Stanley Gibbons SIMPLIFIED CATALOGUE

Stamps of the World

2001 Edition

An illustrated and priced three-volume guide to the postage stamps of the whole world, excluding changes of paper, perforation, shade and watermark

VOLUME 2

COUNTRIES G–N

STANLEY GIBBONS LTD
London and Ringwood

By Appointment to
Her Majesty the Queen
Stanley Gibbons Limited
London
Philatelists

66th Edition

Published in Great Britain by
Stanley Gibbons Ltd
Publications Editorial, Sales Offices and Distribution Centre
5, Parkside, Christchurch Road,
Ringwood, Hampshire BH24 3SH
Telephone 01425 472363

ISBN: 085259-497-6

Published as Stanley Gibbons Simplified Stamp Catalogue from 1934 to 1970, renamed Stamps of the World in 1971, and produced in two (1982–88) or three (from 1989) volumes as Stanley Gibbons Simplified Catalogue of Stamps of the World.
This volume published October 2000

S.G. Item No. 2882 (01)

Origination by Polestar Whitefriars Ltd, Tunbridge Wells, Kent
Printed in Great Britain by Bemrose Security Printing, London & Derby

Stanley Gibbons
SIMPLIFIED CATALOGUE

Stamps of the World

This popular catalogue is a straightforward three-volume listing of the stamps that have been issued everywhere in the world since the very first–Great Britain's famous Penny Black in 1840.

This edition is arranged completely alphabetically in a three-volume format, Volume 1 (Countries A–F) appears in September, Volume 2 (Countries G–N) in October, and Volume 3 (Countries O–Z) in December.

Readers are reminded that the Catalogue Supplements, published in each issue of **Gibbons Stamp Monthly,** can be used to update the listings in **Stamps of the World** as well as our twenty-two part standard catalogue. To make the supplement even more useful the Type numbers given to the illustrations are the same in the Stamps of the World as in the standard catalogues. The first Catalogue Supplement to this Volume appeared in the September 2000 issue of **Gibbons Stamp Monthly.**

Gibbons Stamp Monthly can be obtained through newsagents or on postal subscription from Stanley Gibbons Publications, 5, Parkside, Christchurch Road, Ringwood, Hants BH24 3SH.

The catalogue has many important features:

- As an indication of current values virtually every stamp is priced. Thousands of alterations have been made since the last edition.
- By being set out on a simplified basis that excludes changes of paper, perforation, shade, watermark, gum or printer's and date imprints it is particularly easy to use. (For its exact scope see "Information for users" pages following.)
- The thousands of illustrations and helpful descriptions of stamp designs make it of maximum appeal to collectors with thematic interests.
- Its catalogue numbers are the world-recognised Stanley Gibbons numbers throughout.
- Helpful introductory notes for the collector are included, backed by much historical, geographical and currency information.
- A very detailed index gives instant location of countries in this volume, and a cross-reference to those included in the other volumes.

Over 4,265 stamps and 1,135 new illustrations have been added to the listings in this volume. Last year's three-volume edition contained over 361,220 stamps and 87,170 illustrations.

The listings in this edition are based on the standard catalogues: Part 1 (British Commonwealth) (2001 edition), Part 2 (Austria & Hungary) (5th edition), Part 3 (Balkans) (4th edition), Part 4 (Benelux) (4th edition), Part 5 (Czechoslovakia & Poland) (5th edition), Part 6 (France) (4th edition), Part 7 (Germany) (5th edition), Part 8 (Italy & Switzerland) (5th edition), Part 9 (Portugal & Spain) (4th edition), Part 10 (Russia) (5th edition), Part 11 (Scandinavia) (4th edition), Part 12 (Africa since Independence A-E) (2nd edition), Part 13 (Africa since Independence F-M) (1st edition), Part 14 (Africa since Independence N-Z) (1st edition), Part 15 (Central America) (2nd edition), Part 16 (Central Asia) (3rd edition), Part 17 (China) (6th edition), Part 18 (Japan & Korea) (4th edition), Part 19 (Middle East) (5th edition), Part 20 (South America) (3rd edition), Part 21 (South-East Asia) (3rd edition) and Part 22 (United States) (5th edition).

Important price revisions made specially for this edition include Greenland, Iceland, Liechtenstein, Luxembourg, and Mexico (post 1945).

Stanley Gibbons Stamp Catalogue
Complete List of Parts

1 British Commonwealth
(Annual in two volumes)

Foreign Countries

2 Austria & Hungary (5th edition, 1994)
Austria · Bosnia & Herzegovina · U.N. (Vienna) · Hungary

3 Balkans (4th edition, 1998)
Albania · Bulgaria · Greece & Islands · Rumania · Yugoslavia

4 Benelux (4th edition, 1993)
Belgium & Colonies · Netherlands & Colonies · Luxembourg

5 Czechoslovakia & Poland (5th edition, 1995)
Czechoslovakia · Bohemia & Moravia · Slovakia · Poland

6 France (4th edition, 1993)
France · Colonies · Post Offices · Andorra · Monaco

7 Germany (5th edition, 1996)
Germany · States · Colonies · Post Offices

8 Italy & Switzerland (5th edition, 1997)
Italy & Colonies · Fiume · San Marino · Vatican City · Trieste · Liechtenstein · Switzerland · U.N. (Geneva)

9 Portugal & Spain (4th edition, 1996)
Andorra · Portugal & Colonies · Spain & Colonies

10 Russia (5th edition, 1999)
Russia · Baltic States · Mongolia · Tuva

11 Scandinavia (4th edition, 1994)
Aland Islands · Denmark · Faroe Islands · Finland · Greenland · Iceland · Norway · Sweden

12 Africa since Independence A-E (2nd edition, 1983)
Algeria · Angola · Benin · Bophuthatswana · Burundi · Cameroun · Cape Verde · Central African Republic · Chad · Comoro Islands · Congo · Djibouti · Equatorial Guinea · Ethiopia

13 Africa since Independence F-M (1st edition, 1981)
Gabon · Guinea · Guinea-Bissau · Ivory Coast · Liberia · Libya · Malagasy Republic · Mali · Mauritania · Morocco · Mozambique

14 Africa since Independence N-Z (1st edition, 1981)
Niger Republic · Rwanda · St. Thomas & Prince · Senegal · Somalia · Sudan · Togo · Transkei · Tunisia · Upper Volta · Venda · Zaire

15 Central America (2nd edition, 1984)
Costa Rica · Cuba · Dominican Republic · El Salvador · Guatemala · Haiti · Honduras · Mexico · Nicaragua · Panama

16 Central Asia (3rd edition, 1992)
Afghanistan · Iran · Turkey

17 China (6th edition, 1998)
China · Taiwan · Tibet · Foreign P.O.s

18 Japan & Korea (4th edition, 1997)
Japan · Ryukyus · Korean Empire · South Korea · North Korea

19 Middle East (5th edition, 1996)
Bahrain · Egypt · Iraq · Israel · Jordan · Kuwait · Lebanon · Oman · Qatar · Saudi Arabia · Syria · U.A.E. · Yemen

20 South America (3rd edition, 1989)
Argentina · Bolivia · Brazil · Chile · Colombia · Ecuador · Paraguay · Peru · Surinam · Uruguay · Venezuela

21 South-East Asia (3rd edition, 1995)
Bhutan · Indonesia · Kampuchea · Laos · Myanmar · Nepal · Philippines · Thailand · Vietnam

22 United States (5th edition, 2000)
U.S. & Possessions · Canal Zone · Marshall Islands · Micronesia · Palau · U.N. (New York, Geneva, Vienna)

Thematic Catalogues

Stanley Gibbons Catalogues for use with **Stamps of the World.**
Collect Aircraft on Stamps (1st edition, 1994)
Collect Birds on Stamps (4th edition, 1996)
Collect Chess on Stamps (2nd edition, 1999)
Collect Fish on Stamps (1st edition, 1999)
Collect Fungi on Stamps (2nd edition, 1997)
Collect Railways on Stamps (3rd edition, 1999)
Collect Shells on Stamps (1st edition, 1995)
Collect Ships on Stamps (new edition in preparation)

Information for users

Particular care is advised with Aden Protectorate States, Ajman, Bhutan, Chad, Fujeira, Khor Fakkan, Manama, Ras al Khaima, Sharjah, Umm al Qiwain and Yemen. Totally bogus stamps exist (as explained in Appendix notes) and these are to be avoided also for competition. As distinct from "undesirable stamps" certain categories are not covered in this catalogue purely by reason of its scope (see page v). Consult the particular competition rules to see if such are admissible even though not listed by us.

Where to Look for More Detailed Listings

The present work deliberately omits details of paper, perforation, shade and watermark. But as you become more absorbed in stamp collecting and wish to get greater enjoyment from the hobby you may well want to study these matters.

All the information you require about any particular postage stamp will be found in the main Stanley Gibbons Catalogues.

Commonwealth countries are covered by the Part 1 (British Commonwealth) Catalogue publised annually in two volumes

For | foreign | countries you can easily find which catalogue to consult by looking at the country headings in the present book.

To the right of each country name are code letters specifying which volume of our main catalogues contains that country's listing.

The code letters are as follows:

Pt. 2 Part 2

Pt. 3 Part 3 etc.

(See page iv for complete list of Parts.)

So, for example, if you want to know more about Chinese stamps than is contained in the *Simplified Catalogue of Stamps of the World* the reference to

CHINA Pt. 17

guides you to the Gibbons Part 17 *(China)* Catalogue listing for the details you require.

New editions of Parts 2 to 22 appear at irregular intervals.

Correspondence

Whilst we welcome information and suggestions we must ask correspondents to include the cost of postage for the return of any stamps submitted plus registration where appropriate. Letters should be addressed to The Catalogue Editor at Ringwood.

Where information is solicited purely for the benefit of the enquirer we regret we cannot undertake to reply unless stamps or reply coupons are sent to cover the postage.

Identification of Stamps

We regret we do not give opinions as to the genuineness of stamps, nor do we identify stamps or number them by our Catalogue.

Users of this catalogue are referred to our companion booklet entitled *Stamp Collecting — How to Identify Stamps.* It explains how to look up stamps in this catalogue, contains a full checklist of stamp inscriptions and gives help in dealing with unfamiliar scripts. It is available from Stanley Gibbons at £2.95, postage extra.

Stanley Gibbons would like to complement your collection

At Stanley Gibbons we offer a range of services which are designed to complement your collection.

Our modern stamp shop, the largest in Europe, together with our rare stamp department has one of the most comprehensive stocks of Great Britain in the world, so whether you are a beginner or an experienced philatelist you are certain to find something to suit your special requirements.

Alternatively through our Mail Order services you can control the growth of your collection from the comfort of your own home. Our Postal Sales Department regularly sends out mailings of Special Offers. We can also help with your wants list—so why not ask us for those elusive items?

And don't forget Stanley Gibbons Auctions which holds regular sales each year. Come along in person or send in a written bid for the items you require. For details of current subscription rates for Auction catalogues write to Stanley Gibbons Auctions, 399 Strand, London WC2R 0LX.

Why not take advantage of the many services we have to offer? Visit our premises in the Strand or, for more information, write to the appropriate address on page x.

Stanley Gibbons Holdings Plc Addresses

Stanley Gibbons Limited, Stanley Gibbons Auctions

399 Strand, London WC2R 0LX
Telephone 020 7836 8444, Fax 020 7836 7342,
E-mail: enquires@stanleygibbons.co.uk,
Website: www.stanleygibbons.com for all departments.

Auction Room and Specialist Stamp Departments. Open Monday–Friday 9.30 a.m. to 5 p.m.
Shop. Open Monday–Friday 8.30 a.m. to 6 p.m. and Saturday 9.30 a.m. to 5.30 p.m.

Fraser's

(Autographs, photographs, letters and documents)

399 Strand, London WC2 0LX
Telephone 020 7836 8444, Fax 020 7836 7342,
E-mail: info@frasersautographs.co.uk,
Website: www.frasersautographs.com

Monday-Friday 9 a.m. to 5.30 p.m. and Saturday 10 a.m. to 4 p.m.

Stanley Gibbons Publications

5 Parkside, Christchurch Road, Ringwood, Hants BH24 3SH.
Telephone 01425 472363 (24 hour answerphone service), Fax 01425 470247,
E-mail: info@stanleygibbons.co.uk,
Website: www.stanley gibbons.com

Publications Showroom (at above address). Open Monday–Friday 9 a.m. to 3 p.m.

Publications Mail Order. FREEPHONE 0800 611622. Monday–Friday 8.30 a.m. to 5 p.m.

Stanley Gibbons Publications Overseas Representation

Stanley Gibbons Publications are represented overseas by the following sole distributors (*), distributors (**) or licensees (***).

Australia*
Lighthouse Philatelic (Aust.) Pty. Ltd., P.O. Box 763, Strawberry Hills, New South Wales, 2012 Australia.

Stanley Gibbons (Australia) Pty. Ltd.***
Level 6, 36 Clarence Street, Sydney, New South Wales 2000, Australia.

Belgium and Luxembourg**
Davo c/o Philac, Rue du Midi 48, Bruxelles, 1000 Belgium.

Canada*
Lighthouse Publications (Canada) Ltd., 255 Duke Street, Montreal Quebec, Canada H3C 2M2.

Denmark**
Samlerforum/Davo, Ostergade 3, DK 7470 Karup, Denmark.

Finland**
Davo c/o Suomen Postimerkkeily Ludvingkatu 5 SF-00130 Helsinki, Finland.

France*
Davo France (Casteilla), 10, Rue Leon Foucault, 78184 St. Quentin Yvelines Cesex, France.

Germany and Austria*
Leuchtturm Albenverlag Gmbh u.Co. Am Spakenberg 45, Postfach 1340, D-21495 Geesthacht, Germany.

Hong Kong**
Po-on Stamp Service, G.P.O. Box 2498, Hong Kong.

Israel**
Capital Stamps, P.O. Box 3769, Jerusalem 91036, Israel.

Italy*
Ernesto Marini Srl, Via Struppa 300, I-16165, Genova GE, Italy

Japan**
Japan Philatelic Co. Ltd., P.O. Box 2, Suginami-Minami, Tokyo, Japan.

Netherlands*
Davo Publications, P.O. Box 411, 7400 AK Deventer, Netherlands.

New Zealand***
Mowbray Collectables, P.O. Box 80, Wellington, New Zealand.

Norway**
Davo Norge A/S, P.O. Box 738 Sentrum, N-0105, Oslo, Norway.

Singapore***
Stanley Gibbons (Singapore) Pte Ltd., Raffles City P.O. Box 1689, Singapore 9117.

South Africa**
Republic Coin & Stamp Accessories cc., Republic House, 54A Silwood Road, Bramley 2090, Gauteng, South Africa.

Sweden*
Chr Winther Soerensen AB, Box 43, S-310 Knaered, Sweden.

Switzerland**
Phila Service, Burgstrasse 160, CH 4125, Riehen, Switzerland.

West Indies/Caribbean**
Hugh Dunphy, P.O. Box 413, Kingston 10, Jamaica, West Indies.

Abbreviations

Anniv.	denotes	Anniversary
Assn.	,,	Association
Bis.	,,	Bistre
Bl.	,,	Blue
Bldg.	,,	Building
Blk.	,,	Black
Br.	,,	British *or* Bridge
Brn.	,,	Brown
B.W.I.	,,	British West Indies
C.A.R.I.F.T.A.	,,	Caribbean Free Trade Area
Cent.	,,	Centenary
Chest.	,,	Chestnut
Choc.	,,	Chocolate
Clar.	,,	Claret
Coll.	,,	College
Commem.	,,	Commemoration
Conf.	,,	Conference
Diag.	,,	Diagonally
E.C.A.F.E.	,,	Economic Commission for Asia and Far East
Emer.	,,	Emerald
E.P.T. Conference	,,	European Postal and Telecommunications Conference
Exn.	,,	Exhibition
F.A.O.	,,	Food and Agriculture Organization
Fig.	,,	Figure
G.A.T.T.	,,	General Agreement on Tariffs and Trade
G.B.	,,	Great Britain
Gen.	,,	General
Govt.	,,	Government
Grn.	,,	Green
Horiz.	,,	Horizontal
H.Q.	,,	Headquarters
Imperf.	,,	Imperforate
Inaug.	,,	Inauguration
Ind.	,,	Indigo
Inscr.	,,	Inscribed or inscription
Int.	,,	International
I.A.T.A.	,,	International Air Transport Association
I.C.A.O.	,,	International Civil Aviation Organization
I.C.Y.	,,	International Co-operation Year
I.G.Y.	,,	International Geophysical Year
I.L.O.	,,	International Labour Office (or later, Organization)
I.M.C.O.	,,	Inter-Governmental Maritime Consultative Organization
I.T.U.	,,	International Telecommunication Union
Is.	,,	Islands
Lav.	,,	Lavender
Mar.	,,	Maroon
mm.	,,	Millimetres
Mult.	,,	Multicoloured
Mve.	denotes	Mauve
Nat.	,,	National
N.A.T.O.	,,	North Atlantic Treaty Organization
O.D.E.C.A.	,,	Organization of Central American States
Ol.	,,	Olive
Optd.	,,	Overprinted
Orge. *or* oran.	,,	Orange
P.A.T.A.	,,	Pacific Area Travel Association
Perf.	,,	Perforated
Post.	,,	Postage
Pres.	,,	President
P.U.	,,	Postal Union
Pur.	,,	Purple
R.	,,	River
R.S.A.	,,	Republic of South Africa
Roul.	,,	Rouletted
Sep.	,,	Sepia
S.E.A.T.O.	,,	South East Asia Treaty Organization
Surch.	,,	Surcharged
T.	,,	Type
T.U.C.	,,	Trades Union Congress
Turq.	,,	Turquoise
Ultram.	,,	Ultramarine
U.N.E.S.C.O.	,,	United Nations Educational, Scientific & Cultural Organization
U.N.I.C.E.F.	,,	United Nations Children's Fund
U.N.O.	,,	United Nations Organization
U.N.R.W.A.	,,	United Nations Relief and Works Agency for Palestine Refugees in the Near East
U.N.T.E.A.	,,	United Nations Temporary Executive Authority
U.N.R.R.A.	,,	United Nations Relief and Rehabilitation Administration
U.P.U.	,,	Universal Postal Union
Verm.	,,	Vermilion
Vert.	,,	Vertical
Vio.	,,	Violet
W.F.T.U	,,	World Federation of Trade Unions
W.H.O.	,,	World Health Organization
Yell.	,,	Yellow

Arabic Numerals

As in the case of European figures, the details of the Arabic numerals vary in different stamp designs, but they should be readily recognised with the aid of this illustration:

٠	١	٢	٣	٤
0	1	2	3	4
٥	٦	٧	٨	٩
5	6	7	8	9

Key-Types

(see note on page vii)

French Group

A. " Blanc."

B. " Mouchon."

C. " Merson."

D. " Tablet."

E.

F.

" International Colonial Exhibition."

G.

H.

I. " Faidherbe."

J. " Palms."

K. " Balay."

L. " Natives."

M. " Figure."

German Group

N. " Yacht."

O. " Yacht."

Spanish Group

X. " Alfonso XII."

Y. " Baby."

Z. "Curly Head"

Portuguese Group

P. " Crown."

Q. " Embossed."

R. " Figures."

S. " Carlos."

T. " Manoel."

U. " Ceres."

V. " Newspaper."

W. " Due."

STANLEY GIBBONS SIMPLIFIED CATALOGUE OF STAMPS OF THE WORLD—VOLUME 2 COUNTRIES G–N

GABON Pt. 6; Pt. 13

A French colony on the W. coast of equatorial Africa. Became part of Fr. Equatorial Africa in 1937 and a republic within the French Community in 1958.

100 centimes = 1 franc.

1886. Stamps of French Colonies, "Commerce" type, surch **GAB** surrounded by dots, and value in figures.

1 J 5 on 20 c. red on green £275 £275
2 10 on 20 c. red on green £275 £275
3 25 on 20 c. red on green £275 £275
4 50 on 15 c. blue on light blue . £850 £850
5 75 on 15 c. blue on light blue . £1000 £1000

1888. Stamps of French Colonies, "Commerce" type, surch in figures.

6 J 15 on 10 c. black on lilac . . . £3250 £750
7 15 on 1 f. olive £1300 £600
8 25 on 5 c. green £850 £160
9 25 on 10 c. black on lilac . . . £3250 £1000
10 25 on 75 c. red £1800 £850

1889. Postage Due stamps of French Colonies surch **GABON TIMBRE** and value in figures.

11 U 15 on 5 c. black £160 £140
12 15 on 30 c. black £3250 £2250
13 25 on 20 c. black . . . . . . 70·00 50·00

6

1889. Imperf.

14 6 15 c. black on pink £1000 £675
15 25 c. black on green £650 £525

1904. "Tablet" key-type inscr "GABON" in red (1, 5, 15, 25, 35, 45, 75 c., 1, 2 f.) or blue (others).

16 D 1 c. black on blue 50 55
17 2 c. brown on buff 50 40
18 4 c. brown on grey 70 70
19 5 c. green 80 60
20 10 c. red . . . . 2·50 65
21 15 c. grey . . . . 3·75 75
22 20 c. red on green . . . . . 5·00 4·00
23 25 c. blue . . . . 4·00 3·00
24 30 c. brown on drab . . . . . 8·25 7·00
25 35 c. black on yellow . . . . 14·00 12·50
26 40 c. red on yellow . . . . . 9·50 9·00
27 45 c. black on green . . . . 18·00 18·00
28 50 c. brown on blue . . . . . 7·00 6·50
29 75 c. brown on orange . . . . 11·00 12·00
30 1 f. green . . . . 22·00 20·00
31 2 f. violet on pink . . . . . 48·00 50·00
32 5 f. mauve on lilac . . . . . 95·00 90·00

7 Gabon Warrior 9 Bantu Woman

8 View of Libreville

1910.

33 7 1 c. brown and orange 50 50
34 2 c. black and brown . . . . 1·00 50
35 4 c. violet and blue 70 50
36 5 c. olive and green 50 50
37 10 c. red and lake . . . . . 1·25 1·00
38 20 c. brown and violet . . . . 1·50 3·00
39 8 25 c. brown and blue . . . . 2·00 2·75
40 30 c. red and grey . . . . . 15·00 19·00
41 35 c. green and violet . . . . 9·00 9·00
42 40 c. blue and brown . . . . . 13·00 16·00
43 45 c. violet and red . . . . . 21·00 21·00
44 50 c. grey and green . . . . . 40·00 42·00
45 75 c. brown and orange . . . . 60·00 65·00
46 9 1 f. yellow and brown . . . . 65·00 65·00
47 2 f. brown and red £180 £180
48 5 f. brown and blue £180 £180

1910. As last but inscr "AFRIQUE EQUATORIALE GABON".

49 7 1 c. brown and orange 10 10
50 2 c. black and brown 10 10
51 4 c. violet and blue 20 20
52 5 c. grey and green 35 20
82 5 c. black and yellow 30 45
53 10 c. red and lake 50 40
83 10 c. light green and green . . 30 50
54 15 c. purple and pink 30 50
55 20 c. brown and violet . . . . 5·00 6·75
56 8 25 c. brown and blue 55 50
84 25 c. black and green 75 85
57 30 c. red and grey 50 50
85 30 c. red and carmine 65 70
58 35 c. green and violet 55 55
59 40 c. blue and brown 70 50
60 45 c. violet and red 55 50
86 45 c. red and black 65 80
61 50 c. grey and green 65 70
87 50 c. blue and deep blue 45 50
62 75 c. brown and red . . . . . 1·90 3·00
63 9 1 f. bistre and brown . . . . 1·50 1·75
64 2 f. brown and red . . . . . 2·50 2·25
65 5 f. brown and blue . . . . . 4·50 4·50

1912. "Tablet" key-type surch in figures.

66 D 05 on 2 c. brown on buff . . 50 55
67 05 on 4 c. brown on grey . . 50 55
68 05 on 15 c. grey 15 15
69 05 on 20 c. red on green . . . 25 40
70 05 on 25 c. blue 20 25
71 05 on 30 c. brown on drab . . 50 65
72 10 on 40 c. red on yellow . . . 25 40
73 10 on 45 c. black on green . . 30 55
74 10 on 50 c. brown on blue . . 70 85
75 10 on 75 c. brown on orange . 40 60
76 10 on 1 f. green 40 60
77 10 on 2 f. violet on pink . . . 40 60
78 10 on 5 f. mauve on lilac . . . 1·75 2·00

1915. Surch with red cross and **5c.**

79 7 10 c. + 5 c. (No. 37) . . . . 10·00 10·50
81 10 c. + 5 c. (No. 53) 30 65

1924. Inscr "AFRIQUE EQUATORIALE GABON" and optd **AFRIQUE EQUATORIALE FRANCAISE.**

88 7 1 c. brown and orange . . . 10 20
89 2 c. black and brown 10 30
90 4 c. violet and blue 10 25
91 5 c. black and yellow 10 20
92 10 c. light green and green . . 30 40
93 10 c. blue and brown 15 20
94 15 c. purple and pink 20 40
95 15 c. pink and purple 40 55
96 20 c. brown and violet 20 40
97 8 25 c. black and green 15 30
98 30 c. red and carmine 25 40
99 30 c. yellow and black 25 40
100 30 c. green 65 65
101 35 c. green and violet 20 35
102 40 c. blue and brown 30 25
103 45 c. red and black 45 50
104 50 c. blue and deep blue . . . 30 35
105 50 c. green and red 30 20
106 65 c. red and blue . . . . . 1·00 2·00
107 75 c. brown and orange 50 80
108 90 c. red and scarlet . . . . 1·25 1·40
109 9 1 f. bistre and brown 50 60
110 1 f. 10 red and green . . . . 3·25 3·50
111 1 f. 50 blue and light blue . . 1·00 60
112 2 f. brown and red 80 80
113 3 f. mauve on pink . . . . . 3·00 4·25
114 5 f. brown and blue . . . . . 3·25 4·00

1925. As last, surch in figures.

115 9 65 on 1 f. brown & green . . 35 55
116 85 on 1 f. brown & green . . 35 55
117 8 90 c. on 75 c. pink & red . . 65 1·10
118 9 1 f. 25 on 1 f. ultram & bl . . 45 50
119 1 f. 50 on 1 f. dp blue & blue . 65 80
120 3 f. on 5 f. brown & mve . . 1·50 3·75
121 10 f. on 5 f. green & brown . . 8·00 8·25
122 20 f. on 5 f. red & purple . . 8·25 8·25

1931. "Colonial Exn." key-type inscr "GABON".

123 E 40 c. green . . . . 1·40 1·60
124 F 50 c. mauve . . . . 1·25 1·40
125 G 90 c. orange . . . . 1·40 1·60
126 H 1 f. 50 blue . . . . 2·25 2·50

21 Log Raft on the River Ogowe 22 Count de Brazza

1932.

127 21 1 c. red 15 25
128 2 c. black on red 20 30
129 4 c. green 20 30
130 5 c. blue 20 30
131 10 c. red on yellow 20 30
132 15 c. red on green 50 60
133 20 c. red 50 65
134 25 c. brown 35 45
135 22 30 c. green 80 80
136 40 c. purple 65 65
137 45 c. black on green 85 85
138 50 c. brown 60 40
139 65 c. blue . . . . 3·25 3·00
140 75 c. black on orange . . . 1·75 1·75
141 90 c. red . . . . 2·00 1·90
142 1 f. green on blue . . . . . 10·00 11·00
143 – 1 f. 25 violet . . . . . . 1·25 85
144 – 1 f. 50 blue . . . . 2·00 1·00
145 – 1 f. 75 green . . . . . . 1·60 75
146 – 2 f. red . . . . 13·50 10·50
147 – 3 f. green on blue . . . . . 3·25 2·75
148 – 5 f. brown . . . . 4·00 4·00
149 – 10 f. black on orange . . . 17·00 14·00
150 – 20 f. purple . . . . 30·00 24·00

DESIGN—HORIZ: 1 f. 25 to 20 f. Gabon Village.

25 Prime Minister Leon Mba

1959. 1st Anniv of Republic.

161 25 15 f. brown 40 30
162 – 25 f. green and sepia 40 25

PORTRAIT: 25 f. Prime Minister Mba (profile).

1960. 10th Anniv of African Technical Co-operation Commission. As T **4** of Malagasy Republic.

163 50 f. blue and purple 85 75

27 Dr. Albert Schweitzer (philosopher and missionary), Organ and View of Lambarene

1960. Air.

164 27 200 f. brown, green & bl . . 5·50 2·75

1960. Air. Olympic Games. No. 192 of French Equatorial Africa surch with Olympic rings, **XVIIe OLYMPIADE 1960 REPUBLIQUE GABONAISE 250F** and bars.

165 250 f. on 500 f. bl, blk & grn . . 6·75 6·75

29 Tree Felling

1960. Air. 5th World Forestry Congress, Seattle.

166 29 100 f. brown, black & grn . . 3·00 1·40

30 Flag, Map and U. N. Emblem 32 Combretum

31 Lyre-tailed Honeyguide in flight

1961. Admission into U.N.

167 30 15 f. multicoloured 30 20
168 25 f. multicoloured 35 25
169 85 f. multicoloured . . . . 1·25 80

1961. Air. Birds. Multicoloured.

170 50 f. Type **31** . . . . 3·25 1·40
171 100 f. Madame Verreaux's sun-bird . . . . 6·25 2·00
172 200 f. Blue-headed bee eater . . 12·00 4·25
173 250 f. Crowned eagle . . . . . 15·00 5·75
174 500 f. Narina trogon . . . . . 30·00 11·00

The 200 f., 250 f., and 500 f. are vert designs.

1961.

175 32 50 c. red, purple & grn . . . 10 10
176 – 1 f. red, turquoise & bistre . 10 10
177 – 2 f. yellow and green . . . 10 10
178 – 3 f. yellow, green & olive . . 20 15
179 – 5 f. multicoloured 25 20
180 32 10 f. red, grn & turquoise . . 30 25

FLOWERS—VERT: 1 f., 5 f. Gabonese tulip (tree). HORIZ: 2 f., 3 f. Yellow cassia.

REPUBLIQUE GABONAISE 20F JEUX SPORTIFS

33 President Mba 36 Start of Race

1962.

181 33 15 f. blue, red & green . . . 20 10
182 20 f. sepia, red & green . . 35 15
183 25 f. brown, red & green . . 40 15

1962. Air. "Air Afrique" Airline. As T **42** of Mauritania.

184 500 f. green, ochre & black . . 9·50 5·50

1962. Malaria Eradication. As T **43** of Mauritania.

185 25 f. + 5 f. green 80 80

1962. Sports. Multicoloured.

186 20 f. Type **36** (postage) 45 20
187 50 f. Football 95 60
188 100 f. Long jump (26 × 47 mm) (air) . . . . 2·50 1·10

37 Breguet 14 Biplane

1962. Air. Evolution of Air Transport.

189 37 10 f. blue and red 50 20
190 – 20 f. indigo, blue & brown . 70 35
191 – 60 f. blue, purple & green . 1·60 85
192 – 85 f. indigo, blue & orange . 2·75 1·40

AIRCRAFT: 20 f. De Havilland Dragon Rapide; 60 f. Sud Aviation Caravelle; 85 f. Rocket.

1962. 1st Anniv of Union of African and Malagasy States. As No. 155 of Mauritania.

194 30 f. green . . . . 1·10 80

39 Capt. Ntchorere and Flags

1962. Capt. Ntchorere Commemoration.

195 39 80 f. multicoloured . . . . 1·10 70

1963. Freedom from Hunger. As T **51** of Mauritania.

196 25 f. + 5 f. green, brown & red . 60 60

1963. Air. 50th Anniv of Arrival of Dr Schweitzer in Gabon. Surch **100F JUBILE GABONAIS 1913-1963.**

197 27 100 f. on 200 f. brown, green and blue . . . . 2·75 1·40

43 Libreville Post Office

1963. Air. Cent of Gabon Postal Services.

198 43 100 f. multicoloured . . . . 1·40 85

1963. Air. African and Malagasy Posts and Telecommunications Union. As T **56** of Mauritania.
199 85 f. multicoloured . . . . . . 1·40 80

1963. Space Telecommunications. As Nos. 178/80 of Mauritania.
200 25 f. orange, blue & green . . . 40 35
201 100 f. brown, green & blue . . . 1·60 1·40

1963. Air. 1st Anniv of "Air Afrique" and Inauguration of "DC-8" Service. As T **59** of Mauritania.
202 50 f. multicoloured 90 55

1963. Air. European–African Economic Convention. As T **61** of Mauritania.
203 50 f. multicoloured . . . . . . 1·25 65

1963. 15th Anniv of Declaration of Human Rights. As T **23** of Malagasy Republic.
204 25 f. slate green and brown . . 45 30

49 Rameses and Gods, Wadi-es-Sebua

1964. Air. Nubian Monuments.
205 **49** 10 f. + 5 f. brown & blue . 85 85
206 25 f. + 5 f. blue and red . . 1·00 1·00
207 50 f. + 5 f. pur & myrtle . . 1·50 1·50

1964. World Meteorological Day. As T **24** of Malagasy Republic.
208 25 f. green, blue and bistre . . . 55 35

51 Arms of Gabon **52** Map and African Heads of State

1964.
209 **51** 25 f. multicoloured 50 30

1964. Air. 5th Anniv of Equatorial African Heads of State Conf.
210 **52** 100 f. multicoloured . . . . 1·50 85

53 Atlantic Tarpon **54** Ear of Wheat, Cogwheel and Globe

1964. Gabon Fauna.
211 **53** 30 f. black, blue & brown . 90 45
212 – 60 f. brown, chest & green . 1·50 60
213 – 80 f. brown, green & blue . 1·60 85
DESIGNS—VERT: 60 f. Gorilla. HORIZ: 80 f. African buffalo.

1964. Air. 1st Anniv of "Europafrique".
214 **54** 50 f. blue, olive and red . . 1·25 80

55 Start of Race

1964. Air. Olympic Games, Tokyo.
215 **55** 25 f. green, brown & orge . 60 35
216 – 50 f. brown, orange & grn . 1·10 45
217 – 100 f. violet, pur & olive . . 2·25 90
218 – 200 f. brown, purple & red . 3·50 2·25
DESIGNS—VERT: 50 f. Massaging athlete; 100 f. Anointing before the Games. HORIZ: 200 f. Athletes.

56 Posthorns, Envelope and Radio Mast

1964. Air. Pan-African and Malagasy Posts and Telecommunications Congress, Cairo.
220 **56** 25 f. sepia, red and green . . 55 30

1964. French, African and Malagasy Co-operation. As T **68** of Mauritania.
221 25 f. brown, blue and slate . . . 55 40

58 "Dissotis rotundifolia" **59** Pres. Kennedy

1964. Flowers. Multicoloured.
222 3 f. Type **58** 20 10
223 5 f. "Gloriosa superba" 30 15
224 15 f. "Eulophia horsfallii" . . . 55 25

1964. Air. Pres. Kennedy Commem.
225 **59** 100 f. black, orange & grn . 1·60 1·40

60 Women in Public Service

1964. Air. Social Evolution of Gabonese Women.
227 **60** 50 f. brown, blue & red . . 85 45

61 Sun and I.Q.S.Y. Emblem

1965. International Quiet Sun Year.
228 **61** 85 f. multicoloured . . . . 1·40 85

62 Globe and I.C.Y. Emblem

1965. Air. International Co-operation Year.
229 **62** 50 f. orange, turq & blue . . 85 45

63 17th-cent. Merchantman

1965. Air. Old Ships. Multicoloured.
230 25 f. 16th-cent. galleon . . . . 1·25 55
231 50 f. Type **63** . . . . 2·10 85
232 85 f. 18th-cent. frigate . . . . 3·75 1·40
233 100 f. 19th-cent. brig . . . . 5·25 1·60
The 25 f. and 85 f. are vert.

64 Morse Telegraph Apparatus

1965. Centenary of I.T.U.
234 **64** 30 f. green, orange & blue . 55 35

65 Manganese Mine, Moanda **67** Football

66 Nurse holding Child

1965. "Mining Riches".
235 **65** 15 f. red, violet and blue . . 40 20
236 – 60 f. red and blue . . . . . 1·25 60
DESIGN: 60 f. Uranium mine, Mounana.

1965. Air. Gabon Red Cross.
237 **66** 100 f. brown, red & green . 1·60 85

1965. 1st African Games, Brazzaville.
238 **67** 25 f. blk, red & grn (post) . 55 35
239 – 100 f. purple, red & brown (air) . . . . 1·90 85
DESIGN (27 × 48½ mm): 100 f. Basketball.

68 "Globe", Pylon and "Sun"

1965. Air. "Europafrique".
240 **68** 50 f. multicoloured . . . . 1·40 55

69 President Mba

1965. Air. 5th Anniv of Independence.
241 **69** 25 f. multicoloured 50 30

70 Okoukoue Dance **71** Abraham Lincoln

1965. Gabon Dances.
242 **70** 25 f. yellow, brown & grn . 45 20
243 – 60 f. black, red & brown . . 1·25 60
DESIGN: 60 f. Makudji dance.

1965. Death Cent of Abraham Lincoln.
244 **71** 50 f. multicoloured 80 45

72 Sir Winston Churchill

1965. Air. Churchill Commem.
245 **72** 100 f. multicoloured . . . . 1·60 85

73 Dr. A. Schweitzer and Map

1965. Air. Schweitzer Commem.
246 **73** 1000 f. gold . . . . 48·00 48·00

74 Pope John XXIII

1965. Air. Pope John Commem.
247 **74** 85 f. multicoloured . . . . 1·10 80

75 Mail Carrier, Post Office and Van

1965. Stamp Day.
248 **75** 30 f. brown, green & blue . 50 40

76 Nurse and Patients

1966. Air. Red Cross. Multicoloured.
249 50 f. Type **76** 95 55
250 100 f. Bandaging patient . . . 1·90 85

77 Balumbu Mask **78** W.H.O. Building

1966. World Festival of Negro Arts, Dakar. Multicoloured.
253 5 f. Type **77** 20 15
254 10 f. Statuette—"Ancestor of the Fang (tribe), Byeri" 30 20
255 25 f. Fang mask 70 30
256 30 f. Okuyi Myene mask . . . 90 50
257 85 f. Bakota copper mask . . . 2·10 1·10

1966. Inaug of W.H.O. Headquarters, Geneva.
258 **78** 50 f. black, yellow & blue . 85 40

79 Satellite "A1" and Rocket

1966. Air. "Conquest of Space".
259 **79** 30 f. lake, plum and blue . . 55 30
260 – 90 f. plum, red and purple . 1·40 60
DESIGN: 90 f. Satellite "FR1" and rocket.

80 "Learning the Alphabet"   **81** Footballer

1966. U.N.E.S.C.O. Literacy Campaign.
261 **80** 30 f. multicoloured 55 30

1966. World Cup Football Championships, England.
262 **81** 25 f. bl, grn & lake (postage) 40 20
263 – 90 f. purple and blue . . . . 1·60 70
264 – 100 f. slate and red (air) . . 1·90 90
DESIGNS—VERT: 90 f. Footballer (different). HORIZ: 100 f. Footballers on world map (47½ × 27 mm).

82 Industrial Scenes within leaves of "Plant"   **83** Plywood Mill

1966. Air. "Europafrique".
265 **82** 50 f. multicoloured . . . . 2·75 65

1966. Economic Development.
266 **83** 20 f. lake, purple & green . . 45 30
267 – 85 f. brown, blue & green . . 3·50 1·40
DESIGN: 85 f. "Roger Butin" (oil rig).

1966. Air. Inauguration of Douglas DC-8F Air Services. As T **87** of Mauritania.
268 30 f. grey, black and orange . . 40 20

85 Making Deposit

1966. Savings Bank.
269 **85** 25 f. brown, green & blue . 55 30

86 Scouts and Camp Fire

1966. Scouting.
270 **86** 30 f. brown, red & slate . . 55 35
271 – 50 f. brown, lake & blue . . 1·00 45
DESIGN—VERT: 50 f. Scouts taking oath.

87 Gabonese Scholar

1966. Air. 20th Anniv of U.N.E.S.C.O.
272 **87** 100 f. black, buff & blue . . 1·40 65

88 Libreville Airport

1966. Air.
273 **88** 200 f. brown, red & blue . . 3·25 1·10

89 Sikorsky S-43 Amphibian, Map and Flag (Aeromaritime's First Airmail Service, 1937)

1966. Stamp Day.
274 **89** 30 f. multicoloured 80 50

90 Hippopotami

1967. Gabon Fauna. Multicoloured.
275 1 f. Type **90** 10 10
276 2 f. Crocodiles 15 10
277 3 f. Water chevrotains 15 10
278 5 f. Chimpanzees 20 10
279 10 f. African elephants 65 30
280 20 f. Leopards . . . . 1·25 40

91 Lions Emblem and Anniversary Dates

1967. 50th Anniv of Lions Int. Mult.
281 30 f. Type **91** 55 30
282 50 f. Lions emblem, map and globe 90 40

92 Masked Faces   **93** I.T.Y. Emblem and Transport

1967. Libreville Carnival.
283 **92** 30 f. blue, brown & yellow . 60 30

1967. Int Tourist Year.
284 **93** 30 f. multicoloured . . . . 1·25 40

94 Diving-board (Mexico City)   **96** Atomic Symbol Dove and Globe

95 Farman F.190

1967. Publicity for 1968 Olympic Games, Mexico.
285 **94** 25 f. turq, blue & violet . . 45 20
286 – 30 f. purple, lake & green . . 65 30
287 – 50 f. blue, green & purple . . 1·10 60
DESIGNS: 30 f. Sun and snow crystal. 50f. Ice rink, Grenoble.

1967. Air. Famous Aircraft.
288 **95** 200 f. plum, blue & turq . . 3·25 1·10
289 – 300 f. blue, purple & brn . . 5·50 1·40
290 – 500 f. blue, purple & grn . . 9·50 4·25
AIRCRAFT: 300 f. De Havilland Heron 2; 500 f. Potez 56.

1967. Int Atomic Energy Agency.
291 **96** 30 f. red, blue and green . . 65 30

97 Aircraft on Flight-paths

1967. Air. I.C.A.O. Commem.
292 **97** 100 f. purple, blue & green . 1·50 70

98 Pope Paul VI   **99** Blood Donor and Bank

1967. Papal Encyclical "Populorum Progressio".
293 **98** 30 f. black, blue & green . . 65 35

1967. Air. Red Cross.
294 **99** 50 f. multicoloured . . . . 1·10 45
295 – 100 f. multicoloured . . . . 2·25 95
DESIGN: 100 f. Heart and blood-transfusion apparatus.

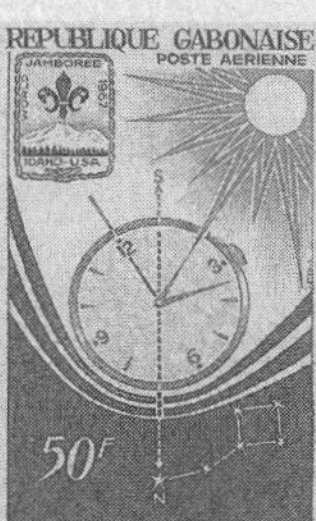

100 Indigenous Emblems   **101** "Europafrique"

1967. World Fair, Montreal.
297 **100** 30 f. brown, green & lake . 55 30

1967. Europafrique.
298 **101** 50 f. multicoloured 85 35

102 Orientation Diagram and Sun

1967. Air. World Scout Jamboree, Idaho.
299 **102** 50 f. green, orge & blue . . 80 50
300 – 100 f. red, green & blue . . 1·40 90
DESIGN: 100 f. U.S. scout greeting Gabon scout on map.

103 U.N. Emblem, Gabon Women and Child

1967. U.N. Status of Women Commission.
301 **103** 75 f. blue, green & brn . . 1·40 55

1967. Air. 5th Anniv of U.A.M.P.T. As T **101** of Mauritania.
302 100 f. red, blue and olive . . . 1·40 65

105 Baraka Mission, Libreville

1967. Air. 125th Anniv of American Missionaries Arrival.
303 **105** 100 f. black, green & blue . 1·60 85

106 U.N. Emblem and Book with Supporters   **107** "Draconea fragans"

1967. Air. U.N. Int. Rights Commission.
304 **106** 60 f. multicoloured 90 55

1967. Gabon Trees.
305 **107** 5 f. brown, green and blue (postage) 20 15
306 – 10 f. green, bronze & blue . 35 20
307 – 20 f. red, green & brown . 55 30
308 – 50 f. green, bistre and blue (air) 95 40
309 – 100 f. multicoloured . . . 1·90 70
DESIGNS: 10 f. "Pycnanthus angolensis"; 20 f. "Disthemonanthus benthamianus". (27 × 48 mm); 50 f. "Baillonella toxisperma"; 100 f. "Aucoumea klaineana".

108 "Belgrano" and "Jean Guiton" (19th-century steam packets)

1967. Stamp Day. Multicoloured.
311 30 f. Type **108** . . . . 1·25 45
312 30 f. "Ango" and "Lucie Delmas" (modern mail carriers) . . . . 1·25 45
Nos. 311/12 were issued together, se-tenant, forming a composite design.

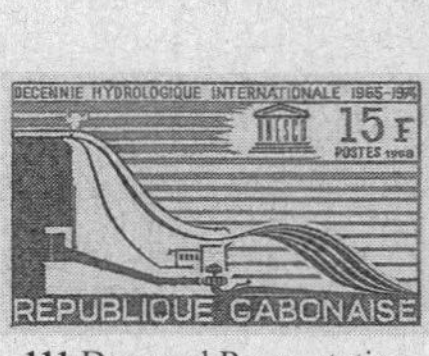

109 Chancellor Adenauer   **110** African W.H.O. Building

1968. Air. Adenauer Commem.
313 **109** 100 f. sepia, red & yellow . 1·90 65

1968. 20th Anniv of W.H.O.
315 **110** 20 f. purple, blue & green . 55 30

111 Dam and Power-station   **112** President Bongo

1968. International Hydrological Decade.
316 **111** 15 f. blue, orange & lake . 45 20

1968.
317 **112** 25 f. black, yellow & grn . 40 20
318 – 30 f. black, turq & pur . . 45 20
DESIGN: 30 f. Pres. Bongo (half-length portrait).

113 "Madonna and Child with Rosary" (Murillo)

1968. Air. Religious Paintings. Multicoloured.
319 60 f. Type **113** 90 45
320 90 f. "Christ in Bonds" (Luis de Morales) 1·40 65
321 100 f. "St. John at Patmos" (Juan Mates) (horiz) 1·60 85

114 Beribboned Rope

1968. Air. 5th Anniv of Europafrique.
322 **114** 50 f. multicoloured 80 40

115 Refinery and Tanker

1968. Inauguration of Petroleum Refinery, Port Gentil, Gabon.
323 **115** 30 f. multicoloured 70 30

116 Distribution to the Needy

1968. Air. Red Cross. Multicoloured.
324 50 f. Type **116** 85 35
325 100 f "Support the Red Cross" 1·90 65

117 High-jumping

1968. Air. Olympic Games, Mexico.
327 **117** 25 f. brown, slate & red 50 30
328 – 30 f. brown, blue & red 60 35
329 – 100 f. brown, yell & blue 1·60 80
330 – 200 f. brown, slate & grn 3·00 1·40
DESIGNS—VERT: 30 f. Cycling; 100 f. Judo. HORIZ: 200 f. Boxing.

118 Open Book **120** Coffee

1968. Literacy Day.
332 **118** 25 f. brown, red & blue 40 20

1968. Agricultural Produce.
333 **120** 20 f. red, myrtle and green 45 15
334 – 40 f. orange, brown & grn 75 35
DESIGNS: 40 f. Cocoa.

121 "Junon" (sail/steam warship) **123** Advocate holding "Charter"

122 President Mba and Flag

1968. Stamp Day.
335 **121** 30 f. violet, green & orge 1·10 55

1968. Air. 1st Death Anniv of Pres. Mba.
336 **122** 1,000 f. multicoloured 18·00 18·00

1968. Human Rights Year.
337 **123** 20 f. black, green & red 45 30

124 President Bongo, Maps of Gabon and Owendo Port

1968. Air. "Laying of 1st Stone". Owendo Port. Multicoloured.
338 25 f. Type **124** 60 25
339 30 f. Harbour Project 75 20

1969. Air. "Philexafrique" Stamp Exn., Abidjan, Ivory Coast (1st issue). As T **113a** of Mauritania.
340 100 f. multicoloured 2·75 2·75
DESIGN: 100 f. "The Cloisters of Ste. Marie des Anges" (F. M. Granet).
See also No. 346.

126 Mahatma Gandhi **128** View of Okanda Gates

1969. Air. "Apostles of Peace".
341 **126** 25 f. black and pink 45 15
342 – 30 f. black and green 55 30
343 – 50 f. black and blue 85 35
344 – 100 f. black and mauve 1·50 60
DESIGNS: 30 f. J. F. Kennedy; 50 f. R. F. Kennedy; 100 f. Martin Luther King.

1969. Air. "Philexafrique" Stamp Exn., Abidjan, Ivory Coast (2nd issue). As T **114a** of Mauritania.
346 50 f. blue, red and green 1·50 1·50
DESIGN: 50 f. Oil refinery. Port Gentil and Gabon stamp of 1932.

1969. African Tourist Year.
347 **128** 10 f. brown, grn & blue 20 10
348 – 15 f. blue, green and red 1·25 25
349 – 25 f. pur, blue & brown 40 20
350 – 30 f. brn, choc & blue 85 35
DESIGNS—HORIZ: 15 f. Great barracuda. VERT: 25 f. Kinguele Falls; 30 f. Hunting trophies.

129 "Battle of Rivoli" (Philippoteaux)

1969. Air. Birth Bicent. of Napoleon Bonaparte. Multicoloured.
351 50 f. Type **129** 1·60 1·10
352 100 f. "Oath of the Army" (J. L. David) 1·90 1·60
353 250 f. "The Emperor Napoleon I on the Terrace at St. Cloud" (Ducis) 7·50 4·50

130 Mvet **132** "Aframomum polyanthum"

131 Refugees and Red Cross Plane

1969. Traditional Musical Instruments from Folk Art Museum, Libreville.
354 **130** 25 f. lake, drab & purple 40 15
355 – 30 f. brown, drab & red 45 20
356 – 50 f. lake, drab & purple 85 35
357 – 100 f. brn, drab & red 1·60 65
DESIGNS: 30 f. Ngombi harp; 50 f. Ebele and Mbe drums; 100 f. Medzang xylophone.

1969. Air. Red Cross. Aid for Biafra. Multicoloured.
359 15 f. Type **131** 40 20
360 20 f. Hospital and supplies van 45 25
361 25 f. Doctor and nurse tending children 50 25
362 30 f. Children and hospital 60 30

1969. Flowers. Multicoloured.
364 1 f. Type **132** 10 10
365 2 f. "Chlamydocola chlamydantha" 15 10
366 5 f. "Costus dinklagei" 20 10
367 10 f. "Cola rostrata" 45 20
368 20 f. "Dischistocalyx grandifolius" 70 45

133 Astronauts and Module on Moon

1969. Air. 1st Man on the Moon. Embossed on gold foil.
369 **133** 1000 f. gold 18·00 18·00

134 Tree and Insignia **135** Oil Derrick

1969. "National Renovation".
370 **134** 25 f. multicoloured 40 30

1969. 20th Anniv of Elf/Spafe Petroleum Consortium.
371 25 f. Type **135** 35 10
372 50 f. Oil rig 90 30

136 African Workers **137** Arms of Lambarene

1969. 50th Anniv of I.L.O.
373 **136** 30 f. green, blue and red 55 30

1969. Town Arms (1st series).
374 **137** 20 f. multicoloured 50 15
375 – 25 f. gold, black & blue 80 15
376 – 30 f. multicoloured 90 45
ARMS: 25 f. Port-Gentil; 30 f. Libreville.
See also Nos. 405/7, 460/2, 504/6, 510/12, 539/41, 596/8, 618/20, 669/71, 684/6, 729/31, 800/2, 898/900, 953/4, 1083 and 1128.

138 Adoumas Mail Pirogue

1969. Stamp Day.
377 **138** 30 f. brown, emer & grn 80 35

139 Satellite and Globe

1970. World Telecommunications Day.
378 **139** 25 f. blue, black & lake 55 35

1970. New U.P.U. Headquarters Building Berne. As T **81** of New Caledonia.
379 30 f. green, purple & brown 50 30

140 Japanese Geisha and African

1970. "EXPO 70" World Fair, Osaka, Japan.
380 **140** 30 f. multicoloured 50 30

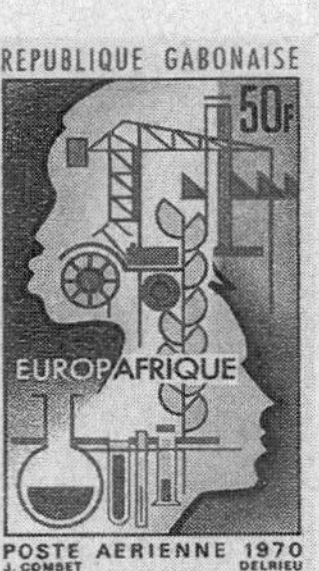

141 "Co-operation" **142** Icarus and the Sun

1970. Air. "Europafrique".
381 **141** 50 f. multicoloured 85 35

1970. Air. History of Flight.
382 **142** 25 f. blue, yellow & red 55 35
383 – 100 f. green, brown & pur 1·40 70
384 – 200 f. blue, red & slate 3·00 1·40
DESIGNS: 100 f. Leonardo da Vinci's design for wings; 200 f. Jules Verne's rocket approaching Moon.

143 U.A.M.P.T. Emblem

1970. Air. U.A.M.P.T. Conf., Libreville.
386 **143** 200 f. gold, green & blue 2·75 1·25

144 Throwing-knives

1970. Air. Gabonaise Weapons, Folk Art Museum, Libreville. All values blue, red and green.
387 25 f. Type **144** 45 30
388 30 f. Assegai and crossbow 55 35
389 50 f. War knives 80 40
390 90 f. Dagger and sheath 1·60 55
Nos. 388/9 are vert.

145 Japanese Masks, Gateway and Mt. Fuji

1970. Air. "Expo. 70" World Fair, Osaka, Japan. Embossed on gold foil.

392 **145** 1000 f. red, black, green and gold . . . . 17·00 17·00

146 President Bongo

1970. Air. 10th Anniv of Independence.

393 **146** 200 f. multicoloured . . . . 3·25 1·60

147 Aircraft, Map and Airport

1970. 10th Anniv (1969) of Aerial Navigation Security Agency for Africa and Madagascar.

394 **147** 100 f. green and blue . . . 1·40 65

148 "Portrait of Young Man" (School of Raphael)

1970. Air. 450th Death Anniv of Raphael. Multicoloured.

395 50 f. Type **148** 90 40
396 100 f. "Jeanne d'Aragon" (Raphael) . . . . 1·60 70
397 200 f. "The Virgin of the Blue Diadem" (Raphael) . . . . 3·25 1·60

149 U.N. Emblem, Globe, Dove and Wheat

1970. 25th Anniv of United Nations.

398 **149** 30 f. multicoloured 55 35

150 Bushbucks

1970. Wild Fauna. Multicoloured.

399 5 f. Type **150** 35 25
400 15 f. Pel's flying squirrel 55 30
401 25 f. White-cheeked mangabey (vert) . . . . 1·40 55
402 40 f. African golden cat . . . . 2·25 1·10
403 60 f. Servaline genet . . . . . 3·25 1·40

151 Presidents Bongo and Pompidou

1971. Air. Visit of Pres. Pompidou of France to Gabon.

404 **151** 50 f. multicoloured . . . . 1·60 85

1971. Town Arms (2nd series). Vert. designs as T **137**. Multicoloured.

405 20 f. multicoloured 40 15
406 25 f. black, green & gold . . . 40 15
407 30 f. multicoloured 55 20

ARMS: 20 f. Mouila; 25 f. Bitam; 30 f. Oyem.

152 Four Races and Emblem

154 Freesias

153 Telecommunications Map

1971. Racial Equality Year.

408 **152** 40 f. black, orange & yell . 55 30

1971. Pan-African Telecommunications Network.

409 **153** 30 f. multicoloured 50 30

1971. Air. "Flowers by Air". Mult.

410 15 f. Type **154** 35 20
411 25 f. Carnations 50 20
412 40 f. Roses 85 35
413 55 f. Daffodils 95 35
414 75 f. Orchids . . . . 1·90 60
415 120 f. Tulips . . . . 2·25 80

155 Napoleon's Death Mask

1971. Air. 150th Death Anniv of Napoleon. Multicoloured.

417 100 f. Type **155** . . . . . . 2·25 60
418 200 f. "Longwood House" (after Marchand) (horiz) . . . . . 3·25 1·40
419 500 f. Napoleon's Tomb . . . . 8·25 4·00

156 "Charaxes smaragdalis"

157 Hertzian Communications Centre, Nkol Ogoum

1971. Butterflies. Multicoloured.

420 5 f. Type **156** 40 30
421 10 f. "Euxanthe crossleyi" . . . 90 40
422 15 f. "Epiphora rectifascia" . . 1·60 45
423 25 f. "Imbrasia bouvieri" . . . 2·00 70

1971. World Telecommunications Day.

424 **157** 40 f. red, blue & green . . 60 35

159 Red Crosses

1971. Air. Red Cross.

426 **159** 50 f. multicoloured 95 40

160 Uranium

1971. Air. Minerals Multicoloured.

427 85 f. Type **160** . . . . 3·25 1·90
428 90 f. Manganese . . . . 4·00 2·25

161 Landing Module above Moon's Surface

1971. Air. Moon Flight of "Apollo 15". Embossed on gold foil.

429 **161** 1500 f. multicoloured . . . 19·00 19·00

162 Mother feeding Child

163 U.N. Emblem and New York Headquarters

1971. 15th Anniv of Social Welfare Fund.

430 **162** 30 f. brn, bis & mve . . . 50 30

1971. 10th Anniv of Gabon's Admission to United Nations.

431 **163** 30 f. multicoloured 45 30

164 Great Egret

1971. Birds. Multicoloured.

432 30 f. Type **164** . . . . 2·00 1·00
433 40 f. Grey parrot . . . . 2·75 1·25
434 50 f. Woodland kingfisher . . . 3·00 1·50
435 75 f. Grey-necked bald crow . . 4·25 1·75
436 100 f. Knysna turaco . . . . . 5·75 2·25

1971. Air. 10th Anniv of African and Malagasy Posts and Telecommunications Union. As T **139a** of Mauritania. Multicoloured.

439 100 f. U.A.M.P.T. building & Bakota copper mask . . . . 1·40 65

167 Ski-jumping

1972. Air. Winter Olympic Games, Sapporo, Japan.

440 **167** 40 f. violet, brown & grn . 65 35
441 – 130 f. green, violet & brn . 1·90 80

DESIGN: 130 f. Speed-skating.

168 "Santa Maria della Salute" (Vanvitelli)

1972. Air. U.N.E.S.C.O. "Save Venice" Campaign. Multicoloured.

443 60 f. "The Basin and Grand Canal" (Vanvitelli) (horiz) . . 1·10 55
444 70 f. "Rialto Bridge" (Canaletto) . . . . 1·60 85
445 140 f. Type **168** . . . . . . 2·75 1·10

On the stamp the design of No. 445 wrongly attributed to Caffi.

170 Hotel Intercontinental

1972. Air. Opening of Hotel Intercontinental.

447 **170** 40 f. brn, grn & blue . . . 60 30

1972. Air. Visit of the Grand Master, Sovereign Order of Malta. No. 289 surch **VISITE OFFICIELLE GRAND MAITRE ORDRE SOUVERAIN DE MALTE 3 MARS 1972 50F** and emblem.

448 50 f. on 300 f. bl, pur & brn . . 80 40

172 "Asystasia vogeliana"

1972. Flowers. Varieties of Acanthus. Multicoloured.

449 5 f. Type **172** 20 20
450 10 f. "Stenandriopsis guineensis" 35 25
451 20 f. "Thomandersia hensii" . . 55 35
452 30 f. "Thomandersia laurifolia" . 85 50
453 40 f. "Physacanthus batanganus" . . . . 1·40 65
454 65 f. "Physacanthus nematosiphon" . . . . 2·25 85

173 "The Discus-thrower" (Alcamene)

174 Pasteur with Microscope

1972. Air. Olympic Games, Munich. Ancient Sculptures.

455 **173** 30 f. grey and red 60 50
456 – 100 f. grey and red . . . . 1·40 70
457 – 140 f. grey and red . . . . 1·90 1·00

DESIGNS: 100 f. "Doryphoros" (Polyclete); 140 f. "Gladiator" (Agasias).

1972. 150th Anniv of Louis Pasteur (scientist).

459 **174** 80 f. purple, green & red . 65 35

1972. Town Arms (3rd series). Vert designs as T **137**. Multicoloured.

460 30 f. multicoloured 40 20
461 40 f. multicoloured 55 20
462 60 f. silver, black & green . . . 90 30

ARMS: 30 f. Franceville; 40 f. Makokou; 60 f. Tchibanga.

175 Global Emblem

1972. World Telecommunications Day.

463 **175** 40 f. black, orge & yell . . 55 30

176 Nat King Cole

1972. Famous Negro Musicians. Mult.

464 40 f. Type **176** 60 30

465 60 f. Sidney Bechet 90 45

466 100 f. Louis Armstrong . . . . 1·60 65

177 "Boiga blandingi"

1972. Reptiles. Multicoloured.

467 1 f. Type **177** 10 10

468 2 f. Sand snake 15 10

469 3 f. Egg-eating snake 20 15

470 15 f. Pit viper 70 25

471 25 f. Jameson's tree asp . . . . 1·40 30

472 50 f. Gabon viper . . . . 2·25 50

178 "The Adoration of the Magi" (Bruegel the Elder)

1972. Air. Christmas. Multicoloured.

473 30 f. Type **178** 60 35

474 40 f. "Madonna and Child" (Basaiti) (vert) . . . 85 45

1972. Air. Olympic Gold Medal Winners. Nos. 455/7 surch as listed below.

475 **125** 40 f. on 30 f. grey & red . . 70 40

476 – 120 f. on 100 f. grey & red . 1·40 65

477 – 170 f. on 140 f. grey & red . 2·10 90

SURCHARGES: No. 475, **MORELON**. No. 476, **KEINO**. No. 477, **SPITZ**.

180 Dr. G. A. Hansen and Hospital, Lambarene

182 "Charaxes candiope"

181 "Thematic Collecting"

1973. Centenary of Dr Hansen's Discovery of Leprosy Bacillus.

478 **180** 30 f. brown, green & blue . 65 35

1973. Air. "PHILEXGABON 73" Int. Stamp Exhibition, Libreville.

479 **181** 100 f. multicoloured . . . 2·40 85

1973. Butterflies. Multicoloured.

481 10 f. Type **182** 40 15

482 15 f. "Eunica pechueli" 50 15

483 20 f. "Cyrestis camillus" 80 30

484 30 f. "Charaxes castor" . . . . 1·10 40

485 40 f. "Charaxes ameliae" . . . 1·25 55

486 50 f. "Pseudacrea boisduvali" . 1·40 80

183 Douglas DC-10–30 over Libreville Airport

1973. Air. Libreville-Paris Air Service by "Air Afrique" "DC 10 Libreville". No gum.

487 **183** 40 f. multicoloured . . . . 1·10 55

184 Montgolfier's Balloon, 1783

186 Interpol Emblem

185 Power Station

1973. History of Flight.

488 **184** 1 f. green, myrtle & brn . 10 10

489 – 2 f. green and blue . . . 10 10

490 – 3 f. new blue, bl & orge . 10 10

491 – 4 f. vio & reddish vio . . 25 15

492 – 5 f green and orange . . 30 20

493 – 10 f. purple and blue . . 45 20

493a – 10 f. blue 45 45

DESIGNS—HORIZ: 2 f. Santos-Dumont's airship "Ballon No. 6", 1901; 3 f. Chanute's glider, 1896; 4 f. Clement Ader's "Avion III" flying-machine, 1897; 5 f. Bleriot's cross-Channel flight, 1909; 10 f. (both) Fabre's seaplane "Hydravion", 1910.

1973. Air. Kinguele Hydro-electric Project.

494 **185** 30 f. green and brown . . 50 25

495 – 40 f. blue, green & brown . 60 25

DESIGN: 40 f. Dam.

1973. 50th Anniv Int. Criminal Police Organization (Interpol).

496 **186** 40 f. blue and red 55 35

187 Dish Aerial and Station

188 Gabon Woman

1973. Inauguration of "2 Decembre" Satellite Earth Station.

497 **187** 40 f. brown, blue & grn . . 55 30

1973. Air. M'Bigou Stone Sculptures.

498 **188** 100 f. brown, blue & blk . 1·50 80

499 – 200 f. green and brown . . 2·75 1·40

DESIGN: 200 f. Gabon man wearing head-dress.

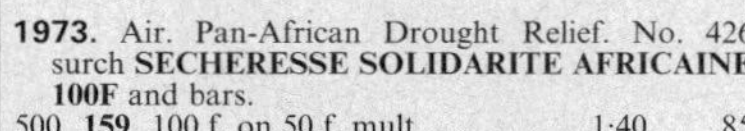

1973. Air. Pan-African Drought Relief. No. 426 surch **SECHERESSE SOLIDARITE AFRICAINE 100F** and bars.

500 **159** 100 f. on 50 f. mult . . . . 1·40 85

190 Party Headquarters

1973. Gabonaise Democratic Party Headquarters, Libreville.

501 **190** 30 f. multicoloured 40 20

191 Astronauts and Lunar Rover

1973. Air. Moon Flight of "Apollo 17".

502 **191** 500 f. multicoloured . . . 6·75 3·25

1973. 12th Anniv of African and Malagasy Posts and Telecommunications Union. As T **155a** of Mauritania.

503 100 f. plum, purple & blue . . . 90 55

1973. Town Arms (4th series). Vert designs as T **137** dated "1973". Multicoloured.

504 30 f. Kango 55 20

505 40 f. Booue 65 30

506 60 f. Koula-Moutou . . . . . 1·00 35

193 St. Theresa of Lisieux

194 Flame Emblem

1973. Birth Cent. of St. Theresa of Lisieux. Stained-glass windows in the Basilica at Lisieux. Multicoloured.

507 30 f. Type **193** 55 25

508 40 f. "St. Theresa with Saviour" 65 30

1973. 25th Anniv of Declaration of Human Rights.

509 **194** 20 f. red, blue & green . . 40 20

1974. Town Arms (5th series). Vert designs as T **137** dated "1974". Multicoloured.

510 5 f. Gamba 15 10

511 10 f. Ogooue-Lolo 15 10

512 15 f. Fougamou 20 15

195 White-collared Mangabey

1974. Monkeys. Multicoloured.

513 40 f. Type **195** 55 30

514 60 f. Moustached Monkey . . . 85 35

515 80 f. Mona Monkey . . . . . 1·40 50

196 De Gaulle and Houphouet-Boigny

1974. Air. 30th Anniv of Brazzaville Conference.

516 **196** 40 f. blue and purple . . . 1·00 55

197 "Pleasure Boats" (Monet)

1974. Air. Impressionist Paintings. Multicoloured.

517 40 f. Type **197** 90 45

518 50 f. "End of an Arabesque" (Degas) (vert) . . . . . . 1·40 65

519 130 f. "Young Girl with Flowers" (Renoir) (vert) . . . 2·25 1·10

198 American Bald Eagle, and Astronaut on Moon

1974. Air. 5th Anniv of First Manned Moon Landing.

520 **198** 200 f. blue, brn & ind . . . 2·75 1·25

199 Ogooue River, Lambarene

1974. Gabon Views. Multicoloured.

521 30 f. Type **199** 35 25

522 50 f. Cape Esterias 50 30

523 75 f. Rope bridge, Poubara . . 85 45

200 U.P.U. Emblem and Letters

1974. Air. Cent. of U.P.U.

524 **200** 150 f. turquoise & blue . . 1·90 80

525 – 300 f. red and orange . . . 3·25 1·60

DESIGN: 300 f. Similar to Type **200**, but with design reversed.

201 "Apollo" and "Soyuz" Spacecraft, Flight Badge and Maps of U.S.A. and U.S.S.R.

1974. Air. Soviet-American Co-operation in Space.

526 **201** 1000 f. green, red & blue . 7·75 5·50

202 Ball and Footballers

1974. Air. World Cup Football Championships, Munich.

527 **202** 40 f. red, green & brown . 50 30

528 – 65 f. green, brown & red . 65 40

529 – 100 f. brown, red & grn . . 1·10 65

DESIGNS: 65 f., 100 f. Football scenes similar to Type **202**.

203 Manioc Plantation

1974. Agriculture. Multicoloured.

531 40 f. Type **203** 50 20

532 50 f. Palm-tree grove 60 20

204 African Leaders, U.D.E.A.C. Headquarters and Flags

1974. 10th Anniv of Central African Customs and Economic Union. Multicoloured.

533 40 f. Type **204** (postage) 50 30
534 100 f. African leaders, U.D.E.A.C. Headquarters Building (air) 85 45

205 "The Visitation"

1974. Air. Christmas. Details from 15th century tapestry of Notre Dame, Beaune. Multicoloured.

535 40 f. Type **205** 80 35
536 50 f. "The Annunciation" (horiz) 90 45

206 Dr. Schweitzer and Lambarene Hospital

1978. Air. Birth Centenary of Dr. Albert Schweitzer.

537 **206** 500 f. green, lilac & brn . . 5·50 3·25

207 Dialogue Hotel

1975. Inauguration of "Hotel du Dialogue", Libreville.

538 **207** 50 f. multicoloured 55 30

1975. Town Arms (6th series). Vert designs as T **137** dated "1975". Multicoloured.

539 5 f. Ogooue-Ivindo 10 10
540 10 f. Moabi 15 10
541 15 f. Moanda 25 10

208 "The Crucifixion" (Bellini)

1975. Air. Easter. Multicoloured.

542 140 f. Type **208** . . . . 1·40 55
543 150 f. "The Resurrection" (Burgundian School) (36 × 49 mm) . . . . 1·90 80

209 Marc Seguin Locomotive, 1829, France (illustration reduced. Actual size 100 × 27 mm)

1975. Air. Scale Drawings of Steam Locomotives.

544 **209** 20 f. blue, brn & brt bl . . 1·10 40
545 – 25 f. red, yellow & blue . . 1·50 50
546 – 40 f. blue, purple & grn . . 1·90 80
547 – 50 f. purple, blue & grn . . 2·75 1·10

Locomotives: 25 f. "Iron Duke", 1847, Great Britain; 40 f. "Thomas Rogers", 1855, U.S.A. (inscr "1895"); 50 f. Class AA steam locomotive, 1934, Russia.

210 Congress Emblem

1975. 17th Lions Club Congress, Libreville.

548 **210** 50 f. multicoloured 70 30

211 Aerial and Network Map

1975. Gabonese Development of Hertzian Wave Radio Links.

549 **211** 40 f. green, brn & blue . . 55 35

212 Man and Woman and I.W.Y. Emblem

1975. International Women's Year.

550 **212** 50 f. brown, red and blue . 1·75 35

213 Ange M'ba (founder of Gabonaise Scouts)

1975. "Nordjamb 75" World Scout Jamboree, Norway.

551 **213** 40 f. black, purple & grn . 45 30
552 – 50 f. purple, green & red . 55 30

DESIGN: 50 f. Scout camp.

214 Pink Snapper

1975. Fishes. Multicoloured.

553 30 f. Type **214** 70 25
554 40 f. Guinean threadfin 85 40
555 50 f. Round sardinella . . . . 1·50 40
556 120 f. West African parrot-fish . 2·50 85

215 Swimming Pool

1975. Air. Olympic Games, Montreal (1976). (1st issue). Multicoloured.

557 100 f. Type **215** . . . . . . 1·00 45
558 150 f. Boxing ring . . . . . . 1·40 65
559 300 f. Aerial view of Games complex . . . . 2·75 1·40

See also Nos. 591/3.

1975. Air. "Apollo-Soyuz" Space Link. Optd **JONCTION 17 Juillet 1975.**

561 **201** 1000 f. grn, red & blue . . 7·25 4·00

217 "The Annunciation" (M. Denis)

1975. Air. Christmas. Multicoloured.

562 40 f. Type **217** 60 30
563 50 f. "Virgin and Child with Two Saints" (Fra Filippo Lippi) . 80 40

218 Franceville Complex

1975. Inauguration of Agro-Industrial Complex, Franceville.

564 **218** 60 f. multicoloured 65 35

219 Concorde

1975. Air.

565 **219** 500 f. ultram, bl & red . . 7·75 4·50

1975. Air. Concorde's First Commercial Flight. Surch **1000F 21 Janv. 1976 1er Vol Commercial de CONCORDE**.

566 **219** 1000 f. on 500 f. ultram, blue and red . . . . . 14·00 9·00

221 Tchibanga Bridge

1975. Gabon Bridges. Multicoloured.

567 5 f. Type **221** 15 10
568 10 f. Mouila Bridge 20 15
569 40 f. Kango Bridges 45 20
570 50 f. Lambarene Bridges (vert) . 60 30

222 A. G. Bell and Early and Modern Telephones

1976. Telephone Centenary.

571 **222** 60 f. grey, green & blue . . 60 30

223 Skiing (slalom)

1976. Air. Winter Olympic Games, Innsbruck.

572 **223** 100 f. brown, blue & blk . 95 45
573 – 250 f. brown, blue & blk . 2·10 1·25

DESIGN: 250 f. Speed skating.

224 "The Crucifixion between Thieves" (wood-carving)

1976. Air. Easter. Multicoloured.

575 120 f. Type **224** . . . . 1·10 60
576 130 f. "Thomas placing finger in Jesus' wounds" (wood-carving) . . . . 1·40 80

225 Monseigneur Jean-Remy Bessieux

1976. Death Centenary of Bessieux.

577 **225** 50 f. brn, blue & grn . . . 50 30

226 Boston Tea Party

1976. Air. Bicent. of American Revolution.

578 **226** 100 f. brn, orge & blue . . 90 50
579 – 150 f. brn, orge & blue . . 1·40 65
580 – 200 f. brn, orge & blue . . 2·00 1·00

DESIGNS: 150 f. Battle scenes at Hudson Bay and New York; 200 f. Wrecking of King George III's statue in New York.

227 Games Emblem

1976. 1st Central African Games.

581 **227** 50 f. multicoloured 45 20
582 60 f. multicoloured 55 30

1976. Air. U.S. Independence Day. Nos. 578/80 optd **4 JUILLET 1976**.

583 **226** 100 f. brn, orge & blue . . 95 55
584 – 150 f. brn, orge & blue . . 1·40 65
585 – 200 f. brn, orge & blue . . 2·00 1·00

229 Motobecane 125–LT3 (France)

1976. Motorcycles.

586 **229** 3 f. black, green & blue . . 15 10
587 – 5 f. black, mve & yell . . 15 15
588 – 10 f. black, grn & blue . . 35 15
589 – 20 f. black, grn & red . . 65 15
590 – 100 f. black, blue & red . . 2·00 70

MOTORCYCLES: 5 f. Bultaco 125 (Spain); 10 f. Suzuki 125 (Japan); 20 f. Kawasaki H2R (Japan); 100 f. Harley-Davidson 750-TX (USA).

230 Running

1976. Air. Olympic Games, Montreal. (2nd issue). Multicoloured.

No.	Type	Description	Unused	Used
591	**230**	100 f. brn, blue & violet	85	45
592	–	200 f. multicoloured	1·60	90
593	–	260 f. brn, grn & myrtle	2·25	1·10

DESIGNS: 200 f. Football; 260 f. High Jumping.

231 Presidents Giscard d'Estaing and Bongo

1976. Air. Visit of Pres. Giscard d'Estaing to Gabon.

No.	Type	Description	Unused	Used
595	**231**	60 f. multicoloured	90	40

1976. Town Arms (7th series). Vert designs as T **137** dated "1976".

No.	Type	Description	Unused	Used
596		15 f. multicoloured	15	10
597		25 f. multicoloured	20	10
598		50 f. black, gold and red	50	15

ARMS: 15 f. Nyanga; 25 f. Mandji; 50 f. Mekambo.

232 Ricefield and Plant

1976. Agriculture. Multicoloured.

No.	Type	Description	Unused	Used
599		50 f. Type **232**	55	20
600		60 f. Pepper grove and plant	65	30

233 "Presentation at the Temple"

1976. Air. Christmas. Wood-carvings. Mult.

No.	Type	Description	Unused	Used
601		50 f. Type **233**	60	30
602		60 f. "The Nativity"	70	35

234 Photograph of Site

1976. Air. Discovery of Oklo Fossil Reactor.

No.	Type	Description	Unused	Used
603	**234**	60 f. multicoloured	65	35

235 "The Last Supper" (Juste de Gand)

1977. Air. Easter. Multicoloured.

No.	Type	Description	Unused	Used
604		50 f. Type **235**	80	45
605		100 f. "The Deposition" (N. Poussin)	1·40	65

1977. Agriculture. As T **232** but dated "1977". Multicoloured.

No.	Type	Description	Unused	Used
606		50 f. Banana plantation	55	20
607		60 f. Groundnuts and market	65	30

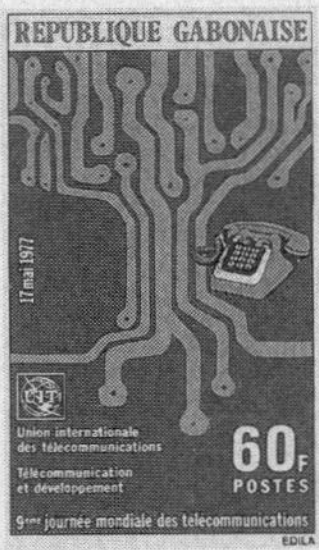

236 Printed Circuit and Telephone

1977. 9th World Telecommunications Day.

No.	Type	Description	Unused	Used
608	**236**	60 f. multicoloured	55	30

237 "Air Gabon" Insignia and Boeing 747

1977. Air. First "Air Gabon" Intercontinental Air Service.

No.	Type	Description	Unused	Used
609	**237**	60 f. blue, yellow & green	70	40

238 Cap Lopez

1977. Gabon Views and Features. Mult.

No.	Type	Description	Unused	Used
610		50 f. Type **238**	45	20
611		60 f. Oyem	45	20
612		70 f. Lebamba grotto	60	25

239 Beethoven and Musical Score

1977. Air. 150th Death Anniv of Beethoven.

No.	Type	Description	Unused	Used
613	**239**	260 f. blue	2·25	1·40

240 Palais des Congres

1977. Organization of African Unity Conference.

No.	Type	Description	Unused	Used
614	**240**	100 f. multicoloured	85	55

241 Gabon Coat of Arms

1977.

No.	Type	Description	Unused	Used
615	**241**	50 f. blue (22 × 36 mm)	65	30
616		60 f. orange	60	30
617		80 f. red	70	35

1977. Town Arms (8th series). As T **137** but dated "1977". Multicoloured.

No.	Type	Description	Unused	Used
618		50 f. Omboue	45	20
619		60 f. Minvoul	50	20
620		90 f. Mayumba	85	35

INDEX

Countries can be quickly located by referring to the index at the end of this volume.

242 Parliament Building, Libreville

1977. National Festival.

No.	Type	Description	Unused	Used
621	**242**	50 f. multicoloured	50	20

243 Renault "Voiturette" of 1902

1977. Birth Centenary of Louis Renault (motor pioneer).

No.	Type	Description	Unused	Used
622	**243**	5 f. blue, red and brown	20	15
623	–	10 f. brown and red	20	15
624	–	30 f. red, green & drab	65	30
625	–	40 f. green, yellow & brn	1·10	35
626	–	100 f. blk, turq & blue	2·25	1·00

DESIGNS: 10 f. Coupe of 1921; 30 f. "Torpedo Scaphandrier" of 1925; 40 f. "Reinastella" of 1929; 100 f. "Nerva Grand Sport" of 1937.

244 Lindbergh and "Spirit of St. Louis"

1977. Air. 50th Anniv of Lindbergh's Transatlantic Flight.

No.	Type	Description	Unused	Used
628	**244**	500 f. bl, brn & lt bl	5·50	3·25

245 Footballer

1977. Air. World Cup Football Championship Qualifying Rounds.

No.	Type	Description	Unused	Used
629	**245**	250 f. multicoloured	2·25	1·25

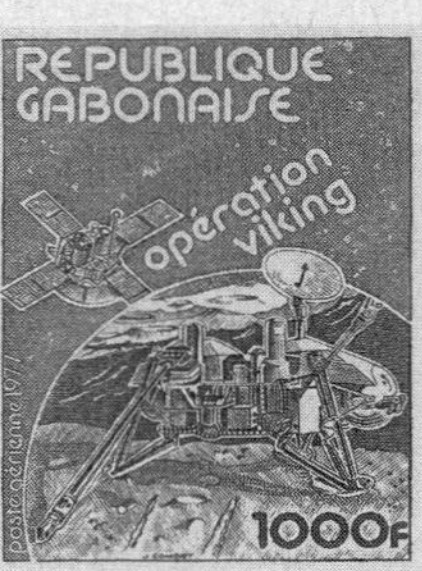

246 "Viking" on Mars

1977. Air. "Operation Viking".

No.	Type	Description	Unused	Used
630	**246**	1000 f. multicoloured	8·25	8·25

1977. Air. First Commercial Paris-New York Flight by "Concorde". Optd **PARIS NEW YORK PREMIER VOL 22.11.77.**

No.	Type	Description	Unused	Used
631	**219**	500 f. ultram., bl & red	7·25	5·00

248 "Study of a Head"

1977. Air. 400th Birth Anniv of Peter Paul Rubens. Multicoloured.

No.	Type	Description	Unused	Used
632		60 f. "Lion Hunt" (horiz)	65	25
633		80 f. "Hippopotamus Hunt" (horiz)	85	40
634		200 f. Type **248**	2·25	1·00

249 "Adoration of the Magi" (Rubens)

1977. Air. Christmas. Multicoloured.

No.	Type	Description	Unused	Used
636		60 f. Type **249**	65	35
637		80 f. "The Flight into Egypt" (Rubens)	90	45

250 "Still Life and Maori Statue"

1978. Air. 75th Death Anniv of Paul Gauguin. Multicoloured.

No.	Type	Description	Unused	Used
638		150 f. Type **250**	1·90	65
639		300 f. "Self-Portrait"	3·25	1·40

251 Globe

1978. World Leprosy Day.

No.	Type	Description	Unused	Used
640	**251**	80 f. green, blue & red	55	30

252 Boeing 747 Airplane, Diesel Locomotive and President

1978. 10th Anniv of National Renewal.

No.	Type	Description	Unused	Used
641	**252**	500 f. multicoloured	10·00	5·25

253 Citroen "Cabriolet", 1922

1978. Birth Centenary of Andre Citroen (motor pioneer).

No.	Type	Description	Unused	Used
642	**253**	10 f. pur, grn and red	30	15
643	–	50 f. green, blue & turq	65	20
644	–	60 f. grey, brn & blue	1·00	40
645	–	80 f. blue, slate & lilac	1·10	45
646	–	200 f. brn, slate & orge	2·75	1·00

DESIGNS: 50 f. "B 14" Taxi, 1927; 60 f. 8 h.p. "Berline", 1932; 80 f. 7 h.p. "Berline" saloon, 1934; 200 f. 2 h.p. "Berline", 1948.

254 Ndjole and L'Ogooue

1978. Views of Gabon. Multicoloured.
648 30 f. Type **254** 20 15
649 40 f. Lambarene, Lake District . . 35 15
650 50 f. Owendo Port 60 15

255 "Sternotomis mirabilis"

1978. Beetles. Multicoloured.
651 20 f. Type **255** 20 15
652 60 f. "Analeptes trifasciata" . . 65 40
653 75 f. "Homoderus mellyi" . . . 85 45
654 80 f. "Stephanorrhina guttata" . 1·00 55

257 Players heading Ball

1978. Air. World Cup Football Championship, Argentina.
660 **257** 100 f. brown, red & grn . . 70 35
661 – 120 f. brown, red & grn . . 85 45
662 – 200 f. brown and red . . . 1·50 70
DESIGNS: 120 f. Players tackling. VERT: 200 f. F.I.F.A. World Cup.

258 Anti-Apartheid Emblem

1978. International Anti-Apartheid Year.
664 **258** 80 f. orange, brn & blue . . 55 35

1978. Air. Argentina's Victory in World Cup Football Championship. Nos. 660/2 optd.
665 **257** 100 f. brown, red & grn . . 70 40
666 – 120 f. brown, red & grn . . 90 50
667 – 200 f. brown and red . . . 1·40 80
OVERPRINTS: 100 f. **ARGENTINE HOLLANDE 3 - 1**. 120 f. **BRESIL ITALIE 2 - 1**. 200 f. **CHAMPION DU MONDE 1978 ARGENTINE**.

1978. Town Arms (9th series). As T **137**, but dated "1978".
669 5 f. multicoloured 15 10
670 40 f. multicoloured 30 15
671 60 f. gold, black and blue . . . 45 15
DESIGNS: 5 f. Oyem; 40 f. Okandja; 60 f. Mimongo.

260 "Self-portrait at 13 years"

1978. Air. 450th Death Anniv of Albrecht Durer (artist).
672 **260** 100 f. grey and red 85 40
673 – 250 f. red and grey . . . . 2·50 1·00
DESIGN: 250 f. "Lucas de Leyde".

261 Parthenon

1978. U.N.E.S.C.O. Campaign for the Preservation of the Acropolis.
674 **261** 80 f. brn, orge & bl 55 35

1978. Air. "Philexafrique" Exhibitions Libreville, Gabon and Int Stamp Fair Essen, W. Germany. As T **262** of Niger. Multicoloured.
675 100 f. White Stork and Saxony 1850 3 f. stamp . . . . . . 1·60 1·40
676 100 f. Gorilla and Gabon 1971 40 f. Grey Parrot stamp . . . 1·60 1·40

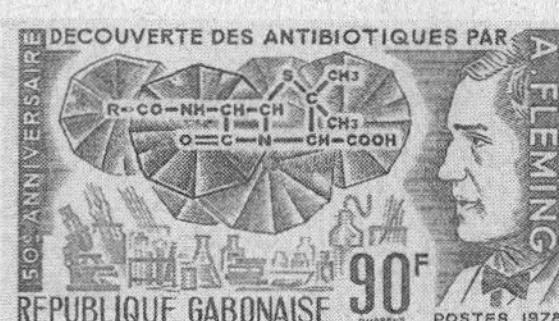

263 Sir Alexander Fleming, Chemical Formula and Laboratory Equipment

1978. 50th Anniv of Fleming's Discovery of Antibiotics.
677 **263** 90 f. brown, orange & grn . 80 40

264 "The Visitation"

1978. Christmas. Sculptures from the Church of St. Michel de Libreville. Multicoloured.
678 60 f. Type **264** 50 20
679 80 f. "Massacre of the Innocents" 60 35

265 Wright Brothers and Flyer 1

1978. Air. 75th Anniv of First Powered Flight.
680 **265** 380 f. brown, blue & red . 3·25 1·40

266 Diesel Train

1978. Inauguration of First Section of Trans-Gabon Railway, Libreville-Njole.
681 **266** 60 f. multicoloured . . . . 1·40 45

267 Pope John Paul II

1979. Air. The Popes of 1978. Multicoloured.
682 100 f. Type **267** . . . . 1·40 65
683 200 f. Popes Paul VI and John Paul I with St. Peter's . . . . 2·50 90

1979. Town Arms (10th series). As T **137**, but dated "1979". Multicoloured.
684 5 f. Ogooue-Maritime 15 10
685 10 f. Lastoursville 15 10
686 15 f. M'Bigou 20 10

268 "The Two Disciples"

1979. Air. Easter. Wood-carvings from St. Michel de Libreville Church. Multicoloured.
687 100 f. Type **268** 75 55
688 150 f. "Jesus appearing to Mary Magdalene" . . . . 1·25 65

269 Long Jumping

1979. Pre-Olympic Year.
689 – 60 f. red, brown & turq . . 45 15
690 **269** 80 f. brown, turq & red . . 55 30
691 – 100 f. turq, red & brn . . . 65 35
DESIGNS—HORIZ: 60 f. Horse Riding; 100 f. Yachting.

270 Sir Rowland Hill, Postal Messenger and Stamp

1979. "Philexafrique 2" Exhibition, Libreville.
693 **270** 50 f. multicoloured 70 55
694 – 80 f. multicoloured . . . . 1·25 85
695 – 150 f. green, blue & brn . . 1·90 1·40
DESIGNS—VERT: 80 f. Bakota mask and tulip flower. HORIZ: 150 f. Canoeist, mail van, U.P.U. emblem and stamps.

272 Child holding Bird

1979. International Year of the Child.
697 **272** 100 f. brown, violet & blue 80 40

273 Captain Cook

1979. Air. Death Bicent of Captain Cook.
698 **273** 500 f. multicoloured . . . 4·50 2·25

274 Louis Bleriot and Channel Flight Route

1979. Air. Aviation History. Multicoloured.
699 250 f. Type **274** (First Channel Flight, 70th anniv) . . . . . 2·25 1·40
700 1000 f. Astronauts and module on Moon and Gabon S.G. 369 (Moon Landing, 10th anniv) . 7·25 4·00

275 "Telecom 79" **276** Carved Head, Map and Rotary Emblem

1979. Third World Telecommunications Exhibition, Geneva.
701 **275** 80 f. bl, orge & dp bl . . . 50 30

1979. Air. 75th Anniv of Rotary International.
702 **276** 80 f. multicoloured 60 35

277 Harvesting Sugar Cane **278** Judo

1979. Agriculture. Multicoloured.
703 25 f. Type **277** 25 10
704 30 f. Igname 35 10

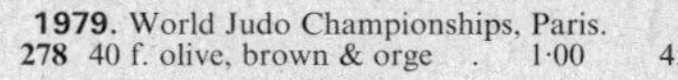

1979. World Judo Championships, Paris.
705 **278** 40 f. olive, brown & orge . 1·00 45

279 Eugene Jamot and Tsetse Fly

1979. Air. Birth Centenary of Eugene Jamot (discovery of sleeping sickness cure).
706 **279** 300 f. black, brn & violet . 2·75 1·40

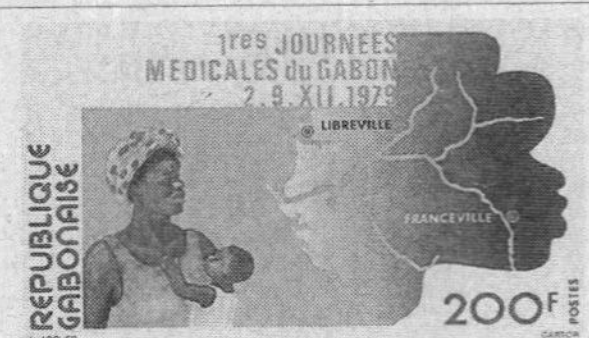

280 Mother with Child and Map of Gabon

1979. First Gabon Medical Days.
707 **280** 200 f. multicoloured . . . . 1·50 65

281 "The Flight into Egypt" **282** Statue of President Bongo

1979. Christmas. Carvings from St. Michael's Church, Libreville. Multicoloured.
708 60 f. Type **281** 50 30
709 80 f. "The Circumcision" 60 30

1979. 44th Anniv of President Bongo.
710 **282** 60 f. multicoloured 55 20
See also No. 714.

283 Bob Sleighing **284** Oil Derrick

1980. Air. Winter Olympic Games, Lake Placid. Multicoloured.
711 100 f. Type **283** 70 40
712 200 f. Ski jumping . . . . . . 1·50 70

1980. Investiture of President. As No. 710 but inscr "INVESTITURE 27 FEVRIER 1980".
714 **282** 80 f. multicoloured . . . . 1·60 1·00

1980. 20th Anniv of O.P.E.C.
715 **284** 50 f. multicoloured 60 30

285 Donguila Church

1980. Easter. Multicoloured.
716 60 f. Type **285** 45 15
717 80 f. Bizangobibere Church . . 55 30

286 Dominique Ingres (artist)

1980. Air. Celebrities' Anniversaries.
718 **286** 100 f. sepia, grn & brn . . . 85 40
719 – 200 f. brown, pur & grey . . 2·25 1·00
720 – 360 f. brn, grn & sepia . . 2·50 1·40
DESIGNS: 100 f. Type **286** (birth cent); 200 f. Jacques Offenbach (composer, death cent); 360 f. Gustave Flaubert (author, death cent).

287 Telephone

1980. Air. World Telecommunications Day.
721 **287** 80 f. multicoloured 60 30

288 Savorgnan de Brazza and Map

1980. Centenary of Franceville.
722 **288** 165 f. multicoloured . . . 1·40 80

289 Dieudonne Costes, Maurice Bellonte and "Point d'Interrogation"

1980. Air. Aviation Anniversaries.
723 **289** 165 f. red, blue & green . . 1·10 55
724 – 1000 f. green, red & blue . 7·25 3·25
DESIGNS: 165 f. Type **289** (50th anniv of first North Atlantic flight); 1000 f. Jean Mermoz and seaplane "Comte de la Vaulx" (50th anniv of first South Atlantic airmail).

290 Running

1980. Air. Olympic Games, Moscow.
725 **290** 50 f. multicoloured 40 15
726 – 100 f. black, red & green . 70 40
727 – 250 f. multicoloured . . . 1·60 85
DESIGNS: 100 f. Pole vaulting; 250 f. Boxing.

1980. District Arms (1st series). Vert. designs as T **137** but dated "1980".
729 10 f. silver, black and gold . . . 15 10
730 20 f. multicoloured 20 15
731 30 f. black, silver and red . . . 20 15
DESIGNS: 10 f. Haut-Ogooue; 20 f. L'Estuaipe; 30 f. Bitam.

291 Leon Mba and El Hadj Omar Bongo

1980. 20th Anniv of Independence.
732 **291** 60 f. multicoloured 60 30

292 Peacock Emblem and Tourist Attractions

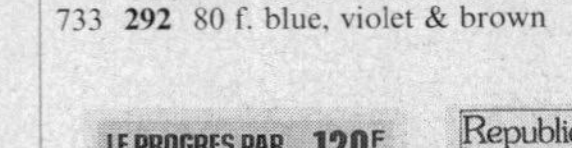

1980. World Tourism Conference, Manila.
733 **292** 80 f. blue, violet & brown . 60 30

293 Figures supporting O.P.E.C. Emblem **295** African River Martin

1980. 20th Anniv of Organization of Petroleum Exporting Countries. Multicoloured.
734 90 f. Globe and O.P.E.C. Emblem (horiz) 85 35
735 120 f. Type **293** . . . . 1·10 50

1980. Air. Olympic Medal Winners. Nos. 725/7 optd.
736 50 f. **YIFTER (Eth.) NYAMBUI (Tanz.) MAANINKA (Finl.) 5000 Metres** 40 20
737 100 f. **KOZIAKIEWICZ (Pol.) (record du monde) VOLKOV (Urss) et SLUSARSKI (Pol.)** . 70 45
738 250 f. **WELTERS ALDAMA (Cuba) MUGABI (Oug.) KRUBER (Rda) et SZCZERDA (Pol.)** . . . . . 1·60 1·00

1980. Birds. Multicoloured.
740 50 f. Type **295** . . . . 1·00 35
741 60 f. White-fronted bee eater . . 1·25 50
742 80 f. African pitta . . . . . . 1·50 70
743 150 f. Pel's fishing owl . . . . . 2·40 1·25

296 Charles de Gaulle

1980. Air. 10th Death Anniv of Charles de Gaulle. Multicoloured.
744 100 f. Type **296** 95 55
745 200 f. Charles and Mme. de Gaulle . . . . 1·90 95

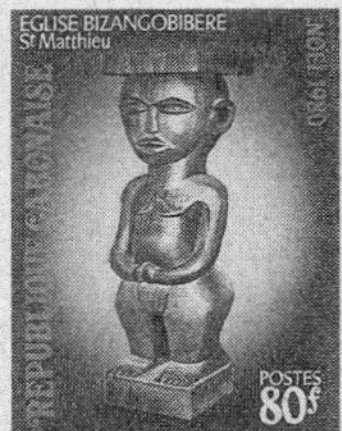

297 St. Matthew

1980. Christmas. Carvings from Bizangobibere Church. Multicoloured.
747 60 f. St. Luke 45 20
748 80 f. Type **297** 65 35

298 Heinrich von Stephan **299** Shooting at Goal

1981. 150th Birth Anniv of Heinrich von Stephan (founder of U.P.U.).
749 **298** 90 f. dp brn, lt brn & brn . 65 35

1981. Air. World Cup Football Championship Eliminators. Multicoloured.
750 60 f. Type **299** 45 30
751 190 f. Players with ball . . . . 1·40 85

300 Palais Renovation

1981. 13th Anniv of National Renewal.
752 **300** 60 f. multicoloured 55 20

301 W. Herschel (Discovery of Uranus Bicent) **302** Lion (St. Mark)

1981. Air. Space Anniversaries. Mult.
753 150 f. Type **301** . . . . 1·10 45
754 250 f. Yuri Gagarin. First man in space (20th anniv) . . . . . 1·60 95
755 500 f. Alan Shepard. First American in space (20th anniv) . . . . 3·25 1·60

1981. Easter. Wood Carvings from Bizangobibere Church. Multicoloured.
757 75 f. Type **302** 55 20
758 100 f. Eagle (St. John) 80 30

303 Port Gentil **304** Caduceus

1981. 23rd Congress of Lions Club District 403 Libreville. Multicoloured.
759 60 f. Type **303** 45 20
760 75 f. District 403 . . . . 55 20
761 80 f. Libreville Cocotiers . . . 55 30
762 100 f. Libreville Hibiscus . . . 80 35
763 165 f. Ekwata . . . . 1·25 55
764 200 f. Haute-Ogooue . . . . . 1·40 65

1981. World Telecommunications Day.
765 **304** 125 f. multicoloured . . . 80 40

305 Map of Africa and Emblems of Gabon Electricity and Water Society and U.P.D.E.A.

1981. Air. 7th Congress of African Electricity Producers and Suppliers.
766 **305** 100 f. multicoloured . . . 70 40

306 Japanese D-51 Locomotive and French Turbotrain TGV 001

1981. Air. Birth Bicent. of George Stephenson.
767 **306** 75 f. grey, orge & brn . . . 1·50 40
768 – 100 f. grn, blk and blue . . 1·75 55
769 – 350 f. grn, brn and red . . 4·25 1·60
DESIGNS: 100 f. Baltimore & Ohio Mallet 7100 and Prussian State Railway T–3 locomotives; 350 f. George Stephenson, his locomotive "Rocket" (1829) and Alsthom diesel locomotive.

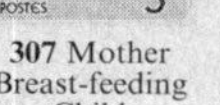

307 Mother Breast-feeding Child **308** R.P. Klaine (70th death anniv)

1981.
772 **307** 5 f. brown and black . . 10 10
773 10 f. mauve and black . . 10 10
774 15 f. green and black . . 10 10
775 20 f. pink and black . . . 10 10
776 25 f. blue and black . . . 15 10
777 40 f. pink and black . . . 25 10
778 50 f. green and black . . 35 10
779 75 f. brown and black . . 45 20
779a 90 f. blue and black . . 55 20
780 100 f. yellow & black . . 60 25
780a 125 f. green and black . . 85 30
780b 150 f. purple & black . . 1·00 25

1981. Religious Personalities. Multicoloured.
781 70 f. Type **308** 50 20
782 90 f. Mgr. Walker (110th birth anniv) 70 30

309 Scout Badge on Map of Gabon **311** "Helping the Disabled"

1981. 4th Pan-African Scout Congress, Abidjan.
783 **309** 75 f. multicoloured 60 30

1981. 28th World Scout Conference, Dakar. Optd **DAKAR 28e CONFERENCE MONDIALE DU SCOUTISME**.
784 **309** 75 f. multicoloured 60 30

1981. International Year of Disabled People.
785 **311** 100 f. red, dp green & grn . 65 35

312 "Hypolimnas salmacis"

1981. Butterflies. Multicoloured.
786 75 f. Type **312** 90 45
787 100 f. "Euphaedra themis" . . . 1·10 45
788 150 f. "Amauris niavius" . . . 1·40 90
789 250 f. "Cymothoe lucasi" . . . 2·50 1·25

313 "Paul as Harlequin" **314** Hand holding Pen

1981. Birth Centenary of Pablo Picasso.
790 **313** 500 f. multicoloured . . . 4·50 1·90

1981. Air. International Letter-writing Week.
791 **314** 200 f. multicoloured . . . 1·40 65

315 Agricultural Scenes, Wheat and F.A.O. Emblem

1981. World Food Day.
792 **315** 350 f. brn, dp brn & bl . . 2·75 1·40

316 Traditional Hairstyle

1981. Traditional Hairstyles.
793 **316** 75 f. red, yellow & blk . . 70 35
794 – 100 f. green, lilac & blk . . 85 40
795 – 125 f. lt grn, grn & blk . . 1·10 60
796 – 200 f. pink, violet & blk . . 1·75 90
DESIGNS: 100 f. to 200 f. Different hairstyles.
See also Nos. 964a and 1046.

317 Dancers around Fire

1981. Christmas. Multicoloured.
798 75 f. Type **317** 55 20
799 100 f. Christmas meal 80 35

1982. District Arms (2nd series). Vert. designs as T **137** but dated "1982". Multicoloured.
800 75 f. Moyen-Ogooue 50 15
801 100 f. Woleu-N'tem 65 15
802 150 f. N'Gounie . . . . 1·00 30

318 Pope John Paul II **319** Alfred de Musset

1982. Papal Visit.
803 **318** 100 f. multicoloured . . . 1·10 65

1982. 125th Death Anniv of Alfred de Musset (writer).
804 **319** 75 f. black 55 20

320 "Leonce Veilvieux" (freighter)

1982. Merchant Ships. Multicoloured.
805 75 f. Type **320** 90 55
806 100 f. "Correze" (container ship) . . . . 1·10 55
807 200 f. Oil tanker . . . . 1·90 85

321 Dr. Robert Koch, Microscope, Bacillus and Guinea Pig

1982. Centenary of Discovery of Tubercle Bacillus.
808 **321** 100 f. multicoloured . . . 90 45

322 Rope Bridge, Poubara **323** Hexagonal Pattern

1982. "Philexfrance 82" International Stamp Exhibition, Paris. Multicoloured.
809 100 f. Type **322** 65 35
810 100 f. Bapounou sculpture . . . 1·40 55

1982. World Telecommunications Day.
811 **323** 75 f. multicoloured 60 35

324 Footballer (Brazil)

1982. World Cup Football Championship, Spain. Multicoloured.
812 100 f. Type **324** 65 30
813 125 f. Footballer (Argentina) . . 85 35
814 200 f. Footballer (England) . . 1·25 50

325 "Caprice des Dames" (Morning)

1982. Flower "Caprice des Dames". Mult.
816 75 f. Type **325** 60 35
817 100 f. Midday 80 35
818 175 f. Evening . . . . 1·40 65

326 Satellites

1982. Second U.N. Conference on Exploration and Peaceful Uses of Outer Space.
819 **326** 250 f. blue, dp bl & red . . 1·90 1·10

1982. World Cup Football Championship Winners. Nos. 812/14 optd.
821 **324** 100 f. multicoloured . . . 65 35
822 – 125 f. multicoloured . . . 85 40
823 – 200 f. multicoloured . . . 1·40 60
OPTS: 100 f. **DEMIE-FINALE POLOGNE 0—ITALIE 2**. 125 f. **DEMIE-FINALE R. F. ALLEMAGNE 3—FRANCE 3**. 200 f. **FINALE ITALIE 3—R. F. ALLEMAGNE 1**.

329 Duplex Murex

1982. Shells. Multicoloured.
825 75 f. Type **329** 80 50
826 100 f. "Chama crenulata" . . . 1·40 60
827 125 f. "Cardium hians" . . . . 2·00 1·10

330 "Still-life with Mandolin" (Braque birth centenary)

1982. Painters' Anniversaries. Mult.
828 300 f. Type **330** . . . . 2·25 70
829 350 f. "Boy blowing Soap Bubbles" (Manet—death cent.) (vert) . . . . 3·25 1·10

331 Okouyi Mask **332** St. Francis Xavier Church, Lambarene

1982. Artifacts. Multicoloured.
830 75 f. Type **331** 45 20
831 100 f. Ondoumbo reliquary . . 65 20
832 150 f. Tsogho statuette . . . . 1·10 40
833 250 f. Forge bellows . . . . . 1·60 60

1982. Christmas.
834 **332** 100 f. multicoloured . . . 65 35

333 Presidents Bongo and Mitterand, Route Map and Diesel Train

1983. Inauguration of Second Stage of Trans-Gabon Railway.
835 **333** 75 f. multicoloured . . . . 1·50 50

334 Stylised Highway and Map of Africa

1983. 5th African Highway Conference.
836 **334** 100 f. multicoloured . . . 65 30

335 Gymnast with Hoop **336** "Epitorium trochiformis" (Estuaire)

1983. Air. Olympic Games, Los Angeles. Multicoloured.
837 90 f. Type **335** 60 30
838 350 f. Wind-surfing . . . . . . 2·50 1·00

1983. Provinces. Multicoloured.
839 75 f. Bakota mask (Ogooue Ivindo) 50 25
840 90 f. African buffalo (Nyanga) . 60 30
841 90 f. "Charaxes druceanus" (Ogooue Lolo) 60 30
842 100 f. Isogho hairstyle (Ngounie) 65 35
843 125 f. Manganese (Haut Ogooue) 85 45
844 125 f. Crocodiles (Moyen Ogooue) 85 45
845 125 f. Atlantic tarpon (Ogooue Maritime) . . . . 1·40 60
846 135 f. Type **336** . . . . 1·00 60
847 135 f. Coffee flowers (Woleu Ntem) . . . . 1·00 60

337 "Ville de Rouen" (container ship) sand I.M.O. Emblem

1983. 25th Anniv of International Maritime Organization.
848 **337** 125 f. multicoloured . . . 1·25 45

338 Water Chevrotain

1983. Fauna. Multicoloured.
849 90 f. Type **338** 60 30
850 125 f. Pink-backed Pelican . . . 2·25 90
851 225 f. African elephant . . . . 1·90 70
852 400 f. Iguana . . . . 2·75 1·40

339 E.C.A. Anniversary Emblem

1983. 25th Anniv of Economic Commission for Africa.
854 **339** 125 f. multicoloured . . . 85 40

340 Telephones 341 "Double Eagle II" crossing Atlantic

1983. World Telecommunications Day. Mult.
855 90 f. Type **340** 85 45
856 90 f. As No. 855 but design inverted 85 45

1983. Air. Ballooning Anniversaries.
857 100 f. grey, orange & blue . . . 80 45
858 125 f. green, purple & blue . . . 90 55
859 350 f. bl, grn & lt grn . . . . 2·75 1·40
DESIGNS: 100 f. Type **341** (5th anniv of first Atlantic crossing); 125 f. Hot-air balloons (Bicentenary of Montgolfier Brothers' balloon); 350 f. Pilatre de Rozier and Montgolfier balloon (Bicentenary of manned flight).

342 "Lady with Unicorn"

1983. Air. 150th Birth Anniv of Raphael.
860 **342** 1000 f. multicoloured . . . 7·25 3·25

343 Nkoltang Satellite Receiving Station

1983. World Communications Year.
861 **343** 125 f. multicoloured . . . 85 35

344 Rapids on the Ivindo River

1983. Tourism.
862 **344** 90 f. blue, brown & grn . . 55 30
863 – 125 f. brown, grn & grey . 85 45
864 – 185 f. grey, orange & grn . 1·25 45
865 – 350 f. brown, grn & blue . 2·40 1·10
DESIGNS: 125 f. Pirogue on the Ogooue River; 185 f. Wonga Wongue Game Reserve; 350 f. Coastal beach.

345 Mahongwe Drum

1983. Music and Dance. Multicoloured.
866 90 f. Type **345** 55 30
867 125 f. Okoukoue dance 85 45
868 135 f. Ngomi bateke . . . . . 1·00 45
869 260 f. Ndoumou dancer . . . . 1·90 90

346 "Glossinidae" 347 "The Adulterous Woman"

1983. Harmful Insects. Multicoloured.
870 90 f. Type **346** 90 45
871 125 f. "Belonogaster junceus" . 1·10 50
872 300 f. "Aedes aegypti" . . . . 2·25 1·25
873 350 f. "Mylabris" . . . . . . 3·25 1·40

1983. Christmas. Wood carvings from St. Michel Church, Libreville. Multicoloured.
874 90 f. Type **347** 55 30
875 125 f. "Parable of the Good Samaritan" 85 40

348 Boeing 747-200 Airliner and Gabon Stamp of 1966

1984. World Post Congress Stamp Exhibition, Hamburg. Multicoloured.
876 125 f. Type **348** 95 45
877 225 f. Douglas DC-10 and German airmail stamp of 1919 . . . . 1·90 90

349 Pylons and Buildings

1984. 3rd Anniv of "Africa 1".
878 **349** 125 f. multicoloured . . . 85 35

350 Ice Hockey

1984. Air. Winter Olympic Games, Sarajevo.
879 **350** 125 f. green, pur & blk . . 1·10 55
880 – 350 f. blue, brown & blk . 2·50 1·10
DESIGN: 350 f. Ice-dancing.

351 Coconut

1984. Fruit Trees. Multicoloured.
881 90 f. Type **351** 70 35
882 100 f. Pawpaw 80 35
883 125 f. Mango . . . . 1·00 45
884 250 f. Banana . . . . 1·90 85

352 Robin Dauphin and Piper Cherokee Six Aircraft

1984. Air. Paris-Libreville Air Rally.
885 **352** 500 f. multicoloured . . . 3·25 1·90

353 "Racehorses"

1984. Air. 150th Birth Anniv of Degas.
886 **353** 500 f. multicoloured . . . 4·50 2·25

354 Water Lily 355 Spectrum

1984. Flowers. Multicoloured.
887 90 f. Type **354** 80 30
888 125 f. Water hyacinth 80 40
889 135 f. Hibiscus . . . . 1·10 45
890 350 f. Bracteate orchid . . . . 2·50 1·40

1984. World Telecommunications Day.
891 **355** 125 f. multicoloured . . . 85 35

356 Basketball 358 Lionel Hampton

1984. Air. Olympic Games, Los Angeles. Multicoloured.
892 90 f. Type **356** 55 35
893 125 f. Steeple-chase 85 45

1984. Jazz Musicians. Multicoloured.
895 90 f. Type **358** . . . . 1·10 55
896 125 f. Charlie Parker . . . . . 1·40 55
897 260 f. Erroll Garner . . . . . 2·75 1·40

1984. District Arms (3rd series). As T **137** but dated "1984". Multicoloured.
898 90 f. Cocobeach 55 15
899 125 f. Mouila 80 15
900 135 f. N'Djole 90 20

359 Medouneu

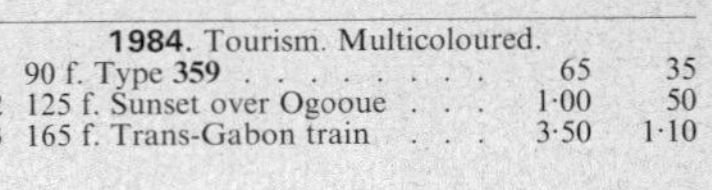

1984. Tourism. Multicoloured.
901 90 f. Type **359** 65 35
902 125 f. Sunset over Ogooue . . . 1·00 50
903 165 f. Trans-Gabon train . . . 3·50 1·10

360 Globe, Post and Emblem 360a Kota Reliquary

1984. Universal Postal Union Day.
905 **360** 125 f. multicoloured . . . 85 35

1984. Traditional Art. Multicoloured.
905a 90 f. Kouble mask . . . . .
905b 125 f. Pounou fan . . . . . .
905c 150 f. Mahongoue reliquary . .
905d 250 f. Type **360a** . . . . . .

361 "Icarus" (Hans Herni)

1984. 40th Anniv of International Civil Aviation Organization.
906 **361** 125 f. dp bl, grn & bl . . . 85 35

362 Tympanum of Saint Michael's Church (left side)

1984. Christmas. Multicoloured.
907 90 f. Type **362** 55 25
908 125 f. Tympanum of Saint Michael's church (right side) . 85 35
Nos. 907/8 were printed together se-tenant forming a composite design.

363 South African Crowned Cranes

1984. Birds. Multicoloured.
909 90 f. Type **363** . . . . 1·50 75
910 125 f. Snowy-breasted humming-bird . . . . 2·50 1·40
911 150 f. Keel-billed toucan . . . 2·75 1·50

364 Leper Colony, Libreville

1985. World Lepers' Day.
912 **364** 125 f. multicoloured . . . 85 40

365 I.Y.Y. Emblem

1985. International Youth Year.
913 **365** 125 f. multicoloured . . . 85 35

367 Profiles and Emblem

1985. 15th Anniv of Cultural and Technical Co-operation Agency.
914 **367** 125 f. bl, red & dp bl . . . 85 35

368 Water Rat

1985. Animals. Multicoloured.
915 90 f. Type **368** 90 35
916 100 f. Porcupine 90 35
917 125 f. Giant pangolin . . . . . 1·25 55
918 350 f. Antelope . . . . 3·00 1·40

369 Score and Aleka

1985. Georges Damas Aleka (composer) Commemoration.
920 **369** 90 f. multicoloured 80 35

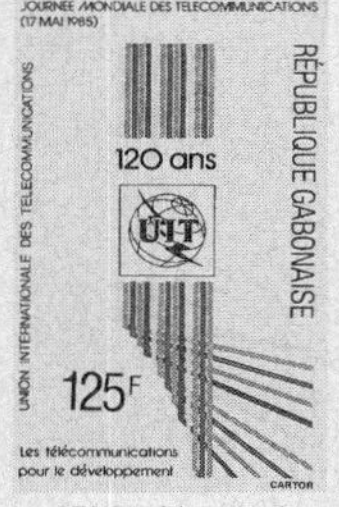

370 Emblem and Coloured Lines

371 Shield

1985. World Telecommunications Day.
921 **370** 125 f. multicoloured . . . 85 35

1985. 30th Anniv of Christian Youth Workers' Movement in Gabon.
922 **371** 90 f. multicoloured 60 30

372 "La Mpassa" (freighter)

1985.
923 **372** 185 f. multicoloured . . . 2·25 85

373 Building and Dish Aerials

1985. 25th Anniv of Posts and Telecommunications Administration.
924 **373** 90 f. multicoloured 60 30

374 President Bongo **375** Dr. Albert Schweitzer

1985. 25th Anniv of Independence.
925 **374** 250 f. multicoloured . . . 2·25 1·10
926 500 f. multicoloured . . . 4·50 2·75

1985. Air. 20th Death Anniv of Dr. Albert Schweitzer.
928 **375** 350 f. multicoloured . . . 2·75 1·25

376 Hand holding U.N. and Gabon Flags

1985. Air. 20th Anniv of Membership of United Nations Organization.
929 **376** 225 f. multicoloured . . . 1·50 70

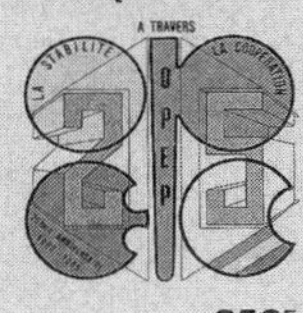

377 O.P.E.C. Emblem

1985. 25th Anniv of Organization of Petroleum Exporting Countries.
930 **377** 350 f. multicoloured . . . 2·50 1·40

378 Boy Scouts around Campfire and Elephant

1985. Air. "Philexafrique" Stamp Exhibition, Lome, Togo. Multicoloured.
931 100 f. Type **378** 85 45
932 150 f. Diesel train, satellite and dish aerial . . . . 3·75 80

379 Central Post Office, Libreville, Gabon Posts and U.P.U. Emblems

1985. Air. World Post Day.
933 **379** 300 f. multicoloured . . . 2·25 1·00

380 Hand holding Globe

1985. Air. 40th Anniv of U.N.O.
934 **380** 350 f. multicoloured . . . 2·50 1·10

381 Centre

1985. International Centre of Bantu Civilisations.
935 **381** 185 f. multicoloured . . . 1·40 60

381a Interior of Church

1985. Christmas. St. Andrew's Church, Libreville. Multicoloured.
935a 90 f. Exterior of church . . .
935b 125 f. Type **381a** . . . . . .

382 Young People within Laurel Wreath

1986. 25th Anniv of U.N.E.S.C.O. National Commission.
936 **382** 100 f. multicoloured . . . 65 30

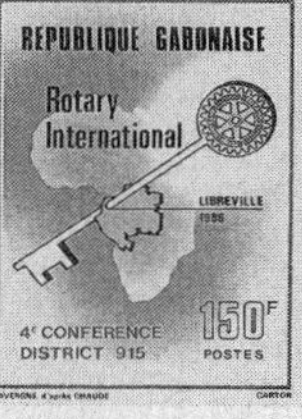

383 "Mother and Child" **385** Key as Emblem and Map

384 Savorgnan de Brazza and Canoe

1986. Air. Gabon's Gift to United Nations Organization.
937 **383** 350 f. multicoloured . . . 2·50 1·10

1986. Air. Centenary of Lastoursville.
938 **384** 100 f. multicoloured . . . 85 45

1986. 4th Rotary International District 915 Conference, Libreville.
939 **385** 150 f. multicoloured . . . 1·10 50

386 Communications Equipment

1986. World Telecommunications Day.
940 **386** 300 f. multicoloured . . . 2·00 1·00

387 Goalkeeper saving Ball

1986. Air. World Cup Football Championship, Mexico. Multicoloured.
941 100 f. Type **387** 65 35
942 150 f. Footballers and Mexican statue . . . . 1·00 45
943 250 f. World Cup trophy, footballers and map . . . . . 1·60 65
944 350 f. Flags, ball and stadium . 2·25 1·00

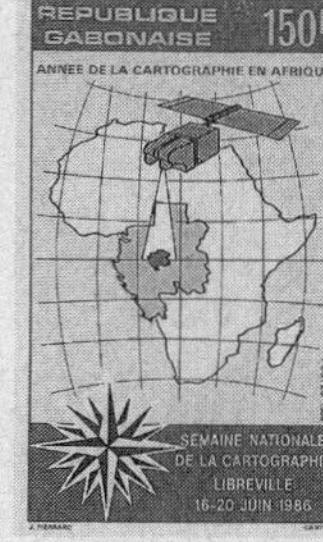

388 Map and Satellite

1986. African Cartography Year and National Cartography Week, Libreville.
946 **388** 150 f. multicoloured . . . 1·10 55

389 "L'Abanga" (container ship)

1986.
947 **389** 250 f. multicoloured . . . 2·25 1·10

390 River and Gabon 1886 50 c. Stamp

1986. Centenary of First Gabon Stamps.
948 **390** 500 f. multicoloured . . . 4·50 2·25

391 "Allamanda neriifolia" **392** Arms of Lambarn

1986. Flowers. Multicoloured.
949 100 f. Type **391** 65 35
950 150 f. "Musa cultivar" . . . . 1·00 50
951 350 f. "Dissotis decumbens" . . 1·10 55
952 350 f. "Campylospermum laeve" . . . . 2·50 1·10

1986. District Arms (4th series). Mult.
953 100 f. Type **392** 65 20
954 160 f. Leconi . . . . 1·10 35

393 Coffee Berries, Flowers and Beans

1986. 25th Anniv of African and Malagasy Coffee Producers Organization.
955 **393** 125 f. multicoloured . . . 95 55

394 "Machaon"

1986. Butterflies. Multicoloured.
956 150 f. Type **394** . . . . 1·90 1·25
957 290 f. "Urania" . . . . 2·75 2·25

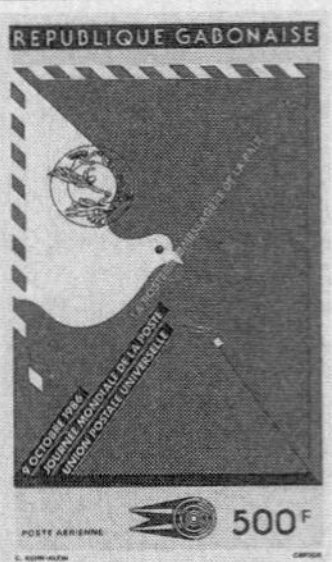
395 Dove and U.P.U. Emblem

1986. Air. World Post Day.
958 **395** 500 f. multicoloured . . . 3·25 1·60

1986. Air. World Cup Football Championship Winners. Nos 941/4 optd **ARGENTINE 3-R.F.A. 2.** Multicoloured.
959 100 f. Type **387** 65 45
960 150 f. Footballers and Mexican statue . . . . 1·00 55
961 250 f. World Cup trophy, footballers and map . . . . . . 1·60 1·00
962 350 f. Flags, ball and stadium . 2·25 1·60

397 St. Peter's Church, Libreville

1986. Christmas.
963 **397** 500 f. multicoloured . . . 3·25 1·60

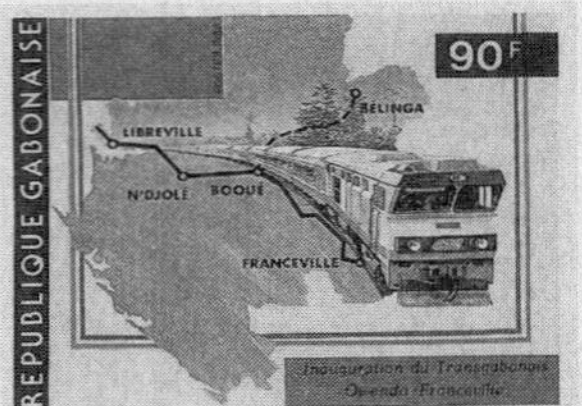
398 Diesel Train and Route Map

1986. Inauguration of Owendo–Franceville Trans-Gabon Railway.
964 **398** 90 f. multicoloured . . . . 3·00 1·10

1986. Traditional Hairstyles. As T **316**.
964a 150 f. black, red and grey . . . 3·25 1·10

399 West African Squirrelfish

1987. Fishes. Multicoloured.
966 90 f. Type **399** 85 45
967 125 f. West African parrotfish . 1·10 65
968 225 f. Flying gurnard . . . . . 2·00 1·10
969 350 f. Marbled stingray . . . . 3·25 2·00

400 Raoul Follereau (leprosy pioneer)

1987. World Leprosy Day.
971 **400** 125 f. multicoloured . . . 1·00 65

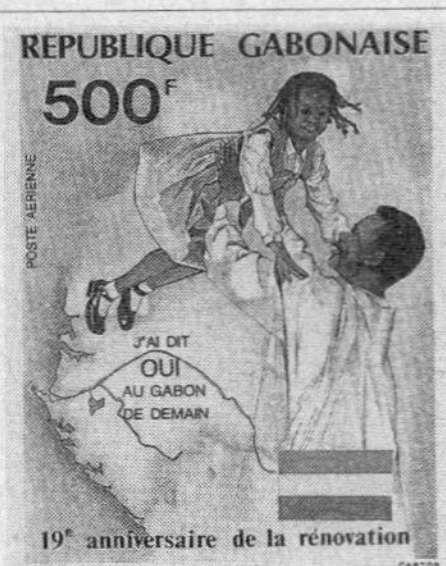
401 Man and Child in front of Map

1987. Air. 19th Anniv of National Renewal.
972 **401** 500 f. multicoloured . . . 4·00 1·60

402 Pres. Bongo receiving Prize

1987. Award of Dag Hammarskjold Peace Prize to Pres. Omar Bongo.
973 **402** 125 f. multicoloured . . . 85 55

403 Konrad Adenauer

404 Symbols of Communication

1987. Air. 20th Death Anniv of Konrad Adenauer (German statesman).
974 **403** 300 f. multicoloured . . . 2·75 1·25

1987. World Telecommunications Day.
975 **404** 90 f. multicoloured 60 35

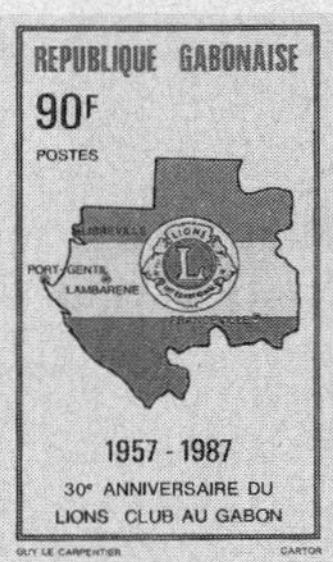
405 Emblem on Map

406 Coubertin and Runner with Torch

1987. 30th Anniv of Lions Club of Gabon.
976 **405** 90 f. multicoloured 60 35

1987. 50th Death Anniv of Pierre de Coubertin (founder of modern Olympic Games).
977 **406** 200 f. multicoloured . . . 1·40 65

407 Map, Emblems and People

408 Globe in Envelope

1987. 70th Anniv of Lions International.
978 **407** 165 f. multicoloured . . . 1·25 65

1987. World Post Day.
979 **408** 125 f. multicoloured . . . 85 35

409 Pres. Bongo and Sam Nujoma

410 Fanel Moon

1987. Solidarity with South-West African Peoples' Organization.
980 **409** 225 f. multicoloured . . . 1·40 55

1987. Sea Shells. Multicoloured.
981 90 f. Type **410** . . . . 1·25 70
982 125 f. Lightning moon ("Natica fulminea cruentata") . . . . 1·50 70
See also Nos. 1018a/b.

411 Man, House and Machinery

1987. International Year of Shelter for the Homeless. World Shelter Day.
984 **411** 90 f. multicoloured 60 35

412 Mission

413 Nurse vaccinating Child

1987. Centenary of St. Anne of Odimba Mission.
985 **412** 90 f. multicoloured 65 35

1987. Universal Vaccination for Children.
986 **413** 100 f. multicoloured . . . 80 40

414 President making Address

1987. 20th Anniv of Installation of President Omar Bongo.
987 **414** 1000 f. multicoloured . . . 6·75 3·25

415 St. Theresa's Church, Oyem

1987. Christmas.
988 **415** 90 f. multicoloured 65 35

416 Skier

1987. Winter Olympic Games, Calgary (1988).
989 **416** 125 f. multicoloured . . . 85 45

417 "Cassia occidentalis"

1988. Medicinal Plants. Multicoloured.
990 90 f. Type **417** 65 45
991 125 f. "Tabernanthe iboga" . . 90 45
992 225 f. "Cassia alata" . . . . . 1·50 80
993 350 f. "Anthocleista schweinfurthii" . . . . 2·75 1·60

418 Obamba Rattle

1988. Traditional Musical Instruments. Mult.
995 90 f. Type **418** 60 35
996 100 f. Fang sanza (vert) 80 45
997 125 f. Mitsogho harp (vert) . . 90 55
998 165 f. Fang xylophone . . . . 1·40 65

419 Elephant with raised Trunk

1988. Endangered Animals. African Elephant Multicoloured.
1000 25 f. Type **419** 30 15
1001 40 f. Elephant family 70 20
1002 50 f. Elephant in vegetation . . 90 20
1003 100 f. Elephant . . . . 1·40 55

420 Postal Delta Building

1988. Inauguration of Postal Delta.
1004 **420** 90 f. multicoloured . . . 65 35

421 Village and Dr. Schweitzer

1988. Air. 75th Anniv of Arrival in Gabon of Dr. Albert Schweitzer.
1005 **421** 500 f. multicoloured . . . 4·00 1·60

422 Players

1988. World Cup Rugby Championship (1987).
1006 **422** 350 f. multicoloured . . . 2·75 1·60

423 Opposing Arrows

1988. World Telecommunications Day.
1007 **423** 125 f. multicoloured . . . 85 40

424 Storming the Bastille, 1789

1988. "Philexfrance 89" Stamp Exhibition, Paris.
1008 **424** 125 f. multicoloured . . . 1·10 55

425 Crops and Agricultural Activities

1988. 10th Anniv of International Agricultural Development Fund.
1009 **425** 350 f. multicoloured . . . 2·75 1·10

426 Emblem and Theatre Staff

1988. 125th Anniv of Red Cross.
1010 **426** 125 f. multicoloured . . . 85 35

427 Refinery

1988. Air. 20th Anniv of Port Gentil Oil Refinery.
1011 **427** 350 f. multicoloured . . . 2·50 1·10

428 Tennis

1988. Olympic Games, Seoul. Multicoloured.
1012 90 f. Type **428** 65 35
1013 100 f. Swimming 65 35
1014 350 f. Running . . . . 2·50 1·00
1015 500 f. Hurdling . . . . 4·00 1·10

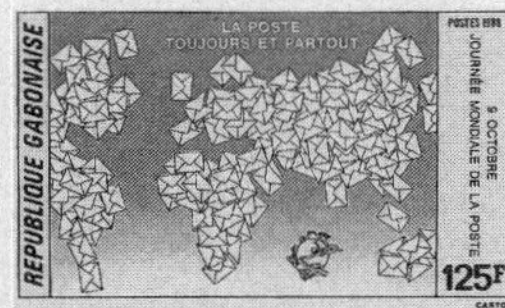

429 Envelopes forming World Map

1988. World Post Day.
1017 **429** 125 f. black, blue & yell . 85 35

430 Medouneu Church **431** Map and Emblem

1988. Christmas.
1018 **430** 200 f. multicoloured . . . 1·40 65

1988. Sea Shells. As T **410**. Multicoloured.
1018a 90 f. Fanel moon ("Natica fanel var") . . . . 1·60 1·10
1018b 125 f. "Natica variolaria" (inscr "Natica sp.") . . . . 2·75 1·60

1989. 10th Anniv of Chaine de Rotisseurs in Gabon.
1019 **431** 175 f. multicoloured . . . 1·10 65

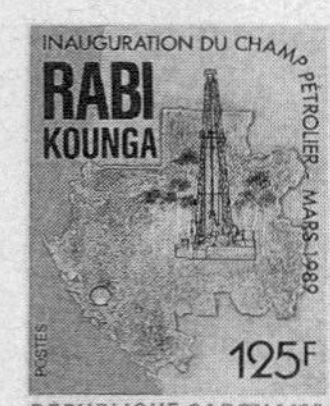

432 Map **434** African Tiger Bittern

433 Boys playing

1989. Inauguration of Rabi Kounga Oil Field.
1020 **432** 125 f. multicoloured . . . 85 50

1989. Traditional Games.
1021 **433** 90 f. multicoloured . . . 60 40

1989. Birds. Multicoloured.
1022 100 f. Type **434** 65 35
1023 175 f. Grey parrot . . . . . . 1·10 65
1024 200 f. Red-billed dwarf hornbill . . . . 1·40 70
1025 500 f. Blue-breasted kingfisher . 3·50 1·75

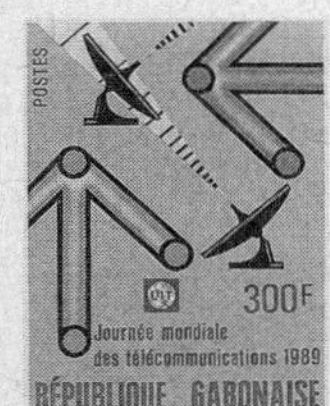

435 Map and Emblem **436** Arrows and Dish Aerials

1989. 8th Lions Club International Multidistrict 403 Convention, Libreville.
1027 **435** 125 f. multicoloured . . . 85 45

1989. World Telecommunications Day.
1028 **436** 300 f. multicoloured . . . 2·25 90

437 Palm-nuts

1989. Fruits. Multicoloured.
1029 90 f. Type **437** 60 35
1030 125 f. Cabosse 85 35
1031 175 f. Pineapple . . . . 1·40 55
1032 250 f. Breadfruit . . . . . . 2·00 1·00

438 "Apples and Oranges"

1989. 150th Birth Anniv of Paul Cezanne (painter).
1034 **438** 500 f. multicoloured . . . 4·00 2·75

439 Phrygian Cap on Tree of Liberty and Sans-culotte

1989. "Philexfrance '89" International Stamp Exhibition, Paris.
1035 **439** 175 f. multicoloured . . . 1·60 65

440 Soldier and Sans-culotte

1989. Bicentenary of French Revolution.
1036 **440** 500 f. multicoloured . . . 4·50 2·75

441 Town Hall

1989. 10th Anniv of International Association of French-speaking Town Halls.
1037 **441** 100 f. multicoloured . . . 90 40

442 Emblem and Map showing Development Programmes

1989. 25th Anniv of African Development Bank.
1038 **442** 100 f. multicoloured . . . 65 40

443 Post Office

1989. 125th Anniv (1987) of Gabon Postal Service.
1039 **443** 90 f. multicoloured . . . 65 35

444 Footballers

1989. World Cup Football Championship, Italy (1990). Multicoloured.
1040 100 f. Type **444** 65 35
1041 175 f. Player tackling . . . . 1·25 55
1042 300 f. Goalkeeper catching ball 2·00 80
1043 500 f. Goalkeeper catching ball (different) . . . . 3·25 1·40

445 Woman and Child posting Letter **447** St. Louis' Church, Port-Gentil

1989. World Post Day.
1045 **445** 175 f. multicoloured . . . 1·10 45

1989. Traditional Hairstyles. As T **316**.
1046 175 f. black, lilac & grey . . . 1·40 55

1989. Christmas.
1047 **447** 100 f. multicoloured . . . 65 30

448 L'Ogooue, N'Gomo

1989.
1048 **448** 100 f. multicoloured . . . 50 25

449 Axehead

1990. Prehistory. Stone Weapons. Mult.
1049 100 f. Type **449** 90 45
1050 175 f. Paring knife . . . . . . 1·40 65
1051 300 f. Flint arrowhead . . . . 2·25 1·10
1052 400 f. Double-edged knife . . 3·50 2·25

450 Arms of Libreville

1990. 22nd Anniv of National Renovation.
1054 **450** 100 f. multicoloured . . . 65 30

451 Penny Black and Beach

1990. 150th Anniv of the Penny Black.
1055 **451** 500 f. multicoloured . . . 4·50 2·75

452 Doctor and Nurse Examining Patient **453** Monkey

1990. World Health Day.
1056 **452** 400 f. multicoloured . . . 2·75 1·40

1990. Animals of Gabon. Multicoloured.
1057 100 f. Type **453** 90 45
1058 175 f. Bush pig (horiz) . . . . 1·40 65
1059 200 f. Antelope (horiz) . . . . 1·60 1·10
1060 500 f. Mandrill . . . . 4·50 2·75

454 De Gaulle and Map

1990. Air. 50th Anniv of De Gaulle's Call to Resist.
1062 **454** 500 f. multicoloured . . . 4·50 2·25

455 Map and Arms on Flag

1990. 30th Anniv of Independence.
1063 **455** 100 f. multicoloured . . . 65 45

456 Morel

1990. Fungi.
1064 **456** 100 f. multicoloured . . . 1·10 55
1065 – 175 f. multicoloured . . . 2·25 1·10
1066 – 300 f. multicoloured . . . 3·25 2·25
1067 – 500 f. multicoloured . . . 4·50 3·25
DESIGNS: 175 f. to 500 f. Various fungi.

457 Flags of Member Countries **458** Envelopes as World Map

1990. 30th Anniv of Organization of Petroleum Exporting Countries.
1068 **457** 200 f. multicoloured . . . 1·40 80

1990. World Post Day.
1069 **458** 175 f. blue, yellow & blk . 1·25 65

459 Makokou Church

1990. Christmas.
1070 **459** 100 f. multicoloured . . . 65 45

460 Frangipani

1991. Flowers. Multicoloured.
1071 100 f. Type **460** 90 45
1072 175 f. Burning bush . . . . . 1·40 65
1073 200 f. Flame tree . . . . . . 1·75 90
1074 300 f. Porcelain rose . . . . . 2·25 1·40

461 "Marseilles Harbour"

1991. Air. Death Cent of Johan Barthold Jongkind (artist).
1076 **461** 500 f. multicoloured . . . 4·00 1·60

462 Lizard **463** Collecting Resin from Rubber Trees

1991. Prehistory. Petroglyphs. Multicoloured.
1077 100 f. Type **462** 70 45
1078 175 f. Triangular figure . . . . 1·10 65
1079 300 f. Abstract pattern . . . . 2·10 1·10
1080 500 f. Circles and chains . . . 3·50 2·25

1991. Agriculture.
1082 **463** 100 f. multicoloured . . . 65 45

1991. District Arms (5th series). As T **392**.
1083 100 f. silver, black & green . . 65 20
DESIGN: 100 f. Port-Gentil.

464 Couple and Arrows **465** Basket Weaving

1991. World Telecommunications Day.
1084 **464** 175 f. multicoloured . . . 1·10 55

1991. Arts and Crafts. Multicoloured.
1085 100 f. Type **465** 65 45
1086 175 f. Stone carving . . . . . 1·40 80
1087 200 f. Weaving . . . . 1·40 80
1088 500 f. Straw plaiting . . . . . 3·50 1·90

466 Women at Riverbank **467** Knight

1991. Washerwomen of the Ngounie.
1089 **466** 100 f. multicoloured . . . 65 45

1991. Order of the Equatorial Star. Mult.
1090 100 f. Type **467** 65 45
1091 175 f. Officer . . . . 1·10 65
1092 200 f. Commander . . . . . . 1·40 90

468 Inspecting Fish Traps **469** Post Box and Globe

1991. Fishing. Multicoloured.
1093 100 f. Type **468** 65 45
1094 175 f. Fishing from canoe . . . 1·10 65
1095 200 f. Casting net . . . . . . 1·40 90
1096 300 f. Pulling in net . . . . . 2·75 1·90

1991. World Post Day.
1098 **469** 175 f. blue, blk & red . . 1·10 45

470 "Phalloid" **471** Dibwangui Church

1991. Termitaries. Multicoloured.
1099 100 f. Type **470** 85 55
1100 175 f. "Cathedral" . . . . . . 1·40 85
1101 200 f. "Mushroom" . . . . . 1·60 1·10
1102 300 f. "Treehouse" . . . . . . 2·25 2·00

1991. Christmas.
1103 **471** 100 f. multicoloured . . . 65 45

472 Neolithic Ceramic Pot **473** Stripping Wood

1992. Prehistory. Pottery. Multicoloured.
1104 100 f. Type **472** 65 45
1105 175 f. Ceramic bottle (8th century) . . . . 1·10 65
1106 200 f. Ceramic vase (late 8th century) . . . . 1·40 90
1107 300 f. Ceramic vase (early 8th century) . . . . 2·25 1·40

1992. Arts and Crafts. Multicoloured.
1109 100 f. Type **473** 65 45
1110 175 f. Metalwork . . . . . . 1·10 65
1111 200 f. Boat building . . . . . 1·40 80
1112 300 f. Hairdressing . . . . . 2·25 1·40

474 Grand Officer of Order of Equatorial Star **475** Konrad Adenauer

1992. Gabonese Honours. Multicoloured.
1114 100 f. Type **474** 65 45
1115 175 f. Grand Cross of Order of Equatorial Star . . . . . . 1·10 65
1116 200 f. Order of Merit . . . . 1·40 90

1992. 25th Death Anniv of Konrad Adenauer (German statesman).
1117 **475** 500 f. blk, stone & grn . . 4·00 2·75

476 Earth and Moon **477** Small Striped Swallowtail

1992. World Telecommunications Day.
1118 **476** 175 f. multicoloured . . . 1·10 45

1992. Butterflies. Multicoloured.
1119 100 f. Type **477** 65 45
1120 175 f. "Acraea egina" . . . . 1·10 65

478 Fang Mask **479** Cycling

1992. Gabonese Masks. Multicoloured.
1121 100 f. Type **478** 65 45
1122 175 f. Mpongwe mask . . . . 1·10 65
1123 200 f. Kwele mask . . . . . . 1·40 95
1124 300 f. Pounou mask . . . . . 1·90 1·40

1992. Olympic Games, Barcelona. Mult.
1125 100 f. Type **479** 65 45
1126 175 f. Boxing . . . . 1·10 65
1127 200 f. Pole vaulting . . . . . 1·40 90

1992. District Arms (6th series). As T **392**.
1128 100 f. silver, black & blue . . . 65 20
DESIGN: 100 f. Medouneu.

1992. World Post Day. As No. 1098 but dated "1992".
1129 **469** 175 f. multicoloured . . . 1·10 55

480 Columbus and Fleet

1992. Air. 500th Anniv of Discovery of America by Columbus.
1130 **480** 500 f. multicoloured . . . 3·25 1·90

481 African Owl **482** Cattle

1992. Birds. Multicoloured.
1131 100 f. Type **481** 65 35
1132 175 f. Speckled mousebird . . 1·10 55
1133 200 f. Palm-nut vulture . . . . 1·40 80
1134 300 f. Giant kingfisher . . . . 2·25 1·40

1992. Beef Production.
1136 **482** 100 f. multicoloured . . . 65 45
1137 – 175 f. multicoloured . . . 1·10 65
1138 – 200 f. multicoloured . . . 1·40 85
DESIGNS: 175, 200 f. Cattle (different).

483 Tchibanga Church **484** Emblems

1992. Christmas.
1139 **483** 100 f. multicoloured . . . 65 35

1992. International Nutrition Conference, Rome.
1140 **484** 100 f. multicoloured . . . 65 45

485 "Giant Hairy Melongena"

1993. Shells. Multicoloured.
1141 100 f. Type **485** 50 30
1142 175 f. Butterfly cone . . . . 1·10 60
1143 200 f. Carpat's spindle . . . . 1·25 70
1144 300 f. "Cymatium linatella" . . 2·00 1·10

486 Crowd with Banner outside Hospital

1993. World Leprosy Day.
1146 **486** 175 f. multicoloured . . . 1·10 50

487 Fritz the Elephant

1993. Fernan-Vaz Mission.

1147 **487** 175 f. multicoloured . . . 1·40 90

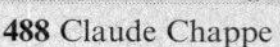

488 Claude Chappe　**489** Schweitzer feeding Animals

1993. Bicentenary of Chappe's Optical Telegraph. Multicoloured.

1148 100 f. Type **488** 45 25
1149 175 f. Signals and table of signs . . . . 1·10 50
1150 200 f. Emile Baudot (inventor of five-unit code telegraph printing system) . . . . . . 1·25 80
1151 300 f. Satellite and fibre-optics . 2·00 1·10

1993. 80th Anniv of First Visit of Albert Schweitzer (medical missionary) to Lambarene. Mult.

1153 250 f. Type **489** . . . . 2·00 1·10
1154 250 f. Schweitzer holding babies . . . . 2·00 1·10
1155 500 f. Schweitzer (36 × 49 mm) . . . . 3·75 2·25

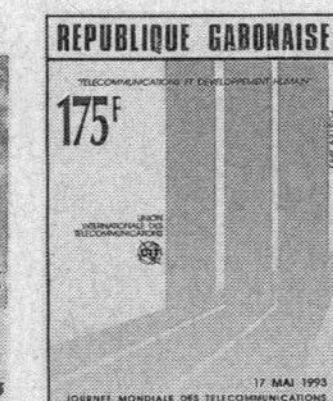

490 Copernicus (astronomer) and illustration from "De Revolutionibus"　**491** Emblem

1993. "Polska'93" International Stamp Exhibition, Poznan.

1156 **490** 175 f. multicoloured . . . 1·10 50

1993. World Telecommunications Day.

1157 **491** 175 f. multicoloured . . . 1·10 50

492 Making Sugar-cane Wine　**493** Lobster

1993. Traditional Wine-making. Mult.

1158 100 f. Type **492** 70 25
1159 175 f. Filling bottle with palm wine . . . . 1·10 50
1160 200 f. Gathering ingredients for palm wine . . . . 1·40 55

1993. Crustaceans. Multicoloured.

1162 100 f. Type **493** 70 25
1163 175 f. Crab . . . . 1·10 50
1164 200 f. Crayfish . . . . 1·25 80
1165 300 f. Sea spider . . . . . . 2·00 1·10

494 Magnifying Glass, Flowers, Stamp and Emblem

1993. First European Stamp Salon, Flower Gardens, Paris.

1166 **494** 100 f. multicoloured . . . 70 50

495 Squirrel Trap　**496** Post Box and Globe

1993. Trapping. Multicoloured.

1167 100 f. Type **495** 70 25
1168 175 f. Small game trap . . . . 1·10 50
1169 200 f. Large game trap . . . . 1·25 80
1170 300 f. Palm squirrel trap . . . 2·00 1·10

1993. World Post Day.

1171 **496** 175 f. multicoloured . . . 80 50

497 Making Model Airplane　**499** Mandji Catholic Mission

498 Leconi Canyon

1993. Bamboo Toys.

1172 **497** 100 f. multicoloured . . . 70 50

1993. Tourism. Multicoloured.

1173 100 f. Type **498** 70 25
1174 175 f. La Lope tourist site . . 1·10 50

1993. Christmas.

1175 **499** 100 f. multicoloured . . . 70 50

OFFICIAL STAMPS

O 119 Map of Gabon River

1968.

O333 **O 119** 1 f. multicoloured . . 10 10
O334 2 f. multicoloured . . 10 10
O335 5 f. multicoloured . . 10 10
O336 10 f. multicoloured . . 15 10
O337 – 25 f. multicoloured . . 35 15
O338 – 30 f. multicoloured . . 40 20
O339 – 50 f. multicoloured . . 55 20
O340 – 85 f. multicoloured . . 1·10 40
O341 – 100 f. multicoloured . 1·40 55
O342 – 200 f. multicoloured . 2·50 1·10

DESIGNS: 25 f., 30 f. Gabon flag; 50 f. to 200 f. Gabon coat of arms.

O 165 Gabon Flag

1971. Flag in actual colours; inscription in blue; background as below.

O436 **O 165** 5 f. blue 10 10
O437 10 f. grey 15 15
O437a 20 f. orange 15 10
O437b 25 f. yellow 20 15
O438 30 f. cobalt 30 10
O439 40 f. orange 55 30
O440 50 f. red 60 20
O441 60 f. brown 70 30
O441a 75 f. grey 55 15
O442 80 f. mauve . . . . 1·10 50
O443 100 f. mauve 80 30
O444 500 f. green . . . . 4·50 1·40

POSTAGE DUE STAMPS

1928. Postage Due type of French Colonies optd **GABON A. E. F.**

D123 U 5 c. blue 10 30
D124 10 c. brown 10 30
D125 20 c. olive 40 60
D126 25 c. red 15 60
D127 30 c. red 15 60
D128 45 c. green 45 90
D129 50 c. red 15 90
D130 60 c. brown 15 90
D131 1 f. purple 15 90
D132 2 f. red . . . . 25 1·00
D133 3 f. violet . . . . . . 40 2·00

D 19 Local Chief　**D 24** Pahquin Woman

1930.

D134 **D 19** 5 c. drab and blue . . . 55 80
D135 10 c. brown and red . . 65 80
D136 20 c. brown & green . . 95 1·25
D137 25 c. brown and blue . 90 1·40
D138 30 c. green & brown . . 90 1·40
D139 45 c. drab and green . . 1·25 1·90
D140 50 c. brown & mve . . 1·40 2·00
D141 60 c. black & violet . . 1·25 3·50
D142 – 1 f. black and brown . . 1·25 5·25
D143 – 2 f. brown & mauve . . 5·00 7·75
D144 – 3 f. brown and red . . 5·00 8·25

DESIGN—VERT: 1 f. to 3 f. Count Savorgnan de Brazza.

1932.

D151 **D 24** 5 c. blue on blue . . . 15 50
D152 10 c. brown 50 70
D153 20 c. brown . . . . . 60 1·40
D154 25 c. green on blue . . 85 1·00
D155 30 c. red . . . . . . 1·25 2·00
D156 45 c. red on yellow . . 3·00 4·50
D157 50 c. purple . . . . . 2·00 3·00
D158 60 c. blue . . . . . . 2·00 3·00
D159 1 f. blk on orange . . . 1·75 3·00
D160 2 f. green . . . . . . 6·25 7·00
D161 3 f. red . . . . 5·50 7·00

D 40 Pineapple

1962. Fruits.

D196 50 c. red, yellow & grn . . . 10 10
D197 50 c. red, yellow & grn . . . 10 10
D198 1 f. mauve, yellow & grn . . . 10 10
D199 1 f. mauve, yellow & grn . . . 10 10
D200 2 f. yellow, brown & grn . . . 10 10
D201 2 f. yellow, brown & grn . . . 10 10
D202 5 f. yellow, green & brn . . . 30 30
D203 5 f. yellow, green & brn . . . 30 30
D204 10 f. multicoloured 60 60
D205 10 f. multicoloured 60 60
D206 25 f. yellow, green & pur . . . 80 80
D207 25 f. yellow, green & pur . . . 80 80

FRUITS: No. D196, Type **D40**. D197, Mangoes D198, Mandarin oranges. D199, Avocado pears. D200, Grapefruit. D201, Coconuts. D202. Oranges. D203, Papaws. D204, Breadfruit. D205, Guavs. D206, Lemons. D207, Bananas.

D 256 "Charaxes candiope"

1978. Butterflies. Multicoloured.

D655 5 f. Type **D 256** 10 10
D656 10 f. "Charaxes ameliae" . . 10 10
D657 25 f. "Cyrestis camillus" . . . 30 15
D658 50 f. "Charaxes castor" . . . 60 35
D659 100 f. "Pseudacrea boisduvali" . . . . 1·10 65

GALAPAGOS ISLANDS　Pt. 20

These islands, noted for their fauna and flora, were annexed by Ecuador, and later (1973) became a province of that country.

100 centavos = 1 sucre.

1 Californian Sealions

1957. Inscr "ISLAS GALAPAGOS".

1 **1** 20 c. brown (postage) 40 15
2 – 50 c. violet 40 15
3 – 1 s. green . . . . 1·25 45
4 – 1 s. blue (air) 30 15
5 – 1 s. 80 purple 65 30
6 – 4 s. 20 black . . . . 1·75 75

DESIGNS—VERT: 50 c. Map of Ecuador coastline. HORIZ: 1 s. (No. 3) Iguana; 1 s. (No. 4) Santa Cruz Island; 1 s. 80, Map of Galapagos Is; 4 s. 20, Giant tortoise.

1959. Air. United Nations Commem. Triangular design as T **316** of Ecuador but inscr "ISLAS GALAPAGOS".

7 2 s. green 50 35

GAMBIA — Pt. 1

A British colony and protectorate on the West coast of Africa. Granted full internal self-government on 4 October 1963, and achieved indepedence on 18 February 1965. Became a republic within the Commonwealth on 24 April 1970.

1869. 12 pence = 1 shilling;
20 shillings = 1 pound.
1971. 100 bututs = 1 dalasy.

1

2

1869. Imperf.

5 **1** 4d. brown £350 £180
8 6d. blue £300 £180

1880. Perf.

11B **1** ½d. orange . . . . 6·50 12·00
12B 1d. purple . . . . 3·75 5·50
13B 2d. pink . . . . 19·00 11·00
14cB 3d. blue . . . . 48·00 26·00
30 4d. brown . . . . 3·00 2·00
17B 6d. blue . . . . 80·00 45·00
19B 1s. green £200 £120

1886.

21 **1** ½d. green . . . . 2·25 2·25
23 1d. red . . . . 4·00 5·50
25 2d. orange . . . . 1·40 8·00
27 2½d. blue . . . . 1·75 1·25
29 3d. grey . . . . 2·50 14·00
34 6d. green . . . . 10·00 45·00
35 1s. violet . . . . 3·25 16·00

1898.

37 **2** ½d. green . . . . 2·50 1·75
38 1d. red . . . . 1·50 75
39 2d. orange and mauve . . . . 5·00 3·50
40 2½d. blue . . . . 1·50 2·00
41 3d. purple and blue . . . . 14·00 12·00
42 4d. brown and blue . . . . 8·50 27·00
43 6d. green and red . . . . 9·50 23·00
44 1s. mauve and green . . . . 26·00 55·00

1902. As T **2**, but portrait of King Edward VII.

57 ½d. green . . . . 4·00 30
46 1d. red . . . . 2·00 85
47 2d. orange and mauve . . . . 3·25 2·00
74 2d. grey . . . . 1·60 9·50
60 2½d. blue . . . . 4·50 4·75
61 3d. purple and blue . . . . 6·00 2·00
75 3d. purple on yellow . . . . 3·00 90
50 4d. brown and blue . . . . 3·00 23·00
76 4d. black and red on yellow . . . 80 65
63 5d. grey and black . . . . 13·00 16·00
77 5d. orange and purple . . . . 1·50 1·25
51 6d. green and red . . . . 3·25 11·00
78 6d. purple . . . . 2·00 2·25
65 7½d. green and red . . . . 9·00 35·00
79 7½d. brown and blue . . . . 2·00 2·50
80 10d. green and red . . . . 2·50 6·50
67 1s. mauve and green . . . . 16·00 48·00
81 1s. black on green . . . . 3·00 17·00
53 1s. 6d. green and red on yellow . . 6·00 17·00
82 1s. 6d. violet and green . . . . 9·50 55·00
54 2s. grey and orange . . . . 48·00 60·00
83 2s. purple and blue on blue . . 14·00 20·00
55 2s. 6d. purple & brn on yell . . 15·00 60·00
84 2s. 6d. black and red on blue . . 21·00 20·00
56 3s. red and green on yellow . . 20·00 60·00
85 3s. yellow and green . . . . 22·00 48·00

1906. Surch in words.

69 ½d. on 2s. 6d. (No. 55) . . . . 45·00 65·00
70 1d. on 3s. (No. 56) . . . . 55·00 30·00

1912. As T **2**, but portrait of King George V.

86 ½d. green . . . . 1·25 1·50
87a 1d. red . . . . 1·50 30
88 1½d. olive and green 30 30
111 2d. grey . . . . 1·00 1·75
112 2½d. blue . . . . 50 4·75
91 3d. purple on yellow 40 30
92c 4d. black and red on yellow . . 1·50 6·00
93 5d. orange and purple . . . . 70 1·75
94 6d. purple . . . . 70 2·00
95 7½d. brown and blue . . . . 1·00 6·50
96a 10d. green and red . . . . 2·00 15·00
97 1s. black on green . . . . 1·75 1·00
98 1s. 6d. violet and green . . . 9·00 10·00
99 2s. purple and blue on blue . . 2·50 6·00
100 2s. 6d. black and red on blue . . 2·75 14·00
101 3s. yellow and green . . . . 7·50 22·00
117 4s. black and red . . . . 60·00 95·00
102 5s. green and red on yellow . . 60·00 95·00

9

10

1922.

122 **9** ½d. black and green 55 40
124 1d. black and brown 70 10
125 1½d. black and red 80 20
126 2d. black and grey . . . . 1·00 2·00
127 **9** 2½d. black and orange . . . 90 11·00
128 3d. black and blue . . . . 1·00 20
118 4d. black and red on yellow . . 2·00 2·25
130 5d. black and olive . . . . 2·00 10·00
131 6d. black and red . . . . 1·25 30
119 7½d. black & pur on yell . . 2·50 6·50
133 10d. black and blue . . . . 4·50 18·00
134 **10** 1s. black & pur on yell . . . 2·25 90
135 1s. 6d. black and blue . . . 9·50 12·00
136 2s. black and purple on blue . . 3·75 4·00
137 2s. 6d. black and green . . . 4·25 9·50
138 3s. black and purple . . . . 11·00 40·00
140 4s. black and brown . . . . 4·75 16·00
141 5s. black and green on yellow . . 12·00 35·00
142 10s. black and olive . . . . 70·00 £100

10a Windsor Castle

1935. Silver Jubilee.

143 **10a** 1½d. blue and red 50 30
144 3d. brown and blue 55 70
145 6d. blue and olive . . . . 90 2·00
146 1s. grey and purple . . . . 2·75 2·50

10b King George VI and Queen Elizabeth

1937. Coronation.

147 **10b** 1d. brown 30 15
148 1½d. red 30 30
149 3d. blue 55 45

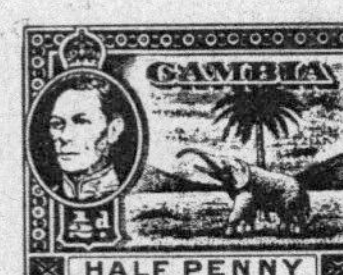

11 Elephant (from Colony Badge)

1938.

150 **11** ½d. black and green 15 60
151 1d. purple and brown . . . 20 50
152b 1½d. pink and red . . . . 30 1·75
152c 1½d. blue and black . . . . 30 1·25
153 2d. blue and black . . . . 2·75 3·00
153a 2d. pink and red . . . . 60 1·75
154 3d. blue 30 10
154a 5d. green and purple . . . 45 45
155 6d. olive and red . . . . 1·50 35
156 1s. blue and purple . . . . 2·00 10
156a 1s. 3d. purple and blue . . . 2·75 2·50
157 2s. red and blue . . . . 4·50 3·25
158 2s. 6d. brown and green . . 12·00 2·00
159 4s. red and purple . . . . 21·00 2·50
160 5s. blue and red . . . . 21·00 4·00
161 10s. orange and black . . . 21·00 7·00

11a Houses of Parliament, London

1946. Victory.

162 **11a** 1½d. black 10 10
163 3d. blue 10 10

11b King George VI and Queen Elizabeth **11c**

1948. Silver Wedding.

164 **11b** 1½d. black 25 10
165 **11c** £1 mauve . . . . 12·00 14·00

11d Hermes, Globe and Forms of Transport

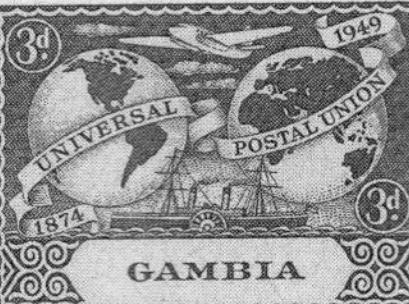

11e Hemispheres, Jetpowered Vickers Viking Airliner and Steamer

11f Hermes and Globe

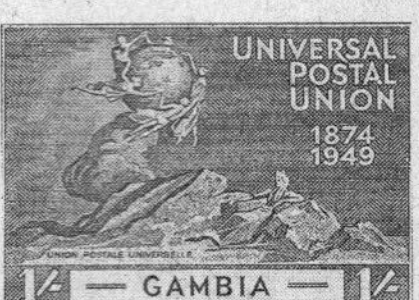

11g U.P.U. Monument

1949. U.P.U.

166 **11d** 1½d. black 40 40
167 **11e** 3d. blue . . . . 1·50 80
168 **11f** 6d. mauve 60 40
169 **11g** 1s. violet 60 30

11h Queen Elizabeth II

12 Tapping for Palm Wine

1953. Coronation.

170 **11h** 1½d. black and blue 50 40

1953. Queen Elizabeth II.

171 **12** ½d. red and green 30 20
172 – 1d. blue and brown 40 30
173 – 1½d. brown and black . . . 20 50
174 – 2½d. black and red 45 70
175 – 3d. blue and lilac 35 10
176 – 4d. black and blue . . . . 60 1·75
177 **12** 6d. brown and purple . . . 35 15
178 – 1s. brown and green 60 50
179 – 1s. 3d. ultramarine and blue . 10·00 50
180 – 2s. blue and red . . . . 7·00 3·50
181 – 2s. 6d. green and brown . . 4·00 1·50
182 – 4s. blue and brown . . . . 11·00 3·00
183 – 5s. brown and blue . . . . 2·50 1·50
184 – 10s. blue and green . . . . 20·00 7·00
185 – £1 green and black . . . . 15·00 9·00

DESIGNS—HORIZ: 1d., 1s. 3d. Cutter (sailing ship); 1½d., 5s. Wollof woman; 2½d., 2s. Barra canoe; 3s., 10s. S.S. "Lady Wright"; 4d., 4s. James Island; 1s., 2s. 6d. Woman hoeing; £1 As Type **11**.

20 Queen Elizabeth II and Palm

20a Protein Foods

1961. Royal Visit.

186 **20** 2d. green and purple 30 15
187 – 3d. turquoise and sepia . . 75 15
188 – 6d. blue and red 75 65
189 **20** 1s. 3d. violet and green . . . 75 1·75

DESIGN: 3d., 6d. Queen Elizabeth II and West African map.

1963. Freedom from Hunger.

190 **20a** 1s. 3d. red 55 15

20b Red Cross Emblem

1963. Centenary of Red Cross.

191 **20b** 2d. red and black 25 10
192 1s. 3d. red and blue 65 45

22 Beautiful Sunbird

36 Gambia Flag and River

22a Shakespeare and Memorial Theatre, Stratford-upon-Avon

1963. Birds. Multicoloured.

193 ½d. Type **22** 30 60
194 1d. Yellow-mantled whydah . . 30 30
195 1½d. Cattle egret . . . . . . 1·75 70
196 2d. Senegal parrot . . . . . 1·75 70
197 3d. Rose-ringed parakeet . . . 1·75 70
198 4d. Violet starling . . . . . 1·75 80
199 6d. Village weaver . . . . . 1·75 10
200 1s. Rufous-crowned roller . . . 1·25 10
201 1s. 3d. Red-eyed dove . . . . 12·00 1·40
202 2s. 6d. Double-spurred francolin 9·00 2·50
203 5s. Palm-nut vulture . . . . 9·00 2·75
204 10s. Orange-checked waxbill . . 13·00 7·00
205 £1 African emerald cuckoo . . 28·00 14·00

1963. New Constitution. Nos. 194, 197 and 200/1 optd **SELF GOVERNMENT 1963**.

206 1d. multicoloured 10 40
207 3d. multicoloured 25 20
208 1s. multicoloured 25 10
209 1s. 3d. multicoloured 30 45

1964. 400th Birth Anniv of Shakespeare.

210 **22a** 6d. blue 20 10

1965. Independence. Multicoloured.

211 ½d. Type **36** 10 40
212 2d. Arms 15 10
213 7½d. Type **36** 40 35
214 1s. 6d. Arms 50 30

1985. Nos 193/205 optd **INDEPENDENCE 1965**.

215 ½d. Type **22** 30 70
216 1d. Yellow-mantled whydah . . 30 20
217 1½d. Cattle egret 60 70
218 2d. Senegal parrot 70 30
219 3d. Rose-ringed parakeet . . . 70 15
220 4d. Violet starling 70 90
221 6d. Village weaver 70 10
222 1s. Rufous-crowned roller . . . 70 10
223 1s. 3d. Red-eyed dove 70 10
224 2s. 6d. Double-spurred francolin 70 60
225 5s. Palm-nut vulture 70 75
226 10s. Orange-checked waxbill . . 1·60 1·50
227 £1 African emerald cuckoo . . 6·00 7·50

39 I.T.U. Emblem and Symbols

1965. Centenary of I.T.U.

228 **39** 1d. silver and blue 25 10
229 1s. 6d. gold and violet . . . 1·00 40

40 Sir Winston Churchill and Houses of Parliament

1966. Churchill Commemoration.

230 **40** 1d. multicoloured 10 10
231 6d. multicoloured 30 15
232 1s. 6d. multicoloured . . . 50 75

41 Red-cheeked Cordon-bleu

1966. Birds. Multicoloured.

233	$\frac{1}{2}$d. Type **41**	90	40
234	1d. White-faced whistling duck	30	50
235	1$\frac{1}{2}$d. Red-throated bee eater	30	40
236	2d. Lesser pied kingfisher	4·25	50
237	3d. Golden bishop	30	10
238	4d. African fish eagle	50	30
239	6d. Yellow-bellied green pigeon	40	10
240	1s. Blue-bellied roller	40	10
241	1s. 6d. African pygmy kingfisher	75	30
242	2s. 6d. Spur-winged goose	75	70
243	5s. Cardinal woodpecker	75	75
244	10s. Violet turaco	75	2·75
245	£1 Pin-tailed whydah ($25 \times 39\frac{1}{2}$ mm)	1·00	6·50

54 Arms, Early Settlement and Modern Buildings

1966. 150th Anniv of Bathurst.

246	**54**	1d. silver, brown and orange	10	10
247		2d. silver, brown and blue	10	10
248		6d. silver, brown and green	10	10
249		1s. 6d. silver, brown & pur	15	15

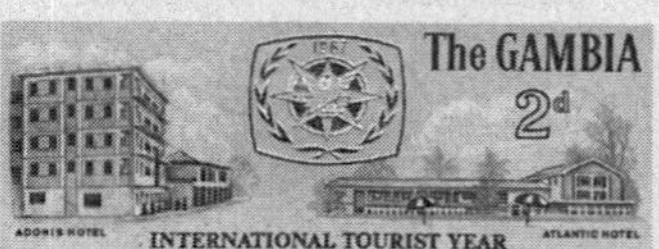

55 I.T.Y. Emblem and Hotels

1967. International Tourist Year.

250	**55**	2d. silver, brown and green	10	10
251		1s. silver, brown and orange	10	10
252		1s. 6d. silver, brn & mve	15	25

56 Handcuffs

1968. Human Rights Year. Multicoloured.

253	1d. Type **56**	10	10
254	1s. Fort Bullen	10	10
255	5s. Methodist Church	30	60

59 Queen Victoria, Queen Elizabeth II and 4d. Stamp of 1869

1969. Gambia Stamp Centenary.

256	**59**	4d. sepia and ochre	20	10
257		6d. blue and green	20	10
258	–	2s. 6d. multicoloured	70	1·40

DESIGN: 2s. 6d. Queen Elizabeth II with 4d. and 6d. stamps of 1869.

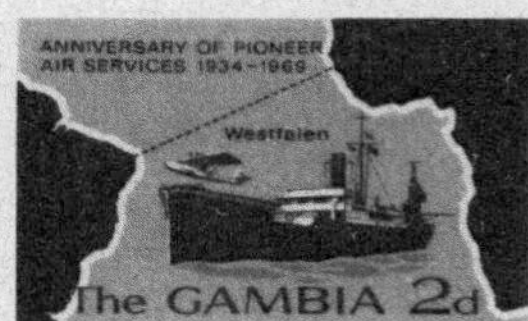

61 Catapult-Ship "Westfalen" launching Dornier Wal

1969. 35th Anniv of Pioneer Air Service. Mult.

259	2d. Type **61**	35	20
260	1s. Dornier Wal flying boat "Boreas"	45	20
261	1s. 6d. Airship "Graf Zeppelin"	55	1·40

63 Athlete and Gambian Flag

1970. 9th British Commonwealth Games, Edinburgh.

262	**63**	1d. multicoloured	10	10
263		1s. multicoloured	10	10
264		5s. multicoloured	30	40

64 President Sir Dawda Kairaba Jawara and State House

1970. Republic Day. Multicoloured.

265	2d. Type **64**	10	10
266	1s. President Sir Dawda Jawara	15	10
267	1s. 6d. President and flag of Gambia	30	35

The 1s. and 1s. 6d. are both vertical designs.

65 Methodist Church, Georgetown

1971. 150th Anniv of Establishment of Methodist Mission. Multicoloured.

268	2d. Type **65**	10	10
269	1s. Map of Africa and Gambian flag (vert)	15	10
270	1s. 6d. John Wesley and scroll	15	35

66 Yellow-finned Tunny

1971. New Currency. Fishes. Multicoloured.

271	2 b. Type **66**	10	50
272	4 b. Peter's mormyrid	10	15
273	6 b. Four-winged flyingfish	15	50
274	8 b. African sleeper goby	15	50
275	10 b. Yellow-tailed snapper	20	15
276	13 b. Rock hind	20	50
277	25 b. West African eel catfish	35	50
278	38 b. Tiger shark	55	45
279	50 b. Electric catfish	70	55
280	63 b. Black swampeel	80	1·50
281	1 d. 25 Small-toothed sawfish	1·40	2·50
282	2 d. 50 Great barracuda	2·00	4·50
283	5 d. Brown bullhead	2·25	7·00

67 Mungo Park in Scotland

1971. Birth Centenary of Mungo Park (explorer). Multicoloured.

284	4 b. Type **67**	20	10
285	25 b. Dug-out canoe	45	35
286	37 b. Death of Mungo Park, Busa Rapids	75	1·50

68 Radio Gambia

1972. 10th Anniv of Radio Gambia.

287	**68**	4 b. brown and black	10	10
288	–	25 b. blue, orange and black	10	25
289	**68**	37 b. green and black	20	70

DESIGN: 25 b. Broadcast-area map.

69 High Jumping

1972. Olympic Games, Munich.

290	**69**	4 b. multicoloured	10	10
291		25 b. multicoloured	20	15
292		37 b. multicoloured	25	20

70 Manding Woman

72 Groundnuts

71 Children carrying Fanal

1972. International Conference on Manding Studies. Multicoloured.

293	2 b. Type **70**	10	10
294	25 b. Musician playing the Kora	15	15
295	37 b. Map of Mail Empire	25	25

1972. Fanals (Model Boats). Multicoloured.

296	2 b. Type **71**	10	10
297	1 d. 25 Fanal with lanterns	30	45

1973. Freedom from Hunger Campaign.

298	**72**	2 b. multicoloured	10	10
299		25 b. multicoloured	15	10
300		37 b. multicoloured	25	20

73 Planting and Drying Rice

74 Oil Palm

1973. Agriculture (1st series). Multicoloured.

301	2 b. Type **73**	10	10
302	25 b. Guinea corn	20	15
303	37 b. Rice	25	25

1973. Agriculture (2nd series). Multicoloured.

304	2 b. Type **74**	10	10
305	25 b. Limes	30	30
306	37 b. Oil palm (fruits)	40	40

75 Cassava

1973. Agriculture (3rd series). Multicoloured.

307	2 b. Type **75**	10	10
308	50 b. Cotton	40	25

76 O.A.U. Emblem

1973. 10th Anniv of O.A.U.

309	**76**	4 b. multicoloured	10	10
310		25 b. multicoloured	15	10
311		37 b. multicoloured	15	20

77 Red Cross

1973. 25th Anniv of Gambian Red Cross.

312	**77**	4 b. red and black	10	10
313		25 b. red, black and blue	15	15
314		37 b. red, black and green	20	20

78 Arms of Banjul

1973. Change of Bathurst's Name to Banjul.

315	**78**	4 b. multicoloured	10	10
316		25 b. multicoloured	15	15
317		37 b. multicoloured	15	20

79 U.P.U. Emblem

1974. Centenary of U.P.U.

318	**79**	4 b. multicoloured	10	10
319		37 b. multicoloured	20	30

80 Churchill as Harrow Schoolboy

1974. Birth Cent of Sir Winston Churchill. Mult.

320	4 b. Type **80**	10	10
321	37 b. Churchill as 4th Hussars officer	25	15
322	50 b. Churchill as Prime Minister	40	60

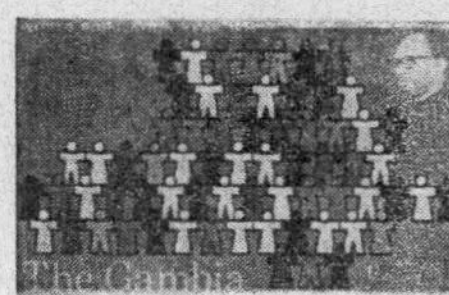

81 "Different Races"

1974. World Population Year. Multicoloured.

323	4 b. Type **81**	10	10
324	37 b. "Multiplication and Division of Races"	15	15
325	50 b. "World Population"	20	25

82 Dr. Schweitzer and River Scene

1975. Birth Centenary of Dr. Albert Schweitzer. Multicoloured.

326	10 b. Type **82**	20	10
327	50 b. Surgery scene	55	25
328	1 d. 25 River journey	1·00	55

83 Dove of Peace

1975. 10th Anniv of Independence. Multicoloured.

329	4 b. Type **83**	10	10
330	10 b. Gambian flag	10	10
331	50 b. Gambian arms	15	10
332	1 d. 25 Map of The Gambia	35	40

84 Development Graph

85 Statue of "David" (Michelangelo)

1975. 10th Anniv of African Development Bank. Multicoloured.

333	10 b. Type **84**	10	10
334	50 b. Symbolic plant	20	15
335	1 d. 25 Bank emblem and symbols	55	60

1975. 500th Birth Anniv of Michelangelo. Mult.
336 10 b. Type **85** 15 10
337 50 b. "Madonna of the Steps" 30 15
338 1 d. 25 "Battle of the Centaurs" (horiz) 50 1·25

86 School Building

1975. Centenary of Gambia High School. Mult.
339 10 b. Type **86** 10 10
340 50 b. Pupil with scientific apparatus 15 10
341 1 d. 50 School crest 35 35

87 "Teaching"

1975. International Women's Year. Multicoloured.
342 4 b. Type **87** 10 10
343 10 b. "Planting rice" 10 10
344 50 b. "Nursing" 35 15
345 1 d. 50 "Directing traffic" 85 35

88 Woman playing Golf

1975. 11th Anniv of Independence. Mult.
346 10 b. Type **88** 55 10
347 50 b. Man playing golf 1·50 20
348 1 d. 50 President playing golf 2·25 70

89 American Militiaman **90** Mother and Child

1976. Bicentenary of American Revolution. Mult.
349 25 b. Type **89** 20 10
350 50 b. Soldier of the Continental Army 30 20
351 1 d. 25 Independence Declaration 40 60

1976. Christmas.
353 **90** 10 b. multicoloured 10 10
354 50 b. multicoloured 15 10
355 1 d. 25 multicoloured 50 45

91 Serval Cat

1976. Abuko Nature Reserve (1st series). Mult.
356 10 b. Type **91** 2·25 20
357 20 b. Bushbuck 3·25 20
358 50 b. Sitatunga (deer) 4·50 40
359 1 d. 25 Leopard 10·00 2·00
See also Nos. 400/3, 431/4 and 460/3.

92 Festival Emblem and Gambian Weaver

1977. 2nd World Black and African Festival of Arts and Culture, Nigeria.
361 **92** 25 b. multicoloured 15 10
362 50 b. multicoloured 20 15
363 1 d. 25 multicoloured 50 70

93 The Spurs and Jewelled Sword

1977. Silver Jubilee. Multicoloured.
365 25 b. The Queen's visit, 1961 25 30
366 50 b. Type **93** 20 25
367 1 d. 25 Oblation of the Sword 30 35

94 Stone Circles, Kuntaur

1977. Tourism. Multicoloured.
368 25 b. Type **94** 10 10
369 50 b. Ruined Fort, James Island 20 20
370 1 d. 25 Mungo Park Monument 70 70

95 Widow of Last Year

1977. Flowers and Shrubs. Multicoloured.
371 2 b. Type **95** 10 15
372 4 b. White water-lily 10 30
373 6 b. Fireball lily 10 30
374 8 b. Cocks-comb 10 15
375 10 b. Broad leaved ground orchid 2·00 30
376 13 b. Fibre plant (yellow background) 15 40
376a 13 b. Fibre plant (grey background) 1·75 3·50
377 25 b. False kapok 15 15
378 38 b. Baobab 25 55
379 50 b. Coral tree 35 35
380 63 b. Gloriosa lily 40 70
381 1 d. 25 Bell-flowered mimosa 45 1·25
382 2 d. 50 Kindin dolo 50 1·25
383 5 d. African tulip tree 60 2·00
Nos. 373/78 and 381/2 are vert designs.

96 Endangered Animals **97** "Flight into Egypt"

1977. Banjul Declaration.
384 **96** 10 b. black and blue 25 10
385 – 25 b. multicoloured 40 10
386 – 50 b. multicoloured 65 20
387 – 1 d. 25 black and red 1·75 75
DESIGNS: 25 b. Extract from Declaration; 50 b. Declaration in full; 1 d. 25, Endangered insects and flowers.

1977. 400th Birth of Rubens. Multicoloured.
388 10 b. Type **97** 15 10
389 25 b. "The Education of the Virgin" 20 10
390 50 b. "Clara Serena Rubens" 35 30
391 1 d. "Madonna with Saints" 65 90

98 Dome of the Rock, Jerusalem

1978. Palestinian Welfare.
392 **98** 8 b. multicoloured 50 15
393 25 b. multicoloured 2·00 85

99 Walking on a Greasy Pole **100** Lion

1978. 13th Anniv of Independence. Multicoloured.
394 10 b. Type **99** 10 10
395 50 b. Pillow fighting 20 10
396 1 d. Long boat rowing 45 45

1978. 25th Anniv of Coronation.
397 – 1 d. black, brown and yellow 20 45
398 – 1 d. multicoloured 20 45
399 **100** 1 d. black, brown and yellow 20 45
DESIGNS: No. 397, White Greyhound of Richmond; No. 398, Queen Elizabeth II.

101 Verreaux's Eagle Owl

1978. Abuko Nature Reserve (2nd series). Multicoloured.
400 20 b. Type **101** 6·00 65
401 25 b. Lizard buzzard 6·00 65
402 50 b. African harrier hawk 9·00 2·25
403 1 d. 25 Long-crested eagle 13·00 9·00

102 M.V. "Lady Wright"

1978. Launching of River Vessel "Lady Chilel Jawara". Multicoloured.
404 8 b. Type **102** 15 10
405 25 b. Sectional view of "Lady Chilel Jawara" 40 25
406 1 d. "Lady Chilel Jawara" 1·25 1·40

103 Police Service

1979. 14th Anniv of Independence. Multicoloured.
407 10 b. Type **103** 60 10
408 50 b. Fire service 1·10 25
409 1 d. 25 Ambulance service 1·40 80

1979. Nos. 376 and 380/1 surch **25b**.
410 25 b. on 13 b. Fibre plant 20 35
411 25 b. on 63 b. Gloriosa lily 15 20
412 25 b. on 1 d. 25 Bell-flowered mimosa 15 20

105 "Ramsgate Sands" (detail showing children playing on beach)

1979. International Year of the Child. "Ramsgate Sands" (William Powell Frith). Multicoloured.
413 10 b. Type **105** 10 10
414 25 b. Detail showing child paddling (vert) 20 10
415 1 d. Complete painting (60 × 23 mm) 60 60

106 1883 2½d. Stamp

1979. Death Centenary of Sir Rowland Hill. Multicoloured.
416 10 b. Type **106** 10 10
417 25 b. 1869 4d. stamp 15 10
418 50 b. 1965 Independence 7½d. commemorative 20 20
419 1 d. 25 1935 Silver Jubilee 1½d. commemorative 40 50

107 Satellite Earth Station under Construction

1979. Abuko Satellite Earth Station. Multicoloured.
421 25 b. Type **107** 20 10
422 50 b. Satellite Earth Station (completed) 30 20
423 1 d. "Intelsat" satellite 65 60

108 "Apollo II" leaving Launch Pad

1979. 10th Anniv of Moon Landing. Multicoloured.
424 25 b. Type **108** 20 10
425 38 b. "Apollo II" in Moon orbit 25 20
426 50 b. Splashdown 30 40
430 2 d. Lunar module on Moon 1·50 2·25
Nos. 424/6 also exist self-adhesive from booklet panes. No. 430 only exists in this form.

109 "Acraea zetes"

1980. Abuko Nature Reserve (3rd series). Butterflies. Multicoloured.
431 25 b. Type **109** 2·50 20
432 50 b. "Precis hierta" 3·00 50
433 1 d. "Graphium leonidas" 5·00 1·00
434 1 d. 25 "Charaxes jasius" 5·00 1·10

110 Steam Launch "Vampire"

1980. "London 1980" International Stamp Exhibition. Multicoloured.
436 10 b. Type **110** 25 10
437 25 b. T.S.S. "Lady Denham" 35 10
438 50 b. T.S.C.M.Y. "Mansa Kila Ba" 40 20
439 1 d. 25 T.S.S. "Prince of Wales" 65 60
Nos. 438 and 439 are larger, 49 × 26 mm.

111 Queen Elizabeth the Queen Mother

1980. 80th Birthday of Queen Elizabeth The Queen Mother.
440 **111** 67 b. multicoloured 30 35

112 Phoenician Trading Vessel

1980. Early Sailing Vessels. Multicoloured.

441 8 b. Type **112** 10 10
442 67 b. Egyptian sea-going vessel 40 20
443 75 b. Portuguese caravel . . . 50 30
444 1 d. Spanish galleon 70 50

113 "Madonna and Child" (Francesco de Mura)

1980. Christmas. Multicoloured.

445 8 b. Type **113** 10 10
446 67 b. "Praying Madonna with Crown of Stars" (workshop of Correggio) 25 25
447 75 b. "La Zingarella" (workshop replica of Correggio painting) 25 30

114 New Atlantic Hotel

1981. World Tourism Conference, Manila. Mult.

448 25 b. Type **114** 15 10
449 75 b. Ancient stone circles . . . 30 40
450 85 b. Conference emblem . . . 40 50

115 1979 Abuko Satellite Earth Station 50 b. Commemorative

1981. World Telecommunications Day.

451 **115** 50 b. multicoloured 30 20
452 – 50 b. multicoloured 30 20
453 – 85 b. black and brown . . 50 45

DESIGNS: No. 452, 1975 Birth centenary of Schweitzer 50 b. commemorative; No. 453 I.T.U. and W.H.O. emblems.

116 Prince Charles in Naval Uniform

1981. Royal Wedding. Multicoloured.

454 75 b. Wedding bouquet from Gambia 20 20
455 1 d. Type **116** 25 30
456 1 d. 25 Prince Charles and Lady Diana Spencer 30 35

117 Planting-out Seedlings

1981. 10th Anniv of West African Rice Development Association. Multicoloured.

457 10 b. Type **117** 10 10
458 50 b. Care of the crops 25 35
459 85 b. Winnowing and drying . . 40 55

118 Bosc's Monitor

1981. Abuko Nature Reserve (4th series). Reptiles. Multicoloured.

460 40 b. Type **118** . . . . 4·00 20
461 60 b. Dwarf crocodile . . . . 4·50 60
462 80 b. Royal python . . . . . 5·50 1·00
463 85 b. Chameleon . . . . . . 5·50 1·00

119 Examination Room

1982. 30th Anniv of West African Examinations Council. Multicoloured.

464 60 b. Type **119** 50 30
465 85 b. First high school 65 45
466 1 d. 10 Council's office 85 55

1982. No. 454 surch **60B**.

467 60 b. on 75 b. Wedding bouquet from Gambia . . . . 75 1·60

121 Tree-planting ("Conservation")

1982. 75th Anniv of Boy Scout Movement. Multicoloured.

468 85 b. Type **121** . . . . 2·00 1·25
469 1 d. 25 Woodworking . . . . 2·25 2·50
470 1 d. 27 Lord Baden-Powell . . . 2·50 3·25

122 Gambia Football Team

1982. World Cup Football Championship, Spain. Multicoloured.

471 10 b. Type **122** 20 10
472 1 d. 10 Gambian team practice 1·10 70
473 1 d. 25 Bernabeu Stadium, Madrid . . . . 1·10 75
474 1 d. 55 FIFA World Cup . . . 1·25 80

123 Gambia Coat of Arms

1982. 21st Birthday of Princess of Wales. Multicoloured.

476 10 b. Type **123** 10 10
477 85 b. Princess at City Hall, Cardiff, October 1981 . . . 30 20
478 1 d. 10 Bride and groom returning to Buckingham Palace . . . 35 35
479 2 d. 50 Formal portrait . . . . 1·25 1·00

124 Vegetable Garden at Yundum Experimental Farm

1982. Economic Community of West African States Development. Multicoloured.

480 10 b. Type **124** 30 15
481 60 b. Banjul/Kaolack microwave tower . . . . 2·00 2·25
482 90 b. Soap factory, Denton Bridge, Banjul . . . . . . 2·00 3·00
483 1 d. 25 Control tower, Yundum Airport . . . . 3·00 3·50

125 "Kassina cassinoides"

1982. Frogs. Multicoloured.

484 10 b. Type **125** 90 20
485 20 b. "Hylarana galamensis" . 1·90 30
486 85 b. "Euphlyctis occipitalis" . 3·00 2·00
487 2 d. "Kassina senegalensis" . . 4·25 8·00

126 Satellite View of Gambia

1983. Commonwealth Day. Multicoloured.

488 10 b. Type **126** 10 10
489 60 b. Batik cloth 20 45
490 1 d. 10 Bagging groundnuts . . 35 65
491 2 d. 10 Gambia flag . . . . . 55 1·25

127 Blessed Anne Marie Javouhey (foundress of Order)

1983. Centenary of Sisters of St. Joseph of Cluny's Work in Gambia. Multicoloured.

492 10 b. Type **127** 10 10
493 85 b. Bathurst Hospital, nun and school children (horiz) . . . 45 50

128 Canoes

1983. River Craft. Multicoloured.

494 1 b. Type **128** 15 40
495 2 b. Upstream ferry 20 40
496 3 b. Dredger 20 40
497 4 b. "Sir Dawda" (harbour launch) 30 40
498 5 b. Cargo liner 30 40
499 10 b. "Lady Dale" (60 ft. launch) 30 10
500 20 b. "Shonga" (container ship) 45 40
501 30 b. Large sailing canoe . . . 45 40
502 40 b. "Lady Wright" (river steamer) 65 55
503 50 b. Container ship (different) 65 55
504 75 b. Fishing boats 75 60
505 1 d. Tug with groundnut barges 90 80
506 1 d. 25 Groundnut canoe . . . 1·00 1·25
507 2 d. 50 "Banjul" (car ferry) . . 1·75 2·50
508 5 d. "Bintang Bolong" (freighter) 2·50 4·00
509 10 d. "Lady Chilel Jawara" (river vessel) . . . . 4·00 6·50

129 Osprey in Tree

1983. The Osprey. Multicoloured.

510 10 b. Type **129** . . . . 1·50 50
511 60 b. Osprey . . . . 2·75 2·50
512 85 b. Osprey with catch . . . 3·25 3·00
513 1 d. 10 In flight . . . . . . 3·50 5·00

130 Local Ferry

1983. World Communications Year. Multicoloured.

514 10 b. Type **130** 10 10
515 85 b. Telex operator 45 50
516 90 b. Radio Gambia 45 50
517 1 d. 10 Loading mail onto Douglas DC-9-80 aircraft . . 1·25 65

131 "St. Paul preaching at Athens" (detail)

1983. 500th Birth Anniv of Raphael.

518 **131** 60 b. multicoloured 35 40
519 – 85 b. multicoloured 45 50
520 – 1 d. multicoloured 50 55

Nos. 519/20 show different details of "St. Paul preaching at Athens".

132 Montgolfier Balloon and Siege of Paris Cover

1983. Bicentenary of Manned Flight. Multicoloured.

522 60 b. Type **132** 35 40
523 85 b. Douglas DC-10 aircraft and flown cover 45 50
524 90 b. Junkers seaplane "Atlantis" and Hans Bertram cover . . 45 50
525 1 d. 25 Lunar module and H. E. Sieger's space cover 65 70
526 4 d. Airship "Graf Zeppelin" . 2·00 3·00

133 Shot-putting 134 Goofy

1984. Olympic Games, Los Angeles (1st issue). Multicoloured.

527 60 b. Type **133** 25 30
528 85 b. High jumping (horiz) . . 35 40
529 90 b. Wrestling 35 40
530 1 d. Gymnastics 40 45
531 1 d. 25 Swimming (horiz) . . . 50 55
532 2 d. Diving 80 85

See also Nos. 555/8.

1984. Easter. Multicoloured.

534 1 b. Type **134** 10 10
535 2 b. Mickey Mouse 10 10
536 3 b. Huey, Dewey and Louie . 10 10
537 4 b. Goofy (different) 10 10
538 5 b. Donald Duck 10 10
539 10 b. Chip 'n' Dale 10 10
540 60 b. Pluto 35 40
541 90 b. Scrooge McDuck 50 60
542 5 d. Morty and Ferdie . . . . 2·25 2·75

Nos. 534/42 show Walt Disney cartoon characters painting eggs.

135 Young Crocodiles Hatching

1984. Endangered Species. The Nile Crocodile. Multicoloured.

544 4 b. Type **135** 55 55
545 6 b. Adult carrying young . . . 55 55
546 90 b. Adult . . . . 4·50 3·00
547 1 d. 50 Crocodile at riverbank . 5·50 7·00

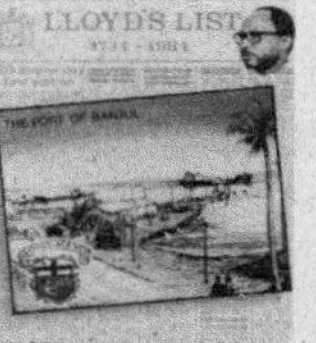

136 Port Banjul

1984. 250th Anniv of "Lloyd's List" (newspaper). Multicoloured.

549 60 b. Type **136** 60 50
550 85 b. Bulk carrier 75 80
551 90 b. Sinking of the "Dagomba" 75 90
552 1 d. 25 19th century frigate . . 1·25 1·60

1984. Universal Postal Union Congress, Hamburg. Nos. 507/8 optd **19th UPU CONGRESS HAMBURG**.

553 2 d. 50 "Banjul" (car ferry) . . 1·00 1·50
554 5 d. "Bintang Bolong" (ferry) . 1·75 2·50

138 Sprinting

1984. Olympic Games, Los Angeles (2nd issue). Multicoloured.

555 60 b. Type **138** 25 30
556 85 b. Long jumping 35 40
557 90 b. Long-distance running . . 35 40
558 1 d. 25 Triple jumping 50 55

139 Airship "Graf Zeppelin"

1984. 50th Anniv of Gambia-South America Trans-Atlantic Flights. Multicoloured.

559 60 b. Type **139** . . . . 1·10 1·00
560 85 b. Dornier Wal on S.S. "Westfalen" . . . . 1·60 1·75
561 90 b. Dornier DO-18 . . . . . 1·75 2·50
562 1 d. 25 Dornier Wal . . . . . 1·75 2·75

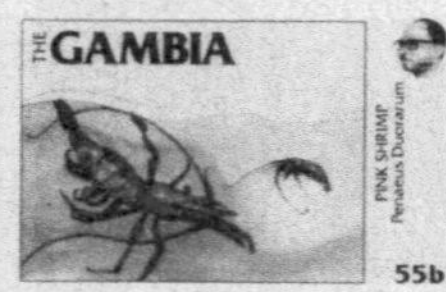

140 Pink Shrimp

1984. Marine Life. Multicoloured.

563 55 b. Type **140** 35 30
564 75 b. Atlantic loggerhead turtle 55 40
565 1 d. 50 Portuguese man-of-war 90 1·00
566 2 d. 35 Fiddler crab . . . . . 1·40 1·60

141 "Antanartia hippomene"

1984. Butterflies. Multicoloured.

568 10 b. Type **141** 30 20
569 85 b. "Pseudacraea eurytus" . . 80 90
570 90 b. "Charaxes lactitinctus" . . 80 90
571 3 d. "Graphium pylades" . . . 2·00 3·75

142 Oral Re-hydration Therapy

1985. Campaign for Child Survival.

573 **142** 10 b. black, blue and brown 10 10
574 – 85 b. multicoloured 35 45
575 – 1 d. 10 multicoloured . . . 45 65
576 – 1 d. 50 multicoloured . . . 60 80

DESIGNS: 85 b. Growth monitoring; 1 d. 10, Health care worker with women and babies ("Promotion of breast feeding"); 1 d. 50, Universal immunisation.

143 Women at Market

1985. Women and Development. Multicoloured.

577 60 b. Type **143** 25 35
578 85 b. Type **143** 35 50
579 1 d. Woman office worker . . . 40 60
580 1 d. 25 As 1 d. 50 90

144 Turkey Vulture **145** The Queen Mother

1985. Birth Bicentenary of John J. Audubon (ornithologist). Designs showing original paintings. Multicoloured.

581 60 b. Type **144** . . . . 1·40 75
582 85 b. American anhinga . . . 1·60 1·50
583 1 d. 50 Green heron . . . . . 2·00 3·25
584 5 d. Wood duck . . . . 3·25 5·50

1985. Life and Times of Queen Elizabeth the Queen Mother. Multicoloured.

586 85 b. The Queen Mother and King George VI reviewing Home Guard 35 30
587 3 d. Type **145** . . . . 1·00 1·00
588 5 d. The Queen Mother with posy 1·75 1·75

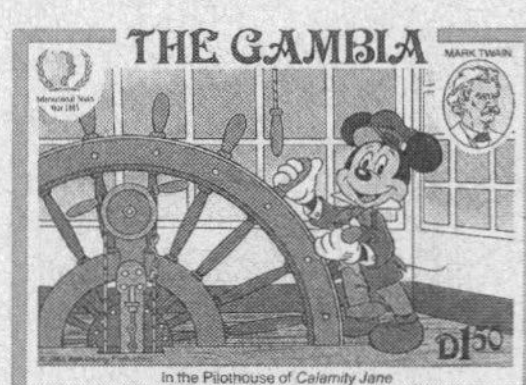

145a Mickey Mouse steering the "Calamity Jane"

1985. 150th Birth Anniv of Mark Twain (author). Designs showing Walt Disney cartoon characters in scenes from "Life on the Mississippi". Multicoloured.

590 1 d. 50 Type **145a** . . . . . 1·25 1·25
591 2 d. Mickey and Minnie Mouse at antebellum mansion . . . . 1·50 1·50
592 2 d. 50 Donald Duck and Goofy heaving the lead . . . . . 1·75 1·75
593 3 d. Poker game aboard the "Gold Dust" . . . . 2·00 2·00

145b The King (Mickey Mouse) and Portrait of the Princess (Minnie Mouse)

1985. Birth Bicentenaries of Grimm Brothers (folklorists). Designs showing Walt Disney cartoon characters in scenes from "Faithful John". Multicoloured.

595 60 b. Type **145b** 40 40
596 85 b. The King showing the Princess his treasures 50 50
597 2 d. 35 Faithful John (Goofy) playing trumpet . . . . . . 1·40 1·40
598 5 d. Faithful John turned to stone . . . . 2·50 2·50

1985. Olympic Gold Medal Winners, Los Angeles. Nos. 527/32 optd.

600 60 b. Type **133** (optd **GOLD MEDALLIST CLAUDIA LOCH WEST GERMANY**) 40 40
601 85 b. High jumping (optd **GOLD MEDALLIST ULRIKE MEYFARTH WEST GERMANY**) 50 50
602 90 b. Wrestling (optd **GOLD MEDALLIST PASQUALE PASSARELLI WEST GERMANY**) 50 50
603 1 d. Gymnastics (optd **GOLD MEDALLIST LI NING CHINA**) 55 55
604 1 d. 25 Swimming (optd **GOLD MEDALLIST MICHAEL GROSS WEST GERMANY**) 70 70
605 2 d. Diving (optd **GOLD MEDALLIST SYLVIE BERNIER CANADA**) . . . 1·00 1·00

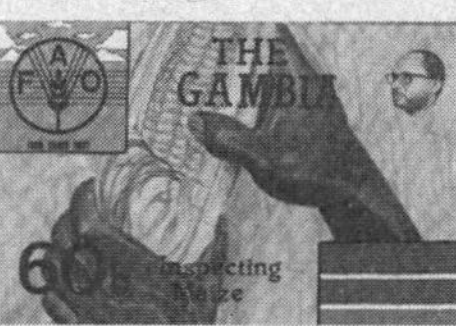

147 Inspecting Maize

1985. United Nations Anniversaries. Multicoloured.

607 60 b. Type **147** 40 35
608 85 b. Football match, Independence Stadium, Banjul 50 40
609 1 d. 10 Rice fields 60 60
610 2 d. Central Bank of The Gambia 85 1·00
611 3 d. Cow and calf . . . . . . 1·50 1·75
612 4 d. Banjul harbour . . . . . 2·00 2·25
613 5 d. Gambian fruits . . . . . 2·25 2·50
614 6 d. Oyster Creek Bridge . . . 2·50 3·00

Nos. 607, 609, 611 and 613 commemorate the 40th anniv of the Food and Agriculture Organization and Nos. 608, 610, 612 and 614 the 40th anniv of the United Nations Organization.

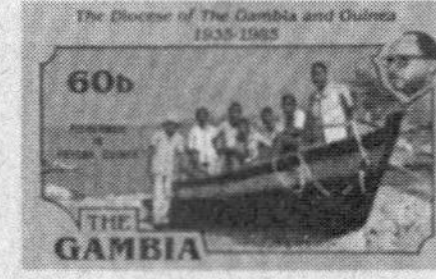

148 Fishermen in Fotoba, Guinea

1985. 50th Anniv of Diocese of The Gambia and Guinea. Multicoloured.

615 60 b. Type **148** 40 30
616 85 b. St. Mary's Primary School, Banjul 40 40
617 1 d. 10 St. Mary's Cathedral, Banjul 40 65
618 1 d. 50 Mobile dispensary at Christy Kunda 60 85

149 "Virgin and Child" (Dieric Bouts)

1985. Christmas. Religious Paintings. Multicoloured.

619 60 b. Type **149** 20 25
620 85 b. "The Annunciation" (Robert Campin) 25 30
621 1 d. 50 "Adoration of the Shepherds" (Gerard David) . 45 50
622 5 d. "The Nativity" (Gerard David) . . . . 1·60 1·75

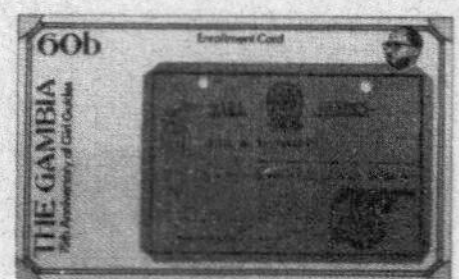

150 Enrolment Card

1985. 75th Anniv of Girl Guide Movement. Multicoloured.

624 60 b. Type **150** 40 30
625 85 b. 2nd Bathurst Company centre 50 35
626 1 d. 50 Lady Baden-Powell (vert) 70 1·00
627 5 d. Miss Rosamond Fowlis (Gambian Guide Association leader) (vert) . . . . 2·00 3·75

151 Girl and Village Scene

1985. International Youth Year. Multicoloured.

629 60 b. Type **151** 30 30
630 85 b. Youth and wrestling bout 35 35
631 1 d. 10 Girl and Griot storyteller 45 1·00
632 1 d. 50 Youth and crocodile pool 70 1·40

151a Maria Mitchell (astronomer) and Kitt Peak National Observatory, Arizona

1986. Appearance of Halley's Comet. Multicoloured.

634 10 b. Type **151a** 40 20
635 20 b. Neil Armstrong, first man on Moon, 1969 . . . . . . 55 25
636 75 b. "Skylab 4" and Comet Kohoutek, 1973 . . . . . . 85 65
637 1 d. N.A.S.A.'s infra-red astronomical satellite and Halley's Comet . . . . . 1·00 80
638 2 d. Comet of 1577 from Turkish painting . . . . 1·50 1·50
639 10 d. N.A.S.A.'s International Cometary Explorer . . . . 4·00 5·50

151b Duke of York and Family, Royal Tournament, 1936

1986. 60th Birthday of Queen Elizabeth II.

641 **151b** 1 d. black and yellow . . 25 30
642 – 2 d. 50 multicoloured . . 65 70
643 – 10 d. multicoloured . . . 2·50 3·50

DESIGNS: Nos. 642, Queen attending christening, 1983; 643, In West Germany, 1978.

152 Two Players competing for Ball

1986. World Cup Football Championship, Mexico. Multicoloured.

645 75 b. Type **152** 75 60
646 1 d. Player kicking ball . . . . 1·00 85
647 2 d. 50 Player kicking ball (different) . . . . 2·00 2·25
648 10 d. Player heading ball . . . 5·00 6·00

153 Mercedes "500" (1986)

1986. "Ameripex" International Stamp Exhibition, Chicago. Centenary (1985) of First Benz Motor Car. Multicoloured.

650 25 b. Type **153** 20 10
651 75 b. Cord "810" (1935) . . . 40 40
652 1 d. Borgward "Isabella Coupe" (1957) 60 60
653 1 d. 25 Lamborghini "Countach" (1985/6) 70 70
654 2 d. Ford "Thunderbird" (1955) 75 1·25
655 2 d. 25 Citroen "DS19" (1956) 75 1·60
656 5 d. Bugatti "Atlante" (1936) . 1·00 3·00
657 10 d. Horch "853" (1936) . . . 1·25 5·00

The 25 b. value is inscribed "MECEDES" and the 10 d. "LARL BENZ".

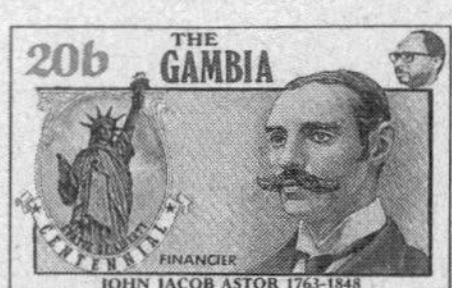

153a John Jacob Astor (financier)

1986. Centenary of Statue of Liberty (1st issue). Multicoloured. Designs showing Statue of Liberty and immigrants to the U.S.A.

659 20 b. Type **153a** 10 10
660 1 d. Jacob Riis (journalist) . . 40 50
661 1 d. 25 Igor Sikorsky (aeronautics engineer) 60 60
662 5 d. Charles Boyer (actor) . . . 2·50 2·50

See also Nos. 705/14.

153b Prince Andrew and Miss Sarah Ferguson

1986. Royal Wedding. Multicoloured.

664 1 d. Type **153b** 40 45
665 2 d. 50 Prince Andrew . . . . 1·00 1·40
666 4 d. Prince Andrew as helicopter pilot . . . . 1·60 2·00

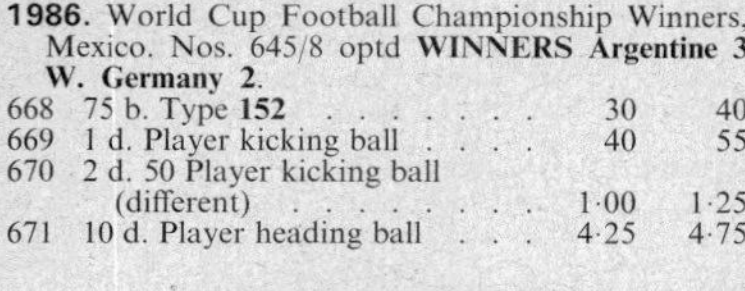

1986. World Cup Football Championship Winners, Mexico. Nos. 645/8 optd **WINNERS Argentine 3 W. Germany 2.**

668 75 b. Type **152** 30 40
669 1 d. Player kicking ball . . . 40 55
670 2 d. 50 Player kicking ball (different) . . . . 1·00 1·25
671 10 d. Player heading ball . . . 4·25 4·75

154 Minnie Mouse (Great Britain)

1986. Christmas. Designs showing Walt Disney cartoon characters posting letters in various countries. Multicoloured.

673 1 d. Type **154** 75 60
674 1 d. 25 Huey (U.S.A.) . . . 80 80
675 2 d. Huey, Dewey and Louie (France) . . . . 1·25 1·40
676 2 d. 35 Kanga and Roo (Australia) . . . . 1·40 1·75
677 5 d. Goofy (Germany) . . . . 2·25 3·00

Nos. 673/7 also show the "Stockholmia '86" International Stamp Exhibition emblem.

1986. Appearance of Halley's Comet (2nd issue). Nos. 634/9 optd **HALLEYS COMET 1985-OFFICIAL-1986.**

679 10 b. Maria Mitchell (astronomer) and Kitt Peak National Observatory, Arizona 30 15
680 20 b. Neil Armstrong, first man on Moon, 1969 . . . . . . 50 20
681 75 b. "Skylab 4" and Comet Kohoutek, 1973 . . . . . . 75 50
682 1 d. N.A.S.A.'s infra-red astronomical satellite and Halley's Comet 85 60
683 2 d. Comet of 1577 from Turkish painting . . . . 1·40 1·75
684 10 d. N.A.S.A.'s International Cometary Explorer . . . . 3·75 6·00

155 Bugarab and Tabala

1987. Manding Musical Instruments. Multicoloured.

686 75 b. Type **155** 15 20
687 1 d. Balaphong and fiddle . . . 15 25
688 1 d. 25 Bolongbato and konting (vert) 20 35
689 10 d. Antique and modern koras (vert) . . . . 1·60 3·00

156 "Snowing"

1987. Birth Centenary of Marc Chagall (artist). Multicoloured.

691 75 b. Type **156** 40 40
692 85 b. "The Boat" 50 50
693 1 d. "Maternity" 65 65
694 1 d. 25 "The Flute Player" . . 75 75
695 2 d. 35 "Lovers and the Beast" . 1·25 1·25
696 4 d. "Fishes at Saint Jean" . . 1·50 2·00
697 5 d. "Entering the Ring" . . . 1·75 2·50
698 10 d. "Three Acrobats" . . . . 2·75 3·75

157 "America", 1851

1987. America's Cup Yachting Championship. Multicoloured.

700 20 b. Type **157** 20 15
701 1 d. "Courageous", 1974 . . . 35 35
702 2 d. 50 "Volunteer", 1887 . . . 75 1·10
703 10 d. "Intrepid", 1967 . . . . 2·25 3·25

158 Arm of Statue of Liberty

159 "Lantana camara"

1987. Centenary of Statue of Liberty (1986) (2nd issue). Multicoloured.

705 1 b. Type **158** 10 10
706 2 b. Launch passing Statue (horiz) 10 10
707 3 b. Schooner passing Statue (horiz) 10 10
708 5 b. U.S.S. "John F. Kennedy" (aircraft carrier) and "Queen Elizabeth 2" (liner) (horiz) . 10 10
709 50 b. Checking Statue for damage 40 40
710 75 b. Cleaning in progress . . . 55 55
711 1 d. Working on Statue 70 70
712 1 d. 25 Statue and fireworks . . 80 80
713 10 d. Statue illuminated . . . . 4·25 4·25
714 12 d. Statue and fireworks (different) . . . . 4·50 4·50

1987. Flowers of Abuko Nature Reserve. Multicoloured.

715 75 b. Type **159** 15 15
716 1 d. "Clerodendrum thomsoniae" 15 20
717 1 d. 50 "Haemanthus multiflorus" 25 30
718 1 d. 70 "Gloriosa simplex" . . 25 35
719 1 d. 75 "Combretum microphyllum" 30 40
720 2 d. 25 "Eulophia quineensis" . 35 45
721 5 d. "Erythrina senegalensis" . . 80 1·25
722 15 d. "Dichrostachys glomerata" 2·40 3·50

160 Front of Mail Bus

161 Basketball

1987. "Capex '87" International Stamp Exhibition, Toronto and 10th Anniv of Gambia Public Transport Corporation. Mail Buses. Mult.

724 20 b. Type **160** 50 20
725 75 b. Bus in Banjul (horiz) . . . 80 45
726 1 d. Passengers queueing for bus (horiz) 80 45
727 10 d. Two buses on rural road . 3·25 5·50

1987. Olympic Games, Seoul (1988) (1st issue). Multicoloured.

729 50 b. Type **161** 35 20
730 1 d. Volleyball 50 35
731 3 d. Hockey (horiz) . . . . . 1·10 85
732 10 d. Handball (horiz) . . . . 2·50 2·25

See also Nos. 779/82.

162 "A Partridge in a Pear Tree"

163 Campfire Singsong

1987. Christmas. Designs showing a Victorian couple in scenes from carol "The Twelve Days of Christmas". Multicoloured.

734 20 b. Type **162** 30 40
735 40 b. "Two turtle doves" 35 45
736 60 b. "Three French hens" . . . 40 50
737 75 b. "Four calling birds" . . . 40 55
738 1 d. "Five golden rings" . . . 40 55
739 1 d. 25 "Six geese a-laying" . . 50 60
740 1 d. 50 "Seven swans a-swimming" 50 60
741 2 d. "Eight maids a-milking" . . 60 70
742 3 d. "Nine ladies dancing" . . 70 75
743 5 d. "Ten lords a-leaping" . . 1·00 1·10
744 10 d. "Eleven pipers piping" . . 1·60 1·75
745 12 d. "Twelve drummers drumming" . . . . 1·90 2·00

1987. World Scout Jamboree, Australia. Multicoloured.

747 75 b. Type **163** 50 30
748 1 d. Scouts examining African katydid 60 40
749 1 d. 25 Scouts watching Red-tailed tropic bird 75 75
750 12 d. Scouts helping bus passenger . . . . 2·75 3·75

163a Morty and Ferdie examining Trevithick's Locomotive, 1804

1987. 60th Anniv of Mickey Mouse (Walt Disney cartoon character) (1st issue). Multicoloured.

752 60 b. Type **163a** 25 25
753 75 b. Clarabelle Cow in "Empire State Express", 1893 . . . . 30 30
754 1 d. Donald Duck inspecting Stephenson's "Rocket", 1829 . . . . 40 40
755 1 d. 25 Piglet and Winnie the Pooh with Santa Fe Railroad locomotive, 1920 . . . . . 45 45
756 2 d. Donald and Daisy Duck with Pennsylvania Railroad Class GG1 electric locomotive, 1933 . . . . 70 70
757 5 d. Mickey Mouse in "Stourbridge Lion", 1829 . . 1·60 1·75
758 10 d. Goofy in "Best Friend of Charleston", 1830 . . . . . 2·75 3·00
759 12 d. Brer Bear and Brer Rabbit with Union Pacific diesel locomotive No. M10001, 1934 . . . . 3·00 3·25

See also Nos. 849/57.

164 Common Duiker and Acacia

165 Wedding Portrait, 1947

1988. Flora and Fauna. Multicoloured.

761 50 b. Type **164** 20 10
762 75 b. Red-billed hornbill and casuarina (vert) 50 30
763 90 b. West African dwarf crocodile and rice 30 20
764 1 d. Leopard and papyrus (vert) 30 20
765 1 d. 25 Crowned crane and millet 50 45
766 2 d. Waterbuck and baobab tree (vert) 40 60
767 3 d. Oribi and Senegal palm . . 50 1·25
768 5 d. Hippopotamus and papaya (vert) . . . . 80 1·75

1988. Royal Ruby Wedding.

770 **165** 75 b. brown, black & orange 30 15
771 – 1 d. brown, black and blue . 40 20
772 – 3 d. multicoloured . . . . 90 1·00
773 – 10 d. multicoloured . . . . 2·25 3·25

DESIGNS: 1 d. Engagement photograph; 3 d. Wedding portrait, 1947 (different); 10 d. Queen Elizabeth II and Prince Philip (photo by Karsh), 1986.

1988. Stamp Exhibitions. Nos. 689, 703, 722 and 726 optd.

775 1 d. Passengers queueing for bus (optd **Independence 40**, Israel) 25 25
776 10 d. Antique and modern koras (optd **FINLANDIA 88**, Helsinki) . . . . 2·00 2·50
777 10 d. "Intrepid" (yacht), 1967 (optd **Praga '88**, Prague) . . 2·00 2·50
778 15 d. "Dichrostachys glomerata" (optd **OLYMPHILEX '88**, Seoul) . . . . 2·75 3·00

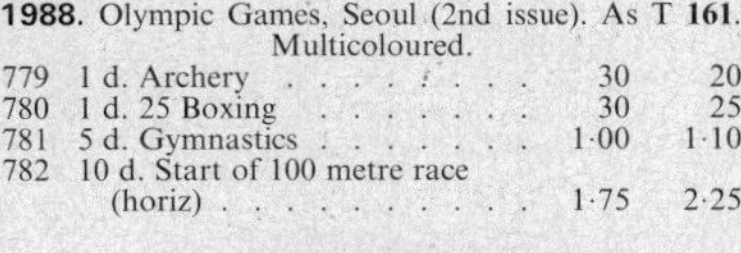

1988. Olympic Games, Seoul (2nd issue). As T **161**. Multicoloured.

779 1 d. Archery 30 20
780 1 d. 25 Boxing 30 25
781 5 d. Gymnastics . . . . . . 1·00 1·10
782 10 d. Start of 100 metre race (horiz) . . . . 1·75 2·25

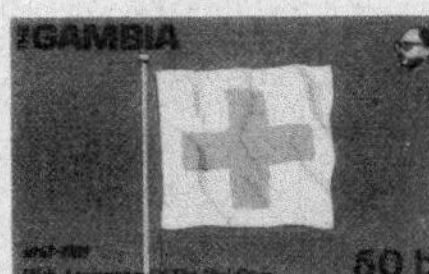

166 Red Cross Flag

1988. Anniversaries and Events. Multicoloured.

784 50 b. Type **166** (125th anniv) . 55 55
785 75 b. "Friendship 7" spacecraft (25th anniv of first American manned Earth orbit) 60 60
786 1 d. British Airways Concorde (10th anniv of Concorde London–New York service) . 1·00 1·00
787 1 d. 25 "Spirit of St. Louis" (60th anniv of first solo transatlantic flight) . . . . 1·00 1·00

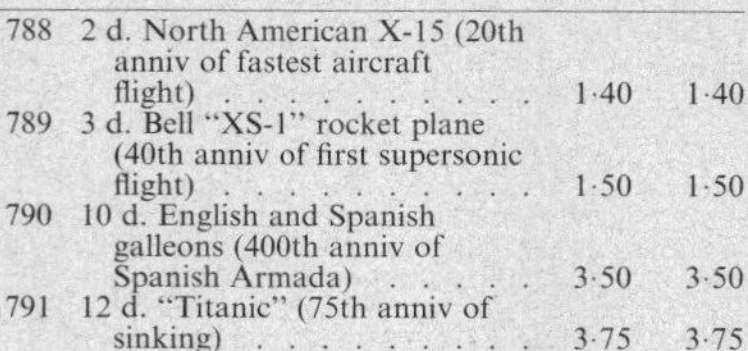

788 2 d. North American X-15 (20th anniv of fastest aircraft flight) . . . . 1·40 1·40
789 3 d. Bell "XS-1" rocket plane (40th anniv of first supersonic flight) . . . . 1·50 1·50
790 10 d. English and Spanish galleons (400th anniv of Spanish Armada) . . . . . 3·50 3·50
791 12 d. "Titanic" (75th anniv of sinking) . . . . 3·75 3·75

166a "Emperor Charles V"

1988. 500th Birth Anniv of Titian (artist). Mult.

793 25 b. Type **166a** 20 20
794 50 b. "St. Margaret and the Dragon" 35 35
795 60 b. "Ranuccio Farnese" . . . 40 40
796 75 b. "Tarquin and Lucretia" . . 55 55
797 1 d. "The Knight of Malta" . . 70 70
798 5 d. "Spain succouring Faith" . 2·25 2·50
799 10 d. Doge Francesco Venier" . 3·50 3·50
800 12 d. "Doge Grimani before the Faith" (detail) . . . . . . 3·75 3·75

167 John Kennedy sailing

1988. 25th Death Anniv of President John F. Kennedy. Multicoloured.

802 75 b. Type **167** 15 15
803 1 d. Kennedy signing Peace Corps legislation, 1962 . . . . . . 15 20
804 1 d. 25 Speaking at U.N., New York (vert) 20 25
805 12 d. Grave and eternal flame, Arlington National Cemetery (vert) . . . . 1·90 2·75

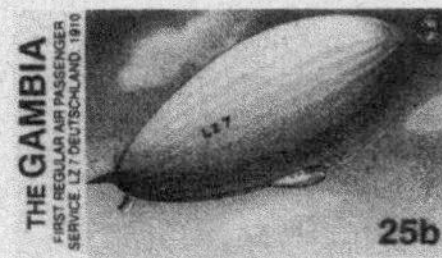

168 Airship "Graf Zeppelin" (first regular air passenger service), 1910

1988. Milestones of Transportation. Multicoloured.

807 25 b. Type **168** 60 35
808 50 b. Stephenson's "Locomotion" (first permanent public railway), 1825 . . . . 90 50
809 75 b. G.M. "Sun Racer" (first world solar challenge), 1987 . 1·00 65
810 1 d. Sprague's "Premiere" (first operational electric tramway), 1888 . . . . 1·25 80
811 1 d. 25 "Gold Rush" Bicycle (holder of man-powered land speed record), 1986 . . . . 1·50 85
812 2 d. 50 Robert Goddard and rocket launcher (first liquid fuel rocket), 1925 . . . . . 1·60 1·25
813 10 d. "Orukter Amphibolos" (first steam traction engine), 1805 . . . . 3·50 3·25
814 12 d. "Sovereign of the Seas" (largest cruise liner), 1988 . . 3·50 3·50

169 Emmett Kelley

170 Prince Henry the Navigator and Caravel

1988. Entertainers. Multicoloured.

816 20 b. Type **169** 10 10
817 1 d. Gambia National Ensemble 25 25
818 1 d. 25 Jackie Gleason 30 30
819 1 d. 50 Laurel and Hardy . . . 40 40
820 2 d. 50 Yul Brynner 75 75
821 3 d. Cary Grant 95 95
822 10 d. Danny Kaye . . . . . . 3·00 3·00
823 20 d. Charlie Chaplin . . . . 5·50 5·50

1988. Exploration of West Africa. Multicoloured.
825 50 b. Type **170** 60 60
826 75 b. Jesse Ramsden's sextant, 1785 . . . . 70 70
827 1 d. 15th-century hourglass . . 80 80
828 1 d. 25 Prince Henry the Navigator and Vasco da Gama 95 95
829 2 d. 50 Vasco da Gama and ship 1·60 1·60
830 5 d. Mungo Park and map of Gambia River (horiz) . . . 2·50 2·50
831 10 d. Map of West Africa, 1563 (horiz) . . . . 3·75 3·75
832 12 d. Portuguese caravel (horiz) 4·00 4·00

171 Projected Space Plane and Ernst Mach (physicist)

1988. 350th Anniv of Publications of Galileo's "Discourses". Space Achievements. Mult.
834 50 b. Type **171** 40 30
835 75 b. OAO III astronomical satellite and Niels Bohr (physicist) 50 40
836 1 d. Space shuttle, projected space station and Robert Goddard (physicist) (horiz) 60 45
837 1 d. 25 Jupiter probe, 1979, and Edward Barnard (astronomer) (horiz) 80 60
838 2 d. Hubble Space Telescope and George Hale (astronomer) . 1·00 75
839 3 d. Earth-to-Moon laser measurement and Albert Michaelson (physicist) (horiz) 1·00 85
840 10 d. HEAO-2 "Einstein" orbital satellite and Albert Einstein "physicist" . . . . 2·50 2·75
841 20 d. "Voyager" (first non-stop round-the-world flight), 1987, and Wright Brothers (aviation pioneers) (horiz) . . . . . . 4·50 5·00

172 Passing Out Parade

1989. Army Day. Multicoloured.
843 75 b. Type **172** 25 25
844 1 d. Standards of The Gambia Regiment 25 25
845 1 d. 25 Side drummer in ceremonial uniform (vert) . . 30 30
846 10 d. Marksman with Atlantic Shooting Cup (vert) . . . . 2·00 2·00
847 15 d. Soldiers on assault course (vert) . . . . 2·75 2·75
848 20 d. Gunner with 105 mm field gun . . . . 3·00 3·00

173 Mickey Mouse, 1928

1989. 60th Birthday of Mickey Mouse (2nd issue). Multicoloured.
849 2 d. Type **173** 65 70
850 2 d. Mickey Mouse, 1931 . . . 65 70
851 2 d. Mickey Mouse, 1936 . . . 65 70
852 2 d. Mickey Mouse, 1955 . . . 65 70
853 2 d. Mickey Mouse, 1947 . . . 65 70
854 2 d. Mickey Mouse as magician, 1940 . . . . 65 70
855 2 d. Mickey Mouse with palette, 1960 . . . . 65 70
856 2 d. Mickey Mouse as Uncle Sam, 1976 . . . . 65 70
857 2 d. Mickey Mouse, 1988 . . . 65 70
Nos. 849/57 were printed together, se-tenant, forming a composite design.

174 "Le Coup de Lance" (detail)

176 "Druryia antimachus"

175 African Emerald Cuckoo

1989. Easter. Religious Paintings by Rubens. Multicoloured.
859 50 b. Type **174** 25 25
860 75 b. "Flagellation of Christ" . 35 35
861 1 d. "Lamentation for Christ" . 35 35
862 1 d. 25 "Descent from the Cross" 40 40
863 2 d. "Holy Trinity" 60 70
864 5 d. "Doubting Thomas" . . . 1·25 1·50
865 10 d. "Lamentation over Christ" 2·00 2·50
866 12 d. "Lamentation with Virgin and St. John" . . . . 2·25 2·75

1989. West African Birds. Multicoloured.
868 20 b. Type **175** 70 30
869 60 b. Grey-headed bush shrike 95 50
870 75 b. South African crowned crane . . . . 1·00 55
871 1 d. Secretary bird . . . . . 1·25 60
872 2 d. Red-billed hornbill . . . . 1·75 1·00
873 5 d. Superb sunbird . . . . . 2·25 2·75
874 10 d. Pearl-spotted owlet ("Little owl") . . . . 3·00 4·00
875 12 d. Bateleur . . . . 3·00 4·00

1989. Butterflies of Gambia. Multicoloured.
877 50 b. Type **176** 30 30
878 75 b. "Euphaedra neophron" . 45 45
879 1 d. "Aterica rabena" 45 45
880 1 d. 25 "Salamis parhassus" . . 55 55
881 5 d. "Precis rhadama" . . . . 1·75 2·00
882 10 d. "Papilio demodocus" . . 2·25 2·50
883 12 d. "Charaxes etesipe" . . . 2·50 2·75
884 15 d. "Danaus formosa" . . . 2·50 2·75

177 Class "River" Steam Locomotive No. 021, 1959, Nigeria

1989. African Steam Locomotive. Multicoloured.
886 50 b. Type **177** 35 35
887 75 b. Class 14A steam locomotive, Rhodesia . . . 45 45
888 1 d. British-built steam locomotive No. 120, Sudan . 55 55
889 1 d. 25 Steam locomotive, 1925, U.S.A. 65 65
890 5 d. North British steam locomotive, 1955 . . . . . 1·75 1·75
891 7 d. Scottish-built steam locomotive No. 120, 1926 . 2·00 2·00
892 10 d. East African Railways Class 1T steam tank locomotive . . . . 2·25 2·25
893 12 d. American-built steam locomotive, Ghana . . . . 2·50 2·50

1989. "Philexfrance '89" Int Stamp Exhibition, Paris. Nos. 686/9 optd **PHILEXFRANCE '89**
895 75 b. Type **155** 10 10
896 1 d. Balaphong and fiddle . . . 15 20
897 1 d. 25 Bolongbato and konting (vert) 20 25
898 10 d. Antique and modern koras (vert) . . . . 1·50 2·25

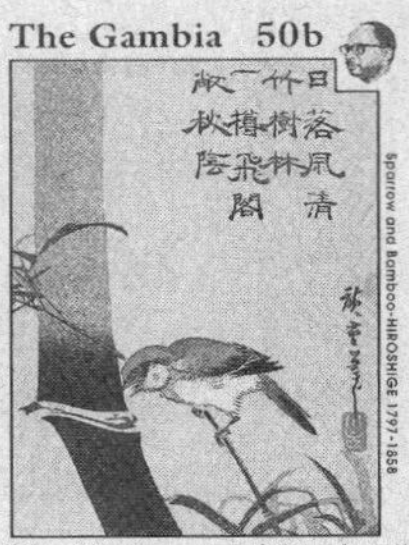

177a "Sparrow and Bamboo" (Hiroshige)

1989. Japanese Art. Multicoloured.
900 50 b. Type **177a** 40 30
901 75 b. "Peonies and a Canary" (Hokusai) 50 40
902 1 d. "Crane and Marsh Grasses" (Hiroshige) 60 45
903 1 d. 25 "Crossbill and Thistle" (Hokusai) 70 60
904 2 d. "Cuckoo and Azalea" (Hokusai) 90 80
905 5 d. "Parrot on a Pine Branch" (Hiroshige) . . . . 1·50 1·75
906 10 d. "Mandarin Ducks in a Stream" (Hiroshige) . . . . 2·25 2·50
907 12 d. "Bullfinch and Drooping Cherry" (Hokusai) . . . . . 2·25 2·50

179 Rialto Bridge, Venice

1989. World Cup Football Championship, Italy (1990) (1st issue). Designs showing landmarks and players. Multicoloured.
909 75 b. Type **179** 45 45
910 1 d. 25 The Baptistery, Pisa . . 60 60
911 7 d. Casino, San Remo . . . . 2·25 2·75
912 12 d. Colosseum, Rome . . . . 3·00 3·50
See also Nos. 1064/7.

180 "Vitex doniana"

1989. Medicinal Plants. Multicoloured.
914 20 b. Type **180** 20 20
915 50 b. "Ricinus communis" . . . 30 30
916 75 b. "Palisota hirsuta" 45 45
917 1 d. "Smilax kraussiana" . . . 55 55
918 1 d. 25 "Aspilia africana" . . . 65 65
919 5 d. "Newbouldia laevis" . . . 1·75 2·00
920 8 d. "Monodora tenuifolia" . . 1·90 2·50
921 10 d. "Gossypium arboreum" . 2·00 2·50

181 Lookdown Fish

1989. Fishes. Multicoloured.
923 20 b. Type **181** 25 25
924 75 b. Boarfish 55 55
925 1 d. Grey triggerfish 65 65
926 1 d. 25 Skipjack tuna 75 75
927 2 d. Striped rudderfish 95 95
928 4 d. Atlantic manta . . . . . 1·60 1·75
929 5 d. Flat-headed grey mullet . . 1·75 1·90
930 10 d. Ladyfish . . . . 2·75 3·25

181a Little Hiawatha on Daniel Muller Indian Pony

1989. "World Stamp Expo '89" International Stamp Exhibition, Washington. Designs showing Walt Disney cartoon characters and American carousel horses. Multicoloured.
932 20 b. Type **181a** 50 30
933 50 b. Morty on Herschell-Spillman stander 70 50
934 75 b. Goofy on Gustav Dentzel stander 85 65
935 1 d. Mickey Mouse on Daniel Muller armoured stander . . 90 70
936 1 d. 25 Minnie Mouse on jumper from Smithsonian Collection 1·00 80
937 2 d. Webby on Illion "American Beauty" . . . . 1·50 1·25
938 8 d. Donald Duck on Zalar jumper . . . . 3·50 4·00
939 10 d. Mickey Mouse on Parker bucking horse . . . . . . 3·50 4·00

183 Mickey and Minnie Mouse in Pierce-Arrow, 1922

1989. Christmas. Designs showing Walt Disney cartoon characters with cars. Multicoloured.
942 20 b. Type **183** 50 25
943 50 b. Goofy in Spyker, 1919 . . 70 45
944 75 b. Donald and Grandma Duck with Packard, 1929 . . . . 80 55
945 1 d. Mickey Mouse driving Daimler, 1920 . . . . 85 65
946 1 d. 25 Mickey Mouse in Hispano "Suiza", 1924 . . . . 90 90
947 2 d. Mickey and Minnie Mouse in Opel "Laubfrosch", 1924 . . 1·25 1·25
948 10 d. Donald Duck driving Vauxhall "30/98", 1927 . . . 3·25 4·00
949 12 d. Goofy with Peerless, 1923 3·25 4·00

184 Charles Nicolle (typhus transmission) and Vaccination

1989. Great Medical Discoveries. Multicoloured.
951 20 b. Type **184** 50 20
952 50 b. Paul Ehrlich (immunization pioneer) and medical examination 70 30
953 75 b. Selman Waksman (discoverer of streptomycin) and T.B. clinic 85 40
954 1 d. Edward Jenner (smallpox vaccination), and Jenner conducting experiment, 1796 1·00 50
955 1 d. 25 Robert Koch (developer of tuberculin test) and Gambian using vaccination gun . . . . 1·25 75
956 5 d. Sir Alexander Fleming (discoverer of penicillin) and doctor giving injection . . . 2·00 2·50
957 8 d. Max Theiler (developer of yellow fever vaccine) and child clinic . . . . 2·50 3·00
958 10 d. Louis Pasteur (bacteriologist) and health survey . . . . 2·50 3·00

185 "Bulbophyllum lepidum"

186 John Newcombe

1989. Orchids. Multicoloured.
960 20 b. Type **185** 30 30
961 75 b. "Tridactyle tridactylites" . 55 55
962 1 d. "Vanilla imperialis" . . . 70 70
963 1 d. 25 "Oeceoclades maculata" . 80 90
964 2 d. "Polystachya affinis" . . . 1·10 1·25
965 4 d. "Ancistrochilus rothschildianus" . . . . . . 1·90 2·25
966 5 d. "Angraecum distichum" . . 2·00 2·25
967 10 d. "Liparis guineensis" . . . 3·50 4·00

1990. Wimbledon Tennis Champions. Multicoloured.
969 20 b. Type **186** 10 10
970 20 b. Mrs. G. W. Hillyard . . . 10 10
971 50 b. Roy Emerson 20 20
972 50 b. Dorothy Chambers . . . 20 20
973 75 b. Donald Budge 30 30
974 75 b. Suzanne Lenglen 30 30

975	1 d. Laurence Doherty	35	35
976	1 d. Helen Wills Moody	35	35
977	1 d. 25 Bjorn Borg	40	40
978	1 d. 25 Maureen Connolly	40	40
979	4 d. Jean Borotra	1·00	1·00
980	4 d. Maria Bueno	1·00	1·00
981	5 d. Anthony Wilding	1·00	1·00
982	5 d. Louise Brough	1·00	1·00
983	7 d. Fred Perry	1·40	1·40
984	7 d. Margaret Court	1·40	1·40
985	10 d. Bill Tilden	2·00	2·00
986	10 d. Billie Jean King	2·00	2·00
987	12 d. Rod Laver	2·25	2·25
988	12 d. Martina Navratilova	2·25	2·25

187 Lunar Module "Eagle"

1990. 20th Anniv (1989) of First Manned Landing on Moon. Multicoloured.

990	20 b. Type **187**	40	20
991	50 b. Lift-off of "Apollo 11" (vert)	50	30
992	75 b. Neil Armstrong stepping on to Moon	65	45
993	1 d. Buzz Aldrin and American flag	70	55
994	1 d. 25 "Apollo 11" emblem (vert)	80	60
995	1 d. 75 Crew of "Apollo 11"	1·00	90
996	8 d. Lunar Module "Eagle" on Moon	2·75	3·25
997	12 d. Recovery of "Apollo 11" after splashdown	3·00	3·50

188 Bristol Type 142 Blenheim Mk I

1990. R.A.F. Aircraft of Second World War. Multicoloured.

999	10 b. Type **188**	40	40
1000	20 b. Fairey Battle	60	40
1001	50 b. Bristol Type 142 Blenheim Mk IV	80	40
1002	60 b. Vickers-Armstrong Wellington Mk 1c	85	40
1003	75 b. Armstrong Whitworth Whitley Mk V	90	40
1004	1 d. Handley Page Hampden Mk 1	90	45
1005	1 d. 25 Supermarine Spitfire Mk 1A and Hawker Hurricane Mk I	1·10	50
1006	2 d. Avro Manchester	1·25	90
1007	3 d. Short Stirling Mk I	1·50	1·40
1008	5 d. Handley Page Halifax Mk I	1·75	2·00
1009	10 d. Avro Lancaster Mk III	2·50	3·00
1010	12 d. De Havilland Mosquito Mk IV	2·50	3·00

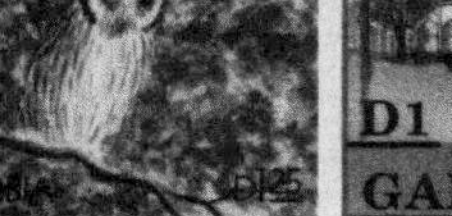

189 White-faced Scops Owl **191** Flag and National Assembly Building

190 Penny Black

1990. African Birds. Multicoloured.

1012	1 d. 25 Type **189**	60	60
1013	1 d. 25 Village weaver	60	60
1014	1 d. 25 Red-throated bee eater	60	60
1015	1 d. 25 Brown harrier eagle	60	60
1016	1 d. 25 Red bishop	60	60
1017	1 d. 25 Scarlet-chested sunbird	60	60
1018	1 d. 25 Red-billed hornbill	60	60
1019	1 d. 25 Mosque swallow	60	60
1020	1 d. 25 White-faced whistling duck	60	60
1021	1 d. 25 African fish eagle	60	60
1022	1 d. 25 Eastern white pelican	60	60
1023	1 d. 25 Carmine bee eater	60	60
1024	1 d. 25 Hadada ibis	60	60
1025	1 d. 25 Egyptian plover	60	60
1026	1 d. 25 Variable sunbird	60	60
1027	1 d. 25 African skimmer	60	60
1028	1 d. 25 Woodland kingfisher	60	60
1029	1 d. 25 African jacana	60	60
1030	1 d. 25 African pygmy goose	60	60
1031	1 d. 25 Hammerkop	60	60

Nos. 1012/31 were printed together, se-tenant, forming a composite design of birds at a lake.

1990. 150th Anniv of the Penny Black.

1032	**190** 1 d. 25 black and blue	85	50
1033	12 d. black and red	3·25	4·00

1990. 25th Anniv of Independence. Multicoloured.

1035	1 d. Type **191**	50	25
1036	3 d. President Sir Dawda Jawara	50	50
1037	12 d. Map of Yundum airport and Boeing 707 airliner	4·00	4·50

192 Baobab Tree

1990. Gambian Life. Multicoloured.

1039	5 b. Type **192**	30	30
1040	10 b. Woodcarving, Albert Market, Banjul	10	30
1041	20 b. President Jawara planting seedling (vert)	10	10
1042	50 b. Sailing canoe and map	50	10
1043	75 b. Batik fabric	20	10
1044	1 d. Hibiscus and Bakau beach	30	20
1045	1 d. 25 Bougainvillea and Tendaba Camp	30	20
1046	2 d. Shrimp fishing and sorting	45	35
1047	5 d. Groundnut oil mill, Denton Bridge	80	1·25
1048	10 d. Handicraft pot and kora (musical instrument)	1·50	2·50
1049	15 d. "Ansellia africana" (orchid) (vert)	4·25	5·00
1050	30 d. "Euriphene gambiae" (butterfly) and ancient stone ring near Georgetown	7·00	8·00

193 Daisy Duck at 10 Downing Street

1990. "Stamp World London 90" International Stamp Exhibition. Walt Disney cartoon characters in England. Multicoloured.

1051	20 b. Type **193**	40	30
1052	50 b. Goofy in Trafalgar Square	45	35
1053	75 b. Mickey Mouse on White Cliffs of Dover (horiz)	60	50
1054	1 d. Mickey Mouse at Tower of London	60	50
1055	5 d. Mickey Mouse and Goofy at Hampton Court Palace (horiz)	2·00	2·25
1056	8 d. Mickey Mouse by Magdalen Tower, Oxford	2·25	2·75
1057	10 d. Mickey Mouse on Old London Bridge (horiz)	2·50	3·00
1058	12 d. Scrooge McDuck and Rosetta Stone, British Museum (horiz)	2·50	3·00

194 Lady Elizabeth Bowes-Lyon in High Chair **195** Vialli, Italy

1990. 90th Birthday of Queen Elizabeth the Queen Mother.

1060	**194** 6 d. black, mauve & yell	1·25	1·60
1061	– 6 d. black, mauve & yell	1·25	1·60
1062	– 6 d. black, mauve & yell	1·25	1·60

DESIGNS: No. 1061, Lady Elizabeth Bowes-Lyon as a young girl; No. 1062, Lady Elizabeth Bowes-Lyon with wild flowers.

1990. World Cup Football Championships, Italy (2nd issue). Multicoloured.

1064	1 d. Type **195**	30	30
1065	1 d. 25 Cannegia, Argentina	35	35
1066	3 d. Marchena, Costa Rica	80	90
1067	5 d. Shaiba, United Arab Emirates	1·10	1·40

195a Men's Discus

1990. Olympic Games, Barcelona (1992) (1st issue). Multicoloured.

1069	20 b. Type **195a**	45	15
1070	50 b. Men's 100 metres	55	20
1071	75 b. Women's 400 metres	65	30
1072	1 d. Men's 200 metres	70	40
1073	1 d. 25 Women's rhythmic gymnastics	75	50
1074	3 d. Football	1·25	1·50
1075	10 d. Men's marathon	2·50	3·25
1076	12 d. "Tornado" class yachting	2·50	3·25

See also Nos. 1289/96 and 1351/62.

195b "The Annunciation with St. Emidius" (detail) (Crivelli)

1990. Christmas. Paintings by Renaissance Masters. Multicoloured.

1078	20 b. Type **195b**	20	10
1079	50 b. "The Annunciation" (detail) (Campin)	30	10
1080	75 b. "The Solly Madonna" (detail) (Raphael)	40	20
1081	1 d. 25 "The Tempi Madonna" (Raphael)	40	30
1082	2 d. "Madonna of the Linen Window" (detail) (Raphael)	60	50
1083	7 d. "The Annunciation, with St. Emidius" (different detail) (Crivelli)	2·00	2·75
1084	10 d. "The Orleans Madonna" (Raphael)	2·00	2·75
1085	15 d. "Madonna and Child" (detail) (Crivelli)	2·75	3·75

195c "The Lion Hunt" (detail)

1990. 350th Death Anniv of Rubens. Multicoloured.

1087	20 b. Type **195c**	15	15
1088	75 b. "The Lion Hunt" (detail)	25	25
1089	1 d. "The Tiger Hunt" (detail)	30	30
1090	1 d. 25 "The Tiger Hunt" (different detail)	35	35
1091	3 d. "The Tiger Hunt" (different detail)	75	80
1092	5 d. "The Boar Hunt" (detail)	1·10	1·25
1093	10 d. "The Lion Hunt" (different detail)	1·75	2·25
1094	15 d. "The Tiger Hunt" (different detail)	2·40	3·00

196 Summit Logo

1991. World Summit for Children, New York.

1096	**196** 1 d. multicoloured	40	40

196a Sir Kay and Wart searching for Lost Arrow

1991. International Literacy Year (1990). Designs showing scenes from Disney cartoon film "The Sword in the Stone". Multicoloured.

1097	3 d. Type **196a**	1·10	1·25
1098	3 d. Merlin the Magician	1·10	1·25
1099	3 d. Merlin teaching Wart	1·10	1·25
1100	3 d. Wart writing on blackboard	1·10	1·25
1101	3 d. Wart transformed into bird and Madame Mim	1·10	1·25
1102	3 d. Merlin and Madame Mim	1·10	1·25
1103	3 d. Madame Mim transformed into dragon	1·10	1·25
1104	3 d. Wart pulling sword from stone	1·10	1·25
1105	3 d. King Arthur on throne	1·10	1·25

197 "Bebearia senegalensis"

1991. Wildlife. Multicoloured.

1107	1 d. Type **197**	45	50
1108	1 d. "Graphium ridleyanus" (butterfly)	45	50
1109	1 d. "Precis antilope" (butterfly)	45	50
1110	1 d. "Charaxes ameliae" (butterfly)	45	50
1111	1 d. Addax	45	50
1112	1 d. Sassaby	45	50
1113	1 d. Civet	45	50
1114	1 d. Green monkey	45	50
1115	1 d. Spur-winged goose	45	50
1116	1 d. Red-billed hornbill	45	50
1117	1 d. Osprey	45	50
1118	1 d. Glossy ibis	45	50
1119	1 d. Egyptian plover	45	50
1120	1 d. Golden-tailed woodpecker	45	50
1121	1 d. Green wood hoopoe	45	50
1122	1 d. Gaboon viper	45	50
1123	1 d. 50 Red-billed fire finch	50	55
1124	1 d. 50 Leaf-love	50	55
1125	1 d. 50 Piapiac	50	55
1126	1 d. 50 African emerald cuckoo	50	55
1127	1 d. 50 Red colobus monkey	50	55
1128	1 d. 50 African elephant	50	55
1129	1 d. 50 Duiker	50	55
1130	1 d. 50 Giant eland	50	55
1131	1 d. 50 Oribi	50	55
1132	1 d. 50 Western African dwarf crocodile	50	55
1133	1 d. 50 Crowned crane	50	55
1134	1 d. 50 Jackal	50	55
1135	1 d. 50 Yellow-throated longclaw	50	55
1136	1 d. 50 Abyssinian ground hornbill	50	55
1137	1 d. 50 "Papilio hesperus"	50	55
1138	1 d. 50 "Papilio antimachus"	50	55
1139	5 d. Martial eagle	1·00	1·10
1140	5 d. Red-checked cordon-bleu	1·00	1·10
1141	5 d. Red bishop	1·00	1·10
1142	5 d. Eastern white pelican	1·00	1·10
1143	5 d. Patas monkey	1·00	1·10
1144	5 d. Vervet monkey	1·00	1·10
1145	5 d. Roan antelope	1·00	1·10
1146	5 d. Western hartebeest	1·00	1·10
1147	5 d. Waterbuck	1·00	1·10
1148	5 d. Warthog	1·00	1·10
1149	5 d. Spotted hyena	1·00	1·10
1150	5 d. Olive baboon	1·00	1·10
1151	5 d. "Palla decius"	1·00	1·10
1152	5 d. "Acraea pharsalus"	1·00	1·10
1153	5 d. "Neptidopsis ophione"	1·00	1·10
1154	5 d. "Acraea caecilia"	1·00	1·10

Nos. 1107/22, 1123/38 and 1139/54 respectively were issued together, se-tenant, forming composite designs.

198 "Papilio dardanus"

1991. Butterflies. Multicoloured.

1156	20 b. Type **198**	60	30
1157	50 b. "Bematistes poggei"	80	40
1158	1 d. "Vanessa cardui"	90	55
1159	1 d. 50 "Amphicallia tigris"	1·00	85
1160	3 d. "Hypolimnas dexithea"	1·75	1·25
1161	8 d. "Acraea egina"	2·25	3·00
1162	10 d. "Salamis temora"	2·25	3·00
1163	15 d. "Precis octavia"	2·75	4·00

198a The Queen and Prince Charles at Windsor Polo Match

1991. 65th Birthday of Queen Elizabeth II. Mult.

No.	Description	Mint	Used
1165	50 b. Type **198a**	30	20
1166	1 d. The Queen and Prince Anne at the Derby, 1988	45	35
1167	1 d. 25 The Queen at the Royal London Hospital, 1970	55	50
1168	12 d. The Queen and Prince Philip at Balmoral, 1976	3·00	3·50

198b Prince and Princess with Sons in June, 1989

1991. 10th Wedding Anniv of Prince and Princess of Wales. Multicoloured.

No.	Description	Mint	Used
1170	20 b. Type **198b**	35	25
1171	75 b. Separate photographs of Prince, Princess and sons	60	50
1172	1 d. 50 Prince Henry on first day of school, 1987, and Prince William at polo match	80	70
1173	15 d. Separate photographs of Prince and Princess of Wales	4·00	4·50

198c Donald Duck and Mickey Mouse playing "go"

1991. "Phila Nippon '91" International Stamp Exhibition, Tokyo. Designs showing Walt Disney cartoon characters playing Japanese sports and games. Multicoloured.

No.	Description	Mint	Used
1175	50 b. Type **198c**	50	30
1176	75 b. Morty, Ferdie and Pete as Sumo wrestlers	60	40
1177	1 d. Minnie Mouse, Clarabelle Cow and Daisy Duck playing battledore and shuttlecock	70	45
1178	1 d. 25 Goofy and Mickey at Okinawa bullfight (vert)	80	55
1179	5 d. Mickey flying hawk (vert)	2·00	2·00
1180	7 d. Mickey, Minnie and Donald playing "jan-ken-pon" (vert)	2·25	2·50
1181	10 d. Goofy as archer	2·50	2·75
1182	15 d. Morty and Ferdie flying kites (vert)	3·00	3·25

198d "How the Whale got his Throat"

1991. International Literacy Year (1990). Designs showing Walt Disney cartoon characters in Kipling's "Just So" stories. Multicoloured.

No.	Description	Mint	Used
1184	50 b. Type **198d**	50	30
1185	75 b. "How the Camel got his Hump"	65	40
1186	1 d. "How the Leopard got his Spots"	70	45
1187	1 d. 25 "The Elephant's Child"	80	55
1188	1 d. 50 "The Singsong of Old Man Kangaroo"	95	80
1189	7 d. "The Crab that played with the Sea"	2·25	2·50
1190	10 d. "The Cat that walked by Himself"	2·50	2·75
1191	15 d. "The Butterfly that Stamped"	3·00	3·25

199 Canadian Pacific Steel Cupola Caboose

1991. Railway Brake-vans. Multicoloured.

No.	Description	Mint	Used
1193	1 d. Type **199**	25	25
1194	1 d. Cumberland and Pennsylvania four-wheeled caboose, U.S.A.	25	25
1195	1 d. Ferrocarril Interoceanico caboose, Mexico	25	25
1196	1 d. Northern Pacific Railroad steel cupola caboose, U.S.A.	25	25
1197	1 d. Morristown and Erie Railroad four-wheeled caboose, U.S.A.	25	25
1198	1 d. Burlington Northern Railroad streamlined cupola caboose, U.S.A.	25	25
1199	1 d. McCloud River Railroad caboose-coach, U.S.A.	25	25
1200	1 d. Santa Fe Railroad wide-vision caboose, U.S.A.	25	25
1201	1 d. Frisco Railroad wide-vision caboose, U.S.A.	25	25
1202	1 d. 50 Colorado and Southern Railroad four-wheeled caboose, U.S.A.	35	40
1203	1 d. 50 Santa Fe Railroad transfer caboose, U.S.A.	35	40
1204	1 d. 50 Canadian National wooden cupola caboose	35	40
1205	1 d. 50 Union Pacific steel transfer caboose, U.S.A.	35	40
1206	1 d. 50 Virginia and Truckee Railroad caboose-coach, U.S.A.	35	40
1207	1 d. 50 British Railways standard brake van	35	40
1208	1 d. 50 International Railways of Central America caboose	35	40
1209	1 d. 50 Northern Pacific Railroad steel cupola caboose, U.S.A.	35	40
1210	1 d. 50 Burlington Northern Railroad wooden caboose, U.S.A.	35	40
1211	2 d. Oahu Railway caboose, Hawaii	40	50
1212	2 d. British Railways standard brake van	40	50
1213	2 d. Union Pacific steel wide-view caboose, U.S.A.	40	50
1214	2 d. Belt Railway of Chicago four-wheeled caboose, U.S.A.	40	50
1215	2 d. McCloud River Railroad four-wheeled caboose, U.S.A.	40	50
1216	2 d. Angelina County Lumber Co caboose, U.S.A.	40	50
1217	2 d. Coahuila & Zacateca caboose, Mexico	40	50
1218	2 d. United Railways of Yucatan caboose, Mexico	40	50
1219	2 d. Rio Grande Railroad steel cupola caboose, U.S.A.	40	50

200 Tiger Shark

1991. Fishes. Multicoloured.

No.	Description	Mint	Used
1221	20 b. Type **200**	15	15
1222	25 b. Common jewelfish	15	15
1223	50 b. Five-spotted cichlid	25	25
1224	75 b. Small-toothed sawfish	25	25
1225	1 d. Spotted tilapia	30	30
1226	1 d. 25 Dwarf jewelfish	35	35
1227	1 d. 50 Five-spotted jewelfish	40	40
1228	3 d. Lion-headed cichlid	65	65
1229	10 d. Egyptian mouthbrooder	2·00	2·50
1230	15 d. Burton's mouthbrooder	2·75	3·50

200a Children waving

1991. Hummel Figurines. Multicoloured.

No.	Description	Mint	Used
1232	20 b. Type **200a**	10	10
1233	75 b. Children under umbrella	15	15
1234	1 d. Girl kissing friend	20	20
1235	1 d. 50 Children at window	30	30
1236	2 d. 50 Two girls in aprons	45	45
1237	5 d. Two boys in bow ties	85	85
1238	10 d. Two girls sitting on fence with birds	1·75	2·00
1239	15 d. Boy and girl in Swiss costume	2·50	3·00

200b "The Old Cemetery Tower at Nuenen in the Snow"

1991. Death Centenary of Vincent van Gogh (artist). Multicoloured.

No.	Description	Mint	Used
1241	20 b. Type **200b**	15	15
1242	25 b. "Head of Peasant Woman with White Cap" (vert)	15	15
1243	50 b. "The Green Parrot" (vert)	20	20
1244	75 b. "Vase with Carnations" (vert)	20	20
1245	1 d. "Vase with Red Gladioli" (vert)	25	25
1246	1 d. 25 "Beach at Scheveningen in Calm Weather"	30	30
1247	1 d. 50 "Boy cutting Grass with Sickle"	35	35
1248	2 d. "Coleus Plant in a Flowerpot" (detail) (vert)	40	40
1249	3 d. "Self-portrait 1887" (vert)	60	60
1250	4 d. "Self-portrait" (different) (vert)	70	70
1251	5 d. "Self-portrait" (different) (vert)	85	85
1252	6 d. "Self-portrait 1887" (different) (vert)	1·25	125
1253	8 d. "Still Life with Bottle, Two Glasses, Cheese and Bread" (detail) (vert)	1·75	1·75
1254	10 d. "Still Life with Cabbage, Clogs and Potatoes"	2·25	2·25
1255	12 d. "Montmartre: The Street Lamps" (vert)	2·75	2·75
1256	15 d. "Head of Peasant Woman with Brownish Cap" (vert)	3·00	3·00

200c "The Madonna of Humility"

1991. Christmas. Religious Paintings by Fra Angelico. Multicoloured.

No.	Description	Mint	Used
1258	20 b. Type **200c**	10	10
1259	50 b. "Madonna and Child with Angels"	20	20
1260	75 b. "Virgin and Child with Angels"	25	25
1261	1 d. "The Annunciation"	30	30
1262	1 d. 25 "Presentation in the Temple"	35	35
1263	5 d. "The Annunciation" (different)	1·25	1·50
1264	10 d. "Madonna della Stella"	2·00	2·50
1265	15 d. "Naming of St. John the Baptist"	2·50	3·25

201 Son House

202 Pope John Paul II

1992. Famous Blues Singers. Multicoloured.

No.	Description	Mint	Used
1267	20 b. Type **201**	15	15
1268	25 b. W. C. Handy	15	15
1269	50 b. Muddy Waters	30	30
1270	75 b. Lightnin Hopkins	40	40
1271	1 d. Ma Rainey	45	45
1272	1 d. 25 Mance Lipscomb	50	50
1273	1 d. 50 Mahalia Jackson	60	60
1274	2 d. Ella Fizgerald	70	70
1275	3 d. Howlin Wolf	85	85
1276	5 d. Bessie Smith	1·25	1·25
1277	7 d. Leadbelly	1·50	1·50
1278	10 d. Joe Willie Wilkins	2·00	2·00

1992. Papal Visit. Multicoloured.

No.	Description	Mint	Used
1280	1 d. Type **202**	40	40
1281	1 d. 25 Pope John Paul II and Pres. Sir Dawda Jawara	50	50
1282	20 d. Gambian and Papal flags	4·75	5·50

202a Pottery Market

1992. 40th Anniv of Queen Elizabeth II's Accession. Multicoloured.

No.	Description	Mint	Used
1284	20 b. Type **202a**	15	10
1285	50 b. Ruins of early fort	25	20
1286	1 d. Fishing boat	40	30
1287	15 d. Canoes on beach	3·25	4·00

203 Nadia Comaneci (Rumania) (combined gymnastic events) and Map of Barcelona

1992. Olympic Games, Barcelona (2nd issue). Past Medal Winners. Multicoloured.

No.	Description	Mint	Used
1289	20 b. Type **203**	10	10
1290	50 b. D. Moorcroft (G.B.) (5000 metres) and map	20	20
1291	75 b. M. Nemeth (Hungary) (javelin) and decorative tiles	25	25
1292	1 d. J. Pedraza (Mexico) (20k walk) and decorative plate	30	30
1293	1 d. 25 "Soling" class yachting (Brazil), state arms and flag	40	40
1294	1 d. 50 Women's hockey (G.D.R.) and Barcelona building	45	45
1295	12 d. M. Jordan (U.S.A.) (basketball) and map	2·50	3·25
1296	15 d. V. Borzov (U.S.S.R.) (100 metres) and galleon	3·00	3·50

204 Mickey Mouse as Christopher Columbus

1992. International Stamp Exhibitions. Walt Disney Cartoon Characters. Multicoloured. (a) "Granada '92", Spain. Voyage of Columbus.

No.	Description	Mint	Used
1298	20 b. Type **204**	30	15
1299	75 b. Mickey's plans derided	45	25
1300	1 d. 50 Mickey lands in America	65	60
1301	15 d. Mickey presents treasure to Minnie	3·25	4·00

(b) World Columbian Stamp "Expo '92". Chicago Landmarks.

No.	Description	Mint	Used
1303	50 b. Navy Pier	20	10
1304	1 d. Wrigley Building	30	25
1305	1 d. 25 University of Chicago	35	30
1306	12 d. Alder Planetarium	2·25	3·25

204a "Christ presented to the People" (Rembrandt)

1992. Easter. Religious Paintings. Multicoloured.

No.	Description	Mint	Used
1308	20 b. Type **204a**	10	10
1309	50 b. "Christ carrying the Cross" (Grunewald)	20	20
1310	75 b. "The Crucifixion" (Grunewald)	25	25
1311	1 d. "The Crucifixion" (Rubens)	30	30
1312	1 d. 25 "The Road to Calvary" (detail) (Tintoretto)	35	35
1313	1 d. 50 "The Road to Calvary" (Tintoretto) (different)	40	40
1314	15 d. "The Crucifixion" (Masaccio)	2·75	3·25
1315	20 d. "The Descent from the Cross" (Rembrandt)	3·50	4·00

205 "Hibiscus rosa-sinensis"

1992. Flowers. Multicoloured.

No.	Description	Mint	Used
1317	20 b. Type **205**	10	10
1318	50 b. "Monodora myristica"	20	20
1319	75 b. "Bombax costatum"	25	25
1320	1 d. "Oncoba spinosa"	30	30
1321	1 d. 25 "Combretum grandiflorum"	35	35
1322	1 d. 50 "Rothmannia longiflora"	40	40
1323	2 d. "Clerodendrum splendens"	55	55
1324	5 d. "Mussaenda erythrophylla"	1·10	1·25
1325	10 d. "Nauclea latifolia"	1·75	2·00
1326	12 d. "Clerodendrum capitatum"	1·90	2·25
1327	15 d. "Costus spectabilis"	2·50	2·75
1328	18 d. "Strophanthus preussii"	2·75	3·00

206 "Joven Antonia" (River Gambia)

1992. River Boats of the World. Multicoloured.

1330 20 b. Type **206** 10 10
1331 50 b. "Dresden" (River Elbe) 20 20
1332 75 b. "Medway Queen" (River Medway) 25 25
1333 1 d. "Lady Wright" (River Gambia) 30 30
1334 1 d. 25 "Devin" (River Vltava) 35 35
1335 1 d. 50 "Lady Chilel Jawara" (River Gambia) 40 50
1336 5 d. "Robert Fulton" (River Hudson) 1·10 1·25
1337 10 d. "Coonawarra" (River Murray) 1·75 2·00
1338 12 d. "Nakusp" (River Columbia) 2·00 2·25
1339 15 d. "Lucy Ashton" (Firth of Clyde) 2·50 2·75

206a U.S.S. "Pennsylvania" (battleship)

1992. 50th Anniv of Japanese Attack on Pearl Harbor. Multicoloured.

1341 2 d. Type **206a** 90 95
1342 2 d. Japanese Mitsubishi A6M Zero-Sen aircraft over Pearl Harbor 90 95
1343 2 d. U.S.S. "Ward" (destroyer) sinking midget submarine 90 95
1344 2 d. Ford Naval Station under attack 90 95
1345 2 d. Agency report of Japanese attack 90 95
1346 2 d. Newspaper headline 90 95
1347 2 d. Japanese troops on Guam 90 95
1348 2 d. U.S. forces regaining Wake Island 90 95
1349 2 d. North American B-25B Mitchell bomber raid on Japan 90 95
1350 2 d. American Douglas Dauntless dive bomber attacking Japanese carrier, Midway 90 95

207 Women's Double Sculls

1992. Winter Olympic Games, Albertville, and Olympic Games, Barcelona (3rd issue). Multicoloured.

1351 20 b. Type **207** 20 15
1352 50 b. Men's kayak (vert) 30 20
1353 75 b. Women's rapid precision pistol shooting 40 30
1354 1 d. Judo (vert) 45 30
1355 1 d. 25 Men's javelin (vert) 55 35
1356 1 d. 50 Men's vaulting horse (vert) 70 40
1357 2 d. Men's downhill skiing (vert) 85 55
1358 3 d. Windsurfing (vert) 1·00 90
1359 5 d. Men's high jump 1·50 1·50
1360 10 d. Four-man bobsled (vert) 2·25 2·50
1361 12 d. 90 meter ski-jump (vert) 2·50 3·00
1362 15 d. Men's slalom skiing 2·75 3·50

207a Dryosaurus

1992. "Genova '92" International Thematic Stamp Exhibition. Dinosaurs. Multicoloured.

1364 20 b. Type **207a** 30 10
1365 25 b. Saurolophus 30 10
1366 50 b. Allosaurus 35 20
1367 75 b. Fabrosaurus 40 25
1368 1 d. Deinonychus 40 30
1369 1 d. 25 Cetiosaurus 50 35
1370 1 d. 50 Camptosaurus 50 35
1371 2 d. Ornithosuchus 55 45
1372 3 d. Spinosaurus 60 60
1373 5 d. Ornithomimus 1·00 1·25
1374 10 d. Kentrosaurus 1·75 2·25
1375 12 d. Schlermochus 1·90 2·50

The Gambia · Christmas 1992
Raphael - THE HOLY FAMILY 50b

207b "The Holy Family" (Raphael)

1992. Christmas. Religious Paintings. Multicoloured.

1378 50 b. Type **207b** 20 20
1379 75 b. "The Little Holy Family" (Raphael) 25 25
1380 1 d. "The Little Holy Family" (detail) (Raphael) 30 30
1381 1 d. 25 "Escape to Egypt" (Melchior Broederlam) 35 35
1382 1 d. 50 "Flight into Egypt" (Adriaen Isenbrant) 35 35
1383 2 d. "The Holy Family" (El Greco) 45 45
1384 2 d. "Flight into Egypt" (detail) (Cosimo Tura) 45 45
1385 2 d. "Flight into Egypt" (detail) (Master of Hoogstraelen) 45 45
1386 4 d. "The Holy Family" (Bernard van Orley) 80 90
1387 5 d. "Holy Family with Infant Jesus Sleeping" (detail) (Charles Le Brun) 95 1·10
1388 10 d. "Rest on The Flight to Egypt" (Orazio Gentileschi) 1·75 2·25
1389 12 d. "Rest on The Flight to Egypt" (detail) (Orazio Gentileschi) 1·90 2·50

207c Goofy in "Orphan's Benefit", 1934

1992. 60th Anniv of Goofy (Disney cartoon character). Multicoloured.

1391 50 b. Type **207c** 30 20
1392 75 b. Goofy and Donald Duck in "Moose Hunters", 1937 40 30
1393 1 d. Goofy in "Mickey's Amateurs", 1937 50 40
1394 1 d. 25 Goofy, Donald and Mickey Mouse in "Lonesome Ghosts", 1937 55 55
1395 5 d. Goofy, Donald and Mickey in "Boat Builders", 1938 1·40 1·40
1396 7 d. Goofy, Donald and Mickey in "The Whalers", 1938 1·75 2·00
1397 10 d. Goofy and Wilbur the grasshopper in "Goofy and Wilbur", 1939 2·00 2·25
1398 15 d. Goofy in "Saludos Amigos", 1941 2·50 2·75

208 Pres. Jawara playing Golf and Map of Australia

209 Launch of European "Ariane 4"

1992. Open Golf Championships. Multicoloured.

1400 20 b. Type **208** 30 15
1401 1 d. Pres. Jawara and Gambia Open trophy 65 45
1402 1 d. 50 Pres. Jawara (winner of Gambia Open, 1985) 90 55
1403 2 d. Pres. Jawara and map of Japan 1·00 70
1404 3 d. Pres. Jawara and map of U.S.A. 1·25 1·00
1405 5 d. Gambia Open trophy 1·75 1·75
1406 10 d. Pres. Jawara and map of Scotland 2·75 3·25
1407 12 d. Pres. Jawara and map of Italy 2·75 3·25

1993. Anniversaries and Events. Multicoloured.

1409 2 d. Type **209** 50 50
1410 2 d. Konrad Adenauer and Berlin Airlift (horiz) 50 50
1411 2 d. Airship "Hindenburg", 1928 (horiz) 50 50
1412 5 d. "Santa Maria" (horiz) 1·25 1·25
1413 6 d. Jentink's duiker (horiz) 1·40 1·40
1414 7 d. World map and emblem (horiz) 1·40 1·40
1415 9 d. Wolfgang Amadeus Mozart 1·75 1·75
1416 10 d. Lions Club emblem 1·75 1·75
1417 10 d. "Enterprise" (yacht), 1930 1·75 1·75
1418 10 d. Imperial amazon ("Sisserou Parrot") 1·75 1·75
1419 12 d. American space shuttle 2·00 2·00
1420 12 d. Fleet of Columbus (horiz) 2·00 2·00
1421 15 d. Adenauer and returning prisoners of war (horiz) 2·40 2·40
1422 18 d. Airship LZ-1, 1900 (horiz) 3·00 3·00

ANNIVERSARIES AND EVENTS: Nos. 1409, 1419, International Space Year; 1410, 1421, 25th death anniv of Konrad Adenauer (German statesman); Nos. 1411, 1422, 75th death anniv of Count Ferdinand von Zeppelin; 1412, 1420, 500th anniv of discovery of America by Columbus; 1413, 1418, Earth Summit '92, Rio; 1414, International Nutrition Conference, Rome; 1415, Death bicentenary of Mozart; 1416, 75th anniv of International Association of Lions Clubs; 1417, Americas Cup Yachting Championship.

209a Elvis Presley

1993. 15th Death Anniv (1992) of Elvis Presley (singer). Multicoloured.

1424 3 d. Type **209a** 70 70
1425 3 d. Elvis with guitar 70 70
1426 3 d. Elvis with microphone 70 70

209b "St. John the Baptist" (Da Vinci)

1993. Bicentenary of the Louvre, Paris. Paintings. Multicoloured.

1427 3 d. Type **209b** 65 70
1428 3 d. "Virgin of the Rocks" (Da Vinci) 65 70
1429 3 d. "Bacchus" (Da Vinci) 65 70
1430 3 d. "Lady of the Court, Milan" (Da Vinci) 65 70
1431 3 d. "Virgin of the Rocks" (detail) (Da Vinci) 65 70
1432 3 d. "Mona Lisa" (Da Vinci) 65 70
1433 3 d. "Mona Lisa" (detail) (Da Vinci) 65 70
1434 3 d. Sketches for "Two Horsemen" (Da Vinci) 65 70
1435 3 d. "The Oath of Horatii" (left detail) (David) 65 70
1436 3 d. "The Oath of Horatii" (right detail) (David) 65 70
1437 3 d. "The Love of Paris and Helen" (detail) (David) 65 70
1438 3 d. "The Sabine Women" (detail) (David) 65 70
1439 3 d. "Leonidas at Thermopylae" (detail) (David) 65 70
1440 3 d. "The Coronation of Napoleon" (left detail) (David) 65 70
1441 3 d. "The Coronation of Napoleon" (centre detail) (David) 65 70
1442 3 d. "The Coronation of Napoleon" (right detail) (David) 65 70
1443 3 d. "Peasant Family at Home" (detail) (L. le Nain) 65 70
1444 3 d. "Smoking Room" (left detail) (L. le Nain) 65 70
1445 3 d. "Smoking Room" (right detail) (L. le Nain) 65 70
1446 3 d. "The Cart" (detail) (L. le Nain) 65 70
1447 3 d. "Peasants' Repast" (detail) (L. le Nain) 65 70
1448 3 d. "Portrait in an Interior" (detail) (L. le Nain) 65 70
1449 3 d. "Portrait in an Interior" (different detail) (L. le Nain) 65 70
1450 3 d. "The Forge" (L. le Nain) 65 70

Nos. 1432/3 are incorrectly inscribed "Monna Lisa".

210 Peace Corps and Gambian Flags

1993. 25th Anniv of U.S. Peace Corps.

1452 **210** 2 d. multicoloured 60 60

211 Jackie Robinson and Ruby Dee ("The Jackie Robinson Story")

1993. Baseball Films. Multicoloured.

1453 3 d. Type **211** 70 80
1454 3 d. Robert DeNiro ("Bang the Drum Slowly") 70 80
1455 3 d. James Earl Jones and Billy Dee Williams ("The Bingo Long Travelling All-Stars and Motor Kings") 70 80
1456 3 d. Kevin Costner and Susan Sarandon ("Bull Durham") 70 80
1457 3 d. Cast photograph ("Eight Men Out") 70 80
1458 3 d. Ray Liotta ("Field of Dreams") 70 80
1459 3 d. Charlie Sheen ("Major League") 70 80
1460 3 d. Tom Selleck ("Mr. Baseball") 70 80
1461 3 d. Wallace Beery, 1927, and Elliott Gould, 1986 ("Casey at the Bat") 70 80
1462 3 d. Anna Nilsson and Babe Ruth ("Babe comes Home") 70 80
1463 3 d. Joe Brown ("Elmer the Great") 70 80
1464 3 d. Bud Abbott and Lou Costello ("The Naughty Nineties") 70 80
1465 3 d. Frank Sinatra, Gene Kelly and Esther Williams ("Take Me Out to the Ball Game") 70 80
1466 3 d. Tab Hunter and Gwen Verdon ("Damn Yankees") 70 80
1467 3 d. Dan Dailey ("The Pride of St. Louis") 70 80
1468 3 d. John Candy and Richard Pryor ("Brewster's Millions") 70 80

212 Giraffe

213 Long-tailed Pangolin hanging by Tail

1993. Animals of West Africa. Multicoloured.

1470 2 d. Type **212** 55 60
1471 2 d. Baboon 55 60
1472 2 d. Caracal 55 60
1473 2 d. Large-spotted genet 55 60
1474 2 d. Bushbuck 55 60
1475 2 d. Red-fronted gazelle 55 60
1476 2 d. Red-flanked duiker 55 60
1477 2 d. Cape buffalo 55 60
1478 2 d. African civet 55 60
1479 2 d. Side-striped jackal 55 60
1480 2 d. Ratel 55 60
1481 2 d. Striped polecat 55 60
1482 5 d. Vervet 85 90
1483 5 d. Blackish-green guenon 85 90
1484 5 d. Long-tailed pangolin 85 90
1485 5 d. Leopard 85 90
1486 5 d. Elephant 85 90
1487 5 d. Hunting dog 85 90
1488 5 d. Spotted hyena 85 90
1489 5 d. Lion 85 90
1490 5 d. Hippopotamus 85 90
1491 5 d. Nile crocodile 85 90
1492 5 d. Aardvark 85 90
1493 5 d. Warthog 85 90

Nos. 1470/81 and 1482/93 were each printed together, se-tenant, with the backgrounds forming composite designs.

1993. Endangered Species. Long-tailed Pangolin. Multicoloured.

1495 1 d. 25 Type **213** 45 25
1496 1 d. 50 Sitting on branch 55 40
1497 2 d. Climbing up branch 65 60
1498 5 d. Climbing down branch 1·60 2·00

214 Osprey

215 Rose-ringed Parakeet

1993. Birds of Prey. Multicoloured.

1500 1 d. 25 Type **214** 90 50
1501 1 d. 50 Egyptian vulture (horiz) 1·00 50
1502 2 d. Martial eagle 1·10 55
1503 3 d. Ruppell's griffon (horiz) 1·40 75
1504 5 d. Augur buzzard 1·75 1·25
1505 8 d. Greater kestrel 2·25 2·50
1506 10 d. Secretary bird 2·25 2·50
1507 15 d. Bateleur (horiz) 2·75 3·50

1993. African Birds. Multicoloured.

1509 2 d. Type **215** 1·10 1·25
1510 2 d. Variable sunbird 1·10 1·25
1511 2 d. Red-billed hornbill 1·10 1·25
1512 2 d. Red-billed fire finch 1·10 1·25
1513 2 d. Go-away bird 1·10 1·25
1514 2 d. Burchell's Gonolek ("Crimson-breasted shrike") 1·10 1·25
1515 2 d. Grey-headed bush shrike 1·10 1·25
1516 2 d. Western nicator 1·10 1·25
1517 2 d. Egyptian plover 1·10 1·25
1518 2 d. Congo peafowl 1·10 1·25
1519 2 d. Painted snipe 1·10 1·25
1520 2 d. South African crowned crane 1·10 1·25

215a Queen Elizabeth II (photograph by Cecil Beaton)

1993. 40th Anniv of Coronation.

1521 **215a** 2 d. multicoloured 85 90
1522 – 5 d. multicoloured 1·40 1·50
1523 – 8 d. brown and black 1·50 1·60
1524 – 10 d. multicoloured 1·75 1·90

DESIGNS—(38 × 47 mm): 5 d. Orb and sceptre; 8 d. Sir Winston Churchill; 10 d. Queen Elizabeth II at Trooping the Colour.

216 Hugo Eckener and "Graf Zeppelin"

1993. Aviation Anniversaries. Multicoloured.

1526 2 d. Type **216** 55 50
1527 2 d. Guyot's balloon, 1785 (vert) 55 50
1528 5 d. Airship "Luftschiffe 3" and crowd 1·00 1·00
1529 5 d. Sopwith Snipe (fighter) 1·00 1·00
1530 8 d. Eckener and "Graf Zeppelin" 1·60 1·75
1531 10 d. "Comte D'Artois" (hot air balloon), 1785 (vert) 1·90 2·00
1532 15 d. Royal Aircraft Factory S.E.5 (fighter) 2·40 2·50

ANNIVERSARIES: Nos. 1526, 1528, 1530, Birth anniv of Hugo Eckener (airship pioneer); Nos. 1527, 1531, Bicentenary of first airmail flight; Nos. 1529, 1532, 75th anniv of Royal Air Force.

217 Henry Ford and "Model T", 1910

1993. Centenaries of Henry Ford's First Petrol Engine (Nos. 1534/45) and Karl Benz's First Four-wheeled Car (Nos. 1546/57). Multicoloured.

1534 2 d. Type **217** 45 50
1535 2 d. Car of 1896 45 50
1536 2 d. Henry Ford with Barney Oldfield and "999", 1902 45 50
1537 2 d. Henry Ford, 1893, and car of 1896 45 50
1538 2 d. "Model A", 1903 45 50
1539 2 d. "Model T" with roof lowered, 1908 45 50
1540 2 d. "Model T" with roof raised, 1908 45 50
1541 2 d. "Model K", 1906 45 50
1542 2 d. "Model A", 1931 45 50
1543 2 d. "Model A", 1906 45 50
1544 2 d. "Model N", 1906 45 50
1545 2 d. "Model F", 1905 45 50
1546 2 d. Benz "Velo", 1894 45 50
1547 2 d. Car of 1894 45 50
1548 2 d. Three-wheeled car of 1885 from side 45 50
1549 2 d. "Mannheim", 1905 45 50
1550 2 d. Car of 1892 45 50
1551 2 d. Car of 1900 from front 45 50
1552 2 d. Racing car of 1911 from side 45 50
1553 2 d. "Velo", 1893 45 50
1554 2 d. Black car of 1900 from side 45 50
1555 2 d. Red car of 1900 from side 45 50
1556 2 d. Racing car of 1911 from front 45 50
1557 2 d. Three-wheeled car of 1885 from back 45 50

Nos. 1534/45 and 1546/57 were each printed together, se-tenant, with the backgrounds forming composite designs.

218 Marilyn Monroe

220 "Woman with a Comb" (Picasso)

219 Siamese

1993. Musical Entertainers.

1559/93 3d. × 35 multicoloured 14·50 15·00

Nos. 1559/93 were issued as four sheetlets, three of nine different designs (Nos. 1559/85) and one of eight (Nos. 1586/93), depicting Marilyn Monroe (Nos. 1559/67), Elvis Presley (Nos. 1568/76), Madonna (Nos. 1577/85) and Buddy Holly, Otis Redding, Bill Haley, Dinah Washington, musical instruments, Ritchie Valens, Clyde McPhatter, Elvis Presley (Nos. 1586/93).

1993. Oriental Cats. Multicoloured.

1594 2 d. Type **219** 80 80
1595 2 d. Colourpoint longhair sitting 80 80
1596 2 d. Burmese 80 80
1597 2 d. Birman 80 80
1598 2 d. Snowshoe 80 80
1599 2 d. Tonkinese 80 80
1600 2 d. Foreign shorthair stretching 80 80
1601 2 d. Balinese 80 80
1602 2 d. Oriental shorthair 80 80
1603 2 d. Foreign shorthair lying 80 80
1604 2 d. Colourpoint longhair with black face standing 80 80
1605 2 d. Colourpoint longhair with white face standing 80 80

Nos. 1594/1605 were printed together, se-tenant, with the background forming a composite design.

1993. Royal Dogs. As T **219**. Multicoloured.

1607 2 d. Shih tzu (Emperor of China) 70 75
1608 2 d. Skye terrier (Queen Victoria) 70 75
1609 2 d. Berner laufhund (King Louis XVI, France) 70 75
1610 2 d. Boxer (King Francis I, France) 70 75
1611 2 d. Welsh corgi (Queen Elizabeth II) 70 75
1612 2 d. Dumfriesshire (Princess Anne) 70 75
1613 2 d. Lurcher (King George VI) 70 75
1614 2 d. Welsh corgi (Princess Anne) 70 75
1615 2 d. Pekinese (Empress Ts'Eu-Hi, China) 70 75
1616 2 d. Papillon (King Louis XIII, France) 70 75
1617 2 d. Otterhound (King John) 70 75
1618 2 d. Pug (Napoleon I, France) 70 75

Nos. 1607/18 were printed together, se-tenant, with the background forming a composite design.

219a National Monument and Statue, Jakarta

1993. Asian International Stamp Exhibitions. Multicoloured. (a) "Indopex '93", Surabaya, Indonesia.

1620 20 b. Type **219a** 20 20
1621 20 b. Pura Taman Ayun Temple, Bali 20 20
1622 2 d. Guardian statue, Singosari Palace, Java 60 60
1623 2 d. Candi Jawi, Java 60 60
1624 5 d. Telek Luh mask 1·40 1·40
1625 5 d. Jero Gde mask 1·40 1·40
1626 5 d. Barong Macan mask 1·40 1·40
1627 5 d. Monkey mask 1·40 1·40
1628 5 d. Mata Gde mask 1·40 1·40
1629 5 d. Jauk Kras mask 1·40 1·40
1630 5 d. "Tree Mask" (Soedibio) 1·40 1·40
1631 5 d. "Dry Lizard" (Hendra Gunawan) 1·40 1·40
1632 5 d. "The Corn Eater" (Sudjana Kerton) 1·40 1·40
1633 5 d. "Night Watchman" (Djoko Pekik) 1·40 1·40
1634 5 d. "Hunger" (Kerton) 1·40 1·40
1635 5 d. "Arje Player" (Soedjojono) 1·40 1·40
1636 5 d. Central Temple, Lara Djonggrang 1·40 1·40
1637 5 d. Irian Jaya Monument, Jakarta 1·40 1·40
1638 15 d. Brahma and Siva Temples, Java 2·75 3·25
1639 15 d. Date of the Year Temple, Java 2·75 3·25

(b) "Taipei '93", Taiwan.

1641 20 b. Fawang Si Pagoda, Henan 20 20
1642 20 b. Wanshoubao Pagoda, Shashi 20 20
1643 2 d. Red Pavilion, Shibaozhai 60 60
1644 2 d. Songyue Si Pagoda, Henan 60 60
1645 5 d. Pottery camel (walking) 1·40 1·40
1646 5 d. Pottery horse and rider 1·40 1·40
1647 5 d. Pottery camel (standing with mouth closed) 1·40 1·40
1648 5 d. Yellow-glazed pottery horse 1·40 1·40
1649 5 d. Pottery camel (standing with mouth open) 1·40 1·40
1650 5 d. Pottery saddled horse 1·40 1·40
1651 5 d. Qianlong vase 1·40 1·40
1652 5 d. Small wine cup 1·40 1·40
1653 5 d. Mei-ping vase 1·40 1·40
1654 5 d. Urn vase 1·40 1·40
1655 5 d. Tureen 1·40 1·40
1656 5 d. Lidded potiche 1·40 1·40
1657 5 d. Tianning Si Pagoda, Beijing 1·40 1·40
1658 5 d. Bond Centre, Hong Kong 1·40 1·40
1659 15 d. Forbidden City pavilion, Beijing 2·75 3·25
1660 15 d. Xuanzhuang Pagoda, Shenxi 2·75 3·25

(c) "Bangkok '93", Thailand.

1662 20 b. Sanctuary of Prasat Phanom Wan 20 20
1663 20 b. Lai Kham Vihan, Chiang Mai 20 20
1664 2 d. Upmarket spirit shrine, Bangkok 60 60
1665 2 d. Walking Buddha statue, Wat Phra Si Ratana Mahathat 60 60
1666 5 d. "Early Fruit Stand" 1·40 1·40
1667 5 d. "Scene Rendered in Chinese Style" 1·40 1·40
1668 5 d. "Buddha descends from Tauatimsa" 1·40 1·40
1669 5 d. "Sang Thong Tales" (detail) 1·40 1·40
1670 5 d. "The Damned in Hell" 1·40 1·40
1671 5 d. "King Sanjaya travels on Elephant" 1·40 1·40
1672 5 d. U Thong C Buddha (bronze) 1·40 1·40
1673 5 d. Seated Buddha (bronze) 1·40 1·40
1674 5 d. Phra Chai Buddha (ivory and gold) 1·40 1·40
1675 5 d. Buddha (bronze) 1·40 1·40
1676 5 d. U Thong A Buddha (bronze) 1·40 1·40
1677 5 d. Crowned Buddha (bronze) 1·40 1·40
1678 5 d. Statue of Buddha, Wat Mahathat 1·40 1·40
1679 5 d. The Gopura of Prasat Phanom Rung 1·40 1·40
1680 15 d. Slender Chedis, Mongkon 2·75 3·25
1681 15 d. The Prang of Prasat Hin Phimai 2·75 3·25

1993. Anniversaries and Events. Mult.

1683 2 d. Type **220** 75 75
1684 2 d. "Niedzica Castle" (horiz) 75 75
1685 5 d. "The Mirror" (Picasso) 1·40 1·40
1686 5 d. Early astronomical instrument 1·40 1·40
1687 7 d. "Woman on a Pillow" (Picasso) 1·60 1·60
1688 10 d. "Pont-Neuf in Paris" (Hanna Rudza-Cybisowa (horiz) 2·25 2·50
1689 10 d. "Honegger's Liturgical Symphony" (Marian Bogusz) (horiz) 2·25 2·50
1690 10 d. Modern telescope 2·25 2·50

ANNIVERSARIES AND EVENTS: Nos. 1683, 1685, 1687, 20th death anniv of Picasso (artist); Nos. 1684, 1688/9, "Polska '93" International Stamp Exhibition, Poznan; Nos. 1686, 1690, 450th death anniv of Copernicus (astronomer).

The captions on Nos. 1684 and 1689 are transposed in error.

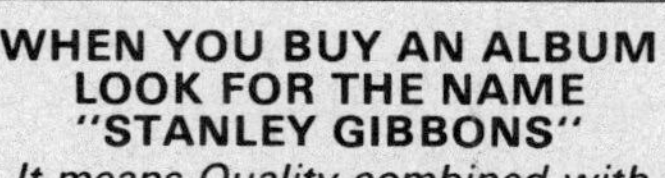

Casey at the Bat
THE GAMBIA D2
Batter up from Mudville.

221 Mudville Player at the Plate

1993. "Casey at the Bat". Scenes from Walt Disney's cartoon film. Multicoloured.

1692 2 d. Type **221** 80 85
1693 2 d. Mudville player out 80 85
1694 2 d. Umpire and player arguing 80 85
1695 2 d. Fans applauding 80 85
1696 2 d. Casey reading newspaper at plate 80 85
1697 2 d. Casey letting second pitch go by 80 85
1698 2 d. Over-confident Casey 80 85
1699 2 d. Casey striking out 80 85
1700 2 d. Casey striking out at night 80 85

221a Hannich (Hungary) and Stopyra (France)

1993. World Cup Football Championship, 1994, U.S.A. (1st issue). Multicoloured.

1702 1 d. 25 Type **221a** 75 40
1703 1 d. 50 Labd (Morocco) and Gary Lineker (England) 85 50
1704 2 d. Segota (Canada) and Morozov (Russia) 1·10 65
1705 3 d. Roger Milla (Cameroun) 1·40 1·25
1706 5 d. Rodax (Austria) and Weiss (Czechoslovakia) 1·75 1·75
1707 10 d. Claesen (Belgium), Bossis and Amoros (France) 2·25 2·50
1708 12 d. Candida (Brazil) and Ramirez (Costa Rica) 2·50 2·75
1709 15 d. Silva (Brazil) and Michel Platini (France) 2·75 3·25

See also Nos. 1882/9.

221b "The Adoration of the Magi" (detail) (Rubens)

1993. Christmas. Religious Paintings. Black, yellow and red (Nos. 1712/13 and 1715/17) or multicoloured (others).

1711 25 b. Type **221b** 20 20
1712 1 d. "The Holy Family with Joachim and Anna" (Durer) 45 20
1713 1 d. 50 "The Annunciation" (Durer) 60 30
1714 2 d. "The Adoration of the Magi" (different detail) (Rubens) 75 60
1715 2 d. "The Virgin Mary worshipped by Albrecht Bonstetten" (Durer) 75 60
1716 7 d. "The Holy Family with Two Angels in a Portico" (detail) (Durer) 2·00 2·75
1717 10 d. "Virgin on a Throne, crowned by an Angel" (Durer) 2·25 2·75
1718 15 d. "The Adoration of the Magi" (different detail) (Rubens) 2·50 3·75

221c "A Man in a Cap" (Rembrandt)

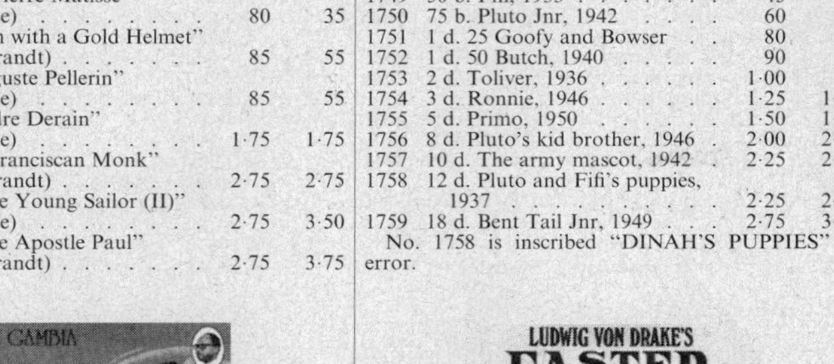

1993. Famous Paintings by Rembrandt and Matisse. Multicoloured.

No.	Description	Unused	Used
1720	50 b. Type **221c**	50	20
1721	1 d. 50 "Pierre Matisse" (Matisse)	80	35
1722	2 d. "Man with a Gold Helmet" (Rembrandt)	85	55
1723	2 d. "Auguste Pellerin" (Matisse)	85	55
1724	5 d. "Andre Derain" (Matisse)	1·75	1·75
1725	7 d. "A Franciscan Monk" (Rembrandt)	2·75	2·75
1726	12 d. "The Young Sailor (II)" (Matisse)	2·75	3·50
1727	15 d. "The Apostle Paul" (Rembrandt)	2·75	3·75

222 Mickey Mouse performing Ski Ballet

1993. Winter Sports. Walt Disney cartoon characters. Multicoloured.

No.	Description	Unused	Used
1729	50 b. Type **222**	40	15
1730	75 b. Clarabelle and Horace ice dancing	50	15
1731	1 d. Donald Duck and Dale speed skating	55	20
1732	1 d. 25 Donald in biathlon	60	20
1733	4 d. Donald and nephews in bob-sled	1·60	1·60
1734	5 d. Goofy on luge	1·75	1·75
1735	7 d. Minnie Mouse figure skating	2·25	2·75
1736	10 d. Goofy downhill skiing	2·50	2·75
1737	15 d. Goofy playing ice hockey	2·75	3·25

222a Hong Kong 1979 $2 Butterflies Stamp and "Spring Garden" (M. Bruce)

1994. "Hong Kong '94" International Stamp Exhibition (1st issue). Multicoloured.

No.	Description	Unused	Used
1739	1 d. 50 Type **222a**	50	65
1740	1 d. 50 Gambia 1990 50 d. Gambian Life stamp and "Spring Garden" (M. Bruce)	50	65

Nos. 1739/40 were printed together, se-tenant, forming the complete painting.

See also Nos. 1742/7.

222b Warriors and Horses

1994. "Hong Kong '94" International Stamp Exhibition (2nd issue). Qin Dynasty Terracotta Figures. Multicoloured.

No.	Description	Unused	Used
1742	1 d. 50 Type **222b**	40	50
1743	1 d. 50 Head of warrior	40	50
1744	1 d. 50 Kneeling warrior	40	50
1745	1 d. 50 Chariot driver	40	50
1746	1 d. 50 Dog	40	50
1747	1 d. 50 Warriors as excavated	40	50

223 Pluto the Racer, 1934–35

1994. Chinese New Year ("Year of the Dog"). Walt Disney cartoon dogs. Multicoloured.

No.	Description	Unused	Used
1748	25 b. Type **223**	30	20
1749	50 b. Fifi, 1933	45	30
1750	75 b. Pluto Jnr, 1942	60	30
1751	1 d. 25 Goofy and Bowser	80	30
1752	1 d. 50 Butch, 1940	90	45
1753	2 d. Toliver, 1936	1·00	60
1754	3 d. Ronnie, 1946	1·25	1·00
1755	5 d. Primo, 1950	1·50	1·40
1756	8 d. Pluto's kid brother, 1946	2·00	2·25
1757	10 d. The army mascot, 1942	2·25	2·50
1758	12 d. Pluto and Fifi's puppies, 1937	2·25	2·75
1759	18 d. Bent Tail Jnr, 1949	2·75	3·50

No. 1758 is inscribed "DINAH'S PUPPIES" in error.

224 Ludwig von Drake and Easter Bunny

1994. Easter. Walt Disney cartoon characters. Multicoloured.

No.	Description	Unused	Used
1761	25 b. Type **224**	30	10
1762	50 b. Minnie Mouse and Daisy Duck carrying banner	45	10
1763	3 d. Mickey Mouse wearing top hat	1·10	85
1764	4 d. Von Drake holding hatching egg	1·25	1·25
1765	5 d. Donald Duck pushing trolley full of eggs	1·40	1·40
1766	8 d. Bunny taking photograph of Von Drake	1·75	2·00
1767	10 d. Goofy dressed as Easter Bunny	2·00	2·50
1768	12 d. Von Drake holding dinosaur egg	2·25	2·75

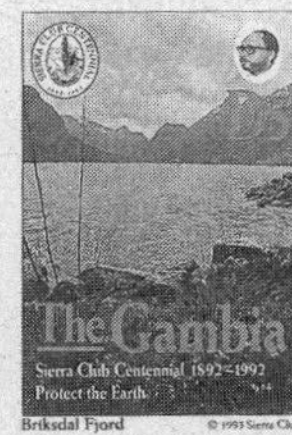

224a Briksdal Fjord

1994. Centenary (1992) of Sierra Club (environmental protection society). Endangered Environments. Multicoloured.

No.	Description	Unused	Used
1770	5 d. Type **224a**	80	90
1771	5 d. Glacier, Briksdal Fjord	80	90
1772	5 d. Waterfall, Briksdal Fjord	80	90
1773	5 d. Frozen lake, Yosemite	80	90
1774	5 d. Cliffs and river, Yosemite	80	90
1775	5 d. Forest, Yosemite	80	90
1776	5 d. Mother and child, Tibetan Plateau	80	90
1777	5 d. Yellowstone in winter	80	90
1778	5 d. Ross Island	80	90
1779	5 d. Mount Erebus	80	90
1780	5 d. Tibetan Plateau	80	90
1781	5 d. Waterfall, Yellowstone	80	90
1782	5 d. Sunset on the Serengeti	80	90
1783	5 d. Dead trees, Ansel Adams Wilderness	80	90
1784	5 d. Ansel Adams Wilderness in winter (horiz)	80	90
1785	5 d. Ansel Adams Wilderness in summer (horiz)	80	90
1786	5 d. Ridge on Mount Erebus (horiz)	80	90
1787	5 d. Mount Erebus from a distance (horiz)	80	90
1788	5 d. Prince William Sound (horiz)	80	90
1789	5 d. Geysers, Yellowstone (horiz)	80	90
1790	5 d. Local dwelling, Tibetan Plateau (horiz)	80	90
1791	5 d. Sierra Club Centennial emblem (horiz)	80	90
1792	5 d. Frozen lake, Prince William Sound (horiz)	80	90
1793	5 d. Forest, Prince William Sound (horiz)	80	90
1794	5 d. Baobab Tree, Serengeti (horiz)	80	90
1795	5 d. Plains, Serengeti (horiz)	80	90
1796	5 d. Volcano, Ross Island (horiz)	80	90
1797	5 d. Mountains, Ross Island (horiz)	80	90

INDEX

Countries can be quickly located by referring to the index at the end of this volume.

225 "Oeceoclades maculata"

226 "Girl with a Kitten" (Perronneau)

1994. Orchids. Multicoloured.

No.	Description	Unused	Used
1798	1 d. Type **225**	35	20
1799	1 d. 25 "Angraecum distichum" (horiz)	45	30
1800	2 d. "Plectrelminthus caudatus"	60	35
1801	5 d. "Tridactyle tridactylites" (horiz)	1·25	1·25
1802	8 d. "Bulbophyllum lepidum" (horiz)	1·40	1·50
1803	10 d. "Angraecum eburneum"	1·60	1·90
1804	12 d. "Eulophia guineensis"	1·75	2·00
1805	15 d. "Angraecum eichleranum" (horiz)	2·00	2·50

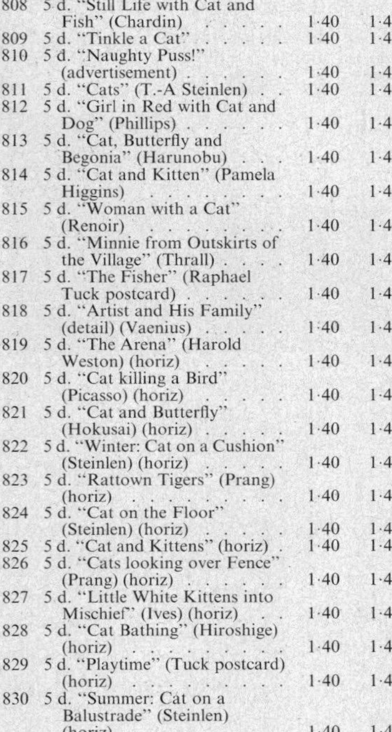

1994. Cats. Paintings of Cats. Multicoloured.

No.	Description	Unused	Used
1807	5 d. Type **226**	1·40	1·40
1808	5 d. "Still Life with Cat and Fish" (Chardin)	1·40	1·40
1809	5 d. "Tinkle a Cat"	1·40	1·40
1810	5 d. "Naughty Puss!" (advertisement)	1·40	1·40
1811	5 d. "Cats" (T.-A Steinlen)	1·40	1·40
1812	5 d. "Girl in Red with Cat and Dog" (Phillips)	1·40	1·40
1813	5 d. "Cat, Butterfly and Begonia" (Harunobu)	1·40	1·40
1814	5 d. "Cat and Kitten" (Pamela Higgins)	1·40	1·40
1815	5 d. "Woman with a Cat" (Renoir)	1·40	1·40
1816	5 d. "Minnie from Outskirts of the Village" (Thrall)	1·40	1·40
1817	5 d. "The Fisher" (Raphael Tuck postcard)	1·40	1·40
1818	5 d. "Artist and His Family" (detail) (Vaenius)	1·40	1·40
1819	5 d. "The Arena" (Harold Weston) (horiz)	1·40	1·40
1820	5 d. "Cat killing a Bird" (Picasso) (horiz)	1·40	1·40
1821	5 d. "Cat and Butterfly" (Hokusai) (horiz)	1·40	1·40
1822	5 d. "Winter: Cat on a Cushion" (Steinlen) (horiz)	1·40	1·40
1823	5 d. "Rattown Tigers" (Prang) (horiz)	1·40	1·40
1824	5 d. "Cat on the Floor" (Steinlen) (horiz)	1·40	1·40
1825	5 d. "Cat and Kittens" (horiz)	1·40	1·40
1826	5 d. "Cats looking over Fence" (Prang) (horiz)	1·40	1·40
1827	5 d. "Little White Kittens into Mischief" (Ives) (horiz)	1·40	1·40
1828	5 d. "Cat Bathing" (Hiroshige) (horiz)	1·40	1·40
1829	5 d. "Playtime" (Tuck postcard) (horiz)	1·40	1·40
1830	5 d. "Summer: Cat on a Balustrade" (Steinlen) (horiz)	1·40	1·40

227 Patas Monkey

1994. Monkeys. Multicoloured.

No.	Description	Unused	Used
1832	1 d. Type **227**	45	20
1833	1 d. 50 Collared mangabey	65	30
1834	2 d. Black and white colobus	75	35
1835	5 d. Mona monkey	1·25	1·10
1836	8 d. Kirk's colobus	1·50	2·00
1837	10 d. Vervet	1·75	2·25
1838	12 d. Red colobus	2·00	2·50
1839	15 d. Guinea baboon	2·25	2·75

227a Yuri Gagarin (first cosmonaut)

1994. 25th Anniv of First Manned Moon Landing. Multicoloured.

No.	Description	Unused	Used
1841	2 d. Type **227a**	60	60
1842	2 d. Valentina Tereshkova (first woman in Space)	60	60
1843	2 d. Ham (first chimpanzee in Space)	60	60
1844	2 d. Aleksei Leonov (first man to walk in Space)	60	60
1845	2 d. Neil Armstrong (first man on Moon)	60	60
1846	2 d. Svetlana Savitskaya (first woman to walk in Space)	60	60
1847	2 d. Marc Garneau (first Canadian in Space)	60	60
1848	2 d. Vladimir Komarov (first Soviet Space casualty)	60	60
1849	2 d. Ulf Merbold (first German in Space)	60	60

227b Daley Thompson (Great Britain) (decathlon), 1980 and 1984

227d Soldiers on Horses

227c "Soema" (Dutch Sloop)

1994. Centenary of International Olympic Committee. Gold Medal Winners. Multicoloured.

No.	Description	Unused	Used
1851	1 d. 50 Type **227b**	40	30
1852	5 d. Heide Marie Rosendohl (Germany) (long jump), 1972	1·10	1·25

1994. 50th Anniv of D-Day. Multicoloured.

No.	Description	Unused	Used
1854	50 b. Type **227c**	50	50
1855	75 b. H.M.S. "Belfast" (cruiser)	60	60
1856	1 d. U.S.S. "Texas" (battleship)	70	70
1857	2 d. "Georges Leygues" (French cruiser)	1·25	1·25

1994. "Philakorea '94" International Stamp Exhibition, Seoul. Screen paintings of the "Sanguozhi". Multicoloured.

No.	Description	Unused	Used
1859	50 b. Kungnakchon Hall (38 × 25 mm)	30	30
1860	1 d. Type **227d**	40	40
1861	1 d. Soldiers defending fort	40	40
1862	1 d. Archers	40	40
1863	1 d. General on horse	40	40
1864	1 d. Three soldiers in battle	40	40
1865	1 d. Army in retreat	40	40
1866	1 d. Archers using fire arrows	40	40
1867	1 d. Horsemen attacking fort	40	40
1868	1 d. Women in summer house	40	40
1869	1 d. Old man, child and house	40	40
1870	2 d. Kettle of Popchusa (38 × 25 mm)	60	60
1871	3 d. Pomun tourist resort (38 × 25 mm)	70	70

228 "Mylothris rhodope"

229 Bobby Charlton (England)

1994. Butterflies. Multicoloured.

No.	Description	Unused	Used
1873	1 d. Type **228**	50	25
1874	1 d. 25 "Iolaphilus menas"	65	35
1875	2 d. "Neptis nemetes"	75	40
1876	5 d. "Antanartia delius"	1·25	1·10
1877	8 d. "Acraea caecilia"	1·50	2·00
1878	10 d. "Papilio nireus"	1·50	2·00
1879	12 d. "Papilio menestheus"	1·75	2·50
1880	15 d. "Iolaphilus julus"	2·00	2·75

1994. World Cup Football Championship, U.S.A. (2nd issue). Multicoloured.

No.	Description	Unused	Used
1882	50 b. Type **229**	40	20
1883	75 b. Ferenc Puskas (Hungary)	55	25
1884	1 d. Paolo Rossi (Italy)	65	25
1885	2 d. Biri Biri (Spain)	90	40
1886	3 d. Diego Maradona (Argentina)	1·00	80
1887	8 d. Johann Cruyff (Netherlands)	1·75	2·00
1888	10 d. Franz Beckenbauer (Germany)	1·75	2·00
1889	15 d. Thomas Dooley (U.S.A.)	2·25	3·00

230 "Suillus luteus" **230a** "Expectant Madonna with St. Joseph" (French 15th-century)

1994. Fungi. Multicoloured.
1891 5 d. Type **230** 90 90
1892 5 d. "Bolbitius vitellinus" . . 90 90
1893 5 d. "Clitocybe nebularis" . . 90 90
1894 5 d. "Omphalotus olearius" . . 90 90
1895 5 d. "Auricularia auricula" . . 90 90
1896 5 d. "Macrolepiota rhacodes" . 90 90
1897 5 d. "Volvariella volvacea" . . 90 90
1898 5 d. "Psilocybe coprophila" . . 90 90
1899 5 d. "Suillus granulatus" . . 90 90
1900 5 d. "Agaricus campestris" . . 90 90
1901 5 d. "Lepista nuda" 90 90
1902 5 d. "Podaxis pistillaris" . . 90 90
1903 5 d. "Oudemansiella radicata" . 90 90
1904 5 d. "Schizophyllum commune" 90 90
1905 5 d. "Chlorophyllum molybdites" 90 90
1906 5 d. "Hypholoma fasciculare" . 90 90
1907 5 d. "Mycena pura" 90 90
1908 5 d. "Ganoderma lucidum" . . 90 90

1994. Christmas. Religious Paintings. Multicoloured.
1910 50 b. Type **230a** 30 10
1911 75 b. "Rest of the Holy Family" (Louis le Nain) 40 20
1912 1 d. "Rest on the Flight into Egypt" (Antoine Watteau) . 85 20
1913 2 d. "Rest on the Flight into Egypt" (Jean-Honore Fragonard) 60 60
1914 2 d. "Rest on the Flight into Egypt" (Francois Boucher) . 60 60
1915 2 d. "Noon" (Claude Lorrain) . 60 60
1916 10 d. "The Holy Family" (Nicolas Poussin) . . . . . 2·00 2·75
1917 12 d. "Mystical Marriage of St. Catherine" (Pierre-Francois Mignard) . . . . 2·00 2·75

231 Marilyn Monroe

1995. Marilyn Monroe (American entertainer) Commemoration. Multicoloured.
1919 4 d. Type **231** 85 90
1920 4 d. Wearing pendant necklace 85 90
1921 4 d. In blue jacket 85 90
1922 4 d. With sun-glasses on head . 85 90
1923 4 d. Looking over right arm . 85 90
1924 4 d. Wearing gold beret and jacket 85 90
1925 4 d. Wearing hooped earrings . 85 90
1926 4 d. Smiling 85 90
1927 4 d. Laughing 85 90

232 Elvis as a Child

1995. 60th Birth Anniv of Elvis Presley (singer). Multicoloured.
1929 4 d. Type **232** 85 90
1930 4 d. Wearing white shirt . . . 85 90
1931 4 d. With his mother Gladys . 85 90
1932 4 d. With his wife Priscilla . 85 90
1933 4 d. With large gold medallion . 85 90
1934 4 d. In army uniform 85 90
1935 4 d. In purple shirt 85 90
1936 4 d. Wearing stetson 85 90
1937 4 d. With his daughter Lisa-Marie 85 90

233 Pteranodon

1995. Prehistoric Animals. Multicoloured.
1938 2 d. Type **233** 50 50
1939 2 d. Archaeopteryx 50 50
1940 2 d. Rhamphorhynchus . . . 50 50
1941 2 d. Ornithomimus 50 50
1942 2 d. Stegosaurus 50 50
1943 2 d. Heterodontosaurus . . . 50 50
1944 2 d. Lystrosaurus 50 50
1945 2 d. Euoplocephalus 50 50
1946 2 d. Coelophysis 50 50
1947 2 d. Staurikosaurus 50 50
1948 2 d. Giantoperis 50 50
1949 2 d. Diarthrognathus 50 50
1950 3 d. Archaeopteryx 55 55
1951 3 d. Vangehuanosaurus . . . 55 55
1952 3 d. Celophysis 55 55
1953 3 d. Plateosaurus 55 55
1954 3 d. Baryonyx 55 55
1955 3 d. Ornitholestes 55 55
1956 3 d. Dryosaurus 55 55
1957 3 d. Estemmenosuchus 55 55
1958 3 d. Macroplata 55 55
1959 3 d. Shonisaurus 55 55
1960 3 d. Muraeonosaurus 55 55
1961 3 d. Archelon 55 55
Nos. 1938/49 and 1950/61 respectively were printed together, se-tenant, forming composite designs.

234 Pig (Chinese characters in green) **236** Rural Road

235 Great White Egret

1995. Chinese New Year ("Year of the Pig").
1963 **234** 3 d. red, black and green . 45 55
1964 – 3 d. multicoloured (characters in blue) . . 45 55
1965 – 3 d. orange, red and black (characters in white) . . 45 55
1966 – 3 d. pink, red and black (characters in black) . . 45 55
DESIGNS: Nos. 1964/6, Different symbolic pigs.

1995. Water Birds. Multicoloured.
1968 2 d. Type **235** 55 55
1969 3 d. Pintails 60 65
1970 3 d. Fulvous whistling duck . . 60 65
1971 3 d. Garganey 60 65
1972 3 d. White-faced whistling duck 60 65
1973 3 d. White-backed duck . . . 60 65
1974 3 d. Egyptian goose 60 65
1975 3 d. African pygmy geese . . . 60 65
1976 3 d. Little bitterns 60 65
1977 3 d. Redshanks 60 65
1978 3 d. Ringed plovers 60 65
1979 3 d. Black-winged stilt . . . 60 65
1980 3 d. Squacco herons 60 65
1981 8 d. Hammerkop . . . . . 1·75 2·00
1982 10 d. Common shovelers . . . 2·00 2·25
1983 12 d. Crowned crane . . . . 2·25 2·50
Nos. 1969/80 were printed together, se-tenant, forming a composite design.

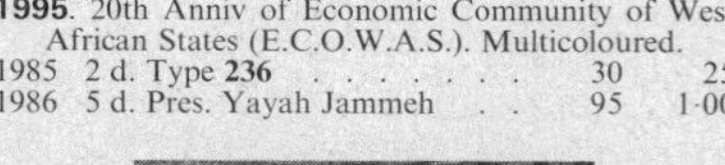

1995. 20th Anniv of Economic Community of West African States (E.C.O.W.A.S.). Multicoloured.
1985 2 d. Type **236** 30 25
1986 5 d. Pres. Yayah Jammeh . . 95 1·00

237 Leather Back Turtle

1995. Marine Life. Multicoloured.
1987 3 d. Type **237** 60 65
1988 3 d. Tiger shark 60 65
1989 3 d. Powder-blue surgeonfish . 60 65
1990 3 d. Emperor angelfish . . . 60 65
1991 3 d. Blue parrotfish 60 65
1992 3 d. Clown triggerfish . . . 60 65
1993 3 d. Sea horses 60 65
1994 3 d. Lionfish 60 65
1995 3 d. Moray eel 60 65
1996 3 d. Melon butterflyfish . . . 60 65
1997 3 d. Octopus 60 65
1998 3 d. Common stingray 60 65
1999 8 d. Stoplight parrotfish ("Multicoloured Parrot Fish") (vert) . . . . . . 1·75 2·00
2000 8 d. Stoplight parrotfish ("Sparisoma Viride") (vert) . 1·75 2·00
2001 8 d. Queen parrotfish (vert) . . 1·75 2·00
2002 8 d. Bicoloured parrotfish (vert) . . . . 1·75 2·00
Nos. 1987/98 and 1999/2002 respectively were printed together, se-tenant, forming composite designs.
No. 1991 is inscribed "BLUE PARRO FISH" in error.

237a Peter Lawford

1995. 50th Anniv of End of Second World War in Europe. Film Stars. Black and red (Nos. 2008 and 2010) or multicoloured (others).
2006 3 d. Type **237a** 60 60
2007 3 d. Gene Tierney and Dana Andrews 60 60
2008 3 d. Groucho and Harpo Marx 60 60
2009 3 d. James Stewart 60 60
2010 3 d. Chico and Zeppo Marx . 60 60
2011 3 d. Tyrone Power 60 60
2012 3 d. Cary Grant and Ingrid Bergman 60 60
2013 3 d. Veronica Lake 60 60
No. 2012 is inscribed "BERMAN" in error.

237b Children in Class

1995. 50th Anniv of United Nations. Multicoloured.
2015 3 d. Type **237b** 80 80
2016 3 d. Teacher helping child . . 80 80
2017 3 d. Child writing on blackboard 80 80
Nos. 2015/17 were printed together, se-tenant, forming a composite design.

237c Woman carrying Sack

1995. 50th Anniv of F.A.O. Multicoloured.
2019 3 d. Type **237c** 80 80
2020 3 d. Two men carrying sacks . 80 80
2021 3 d. Man carrying sack . . . 80 80
Nos. 2019/21 were printed together, se-tenant, forming a composite design.

239 Paul Harris (founder) and Rotary Emblem

1995. 90th Anniv of Rotary International.
2023 **239** 15 d. multicoloured . . . 2·00 2·50

239a Queen Elizabeth the Queen Mother (pastel drawing)

1995. 95th Birthday of Queen Elizabeth the Queen Mother.
2025 **239a** 5 d. brown, light brown and black . . . . . 1·00 1·10
2026 – 5 d. multicoloured . . . 1·00 1·10
2027 – 5 d. multicoloured . . . 1·00 1·10
2028 – 5 d. multicoloured . . . 1·00 1·10
DESIGNS: Nos. 2026, Wearing blue hat and dress; 2027, At desk (oil painting); 2028, Wearing green hat and dress.

239b Fairey Firefly

1995. 50th Anniv of End of Second World War in the Pacific. Multicoloured.
2030 5 d. Type **239b** . . . . . . 1·00 1·10
2031 5 d. Fairey Barracuda Mk III . 1·00 1·10
2032 5 d. Supermarine Seafire II . . 1·00 1·10
2033 5 d. H.M.S. "Repulse" (battle cruiser) . . . . 1·00 1·10
2034 5 d. H.M.S. "Illustrious" (aircraft carrier) . . . . 1·00 1·10
2035 5 d. H.M.S. "Exeter" (cruiser) . 1·00 1·10

240 Kenichi Fukui (1981 Chemistry)

1995. Centenary of Nobel Prize Trust Fund. Past Prize Winners. Multicoloured.
2037 2 d. Type **240** 40 40
2038 3 d. Gustav Stresemann (1929 Peace) 50 50
2039 5 d. Thomas Mann (1929 Literature) 80 85
2040 5 d. Marie Curie (1911 Chemistry) 80 85
2041 5 d. Adolf Butenandt (1939 Chemistry) 80 85
2042 5 d. Susumu Tonegwa (1987 Medicine) 80 85
2043 5 d. Nelly Sachs (1966 Literature) 80 85
2044 5 d. Yasunari Kawabata (1968 Literature) 80 85
2045 5 d. Hideki Yukawa (1949 Physics) 80 85
2046 5 d. Paul Ehrlich (1908 Medicine) 80 85
2047 5 d. Bisaku Sato (1974 Peace) . 80 85
2048 5 d. Carl von Ossietsky (1935 Peace) 80 85
2049 8 d. Albert Schweitzer (1952 Peace) . . . . 1·40 1·50
2050 12 d. Leo Esaki (1973 Physics) . . . . 1·75 2·00
2051 15 d. Lech Walesa (1983 Peace) . . . . 2·00 2·50
Nos. 2040/8 were printed together, se-tenant, forming a composite design.
No. 2048 is dated "1974" and No. 2051 inscribed "Lech Walsea", both in error.

241 Bruce Jenner (U.S.A.) (decathlon)

1995. Olympic Games, Atlanta (1996) (1st issue). Multicoloured.
2053 1 d. Type **241** 20 30
2054 1 d. 25 Greg Louganis (U.S.A.) (diving) 20 30
2055 1 d. 50 Michael Gross (Germany) (50 metre butterfly) 25 30
2056 2 d. Vasily Alexeev (Russia) (weightlifting) 30 30
2057 3 d. Ewing (U.S.A.) and Corbalan (Spain) (basketball) 50 50
2058 3 d. Stefano Cerioni (Italy) (fencing) (vert) 50 55
2059 3 d. Alberto Cova (Italy) (10000 metres) (vert) 50 55
2060 3 d. Mary Lou Retton (U.S.A.) (gymnastics) (vert) 50 55
2061 3 d. Vladimir Artemov (Russia) (gymnastics) (vert) 50 55
2062 3 d. Florence Griffith-Joyner (U.S.A.) (400 metre relay) (vert) 50 55
2063 3 d. Brazil (football) (vert) . . 50 55
2064 3 d. Nelson Vails (U.S.A.) (sprint cycling) (vert) . . . 50 55
2065 3 d. Cheryl Miller (U.S.A.) (basketball) (vert) 50 55

2066 5 d. U.S.A. v Brazil (men's volleyball) 85 95
2067 10 d. Svenden (West Germany) and Fernandez (U.S.A.) (water polo) . . . . 1·50 1·75
2068 15 d. Pertii Karppinen (Finland) (single sculls) . . . . . . 2·25 2·75

No. 2059 is inscribed "Alberto Covo" and No. 2064 "Nelson Valis", both in error.

See also Nos. 2281/2302.

242 Rotary Emblem and Rotarians supporting School for the Deaf

1995. Local Rotary and Boy Scout Projects. Multicoloured.

2070 2 d. Type **242** 30 30
2071 5 d. Scout wood badge course, 1980 . . . . 85 95
2072 5 d. Scout Commissioner M. J. E. Sambou (vert) . . 85 95

243 "Zantedeschia rehmannii"

1995. African Flowers. Multicoloured.

2073 2 d. Type **243** 45 45
2074 3 d. "Kigelia africana" 50 55
2075 3 d. "Hibiscus schizopelatus" . 50 55
2076 3 d. "Dombeya mastersii" . . 50 55
2077 3 d. "Agapanthus orientalis" . 50 55
2078 3 d. "Strelitzia reginae" . . . 50 55
2079 3 d. "Spathodea companulata" 50 55
2080 3 d. "Rhodolaena bakeriana" . 50 55
2081 3 d. "Gazania rigens" 50 55
2082 3 d. "Ixianthes retzioides" . . 50 55
2083 3 d. "Canarina abyssinica" . . 50 55
2084 3 d. "Nerine bowdenii" . . . 50 55
2085 3 d. "Zantedeschia aethiopica" 50 55
2086 3 d. "Aframomum sceptrum" . 50 55
2087 3 d. "Schotia brachypetala" . 50 55
2088 3 d. "Catharanthus roseus" . . 50 55
2089 3 d. "Protea grandiceps" . . . 50 55
2090 3 d. "Plumbago capensis" . . . 50 55
2091 3 d. "Uncarina grandidieri" . . 50 55
2092 5 d. "Euadenia eminens" . . . 85 95
2093 10 d. "Passiflora vitifolia" . . 1·50 1·75
2094 15 d. "Dietes grandiflora" . . 2·25 2·75

Nos. 2074/82 and 2083/91 respectively were printed together, se-tenant, forming composite background designs.

244 Children outside Huts

1995. Kinderdorf International S.O.S. Children's Villages. Multicoloured.

2096 2 d. Type **244** 30 35
2097 2 d. Charity worker with children (vert) 30 35
2098 5 d. Children at party 80 95

245 Roy Orbison

1995. History of Rock n' Roll Music. Multicoloured.

2099 3 d. Type **245** 55 55
2100 3 d. Mick Jagger 55 55
2101 3 d. Bruce Springsteen 55 55
2102 3 d. Jimi Hendrix 55 55
2103 3 d. Bill Haley 55 55
2104 3 d. Gene Vincent 55 55
2105 3 d. Buddy Holly 55 55
2106 3 d. Jerry Lee Lewis 55 55
2107 3 d. Chuck Berry 55 55

Nos. 2099/2107 were printed together, se-tenant, forming a composite design.

1995. Centenary of Cinema. As T **245** but depicting James Dean. Multicoloured.

2109 3 d. As a boy 55 55
2110 3 d. On motorbike 55 55
2111 3 d. With sports car and trophy 55 55
2112 3 d. Close-up portrait 55 55
2113 3 d. Facing left 55 55
2114 3 d. Holding girl 55 55
2115 3 d. "Rebel without a Cause" (film) 55 55
2116 3 d. "Giant" (film) 55 55
2117 3 d. "East of Eden" (film) . . . 55 55

Nos. 2109/17 were printed together, se-tenant, forming a composite design.

245a "Madonna and Child" (Maria della Vallicella)

1995. Christmas. Religious Paintings. Multicoloured.

2119 75 b. Type **245a** 20 10
2120 1 d. "Madonna" (Giotto) . . 20 10
2121 2 d. "The Flight into Egypt" (Luca Giordano) 35 25
2122 5 d. "The Epiphany" (Bondone) 80 75
2123 8 d. "Virgin and Child" (Burgkmair) . . . . 1·40 1·75
2124 12 d. "Madonna" (Bellini) . . 1·75 2·25

246 Terminal Building

1995. Opening of New Terminal Building, Banjul International Airport.

2126 **246** 1 d. multicoloured 20 10
2127 2 d. multicoloured 35 25
2128 3 d. multicoloured 45 45
2129 5 d. multicoloured . . . . 75 1·00

247 U.P.U. Emblem

1995. 121st Anniv of Universal Postal Union.

2130 **247** 1 d. black and violet . . . 20 10
2131 2 d. black and blue . . . 35 25
2132 3 d. black and red 45 45
2133 7 d. black and green . . . 1·25 1·50

248 Commerson's Dolphin

1995. Whales and Dolphins. Multicoloured.

2134 2 d. Type **248** 20 25
2135 3 d. Bryde's whale 35 40
2136 3 d. Sperm whale 35 40
2137 3 d. Humpback whale 35 40
2138 3 d. Sei whale 35 40
2139 3 d. Blue whale 35 40
2140 3 d. Grey whale 35 40
2141 3 d. Fin whale 35 40
2142 3 d. Killer whale 35 40
2143 3 d. Right whale 35 40
2144 3 d. Northern right whale dolphin 35 40
2145 3 d. Spotted dolphin 35 40
2146 3 d. Common dolphin 35 40
2147 3 d. Pacific white-sided dolphin 35 40
2148 3 d. Atlantic humpbacked dolphin 35 40
2149 3 d. Atlantic white-sided dolphin 35 40
2150 3 d. White-beaked dolphin . . 35 40
2151 3 d. Striped dolphin 35 40
2152 3 d. Risso's dolphin 35 40
2153 5 d. Narwhal 60 65
2154 8 d. True's beaked whale . . . 90 95
2155 10 d. Rough-toothed dolphin . 1·10 1·25

Nos. 2135/43 and 2144/52 respectively were printed together, se-tenant, forming composite designs.

249 Big Pete as Seminole with Alligator

1995. Disney Cowboys and Indians. Walt Disney Cartoon Characters. Multicoloured.

2157 15 b. Type **249** 10 10
2158 20 b. Donald Duck as Chinook fisherman 10 10
2159 25 b. Huey, Dewey and Louie as Blackfoot braves 10 10
2160 30 b. Minnie Mouse shooting bottles 10 10
2161 40 b. Donald riding bull . . . 10 10
2162 50 b. Mickey Mouse branding steer 10 10
2163 2 d. Donald in Tlingit mask . 30 25
2164 3 d. Mickey bronco-busting . 45 40
2165 12 d. Grandma Duck with lasso . . . . 2·00 2·00
2166 15 d. Mickey in Pomo canoe . 2·50 2·50
2167 15 d. Goofy as ranch hand . . 2·50 2·50
2168 20 d. Goofy and Minnie with Navaho weavin . . . . . 2·75 2·75

250 Rat

1996. Chinese New Year ("Year of the Rat").

2170 **250** 63 b. multicoloured . . . 10 10
2171 – 75 b. multicoloured . . . 10 10
2172 – 1 d. 50 multicoloured . . 20 25
2173 – 4 d. multicoloured 45 50

DESIGNS: 75 b. to 4 d. Different stylised rats.

251 "Don Tiburcio Perez y Cuervo" (detail) (Goya)

1996. 125th Anniv of Metropolitan Museum of Art, New York. Multicoloured.

2176/83 4 d. × 8 (Type **251**; "Jean Antoine Moltedo" (Ingres); "The Letter" (Corot); "General Etienne Gerard" (David); "Portrait of the Artist" (Van Gogh); "Joseph Henri Altes" (Degas); "Princess de Broglie" (Ingres); "Lady at the Table" (Cassatt))

2184/91 4 d. × 8 ("Broken Eggs" (Greuze); "Johann Joachim Winckleman" (Mengs); "Col. George Coussmaker" (Reynolds); "Self Portrait with Pupils" (Labille-Guiard); "Courtesan holding a Fan" (Utamaro); "The Woodgatherers" (Gainsborough); "Mrs Grace Elliott" (Gainsborough); "The Drummond Children" (Raeburn))

2192/9 4 d. × 8 ("Sunflowers" (Monet); "Still Life with Pansies" (Fantin-Latour); "Parisians enjoying the Parc" (Monet); "La Mere Larcheveque" (Pissarro); "Rue de L'Epicerie, Rouen" (Pissarro); "The Abduction of Rebecca" (Delacroix); "Daughter, Abraham-Ben-Chimol" (Delacroix); "Christ on Lake of Gennesaret" (Delacroix))

2200/7 4 d. × 8 ("Henry Prince of Wales" (Peake); "Saints Peter, Martha, Mary and Leonard" (Correggio); "Marriage Feast at Cana" (Juan de Flandes); "Portrait of One of Wedigh Family" (Holbein); "Guillaume Bude" (Clouet); "Portrait of a Cardinal" (El Greco); "St. Jerome as a Cardinal" (El Greco); "Portrait of a Man" (Titian))

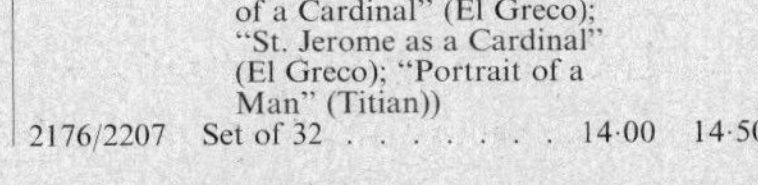
2176/2207 Set of 32 . . . . 14·00 14·50

252 Fire-eater

253 Bruce Lee

1996. Fire-eating in the Gambia.

2209 **252** 1 d. multicoloured 10 10
2210 – 2 d. multicoloured 20 25
2211 – 3 d. multicoloured 35 40
2212 – 7 d. multicoloured 80 85

DESIGNS: 2 d. to 7 d. Various fire-eating scenes, the 2 d. and 7 d. being horiz.

1996. Bruce Lee (film star) Commemoration. Different portraits. Multicoloured.

2213 3 d. Wearing cap and mask . . 35 40
2214 3 d. Type **253** 35 40
2215 3 d. Facing left 35 40
2216 3 d. Wearing blue jumper and with hand to face 35 40
2217 3 d. Wearing buff jacket . . . 35 40
2218 3 d. Wearing brown jacket (Chinese characters in brown) 35 40
2219 3 d. Wearing black shirt (Chinese characters in lilac) . 35 40
2220 3 d. Wearing white shirt . . . 35 40
2221 3 d. Bare-chested 35 40

254 Donald Duck and Big Pete giving Blood

1996. Voluntary Activities. Walt Disney Cartoon Characters. Multicoloured.

2223 1 d. Type **254** 15 10
2224 4 d. Daisy Duck and Minnie Mouse adopting pets . . . 65 50
2225 5 d. Goofy as one-man band raising money for the needy . 75 65
2226 10 d. Goofy teaching outdoor skills . . . . 1·40 1·60
2227 15 d. Minnie teaching reading . 2·00 2·50
2228 20 d. Donald, Mickey and Goofy as volunteer fire fighters . . . . 2·50 2·75

255 Roan Antelope

1996. Wildlife. Multicoloured.

2230 3 d. Type **255** 35 40
2231 3 d. Lesser bushbaby 35 40
2232 3 d. Black leopard 35 40
2233 3 d. Guinea forest red colobus 35 40
2234 3 d. Kobs 35 40
2235 3 d. Common eland 35 40
2236 4 d. African buffalo 45 50
2237 4 d. Herd of topi 45 50
2238 4 d. Vervet 45 50
2239 4 d. Hippopotamuses 45 50
2240 4 d. Waterbuck 45 50
2241 4 d. Senegal chameleon . . . 45 50
2242 4 d. Western green mamba . . 45 50
2243 4 d. Slender-snouted crocodile 45 50
2244 4 d. Adanson's mud turtle . . 45 50
2245 15 d. African civet . . . . . 1·75 1·90

Nos. 2230/5 and 2236/44 respectively were printed together, se-tenant, Nos. 2236/44 forming a composite design.

255a Queen Elizabeth II

1996. 70th Birthday of Queen Elizabeth II. Mult.
2247 8 d. Type **255a** 90 95
2248 8 d. Wearing tiara facing right . 90 95
2249 8 d. Wearing tiara facing left . 90 95

256 Pumper Hose Cart, U.S.A. (1850)

1996. Classic Road Transport. Fire Engines (Nos. 2251/6) or Cars (Nos. 2257/62). Multicoloured.
2251 4 d. Type **256** 45 50
2252 4 d. Steam fire engine, U.S.A. (1891) 45 50
2253 4 d. Lausitzer engine, Germany (1864) 45 50
2254 4 d. Chemical engine, Great Britain (1902) 45 50
2255 4 d. Motor fire engine, Great Britain (1904) 45 50
2256 4 d. Colonia No. 5 engine, Germany (1860) 45 50
2257 4 d. Fiat Tipo 510, Italy (1912) . 45 50
2258 4 d. Toyota Model 4B Phaeton, Japan (1936) 45 50
2259 4 d. Nag C4B, Germany (1924) 45 50
2260 4 d. Cadillac, U.S.A. (1903) . 45 50
2261 4 d. Bentley, Great Britain (1925) 45 50
2262 4 d. Renault Model AX, France (1909) 45 50

257 Bulgarian Team

1996. European Football Championship, England. Multicoloured.
2264 2 d. Type **257** 20 25
2265 2 d. Croatian team 20 25
2266 2 d. Czech Republic team . . 20 25
2267 2 d. Danish team 20 25
2268 2 d. English team 20 25
2269 2 d. French team 20 25
2270 2 d. German team 20 25
2271 2 d. Dutch team 20 25
2272 2 d. Italian team 20 25
2273 2 d. Portuguese team 20 25
2274 2 d. Rumanian team 20 25
2275 2 d. Russian team 20 25
2276 2 d. Scottish team 20 25
2277 2 d. Spanish team 20 25
2278 2 d. Swiss team 20 25
2279 2 d. Turkish team 20 25

258 Ray Ewry (U.S.A.) (standing high jump), 1912

258a Boy holding Shoes

259 Roman Officer and Pillar of Absalom

1996. Olympic Games, Atlanta (2nd issue). Previous Gold Medal Winners. Multicoloured.
2281 1 d. Type **258** 10 10
2282 2 d. Fanny Durack (Australia) (100m freestyle swimming), 1912 . . . . 20 25
2283 3 d. Fu Mingxia (China) (platform diving), 1992 . . 30 35
2284 3 d. H. Henkel (Germany) (high jump), 1992 . . . . . . 30 35
2285 3 d. Spanish team (soccer), 1992 . . . . 30 35
2286 3 d. Jackie Joyner-Kersee (U.S.A.) (heptathlon), 1988 and 1992 . . . . 30 35
2287 3 d. T. Gutsu (Russia) (gymnastics), 1992 . . . . 30 35
2288 3 d. M. Johnson (U.S.A.) (400m running), 1992 . . . . . . 30 35
2289 3 d. Lin Li (China) (200m medley swimming), 1992 . . 30 35
2290 3 d. G. Devers (U.S.A.) (100m running), 1992 . . . . . . 30 35
2291 3 d. Michael Powell (U.S.A.) (long jump), 1992 . . . . . 30 35
2292 3 d. Japanese volleyball team, 1964 . . . . 30 35
2293 3 d. Li Neng (China) (floor exercises), 1984 . . . . . . 30 35
2294 3 d. S. Bubka (U.S.S.R.) (pole vault), 1988 . . . . 30 35
2295 3 d. Nadia Comaneci (Romania) (gymnastics), 1976 . . . . 30 35
2296 3 d. Edwin Moses (U.S.A.) (400m hurdles), 1984 . . . 30 35
2297 3 d. Victor Scherbo (Russia) (gymnastics), 1992 . . . . 30 35
2298 3 d. Evelyn Ashford (U.S.A.) (100m running), 1984 . . . 30 35
2299 3 d. Mohammed Ali (U.S.A.) (light heavyweight boxing), 1960 . . . . 30 35
2300 3 d. Carl Lewis and C. Smith (U.S.A.) (400m relay), 1984 . 30 35
2301 5 d. Stockholm Olympic arena, 1912 . . . . 60 65
2302 10 d. Jim Thorpe (U.S.A.) (decathalon and pentathlon), 1912 . . . . 1·10 1·25

1996. 50th Anniv of U.N.I.C.E.F. Multicoloured.
2304 63 b. Type **258a** 10 10
2305 3 d. Girl being inoculated . . 35 40
2306 8 d. Boy holding ladle 90 95
2307 10 d. Child with blanket . . . 1·10 1·25

1996. 3000th Anniv of Jerusalem. Multicoloured.
2309 1 d. 50 Type **259** 20 25
2310 2 d. Turk and Gate of Mercy . 20 25
2311 3 d. Ancient Greek and Church of the Holy Sepulchre . . . 35 40
2312 10 d. Modern Hasidic Jew at Wailing Wall . . . . . . 1·10 1·25

259a Glenn Miller

1996. Centenary of Radio. Entertainers. Mult.
2314 1 d. Type **259a** 10 10
2315 4 d. Louis Armstrong 45 50
2316 5 d. Nat "King" Cole 60 65
2317 10 d. The Andrew Sisters . . . 1·10 1·25
No. 2314 is inscribed "Glen Miller" in error.

260 Jacqueline Kennedy Onassis in Wedding Dress

1996. Famous People of the 20th Century. Multicoloured.
2319 5 d. Type **260** 60 65
2320 5 d. Jaqueline Kennedy and White House 60 65
2321 5 d. Jaqueline Kennedy wearing pink hat 60 65
2322 5 d. Jaqueline Kennedy and motor yacht 60 65
2323 5 d. Jacqueline Kennedy wearing red jumper 60 65
2324 5 d. Jacqueline Kennedy and horse 60 65
2325 5 d. Jacqueline Kennedy on book 60 65
2326 5 d. Jacqueline Kennedy in blue dress and three rows of pearls 60 65
2327 5 d. Jacqueline Kennedy and corner of fountain 60 65
2328 5 d. President John Kennedy . 60 65
2329 5 d. Jacqueline Kennedy (inscr in capitals) 60 65
2330 5 d. Willy Brandt 60 65
2331 5 d. Marilyn Monroe 60 65
2332 5 d. Mao Tse-tung 60 65
2333 5 d. Sung Ching Ling 60 65
2334 5 d. Charles De Gaulle . . . 60 65
2335 5 d. Marlene Dietrich 60 65
No. 2330 is inscr "WILLIE BRANDT", No. 2331 "MARYLYN MONROE" and No. 2332 "MAO TSE TONG", all in error.

261 Richard Petty's 1969 Ford

1996. Richard Petty (stock car driver) Commem. Multicoloured.
2337 5 d. Type **261** 60 65
2338 5 d. Richard Petty 60 65
2339 5 d. Dodge Magnum, 1978 . . 60 65
2340 5 d. Pontiac, 1987 . . . . . 60 65
2341 5 d. Pontiac, 1989 . . . . . 60 65
2342 5 d. Dodge Daytona, 1975 . . 60 65

1996. Results of European Football Championships, England. As Nos. 2265/6, 2268, 2270, 2272 and 2275, but each additionally inscribed with date and match result. Multicoloured.
2344 2 d. Croatian team ("23/6/96 Germany 2, Croatia 1") . . 20 25
2345 2 d. Czech Republic team ("9/6/96 Germany 2, Czech Rep. 0") 20 25
2346 2 d. English team ("26/6/96 Germany 6, England 5") . . 20 25
2347 2 d. German team ("30/6/96 Germany 2, Czech Rep. 1") . 20 25
2348 2 d. Italian team ("19/6/96 Germany 0, Italy 0") . . . 20 25
2349 2 d. Russian team ("16/6/96 Germany 3, Russia 0") . . 20 25

262 Elvis Presley with Microphone

263 Bob Dylan

1996. Elvis Presley Commemoration. Different Portraits. Multicoloured.
2351 5 d. Type **262** 60 65
2352 5 d. In dinner jacket 60 65
2353 5 d. In Mexican outfit 60 65
2354 5 d. Wearing blue jumper . . 60 65
2355 5 d. In leather jacket 60 65
2356 5 d. Wearing lei 60 65

1996. Rock and Roll Legends. Bob Dylan.
2357 **263** 5 d. multicoloured . . . 60 65

264 Supermarine Spitfire Prototype K5054

1996. 65th Anniv of Britain's Victory in Schneider Trophy Air Race. Multicoloured.
2358 4 d. Type **264** 45 50
2359 4 d. First production Spitfire K9787 . . . . 45 50
2360 4 d. Spitfire Mk 1A in Battle of Britain 45 50
2361 4 d. Spitfire Lfmk IXE with D-Day markings 45 50
2362 4 d. Spitfire Mk XII (first with "Griffon" engine) 45 50
2363 4 d. Spitfire Mk XIVC with jungle markings 45 50
2364 4 d. Spitfire XIX of Royal Swedish Air Force 45 50
2365 4 d. Spitfire Mk XIX 45 50
2366 4 d. Spitfire FMk 22/24 (final variant) 45 50
2367 4 d. Spitfire Mk XIX of Royal Swedish Air Force (from below) 45 50
2368 4 d. Spitfire Mk VB of United States Army Air Corps . . 45 50
2369 4 d. Spitfire Mk VC of French Air Force 45 50
2370 4 d. Spitfire Mk VB of Soviet Air Force 45 50
2371 4 d. Spitfire Mk IXE of Netherlands East Indies Air Force 45 50
2372 4 d. Spitfire Mk IXE of Israeli Air Force 45 50
2373 4 d. Spitfire Mk VIII of Royal Australian Air Force . . . 45 50
2374 4 d. Siptfire Mk VB of Turkish Air Force 45 50
2375 4 d. Spitfire Mk XI of Royal Danish Air Force 45 50

265 Egyptian Plover

1996. Birds. Multicoloured.
2377 50 b. Type **265** 10 10
2378 63 b. Painted snipe 10 10
2379 75 b. Golden-breasted bunting 10 10
2380 1 d. Bateleur 10 10
2381 1 d. 50 Didric cuckoo . . . 20 25
2382 2 d. Turtle dove 20 25
2383 3 d. Village weaver 35 40
2384 4 d. Common roller 45 50
2385 5 d. Cut-throat 60 65
2386 10 d. Hoopoe . . . . 1·10 1·25
2387 15 d. White-faced scops owl . 1·75 1·90
2388 20 d. Narina trogon . . . . 2·25 2·40
2389 25 d. Lesser pied kingfisher . 3·00 3·25
2390 30 d. Common kestrel . . . 3·50 3·75
2391 40 d. Temminck's courser . . 4·75 5·00
2392 50 d. European bee-eater . . 5·75 6·00
2392a 100 d. Green-winged teal . . 11·50 12·50
No. 2388 is inscribed "TROGAN" in error.

265a "Assumption of the Madonna" (detail)

1996. Christmas. Religious Paintings.
2393 **265a** 1 d. multicoloured . . . 10 10
2394 – 1 d. 50 multicoloured . . 20 25
2395 – 2 d. multicoloured . . . 20 25
2396 – 3 d. multicoloured . . . 35 40
2397 – 10 d. multicoloured . . . 1·10 1·25
2398 – 15 d. multicoloured . . . 1·75 1·90
DESIGNS: 1 d. 50 to 15 d. Different details of "Assumption of the Madonna" (Tiziano Vecellio).

267 Ox

268 "Arch 22" Monument

1997. Chinese New Year ("Year of the Ox").
2401 **267** 63 b. multicoloured . . . 10 10
2402 – 75 b. multicoloured . . . 10 10
2403 – 1 d. 50 multicoloured . . 20 25
2404 – 4 d. multicoloured . . . 45 50
DESIGNS: 75 b. to 4 d. Symbolic oxen.

1997. Economic Development. Multicoloured.
2407 63 b. Type **268** 10 10
2408 1 d. Tractor (horiz) 10 10
2409 1 d. 50 Man planting rice . . 20 25
2410 2 d. As Type **268**, but with white panel at top 20 25
2411 3 d. Model of Banjul International Airport terminal building (horiz) . . 35 40
2412 5 d. Chamoi Bridge (horiz) . . 60 65

269 Monkey King extinguishing Fire on Flame Mountain

1997. Mickey Mouse's Journey to the West. Disney Cartoon Characters. Multicoloured.
2414 2 d. Type **269** 40 40
2415 2 d. Demon Ox and Monkey King fighting 40 40
2416 2 d. Mickey, Donald, Monkey King and Master San Tsang 40 40
2417 2 d. Fighting the Spider Demon 40 40
2418 2 d. Fighting the White Skeleton Demon 40 40

2419 2 d. The real and the fake Monkey King 40 40
2420 3 d. Monkey King trapped in furnace 50 50
2421 3 d. Monkey King with magic weapon 50 50
2422 3 d. Type **269** 50 50
2423 3 d. At the Gate of South Heaven 50 50
2424 3 d. Tasting the celestial peaches 50 50
2425 3 d. Monkey King rescued from Five-Finger Mountain 50 50

270 Jackie Chan

1997. "HONG KONG '97" International Stamp Exhibition. Jackie Chan (film star). Multicoloured.
2427 4 d. Type **270** 45 50
2428 4 d. Wearing red jacket 45 50
2429 4 d. In open-necked shirt 45 50
2430 4 d. Bare-chested 45 50
2431 4 d. Wearing black jacket 45 50
2432 4 d. Wearing black and white spotted shirt 45 50
2433 4 d. Wearing white T-shirt and red anorak 45 50
2434 4 d. Wearing white sleeveless T-shirt 45 50

271 Clouded Leopard

1997. Endangered Species. Multicoloured.
2436 1 d. 50 Type **271** 20 25
2437 1 d. 50 Audouin's gull 20 25
2438 1 d. 50 Leatherback turtle 20 25
2439 1 d. 50 White-eared pheasant 20 25
2440 1 d. 50 Kakapo 20 25
2441 1 d. 50 Right whale 20 25
2442 1 d. 50 Black-footed ferret 20 25
2443 1 d. 50 Dwarf lemur 20 25
2444 1 d. 50 Peacock-pheasant 20 25
2445 1 d. 50 Brown hyena 20 25
2446 1 d. 50 Cougar 20 25
2447 1 d. 50 Gharial 20 25
2448 1 d. 50 Monk seal 20 25
2449 1 d. 50 Mountain gorilla 20 25
2450 1 d. 50 Blyth's tragopan 20 25
2451 1 d. 50 Malayan tapir 20 25
2452 1 d. 50 Black rhinoceros 20 25
2453 1 d. 50 Polar bear 20 25
2454 1 d. 50 Red colobus 20 25
2455 1 d. 50 Tiger 20 25
2456 1 d. 50 Arabian oryx 20 25
2457 1 d. 50 Baiji 20 25
2458 1 d. 50 Ruffed lemur 20 25
2459 1 d. 50 California condor 20 25
2460 1 d. 50 Blue-headed quail dove 20 25
2461 1 d. 50 Numbat 20 25
2462 1 d. 50 Congo peacock 20 25
2463 1 d. 50 White uakari 20 25
2464 1 d. 50 Eskimo curlew 20 25
2465 1 d. 50 Gouldian finch 20 25
2466 1 d. 50 Coelacanth 20 25
2467 1 d. 50 Toucan barbet 20 25
2468 1 d. 50 Snow leopard 20 25
2469 1 d. 50 Queen Alexandra's birdwing 20 25
2470 1 d. 50 Dalmatian pelican 20 25
2471 1 d. 50 Chaco tortoise 20 25
2472 1 d. 50 Mekong catfish 20 25
2473 1 d. 50 Helmeted hornbill 20 25
2474 1 d. 50 White-eyed river martin 20 25
2475 1 d. 50 Fluminense swallowtail 20 25

272 Monkey

1997. "The Jungle Book" by Rudyard Kipling. Multicoloured.
2477 3 d. Type **272** 35 40
2478 3 d. Baloo (bear) 35 40
2479 3 d. Elephant 35 40
2480 3 d. Monkey and temple 35 40
2481 3 d. Bagheera (panther) 35 40
2482 3 d. Buffalo 35 40
2483 3 d. Mandrill 35 40
2484 3 d. Shere Khan (tiger) 35 40
2485 3 d. Rama (wolf) 35 40
2486 3 d. Kaa (cobra) 35 40
2487 3 d. Mongoose 35 40
2488 3 d. Mowgli 35 40
Nos. 2477/88 were printed together, se-tenant, with the backgrounds forming a composite design.

273 "Polyporus squamosus"

1997. Fungi. Multicoloured.
2489 1 d. Type **273** 10 15
2490 3 d. "Armillaria tabescens" 35 40
2491 4 d. "Amanita caesarea" (vert) 45 50
2492 4 d. "Lepiota procera" (vert) 45 50
2493 4 d. "Hygrophorus psittacinus" (vert) 45 50
2494 4 d. "Russula xerampelina" (vert) 45 50
2495 4 d. "Laccaria amethystina" (vert) 45 50
2496 4 d. "Coprinus micaceus" (vert) 45 50
2497 4 d. "Boletus edulis" (vert) 45 50
2498 4 d. "Morchella esculenta" (vert) 45 50
2499 4 d. "Otidea auricula" (vert) 45 50
2500 5 d. "Collybia velutipes" 60 65
2501 10 d. "Sarcoscypha coccinea" 1·10 1·25

50th Anniversary of UNESCO
273a Cloister, Horyu-ji, Japan

1997. 50th Anniv of U.N.E.S.C.O. Multicoloured.
2503 1 d. Type **273a** 10 15
2504 2 d. Great Wall, China 20 25
2505 3 d. Statues, Ayutthaya, Thailand 35 40
2506 4 d. Ascension Convent, Santa Maria, Philippines 45 50
2507 4 d. Mount Nimba Nature Reserve, Guinea (vert) 45 50
2508 4 d. Banc d'Arguin National Park, Mauritania (vert) 45 50
2509 4 d. Doorway, Marrakesh, Morocco (vert) 45 50
2510 4 d. Ichkeul National Park, Tunisia (vert) 45 50
2511 4 d. Village pottery, Mali (vert) 45 50
2512 4 d. Hippopotamus, Salonga National Park, Zaire (vert) 45 50
2513 4 d. Timgad Roman Ruins, Algeria (vert) 45 50
2514 4 d. Wooden statue, Benin (vert) 45 50
2515 4 d. Temple, Magao Caves, China (vert) 45 50
2516 4 d. Statue, Magao Caves (vert) 45 50
2517 4 d. Domes, Magao Caves (vert) 45 50
2518 4 d. Great Wall from air, China (vert) 45 50
2519 4 d. Statue, Great Wall (vert) 45 50
2520 4 d. Bronze Bird, Imperial Palace, China (vert) 45 50
2521 4 d. Temples, Imperial Palace, China (vert) 45 50
2522 4 d. Dragon statue, Imperial Palace (vert) 45 50
2523 4 d. Kyoto Gardens, Japan (vert) 45 50
2524 4 d. Himeji Castle, Japan (vert) 45 50
2525 4 d. Horyu-ji Temple, Japan (vert) 45 50
2526 4 d. Buddha, Horyu-ji, Japan (vert) 45 50
2527 4 d. Yakushima Forest, Japan (vert) 45 50
2528 4 d. Ancient tree, Yakushima Forest, Japan (vert) 45 50
2529 4 d. Temple, Kyoto, Japan (vert) 45 50
2530 4 d. Pavilion, Kyoto, Japan (vert) 45 50
2531 5 d. Riverside houses, Inselstadt, Germany 60 65
2532 5 d. Rosaleda Gardens, Bamberg, Germany 60 65
2533 5 d. Bamberg Cathedral, Germany 60 65
2534 5 d. Timbered house, Maulbronn, Germany 60 65
2535 5 d. Maulbronn Monastry, Germany 60 65
2536 5 d. Ruins at Delphi, Greece 60 65
2537 5 d. Rhodes waterfront, Greece 60 65
2538 5 d. Knights' Hospital, Rhodes, Greece 60 65
2539 5 d. Temple, Delphi, Greece 60 65
2540 5 d. Delphi from air, Greece 60 65
2541 5 d. Foliage, Shirakami-Sanchi, Japan 60 65
2542 5 d. Notice board, Shirakami-Sanchi, Japan 60 65
2543 5 d. Tower, Himeji Castle, Japan 60 65
2544 5 d. Roof tops, Himeji Castle, Japan 60 65
2545 5 d. Gateway, Himeji Castle, Japan 60 65
2546 10 d. Komodo Dragons, Indonesia 1·10 1·40
2547 15 d. Ancient hut, Timbuktu, Mali 1·75 1·90

274 Minnie Mouse, 1928

1997. Minnie Mouse Through the Years. Designs showing Disney cartoon character in years stated. Multicoloured.
2549 4 d. Type **274** 70 75
2550 4 d. In 1933 70 75
2551 4 d. In 1934 70 75
2552 4 d. In 1937 70 75
2553 4 d. In 1938 70 75
2554 4 d. In 1941 70 75
2555 4 d. In 1950 70 75
2556 4 d. In 1990 70 75
2557 4 d. In 1997 70 75

275 Dipstick

1997. "101 Dalmatians". Disney cartoon characters. Multicoloured.
2559 50 b. Type **275** 20 20
2560 50 b. Fidget 20 20
2561 50 b. Jewel 20 20
2562 50 b. Lucky 20 20
2563 50 b. Two-Tone 20 20
2564 50 b. Wizzer 20 20
2565 2 d. Two puppies playing (horiz) 35 35
2566 2 d. Puppy and pig (horiz) 35 35
2567 2 d. Two puppies with butterfly (horiz) 35 35
2568 2 d. Puppy lying on back (horiz) 35 35
2569 2 d. Puppy with ball (horiz) 35 35
2570 2 d. Puppy with bone (horiz) 35 35
2571 2 d. One puppy pulling another puppy's tail (horiz) 35 35
2572 2 d. Two puppies pulling third puppy's ears (horiz) 35 35
2573 2 d. Puppy with teddy bear (horiz) 35 35
2574 3 d. Puppy asleep on biscuit box (horiz) 45 45
2575 3 d. Puppy with hose (horiz) 45 45
2576 3 d. Puppy and bottle (horiz) 45 45
2577 3 d. Puppy and biscuit bowl (horiz) 45 45
2578 3 d. Puppy wearing hat (horiz) 45 45
2579 3 d. Three puppies with lipstick (horiz) 45 45
2580 3 d. Puppy tying another up with string (horiz) 45 45
2581 3 d. Two puppies and lunch box (horiz) 45 45
2582 3 d. Three puppies and computer (horiz) 45 45

276 Juventus Team, 1897

1997. Centenary of Juventus Football Team. Multicoloured.
2584 5 d. Type **276** 60 65
2585 5 d. Centenary emblem and player 60 65
2586 5 d. Giampiero Boniperti 60 65
2587 5 d. Roberto Bettega 60 65
2588 5 d. Juventus team, 1996 60 65
2589 5 d. Juventus '97 logo 60 65

276a Child's Face and U.N.E.S.C.O. Emblem

1997. 10th Anniv of Chernobyl Nuclear Disaster. Multicoloured.
2591 15 d. Type **276a** 1·75 1·90
2592 15 d. As No. 2591 but inscribed "CHABAD'S CHILDREN OF CHERNOBYL" 1·75 1·90

276b Rotary President Sydney Pascall planting Tree of Friendship

1997. 50th Death Anniv of Paul Harris (founder of Rotary International).
2593 **276b** 10 d. multicoloured 1·10 1·25

276c Queen Elizabeth II

1997. Golden Wedding of Queen Elizabeth and Prince Philip. Multicoloured.
2595 4 d. Type **276c** 45 50
2596 4 d. Royal coat of arms 45 50
2597 4 d. Queen Elizabeth and Prince Philip applauding 45 50
2598 4 d. Queen Elizabeth and Prince Philip taking the salute 45 50
2599 4 d. Royal Yacht "Britannia" 45 50
2600 4 d. Prince Philip 45 50

276d Von Stephan and Otto von Bismarck

1997. "Pacific '97" International Stamp Exhibition, San Francisco. Death Centenary of Henrich von Stephan (founder of U.P.U.).
2602 **276d** 5 d. mauve 60 65
2603 – 5 d. brown 60 65
2604 – 5 d. green and black 60 65
DESIGNS: Nos. 2603, Von Stephan and Mercury; 2604, Mail wagon, Boston, 1900.

277 "Morning Glory and Cricket"

1997. Birth Bicentenary of Hiroshige (Japanese painter). Multicoloured.
2606/11 4 d. × 6 (Type **277**; "Dragonfly and Begonia"; "Two Ducks swimming among Reeds"; "A Black-naped Oriole perched on a Stem of Rose Mallow"; "A Pheasant on a Snow-covered Pine"; "A Cuckoo flying through the Rain")

2612/17 4 d. × 6 ("An Egret among Rushes"; "Peacock and Peonies"; "Three Wild Geese flying across the Moon"; "A Cock in the Snow"; "A Pheasant and Bracken"; "Peonies")
2618/23 4 d. × 6 ("Sparrow and Bamboo"; "Mandarin Ducks on an Icy Pond with Brown Leaves falling"; "Blossoming Plum Tree"; "Java Sparrow and Magnolia"; "Chinese Bellflowers and Miscanthus"; "A Small Black Bird clinging to a Tendril of Ivy")
2624/9 5 d. × 6 ("Sparrows and Camellia in Snow", "Parrot on a Branch of Pine"; "A Long-tailed Blue Bird on a Branch of Flowering Plum"; "Sparrow and Bamboo"; "Bird in a Tree"; "A Wild Duck swimming beneath Snow-laden reeds")
2630/5 5 d. × 6 ("Kingfisher above a Yellow-flowered Water Plant"; "Wagtail and Roses"; "A Mandarin Duck on a Snowy Bank"; "A Japanese White-eye on a Persimmon Branch"; "Sparrows and Camellia in Snow"; "Kingfisher and Moon above a Yellow-flowered Water Plant")
2636/41 5 d. × 6 ("Sparrow and Bamboo by Night"; "Birds Flying over Waves"; "Blossoming Plum Tree with Full Moon"; "Kingfisher and Iris"; "A Blue-and-White Flycatcher on a Hibiscus Flower"; "Mandarin Ducks in Snowfall")
2606/41 Set of 35 15·00 16·00

277a Grandma's Cottage

1997. 175th Anniv of Brothers Grimm's Third Collection of Fairy Tales. Little Red Riding Hood. Multicoloured.

2643 10 d. Type **277a** 1·10 1·25
2644 10 d. Little Red Riding Hood 1·10 1·25
2645 10 d. The Wolf 1·10 1·25

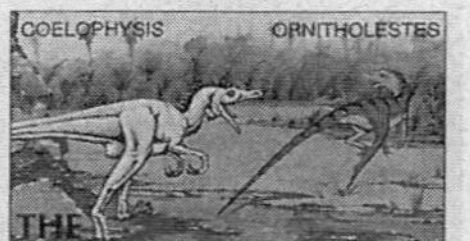

278 Coelophysis chasing Ornitholestes

1997. Dinosaurs. Multicoloured.

2647 50 b. Type **278** 10 10
2648 63 b. Spinosauru 10 10
2649 75 b. Kentrosaurs 10 10
2650 1 d. Ceratosaurus 10 10
2651 1 d. 50 Stygimoloch 20 25
2652 2 d. Troodon 20 25
2653 3 d. Velociraptor 35 40
2654 4 d. Triceratops 45 50
2655 4 d. Anurognathus 45 50
2656 4 d. Pteranodon 45 50
2657 4 d. Pterosaurus 45 50
2658 4 d. Saltasaurus 45 50
2659 4 d. Agathaumus 45 50
2660 4 d. Stegosaurus 45 50
2661 4 d. Albertosaurus libratus 45 50
2662 4 d. Three Lesothosauruses running 45 50
2663 4 d. Five Lesothosauruses running 45 50
2664 4 d. Tarbosaurus bataar 45 50
2665 4 d. Brachiosaurus 45 50
2666 4 d. Styracosasaurus 45 50
2667 4 d. Baryonyx 45 50
2668 4 d. Coelophysis 45 50
2669 4 d. Carnotaurus 45 50
2670 4 d. Compsognathus longipes 45 50
2671 4 d. Compsognathus "Elegant Jaw" 45 50
2672 4 d. Stenonychosaurus 45 50
2673 4 d. Protoceratops 60 65
2674 10 d. Ornithomimus 1·10 1·25
2675 15 d. Stegosaurus 1·75 1·90
2676 20 d. Ankylosaurus saichania 2·25 2·40

Nos. 2655/63 and 2664/72 respectively were printed together, se-tenant, with the backgrounds forming composite designs.

279 Margaret Thatcher and Deng Xiaoping toasting Joint Declaration, 1984

1997. Return of Hong Kong to China. Multicoloured.

2678 3 d. Type **279** 35 40
2679 3 d. Signing Joint Declaration on Hong Kong, 1984 35 40
2680 3 d. Signing Joint Declaration on Macao, 1987 35 40
2681 3 d. Deng Xiaoping toasting Prime Minister Anibal Silva of Portugal 35 40
2682 4 d. Hong Kong in 1843 and Governor Sir Henry Pottinger 45 50
2683 4 d. Kowloon in 1860 and Governor Sir Hercules Robinson 45 50
2684 4 d. Reception in New Territories, 1898, and Governor Sir Henry Blake 45 50
2685 5 d. Governor Sir Henry Pottinger and British warship 60 65
2686 5 d. Governor Christopher Patten and Lantau Bridge 60 65
2687 5 d. Chief Executive C.H. Tung and Hong Kong by night 60 65
2688 6 d. Signing the Treaty of Nanking, 1842 70 75
2689 6 d. Signing the Japanese Surrender of Hong Kong, 1945 70 75
2690 6 d. Signing of the Sino-British Joint Declaration, 1984 70 75

280 Great Mosque, Samarra, Iran

1997. Natural and Man-made Wonders of the World. Multicoloured.

2691 63 b. Type **280** 10 10
2692 75 b. Moai statues, Easter Island (horiz) 10 10
2693 1 d. Golden Gate Bridge, San Francisco (horiz) 10 10
2694 1 d. 50 The Statue of Liberty, New York 20 25
2695 2 d. The Parthenon, Athens (horiz) 20 25
2696 3 d. Pyramid of the Sun, Mexico (horiz) 35 40
2697 5 d. The Rock of Gibraltar (horiz) 60 65
2698 5 d. St. Peter's Basilica, Rome (horiz) 60 65
2699 5 d. Santa Sophia, Istanbul (horiz) 60 65
2700 5 d. "Gateway to the West" monument, St. Louis (horiz) 60 65
2701 5 d. Great Wall of China (horiz) 60 65
2702 5 d. City of Carcassonne, France (horiz) 60 65
2703 5 d. Stonehenge, England (horiz) 60 65
2704 5 d. Hughes HK-1 "Spruce Goose" flying boat (World's largest aircraft) (horiz) 60 65
2705 5 d. Hoverspeed "Seacat" catamaran (fastest Atlantic crossing by a commercial catamaran) (horiz) 60 65
2706 5 d. "Thrust 2" car (official land speed record) (horiz) 60 65
2707 5 d. Stepped Pyramid, Egypt (horiz) 60 65
2708 5 d. L.N.E.R. Clas A4 "Mallard" (fastest steam locomotive), 1938 (horiz) 60 65

No. 2702 is inscribed "CARCASSONNNE" in error.

281 Downhill Skiing

1997. Winter Olympic Games, Nagano (1998). Multicoloured.

2710 5 d. Type **281** 60 65
2711 5 d. Two-man bobsleigh (vert) 60 65
2712 5 d. Freestyle skiing (vert) 60 65
2713 5 d. Speed skating (vert) 60 65
2714 5 d. Downhill skiing (No. 8 on bib) (vert) 60 65
2715 5 d. Womens figure skating (vert) 60 65
2716 5 d. Downhill skiing (No. 4 on bib) (vert) 60 65
2717 5 d. Pairs figure skating (vert) 60 65
2718 5 d. Cross-country (vert) 60 65
2719 5 d. Ski jumping (vert) 60 65
2720 5 d. One-man luge 60 65
2721 5 d. Ice hockey 60 65
2722 5 d. Four-man bobsleigh 60 65
2723 5 d. Ski-jumping 60 65
2724 5 d. Curling 60 65
2725 5 d. Figure skating 60 65
2726 5 d. Speed skating 60 65
2727 5 d. Biathlon 60 65
2728 5 d. Downhill skiing (different) 60 65
2729 10 d. One-man luge 1·10 1·25
2730 15 d. Speed skating 1·75 1·90
2731 20 d. Ice hockey 2·25 2·40

282 Brown Pelican

1997. Sea Birds. Multicoloured.

2733 3 d. Type **282** 35 40
2734 3 d. Galapagos penguin 35 40
2735 3 d. Red-billed tropic bird 35 40
2736 3 d. Little tern 35 40
2737 3 d. Dunlin 35 40
2738 3 d. Kittiwake 35 40
2739 3 d. Atlantic puffin 35 40
2740 3 d. Wandering albatross 35 40
2741 3 d. Masked booby 35 40
2742 3 d. Galucous winged tern 35 40
2743 3 d. Arctic tern 35 40
2744 3 d. Piping plover 35 40
2745 5 d. Roseate tern 60 65
2746 10 d. Red-legged cormorant 1·10 1·25
2747 15 d. Blue-footed booby 1·75 1·90
2748 20 d. Sanderling 2·25 2·40

No. 2743 is inscribed "ARTIC TEN" and the captions on Nos. 2745/6 are transposed, both in error.

283 Scottish Fold Cat

1997. Cats and Dogs. Multicoloured.

2750 63 b. Type **283** 10 10
2751 75 b. Dalmatian 10 10
2752 1 d. Rottweiler 10 15
2753 1 d. 50 American curl cat 20 25
2754 2 d. British bi-colour cat 20 25
2755 3 d. Newfoundland 35 40
2756 3 d. Devon Rex cat 35 40
2757 4 d. Great Dane 45 50
2758 5 d. Burmilla cat 60 65
2759 5 d. Blue Burmese cat 60 65
2760 5 d. Korat cat 60 65
2761 5 d. British tabby cat 60 65
2762 5 d. Foreign white cat 60 65
2763 5 d. Somali cat 60 65
2764 5 d. Akita 60 65
2765 5 d. Welsh corgi 60 65
2766 5 d. German shepherd 60 65
2767 5 d. Saint Bernard 60 65
2768 5 d. Bullmastiff 60 65
2769 5 d. Malamute 60 65
2770 6 d. Silver tabby cat 70 75
2771 10 d. Old English sheepdog 1·10 1·25
2772 15 d. Queensland heeler cat 1·75 1·90
2773 20 d. Abyssinian cat 2·25 2·40

283a Uruguay Team, 1950

1997. World Cup Football Championship, France (1998).

2775 **283a** 1 d. black 10 10
2776 – 1 d. 50 black 20 25
2777 – 2 d. black 20 25
2778 – 3 d. black 35 40
2779/86 – 4 d. × 8 mult or brown (Nos. 2782/3) 3·50
2787/94 – 4 d. × 8 mult or black (No. 2788) 3·50
2795/2802 – 4 d. × 8 brown (Nos. 2795/6, 2800 and 2802) or mult 3·50
2803/10 – 4 d. × 8 mult 3·50
2811 – 5 d. black 60 65
2812 – 10 d. black 1·10 1·25

DESIGNS—HORIZ: No. 2776, West German team, 1954; 2777, Brazilian team, 1970; 2778, Brazilian team, 1962; 2779, Brazilian team, 1994; 2780, Argentine team, 1986; 2781, Brazilian team, 1970; 2782, Italian team, 1934; 2783, Uruguay team, 1958; 2784, English team, 1966; 2785, Brazilian team, 1962; 2786, West German team, 1990; 2787, Mario Kempes, Argentina (1978); 2788, Joseph Gaetjens, U.S.A. (1950) (inscr "ADEMIR BRAZIL" in error); 2789, Muller, West Germany (1970); 2790, Lineker, England (1986); 2791, Eusebio, Portugal (1966); 2792, Schillaci, Italy (1990); 2793, Lato, Poland (1974); 2794, Rossi, Italy (1982); 2811, Italian team, 1938; 2812, Uruguay team, 1930. VERT: No. 2795, Moore, England (1966); 2796, Fritzwalter, West Germany (1954); 2797, Beckenbauer, West Germany (1974); 2798, Zoff, Italy (1982); 2799, Maradona, Argentina (1986); 2800, Passarella, Argentina (1978); 2801, Matthaus, West Germany (1990); 2802, Dunga, Brazil (1994); 2803, Kinkladze, Georgia; 2804, Shearer, England; 2805, Dani, Portugal; 2806, Weah, Portugal; 2807, Ravanelli, Italy; 2808, Raducioiu, Rumania; 2809, Schmeichel, Denmark; 2810, Bergkamp, Holland.

284 Diana, Princess of Wales

285 Tiger

284a "Angel" (Rembrandt)

1997. Diana, Princess of Wales Commemoration. Each brown and black.

2814 10 d. Type **284** 1·10 1·25
2815 10 d. Wearing open-necked shirt 1·10 1·25
2816 10 d. Wearing polo-neck jumper 1·10 1·25
2817 10 d. Wearing diamond-drop earrings 1·10 1·25

1997. Christmas. Paintings. Multicoloured.

2819 1 d. Type **284a** 10 15
2820 1 d. 50 "Initiation into the Rites of Dionysus" at Villa dei Misteri 20 25
2821 2 d. "Pair of Erotes with Purple Cloaks" 20 25
2822 3 d. "The Ecstasy of Saint Theresa" (Gianlorenzo Bernini) 35 40
2823 5 d. "Virgin and Child with Angels" (Matthias Grunewald) 60 65
2824 10 d. "Angel playing the Organ" (Stefan Lochner) 1·10 1·25

1998. Chinese New Year ("Year of the Tiger"). Multicoloured.

2826 3 d. Type **285** ("GAMBIA" in green) 35 40
2827 3 d. Tiger ("GAMBIA" in mauve) 35 40
2828 3 d. Tiger ("GAMBIA" in lilac) 35 40
2829 3 d. Tiger ("GAMBIA" in blue) 35 40

286 Class 91 Electric Train, Great Britian

1998. Trains of the World. Multicoloured.

2831 5 d. Type **286** 60 65
2832 5 d. Class 26 steam locomotive No. 3450 "Red Devil", South Africa 60 65
2833 5 d. TGV express train, France 60 65
2834 5 d. People Mover railcar, Great Britain 60 65
2835 5 d. ICE high speed train, Germany 60 65
2836 5 d. Montmartre funicular car, France 60 65
2837 5 d. Burlington Northern SD70 diesel locomotive No. 9716, U.S.A. 60 65
2838 5 d. L.N.E.R. Class A4 steam locomotive "Mallard", 1938 60 65
2839 5 d. Baldwin steam locomotive, Peru 60 65

2840 5 d. Amtrak Class ARM-7 electric locomotive, U.S.A. 60 65
2841 5 d. Rack steam locomotive No. B2503, Amberawa, Java 60 65
2842 5 d. Beyer-Peacock steam locomotive No. 3108, Pakistan 60 65

No. 2832 is inscribed "BEACONSFIELD CHINA", No. 2836 "MOUNTMAETRE FUNICULAR" and No. 2840 "SWEDEN RAIL 125 MPH", all in error.

287 Yellow Orchid **289** Mulan

288 Wright "Flyer I", 1903

1998. African Flowers. Multicoloured.
2844 75 b. Type **287** 10 10
2845 1 d. 50 Transvaal daisy 20 25
2846 3 d. Torch lily 35 40
2847 4 d. "Ancistrochilus rothschildianus" 45 50
2848 5 d. "Adenium multiflorum" (horiz) 60 65
2849 5 d. "Huernia namaquensis" (horiz) 60 65
2850 5 d. "Gloriosa superba" (horiz) 60 65
2851 5 d. "Strelitzia reginae" (horiz) 60 65
2852 5 d. "Passiflora mollissima" (horiz) 60 65
2853 5 d. "Bauhinia variegata" (horiz) 60 65
2854 10 d. "Polystachya vulcanica" 1·10 1·25
2855 15 d. Gladiolus 1·75 1·90

Nos. 2848/53 were printed together, se-tenant, forming a composite background design.

1998. History of Aviation. Multicoloured.
2857 5 d. Type **288** 60 65
2858 5 d. Curtiss A-1 seaplane, 1910 60 65
2859 5 d. Farman biplane, 1907 60 65
2860 5 d. Bristol monoplane, 1911 60 65
2861 5 d. Antoinette IV, 1908 60 65
2862 5 d. Sopwith "Bat Boat" amphibian, 1912 60 65
2863 5 d. Short Type 38, 1913 60 65
2864 5 d. Fokker F.VIIb/3m, 1925 60 65
2865 5 d. Junkers J.13, 1919 60 65
2866 5 d. Pitcairn "Mailwing", 1927 60 65
2867 5 d. Douglas, 1920 60 65
2868 5 d. Curtiss T-32 Condor II airliner, 1934 60 65

Nos. 2857/62 and 2863/8 respectively were printed together, se-tenant, forming composite background designs.

No. 2857 is dated "1902" in error.

1998. "Mulan" (film). Multicoloured.
2870 4 d. Type **289** 45 50
2871 4 d. Mushu 45 50
2872 4 d. Little Brother 45 50
2873 4 d. Cri-kee 45 50
2874 4 d. Grandmother Fa 45 50
2875 4 d. Fa Li 45 50
2876 4 d. Fa Zhou 45 50
2877 4 d. Mulan and Khan 45 50
2878 5 d. Mulan riding Khan 60 65
2879 5 d. Shang 60 65
2880 5 d. Chi-fu 60 65
2881 5 d. Chien-po 60 65
2882 5 d. Yao 60 65
2883 5 d. Ling 60 65
2884 5 d. Shan-yu 60 65
2885 5 d. Mulan, Shang and Mushu 60 65

289a Sidney Bechet

1998. Millennium Series. Famous People of the Twentieth Century. Multicoloured. (a) Famous Jazz Musicians.
2887 4 d. Type **289a** 45 50
2888 4 d. Sidney Bechet playing saxophone (53 × 38 mm) 45 50
2889 4 d. Duke Ellington conducting (53 × 38 mm) 45 50
2890 4 d. Duke Ellington 45 50
2891 4 d. Louis Armstrong 45 50
2892 4 d. Louis Armstrong playing trumpet (53 × 38 mm) 45 50
2893 4 d. Charlie "Bird" Parker playing saxophone (53 × 38 mm) 45 50
2894 4 d. Charlie "Bird" Parker 45 50

(b) Famous Theatrical Composers.
2895 4 d. Cole Porter 45 50
2896 4 d. "Born to Dance" (Cole Porter) (53 × 38 mm) 45 50
2897 4 d. "Porgy and Bess" (George Gershwin) (53 × 38 mm) 45 50
2898 4 d. George Gershwin 45 50
2899 4 d. Rogers and Hammerstein 45 50
2900 4 d. "The King and I" (Rogers and Hammerstein) (53 × 38 mm) 45 50
2901 4 d. "West Side Story" (Leonard Bernstein) (53 × 38 mm) 45 50
2902 4 d. Leonard Bernstein 45 50

290 Chinese Junk **291** Captain Edward Smith

1998. Ships. Multicoloured.
2904 2 d. Type **290** 20 25
2905 3 d. H.M.S. "Victory" (ship of the line, 1765) 35 40
2906 5 d. "Santa Maria" (Columbus) 60 65
2907 5 d. "Mary Rose" (galleon) 60 65
2908 5 d. "Mayflower" (Pilgrim Fathers) 60 65
2909 5 d. "Ark Royal" (galleon, 1587) 60 65
2910 5 d. H.M.S. "Beagle" (Darwin) 60 65
2911 5 d. H.M.S. "Bounty" (Bligh) 60 65
2912 5 d. H.M.S. "Dreadnought" (battleship) 60 65
2913 5 d. American "Truxton" Class cruiser 60 65
2914 5 d. "Queen Mary" (liner) 60 65
2915 5 d. "Canberra" (liner) 60 65
2916 5 d. "Queen Elizabeth" (liner) 60 65
2917 5 d. "Queen Elizabeth II" (liner) 60 65
2918 10 d. British "County" Class destroyer 1·10 1·25
2919 15 d. Viking longship 1·75 1·90

1998. "Titanic" Commemoration.
2921 **291** 5 d. brown, black and blue 60 65
2922 – 5 d. brown, black and blue 60 65
2923 – 5 d. brown and black 60 65
2924 – 5 d. blue and black 60 65
2925 – 5 d. mauve and black 60 65
2926 – 5 d. mauve and black 60 65

DESIGNS: No. 2922, Mrs. J. J. "Molly" Brown (passenger); 2923, Newspaper boy with placard; 2924, Benjamin Guggenheim (passenger); 2925, Isidor Strauss (passenger); 2926, Ida Strauss (passenger).

291a "Death of Casagemas"

1998. 25th Death Anniv of Pablo Picasso (painter). Multicoloured.
2928 3 d. Type **291a** 35 40
2929 5 d. "Seated Woman" (vert) 60 65
2930 10 d. "Mother and Child" (vert) 1·10 1·25

291b Scout Handshake **292** Mahatma Gandhi

1998. 19th World Scout Jamboree, Chile. Mult.
2932 10 d. Type **291b** 1·10 1·25
2933 10 d. Dinghy sailing 1·10 1·25
2934 10 d. Scout salute 1·10 1·25

1998. 50th Death Anniv of Mahatma Gandhi. Multicoloured.
2936 10 d. Type **292** 1·10 1·25
2937 10 d. Gandhi on Salt March with Mrs. Sarojini Naidu (53 × 38 mm) 1·10 1·25
2938 10 d. Gandhi spinning yarn (53 × 38 mm) 1·10 1·25
2939 10 d. Gandhi in 1916 1·10 1·25

292a Sepecat Jaguar GR1A

1998. 80th Anniv of Royal Air Force. Multicoloured.
2941 5 d. Type **292b** 60 65
2942 5 d. Panavia Tornado GR1A 60 65
2943 5 d. Sepecat Jaguar GR1A (side view) 60 65
2944 5 d. BAe Hawk 200 60 65
2945 5 d. Sepecat Jaguar GR1A firing Sparrow missile 60 65
2946 5 d. BAe Harrier GR7 firing SNEB rockets 60 65
2947 5 d. Panavia Tornado GR1 firing AIM-9L missile 60 65
2948 5 d. Panavia Tornado GR1 in low level flight 60 65
2949 7 d. Panavia Tornado GR1 (facing left) 80 85
2950 7 d. BAe Hawk T1A 80 85
2951 7 d. Sepecat Jaguar GR1A 80 85
2952 7 d. Panavia Tornado GR1 (facing right) 80 85

293 "Mule-drivers from Tetuan"

1998. Birth Bicentenary of Eugene Delacroix (painter). Multicoloured.
2954 4 d. Type **293** 45 50
2955 4 d. "Encampment of Arab Mule-drivers" 45 50
2956 4 d. "An Orange Seller" 45 50
2957 4 d. "The Banks of the River" 45 50
2958 4 d. "View of Tangier from the Seashore" 45 50
2959 4 d. "Arab Horses fighting in a Stable" 45 50
2960 4 d. "Horses at the Trough" 45 50
2961 4 d. "The Combat of Giaour and Hassan" 45 50
2962 4 d. "Turk on a Sofa, Smoking" 45 50
2963 4 d. "View of Tangier" 45 50
2964 4 d. "The Spanish Coast at Salobrena" 45 50
2965 4 d. "The Aissaouas" 45 50
2966 4 d. "The Sea from the Cliffs of Dieppe" 45 50
2967 4 d. "The Fanatics of Tangier" 45 50
2968 4 d. "Arab Musicians" 45 50
2969 4 d. "An Arab Camp at Night" 45 50
2970 4 d. "Moroccan from Tangier, standing" (vert) 45 50
2971 4 d. "A Man of Tangier" (vert) 45 50
2972 4 d. "Young Arab standing with a Rifle" (vert) 45 50
2973 4 d. "Moroccan Chieftain" (vert) 45 50
2974 4 d. "Jewish Bride, Tangier" (vert) 45 50
2975 4 d. "Seated Jewess from Morocco" (vert) 45 50
2976 4 d. "Young Arab seated by a Wall" (vert) 45 50
2977 4 d. "Arab Dancer" (vert) 45 50

293a Diana, Princess of Wales

1998. First Death Anniv of Diana, Princess of Wales.
2979 **293a** 10 d. multicoloured 1·10 1·25

294 Puppy in Stocking **295** Rabbit

1998. Christmas. Multicoloured.
2980 1 d. Type **294** 10 15
2981 2 d. Giraffe in Christmas wreath 20 25
2982 3 d. Rainbow bee eater (bird) with bauble 35 40
2983 4 d. Deer 45 50
2984 5 d. Fawn 60 65
2985 10 d. Puppy in gift box 1·10 1·25

1999. Chinese New Year ("Year of the Rabbit"). Multicoloured.
2987 3 d. Type **295** 35 40
2988 3 d. Rabbit looking over shoulder 35 40
2989 3 d. Rabbit facing left 35 40
2990 3 d. Rabbit running 35 40

296 Mowgli and Baloo (bear)

1999. "The Jungle Book" (film). Walt Disney Cartoon Characters. Multicoloured.
2992 5 d. Type **296** 60 65
2993 5 d. Kaa (snake) and Mowgli 60 65
2994 5 d. King Louie at ruined temple 60 65
2995 5 d. Monkey playing leaf "guitar" 60 65
2996 5 d. Village girl collecting water 60 65
2997 5 d. King Louie on throne with Mowgli 60 65
2998 5 d. Mowgli and vultures 60 65
2999 5 d. Shere Khan (tiger) 60 65

297 "Danaus chrysippus"

1999. "Australia '99" World Stamp Exhibition, Melbourne. African Butterflies. Multicoloured.
3001 6 d. Type **297** 70 75
3002 6 d. "Papilio zalmoxis" 70 75
3003 6 d. "Papilio menestheus" 70 75
3004 6 d. "Poecilmitis thysbe" 70 75
3005 6 d. "Euxanthe wakefieldii" 70 75
3006 6 d. "Pseudacraea boisduvali" 70 75
3007 6 d. "Eurytela dryope" 70 75
3008 6 d. "Papilio demodocus" 70 75
3009 6 d. "Hemiolaus coeculus" 70 75
3010 6 d. "Charaxes jasius" 70 75
3011 6 d. "Junonia orithya" 70 75
3012 6 d. "Kallimoides rumia" 70 75

No. 3003 is inscribed "Papilio mnestheus" in error.

298 Prince Edward and Miss Sophie Rhys-Jones

1999. Royal Wedding. Multicoloured.
3014 10 d. Type **298** 1·10 1·25
3015 10 d. Prince Edward and Miss Sophie Rhys-Jones (with long hair) 1·10 1·25
3016 10 d. Prince Edward and Miss Sophie Rhys-Jones (wearing a red jacket) 1·10 1·25

298a Railway locomotive "Adler", 1835, and Samoa 1914 G.R.I. 2½d. on 20 pf. variety

1999. "iBRA '99" International Stamp Exhibition, Nuremberg. Multicoloured.

3018 4 d. Type **298a** 45 50
3019 5 d. Railway locomotive "Adler", 1835, and Samoa 1900 25 pf. optd on Germany 60 65
3020 10 d. "Friedrech August" (full-rigged ship) and Samoa 1900 Yacht type 50 and 80 pf. stamps . . . . 1·10 1·25
3021 15 d. "Friedrech August" (full-rigged ship) and Samoa 1900 Yacht type 2 m. stamp . . . 1·75 1·90

298b "Exotic Beauty"

1999. 150th Death Anniv of Katsushika Hokusai (Japanese artist). Multicoloured.

3023 5 d. Type **298b** 60 65
3024 5 d. "Wind" (two people) . . . 60 65
3025 5 d. "Dancing Monkey" . . . 60 65
3026 5 d. "Lady and Maiden on an Outing" 60 65
3027 5 d. "Wind" (three people) . . 60 65
3028 5 d. "Courtesan with Fan" . . 60 65
3029 5 d. "Bunshosei" 60 65
3030 5 d. "Overthrower of Castles, Overthrower of Nations" . . 60 65
3031 5 d. "Bee on Wild Rose" . . . 60 65
3032 5 d. "Sei Shonagon" 60 65
3033 5 d. "Kuan-yu" 60 65
3034 5 d. "The Fifth Month" . . . 60 65

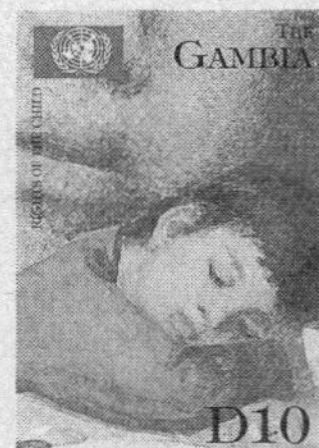

298c Child asleep

1999. 10th Anniv of United Nations Rights of the Child Convention. Multicoloured.

3036 10 d. Type **298c** . . . . 1·10 1·25
3037 10 d. Child drinking . . . . . 1·10 1·25
3038 10 d. Child drawing . . . . . 1·10 1·25

Nos. 3036/8 were printed together, se-tenant, forming a composite design.

298d Faust quaffs the Spirit's Nectar

1999. 250th Birth Anniv of Johann von Goethe (German writer).

3041 **298d** 15 d. violet, black and purple . . . . . . 1·75 1·90
3042 – 15 d. blue and black . . 1·75 1·90
3043 – 15 d. brown, black and green . . . . . . 1·75 1·90

DESIGNS: No. 3042, Von Goethe and Von Schiller; 3043, Faust contemplates mortality.

MORE DETAILED LISTS
are given in the Stanley Gibbons Catalogues referred to in the country headings.
For lists of current volumes see Introduction.

298e Bell X-14A VTOL Aircraft

1999. 30th Anniv of First Manned Landing on Moon. Multicoloured.

3045 6 d. Type **298e** 70 75
3046 6 d. Lunar landing practice rig . 70 75
3047 6 d. Early prototype lander . . 70 75
3048 6 d. Astronaut during zero gravity training 70 75
3049 6 d. Jet pack training 70 75
3050 6 d. Lunar lander pilot training 70 75

Nos. 3045/50 were printed together, se-tenant, forming a composite design.

299 Swallow-tailed Gull

1999. Marine Life of the Galapagos Islands. Multicoloured.

3052 1 d. 50 Type **299** 20 25
3053 1 d. 50 Frigate birds 20 25
3054 1 d. 50 Red-footed booby . . . 20 25
3055 1 d. 50 Galapagos hawk . . . 20 25
3056 1 d. 50 Great blue heron . . . 20 25
3057 1 d. 50 Masked booby 20 25
3058 1 d. 50 Bottlenose dolphins . . 20 25
3059 1 d. 50 Black grunts 20 25
3060 1 d. 50 Surgeonfish 20 25
3061 1 d. 50 Stingray 20 25
3062 1 d. 50 Short-finned pilot whales 20 25
3063 1 d. 50 Pacific green sea turtle . 20 25
3064 1 d. 50 Great white shark . . . 20 25
3065 1 d. 50 Sealion 20 25
3066 1 d. 50 Marine iguana 20 25
3067 1 d. 50 Pacific manta ray . . . 20 25
3068 1 d. 50 Moorish idol 20 25
3069 1 d. 50 Galapagos penguins . . 20 25
3070 1 d. 50 Silver grunts 20 25
3071 1 d. 50 Sea urchin 20 25
3072 1 d. 50 Wrasse 20 25
3073 1 d. 50 Almaco amber jack . . 20 25
3074 1 d. 50 Blue parrotfish 20 25
3075 1 d. 50 Yellow sea urchin . . . 20 25
3076 1 d. 50 Lobster 20 25
3077 1 d. 50 Grouper 20 25
3078 1 d. 50 Scorpionfish 20 25
3079 1 d. 50 Squirrelfish 20 25
3080 1 d. 50 Octopus 20 25
3081 1 d. 50 King angelfish 20 25
3082 1 d. 50 Horned shark 20 25
3083 1 d. 50 Galapagos hogfish . . . 20 25
3084 1 d. 50 Pufferfish 20 25
3085 1 d. 50 Moray eel 20 25
3086 1 d. 50 Orange tube coral . . . 20 25
3087 1 d. 50 Whitestripe chromis . . 20 25
3088 1 d. 50 Long-nosed hawkfish . . 20 25
3089 1 d. 50 Sea cucumbers 20 25
3090 1 d. 50 Spotted hawkfish . . . 20 25
3091 1 d. 50 Zebra moray eel . . . 20 25

Nos. 3052/91 respectively were printed together, se-tenant, forming a composite design.

300 "Telstar 1" Satellite, 1962

1999. History of Space Exploration. Multicoloured.

3093 1 d. Type **300** 10 15
3094 1 d. 50 "Skylab", 1973 (vert) . 20 25
3095 2 d. "Mars 3" spacecraft, 1971 (vert) 20 25
3096 3 d. "Cobe", 1989 (vert) . . . 35 40
3097 6 d. "Mariner 4", 1964 . . . 70 75
3098 6 d. "Viking" Mars Orbiter, 1975 . . . . 70 75
3099 6 d. Giotto, 1985 . . . . . . 70 75
3100 6 d. "Luna 9", 1966 . . . . . 70 75
3101 6 d. "Voyager 1", 1977 . . . . 70 75
3102 6 d. Galileo, 1989 . . . . . . 70 75
3103 6 d. Soviet "Vostok 1", 1961 . 70 75
3104 6 d. "Apollo" command and service module, 1968 . . . 70 75
3105 6 d. "Mercury" capsule, 1961 . 70 75
3106 6 d. "Apollo 16" lunar module, 1972 . . . . 70 75
3107 6 d. "Gemini 8", 1966 . . . . 70 75
3108 6 d. Soviet "Soyuz", 1975 . . 70 75
3109 6 d. German "V 2" rocket, 1942 (vert) 70 75
3110 6 d. "Delta Straight 8", 1972 (vert) 70 75
3111 6 d. "Ariane 4", 1988 (vert) . . 70 75
3112 6 d. "Mercury MA-A Atlas", 1962 (vert) 70 75
3113 6 d. "Saturn 1B", 1975 (vert) . 70 75
3114 6 d. "Cassini", 1997 (vert) . . 70 75
3115 10 d. Bruce McCandless outside shuttle, 1984 (vert) . . . . 1·10 1·25
3116 15 d. "Apollo 13" after splash-down, 1970 (vert) . . . . . 1·75 1·90

301 Carnotaurus

1999. Prehistoric Animals. Multicoloured.

3118 3 d. Type **301** 35 40
3119 3 d. Quetzalcoatlus 35 40
3120 3 d. Peteinosaurus 35 40
3121 3 d. Prenocephale 35 40
3122 3 d. Hesperornis 35 40
3123 3 d. Coelophysis 35 40
3124 3 d. Camptosaurus 35 40
3125 3 d. Panderichthys 35 40
3126 3 d. Garudimimus 35 40
3127 3 d. Cacops 35 40
3128 3 d. Ichthyostega 35 40
3129 3 d. Scutellosaurus 35 40
3130 3 d. Diatryma 35 40
3131 3 d. Pteranodon 35 40
3132 3 d. Stegodon 35 40
3133 3 d. Icaronycthris 35 40
3134 3 d. Archaeopteryx 35 40
3135 3 d. Chasmatosaurus 35 40
3136 3 d. Tytthostonyx 35 40
3137 3 d. Hyaenodon 35 40
3138 3 d. Uintatherium 35 40
3139 3 d. Hesperocyon 35 40
3140 3 d. Ambelodon 35 40
3141 3 d. Indricotherium 35 40

Nos. 3118/29 and 3130/41 respectively, were printed together, se-tenant, forming composite designs.

302 Seagull

1999. Marine Life. Multicoloured.

3143 1 d. Type **302** 10 15
3144 1 d. 50 Portugese man-o-war . 20 25
3145 3 d. Whale shark 35 40
3146 3 d. Grey reef shark 35 40
3147 3 d. New England octopus . . 35 40
3148 3 d. Pufferfish 35 40
3149 3 d. Lionfish 35 40
3150 3 d. Squid 35 40
3151 3 d. Chambered nautilus . . . 35 40
3152 3 d. Clownfish 35 40
3153 3 d. Moray eel 35 40
3154 3 d. Spiny lobster 35 40
3155 3 d. Spotted ray 35 40
3156 3 d. Clown anemone 35 40
3157 3 d. Angelfish 35 40
3158 3 d. Leafy seadragon 35 40
3159 3 d. Hawksbill turtle 35 40
3160 3 d. Mandarinfish 35 40
3161 3 d. Candy cane sea star . . . 35 40
3162 3 d. Plate coral 35 40
3163 3 d. Butterflyfish 35 40
3164 3 d. Coral polyp 35 40
3165 3 d. Hermit crab 35 40
3166 3 d. Strawberry shrimp 35 40
3167 3 d. Giant blue clam 35 40
3168 3 d. Sea cucumber 35 40
3169 5 d. Walrus 60 65
3170 10 d. Manatee . . . . 1·10 1·25

Nos. 3145/56 and 3157/68 respectively were printed together, se-tenant, forming composite designs.

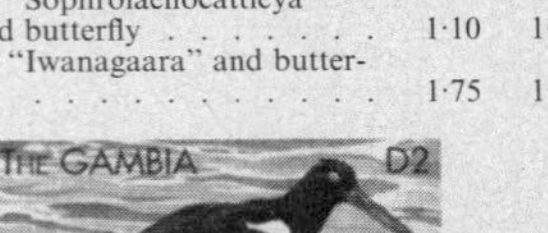

303 "Sophrocattleya"

1999. Orchids of the World. Multicoloured.

3172 2 d. Type **303** 20 25
3173 3 d. "Cattleya" and butterfly . 35 40
3174 4 d. "Brassolaeliocattleya" (pink) 45 50
3175 5 d. "Brassoepidendrum" . . . 60 65
3176 6 d. "Brassolaeliocattleya" (yellow) 70 75
3177 6 d. "Cattleytonia" 70 75
3178 6 d. "Lacliocattleya" 70 75
3179 6 d. "Miltonia" 70 75
3180 6 d. "Cattleya forbesii" . . . 70 75
3181 6 d. "Odontoglossum cervantesii" 70 75
3182 6 d. "Lycaste macrobulbon" . . 70 75
3183 6 d. "Laeliocattleya" 70 75
3184 6 d. "Brassocattleya" (pink) . . 70 75
3185 6 d. "Cattleya" 70 75
3186 6 d. "Brassocattleya" (red spotted) 70 75
3187 6 d. "Brassolaeliocattleya" (yellow and red) 70 75
3188 10 d. "Sophrolaeliocattleya" and butterfly . . . . . . 1·10 1·25
3189 15 d. "Iwanagaara" and butterfly . . . . 1·75 1·90

304 American Black Oystercatcher

1999. Sea Birds. Multicoloured.

3191 2 d. Type **304** 20 25
3192 3 d. Blue-footed booby 35 40
3193 4 d. Atlantic puffin 45 50
3194 4 d. Red-tailed tropic bird . . 45 50
3195 4 d. Reddish egret 45 50
3196 4 d. Laughing gull 45 50
3197 4 d. Great egret 45 50
3198 4 d. Northern gannet 45 50
3199 4 d. Forster's tern 45 50
3200 4 d. Common cormorant ("Great Cormorant") . . . 45 50
3201 4 d. Razorbill (perched on rocks) 45 50
3202 4 d. Adelie penguin 45 50
3203 4 d. Black skimmer 45 50
3204 4 d. Big crested penguin . . . 45 50
3205 4 d. Heermann's gull 45 50
3206 4 d. Glaucous gull 45 50
3207 4 d. Laysan albatross 45 50
3208 4 d. American white pelican . . 45 50
3209 4 d. Tufted puffin 45 50
3210 4 d. Black guillemot 45 50
3211 5 d. Razorbill (in flight) . . . 60 65
3212 5 d. Shelduck 60 65
3213 5 d. Sandwich tern 60 65
3214 5 d. Arctic skua 60 65
3215 5 d. Gannet 60 65
3216 5 d. Common gull 60 65
3217 10 d. Western gull . . . . . 1·10 1·25
3218 15 d. Brown pelican . . . . . 1·75 1·90

Nos. 3211/16 were printed together, se-tenant, forming a composite design.

Nos. 3202 and 3207 are inscribed "ADELIES PENGUIN" or "LAYSON ALBATROSS", both in error.

304a Duchess of York and Princess Elizabeth, 1928

1999. "Queen Elizabeth the Queen Mother's Century".

3220 **304a** 10 d. multicoloured . . . 1·10 1·25
3221 – 10 d. black and gold . . 1·10 1·25
3222 – 10 d. black and gold . . 1·10 1·25
3223 – 10 d. multicoloured . . . 1·10 1·25

DESIGNS: No. 3221, Lady Elizabeth Bowes-Lyon, 1923; 3222, Queen Elizabeth, 1946; 3223, Queen Mother and Prince Harry.

305 Temple of A-Ma

1999. "China '99" International Stamp Exhibition, Beijing. Return of Macao to China. Multicoloured.

3225 7 d. Type **305** 80 85
3226 7 d. Border Gate 80 85
3227 7 d. Ruins of St. Paul's 80 85

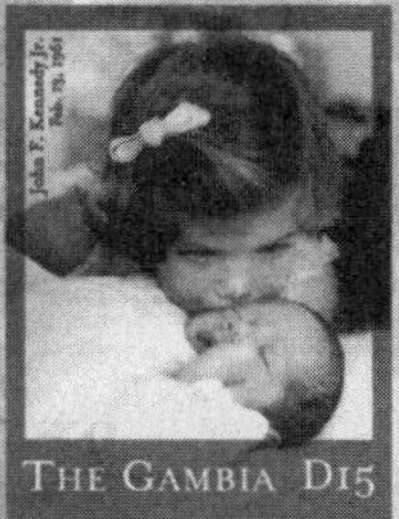

306 John F. Kennedy Jr. as Baby, 1961

1999. John F. Kennedy Jr. Commemoration. Each brown, blue and black.

3228 15 d. Type **306** . . . . . . 1·75 1·90
3229 15 d. John F. Kennedy Jr. as teenager . . . . 1·75 1·90
3230 15 d. John F. Kennedy Jr. in 1997 . . . . 1·75 1·90

GAZA Pt.19

EGYPTIAN OCCUPATION

A strip of territory along the coast from Gaza to the Egyptian frontier, seized by Egypt when the British Mandate for Palestine ended in May 1948.

In 1967 Israeli troops seized the Gaza Strip and from that date Israeli stamps were used.

In May 1994 the area became autonomous under the Palestinian National Authority.

1000 milliemes = £1 (Egyptian).

1948. Various stamps of Egypt optd **PALESTINE** in English and Arabic.

1 **91** 1 m. brown (postage) . . . 40 55
2 2 m. red 40 55
3 **78** 3 m. brown 40 55
4 **91** 4 m. green 40 55
5 5 m. brown 40 60
6 **78** 6 m. green 55 60
7 **91** 10 m. violet 40 60
8 **78** 13 m. red . . . . 80 1·00
9 **91** 15 m. purple 50 60
10 17 m. green 60 65
11 20 m. violet . . . . . . 75 1·10
12 22 m. blue . . . . 80 1·10
13 – 30 m. green (No 340) . . . 80 1·10
14 **106** 40 m. brown . . . . . . 1·25 1·40
15 – 50 m. blue (No. 342) . . . 1·75 1·75
16 – 100 m. purple (No. 280) . . 6·00 6·50
17 – 200 m. violet (No. 281) . . 12·00 14·00
18 **86** 50 p. brown and green . . . 17·00 18·00
19 **87** £El brown and blue . . . . 30·00 32·00
20 **101** 2 m. red (air) 40 55
21 3 m. brown 40 55
22 5 m. red 40 45
23 7 m. brown 40 45
24 8 m. green 40 45
25 10 m. violet 40 45
26 20 m. blue 60 65
27 30 m. purple 80 85
28 40 m. red . . . . 1·40 1·50
29 50 m. blue . . . . 1·60 1·75
30 100 m. green . . . . . . 2·25 2·75
31 200 m. grey . . . . . . 18·00 22·00

1953. As above but with portrait obliterated by three horiz bars. (a) Postage.

32 **91** 1 m. brown 40 50
33 2 m. red 40 50
34 **78** 3 m. brown 40 50
35 **91** 4 m. green 40 50
36 5 m. brown 40 50
37 **78** 6 m. green 40 50
38 **91** 10 m. violet 40 60
39 **78** 13 m. red 80 95
40 **91** 15 m. purple 80 95
41 17 m. green 80 95
42 20 m. violet 80 95
43 22 m. blue . . . . 1·25 1·40
44 – 30 m. green . . . . . . 2·00 2·25
45 **106** 40 m. brown . . . . . . 2·75 3·00
46 – 50 m. blue . . . . 4·00 4·25
47 – 100 m. purple . . . . . . 8·00 10·00
48 – 200 m. violet . . . . . . 16·00 22·00
49 **86** 50 p. brown and green . . . 32·00 38·00
50 **87** £El brown and blue . . . . 90·00 95·00

(b) Air.

51 **101** 2 m. red . . . . 1·75 2·10
52 3 m. brown 45 75
53 5 m. red . . . . 10·00 11·00
54 7 m. brown 65 90
55 8 m. green . . . . 1·75 1·90
56 10 m. violet . . . . 1·75 1·90
57 20 m. blue . . . . 1·75 1·90
58 30 m. purple . . . . . . 1·75 1·90
59 40 m. red . . . . 1·40 1·50
60 50 m. blue . . . . 14·00 15·00
61 100 m. green . . . . . . 55·00 60·00
62 200 m. grey . . . . . . 14·00 19·00

1953. Air. Nos. 480/2, 485 and 489/90 of Egypt optd **PALESTINE** in English and Arabic.

63 **101** 2 m. red 40 55
64 3 m. brown . . . . 8·75 10·00
65 5 m. red 60 65
66 10 m. violet . . . . 20·00 21·00
67 50 m. blue . . . . 4·00 4·50
68 100 m. olive . . . . . . 33·00 38·00

1955. Stamps of Egypt, 1953/4, optd **PALESTINE** in English and Arabic.

69 **137** 1 m. brown 40 45
70 2 m. purple 40 45
71 3 m. blue 40 45
72 4 m. green 40 45
73 5 m. red 40 45
74 **130** 10 m. sepia (B) 40 45
75 15 m. grey 60 70
76 17 m. turquoise 60 70
77 20 m. violet 60 70
78 **131** 30 m. green . . . . 1·00 1·10
79 32 m. blue . . . . 1·00 1·10
80 35 m. violet . . . . 1·00 1·10
81 40 m. brown . . . . 1·75 1·90
82 50 m. purple . . . . . . 2·00 2·10
83 **132** 100 m. brown . . . . . . 5·00 5·25
84 200 m. turquoise . . . . . 11·00 11·50
85 500 m. violet . . . . . . 40·00 40·00
86 £E1 red and green . . . . 70·00 70·00

1955. Air. Nos. 433/4 of Egypt optd **PALESTINE** in English and Arabic.

86a **133** 5 m. brown . . . . 4·00 5·25
86b 15 m. green . . . . 5·00 6·00

Types of Egypt (sometimes with colours changed) overprinted **PALESTINE** in English and Arabic.

1957. Re-occupation of Gaza Strip.

87 **152** 10 m. green . . . . 4·00 4·75

1958. Stamps of 1957.

88 – 1 m. turq (No. 538) 10 20
89 – 5 m. sepia (No. 541) 40 40
90 **160** 10 m. violet 40 40

UNITED ARAB REPUBLIC

1958. Stamps of 1958 (inscr "U A R EGYPT").

91 – 1 m. red (No. 553) 10 10
92 – 2 m. blue (No. 554) 10 10
93 **168** 3 m. brown 15 15
94 – 4 m. green (No. 556) . . . 15 15
95 – 5 m. sepia (No. 557) . . . 20 20
96 **160** 10 m. violet (No. 558) . . . 20 20
96a – 35 m. blue (No. 559) . . . 2·75 1·75

1958. 5th Anniv of Republic.

97 **172** 10 m. brown . . . . 1·75 1·75

1958. 10th Anniv of Declaration of Human Rights.

98 **178** 10 m. purple . . . . 2·00 3·25
99 35 m. brown . . . . 5·00 5·50

1959. No. 588.

100 **132** 55 m. on 100 m. red . . . 3·00 4·50

Types of Egypt with some colours changed and additionally inscribed "PALESTINE" in English and Arabic.

1960. As Nos. 603, etc.

101 **160** 1 m. orange 10 10
104 – 4 m. brown 10 10
105 – 5 m. violet 15 15
106 – 10 m. green 20 20

1960. World Refugee Year.

109 **205** 10 m. brown 30 30
110 35 m. black . . . . 1·50 1·25

1961. World Health Day.

111 **213** 10 m. blue . . . . 1·00 1·00

1961. Palestine Day.

112 **215** 10 m. violet 25 20

1961. U.N. Technical Co-operation Programme and 16th Anniv of U.N.O.

113 – 10 m. blue & orange . . . 50 30
114 **220** 35 m. purple and red . . . 80 50

1961. Education Day.

115 **223** 10 m. brown 80 50

1961. Victory Day.

116 **224** 10 m. brown & chest. . . . 30 25

1962. 5th Anniv of Egyptian Occupation of Gaza.

117 **229** 10 m. brown 30 25

1962. Arab League Week.

118 **231** 10 m. purple 30 25

1962. Malaria Eradication.

119 **235** 10 m. red and brown . . . 25 25
120 – 35 m. yellow and black . . 1·00 75

1962. 17th Anniv of U.N.O. and Hammarskjold Commemoration.

121 **245** 5 m. blue and pink 20 20
122 10 m. blue and brown . . . 35 30
123 35 m. indigo and blue . . . 1·00 80

1963. As No. 739.

124 4 m. blue, orge & blk 20 20

1963. Freedom from Hunger.

125 **252** 5 m. brown and green . . . 15 10
126 – 10 m. yellow and green . . 30 20
127 – 35 m. yellow & purple . . 1·25 80

1963. Centenary of Red Cross.

128 **253** 10 m. red, purple & blue . . 50 30
129 – 35 m. ultram, blue & red . 1·00 80

1963. U.N.E.S.C.O. Campaign for Preservation of Nubian Monuments (4th issue).

130 **256** 5 m. yellow and purple . . 15 10
131 – 10 m. yellow and black . . 20 15
132 – 35 m. yellow and violet . . 1·00 80

1963. Air. As Nos. 758, 760 and 761/2.

133 50 m. purple and blue 80 75
134 80 m. indigo and blue . . . . . 1·25 1·10
135 115 m. yellow and black . . . . 2·00 1·75
136 140 m. red and blue . . . . . 2·50 2·25

1963. 15th Anniv of Declaration of Human Rights.

137 **259a** 5 m. yellow and sepia . . 15 15
138 – 10 m. blk, grey & pur . . 20 20
139 – 35 m. blk, grn & turq . . 80 80

1964. As No. 769, etc.

140 – 1 m. violet and green . . . 10 10
141 – 2 m. blue and orange . . . 10 10
142 – 3 m. blue, brown & lt bl . . 10 10
143 – 4 m. green, brn & pink . . 15 10
144 – 5 m. red, blue and pink . . 15 10
145 – 10 m. red, brown & grn . . 20 15
146 – 15 m. yell, vio & lilac . . 20 15
147 – 20 m. green and violet . . 40 15
148 **261** 30 m. blue and orange . . . 80 15
149 – 35 m. brn, grn & orge . . . 60 30
150 – 40 m. blue and green . . . 80 30
151 – 60 m. brown and blue . . . 1·25 70
152 **263** 100 m. brown and blue . . 1·75 1·40

1964. Arab League Heads of State Congress, Cairo.

153 **266** 10 m. black and olive . . . 15 15

1964. Ramadan Festival.

154 **267** 4 m. olive, red & lake . . . 15 15

1964. 10th Anniv of Arab Postal Union's Permanent Office.

155 **271** 10 m. blue and green . . . 15 10

1964. World Health Day.

156 **272** 10 m. purple and red . . . 15 10

1965. Ramadan Festival. As No. 834.

157 – 4 m. brown and green . . . 30 15

1965. 20th Anniv of Arab League.

158 **289** 10 m. green and red . . . 15 15
159 – 20 m. brown & green . . . 20 20

1965. Air. World Meteorological Day.

160 **290** 80 m. orange and blue . . 2·00 1·50

1965. World Health Day.

161 **291** 10 m. red and green 30 20

1965. Deir Yassin Massacre.

162 **292** 10 m. red and blue 50 20

1965. Cent of I.T.U.

163 **293** 5 m. blue, yellow & grn . . 30 15
164 10 m. rose, blue and red . . 40 20
165 35 m. bl, yell & ultram . . 1·00 60

1965. Air. Re-establishment of Egyptian Civil Airlines "MISRAIR".

166 **295** 10 m. green and orange . . 40 30

1966. U.N. Day.

167 **321** 5 m. violet and red 10 10
168 – 10 m. violet & brown . . . 20 15
169 – 35 m. violet and green . . 60 30

1966. Victory Day.

170 **324** 10 m. red and olive 15 10

1967. Arab Publicity Week.

171 **328** 10 m. brown and blue . . . 15 10

1967. Labour Day.

172 **331** 10 m. sepia and olive . . . 15 10

EXPRESS LETTER STAMP

1948. Express Letter stamp of Egypt optd **PALESTINE** in English and Arabic.

E32 E **52** 40 m. black & brown . . 7·00 7·50

POSTAGE DUE STAMPS

1948. Postage Due stamps of Egypt optd **PALESTINE** in English and Arabic.

D32 D **59** 2 m. orange . . . . . . 1·25 1·40
D33 4 m. green . . . . . . 1·00 1·10
D34 6 m. green . . . . . . 1·00 1·10
D35 8 m. purple . . . . . . 1·00 1·10
D36 10 m. lake . . . . . . 1·00 1·10
D37 12 m. red . . . . . . 1·00 1·10
D38 30 m. violet . . . . . 3·00 5·50

This area was occupied by Israel on 6th June 1967. Post Offices were opened in July 1967 and Israeli stamps are now used.

GEORGIA Pt.10

Formerly part of Russia, Georgia declared its independence after the Russian Revolution. In 1921 it became a Soviet Republic and in 1922 joined with Armenia and Azerbaijan to form the Transcaucasian Federation, whose stamps were used from September 1923. After absorption into the U.S.S.R. Russian stamps were used from 1924.

With the dissolution of the Soviet Union in 1991 Georgia again became an independent state.

1919. 100 kopeks = 1 rouble.
1993. kupon.
1995. 100 tetri = 1 lari.

1 St. George   **3** Queen Tamara (A.D. 1184–1212)

1919. Imperf or perf.

10 **1** 10 k. blue . . . . 20 1·00
11 40 k. red . . . . 20 1·00
12 50 k. green . . . . 20 1·00
13 60 k. red . . . . 20 1·00
14 70 k. mauve . . . . 20 1·00
15 – 1 r. brown (20 × 25 mm) . . 20 1·00
16 **3** 2 r. brown 30 75
17a 3 r. blue . . . . 20 1·00
18 5 r. yellow . . . . 50 1·00

4 Soldier   **6** Industry and agriculture

1922. Perf.

28a **4** 500 r. red . . . . 2·00 4·00
29 – 1000 r. brown (Sower) . . . 2·75 3·50
30 **6** 2000 r. grey . . . . 3·25 3·50
31 3000 r. brown . . . . . . 3·00 3·50
32 5000 r. green . . . . . . 3·00 3·50

7

1922. Famine Relief. Designs as T **7**. Surch.

33 – 100 r. on 50 r. violet . . . . 50 2·00
34 – 3000 r. on 100 r. red . . . . 50 2·00
35 – 5000 r. on 250 r. green . . . 50 2·00
36 **7** 10,000 r. on 25 r. blue . . . 50 3·00

1923. Surch.

37 – 10,000 r. on 1000 r. (No. 29) . 2·75 1·00
38 **6** 15,000 r. on 2000 r. grey . . 3·00 1·25
44 **4** 20,000 r. on 500 r. red . . . 75 1·25
40a **6** 40,000 r. on 5000 r. green . . 1·25 1·00
46 80,000 r. on 3000 r. brown . . 1·75 2·00

1923. Surch (a) On Arms types of Russia.

47 **22** 10,000 r. on 7 k. blue . . . . 32·00 32·00
48 **10** 15,000 r. on 15 k. bl & brn . . 3·00 3·50

(b) On No. 75B of Armenia.

49 **10** 1,5000 r. on 5 r. on 15 k. blue and brown . . . . 22·00 20·00

1923. Arms types of Russia surch with hammer and sickle and value. Imperf or perf.

50 **22** 75,000 r. on 1 k. orange . . . 4·00 4·50
52 20,0000 r. on 5 k. red . . . . 3·00 4·00
53 **14** 30,0000 r. on 20 k. red & bl . 2·75 3·00
54 **22** 35,0000 r. on 3 k. red . . . . 3·50 4·25
57 700,000 r. on 2 k. green . . . 5·00 5·00

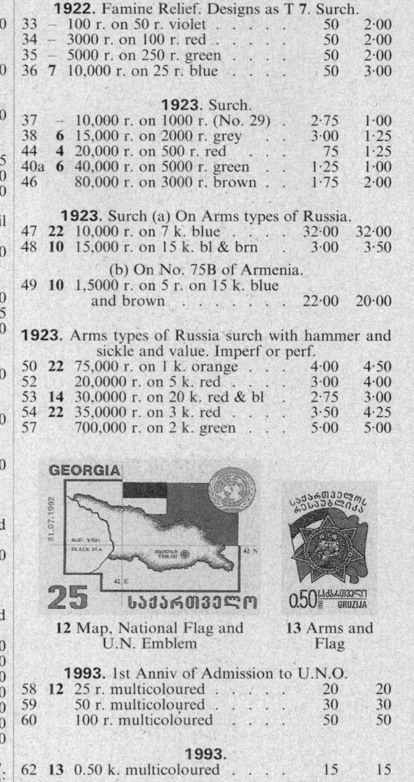

12 Map, National Flag and U.N. Emblem   **13** Arms and Flag

1993. 1st Anniv of Admission to U.N.O.

58 **12** 25 r. multicoloured 20 20
59 50 r. multicoloured 30 30
60 100 r. multicoloured 50 50

1993.

62 **13** 0.50 k. multicoloured 15 15

14 18th-century Fresco in Gold   **15** "Apostle Simon" (icon)

1993. Treasures of the National Museum.

63 **14** 0.50 k. multicoloured 15 15

1993. Ancient Art.

64 **15** 1 r. multicoloured 15 15

16 "Three Women" (Lado Gudiashvili)   **17** Juari Monastery, Mtskheta

1993. National Paintings.

65 **16** 1 k. multicoloured 15 15

1993. Places of Worship.

66 **17** 30 k. blue 10 10
67 – 40 k. brown 15 15
68 – 50 k. brown 20 20
69 – 60 k. red 20 20
70 – 70 k. lilac 25 25
71 – 80 k. green 30 30
72 – 90 k. black 35 35

DESIGNS: 40 k. Gelati Church; 50 k. Nikortsminda Church; 60 k. Ikorta Church; 70 k. Samtavisi church; 80 k. Bolnisi Zion Synagogue; 90 k. Gremi Citadel Church.

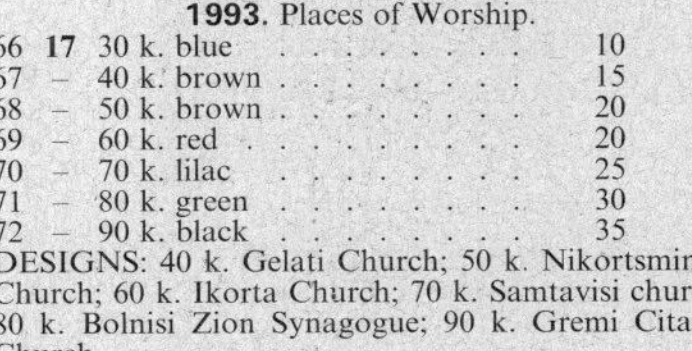

MINIMUM PRICE

The minimum price quoted is 10p which represents a handling charge rather than a basis for valuing common stamps. For further notes about prices see introductory pages.

18 Emblem 19 Emblem

1994. 2nd Anniv of International Olympic Committee Recognition of Georgian National Olympic Committee.
73 **18** 100 k. + 50 k. multicoloured 25 25

1994. Admission (1993) of Georgia to U.P.U.
74 **19** 200 k. multicoloured 40 40

20 Window and Nikoladze

1994. 150th Birth Anniv (1993) of Niko Nikoladze (journalist).
75 **20** 150 k. multicoloured 30 30

1994. Nos. 62/5 surch.
76 **13** 5000 k. on 0.50 k. mult . . . 10 10
77 **14** 5000 k. on 0.50 k. mult . . . 10 10
78 **15** 10000 k. on 1 k. mult 20 20
79 **16** 10000 k. on 1 k. mult 30 30

22 "Barba and the Lion" **24** Olympic Rings and Colours

1994. All-Georgian Congress.
80 **22** 100 k. brown and pink . . . 70 70
81 – 200 k. deep blue & blue . . . 70 70
DESIGN: 200 k. Equestrian statue

1994. Nos: 63/5 surch **Georgia** and new value.
82 **14** 200 k. on 0.50 k. mult . . . 25 25
83 **15** 300 k. on 1 k. mult 45 45
84 **16** 500 k. on 1 k. mult 70 70

1995. Centenary of International Olympic Committee. Multicoloured.
85 10 k. Type **24** (International Year of Sport) 20 20
86 15 k. Emblem symbolising founding congress 30 30
87 20 k. Anniversary emblem . . . 40 40
88 25 k. Olympic rings and peace dove ("Olympic Truce") . . . 50 50

25 "Giraffe"

1995. 77th Death Anniv of Niko Pirosmanashvili (painter). Multicoloured.
89 20 k. Type **25** 50 50
90 20 k. "Three Princes Carousing on the Grass" (horiz) 50 50
91 20 k. "Brooder with Chicks" (horiz) 50 50
92 20 k. "Boy on a Donkey" 50 50
93 20 k. "Fisherman" 50 50
94 20 k. "Woman with a Tankard of Beer" 50 50
95 20 k. "Bear on a Moonlit Night" . . 50 50
96 20 k. "Georgian woman with a Tambourine" 50 50
97 20 k. "Still Life" (horiz) 50 50
98 20 k. "Deer" 50 50

26 Alaverdi **27** Sveti-Zchoveli Cathedral, Mtskheta

28 Bitschvinta

1995. Monasteries. Value expressed by letter.
100 **26** A blue and black 60 60
101 – A green and black 60 60
102 **27** I lilac and black 60 60
103 – I brown and black 60 60
104 – I green and black 60 60
105 **28** U brown and black 60 60
106 – U brown and black 60 60
DESIGNS: No. 101, Ananuri; 103, Kumurdo; 104, Dranda; 106, Metechi.
The stamps are inscribed with letters of the Georgian alphabet

1995. Monasteries. As Nos. 106, 100 and 104 but with value expressed by figure.
107 1 purple and black 60 60
108 2 brown and black 60 60
109 3 brown and black 60 60
DESIGNS: No. 107, Metechi; 108, Alaverdi; 109, Dranda.
The numbers on Nos. 107/9 represent classes of postage rather than the face value of the stamps.

29 Iashvili and Family

1995. Birth Centenary (1994) of Paolo Iashvili (writer).
110 **29** 300 k. brown and black . . 60 60

30 Brontosaurus

1995. Prehistoric Animals. Multicoloured.
111 15 k. Type **30** 30 30
112 15 k. Ceratosaurus 30 30
113 15 k. Deinonichus 30 30
114 15 k. Parasaurolophus 30 30
115 15 k. Saurolophus 30 30
116 15 k. Scolosaurus 30 30
117 15 k. Stegosaurus 30 30
118 15 k. Triceratops 30 30
119 15 k. Tyrannosaurus 30 30

31 Slipperbill, Deer and Parrot

1995. Wildlife. Multicoloured.
121 15 k. Heads of horse, monkey, eagle, deer, bird, lynx and elephant 20 20
122 15 k. Dragonfly and butterfly at left, mosquitoes and fishes among heads of birds including flamingo 20 20
123 15 k. Fishes and butterfly with heads of lioness, cow, parrot, monkey, owl with egret at right 20 20
124 15 k. Fox's face at left, birds, skunk and fish 20 20
125 15 k. Butterfly, scorpion, birds, fishes and elephant's trunk at right 20 20
126 15 k. Type **31** 20 20
127 15 k. Fishes, shells, antelope, dogs, dolphin and birds . . . 20 20
128 15 k. Body of pipefish, birds including peacock and duck, fox and fly 20 20
129 15 k. Rhinoceros, seahorse, dolphin and birds 20 20
130 15 k. Zebra, hippopotamus, deer, fishes and moth 20 20
131 15 k. Dog's head, birds including hornbill, lobster, fishes and other mammals 20 20
132 15 k. Seal, warthog, rabbits, fishes, beetle and bird 20 20
133 15 k. Emu, other birds, fish and lion's face 20 20
134 15 k. Snake's head, fishes, bird, beetle, giraffe's head and frog 20 20
135 15 k. Sheep, antelope, fishes, ant and birds including dove . . 20 20
136 15 k. Whale, stoat, birds including parrot, butterfly and lizard 20 20
Nos. 121/36 were issued together, se-tenant, forming a composite design.

32 Bagrati Cathedral

1995. U.N.E.S.C.O. World Heritage Sites.
137 **32** 100 k. multicoloured . . . 60 60

33 Pterodactylus

1995. Prehistoric Animals. Multicoloured.
139 15 t. Type **33** 35 35
140 15 t. Rhamphorhynchus (inscr "Rhamphorhynghus") . . . 35 35
141 15 t. Pteranodon 35 35
142 15 t. Spinosaurus 35 35
143 15 t. Tyrannosaurus 35 35
144 15 t. Velociraptor 35 35
145 15 t. Monoklonius 35 35
146 15 t. Ornithomimus 35 35
147 15 t. Mastodon 35 35
Nos. 139/47 were issued together, se-tenant, forming a composite design.

34 Barn Swallows

1996. Birds. Multicoloured.
148 15 t. Type **34** 20 20
149 15 t. Redwing (spotted breast) . 20 20
150 15 t. Common starling (black with greenish wing) 20 20
151 15 t. Hawfinch (brown with black patch on neck) 20 20
152 15 t. Tree pipit (black and white bird on twig) 20 20
153 15 t. Golden oriole (yellow with black wing) 20 20
154 15 t. Collared flycatcher (black and white bird on trunk of tree) 20 20
155 15 t. Chaffinch (chestnut front and back and small crest) . . 20 20
156 15 t. Crested tit (brown body, black and white head and crest) 20 20
157 15 t. Yellowhammer (speckled black and yellow) 20 20
158 15 t. Pied wagtail (white with black chest, nape and wings) . 20 20
159 15 t. Blackbird (black with yellow beak) 20 20
160 15 t. Redstart (grey and black head, chestnut patch on front) 20 20
161 15 t. European robin (red face and chest) 20 20
162 15 t. European nuthatch (bird with black stripe across eye, on tree trunk) 20 20
163 15 t. Blue tit (blue head, wings and tail and green back) . . 20 20
164 15 t. White-tailed sea eagle (white tail) 20 20
165 15 t. Osprey (black and white bird in flight) 20 20
166 15 t. Short-toed eagle (speckled brown and white on tip of branch) 20 20
167 15 t. Common buzzard (chestnut) 20 20
168 15 t. Red kite (red tail, in flight) 20 20
169 15 t. Marsh harrier (white tail and white wings tipped with brown, in flight) 20 20
170 15 t. Northern goshawk (grey bird with black eye stripe, on branch) 20 20
171 15 t. Ural owl (on branch, tips of fir trees) 20 20
172 15 t. European hobby (black and white bird on branch overhanging water) 20 20
173 15 t. Common kestrel (black head and tail and brown body, valley in background) 20 20
174 15 t. Screech owl (with large ears sitting upright) 20 20
175 15 t. Great grey owl (on top of tree stump, fir trees behind) . 20 20
176 15 t. Golden eagle (both wings raised above body and flying over water) 20 20
177 15 t. Lesser spotted eagle (brown bird with white wing-tips on branch overhanging water) . . 20 20
178 15 t. Tawny owl (white owl on thick branch at water's edge) . 20 20
179 15 t. Eagle owl (brown bird with ears spreading wings) 20 20
Nos. 148/63 and 164/79 were issued respectively together, se-tenant, forming composite designs.

35 Head of Crane

1996. Animals. Multicoloured.
181 10 t. Type **35** 20 20
182 10 t. Body of crane 20 20
183 10 t. Head of snake 20 20
184 10 t. Body of snake and moth . . 20 20
185 10 t. Lizard 20 20
186 10 t. Two birds 20 20
187 10 t. Dragonfly 20 20
188 10 t. Bees on clover and body of snake 20 20
189 10 t. Butterfly 20 20
190 10 t. Frog 20 20
191 10 t. Snail 20 20
192 10 t. Turtle 20 20
193 10 t. Crayfish 20 20
194 10 t. Water plant and head of salamander 20 20
195 10 t. Crested salamander and body of salamander 20 20
196 10 t. Speckled salamander on trunk 20 20
Nos. 181/96 were issued together, se-tenant, forming a composite design of a pond.

36 Apatosaurus

1996. Prehistoric Animals. Multicoloured.
197 10 t. Type **36** 25 25
198 10 t. Archaeopteryx (bird) . . . 25 25
199 10 t. Leptoceratops (on rocks at entrance to cave) 25 25
200 10 t. Parasaurolophus (pair) and body of apatosaurus 25 25
201 10 t. Pentaceratops (with horns and neck flap) 25 25
202 10 t. Hererasaurus (with mouth gaping, fronds in background) 25 25
203 10 t. Hadrosaurus and nest with eggs 25 25
204 10 t. Montanoceratops (green dinosaur with different dinosaur in background) 25 25
205 10 t. Fulgoloterium (red dinosaur) 25 25
Nos. 197/205 were issued together, se-tenant, forming a composite design.

37 "Citizens of Paris" (Lado Gudiashvili)

1996. Paintings. Multicoloured.
206 10 t. Type **37** 15 15
207 20 t. "Abstract" (Wassily Kandinsky) 30 30
208 30 t. "Still-life" (David Kakabadze) 45 45
209 50 t. "Three Painters" (Shalva Kikodze) 80 80

38 Helsinki, 1952

1996. Cent of Modern Olympic Games. Mult.

211 1 t. Type **38** 10 10
212 2 t. Melbourne, 1956 . . . . . . 10 10
213 3 t. Rome, 1960 . . . . . . 10 10
214 4 t. Tokyo, 1964 . . . . . . 15 15
215 5 t. Mexico, 1968 . . . . . . 20 20
216 6 t. Munich, 1972 . . . . . . 25 25
217 7 t. Montreal, 1976 . . . . . . 30 30
218 8 t. Moscow, 1980 . . . . . . 35 35
219 9 t. Seoul, 1988 . . . . . . 35 35
220 10 t. Barcelona, 1992 . . . . . 40 40

Each stamp is also inscribed with the names of Georgian gold medal winners at the relevant games.

39 Anniversary Emblem

1997. 50th Anniv of U.N.O.

222 **39** 30 t. blue and purple . . . 40 40
223 125 t. blue and red . . . . 1·60 1·60

40 Javakhishvili and University

1997. 120th Birth Anniv (1996) of Ivane Javakhishvili (first director of Tbilisi University).

224 **40** 50 t. multicoloured . . . . 1·00 1·00

41 Anton I — 42 Railway Track and Tunnel

1997. 210th Death Anniv (1998) of Anton I (head of Georgian Orthodox Church).

225 **41** 30 t. brown 75 75

1997. 50th Anniv (1996) of U.N.I.C.E.F. Children's Paintings. Multicoloured.

226 20 t. + 5 r. Type **42** 50 50
227 30 t. + 10 r. Creature (horiz) . . 75 75

GEORGIA 1996
10
ROTTWEILER

43 Rottweiler

1997. Dogs. Multicoloured.

228 10 t. Type **43** 15 15
229 30 t. Gordon setter 45 45
230 50 t. St. Bernard 75 75
231 60 t. English bulldog 90 90
232 70 t. Caucasian sheepdog . . . 1·00 1·00
233 125 t. Caucasian sheepdog (different) . . . . 1·75 1·75

44 Two Mice

1997. Animated Cartoon Characters. Mult.

235 20 t. Type **44** 30 30
236 30 t. Man in bed 45 45
237 40 t. Girl and rabbit on cloud with balloons 60 60
238 50 t. Dancing animals 75 75
239 60 t. Duck wearing dress . . . 90 90

46 Map of Caucasus, 1745

1997. 300th Birth Anniv (1996) of Prince Vakhushti Bagration. Multicoloured.

241 40 t. Type **46** 60 60
242 80 t. Prince Vakhushti Bagration (vert) . . . . 1·25 1·25

47 Tiflis Town Post — 48 Congress and Cultural Emblems

1997. "Moscow '97" Int Stamp Exn.

243 **47** 80 t. multicoloured . . . . 1·25 1·25

1997. 1st World Junior (40 t.) and Second World (80 t.) Delphic Congresses, Tbilisi. Multicoloured.

245 40 t. Type **48** 60 60
246 80 t. Emblem and church, Mzcheta . . . . 1·25 1·25

49 Snow-shoe and Hat

1998. Winter Olympic Games, Nagano, Japan. Mult.

(a) Clothes and accessories.

247 20 t. Type **49** 35 35
248 30 t. Glove and snow-shoe . . . 50 50
249 40 t. Sledge and gloves 70 70
250 50 t. Scarf and skates . . . . . 1·50 1·50

(b) Ski Jumping.

251 20 t. Ski jumper 35 35
252 30 t. As No. 251 . . . . 50 50
253 40 t. As No. 251 . . . . 70 70
254 50 t. As No. 251 . . . . 1·50 1·50

50 Greek Galley (terracotta plate)

1998. Voyage of the Argonauts (ancient Greek legend). Multicoloured.

256 30 t. Type **50** 45 45
257 40 t. Preparation for battle . . . 60 60
258 50 t. Boreads, Phineus (blind seer) and Harpy 75 75
259 60 t. Punishment of King Amicus 90 90
260 70 t. Argonauts in Colchis . . . 1·00 1·00
261 80 t. The dragon vomiting Jason . . . . 1·25 1·25

Nos. 257/61 show vase paintings.

51 Brown Horse

1998. Horses. Multicoloured.

262 10 t. Type **51** 15 15
263 40 t. Black horse 75 75
264 70 t. Chestnut . . . . 1·00 1·00
265 80 t. White horse . . . . 2·75 2·75

52 Class VL8 No. 888

1998. Electric Railway Locomotives built at Tbilisi. Multicoloured.

267 10 t. Type **52** 15 15
268 30 t. Class VL10 No. 580 . . . 45 45
269 40 t. Class VL11 No. 500A . . 60 60
270 50 t. Class VL11 No. 001B . . . 75 75
271 80 t. Class VL10u No. 591 . . . 1·25 1·25

53 Flag and "26 May"

1998. 80th Anniv of Declaration of National Republic.

273 **53** 80 t. multicoloured . . . . 1·25 1·25

54 Berikaoba

1998. Europa. National Festivals. Value expressed by letter of Georgian alphabet.

274 A (80 t.) Type **54** . . . . . . 1·25 1·25
275 B (100 t.) Chiakokononba . . 1·75 1·75

55 Marbled Polecat

1999. Mammals. Multicoloured.

276 10 t. Type **55** 15 15
277 40 t. Striped hyena 60 60
278 80 t. Brown bear . . . . 1·25 1·25

56 Michael Bridge

1999. Bridges in Tbilisi. Multicoloured.

280 10 t. Type **56** 15 15
281 40 t. Saarbruken 60 60
282 50 t. N. Baratashvili Bridge . . 75 75
283 60 t. Mukhrani railway bridge . 90 90
284 70 t. Avlabari Bridge . . . . . 1·00 1·00
285 80 t. Metekhi Bridge . . . . . 1·25 1·25

57 Mink

1999. The European Mink. Values expressed by letter of Georgian alphabet. Multicoloured.

286 A (10 t.) Type **57** 25 25
287 B (20 t.) Mink with fish . . . 45 45
288 G (30 t.) Two mink 65 65
289 D (60 t.) Mink emerging from burrow . . . . 1·40 1·40

58 Batsara-Babaneury Reserve

1999. Europa. Parks and Gardens. Value indicated by letter of Georgian alphabet. Multicoloured.

290 A (80 t.) Type **58** . . . . . . 1·25 1·25
291 B (100 t.) Lagodekhy Reserve . 1·75 1·75

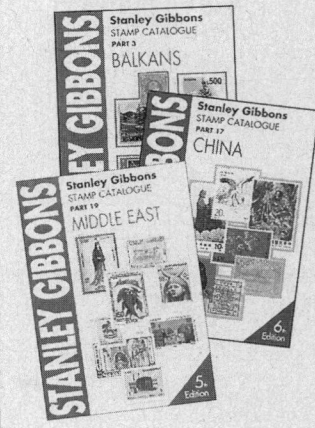

GERMAN COMMANDS Pt. 7

EASTERN COMMAND

German occupation of Estonia, Latvia and Lithuania during the war of 1914–18.

100 pfennig = 1 mark.

1916. Stamps of Germany inscr "DEUTSCHES REICH" optd **Postgebiet Ob. Ost.**

1	24	$2\frac{1}{2}$ pf. grey	30	40
2	10	3 pf. brown	25	25
3		5 pf. green	30	40
4	24	$7\frac{1}{2}$ pf. orange	30	40
5	10	10 pf. red	45	80
6	24	15 pf. brown	4·50	3·00
7		15 pf. violet	25	35
8	10	20 pf. blue	50	60
9		25 pf. black & red on yell	30	50
10		40 pf. black and red	1·00	2·75
11		50 pf. black & pur on buff	1·00	1·25
12a	12	1 m. red	10·00	3·25

WESTERN COMMAND

For Forces in Belgium and Northern France.

100 centimes = 1 franc.

1916. Stamps of Germany surch with new values as **2 Cent.**, 1F. or **1F.25 Cent.**

1	10	3 c. on 3 pf. brown	25	50
2		5 c. on 5 pf. green	25	55
3	24	8 c. on $7\frac{1}{2}$ pf. orange	40	80
4	10	10 c. on 10 pf. red	1·25	3·00
5	24	15 c. on 15 pf. brown	25	45
6	10	25 c. on 20 pf. blue	85	2·00
7		40 c. on 30 pf. black and orange on buff	70	1·40
8		50 c. on 40 pf. blk & red	1·00	2·00
9		75 c. on 60 pf. purple	3·25	6·50
10		1 f. on 80 pf. black and red on red	4·00	7·50
11a	12	1 f. 25 on 1 m. red	18·00	18·00
12	13	2 f. 50 on 2 m. blue	18·00	16·00

GERMAN EAST AFRICA Pt. 7

A German colony on the east coast of Africa. Placed under British mandate after the First World War.

1893. 64 pesa = 1 rupee.
1905. 100 heller = 1 rupee.

1893. Stamps of Germany surch with value in "PESA".

1	8	2 p. on 3 pf. brown	42·00	65·00
2		3 p. on 5 pf. green	55·00	65·00
4	9	5 p. on 10 pf. red	30·00	17·00
5		10 p. on 20 pf. blue	23·00	14·00
6		25 p. on 50 pf. brown	40·00	35·00

1896. Stamps of Germany surch **Deutsch-Ostafrika** and value in "Pesa".

7	8	2 p. on 3 pf. brown	1·60	6·50
10		3 p. on 5 pf. green	2·25	4·50
11	9	5 p. on 10 pf. red	2·25	4·50
13		10 p. on 20 pf. blue	5·50	6·00
14		25 p. on 50 pf. brown	22·00	32·00

1901. "Yacht", key-type inscr "DEUTSCH-OSTAFRIKA". Currency in pesa and rupees.

15	N	2 p. brown	3·00	2·25
16		3 p. green	3·00	2·25
17		5 p. red	3·25	3·00
18		10 p. blue	4·75	5·50
19		15 p. black & orge on buff	4·75	7·00
20		20 p. black and red	7·50	18·00
21		25 p. black & pur on buff	7·50	18·00
22		40 p. black & red on rose	8·00	26·00
23	O	1 r. red	23·00	65·00
24		2 r. green	11·00	£120
44		3 r. black and red	40·00	£225

1905. "Yacht" key-types inscr "DEUTSCH-OSTAFRIKA". Currency in heller.

34	N	$2\frac{1}{2}$ h. brown	90	80
35		4 h. green	90	60
36		$7\frac{1}{2}$ h. red	1·00	50
37		15 h. blue	2·25	1·00
38		20 h. blk & red on yellow	2·75	14·00
39		30 h. black and red	2·75	8·00
32a		45 h. black and mauve	15·00	32·00
33		60 h. black & red on rose	20·00	£110

For stamps issued for this territory under British auspices since 1915 see under Tanganyika in Volume 3.

GERMAN NEW GUINEA Pt. 7

A German Colony, part of the island of New Guinea.

100 pfennig = 1 mark.

1898. Stamps of Germany optd **Deutsch-Neu-Guinea.**

1a	8	3 pf. brown	7·00	11·00
2		5 pf. green	3·00	5·00
3	9	10 pf. red	6·00	8·50
4		20 pf. blue	9·00	13·00
5		25 pf. orange	32·00	60·00
6		50 pf. brown	32·00	50·00

1901. "Yacht" key-types inscr "DEUTSCH-NEU-GUINEA".

7	N	3 pf. brown	1·00	1·10
8		5 pf. green	9·00	1·10
9		10 pf. red	35·00	1·75
10	N	20 pf. blue	1·00	2·25
11		25 pf. blk & red on yell	1·00	15·00
12		30 pf. blk & orge on buff	1·00	22·00
13		40 pf. black and red	1·00	26·00
14		50 pf. blk & pur on buff	1·75	22·00
15		80 pf. black & red on rose	3·25	30·00
16	O	1 m. red	3·50	60·00
17		2 m. blue	5·00	85·00
18		3 m. black	7·50	£190
19		5 m. red and black	£130	£500

Australian forces occupied German New Guinea in 1914 and it was administered as a League of Nations mandate from 1920. For stamps issued since 1914 see under New Guinea.

GERMAN OCCUPATION OF ALSACE Pt. 7

100 pfennig = 1 mark.

1940. Stamps of Germany optd **Elsaß.**

1	94	3 pf. brown	20	40
2		4 pf. slate	30	1·00
3		5 pf. green	20	45
4		6 pf. green	20	45
5		8 pf. orange	20	45
6		10 pf. brown	25	70
7		12 pf. red	25	60
8		15 pf. red	35	90
9		20 pf. blue	35	90
10		25 pf. blue	40	1·25
11		30 pf. olive	90	1·40
12		40 pf. mauve	90	1·40
13		50 pf. black and green	1·40	2·00
14		60 pf. black and red	1·50	3·00
15		80 pf. black and blue	1·75	4·25
16		100 pf. black and yellow	3·00	3·25

GERMAN OCCUPATION OF BELGIUM Pt. 4

German occupation of E. Belgium during the war of 1914–18.

100 centimes = 1 franc.

Stamps of Germany inscr "DEUTSCHES REICH" surcharged.

1914. Surch **Belgien** and value thus: **3 Centimes, 1Franc** or **1Fr.25C.**

1	10	3 c. on 3 pf. brown	25	30
2		5 c. on 5 pf. green	25	30
3		10 c. on 10 pf. red	50	30
4		25 c. on 20 pf. blue	60	35
5		50 c. on 40 pf. black & red	2·00	1·25
6		75 c. on 60 pf. purple	1·00	1·10
7		1 f. on 80 pf. black and red on rose	2·25	2·00
8	12	1 f. 25 on 1 m. red	17·00	15·00
9	13	2 f. 50 on 2 m. blue	16·00	17·00

1916. Surch **Belgien** and value, thus: **2 Cent., 1F.,** or **1F.25Cent.**

10	24	2 c. on 2 pf. grey	15	30
11	10	3 c. on 3 pf. brown	15	20
12		5 c. on 5 pf. green	25	30
13	24	8 c. on $7\frac{1}{2}$ pf. orange	40	50
14	10	10 c. on 10 pf. red	25	40
15	24	15 c. on 15 pf. brown	25	30
16		15 c. on 15 pf. violet	20	40
17	10	20 c. on 25 pf. black and red on yellow	15	25
18		25 c. on 20 pf. blue	15	25
19		40 c. on 30 pf. black and orange on buff	15	20
20		50 c. on 40 pf. blk & red	30	35
21		75 c. on 60 pf. mauve	1·40	1·40
22		1 f. on 80 f. black and red on rose	1·40	4·50
23a	12	1 f. 25 on 1 m. red	2·75	2·50
24	13	2 f. 50 on 2 m. blue	25·00	25·00
25	15	6 f. 25 on 5 m. red & black	26·00	30·00

GERMAN OCCUPATION OF DALMATIA Pt. 3

Areas formerly under Italian control which were occupied by the Germans in 1943.

A. ZARA (Zadar)

100 centesimi = 1 lira.

1943. Imperial series of Italy, 1929, optd **Deutsche Besetzung Zara.**

1	98	5 c. brown	28·00	£100
2	–	10 c. brown	2·50	9·00
3	–	15 c. green	5·00	15·00
4	99	20 c. red	2·50	10·00
5	–	25 c. green	2·50	10·00
6	103	30 c. brown	2·50	10·00
7	–	35 c. blue	95·00	£375
8	–	75 c. red	7·50	25·00
9	99	1 l. violet	2·50	10·00
10		1 l. 25 blue	5·00	15·00
11		1 l. 75 red	10·50	45·00
12	–	2 l. red	22·00	75·00
13	98	2 l. 55 green	£140	£475
14		3 l. 70 violet	£1300	£3000
15		5 l. red	22·00	75·00
16	–	10 l. violet	£450	£600
17	99	20 l. green	£6000	£12000
18	–	25 l. black	£24000	£20000
19	–	50 l. violet	£20000	£14000

1943. War Propaganda stamps of Italy (Nos. 571/4) optd **Deutsche Besetzung Zara** on stamp and label.

20	103	50 c. violet (Navy)	4·00	15·00
21		50 c. violet (Army)	4·00	15·00
22		50 c. violet (Air Force)	4·00	15·00
23		50 c. violet (Militia)	4·00	15·00

1943. Air. Nos. 270/7 of Italy optd **Deutsche Besetzung Zara.**

26	–	25 c. green	5·00	15·00
27	110	50 c. brown	5·00	15·00
28	–	75 c. brown	£150	£450
29	–	80 c. red	17·00	£600
30	–	1 l. violet	5·00	15·00
31	113	2 l. blue	12·00	35·00
32	110	5 l. green	£2250	£4250
33		10 l. red	£7000	£14000

1943. Imperial series of Italy, 1929, optd **ZARA** within pattern of bars.

46	103	50 c. violet	3·50	15·00
47	–	75 c. red	3·50	5·00
48	–	1 l. 25 blue	30·00	£100

1943. War Propaganda stamps of Italy (Nos. 563/70) optd **ZARA** within pattern of bars on stamp and label.

49	–	25 c. green (Navy)	5·00	17·00
50	–	25 c. green (Army)	5·00	17·00
51	–	25 c. green (Air Force)	5·00	17·00
52	–	25 c. green (Militia)	5·00	17·00
53	103	30 c. brown (Navy)	5·00	17·00
54		30 c. brown (Army)	5·00	17·00
55		30 c. brown (Air Force)	5·00	17·00
56		30 c. brown (Militia)	5·00	17·00

EXPRESS LETTER STAMPS

1943. Nos. E350/1 of Italy optd **Deutsche Besetzung Zara.**

E24	E 132	1 l. 25 green	7·00	25·00
E25		2 l. 50 orange	35·00	95·00

1943. Air. No. E370 of Italy optd **Deutsche Besetzung Zara.**

E34	E 133	2 l. black	12·00	35·00

1943. Nos. E350/1 of Italy optd **ZARA** within pattern of bars, twice.

E57	E 132	1 l. 25 green	7·00	25·00
E58		2 l. 50 orange	48·00	£120

POSTAGE DUE STAMPS

1943. Italian Postage Due stamps optd **Deutsche Besetzung Zara.**

D35	D 141	5 c. brown	13·00	65·00
D36		10 c. blue	13·00	65·00
D37		20 c. red	13·00	65·00
D38		25 c. green	£350	£650
D39		30 c. red	13·00	65·00
D40		40 c. brown	13·00	65·00
D41		50 c. violet	13·00	65·00
D42		60 c. blue	£350	£650
D43	D 142	1 l. orange	£350	£650
D44		2 l. green	£400	£900
D45		5 l. violet	£350	£650

B. GULF OF KOTOR

Italian and German currency.

1944. Imperial series of Italy, 1929, surch **Deutsche Militar-verwaltung Kotor** and new value in lire.

1	–	0.50 LIT. on 10 c. brown	23·00	60·00
2	–	1 LIT. on 25 c. green	23·00	60·00
3	103	1.50 LIT. on 50 c. violet	23·00	60·00
4		3 LIT. on 30 c. brown	23·00	60·00
5	99	4 LIT. on 20 c. red	23·00	60·00
6		10 LIT. on 20 c. red	23·00	60·00

1944. Nos. 419/20 of Yugoslavia (King Petar II) surch **Boka Kotorska** and new value in Reichsmarks.

7	99	0,10 R.M. on 3 d. brown	2·00	4·00
8		0,15 R.M. on 3 d. brown	2·00	4·00
9		0,25 R.M. on 4 d. blue	3·25	7·50
10		0,50 R.M. on 4 d. blue	4·00	10·50

GERMAN OCCUPATION OF ESTONIA Pt. 10

100 kopeks = 1 rouble.

1

2 "Long Hermann" Tower, Reval (Tallinn)

1941. Tartu issue.

3	1	15 (k.) brown	7·50	10·00
4		20 (k.) green	7·50	10·00
5		30 (k.) blue	7·50	10·00

Originally issued for local use, the above were made available for use throughout Estonia from 29.9.41 to 30.4.42. However, not many were used since the German **OSTLAND** stamps were used from 1 December 1941.

1941. Reconstruction Fund.

6	2	15 + 15 (k.) sepia & brown	15	3·00
7	–	20 + 20 (k.) purple & brown	15	3·00
8	–	30 + 30 (k.) blue & brown	15	3·00
9	–	50 + 50 (k.) green and brown	20	5·00
10	–	60 + 60 (k.) red and brown	30	5·00
11	–	100 + 100 (k.) slate & brown	55	5·00

DESIGNS—HORIZ: 20 k. Stone Bridge, Tartu; 30 k. Two Narva Castles; 50 k. View of Tallinn. VERT: 60 k. Tartu University; 100 k. Hermann Castle, Narva.

German stamps optd **OSTLAND** (see German Occupation of Russia, Nos. 1/20) were used from 1 December 1941 until the Russian re-occupation of Estonia in 1944. Since then Russian stamps have been in use.

GERMAN OCCUPATION OF LATVIA Pt. 10

100 kopeks = 1 rouble.

1941. Russian stamps of 1936–39 optd **LATVIJA 1941. 1. VII.**

1		5 k. red (No. 847a)	50	3·00
2		10 k. blue (No. 727f)	50	3·00
3		15 k. green (No. 847c)	15·00	60·00
4		20 k. green (No. 727h)	50	3·00
5		30 k. blue (No. 847d)	50	3·00
6		50 k. brown on buff (No. 727m)	1·00	7·50

German stamps optd **OSTLAND** (see German Occupation of Russia Nos. 1/20) were used from 4th November, 1941, until the Russian re-occupation of Latvia in 1944–45. Since then Russian stamps have been in use.

GERMAN OCCUPATION OF LITHUANIA Pt. 10

100 kopeks = 1 rouble.

1941. Russian stamps of 1936–40 optd **NEPRIKLAUSOMA LIETUVA 1941-VI-23.**

1		2 k. green (No. 542)	22·00	£120
2		5 k. red (No. 847a)	60	10·00
3		10 k. blue (No. 727f)	60	10·00
4		15 k. green (No. 847c)	60	10·00
5		20 k. green (No. 727h)	60	10·00
6		30 k. blue (No. 847d)	60	10·00
7		50 k. brown on buff (No. 727m)	1·50	16·00
8		60 k. red (No. 847f)	4·00	30·00
9		80 k. blue (No. 905)	9·00	40·00

1941. Issue for Vilnius and South Lithuania. Russian stamps of 1936–39 optd **VILNIUS.**

10		5 k. red (No. 847a)	1·10	3·00
11		10 k. blue (No. 727f)	1·10	3·00
12		15 k. green (No. 847c)	1·10	3·00
13		20 k. green (No. 727h)	4·00	11·00
14		30 k. blue (No. 847d)	2·25	7·00
15		50 k. brown on buff (No. 727m)	3·25	7·00
16		60 k. red (No. 847f)	4·00	8·50
17		80 k. red and deep red (No. 772)	£150	£225
18		1 r. black and red (No. 779)	£475	£650

German stamps optd **OSTLAND** (see German Occupation of Russia Nos. 1/20) were used from 4th November. 1941, till the Russian re-occupation of Lithuania in 1944. Since then Russian stamps have been in use.

GERMAN OCCUPATION OF LORRAINE Pt. 7

100 pfennig = 1 mark.

1940. Stamps of Germany optd **Lothringen.**

1	94	3 pf. brown	30	75
2		4 pf. slate	35	75
3		5 pf. green	35	75
4		6 pf. green	35	35
5		8 pf. orange	35	75
6		10 pf. brown	35	50
7		12 pf. red	40	50
8		15 pf. lake	50	90
9		20 pf. blue	50	1·10
10		25 pf. blue	60	1·10
11		30 pf. olive	75	1·25
12		40 pf. mauve	75	1·25
13		50 pf. black and green	1·25	2·25
14		60 pf. black and red	1·25	2·75
15		80 pf. black and blue	1·60	3·25
16		100 pf. black and yellow	2·00	5·50

GERMAN OCCUPATION OF POLAND Pt. 5

German occupation of Poland, 1915–1918.

100 pfennig = 1 mark.

1915. Stamps of Germany inscr "DEUTSCHES REICH" optd **Russisch-Polen.**

1	10	3 pf. brown	60	30
2		5 pf. green	75	35
3		10 pf. red	75	35
4		20 pf. blue	1·10	50
5		40 pf. black and red	6·00	2·50

1916. Stamps of Germany inscr "DEUTSCHES REICH" optd **Gen.-Gouv. Warschau.**
6 **24** 2½ pf. grey 25 30
7 **10** 3 pf. brown . . . . 70 1·00
8 5 pf. green 70 70
9 **24** 7½ pf. orange 40 25
10 **10** 10 pf. red 55 50
11 **24** 15 pf. brown . . . . 2·50 2·50
12 15 pf. violet 35 90
13 **10** 20 pf. blue . . . . 1·00 90
14 30 pf. blk & orge on buff . . 3·75 4·00
15 40 pf. black and red . . . . 1·40 30
16 60 pf. purple . . . . 2·00 2·00

GERMAN OCCUPATION OF RUMANIA Pt. 3

German occupation of Rumania. 1917–1918.

100 bani = 1 leu.

Stamps of Germany inscr "DEUTSCHES REICH".

1917. Surch **M.V.i.R.** in frame and value in "Bani".
1 **24** 15 b. on 15 pf. violet . . . . 70 1·00
2 **10** 25 b. on 20 pf. blue . . . . 70 1·00
3 40 b. on 30 pf. black and orange on buff . . . . . . 22·00 35·00

1917. Surch **M.V.i.R.** (not in frame) and value in "Bani".
4 **10** 10 b. on 10 pf. red . . . . 1·00 1·25
5 **24** 15 b. on 15 pf. violet . . . . 3·00 5·50
6 **10** 25 b. on 20 pf. blue . . . . 1·00 1·25
7 40 b. on 30 pf. black and orange on buff . . . . . . 1·25 1·10

1918. Surch **Rumanien** and value in "Bani".
8 **10** 5 b. on 5 pf. green 25 30
9 10 b. on 10 pf. red 25 40
10 **24** 15 b. on 15 pf. violet 10 15
11 **10** 25 b. on 20 pf. blue . . . . 50 1·00
12 40 b. on 30 pf. black and orange on buff 30 30

1918. Stamps of Germany inscr "DEUTSCHES REICH" optd **Gultig 9. Armee** in frame.
13 **10** 10 pf. red . . . . 9·00 20·00
14 **24** 15 pf. violet . . . . 16·00 28·00
15 **10** 20 pf. blue . . . . 1·25 2·00
16 30 pf. blk & orge on buff . . 12·00 22·00

POSTAGE DUE STAMPS

1918. Postage Due stamps of Rumania optd **M.V.i.R.** in frame.
D1 **D 38** 5 b. blue on green . . . . 4·00 7·00
D2 10 b. blue on green . . . 4·00 7·00
D3 20 b. blue on green . . . 2·00 3·00
D4 30 b. blue on green . . . 2·00 3·00
D5 50 b. blue on green . . . 2·00 3·00

GERMAN OCCUPATION OF RUSSIA Pt. 10

100 pfennig = 1 reichsmark.

1941. Issue for Ostland. Stamps of Germany of 1941 optd **OSTLAND.**
1 **173** 1 pf. grey 10 15
2 3 pf. brown 10 15
3 4 pf. slate 10 15
4 5 pf. green 10 15
5 6 pf. violet 10 15
6 8 pf. red 10 15
7 10 pf. brown . . . . 60 1·25
9 12 pf. red . . . . 60 1·25
11 15 pf. lake 10 15
12 16 pf. green 10 25
13 20 pf. blue 10 15
14 24 pf. brown 10 25
15 25 pf. blue 10 15
16 30 pf. olive 10 15
17 40 pf. mauve 10 20
18 50 pf. green 10 20
19 60 pf. brown 10 20
20 80 pf. blue 10 45

1941. Issue for Ukraine. Stamps of Germany of 1941 optd **UKRAINE.**
21 **173** 1 pf. grey 10 15
22 3 pf. brown 10 15
23 4 pf. slate 10 15
24 5 pf. green 10 15
25 6 pf. violet 10 15
26 8 pf. red 10 15
27 10 pf. brown . . . . 50 1·60
29 12 pf. red . . . . 50 1·60
31 15 pf. lake 10 15
32 16 pf. green 10 20
33 20 pf. blue 10 15
34 24 pf. brown 10 20
35 25 pf. blue 10 15
36 30 pf. olive 10 15
37 40 pf. mauve 10 20
38 50 pf. green 10 15
39 60 pf. brown 10 20
40 80 pf. blue 10 25

GERMAN OCCUPATION OF ZANTE Pt. 3

German occupation of Ionian Islands, 1943–44.

100 centesimi = 1 lira = 8 drachma.

(1)

1943. Stamps of Italian Occupation of Ionian Islands further optd with T **1**.
1 – 25 c. green (postage) . . . . 10·00 25·00
2 **103** 50 c. violet . . . . 10·00 25·00
3 **110** 50 c. brown (air) . . . . . . 10·00 25·00

GERMAN POST OFFICES IN CHINA Pt. 7

German post offices in China, now closed.

1898. 100 pfennig = 1 mark.
1905. 100 cents = 1 dollar.

1898. Stamps of Germany optd **China.**
7 **8** 3 pf. brown . . . . 6·00 6·00
8 5 pf. green . . . . 3·50 3·00
9 **9** 10 pf. red . . . . 8·00 7·50
4 20 pf. blue . . . . 18·00 10·00
11 25 pf. orange . . . . 38·00 35·00
12 50 pf. brown . . . . 18·00 14·00

1901. Stamps of Germany inscr "REICHSPOST" optd **China.**
22 **10** 3 pf. brown . . . . 1·50 1·75
23 5 pf. green . . . . 1·50 1·00
24 10 pf. red . . . . 2·50 1·00
25 20 pf. blue . . . . 2·75 1·25
26 25 pf. blk & red on yell . . 12·00 18·00
27 30 pf. blk & orge on pink . . 13·00 14·00
28 40 pf. black and red . . . . 12·00 11·00
29 50 pf. blk & pur on pink . . 12·00 11·00
30 80 pf. blk & red on pink . . 14·00 12·00
31 **12** 1 m. red . . . . 35·00 35·00
32 **13** 2 m. blue . . . . 30·00 32·00
33 **14** 3 m. black . . . . 45·00 60·00
35a **15** 5 m. red and black £180 £325

1905. Stamps of Germany inscr "DEUTSCHES REICH" surch **China** and new value.
46 **10** 1 c. on 3 pf. brown 35 75
47 2c. on 5 pf. green 35 70
48 4c. on 10 pf. red 35 70
39 10c. on 20 pf. blue . . . . 3·00 1·40
50 20c. on 40 pf. black and red 1·00 3·00
51 40c. on 80 pf. black and red on rose . . . . 1·25 45·00
42 **12** ½ d. on 1 m. red . . . . . 18·00 25·00
53 **13** 1 d. on 2 m. blue . . . . . 12·00 32·00
44a **14** 1½ d. on 3 m. black . . . . 24·00 50·00
55 **15** 2½ d. on 5 m. red and black . 60·00 £110

GERMAN POST OFFICES IN MOROCCO Pt. 7

German Post Offices in Morocco, now closed.

100 centimos = 1 peseta.

Stamps of Germany surcharged **Marocco** (or **Marokko**) and new value.

1889. Spelt **Marocco.**
1 **8** 3 c. on 3 pf. brown . . . . . . 2·75 3·00
2 5 c. on 5 pf. green . . . . . 2·75 3·00
3 **9** 10 c. on 10 pf. red . . . . . 5·50 6·00
4 25 c. on 20 pf. blue . . . . . 12·00 16·00
5 30 c. on 25 pf. orange . . . . 23·00 35·00
6 60 c. on 50 pf. brown . . . . 18·00 45·00

1900. Inscr "REICHSPOST" surch **Marocco** (3 c. to 1 p.) or **Marocco Marocco** (others).
7 **10** 3 c. on 3 pf. brown . . . . 1·10 1·75
8 5 c. on 5 pf. green . . . . 1·10 80
9 10 c. on 10 pf. red . . . . 1·75 80
10 25 c. on 20 pf. blue . . . . 2·25 2·25
11 30 c. on 25 pf. black and red on yellow . . . . . . 9·00 14·00
12 35 c. on 30 pf. black and orange on rose . . . . . 6·50 5·50
13 50 c. on 40 pf. blk & red . . 6·50 5·50
14 60 c. on 50 pf. black and purple on rose . . . . . 15·00 32·00
15 1 p. on 80 pf. black and red on rose . . . . 11·00 11·00
16 **12** 1 p. 25 c. on 1 m. red . . . 28·00 40·00
17 **13** 2 p. 50 c. on 2 m. blue . . . 30·00 48·00
18 **14** 3 p. 75 c. on 3 m. black . . . 40·00 60·00
19b **15** 6 p. 25 c. on 5 m. red and black £160 £300

1905. Inscr "DEUTSCHES REICH" surch **Marocco** (3 c. to 1 p.) or **Marocco Marocco** (others).
26 **10** 3 c. on 3 pf. brown . . . . 2·50 2·50
27 5 c. on 5 pf. green . . . . 5·00 85
28 10 c. on 10 pf. red . . . . 10·00 65
42 25 c. on 20 pf. blue . . . . 19·00 3·50
30 30 c. on 25 pf. black and red on yellow . . . . . . 6·00 4·50
31 35 c. on 30 pf. black and orange on buff . . . . . 10·00 5·50
32 **10** 50 c. on 40 pf. black & red . . 9·50 8·50
46 60 c. on 50 pf. black and purple on buff . . . . 25·00 15·00
34 1 p. on 80 pf. black and red on rose . . . . 32·00 20·00
35a **12** 1 p. 25 on 1 m. red . . . . 40·00 30·00
36 **13** 2 p. 50 on 2 m. blue . . . . 80·00 £140
37a **14** 3 p. 75 on 3 m. black . . . . 45·00 42·00
38 **15** 6 p. 25 on 5 m. red and black £120 £160

1911. Inscr "DEUTSCHES REICH". Spelt **Marokko.**
51 **10** 3 c. on 3 pf. brown 45 65
52 5 c. on 5 pf. green 45 75
53 10 c. on 10 pf. red 45 80
54 25 c. on 20 pf. blue 55 85
55 30 c. on 25 pf. black and red on yellow . . . . 1·25 17·00
56 35 c. on 30 pf. black and orange on buff . . . . . 1·10 8·50
57 50 c. on 40 pf. black & red . 1·10 4·50
58 60 c. on 50 pf. black and purple on buff . . . . . . 1·50 35·00
59 1 p. on 80 pf. black and red on rose . . . . 1·60 28·00
60 **12** 1 p. 25 c. on 1 m. red . . . . 3·00 65·00
61 **13** 2 p. 50 c. on 2 m. blue . . . 4·50 55·00
62 **14** 3 p. 75 c. on 3 m. black . . . 9·00 £250
63 **15** 6 p. 25 c. on 5 m. red and black . . . . 16·00 £325

GERMAN POST OFFICES IN THE TURKISH EMPIRE Pt. 7

German Post Offices in the Turkish Empire, now closed.

1884. 40 para = 1 piastre.
1908. 100 centimes = 1 franc.

1884. Stamps of Germany surch with new value. ("PFENNIG" without final "E".)
1 **5** 10 pa. on 5 pf. mauve . . . . 30·00 24·00
2 **6** 20 pa. on 10 pf. red . . . . . 65·00 60·00
3 1 pi. on 20 pf. blue . . . . . 48·00 2·25
4 1¼ pi. on 25 pf. brown £120 £190
6 2½ pi. on 50 pf. green . . . . £100 65·00

1889. Stamps of Germany surch.
10 **8** 10 pa. on 5 pf. green . . . . 2·75 3·25
11 **9** 20 pa. on 10 pf. red . . . . 7·00 1·50
12 1 pi. on 20 pf. blue . . . . 4·50 85
14 1¼ pi. on 25 pf. orange . . . . 27·00 15·00
16 2½ pi. on 50 pf. brown . . . . 32·00 23·00

1900. Stamps of Germany inscr "REICHSPOST" surch in **PARA** or **PIASTER.**
17 **10** 10 pa. on 5 pf. green . . . 1·40 1·40
18 20 pa. on 10 pf. red . . . 1·75 1·75
19 1 pi. on 20 pf. blue . . . 3·50 1·25
20 1¼ pi. on 25 pf. black and red on yellow . . . . . . 7·00 4·00
21 1½ pi. on 30 pf. black and orange on buff . . . . . 7·00 4·00
22 2 pi. on 40 pf. black & red . 7·00 4·00
23 2½ pi. on 50 pf. black and purple on buff . . . . . 13·00 13·00
24 4 pi. on 80 pf. black and red on rose . . . . 17·00 13·00
25 **12** 5 pi. on 1 m. red . . . . . 32·00 40·00
26 **13** 10 pi. on 2 m. blue . . . . 32·00 45·00
27 **14** 15 pi. on 3 m. black . . . . 55·00 £100
28b **15** 25 pi. on 5 m. red & black . . £160 £275

1905. Stamps of Germany inscr "DEUTSCHES REICH" surch in **Para** or **Piaster.**
47 **10** 10 pa. on 5 pf. green . . . . 1·60 40
48 20 pa. on 10 pf. red . . . . 2·00 40
49 1 pi. on 20 pf. blue . . . . 3·25 40
38 1¼ pi. on 25 pf. black and red on yellow . . . . 11·00 7·00
51 1½ pi. on 30 pf. black and orange on buff . . . . . 10·00 6·50
52 2 pi. on 40 pf. black & red . . 4·50 1·00
53 2½ pi. on 50 pf. black and purple on buff . . . . . . 11·00 7·00
54 4 pi. on 80 pf. black and red on pink . . . . 10·00 18·00
55 **12** 5 pi. on 1 m. red . . . . . 18·00 32·00
56 **13** 10 pi. on 2 m. blue . . . . 18·00 48·00
45 **14** 15 pi. on 3 m. black . . . . 50·00 50·00
58 **15** 25 pi. on 5 m. red & black . . 24·00 60·00

1908. Stamps of Germany inscr "DEUTSCHES REICH", surch in **Centimes.**
60 **10** 5 c. on 5 pf. green . . . . 1·25 2·00
61 10 c. on 10 pf. red . . . . 3·25 5·00
62 25 c. on 20 pf. blue . . . . 7·00 35·00
63 50 c. on 40 pf. black & red . 32·00 70·00
64 100 c. on 80 pf. black and red on rose . . . . 70·00 90·00

GERMAN SOUTH WEST AFRICA Pt. 7

A German colony in S.W. Africa.

100 pfennig = 1 mark.

1897. Stamps of Germany optd.
(a) **Deutsch-Sudwest-Afrika.**
1 **8** 3 pf. brown . . . . 6·00 12·00
2 5 pf. green . . . . 3·25 3·75
3 **9** 10 pf. red . . . . 16·00 17·00
4 20 pf. blue . . . . 3·50 4·50

(b) **Deutsch- Sudwestafrika.**
5 **8** 3 pf. brown . . . . 6·00 12·00
6 5 pf. green . . . . 2·75 2·25
7 **9** 10 pf. red . . . . 2·75 3·00
8 20 pf. blue . . . . 13·00 16·00
9 25 pf. orange £325 £475
10 50 pf. brown . . . . 12·00 12·00

1900. "Yacht" key-types inscr "DEUTSCH-SUDWESTAFRIKA".
24 N 3 pf. brown . . . . 75 1·25
25 5 pf. green . . . . 75 1·25
26 10 pf. red . . . . 75 1·50
27 20 pf. blue . . . . 90 1·00
15 25 pf. black & red on yell . . 1·40 5·00
16 30 pf. blk & orge on buff . . 12·00 2·75
17 40 pf. black and red . . . . 1·40 3·25
18 50 pf. blk & pur on buff . . 1·75 2·25
19 80 pf. black & red on rose . . 1·75 8·00
29 O 1 m. red . . . . 12·00 32·00
30 2 m. blue . . . . 11·00 32·00
22 3 m. black . . . . 32·00 55·00
32 5 m. red and black . . . . 22·00 £300

South Africa occupied the colony in 1914 and administered the territory under a League of Nations mandate from 1920. For stamps issued from 1923 see under South West Africa in Volume 3.

GERMANY Pt. 7

A country in Northern Central Europe. A federation of states forming the German Reich. An empire till November 1918 and then a republic until the collapse of Germany in 1945. Until 1949 under Allied Military Control when the German Federal Republic was set up for W. Germany and the German Democratic Republic for E. Germany. See also notes before No. 899.

I. GERMANY 1871–1945

1872. Northern areas including Alsace and Lorraine: 30 groschen = 1 thaler. Southern areas: 90 kreuzer = 1 gulden.
1875. Throughout Germany: 100 pfennig = 1 mark.
1923. 100 renten-pfennig = 1 rentenmark (gold currency).
1928. 100 pfennig = 1 reichsmark.

1

A

1872. Arms embossed as Type A.
1 **1** ¼ g. violet . . . . £170 80·00
2 ⅓ g. green . . . . £325 30·00
3 ½ g. red . . . . £1000 35·00
4 ½ g. yellow . . . . £1000 40·00
5 1 g. red . . . . £250 3·00
6 2 g. blue . . . . £900 9·00
7 5 g. bistre . . . . £475 80·00
8 1 k. green . . . . £500 50·00
9 2 k. red £550 £250
10 2 k. yellow . . . . 30·00 £160
11 3 k. red . . . . £1000 9·75
12 7 k. blue . . . . £1800 80·00
13 18 k. bistre £500 £350

2

B

1872.
14 **2** 10 g. grey . . . . 55·00 £100
15 – 30 g. blue £100 £400
38d **2** 2 m. purple . . . . 45·00 1·75

On the 30 g. the figures are in a rectangular frame.

1872. Arms embossed as Type B.
16 **1** ¼ g. purple . . . . 55·00 £100
17 ⅓ g. green . . . . 25·00 12·00
18 ½ g. orange . . . . 27·00 3·50
19 1 g. red . . . . 38·00 1·00
20 2 g. blue . . . . 20·00 3·75
21 2½ g. brown . . . . £2000 50·00
22 5 g. olive . . . . 26·00 28·00
23 1 k. green . . . . 30·00 28·00
24 2 k. orange £400 £2250
25 3 k. red . . . . 20·00 3·00
26 7 k. blue . . . . 28·00 65·00
27 9 k. brown £225 £170
28 18 k. olive . . . . 30·00 £2000

1874. Surch with bold figures over arms.
29 **1** "2½" on 2½ g. brown . . . . 28·00 32·00
30 "9" on 9 k. brown . . . . . 60·00 £300

5

6

1875. "PFENNIGE" with final "E".
31 **5** 3 pf. green . . . . 60·00 5·00
32 5 pf. mauve . . . . 95·00 2·00
33 **6** 10 pf. red . . . . 38·00 30
34 20 pf. blue £300 90
35 25 pf. brown . . . . £450 16·00
36a 50 pf. grey . . . . £900 10·00
37 50 pf. green . . . . £1600 15·00

1880. "PFENNIG" without final "E"

39a	5	3 pf. green	2·75	40
40a		5 pf. purple	1·50	30
41b	6	10 pf. red	9·00	10
42a		20 pf. blue	7·00	10
43b		25 pf. brown	17·00	2·75
44a		50 pf. green	7·00	65

8 9

1889.

45	8	2 pf. grey	50	70
46		3 pf. brown	1·75	10
47a		5 pf. green	1·25	20
48b	9	10 pf. red	1·75	20
49		20 pf. blue	9·00	20
50b		25 pf. yellow	35·00	1·25
51b		50 pf. brown	35·00	30

10 "Germania" **12** General Post Office, Berlin

13 Allegory of Union of N and S Germany (after Anton von Werner)

14 Unveiling of Kaiser Wilhelm I Memorial in Berlin (after W Pape)

15 25th Anniv of German Empire Address by Wilhelm II (after W Pape)

1899. Types **10** to **15** inscr "REICHSPOST".

52	10	2 pf. grey	50	60
53		3 pf. brown	50	30
54		5 pf. green	1·00	30
55		10 pf. red	1·75	30
56		20 pf. blue	6·00	30
57		25 pf. blk & red on yell	12·00	6·00
58		30 pf. blk & orge on rose	22·00	60
59		40 pf. black and red	26·00	1·40
60		50 pf. blk & pur on rose	26·00	1·00
61		80 pf. blk & red on rose	35·00	2·25
62	12	1 m. red	60·00	1·40
63	13	2 m. blue	65·00	5·00
64	14	3 m. black	90·00	42·00
65b	15	5 m. red and black	£300	£325

1902. T **10** to **15** inscr "DEUTSCHES REICH".

67	10	2 pf. grey	1·25	60
83a		3 pf. brown	25	10
84a		5 pf. green	25	10
85a		10 pf. red	60	10
86d		20 pf. blue	30	10
87		25 pf. blk & red on yell	30	15
88a		30 pf. blk & orge on buff	30	15
89a		40 pf. black and red	65	15
90a		50 pf. blk & pur on buff	30	10
91a		60 pf. purple	1·00	50
92a		80 pf. blk & red on rose	70	1·90
93	12	1 m. red	1·75	40
94	13	2 m. blue	3·50	4·50
95	14	3 m. black	1·00	3·75
96	15	5 m. red and black	80	2·75

No. 93 has three pedestrians in front of the carriage in the right foreground and has no tram in the background. See No. 113 for redrawn design.

24 Unshaded background

1916. Inscr "DEUTSCHES REICH".

97	24	2 pf. grey	15	2·40
98		$2\frac{1}{2}$ pf. grey	15	40
140	10	5 pf. brown	15	1·00
99a	24	$7\frac{1}{2}$ pf. yellow	20	70
141a	10	10 pf. orange	10	50
100	24	15 pf. brown	2·25	80
101		15 pf. violet	15	50
102		15 pf. purple	20	85
142	10	20 pf. green	10	80
143a		30 pf. blue	10	75
103	24	35 pf. brown	15	1·00
144a	10	40 pf. red	10	75
145a		50 pf. purple	40	1·60
146		60 pf. olive	10	60
104		75 pf. black and green	15	60
147a	10	75 pf. purple	10	1·00
148a		80 pf. blue	10	1·10
149		1 m. green and violet	10	65
113	12	1 m. red	1·75	1·25
150	10	$1\frac{1}{4}$ m. purple and red	10	70
114	12	1 m. 25 green	1·50	1·00
115		1 m. 50 brown	40	1·10
151	10	2 m. blue and red	45	85
116a	13	2 m. 50 red	10	1·00
152	10	4 m. red and black	10	1·40

No. 113 has one pedestrian behind the carriage in the right foreground and a tram in the background.

1919. War Wounded Fund. Surch **5 Pf. fur Kriegs = beschadigte**.

105	10	10 pf. + 5 pf. (No. 85a)	50	6·00
106	24	15 pf. + 5 pf. (No. 101)	50	7·00

26 27 28

1919. National Assembly, Weimar.

107	26	10 pf. red	10	1·25
108	27	15 pf. blue and brown	10	1·25
109	28	25 pf. red and green	10	1·25
110		30 pf. red and purple	10	1·25

29 **30** L.V.G. Schneider Biplane

1919. Air.

111	29	10 pf. orange	10	2·50
112	30	40 pf. green	10	2·50

1920. Stamps of Bavaria optd **Deutsches Reich**.

117	26	5 pf. green	10	1·25
118		10 pf. orange	10	1·10
119		15 pf. red	10	1·10
120	27	20 pf. purple	10	80
121		30 pf. blue	10	80
122		40 pf. brown	10	80
123	28	50 pf. red	10	2·00
124		60 pf. green	10	80
125		75 pf. purple	35	4·00
126		80 pf. blue	20	2·50
127	29	1 m. red and grey	30	2·00
128		$1\frac{1}{4}$ m. blue and bistre	30	1·60
129		$1\frac{1}{2}$ m. green and grey	30	2·00
130		2 m. violet and bistre	65	3·50
131		$2\frac{1}{2}$ m. black and grey	10	2·25
132	30	3 m. blue	2·75	6·50
133		4 m. red	3·25	12·00
134		5 m. yellow	2·50	8·50
135		10 m. green	3·00	12·00
136		20 m. black	5·25	15·00

1920. Surch with new value and stars.

137	12	1 m. 25 on 1 m. green	30	7·00
138		1 m. 50 on 1 m. brown	30	7·00
139	13	2 m. 50 on 2 m. purple	7·00	£200

35 **36** Blacksmiths **37** Miners

38 Reapers 40

41 Ploughman **39** Posthorn

1921.

153	35	5 pf. red	10	1·40
154		10 pf. olive	10	80
155		15 pf. blue	10	60
156		25 pf. brown	10	50
157		30 pf. green	10	50
158		40 pf. orange	10	45
182		50 pf. purple	10	80
160	36	60 pf. red	10	60
184	35	75 pf. blue	10	3·25
161	36	80 pf. red	10	7·00
186	37	100 pf. green	10	55
163		120 pf. blue	10	60
188	38	150 pf. orange	10	70
165		160 pf. green	10	11·00
193	40	5 m. orange	15	1·25
170		10 m. red	30	1·50
195	41	20 m. blue and green	10	3·00

1921. 1902 stamps surch.

172	10	1 m. 60 on 5 pf. brown	10	1·10
173		3 m. on $1\frac{1}{4}$ m. pur & red	10	1·10
174		5 m. on 75 pf. purple	10	1·10
175		10 m. on 75 pf. purple	30	1·50

1921.

190	39	2 m. violet and pink	10	60
204		2 m. purple	10	90
191		3 m. red and yellow	15	85
205		3 m. red	10	60
192		4 m. green & light green	10	85
206		4 m. green	10	80
207		5 m. orange and yellow	10	1·40
208		5 m. orange	10	80
209		6 m. blue	10	90
210		8 m. green	10	80
211		10 m. red and pink	10	60
212		20 m. violet and red	10	90
213		20 m. violet	10	95
214		30 m. brown and yellow	10	80
215		30 m. brown	15	6·50
216		40 m. green	10	1·00
217		50 m. green and purple	10	80

47 Arms of Munich 48

1922. Munich Exhibition.

198	47	$1\frac{1}{4}$ m. red	20	1·25
199		2 m. violet	20	1·25
200		3 m. red	30	1·40
201		4 m. blue	20	1·40
202		10 m. brown on buff	50	2·25
203		20 m. red on rose	2·75	10·00

1922. Air.

218	48	25 pf. brown	30	17·00
219		40 pf. orange	30	25·00
220		50 pf. purple	15	10·00
221		60 pf. red	35	20·00
222		80 pf. green	35	18·00
223	–	1 m. green	10	4·00
224	–	2 m. red and grey	10	4·00
225	–	3 m. blue and grey	10	4·50
226	–	5 m. orange and yellow	10	4·00
227	–	10 m. purple and red	15	12·00
228	–	25 m. brown and yellow	15	10·00
229	–	100 m. olive and red	15	8·50

The mark values are larger (21 × 27 mm).
See also Nos. 269/73 and 358/64.

1922. New values.

235	40	50 m. black	10	1·40
230		100 m. purple on buff	20	1·00
237		200 m. red on buff	10	65
238		300 m. green on buff	10	60
239		400 m. brown on buff	10	60
240		500 m. orange on buff	10	60
241		1000 m. grey	10	60
242		2000 m. blue	10	80
243		3000 m. brown	10	1·25
244		4000 m. violet	20	1·40
245		5000 m. green	30	1·75
246		100000 m. red	10	1·40

50 Allegory of Charity **51** Miners 54

1922. Fund for the Old and for Children.

247	50	6 m. + 4 m. bl & bistre	15	20·00
248		12 m. + 8 m. red & lilac	15	20·00

1923.

249	51	5 m. orange	10	16·00
250	38	10 m. blue	10	55
251		12 m. red	10	1·00
252	51	20 m. purple	10	85
253	38	25 m. bistre	10	40
254	51	30 m. olive	10	1·75
255	38	40 m. green	10	95
256	51	50 m. blue	25	£120

1923. Relief Fund for Sufferers in the Rhine and Ruhr Occupation Districts. Surch **Rhein = Ruhr = Hilfe** and premium.

257	51	5 + 100 m. orange	10	10·00
258	38	25 + 500 m. bistre	10	26·00
259	41	20 + 1000 m. blue & green	1·75	£100

1923. T = Tausend (thousand).

261	54	100 m. purple	10	60
262		200 m. red	10	75
263		300 m. green	10	1·00
264		400 m. brown	10	6·00
265		500 m. red	10	5·50
266		1000 m. grey	10	1·10
312		5 T. blue	10	16·00
313		50 T. brown	10	60
314		75 T. purple	10	12·00

55 Wartburg Castle 62

1923.

267	55	5000 m. blue	15	2·50
268	–	10,000 m. olive	15	3·50

DESIGN—VERT: 10,000 m. Cologne Cathedral.

1923. Air. As T **48**, but larger (21 × 27 mm).

269	5 m. orange	10	45·00
270	10 m. purple	10	9·50
271	25 m. brown	10	10·00
272	100 m. green	10	8·50
273	200 m. blue	10	40·00

1923. Surch with new value in **Tausend** or **Millionen** (marks). Perf or rouletted.

274	35	5 T. on 40 pf. orange	10	1·50
275a		8 T. on 30 pf. green	10	1·75
276	38	15 T. on 40 m. green	10	90
277		20 T. on 12 m. red	10	1·25
278		20 T. on 25 m. brown	10	2·25
279	54	20 T. on 200 m. red	10	1·25
280	38	25 T. on 25 m. brown	10	18·00
281		30 T. on 10 m. blue	10	1·00
282	54	30 T. on 200 m. blue	10	1·40
283		75 T. on 300 m. green	10	19·00
284		75 T. on 400 m. green	10	85
285		75 T. on 1000 m. green	10	85
286		100 T. on 100 m. purple	10	1·75
287		100 T. on 400 m. green	10	70
288		125 T. on 1000 m. red	10	1·40
289		250 T. on 200 m. red	10	4·00
290		250 T. on 300 m. green	10	18·00
291		250 T. on 400 m. brown	10	20·00
292		250 T. on 500 m. pink	10	70
293		250 T. on 500 m. orange	10	20·00
306	35	400 T. on 15 pf. brown	10	4·00
307		400 T. on 25 pf. brown	10	4·00
308		400 T. on 30 pf. brown	10	4·00
309		400 T. on 40 pf. brown	10	4·00
294		800 T. on 5 pf. green	10	5·00
295		800 T. on 10 pf. green	10	5·00
296	54	800 T. on 200 m. red	10	60·00
297		800 T. on 300 m. green	10	4·50
298		800 T. on 400 m. green	10	4·00
299		800 T. on 400 m. brown	10	18·00
300		800 T. on 500 m. green	20	£1200
301		800 T. on 1000 m. green	10	90
302		2 M. on 200 m. red	10	85
303		2 M. on 300 m. green	10	2·00
304		2 M. on 500 m. red	10	6·00
305		2 M. on 5 T. red	10	1·00

1923. Perf or rouletted.

315	62	500 T. brown	10	3·00
316		1 M. blue	10	70
317		2 M. purple	10	25·00
318		4 M. green	10	2·00
319		5 M. red	10	65
320		10 M. red	10	65
321		20 M. blue	10	75
322		30 M. purple	10	10·00
323		50 M. green	10	80
324		100 M. grey	10	80
325		200 M. brown	10	1·00
326		500 M. olive	10	90

1923. As T **62**, but value in "Milliarden". Perf or roul.

327	62	1 Md. brown	10	1·00
328		2 Md. green and flesh	10	1·00
329		5 Md. brown and yellow	10	1·00
330		10 Md. green & lt green	10	1·25
331		20 Md. brown and green	10	1·60
332		50 Md. blue	40	30·00

1923. Surch in **Milliarden**. Perf or roul.

342	54	1 Md. on 100 m. purple	10	26·00
343	62	5 Md. on 2 M. purple	20	£140
344		5 Md. on 4 M. green	10	27·00
345		5 Md. on 10 M. red	10	2·25
346		10 Md. on 20 M. blue	25	2·50
347		10 Md. on 50 M. green	10	2·25
348		10 Md. on 100 M. grey	10	7·50

1923. As T **62**, but without value in words and tablet blank.

352	62	3 pf. brown	40	20
353		5 pf. green	40	20
354		10 pf. red	40	20
355		20 pf. blue	90	25
356		50 pf. orange	2·75	60
357		100 pf. purple	8·00	70

The values of this and the following issues are expressed on the basis of the gold mark.

1924. Air.

358	48	5 pf. green	1·50	1·25
359		10 pf. red	1·50	1·60
360		20 pf. blue	3·25	5·00
361		50 pf. orange	12·00	20·00
362		100 pf. purple	30·00	55·00
363		200 pf. blue	60·00	75·00
364		300 pf. grey	95·00	£110

65

66

1924. Welfare Fund.
365 **65** 5+15 pf. green . . . . . . 1·00 2·00
366 – 10+30 pf. red . . . . . . 1·00 2·00
367 – 20+60 pf. blue . . . . . . 6·00 7·00
368 – 50+1 m. 50 pf. brown . . . 26·00 60·00
DESIGNS: St. Elizabeth feeding the hungry (5 pf.); giving drink to the thirsty (10 pf.); clothing the naked (20 pf.); and caring for the sick (50 pf.).

1924.
369 **66** 3 pf. brown 20 15
370 5 pf. green 20 10
371 10 pf. red 30 10
372 20 pf. blue . . . . 1·50 15
373 30 pf. red . . . . 2·25 40
374 40 pf. olive . . . . 15·00 80
375 50 pf. orange . . . . 15·00 1·50

67 Rheinstein

1924.
376 **67** 1 m. green . . . . 15·00 2·00
377 – 2 m. blue (A) . . . . 23·00 2·00
458 – 2 m. blue (B) . . . . 35·00 17·00
378 – 3 m. red . . . . 23·00 5·50
379 – 5 m. green . . . . 32·00 15·00
DESIGNS: 2 m. Cologne. (A) inscr "Zwei Mark"; (B) inscr "ZWEI REICHSMARK"; 3 m. Marienburg; 5 m. Speyer Cathedral.

71 Dr. von Stephan 73 German Eagle and Rhine 74

1924. 50th Anniv of U.P.U.
380 **71** 10 pf. green 50 15
381 20 pf. blue . . . . . . 1·00 50
382 – 60 pf. brown . . . . . . 5·00 20
383 – 80 pf. deep green . . . . 10·00 1·40
DESIGNS: Nos. 382/3. Similar to Type **71** but with border changed.

1925. Rhineland Millenary.
384 **73** 5 pf. green 40 20
385 10 pf. red 80 20
386 20 pf. blue . . . . 4·50 90

1925. Munich Exhibition.
387 **74** 5 pf. green . . . . 3·00 6·50
388 10 pf. red . . . . 4·00 9·00

75 Arms of Prussia 76 78 Goethe

1925. Welfare Fund. Arms dated "1925".
389 **75** 5 pf.+5 pf. yell, blk & grn . . 35 85
390 – 10 pf.+10 pf. brn, bl & red . 1·00 1·00
391 – 20 pf.+20 pf. brn, grn & bl . 6·00 16·00
ARMS: 10 pf. Bavaria; 20 pf. Saxony.
See also Nos. 413/16a, 446/50 and 451/5.

1926. Air.
392 **76** 5 pf. green 65 50
393 10 pf. red 65 50
394 15 pf. purple . . . . . . 1·50 1·00
395 20 pf. blue . . . . . . 1·50 1·25
396 50 pf. orange . . . . . . 20·00 5·00
397 1 m. red and black . . . . 18·00 6·00
398 2 m. blue and black . . . 19·00 22·00
399 3 m. olive and black . . . 55·00 70·00

1926. Portraits.
400 **78** 3 pf. brown 40 15
402 – 5 pf. green (Schiller) . . . 90 15
404 – 8 pf. green (Beethoven) . . . 2·00 15
405 – 10 pf. red (Frederick the Great) 90 15
406 – 15 pf. red (Kant) . . . . . 2·00 20
407 – 20 pf. deep green (Beethoven) . . . . . . 18·00 1·00
408 **78** 25 pf. blue . . . . . . 3·25 50
409 – 30 pf. olive (Lessing) . . . 6·50 25
410 – 40 pf. violet (Leibniz) . . . 14·00 50
411 – 50 pf. brown (Bach) . . . 23·00 8·00
412 – 80 pf. brown (Durer) . . . 32·00 6·00

1926. Welfare Fund. As T **75**. Arms, dated "1926".
413 5 pf.+5 pf. multicoloured . . 1·00 1·10
414 10 pf.+10 pf. red, gold and rose . . . . 1·50 2·00
415 25 pf.+25 pf. bl, yell & red . . 12·00 22·00
416a 50 pf+50 pf. multicoloured . . 50·00 85·00
ARMS: 5 pf. Wurttemberg; 10 pf. Baden; 25 pf. Thuringia; 50 pf. Hesse.

79 Pres. von Hindenburg 81 Pres. Ebert 82 Pres. von Hindenburg

1927. Welfare Fund. President's 80th Birthday.
417 **79** 8 pf.+7 pf. green . . . . 65 1·40
418 15 pf.+15 pf. red . . . . 80 2·00
419 25 pf.+25 pf. blue . . . . 8·00 20·00
420 50 pf.+50 pf. brown . . . 12·00 24·00

1927. International Labour Office Session, Berlin. Optd **I.A.A. 10.–15. 10. 1927**.
421 – 8 pf. green (No. 404) . . . 20·00 60·00
422 – 15 pf. red (No. 406) . . . 20·00 60·00
423 **78** 25 pf. blue . . . . 20·00 60·00

1928.
424 **81** 3 pf. brown 20 15
425 **82** 4 pf. blue 40 20
426 5 pf. green 25 10
427 **81** 6 pf. olive 50 15
428 8 pf. green 15 10
429 10 pf. red . . . . 1·75 1·60
430 10 pf. purple . . . . . . 1·00 25
431 **82** 12 pf. orange . . . . . . 1·00 20
432 15 pf. red 45 10
433 **81** 20 pf. deep green . . . . . 6·00 2·75
434 20 pf. grey . . . . 7·00 30
435 **82** 25 pf. blue . . . . 10·00 40
436 **81** 30 pf. olive . . . . 6·00 25
437 **82** 40 pf. violet . . . . . . 17·00 40
438 **81** 45 pf. orange . . . . . . 10·00 3·00
439 **82** 50 pf. brown . . . . . . 10·00 1·25
440 **81** 60 pf. brown . . . . . . 13·00 2·75
441 **82** 80 pf. brown . . . . . . 28·00 6·00
442 80 pf. yellow . . . . . . 12·00 1·50

83 Airship "Graf Zeppelin"

1928. Air.
443 **83** 1 m. red . . . . 28·00 40·00
444 2 m. blue . . . . 45·00 55·00
445 4 m. brown . . . . 27·00 35·00

1928. Welfare Fund. As T **75**, dated "1928".
446 5 pf.+5 pf. green, red & yell . . 50 2·75
447 8 pf.+7 pf. multicoloured . . . 50 2·75
448 15 pf.+15 pf. red, bl & yellow . 1·40 2·75
449 25 pf.+25 pf. bl, red & yell . . 9·00 30·00
450 50 pf.+50 pf. multicoloured . . 45·00 80·00
ARMS: 5 pf. Hamburg; 8 pf. Mecklenburg-Schwerin; 15 pf. Oldenburg; 25 pf. Brunswick; 50 pf. Anhalt.

1929. Welfare Fund. As T **75**, dated "1929".
451 5 pf.+2 pf. green, yell & red . . 50 1·75
452 8 pf.+4 pf. yellow, red & grn . . 50 1·75
453 15 pf.+5 pf. yell, blk & red . . 60 1·75
454 25 pf.+10 pf. multicoloured . . 12·00 32·00
455 50 pf.+40 pf. yell, red & brn . . 45·00 85·00
ARMS: 5 pf. Bremen; 8 pf. Lippe; 15 pf. Lubeck; 25 pf. Mecklenburg-Strelitz; 50 pf. Schaumburg-Lippe.

1930. Air. "Graf Zeppelin" 1st S. American Flight. T **83** inscr "I. SUDAMERIKA FAHRT".
456 2 m. blue £170 £275
457a 4 m. brown £225 £275

1930. Evacuation of Rhineland by Allied Forces. Optd **30. JUNI 1930**.
459 **81** 8 pf. green 70 30
460 **82** 15 pf. red 80 50

86 Aachen 92 Heidelberg Castle

1930. Welfare Fund.
465 **86** 8 pf.+4 pf. green 40 60
466 – 15 pf.+5 pf. red 60 80
467 – 25 pf.+10 pf. blue . . . . 8·50 20·00
468 – 50 pf.+40 pf. brown . . . 23·00 50·00
DESIGNS: 15 pf. Berlin; 25 pf. Marienwerder; 50 pf. Wurzburg.

1931. Air. "Graf Zeppelin" Polar Flight. Optd **POLAR-FAHRT 1931**.
469 **83** 1 m. red . . . . 90·00 75·00
470 2 m. blue £140 £190
471 4 m. brown £300 £600

1931. Welfare Fund.
472 – 8 pf.+4 pf. green 40 80
473 – 15 pf.+5 pf. red 40 90
474 **92** 25 pf.+10 pf. blue . . . . 10·00 22·00
475 – 50 pf.+40 pf. brown . . . 30·00 70·00
DESIGNS—VERT: 8 pf. The Zwinger, Dresden; 15 pf. Town Hall, Breslau; 50 pf. The Holstentor, Lubeck.
See also Nos. 485/9.

1932. Welfare Fund. Nos. 472/3 surch.
476 6+4 pf. on 8 pf.+4 pf. green . 5·00 12·00
477 12+3 pf. on 15 pf.+5 pf. red . 6·00 14·00

94 President von Hindenburg 96 Frederick the Great (after A von Menzel)

1932. 85th Birthday of Pres. von Hindenburg.
478 **94** 4 pf. blue 60 25
496B 5 pf. green 10 20
480 12 pf. orange . . . . . . 5·00 20
481 15 pf. red . . . . 4·00 12·00
503B 25 pf. blue 35 20
483 40 pf. violet . . . . . . 17·00 2·00
484 50 pf. brown . . . . . . 9·00 12·00
See also Nos. 493/509 and 545/50.

1932. Welfare Fund. As T **92**.
485 4 pf.+2 pf. blue 30 60
486 6 pf.+4 pf. olive 30 60
487 12 pf.+3 pf. red 50 90
488 25 pf.+10 pf. blue . . . . . 8·00 18·00
489 40 pf.+40 pf. purple . . . . 28·00 60·00
CASTLES: 4 pf. Wartburg; 6 pf. Stolzenfels; 12 pf. Nuremberg; 25 pf. Lichtenstein; 40 pf. Marburg.

1933. Opening of Reichstag in Potsdam.
490 **96** 6 pf. green 50 90
491 12 pf. red 50 90
492 25 pf. blue . . . . 35·00 20·00

1933.
493B **94** 1 pf. black 30 20
494B 3 pf. brown 10 20
495B 4 pf. grey 10 20
497B 6 pf. green 10 20
498B 8 pf. orange 10 20
499B 10 pf. brown 30 20
500B 12 pf. red 20 20
501B 15 pf. red 30 20
502B 20 pf. blue 35 20
504B 30 pf. green 70 20
505B 40 pf. mauve 70 30
506B 50 pf. black and green . . . 1·00 35
507B 60 pf. black and red . . . 90 40
508B 80 pf. black and blue . . . 2·50 1·25
509B 100 pf. black & yellow . . . 5·50 75

1933. Air. "Graf Zeppelin" Chicago World Exhibition Flight. Optd **Chicagofahrt Weltausstellung 1933**.
510 **83** 1 m. red £425 £275
511 2 m. blue . . . . 48·00 £150
512 4 m. brown . . . . 45·00 £150

99 Tannhauser

1933. Welfare Fund. Wagner's Operas.
513 **99** 3 pf.+2 pf. brown . . . . 1·90 5·50
514 – 4 pf.+2 pf. blue . . . . 1·50 1·75
515 – 5 pf.+2 pf. green . . . . 3·75 6·50
516 – 6 pf.+4 pf. green . . . . 1·40 1·25
517 – 8 pf.+4 pf. orange . . . . 2·25 3·25
518 – 12 pf.+3 pf. red . . . . 2·25 1·75
519 – 20 pf.+10 pf. light blue . . . £150 £160
520 – 25 pf.+15 pf. blue . . . 34·00 35·00
521 – 40 pf.+35 pf. mauve . . . £125 £120
OPERAS: 4 pf. "The Flying Dutchman"; 5 pf. "Rhinegold"; 6 pf. "The Mastersingers"; 8 pf. "The Valkyries"; 12 pf. "Siegfried"; 20 pf. "Tristan and Isolde"; 25 pf. "Lohengrin"; 40 pf. "Parsifal".

1933. Welfare Fund. Stamps as 1924, issued together in sheets of four, each stamp optd **1923–1933**.
522 **65** 5+15 pf. green . . . . . 75·00 £225
523 – 10+30 pf. red . . . . . 75·00 £225
524 – 20+60 pf. blue . . . . . 75·00 £225
525 – 50 pf.+1.50 m. brown . . . 75·00 £225

100 Golden Eagle, Globe and Swastika 101 Count Zeppelin and "Graf Zeppelin"

1934. Air.
526A **100** 5 pf. green 75 40
527A 10 pf. red 75 55
528A 15 pf. blue . . . . . . 1·10 60
529A 20 pf. blue . . . . . . 2·00 1·40
530A 25 pf. brown . . . . . . 2·75 1·25
531A 40 pf. mauve . . . . . . 5·50 1·00
532A 50 pf. green . . . . . . 4·00 65
533A 80 pf. yellow . . . . . . 5·00 4·50
534A **100** 100 pf. black . . . . . 6·00 2·50
535A 2 m. grey and green . . . 16·00 20·00
536A **101** 3 m. grey and blue . . . 35·00 38·00
DESIGN—As Type **101**: 2 m. Otto Lilienthal and biplane glider.

Franz A. E. ...deritz 104 "Saar Ownership" 105 Nuremberg Castle

537 **934**. German Colonizers' Jubilee.
538 pf. brown & chocolate . . 2·75 6·50
539 brown and green . . 1·00 1·00
540 brown and red . . . 1·50 65
DESIG brown and blue . . 8·50 16·00
Peters; Gustav Nachtigal; 12 pf. Karl
ann von Wissmann.

541 **104** Saar Plebiscite.
542 – . . . . . . 3·00 30
DESIGN: . . . . . . 5·00 30
a swastika-e scribed "Saar" in rays from

543 **105** 6 pf.
544 12 pf Congress.
. . . 2·75 30
1934. Hindenb . . . 4·00 30

545 **94** 3 pf. bro
546 5 pf. gree ortrait with black
547 6 pf. green
548 8 pf. orang
549 12 pf. red 90 35
550 25 pf. blue . 90 50
1·40 30
2·50 30
·25 25
00 7·50

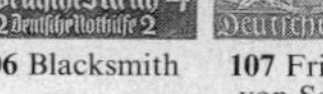
106 Blacksmith 107 Fried... von Schil...

1934. Welfare ...
551 – 3 pf.+2 pf. brown .
552 **106** 4 pf.+2 pf. black . .
553 – 5 pf.+2 pf. green . .
554 – 6 pf.+4 pf. green . .
555 – 8 pf.+4 pf. red . . .
556 – 12 pf.+3 pf. red . . . .
557 – 20 pf.+10 pf. green . .
558 – 25 pf.+15 pf. blue . . .
559 – 40 pf.+35 pf. lilac . . . .
DESIGNS: 3 pf. Merchant; 5 pf. Maso... 8 pf. Architect; 12 pf. Farmer; 20 pf. Sc... Sculptor 40 pf. Judge.

1934. 175th Birth Anniv of Schiller.
560 **107** 6 pf. green . . . . 2·75
561 12 pf. red . . . . 4·50

1935. Saar Restoration.
562 **108** 3 pf. brown . . . . 75 1·00
563 6 pf. green 75 30
564 12 pf. red . . . . 5·00 30
565 25 pf. blue . . . . 8·50 6·00

109 "Steel helmet" 110 "Victor's Crown"

1935. War Heroes' Day.
566 **109** 6 pf. green . . . . . . 1·00 1·60
567 12 pf. red . . . . 1·00 1·60

1935. Apprentices Vocational Contest.
568 **110** 6 pf. green . . . . . . 75 1·25
569 12 pf. red . . . . 1·00 1·25

111 Heinrich Schutz 112 Allenstein Castle

1935. Musicians' Anniversaries.
570 **111** 6 pf. green . . . . 1·25 20
571 – 12 pf. red (Bach) . . . . . 1·40 20
572 – 25 pf. blue (Handel) . . . . 2·00 80

1935. Int. Philatelic Exn., Konigsberg. In miniature sheets.
573 **112** 3 pf. brown . . . . . . 35·00 40·00
574 – 6 pf. green . . . . . . 35·00 40·00
575 – 12 pf. red . . . . . . 35·00 40·00
576 – 25 pf. blue . . . . . . 35·00 40·00
DESIGNS: 6 pf. Tannenberg Memorial; 12 pf. Konigsberg Castle; 25 pf. Heilsberg Castle.

113 "Adler", 1835

114 Trumpeter

1935. German Railway Cent. Locomotive types inscr "1835–1935".

577 **113** 6 pf. green . . . . 1·50 40
578 – 12 pf. red . . . . 1·50 1·50
579 – 25 pf. blue . . . . 12·00 1·75
580 – 40 pf. purple . . . . 14·25 pf.

DESIGNS: 12 pf. Class 03 steam train; 25 pf. Class 05 Diesel train "Flying Hamburger"; 40 pf. streamlined steam locomotive No. 00...

1935. World Jamboree of ...uth".

581 **114** 6 pf. green . . . . 1·50 2·25
582 15 pf. red . . . . 1·75 2·75

116 East Prussia

...berg Congress.

. . . . 80 40
. . . . 1·25 40

...und. Provincial Costumes.

58... brown 20 25
...f. blue . . . . 1·25 1·00
... pf. green 20 50
... pf. green 25 20
...4 pf. brown . . . . 2·00 1·25
... + 6 pf. red 20 20
... + 10 pf. brown . . . 5·00 5·00
...f. + 15 pf. blue . . . . 7·50 5·00
... pf. + 20 pf. grey . . . . 19·00 20·00
... pf. + 35 pf. mauve . . . 14·00 14·00

...ES: 4 pf. Silesia; 5 pf. Rhineland; 6 pf. ...xony; 8 pf. Kurmark; 12 pf. Black Forest; ...esse; 25 pf. Upper Bavaria; 30 pf. Friesland; ...ranconia.

117 S.A. Man and Feldherrnhalle, Munich

118 Skating

1935. 12th Anniv of 1st Hitler Putsch.

595 **117** 3 pf. brown . . . . 1·00 60
596 12 pf. red . . . . 1·50 50

1935. Winter Olympic Games, Garmisch-Partenkirchen.

597 **118** 6 pf. + 4 pf. green 70 50
598 – 12 pf. + 6 pf. red . . . . 1·50 75
599 – 25 pf. + 15 pf. blue . . . . 7·00 8·75

DESIGNS: 12 pf. Ski jumping; 25 pf. Bobsleighing.

119 Heinkel He 70 Blitz

120 Gottlieb Daimler

1936. 10th Anniv of Lufthansa Airways.

600 **119** 40 pf. blue . . . . 7·00 1·50

1936. Berlin Motor Show. 50th Anniv of Invention of First Motor Car.

601 **120** 6 pf. green 50 40
602 12 pf. red (Carl Benz) . . . 75 60

121 Airship "Hindenburg"

122 Otto von Guericke

1936. Air.

603 **121** 50 pf. blue . . . . 15·00 60
604 75 pf. green . . . . 20·00 60

1936. 250th Death Anniv of Otto von Guericke (scientist).

605 **122** 6 pf. green 30 45

123 Gymnastics

124 Symbolical of Local Government

1936. Summer Olympic Games, Berlin.

606 **123** 3 pf. + 2 pf. brown 20 30
607 – 4 pf. + 3 pf. blue 20 65
608 – 6 pf. + 4 pf. green 30 15
609 – 8 pf. + 4 pf. red . . . . 4·50 1·40
610 – 12 pf. + 6 pf. red 40 15
611 – 15 pf. + 10 pf. red . . . . 8·50 3·75
612 – 25 pf. + 15 pf. blue . . . . 11·00 7·50
613 – 40 pf. + 35 pf. violet . . . . 26·00 15·00

DESIGNS: 4 pf. Diver; 6 pf. Footballer; 8 pf. Javelin thrower; 12 pf. Olympic torchbearer; 15 pf. Fencer; 25 pf. Double scullers; 40 pf. Show jumper.

1936. 6th Int. Local Government Congress.

614 **124** 3 pf. brown 25 20
615 5 pf. green 30 20
616 12 pf. red 40 30
617 25 pf. blue . . . . 1·00 85

125 "Brown Ribbon" Race

126 "Leisure Time"

1936. "Brown Ribbon of Germany". Single stamp in miniature sheet.

MS618 **125** 42 pf. brown . . . . . . 7·50 16·00

1936. Int. Recreational Congress, Hamburg.

619 **126** 6 pf. green 50 60
620 15 pf. red 75 80

127 Saluting the Swastika

128 Luitpoldhain Heroes Memorial, Nuremberg

1936. Nuremberg Congress.

621 **127** 6 pf. green 50 40
622 12 pf. red 75 60

1936. Winter Relief Fund.

623 3 pf. + 2 pf. brown 15 20
624 – 4 pf. + 3 pf. black 30 70
625 **128** 5 pf. + 3 pf. green 20 20
626 – 6 pf. + 4 pf. green 20 20
627 – 8 pf. + 4 pf. brown . . . . 1·00 1·75
628 – 12 pf. + 6 pf. red 20 20
629 – 15 pf. + 10 pf. brown . . . 3·00 5·50
630 – 25 pf. + 15 pf. blue . . . 2·75 3·25
631 – 40 pf. + 35 pf. mauve . . . 3·75 6·00

DESIGNS: 3 pf. Munich frontier road; 4 pf. Air Ministry, Berlin; 6 pf. Bridge over River Saale; 8 pf. Deutschlandhalle. Berlin; 12 pf. Alpine road; 15 pf. Fuhrerhaus. Munich; 25 pf. Bridge over River Mangfall; 40 pf. German Art Museum. Munich.

129 R(eichs) L(uftschutz) B(und) = Civil Defence Union

1937. 4th Anniv of Civil Defence Union.

632 **129** 3 pf. brown 20 30
633 6 pf. green 40 25
634 12 pf. red 60 60

131 Fishing Smacks

132 Hitler Youth

1937. Winter Relief Fund.

639 – 3 pf. + 2 pf. brown 20 30
640 – 4 pf. + 3 pf. black . . . . 1·00 1·00
641 **131** 5 pf. + 3 pf. green 20 30
642 – 6 pf. + 4 pf. green 20 45
643 – 8 pf. + 4 pf. orange . . . . 1·40 1·50
644 – 12 pf. + 6 pf. red 30 25
645 – 15 pf. + 10 pf. brown . . . 6·00 4·25
646 – 25 pf. + 15 pf. blue . . . 9·50 4·25
647 – 40 pf. + 35 pf. purple . . . 7·50 9·00

DESIGNS: 3 pf. Lifeboat "Bremen"; 4 pf. Light-ship "Burgermeister Oswald"; 6 pf. Liner "Wilhelm Gustloff"; 8 pf. Barque "Padua"; 12 pf. Liner "Tannenberg"; 15 pf. Train ferry "Schwerin"; 25 pf. Liner "Hamburg"; 40 pf. Liner "Europa".

1938. Hitler Culture Fund. 5th Anniv of Hitler's Leadership.

648 **132** 6 pf. + 4 pf. green . . . . 85 1·00
649 12 pf. + 8 pf. red . . . . 1·40 1·60

133 "Unity"

134 Adolf Hitler

1938. Austrian Plebiscite.

650 **133** 6 pf. green 15 40

1938. Hitler's Culture Fund and 49th Birthday.

652 **134** 12 pf. + 38 pf. red . . . . 2·50 2·50

See also No. 660.

135 Breslau Cathedral

136 Airship Gondola and "Graf Zeppelin"

1938. 16th German Sports Tournament, Breslau. Inscr as in T 135.

653 **135** 3 pf. brown 25 30
654 – 6 pf. green 40 30
655 – 12 pf. red 60 30
656 – 15 pf. brown . . . . 90 1·00

DESIGNS: 6 pf. Hermann Goering Stadium; 12 pf. Breslau Town Hall; 15 pf. Centenary Hall.

1938. Air. Birth Cent of Count Zeppelin.

657 – 25 pf. blue . . . . 4·25 1·00
658 **136** 50 pf. green . . . . 5·75 1·00

DESIGN: 25 pf. Count Zeppelin in primitive airship gondola and airship LZ-5.

137 Horsewoman

138 Saarpfalz Gautheater, Saarbrucken

1938. "Brown Ribbon of Germany".

659 **137** 42 pf. + 108 pf. brown . . 32·00 40·00

1938. Nuremberg Congress and Hitler's Culture Fund. As No. 652, but inscr "Reichsparteitag 1938".

660 **134** 6 pf. + 19 pf. green . . . . 3·00 3·75

1938. Opening of Gautheater and Hitler's Culture Fund.

661 **138** 6 pf. + 4 pf. green . . . . 1·50 2·00
662 12 pf. + 8 pf. red . . . . 2·25 3·00

139 Forchtenstein Castle, Burgenland

140 Sudeten Miner and Wife

1938. Winter Relief.

663 **139** 3 pf. + 2 pf. brown 20 30
664 – 4 pf. + 3 pf. blue . . . . 2·40 1·75
665 – 5 pf. + 3 pf. green 15 40
666 – 6 pf. + 4 pf. green 15 20
667 – 8 pf. + 4 pf. red . . . . 2·00 1·75
668 – 12 pf. + 6 pf. red 25 30
669 – 15 pf. + 10 pf. red . . . . 5·00 5·75
670 – 25 pf. + 15 pf. blue . . . . 4·00 5·75
671 – 40 pf. + 35 pf. mauve . . . 10·00 11·00

DESIGNS: 4 pf. Flexenstrasse; 5 pf. Zell am See; 6 pf. Grossglockner; 8 pf. Augstein Castle, Wachau; 12 pf. Wien (Prince Eugene Statue, Vienna); 15 pf. Erzberg, Steiermark; 25 pf. Hall-in-Tirol; 40 pf. Braunau.

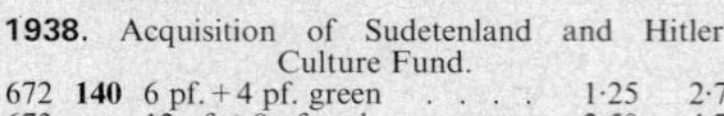

1938. Acquisition of Sudetenland and Hitler's Culture Fund.

672 **140** 6 pf. + 4 pf. green . . . . 1·25 2·75
673 12 pf. + 8 pf. red . . . . 2·50 4·75

141 Racing Cars

142 Eagle and Laurel Wreath

1939. Int. Motor Show, Berlin, and Hitler's Culture Fund. Inscr "Internationale Automobil—und Motorrad—Ausstellung Berlin 1939".

674 – 6 pf. + 4 pf. green . . . . 3·75 3·50
675 **141** 12 pf. + 8 pf. red . . . . 4·00 3·75
676 – 25 pf. + 10 pf. blue . . . . 11·00 6·50

DESIGNS: 6 pf. Early Benz and Daimler cars; 25 pf. Volkswagen car.

1939. Apprentices' Vocational Contest.

677 **142** 6 pf. green . . . . 1·75 3·25
678 12 pf. red . . . . 2·00 3·25

143 Adolf Hitler in Braunau

144 Horticultural Exhibition Entrance and Arms of Stuttgart

1939. Hitler's 50th Birthday and Culture Fund.

679 **143** 12 pf. + 38 pf. red . . . . 2·50 5·50

1939. Stuttgart Horticultural Exhibition and Hitler's Culture Fund.

680 **144** 6 pf. + 4 pf. green . . . . 1·50 2·25
681 15 pf. + 5 pf. red . . . . 1·50 2·25

145 Adolf Hitler Speaking

147 "Investment" and Jockey

1939. National Labour Day and Hitler's Culture Fund.

682 **145** 6 pf. + 19 pf. brown . . . 2·75 5·75

See also No. 689.

1939. Nurburgring Races and Hitler's Culture Fund. Nos. 674/6 optd **Nurburgring-Rennen**.

683 – 6 pf. + 4 pf. green . . . . 30·00 32·00
684 **141** 12 pf. + 8 pf. red . . . . 30·00 32·00
685 – 25 pf. + 10 pf. blue . . . . 30·00 32·00

1939. 70th Anniv of German Derby.

686 **147** 25 pf. + 50 pf. blue . . . . 20·00 20·00

148 Training Thoroughbred Horses

149 "Young Venetian Woman" after Durer

1939. "Brown Ribbon of Germany" and Hitler's Culture Fund.

687 **148** 42 pf. + 108 pf. brown . . 17·00 30·00

1939. German Art Day.

688 **149** 6 pf. + 19 pf. green . . . . 5·50 9·00

1939. Nuremberg Congress and Hitler's Culture Fund. As T 145, but inscr "REICHS-/PARTEITAG/1939".

689 6 pf. + 19 pf. brown . . . . . 3·75 9·00

150 Mechanics at Work and Play

151 St. Mary's Church, Danzig

1939. Postal Employees' and Hitler's Culture Funds. Inscr "Kameradschaftsblock der Deutschen Reichspost".

690 – 3 pf. + 2 pf. brown . . . . 4·00 6·00
691 – 4 pf. + 3 pf. blue . . . . 4·00 6·00
692 **150** 5 pf. + 3 pf. green . . . . 1·00 1·50
693 – 6 pf. + 4 pf. green . . . . 1·00 1·50
694 – 8 pf. + 4 pf. orange . . . . 1·00 1·75
695 – 10 pf. + 5 pf. brown . . . . 1·00 2·25
696 – 12 pf. + 6 pf. red . . . . 1·00 2·25
697 – 15 pf. + 10 pf. red . . . . 1·00 2·50
698 – 16 pf. + 10 pf. green . . . 1·25 2·25
699 – 20 pf. + 10 pf. blue . . . . 1·00 2·25
700 – 24 pf. + 10 pf. olive . . . 3·50 4·00
701 – 25 pf. + 15 pf. blue . . . . 3·50 5·00

DESIGNS: 3 pf. Postal employees' rally; 4 pf. Review in Vienna; 6 pf. Youths on parade; 8 pf. Flag bearers; 10 pf. Distributing prizes; 12 pf. Motor race; 15 pf. Women athletes; 16 pf. Postal police; 20 pf. Glider workshop; 24 pf. Mail coach; 25 pf. Sanatorium, Konigstein.

See also Nos. 761/6 and 876/81.

1939. Occupation of Danzig. Inscr "DANZIG IST DEUTSCH".

702	**151**	6 pf. green	30	50
703	–	12 pf. red (Crane Gate)	40	60

1939. Stamps of Danzig surch **Deutsches Reich** and new values.

704	**28**	Rpf. on 3 pf. brown	1·00	2·25
705		4 Rpf. on 35 pf. blue	1·00	2·25
706		Rpf. on 5 pf. orange	1·00	2·25
707		Rpf. on 8 pf. green	1·75	4·00
708		Rpf. on 10 pf. green	2·00	4·00
709		12 Rpf. on 7 pf. green	1·25	2·25
710		Rpf. on 15 pf. red	6·00	12·00
711		Rpf. on 20 pf. grey	3·50	8·00
712		Rpf. on 25 pf. red	6·00	12·00
713		Rpf. on 30 pf. purple	1·75	4·50
714		Rpf. on 40 pf. blue	1·90	5·50
715		Rpf. on 50 pf. red and blue	4·00	8·00
716	**42**	1 Rm on 1 g. blk & orge	14·00	28·00
717		2 Rm. on 2 g. black and red (No. 206)	20·00	45·00

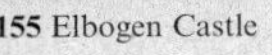
155 Elbogen Castle

156 Leipzig Library and Gutenberg

1939. Winter Relief Fund.

718	**155**	3 pf. + 2 pf. brown	15	30
719	–	4 pf. + 3 pf. black	2·00	2·25
720	–	5 pf. + 3 pf. green	20	40
721	–	6 pf. + 4 pf. green	20	30
722	–	8 pf. + 4 pf. red	2·00	1·40
723	–	12 pf. + 6 pf. red	25	30
724	–	15 pf. + 10 pf. brown	3·75	6·00
725	–	25 pf. + 15 pf. blue	2·75	5·75
726	–	40 pf. + 35 pf. purple	4·00	7·50

DESIGNS: 4 pf. Drachenfels; 5 pf. Goslar Castle; 6 pf. Clocktower, Graz; 8 pf. The Romer, Frankfurt; 12 pf. City Hall, Klagenfurt; 15 pf. Ruins of Schreckenstein Castle; 25 pf. Salzburg Fortress; 40 pf. Hohentwiel Castle.

1940. Leipzig Fair.

727	**156**	3 pf. brown	25	60
728	–	6 pf. green	30	60
729	–	12 pf. red	30	60
730	–	25 pf. blue	60	1·25

DESIGNS: 6 pf. Augustusplatz; 12 pf. Old Town Hall; 25 pf. View of Fair.

157 Courtyard of Chancellery, Berlin

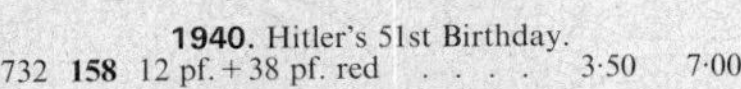
158 Hitler and Child

1940. 2nd Berlin Philatelic Exhibition.

731	**157**	24 pf. + 76 pf. green	7·50	16·00

1940. Hitler's 51st Birthday.

732	**158**	12 pf. + 38 pf. red	3·50	7·00

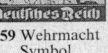

159 Wehrmacht Symbol

160 Horseman

1940. National Fete Day and Hitler's Culture Fund.

733	**159**	6 pf. + 4 pf. green	40	85

1940. Hamburg Derby and Hitler's Culture Fund.

734	**160**	25 pf. + 100 pf. blue	4·50	12·00

161 Chariot

162 Malmedy

1940. Hitler's Culture Fund and "Brown Ribbon" Race.

735	**161**	42 pf. + 108 pf. brown	18·00	30·00

1940. Eupen and Malmedy reincorporated in Germany, and Hitler's Culture Fund. Inscr "Eupen-Malmedy wieder deutsch".

736	**162**	6 pf. + 4 pf. green	80	2·75
737	–	12 pf. + 8 pf. red	80	2·75

DESIGNS: 12 pf. View of Eupen.

163 Heligoland

164 Artushof, Danzig

1940. 50th Anniv of Cession of Heligoland to Germany and Hitler's Culture Fund.

738	**163**	6 pf. + 94 pf. red & green	4·50	8·50

1940. Winter Relief Fund.

739	**164**	3 pf. + 2 pf. brown	15	30
740	–	4 pf. + 3 pf. blue	1·00	1·00
741	–	5 pf. + 3 pf. green	20	50
742	–	6 pf. + 4 pf. green	25	15
743	–	8 pf. + 4 pf. orange	1·50	1·00
744	–	12 pf. + 6 pf. red	20	15
745	–	15 pf. + 10 pf. brown	1·50	2·75
746	–	25 pf. + 15 pf. blue	2·00	3·00
747	–	40 pf. + 35 pf. purple	3·00	6·00

DESIGNS: 4 pf. Town Hall, Thorn; 5 pf. Kaub Castle; 6 pf. City Theatre, Posen; 8 pf. Heidelberg Castle; 12 pf. Porta Nigra, Trier; 15 pf. New Theatre, Prague; 25 pf. Town Hall, Bremen; 40 pf. Town Hall, Munster.

165 Emil von Behring (bacteriologist)

166 Postilion and Globe

1940. 50th Anniv of Development of Diphtheria Antitoxin.

748	**165**	6 pf. + 4 pf. green	80	1·40
749		25 pf. + 10 pf. blue	1·25	3·00

1941. Stamp Day.

750	**166**	6 pf. + 24 pf. green	75	2·00

167 Mussolini and Hitler

168 House of Nations, Leipzig

1941. Hitler's Culture Fund.

751	**167**	12 pf. + 38 pf. red	1·50	3·50

1941. Leipzig Fair. Buildings. Inscr "REICHSMESSE LEIPZIG 1941".

752	**168**	3 pf. brown	30	60
753	–	6 pf. green	30	60
754	–	12 pf. red	40	90
755	–	25 pf. blue	1·00	1·25

DESIGNS: 6 pf. Cloth Hall; 12 pf. Exhibition Building; 25 pf. Railway Station.

169 Dancer

170 Adolf Hitler

1941. Vienna Fair.

756	**169**	3 pf. brown	25	60
757	–	6 pf. green	25	60
758	–	12 pf. red	35	70
759	–	25 pf. blue	80	2·00

DESIGNS: 6 pf. Arms and Exhibition Building; 12 pf. Allegory and Municipal Theatre; 25 pf. Prince Eugene's Equestrian Monument.

1941. Hitler's 52nd Birthday and Culture Fund.

760	**170**	12 pf. + 38 pf. red	2·00	3·00

1941. Postal Employees' and Hitler's Culture Funds. Inscr "Kameradschaftsblock der Deutschen Reichspost" as Nos. 693/4, 696 and 698/700, but premium values and colours changed.

761	6 pf. + 9 pf. green	80	1·40
762	8 pf. + 12 pf. red	80	1·25
763	12 pf. + 18 pf. red	80	1·25
764	16 pf. + 24 pf. black	1·50	3·50
765	20 pf. + 30 pf. blue	1·50	3·50
766	24 pf. + 36 pf. violet	4·00	12·50

171 Racehorse

172 Two Amazons

1941. 72nd Anniv of Hamburg Derby.

767	**171**	25 pf. + 100 pf. blue	4·50	7·50

1941. "Brown Ribbon of Germany".

768	**172**	42 pf. + 108 pf. brown	3·00	5·75

173 Adolf Hitler

174 Brandenburg Gate, Berlin

1941.

769	**173**	1 pf. grey	10	15
770		3 pf. brown	10	15
771		4 pf. slate	10	15
772		5 pf. green	10	15
773		6 pf. violet	10	15
774		8 pf. red	10	15
775		10 pf. brown	15	30
776		12 pf. red	10	30
779		15 pf. lake	10	20
780		16 pf. green	20	1·25
781		20 pf. blue	10	20
782		24 pf. brown	10	1·25
783		25 pf. blue	10	20
784		30 pf. olive	10	20
785		40 pf. mauve	15	20
786		50 pf. green	15	20
787		60 pf. brown	15	20
788		80 pf. blue	15	20

Nos. 783/8 are larger (21½ × 26 mm)

1941. Berlin Grand Prix and Hitler's Culture Fund.

789	**174**	25 pf. + 50 pf. blue	3·00	6·50

175 Belvedere Palace, Vienna

176 Belvedere Gardens, Vienna

1941. Vienna Fair and Hitler's Culture Fund.

790	**175**	12 pf. + 8 pf. red	75	2·50
791	**176**	15 pf. + 10 pf. violet	1·00	2·75

177 Marburg

178 Veldes

1941. Annexation of Northern Slovenia, and Hitler's Culture Fund.

792	**177**	3 pf. + 7 pf. brown	80	1·25
793	**178**	6 pf. + 9 pf. violet	70	1·60
794	–	12 pf. + 13 pf. red	80	1·75
795	–	25 pf. + 15 pf. blue	2·00	3·50

DESIGNS: 12 pf. Pettau; 25 pf. Triglav.

179 Mozart

180 Philatelist

1941. 150th Death Anniv of Mozart and Hitler's Culture Fund.

796	**179**	6 pf. + 4 pf. purple	30	50

1942. Stamp Day and Hitler's Culture Fund.

797	**180**	6 pf. + 24 pf. violet	55	2·50

181 Symbolical of Heroism

182 Adolf Hitler

1942. Heroes' Remembrance Day and Hitler's Culture Fund.

798	**181**	12 pf. + 38 pf. slate	40	1·50

1942.

799	**182**	1 m. green	20	75
800		2 m. violet	70	1·50
801		3 m. red	70	1·75
802		5 m. blue	1·25	4·00

183 Adolf Hitler

184 Jockey and Three-year-old Horse

1942. Hitler's 53rd Birthday and Culture Fund.

803	**183**	12 pf. + 38 pf. red	3·00	6·00

1942. Hamburg Derby and Hitler's Culture Fund.

804	**184**	25 pf. + 100 pf. blue	6·00	14·00

185 Equine Trio

186 Cream Jug and Loving Cup

1942. "Brown Ribbon of Germany" and Hitler's Culture Fund.

805	**185**	42 pf. + 108 pf. brown	2·25	7·00

1942. 10th Anniv of National Goldsmiths' Institution.

806	**186**	6 pf. + 4 pf. red	30	1·00
807		12 pf. + 88 pf. green	50	2·00

187 Badge of Armed S.A.

188 Peter Henlein

1942. S.A. Military Training Month.

808	**187**	6 pf. violet	20	90

1942. 400th Death Anniv of Henlein (inventor of the watch).

809	**188**	6 pf. + 24 pf. violet	50	1·25

189 Mounted Postilion

1942. European Postal Congress, Vienna.

810	–	3 pf. + 7 pf. blue	30	1·75
811	–	6 pf. + 14 pf. brown & bl	40	1·75
812	**189**	12 pf. + 38 pf. brn & red	75	2·75

DESIGNS—HORIZ: 3 pf. Postilion and map of Europe. VERT: 6 pf. Mounted postilion and globe.

1942. Signing of European Postal Union Agreement. Nos. 810/2 optd **19.Okt.1942.**

813	–	3 pf. + 7 pf. blue	75	2·75
814	–	6 pf. + 14 pf. brn & bl	75	2·75
815	**189**	12 pf. + 38 pf. brn & red	1·00	5·50

191 Mail Coach

192 Brandenburg Gate and Torchlight Parade

1943. Stamp Day and Hitler's Culture Fund.

816	**191**	6 pf. + 24 pf. brn, yell & bl	25	80

1943. 10th Anniv of Third Reich.

817	**192**	54 pf. + 96 pf. red	35	2·00

193

194 Machine Gunners

1943. Philatelic Cancellation Premium.
818 **193** 3 pf. + 2 pf. bistre 20 60

1943. Armed Forces' and Heroes' Day.
819 – 3 pf. + 2 pf. brown . . . . 50 1·25
820 **194** 4 pf. + 3 pf. brown 40 60
821 – 5 pf. + 4 pf. green 40 70
822 – 6 pf. + 9 pf. violet 50 70
823 – 8 pf. + 7 pf. red 50 70
824 – 12 pf. + 8 pf. red 50 80
825 – 15 pf. + 10 pf. purple . . . 50 80
826 – 20 pf. + 14 pf. blue . . . 60 1·00
827 – 25 pf. + 15 pf. blue . . . 70 1·00
828 – 30 pf. + 30 pf. green . . . 75 1·40
829 – 40 pf. + 40 pf. purple . . . 75 2·00
830 – 50 pf. + 50 pf. green . . . 1·00 3·00
DESIGNS: 3 pf. U-boat Type VIIA; 5 pf. Armed motor cyclists; 6 pf. Wireless operators; 8 pf. Engineers making pontoon; 12 pf. Grenade thrower; 15 pf. Heavy artillery; 20 pf. Anti-aircraft gunners; 25 pf. Junkers Ju 87B "Stuka" dive bombers; 30 pf. Parachutists; 40 pf. Tank; 50 pf. "S-22" (motor torpedo-boat).

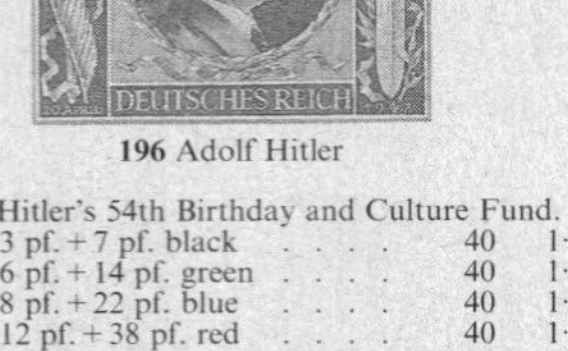

195 Hitler Youth

1943. Youth Dedication Day.
831 **195** 6 pf. + 4 pf. green 25 90

196 Adolf Hitler

1943. Hitler's 54th Birthday and Culture Fund.
832 **196** 3 pf. + 7 pf. black . . . . 40 1·00
833 6 pf. + 14 pf. green . . . . 40 1·00
834 8 pf. + 22 pf. blue . . . . 40 1·00
835 12 pf. + 38 pf. red . . . . 40 1·00
836 24 pf. + 76 pf. purple . . . 1·00 3·00
837 40 pf. + 160 pf. olive . . . 1·00 3·50

197 Attestation **198** Huntsman

1943. Labour Corps.
838 **197** 3 pf. + 7 pf. brown 15 50
839 – 5 pf. + 10 pf. green 15 50
840 – 6 pf. + 14 pf. blue 15 65
841 – 12 pf. + 18 pf. red . . . . 30 1·25
DESIGNS: 5 pf. Harvester sharpening scythe; 6 pf. Labourer wielding sledge-hammer; 12 pf. "Pick and shovel fatigue".

1943. "Brown Ribbon of Germany".
842 **198** 42 pf. + 108 pf. brown . . 30 1·25

199 Birthplace of Peter Rosegger **200** Peter Rosegger

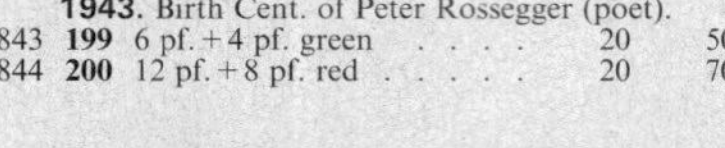
1943. Birth Cent. of Peter Rossegger (poet).
843 **199** 6 pf. + 4 pf. green 20 50
844 **200** 12 pf. + 8 pf. red 20 70

201 Racehorse **202** Mother and Children

1943. Grand Prix, Vienna.
845 **201** 6 pf. + 4 pf. violet . . . . 20 1·00
846 12 pf. + 88 pf. red . . . . 20 1·00

1943. 10th Anniv of Winter Relief Fund.
847 **202** 12 pf. + 38 pf. red . . . . 25 1·00

203 St George and the Dragon **204** Lubeck

1943. 11th Anniv of National Goldsmiths' Institution.
848 **203** 6 pf. + 4 pf. green 20 60
849 12 pf. + 88 pf. purple . . . 20 1·00

1943. 800th Anniv of Lubeck.
850 **204** 12 pf. + 8 pf. red 20 75

205

1943. 20th Anniv of Munich Rising.
851 **205** 24 pf. + 26 pf. red 20 80

206 Dr. Robert Koch **207** Adolf Hitler

1944. Birth Centenary of Dr. Robert Koch (bacteriologist).
852 **206** 12 pf. + 38 pf. sepia 25 80

1944. 11th Anniv of Third Reich.
853 **207** 54 pf. + 96 pf. brown . . . 25 1·25

208 Focke Wulf Condor over Tempelhof Airport **209** Dornier Do-26 Flying Boat

1944. 25th Anniv of Air Mail Services.
854 **208** 6 pf. + 4 pf. green 20 60
855 **209** 12 pf. + 8 pf. purple . . . 20 90
856 – 42 pf. + 108 pf. blue . . . 30 2·25
DESIGN—VERT: 42 pf. Junkers Ju 90B airplane seen from above.

210 Day Nursery **211** "Mothers' Help"

1944. 10th Anniv of "Mother and Child" Organization.
857 **210** 3 pf. + 2 pf. brown 15 35
858 **211** 6 pf. + 4 pf. green 15 35
859 – 12 pf. + 8 pf. red 20 35
860 – 15 pf. + 10 pf. purple . . . 25 65
DESIGNS: 12 pf. Child auscultation; 15 pf. Mothers at convalescent home.

212 Landing Craft **213** Fulda Monument

1944. Armed Forces' and Heroes' Day.
861 **212** 3 pf. + 2 pf. brown . . . . 50 1·25
862 – 4 pf. + 3 pf. blue 30 60
863 – 5 pf. + 3 pf. green 30 60
864 – 6 pf. + 4 pf. violet 30 60
865 – 8 pf. + 4 pf. red 30 60
866 – 10 pf. + 5 pf. brown . . . 30 60
867 – 12 pf. + 6 pf. red 30 60
868 – 15 pf. + 10 pf. purple . . . 30 60
869 – 16 pf. + 10 pf. green . . . 40 1·25
870 – 20 pf. + 10 pf. blue . . . 45 1·25
871 – 24 pf. + 10 pf. brown . . . 70 1·25
872 – 25 pf. + 15 pf. blue . . . 1·00 1·25
873 – 30 pf. + 20 pf. olive . . . 1·00 3·75
DESIGNS: 4 pf. Caterpillar tricar; 5 pf. Parachutists; 6 pf. Submarine officer; 8 pf. Mortar-firing party; 10 pf. Searchlight unit; 12 pf. Machine gunners; 15 pf. Tank; 16 pf. "S-128" (motor torpedo-boat); 20 pf. Arado Ar 196A seaplane; 24 pf. Armoured train; 25 pf. Rocket projectiles; 30 pf. Alpine trooper.

1944. 1200th Anniv of Fulda.
874 **213** 12 pf. + 38 pf. brown . . . 25 85

214 Adolf Hitler **215** Postwoman

1944. Hitler's 55th Birthday.
875 **214** 54 pf. + 96 pf. red . . . . 40 1·60

1944. Postal Employees' and Hitler's Culture Funds. Inscr "Kameradschaftsblock der Deutschen Reichspost".
876 **215** 6 pf. + 9 pf. blue 15 35
877 – 8 pf. + 12 pf. grey 15 35
878 – 12 pf. + 18 pf. mauve . . . 15 55
879 – 16 pf. + 24 pf. green . . . 15 60
880 – 20 pf. + 30 pf. blue . . . 25 1·25
881 – 24 pf. + 36 pf. violet . . . 25 1·40
DESIGNS: As Type **150**–8 pf. Mail coach; 16 pf. Motor-car race; 20 pf. Postal police march; 24 pf. Glider workshop. As Type **215**–12 pf. The Field Post on Eastern Front.

216 Girl Worker **217** Labourer

1944. Labour Corps.
882 **216** 6 pf. + 4 pf. green 10 55
883 **217** 12 pf. + 8 pf. red 10 65

218 Riflemen **219** Duke Albrecht

1944. 7th Innsbruck Shooting Competition.
884 **218** 6 pf. + 4 pf. green 10 55
885 12 pf. + 8 pf. red 35 65

1944. 400th Anniv of Albert University, Konigsberg.
886 **219** 6 pf. + 4 pf. green . . . . 25 1·25

220 Racehorse and Foal

1944. "Brown Ribbon of Germany".
887 **220** 42 pf. + 108 pf. brown . . 30 1·40

221 Racehorse and Laurel Wreath **222** Chambered Nautilus Beaker

1944. Vienna Grand Prix.
888 **221** 6 pf. + 4 pf. green . . . . 10 1·25
889 12 pf. + 88 pf. red . . . . 15 1·50

1944. National Goldsmiths' Institution.
890 **222** 6 pf. + 4 pf. green . . . . 10 1·25
891 12 pf. + 88 pf. red . . . . 20 1·50

223 Posthorn **224** Eagle and Dragon

1944. Stamp Day.
892 **223** 6 pf. + 24 pf. green . . . . 25 1·25

1944. 21st Anniv of Munich Rising.
893 **224** 12 pf. + 8 pf. red . . . . 25 1·25

225 Adolf Hitler **226** Count Anton Gunther

1944.
894 **225** 42 pf. green . . . . . . 15 1·25

1945. 600th Anniv of Oldenburg.
895 **226** 6 pf. + 14 pf. purple . . . 25 1·40

227 "Home Guard" **228** S.S. Troopers

1945. Mobilization of "Home Guard".
896 **227** 12 pf. + 8 pf. red . . . . 40 1·75

1945. 12th Anniv of Third Reich.
897 **228** 12 pf. + 38 pf. red . . . . 12·00 35·00
898 – 12 pf. + 38 pf. red . . . . 12·00 40·00
DESIGN: No. 898, S.A. man with torch.

For Nos. 899 onwards see section B of Allied Occupation.

MILITARY FIELDPOST STAMPS

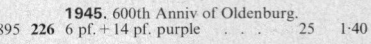

M 184 Junkers Ju 52/3m **M 185**

1942. Air. No value indicated. Perf. or roul.
M804 **M 184** (–) blue 20 20

1942. Parcel Post. Size 28 × 23 mm. No value indicated. Perf. or roul.
M805 **M 185** (–) brown 20 40

Nos. M804/5 also exist overprinted **INSELPOST** in various types for use in Crete and the Aegean Islands and there are various other local fieldpost issues.

1944. Christmas Parcel Post. Size 22½ × 18 mm. No value indicated. Perf.
M895 **M 185** (–) green . . . . . . 50 1·50

1944. For 2 kilo parcels. No value indicated. No. 785 optd **FELDPOST 2kg.**
M896 **173** (–) on 40 pf. mauve . . . 50 1·60

NEWSPAPER STAMPS

N 156 Newspaper Messenger and Globe

1939.
N727 **N 156** 5 pf. green . . . . . 50 2·75
N728 10 pf. brown . . . . . 50 2·75

OFFICIAL STAMPS

O 23 **O 24**

1903.
O82 **O 23** 2 pf. grey . . . . . . 1·25 6·00
O83 3 pf. brown . . . . . . 1·25 6·00
O84 5 pf. green 30 30
O85 10 pf. red 30 30
O86 20 pf. blue 30 30
O87 25 pf. black and red on yellow 30 30
O88 40 pf. black and red . . . 30 1·50
O89 50 pf. black and purple on buff . . . . . . 40 1·75

1905.

O90	**O 24**	2 pf. grey	60·00	75·00
O91		3 pf. brown	6·00	6·00
O92		5 pf. green	4·00	5·00
O93		10 pf. red	1·00	2·25
O94		20 pf. blue	1·40	2·25
O95		25 pf. black and red on yellow	35·00	40·00

O 31 O 32

1920. Numeral designs as Types **O 31** and **O 32**.

O117	5 pf. green	30	2·50
O118	10 pf. red	60	1·25
O119	15 pf. brown	20	1·00
O120	20 pf. blue	20	70
O121	30 pf. orange on pink	15	80
O122	50 pf. violet on pink	35	75
O123	1 m. red on pink	8·00	4·50

1920. Similar designs but without figures "21".

O124	5 pf. green	1·00	10·00
O125	10 pf. red	10	40
O126	10 pf. orange	35	£350
O127	15 pf. purple	10	65
O128	20 pf. blue	10	50
O129	30 pf. orange on pink	10	50
O130	40 pf. red	10	50
O131	50 pf. violet on pink	10	50
O132	60 pf. brown	10	1·00
O133	1 m. red on pink	10	50
O134	1 m. 25 blue on yellow	10	90
O135a	2 m. blue	10	50
O136	5 m. brown on yellow	10	90

1920. Official stamps of Bavaria optd **Deutsches Reich.**

O137	**O 31**	5 pf. green	10	2·00
O138		10 pf. orange	10	1·50
O139		15 pf. red	10	1·50
O140		20 pf. purple	10	1·10
O141		30 pf. blue	10	50
O142		40 pf. brown	10	50
O143	**O 32**	50 pf. red	10	50
O144		60 pf. green	10	50
O145		70 pf. violet	1·60	2·75
O146		75 pf. red	35	1·10
O147		80 pf. blue	10	85
O148		90 pf. olive	1·40	6·75
O149	**O 33**	1 m. brown	10	45
O150		1¼ m. green	10	45
O151		1½ m. red	10	45
O152		2½ m. blue	15	85
O153		3 m. red	15	95
O154		5 m. black	8·50	30·00

1920. Municipal Service stamps of Wurttemberg optd **Deutsches Reich.**

O155	**M 5**	5 pf. green	3·50	7·00
O156		10 pf. red	2·00	4·25
O157		15 pf. violet	2·00	4·25
O158		20 pf. blue	3·50	10·00
O159		50 pf. purple	5·00	14·00

1920. Official stamps of Wurttemberg optd **Deutsches Reich.**

O160	**O 5**	5 pf. green	25	2·50
O161		10 pf. red	10	1·25
O162		15 pf. purple	10	1·00
O163		20 pf. blue	10	1·00
O164		30 pf. black & orange	10	1·00
O165		40 pf. black and red	15	1·00
O166		50 pf. purple	15	1·60
O167		1 m. black and grey	20	3·25

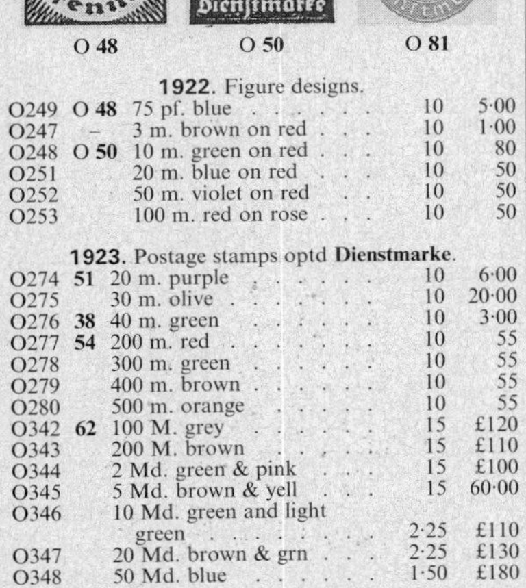

O 48 O 50 O 81

1922. Figure designs.

O249	**O 48**	75 pf. blue	10	5·00
O247	–	3 m. brown on red	10	1·00
O248	**O 50**	10 m. green on red	10	80
O251		20 m. blue on red	10	50
O252		50 m. violet on red	10	50
O253		100 m. red on rose	10	50

1923. Postage stamps optd **Dienstmarke.**

O274	**51**	20 m. purple	10	6·00
O275		30 m. olive	10	20·00
O276	**38**	40 m. green	10	3·00
O277	**54**	200 m. red	10	55
O278		300 m. green	10	55
O279		400 m. brown	10	55
O280		500 m. orange	10	55
O342	**62**	100 M. grey	15	£120
O343		200 M. brown	15	£110
O344		2 Md. green & pink	15	£100
O345		5 Md. brown & yell	15	60·00
O346		10 Md. green and light green	2·25	£110
O347		20 Md. brown & grn	2·25	£130
O348		50 Md. blue	1·50	£180

1923. Official stamps of 1920 and 1922 surch, **Tausend** or **Millionen** and figure.

O312	–	5 T. on 5 m. brown on yellow	10	2·50
O313	–	20 T. on 30 pf. orge on rose (No. O129)	10	2·50
O317	**O 50**	75 T. on 50 m. vio on rose	10	2·50
O314	–	100 T. on 15 pf. pur	10	2·50
O315	–	250 T. on 10 pf. red (No. O125)	10	2·50
O318	–	400 T. on 15 pf. pur	10	32·00
O319	–	800 T. on 30 pf. orge on rose (No. O129)	10	2·75
O320	**O 48**	1 M. on 75 pf. blue	10	42·00
O321	–	2 M. on 10 pf. red (No. O125)	10	3·00
O322	**O 50**	5 M. on 100 m. red on rose	10	5·00

1923. Nos. 352/7 optd **Dienstmarke.**

O358	**64**	3 pf. brown	15	20
O359		5 pf. green	15	20
O360		10 pf. red	25	10
O361		20 pf. blue	55	20
O362		50 pf. orange	55	65
O363		100 pf. purple	3·00	5·50

1924. Optd **Dienstmarke.**

O376	**66**	3 pf. brown	30	60
O377		5 pf. green	30	20
O378		10 pf. red	30	20
O379		20 pf. blue	30	20
O380		30 pf. red	60	40
O381		40 pf. olive	60	40
O382		50 pf. orange	3·00	1·75
O384	**72**	60 pf. brown	1·50	2·50
O385		80 pf. grey	7·75	27·00

1927.

O424	**O 81**	3 pf. brown	30	10
O425		4 pf. blue	25	15
O427		5 pf. green	15	10
O428		6 pf. green	25	10
O429		8 pf. green	15	10
O430		10 pf. red	8·00	6·00
O432		10 pf. mauve	30	25
O433		10 pf. brown	2·00	3·25
O434		12 pf. orange	30	10
O436		15 pf. red	30	10
O437		20 pf. green	3·00	1·50
O438		20 pf. grey	50	30
O439		30 pf. green	85	15
O440		40 pf. violet	85	20
O441		60 pf. brown	1·00	80

O 100

1934.

O526	**O 100**	3 pf. brown	15	30
O527		4 pf. blue	15	30
O528		5 pf. green	15	30
O529		6 pf. green	15	30
O812		6 pf. violet	15	30
O530		8 pf. red	30	30
O531		10 pf. brown	25	30
O532		12 pf. red	65	30
O533		15 pf. red	65	2·25
O534		20 pf. blue	20	35
O818		30 pf. green	20	60
O819		40 pf. mauve	20	60
O537		50 pf. yellow	30	35
O820		50 pf. green	2·00	5·50

SPECIAL STAMPS FOR USE BY OFFICIALS OF THE NATIONAL SOCIALIST GERMAN WORKERS' PARTY.

P 132 Party Badge

1938.

O798	**P 132**	1 pf. black	50	1·25
O799		3 pf. brown	20	30
O800		4 pf. blue	20	30
O801		5 pf. green	20	1·50
O652		6 pf. green	60	75
O802		6 pf. violet	20	30
O803		8 pf. red	20	30
O804		12 pf. red	25	30
O655		16 pf. grey	1·00	14·00
O805		16 pf. blue	3·00	6·00
O656		24 pf. green	2·00	6·00
O806		24 pf. brown	45	1·00
O807		30 pf. green	45	1·50
O808		40 pf. mauve	70	2·00

II. ALLIED OCCUPATION

The defeat of Germany in May 1945 resulted in the division of the country into four zones of occupation (British, American, French and Russian), while Berlin was placed under joint allied control. Allied Military Post Stamps came into use in the British and American zones, the French issued special stamps in their zone and in the Russian zone the first issues were made by local administrations.

The territory occupied by the Anglo-American and French Zones subsequently became the German Federal Republic (West Germany) which was set up in September 1949. By the Nine Power Agreement of 3 October 1954, the occupation of West Germany was ended and full sovereignty was granted to the German Federal Government as from 5 May 1955 (see Section III).

The territory in the Russian Zone became the German Democratic Republic (East Germany) which was set up on 7 October 1949 (see Section V).

Separate issues for the Western Sectors of Berlin came into being in 1948 (see Section IV). The Russian Zone issues inscribed "STADT BERLIN" were for use in the Russian sector of the city and Brandenburg and these were superseded first by the General Issues of the Russian Zone and then by the stamps of East Germany.

100 pfennige = 1 Reichsmark.
21.6.48. 100 pfennige = 1 Deutsche Mark (West).
24.6.48. 100 pfennige = 1 Deutsche Mark (East).

A. Allied Military Post (British and American Zones)

A 1

1945.

A16	**A 1**	1 pf. black	20	50
A 1		3 pf. violet	20	20
A 2		4 pf. grey	20	20
A 3		5 pf. green	20	20
A 4		6 pf. yellow	20	20
A 5		8 pf. orange	20	20
A 6		10 pf. brown	20	20
A 7		12 pf. purple	20	20
A 8		15 pf. red	20	20
A25		16 pf. green	20	20
A26		20 pf. blue	20	20
A27		24 pf. brown	30	20
A 9		25 pf. blue	20	20
A29		30 pf. olive	25	60
A30		40 pf. mauve	25	50
A31		42 pf. green	25	50
A32		50 pf. slate	25	60
A33		60 pf. plum	25	1·50
A34		80 pf. blue	22·00	30·00
A35		1 m. green	3·50	7·50

Values 30 pf. to 80 pf. are size 22 × 25 mm. and 1 m. size 25 × 29½ mm.

Nos. A36 etc continue in Section C.

B. American, British and Russian Zones 1946–48

From February 1946 to June 1948 these zones used the same stamps (Nos. 899/956). It had been intended that they should be used throughout all four zones but until the creation of the German Federal Republic, in September 1949, the French Zone always had its own stamps, while after the revaluation of the currency in June 1948 separate stamps were again issued for the Russian Zone.

229 Numeral 231 1160: Leipzig obtains Charter

1946.

899	**229**	1 pf. black	10	60
900		2 pf. black	10	10
901		3 pf. brown	10	60
902		4 pf. blue	10	70
903		5 pf. green	10	10
904		6 pf. violet	10	10
905		8 pf. red	10	10
906		10 pf. brown	10	10
907		12 pf. red	10	10
908		12 pf. grey	10	10
909		15 pf. red	15	1·00
910		15 pf. green	10	10
911		16 pf. green	10	10
912		20 pf. blue	10	10
913		24 pf. brown	15	10
914		25 pf. blue	10	1·25
915		25 pf. orange	10	50
916		30 pf. green	10	25
917		40 pf. purple	10	25
918		42 pf. green	1·25	7·50
919		45 pf. red	10	30
920		50 pf. green	10	20
921		60 pf. red	15	30
922		75 pf. blue	20	30
923		80 pf. blue	15	30
924		84 pf. green	10	30
925		1 m. green (24 × 30 mm)	15	60

1947. Leipzig Spring Fair. Inscr "LEIPZIGER MESSE 1947".

926	**231**	24 pf. + 26 pf. brown	25	1·00
927	–	60 pf. + 40 pf. blue	35	1·50

DESIGN: 60 pf. 1268: Foreign merchants at Leipzig Fair.

See also Nos. 951/4.

233 Gardener

237 "Dove of Peace"

1947.

928	**233**	2 pf. black	10	40
929		6 pf. violet	10	15
930	A	8 pf. red	10	15
931		10 pf. green	10	30
932	B	12 pf. grey	10	15
933	**233**	15 pf. brown	20	1·25
934	C	16 pf. green	10	15
935	A	20 pf. blue	10	20
936	C	24 pf. brown	10	15
937	**233**	25 pf. orange	10	25
938	B	30 pf. red	30	50
939	A	40 pf. mauve	10	30
940	C	50 pf. blue	30	60
941	B	60 pf. red	10	50
942		60 pf. brown	15	50
943		80 pf. blue	10	30
944	C	84 pf. green	30	30
945	**237**	1 m. green	10	30
946		2 m. violet	15	50
947		3 m. lake	15	1·10
948		5 m. blue	1·25	2·00

DESIGNS: A, Sower; B, Labourer; C, Bricklayer and reaper.

238 Dr. von Stephan

1947. 50th Death Anniv of Von Stephan.

949	**238**	24 pf. brown	15	35
950		75 pf. blue	20	55

1947. Leipzig Autumn Fair. As T **231**.

951	12 pf. red	20	60
952	75 pf. blue	20	80

DESIGNS: 12 pf. 1497: Maximilian I granting Charter; 75 pf. 1365: Assessment and Collection of Ground Rents.

1948. Leipzig Spring Fair. As T **231** but dated "1948".

953	50 pf. blue	20	65
954	84 pf. green	20	85

DESIGNS: 50 pf. 1388: At the customs barrier; 84 pf. 1433: Bringing merchandise.

For similar types, dated "1948", "1949" or "1950", but with premium values, see Nos. R31/2, R51/2, R60/1 of Russian Zone and E7/8 of East Germany.

239 Weighing Goods

1948. Hanover Trade Fair.

955	**239**	24 pf. red	10	55
956		50 pf. blue	20	75

C. British and American Zones 1948–49

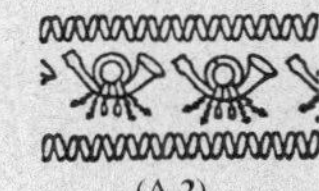

(A 2)

1948. Currency Reform. Optd I with Type A **2** or II with multiple posthorns over whole stamp.

(a) On Pictorial issue of 1947, Nos. 928/44.

		I		II	
A36	2 pf. black	10	10	1·00	1·40
A37	6 pf. violet	10	10	1·25	1·40
A38	8 pf. red	10	10	1·00	1·25
A39	10 pf. green	20	20	15	15
A40	12 pf. grey	20	10	1·25	1·25
A41	15 pf. brown	8·00	13·00	30	35
A42	16 pf. green	1·25	2·00	30	20
A43	20 pf. blue	60	60	30	20
A44	24 pf. brown	15	10	75	1·00
A45	25 pf. orange	40	40	8·50	13·00
A46	30 pf. red	2·25	4·00	30	40
A47	40 pf. mauve	80	90	40	30
A48	50 pf. blue	80	80	50	25
A49	60 pf. brown	80	80	50	25
A50	60 pf. red	55·00	£225	2·25	3·00
A51	80 pf. blue	1·40	2·00	45	25
A52	84 pf. green	4·25	6·00	1·00	1·40

(b) On Numeral issue of 1946, Nos. 900 to 924.

			I		II	
A53	**229**	2 pf. blk	6·00	20·00	22·00	55·00
A54		8 pf. red	14·00	50·00	42·00	95·00
A55		10 pf. brn	1·00	3·50	35·00	95·00
A56		12 pf. red	10·00	35·00	14·00	42·00
A57		12 pf. grey	£160	£450	£300	£800
A58		15 pf. red	11·00	35·00	16·00	35·00
A59		15 pf. grn	3·50	12·00	90	6·00
A60		16 pf. grn	50·00	£150	48·00	£130
A61		24 pf. brn	95·00	£170	55·00	£170
A62		25 pf. blue	18·00	48·00	18·00	45·00
A63		25 pf. orge	1·75	6·50	48·00	£140
A64		30 pf. olive	1·50	4·75	1·75	3·25
A65		40 pf. pur	70·00	£170	65·00	£190
A66		45 pf. red	2·40	7·00	3·00	9·00
A67		50 pf. grn	2·10	4·00	3·00	9·00
A68		75 pf. blue	6·00	12·00	3·50	8·00
A69		84 pf. grn	6·00	20·00	3·00	11·00

A 4 Crowned Head

A 7 Cologne Cathedral

1948. 700th Anniv of Cologne Cathedral and Restoration Fund.

A70	A 4	6 pf. + 4 pf. brown	60	70
A71	–	12 pf. + 8 pf. blue	1·40	1·50
A72	–	24 pf. + 16 pf. red	3·25	3·50
A73	A 7	50 pf. + 50 pf. blue	7·50	8·00

DESIGNS—As Type A **4**. 12 pf. The Three Wise Men; 24 pf. Cologne Cathedral.

A **9** The Romer, Frankfurt-on-Main

A **10** Frauenkirche, Munich

A **13** Holstentor Lubeck

1948. Various designs.

A 74	A 9	2 pf. black	10	10
A 75	A 10	4 pf. brown	20	10
A 76a	A	5 pf. blue	20	10
A 77	A 10	6 pf. brown	15	40
A 78		6 pf. orange	30	10
A 79	A 9	8 pf. yellow	35	40
A 80	A 10	8 pf. slate	30	10
A 81a	A	10 pf. green	35	10
A 82	A 10	15 pf. orange	2·00	3·00
A 83	A 9	15 pf. violet	1·25	10
A 84		16 pf. green	40	60
A 85		20 pf. blue	75	1·25
A 86	B	20 pf. red	65	10
A 87		24 pf. red	25	25
A 88	A	25 pf. red	1·00	10
A 89	B	30 pf. blue	1·40	10
A 90	A 10	30 pf. red	2·75	3·25
A 91	A	40 pf. mauve	2·00	10
A 92	B	50 pf. blue	1·00	1·50
A 93	A 10	50 pf. green	2·00	10
A 94	A	60 pf. purple	2·75	10
A 95	B	80 pf. mauve	3·00	10
A 96	A 10	84 pf. purple	2·75	3·75
A 97	A	90 pf. mauve	3·00	10
A 98	A 13	1 Dm. green	29·00	60
A 99		2 Dm. violet	25·00	60
A100		3 Dm. mauve	28·00	2·75
A101		5 Dm. blue	45·00	18·00

DESIGNS—As Type A **9/10**: A, Cologne Cathedral; B, Brandenburg Gate.

A **15** Brandenburg Gate, Berlin

1948. Aid to Berlin.

A106	A 15	10 pf. + 5 pf. green	5·50	6·00
A107		20 pf. + 10 pf. red	5·50	6·00

A **16** Herman Hillebrant Wedigh (after Holbein)

A **17** Racing Cyclists

1949. Hanover Trade Fair.

A108	A 16	10 pf. green	3·00	3·00
A109		20 pf. red	3·00	3·00
A110		30 pf. blue	4·00	4·00

1949. Trans-Germany Cycle Race.

A112	A 17	10 pf. + 5 pf. green	5·00	5·00
A113		20 pf. + 10 pf. brown	14·00	16·00

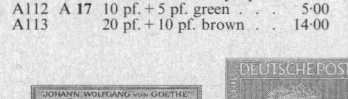

A **18** Goethe in Italy

A **19** Goethe

1949. Birth Bicentenary of Goethe (poet).

A114	A 18	10 pf. + 5 pf. green	4·00	7·50
A115	A 19	20 pf. + 10 pf. red	5·00	8·00
A116	–	30 pf. + 15 pf. blue	18·00	15·00

DESIGN—VERT: 30 pf. Profile portrait.

OBLIGATORY TAX STAMPS

AT 14

1948. Aid for Berlin. Perf of imperf.

T1103	AT 14	2 pf. blue	20	10

The Anglo-American Zones, together with the French Zone, became the Federal German Republic (West Germany) in September, 1949.

D. French Zone.

(a) General Issues, 1945–46.

F **1** Arms of the Palatinate

F **2** Goethe

1945. (a) Arms.

F 1	F 1	1 pf. green, blk & yell	10	25
F 2	–	3 pf. yellow, blk & red	10	10
F 3	–	5 pf. black, yell & brn	10	10
F 4	–	8 pf. red, yellow & brn	10	10
F 5	F 1	10 pf. green, brn & yell	5·00	16·00
F 6	–	12 pf. yellow, blk & red	10	10
F 7	–	15 pf. blue, blk & red	10	10
F 8	–	20 pf. black, yell & red	10	20
F 9	–	24 pf. blue, blk & red	10	10
F10	–	30 pf. red, yell & blk	10	20

ARMS: 3, 12 pf. Rhineland; 5, 20 pf. Wurttemberg; 8, 30 pf. Baden; 15, 24 pf. Saar.

(b) Poets.

F11	F 2	1 m. brown	1·50	6·00
F12	–	2 m. blue (Schiller)	1·00	10·00
F13	–	5 m. red (Heine)	1·25	10·00

(b) Baden, 1947–49.

FB **1** J. P. Hebel

FB **2** Rastatt Castle

FB **3** Hollental Black Forest

FB **4** Freiburg Cathedral

1947. Inscr "BADEN".

FB 1	FB 1	2 pf. grey	10	15
FB 2	–	3 pf. brown	10	15
FB 3	–	10 pf. blue	10	15
FB 4	FB 1	12 pf. green	10	15
FB 5	–	15 pf. violet	10	30
FB 6	FB 2	16 pf. green	10	90
FB 7	–	20 pf. blue	10	20
FB 8	FB 2	24 pf. red	10	25
FB 9	–	45 pf. mauve	10	30
FB10	FB 1	60 pf. orange	10	20
FB11	–	75 pf. blue	10	60
FB12	FB 3	84 pf. green	15	1·00
FB13	FB 4	1 m. brown	15	30

DESIGNS—18 × 23 mm: 3, 15, 45 pf. Badensian girl and yachts; 10, 20, 75 pf. Hans Baldung Grien.

1948. Currency Reform. As 1947 issue.

(a) Value in "PF."

FB14	FB 1	2 pf. orange	25	35
FB15	–	6 pf. brown	25	15
FB16	–	10 pf. brown	45	15
FB17	FB 1	12 pf. red	45	15
FB18	–	15 pf. blue	50	35
FB19	FB 2	24 pf. green	70	10
FB20	–	30 pf. mauve	1·40	85
FB21	–	50 pf. blue	1·40	15

(b) New currency. Value in "D.PF" or "D.M." (= "Deutschpfennig" or "Deutschmark").

FB22	–	8 dpf. green	70	1·25
FB23	FB 2	16 dpf. violet	1·00	1·75
FB24	–	20 dpf. brown	4·50	1·10
FB25	FB 1	60 dpf. grey	4·00	20
FB26	FB 3	84 dpf. red	7·00	3·00
FB27	FB 4	1 dm. blue	7·00	2·75

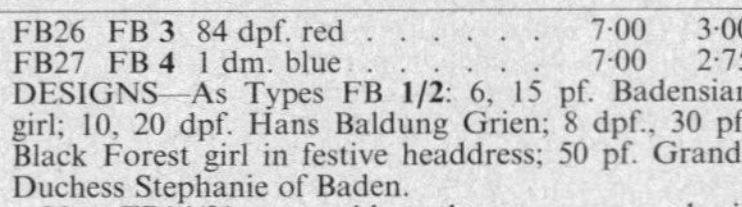

DESIGNS—As Types FB **1/2**: 6, 15 pf. Badensian girl; 10, 20 dpf. Hans Baldung Grien; 8 dpf., 30 pf. Black Forest girl in festive headdress; 50 pf. Grand-Duchess Stephanie of Baden.

Nos. FB14/21 were sold on the new currency basis though not inscribed "D.PF."

1948. As 1947 issue, but "PF" omitted.

FB28	FB 1	2 pf. orange	70	50
FB29	–	4 pf. violet	35	35
FB30	–	5 pf. blue	1·00	70
FB31	–	6 pf. brown	24·00	12·00
FB32	–	8 pf. brown	1·00	80
FB33	–	10 pf. green	1·00	15
FB34	–	20 pf. mauve	1·75	25
FB35	–	40 pf. brown	55·00	60·00
FB36	FB 1	80 pf. red	11·00	7·00
FB37	FB 3	90 pf. red	65·00	80·00

DESIGNS—18 × 23 mm: 4 pf., 40 pf. Rastatt; 5 pf., 6 pf. Badensian girl and yachts; 8 pf. Black Forest girl in festive headdress; 10 pf., 20 pf. Portrait of Hans Baldung Grien.

FB **5** Cornhouse, Freiburg

FB **6** Arms of Baden

1949. Freiburg Rebuilding Fund.

FB38	FB 5	4 pf. + 16 pf. violet	7·50	30·00
FB39	–	10 pf. + 20 pf. green	11·00	30·00
FB40	–	20 pf. + 30 pf. red	14·00	30·00
FB41	–	30 pf. + 50 pf. blue	19·00	40·00

DESIGNS: 10 pf. Freiburg Cathedral; 20 pf. Trumpeting angel, Freiburg; 30 pf. "Fischbrunnen," Freiburg.

1949. Red Cross Fund.

FB42	FB 6	10 pf. + 20 pf. green	18·00	75·00
FB43		20 pf. + 40 pf. lilac	18·00	75·00
FB44		30 pf. + 60 pf. blue	18·00	75·00
FB45		40 pf. + 80 pf. grey	18·00	75·00

FB **7** Seehof Hotel, Constance

1949. Engineers' Congress, Constance.

FB46	FB 7	30 pf. blue	24·00	65·00

FB **8** Goethe

FB **9** Carl Schurz and Revolutionary Scene

FB **10** Conradin Kreutzer

1949. Birth Bicentenary of Goethe (poet).

FB47	FB 8	10 pf. + 5 pf. green	8·50	17·00
FB48	–	20 pf. + 10 pf. red	8·50	17·00
FB49	–	30 pf. + 15 pf. blue	10·00	35·00

1949. Cent of Rastatt Insurrection.

FB50	FB 9	10 pf. + 5 pf. green	11·00	24·00
FB51		20 pf. + 10 pf. mauve	11·00	24·00
FB52		30 pf. + 15 pf. blue	11·00	24·00

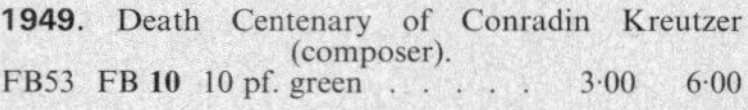

1949. Death Centenary of Conradin Kreutzer (composer).

FB53	FB 10	10 pf. green	3·00	6·00

FB **11** 1849 Mail Coach

FB **12** Posthorn and Globe

1949. German Stamp Centenary.

FB54	FB 11	10 pf. green	5·50	10·00
FB55	–	20 pf. brown	5·50	10·00

DESIGN: 20 pf. Postal motor-coach with trailer and Douglas DC-4 airliner.

1949. 75th Anniv of U.P.U.

FB56	FB 12	20 pf. red	5·50	10·00
FB57		30 pf. blue	5·50	8·25

(c) Rhineland Palatinate, 1947–49.

FR **1** "Porta Nigra" Trier

FR **2** Karl Marx

FR **4** Statue of Charlemagne

FR **5** St. Martin

1947. Inscr "RHEINLAND-PFALZ".

FR 1	–	2 pf. grey	10	15
FR 2	–	3 pf. brown	10	15
FR 3	–	10 pf. blue	10	15
FR 4	FR 1	12 pf. green	10	10
FR 5	FR 2	15 pf. violet	10	15
FR 6	–	16 pf. green	10	20
FR 7	–	20 pf. blue	10	10
FR 8	–	24 pf. red	10	10
FR 9	–	30 pf. mauve	10	80
FR10	–	45 pf. mauve	10	20
FR11	–	50 pf. blue	10	90
FR12	–	60 pf. orange	10	15
FR13	–	75 pf. blue	10	30
FR14	–	84 pf. green	10	70
FR15	FR 4	1 m. brown	10	30

DESIGNS—SMALL SIZE: 2 pf., 60 pf. Beethoven's death mask; 3 pf. Baron von Ketteler, Bishop of Mainz; 10 pf. Girl vintager; 16 pf. Rocks at Arnweiler; 20 pf. Palatinate village house; 24 pf. Worms Cathedral; 30 pf., 75 pf. Gutenberg (printer); 45 pf., 50 pf. Mainz Cathedral. LARGE SIZE—HORIZ: 84 pf. Gutenfels Castle and Rhine.

1948. Currency Reform. As 1947 issue.

(a) Value in "PF."

FR16	–	2 pf. orange	25	40
FR17	–	6 pf. brown	25	30
FR18	–	10 pf. brown	60	10
FR19	FR 1	12 pf. red	50	10
FR20	FR 2	15 pf. blue	1·10	70
FR21	–	24 pf. green	65	10
FR22	–	30 pf. mauve	1·10	30
FR23	–	50 pf. blue	1·60	30

(b) New currency. Value in "D.PF." or "D.M." (= "Deutschpfennig" or "Deutschmark").

FR24	FR 1	8 dpf. green	75	1·50
FR25	–	16 dpf. violet	80	1·25
FR26	–	20 dpf. brown	2·50	40
FR27	–	60 dpf. grey	11·00	30
FR28	–	84 dpf. red	5·00	4·00
FR29	FR 4	1 dm. blue	5·50	4·00

DESIGNS—SMALL SIZE: 6 pf. Baron von Ketteler; 30 pf. Mainz Cathedral; 50 pf. Gutenberg (printer). Others as 1947 issue.

Nos. FR16/23 were sold on the new currency basis though not inscribed "D.PF.".

1948. Ludwigshafen Explosion Relief Fund.

FR30	FR 5	20 pf. + 30 pf. mauve	1·40	20·00
FR31	–	30 pf. + 50 pf. blue	1·40	20·00

DESIGN: 30 pf. St. Christopher.

1948. Inscr "RHEINLAND-PFALZ". As 1947 issue, but "PF" omitted.

FR32	–	2 pf. orange	30	35
FR33	–	4 pf. violet	40	20
FR34	FR 2	5 pf. blue	75	50
FR35	–	6 pf. brown	28·00	14·00
FR36	FR 1	8 pf. red	75·00	£150
FR37	–	10 pf. green	80	15
FR38	–	20 pf. mauve	85	15
FR39	–	40 pf. brown	2·25	3·00
FR40	FR 1	80 pf. red	3·00	4·50
FR41	–	90 pf. red	5·00	14·00

DESIGNS—SMALL SIZE: 4 pf. Rocks at Arnweiler; 40 pf. Worms Cathedral. LARGE SIZE—HORIZ: 90 pf. Gutenfels Castle and Rhine. Others as 1947–48 issues.

1949. Red Cross Fund. As Type FB **6** of Baden, but Arms of Rhineland and inscr "RHEINLAND/PFALZ".

FR42	10 pf. + 20 pf. green	20·00	85·00
FR43	20 pf. + 40 pf. lilac	20·00	85·00
FR44	30 pf. + 60 pf. blue	20·00	85·00
FR45	40 pf. + 80 pf. grey	20·00	85·00

1949. Birth Bicent. of Goethe. As Nos. FB47/9 of Baden.

FR46	10 pf. + 5 pf. green	6·00	16·00
FR47	20 pf. + 10 pf. mauve	6·00	16·00
FR48	30 pf. + 15 pf. blue	12·00	38·00

1949. Centenary of German Postage Stamp. As Nos. FB54/5 of Baden.

FR49	10 pf. green	8·75	19·00
FR50	20 pf. brown	8·75	19·00

1949. 75th Anniv of U.P.U. As Nos. FB56/7 of Baden.

FR51	20 pf. red	5·00	10·00
FR52	30 pf. blue	5·00	9·00

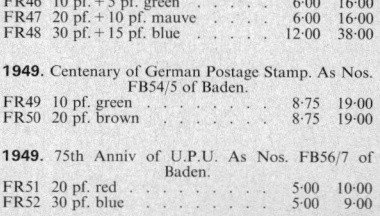

(d) Saar, 1945–7.

The Saar District, from 1945 to 1947 part of the French Zone, also had its own stamps, but as it was in a different political category, we list its stamps for convenience of reference all together under **SAAR**.

(e) Wurttemberg, 1947–49.

FW **1** Fr. von Schiller — FW **2** Bebenhausen Monastery — FW **3** Lichtenstein Castle

1947. Inscr "WURTTEMBERG".

No.	Type	Description	Unused	Used
FW 1	FW **1**	2 pf. grey	10	10
FW 2	–	3 pf. brown	10	10
FW 3	–	10 pf. blue	10	10
FW 4	FW **1**	12 pf. green	10	10
FW 5	–	15 pf. violet	10	20
FW 6	FW **2**	16 pf. green	10	50
FW 7	–	20 pf. blue	10	50
FW 8	FW **2**	24 pf. red	10	10
FW 9	–	45 pf. mauve	15	30
FW10	FW **1**	60 pf. orange	15	45
FW11	–	75 pf. blue	15	50
FW12	FW **3**	84 pf. green	20	60
FW13	–	1 m. brown	20	45

DESIGNS—SMALL SIZE: 3 pf., 15 pf., 45 pf. Holderlin (poet); 10 pf., 20 pf., 75 pf. Wangen Gate. LARGE SIZE—VERT: 1 m. Zwiefalten Monastery Church.

1948. Currency Reform. As 1947 issue.

(a) Value in "PF."

No.	Type	Description	Unused	Used
FW14	FW **1**	2 pf. orange	20	55
FW15	–	6 pf. brown	20	15
FW16	–	10 pf. brown	25	30
FW17	FW **1**	12 pf. red	25	10
FW18	–	15 pf. blue	70	35
FW19	FW **2**	24 pf. green	80	10
FW20	–	30 pf. mauve	1·25	30
FW21	–	50 pf. blue	2·00	30

(b) Value in "D.PF" (= Deutsch Pfennig) or "D.M." (= Deutsch Mark).

No.	Type	Description	Unused	Used
FW22	–	8 dpf. green	1·00	2·00
FW23	FW **2**	16 dpf. violet	90	1·75
FW24	–	20 dpf. brown	1·90	1·10
FW25	FW **1**	60 dpf. grey	13·00	30
FW26	FW **3**	84 dpf. red	4·25	4·00
FW27	–	1 dm. blue	4·25	4·00

DESIGNS—SMALL SIZE: 6 pf., 15 pf. Fr. Holderlin (poet); 8 dpf., 30 pf. Waldsee Castle; 50 pf. Ludwig Uhland (poet). Others as 1947 issue.

Nos. FW14/21 were sold on the new currency basis though not inscribed "D.PF."

1948. Inscr "WURTTEMBERG". As 1947 issue, but "PF" omitted.

No.	Type	Description	Unused	Used
FW28	FW **1**	2 pf. orange	1·25	40
FW29	FW **2**	4 pf. violet	1·00	30
FW30	–	5 pf. blue	5·00	1·75
FW31	–	6 pf. brown	8·00	4·25
FW32	–	8 pf. red	7·00	1·75
FW33	–	10 pf. green	7·00	10
FW34	–	20 pf. mauve	7·00	10
FW35	FW **2**	40 pf. brown	23·00	40·00
FW36	FW **1**	80 pf. red	50·00	40·00
FW37	FW **3**	90 pf. red	70·00	£100

DESIGNS—SMALL SIZE: 5 pf., 6 pf. Holderlin. Others as 1947 and 1948 issues.

FW **4** Isny and Coat of Arms — FW **5** Gustav Werner

1949. Ski Championships (Northern Combination) at Isny/Allgau.

No.	Type	Description	Unused	Used
FW38	FW **4**	10 pf. + 4 pf. green	5·00	14·00
FW39	–	20 pf. + 6 pf. lake	5·00	14·00

DESIGN: 20 pf. Skier and view of Isny.

1949. Red Cross Fund. As Type FB **6** of Baden, but Arms of Wurttemberg and inscr "WURTTEMBERG".

No.	Description	Unused	Used
FW40	10 pf. + 20 pf. green	28·00	85·00
FW41	20 pf. + 40 pf. lilac	28·00	85·00
FW42	30 pf. + 60 pf. blue	28·00	85·00
FW43	40 pf. + 80 pf. grey	28·00	85·00

1949. Birth Bicent. of Goethe. As Nos. FB47/9 of Baden.

No.	Description	Unused	Used
FW44	10 pf. + 5 pf. green	7·50	14·00
FW45	20 pf. + 10 pf. mauve	8·00	22·00
FW46	30 pf. + 15 pf. blue	11·00	30·00

1949. Centenary of Christian Institution "Zum Bruderhaus".

No.	Type	Description	Unused	Used
FW47	FW **5**	10 pf. + 5 pf. green	5·00	12·00
FW48		20 pf. + 10 pf. purple	5·00	12·00

1949. German Stamp Centenary. As Nos. FB54/5 of Baden.

No.	Description	Unused	Used
FW49	10 pf. green	6·00	10·00
FW50	20 pf. brown	6·00	13·00

1949. 75th Anniv of U.P.U. As Nos. FB56/7 of Baden.

No.	Description	Unused	Used
FW51	20 pf. red	5·00	10·00
FW52	30 pf. blue	5·00	7·50

The French Zone was incorporated in West Germany in September, 1949.

E. Russian Zone.

For a list of the stamps issued by the Russian Zone Provincial Administrations of Berlin (Brandenburg), Mecklenburg – Vorpommern, Saxony (Halle, Leipzig and Dresden) and Thuringia, see Stanley Gibbons Part 7 (Germany) Catalogue.

General Issues.

In February 1946, the Provincial Issues were replaced by the General Issues, Nos. 899/956 until the revaluation of the currency in June 1948, when Nos. 928/44 were brought into use handstamped with District names and numbers as a control measure pending the introduction of the following overprinted stamps on 3rd July. There are over 1,900 different types of district handstamp.

R **1** Arms of Berlin — R **3** Kathe Kollwitz

1948. Optd **Sowjetische Besatzungs Zone.**

(a) On Pictorial issue of 1947, Nos. 928/44.

No.	Description	Unused	Used
R 1	2 pf. black	15	25
R 2	6 pf. violet	15	20
R 3	8 pf. red	15	20
R 4	10 pf. green	15	20
R 5	12 pf. grey	15	20
R 6	15 pf. brown	15	25
R 7	16 pf. green	15	30
R 8	20 pf. blue	15	20
R 9	24 pf. brown	15	20
R10	25 pf. orange	15	30
R11	30 pf. red	30	30
R12	40 pf. mauve	30	30
R13	50 pf. blue	30	50
R14	60 pf. brown	50	50
R15	60 pf. red	40·00	70·00
R16	80 pf. blue	70	70
R17	84 pf. green	70	90

(b) On Numerical issue of 1946, Nos. 903, etc.

No.	Type	Description	Unused	Used
R18	**229**	5 pf. green	25	30
R19		30 pf. olive	50	1·10
R20		45 pf. red	30	50
R21		75 pf. blue	30	50
R22		84 pf. green	70	50

(c) On stamps inscr "STADT BERLIN".

No.	Type	Description	Unused	Used
R23	R **1**	5 pf. green	20	50
R25	–	6 pf. violet	20	50
R26	–	8 pf. orange	20	30
R27	–	10 pf. brown	20	50
R28	–	12 pf. red	20	50
R29	–	20 pf. blue	50	1·00
R30	–	30 pf. olive	35	60

DESIGNS: 6 pf. Bear with spade; 8 pf. Bear on shield; 10 pf. Bear holding brick; 12 pf. Bear carrying plank; 20 pf. Bear on small shield; 30 pf. Oak sapling amid ruins.

1948. Leipzig Autumn Fair. As T **231** but dated "1948".

No.	Description	Unused	Used
R31	16 pf. + 9 pf. purple	30	40
R32	50 pf. + 25 pf. blue	30	40

DESIGNS: 16 pf. 1459: The first Spring Fair; 50 pf. 1469: Foreign merchants displaying cloth.

1948. Politicians, Artists and Scientists.

No.	Type	Description	Unused	Used
R33	R **3**	2 pf. grey	15	15
R34	–	6 pf. violet	20	15
R35	–	8 pf. red	45	25
R36	–	10 pf. green	20	25
R37	–	12 pf. blue	4·00	25
R38	–	15 pf. brown	55	1·10
R39	–	16 pf. blue	40	35
R40	R **3**	20 pf. purple	40	70
R41	–	24 pf. red	5·00	25
R42	–	25 pf. olive	80	1·40
R43	–	30 pf. red	80	1·00
R44	–	40 pf. purple	55	60
R45	–	50 pf. blue	55	40
R46	–	60 pf. green	2·00	40
R47	–	80 pf. blue	1·10	40
E95	–	80 pf. red	8·25	9·00
R48	–	84 pf. brown	2·00	2·00

PORTRAITS: 6, 40 pf. Gerhart Hauptmann; 8, 50 pf. Karl Marx; 10, 84 pf. August Bebel; 12, 30 pf. Friedrich Engels; 15, 60 pf. G. F. W. Hegel; 16, 25 pf. Rudolf Virchow; 24, 80 pf. Ernst Thalmann.

R **4** — R **5** Liebknecht and Rosa Luxemburg

1948. Stamp Day.

No.	Type	Description	Unused	Used
R49	R **4**	12 pf. + 3 pf. red	20	40

1949. 30th Death Anniv of Karl Liebknecht and Rosa Luxemburg (revolutionaries).

No.	Type	Description	Unused	Used
R50	R **5**	24 pf. red	30	60

1949. Leipzig Spring Fair. As T **231** but dated "1949".

No.	Description	Unused	Used
R51	30 pf. + 15 pf. red	2·75	3·25
R52	50 pf. + 25 pf. blue	3·00	3·75

DESIGNS: 30 pf. 1st Neubau Town Hall bazaar, 1556; 50 pf. Italian merchants at Leipzig, 1536.

R **6** Dove — R **8** Goethe

1949. 3rd German Peoples' Congress.

No.	Type	Description	Unused	Used
R53	R **6**	24 pf. red	80	1·25

1949. Optd **3. Deutscher Volkskongreß 29.-30 Mai 1949.**

No.	Type	Description	Unused	Used
R54	R **6**	24 pf. red	1·00	1·40

1949. Birth Bicent. of Goethe. Portraits of Goethe.

No.	Type	Description	Unused	Used
R55	R **8**	6 pf. + 4 pf. violet	2·00	2·00
R56	–	12 pf. + 8 pf. brown	2·00	2·00
R57	–	24 pf. + 16 pf. lake	1·75	1·75
R58	–	50 pf. + 25 pf. blue	1·75	1·75
R59	–	84 pf. + 36 pf. grey	3·00	3·00

1949. Leipzig Autumn Fair. As T **231** but dated "1949".

No.	Description	Unused	Used
R60	12 pf. + 8 pf. slate	3·00	5·00
R61	24 pf. + 16 pf. lake	4·00	7·50

DESIGNS: 12 pf. Russian merchants, 1650; 24 pf. Goethe at Fair, 1765.

The Russian Zone was incorporated in East Germany in October, 1949.

III. GERMAN FEDERAL REPUBLIC

The Federal Republic was set up on 23 May, 1949. Until October 1990 it comprised the territory which formerly came under the British, American and French Zones. On 3 October 1990 the former territory of East Germany (German Democratic Republic) was absorbed into the Federal Republic.

100 pfennig = 1 Deutsche Mark (West)

257 Constructing Parliament Building — **258** Reproduction of T **1** of Bavaria

1949. Opening of West German Parliament, Bonn.

No.	Type	Description	Unused	Used
1033	**257**	10 pf. green	42·00	20·00
1034		20 pf. red	50·00	28·00

1949. Centenary of 1st German Stamps.

No.	Type	Description	Unused	Used
1035	**258**	10 pf. + 2 pf. blk & grn	10·00	12·00
1036	–	20 pf. blue and red	35·00	35·00
1037	–	30 pf. brown and blue	50·00	60·00

DESIGNS: 20 pf., 30 pf. Reproductions of T **2** of Bavaria.

259 Dr. von Stephan, Old GPO, Berlin and Standehaus, Berne — **260** St. Elisabeth of Thuringia

1949. 75th Anniv of U.P.U.

No.	Type	Description	Unused	Used
1038	**259**	30 pf. blue	65·00	45·00

1949. Refugees' Relief Fund. Inscr as in T **260**.

No.	Type	Description	Unused	Used
1039	**260**	8 pf. + 2 pf. purple	18·00	23·00
1040	–	10 pf. + 5 pf. green	13·00	13·00
1041	–	20 pf. + 10 pf. red	13·00	13·00
1042	–	30 pf. + 15 pf. blue	85·00	£100

PORTRAITS: 10 pf. Paracelsus von Hohenheim; 20 pf. F. W. A. Froebel; 30 pf. J. H. Wichern.

261 J. S. Bach's Seal — **262** Numeral and Posthorn

1950. Death Bicent of Bach (composer).

No.	Type	Description	Unused	Used
1043	**261**	10 pf. + 2 pf. green	60·00	40·00
1044		20 pf. + 3 pf. red	70·00	42·00

1951.

No.	Type	Description	Unused	Used
1045	**262**	2 pf. green	3·25	75
1046		4 pf. brown	2·50	10
1047		5 pf. purple	6·50	10
1048		6 pf. orange	16·00	3·00
1049		8 pf. grey	18·00	8·25
1050		10 pf. green	2·50	10262
1051	**262**	15 pf. violet	30·00	90
1052		20 pf. red	3·50	10
1053		25 pf. plum	85·00	4·00
1054		30 pf. blue	45·00	20
1055		40 pf. purple	£120	20
1056		50 pf. grey	£150	20
1057		60 pf. brown	£120	20
1058		70 pf. yellow	£500	12·00
1059		80 pf. red	£400	1·75
1060		90 pf. green	£600	2·00

The 30 pf. to 90 pf. are 20 × 24½ mm.

264 Figures — **265** Stamps under Magnifier

1951. 700th Anniv of St. Mary's Church, Lubeck.

No.	Type	Description	Unused	Used
1065	**264**	10 pf. + 5 pf. blk & grn	£100	70·00
1066		20 pf. + 5 pf. blk & red	£100	80·00

1951. National Philatelic Exn., Wuppertal.

No.	Type	Description	Unused	Used
1067	**265**	10 pf. + 2 pf. yellow, black and green	45·00	40·00
1068		20 pf. + 3 pf. yellow, black and red	45·00	40·00

266 St. Vincent de Paul — **267** W. C. Rontgen (physicist)

1951. Humanitarian Relief Fund.

No.	Type	Description	Unused	Used
1069	**266**	4 pf. + 2 pf. brown	8·00	10·00
1070	–	10 pf. + 3 pf. green	14·00	8·00
1071	–	20 pf. + 5 pf. red	14·00	7·00
1072	–	30 pf. + 10 pf. blue	£120	£110

PORTRAITS: 10 pf. F. Von Bodelschwingh; 20 pf. Elsa Brandstrom; 30 pf. J. H. Pestalozzi.

1951. 50th Anniv of Award to Rontgen of 1st Nobel Prize for Physics.

No.	Type	Description	Unused	Used
1073	**267**	30 pf. blue	80·00	18·00

268 Mona Lisa — **269** Martin Luther

1952. 500th Birth Anniv of Leonardo da Vinci.

No.	Type	Description	Unused	Used
1074	**268**	5 pf. multicoloured	1·00	1·00

1952. Lutheran World Federation Assembly, Hanover.

No.	Type	Description	Unused	Used
1075	**269**	10 pf. green	11·50	5·00

270 A. N. Otto and Diagram — **271** Nuremberg Madonna

1952. 75th Anniv of Otto Gas Engine.

No.	Type	Description	Unused	Used
1076	**270**	30 pf. blue	30·00	15·00

1952. Centenary of German National Museum, Nuremberg.

No.	Type	Description	Unused	Used
1077	**271**	10 pf. + 5 pf. green	15·00	20·00

272 Trawler "Senator Schaffer" off Heligoland — **273** Carl Schurz

1952. Rehabilitation of Heligoland.

No.	Type	Description	Unused	Used
1078	**272**	20 pf. red	15·00	3·75

1952. Centenary of Arrival of Schurz in America.

No.	Type	Description	Unused	Used
1079	**273**	20 pf. pink, black & bl	16·00	6·50

274 Boy Hikers

275 Elizabeth Fry

1952. Youth Hostels Fund. Inscr "JUGENDMARKE 1952".
1080 **274** 10 pf. + 2 pf. green . . . 18·00 21·00
1081 – 20 pf. + 3 pf. red . . . . 18·00 21·00
DESIGN: 20 pf. Girl hikers.

1952. Humanitarian Relief Fund.
1082 **275** 4 pf. + 2 pf. brown . . . 8·00 8·00
1083 – 10 pf. + 5 pf. green . . . 6·50 5·00
1084 – 20 pf. + 10 pf. lake . . . 18·00 16·00
1085 – 30 pf. + 10 pf. blue . . . 90·00 75·00
PORTRAITS: 10 pf. Dr. C. Sonnenschein; 20 pf. T. Fliedner; 30 pf. H. Dunant.

276 Postman, 1852

277 P. Reis

1952. Thurn and Taxis Stamp Cent.
1086 **276** 10 pf. multicoloured . . . 7·25 2·50

1952. 75th Anniv of German Telephone Service.
1087 **277** 30 pf. blue . . . . 40·00 15·00

278 Road Accident Victim

279

1953. Road Safety Campaign.
1088 **278** 20 pf. multicoloured . . . 15·00 4·50

1953. 50th Anniv of Science Museum, Munich.
1089 **279** 10 pf. + 5 pf. green . . . 28·00 28·00

280 Red Cross and Compass

281 Prisoner of War

1953. 125th Birth Anniv of Henri Dunant (founder of Red Cross).
1090 **280** 10 pf. red and green . . . 17·00 6·50

1953. Commemorating Prisoners of War.
1091 **281** 10 pf. black and grey . . . 6·00 20

282 J. von Liebig

283 "Rail Transport"

1953. 150th Birth Anniv of Liebig (chemist).
1092 **282** 30 pf. blue . . . . 35·00 20·00

1953. Transport Exn., Munich. Inscr as in T **283**.
1093 **283** 4 pf. brown . . . . . . 8·50 6·00
1094 – 10 pf. green . . . . . . 15·00 6·00
1095 – 20 pf. red . . . . . . 18·00 8·00
1096 – 30 pf. blue . . . . . . 40·00 18·00
DESIGNS: 10 pf. "Air" (dove and aeroplanes); 20 pf. "Road" (traffic lights and cars); 30 pf. "Sea" (buoy and ships).

284 Gateway, Thurn and Taxis Palace

285 A. H. Francke

1953. Int. Philatelic Exhibition, Frankfurt-on-Main. Inscr "IFRABA 1953".
1097 **284** 10 pf. + 2 pf. brown, black and green . . . . . . 23·00 26·00
1098 – 20 pf. + 3 pf. grey, blue and red . . . . . . 26·00 26·00
DESIGN: 20 pf. Telecommunications Buildings, Frankfurt-on-Main.

1953. Humanitarian Relief Fund.
1099 **285** 4 pf. + 2 pf. brown . . . 5·00 5·00
1100 – 10 pf. + 5 pf. green . . . 8·00 8·00
1101 – 20 pf. + 10 pf. red . . . 12·00 10·00
1102 – 30 pf. + 10 pf. blue . . . 55·00 60·00
PORTRAITS: 10 pf. S. Kneipp; 20 pf. J. C. Senckenberg; 30 pf. F. Nansen.

286 Pres. Heuss

1954. (a) Size $18\frac{1}{2} \times 22\frac{1}{2}$ mm. or 18 × 22 mm.
1103 **286** 2 pf. green 10 10
1104 4 pf. brown 30 10
1105 5 pf. mauve 20 10
1106 6 pf. brown 10 60
1107 7 pf. green 25 10
1108 8 pf. grey 20 30
1109 10 pf. green 15 10
1110 15 pf. blue 45 20
1111 20 pf. red 20 10
1112 25 pf. purple 70 50
1122a 30 pf. green 50 50
1122c 40 pf. blue . . . . . . 2·50 35
1122e 50 pf. olive . . . . . . 1·10 35
1122f 60 pf. brown . . . . . . 3·00 35
1122g 70 pf. violet . . . . . . 7·25 35
1122h 80 pf. orange . . . . . . 4·50 2·50
1122i 90 pf. green . . . . . . 13·00 70

(b) Size 20 × 24 mm.
1113 **286** 30 pf. blue . . . . . . 15·00 4·00
1114 40 pf. purple . . . . . . 5·00 10
1115 50 pf. slate £225 35
1116 60 pf. brown . . . . . . 45·00 40
1117 70 pf. olive . . . . . . 18·00 1·50
1118 80 pf. red . . . . . . 3·75 4·50
1119 90 pf. green . . . . . . 18·00 3·00

(c) Size 25 × 30 mm.
1120 **286** 1 Dm. olive . . . . . . 2·00 10
1121 2 Dm. lavender . . . . . . 3·50 1·60
1122 3 Dm. purple . . . . . . 7·25 3·00

287 P. Ehrlich and E. von Behring

288 Gutenburg and Printing-press

1954. Birth Centenaries of Ehrlich and Von Behring (bacteriologists).
1123 **287** 10 pf. green . . . . . . 11·50 3·50

1954. 500th Anniv of Gutenberg Bible.
1124 **288** 4 pf. brown . . . . . . 1·10 30

289 Sword-pierced Mitre

290 Kathe Kollwitz

1954. 1,200th Anniv of Martyrdrom of St. Boniface.
1125 **289** 20 pf. red and brown . . 6·50 4·25

1954. Humanitarian Relief Fund.
1126 **290** 7 pf. + 3 pf. brown . . . 3·00 3·75
1127 – 10 pf. + 5 pf. green . . . 2·25 2·00
1128 – 20 pf. + 10 pf. red . . . 10·00 4·00
1129 – 40 pf. + 10 pf. blue . . . 35·00 40·00
PORTRAITS: 10 pf. L. Werthmann; 20 pf. J. F. Oberlin; 40 pf. Bertha Pappenheim.

291 C. F. Gauss

292 "Flight"

1955. Death Cent. of Gauss (mathematician).
1130 **291** 10 pf. green . . . . . . 5·00 60

1955. Re-establishment of "Lufthansa" Airways.
1131 **292** 5 pf. mauve and black . . 1·00 70
1132 10 pf. green and black . . 1·40 1·00
1133 15 pf. blue and black . . 6·50 7·25
1134 20 pf. red and black . . . 22·00 10·00

293 O. von Miller

295 Schiller

1955. Birth Centenary of Von Miller (electrical engineer).
1135 **293** 10 f. green . . . . . . 5·00 1·50

1955. 150th Death Anniv of Schiller (poet).
1136 **295** 40 pf. blue . . . . . . 15·00 5·50

296 Motor-coach, 1906

297 Arms of Baden-Wurttemberg

1955. 50th Anniv of Postal Motor Transport.
1137 **296** 20 pf. black and red . . . 10·50 5·25

1955. Baden-Wurttemberg Agricultural Exhibition, Stuttgart.
1138 **297** 7 pf. blk brn & bistre . . 2·50 3·00
1139 10 pf. blk grn & bistre . . 6·00 2·00

298 "Earth and Atom"

299 Refugees

1955. Cosmic Research.
1140 **298** 20 pf. lake . . . . . . 8·25 1·00

1955. 10th Anniv of Expulsion of Germans from beyond the Oder-Neisse Line.
1141 **299** 20 pf. red . . . . . . 3·25 55
See also No. 1400.

300 Orb, Arrows and Waves

301 Magnifying Glass and Carrier Pigeon

1955. Millenary of Battle of Lechfeld.
1142 **300** 20 pf. purple . . . . . . 8·25 4·50

1955. West European Postage Stamp Exn.
1143 **301** 10 pf. + 2 pf. green . . . 4·00 6·00
1144 – 20 pf. + 3 pf. red . . . 9·25 11·00
DESIGN: 20 pf. Tweezers and posthorn.

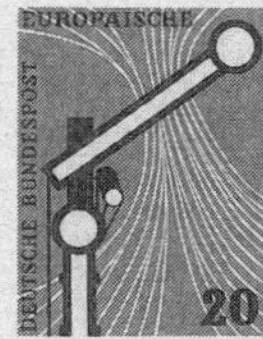

302 Railway Signal

303 Stifter Monument

1955. Railway Timetable Conference.
1145 **302** 20 pf. black and red . . . 10·00 1·00

1955. 150th Birth Anniv of Stifter (Austrian poet).
1146 **303** 10 pf. green . . . . . . 3·25 2·00

304 U.N. Emblem

305 Amalie Sieveking

1955. U.N. Day.
1147 **304** 10 pf. green & brown . . . 3·75 4·25

1955. Humanitarian Relief Fund.
1148 **305** 7 pf. + 3 pf. brown . . . 3·00 2·00
1149 – 10 pf. + 5 pf. green . . . 2·00 1·00
1150 – 20 pf. + 10 pf. red . . . 2·00 1·00
1151 – 40 pf. + 10 pf. blue . . . 32·00 35·00
PORTRAITS: 10 pf. A. Kolping; 20 pf. Dr. S. Hahnemann; 40 pf. Florence Nightingale.

306

307 Von Stephan's Signature

1955.
1152 **306** 1 pf. grey 10 10

1955. 125th Birth Anniv H. von Stephan.
1153 **307** 20 pf. red . . . . . . 6·00 2·50

308 Spinet and Opening Bars of Minuet

309 Heinrich Heine

1956. Birth Bicent of Mozart (composer).
1154 **308** 10 pf. black and lilac . . 60 10

1956. Death Cent of Heine (poet).
1155 **309** 10 pf. green & black . . . 2·50 2·75

310 Old Houses and Crane

OLYMPISCHES JAHR 1956
DEUTSCHE BUNDESPOST
311

1956. Millenary of Luneburg.
1156 **310** 20 pf. red . . . . . . 6·50 5·75

1956. Olympic Year.
1157 **311** 10 pf. green 45 15

312 Boy and Dove

100 Jahre † 29 Juli 1856
Robert Schumann
BUNDESPOST
10 DEUTSCHE
313 Robert Schumann

1956. Youth Hostels' Fund. Inscr "JUGEND".
1158 **312** 7 pf. + 3 pf. grey, black and brown . . . . . . 2·00 2·50
1159 – 10 pf. + 5 pf. grey black and green . . . . . . 5·00 6·50
DESIGN: 10 pf. Girl playing flute and flowers.

1956. Death Cent. of Schumann (composer).
1160 **313** 10 pf. blk, red & bistre . . 50 20

314

315 T. Mann (author)

1956. Evangelical Church Convention, Frankfurt-on-Main.
1161 **314** 10 pf. green . . . . . . 3·00 4·00
1162 20 pf. red . . . . . . 3·50 4·75

1956. Thomas Mann Commem.
1163 **315** 20 pf. red . . . . . . 2·50 2·00

316

317 Ground Plan of Cologne Cathedral and Hand

1956. 800th Anniv of Maria Laach Abbey.
1164 **316** 20 pf. grey and red . . . 1·75 1·90

1956. 77th Meeting of German Catholics, Cologne.
1165 **317** 10 pf. green and brown . 2·00 2·25

318 **320** Nurse and Baby

1956. Int. Police Exhibition, Essen.
1166 **318** 20 pf. grn, orge & blk . . 2·50 2·50

1956. Europa. As T **320** of Belgium.
1167 10 pf. green . . . . 1·00 10
1168 40 pf. blue . . . . 6·50 1·00

1956. Humanitarian Relief Fund. Centres in black.
1169 **320** 7 pf. + 3 pf. brown . . . 1·25 2·00
1170 – 10 pf. + 5 pf. green . . . 80 55
1171 – 20 pf. + 10 pf. red . . . . 1·00 40
1172 – 40 pf. + 10 pf. blue . . . 13·00 16·00
DESIGNS: 10 pf. I. P. Semmelweis and cot; 20 pf. Mother, and baby in cradle; 40 f. Nurse maid and children.

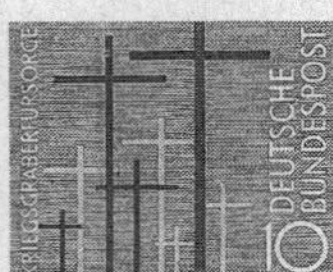

321 Carrier Pigeon **322** "Military Graves"

1956. Stamp Day.
1173 **321** 10 pf. green . . . . . . 1·25 40

1956. War Graves Commission.
1174 **322** 10 pf. green . . . . . . 1·00 30

323 Arms **324** Children with Luggage

1957. Return of the Saar to West Germany.
1175 **323** 10 pf. brown & green . . 40 30

1957. Berlin Children's Holiday Fund.
1176 **324** 10 pf. + 5 pf. orange and green . . . . 1·25 2·25
1177 – 20 pf. + 10 pf. blue and orange . . . . 2·25 3·75
DESIGN: 20 pf. Girl returning from holiday.

325 Heinrich Hertz **326** Paul Gerhardt

1957. Birth Cent of Hertz (physicist).
1178 **325** 10 pf. black & green . . . 1·00 40

1957. 350th Birth Anniv of Paul Gerhardt (hymn-writer).
1179 **326** 20 pf. red 40 30

327 "Flora and Philately" **328** Emblem of Aschaffenburg

1957. Exhibition and 8th Congress of Int. Federation of "Constructive Philately".
1180 **327** 20 pf. orange 40 30

1957. Millenary of Aschaffenburg.
1181 **328** 20 pf. red and black . . . 40 30

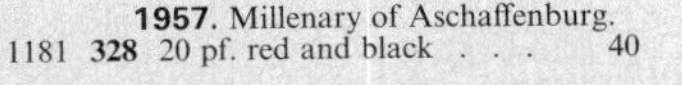

329 University Class

1957. 500th Anniv of Freiburg University.
1182 **329** 10 pf. black, red & grn . . 25 10

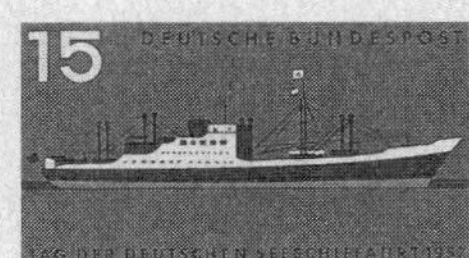

330 "Bayernstein" (freighter)

1957. German Merchant Shipping Day.
1183 **330** 15 pf. black, red & blue . 1·25 1·25

331 Justus Liebig University **332** Albert Ballin

1957. 350th Anniv of Justus Liebig University, Giessen.
1184 **331** 10 pf. green 30 20

1957. Birth Cent. of Albert Ballin (director of Hamburg-America Shipping Line).
1185 **332** 20 pf. black and red . . . 1·10 30

333 Television Screen **334** "Europa" Tree

1957. Publicizing West German Television Service.
1186 **333** 10 pf. green and blue . . 30 20

1957. Europa.
1187 **334** 10 pf. green and blue . . 40 10
1188 40 pf. blue . . . . 3·50 30

335 Young Miner **336** Water Lily

1957. Humanitarian Relief Fund.
1189 **335** 7 pf. + 3 pf. blk & brn . . 1·60 2·00
1190 – 10 pf. + 5 pf. blk & grn . . 90 55
1191 – 20 pf. + 10 pf. blk & red . . 1·10 55
1192 – 40 pf. + 10 pf. blk & bl . . 15·00 18·00
DESIGNS: 10 pf. Miner drilling coal-face; 20 pf. Miner with coal-cutting machine; 40 pf. Operator at mine lift-shaft.

1957. Nature Protection Day.
1193 **336** 10 pf. orge, yell & grn . . 30 20
1194 – 20 pf. multicoloured . . . 60 40
DESIGN—VERT: 20 pf. European robin.

337 Carrier Pigeons **338** Baron von Stein

1957. Int. Correspondence Week.
1195 **337** 20 pf. black and red . . . 80 30

1957. Birth Bicentenary of Baron von Stein (statesman).
1196 **338** 20 pf. red . . . . 1·25 60

339 Dr Leo Baeck (philosopher) **340** Wurttemberg Parliament House

1957. 1st Death Anniv of Dr. Leo Baeck.
1197 **339** 20 pf. red . . . . 1·25 60

1957. 500th Anniv of First Wurttemberg Parliament.
1198 **340** 10 pf. olive and green . . 70 30

341 Stage Coach **342** "Max and Moritz" (cartoon characters)

1957. Death Centenary of Joseph von Eichendorff (novelist).
1199 **341** 10 pf. green 65 30

1958. 50th Death Anniv of Wilhelm Busch (writer and illustrator).
1200 **342** 10 pf. olive and black . . 20 20
1201 – 20 pf. red and black . . . 40 30
DESIGN: 20 pf. Wilhelm Busch.

343 "Prevent Forest Fires"

1958. Forest Fires Prevention Campaign.
1202 **343** 20 pf. black and red . . . 45 30

344 Rudolf Diesel and First Oil Engine **345** "The Fox who stole the Goose"

1958. Birth Cent. of Rudolf Diesel (engineer).
1203 **344** 10 pf. myrtle 25 20

1958. Berlin Students' Fund. Inscr "Fur die Jugend".
1204 **345** 10 pf. + 5 pf. red, black and green . . . . . . 1·00 2·25
1205 – 20 pf. + 10 pf. brown, green and red . . . . 2·25 3·50
DESIGN: 20 pf. "A hunter from the Palatinate" (horseman).

346 Giraffe and Lion **347** Old Munich

1958. Cent. of Frankfurt-am-Main Zoo.
1206 **346** 10 pf. black & green . . . 40 30

1958. 800th Anniv of Munich.
1207 **347** 20 pf. red 40 20

348 Trier and Market Cross **349** Deutsche Mark (coin)

1958. Millenary of Trier Market.
1208 **348** 20 pf. red and black . . . 40 20

1958. 10th Anniv of Currency Reform.
1209 **349** 20 pf. black & orange . . 40 20

350 Emblem of Gymnastics **351** H. Schulze-Delitzsch

1958. 150th Anniv of German Gymnastics.
1210 **350** 10 pf. blk, grn. & grey . . 20 20

1958. 150th Birth Anniv of Schulze-Delitzsch (pioneer of German co-operative movement).
1211 **351** 10 pf. green 30 10

1958. Europa. As T **345** of Belgium. Size 24½ × 30 mm.
1212 10 pf. blue and green 20 10
1213 40 pf. red and blue . . . . 2·25 40

352 Friedrich Raiffeisen (philanthropist) **353** Dairymaid

1958. Humanitarian Relief and Welfare Funds.
1214 **352** 7 pf. + 3 pf. brown, dp brown and chestnut . . 40 70
1215 **353** 10 pf. + 5 pf. red, yellow and green 35 20
1216 – 20 pf. + 10 pf. blue, green and red 45 30
1217 – 40 pf. + 10 pf. yellow, orange and blue . . . 6·00 7·50
DESIGNS: As Type **353**: 20 pf. Vine-dresser; 40 pf. Farm labourer.

354 Cardinal Nicholas of Cues (founder) **355** Jakob Fugger (merchant prince)

1958. 500th Anniv of Hospice of St. Nicholas.
1218 **354** 20 pf. black & mauve . . 30 10

1959. As Type B **53** of West Berlin but without "BERLIN".
1219 7 pf. green 30 10
1220 10 pf. green 40 10
1221 20 pf. red 50 10
1222 40 pf. blue . . . . 12·00 45
1223 70 pf. violet . . . . 3·75 20

1959. 500th Birth Anniv of Jakob Fugger.
1224 **355** 20 pf. black and red . . . 30 20

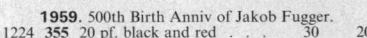

356 Adam Riese (mathematician) **357** A. von Humboldt (naturalist)

1959. 400th Death Anniv of Adam Riese.
1225 **356** 10 pf. black & green . . . 15 15

1959. Death Cent. of Alexander von Humboldt.
1226 **357** 40 pf. blue . . . . 1·25 1·00

358 First Hamburg Stamp of 1859 **359** Buxtehude

1959. International Stamp Exhibition, Hamburg, and Centenary of First Stamps of Hamburg and Lubeck.
1228 **358** 10 pf. + 5 pf. brn & grn . 20 25
1230 – 20 pf. + 10 pf. brn & red . 20 60
DESIGN: 20 pf. First Lubeck stamp of 1859.

1959. Millenary of Buxtehude.
1231 **359** 20 pf. red, black and blue . 20 20

360 Holy Tunic of Trier **361** Congress Emblem

1959. Holy Tunic of Trier Exhibition.
1232 **360** 20 pf. black, buff & pur . 20 20

1959. German Evangelical Church Day and Congress, Munich.
1233 **361** 10 pf. violet, grn & blk . . 10 10

1959. Europa. As T **360** of Belgium but size 24½ × 30 mm.
1234 10 pf. green 15 10
1235 40 pf. blue 80 40

362 "Feeding the Poor"

363 "Uprooted Tree"

1959. Humanitarian Relief and Welfare Funds.
1236 **362** 7 pf. + 3 pf. sep & yell . . 15 40
1237 – 10 pf. + 5 pf. grn & yell . . 20 20
1238 – 20 pf. + 10 pf. red & yell . . 30 20
1239 – 40 pf. + 10 pf. mult . . . 3·00 4·00
DESIGNS: 10 pf. "Clothing the Naked"; 20 pf. "Bounty from Heaven" (scenes from the Brothers Grimm story "The Star Thaler"); 40 pf. The Brothers Grimm.

1960. World Refugee Year.
1240 **363** 10 pf. blk, pur & grn . . 20 10
1241 40 pf. blk, red & blue . . 1·25 1·75

364 P. Melanchthon

365 Cross and Symbols of the Crucifixion

1960. 400th Death Anniv of Philip Melanchthon. (Protestant reformer).
1242 **364** 20 pf. black and red . . . 1·00 90

1960. Oberammergau Passion Play.
1243 **365** 10 pf. grey, ochre and blue 20 20

366

367 Wrestling

1960. 37th World Eucharistic Congress, Munich.
1244 **366** 10 pf. green 50 30
1245 20 pf. red 70 40

1960. Olympic Year. Inscr as in T **367**.
1246 **367** 7 pf. brown 15 20
1247 – 10 pf. green 25 15
1248 – 20 pf. red 30 10
1249 – 40 pf. blue . . . . . . 1·00 1·10
DESIGNS: 10 pf. Running; 20 pf. Javelin and discus-throwing; 40 pf. Chariot-racing.

368 Hildesheim Cathedral

369 Little Red Riding Hood meeting Wolf

1960. Birth Millenary of Bishops St. Bernward and St. Godehard.
1250 **368** 20 pf. purple 40 40

1960. Europa. As T **373** of Belgium.
1251 10 pf. green & olive 20 10
1252 20 pf. vermilion and red . . . 60 20
1253 40 pf. light blue and blue . . . 1·10 60

1960. Humanitarian Relief and Welfare Funds.
1254 **369** 7 pf. + 3 pf. black, red and bistre 30 50
1255 – 10 pf. + 5 pf. black, red and green 30 15
1256 – 20 pf. + 10 pf. black, green and red 30 20
1257 – 40 pf. + 20 pf. black, red and blue . . . . . . 2·10 3·25
DESIGNS: 10 pf. Red Riding Hood and wolf disguised as grandmother; 20 pf. Woodcutter and dead wolf; 40 pf. Red Riding Hood with grandmother.

1960. 1st Death Anniv of Gen. George C. Marshall. Portrait as T **364**.
1258 40 pf. black and blue . . . . 2·10 1·75

371 "Adler", 1835

372 St. George and the Dragon

1960. 125th Anniv of German Railway.
1259 **371** 10 pf. black & bistre . . . 50 20

1961. Pathfinders (German Boy Scouts). Commemoration.
1260 **372** 10 pf. green 10 10

1961. Famous Germans. As Nos. B194, etc. of West Berlin but without "BERLIN".
1261 5 pf. olive 10 10
1262 7 pf. brown 10 10
1263 8 pf. violet 10 15
1264 10 pf. green 10 10
1265 15 pf. blue 10 10
1266 20 pf. red 10 10
1267 25 pf. brown 15 10
1268 30 pf. sepia 20 10
1269 40 pf. blue 20 10
1270 50 pf. brown 45 10
1271 60 pf. red 35 20
1272 70 pf. green 35 10
1273 80 pf. brown 60 20
1274 90 pf. bistre 60 40
1275 1 Dm. violet 75 10
1276 2 Dm. green . . . . 3·00 30
PORTRAIT: 90 pf. Franz Oppenheimer (economist).

373 Early Daimler Motor Car

374 Nuremberg Messenger of 1700

1961. 75th Anniv of Daimler-Benz Patent.
1277 **373** 10 pf. green and black . . 10 10
1278 – 20 pf. red and black . . . 20 15
DESIGN: 20 pf. Early Benz motor car.

1961. "The Letter during Five Centuries" Exhibition, Nuremberg.
1279 **374** 7 pf. black and red . . . 10 10

375 Speyer Cathedral

376 Doves

1961. 900th Anniv of Speyer Cathedral.
1280 **375** 20 pf. red 20 10

1961. Europa.
1281 **376** 10 pf. green 10 10
1282 40 pf. blue 40 40

377 Hansel and Gretel in the Wood

378 Telephone Apparatus

1961. Humanitarian Relief and Welfare Funds. Multicoloured.
1283 7 pf. + 3 pf. Type **377** 20 30
1284 10 pf. + 5 pf. Hansel, Gretel and the Witch 15 15
1285 20 pf. + 10 pf. Hansel in the Witch's cage 15 15
1286 40 pf. + 20 pf. Hansel and Gretel reunited with their father . . . . 1·00 1·75

1961. Centenary of Philipp Reis's Telephone.
1287 **378** 10 pf. green 15 10

379 Baron W. E. von Ketteler

380 Drusus Stone

1961. 150th Birth Anniv of Baron W. E. von Ketteler (Catholic leader).
1288 **379** 10 pf. black & green . . . 10 10

1962. Bimillenary of Mainz.
1289 **380** 20 pf. purple 10 10

381 Apollo

382 Part of "In Dulci Jubilo", from "Musæ Sionæ" (M. Praetorius)

1962. Child Welfare. Butterflies. Mult.
1290 7 pf. + 3 pf. Type **381** 35 45
1291 10 pf. + 5 pf. Camberwell beauty 40 45
1292 20 pf. + 10 pf. Small tortoise-shell . . . . 1·00 90
1293 40 pf. + 20 pf. Scarce swallow-tail . . . . 1·40 1·40

1962. "Song and Choir" (Summer Music Festivals).
1294 **382** 20 pf. red and black . . . 20 10

383 "Belief, Thanksgiving and Service"

384 Open Bible

1962. Catholics' Day.
1295 **383** 20 pf. mauve 10 10

1962. 150th Anniv of Wurttembergische Bibelanstalt (Bible publishers).
1296 **384** 20 pf. black and red . . . 10 10

385 Europa "Tree"

386 Snow White and Seven Dwarfs

1962. Europa.
1297 **385** 10 pf. green 10 10
1298 40 pf. blue 25 15

1962. Humanitarian Relief and Welfare Funds. Scenes from "Snow White and the Seven Dwarfs" (Brothers Grimm). Multicoloured.
1299 7 pf. + 3 pf. The "Magic Mirror" 20 30
1300 10 pf. + 5 pf. Type **386** 20 10
1301 20 pf. + 10 pf. "The Poisoned Apple" 20 15
1302 40 pf. + 20 pf. Snow White and Prince Charming . . . . . 95 1·25

387 "Bread for the World"

388 Relief Distribution

1963. Freedom from Hunger.
1303 **387** 20 pf. brown & black . . 10 10

1963. CRALOG and CARE Relief Organizations.
1304 **388** 20 pf. red 10 10

389 Ears of Wheat, Cross and Globe

390 Snake's Head Lily

1963. Freedom from Hunger.
1305 **389** 20 pf. black, red & grey . 15 15

1963. "Flora and Philately" Exhibition, Hamburg. Multicoloured.
1306 10 pf. Type **390** 15 10
1307 15 pf. Lady's slipper orchid . . 15 10
1308 20 pf. Columbine 15 10
1309 40 pf. Sea holly 30 20

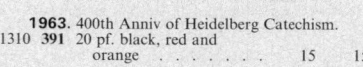

391 "Heidelberger Catechismus"

392 Cross, Sun and Moon

1963. 400th Anniv of Heidelberg Catechism.
1310 **391** 20 pf. black, red and orange 15 15

1963. Consecration of Regina Martyrum Church, Berlin.
1311 **392** 10 pf. multicoloured . . . 10 10

393 Emblems of Conference Participating Countries

394 Map and Flags

1963. Cent of Paris Postal Conference.
1312 **393** 40 pf. blue 10 15

1963. Opening of Denmark—Germany Railway ("Vogelfluglinie").
1313 **394** 20 pf. multicoloured . . . 20 15

395 Red Cross Emblem

396 Hoopoe

1963. Red Cross Cent.
1314 **395** 20 pf. red, purple & yell . 10 10

1963. Child Welfare. Bird designs inscr "FUR DIE JUGEND 1963". Multicoloured.
1315 10 pf. + 5 pf. Type **396** 70 70
1316 15 pf. + 5 pf. Golden Oriole . . 50 60
1317 20 pf. + 10 pf. Bullfinch 55 70
1318 40 pf. + 20 pf. Common Kingfisher . . . . 1·90 2·25

397 Congress Emblem

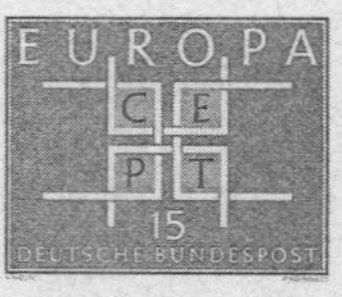
398 "Co-operation"

1963. German Evangelical Church Day and Congress, Dortmund.
1319 **397** 20 pf. black & brown . . 15 20

1963. Europa.
1320 **398** 15 pf. green 10 10
1321 20 pf. red 10 10

399 Mother Goat warning kids

400 Atlantic Herring

1963. Humanitarian Relief and Welfare Funds.
1322 **399** 10 pf. + 5 pf. mult 10 20
1323 – 15 pf. + 5 pf. mult 10 15
1324 – 20 pf. + 10 pf. mult . . . 15 15
1325 – 40 pf. + 20 pf. mult . . . 65 90
DESIGNS: 15 pf. Wolf entering house; 20 pf. Wolf in house, threatening kids; 40 pf. Mother Goat and Kids dancing round wolf in well. From Grimm's "Wolf and the Seven Kids".

1964. Child Welfare. Fish designs inscr "Fur die Jugend 1964". Multicoloured.
1326 10 pf. + 5 pf. Type **400** 20 40
1327 15 pf. + 5 pf. Redfish 20 30
1328 20 pf. + 10 pf. Mirror carp . . 40 30
1329 40 pf. + 20 pf. Atlantic cod . . 1·10 1·50

401 Old Town Hall, Hanover

402 Ottobeuren Abbey

1964. Capitals of the Federal Lands. Mult.
1330 20 pf. Type **401** 20 15
1331 20 pf. Hamburg 20 15
1332 20 pf. Kiel 20 15
1333 20 pf. Munich 20 15
1334 20 pf. Wiesbaden 20 15
1335 20 pf. Berlin 20 15
1336 20 pf. Mainz 20 15
1337 20 pf. Dusseldorf 20 15
1338 20 pf. Bonn 20 15
1339 20 pf. Bremen 20 15
1340 20 pf. Stuttgart 20 15
1340a 20 pf. Saarbrucken 20 15
DESIGNS: No. 1331, Liner "Lichtenfels" and St. Michael's Church (775th anniv); No. 1332, Ferry "Kronprinz Harald"; No. 1333, National Theatre; No. 1334, Kurhaus; No. 1335, Reichstag; No. 1336, Gutenberg Museum; No. 1337, Jan Wellen's Monument and Town Hall; No. 1338, Town Hall; No. 1339, Market Hall; No. 1340, Town view; No. 1340a, Ludwig's Church.

1964. 1200th Anniv of Benedictine Abbey, Ottobeuren.
1341 **402** 20 pf. black, red & pink . 10 10

1964. Re-election of Pres. Lubke. As Type B **67** of West Berlin, inscr "DEUTSCHE BUNDESPOST" only.
1342 20 pf. red 10 10
1343 40 pf. blue 10 10

402b Sophie Scholl

1964. 20th Anniv of Attempt on Hitler's Life. Anti-Hitlerite Martyrs. Each black and grey.
1343a 20 pf. Type **402b** . . . . . 65 1·40
1343b 20 pf. Ludwig Beck . . . . . 65 1·40
1343c 20 pf. Dietrich Bonhoeffer . . 65 1·40
1343d 20 pf. Alfred Delp . . . . . 65 1·40
1343e 20 pf. Karl Friedrich Goerdeler . . . . 65 1·40
1343f 20 pf. Wilhelm Leuschner . . 65 1·40
1343g 20 pf. Helmuth James (Von Moltke) . . . . 65 1·40
1343h 20 pf. Claus Schenk (Von Stauffenberg) . . . . . . 65 1·40

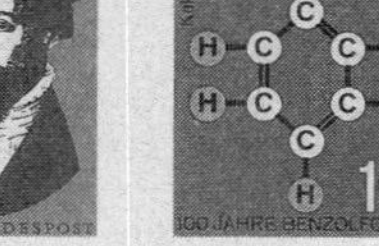

403 Calvin **404** Diagram of Benzene Formula

1964. World Council of Reformed Churches.
1344 **403** 20 pf. black and red . . . 10 10

1964. Scientific Anniversaries (1st series).
1345 10 pf. green, black & brown . . 10 10
1346 15 pf. multicoloured 10 10
1347 20 pf. green, black and red . . 10 10
DESIGNS: 10 pf. Type **404** (centenary of publication of Kekule's benzene formula); 15 pf. Diagram of nuclear reaction (25th anniv of publication of Hahn-Strassman treatise on splitting the nucleus of the atom); 20 pf. Gas engine (centenary of Otto-Langen internal-combustion engine)..

See also Nos. 1426/7 and 1451/3.

405 F. Lassalle **406** "The Sun"

1964. Death Centenary of Ferdinand Lassalle (Socialist founder and leader).
1348 **405** 20 pf. black and blue . . 10 10

1964. 80th Catholics' Day.
1349 **406** 20 pf. red and blue . . . 10 10

407 Europa "Flower" **408** "The Sleeping Beauty"

1964. Europa.
1350 **407** 15 pf. violet and green . . 10 20
1351 20 pf. violet and red . . . 10 10

1964. Humanitarian Relief and Welfare Funds.
1352 **408** 10 pf. + 5 pf. mult 15 20
1353 – 15 pf. + 5 pf. mult 15 15
1354 – 20 pf. + 10 pf. mult 15 15
1355 – 40 pf. + 20 pf. mult . . . 45 90
DESIGNS: 15 pf., 20 pf., 40 pf. Various scenes from Grimm's "The Sleeping Beauty".

409 Judo **410** Prussian Eagle

1964. "Olympic Year".
1356 **409** 20 pf. multicoloured . . . 20 10

1964. 250th Anniv of German Court of Accounts.
1357 **410** 20 pf. orange & black . . 30 10

411 Pres. Kennedy **412** Castle Gateway Ellwangen (Jagst)

1964. Pres. Kennedy Commem.
1358 **411** 40 pf. blue 20 10

1964. Twelve Centuries of German Architecture.
(a) Size $18\frac{1}{2} \times 22$ mm. Plain background.
1359 – 10 pf brown 15 10
1360 – 15 pf. green 15 10
1361 – 20 pf. brown 15 10
1362 – 40 pf. blue 30 10
1363 **412** 50 pf. brown 60 10
1364 – 60 pf. red 75 45
1365 – 70 pf. green . . . . . . 1·00 45
1366 – 80 pf. brown 85 10
(b) Size $19\frac{1}{2} \times 24$ mm. Coloured background.
1367 – 5 pf. brown 10 10
1368 – 10 pf. brown 10 10
1369 – 20 pf. green 20 10
1370 – 30 pf. green 15 10
1371 – 30 pf. red 30 10
1372 – 40 pf. brown 35 10
1373 – 50 pf. blue 50 10
1374 – 60 pf. orange . . . . . . 2·25 1·25
1375 – 70 pf. green 85 10
1376 – 80 pf. brown . . . . . . 2·25 1·25
1377 – 90 pf. black 70 10
1378 – 1 Dm. blue 85 10
1379 – 1 Dm. 10 brown . . . . . 1·25 15
1380 – 1 Dm. 30 green . . . . . 2·75 60
1381 – 2 Dm. purple . . . . . . 1·40 30
BUILDINGS: 5 pf. Berlin Gate, Stettin; 10 pf. Zwinger pavilion, Dresden; 15 pf. Tegel Castle, Berlin; 20 pf. Monastery Gate, Lorsch; 30 pf. North Gate, Flensburg; 40 pf. Trifels Castle (Palatinate); 60 pf. Treptow Portal, Neubrandenburg; 70 pf. Osthofen Gate, Soest; 80 pf. Ellingen Portal, Weissenburg (Bavaria); 90 pf. Zschokk's Convent, Konigsberg; 1 Dm. Melanchthon House, Wittenberg; 1 Dm. 10, Trinity Hospital, Hildesheim; 1 Dm. 30, Tegel Castle, Berlin (diff); 2 Dm. Burghers' Hall, Lowenberg Town Hall (Silesia).

413 Owl, Hat, Walking-stick and Satchel **414** Woodcock

1965. 150th Death Anniv of Matthias Claudius (poet).
1383 **413** 20 pf. black and red on grey 15 10

1965. Child Welfare. Inscr "FUR DIE JUGEND 1965". Multicoloured.
1384 10 pf. + 5 pf. Type **414** 20 20
1385 15 pf. + 5 pf. Ring-necked Pheasant 20 25
1386 20 pf. + 10 pf. Black Grouse . . 30 25
1387 40 pf. + 20 pf. Capercaillie . . 60 70

415 Bismarck (statesman) **416** Boeing 727-100 Airliner and Space Capsule

1965. 150th Birth Anniv of Otto von Bismarck.
1388 **415** 20 pf. black and red . . . 10 10

1965. Int. Transport Exn., Munich. Mult.
1389 5 pf. Traffic lights and road signs 10 10
1390 10 pf. "Syncom" satellite and tracking station 10 10
1391 15 pf. Old and modern postal buses 10 10
1392 20 pf. Old semaphore station and modern signal tower . . 10 10
1393 40 pf. Locomotive "Adler" (1835) and Class E.10.12 electric locomotive (1960s) . . . 25 15
1394 60 pf. Type **416** 30 20
1395 70 pf. "Bremen" (liner) and "Hammonia" (19th-century steamship) 50 15
No. 1394 was also issued to mark the 10th anniv of Lufthansa's renewed air services.

HAVE YOU READ THE NOTES AT THE BEGINNING OF THIS CATALOGUE?
These often provide answers to the enquiries we receive.

417 Bouquet **418** ITU Emblem

1965. 75th Anniv of "May 1st" (Labour Day).
1396 **417** 15 pf. multicoloured . . . 10 10

1965. Centenary of I.T.U.
1397 **418** 40 pf. black and blue . . 25 10

419 A. Kopling **420** Rescue Vessel "Theodor Heuss"

1965. Death Centenary of Adolf Kolping (miners' padre).
1398 **419** 20 pf. black, red & grey . . 10 10

1965. Cent. of German Sea-Rescue Service.
1399 **420** 20 pf. violet, blk & red . . 20 10

1965. 20th Anniv of Influx of East German Refugees. As T **299** but inscr "ZWANZIG JAHRE VERTREIBUNG 1945 1965".
1400 20 pf. purple 10 10

421 Evangelical Church Emblem **422** Radio Tower

1965. German Evangelical Church Day and Synod, Cologne.
1401 **421** 20 pf. black, turq & bl . . 10 10

1965. Radio Exhib., Stuttgart.
1402 **422** 20 pf. blk, blue & mve . . 10 10

423 Thurn and Taxis 1, 2, and 5 sgr. Stamps of 1852

1965. 125th Anniv of 1st Postage Stamp.
1403 **423** 20 pf. multicoloured . . . 10 10

424 Europa "Sprig"

1965. Europa.
1404 **424** 15 pf. green 20 10
1405 20 pf. red 20 10

425 Cinderella with Birds **426** N. Soderblom

1965. Humanitarian Relief Funds. Mult.
1406 10 pf. + 5 pf. Type **425** 15 10
1407 15 pf. + 5 pf. Cinderella and birds with dress 15 10
1408 20 pf. + 10 pf. Prince offering slipper to Cinderella 20 10
1409 40 pf. + 20 pf. Cinderella and Prince on horse 50 70

1966. Birth Centenary of Nathan Soderblom (Archbishop of Uppsala).
1410 **426** 20 pf. black and lilac . . 10 10

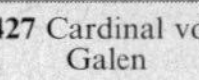

427 Cardinal von Galen **428** Brandenburg Gate, Berlin

1966. 20th Death Anniv of Cardinal Clemens von Galen.
1411 **427** 20 pf. red, mauve & black . 10 10

1966.
1412 **428** 10 pf. brown 10 10
1413 20 pf. green 15 10
1414 30 pf. red 25 10
1415 50 pf. blue . . . . . . 1·25 10
1415a 100 pf. blue . . . . . . 8·25 50

429 Roe deer **430** Christ and Fishermen (Miracle of the Fishes)

1966. Child Welfare. Multicoloured.
1416 10 pf. + 5 pf. Type **429** 15 25
1417 20 pf. + 10 pf. Chamois 15 15
1418 30 pf. + 15 pf. Fallow deer . . . 25 35
1419 50 pf. + 25 pf. Red deer . . . 55 1·00

1966. Catholics' Day.
1420 **430** 30 pf. black & salmon . . 10 10

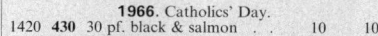

431 19th-cent Postman **432** G. W. Leibniz

1966. F.I.P. Meeting, Munich. Multicoloured.
1421 30 pf. + 15 pf. Bavarian mail coach 30 70
1422 50 pf. + 25 pf. Type **431** . . . 45 55

1966. 250th Death Anniv of Gottfried Leibniz (scientist).
1423 **432** 30 pf. black & mauve . . 10 10

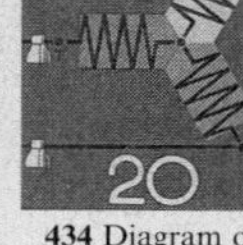

433 Europa "Ship" **434** Diagram of A.C. Transmission (75th Anniv)

1966. Europa.
1424 **433** 20 pf. multicoloured . . . 10 15
1425 30 pf. multicoloured . . . 10 10

1966. Scientific Annivs. (2nd series). Mult.
1426 20 pf. Type **434** 10 10
1427 30 pf. Diagram of electric dynamo (cent.) 10 10

435 Princess and Frog **436** UNICEF Emblem

1966. Humanitarian Relief Funds. Mult.
1428 10 pf. + 5 pf. Type **435** 10 20
1429 20 pf. + 10 pf. Frog dining with Princess 10 10
1430 30 pf. + 15 pf. Prince and Princess 15 20
1431 50 pf. + 25 pf. In coach 35 90
Designs from Grimm's "The Frog Prince".

1966. Award of Nobel Peace Prize to United Nations Children's Fund.
1432 **436** 30 pf. sepia, blk & red . . 10 10

437 W. von Siemens (electrical engineer) **438** Common rabbit

1966. 150th Birth Anniv of Werner von Siemens (electrical engineer).
1433 **437** 30 pf. red 20 15

1967. Child Welfare. Multicoloured.
1434 10 pf. + 5 pf. Type **438** 20 40
1435 20 pf. + 10 pf. Stoat 20 25
1436 30 pf. + 15 pf. Common hamster 30 50
1437 50 pf. + 25 pf. Red fox . . . . 80 1·25
See also Nos. 1454/7.

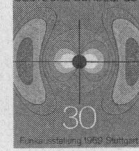

439 Cogwheels **440** Francis of Taxis

1967. Europa.
1438 **439** 20 pf. multicoloured . . . 10 20
1439 30 pf. multicoloured . . . 10 10

1967. 450th Death Anniv of Francis of Taxis.
1440 **440** 30 pf. black & orange . . 10 10

441 Evangelical Symbols **442** Friedrich von Bodelschwingh (Head of Hospital 1910–46)

1967. 13th German Evangelical Churches Day.
1441 **441** 30 pf. black & mauve . . 10 10

1967. Cent of Bethel Hospital, Bielefeld.
1442 **442** 30 pf. black and brown . . 10 10

443 Frau Holle at Spinning-wheel **444** Wartburg (castle), Eisenach

1967. Humanitarian Relief Funds. Mult.
1443 10 pf. + 5 pf. Type **443** 15 30
1444 20 pf. + 10 pf. In the clouds . . 15 15
1445 30 pf. + 15 pf. With shopping-basket and cockerel 20 30
1446 50 pf. + 25 pf. Covered with soot 40 75
Designs from Grimm's "Frau Holle" ("Mother Carey").

1967. Re-election of Pres. Lubke. As Type B **67** of West Berlin, but inscr "DEUTSCHE BUNDESPOST".
1447 30 pf. red 10 10
1448 50 pf. blue 15 10

1967. 450th Anniv of Luther's "Theses" and the Reformation.
1449 **444** 30 pf. red 10 10

445 Cross on South American Map **446** Koenig's Printing Machine

1967. "Adveniat" (Aid for Catholic Church in Latin America).
1450 **445** 30 pf. multicoloured . . . 10 10

1968. Scientific Anniv (3rd series). Mult.
1451 10 pf. Type **446** 10 10
1452 20 pf. Ore Crystals 10 10
1453 30 pf. Lens Refraction 10 10
ANNIVS: 10 pf. 150th anniv; 20 pf. Millenary of ore mining in Harz Mountains; 30 pf. Centenary of Abbe-Zeiss Scientific Microscope.

1968. Child Welfare. As T **438** but inscr "1968". Multicoloured.
1454 10 pf. + 5 pf. Wildcat 30 55
1455 20 pf. + 10 pf. European otter . 35 65
1456 30 pf. + 15 pf. Eurasian badger . 65 1·10
1457 50 pf. + 25 pf. Eurasian beaver . 1·50 2·75

447 Trade Symbols

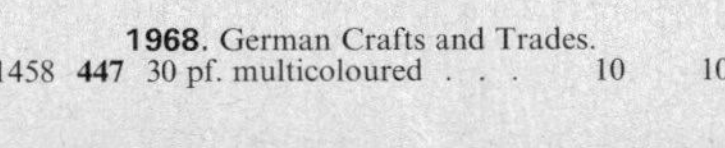
1968. German Crafts and Trades.
1458 **447** 30 pf. multicoloured . . . 10 10

449 Europa "Key" **450** Karl Marx

1968. Europa.
1460 **449** 20 pf. yellow, brn & grn . . 10 10
1461 30 pf. yellow, brn & red . . 10 10

1968. 150th Birth Anniv of Karl Marx.
1462 **450** 30 pf. red, black & grey . . 10 10

451 F. von Langen (horseman)

1968. Olympic Games (1972) Promotion Fund (1st series).
1463 **451** 10 pf. + 5 pf. blk & grn . . 30 30
1464 – 20 pf. + 10 pf. blk & grn . 30 30
1465 – 30 pf. black & lilac . . . 20 10
1466 – 30 pf. + 15 pf. blk & red . 40 40
1467 – 50 pf. + 25 pf. blk & bl . . 60 70
DESIGN: 20 pf. R. Harbig (runner); 30 pf. (No. 1465) Pierre de Coubertin (founder of Olympics); 30 pf. (No. 1466) Helene Mayer (fencer); 50 pf. Carl Diem (sports organiser).
See also Nos. 1493/6, 1524/7, 1589/92, 1621/4 and 1629/32.

452 Opening Bars of "The Mastersingers" **453** Dr. Adenauer

1968. Cent. of 1st Performance of Richard Wagner's Opera "The Mastersingers".
1468 **452** 30 pf. multicoloured . . . 30 15

1968. Adenauer Commem.
1469 **453** 30 pf. black & orange . . 20 10

454 Cross, Dove and "The Universe" **455** Northern District 1 g. and Southern District 7 k. stamps of 1868

1968. Catholics' Day.
1470 **454** 20 pf. vio, yell & grn . . . 20 10

1968. Cent of North German Postal Confederation and First Stamps.
1471 **455** 30 pf. red, blue & black . 20 10

456 Arrows **457** Doll of 1878

1968. Cent of German Trade Unions.
1472 **456** 30 pf. multicoloured . . . 10 10

1968. Humanitarian Relief Funds. Mult.
1473 10 pf. + 5 pf. Type **457** . . . 10 20
1474 20 pf. + 10 pf. Doll of 1850 . . 10 15
1475 30 pf. + 15 pf. Doll of 1870 . . 15 20
1476 50 pf. + 25 pf. Doll of 1885 . . 40 90

458 Human Rights Emblem **459** Pony

1968. Human Rights Year.
1477 **458** 30 pf. multicoloured . . . 10 10

1969. Child Welfare.
1478 **459** 10 pf. + 5 pf. brown, black and yellow 30 35
1479 – 20 pf. + 10 pf. brown black and buff 40 30
1480 – 30 pf. + 15 pf. brown, black and red 55 55
1481 – 50 pf. + 25 pf. mult . . . 1·50 1·50
HORSES: 20 pf. Draught-horse; 30 pf. Saddle-horse; 50 pf. Thoroughbred.

460 Junkers Ju 52/3m "Boelke"

1969. 50th Anniv of German Airmail Services. Multicoloured.
1482 20 pf. Type **460** 30 10
1483 30 pf. Boeing 707 airliner . . . 40 10

461 Colonnade **462** "The Five Continents"

1969. Europa.
1484 **461** 20 pf. yellow, grn & bl . . 10 10
1485 30 pf. yellow, red & vio . . 15 10

1969. 50th Anniv of I.L.O.
1486 **462** 30 pf. multicoloured . . . 15 10

463 Eagle Emblems of Weimar and Federal Republics **464** "War Graves"

1969. 20th Anniv of German Federal Republic.
1487 **463** 30 pf. black, gold & red . 75 10

1969. 50th Anniv of German War Graves Commission.
1488 **464** 30 pf. blue & yellow . . . 20 10

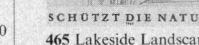

465 Lakeside Landscape **466** "Running Track"

1969. Nature Protection. Multicoloured.
1489 10 pf. Type **465** 10 10
1490 20 pf. Highland landscape . . 60 20
1491 30 pf. Alpine landscape . . . 45 15
1492 50 pf. River landscape 70 35

1969. Olympic Games (1972). Promotion Fund (2nd series). Multicoloured.
1493 10 pf. + 5 pf. Type **466** 20 20
1494 20 pf. + 15 pf. "Hockey" . . . 30 40
1495 30 pf. + 15 pf. "Shooting target" 45 45
1496 50 pf. + 25 pf. "Sailing" . . . 80 75

467 "Longing for Justice" **468** "Electro-magnetic Field"

1969. 14th German Protestant Congress, Stuttgart.
1497 **467** 30 pf. multicoloured . . . 15 10

1969. German Radio Exn., Stuttgart.
1498 **468** 30 pf. multicoloured . . . 15 10

470 Maltese Cross Symbol **471** Bavaria 3 k. Stamp of 1867

1969. "Malteser Hilfsdienst" (welfare organization).
1500 **470** 30 pf. red and black . . . 15 10

1969. German Philatelic Federation Congress and Exn., Garmisch-Partenkirchen.
1501 **471** 30 pf. red and slate . . . 40 10

472 Map of Pipeline

1969. 350th Anniv of Bad Reichenhall-Traunstein Brine Pipeline.
1502 **472** 20 pf. multicoloured . . . 10 10

473 Rothenburg ob der Tauber

1969. Tourism.
1503 **473** 30 pf. black and red . . . 15 10
See also Nos. 1523, 1558, 1564, 1587, 1606, 1641/2, 1655/6 and 1680/2.

474 Mahatma Gandhi **475** Pope John XXIII

1969. Birth Cent. of Mahatma Gandhi.
1504 **474** 20 pf. black & green . . . 15 10

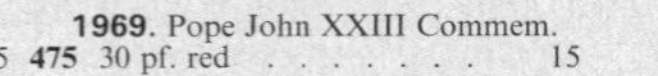
1969. Pope John XXIII Commem.
1505 **475** 30 pf. red 15 10

476 "Adler" (1835) **477** E. M. Arndt

1969. Humanitarian Relief Funds. Pewter Figurines. Multicoloured.
(a) Inscr "WOHLFAHRTSMARKE".
1506 10 pf. + 5 pf. Type **476** 35 25
1507 20 pf. + 10 pf. Woman watering flowers (1780) 20 15
1508 30 pf. + 15 pf. Bird salesman (1850) 30 25
1509 50 pf. + 25 pf. Mounted dignitary (1840) 70 70
(b) Christmas. Inscr "WEIHNACHTSMARKE".
1510 10 pf. + 5 pf. "Child Jesus in crib" (1850) 10 15

1969. Birth Bicent. of Ernst Arndt (writer).
1511 **477** 30 pf. lake and bistre . . 15 10

478 "H von Rugge"

1970. Child Welfare. Minnesinger Themes. Multicoloured.
1512 10 pf. + 5 pf. Type **478** 40 40
1513 20 pf. + 10 pf. "W. von Eschenbach" 50 40
1514 30 pf. + 15 pf. "W. von Metz" . 60 55
1515 50 pf. + 25 pf. "W. von der Vogelweide" . . . . 1·50 1·40

479 Beethoven **480** Saar 1 m. Stamp of 1947

1970. Birth Bicents.
1516 **479** 10 pf. black & blue . . . 50 15
1517 – 20 pf. black & olive . . . 20 10
1518 – 30 pf. black and pink . . 30 10
DESIGNS: 20 pf. G. W. Hegel (philosopher); 30 pf. F. Holderlin (poet).

1970. "Sabria 70" Stamp Exn., Saarbrucken.
1519 **480** 30 pf. green, blk & red . . 15 10

481 "Flaming Sun" **482** Von Munchhausen on Severed Horse

1970. Europa.
1520 **481** 20 pf. green 20 10
1521 30 pf. red 40 10

1970. 250th Birth Anniv of Baron H. von Munchhausen.
1522 **482** 20 pf. multicoloured . . . 15 10

1970. Tourism. Horiz. design as T **473**, but with view of Oberammergau.
1523 30 pf. black and orange . . . 15 10

483 Royal Palace

1970. Olympic Games (1972). Promotion Fund (3rd series).
1524 **483** 10 pf. + 5 pf. brown . . . 20 30
1525 – 20 pf. + 10 pf. turquoise . . 30 40
1526 – 30 pf. + 15 pf. red 50 50
1527 – 50 pf. + 25 pf. blue . . . 80 80
DESIGNS (Munich buildings): 20 pf. Propylaea; 30 pf. Glyptothek; 50 pf. "Bavaria" (statue and colonnade).

484 Liner "Kungsholm IV" and Road-tunnel **485** Nurse with Invalid

1970. 75th Anniv of Kiel Canal.
1528 **484** 20 pf. multicoloured . . . 25 10

1970. Voluntary Relief Services. Mult.
1529 5 pf. Oxygen-lance operator . . 10 10
1530 10 pf. Mountain rescue 15 10
1531 20 pf. Type **485** 15 10
1532 30 pf. Fireman with hose . . . 35 10
1533 50 pf. Road-accident casualty . 60 55
1534 70 pf. Rescue from drowning . 75 55

486 President Heinemann **487** Illuminated Cross

1970.
1535 **486** 5 pf. black 10 10
1536 10 pf. brown 15 10
1537 20 pf. green 15 10
1538 25 pf. green 30 10
1539 30 pf. brown 35 10
1540 40 pf. orange 35 10
1541 50 pf. blue . . . . . . 1·60 10
1542 60 pf. blue 55 10
1543 70 pf. brown 60 10
1544 80 pf. green 70 15
1545 90 pf. red . . . . 1·25 1·25
1546 1 Dm. green 95 35
1547 110 pf. grey . . . . . . 1·10 50
1548 120 pf. brown 90 55
1549 130 pf. brown 90 60
1550 140 pf. green . . . . . 1·60 1·00
1551 150 pf. red . . . . . . 1·40 40
1552 160 pf. orange . . . . . 1·50 75
1553 170 pf. orange . . . . . 1·60 70
1554 190 pf. purple . . . . . 2·25 1·25
1555 2 Dm. violet . . . . . 1·60 40

1970. Catholic Church World Mission.
1556 **487** 20 pf. yellow & green . . 15 10

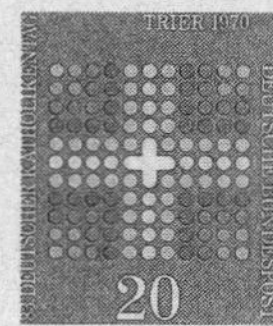

488 Stylised Cross **489** "Jester"

1970. Catholics Day and 83rd German Catholic Congress, Trier.
1557 **488** 20 pf. multicoloured . . . 15 10

1970. Tourism. As T **473**.
1558 20 pf. black and green 20 10
DESIGN: 20 pf. View of Cochem.

1970. Humanitarian Relief Funds. Puppets. Multicoloured.
(a) Relief Funds
1559 10 pf. + 5 pf. Type **489** 15 15
1560 20 pf. + 10 pf. "Buffoon" . . . 20 20
1561 30 pf. + 15 pf. "Clown" . . . 30 30
1562 50 pf. + 25 pf. "Harlequin" . . 85 85
(b) Christmas.
1563 10 pf. + 5 pf. "Angel" 10 15

1970. Tourism. Horiz design as T **473**, but with view of Freiburg im Breisgau.
1564 20 pf. brown and green 20 10

490 A. J. Comenius (scholar) **491** Engels as Young Man

1970. Int. Education Year and 300th Death Anniv of Comenius (Jan Komensky).
1565 **490** 30 pf. red and black . . . 20 10

1970. 150th Birth Anniv of Friedrich Engels.
1566 **491** 50 pf. blue and red . . . 1·00 60

492 German Eagle **493** "Ebert" Stamp of 1928 and inscr "To the German People"

1971. Cent. of German Unification.
1567 **492** 30 pf. black, red & orange 75 10

1971. Birth Centenary of Friedrich Ebert (Chancellor 1918 and President 1919–25).
1568 **493** 30 pf. green, black & red . 85 10

494 "King of Blackamoors" **495** Molecular Chain

1971. Child Welfare. Children's Drawings. Multicoloured.
1569 10 pf. + 5 pf. Type **494** . . . 30 35
1570 20 pf. + 10 pf. "Flea" 40 50
1571 30 pf. + 15 pf. "Puss-in-Boots" . 70 85
1572 50 pf. + 25 pf. "Serpent" . . 1·00 1·00

1971. 125 Years of Chemical Fibre Research.
1573 **495** 20 pf. black, red & green . 15 10

496 Road-crossing Patrol **497** Luther before Charles V

1971. New Road Traffic Regulations (1st series).
1574 **496** 10 pf. blk, blue & red . . 15 10
1575 – 20 pf. black, red & grn . . 30 15
1576 – 30 pf. red, blk & grey . . 45 15
1577 – 50 pf. blk, blue & red . . 50 50
ROAD SIGNS: 20 pf. "Right-of-way across junction"; 30 pf. "STOP"; 50 pf. "Pedestrian Crossing".
See also Nos. 1579/82.

1971. 450th Anniv of Diet of Worms.
1578 **497** 30 pf. black and red . . . 30 10

1971. New Traffic Regulations (2nd series). Horiz designs similar to T **496**.
1579 5 pf. red, black and blue . . 10 10
1580 10 pf. multicoloured 15 10
1581 20 pf. red, black & green . . 25 15
1582 30 pf. yellow, black & red . . 40 25
NEW HIGHWAY CODE: 5 pf. Overtaking; 10 pf. Warning of obstruction; 20 pf. Lane discipline; 30 pf. Pedestrian Crossing.

498 Europa Chain **499** Thomas a Kempis writing "The Imitation of Christ"

1971. Europa.
1583 **498** 20 pf. gold, grn & blk . . 30 10
1584 30 pf. gold, red & blk . . 35 10

1971. 500th Death Anniv of Thomas a Kempis (devotional writer).
1585 **499** 30 pf. black and red . . . 20 10

500 Durer's Monogram **501** Meeting Emblem

1971. 500th Birth Anniv of Albrecht Durer.
1586 **500** 30 pf. brown & red . . . 90 10

1971. Tourism. As T **473**, but with view of Nuremburg.
1587 30 pf. black and red 30 10

1971. Whitsun Ecumenical Meeting, Augsburg.
1588 **501** 30 pf. black, orange & red 20 10

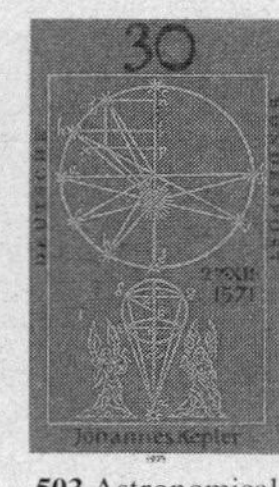

502 Ski Jumping **503** Astronomical Calculus

1971. Olympic Games (1972). Promotion Fund (4th series). Winter Games, Sapporo.
1589 **502** 10 pf. + 5 pf. blk & brn . . 30 40
1590 – 20 pf. + 10 pf. blk & grn . 55 75
1591 – 30 pf. + 15 pf. blk & red . 70 85
1592 – 50 pf. + 25 pf. blk & bl . 1·40 1·60
DESIGNS: 20 pf. Ice dancing; 30 pf. Skiing start; 50 pf. Ice hockey.

1971. 400th Birth Anniv of Johann Kepler (astronomer).
1594 **503** 30 pf. gold, red & blk . . 30 10

504 Dante **505** Alcohol and front of Car ("Don't Drink and Drive")

1971. 650th Death Anniv of Dante Alighieri.
1595 **504** 10 pf. black 10 10

1971. Accident Prevention.
1596 – 5 pf. orange 30 10
1597 – 10 pf. brown 15 10
1598 – 20 pf. violet 30 10
1599 **505** 25 pf. green 50 10
1600 – 30 pf. red 30 10
1601 – 40 pf. mauve 40 10
1602 – 50 pf. blue . . . . . . 2·00 10
1603 – 60 pf. blue . . . . . . 1·00 35
1603a – 70 pf. blue and green . . 1·00 10
1604 – 1 Dm. green . . . . . 1·40 10
1605 – 1 Dm. 50 brown . . . . 4·75 70
DESIGNS: 5 pf. Man within flame, and spent match ("Fire Prevention"); 10 pf. Fall from ladder; 20 pf. Unguarded machinery ("Factory Safety"); 30 pf. Falling brick and protective helmet; 40 pf. Faulty electric plug; 50 pf. Protruding nail in plank; 60 pf., 70 pf. Ball in front of car ("Child Road Safety"); 1 Dm. Crate on hoist; 1 Dm. 50, Open manhole.

1971. Tourism. As T **473** but with view of Goslar.
1606 20 pf. black and green 30 10

506 Women churning Butter **507** Deaconess and Nurse

1971. Humanitarian Relief Funds. Wooden Toys. Multicoloured.
(a) Inscr "WOHLFAHRTSMARKE".
1607 20 pf. + 10 pf. Type **506** . . . 20 25
1608 25 pf. + 10 pf. Horseman on wheels 20 25
1609 30 pf. + 15 pf. Nutcracker man 30 30
1610 60 pf. + 30 pf. Dovecote . . . 90 1·10
(b) Christmas. Inscr "WEIHNACHTSMARKE".
1611 20 pf. + 10 pf. Angel with three candles 20 20

1972. Death Cent. of Johann Wilhelm Lohe (founder of Deaconesses Mission, Neuendettelsau).
1612 **507** 25 pf. slate, black & green 15 10

508 Ducks crossing Road **509** Senefelder's Press

1972. Child Welfare. Annimal Protection Multicoloured.
1613 20 pf. + 10 pf. Type **508** . . . 45 45
1614 25 pf. + 10 pf. Hunter scaring deer 40 40
1615 30 pf. + 15 pf. Child protecting bird from cat 70 70
1616 60 pf + 30 pf. Boy annoying mute swans . . . . 1·90 1·90

1972. "175 Years of Offset Lithography".
1617 **509** 25 pf. multicoloured . . . 15 10

510 "Communications" **511** Lucas Cranach

1972. Europa.
1618 **510** 25 pf. multicoloured . . . 30 15
1619 30 pf. multicoloured . . . 40 15

1972. 500th Birth Anniv of Lucas Cranach the Elder (painter).
1620 **511** 25 pf. blk, stone & grn . . 25 10

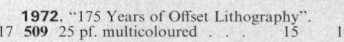

512 Wrestling **514** Invalid Archer

1972. Olympic Games, Munich (5th series). Multicoloured.
1621 20 pf. + 10 pf. Type **512** . . . 25 25
1622 25 pf. + 10 pf. Sailing 35 35
1623 30 pf. + 15 pf. Gymnastics . . 50 50
1624 60 pf. + 30 pf. Swimming . . 1·40 1·40
See also Nos. 1629/32.

1972. 21st Int. Games for the Paralysed, Heidelberg.
1626 **514** 40 pf. red, black & yell . . 30 15

515 Posthorn and Decree **516** K. Schumacher

1972. Cent. of German Postal Museum.
1627 **515** 40 pf. multicoloured . . . 55 10

1972. 20th Death Anniv of Kurt Schumacher (politician).
1628 **516** 40 pf. black and red . . . 90 10

1972. Olympic Games, Munich (7th series). As Type **512**. Multicoloured.
1629 25 pf. + 5 pf. Long jumping . . 75 75
1630 30 pf. + 10 pf. Basketball . . . 75 75
1631 40 pf. + 10 pf. Throwing the discus 75 75
1632 70 pf. + 10 pf. Canoeing . . . 75 75

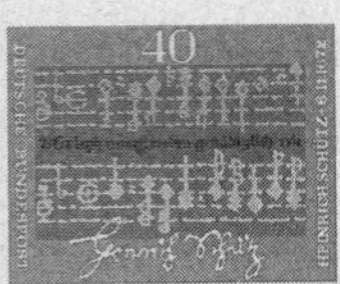

517 Open Book **518** Music and Signature

1972. Int. Book Year.
1634 **517** 40 pf. multicoloured . . . 30 10

1972. 300th Death Anniv of Heinrich Schutz (composer).
1635 **518** 40 pf. multicoloured . . . 40 10

519 Knight **520** Revellers

1972. Humanitarian Relief Funds. Mult.
(a) 19th-century Faience Chessmen. Inscr "WOHLFAHRTSMARKE".
1636 25 pf. + 10 pf. Type **519** . . . 40 40
1637 30 pf. + 15 pf. Rook 50 50
1638 40 pf. + 20 pf. Queen 60 60
1639 70 pf. + 35 pf. King . . . . . 2·00 2·00

(b) Christmas. Inscr "WEIHNACHTSMARKE".
1640 30 pf. + 15 pf. "The Three Wise Men" (horiz) 30 40

1972. Tourism. As T **473**.
1641 30 pf. black and green 30 15
1642 40 pf. black and orange . . . 40 15
VIEWS: 30 pf. Heligoland; 40 pf. Heidelberg.

1972. 150th Anniv of Cologne Carnival.
1643 **520** 40 pf. multicoloured . . . 60 10

521 H. Heine

1972. 175th Birth Anniv of Heinrich Heine (poet).
1644 **521** 40 pf. black, red & pink . 50 10

522 "Brot fur die Welt" **523** Wurzburg Cathedral (seal)

1972. Freedom from Hunger Campaign.
1645 **522** 30 pf. red and green . . . 30 30

1972. Catholic Synod '72.
1646 **523** 40 pf. black, pur & red . . 30 10

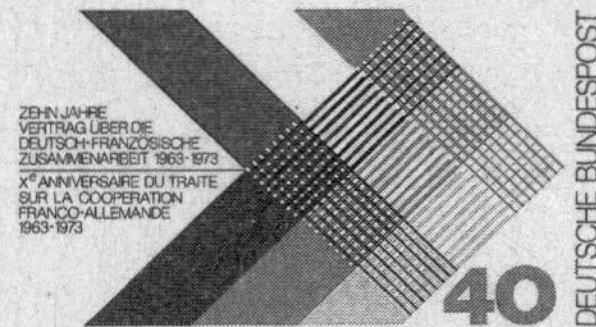

524 National Colours of France and Germany

1973. 10th Anniv of Franco-German Treaty.
1647 **524** 40 pf. multicoloured . . . 80 15

525 Osprey **527** Radio Mast and Transmission

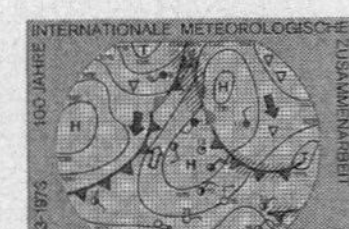

526 Copernicus

1973. Youth Welfare. Birds of Prey. Multicoloured.
1648 25 pf. + 10 pf. Type **525** . . . 1·50 1·50
1649 30 pf. + 15 pf. Common Buzzard . . . . 2·00 2·00
1650 40 pf. + 20 pf. Red Kite . . . 3·00 3·00
1651 70 pf. + 35 pf. Montagu's Harrier . . . . 6·00 6·00

1973. 500th Birth Anniv of Copernicus.
1652 **526** 40 pf black and red . . . 80 10

1973. 50th Anniv of Interpol.
1653 **527** 40 pf. blk, red & grey . . 40 10

528 Weather Chart **529** "Gymnast" (poster)

1973. Cent of Int Meteorological Organization.
1654 **528** 30 pf. multicoloured . . . 30 10

1973. Tourism. As T **473**.
1655 40 pf. black and red 60 15
1656 40 pf. black and orange . . . 50 15
VIEWS: No. 1655, Hamburg;. No. 1656, Rudesheim.

1973. Gymnastics Festival, Stuttgart.
1657 **529** 40 pf. multicoloured . . . 30 10

530 Kassel (Hesse) Sign **532** "R" Motif

531 Europa "Posthorn"

1973. "I.B.R.A. Munchen 73" Int Stamp Exhib., Munich. F.I.P. Congress. Post-house Signs. Multicoloured.
1658 40 pf. + 20 pf. Type **530** . . . 80 80
1659 70 pf. + 35 pf. Prussia . . . . 1·00 1·00

1973. Europa.
1661 **531** 30 pf. yell, myrtle & grn . 40 20
1662 40 pf. yell, lake & pink . . 60 10

1973. 1000th Death Anniv of Roswitha von Gandersheim (poetess).
1663 **532** 40 pf. yellow, blk & red . . 30 10

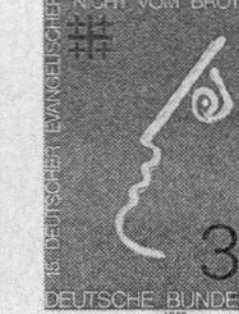

533 M. Kolbe **534** "Profile" (from poster)

1973. Father Maximilian Kolbe (Concentration camp victim) Commemoration.
1664 **533** 40 pf. red, brown & blk . . 40 10

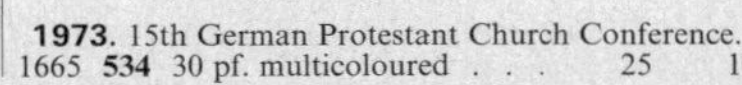

1973. 15th German Protestant Church Conference.
1665 **534** 30 pf. multicoloured . . . 25 10

535 Environmental Conference Emblem and Waste

1973. "Protection of the Environment". Multicoloured.
1666 25 pf. Type **535** 30 15
1667 30 pf. Emblem and "Water" . . 35 15
1668 40 pf. Emblem and "Noise" . . 50 15
1669 70 pf. Emblem and "Air" . . . 95 75

536 Schickard's Calculating Machine **537** Otto Wels

1973. 350th Anniv of Schickard's Calculating Machine.
1670 **536** 40 pf. black, red and orange 45 40

1973. Birth Centenary of Otto Wels (Social Democratic Party leader).
1671 **537** 40 pf. purple and lilac . . 40 10

538 Lubeck Cathedral

1973. 800th Anniv of Lubeck Cathedral
1672 **538** 40 pf. multicoloured . . . 75 10

539 U.N. and German Eagle Emblems

1973. Admission of German Federal Republic to U.N. Organization.
1673 **539** 40 pf. multicoloured . . . 1·10 10

540 French Horn

1973. Humanitarian Relief Funds. Multicoloured.
(a) Musical Instruments. Inscr "WOHLFAHRTSMARKE".
1674 25 pf. + 10 pf. Type **540** . . . 50 35
1675 30 pf. + 15 pf. Grand piano . . 50 30
1676 40 pf. + 20 pf. Violin 60 45
1677 70 pf. + 70 pf. Harp . . . . . 1·75 1·75

(b) Christmas. Inscr "WEIHNACHTSMARKE".
1678 30 pf. + 15 pf. Christmas star . 50 40

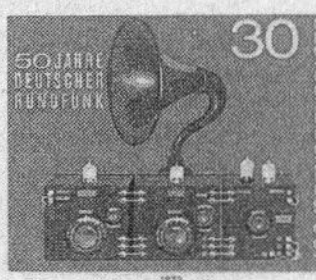

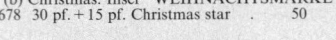

541 Radio set of 1923

1973. "50 Years of German Broadcasting".
1679 **541** 30 pf. multicoloured . . . 25 15

1974. Tourism. As Type **473**.
1680 30 pf. black and green 50 15
1681 40 pf. black and red 50 15
1682 40 pf. black and red 50 15
VIEWS: No. 1680, Saarbrucken; No. 1681, Aachen; No. 1682, Bremen.

542 Louise Otto-Peters

1974. Women in German Politics. Each black and orange.
1683 40 pf. Type **542** 50 45
1684 40 pf. Helene Lange 50 45
1685 40 pf. Rosa Luxemburg 50 45
1686 40 pf. Gertrud Baumer 50 45

543 Drop of Blood and Emergency Light

1974. Blood Donor and Accident/Rescue Services.
1687 **543** 40 pf. red and blue . . . 50 15

544 "Deer in Red" (Franz Marc)

1974. German Expressionist Paintings. Mult.
1688 30 pf. Type **544** 35 15
1689 30 pf. "Girls under Trees" (A. Macke) 50 15
1690 40 pf. "Portrait in Blue" (A. von Jawiensky) (vert) . . . 50 20
1691 50 pf. "Pechstein asleep" (E. Heckel) (vert) 45 25
1692 70 pf. "Still Life with Telescope" (Max Beckmann) 65 50
1693 120 pf. "Old Peasant" (L. Kirchner) (vert) . . . . . . 1·40 1·50

545 St. Thomas teaching Pupils

1974. 700th Death Anniv of St. Thomas Aquinas.
1694 **545** 40 pf. black and red . . . 30 10

546 Disabled Persons in Outline

1974. Rehabilitation of the Handicapped.
1695 **546** 40 pf. red and black . . . 55 15

547 Construction (Bricklayer) **548** "Ascending Youth" (W. Lehmbruck)

1974. Youth Welfare. Youth Activities. Multicoloured.
1696 25 pf. + 10 pf. Type **547** . . . 50 50
1697 30 pf. + 15 pf. Folk dancing . . 1·00 1·00
1698 40 pf. + 20 pf. Study . . . . 1·50 1·50
1699 70 pf. + 35 pf. Research . . . 2·50 2·50

1974. Europa.
1700 **548** 30 pf. blk, grn & silver . . 25 20
1701 – 40 pf. blk, red & lilac . . 35 15
DESIGN: 40 pf. "Kneeling Woman" (W. Lehmbruck).

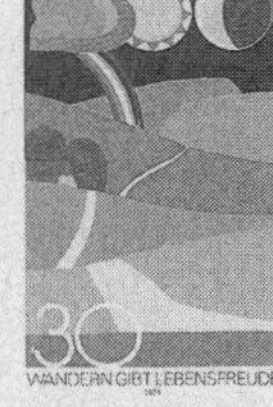

549 Immanuel Kant **551** Country Road

1974. 250th Birth Anniv of Immanuel Kant (philosopher).
1702 **549** 90 pf. red . . . . 1·25 20

1974. Rambling, and Birth Centenaries of Richard Schirrman and Wilhelm Munker (founders of Youth Hostelling Assn.).
1704 **551** 30 pf. multicoloured . . . 30 15

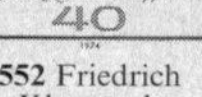

552 Friedrich Klopstock
553 "Crowned Cross" Symbol

1974. 250th Birth Anniv of Friedrich Gottlieb Klopstock (poet).
1705 **552** 40 pf. black and red . . . 40 15

1974. 125th Anniv of German Protestant Church Diaconal Association (Charitable organization).
1706 **553** 40p. multicoloured . . . 30 15

554 Goalkeeper saving Goal

1974. World Cup Football Championships. Multicoloured.
1707 30 pf. Type **554** 80 20
1708 40 pf. Mid-field melee . . . . 1·10 20

555 Hans Holbein (self-portrait)
556 Broken Bars of Prison Window

1974. 450th Death Anniv of Hans Holbein the Elder (painter).
1709 **555** 50 pf. black and red . . . 55 15

1974. Amnesty International Commemoration.
1710 **556** 70 pf. black and blue . . 80 30

557 "Man and Woman looking at the Moon"

1974. Birth Bicentenary of Caspar David Friedrich (artist).
1711 **557** 50 pf. multicoloured . . . 75 25

558 Campion
559 Early German Post-boxes

1974. Humanitarian Relief Funds. Flowers. Multicoloured.
(a) 25th Anniv of Welfare Stamps. Inscr "25 JAHRE WOHLFAHRTSMARKE".
1712 30 pf. + 15 pf. Type **558** . . . 35 35
1713 40 pf. + 20 pf. Foxglove . . . 45 45
1714 50 pf. + 25 pf. Mallow . . . 55 55
1715 70 pf. + 35 pf. Campanula . . 1·25 1·25
(b) Christmas. Inscr "WEIHNACHTSMARKE".
1716 40 pf. + 20 pf. Poinsettia . . . 60 60

1974. Cent of Universal Postal Union.
1717 **559** 50 pf. multicoloured . . . 85 30

560 Annette Kolb
562 Mother and Child and Emblem

561 Hans Bockler (Trade Union leader)

1975. International Women's Year. Women Writers.
1718 30 pf. Type **560** 35 25
1719 40 pf. Ricarda Huch 45 20
1720 50 pf. Else Lasker-Schuler . . 55 20
1721 70 pf. Gertrud von le Fort . . 90 90

1975. Birth Centenaries.
1722 **561** 40 pf. black and green . . 40 15
1723 – 50 pf. black and red . . 50 15
1724 – 70 pf. black and blue . . 1·50 40
DESIGNS: 50 pf. Matthias Erzberger (statesman); 70 pf. Albert Schweitzer (medical missionary).

1975. 25th Anniv of Organization for the Rest and Recuperation of Mothers.
1725 **562** 50 pf. multicoloured . . . 40 15

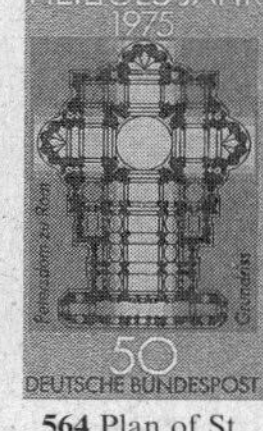

563 Detail of Ceiling Painting, Sistine Chapel
564 Plan of St. Peter's, Rome within a cross

1975. 500th Birth Anniv of Michelangelo.
1726 **563** 70 pf. black and blue . . 1·00 1·00

1975. "Holy Year (Year of Reconcillation)".
1727 **564** 50 pf. multicoloured . . . 30 15

565 Ice Hockey

1975. World Ice Hockey Championships, Munich and Dusseldorf.
1728 **565** 50 pf. multicoloured . . . 60 15

566 Class 218 Diesel Locomotive

1975. Youth Welfare. Railway Locomotives. Multicoloured.
1729 30 pf. + 15 pf. Type **566** . . . 90 80
1730 40 pf. + 20 pf. Class 103 electric locomotive . . . . 1·10 95
1731 50 pf. + 25 pf. Class 403 electric railcar . . . . 1·75 1·50
1732 70 pf. + 35 pf. Transrapid Maglev train (model) . . . 2·40 2·00

567 "Concentric Group"
569 "Nuis" (wood-carving)

568 Morike's Silhouette and Signature

1975. Europa. Paintings by Oskar Schlemmer. Multicoloured.
1733 40 pf. Type **567** 30 20
1734 50 pf. "Bauhaus Staircase" . . 60 10

1975. Death Cent of Eduard Morike (writer).
1735 **568** 40 pf. multicoloured . . . 30 15

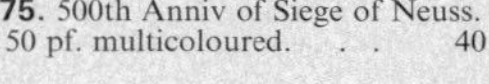

1975. 500th Anniv of Siege of Neuss.
1736 **569** 50 pf. multicoloured. . . 40 15

570 Jousting Contest

1975. 500th Anniv of "Landshut Wedding" (festival).
1737 **570** 50 pf. multicoloured . . . 60 15

571 Mainz Cathedral
572 Tele-communication Satellite

1975. Millenary of Mainz Cathedral.
1738 **571** 40 pf. multicoloured. . . 60 15

1975. Industry and Technology.
1739 **572** 5 pf. green 10 10
1740 – 10 pf. mauve 15 10
1741 – 20 pf. red 20 10
1742 – 30 pf. lilac 30 10
1743 – 40 pf. green 40 10
1744 – 50 pf. mauve 45 10
1745 – 60 pf. red 65 10
1746 – 70 pf. blue 55 10
1747 – 80 pf. green 65 10
1748 – 100 pf. brown 80 10
1748a – 110 pf. purple . . . . . 1·40 25
1749 – 120 pf. blue . . . . . 1·00 25
1749a – 130 pf. red . . . . . 1·60 25
1750 – 140 pf. red . . . . . 1·10 30
1751 – 150 pf. red . . . . . 2·00 50
1752 – 160 pf. green . . . . . 1·75 40
1753 – 180 pf. brown . . . . . 1·75 60
1753a – 190 pf. brown . . . . . 2·25 60
1754 – 200 pf. purple . . . . . 1·50 15
1754a – 230 pf. purple . . . . . 2·40 60
1754b – 250 pf. green . . . . . 3·00 80
1754c – 300 pf. green . . . . . 4·25 1·10
1755 – 500 pf. black . . . . . 4·00 50
DESIGNS: 10 pf. Electric train; 20 pf. Modern lighthouse; 30 pf. MBB-Bolkow Bo 105C rescue helicopter; 40 pf. Space laboratory; 50 pf. Dish aerial; 60 pf. X-ray apparatus; 70 pf. Ship-building; 80 pf. Farm tractor; 100 pf. Lignite excavator; 110 pf. Colour television camera; 120 pf. Chemical plant; 130 pf. Brewery plant; 140 pf. Power station; 150, 190 pf. Mechanical shovel; 160 pf. Blast furnace, 180 pf. Wheel loader; 200 pf. Marine drilling platform; 230, 250 pf. Frankfurt Airport; 300 pf. Electromagnetic monorail; 500 pf. Radio telescope.

573 Town Hall and Market, Alsfeld

1975. European Architectural Heritage Year. German Buildings. Multicoloured.
1756 50 pf. Type **573** 60 60
1757 50 pf. Plonlein corner, Siebers tower and Kobelzeller gate, Rothenburg-on-Tauber . . . 60 60
1758 50 pf. Town Hall ("The Steipe") Trier 60 60
1759 50 pf. View of Xanten 60 60

574 Effects of Drug-taking

1975. Campaign to Fight the Abuse of Drugs and Intoxicants.
1760 **574** 40 pf. multicoloured . . . 40 15

575 Posthouse Sign, Royal Prussian Establishment for Transport 1776
576 Edelweiss

1975. Stamp Day.
1761 **575** 10 pf. multicoloured . . . 15 10

1975. Humanitarian Relief Funds. Alpine Flowers. Multicoloured.
(a) Inscr "Wohlfartsmarke 1975".
1762 30 pf. + 15 pf. Type **576** . . . 35 35
1763 40 pf. + 20 pf. Trollflower . . . 50 50
1764 50 pf. + 25 pf. Alpine rose . . 60 60
1765 70 pf. + 35 pf. Pasque-flower . 1·40 1·40
(b) Inscr "Weihnachtsmarke 1975".
1766 **576** 40 pf. + 20 pf. Christmas rose 55 55
See also Nos. 1796/9, 1839/42, 1873/6 and 1905/8.

578 Stylised Ski-runners
579 Konrad Adenauer

1975. Winter Olympic Games, Innsbruck.
1768 **578** 50 pf. multicoloured . . . 50 15

1976. Birth Centenary of Konrad Adenauer (Chancellor 1949–63).
1769 **579** 50 pf. green . . . . . . 1·10 15

580 Cover Pages from Hans Sachs' Books
581 Junkers F-13 "Herta"

1976. 400th Death Anniv of Hans Sachs (poet and composer).
1770 **580** 40 pf. multicoloured . . . 35 10

1976. 50th Anniv of Lufthansa (German civil airline).
1771 **581** 50 pf. multicoloured . . . 70 15

582 Emblem and Commemorative Inscription
583 Letters "E G" representing Steel Girders

1976. 25th Anniv of Federal Constitutional Court.
1772 **582** 50 pf. multicoloured . . . 45 15

1976. 25th Anniv of European Coal and Steel Community.
1773 **583** 40 pf. multicoloured . . . 40 10

584 Monorail Train
585 Basketball

1976. 75th Anniv of Wuppertal Monorailway.
1774 **584** 50 pf. multicoloured . . . 70 15

1976. Youth Welfare. Training for the Olympics. Multicoloured.
1775 30 pf. + 15 pf. Type **585** . . . 35 35
1776 40 pf. + 20 pf. Rowing 65 65
1777 50 pf. + 25 pf. Gymnastics . . 75 75
1778 70 pf. + 35 pf. Volleyball . . . 1·25 1·25

586 Swimming

1976. Olympic Games, Montreal. Mult.
1779 40 pf. + 25 pf. Type **586** . . . 55 65
1780 50 pf. + 25 pf. High jumping . 70 80

587 Girl selling Trinkets and Copperplate Prints
588 Carl Sonnenschein

1976. Europa. Ludwigsburg China Figures. Multicoloured.
1782 40 pf. Type **587** 40 15
1783 50 pf. Boy selling copperplate prints 60 10

1976. Birthday Centenary of Dr. Carl Sonnenschein (clergyman).
1784 **588** 50 pf. multicoloured . . . 35 15

589 Opening bars of Hymn "Entrust Yourself to God"

1976. 300th Birth Anniv of Paul Gerhardt (composer).
1785 **589** 40 pf. multicoloured . . . 40 15

590 Carl Maria von Weber conducting

1976. 150th Death Anniv of Carl Maria von Weber (composer).
1786 **590** 50 pf. black & brown . . 65 15

591 Carl Schurz

1976. Bicent of American Revolution.
1787 **591** 70 pf. multicoloured . . . 65 30

592 Wagnerian Stage

1976. Centenary of Bayreuth Festival.
1788 **592** 50 pf. multicoloured . . . 80 15

593 Bronze Ritual Chariot

1976. Archaeological Heritage. Mult.
1789 30 pf. Type **593** 35 20
1790 40 pf. Gold-ornamental bowl . 45 20
1791 50 pf. Silver necklet 60 25
1792 120 pf. Roman gold goblet . . 1·75 1·75

594 Golden Plover
595 Mythical Creature

1976. Bird Protection.
1793 **594** 50 pf. multicoloured . . . 1·00 20

1976. 300th Death Anniv of J. J. C. von Grimmelshausen (writer).
1794 **595** 40 pf. multicoloured . . . 75 15

596 18th-century Posthouse Sign, Hochst-am-Main
597 Sophie Schroder ("Sappho")

1976. Stamp Day.
1795 **596** 10 pf. multicoloured . . . 10 10

1976. Humanitarian Relief Funds. Garden Flowers. Designs similar to T **576**. Multicoloured.
1796 30 pf. + 15 pf. Phlox 40 40
1797 40 pf. + 20 pf. Marigolds . . . 50 50
1798 50 pf. + 25 pf. Dahlias 65 65
1799 70 pf. + 35 pf. Pansies . . . . 1·00 1·00

1976. Famous German Actresses. Mult.
1800 30 pf. Carolin Neuber ("Medea") 35 15
1801 40 pf. Type **597** 45 30
1802 50 pf. Louise Dumont ("Hedda Gabler") 60 30
1803 70 pf. Hermine Korner ("Macbeth") 90 90

599 Eltz Castle
600 Palais de l'Europe

1977. German Castles.
1805 – 10 pf. blue 10 10
1805c – 20 pf. orange 15 10
1805d – 25 pf. red 25 10
1806 – 30 pf. bistre 25 10
1806c – 35 pf. red 50 10
1807 **599** 40 pf. green 50 10
1807a – 40 pf. brown 35 10
1808 – 50 pf. red 45 10
1808b – 50 pf. green 50 10
1809 – 60 pf. brown 75 15
1809a – 60 pf. red 70 10
1810 – 70 pf. blue 60 15
1810a – 80 pf. green 80 20
1810c – 90 pf. blue 90 25
1810d – 120 pf. violet . . . . . 1·50 30
1811 – 190 pf. red . . . . . . 1·50 50
1812 – 200 pf. green . . . . . 1·75 55
1812a – 210 pf. brown . . . . . 2·40 70
1812b – 230 pf. green . . . . . 2·50 70
1812c – 280 pf. blue . . . . . 3·25 85
1812d – 300 pf. orange . . . . . 3·50 1·00
DESIGNS: 10 pf. Glucksburg; 20, 190 pf. Pfaueninsel, Berlin; 25 pf. Gemen; 30 pf. Ludwigstein, Werratal; 35 pf. Lichtenstein; 40 pf. (1807a) Wolfsburg; 50 pf. (1808) Neuschwanstein; 50 pf. (1808b) Inzlingen; 60 pf. (1809) Marksburg; 60 pf. (1809a) Rheydt; 70 pf. Mespelbrunn; 80 pf. Wilhelmsthal; 90 pf. Vischering; 120 pf. Charlottenburg, Berlin; 200 pf. Burresheim; 210 pf. Schwanenburg; 230 pf. Lichtenberg; 280 pf. Ahrensburg; 300 pf. Herrenhausen, Hanover.

1977. Inauguration of Palais de l'Europe (council of Europe buildings), Strasbourg.
1813 **600** 140 pf. green and black . 1·25 40

601 Book Illustrations
603 Jean Monnet

1977. "Till Eulenspiegel" (popular fable).
1814 **601** 50 pf. multicoloured . . . 50 15

1977. Award of "Citizen of Europe" honour to Jean Monnet (French statesman).
1816 **603** 50 pf. black, grey & yell . 40 15

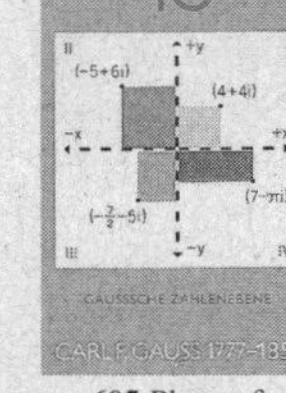

604 "Flower"
605 Plane of Complex Numbers

1977. 25th Anniv of Federal Horticultural Show.
1817 **604** 50 pf. multicoloured . . . 40 15

1977. Birth Bicentenary of Carl Friedrich Gauss (mathematician).
1818 **605** 40 pf. multicoloured . . . 90 15

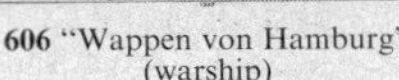

606 "Wappen von Hamburg" (warship)
607 Head of Barbarossa

1977. Youth Welfare. Ships. Multicoloured.
1819 30 pf. + 15 pf. Type **606** . . . 75 85
1820 40 pf. + 20 pf. "Preussen" (full-rigged sailing ship) . . . . 1·00 1·10
1821 50 pf. + 25 pf. "Bremen" (liner) 1·25 1·50
1822 70 pf. + 35 pf. "Sturmfels" (container ship) . . . . 1·60 1·75

1977. Staufer Year, Baden-Wurttemberg.
1823 **607** 40 pf. multicoloured . . . 80 15

608 Rhon Autobahn
609 "Self-Portrait" (Rubens)

1977. Europa.
1824 **608** 40 pf. black and green . . 40 15
1825 – 50 pf. black and red . . . 70 10
DESIGN: 50 pf. Rhine landscape.

1977. 400th Birth Anniv of Peter Paul Rubens.
1826 **609** 30 pf. black 70 10

610 Ulm Cathedral
611 Rector's Seal, Mainz University (500th Anniv)

1977. 600th Anniv of Ulm Cathedral.
1827 **610** 40 pf. brn, grn & bl . . . 30 15

1977. University Anniversaries.
1828 **611** 50 pf. black and red . . . 65 15
1829 – 50 pf. black and red . . . 65 15
1830 – 50 pf. black and red . . . 65 15
DESIGNS: No. 1829, Great Seal, Marburg University (450th anniv); No. 1830, Great Seal, Tubingen University (500th anniv).

612 "Morning"

1977. Birth Bicentenary of Phillipp Otto Runge (artist).
1831 **612** 60 pf. multicoloured . . . 55 30

613 Ketteler's Coat of Arms
614 Fritz von Bodelschwingh

1977. Death Centenary of Bishop Wilhelm Emmanuel von Ketteler.
1832 **613** 50 pf. multicoloured . . . 50 15

1977. Birth Centenary of Pastor Fritz von Bodelschwingh (pioneer of welfare work for the disabled).
1833 **614** 50 pf. multicoloured . . . 50 15

615 Golden Hat

1977. Archaeological Heritage. Multicoloured.
1834 30 pf. Type **615** 50 10
1835 120 pf. Gilt helmet . . . . . 90 1·10
1836 200 pf. Bronze centaur head . . 1·40 1·40

616 Operator and Switchboard
617 19th-century Posthouse Sign, Hamburg

1977. Centenary of Telephone in Germany.
1837 **616** 50 pf. multicoloured . . . 80 15

1977. Stamp Day.
1838 **617** 10 pf. multicoloured . . . 15 10

1977. Humanitarian Relief Funds. Meadow Flowers. As T **576**. Multicoloured.
1839 30 pf. + 15 pf. Caraway 35 40
1840 40 pf. + 20 pf. Dandelion . . . 50 55
1841 50 pf. + 25 pf. Red clover . . . 60 70
1842 70 pf. + 35 pf. Meadow sage . . 1·00 1·10

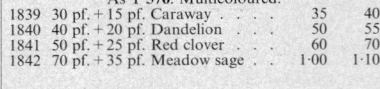

618 Travelling Surgeon
619 Wilhelm Hauff

1977. 250th Death Anniv of Dr. Johann Andreas Eisenbarth.
1843 **618** 50 pf. multicoloured . . . 55 15

1977. 150th Death Anniv of Wilhelm Hauff (poet and novelist).
1844 **619** 40 pf. multicoloured . . . 40 15

621 Book Cover Designs
622 Refugees

1978. Birth Centenary of Rudolph Alexander Schroder (writer).
1846 **621** 50 pf. multicoloured . . . 40 15

1978. 20th Anniv of Friedland Aid Society.
1847 **622** 50 pf. multicoloured . . . 40 15

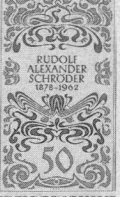

623 Skiing

1978. Sport Promotion Fund. Multicoloured.
1848 50 pf. + 25 pf. Type **623** . . . 1·00 1·00
1849 70 pf. + 35 pf. Show jumping . 2·50 2·50

624 Gerhart Hauptmann 625 Martin Buber

1978. German Winners of Nobel Prize for Literature. Multicoloured.

1850 30 pf. Type **624** 25 25
1851 50 pf. Hermann Hesse 45 45
1852 70 pf. Thomas Mann 60 60

1978. Birth Centenary of Martin Buber (religious philosopher).

1854 **625** 50 pf. multicoloured . . . 40 15

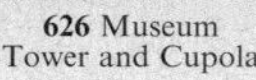

626 Museum Tower and Cupola **627** Wilhelmine Reichart's Balloon, Munich October Festival, 1820

1978. 75th Anniv of German Scientific and Technical Museum, Munich.

1855 **626** 50 pf. blk, yell & red . . . 40 15

1978. Youth Welfare. Aviation History (1st series). Multicoloured.

1856 30 pf. + 15 pf. Type **627** . . . 70 80
1857 40 pf. + 20 pf. Airship LZ-1, 1900 . . . . 80 90
1858 50 pf. + 25 pf. Bleriot XI monoplane, 1909 . . . . . 75 75
1859 70 pf. + 35 pf. Hans Grade's monoplane, 1909 . . . . . 1·00 1·00

See also Nos. 1886/9 and 1918/21.

628 Old Town Hall, Bamberg

1978. Europa. Multicoloured.

1860 40 pf. Type **628** 60 15
1861 50 pf. Old Town Hall, Regensburg 75 10
1862 70 pf. Old Town Hall, Esslingen am Neckar . . . . . . 1·00 50

629 Piper and Children

1978. Pied Piper of Hamelin.

1863 **629** 50 pf. multicoloured . . . 70 15

630 Janusz Korczak **631** Fossil Bat

1978. Birth Centenary of Janusz Korczak (educational reformer).

1864 **630** 90 pf. multicoloured . . . 95 35

1978. Archaeological Heritage, Fossils. Multicoloured.

1865 80 pf. Type **631** . . . . 1·50 1·00
1866 200 pf. Horse ("eohippus") skeleton . . . . 1·50 1·50

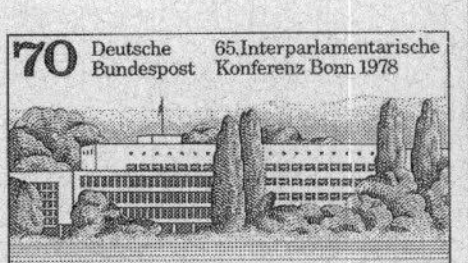

632 Parliament Building, Bonn **633** Rose Window, Freiburg Minster

1978. 65th Interparliamentary Union Conference, Bonn.

1867 **632** 70 pf. multicoloured . . . 90 30

1978. 85th Conference of German Catholics, Freiburg.

1868 **633** 40 pf. multicoloured . . . 40 15

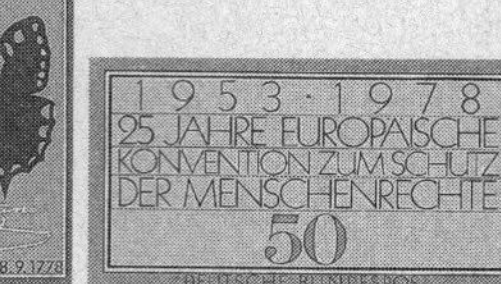

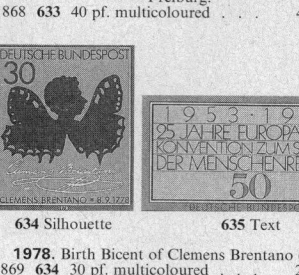

634 Silhouette **635** Text

1978. Birth Bicent of Clemens Brentano (poet).

1869 **634** 30 pf. multicoloured . . . 25 15

1978. 25th Anniv of European Convention for the Protection of Human Rights.

1870 **635** 50 pf. multicoloured . . . 40 15

636 Baden Posthouse Sign **639** Child

637 "Easter at the Walchensee" (Lovis Corinth)

1978. Stamp Day and World Philatelic Movement. Multicoloured.

1871 40 pf. Type **636** 50 25
1872 50 pf. 1850 3 pf. stamp of Saxony 50 25

1978. Humanitarian Relief Funds. Woodland Flowers. As T **576**. Multicoloured.

1873 30 pf. + 15 pf. Arum 35 35
1874 40 pf. + 20 pf. Weasel-snout . 45 45
1875 50 pf. + 25 pf. Turk's-cap lily . 60 60
1876 70 pf. + 35 pf. Liverwort . . . 95 95

1978. Impressionist Paintings. Multicoloured.

1877 50 pf. Type **637** 50 30
1878 70 pf. "Horseman on the Shore turning Left" (Max Liebermann) (vert) 75 60
1879 120 pf. "Lady with a Cat" (Max Slevogt) (vert) . . . . 1·40 1·40

1979. International Year of the Child.

1881 **639** 60 pf. multicoloured . . . 60 15

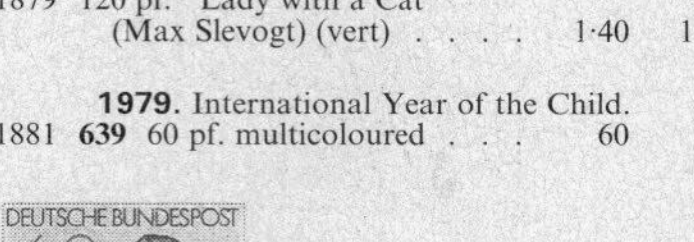
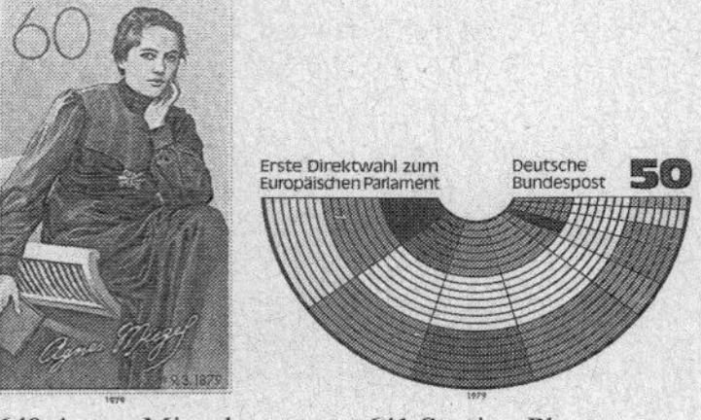

640 Agnes Miegel **641** Seating Plan

1979. Birth Cent of Agnes Miegel (poet).

1882 **640** 60 pf. multicoloured . . . 40 15

1979. First Direct Elections to European Parliament.

1883 **641** 50 pf. multicoloured . . . 45 15

642 Film **643** Rescue Services Emblems

1979. 25th West German Short Film Festival.

1884 **642** 50 pf. black and turq . . 60 15

1979. Rescue Services on the Road.

1885 **643** 50 pf. multicoloured . . . 55 15

1979. Youth Welfare. History of Aviation (2nd series). As T **627**. Multicoloured.

1886 40 pf. + 20 pf. Dornier Do-J Wal flying boat, 1922 . . . 80 80
1887 50 pf. + 25 pf. Heinkel He 70 Blitz, 1932 . . . . 90 1·00
1888 60 pf. + 30 pf. Junkers W.33 "Bremen", 1928 . . . . . 1·25 1·25
1889 90 pf. + 45 pf. Focke Achgelis Fa 61 helicopter, 1936 . . . 1·75 1·60

644 Handball

1979. Sport Promotion Fund. Multicoloured.

1890 60 pf. + 30 pf. Type **644** . . . 1·00 1·00
1891 90 pf. + 45 pf. Canoeing . . . 1·10 1·10

645 Telegraph Office, 1863 **646** Anne Frank

1979. Europa. Multicoloured.

1892 50 pf. Type **645** 50 15
1893 60 pf. Post Office counter, 1854 . . . . 60 10

1979. 50th Birth Anniv of Anne Frank (concentration camp victim and diary writer).

1894 **646** 60 pf. black, grey & red . . . 60 15

647 Werner von Siemens's Electric Railway, 1879

1979. International Transport Exhibition. Hamburg.

1895 **647** 60 pf. multicoloured . . . 75 15

648 Hand operating Radio Dial

1979. World Administrative Radio Conference, Geneva.

1896 **648** 60 f. multicoloured . . . 65 15

649 "Moses receiving the Tablets of the Law" (woodcut, Cranach the Elder) **650** Cross and Orb

1979. 450th Anniv of Publication of Martin Luther's Catechisms.

1897 **649** 50 pf. black & green . . . 75 15

1979. Pilgrimage to Aachen.

1898 **650** 50 pf. multicoloured . . . 40 15

651 Hildegard von Bingen

1979. 800th Death Anniv of Hildegard von Bingen (writer and mystic).

1899 **651** 110 pf. multicoloured . . 1·00 55

652 Photo-electric Effect

1979. Birth Centenaries of Nobel Prize Winners. Multicoloured.

1900 60 pf. Type **652** (Albert Einstein, Physics, 1921) . . 70 35
1901 60 pf. Splitting of uranium nucleus (Otto Hahn, Chemistry, 1944) 70 35
1902 60 pf. Diffraction pattern of X-rays passed through crystal (Max von Laue, Physics, 1914) 70 35

653 Pilot and Helmsman **654** Posthouse Sign, Altheim, Saar (German side), 1754

1979. 300th Anniv of 1st Pilotage Regulations.

1903 **653** 60 pf. brown & claret . . 55 15

1979. Stamp Day.

1904 **654** 60 pf. + 30 pf. mult . . . 1·00 1·00

1979. Humanitarian Relief Funds. Woodland Flowers and Fruit. As T **576**. Multicoloured.

1905 40 pf. + 20 pf. Red beech (horiz) 60 50
1906 50 pf. + 25 pf. English oak (horiz) 75 65
1907 60 pf. + 30 pf. Hawthorn (horiz) 80 70
1908 90 pf. + 45 pf. Mountain pine (horiz) . . . . 1·25 1·10

656 "Bird Garden"

1979. Birth Cent of Paul Klee (artist).

1909 **656** 90 pf. multicoloured . . . 80 45

657 Faust and Mephistopheles **658** Lightbulb

1979. Doctor Johannes Faust.

1910 **657** 60 pf. multicoloured . . . 90 15

1979. "Save Energy".

1911 **658** 40 pf. multicoloured . . . 40 15

659 "Nativity" (Altenberg medieval manuscript)

1979. Christmas.

1912 **659** 60 pf. + 30 pf. mult . . . 90 65

660 "Iphigenia"

1980. Death Centenary of Anselm Feuerbach (artist).

1913 **660** 50 pf. multicoloured . . . 80 15

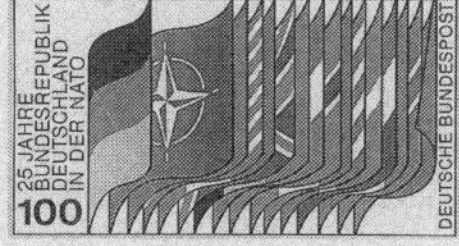

661 Flags of NATO Members

1980. 25th Anniv of NATO Membership.

1914 **661** 100 pf. multicoloured . . 1·25 60

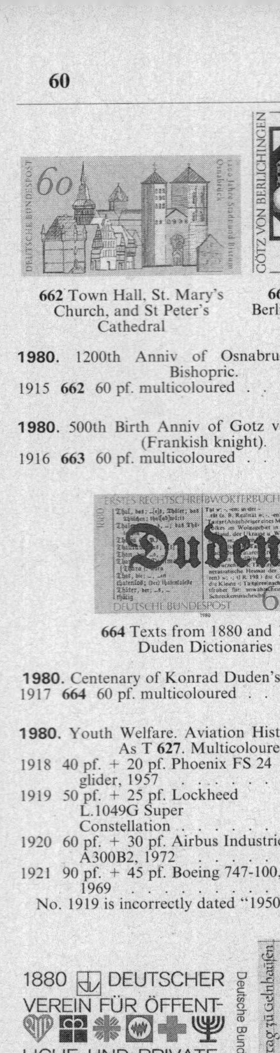

662 Town Hall, St. Mary's Church, and St Peter's Cathedral

663 "Gotz von Berlichingen" (glass picture)

1980. 1200th Anniv of Osnabruck Town and Bishopric.
1915 **662** 60 pf. multicoloured . . . 55 20

1980. 500th Birth Anniv of Gotz von Berlichingen (Frankish knight).
1916 **663** 60 pf. multicoloured . . . 45 20

664 Texts from 1880 and 1980 Duden Dictionaries

1980. Centenary of Konrad Duden's 1st Dictionary.
1917 **664** 60 pf. multicoloured . . . 65 15

1980. Youth Welfare. Aviation History (3rd series). As T **627**. Multicoloured.
1918 40 pf. + 20 pf. Phoenix FS 24 glider, 1957 . . . . 60 50
1919 50 pf. + 25 pf. Lockheed L.1049G Super Constellation 80 70
1920 60 pf. + 30 pf. Airbus Industrie A300B2, 1972 . . . . . . 90 90
1921 90 pf. + 45 pf. Boeing 747-100, 1969 . . . . 1·40 1·40
No. 1919 is incorrectly dated "1950".

665 Emblems of Association Members

666 "Frederick I with his sons" (Welf Chronicle)

1980. Centenary of German Association of Welfare Societies.
1922 **665** 60 pf. blue, red & black . 45 15

1980. 800th Anniv of Imperial Diet of Gelnhausen.
1923 **666** 60 pf. multicoloured . . . 60 15

667 Football

1980. Sport Promotion Fund. Multicoloured.
1924 50 pf. + 25 pf. Type **667** . . . 60 70
1925 60 pf. + 30 pf. Dressage . . . 75 75
1926 90 pf. + 45 pf. Skiing . . . . 1·25 1·25

668 Albertus Magnus (scholar)

669 Reading the Augsburg Confession (engraving, G Kohler)

1980. Europa. Multicoloured.
1927 50 pf. Type **668** 60 10
1928 60 pf. Gottfried Leibniz (philosopher) 80 15

1980. 450th Anniv of Augsburg Confession.
1929 **669** 50 pf. blk, yell & grn . . 45 15

670 Nature Reserve

1980. Nature Conservation.
1930 **670** 40 pf. multicoloured . . . 75 15

671 Ear and Oscillogram Pulses

1980. International Congress for the Training and Education of the Hard of Hearing, Hamburg.
1931 **671** 90 pf. multicoloured . . . 90 30

672 First Book of Daily Bible Readings, 1731

673 St. Benedict

1980. 250th Anniv of Moravian Brethren's Book of Daily Bible Readings.
1932 **672** 50 pf. multicoloured . . . 55 15

1980. 1500th Birth Anniv of St. Benedict of Nursia (founder of Benedictine Order).
1933 **673** 50 pf. multicoloured . . . 55 15

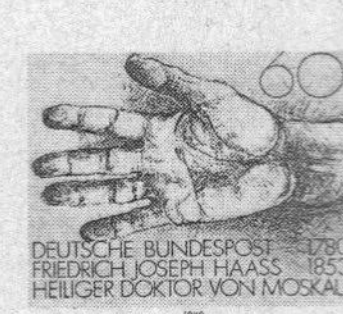

674 Helping Hand

675 Marie von Ebner-Eschenbach

1980. Birth Bicentenary of Friedrich Joseph Haass (philanthropist).
1934 **674** 60 pf. multicoloured . . . 60 15

1980. 150th Birth Anniv of Marie von Ebner-Eschenbach (novelist).
1935 **675** 60 pf. buff, blk & orge . . 60 15

676 Rigging

1980. Birth Centenary of Johan Kinau ("Gorch Fock") (poet).
1936 **676** 60 pf. multicoloured . . . 1·10 15

677 Positioning Keystone of South Tower Finial (engraving)

678 "Ceratocephalus falcatus"

1980. Centenary of Completion of Cologne Cathedral.
1937 **677** 60 pf. multicoloured . . . 1·25 15

1980. Humanitarian Relief Funds. Endangered Wildflowers. Multicoloured.
1938 40 pf. + 20 pf. Type **678** . . . 50 50
1939 50 pf. + 25 pf. Yellow Vetchling 65 65
1940 60 pf. + 30 pf. Corn Cockle . 90 90
1941 90 pf. + 45 pf. Tassel Hyacinth . . . . 1·25 1·25
See also Nos. 1972/5.

679 Wine-making (woodcuts)

1980. Bimillenary of Vine Growing in Central Europe.
1942 **679** 50 pf. multicoloured . . . 55 15

680 Posthouse Sign, Altheim, Saar, 1754 (French side)

681 "Nativity" (Altomunster manuscript)

1980. 49th International Philatelic Federation Congress, Essen.
1943 **680** 60 pf. + 30 pf. mult . . 45 60

1980. Christmas.
1944 **681** 60 pf. + 30 pf. mult . . . 80 70

682 "Landscape with Two Fir Trees" (etching)

683 Elly Heuss-Knapp

1980. 500th Birth Anniv of Albrecht Altdorfer (painter, engraver and architect).
1945 **682** 40 pf. lt brn, blk & brn . . 40 15

1981. Birth Centenary of Elly Heuss-Knapp (social reformer).
1946 **683** 60 pf. multicoloured . . . 50 15

684 Society accepting the Handicapped

1981. International Year of Disabled Persons.
1947 **684** 60 pf. multicoloured . . . 50 15

685 Old Town Houses

1981. European Campaign for Urban Renaissance.
1948 **685** 60 pf. multicoloured . . . 55 15

686 Telemann and Title Page of "Singet dem Herrn"

1981. 300th Birth Anniv of Georg Philipp Telemann (composer).
1949 **686** 60 pf. multicoloured . . . 70 15

687 Visiting a Foreign Family

1981. Integration of Guest Worker Families.
1950 **687** 50 pf. multicoloured . . . 55 15

688 Polluted Butterfly, Fish and Plant

1981. Preservation of the Environment.
1951 **688** 60 pf. multicoloured . . . 75 15

689 Patent Office Emblem and Scientific Signs

1981. Establishment of European Patent Office, Munich.
1952 **689** 60 pf. grey, red & black . 60 15

690 Scintigram showing Distribution of Radioactive Isotope

691 Borda Circle, 1800

1981. Cancer Prevention through Medical Check-ups.
1953 **690** 40 pf. multicoloured . . . 40 15

1981. Youth Welfare. Optical Instruments. Multicoloured.
1954 40 pf. + 20 pf. Type **691** . . . 60 60
1955 50 pf. + 25 pf. Reflecting telescope, 1770 . . . . 90 70
1956 60 pf. + 30 pf. Binocular microscope, 1860 . . . . . 90 80
1957 90 pf. + 45 pf. Octant, 1775 . 1·50 1·40

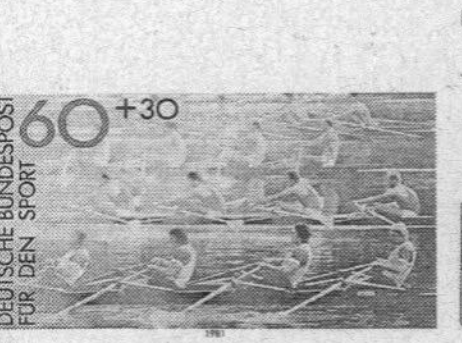

692 Rowing

693 South German Dancers

1981. Sport Promotion Fund. Multicoloured.
1958 60 pf. + 30 pf. Type **692** . . . 75 70
1959 90 pf. + 45 pf. Gliding . . . . 1·00 90

1981. Europa. Multicoloured.
1960 50 pf. Type **693** 60 15
1961 60 pf. North German dancers . 70 15

694 Convention Cross

695 Group from Crucifixion Altar

1981. 19th German Protestant Convention, Hamburg.
1962 **694** 50 pf. multicoloured . . . 50 15

1981. 450th Death Anniv of Tilman Riemenschneider (woodcarver).
1963 **695** 60 pf. multicoloured . . . 60 15

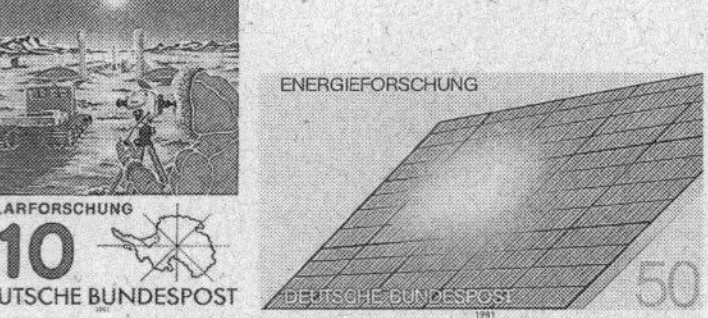

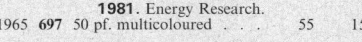

696 Georg von Neumayer Antarctic Research Station

697 Solar Generator

1981. Polar Research.
1964 **696** 110 pf. multicoloured . . 1·75 50

1981. Energy Research.
1965 **697** 50 pf. multicoloured . . . 55 15

698 Hand holding Baby Coot

700 Wilhelm Raabe

699 Arms of different Races forming Square

1981. Animal Protection.
1966 **698** 60 pf. multicoloured . . . 1·00 15

1981. Co-operation with Developing Countries.
1967 **699** 90 pf. multicoloured . . . 80 40

1981. 150th Birth Anniv of Wilhelm Raabe (poet).
1968 **700** 50 pf. lt green & green . . 50 15

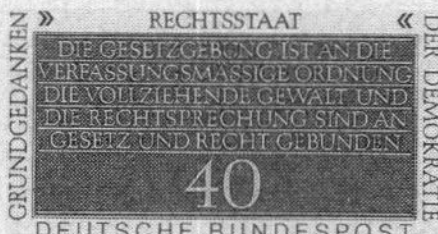

701 Constitutional Freedom

1981. Fundamental Concepts of Democracy. Article 20 of the Basic Law. Multicoloured.
1969 40 pf. Type **701** 40 15
1970 50 pf. Separation of Powers . . 50 15
1971 60 pf. Sovereignty of the People 60 20

1981. Humanitarian Relief Funds. Endangered Wildflowers. As T **678**. Multicoloured.
1972 40 pf. + 20 pf. Water nut . . 60 50
1973 50 pf. + 25 pf. Floating Heart 75 60
1974 60 pf. + 30 pf. Water gilly-flower 80 75
1975 90 pf. + 45 pf. Water lobelia . 1·40 1·25

702 Posthouse Scene c. 1855 **703** "Nativity" (glass painting)

1981. Stamp Day.
1976 **702** 60 pf. multicoloured . . . 1·10 15

1981. Christmas.
1977 **703** 60 pf. + 30 pf. mult . . . 85 65

704 St. Elisabeth **705** Clausewitz (after W. Wach)

1981. 750th Death Anniv of St. Elisabeth of Thuringia.
1978 **704** 50 pf. multicoloured . . . 75 15

1981. 150th Death Anniv of General Carl von Clausewitz (military writer).
1979 **705** 60 pf. multicoloured . . . 65 15

706 People forming Figure "100" **707** Map of Antarctica

1981. Cent of Social Insurance.
1980 **706** 60 pf. multicoloured . . . 60 15

1981. 20th Anniv of Antarctic Treaty.
1981 **707** 100 pf. bl, lt bl & blk . . 1·50 40

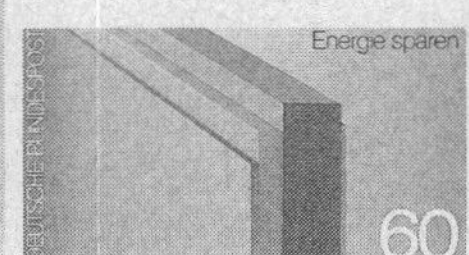

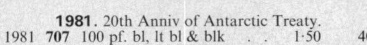

708 Pot with Lid **709** Insulated Wall

1982. 300th Birth Anniv of Johann Friedrich Bottger (founder of Meissen China Works).
1982 **708** 60 pf. multicoloured . . . 55 15

1982. Energy Conservation.
1983 **709** 60 pf. multicoloured . . . 60 15

710 Silhouette (Dora Brandenburg-Polster) **711** Goethe (after Georg Melchior Kraus)

1982. "The Town Band of Bremen" (German fairy tale).
1984 **710** 40 pf. black and red . . . 50 15

1982. 150th Death Anniv of Johann Wolfgang von Goethe (writer).
1985 **711** 60 pf. multicoloured . . . 1·50 20

712 Robert Koch

1982. Centenary of Discovery of Tubercle Bacillus.
1986 **712** 50 pf. multicoloured . . . 2·10 15

713 Benz Patent "Motorwagen", 1886

1982. Youth Welfare. Motor Cars. Mult.
1987 40 pf. + 20 pf. Type **713** . . . 70 65
1988 50 pf. + 25 pf. Mercedes "Tourenwagen", 1913 . . . 80 70
1989 60 pf. + 30 pf. Hannomag "Kommissbrot", 1925 . . . 1·10 1·00
1990 90 pf. + 45 pf. Opel "Olympia", 1937 . . . . . 1·60 1·40

714 Jogging

1982. Sport Promotion Fund. Multicoloured.
1991 60 pf. + 30 pf. Type **714** . . . 1·00 95
1992 90 pf. + 45 pf. Disabled archers . . . . 1·25 1·25

715 "Good Helene"

1982. 150th Birth Anniv of Wilhelm Busch (writer and illustrator).
1993 **715** 50 pf. blk, grn & yell . . 65 15

716 "Procession to Hambach Castle, 1832" (wood engraving)

1982. Europa.
1994 **716** 50 pf. black, yellow & red 90 20
1995 – 60 pf. multicoloured . . . 1·25 20
DESIGN: 60 pf. Excerpt from Treaty of Rome (instituting European Economic Community), 1957, and flags.

717 Racing Yachts

1982. Centenary of Kiel Regatta Week,
1996 **717** 60 pf. multicoloured . . . 1·00 25

718 Young Couple

1982. Centenary of Young Men's Christian Association in Germany.
1997 **718** 50 pf. multicoloured . . . 55 15

719 Polluted Sea

1982. "Prevent the Pollution of the Sea".
1998 **719** 120 pf. multicoloured . . 1·75 40

720 Battered Licence Plate

1982. "Don't Drink and Drive".
1999 **720** 80 pf. multicoloured . . . 1·00 25

721 Doctor examining Leper **722** Franck and Born

1982. 25th Anniv of German Lepers' Welfare Organization.
2000 **721** 80 pf. multicoloured . . . 95 25

1982. Birth Centenaries of James Franck and Max Born (physicists and Nobel Prize Winners).
2001 **722** 80 pf. grey, black and red . 95 25

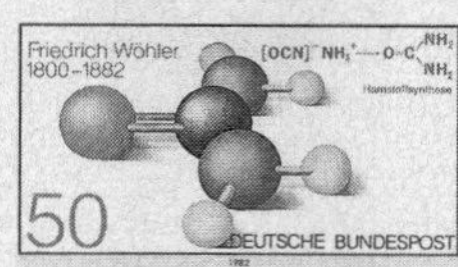

723 Atomic Model of Urea

1982. Death Centenary of Friedrich Wohler (chemist).
2002 **723** 50 pf. multicoloured . . . 55 10

724 "St. Francis preaching to the Birds" (fresco by Giotto) **725** Hybrid Tea Rose

1982. 87th German Catholics' Congress, Dusseldorf and 800th Birth Anniv of St. Francis of Assisi.
2003 **724** 60 pf. multicoloured . . . 70 20

1982. Humanitarian Relief Funds. Roses. Multicoloured.
2004 50 pf. + 20 pf. Type **725** . . . 60 60
2005 60 pf. + 30 pf. Floribunda . . 70 70
2006 80 pf. + 40 pf. Bourbon . . . 90 90
2007 120 pf. + 60 pf. Polyantha hybrid . . . . 1·50 1·50

726 Letters on Desk **727** Gregorian Calendar by Johannes Rasch, 1586

1982. Stamp Day.
2008 **726** 80 pf. multicoloured . . . 1·25 25

1982. 400th Anniv of Gregorian Calendar.
2009 **727** 60 pf. multicoloured . . . 65 20

729 "Nativity" (detail from St. Peter Altar by Master Bertram) **730** Edith Stein

1982. Christmas.
2011 **729** 80 pf. + 40 pf. mult . . . 1·25 95

1983. 40th Death Anniv (1982) of Edith Stein (philosopher).
2012 **730** 80 pf. lt grey, grey & blk . 1·10 25

731 White Rose and Barbed Wire

1983. Persecution and Resistance 1933–1945.
2013 **731** 80 pf. multicoloured . . . 1·00 25

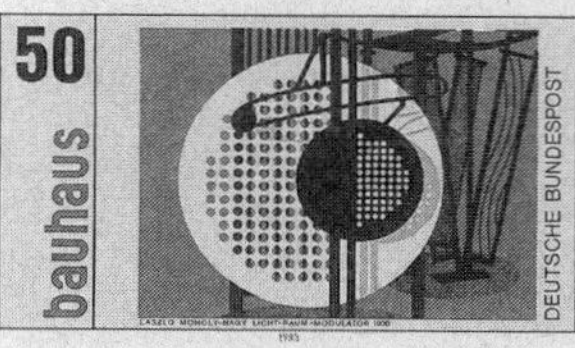

732 "Light Space Modulator" (Laszlo Moholy-Nagy)

1983. Birth Cent of Walter Gropius (founder of Bauhaus School of Art, Weimar). Bauhaus Art. Multicoloured.
2014 50 pf. Type **732** 55 20
2015 60 pf. "Sanctuary" (lithograph by Josef Albers) 65 25
2016 80 pf. Skylights from Bauhaus Archives, Berlin (Walter Gropius) 90 30

733 Federahannes (Rottweil carnival figure) **734** Daimler-Maybach, 1885

1983. Carnival.
2017 **733** 60 pf. multicoloured . . . 65 20

1983. Youth Welfare. Motor Cycles. Mult.
2018 50 pf. + 20 pf. Type **734** . . . 50 50
2019 60 pf. + 30 pf. N.S.U., 1901 . . 65 60
2020 80 pf. + 40 pf. Megola "Sport", 1922 . . . . . . 1·00 1·00
2021 120 pf. + 60 pf. B.M.W. world record holder, 1936 . . . . 1·50 1·50

735 Gymnastics (German Festival, Frankfurt am Main)

1983. Sports Promotion Fund. Multicoloured.
2022 80 pf. + 40 pf. Type **735** . . . 85 50
2023 120 pf. + 60 pf. Modern pentathlon (world championships, Warendorf) . . . . . 1·50 80

736 Stylized Flower

1983. 4th International Horticultural Show. Munich.
2024 **736** 60 pf. multicoloured . . . 80 20

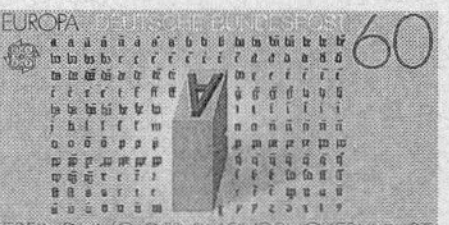

737 Modern Type and Gutenberg Letters

1983. Europa. Multicoloured.
2025 60 pf. Type **737** 1·50 20
2026 80 pf. Resonant circuit and electric flux lines 1·50 20

738 Johannes Brahms

1983. 150th Birth Anniv of Johannes Brahms (composer).
2027 **738** 80 pf. multicoloured 1·25 25

739 Kafka's Signature and Teyn Church, Prague

1983. Birth Cent of Franz Kafka (writer).
2028 **739** 80 pf. multicoloured 1·10 25

740 Brewing (frontispiece of 1677 treatise)

1983. 450th Anniv of Beer Purity Law.
2029 **740** 80 pf. multicoloured 1·10 25

741 "Concord"

1983. 300th Anniv of First German Settlers in America.
2030 **741** 80 pf. multicoloured 1·75 25

742 Children crossing Road

1983. Children and Road Traffic.
2031 **742** 80 pf. multicoloured 1·10 25

743 Flags forming Car

1983. 50th International Motor Show, Frankfurt-on-Main.
2032 **743** 60 pf. multicoloured 75 20

744 Warburg (after Oberland)
745 Wieland (after G. B. Bosio)

1983. Birth Centenary of Otto Warburg. (physiologist and chemist).
2033 **744** 50 pf. multicoloured 60 20

1983. 250th Birth Anniv of Cristoph Martin Wieland (writer).
2034 **745** 80 pf. multicoloured 90 25

746 Rosette in National Colours

1983. 10th Anniv of U.N. Membership.
2035 **746** 80 pf. multicoloured 1·10 30

747 "Das Rauhe Haus" and Children

1983. 150th Anniv of "Das Rauhe Haus" (children's home, Hamburg).
2036 **747** 80 pf. multicoloured 1·00 25

748 Surveying Maps

1983. International Geodesy and Geophysics Union General Assembly, Hamburg.
2037 **748** 120 pf. multicoloured 1·60 60

749 Swiss Androsace
750 Horseman with Posthorn

1983. Humanitarian Relief Funds. Endangered Alpine Flowers. Multicoloured.
2038 50 pf. + 20 pf. Type **749** 70 70
2039 60 pf. + 30 pf. Krain groundsel 95 95
2040 80 pf. + 40 pf. Fleischer's willow herb 1·25 1·25
2041 120 pf. + 60 pf. Alpine sowthistle 2·00 2·00

1983. Stamp Day.
2042 **750** 80 pf. multicoloured 1·40 25

751 Luther (engraving by G. Konig after Cranach)

1983. 500th Birth Anniv of Martin Luther (Protestant reformer).
2043 **751** 80 pf. multicoloured 2·00 25

752 Interwoven National Colours

1983. Federation, Lander and Communities Co-operation.
2044 **752** 80 pf. multicoloured 1·40 25

753 Customs Stamps
754 Epiphany Carol Singers

1983. 150th Anniv of German Customs Union.
2045 **753** 60 pf. multicoloured 1·50 20

1983. Christmas.
2046 **754** 80 pf. + 40 pf. mult 1·25 1·10

755 Black Gate, Trier
756 Reis and Telephone Apparatus

1984. 2000th Anniv of Trier.
2047 **755** 80 pf. multicoloured 1·40 30

1984. 150th Birth Anniv of Philipp Reis (telephone pioneer).
2048 **756** 80 pf. multicoloured 1·10 30

757 Mendel and Genetic Diagram

1984. Death Cent. of Gregor Mendel (geneticist).
2049 **757** 50 pf. multicoloured 80 20

758 Town Hall
759 Cloth draped on Cross

1984. 500th Anniv of Michelstadt Town Hall.
2050 **758** 60 pf. multicoloured 75 20

1984. 350th Anniv of Oberammergau Passion Play.
2051 **759** 60 pf. multicoloured 75 20

760 Bee-eating Beetle
761 Throwing the Discus

1984. Youth Welfare. Pollinating Insects. Multicoloured.
2052 50 pf. + 20 pf. Type **760** 80 80
2053 60 pf. + 30 pf. Red admiral 1·10 1·10
2054 80 pf. + 40 pf. Honey bee 1·40 1·40
2055 120 pf. + 60 pf. "Chrysotoxum festivium" (hover fly) 2·25 2·25

1984. Sport Promotion Fund. Multicoloured.
2056 60 pf. + 30 pf. Type **761** 1·00 90
2057 80 pf. + 40 pf. Rhythmic gymnastics 1·40 1·25
2058 120 pf. + 60 pf. Windsurfing 2·25 2·25

762 Parliament Emblem
763 Bridge

1984. Second Direct Elections to European Parliament.
2059 **762** 80 pf. yellow, blue and light blue 1·40 25

1984. Europa. 25th Anniv of European Post and Telecommunications Conference.
2060 **763** 60 pf. bl, lt bl & blk 95 25
2061 80 pf. pur, red & blk 1·10 25

764 St. Norbert (sculpture)
765 Nursery Rhyme Illustration

1984. 850th Death Anniv of St. Norbert von Xanten.
2062 **764** 80 pf. green & dp green 85 25

1984. Death Centenary of Ludwig Richter (illustrator).
2063 **765** 60 pf. black & brown 60 20

766 Cross and Shadow

1984. 50th Anniv of Protestant Churches' Barmen Theological Declaration.
2064 **766** 80 pf. multicoloured 85 20

768 Groom leading Horse (detail from tomb of Oclatius)
769 Bessel

1984. 2000th Anniv of Neuss.
2066 **768** 80 pf. multicoloured 85 20

1984. Birth Bicentenary of Friedrich Wilhelm Bessel (astronomer and mathematician).
2067 **769** 80 pf. grey, black and red 95 20

770 Eugenio Pacelli (Pope Pius XII)

1984. 88th German Catholics' Congress, Munich.
2068 **770** 60 pf. multicoloured 65 20

771 Town Hall
772 Medieval Document and Visual Display Unit

1984. 750th Anniv of Duderstadt Town Hall.
2069 **771** 60 pf. multicoloured 65 20

1984. 10th International Archives Congress, Bonn.
2070 **772** 70 pf. multicoloured 90 20

773 Knoop Lock

1984. Bicent of Schleswig-Holstein Canal.
2071 **773** 80 pf. multicoloured 1·00 20

774 Research Centre and Storage Rings

1984. 25th Anniv of German Electron Synchrotron (physics research centre), Hamburg–Bahrenfeld.
2072 **774** 80 pf. multicoloured 90 20

775 "Aceras anthropophorum"

1984. Humanitarian Relief Funds. Orchids. Multicoloured.
2073 50 pf. + 20 pf. Type **775** 1·00 80
2074 60 pf. + 30 pf. "Orchis ustulata" 1·10 1·10
2075 80 pf. + 40 pf. "Limodorum abortivum" 1·60 1·40
2076 120 pf. + 60 pf. "Dactylorhiza sambucina" 2·10 2·00

776 Taxis Posthouse, Augsburg

1984. Stamp Day.
2077 **776** 80 pf. multicoloured 1·50 30

777 Burning Match

1984. Anti-smoking Campaign.
2078 **777** 60 pf. multicoloured . . . 90 30

778 Male and Female Symbols

1984. Equal Rights for Men and Women.
2079 **778** 80 pf. blk, mve & bl . . . 90 30

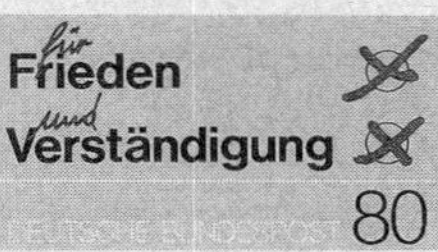

779 Ballot Slip

1984. For Peace and Understanding.
2080 **779** 80 pf. grey, blk & bl . . . 90 30

780 St. Martin giving Cloak to Beggar

1984. Christmas.
2081 **780** 80 pf. + 40 pf. mult . . . 1·25 1·25

781 Emperor Augustus (bust), Buildings and Arms

1985. 2000th Anniv of Augsburg.
2082 **781** 80 pf. multicoloured . . . 90 30

782 Spener (engraving by Bartholome Kilian after Johann Georg Wagner)

1985. 350th Birth Anniv of Philipp Jakob Spener (church reformer).
2083 **782** 80 pf. black & green . . . 90 30

783 Grimm Brothers (engraving by Lazarus Sichling)

1985. Birth Bicentenaries of Grimm Brothers (folklorists) and 7th International Union for German Linguistics and Literature Congress, Gottingen.
2084 **783** 80 pf. black, grey and red . 1·25 30

784 Romano Guardini

1985. Birth Centenary of Romano Guardini (theologian).
2085 **784** 80 pf. multicoloured . . . 90 30

785 Verden

1985. Millenary of Market and Coinage Rights in Verden.
2086 **785** 60 pf. multicoloured . . . 1·10 20

786 Flags and German-Danish Border

1985. 30th Anniv of Bonn-Copenhagen Declarations.
2087 **786** 80 pf. multicoloured . . . 1·00 30

787 Bowling

1985. Sport Promotion Fund. Multicoloured.
2088 80 pf. + 40 pf. Type **787** (cent. of German Nine-pin Bowling Association) . . . . 1·40 1·25
2089 120 pf. + 60 pf. Kayak (world rapid-river and slalom canoeing championships) . . . . 2·25 2·25

788 Kisch

789 "Hebel and the Margravine"

1985. Birth Centenary of Egon Erwin Kisch (journalist).
2090 **788** 60 pf. multicoloured . . . 75 20

1985. 225th Birth Anniv of Johann Peter Hebel (poet).
2091 **789** 80 pf. multicoloured . . . 1·00 30

790 Draisienne Bicycle, 1817

791 Handel

1985. Youth Welfare International Youth Year. Cycles. Multicoloured.
2092 50 pf. + 20 pf. Type **790** . . . 85 75
2093 60 pf. + 30 pf. NSU Germania "ordinary", 1866 . . . . . 1·25 1·10
2094 80 pf. + 40 pf. Cross-frame low bicycle, 1887 . . . . 1·50 1·50
2095 120 pf. + 60 pf. Adler tricycle, 1888 . . . . 2·75 2·75

1985. Europa. Composers' 300th Birth Anniversaries. Multicoloured.
2096 60 pf. Type **791** . . . . 1·50 30
2097 80 pf. Bach . . . . 1·50 30

792 Saint George's Cathedral

793 Capital (presbytery, "Wies" Church)

1985. 750th Anniv of Limburg Cathedral.
2098 **792** 60 pf. multicoloured . . . 90 20

1985. 300th Birth Anniv of Dominikus Zimmermann (architect).
2099 **793** 70 pf. multicoloured . . . 90 25

794 Josef Kentenich

1985. Birth Centenary of Father Josef Kentenich (founder of International Schonstatt (Catholic laymen's) Movement).
2100 **794** 80 pf. multicoloured . . . 1·00 30

795 Clock and Forest

1985. Save the Forests.
2101 **795** 80 pf. multicoloured . . . 1·10 30

796 Tug of War and Scouting Emblem

1985. 30th World Scouts Conference, Munich.
2102 **796** 60 pf. multicoloured . . . 85 20

797 "Sunday Walk"

1985. Death Cent of Carl Spitzweg (artist).
2103 **797** 60 pf. multicoloured . . . 1·10 20

798 Horses and Postilion

1985. "Mophila 1985" Stamp Exhibition, Hamburg. Multicoloured.
2104 60 pf. + 20 pf. Type **798** . . . 2·10 2·10
2105 80 pf. + 20 pf. Mail coach . . 2·40 2·40
Nos. 2104/5 were printed se-tenant, forming a composite design.

799 Stock Exchange

1985. 400th Anniv of Frankfurt Stock Exchange.
2106 **799** 80 pf. black, red and grey . 95 30

800 Flowers and Butterfly

801 Fritz Reuter

1985. Humanitarian Relief Funds. Designs depict motifs from borders of medieval prayer book. Multicoloured.
2107 50 pf. + 20 pf. Type **800** . . . 60 60
2108 60 pf. + 30 pf. Flowers, bird and butterfly 75 75
2109 80 pf. + 40 pf. Flowers, berries and snail . . . . 1·00 1·00
2110 120 pf. + 60 pf. Flowers, snail and butterfly . . . . 1·60 1·60

1985. 175th Death Anniv of Fritz Reuter (writer).
2111 **801** 80 pf. black, grey and blue . . . . 1·25 30

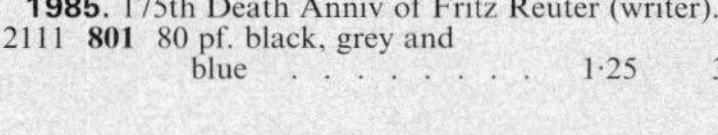

802 "Inauguration of First German Railway" (Heim)

1985. 150th Anniv of German Railways and Birth Bicent. of Johannes Scharrer (joint founder).
2112 **802** 80 pf. multicoloured . . . 1·40 30

803 Carpentry Joint in National Colours

805 "Nativity" (detail, High Altar, Freiburg)

804 Iron Cross and National Colours

1985. 40th Anniv of Integration of Refugees.
2113 **803** 80 pf. multicoloured . . . 1·25 30

1985. 30th Anniv of Federal Armed Forces.
2114 **804** 80 pf. red, blk & yell . . . 1·75 30

1985. Christmas. 500th Birth Anniversary of Hans Baldung Grien (artist).
2115 **805** 80 pf. + 40 pf. mult . . . 1·10 1·10

806 Early and Modern Cars

1986. Centenary of Motor Car.
2116 **806** 80 pf. multicoloured . . . 1·25 30

807 Town Buildings

808 "Self-portrait"

1986. 1250th Anniv of Bad Hersfeld.
2117 **807** 60 pf. multicoloured . . . 95 30

1986. Birth Centenary of Oskar Kokoschka (artist and writer).
2118 **808** 80 pf. black, grey and red . 95 30

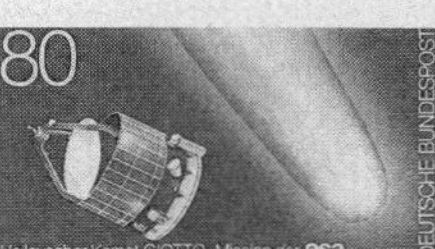

809 Comet and "Giotto" Space Probe

1986. Appearance of Halley's Comet.
2119 **809** 80 pf. multicoloured . . . 1·25 30

810 Running

1986. Sport Promotion Fund. Multicoloured.
2120 80 pf. + 40 pf. Type **810** (European Athletics Championships, Stuttgart) . 1·25 1·25
2121 120 pf. + 55 pf. Bobsleigh (World Championships, Konigsee) . . . . 2·00 2·00

811 Optician

1986. Youth Welfare. Trades (1st series). Multicoloured.
2122 50 pf. + 25 pf. Type **811** . . 75 75
2123 60 pf. + 30 pf. Bricklayer . . 95 95
2124 70 pf. + 35 pf. Hairdresser . . 1·40 1·40
2125 80 pf. + 40 pf. Baker . . . 2·00 2·00
See also Nos. 2179/82.

812 Walsrode Monastery

1986. Millenary of Walsrode.
2126 **812** 60 pf. multicoloured . . . 95 20

813 Ludwig and Neuschwanstein Castle

1986. Death Centenary of King Ludwig II of Bavaria.
2127 **813** 60 pf. multicoloured . . . 1·40 25

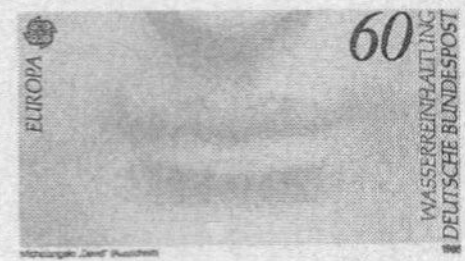

814 Mouth

1986. Europa. Details of "David" (sculpture) by Michelangelo. Multicoloured.
2128 60 pf. Type **814** . . . . 1·00 20
2129 80 pf. Nose . . . . 1·40 25

815 Karl Barth **817** Weber and Score of "Gloria"

816 Ribbons

1986. Birth Centenary of Karl Barth (theologian).
2130 **815** 80 pf. blk, red & pur . . . 1·00 30

1986. Union of German Catholic Students' Societies 100th Assembly, Frankfurt am Main.
2131 **816** 80 pf. multicoloured . . . 1·00 30

1986. Birth Bicentenary of Carl Maria von Weber (composer).
2132 **817** 80 pf. brn, blk & red . . . 1·40 30

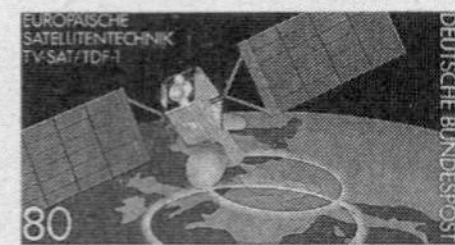

818 "TV-Sat" and Earth

1986. Launch of German "TV-Sat" and French "TDF-1" Broadcasting Satellites.
2133 **818** 80 pf. multicoloured . . . 1·40 30

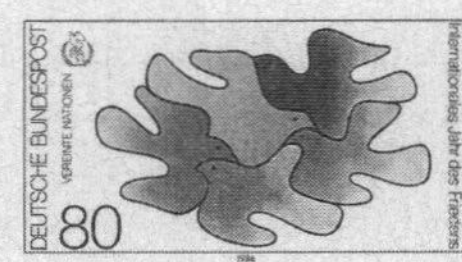

819 Doves

1986. International Peace Year.
2134 **819** 80 pf. multicoloured . . . 1·25 30

820 Liszt

1986. Death Centenary of Franz Liszt (composer).
2135 **820** 80 pf. blue & orange . . . 1·50 30

822 Pollution Damage of Stained Glass Window

1986. Protection of Monuments.
2137 **822** 80 pf. multicoloured . . . 1·25 30

823 Frederick the Great (after Anton Graff) **824** Congress Card

1986. Death Bicentenary of Frederick the Great.
2138 **823** 80 pf. multicoloured . . . 2·00 30

1986. Centenary of First German Skat Congress and 24th Congress, Cologne.
2139 **824** 80 pf. multicoloured . . . 1·25 30

825 Opposing Arrows

1986. 25th Anniv of Organization for Economic Co-operation and Development.
2140 **825** 80 pf. multicoloured . . . 1·00 30

826 Old University

1986. 600th Anniv of Heidelberg University.
2141 **826** 80 pf. multicoloured . . . 1·25 30

827 Fan of Stamps behind Stagecoach

1986. 50th Anniv of Stamp Day.
2142 **827** 80 pf. multicoloured . . . 1·25 35

828 Ornamental Flask, 300 AD **829** "Dance in Silence" from "Autumnal Dances"

1986. Humanitarian Relief Funds. Glassware. Multicoloured.
2143 50 pf. + 25 pf. Type **828** . . . 70 70
2144 60 pf. + 30 pf. Goblet with decorated stem, 1650 . . . 85 85
2145 70 pf. + 35 pf. Imperial Eagle tankard, 1662 . . . . . . 1·00 1·00
2146 80 pf. + 40 pf. Engraved goblet, 1720 . . . . 1·25 1·25

1986. Birth Centenary of Mary Wigman (dancer).
2147 **829** 70 pf. multicoloured . . . 90 25

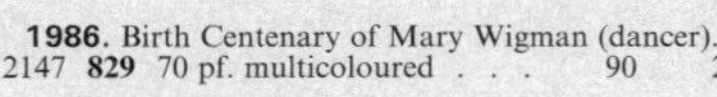

830 Cross over Map

1986. 25th Anniv of Adveniat (Advent collection for Latin America).
2148 **830** 80 pf. grn, bl & blk . . . 85 30

831 "Adoration of the Infant Jesus" (Ortenberg altarpiece) **832** Christine Teusch (politician)

1986. Christmas.
2149 **831** 80 pf. + 40 pf. mult . . . 1·25 1·25

1986. Famous German Women. Inscr "Deutsche Bundespost".

2150	–	5 pf. brown and grey	20	10
2151	–	10 pf. brown & violet	20	10
2152	–	20 pf. blue and red	25	10
2152a	–	30 pf. bistre & purple	30	10
2153	–	40 pf. red and blue	40	10
2154	**832**	50 pf. green & brown	50	10
2155	–	60 pf. lilac and green	50	15
2155a	–	70 pf. green and red	85	20
2156	–	80 pf. brown & green	90	20
2156a	–	80 pf. brown & blue	65	25
2157	–	100 pf. grey and red	80	25
2157a	–	100 pf. bistre & lilac	60	30
2158	–	120 pf. green & brn	90	25
2159	–	130 pf. violet & blue	1·60	30
2160	–	140 pf. ochre & blue	2·10	60
2161	–	150 pf. blue and red	2·40	65
2162	–	170 pf. purple & grn	1·40	35
2163	–	180 pf. purple & blue	1·50	40
2164	–	200 pf. red & brown	1·00	45
2165	–	240 pf. brown & grn	2·00	50
2166	–	250 pf. blue & mauve	3·00	55
2167	–	300 pf. green & pur	1·75	65
2168	–	350 pf. brown & blk	3·25	80
2168a	–	400 pf. black and red	3·75	95
2168b	–	450 pf. ultram & blue	4·00	1·50
2169	–	500 pf. red and green	4·25	1·50

DESIGNS: 5 pf. Emma Ihrer (politician and trade unionist); 10 pf. Paula Modersohn-Becker (painter); 20 pf. Cilly Aussem (tennis player); 30 pf. Kathe Kollwitz (artist); 40 pf. Maria Sibylla Merian (artist and naturalist); 60 pf. Dorothea Erxleben (first German woman Doctor of Medicine); 70 pf. Elisabet Boehm (founder of Agricultural Association of Housewives); 80 pf. (2156), Clara Schumann (pianist and composer); 80 pf. (2156a), Rahel Varnhagen von Ense (humanist) (after Wilhelm Hensel); 100 pf. (2157), Therese Giehse (actress); 100 pf. (2157a), Luise Henriette of Orange (mother of King Friedrich I of Prussia) (after Gerhard von Honthorst); 120 pf. Elisabeth Selbert (politician); 130 pf. Lise Meitner (physicist); 140 pf. Cecile Vogt (medical researcher); 150 pf. Sophie Scholl (resistance member); 170 pf. Hannah Arendt (sociologist); 180 pf. Lotte Lenmann (opera singer); 200 pf. Bertha von Suttner (novelist and pacifist); 240 pf. Mathilda Franziska Anneke (women's rights activist); 250 pf. Queen Louise of Prussia; 300 pf. Fanny Hensel (composer) (after Eduard Magnus); 350 pf. Hedwig Dransfeld (politician); 400 pf. Charlotte von Stein (friend of Goethe); 450 pf. Hedwig Courths-Mahler (novelist); 500 pf. Alice Salomon (women's rights activist).

For similar designs inscribed "Deutschland", see Nos. 2786/90.

833 Berlin Landmarks

1987. 750th Anniv of Berlin.
2170 **833** 80 pf. multicoloured . . . 1·60 35

834 Staircase, Residenz Palace, Wurzburg **835** Erhard

1987. 300th Birth Anniv of Balthasar Neumann (architect).
2171 **834** 80 pf. grey, black and red . 1·00 30

1987. 90th Birth Anniv of Ludwig Erhard (former Chancellor).
2172 **835** 80 pf. multicoloured . . . 1·25 30

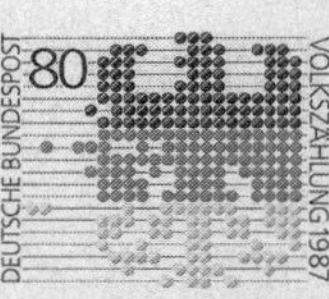

836 Abacus Beads forming Eagle **838** Chief Winnetou (from book cover)

837 Clemenswerth Castle

1987. Census.
2173 **836** 80 pf. multicoloured . . . 1·00 30

1987. 250th Anniv of Clemenswerth Castle.
2174 **837** 60 pf. multicoloured . . . 90 30

1987. 75th Death Anniv of Karl May (writer).
2175 **838** 80 pf. multicoloured . . . 1·00 30

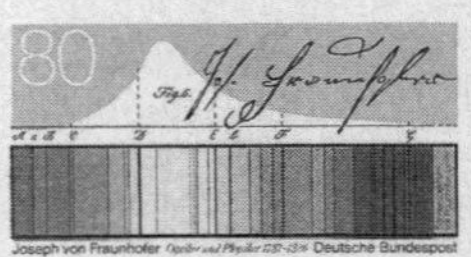

839 Solar Spectrum

1987. Birth Bicentenary of Joseph von Fraunhofer (optician and physicist).
2176 **839** 80 pf. multicoloured . . . 90 30

840 World Sailing Championships, Kiel

1987. Sport Promotion Fund. Multicoloured.
2177 80 pf. + 40 pf. Type **840** . . . 1·25 1·25
2178 120 pf. + 55 pf. World Nordic Skiing Championships, Oberstdorf . . . . 1·75 1·75

1987. Youth Welfare. Trades (2nd series). As T **811**. Multicoloured.
2179 50 pf. + 25 pf. Plumber . . . 85 85
2180 60 pf. + 30 pf. Dental technician . . . . 1·00 1·00
2181 70 pf. + 35 pf. Butcher . . . 1·25 1·25
2182 80 pf. + 40 pf. Bookbinder . . 1·75 1·60

841 Clefs, Notes and Leaves

1987. 125th Anniv of German Choir Association.
2183 **841** 80 pf. multicoloured . . . 1·00 30

842 Pope's Arms, Madonna and Child and Kevelaer

1987. Visit of Pope John Paul II to Kevelaer (venue for 17th Marian and 10th Mariological Congresses).
2184 **842** 80 pf. multicoloured . . . 1·00 30

843 Dulmen's Wild Horses

1987. European Environment Year.
2185 **843** 60 pf. multicoloured . . . 1·25 35

844 German Pavilion, International Exhibition, Barcelona, 1929 (Ludwig Mies van der Rohe)

1987. Europa. Architecture. Multicoloured.
2186 60 pf. Type **844** 85 25
2187 80 pf. Kohlbrand Bridge, Hamburg (Thyssen Engineering) . . . . 1·10 30

845 Emblem and Globe

1987. Rotary International Convention, Munich.
2188 **845** 70 pf. ultram, yell & bl . . 1·00 30

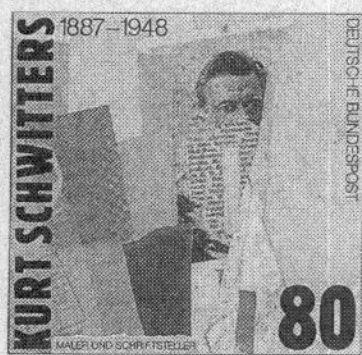

846 "Without Title (With an Early Portrait)"
847 Organ Pipes and Signature

1987. Birth Centenary of Kurt Schwitters (artist and writer).
2189 **846** 80 pf. multicoloured . . . 1·00 30

1987. 350th Birth Anniv of Dietrich Buxtehude (composer).
2190 **847** 80 pf. black, stone and red . . . . 1·00 30

848 Bengel
849 Wilhelm Kaisen

1987. 300th Birth Anniv of Johann Albrecht Bengel (theologian).
2191 **848** 80 pf. brn, ochre & blk . . 1·00 30

1987. Birth Centenary of Wilhelm Kaisen (Senate president and Mayor of Bremen).
2192 **849** 80 pf. multicoloured . . . . 1·00 30

850 Charlemagne, Bishop Willehad, Bremen Cathedral and City Arms (after mural)

1987. 1200th Anniv of Bremen Bishopric.
2193 **850** 80 pf. multicoloured . . . 90 30

851 Target, Crossed Rifles and Wreath

1987. 7th European Riflemen's Festival, Lippstadt.
2194 **851** 80 pf. multicoloured . . . 80 30

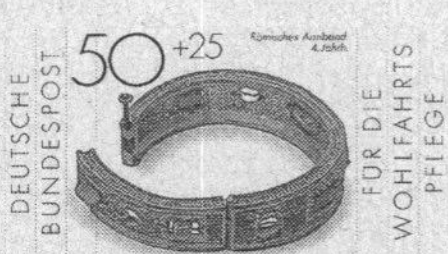

852 4th-century Roman Bracelet

1987. Humanitarian Relief Funds. Precious Metal Work. Multicoloured.
2195 50 pf. + 25 pf. Type **852** . . . 1·00 65
2196 60 pf. + 30 pf. 6th-century East Gothic buckle . . . . . . 1·10 75
2197 70 pf. + 35 pf. 7th-century Merovingian disc fibula . . 1·25 95
2198 80 pf. + 40 pf. 8th-century reliquary . . . . 1·60 1·10

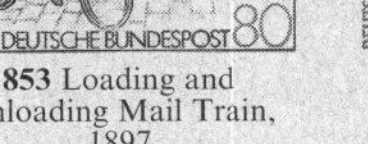

853 Loading and Unloading Mail Train, 1897
854 Corner Tower, Celle Castle

1987. Stamp Day.
2199 **853** 80 pf. multicoloured . . . 90 35

1987. Tourist Sights. Inscr "DEUTSCHE BUNDESPOST".

2200	–	5 pf. blue and grey . . .	10	10
2201	–	10 pf. blue & indigo . .	10	10
2202	–	20 pf. pink and blue . .	15	10
2203	**854**	30 pf. brown & green . .	20	10
2204	–	33 pf. green and red . .	40	10
2205	–	38 pf. grey and blue . .	60	10
2206	–	40 pf. brn, red & bl . . .	30	10
2206a	–	41 pf. grey & yellow . .	30	10
2207	–	45 pf. pink and blue . .	30	10
2208	–	50 pf. brown & blue . .	35	10
2209	–	60 pf. green & black . .	40	15
2210	–	70 pf. pink and blue . .	85	20
2210a	–	70 pf. brown & blue . .	50	20
2211	–	80 pf. grey and green . .	55	20
2212	–	90 pf. bistre & yellow . .	1·10	20
2213	–	100 pf. green & orge . .	80	25
2214	–	120 pf. green and red . .	1·40	25
2215	–	140 pf. bistre & yell . .	1·60	30
2216	–	170 pf. grey & yellow . .	1·75	35
2216a	–	200 pf. blue & brown . .	1·10	60
2217	–	280 pf. grey and blue . .	3·00	60
2218	–	300 pf. pink & brown . .	1·60	65
2219	–	350 pf. grey and blue . .	2·25	80
2220	–	400 pf. red & brown . .	2·50	90
2220a	–	450 pf. blue & brown . .	2·75	1·40
2220b	–	500 pf. stone & pur . . .	3·00	1·75
2220c	–	550 pf. brown & blue . .	3·25	2·00
2220d	–	700 pf. green & yell . .	4·00	3·00

DESIGNS: 5 pf. Brunswick Lion; 10 pf. Frankfurt airport; 20, 70 (2210) pf. Head of Nefertiti, Berlin Museum; 33, 120 pf. Schleswig Cathedral; 38, 280 pf. Statue of Roland, Bremen; 40 pf. Chile House, Hamburg; 41, 170 pf. Russian Church, Wiesbaden; 45 pf. Rastatt Castle; 50 pf. Freiburg Cathedral; 60 pf. "Bavaria" (bronze statue), Munich; 70 pf. (2210a) Heligoland; 80 pf. Zollern II Dortmund Mine Industrial Museum, Westphalia; 90, 140 pf. Bronze flagon, Reinheim; 100 pf. Pilgrimage Chapel, Altotting; 200 pf. Magdeburg Cathedral; 300 pf. Hambach Castle; 350 pf. Externsteine (rock formation), Horn-Bad Meinberg; 400 pf. Dresden Opera House; 450 pf. New Gate, Neubrandenburg; 500 pf. Cottbus State Theatre; 550 pf. Suhl-Heinrichs Town Hall, Thuringia; 700 pf. National Theatre, Berlin.

The 10, 60, 80 and 100 pf. also exist imperforate and self-adhesive from booklets.

For similar designs inscribed "DEUTSCHLAND", see Nos. 2665/6.

855 Gluck and Score of "Armide"

1987. Death Bicentenary of Christoph Willibald Gluck (composer).
2221 **855** 60 pf. black, grey and red . 75 20

856 Poster by Emil Orlik for "The Weavers"

1987. 125th Birth Anniv of Gerhart Hauptmann (playwright).
2222 **856** 80 pf. lt red, blk & red . . 1·00 30

857 Paddy Field

1987. 25th Anniv of German Famine Aid.
2223 **857** 80 pf. multicoloured . . . 1·00 30

858 "Birth of Christ" (13th-century Book of Psalms)

1987. Christmas.
2224 **858** 80 pf. + 40 pf. mult . . . 1·00 1·10

859 Jester
860 Kaiser

1988. 150th Anniv of Mainz Carnival.
2225 **859** 60 pf. multicoloured . . . 80 20

1988. Birth Centenary of Jakob Kaiser (trade unionist and politician).
2226 **860** 80 pf. black and grey . . 85 30

861 Stein and Mayer

1988. Beatification of Edith Stein and Father Rupert Mayer.
2227 **861** 80 pf. multicoloured . . . 1·00 30

862 Dr Konrad Adenauer (West German Chancellor) and Charles de Gaulle (French President)

1988. 25th Anniv of Franco–German Co-operation Treaty.
2228 **862** 80 pf. purple & black . . 1·25 35

863 "Solitude of the Green Woods" (woodcut of poem, Ludwig Richter)
865 Schopenhauer

864 Raiffeisen and Ploughed Field

1988. Birth Bicentenary of Joseph von Eichendorff (writer).
2229 **863** 60 pf. multicoloured . . . 80 20

1988. Death Centenary of Friedrich Wilhelm Raiffeisen (philanthropist and agricultural co-operative founder).
2230 **864** 80 pf. green and black . . 1·25 30

1988. Birth Bicentenary of Arthur Schopenhauer (philosopher).
2231 **865** 80 pf. brown and black . 90 30

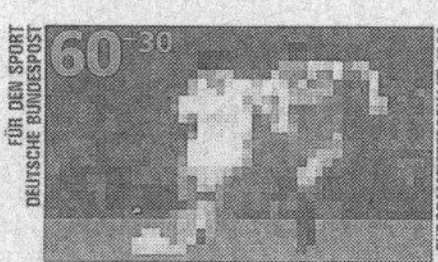

866 Football (European Championship)

1988. Sport Promotion Fund. Multicoloured.
2232 60 pf. + 30 pf. Type **866** . . . 85 75
2233 80 pf. + 40 pf. Tennis (Olympic Games) . . . . 1·10 1·00
2234 120 pf. + 55 pf. Diving (Olympic Games) . . . . . 1·75 1·60

867 Buddy Holly

1988. Youth Welfare. Pop Music. Mult.
2235 50 pf. + 25 pf. Type **867** . . 1·25 1·00
2236 60 pf. + 30 pf. Elvis Presley . 2·75 2·00
2237 70 pf. + 35 pf. Jim Morrison . 1·50 1·00
2238 80 pf. + 40 pf. John Lennon . 2·50 1·50

868 Hutten (wood engraving from "Conquestiones")

1988. 500th Birth Anniv of Ulrich von Hutten (writer).
2239 **868** 80 pf. multicoloured . . . 90 30

869 City Buildings and Jan Wellem Monument

1988. 700th Anniv of Dusseldorf.
2240 **869** 60 pf. multicoloured . . . 75 20

870 Airbus Industrie A320 and Manufacturing Nations' Flag

1988. Europa. Transport and Communications. Multicoloured.
2241 60 pf. Type **870** . . . . 1·25 30
2242 80 pf. Diagram of Integrated Services Digital Network . . 85 35

871 University Buildings and City Landmarks
872 Monnet

1988. 600th Anniv of Cologne University.
2243 **871** 80 pf. multicoloured . . . 90 30

1988. Birth Centenary of Jean Monnet (statesman).
2244 **872** 80 pf. multicoloured . . . 90 30

873 Storm

1988. Death Centenary of Theodor Storm (writer).
2245 **873** 80 pf. multicoloured . . . 80 30

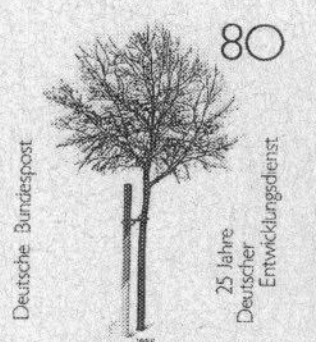

874 Tree supported by Stake in National Colours
876 Gmelin

875 Meersburg

1988. 25th Anniv of German Volunteer Service.
2246 **874** 80 pf. multicoloured . . . 80 30

1988. Millenary of Meersburg.
2247 **875** 60 pf. multicoloured . . . 65 20

1988. Birth Bicentenary of Leopold Gmelin (chemist).
2248 **876** 80 pf. multicoloured . . . 80 30

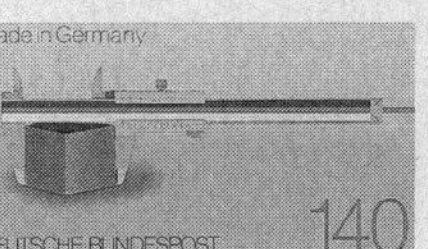

877 Vernier Caliper Rule in National Colours

1988. "Made in Germany".
2249 **877** 140 pf. multicoloured . . 1·60 55

878 Bebel

1988. 75th Death Anniv of August Bebel (Social Democratic Labour Party co-founder).
2250 **878** 80 pf. mauve, bl & silver . . 1·00 30

879 Carrier Pigeon

880 13th-century Rock Crystal Reliquary

1988. Stamp Day.
2251 **879** 20 pf. multicoloured . . . 50 10

1988. Humanitarian Relief Funds. Precious Metal Work. Multicoloured.
2252 50 pf. + 25 pf. Type **880** . . . 70 55
2253 60 pf. + 30 pf. 14th-century bust of Charlemagne 85 70
2254 70 pf. + 35 pf. 10th-cent. crown of Otto III . . . . . 1·00 85
2255 80 pf. + 40 pf. 17th-cent. jewelled flowers . . . . 1·25 1·10

881 Red Cross

882 Burning Synagogue, Baden-Baden

1988. 125th Anniv of Red Cross.
2256 **881** 80 pf. red and black . . . 1·00 30

1988. 50th Anniv of "Kristallnacht" (Nazi pogrom).
2257 **882** 80 pf. purple & black . . 85 30

883 Cancelled Postage Stamps

1988. Centenary of Collection of Used Stamps for the Bethel Charity.
2258 **883** 60 pf. multicoloured . . . 90 20

884 Linked Arms

1988. Centenary of Samaritan Workers' (first aid) Association.
2259 **884** 80 pf. multicoloured . . . 85 30

885 "Adoration of the Magi" (illus from Henry the Lion's Gospel Book)

1988. Christmas.
2260 **885** 80 pf. + 40 pf. mult . . . 1·10 1·00

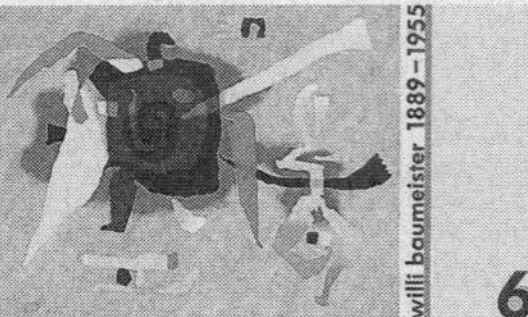

886 "Bluxao I"

1989. Birth Centenary of Willi Baumeister (painter).
2261 **886** 60 pf. multicoloured . . . 70 20

887 Bonn

1988. 2000th Anniv of Bonn.
2262 **887** 80 pf. multicoloured . . . 1·25 30

888 Grass growing from Dry, Cracked Earth

1989. 30th Anniversaries of Misereor and Bread for the World (Third World relief organizations).
2263 **888** 80 pf. multicoloured . . . 80 30

889 "Cats in the Attic" (woodcut)

1989. Birth Cent of Gerhard Marcks (artist).
2264 **889** 60 pf. blk, stone & red . . 65 20

890 Table Tennis (World Championships)

1989. Sport Promotion Fund. Multicoloured.
2265 100 pf. + 50 pf. Type **890** . . 1·50 1·25
2266 140 pf. + 60 pf. Gymnastics (World Championships) . . 2·25 2·00

891 Elephants

1989. Youth Welfare. Circus. Multicoloured.
2267 60 pf. + 30 pf. Type **891** . . . 1·50 80
2268 70 pf. + 30 pf. Acrobat on horseback . . . . . . 2·00 90
2269 80 pf. + 35 pf. Clown . . . . . 2·50 1·40
2270 100 pf. + 50 pf. Caravans and Big Top . . . . 4·00 1·90

892 Posthorn and Book of Stamps

1989. "IPHLA '89" International Philatelic Literature Exhibition, Frankfurt.
2271 **892** 100 pf. + 50 pf. mult . . 2·00 1·75

893 European and Members' Flags

1989. 3rd Direct Elections to European Parliament.
2272 **893** 100 pf. multicoloured . . 1·60 60

894 Shipping

1989. 800th Anniv of Hamburg Harbour.
2273 **894** 60 pf. multicoloured . . . 1·00 20

895 Asam (detail of fresco, Weltenburg Abbey)

1989. 250th Death Anniv of Cosmas Damian Asam (painter and architect).
2274 **895** 60 pf. multicoloured . . . 75 20

896 Kites

1989. Europa. Children's Toys. Multicoloured.
2275 60 pf. Type **896** 85 20
2276 100 pf. Puppet show . . . . . 1·40 30

897 Emblem, National Colours and Presidents' Signatures

1989. 40th Anniv of German Federal Republic.
2277 **897** 100 pf. multicoloured . . 1·50 35

898 Council Assembly and Stars

1989. 40th Anniv of Council of Europe.
2278 **898** 100 pf. blue and gold . . 1·25 35

899 Gabelsberger and Shorthand

1989. Birth Bicentenary of Franz Xaver Gabelsberger (shorthand pioneer).
2279 **899** 100 pf. multicoloured . . 1·10 35

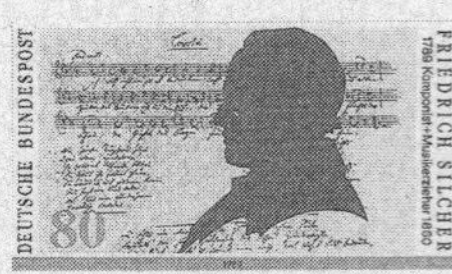

900 Score of "Lorelei" and Silhouette of Silcher

1989. Birth Bicentenary of Friedrich Silcher (composer).
2280 **900** 80 pf. multicoloured . . . 1·00 30

901 Saints Kilian, Totnan and Colman (from 12th-century German manuscript)

1989. 1300th Death Anniversaries of Saints Kilian, Colman and Totnan (Irish missionaries to Franconia).
2281 **901** 100 pf. multicoloured . . 1·25 35

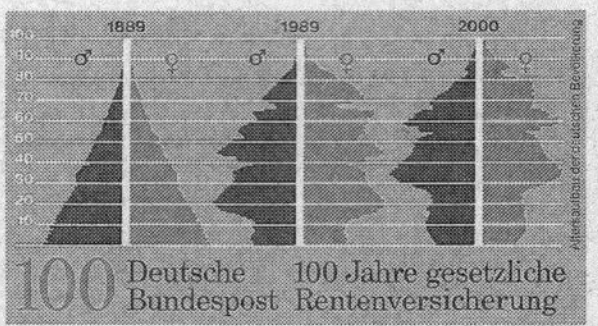

902 Age Graphs of Men and Women

1989. Centenary of National Insurance.
2282 **902** 100 p. blue, red & lt bl . . 1·25 35

903 "Summer Evening" (Heinrich Vogler)

1989. Cent of Worpswede Artists' Village.
2283 **903** 60 pf. multicoloured . . . 80 20

904 Schneider

905 List (after Kriehuber) and Train

1989. 50th Death Anniv of Reverend Paul Schneider (concentration camp victim).
2284 **904** 100 pf. blk, lt grey & grey 1·00 35

1989. Birth Bicentenary of Friedrich List (economist).
2285 **905** 170 pf. black and red . . 2·00 60

906 Cathedral

907 Children building House

1989. 750th Anniv of Frankfurt Cathedral.
2286 **906** 60 pf. multicoloured . . . 1·00 20

1989. "Don't Forget the Children".
2287 **907** 100 pf. multicoloured . . 1·25 35

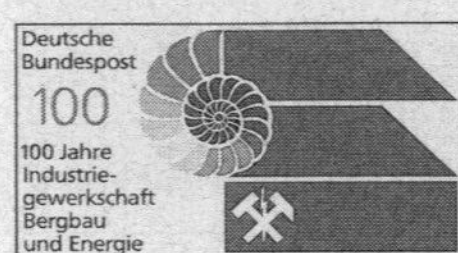

908 Ammonite and Union Emblem

1989. Centenary of Mining and Power Industries Trade Union.
2288 **908** 100 pf. multicoloured . . 1·50 45

909 18th-century Mounted Courier, Thurn and Taxis

910 Maier

1989. Humanitarian Relief Funds. Postal Deliveries. Multicoloured.
2289 60 pf. + 30 pf. Type **909** . . . 1·10 1·10
2290 80 pf. + 35 pf. Hamburg postal messenger, 1808 . . . . . . 1·25 1·25
2291 100 pf. + 50 pf. Bavarian mail coach, 1900 . . . . 1·75 1·75

1989. Birth Centenary of Reinhold Maier (politician).
2292 **910** 100 pf. multicoloured . . 1·10 35

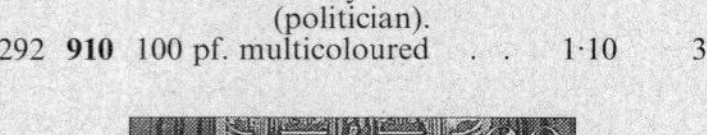

911 Organ Pipes

1989. 300th Anniv of Arp Schnitger Organ, St. James's Church, Hamburg.
2293 **911** 60 pf. multicoloured . . . 75 20

912 Angel

1989. Christmas. 16th-century Carvings by Veit Stoss, St. Lawrence's Church, Nuremberg. Multicoloured.

2294 60 pf. + 30 pf. Type **912** . . . 90 90
2295 100 pf. + 50 pf. "Nativity" . . 1·60 1·60

913 Speyer 914 "Courier" (Albrecht Durer)

1990. 2000th Anniv of Speyer.

2296 **913** 60 pf. multicoloured . . . 1·00 20

1990. 500th Anniv of Regular European Postal Services.

2297 **914** 100 pf. deep brown, light brown and brown . . . 1·50 35

915 Vine forming Initial "R".

1990. 500 Years of Riesling Grape Cultivation.

2298 **915** 100 pf. multicoloured . . 1·00 35

916 Old Lubeck

1990. U.N.E.S.C.O. World Heritage Site, Old Lubeck.

2299 **916** 100 pf. multicoloured . . 1·00 35

917 15th-century Seal and Grand Master's Arms

1990. 800th Anniv of Teutonic Order.

2300 **917** 100 pf. multicoloured . . 1·25 35

918 Frederick II's Seal and Fair Entrance Hall

1990. 750th Anniv of Granting of Fair Privileges to Frankfurt.

2301 **918** 100 pf. multicoloured . . 1·25 35

919 Maze

1990. 25th Anniv of Youth Research Science Competition.

2302 **919** 100 pf. multicoloured . . 1·00 35

920 Wildlife

1990. North Sea Protection.

2303 **920** 100 pf. multicoloured . . 1·40 45

921 Handball

1990. Sport Promotion Fund. Multicoloured.

2304 100 pf. + 50 pf. Type **921** . . 2·00 1·40
2305 140 pf. + 60 pf. Keep-fit . . . 2·50 1·60

922 Widow Bolte

1990. Youth Welfare. 125th Anniv of Max and Moritz (characters from books by Wilhelm Busch). Multicoloured.

2306 60 pf. + 30 pf. Type **922** . . . 1·00 80
2307 70 pf. + 30 pf. Max asleep . . 1·25 1·00
2308 80 pf. + 35 pf. Moritz watching Max sawing through bridge . 1·25 1·10
2309 100 pf. + 50 pf. Max and Moritz . . . . 1·60 1·40

923 "1.MAI" and Factory Silhouette

1990. Centenary of Labour Day.

2310 **923** 100 pf. red and black . . 1·00 35

924 Woman's Face

1990. 75th Anniv of German Association of Housewives.

2311 **924** 100 pf. multicoloured . . 1·00 35

925 Collection Box

1990. 125th Anniv of German Lifeboat Institution.

2312 **925** 60 pf. multicoloured . . . 1·10 20

926 Thurn and Taxis Palace, Frankfurt

1990. Europa. Post Office Buildings. Mult.

2313 60 pf. Type **926** 90 20
2314 100 pf. Postal Giro Office, Frankfurt . . . . 1·25 35

927 St Philip's Church, Protestant Church Flag and Candle Flames

1990. Centenary of Rummelsberg Diaconal Institution.

2315 **927** 100 pf. multicoloured . . 1·00 35

928 Leuschner 929 Globe

1990. Birth Centenary of Wilhelm Leuschner (trade unionist and member of anti-Hitler Resistance).

2316 **928** 100 pf. black and lilac . . 1·25 35

1990. 125th Anniv of I.T.U.

2317 **929** 100 pf. multicoloured . . 1·00 35

930 National Colours and Students

1990. 175th Anniv of German Students' Fraternity and of their Colours (now national colours).

2318 **930** 100 pf. multicoloured . . 1·40 35

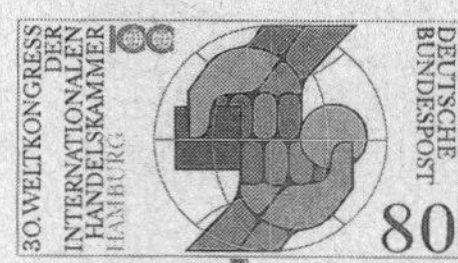

931 Hands exchanging Money and Goods

1990. 30th World Congress of International Chamber of Commerce, Hamburg.

2319 **931** 80 pf. multicoloured . . . 70 25

932 Closing Sentence of Charter

1990. 40th Anniv of Expelled Germans Charter.

2320 **932** 100 pf. multicoloured . . 90 30

934 Claudius 935 Mail Motor Wagon, 1900

1990. 250th Birth Anniv of Matthias Claudius (writer).

2322 **934** 100 pf. blue, blk & red . . 1·10 30

1990. Humanitarian Relief Funds. Posts and Telecommunications. Multicoloured.

2323 60 pf + 30 pf. Type **935** . . . 1·00 75
2324 80 pf. + 35 pf. Telephone exchange, 1890 . . . . . . 1·25 90
2325 100 pf. + 50 pf. Parcel sorting office, 1900 . . . . 1·40 1·25

936 "German Unity" and National Colours

1990. Reunification of Germany.

2326 **936** 50 pf. black, red & yell . . 60 15
2327 100 pf. blk, red & yell . . 1·25 30

937 Schliemann and Lion Gate, Mycenae

1990. Death Centenary of Heinrich Schliemann (archaeologist).

2328 **937** 60 pf. multicoloured . . . 70 20

938 Penny Black, Bavaria 1 k. and West Germany 1989 100 pf. Stamps

1990. Stamp Day. 150th Anniv of the Penny Black.

2329 **938** 100 pf. multicoloured . . 1·25 30

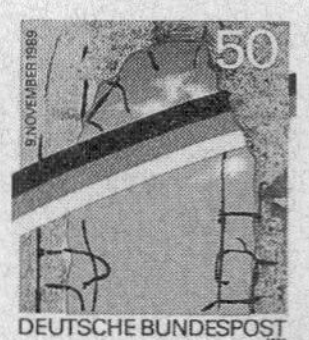

939 National Colours spanning Breach in Wall 940 Angel with Candles

1990. 1st Anniv of Opening of Berlin Wall.

2330 50 pf. Type **939** 50 15
2331 100 pf. Brandenburg Gate and crowd . . . . 1·00 30

1990. Christmas. Multicoloured.

2333 50 pf. + 20 pf. Type **940** . . . 65 60
2334 60 pf. + 30 pf. Figure of man smoking 85 70
2335 70 pf. + 30 pf. "Soldier" nut-crackers . . . . 1·00 85
2336 100 pf. + 50 pf. Tinsel angel . 1·50 1·25

941 Kathe Dorsch in "Mrs Warren's Profession" 942 View of City

1990. Birth Centenary of Kathe Dorsch (actress).

2337 **941** 100 pf. violet and red . . 1·00 30

1991. 750th Anniv of Hanover.

2338 **942** 60 pf. multicoloured . . . 85 20

943 "Three Golden Circles with a Full Circle in Blue" (relief in wood) 944 Miniature from 13th-century French Code

1991. Birth Centenary of Erich Buchholz (artist).

2339 **943** 60 pf. multicoloured . . . 75 20

1991. 750th Anniv of Promulgation of Pharmaceutical Ethics in Germany.

2340 **944** 100 pf. multicoloured . . 1·25 30

945 Brandenburg Gate (from "Old Engravings of Berlin")

1991. Bicentenary of Brandenburg Gate.

2341 **945** 100 pf. black, red & grey . 1·40 30

946 Eucken 947 Globe and "25" (poster)

1991. Birth Centenary of Walter Eucken (economist).

2342 **946** 100 pf. multicoloured . . 90 30

1991. 25th International Tourism Fair, Berlin.

2343 **947** 100 pf. multicoloured . . 90 30

949 Weightlifting (World Championships)

1991. Sport Promotion Fund. Multicoloured.

2345 70 pf. + 30 pf. Type **949** . . . 90 75
2346 100 pf. + 50 pf. Cycling (world championships) . . . 1·25 1·10
2347 140 pf. + 60 pf. Basketball (centenary) . . . 1·75 1·50
2348 170 pf. + 80 pf. Wrestling (European championships) . 2·00 1·75

950 Title Page of "Cautio Criminalis" (tract against witch trials), Langenfeld and Score of "Trutz-Nachtigall"

1991. 400th Birth Anniv of Friedrich Spee von Langenfeld (poet and human rights pioneer).

2349 **950** 100 pf. multicoloured . . 90 30

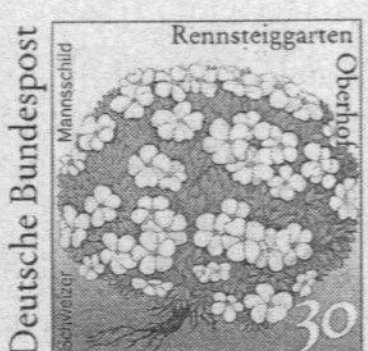

951 Androsace **952** Werth (attr Wenzel Hollar)

1991. Plants in Rennsteiggarten (botanical garden), Oberhof. Multicoloured.

2350 30 pf. Type **951** 35 15
2351 50 pf. Primula 50 20
2352 80 pf. Gentian 70 25
2353 100 pf. Cranberry 90 30
2354 350 pf. Edelweiss . . . . . . 3·25 1·75

1991. 400th Birth Anniv of Jan von Werth (military commander).

2355 **952** 60 pf. multicoloured . . . 50 20

953 Windthorst **955** Mountain Clouded Yellow

954 Junkers F-13, 1930

1991. Death Centenary of Ludwig Windthorst (politician).

2356 **953** 100 pf. multicoloured . . 90 30

1991. Historic Mail Aircraft. Multicoloured.

2357 30 pf. Type **954** 40 20
2358 50 pf. Hans Grade's mono-plane, 1909 . . . . . 60 30
2359 100 pf. Fokker F.III, 1922 . . 1·00 40
2360 165 pf. Airship "Graf Zeppelin", 1928 . . . . . 2·00 1·40

1991. Youth Welfare. Endangered Butterflies. Multicoloured.

2361 30 pf. + 15 pf. Type **955** . . . 40 40
2362 50 pf. + 25 pf. Poplar admiral 60 60
2363 60 pf. + 30 pf. Purple emperor 70 60
2364 70 pf. + 30 pf. Violet copper . 1·10 95
2365 80 pf. + 35 pf. Swallowtail . . 1·25 1·10
2366 90 pf. + 45 pf. Small apollo . 1·40 1·25
2367 100 pf. + 50 pf. Moorland clouded yellow . . . . . 2·00 1·40
2368 140 pf. + 60 pf. Large copper . 2·50 1·90

See also Nos. 2449/53.

956 Academy Building, 1830

1991. Bicentenary of Choral Academy, Berlin.

2369 **956** 100 pf. multicoloured . . 90 30

957 Typesetting School, 1875

1991. 125th Anniv of Lette Foundation (institute for professional training of women).

2370 **957** 100 pf. multicoloured . . 90 30

958 Battle (detail of miniature, Schlackenwerth Codex, 1350)

1991. 750th Anniv of Battle of Legnica.

2371 **958** 100 pf. multicoloured . . 90 40

959 Arms

1991. 700th Anniv of Granting of Charters to Six Towns of Trier.

2372 **959** 60 pf. multicoloured . . . 50 20

960 Speeding Train

1991. Inauguration of Inter-City Express (ICE) Railway Service.

2373 **960** 60 pf. multicoloured . . . 70 20

961 "ERS-1" European Remote Sensing Satellite

1991. Europa. Europe in Space. Mult.

2374 60 pf. Type **961** 75 15
2375 100 pf. "Kopernikus" telecom-munications satellite . . . 1·40 40

962 Reger and Organ Pipes **963** Ruffs

1991. 75th Death Anniv of Max Reger (composer).

2376 **962** 100 pf. multicoloured . . 90 30

1991. Seabirds. Multicoloured.

2390 60 pf. Type **963** 75 25
2391 80 pf. Little terns 95 40
2392 100 pf. Brent geese . . . . . 1·25 45
2393 140 pf. White-tailed sea eagles . 1·75 1·40

964 Wilhelm August Lampadius (gas pioneer)

1991. 18th World Gas Congress, Berlin. Each black and blue.

2394 60 pf. Type **964** 50 20
2395 100 pf. Gas street lamp, Berlin . 90 30

965 Wallot (after Franz Wurbel) and Reichstag Building, Berlin

1991. 150th Birth Anniv of Paul Wallot (architect).

2396 **965** 100 pf. multicoloured . . 90 40

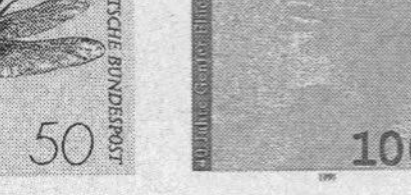

966 "Libellula depressa" **967** Hand clutching Cloak

1991. Dragonflies. Multicoloured.

2397 50 pf. Type **966** 50 20
2398 60 pf. Type **966** 60 40
2399 60 pf. "Sympetrum sanguineum" 60 40
2400 60 pf. "Cordulegaster boltonii" 60 40
2401 60 pf. "Aeshna viridis" 60 40
2402 70 pf. As No. 2399 . . . . 70 30
2403 80 pf. As No. 2400 . . . . 80 40
2404 100 pf. As No. 2401 . . . . 1·00 50

1991. 40th Anniv of Geneva Convention on Refugees.

2405 **967** 100 pf. lilac and black . . 90 30

968 Radio Waves and Mast

1991. International Radio Exhibition, Berlin.

2406 **968** 100 pf. multicoloured . . 90 30

969 Pedestrians and Traffic

1991. Road Safety Campaign.

2407 **969** 100 pf. multicoloured . . 1·25 40

971 August Heinrich Hoffmann von Fallersleben (lyricist) and Third Verse

1991. 150th Anniv of "Song of the Germans" (national anthem).

2409 **971** 100 pf. red, black & grn . 1·00 30

972 Thadden-Trieglaff

1991. Birth Cent of Reinold von Thadden-Trieglaff (founder of German Protestant Convention).

2410 **972** 100 pf. multicoloured . . 1·00 30

973 Transmission Test between Lauffen-on-Neckar and Frankfurt-on-Main

1991. Centenary of Three-phase Energy Transmission.

2411 **973** 170 pf. multicoloured . . 1·75 60

975 Albers in "The Winner"

1991. Birth Centenary of Hans Albers (actor).

2413 **975** 100 pf. multicoloured . . 1·40 30

976 Harbour

1991. 275th Anniv of Rhine-Ruhr Port, Duisburg.

2414 **976** 100 pf. multicoloured . . 1·25 35

977 Bethel Post Office **978** Postal Delivery in Spreewald Region

1991. Humanitarian Relief Funds. Postal Buildings. Multicoloured.

2415 30 pf. + 15 pf. Type **977** . . . 50 40
2416 60 pf. + 30 pf. Budingen post station 80 70
2417 70 pf. + 30 pf. Stralsund post office . . . . 1·10 90
2418 80 pf. + 35 pf. Lauscha post office . . . . 1·40 1·00
2419 100 pf. + 50 pf. Bonn post office . . . . 1·75 1·40
2420 140 pf. + 60 pf. Weilburg post office . . . . 2·10 1·75

1991. Stamp Day.

2421 **978** 100 pf. multicoloured . . 1·25 40

979 "Bird Monument" (detail) **980** "Portrait of the Dancer Anita Berber"

1991. Birth Centenary of Max Ernst (painter).

2422 **979** 100 pf. multicoloured . . 1·00 30

1991. Birth Cent of Otto Dix (painter). Mult.

2423 60 pf. Type **980** 75 25
2424 100 pf. "Self-portrait in Right Profile" . . . . 1·25 30

981 "The Violinist and the Water Sprite" **982** Angel (detail of "The Annunciation")

1991. Sorbian Legends. Multicoloured.

2425 60 pf. Type **981** 70 15
2426 100 pf. "The Midday Woman and the Woman from Nochten" . . . . 1·00 30

1991. Christmas. Works by Martin Schongauer. Multicoloured.

2427 60 pf. + 30 pf. Type **982** . . . 90 70
2428 70 pf. + 30 pf. Virgin Mary (detail of "The Annunciation") . . . . . . 1·25 90
2429 80 pf. + 35 pf. Angel (detail of "Madonna in a Rose Garden") . . . . . . 1·40 90
2430 100 pf. + 50 pf. "Nativity" . . 2·00 1·40

983 Leber **984** Nelly Sachs

1991. Birth Cent of Julius Leber (politician).
2431 **983** 100 pf. multicoloured . . 1·25 30

1991. Birth Centenary of Nelly Sachs (writer).
2432 **984** 100 pf. dp violet & violet . 1·00 30

986 Base of William I Monument and City Silhouette

1992. 2000th Anniv of Koblenz.
2434 **986** 60 pf. multicoloured . . . 80 20

987 Niemoller **988** Child's Eyes

1992. Birth Centenary of Martin Niemoller (theologian).
2435 **987** 100 pf. multicoloured . . 1·00 30

1992. 25th Anniv of Terre des Hommes (child welfare organization) in Germany.
2436 **988** 100 pf. multicoloured . . 1·00 30

989 Arms of Baden-Wurttemberg

1992. Lander of the Federal Republic.
2437 **989** 100 pf. multicoloured . . . 1·00 40
See also Nos. 2448, 2465, 2470, 2474, 2479, 2506, 2526, 2527, 2534, 2539, 2556, 2567, 2580, 2584 and 2597.

990 Fencing **991** Honegger and Score of Ballet "Semiramis"

1992. Sport Promotion Fund. Olympic Games, Albertville and Barcelona. Multicoloured.
2438 60 pf. + 30 pf. Type **990** . . 70 70
2439 80 pf. + 40 pf. Rowing eight . 1·10 1·00
2440 100 pf. + 50 pf. Dressage . . 1·75 1·25
2441 170 pf. + 80 pf. Skiing (slalom) . . . . 2·40 1·50

1992. Birth Centenary of Arthur Honegger (composer).
2442 **991** 100 pf. black & brown . . 1·00 30

992 Zeppelin and "Graf Zeppelin"

1992. 75th Death Anniv of Ferdinand von Zeppelin (airship manufacturer).
2443 **992** 165 pf. multicoloured . . 2·00 60

993 Kiel City and Harbour

1992. 750th Anniv of Kiel.
2444 **993** 60 pf. multicoloured . . . 65 25

994 Andreas Marggraf, Beet, Franz Achard and Carl Scheibler

1992. 125th Anniv of Berlin Sugar Institute.
2445 **994** 100 pf. multicoloured . . 90 35
The stamp depicts the discoverer of beet sugar, the founder of the beet sugar industry and the founder of the Institute respectively.

995 Horses and Renz **996** Adenauer

1992. Death Centenary of Ernst Jakob Renz (circus director).
2446 **995** 100 pf. multicoloured . . 90 35

1992. 25th Death Anniv of Konrad Adenauer (Chancellor, 1949–63).
2447 **996** 100 pf. brn & cinnamon . 1·00 35

1992. Lander of the Federal Republic. As T **989**. Multicoloured.
2448 100 pf. Bavaria . . . . 1·25 35

1992. Youth Welfare. Endangered Moths. As T **955**. Multicoloured.
2449 60 pf. + 30 pf. Purple tiger moth . . . . 1·25 1·25
2450 70 pf. + 30 pf. Hawk moth . . 1·40 1·40
2451 80 pf. + 40 pf. "Noctuidae sp." . . . . 1·75 1·75
2452 100 pf. + 50 pf. Tiger moth . . 1·90 1·90
2453 170 pf. + 80 pf. "Arichanna melanaria" . . . . 2·50 2·50

997 Schall

1992. 400th Birth Anniv of Adam Schall (missionary astronomer).
2454 **997** 140 pf. black, yell & bl . . 1·25 55

998 Cathedral and St. Severus's Church **999** Woodcut from 1493 Edition of Columbus's Letters

1992. 1250th Anniv of Erfurt.
2455 **998** 60 pf. multicoloured . . . 60 25

1992. Europa. 500th Anniv of Discovery of America by Columbus. Multicoloured.
2456 60 pf. Type **999** 65 25
2457 100 pf. "Rene de Laudonniere and Chief Athore" (Jacques le Moyne de Morgues, 1564) 90 40

1000 "Consecration of St. Ludgerus" (from "Vita Liudgeri" by Altfridus) **1001** Arithmetic Sum

1992. 1250th Birth Anniv of St. Ludgerus (first Bishop of Munster).
2458 **1000** 100 pf. multicoloured . . 1·10 35

1992. 500th Birth Anniv of Adam Riese (mathematician).
2459 **1001** 100 pf. multicoloured . . 90 40

1002 Order of Merit

1992. 150th Anniv of Civil Class of Order of Merit (for scientific or artistic achievement).
2460 **1002** 100 pf. multicoloured . . 85 35

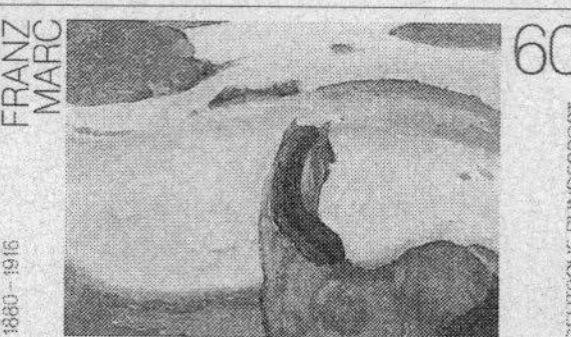

1003 "Landscape with Horse" (Franz Marc)

1992. 20th-century German Paintings (1st series). Multicoloured.
2461 60 pf. Type **1003** 50 25
2462 100 pf. "Fashion Shop" (August Macke) 85 40
2463 170 pf. "Murnau with Rainbow" (Wassily Kandinsky) . . . . . . 1·40 65
See also Nos. 2507/9, 2590/2, 2615/17 and 2704/6.

1004 Lichtenberg **1005** Rainforest

1992. 250th Birth Anniv of Georg Christoph Lichtenberg (physicist and essayist).
2464 **1004** 100 pf. multicoloured . . 90 40

1992. Lander of the Federal Republic. As T **989**. Multicoloured.
2465 100 pf. Berlin 85 40

1992. "Save the Tropical Rain Forest".
2466 **1005** 100 pf. + 50 pf. mult . . 1·25 1·10
The premium was for the benefit of environmental projects.

1006 Garden

1992. Leipzig Botanical Garden.
2467 **1006** 60 pf. multicoloured . . 60 25

1007 Stylized House and Globe

1992. 17th International Home Economics Congress, Hanover.
2468 **1007** 100 pf. multicoloured . . 90 40

1008 Family **1009** "Assumption of the Virgin Mary" (Rohr Monastery Church)

1992. Family Life.
2469 **1008** 100 pf. multicoloured . . 90 40

1992. Lander of the Federal Republic. As T **989**. Multicoloured.
2470 100 pf. Brandenburg 85 40

1992. 300th Birth Anniv of Egid Quirin Asam (sculptor).
2471 **1009** 60 pf. multicoloured . . 60 25

1010 Opera House (Georg von Knobelsdorff) **1011** Masked Actors

1992. 250th Anniv of German State Opera House, Berlin.
2472 **1010** 80 pf. multicoloured . . 1·00 35

1992. Centenary of German Amateur Theatres Federation.
2473 **1011** 100 pf. multicoloured . . 90 40

1992. Lander of the Federal Republic. As T **989**. Multicoloured.
2474 100 pf. Bremen 85 40

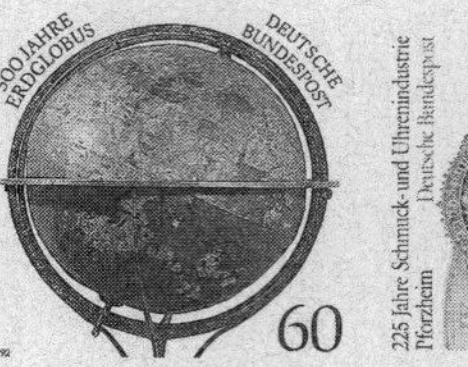

1012 Globe **1013** 1890 Pendant and 1990 Clock

1992. 500th Anniv of Martin Behaim's Terrestrial Globe.
2475 **1012** 60 pf. multicoloured . . 90 25

1992. 225th Anniv of Jewellery and Watch-making in Pforzheim.
2476 **1013** 100 pf. multicoloured . . 90 40

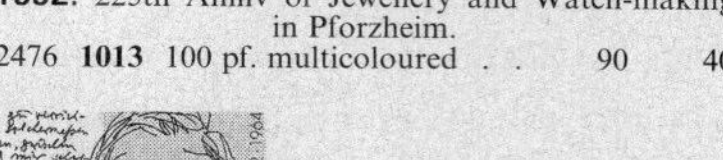

1014 Bergengruen (after Hanni Fries) **1015** Neue Holzbrucke Bridge, nr Essing

1992. Birth Centenary of Werner Bergengruen (writer).
2477 **1014** 100 pf. grey, blue & blk . 90 40

1992. Inauguration of Main–Donau Canal.
2478 **1015** 100 pf. multicoloured . . 90 40

1992. Lander of the Federal Republic. As T **989**. Multicoloured.
2479 100 pf. Hamburg 85 40

1016 Turret Clock, 1400

1992. Humanitarian Relief Funds. Clocks. Multicoloured.
2480 60 pf. + 30 pf. Type **1016** . . 85 85
2481 70 pf. + 30 pf. Astronomical mantel clock, 1738 . . . . 1·00 1·00
2482 80 pf. + 40 pf. Flute clock, 1790 . . . . 1·10 1·10
2483 100 pf. + 50 pf. Figurine clock, 1580 . . . . 1·50 1·50
2484 170 pf. + 80 pf. Table clock, 1550 . . . . 2·25 2·25

1017 Distler and Score of "We Praise Our Lord Jesus Christ" **1018** Balloon Post

1992. 50th Death Anniv of Hugo Distler (composer).
2485 **1017** 100 pf. black & violet . . 90 40

1992. Stamp Day.
2486 **1018** 100 pf. multicoloured . . 90 40

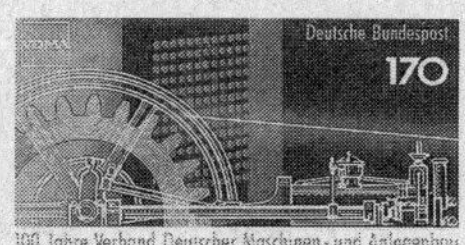

1019 Otto Engine, 1892, Cogwheel and Laser Beam

1992. Centenary of German Plant and Machine Builders Association.
2487 **1019** 170 pf. multicoloured . . 1·40 65

1020 "Adoration of the Magi" **1021** Blucher (after Simon Meister)

1992. Christmas. Carvings by Franz Maidburg, St. Anne's Church, Annaberg-Buchholz. Mult.

2488 60 pf. + 30 pf. Type **1020** . . 75 75
2489 100 pf. + 50 pf. "Birth of Christ" . . . . 1·10 1·10

1992. 250th Birth Anniv of Field Marshal Gebhard Leberecht von Blucher.

2490 **1021** 100 pf. multicoloured . . 90 40

1022 Werner von Siemens

1023 Klepper

1992. Death Centenary of Werner von Siemens (electrical engineer).

2491 **1022** 100 pf. brown & dp brn . 90 40

1992. 50th Death Anniv of Jochen Klepper (writer).

2492 **1023** 100 pf. multicoloured . . 90 40

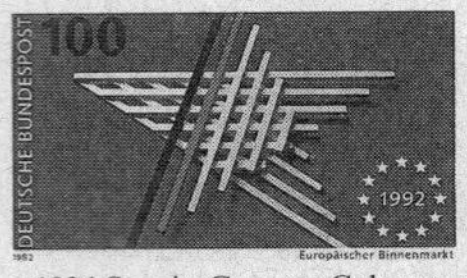

1024 Star in German Colours

1992. European Single Market.

2493 **1024** 100 pf. multicoloured . . 90 40

1025 Cathedral and Uberwasser Church

1993. 1200th Anniv of Munster.

2494 **1025** 60 pf. multicoloured . . 60 35

1026 Newton, Sketch of Refraction of Light and Formula

1993. 350th Birth Anniv of Sir Isaac Newton (scientist).

2495 **1026** 100 pf. multicoloured . . 90 40

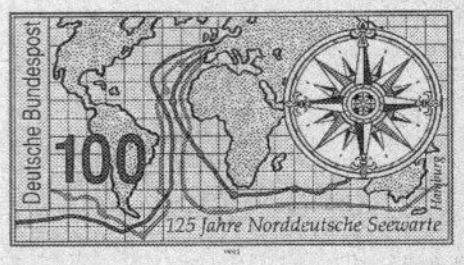

1027 Route Map and Compass Rose

1028 Emblem and Safety Stripes

1993. 125th Anniv of North German Naval Observatory, Hamburg.

2496 **1027** 100 pf. multicoloured . . 90 40

1993. European Year of Health, Hygiene and Safety in the Workplace.

2497 **1028** 100 pf. blue, yell & blk . 90 40

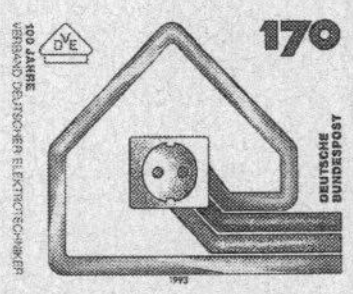

1029 Wires and Wall Socket forming House

1030 Ski-jumping Hill, Garmisch-Partenkirchen

1993. Centenary of German Association of Electrical Engineers.

2498 **1029** 170 pf. multicoloured . . 1·40 65

1993. Sport Promotion Fund. German Olympic Venues. Multicoloured.

2499 60 pf. + 30 pf. Type **1030** . 85 85
2500 80 pf. + 40 pf. Olympia-park, Munich . . . . 1·25 1·25
2501 100 pf. + 50 pf. Olympic Stadium, Berlin . . . . . 1·40 1·40
2502 170 pf. + 80 pf. Olympic Harbour, Kiel . . . . . . 2·25 2·25

1031 Stylised Sound Vibration

1993. 250th Anniv of Leipzig Gewandhaus Orchestra.

2503 **1031** 100 pf. gold and black . 90 40

1032 Statue of St. John and Charles Bridge, Prague

1993. 600th Death Anniv of St. John of Nepomuk.

2504 **1032** 100 pf. multicoloured . . 90 40

1033 Diagram explaining New Postcodes

1993. Introduction of Five-digit Postcode System.

2505 **1033** 100 pf. multicoloured . . 90 40

1993. Lander of the Federal Republic. As T **989**. Multicoloured.

2506 100 pf. Hesse 85 40

1993. 20th-century German Paintings (2nd series). As T **1003**. Multicoloured.

2507 100 pf. multicoloured 90 40
2508 100 pf. black, grey & mauve . . 90 40
2509 100 pf. multicoloured 90 40

DESIGNS: No. 2507, "Cafe" (George Grosz); 2508, "Sea and Sun" (Otto Pankok); 2509, "Audience" (Andreas Paul Weber).

1034 Abbeys

1993. 900th Anniversaries of Maria Laach and Bursfelde Benedictine Abbeys.

2510 **1034** 80 pf. multicoloured . . 85 30

1035 Alpine Longhorn Beetle

1993. Youth Welfare. Endangered Beetles. Multicoloured.

2511 80 pf. + 40 f. Type **1035** . . 1·10 1·10
2512 80 pf. + 40 pf. Rose chafer . . 1·10 1·10
2513 100 pf. + 50 pf. Stag beetle . . 1·40 1·40
2514 100 pf. + 50 pf. Tiger beetle . 1·40 1·40
2515 200 pf. + 50 pf. Cockchafer . 1·90 1·90

1036 Plants

1993. 5th International Horticultural Show, Stuttgart.

2516 **1036** 100 pf. multicoloured . . 90 40

1037 Horse Race

1993. 125th Anniv of Hoppegarten Racecourse.

2517 **1037** 80 pf. multicoloured . . 60 30

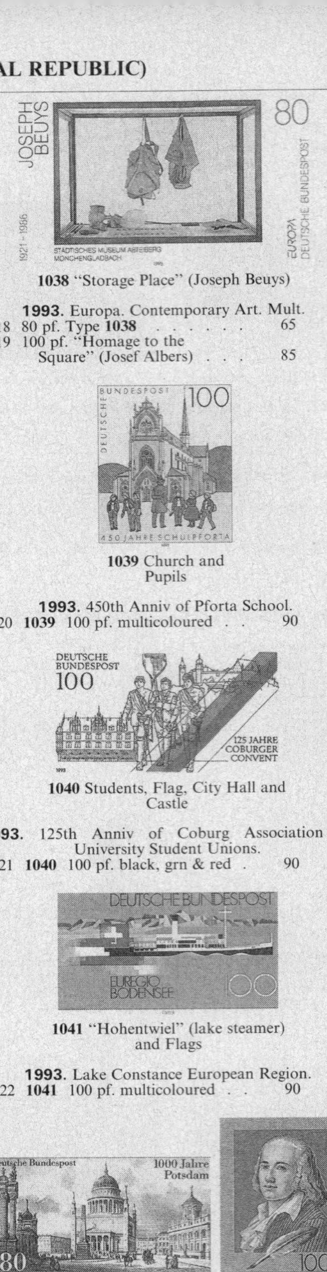

1038 "Storage Place" (Joseph Beuys)

1993. Europa. Contemporary Art. Mult.

2518 80 pf. Type **1038** 65 30
2519 100 pf. "Homage to the Square" (Josef Albers) . . . 85 40

1039 Church and Pupils

1993. 450th Anniv of Pforta School.

2520 **1039** 100 pf. multicoloured . . 90 40

1040 Students, Flag, City Hall and Castle

1993. 125th Anniv of Coburg Association of University Student Unions.

2521 **1040** 100 pf. black, grn & red . 90 40

1041 "Hohentwiel" (lake steamer) and Flags

1993. Lake Constance European Region.

2522 **1041** 100 pf. multicoloured . . 90 40

1042 "Old Market—View of St. Nicholas's Church" (detail, Ferdinand von Arnim)

1043 Holderlin (after Franz Hiemer)

1993. Millenary of Potsdam.

2523 **1042** 80 pf. multicoloured . . 90 40

1993. 150th Death Anniv of Friedrich Holderlin (poet).

2524 **1043** 100 pf. multicoloured . . 90 40

1044 "If People can fly to the Moon, why can't they do anything about so many Children dying?"

1993. 40th Anniv of German United Nations Children's Fund Committee.

2525 **1044** 100 pf. multicoloured . . 90 40

1993. Lander of the Federal Republic. As T **989**. Multicoloured.

2526 100 pf. Mecklenburg–Vorpommern 85 40

1993. Lander of the Federal Republic. As T **989**. Multicoloured.

2527 100 pf. Lower Saxony 85 40

1045 Fallada (after E. O. Plauen)

1993. Birth Centenary of Hans Fallada (writer).

2528 **1045** 100 pf. grn, brn & red . 90 40

1046 Harz Mountain Range

1993. Landscapes (1st series). Multicoloured.

2529 100 pf. Type **1046** 85 40
2530 100 pf. Rugen 85 40
2531 100 pf. Hohe Rhon 85 40

See also Nos. 2585/8, 2646/9, 2709/12 and 2806/8.

1047 Stages of Manufacture

1993. 250th Death Anniv of Mathias Klotz (violin maker).

2532 **1047** 80 pf. multicoloured . . 65 30

1048 George as Gotz von Berlichingen in Goethe's "Urgotz"

1050 Swedish Flag, Heart and Cross

1049 Digitalised Eye and Ear

1993. Birth Centenary of Heinrich George (actor).

2533 **1048** 100 pf. multicoloured . . 85 40

1993. Lander of the Federal Republic. As T **989**. Multicoloured.

2534 100 pf. Nordrhein–Westfalen . 85 40

1993. International Radio Exhibition, Berlin.

2535 **1049** 100 pf. multicoloured . . 85 40

1993. Birth Centenary of Birger Forell (founder of Espelkamp (town for war refugees)).

2536 **1050** 100 pf. yell, ultram & bl . 85 40

1051 "Tuledu Bridge" (engraving)

1993. Birth Centenary of Hans Leip (writer and artist).

2537 **1051** 100 pf. black, red & bl . 85 40

1993. Lander of the Federal Republic. As T **989**. Multicoloured.

2539 100 pf. Rheinland–Pfalz . . . 85 40

1053 Postman delivering Letter

1993. Stamp Day.

2540 **1053** 100 pf. + 50 pf. mult . . 1·10 1·10

1054 "Swan Lake"

1993. Death Centenary of Pyotr Tchaikovsky (composer).

2541 **1054** 80 pf. multicoloured . . 65 30

1055 Fohr, Schleswig-Holstein

1056 St. Jadwiga (miniature, Schlackenwerther Codex)

1993. Humanitarian Relief Funds. Traditional Costumes (1st series). Multicoloured.

2542 80 pf. + 40 pf. Type **1055** . . 1·00 1·00
2543 80 pf. + 40 pf. Rugen, Mecklenburg–Vorpommern . 1·00 1·00
2544 100 pf. + 50 pf. Oberndorf, Bavaria . . . . 1·40 1·40
2545 100 pf. + 50 pf. Schwalm, Hesse . . . . 1·40 1·40
2546 200 pf. + 40 pf. Ernstroda, Thuringia . . . . 2·00 2·00

See also Nos. 2598/2602.

1993. 750th Death Anniv of St. Jadwiga of Silesia.

2547 **1056** 100 pf. multicoloured . . 85 40

1057 Reinhardt on Stage

1058 Brandt

1993. 50th Death Anniv of Max Reinhardt (theatrical producer).

2548 **1057** 100 pf. black, brn & red . . 85 40

1993. 80th Birth Anniv of Willy Brandt (statesman).

2549 **1058** 100 pf. multicoloured . . 85 40

1059 Monteverdi

1993. 350th Death Anniv of Claudio Monteverdi (composer).

2550 **1059** 100 pf. multicoloured . . 85 40

1060 Paracelsus (after Augustin Hirschvogel)

1061 "Adoration of the Magi"

1993. 500th Birth Anniv of Paracelsus (physician and philosopher).

2551 **1060** 100 pf. ochre, brown and green 85 40

1993. Christmas. Carvings from Altar Triptych, Blaubeuren Minster. Multicoloured.

2552 80 pf. + 40 pf. Type **1061** . . 1·00 1·00
2553 100 pf. + 50 pf. "Birth of Christ" . . . . 1·40 1·40

1062 Quayside Buildings, Town Hall and St. Cosmas's Church

1994. Millenary of Stade.

2554 **1062** 80 pf. red, brown & blue 65 35

1063 "FAMILIE"

1994. International Year of the Family.

2555 **1063** 100 pf. multicoloured . . 85 40

1994. Lander of the Federal Republic. As T **989**. Multicoloured.

2556 100 pf. Saarland 85 40

1064 Hertz and Electromagnetic Waves

1994. Death Centenary of Heinrich Hertz (physicist).

2557 **1064** 200 pf. black, red and drab . . . . 1·75 1·00

1065 Frankfurt am Main

1994. 1200th Anniv of Frankfurt am Main.

2558 **1065** 80 pf. multicoloured . . 70 35

1066 Ice Skating

1994. Sport Promotion Fund. Sporting Events and Anniversaries. Multicoloured.

2559 80 pf. + 40 pf. Type **1066** (Winter Olympic Games, Lillehammer, Norway) . . . 1·10 1·10
2560 100 pf. + 50 pf. Football and trophy (World Cup Football Championship, U.S.A.) . . 1·40 1·40
2561 100 pf. + 50 pf. Flame (cent of International Olympic Committee) . . . . 1·40 1·40
2562 200 pf. + 80 pf. Skier (Winter Paralympic Games, Lillehammer) . . . . 2·50 2·50

1067 Cathedral, St. Michael's Church and Castle

1994. 1250th Anniv of Fulda.

2563 **1067** 80 pf. multicoloured . . 70 35

1068 Council Emblem

1994. Cent of Federation of German Women's Associations—German Women's Council.

2564 **1068** 100 pf. blk, red & yell . . 85 40

1069 Members' Flags as Stars

1994. 4th Direct Elections to European Parliament.

2565 **1069** 100 pf. multicoloured . . 85 40

1070 People holding Banner

1994. "Living Together" (integration of foreign workers in Germany).

2566 **1070** 100 pf. multicoloured . . 85 40

1994. Lander of the Federal Republic. As T **989**. Multicoloured.

2567 100 pf. Saxony 85 40

1071 Johnny Head-in-the-Air

1994. Youth Welfare. Death Centenary of Heinrich Hoffmann (writer). Designs illustrating characters from "Slovenly Peter". Multicoloured.

2568 80 pf. + 40 pf. Type **1071** . . 1·10 1·10
2569 80 pf. + 40 pf. Little Pauline . 1·10 1·10
2570 100 pf. + 50 pf. Naughty Friederich . . . . 1·25 1·25
2571 100 pf. + 50 pf. Slovenly Peter 1·25 1·25
2572 200 pf. + 80 pf. Fidget-Philipp 2·50 2·50

1072 Frauenkirche

1994. 500th Anniv of Frauenkirche, Munich.

2573 **1072** 100 pf. multicoloured . . 85 40

1073 Resistor and Formula

1074 Pfitzner (after Emil Orlik)

1994. Europa. Discoveries. Multicoloured.

2574 80 pf. Type **1073** (Ohm's Law) . 70 35
2575 100 pf. Radiation from black body and formula (Max Planck's Quantum Theory) . 85 40

1994. 125th Birth Anniv of Hans Pfitzner (composer).

2576 **1074** 100 pf. deep blue, blue and red 85 40

1076 Spandau Castle

1994. 400th Anniv of Spandau Castle.

2578 **1076** 80 pf. multicoloured . . 70 35

1077 Village Sign showing Society Emblem

1994. Centenary of Herzogsagmuhle (Society for the Domestic Missions welfare village).

2579 **1077** 100 pf. multicoloured . . 85 40

1994. Lander of the Federal Republic. As T **989**. Multicoloured.

2580 100 pf. Saxony-Anhalt 85 40

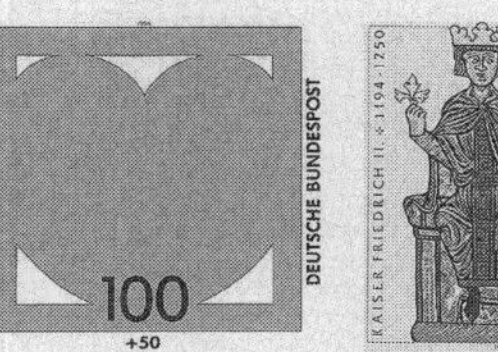

1078 Heart inside Square

1079 Friedrich II (13th-century miniature, "Book of Falcons")

1994. Environmental Protection.

2581 **1078** 100 pf. + 50 pf. green and black . . . . . . 1·25 1·25

1994. 800th Birth Anniv of Emperor Friedrich II.

2582 **1079** 400 pf. multicoloured . . 3·50 2·50

1994. Lander of the Federal Republic. As T **989**. Multicoloured.

2584 100 pf. Schleswig-Holstein . . 85 40

1994. Landscapes (2nd series). As T **1046**. Multicoloured.

2585 100 pf. The Alps 85 40
2586 100 pf. Erzgebirge 85 40
2587 100 pf. Main valley 85 40
2588 100 pf. Mecklenburg lakes . . 85 40

1081 Herder (after Anton Graff)

1994. 250th Birth Anniv of Johann Gottfried Herder (philosopher).

2589 **1081** 80 pf. multicoloured . . 70 35

1994. 20th-century German Paintings (3rd series). As T **1003**. Multicoloured.

2590 100 pf. "Maika" (Christian Schad) 85 40
2591 200 pf. "Dresden Landscape" (Erich Heckel) . . . . . 1·75 85
2592 300 pf. "Aleksei Javlensky and Marianne Werefkin" (Gabriele Munter) . . . . . 2·75 1·25

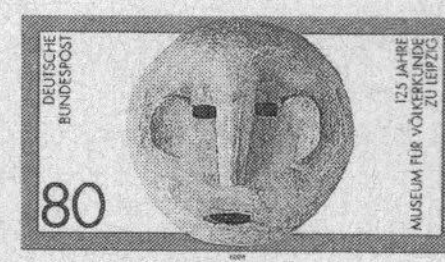

1082 Early 20th-century Makonde Mask (Tanzania)

1994. 125th Anniv of Leipzig Ethnology Museum.

2593 **1082** 80 pf. multicoloured . . 70 30

1083 Helmholtz, Eye and Colour Triangle

1994. Death Centenary of Hermann von Helmholtz (physicist).

2594 **1083** 100 pf. multicoloured . . 85 40

1084 Richter

1086 St. Wolfgang with Church Model (woodcut)

1994. Birth Cent of Willi Richter (President of Confederation of German Trade Unions).

2595 **1084** 100 pf. brown, purple and black 85 40

1994. Lander of the Federal Republic. As T **989**. Multicoloured.

2597 100 pf. Thuringia 85 40

1994. Humanitarian Relief Funds. Traditional Costumes (2nd series). As T **1055**. Multicoloured.

2598 80 pf. + 40 pf. Buckeburg . . 1·10 1·10
2599 80 pf. + 40 pf. Halle an der Saale . . . . 1·10 1·10
2600 100 pf. + 50 pf. Minden . . . 1·25 1·25
2601 100 pf. + 50 pf. Hoyerswerda . 1·25 1·25
2602 200 pf. + 70 pf. Betzingen . . 2·40 2·40

1994. Death Millenary of St. Wolfgang, Bishop of Regensburg.

2603 **1086** 100 pf. gold, cream and black 85 40

1087 Sachs

1088 Spreewald Postman, 1900

1994. 500th Birth Anniv of Hans Sachs (mastersinger and poet).

2604 **1087** 100 pf. purple and green on greyish 85 40

1994. Stamp Day.

2605 **1088** 100 pf. multicoloured . . 85 40

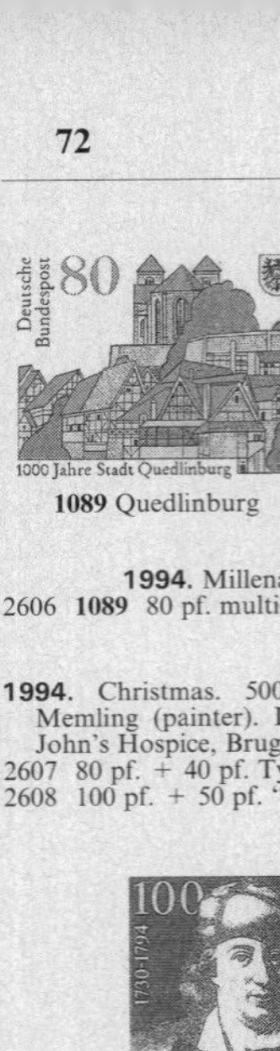

1089 Quedlinburg

1090 "Adoration of the Magi"

1994. Millenary of Quedlinburg.

2606 **1089** 80 pf. multicoloured . . 70 35

1994. Christmas. 500th Death Anniv of Hans Memling (painter). Details of his triptych in St. John's Hospice, Bruges. Multicoloured.

2607 80 pf. + 40 pf. Type **1090** . . 1·10 1·10
2608 100 pf. + 50 pf. "Nativity" . . 1·25 1·25

1091 Steuben and "Surrender of Cornwallis at Yorktown" (detail, John Trumbull)

1994. Death Bicentenary of Gen. Friedrich Wilhelm von Steuben (Inspector General of Washington's Army).

2609 **1091** 100 pf. multicoloured . . 85 40

1092 Cemetery

1994. 75th Anniv of National Assn for the Preservation of German Graves Abroad.

2610 **1092** 100 pf. black and red . . 85 40

1093 Obersuhl Checkpoint, 11 November 1989

1994. 5th Anniv of Opening of Borders between East and West Germany.

2611 **1093** 100 pf. multicoloured . . 85 40

1094 Fontane (after Max Liebermann) and Lines from "Prussian Song"

1095 Simson Fountain, Town Hall and St. Mary's and St Salvator's Churches

1994. 175th Birth Anniv of Theodor Fontane (writer).

2612 **1094** 100 pf. green, black and mauve 85 40

1995. Millenary of Gera.

2613 **1095** 80 pf. multicoloured . . 70 35

1096 Emperor Friedrich III, First Page of "Libellus" and Zur Munze (venue)

1995. 500th Anniv of Diet of Worms.

2614 **1096** 100 pf. black and red . . 85 40

1995. 20th-century German Paintings (4th series). As T **1003**. Multicoloured.

2615 100 pf. "The Water Tower, Bremen" (Franz Radziwill) . 85 40
2616 200 pf. "Still Life with Cat" (Georg Schrimpf) . . . . . 1·50 1·50
2617 300 pf. "Estate in Dangast" (Karl Schmidt-Rottluff) . . 2·50 2·50

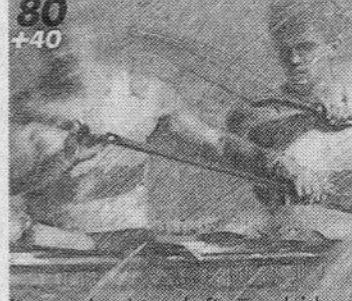

1097 Canoeing

1098 Friedrich Wilhelm (after A. Romandon)

1995. Sport Promotion Fund. Multicoloured.

2618 80 pf. + 40 pf. Type **1097** (27th World Canoeing Championships, Duisburg) . 85 85
2619 100 pf. + 50 pf. Hoop exercises (10th Int Gymnastics Festival, Berlin) . . . . . . 1·00 1·00
2620 100 pf. + 50 pf. Boxing (8th World Amateur Boxing Championships, Berlin) . . 1·00 1·00
2621 200 pf. + 80 pf. Volleyball (centenary) . . . . 2·00 2·00

1995. 375th Birth Anniv of Friedrich Wilhelm of Brandenburg, The Great Elector.

2622 **1098** 300 pf. multicoloured . . 2·40 1·60

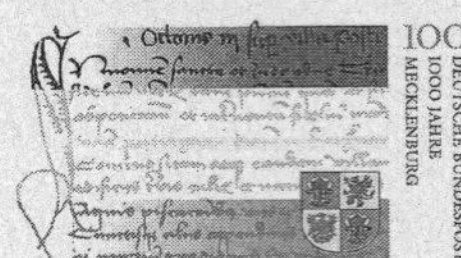

1099 Deed of Donation (995) and Arms of Mecklenburg-Vorpommern

1995. Millenary of Mecklenburg.

2623 **1099** 100 pf. multicoloured . . 85 40

1100 Computer Image of Terminal and Lion

1995. 250th Anniv of Carolo-Wilhelmina Technical University, Braunschweig.

2624 **1100** 100 pf. multicoloured . . 85 40

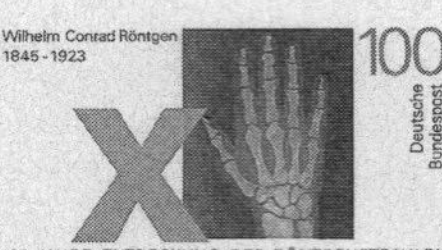

1101 X-ray of Hand

1995. 150th Birth Anniv of Wilhelm Rontgen and Centenary of his Discovery of X-rays.

2625 **1101** 100 pf. multicoloured . . 85 40

1102 Globe and Rainbow

1995. 1st Conference of Signatories to General Convention on Climate, Berlin.

2626 **1102** 100 pf. multicoloured . . 85 40

1103 Old Town Hall Reliefs

1995. 750th Anniv of Regensburg.

2627 **1103** 80 pf. multicoloured . . 70 35

1104 Bonhoeffer

1995. 50th Death Anniv of Dietrich Bonhoeffer (theologian).

2628 **1104** 100 pf. black, bl & grey . 85 40

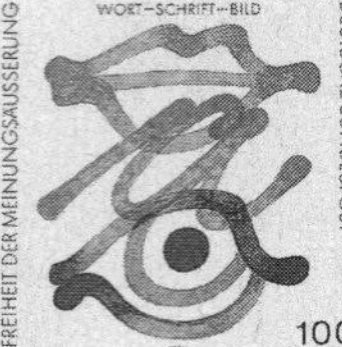

1105 Symbols of Speech, Writing and Pictures

1995. Freedom of Expression.

2629 **1105** 100 pf. multicoloured . . 85 40

1106 St. Clement's Church, Munster

1995. 300th Birth Anniv of Johann Conrad Schlaun (architect).

2630 **1106** 200 pf. multicoloured . . 1·50 85

1107 Friedrich Schiller, Signature and Schiller Museum, Marbach

1108 St. Vincent de Paul

1995. Centenary of German Schiller Society.

2631 **1107** 100 pf. multicoloured . . 90 45

1995. 150th Anniv of Vincent Conferences (charitable organization) in Germany.

2632 **1108** 100 pf. multicoloured . . 90 45

1111 Returning Soldiers ("End of War")

1112 Shipping Routes before and after 1895

1995. Europa. Peace and Freedom.

2635 **1111** 100 pf. black and red . . 90 45
2636 – 200 pf. bl, yell & blk . . 1·50 85

DESIGN: 200 pf. Emblem of European Community ("Moving towards Europe").

1995. Centenary of Kiel Canal.

2637 **1112** 80 pf. multicoloured . . 70 35

1113 Guglielmo Marconi and Wireless Equipment

1995. 100 Years of Radio.

2638 **1113** 100 pf. multicoloured . . 90 45

1114 U.N. Emblem

1995. 50th Anniv of U.N.O.

2639 **1114** 100 pf. lilac, gold and grey 90 45

MINIMUM PRICE

The minimum price quoted is 10p which represents a handling charge rather than a basis for valuing common stamps. For further notes about prices see introductory pages.

1115 Munsterlander

1116 Opening Bars of "Carmina Burana" and Characters

1995. Youth Welfare. Dogs (1st series). Mult.

2640 80 pf. + 40 pf. Type **1115** . . 85 85
2641 80 pf. + 40 pf. Giant schnauzer 85 85
2642 100 pf. + 50 pf. Wire-haired dachshund . . . . 1·00 1·00
2643 100 pf. + 50 pf. German shepherd . . . . 1·00 1·00
2644 200 pf. + 80 pf. Keeshund . . 2·00 2·00

See also Nos. 2696/2700.

1995. Birth Centenary of Carl Orff (composer).

2645 **1116** 100 pf. multicoloured . . 90 45

1995. Landscapes (3rd series). As T **1046**. Multicoloured.

2646 100 pf. Franconian Switzerland 65 45
2647 100 pf. River Havel, Berlin . . 65 45
2648 100 pf. Oberlausitz 65 45
2649 100 pf. Sauerland 65 45

1117 Lion (from 12th-century coin)

1118 Kaiser Wilhelm Memorial Church

1995. 800th Death Anniv of Henry the Lion, Duke of Saxony and Bavaria.

2650 **1117** 400 pf. multicoloured . . 2·75 2·25

1995. Centenary of Kaiser Wilhelm Memorial Church, Berlin.

2651 **1118** 100 pf. multicoloured . . 90 45

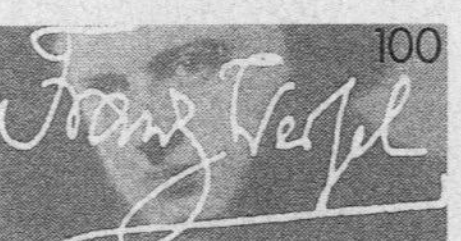

1119 Werfel and Signature

1995. 50th Death Anniv of Franz Werfel (writer).

2652 **1119** 100 pf. mve, bl & blk . . 65 45

1995. Tourist Sights. As T **854** but inscr "DEUTSCHLAND".

2654 47 pf. green and black 30 15
2656 100 pf. blue and black 55 35
2657 110 pf. cinnamon & brown . . 65 35
2658 110 pf. orange and blue . . . 80 40
2659 220 pf. green and black . . . 1·25 75
2661 440 pf. orange and blue . . . 2·50 1·50
2663 510 pf. red and blue . . . . . 3·00 1·75
2665 640 pf. blue and brown . . . . 3·75 2·50
2666 690 pf. black and green . . . 4·00 2·75

DESIGNS: 47 pf. Berus Monument, Uberherrn; 100 pf. Goethe-Schiller Monument, Weimar; 110 pf. (2657) Bellevue Castle, Berlin; 110 pf. (2658) Emblem of "Expo 2000" World's Fair, Hanover; 220 pf. Bruhl's Terrace, Dresden; 440 pf. Town Hall, Bremen; 510 pf. Holsten Gate, Lubeck; 640 pf. Speyer Cathedral; 690 pf. St. Michael's Church, Hamburg.

1120 Strauss

1995. 80th Birth Anniv of Franz Josef Strauss (politician).

2675 **1120** 100 pf. multicoloured . . 65 45

1121 Postwoman

1995. Stamp Day.

2676 **1121** 200 pf. + 100 pf. mult . 2·10 2·10

1123 Eifel

1995. Humanitarian Relief Funds. Farmhouses (1st series). Multicoloured.
2678 80 pf. + 40 pf. Type **1123** . . 85 85
2679 80 pf. + 40 pf. Saxony 85 85
2680 100 pf. + 50 pf. Lower Germany . . . . 1·00 1·00
2681 100 pf. + 50 pf. Upper Bavaria . . . . 1·00 1·00
2682 200 pf. + 70 pf. Mecklenburg . 2·00 2·00
See also Nos. 2742/6.

1124 Schumacher 1126 Ranke

1995. Birth Centenary of Kurt Schumacher (politician).
2683 **1124** 100 pf. multicoloured . . 65 45

1995. Birth Bicentenary of Leopold von Ranke (historian).
2685 **1126** 80 pf. multicoloured . . 70 35

1127 Hindemith

1995. Birth Centenary of Paul Hindemith (composer).
2686 **1127** 100 pf. multicoloured . . 65 45

1128 Alfred Nobel and Will

1995. Centenary of Nobel Prize Trust Fund.
2687 **1128** 100 pf. multicoloured . . 90 45

1129 "CARE" in American Colours

1995. 50th Anniv of CARE (Co-operative for Assistance and Remittances Overseas).
2688 **1129** 100 pf. multicoloured . . 65 45

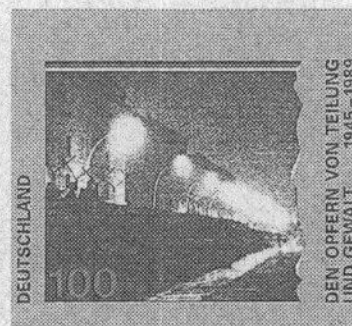

1130 Berlin Wall

1995. Commemorating Victims of Political Oppression, 1945–89.
2689 **1130** 100 pf. multicoloured . . 65 45

1131 "The Annunciation"

1995. Christmas. Stained Glass Windows in Augsburg Cathedral. Multicoloured.
2690 80 pf. + 40 pf. Type **1131** . . 85 85
2691 100 pf. + 50 pf. "Nativity" . . 1·25 1·25

1132 Dribbling

1995. Borussia Dortmund, German Football Champion.
2692 **1132** 100 pf. multicoloured . . 90 45

1133 Auguste von Sartorius (founder)

1996. 150th Anniv of German Institute for Children's Missionary Work.
2693 **1133** 100 pf. multicoloured . . 65 45

1134 Bodelschwingh

1996. 50th Death Anniv of Friedrich von Bodelschwingh (theologian).
2694 **1134** 100 pf. black and red . . 65 45

1135 Luther (after Lucas Cranach)

1996. 450th Death Anniv of Martin Luther (Protestant reformer).
2695 **1135** 100 pf. multicoloured . . 65 45

1996. Youth Welfare. Dogs (2nd series). As T **1115**. Multicoloured.
2696 80 pf. + 40 pf. Borzoi 85 85
2697 80 pf. + 40 pf. Chow chow . . 85 85
2698 100 pf. + 50 pf. St. Bernard . 1·00 1·00
2699 100 pf. + 50 pf. Rough collie . 1·00 1·00
2700 200 pf. + 80 pf. Briard . . . 2·00 2·00

1136 Siebold

1996. Birth Bicentenary of Philipp Franz von Siebold (physician and Japanologist).
2701 **1136** 100 pf. multicoloured . . 65 45

1137 Cathedral Square

1996. Millenary of Cathedral Square, Halberstadt.
2702 **1137** 80 pf. multicoloured . . 45 35

1138 Galen

1996. 50th Death Anniv of Cardinal Count Clemens von Galen, Bishop of Munster.
2703 **1138** 100 pf. grey, bl & gold . 65 45

1996. 20th-century German Paintings (5th series). As T **1003**. Multicoloured.
2704 100 pf. "Seated Female Nude" (Max Pechstein) 65 45
2705 200 pf. "For Wilhelm Runge" (Georg Muche) . . . . . . 1·40 85
2706 300 pf. "Still Life with Guitar, Book and Vase" (Helmut Kolle) . . . . 1·90 1·25

1139 Detail of Ceiling Fresco, Prince-bishop's Residence, Wurzburg

1996. 300th Birth Anniv of Giovanni Battista Tiepolo (artist).
2707 **1139** 200 pf. multicoloured . . 1·25 85

1996. Landscapes (4th series). As T **1046**. Multicoloured.
2709 100 pf. Eifel 55 40
2710 100 pf. Holstein Switzerland . 55 40
2711 100 pf. Saale 55 40
2712 100 pf. Spreewald 55 40

1141 Paula Modersohn-Becker (self-portrait)

1996. Europa. Famous Women.
2713 **1141** 80 pf. multicoloured . . 40 30
2714 – 100 pf. black, grey and mauve 55 40
DESIGN: 100 pf. Kathe Kollwitz (self-portrait).

1142 Opening Lines of Document and Town (1642 engraving, Matthaeus Merian)

1996. Millenary of Granting to Freising the Right to hold Markets.
2715 **1142** 100 pf. multicoloured . . 55 40

1143 Borchert

1996. 75th Birth Anniv of Wolfgang Borchert (writer).
2716 **1143** 100 pf. multicoloured . . 55 40

1144 Emblem

1996. 50th Anniv of Ruhr Festival, Recklinghausen.
2717 **1144** 100 pf. multicoloured . . 55 40

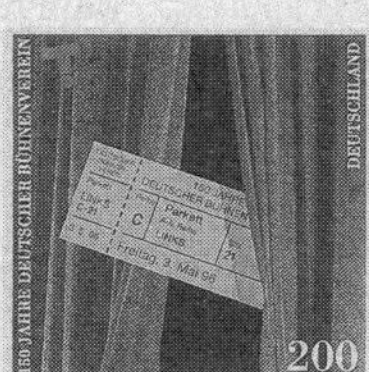

1145 Ticket and Stage Curtain

1996. 150th Anniv of German Theatre Assn.
2718 **1145** 200 pf. multicoloured . . 1·25 80

1146 Leibniz and Mathematical Diagram

1996. 350th Birth Anniv of Gottfried Leibniz.
2719 **1146** 100 pf. red and black . . 55 40

1147 Kneeling Figure and Motto forming "A"

1996. 300th Anniv of Berlin Academy of Arts.
2720 **1147** 100 pf. multicoloured . . 55 40

1148 Carl Schuhmann (wrestling, equestrian sports and gymnastics, 1896)

1996. Sport Promotion Fund. Centenary of Modern Olympic Games. German Olympic Champions. Multicoloured.
2721 80 pf. + 40 pf. Type **1148** . . 75 75
2722 100 pf. + 50 pf. Josef Neckermann (dressage, 1964 and 1968) . . . . 1·00 1·00
2723 100 pf. + 50 pf. Annie Hubler-Horn (ice skating, 1908) . . 1·00 1·00
2724 200 pf. + 80 pf. Alfred and Gustav Flatow (gymnastics, 1896) . . . . 1·90 1·90

1149 Townscape

1996. 800th Anniv of Heidelberg.
2725 **1149** 100 pf. multicoloured . . 55 40

1150 Children's Handprints

1996. 50th Anniv of U.N.I.C.E.F.
2726 **1150** 100 pf. multicoloured . . 55 40

1151 "Wedding" (illustration by Bruno Paul)

1996. 75th Death Anniv of Ludwig Thoma (satirist).
2727 **1151** 100 pf. multicoloured . . 55 40

1153 Map and Tropical Wildlife

1996. Environmental Protection. Preservation of Tropical Habitats.
2729 **1153** 100 pf. + 50 pf. mult . . 95 95

1154 Volklingen Blast Furnace

1996. U.N.E.S.C.O. World Heritage Sites.
2730 **1154** 100 pf. multicoloured . . 55 40

1155 Lincke

1996. 50th Death Anniv of Paul Lincke (composer and conductor).
2731 **1155** 100 pf. multicoloured . . 55 40

1156 Gendarmenmarkt, Berlin

1996.
2732 **1156** 100 pf. multicoloured . . 55 40

1157 "50" comprising Stamp under Magnifying Glass

1996. 50th Anniv of Association of German Philatelists.
2733 **1157** 100 pf. multicoloured . . 55 40

1158 Book

1996. Centenary of German Civil Code.
2734 **1158** 300 pf. multicoloured . . 1·75 1·25

1159 Players

1996. Borussia Dortmund, German Football Champion.
2735 **1159** 100 pf. multicoloured . . 55 40

1160 Bamburg Old Town

1996. U.N.E.S.C.O. World Heritage Sites.
2736 **1160** 100 pf. multicoloured . . 55 40

1161 Eyes

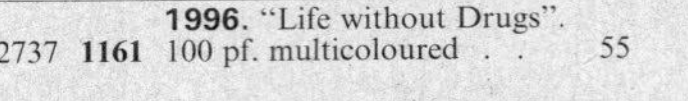

1996. "Life without Drugs".
2737 **1161** 100 pf. multicoloured . . 55 40

1162 "Like will Cure Like" and Samuel Hahnemann (developer of principle)

1163 Bruckner and Symphony No. III

1996. Bicentenary of Homeopathy.
2738 **1162** 400 pf. multicoloured . . 2·25 1·60

1996. Death Centenary of Anton Bruckner (composer).
2739 **1163** 100 pf. multicoloured . . 55 40

1164 Mueller, Map and Plants

1996. Death Centenary of Baron Ferdinand von Mueller (botanist).
2740 **1164** 100 pf. multicoloured . . 55 40

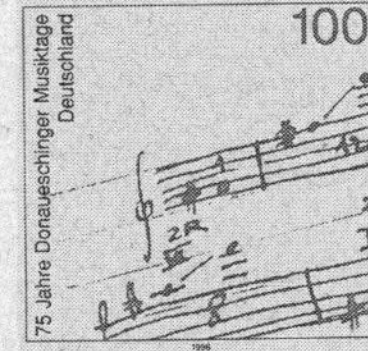

1165 Score by John Cage

1996. 75th Anniv of Donaueschingen Music Festival.
2741 **1165** 100 pf. blue, blk & mve . 55 40

1996. Humanitarian Relief Funds. Farmhouses (2nd series). As T **1123**. Multicoloured.
2742 80 pf. + 40 pf. Spree Forest . 75 75
2743 80 pf. + 40 pf. Thuringia . . . 75 75
2744 100 pf. + 50 pf. Black Forest . 1·00 1·00
2745 100 pf. + 50 pf. Westphalia . . 1·00 1·00
2746 200 pf. + 70 pf. Schleswig-Holstein . . . . 1·75 1·75

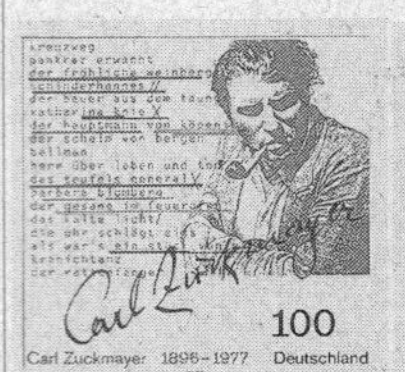

1166 Titles of Plays and Zuckmayer

1167 "Adoration of the Magi"

1996. Birth Centenary of Carl Zuckmayer (dramatist).
2747 **1166** 100 pf. multicoloured . . 50 35

1996. Christmas. Illustrations from Henry II's "Book of Pericopes" (illuminated manuscript of readings from the Gospels). Multicoloured.
2748 80 pf. + 40 pf. Type **1167** . . 60 60
2749 100 pf. + 50 pf. "Nativity" . . 80 80

1168 Schmid

1996. Birth Centenary of Carlo Schmid (politician and writer).
2750 **1168** 100 pf. multicoloured . . 55 35

1169 "Friends of Schubert in Afzenbrugg" (detail, L. Kupelwieser)

1170 Pitch, Player and Herberger

1997. Birth Bicentenary of Franz Schubert (composer).
2751 **1169** 100 pf. multicoloured . . 55 35

1997. Birth Centenary of Sepp Herberger (national football team coach, 1936–64).
2752 **1170** 100 pf. green, red & blk . 55 35

1171 Motor Cars

1997. "More Safety for Children" (road safety campaign).
2753 **1171** 100 pf. multicoloured . . 55 35
See also No. 2812.

1172 Melanchthon (after Lucas Cranach the younger)

1173 Revellers "Wiggling"

1997. 500th Birth Anniv of Philipp Melanchthon (religious reformer).
2754 **1172** 100 pf. multicoloured . . 55 35

1997. 175th Anniv of Cologne Carnival.
2755 **1173** 100 pf. multicoloured . . 55 35

1174 Erhard

1997. Birth Centenary of Ludwig Erhard (Chancellor, 1963–66).
2756 **1174** 100 pf. black and red . . 55 35

1175 Aerobics

1997. Sport Promotion Fund. Fun Sports. Multicoloured.
2757 80 pf. + 40 pf. Type **1175** . . 80 80
2758 100 pf. + 50 pf. Inline skating . 1·00 1·00
2759 100 pf. + 50 pf. Streetball . . 1·00 1·00
2760 200 pf. + 80 pf. Free-climbing . 1·75 1·75

1176 New Pavilion

1997. 500th Anniv of Granting of Imperial Fair Privilege to Leipzig.
2761 **1176** 100 pf. silver, red & blue 55 35

1178 Straubing

1997. 1100th Anniv of Straubing.
2763 **1178** 100 pf. multicoloured . . 55 35

1179 Stephan, Telephone and Postcards

1997. Death Centenary of Heinrich von Stephan (founder of U.P.U.).
2764 **1179** 100 pf. multicoloured . . 55 35

1180 Augustusburg and Falkenlust Castles

1997. U.N.E.S.C.O. World Heritage Sites.
2765 **1180** 100 pf. multicoloured . . 55 35

1181 Diamonds

1182 St. Adalbert

1997. 500th Anniv of Idar-Oberstein Region Gem Industry.
2766 **1181** 300 pf. multicoloured . . 1·75 1·00

1997. Death Millenary of St. Adalbert (Bishop of Prague).
2767 **1182** 100 pf. lilac 55 35

1183 "The Fisherman and His Wife" (Brothers Grimm)

1997. Europa. Tales and Legends. Mult.
2768 80 pf. Type **1183** 45 25
2769 100 pf. Rubezahl 55 35

1184 Knotted Ribbons

1997. 50th Anniv of Town Twinning Movement.
2770 **1184** 100 pf. multicoloured . . 55 35

1186 Kneipp

1997. Death Cent of Father Sebastian Kneipp (developer of naturopathic treatments).
2772 **1186** 100 pf. multicoloured . . 55 35

1187 United States Flag, George Marshall and Bomb Site

1997. 50th Anniv of Marshall Plan (European Recovery Program).
2773 **1187** 100 pf. multicoloured . . 55 35

1188 Rheno-German Heavy Horse

1997. Youth Welfare. Horses. Multicoloured.

2774 80 pf. + 40 pf. Type **1188** . . 80 80
2775 80 pf. + 40 pf. Shetland ponies 80 80
2776 100 pf. + 50 pf. Frisian . . . 1·00 1·00
2777 100 pf. + 50 pf. Haflinger . . 1·00 1·00
2778 200 pf. + 80 pf. Hanoverian with foal . . . . 1·90 1·90

1189 Bridge

1997. Centenary of Mungsten Railway Bridge.

2779 **1189** 100 pf. multicoloured . . 70 35

1997. Famous Women. As T **832** but inscr "Deutschland".

2785 100 pf. brown and green . . . 70 35
2786 110 pf. drab and violet . . . 65 50
2790 220 pf. ultramarine & blue . . 1·25 75
2792 300 pf. brown and blue . . . . 2·10 1·00
2795 440 pf. brown and violet . . . 3·25 1·60

DESIGNS: 100 pf. Elisabeth Schwarzhaupt (politician); 110 pf. Marlene Dietrich (actress); 220 pf. Marie-Elisabeth Luders (politician); 300 pf. Maria Probst (social reformer and politician); 440 pf. Gret Palucca (dancer).

1192 Arms of Brandenburg

1997. Flood Relief Funds.

2805 **1192** 110 pf. + 90 pf. mult . . 1·25 1·25

1997. Landscapes (5th series). As T **1046**. Multicoloured.

2806 110 pf. Bavarian Forest . . . 65 35
2807 110 pf. North German Moors . 65 35
2808 110 pf. Luneburg Heath . . . 65 35

1193 Rudolf Diesel and Engine

1997. Centenary of Diesel Engine.

2809 **1193** 300 pf. black and blue . 2·00 1·00

1194 Potato Plant and Cultivation

1997. 350th Anniv of Introduction of the Potato to Germany.

2810 **1194** 300 pf. multicoloured . . 2·10 1·00

1997. As No. 2753 but with face value changed.

2812 **1171** 10 pf. multicoloured . . 10 10

1196 Mendelssohn-Bartholdy

1997. 150th Death Anniv of Felix Mendelssohn-Bartholdy (composer).

2813 **1196** 110 pf. green, ol & yell . 80 40

1197 Watermill, Black Forest

1997. Humanitarian Relief Funds. Mills. Multicoloured.

2814 100 pf. + 50 pf. Type **1197** . . 1·10 1·10
2815 110 pf. + 50 pf. Watermill, Hesse . . . . 1·10 1·10
2816 110 pf. + 50 pf. Post mill, Lower Rhine . . . . 1·10 1·10
2817 110 pf. + 50 pf. Scoop wind-mill, Schleswig-Holstein . . 1·10 1·10
2818 220 pf. + 80 pf. Dutch wind-mill . . . . 2·10 2·10

1198 Emblem

1997. Saar-Lor-Lux European Region.

2819 **1198** 110 pf. multicoloured . . 80 40

1199 Team celebrating

1997. Bayern Munchen, German Football Champion.

2820 **1199** 110 pf. multicoloured . . 80 40

1200 Dehler

1997. Birth Centenary of Thomas Dehler (politician).

2821 **1200** 110 pf. multicoloured . . 80 40

1201 Heine (after Wilhelm Hensel)

1997. Birth Bicentenary of Heinrich Heine (journalist and poet).

2822 **1201** 110 pf. multicoloured . . 80 40

1202 Tree and Title of Hymn

1997. 300th Birth Anniv of Gerhard Tersteegen (religious reformer).

2823 **1202** 110 pf. brown, grey and black 80 40

1203 Emblem

1997. Cent of Deutscher Caritas Verband (Catholic charitable association).

2824 **1203** 110 pf. multicoloured . . 80 40

1204 Wise Men

1997. Christmas. Multicoloured.

2825 100 pf. + 50 pf. Type **1204** . . 1·10 1·10
2826 110 pf. + 50 pf. Nativity . . . 1·10 1·10

The premium was for the benefit of the Federal Association of Free Welfare Work, Bonn.

1205 Monastery Plan and Church

1998. U.N.E.S.C.O. World Heritage Site. Maulbronn Monastery.

2827 **1205** 100 pf. multicoloured . . 70 35

1206 Walled City

1998. 1100th Anniv of Nordlingen.

2828 **1206** 110 pf. multicoloured . . 80 40

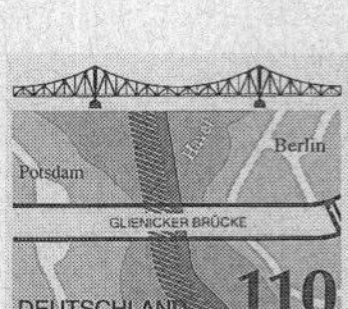

1207 Glienicke Bridge, Potsdam–Berlin **1209** Characters in Brecht's Head

1208 Football

1998. Bridges.

2829 **1207** 110 pf. multicoloured . . 80 40

1998. Sport Promotion Fund. International Championships. Multicoloured.

2830 100 pf. + 50 pf. Type **1208** (World Cup Football Championship, France) . . 1·10 1·10
2831 110 pf. + 50 pf. Ski jumping (Winter Olympic Games, Nagano, Japan) . . . . . . 1·10 1·10
2832 110 pf. + 50 pf. Rowing (World Rowing Championships, Cologne) . 1·10 1·10
2833 300 pf. + 100 pf. Disabled skier (Winter Paralympic Games, Nagano) . . . . 2·75 2·75

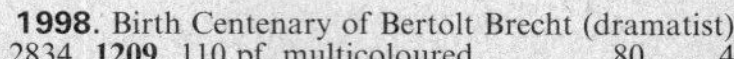

1998. Birth Centenary of Bertolt Brecht (dramatist).

2834 **1209** 110 pf. multicoloured . . 80 40

1210 X-ray Photographs of Moon, Ionic Lattice Structure and Nerve of Goldfish and Founding Assembly

1998. 50th Anniv of Max Planck Society for the Advancement of Science.

2835 **1210** 110 pf. multicoloured . . 80 40

1211 Bad Frankenhausen

1998. Millenary of First Documentary Mention of Bad Frankenhausen.

2836 **1211** 110 pf. multicoloured . . 80 40

1212 Signatories

1998. 350th Anniv of Peace of Westphalia (settlements ending Thirty Years' War).

2837 **1212** 110 pf. blk, grey & mve . 80 40

1213 Baden-Wurttemberg (Kurt Viertel)

1998. Federal State Parliament Buildings. Multicoloured.

2838 110 pf. Type **1213** 80 40
2839 110 pf. Bavaria (designed Friedrich Burklein) 80 40
2840 110 pf. Chamber of Deputies, Berlin (Friedrich Schulze) . . 80 40
2841 110 pf. Brandenburg (Franz Schwechten) 80 40

See also Nos. 2885, 2893/4 and 2897.

1214 Hildegard's Vision of Life Cycle

1998. 900th Birth Anniv of Hildegard of Bingen (mystic).

2842 **1214** 100 pf. multicoloured . . 70 35

1216 St. Marienstern Abbey

1998. 750th Anniv of St. Marienstern Abbey, Panschwitz-Kuckau.

2844 **1216** 110 pf. multicoloured . . 80 40

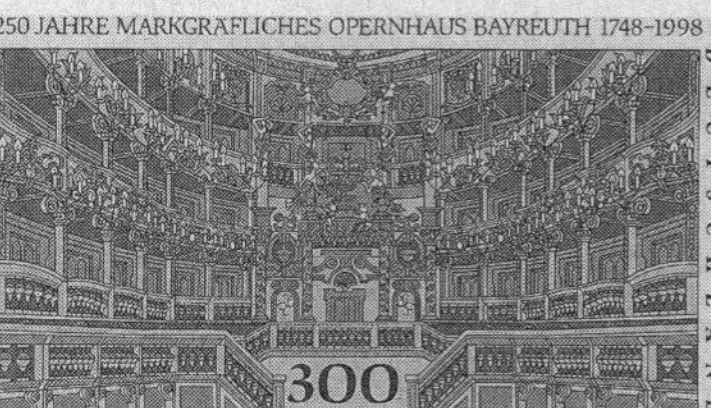

1217 Auditorium

1998. 250th Anniv of Bayreuth Opera House.

2845 **1217** 300 pf. multicoloured . . 2·10 1·00

1218 Junger **1219** Doves and Tree (German Unification Day)

1998. Ernst Junger (writer) Commemoration.

2846 **1218** 110 pf. multicoloured . . 80 40

1998. Europa. National Festivals.

2847 **1219** 110 pf. multicoloured . . 80 40

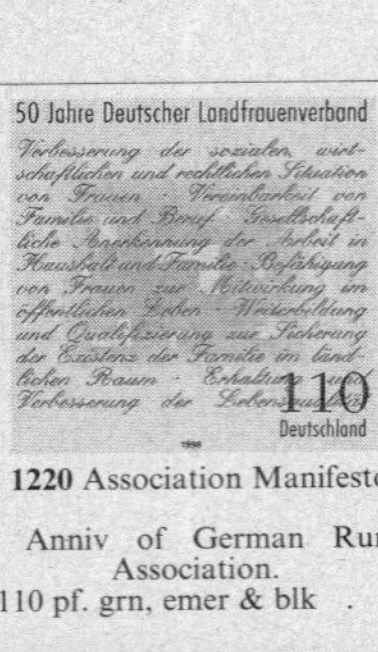

1220 Association Manifesto

1998. 50th Anniv of German Rural Women's Association.
2848 **1220** 110 pf. grn, emer & blk . 80 40

1222 Coast and Ocean

1998. Environmental Protection.
2850 **1222** 110 pf. + 50 pf. mult . . 1·10 1·10

1223 "The Mouse" **1224** Crowds of People and Cross

1998. Youth Welfare. Children's Cartoons. Multicoloured.
2851 100 pf. + 50 pf. Type **1223** . . 1·10 1·10
2852 100 pf. + 50 pf. "The Sandman" . . . . 1·10 1·10
2853 110 pf. + 50 pf. "Maja the Bee" . . . . 1·10 1·10
2854 110 pf. + 50 pf. "Captain Bluebear" . . . . 1·10 1·10
2855 220 pf. + 80 pf. "Pumuckl" . 2·10 2·10

1998. 150th Anniv of First Congress of German Catholics.
2856 **1224** 110 pf. multicoloured . . 80 40

1225 One Deutschmark Coin

1998. 50th Anniv of the Deutschmark.
2857 **1225** 110 pf. multicoloured . . 80 40

1226 Harvesting Hops

1998. 1100 Years of Hop Cultivation in Germany.
2858 **1226** 110 pf. multicoloured . . 80 40

1227 Euro Banknotes forming "EZB"

1998. Inauguration of European Central Bank, Frankfurt-on-Main.
2859 **1227** 110 pf. multicoloured . . 80 40

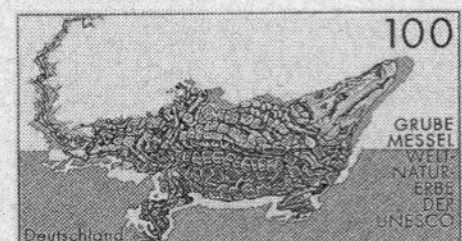

1229 Skeleton of Crocodile

1998. U.N.E.S.C.O. World Heritage Sites. Grube Messel Fossil Deposits.
2861 **1229** 100 pf. multicoloured . . . 70 35

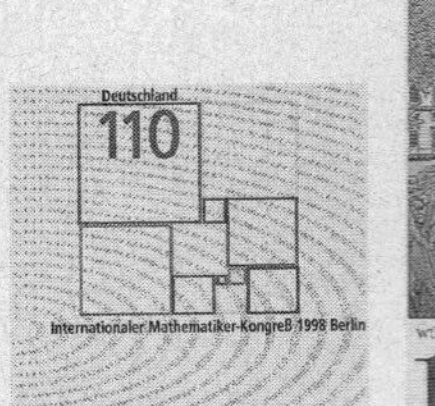

1230 Coloured Squares and Ludolphian Number **1231** Wurzburg Palace

1998. 23rd International Congress of Mathematicians, Berlin.
2862 **1230** 110 pf. multicoloured . . 80 40

1998. U.N.E.S.C.O. World Heritage Sites. Multicoloured.
2863 110 pf. Type **1231** 80 40
2864 110 pf. Puning Temple, Chengde, China 80 40

1233 Players, Ball and Pitch

1998. 1. FC Kaiserslautern, National Football Champion, 1998.
2866 **1233** 110 pf. multicoloured . . 80 40

1234 Main Building **1235** Hausmann and Book Cover

1998. 300th Anniv of Francke Charitable Institutions, Halle.
2867 **1234** 110 pf. multicoloured . . 80 40

1998. Birth Centenary of Manfred Hausmann (writer).
2688 **1235** 100 pf. multicoloured . . 80 40

1236 Hands on T-shirt **1237** Hen Harriers and Chicks

1998. Child Protection.
2869 **1236** 110 pf. red and black . . 80 40

1998. Humanitarian Relief Funds. Birds. Multicoloured.
2870 100 pf. + 50 pf. Type **1237** . . 1·10 1·10
2871 110 pf. + 50 pf. Great bustards . . . . 1·10 1·10
2872 110 pf. + 50 pf. White-eyed ducks . . . . 1·10 1·10
2873 110 pf. + 50 pf. Sedge warblers on reeds . . . . 1·10 1·10
2874 220 pf. + 80 pf. Woodchat shrike . . . . 2·10 2·10

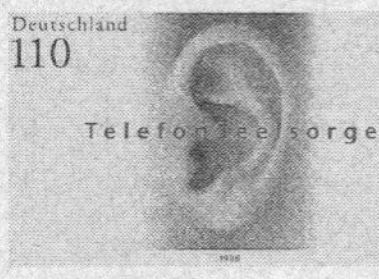

1238 Ear

1998. Telephone Help Lines.
2875 **1238** 110 pf. black & orange . 80 40

1239 "Hiorten" (sailing packet), 1692

1998. Stamp Day.
2876 **1239** 110 pf. multicoloured . . 80 40

1240 Ramin

1998. Birth Centenary of Gunther Ramin (choir leader and organist).
2877 **1240** 300 pf. multicoloured . . 2·10 1·00

1241 Shepherds following Star

1998. Christmas. Multicoloured.
2878 100 pf. + 50 pf. Type **1241** . . 11·10 1·10
2879 110 pf. + 50 pf. Baby Jesus . . 1·10 1·10

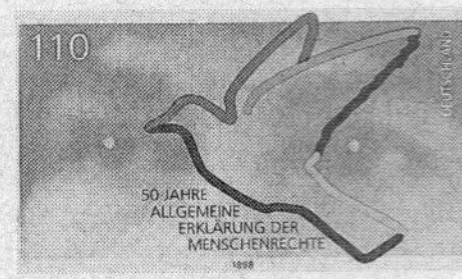

1242 Dove

1998. 50th Anniv of Declaration of Human Rights.
2880 **1242** 110 pf. multicoloured . . 80 80
For this design with charity premium see No. 2899.

1243 Conductor's Hands and Baton

1998. 450th Anniv of Saxon State Orchestra, Dresden.
2881 **1243** 300 pf. multicoloured . . 2·10 1·00

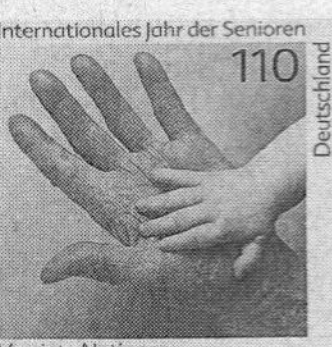

1244 National Theatre, Schiller, Goethe, Wieland and Herder **1245** Hands of Elderly Person and Child

1999. 1100th Anniv of Weimar. European City of Culture.
2882 **1244** 100 pf. multicoloured . . 70 35

1999. International Year of the Elderly.
2883 **1245** 110 pf. multicoloured . . 80 40

1246 Katharina von Bora

1999. 500th Birth Anniv of Katharina von Bora (wife of Martin Luther).
2884 **1246** 110 pf. multicoloured . . 80 40

1999. Federal State Parliament Buildings (2nd series). As T **1213**.
2885 110 pf. Hesse (Richard Goerz) (former palace of Dukes of Hesse) 80 40

1247 Cycle Racing

1999. Sport Promotion Fund. Multicoloured.
2886 100 pf. + 50 pf. Type **1247** . . 1·00 1·00
2887 110 pf. + 50 pf. Horse racing . 1·10 1·10
2888 110 pf. + 50 pf. Motor racing . 1·10 1·10
2889 300 pf. + 100 pf. Motor cycle racing . . . . 2·50 2·50

1248 Cover Illustration (by Walter Trier) of "Emil and the Detectives" (novel)

1999. Birth Centenary of Erich Kastner (writer).
2890 **1248** 300 pf. multicoloured . . 2·00 1·00

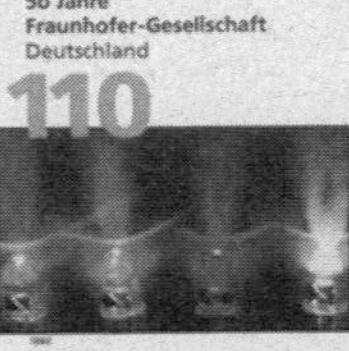

1249 Coloured Diodes

1999. 50th Anniv of Fraunhofer Society (for applied research).
2891 **1249** 110 pf. multicoloured . . 70 35

1250 Emblem and Initials

1999. 50th Anniv of North Atlantic Treaty Organization.
2892 **1250** 110 pf. multicoloured . . 70 35

1999. Federal State Parliament Buildings (3rd series). As T **1213**. Multicoloured.
2893 110 pf. City Parliament of Hamburg 70 35
2894 110 pf. Mecklenburg-Western Pomerania (Schwerin Castle, rebuilt by Georg Demmler and Friedrich Stuler) 70 35

1251 Maybach Cabriolet of 1936 and Club Emblem

1999. Centenary of German Automobile Club.
2895 **1251** 110 pf. multicoloured . . 70 35

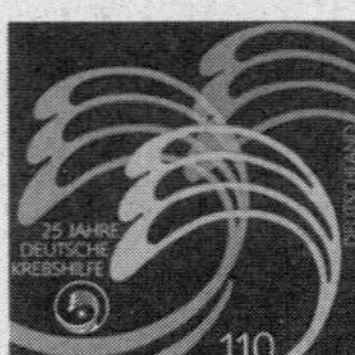

1252 Emblem

1999. 25th Anniv of German Cancer Relief.
2896 **1252** 110 pf. multicoloured . . 70 35

1999. Federal State Parliament Buildings (4th series). As T **1213**.
2897 110 pf. Bremen (Wassili Luckhardt) 70 35

1253 "Man, Nature, Technology"

1999. "EXPO 2000" World's Fair, Hanover.
2898 **1253** 110 pf. multicoloured . . 70 35
See also No. 2936.

1999. Kosovo Relief Fund. As T **1242** but with inscription changed to "Kosovo–HILFE 1999".
2899 110 pf. + 100 pf. mult . . 1·40 1·40

1256 Cross of St. John

1999. 900th Anniv of Order of Knights of St. John of Jerusalem and of Malta.
2902 **1256** 110 pf. multicoloured . . 70 35

1257 Flags and Children

1999. 50th Anniv of Berlin Airlift of 1948–49.
2903 **1257** 110 pf. multicoloured . . 70 35

1258 Emblem

1999. 50th Anniv of Council of Europe.
2904 **1258** 110 pf. multicoloured . . 70 35

1261 Lars, the Little Polar Bear

1999. Youth Welfare. Cartoons Characters. Mult.
2907 100 pf. + 50 pf. Type **1261** . . 1·00 1·00
2908 100 pf. + 50 pf. Rudi the Crow . . . . 1·00 1·00
2909 110 pf. + 50 pf. Twipsy (mascot of "Expo 2000" World's Fair, Hanover) . . 1·10 1·10
2910 110 pf. + 50 pf. Mecki (hedgehog) . . . . 1·10 1·10
2911 220 pf. + 80 pf. Tabaluga (dragon) . . . . 2·00 2·00

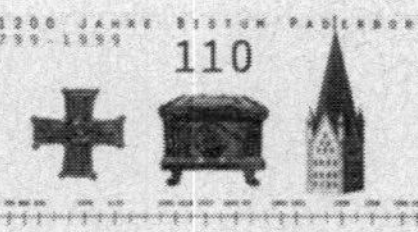

1262 Cross Clasp, Altar, Cathedral Spire and Time-line

1999. 1200th Anniv of Paderborn Diocese.
2912 **1262** 110 pf. multicoloured . . 70 35

1263 House (child's painting)

1264 "Ball at the Viennese Hofburg" and Score

1999. 50th Anniv of S.O.S. Children's Villages.
2913 **1263** 110 pf. multicoloured . . 70 35

1999. Death Centenary of Johann Strauss the younger (composer).
2914 **1264** 300 pf. multicoloured . . 2·00 1·00

1265 Children at Desks (tapestry)

1999. 115th Anniv of Dominikus-Ringeisen Institute for Disabled People, Ursberg.
2915 **1265** 110 pf. multicoloured . . 70 35

1266 Heinemann

1999. Birth Centenary of Gustav Heinemann (President 1969–74).
2916 **1266** 110 pf. grey and red . . 70 35

1267 "Old Woman laughing" (Ernst Barlach)

1999. Cultural Foundation of the Federal States. Sculptures. Multicoloured.
2917 110 pf. Type **1267** 70 35
2918 220 pf. "Bust of a Thinker" (Wilhelm Lehmbruck) . . . 1·40 70

1268 Participating Countries and Dove

1999. Centenary of First Peace Conference, The Hague.
2919 **1268** 300 pf. grey, red and blue . . . . 2·00 1·00

1269 Goethe (after J. K. Stieler)

1999. 250th Birth Anniv of Johann Wolfgang von Goethe (poet and playwright).
2920 **1269** 110 pf. multicoloured . . 70 35

1272 Player

1999. FC Bayern Munich, National Football Champion, 1999.
2923 **1272** 110 pf. multicoloured . . 70 35

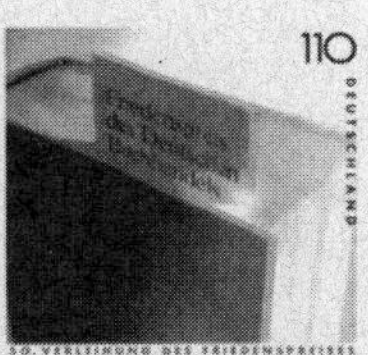

1273 Book and Bookmark

1999. 50th Anniv of Federal Association of German Book Traders' Peace Prize.
2924 **1273** 110 pf. multicoloured . . 70 35

1274 Strauss with Character and Poster from "Salome" (opera)

1999. 50th Death Anniv of Richard Strauss (composer).
2925 **1274** 300 pf. multicoloured . . 2·00 1·00

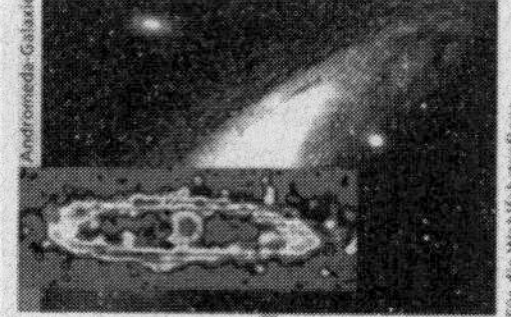

1275 Andromeda Galaxy

1999. Humanitarian Relief Funds. Outer Space. Multicoloured.
2926 100 pf. + 50 pf. Type **1275** . . 1·00 50
2927 100 pf. + 50 pf. Swan constellation . . . . 1·00 50
2928 110 pf. + 50 pf. X-ray image of exploding star . . . . . . 1·10 55
2929 110 pf. + 50 pf. Comet colliding with Jupiter . . . . . . 1·10 55
2930 300 pf. + 100 pf. Gamma ray image of sky . . . . 2·50 1·25

1276 Goltzsch Valley Railway Bridge

1999. Bridges.
2931 **1276** 110 pf. multicoloured . . 70 35

1277 "DGB"

1999. 50th Anniv of German Federation of Trade Unions.
2932 **1277** 110 pf. black and bright red 70 35

1278 Greater Horseshoe Bats

1999. Endangered Species.
2933 **1278** 100 pf. multicoloured . . 65 30

1279 The Annunciation

1999 . Christmas. Multicoloured.
2934 100 pf. + 50 pf. Type **1279** . . 1·00 50
2935 110 pf. + 50 pf. Nativity . . . 1·10 55

1280 Emblem and Eye

2000. "EXPO 2000" World's Fair, Hanover (2nd issue).
2936 **280** 100 pf. multicoloured . . 65 30

1281 Emblem

2000. Holy Year 2000.
2937 **1281** 110 pf. multicoloured . . 70 35

1282 Charlemagne and Plan of Palace Chapel

2000. 1200th Anniv of Aachen Cathedral.
2938 **1282** 110 pf. multicoloured . . 70 35

1283 Schweitzer and Signature

2000. 125th Birth Anniv of Albert Schweitzer (missionary doctor).
2939 **1283** 110 pf. multicoloured . . 70 35

1284 Football

2000. Centenary of German Football Association.
2940 **1284** 110 pf. multicoloured . . 70 35

1285 Wehner

2000. Tenth Death Anniv of Herbert Wehner (politician).
2941 **1285** 110 pf. multicoloured . . 70 35

IV. WEST BERLIN.

The Russian Government withdrew from the four-power control of Berlin on 1 July 1948, with the Western Sectors remaining under American, British and French control. West Berlin was constituted a "Land" of the Federal Republic in 1 September 1950.

The Russian Zone issues inscribed "STADT BERLIN" (which we do not list unoverprinted in this Catalogue), were not intended for use throughout Berlin, but were for the Russian sector of the city and for Brandenburg.

The first stamps to be used in the Western Sectors were Nos. A4/5 and A7 of the Anglo-American Zones, followed by Nos. A36/52, which were on sale from 24 June to 31 August 1948, and remained valid until 19 September 1948.

1948. 100 pfennig = 1 Deutsche Mark (East).
1949. 100 pfennig = 1 Deutsche Mark (West).

1948. Pictorial issue of 1947 (Nos. 928/48) optd **BERLIN.**

B21	2 pf. black	2·75	1·40
B 2	6 pf. violet	85	3·00
B 3	8 pf. red	85	2·75
B 4	10 pf. green	60	80
B 5	12 pf. grey	60	40
B25	15 pf. brown	8·00	2·00
B 7	16 pf. green	1·00	1·75
B26	20 pf. blue	2·75	50
B 9	24 pf. brown	90	40
B10	25 pf. orange	22·00	45·00
B11	30 pf. red	3·50	7·00
B12	40 pf. mauve	4·00	3·00
B13	50 pf. blue	8·00	30·00
B14	60 pf. brown	2·25	20
B15	80 pf. blue	8·00	26·00
B16	84 pf. green	16·00	95·00
B17	1 m. olive	50·00	£160
B18	2 m. violet	60·00	£475
B19	3 m. red	80·00	£650
B20	5 m. blue	90·00	£700

B 2 Schoneberg

B 3 Douglas C-54 Skymaster Transport over Tempelhof Airport

1949. Insc "DEUTSCHE POST". Berlin Views.

(a) Small size.

B35	–	1 pf. grey	15	10
B36	B 2	4 pf. brown	70	10
B36c	–	4 pf. brown	5·50	4·00
B37	–	5 pf. green	1·00	10
B38	–	6 pf. purple	1·50	80
B39	B 2	8 pf. orange	1·60	1·25
B40	–	10 pf. green	1·00	10
B41	B 3	15 pf. brown	14·50	50
B42	–	20 pf. red	6·25	10
B42b	–	20 pf. red	65·00	60
B43	–	25 pf. yellow	28·00	90
B44	–	30 pf. blue	14·00	60
B45	B 2	40 pf. lake	19·00	30
B46	–	50 pf. olive	20·00	20
B47	–	60 pf. red	60·00	20
B48	–	80 pf. blue	17·00	95
B49	–	90 pf. green	19·00	80

(b) Large size.

B50	B 3	1 Dm. olive	29·00	80
B51	–	2 Dm. purple	75·00	1·25
B52	–	3 Dm. red	£275	14·00
B53	–	5 Dm. blue	£160	15·00

DESIGNS—As Type **B 2**: 1 pf. Brandenburg Gate; 4 pf. (B36c) Exhibition Building; 5, 25 pf. "Tegel Schloss". 6, 50 pf. Reichstag Building. 10, 30 pf. "Kleistpark". 20 (B42), 80, 90 pf. Technical High School; 20 pf. (B42b) Olympia Stadium; 60 pf. National Gallery. As Type **B 3**: 2 Dm. "Gendarmenmarkt"; 3 Dm. Brandenburg Gate; 5 Dm. "Tegel Schloss".

For similar views inscribed "DEUTSCHE POST BERLIN" see Nos. B118/19.

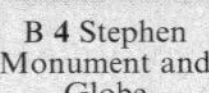

B 4 Stephen Monument and Globe

B 5 Heinrich von Stephen Monument

1949. 75th Anniv of U.P.U.

B54	B 4	12 pf. grey	23·00	7·50
B55		16 pf. green	45·00	16·00
B56		24 pf. orange	30·00	80
B57		50 pf. olive	£190	35·00
B58		60 pf. brown	£240	35·00
B59	B 5	1 Dm. olive	£140	£120
B60		2 Dm. purple	£150	70·00

MINIMUM PRICE

The minimum price quoted is 10p which represents a handling charge rather than a basis for valuing common stamps. For further notes about prices see introductory pages.

B 6 Goethe and Scene from "Iphigenie"

B 9 Alms Bowl and Bear

1949. Birth Bicent. of Goethe (poet). Portraits of Goethe and scenes from his works.

B61	B 6	10 pf. green	£130	70·00
B62	–	20 pf. red	£140	80·00
B63	–	30 pf. blue	35·00	50·00

DESIGNS: Scenes from—20 pf. "Reineke Fuchs" or—30 pf. "Faust".

1949. Numeral and pictorial issues of 1946/7 surch **BERLIN** and bold figures.

B64	229	5 pf. on 45 pf. red	3·50	10
B65	C	10 pf. on 24 pf. brown	14·00	20
B66	B	20 pf. on 80 pf. blue	70·00	17·00
B67	237	1 m. on 3 m. lake	£160	18·00

1949. Berlin Relief Fund.

B68	B 9	10 pf. + 5 pf. green	£110	£175
B69		20 pf. + 5 pf. red	£120	£175
B70		30 pf. + 5 pf. blue	£120	£200

B 10

B 11 Harp

1950. European Recovery Programme.

B71	B 10	20 pf. red	85·00	40·00

1950. Restablishment of Berlin Philharmonic Orchestra.

B72	B 11	10 pf. + 5 pf. green	50·00	40·00
B73	–	30 pf. + 5 pf. blue	90·00	80·00

DESIGN: 30 pf. "Singing Angels" (after H. and J. van Eyck).

B 13 G. A. Lortzing

B 14 Freedom Bell

1951. Death Cent. of Lortzing (composer).

B74	B 13	20 pf. brown	60·00	50·00

1951. (a) Clapper at left.

B75	B 14	5 pf. brown	2·00	8·00
B76		10 pf. green	15·00	24·00
B77		20 pf. red	7·50	17·00
B78		30 pf. blue	50·00	70·00
B79		40 pf. purple	13·00	40·00

(b) Clapper at right.

B82	B 14	5 pf. green	2·50	1·40
B83		10 pf. green	7·50	5·00
B84		20 pf. red	25·00	18·00
B85		30 pf. blue	55·00	42·00
B86		40 pf. red	21·00	16·00

(c) Clapper in centre.

B101	B 14	5 pf. brown	1·40	85
B102		10 pf. green	4·00	1·40
B103		20 pf. red	7·00	3·75
B104		30 pf. blue	12·50	12·00
B105		40 pf. violet	55·00	35·00

B 15 Boy Stamp Collectors

B 16 Mask of Beethoven (taken from life, 1812)

1951. Stamp Day.

B80	B 15	10 pf. + 3 pf. green	24·00	29·00
B81		20 pf. + 2 pf. red	30·00	35·00

1952. 125th Death Anniv of Beethoven (composer).

B87	B 16	30 pf. blue	45·00	32·00

B 17 Olympic Torch

B 18 W. von Siemens (electrical engineer)

1952. Olympic Games Festival, Berlin.

B88	B 17	4 pf. brown	1·00	2·50
B89		10 pf. green	10·50	14·00
B90		20 pf. red	16·00	21·00

1952. Famous Berliners.

B 91	–	4 pf. brown	55	15
B 92	–	5 pf. blue	90	30
B 93	–	6 pf. purple	6·00	9·00
B 94	–	8 pf. brown	2·00	2·00
B 95	–	10 pf. green	3·00	55
B 96		15 pf. lilac	16·00	15·00
B 97	B 18	20 pf. red	3·00	60
B 98	–	25 pf. green	50·00	6·00
B 99	–	30 pf. purple	17·00	8·00
B100	–	40 pf. black	27·00	3·00

PORTRAITS: 4 pf. Zelter (musician); 5 pf. Lilienthal (aviator); 6 pf. Rathenau (statesman); 8 pf. Fontane (writer); 10 pf. Von Menzel (artist); 15 pf. Virchow (pathologist); 25 pf. Schinkel (architect); 30 pf. Planck (physicist); 40 pf. W. von Humboldt (philologist).

B 19 Church before Bombing

B 20 Chainbreaker

1953. Kaiser Wilhelm Memorial Church Reconstruction Fund.

B106	B 19	4 pf. + 1 pf. brown	30	13·00
B107		10 pf. + 5 pf. green	1·50	40·00
B108	–	20 pf. + 10 pf. red	3·00	50·00
B109	–	30 pf. + 15 pf. blue	16·00	£100

DESIGN: 20 pf., 30 pf. Church after bombing.

1953. East German Uprising. Inscr "17 JUNI 1953".

B110	B 20	20 pf. black	5·00	2·10
B111	–	30 pf. red	30·00	28·00

DESIGN: 30 pf. Brandenburg Gate.

B 21 Ernst Reuter

B 22 Conference Buildings

1954. Death of Ernst Reuter (Mayor of West Berlin).

B112	B 21	20 pf. brown	7·50	1·75

1954. Four-Power Conference, Berlin.

B113	B 22	20 pf. red	7·75	5·00

B 23 O. Mergenthaler and Linotype Machine

B 25 "Germany in Bondage"

1954. Birth Cent. of Mergenthaler (inventor).

B114	B 23	10 pf. green	2·50	2·75

1954. West German Presidential Election. No. B103 optd **Wahl des Bundesprasidenten in Berlin 17. Juli 1954.**

B115	B 14	20 pf. red	3·75	4·75

1954. 10th Anniv of Attempt on Hitler's Life.

B116	B 25	20 pf. grey and red	5·00	4·75

B 26 Prussian Postilion, 1827

B 27 Memorial Library

1954. National Stamp Exhibition.

B117	B 26	20 pf. + 10 pf. mult	15·00	35·00

1954. Berlin Views. As Type **B 4** but inscr "DEUTSCHE POST BERLIN".

B118	7 pf. green	7·50	30
B119	70 pf. olive	£110	21·00

DESIGNS: 7 pf. Exhibition building; 70 pf. Grunewald hunting lodge.

1954.

B120	B 27	40 pf. purple	10·50	3·25

B 28 Richard Strauss

B 29 Blacksmiths forging Rail

1954. 5th Death Anniv of Strauss (composer).

B121	B 28	40 pf. blue	11·00	3·50

1954. Death Cent. of A. Borsig (industrialist).

B122	B 29	20 pf. brown	6·00	1·25

B 30 Liner "Berlin"

B 31 Wilhelm Furtwangler (conductor)

1955.

B123	B 30	10 pf. green	1·25	30
B124		25 pf. blue	6·50	3·75

1955. 1st Death Anniv of Furtwangler.

B125	B 31	40 pf. blue	20·00	20·00

B 32

B 33 Prussian Rural Postilion, 1760

1955. Federal Parliament Session, Berlin.

B126	B 32	10 pf. blk, yell & red	30	25
B127		20 pf. blk, yell & red	5·00	8·75

1955. Stamp Day and Philatelic Fund.

B128	B 33	25 pf. + 10 pf. mult	6·00	14·00

B 34 St Otto

B 35 Radio Tower and Exhibition Hall

1955. 25th Anniv of Berlin Bishopric.

B129	B 34	7 pf. + 3 pf. brown	60	2·25
B130	–	10 pf. + 5 pf. green	1·25	3·00
B131	–	20 pf. + 10 pf. mve	1·50	4·00

DESIGNS: 10 pf. St. Hedwig; 20 pf. St. Peter.

1956. Berlin Buildings and Monuments.

B133	–	1 pf. grey	10	10
B133b	–	3 pf. violet	15	10
B134	–	5 pf. mauve	15	10
B132	B 35	7 pf. turq (A)	8·25	2·40
B135	–	7 pf. turq (B)	20	10
B136	–	8 pf. grey	30	55
B136a	–	8 pf. red	30	20
B137	–	10 pf. green	15	10
B138	–	15 pf. blue	25	30
B139	–	20 pf. red	15	10
B140	–	25 pf. brown	35	30
B141	–	30 pf. green	50	55
B142	–	40 pf. blue	9·00	7·50
B143	–	50 pf. green	50	50
B144	–	60 pf. brown	65	1·00
B145	–	70 pf. violet	24·00	13·00
B146	–	1 Dm. green	2·00	3·00
B146a	–	3 Dm. red	5·00	11·00

7 pf. (A) Type **B 35**. (B) As Type **B 35** but with inscription at top.

DESIGNS—As Type **B 35** (B)—HORIZ: 1 pf., 3 pf. Brandenburg Gate; 5 pf. P.O. Headquarters; 20 pf. Free University; 40 pf. Charlottenburg Castle; 60 pf. Chamber of Commerce and Bourse; 70 pf. Schiller Theatre. VERT: 8 pf. Town Hall, Neukollin; 10 pf. Kaiser Wilhelm Memorial Church; 15 pf. Airlift Monument; 25 pf. Lilienthal Monument; 30 pf. Pfaueninsel Castle; 50 pf. Reuter Power-station. LARGER (24 × 30 mm): 1 Dm. "The Great Elector" (statue, after Schluter). ($29\frac{1}{2}$ × 25 mm): 3 Dm. Congress Hall, Berlin.

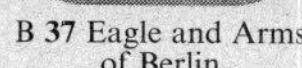

B 37 Eagle and Arms of Berlin

B 38

1956. Federal Council Meeting.
B147 B 37 10 pf. blk, yell & red . . 85 40
B148 25 pf. blk, yell & red . . 4·00 4·25

1956. Cent. of German Engineers' Union.
B149 B 38 10 pf. green . . . . . . 2·00 1·50
B150 20 pf. red . . . . 4·00 4·50

1956. Flood Relief Fund. As No. B 77 (colour changed) surch **+10 Berlinhilfe fur die Hochwassergeschadigten DEUTSCHE BUNDESPOST-BERLIN** and bar.
B151 B 14 20 pf. + 10 pf. bistre . . 2·50 3·00

B 40 P. Lincke

B 41 Wireless Transmitter

1956. 10th Death Anniv of Lincke (composer).
B152 B 40 20 pf. red . . . . 2·10 2·75

1956. Industrial Exhibition.
B153 B 41 25 pf. brown . . . . . 5·75 9·25

B 42 Brandenburg Postilion, 1700

B 43 Spandau

1956. Stamp Day and Philatelic Fund.
B154 B 42 25 pf. + 10 pf. mult . . 2·25 3·50

1957. 725th Anniv of Spandau.
B155 B 43 20 pf. olive & brown . . 40 60

B 44 Model of Hansa District

B 45 Friedrich K. von Savigny (jurist)

1957. Int Building Exn., Berlin.
B156 B 44 7 pf. brown 45 30
B157 – 20 pf. red 70 60
B158 – 40 pf. blue . . . . . . 1·50 2·00
DESIGNS—HORIZ: 20 pf. Aerial view of Exhibition; 40 pf. Exhibition Congress Hall.

1957. Portraits as Type B 45.
B159 – 7 pf. brown & green . . 10 10
B160 – 8 pf. brown & grey . . . 10 25
B161 – 10 pf. brn & green . . . 10 10
B162 – 15 pf. sepia and blue . . 50 80
B163 – 20 pf. + 10 pf. sepia and red 20 60
B164 – 20 pf. brown & red . . . 15 15
B165 – 25 pf. sepia and lake . . 80 1·00
B166 B 45 30 pf. sepia & grn . . . 1·60 2·00
B167 – 40 pf. sepia & blue . . . 80 75
B168 – 50 pf. sepia & olive . . . 4·00 7·00
PORTRAITS—VERT: 7 pf. T. Mommsen (historian); 8 pf. H. Zille (painter); 10 pf. E. Reuter (Mayor of Berlin); 15 pf. F. Haber (chemist); 20 pf. (No. B164), F. Schleiermacher (theologian); 20 pf. (B163), L. Heck (zoologist); 25 pf. Max Reinhardt (theatrical producer); 40 pf. A. von Humboldt (naturalist); 50 pf. C. D. Rauch (sculptor).
The premium on No. B163 was for the Berlin Zoo. No. B167 commemorates Humboldt's death centenary.

B 46 Uta von Naumburg (statue)

B 47 "Unity Justice and Freedom"

1957. German Cultural Congress.
B169 B 46 25 pf. brown 75 90

1957. 3rd Federal Parliament Assembly.
B170 B 47 10 pf. blk, ochre & red . 30 40
B171 20 pf. blk, ochre & red . 1·75 2·50

B 48 Postilion, 1897–1925

B 49 Torch of Remembrance

1957. Stamp Day.
B172 B 48 20 pf. multicoloured . . 45 75

1957. 7th World War Veterans Congress.
B173 B 49 20 pf. myrtle, yell & grn . 75 60

B 50 Elly Heuss-Knapp (social worker)

B 51 Christ and Symbols of the Cosmos

1957. Mothers' Convalescence Fund.
B174 B 50 20 pf. + 10 pf. red . . . 90 1·75

1958. German Catholics' Day.
B175 B 51 10 pf. black & green . . 25 50
B176 20 pf. black & mauve . . 85 1·25

B 52 Otto Suhr

B 53 Pres. Heuss

1958. 1st Death Anniv of Burgomaster Otto Suhr.
B177 B 52 20 pf. red . . . . 85 1·40
See also Nos. B187 and B193.

1959.
B178 B 53 7 pf. green 40 30
B179 10 pf. green 30 10
B180 20 pf. red 75 10
B181 40 pf. blue . . . . . . 2·50 4·75
B182 70 pf. violet . . . . . 8·00 11·00

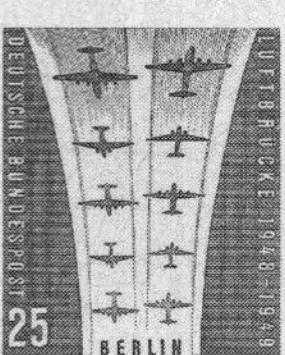

B 54 Symbolic Airlift

B 55 Brandenburg Gate, Berlin

1959. 10th Anniv of Berlin Airlift.
B183 B 54 25 pf. blk and red . . . 50 35

1959. 14th World Communities Congress, Berlin.
B184 B 55 20 pf. bl, red & lt bl . . 75 30

B 56 Schiller

B 57 Robert Koch

1959. Birth Bicent. of Schiller (poet).
B185 B 56 20 pf. brn & red 20 20

1960. 50th Death Anniv of Robert Koch (bacteriologist).
B186 B 57 20 pf. purple 20 25

1960. 4th Death Anniv of Walther Schreiber (Mayor of Berlin, 1951–53). As Type B 52.
B187 20 pf. red 30 45
DESIGN: Portrait of Schreiber.

B 58 Boy at Window

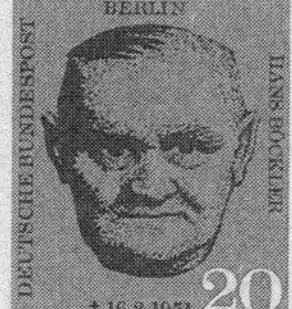

B 59 Hans Boeckler

1960. Berlin Children's Holiday Fund. Inscr "FERIENPLATZE FUR BERLINER KINDER".
B188 B 58 7 pf. + 3 pf. dp brown, brown & lt brown . . 15 40
B189 – 10 pf. + 5 pf. deep green, olive & green . 15 50
B190 – 20 pf. + 10 pf. brown, red and pink 25 65
B191 – 40 pf. + 20 pf. deep blue, blue & lt blue . . 80 3·00
DESIGNS: 10 pf. Girl in street; 20 pf. Girl blowing on Alpine flower; 40 pf. Boy on beach.

1961. 10th Anniv of Hans Boeckler (politician).
B192 B 59 20 pf. black and red . . 10 10

1961. Louise Schroeder Commemoration. As Type B 52.
B193 20 pf. brown 15 25
DESIGN: Portrait of Schroeder.

B 60 Durer

B 61 "Five Crosses" Symbol and St. Mary's Church

1961. Famous Germans.
B194 5 pf. olive (Magnus) 10 15
B195 7 pf. brown (St. Elizabeth of Thuringia) 10 30
B196 8 pf. violet (Gutenberg) . . . 10 30
B197 10 pf. green (Type B 60) . . . 10 10
B198 15 pf. blue (Luther) 20 25
B199 20 pf. red (Bach) 30 10
B200 25 pf. brown (Neumann) . . . 20 35
B201 30 pf. brown (Kant) 20 25
B202 40 pf. blue (Lessing) 40 55
B203 50 pf. brown (Goethe) 40 60
B204 60 pf. red (Schiller) 40 70
B205 70 pf. green (Beethoven) . . . 90 70
B206 80 pf. brown (Kleist) . . . . 3·50 7·25
B207 1 Dm. violet (Annette von Droste-Hulshoff) . . . . 1·60 2·50
B208 2 Dm. green (Hauptmann) . . 1·75 4·50

1961. 10th Evangelical Churches' Day. Crosses in violet.
B210 B 61 10 pf. green 10 15
B211 20 pf. purple 10 20
DESIGN: 20 pf. "Five Crosses" and Kaiser Wilhelm Memorial Church.

B 62 Exhibition Emblem

1961. West Berlin Radio and Television Exn.
B212 B 62 20 pf. brown & red . . . 10 15

B 63 "Die Linden" (1650)

B 64 Euler Gelberhund Biplane, 1912, and Boeing 707 Airliner

1962. "Old Berlin" series.
B213 B 63 7 pf. sepia & brown . . 10 10
B214 – 10 pf. sepia & green . . 10 10
B215 – 15 pf. black & blue . . 15 10
B216 – 20 pf. sepia & brown . . 25 10
B217 – 25 pf. sepia & olive . . 20 30
B218 – 40 pf. black & blue . . 30 25
B219 – 50 pf. sepia & purple . . 40 35
B220 – 60 pf. sepia & mauve . . 35 50
B221 – 70 pf. black & purple . . 30 50
B222 – 80 pf. sepia and red . . 40 60
B223 – 90 pf. sepia & brown . . 70 80
B224 – 1 Dm. sepia & green . . 65 1·00
DESIGNS: 10 pf. "Waisenbrucke" (Orphans' Bridge), 1783; 15 pf. Mauerstrasse, 1780; 20 pf. Berlin Castle, 1703; 25 pf. Potsdamer Platz, 1825; 40 pf. Bellevue Castle, circa 1800; 50 pf. Fischer Bridge, 1830; 60 pf. Halle Gate, 1880; 70 pf. Parochial Church, 1780; 80 pf. University, 1825; 90 pf. Opera House, 1780; 1 Dm. Grunewald Lake, circa 1790.

1962. 50th Anniv of German Airmail Transport.
B225 B 64 60 pf. black & blue . . . 40 40

B 65 Exhibition Emblem

B 66 Town Hall Schoneberg

1963. West Berlin Broadcasting Exn.
B226 B 65 20 pf. ultram, grey & bl . 15 20

1964. 700th Anniv of Schoneberg.
B227 B 66 20 pf. brown 15 15

B 67 Pres. Lubke

B 68 Kaiser Wilhelm Memorial Church

1964. Re-election of Pres. Lubke.
B228 B 67 20 pf. red 10 10
B229 40 pf. blue 20 25
See also Nos. B 308/9.

WEST BERLIN DESIGNS: Except where illustrated the following are the same or similar designs to German Federal Republic additonally inscr "BERLIN".

1964. Capitals of the Federal Lands. As No. 1335.
B230 20 pf. multicoloured 20 25

1964. Humanitarian Relief and Welfare Funds. As Nos. 1352/5.
B231 10 pf. + 5 pf. mult 15 20
B232 15 pf. + 5 pf. mult 15 20
B233 20 pf. + 10 pf. mult 20 20
B234 40 pf. + 20 pf. mult 50 90

1964. Pres. Kennedy Commem. As Type **411**.
B235 40 pf. blue 20 30

1964. Twelve Centuries of German Architecture.
(a) Size $18\frac{1}{2} \times 22\frac{1}{2}$ mm. As Nos. 1359/66. Plain backgrounds.
B236 10 pf. brown 10 10
B237 15 pf. green 20 15
B238 20 pf. red 20 15
B239 40 pf. blue 70 80
B240 50 pf. bistre . . . . 1·40 1·50
B241 60 pf. red . . . . 1·00 90
B242 70 pf. green . . . . 2·25 3·00
B243 80 pf. brown . . . . 1·50 1·60

(b) Size $19\frac{1}{2} \times 24$ mm. As Nos. 1367/81. Coloured backgrounds.
B244 5 pf. bistre 10 15
B245 8 pf. red 10 30
B246 10 pf. purple 15 10
B247 20 pf. green 20 15
B248 30 pf. olive 30 30
B249 30 pf. red 25 10
B250 40 pf. bistre 55 75
B251 50 pf. blue 40 55
B252 60 pf. red . . . . 1·50 2·00
B253 70 pf. bronze 70 80
B254 80 pf. brown . . . . 1·00 1·60
B255 90 pf. black 70 90
B256 1 Dm. blue 60 75
B257 1 Dm. 10 brown . . . . . 1·25 1·25
B258 1 Dm. 30 green . . . . . 2·00 1·75
B259 2 Dm. purple . . . . 2·00 1·60
BUILDINGS: 8 pf. Palatine Castle, Kaub. Others as Nos. 1359/81 of German Federal Republic.

1965. Child Welfare. As Nos. 1384/7.
B261 10 pf. + 5 pf. Woodcock . . . 15 20
B262 15 pf. + 5 pf. Ringnecked pheasant 15 20
B263 20 pf. + 10 pf. Black grouse . . 25 25
B264 40 pf. + 20 pf. Capercaillie . . 60 65

1965. "New Berlin". Multicoloured.
B265 10 pf. Type B **68** 15 10
B266 15 pf. Opera House 15 10
B267 20 pf. Philharmonic Hall . . . 15 10
B268 30 pf. Jewish Community Centre 30 10
B269 40 pf. Regina Martyrum Memorial Church 25 20
B270 50 pf. Ernst-Reuter Square . . 30 20
B271 60 pf. Europa Centre 30 40
B272 70 pf. Technical University, Charlottenburg 45 60
B273 80 pf. City Motorway 40 25
B274 90 pf. Planetarium 50 30
B275 1 Dm. Telecommunications, Tower 50 60
B276 1 Dm. 10 University Clinic, Steglitz 50 60
Nos. B266/270, B272, B274 and B276 are horiz.

1965. Humanitarian Relief Funds. As Nos. 1406/9.
B277 10 pf. + 5 pf. Type **425** . . . 10 30
B278 15 pf. + 5 pf. Cinderella and birds with dress 10 30
B279 20 pf. + 10 pf. Prince offering slipper to Cinderella 15 30
B280 40 pf. + 20 pf. Cinderella and Prince on horse 40 75

1966. As Nos. 1412/5a.
B281 10 pf. brown 10 10
B282 20 pf. green 30 15
B283 30 pf. red 30 10
B284 50 pf. blue 80 55
B284a 100 pf. blue . . . . 5·50 4·00

1966. Child Welfare. As Nos. 1416/9.
B285 10 pf. + 5 pf. Type **429** . . . 20 30
B286 20 pf. + 10 pf. Chamois . . . 20 30
B287 30 pf. + 15 pf. Fallow deer . . . 30 50
B288 50 pf. + 25 pf. Red deer . . . 50 75

1966. Humanitarian Relief Funds. As Nos. 1428/31.
B289 10 pf. + 5 pf. Type **435** . . . 15 30
B290 20 pf. + 10 pf. Frog dining with Princess 15 30
B291 30 pf. + 15 pf. Frog Prince and Princess 20 30
B292 50 pf. + 25 pf. In coach . . . 35 80
Designs from Grimm's "The Frog Prince".

1967. Child Welfare. As Nos. 1434/7.
B293 10 pf. + 5 pf. Common rabbit 25 40
B294 20 pf. + 10 pf. Stoat 30 40
B295 30 pf. + 15 pf. Common hamster 40 50
B296 50 pf. + 25 pf. Red fox . . . 65 1·25

B 69 "Bust of a Young Man" (after C. Meit)

B 70 Broadcasting Tower and TV Screen

1967. Berlin Art Treasures.
B297 B **69** 10 pf. sepia & bistre . . 15 15
B298 – 20 pf. olive and blue . . 20 20
B299 – 30 pf. brown & olive . . 20 30
B300 – 50 pf. sepia and grey . . 30 40
B301 – 1 Dm. black & blue . . 50 65
B302 – 1 Dm. 10 brown and chestnut 75 90
DESIGNS: 20 pf. Head of "The Elector of Brandenburg" (statue by Schluter); 30 pf. "St. Mark" (statue by Riemenschneider); 50 pf. Head from Quadriga, Brandenburg Gate. 1 Dm. "Madonna" (carving by Feuchtmayer). ($22\frac{1}{2} \times 39$ mm) 1 Dm. 10, "Christ and St. John" (after carving from Upper Swabia, circa 1320).

1967. West Berlin Broadcasting Exn.
B303 B **70** 30 pf. multicoloured . . 20 30

1967. Humanitarian Relief Funds. As Nos. 1443/6.
B304 10 pf. + 5 pf. mult 20 30
B305 20 pf. + 10 pf. mult 20 30
B306 30 pf. + 15 pf. mult 30 40
B307 50 pf. + 25 pf. mult 50 90

1967. Re-election of President Lubke. As Type B **67**.
B308 B **67** 30 pf. red 20 30
B309 50 pf. blue 30 40

1968. Child Welfare. As Nos. 1454/7.
B310 10 pf. + 5 pf. Wild cat . . . 30 65
B311 20 pf. + 10 pf. European otter 40 65
B312 30 pf. + 15 pf. Eurasian badger 65 85
B313 50 pf. + 25 pf. Eurasian beaver . . . . 1·50 2·25

B 71 Former Courthouse

B 72 Festival Emblems

1968. 500th Anniv of Berlin Magistrate's Court.
B314 B **71** 30 pf. black 20 30

1968. Athletics Festival, Berlin.
B315 B **72** 20 f. red, blk & grey . . 15 30

1968. Humanitarian Relief Funds. As Nos. 1473/6.
B316 10 pf. + 5 pf. Doll of 1878 . . 15 25
B317 20 pf. + 10 pf. Doll of 1850 . 20 15
B318 30 pf. + 15 pf. Doll of 1870 . 25 20
B319 50 pf. + 25 pf. Doll of 1885 . 60 80

B 74 "The Newspaper Seller" (C. W. Allers, 1889)

1969. 19th-Cent. Berliners. Contemporary Art.
B320 – 5 pf. black 10 15
B321 B **74** 10 pf. purple 15 20
B322 – 10 pf. brown 15 20
B323 – 20 pf. green 15 20
B324 – 20 pf. turquoise 15 20
B325 – 30 pf. brown 55 60
B326 – 30 pf. brown 40 50
B327 – 50 pf. blue . . . . . 1·75 1·90
DESIGNS—HORIZ: 5 pf. "The Cab-driver" (H. Zille, 1875). VERT: 10 pf. "The Bus-driver" (C. W. Allers, 1890); 20 pf. (No. B323) "The Cobblers Boy" (F. Kruger, 1839); 20 pf. (No. B324) "The Cobbler" (A. von Menzel, 1833); 30 pf. (No. B325) "The Borsig Forge" (P. Meyerheim, 1878); 30 pf. (No. B326) "Three Berlin Ladies" (F. Kurger, 1839); 50 pf. "At the Brandenburg Gate" (C.W. Allers, 1889).

1969. Child Welfare. As Nos. 1478/81.
B328 10 pf. + 5 pf. brn, blk & yell . 25 40
B329 20 pf. + 10 pf. brown, black and buff 35 50
B330 30 pf. + 15 pf. brn, blk & red . 50 70
B331 50 pf. + 25 pf. grey, yellow, black and blue . . . . 1·25 1·50

B 76 Postman

B 77 J. Joachim (violinist & director, after A. von Menzel)

1969. 20th Congress of Post Office Trade Union Federation (I.P.T.T.), Berlin.
B333 B **76** 10 pf. olive 15 25
B334 – 20 pf. brown & buff . . 25 35
B335 – 30 pf. violet & ochre . . 60 60
B336 – 50 pf. blue & lt blue . . 80 80
DESIGNS: 20 pf. Telephonist; 30 pf. Technician; 50 pf. Airmail Handlers.

1969. Anniversaries. Multicoloured.
B337 30 pf. Type B **77** 50 40
B338 50 pf. Alexander von Humboldt (after J. Stieler) . . 60 40
ANNIVERSARIES: 30 pf. Centenary of Berlin Academy of Music; 50 pf. Birth bicentenary of Humboldt.

B 78 Railway Carriage (1835)

B 79 T. Fontane

1969. Humanitarian Relief Funds. Pewter Figurines. Multicoloured.
(a) Inscr "WOHLFAHRTSMARKE".
B339 10 pf. + 5 pf. Type B **78** . . . 35 40
B340 20 pf. + 10 pf. Woman feeding chicken (1850) 25 30
B341 30 pf. + 15 pf. Market stall (1850) 40 50
B342 50 pf. + 25 pf. Mounted postilion (1860) 80 90
(b) Christmas. Inscr "WEIHNACHTSMARKE".
B343 10 pf. + 5 pf. "The Three Kings" 20 30

1970. 150th Birth Anniv of Theodor Fontane (writer).
B344 B **79** 20 pf. multicoloured . . 25 25

B 80 Heinrich von Stretlingen

B 81 Film "Title"

1970. Miniatures of Minnesingers. Mult.
B345 10 pf. + 5 pf. Type B **80** . . . 20 40
B346 20 pf. + 10 pf. Meinloh von Sevelingen 35 50
B347 30 pf. + 15 pf. Burkhart von Hohenfels 60 85
B348 50 pf. + 25 pf. Albrecht von Johannsdorf . . . . 1·00 1·40

1970. 20th Int. Film Festival, Berlin.
B349 B **81** 30 pf. multicoloured . . 20 30

1970. Pres. Heinemann. As Nos. 1535/1555.
B350 **486** 5 pf. black 15 10
B351 8 pf. brown 60 75
B352 10 pf. brown 15 10
B353 15 pf. bistre 25 20
B354 20 pf. green 15 10
B355 25 pf. green 80 50
B356 30 pf. brown . . . . . . 1·00 30
B357 40 pf. orange 35 25
B358 50 pf. blue 40 25
B359 60 pf. blue 70 40
B360 70 pf. brown 50 40
B361 80 pf. green 75 75
B362 90 pf. red . . . . . . 1·75 2·00
B363 1 Dm. green 85 60
B364 1 Dm. 10 grey . . . . . 1·25 1·25
B365 1 Dm. 20 brown . . . . . 1·10 1·00
B366 1 Dm. 30 brown . . . . . 1·50 1·50
B367 1 Dm. 40 green . . . . . 1·50 1·60
B368 1 Dm. 50 red . . . . . 1·50 65
B369 1 Dm. 60 orange . . . . . 2·00 2·00
B370 1 Dm. 70 orange . . . . . 1·75 1·50
B371 1 Dm. 90 purple . . . . . 2·00 1·50
B372 2 Dm. violet . . . . . . 2·00 1·25

B 82 Allegory of Folklore

B 83 "Caspar"

1970. 20th Berlin Folklore Week.
B373 B **82** 30 pf. multicoloured . . 30 30

1970. Humanitarian Relief Funds. Puppets. Multicoloured.
(a) Relief Funds.
B374 10 pf. + 5 pf. Type B **83** . . . 15 20
B375 20 pf. + 10 pf. "Polichinelle" . 20 35
B376 30 pf. + 15 pf. "Punch" . . . 30 35
B377 50 pf. + 25 pf. "Pulcinella" . 60 90
(b) Christmas.
B378 10 pf. + 5 pf. "Angel" . . . 20 20

B 84 L. von Ranke (after painting by J. Schrader)

B 85 Class ET 165.8 Electric Train, 1933

1970. 175th Birth Anniv of Leopold von Ranke (historian).
B379 B **84** 30 pf. multicoloured . . 25 30

1971. Centenary of German Unification.
B380 **492** 30 pf. black, red & orge . 30 40

1971. Berlin Rail Transport. Multicoloured.
B381 5 pf. Class T.12 steam train, 1925 . . . . 20 25
B382 10 pf. Electric tram, 1890 . . . 30 25
B383 20 pf. Horse tram, 1890 . . . 50 40
B384 30 pf. Type B **85** 55 55
B385 50 pf. Electric tram, 1950 . . . 1·75 2·00
B386 1 Dm. Underground train No. 2431, 1971 . . . . 2·25 2·75

B 86 "Fly"

B 87 "The Bagpiper" (copper engraving, Durer, c. 1514)

1971. Child Welfare Children's Drawings. Multicoloured.
B387 10 pf. + 5 pf. Type B **86** . . 30 40
B388 20 pf. + 10 pf. "Fish" . . . 30 45
B389 30 pf. + 15 pf. "Porcupine" . . 40 70
B390 50 pf. + 25 pf. "Cockerel" . . 90 1·25

1971. 500th Birth Anniv of Albrecht Durer.
B391 B **87** 10 pf. black & brown . . 30 20

B 88 Communications Tower and Dish Aerials

B 89 Bach and part of 2nd Brandenburg Concerto

1971. West Berlin Broadcasting Exhib.
B392 B **88** 30 pf. indigo, bl & red . 65 55

1971. 250th Anniv of Bach's Brandenburg Concertos.
B393 B **89** 30 pf. multicoloured . . 80 35

B 90 H. von Helmholtz (from painting by K. Morell-Kramer)

B 92 Dancing Men

1971. 150th Anniv of Hermann von Helmholtz (scientist).
B394 B **90** 25 pf. multicoloured . . 35 40

1971. Accident Prevention. As Nos. 1596/1605.
B396 5 pf. orange 30 35
B397 10 pf. brown 30 20
B398 20 pf. violet 30 30
B399 25 pf. green 60 55
B400 30 pf. red 40 15
B401 40 pf. mauve 40 20
B402 50 pf. blue . . . . 2·00 1·50
B403 60 pf. blue . . . . 1·75 1·75
B404 70 pf. blue and green . . . . 1·25 1·10
B405 100 pf. green . . . . 1·75 1·75
B406 150 pf. brown . . . . 5·25 4·50

1971. Humanitarian Relief Funds. Wooden Toys. Multicoloured.
(a) Inscr "WOHLFAHRTSMARKE".
B407 10 pf. + 5 pf. Type B **92** . . . 15 20
B408 25 pf. + 10 pf. Horseman on wheels 25 35
B409 30 pf. + 15 pf. Acrobat . . . 50 50
B410 60 pf. + 30 pf. Nurse and babies 75 90
(b) Christmas. Inscr "WEIHNACHTSMARKE".
B411 10 pf. + 5 pf. Angel with two candles 20 30

B 93 Microscope

B 94 F. Gilly (after bust by Schadow)

1971. Birth Centenary of Material-Testing Laboratory, Berlin.
B412 B **93** 30 pf. multicoloured . . 30 30

1972. Birth Bicentenary of Friedrich Gilly (architect).
B413 B **94** 30 pf. black & blue . . . 30 30

B 95 Boy raiding Bird's-nest

B 97 E. T. A. Hoffman

B 96 "Grunewaldsee" (A. von Riesen)

1972. Child Welfare. Animal Protection. Multicoloured.
B414 10 pf. + 5 pf. Type B **95** . . . 25 30
B415 25 pf. + 10 pf. Care of kittens 40 50
B416 30 pf. + 15 pf. Man beating watch-dog 60 75
B417 60 pf. + 30 pf. Animals crossing road at night . . . . . 1·25 1·25

1972. Paintings of Berlin Lakes. Mult.
B418 10 pf. Type B **96** 15 10
B419 25 pf. "Wannsee" (Max Liebermann) 35 30
B420 30 pf. "Schlachtensee" (W. Leistikow) 50 45

1972. 150th Death Anniv of E. T. A. Hoffman (poet and musician).
B421 B **97** 60 pf. blk & violet . . . 80 85

B 98 Max Liebermann (self-portrait)

B 99 Stamp Printing-press

1972. 125th Birth Anniv of Max Liebermann (painter).

B422 B **98** 40 pf. multicoloured . . 65 30

1972. Stamp Day.

B423 B **99** 20 pf. blue, blk & red . . 25 15

1972. Humanitarian Relief Funds. Multicoloured. (a) 19th-century Faience Chessmen. As Nos. 1636/40 of West Germany. Inscr "WOLHFAHRTSMARKE".

B424 20 pf. + 10 pf. Knight 30 30
B425 30 pf. + 15 pf. Rook 40 40
B426 40 pf. + 20 pf. Queen . . . . 1·10 1·10
B427 70 pf. + 35 pf. King . . . . 1·50 1·25

(b) Christmas. Inscr "WEIHNACHTSMARKE".

B428 20 pf. + 10 pf. "The Holy Family" 35 40

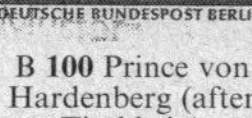

B 100 Prince von Hardenberg (after Tischbein)

B 101 Northern Goshawk

1972. 150th Death Anniv of Karl August von Hardenberg (statesman).

B429 B **100** 40 pf. multicoloured . . 45 30

1973. Youth Welfare. Birds of Prey. Mult.

B430 20 pf. + 10 pf. Type B **101** . . 75 75
B431 30 pf. + 15 pf. Peregrine falcon . . . . 1·10 1·10
B432 40 pf. + 20 pf. European sparrow hawk . . . . . 1·75 1·75
B433 70 pf. + 35 pf. Golden eagle . 2·50 2·50

B 102 Horse-bus, 1907

1973. Berlin Buses. Multicoloured.

B434 20 pf. Type B **102** 30 20
B435 20 pf. Trolley bus, 1933 . . . 30 20
B436 30 pf. Motor bus, 1919 . . . 75 60
B437 30 pf. Double-decker, 1970 . . 90 45
B438 40 pf. Double-decker, 1925 . . 1·40 75
B439 40 pf. "Standard" bus, 1973 . 1·40 65

B 103 L. Tieck

B 104 J. J. Quantz

1973. Birth Bicentenary of Ludwig Tieck (poet and writer).

B440 B **103** 40 pf. multicoloured . . 40 30

1973. Death Bicentenary of Johann Quantz (composer).

B441 B **104** 40 pf. black 85 50

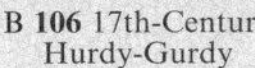

B 106 17th-Century Hurdy-Gurdy

B 107 G. W. Knobelsdorff

1973. Humanitarian Relief Funds. Mult. (a) Musical Instruments. Inscr "WOHLFAHRTSMARKE".

B443 20 pf. + 10 pf. Type B **106** . . 35 30
B444 30 pf. + 15 pf. 16th century drum 50 40
B445 40 pf. + 20 pf. 18th century lute 80 50
B446 70 pf. + 35 pf. 16th century organ . . . . 1·00 1·10

(b) Christmas. Inscr "WEIHNACHTSMARKE".

B447 20 pf. + 10 pf. Christmas star 40 30

1974. 275th Birth Anniv of Georg W. von Knobelsdorff (architect).

B448 B **107** 20 pf. brown 25 20

B 108 G. R. Kirchhoff

B 109 A. Slaby

1974. 150th Birth Anniv of Gustav R. Kirchhoff (physicist).

B449 B **108** 30 pf. green & grey . . 30 25

1974. 125th Birth Anniv of Adolf Slaby (radio pioneer).

B450 B **109** 40 pf. black & red . . . 40 40

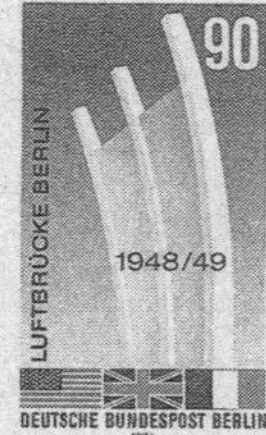

B 110 Airlift Memorial

B 111 Photography

1974. 25th Anniv of Berlin Airlift.

B451 B **110** 90 pf. mult . . . . . 1·60 1·50

1974. Youth Welfare. Youth Activities. Multicoloured.

B452 20 pf. + 10 pf. Type B **111** . . 50 55
B453 30 pf. + 15 pf. Athletics . . . 60 40
B454 40 pf. + 20 pf. Music 75 75
B455 70 pf. + 35 pf. Voluntary service (Nurse) . . . . 1·25 1·25

B 112 School Seal

B 113 Spring Bouquet

1974. 400th Anniv of Evangelical Grammar School, Berlin.

B456 B **112** 50 pf. grey, brn & gold . 40 35

1974. Humanitarian Relief Funds. Flowers. Multicoloured. (a) 25th Anniv of Humanitarian Relief Stamps. Inscr "25 JAHRE WOHLFAHRTSMARKE".

B457 30 pf. + 15 pf. Type B **113** . . 30 40
B458 40 pf. + 20 pf. Autumn bouquet 40 45
B459 50 pf. + 25 pf. Bouquet of roses 70 55
B460 70 pf. + 35 pf. Winter bouquet . . . . 1·10 1·10

(b) Christmas. Inscr "WEIHNACHTSMARKE."

B461 30 pf. + 15 pf. Christmas bouquet 60 40

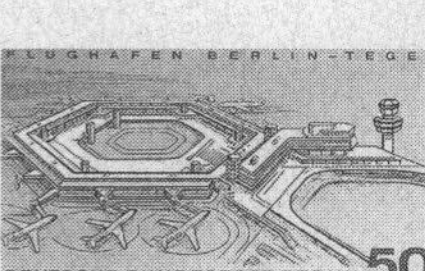

B 114 Tegel Airport

B 115 "Venus" (F. E. Meyer)

1974. Opening of Tegel Airport. Berlin.

B462 B **114** 50 pf. vio, bl & grn . . 90 45

1974. Berlin Porcelain Figures. Mult.

B463 30 pf. Type B **115** 35 25
B464 40 pf. "Astronomy" (W. C. Meyer) 40 45
B465 50 pf. "Justice" (J. G. Muller) . 50 50

B 116 Gottfried Schadow

B 117 "Prinzess Charlotte"

1975. 125th Death Anniv of Gottfried Schadow (sculptor).

B466 B **116** 50 pf. brown 45 40

1975. Berlin Pleasure Boats. Multicoloured.

B467 30 pf. Type B **117** 50 35
B468 40 pf. "Siegfried" 75 60
B469 50 pf. "Sperber" . . . . . 1·00 65
B470 60 pf. "Vaterland" . . . . . 1·25 75
B471 70 pf. "Moby Dick" . . . . . 1·50 1·25

B 118 Steam Locomotive "Drache", 1848

1975. Youth Welfare. Railway Locomotives. Multicoloured.

B472 30 pf. + 15 pf. Type B **118** . . 1·00 80
B473 40 pf. + 20 pf. Class 89 tank locomotive . . . . 1·25 1·10
B474 50 pf. + 25 pf. Class 050 steam locomotive . . . . 1·90 1·60
B475 70 pf. + 35 pf. Class 010 steam locomotive . . . . 2·75 2·75

B 119 Ferdinand Sauerbruch (surgeon)

B 120 Gymnastics Emblem

1975. Birth Cent. of Ferdinand Sauerbruch.

B476 B **119** 50 pf. dp brn, brn & pk 55 40

1975. Gymnaestrada (Gymnastic Games), Berlin.

B477 B **120** 40 pf. black, gold and green 45 35

1975. Industry and Technology. As Nos. 1742/55.

B478 – 5 pf. green 10 10
B479 – 10 pf. purple 10 10
B480 – 20 pf. red 25 10
B481 – 30 pf. violet 30 15
B482 **572** 40 pf. green 45 25
B483 – 50 pf. red 55 15
B483a – 60 pf. red . . . . . . 1·00 25
B484 – 70 pf. blue 70 25
B485 – 80 pf. green 80 20
B486 – 100 pf. brown 90 35
B486a – 110 pf. purple . . . . . 1·25 85
B487 – 120 pf. blue . . . . . 1·25 95
B487a – 130 pf. red . . . . . . 2·00 95
B488 – 140 pf. red . . . . . . 1·25 1·25
B488a – 150 pf. red . . . . . . 2·75 1·25
B489 – 160 pf. green . . . . . 2·40 1·10
B489a – 180 pf. brown . . . . . 2·50 2·00
B489b – 190 pf. brown . . . . . 2·50 1·75
B490 – 200 pf. purple . . . . . 1·50 50
B490a – 230 pf. purple . . . . . 2·25 1·90
B490b – 250 pf. green . . . . . 3·50 1·75
B490c – 300 pf. green . . . . . 3·75 2·00
B491 – 500 pf. black . . . . . 5·25 3·50

B 121 "Lovis Corinth" (self-portrait)

B 122 Buildings in Naunynstrasse, Berlin-Kreuzberg

1975. 50th Death Anniv of Lovis Corinth (painter).

B492 B **121** 50 pf. multicoloured . . 60 40

1975. European Architectural Heritage Year.

B493 B **122** 50 pf. multicoloured . . 50 35

B 123 Yellow Gentian

B 124 Paul Lobe

1975. Humanitarian Relief Funds. Alpine Flowers. Multicoloured.

B494 30 pf. + 15 pf. Type B **123** . . 45 35
B495 40 pf. + 20 pf. Arnica 50 45
B496 50 pf. + 25 pf. Cyclamen . . 65 60
B497 70 pf. + 35 pf. Blue gentian . 1·25 95

1975. Christmas. As Type B **123**. inscr "WEIHNACHTSMARKE". Mult.

B498 30 pf. + 15 pf. Snow heather 55 55

See also Nos. B508/11, B540/3 and B557/60.

1975. Birth Cent of Paul Lobe (politician).

B499 B **124** 50 pf. red 55 45

B 125 Ears of Wheat, with inscription "Grune Woche"

B 126 Putting the Shot

1976. "International Agriculture Week", Berlin.

B500 B **125** 70 pf. yellow & green . 60 60

1976. Youth Welfare. Training for the Olympics. Multicoloured.

B501 30 pf. + 15 pf. Type B **126** . . 60 60
B502 40 pf. + 20 pf. Hockey . . . 70 70
B503 50 pf. + 25 pf. Handball . . . 90 90
B504 70 pf. + 35 pf. Swimming . . 1·40 1·40

B 127 Hockey

B 128 Treble Clef

1976. Women's World Hockey Championships.

B505 B **127** 30 pf. green 60 35

1976. German Choristers' Festival.

B506 B **128** 40 pf. multicoloured . . 70 40

B 129 Fire Service Emblem

B 130 Julius Tower, Spandau

1976. 125th Anniv of Berlin Fire Service.

B507 B **129** 50 pf. multicoloured . 1·00 75

1976. Humanitarian Relief Funds. Garden Flowers. As Type B **123**. Multicoloured.

B508 30 pf. + 15 pf. Iris 40 40
B509 40 pf. + 20 pf. Wallflower . . 50 50
B510 50 pf. + 25 pf. Dahlia . . . 60 60
B511 70 pf. + 35 pf. Larkspur . . . 1·00 1·00

1976. Berlin Views (1st series).

B512 – 30 pf. black & blue . . 50 25
B513 B **130** 40 pf. black & brown . . 60 35
B514 – 50 pf. black & green . . 70 50

DESIGNS: 30 pf. Yacht on the Havel; 50 pf. Lake and Victory Column, Tiergarten park.

See also Nos. B562/4, B605/7 and B647/9.

1977. Coil Stamps. German Castles. As Nos. 1805/12d. of Germany.

B516 10 pf. blue 10 10
B517 20 pf. orange 20 10
B517a 25 pf. red 50 20
B518 30 pf. brown 30 10
B518c 35 pf. red 55 15
B519 40 pf. green 45 15
B519a 40 pf. brown 35 15
B520 50 pf. red 55 15
B520b 50 pf. green 45 15
B521 60 pf. brown . . . . . . 1·00 20
B521a 60 pf. red 85 15
B522 70 pf. blue 90 30
B522a 80 pf. green . . . . . . 1·00 25
B522b 90 pf. blue . . . . 1·00 40
B522c 120 pf. violet . . . . . . 1·10 50
B523 190 pf. red . . . . 1·60 80
B524 200 pf. green . . . . . . 2·00 80
B524a 210 pf. brown . . . . . . 2·50 1·25
B524b 230 pf. green . . . . . . 2·50 1·00
B524c 280 pf. blue . . . . . . 3·25 2·00
B524d 300 pf. orange . . . . . 3·50 2·25

B 132 "Eugenie d' Alton" (Cristian Rauch)

B 133 "Eduard Gaertner" (self-portrait)

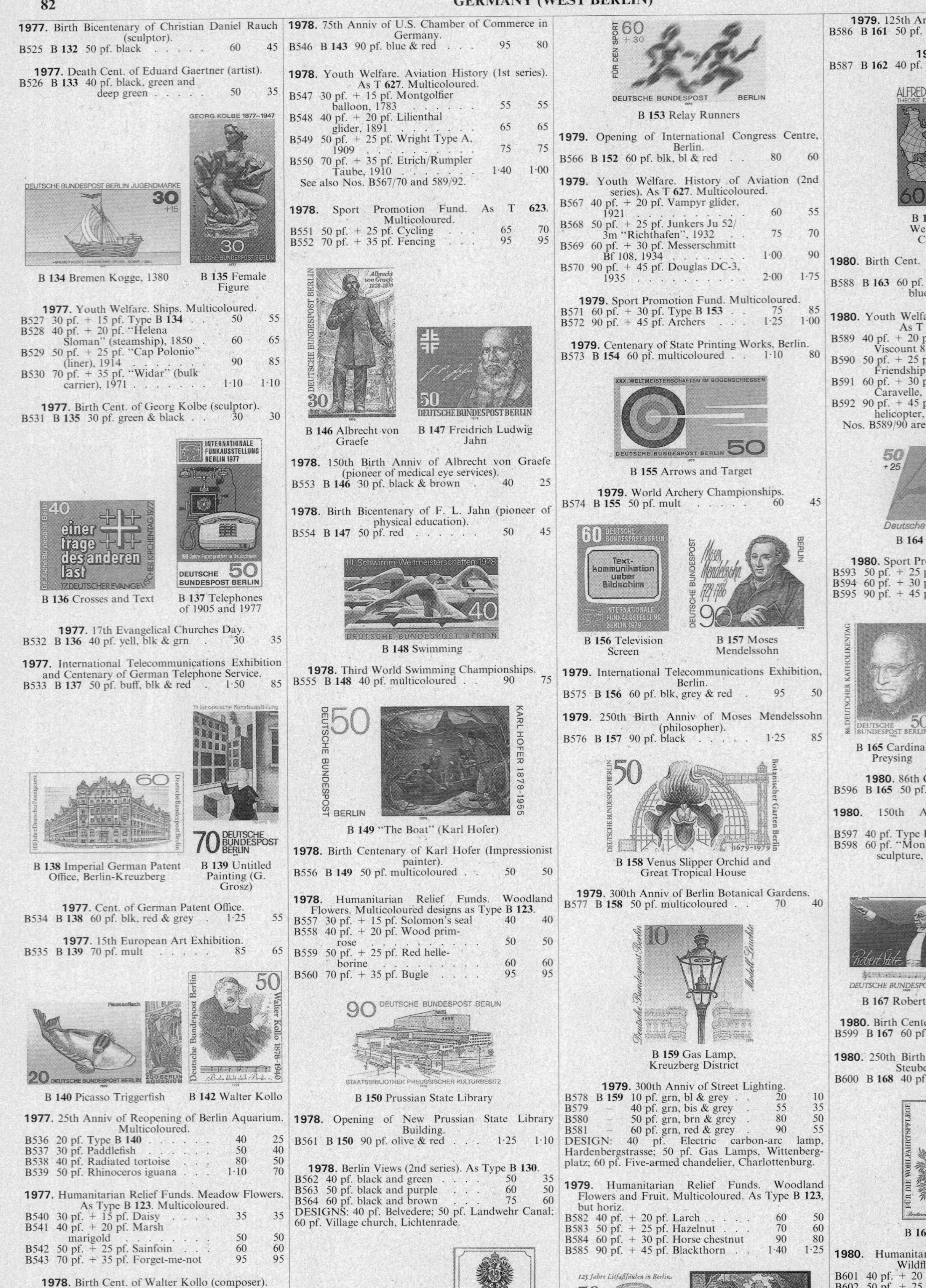

1977. Birth Bicentenary of Christian Daniel Rauch (sculptor).
B525 B **132** 50 pf. black 60 45

1977. Death Cent. of Eduard Gaertner (artist).
B526 B **133** 40 pf. black, green and deep green 50 35

B 134 Bremen Kogge, 1380

B 135 Female Figure

1977. Youth Welfare. Ships. Multicoloured.
B527 30 pf. + 15 pf. Type B **134** . . 50 55
B528 40 pf. + 20 pf. "Helena Sloman" (steamship), 1850 . . 60 65
B529 50 pf. + 25 pf. "Cap Polonio" (liner), 1914 . . . . . . 90 85
B530 70 pf. + 35 pf. "Widar" (bulk carrier), 1971 . . . . 1·10 1·10

1977. Birth Cent. of Georg Kolbe (sculptor).
B531 B **135** 30 pf. green & black . . 30 30

B 136 Crosses and Text

B 137 Telephones of 1905 and 1977

1977. 17th Evangelical Churches Day.
B532 B **136** 40 pf. yell, blk & grn . 30 35

1977. International Telecommunications Exhibition and Centenary of German Telephone Service.
B533 B **137** 50 pf. buff, blk & red . 1·50 85

B 138 Imperial German Patent Office, Berlin-Kreuzberg

B 139 Untitled Painting (G. Grosz)

1977. Cent. of German Patent Office.
B534 B **138** 60 pf. blk, red & grey . 1·25 55

1977. 15th European Art Exhibition.
B535 B **139** 70 pf. mult 85 65

B 140 Picasso Triggerfish

B 142 Walter Kollo

1977. 25th Anniv of Reopening of Berlin Aquarium. Multicoloured.
B536 20 pf. Type B **140** 40 25
B537 30 pf. Paddlefish 50 40
B538 40 pf. Radiated tortoise . . . 80 50
B539 50 pf. Rhinoceros iguana . . . 1·10 70

1977. Humanitarian Relief Funds. Meadow Flowers. As Type B **123**. Multicoloured.
B540 30 pf. + 15 pf. Daisy 35 35
B541 40 pf. + 20 pf. Marsh marigold 50 50
B542 50 pf. + 25 pf. Sainfoin . . . 60 60
B543 70 pf. + 35 pf. Forget-me-not 95 95

1978. Birth Cent. of Walter Kollo (composer).
B545 B **142** 50 pf. brn & red 90 60

B 143 Emblem of U.S. Chamber of Commerce

1978. 75th Anniv of U.S. Chamber of Commerce in Germany.
B546 B **143** 90 pf. blue & red . . . 95 80

1978. Youth Welfare. Aviation History (1st series). As T **627**. Multicoloured.
B547 30 pf. + 15 pf. Montgolfier balloon, 1783 . . . . . . 55 55
B548 40 pf. + 20 pf. Lilienthal glider, 1891 . . . . 65 65
B549 50 pf. + 25 pf. Wright Type A, 1909 . . . . 75 75
B550 70 pf. + 35 pf. Etrich/Rumpler Taube, 1910 . . . . 1·40 1·00
See also Nos. B567/70 and 589/92.

1978. Sport Promotion Fund. As T **623**. Multicoloured.
B551 50 pf. + 25 pf. Cycling . . . 65 70
B552 70 pf. + 35 pf. Fencing . . . 95 95

B 146 Albrecht von Graefe

B 147 Friedrich Ludwig Jahn

1978. 150th Birth Anniv of Albrecht von Graefe (pioneer of medical eye services).
B553 B **146** 30 pf. black & brown . 40 25

1978. Birth Bicentenary of F. L. Jahn (pioneer of physical education).
B554 B **147** 50 pf. red 50 45

B 148 Swimming

1978. Third World Swimming Championships.
B555 B **148** 40 pf. multicoloured . . 90 75

B 149 "The Boat" (Karl Hofer)

1978. Birth Centenary of Karl Hofer (Impressionist painter).
B556 B **149** 50 pf. multicoloured . . 50 50

1978. Humanitarian Relief Funds. Woodland Flowers. Multicoloured designs as Type B **123**.
B557 30 pf. + 15 pf. Solomon's seal 40 40
B558 40 pf. + 20 pf. Wood primrose 50 50
B559 50 pf. + 25 pf. Red helleborine 60 60
B560 70 pf. + 35 pf. Bugle 95 95

B 150 Prussian State Library

1978. Opening of New Prussian State Library Building.
B561 B **150** 90 pf. olive & red . . . 1·25 1·10

1978. Berlin Views (2nd series). As Type B **130**.
B562 40 pf. black and green 50 35
B563 50 pf. black and purple . . . 60 50
B564 60 pf. black and brown . . . 75 60
DESIGNS: 40 pf. Belvedere; 50 pf. Landwehr Canal; 60 pf. Village church, Lichtenrade.

B 152 Congress Centre

B 154 Old and New Arms

B 153 Relay Runners

1979. Opening of International Congress Centre, Berlin.
B566 B **152** 60 pf. blk, bl & red . . 80 60

1979. Youth Welfare. History of Aviation (2nd series). As T **627**. Multicoloured.
B567 40 pf. + 20 pf. Vampyr glider, 1921 . . . . 60 55
B568 50 pf. + 25 pf. Junkers Ju 52/3m "Richthafen", 1932 . . 75 70
B569 60 pf. + 30 pf. Messerschmitt Bf 108, 1934 . . . . . . 1·00 90
B570 90 pf. + 45 pf. Douglas DC-3, 1935 . . . . 2·00 1·75

1979. Sport Promotion Fund. Multicoloured.
B571 60 pf. + 30 pf. Type B **153** . . 75 85
B572 90 pf. + 45 pf. Archers . . . 1·25 1·00

1979. Centenary of State Printing Works, Berlin.
B573 B **154** 60 pf. multicoloured . . 1·10 80

B 155 Arrows and Target

1979. World Archery Championships.
B574 B **155** 50 pf. mult 60 45

B 156 Television Screen

B 157 Moses Mendelssohn

1979. International Telecommunications Exhibition, Berlin.
B575 B **156** 60 pf. blk, grey & red . 95 50

1979. 250th Birth Anniv of Moses Mendelssohn (philosopher).
B576 B **157** 90 pf. black . . . . . 1·25 85

B 158 Venus Slipper Orchid and Great Tropical House

1979. 300th Anniv of Berlin Botanical Gardens.
B577 B **158** 50 pf. multicoloured . . 70 40

B 159 Gas Lamp, Kreuzberg District

1979. 300th Anniv of Street Lighting.
B578 B **159** 10 pf. grn, bl & grey . . 20 10
B579 – 40 pf. grn, bis & grey . 55 35
B580 – 50 pf. grn, brn & grey . 80 50
B581 – 60 pf. grn, red & grey . 90 55
DESIGN: 40 pf. Electric carbon-arc lamp, Hardenbergstrasse; 50 pf. Gas Lamps, Wittenbergplatz; 60 pf. Five-armed chandelier, Charlottenburg.

1979. Humanitarian Relief Funds. Woodland Flowers and Fruit. Multicoloured. As Type B **123**, but horiz.
B582 40 pf. + 20 pf. Larch 60 50
B583 50 pf. + 25 pf. Hazelnut . . . 70 60
B584 60 pf. + 30 pf. Horse chestnut 90 80
B585 90 pf. + 45 pf. Blackthorn . . 1·40 1·25

B 161 Advertisement Pillar

B 162 "Nativity" (Altenberg medieval manuscript)

1979. 125th Anniv of Advertisement Pillars.
B586 B **161** 50 pf. red and lilac . . 1·00 60

1979. Christmas.
B587 B **162** 40 pf. + 20 pf. mult . . 60 70

B 163 Map showing Wegener's Theory of Continental Drift

1980. Birth Cent. of Alfred Wegener (explorer and geophysicist).
B588 B **163** 60 pf. black, orange and blue . . . . 1·10 80

1980. Youth Welfare. Aviation History (3rd series). As T **627**. Multicoloured.
B589 40 pf. + 20 pf. Vickers Viscount 810 . . . . 75 75
B590 50 pf. + 25 pf. Fokker Friendship "Condor" . . . 90 90
B591 60 pf. + 30 pf. Sud Aviation Caravelle, 1955 . . . . . . 1·25 1·25
B592 90 pf. + 45 pf. Sikorsky S-55 helicopter, 1949 . . . . . 1·75 1·75
Nos. B589/90 are incorrectly dated.

B 164 Throwing the Javelin

1980. Sport Promotion Fund. Multicoloured.
B593 50 pf. + 25 pf. Type B **164** . . 60 70
B594 60 pf. + 30 pf. Weightlifting . 80 85
B595 90 pf. + 45 pf. Water polo . . 1·00 1·00

B 165 Cardinal Preysing

B 166 "Operatio" (enamel medallion)

1980. 86th German Catholics Congress.
B596 B **165** 50 pf. red & black . . . 65 45

1980. 150th Anniv of Prussian Museums. Multicoloured.
B597 40 pf. Type B **166** 60 30
B598 60 pf. "Monks Reading" (oak sculpture, Ernst Barlach) . . 75 55

B 167 Robert Stolz

B 168 Von Steuben

1980. Birth Centenary of Robert Stolz (composer).
B599 B **167** 60 pf. multicoloured . . 1·00 70

1980. 250th Birth Anniv of Friedrich Wilhelm von Steuben (American general).
B600 B **168** 40 pf. multicoloured . . 90 45

B 169 Orlaya grandiflora

1980. Humanitarian Relief Funds. Endangered Wildflowers. Multicoloured.
B601 40 pf. + 20 pf. Type B **169** . . 60 60
B602 50 pf. + 25 pf. Yellow gagae . 65 65
B603 60 pf. + 30 pf. Summer pheasant's-eye 85 85
B604 90 p. + 45 pf. Venus's looking-glass . . . . 1·25 1·25
See also Nos. B622/5

1980. Berlin Views (3rd series). As Type B **130**.
B605 40 pf. black and green 50 35
B606 50 pf. black and brown . . . 65 45
B607 60 pf. black and blue . . . 1·10 60
DESIGNS: 40 pf. Lilienthal Monument; 50 pf. "Grosse Neugierde"; 60 pf. Grunewald Tower.

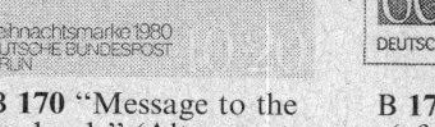

B **170** "Message to the Shepherds" (Altomunster manuscript)
B **171** Von Arnim (after Strohling)

1980. Christmas.
B608 B **170** 40 pf. + 20 pf. mult . . 70 80

1981. Birth Bicentenary of Achim von Arnim (poet).
B609 B **171** 60 pf. green 50 50

B **172** Von Chamisso (bronze medallion, David d'Angers)
B **173** Von Gontard

1981. Birth Bicentenary of Adelbert von Chamisso (poet and naturalist).
B610 B **172** 60 pf. brown, deep brown and ochre . . 50 50

1981. 250th Birth Anniv of Karl Phillipp von Gontard (architect).
B611 B **173** 50 pf. red, blk & grey . 55 55

B **174** Kreuzberg War Memorial
B **175** Theodolite, c. 1810

1981. Birth Bicentenary of Karl Friedrich Schinkel (architect).
B612 B **174** 40 pf. green & brown . 85 65

1981. Youth Welfare. Optical Instruments. Multicoloured.
B613 40 pf. + 20 pf. Type B **175** . . 55 55
B614 50 pf. + 25 pf. Equatorial telescope, 1820 . . . . 75 75
B615 60 pf. + 30 pf. Microscope, 1790 . . . . 90 90
B616 90 pf. + 45 pf. Sextant, 1830 . 1·50 1·50

B **176** Group Gymnastics

1981. Sport Promotion Fund. Multicoloured.
B617 60 pf. + 30 pf. Type B **176** . . 90 60
B618 90 pf. + 45 pf. Cross-country race . . . . 1·25 1·00

B **177** "Cupid and Psyche"
B **178** Badge of Order "Pour le Merite"

1981. 150th Birth Anniv of Reinhold Begas (sculptor).
B619 B **177** 50 pf. black & blue . . 50 40

1981. Prussian Exhibition, Berlin-Krevzberg.
B620 B **178** 40 pf. multicoloured . . 50 30

B **179** Broadcasting House, Charlottenburg
B **180** "Three Kings" (glass painting)

1981. International Telecommunications Exhibition, Berlin.
B621 B **179** 60 pf. multicoloured . . 1·00 65

1981. Humanitarian Relief Funds. Endangered Wildflowers. Designs as Type B **169**. Multicoloured.
B622 40 pf + 20 pf. Common bistort 60 60
B623 50 pf. + 25 pf. Moor-king . . 70 70
B624 60 pf. + 30 pf. "Gladiolus palustris" 90 90
B625 90 pf. + 45 pf. Siberian iris . . 1·60 1·60

1981. Christmas.
B626 B **180** 40 pf. + 20 pf. mult . . 55 55

B **181** Peter Beuth
B **182** "Dancer Nijinsky" (Georg Kolbe)

1981. Birth Bicentenary of Peter Beuth (constitutional lawyer).
B627 B **181** 60 pf. black & brown . 55 55

1981. 20th Century Sculptures. Mult.
B628 40 pf. Type B **182** 40 30
B629 60 pf. "Mother Earth II" (Ernst Barlach) 70 55
B630 90 pf. "Flora Kneeling" (Richard Scheibe) . . . . . 1·25 85

B **183** Arms and View of Spandau, c. 1700

1982. 750th Anniv of Spandau.
B631 B **183** 60 pf. multicoloured . . 90 90

B **184** Daimler Steel-wheeled Car, 1889

1982. Youth Welfare Fund. Motor Cars. Multicoloured.
B632 40 pf. + 20 pf. Type B **184** . . 80 65
B633 50 pf. + 25 pf. Wanderer "Puppchen", 1911 . . . . . 95 70
B634 60 pf. + 30 p. Adler limousine, 1913 . . . . 1·00 1·00
B635 90 pf. + 45 pf. DKW "F 1", 1913 . . . . 1·40 1·40

B **185** Sprinting

1982. Sport Promotion Fund. Multicoloured.
B636 60 pf. + 30 pf. Type B **185** . . 75 60
B637 90 pf. + 45 pf. Volleyball . . 1·40 1·10

B **186** Harp
B **187** "Emigrants reaching Prussian Frontier" (woodcut after drawing by Adolph von Menzel)

1982. Centenary of Berlin Philharmonic Orchestra.
B638 B **186** 60 pf. grey, red & grn . . 80 70

1982. 250th Anniv of Salzburg Emigrants' Arrival in Prussia.
B639 B **187** 50 pf. stone, deep brown and brown 50 40

B **188** "Italian Stone Carriers" (Max Pechstein)

1982. Paintings. Multicoloured.
B640 50 pf. Type B **188** 85 70
B641 80 pf. "Two Girls Bathing" (Otto Mueller) . . . . . . 1·00 1·00

B **189** Floribunda-Grandiflora
B **191** "Adoration of the Kings" (detail from St. Peter altar by Master Bertram)

B **190** Castle Theatre, Charlottenburg

1982. Humanitarian Relief Funds. Roses. Multicoloured.
B642 50 pf. + 20 pf. Type B **189** . . 75 65
B643 60 pf. + 30 pf. Hybrid tea . . 1·00 90
B644 80 pf. + 40 pf. Floribunda . . 1·50 1·10
B645 120 pf. + 60 pf. Miniature rose . . . . 2·25 2·00

1982. 250th Birth Anniv of Carl Gotthard Langhans (architect).
B646 B **190** 80 pf. red, grey and black . . . . 1·40 1·25

1982. Berlin Views (4th series). As Type B **130**.
B647 50 pf. black and blue . . . . 1·00 40
B648 60 pf. black and red . . . . 1·10 70
B649 80 pf. black and brown . . . 1·25 95
DESIGNS: 50 pf. Villa Borsig; 60 pf. Sts. Peter and Paul Church; 80 pf. Villa von der Heydt.

1982. Christmas.
B650 B **191** 50 pf. + 20 pf. mult . . 80 75

B **192** Water Pump, Klausenerplatz
B **193** Royal Prussian Telegraphy Inspectors at St. Anne's Church

1983. Street Water Pumps. Multicoloured.
B651 50 pf. Type B **192** 80 45
B652 60 pf. Chamissoplatz . . . . 1·00 60
B653 80 pf. Schloss-strasse . . . 1·25 85
B654 120 pf. Kuerfurstendamm . . 2·00 1·25

1983. 150th Anniv of Berlin-Coblenz Optical-Mechanical Telegraph.
B655 B **193** 80 pf. brown . . . . . 1·50 1·00

B **194** Hildebrand & Wolfmuller, 1894

1983. Youth Welfare. Motor Cycles. Mult.
B656 50 pf. + 20 pf. Type B **194** . . 1·00 80
B657 60 pf. + 30 pf. Wanderer, 1908 . . . . 1·40 1·10
B658 80 pf. + 40 pf. D.K.W.-Lomos, 1922 . . . . . . 1·50 1·25
B659 120 pf. + 60 pf. Mars, 1925 . . 2·25 1·90

B **195** Latin-American Dancing

1983. Sport Promotion Fund. Multicoloured.
B660 80 pf. + 40 pf. Type B **195** . . 1·25 1·00
B661 120 pf. + 60 pf. Ice hockey . . 2·00 1·60

B **196** "La Barbarina" (painting of Barbara Campanini)
B **197** Ringelnatz (silhouette by E. M. Engert)

1983. 300th Birth Anniv of Antoine Pesne (artist).
B662 B **196** 50 pf. multicoloured . . 70 60

1983. Birth Centenary of Joachim Ringelnatz (poet and painter).
B663 B **197** 50 pf. grn, brn & red . 70 60

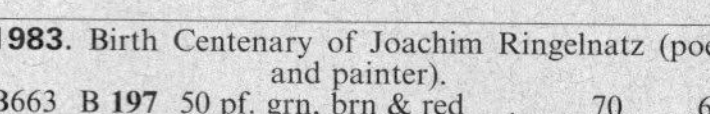

B **198** Paul Nipkow's Picture Transmission System, 1884

1983. International Broadcasting Exn, Berlin.
B664 B **198** 80 pf. multicoloured . . 1·40 90

B **199** Mountain Windflower
B **200** Nigerian Yoruba Crib

1983. Humanitarian Relief Funds. Endangered Alpine Flowers. Multicoloured.
B665 50 pf. + 20 pf. Type B **199** . . 1·00 1·00
B666 60 pf. + 30 pf. Alpine auricula . . . . 1·25 1·25
B667 80 pf. + 40 pf. Little primrose 1·75 1·60
B668 120 pf. + 60 pf. Einsele's aquilegia . . . . 2·10 1·75

1983. Christmas.
B669 B **200** 50 pf. + 20 pf. mult . . 90 70

B **201** Queen Cleopatra VII (Antikenmuseum)

1984. Art Objects in Berlin Museums. Multicoloured.
B670 30 pf. Type B **201** . . . . . . 1·00 1·00
B671 50 pf. Statue of seated couple from Giza Necropolis (Egyptian Museum) . . . . 1·25 1·10
B672 60 pf. Goddess with pearl turban (Ethnology Museum) . . . . 1·40 1·25
B673 80 pf. Majolica dish (Applied Arts Museum) . . . . . . 2·00 1·75

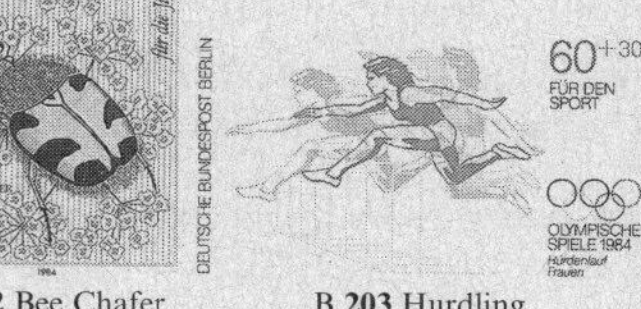

B **202** Bee Chafer
B **203** Hurdling

1984. Youth Welfare. Pollinating Insects. Multicoloured.
B674 50 pf. + 20 pf. Type B **202** . . 1·25 1·00
B675 60 pf. + 30 pf. Common burnet (moth) . . . . . 1·25 1·25
B676 80 pf. + 40 pf. Buff-tailed bumble bee . . . . 2·00 1·50
B677 120 pf. + 60 pf. Drone-fly . . 2·25 2·25

1984. Sport Promotion Fund. Multicoloured.
B678 60 pf. + 30 pf. Type B **203** . . 1·25 1·10
B679 80 pf. + 40 pf. Cycling . . . 2·00 1·60
B680 120 pf. + 60 pf. Four-seater kayaks . . . . 2·50 2·25

B **204** Klausener
B **205** "Electric Power" (K. Sutterlin)

1984. 50th Death Anniv of Dr. Erich Klausener (chairman of Catholic Action).
B681 B **204** 80 pf. grn & dp grn . . 80 80

1984. Cent. of Berlin Electricity Supply.
B682 B **205** 50 pf. yell, orge & blk . . 60 50

B 206 Conference Emblem

B 207 Brehm and White Stork

1984. 4th European Ministers of Culture Conference, Berlin.
B683 B **206** 60 pf. multicoloured . . 70 60

1984. Death Centenary of Alfred Brehm (zoologist).
B684 B **207** 80 pf. multicoloured . . 1·75 1·10

B 208 Heim (bust, Friedrich Tieck)

B 209 "Listera cordata"

1984. 150th Death Anniv of Ernst Ludwig Heim (medical pioneer).
B685 B **208** 50 pf. black and red . . 70 60

1984. Humanitarian Relief Funds. Orchids. Multicoloured.
B686 50 pf. + 20 pf. Type B **209** . . 1·25 1·25
B687 60 pf. + 30 pf. "Ophrys insectifera" . . . . 1·40 1·40
B688 80 pf. + 40 pf. "Epipactis palustris" . . . . 2·25 2·25
B689 120 pf. + 60 pf. "Ophrys coriophora" . . . . 3·50 3·25

B 210 "Sunflowers on Grey Background"

B 211 St. Nicholas

1984. Birth Centenary of Karl Schmidt-Rottluff (artist).
B690 B **210** 60 pf. multicoloured . . 90 70

1984. Christmas.
B691 B **211** 50 pf. + 20 pf. mult . . 1·00 1·00

B 212 Bettina von Arnim

B 213 Humboldt (statue, Paul Otto)

1985. Birth Bicentenary of Bettina von Arnim (writer).
B692 B **212** 50 pf. blk, brn & red . 80 60

1985. 50th Death Anniv of Wilhelm von Humboldt (philologist).
B693 B **213** 80 pf. blk, bl & red . . 1·25 90

B 214 Ball in Net

1985. Sport Promotion Fund. Multicoloured.
B694 80 pf. + 40 pf. Type B **214** (50th anniv of basketball in Germany and European championships, Stuttgart) . 1·25 1·00
B695 120 pf. + 60 pf. Table tennis (60th anniv of German Table Tennis Association) . . . . 2·10 1·50

B 215 Stylized Flower

B 216 Bussing Bicycle, 1868

1985. Federal Horticultural Show, Berlin.
B696 B **215** 80 pf. multicoloured . . 1·00 80

1985. Youth Welfare. International Youth Year. Bicycles. Multicoloured.
B697 50 pf. + 20 pf. Type B **216** . . 1·25 1·00
B698 60 pf. + 30 pf. Child's tricycle, 1885 . . . . 1·40 1·25
B699 80 pf. + 40 pf. Jaray bicycle, 1925 . . . . 1·75 1·50
B700 120 pf. + 60 pf. Opel racing bicycle, 1925 . . . . 2·75 2·25

B 217 Stock Exchange, 1863–1945

1985. 300th Anniv of Berlin Stock Exchange.
B701 B **217** 50 pf. multicoloured . . 75 55

B 218 Otto Klemperer

1985. Birth Centenary of Otto Klemperer (orchestral conductor).
B702 B **218** 60 pf. blue . . . . . . 1·25 90

B 219 Association Emblem

1985. 11th International Gynaecology and Obstetrics Association Congress, Berlin.
B703 B **219** 60 pf. multicoloured . . 75 60

B 220 "FE 3" Television Camera, 1935

1985. International Broadcasting Exn, Berlin.
B704 B **220** 80 pf. multicoloured . . 1·50 1·10

B 221 Seal of Brandenburg-Prussia and Preamble of Edict

1985. 300th Anniv of Edict of Potsdam (admitting Huguenots to Prussia).
B705 B **221** 50 pf. lilac & black . . 60 45

B 222 Flowers, Strawberries and Ladybirds

1985. Humanitarian Relief Funds. Designs depict motifs from borders of Medieval Prayer book. Multicoloured.
B706 50 pf. + 20 pf. Type B **222** . . 90 80
B707 60 pf. + 30 pf. Flowers, bird and butterfly . . . . 1·25 1·00
B708 80 pf. + 40 pf. Flowers, bee and butterfly . . . . 1·50 1·25
B709 120 pf. + 60 pf. Flowers, berries, butterfly and snail . . . 2·25 2·25

B 223 "Adoration of the Kings" (detail, Epiphany Altar)

B 224 Kurt Tucholsky

1985. Christmas. 500th Birth Anniv of Hans Baldung Grien (artist).
B710 B **223** 50 pf. + 20 pf. mult . . 1·00 1·00

1985. 50th Death Anniv of Kurt Tucholsky (writer and journalist).
B711 B **224** 80 pf. multicoloured . . 1·40 1·25

B 225 Furtwangler and Score

1986. Birth Centenary of Wilhelm Furtwangler (composer and conductor).
B712 B **225** 80 pf. multicoloured . . 1·75 1·40

B 226 Rohe and National Gallery

1986. Birth Centenary of Ludwig Mies van der Rohe (architect).
B713 B **226** 50 pf. multicoloured . . 85 60

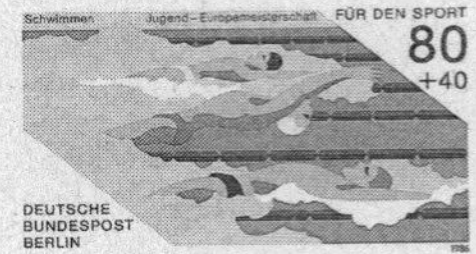

B 227 Swimming

1986. Sport Promotion Fund. Multicoloured.
B714 80 pf. + 40 pf. Type B **227** (European Youth Championships, Berlin) . . 1·60 1·60
B715 120 pf. + 55 pf. Show-jumping (World Championships, Aachen) . . . . 2·25 2·25

B 228 Glazier

1986. Youth Charity. Trades (1st series). Multicoloured.
B716 50 pf. + 25 pf. Type B **228** . . 1·00 90
B717 60 pf. + 30 pf. Locksmith . . 1·50 1·40
B718 70 pf. + 35 pf. Tailor . . . . 1·75 1·60
B719 80 pf. + 40 pf. Carpenter . . 1·90 1·75
See also Nos. B765/8.

B 229 Flags

1986. 16th European Communities Day.
B720 B **229** 60 pf. multicoloured . . 75 55

B 230 Ranke

B 231 Benn

1986. Death Centenary of Leopold von Ranke (historian).
B721 B **230** 80 pf. brown & grey . . 1·25 1·00

1986. Birth Centenary of Gottfried Benn (poet).
B722 B **231** 80 pf. blue . . . . . . 1·25 1·00

B 232 Charlottenburg Gate

B 233 "The Flute Concert" (detail, Adolph von Menzel)

1986. Gateways. Multicoloured.
B723 50 pf. Type B **232** . . . . . . 1·10 65
B724 60 pf. Griffin Gate, Glienicke Palace . . . . 1·25 95
B725 80 pf. Elephant Gate, Berlin Zoo . . . . 1·50 1·25

1986. Death Bicentenary of Frederick the Great.
B726 B **233** 80 pf. multicoloured . . 1·25 80

B 234 Cantharus, 1st century A.D.

B 235 "Adoration of the Three Kings" (Ortenberg altarpiece)

1986. Humanitarian Relief Funds. Glassware. Multicoloured.
B727 50 pf. + 25 pf. Type B **234** . . 1·00 75
B728 60 pf. + 30 pf. Beaker, 200 A.D. . . . . 1·40 1·00
B729 70 pf. + 35 pf. Jug, 3rd century A.D. . . . . 1·50 1·25
B730 80 pf. + 40 pf. Diatreta 4th century A.D. . . . . 1·75 1·40

1986. Christmas.
B731 B **235** 50 pf. + 25 pf. mult . . 1·00 1·00

1986. Famous German Women. As Nos. 2149a/2154, 2158, 2161, 2166/9a.
B732 5 pf. brown and grey . . . . 15 1·50
B733 10 pf. brown and violet . . . 25 1·10
B734 20 pf. blue and red . . . . . 65 3·00
B735 40 pf. red and blue . . . . . 1·00 2·75
B736 50 pf. green and brown . . . 1·25 2·25
B737 60 pf. lilac and green . . . . 60 3·00
B738 80 pf. brown and green . . . 1·10 1·40
B739 100 pf. grey and red . . . . 1·50 1·00
B740 130 pf. violet and blue . . . 3·50 8·00
B741 140 pf. brown and blue . . . 3·75 9·50
B742 170 pf. purple & green . . . 2·40 8·00
B743 180 pf. purple and blue . . . 4·00 9·50
B744 240 pf. brown and blue . . . 3·25 9·50
B745 250 pf. blue and mauve . . . 6·50 14·00
B746 300 pf. green and plum . . . 7·25 14·00
B747 350 pf. brown & black . . . 6·50 11·00
B748 500 pf. red and green . . . 8·25 24·00

1987. 750th Anniv of Berlin. As No. 2170.
B760 **833** 80 pf. multicoloured . . . 1·40 1·00

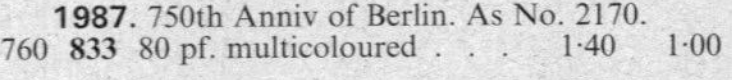

B 237 Louise Schroeder

B 239 "Bohemian Refugees" (detail of relief, King Friedrich Wilhelm Monument, Berlin-Neukolln)

B 238 German Gymnastics Festival, Berlin

1987. Birth Centenary of Louise Schroeder (Mayor of Berlin).
B762 B **237** 50 pf. brown and orange on light brown . . . 80 70

1987. Sport Promotion Fund. Multicoloured.
B763 80 pf. + 40 pf. Type B **238** . . 1·50 1·50
B764 120 pf. + 55 pf. World Judo Championships, Essen . . . 2·25 2·00

1987. Youth Welfare. Trades (2nd series). As Type B **228**. Multicoloured.
B765 50 pf. + 25 pf. Cooper . . . 1·25 90
B766 60 pf. + 30 pf. Stonemason . 1·40 1·25
B767 70 pf. + 35 pf. Furrier . . . 1·60 1·40
B768 80 pf. + 40 pf. Painter/lacquerer . . . . 1·75 1·50

1987. 250th Anniv of Bohemian Settlement, Rixdorf.
B769 B **239** 50 pf. brn & grn . . . 60 45

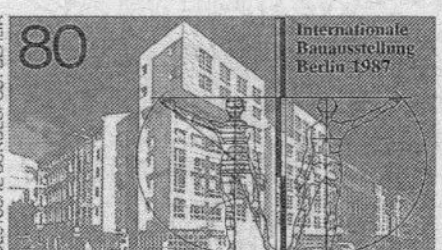

B 240 New Buildings

1987. International Building Exhibition, Berlin.
B770 B **240** 80 pf. sil, blk & bl . . 95 60

B 241 Tree in Arrow Circle

B 242 Compact Disc and Gramophone

1987. 14th International Botanical Congress, Berlin.
B771 B **241** 60 pf. multicoloured . . 80 60

1987. International Broadcasting Exhibition, Berlin. Centenary of Gramophone Record.
B772 B **242** 80 pf. multicoloured . . 1·00 70

B **243** 5th-century Bonnet Ornament

1987. Humanitarian Relief Funds. Precious Metal Work. Multicoloured.
B773 50 pf + 25 pf. Type B **243** . . 90 80
B774 60 pf. + 30 pf. Athene plate, 1st-century B.C. . . . . . 1·00 90
B775 70 pf. + 35 pf. "Armilla" armlet, 1180 . . . . . . 1·25 1·00
B776 80 pf. + 40 pf. Snake bracelet, 300 B.C. . . . . 1·40 1·25

1987. Tourist Sights. As Nos. 2200/19.
B777 5 pf. blue and grey 20 30
B778 10 pf. blue and indigo 15 25
B779 20 pf. flesh and blue 30 40
B780 30 pf. brown and green . . . 80 70
B781 40 pf. brown, red & blue . . . 75 1·75
B782 50 pf. ochre and blue . . . . 1·00 90
B783 60 pf. green and black . . . . 1·00 85
B784 70 pf. flesh and blue . . . . 1·00 2·25
B785 70 pf. brown and blue . . . . 2·00 3·25
B786 80 pf. grey and green . . . . 1·00 90
B787 100 pf. green and orange . . . 1·00 1·40
B788 120 pf. green and red . . . 1·90 3·25
B789 140 pf. bistre and yellow . . . 2·00 3·25
B790 300 pf. flesh and brown . . . 4·75 8·00
B791 350 pf. brown and blue . . . 4·50 9·00

B **244** "Adoration of the Magi" (13th-century Book of Psalms)

B **245** Heraldic Bear

1987. Christmas.
B797 B **244** 50 pf. + 25 pf. mult . . 80 75

1988. Berlin, European City of Culture.
B798 B **245** 80 pf. multicoloured . . 1·50 1·00

B **246** Old and New Buildings

1988. Centenary of Urania Science Museum.
B799 B **246** 50 pf. multicoloured . . 1·00 70

B **247** "Large Pure-bred Foal" (bronze)

1988. Birth Centenary of Rene Sintenis (sculptor).
B800 B **247** 60 pf. multicoloured . . 75 60

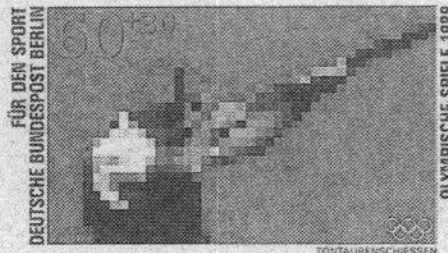

B **248** Clay-pigeon Shooting

1988. Sport Promotion Fund. Olympic Games. Multicoloured.
B801 60 pf. + 30 pf. Type B **248** . . 1·25 1·25
B802 80 pf. + 40 pf. Figure skating (pairs) . . . . 1·40 1·40
B803 120 pf. + 55 pf. Throwing the hammer . . . . 1·75 1·75

B **249** Piano, Violin and Cello

1988. Youth Welfare. Music. Multicoloured.
B804 50 pf. + 25 pf. Type B **249** . . 1·25 1·00
B805 60 pf. + 30 pf. Wind quintet . . 1·50 1·25
B806 70 pf. + 35 pf. Guitar, recorder and mandolin . . . . . . 1·60 1·60
B807 80 pf. + 40 pf. Children's choir . . . . 2·00 1·75

B **250** Great Elector and Family in Berlin Castle Gardens

B **251** Globe

1988. 300th Death Anniv of Friedrich Wilhelm, Great Elector of Brandenburg.
B808 B **250** 50 pf. multicoloured . . 90 80

1988. International Monetary Fund and World Bank Boards of Governors Annual Meetings, Berlin.
B809 B **251** 70 pf. multicoloured . . 1·00 80

B **252** First Train leaving Potsdam Station

1988. 150th Anniv of Berlin–Potsdam Railway.
B810 B **252** 10 pf. multicoloured . . 60 40

B **253** "The Collector" (bronze statue)

B **254** 18th-century Breast Ornament

1988. 50th Death Anniv of Ernst Barlach (artist).
B811 B **253** 40 pf. multicoloured . . 60 40

1988. Humanitarian Relief Funds. Precious Metal Work. Multicoloured.
B812 50 pf. + 25 pf. Type B **254** . . 1·00 1·00
B813 60 pf. + 30 pf. 16th-century lion-shaped jug . . . . . . 1·25 1·25
B814 70 pf. + 35 pf. 16th-century goblet . . . . 1·25 1·25
B815 80 pf. + 40 pf. 15th-century cope clasp . . . . 1·50 1·50

B **255** "Annunciation to the Shepherds" (illus from Henry the Lion's Gospel Book)

1988. Christmas.
B816 B **255** 50 pf. + 25 pf. mult . . 1·00 90

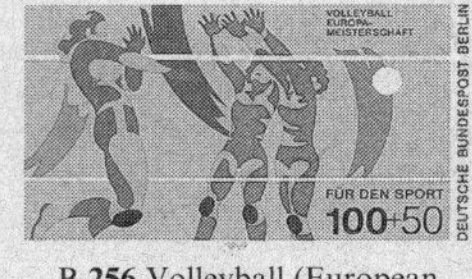

B **256** Volleyball (European Championships)

1989. Sport Promotion Fund. Multicoloured.
B817 100 pf. + 50 pf. Type B **256** . 2·25 2·25
B818 140 pf. + 60 pf. Hockey (Champions Trophy) . . . 2·75 2·75

B **257** Tigers and Tamer

1989. Youth Welfare. Circus. Multicoloured.
B819 60 pf. + 30 pf. Type B **257** . . 1·50 1·50
B820 70 pf. + 30 pf. Trapeze artistes . . . . 1·60 1·60
B821 80 pf. + 35 pf. Sealions . . . . . 2·25 2·25
B822 100 pf. + 50 pf. Jugglers . . . 2·75 2·75

B **258** U.S. and U.K. Flags forming Airplane

B **259** Emblem

1989. 40th Anniv of Berlin Airlift.
B823 B **258** 60 pf. multicoloured . . 75 50

1989. 13th International Organization of Chief Accountants Congress.
B824 B **259** 80 pf. multicoloured . . 1·00 50

B **260** Reuter

1989. Birth Centenary of Ernst Reuter (politician and Mayor of Berlin).
B825 B **260** 100 pf. mult . . . . . 1·25 1·00

B **261** Satellite Radio Waves and TV Screen

1989. International Broadcasting Exn, Berlin.
B826 B **261** 100 pf. mult . . . . . 1·25 85

B **262** Plan of Berlin Zoo and Lenne

1989. Birth Bicentenary of Peter Joseph Lenne (landscape designer).
B827 B **262** 60 pf. multicoloured . . 1·25 80

B **263** Ossietzky and Masthead of "Die Weltbuhne"

1989. Birth Centenary of Carl von Ossietzky (journalist and peace activist).
B828 B **263** 100 pf. mult . . . . . 1·25 80

B **264** Former School Building

B **265** St. Nicholas's Church, Berlin-Spandau

1989. 300th Anniv of Berlin Lycee Francais.
B829 B **264** 40 pf. multicoloured . . 75 60

1989. 450th Anniv of Reformation.
B830 B **265** 60 pf. multicoloured . . 75 60

B **266** 15th-century Letter Messenger

B **267** "Journalists"

1989. Humanitarian Relief Funds. Postal Deliveries. Multicoloured.
B831 60 pf. + 30 pf. Type B **266** . . 2·00 2·00
B832 80 pf. + 35 pf. Brandenburg mail coach, 1700 . . . . 2·50 2·50
B833 100 pf. + 50 pf. 19th-century Prussian postal messengers . . 3·00 3·00

1989. Birth Centenary of Hannah Hoch (painter).
B834 B **267** 100 pf. mult . . . . . 1·60 1·25

B **268** Angel

1989. Christmas. 16th-century Carvings by Veit Stoss, St. Lawrence's Church, Nuremberg. Multicoloured.
B835 40 pf. + 20 pf. Type B **268** . . 1·00 1·00
B836 60 pf. + 30 pf. "Adoration of the Magi" . . . . 1·50 1·50

B **269** Horse-drawn Passenger Vehicle

1990. 250th Anniv of Public Transport in Berlin.
B837 B **269** 60 pf. multicoloured . . 1·50 1·00

B **270** Rudorff

1990. 150th Birth Anniv of Ernst Rudorff (founder of conservation movement).
B838 B **270** 60 pf. multicoloured . . 1·50 1·00

1990. 500th Anniv of Regular European Postal Services. As No. 2297.
B839 **914** 100 pf. deep brown, light brown and brown . . . 1·50 1·00

B **271** Curtain and Theatre

1990. Cent of National Free Theatre, Berlin.
B840 B **271** 100 pf. mult . . . . . 1·50 1·25

B **272** Facade

1990. 40th Anniv of Bundeshaus, Berlin.
B841 B **272** 100 pf. mult . . . . . 2·25 1·75

B **273** Water Polo

1990. Sport Promotion Fund. Multicoloured.
B842 100 pf. + 50 pf. Type B **273** . 3·00 3·00
B843 140 pf. + 60 pf. Wheelchair basketball . . . . 4·00 4·00

B **274** Moritz filling Pipe with Gunpowder

1990. Youth Welfare. 125th Anniv of Max and Moritz (characters from books by Wilhelm Busch). Multicoloured.
B844 60 pf. + 30 pf. Type B **274** . . 1·75 1·75
B845 70 pf. + 30 pf. Max and Moritz running off . . . . 2·00 2·00
B846 80 pf. + 35 pf. Moritz slashing sack open . . . . 2·25 2·25
B847 100 pf. + 50 pf. Insect on Uncle Fritz's nose . . . . . 2·50 2·50

B **275** Poster

B **276** "Street Singer" (etching, Ludwig Knaus)

1990. 90th German Catholic Day.
B848 B **275** 60 pf. multicoloured . . 1·25 1·00

1990. Bicentenary of Barrel-organ.
B849 B **276** 100 pf. mult . . . . . 1·40 1·00

B **277** Pestle and Mortar and Diagram of Aspirin Molecule

B **278** Diesterweg

1990. Centenary of German Pharmaceutical Society.
B850 B **277** 100 pf. mult . . . . . 3·25 2·50

1990. Birth Bicentenary of Adolph Diesterweg (educationist).
B851 B **278** 60 pf. multicoloured . . 2·00 1·75

B **279** Travelling Post Office, 1900

1990. Humanitarian Relief Funds. Posts and Telecommunications. Multicoloured.
B852 60 pf. + 30 pf. Type B **279** . . 2·50 2·50
B853 80 pf. + 35 pf. Installing telephone lines, 1900 . . . . . 2·50 2·50
B854 100 pf. + 50 pf. Electric parcels van, 1930 . . . . 3·00 3·00

With the absorption of East Germany into the Federal Republic of Germany on 3 October 1990, separate issues for West Berlin ceased.

V. GERMAN DEMOCRATIC REPUBLIC (East Germany)

The German Democratic Republic was set up in October 1949 and comprised the former Russian Zone. Its stamps were used in East Berlin.
On 3 October 1990 the territory was absorbed into the German Federal Republic.

1949. 100 pfennig = 1 Deutsche mark (East).
1990. 100 pfennig = 1 Deutsche mark (West).

E **1** Pigeon and Globe

E **2** Postal Workers and Globe

1949. 75th Anniv of U.P.U.
E1 E **1** 50 pf. blue & dp blue . . . 9·50 10·00

1949. Postal Workers' Congress.
E2 E **2** 12 pf. blue . . . . 8·25 8·25
E3 30 pf. red . . . . 13·00 15·00

E **3** T **1** of Bavaria and Magnifying Glass

E **4** Skier

1949. Stamp Day.
E4 E **3** 12 pf. + 3 pf. black . . . . 6·00 5·50

1950. 1st Winter Sports Meeting, Schierke.
E5 E **4** 12 pf. violet . . . . 6·50 4·50
E6 – 24 pf. blue . . . . 8·25 7·75
DESIGN: 24 pf. Girl skater.

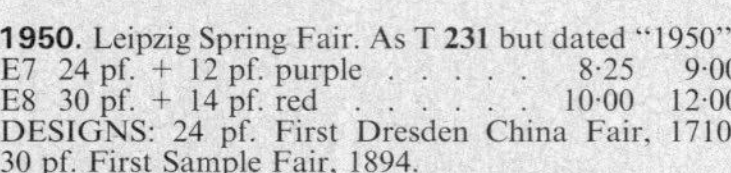

1950. Leipzig Spring Fair. As T **231** but dated "1950".
E7 24 pf. + 12 pf. purple . . . . . 8·25 9·00
E8 30 pf. + 14 pf. red . . . . . 10·00 12·00
DESIGNS: 24 pf. First Dresden China Fair, 1710; 30 pf. First Sample Fair, 1894.

E **5** Globe and Sun

E **6** Wilhelm Pieck

E **7** Wilhelm Pieck

E **8** Shepherd Playing Pipes

1950. 60th Anniv of Labour Day.
E9 E **5** 30 pf. red . . . . 19·00 17·00

1950.
E68 E **6** 5 pf. green . . . . 6·50 3·00
E69 12 pf. blue . . . . 20·00 1·60
E70 24 pf. brown . . . . . . 20·00 1·60
E12 E **7** 1 Dm. green . . . . . . 26·00 3·25
E13 2 Dm. red . . . . 16·00 3·25
E14 5 Dm. blue . . . . 6·50 1·00
For 1 and 2 Dm. with different portrait of president, see Nos. E320/1 (1953).

1950. Death Bicentenary of J. S. Bach (composer).
E15 E **8** 12 pf. + 4 pf. green . . . 5·50 4·50
E16 – 24 pf. + 6 pf. olive . . . 6·00 5·25
E17 – 30 pf. + 8 pf. red . . . . 11·00 9·00
E18 – 50 pf. + 16 pf. blue . . . 16·00 11·00
DESIGNS: 24 pf. Girl playing hand-organ; 30 pf. Bach; 50 pf. Three singers.

E **9** Dove, Globe and Stamp

E **10** L. Euler

1950. Philatelic Exhibition (DEBRIA), Leipzig.
E19 E **9** 84 pf. + 41 pf. red . . . . 45·00 12·00

1950. 250th Anniv of Academy of Science, Berlin.
E20 E **10** 1 pf. grey . . . . 4·25 1·75
E21 – 5 pf. green . . . . 6·00 4·00
E22 – 6 pf. violet . . . . 10·00 4·00
E23 – 8 pf. brown . . . . 16·00 11·00
E24 – 10 pf. green . . . . . . 13·00 11·00
E25 – 12 pf. blue . . . . 4·25 3·25
E26 – 16 pf. blue . . . . 20·00 18·00
E27 – 20 pf. purple . . . . . . 16·00 16·00
E28 – 24 pf. red . . . . 20·00 3·25
E29 – 50 pf. blue . . . . 26·00 20·00
PORTRAITS: 5 pf. A. von Humboldt; 6 pf. T. Mommsen; 8 pf. W. von Humboldt; 10 pf. H. von Helmholtz; 12 pf. M. Planck; 16 pf. J. Grimm; 20 pf. W. Nernst; 24 pf. G. W. Leibniz; 50 pf. A. von Harnack.

E **11** Miner

E **12** Ballot Box

1950. 750th Anniv of Mansfeld Copper Mines.
E30 E **11** 12 pf. blue . . . . 5·25 8·00
E31 – 24 pf. red . . . . 8·50 9·00
DESIGN: 24 pf. Copper smelting.

1950. East German Elections.
E32 E **12** 24 pf. brown . . . . . . 15·00 5·25

E **13** Hand, Dove and Burning Buildings

E **14** Tobogganing

1950. Peace Propaganda. Inscr "ERKAMPFT DEN FRIEDEN".
E33 – 6 pf. blue . . . . 4·00 3·75
E34 E **13** 8 pf. brown . . . . 3·25 1·50
E35 – 12 pf. blue . . . . 6·00 3·25
E36 – 24 pf. red . . . . 5·25 1·50
DESIGNS (all include hand and dove): 6 pf. Tank; 12 pf. Atom bomb Explosion; 24 pf. Rows of gravestones.

1951. 2nd Winter Sports Meeting, Oberhof.
E37 E **14** 12 pf. blue . . . . 8·25 7·50
E38 – 24 f. red (ski jumper) . . 11·00 9·00

E **15**

1951. Leipzig Spring Fair.
E39 E **15** 24 pf. red . . . . 18·00 15·00
E40 50 pf. blue . . . . 18·00 15·00

E **16** Presidents Pieck and Bierut

1951. Visit of Polish President to Berlin.
E41 E **16** 24 pf. red . . . . 19·00 16·00
E42 50 pf. blue . . . . 19·00 16·00

E **17** Mao Tse-tung

E **18** Chinese Land Reform

1951. Friendship with China.
E43 E **17** 12 pf. green . . . . . . £100 24·00
E44 E **18** 24 pf. red . . . . £150 32·00
E45 E **17** 50 pf. blue . . . . £100 24·00

E **19** Youth Hoisting Flag

E **20** Symbols of Agriculture & Industry

1951. 3rd World Youth Festival. Inscr as in Type E **19**. On coloured papers.
E46 E **19** 12 pf. brown . . . . . . 11·00 4·00
E47 – 24 pf. green & red . . . 11·00 4·00
E48 E **19** 30 pf. buff and green . . 15·00 8·25
E49 – 50 pf. red and blue . . . 13·00 8·25
DESIGN: 24 pf., 50 pf. Three girls dancing.

1951. Five Year Plan.
E50 E **20** 24 pf. multicoloured . . . 5·00 1·75

E **21** K. Liebknecht

E **22** Instructing Young Collectors

1951. 80th Birth Anniv of Liebknecht (revolutionary).
E51 E **21** 24 pf. slate and red . . . 5·75 2·00

1951. Stamp Day.
E52 E **22** 12 pf. blue . . . . 5·50 2·00

E **23** P. Bykow and E. Wirth

1951. German-Soviet Friendship.
E53 E **23** 12 pf. blue . . . . 4·00 3·50
E54 – 24 pf. red . . . . 5·00 5·25
DESIGN: 24 pf. Stalin and Pres. Pieck.

E **24** Skier

E **25** Beethoven

1952. 3rd Winter Sports Meeting. Oberhof.
E55 E **24** 12 pf. green . . . . . . 6·25 3·00
E56 – 24 pf. blue . . . . 6·25 3·50
DESIGN: 24 pf. Ski jumper.

1952. 125th Death Anniv of Beethoven (composer).
E57 – 12 pf. bl & lt bl . . . . . 2·00 50
E58 E **25** 24 pf. brn & grey . . . . 3·00 70
DESIGN: 12 pf. Full face portrait.

E **26** President Gottwald

E **27** Bricklayers

1952. Czechoslovak-German Friendship.
E59 E **26** 24 pf. blue . . . . 2·50 1·75

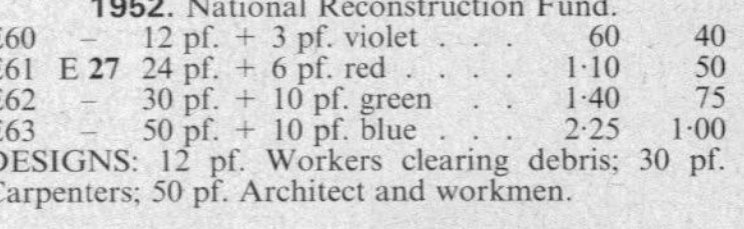

1952. National Reconstruction Fund.
E60 – 12 pf. + 3 pf. violet . . . 60 40
E61 E **27** 24 pf. + 6 pf. red . . . . 1·10 50
E62 – 30 pf. + 10 pf. green . . 1·40 75
E63 – 50 pf. + 10 pf. blue . . . 2·25 1·00
DESIGNS: 12 pf. Workers clearing debris; 30 pf. Carpenters; 50 pf. Architect and workmen.

E **28** Cyclists

E **29** Handel

1952. 5th Warsaw–Berlin–Prague Cycle Race.
E64 E **28** 12 pf. blue . . . . 2·75 1·25

1952. Handel Festival, Halle.
E65 E **29** 6 pf. brown . . . . 1·60 1·40
E66 – 8 pf. red . . . . 2·50 1·90
E67 – 50 pf. blue . . . . 3·50 2·50
COMPOSERS: 8 pf. Lortzing; 50 pf. Weber.

E **31** Victor Hugo

E **32** Machinery, Dove and Globe

1952. Cultural Anniversaries.
E73 E **31** 12 pf. brown . . . . . . 3·00 3·50
E74 – 20 pf. green . . . . . . 3·00 3·50
E75 – 24 pf. red . . . . 3·00 3·50
E76 – 35 pf. blue . . . . 4·00 6·00
PORTRAITS: 20 pf. Leonardo da Vinci; 24 pf. N. Gogol; 35 pf. Avicenna.

1952. Leipzig Autumn Fair.
E77 E **32** 24 pf. red . . . . 1·40 30
E78 35 pf. blue . . . . 2·10 1·50

E **33** F. L. Jahn

E **34** University Building

1952. Death Cent of Jahn (patriot).
E79 E **33** 12 pf. blue . . . . 1·75 90

1952. 450th Anniv of Halle-Wittenberg University.
E80 E **34** 24 pf. green . . . . . . 2·00 90

E **35** Dove, Stamp and Flags

E **36** Dove, Globe and St. Stephen's Cathedral, Vienna

1952. Stamp Day.
E81 E **35** 24 pf. brown . . . . . . 2·10 80

1952. Vienna Peace Congress.
E97 E **36** 24 pf. red . . . . 1·00 1·90
E98 35 pf. blue . . . . 1·75 3·25

E **37** President Pieck

E **38** Karl Marx

1953. President's Birthday.
E320 E **37** 1 Dm. olive . . . . . . 1·50 10
E321 2 Dm. brown . . . . . 4·50 50

1953. 70th Death Anniv of Marx.
E102 – 6 pf. red & green . . . 60 30
E103 – 10 pf. brown & green . . 4·75 50
E104 – 12 pf. red & green . . . 60 50
E105 – 16 pf. blue and red . . . 2·50 1·50
E106 – 20 pf. brown & yellow . . 80 80
E107 E **38** 24 pf. brown & red . . . 2·75 60
E108 – 35 pf. yellow & purple . . 3·00 2·25
E109 – 48 pf. brown & green . . 1·25 60
E110 – 60 pf. red & brown . . . 5·00 2·75
E111 – 84 pf. brown & blue . . 3·50 1·75
DESIGNS—VERT: 6 pf. Flag and foundry; 12 pf. Flag and Spassky Tower, Kremlin; 20 pf. Marx reading from "Das Kapital"; 35 pf. Marx addressing meeting; 48 pf. Marx and Engels. HORIZ: 10 pf. Marx, Engels and "Communist Manifesto"; 16 pf. Marching crowd; 60 pf. Flag and workers; 84 pf. Marx in medallion and Stalin Avenue, Berlin.
In each case the flag shows heads of Marx, Engels, Lenin and Stalin.

E **39** Gorky

E **40** Cyclists

1953. 85th Birth Anniv of Maksim Gorky (writer).
E112 E **39** 35 pf. brown 20 20

1953. 6th Int. Cycle Race.
E113 E **40** 24 pf. green . . . . . . 1·90 1·75
E114 – 35 pf. blue . . . . . . 1·25 1·00
E115 – 60 pf. brown . . . . . 1·50 1·25
DESIGNS—VERT: 35 pf. Cyclists and countryside; 60 pf. Cyclists in town.

E **41** H. Von Kleist

E **42** Miner

1953. 700th Anniv of Frankfurt-on-Oder.
E116 E **41** 16 pf. brown . . . . . 1·25 1·60
E117 – 20 pf. green . . . . . . 1·00 75
E118 – 24 pf. red . . . . . . 1·75 1·50
E119 – 35 pf. blue . . . . . 1·25 1·50
DESIGNS—HORIZ: 20 pf. St. Mary's Church; 24 pf. Frankfurt from R. Oder; 35 pf. Frankfurt Town Hall and coat of arms.

1953. Five Year Plan. (a) Design in minute dots.
E120 E **42** 1 pf. black . . . . . . 1·10 20
E121 – 5 pf. green . . . . . . 1·75 1·00
E122 – 6 pf. violet . . . . . . 1·75 70
E123 – 8 pf. brown . . . . . . 2·40 1·00
E124 – 10 pf. green . . . . . . 1·75 75
E125 – 12 pf. blue . . . . . . 1·75 80
E126 – 15 pf. violet . . . . . 3·00 2·10
E127 – 16 pf. violet . . . . . 3·50 2·50
E128 – 20 pf. green . . . . . 3·75 2·75
E129 – 24 pf. red . . . . . . 8·50 70
E130 – 25 pf. green . . . . . 6·00 2·00
E131 – 30 pf. red . . . . . . 5·00 2·25
E132 – 35 pf. blue . . . . . 10·00 2·50
E133 – 40 pf. red . . . . . . 10·00 1·60
E134 – 48 pf. mauve . . . . . 12·50 3·00
E135 – 60 pf. blue . . . . . . 12·50 4·00
E136 – 80 pf. turquoise . . . . 14·00 4·00
E137 – 84 pf. brown . . . . . 14·00 7·50

(b) Design in lines.
E153 E **42** 1 pf. black 70 10
E310 – 5 pf. green 10 10
E155 – 6 pf. violet . . . . . 3·00 30
E156 – 8 pf. brown . . . . . 3·00 30
E312 – 10 pf. green 45 10
E311 – 10 pf. blue 15 30
E159 – 12 pf. turquoise . . . . 3·00 20
E160 – 15 pf. lilac . . . . . 8·50 40
E313 – 15 pf. violet 10 10
E162 – 16 pf. violet . . . . . 3·00 50
E163 – 20 pf. green . . . . . 45·00 50
E314 – 20 pf. red 25 10
E165 – 24 pf. red . . . . . . 6·50 20
E315 – 25 pf. green 50 20
E316 – 30 pf. red 10 10
E168 – 35 pf. blue . . . . . 3·00 55
E169 – 40 pf. red . . . . . . 11·00 70

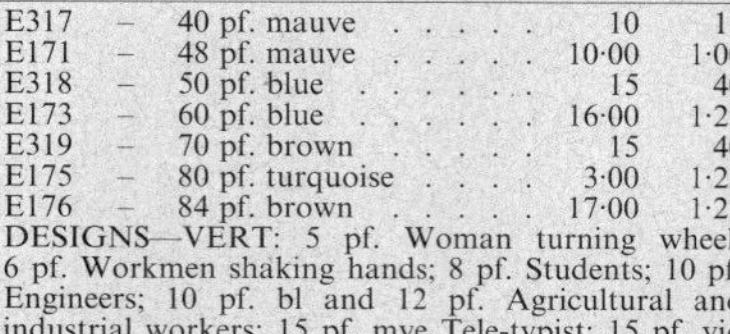

E317 – 40 pf. mauve 10 15
E171 – 48 pf. mauve . . . . . 10·00 1·00
E318 – 50 pf. blue 15 40
E173 – 60 pf. blue . . . . . . 16·00 1·25
E319 – 70 pf. brown 15 40
E175 – 80 pf. turquoise . . . . 3·00 1·25
E176 – 84 pf. brown . . . . . 17·00 1·25
DESIGNS—VERT: 5 pf. Woman turning wheel; 6 pf. Workmen shaking hands; 8 pf. Students; 10 pf. Engineers; 10 pf. bl and 12 pf. Agricultural and industrial workers; 15 pf. mve Tele-typist; 15 pf. vio and 16 pf. Foundry worker; 20 pf. grn Workers' health centre, Elster; 20 pf. red and 24 pf. Stalin Avenue, Berlin; 25 pf. Railway engineers; 30 pf. Folk dancers; 35 pf. Stadium; 40 pf. red, Scientist; 40 pf. mve, 48 pf. Zwinger, Dresden; 50 pf., 60 pf. Launching ship; 80 pf. Farm workers; 70 pf., 84 pf. Workman and family.

E **43** Mechanical Grab

1953. Leipzig Autumn Fair.
E138 E **43** 24 pf. brown . . . . . 1·60 80
E139 – 35 pf. green . . . . . . 2·50 2·10
DESIGN: 35 pf. Potato-harvester.

E **44** G. W. von Knobelsdorff and Opera House, Berlin

1953. German Architects.
E140 E **44** 24 pf. mauve . . . . . 1·40 50
E141 – 35 pf. slate . . . . . . 1·75 1·10
DESIGN: 35 pf. B. Neumann and Wurzburg Palace.

E **45** Lucas Cranach

E **46** Nurse and Patient

1953. 400th Death Anniv of Cranach (painter).
E142 E **45** 24 pf. brown . . . . . 3·25 1·00

1953. Red Cross.
E143 E **46** 24 pf. red & brown . . . 2·40 1·50

E **47** Postman delivering Letters

E **48** Lion and Lioness

1953. Stamp Day.
E144 E **47** 24 pf. blue . . . . . . 2·50 75

1953. 75th Anniv of Leipzig Zoo.
E145 E **48** 24 pf. brown . . . . . 1·75 50

E **49** Muntzer and Peasants

E **50** Franz Schubert

1953. German Patriots.
E146 E **49** 12 pf. brown . . . . . 1·00 50
E147 – 16 pf. brown . . . . . 1·00 50
E148 – 20 pf. red 90 20
E149 – 24 pf. blue . . . . . 1·00 20
E150 – 35 pf. green . . . . . 2·00 1·25
E151 – 48 pf. sepia . . . . . 2·00 90
DESIGNS: 16 pf. Baron vom Stein and scroll; 20 pf. Von Schill and cavalry; 24 pf. Blucher and infantry; 35 pf. Students marching; 48 pf. Barricade, 1848 Revolution.

1953. 125th Death Anniv of Schubert.
E152 E **50** 48 pf. brown . . . . . 2·50 1·10

E **52** G. E. Lessing (writer)

E **53** Conference Table and Crowd

1954. 225th Birth Anniv of Lessing.
E177 E **52** 20 pf. green . . . . . . 1·75 60

1954. Four-Power Conference, Berlin.
E178 E **53** 12 pf. blue . . . . . . 1·50 50

E **54** Stalin

E **55** Racing Cyclists

1954. 1st Death Anniv of Stalin.
E179 E **54** 20 pf. brown orange & grey . . . . 2·50 60

1954. 7th International Cycle Race.
E180 E **55** 12 pf. brown . . . . . 1·25 80
E181 – 24 pf. green . . . . . . 1·60 1·00
DESIGN: 24 pf. Cyclists racing through countryside.

E **56** Folk Dancing

E **57** F. Reuter

1954. 2nd German Youth Assembly.
E182 E **56** 12 pf. green 80 55
E183 – 24 pf. red 80 55
DESIGN: 24 pf. Young people and flag.

1954. 80th Death Anniv of Reuter (author).
E184 E **57** 24 pf. brown . . . . . 1·40 80

E **58** Dam and Forest

E **59** E. Thalmann

1954. Flood Relief Fund.
E185 E **58** 24 pf. + 6 pf. green . . . 60 60

1954. 10th Death Anniv of Thalmann (politician)
E186 E **59** 24 pf. brn, bl & orge . . 75 40

E **60** Exhibition Buildings

1954. Leipzig Autumn Fair.
E187 E **60** 24 pf. red 40 20
E188 35 pf. blue 70 35

1954. (a) Nos. E155, etc surch in figures.
E189 5 pf. on 6 pf. violet 40 10
E190 5 pf. on 8 pf. brown 40 10
E191 10 pf. on 12 pf. turq 60 20
E192 15 pf. on 16 pf. lilac 50 20
E194 20 pf. on 24 pf. red 50 20
E195 40 pf. on 48 pf. mauve . . . 2·40 1·00
E196 50 pf. on 60 pf. blue . . . . 2·50 1·00
E197 70 pf. on 84 pf. brown . . . 9·00 1·00

(b) No. E129 similarly surch.
E193a 20 pf. on 24 pf. red 50 25

E **62** President Pieck

1954. 5th Anniv of German Democratic Republic.
E198 E **62** 20 pf. brown . . . . . 1·90 80
E199 35 pf. blue . . . . . . 2·25 1·25

E **63** Stamp of 1953

E **64** Russian Pavilion

1954. Stamp Day.
E200 E **63** 20 pf. mauve . . . . . 1·25 50

1955. Leipzig Spring Fair.
E201 E **64** 20 pf. purple 50 30
E202 – 35 pf. blue (Chinese Pavilion) . . . . . . 1·25 80

1955. Flood Relief Fund. Surch in figures.
E203 E **58** 20 + 5 pf. on 24 pf. + 6 pf. green 60 40

E **66** "Women of All Nations"

1955. 45th Anniv of Int Women's Day.
E204 E **66** 10 pf. green 60 30
E205 20 pf. red 70 40

E **67** Parade of Workers

E **68** Monument to Fascist Victims, Brandenburg

1955. International Conference of Municipal Workers, Vienna.
E206 E **67** 10 pf. black & red . . . 80 60

1955. Int Liberation Day.
E207 E **68** 10 pf. blue 60 80
E208 20 pf. mauve . . . . . 80 1·00

E **69** Monument to Russian Soldiers, Treptow

E **70** Schiller (poet)

1955. 10th Anniv of Liberation.
E209 E **69** 20 pf. mauve . . . . . 1·25 80

1955. 150th Death Anniv of Schiller.
E210 E **70** 5 pf. green . . . . . . 2·75 2·25
E211 – 10 pf. blue 55 20
E212 – 20 pf. brown 55 20
PORTRAITS OF SCHILLER: 10 pf. Full-face; 20 pf. Facing left.

E **71** Cyclists

E **72** Karl Liebknecht

1955. 8th Int. Cycle Race.
E213 E **71** 10 pf. turquoise 60 30
E214 20 pf. red 70 50

1955. German Labour Leaders.
E215 E **72** 5 pf. green 15 20
E216 – 10 pf. blue 20 20
E217 – 15 pf. violet . . . . . 7·00 3·00
E218 – 20 pf. red 20 10
E219 – 25 pf. blue 30 10
E220 – 40 pf. red . . . . . . 1·10 10
E221 – 60 pf. brown 30 20
PORTRAITS: 10 pf. A. Bebel; 15 pf. F. Mehring; 20 pf. E. Thalmann; 25 pf. Clara Zetkin; 40 pf. Wilhelm Liebknecht; 60 pf. Rosa Luxemburg.

E **73** Pottery

E **74** Workers and Charter

1955. Leipzig Autumn Fair.

E222 – 10 pf. blue 50 30
E223 E **73** 20 pf. green 50 30
DESIGN: 10 pf. Camera and microscope.

1955. 10th Anniv of Land Reform.

E224 E **74** 5 pf. green . . . . . . 5·00 4·50
E225 – 10 pf. blue 60 20
E226 – 20 pf. red 70 20
DESIGNS—VERT: 10 pf. Bricklayers at work. HORIZ: 20 pf. Combine-harvesters.

E **75** "Solidarity" E **76** Engels Speaking

1955. 10th Anniv of People's Solidarity Movement.

E227 E **75** 10 pf. blue 50 20

1955. 135th Birth Anniv of Engels.

E228 E **76** 5 pf. blue & yellow . . . 30 10
E229 – 10 pf. violet & yellow . . 60 10
E230 – 15 pf. green & yellow . . 70 10
E231 – 20 pf. brown & orange . 1·40 20
E232 – 30 pf. brown & grey . 8·00 6·00
E233 – 70 pf. green & red . . 2·50 30
DESIGNS: 10 pf. Engels and Marx; 15 pf. Engels and newspaper; 20 pf. Portrait facing right; 30 pf. Portrait facing left; 70 pf. 1848 Revolution scene.

E **77** Magdeburg Cathedral E **78** Georg Agricola

1955. Historic Buildings.

E234 E **77** 5 pf. sepia 40 10
E235 – 10 pf. green 40 10
E236 – 15 pf. purple 40 10
E237 – 20 pf. red 40 10
E238 – 30 pf. brown . . . . 12·00 11·00
E239 – 40 pf. blue . . . . . 1·10 75
DESIGNS: 10 pf. State Opera House, Berlin; 15 pf. Old Town Hall, Leipzig; 20 pf. Town Hall, Berlin; 30 pf. Erfurt Cathedral; 40 pf. Zwinger, Dresden.

1955. 400th Death Anniv of Agricola (scholar).

E240 E **78** 10 pf. brown 50 30

E **79** "Portrait of a Young Man" (Durer) E **80** Mozart

1955. Dresden Gallery Paintings. (1st series).

E241 E **79** 5 pf. brown 60 10
E242 – 10 pf. brown 60 10
E243 – 15 pf. purple . . . . . 30·00 24·00
E244 – 20 pf. sepia 85 20
E245 – 40 pf. green 85 40
E246 – 70 pf. blue . . . . . . 2·50 80
PAINTINGS: 10 pf. "The Chocolate Girl" (Liotard); 15 pf. "Portrait of a Boy" (Pinturicchio); 20 pf. "Self-portrait with Saskia" (Rembrandt); 40 pf. "Maiden with Letter" (Vermeer); 70 pf. "Sistine Madonna" (Raphael).
See also Nos. E 325/30 and E 427/31.

1956. Birth Bicent of Mozart (composer).

E247 E **80** 10 pf. green . . . . . . 10·00 8·00
E248 – 20 pf. brown . . . . . . 3·00 1·60
PORTRAIT: 20 pf. Facing left.

E **81** Ilyushin Il-14P E **82** Heinrich Heine (poet)

1956. Establishment of East German Lufthansa Airways.

E249 – 5 pf. multicoloured . . . 12·00 9·00
E250 E **81** 10 pf. green 30 10
E251 – 15 pf. blue 30 10
E252 – 20 pf. red 30 10
DESIGNS: 5 pf. Lufthansa flag; 15 pf. View of Ilyushin Il-14P airplane from below; 20 pf. Ilyushin Il-14P airplane facing left.

1956. Death Cent. of Heine.

E253 E **82** 10 pf. green . . . . . . 10·50 5·50
E254 – 20 pf. red . . . . . . 2·25 50
PORTRAIT: 20 pf. Full-face.

E **83** Mobile Cranes E **84** E Thalmann

1956. Leipzig Spring Fair.

E255 E **83** 20 pf. red 75 30
E256 35 pf. blue . . . . . . 1·00 60

1956. 70th Birth Anniv of Thalmann (communist leader).

E257 E **84** 20 pf. blk, brn & red . . 50 20

E **85** Hand, Laurels and Cycle Wheel E **86** New Buildings, Old Market-place

1956. 9th Int. Cycle Race.

E258 E **85** 10 pf. green 50 15
E259 – 20 pf. red 50 15
DESIGN: 20 pf. Arms of Warsaw, Berlin and Prague and cycle wheel.

1956. 750th Anniv of Dresden.

E260 E **86** 10 pf. green 45 20
E261 – 20 pf. red 30 10
E262 – 40 pf. violet . . . . . 2·00 2·00
DESIGNS: 20 pf. Elbe Bridge; 40 pf. Technical High School.

E **87** Workman

1956. 10th Anniv of Industrial Reforms.

E263 E **87** 20 pf. red 30 20

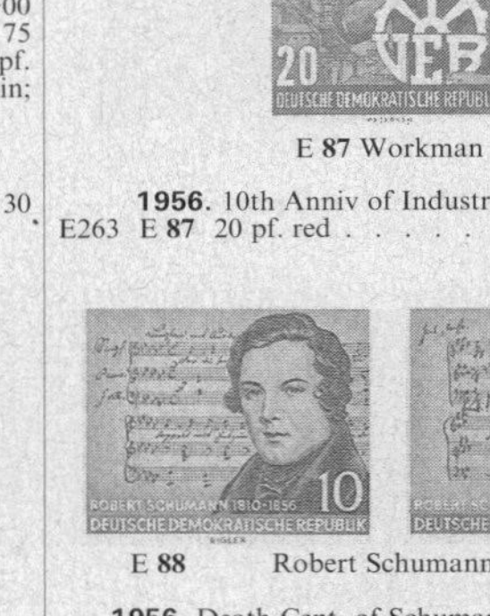

E **88** Robert Schumann E **88a**

1956. Death Cent. of Schumann (composer).

(a) Type E **88** (wrong music).

E264 E **88** 10 pf. green . . . . . 2·00 1·25
E265 20 pf. red 50 15

(b) Type E **88a** (correct music).

E266 E **88a** 10 pf. green . . . . . 5·00 1·40
E267 20 pf. red . . . . . . 2·40 35

E **89** Footballers E **90** T. Mann (author)

1956. 2nd Sports Festival, Leipzig.

E268 E **89** 5 pf. green 20 10
E269 – 10 pf. blue 20 10
E270 – 15 pf. purple . . . . . 2·00 1·10
E271 – 20 pf. red 20 10
DESIGNS: 10 pf. Javelin thrower; 15 pf. Hurdlers; 20 pf. Gymnast.

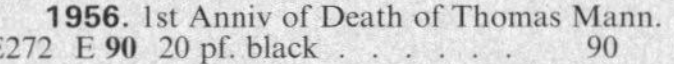

1956. 1st Anniv of Death of Thomas Mann.

E272 E **90** 20 pf. black 90 40

E **91** J. B. Cisinski E **92** Lace

1956. Birth Cent. of Cisinski (poet).

E273 E **91** 50 pf. brown 80 25

1956. Leipzig Autumn Fair.

E274 E **92** 10 pf. green & black . . 15 10
E275 – 20 pf. pink & black (Sailing dinghy) . . . 20 15

E **93** Buchenwald Memorial

1956. Concentration Camp Memorials Fund.

E276 E **93** 20 pf. + 80 pf. red . . . 1·25 2·10
For similar stamp see No. E390.

E **94** Torch and Olympic Rings E **95**

1956. Olympic Games.

E277 E **94** 20 pf. brown 30 10
E278 – 35 pf. slate 40 20
DESIGN: 35 pf. Greek athlete.

1956. 500th Anniv of Greifswald University.

E279 E **95** 20 pf. red 40 15

E **96** Postal Carrier, 1450 E **97** E. Abbe

1956. Stamp Day.

E280 E **96** 20 pf. red 40 15

1956. 110th Anniv of Zeiss Factory, Jena.

E281 E **97** 10 pf. green 15 10
E282 – 20 pf. brown 15 10
E283 – 25 pf. blue 25 15
DESIGNS—HORIZ: 20 pf. Factory buildings; 25 pf. Carl Zeiss.

E **98** "Negro" E **99** Indian Elephants

1956. Human Rights Day.

E284 – 5 pf. green on olive . . . 1·00 1·00
E285 E **98** 10 pf. brown on pink . . 15 10
E286 – 25 pf. blue on lav. . . . 15 10
DESIGNS: 5 pf. "Chinese"; 25 pf. "European".

1956. Berlin Zoological Gardens. Centres in grey.

E287 E **99** 5 pf. black 15 10
E288 – 10 pf. green 30 10
E289 – 15 pf. purple . . . . . 4·00 3·00
E290 – 20 pf. red 20 10
E291 – 25 pf. brown 30 15
E292 – 30 pf. blue 30 15
DESIGNS: 10 pf. Greater Flamingoes; 15 pf. Black rhinoceros; 20 pf. Mouflon; 25 pf. European bison; 30 pf. Polar bear.

1956. Egyptian Relief Fund. No. E237 surch **HELFT AGYPTEN + 10.**

E293 20 pf. + 10 pf. red 40 20

1956. Hungarian Socialists' Relief Fund. No. E237 surch **HELFT DEM SOZIALISTISCHEN UNGARN + 10.**

E294 20 pf. + 10 pf. red 40 20

E **103** "Frieden" (freighter)

1957. Leipzig Spring Fair.

E295 E **103** 20 pf. red 25 10
E296 – 25 pf. blue 40 15
DESIGN: 25 pf. Class E251 electric locomotive.

E **104** Silver Thistle

1957. Nature Protection Week.

E297 E **104** 5 pf. brown 15 10
E298 – 10 pf. green . . . . . 2·40 2·00
E299 – 20 pf. brown 30 10
DESIGNS: 10 pf. Green lizard; 20 pf. Lady's slipper orchid.

E **105** Friedrich Froebel and Children

1957. 175th Birth Anniv of Froebel (educator).

E300 – 10 pf. black & green . . 1·00 1·00
E301 E **105** 20 pf. black & brown . . 20 10
DESIGN: 10 pf. Children at play.

E **106** Ravensbruck Memorial E **107** Cycle Race Route

1957. Concentration Camp Memorials Fund.

E302 E **106** 5 pf. + 5 pf. green . . 15 15
E303 – 20 pf. + 10 pf. red . . 20 30
DESIGN—HORIZ: 20 pf. Memorial and environs.
For similar stamp to No. E 303 see No. E 453.

1957. 10th Int Cycle Race.

E304 E **107** 5 pf. orange 30 15

E **108** Miner E **109** Henri Dunant and Globe

1957. Coal Mining Industry.

E305 – 10 pf. green 15 10
E306 – 20 pf. brown 15 10
E307 E **108** 25 pf. blue . . . . . 2·00 80
DESIGNS: (39 × 21 mm): 10 pf. Mechanical shovel; 20 pf. Gantry.

1957. Int. Red Cross Day. Cross in red.

E308 E **109** 10 pf. brown & green . 15 10
E309 – 25 pf. brn & blue . . . 20 15
DESIGN: 25 pf. H. Dunant wearing hat, and globe.

E **110** Joachim Jungius (botanist) E **111** Clara Zetkin and Flower

1957. Scientists' Anniversaries.

E322 E **110** 5 pf. brown . . . . . 1·40 75
E323 – 10 pf. green 15 10
E324 – 20 pf. brown 15 10
PORTRAITS: 10 pf. L. Euler (mathematician); 20 pf. H. Hertz (physicist).

1957. Dresden Gallery Paintings (2nd series). As Type E **79**.
E325 5 pf. sepia 15 10
E326 10 pf. green 15 10
E327 15 pf. brown 15 10
E328 20 pf. red 15 10
E329 25 pf. purple 30 10
E330 40 pf. grey . . . . 4·75 2·00
PAINTINGS—VERT: 5 pf. "The Holy Family" (Mantegna); 10 pf. "The Dancer, Barbarina Campani" (Carriera); 15 pf. "Portrait of Morette" (Holbein the Younger); 20 pf. "The Tribute Money" (Titian); 25 pf. "Saskia with a Red Flower" (Rembrandt); 40 pf. "A Young Standard-bearer" (Piazetta).

1957. Birth Cent of Clara Zetkin (patriot).
E331 E **111** 10 pf. green & red . . . 50 20

E **112** Bertolt Brecht (dramatist)
E **113** Congress Emblem

1957. 1st Death Anniv of Bertolt Brecht.
E332 E **112** 10 pf. green 20 15
E333 25 pf. blue 40 15

1957. 4th World Trade Unions Congress.
E334 E **113** 20 pf. black & red . . . 50 25

E **114** Fair Emblem

E **115** Savings Bank Book

1957. Leipzig Autumn Fair.
E335 E **114** 20 pf. red 20 10
E336 25 pf. blue 25 10

1957. Savings Week.
E337 E **115** 10 pf. black and green on grey 75 65
E338 20 pf. black and mauve on grey 25 15

E **116** Postrider of 1563

E **117** Revolutionary's Rifle and Red Flag

1957. Stamp Day.
E339 E **116** 5 pf. blue on brown . . 40 15

1957. 40th Anniv of Russian Revolution.
E340 E **117** 10 pf. green & red . . . 15 10
E341 25 pf. blue & red . . . 25 20

E **118** Artificial Satellite

E **119** Professor Ramin

1957. Int Geophysical Year.
E342 E **118** 10 pf. blue 30 15
E343 – 20 pf. red 30 15
E344 – 25 pf. blue . . . . . . 2·25 1·25
DESIGNS: 20 pf. Stratosphere balloon; 25 pf. Ship using echo-sounder.

1957. "National Prize" Composers.
E345 E **119** 10 pf. black & green . . 75 75
E346 – 20 pf. black & orange . . 25 25
PORTRAIT: 20 pf. Professor Abendroth.

E **120** Ernst Thalmann

1957. National Memorials Fund. East German War Victims. Portraits in grey.
E347 E **120** 20 pf. + 10 pf. mauve . 10 15
E348 – 25 pf. + 15 pf. blue . . 15 20
E349 – 40 pf. + 20 pf. violet . 30 35
PORTRAITS: 25 pf. R. Breitscheid; 40 pf. Father P. Schneider.
For other stamps as Type E **120** see Nos. E374/8, E448/52, E485/7, E496/500, E540/4 and E588/92.

E **121**

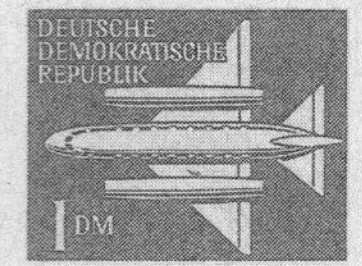

E **122**

1957. Air.
E350 E **121** 5 pf. black & grey . . . 50 10
E351 20 pf. black & red . . . 30 10
E352 35 pf. black & vio . . 15 10
E353 50 pf. black & brn . . 20 15
E354 E **122** 1 Dm. olive & yell . . 1·50 10
E355 3 Dm. brn & yell . . . 2·50 20
E356 5 Dm. blue & yell . . . 4·75 25

E **123** Fair Emblem

1958. Leipzig Spring Fair.
E357 E **123** 20 pf. red 25 15
E358 25 pf. blue 25 15

E **124** Transmitting Aerial and Posthorn

E **125** "Zille at play"

1958. Communist Postal Conf., Moscow.
E359 E **124** 5 pf. black and grey . . 65 55
E360 – 20 pf. red 25 10
DESIGN—HORIZ: 20 pf. Aerial as in 5 pf. but posthorn above figures of value.

1958. Birth Cent. of Heinrich Zille (painter).
E361 E **125** 10 pf. drab & green . . 2·40 1·25
E362 – 20 pf. drab and red . . 65 15
DESIGN—VERT: 20 pf. Self-portrait of Zille.

E **126** Max Planck

E **127** Breeding Cow

1958. Birth Cent. of Max Planck (physicist).
E363 – 10 pf. olive . . . . . 1·10 1·10
E364 E **126** 20 pf. mauve 30 15
DESIGN—VERT: 10 pf. "h" (symbol of Planck's Constant).

1958. 6th Markkleeberg Agricultural Exn. Inscr "6 Landwirtschaftausstellung der DDR in Markkleeberg".
E365 E **127** 5 pf. grey . . . . . . 2·00 1·25
E366 – 10 pf. green 15 10
E367 – 20 pf. red 15 10
DESIGNS (39 × 22½ mm): 10 pf. Chaff-cutter; 20 pf. Beet-harvester.

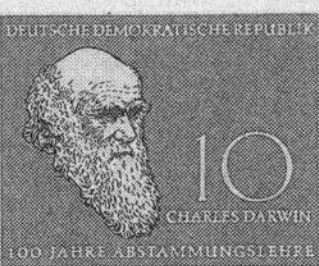

E **128** Charles Darwin

E **129** Congress Emblem

1958. Cent. of Darwin's Theory of Evolution and Bicent. of Linnaeus's Plant Classification System. Portraits in black.
E368 E **128** 10 pf. green . . . . 1·40 1·10
E369 – 20 pf. red 15 15
PORTRAIT—HORIZ: 20 pf. Linnaeus (Carl von Linne) inscr "200 JAHRE SYSTEMA NATURAE".

1958. 5th German Socialist Unity Party Congress.
E370 E **129** 10 pf. red 25 20

E **130** "The Seven Towers of Rostock", Liner and Freighters

E **131** Mare and Foal

1958. Rostock Port Reconstruction.
E371 – 10 pf. green 20 10
E372 E **130** 20 pf. orange 30 10
E373 – 25 pf. blue . . . . . 1·00 1·25
DESIGNS: 10 pf. "Freundschaft" (freighter) at quayside; 25 pf. "Frieden" (freighter) in Rostock harbour.

1958. "Resistance Fighters". As Type E **120**. Portraits in grey.
E374 5 pf. + 5 pf. brown 10 15
E375 10 pf. + 5 pf. green 10 15
E376 15 pf. + 10 pf. violet . . . . 15 2·50
E377 20 pf. + 10 pf. brown 15 40
E378 25 pf. + 15 pf. black . . . . 55 9·50
PORTRAITS—VERT: 5 pf. A. Kuntz; 10 pf. R. Arndt; 15 pf. Dr. K. Adams; 20 pf. R. Renner; 25 pf. W. Stoecker.

1958. "Grand Prix of the D.D.R." Horse Show.
E379 E **131** 5 pf. sepia . . . . . 2·25 2·50
E380 – 10 pf. green 15 10
E381 – 20 pf. brown 15 10
DESIGNS: 10 pf. Horse-trotting; 20 pf. Racing horses.

E **132** J. A. Komensky ("Comenius")

E **133** Camp Bugler

1958. Komensky Commem. Centres in black.
E382 E **132** 10 pf. green . . . . . 1·40 1·10
E383 – 20 pf. brown 15 10
DESIGN: 20 pf. Komensky with pupils (from an old engraving).

1958. 10th Anniv of East German "Pioneer" Organization.
E384 E **133** 10 pf. + 5 pf. green . . 25 15
E385 – 20 pf. + 10 pf. red . . 25 20
DESIGN—VERT: 20 pf. Young Pioneer saluting.

E **134** University Seal

1958. 400th Anniv of Friedrich Schiller University, Jena.
E386 E **134** 5 pf. black & grey . . . 1·40 1·10
E387 – 20 pf. grey and red . . 35 10
DESIGN: 20 pf. University building.

E **135** Model with Hamster-lined Coat, and Leipzig Central Railway Station

E **136** Soldier climbing Wall

1958. Leipzig Autumn Fair.
E388 E **135** 10 pf. brown & green . 20 10
E389 – 25 pf. black & blue . . 20 20
DESIGN: 25 pf. Model with Karakul fur coat, and Leipzig Old Town Hall.

1958. Concentration Camp Memorials Fund. As Type E **93** but additionally inscr "14. SEPTEMBER 1958" in black.
E390 20 pf. + 20 pf. red 35 35

1958. 1st Summer Military Games, Leipzig.
E391 E **136** 10 pf. brn & green . . 1·50 1·00
E392 – 20 pf. yell & brown . . 10 10
E393 – 25 pf. red & blue . . . 10 10
DESIGNS: 20 pf. Games emblem; 25 pf. Marching athletes with banner.

E **137** Warding off the Atomic Bomb

1958. Campaign Against Atomic Warfare.
E394 E **137** 20 pf. red 20 10
E395 25 pf. blue 40 15

E **138** 17th-century Mail Cart

1958. Stamp Day.
E396 E **138** 10 pf. green . . . . . 2·25 1·40
E397 – 20 pf. red 30 10
DESIGN: 20 pf. Modern postal sorting train and Baade-Bonin 152 jetliner.

E **139** Revolutionary and Soldier

E **140** Brandenburg Gate, Berlin

1958. 40th Anniv of November Revolution.
E398 E **139** 20 pf. purple & red . . 9·50 20·00

1958. Brandenburg Gate Commem.
E399 E **140** 20 pf. red 35 10
E400 25 pf. blue . . . . . . 2·40 1·75

E **141** "Girl's Head" (bas-relief)

E **142** Negro and European Youths

1958. Antique Art Treasures.
E401 E **141** 10 pf. black & green . . 1·00 1·00
E402 – 20 pf. black & red . . . 35 15
DESIGN: 20 pf. "Large Head" (from Pergamon frieze).
See also Nos. E475/8.

1958. 10th Anniv of Declaration of Human Rights.
E403 E **142** 10 pf. black & green . . 15 15
E404 – 25 pf. black & blue . . 1·40 1·00
DESIGN: 25 pf. Chinese and European girls.

E **143** O. Nuschke

E **144** "The Red Flag" (Party Newspaper)

1958. 1st Death Anniv of Vice-Premier Otto Nuschke.
E405 E **143** 20 pf. red 25 15

1958. 40th Anniv of German Communist Party.
E406 E **144** 20 pf. red 30 10

E **145** Pres. Pieck

E **146** Rosa Luxemburg (revolutionary)

1959. Pres. Pieck's 83rd Birthday.
E407 E **145** 20 pf. red 30 15
For 20 pf. black see No. E517.

1959. 40th Death Anniv of Rosa Luxemburg and Karl Liebknecht. Centres in black.
E408 E **146** 10 pf. green . . . . . 2·00 1·40
E409 – 20 pf. red 35 15
DESIGN—HORIZ: 20 pf. Liebknecht (revolutionary).

E **147** Concert Hall, Leipzig

1959. 150th Birth Anniv of Felix Mendelssohn-Bartholdy (composer).
E410 E **147** 10 pf. green on green . 25 35
E411 – 25 pf. blue on blue . . 1·50 2·00
DESIGN—HORIZ: 25 pf. Opening theme of Symphony in A Major ("The Italian").

E **148** "Schwarze Pumpe" plant
E **149** Boy holding Book for Girl

1959. Leipzig Spring Fair. Inscr as in Type E **148**.
E412 E **148** 20 pf. red 10 10
E413 – 25 pf. blue 30 15
DESIGN—HORIZ: 25 pf. Various cameras.

1959. 5th Anniv of "Youth Consecration".
E414 E **149** 10 pf. black on green . 1·40 1·00
E415 – 20 pf. blk on salm . . . 15 10
DESIGN: 20 pf. Girl holding book for boy.

E **150** Handel's Statue, Oboe and Arms of Halle
E **151** A. von Humboldt and Jungle Scene

1959. Death Bicentenary of Handel. Centre in black.
E416 E **150** 10 pf. green . . . . . 1·50 1·10
E417 – 20 pf. red 15 10
DESIGN: 20 pf. Portrait of Handel (after oil painting by Thomas Hudson).

1959. Death Centenary of Alexander von Humboldt (naturalist).
E418 E **151** 10 pf. green . . . . . 1·40 1·00
E419 – 20 pf. red 20 45
DESIGN: 20 pf. As Type E **151** but with view of sleigh in forest.

E **152** Posthorn
E **153** Grey Heron

1959. Socialist Countries' Postal Ministers Conference, Berlin.
E420 E **152** 20 pf. blk, yell & red . 15 10
E421 25 pf. blk, yell & bl . 75 75

1959. Nature Preservation.
E422 E **153** 5 pf. lil, blk & bl . . . 40 10
E423 – 10 pf. brn, sep & turq . 40 10
E424 – 20 pf. multicoloured . . 25 10
E425 – 25 pf. multicoloured . . 35 15
E426 – 40 pf. yell, blk & grey . 5·50 3·00
DESIGNS: 10 pf. Eurasian bittern; 20 pf. Lily of the valley and peacock (butterfly); 25 pf. Eurasian beaver; 40 pf. Honey bee and willow catkin.

1959. Dresden Gallery Paintings as Type E **79** (3rd series).
E427 5 pf. olive 10 10
E428 10 pf. green 10 10
E429 20 pf. orange 10 10
E430 25 pf. brown 20 10
E431 40 pf. red . . . . 5·25 2·75
PAINTINGS—VERT: 5 pf. "The Vestal Virgin" (Kauffman); 10 pf. "The Needlewoman" (Metsu); 20 pf. "Mlle. Lavergne reading a letter" (Liotard); 25 pf. "Old woman with a brazier" (Rubens); 40 pf. "Young man in black coat" (Hals).

E **154** Common Cormorant
E **155**

1959. "Birds of the Homeland". Centres and inscriptions in black.
E432 E **154** 5 pf. yellow 10 10
E433 – 10 pf. green 15 10
E434 – 15 pf. violet . . . . . 5·00 2·50
E435 – 20 pf. pink 20 10
E436 – 25 pf. blue 25 10
E437 – 40 pf. red 55 15
BIRDS: 10 pf. Black Stork; 15 pf. Eagle Owl; 20 pf. Black Grouse; 25 pf. Hoopoe; 40 pf. Peregrine Falcon.

1959. 7th World Youth Festival, Vienna.
E438 E **155** 20 pf. red 20 20
E439 – 25 pf. blue 45 35
DESIGN—HORIZ: 25 pf. White girl embracing negro girl.

E **156** Hoop Exercises

1959. 3rd German Gymnastic and Sports Festival, Leipzig.
E440 E **156** 5 pf. + 5 pf. brown . . 10 10
E441 – 10 pf. + 5 pf. green . . 10 10
E442 – 20 pf. + 10 pf. red . . 10 10
E443 – 25 pf. + 10 pf. blue . . 20 10
E444 – 40 pf. + 20 pf. pur . . 2·00 75
DESIGNS: 10 pf. High jumping; 20 pf. Vaulting; 25 pf. Club exercises; 40 pf. Fireworks over Leipzig Stadium.

E **157** Modern Leipzig Building

1959. Leipzig Autumn Fair.
E445 E **157** 20 pf. grey & red . . . 20 15
See also Nos. E483/4.

E **158** Glass Tea-set

1959. 75 Years of Jena Glassware.
E446 E **158** 10 pf. turquoise . . . 25 10
E447 – 25 pf. blue . . . . . . 1·90 75
DESIGN—VERT: 25 pf. Laboratory retorts.

1959. Ravensbruck Concentration Camp Victims. As Type E **120**. Portraits in black.
E448 5 pf. + 5 pf. brown 10 10
E449 10 pf. + 5 pf. green 15 10
E450 15 pf. + 10 pf. violet 15 10
E451 20 pf. + 10 pf. mauve 15 10
E452 25 pf. + 15 pf. blue . . . . . 50 1·00
PORTRAITS: 5 pf. T. Klose; 10 pf. K. Niederkirchner; 15 pf. C. Eisenblatter; 20 pf. O. Benario-Prestes; 25 pf. M. Grollmuss.

1959. Concentration Camp Memorials Fund. As No. E303 but inscr "12. SEPTEMBER 1959" in black.
E453 20 pf. + 10 pf red 35 15

E **159** "Russian Pennant on the Moon"

1959. Landing of Russian Rocket on the Moon.
E454 E **159** 20 pf. red 55 25

E **160** E. German Flag & Combine-harvester
E **161** J. R. Becher

1959. 10th Anniv of German Democratic Republic. Designs as Type E **160** showing E. German Flag in black, red and yellow. Inscriptions in black and red on coloured paper.
E455 E **160** 5 pf. buff 10 10
E456 – 10 pf. grey 10 10
E457 – 15 pf. pale yellow 10 10
E458 – 20 pf. lilac 10 10
E459 – 25 pf. pale olive 15 15
E460 – 40 pf. yellow 20 20
E461 – 50 pf. salmon 25 25
E462 – 60 pf. turquoise . . . 25 25
E463 – 70 pf. pale green . . . 25 25
E464 – 1 Dm. brown 50 50
DESIGNS—East German flag and: 10 pf. "Fritz Heckert" convalescent home; 15 pf. Zwinger Palace, Dresden; 20 pf. Steel worker; 25 pf. Industrial chemist; 40 pf. Leipzig Stadium; 50 pf. Woman tractor-driver; 60 pf. Ilyushin Il-14M airplane; 70 pf. Shipbuilding; 1 Dm. East Germany's first atomic reactor.

1959. 1st Death Anniv of Becher (poet).
E465 E **161** 20 pf. slate and red . . 1·25 15

E **162** Schiller
E **163** 18th-century Courier and Milestone

1959. Birth Bicent. of Schiller (poet).
E466 – 10 pf. green on green . 1·50 1·10
E467 E **162** 20 pf. lake on pink . . 50 10
DESIGN: 10 pf. Schiller's house, Weimar.

1959. Stamp Day.
E468 E **163** 10 pf. green . . . . . 1·10 75
E469 – 20 pf. lake 15 10
DESIGN: 20 pf. Postwoman on motor cycle.

E **164** Eurasian Red Squirrels

1959. Forest Animals.
E470 E **164** 5 pf. red, brn & grey . 15 10
E471 – 10 pf. lt brn, brn & grn 15 10
E472 – 20 pf. multicoloured . . 15 10
E473 – 25 pf. multicoloured . . 15 10
E474 – 40 pf. yellow, brown and blue . . . . . 10·00 2·75
ANIMALS: 10 pf. Brown hares; 20 pf. Roe deer; 25 pf. Red deer; 40 pf. Lynx.

1959. Antique Art Treasures (2nd series). As Type E **141**.
E475 5 pf. black and yellow 10 10
E476 10 pf. black and green 10 10
E477 20 pf. black and red 10 10
E478 25 pf. black and blue . . . . 1·10 50
DESIGNS: 5 pf. Attic goddess (about 580 B.C.); 10 pf. Princess of Tell el-Amarna (about 1360 B.C.); 20 pf. Bronze horse of Toprak-Kale, Armenia (7th-century B.C.). HORIZ: (49 × 28 mm): 25 pf. Altar of Zeus, Pergamon (about 160 B.C.).

E **165** Boxing

1960. Olympic Games. As Type E **165** inscr "OLYMPISCHE SOMMERSPIELE 1960" or "WINTERSPIELE" etc. (20 pf). Centres and inscriptions in bistre.
E479 E **165** 5 pf. brown . . . . . 4·75 2·50
E480 – 10 pf. green 10 10
E481 – 20 pf. red 10 10
E482 – 25 pf. blue 15 10
DESIGNS: 10 pf. Running; 20 pf. Ski jumping; 25 pf. Sailing.

1960. Leipzig Spring Fair. As Type E **157** but inscr "LEIPZIGER FRUHJAHRSMESSE 1960".
E483 20 pf. grey and red 15 10
E484 25 pf. grey and blue 20 10
DESIGNS: 20 pf. Northern Entrance, Technical Fair; 25 pf. Ring Fair Building.

1960. Sachsenhausen Concentration Camp Victims (1st issue). As Type E **120**. Portraits in black.
E485 5 pf. + 5 pf. drab 10 10
E486 10 pf. + 5 pf. myrtle 10 10
E487 20 pf. + 10 pf. purple 10 10
PORTRAITS: 5 pf. L. Erdmann; 10 pf. E. Schneller; 20 pf. L. Horn.
See also Nos. E 496/500.

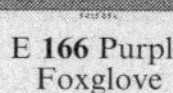

E **166** Purple Foxglove
E **167** Lenin

1960. Medicinal Flowers. Background in pale drab.
E488 E **166** 5 pf. red and green . . 10 10
E489 – 10 pf. olive & green . . 10 10
E490 – 15 pf. red & green . . . 15 10
E491 – 20 pf. violet & turq . . 15 10
E492 – 40 pf. red, grn & brn . 4·50 2·40
FLOWERS: 10 pf. Camomile; 15 pf. Peppermint; 20 pf. Poppy; 40 pf. Wild Rose.

1960. 90th Birth Anniv of Lenin.
E493 E **167** 20 pf. red 20 10

1960. Re-opening of Rostock Port. No. E371 optd **Inbetriebnahme des Hochsee-hafens 1. Mai 1960**.
E494 10 pf. green 25 20

E **169** Russian Soldier and Liberated Prisoner

1960. 15th Anniv of Liberation.
E495 E **169** 20 pf. red 75 15

1960. Sachsenhausen Concentration Camp Victims (2nd issue). As Type E **120**. Portraits in black.
E496 10 pf. + 5 pf. green 10 10
E497 15 pf. + 5 pf. violet 70 65
E498 20 pf. + 10 pf. lake 10 10
E499 25 pf. + 10 pf. blue 20 15
E500 40 pf. + 20 pf. brown . . . . 2·10 1·60
PORTRAITS: 10 pf. M. Lademann; 15 pf. L. Breunig; 20 pf. M. Thesen; 25 pf. G. Sandtner; 40 pf. H. Rothbarth.

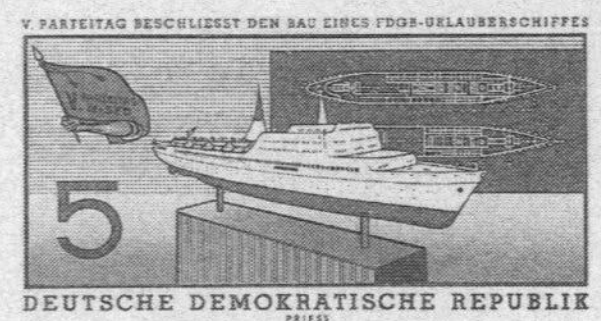

E **170** Model and Plan of Liner

1960. Launching of Cruise Liner "Fritz Heckert".
E501 E **170** 5 pf. slate, red & yell . 15 10
E502 – 10 pf. + 5 pf. black, red and yellow 15 10
E503 – 20 pf. + 10 pf. black, red and blue 20 10
E504 – 25 pf. black, yellow and blue . . . . . . 4·25 4·00
DESIGNS: 10 pf. Liner under construction at Wismar; 20 pf. Liner off Stubbenkammer; 25 pf. Liner and Russian cruiser "Aurora" at Leningrad.

E **171** Lenin Statue, Eisleben
E **172** Masked Dancer (statuette)

1960. Lenin-Thalmann Statues.
E505 E **171** 10 pf. green 15 15
E506 – 20 pf. red 25 25
DESIGN: 20 pf. Thalmann statue, Pushkin, U.S.S.R.

1960. 250th Anniv of Porcelain Industry, Meissen. Centres and inscriptions in blue. Figures in colours given.
E507 E **172** 5 pf. orange 10 10
E508 – 10 pf. green 10 10
E509 – 15 pf. purple . . . . . 4·00 3·00
E510 – 20 pf. red 15 10
E511 – 25 pf. olive 15 10
DESIGNS: 10 pf. Dish inscr with swords and years "1710 1960"; 15 pf. Otter; 20 pf. Potter; 25 pf. Coffee-pot.

E **173** Racing Cyclist

1960. World Cycling Championships.
E512 E **173** 20 pf. + 10 pf. mult . . 25 15
E513 – 25 pf. + 10 pf. brown, drab and blue . . . 1·40 2·10
DESIGN (38½ × 21 mm): 25 pf. Racing cyclists on track.

E **174** Opera House, Leipzig

1960. Leipzig Autumn Fair.
E514 E **174** 20 pf. grey and red . . . 15 10
E515 – 25 pf. brown & blue . . 35 20
DESIGN: 25 pf. Export goods.

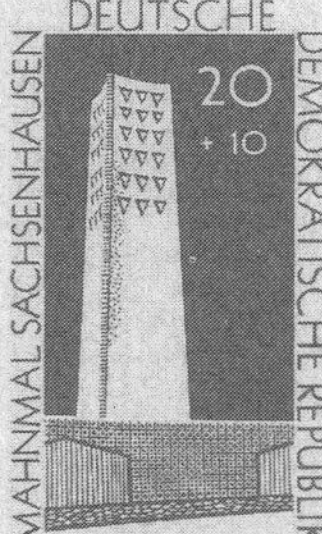

E **175** Sachsenhausen Memorial
E **176** 18th-century Rook

1960. Concentration Camp Memorials Fund.
E516 E **175** 20 pf. + 10 pf. red . . 30 20

1960. President Pieck Mourning issue.
E517 E **145** 20 pf. black 35 20

1960. 14th Chess Olympiad, Leipzig. German Chessmen.
E518 E **176** 10 pf. + 5 pf. green . . 20 15
E519 – 20 pf. + 10 pf. pur . . 20 15
E520 – 25 pf. + 10 pf. blue . . 1·50 2·00
DESIGNS: 20 pf. 18th-century knight; 25 pf. 14th-century knight.

E **177** Mail Vans

1960. Stamp Day.
E521 E **177** 20 pf. yell, blk & mve . . 30 10
E522 – 25 pf. mve, blk & bl . . 2·00 1·60
DESIGN: 25 pf. 19th-century railway mail coach.

E **178** Medal of 1518 showing Hans Burgkmair (painter)
E **179** Count N. von Gneisenau

1960. 400th Anniv of Dresden Art Collections.
E523 E **178** 20 pf. ochre, green and buff 10 10
E524 – 25 pf. black & blue . . 1·40 1·40
DESIGN: 25 pf. "Dancing Peasants" (after Durer).

1960. Birth Bicent of Count N. von Gneisenau.
E525 E **179** 20 pf. black & red . . . 15 10
E526 – 25 pf. blue . . . . . . 1·10 90
DESIGN: 25 pf. Similar portrait but vert.

E **180** R. Virchow

1960. 250th Anniv of Berlin Charity and 150th Anniv of Humboldt University, Berlin. Centres in black.
E527 E **180** 5 pf. ochre 15 10
E528 – 10 pf. green 15 10
E529 – 20 pf. brown 15 10
E530 – 25 pf. blue 15 15
E531 – 40 pf. red . . . . . . 2·50 1·40
DESIGNS—As Type E **180** (Berlin Charity); 10 pf. Robert Koch; 40 pf. W. Griesinger. (Humboldt University); 20 pf. University building and statues of William and Alexander von Humboldt; 25 pf. Plaque with profiles of Von Humboldt brothers.

E **181** Scientist with notebook

1960. Chemical Workers' Day.
E532 E **181** 5 pf. grey & red . . . 10 10
E533 – 10 pf. grn & orge . . . 10 10
E534 – 20 pf. red & blue . . . 10 10
E535 – 25 pf. blue & yellow . . 1·90 1·40
DESIGNS: 10 pf. Chemical worker with fertiliser; 20 pf. Girl worker with jar, and Trabant car; 25 pf. Laboratory assistant and synthetic dress.

E **182** "Young Socialists' Express" (double-deck train)
E **183** President Pieck

1960. 125th Anniv of German Railways.
E536 E **182** 10 pf. black and green . 15 10
E537 – 20 pf. black & red . . . 40 10
E538 – 25 pf. black & blue . . 4·00 3·75
DESIGNS—As Type E **182**: 25 pf. Locomotive "Adler" (1835) and Class V180 diesel locomotive with train. (43 × 25½ mm): 20 pf. Sassnitz Harbour station and train ferry "Sassnitz".

1961. 85th Birth Anniv of President Pieck.
E539 E **183** 20 pf. red & black . . . 35 20

1961. Concentration Camp Victims. As Type E **120**. Portraits in black.
E540 5 pf. + 5 pf. green 10 10
E541 10 pf. + 5 pf. green 10 10
E542 15 pf. + 5 pf. violet . . . . 1·00 2·75
E543 20 pf. + 10 pf. red 10 10
E544 25 pf. + 10 pf. blue 10 10
PORTRAITS: 5 pf. W. Kube; 10 pf. H. Gunther; 15 pf. Elvira Eisenschneider; 20 pf. Hertha Lindner; 25 pf. H. Tschape.

E **184** High-voltage Switchgear
E **185** Lilienstein Saxony

1961. Leipzig Spring Fair. Inscr as in Type E **184**.
E545 E **184** 10 pf. slate & green . . 15 10
E546 – 25 pf. slate & blue . . 35 20
DESIGN: 25 pf. Fair Press Centre.

1961. Landscapes and Historical Buildings.
E547 – 5 pf. grey 10 10
E548 – 10 pf. green 10 10
E549 E **185** 20 pf. brown 10 10
E550 – 20 pf. red 10 10
E551 – 25 pf. blue 15 10
DESIGNS—VERT: 5 pf. Ruins of Rudelsburg; 10 pf. Wartburg; 20 pf. (No. E550), Town Hall, Wernigerode. HORIZ: 25 pf. Brocken, Oberharz.

E **186** Trawler "Ros"

1961. Deep Sea Fishing Industry.
E552 E **186** 10 pf. green 20 10
E553 – 20 pf. purple 10 10
E554 – 25 pf. blue 20 10
E555 – 40 pf. violet . . . . . 2·50 1·60
DESIGNS: 20 pf. Hauling nets; 25 pf. Trawler "Robert Koch"; 40 pf. Fish-processing machine.

E **187** Cosmonaut in Capsule

1961. 1st Manned Space Flight. Inscr "12.4.1961".
E556 – 10 pf. red & green . . . 25 10
E557 E **187** 20 pf. red 25 10
E558 – 25 pf. blue . . . . . 4·50 5·00
DESIGNS: 10 pf. Space rocket leaving globe; 25 pf. Capsule's parachute descent.

E **188** Marx, Engels, Lenin and Demonstrators

1961. 15th Anniv of German Socialist Unity Party.
E559 E **188** 20 pf. red 40 20

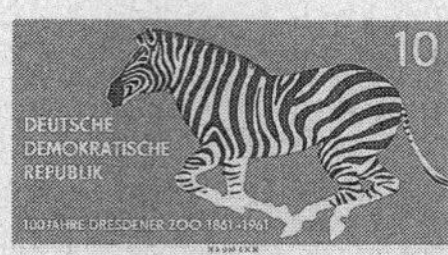

E **189** Common Zebra

1961. Centenary of Dresden Zoo.
E560 E **189** 10 pf. black & green . . 4·50 4·00
E561 – 20 pf. black & mauve . . 30 30
DESIGN: 20 pf. Eastern black-and-white colobus.

E **190** Pioneers playing Volleyball

1961. Young Pioneers Meeting; Erfurt. Multicoloured.
E562 10 pf. + 5 pf. Type E **190** . . 10 10
E563 20 pf. + 10 pf. Folk dancing . 10 10
E564 25 pf. + 10 pf. Model airplane construction . . . . 3·00 2·25

E **191** High Jump
E **192** Salt Miners and Castle

1961. 3rd European Women's Gymnastic Championships, Leipzig.
E565 E **191** 10 pf. green 15 10
E566 – 20 pf. mauve 15 10
E567 – 25 pf. blue . . . . . 4·75 4·25
DESIGNS—VERT: 20 pf. Gymnast. HORIZ: 25 pf. Exercise on parallel bars.

1961. Halle (Saale) Millenary.
E568 E **192** 10 pf. blk, yell & grn . 2·50 1·25
E569 – 20 pf. blk, yell & red . 15 10
DESIGNS: 20 pf. Scientist and Five Towers of Halle.

E **193** Canadian Canoe

1961. World Canoeing Championships.
E570 – 5 pf. blue & grey . . . 2·75 2·50
E571 E **193** 10 pf. green & grey . . 10 10
E572 – 20 pf. pur & grey . . . 10 10
DESIGNS: 5 pf. Folding canoe; 20 pf. Canadian two-seater canoe.

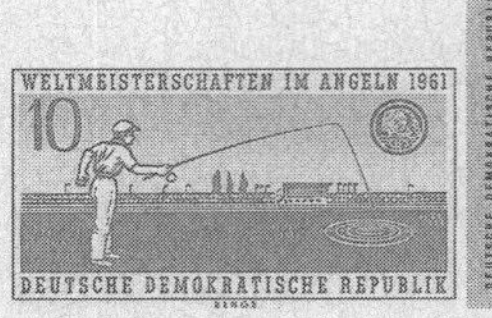

E **194** Line-casting
E **195** Old Weigh-house, Leipzig

1961. World Angling Championships.
E573 E **194** 10 pf. green & blue . . 2·10 1·75
E574 – 20 pf. lake & blue . . . 15 15
DESIGN: 20 pf. River-fishing.

1961. Leipzig Autumn Fair.
E575 E **195** 10 pf. olive & green . . 20 10
E576 – 25 pf. blue & ultram. . 60 10
DESIGNS: 25 pf. Old Stock Exchange, Leipzig.
See also Nos. E612/14.

E **196** Walter Ulbricht
E **197** Dahlia

1961. Type E **196** or larger, 24 × 29 mm. (Dm. values).
E577 5 pf. blue 10 10
E578 10 pf. green 15 10
E579 15 pf. purple 20 15
E580 20 pf. red 65 30
E581 25 pf. turquoise 15 10
E582 30 pf. red 20 10
E582a 35 pf. green 30 10
E583 40 pf. violet 20 10
E584 50 pf. blue 30 10
E584a 60 pf. green 40 10
E585 70 pf. brown 40 10
E585a 80 pf. blue 55 10
E586 1 DM. green 50 15
E587 2 DM. brown . . . . . . 1·25 15
See also Nos. E805/6, E1197/8 and E1255.

1961. Concentration Camps Memorials Fund. As Type E **120**. Portraits in grey and black.
E588 5 pf. + 5 pf. green 10 15
E589 10 pf. + 5 pf. green 10 15
E590 20 pf. + 10 pf. mauve . . . 15 30
E591 25 pf. + 10 pf. blue 25 30
E592 40 pf. + 20 pf. lake . . . . 2·00 5·50
PORTRAITS: 5 pf. C. Schonhaar; 10 pf. H. Baum; 20 pf. Liselotte Herrmann. HORIZ: (41 × 32½ mm): 25 pf. Sophie and Hans Scholl; 40 pf. Hilde and Hans Coppi.

1961. Int Horticultural Exn.
E593 – 10 pf. red, yell & grn . 15 10
E594 E **197** 20 pf. red, yell & brn . 30 15
E595 – 40 pf. red, yell & bl . . 7·50 8·00
FLOWERS: 10 pf. Tulip. 40 pf. Rose.

E **198** Liszt and Berlioz (after Von Kaulbach and Prinzhofer)
E **199** TV Camera and Screen

1961. 150th Birth Anniv of Liszt (composer).
E596 E **198** 5 pf. black 15 15
E597 – 10 pf. green . . . . . 1·90 1·75
E598 – 20 pf. red 15 15
E599 – 25 pf. blue . . . . . . 2·25 2·00
DESIGNS: 10 pf. Young hand of Liszt (from French sculpture, Liszt Museum, Budapest); 20 pf. Liszt (after Rietschel); 25 pf. Liszt and Chopin (after Bartolini and Bovy).

1961. Stamp Day.
E600 E **199** 10 pf. black & green . . 1·40 1·90
E601 – 20 pf. black & red . . 15 15
DESIGNS: 20 pf. Studio microphone and radio tuning-scale.

E **200** G. S. Titov with Young Pioneers

1961. 2nd Russian Manned Space Flight.
E602 E **200** 5 pf. violet & red . . . 15 10
E603 – 10 pf. green & red . . . 15 10
E604 – 15 pf. mve & blue . . . 7·50 8·00
E605 – 20 pf. red and blue . . 15 10
E606 – 25 pf. blue and red . . 15 10
E607 – 40 pf. blue and red . . 1·00 15
DESIGNS—HORIZ: 15 pf. Titov in space-suit; 20 pf. Titov receiving Karl Marx Order from Ulbricht; 25 pf. "Vostok 2" rocket in flight; 40 pf. Titov and Ulbricht in Berlin. VERT: 10 pf. Titov in Leipzig.

E **201** Red Wood Ants

1962. Fauna Protection Campaign (1st series).
E608 E **201** 5 pf. yell, brn & blk . . 3·25 4·50
E609 – 10 pf. brown & green . . 15 10
E610 – 20 pf. brown & red . . 15 10
E611 – 40 pf. yell, blk & vio . . 50 10
DESIGNS: 10 pf. Weasels; 20 pf. Eurasian common shrews; 40 pf. Common long-eared bat.
See also Nos. E699/703.

1962. Leipzig Spring Fair. As Type E **195**.
E612 10 pf. sepia and green 20 10
E613 20 pf. black and red 25 10
E614 25 pf. purple and blue 75 50
BUILDINGS: 10 pf. Zum Kaffeebaum; 20 pf. Gobliser Schlosschen; 25 pf. Romanus-Haus.

E **203** Pilot and Mikoyan Gurevich MiG-17 Jet Fighters

E **204** Danielle Casanova

1962. 6th Anniv of East German People's Army.
E615 E **203** 5 pf. blue 10 10
E616 – 10 pf. green 10 10
E617 – 20 pf. red 15 10
E618 – 25 pf. blue 20 15
E619 – 40 pf. brown . . . . . 1·60 1·25
DESIGNS: 10 pf. Soldier and armoured car; 20 pf. Factory guard; 25 pf. Sailor and Habich I class minesweeper; 40 pf. Tank and driver.

1962. Concentration Camps Memorial Fund. Camp Victims.
E620 E **204** 5 pf. + 5 pf. black . . 10 15
E621 – 10 pf. + 5 pf. grn . . . 10 15
E622 – 20 pf. + 10 pf. pur . . . 10 15
E623 – 25 pf. + 10 pf. blue . . 20 25
E624 – 40 pf. + 20 pf. pur . . 1·60 1·60
PORTRAITS: 10 pf. Julius Fucik; 20 pf. Johanna J. Schaft; 25 pf. Pawel Finder; 40 pf. Soja A. Kosmodemjanskaja.

E **205** Racing Cyclists and Prague Castle

1962. 15th Int Peace Cycle Race. Mult.
E625 10 pf. Type E **205** 10 10
E626 20 pf. + 10 pf. Cyclists and Palace of Culture and Science, Warsaw 10 10
E627 25 pf. Cyclist and Town Hall, East Berlin . . . . 1·50 1·50

E **206** Johann Fichte

1962. Birth Bicent of Fichte (philosopher).
E628 – 10 pf. green & black . . 1·25 1·50
E629 E **206** 20 pf. red and blk . . . 15 15
DESIGNS: 10 pf. Fichte's birthplace, Ramenau.

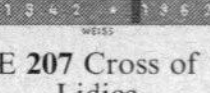

E **207** Cross of Lidice

E **208** Dimitrov at Leipzig

1962. 20th Anniv of Destruction of Lidice.
E630 E **207** 20 pf. red & black . . . 15 10
E631 25 pf. blue & black . . 1·00 70

1962. 80th Birth Anniv of G. Dimitrov (Bulgarian statesman).
E632 E **208** 5 pf. black & turq . . . 55 55
E633 – 20 pf. black & red . . . 10 10
DESIGN: 20 pf. Dimitrov as Premier of Bulgaria.

E **209** Maize-planting machine

1962. 10th D.D.R. Agricultural Exn., Markkleeberg. Multicoloured.
E634 10 pf. Type E **209** 15 10
E635 20 pf. Milking shed 15 10
E636 40 pf. Combine-harvester . . . 1·40 1·40

E **210** Freighter "Frieden"

1962. 5th Baltic Sea Week, Rostock.
E637 – 10 pf. turq & blue . . . 15 10
E638 – 20 pf. red & yellow . . 20 10
E639 E **210** 25 pf. bistre & blue . . 2·50 2·00
DESIGNS—HORIZ: 10 pf. Map of Baltic Sea inscr "Meer des Friedens" ("Sea of Peace"). VERT: 20 pf. Hochhaus, Rostock.

E **215** Dove

E **216** National Theatre, Helsinki

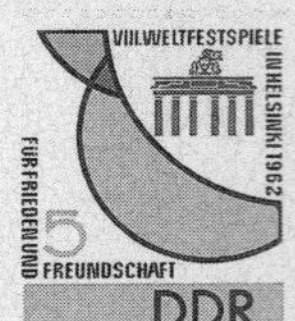

E **211** Brandenburg Gate, Berlin

E **212** Youth of Three Races

E **213** Folk Dancers

E **214** Youth of Three Nations

1962. World Youth Festival Games, Helsinki. Multicoloured.
E640 E **211** 5 pf. . . . . 1·50 1·75
E641 E **212** 5 pf. . . . . 1·50 1·75
E642 E **213** 10 pf. + 5 pf. 50 25
E643 E **214** 15 pf. + 5 pf. 50 25
E644 E **215** 20 pf. . . . . 1·50 1·75
E645 E **216** 20 pf. . . . . 1·50 1·75

E **217** Free-style Swimming

E **218** Municipal Store, Leipzig

1962. 10th European Swimming Championships, Leipzig. Design in blue: value colours given.
E646 E **217** 5 pf. orange 10 10
E647 – 10 pf. blue 10 10
E648 – 20 pf. + 10 pf. mve . . 10 10
E649 – 25 pf. blue 10 10
E650 – 40 pf. violet . . . . . 1·10 1·10
E651 – 70 pf. brown 15 10
DESIGNS: 10 pf. Back stroke; 20 pf. High diving; 25 pf. Butterfly stroke; 40 pf. Breast stroke; 70 pf. Water-polo. On Nos. E649/51 the value, etc., appears at the foot of the design.

1962. Leipzig Autumn Fair.
E652 E **218** 10 pf. black & green . . 20 15
E653 – 20 pf. black & red . . . 30 15
E654 – 25 pf. black & blue . . 50 30
DESIGNS: 20 pf. Madler Arcade, Leipzig; 25 pf. Leipzig Airport and Ilyushin Il-14M airplane.

E **219** "Transport and Communications"

E **220** Rene Blieck

1962. 10th Anniv of "Friedrich List" Transport High School, Dresden.
E655 E **219** 5 pf. black & blue . . . 30 20

1962. Concentration Camp Victims. Memorials Fund.
E656 E **220** 5 pf. + 5 pf. blue . . . 10 10
E657 – 10 pf. + 5 pf. green . . 10 10
E658 – 15 pf. + 5 pf. violet . . 15 15
E659 – 20 pf. + 10 pf. pur . . 15 15
E660 – 70 pf. + 30 pf. brn . . 1·90 2·10
PORTRAITS—As Type E **220**: 10 pf. Dr. A. Klahr; 15 pf. J. Diaz; 20 pf. J. Alpari. HORIZ: (39 × 21 mm): 70 pf. Seven Cervi brothers.

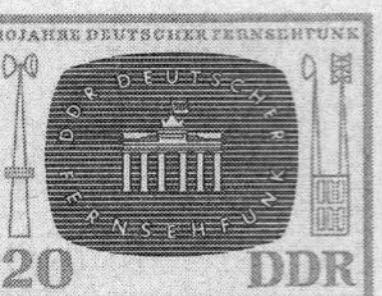

E **221** Television Screen and Call-sign

E **222** G. Hauptmann

1962. Stamp Day and 10th Anniv of German Television.
E661 E **221** 20 pf. purple & grn . . 15 10
E662 – 40 pf. purple & mve . . 1·75 1·75
DESIGN: 40 pf. Children with stamp album (inscr "TAG DER BRIEFMARKE 1962").

1962. Birth Centenary of Gerhart Hauptmann (author).
E663 E **222** 20 pf. black and red . . 35 15

E **223** Pierre de Coubertin

E **224** Party Flag

1963. Birth Cent of Pierre de Coubertin (reviver of Olympic Games).
E664 E **223** 20 pf. red & grey . . . 10 10
E665 – 25 pf. blue & ochre . . 1·50 2·10
DESIGN: 25 pf. Stadium.

1963. 6th Socialists Unity Party Day.
E666 E **224** 10 pf. red, blk & yell . 30 10

E **225** Insecticide Sprayer

1963. Malaria Eradication.
E667 E **225** 20 pf. blk, red & orge . 10 10
E668 – 25 pf. multicoloured . . 10 10
E669 – 50 pf. multicoloured . . 1·25 1·40
DESIGNS: 25 pf. Rod of Aesculapius; 50 pf. Mosquito. Map is common to all values.

E **226** Red Fox

E **227** Barthels Hof, Leipzig (1748–1872)

1963. Int Fur Auctions, Leipzig.
E670 E **226** 20 pf. blue and red . . 20 15
E671 – 25 pf. indigo & blue . . 1·40 1·90
DESIGN: 25 pf. Karakul lamb.

1963. Leipzig Spring Fair.
E672 E **227** 10 pf. black & yell . . 15 10
E673 – 20 pf. black & brn . . 25 25
E674 – 25 pf. black & blue . . 95 95
LEIPZIG BUILDINGS: 20 pf. New Town Hall; 25 pf. Clock-tower, Karl-Marx Square.

E **228** J. G. Seume (poet) and Scene from "Syracuse Walk" (Birth Bicent)

1963. Cultural Anniversaries. Design and portrait in black.
E675 E **228** 5 pf. yellow 15 10
E676 – 10 pf. turquoise 15 10
E677 – 20 pf. orange 15 10
E678 – 25 pf. blue . . . . . . 1·75 1·60
DESIGNS: 10 pf. F. Hebbel (poet) and scene from "Mary Magdalene" (150th birth anniv); 20 pf. G. Buchner (poet) and scene from "Woyzeck" (150th birth anniv); 25 pf. R. Wagner (composer) and scene from "The Flying Dutchman" (150th birth anniv).

E **229** Nurse bandaging Patient

E **230** W. Bohne (runner)

1963. Centenary of Red Cross.
E679 E **229** 10 pf. mult 95 75
E680 – 20 pf. black, grey and red 10 10
DESIGNS: 20 pf. Barkas type "B 1000" ambulance.

1963. Concentration Camps Memorial Fund. Sportsmen Victims (1st series). Designs in black.
E681 E **230** 5 pf. + 5 pf. yellow . . 15 10
E682 – 10 pf. + 5 pf. green . . 15 10
E683 – 15 pf. + 5 pf. mve . . . 15 15
E684 – 20 pf. + 10 pf. pink . . 15 15
E685 – 25 pf. + 10 pf. blue . . 1·90 3·75
SPORTSMEN: 10 pf. W. Seelenbinder (wrestler); 15 pf. A. Richter (cyclist); 20 pf. H. Steyer (footballer); 25 pf. K. Schlosser (mountaineer).
See also Nos. E704/8.

E **231** Gymnastics

E **232** E. Pottier (lyricist) and Opening Bars of the "Internationale"

1963. 4th East German Gymnastics and Sports Festival, Leipzig. Inscr in black.
E686 E **231** 10 pf. + 5 pf. yellow and green 15 10
E687 – 20 pf. + 10 pf. violet and red 20 15
E688 – 25 pf. + 10 pf. green and blue . . . . 3·25 3·00
DESIGNS: 20 pf. Dederon kerchief exercises; 25 pf. Relay-racing.

1963. 75th Anniv of "Internationale" (song).
E689 E **232** 20 pf. black & red . . . 15 10
E690 – 25 pf. blk & blue . . . 95 1·25
DESIGN: 25 pf. As 20 pf. but portrait of P.-C. Degeyter.

E **233** V Tereshkova and "Vostok 6"

E **234** V Bykovsky and "Vostok 5"

1963. 2nd "Team" Manned Space Flights.
E691 E **233** 20 pf. blk, grey & bl . . 65 10
E692 E **234** 20 pf. blk, grey & bl . . 65 10
Nos. E691/2 were printed together, se-tenant, forming a composite design.

E **235** Motor Cyclist competing in "Motocross", Apolda

E **236** Treblinka Memorial

1963. World Motor Cycle Racing Championships.
E693 E **235** 10 pf. emer & grn . . . 3·50 3·75
E694 – 20 pf. red and pink . . 25 15
E695 – 25 pf. blue & lt blue . . 25 20
DESIGNS—HORIZ: (39 × 22 mm): 20 pf. Motor cyclist; 25 pf. Two motor cyclists cornering.

1963. Erection of Treblinka Memorial, Poland.
E696 E **236** 20 pf. blue & red . . . 25 15

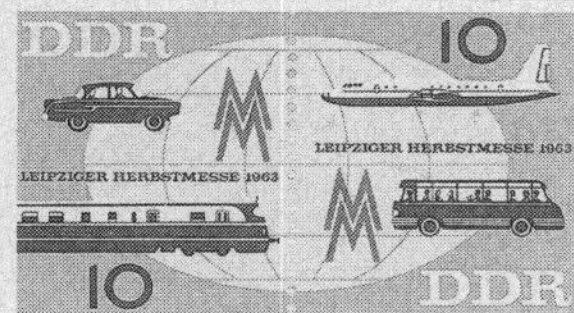

E **237** Transport E **238**

1963. Leipzig Autumn Fair.
E697 E **237** 10 pf. multicoloured . . 75 10
E698 E **238** 10 pf. multicoloured . . 75 10
Nos. E697/8 were printed together, se-tenant, forming a composite design.

1963. Fauna Protection Campaign (2nd series). As Type E **201**. Fauna in natural colours, background colours given.
E699 10 pf. green 20 10
E700 20 pf. red 20 10
E701 30 pf. red 30 10
E702 50 pf. blue . . . . 3·25 3·00
E703 70 pf. brown 40 30
DESIGNS: 10 pf. Stag-beetle; 20 pf. Salamander; 30 pf. European pond tortoise; 50 pf. Green toad; 70 pf. West European hedgehogs.

1963. Concentration Camps Memorial Fund. Sportsmen Victims (2nd series). As Type E **230**. Designs in black.
E704 5 pf. + 5 pf. yellow 15 15
E705 10 pf. + 5 pf. green 15 15
E706 15 pf. + 5 pf. violet 15 20
E707 20 pf. 10 pf. red 15 20
E708 40 pf. + 20 pf. blue . . . . . 2·75 3·00
SPORTSMEN: 5 pf. H. Tops (Gymnast); 10 pf. Kate Tucholla (hockey-player); 15 pf. R. Seiffert (swimmer); 20 pf. E. Grube (athlete); 40 pf. K. Biedermann (canoeist).

E **239** N. von Gneisenau and G. L. von Blucher

1963. 150th Anniv of German War of Liberation.
E709 E **239** 5 pf. blk, buff & yell . . 15 10
E710 – 10 pf. blk, buff & grn . 15 10
E711 – 20 pf. blk, buff & orge . 15 10
E712 – 25 pf. blk, buff & bl . . 15 10
E713 – 40 pf. blk, buff & red . 1·75 85
DESIGNS: 10 pf. "Cossacks and (German) Soldiers in Berlin" (Ludwig Wolf); 20 pf. E. M. Arndt and Baron vom Stein; 25 pf. Lutzow corps in battle order (detail from painting by Hans Kohlschein); 40 pf. G. von Scharnhorst and Prince Kutuzov.

E **240** V. Tereshkova E **241** Synagogue aflame

1963. Visit of Soviet Cosmonauts to East Berlin.
E714 E **240** 10 pf. green & blue . . 15 10
E715 – 20 pf. blk, red & buff . 15 10
E716 – 20 pf. grn, red & buff . 15 10
E717 – 25 pf. orange and blue . 3·50 2·00
DESIGNS—SQUARE: No. E717, Tereshkova in capsule. VERT: (24 × 32 mm). No. E715, Tereshkova with bouquet; No. E716, Gagarin (visit to Berlin).

1963. 25th Anniv of "Kristallnacht" (Nazi pogrom).
E718 E **241** 10 pf. multicoloured . . 25 15

E **242** Letter-sorting Machine

1963. Stamp Day. Multicoloured.
E719 10 pf. Type E **242** . . . . . 1·10 1·10
E720 20 pf. Fork-lift truck loading mail train 35 10

E **243** Ski Jumper commencing Run E **244** Red Admiral

1963. Winter Olympic Games, Innsbruck, 1964. Rings in different colours; skier in black.
E721 E **243** 5 pf. yellow 20 10
E722 – 10 pf. green 20 10
E723 – 20 pf. + 10 pf. red . . . 20 10
E724 – 25 pf. blue . . . . . 1·90 1·60
DESIGNS: Ski jumper—10 pf. Taking-off; 20 pf. In mid-air; 25 pf. Landing.

1964. Butterflies. Butterflies in natural colours; inscr in black.
E725 E **244** 10 pf. olive 15 10
E726 – 15 pf. lilac 15 10
E727 – 20 pf. orange 20 10
E728 – 25 pf. blue 30 10
E729 – 40 pf. blue . . . . . 5·00 2·50
BUTTERFLIES: 15 pf. Small apollo; 20 pf. Swallowtail; 25 pf. Clouded yellow; 40 pf. Large tortoiseshell.

E **245** Shakespeare (b. 1564)

1964. Cultural Anniversaries.
E730 – 20 pf. blue & pink . . 15 10
E731 – 25 pf. purple & blue . . 15 10
E732 E **245** 40 pf. blue & lilac . . 1·00 90
DESIGNS: 20 pf. Quadriga, Brandenburg Gate (J. G. Schadow, sculptor, b. 1764); 25 pf. Portal keystone, German Historical Museum (A. Schluter, sculptor, b. 1664).

E **246** "Elektrotecknik" Hall

1964. Leipzig Spring Fair.
E733 E **246** 10 pf. black & grn . . 1·75 10
E734 – 20 pf. black & red . . 2·50 10
DESIGNS: 20 pf. Braunigkes Hof, c. 1700.

E **247** A. Saefkow

1964. Concentration Camp Victims. Memorials Fund.
E735 E **247** 5 pf. + 5 pf. brn & bl . 15 10
E736 – 10 pf. + 5 pf. brn & ol . 15 10
E737 – 15 pf. + 5 pf. brn & vio . 15 10
E738 – 20 pf. + 5 pf. olive and red 15 10
E739 – 25 pf. + 10 pf. bl & ol . 20 15
E740 – 40 pf. + 10 pf. ol & brn . 1·25 1·50
PORTRAITS—As Type E **247**: 10 pf. F. Jacob; 15 pf. B. Bastlein; 20 pf. H. Schulze-Boysen; 25 pf. Dr. A. Kuckhoff. (49 × 27½ mm): 40 pf. Dr. A. and Mildred Harnack.

E **248** Mr. Khrushchev with East German Officials E **249** Boys and Girls

1964. Mr. Khrushchev's 70th Birthday.
E741 E **248** 25 pf. blue 15 10
E742 – 40 pf. black & purple . 2·50 2·25
DESIGN: 40 pf. Mr. Khrushchev with cosmonauts Tereshkova and Gagarin.

1964. German Youth Meeting, Berlin. Multicoloured.
E743 10 pf. Type E **249** 10 10
E744 20 pf. Young gymnasts . . . 20 10
E745 25 pf. Youth with accordion and girl with flowers . . . . 1·50 65

E **250** Flax, Krumel and Struppi, the dog

1964. Children's Day. Multicoloured.
E746 5 pf. Type E **250** 10 10
E747 10 pf. Master Nadelohr . . . 10 10
E748 15 pf. Pittiplatsch 10 10
E749 20 pf. Sandmannschen (sandman) 10 10
E750 40 pf. Bummi (teddy bear) and Schnatterinchen (duckling) . 1·50 1·50
The designs show characters from children's T.V. programmes.

E **251** Governess and Child (with portrait of Jenny Marx)

1964. East German Women's Congress. Mult.
E751 20 pf. Type E **251** 10 10
E752 25 pf. Switchboard technicians 1·10 80
E753 70 pf. Farm girls 15 10

E **252** Cycling E **253** Diving

1964. Olympic Games, Tokyo. Multicoloured.
(a) 1st Series. As Type E **252**.
E754 5 pf. Type E **252** 10 10
E755 10 pf. Volleyball 10 10
E756 20 pf. Judo 10 10
E757 25 pf. Diving 10 10
E758 40 pf. + 20 pf. Running . . 30 10
E759 70 pf. Horse-jumping . . . . 1·60 1·50
(b) 2nd Series. As Type E **253**.
E760 10 pf. Type E **253** . . . . . 2·10 2·25
E761 10 pf. + 5 pf. Horse-jumping . 2·10 2·25
E762 10 pf. Volleyball . . . . . 2·10 2·25
E763 10 pf. Cycling . . . . . . 2·10 2·25
E764 10 pf. + 5 pf. Running . . . 2·10 2·25
E765 10 pf. Judo . . . . 2·10 2·25
Nos. E760/5 were printed together in se-tenant blocks of six (3 × 2) within sheets of 60 (6 × 10), and with an overall pattern of the five Olympic "rings" in each block.

E **254** Young Artists

1964. 5th Young Pioneer's Meeting, East Berlin. Multicoloured.
E766 10 pf. + 5 pf. Type E **254** . . . 20 10
E767 20 pf. + 10 pf. Planting tree . . 50 10
E768 25 pf. + 10 pf. Playing with ball . . . . 2·25 1·10

E **255** Leningrad Memorial E **256** F. Joliot-Curie

1964. Victims of Leningrad Siege Commem.
E769 E **255** 25 pf. black, yellow and blue 60 15

1964. "World Peace".
E770 E **256** 20 pf. sepia & red . . . 15 10
E771 – 25 pf. black & blue . . 15 10
E772 – 50 pf. black & lilac . . 1·10 65
PORTRAITS: (Campaigners for "World Peace"): 25 pf. B. von Suttner; 50 pf. C. von Ossietzky.

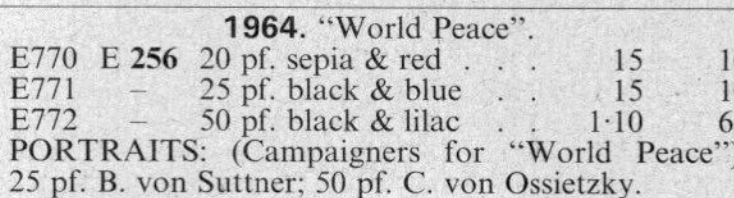

E **257** Ancient Glazier's Shop E **258** I.W.M.A. Cachet

1964. Leipzig Autumn Fair. Multicoloured.
E773 10 pf. Type E **257** 55 10
E774 15 pf. Jena glass factory . . . 55 10

1964. Centenary of "First International".
E775 E **258** 20 pf. black & red . . 10 10
E776 25 pf. black & blue . . 70 60

E **259** "Rostock Port" Stamp of 1958 E **260** Modern Buildings and Flag ("Reconstruction")

1964. National Stamp Exn., East Berlin.
E777 E **259** 10 pf. + 5 pf. green and orange 20 10
E778 – 20 pf. + 10 pf. blue and purple 20 10
E779 – 50 pf. brown and grey . 2·50 1·50
DESIGNS: 20 pf., 12 pf. "Peace" stamp of 1950; 50 pf., 5 pf. "Dresden Paintings" stamp of 1955.

1964. 15th Anniv of German Democratic Republic. Multicoloured.
E780 10 pf. Type E **260** 20 15
E781 10 pf. Surveyor and conveyor ("Coal") 20 15
E782 10 pf. Scientist and chemical works ("Chemical Industry") 20 15
E783 10 pf. Guard and chemical works ("Chemical Industry") 20 15
E784 10 pf. Milkmaid and dairy pen ("Agriculture") 20 15
E785 10 pf. Furnaceman and mills ("Steel") 20 15
E786 10 pf. Student with microscope, and lecture hall ("Education") 20 15
E787 10 pf. Operator and lathe ("Engineering") 20 15
E788 10 pf. Scientist and planetarium ("Optics") 20 15
E789 10 pf. Girl with cloth, and loom ("Textiles") 20 15
E790 10 pf. Docker and ship at quay-side ("Shipping") 45 15
E791 10 pf. Leipzig buildings and "businessmen" formed of Fair emblem ("Exports") . . 20 15
E792 10 pf. Building worker and flats ("New Construction") . . . 20 15
E793 10 pf. Sculptor modelling and Dresden gateway ("Culture") 20 15
E794 10 pf. Girl skier and holiday resort ("Recreation") . . . 20 15

E **261** Monchgut (Rugen) Costume E **262** Dr. Schweitzer and Lambarene River

1964. Provincial costumes (1st series). Mult.
E795 5 pf. Type E **261** . . . . . 8·25 6·25
E796 5 pf. Monchgut (male) . . . . 8·25 6·25
E797 10 pf. Spreewald (female) . . . 35 15
E798 10 pf. Spreewald (male) . . . 35 15
E799 20 pf. Thuringen (female) . . . 65 30
E800 20 pf. Thuringen (male) . . . 65 30
See Nos. E932/7 and E1073/6.

1965. 90th Birthday of Dr. Albert Schweitzer.

E802 E **262** 10 pf. yell, blk & grn . . 15 10
E803 – 20 pf. yell, blk & red . . 15 10
E804 – 25 pf. yell, blk & bl . . 2·75 1·75

DESIGNS: 20 pf. Schweitzer and "nuclear disarmament" marchers; 25 pf. Schweitzer and part of a Bach organ prelude.

1965. As Nos. E586/7 but values expressed in "MDN" (Deutschen Notenbank Marks) instead of "DM".

E805 1 MDN. green 35 10
E806 2 MDN. brown 55 10

E **263** A. Bebel   E **264** Fair Medal (obverse)

1965. 125th Birth Anniv of August Bebel (founder of Social Democratic Party).

E307 E **263** 20 pf. yell, brn & red . . 35 10

See also Nos. E814/5, E839, E842 and E871.

1965. Leipzig Spring Fair and 800th Anniv of Leipzig Fair.

E808 E **264** 10 pf. gold & mve . . . 15 10
E809 – 15 pf. gold & mve . . . 20 10
E810 – 25 pf. mult 50 15

DESIGNS: 15 pf. Fair medal (reverse); 25 pf. Chemical Works.

E **265** Giraffe   E **266** Belyaev and Leonov

1965. 10th Anniv of East Berlin Zoo.

E811 E **265** 10 pf. grey & grn . . . 20 10
E812 – 25 pf. grey & blue . . . 30 15
E813 – 30 pf. grey & sepia . . 2·10 1·25

ANIMALS—HORIZ: 25 pf. Iguana; 30 pf. Black wildebeest.

1965. 120th Birth Anniv of W. C. Rontgen (physicist). As Type E **263** but portrait of Rontgen.

E814 10 pf. yellow, brn & grn . . . 40 10

1985. 700th Birth Anniv of Dante. As Type E **263** but portrait of Dante.

E815 50 pf. yell, brn & lemon . . . 1·00 15

1965. Space Flight of "Voskhod 2".

E816 E **266** 10 pf. red 20 10
E817 – 25 pf. blue . . . . . . 2·10 1·60

DESIGN: 25 pf. Leonov in space.

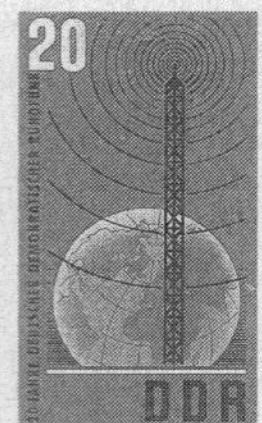

E **267** Boxing Gloves   E **269** Transmitter Aerial and Globe

E **268** Dimitrov denouncing Fascism

1965. European Boxing Championships, Berlin.

E818 E **267** 10 pf. + 5 pf. mult . . . 15 10
E819 – 20 pf. gold, black and red 75 75

DESIGN: 20 pf. Boxing glove.

1965. 20th Anniv of Liberation. Multicoloured.

E820 5 pf. + 5 pf. Type E **268** . . . 10 10
E821 10 pf. + 5 pf. Distributing "Communist Manifesto" . . 10 10
E822 15 pf. + 5 pf. Soldiers of International Brigade fighting in Spain 10 10
E823 20 pf. + 10 pf. "Freedom for Ernst Thalmann" demonstration 10 10
E824 25 pf. + 10 pf. Founding of "Free Germany" National Committee (Moscow) . . . 10 10
E825 40 pf. Ulbricht and Weinert distributing "Manifesto" on Eastern Front 15 10
E826 50 pf. Liberation of concentration camps 15 10
E827 60 pf. Hoisting Red Flag on Reichstag . . . . 2·00 1·75
E828 70 pf. Bilateral demonstration of Communist and Socialist parties 20 10

1965. 20th Anniv of East German Broadcasting Service.

E829 E **269** 20 pf. black, red and cerise 20 10
E830 – 40 pf. black & blue . . 1·25 40

DESIGN: 40 pf. Radio workers.

E **270** I.T.U. Emblem and Radio Circuit Diagram   E **271** F.D.G.B. Emblem

1965. Centenary of I.T.U.

E831 E **270** 20 pf. blk, yell & ol . . 30 10
E832 – 25 pf. blk, mve & vio . 1·75 40

DESIGN: 25 pf. I.T.U. emblem and switch diagram.

1965. 20th Anniv of Free German (F.D.G.B.) and World Trade Unions.

E833 E **271** 20 pf. gold and red . . 15 10
E834 – 25 pf. blk, bl & gold . . 75 50

DESIGN—HORIZ: (39 × 21½ mm): 25 pf. Workers of "two hemispheres" (inscr "20 JAHRE WELTGEWERKSCHAFTSBUND").

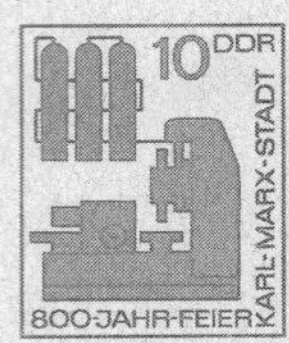

E **272** Industrial Machine   E **273** Marx and Lenin

1965. 800th Anniv of Karl-Marx-Stadt (formerly Chemnitz).

E835 E **272** 10 pf. green & gold . . 15 10
E836 – 20 pf. red and gold . . 20 10
E837 – 25 pf. blue & gold . . 70 30

DESIGNS: 20 pf. Red Tower, Chemnitz; 25 pf. Town Hall, Chemnitz.

1965. Socialist Countries' Postal Ministers Conference, Peking.

E838 E **273** 20 pf. blk, yell & red . 25 10

1965. 90th Birth Anniv of Dr Wilhelm Kulz (politician). As Type E **263** but portrait of Kulz.

E839 25 pf. yellow, brown & bl . . 65 10

E **274** Congress Emblem

1965. World Peace Congress, Helsinki.

E840 E **274** 10 pf. + 5 pf. green and blue 10 10
E841 20 pf. + 5 pf. blue and red 60 40

1965. 75th Birth Anniv of Erich Weinert (poet). As Type E **263**, but portrait of Weinert.

E842 40 pf. yell, brn & red 40 10

1965. "Help for Vietnam". Surch **Hilfe fur VIETNAM + 10.**

E843 E **260** 10 pf. + 10 pf. mult . . 35 10

E **276** Rebuilt Weigh-house and Modern Buildings, Katharinenstrasse

1965. 800th Anniv of Leipzig.

E844 E **276** 10 pf. pur, bl & gold . 10 10
E845 – 25 pf. orge, sep & gold . 10 10
E846 – 40 pf. multicoloured . . 10 10
E847 – 70 pf. blue & gold . . 1·50 1·00

DESIGNS: 25 pf. Old Town Hall; 40 pf. Opera House and new G.P.O.; 70 pf. "Stadt Leipzig" Hotel.

E **277** "Praktica" and "Praktisix" Cameras   E **278** Show Jumping

1965. Leipzig Autumn Fair.

E848 E **277** 10 pf. blk, gold & grn . . 10 10
E849 – 15 pf. mult 10 10
E850 – 25 pf. mult 60 15

DESIGNS: 15 pf. Clavichord and electric guitar; 25 pf. "Zeiss" microscope.

1965. World Modern Pentathlon Championships, Leipzig. Multicoloured.

E852 10 pf. Type E **278** 20 10
E853 10 pf. Swimming 20 10
E854 10 pf. Running . . . . . . 3·00 2·25
E855 10 pf. + 5 pf. Fencing 20 10
E856 10 pf. + 5 pf. Pistol-shooting . 20 10

E **279** E. Leonov   E **280** Memorial at Putten, Netherlands

1965. Soviet Cosmonauts Visit to East Germany.

E857 E **279** 20 pf. bl, sil & red . . 50 50
E858 – 20 pf. bl, sil & red . . 50 50
E859 – 25 pf. multicoloured . . 50 50

DESIGNS—As Type E **275**. No. E858, Belyaev. HORIZ: (48 × 29 mm): No. E859, "Voskhod 2" and Leonov in space.

1965. Putten War Victims Commem.

E860 E **280** 25 pf. blk, yell & bl . . 45 10

E **281** Stoking Furnace (from old engraving)   E **282** Red Kite

1965. Bicent. of Mining School, Freiberg. Multicoloured.

E861 10 pf. Type E **281** 10 10
E862 15 pf. Mining ore (old engraving) 90 90
E863 20 pf. Ore 15 10
E864 25 pf. Sulphur 15 10

1965. Birds of Prey. Multicoloured.

E865 5 pf. Type E **282** 10 10
E866 10 pf. Lammergeier 15 10
E867 20 pf. Common Buzzard . . . 20 10
E868 25 pf. Common Kestrel . . . 20 10
E869 40 pf. Northern Goshawk . . 30 10
E870 70 pf. Golden Eagle . . . . 5·75 2·40

1965. 150th Birth Anniv of A. von Menzel (painter). As Type E **263** but portrait of Menzel.

E871 10 pf. yellow, brown and red . 45 10

E **283** Otto Grotewohl   E **285** Ladies' Single-seater

1965. Grotewohl Commem.

E872 E **283** 20 f. black 45 10

1966. World Tobogganing Championships, Friedrichroda.

E874 E **285** 10 pf. green & olive . . 10 10
E875 – 20 pf. blue & red . . . 25 10
E876 – 25 pf. indigo & blue . . 1·10 75

DESIGNS: 20 pf. Men's double-seater; 25 pf. Men's single seater.

E **286** Electronic Punch-card Computer

1966. Leipzig Spring Fair. Multicoloured.

E877 10 pf. Type E **286** 25 10
E878 15 pf. Drilling and milling plant 50 10

E **287** Soldier and National Gallery Berlin   E **288** J. A. Smoler (Sorb patriot and savant)

1966. 10th Anniv of National People's Army.

E879 E **287** 5 pf. blk, ol & yell . . 10 10
E880 – 10 pf. blk, ol & yell . . 10 10
E881 – 20 pf. blk, ol & yell . . 20 10
E882 – 25 pf. blk, ol & yell . . 1·10 75

DESIGNS: Soldier and—10 pf. Brandenburg Gate; 20 pf. Industrial plant; 25 pf. Combine-harvester.

1966. 150th Birth Anniv of Jan Smoler.

E883 E **288** 20 pf. blk, red & bl . . 10 10
E884 – 25 pf. blk, red & bl . . 40 45

DESIGN: 25 pf. House of the Sorbs, Bautzen.

E **289** "Good Knowledge" Badge   E **290** "Luna 9" on Moon

1966. 20th Anniv of "Freie Deutsche Jugend" (Socialist Youth Movement).

E885 E **289** 20 pf. multicoloured . . 35 10

1966. Moon Landing of "Luna 9".

E886 E **290** 20 pf. multicoloured . . 1·75 25

E **291** Road Signs

1966. Road Safety.

E887 E **291** 10 pf. red, bl & ultram . 10 10
E888 – 15 pf. blk, yell & grn . 10 10
E889 – 25 pf. blk, bl & bis . . 10 10
E890 – 50 pf. blk, yell & red . 1·10 50

DESIGNS: 15 pf. Child on scooter crossing in front of car; 25 pf. Cyclist and hand-signal; 50 pf. Motor cyclist, glass of beer and ambulance.

E **292** Marx and Lenin Banner

1966. 20th Anniv of Socialist Unity Party (S.E.D.).

E891 – 5 pf. multicoloured . . 10 10
E892 E **292** 10 pf. yell, blk & red . . 10 10
E893 – 15 pf. black & green . . 10 10
E894 – 20 pf. black & red . . 15 10
E895 – 25 pf. blk, yell & red . 1·25 1·00

DESIGNS—VERT: 5 pf. Party badge and demonstrators; 15 pf. Marx, Engels and manifesto; 20 pf. Pieck and Grotewohl. HORIZ: 25 pf. Workers greeting Ulbricht.

E **293** W.H.O. Building

1966. Inaug of W.H.O. Headquarters, Geneva.

E896 E **293** 20 pf. multicoloured . . 30 20

E **294** Spreewald

1966. National Parks. Multicoloured.

E897 10 pf. Type E **294** 10 10
E898 15 pf. Konigsstuhl (Isle of Rugen) 10 10
E899 20 pf. Sachsische Schweiz . . 10 10
E900 25 pf. Westdarss 20 10
E901 30 pf. Teufelsmauer 20 10
E902 50 pf. Feldberg Lakes . . . . 1·60 1·00

E **295** Lace "Flower" E **296** Lily of the Valley

1966. Plauen Lace. Floral Patterns as Type E **295**.

E903 E **295** 10 pf. myrtle & grn . . 10 10
E904 – 20 pf. indigo & blue . . 20 10
E905 – 25 pf. red & rose . . . 25 10
E906 – 50 pf. violet & lilac . . 2·25 1·10

1966. Int Horticultural Show, Erfurt. Mult.

E907 20 pf. Type E **296** 10 10
E908 25 pf. Rhododendrons 20 10
E909 40 pf. Dahlias 20 10
E910 50 pf. Cyclamen . . . . . . 3·50 3·00

E **297** Parachutist on Target

1966. 8th World Parachute Jumping Championships, Leipzig.

E911 E **297** 10 pf. bl, blk & bis . . . 10 10
E912 – 15 pf. multicoloured . . 50 50
E913 – 20 pf. blk, bis & bl . . 10 10
DESIGNS: 15 pf. Group descent; 20 pf. Free fall.

E **298** Hans Kahle and Music of "The Thalmann Column"

1966. 30th Anniv of Int. Brigade in Spain. Multicoloured.

E914 5 pf. Type E **298** 10 10
E915 10 pf. + 5 pf. W. Bredel and open-air class 10 10
E916 15 pf. H. Beimler and Madrid street-fighting 10 10
E917 20 pf. + 10 pf. H. Rau and march-past after Battle of Brunete 20 10
E918 25 pf. + 10 pf. H. Marchwitza and soldiers 25 10
E919 40 pf. + 10 pf. A. Becker and Ebro battle . . . . 1·50 95

E **299** Canoeing

1966. World Canoeing Championships, Berlin. Multicoloured.

E920 10 pf. + 5 pf. Type E **299** . . 10 10
E921 15 pf. Kayak doubles . . . . 1·00 1·00

E **300** Television Set

1966. Leipzig Autumn Fair. Multicoloured.

E922 10 pf. Type E **300** 30 10
E923 15 pf. Electric typewriter . . . 50 10

E **301** Oradour Memorial

1966. Oradour-sur-Glane War Victims. Commem.

E924 E **301** 25 pf. blk, bl & red . . 20 10

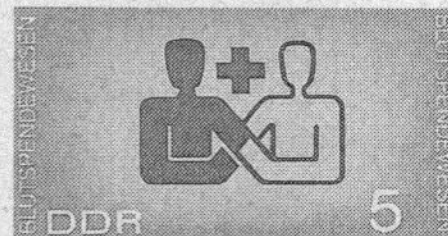

E **302** "Blood Donors"

1966. Int. Health Co-operation.

E925 E **302** 5 pf. red and green . . 10 10
E926 – 20 pf. + 10 pf. red and violet 10 10
E927 – 40 pf. red and blue . . 1·10 40
DESIGNS—HORIZ: 20 pf. I.C.Y. emblem. VERT: 40 pf. Health symbol.

E **303** Weightlifting ("snatch") E **304** Congress Hall

1966. World and European Weightlifting Championships, Berlin.

E928 E **303** 15 pf. black & brn . . 1·10 1·25
E929 – 20 pf. + 5 pf. black and blue 15 10
DESIGN: 20 pf. Weightlifting ("jerk").

1966. 6th Int. Journalists' Congress, Berlin.

E930 E **304** 10 pf. multicoloured . . 35 20
E931 – 20 pf. yellow & blue . . 15 10
DESIGN—VERT: 20 pf. Emblem of Int Organization of journalists.

1966. Provincial Costumes (2nd series). As Type E **261**. Multicoloured.

E932 5 pf. Altenburg (female) . . . 15 15
E933 10 pf. Altenburg (male) . . . 15 15
E934 10 pf. Mecklenburg (female) . 15 15
E935 15 pf. Mecklenburg (male) . . 15 15
E936 20 pf. Magdeburger Borde (female) . . . . 2·00 2·00
E937 30 pf. Magdeburger Borde (male) . . . . 2·00 2·00

E **305** "Vietnam is Invincible"

1966. Aid for Vietnam.

E938 E **305** 20 pf. + 5 pf. black and pink 25 10

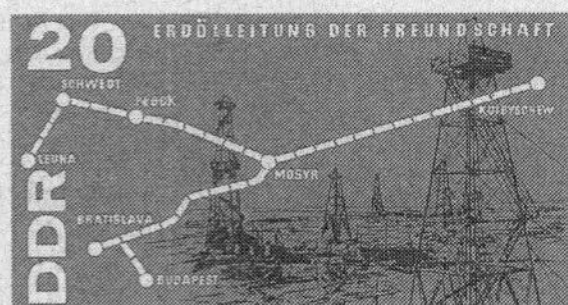

E **306** Oil Rigs and Pipeline Map

1966. Inaug of Int "Friendship" Oil Pipeline.

E939 E **306** 20 pf. black & red . . . 10 10
E940 – 25 pf. black & blue . . 50 30
DESIGN: 25 pf. "Walter Ulbricht" Oil Works, Leuna and pipeline map.

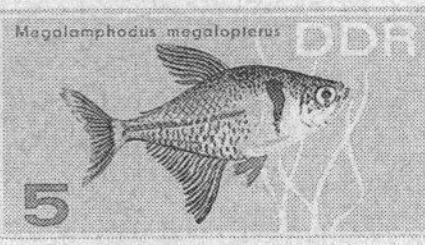

E **307** Black Phantom Tetra

1966. Aquarium Fishes. Multicoloured.

E941 5 pf. Type E **307** 10 10
E942 10 pf. Cardinal tetra 10 10
E943 15 pf. Rio Grande cichlid . . 2·40 2·00
E944 20 pf. Blue gularis 15 10
E945 25 pf. Ramirez's dwarf cichlid . 20 10
E946 40 pf. Honey gourami 30 15

E **308** "Horse" (detail from Ishtar Gate)

1966. Babylonian Art Treasures, Vorderasiatisches Museum, Berlin. Multicoloured.

E947 10 pf. Type E **308** 10 10
E948 20 pf. Mythological animal, Ishtar Gate 10 10
E949 25 pf. Lion facing right (vert) . 10 10
E950 50 pf. Lion facing left (vert) . . 85 85

E **309** The Wartburg from the East E **310** "Gentiana pneumonanthe"

1966. 900th Anniv of Wartburg Castle.

E951 E **309** 10 pf. + 5 pf. slate . . 10 10
E952 – 20 pf. green 10 10
E953 – 25 pf. purple 60 35
DESIGNS: 20 pf. Castle bailiwick; 25 pf. Residence.

1966. Protected Plants (1st series). Mult.

E954 10 pf. Type E **310** 10 10
E955 20 pf. "Cephalanthera rubra" . 15 10
E956 25 pf. "Arnica montana" . . . 1·40 80
See also Nos. E1177/82 and E1284/9.

E **311** Son leaves Home E **312** Worlitz Castle

1966. Fairy Tales (1st series). "The Wishing Table". Multicoloured.

E957 5 pf. Type E **311** 30 30
E958 10 pf. Setting the table 30 30
E959 20 pf. The thieving inn-keeper . 30 30
E960 25 pf. The magic donkey . . . 30 30
E961 30 pf. The cudgel in the sack . 30 30
E962 50 pf. Return of the son . . . 30 30
See also Nos. E1045/50, E1147/52, E1171/6, E1266/71, E1437/42, E1525/30, E1623/8, E1711/16, E1811/13, E1902/7, E1996/2001 and E2092/7.

1967. Principal East German Buildings. (1st series). Multicoloured.

E964 5 pf. Type E **312** 10 10
E965 10 pf. Stralsund Town Hall . . 10 10
E966 15 pf. Chorin Monastery . . . 10 10
E967 20 pf. Ribbeck House, Berlin . 10 10
E968 25 pf. Moritzburg, Zeitz . . . 10 10
E969 40 pf. Old Town Hall Potsdam . . . . 1·10 90
The 10 pf., 15 pf., 25 pf. and 40 pf. are vert.
See also Nos. E1100/3 and E1155/60.

E **313** Rifle-shooting

1967. World Biathlon Championships, Altenburg.

E970 E **313** 10 pf. bl, drab & mve . . 10 10
E971 – 20 pf. ol, bl & grn . . . 15 10
E972 – 25 pf. grn, bl & ol . . . 1·00 65
DESIGNS: 20 pf. Shooting on skis; 25 pf. Riflemen racing on skis.

E **314** "Multilock" Loom

1967. Leipzig Spring Fair.

E973 E **314** 10 pf. grn, grey & pur . . 15 10
E974 – 15 pf. bistre & blue . . 35 10
DESIGN: 15 pf. Zeiss tracking telescope.

E **315** Mother and Child E **317** "Portrait of a Girl" (after F Hodler)

E **316** Industrial Control Desk

1967. 20th Anniv of German Democratic Women's Federation.

E975 E **315** 20 pf. grey, red and purple 10 10
E976 – 25 pf. brown, turq and brown 75 60
DESIGN: 25 pf. Professional woman.

1967. Socialist Party Rally. Multicoloured.

(a) 1st series.

E977 10 pf. Type E **316** 10 10
E978 20 pf. Ulbricht meeting workers 10 10
E979 25 pf. Servicemen guarding industrial plants 10 10
E980 40 pf. Agricultural workers and harvesters 65 55
Each with inset portraits of Marx, Engels and Lenin.

(b) 2nd series. As Type E **316** but vert.

E981 5 pf. Agricultural worker . . . 10 10
E982 10 pf. Teacher and pupil . . . 10 10
E983 15 pf. Socialist family 40 40
E984 20 pf. Servicemen 10 10
Each with inset portraits as above.

1967. Dresden Gallery Paintings (1st series). Multicoloured.

E985 20 pf. Type E **317** 10 10
E986 25 pf. "Peter at the Zoo" (H. Hakenbeck) 10 10
E987 30 pf. "Venetian Episode" (R. Bergander) 10 10
E988 40 pf. "Tahitian Women" (Gauguin) 10 10
E989 50 pf. "The Grandchild" (J. Scholtz) . . . . 1·60 1·60
E990 70 pf. "Cairn in the Snow" (C. D. Friedrich) 15 15
The 40 pf. and 70 pf. are horiz.
See also Nos. E1114/19 and E1249/54.

E **318** Barn Owl E **319** Cycle Wheels

1967. Protected Birds. Multicoloured.

E991 5 pf. Type E **318** 20 10
E992 10 pf. Common Crane 20 10
E993 20 pf. Peregrine Falcon . . . 30 10
E994 25 pf. Bullfinches 40 10
E995 30 pf. Common Kingfisher . . 4·75 2·50
E996 40 pf. Common Roller 25 10

1967. 20th Warsaw-Berlin-Prague Cycle Race.

E997 E **319** 10 pf. violet, black and yellow 10 10
E998 – 25 pf. red and blue . . 45 35
DESIGN: 25 pf. Racing cyclists.

E **320** "Tom Cat"

1967. Int Children's Day. Multicoloured.

E 999 5 pf. Type E **320** 10 10
E1000 10 pf. "Snow White" 10 10
E1001 15 pf. "Fire Brigade" 10 10
E1002 20 pf. "Cockerel" 10 10
E1003 25 pf. "Vase of Flowers" . . . 15 15
E1004 30 pf. "Children Playing with Ball" . . . . 1·00 65

E **321** "Girl with Grapes" (Gerard Dou)   E **322** Exhibition Emblem

1967. Paintings Missing from German National Galleries (after World War II).

E1005 5 pf. blue 10 10
E1006 10 pf. brown 10 10
E1007 20 pf. green 10 10
E1008 25 pf. purple 10 10
E1009 40 pf. olive 15 10
E1010 50 pf. sepia . . . . 1·60 1·40

DESIGNS—VERT: 10 pf. Type E **321**; 25 pf. "Portrait of W Schroeder-Devrient" (after K. Begas); 40 pf. "Young Girl in Straw Hat" (after S. Bray); 50 pf. "The Four Evangelists" (after Jordaens). HORIZ: 5 pf. "Three Horsemen" (after Rubens); 20 pf. "Spring Idyll" (after H. Thoma).

1967. 15th Agricultural Exn., Markkleeberg.

E1011 E **322** 20 pf. red, green and yellow 20 10

E **323** Marie Curie (Birth Cent)   E **324** Jack of Diamonds

1967. Birth Anniversaries.

E1012 – 5 pf. brown 10 10
E1013 E **323** 10 pf. blue 10 10
E1014 – 20 pf. red 10 10
E1015 – 25 pf. sepia 10 10
E1016 – 40 pf. green 80 55

PORTRAITS: 5 pf. G. Herwegh (poet—150th); 20 pf. Kathe Kollwitz (artist—cent); 25 pf. J. J. Winckelmann (archaeologist—250th); 40 pf. T. Storm (poet—150th).

1967. German Playing-Cards. Multicoloured.

E1017 5 pf. Type E **324** 15 10
E1018 10 pf. Jack of Hearts 15 10
E1019 20 pf. Jack of Spades 35 10
E1020 25 pf. Jack of Clubs . . . . 4·25 2·75

E **325** Mare and Filly

1967. Thoroughbred Horse Meeting, Berlin Multicoloured

E1021 5 pf. Type E **325** 10 10
E1022 10 pf. Stallion 10 10
E1023 20 pf. Horse-racing 30 10
E1024 50 pf. Two fillies (vert) . . . 2·75 1·75

E **326** Kitchen Equipment   E **328** Kragujevac Memorial

E **327** Max Reichpietsch and "Friedrich der Grosse" (battleship)

1967. Leipzig Autumn Fair. Multicoloured.

E1025 10 pf. Type E **326** 40 10
E1026 15 pf. Fur coat and "Interpelz" brand-mark . . 60 15

1967. 50th Anniv of Revolutionary Sailors' Movement. Multicoloured.

E1027 10 pf. Type E **327** 15 10
E1028 15 pf. Albin Kobis and battle-ship "Prinzregent Luitpold" . . . . . . 1·00 40
E1029 20 pf. Sailors' demonstration with battle cruiser "Seydlitz" 30 10

1967. Victims of Kragujevac (Yugoslavia) Massacre.

E1030 E **328** 25 pf. black, yellow & red 45 20

E **329** Worker and Dam ("Electrification")   E **330** Martin Luther (from engraving by Lucas Cranach the Elder)

1967. 50th Anniv of October Revolution.

E1031 5 pf. black, orange & red . . 10 10
E1032 10 pf. black, red & bistre . . 10 10
E1033 15 pf. black, red & grey . . 10 10
E1034 20 pf. black, red & orange . . 20 10
E1035 40 pf. black, red & orange . . 2·50 1·90

DESIGNS: 5 pf. Worker and newspaper headline "Hands off Soviet Russia!"; 10 pf. Type E **329**. 15 pf. Treptow Memorial ("Victory over Fascism"); 20 pf. German and Soviet soldiers ("Friendship"); 40 pf. Lenin and cruiser "Aurora". Each with hammer and sickle.

1967. 450th Anniv of Reformation.

E1037 E **330** 20 pf. black & mauve . 10 10
E1038 – 25 pf. black & blue . . 10 10
E1039 – 40 pf. black & bistre . 1·90 1·00

DESIGNS—HORIZ: 25 pf. Luther's house, Wittenberg. VERT: 40 pf. Castle church, Wittenberg.

E **331** Young Workers   E **332** Goethe's House Weimar

1967. 10th "Masters of Tomorrow" Fair, Leipzig.

E1040 20 pf. black, gold & blue . . 40 35
E1041 20 pf. black, gold & blue . . 40 35
E1042 25 pf. multicoloured 40 35

DESIGNS—VERT: No. E1040, Type E **331**; No. E1041, Young man and woman. HORIZ:—(51 × 29 mm): No. E1042, Presentation of awards.

1967. Cultural Places.

E1043 E **332** 20 pf. blk, brn & grey . 15 10
E1044 – 25 pf. ol, brn & yell . 1·40 50

DESIGN: 25 pf. Schiller's House, Weimar.

E **333** Queen and Courtiers   E **335** Nutcracker and Two "Smokers"

E **334** Peasants and Modern Farm Buildings

1967. Fairy Tales (2nd series). "King Thrushbeard". Designs showing different scenes.

E1045 E **333** 5 pf. multicoloured . 25 25
E1046 – 10 pf. multicoloured . 25 25
E1047 – 15 pf. multicoloured . 25 25
E1048 – 20 pf. multicoloured . 25 25
E1049 – 25 pf. multicoloured . 25 25
E1050 – 30 pf. multicoloured . 25 25

1967. 15th Anniv of Agricultural Co-operatives.

E1052 E **334** 10 pf. sepia, green and olive 20 10

1967. Popular Art of the Erzgebirge. Multicoloured.

E1053 10 pf. Type E **335** 55 25
E1054 20 pf. "Angel" and miner with candles (carved figures) . . 10 10

E **336** Ice Skating   E **337** Actinometer

1968. Winter Olympic Games, Grenoble.

E1055 E **336** 5 pf. blue, red and light blue 10 10
E1056 – 10 pf. + 5 pf. blue, red & turquoise 10 10
E1057 – 15 pf. mult 20 10
E1058 – 20 pf. ultramarine, red and blue 20 10
E1059 – 25 pf. mult 30 10
E1060 – 30 pf. ultram, red and blue . . . . . . 2·50 1·60

DESIGNS: 10 pf. Tobogganning; 15 pf. Slalom; 20 pf. Ice hockey; 25 pf. Figure skating (pairs); 30 pf. Cross-country skiing.

1968. 75th Anniv of Potsdam Meteorological Observatory and World Meteorological Day (23 March).

E1061 E **337** 10 pf. blk, red & pur . 35 35
E1062 – 20 pf. mult 35 35
E1063 – 25 pf. blk, yell & grn . 35 35

DESIGNS—VERT: 25 pf. Cornfield by day and night. HORIZ:—(50 × 28 mm): 20 pf. Satellite picture of clouds.

E **338** "Venus 4"

1968. Soviet Space Achievements. Mult.

E1064 20 pf. Type E **338** 20 10
E1065 25 pf. Coupled satellites "Cosmos 186" and "188" . 1·00 30

E **339** "Illegal Struggle" (man, wife and child)   E **341** Gorky

E **340** Type DE1 Diesel-electric Locomotive

1968. Stained-glass Windows, Sachsenhausen National Memorial Museum. Multicoloured.

E1066 10 pf. Type E **339** 10 10
E1067 20 pf. "Liberation" 10 10
E1068 25 pf. "Partisans' Struggle" . 50 40

1968. Leipzig Spring Fair. Multicoloured.

E1069 10 pf. Type E **340** 40 15
E1070 15 pf. Deep sea trawler . . . 75 30

1968. Birth Cent of Maxim Gorky (writer).

E1071 E **341** 20 pf. pur & red . . . 10 10
E1072 – 25 pf. pur & red . . . 60 40

DESIGN: 25 pf. Fulmar (from "Song of the Stormy Petrel"—poem).

1968. Provincial Costumes (3rd series). As Type E **261**. Multicoloured.

E1073 10 pf. Hoyerswerda (female) . . 10 10
E1074 20 pf. Schleife (female) . . . 10 10
E1075 40 pf. Crostwitz (female) . . 10 10
E1076 50 pf. Spreewald (female) . . 2·25 90

E **342** Ring-necked Pheasants   E **343** Karl Marx

1968. Small Game. Multicoloured.

E1077 10 pf. Type E **342** 40 10
E1078 15 pf. Grey Partridges . . . 40 10
E1079 20 pf. Mallards 40 10
E1080 25 pf. Greylag Geese 40 10
E1081 30 pf. Wood Pigeon 50 15
E1082 40 pf. Brown hares . . . . . 3·00 5·00

1968. 150th Birth Anniv of Karl Marx.

E1083 – 10 pf. blk & grn . . . 75 75
E1084 E **343** 20 pf. blk, yell & red . 75 75
E1085 – 25 pf. blk, brn & yell . 75 75

DESIGNS: 10 pf. Title-page of "Communist Manifesto"; 25 pf. Title-page of "Das Kapital".

E **344** "Fritz Heckert" (after E. Hering)   E **345** Hammer and Anvil ("The right to work")

1968. 7th Confederation of Free German Trade Unions Congress. Multicoloured.

E1087 10 pf. Type E **344** 15 10
E1088 20 pf. Young workers and new tenements 20 20

1968. Human Rights Year.

E1089 E **345** 5 pf. mve & pur . . . 10 10
E1090 – 10 pf. bistre & brn . . 10 10
E1091 – 25 pf. bl & turq . . 60 35

DESIGNS: 10 pf. Tree and Globe ("The right to live"); 25 pf. Dove and Sun ("The right to peace").

E **346** Vietnamese Mother and Child

1968. Aid for Vietnam.

E1092 E **346** 10 pf. + 5 pf. mult . . 15 10

E **347** Angling (World Angling Championships, Gustrow)

1968. Sporting Events.

E1093 E **347** 20 pf. bl, grn & red . . 70 70
E1094 – 20 pf. blue, turq & grn 10 10
E1095 – 20 pf. pur, red & bl . . 10 10

DESIGNS: No. E1094, Sculling (European Women's Rowing Championships, Berlin); No. E1095, High jumping (2nd European Youth Athletic Competitions).

E **348** Brandenburg Gate and Torch   E **349** Festival Emblem

1968. German Youth Sports Day. Mult.

E1096 10 pf. Type E **348** 10 10
E1097 25 pf. Stadium plan and torch 90 65

1968. Peace Festival, Sofia.

E1098 E **349** 20 pf. + 5 pf. mult . . 10 10
E1099 25 pf. multicoloured . . 70 35

1968. Principal East German Buildings (2nd series). As Type E **312**. Multicoloured.
E1100 10 pf. Town Hall, Wernigerode 10 10
E1101 20 pf. Moritzburg Castle, Dresden 10 10
E1102 25 pf. Town Hall, Greifswald 10 10
E1103 30 pf. New Palace, Potsdam . 80 85
DESIGN SIZES—VERT: 10 pf., 25 pf. (24 × 29 mm). HORIZ: 20 pf., 30 pf. (51½ × 29½ mm).

E **350** Walter Ulbricht

1968. 75th Birthday of Walter Ulbricht (Chairman of Council of State).
E1104 E **350** 20 pf. black, red and orange 20 10

E **351** Ancient Rostock

1968. 750th Anniv of Rostock. Mult.
E1105 20 pf. Type E **351** 20 10
E1106 25 pf. Rostock, 1968 . . . . 50 50

E **352** Dr K. Landsteiner (physician and pathologist, birth cent)

1968. Celebrities' Annivs. (1st series).
E1107 E **352** 10 pf. grey 10 10
E1108 – 15 pf. black 20 10
E1109 – 20 pf. brown 10 10
E1110 – 25 pf. blue 10 10
E1111 – 40 pf. red 80 65
DESIGNS: 15 pf. Emanuel Lasker (chess master, birth cent); 20 pf. Hans Eisler (composer, 70th birth anniv); 25 pf. Ignaz Semmelweis (physician, 150th birth anniv); 40 pf. Max von Pettenkofer (hygienist, 150th birth anniv).
See also Nos. E1161/4 and E1256/61.

E **353** Zlin Z-226 Trener 6 looping

E **354** "At the Seaside" (Womacka)

1963. Aerobatics World Championships, Magdeburg. Multicoloured.
E1112 10 pf. Type E **353** 10 10
E1113 25 pf. Stunt flying 60 50

1968. Dresden Gallery Paintings (2nd series). Multicoloured.
E1114 10 pf. Type E **354** 10 10
E1115 15 pf. "Peasants Mowing Mountain Meadow" (Egger-Lienz) 10 10
E1116 20 pf. "Portrait of a Farmer's Wife" (Liebl) 10 10
E1117 40 pf. "Portrait of my Daughter" (Venturelli) . . 15 10
E1118 50 pf. "High-School Girl" (Michaelis) 15 15
E1119 70 pf. "Girl with Guitar" (Castelli) . . . . 2·10 1·40
The 20 pf. to 70 pf. are vert.

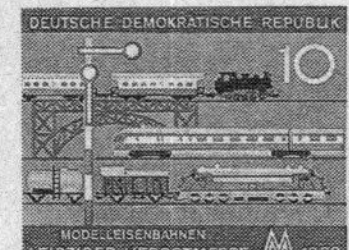

E **355** Model Trains

1968. Leipzig Autumn Fair.
E1120 E **355** 10 pf. multicoloured . 25 10

E **356** Spremberg Dam

1968. East German Post-War Dams. Multicoloured.
E1121 5 pf. Type E **356** 10 10
E1122 10 pf. Pohl Dam 10 10
E1123 15 pf. Ohra Valley Dam . . . 50 50
E1124 20 pf. Rappbode Dam . . . 10 10
The 10 pf. and 15 pf. are vert.

E **357** Sprinting

1968. Olympic Games, Mexico. Multicoloured.
E1125 5 pf. Type E **357** 10 10
E1126 10 pf. + 5 pf. Pole-vaulting . 10 10
E1127 20 pf. + 10 pf. Football . . 10 10
E1128 25 pf. Gymnastics 20 10
E1129 40 pf. Water-polo 30 10
E1130 70 pf. Sculling . . . . 1·50 1·50
The 10, 20, 25 and 40 pf. are vert.

E **358** Breendonk Memorial, Belgium

E **359** Green Tiger Beetle

1968. Breendonk War Victims. Commem.
E1131 E **358** 25 pf. mult 20 10

1968. "Useful Beetles". Multicoloured.
E1132 10 pf. Type E **359** 10 10
E1133 15 pf. Cyprus beetle 10 10
E1134 20 pf. Two spotted ladybird . 20 10
E1135 25 pf. Field ground beetle . . 3·00 1·60
E1136 30 pf. Hister beetle 30 10
E1137 40 pf. "Pseudoclerops mutillarius" 40 10

E **360** Lenin and Letter to Spartacus Group

1968. 50th Anniv of German November Revolution.
E1138 10 pf. black, red and yellow . 10 10
E1139 20 pf. black, red and yellow . 10 10
E1140 25 pf. black, red and yellow . 40 40
DESIGNS: 10 pf. Type E **360**; 20 pf. Revolutionaries and title of Spartacus newspaper "Die Rote Fahne"; 25 pf. Karl Liebknecht and Rose Luxemburg.

E **361** "Lailio-cattleya alba rubra" ("Maggie Raphaela")

1968. Orchids. Multicoloured.
E1141 5 pf. Type E **361** 10 10
E1142 10 pf. "Paphiopedilum albertianum" 10 10
E1143 15 pf. "Cattleya fabia" . . . 10 10
E1144 20 pf. "Cattleya aclaniae" . . 15 10
E1145 40 pf. "Sobralia macrantha" . 15 15
E1146 50 pf. "Dendrobium alpha" . 2·00 1·60

E **362** Trying on the Boots

1968. Fairy Tales (3rd series). "Puss in Boots". As Type E **362**. Designs showing different scenes.
E1147 5 pf. multicoloured 35 35
E1148 10 pf. multicoloured 35 35
E1149 15 pf. multicoloured 35 35
E1150 20 pf. multicoloured 35 35
E1151 25 pf. multicoloured 35 35
E1152 30 pf. multicoloured 35 35

E **363** Young Pioneers

1968. 20th Anniv of Ernst Thalmann's "Young Pioneers." Multicoloured.
E1153 10 pf. Type E **363** 10 10
E1154 15 pf. Young pioneers (diff) . 35 25

1969. Principal East German Buildings (3rd series). As Type E **312**. Multicoloured.
E1155 5 pf. Town Hall, Tangermunde 10 10
E1156 10 pf. State Opera House, Berlin 10 10
E1157 20 pf. Rampart Pavilion, Dresden Castle 10 10
E1158 25 pf. Patrician's House, Luckau . . . . 1·00 80
E1159 30 pf. Dornburg Castle . . . 15 10
E1160 40 pf. "Zum Stockfisch" Inn, Erfurt 15 15
The 5, 20, 25 and 40 pf. are vert.

1969. Celebrities' Annivs. (2nd series). As Type E **352**.
E1161 10 pf. olive 10 10
E1162 20 pf. brown 10 10
E1163 25 pf. blue 80 55
E1164 40 pf. brown 10 10
DESIGNS: 10 pf. M. A. Nexo (Danish poet—birth cent.); 20 pf. O. Nagel (painter—75th birth anniv); 25 pf. A. von Humboldt (naturalist—bicent. of birth); 40 pf. T. Fontane (writer—150th birth anniv).

E **364** Pedestrian Crossing

1969. Road Safety. Multicoloured.
E1165 5 pf. Type E **364** 10 10
E1166 10 pf. Traffic lights 10 10
E1167 20 pf. Level-crossing sign . . 20 10
E1168 25 pf. Motor-vehicle overtaking 55 35

E **365** "E-512" Combine-harvester

1969. Leipzig Spring Fair. Multicoloured.
E1169 10 pf. Type E **365** 10 10
E1170 15 pf. "Planeta-Variant" lithograph printing-press . 15 15

E **366** Jorinde and Joringel

E **367** Spring Snowflake

1969. Fairy Tales (4th series). "Jorinde and Joringel". As Type E **366**, showing different scenes.
E1171 5 pf. multicoloured 25 25
E1172 10 pf. multicoloured 25 25
E1173 15 pf. multicoloured 25 25
E1174 20 pf. multicoloured 25 25
E1175 25 pf. multicoloured 25 25
E1176 30 pf. multicoloured 25 25

1969. Protected Plants (2nd series). Mult.
E1177 5 pf. Type E **367** 10 10
E1178 10 pf. Yellow pheasant's-eye ("Adonis vernalis") . . . 10 10
E1179 15 pf. Globe flower ("Trollius europaeus") 10 10
E1180 20 pf. Martagon lily ("Lilium martagon") 15 10
E1181 25 pf. Sea holly ("Eryngium maritmum") . . . . . . 2·50 1·50
E1182 30 pf. "Dactylorchis latifolia" 25 10
See also Nos. E1284/9.

MINIMUM PRICE

The minimum price quoted is 10p which represents a handling charge rather than a basis for valuing common stamps. For further notes about prices see introductory pages.

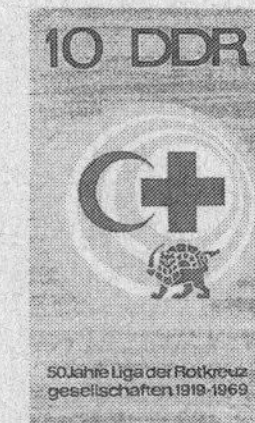

E **368** Plantation of Young Conifers

E **369** Symbols of the Societies

1969. Forest Fires Prevention. Mult.
E1183 5 pf. Type E **368** 10 10
E1184 10 pf. Lumber, and resin extraction 20 10
E1185 20 pf. Forest stream 20 10
E1186 25 pf. Woodland camp . . . 1·25 45

1969. 50th Anniv of League of Red Cross Societies. Multicoloured.
E1187 10 pf. Type E **369** 20 10
E1188 15 pf. Similar design with symbols in oblong 65 20

E **370** Erythrite (Schneeberg)

E **371** Women and Symbols

1969. East German Minerals. Multicoloured.
E1189 5 pf. Type E **370** 10 10
E1190 10 pf. Fluorite (Hals-brucke) . 10 10
E1191 15 pf. Galena (Neudorf) . . . 10 10
E1192 20 pf. Smoky Quartz (Lichtenberg) 10 10
E1193 25 pf. Calcite (Niederrabenstein) . . . . 1·10 1·10
E1194 50 pf. Silver (Freiberg) . . . 15 10

1969. 2nd D.D.R. Women's Congress.
E1195 E **371** 20 pf., red & blue . . 10 10
E1196 – 25 pf. blue & red . . . 50 25
DESIGN: 25 pf. Woman and Symbols (different).

1969. As Nos. E586/7 (Ulbricht), but with face values expressed in "M" (Mark).
E1197 1 M green 35 20
E1198 2 M. brown 65 50

E **372** Badge of D.D.R. Philatelists' Association

E **373** Armed Volunteers

1969. 20th Anniv of DDR Stamp Exhibition, Magdeburg (1st issue).
E1199 E **372** 10 pf. gold, blue and red 15 10
See also Nos. E1233/4.

1969. Aid for Vietnam.
E1200 E **373** 10 pf. + 5 pf. mult . . 15 10

E **374** "Development of Youth"

E **375** Inaugural Ceremony

1969. Int Peace Meeting, East Berlin. Mult.
E1201 10 pf. Type E **374** 45 45
E1202 20 pf. + 5 pf. Berlin landmarks (50 × 28 mm) . . . 45 45
E1203 25 pf. "Workers of the World" 45 45

1969. 5th Gymnastics and Athletic Meeting, Leipzig. Multicoloured.
E1204 5 pf. Type E **375** 10 10
E1205 10 pf. + 5 pf. Gymnastics . . 10 10
E1206 15 pf. Athletes' parade . . . 10 10
E1207 20 pf. + 5 pf. "Sport" Art Exhibition 10 10
E1208 25 pf. Athletic events . . . . 1·40 50
E1209 30 pf. Presentation of colours 10 10

E 376 Pierre de Coubertin (from bust by W. Forster)

E 377 Knight

1969. 75th Anniv of Pierre de Coubertin's Revival of Olympic Games' Movement.
E1210 E 376 10 pf. sep, blk & bl 10 10
E1211 – 25 pf. sep, blk & red 70 50
DESIGN: 25 pf. Coubertin monument, Olympia.

1969. World Sports Championships. Mult.
E1212 E 377 20 pf. gold, red & pur 30 15
E1213 – 20 pf. mult 15 15
E1214 – 20 pf. mult 15 15
DESIGNS AND EVENTS: No. E1212, 16th World Students' Team Championship, Dresden; No. E1213, Cycle Wheel (World Covered Court Cycling Championships, Erfurt); No. E1214, Ball and net (2nd World Volleyball Cup-ties).

E 378 Fair Display Samples

E 381 TV Tower, East Berlin

E 379 Rostock

1969. Leipzig Autumn Fair.
E1215 E 378 10 pf. mult 15 15

1969. 20th Anniv of German Democratic Republic. Multicoloured.
(a) 1st Issue. As Type E 379.
E1216 10 pf. Type E 379 10 10
E1217 10 pf. Neubrandenburg 10 10
E1218 10 pf. Potsdam 10 15
E1219 10 pf. Eisenhuttenstadt 10 15
E1220 10 pf. Hoyerswerda 10 15
E1221 10 pf. Magdeburg 10 15
E1222 10 pf. Halle-Neustadt 10 10
E1223 10 pf. Suhl 10 10
E1224 10 pf. Dresden 10 10
E1225 10 pf. Leipzig 20 10
E1226 10 pf. Karl-Marx Stadt 10 10
E1227 10 pf. East Berlin 10 10
(b) 2nd Issue. As Type E 381.
E1230 10 pf. Type E 381 10 10
E1231 20 pf. "Globe" of Tower with TV Screen 20 15

E 382 O. von Guericke Memorial, Cathedral and Hotel International, Magdeburg

1969. 20th Anniv of D.D.R. Stamp Exhibition, Magdeburg (2nd issue). Multicoloured.
E1233 20 pf. Type E 382 10 10
E1234 40 pf. + 10 pf. Von Guericke's vacuum experiment 55 40

E 383 Ryvangen Memorial

E 384 U.F.I. Emblem

1969. War Victims' Memorial, Ryvangen (Copenhagen).
E1235 E 383 25 pf. multicoloured 30 10

1969. 36th Int. Fairs Union (U.F.I.) Congress, Leipzig.
E1236 E 384 10 pf. multicoloured 20 10
E1237 15 pf. multicoloured 1·25 25

E 385 I.L.O. Emblem

E 386 University Seal and Building

1969. 50th Anniv of I.L.O.
E1238 E 385 20 pf. silver & grn 15 10
E1239 25 pf. silv. & mve 80 30

1969. 550th Anniv of Rostock University. Multicoloured.
E1240 10 pf. Type E 386 20 10
E1241 15 pf. Steam-turbine rotor and curve (University emblem) 65 20

E 387 "Horseman" Pastry-mould

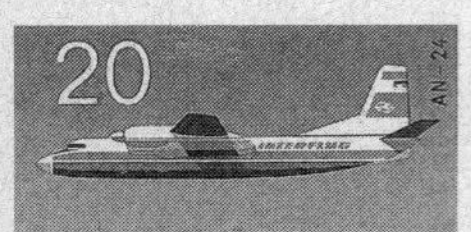

E 388 Antonov An-24B

1969. Lausitz Folk Art.
E1242 E 387 10 pf. brn, blk & flesh 1·00 90
E1243 – 20 pf. + 5 pf. mult 15 15
E1244 – 50 pf. mult 1·50 1·25
DESIGNS: 20 pf. Plate; 50 pf. Pastry in form of Negro couple.

1969. Interflug Aircraft. Multicoloured.
E1245 20 pf. Type E 388 10 10
E1246 25 pf. Ilyushin Il-18 1·25 1·25
E1247 30 pf. Tupolev Tu-134 15 15
E1248 50 pf. Mil Mi-8 helicopter 15 15

E 389 "Siberian Teacher" (Svechnikov)

1969. Dresden Gallery Paintings (3rd series). Multicoloured.
E1249 5 pf. Type E 389 10 10
E1250 10 pf. "Steel-worker" (Serov) 10 10
E1251 20 pf. "Still Life" (Aslamasjan) 10 10
E1252 25 pf. "A Warm Day" (Romas) 1·00 1·25
E1253 40 pf. "Springtime Again" (Kabatchek) 15 10
E1254 50 pf. "Man by the River" (Makovsky) 20 10

1970. Coil Stamp. As Nos. E577 etc., but value expressed in "M".
E1255 E 196 1 m. olive 45 10

1970. Celebrities Annivs. (3rd series). As Type E 352.
E1256 5 pf. blue 10 10
E1257 10 pf. brown 10 10
E1258 15 pf. blue 10 10
E1259 20 pf. purple 15 10
E1260 25 pf. blue 2·10 60
E1261 40 pf. red 30 10
DESIGNS: 5 pf. E. Barlach (sculptor and playwright; birth cent.); 10 pf. J. Gutenberg (printer; 500th death anniv) (1968); 15 pf. K. Tucholsky (author; 80th birth anniv); 20 pf. Beethoven (birth bicent.); 25 pf. F. Holderlin (poet; birth bicent.); 40 pf G. W. F. Hegel (philosopher; birth bicent.).

E 390 Red fox

1970. Int Fur Auction, Leipzig. Mult.
E1262 10 pf. Rabbit 20 10
E1263 20 pf. Type E 390 20 10
E1264 25 pf. European mink 3·00 2·25
E1265 40 pf. Common hamster 40 10

E 391 "Little Brother and Little Sister"

1970. Fairy Tales (5th series). "Little Brother and Little Sister". As Type E 391. showing different scenes.
E1266 5 pf. multicoloured 25 25
E1267 10 pf. multicoloured 25 25
E1268 15 pf. multicoloured 25 25
E1269 20 pf. multicoloured 25 25
E1270 25 pf. multicoloured 25 25
E1271 30 pf. multicoloured 25 25

E 392 Telephone and Electrical Switchgear

1970. Leipzig Spring Fair. Multicoloured.
E1272 10 pf. Type E 392 10 10
E1273 15 pf. High-voltage transformer (vert) 30 10

E 393 Horseman's Gravestone (A.D. 700)

1970. Archaeological Discoveries.
E1274 E 393 10 pf. ol, blk & grn 10 10
E1275 – 20 pf. blk, yell & red 10 10
E1276 – 25 pf. grn, blk & yell 80 80
E1277 – 40 pf. chestnut, black and brown 15 15
DESIGNS: 20 pf. Helmet (A.D. 500); 25 pf. Bronze basin (1000 B.C.); 40 pf. Clay drum (2500 B.C.).

E 394 Lenin and "Iskra" (= the Spark) press

1970. Birth Cent. Lenin. Multicoloured.
E1278 10 pf. Type E 394 10 10
E1279 20 pf. Lenin and Clara Zetkin 10 10
E1280 25 pf. Lenin and "State & Revolution" (book) 1·90 90
E1281 40 pf. Lenin Monument, Eisleben 10 10
E1282 70 pf. Lenin Square, East Berlin 20 15

1970. Protected Plants (3rd series). Vert designs as Type E 367. Multicoloured.
E1284 10 pf. Sea kale ("Crambe maritima") 10 10
E1285 20 pf. Pasque flower ("Pulsatilla vulgaris") 15 10
E1286 25 pf. Fringed gentian ("Gentiana ciliata") 1·60 1·75
E1287 30 pf. Military orchid ("Orchis militaris") 15 10
E1288 40 pf. Labrador tea ("Ledum palustre") 15 15
E1289 70 pf. Round-leaved wintergreen ("Pyrola rotundifolia") 30 10

E 395 Capture of the Reichstag, 1945

E 396 Shortwave Aerial

1970. 25th Anniv of "Liberation from Fascism". Multicoloured.
E1290 10 pf. Type E 395 10 10
E1291 20 pf. Newspaper headline, Kremlin and State Building, East Berlin 10 10
E1292 25 pf. C.M.E.A. Building, Moscow and flags 1·40 45

1970. 25th Anniv of D.D.R. Broadcasting Service. Multicoloured.
E1294 10 pf. Type E 396 40 40
E1295 15 pf. Radio Station, East Berlin 60 60
No. E1295 is a horiz. design, size 50 × 28 mm.

E 397 Globe and Ear of Corn

E 398 Fritz Heckert Medal

1970. 5th World Corn and Bread Congress, Dresden. Multicoloured.
E1296 20 pf. Type E 397 80 80
E1297 25 pf. Palace of Culture and ear of corn 80 80

1970. 25th Annivs. of German Confederation of Trade Unions and World Trade Union Federation ("Federation Syndicale Mondiale"). Mult.
E1298 20 pf. Type E 398 10 10
E1299 25 pf. F.S.M. Emblem 50 40

E 399 Gods Amon, Shu and Tefnut

1970. Sudanese Archaeological Excavations by Humboldt University Expedition. Multicoloured.
E1300 10 pf. Type E 399 10 10
E1301 15 pf. King Arnekhamani 10 10
E1302 20 pf. Cattle frieze 10 10
E1303 25 pf. Prince Arka 1·10 65
E1304 30 pf. God Arensnuphis (vert) 10 10
E1305 40 pf. War elephants and prisoners 15 10
E1306 50 pf. God Apedemak 15 10
The above designs reproduce carvings unearthed at the Lions' Temple, Musawwarat, Sudan.

E 400 Road Patrol

E 401 D.K.B. Emblem

1970. 25th Anniv of "Deutsche Volkspolizei" (police force). Multicoloured.
E1307 5 pf. Type E 400 10 10
E1308 10 pf. Policeman with children 10 10
E1309 15 pf. Radio patrol car 15 10
E1310 20 pf. Railway policeman 30 10
E1311 25 pf. River police in patrol boat 1·25 55

1970. 25th Anniv of "Deutscher Kulturbund" (cultural assn.).
E1312 E 401 10 pf. brn, silver and blue 1·60 2·00
E1313 – 25 pf. brown, gold and blue 1·60 2·00
DESIGN: 25 pf. Johannes Becher medal.

E **402** Arms of D.D.R. and Poland

1970. 20th Anniv of Gorlitz Agreement on Oder-Neisse Border.
E1314 E **402** 20 pf. mult 25 10

E **403** Vaulting

E **405** Cecilienhof Castle

E **404** Boy Pioneer with Neckerchief

1970. 3rd Children and Young People's Sports Days. Multicoloured.
E1315 10 pf. Type E **403** 10 10
E1316 20 pf. + 5 pf. Hurdling . . . 20 15

1970. 6th Young Pioneers Meeting. Cottbus. Multicoloured.
E1317 10 pf. + 5 pf. Type E **404** . . 20 20
E1318 25 pf. + 5 pf. Girl pioneer with neckerchief 20 20
Nos. E1317/18 were issued together, se-tenant, forming a composite design.

1970. 25th Anniv of Potsdam Agreement.
E1319 E **405** 10 pf. yellow, red and black 15 15
E1320 – 20 pf. black, red and yellow 15 15
E1321 – 25 pf. black & red . . 15 15
DESIGNS—VERT: 20 pf. "Potsdam Agreement" in four languages. HORIZ: (77 × 28 mm): 25 pf. Conference delegates around the table.

E **406** Pocket-watch and Wristwatch

E **407** T. Neubauer and M. Poser

1970. Leipzig Autumn Fair.
E1322 E **406** 10 pf. multicoloured . 20 10

1970. "Anti-Fascist Resistance".
E1323 E **407** 20 pf. pur, red & bl . . 15 10
E1324 – 25 pf. olive & red . . 25 20
DESIGN—VERT: 25 pf. "Motherland"—detail from Soviet War Memorial, Treptow, Berlin.

E **408** Pres. Ho-Chi-Minh

E **409** Compass and Map

1970. Aid for Vietnam and Ho-Chi-Minh. Commemoration.
E1325 E **408** 20 pf. + 5 pf. blk, red and pink 20 10

1970. World "Orienteering" Championships. East Germany. Multicoloured.
E1326 10 pf. Type E **409** 10 10
E1327 25 pf. Runner and three map sections 60 30

E **410** "Forester Scharf's Birthday" (Nagel)

1970. "The Art of Otto Nagel, Kathe Kollwitz and Ernst Barlach".
E1328 E **410** 10 pf. multicoloured . 10 10
E1329 – 20 pf. multicoloured . 10 10
E1330 – 25 pf. brn & mve . . 1·10 1·10
E1331 – 30 pf. black & pink . 10 10
E1332 – 40 pf. black & yellow . 15 10
E1333 – 50 pf. black & yellow . 15 10
DESIGNS: 20 pf. "Portrait of a Young Girl" (Nagel); 25 pf. "No More War" (Kollwitz); 30 pf. "Mother and Child" (Kollwitz); 40 pf. Sculptured head from Gustrow Cenotaph (Barlach); 50 pf. "The Flute-player" (Barlach).

E **411** "The Little Trumpeter" (Weineck Memorial, Halle)

E **413** Musk Ox

E **412** Flags Emblem

1970. 2nd National Youth Stamp Exhibition, Karl-Marx-Stadt. Multicoloured.
E1334 10 pf. Type E **411** 15 10
E1335 15 pf. + 5 pf. East German 25 pf. stamp of 1959 . . . 20 20

1970. "Comrades-in-Arms". Warsaw Pact Military Manoeuvres.
E1336 E **412** 10 pf. multicoloured . 10 10
E1337 20 pf. multicoloured . 15 10

1970. Animals in East Berlin "Tierpark" (Zoo). Multicoloured.
E1338 10 pf. Type E **413** 30 10
E1339 15 pf. Whale-headed Stork . 90 10
E1340 20 pf. Addax 75 30
E1341 25 pf. Sun bear . . . . . . 4·50 4·00

E **414** U.N. Emblem and Headquarters, New York

E **415** Engels

1970. 25th Anniv of United Nations.
E1342 E **414** 20 pf. multicoloured . 45 15

1970. 150th Birth Anniv of Friedrich Engels.
E1343 E **415** 10 pf. black, grey and orange 20 10
E1344 – 20 pf. blk, grn & orge . 20 10
E1345 – 25 pf. blk, red & orge . 1·00 55
DESIGNS: 20 pf. Engels, Marx and "Communist Manifesto"; 25 pf. Engels and "Anti Duhring".

HAVE YOU READ THE NOTES AT THE BEGINNING OF THIS CATALOGUE?
These often provide answers to the enquiries we receive.

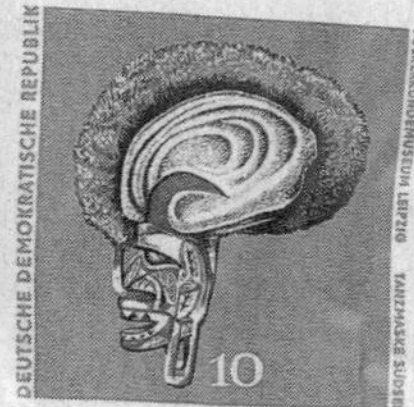

E **416** "Epiphyllum hybr"

E **417** Dancer's Mask, Bismarck Archipelago

1970. Cacti Cultivation in D.D.R. Mult.
E1346 5 pf. Type E **416** 10 10
E1347 10 pf. "Astrophytum myriostigma" 10 10
E1348 15 pf. "Echinocereus salm-dyckianus" 10 10
E1349 20 pf. "Selenicereus grandiflorus" 10 10
E1350 25 pf. "Hamatoc setispinus" . 1·60 1·40
E1351 30 pf. "Mamillaria boolii" . . 20 10

1971. Exhibits from the Ethnological Museum, Leipzig.
E1353 E **417** 10 pf. multicoloured . 10 10
E1354 – 20 pf. brn & orge . . 10 10
E1355 – 25 pf. multicoloured . 80 80
E1356 – 40 pf. brown & red . . 10 10
DESIGNS: 20 pf. Bronze head, Benin; 25 pf. Tea-pot, Thailand; 40 pf. Zapotec earthenware Jaguar-god, Mexico.

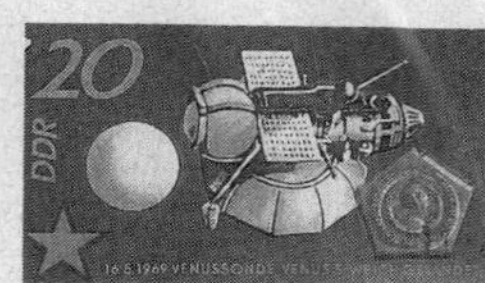

E **418** "Venus 5"

1971. Soviet Space Research. Multicoloured.
E1357 20 pf. Type E **418** 30 30
E1358 20 pf. Orbital space station . 30 30
E1359 20 pf. "Luna 10" and "Luna 16" 30 30
E1360 20 pf. Various "Soyuz" space-craft 30 30
E1361 20 pf. "Proton 1" satellite and "Vostok" rocket 30 30
E1362 20 pf. "Molniya 1" communi-cations satellite 30 30
E1363 20 pf. Gagarin and "Vostok 1" 30 30
E1364 20 pf. Leonov in space . . . 30 30

E **419** K. Liebknecht

R **420** J. R. Becher (poet)

1971. Birth Centenaries of Karl Liebknecht and Rosa Luxemburg (revolutionaries).
E1365 E **419** 20 pf. mauve, gold and black 40 40
E1366 – 25 pf. mauve, gold and black 40 40
DESIGN: 25 pf. Rosa Luxemburg.

1971. Celebrities' Birth Anniversaries.
E1367 E **420** 5 pf. brown 10 10
E1368 – 10 pf. blue 10 10
E1369 – 15 pf. black 10 10
E1370 – 20 pf. purple 10 10
E1371 – 25 pf. green 80 65
E1372 – 50 pf. blue 10 10
DESIGNS: 5 pf. (80th birth anniv); 10 pf. H. Mann (writer—birth cent); 15 pf. J. Heartfield (artist—80th birth anniv); 20 pf. W. Bredel (70th birth anniv); 25 pf. F. Mehring (politician—125th birth anniv); 50 pf. J. Kepler (astronomer—400th birth anniv).
See also Nos. E1427 and E1451/5.

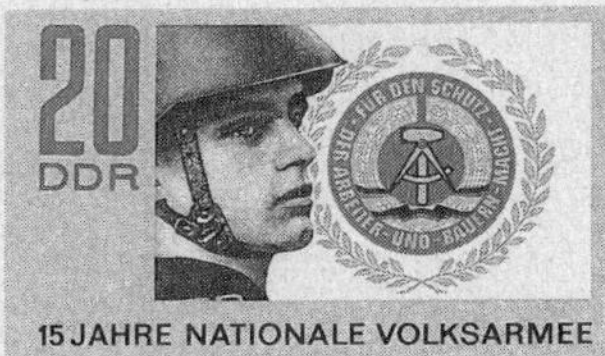

E **421** Soldier and Army Badge

1971. 15th Anniv of National People's Army.
E1373 E **421** 20 pf. multicoloured . 20 10

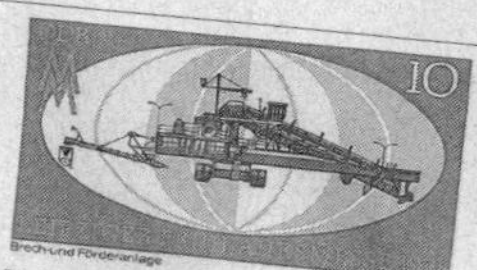

E **422** "Sket" Mobile Ore-crusher

1971. Leipzig Spring Fair. Multicoloured.
E1374 10 pf. Type E **422** 10 10
E1375 15 pf. Dredger "Takraf" . . 15 10

E **423** Proclam... Commu... the

E **425** St. Mary's Church

E **424** "Lunokhod 1" on

1971. Centenary of Paris ...ce
E1376 E **423** 10 pf. black, brown and red . . . .
E1377 – 20 pf. black, brown and red . . . . .
E1378 – 25 pf. black, brown and red *10*
E1379 – 30 pf. black, grey and red . . . .
DESIGNS: 20 pf. Women at the Place barricade; 25 pf. Cover of "L'Internationale Title page of Karl Marx's "The Civil France".

1971. Moon Mission of "Lunokhod 1".
E1380 E **424** 20 pf. turquoise, blue and red 40 20

1971. Berlin Buildings. Multicoloured.
E1381 10 pf. Type E **425** 10 10
E1382 15 pf. Kopenick Castle (horiz) 10 10
E1383 20 pf. Old Library (horiz) . . 10 10
E1384 25 pf. Ermeler House . . . . 2·50 2·00
E1385 50 pf. New Guardhouse (horiz) 25 10
E1386 70 pf. National Gallery (horiz) 30 15

E **426** "The Discus-thrower"

1971. 20th Anniv of D.D.R. National Olympics Committee.
E1387 E **426** 20 pf. mult 45 15

E **427** Handclasp and XXV Emblem

E **428** Schleife Costume

1971. 25th Anniv of Socialist Unity Party.
E1388 E **427** 20 pf. black, red and gold 20 10

1971. Sorbian Dance Costumes. Mult.
E1389 10 pf. Type E **428** 10 10
E1390 20 pf. Hoyerswerda 15 10
E1391 25 pf. Cottbus 80 75
E1392 40 pf. Kamenz 25 10
For 10 pf. and 20 pf. in smaller size, see Nos. E1443/4.

E 429 Self-portrait, c. 1500

E 432 "Internees"

E 430 Constr... tion Work...

...3 Cherry stone with 180 Carved Heads

1971. 50... Anniv of Albrecht Durer. ...gs. Multicoloured.
... E 429 . . . . . 10 10
... "Three Peasants" . 25 10
...hilipp
E1393 ...ichthon" . . . . . 1·25 1·00
E139...
E1...

...71. 8th S.E.D. Party Conference.
...30 5 pf. multicoloured . . 10 10
– 10 pf. multicoloured . 10 10
– 20 pf. multicoloured . 10 10
– 20 pf. gold, red & mauve 20 10
...99 – 25 pf. multicoloured . 40 40
...SIGNS: 10 pf. Technician; 20 pf. (No. E1398) ...arm girl; 20 pf. (No. E1400) Conference emblem (smaller, 23 × 29 mm); 25 pf. Soldier.

1971. 20th Anniv of International Resistance Federation (F.I.R.). Lithographs from Fritz Cremer's "Buchenwaldzyklus".
E1401 E **432** 20 pf. black & yell . . 50 55
E1402 – 25 pf. black & blue . . 50 55
DESIGN: 25 pf. "Attack on Guard".

1971. Art Treasures of Dresden's Green Vaults. Multicoloured.
E1403 5 pf. Type E **433** 10 10
E1404 10 pf. Insignia of the Golden Fleece, c. 1730 . . . . . . 10 10
E1405 15 pf. Nuremberg jug, c. 1530 . . . . 10 10
E1406 20 pf. Mounted Moorish drummer figurine, c. 1720 . . 15 10
E1407 25 pf. Writing-case, 1562 . . 90 90
E1408 30 pf. St. George medallion, c. 1570 . . . . 15 10

E **434** Mongolian Arms

E **435** Child's Face

1971. 50th Anniv of Mongolian People's Republic.
E1409 E **434** 20 pf. multicoloured . 20 10

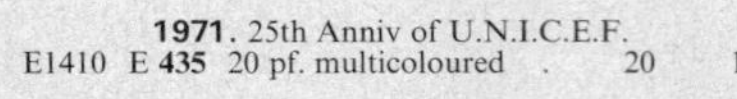

1971. 25th Anniv of U.N.I.C.E.F.
E1410 E **435** 20 pf. multicoloured . 20 10

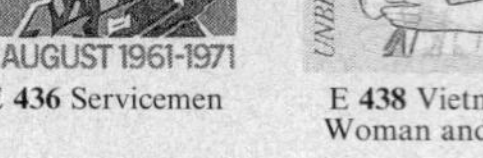

E **436** Servicemen

E **438** Vietnamese Woman and Child

E **437** Liner "Ivan Franko"

1971. 10th Anniv of Berlin Wall. Mult.
E1411 20 pf. Type E **436** 65 30
E1412 35 pf. Brandenburg Gate . . 1·25 80

1971. East German Shipbuilding Industry.
E1413 E **437** 10 pf. brown 15 10
E1414 – 15 pf. blue & brown . 15 10
E1415 – 20 pf. green 20 10
E1416 – 25 pf. blue . . . . 1·50 1·25
E1417 – 40 pf. brown 20 10
E1418 – 50 pf. blue 25 10
DESIGNS: 15 pf. Freighter "Irkutsk"; 20 pf. Freighter "Rostock"; 25 pf. Fish-factory ship "Junge Welt"; 40 pf. Container ship "Hansel"; 50 pf. Research ship "Akademik Kurchatov".

1971. Aid for Vietnam.
E1419 E **438** 10 pf. + 5 pf. mult . . 20 10

E **439** MAG-Butadien Plant

E **440** Upraised Arms (motif by J. Heartfield)

1971. Leipzig Autumn Fair.
E1420 E **439** 10 pf. vio, mve & grn . 10 10
E1421 – 25 pf. vio, grn & bl . . 20 15
DESIGN: 25 pf. SKL reactor plant.

1971. Racial Equality Year.
E1422 E **440** 35 pf. blk, silver & bl . 25 10

E **441** Tupolev Tu-134 Mail Plane at Airport

1971. Philatelists' Day.
E1423 E **441** 10 pf. + 5 pf. blue, red and green 20 10
E1424 – 25 pf. red, grn & bl . . 40 35
DESIGN: 25 pf. Milestone and Zurner's measuring cart.

E **442** Wiltz Memorial, Luxembourg

E **443** German Violin

1971. Monuments. Multicoloured.
E1425 25 pf. Type E **442** 20 10
E1426 35 pf. Karl Marx monument, Karl-Marx-Stadt 30 10

1971. 150th Birth Anniv of R. Virchow (physician). As Type E **420**.
E1427 40 pf. plum 30 10

1971. Musical Instruments in Markneukirchen Museum. Multicoloured.
E1428 10 pf. North African "darbuka" 10 10
E1429 15 pf. Mongolian "morin chuur" 10 10
E1430 20 pf. Type E **443** 15 10
E1431 25 pf. Italian mandolin . . . 15 10
E1432 40 pf. Bohemian bagpies . . . 15 10
E1433 50 pf. Sudanese "kasso" . . 1·10 1·10

E **444** "Dahlta O 10 A" Theodolite

E **445** Donkey and Windmill

1971. 125th Anniv of Carl Zeiss Optical Works, Jena.
E1434 E **444** 10 pf. blk, red & bl . . 40 40
E1435 – 20 pf. blk, red & bl . . 40 40
E1436 – 25 pf. blue, yellow and ultramarine 40 40
DESIGNS—VERT: 20 pf. "Ergaval" microscope. HORIZ: (52 × 29 mm) 25 pf. Planetarium.

1971. Fairy Tales (6th series). As Type E **445**. "The Town Musicians of Bremen".
E1437 5 pf. multicoloured 30 30
E1438 10 pf. multicoloured 30 30
E1439 15 pf. multicoloured 30 30
E1440 20 pf. multicoloured 30 30
E1441 25 pf. multicoloured 30 30
E1442 30 pf. multicoloured 30 30

1971. Sorbian Dance Costumes. As Nos. E1389/90 but smaller, size 23 × 28 mm.
E1443 E **428** 10 pf. mult 10 10
E1444 – 20 pf. mult 55 35

E **446** Tobogganing

1971. Winter Olympic Games, Sapporo, Japan (1972).
E1445 5 pf. black, green & mve . . 10 10
E1446 10 pf. + 5 pf. blk, bl & mve . . 10 10
E1447 15 pf. + 5 pf. blk, grn & bl . . 10 10
E1448 20 pf. black, mve & vio . . . 15 10
E1449 25 pf. black, vio & mve . . . 1·40 1·00
E1450 70 pf. black, blue & vio . . . 30 15
DESIGNS: 5 pf. Type E **446**; 10 pf. Figure skating; 15 pf. Speed skating; 20 pf. Cross-country skiing; 25 pf. Biathlon; 70 pf. Ski jumping.

1972. German Celebrities. As Type E **420**.
E1451 10 pf. green 10 10
E1452 20 pf. mauve 10 10
E1453 25 pf. blue 10 10
E1454 35 pf. brown 10 10
E1455 50 pf. lilac . . . . 1·00 1·00
CELEBRITIES: 10 pf. J. Tralow (writer); 20 pf. L. Frank (writer); 25 pf. K. A. Kocor (composer); 35 pf. H. Schliemann (archaeologist); 50 pf. Caroline Neuber (actress).

E **447** Gypsum from Eisleben

1972. Minerals. Multicoloured.
E1456 5 pf. Type E **447** 10 10
E1457 10 pf. Zinnwaldite, Zinnwald . 10 10
E1458 20 pf. Malachite, Ullersreuth . 15 10
E1459 25 pf. Amethyst, Wiesenbad . 15 10
E1460 35 pf. Halite, Merkers . . . 20 10
E1461 50 pf. Proustite, Schneeberg . 1·00 80

E **448** Vietnamese Woman

E **449** Soviet Exhibition Hall

1972. Aid for Vietnam.
E1462 E **448** 10 pf. + 5 pf. mult . . 20 10

1972. Leipzig Spring Fair. Multicoloured.
E1463 10 pf. Type E **449** 10 10
E1464 25 pf. East German and Soviet flags 20 15

E **451** W.H.O. Emblem

1972. World Health Day.
E1466 E **451** 35 pf. ultramarine, silver & blue . . . 25 10

E **452** Kamov Ka-26 Helicopter

1972. East German Aircraft. Multicoloured.
E1467 5 pf. Type E **452** 20 10
E1468 10 pf. Letov Z-37 Cmelak crop-sprayer 20 10
E1469 35 pf. Ilyushin Il-62M . . . 30 10
E1470 1 m. Ilyushin Il-62M . . . . 1·60 1·25

E **453** Wrestling

1972. Olympic Games, Munich. Mult.
E1471 5 pf. Type E **453** 10 10
E1472 10 pf. + 5 pf. High-diving . . 20 10
E1473 20 pf. Pole-vaulting 20 10
E1474 25 pf. + 10 pf. Rowing . . . 20 10
E1475 35 pf. Handball 30 10
E1476 70 pf. Gymnastics . . . . . 2·40 1·50

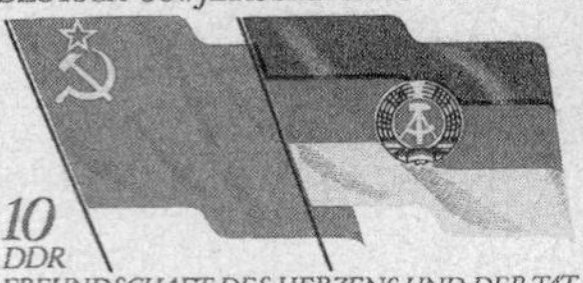

E **454** Soviet and East German Flags

1972. 25th Anniv of German-Soviet Friendship Society. Multicoloured.
E1477 10 pf. Type E **454** 30 20
E1478 20 pf. Brezhnev (U.S.S.R.) and Honecker (D.D.R.) . . 50 30

E **455** Steel Workers

E **456** "Karneol" Rose

1972. Trade Unions Federation Congress.
E1479 E **455** 10 pf. pur, orge & brn 15 15
E1480 – 35 pf. blue & brown . 15 15
DESIGNS: 35 pf. Students.

1972. Int Rose Exhib. German Species. Multicoloured.
E1481 5 pf. Type E **456** 10 10
E1482 10 pf. "Berger's Rose" . . . 10 10
E1497 10 pf. "Berger's Rose" . . . 15 10
E1483 15 pf. "Charme" . . . . . . 1·60 1·40
E1484 20 pf. "Izetka Spreeathen" . 10 10
E1485 25 pf. "Kopernicker Sommer" 10 10
E1498 25 pf. "Kopernicker Sommer" . . . . 1·00 35
E1486 35 pf. "Professor Knoll" . . 15 10
E1499 35 pf. "Professor Knoll" . . 1·00 35
Nos. E1497/9 are smaller, size 24 × 28 mm.

E **457** "Portrait of Young Man"

1972. 500th Birth Anniv of Lucas Cranach the Elder. Multicoloured.
E1487 5 pf. Type E **457** 10 10
E1488 20 pf. "Mother and Child" . 10 10
E1489 25 pf. "Margarete Luther" . 15 10
E1490 70 pf. "Nymph" (horiz) . . . 2·00 2·10

E **458** Compass and Motor Cyclist

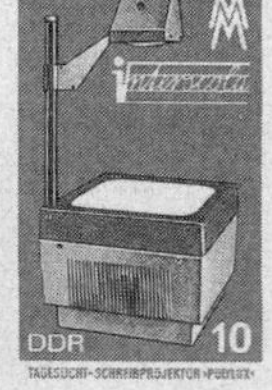

E **460** Overhead Projector

E **459** "Young Worker Reading" (J. Damme)

1972. Sports and Technical Sciences Association. Multicoloured.
E1491 5 pf. Type E **458** 10 10
E1492 10 pf. Light airplane and parachute 10 10
E1493 20 pf. Target and obstacle race 15 10
E1494 25 pf. Radio set and Morse key 80 80
E1495 35 pf. Brigantine "Wilhelm Pieck" and propeller . . . 20 10

1972. Int Book Year.
E1496 E **459** 50 pf. multicoloured . 45 15

1972. Leipzig Autumn Fair.
E1500 E **460** 10 pf. black & red . . 10 10
E1501 – 25 pf. black & grn . . 20 15
DESIGN—HORIZ: 25 pf. Slide projector.

E **461** G. Dimitrov E **462** "Catching Birds" (Egyptian relief painting, c. 2400 B.C.)

1972. 90th Birth Anniv of Georgi Dimitrov (Bulgarian statesman).
E1502 E **461** 20 pf. black & red . . 25 10

1972. "Interartes" Stamp Exhib, East Berlin. Multicoloured.
E1503 10 pf. Type E **462** 10 10
E1504 15 pf. + 5 pf. "Persian Spearman" (glazed tile, c. 500 B.C.) . . . . 1·00 90
E1505 20 pf. Anatolian tapestry c. 1400 B.C. 10 10
E1506 35 pf. + 5 pf. "The Grapesellers" (Max Lingner, 1949) (horiz) . . 10 10

E **463** Red Cross Team and Patient E **464** Terrestrial Globe (J. Praetorius, 1568)

1972. East German Red Cross.
E1507 E **463** 10 pf. ultramarine, blue and red 25 25
E1508 – 15 pf. ultramarine, blue and red 30 25
E1509 – 35 pf. red, blue and ultramarine 35 25
DESIGNS—VERT: 15 pf. Sea-rescue launch. HORIZ: ($50\frac{1}{2} \times 28$ mm): 35 pf. World map on cross, and transport.

1972. Terrestrial and Celestial Globes. Multicoloured.
E1510 5 pf. Arab celestial globe, 1279 . . . . 10 10
E1511 10 pf. Type E **464** 10 10
E1512 15 pf. Globe clock (J. Reinhold and G. Roll, 1586) . . . . 2·00 2·00
E1513 20 pf. Globe clock (J. Burgi, 1590) 15 15
E1514 25 pf. Armillary sphere (J. Moeller, 1687) 20 15
E1515 35 pf. Heraldic celestial globe, 1690 . . . . 30 20

E **465** Monument E **467** "Mauz and Hoppel" (Cat and Hare)

E **466** Educating Juveniles

1972. German-Polish Resistance Memorial. Berlin. Inauguration.
E1516 E **465** 25 pf. mult 25 15

1972. Juvenile Inventions Exhib. Mult.
E1517 10 pf. Type E **466** 15 15
E1518 25 pf. Youths with welding machine 15 15

1972. Children's T.V. Characters. Mult.
E1519 5 pf. Type E **467** 30 30
E1520 10 pf. "Fuchs and Elster" (Fox and Magpie) 30 30
E1521 15 pf. "Herr Uhu" (Eagle Owl) 30 30
E1522 20 pf. "Frau Igel and Borstel" (Hedgehogs) 30 30
E1523 25 pf. "Schuffel and Pieps" (Dog and Mouse) 30 30
E1524 35 pf. "Paulchen" (Paul from the children's library) . . . 30 30

E **468** "The Snow Queen" E **470** Arms of U.S.S.R.

1972. Fairy Tales (7th series). As Type E **468**. "The Snow Queen" (Hans Christian Andersen).
E1525 5 pf. multicoloured 30 30
E1526 10 pf. multicoloured 30 30
E1527 15 pf. multicoloured 30 30
E1528 20 pf. multicoloured 30 30
E1529 25 pf. multicoloured 30 30
E1530 35 pf. multicoloured 30 30

1972. 50th Anniv of U.S.S.R.
E1532 E **470** 20 pf. mult 30 10

E **471** Leninplatz, East Berlin E **472** M. da Caravaggio

1973. (a) Size 29 × 24 mm.
E1533 – 5 pf. green 50 10
E1534 – 10 pf. green 35 10
E1535 – 15 pf. mauve 25 10
E1536 E **471** 20 pf. mauve 45 10
E1537 – 25 pf. green 70 10
E1538 – 30 pf. orange 60 10
E1539 – 35 pf. blue 80 10
E1540 – 40 pf. violet 35 10
E1541 – 50 pf. blue 50 10
E1542 – 60 pf. purple 80 10
E1543 – 70 pf. brown 75 10
E1544 – 80 pf. blue 75 10
E1545 – 1 m. green . . . . . 1·00 10
E1546 – 2 m. red . . . . . . 1·75 10
E1546a – 3 m. mauve . . . . 2·50 40

(b) Size 22 × 18 mm.
E2197 – 5 pf. green 40 10
E1548 – 10 pf. green 30 10
E2198 – 10 pf. green 15 10
E2199 – 15 pf. mauve 30 10
E2200 E **471** 20 pf. mauve 60 10
E1549a – 25 pf. green 35 15
E2202 – 30 pf. orange 40 15
E2203 – 35 pf. blue 45 15
E2204 – 40 pf. violet 65 15
E2205 – 50 pf. blue 50 15
E2206 – 60 pf. purple 50 15
E2207 – 70 pf. brown 50 25
E2208 – 80 pf. blue 85 20
E2209 – 1 m. green 85 35
E2210 – 2 m. red . . . . . . 1·40 50
E2211 – 3 m. mauve . . . . 2·40 65

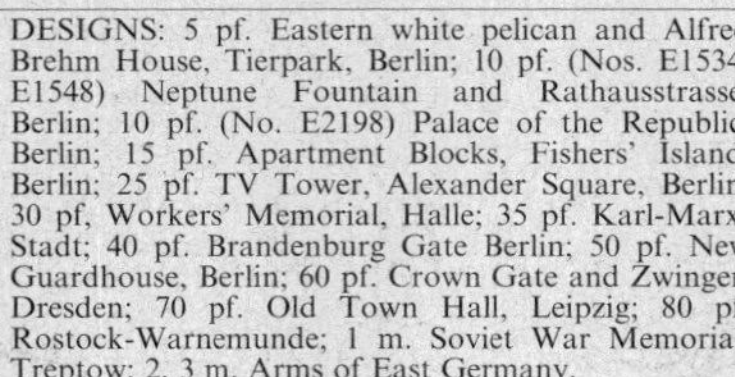
DESIGNS: 5 pf. Eastern white pelican and Alfred Brehm House, Tierpark, Berlin; 10 pf. (Nos. E1534, E1548) Neptune Fountain and Rathausstrasse, Berlin; 10 pf. (No. E2198) Palace of the Republic, Berlin; 15 pf. Apartment Blocks, Fishers' Island, Berlin; 25 pf. TV Tower, Alexander Square, Berlin; 30 pf, Workers' Memorial, Halle; 35 pf. Karl-Marx-Stadt; 40 pf. Brandenburg Gate Berlin; 50 pf. New Guardhouse, Berlin; 60 pf. Crown Gate and Zwinger, Dresden; 70 pf. Old Town Hall, Leipzig; 80 pf. Rostock-Warnemunde; 1 m. Soviet War Memorial, Treptow; 2, 3 m. Arms of East Germany.

1973. Cultural Anniversaries.
E1551 E **472** 5 pf. brown 75 80
E1552 – 10 pf. green 15 10
E1553 – 20 pf. purple 15 10
E1554 – 25 pf. blue 15 10
E1555 – 35 pf. red 15 10
PORTRAITS AND ANNIVERSARIES: 5 pf. (painter, 400th birth anniv); 10 pf. Friedrich Wolf (dramatist, 85th birth anniv); 20 pf. Max Reger (composer, birth cent.); 25 pf. Max Reinhardt (impressario, birth cent.); 35 pf. Johannes Dieckmann (politician, 80th birth anniv).

E **473** "Lebachia speciosa"

1973. Fossils in Palaeontological Collection, Berlin Natural History Museum. Multicoloured.
E1556 10 pf. Type E **473** 10 10
E1557 15 pf. "Spheronopteris hollandica" 10 10
E1558 20 pf. "Pterodactylus kochi" . 10 10
E1559 25 pf. "Botryopteris" 15 10
E1560 35 pf. "Archaeopteryx lithographica" 30 10
E1561 70 pf. "Odontopleura ovata" . 1·75 1·60

E **474** Copernicus
(Illustration reduced. Actual size $77\frac{1}{2} \times 29$ mm)

1973. 500th Birth Anniv of Copernicus.
E1562 E **474** 70 pf. multicoloured . 65 25

E **475** National Flags E **476** Bobsleigh Course

1973. 10th World Youth Festival, Berlin (1st issue). Multicoloured.
E1563 10 pf. + 5 pf. Type E **475** . . 15 10
E1564 25 pf. + 5 pf. Youths and peace dove 25 15
See also Nos. E1592/6.

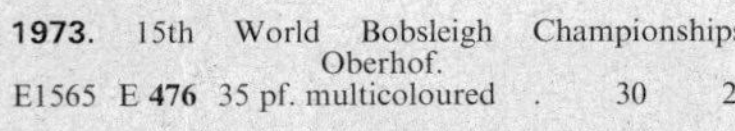
1973. 15th World Bobsleigh Championships, Oberhof.
E1565 E **476** 35 pf. multicoloured . 30 20

E **477** Combine Harvester

1973. Leipzig Spring Fair. Multicoloured.
E1566 10 pf. Type E **477** 10 10
E1567 25 pf. Automatic lathe . . . 20 15

E **478** Firecrests

1973. Songbirds. Multicoloured.
E1568 5 pf. Type E **478** 20 10
E1569 10 pf. White-winged crossbill . 25 10
E1570 15 pf. Bohemian waxwing . . 25 10
E1571 20 pf. Bluethroats 25 10
E1572 25 pf. Goldfinch 30 10
E1573 35 pf. Golden oriole 30 10
E1574 40 pf. Grey wagtail 35 15
E1575 60 pf. Wallcreeper . . . . . 4·75 2·50

E **479** Class 211 Electric Locomotive No 200–3

1973. Railway Rolling Stock. Multicoloured.
E1576 5 pf. Type E **479** 20 10
E1577 10 pf. Refrigerator wagon . . 20 10
E1578 20 pf. Long-distance passenger carriage 20 10
E1579 25 pf. Tank wagon 20 10
E1580 35 pf. Double-deck carriage . 30 15
E1581 85 pf. Passenger carriage . . 3·50 2·50

E **480** "King Lear" (directed by W. Langhoff) E **481** H. Matern

1973. Famous Theatrical Productions. Mult.
E1582 10 pf. Type E **480** 10 10
E1583 25 pf. "A Midsummer Night's Dream" (opera) (Benjamin Britten) (directed by Walter Felsenstein) 10 10
E1584 35 pf. "Mother Courage" (directed by Berthold Brecht) 75 75

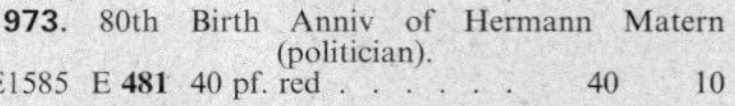
1973. 80th Birth Anniv of Hermann Matern (politician).
E1585 E **481** 40 pf. red 40 10

E **482** Goethe and House E **483** Firework Display

1973. Cultural Celebrities and Houses in Weimar. Multicoloured.
E1586 10 pf. Type E **482** 10 10
E1587 15 pf. C. M. Wieland (writer) 10 10
E1588 20 pf. F. Schiller (writer) . . 10 10
E1589 25 pf. J. G. Herder (writer) . 10 10
E1590 35 pf. Lucas Cranach the Elder (painter) 15 10
E1591 50 pf. Franz Liszt (composer) 1·60 85

1973. World Festival of Youth and Students, East Berlin (2nd issue). Multicoloured.
E1592 5 pf. Type E **483** 10 10
E1593 15 pf. Students ("Int. Solidarity") 10 10
E1594 20 pf. Young workers ("Economic Integration") . 10 10
E1595 30 pf. Students ("Aid for Young Nations") 90 35
E1596 35 pf. Youth and Students' Emblems 10 10

E **484** W. Ulbricht E **485** Power Network

1973. Death of Walter Ulbricht.
E1598 E **484** 20 pf. black 25 15

1973. 10th Anniv of "Peace" United Energy Supply System.
E1599 E **485** 35 pf. orge, pur & bl . 30 20

E **486** "Leisure Activities"

1973. Leipzig Autumn Fair. Multicoloured.
E1600 10 pf. Type E **486** 10 10
E1601 25 pf. Yacht, guitar and power drill 20 15

E **487** Militiaman and Emblem

1973. 20th Anniv of Workers Militia. Mult.
E1602 10 pf. Type E **487** 10 10
E1603 20 pf. Militia guard 25 20

E **488** Red Flag encircling Globe
E **489** Langenstein-Zwieberge Memorial

1973. 15th Anniv of "Problems of Peace and Socialism".
E1605 E **488** 20 pf. red & gold . . 25 10

1973. Langenstein-Zwieberge Monument.
E1606 E **489** 25 pf. multicoloured . 25 15

E **490** U.N. H.Q. and Emblems
E **491** "Young Couple" (G. Glombitza)

1973. Admission of German Democratic Republic to United Nations Organization.
E1607 E **490** 35 pf. mult 30 15

1973. Philatelists' Day and 3rd Young Philatelists' Stamp Exhibition, Halle.
E1608 E **491** 20 pf. + 5 pf. mult . . 25 15

E **492** Congress Emblem
E **493** Vietnamese Child

1973. 8th World Trade Union Congress, Varna, Bulgaria.
E1609 E **492** 35 pf. multicoloured . 30 20

1973. "Solidarity with Vietnam".
E1610 E **493** 10 pf. + 5 pf. mult . . 20 15

E **494** Launching Rocket

1973. Soviet Science and Technology Days. Multicoloured.
E1611 10 pf. Type E **494** 15 10
E1612 20 pf. Soviet map and emblem (horiz) 20 10
E1612 25 pf. Oil refinery 85 55

E **495** L. Corvalan
E **496** "Child with Doll" (C. L. Vogel)

1973. Solidarity with the Chilean People. Multicoloured.
E1614 10 pf. + 5 pf. Type E **495** . . 10 10
E1615 25 pf. + 5 pf. Pres. Allende . 30 30

1973. Paintings by Old Masters. Mult.
E1616 10 pf. Type E **496** 10 10
E1617 15 pf. "Madonna with Rose" (Parmigianino) 10 10
E1618 20 pf. "Woman with Fair Hair" (Rubens) 10 10
E1619 25 pf. "Lady in White" (Titian) 10 10
E1620 35 pf. "Archimedes" (D. Fetti) 15 10
E1621 70 pf. "Flower Arrangement" (Jan D. de Heem) . . . . 2·00 1·50

E **497** Flame Emblem
E **498** "Catching the Pike"

1973. 25th Anniv of Declaration of Human Rights.
E1622 E **497** 35 pf. multicoloured . . 30 15

1973. Fairy Tales (8th series). As Type E **498**. "At the Bidding of the Pike".
E1623 5 pf. multicoloured 55 30
E1624 10 pf. multicoloured 55 30
E1625 15 pf. multicoloured 55 30
E1626 20 pf. multicoloured 55 30
E1627 25 pf. multicoloured 55 30
E1628 35 pf. multicoloured 55 30

E **499** E. Hoernle
E **500** Pablo Neruda

1974. Socialist Personalities.
E1629 E **499** 10 pf. grey 10 10
E1630 – 10 pf. lilac 10 10
E1631 – 10 pf. blue 10 10
E1632 – 10 pf. brown 10 10
E1633 – 10 pf. green 10 10
E1634 – 10 pf. brown 10 10
E1635 – 10 pf. blue 10 10
E1636 – 10 pf. brown 10 10
PERSONALITIES: No. E1630, Etkar Andre; E1631, Paul Merker; E1632, Hermann Duncker; E1633, Fritz Heckert; E1634, Otto Grotewohl; E1635, Wilhelm Florin; E1636, Georg Handke.
See also Nos. E1682/4.

1974. Pablo Neruda (Chilean poet) Commem.
E1637 E **500** 20 pf. multicoloured . . 20 15

E **501** "Comecon" Emblem
E **502** "Echinopsis multiplex"

1974. 25th Anniv of Council for Mutual Economic Aid.
E1638 E **501** 20 pf. mult 40 10

1974. Cacti. Multicoloured.
E1639 5 pf. Type E **502** 10 10
E1640 10 pf. "Lobivia haageana" . . 10 10
E1641 15 pf. "Parodia sanguiniflora" . . . . 2·00 2·00
E1642 20 pf. "Gymnocal monvillei" 15 10
E1643 25 pf. "Neoporteria rapifera" 25 10
E1644 35 pf. "Notocactus concinnus" 30 15

E **503** Handball Players
E **504** High-tension Testing Plant

1974. Eighth Men's World Indoor Handball Championships.
E1645 E **503** 5 pf. multicoloured . . 25 25
E1646 – 10 pf. multicoloured . 25 25
E1647 – 35 pf. multicoloured . 25 25
Nos. E1645/7 were issued together, se-tenant, forming a composite design of a handball match.

1974. Leipzig Spring Fair. Multicoloured.
E1648 10 pf. Type E **504** 10 10
E1649 25 pf. "Robotron" computer (horiz) 20 15

E **505** Leaden Entoloma
E **506** Gustav Kirchhoff

1974. Poisonous Fungi. Multicoloured.
E1650 5 pf. Type E **505** 10 10
E1651 10 pf. Devil's boletus 15 10
E1652 15 pf. False blusher 20 10
E1653 20 pf. Fly agaric 30 10
E1654 25 pf. Beefsteak morel . . . 35 10
E1655 30 pf. Red-staining inocybe . 40 15
E1656 35 pf. Death cap 50 15
E1657 40 pf. "Clitocybe dealbata" . 2·75 1·10

1974. Celebrities. Birth Anniversaries.
E1658 E **506** 5 pf. blk, & grey . . . 10 10
E1659 – 10 pf. ultram. & bl . . 10 10
E1660 – 20 pf. red & pink . . 10 10
E1661 – 25 pf. grn & turq . . 15 10
E1662 – 35 pf. choc & brn . . 75 50
PORTRAITS AND ANNIVERSARIES: 5 pf. (physicist, 150th); 10 pf. Immanuel Kant (philosopher, 250th); 20 pf. Elm Welk (writer, 90th); 25 pf. Johann Herder (author, 230th); 35 pf. Lion Feuchtwanger (novelist, 90th).

E **507** Globe and "PEACE"

1974. 25th Anniv of 1st World Peace Congress.
E1663 E **507** 35 pf. mult 30 20

E **508** Tractor Driver
E **509** Buk Lighthouse, 1878

1974. 25th Anniv of German Democratic Republic. Multicoloured.
E1664 10 pf. Type E **508** 10 10
E1665 20 pf. Students 10 10
E1666 25 pf. Woman worker . . . 15 10
E1667 35 pf. East German family . . 90 90

1974. Lighthouses (1st series). Multicoloured.
E1668 10 pf. Type E **509** 10 10
E1669 15 pf. Warnemunde lighthouse, 1898 . . . . . . 25 10
E1670 20 pf. Darsser Ort lighthouse, 1848 . . . . . . 10 10
E1671 35 pf. Arkona lighthouse in 1827 and 1902 . . . . 15 10
E1672 40 pf. Greifswalder Oie lighthouse, 1855 . . . . . . 1·00 65
See also Nos. E1760/4.

E **510** "Man and Woman looking at the Moon"

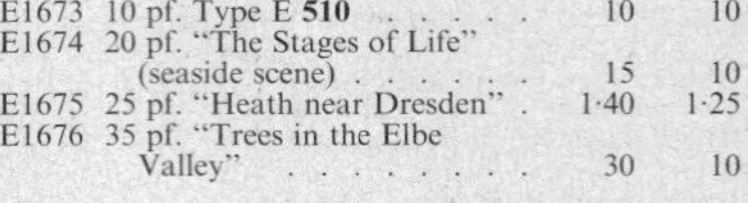

1974. Birth Bicentary of Caspar Friedrich (painter). Multicoloured.
E1673 10 pf. Type E **510** 10 10
E1674 20 pf. "The Stages of Life" (seaside scene) 15 10
E1675 25 pf. "Heath near Dresden" . 1·40 1·25
E1676 35 pf. "Trees in the Elbe Valley" 30 10

E **512** Lace Pattern
E **513** Show Jumping

1974. Plauen Lace.
E1678 E **512** 10 pf. black & vio . . 10 10
E1679 – 20 pf. brown, black and bistre 10 10
E1680 – 25 pf. black, blue and turquoise . . . 1·10 1·00
E1681 – 35 pf. black, mauve and pink 25 10
DESIGNS: Nos. E1679/81, Lace patterns similar to Type E **512**.

1974. Socialist Personalities. As Type E **499**.
E1682 10 pf. blue 10 10
E1683 10 pf. violet 10 10
E1684 10 pf. brown 10 10
DESIGNS: No. E1682, R. Breitscheid; No. E1683, K. Burger; No. E1684, C. Moltmann.

1974. Int. Horse-breeders' Congress, Berlin. Multicoloured.
E1685 10 pf. Type E **513** 10 10
E1686 20 pf. Horse & trap (horiz) . 10 10
E1687 25 pf. Haflinger draught horses (horiz) . . . . . 1·60 1·40
E1688 35 pf. Horse-racing (horiz) . . 15 15

E **514** Mobile Railway Crane

1974. Leipzig Autumn Fair. Multicoloured.
E1689 10 pf. Type E **514** 15 10
E1690 25 pf. Agricultural machine . 25 15

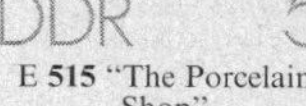

E **515** "The Porcelain Shop"
E **518** Paddle-steamer "James Watt" and Modern Freighter

E **516** Ardeatine Caves Memorial, Rome

1974. "Mon Plaisir". Exhibits in Dolls' Village, Castle Museum, Arnstadt. Mult.

E1691 5 pf. Type E **515** 10 10
E1692 10 pf. "Fairground Crier" . . 10 10
E1693 15 pf. "Wine-tasting in Cellar" 10 10
E1694 20 pf. "Cooper and Apprentice" 10 10
E1695 25 pf. "Bagpiper playing for Dancing Bear" . . . . . 1·60 1·25
E1696 35 pf. "Butcher's Wife and Crone" 30 15

1974. International War Memorials.

E1697 E **516** 35 pf. blk, grn & red . 25 20
E1698 – 35 pf. blk, bl & red . . 25 20
DESIGN: No. E1698, Resistance Memorial, Chateaubriant, France.

1974. Centenary of U.P.U. Multicoloured.

E1700 10 pf. Type E **518** 10 10
E1701 20 pf. Steam and diesel railway locomotives 30 15
E1702 25 pf. Early and Tupolev Tu-134 airliners 20 10
E1703 35 pf. Early mail coach and modern truck . . . . . . 1·25 70

E **519** "The Revolutionaries" (E. Rossdeutscher)

E **520** "The Sun shines for all" (G. Milosch)

1974. "DDR 74" Stamp Exhibition. Sculptures in Karl-Marx-Stadt. Each black, bistre and green.

E1704 10 pf. + 5 pf. Type E **519** . . 15 15
E1705 20 pf. "The Dialectics" . . . 15 15
E1706 25 pf. "The Party" 15 15

1974. Children's Paintings. Multicoloured.

E1707 20 pf. Type E **520** 25 20
E1708 20 pf. "My Friend Sascha" (B. Ozminski) 25 20
E1709 20 pf. "Carsten the Best Swimmer" (M. Kluge) . . 25 20
E1710 20 pf. "Me and the Blackboard" (P. Westphal) 25 20

E **521** "The Woodchopper"

E **523** Banded Jasper

E **522** "Still Life" (R. Paris)

1974. Fairy Tales (9th series). "Twittering To and Fro" by A. Tolstoi.

E1711 E **521** 10 pf. mult 30 30
E1712 – 15 pf. mult 30 30
E1713 – 20 pf. mult 30 30
E1714 – 30 pf. mult 30 30
E1715 – 35 pf. mult 30 30
E1716 – 40 pf. mult 30 30
DESIGNS: Nos. E1712/6, Scenes from "Twittering To and Fro" fairy tale, similar to Type E **521**.

1974. Paintings from Berlin Museums. Mult.

E1717 10 pf. Type E **522** 10 10
E1718 15 pf. "Girl in Meditation" (W. Lachnit) (vert) . . . 10 10
E1719 20 pf. "Fisherman's House" (H. Hakenbeck) (vert) . . 10 10
E1720 35 pf. "Girl in Red" (R. Bergander) 15 10
E1721 70 pf. "Parents" (W. Sitte) (vert) . . . . 1·50 1·50

1974. Gem-stones in Freiberg Mining Academy Collection. Multicoloured.

E1722 10 pf. Type E **523** 10 10
E1723 15 pf. Smoky quartz 10 10
E1724 20 pf. Topaz 10 10
E1725 25 pf. Amethyst 15 15
E1726 35 pf. Aquamarine 15 15
E1727 70 pf. Agate . . . . 1·25 1·25

E **524** Martha Arendsee

E **525** Peasants doing Forced Labour

1975. 90th Birth Anniv of Martha Arendsee (Socialist).

E1728 E **524** 10 pf. red 15 10

1975. 450th Anniv of Peasants' War.

E1729 E **525** 5 pf. black, green and grey 30 30
E1730 – 10 pf. black, brown and grey 30 30
E1731 – 20 pf. black, blue and grey 30 30
E1732 – 25 pf. black, yellow and grey 50 50
E1733 – 35 pf. black, lilac and grey 50 50
E1734 – 50 pf. black, grey and light grey 30 30
DESIGNS: 10 pf. "Paying Tithe"; 20 pf. Thomas Muntzer (leader); 25 pf. "Armed Peasants"; 35 pf. "Liberty" flag; 50 pf. Peasants on trial.

E **526** Women and Emblem

E **527** Pentakta "A-100" (microfilm camera)

1975. International Women's Year.

E1735 E **526** 10 pf. mult 20 20
E1736 – 20 pf. mult 20 20
E1737 – 25 pf. mult 20 20
DESIGNS: 20 pf., 25 pf. Similar to Type E **526**.

1975. Leipzig Spring Fair. Multicoloured.

E1738 10 pf. Type E **527** 10 10
E1739 25 pf. "SKET" (cement works) 20 15

E **528** Hans Otto (actor) (1900–1933)

E **529** Blue and Yellow Macaws

1975. Celebrities' Birth Anniversaries.

E1740 E **528** 5 pf. blue 10 10
E1741 – 10 pf. red 10 10
E1742 – 20 pf. green 10 10
E1743 – 25 pf. brown 15 10
E1744 – 35 pf. blue 75 60
PORTRAITS AND ANNIVERSARIES: 10 pf. Thomas Mann, author (1875–1955); 20 pf. Dr. A. Schweitzer (1875–1965); 25 pf. Michelangelo (1475–1564); 35 pf. Andre-Marie Ampere, scientist (1775–1836).

1975. Zoo Animals. Multicoloured.

E1745 5 pf. Type E **529** 40 10
E1746 10 pf. Orang-utans 10 10
E1747 15 pf. Ibex 10 10
E1748 20 pf. Indian rhinoceros (horiz) 20 10
E1749 25 pf. Pygmy hippopotamus (horiz) 20 10
E1750 30 pf. Grey seals (horiz) . . . 20 10
E1751 35 pf. Tiger (horiz) 35 15
E1752 50 pf. Common zebra . . . . 1·90 1·75

E **530** Soldiers, "Industry" and "Agriculture"

1975. 20th Anniv of Warsaw Treaty.

E1753 E **530** 20 pf. multicoloured . 45 10

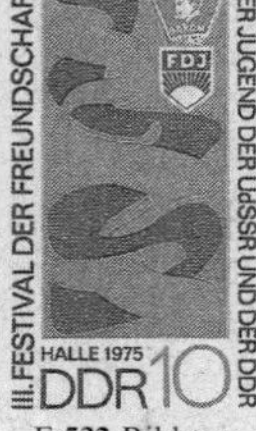

E **531** Soviet Memorial, Berlin-Treptow

E **532** Ribbons with "Komsomol" and "F.D.J." Badges

1975. 30th Anniv of Liberation. Mult.

E1754 10 pf. Type E **531** 10 10
E1755 20 pf. Detail of Buchenwald memorial 10 10
E1756 25 pf. Woman voluntary worker 10 10
E1757 55 pf. "Socialist economic integration" 65 60

1975. 3rd Youth Friendship Festival, Halle.

E1759 E **532** 10 pf. mult 20 10

1975. Lighthouses (2nd series). As Type E **509**. Multicoloured.

E1760 5 pf. Trimmendorf lighthouse . 10 10
E1761 10 pf. Gellen lighthouse . . . 10 10
E1762 20 pf. Sassnitz lighthouse . . 25 10
E1763 25 pf. Dornbusch lighthouse . 15 10
E1764 35 pf. Peenemunde lighthouse 80 50

E **533** Wilhelm Leibknecht and August Bebel

E **534** Dove and "Scientific Co-operation between Socialist Countries"

1975. Centenary of Marx's "Programmkritik" and Gotha Unity Congress.

E1765 E **533** 10 pf. deep brown, brown and red . . 15 15
E1766 – 20 pf. mult 15 15
E1767 – 25 pf. deep brown, brown and red . . 15 15
DESIGNS: 20 pf. Tivoli (meeting place at Gotha) and title-page of Minutes of Unity Congress; 25 pf. Karl Marx and Friedrich Engels.

1975. 25th Anniv of Eisenhuettenstadt.

E1768 E **534** 20 pf. mult 15 10

E **535** Construction Workers

E **536** Automatic Clock, 1585

1975. 30th Anniv of Free-German Trade Union Association.

E1769 E **535** 20 pf. mult 15 10

1975. Ancient Clocks. Multicoloured.

E1770 5 pf. Type E **536** 10 10
E1771 10 pf. Astronomical Mantlepiece clock, 1560 . . 10 10
E1772 15 pf. Automatic clock, 1600 . . 1·50 1·60
E1773 20 pf. Mantlepiece Clock, 1720 . . . . 10 10
E1774 25 pf. Mantlepiece Clock, 1700 . . . . 10 10
E1775 35 pf. Astronomical Clock, 1738 . . . . 15 15

INDEX

Countries can be quickly located by referring to the index at the end of this volume.

E **537** Jacob and Wilhelm Grimm's German Dictionary

1975. 275th Anniv of Academy of Science.

E1776 E **537** 10 pf. blk, grn & red . 10 10
E1777 – 20 pf. black & bl . . . 10 10
E1778 – 25 pf. blk, yell & grn . 10 10
E1779 – 35 pf. mult . . . . 1·00 65
DESIGNS: 20 pf. Karl Schwarzschildt observatory, Tautenberg; 25 pf. Electron microscope and chemical plant; 35 pf. Intercosmic satellite.

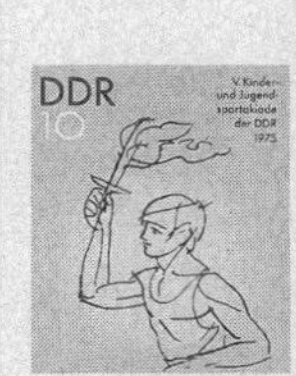

E **538** Runner with Torch

E **539** Map of Europe

1975. 5th National Youth Sports Day.

E1780 E **538** 10 pf. black & pink . 10 10
E1781 – 20 pf. black & yell . . 10 10
E1782 – 25 pf. black & blue . . 15 10
E1783 – 35 pf. black & green . 80 65
DESIGNS: 20 pf. Hurdling; 25 pf. Swimming; 35 pf. Gymnastics.

1975. European Security and Co-operation Conference, Helsinki.

E1784 E **539** 20 pf. multicoloured . 20 10

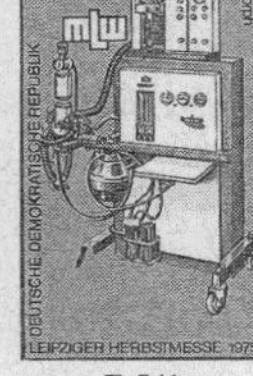

E **540** Asters

E **541** "Medimorph" (Anaesthetizing machine)

1975. Flowers. Multicoloured.

E1785 5 pf. Type E **540** 10 10
E1786 10 pf. Pelargoniums 10 10
E1787 20 pf. Gerberas 10 10
E1788 25 pf. Carnation 10 10
E1789 35 pf. Chrysanthemum . . . 20 15
E1790 70 pf. Pansies . . . . 2·25 1·75

1975. Leipzig Autumn Fair. Multicoloured.

E1791 10 pf. Type E **541** 15 10
E1792 25 pf. Zschopau "TS-250" motor-cycle (horiz) 25 20

E **542** School Crossing

1975. Road Safety. Multicoloured.

E1793 10 pf. Type E **542** 10 10
E1794 15 pf. Policewoman controlling traffic . . . . . . 1·00 50
E1795 20 pf. Policeman assisting motorist 10 10
E1796 25 pf. Car having check-up . 10 10
E1797 35 pf. Road safety instruction 35 15

E **543** Launch of "Soyuz"

E **544** Clenched Fist and Red Star

1975. "Apollo"–"Soyuz" Space Link. Mult.

E1798 10 pf. Type E **543** 10 10
E1799 20 pf. Spaceships in linking manoeuvre 15 10
E1800 70 pf. The completed link (88 × 33 mm) . . . . . . 1·60 1·00

1975. "International Solidarity".
E1801 E **544** 10 pf.+5 pf. black, red and olive 20 10

E **545** "Weimar in 1650" (Merian)

1975. Millenary of Weimar.
E1802 E **545** 10 pf. brown, light green and green . . 10 10
E1803 – 20 pf. mult 10 10
E1804 – 35 pf. mult 50 40
DESIGNS:—VERT: 20 pf. Buchenwald memorial. HORIZ: 35 pf. Weimar buildings (975–1975).

E **546** Vienna Memorial (F. Cremer) E **547** Louis Braille

1975. Austrian Patriots Monument, Vienna.
E1805 E **546** 35 pf. multicoloured . . . 30 10

1975. International Braille Year. Mult.
E1806 20 pf. Type E **547** 10 10
E1807 35 pf. Hands reading braille . 15 10
E1808 50 pf. An eye-ball, eye shade and safety goggles . . . . 1·10 95

E **548** Post Office Gate, Wurzen

1975. National Philatelists' Day. Mult.
E1809 10 pf.+5 pf. Type E **548** . . 50 30
E1810 20 pf. Post Office, Barenfels . 10 10

E **549** Hans Christian Andersen and scene from "The Emperor's New Clothes" (Actual size 70 × 25 mm)

1975. Fairy Tales (10th series). "The Emperor's New Clothes".
E1811 E **549** 20 pf. multicoloured . 30 30
E1812 – 35 pf. multicoloured . 40 40
E1813 – 50 pf. multicoloured . 40 40
DESIGNS: 35, 50 pf. Different scenes.

E **550** Tobogganing

1975. Winter Olympic Games, Innsbruck (1976). Multicoloured.
E1814 5 pf. Type E **550** 10 10
E1815 10 pf.+5 pf. Bobsleigh track . 10 10
E1816 20 pf. Speed-skating rink . . 10 10
E1817 25 pf.+5 pf. Ski-jump . . . 15 10
E1818 35 pf. Skating-rink 15 10
E1819 70 pf. Skiing . . . . 1·90 1·25

E **551** W. Pieck E **552** Organ, Rotha

1975. Birth Cent. of President Pieck (statesman).
E1821 E **551** 10 pf. brn & blue . . 15 10

1976. Members of German Workers' Movement. As Type E **551**.
E1822 10 pf. brown and red 10 10
E1823 10 pf. brown and green . . . 10 10
E1824 10 pf. brown & orange . . . 10 10
E1825 10 pf. brown and violet . . . 10 10
PORTRAITS: No. E1822, Ernst Thalmann; E1823, Georg Schumann; E1824, Wilhelm Koenen; E1825, John Schehr.

1976. Gottfried Silbermann (organ builder) Commemoration. Multicoloured.
E1826 10 pf. Type E **552** 10 10
E1827 20 pf. Organ, Freiberg . . . 10 10
E1828 35 pf. Organ, Fraureuth . . . 15 15
E1829 50 pf. Organ, Dresden . . . 1·25 55

E **554** Servicemen and Emblem

1976. 20th Anniv of National Forces (NVA). Multicoloured.
E1831 10 pf. Type E **554** 15 10
E1832 20 pf. N.V.A. equipment . . 30 15

E **555** Telephone and Inscription E **556** Block of Flats, Leipzig

1976. Centenary of Telephone.
E1833 E **555** 20 pf. blue 20 10

1976. Leipzig Spring Fair. Multicoloured.
E1834 10 pf. Type E **556** 15 10
E1835 25 pf. "Prometey" deep sea trawler (horiz) 30 15

E **557** Palace of the Republic, Berlin

1976. Opening of Palace of Republic, Berlin.
E1836 E **557** 10 pf. multicoloured . 50 10

E **558** Telecommunications Satellite Tracking Radar E **559** Marx, Engels, Lenin and Socialist Party Emblem

1976. "Intersputnik".
E1837 E **558** 20 pf. multicoloured . 25 10

1976. 9th East German Socialist Party Congress.
E1838 E **559** 10 pf. red, gold and deep red 20 10
E1839 – 20 pf. multicoloured . 30 10
DESIGN—HORIZ: 20 pf. Industrial site, housing complex and emblem.

E **560** Cycling

1976. Olympic Games, Montreal. Mult.
E1841 5 pf. Type E **560** 10 10
E1842 10 pf.+5 pf. Modern swimming pool 10 10
E1843 20 pf. Modern sports hall . . 10 10
E1844 25 pf. Regatta course . . . 15 10
E1845 35 pf.+10 pf. Rifle-range . . 20 15
E1846 70 pf. Athletics . . . . . . 2·00 1·10

E **561** Intertwined Ribbon and Emblem

1976. 10th Youth Parliament Conference, Berlin. Multicoloured.
E1848 10 pf. Type E **561** 15 10
E1849 20 pf. Members of Youth Parliament and stylised industrial plant 30 15

E **562** "Himantoglossum bircinum" E **564** Marx, Engels, Lenin and Red Flag

E **563** "Shetland Pony" (H. Drake)

1976. Flowers. Multicoloured.
E1850 10 pf. Type E **562** 10 10
E1851 20 pf. "Dactylorhiza incarnata" 10 10
E1852 25 pf. "Anacamptis pyramidalis" 15 10
E1853 35 pf. "Dactylorhiza sambucina" 25 15
E1854 40 pf. "Orchis coriophora" . 30 15
E1855 50 pf. "Cypripedium calceolus" . . . . 2·50 2·00

1976. Statuettes from Berlin Museums.
E1856 E **563** 10 pf. black & blue . . 10 10
E1857 – 20 pf. black & brn . . 10 10
E1858 – 25 pf. black & orge . . 10 10
E1859 – 35 pf. black & grn . . 15 15
E1860 – 50 pf. black & pink . 1·50 1·25
STATUETTES—VERT: 20 pf. "Tanzpause" (W. Arnold); 25 pf. "Am Strand" (L. Englehardt); 35 pf. "Herman Duncker" (W. Howard); 50 pf. "Das Gesprach" (G. Weidanz).

1976. European Communist Parties' Conference.
E1861 E **564** 20 pf. blue, deep red and red 25 10

E **565** State Carriage, 1790

1976. 19th Century Horse-drawn Vehicles. Multicoloured.
E1862 10 pf. Type E **565** 10 10
E1863 20 pf. Russian trap, 1800 . . 10 10
E1864 25 pf. Carriage, 1840 . . . . 10 10
E1865 35 pf. State carriage, 1860 . . 10 10
E1866 40 pf. Stagecoach, 1850 . . . 15 15
E1867 50 pf. Carriage, 1889 . . . . 2·00 2·00

E **566** Gera, circa 1652

1976. National Philatelists' Day, Gera. Mult.
E1868 10 pf. + 5 pf. Type E **566** . . 15 15
E1869 20 pf. Gera buildings 15 15

E **567** Boxer

1976. Domestic Dogs. Multicoloured.
E1870 5 pf. Type E **567** 10 10
E1871 10 pf. Airedale Terrier . . . 10 10
E1872 20 pf. Alsatian 10 10
E1873 25 pf. Collie 10 10
E1874 35 pf. Schnauzer 15 10
E1875 70 pf. Great Dane . . . . . 2·25 2·25

E **568** Oil Refinery

1976. Autumn Fair, Leipzig. Multicoloured.
E1876 10 pf. Type E **568** 15 10
E1877 25 pf. Library, Leipzig . . . 25 10

E **569** Templin Lake Bridge

1976. East German Bridges. Multicoloured.
E1878 10 pf Type E **569** 20 10
E1879 15 pf. Adlergestell Bridge, Berlin 20 10
E1880 20 pf. Elbe River Bridge, Rosslau 30 10
E1881 25 pf. Goltzschtal Viaduct . . 30 10
E1882 35 pf. Elbe River Bridge, Magdeburg 30 15
E1883 50 pf. Grosser Dreesch Bridge, Scherwin . . . . 2·00 1·60

E **570** Memorial Figures

1976. Patriot's Memorial, Budapest.
E1884 E **570** 35 pf. multicoloured . 30 10

E **571** Brass Jug, c. 1500 E **572** Berlin T.V. Tower

1976. Exhibits from Applied Arts Museum, Kopenick Castle, Berlin. Multicoloured.
E1885 10 pf. Type E **571** 10 10
E1886 20 pf. Faience covered vase, c. 1710 . . . . 10 10
E1887 25 pf. Porcelain "fruit-seller" table centre, c. 1768 . . . 10 10
E1888 35 pf. Silver "basket-carrier" statuette, c. 1700 . . . . . 10 10
E1889 70 pf. Coloured glass vase, c. 1900 . . . . 1·60 1·60

1976. "Sozphilex 77" Stamp Exhibition. East Berlin (1st issue).
E1890 E **572** 10 pf. + 5 pf. blue, black and red . . . 20 10
See also Nos. E1962/3.

E **573** Spade-tailed Guppy E **575** The Miller and the King

E **574** Clay Pots c. 3000 B.C.

1976. Aquarium Fishes – Guppies. Mult.
E1891 10 pf. Type E **573** 10 10
E1892 15 pf. Lyre-tailed 10 10
E1893 20 pf. Flag-tailed 10 10
E1894 25 pf. Sword-tailed 15 10
E1895 35 pf. Delta 20 10
E1896 70 pf. Round-tailed . . . . 2·10 1·10

1976. Archaeological Discoveries in D.D.R. Multicoloured.
E1897 10 pf. Type E **574** 10 10
E1898 20 pf. Bronze cult vessel on wheels, c. 1300 B.C. . . . 10 10
E1899 25 pf. Roman gold aureus of Tetricus I, A.D. 270–273 . 10 10
E1900 35 pf. Viking cross-shaped pendant. 10th century A.D. 10 10
E1901 70 pf. Roman glass beaker, 3rd century A.D. . . . . 1·90 1·40

1976. Fairy Tales (11th series). "Rumpelstiltskin".
E1902 E **575** 5 pf. mult 25 25
E1903 – 10 pf. mult 25 25
E1904 – 15 pf. mult 25 25
E1905 – 20 pf. mult 25 25
E1906 – 25 pf. mult 25 25
E1907 – 30 pf. mult 25 25
DESIGNS: 10 pf. to 30 pf. Scenes from the fairy tale.

E **576** "The Air" (R. Carriera)   E **577** Arnold Zweig (author)

1976. Paintings by Old Masters from the National Art Collection, Dresden. Mult.
E1908 10 pf. Type E **576** 10 10
E1909 15 pf. "Madonna and Child" (Murillo) 10 10
E1910 20 pf. "Viola Player" (B. Strozzi) 10 10
E1911 25 pf. "Ariadne Forsaken" (A. Kauffman) 10 10
E1912 35 pf. "Old Man in Black Cap" (B. Nazzari) 15 10
E1913 70 pf. "Officer reading a Letter" (G. Terborch) . . 1·90 1·25

1977. German Celebrities.
E1914 E **577** 10 pf. black & pink . . 10 10
E1915 – 20 pf. black & grey . . 10 10
E1916 – 35 pf. black & grn . . 10 10
E1917 – 40 pf. black & blue . . 75 50
DESIGNS: 20 pf. Otto von Guericke (scientist); 35 pf. Albrecht D. Thaer (agriculturalist); 40 pf. Gustav Hertz (physicist).

E **578** Spring near Plaue, Thuringia   E **579** Book Fair Building

1977. Natural Phenomena. Multicoloured.
E1918 10 pf. Type E **578** 10 10
E1919 20 pf. Rock face near Jonsdorf 10 10
E1920 25 pf. Oaks near Reuterstadt Stavenhagen 10 10
E1921 35 pf. Rocky ledge near Saalburg 10 10
E1922 50 pf. Erratic boulder near Furstenwalde/Spree . . . 1·25 1·10

1977. Leipzig Spring Fair. Multicoloured.
E1923 10 pf. Type E **579** 10 10
E1924 25 pf. Aluminium casting machine 25 15

E **580** Senftenberg Costume, Zly Komorrow   E **581** Carl Friedrich Gauss

1977. Sorbian Historical Costumes. Mult.
E1925 10 pf. Type E **580** 10 10
E1926 20 pf. Bautzen, Budysin . . . 10 10
E1927 25 pf. Klitten, Kletno . . . 10 10
E1928 35 pf. Nochten, Wochozy . . . 15 10
E1929 70 pf. Muskau, Muzakow . . 1·90 1·25

1977. Birth Bicentenary of Carl Friedrich Gauss (mathematician).
E1930 E **581** 20 pf. black & blue . . 30 10

E **582** Start of Race   E **583** Three Flags

1977. 30th International Peace Cycle Race. Multicoloured.
E1931 10 pf. Type E **582** 25 25
E1932 20 pf. Spurt 25 25
E1933 35 pf. Race finish 25 25

1977. 9th Congress of Free German Trade Unions Association.
E1934 E **583** 20 pf. mult 25 10

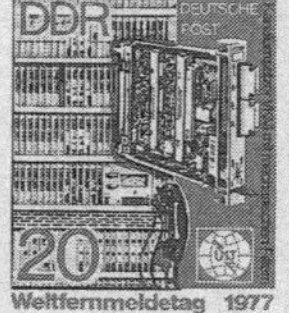

E **584** VKM Channel Converter and Filters   E **585** Shooting

1977. World Telecommunications Day.
E1935 E **584** 20 pf. black, blue and red 20 10

1977. 25th Anniv of Sports and Technical Sciences Association.
E1936 E **585** 10 pf. blk, grn & red . 10 10
E1937 – 20 pf. blk, bl & mve . 10 10
E1938 – 35 pf. blk, pk & grn . 75 75
DESIGNS: 20 pf. Skin diving; 25 pf. Radio-controlled model boat.

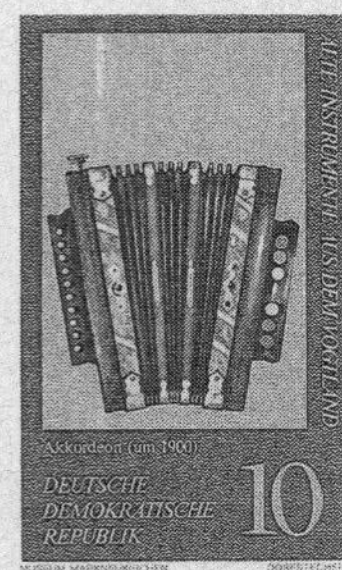

E **586** Accordion, 1900   E **587** "Bathsheba at the Fountain"

1977. Old Musical Instruments from Vogtland. Multicoloured.
E1939 10 pf. Type E **586** 10 10
E1940 20 pf. Treble viola da gamba, 1747 . . . . 10 10
E1941 25 pf. Oboe, 1785, Clarinet, 1830, Flute, 1817 . . . 10 10
E1942 35 pf. Concert zither, 1891 . . 10 10
E1943 70 pf. Trumpet, 1860 . . . . 1·75 1·60

1977. 400th Birth Anniv of Peter Paul Rubens. Dresden Gallery Paintings. Multicoloured.
E1944 10 pf. Type E **587** 10 10
E1945 15 pf. "Mercury and Argus" (horiz) 10 10
E1946 20 pf. "The Drunk Hercules" . . 15 10
E1947 25 pf. "Diana's Return from Hunting" (horiz) 15 10
E1948 35 pf. "The Old Woman with the Brazier" 30 10
E1949 50 pf. "Leda with the Swan" (horiz) . . . . 2·50 2·10

E **589** Tractor and Plough

1977. Modern Agricultural Techniques. Multicoloured.
E1951 10 pf. Type E **589** 10 10
E1952 20 pf. Fertilizer spreader on truck 15 10
E1953 25 pf. Potato digger and loader 15 10
E1954 35 pf. High pressure collecting press 25 10
E1955 50 pf. Milking machine . . . 1·75 1·50

E **590** High Jump   E **591** "Bread for Everybody" (Wolfram Schubert)

1977. 6th Gymnastics and Athletic Meeting and 6th Children and Young People's Sports Days, Leipzig. Multicoloured.
E1956 5 pf. Type E **590** 15 10
E1957 10 pf. + 5 pf. Running . . . 15 10
E1958 20 pf. Hurdling 15 10
E1959 25 pf. + 5 pf. Gymnastics . . 15 10
E1960 35 pf. Dancing 20 10
E1961 40 pf. Torch bearer and flags . 1·75 1·50

1977. "Sozphilex 77" Stamp Exhibition, East Berlin (2nd issue). Multicoloured.
E1962 10 pf. Type E **591** 15 10
E1963 25 pf. "...when Communists are Dreaming" (Walter Womacka) 30 25

E **592** "Konsument" Department Store, Leipzig

1977. Leipzig Autumn Fair. Multicoloured.
E1966 10 pf. Type E **592** 10 10
E1967 25 pf. Carved bowl and Thuringian blown-glass vases 30 20

E **594** Steam Locomotive "Muldenthal", 1861

1977. Transport Museum, Dresden. Mult.
E1969 5 pf. Type E **594** 35 10
E1970 10 pf. Dresden tram, 1896 . . 35 10
E1971 20 pf. Hans Grade's monoplane, 1909 . . . . 20 10
E1972 25 pf. Phanomobil tricar, 1924 . . . . 30 10
E1973 35 pf. River Elbe passenger steamer, 1837 . . . . . . 2·25 1·50

E **595** Cruiser "Aurora"

1977. 60th Anniv of October Revolution. Multicoloured.
E1974 10 pf. Type E **595** 30 20
E1975 25 pf. Assault on Winter Palace 30 20

E **596** Soviet Memorial   E **597** Flaming Torch

1977. Soviet Memorial, Berlin-Schoenholz.
E1977 E **596** 35 pf. mult 25 10

1977. "Solidarity".
E1978 E **597** 10 pf. + 5 pf. mult . . 20 10

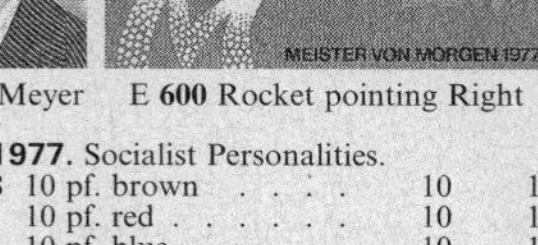

E **598** Ernst Meyer   E **600** Rocket pointing Right

1977. Socialist Personalities.
E1979 E **598** 10 pf. brown 10 10
E1980 – 10 pf. red 10 10
E1981 – 10 pf. blue 10 10
PERSONALITIES: No. E1980, A. Frolich; No. E1981, G. Eisler.

1977. 20th "Masters of Tomorrow" Fair, Leipzig.
E1983 E **600** 10 pf. red, silver and black 15 15
E1984 – 20 pf. blue, gold and black 15 15
DESIGN: 20 pf. Rocket pointing left.

E **601** Mouflon   E **602** Firemen with Scaling Ladders

1977. Hunting. Multicoloured.
E1985 10 pf. Type E **601** 10 10
E1986 15 pf. Red deer . . . . . . 2·10 1·60
E1987 20 pf. Shooting ring-necked pheasant 40 10
E1988 25 pf. Red fox and mallard . . 30 10
E1989 35 pf. Tractor driver with roe deer fawn 30 15
E1990 70 pf. Wild boars 50 20

1977. Fire Brigade. Multicoloured.
E1991 10 pf. Type E **602** 10 10
E1992 20 pf. Children visiting fire brigade (vert) 15 10
E1993 25 pf. Fire engines in country-side 15 10
E1994 35 pf. Artificial respiration (vert) 20 15
E1995 50 pf. Fire-fighting tug . . . 2·25 2·00

E **603** Traveller and King   E **605** Amilcar Cabral

E **604** Rosehips

1977. Fairy Tales (12th series). "Six World Travellers" (Brothers Grimm).
E1996 E **603** 5 pf. multicoloured . . 30 30
E1997 – 10 pf. multicoloured . 30 30
E1998 – 20 pf. multicoloured . 30 30
E1999 – 25 pf. multicoloured . 30 30
E2000 – 35 pf. multicoloured . 30 30
E2001 – 60 pf. multicoloured . 30 30
DESIGNS: 10 pf. to 60 pf. Scenes from the fairy tale.

1978. Medicinal Plants. Multicoloured.
E2002 10 pf. Type E **604** 10 10
E2003 15 pf. Birch leaves 10 10
E2004 20 pf. Camomile flowers . . 10 10
E2005 25 pf. Coltsfoot 10 10
E2006 35 pf. Lime flowers 15 10
E2007 50 pf. Elder flowers . . . . 2·00 1·50

1978. Amilcar Cabral (nationalist leader of Guinea-Bissau) Commemoration.
E2008 E **605** 20 pf. multicoloured . 20 10

E **606** Town Hall, Suhl-Heinrichs   E **608** Ear-pendant, 11th century

E **607** Post Office Van, 1921

1978. Half-timbered Buildings. Multicoloured.
E2009 10 pf. Type E **606** 10 10
E2010 20 pf. Farmhouse, Niederoderwitz 10 10
E2011 25 pf. Farmhouse, Strassen . . 10 10
E2012 35 pf. House, Quedlinburg . . 15 10
E2013 40 pf. House, Eisenach . . . 1·40 1·25

1978. Postal Transport. Multicoloured.
E2014 10 pf. Type **607** 15 15
E2015 20 pf. Postal truck, 1978 . . 30 30
E2016 25 pf. Railway mail coach, 1896 . . . . 1·00 80
E2017 35 pf. Railway mail coach, 1978 . . . . 1·00 80

1978. Slavonic Treasures. Multicoloured.
E2018 10 pf. Type E **608** 10 10
E2019 20 pf. Ear-ring, 10th century . 10 10
E2020 25 pf. Bronze tag, 10th century 10 10
E2021 35 pf. Bronze horse, 12th century 10 10
E2022 70 pf. Arabian coin, 8th century . . . . 1·40 1·25

E **609** "Royal House" Market Square, Leipzig
E **610** "M-100" Meteorological Rocket

1978. Leipzig Spring Fair.
E2023 E **609** 10 pf. yell, blk & red . 15 10
E2024 – 25 pf. grn, blk & red . 30 20
DESIGN: 25 pf. Universal measuring instrument, UMK 10/1318.

1978. "Interkosmos" Space Programme. Multicoloured.
E2025 10 pf. Type E **610** 15 10
E2026 20 pf. "Interkosmos 1" satellite 20 10
E2027 35 pf. "Meteor" satellite with Fourier spectrometer . . . 1·00 65

E **611** Samuel Heinicke (founder)

1978. Bicentenary of First National Deaf and Dumb Educational Institution.
E2029 20 pf. Type E **611** 10 10
E2030 25 pf. Child learning alphabet 70 70

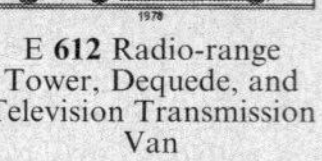

E **612** Radio-range Tower, Dequede, and Television Transmission Van
E **613** Saxon miner in Gala Uniform

1978. World Telecommunications Day. Mult.
E2031 10 pf. Type E **612** 10 10
E2032 20 pf. Equipment in Berlin television tower and Dresden television tower 25 20

1978. 19th-Century Gala Uniforms of Mining and Metallurgical Industries. Multicoloured.
E2033 10 pf. Type E **613** 10 10
E2034 20 pf. Freiberg foundry worker 10 10
E2035 25 pf. School of Mining academician 10 10
E2036 35 pf. Chief Inspector of Mines . . . . 1·25 80

E **614** Lion Cub
E **615** Loading Container

1978. Leipzig Zoo Cent. Multicoloured.
E2037 10 pf. Type E **614** 10 10
E2038 20 pf. Leopard cub 15 10
E2039 35 pf. Tiger cub 20 10
E2040 50 pf. Snow leopard cub . . 1·25 95

1978. Container Goods Traffic. Multicoloured.
E2041 10 pf. Type E **615** 10 10
E2042 20 pf. Placing container on truck 10 10
E2043 35 pf. Container sidings . . . 35 15
E2044 70 pf. Placing containers on "Boltenhagen" . . . . . 1·60 1·50

E **616** Clay Ox (Egyptian Museum, Leipzig)

1978. Ancient African Works of Art in Egyptian Museums at Leipzig and Berlin. Multicoloured.
E2045 5 pf. Type E **616** 10 10
E2046 10 pf. Clay head of woman (Leipzig) 10 10
E2047 20 pf. Gold bangle (Berlin) (horiz) 10 10
E2048 25 pf. Gold ring plate (Berlin) 10 10
E2049 35 pf. Gold signet-ring plate (Berlin) 10 10
E2050 40 pf. Necklace (Berlin) (horiz) . . . . 1·40 1·10

E **617** Justus von Liebig (agricultural chemist, 175th birth anniv)

1978. Celebrities' Birth Anniversaries.
E2051 E **617** 5 pf. black & ochre . . 10 10
E2052 – 10 pf. black & blue . . 10 10
E2053 – 15 pf. black & grn . . 10 10
E2054 – 20 pf. black & blue . . 10 10
E2055 – 25 pf. black & red . . 10 10
E2056 – 35 pf. black & grn . . 10 10
E2057 – 70 pf. black & drab . 1·40 1·10
DESIGNS: 10 pf. Joseph Dietzgen (writer, 150th); 15 pf. Alfred Doblin (novelist, 100th); 20 pf. Hans Loch (politician, 80th); 25 pf. Theodor Brugsch (scientist, 100th); 35 pf. Friedrich Ludwig Jahn (gymnast, 200th); 70 pf. Albrecht von Graefe (ophthalmotician, 150th).

E **618** Cottbus, 1730

1978. 5th National Youth Stamp Exhibition, Cottbus. Multicoloured.
E2058 10 pf. + 5 pf. Type E **618** . . 25 10
E2059 20 pf. Modern Cottbus . . . 25 10

E **619** Havana Buildings and Festival Emblem

1978. 11th World Youth and Students' Festival, Havana. Multicoloured.
E2060 20 pf. Type E **619** 30 30
E2061 35 pf. Festival emblem and East Berlin buildings . . . 30 30

E **621** "Multicar 25" Truck

1978. Leipzig Autumn Fair. Multicoloured.
E2063 10 pf. Type E **621** 10 10
E2064 25 pf. "Three Kings" Fair building, Petersstrasse . . 25 20

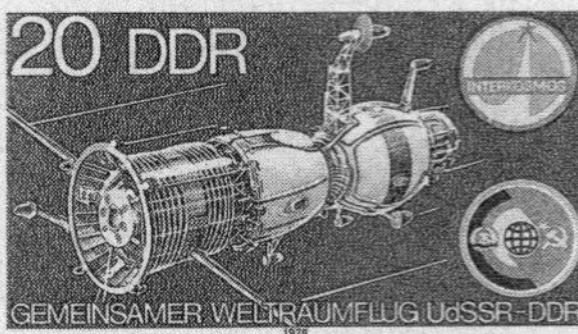

E **622** "Soyuz" Spaceship and Emblems

1978. Soviet–East German Space Flight (1st issue).
E2065 E **622** 20 pf. mult 40 10
See also Nos. E2069/72

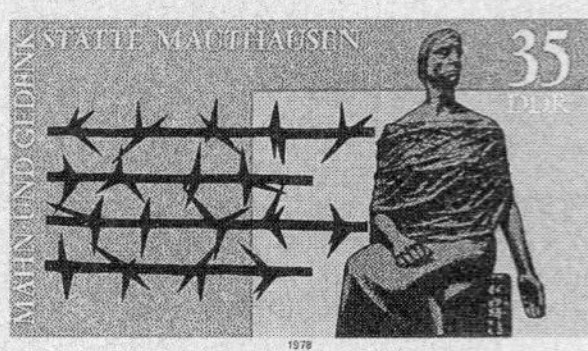

E **623** Mautnausen Memorial

1978. War Victims' Memorial, Mauthausen, Austria.
E2066 E **623** 35 pf. mult 30 10

E **624** W.M.S. Unit on the March

1978. 25th Anniv of Workers' Militia Squads.
E2067 20 pf. Type E **624** 40 40
E2068 35 pf. Members of Red Army, National People's Army and W.M.S. 40 40

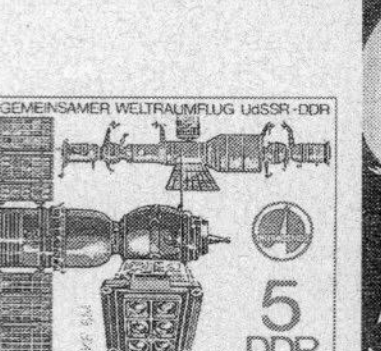

E **625** "Soyuz" "MKF 6M" Camera and Space Station
E **626** Human Pyramid

1978. Soviet–East German Space Flight (2nd issue). Multicoloured.
E2069 5 pf. Type E **625** 10 10
E2070 10 pf. Albert Einstein and "Soyuz" 15 10
E2071 20 pf. Sigmund Jahn (first East German cosmonaut) (vert) 20 10
E2072 35 pf. "Salyut", "Soyuz" and Otto Lilienthal monoplane glider . . . . 1·25 1·10

1978. The Circus. Multicoloured.
E2074 5 pf. Type E **626** 15 30
E2075 10 pf. Elephant on tricycle . . 50 65
E2076 20 pf. Performing horse . . . 70 85
E2077 35 pf. Polar bear kissing girl . 1·50 1·60

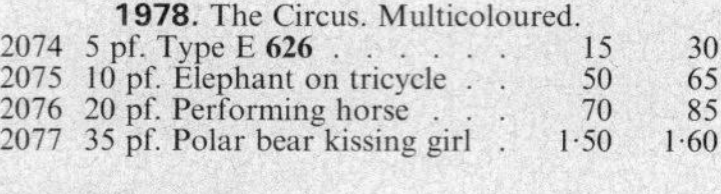

E **627** African behind Barbed Wire
E **628** Construction of Natural Gas Pipe Line

1978. International Anti-Apartheid Year.
E2078 E **627** 20 pf. mult 20 10

1978. Construction of "Friendship Line" (Drushba-Trasse) by East German Youth.
E2079 E **628** 20 pf. mult 30 10

E **629** "Papilio hahneli"
E **631** Old Woman and Youth

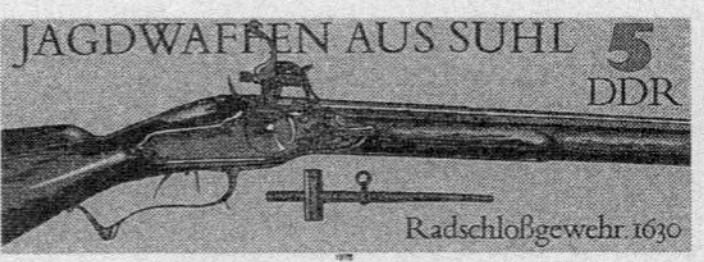

E **630** Wheel-lock Gun, 1630

1978. 250th Anniv of Dresden Scientific Museums. Multicoloured.
E2080 10 pf. Type E **629** 20 10
E2081 20 pf. "Agama lehmanni" . . 20 10
E2082 25 pf. Agate 25 10
E2083 35 pf. "Palaeobatrachus diluvianus" 30 10
E2084 40 pf. Mantlepiece clock, c. 1720 . . . . 30 10
E2085 50 pf. Table telescope, c. 1750 . . . . 2·40 2·00

1978. Sporting Guns from Suhl. Multicoloured.
E2086 5 pf. Type E **630** 10 10
E2087 10 pf. Double-barrelled gun, 1978 . . . . 15 15
E2088 20 pf. Spring-cock gun, 1780 . 25 25
E2089 25 pf. Superimposed double-barrelled gun, 1978 . . . . 40 40
E2090 35 pf. Percussion gun, 1850 . . 50 50
E2091 70 pf. Three-barrelled gun, 1978 . . . . 90 90

1978. Fairy Tales. "Rapunzel". Multicoloured
E2092 10 pf. Type E **631** 40 40
E2093 15 pf. Old Woman climbing tower on Rapunzel's hair . 40 40
E2094 20 pf. Prince calling to Rapunzel 40 40
E2095 25 pf. Prince climbing through window 40 40
E2096 35 pf. Old woman about to cut Rapunzel's hair . . . 40 40
E2097 50 pf. "Happy ever after" . . 40 40

E **632** Chaffinches
E **633** Chabo

1979. Songbirds. Multicoloured.
E2098 5 pf. Type E **632** 15 10
E2099 10 pf. European nuthatch . . 15 10
E2100 20 pf. European robin . . . 20 10
E2101 25 pf. Common rosefinch . . 30 10
E2102 35 pf. Blue tit 45 15
E2103 50 pf. Linnet . . . . 3·75 2·25

1979. Poultry. Multicoloured.
E2104 10 pf. Type E **633** 15 10
E2105 15 pf. Crows head 15 10
E2106 20 pf. Porcelain-colour Feather-footed dwarf . . . 15 10
E2107 25 pf. Saxonian 20 10
E2108 35 pf. Phoenix 25 10
E2109 50 pf. Striped Italian . . . . 2·25 1·60

E **634** Telephone Exchanges in 1900 and 1979

1979. Telephone and Telegraphs Communications. Multicoloured.
E2110 20 pf. Type E **634** 10 10
E2111 35 pf. Transmitting telegrams in 1800 and 1979 . . . . 75 45

MORE DETAILED LISTS
are given in the Stanley Gibbons Catalogues referred to in the country headings.
For lists of current volumes see Introduction.

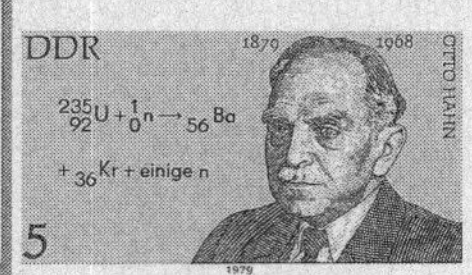

E **636** Max Klinger Exhibition House, Leipzig

E **637** Otto Hahn (physicist, centenary)

1979. Leipzig Spring Fair. Multicoloured.

E2113 10 pf. Type E **636** 15 10
E2114 25 pf. Horizontal drill and milling machine 30 20

1979. Celebrities' Birth Anniversaries.

E2115 E **637** 5 pf. black & pink . . 10 10
E2116 – 10 pf. black & blue . . 10 10
E2117 – 20 pf. black & yell . . 10 10
E2118 – 25 pf. black & grn . . 10 10
E2119 – 35 pf. black & blue . . 40 15
E2120 – 70 pf. black & pink . 1·50 1·10

DESIGNS: 10 pf. Max von Laue (physicist, centenary); 20 pf. Arthur Scheunert (physiologist, centenary); 25 pf. Friedrich August Kekule (chemist, 150th); 35 pf. Georg Forster (explorer and writer, 225th); 70 pf. Gotth Ephraim Lessing (playwright and essayist, 250th).

E **638** "Radebeul" (container ship), "Sturmvogol" (tug) and Shipping Route Map

1979. World Navigation Day.

E2121 E **638** 20 pf. multicoloured . 40 25

E **639** Horch "8", 1911

1979. Zwickau Motor Industry. Multicoloured.

E2122 20 pf. Type E **639** 50 30
E2123 35 pf. Trabant "601 S de luxe", 1978 . . . . 80 60

E **640** MXA Electric Train

1979. East German Locomotives and Wagons. Multicoloured.

E2124 5 pf. Type E **640** 10 10
E2125 10 pf. Self-discharging wagon 10 10
E2126 20 pf. Diesel locomotive No. 110836.4 . . . . 20 10
E2127 35 pf. Railway car transporter . . . . 2·40 2·00

E **641** Durga (18th century)

E **642** Children Playing

1979. Indian Miniatures. Multicoloured.

E2128 20 pf. Type E **641** 10 10
E2129 35 pf. Mahavira (15th/16th century) 15 10
E2130 50 pf. Todi Ragini (17th century) 20 15
E2131 70 pf. Asavari Ragini (17th century) . . . . 1·90 1·50

1979. International Year of the Child. Multicoloured.

E2132 10 pf. Type E **642** 10 10
E2133 20 pf. Overseas aid for children 55 35

E **643** Construction Work on Leipziger Strasse Complex

1979. "Berlin Project" of Free German Youth Organization. Multicoloured.

E2134 10 pf. Type E **643** 10 10
E2135 20 pf. Berlin-Marzahn building site 40 25

E **644** Torch-light Procession of Free German Youth, 1949

1979. National Youth Festival. Mult.

E2136 10 pf. + 5 pf. Type E **644** . . 25 20
E2137 20 pf. Youth rally 25 20

E **645** Exhibition Symbol

1979. "agra 79" Agricultural Exhibition, Markkleeberg.

E2138 E **645** 10 pf. multicoloured . 20 10

E **646** Train Ferry "Rostock"

1979. 70th Anniv of Sassnitz–Trelleborg Railway Ferry. Multicoloured.

E2139 20 pf. Type E **646** 80 65
E2140 35 pf. Train ferry "Rugen" . 80 65

E **647** Hospital Classroom

1979. Rehabilitation. Multicoloured.

E2141 10 pf. Type E **647** 10 10
E2142 35 pf. Wheelchair-bound factory worker 50 35

E **648** Cycling

1979. 7th Children's and Young People's Sports Day, Berlin. Multicoloured.

E2143 10 pf. Type E **648** 15 10
E2144 20 pf. Roller-skating 50 40

E **649** Dahlia "Rubens"

E **650** Goose-thief Fountain, Dresden

1979. "iga" International Garden Exhibition, Erfurt. Dahlias. Multicoloured.

E2145 10 pf. Type E **649** 10 10
E2146 20 pf. "Rosalie" 10 10
E2147 25 pf. "Corinna" 10 10
E2148 35 pf. "Enzett-Dolli" . . . 15 10
E2149 50 pf. "Enzett-Carola" . . . 25 15
E2150 70 pf. "Don Lorenzo" . . . 2·75 2·10

1979. National Stamp Exhibition, Dresden. Multicoloured.

E2151 10 pf. + 5 pf. Type E **650** . . 50 30
E2152 20 pf. Dandelion fountain, Dresden 10 10

E **651** World Map and Russian Alphabet

1979. 4th International Congress of Russian Language and Literature Teachers, Berlin.

E2154 E **651** 20 pf. multicoloured . 15 10

E **652** Italian Lira de Gamba, 1592

1979. Musical Instruments in Leipzig Museum. Multicoloured.

E2155 20 pf. Type E **652** 15 10
E2156 25 pf. French serpent, 17th/18th century 20 10
E2157 40 pf. French barrel-lyre, 1750 . . . . 25 10
E2158 85 pf. German tenor flugelhorn, 1850 . . . . 2·10 1·50

E **653** Horseracing

1979. 30th International Congress on Horsebreeding in Socialist Countries, Berlin. Multicoloured.

E2159 10 pf. Type E **653** 15 10
E2160 25 pf. Dressage (pas de deux) 1·00 50

E **654** Mittelbau-Dora Memorial

E **655** Teddy Bear

1979. Mittelbau-Dora Memorial, Nordhausen.

E2161 E **654** 35 pf. blk & vio . . . 30 10

1979. Leipzig Autumn Fair. Multicoloured.

E2162 10 pf. Type E **655** 10 10
E2163 25 pf. Grosser Blumenberg building, Richard Wagner Square 35 10

E **656** Philipp Dengel

E **657** Building Worker and Flats

1979. Socialist Personalities.

E2164 E **656** 10 pf. black, green and deep green 15 10
E2165 – 10 pf. blk, bl & ind . . 15 10
E2166 – 10 pf. blk, stone & bis 15 10
E2167 – 10 pf. blk, red & brn . 15 10

DESIGNS: No. E2165, Otto Buchwitz; No. E2166, Bernard Koenen; No. E2167, Heinrich Rau.

1979. 30th Anniv of German Democratic Republic. Multicoloured.

E2168 5 pf. Type E **657** 10 10
E2169 10 pf. Boy and girl 10 10
E2170 15 pf. Soldiers 50 35
E2171 20 pf. Miner and Soviet soldier 10 10

E **658** Girl applying Lipstick (1966/7)

E **659** Vietnamese Soldier, Mother and Child

1979. Meissen Porcelain. Multicoloured.

E2173 5 pf. Type E **658** 10 10
E2174 10 pf. "Altozier" coffee pot (18th cent.) 10 10
E2175 15 pf. "Gosser Ausschnitt" coffee pot (1973/4) 25 20
E2176 20 pf. Vase with lid (18th century) 30 25
E2177 25 pf. Parrot with cherry (18th century) 40 25
E2178 35 pf. Harlequin with tankard (18th century) 50 50
E2179 50 pf. Flower girl (18th century) 80 70
E2180 70 pf. Sake bottle (18th century) . . . . 1·25 1·00

1979. "Invincible Vietnam".

E2181 E **659** 10 pf. + 5 pf. black and red 20 10

E **660** Rag-doll, 1800

E **661** "Balance on Ice" (Johanna Starke)

1979. Dolls. Multicoloured.

E2182 10 pf. Type E **660** 35 35
E2183 15 pf. Ceramic doll, 1960 . . 35 35
E2184 20 pf. Wooden doll, 1780 . . 35 35
E2185 35 pf. Straw puppet, 1900 . . 35 35
E2186 50 pf. Jointed doll, 1800 . . 35 35
E2187 70 pf. Tumbler-doll, 1820 . . 35 35

1980. Winter Olympic Games, Lake Placid. Multicoloured.

E2188 10 pf. "Bobsleigh Start" (Gunter Rechn) (horiz) . . 10 10
E2189 20 pf. Type E **661** 10 10
E2190 25 pf. + 10 pf. "Ski jumpers" (plastic sculpture, Gunter Schultz) 15 10
E2191 35 pf. "Speed Skaters at the Start" (Axel Wunsch) . . . 1·00 70

E **662** Stille Musik Rock Garden, Grosssedlitz

1980. Baroque Gardens. Multicoloured.

E2193 10 pf. Type E **662** 10 10
E2194 20 pf. Belvedere Orangery, Weimar 10 10
E2195 50 pf. Flower garden, Dornburg Castle 20 15
E2196 70 pf. Park, Rheinsberg Castle . . . . 1·25 1·25

E 663 Cable-laying Machine and Dish Aerial

1980. Post Office Activities. Multicoloured.
E2212 10 pf. Type E **663** 10 10
E2213 20 pf. T.V. Tower, Berlin, and television 20 15

E 664 Johann Wolfgang Dobereiner (chemist, bicent)

1980. Celebrities. Birth Anniversaries.
E2214 E **664** 5 pf. black & bistre . . 15 10
E2215 – 10 pf. black & red . . 25 10
E2216 – 20 pf. black & grn . . 60 10
E2217 – 25 pf. black & blue . . 20 10
E2218 – 35 pf. black & blue . . 25 15
E2219 – 70 pf. black & red . . 1·25 1·00
DESIGNS: 10 pf. Frederic Joliot-Curie (physicist, and chemist, 80th anniv); 20 pf. Johann Friedrich Naumann (zoologist, bicent); 25 pf. Alfred Wegener (explorer and geophysicist, cent); 35 pf. Carl von Clausewitz (Prussian general, bicent); 70 pf. Helene Weigel (actress, 80th anniv).

E 665 Karl Marx University, Leipzig
E 666 Werner Eggerath

1980. Leipzig Spring Fair. Multicoloured.
E2220 10 pf. Type E **665** 10 10
E2221 25 pf. "ZT 303" tractor . . . 25 20

1980. 80th Birth Anniv of Werner Eggerath (socialist).
E2222 E **666** 10 pf. brown and red . 30 10

E 668 "On the Horizontal Beam" (sculpture, Erich Wurzer)

1980. Olympic Games, Moscow (1st issue). Multicoloured.
E2224 10 pf. Type E **668** 10 10
E2225 20 pf. + 5 pf. "Runners before the Winning Post" (Lothar Zitzmann) 10 10
E2226 50 pf. "Coxless Four" (Wilfred Falkenthal) . . . 95 65
See also Nos. E2247/9.

E 669 Flags of Member States
E 670 Co-operative Society Building (W Gropius)

1980. 25th Anniv of Warsaw Pact.
E2227 E **669** 20 pf. multicoloured . . 30 10

1980. Bauhaus Architecture. Multicoloured.
E2228 5 pf. Type E **670** 10 10
E2229 10 pf. Socialists' Memorial Place (M. v. d. Rhode) (horiz) 10 10
E2230 15 pf. Monument to the Fallen of March 1922 (W. Gropius) 10 10
E2231 20 pf. Steel Building 1926 (G. Muche and R. Paulick) (horiz) 10 10
E2232 50 pf. Trade Union school (H. Meyer) 20 15
E2233 70 pf. Bauhaus building (W. Gropius) (horiz) . . . . . 2·00 1·10

E 671 Rostock Buildings

1980. 18th Workers' Festival, Rostock. Mult.
E2234 10 pf. Type E **671** 10 10
E2235 20 pf. Costumed dancers . . 20 10

E 672 Radar Complex, Berlin-Schoenefeld Airport

1980. "Aerosozphilex 1980" International Airmail Exhibition, Berlin. Multicoloured.
E2236 20 pf. Type E **672** 40 40
E2237 25 pf. Ilyushin Il-62M at Schonfeld Airport 50 50
E2238 35 pf. PZL-106A Kruk crop-spraying airplane 60 60
E2239 70 pf. Antonov An-2 aerial photography biplane and multispectrum camera . . 1·00 1·00

E 673 Okapi

1980. Endangered Animals. Multicoloured.
E2241 5 pf. Type E **673** 15 10
E2242 10 pf. Lesser pandas 15 10
E2243 15 pf. Maned wolf 20 10
E2244 20 pf. Arabian oryx 25 10
E2245 25 pf. White-eared pheasant . 60 15
E2246 35 pf. Musk oxen . . . . . 2·00 1·25

1980. Olympic Games, Moscow (2nd issue). As Type E **668**. Multicoloured.
E2247 10 pf. "Judo" (Erhard Schmidt) 10 10
E2248 20 pf. + 10 pf. "Swimmer" (Willi Sitte) (vert) 15 10
E2249 50 pf. "Spurt" (sculpture, Siegfried Schreiber) . . . 1·25 75

E 674 Suhl, 1700
E 675 Huntley Microscope

1980. Sixth National Youth Stamp Exhibition, Suhl. Multicoloured.
E2251 10 pf. + 5 pf. Type E **674** . . 25 25
E2252 20 pf. Modern Suhl 25 25

1980. Carl Zeiss Optical Museum, Jena. Mult.
E2253 20 pf. Type E **675** 30 15
E2254 25 pf. Magny microscope, 1751 . . . . 30 30
E2255 35 pf. Amici microscope, 1845 . . . . 65 30
E2256 70 pf. Zeiss microscope, 1873 . 65 65

E 676 Majdanek Memorial

1980. War Victims' Memorial, Majdanek, Poland.
E2257 E **676** 35 pf. multicoloured . 40 15

E 677 Information Centre, Leipzig

1980. Leipzig Autumn Fair. Multicoloured.
E2258 10 pf. Type E **677** 10 10
E2259 25 pf. Carpet-knitting machine 30 10

E 678 Palace of Republic, Berlin

1980. 67th Interparliamentary Conference, Berlin.
E2260 E **678** 20 pf. mult 60 10

E 679 "Laughing Boy with Flute"
E 680 Clenched Fist and Star

1980. 400th Anniv of Frans Hals (artist). Multicoloured.
E2261 10 pf. Type E **679** 10 10
E2262 20 pf. "Portrait of Young Man in Drab Coat" . . . 10 10
E2263 25 pf. "The Mulatto" 10 10
E2264 35 pf. "Portrait of Young Man in Black Coat" . . . 80 60

1980. "Solidarity".
E2266 E **680** 10 pf. + 5 pf. turq & red 20 10

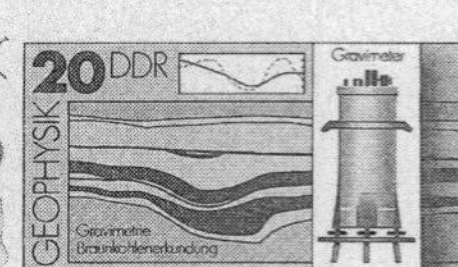

E 681 Red Cap
E 682 Gravimetry

1980. Edible Mushrooms. Multicoloured.
E2267 5 pf. Type E **681** 10 10
E2268 10 pf. Flaky-stemmed witches' mushroom 10 10
E2269 15 pf. Field mushroom . . . 45 15
E2270 20 pf. Chestnut mushroom . . 15 10
E2271 35 pf. Cep 20 10
E2272 70 pf. Chanterelle . . . . . 2·50 1·50

1980. Geophysics. Multicoloured.
E2273 20 pf. Type E **682** 25 25
E2274 25 pf. Bore-hole measuring . . 30 30
E2275 35 pf. Seismic prospecting . . 50 50
E2276 50 pf. Seismology 65 65

E 683 Radebeul–Radeburg Steam Locomotive
E 684 Toy Steam Locomotive, 1850

1980. Narrow-gauge Railways (1st series). Multicoloured.
E2277 20 pf. Type E **683** . . . . 1·40 65
E2278 20 pf. Bad Doberan–Ostseebad Kuhlungsborn steam locomotive . . . 1·40 65
E2279 25 pf. Radebeul–Radeburg passenger carriage . . . . 1·40 65
E2280 35 pf. Bad Doberan–Ostseebad Kuhlungsborn passenger carriage . . . . 1·60 70
See also Nos. E2342/5, E2509/12 and E2576/9.

1980. Historical Toys. Multicoloured.
E2281 10 pf. Type E **684** 70 70
E2282 20 pf. Aeroplane, 1914 . . . 45 45
E2283 25 pf. Steam-roller, 1920 . . 45 45
E2284 35 pf. Sailing ship, 1825 . . 45 45
E2285 40 pf. Car, 1900 . . . . . 45 45
E2286 50 pf. Balloon, 1920 . . . . 45 45

E 686 "Malus pumila"
E 687 Heinrich von Stephan

1981. Rare Plants in Berlin Arboretum. Mult.
E2288 5 pf. Type E **686** 10 10
E2289 10 pf. "Halesia carolina" (horiz) 10 10
E2290 20 pf. "Colutea arborescens" . 10 10
E2291 25 pf. "Paulownia tomentosa" 10 10
E2292 35 pf. "Lonicera periclymenum" (horiz) 20 10
E2293 50 pf. "Calycanthus floridus" . 2·00 1·60

1981. 150th Birth Anniv of Heinrich von Stephan (founder of U.P.U.).
E2294 E **687** 10 pf. black & yell . . 25 10

E 688 Soldiers on Parade

1981. 25th Anniv of National People's Army. Multicoloured.
E2295 10 pf. Type E **688** 15 10
E2296 20 pf. Marching soldiers . . 20 15

E 689 Marx and Lenin

1981. 10th East German Socialist Party Congress (1st series).
E2297 E **689** 10 pf. multicoloured . 15 10
See Nos. E2309/12.

E 690 Counter Clerks

1981. Post Office Training. Multicoloured.
E2298 5 pf. Type E **690** 10 10
E2299 10 pf. Telephone engineers . . 10 10
E2300 15 pf. Radio communications 10 10
E2301 20 pf. Rosa Luxemburg Engineering School, Leipzig 10 10
E2302 25 pf. Freidrich List Communications School, Dresden . . . . 1·10 65

E 691 Erich Baron
E 692 Hotel Merkur Leipzig

1981. Socialist Personalities.
E2303 E **691** 10 pf. black & grn . . 10 10
E2304 – 10 pf. black & yell . . 10 10
E2305 – 10 pf. black & blue . . 10 10
E2306 – 10 pf. black & brn . . 10 10
DESIGNS: No. E2304, Conrad Blenkle; E2305, Arthur Ewert; E2306, Walter Stoecker.

1981. Leipzig Spring Fair. Multicoloured.
E2307 10 pf. Type E **692** 15 10
E2308 25 pf. Open-cast mining machine 35 20

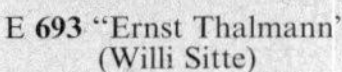
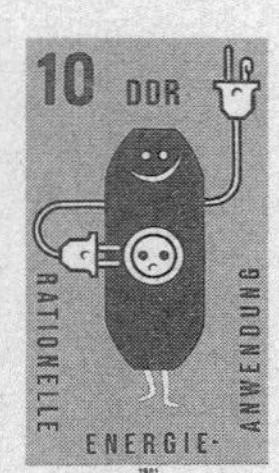

E 693 "Ernst Thalmann" (Willi Sitte)
E 695 Plugs and Socket

1981. 10th East German Socialist Party Congress (2nd series). Multicoloured.

E2309 10 pf. Type E **693** 10 10
E2310 20 pf. "Brigadier" (Bernhard Heisig) 10 10
E2311 25 pf. "Festival Day" (Rudolf Bergander) 75 60
E2312 35 pf. "Comrades in Arms" (Paul Michaelis) 15 10

1981. Conservation of Energy.

E2315 E **695** 10 pf. blk & orge . . 15 10

E 696 Heinrich Barkhausen

1981. Celebrities' Birth Anniversaries.

E2316 E **696** 10 pf. black & blue . . 10 10
E2317 – 20 pf. black & red . . 10 10
E2318 – 25 pf. black & brn . . 2·00 1·10
E2319 – 35 pf. black & vio . . 15 10
E2320 – 50 pf. black & grn . . 20 10
E2321 – 70 pf. black & brn . . 20 15

DESIGNS: 10 pf. Type E **696** (physicist, birth centenary); 20 pf. Johannes R. Becher (writer, 90th birth anniv); 25 pf. Richard Dedekind (mathematician, 150th birth anniv); 35 pf. Georg Philipp Telemann (composer, 300th anniv); 50 pf. Adelbert V. Chamisso (poet and naturalist, bicentenary); 70 pf. Wilhelm Raabe (novelist, 150th birth anniv).

E 697 Free German Youth Members and Banner
E 698 Worlitz Park

1981. 11th Free German Youth Parliament. Multicoloured.

E2322 10 pf. Type E **697** 15 15
E2323 20 pf. Free German Youth members instructing foreign students 15 15

1981. Landscaped Parks. Multicoloured.

E2324 5 pf. Type E **698** 10 10
E2325 10 pf. Tiefurt Park, Weimar . 10 10
E2326 15 pf. Marxwalde 10 10
E2327 20 pf. Branitz Park 10 10
E2328 25 pf. Treptow Park, Berlin . 1·50 1·00
E2329 35 pf. Wiesenburg Park . . . 20 15

E 699 Children at Play and Sport

1981. 8th Children's and Young People's Sports Days, Berlin. Multicoloured.

E2330 10 pf. + 5 pf. Type E **699** . . 55 35
E2331 20 pf. Artistic gymnastics . . 10 10

E 700 Berlin Theatre

1981. Birth Bicentenary of Karl Friedrich Schinkel (architect).

E2332 E **700** 10 pf. stone & black . 65 15
E2333 – 25 pf. stone & black . 1·60 65

DESIGN: 25 pf. Old Museum, Berlin.

E 701 Throwing the Javelin from a Wheel chair
E 702 House, Zaulsdorf

1981. International Year of Disabled Persons. Multicoloured.

E2334 5 pf. Type E **701** 15 15
E2335 15 pf. Disabled people in art gallery 15 15

1981. Half-timbered Buildings. Multicoloured.

E2336 10 pf. Type E **702** 10 10
E2337 20 pf. "Sugar-loaf" cottage, Gross Zicker (horiz) . . . 15 10
E2338 25 pf. Farmhouse, Weckersdorf 20 10
E2339 35 pf. House, Pillgram (horiz) 25 15
E2340 50 pf. House, Eschenbach . . 30 15
E2341 70 pf. House, Ludersdorf (horiz) . . . . 3·00 1·90

1981. Narrow-Gauge Railways (2nd series). As Type E **683**. Multicoloured.

E2342 5 pf. black and red 75 50
E2343 5 pf. black and red 75 50
E2344 15 pf. multicoloured 75 50
E2345 20 pf. multicoloured 80 50

DESIGNS: Nos. E2342, Freital–Kurort Kipsdorf steam locomotive; E2343, Putbus–Gohren steam locomotive; E2344, Freital–Kurort Kipsdorf luggage van; E2345, Putbus–Gohren passenger carriage.

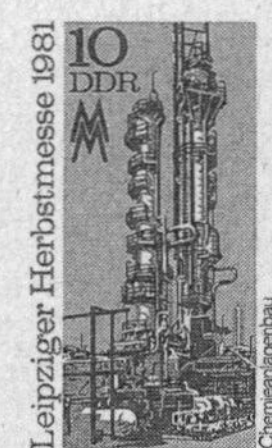

E 703 Chemical Works
E 704 Ebers Papyrus (Leipzig University Library)

1981. Leipzig Autumn Fair. Multicoloured.

E2346 10 pf. Type E **703** 10 10
E2347 25 pf. New Draper's Hall (horiz) 35 25

1981. Precious Books from East German Libraries. Multicoloured.

E2348 20 pf. Type E **704** 10 10
E2349 35 pf. Maya manuscript (Dresden Library) 20 10
E2350 50 pf. Miniature from "Les six visions Messire Francoys Petrarque" (Berlin State Library) . . . . 1·25 80

E 705 Sassnitz Memorial
E 706 Henbane and Incense Burner

1981. Resistance Fighters' Memorial, Sassnitz.

E2351 E **705** 35 pf. multicoloured . 40 10

1981. Early Medical Equipment in the Karl–Sudhoff Institute, Leipzig. Multicoloured.

E2352 10 pf. Type E **706** 10 10
E2353 20 pf. Dental instruments . . 10 10
E2354 25 pf. Forceps 10 10
E2355 35 pf. Bladder knife and hernia shears 20 10
E2356 50 pf. Speculum and gynaecological forceps (vert) . . . 2·10 1·50
E2357 85 pf. Triploid elevators (vert) 35 15

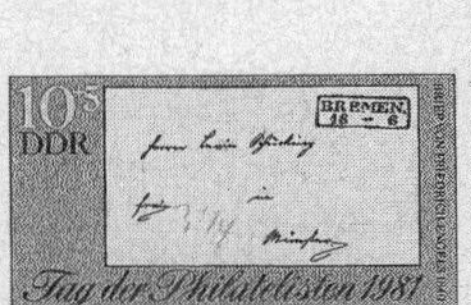

E 707 Letter from Friedrich Engels, 1840
E 708 African breaking Chains

1981. Stamp Day. Multicoloured.

E2358 10 pf. + 5 pf. Type E **707** . . 65 40
E2359 20 pf. Postcard from Karl Marx, 1878 . . . . 15 10

1981. "Solidarity".

E2360 E **708** 10 pf. + 5 pf. mult . . 20 10

E 709 Tug
E 710 Windmill, Dabel

1981. Inland Shipping. Multicoloured.

E2361 10 pf. Type E **709** 10 10
E2362 20 pf. Tug and barges 10 10
E2363 25 pf. Diesel-electric paddle-ferry on the Elbe 15 10
E2364 35 pf. Ice-breaker in the Oder estuary 20 10
E2365 50 pf. Motor barge "Schonewalde" 25 20
E2366 85 pf. Dredger . . . . . . 2·75 2·50

1981. Windmills. Multicoloured.

E2367 10 pf. Type E **710** 10 10
E2368 20 pf. Pahrenz 10 10
E2369 25 pf. Dresden-Gohlis . . . 10 10
E2370 70 pf. Ballstadt . . . . . . 1·40 1·10

E 711 Snake, 1850
E 712 Coffee Pot, 1715

1981. Historical Toys. Multicoloured.

E2371 10 pf. Type E **711** 50 50
E2372 20 pf. Teddy bear, 1910 . . . 50 50
E2373 25 pf. Goldfish, 1935 . . . . 50 50
E2374 35 pf. Hobby-horse, 1850 . . 50 50
E2375 40 pf. Pull-along duck, 1800 . 50 50
E2376 70 pf. Clockwork frog, 1930 . 50 50

1982. 300th Birth Anniv of Johann Friedrich Bottger (founder of Meissen China Works). Multicoloured.

E2377 10 pf. Type E **712** 15 15
E2378 20 pf. Vase decorated with flowers, 1715 . . . . 30 30
E2379 25 pf. "Oberon" (figurine), 1969 . . . . 40 40
E2380 35 pf. Vase "Day and Night", 1979 . . . . 60 60

E 713 Post Office, Bad Liebenstein

1982. Post Office Building. Multicoloured.

E2382 20 pf. Type E **713** 10 10
E2383 25 pf. Telecommunications Centre, Berlin 10 10
E2384 35 pf. Head Post Office, Erfurt 20 10
E2385 50 pf. Head Post Office, Dresden 6 . . . . 1·25 1·00

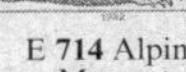

E 714 Alpine Marmot
E 718 Max Fechner

E 716 West Entrance to Fairground

1982. International Fur Auction, Leipzig. Multicoloured.

E2386 10 pf. Type E **714** 15 10
E2387 20 pf. Polecat 20 10
E2388 25 pf. European mink . . . 25 10
E2389 35 pf. Beech marten . . . . 1·60 1·10

1982. Leipzig Spring Fair. Multicoloured.

E2391 10 pf. Type E **716** 15 10
E2392 25 pf. Seamless steel tube plant, Riesa Zeithain . . . 30 15

1982. Socialist Personalities.

E2394 E **718** 10 pf. brown 10 10
E2395 – 10 pf. green 10 10
E2396 – 10 pf. lilac 10 10
E2397 – 10 pf. blue 10 10
E2398 – 10 pf. green 10 10

DESIGNS: No. E2395, Ottomar Geschke; E2396, Helmut Lehmann; E2397, Herbert Warnke; E2398, Otto Winzer.

E 719 Meadow Saffron
E 720 Decorative Initial "I"

1982. Poisonous Plants. Multicoloured.

E2399 10 pf. Type E **719** 15 10
E2400 15 pf. Bog arum 15 10
E2401 20 pf. Labrador tea 20 10
E2402 25 pf. Bryony 25 10
E2403 35 pf. Monkshood 30 10
E2404 50 pf. Henbane . . . . . . 1·50 1·10

1982. International "Art of the Book" Exhibition, Leipzig.

E2405 E **720** 15 pf. multicoloured . 40 40
E2406 – 35 pf. brn, red & blk . 40 40

DESIGN: 35 pf. Exhibition emblem.

E 721 "Mother with Child" (W. Womacka)
E 722 Osprey

1982. 10th Free German Trade Unions Association Congress, Berlin.

E2407 E **721** 10 pf. black, red and yellow 10 10
E2408 – 20 pf. multicoloured . 10 10
E2409 – 25 pf. multicoloured . 65 55

DESIGNS—HORIZ: 20 pf. "Discussion by Collective of Innovators" (Willi Neubert). VERT: 25 pf. "Young Couple" (Karl-Heinz Jakob).

1982. Protected Birds. Multicoloured.

E2410 10 pf. Type E **722** 25 10
E2411 20 pf. White-tailed sea eagle (horiz) 35 10
E2412 25 pf. Little owl 40 15
E2413 35 pf. Eagle owl . . . . . . 3·25 1·60

E 723 Old and Modern Buildings

1982. 19th Workers' Festival, Neubrandenburg. Multicoloured.

E2414 10 pf. Type E **723** 15 10
E2415 20 pf. Couple in traditional costume 30 20

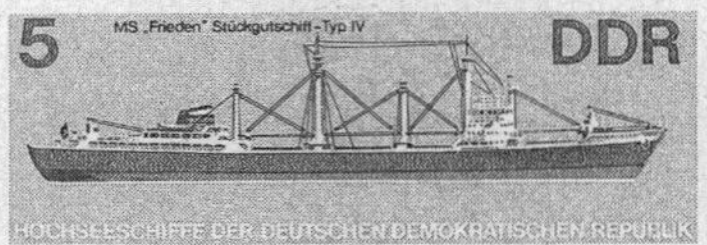

E 725 Freighter "Frieden"

1982. Ocean-going Ships. Multicoloured.

E2417 5 pf. Type E **725** 10 10
E2418 10 pf. Roll-on roll-off freighter "Fichtelberg" 10 10
E2419 15 pf. Heavy cargo carrier "Brocken" 15 10
E2420 20 pf. Container ship "Weimar" 20 10
E2421 25 pf. First DSR freighter "Vorwarts" 20 10
E2422 35 pf. Container ship "Berlin" . . . . 1·75 1·50

E **726** Members' Activities

1982. 30th Anniv of Sports and Science Association.

E2423 E **726** 20 pf. multicoloured . . . 40 10

E **727** Bird Wedding

1982. Sorbian Folk Customs. Multicoloured.

E2424 10 pf. Type E **727** 15 15
E2425 20 pf. Shrove Tuesday procession 30 30
E2426 25 pf. Egg rolling 40 40
E2427 35 pf. Painted Easter eggs . . 50 50
E2428 40 pf. St. John's Day riders . . 55 55
E2429 50 pf. Distribution of Christmas gifts to hard-working children 65 65

E **728** Schwerin, 1640

1982. 7th National Youth Stamp Exhibition, Schwerin. Multicoloured.

E2430 10 pf. + 5 pf. Type E **728** . . 25 25
E2431 20 pf. Modern Schwerin . . . 25 25

E **729** Flag and Pioneers

1982. 7th Pioneers Meeting, Dresden. Mult.

E2432 10 pf. + 5 pf. Type E **729** . . 50 25
E2433 20 pf. Trumpet and drum . . 10 10

E **730** "Stormy Sea" (Ludolf Backhuysen)

1982. Paintings in Schwerin State Museum. Multicoloured.

E2434 5 pf. Type E **730** 15 10
E2435 10 pf. "Music making at Home" (Frans van Mieris) (vert) 15 10
E2436 20 pf. "The Watchman" (Carel Fabritius) (vert) . . 20 10
E2437 25 pf. "Company of Peasants" (Adriaen Brouwer) 20 15
E2438 35 pf. "Breakfast Table with Ham" (Willem Claesz Heda) 30 15
E2439 70 pf. "River Landscape" (Jan van Goyen) . . . . . . 1·90 1·50

E **731** Karl-Marx-Stadt

1982. 13th Socialist Countries' Postal Ministers Conference, Karl-Marx-Stadt.

E2440 E **731** 10 pf. multicoloured . . 15 10

E **732** Stentzlers Hof

1982. Leipzig Autumn Fair. Multicoloured.

E2441 10 pf. Type E **732** 10 10
E2442 25 pf. Amber box, ring and pendant 25 10

E **733** Auschwitz-Birkenau Memorial
E **734** Federation Badge

1982. War Victims' Memorial, Auschwitz-Birkenau.

E2443 E **733** 35 pf. bl, blk & red . . 25 10

1982. 9th International Federation of Resistance Fighters Congress, Berlin.

E2444 E **734** 10 pf. multicoloured . . 25 10

E **735** "Anemone hupehensis"
E **736** Palestinian Family

1982. Autumn Flowers. Multicoloured.

E2445 5 pf. Type E **735** 15 10
E2446 10 pf. French marigolds . . . 15 10
E2447 15 pf. Gazania 20 10
E2448 20 pf. Sunflower 25 10
E2449 25 pf. Annual chrysanthemum 30 10
E2450 35 pf. Cosmea . . . . 2·25 1·25

1982. Solidarity with Palestinian People.

E2451 E **736** 10 pf. + 5 pf. mult . . 30 10

E **737** "B 1000" Ambulance
E **738** Fair Emblem

1982. IFA Vehicles. Multicoloured.

E2452 5 pf. Type E **737** 10 10
E2453 10 pf. Road cleaner 15 10
E2454 20 pf. "LD 3000" omnibus . . 20 10
E2455 25 pf. "LD 3000" lorry . . . 25 10
E2456 35 pf. "W 50" lorry 30 10
E2457 85 pf. "W 50" milk tanker . . 2·25 1·75

1982. 25th "Masters of Tomorrow" Fair, Leipzig.

E2458 E **738** 20 pf. multicoloured . . 20 10

E **739** Aircraft and Envelope
E **740** Seal of Eisleben, 1500

1982. Air.

E2459 E **739** 5 pf. black and blue . 15 10
E2460 15 pf. black & mauve . 20 10
E2461 20 pf. black & orange . 20 15
E2462 25 pf. blk & bistre . 30 15
E2463 30 pf. black & green . 20 10
E2464 40 pf. black & green . 25 10
E2465 1 m. black & blue . . 65 25
E2466 3 m. black & brown . 2·50 90
E2467 5 m. black and red . . 4·25 90

1982. 500th Birth Anniv of Martin Luther (Protestant reformer).

E2471 10 pf. Type E **740** 10 10
E2472 20 pf. Luther as Junker Jog, 1521 . . . . 20 10
E2473 35 pf. Seal of Wittenberg, 1500 . . . . 30 10
E2474 85 pf. Luther (after Cranach) 2·50 1·75

E **741** Carpenter

1982. Mechanical Toys. Multicoloured.

E2475 10 pf. Type E **741** 40 40
E2476 20 pf. Shoemaker 40 40
E2477 25 pf. Baker 40 40
E2478 35 pf. Cooper 40 40
E2479 40 pf. Tanner 40 40
E2480 70 pf. Wheelwright 40 40

E **743** Franz Dahlem
E **744** Telephone Handset and Push-buttons

1983. Socialist Personalities.

E2482 E **743** 10 pf. brown 10 10
E2483 – 10 pf. green 10 10
E2484 – 10 pf. green 10 10
E2485 – 10 pf. lilac 10 10
E2486 – 10 pf. blue 10 10

DESIGN: No. E2483, Karl Maron; E2484, Josef Miller; E2485, Fred Oelssner; E2486, Siegfried Radel.

1983. World Communications Year.

E2487 E **744** 5 pf. brown, black and deep brown 10 10
E2488 – 10 pf. blue, turquoise and deep blue . . . 20 10
E2489 – 20 pf. green, deep green and black . . 30 10
E2490 – 35 pf. multicoloured . . 1·10 75

DESIGNS: 10 pf. Aerials and tankers (Rugen Radio); 20 pf. Aircraft, container ship, letter and parcel; 35 pf. Optical fibre cables.

E **745** Otto Nuschke
E **746** Stolberg Town Hall

1983. Birth Cent of Otto Nuschke (politician).

E2491 E **745** 20 pf. light brown, black and brown . . 20 10

1983. Historic Town Halls. Multicoloured.

E2492 10 pf. Type E **746** 10 10
E2493 20 pf. Gera (vert) 10 10
E2494 25 pf. Possneck (vert) 10 10
E2495 35 pf. Berlin . . . . 1·40 1·00

E **747** Petershof

1983. Leipzig Spring Fair. Multicoloured.

E2496 10 pf. Type E **747** 10 10
E2497 25 pf. Robotron micro-electronic calculator . . . 25 10

E **748** Paul Robeson

1983. 85th Birth Anniv of Paul Robeson (singer).

E2498 E **748** 20 pf. multicoloured . . 25 10

E **750** Karl Marx and Newspaper Mastheads

1983. Death Cent of Karl Marx. Multicoloured.

E2500 10 pf. Type E **750** 10 10
E2501 20 pf. Marx, Lyons silk weavers and title page of "Deutsche-Franzosische Jahrbucher" 10 10
E2502 35 pf. Marx, Engels and "Communist Manifesto" . 20 10
E2503 50 pf. Marx and German, Russian and French versions of "Das Kapital" . . 20 10
E2504 70 pf. Marx and part of letter to Wilhelm Bracke containing commentary on German Workers' Party Programme 25 20
E2505 85 pf. Globe and banner portraying Marx, Engels, Lenin . . . . 2·50 2·40

E **751** "Athene"
E **752** Chancery Hourglass with Wallmount, 1674

1983. Sculptures in State Museum, Berlin.

E2507 E **751** 10 pf. brown, light brown and blue . . 10 10
E2508 – 20 pf. brown, light brown and green . . 25 10

DESIGN: 20 pf. "Amazon".

1983. Narrow-gauge Railways (3rd series). As Type E **683**.

E2509 15 pf. grey, black & red . . . 1·60 90
E2510 20 pf. multicoloured . . . . 1·60 90
E2511 20 pf. grey, black & red . . . 1·60 90
E2512 50 pf. brown, black & grey . 1·60 90

DESIGNS: No. E2509, Wernigerode-Nordhausen steam locomotive; E2510, Wernigerode-Nordhausen passenger carriage; E2511, Zittau-Kurort Oybin/Kurort Jonsdorf steam locomotive; E2512, Zittau-Kurort Oybib/Kurort Jonsdorf luggage van.

1983. Hourglasses and Sundials. Multicoloured.

E2513 5 pf. Type E **752** 10 10
E2514 10 pf. Chancery hour-glass, 1700 . . . . 10 10
E2515 20 pf. Horizontal table sundial, 1611 . . . . . . 10 10
E2516 30 pf. Equatorial sundial, 1750 . . . . 15 10
E2517 50 pf. Equatorial sundial, 1760 . . . . 25 20
E2518 85 pf. "Noon Gun" table sundial, 1800 . . . . . . 2·50 1·75

E **753** "Coryphantha elephantidens"
E **755** "Glasewaldt and Zinna defending the Barricade, Berlin, 1848" (Theodor Hosemann)

E **754** Thimo and Wilhelm

1983. Cultivated Cacti. Multicoloured.

E2519 5 pf. Type E **753** 10 10
E2520 10 pf. "Thelocactus schwarzii" 10 10
E2521 20 pf. "Leuchtenbergia principis" 10 10
E2522 25 pf. "Submatucana madisoniorum" 10 10
E2523 35 pf. "Oroya peruviana" . . 15 10
E2524 50 pf. "Copiapoa cinerea" . . 2·00 1·25

1983. Founders of Naumberg Cathedral. Statues in the West Choir. Multicoloured.

E2525 20 pf. Type E **754** 35 35
E2526 25 pf. Gepa and Gerburg . . 35 35
E2527 35 pf. Hermann and Reglindis 35 35
E2528 85 pf. Eckehard and Uta . . 1·25 1·25

1983. "Junior Sozphilex 1983" Stamp Exhibition, Berlin.

E2529 E **755** 10 pf. + 5 pf. brown, black and red . . . 60 55
E2350 – 20 pf. multicoloured . . 10 10

DESIGN—HORIZ: 20 pf. "Instruction at Polytechnic" (Harald Metzkes).

E **756** Simon Bolivar and Alexander von Humboldt

1983. Birth Bicent. of Simon Bolivar.
E2531 E **756** 35 pf. black, brown and deep brown . . 40 15

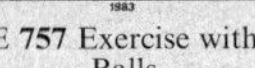

E **757** Exercise with Balls

E **758** Arms of Cottbus

1983. 7th Gymnastics and Sports Festival and 9th Children and Young People's Sports Days, Leipzig. Multicoloured.
E2532 10 pf. + 5 pf. Type E **757** . . 50 35
E2533 20 pf. Volleyball 10 10

1983. Town Arms (1st series).
E2534 E **758** 50 pf. mult 65 60
E2535 – 50 pf. mult 65 60
E2536 – 50 pf. red, black and silver 65 60
E2537 – 50 pf. mult 65 60
E2568 – 50 pf. black, red and silver 65 60
DESIGNS: No. E2535, Dresden; E2536, Erfurt; E2537, Frankfurt-on-Oder. (21 × 39 mm); No. E2538, Berlin.
See also Nos. E2569/73 and E2644/8.

E **759** Central Fair Palace

1983. Leipzig Autumn Fair. Multicoloured.
E2539 10 pf. Type E **759** 15 10
E2540 25 pf. Microchip 30 10

E **761** Euler, Formula and Model

1983. Death Bicentenary of Leonhard Euler (mathematician).
E2542 E **761** 20 pf. blue and black . 30 15

E **762** Sanssouci Castle

1983. Public Palaces and Gardens of Potsdam-Sanssouci. Multicoloured.
E2543 10 pf. Type E **762** 10 10
E2544 20 pf. Chinese tea house . . 10 10
E2545 40 pf. Charlottenhof Palace . 30 15
E2546 50 pf. Film museum (former stables) . . . . 2·25 1·90

E **763** "Mother Homeland" (Yevgeni Vuzhetich)

E **765** Learning to Read and Write

1983. Volograd War Memorial.
E2547 E **763** 35 pf. blue, blk & grn . 40 15

1983. "Solidarity with Nicaragua".
E2549 E **765** 10 pf. + 5 pf. mult . . 30 10

E **766** Cockerel

1983. Thuringian Glass. Multicoloured.
E2550 10 pf. Type E **766** 10 10
E2551 20 pf. Beaker 10 10
E2552 25 pf. Vase 10 10
E2553 70 pf. Goblet . . . . 1·75 1·40

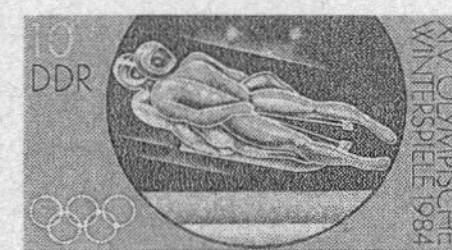

E **767** Luge

1983. Winter Olympic Games, Sarajevo (1984). Multicoloured.
E2554 10 pf. + 5 pf. Type E **767** . . 15 10
E2555 20 pf. + 10 pf. Cross-country skiing and ski jumping . . 20 10
E2556 25 pf. Cross-country skiing . 20 10
E2557 35 pf. Biathlon . . . . . . 1·40 1·00

E **769** Dr. Otto Schott (chemist)

E **770** Friedrich Ebert

1984. Centenary of Jena Glass.
E2560 E **769** 20 pf. mult 20 10

1984. Socialist Personalities.
E2561 E **770** 10 pf. black 10 10
E2562 – 10 pf. green 10 10
E2563 – 10 pf. black 10 10
DESIGNS: No. E2562, Fritz Grosse; E2563, Albert Norden.

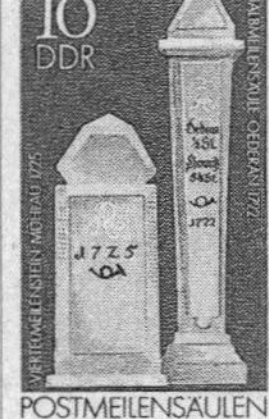

E **772** Milestones, Muhlau and Oederan

E **773** Old Town Hall, Leipzig

1984. Postal Milestones. Multicoloured.
E2565 10 pf. Type E **772** 10 10
E2566 20 pf. Milestones, Johanngeorgenstadt and Schonbrunn 20 20
E2567 35 pf. Distance column, Freiberg 30 30
E2568 85 pf. Distance column, Pegau 80 50

1984. Town Arms (2nd series). As Type E **758**.
E2569 50 pf. multicoloured . . . 40 40
E2570 50 pf. red, black and silver . . 40 40
E2571 50 pf. multicoloured 40 40
E2572 50 pf. multicoloured 40 40
E2573 50 pf. multicoloured 40 40
DESIGNS: No. E2569, Gera; E2570, Halle; E2571, Karl-Marx-Stadt; E2572, Leipzig; E2573, Magdeburg.

1984. Leipzig Spring Fair. Multicoloured.
E2574 10 pf. Type E **773** 10 10
E2575 25 pf. Body stamping press . 20 10

1984. Narrow-gauge Railways (4th series). As Type E **683**.
E2576 30 pf. grey, black and red . . 1·25 30
E2577 40 pf. grey, black and red . . 1·25 30
E2578 60 pf. multicoloured . . . . 1·25 30
E2579 80 pf. multicoloured . . . . 1·25 30
DESIGNS: 30 pf. Cranzahl–Kurort Oberwiesenthal steam locomotive; 40 pf. Selketalbahn steam locomotive; 60 pf. Selketalbahn passenger carriage; 80 pf. Cranzahl–Kurort Oberwiesenthal passenger carriage.

E **774** Town Hall, Rostock

E **775** Telephone, Letter, Pencil and Headquarters

1984. 7th International Society for Preservation of Monuments General Assembly, Rostock and Dresden. Multicoloured.
E2580 10 pf. Type E **774** 10 10
E2581 15 pf. Albrecht Castle, Meissen 10 10
E2582 40 pf. Gateway, Rostock (vert) 30 30
E2583 85 pf. Stables, Dresden . . . 75 75

1984. 25th Meeting of Posts and Telecommunications Commission of Council of Mutual Economic Aid, Cracow.
E2584 E **775** 70 pf. multicoloured . 50 30

E **776** Cast Iron Bowl

E **777** String Puppet

1984. Cast Iron from Lauchhammer. Multicoloured.
E2585 20 pf. Type E **776** 30 30
E2586 85 pf. "Climber" (Fritz Cremer) 50 50

1984. Puppets. Multicoloured.
E2587 50 pf. Type E **777** 40 40
E2588 80 pf. Hand puppet 70 70

E **778** Marchers with Flags

1984. National Youth Festival, Berlin. Multicoloured.
E2589 10 pf. + 5 pf. Type E **778** . . 10 10
E2590 20 pf. Young construction workers 10 10

E **779** Gera Buildings

1984. 20th Workers' Festival, Gera. Multicoloured.
E2591 10 pf. Type E **779** 10 10
E2592 20 pf. Couple in traditional costume 15 15

E **780** Salt Carrier

E **781** Bakers' Seal, Berlin

1984. National Stamp Exhibition, Halle. Mult.
E2593 10 pf. + 5 pf. Type E **780** . . 15 10
E2594 20 pf. Citizen of Halle with his bride 20 10

1984. Historical Seals of 1442. Multicoloured.
E2595 5 pf. Type E **781** 50 15
E2596 10 pf. Wool weavers, Berlin . 70 20
E2597 20 pf. Wool weavers, Colln on Spree . . . . 1·00 35
E2598 35 pf. Shoemakers, Colln on Spree . . . . 1·75 1·25

E **782** New Flats and Restored Terrace

E **783** Frege House, Katherine Street

1984. 35th Anniv of German Democratic Republic (1st issue). Multicoloured.
E2599 10 pf. Type E **782** 10 10
E2600 20 pf. Surface mining 20 15
See also Nos. E2604/6 and E2609/12.

1984. Leipzig Autumn Fair. Multicoloured.
E2602 10 pf. Type E **783** 10 10
E2603 25 pf. Crystal jar from Olbernhau 25 10

E **784** East Ironworks

1984. 35th Anniv of German Democratic Republic (2nd issue). Multicoloured.
E2604 10 pf. Type E **784** 10 10
E2605 20 pf. Soldiers, Mil Mi-8 helicopter, tank and warship . 20 20
E2606 25 pf. Petro-chemical complex, Schwedt 30 30

E **785** "Members of the Resistance" (Arno Wittig)

1984. Resistance Memorial, Georg-Schumann Building, Technical University of Dresden.
E2608 E **785** 35 pf. multicoloured . 50 10

E **786** Construction Workers

1984. 35th Anniv of German Democratic Republic (3rd issue). Multicoloured.
E2609 10 pf. Type E **786** 10 10
E2610 20 pf. Soldiers 15 10
E2611 25 pf. Industrial workers . . 20 20
E2612 35 pf. Agricultural workers . 35 30

E **787** Magdeburg, 1551

1984. Eighth National Youth Exhibition, Magdeburg. Multicoloured.
E2614 10 pf. + 5 pf. Type E **787** . . 10 10
E2615 20 pf. Modern Magdeburg . . 15 15

E **788** "Spring"

E **789** Entwined Cable and Red Star

1984. Statuettes by Balthasar Permoser in Green Vault, Dresden. Multicoloured.
E2616 10 pf. Type E **788** 15 15
E2617 20 pf. "Summer" 20 20
E2618 35 pf. "Autumn" 40 40
E2619 70 pf. "Winter" 65 65

1984. "Solidarity".
E2621 E **789** 10 pf. + 5 pf. mult . . 30 10

E **790** Falkenstein Castle

1984. Castles (1st series). Multicoloured.

E2622 10 pf. Type E **790** 10 10
E2623 20 pf. Kriebstein Castle . . . 20 20
E2624 35 pf. Ranis Castle 50 30
E2625 80 pf. Neuenburg 65 50

See also Nos. E2686/9 and E2742/5.

E **791** Queen and Princess

1984. Fairy Tales. "Dead Tsar's Daughter and the Seven Warriors" by Pushkin. Multicoloured.

E2626 5 pf. Type E **791** 30 15
E2627 10 pf. Princess and dog outside cottage 45 25
E2628 15 pf. Princess and seven warriors 75 40
E2629 20 pf. Princess holding poisoned apple . . . . . . 1·10 50
E2630 35 pf. Princess awakened by Prince . . . . 1·75 90
E2631 50 pf. Prince and Princess on horse . . . . 2·25 1·10

E **792** Anton Ackermann — E **794** Letter-box, 1850

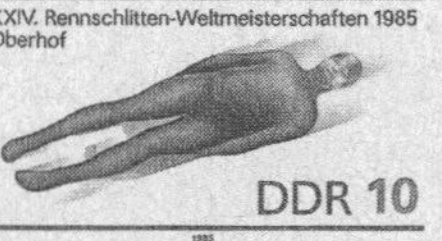

E **793** Luge

1985. Socialist Personalities.

E2632 E **792** 10 pf. black 10 10
E2633 10 pf. brown 10 10
E2634 10 pf. purple 10 10

DESIGNS: No. E2633, Alfred Kurella; E2634, Otto Schon.

1985. 24th World Luge Championships, Oberhof.

E2635 E **793** 10 pf. multicoloured . 30 10

1984. Letter-boxes.

E2636 E **794** 10 pf. brown & blk . . 10 10
E2637 – 20 pf. black, brown and red 20 20
E2638 – 35 pf. multicoloured . 30 30
E2639 – 50 pf. brown, black and grey 40 40

DESIGNS: 20 pf. Letter-box, 1860; 35 pf. Letter-box, 1900; 50 pf. Letter-box, 1920.

E **796** Bach Statue, Leipzig — E **798** Liberation Monument

1985. Leipzig Spring Fair. Multicoloured.

E2641 10 pf. Type E **796** 10 10
E2642 25 pf. Meissen porcelain pot . 20 10

1985. Town Arms (3rd series). As Type E **758**. Multicoloured.

E2644 50 pf. Neubrandenburg . . . 40 30
E2645 50 pf. Potsdam 40 30
E2646 50 pf. Rostock 40 30
E2647 50 pf. Schwerin 40 30
E2648 50 pf. Suhl 40 30

1985. Liberation Monument, Seelow Heights.

E2649 E **798** 35 pf. mult 30 15

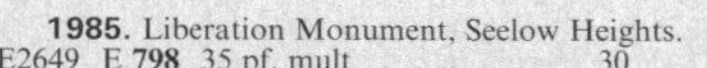

E **799** Egon Erwin Kisch

1985. Birth Centenary of Egon Erwin Kisch (journalist).

E2650 E **799** 35 pf. multicoloured . 40 25

E **800** Sigmund Jahn and Valeri Bykovski

1985. 40th Anniv of Defeat of Fascism. Multicoloured.

E2651 10 pf. Type E **800** 10 10
E2652 20 pf. Adolf Hennecke as miner 15 15
E2653 25 pf. Agricultural workers reading paper 20 20
E2654 50 pf. Laboratory technicians 45 45

E **801** Flags forming "Frieden" (Peace)

1985. 30th Anniv of Warsaw Pact.

E2656 E **801** 20 pf. multicoloured . 20 10

E **802** Emblem and Berlin Buildings

1985. 12th Free German Youth Parliament, Berlin. Multicoloured.

E2657 10 pf. + 5 pf. Type E **802** . . 10 10
E2658 20 pf. Flags, Ernst Thalmann and emblem 20 20

E **803** "Solidarity" and Dove on Globe — E **804** Olympic Flag

1985. "Solidarity".

E2659 E **803** 10 pf + 5 pf. mult . . 15 10

1985. 90th International Olympic Committee Meeting, Berlin.

E2660 E **804** 35 pf. multicoloured . 40 30

E **805** "40" and Emblem — E **806** Harpy Eagle

1985. 40th Anniv of Free German Trade Unions Federation.

E2661 E **805** 20 pf. multicoloured . 20 10

1985. Protected Animals. Multicoloured.

E2662 5 pf. Type E **806** 55 10
E2663 10 pf. Red-breasted geese (horiz) 80 30
E2664 20 pf. Spectacled bear (horiz) 30 25
E2665 50 pf. Bantengs (horiz) . . . 60 60
E2666 85 pf. Sunda gavial (horiz) . . 1·00 75

E **807** Support Steam-engine, Gera, 1833 — E **808** Students reading

1985. Steam Engines. Multicoloured.

E2667 10 pf. Type E **807** 10 10
E2668 85 pf. Balance steam-engine, Frieberg, 1848 . . . . . . 75 75

1985. 12th World Youth and Students' Festival, Moscow. Multicoloured.

E2669 20 pf. + 5 pf. Type E **808** . . 20 20
E2670 50 pf. Students with raised arms 40 40

E **809** Diver at Turning Post

1985. Second World Orienteering Diving Championship, Neuglobsow. Multicoloured.

E2671 10 pf. Type E **809** 10 10
E2672 70 pf. Divers 65 65

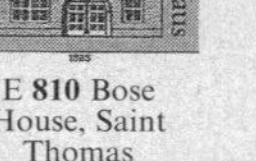

E **810** Bose House, Saint Thomas Churchyard — E **811** Passenger Mail Coach (relief, Hermann Steinemann)

1985. Leipzig Autumn Fair. Multicoloured.

E2673 10 pf. Type E **810** 10 10
E2674 25 pf. J. Scherzer Bach-trumpet 30 10

1985. "Sozphilex '85" Stamp Exhibition, Berlin. Multicoloured.

E2675 5 pf. Type E **811** 10 10
E2676 20 pf. + 5 pf. Team of horses 25 25

Nos. E2675/6 were printed together, se-tenant, forming a composite design.

E **812** Electrification of Railway — E **813** Gertrauden Bridge

1985. Railways. Multicoloured.

E2677 20 pf. Signal box 45 20
E2678 25 pf. Andreas Schubert (engineer), his locomotive "Saxonia", 1838, and electric locomotive Type BR 250 . . . . 55 30
E2679 50 pf. Type E **812** 85 65
E2680 85 pf. Leipzig Central Station 1·75 65

1985. Berlin Bridges. Multicoloured.

E2681 10 pf. Type E **813** 10 10
E2682 20 pf. Jungfern Bridge . . . 15 15
E2683 35 pf. Weidendammer Bridge 50 50
E2684 70 pf. Marx-Engels Bridge . . 70 70

1985. Castles (2nd series). As Type E **790**. Multicoloured.

E2686 10 pf. Hohnstein Castle . . . 10 10
E2687 20 pf. Rochsburg 15 15
E2688 35 pf. Schwarzenberg Castle . 30 30
E2689 80 pf. Stein Castle 80 80

E **814** Humboldt University — E **815** Cecilienhof Castle and U.N. Emblem

1985. Anniversaries. Multicoloured.

E2690 20 pf. Type E **814** (175th anniv of Humboldt University, Berlin) 30 15
E2691 85 pf. New and old Charite buildings (275th anniv of Berlin Charite (training clinic)) 65 65

1985. 40th Anniv of U.N.O.

E2692 E **815** 85 pf. multicoloured . 85 40

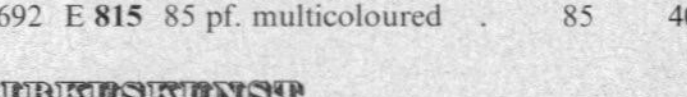

E **816** Elephants on Balls — E **817** Grimm Brothers

1985. Circus. Multicoloured.

E2693 10 pf. Type E **816** 20 20
E2694 20 pf. Trapeze artiste 30 30
E2695 35 pf. Acrobats on monocycles . . . . 1·00 1·00
E2696 50 pf. Tigers and trainer . . 1·25 1·25

1985. Birth Bicentenaries of Jacob and Wilhelm Grimm (folklorists). Multicoloured.

E2697 5 pf. Type E **817** 10 10
E2698 10 pf. "The Valiant Tailor" . . 10 10
E2699 20 pf. "Lucky John" 20 20
E2700 25 pf. "Puss in Boots" . . . 30 30
E2701 35 pf. "The Seven Ravens" . . 35 35
E2702 85 pf. "The Sweet Pap" . . . 65 65

E **818** Water Pump, Berlin, 1900 — E **819** Saxon Postilion

1986. Water Supply.

E2703 E **818** 10 pf. green and red . 10 10
E2704 – 35 pf. deep brown, brown and green . . 20 20
E2705 – 50 pf. purple & grn . . 30 30
E2706 – 70 pf. blue & brown . . 65 65

DESIGNS: 35 pf. Water tower, Berlin-Altglienicke, 1906; 50 pf. Waterworks, Berlin-Friedrichshagen, 1893; 70 pf. Rappbode dam, 1959.

1986. Postal Uniforms of 1850. Multicoloured.

E2707 10 pf. Type E **819** 15 15
E2708 20 pf. Prussian postman . . . 50 30
E2709 85 pf. Prussian postal official . 1·00 1·00
E2710 1 m. Postal official from Mecklenburg region . . . 1·25 1·25

E **820** Flag

1986. 40th Anniv of Free German Youth.

E2711 E **820** 20 pf. yell, bl & blk . 20 10

E **821** Flag

1986. 30th Anniv of National People's Army.

E2712 E **821** 20 pf. multicoloured . 30 10

E **822** Exhibition Hall

1986. Leipzig Spring Fair. Multicoloured.
E2713 35 pf. Type E **822** 30 15
E2714 50 pf. Factory trawler "Atlantik 488" 65 35

E **823** Yuri Gagarin and "Vostok"

1986. 25th Anniv of Manned Space Flight. Multicoloured.
E2715 40 pf. Type E **823** (first man in space) 15 15
E2716 50 pf. Cosmonauts Valeri Bykovski and Sigmund Jahn, space station and "Interkosmos" emblem . . 30 30
E2717 70 pf. Space probe "Venera", orbit around Venus and spectrometer 40 40
E2718 85 pf. Reconnaissance camera MKF-6, photo, "Soyuz 22" spaceship, airplane and ship 75 65

E **824** Marx, Engels and Lenin

E **825** Memorial

1986. 11th Socialist Unity Party of Germany Day.
E2719 E **824** 10 pf. black, red and silver 10 10
E2720 – 20 pf. red, black and silver 20 20
E2721 – 50 pf. multicoloured . 30 30
E2722 – 85 pf. black, red and silver 65 65
DESIGNS: 20 pf. Ernst Thalmann (birth centenary); 50 pf. Wilhelm Pieck and Otto Grotewohl, April 1946; 85 pf. Family.

1986. Opening of Ernst Thalmann Park, Berlin.
E2724 E **825** 20 pf. multicoloured . 20 10

E **826** Horse Tram, Dresden, 1886

1986. Trams. Multicoloured.
E2725 10 pf. Type E **826** 25 15
E2726 20 pf. Leipzig, 1896 . . . . . 35 25
E2727 40 pf. Berlin, 1919 . . . . . 85 50
E2728 70 pf. Halle, 1928 . . . . . 1·60 90

E **827** Orang-utan

E **828** City Seal, 1253

1986. 125th Anniv of Dresden Zoo. Multicoloured.
E2729 10 pf. Type E **827** 15 10
E2730 20 pf. Eastern black-and-white colobus 30 20
E2731 50 pf. Mandrill 65 30
E2732 70 pf. Ring-tailed lemurs . . 80 65

1986. 750th Anniv of Berlin (1st issue).
E2733 E **828** 10 pf. deep brown, bistre and brown . . 15 10
E2734 – 20 pf. ol, grn & brn . 30 20
E2735 – 50 pf. blk, brn & red . 85 50
E2736 – 70 pf. grn & brn . . . 1·60 85
DESIGNS—HORIZ: 20 pf. City map, 1648; 50 pf. Oldest City arms. VERT: 70 pf. St. Nicholas's Church, 1832.
See also Nos. E2780/3.

E **829** Couple, Tractor and House

1986. 21st Workers' Festival, Magdeburg. Multicoloured.
E2738 20 pf. Type E **829** 20 20
E2739 50 pf. Port and town of Magdeburg 65 65

E **830** Berlin, 1652

1986. 9th Youth Stamp Exhibition, Berlin. Multicoloured.
E2740 10 pf. + 5 pf. Type E **830** . . 10 10
E2741 20 pf. Historic and modern Berlin buildings 15 15

E **831** Schwerin Castle

1986. Castles (3rd series). Multicoloured.
E2742 10 pf. Type E **831** 15 15
E2743 20 pf. Gustrow castle 30 30
E2744 85 pf. Rheinsberg castle . . . 85 85
E2745 1 m. Ludwigslust castle . . . 1·00 1·00

E **832** Soldiers and Girl before Brandenburg Gate

1986. 25th Anniv of Berlin Wall.
E2746 E **832** 20 pf. multicoloured . 40 20

E **833** Doves flying from Emblem

1986. International Peace Year.
E2747 E **833** 35 pf. multicoloured . 40 20

E **835** Rostock, 1637

E **836** Man with Rifle

1986. Coins.
E2749 E **835** 10 pf. black, silver and red 15 10
E2750 – 35 pf. black, silver and blue 30 30
E2751 – 50 pf. multicoloured . 50 40
E2752 – 85 pf. black, silver and blue 65 50
E2753 – 1 m. black, silver and green . . . . . . 1·00 1·00
DESIGNS: 35 pf. Nordhausen, 1660; 50 pf. Erfurt, 1633; 85 pf. Magdeburg, 1638; 1 m. Stralsund, 1622;

1986. 44th World Sports Shooting Championships, Suhl.
E2754 E **836** 20 pf. black, green and grey 15 15
E2755 – 70 pf. black, red and grey 65 65
E2756 – 85 pf. black, blue and grey 85 85
DESIGNS: 70 pf. Woman with pistol; 85 pf. Man with double-barrelled shotgun.

E **837** Guard and Boundary Post

E **838** Hemispheres and Red Banner

1986. 40th Anniv of Border Guards.
E2757 E **837** 20 pf. multicoloured . 20 15

1986. 11th World Trade Unions Congress, Berlin.
E2758 E **838** 70 pf. multicoloured . 80 60

E **839** German Members Memorial, Friedrichshain

E **840** Memorial

1986. 50th Anniv of Formation of International Brigades in Spain.
E2759 E **839** 20 pf. brown, black and red 25 10

1986. 25th Anniv of Sachsenhausen Memorial.
E2760 E **840** 35 pf. blk, grn & bl . . 30 15

E **841** Double-deck Loading Ramps

1986. Opening of Mukran–Klaipeda Railway Ferry Service. Multicoloured.
E2761 50 pf. Type E **841** 90 70
E2762 50 pf. "Mukran" (train ferry) 90 70
Nos. E2761/2 were printed together, se-tenant, forming a composite design.

E **842** "Help for Developing Countries"

1986. "Solidarity".
E2763 E **842** 10 pf. + 5 pf. mult . . 20 15

E **844** Indira Gandhi

E **845** Candle Holder, 1778

1986. 2nd Death Anniv of Indira Gandhi (Indian Prime Minister).
E2765 E **844** 10 pf. stone & brn . . 15 10

1986. Candle Holders from the Erzgebirge. Multicoloured.
E2766 10 pf. Type E **845** 10 10
E2767 20 pf. Candle holder, 1796 . . 15 15
E2768 25 pf. Candle holder, 1810 . . 15 15
E2769 35 pf. Candle holder, 1821 . . 25 25
E2770 40 pf. Candle holder, 1830 . . 30 30
E2771 85 pf. Candle holder, 1925 . . 65 65

E **846** Roland Statue, Stendal

E **847** Post Office, Freiberg

1987. Statues of Roland (1st series).
E2772 10 pf. lt brn, brn & yell . . . 10 10
E2773 20 pf. lt brn, brn & bl . . . 20 10
E2774 35 pf. lt brn, brn & orge . . 35 30
E2775 50 pf. lt brn, brn & grn . . . 50 45
DESIGNS: Statues at—10 pf. Type E **846**.; 20 pf. Halle; 35 pf. Brandenburg; 50 pf. Quedlinburg.
See also Nos. E2984/7.

1987. Post Offices.
E2776 E **847** 10 pf. black, red and blue 15 15
E2777 – 20 pf. multicoloured . 30 25
E2778 – 70 pf. multicoloured . 80 75
E2779 – 1 m. 20 multicoloured 95 85
DESIGNS: 20 pf. Perleberg; 70 pf. Weimar; 1 m. 20, Kirschau.

1987. 750th Anniv of Berlin (2nd issue). As Type E **828**.
E2780 20 pf. brown and green . . . 15 15
E2781 35 pf. green and red 30 25
E2782 70 pf. blue and red 65 55
E2783 85 pf. olive and green 85 70
DESIGNS—VERT: 20 pf. Ephraim Palace. HORIZ: 35 pf. New buildings, Alt Marzahn; 70 pf. Marx-Engels Forum; 85 pf. Friedrichstadtpalast.

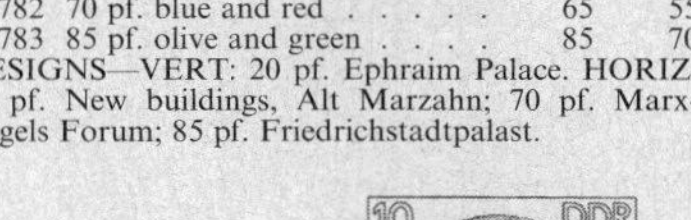

E **848** Woman with Flower in Hair

E **850** Clara Zetkin

E **849** Fair Hall 20

1987. 40th Anniv and 12th Congress (Berlin) of German Democratic Women's Federation.
E2785 E **848** 10 pf. blue, red & sil . 15 10

1987. Leipzig Spring Fair. Multicoloured.
E2786 35 pf. Type E **849** 30 30
E2787 50 pf. "Traders at Weighbridge, 1804" (Christian Geissler) 50 50

1987. Socialist Personalities. Multicoloured.
E2788 E **850** 10 pf. purple 10 10
E2789 – 10 pf. black 10 10
E2790 – 10 pf. black 10 10
E2791 – 10 pf. green 10 10
DESIGNS: No. E2789, Fritz Gabler; E2790, Walter Vesper; E2791, Robert Siewert.

E **851** Construction Industry

1987. 11th Federation of Free German Trade Unions Congress, Berlin. Multicoloured.
E2792 20 pf. Type E **851** 15 15
E2793 50 pf. Communications industry 40 40

E **852** Flag, World Map and Doves

1987. 10th German Red Cross Congress, Dresden.
E2794 E **852** 35 pf. multicoloured . 40 10

E **853** Museum and Karl August Lingner (founder) (after Robert Sterl)

1987. 75th Anniv of German Hygiene Museum, Dresden.
E2795 E **853** 85 pf. multicoloured . 65 40

INDEX

Countries can be quickly located by referring to the index at the end of this volume.

E **854** Old and New Farming Methods

1987. 35th Anniv of Agricultural Co-operatives.
E2796 E **854** 20 pf. multicoloured . 20 10

E **855** Ludwig Uhland (poet)

1987. Birth Anniversaries. Multicoloured.
E2797 10 pf. Type E **855** (bicent) . . 10 10
E2798 20 pf. Arnold Zweig (writer, centenary) 25 20
E2799 35 pf. Gerhart Hauptmann (writer, 125th anniv) . . 30 25
E2800 50 pf. Gustav Hertz (physicist, centenary) 60 45

E **856** Bream

1987. Freshwater Fishes. Multicoloured.
E2801 5 pf. Type **856** 10 10
E2802 10 pf. Brown trout 10 10
E2803 20 pf. Wels 25 20
E2804 35 pf. European grayling . . 35 30
E2805 50 pf. Barbel 60 50
E2806 70 pf. Northern pike . . . . 1·10 75

E **857** Woman holding Baby

1987. "Solidarity" Anti-apartheid Campaign.
E2807 E **857** 10 pf. + 5 pf. mult . . 15 10

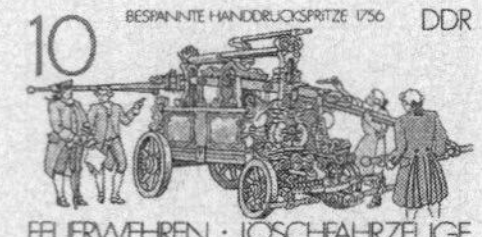

E **858** Horse-drawn Hand-pumped Fire Engine, 1756

1987. Fire Engines. Multicoloured.
E2808 10 pf. Type E **858** 15 15
E2809 25 pf. Steam engine, 1903 . . 30 30
E2810 40 pf. Model "LF 15", 1919 . . 30 30
E2811 70 pf. Model "LF 16-TS 8", 1971 . . . . 65 50

E **860** Otters

1987. Endangered Animals. European Otter. Multicoloured.
E2813 10 pf. Type E **860** 10 10
E2814 25 pf. Otter swimming . . . 15 15
E2815 35 pf. Otter 40 40
E2816 60 pf. Otter's head 65 65

E **861** Tug-of-War

1987. 8th Gymnastics and Sports Festival and 11th Children and Young People's Sports Days, Leipzig. Multicoloured.
E2817 5 pf. Type E **861** 10 10
E2818 10 pf. Handball 15 15
E2819 20 pf. + 5 pf. Long jumping . 20 20
E2820 35 pf. Table tennis 30 30
E2821 40 pf. Bowling 40 40
E2822 70 pf. Running 75 75

E **862** Association Activities

1987. 35th Anniv of Association of Sports and Technical Sciences.
E2823 E **862** 10 pf. multicoloured . 15 10

E **863** Head Post Office, Berlin, 1760

1987. Stamp Day. Multicoloured.
E2824 10 pf. + 5 pf. Type E **863** . . 10 10
E2825 20 pf. Wartenberg Palace . . 15 15

E **865** Memorial Statue (Jozsef Somogyi)

E **867** "Weidendamm Bridge" (Arno Mohr)

1987. War Victims' Memorial, Budapest.
E2827 E **865** 35 pf. multicoloured . 30 15

1987. 10th Art Exhibition, Dresden. Mult.
E2829 10 pf. Type E **867** 10 10
E2830 50 pf. "They only wanted to learn Reading and Writing (Nicaragua)" (Willi Sitte) . 50 50
E2831 70 pf. "Big Mourning Man" (Wieland Forster) 65 65
E2832 1 m. Vase (Gerd Lucke) (horiz) 85 85

E **868** Red Flag, Smolny Building (Leningrad), "Aurora" and Lenin

1987. 70th Anniv of Russian Revolution. Multicoloured.
E2833 10 pf. Type E **868** 10 10
E2834 20 pf. Moscow Kremlin towers 20 10

E **869** Youth using Personal Computer

E **870** Annaberg, 1810

1987. 39th "Masters of Tomorrow" Fair, Leipzig. Multicoloured.
E2835 10 pf. Type E **869** 10 10
E2836 20 pf. "ZIM 10-S" robot-welder 20 10

1987. Christmas Pyramids from Erzgebirge. Multicoloured.
E2837 10 pf. Type E **870** 10 10
E2838 20 pf. Freiberg, 1830 . . . . 15 15
E2839 25 pf. Neustadtel, 1870 . . . 20 20
E2840 35 pf. Schneeberg, 1870 . . . 25 25
E2841 40 pf. Lossnitz, 1880 . . . . 30 30
E2842 85 pf. Seiffen, 1910 . . . . . 65 65

E **871** Ski Jumping

E **874** "Tillandsia macrochlamys"

E **872** Berlin-Buch Post Office

1988. Winter Olympic Games, Calgary. Mult.
E2843 5 pf. Type E **871** 10 10
E2844 10 pf. Speed skating 15 10
E2845 20 pf. + 10 pf. Four-man bobsleigh 30 25
E2846 35 pf. Biathlon 50 30

1988. Postal Buildings. Multicoloured.
E2848 15 pf. Type E **872** 15 15
E2849 20 pf. Postal museum 30 20
E2850 50 pf. Berlin-Marzahn general post office 65 50

1988. Bromeliads. Multicoloured.
E2852 10 pf. Type E **874** 10 10
E2853 25 pf. "Tillandsia bulbosa" . . 25 25
E2854 40 pf. "Tillandsia kalmbacheri" 40 30
E2855 70 pf. "Guzmania blassii" . . 65 50

E **875** Madler-passage Entrance

E **877** Saddler, Muhlhausen, 1565

1988. Leipzig Spring Fair. 75th Anniv of Madler-passage (fair building). Each brown, orange and pink.
E2856 20 pf. Type E **875** 15 15
E2857 70 pf. "Faust and Mephistopheles" (bronze statue, Matthieu Molitor) . 65 50

1988. Historic Seals. Multicoloured.
E2859 10 pf. Type E **877** 10 10
E2860 25 pf. Butcher, Dresden, 1564 . . . . 20 15
E2861 35 pf. Smith, Nauen, 16th-century 25 20
E2862 50 pf. Clothier, Frankfurt on Oder, 16th-century 40 35

E **878** Georg Forster Antarctic Research Station

1988. 12th Anniv of Georg Forster Antarctic Research Station.
E2863 E **878** 35 pf. multicoloured . 30 15

E **879** Wismar

1988. Northern Towns of the Democratic Republic.
E2864 5 pf. black, green & turq . . 10 10
E2865 10 pf. black, ochre & brn . . 10 10
E2866 25 pf. black, lt blue & blue . 20 15
E2867 60 pf. black, pink and red . . 50 40
E2868 90 pf. black, lt green & green . 75 60
E2869 1 m. 20 black, brown & red . 1·10 1·00
DESIGNS: 5 pf. Type E **879**.; 10 pf. Anklam; 25 pf. Ribnitz-Damgarten; 60 pf. Stralsund; 90 pf. Bergen; 1 m. 20, Greifswald.

E **881** Chorin and Neuzelle Monasteries, Industrial and Agricultural Symbols

1988. 22nd Workers' Arts Festival, Frankfurt-on-Oder. Multicoloured.
E2871 20 pf. Type E **881** 15 15
E2872 50 pf. Buildings of Frankfurt . 45 45

E **882** Cosmonauts Sigmund Jahn and Valery Bykovski

1988. 10th Anniv of U.S.S.R.–East German Manned Space Flight (1st issue). Multicoloured.
E2873 5 pf. Type E **882** 10 10
E2874 10 pf. "MKS-M" multi-channel spectrometer . . . 10 10
E2875 20 pf. "Mir"–"Soyuz" space complex 15 15
See also Nos. E2894/6.

E **883** Erfurt, 1520

1988. 10th Youth Stamp Exhibition, Erfurt and Karl-Marx-Stadt. Multicoloured.
E2876 10 pf. + 5 pf. Type E **883** . . 10 10
E2877 20 pf. + 5 pf. Chemnitz, 1620 . . . . 20 20
E2878 25 pf. Modern view of Erfurt 20 20
E2879 50 pf. Modern view of Karl-Marx-Stadt (formerly Chemnitz) 45 45

E **884** Swearing-in Ceremony

1988. 35th Anniv of Workers' Militia Squads. Multicoloured.
E2880 5 pf. Type E **884** 10 10
E2881 10 pf. Tribute to Ernst Thalmann 10 10
E2882 15 pf. Parade 15 15
E2883 20 pf. Arms distribution . . . 20 20

E **885** Balloons and Doves over Karl-Marx-Stadt

1988. 8th Pioneers Meeting, Karl-Marx-Stadt. Multicoloured.
E2884 10 pf. Type E **885** 10 10
E2885 10 pf. + 5 pf. Doves, balloons and Pioneers 15 15

E **886** Swimming

1988. Olympic Games, Seoul. Multicoloured.
E2886 5 pf. Type E **886** 10 10
E2887 10 pf. Handball 15 15
E2888 20 pf. + 10 pf. Hurdling . . 30 30
E2889 25 pf. Rowing 30 30
E2890 35 pf. Boxing 45 45
E2891 50 pf. + 20 pf. Cycling . . . 65 65

1988. 10th Anniv of U.S.S.R.–East German Manned space Flight (2nd issue). As Nos. E2873/5 but values changed. Multicoloured.
E2894 10 pf. Type E **882** 10 10
E2895 20 pf. As No. E2874 . . . . 25 25
E2896 35 pf. As No. E2875 . . . . 35 35

E **888** Buchenwald Memorial (Fritz Cremer)

1988. War Memorials.
E2897 E **888** 10 pf. green, black and brown 10 10
E2898 – 35 pf. multicoloured . 30 15
DESIGN: 35 pf. Resistance Monument, Lake Como, Italy (Gianni Colombo)

E **889** "'Adolph Friedrich' at Stralsund: Captain C. Leplow" (E. Laschke)

1988. 500th Anniv of Stralsund Shipping Company. Captains' Paintings. Multicoloured.
E2899 5 pf. Type E **889** 15 15
E2900 10 pf. "'Gartenlaube' of Stralsund: Captain J. F. Kruger" (A. Luschky) . . 30 30
E2901 70 pf. "Brigantina 'Auguste Mathilde' of Stralsund: Captain I. C. Grunwaldt" (Johnsen-Seby Bergen) . . 90 90
E2902 1 m. 20 "Brig 'Hoffnung' of Cologne-on-Rhine: Captain G. A. Luther" (anon) . . . 1·60 1·60

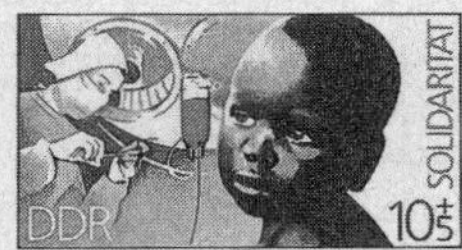

E **890** Medical Scene and African Child

1988. "Solidarity".
E2903 E **890** 10 pf. + 5 pf. mult . . 40 30

E **891** Bridge, Magdeburg E **892** Menorah

1988. Drawbridges and Ship Lifts. Mult.
E2904 5 pf. Type E **891** 20 10
E2905 10 pf. Lift, Magdeburg-Rothensee Canal 10 10
E2906 35 pf. Lift, Niederfinow . . . 20 20
E2907 70 pf. Bridge and lock, Altfriesack 50 30
E2908 90 pf. Drawbridge, Rugendamm 90 80

1988. 50th Anniv of "Kristallnacht" (Nazi pogrom).
E2909 E **892** 35 pf. purple, yellow and black 40 10

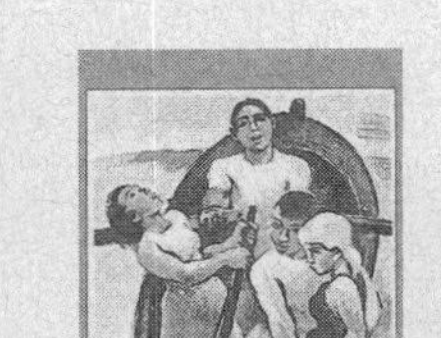

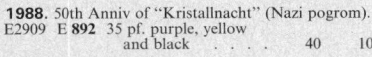

E **893** "In the Boat" E **894** Lace (Regine Wengler)

1988. Birth Centenary of Max Lingner (artist). Multicoloured.
E2910 5 pf. Type E **893** 10 10
E2911 10 pf. "Mademoiselle Yvonne" 15 10
E2912 20 pf. "Free, Strong and Happy" 20 15
E2913 85 pf. "New Harvest" . . . 85 30

1988. Bobbin Lace from Erzgebirge. Pieces by lacemakers named. Each black, brown and yellow.
E2914 20 pf. Type E **894** 10 10
E2915 25 pf. Wally Tilp 10 10
E2916 35 pf. Elisabeth Mehnert-Pfabe 25 25
E2917 40 pf. Ute Siewert 30 30
E2918 50 pf. Regine Siebdraht . . . 50 50
E2919 85 pf. Elise Schubert 65 65

E **895** W.H.O. Emblem E **897** Members' Flags

1988. 40th Anniv of W.H.O.
E2920 E **895** 85 pf. sil, blue & grey . 65 30

1989. 40th Anniv of Council of Mutual Economic Aid.
E2922 E **897** 20 pf. multicoloured . 20 10

E **898** Edith Baumann E **899** Philipp Reis Telephone, 1861

1989. Socialist Personalities.
E2923 E **898** 10 pf. brown 10 10
E2924 – 10 pf. green 10 10
E2925 – 10 pf. brown 10 10
E2926 – 10 pf. blue 10 10
DESIGNS: No. E2924, Otto Meier; E2925, Alfred Oelssner; E2926, Fritz Selbmann.

1989. Telephones. Multicoloured.
E2927 10 pf. Type E **899** 10 10
E2928 20 pf. Siemens & Halske wall telephone, 1882 . . . . 20 20
E2929 50 pf. "OB 03" wall telephone, 1903 . . . . 60 60
E2930 85 pf. "OB 05" desk telephone, 1905 . . . . 90 90

E **900** Johann Beckmann (technologist, 250th anniv)

1989. Birth Anniversaries. Multicoloured.
E2931 10 pf. Type E **900** 10 10
E2932 10 pf. Rudolf Mauersberger and church choir (musician, cent) 10 10
E2933 10 pf. Carl von Ossietzky and masthead of "Die Weltbuhne" (journalist and peace activist, centenary) . 10 10
E2934 10 pf. Ludwig Renn and International Brigades flag (writer, centenary) 10 10
E2935 10 pf. Adam Scharrer and cover of "Stateless People" (novelist, centenary) . . . 10 10

E **901** Handelshof Fair Building

1989. Leipzig Spring Fair. Multicoloured.
E2936 70 pf. Type E **901** (80th anniv) 50 50
E2937 85 pf. Naschmarkt bake-house and bread shop, 1690 . . . 85 85

E **903** Friedrich List (economist and promoter of railway system)

1989. 150th Anniv of Leipzig–Dresden Railway (first German long-distance service).
E2939 E **903** 15 pf. brown, pale brown and green . . 15 15
E2940 – 20 pf. black, green and red 30 25
E2941 – 50 pf. black, brown and deep brown . . 1·10 1·00
DESIGNS: 20 pf. Dresdner Station, Leipzig, 1839; 50 pf. Leipziger Station, Dresden, 1839.

E **904** Tea Caddy E **905** Renaissance Initial "I"

1989. Meissen Porcelain. 250th Anniv of Onion Design. Each brown, blue and ultramarine.
E2942 10 pf. Type E **904** 10 10
E2943 20 pf. Vase 25 10
E2944 35 pf. Bread board 40 25
E2945 70 pf. Coffee pot 75 50

1989. 7th International Typography Exhibition, Leipzig.
E2946 E **905** 20 pf. mult 15 15
E2947 – 50 pf. black, yellow and green 65 50
E2948 – 1 m. 35 red, black and grey . . . . 1·00 1·00
DESIGNS: 50 pf. Art Nouveau initial "B"; 1 m. 35, Modern initial "A".

E **906** Chollima Statue, Pyongyang E **907** "Princess Louise"

1989. 13th World Youth and Students' Festival, Pyongyang (E2949) and Free German Youth Whitsun Festival, Berlin (E2950). Multicoloured.
E2949 20 pf. Type E **906** 20 20
E2950 20 pf. + 5 pf. Berlin buildings 20 20

1989. 225th Birth Anniv of Johann Gottfried Schadow (sculptor). Details of "Princesses". Multicoloured.
E2951 50 pf. Type E **907** 60 40
E2952 85 pf. "Princess Friederike" . 90 75

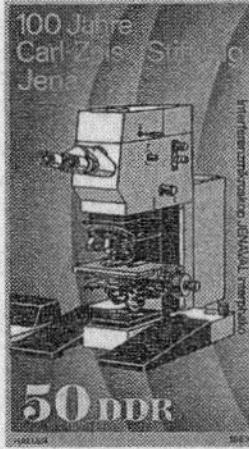

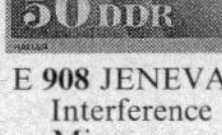

E **908** JENEVAL Interference Microscope E **909** Front Page of Address

1989. Centenary of Carl Zeiss Foundation, Jena. Multicoloured.
E2953 50 pf. Type E **908** 50 50
E2954 85 pf. "ZKM 01-250 C" bi-coordinate measuring instrument 65 65

1989. Bicentenary of Inaugural Address to Jena University by Friedrich Schiller (writer and philosopher). Each brown, black & grey.
E2955 25 pf. Type E **909** 30 30
E2956 85 pf. Part of address 65 65

E **911** Storming the Bastille

1989. Bicent of French Revolution. Mult.
E2958 5 pf. Type E **911** 10 10
E2959 20 pf. Sans-culottes 25 25
E2960 90 pf. Invading the Tuileries . 90 90

E **912** Haflingers

1989. 40th International Horse Breeding in Socialist States Congress, Berlin. Multicoloured.
E2961 10 pf. Type E **912** 10 10
E2962 20 pf. English thoroughbreds (racehorses) 20 20
E2963 70 pf. Heavy horses (plough team) 50 50
E2964 110 pf. Thoroughbreds (dressage) . . . . 1·00 1·00

E **913** Till Eulenspiegel Fountain

1989. National Stamp Exn, Magdeburg. Fountains by Heinrich Apel. Multicoloured.
E2965 20 pf. Type E **913** 25 25
E2966 70 pf. + 5 pf. Devil's fountain 70 70

E **914** "Annunciation to the Peasants" E **916** African Children

1989. 500th Birth Anniv of Thomas Muntzer (Protestant reformer) (2nd issue). Details of "Early Bourgeois Revolution in Germany" by Werner Tubke. Multicoloured.
E2967 5 pf. Type E **914** 10 10
E2968 10 pf. "Fountain of Life" . . 10 10
E2969 20 pf. "Muntzer in the Battle" 25 25
E2970 50 pf. "Lutheran Cat Battle" . 45 45
E2971 85 pf. "Justice, Jester" . . . 90 90

1989. "Solidarity".
E2974 E **916** 10 pf. + 5 pf. mult . . 15 10

E **917** "Mother Group" (Fritz Cremer) E **918** "Adriana"

1989. 30th Anniv of Ravensbruck War Victims' Memorial.
E2975 E **917** 35 pf. multicoloured . 30 15

1989. Epiphyllums. Multicoloured.
E2976 10 pf. Type E **918** 10 10
E2977 35 pf. "Fire Magic" 25 25
E2978 50 pf. "Franzisko" 45 45

E **919** Dove, Flag and Schoolchildren

1989. 40th Anniv of German Democratic Republic. Multicoloured.
E2979 5 pf. Type E **919** 10 10
E2980 10 pf. Combine harvester and agricultural workers . . . 10 10
E2981 20 pf. Political activists working together 20 20
E2982 25 pf. Industrial workers . . 25 25

1989. Statues of Roland (2nd series). As Type E **846**. Multicoloured.

E2984		5 pf. Zerbst	10	10
E2985		10 pf. Halberstadt	15	15
E2986		20 pf. Buch-Altmark	20	20
E2987		50 pf. Perleberg	50	50

E **920** Nehru

E **921** Schneeberg, 1860

1989. Birth Centenary of Jawaharlal Nehru (Indian statesman).

E2988	E **920**	35 pf. brown & black	40	25

1989. Chandeliers from the Erzgebirge. Mult.

E2989		10 pf. Type E **921**	10	10
E2990		20 pf. Schwarzenberg, 1850	15	15
E2991		25 pf. Annaberg, 1880	20	20
E2992		35 pf. Seiffen, 1900	30	30
E2993		50 pf. Seiffen, 1930	40	40
E2994		70 pf. Annaberg, 1925	75	75

E **922** Bee on Apple Blossom

E **923** "Courier" (Albrecht Durer)

1990. The Honey Bee. Multicoloured.

E2995		5 pf. Type E **922**	10	10
E2996		10 pf. Bee on heather	10	10
E2997		20 pf. Bee on rape	15	15
E2998		50 pf. Bee on clover	65	50

1990. 500th Anniv of Regular European Postal Services.

E2999	E **923**	35 pf. chocolate, light brown and brown	50	30

E **924** Erich Weinert

E **925** 19th-century Sign, Blankenburg

1990. Socialist Personalities.

E3000	E **924**	10 pf. blue	25	10
E3001	–	10 pf. brown	25	10

DESIGN: No. E3001, Bruno Leuschner.

1990. Posthouse Signs. Multicoloured.

E3002		10 pf. Type E **925**	15	15
E3003		20 pf. Royal Saxony sign (19th century)	20	20
E3004		50 pf. German Empire sign (1870s)	65	65
E3005		110 pf. German Empire auxiliary station sign (1900s)	85	85

E **926** Bebel

E **927** Drawings by Leonardo da Vinci

1990. 150th Birth Anniv of August Bebel (politician).

E3006	E **926**	20 pf. black, grey and red	30	20

1990. "Lilienthal '91" European Airmail Exhibition. Historic Flying Machine Designs. Multicoloured.

E3007		20 pf. Type E **927**	35	35
E3008		35 pf. + 5 pf. Melchior Bauer's man-powered airplane design, 1764	60	60
E3009		50 pf. Albrecht-Ludwig Berblinger's manpowered flying machine, 1811	75	75
E3010		90 pf. Otto Lilienthal's design for monoplane glider	1·25	1·25

E **928** St. Nicholas's Church, Leipzig, and Demonstrators

E **929** Warrior's Head

1990. "We Are The People".

E3011	E **928**	35 pf. + 15 pf. mult	65	50

1990. Museum of German History, Berlin. Stone Reliefs by Andreas Schluter.

E3012	E **929**	40 pf. yell, grn & blk	30	30
E3013	–	70 pf. multicoloured	65	65

DESIGN: 70 pf. Warrior's head (different).

E **930** Fair Seal, 1268

E **931** Kurt Tucholsky (writer, centenary)

1990. Leipzig Spring Fair and 825th Anniv of Leipzig. Multicoloured.

E3014		70 pf. Type E **930**	80	65
E3015		85 pf. Fair seal, 1497	1·00	65

1990. Birth Anniversaries.

E3016	E **931**	10 pf. black, green and deep green	20	15
E3017	–	10 pf. black, brown and red	20	15

DESIGN: No. E3017, Friedrich Adolph Wilhelm Diesterweg (educationist, bicent).

E **932** "Solidarity of Labour" (Walter Crane)

E **933** Dicraeosaurus

1990. Centenary of Labour Day.

E3018	E **932**	10 pf. grey, black and red	30	25
E3019	–	20 pf. red, grey and black	65	40

DESIGN: 20 pf. Red carnation.

1990. Centenary of Natural Science Museum, Berlin. Dinosaur Skeletons. Multicoloured.

E3020		10 pf. Type E **933**	10	10
E3021		25 pf. Kentrurosaurus	20	20
E3022		35 pf. Dysalotosaurus	30	30
E3023		50 pf. Brachiosaurus (vert)	50	50
E3024		85 pf. Skull of brachiosaurus (vert)	75	75

E **934** Penny Black

E **935** Edward Hughes and 1855 Printing Telegraph

1990. 150th Anniv of the Penny Black.

E3025	E **934**	20 pf. black, mve & magenta	30	30
E3026	–	35 pf. + 15 pf. red, lilac and black	65	65
E3027	–	110 pf. multicoloured	1·60	1·60

DESIGNS: 35 pf. Saxony 1850 3 pf. stamp; 110 pf. First East Germany stamp, 1949.

1990. 125th Anniv of I.T.U. Multicoloured.

E3028		10 pf. Type E **935**	10	10
E3029		20 pf. Distribution rods from Berlin-Kopenick post office	30	30
E3030		25 pf. Transmitting tower and radio control desk	40	40
E3031		50 pf. "Molniya" communications satellite and globe	50	50

E **936** Pope John Paul II

1990. Pope's 70th Birthday.

E3033	E **936**	35 pf. multicoloured	40	30

E **937** Halle (18th-century)

1990. 11th National Youth Stamp Exhibition, Halle. Multicoloured.

E3034		10 pf. + 5 pf. Type E **937**	20	20
E3035		20 pf. Modern Halle	25	25

E **938** Rules of Order of Teutonic Knights, 1264

E **939** Albrechts Castle and Cathedral, Meissen

1990. Exhibits in German State Library, Berlin. Multicoloured.

E3036		20 pf. Type E **938**	30	30
E3037		25 pf. World map from "Rudimentum Novitiorum", 1475	40	30
E3038		40 pf. "Chosrou and Schirin" by Nizami (18th century Persian manuscript)	80	65
E3039		110 pf. Book cover from Amalia musical library	1·50	1·00

WEST GERMAN CURRENCY

On 1 July 1990 the Ostmark was abolished and replaced by the West German Deutsche Mark.

1990. Tourist Sights.

E3040	E **939**	10 pf. blue	10	10
E3041	–	30 pf. green	25	15
E3042	–	50 pf. green	40	25
E3043	–	60 pf. brown	60	30
E3044	–	70 pf. brown	60	30
E3045	–	80 pf. red	65	40
E3046	–	100 pf. red	1·00	50
E3047	–	200 pf. violet	2·00	1·60
E3048	–	500 pf. green	3·75	3·00

DESIGNS: 30 pf. Goethe-Schiller Monument, Weimar; 50 pf. Brandenburg Gate, Berlin; 60 pf. Kyffhauser Monument; 70 pf. Semper Opera House, Dresden; 80 pf. Sanssouci Palace, Potsdam; 100 pf. Wartburg Castle, Eisenach; 200 pf. Magdeburg Cathedral; 500 pf. Schwerin Castle.

E **940** Different Alphabets

E **942** Louis Lewandowski (choir conductor)

E **941** Letter-carrier (from playing card) and Messenger, 1486

1990. International Literacy Year.

E3049	E **940**	30 pf. + 5 pf. on 10 pf. + 5 pf. mult	1·00	1·00

No. E3049 was not issued without surcharge.

1990. 500th Anniv of Regular European Postal Services.

E3050	E **941**	30 pf. blk, brn & grn	30	15
E3051	–	50 pf. black, red and blue	65	65
E3052	–	70 pf. black, brown and red	65	65
E3053	–	100 pf. blk, grn & bl	2·50	2·50

DESIGNS: 50 pf. "Courier" (Albrecht Durer) and post rider, 1590; 70 pf. Open wagon, 1595, and mail carriage, 1750; 100 pf. Travelling post offices, 1842 and 1900.

1990. Reconstruction of New Synagogue, Berlin. Multicoloured.

E3054		30 pf. Type E **942**	30	30
E3055		50 pf. + 15 pf. New Synagogue	65	50

E **943** Schliemann and Two-handled Vessel

E **944** Dresden

1990. Death Cent of Heinrich Schliemann (archaeologist). Multicoloured.

E3056		30 pf. Type E **943**	45	45
E3057		50 pf. Schliemann and double pot (horiz)	60	50

1990. 41st International Astronautics Federation Congress, Dresden.

E3058	E **944**	30 pf. black & grey	30	30
E3059	–	50 pf. multicoloured	50	30
E3060	–	70 pf. dp bl, grn & bl	65	50
E3061	–	100 pf. mult	85	85

DESIGNS: 50 pf. Earth; 70 pf. Moon; 100 pf. Mars.

On 3 October 1990 the territory of the Democratic Republic was absorbed into the Federal Republic of Germany, whose stamps have been used since then.

OFFICIAL STAMPS

EO **58** (Cross-piece projects to left)

EO **59** (Cross-piece projects to right)

EO **84**

1954. (a) Design in minute dots.

EO185	EO **58**	5 pf. green	—	15
EO186		6 pf. violet	—	1·40
EO187		8 pf. brown	—	10
EO188		10 pf. turquoise	—	10
EO189		12 pf. blue	—	10
EO190		15 pf. violet	—	10
EO191		16 pf. violet	—	1·25
EO192		20 pf. olive	—	10
EO193		24 pf. red	—	50
EO194		25 pf. turquoise	—	40
EO195		30 pf. red	—	35
EO196		40 pf. red	—	20
EO197		48 pf. lilac	—	8·00
EO198		50 pf. lilac	—	50
EO199		60 pf. blue	—	65
EO200		70 pf. brown	—	50
EO201		84 pf. brown	—	20·00

(b) Design in lines.

EO295	EO **59**	5 pf. green	—	10
EO296		10 pf. turquoise	—	10
EO204		12 pf. turquoise	—	15
EO297		15 pf. violet	—	10
EO298		20 pf. olive	—	10
EO212	EO **58**	20 pf. olive	—	20
EO207	EO **59**	25 pf. green	—	1·60
EO299		30 pf. red	—	10
EO300		40 pf. red	—	10
EO301		50 pf. lilac	—	10
EO302		70 pf. brown	—	10

1956. For internal use.

EO257	EO **84**	5 pf. black	—	10
EO258		10 pf. black	—	10
EO259		20 pf. black	—	10
EO260		40 pf. black	—	10
EO261		70 pf. black	—	10

Nos. EO257/61 were not on sale to the public in unused condition, although specimens of all values are available on the market. The used prices are for cancelled-to-order, with segments across the corners of the stamps. Postally used are worth more.

OFFICIAL CENTRAL COURIER SERVICE STAMPS

These were for use on special postal services for confidential mail between Government officials and state-owned enterprises.

EO **95**

1956. With or without control figures.

EO303	EO **95**	10 pf. black & pur	50	30
EO304		20 pf. black & pur	60	30
EO305		40 pf. black & pur	60	25
EO306		70 pf. black & pur	1·50	2·25

EO **123**

1958. With various control figures.
(a) With one bar (thick or thin) each side of figure.
EO357 EO **123** (10 pf.) red and yell . . 6·50 4·25
EO373 (10 pf.) brn & bl . . 6·50 5·00
EO375 (10 pf.) violet and orange . . . . . 6·50 6·00
EO377 (10 pf.) red and green . . . . . 7·00 7·00

(b) With two bars (thick or thin) each side of figure.
EO358 EO **123** (20 pf.) red and yell 13·00 2·25
EO374 (20 pf.) brn & bl . . 32·00 3·25
EO376 (20 pf.) violet and orange . . . . . 23·00 4·25
EO378 (20 pf.) red and green . . . . . 16·00 3·25

EO **149**

1959. With various control figures.
(a) With one bar each side of figure.
EO414 EO **149** (10 pf.) red, violet and green . . . 8·25 6·00
EO416 (10 pf.) blk & bl . . 11·50 18·00
EO418 (10 pf.) black, brown and blue . . . . 23·00 15·00

(b) With two bars each side of figure.
EO415 EO **149** (20 pf.) blue, brown and yellow . . . 11·50 4·25
EO417 (20 pf.) green, blue and red . . . . 16·00 6·50
EO419 (20 pf.) violet, black and brown . . . 26·00 4·00

REGISTRATION STAMPS

SELF-SERVICE POST OFFICE

These registration labels embody a face value to cover the registration fee and have franking value to this extent. They are issued in pairs from automatic machines together with a certificate of posting against a 50 pf. coin. The stamps are serially numbered in pairs and inscribed with the name of the town of issue.

The procedure is to affix one label to the letter (already franked with stamps for carriage of the letter) and complete page 1 of the certificate of posting which is then placed in the box provided together with the letter. The duplicate label is affixed to the second page of the certificate and retained for production as evidence in the event of a claim.

They are not obtainable over the post office counter.

Unused prices are for pairs.

ER **318**

1967.
ER992 ER **318** 50 pf. red & black . . . . 4·00

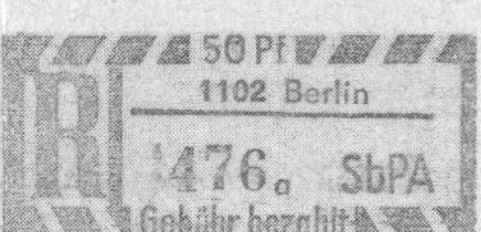

ER **319**

1968.
ER993 ER **319** 50 pf. red . . . . 1·25

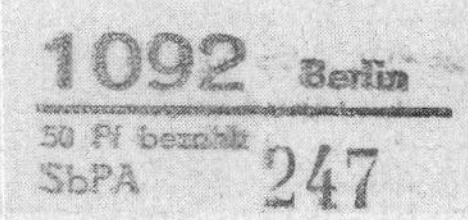

ER **345**

1968. For Parcel Post.
ER1089 ER **345** 50 pf. black . . . . . . 7·00

GHADAMES Pt. 6

A caravan halting place in the Libyan desert, under French administration from 1943 until 1951 when the area reverted to Libya. From 1943 to 1948 stamps of Fezzan were used.

100 centimes = 1 franc.

1 Cross of Agadem

1949.
1 **1** 4 f. chestnut & brn (postage) . 1·50 3·00
2 5 f. green and blue . . . . . 1·50 3·00
3 8 f. chestnut and brown . . . 2·50 4·00
4 10 f. blue and black . . . . . 2·50 4·00
5 12 f. mauve and purple . . . 5·00 7·75
6 15 f. chestnut and brown . . . 5·00 7·00
7 20 f. green and brown . . . . 5·00 7·00
8 25 f. blue and brown . . . . 5·00 7·00
9 50 f. cerise and purple (air) . . 5·00 7·00
10 100 f. purple and brown . . . 5·00 7·00

GHANA Pt. 1

Formerly the British Colony of Gold Coast. Attained Dominion status on 6 March 1957, and became a republic within the British Commonwealth in 1960.

1957. 12 pence = 1 shilling;
20 shillings = 1 pound.
1965. 100 pesewas = 1 cedi.
1967. 100 new pesewas = 1 new cedi.
1972. 100 pesewas = 1 cedi = 0.8 (1967) new cedi.

CANCELLED REMAINDERS. In 1961 remainders of some issues of 1957 to 1960 were put on the market cancelled-to-order in such a way as to be indistinguishable from genuine postally used copies. Our used quotations which are indicated by an asterisk are, therefore, for cancelled-to-order copies.

29 Dr. Kwame Nkrumah, Palm-nut Vulture and Map of Africa

1957. Independence Commemoration.
166 **29** 2d. red 10 10*
167 2½d. green 10 15*
168 4d. brown 10 15*
169 1s. 3d. blue 15 15*

1957. Queen Elizabeth stamps of 1952 of Gold Coast optd **GHANA INDEPENDENCE 6TH. MARCH, 1957.**
170 ½d. brown and red 10 10*
171 1d. blue 10 10*
172 1½d. green 10 10*
173 2d. brown 30 30
174 2½d. red . . . . 1·00 1·25
175 3d. mauve 30 10*
176 4d. blue . . . . 3·75 6·00
177 6d. black and orange 10 10*
178 1s. black and red 10 10*
179 2s. olive and red 60 10*
180 5s. purple and black 75 10*
181 10s. black and olive 75 60*

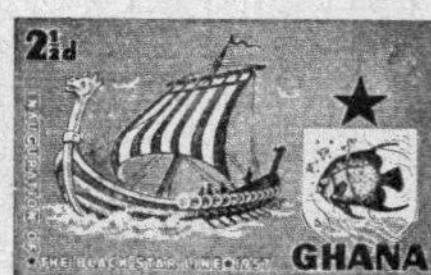

31 Viking Ship

1957. Inauguration of Black Star Shipping Line.
182 **31** 2½d. green 70 20
183 – 1s. 3d. blue . . . . 75 1·25
184 – 5s. purple . . . . 1·00 3·00
DESIGNS—HORIZ: 1s. 3d. Galleon; 5s. M.V. "Volta River".

34 Ambassador Hotel, Accra

1958. 1st Anniv of Independence. Flag and Coat of Arms in national colours.
185 **34** ½d. black and red 10 10
186 – 2½d. black, red and yellow . . 10 10
187 – 1s. 3d. black and blue . . . 30 10
188 – 2s. yellow and black 45 35
DESIGNS—HORIZ: 2½d. State Opening of Parliament; 1s. 3d. National Monument. VERT: 2s. Ghana Coat of Arms.

38 Map showing the Independent African States

40 Palm-nut Vulture over Globe

41 Bristol Britannia

1958. 1st Conference of Independent African States, Accra. Star in black and yellow.
189 **38** 2½d. red and yellow 10 10
190 3d. green and brown 10 10
191 – 1s. blue, yellow and orange . 20 10
192 – 2s. 6d. purple, yell & orge . 40 35
DESIGN—VERT: 1s., 2s. 6d. Map of Africa and flaming torch.

1958. Inauguration of Ghana Airways. Inscr as in T **40/41**.
193 **40** 2½d. black, bistre and red . . 45 10
194 **41** 1s. 3d. multicoloured . . . 90 20
195 – 2s. multicoloured . . . . . 1·00 55
196 – 2s. 6d. black and bistre . . . 1·00 95
DESIGNS—(As Type **41**): 2s. Boeing Stratocruiser and yellow-nosed albatross. (As Type **40**): 2s. 6d. Palm-nut vulture and Vickers VC-10 aircraft.

1958. Prime Minister's Visit to United States and Canada. Optd **PRIME MINISTER'S VISIT, U.S.A. AND CANADA**.
197 **29** 2d. red 10 10
198 2½d. green 10 10
199 4d. brown 10 15
200 1s. 3d. blue 15 25

45

46 Dr. Nkrumah and Lincoln Statue, Washington

1958. United Nations Day.
201 **45** 2½d. brown, green and black . 10 10
202 1s. 3d. brown, blue and black . 20 10
203 2s. 6d. brown, violet & blk . 25 35

1959. 150th Birth Anniv of Abraham Lincoln.
204 **46** 2½d. pink and purple 15 10
205 1s. 3d. light blue and blue . . 15 10
206 2s. 6d. yellow and olive . . 20 25

49 Talking Drums and Elephant-horn Blower

1959. Independence. Inscr "SECOND ANNIVERSARY OF INDEPENDENCE".
207 – ½d. multicoloured 10 10
208 **49** 2½d. multicoloured 10 10
209 – 1s. 3d. multicoloured . . . 15 10
210 – 2s. multicoloured . . . . . 30 1·25
DESIGNS—HORIZ: ½d. Kente cloth and traditional symbols; 2s. Map of Africa, Ghana flag and palms. VERT: 1s. 3d. "Symbols of Greeting".

52 Globe and Flags

1959. Africa Freedom Day.
211 **52** 2½d. multicoloured 15 10
212 8½d. multicoloured 15 20

54 Nkrumah Statue, Accra

55 Ghana Timber

65a Red-fronted Gazelle

1959. Multicoloured.
213 ½d. "God's Omnipotence" (postage) 10 10
213a ½d. "Gye Nyame" 30 10
214 1d. Type **54** 10 10
215 1½d. Type **55** 10 10
216 2d. Volta river 10 10
217 2½d. Cocoa bean 10 10
218 3d. "God's Omnipotence" . . 10 10
218a 3d. "Gye Nyame" 30 10
219 4d. Diamond and mine . . . 4·50 65
220 6d. Red-crowned bishop (bird) 50 10
221 11d. Golden-spider lily . . . 25 10
222 1s. Shell ginger 25 10
223 2s. 6d. Giant blue turaco . . . 2·25 15
224 5s. Tiger orchid . . . . . . 4·00 50
225 10s. Jewel cichlid . . . . . . 1·00 70
225a £1 Type **65a** . . . . 8·00 4·75
226 1s. 3d. Pennant-winged nightjar (air) . . . . 2·50 10
227 2s. Crowned cranes . . . . . 1·75 10
SIZES—HORIZ (As Type **54**): ½d. (As Type **55**): 2d., 2½d., 3d., 4d., 6d., 1s. 3d., 2s. 6d. (As Type **65a**): 10s. VERT (As Type **55**): 11d., 1s., 2s., 5s.
The 3d. is a different symbolic design from the ½d.

68 Gold Cup and West African Map

1959. West African Football Competition, 1959. Multicoloured.
228 ½d. Type **68** 10 10*
229 1d. Footballers 10 10*
230 3d. Goalkeeper saving ball . . 10 10*
231 8d. Forward attacking goal . . 60 15*
232 2s. 6d. "Kwame Nkrumah" Gold Cup 70 15*
Nos. 229 and 232 are vert and the rest horiz.

73 Duke of Edinburgh and Arms of Ghana

1959. Visit of the Duke of Edinburgh.
233 **73** 3d. black and mauve . . . 30 10*

74 Ghana Flag and Talking Drums

1959. U.N. Trusteeship Council. Multicoloured.
234 3d. Type **74** 10 10*
235 6d. Ghana flag and U.N. emblem 10 10*
236 1s. 3d. As 6d. but emblem above flag 30 15*
237 2s. 6d. "Totem pole" 40 15*
Nos. 235/7 are vert.

78 Eagles in Flight

85 Dr. Nkrumah

82 Flags and Map forming letter "A"

1960. 3rd Anniv of Independence. Mult.
238 ½d. Type **78** 10 10*
239 3d. Fireworks 10 10*
240 1s. 3d. "Third Anniversary" . . 30 10*
241 2s. "Ship of State" 30 15*

1960. African Freedom Day. Multicoloured.
242 3d. Type **82** 10 10*
243 6d. Letter "f" 20 10*
244 1s. Letter "d" 20 10*

1960. Republic Day. Inscr "REPUBLIC DAY 1ST JULY 1960". Multicoloured.
245 3d. Type **85** 10 10
246 1s. 3d. Ghana flag 25 10
247 2s. Torch of Freedom 30 20
248 10s. Ghana arms . . . . . . 70 1·25
The 10s. is horiz and the rest vert.

90 Athlete

1960. Olympic Games.
249 – 3d. multicoloured 10 10
250 – 6d. multicoloured 15 10
251 **90** 1s. 3d. multicoloured . . . 25 10
252 2s. 6d. multicoloured . . . 35 60
DESIGN—VERT: 3d., 6d. Olympic torch.

91 President Nkrumah

1960. Founder's Day. Inscribed as in T **91**.
253 **91** 3d. multicoloured 10 10
254 – 6d. multicoloured 10 10
255 – 1s. 3d. multicoloured . . . 20 20
DESIGNS—VERT: 6d. President Nkumah within star; 1s. 3d. Map of Africa and column.

94 U.N. Emblem and Ghana Flag

97 Talking Drums

1960. Human Rights Day.
256 **94** 3d. multicoloured 10 10
257 – 6d. yellow, black and blue . . 20 10
258 – 1s. 3d. multicoloured . . . 40 30
DESIGNS: U.N. Emblem with torch (6d.) or within laurel (1s. 3d.).

1961. Africa Freedom Day. Inscr "15th APRIL 1961".
259 **97** 3d. multicoloured 10 10
260 – 6d. red, black and green . . 20 10
261 – 2s. multicoloured 50 45
DESIGNS—VERT: 6d. Map of Africa. HORIZ: 2s. Flags and map.

100 Eagle on Column

103 Dove with Olive Branch

1961. 1st Anniv of Republic. Multicoloured.
262 3d. Type **100** 10 10
263 1s. 3d. "Flower" 10 10
264 2s. Ghana flags 20 80

1961. Belgrade Conference.
265 **103** 3d. green 10 10
266 – 1s. 3d. blue 15 10
267 – 5s. purple 60 70
DESIGNS—HORIZ: 1s. 3d. World map, chain and olive branch; 5s. Rostrum, Conference room.

106 President Nkrumah and Globe

1961. Founder's Day. Multicoloured.
268 3d. Type **106** 10 10
269 1s. 3d. President in Kente cloth 25 10
270 5s. President in national costume 95 2·50
Nos. 269/70 are vert.

109 Queen Elizabeth II and African Map

1961. Royal Visit.
271 **109** 3d. multicoloured 15 10
272 1s. 3d. multicoloured . . . 50 20
273 5s. multicoloured . . . . 1·60 3·00

110 Ships in Tema Harbour

1962. Opening of Tema Harbour. Multicoloured.
274 **110** 3d. Type **110** (postage) . . 15 10
275 – 1s. 3d. Douglas DC-8 aircraft and ships at Tema (air) . 80 15
276 – 2s. 6d. As No. 275 . . . . 1·00 2·00

112 Africa and Peace Dove

1962. 1st Anniv of Casablanca Conference.
277 **112** 3d. multicoloured (post) . . 10 10
278 1s. 3d. multicoloured (air) . 30 15
279 2s. 6d. multicoloured . . . 40 1·40

113 Compass over Africa

115 Atomic Bomb-burst "Skull"

1962. Africa Freedom Day.
280 **113** 3d. sepia, turquoise & pur . 10 10
281 6d. sepia, turquoise & brn . 10 15
282 1s. 3d. sepia, turq & red . . 15 15

1962. The Accra Assembly.
283 – 3d. black and lake 10 10
284 **115** 6d. black and red 25 35
285 – 1s. 3d. turquoise 30 50
DESIGNS: 3d. Ghana Star over "five continents"; 1s. 3d. Dove of Peace.

117 Patrice Lumumba

1962. 1st Death Anniv of Lumumba.
286 **117** 3d. black and yellow . . . 10 10
287 6d. black, green and slate . 10 30
288 1s. 3d. black, pink and green 15 35

118 Star over Two Columns

121 President Nkrumah

1962. 2nd Anniv of Republic. Inscribed "1st JULY 1962". Multicoloured.
289 3d. Type **118** 10 10
290 6d. Flaming torch 20 30
291 1s. 3d. Eagle trailing flag . . . 40 55
The 1s. 3d. is horiz.

1962. Founder's Day.
292 **121** 1d. multicoloured 10 10
293 – 3d. multicoloured 10 10
294 – 1s. 3d. black and blue . . . 30 15
295 – 2s. multicoloured 30 60
DESIGNS: 3d. Nkrumah medallion; 1s. 3d. President and Ghana Star; 2s. Laying "Ghana" brick.

125 Campaign Emblem

126 Campaign Emblem

1962. Malaria Eradication.
296 **125** 1d. red 15 10
297 4d. green . . . . 40 1·00
298 6d. bistre 40 30
299 1s. 3d. violet 40 90

1963. Freedom from Hunger.
300 **126** 1d. multicoloured 15 10
301 – 4d. sepia, yellow and orange 75 45
302 – 1s. 3d. ochre, blk & grn . . 1·60 80
DESIGNS—HORIZ: 4d. Emblem in hands; 1s. 3d. World map and emblem.

129 Map of Africa

133 Red Cross

1963. Africa Freedom Day.
303 **129** 1d. gold and red 10 10
304 – 4d. red, black and yellow . 10 10
305 – 1s. 3d. multicoloured . . . 35 10
306 – 2s. 6d. multicoloured . . . 50 1·25
DESIGNS—HORIZ: 4d. Carved stool. VERT: 1s. 3d. Map and bowl of fire; 2s. 6d. Topi (antelope) and flag.

1963. Centenary of Red Cross. Multicoloured.
307 1d. Type **133** 60 15
308 1½d. Centenary emblem . . . . 90 1·25
309 4d. Nurses and child . . . . 2·25 20
310 1s. 3d. Emblem, globe and laurel 3·50 2·00
The 1½d. and 4d. are horiz.

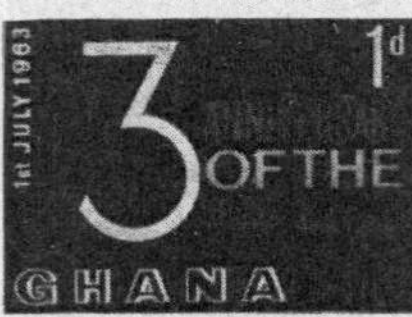

137 "3rd Anniversary"

1963. 3rd Anniv of Republic. Multicoloured.
311 1d. Type **137** 10 10
312 4d. Three Ghanian flags . . . 10 10
313 1s. 3d. Map, flag and star (vert) 35 15
314 2s. 6d. Flag and torch (vert) . . 55 1·50

141 President Nkrumah and Ghana Flag

145 Rameses II, Abu Simbel

1963. Founder's Day.
315 **141** 1d. multicoloured 10 10
316 – 4d. multicoloured 15 10
317 – 1s. 3d. multicoloured . . . 30 10
318 – 5s. yellow and mauve . . . 65 75
DESIGNS—VERT: 4d. Type **141** but with larger flag behind President Nkrumah. HORIZ: 1s. 3d. President Nkrumah and fireworks; 5s. Native symbol of wisdom.

1963. Preservation of Nubian Monuments. Multicoloured.
319 1d. Type **145** 15 10
320 1½d. Rock paintings 20 65
321 2d. Queen Nefertari 20 10
322 4d. Sphinx, Sebua 35 15
323 1s. 3d. Rock Temple, Abu Simbel 80 90
The 1d. and 4d. are vert, the rest are horiz.

150 Class 248 Steam Locomotive and Diesel-electric Locomotive No. 1401

1963. 60th Anniv of Ghana Railway.
324 **150** 1d. multicoloured 10 10
325 6d. multicoloured 60 10
326 1s. 3d. multicoloured . . . 1·00 60
327 2s. 6d. multicoloured . . . 1·75 2·25

151 Eleanor Roosevelt and "Flame of Freedom"

154 Sun and Globe Emblem

1963. 5th Anniv of Declaration of Human Rights. Multicoloured.
328 1d. Type **151** 10 10
329 4d. Type **151** 10 30
330 6d. Eleanor Roosevelt 10 10
331 1s. 3d. Eleanor Roosevelt and emblems (horiz) 15 15

1964. International Quiet Sun Years.
332 **154** 3d. multicoloured 15 10
333 6d. multicoloured 25 10
334 1s. 3d. multicoloured . . . 25 15

155 Harvesting Corn on State Farm

1964. 4th Anniv of Republic.
335 **155** 3d. olive, brown and yellow 10 10
336 – 6d. green, brown & turq . . 10 10
337 – 1s. 3d. red, brn & salmon . 10 10
338 – 5s. multicoloured 40 70
DESIGNS: 6d. Oil refinery, Tema; 1s. 3d. "Communal Labour"; 5s. Procession headed by flag.

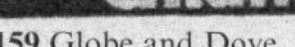

159 Globe and Dove

163 President Nkrumah and Hibiscus Flowers

1964. 1st Anniv of African Unity Charter.
339 **159** 3d. multicoloured 10 10
340 – 6d. green and red 10 10
341 – 1s. 3d. multicoloured . . . 15 10
342 – 5s. multicoloured 45 70
DESIGNS—VERT: 6d. Map of Africa and quill pen; 5s. Planting flower. HORIZ: 1s. 3d. Hitched rope on map of Africa.

1964. Founder's Day.
343 **163** 3d. multicoloured 10 10
344 6d. multicoloured 15 10
345 1s. 3d. multicoloured . . . 25 10
346 2s. 6d. multicoloured . . . 40 60

164 Hurdling

1964. Olympic Games, Tokyo. Multicoloured.
347 1d. Type **164** 10 10
348 2½d. Running . . . . 10 1·25
349 3d. Boxing 10 10
350 4d. Long-jumping 10 10
351 6d. Football 15 10
352 1s. 3d. Athlete holding Olympic Torch 20 10
353 5s. Olympic "Rings" and flags . 85 3·25
Nos. 249/52 are vert.

171 G. Washington Carver (botanist) and Plant

1964. UNESCO Week.
354 **171** 6d. blue and green 15 10
355 – 1s. 3d. purple and blue . . 60 10
356 **171** 5s. sepia and red . . . . . 1·25 4·00
DESIGN: 1s. 3d. Albert Einstein (scientist) and Atomic symbol.

173 African Elephant 181 I.C.Y. Emblem

1964. Multicoloured.
357 1d. Type **173** 50 50
358 1½d. Secretary bird (horiz) . . . 1·00 2·25
359 2½d. Purple wreath (flower) . . 60 2·25
360 3d. Grey parrot . . . . 1·50 50
361 4d. Blue-naped mousebird (horiz) . . . . 1·50 70
362 6d. African tulip tree (horiz) . . 60 30
363 1s. 3d. Violet starling (horiz) . . 1·75 1·25
364 2s. 6d. Hippopotamus (horiz) . 1·75 5·50

1965. International Co-operation Year.
365 **181** 1d. multicoloured 35 60
366 4d. multicoloured . . . . 1·50 1·40
367 6d. multicoloured . . . . 1·50 60
368 1s. 3d. multicoloured . . . 1·75 2·75

182 I.T.U. Emblem and Symbols

1965. Centenary of I.T.U.
369 **182** 1d. multicoloured 15 15
370 6d. multicoloured 55 15
371 1s. 3d. multicoloured . . . 1·00 25
372 5s. multicoloured . . . . 2·25 2·75

183 Lincoln's Home

1965. Death Centenary of Abraham Lincoln.
373 **183** 6d. multicoloured 15 10
374 – 1s. 3d. black, red and blue 25 15
375 – 2s. black, brown and yellow 30 30
376 – 3s. black and red . . . . 70 1·50
DESIGNS: 1s. 3d. Lincoln's Inaugural Address; 2s. Abraham Lincoln; 5s. Adaption of U.S. 90 c. Lincoln stamp of 1869.

187 Obverse (President Nkrumah) and Reverse of 5 p. Coin

1965. Introduction of Decimal Currency. Multicoloured designs showing coins expressed in the same denominations as on the stamps.
377 5 p. Type **187** 25 10
378 10 p. As Type **187** 30 10
379 25 p. Size 63 × 39 mm . . . . 1·00 1·00
380 50 p. Size 71 × 43½ mm . . . . 2·00 2·25

1965. Nos. 214/27 surch **Ghana New Currency 19th July. 1965.** and value. Multicoloured.
381 **54** 1 p. on 1d. (postage) . . . 10 10
382 – 2 p. on 2d. 10 10
383 – 3 p. on 3d. (No. 218a) . . 95 4·50
384 – 4 p. on 4d. . . . . 4·00 45
385 – 6 p. on 6d. 50 10
386 – 11 p. on 11d. 25 10
387 – 12 p. on 1s. 25 10
388 – 30 p. on 2s. 6d. . . . . . 3·00 2·75
389 – 60 p. on 5s. . . . . 4·50 70
390 – 1 c. 20 on 10s. . . . . . 75 2·25
391 **65a** 2 c. 40 on £1 . . . . . . 1·00 6·00
392 – 15 p. on 1s. 3d. (air) . . . 2·50 70
393 – 24 p. on 2s. . . . . 2·50 30

189 "OAU" and Flag

1965. O.A.U. Summit Conf, Accra. Mult.
394 1 p. Type **189** 10 10
395 2 p. "OAU" heads and flag . . 10 10
396 5 p. OAU emblem and flag . . 10 10
397 6 p. African map and flag . . . 10 10
398 15 p. "Sunburst" and flag . . . 20 30
399 24 p. "O.A.U." on map, and flag 35 60
Nos. 397/9 are horiz, 37½ × 27½ mm.

195 Goalkeeper saving Ball

1965. African Soccer Cup Competition. Mult.
400 6 p. Type **195** 25 10
401 15 p. Player with ball (vert) . . 40 25
402 24 p. Player, ball and Soccer Cup 45 50

198 President Kennedy and Grave Memorial

1965. 2nd Death Anniv of President Kennedy.
403 **198** 6 p. multicoloured 15 10
404 – 15 p. violet, red and green 25 35
405 – 24 p. black and purple . . 30 60
406 – 30 p. purple and black . . 40 75
DESIGNS: 15 p. President Kennedy and Eternal Flame; 24 p. President Kennedy and Memorial Inscription; 30 p. President Kennedy.

202 Section of Dam and Generators

1966. Volta River Project.
408 **202** 6 p. multicoloured 15 10
409 – 15 p. multicoloured 20 15
410 – 24 p. multicoloured 25 20
411 – 30 p. black and blue . . . 35 50
DESIGNS: 15 p. Dam and Lake Volta; 24 p. Word "GHANA" as Dam; 30 p. "Fertility".

1966. "Black Stars" Victory in African Soccer Cup Competition. Optd **Black Stars Retain Africa Cup 21st Nov. 1965.**
412 **195** 6 p. multicoloured 25 10
413 – 15 p. multicoloured 40 20
414 – 24 p. multicoloured 45 35

207 W.H.O. Building and Ghana Flag

1966. Inaug of W.H.O. Headquarters, Geneva. Mult.
415 6 p. Type **207** 50 10
416 15 p. Type **207** . . . . 1·25 65
417 24 p. W.H.O. Building and emblem . . . . 1·40 1·25
418 30 p. W.H.O. Building and emblem . . . . 1·60 2·50

209 Atlantic Herring

1966. Freedom from Hunger. Multicoloured.
420 6 p. Type **209** 20 10
421 15 p. Turbot 45 15
422 24 p. Spadefish 75 35
423 30 p. Red snapper . . . . . . 80 1·10
424 60 p. Blue-finned tuna . . . . 2·00 4·00

214 African "Links" and Ghana Flag

1966. 3rd Anniv of African Charter. Multicoloured.
426 6 p. Type **214** 15 10
427 15 p. Flags as "Quill" and diamond (horiz) 35 55
428 24 p. Ship's wheel, map and cocoa bean (horiz) 40 70

217 Player heading Ball, and Jules Rimet Cup

1966. World Cup Football Championships. Multicoloured.
429 5 p. Type **217** 30 10
430 15 p. Goalkeeper clearing ball . 70 20
431 24 p. Player and Jules Rimet Cup (replica) 85 35
432 30 p. Players and Jules Rimet Cup (replica) . . . . 1·10 1·25
433 60 p. Players with ball . . . . 1·75 5·50

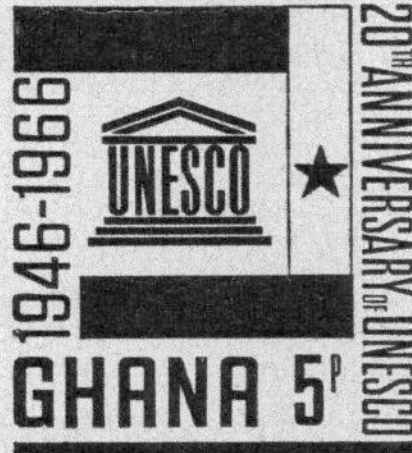

222 U.N.E.S.C.O. Emblem

1966. 20th Anniv of U.N.E.S.C.O.
435 **222** 5 p. multicoloured 25 15
436 15 p. multicoloured 70 40
437 24 p. multicoloured . . . . 1·00 85
438 30 p. multicoloured . . . . 1·40 2·50
439 60 p. multicoloured . . . . 2·25 5·00

223 Fair Emblem and Crates

1967. Ghana Trade Fair, Accra. Multicoloured.
441 5 p. Type **223** 10 10
442 15 p. Fair emblem and world map 15 20
443 24 p. Shipping and flags 25 30
444 36 p. Fair emblem and hand-held hoist . . . . 40 2·25

1967. New Currency. Nos. 216/26 and 393 surch with new value.
445 1½ n.p. on 2d. (postage) . . . . 3·00 4·00
446 3½ n.p. on 4d. . . . . 4·50 1·25
447 5 n.p. on 6d. . . . . 1·25 50
448 9 n.p. on 11d. 30 20
449 10 n.p. on 1s. 30 30
450 25 n.p. on 2s. 6d. . . . . . . 3·50 5·00
451 1 n.c. on 10s. . . . . 3·00 14·00
452 2 n.c. on £1 . . . . 6·00 24·00
453 12½ n.p. on 1 s. 3d. (air) . . . . 4·00 2·25
454 20 n.p. on 24 p. on 2s. . . . . 4·75 3·50

229 Ghana Eagle and Flag

1967. 1st Anniv of 24 February Revolution.
455 **229** 1 n.p. multicoloured . . . 10 30
456 4 n.p. multicoloured . . . 10 10
457 12½ n.p. multicoloured . . . 40 60
458 25 n.p. multicoloured . . . 85 2·75

230 Maize 232 The Ghana Mace

1967. Multicoloured.
460 1 n.p. Type **230** 10 10
461 1½ n.p. Forest kingfisher . . . 90 2·00
462 2 n.p. Type **232** 10 10
463 2½ n.p. Commelina 35 10
464 3 n.p. West African lungfish . . 20 40
465 4 n.p. Rufous-crowned roller . 1·50 10
466 6 n.p. Akosombo Dam 15 75
467 8 n.p. Adomi Bridge 15 10
468 9 n.p. Chameleon 75 10
469 10 n.p. Tema Harbour 15 10
470 20 n.p. Bush hare (blue) . . . 20 10
471 50 n.p. Black-winged stilt . . . 5·00 1·75
472 1 n.c. Wooden stool . . . . . 2·25 75
473 2 n.c. Frangipani . . . . . . 2·00 3·50
474 2 n.c. 50 Seat of State . . . . 3·00 7·50
SIZES—VERT (As Type **230**): 4 n.p. (As Type **232**): 1½ n.p.; 2½ n.p., 20 n.p., 2 n.c., 2 n.c. 50. HORIZ (as Type **230**): 8 n.p. (As Type **232**): 3 n.p., 6 n.p., 9 n.p., 10 n.p., 50 n.p., 1 n.c.

245 Kumasi Fort

1967. Castles and Forts.
475 **245** 4 n.p. multicoloured . . . 25 10
476 – 12½ n.p. multicoloured . . 1·00 1·00
477 – 20 n.p. multicoloured . . 1·40 2·75
478 – 25 n.p. multicoloured . . 1·75 3·50
DESIGNS: 12½ n.p. Christiansborg Castle and British galleon; 20 n.p. Elmina Castle and Portuguese galleon; 25 n.p. Cape Coast Castle and Spanish galleon.

249 "Luna 10"

255 U.N. Headquarters Building

252 Scouts and Campfire

1967. "Peaceful Use of Outer Space". Multicoloured.
479 4 n.p. Type **249** 10 10
480 10 n.p. "Orbiter 1" 10 45
481 12½ n.p. Man in Space 20 80

1967. 50th Anniv of Ghanaian Scout Movement. Multicoloured.
483 4 n.p. Type **252** 20 10
484 10 n.p. Scout on march 50 50
485 12½ n.p. Lord Baden-Powell 70 1·75

1967. United Nations Day (24 October).
487 **255** 4 n.p. multicoloured 10 10
488 10 n.p. multicoloured 10 15
489 – 50 n.p. multicoloured 30 70
490 – 2 n.c. 50 multicoloured 1·00 4·00
DESIGN: 50 n.p., 2 n.c. 50, General view of U.N. H.Q., Manhattan.

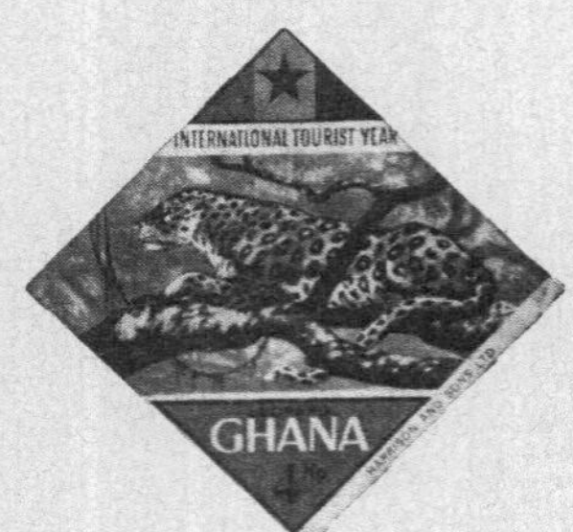

257 Leopard

1967. International Tourist Year. Multicoloured.
492 4 n.p. Type **257** 1·00 20
493 12½ n.p. "Papilio demodocus" (butterfly) 2·50 1·50
494 20 n.p. Carmine bee eater 3·00 3·50
495 50 n.p. Waterbuck 3·00 7·00

261 Revolutionaries entering Accra

1968. 2nd Anniv of February Revolution. Mult.
497 4 n.p. Type **261** 10 10
498 12½ n.p. Marching troops 20 20
499 20 n.p. Cheering people 30 40
500 40 n.p. Victory celebrations 50 1·50

265 Microscope and Cocoa Beans

1968. Cocoa Research.
501 **265** 2½ n.p. multicoloured 10 60
502 – 4 n.p. multicoloured 10 10
503 **265** 10 n.p. multicoloured 15 20
504 – 25 n.p. multicoloured 60 1·10
DESIGNS: 4 n.p. and 25 n.p. Microscope and cocoa tree, beans and pods.

267 Kotoka and Flowers

1968. 1st Death Anniv of Lt.-Gen. E. K. Kotoka. Multicoloured.
506 4 n.p. Type **267** 10 10
507 12½ n.p. Kotoka and wreath 20 30
508 20 n.p. Kotoka in civilian clothes 35 75
509 40 n.p. Lt.-Gen. Kotoka 50 1·60

271 Tobacco **277** Hurdling

276 Surgeons, Flag and W.H.O. Emblem

1968. Flora and Fauna. Multicoloured.
510 4 n.p. Type **271** 15 10
511 5 n.p. North African crested porcupine 15 60
512 12½ n.p. Rubber 50 75
513 20 n.p. "Cymothoe sangaris" (butterfly) 2·25 2·75
514 40 n.p. "Charaxes ameliae" (butterfly) 2·50 4·75

1968. 20th Anniv of W.H.O.
516 **276** 4 n.p. multicoloured 25 10
517 12½ n.p. multicoloured 60 40
518 20 n.p. multicoloured 95 1·25
519 40 n.p. multicoloured 1·50 3·25

1969. Olympic Games, Mexico (1968). Multicoloured.
521 4 n.p. Type **277** 10 10
522 12½ n.p. Boxing 20 30
523 20 n.p. Torch, Olympic Rings and flags 40 75
524 40 n.p. Football 70 2·75

281 U.N. Building **285** Dr. J. B. Danquah

1969. United Nations Day. Multicoloured.
526 4 n.p. Type **281** 10 10
527 12½ n.p. Native stool, staff and U.N. emblem 15 25
528 20 n.p. U.N. building and emblem over Ghanian Flag 20 40
529 40 n.p. U.N. emblem encircled by flags 40 1·50

1969. Human Rights Year. Multicoloured.
531 4 n.p. Type **285** 10 10
532 12½ n.p. Dr. Martin Luther King 20 35
533 20 n.p. As 12½ n.p. 35 75
534 40 n.p. Type **285** 50 1·60

287 Constituent Assembly Building

1969. 3rd Anniv of Revolution. Multicoloured.
536 4 n.p. Type **287** 10 10
537 12½ n.p. Arms of Ghana 10 15
538 20 n.p. Type **287** 15 20
539 40 n.p. As 12½ n.p. 20 15

1969. New Constitution. Nos. 460/74 optd **NEW CONSTITUTION 1969.**
541 **230** 1 n.p. multicoloured 10 1·25
542 – 1½ n.p. multicoloured 85 2·25
543 **232** 2 n.p. multicoloured 10 2·00
544 – 2½ n.p. multicoloured 10 1·50
545 – 3 n.p. multicoloured 60 1·75
546 – 4 n.p. multicoloured 2·25 30
547 – 6 n.p. multicoloured 15 1·75
548 – 8 n.p. multicoloured 15 1·40
549 – 9 n.p. multicoloured 15 1·75
550 – 10 n.p. multicoloured 20 1·25
551 – 20 n.p. multicoloured 35 1·25
552 – 50 n.p. multicoloured 5·00 6·00
553 – 1 n.c. multicoloured 1·75 7·00
554 – 2 n.c. multicoloured 2·75 8·50
555 – 2 n.c. 50 multicoloured 2·75 9·50
On Nos. 541, 545, 547/50 and 552/3 the opt is horiz. The rest are vert.

MINIMUM PRICE

The minimum price quoted is 10p which represents a handling charge rather than a basis for valuing common stamps. For further notes about prices see introductory pages.

290 Map of Africa and Flags **294** Red Cross and Globe

293 I.L.O. Emblem and Cogwheels

1969. Inauguration of 2nd Republic. Multicoloured.
556 4 n.p. Type **290** 10 10
557 12½ n.p. Figure "2", branch and Ghanaian colours 20 10
558 20 n.p. Hands receiving egg 35 30
559 40 n.p. Type **290** 60 70

1970. 50th Anniv of I.L.O.
560 **293** 4 n.p. multicoloured 10 10
561 12½ n.p. multicoloured 20 30
562 20 n.p. multicoloured 30 55

1970. 50th Anniv of League of Red Cross Societies. Multicoloured.
564 4 n.p. Type **294** 30 10
565 12½ n.p. Henri Dunant and Red Cross emblem 35 20
566 20 n.p. Patient receiving medicine 40 55
567 40 n.p. Patient having arm bandaged 60 1·40
Nos. 565/7 are horiz.

298 General Kotoka, Vickers VC-10 and Airport **302** Lunar Module landing on Moon

1970. Inauguration of Kotoka Airport. Mult.
569 4 n.p. Type **298** 15 10
570 12½ n.p. Control tower and tail of Vickers VC-10 25 15
571 20 n.p. Aerial view of airport 40 30
572 40 n.p. Airport and flags 75 80

1970. Moon Landing. Multicoloured.
573 4 n.p. Type **302** 30 10
574 12½ n.p. Astronaut's first step onto the Moon 85 60
575 20 n.p. Astronaut with equipment on Moon 1·25 1·40
576 40 n.p. Astronauts 1·75 3·00
Nos. 575/6 are horiz.

306 Adult Education

1970. International Education Year. Multicoloured.
578 4 n.p. Type **306** 10 10
579 12½ n.p. International education 20 20
580 20 n.p. "Ntesie" and I.E.Y. symbols 35 30
581 40 n.p. Nursery schools 60 85

310 Saluting March-Past

1970. 1st Anniv of Second Republic. Multicoloured
582 4 n.p. Type **310** 10 10
583 12½ n.p. Busia Declaration 15 15
584 20 n.p. Doves symbol 25 30
585 40 n.p. Opening of Parliament 50 65

314 "Crinum ornatum"

1970. Flora and Fauna. Multicoloured.
586 4 n.p. Type **314** 1·50 10
587 12½ n.p. Lioness 1·50 85
588 20 n.p. "Anselia africana" (flower) 1·60 1·25
589 40 n.p. African elephant 4·75 5·50

315 Kuduo Brass Casket

1970. Monuments and Archaeological Sites in Ghana. Multicoloured.
590 4 n.p. Type **315** 15 10
591 12½ n.p. Akan traditional house 40 20
592 20 n.p. Larabanga Mosque 55 50
593 40 n.p. Funerary clay head 70 1·10

316 Trade Fair Building

1971. International Trade Fair, Accra. Multicoloured.
595 4 n.p. Type **316** 10 10
596 12½ n.p. Cosmetic and pharmaceutical goods 60 20
597 20 n.p. Vehicles 65 25
598 40 n.p. Construction equipment 95 95
599 50 n.p. Transport and packing case (vert) 1·10 1·10

317 Christ on the Cross **318** Corn Cob

1971. Easter. Multicoloured.
600 4 n.p. Type **317** 20 10
601 12½ n.p. Christ and Disciples 45 45
602 20 n.p. Christ blessing Disciples 65 1·10

1971. Freedom from Hunger Campaign.
603 **318** 4 n.p. multicoloured 10 10
604 12½ n.p. multicoloured 35 70
605 20 n.p. multicoloured 65 1·40
Remainder stocks of the above stamps were optd on the occasion of the death of Lord Boyd Orr and further surch 12½, 20 and 60 n.p.
It is understood that 8070 sets from the agency were overprinted locally and returned to New York. Limited remainders of these stamps (only 330 of 60 n.p.) were sold at the G.P.O. We do not list these as they were not freely on sale in Ghana.

319 Guides Emblem and Ghana Flag

1971. Golden Jubilee of Ghana Girl Guides. Each design includes Guides emblem. Mult.
606 4 n.p. Type **319** 20 10
607 12½ n.p. Mrs E. Ofuatey-Kodjoe (founder) and guides with flags 60 50
608 20 n.p. Guides laying stones 90 90
609 40 n.p. Camp-fire and tent 1·50 1·75
610 50 n.p. Signallers 1·75 2·00

320 Child-care Centre

1971. Y.W.C.A. World Council Meeting, Accra. Multicoloured.
612 4 n.p. Type **320** 10 10
613 $12\frac{1}{2}$ n.p. Council meeting . . . 10 15
614 20 n.p. School typing class . . . 15 30
615 40 n.p. Building Fund Day . . 30 60

321 Firework Display **322** Weighing Baby

1971. Christmas. Multicoloured.
617 1 n.p. Type **321** 10 60
618 3 n.p. African Nativity 15 70
619 6 n.p. The Flight into Egypt . . 15 70

1971. 25th Anniv of U.N.I.C.E.F. Multicoloured.
620 5 n.p. Type **322** 10 10
621 15 n.p. Mother and child (horiz) 20 30
622 30 n.p. Nurse 30 70
623 50 n.p. Young boy (horiz) . . . 50 2·25

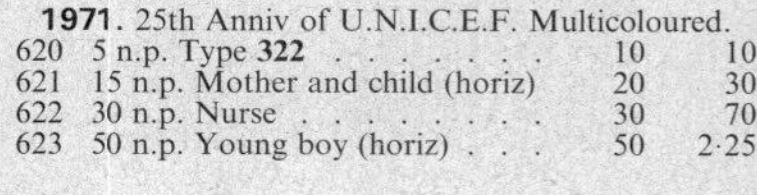

323 Unity Symbol and Trade Fair Emblem

1972. All African Trade Fair. Multicoloured.
625 5 n.p. Type **323** 10 10
626 15 n.p. Horn of Plenty 15 30
627 30 n.p. Fireworks on map of Africa 25 70
628 60 n.p. "Participating Nations" 35 2·00
629 1 n.c. As No. 628 . . . . . . 50 2·50

On 24 June 1972, on the occasion of the Belgian International Philatelic Exhibition, Nos. 625/9 were issued optd **BELGICA 72**. Only very limited supplies were sent to Ghana (we understand not more than 900 sets), and for this reason we do not list them.

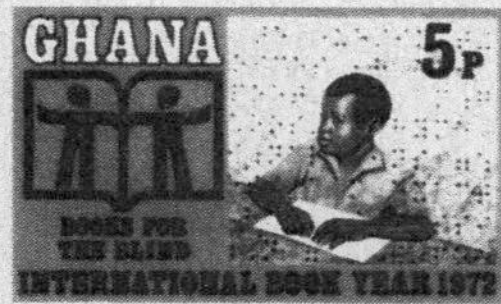

324 Books for the Blind

1972. International Book Year. Multicoloured.
630 5 p. Type **324** 20 10
631 15 p. Children's books 55 50
632 30 p. Books for recreation . . 1·00 1·25
633 50 p. Books for students . . . 1·75 2·75
634 1 c. Book and flame of knowledge (vert) . . . . 2·50 3·75

325 "Hypoxis urceolata"

1972. Flora and Fauna. Multicoloured.
636 5 p. Type **325** 30 10
637 15 p. Mona monkey 65 65
638 30 p. "Crinum ornatum" . . . 5·50 4·00
639 1 c. De Winton's tree squirrel . 6·00 8·00

326 Football

1972. Olympic Games, Munich. Multicoloured.
640 5 p. Type **326** 20 10
641 15 p. Running 35 20
642 30 p. Boxing 60 65
643 50 p. Long-jumping . . . . . 80 2·25
644 1 c. High-jumping . . . . . . 1·40 3·50

327 Senior Scout and Cub

1972. 65th Anniv of Boy Scouts. Multicoloured.
646 5 p. Type **327** 30 10
647 15 p. Scout and tent 65 45
648 30 p. Sea scouts . . . . 1·00 1·25
649 50 p. Leader with cubs . . . . 1·40 2·00
650 1 c. Training school . . . . . 2·25 3·50

328 "The Holy Night" (Correggio) **330** Under 5's Clinic

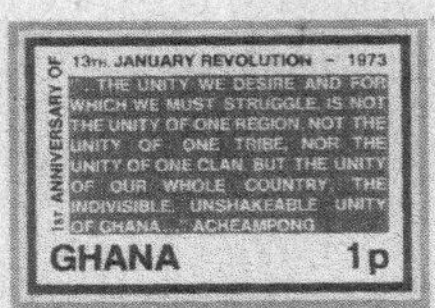

329 Extract from Speech

1972. Christmas. Multicoloured.
652 1 p. Type **328** 10 10
653 3 p. "Adoration of the Kings" (Holbein the Elder) 10 10
654 15 p. "Madonna of the Passion" (School of Ricco) 40 30
655 30 p. "King Melchior" 70 70
656 60 p. "King Gaspar, Mary and Jesus" . . . . 1·00 2·00
657 1 c. "King Balthasar" . . . . 1·50 3·00

1973. 1st Anniv of 13 January Revolution. Multicoloured.
659 1 p. Type **329** 10 10
660 3 p. Market scene 10 10
661 5 p. Selling bananas (vert) . . . 10 10
662 15 p. Farmer with hoe and produce (vert) 20 25
663 30 p. Market traders 30 40
664 1 c. Farmer cutting palm-nuts . 70 1·40

1973. 25th Anniv of W.H.O. Multicoloured.
666 5 p. Type **330** 10 10
667 15 p. Radiography 25 30
668 30 p. Immunisation 35 50
669 50 p. Starving child . . . . . 50 1·25
670 1 c. W.H.O. H.Q., Geneva . . 75 2·25

1973. World Scouting Conference. Nairobi/Addis Ababa. Nos. 646/50 optd **1st WORLD SCOUTING CONFERENCE IN AFRICA**.
671 **327** 5 p. multicoloured 10 15
672 – 15 p. multicoloured 35 60
673 – 30 p. multicoloured . . . . 60 1·40
674 – 50 p. multicoloured . . . . 80 2·00
675 – 1 c. multicoloured . . . . 1·50 3·00

332 Poultry Farming

1973. 10th Anniv of World Food Programme. Multicoloured.
677 5 p. Type **332** 10 10
678 15 p. Mechanisation 15 15
679 50 p. Cocoa harvest 40 90
680 1 c. F.A.O. H.Q., Rome . . . 60 1·90

333 "Green Alert"

1973. 50th Anniv of Interpol. Multicoloured.
682 5 p. Type **333** 15 10
683 30 p. "Red Alert" 75 80
684 50 p. "Blue Alert" . . . . . . 1·50 1·75
685 1 c. "Black Alert" . . . . . . 3·00 4·00

334 Handshake

1973. 10th Anniv of O.A.U. Multicoloured.
686 5 p. Type **334** 10 10
687 30 p. Africa Hall, Addis Ababa 15 30
688 50 p. O.A.U. emblem . . . . 20 1·00
689 1 c. "X" in colours of Ghana flag 35 1·50

335 Weather Balloon

1973. Centenary of I.M.O./W.M.O. Multicoloured.
690 5 p. Type **335** 10 10
691 15 p. Satellite "Tiros" 15 20
692 30 p. Computer weather map . 30 65
693 1 c. Radar screen . . . . . . 60 2·25

336 Epiphany Scene **337** "Christ carrying the Cross" (Thomas de Kolozsvar)

1973. Christmas. Multicoloured.
695 1 p. Type **336** 10 10
696 3 p. Madonna and Child . . . 10 10
697 30 p. "Madonna and Child" (Murillo) 30 75
698 50 p. "Adoration of the Magi" (Tiepolo) . . . . 45 1·00

1974. Easter.
700 **337** 5 p. multicoloured 10 10
701 – 30 p. blue, silver and brown 20 35
702 – 50 p. red, silver and brown 30 60
703 – 1 c. green, silver and brown 50 1·25

DESIGNS (from 15th-century English carved alabaster): 30 p. "The Betrayal"; 50 p. "The Deposition"; 1 c. "The Risen Christ and Mary Magdalene".

338 Letters

1974. Centenary of U.P.U. Multicoloured.
705 5 p. Type **338** 10 10
706 9 p. U.P.U. Monument and H.Q. 10 15
707 50 p. Airmail letter . . . . . 35 1·00
708 1 c. U.P.U. Monument and Ghana stamp . . . . 60 1·75

1974. "Internaba 1974" Stamp Exhibition. As Nos. 705/8 additionally inscr "INTERNABA 1974".
710 5 p. multicoloured 10 10
711 9 p. multicoloured 10 15
712 50 p. multicoloured . . . . . 30 1·00
713 1 c. multicoloured . . . . . . 45 1·75

339 Footballers

1974. World Cup Football Championships.
715 **339** 5 p. multicoloured 10 10
716 – 30 p. multicoloured 20 60
717 – 50 p. multicoloured 25 85
718 – 1 c. multicoloured . . . . 30 1·50

DESIGNS: As Type **339** showing footballers in action.

340 Roundabout

1974. Change to Driving on the Right.
720 **340** 5 p. green, red and black . 10 10
721 – 15 p. purple, red and black 25 35
722 – 30 p. multicoloured 45 60
723 – 50 p. multicoloured . . . . 70 1·10
724 – 1 c. multicoloured . . . . 1·40 2·00

DESIGNS—HORIZ: 15 p. Warning triangle sign. VERT: 30 p. Highway arrow and slogan; 50 p. Warning hands; 1 c. Car on symbolic hands.

1974. West Germany's Victory in World Cup. Nos. 715/18 optd **WEST GERMANY WINNERS**.
725 5 p. multicoloured 10 10
726 30 p. multicoloured 35 40
727 50 p. multicoloured 50 55
728 1 c. multicoloured . . . . . . 90 1·25

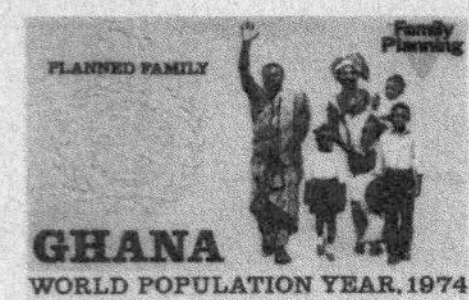

342 "Planned Family"

1974. World Population Year. Multicoloured.
730 5 p. Type **342** 10 10
731 30 p. Family planning clinic . . 25 35
732 50 p. Immunization 35 60
733 1 c. Population census enumeration . . . . 60 1·40

343 Angel **346** Angel

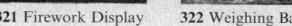

345 Tractor Driver

1974. Christmas. Multicoloured.
734 5 p. Type **343** 10 10
735 7 p. The Magi (diamond 47 × 47 mm) 10 10
736 9 p. The Nativity 10 10
737 1 c. The Annunciation . . . . 60 1·40

1975. "Apollo-Soyuz" Space Link. Nos. 715/18 optd **APOLLO SOYUZ JULY 15, 1975**.
739 **339** 5 p. multicoloured 10 10
740 – 30 p. multicoloured 25 25
741 – 50 p. multicoloured 45 55
742 – 1 c. multicoloured 70 80

1975. International Women's Year. Multicoloured.
744 7 p. Type **345** 35 10
745 30 p. Motor mechanic 85 35
746 60 p. Factory workers . . . . 1·00 80
747 1 c. Cocoa research . . . . . 1·25 1·40

1975. Christmas.
749 **346** 2 p. multicoloured 10 10
750 – 5 p. yellow and green . . . 10 10
751 – 7 p. yellow and green . . . 10 10
752 – 30 p. yellow and green . . 20 20
753 – 1 c. yellow and green . . . 50 1·00

DESIGNS: 5 p. Angle with harp; 7 p. Angel with lute; 30 p. Angel with violin; 1 c. Angel with trumpet.

347 Map Reading

1976. 14th World Scout Jamboree, Norway. Multicoloured.
755 7 p. Type **347** 20 10
756 30 p. Sailing 60 90
757 60 p. Hiking . . . . 90 2·25
758 1 c. Life-saving . . . . 1·10 2·50

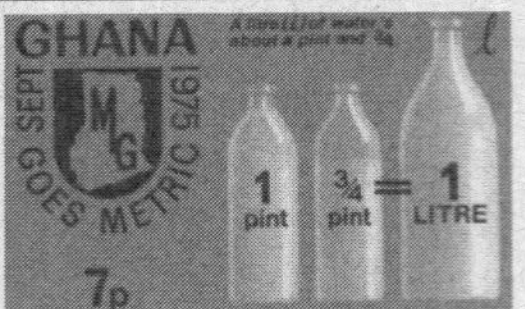

348 Bottles (litre)

1976. Metrication Publicity. Multicoloured.
760 7 p. Type **348** 15 10
761 30 p. Scales (kilogramme) . . . 40 40
762 60 p. Tape measure and bale of cloth (metre) . . . . 80 1·00
763 1 c. Ice, thermometer and kettle (temperature) . . . . 1·25 1·75

349 Fair Site

1976. International Trade Fair, Accra.
764 **349** 7 p. multicoloured 10 10
765 – 30 p. multicoloured 20 20
766 – 60 p. multicoloured 35 60
767 – 1 c. multicoloured . . . . 55 1·00
DESIGNS: As Type **349** showing different views of the Fair.

1976. Interphil Stamp Exhibition. Nos. 755/8 optd **'INTERPHIL' 76 BICENTENNIAL EXHIBITION**.
768 **347** 7 p. multicoloured 15 15
769 – 30 p. multicoloured 35 50
770 – 60 p. multicoloured 55 75
771 – 1 c. multicoloured . . . . 80 1·25

351 Shot-put

1976. Olympic Games, Montreal. Multicoloured.
773 7 p. Type **351** 15 10
774 30 p. Football 30 25
775 60 p. Women's 1500 metres . . 45 50
776 1 c. Boxing 60 80

352 Supreme Court

1976. Centenary of Supreme Court.
778 **352** 8 p. multicoloured 10 10
779 – 30 p. multicoloured 20 25
780 – 60 p. multicoloured 35 50
781 – 1 c. multicoloured . . . . 60 1·00
DESIGNS: As Type **352** showing different views of the Court Buildings.

353 Examination for River Blindness

1976. Prevention of Blindness. Multicoloured.
782 7 p. Type **353** 65 10
783 30 p. Entomologist . . . . . 1·75 1·40
784 60 p. Normal vision . . . . . 2·75 2·75
785 1 c. Blackfly eradication . . . 4·25 4·50

354 Fireworks Party, Christmas Eve

1976. Christmas. Multicoloured.
786 6 p. Type **354** 15 10
787 8 p. Children and gifts 15 10
788 30 p. Christmas feast 35 30
789 1 c. As 8 p. . . . . 75 1·75

355 "Gallows Frame" Telephone and Alexander Graham Bell

1976. Centenary of Telephone. Multicoloured.
791 8 p. Type **355** 15 10
792 30 p. Bell and 1895 telephone . 20 30
793 60 p. Bell and 1929 telephone . 40 70
794 1 c. Bell and 1976 telephone . . 60 1·25

1977. Olympic Winners. Nos. 773/6 optd **WINNERS** and country name.
796 **351** 7 p. multicoloured 15 15
797 – 30 p. multicoloured 35 40
798 – 60 p. multicoloured 45 85
799 – 1 c. multicoloured . . . . 65 1·50
OPTD: 7 p., 30 p. **EAST GERMANY**; 60 p. **U.S.S.R.**; 1 c. **U.S.A.**

357 Dipo Dancers and Drum Ensemble

1977. Second World Black and African Festival of Arts and Culture, Nigeria. Multicoloured.
801 8 p. Type **357** 15 15
802 30 p. Arts and crafts 30 60
803 60 p. Acon music and dancing priests . . . . 50 1·25
804 1 c. African huts . . . . . . 60 2·00

1977. Prince Charles's Visit to Ghana. Nos. 791/94 optd **PRINCE CHARLES VISITS GHANA 17th TO 25th MARCH, 1977**.
806 8 p. Type **355** 50 55
807 30 p. 1895 telephone . . . . . 1·25 1·00
808 60 p. 1929 telephone . . . . . 1·75 2·00
809 1 c. 1976 telephone . . . . . 2·25 2·50

359 Olive Colobus Monkey

1977. Wildlife. Multicoloured.
811 8 p. Type **359** 45 15
812 20 p. Temminck's giant squirrel 1·25 80
813 30 p. Hunting dog . . . . . . 1·75 1·25
814 60 p. African manatee (sea cow) 3·00 2·75

360 "Le Chapeau de Paille" (Rubens—400th Birth Anniv)
361 The Magi, Madonna and Child

1977. Painters' Anniversaries. Multicoloured.
816 8 p. Type **360** 25 10
817 30 p. "Isabella of Portugal" (Titian—500th birth anniv) . 40 40
818 60 p. "Duke and Duchess of Cumberland" (Gainsborough—250th birth anniv) . 55 65
819 1 c. "Rubens and Isabella Brandt" . . . . 75 1·25

1977. Christmas. Multicoloured.
821 1 p. Type **361** 10 10
822 2 p. Choir, St. Andrew's Anglican Church, Abossey Okai . . . 10 10
823 6 p. Methodist Church, Wesley, Accra 10 10
824 8 p. Madonna and Child . . . 10 10
825 30 p. Holy Spirit Cathedral, Accra 30 50
826 1 c. Ebenezer Presbyterian Church, Accra . . . . . . 1·00 1·60

1978. Referendum. Nos. 821/26 optd **REFERENDUM 1978 VOTE EARLY**.
828 1 p. Type **361** 10 10
829 2 p. Choir, St. Andrew's Anglican Church, Abossey Okai . . . 10 10
830 6 p. Methodist Church, Wesley, Accra 10 10
831 8 p. Madonna and Child . . . 10 10
832 30 p. Holy Spirit Cathedral, Accra 30 50
833 1 c. Ebenezer Presbyterian Church, Accra . . . . . . 1·00 1·50

363 Cutting Bananas

1978. Operation "Feed Yourself". Multicoloured.
835 2 p. Type **363** 10 10
836 8 p. Home produce 10 10
837 30 p. Market 25 35
838 60 p. Fishing 60 60
839 1 c. Mechanisation . . . . . . 80 1·25

364 Wright Flyer III
367 "The Betrayal"

366 Players and African Cup Emblem

1978. 75th Anniv of Powered Flight.
840 **364** 8 p. black, brown and ochre 20 10
841 – 30 p. black, brown and green 30 30
842 – 60 p. black, brown and red 40 60
843 – 1 c. black, brown and blue 1·50 1·10
DESIGNS: 30 p. Handley Page H.P.42; 60 p. De Havilland Comet 1; 1 c. Concorde.

1978. "CAPEX 1978" International Stamp Exhibition, Toronto. Nos. 840/3 optd **"CAPEX 78 JUNE 9-18 1978"**.
845 **364** 8 p. black, brown and ochre 15 15
846 – 30 p. black, brown and green 25 25
847 – 60 p. black, brown and red 50 50
848 – 1 c. black, brown and blue 1·10 80

1978. Football Championships. Multicoloured.
850 8 p. Type **366** 20 15
851 30 p. Players and African Cup emblem (different) 25 30
852 60 p. Players and World Cup emblem 40 60
853 1 c. Goalkeeper and World Cup emblem . . . . 55 1·00

1978. Easter. Drawings by Durer.
855 **367** 11 p. black and mauve . . 10 10
856 – 39 p. black and flesh . . . 25 30
857 – 60 p. black and yellow . . 40 45
858 – 1 c. black and green . . . 60 65
DESIGNS: 39 p. "The Crucifixion"; 60 p. "The Deposition"; 1 c. "The Resurrection".

1978. Football Victories of Ghana and Argentina. Nos. 850/3 optd **"GHANA WINNERS"** (8, 30 p.) or **"ARGENTINA WINS"** (others).
859 **366** 8 p. multicoloured 25 15
860 – 30 p. multicoloured 35 30
861 – 60 p. multicoloured 45 45
862 – 1 c. multicoloured 55 75

369 "Bauhinia purpurea"

1978. Flowers. Multicoloured.
864 11 p. Type **369** 15 10
865 39 p. "Cassia fistula" 30 55
866 60 p. "Plumeria acutifolia" . . 40 70
867 1 c. "Jacaranda mimosifolia" . 45 1·00

370 Mail Van

1978. 75th Anniv of Ghana Railways. Multicoloured.
868 11 p. Type **370** 25 10
869 39 p. Pay and bank car 35 65
870 60 p. Steam locomotive No. 1 "Amanful", 1922 . . . . . 40 1·00
871 1 c. Diesel-electric locomotive No. 1651, 1960 . . . . . . 40 1·40

371 "Orbiter" Spacecraft

1979. "Pioneer" Venus Space Project. Multicoloured.
872 11 p. Type **371** 15 10
873 39 p. "Multiprobe" space craft 25 30
874 60 p. "Orbiter" and "Multiprobe" spacecraft in Venus orbit 40 45
875 3 c. Radar chart of Venus . . . 60 1·40

372 "O Come All Ye Faithful"

1979. Christmas. Lines and Scenes from Christmas Carols. Multicoloured.
877 8 p. Type **372** 10 10
878 10 p. "O Little Town of Bethlehem" 10 10
879 15 p. "We Three Kings of Orient Are" 10 10
880 20 p. "I Saw Three Ships come Sailing By" 10 10
881 2 c. "Away In a Manger" . . . 30 80
882 4 c. "Ding Dong Merrily on High" . . . . 50 1·40

373 Dr. J. B. Danquah (lawyer and nationalist)
375 Children in Classroom

374 Tribesman ringing Clack Bells

1980. Famous Ghanaians. Multicoloured.
884 20 p. Type **373** 10 10
885 65 p. John Mensah Sarbah (nationalist) 15 20
886 80 p. Dr. J. E. K. Aggrey (educationalist) 15 30
887 2 c. Dr. Kwame Nkrumah (nationalist) 30 40
888 4 c. G. E. (Paa) Grant (lawyer) . 60 1·10

1980. Death Centenary of Sir Rowland Hill (1979). Multicoloured.
889 20 p. Type **374** 15 15
893 25 p. Type **374** 15 20
894 50 p. Chieftain with Golden Elephant staff 25 40
890 65 p. As 50 p. 30 30
895 1 c. Signalling with drums . . . 40 85
891 2 c. As 1 c. . . . . 50 1·00
892 4 c. Chieftain with ivory and gold staff . . . . 75 2·00
896 5 c. As 4 c. . . . . 1·00 3·00

1980. International Year of the Child (1979). Multicoloured.

898	20 p. Type **375**	15	15
899	65 p. Playing football	25	45
900	2 c. Playing in a boat	40	1·00
901	4 c. Mother and child	60	1·75

1980. "London 1980" International Stamp Exhibition. Nos. 889/96 optd **"LONDON 1980" 6th - 14th May 1980.**

903 **374**	20 p. multicoloured	15	15
907 –	25 p. multicoloured	80	1·00
908 –	50 p. multicoloured	1·10	1·75
904 –	65 p. multicoloured	25	50
909 –	1 c. multicoloured	2·00	2·50
905 –	2 c. multicoloured	50	1·25
906 –	4 c. multicoloured	75	2·25
910 –	5 c. multicoloured	3·75	5·00

1980. Papal Visit. Nos. 898/901 optd **"PAPAL VISIT" 8th - 9th May 1980.**

912 **375**	20 p. multicoloured	55	35
913 –	65 p. multicoloured	1·00	60
914 –	2 c. multicoloured	1·75	1·40
915 –	4 c. multicoloured	2·50	2·50

378 Parliament House

1980. 3rd Republic Commemoration. Multicoloured.

917	20 p. Type **378**	10	10
918	65 p. Supreme Court	20	25
919	2 c. The Castle	40	70

379 Boeing 737 Airliner and Map of West Africa

1980. 5th Anniv of Economic Community of West African States. Multicoloured.

921	20 p. Type **379**	10	10
922	65 p. Antenna and map	15	20
923	80 p. Cog-wheels and map	20	25
924	2 c. Corn and map	35	50

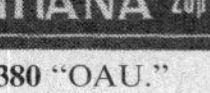

380 "OAU." **381** "The Adoration of the Magi"

1980. First Organization of African Unity Economic Summit Conference, Nigeria.

925 **380**	20 p. multicoloured	10	10
926 –	65 p. multicoloured	15	20
927 –	80 p. deep red, red and black	15	25
928 –	2 c. multicoloured	20	65

DESIGNS: 65 p. Maps of Africa and Ghana and banner; 80 p. Map of Africa; 2 c. Map of Africa, banner and Ghanaian flag.

1980. Christmas. Paintings by Fra Angelico. Multicoloured.

929	15 p. Type **381**	10	10
930	20 p. "The Virgin and Child, enthroned with Four Angels"	10	10
931	2 c. "The Virgin and Child enthroned with Eight Angels"	35	80
932	4 c. "The Annunciation"	60	1·60

382 "Health"

1980. 75th Anniv of Rotary International. Multicoloured.

934	20 p. Type **382**	10	10
935	65 p. Rotary emblem and motto with maps of World and Ghana	15	30
936	2 c. Rotary emblem, globe and outstretched hands	35	85
937	4 c. "Eradication of Hunger"	60	1·50

383 Narina Trogon **385** Royal Yacht "Britannia"

384 Pope John Paul II, Archbishop of Canterbury and President Limann during Papal Visit

1981. Birds. Multicoloured.

939	20 p. Type **383**	1·25	15
940	65 p. White-crowned robin chat	2·25	50
941	2 c. Swallow-tailed bee eater	2·75	1·75
942	4 c. Rose-ringed parakeet	4·25	3·25

1981. 1st Anniv of Papal Visit.

944 **384**	20 p. multicoloured	25	15
945	65 p. multicoloured	45	55
946	80 p. multicoloured	60	70
947	2 c. multicoloured	1·10	2·00

1981. Royal Wedding. Multicoloured.

948	20 p. Prince Charles and Lady Diana Spencer	10	10
952	65 p. As 20 p.	15	25
949	80 p. Prince Charles on visit to Ghana	15	20
953	1 c. As 80 p.	25	35
955	2 c. Type **385**	1·00	1·50
954	3 c. Type **385**	70	1·10
950	4 c. Type **385**	50	80
956	5 c. As 20 p.	1·00	2·75

386 Earth Satellite Station **388** "The Betrothal of St. Catherine of Alexandria" (Lucas Cranach)

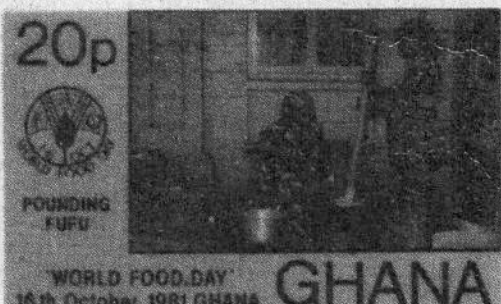

387 Pounding Fufu

1981. Commissioning of Earth Satellite Station. Mult.

957	20 p. Type **386**	10	10
958	65 p. Satellites beaming signals to Earth	15	15
959	80 p. Satellite	15	20
960	4 c. Satellite orbiting Earth	1·00	1·50

1981. World Food Day. Multicoloured.

962	20 p. Type **387**	10	10
963	65 p. Plucking cocoa	25	35
964	80 p. Preparing banku	35	40
965	2 c. Garri processing	75	2·25

1981. Christmas. Details from Paintings. Multicoloured.

967	15 p. Type **388**	15	10
968	20 p. "Angelic Musicians play for Mary and Child" (Aachener Altares)	15	10
969	65 p. "Child Jesus embracing his Mother" (Gabriel Metsu)	20	15
970	80 p. "Madonna and Child" (Fra Filippo Lippi)	20	20
971	2 c. "The Madonna with Infant Jesus" (Barnaba da Modena)	40	70
972	4 c. "The Immaculate Conception" (Murillo)	45	1·10

389 Blind Person

1982. International Year for Disabled Persons. Multicoloured.

974	20 p. Type **389**	10	10
975	65 p. Disabled person with crutches	30	35
976	80 p. Blind child reading braille	40	45
977	4 c. Disabled people helping one another	1·75	2·25

390 African Clawless Otter **391** "Precis westermanni"

1982. Flora and Fauna. Multicoloured.

979	20 p. Type **390**	25	15
980	65 p. Bushbuck	60	40
981	80 p. Aardvark	70	50
982	1 c. Scarlet bell tree	85	60
983	2 c. Glory-lilies	1·60	1·25
984	4 c. Blue-pea	2·75	2·25

1982. Butterflies. Multicoloured.

986	20 p. Type **391**	70	15
987	65 p. "Papilio menestheus"	1·50	1·00
988	2 c. "Antanartia delius"	2·50	3·50
989	4 c. "Charaxes castor"	4·00	4·75

392 Scouts planting Tree

1982. 75th Anniv of Boy Scout Movement. Multicoloured.

991	20 p. Type **392**	25	15
992	65 p. Scouts cooking on campfire	70	65
993	80 p. Sea Scouts sailing	90	85
994	3 c. Scouts observing African elephant	2·25	3·25

393 Initial Stages of Construction

1982. Kpong Hydro-Electric Project. Multicoloured.

996	20 p. Type **393**	65	10
997	65 p. Truck removing rubble	1·40	45
998	80 p. Hydro-electric turbines	1·60	65
999	2 c. Aerial view of completed plant	3·00	1·60

394 Footballers

1982. World Cup Football Championship, Spain.

1000 **394**	20 p. multicoloured	20	10
1005	30 p. multicoloured	20	20
1001 –	65 p. multicoloured	45	35
1002 –	80 p. multicoloured (Heading)	60	45
1006 –	80 p. multicoloured (Three footballers)	35	45
1007 –	1 c. multicoloured	40	55
1008 –	3 c. multicoloured	1·00	1·60
1003 –	4 c. multicoloured	1·50	2·00

DESIGNS: 65 p. to 4 c. Scenes showing footballers.

395 The Fight against Tuberculosis

1982. Centenary of Robert Koch's Discovery of Tubercle Bacillus. Multicoloured.

1009	20 p. Type **395**	70	20
1010	65 p. Robert Koch	1·60	1·25
1011	80 p. Robert Koch in Africa	2·00	1·75
1012	1 c. Centenary of discovery of Tuberculosis	2·25	2·75
1013	2 c. Robert Koch and Nobel Prize, 1905	3·25	4·00

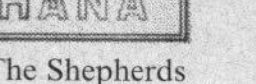

396 The Shepherds worship Jesus **397** Ghana and Commonwealth Flags with Coat of Arms

1982. Christmas. Multicoloured.

1014	15 p. Type **396**	10	10
1015	20 p. Mary, Joseph and baby Jesus	10	10
1016	65 p. The Three Kings sight star	25	30
1017	4 c. Winged Angel	1·00	1·75

1983. Commonwealth Day. Multicoloured.

1019	20 p. Type **397**	25	15
1020	55 p. Satellite view of Ghana	45	65
1021	80 p. Minerals of Ghana	1·00	1·25
1022	3 c. African fish eagle	1·50	4·25

1983. Italy's Victory in World Cup Football Championships (1982). Nos. 1000/8 optd **WINNER ITALY 3-1.**

1023	20 p. multicoloured	15	10
1028	30 p. multicoloured	20	40
1024	65 p. multicoloured	25	15
1025	80 p. multicoloured	25	20
1029	80 p. multicoloured	60	1·00
1030	1 c. multicoloured	70	1·10
1031	3 c. multicoloured	1·50	2·25
1026	4 c. multicoloured	1·40	1·75

1983. No. 470 surch **C1.**

1031a	1 c. on 20 n.p. Bush hare (blue)	40	40

399 Short-finned Pilot Whale

1983. Coastal Marine Mammals. Multicoloured.

1032	1 c. Type **399**	1·00	1·00
1033	1 c. 40 Risso's dolphin	1·10	1·10
1034	2 c. False killer whale	1·25	1·25
1035	3 c. Spinner dolphin	1·60	1·60
1036	4 c. Atlantic hump-backed dolphin	2·00	2·00

400 Banded Jewelfish **401** Communication Devices

1983.

1038 **400**	5 p. multicoloured	30	20
1039 –	10 p. multicoloured	30	20
1040 –	20 p. multicoloured	40	20
1041 –	50 p. green, orange & blk	40	30
1042 –	1 c. orange, blue and black	50	20
1043 –	2 c. multicoloured	50	30
1044 –	3 c. multicoloured	90	30
1045 –	4 c. multicoloured	40	40
1046 –	5 c. multicoloured	50	40
1047 –	10 c. multicoloured	65	1·00

DESIGNS—HORIZ: 10 p. Banded jewelfish (different); 2 c. Jet airliner. VERT: 20 p. "Haemanthus rupestris"; 50 p. Mounted warrior; 1 c. Scorpion; 3 c. White-collared mangabey; 4 c. Demidoff's galago; 5 c. "Kaemferia nigerica"; 10 c. Grey-backed camaroptera.

1983. World Communications Year. Multicoloured.

1048	1 c. Type **401**	15	25
1049	1 c. 40 Satellite dish aerial	20	30
1050	2 c. 30 Cable and "Long Lines" (cable ship)	35	55
1051	3 c. Switchboard operators	40	65
1052	5 c. Aircraft cockpit and air traffic controllers	55	85

402 Children receiving Presents

1983. Christmas. Multicoloured.

1054	70 p. Type **402**	15	10
1055	1 c. Nativity and Star of Bethlehem (vert)	15	10

1056 1 c. 40 Children celebrating (vert) 25 55
1057 2 c. 30 Family praying together (vert) 35 1·00
1058 3 c. Dancing to bongo drum 45 1·25

403 Soldiers with Rifles

407 Cross and Crown of Thorns

1983. Namibia Day.
1060 **403** 50 p. green and black 10 10
1061 – 1 c. multicoloured 10 10
1062 – 1 c. 40 blue, lt blue & blk 15 15
1063 – 2 c. 30 multicoloured 20 25
1064 – 3 c. multicoloured 25 30
DESIGNS: 1 c. Soldiers supported by tank; 1 c. 40, Machete cutting chains; 2 c. 30, Peasant woman; 3 c. Soldiers and artillery support.

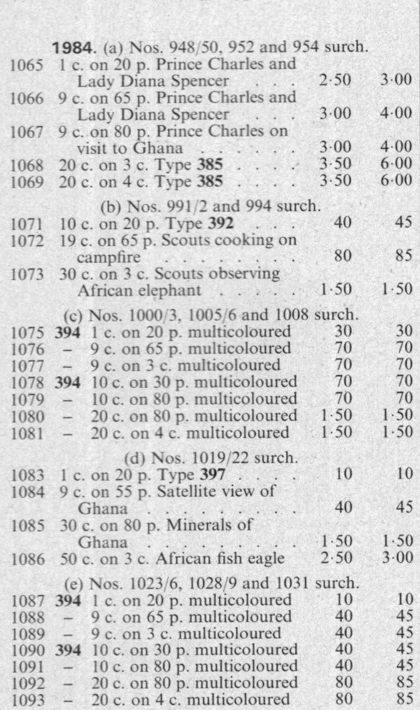

1984. (a) Nos. 948/50, 952 and 954 surch.
1065 1 c. on 20 p. Prince Charles and Lady Diana Spencer 2·50 3·00
1066 9 c. on 65 p. Prince Charles and Lady Diana Spencer 3·00 4·00
1067 9 c. on 80 p. Prince Charles on visit to Ghana 3·00 4·00
1068 20 c. on 3 c. Type **385** 3·50 6·00
1069 20 c. on 4 c. Type **385** 3·50 6·00

(b) Nos. 991/2 and 994 surch.
1071 10 c. on 20 p. Type **392** 40 45
1072 19 c. on 65 p. Scouts cooking on campfire 80 85
1073 30 c. on 3 c. Scouts observing African elephant 1·50 1·50

(c) Nos. 1000/3, 1005/6 and 1008 surch.
1075 **394** 1 c. on 20 p. multicoloured 30 30
1076 – 9 c. on 65 p. multicoloured 70 70
1077 – 9 c. on 3 c. multicoloured 70 70
1078 **394** 10 c. on 30 p. multicoloured 70 70
1079 – 10 c. on 80 p. multicoloured 70 70
1080 – 20 c. on 80 p. multicoloured 1·50 1·50
1081 – 20 c. on 4 c. multicoloured 1·50 1·50

(d) Nos. 1019/22 surch.
1083 1 c. on 20 p. Type **397** 10 10
1084 9 c. on 55 p. Satellite view of Ghana 40 45
1085 30 c. on 80 p. Minerals of Ghana 1·50 1·50
1086 50 c. on 3 c. African fish eagle 2·50 3·00

(e) Nos. 1023/6, 1028/9 and 1031 surch.
1087 **394** 1 c. on 20 p. multicoloured 10 10
1088 – 9 c. on 65 p. multicoloured 40 45
1089 – 9 c. on 3 c. multicoloured 40 45
1090 **394** 10 c. on 30 p. multicoloured 40 45
1091 – 10 c. on 80 p. multicoloured 40 45
1092 – 20 c. on 80 p. multicoloured 80 85
1093 – 20 c. on 4 c. multicoloured 80 85

1984. Universal Postal Union Congress, Hamburg. Nos. 1035/6 surch **19th U.P.U. CONGRESS – HAMBURG**, emblem and new value.
1095 10 c. on 3 c. Spinner dolphin 40 45
1096 50 c. on 5 c. Atlantic humpbacked dolphin 2·10 2·25

1984. Easter. Multicoloured.
1098 1 c. Type **407** 10 10
1099 1 c. 40 Christ praying 10 10
1100 2 c. 30 The Resurrection 10 10
1101 3 c. Palm Sunday 10 15
1102 50 c. Christ on the road to Emmaus 1·10 2·25

408 Women's 400 Metre Race

409 "Amorphophallus johnsonii"

1984. Olympic Games, Los Angeles. Multicoloured.
1104 1 c. Type **408** 10 10
1105 1 c. 40 Boxing 15 10
1106 2 c. 30 Hockey 20 15
1107 3 c. Men's 400 metre hurdles race 20 15
1108 50 c. Rhythmic gymnastics 1·75 3·50

1984. Flowers. Multicoloured.
1110 1 c. Type **409** 10 10
1111 1 c. 40 "Pancratium trianthum" 10 10
1112 2 c. 30 "Eulophia cucullata" 15 15
1113 3 c. "Amorphophallus abyssinicus" 15 15
1114 50 c. "Chlorophytum togoense" 2·50 5·00

410 Young Bongo

1984. Endangered Antelopes. Multicoloured.
1116 1 c. Type **410** 30 20
1117 2 c. 30 Bongo bucks fighting 55 55
1118 3 c. Bongo family 70 70
1119 20 c. Bongo herd in high grass 2·50 3·50

411 Dipo Girl

412 The Three Wise Men bringing Gifts

1984. Ghanaian Culture. Multicoloured.
1121 1 c. Type **411** 10 10
1122 1 c. 40 Adowa dancer 10 10
1123 2 c. 30 Agbadza dancer 10 15
1124 3 c. Damba dancer 10 15
1125 50 c. Dipo dancer 1·40 3·00

1984. Christmas. Multicoloured.
1127 70 p. Type **412** 10 10
1128 1 c. Choir of angels 10 10
1129 1 c. 40 Mary and shepherds at manger 10 10
1130 2 c. 30 The flight into Egypt 10 10
1131 3 c. Simeon blessing Jesus 10 15
1132 50 c. Holy Family and angels 1·40 3·00

1984. Olympic Winners. Nos. 1104/8 optd
1134 1 c. Type **408** (optd **VALERIE BRISCO-HOOKS U.S.A.**) 10 10
1135 1 c. 40 Boxing (optd **U.S. WINNERS**) 10 10
1136 2 c. 30 Hockey (optd **PAKISTAN (FIELD HOCKEY)**) 10 10
1137 3 c. Men's 400 metre hurdles race (optd **EDWIN MOSES U.S.A.**) 10 10
1138 50 c. Rhythmic gymnastics (optd **LAURI FUNG CANADA**) 1·50 1·60

414 The Queen Mother attending Church Service

415 Moslems going to Mosque

1985. Life and Times of Queen Elizabeth the Queen Mother. Multicoloured.
1140 5 c. Type **414** 10 15
1141 12 c. At Ascot Races 25 30
1142 100 c. At Clarence House on her 84th birthday 1·75 2·50
Stamps as Nos. 1140/2 but with face values of 8 c., 20 c. and 70 c. exist from additional sheetlets with changed background colours.

1985. Islamic Festival of Id-el-Fitr. Multicoloured.
1144 5 c. Type **415** 25 20
1145 8 c. Moslems at prayer 35 30
1146 12 c. Pilgrims visiting the Dome of the Rock 55 45
1147 18 c. Preaching the Koran 70 60
1148 50 c. Banda Nkwanta Mosque, Accra, and map of Ghana 1·75 1·60

416 Youths clearing Refuse ("Make Ghana Clean")

418 Fork-tailed Flycatcher

417 Honda "Interceptor", 1984

1985. International Youth Year. Multicoloured.
1149 5 c. Type **416** 10 10
1150 8 c. Planting sapling ("Make Ghana Green") 15 15
1151 12 c. Youth carrying bananas ("Feed Ghana") 20 25
1152 100 c. Open-air class ("Educate Ghana") 90 2·25

1985. Centenary of the Motorcycle. Multicoloured.
1154 5 c. Type **417** 55 55
1155 8 c. DKW, 1938 65 75
1156 12 c. BMW "R 32", 1923 1·00 1·00
1157 100 c. NSU, 1900 5·50 7·00

1985. Birth Bicentenary of John J. Audubon (ornithologist). Designs showing original paintings. Multicoloured.
1159 5 c. Type **418** 1·25 50
1160 8 c. Barred owl 2·25 2·00
1161 12 c. Black-throated mango 2·25 2·00
1162 100 c. White-crowned pigeon 6·50 9·50
No. 1159 is inscribed "York-tailed fly catcher" in error

419 United Nations Building, New York

1985. 40th Anniv of U.N.O. Multicoloured.
1164 5 c. Type **419** 10 10
1165 8 c. Flags of member nations and U.N. Building 10 15
1166 12 c. Dove with olive branch 10 25
1167 18 c. General Assembly 15 35
1168 100 c. Flags of Ghana and United Nations 90 1·75

420 Coffee

1985. 20th Anniv of United Nations Conference on Trade and Development. Designs showing export products. Multicoloured.
1170 5 c. Type **420** 10 10
1171 8 c. Cocoa 15 15
1172 12 c. Timber 25 25
1173 18 c. Bauxite 1·25 90
1174 100 c. Gold 6·50 8·50

421 Growth Monitoring

1985. U.N.I.C.E.F. Child Survival Campaign. Multicoloured.
1176 5 c. Type **421** 30 10
1177 8 c. Oral rehydration therapy 50 30
1178 12 c. Breast feeding 70 40
1179 100 c. Immunization 2·50 4·50

422 Airline Stewardess and Boys with Stamp Album

1986. "Ameripex" International Stamp Exhibition, Chicago. Multicoloured.
1181 5 c. Type **422** 15 15
1182 25 c. Globe and Douglas DC-10 airplane 60 45
1183 100 c. Ghana Airways stewardess (vert) 2·25 3·00

MINIMUM PRICE

The minimum price quoted is 10p which represents a handling charge rather than a basis for valuing common stamps. For further notes about prices see introductory pages.

423 Kejetia Roundabout, Kumasi

1986. "Inter-Tourism '86" Conference. Mult.
1185 5 c. Type **423** 10 10
1186 15 c. Fort St. Jago, Elmina 30 30
1187 25 c. Tribal warriors 45 45
1188 100 c. Chief holding audience 1·75 3·25

424 Tackling **425** Fertility Doll

1987. World Cup Football Championship, Mexico (1986). Multicoloured.
1190 5 c. Type **424** 20 10
1191 15 c. Player taking control of ball 30 15
1192 25 c. Player kicking ball 50 25
1193 100 c. Player with ball 1·50 1·25

1987. Ghanaian Fertility Dolls. Designs showing different dolls.
1195 **425** 5 c. multicoloured 10 10
1196 – 15 c. multicoloured 20 15
1197 – 25 c. multicoloured 35 25
1198 – 100 c. multicoloured 1·25 1·50

426 Children of Different Races, Peace Doves and Sun

1987. International Peace Year (1986). Multicoloured.
1200 5 c. Type **426** 15 10
1201 25 c. Plough, peace dove and rising sun 75 25
1202 100 c. Peace dove, olive branch and globe (vert) 2·50 3·00

427 Lumber and House under Construction

1987. "Gifex '87" International Forestry Exposition, Accra. Multicoloured.
1204 5 c. Type **427** 10 10
1205 15 c. Planks and furniture 15 15
1206 25 c. Felled trees 30 25
1207 200 c. Logs and wood carvings 1·90 2·25

1987. Appearance of Halley's Comet (1986). As T **151a** of Gambia. Multicoloured.
1208 5 c. Mikhail Lomonosov (scientist) and Chamber of Curiosities, St. Petersburg 20 10
1209 25 c. Lunar probe "Surveyor 3", 1966 70 30
1210 200 c. Wedgwood plaques for Isaac Newton, 1790 and "Apollo 11" Moon landing, 1968 3·25 2·25

428 Demonstrator and Arms breaking Shackles

1987. Solidarity with the People of Southern Africa. Multicoloured.
1212 5 c. Type **428** 10 10
1213 15 c. Miner and gold bars 40 15
1214 25 c. Xhosa warriors 30 25
1215 100 c. Nelson Mandela and shackles 1·25 2·00

429 Aerophones

1987. Musical Instruments. Multicoloured.
1217 5 c. Type **429** 10 10
1218 15 c. Xylophone 15 15
1219 25 c. Chordophones 30 25
1220 100 c. Membranophones . . . 1·00 1·25

430 Woman filling Water Pot at Pump

1987. Int Year of Shelter for the Homeless. Mult.
1222 5 c. Type **430** 10 10
1223 15 c. Building house from breeze blocks 15 15
1224 25 c. Modern village with stream 25 25
1225 100 c. Modern houses with verandahs . . . . 1·25 1·25

431 Ga Women preparing Kpokpoi for Homowo Festival

1988. Ghana Festivals. Multicoloured.
1226 5 c. Type **431** 10 10
1227 15 c. Efute hunters with deer, Aboakyir festival 15 15
1228 25 c. Fanti chief dancing at Odwira festival 25 25
1229 100 c. Chief in palanquin, Yam festival . . . . 90 1·25

432 Port Installation

1988. 5th Anniv (1987) of 31 December Revolution. Multicoloured.
1230 5 c. Type **432** . . . . 1·25 40
1231 15 c. Repairing railway line . . 9·00 2·25
1232 25 c. Planting cocoa . . . . . 1·75 55
1233 100 c. Miners with ore truck . . 10·00 10·00

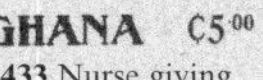

433 Nurse giving Injection

435 Akwadjan Men

434 Fishing

1988. U.N.I.C.E.F. Global Immunization Campaign. Multicoloured.
1234 5 c. Type **433** 20 10
1235 15 c. Girl receiving injection . 25 20
1236 25 c. Schoolgirl crippled by polio 35 50
1237 100 c. Nurse giving oral vaccine to baby . . . . 60 2·25

1988. 10th Anniv of International Fund for Agricultural Development. Multicoloured.
1238 5 c. Type **434** 55 20
1239 15 c. Women harvesting crops . 85 30
1240 25 c. Cattle . . . . 1·10 40
1241 100 c. Village granaries . . . 3·00 5·00

1988. Tribal Costumes. Multicoloured.
1242 5 c. Type **435** 15 10
1243 25 c. Banaa man 35 20
1244 250 c. Agwasen woman . . . 1·50 2·00

1988. Nos. 460, 464/6, 469/70, 1031a, 1038/42, 1044 and 1046 surch.
1245 – 20 c. on 50 p. green, orange and black (No. 1041) . 30 15
1246 – 20 c. on 1 c. orange, blue and black (No. 1042) . 30 15
1247 – 50 c. on 10 n.p. mult (No. 469) 30 25
1248 – 50 c. on 20 n.p. deep blue and blue (No. 470) (surch **C50**) . . . . . 3·00 45
1249 – 50 c. on 20 n.p. deep blue and blue (No. 470) (surch **C50.00**) . . . . 3·00 45
1250 – 50 c. on 10 p. mult (No. 1039) 30 15
1251 – 50 c. on 1 c. on 20 n.p. deep blue and blue (No. 1031a) (surch **C50**) . . . . . 3·00 45
1252 – 50 c. on 1 c. on 20 n.p. deep blue and blue (No. 1031a) (surch **C50.00**) . . . . 3·00 45
1254 – 50 c. on 1 c. orange, blue and black (No. 1042) . 3·00 45
1255 **230** 60 c. on 1 n.p. mult . . . 3·00 45
1256 – 60 c. on 4 n.p. mult (No. 465) . . . . . . 3·00 30
1257 – 60 c. on 3 c. mult (No. 1044) 50 30
1258 **400** 80 c. on 5 p. mult 55 35
1259 – 80 c. on 5 c. mult (No. 1046) 3·75 4·00
1260 – 100 c. on 3 n.p. mult (No. 464) . . . . . . 6·50 6·50
1261 – 100 c. on 20 n.p. deep blue and blue (No. 470) . . 50 55
1262 – 100 c. on 20 p. mult (No. 1040) 50 55
1263 – 100 c. on 3 c. mult (No. 1044) 50 55
1264 – 200 c. on 6 n.p. mult (No. 466) 50 65

440 Boxing

1988. Olympic Games, Seoul. Multicoloured.
1265 20 c. Type **440** 20 15
1266 60 c. Athletics 55 55
1267 80 c. Discus-throwing 60 80
1268 100 c. Javelin-throwing . . . 70 1·10
1269 350 c. Weightlifting . . . . . 1·75 3·00

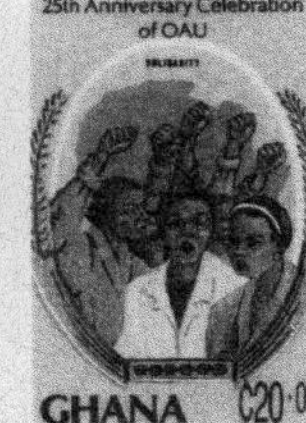

441 Nutrition Lecture

443 "African Solidarity"

442 Tropical Forest

1988. 125th Anniv of Int Red Cross. Mult.
1271 20 c. Type **441** 40 15
1272 50 c. Red Cross volunteer with blind woman 90 90
1273 60 c. Distributing flood relief supplies . . . . 1·00 1·00
1274 200 c. Giving first aid . . . . 2·50 3·25

1988. Christmas. Multicoloured.
1275 20 c. Type **442** 15 10
1276 60 c. Christ Child (vert) . . . 35 35
1277 80 c. Virgin and Child with Star (vert) 50 50
1278 100 c. Three Wise Men following Star 60 70
1279 350 c. Symbolic Crucifixion (vert) . . . . 2·00 2·50

1989. 25th Anniv (1988) of Organization of African Unity. Multicoloured.
1281 20 c. Type **443** 10 10
1282 50 c. O.A.U. Headquarters Addis Ababa 15 20
1283 60 c. Emperor Haile Selassie and Ethiopian flag (horiz) . . . 20 25
1284 200 c. Kwame Nkrumah (former Ghanaian President) and flag (horiz) 60 85

444 "Amor"

1989. 500th Birth Anniv of Titian (artist). Multicoloured.
1285 20 c. Type **444** 40 15
1286 60 c. "The Appeal" 80 65
1287 80 c. "Bacchus and Ariadne" (detail) 90 85
1288 100 c. "Portrait of a Musician" 1·00 1·60
1289 350 c. "Philip II seated" . . . 2·25 4·50

1989. Olympic Medal Winners, Seoul. Nos. 1251/5 optd.
1291 20 c. Type **436** (optd **A. ZUELOW DDR 60 KG**) . 15 10
1292 20 c. Athletics (optd **G. BORDIN ITALY MARATHON**) 25 25
1293 80 c. Discus-throwing (optd **J. SCHULT DDR**) 30 30
1294 100 c. Javelin-throwing (optd **T. KORJUS FINLAND**) . . 35 35
1295 350 c. Weightlifting (optd **B. GUIDIKOV BULGARIA 75 KG**) . . . . 1·25 1·10

1989. Various stamps surch. (a) Nos. 949/50 and 952/4
1297 80 c. on 65 p. Prince Charles and Lady Diana Spencer . . . 35 40
1298 100 c. on 80 p. Prince Charles on visit to Ghana 45 50
1299 100 c. on 1 c. Prince Charles on visit to Ghana 45 50
1300 300 c. on 3 c. Type **385** . . . 1·25 1·60
1301 500 c. on 4 c. Type **385** . . . 2·25 2·75

(b) Nos. 1048/51
1302 60 c. on 1 c. Type **401** 50 50
1303 80 c. on 1 c. 40 Satellite dish aerial 65 65
1304 200 c. on 2 c. 30 Cable and cable-laying ship . . . . 1·75 2·00
1305 300 c. on 3 c. Switchboard operators . . . . 2·00 2·25

(c) Nos. 1104/7
1307 60 c. on 1 c. Type **408** 30 30
1308 80 c. on 1 c. 40 Boxing . . . 40 40
1309 200 c. on 2 c. 30 Hockey . . . 1·25 1·60
1310 300 c. on 3 c. Men's 400 metre hurdles race . . . . 1·40 1·75

(d) Nos. 1134/7
1312 60 c. on 1 c. Type **408** (optd **VALERIE BRISCO-HOOKS U.S.A.**) 85 90
1313 80 c. on 1 c. 40 Boxing (optd **U.S. WINNERS**) . . . . . 1·10 1·25
1314 200 c. on 2 c. 30 Field hockey (optd **PAKISTAN (FIELD HOCKEY)**) . . . . 3·25 3·50
1315 300 c. on 3 c. Men's 400 metre hurdles race (optd **EDWIN MOSES U.S.A.**) . . . . . 3·50 3·75

(e) Nos. 1140/2
1317 80 c. on 5 c. Type **414** 35 40
1318 250 c. on 12 c. At Ascot Races 1·10 1·75
1319 300 c. on 100 c. At Clarence House on her 84th birthday 1·25 1·75

(f) Nos. 1159/61
1321 80 c. on 5 c. Type **418** . . . . 1·00 1·00
1322 100 c. on 8 c. Barred owl . . . 2·25 2·25
1323 300 c. on 12 c. Black-throated mango . . . . 2·50 3·00

(g) Nos. 1190/2
1325 60 c. on 5 c. Type **424** 45 45
1326 200 c. on 15 c. Player taking control of ball . . . . . . 1·50 2·00
1327 300 c. on 25 c. Player kicking ball . . . . 2·00 2·50

(h) As Nos. 1190/2 but with unissued opt **WINNERS Argentina 3 W. Germany 2**
1329 60 c. on 5 c. Type **424** 30 30
1330 200 c. on 15 c. Player taking control of ball . . . . . . 1·00 1·50
1331 300 c. on 25 c. Player kicking ball . . . . 1·40 2·00

(i) Nos. 1208/10
1333 60 c. on 5 c. Mikhail Lomonosov (scientist) and Chamber of Curiosities, St. Petersburg 65 55
1334 80 c. on 25 c. Lunar probe "Surveyor 3", 1966 . . . . 85 70
1335 500 c. on 200 c. Wedgwood plaques for Isaac Newton, 1790, and "Apollo 11" Moon landing, 1968 . . . . . . 3·25 4·50

(j) As Nos. 1208/10 optd **HALLEYS COMET 1985 – OFFICIAL – 1996** and emblem.
1337 60 c. on 5 c. Mikhail Lomonosov (scientist) and Chamber of Curiosities, St. Petersburg . 35 40
1338 80 c. on 25 c. Lunar probe "Surveyor 3", 1966 . . . . 45 50
1339 500 c. on 200 c. Wedgwood plaques for Isaac Newton, 1790, and "Apollo 11" Moon landing, 1968 . . . . . . 2·50 4·00

448 French Royal Standard and Field Gun

449 Storming the Bastille

1989. "Philexfrance 89" International Stamp Exhibition, Paris. Multicoloured.
1341 20 c. Type **448** 50 25
1342 60 c. Regimental standard, 1789, and French infantry- man . 1·00 90
1343 80 c. Revolutionary standard, 1789, and pistol . . . . . 1·25 1·00
1344 350 c. Tricolour, 1794, and musket . . . . 3·25 5·00

1989. Japanese Art. Portraits. As T **177a** of Gambia. Multicoloured.
1346 20 c. "Minamoto-no-Yoritomo" (Fujiwara-no-Takanobu) (vert) 25 20
1347 50 c. "Takami Senseki" (Watanabe Kazan) (vert) . . 35 30
1348 60 c. "Ikkyu Sojun" (study) (Bokusai) (vert) 40 35
1349 75 c. "Nakamura Kuranosuka" (Ogata Korin) (vert) . . . 45 40
1350 125 c. "Portrait of a Lady" (Kyoto branch, Kano School) (vert) 75 75
1351 150 c. "Portrait of Zemmui" (anon, 12th-century) (vert) . 80 80
1352 200 c. "Ono no Komachi the Poetess" (Hokusai) (vert) . 1·00 1·25
1353 500 c. "Kobo Daisi as a Child" (anon) (vert) . . . . 2·50 3·50

1989. Bicentenary of the French Revolution. Multicoloured.
1355 20 c. Type **449** 40 20
1356 60 c. Declaration of Human Rights 70 50
1357 80 c. Storming the Bastille (horiz) 90 75
1358 200 c. Revolution monument (horiz) . . . . 2·00 2·25
1359 350 c. Tree of Liberty (horiz) . . 2·75 3·50

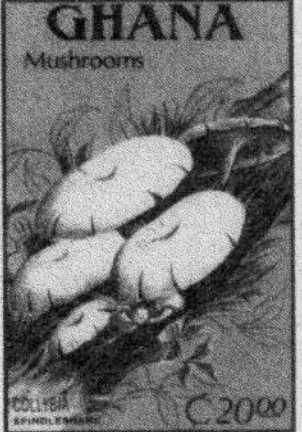

450 "Collybia fusipes"

451 "The Curse of True Love....."

1989. Fungi (1st series). Multicoloured.
1360 20 c. Type **450** 25 25
1361 50 c. "Coprinus comatus" . . 40 40
1362 60 c. "Xerocomus subtomentosus" 45 45
1363 80 c. "Lepista nuda" 55 55
1364 150 c. "Suillus placidus" . . . 95 95
1365 200 c. "Lepista nuda" (different) . . . . 1·25 1·25
1366 300 c. "Marasmius oreades" . 1·75 1·75
1367 500 c. "Agaricus campestris" . 3·00 3·00
See also Nos. 1489/96.

1989. 425th Birth Anniv of Shakespeare. Verses and scenes from "A Mid-summer Night's Dream". Multicoloured.
1369 40 c. Type **451** 65 65
1370 40 c. "Love looks not with the eye but with the mind" . . 65 65
1371 40 c. "Nature here shows art" 65 65
1372 40 c. "Things growing are not ripe till their season" . . . 65 65
1373 40 c. "He is defiled that draws a sword on thee" 65 65
1374 40 c. "It is not enough to speak, but to speak true" 65 65
1375 40 c. "Thou art as wise as thou are beautiful" 65 65
1376 40 c. Wildcat in wood (face value at left) 65 65
1377 40 c. Man 65 65
1378 40 c. Woman with flower . . . 65 65
1379 40 c. King and queen 65 65
1380 40 c. Bottom 65 65
1381 40 c. Wildcat in wood (face value at right) 65 65
1382 40 c. Woman 65 65
1383 40 c. Leopard 65 65
1384 40 c. Tree trunk and man . . . 65 65

1385 40 c. Meadow flowers 65 65
1386 40 c. Mauve flowers 65 65
1387 40 c. Plants 65 65
1388 40 c. Lion 65 65
1389 40 c. Fern and flowers 65 65

Nos. 1369/89 were printed together, forming a composite design.

451a Bronze Mannikin

1989. Birds. Multicoloured.

1390 20 c. Type **451a** 30 10
1391 50 c. African pied wagtail . . 45 30
1392 60 c. African pygmy kingfisher (inscr "Halcyon malimbicus") . . . . 1·25 1·75
1392a 60 c. African pygmy kingfisher (inscr "Ispidina picta") . . 2·00 2·00
1393 80 c. Blue-breasted kingfisher (inscr "Ispidina picta") . . 1·75 2·25
1393a 80 c. Blue-breasted kingfisher (inscr "Halcyon malimbicus") . . . . 2·00 2·50
1394 150 c. Striped kingfisher (vert) . . . . 1·10 1·25
1395 200 c. Shikra (vert) . . . . 1·25 1·40
1396 300 c. Grey parrot (vert) . . 1·50 1·75
1397 500 c. Black kite (vert) . . . 2·50 3·25

452 Command Module "Columbia" orbiting Moon

1989. 20th Anniv of First Manned Landing on Moon. Multicoloured.

1399 20 c. Type **452** 30 15
1400 80 c. Neil Armstrong's footprint on Moon 50 60
1401 200 c. Edwin Aldrin on Moon 1·25 1·75
1402 300 c. "Apollo 11" capsule on parachutes . . . . 1·60 2·00

453 Desertification of Pasture

1989. World Environment Day. Multicoloured.

1404 20 c. Type **453** 50 15
1405 60 c. Wildlife fleeing bush fire 90 80
1406 400 c. Industrial pollution . . 2·75 3·50
1407 500 c. Erosion . . . . 3·00 3·75

454 "Bebearia arcadius"

1990. Butterflies. Multicoloured.

1408 20 c. Type **454** 35 20
1409 60 c. "Charaxes laodice" . . . 50 40
1410 80 c. "Euryphura porphyrion" 60 45
1411 100 c. "Neptis nicomedes" . . 70 50
1412 150 c. "Citrinophila erastus" . . 90 90
1413 200 c. "Aethiopana honorius" . 1·25 1·25
1414 300 c. "Precis westermanni" . 1·50 1·75
1415 500 c. "Cymothoe hypatha" . 2·00 2·50

455 Great Ribbed Cockle

1990. Seashells. Multicoloured.

1417 20 c. Type **455** 60 25
1418 60 c. Elephant's snout 75 40
1419 80 c. Garter cone 85 80
1420 200 c. Tankerville's ancilla . . 2·25 2·50
1421 350 c. Coronate prickly-winkle . . . . 3·00 4·00

456 Nehru welcoming President Nkrumah of Ghana

1990. Birth Centenary of Jawaharlal Nehru (Indian statesman). Multicoloured.

1422 20 c. Type **456** 60 25
1423 60 c. Nehru addressing Bandung Conference, 1955 . . . . 75 30
1424 80 c. Nehru with garland and flowers (vert) 80 55
1425 200 c. Nehru releasing pigeon (vert) . . . . 1·25 1·50
1426 350 c. Nehru (vert) . . . . 1·75 2·75

457 Wyon Medal, 1838

1990. 150th Anniv of the Penny Black.

1427 **457** 20 c. black and violet . . 30 20
1428 – 60 c. black and green . . 55 30
1429 – 80 c. black and violet . . 70 35
1430 – 200 c. black and green . . 1·50 1·25
1431 – 350 c. black and green . . 2·00 2·50
1432 – 400 c. black and red . . . 2·00 2·50

DESIGNS: 60 c. Bath mail coach, 1840; 80 c. Leeds mail coach, 1840; 200 c. Proof of Queen's head engraved by Heath, 1840; 350 c. Master die, 1840; 400 c. London mail coach, 1840.

458 Anniversary Emblem

459 Map of Africa and Satellite Network

1990. 10th Anniv (1989) of 4 June Revolution. Multicoloured.

1434 20 c. Type **458** 15 15
1435 60 c. Foodstuffs 20 20
1436 80 c. Cocoa 25 30
1437 200 c. Mining . . . . 1·50 1·75
1438 350 c. Scales of Justice and sword . . . . 1·75 2·25

1990. 25th Anniv of Intelsat Satellite System. Multicoloured.

1439 20 c. Type **459** 20 20
1440 60 c. Map of Americas . . . 30 30
1441 80 c. Map of Asia and Pacific 35 35
1442 200 c. Map of South America and Africa . . . . 90 1·00
1443 350 c. Map of Indian Ocean and Pacific . . . . 1·50 2·00

460 Housewife using Telephone

1990. 2nd Anniv of Introduction of International Direct Dialling Service. Multicoloured.

1444 20 c. Type **460** 25 20
1445 60 c. Businessman using telephone 35 35
1446 80 c. Man using phonecard telephone 40 40
1447 200 c. Public telephones for internal and IDD services . 90 1·00
1448 350 c. Satellite station . . . . 1·50 2·00

461 Blue Flycatcher

463 "Eulophia guineensis"

462 Jupiter

1990. African Tropical Rain Forest. Multicoloured.

1449 40 c. Type **461** 60 65
1450 40 c. Boomslang (snake) . . . 60 65
1451 40 c. Superb sunbird 60 65
1452 40 c. Bateleur 60 65
1453 40 c. Yellow-casqued hornbill 60 65
1454 40 c. "Salamis temora" (butterfly) 60 65
1455 40 c. Potto 60 65
1456 40 c. Leopard 60 65
1457 40 c. Bongo 60 65
1458 40 c. Grey parrot 60 65
1459 40 c. Okapi 60 65
1460 40 c. Gorilla 60 65
1461 40 c. Flap-necked chameleon . 60 65
1462 40 c. West African dwarf crocodile 60 65
1463 40 c. Python 60 65
1464 40 c. Giant ground pangolin . 60 65
1465 40 c. "Pseudacraea boisduvali" (butterfly) 60 65
1466 40 c. North African crested porcupine 60 65
1467 40 c. Rosy-columned aerangis (orchid) 60 65
1468 40 c. "Cymothoe sangaris" (butterfly) 60 65

Nos. 1449/68 were printed together, se-tenant, forming a composite design.

1990. Space Flight of "Voyager 2". Multicoloured.

1470 100 c. Type **462** 70 70
1471 100 c. Neptune and Triton . . 70 70
1472 100 c. Ariel, moon of Uranus 70 70
1473 100 c. Saturn from Mimas . . 70 70
1474 100 c. Saturn 70 70
1475 100 c. Rings of Saturn 70 70
1476 100 c. Neptune 70 70
1477 100 c. Uranus from Miranda 70 70
1478 100 c. Volcano on Io 70 70

1990. Orchids. Multicoloured.

1480 20 c. Type **463** 45 45
1481 40 c. "Eurychone rothschildiana" 60 60
1482 60 c. "Bulbophyllum barbigerum" 80 80
1483 80 c. "Polystachya galeata" . . 1·10 1·10
1484 200 c. "Diaphananthe kamerunensis" . . . . 1·75 1·75
1485 300 c. "Podangis dactyloceras" . . . . 2·00 2·00
1486 400 c. "Ancistrochilus rothschildianus" . . . . 2·00 2·00
1487 500 c. "Rangaeris muscicola" . 2·00 2·00

464 "Coprinus atramentarius"

1990. Fungi (2nd series). Multicoloured.

1489 20 c. Type **464** 70 45
1490 50 c. "Marasmius oreades" . . 90 65
1491 60 c. "Oudemansiella radicata" 1·00 70
1492 80 c. "Boletus edulis" (Cep) . 1·25 90
1493 150 c. "Hebeloma crustuliniforme" . . . . 1·75 1·50
1494 200 c. "Coprinus micaceus" . 2·00 2·00
1495 300 c. "Macrolepiota procera" ("Lepiota procera") . . . . 2·25 2·50
1496 500 c. "Amanita phalloides" . 2·50 3·00

465 Italian and Swedish Players chasing Ball

1990. World Cup Football Championship, Italy. Multicoloured.

1498 20 c. Type **465** 45 20
1499 50 c. Egyptian player penetrating Irish defence . . 55 30
1500 60 c. Cameroon players celebrating 60 30
1501 80 c. Rumanian player beating challenge 70 40
1502 100 c. Russian goalkeeper Dassayev 85 65
1503 150 c. Roger Milla of Cameroon (vert) . . . . 1·40 1·10
1504 400 c. South Korean player challenging opponent . . . 2·25 2·50
1505 600 c. Klinsman of West Germany celebrating . . . 2·75 3·50

1990. 350th Death Anniv of Rubens. As T **195c** of Gambia, but vert. Multicoloured.

1507 20 c. "Duke of Mantua" . . . 30 20
1508 50 c. "Jan Brant" 40 30
1509 60 c. "Portraits of a Young Man" 40 30
1510 80 c. "Michel Ophovius" . . . 55 40
1511 100 c. "Caspar Gevaerts" . . 65 55
1512 200 c. "Head of Warrior" (detail) . . . . 1·00 1·25
1513 300 c. "Study of a Bearded Man" . . . . 1·50 1·75
1514 400 c. "Paracelsus" . . . . 1·90 2·50

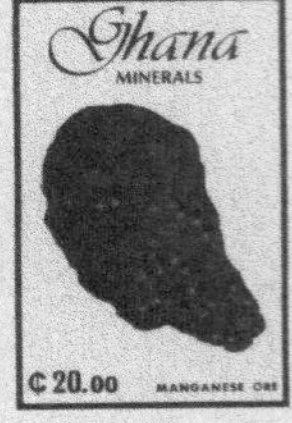

466 Manganese Ore

467 Dance Drums

1991. Minerals. Multicoloured.

1516 20 c. Type **466** 55 30
1517 60 c. Iron ore 70 60
1518 80 c. Bauxite ore 90 75
1519 200 c. Gold ore . . . . 2·00 2·00
1520 350 c. Diamond . . . . 3·00 4·00

1991. Tribal Drums. Multicoloured.

1522 20 c. Type **467** 20 20
1523 60 c. Message drums 50 40
1524 80 c. War drums 60 50
1525 200 c. Dance drums (different) 1·50 1·75
1526 350 c. Ceremonial drums . . . 2·00 3·00

468 "Amorphophallus dracontioides"

469 Transport and Telecommunication Symbols

1991. Flowers (1st series). Multicoloured.

1528 20 c. Type **468** 65 25
1529 60 c. "Anchomanes difformis" 85 50
1530 80 c. "Kaemferia nigerica" . . 1·00 70
1531 200 c. "Aframomum sceptrum" 2·00 2·50
1532 350 c. "Amorphophallus flavovirens" . . . . 2·50 3·50

1991. Flowers (2nd series). As T **468** but inscr "GHANA" in capitals. Multicoloured.

1534 20 c. "Urginea indica" 45 25
1535 60 c. "Hymencallis littoralis" . 85 50
1536 80 c. "Crinum jagus" . . . . 1·50 70
1537 200 c. "Dipcadi tacazzeanum" 2·00 2·50
1538 350 c. "Haemanthus rupestris" 2·50 3·25

1991. 40th Anniv of United Nations Development Programme. Multicoloured.

1540 20 c. Type **469** 30 20
1541 60 c. Agricultural research . . 50 40
1542 80 c. Literacy 60 55
1543 200 c. Advances in agricultural crop growth . . . . 1·40 1·60
1544 350 c. Industrial symbols . . . 1·90 2·75

470 Drawing of Scout from First Handbook

471 Women sorting Fish

1991. 50th Death Anniv of Lord Baden-Powell.

1545 **470** 20 c. black and buff . . . 50 20
1546 – 50 c. grey, blue and black 70 40
1547 – 60 c. multicoloured . . . 70 45
1548 – 80 c. black and buff . . . 80 55
1549 – 100 c. multicoloured . . . 1·10 75
1550 – 200 c. multicoloured . . . 1·75 1·75
1551 – 500 c. multicoloured . . . 2·50 3·25
1552 – 600 c. multicoloured . . . 3·00 4·00

DESIGNS—VERT: 50 c. Lord Baden-Powell; 80 c. Handbook illustrations by Norman Rockwell; 500 c. Scout at prayer. HORIZ: 60 c. Hands holding Boy Scout emblem; 100 c. Mafeking Siege 1d. Goodyear stamp and African runner; 200 c. Scouts with Blitz victim, London, 1944; 600 c. Mafeking Siege 1d. Goodyear stamp.

1991. Chorkor Smoker (fish smoking process). Multicoloured.

1554 20 c. Type **471** 30 20
1555 60 c. Cleaning the ovens . . . 55 40
1556 80 c. Washing fish 65 55
1557 200 c. Laying fish on pallets . 1·25 1·50
1558 350 c. Stacking pallets over ovens . . . . 1·75 2·50

472 African Hind

1991. Fishes. Multicoloured.
1559 20 c. Type **472** 25 25
1560 50 c. Shrew squeaker 40 40
1561 80 c. West African triggerfish . 55 55
1562 100 c. Stonehead 70 70
1563 200 c. Lesser pipefish . . . . 1·50 1·50
1564 300 c. Aba . . . . 1·60 1·60
1565 400 c. Jewel cichlid . . . . . 1·75 1·75
1566 500 c. Smooth hammerhead . 1·90 1·90

1991. Death Centenary (1990) of Vincent van Gogh (artist). As T **200b** of Gambia. Multicoloured.
1568 20 c. "Reaper with Sickle" . . 35 25
1569 50 c. "The Thresher" 55 40
1570 60 c. "The Sheaf-Binder" . . 60 50
1571 80 c. "The Sheep-Shearers" . . 70 65
1572 100 c. "Peasant Woman cutting Straw" 85 80
1573 200 c. "The Sower" . . . . . 1·60 1·75
1574 500 c. "The Plough and the Harrow" (horiz) . . . . 2·25 2·50
1575 600 c. "The Woodcutter" . . 2·25 2·50

473 Gamal Nasser (Egypt) and Conference Hall

1991. 10th Non-Aligned Ministers' Conference, Accra. Statesmen. Multicoloured.
1577 20 c. Type **473** 50 30
1578 60 c. Josip Tito (Yugoslavia) . 55 45
1579 80 c. Pandit Nehru (India) . . 1·75 1·25
1580 200 c. Kwame Nkrumah (Ghana) . . . . 1·75 2·25
1581 350 c. Achmad Sukarno (Indonesia) . . . . 1·90 3·00

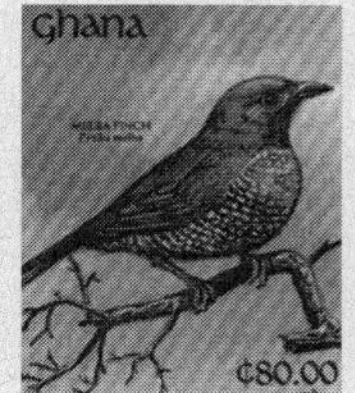

474 Green-winged Pytilia

1991. Birds. As T **474**. Multicoloured.
1582/1629 80 c. × 16, 100 c. × 32 Set of 48 22·00 25·00

Nos. 1582/1629 were issued together, se-tenant, as three sheetlets of 16 forming composite designs. The 80 c. values show Green-winged pytilia, Orange-cheeked waxbill, African paradise flycatcher, Great blue turaco ("Blue plantain-eater"), Red bishop, Splendid glossy starling, Red-faced lovebird, African palm swift, Narina trogon, Tawny eagle, Bateleur, Hoopoe, Secretary bird, African white-backed vulture, White-necked bald crow ("Bare-headed rockfowl"), Abyssinian ground hornbill, and the 100 c. African open-bill stork, African spoonbill, Pink-backed pelican, Little bittern, Purple swamphen ("King reed-hen"), Saddle-bill stork, Glossy ibis, White-faced whistling duck, Black-headed heron, Hammerkop, African darter, Woolly-necked stork, Yellow-billed stork, Black-winged stilt, Goliath heron, African jacana ("Lily trotter"), Shikra, Abyssinian roller, Carmine bee eater, Pin-tailed whydah, Purple glossy starling, Yellow-mantled whydah, Pel's fishing owl, Crested touraco, Red-cheeked cordon-bleu, Olive-bellied sunbird, Red-billed hornbill, Red-billed quelea, South African crowned crane, Blue quail, Egyptian vulture and Helmet guineafowl.

475 "Nularda" (beetle)

476 Boti Falls

1991. Insects. Multicoloured.
1631 20 c. Type **475** 50 20
1632 50 c. "Zonocrus" (grasshopper) 65 30
1633 60 c. "Gryllotalpa africana" (mole cricket) 70 30
1634 80 c. Weevil 80 60
1635 100 c. "Coenagrion" (dragonfly) 90 70
1636 150 c. "Sahlbergella" (fly) . . 1·25 1·60
1637 200 c. "Anthia" (ant) . . . . 1·40 1·75
1638 350 c. "Megacephala" (beetle) 2·00 2·75

1991. Multicoloured.
1639a 20 c. Oil palm fruit 10 10
1640 50 c. Type **476** 20 10
1641 60 c. Larabanga Mosque (horiz) 10 10
1642 80 c. Fort Sebastian, Shama (horiz) 10 10
1643 100 c. Cape Coast Castle (horiz) 20 20
1644 200 c. White-toothed cowrie (horiz) 60 30
1645 400 c. True achatina (horiz) . 1·00 55

1991. Christmas. Religious Paintings. As T **200c** of Gambia. Multicoloured.
1646 20 c. "Adoration of the Magi" (Bosch) 35 20
1647 50 c. "The Annunciation" (Campin) 50 30
1648 60 c. "Virgin and Child" (detail) (Bouts) 55 30
1649 80 c. "Presentation in the Temple" (Memling) 65 50
1650 100 c. "Virgin and Child enthroned with Angel and Donor" (Memling) 85 65
1651 200 c. "Virgin and Child with Saints and Donor" (Van Eyck) . . . . 1·50 1·75
1652 400 c. "St. Luke painting the Virgin" (Van der Weyden) . 2·50 3·00
1653 700 c. "Virgin and Child" (Bouts) . . . . 3·50 4·50

477 Women collecting Water from Bore Hole

1992. Decade of Revolutionary Progress. Multicoloured.
1655 20 c. Type **477** 15 10
1656 50 c. Miners 20 15
1657 60 c. Wood carver 20 15
1658 80 c. Forestry 25 20
1659 200 c. Cacao tree 50 75
1660 350 c. Village electrification . . 75 1·00

478 Mount Fuji and Flying Fish

1992. "Phila Nippon '91" International Stamp Exhibition, Tokyo. Multicoloured.
1661 20 c. Type **478** 35 30
1662 60 c. Itsukushima Jingu Shrine 45 40
1663 80 c. Geisha 60 50
1664 100 c. Samurai house 80 70
1665 200 c. Bonsai tree . . . . . 1·50 1·50
1666 400 c. Olympic Sports Hall . 2·00 2·25
1667 500 c. Great Buddha (statue) . 2·25 2·50
1668 600 c. Nagoya Castle . . . . 2·40 2·75

479 East and West Germans celebrating

1992. Reunification of Germany. Multicoloured.
1670 20 c. Type **479** 30 20
1671 60 c. Signing Reunification Treaty 40 40
1672 80 c. Chariot on Brandenburg Gate and fireworks 45 45
1673 1000 c. Germans with unified currency . . . . 6·00 8·00

480 Steam Side-tank Locomotive, 1903

1992. Ghanaian Railways. Multicoloured.
1675 20 c. Type **480** 40 30
1676 50 c. AIA-AIA diesel locomotive 60 40
1677 60 c. First class coach, 1931 . 60 45
1678 80 c. Railway inspection coach No. 2212 . . . . . 70 70
1679 100 c. Steam locomotive No. 401 on Kumasi turntable . . . 90 90
1680 200 c. Cocoa wagon, 1921 . . 1·40 1·50
1681 500 c. Steam locomotive No. 223 "Prince of Wales" . . . 2·25 2·75
1682 600 c. Cattle wagon . . . . . 2·25 2·75

1992. Olympic Games, Albertville and Barcelona. Past Medal Winners. As T **203** of Gambia. Mutlcoloured.
1684 20 c. E. Blay (Ghana) (boxing) and windmill 30 20
1685 60 c. M. Ahey (Ghana) (athletics) and Catalan coat of arms 50 35
1686 80 c. T. Wilson (U.S.A.) (70 metres ski jump) and grapes . 70 50
1687 100 c. Four-man bobsleighing (East Germany) and passport 85 75
1688 200 c. G. Louganis (U.S.A.) (platform diving) and decorative vase . . . . . . 1·50 1·25
1689 300 c. L. Visser (Netherlands) (5000 metres speed skating) and wine bottle cork . . . 1·75 1·75
1690 350 c. J. Passler (Italy) (biathlon) and lily . . . . 1·90 2·00
1691 400 c. M. Retton (U.S.A.) (gymnastics) and silhouette of castle . . . . 2·00 2·25
1692 500 c. J. Hingsen (West Germany) (decathlon) and gold and silver coins . . . 2·00 2·25
1693 600 c. R. Neubert (West Germany) (heptathlon) and leather work . . . . 2·00 2·25

481 "Angides lugubris"

1992. Reptiles. Multicoloured.
1695 20 c. Type **481** 20 20
1696 50 c. "Kinixys erosa" (tortoise) 30 30
1697 60 c. "Agama agama" (lizard) . 30 30
1698 80 c. "Chameleo gracilis" (chameleon) 40 40
1699 100 c. "Naja melanleuca" (snake) 50 50
1700 200 c. "Crocodylus niloticus" (crocodile) . . . . 90 1·10
1701 400 c. "Chelonia mydas" (turtle) . . . . 1·75 2·25
1702 500 c. "Varanus exanthematicus" (lizard) . . 1·90 2·50

1992. Easter. Religious Paintings. As T **204a** of Gambia but vert designs. Multicoloured.
1704 20 c. "The Four Apostles" (detail) (Durer) 25 20
1705 50 c. "The Last Judgement" (detail) (Rubens) 35 30
1706 60 c. "The Four Apostles" (different detail) (Durer) . . 35 30
1707 80 c. "The Last Judgement" (different detail) (Rubens) . 50 40
1708 100 c. "Crucifixion" (Rubens) . 60 50
1709 200 c. "The Last Judgement" (different detail) (Rubens) . 1·10 1·25
1710 500 c. "Christum Videre" (Rubens) . . . . 2·00 2·50
1711 600 c. "The Last Judgement" (different detail) (Rubens) . 2·25 2·75

481a "Two Men at Table" (Velazquez)

1992. "Granada '92" International Stamp Exhibition, Spain. Spanish Paintings. Mult.
1713 20 c. Type **481a** 20 20
1714 60 c. "Christ in the House of Mary and Martha" (detail) (Velazquez) 30 30
1715 80 c. "The Supper at Emmaus" (Velazquez) 40 40
1716 100 c. "Three Musicians" (Velazquez) 50 50
1717 200 c. "Old Woman cooking Eggs" (Velazquez) (vert) . . 90 90
1718 400 c. "Old Woman cooking Eggs" (detail) (Velazquez) (vert) . . . . 1·60 1·75
1719 500 c. "The Surrender of Breda" (detail) (Velazquez) (vert) . 1·75 1·90
1720 700 c. "The Surrender of Breda" (different detail) (Velazquez) (vert) . . . . 2·00 2·50

482 "Danaus chrysippus"

483 Martin Pinzon and "Pinta"

1992. "Genova '92" International Thematic Stamp Exhibition. Butterflies. Mult.
1722 20 c. Type **482** 50 30
1723 60 c. "Papilio dardanus" . . . 80 45
1724 80 c. "Cynthia cardui" 90 60
1725 100 c. "Meneris tulbaghia" . . 1·00 75
1726 200 c. "Salamis temora" . . . 1·50 1·60
1727 400 c. "Charaxes jasius" . . . 2·00 2·50
1728 500 c. "Precis oenone" . . . . 2·25 2·50
1729 700 c. "Precis sophia" . . . . 2·50 2·75

1992. Prehistoric Animals. As T **207a** of Gambia. Multicoloured.
1731 20 c. Iguanodon 35 25
1732 50 c. Anchisaurus 50 35
1733 60 c. Heterodontosaurus . . . 55 35
1734 80 c. Ouranosaurus 60 45
1735 100 c. Anatosaurus 75 55
1736 200 c. Elaphrosaurus . . . . 1·25 1·50
1737 500 c. Coelophysis . . . . . 2·25 2·75
1738 600 c. Rhamphorynchus . . . 2·50 3·00

1992. World Columbian Stamp "Expo '92", Chicago. 500th Anniv of Discovery of America by Columbus. Multicoloured.
1740 200 c. Type **483** . . . . . . 90 1·00
1741 200 c. Vincente Pinzon and "Nina" . . . . 90 1·00
1742 200 c. Columbus and Father Marchena at La Rabida . . 90 1·00
1743 200 c. Columbus in his cabin . 90 1·00
1744 200 c. Fleet sights land . . . 90 1·00
1745 200 c. Columbus on Samana Cay . . . . 90 1·00
1746 200 c. Wreck of "Santa Maria" . . . . 90 1·00
1747 200 c. Amerindians at Spanish Court . . . . 90 1·00

484 Olive-grey Ancilla

485 "Presentation in the Temple" (Master of the Braunschweiti)

1992. Shells. Multicoloured.
1749 20 c. Type **484** 20 20
1750 20 c. Radula cerith 20 20
1751 60 c. Rugose donex 30 30
1752 60 c. Horned murex 30 30
1753 80 c. Concave ear moon . . . 40 40
1754 80 c. Triple twella 40 40
1755 200 c. "Pila africana" . . . . 90 1·00
1756 200 c. Rat cowrie . . . . . . 90 1·00
1757 350 c. "Thais hiatula" . . . . 1·60 1·90
1758 350 c. West African helmet . . 1·60 1·90

1992. Christmas. Religious Paintings. Mult.
1760 20 c. Type **485** 25 20
1761 50 c. "Presentation in the Temple" (detail) (Master of St. Severin) 35 30
1762 60 c. "The Visitation" (Sebastiano del Piombo) . . 35 30
1763 80 c. "The Visitation" (detail) (Giotto) 45 40
1764 100 c. "The Circumcision" (detail) (Studio of Bellini) . 55 50
1765 200 c. "The Circumcision" (Studio of Garofalo) . . . 1·10 1·10
1766 500 c. "The Visitation" (Studio of Van der Weyden) . . . 1·90 2·25
1767 800 c. "The Visitation" (detail) (Studio of Van der Weyden) . 2·40 3·00

486 "Calappa rubroguttata"

1993. Crabs. Multicoloured.
1769 20 c. Type **486** 40 20
1770 60 c. "Cardisoma amatum" . . 70 25
1771 80 c. "Maia squinado" . . . 80 30
1772 400 c. "Ocypoda cursor" . . . 1·40 1·75
1773 800 c. "Grapus grapus" . . . 2·25 3·00

487 "Clerodendrum thomsoniae"

1993. Flowers. Multicoloured.

1775	20 c. Type **487**	20	15
1776	20 c. "Lagerstroemia flos-reginae"	20	15
1777	60 c. "Cassia fistula"	35	25
1778	60 c. "Spathodea campanulata"	35	25
1779	80 c. "Hildegardia barteri"	40	25
1780	80 c. "Mellitea ferrugenea"	40	25
1781	200 c. "Petrea volubilis"	60	85
1782	200 c. "Ipomoea asarifolia"	60	85
1783	350 c. "Bryphyllum pinnatum"	90	1·25
1784	350 c. "Ritchiea reflexa"	90	1·25

488 Zeppelin "LZ-3" entering Floating Hangar, Lake Constance

1993. Anniversaries and Events. Multicoloured.

1786	20 c. Type **488**	60	30
1787	100 c. Launch of European "Ariane 4" rocket (vert)	1·00	75
1788	200 c. Leopard	1·75	1·75
1789	300 c. Colosseum and fruit	1·90	2·00
1790	400 c. Mozart (vert)	2·50	2·50
1791	600 c. Launch of Japanese "H-1" rocket (vert)	2·75	3·25
1792	800 c. Zeppelin "LZ-10" "Schwaben"	3·00	3·50

ANNIVERSARIES AND EVENTS: Nos. 1786, 1792, 75th death anniv of Count Ferdinand von Zeppelin; Nos. 1787, 1791, International Space Year; No. 1788, Earth Summit '92, Rio; No. 1789, International Conference on Nutrition, Rome; No. 1790, Death bicentenary of Mozart.

1993. Bicentenary of the Louvre, Paris. As T **209b** of Gambia. Multicoloured.

1794	200 c. "Carnival Minuet" (left detail) (Giovanni Domenico Tiepolo)	85	1·00
1795	200 c. "Carnival Minuet" (centre detail) (Giovanni Domenico Tiepolo)	85	1·00
1796	200 c. "Carnival Minuet" (right detail) (Giovanni Domenico Tiepolo)	85	1·00
1797	200 c. "The Tooth Puller" (left detail) (Giovanni Domenico Tiepolo)	85	1·00
1798	200 c. "The Tooth Puller" (right detail) (Giovanni Domenico Tiepolo)	85	1·00
1799	200 c. "Rebecca at the Well" (Giovanni Battista Tiepolo)	85	1·00
1800	200 c. "Presenting Christ to the People" (left detail) (Giovanni Battista Tiepolo)	85	1·00
1801	200 c. "Presenting Christ to the People" (right detail) (Giovanni Battista Tiepolo)	85	1·00

489 Energy Foods

1993. Int Conference on Nutrition, Rome. Mult.

1803	20 c. Type **489**	20	15
1804	60 c. Body-building foods	30	20
1805	80 c. Protective foods	35	25
1806	200 c. Disease prevention equipment	80	1·00
1807	400 c. Quality control and preservation of fish products	1·50	2·00

490 Kwame Nkrumah Mausoleum

1993. Proclamation of 4th Republic. Mult.

1808	50 c. Type **490**	20	15
1809	100 c. Kwame Nkrumah Conference Centre	35	25
1810	200 c. Book of Constitution (vert)	80	80
1811	350 c. Independence Square (vert)	1·60	2·00
1812	400 c. Christiansborg Castle (vert)	1·75	2·00

491 Resurrection Egg

491b Airship "Graf Zeppelin" over Alps

491a Mercedes Benz "300 SLR", Mille Migla, 1955

1993. Easter. Faberge Eggs. Multicoloured.

1813	50 c. Type **491**	40	15
1814	80 c. Imperial Red Cross egg with Resurrection triptych	65	25
1815	100 c. Imperial Uspensky Cathedral egg	75	25
1816	150 c. Imperial Red Cross egg with portraits	1·10	65
1817	200 c. Orange Tree egg	1·25	1·25
1818	250 c. Rabbit egg	1·25	1·50
1819	400 c. Imperial Coronation egg	2·00	2·50
1820	900 c. Silver-gilt enamel Easter egg	3·25	5·00

1993. Centenaries of Henry Ford's First Petrol Engine (Nos. 1823/4) and Karl Benz's First Four-wheeled Car (others). Multicoloured.

1822	150 c. Type **491a**	75	50
1823	400 c. Ford "Depot Wagon", 1920	1·75	1·75
1824	600 c. Ford "Mach 1 Mustang", 1970	2·25	2·75
1825	800 c. Mercedes Benz racing car, Monaco Grand Prix, 1937	3·50	4·50

1993. Aviation Anniversaries. Multicoloured.

1827	50 c. Type **491b**	50	30
1828	150 c. Airship "LZ-7" "Deutschland" (horiz)	85	55
1829	400 c. Avro Vulcan jet bomber (horiz)	1·75	1·75
1830	400 c. U.S. Mail Ford Trimotor (horiz)	1·75	1·75
1831	600 c. Nieuport 27 biplane	2·25	2·25
1832	600 c. Loading mail on "Graf Zeppelin"	2·25	2·25
1833	800 c. Airship "LZ-10" "Schwaben" (horiz)	3·50	4·00

ANNIVERSARIES: Nos. 1827/28, 1833, 125th birth anniv of Hugo Eckener (airship commander); Nos. 1829, 1831, 75th anniv of Royal Air Force; Nos. 1830, 1832, Bicentenary of first airmail flight.

492 African Buffalo

1993. Wild Animals. Multicoloured.

1835	20 c. Type **492**	25	15
1836	50 c. Giant forest hog	30	20
1837	60 c. Potto	40	25
1838	80 c. Bay duiker	50	30
1839	100 c. Royal antelope	60	35
1840	200 c. Serval	90	90
1841	500 c. Golden cat	1·75	2·00
1842	800 c. "Megaloglossus woermanni" (bat)	3·00	3·50

1993. 40th Anniv of Coronation. Nos. 1549/52 optd **40TH ANNIVERSARY OF CORONATION H.M. ELIZABETH II**.

1844	100 c. multicoloured	60	25
1845	200 c. multicoloured	1·00	70
1846	500 c. multicoloured	2·75	3·00
1847	600 c. multicoloured	3·00	3·25

1993. 35th Anniv of Rotary International and 60th Anniv of Ghana Red Cross Society (1992). Nos. 1562 and 1564/6 optd **35 YEARS OF ROTARY INTERNATIONAL GHANA 1958** (Nos. 1849, 1852) or **GHANA RED CROSS SOCIETY FOUNDED 1932** and cross (others).

1849	100 c. Stonehead	60	30
1850	300 c. Aba	1·75	1·75
1851	400 c. Jewel cichlid	2·00	2·00
1852	500 c. Smooth hammerhead	2·25	2·50

496 "Cantharellus cibarius"

1993. Mushrooms. Multicoloured.

1854	20 c. Type **496**	40	25
1855	50 c. "Russula cyanoxantha"	50	30
1856	60 c. "Clitocybe rivulosa"	55	30
1857	80 c. "Cortinarius elatior"	60	35
1858	80 c. "Mycena galericulata"	60	35
1859	200 c. "Tricholoma gambosum"	1·00	1·00
1860	200 c. "Boletus edulis"	1·00	1·00
1861	200 c. "Lepista saeva"	1·00	1·00
1862	250 c. "Gyroporus castaneus"	1·10	1·10
1863	300 c. "Boletus chrysenteron"	1·25	1·25
1864	350 c. "Nolanea sericea"	1·40	1·40
1865	350 c. "Hygrophorus punicea" ("Hygrophorus puiceus")	1·40	1·40
1866	500 c. "Gomphidius glutinosus"	1·60	1·75
1867	600 c. "Russula olivacea"	1·75	2·00
1868	1000 c. "Russula aurata"	2·25	2·75

497 "The Actor" (Picasso)

498 Abedi Pele (Ghana)

1993. Anniversaries and Events. Multicoloured.

1870	20 c. Type **497**	40	20
1871	20 c. Early astronomical equipment	40	20
1872	80 c. "Portrait of Allan Stein" (Picasso)	50	30
1873	200 c. Modern telescope	90	1·00
1874	200 c. "Tattoo" (Lesek Sobocki)	90	1·00
1875	600 c. "Prison" (Sasza Blonder)	2·25	3·00
1876	800 c. "Seated Male Nude" (Picasso)	3·00	3·50

ANNIVERSARIES AND EVENTS: Nos. 1870, 1872, 1876, 20th death anniv of Picasso (artist); Nos. 1871, 1873, 450th death anniv of Copernicus (astronomer); Nos. 1874/5, "Polska '93" International Stamp Exhibition, Poznan.

1993. World Cup Football Championship, U.S.A. (1st issue). Multicoloured.

1878	50 c. Type **498**	60	35
1879	80 c. Pedro Troglio (Argentina)	70	40
1880	100 c. Fernando Alvez (Uruguay)	80	40
1881	200 c. Franco Baresi (Italy)	1·50	1·25
1882	250 c. Gomez (Colombia) and Katanec (Yugoslavia)	1·50	1·50
1883	600 c. Diego Maradona (Argentina)	3·00	3·25
1884	800 c. Hasek (Czechoslovakia) and Wynalda (U.S.A.)	3·00	3·75
1885	1000 c. Lothar Matthaeus (Germany)	3·75	4·50

See also Nos. 2037/42.

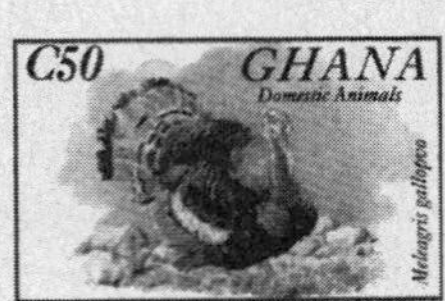

499 Common Turkey

1993. Domestic Animals. Multicoloured.

1887	50 c. Type **499**	50	25
1888	100 c. Goats	70	40
1889	150 c. Muscovy ducks	1·00	75
1890	200 c. Donkeys	1·25	1·00
1891	250 c. Red junglefowl cock	1·25	1·25
1892	300 c. Pigs	1·40	1·40
1893	400 c. Helmet guineafowl	1·75	1·75
1894	600 c. Dog	2·50	2·75
1895	800 c. Red junglefowl hen	3·00	3·50
1896	1000 c. Sheep	3·50	4·00

1993. Christmas. Religious Paintings. As T **221b** of Gambia. Black, yellow and red (Nos. 1898, 1900/1 and 1905) or multicoloured (others).

1898	50 c. "Adoration of the Magi" (Durer)	50	20
1899	100 c. "The Virgin and Child with St. John and an Angel" (Botticelli)	70	25
1900	150 c. "Mary as Queen of Heaven" (Durer)	90	45
1901	200 c. "Saint Anne" (Durer)	1·00	65
1902	250 c. "The Madonna of the Magnificat" (Botticelli)	1·10	75
1903	400 c. "The Madonna of the Goldfinch" (Botticelli)	1·75	2·00
1904	600 c. "The Virgin and Child with the young St. John the Baptist" (Botticelli)	2·25	3·00
1905	1000 c. "Adoration of the Shepherds" (Durer)	3·00	5·00

500 Doll

501 Mickey Mouse in "Steamboat Willie", 1928

1994. Traditional Crafts. Multicoloured.

1907	50 c. Type **500**	30	20
1908	50 c. Pot with "head" lid	30	20
1909	200 c. Bead necklace	70	70
1910	200 c. Snake charmers (statuette)	70	70
1911	250 c. Hoe	70	70
1912	250 c. Scabbard	70	70
1913	600 c. Pipe	1·75	2·00
1914	600 c. Deer (carving)	1·75	2·00
1915	1000 c. Mask	2·50	3·00
1916	1000 c. Doll (different)	2·50	3·00

1994. "Hong Kong '94" International Stamp Exhibition (1st issue). As T **222a** of Gambia. Multicoloured.

1918	200 c. Hong Kong 1986 50 c. "Expo '86" stamp and tram	90	1·00
1919	200 c. Ghana 1992 20 c. Railways stamp and tram	90	1·00

Nos. 1918/19 were printed together, se-tenant, forming a complete design.

See also Nos. 1920/25.

1994. "Hong Kong '94" International Stamp Exhibition (2nd issue). Imperial Palace Clocks. As T **222b** of Gambia. Multicoloured.

1920	600 c. Windmill clock	70	80
1921	600 c. Horse clock	70	80
1922	600 c. Balloon clock	70	80
1923	600 c. Zodiac clock	70	80
1924	100 c. Shar-pei dog clock	70	80
1925	100 c. Cat clock	70	80

1994. 65th Anniv (1993) of Mickey Mouse (Walt Disney cartoon character) (1993). Scenes from various cartoon films.

1926	50 c. Type **501**	30	15
1927	100 c. "The Band Concert", 1935	40	20
1928	150 c. "Moose Hunters", 1937	55	35
1929	200 c. "Brave Little Tailor", 1938	65	50
1930	250 c. "Fantasia", 1940	70	60
1931	400 c. "The Nifty Nineties", 1941	1·50	1·75
1932	600 c. "Canine Caddy", 1941	1·75	2·00
1933	1000 c. "Mickey's Christmas Carol", 1983	2·50	3·00

No. 1929 is inscribed "TAYLOR" in error. The dates on Nos. 1927 and 1932 are incorrectly shown as "1937" and "1944".

501a Boy Hiker

1994. Easter. Hummel Figurines. Multicoloured.

1935	50 c. Type **501a**	30	15
1936	100 c. Girl with basket behind back	40	20
1937	150 c. Boy with rabbits	55	35
1938	200 c. Boy holding basket	65	50
1939	250 c. Girl with chicks	70	60
1940	400 c. Girl with lamb	1·50	1·75
1941	600 c. Girl waving red handkerchief with lamb	1·75	2·00
1942	1000 c. Girl with basket and posy	2·50	3·00

502 Diana Monkey with Young

1994. Wildlife. Multicoloured.

1944	50 c. Type **502**	40	15
1945	100 c. Bushbuck (horiz)	40	20
1946	150 c. Spotted hyena (horiz)	55	35
1947	200 c. Diana monkey on branch facing left	75	50
1948	500 c. Diana monkey on branch facing right	1·25	1·50
1949	800 c. Head of Diana monkey	1·75	2·00
1950	1000 c. Aardvark (horiz)	2·00	2·50

Designs of Nos. 1944 and 1947/9 include the W.W.F. Panda emblem.

503 Norwegian Forest Cat

1994. Cats. Multicoloured.
1952 200 c. Type **503** 50 50
1953 200 c. Blue longhair 50 50
1954 200 c. Red self longhair 50 50
1955 200 c. Black longhair 50 50
1956 200 c. Chinchilla 50 50
1957 200 c. Dilute calico longhair 50 50
1958 200 c. Blue tabby and white longhair 50 50
1959 200 c. Ruby Somali 50 50
1960 200 c. Blue smoke longhair 50 50
1961 200 c. Calico longhair 50 50
1962 200 c. Brown tabby longhair 50 50
1963 200 c. Balinese 50 50
1964 200 c. Sorrel Abyssinian 50 50
1965 200 c. Silver classic tabby 50 50
1966 200 c. Chocolate-point Siamese 50 50
1967 200 c. Brown tortie Burmese 50 50
1968 200 c. Exotic shorthair 50 50
1969 200 c. Havana brown 50 50
1970 200 c. Devon rex 50 50
1971 200 c. Black Manx 50 50
1972 200 c. British blue shorthair 50 50
1973 200 c. Calico American wirehair 50 50
1974 200 c. Spotted oriental Siamese 50 50
1975 200 c. Red classic tabby 50 50
No. 1957 is inscribed "Dilut" in error.

504 Red-bellied Paradise Flycatcher

1994. Birds. Multicoloured.
1977 200 c. Type **504** 55 55
1978 200 c. Many-coloured bush shrike 55 55
1979 200 c. Broad-tailed paradise whydah 55 55
1980 200 c. White-crowned robin chat 55 55
1981 200 c. Violet turaco ("Violet plantain-eater") 55 55
1982 200 c. Village weaver 55 55
1983 200 c. Red-crowned bishop 55 55
1984 200 c. Common shoveler 55 55
1985 200 c. Spur-winged goose 55 55
1986 200 c. African crake 55 55
1987 200 c. Purple swamphen ("King reed-hen") 55 55
1988 200 c. African tiger bittern 55 55
1989 200 c. Oriole warbler ("Moho") 55 55
1990 200 c. Superb sunbird 55 55
1991 200 c. Blue-breasted kingfisher 55 55
1992 200 c. African blue cuckoo shrike 55 55
1993 200 c. Great blue turaco ("Blue plantain-eater") 55 55
1994 200 c. Greater flamingo 55 55
1995 200 c. African jacana ("Lily-trotter") 55 55
1996 200 c. Black-crowned night heron 55 55
1997 200 c. Black-winged stilt 55 55
1998 200 c. White-spotted crake 55 55
1999 200 c. African pygmy goose 55 55
2000 200 c. African pitta 55 55

505 Women at Stand-pipe

1994. 1st Anniv of Fourth Republic. Multicoloured.
2002 50 c. Type **505** 25 15
2003 100 c. Presenting certificate to farmers 35 20
2004 200 c. Village electricity supply 50 35
2005 600 c. Bridge 1·25 1·75
2006 800 c. National Theatre 1·50 2·00
2007 1000 c. Lighting perpetual flame 1·75 2·25

1994. 25th Anniv of First Manned Moon Landing. As T **326** of Antigua showing scientists. Mult.
2008 300 c. Sigmund Jahn 90 1·00
2009 300 c. Ulf Merbold 90 1·00
2010 300 c. Hans Wilhelm Schegal 90 1·00
2011 300 c. Ulrich Walter 90 1·00
2012 300 c. Reinhard Furrer 90 1·00
2013 300 c. Ernst Messerschmid 90 1·00
2014 300 c. Mamoru Mohri 90 1·00
2015 300 c. Klaus-Dietrich Flade 90 1·00
2016 300 c. Chaiki Naito-Mukai 90 1·00

1994. Centenary of International Olympic Committee. Gold Medal Winners. As T **227b** of Gambia, but vert. Multicoloured.
2018 300 c. Dieter Modenburg (Germany) (high jump), 1984 60 65
2019 400 c. Ruth Fuchs (Germany) (javelin), 1972 and 1976 80 85

1994. 50th Anniv of D-Day. As T **331** of Antigua. Multicoloured.
2021 60 c. H.M.S. "Roberts" (monitor) 80 60
2022 100 c. H.M.S. "Warspite" (battleship) 1·10 90
2023 200 c. U.S.S. "Augusta" (cruiser) 1·75 2·00

1994. "Philakorea '94" International Stamp Exn, Seoul. As T **227d** of Gambia. Mult.
2025 20 c. Ch'unghak-dong village elder in traditional costume, (24½ × 38 mm) 15 15
2026 150 c. Stone Pagoda, Punhwangsa (24½ × 38 mm) 40 40
2027 250 c. Character with eggs 45 50
2028 250 c. Character with pair of birds on house 45 50
2029 250 c. Character with cock 45 50
2030 250 c. Character with dragon and pagoda 45 50
2031 250 c. Character with orange flowers 45 50
2032 250 c. Character with parrot and pagoda 45 50
2033 250 c. Character with plant 45 50
2034 250 c. Character with fish 45 50
2035 300 c. Traditional country house, Andong (24½ × 34 mm) 50 55

506 Dennis Bergkamp (Netherlands)

1994. World Cup Football Championship, U.S.A. (2nd issue). Multicoloured.
2037 200 c. Type **506** 50 60
2038 200 c. Lothar Matthaus (Germany) 50 60
2039 200 c. Giuseppe Signori (Italy) 50 60
2040 200 c. Carlos Valderama (Colombia) 50 60
2041 200 c. Jorge Campos (Mexico) 50 60
2042 200 c. Tony Meola (U.S.A.) 50 60

507 Common ("Crowned") Duiker

1994. Duikers (antelopes). Multicoloured.
2044 50 c. Type **507** 30 15
2045 100 c. Red-flanked duiker 40 25
2046 200 c. Yellow-backed duiker 60 40
2047 400 c. Ogilby's duiker 1·00 1·25
2048 600 c. Bay duiker 1·25 1·75
2049 800 c. Jentink's duiker 1·50 2·00

1994. Christmas. Religious Paintings. As T **231a** of Gambia. Multicoloured.
2051 100 c. "Madonna of the Annunciation" (Simone Martini) 30 15
2052 200 c. "Madonna and Child" (Niccolo di Pietro Gerini) 45 20
2053 250 c. "Virgin and Child on the Throne with Angels and Saints" (Raffaello Botticini) 55 45
2054 300 c. "Madonna and Child with Saints" (Antonio Fiorentino) 75 75
2055 400 c. "Adoration of the Magi" (Bartolo di Fredi) 90 90
2056 500 c. "The Annunciation" (Cima da Congeliano) 1·00 1·00
2057 600 c. "Virgin and Child with the Young St. John the Baptist" (workshop of Botticelli) 1·25 1·50
2058 1000 c. "The Holy Family" (Giorgione) 1·75 2·50

508 Northern Region Dancer

510 Fertility Doll

509 Red Cross Stretcher-bearers

1994. Panafest '94 (2nd Pan-African Historical Theatre Festival). Multicoloured.
2060 50 c. Type **508** 20 15
2061 100 c. Traditional artefacts 35 25
2062 200 c. Chief with courtiers 65 60
2063 400 c. Woman in ceremonial costume 1·25 1·25
2064 600 c. Cape Coast Castle 1·75 2·25
2065 800 c. Clay figurines 2·25 3·00

1994. 75th Anniv of Red Cross. Multicoloured.
2066 50 c. Type **509** 30 15
2067 200 c. Worker with children 60 35
2068 600 c. Workers erecting tents 1·50 2·00

1994. Fertility Dolls.
2070 **510** 50 c. multicoloured 20 10
2071 – 100 c. multicoloured 30 15
2072 – 150 c. multicoloured 45 30
2073 – 200 c. multicoloured 50 30
2074 – 400 c. multicoloured 80 70
2075 – 600 c. multicoloured 1·00 1·10
2076 – 800 c. multicoloured 1·25 1·50
2077 – 1000 c. multicoloured 1·40 1·75
DESIGNS: 100 c. to 1000 c. Different dolls.

511 Ghanaian Family

1994. International Year of the Family. Mult.
2079 50 c. Type **511** 20 15
2080 100 c. Teaching carpentry 30 15
2081 200 c. Child care 50 25
2082 400 c. Care for the elderly 80 70
2083 600 c. Learning pottery 1·00 1·25
2084 1000 c. Adult education students 1·50 2·00

512 Control Tower and Emblem

1995. 50th Anniv of I.C.A.O. Mult. (a) Inscr "50 Anniversary Of Ghana Civil Aviation Authority".
2085 100 c. Type **512** 30
2086 400 c. Communications equipment 80
2087 1000 c. Airliner taking off 1·60

(b) Inscr "50th Anniversary Of The International Civil Aviation Organisation (I.C.A.O.)."
2088 100 c. Type **512** 30 20
2089 400 c. Communications equipment 80 80
2090 1000 c. Airliner taking off 1·60 1·75

513 Pluto, Donald Duck and Chip n' Dale around Table

1995. 60th Anniv of Donald Duck. Walt Disney Cartoon Characters at Birthday Party. Mult.
2091 40 c. Type **513** 25 15
2092 50 c. Mickey Mouse and pup with banner 25 15
2093 60 c. Daisy Duck with balloons 25 20
2094 100 c. Goofy making cake 30 20
2095 150 c. Goofy on roller blades delivering cake 40 30
2096 250 c. Donald pinning donkey tail on Goofy 50 50
2097 400 c. Ludwig von Drake singing to Pluto 70 70
2098 500 c. Grandma Duck giving cake to puppies 80 80
2099 1000 c. Mickey and Minnie Mouse at piano 1·40 1·75
2100 1500 c. Pluto with bone and ball 2·25 2·75

514 Fort Appolonia, Beyin

1995. Forts and Castles of Ghana. Multicoloured.
2102 50 c. Type **514** 10 10
2103 200 c. Fort Patience, Apam 20 15
2104 250 c. Fort Amsterdam, Kormantin 25 25
2105 300 c. Fort St. Jago, Elmina 30 30
2106 400 c. Fort William, Anomabo 40 40
2107 600 c. Kumasi Fort 55 65

515 Cochem Castle, Germany

1995. Castles of the World. Multicoloured.
2109 150 c. Type **515** 30 30
2110 500 c. Windsor Castle, England 50 50
2111 500 c. Osaka Castle, Japan 50 50
2112 500 c. Vaj Dahunyad Castle, Hungary 50 50
2113 500 c. Karlstejn Castle, Czech Republic 50 50
2114 500 c. Kronborg Castle, Denmark 50 50
2115 500 c. Alcazar of Segovia, Spain 50 50
2116 500 c. Chambourd Castle, France 50 50
2117 500 c. Linderhof Castle, Germany 50 50
2118 500 c. Red Fort, Delhi, India 50 50
2119 600 c. Hohenzollern Castle, Germany 60 60
2120 800 c. Uwajima Castle, Japan 80 80
2121 1000 c. Hohenschwangau Castle, Germany 90 90

516 European Pochard ("Eurasian Pochard")

1995. Ducks. Multicoloured.
2123 200 c. Type **516** 35 35
2124 400 c. African pygmy goose 55 55
2125 400 c. Southern pochard 55 55
2126 400 c. Cape teal 55 55
2127 400 c. Ruddy shelduck 55 55
2128 400 c. Fulvous whistling duck 55 55
2129 400 c. White-faced whistling duck 55 55
2130 400 c. Ferruginous duck ("Ferruginous white-eye") 55 55
2131 400 c. Hottentot teal 55 55
2132 400 c. African black duck 55 55
2133 400 c. African yellow-bill 55 55
2134 400 c. Bahama pintail ("White-checked pintail duck") 55 55
2135 400 c. Hartlaub's duck 55 55
2136 500 c. Maccoa duck 60 60
2137 800 c. Cape shoveler 80 80
2138 1000 c. Red-crested pochard 90 90
Nos. 2124/35 were printed together, se-tenant, forming a composite design.
No. 2128 is inscribed "Wistling" in error.

517 Cycling

518 "Cymothoe beckeri" (butterfly)

1995. Olympic Games, Atlanta (1996) (1st issue). Multicoloured.
2140 300 c. Type **517** 40 40
2141 300 c. Archery 40 40
2142 300 c. Diving 40 40
2143 300 c. Swimming 40 40
2144 300 c. Women's gymnastics 40 40
2145 300 c. Fencing 40 40
2146 300 c. Boxing 40 40
2147 300 c. Men's gymnastics 40 40
2148 300 c. Javelin 40 40
2149 300 c. Tennis 40 40
2150 300 c. Football 40 40
2151 300 c. Equestrian 40 40
2152 500 c. Carl Lewis (U.S.A.) 50 50
2153 800 c. Eric Liddell (Great Britain) 75 75
2154 900 c. Jesse Owens (U.S.A.) 85 85
2155 1000 c. Jim Thorpe (U.S.A.) 90 90
Nos. 2140/51 were printed together, se-tenant, forming a composite design.
See also Nos. 2334/55.

1995. Multicoloured.
2157 400 c. Type **518** 15 20
2158 500 c. "Graphium policenes" (butterfly) 20 25
2158a 550 c. Atumpan drums (vert) 20 25
2158b 800 c. "Cyrestis camillus" (butterfly) (vert) 30 35
2159 1000 c. African long-tailed hawk (vert) 35 40
2159a 1100 c. Kente cloth 40 45
2160 2000 c. Swordfish 70 75
2161 3000 c. Guinean fingerfish 1·10 1·25
2162 5000 c. Purple heron (vert) 1·90 2·00

519 Ghanaian Scouts

520 Trygve Lie (1946–52) and United Nations Building

1995. 18th World Scout Jamboree, Netherlands.
2163 **519** 400 c. multicoloured . . . 70 80
2164 – 800 c. multicoloured . . . 90 1·00
2165 – 1000 c. multicoloured . . . 1·00 1·25
DESIGNS: 800 c. to 1000 c. Ghanaian scouts (different).

1995. 50th Anniv of End of Second World War in Europe. As T **237a** of Gambia. Multicoloured.
2167 400 c. Winston Churchill . . . 65 65
2168 400 c. Gen. Dwight D. Eisenhower . . . 65 65
2169 400 c. Air Marshal Sir Arthur Tedder . . . 65 65
2170 400 c. Field-Marshal Sir Bernard Montgomery . . . 65 65
2171 400 c. Gen. Omar Bradley . . . 65 65
2172 400 c. Gen. Charles de Gaulle . . 65 65
2173 400 c. French resistance fighters . . . 65 65
2174 400 c. Gen. George S. Patton . . 65 65

1995. 50th Anniv of United Nations. Secretary-Generals. Multicoloured.
2176 200 c. Type **520** . . . 30 40
2177 300 c. Dag Hammarskjold (1953–61) . . . 40 50
2178 400 c. U. Thant (1961–71) . . 50 60
2179 500 c. Kurt Waldheim (1972–81) . . . 60 70
2180 600 c. Javier Perez de Cuellar (1982–91) . . . 70 80
2181 800 c. Boutrous Boutrous-Ghali (1992) . . . 80 90

521 Preserving Fish

1995. 50th Anniv of F.A.O. Multicoloured.
2183 200 c. Type **521** . . . 40 15
2184 300 c. Fishermen with fish traps . . . 50 30
2185 400 c. Ox-drawn plough . . . 60 50
2186 600 c. Harvesting bananas . . 70 80
2187 800 c. Planting saplings . . . 80 90

522 National Flag and Rotary Emblem

1995. 90th Anniv of Rotary International.
2189 **522** 600 c. multicoloured . . . 70 80

1995. 95th Birthday of Queen Elizabeth the Queen Mother. As T **239a** of Gambia. Multicoloured.
2191 600 c. brown, light brown and black . . . 90 90
2192 600 c. multicoloured . . . 90 90
2193 600 c. multicoloured . . . 90 90
2194 600 c. multicoloured . . . 90 90
DESIGNS: No. 2191, Queen Elizabeth the Queen Mother (pastel drawing); 2192, Wearing light blue hat and floral dress; 2193, At desk (oil painting); 2194, Wearing red hat and dress.

1995. 50th Anniv of End of Second World War in the Pacific. Medals. As T **229b** of Gambia. Mult.
2196 500 c. Navy Cross and Purple Heart, U.S.A. . . . 80 80
2197 500 c. Air Force Cross and Distinguished Flying Cross, Great Britain . . . 80 80
2198 500 c. Navy and Marine Corps Medal and Distinguished Service Cross, U.S.A. . . . 80 80
2199 500 c. Distinguished Service Medal and Distinguished Conduct Medal, Great Britain . . . 80 80
2200 500 c. Military Medal and Military Cross, Great Britain . . . 80 80
2201 500 c. Distinguished Service Cross and Distinguished Service Order, Great Britain . . . 80 80

523 Seismosaurus

524 Arms of Otumfuo Opoku Ware II

1995. "Singapore '95" International Stamp Exhibition. Prehistoric Animals. Multicoloured.
2203 400 c. Type **523** . . . 65 65
2204 400 c. Supersaurus . . . 65 65
2205 400 c. Ultrasaurus . . . 65 65
2206 400 c. Saurolophus . . . 65 65
2207 400 c. Lambeosaurus . . . 65 65
2208 400 c. Parasaurolophus . . . 65 65
2209 400 c. Triceratops . . . 65 65
2210 400 c. Styracosaurus . . . 65 65
2211 400 c. Pachyrhinosaurus . . . 65 65
2212 400 c. Peteinosaurus . . . 65 65
2213 400 c. Quetzalcoatlus . . . 65 65
2214 400 c. Eudimorphodon . . . 65 65
2215 400 c. Allosaurus . . . 65 65
2216 400 c. Daspletosaurus . . . 65 65
2217 400 c. Tarbosaurus bataar . . 65 65
2218 400 c. Velociraptor mongoliensis . . . 65 65
2219 400 c. Herrerasaurus . . . 65 65
2220 400 c. Coelophysis . . . 65 65
Nos. 2203/11 and 2212/20 respectively were printed together, se-tenant, forming composite designs.

1995. Silver Jubilee of Otumfuo Opoku Ware II (King of Ashanti). Multicoloured.
2222 50 c. Type **524** . . . 10 10
2223 100 c. Silver casket . . . 15 10
2224 200 c. Golden stool . . . 25 20
2225 400 c. Busummuru sword bearer . . . 45 45
2226 600 c. Otumfuo Opoku Ware II . . . 65 75
2227 800 c. Otumfuo Opoku Ware II under umbrella . . . 80 90
2228 1000 c. Mponponsuo sword bearer . . . 90 1·00

525 Nelson Mandela (1993 Peace)

1995. Centenary of Nobel Prize Trust Fund. Past Prize Winners. Multicoloured.
2229 400 c. Type **525** . . . 60 60
2230 400 c. Albert Schweitzer (1952 Peace) . . . 60 60
2231 400 c. Wole Soyinka (1986 Literature) . . . 60 60
2232 400 c. Emil Fischer (1902 Chemistry) . . . 60 60
2233 400 c. Rudolf Mossbauer (1961 Physics) . . . 60 60
2234 400 c. Archbishop Desmond Tutu (1984 Peace) . . . 60 60
2235 400 c. Max Born (1954 Physics) . . . 60 60
2236 400 c. Max Planck (1918 Physics) . . . 60 60
2237 400 c. Hermann Hesse (1946 Literature) . . . 60 60

1995. Christmas. Religious Paintings. As T **245a** of Gambia. Multicoloured.
2239 50 c. "The Child Jesus and the Young St. John" (Murillo) . 15 10
2240 80 c. "Rest on the Flight into Egypt" (Memling) . . . 15 10
2241 300 c. "Holy Family" (Van Dyck) . . . 40 35
2242 600 c. "Enthroned Madonna and Child" (Uccello) . . . 70 80
2243 800 c. "Madonna and Child" (Van Eyck) . . . 85 1·00
2244 1000 c. "Head of Christ" (Rembrandt) . . . 1·00 1·25

526 Ernemann Camera (1903)

1995. Centenary of Cinema. Multicoloured.
2246 400 c. Type **526** . . . 65 65
2247 400 c. Charlie Chaplin . . . 65 65
2248 400 c. Rudolph Valentino . . . 65 65
2249 400 c. Will Rogers . . . 65 65
2250 400 c. Greta Garbo . . . 65 65
2251 400 c. Jackie Cooper . . . 65 65
2252 400 c. Bette Davis . . . 65 65
2253 400 c. John Barrymore . . . 65 65
2254 400 c. Shirley Temple . . . 65 65
No. 2246 is inscribed "ERNMANN" in error.

527 John Lennon

1995. John Lennon (musician) Commemoration. Multicoloured.
2256 400 c. Type **527** . . . 1·10 1·10
2257 400 c. Full face portrait (green background) . . . 1·10 1·10
2258 400 c. With guitar . . . 1·10 1·10
2259 400 c. Wearing glasses and caftan . . . 1·10 1·10
2260 400 c. Full face portrait (red background) . . . 1·10 1·10
2261 400 c. Wearing headphones . . 1·10 1·10
2262 400 c. Wearing purple T-shirt . 1·10 1·10
2263 400 c. Full face portrait (blue background) . . . 1·10 1·10
2264 400 c. Facing right . . . 1·10 1·10
2265 400 c. As No. 2263, but smaller (24 × 39 mm) . . . 1·10 1·10

528 Louis Pasteur in Laboratory

529 Rat Musicians

1995. Death Centenary of Louis Pasteur (scientist). Multicoloured.
2267 600 c. Type **528** . . . 1·10 1·10
2268 600 c. Pasteur injecting rabid dog . . . 1·10 1·10
2269 600 c. Pasteur and microscope slide . . . 1·10 1·10
2270 600 c. Laboratory equipment and birds . . . 1·10 1·10
2271 600 c. Yeast vats . . . 1·10 1·10

1996. Chinese New Year ("Year of the Rat").
2272 **529** 250 c. brown, violet and red . . . 10 15
2273 – 250 c. brown, violet and red . . . 10 15
2274 – 250 c. brown, violet and red . . . 10 15
2275 – 250 c. brown, violet and red . . . 10 15
DESIGNS: No. 2273, Rats carrying banners; 2274, Rats carrying palanquin; 2275, Rats with offerings.

1996. 125th Anniv of Metropolitan Museum of Art, New York. As T **251** of Gambia. Multicoloured.
2278 400 c. "Portrait of a Man" (Van der Goes) . . . 15 20
2279 400 c. "Paradise" (detail) (Di Paolo) . . . 15 20
2280 400 c. "Portrait of a Young Man" (Messina) . . . 15 20
2281 400 c. "Tommaso Portinari" (detail) (Memling) . . . 15 20
2282 400 c. "Maria Portinari" (detail) (Memling) . . . 15 20
2283 400 c. "Portrait of a Lady" (detail) (Ghirlandaio) . . . 15 20
2284 400 c. "St. Christopher and the Infant Christ" (Ghirlandaio) . . . 15 20
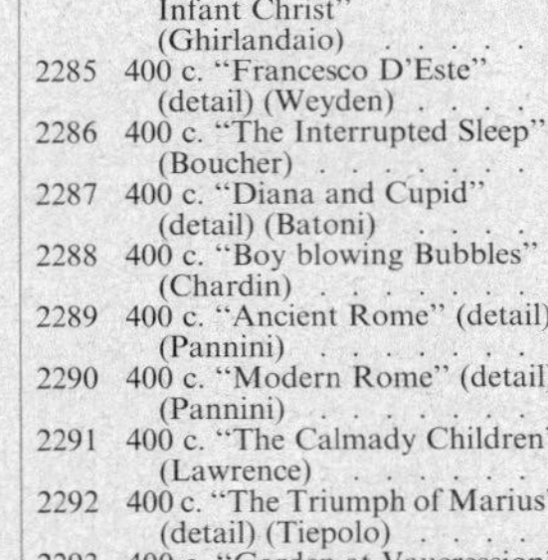
2285 400 c. "Francesco D'Este" (detail) (Weyden) . . . 15 20
2286 400 c. "The Interrupted Sleep" (Boucher) . . . 15 20
2287 400 c. "Diana and Cupid" (detail) (Batoni) . . . 15 20
2288 400 c. "Boy blowing Bubbles" (Chardin) . . . 15 20
2289 400 c. "Ancient Rome" (detail) (Pannini) . . . 15 20
2290 400 c. "Modern Rome" (detail) (Pannini) . . . 15 20
2291 400 c. "The Calmady Children" (Lawrence) . . . 15 20
2292 400 c. "The Triumph of Marius" (detail) (Tiepolo) . . . 15 20
2293 400 c. "Garden at Vaucression" (detail) (Vuillard) . . . 15 20

530 Toco Toucan

1996. Wildlife of the Rainforest. Multicoloured.
2295 400 c. Type **530** . . . 15 20
2296 400 c. Two-toed sloth . . . 15 20
2297 400 c. Orang-utan . . . 15 20
2298 400 c. Crested hawk eagle . . 15 20
2299 400 c. Tiger . . . 15 20
2300 400 c. Yellow-billed stork . . 15 20
2301 400 c. Green-winged macaw . 15 20
2302 400 c. Common squirrel-monkey . . . 15 20
2303 400 c. Crab-eating macaque . 15 20
2304 400 c. "Cithaerias menander" and "Ithomiidae" (butterflies) . . . 15 20
2305 400 c. "Coryptophanes cristatus" and "Gekkonidae" (lizards) . . . 15 20
2306 400 c. Boa constrictor . . . 15 20
2307 400 c. Hoatzin . . . 15 20
2308 400 c. Western tarsier . . . 15 20
2309 400 c. Golden Lion tamarin . 15 20
2310 400 c. "Pteropus gouldii" (bat) . . . 15 20
2311 400 c. Guianan cock of the rock . . . 15 20
2312 400 c. Resplendent quetzal . . 15 20
2313 400 c. Tree frog and poison-arrow frog . . . 15 20
2314 400 c. Ring-tailed lemur . . 15 20
2315 400 c. Iguana . . . 15 20
2316 400 c. "Heliconius burneyi" (butterfly) . . . 15 20
2317 400 c. Vervain hummingbird . 15 20
2318 400 c. Verreaux's sifaka . . . 15 20

531 Pagoda of Kaiyan Si Temple, Fujian

532 Serafim Todorow (Bulgaria)

1996. "CHINA '96" 9th Asian International Stamp Exhibition. Pagodas. Multicoloured.
2320 400 c. Type **531** . . . 15 20
2321 400 c. Kaiyuan Si Temple, Hebei . . . 15 20
2322 400 c. Fogong Si Temple, Shanxi . . . 15 20
2323 400 c. Xiangshan, Beijing . . 15 20

1996. 70th Birthday of Queen Elizabeth II. As T **255a** of Gambia showing different photographs. Multicoloured.
2325 1000 c. Queen Elizabeth II . . 35 40
2326 1000 c. In blue hat and coat . 35 40
2327 1000 c. Wearing straw hat and carrying bouquet . . . 35 40

1996. 50th Anniv of International Amateur Boxing Association. Multicoloured.
2329 300 c. Type **532** . . . 10 15
2330 400 c. Oscar de la Hoya (U.S.A.) . . . 15 20
2331 800 c. Ariel Hernandez (Cuba) . 30 35
2332 1500 c. Arnoldo Mesa (Cuba) . 55 60

533 Ancient Greek Wrestlers

1996. Olympic Games, Atlanta (2nd issue). Previous Medal Winners. Multicoloured.
2334 300 c. Type **533** . . . 10 15
2335 400 c. Aileen Riggin, 1920 (U.S.A.) . . . 15 20
2336 400 c. Pat McCormick, 1952 (U.S.A.) . . . 15 20
2337 400 c. Dawn Fraser, 1956 (Australia) . . . 15 20
2338 400 c. Chris von Saltza, 1960 (U.S.A.) . . . 15 20
2339 400 c. Anita Lonsbrough, 1960 (Great Britain) . . . 15 20
2340 400 c. Debbie Meyer, 1968 (U.S.A.) . . . 15 20
2341 400 c. Shane Gould, 1972 (Australia) . . . 15 20
2342 400 c. Petra Thuemer, 1976 (Germany) . . . 15 20
2343 400 c. Marjorie Gestring, 1936 (U.S.A.) . . . 15 20

2344 400 c. Abedi Pele (Ghana) (vert) 15 20
2345 400 c. Quico Navarez (Spain) (vert) 15 20
2346 400 c. Heino Hanson (Denmark) (vert) 15 20
2347 400 c. Mostafa Ismail (Egypt) (vert) 15 20
2348 400 c. Anthony Yeboah (Ghana) (vert) 15 20
2349 400 c. Jurgen Klinsmann (Germany) (vert) 15 20
2350 400 c. Cobi Jones (U.S.A.) (vert) 15 20
2351 400 c. Franco Baresi (Italy) (vert) 15 20
2352 400 c. Igor Dobrovolski (Russia) (vert) 15 20
2353 500 c. Wilma Rudolph (U.S.A.) (track and field, 1960) 20 25
2354 600 c. Olympic Stadium, 1960, and Roman landmarks 20 25
2355 800 c. Ladies Kayak pairs, 1960 (Soviet Union) 30 35

Nos. 2335/43 (swimming and diving), and 2344/52 (football) respectively were printed together, se-tenant, with the backgrounds forming composite designs.

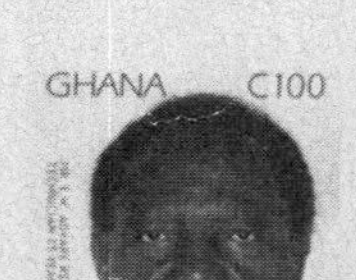

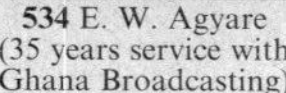

534 E. W. Agyare (35 years service with Ghana Broadcasting)

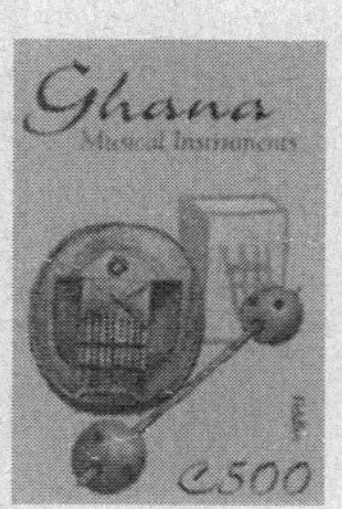

535 Fiddles

1996. Local Broadcasting.
2357 **534** 100 c. multicoloured 10 10

1996. 50th Anniv of U.N.I.C.E.F. As T **258a** of Gambia. Multicoloured.
2358 400 c. Ghanaian child 15 20
2359 500 c. Mother and child 20 25
2360 600 c. Mother and child drinking 20 25

534a St. Stephen's Gate and "Jasminum mesyni"

1996. 3000th Anniv of Jerusalem. Multicoloured.
2362 400 c. Type **534a** 15 20
2363 600 c. The Citadel, Tower of David and "Nerium oleander" 20 25
2364 800 c. Chapel of the Ascension and "Romulea bulbocodium" 30 35

1996. Centenary of Radio. Entertainers. As T **259a** of Gambia. Multicoloured.
2366 500 c. Frank Sinatra 20 25
2367 600 c. Judy Garland 20 25
2368 600 c. Bing Crosby 20 25
2369 800 c. Martin and Lewis 30 35

1996. 50th Anniv of U.N.E.S.C.O. As T **273a** of Gambia. Multicoloured.
2371 400 c. The Citadel, Haiti (vert) 15 20
2372 800 c. Ait-Ben-Hadou (fortified village), Morocco (vert) 30 35
2373 1000 c. Spissky Hrad, Slovakia 35 40

1996. Musical Insruments. Multicoloured.
2375 500 c. Type **535** 20 25
2376 500 c. Proverbial drum 20 25
2377 500 c. Double clapless bell and castanet 20 25
2378 500 c. Gourd rattle 20 25
2379 500 c. Horns 20 25

536 Ariel, Flounder and Sebastian

1996. Disney Friends. Disney Cartoon Characters. Multicoloured.
2380 60 c. Type **536** 30 30
2381 60 c. Pinocchio and Jiminy Cricket 30 30
2382 60 c. Cogsworth and Lumiere 30 30
2383 60 c. Copper and Tod 30 30
2384 60 c. Pocahontas, Meeko and Flit 30 30
2385 60 c. Bambi, Flower and Thumper 30 30
2386 150 c. As No. 2381 50 50
2387 200 c. Type **536** 50 50
2388 200 c. As No. 2383 50 50
2389 300 c. As No. 2385 60 60
2390 350 c. As No. 2382 60 60
2391 450 c. As No. 2384 65 65
2392 600 c. Aladdin and Abu 70 70
2393 700 c. Penny and Rufus 75 75
2394 800 c. Mowgli and Baloo 80 80

537 Herd Boy and Ox

1997. Chinese New Year ("Year of the Ox"). "The Herd Boy and Weaver". Each brown, silver and black.
2397 500 c. Type **537** 20 25
2398 500 c. Ox and weaver in lake 20 25
2399 500 c. Weaver at work 20 25
2400 500 c. Herd boy with dying Ox 20 25
2401 500 c. Weaver flying out of window 20 25
2402 500 c. Herd boy carrying children 20 25
2403 500 c. Family separated by "river" 20 25
2404 500 c. Petitioning the emperor 20 25
2405 500 c. Family reunited 20 25

538 The Tomb of Dr. Hideyo Noguchi

539 Dipo Hairstyle

1997. 120th Birth Anniv of Dr. Hideyo Noguchi (bacteriologist). Multicoloured.
2406 1000 c. Type **538** 35 40
2407 1000 c. Dr. Hideyo Noguchi 35 40
2408 1000 c. Birthplace of Dr. Noguchi at Sanjogarta 35 40
2409 1000 c. Noguchi Institute, Legon 35 40
2410 1000 c. Noguchi Gardens, Accra 35 40

1997. Ghanaian Women's Hairstyle. Multicoloured.
2412 1000 c. Type **539** 35 40
2413 1000 c. Oduku with flowers 35 40
2414 1000 c. Dansinkran 35 40
2415 1000 c. Mbobom 35 40
2416 1000 c. Oduku with hair pins 35 40
2417 1000 c. African corn row 35 40
2418 1000 c. Chinese raster 35 40
2419 1000 c. Chinese raster with top knot 35 40
2420 1000 c. Corn row 35 40
2421 1000 c. Mbakaa 35 40

540 Independence Anniversary Emblem

1997. 40th Anniv of Independence. Multicoloured.
2422 200 c. Type **540** 10 10
2423 200 c. President J. J. Rawlings (vert) 1·50 1·50
2424 550 c. Dr. Kwane Nkrumah (first President) (vert) 30 35
2425 800 c. Children in class 40 45
2426 1100 c. Akosombo Dam 55 60

No. 2425 is inscribed "Acheivement" in error.

1997. 10th Anniv of Chernobyl Nuclear Disaster. As T **276a** of Gambia. Multicoloured.
2428 800 c. Child's face and U.N.E.S.C.O. emblem 30 35
2429 1000 c. As No. 2428, but inscribed "CHABAD'S CHILDREN OF CHERNOBYL" at foot 35 40

541 Deng Xiaoping

1997. Deng Xiaoping (Chinese statesman) Commemoration. Different portraits. Multicoloured.
2430 300 c. Type **541** 10 15
2431 500 c. Looking thoughtful 20 25
2432 600 c. Wearing glasses 20 25
2433 600 c. Delivering speech 20 25
2434 800 c. As No. 2432 20 25
2435 800 c. As No. 2433 20 25
2436 1000 c. Type **541** 35 40
2437 1000 c. As No. 2431 35 40

1997. 50th Death Anniv of Paul Harris (founder of Rotary International). As T **276b** of Gambia. Multicoloured.
2439 2000 c. Paul Harris and Egyptian patient receiving polio vaccination 70 75

1997. Golden Wedding of Queen Elizabeth and Prince Philip. As T **276c** of Gambia. Multicoloured.
2441 800 c. Queen Elizabeth II 30 35
2442 800 c. Royal coat of arms 30 35
2443 800 c. Queen Elizabeth and Prince Philip waving 30 35
2444 800 c. Queen Elizabeth and Prince Philip on official visit 30 35
2445 800 c. Queen in Irish State Coach 30 35
2446 800 c. Prince Philip in 1947 30 35

1997. "Pacific '97" International Stamp Exhibition, San Francisco. Death Centenary of Heinrich von Stephan (founder of the U.P.U.). As T **276d** of Gambia.
2448 1000 c. blue 35 40
2449 1000 c. brown 35 40
2450 1000 c. red 35 40

DESIGNS: No. 2448, Early motor car; 2449, Von Stephan and Mercury; 2450, Blanchard's balloon flight, 1784.

541a "Nihonbashi Bridge and Edobashi Bridge"

1997. Birth Bicentenary of Hiroshige (Japanese painter). "One Hundred Famous Views of Edo". Multicoloured.
2452 600 c. Type **541a** 20 25
2453 600 c. "View of Nihonbashi Tori 1-chome" 20 25
2454 600 c. "Open Garden at Fukagawa Hachiman Shrine" 20 25
2455 600 c. "Inari Bridge and Minato Shrine, Teppozu" 20 25
2456 600 c. "Bamboo Yards, Kyobashi Bridge" 20 25
2457 600 c. "Hall of Thirty-Three Bays, Fukagawa" 20 25

542 Jackie Gleason

1997. Famous Comedians. Multicoloured.
2459 600 c. Type **542** 70 70
2460 600 c. Danny Kaye 70 70
2461 600 c. John Cleese 70 70
2462 600 c. Lucille Ball 70 70
2463 600 c. Jerry Lewis 70 70
2464 600 c. Sidney James 70 70
2465 600 c. Louis Defuenes 70 70
2466 600 c. Mae West 70 70
2467 600 c. Bob Hope 70 70

543 "Galerina calyptrata"

545 Ghanaian Players holding Trophy

544 African Pygmy Angelfish

1997. Fungi of the World. Multicoloured.
2469 200 c. Type **543** 10 10
2470 300 c. "Lepiota ignivolvata" 10 15
2471 400 c. "Omphalotus olearius" 15 20
2472 550 c. "Amanita phalloides" 20 25
2473 600 c. "Entoloma conferendum" 20 25
2474 800 c. "Entoloma nitidum" 30 35
2475 800 c. "Coprinus picaceus" 30 35
2476 800 c. "Stropharia aurantiaca" 30 35
2477 800 c. "Cortinarius splendens" 30 35
2478 800 c. "Gomphidius roseus" 30 35
2479 800 c. "Russula sardonia" 30 35
2480 800 c. "Geastrum schmidelia" 30 35

1997. World Football Championship, France (1998). As T **283a** of Gambia. Multicoloured.
2482 200 c. Azteca Stadium, Mexico 10 10
2483 300 c. The Rose Bowl, U.S.A. 10 15
2484 400 c. Stadio Giuseppe Meazza, Italy 15 20
2485 500 c. Olympiastadion, Germany 20 25
2486 600 c. Patrick Kluivert, Netherlands 20 25
2487 600 c. Roy Keane, Republic of Ireland 20 25
2488 600 c. Abedi Ayew Pele, Ghana 20 25
2489 600 c. Peter Schmeichel, Denmark 20 25
2490 600 c. Roberto di Matteo, Italy 20 25
2491 600 c. Bebeto, Brazil 20 25
2492 600 c. Steve McManaman, England 20 25
2493 600 c. George Oppon Weah, Liberia 20 25
2494 1000 c. Maracana Stadium, Brazil 35 40
2495 2000 c. Bernabeu Stadium, Spain 70 75

1997. Marine Life. Multicoloured.
2497 400 c. Type **544** 15 20
2498 500 c. Violet-crested turaco 20 25
2499 500 c. Pied avocet 20 25
2500 500 c. Bottle-nosed dolphin 20 25
2501 500 c. Bottle-nosed dolphin and long-toed lapwing 20 25
2502 500 c. Longfinned spadefish 20 25
2503 500 c. Imperial angelfish and manta 20 25
2504 500 c. Racoon butterflyfish and African pompano 20 25
2505 500 c. Silvertip shark 20 25
2506 500 c. Longfin banner fish 20 25
2507 500 c. Longfin banner fish and manta 20 25
2508 500 c. Rust parrotfish 20 25
2509 500 c. Coral trout 20 25
2510 600 c. Angelfish 20 25
2511 800 c. Broomtail wrasse 30 35
2512 1000 c. Indian butterflyfish 35 40

Nos. 2498/2509 were printed together, se-tenant, with the backgrounds forming a composite design.

1997. J.V.C. Under-17 World Soccer Champions (1995). Multicoloured.
2514 200 c. + 50 c. Type **545** 10 10
2515 550 c. + 50 c. Ghana football team (horiz) 20 25
2516 800 c. + 50 c. Abu Iddrisu 30 35
2517 1000 c. + 50 c. Emmanuel Bentil (captain) 40 45
2518 1500 c. + 50 c. Basiru Gambo 55 60

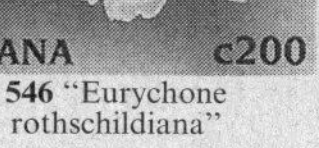

546 "Eurychone rothschildiana"

547 Goldfinch

1997. Flowers of the World. Multicoloured.

2519 200 c. Type **546** 10 10
2520 550 c. "Bulbophyllum lepidum" 20 25
2521 800 c. "Ansellia africana" . . 30 35
2522 800 c. "Strophanthus preusii" (vert) 30 35
2523 800 c. "Ancistrochilus rothschildianus" (vert) . . . 30 35
2524 800 c. "Mussaendra arcuata" (vert) 30 35
2525 800 c. "Micrococlia guyoniane" (vert) 30 35
2526 800 c. "Gloriosa simplex" (vert) 30 35
2527 800 c. "Brachycorythis kalbreyeri" (vert) 30 35
2528 800 c. "Aframomum sceptrum" (vert) 30 35
2529 800 c. "Thunbergia alata" (vert) 30 35
2530 800 c. "Clerodendrum thomsoniae" (vert) 30 35
2531 1100 c. "Combbretum grandiflorum" 40 45

Nos. 2522/30 were printed together, se-tenant, with the backgrounds forming a composite design.

1997. Birds of Africa. Multicoloured.

2533 200 c. Type **547** 10 10
2534 300 c. Cape puff-back flycatcher ("Batis") 10 15
2535 400 c. Red-headed barbet . . 15 20
2536 500 c. African white-necked raven 20 25
2537 600 c. Purple grenadier . . . 20 25
2538 800 c. Black bustard 30 35
2539 800 c. Lapwing 30 35
2540 800 c. Lichtenstein's sandgrouse 30 35
2541 800 c. Red-crested turaco . . 30 35
2542 800 c. White-browed coucal . . 30 35
2543 800 c. Lilac-breasted roller . . 30 35
2544 800 c. Golden pipit 30 35
2545 800 c. Burchell's gonolek . . . 30 35
2546 800 c. Blackcap 30 35
2547 1000 c. Zebra waxbill 35 40

548 Havana Cat

1997. Cats and Dogs. Multicoloured.

2549 20 c. Type **548** 10 10
2550 50 c. Singapura cat 10 10
2551 80 c. Papillon 10 10
2552 100 c. Sphinx cat 10 10
2553 150 c. British white cat . . . 10 10
2554 200 c. Bulldog 10 10
2555 300 c. Snowshoe cat 10 15
2556 400 c. Shetland sheepdog . . . 15 20
2557 500 c. Schnauzer 20 25
2558 600 c. Persian cat 20 25
2559 800 c. Shih tzu 30 35
2560 1000 c. Russian wolfhound . . 35 40
2561 1000 c. Birman cat 35 40
2562 1000 c. Basset hound 35 40
2563 1000 c. Silver tabby cat . . . 35 40
2564 1000 c. Afghan 35 40
2565 1000 c. Burmilla cat 35 40
2566 1000 c. Abyssinian cat 35 40
2567 1000 c. Border terrier 35 40
2568 1000 c. Scottish fold cat . . . 35 40
2569 1000 c. Boston terrier 35 40
2570 1000 c. Oriental cat 35 40
2571 1000 c. Keeshond 35 40
2572 2000 c. Chow Chow 70 75

549 "Landscape" (Huang Binhong)

550 Diana, Princess of Wales

1997. Return of Hong Kong to China.

2574 **549** 200 c. multicoloured . . 10 10
2575 – 300 c. multicoloured . . 10 15
2576 – 400 c. multicoloured . . 15 20
2577 – 500 c. multicoloured . . 20 25
2578 – 600 c. multicoloured . . 20 25
2579 – 800 c. multicoloured . . 30 35
2580 – 1000 c. multicoloured . . 35 40
2581 – 2000 c. multicoloured . . 70 75

DESIGNS: 300 c. to 2000 c. Landscape paintings by Huang Binhong.

1997. Christmas. Paintings. As T **284a** of Gambia. Multicoloured.

2584 200 c. "Cupid" (Botticelli) . . 10 10
2585 550 c. "Zephyr and Chloris" (Botticelli) 20 25
2586 800 c. "Triumphant Cupid" (Caravaggio) 30 35
2587 1100 c. "The Seven Works of Mercy" (Caravaggio) . . . 40 45
2588 1500 c. "The Toilet of Venus" (Diego Velazquez) 55 60
2589 2000 c. "Freeing of St. Peter" (Raphael) 70 75

1997. Diana, Princess of Wales Commemoration. Multicoloured (except Nos. 2591, 2596, 2602).

2591 1200 c. Type **550** (red) 45 50
2592 1200 c. Wearing blue suit and holding flowers 45 50
2593 1200 c. Looking right 45 50
2594 1200 c. Sitting crossed-legged . 45 50
2595 1200 c. With Prince William . 45 50
2596 1200 c. Wearing spotted scarf (blue and black) 45 50
2597 1200 c. Wearing pink shirt . . 45 50
2598 1200 c. Wearing red dress . . 45 50
2599 1200 c. Carrying bouquet . . 45 50
2600 1200 c. Wearing sunglasses . . 45 50
2601 1200 c. With children 45 50
2602 1200 c. Wearing hat (brown and black) 45 50

551 Horse

1998. Animals of the Chinese Lunar Calendar. Multicoloured.

2604 400 c. Type **551** 15 20
2605 400 c. Monkey 15 20
2606 400 c. Ram 15 20
2607 400 c. Cock 15 20
2608 400 c. Dog 15 20
2609 400 c. Ox 15 20
2610 400 c. Rabbit 15 20
2611 400 c. Pig 15 20
2612 400 c. Snake 15 20
2613 400 c. Dragon 15 20
2614 400 c. Tiger 15 20
2615 400 c. Rat 15 20

552 Mortie and Ferdie (January)

554 Maya Agelou

553 Union Pacific SD60M Diesel Locomotive No. 6331, U.S.A.

1998. A Year in the Life of Mickey Mouse and Friends. Walt Disney cartoon characters. Multicoloured.

2616 1000 c. Type **552** . . . . . . 1·00 1·00
2617 1000 c. Minnie on Valentine's Day (February) . . . . . 1·00 1·00
2618 1000 c. Goofy with kite (March) 1·00 1·00
2619 1000 c. Mickey, Minnie and Pluto in rain (April) . . . . 1·00 1·00
2620 1000 c. Minnie with flowers (May) . . . . 1·00 1·00
2621 1000 c. Daisy watering garden (June) . . . . 1·00 1·00
2622 1000 c. Donald at Independance Day celebrations (July) . . 1·00 1·00
2623 1000 c. Donald and Daisy on the beach (August) . . . . 1·00 1·00
2624 1000 c. Morty and Ferdie returning to school (September) . . . . . . 1·00 1·00
2625 1000 c. Hewey, Dewey and Louie at Hallowe'en (October) . . . . 1·00 1·00
2626 1000 c. Mickey on Thanksgiving Day (November) . . . . 1·00 1·00
2627 1000 c. Mickey and Minnie at Christmas (December) . . . 1·00 1·00

1998. Trains of the World. Multicoloured.

2629 300 c. Type **553** 10 15
2630 500 c. ETR 450 high-speed train, Italy 20 25
2631 800 c. X200 high-speed train, Sweden 30 35
2632 800 c. SPS steam locomotive, Pakistan 30 35
2633 800 c. Class WP steam locomotive, India 30 35
2634 800 c. Class QJ steam locomotive, China 30 35
2635 800 c. Type 12 steam locomotive, Belgium . . . 30 35
2636 800 c. Class P8 steam locomotive, Germany . . . 30 35
2637 800 c. Class "Castle" steam locomotive, Great Britain . 30 35
2638 800 c. Tank locomotive, Austria 30 35
2639 800 c. Class P36 steam locomotive, Russia 30 35
2640 800 c. Steam locomotive "William Mason", U.S.A. . 30 35
2641 800 c. AVE high-speed train, Spain 30 35
2642 800 c. Diesel locomotive No. 1602, Luxembourg 30 35
2643 800 c. "Hikari" express train, Japan 30 35
2644 800 c. Santa Fe Railroad GM F7 "Warbonnet" diesel locomotive, U.S.A. 30 35
2645 800 c. Class E1500 diesel locomotive, Morocco . . . 30 35
2646 800 c. Class "Deltic" diesel locomotive, Great Britain . 30 35
2647 800 c. XPT high-speed train, Australia 30 35
2648 800 c. Channel Tunnel shuttle train, France and Great Britain 30 35
2649 800 c. Class 201 diesel locomotive, Ireland 30 35
2650 1000 c. TGV Duplex high-speed train, France 35 40
2651 2000 c. Class EL diesel locomotive, Australia . . . 70 75
2652 3000 c. Eurostar high-speed train, Great Britain . . . . 1·10 1·25

1998. Great Writers of the 20th Century. Mult.

2654 350 c. Type **554** 15 20
2655 350 c. Alex Haley 15 20
2656 350 c. Charles Johnson 15 20
2657 350 c. Richard Wright 15 20
2658 350 c. Toni Cade Bambara . . 15 20
2659 350 c. Henri Louis Gates Jr . . 15 20

555 Breguet Br 14 B2, France

1998. History of Aviation. Multicoloured.

2660 800 c. Type **555** 30 35
2661 800 c. Curtiss BF2C-1 Goshawk, U.S.A. 30 35
2662 800 c. Supermarine Spitfire Mk IX, Great Britain . . . 30 35
2663 800 c. Fiat G.50, Italy 30 35
2664 800 c. Douglas B-18A, U.S.A. . 30 35
2665 800 c. Boeing FB-5, U.S.A. . . 30 35
2666 800 c. Bristol F2B "Brisfit", Great Britain 30 35
2667 800 c. Hawker Fury 1, Great Britain 30 35
2668 800 c. Fiat CR-42, Italy . . . 30 35
2669 800 c. Messerschmitt Bf 109 E-7, Germany 30 35
2670 800 c. Lockheed PV-2 Harpoon, U.S.A. 30 35
2671 800 c. Airspeed Oxford Mk 1, Great Britain 30 35
2672 800 c. Junkers Ju 87D-1, Germany 30 35
2673 800 c. Yakovlev Yak-9D, U.S.S.R. 30 35
2674 800 c. North American P-51D Mustang, U.S.A. 30 35
2675 800 c. Douglas A-206 Havoc, U.S.A. 30 35
2676 800 c. Supermarine Attacker F1, Great Britain 30 35
2677 800 c. Mikoyan Gurevich MiG-15, U.S.S.R. 30 35

556 "Empress of Ireland" (liner)

1998. Famous Ships. Multicoloured.

2679 800 c. Type **556** 30 35
2680 800 c. "Transylvania" (liner) . 30 35
2681 800 c. "Mauretania I" (liner) . 30 35
2682 800 c. "Reliance" (liner) . . . 30 35
2683 800 c. "Aquitania" (liner) . . 30 35
2684 800 c. "Lapland" (liner) . . . 30 35
2685 800 c. "Cap Polonio" (liner) . 30 35
2686 800 c. "France I", 1910 (liner) . 30 35
2687 800 c. "Imperator" (liner) . . 30 35
2688 800 c. H.M.S. "Rodney" (battleship) 30 35
2689 800 c. U.S.S. "Alabama" (battleship) 30 35
2690 800 c. H.M.S. "Nelson" (battleship) 30 35
2691 800 c. "Ormonde" (camouflaged liner) 30 35
2692 800 c. U.S.S. "Radford" (destroyer) 30 35
2693 800 c. "Empress of Russia" (camouflaged liner) 30 35
2694 800 c. Type XIV U-boat . . . 30 35
2695 800 c. Japanese Type A midget submarine 30 35
2696 800 c. "Brin" (Italian submarine) 30 35

No. 2681 is inscribed "MAURITANIA" in error.

1998. "Israel 98" International Stamp Exhibition, Tel-Aviv. Nos. 2362/4 optd with Emblem.

2698 400 c. St. Stephen's Gate and "Jasminum mesnyi" 15 20
2699 600 c. The Citadel, Tower of David and "Nerium oleander" 20 25
2700 800 c. Chapel of the Ascension and "Romulea bulbocodium" 30 35

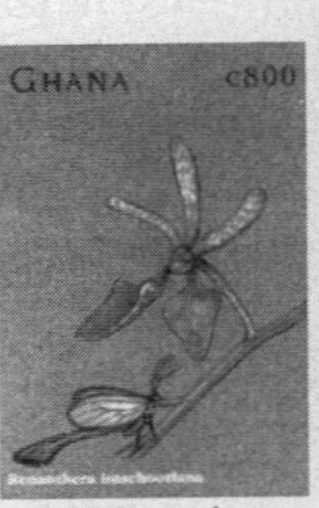

558 "Renanthera imschootiana"

559 Elvis Presley

1998. Orchids of the World. Multicoloured.

2702 800 c. Type **558** 30 35
2703 800 c. "Arachnis flos-aeris" . . 30 35
2704 800 c. "Restrepia lansbergi" . . 30 35
2705 800 c. "Paphiopedilum tonsum" 30 35
2706 800 c. "Phalaenopsis ebauche" 30 35
2707 800 c. "Pleione limprichti" . . 30 35
2708 800 c. "Phragmipedium schroderae" 30 35
2709 800 c. "Zygopetalum clayii" . . 30 35
2710 800 c. "Vanda coerulea" . . . 30 35
2711 800 c. "Odontonia boussole" . . 30 35
2712 800 c. "Disa uniflora" 30 35
2713 800 c. "Dendrobium bigibbum" 30 35

1998. 30th Anniv of Elvis Presley's "68 Special" Television Programme. Multicoloured.

2715 800 c. Type **559** 30 35
2716 800 c. Elvis in white suit . . . 30 35
2717 800 c. In leather jacket, holding microphone 30 35
2718 800 c. Wearing light blue jacket 30 35
2719 800 c. Elvis with silhouetted figures in background . . . 30 35
2720 800 c. Elvis with guitar and microphone 30 35

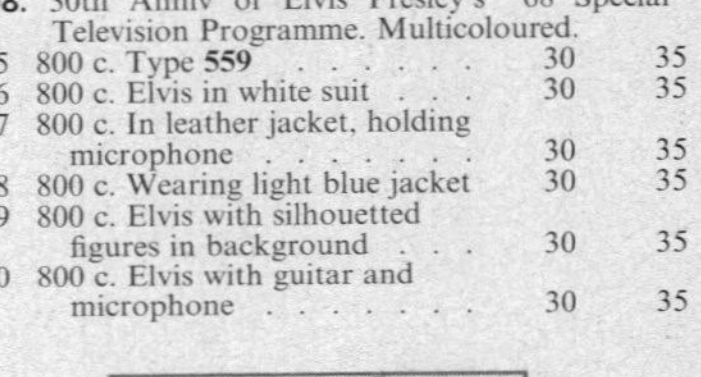

560 Crest of Accra Metropolitan Assembly and Surf Boats

1998. Centenary of Accra Metropolitan Assembly. Multicoloured.

2721 200 c. Type **560** 10 10
2722 550 c. King Tackie Tawiah I . 20 25
2723 800 c. Achimota School . . . 30 35
2724 1100 c. Korle Bu Hospital . . 40 45
2725 1500 c. Christianborg Castle . 55 60

561 Tetteh Quarshie (cocoa industry pioneer)

1998. 50th Anniv of Ghana Cocoa Board. Multicoloured.

2726 200 c. Type **561** 10 10
2727 550 c. Ripe hybrid cocoa pods . 20 25
2728 800 c. Opening cocoa pods . . 30 35
2729 1100 c. Fermenting cocoa beans 40 45
2730 1500 c. Loading freighter with cocoa 55 60

MINIMUM PRICE

The minimum price quoted is 10p which represents a handling charge rather than a basis for valuing common stamps. For further notes about prices see introductory pages.

562 Bamboo

1998. Oriental Flowers. Multicoloured.
2731 2000 c. Type **562** 70 75
2732 2000 c. Cherry blossom . . . 70 75
2733 2000 c. Yellow chrysanthemum 70 75
2734 2000 c. Orchid 70 75
2735 2000 c. Green peony 70 75
2736 2000 c. Red peony 70 75
2737 2000 c. Pink peony 70 75
2738 2000 c. White peony 70 75

563 Two Dolphins

1998. International Year of the Ocean. Multicoloured.
2740 500 c. Type **563** 20 25
2741 500 c. Dolphin 20 25
2742 500 c. Seagull 20 25
2743 500 c. Least tern 20 25
2744 500 c. Emperor angelfish . . . 20 25
2745 500 c. White ear (juvenile) . . 20 25
2746 500 c. Blue shark and diver . . 20 25
2747 500 c. Parrotfish 20 25
2748 500 c. Dottyback 20 25
2749 500 c. Blue-spotted stingray . . 20 25
2750 500 c. Masked butterflyfish . . 20 25
2751 500 c. Jackknife-fish 20 25
2752 500 c. Octopus 20 25
2753 500 c. Lionfish 20 25
2754 500 c. Seadragon 20 25
2755 500 c. Rock cod 20 25

Nos. 2740/55 were printed together, se-tenant, with the backgrounds forming a composite design.
No. 2745 is inscribed "Whit Ear" in error.

1998. Millennium Series. Famous People of the Twentieth Century. Inventors. As T **289a** of Gambia. Multicoloured.
2757 1000 c. Thomas Edison 35 40
2758 1000 c. Peephole kinetoscope (Edison) (53 × 38 mm) . . . 35 40
2759 1000 c. Tesla coil (53 × 38 mm) 35 40
2760 1000 c. Nikola Tesla 35 40
2761 1000 c. Gottlieb Daimler . . . 35 40
2762 1000 c. Motorcycle (Daimler) (53 × 38 mm) 35 40
2763 1000 c. Early transmitter circuit (Marconi) and dish aerial (53 × 38 mm) 35 40
2764 1000 c. Guglielmo Marconi . . 35 40
2765 1000 c. Orville and Wilbur Wright 35 40
2766 1000 c. "Flyer I" (Wright Brothers) (53 × 38 mm) . . . 35 40
2767 1000 c. Neon lights and signs (Claude) (53 × 38 mm) . . . 35 40
2768 1000 c. Georges Claude . . . 35 40
2769 1000 c. Alexander Graham Bell 35 40
2770 1000 c. Early telephone transmitter (Bell) (53 × 38 mm) . . 35 40
2771 1000 c. Uses of lasers (Townes) (53 × 38 mm) 35 40
2772 1000 c. Charles Townes . . . 35 40

564 British Colourpoint with Tree Decoration

1998. Christmas. Cats and Dogs. Multicoloured.
2774 500 c. Type **564** 20 25
2775 600 c. American shorthair kitten with basket 20 25
2776 800 c. Peke-faced Persian on piano keys 30 35
2777 1000 c. German spitz dog in box 35 40
2778 2000 c. British shorthair Blue with antlers 70 75
2779 3000 c. Persian in sleigh . . . 1·10 1·25

1999. 25th Death Anniv of Pablo Picasso (painter). As T **293a** of Gambia. Multicoloured.
2781 1000 c. "Composition with Butterfly" 35 40
2782 1000 c. "Mandolin and Clarinet" (vert) 35 40
2783 2000 c. "Woman throwing a Stone" 70 75

564a Lampredi

1999. Birth Centenary of Enzo Ferrari (car manufacturer). Multicoloured.
2785 2000 c. Type **564a** 70 75
2786 2000 c. 250 GT Cabriolet . . . 70 75
2787 2000 c. 121 LM 70 75

1999. 19th World Scout Jamboree, Chile. As T **291b** of Gambia. Multicoloured.
2789 2000 c. Scout salute 70 75
2790 2000 c. Scout with backpack . 70 75
2791 2000 c. Bowline knot 70 75

1999. 50th Death Anniv of Mahatma Gandhi. As T **292** of Gambia. Multicoloured.
2793 2000 c. Gandhi, 1931 . . . . 70 75
2794 2000 c. On Salt March, 1930 (53 × 38 mm) 70 75
2795 2000 c. Collecting natural salt, 1930 (53 × 38 mm) 70 75
2796 2000 c. After graduating from high school, 1887 . . . . 70 75

1999. 80th Anniv of Royal Air Force. As T **292** of Gambia. Multicoloured.
2798 2000 c. C-130 Hercules on tarmac 70 75
2799 2000 c. HC2 Chinook helicopter 70 75
2800 2000 c. C-130 Hercules W2 taking off 70 75
2801 2000 c. Panavia Tornado F3 . 70 75

1999. 1st Death Anniv of Diana, Princess of Wales. As T **293a** of Gambia.
2803 1000 c. multicoloured 35 40

565 Farmer working

1999. Chinese New Year ("Year of the Rabbit"). "Farmer and the Hare" (Han Fei Tzu). Mult.
2804 1400 c. Type **565** 50 55
2805 1400 c. Farmer watching hare hit tree 50 55
2806 1400 c. Farmer with dead hare . 50 55
2807 1400 c. Farmer asleep under tree 50 55

566 Shirley Temple praying

1999. 70th Birthday of Shirley Temple (actress). Showing film scenes from "Curly Top". Multicoloured.
2808 1000 c. Type **566** 35 40
2809 1000 c. Man looking at painting 35 40
2810 1000 c. With butler 35 40
2811 1000 c. As old woman in rocking chair 35 40
2812 1000 c. With mother (horiz) . . 35 40
2813 1000 c. Wearing brown coat and bowler hat (horiz) . . . 35 40
2814 1000 c. With cuddly toys (horiz) 35 40
2815 1000 c. Pulling father's tie (horiz) 35 40
2816 1000 c. With family (horiz) . . 35 40
2817 1000 c. Watching parents (horiz) 35 40

567 Corythosaurus

1999. Prehistoric Animals. Multicoloured.
2819 400 c. Type **567** 15 20
2820 600 c. Struthiomimus 20 25
2821 800 c. Pterodactylus 30 35
2822 800 c. Scelidosaurus 30 35
2823 800 c. Pteranodon 30 35
2824 800 c. Plateosaurus 30 35
2825 800 c. Ornithosuchus 30 35
2826 800 c. Kentrosaurus 30 35
2827 800 c. Hypsognathus 30 35
2828 800 c. Erythrosuchus 30 35
2829 800 c. Stegoceras 30 35
2830 800 c. Ankylosaurus 30 35
2831 800 c. Anatosaurus 30 35
2832 800 c. Diplodocus 30 35
2833 800 c. Monoclonius 30 35
2834 800 c. Tyrannosaurus 30 35
2835 800 c. Camptosaurus 30 35
2836 800 c. Ornitholestes 30 35
2837 800 c. Archaeopteryx 30 25
2838 800 c. Allosaurus 30 35
2839 1000 c. Lambeosaurus 35 40
2840 2000 c. Hesperasuchus 70 75

Nos. 2821/9 and 2830/8 respectively were printed together, se-tenant, with the backgrounds forming composite designs.

568 Badgers

1999. Endangered Species. Multicoloured.
2842 200 c. Type **568** 10 15
2843 400 c. Azure-winged magpie . . 15 20
2844 600 c. White stork 20 25
2845 800 c. Red fox 30 30
2846 1000 c. European bee eater ("Merops apiaster") 35 40
2847 1000 c. Hoopoe ("Upupa epops") 35 40
2848 1000 c. Red deer 35 40
2849 1000 c. Short-toed eagle ("Cycaetus gallicus") 35 40
2850 1000 c. Lacerta oceliata (lizard) 35 40
2851 1000 c. Lynx 35 40
2852 1000 c. Pine martin 35 40
2853 1000 c. Tawny owl ("Strix aluco") 35 40
2854 1000 c. Wiid boar 35 40
2855 1000 c. Northern goshawk ("Accipiter gentilis") . . . 35 40
2856 1000 c. Garden dormouse . . . 35 40
2857 1000 c. Stag beetles 35 40
2858 2000 c. European black vulture (vert) 35 40
2859 3000 c. Jay (vert) 35 40

Nos. 2846/51 and 2852/7 respectively were printed together, se-tenant, with the backgrounds forming composite designs.

569 California Sister Butterfly

1999. "Australia '99" International Stamp Exhibition, Melbourne. Butterflies. Multicoloured.
2861 300 c. Type **569** 10 15
2862 500 c. Red-splashed sulphur . . 20 20
2863 600 c. Checked white 20 25
2864 800 c. Blue emperor 30 30
2865 1000 c. Red admiral (vert) . . 35 40
2866 1000 c. Buckeye (vert) 35 40
2867 1000 c. Desert chequered skipper (vert) 35 40
2868 1000 c. Orange sulphur (vert) . 35 40
2869 1000 c. Tiger swallowtail (vert) 35 40
2870 1000 c. Orange-bordered blue (vert) 35 40
2871 1000 c. Gulf fritillary "vanillae") (vert) 35 40
2872 1000 c. Monarch (vert) 35 40
2873 1000 c. Small tortoiseshell (vert) 35 40
2874 1000 c. Brimstone (vert) . . . 35 40
2875 1000 c. Camberwell beauty (vert) 35 40
2876 1000 c. Marbled white (vert) . . 35 40
2877 1000 c. Purple Emperor (vert) . 35 40
2878 1000 c. Clouded yellow (vert) . 35 40
2879 1000 c. Ladoga camilla (vert) . 35 40
2880 1000 c. Marsh fritillary (vert) . 35 40

Nos. 2865/72 and 2873/80 respectively were printed together, se-tenant, with the backgrounds forming composite designs.
No. 2862 is inscribed "Red-splashed Sulfer" and No. 2864 "Blue Emperorl", both in error.

570 "Amorphophallus flavovirens"

571 ICE 2 (Germany), 1966

1999.
2882 **570** 200 c. multicoloured . . . 10 15

1999. Railways of the World. Multicoloured.
2883 400 c. Type **571** 15 20
2884 500 c. M41 No. 2112 (Hungary), 1982 . . . . . 20 20
2885 600 c. DVR No. 2526 (Finland), 1963 . . . . . . 20 25
2886 1000 c. Class AVE 100 (Spain), 1992 . . . . 35 40
2887 1300 c. Conrail EMD SD80 No. 4110 (U.S.A.), 1993 . . 50 55
2888 1300 c. Columbus and Greenville EMD SDP35 No. 701 (U.S.A.), 1964–6 . . . . 50 55
2889 1300 c. Providence and Worcester MLW M420 (U.S.A.), 1973–77 . . . . . 50 55
2890 1300 c. Missouri Pacific C36-7 No. 9044 (U.S.A.), 1978–85 . 50 55
2891 1300 c. Virginia and Maryland ALCO C-420 No. 203 (U.S.A.), 1963–68 . . . . . 50 55
2892 1300 c. Reading EMD GP30 No. 3615 (U.S.A.), 1961–63 . 50 55
2893 1300 c. Illinois Terminal EMD GP7 No. 1506 (U.S.A.), 1949/54 . . . . 50 55
2894 1300 c. Canadian Pacific EMD SD 38-2 (Canada), 1972–79 . 50 55
2895 1300 c. EMD SD 60M 500 No. 6058 (U.S.A.), 1989–96 . . . 50 55
2896 1300 c. GE U25C No. 2808 (U.S.A.), 1963–65 . . . . . 50 55
2897 1300 c. EMD GP 28 (U.S.A.), 1961–63 . . . . 50 55
2898 1300 c. EMD SD 9 No. 162 (U.S.A.), 1954–59 . . . . . 50 55

1999. "iBRA '99" International Stamp Exhibition, Nuremberg. Multicoloured. As T **298a** of Gambia.
2900 500 c. "Schomberg" (sailing ship) and Hanover 1850 1 ggr. stamp 20 25
2901 800 c. Class P8 railway locomotive and Hamburg 1859 ½ s. . 30 35
2902 1000 c. "Schomberg" (sailing ship) and Lubeck 1859 ½ s. . 35 40
2903 2000 c. Class P8 railway locomotive and Heligoland 1867 ½ s. 70 75

1999. 150th Death Anniv of Katsushika Hokusai (Japanese artist). Multicoloured as T **298b** of Gambia, but horiz.
2905 1300 c. "Girl picking Plum Blossoms" 50 55
2906 1300 c. "Surveying a Region" . 50 55
2907 1300 c. "Sumo Wrestler" (bending down) 50 55
2908 1300 c. "Sumo Wrestler" (dancing) 50 55
2909 1300 c. "Landscape with Seaside Village" 50 55
2910 1300 c. "Courtiers crossing a Bridge" 50 55
2911 1300 c. "Climbing the Mountain" 50 55
2912 1300 c. "Nakahara in Sagami Province" 50 55
2913 1300 c. "Sumo Wrestlers" . . 50 55
2914 1300 c. "An Oiran and Maid by a Fence" 50 55
2915 1300 c. "Fujiwara Yoshitaka" . 50 55

1999. 10th Anniv of United Nations Rights of the Child Convention. Vert designs as T **298c** of Gambia. Multicoloured.
2917 3000 c. Boy smiling and U.N. Headquarters Building . . . 1·10 1·25
2918 3000 c. Dove and Earth . . . 1·10 1·25
2919 3000 c. Mother and baby . . . 1·10 1·25

Nos. 2917/19 were printed together, se-tenant, forming a composite design.

1999. 250th Birth Anniv of Johann von Goethe (German writer). As T **298d** of Gambia. Multicoloured.
2922 2000 c. Wagner entreats Faust in his study 70 75
2923 2000 c. Von Goethe and Von Schiller 70 75
2924 2000 c. Mephistopheles disguised as the Fool . . . 70 75

1999. 30th Anniv of First Manned Landing on Moon. T **298e** of Gambia. Multicoloured.
2926 1300 c. Command module . . 50 55
2927 1300 c. Lunar module ascending 50 55
2928 1300 c. Giant moon rock . . . 50 55
2929 1300 c. Lunar module's aerials and Earth from Moon . . 50 55
2930 1300 c. Neil Armstrong . . . 50 55
2931 1300 c. "One small step" (alighting on lunar surface) . 50 55

Nos 2926/31 were printed together, se-tenant, forming a composite design.
No. 2927 is inscribed "LUNAR MODULE ASCENSION" in error.

572 Gate of Understanding, Macao

1999. "China '99" World Philatelic Exhibition, Beijing. Return of Macao to China.
2933 **572** 1000 c. multicoloured . . . 35 40

1999. "Queen Elizabeth the Queen Mother's Century". As T **304a** of Gambia.
2934 2000 c. black and gold 70 75
2935 2000 c. black and gold 70 75
2936 2000 c. multicoloured 70 75
2937 2000 c. multicoloured 70 75
DESIGNS: No. 2934, Lady Elizabeth Bowes-Lyon with her brother, David, 1904; 2935, Queen Mother in Rhodesia, 1957; 2936, Queen Mother seated, 1970; 2937, Queen Mother holding bouquet, 1992.

573 Dr. Ephraim Apu

1999. Birth Centenary of Dr. Ephraim Apu (traditional musicologist). Multicoloured.
2939 200 c. Type **573** 10 15
2940 800 c. Playing Odurugya flute . . 30 35
2941 1100 c. Indigenous flutes 40 45

574 Grandma Alice and Village

1999. 25th Anniv of S.O.S. in Ghana (200, 1100 c.) and 50th Anniv of S.O.S. Kinderdorf International (children's villages) (others). Multicoloured.
2942 200 c. Type **574** 10 15
2943 550 c. Kindergarten 20 25
2944 800 c. Hermann Gneiner (founder) and Asiakwa S.O.S. building 30 35
2945 1100 c. Preparing food 40 45

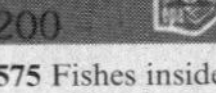

575 Fishes inside Cloud
576 Peace Doves flying from Ghana

1999. Save the Ozone Layer Campaign. Mult.
2946 200 c. Type **575** 10 15
2947 550 c. African looking at diagram of ozone layer . . . 10 25
2948 800 c. Earth weeping 30 35
2949 1100 c. Africans shielding Earth 40 45
2950 1500 c. CFC and no-CFC appliances 55 60

1999. New Millennium. Multicoloured.
2951 300 c. Type **576** 10 15
2952 700 c. Kwame Nkrumah (first President) speaking (horiz) . 25 30
2953 1200 c. Clock tower, University of Ghana 45 50

577 Liu-Yi meets Daughter of the Dragon King

2000. Chinese New Year ("Year of the Dragon"). Vert designs showing scenes from "Daughter of the Dragon King". Each design brown and silver.
2954 1600 c. Type **577** 60 65
2955 1600 c. Liu-Yi and Fairy Soldier 60 65
2956 1600 c. Liu-Yi and the Dragon King 60 65
2957 1600 c. Liu-Yi, Dragon King and Red Dragon 60 65
2958 1600 c. Red Dragon and Dragon of Jing River fighting 60 65
2959 1600 c. Dragon King with his daughter and brother . . . 60 65
2960 1700 c. Dragon King's brother inviting Liu-Yi to marry his niece 65 70
2961 1700 c. Liu-Yi bidding farewell to Dragon King 65 70
2962 1700 c. Liu-Yi with gifts from Dragon King 65 70
2963 1700 c. Liu-Yi with third wife . 65 70
2964 1700 c. Liu-Yi with third wife and son 65 70
2965 1700 c. Liu-Yi realises that third wife is Daughter of the Dragon King 65 70

578 Black-faced Impala

2000. African Wildlife. Multicoloured.
2966 300 c. Type **578** 10 15
2967 500 c. Cheetah 15 20
2968 1000 c. Wildebeest 35 40
2969 1100 c. Chimpanzee (vert) . . 40 45
2970 1100 c. Boomslang tree snake (vert) 40 45
2971 1100 c. Vulture (vert) 40 45
2972 1100 c. Leopard (vert) 40 45
2973 1100 c. African rhinoceros (vert) 40 45
2974 1100 c. Zebra (vert) 40 45
2975 1100 c. Crowned crane (vert) . 40 45
2976 1100 c. Female lesser Kudu (vert) 40 45
2977 1200 c. Purple roller (vert) . . 45 50
2978 1200 c. Pelicans (vert) 45 50
2979 1200 c. Egrets (vert) 45 50
2980 1200 c. Orange-breasted waxbill (vert) 45 50
2981 1200 c. Giraffe (vert) 45 50
2982 1200 c. African buffalo (vert) . 45 50
2983 1200 c. Elelphant (vert) 45 50
2984 1200 c. African lion (vert) . . . 45 50
2985 3000 c. Hippopotamus . . . . 1·10 1·25
Nos. 2969/76 and 2977/84 were each printed together, se-tenant, with the backgrounds forming composite designs.

POSTAGE DUE STAMPS

1958. Postage Due stamps of Gold Coast optd **GHANA** and bar.
D 9 **D 1** 1d. black 10 20
D10 2d. black 10 25
D11 3d. black 10 30
D12 6d. black 15 65
D13 1s. black . . . . 20 1·25

D 3

1958.
D14 **D 3** 1d. red 10 30
D15 2d. green 10 30
D16 3d. orange 10 30
D17 6d. blue 10 50
D18 1s. violet . . . . 15 2·00

1965. Surch **Ghana New Currency 19th July, 1965.** and value.
D19 **D 3** 1 p. on 1d. 10 60
D20 2 p. on 2d. 10 60
D21 3 p. on 3d. 10 60
D22 6 p. on 6d. . . . . . . 10 1·50
D23 12 p. on 1s. . . . . . . 15 2·00

1968. Nos. D20/2 additionally surch.
D24 **D 3** $1\frac{1}{2}$ n.p. on 2 p. on 2d. . . 5·50 4·25
D25 $2\frac{1}{2}$ n.p. on 3 p. on 3d. . . 1·00 5·00
D26 5 n.p. on 6 p. on 6d. . . . 1·00

1970. Inscr in new currency.
D27 **D 3** 1 n.p. red . . . . . . 1·00 3·50
D28 $1\frac{1}{2}$ n.p. green . . . . . 1·00 4·00
D29 $2\frac{1}{2}$ n.p. orange . . . . 1·40 4·50
D30 5 n.p. blue . . . . . . 2·00 4·75
D31 10 n.p. violet . . . . . 2·75 6·00

1980. Currency described as "p".
D32 **D 3** 2p. orange . . . . . . 1·00 2·75
D33 3 p. brown . . . . . . 1·00 2·75

GIBRALTAR Pt. 1

A British colony at the W. entrance to the Mediterranean.

1886. 12 pence = 1 shilling;
20 shillings = 1 pound.
1971. 100 (new) pence = 1 pound.

1886. Stamps of Bermuda (Queen Victoria) optd **GIBRALTAR**.

No.	Type	Description	Unused	Used
1	9	½d. green	9·50	6·50
2		1d. red	50·00	4·25
3		2d. purple	£100	75·00
4		2½d. blue	£120	3·25
5		4d. orange	£120	85·00
6		6d. lilac	£200	£180
7		1s. brown	£425	£350

2

7

1886. Various frames.

No.	Type	Description	Unused	Used
39	2	½d. green	4·00	1·25
40		1d. red	5·50	35
10		2d. purple	30·00	17·00
42		2½d. blue	24·00	40
12		4d. brown	75·00	75·00
13		6d. lilac	£100	£100
14		1s. brown	£180	£180

1889. Surch with new value in **CENTIMOS**.

No.	Type	Description	Unused	Used
15	2	5 c. on ½d. green	6·00	14·00
16		10 c. on 1d. red	11·00	6·50
17		25 c. on 2d. purple	4·50	5·00
18		25 c. on 2½d. blue	25·00	2·25
19		40 c. on 4d. brown	60·00	80·00
20		50 c. on 6d. lilac	60·00	80·00
21		75 c. on 1s. brown	65·00	75·00

1889.

No.	Type	Description	Unused	Used
22	7	5 c. green	4·00	70
23		10 c. red	4·00	45
24		20 c. green and brown	38·00	18·00
25		20 c. green	10·00	50·00
26		25 c. blue	13·00	70
27		40 c. brown	3·50	2·50
28		50 c. lilac	3·00	1·75
29		75 c. green	32·00	32·00
30		1 p. brown	75·00	20·00
31		1 p. brown and blue	4·50	3·75
32		2 p. black and red	9·50	26·00
33		5 p. grey	42·00	£100

1898. As 1886.

No.	Type	Description	Unused	Used
41	2	2d. purple and blue	21·00	1·50
43		4d. brown and green	18·00	6·50
44		6d. violet and red	40·00	20·00
45		1s. brown and red	35·00	16·00

8

9

1903.

No.	Type	Description	Unused	Used
66	8	½d. green	2·50	90
57c		1d. purple on red	3·25	85
58a		2d. green and red	8·00	3·75
49		2½d. purple and black on blue	4·25	60
60a		6d. purple and violet	22·00	8·50
61		1s. black and red	42·00	11·00
62	9	2s. green and blue	65·00	85·00
53		4s. purple and green	80·00	£140
54		8s. purple and black on blue	£110	£140
55		£1 purple and black on red	£475	£550

1907.

No.	Type	Description	Unused	Used
67	8	1d. red	5·00	45
68		2d. grey	7·50	9·00
69		2½d. blue	5·00	1·40
70		6d. purple	£120	£375
71		1s. black on green	22·00	20·00
72	9	2s. purple and blue on blue	48·00	45·00
73		4s. black and red	90·00	£130
74		8s. purple and green	£180	£180

1912. As T 8/9, but portrait of King George V. (3d. A. Inscr "3 PENCE". B. Inscr "THREE PENCE").

No.	Type	Description	Unused	Used
89		½d. green	1·25	1·25
90		1d. red	1·50	80
91a		1½a. brown	1·50	30
93		2d. grey	1·25	1·00
79		2½d. blue	4·00	2·00
95a		3d. blue (A)	2·00	1·50
109		3d. blue (B)	7·50	2·00
97a		6d. purple	1·60	3·50
81		1s. black on green	8·00	3·25
102a		1s. olive and black	14·00	12·00
82		2s. purple and blue on blue	26·00	3·50
103		2s. brown and black	9·50	29·00
104		2s. 6d. green and black	9·50	17·00
83		4s. black and red	30·00	55·00
105		5s. red and black	14·00	50·00
84		8s. purple and green	75·00	90·00
106		10s. blue and black	32·00	70·00
85		£1 purple and black on red	£140	£190
107		£1 orange and black	£140	£180
108		£5 violet and black	£1400	£3500

1918 Optd **WAR TAX**.

No.	Type	Description	Unused	Used
86		½d. green (No. 89)	70	1·75

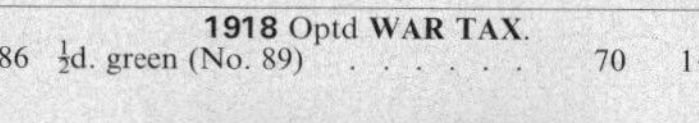

13 The Rock of Gibraltar

1931.

No.	Type	Description	Unused	Used
110	13	1d. red	2·25	2·50
111		1½d. brown	1·75	2·25
112		2d. grey	5·00	1·25
113		3d. blue	5·00	2·75

1935. Silver Jubilee. As T **10a** of Gambia.

No.	Type	Description	Unused	Used
114		2d. blue and black	1·60	2·50
115		3d. brown and blue	3·25	3·50
116		6d. green and blue	9·50	12·00
117		1s. grey and purple	9·50	9·50

1937. Coronation. As T **10b** of Gambia.

No.	Type	Description	Unused	Used
118		½d. green	25	15
119		2d. grey	80	2·25
120		3d. blue	2·00	2·25

14 King George VI

15 Rock of Gibraltar

1938. King George VI.

No.	Type	Description	Unused	Used
121	14	½d. green	10	40
122b	15	1d. brown	50	55
123		1½d. red	35·00	75
123b	–	1½d. violet	30	1·00
124a	–	2d. grey	55	35
124c	–	2d. red	40	60
125b	–	3d. blue	30	30
125c	–	5d. orange	70	1·25
126b	–	6d. red and violet	2·25	1·75
127b	–	1s. black and green	3·00	4·00
128b	–	2s. black and brown	4·00	6·50
129b	–	5s. black and red	12·00	17·00
130a	–	10s. black and blue	35·00	25·00
131	14	£1 orange	38·00	45·00

DESIGNS—HORIZ: 2d. The Rock (North side); 3d., 5d. Europa Point; 6d. Moorish Castle; 1s. Southport Gate; 2s. Eliott Memorial; 5s. Government House; 10s. Catalan Bay.

1946. Victory. As T **11a** of Gambia.

No.	Type	Description	Unused	Used
132		½d. green	10	15
133		3d. blue	30	40

1948. Silver Wedding. As T **11b/11c** of Gambia.

No.	Type	Description	Unused	Used
134		½d. green	70	1·00
135		£1 orange	50·00	65·00

1949. U.P.U. As T **11d/11g** of Gambia.

No.	Type	Description	Unused	Used
136		2d. red	1·00	1·25
137		3d. blue	2·50	1·25
138		6d. purple	2·00	1·25
139		1s. green	1·60	2·75

1950. Inauguration of Legislative Council. Optd **NEW CONSTITUTION 1950**.

No.	Type	Description	Unused	Used
140		2d. red (No. 124c)	30	1·00
141		3d. blue (No. 125b)	55	1·00
142		6d. red and violet (No. 126b)	65	1·60
143		1s. black and green (No. 127b)	65	1·60

1953. Coronation. As T **11h** of Gambia.

No.	Type	Description	Unused	Used
144		½d. black and green	30	1·00

24 Cargo and Passenger Wharves

1953.

No.	Type	Description	Unused	Used
145	24	½d. blue and green	15	30
146	–	1d. green	1·50	30
147	–	1½d. black	90	90
148	–	2d. brown	1·50	50
149a	–	2½d. red	2·75	80
150	–	3d. blue	3·75	10
151	–	4d. blue	2·50	2·00
152	–	5d. purple	70	70
153	–	6d. black and blue	65	60
154a	–	1s. blue and brown	30	60
155a	–	2s. orange and violet	19·00	3·75
156	–	5s. brown	26·00	12·00
157	–	10s. brown and blue	50·00	35·00
158	–	£1 red and yellow	50·00	38·00

DESIGNS—HORIZ: 1d. South view from Straits; 1½d. Tuna fishing industry; 2d. Southport Gate; 2½d. Sailing in the Bay; 3d. Liner; 4d. Coaling wharf; 5d. Airport; 6d. Europa Point; 1s. Straits from Buena Vista; 2s. Rosia Bay and Straits; 5s. Main entrance, Government House. VERT: 10s. Tower of Homage, Moorish Castle; £1 Arms of Gibraltar.

1954. Royal Visit. As No. 150, but inscr "ROYAL VISIT 1954".

No.	Type	Description	Unused	Used
159		3d. blue	15	20

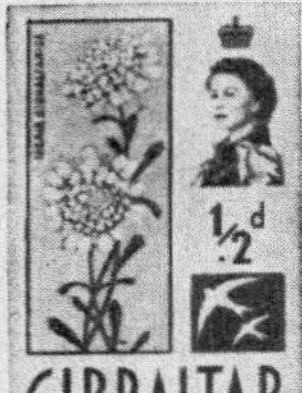

38 Gibraltar Candytuft

40 Rock and Badge of Gibraltar Regiment

1960.

No.	Type	Description	Unused	Used
160	38	½d. purple and green	15	30
161	–	1d. black and green	20	10
162	–	2d. blue and brown	30	20
163a	–	2½d. black and blue	40	30
164	–	3d. blue and orange	30	10
199	–	4d. brown and turquoise	30	70
166	–	6d. brown and green	70	60
167	–	7d. blue and red	90	90
168	–	9d. blue and turquoise	50	60
169	–	1s. brown and green	1·00	50
170	–	2s. brown and blue	14·00	2·50
171	–	5s. blue and green	8·00	6·00
172	–	10s. yellow and blue	16·00	11·00
173	40	£1 black and brown	17·00	12·00

DESIGNS (As Type 38):—HORIZ: 1d. Moorish Castle; 2d. St George's Hall; 3d. The Rock by moonlight; 4d. Catalan Bay; 1s. Barbary ape; 2s. Barbary Partridge; 5s. Blue Rock Thrush. VERT: 2½d. The keys; 6d. Map of Gibraltar; 7d. Air terminal; 9d. American War Memorial; 10s. Rock lily.

1963. Freedom from Hunger. As T **20a** of Gambia.

No.	Type	Description	Unused	Used
174		9d. sepia	9·00	1·50

1963. Centenary of Red Cross. As T **20b** of Gambia.

No.	Type	Description	Unused	Used
175		1d. red and black	1·50	1·75
176		9d. red and blue	14·00	3·50

1964. 400th Birth Anniv of Shakespeare. As T **22a** of Gambia.

No.	Type	Description	Unused	Used
177		7d. bistre	50	20

1964. New Constitution. Nos. 164 and 166 optd **NEW CONSTITUTION 1964.**

No.	Type	Description	Unused	Used
178		3d. blue and orange	20	10
179		6d. sepia and green	20	40

44 I.T.U. Emblem

1965. Centenary of I.T.U.

No.	Type	Description	Unused	Used
180	44	4d. green and yellow	4·00	50
181		2s. green and blue	11·00	3·25

45 I.C.Y. Emblem

1965. I.C.Y.

No.	Type	Description	Unused	Used
182	45	½d. green and lavender	20	1·50
183		4d. purple and turquoise	1·25	80

The value of the ½d. stamp is shown as "1/2".

46 Winston Churchill and St. Paul's Cathedral in Wartime

1966. Churchill Commemoration.

No.	Type	Description	Unused	Used
184	46	½d. blue	20	1·50
185		1d. green	30	10
186		4d. brown	1·25	10
187		9d. violet	1·25	2·25

47 Footballer's Legs, Ball and Jules Rimet Cup

1966. World Cup Football Championships.

No.	Type	Description	Unused	Used
188	47	2½d. multicoloured	75	50
189		6d. multicoloured	1·00	50

53 Red Seabream

1966. European Sea Angling Championships. Gibraltar.

No.	Type	Description	Unused	Used
190	53	4d. red, blue and black	30	10
191	–	7d. red, green and black	30	50
192	–	1s. brown, green and black	40	30

DESIGNS—HORIZ: 7d. Red scorpionfish. VERT: 1s. Stone bass.

54 W.H.O. Building

1966. Inauguration of W.H.O. Headquarters, Geneva.

No.	Type	Description	Unused	Used
193	54	6d. black, green and blue	2·75	1·75
194		9d. black, purple and ochre	3·25	1·75

56 "Our Lady of Europa"

1966. Centenary of Re-enthronement of "Our Lady of Europa".

No.	Type	Description	Unused	Used
195	56	2s. blue and black	30	80

56a "Education"

56b "Science"

56c "Culture"

1966. 20th Anniv of U.N.E.S.C.O.

No.	Type	Description	Unused	Used
196	56a	2d. multicoloured	25	10
197	56b	7d. yellow, violet and olive	80	10
198	56c	5s. black, purple and orange	3·25	3·00

57 H.M.S. "Victory"

1967. Multicoloured.

No.	Type	Description	Unused	Used
200		½d. Type 57	10	15
201		1d. "Arab" (early steamer)	10	10
202		2d. H.M.S. "Carmania" (merchant cruiser)	15	10
203		2½d. "Mons Calpe" (ferry)	30	30
204		3d. "Canberra" (liner)	20	10
205		4d. H.M.S. "Hood" (battle cruiser)	30	10
205a		5d. "Mirror" (cable ship)	3·25	55
206		6d. Xebec (sailing vessel)	30	50
207		7d. "Amerigo Vespucci" (Italian cadet ship)	30	45
208		9d. "Raffaello" (liner)	30	60
209		1s. "Royal Katherine" (galleon)	30	35
210		2s. H.M.S. "Ark Royal" (aircraft carrier, 1937)	3·50	2·50
211		5s. H.M.S. "Dreadnought" (nuclear submarine)	3·50	6·50
212		10s. "Neuralia" (liner)	14·00	22·00
213		£1 "Mary Celeste" (sailing vessel)	14·00	22·00

58 Aerial Ropeway

59 Mary, Joseph and Child Jesus

1967. International Tourist Year. Multicoloured.
214 7d. Type **58** 15 10
215 9d. Shark fishing (horiz) . . . 15 10
216 1s. Skin-diving (horiz) 20 15

1967. Christmas. Multicoloured.
217 2d. Type **59** 15 10
218 6d. Church window (vert) . . . 15 10

61 General Eliott and Route Map

1967. 250th Birth Anniv of General Eliott. Multicoloured.
219 4d. Type **61** 15 10
220 9d. Heathfield Tower and Monument, Sussex 20 10
221 1s. General Eliott (vert) 20 10
222 2s. Eliott directing rescue operations 40 50
No. 222 is 55×21 mm.

65 Lord Baden-Powell

1968. 60th Anniv of Gibraltar Scout Association.
223 **65** 4d. buff and violet 20 10
224 – 7d. ochre and green 20 20
225 – 9d. blue, orange and black . . 25 30
226 – 1s. yellow and green 25 30
DESIGNS: 7d. Scout flag over the Rock; 9d. Tent, Scouts and salute; 1s. Scout badges.

66 Nurse and W.H.O. Emblem

1968. 20th Anniv of W.H.O. Multicoloured.
227 2d. Type **66** 10 15
228 4d. Doctor and W.H.O. emblem 10 15

68 King John signing Magna Carta

70 Shepherd, Lamb and Star

1968. Human Rights Year.
229 **68** 1s. orange, brown and gold 15 10
230 – 2s. myrtle and gold 15 20
DESIGN: 2s. "Freedom" and Rock of Gibraltar.

1968. Christmas. Multicoloured.
231 4d. Type **70** 20 15
232 9d. Mary holding Holy Child . 20 15

72 Parliament Houses

1969. Commonwealth Parliamentary Association Conference.
233 **72** 4d. green and gold 10 10
234 – 9d. violet and gold 10 10
235 – 2s. red, gold and blue . . . 15 20
DESIGNS—HORIZ: 9d. Parliamentary emblem and outline of "The Rock". VERT: 2s. Clock Tower, Westminster (Big Ben) and Arms of Gibraltar.

75 Silhouette of Rock and Queen Elizabeth II

1969. New Constitution.
236 **75** $\frac{1}{2}$d. gold and orange 10 10
237 5d. silver and green 25 10
238 7d. silver and purple 25 10
239 5s. silver and blue . . . . 1·00 1·10

77 Soldier and Cap Badge, Royal Anglian Regiment, 1969

80 "Madonna of the Chair" (detail, Raphael)

1969. Military Uniforms (1st series). Multicoloured.
240 1d. Royal Artillery Officer, 1758, and modern cap badge . . . 20 10
241 6d. Type **77** 45 20
242 9d. Royal Engineers' Artificer, 1786, and modern cap badge 55 30
243 2s. Private, Fox's Marines, 1704, and modern Royal Marines' cap badge . . . . 2·00 1·25
See also Nos. 248/51, 290/3, 300/303, 313/16, 331/4, 340/3 and 363/6.

1969. Christmas. Multicoloured.
244 5d. Type **80** 10 20
245 7d. "Virgin and Child" (detail, Morales) 20 20
246 1s. "The Virgin of the Rocks" (detail, Leonardo da Vinci) . 20 20

83 Europa Point

88 Stamp and Rock of Gibraltar

1970. Europa Point.
247 **83** 2s. multicoloured 45 30

1970. Military Uniforms (2nd series). As T **77**. Multicoloured
248 2d. Royal Scots Officer (1839) and cap badge 35 10
249 5d. South Wales Borderers Private (1763) and cap badge 70 10
250 7d. Queen's Royal Regiment Private (1742) and cap badge 70 15
251 2s. Royal Irish Rangers piper (1969) and cap badge . . . 2·75 1·25

1970. "Philympia 70" Stamp Exhibition, London.
252 **88** 1s. red and green 15 10
253 – 2s. blue and mauve 25 65
DESIGN: 2s. Stamp and Moorish Castle.
The stamps shown in the designs are well-known varieties with values omitted.

90 "The Virgin and Mary" (stained-glass window, Gabriel Loire)

1970. Christmas.
254 **90** 2s. multicoloured 30 30

91 Saluting Battery, Rosia

92 Saluting Battery, Rosia, Modern View

1971. Decimal Currency.

No.	Type	Description	Unused	Used
255	**91**	$\frac{1}{2}$p. multicoloured	20	30
256	**92**	$\frac{1}{2}$p. multicoloured	20	30
257	–	1p. multicoloured	80	30
258	–	1p. multicoloured	80	30
259	–	$1\frac{1}{2}$p. multicoloured	20	50
260	–	$1\frac{1}{2}$p. multicoloured	20	50
317	–	2p. multicoloured	1·25	2·00
318	–	2p. multicoloured	1·25	2·00
263a	–	$2\frac{1}{2}$p. multicoloured	20	50
264	–	$2\frac{1}{2}$p. multicoloured	20	50
265	–	3p. multicoloured	20	20
266	–	3p. multicoloured	20	20
319	–	4p. multicoloured	1·40	2·25
320	–	4p. multicoloured	1·40	2·25
269	–	5p. multicoloured	35	35
270	–	5p. multicoloured	35	35
271	–	7p. multicoloured	65	65
272	–	7p. multicoloured	65	65
273	–	8p. multicoloured	70	80
274	–	8p. multicoloured	70	80
275	–	9p. multicoloured	70	80
276	–	9p. multicoloured	70	80
277	–	10p. multicoloured	80	80
278	–	10p. multicoloured	80	80
279	–	$12\frac{1}{2}$p. multicoloured	1·00	1·75
280	–	$12\frac{1}{2}$p. multicoloured	1·00	1·75
281	–	25p. multicoloured	1·10	1·75
282	–	25p. multicoloured	1·10	1·75
283	–	50p. multicoloured	1·25	2·50
284	–	50p. multicoloured	1·25	2·50
285	–	£1 multicoloured	2·00	4·00
286	–	£1 multicoloured	2·00	4·00

DESIGNS: (The two versions of each value show the same Gibraltar view taken from an early 19th-century print (first design) or modern photograph (second design)): HORIZ: 1p. Prince George of Cambridge Quarters and Trinity Church; $1\frac{1}{2}$p. The Wellington Bust, Alameda Gardens; 2p. Gibraltar from the North Bastion; $2\frac{1}{2}$p. Catalan Bay; 3p. Convent Garden; 4p. The Exchange and Spanish Chapel; 5p. Commercial Square and Library; 7p. South Barracks and Rosia Magazine; 8p. Moorish Mosque and Castle; 9p. Europa Pass Road; 10p. South Barracks from Rosia Bay; $12\frac{1}{2}$p. Southport Gates; 25p. Trooping the Colour, The Alameda. VERT: 50p. Europa Pass Gorge; £1 Prince Edward's Gate.

93

94 Regimental Arms

1971. Coil Stamps.
287 **93** $\frac{1}{2}$p. orange 15 30
288 1p. blue 15 30
289 2p. green . . . . 50 1·10

1971. Military Uniforms (3rd series). As T **77**. Multicoloured.
290 1p. The Black Watch (1845) . . 35 30
291 2p. Royal Regimental of Fusiliers (1971) 65 30
292 4p. King's Own Royal Border Regiment (1704) . . 1·25 50
293 10p. Devonshire and Dorset Regiment (1801) . . . . 3·75 3·00

1971. Presentation of Colours to the Gibraltar Regiment.
294 **94** 3p. black, gold and red . . . 45 30

95 Nativity Scene

1971. Christmas. Multicoloured.
295 3p. Type **95** 60 60
296 5p. Mary and Joseph going to Bethlehem 65 65

MORE DETAILED LISTS
are given in the Stanley Gibbons Catalogues referred to in the country headings.
For lists of current volumes see Introduction.

96 Soldier Artificer, 1773

97 "Our Lady of Europa"

1972. Bicentenary of Royal Engineers in Gibraltar. Multicoloured.
297 1p. Type **96** 65 60
298 3p. Modern tunneller 80 80
299 5p. Old and new uniforms and badge (horiz) . . . . 1·00 90

1972. Military Uniforms (4th series). As T **77**. Multicoloured.
300 1p. The Duke of Cornwall's Light Infantry, 1704 . . . . 60 20
301 3p. King's Royal Rifle Corps, 1830 . . . . 1·75 40
302 7p. 37th North Hampshire, Officer, 1825 . . . . 2·75 70
303 10p. Royal Navy, 1972 . . . . 3·25 1·50

1972. Christmas.
304 **97** 3p. multicoloured 10 20
305 5p. multicoloured 10 35

98 Keys of Gibraltar and "Narcissus niveus"

1972. Royal Silver Wedding.
306 **98** 5p. red 25 20
307 7p. green 25 20

99 Flags of Member Nations and E.E.C. Symbol

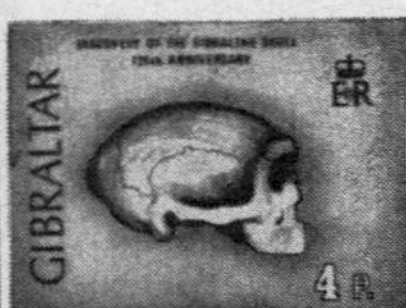

100 Skull

1973. Britain's Entry into E.E.C.
308 **99** 5p. multicoloured 70 50
309 10p. multicoloured . . . . 80 1·00

1973. 125th Anniv of Gibraltar Skull Discovery. Multicoloured.
310 4p. Type **100** . . . . 1·25 50
311 6p. Prehistoric man . . . . 1·25 70
312 10p. Prehistoric family . . . . 1·75 1·25
No. 312 is size 40 × 26 mm.

1973. Military Uniforms (5th series). As T **77**. Multicoloured.
313 1p. King's Own Scottish Borderers, 1770 . . . . 50 50
314 4p. Royal Welsh Fusiliers, 1800 . 1·50 1·10
315 60p. Royal Northumberland Fusiliers, 1736 . . . . 2·25 2·25
316 10p. Grenadier Guards, 1898 . 3·00 4·50

101 "Nativity" (Danckerts)

1973. Christmas.
321 **101** 4p. violet and red 40 15
322 6p. mauve and blue . . . . 60 1·10

101a Princess Anne and Captain Mark Phillips

1973. Royal Wedding.

323	**101a**	6p. multicoloured	10	10
324		14p. multicoloured	20	20

102 Victorian Pillar-box

103 "Madonna with the Green Cushion" (Solario)

1974. Centenary of U.P.U. Multicoloured.

325		2p. Type **102**	15	30
326		6p. Pillar-box of George VI	30	35
327		14p. Pillar-box of Elizabeth II	50	80

Nos. 325/7 also come self-adhesive from booklet panes.

1974. Military Uniforms (6th series). As T **77**. Multicoloured.

331		4p. East Lancashire Regiment, 1742	50	50
332		6p. Somerset Light Infantry, 1833	70	70
333		10p. Royal Sussex Regiment, 1790	1·00	1·40
334		16p. R.A.F. officer, 1974	2·25	4·00

1974. Christmas. Multicoloured.

335		4p. Type **103**	40	30
336		6p. "Madonna of the Meadow" (Bellini)	60	95

104 Churchill and Houses of Parliament

1974. Birth Centenary of Sir Winston Churchill. Multicoloured.

337	**104**	6p. black, purple and lavender	25	15
338	–	20p. black, brown and red	50	85

DESIGN: 20p. Churchill and "King George V" (battleship).

1975. Military Uniforms (7th series). As T **77**. Multicoloured.

340		4p. East Surrey Regiment, 1846	40	30
341		6p. Highland Light Infantry, 1777	60	50
342		10 p. Coldstream Guards, 1704	80	90
343		20p. Gibraltar Regiment, 1974	1·50	2·75

105 Girl Guides' Badge

1975. 50th Anniversary of Gibraltar Girl Guides.

346	**105**	5p. gold, blue and violet	35	55
347		7p. gold, brown and light brown	45	60
348	–	15p. silver, black and brown	75	1·25

No. 348 is as Type **105** but shows a different badge.

106 Child at Prayer

107 Bruges Madonna

1975. Christmas. Multicoloured.

349		6p. Type **106**	40	60
350		6p. Angel with lute	40	60
351		6p. Child singing carols	40	60
352		6p. Three children	40	60
353		6p. Girl at prayer	40	60
354		6p. Boy and lamb	40	60

1975. 500th Birth Anniv of Michelangelo. Multicoloured.

355		6p. Type **107**	25	25
356		9p. Taddei Madonna	30	40
357		15p. Pieta	40	1·10

Nos. 355/7 also come self-adhesive from booklet panes.

108 Bicentennial Emblem and Arms of Gibraltar

109 The Holy Family

1976. Bicentenary of American Revolution.

361	**108**	25p. multicoloured	50	50

1976. Military Uniforms (8th series). As T **24**. Multicoloured.

363		1p. Suffolk Regiment, 1795	25	15
364		6p. Northamptonshire Regiment, 1779	60	30
365		12p. Lancashire Fusiliers, 1793	85	55
366		25p. Ordnance Corps, 1896	1·25	1·10

1976. Christmas. Multicoloured.

367		6p. Type **109**	25	15
368		9p. Madonna and Child	35	25
369		12p. St. Bernard	50	60
370		20p. Archangel Michael	85	1·25

Nos. 367/70 show different stained-glass windows from St. Joseph's Church, Gibraltar.

110 Queen Elizabeth II, Royal Arms and Gibraltar Arms

111 Toothed Orchid

1977. Silver Jubilee. Multicoloured.

371	**110**	6p. red	25	20
372		£1 blue	1·40	2·25

1977. Birds, Flowers, Fish and Butterflies. Multicoloured.

374		½p. Type **111**	60	1·75
375		1p. Red mullet (horiz)	15	30
376		2p. "Maculinea arion" (butterfly) (horiz)	30	70
377		2½p. Sardinian warbler	40	1·50
378		3p. Giant squill	20	10
379		4p. Grey wrasse (horiz)	30	10
380		5p. "Vanessa atalanta" (butterfly) (horiz)	50	90
381		6p. Black kite	1·25	30
382		9p. Shrubby scorpion-vetch	70	70
383		10p. John dory (fish) (horiz)	40	20
384		12p. "Colias crocea" (butterfly) (horiz)	1·00	35
384b		15p. Winged asparagus pea	1·50	55
385		20p. Audouin's gull	1·50	2·25
386		25p. Barbary nut (iris)	1·25	2·00
387		50p. Swordfish (fish) (horiz)	2·00	95
388		£1 "Papilio machaon" (butterfly) (horiz)	4·25	4·50
389		£2 Hoopoe	8·50	10·00
389a		£5 Arms of Gibraltar	10·00	11·00

112 "Our Lady of Europa" Stamp

1977. "Amphilex '77" Stamp Exhibition, Amsterdam. Multicoloured.

390		6p. Type **112**	10	20
391		12p. "Europa Point" stamp	15	30
392		25p. "E.E.C. Entry" stamp	20	50

113 "The Annunciation" (Rubens)

1977. Christmas and 400th Birth Anniv of Rubens. Multicoloured.

393		3p. Type **113**	10	10
394		9p. "The Adoration of the Magi"	25	20
395		12p. "The Adoration of the Magi" (horiz)	30	30
396		15p. "The Holy Family under the Apple Tree"	30	40

114 Aerial View of Gibraltar

1978. Gibraltar from Space.

398	**114**	12p. multicoloured	25	50

115 Holyroodhouse

1978. 25th Anniv of Coronation. Multicoloured.

400		6p. Type **115**	20	15
401		9p. St. James's Palace	25	15
402		12p. Sandringham	30	30
403		18p. Balmoral	40	75
406		25p. Windsor Castle	90	1·75

Nos. 402/3 also exist as self-adhesive stamps from booklet panes, No. 406 only coming in this form.

116 Short S.25 Sunderland, 1938–58

1978. 60th Anniv of Royal Air Force. Multicoloured.

407		3p. Type **116**	15	10
408		9p. Caudron G-3, 1918	35	40
409		12p. Avro Shackleton M.R.2, 1953–66	40	55
410		16p. Hawker Hunter F.6, 1954–77	45	80
411		18p. Hawker Siddeley Nimrod M.R.1, 1969–78	50	90

117 "Madonna with Animals"

1978. Christmas. Paintings by Durer. Multicoloured.

412		5p. Type **117**	20	10
413		9p. "The Nativity"	25	15
414		12p. "Madonna of the Goldfinch"	30	40
415		15p. "Adoration of the Magi"	35	75

118 Sir Rowland Hill and 1d. Stamp of 1886

1979. Death Centenary of Sir Rowland Hill.

416	**118**	3p. multicoloured	10	10
417	–	9p. multicoloured	20	15
418	–	12p. multicoloured	25	20
419	–	25p. black, purple & yell	35	50

DESIGNS: 9p. 1971 1p. coil stamp; 12p. 1840 Post Office Regulations; 25p. "G" cancellation.

119 Posthorn, Dish Antenna and Early Telephone

1979. Europa. Communications.

420	**119**	3p. green and pale green	15	10
421		9p. brown and ochre	30	90
422		12p. blue and violet	35	1·25

120 African Child

121 Early Policeman

1979. Christmas. International Year of the Child. Multicoloured.

423		12p. Type **120**	25	30
424		12p. Asian child	25	30
425		12p. Polynesian child	25	30
426		12p. American Indian child	25	30
427		12p. Nativity and children of different races	25	30
428		12p. European child	25	30

1980. 150th Anniv of Gibraltar Police Force. Multicoloured.

429		3p. Type **121**	20	10
430		6p. Policemen of 1895, early 1900s and 1980	20	15
431		12p. Police officer and police ambulance	25	20
432		37p. Policewoman and police motor-cyclist	55	1·25

122 Peter Amigo (Archbishop)

124 "Horatio Nelson" (J. F. Rigaud)

123 Queen Elizabeth the Queen Mother

1980. Europa. Personalities. Multicoloured.

433		12p. Type **122**	20	30
434		12p. Gustavo Bacarisas (artist)	20	30
435		12p. John Mackintosh (philanthropist)	20	30

1980. 80th Birthday of The Queen Mother.

436	**123**	15p. multicoloured	30	30

1980. 175th Death Anniv of Nelson. Paintings. Multicoloured.

437		3p. Type **124**	15	10
438		9p. "H.M.S. Victory" (horiz)	25	25
439		15p. "Horatio Nelson" (Sir William Beechey)	35	35
440		40p. "'H.M.S. Victory' being towed into Gibraltar" (Clarkson Stanfield) (horiz)	80	1·00

125 Three Kings

1980. Christmas.
442 **125** 15p. brown and yellow . . 25 35
443 – 15p. brown and yellow . . 25 35
DESIGN: No. 443, Nativity scene.

126 Hercules creating the Mediterranean
127 Dining-room

1981. Europa. Multicoloured.
444 9p. Type **126** 20 15
445 15p. Hercules and Pillars of Hercules 25 35

1981. 450th Anniv of The Convent (Govenor's Residence). Multicoloured.
446 4p. Type **127** 10 10
447 14p. King's Chapel 15 15
448 15p. The Convent 15 15
449 55p. Cloister 60 80

128 Prince Charles and Lady Diana Spencer
129

1981. Royal Wedding.
450 **128** £1 multicoloured . . . . . 1·50 1·50

1981.
451 **129** 1p. black 30 30
452 4p. blue 30 30
453 15p. green 30 30

130 Paper Airplane

1981. 50th Anniv of Gibraltar Airmail Service. Multicoloured
454 14p. Type **130** 15 15
455 15p. Airmail letters, post box and aircraft tail fin 15 15
456 55p. Jet airliner circling globe . . 60 70

131 Carol Singers

1981. Christmas. Children's Drawings. Multicoloured.
457 15p. Type **131** 30 15
458 55p. Postbox (vert) . . . . . 1·00 85

132 I.Y.D.P. Emblem and Stylised Faces

1981. International Year for Disabled Persons.
459 **132** 14p. multicoloured 30 30

133 Douglas DC-3

1982. Aircraft. Multicoloured.
460 1p. Type **133** . . . . 25 1·00
461 2p. Vickers Viking 1B . . . . 30 1·00
462 3p. Airspeed Ambassador AS.57 . . . . 30 90
463 4p. Vickers Viscount 800 . . . 40 20
464 5p. Boeing 727-100 . . . . . 90 60
465 10p. Vickers Vanguard . . . . 1·75 50
466 14p. Short Solent 2 . . . . . 1·25 2·50
467 15p. Fokker F.27 Friendship . . 2·50 2·25
468 17p. Boeing 737 . . . . 1·00 55
469 20p. B.A.C. One Eleven . . . 1·00 50
470 25p. Lockheed Constellation . . 4·00 3·00
471 50p. Hawker Siddeley Comet 4B . 4·00 2·25
472 £1 Saro Windhover . . . . . 5·50 2·25
473 £2 Hawker Siddeley Trident 2E 6·50 5·00
474 £5 De Havilland D.H.89A Dragon Rapide . . . . . . 9·00 14·00

134 Crest, H.M.S. "Opossum"
136 Gibraltar Chamber of Commerce Centenary

135 Hawker Hurricane Mk I and Supermarine Spitfires at Gibraltar

1982. Naval Crests (1st series). Multicoloured.
475 ½p. Type **134** 10 10
476 15½p. H.M.S. "Norfolk" . . . 55 65
477 17p. H.M.S. "Fearless" 60 70
478 60p. H.M.S. "Rooke" . . . . 1·40 2·75
See also Nos. 493/6, 510/13, 522/5, 541/4, 565/8, 592/5, 616/19 and 651/4.

1982. Europa. Operation Torch. Multicoloured.
479 14p. Type **135** 25 70
480 17p. General Giraud, General Eisenhower and Gibraltar . . 35 80

1982. Anniversaries. Multicoloured.
481 ½p. Type **136** 10 10
482 15½p. British Forces Postal Service centenary 30 25
483 60p. 75th anniv of Gibraltar Scout Association . . . . . 1·10 1·25

137 Printed Circuit forming Map of World

1982. International Direct Dialling.
484 **137** 17p. black, blue and orange 35 35

138 Gibraltar illuminated at Night and Holly

1982. Christmas. Multicoloured.
485 14p. Type **138** 45 30
486 17p. Gibraltar illuminated at night and mistletoe 50 35

139 Yacht Marina

1983. Commonwealth Day. Multicoloured.
487 4p. Type **139** 10 10
488 14p. Scouts and Guides Commonwealth Day Parade 20 15
489 17p. Flag of Gibraltar (vert) . . 25 20
490 60p. Queen Elizabeth II (from photo by Tim Graham) (vert) 70 1·00

140 St. George's Hall Gallery

1983. Europa.
491 **140** 16p. black and brown . . . 35 35
492 – 19p. black and blue 40 40
DESIGN: 19p. Water catchment slope.

1983. Naval Crests (2nd series). As T **134**. Multicoloured.
493 4p. H.M.S. "Faulknor" 30 10
494 14p. H.M.S. "Renown" 70 35
495 17p. H.M.S. "Ark Royal" . . . 75 40
496 60p. H.M.S. "Sheffield" . . . 1·75 1·50

141 Landport Gate, 1729

1983. Fortress Gibraltar in the 18th Century. Multicoloured.
497 4p. Type **141** 15 10
498 17p. Koehler Gun, 1782 . . . 35 30
499 77p. King's Bastion, 1779 . . . 1·00 1·25

142 "Adoration of the Magi" (Raphael)

1983. Christmas. 500th Birth Anniv of Raphael. Multicoloured.
501 4p. Type **142** 25 10
502 17p. "Madonna of Foligno" (vert) 70 35
503 60p. "Sistine Madonna" (vert) 1·75 1·40

143 1932 2d. Stamp and Globe

1984. Europa, Posts and Telecommunications. Multicoloured.
504 17p. Type **143** 35 50
505 23p. Circuit board and globe . . 45 1·00

144 Hockey

1984. Sports. Multicoloured.
506 20p. Type **144** 55 65
507 21p. Basketball 55 65
508 26p. Rowing . . . . 65 1·00
509 29p. Football . . . . 70 1·10

1984. Naval Crests (3rd series). As T **134**. Multicoloured.
510 20p. H.M.S. "Active" . . . . 1·60 1·75
511 21p. H.M.S. "Foxhound" . . . 1·60 2·00
512 26p. H.M.S. "Valiant" . . . . 1·75 2·00
513 29p. H.M.S. "Hood" . . . . . 1·90 2·25

145 Mississippi River Boat Float

1984. Christmas. Epiphany Floats. Multicoloured.
514 20p. Type **145** 30 30
515 80p. Roman Temple float . . . 1·40 2·25

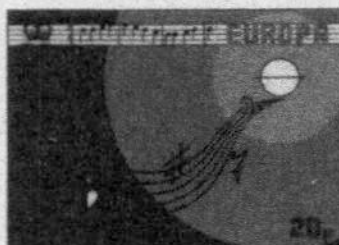

146 Musical Symbols, and Score from Beethoven's 9th (Choral) Symphony

1985. Europa. European Music Year. Multicoloured.
516 **146** 20p. multicoloured 35 30
517 – 29p. multicoloured . . . . 55 1·50
DESIGN: The 29p. is as T **146**, but shows different symbols.

147 Globe and Stop Polio Campaign Logo

1985. Stop Polio Campaign.
518 26p. multicoloured (Type **147**) . 90 1·25
519 26p. multicoloured ("ST" visible) 90 1·25
520 26p. multicoloured ("STO" visible) . . . . 90 1·25
521 26p. multicoloured ("STOP" visible) . . . . 90 1·25

Each design differs in the position of the logo across the centre of the globe. On No. 518 only the letter "S" is fully visible, on No. 519 "ST", on No. 520 "STO" and on No. 521 "STOP". Other features of the design also differ, so that the word "Year" moves towards the top of the stamp and on No. 521 the upper logo is omitted.

1985. Naval Crests (4th series). As T **134**. Multicoloured.
522 4p. H.M.S. "Duncan" 60 10
523 9p. H.M.S. "Fury" 90 50
524 21p. H.M.S. "Firedrake" . . . 2·00 2·00
525 80p. H.M.S. "Malaya" . . . . 4·00 6·00

148 I.Y.Y. Logo
149 St. Joseph

1985. International Youth Year. Multicoloured.
526 4p. Type **148** 25 10
527 20p. Hands passing diamond . 95 1·10
528 80p. 75th anniv logo of Girl Guide Movement . . . . . 2·50 3·25

1985. Christmas. Centenary of St. Joseph's Parish Church. Multicoloured.
529 4p. Type **149** 65 90
530 4p. St. Joseph's Parish Church . 65 90
531 80p. Nativity crib . . . . . . 3·50 4·00

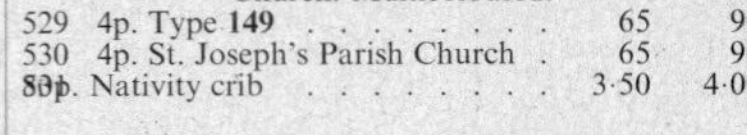

150 "Papilio machaon" (butterfly) and The Convent

1986. Europa. Nature and the Environment. Multicoloured.
532 22p. Type **150** . . . . 1·25 50
533 29p. Herring gull and Europa Point . . . . 1·75 4·25

151 1887 Queen Victoria 6d. Stamp
152 Queen Elizabeth II in Robes of Order of the Bath

1986. Centenary of First Gibraltar Postage Stamps. Designs showing stamps. Multicoloured.
534 4p. Type **151** . . . 30 10
535 22p. 1903 Edward VII 2½d. . . 1·00 1·00
536 32p. 1912 George V 1d. . . 1·50 2·00
537 36p. 1938 George VI £1 . . 1·60 2·50
538 44p. 1953 Coronation ½d. (29 × 46 mm) . . 2·00 3·00

1986. 60th Birthday of Queen Elizabeth II.
540 **152** £1 multicoloured . . 1·60 3·00

1986. Naval Crests (5th series). As T **134**. Multicoloured.
541 22p. H.M.S. "Lightning" . . 1·75 1·00
542 29p. H.M.S. "Hermione" . . 2·00 1·75
543 32p. H.M.S. "Laforey" . . 2·25 3·25
544 44p. H.M.S. "Nelson" . . 2·75 4·00

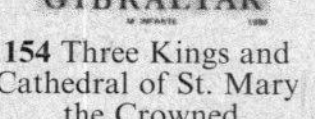

154 Three Kings and Cathedral of St. Mary the Crowned
155 Neptune House

1986. Christmas. International Peace Year. Multicoloured.
546 18p. Type **154** . . . 1·00 50
547 32p. St. Andrew's Church . . 1·50 2·75

1987. Europa. Architecture. Multicoloured.
563 22p. Type **155** . . . 1·50 50
564 29p. Ocean Heights . . 2·50 4·00

1987. Naval Crests (6th series). As T **134**. Multicoloured.
565 18p. H.M.S. "Wishart" . . 1·25 75
566 22p. H.M.S. "Charybdis" . . 1·40 1·10
567 32p. H.M.S. "Antelope" . . 1·90 3·00
568 44p. H.M.S. "Eagle" . . 2·50 4·00

156 13-inch Mortar, 1783
157 Victoria Stadium

1987. Guns. Multicoloured.
569 1p. Type **156** . . . 20 60
570 2p. 6-inch coastal gun, 1909 . . 30 60
571 3p. 8-inch howitzer, 1783 . . 30 60
572 4p. Bofors "L40/70" AA gun, 1951 . . . 40 10
573 5p. 100 ton rifled muzzle-loader, 1882 . . . 40 50
574 10p. 5.25 inch heavy AA gun, 1953 . . . 40 55
575 18p. 25-pounder gun-how, 1943 65 90
576 19p. 64-pounder rifled muzzle-loader, 1873 . . . 70 1·00
577 22p. 12-pounder gun, 1758 . . 70 50
578 50p. 10-inch rifled muzzle-loader, 1870 . . . 1·40 3·00
579 £1 Russian 24-pounder gun, 1854 2·50 2·50
580 £3 9.2 inch "Mk 10" coastal gun, 1935 . . . 5·00 14·00
581 £5 24-pounder gun, 1779 . . 8·00 16·00

1987. Bicentenary of Royal Engineers' Royal Warrant. Multicoloured.
582 18p. Type **157** . . . 1·25 65
583 32p. Freedom of Gibraltar scroll and casket . . . 1·75 3·00
584 44p. Royal Engineers' badge . . 2·50 4·00

158 The Three Kings

1987. Christmas. Multicoloured.
585 4p. Type **158** . . . 15 10
586 22p. The Holy Family . . 90 1·00
587 44p. The Shepherds . . 1·75 3·25

159 "Canberra" (liner) passing Gibraltar

1988. Europa. Transport and Communications. Multicoloured.
588 22p. Type **159** . . . 1·50 2·25
589 22p. "Gibline I" (ferry), dish aerial and Boeing 737 airliner . . . 1·50 2·25
590 32p. Horse-drawn carriage and modern coach . . . 2·00 2·75
591 32p. Car, telephone and Rock of Gibraltar . . . 2·00 2·75

1988. Naval Crests (7th series). As T **134**.
592 18p. multicoloured . . . 1·50 65
593 22p. black, brown and gold . . 2·00 1·25
594 32p. multicoloured . . . 2·25 3·25
595 44p. multicoloured . . . 3·00 4·50
DESIGNS: 18p. H.M.S. "Clyde"; 22p. H.M.S. "Foresight"; 32p. H.M.S. "Severn"; 44p. H.M.S. "Rodney".

160 European Bee Eater

1988. Birds. Multicoloured.
596 4p. Type **160** . . . 65 20
597 22p. Atlantic puffin . . 1·50 90
598 32p. Honey buzzard . . 2·00 3·00
599 44p. Blue rock thrush . . 2·50 4·25

161 "Zebu" (brigantine)

1989. Operation Raleigh. Multicoloured.
600 19p. Type **161** . . . 65 60
601 22p. Miniature of Sir Walter Raleigh and logo . . . 75 70
602 32p. "Sir Walter Raleigh" (expedition ship) and world map . . . 1·10 1·75

162 "Snowman" (Rebecca Falero)

1988. Christmas. Children's Paintings. Multicoloured.
604 4p. Type **162** . . . 15 10
605 22p. "The Nativity" (Dennis Penalver) . . . 55 60
606 44p. "Father Christmas" (Gavin Key) (23 × 31 mm) . . 1·00 1·50

163 Soft Toys and Toy Train

1989. Europa. Children's Toys. Multicoloured.
607 25p. Type **163** . . . 1·25 75
608 32p. Soft toys, toy boat and doll's house . . . 1·75 2·75

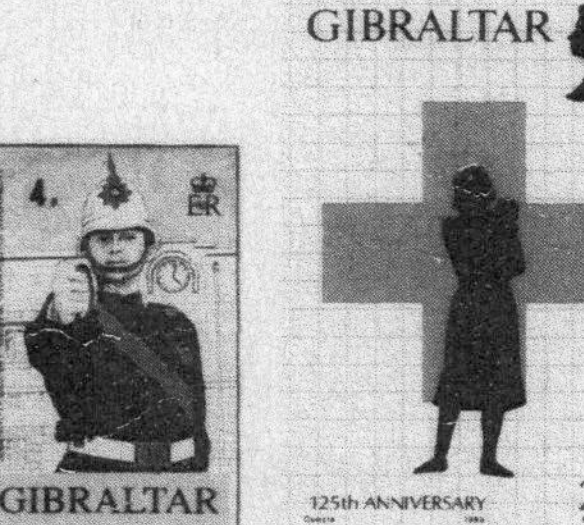

164 Port Sergeant with Keys
165 Nurse and Baby

1989. 50th Anniv of Gibraltar Regiment. Mult.
609 4p. Type **164** . . . 40 10
610 22p. Regimental badge and colours . . . 1·25 1·10
611 32p. Drum major . . . 1·75 2·75

1989. 125th Anniv of International Red Cross.
613 **165** 25p. black, red and brown 75 60
614 – 32p. black, red and brown 95 1·60
615 – 44p. black, red and brown 1·25 2·75
DESIGNS: 32p. Famine victims; 44p. Accident victims.

1989. Naval Crests (8th series). As T **134**.
616 22p. multicoloured . . . 1·50 75
617 25p. black and gold . . . 1·50 1·50
618 32p. gold, black and red . . 2·00 2·50
619 44p. multicoloured . . . 3·00 4·00
DESIGNS: 22p. H.M.S. "Blankney"; 25p. H.M.S. "Deptford"; 32p. H.M.S. "Exmoor"; 44p. H.M.S. "Stork".

167 Father Christmas in Sleigh

1989. Christmas. Multicoloured.
622 4p. Type **167** . . . 15 10
623 22p. Shepherds and sheep . . 70 70
624 32p. The Nativity . . . 1·10 1·75
625 44p. The Three Wise Men . . 1·75 3·00

168 General Post Office Entrance
169 19th-century Firemen

1990. Europa. Post Office Buildings. Multicoloured.
626 22p. Type **168** . . . 1·00 1·50
627 22p. Interior of General Post Office . . . 1·00 1·50
628 32p. Interior of South District Post Office . . . 1·50 2·25
629 32p. South District Post Office 1·50 2·25

1990. 125th Anniv of Gibraltar Fire Service. Multicoloured.
630 4p. Type **169** . . . 60 15
631 20p. Early fire engine (horiz) . . 1·50 1·10
632 42p. Modern fire engine (horiz) 1·75 3·00
633 44p. Modern fireman in breathing apparatus . . . 2·00 3·00

170 Henry Corbould (artist) and Penny Black
172 Candle and Holly

171 Model of Europort Development

1990. 150th Anniv of the Penny Black. Multicoloured.
634 19p. Type **170** . . . 95 80
635 22p. Bath Royal Mail coach . 1·00 90
636 32p. Sir Rowland Hill and Penny Black . . . 2·25 3·50

1990. Naval Crests (9th series). As T **134**. Multicoloured.
638 22p. H.M.S. "Calpe" . . . 1·50 70
639 25p. H.M.S. "Gallant" . . . 1·60 1·75
640 32p. H.M.S. "Wrestler" . . 2·00 2·75
641 44p. H.M.S. "Greyhound" . . 2·50 4·25

1990. Development Projects. Multicoloured.
642 22p. Type **171** . . . 75 80
643 23p. Construction of building material factory . . . 75 1·40
644 25p. Land reclamation . . . 95 1·40

1990. Christmas. Multicoloured.
645 4p. Type **172** . . . 15 10
646 22p. Father Christmas . . . 75 65
647 42p. Christmas tree . . . 1·50 2·25
648 44p. Nativity crib . . . 1·50 2·25

173 Space Laboratory and Spaceplane (Columbus Development Programme)

1991. Europa. Europe in Space. Multicoloured.
649 25p. Type **173** . . . 75 75
650 32p. "ERS-1" earth resources remote sensing satellite . . 1·00 2·00

1991. Naval Crests (10th series). As T **134**.
651 4p. black, blue and gold . . 35 10
652 21p. multicoloured . . . 1·25 1·25
653 22p. multicoloured . . . 1·25 1·25
654 62p. multicoloured . . . 3·25 6·00
DESIGNS: 4p. H.M.S. "Hesperus"; 21p. H.M.S. "Forester"; 22p. H.M.S. "Furious"; 62p. H.M.S. "Scylla".

174 Shag

1991. Endangered Species. Birds. Multicoloured.
655 13p. Type **174** . . . 85 1·10
656 13p. Barbary partridge . . 85 1·10
657 13p. Egyptian vulture . . 85 1·10
658 13p. Black stork . . . 85 1·10

1991. No. 580 surch **£1.05**.
659 £1.05 on £3 9.2-inch "Mk.10" coastal gun, 1935 . . . 3·50 1·60

176 "North View of Gibraltar" (Gustavo Bacarisas)

1991. Local Paintings. Multicoloured.
660 22p. Type **176** . . . 85 50
661 26p. "Parson's Lodge" (Elena Mifsud) . . . 1·00 1·00
662 32p. "Governor's Parade" (Jacobo Azagury) . . 1·50 2·25
663 42p. "Waterport Wharf" (Rudesindo Mannia) (vert) . 2·25 3·50

177 "Once in Royal David's City"

1991. Christmas. Carols. Multicoloured.
664 4p. Type **177** . . . 25 10
665 24p. "Silent Night" . . . 1·25 70
666 25p. "Angels We Have Heard on High" . . . 1·25 1·25
667 49p. "O Come All Ye Faithful" 2·00 3·50

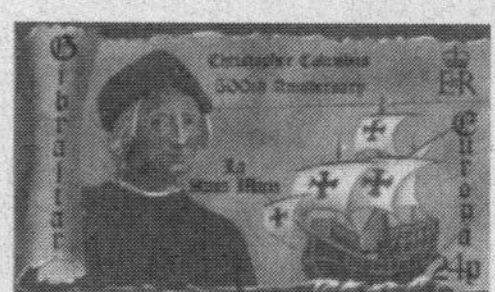

179 Columbus and "Santa Maria"

1992. Europa. 500th Anniv of Discovery of America by Columbus. Multicoloured.
669 24p. Type **179** . . . 1·25 1·75
670 24p. Map of Old World and "Nina" . . . 1·25 1·75
671 34p. Map of New World and "Pinta" . . . 1·50 2·00
672 34p. Map of Old World and look-out . . . 1·50 2·00
Nos. 669/70 and 671/2 were issued together, se-tenant, each pair forming a composite design.

179a Gibraltar from North

1992. 40th Anniv of Queen Elizabeth II's Accession. Multicoloured.
673 4p. Type **179a** . . . 15 10
674 20p. H.M.S. "Arrow" (frigate) and Gibraltar from south . . 60 60
675 24p. Southport Gates . . . 75 80
676 44p. Three portraits of Queen Elizabeth . . . 1·25 1·60
677 54p. Queen Elizabeth II . . . 1·60 1·90

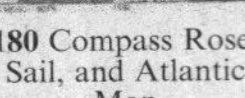

180 Compass Rose, Sail, and Atlantic Map

181 Holy Trinity Cathedral

1992. Round the World Yacht Rally. Multicoloured designs, each incorporating compass rose and sail.

678 21p. Type **180** 75 80
679 24p. Map of Indonesian Archipelago (horiz) . . . . 95 1·40
680 25p. Map of India Ocean (horiz) 95 1·75

1992. 150th Anniv of Anglican Diocese of Gibraltar-in-Europe. Multicoloured.

682 4p. Type **181** 20 10
683 24p. Diocesan crest and map (horiz) . . . . 1·00 65
684 44p. Construction of Cathedral and Sir George Don (horiz) . 1·75 2·75
685 54p. Bishop Tomlinson . . . 2·00 3·00

182 Sacred Heart of Jesus Church

183 "Drama and Music"

1992. Christmas. Churches. Multicoloured.

686 4p. Type **182** 25 10
687 24p. Cathedral of St. Mary the Crowned . . . . 1·25 55
688 34p. St. Andrew's Church of Scotland . . . . 1·75 2·50
689 49p. St. Joseph's Church . . . 2·50 4·25

1993. Europa. Contemporary Art. Multicoloured.

690 24p. Type **183** . . . . 1·50 1·75
691 24p. "Sculpture, Art and Pottery" . . . . 1·50 1·75
692 34p. "Architecture" . . . . 2·00 2·50
693 34p. "Printing and Photo-graphy" . . . . 2·00 2·50

185 Landport Gate

186 £sd and Decimal British Coins (25th anniv of decimal currency)

1993. Architectural Heritage. Multicoloured.

695 1p. Type **185** 10 20
696 2p. St. Mary the Crowned Church (horiz) 20 20
697 3p. Parsons Lodge Battery (horiz) 20 20
698 4p. Moorish Castle (horiz) . . 20 20
699 5p. General Post Office . . . 20 10
699a 6p. House of Assembley . . . 30 30
699b 7p. Bleak House (horiz) . . . 30 30
699c 8p. General Eliott Memorial . 30 30
699d 9p. Supreme Court Building (horiz) 30 30
700 10p. South Barracks (horiz) . 30 30
700a 20p. The Convent (horiz) . . 60 55
701 21p. American War Memorial . 60 55
702 24p. Garrison Library (horiz) . 70 55
703 25p. Southport Gates 70 55
704 26p. Casemates Gate (horiz) . 70 55
704a 30p. St. Bernard's Hospital . . 75 65
704b 40p. City Hall (horiz) . . . . 1·00 1·00
705 50p. Central Police Station (horiz) . . . . 1·50 1·25
706 £1 Prince Edward's Gate . . 2·00 2·50
706a £2 Church of the Sacred Heart of Jesus . . . . 4·00 4·50
707 £3 Lighthouse, Europa Point . 6·50 6·75
708 £5 Coat of Arms and fortress keys . . . . 10·00 10·50

1993. Anniversaries. Multicoloured.

709 21p. Type **186** 75 65
710 24p. R.A.F. crest with Handley Page 0/400 and Panavia Tornado F Mk 3 (75th anniv) 1·25 75
711 34p. Garrison Library badge and building (bicent) . . . . . . 1·40 2·00
712 49p. Sir Winston Churchill and air raid (50th anniv of visit) . 2·25 3·50

187 Mice decorating Christmas Tree

1993. Christmas. Multicoloured.

713 5p. Type **187** 20 10
714 24p. Mice pulling cracker . . . 90 70
715 44p. Mice singing carols . . . 1·75 2·50
716 49p. Mice building snowman . . 1·90 2·75

188 Exploding Atom (Lord Penney)

1994. Europa. Scientific Discoveries. Mult.

717 24p. Type **188** . . . . 1·00 1·25
718 24p. Polonium and radium experiment (Marie Curie) . . 1·00 1·25
719 34p. First oil engine (Rudolph Diesel) . . . . 1·25 1·75
720 34p. Early telescope (Galileo) . . 1·25 1·75

189 World Cup and Map of U.S.A.

1994. World Cup Football Championship, U.S.A. Multicoloured.

721 26p. Type **189** 80 55
722 39p. Players and pitch in shape of U.S.A. . . . . 1·25 1·75
723 49p. Player's legs (vert) . . . . 1·60 2·50

191 Golden Star Coral

193 Great Tit

192 Throwing the Discus and Centenary Emblem

1994. Marine Life. Multicoloured.

726 21p. Type **191** 75 45
727 24p. Star fish 90 55
728 34p. Gorgonian sea-fan . . . . 1·50 2·25
729 49p. Peacock wrasse ("Turkish wrasse") . . . . 2·00 3·25

1994. Centenary of Int Olympic Committee. Mult.

730 49p. Type **192** . . . . 1·75 2·25
731 54p. Javelin throwing and emblem . . . . 1·75 2·50

1994. Christmas. Songbirds. Multicoloured.

732 5p. Type **193** 40 10
733 24p. European robin (horiz) . . 1·25 70
734 34p. Blue tit (horiz) . . . . 1·50 1·50
735 54p. Goldfinch . . . . 2·25 3·25

194 Austrian Flag, Hand and Star

1995. Expansion of European Union. Multicoloured.

736 24p. Type **194** 60 55
737 26p. Finnish flag, hand and star . 60 60
738 34p. Swedish flag, hand and star . . . . 90 1·50
739 49p. Flags of new members and European Union emblem . . 1·60 3·00

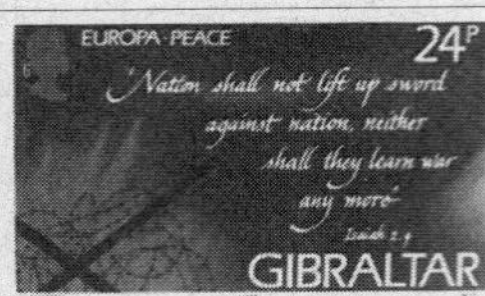

195 Barbed Wire and Quote from Isaiah Ch 2.4

1995. Europa. Peace and Freedom. Multicoloured.

740 24p. Type **195** . . . . 90 1·25
741 24p. Rainbow and hands releasing peace dove . . . . 90 1·25
742 34p. Shackles on wall and quote from Isaiah ch 61.1 . . . . 1·25 1·75
743 34p. Hands and sea birds . . . 1·25 1·75

197 Yachting

198 Bee Orchid

1995. Island Games '95. Multicoloured.

745 24p. Type **197** 70 60
746 44p. Athlete on starting blocks . 1·60 2·50
747 49p. Swimmer at start of race . 1·60 2·50

1995. "Singapore '95" International Stamp Exhibition. Orchids. Multicoloured.

749 22p. Type **198** . . . . 1·00 1·10
750 23p. Brown bee orchid . . . . 1·00 1·10
751 24p. Pyramidal orchid . . . . 1·00 1·10
752 25p. Mirror orchid . . . . . . 1·00 1·10
753 26p. Sawfly orchid . . . . . . 1·00 1·10

199 Handshake and United Nations Emblem

1995. 50th Anniv of United Nations. Multicoloured.

754 34p. Type **199** . . . . 1·25 1·10
755 49p. Peace dove and U.N. emblem . . . . 1·50 2·25

201 Father Christmas

1995. Christmas. Multicoloured.

757 5p. Type **201** 20 10
758 24p. Toys in sack 75 55
759 34p. Reindeer . . . . 1·00 1·25
760 54p. Sleigh over houses . . . . 1·60 2·50

202 Shih Tzu

1996. Puppies. Multicoloured.

761 5p. Type **202** 40 60
762 21p. Dalmatians 75 85
763 24p. Cocker spaniels 80 90
764 25p. West Highland white terriers 80 90
765 34p. Labrador 90 95
766 35p. Boxer 90 95

No. 762 is inscr "Dalmation" in error.

203 Princess Anne

1996. Europa. Famous Women.

767 **203** 24p. black and yellow . . . 85 85
768 – 24p. black and green . . . 85 85
769 – 34p. black and red . . . . 1·25 1·75
770 – 34p. black and purple . . . 1·25 1·75

DETAILS: No. 768, Princess Diana; 769, Queen Elizabeth II; 770, Queen Elizabeth the Queen Mother.

204 West German Player, 1980

205 Ancient Greek Athletes

1996. European Football Championship, England. Players from previous winning teams. Multicoloured.

771 21p. Type **204** 55 45
772 24p. French player, 1984 . . . 65 55
773 34p. Dutch player, 1988 . . . 95 1·10
774 £1.20 Danish player, 1992 . . . 3·00 4·25

1996. Centenary of Modern Olympic Games.

776 **205** 34p. black, purple and orange 95 90
777 – 49p. black and brown . . . 1·40 1·75
778 – £1.05 multicoloured . . . 2·75 3·50

DESIGNS: 49p. Start of early race; £1.05, Start of modern race

206 Asian Children

1996. 50th Anniv of U.N.I.C.E.F.

780 **206** 21p. multicoloured 60 80
781 – 24p. multicoloured 70 90
782 – 49p. multicoloured . . . . 1·25 1·40
783 – 54p. multicoloured . . . . 1·40 1·60

DESIGNS: 24p. to 54p. Children from different continents.

207 Red Kites in Flight

1996. Endangered Species. Red Kite. Multicoloured.

784 34p. Type **207** . . . . 1·00 1·25
785 34p. Red kite on ground . . . 1·00 1·25
786 34p. On rock . . . . 1·00 1·25
787 34p. Pair at nest . . . . . . 1·00 1·25

208 Christmas Pudding

1996. Christmas. Designs created from "Lego" Blocks. Multicoloured.

788 5p. Type **208** 15 15
789 21p. Snowman face 70 45
790 24p. Present 80 55
791 34p. Father Christmas face . . 1·10 1·25
792 54p. Candle . . . . 1·50 2·50

209 "Mary Celeste" passing Gibraltar

211 "Anthocharis belia euphenoides"

210 American Shorthair Silver Tabby

1997. Europa. Tales and Legends. "The Mary Celeste". Multicoloured.

793 28p. Type **209** 80 90
794 28p. Boarding the "Mary Celeste" 80 90
795 30p. Crew leaving "Mary Celeste" . . . . 90 1·10
796 30p. "Mary Celeste" found by "Dei Gratia" . . . . . . 90 1·10

1997. Kittens. Multicoloured.
797 5p. Type **210** 40 60
798 24p. Rumpy Manx red tabby . 75 85
799 26p. Blue point birmans . . . 75 85
800 28p. Red self longhair 80 90
801 30p. British shorthair tortoiseshell and white . . . 80 90
802 35p. British bicolour shorthairs . 90 1·10

1997. Butterflies. Multicoloured.
804 23p. Type **211** 70 50
805 26p. "Charaxes jasius" 85 60
806 30p. "Vanessa cardui" 95 90
807 £1.20 "Iphiclides podalirius" . . 3·25 4·50

212 Queen Elizabeth and Prince Philip at Carriage-driving Trials

1997. Golden Wedding of Queen Elizabeth and Prince Philip. Multicoloured.
810 £1.20 Type **212** . . . . 3·25 3·75
811 £1.40 Queen Elizabeth in Trooping the Colour uniform . . . . 3·25 3·75

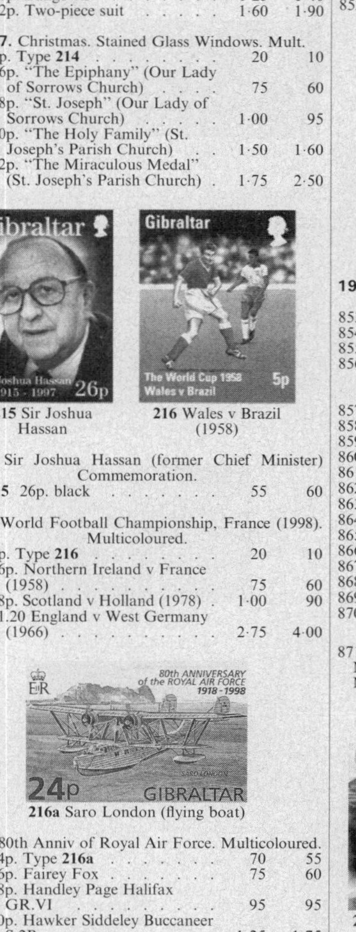

213 Christian Dior Evening Dress

214 "Our Lady and St. Bernard" (St. Joseph's Parish Church)

1997. Christian Dior Spring/Summer '97 Collection. Multicoloured.
812 30p. Type **213** . . . . 80 1·10
813 35p. Tunic top and skirt . . . 1·10 1·50
814 50p. Ballgown . . . . 1·25 1·40
815 62p. Two-piece suit . . . . . 1·60 1·90

1997. Christmas. Stained Glass Windows. Mult.
817 5p. Type **214** 20 10
818 26p. "The Epiphany" (Our Lady of Sorrows Church) 75 60
819 38p. "St. Joseph" (Our Lady of Sorrows Church) . . . . . 1·00 95
820 50p. "The Holy Family" (St. Joseph's Parish Church) . . 1·50 1·60
821 62p. "The Miraculous Medal" (St. Joseph's Parish Church) . 1·75 2·50

215 Sir Joshua Hassan

216 Wales v Brazil (1958)

1997. Sir Joshua Hassan (former Chief Minister) Commemoration.
822 **215** 26p. black 55 60

1998. World Football Championship, France (1998). Multicoloured.
823 5p. Type **216** 20 10
824 26p. Northern Ireland v France (1958) 75 60
825 38p. Scotland v Holland (1978) . 1·00 90
826 £1.20 England v West Germany (1966) . . . . 2·75 4·00

216a Saro London (flying boat)

1998. 80th Anniv of Royal Air Force. Multicoloured.
829 24p. Type **216a** 70 55
830 26p. Fairey Fox 75 60
831 38p. Handley Page Halifax GR.VI 95 95
832 50p. Hawker Siddeley Buccaneer S.2B . . . . 1·25 1·75

217 Miss Gibraltar saluting

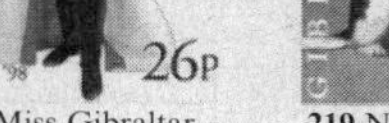

219 Nileus (dog) with Hat and Telescope

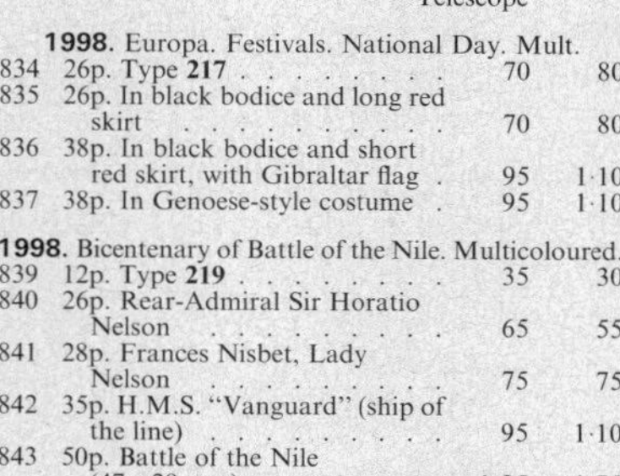

1998. Europa. Festivals. National Day. Mult.
834 26p. Type **217** 70 80
835 26p. In black bodice and long red skirt 70 80
836 38p. In black bodice and short red skirt, with Gibraltar flag . 95 1·10
837 38p. In Genoese-style costume . 95 1·10

1998. Bicentenary of Battle of the Nile. Multicoloured.
839 12p. Type **219** 35 30
840 26p. Rear-Admiral Sir Horatio Nelson 65 55
841 28p. Frances Nisbet, Lady Nelson 75 75
842 35p. H.M.S. "Vanguard" (ship of the line) . . . . 95 1·10
843 50p. Battle of the Nile (47 × 29 mm) . . . . 1·25 1·75

220 "Love comforts like Sunshine after Rain" (William Shakespeare)

221 The Nativity

1998. Famous Quotations. Multicoloured.
844 26p. Type **220** 70 80
845 26p. "The price of greatness is responsibility" (Sir Winston Churchill) 70 80
846 38p. "Hate the sin, love the sinner" (Mahatma Gandhi) . 90 1·00
847 38p. "Imagination is more important than knowledge" (Albert Einstein) . . . . . 90 1·00

1998. Christmas. Multicoloured.
848 5p. Type **221** 15 10
849 26p. Star and stable 75 70
850 30p. King with gold 90 75
851 35p. King with myrrh . . . . 1·00 85
852 50p. King with frankincense . . 1·40 1·75

222 Barbary Macaque

223 Queen Elizabeth II

1999. Europa. Parks and Gardens. Upper Rock Nature Reserve. Multicoloured.
853 30p. Type **222** 80 90
854 30p. Dartford warbler 80 90
855 42p. Dusky grouper . . . . . 1·10 1·25
856 42p. Common kingfisher . . . 1·10 1·25

1999. (a) Ordinary gum.
857 **223** 1p. purple 10 10
858 2p. brown 10 10
859 4p. blue 10 10
860 5p. green 10 10
861 10p. orange 20 25
862 12p. red 25 30
863 20p. green 40 45
864 28p. mauve 55 60
865 30p. orange 60 65
866 40p. grey 80 85
867 42p. green 85 90
868 50p. bistre . . . . 1·00 1·10
869 £1 black . . . . 2·00 2·10
870 £3 blue . . . . 6·00 6·25

(b) Self-adhesive.
871 **223** (1st) orange 55 60

Nos. 868/71 are larger, 25 × 30 mm.
No. 871 was initially sold at 26p.

224 Roman Marine and Galley

225 John Lennon (musician)

1999. Maritime Heritage. Multicoloured.
872 5p. Type **224** 10 10
873 30p. Arab sailor, medieval galley house and dhow 60 65
874 42p. Marine officer and British ship of the line (1779–83) . . 85 90
875 $1.20 Naval rating, Queen Alexandra Dry Dock and H.M.S. "Berwick" (cruiser) (1904) . . . . 2·40 2·50

1999. 30th Wedding Anniv of John Lennon and Yoko Ono. Designs showing John Lennon.
877 **225** 20p. multicoloured 40 45
878 – 30p. black and blue . . . 60 65
879 – 40p. multicoloured 80 85

DESIGNS 20p. With flower over left eye; 40p. Wearing orange glasses.

226 Postal Van at Dockside, 1930s

1999. 125th Anniv of U.P.U. Multicoloured.
881 5p. Type **226** 15 10
882 30p. Space shuttle and station . 75 80

227 EF-2000 Eurofighter

1999. Wings of Prey. Birds of Prey and R.A.F. Fighter Aircraft. Multicoloured.
883 30p. Type **227** 80 90
884 30p. Panavia Tornado F3 . . . 80 90
885 30p. BAe Harrier II GR7 . . . 80 90
886 42p. Lesser kestrel . . . . . 90 1·00
887 42p. Peregrine falcon . . . . 90 1·00
888 42p. Common kestrel . . . . 90 1·00

228 Prince Edward and Sophie Rhys-Jones

1999. Royal Wedding. Multicoloured.
890 30p. Type **228** 70 65
891 42p. Prince Edward and Sophie Rhys-Jones holding hands (vert) . . . . 1·00 90
892 54p. In carriage on wedding day 1·40 1·50
893 66p. On Chapel steps after wedding (vert) . . . . . . 1·50 1·60

229 Football

230 "Seasons Greetings"

1999. Local Sporting Centenaries. Multicoloured.
894 30p. Type **229** 75 65
895 42p. Rowing . . . . 1·00 90
896 £1.20, Cricket . . . . 2·75 3·00

1999. Christmas. Multicoloured.
897 5p. Type **230** 10 10
898 5p. "Happy Christmas" 10 10
899 30p. "Happy Millennium" . . . 60 65
900 30p. "Happy Christmas" and Santa with reindeer 60 65
901 42p. Santa Claus in chimney . . 85 90
902 54p. Santa Claus leaving presents . . . . 1·10 1·25

231 "People travelling with Environmentally-friendly Jet-packs" (Colin Grech)

2000. "Stampin' the Future" (children's stamp design competition). Multicoloured.
903 30p. Type **231** 60 65
904 42p. "Robotic Postman" (Kim Barea) 85 90
905 54p. "Living on the Moon" (Stephan Williamson-Fa) . . 1·10 1·25
906 66p. "Jet-powered Cars" (Michael Podesta) . . . . . 1·50 1·60

POSTAGE DUE STAMPS

D 1

D 2

1956.
D1 **D 1** 1d. green . . . . 2·50 4·00
D2 2d. brown . . . . 2·50 3·75
D3 4d. blue . . . . 3·25 6·75

1971. As Nos. D1/3, but inscr in decimal currency.
D4 ½p. green 30 80
D5 1p. brown 30 70
D6 2p. blue 30 80

1976.
D 7 **D 2** 1p. orange 15 60
D 8 3p. blue 15 75
D 9 5p. red 20 75
D10 7p. violet 25 75
D11 10p. green 35 75
D12 20p. green . . . . 70 1·00

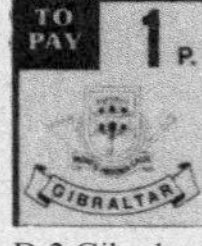

D 3 Gibraltar Coat of Arms

D 4 Water Port Gates

1984.
D13 **D 3** 1p. black 25 50
D14 3p. red 35 50
D15 5p. blue 40 50
D16 10p. blue 50 50
D17 25p. mauve . . . . 90 1·00
D18 50p. orange . . . . . . 1·40 1·50
D19 £1 green . . . . 2·25 2·75

1996. Gibraltar Landmarks.
D20 **D 4** 1p. black, emerald and green 10 10
D21 – 10p. black and grey . . . 20 25
D22 – 25p. black, brown and chestnut 50 55
D23 – 50p. black and lilac . . . 1·00 1·10
D24 – £1 black, brown and chestnut . . . . 2·00 2·10
D25 – £2 black and blue . . . . 4·00 4·25

DESIGNS: 10p. Naval Dockyard; 25p. Military Hospital; 50p. Governor's Cottage; £1 Swans on the Laguna; £2 Catalan Bay.

GILBERT AND ELLICE ISLANDS Pt. 1

A British colony in the South Pacific.

1911. 12 pence = 1 shilling;
20 shillings = 1 pound.
1966. 100 cents = $1 Australian.

1911. Stamps of Fiji (King Edward VII) optd **GILBERT & ELLICE PROTECTORATE.**

1 **23** ½d. green . . . . 4·50 40·00
2 1d. red . . . . 45·00 27·00
3 2d grey . . . . 8·50 14·00
4 2½d. blue . . . . 12·00 25·00
5 5d. purple and green . . . . 38·00 65·00
6 6d. purple . . . . 20·00 40·00
7 1s. black on green . . . . . . 20·00 50·00

2 Pandanus Pine

3

1911

8 **2** ½d. green . . . . 4·25 12·00
9 1d. red . . . . 2·00 6·50
10 2d. grey . . . . 1·50 6·50
11 2½d. blue . . . . 4·00 9·50

1912.

27 **3** ½d. green . . . . 2·50 2·50
13 1d. red . . . . 2·00 4·25
28 1d. violet . . . . 3·75 4·25
29 1½d. red . . . . 3·75 1·75
30 2d. grey . . . . 6·00 22·00
15 2½d. blue . . . . 1·75 11·00
16 3d. purple on yellow . . . . . 2·50 8·50
17 4d. black & red on yellow . . 60 6·00
18 5d. purple and green . . . . 1·50 7·00
19 6d. purple . . . . 1·25 7·50
20 1s. black on green . . . . . . 1·25 5·50
21 2s. purple & blue on blue . . . 14·00 30·00
22 2s. 6d. black & red on blue . . 15·00 25·00
23 5s. green & red on yellow . . 32·00 55·00
35 10s. green & red on green . . £160 £350
24 £1 purple and black on red . . £600 £1400

1918. Optd **WAR TAX.**

26 **3** 1d. red . . . . 30 6·50

1935. Silver Jubilee. As T **10a** of Gambia.

36 1d. blue and black . . . . . . 2·25 9·00
37 1½d. blue and red . . . . . . 1·75 3·75
38 3d. brown and blue . . . . . . 5·50 11·00
39 1s. grey and purple . . . . . . 35·00 24·00

1937. Coronation. As T **10b** of Gambia.

40 1d. violet 35 65
41 1½d. red 35 65
42 3d. blue 40 70

6 Great Frigate Bird

7 Pandanus Pine

1939

43 **6** ½d. blue and green 30 85
44 **7** 1d. green and purple . . . . 30 1·50
45 – 1½d. black and red 30 90
46 – 2d. brown and black . . . . 60 1·00
47 – 2½d. black and green 40 70
48 – 3d. black and blue . . . . . 45 1·00
49 – 5d. blue and brown . . . . . 4·25 1·25
50 – 6d. green and violet 40 50
51a – 1s. black and turquoise . . . 4·50 2·25
52 – 2s. blue and red . . . . . . 16·00 12·00
53 – 2s. 6d. blue and green . . . 17·00 14·00
54 – 5s. red and blue . . . . . . 18·00 16·00

DESIGNS: 1½d. Canoe crossing reef; 2d. Canoe and boat-house; 2½d. Native house; 3d. Seascape; 5d. Ellice Is. canoe; 6d. Coconut palms; 1s. Jetty, Ocean Is.; 2s. H.M.C.S. "Nimanoa"; 2s. 6d. Gilbert Is. canoe; 5s. Coat of arms.

1946. Victory. At T **11a** of Gambia.

55 1d. purple 15 40
56 3d. blue 15 40

1949. Silver Wedding. As T **11b/c** of Gambia.

57 1d. violet 40 50
58 £1 red . . . . 15·00 18·00

1949. U.P.U. As T **11d/g** of Gambia.

59 1d. purple 55 90
60 2d. black . . . . 2·25 2·25
61 3d. blue . . . . 1·00 2·00
62 1s. blue . . . . 1·25 2·00

1953. Coronation. As T **11h** of Gambia.

63 2d. black and grey . . . . . . 55 2·25

18 Great Frigate Bird

1956. As 1939 issue but with portrait of Queen Elizabeth II as in T **18** and colours changed.

64 **18** ½d. black and blue . . . . . 45 1·25
65 **7** 1d. olive and violet 60 70
85 – 2d. green and purple . . . . 75 2·00
67 – 2½d. black and green 50 60
68 – 3d. black and red 50 60
69 – 5d. blue and orange . . . . 8·50 1·75
70 – 6d. brown and black . . . . 55 2·00
71 – 1s. black and olive . . . . . 1·75 60
72 – 2s. blue and sepia . . . . . 8·50 5·50
73 – 2s. 6d. red and blue . . . . 10·00 5·50
74 – 5s. blue and green . . . . . 12·00 9·00
75 – 10s. black & turq (as 1½d.) . . 28·00 15·00

19 Loading Phosphate from Cantilever

1960. Diamond Jubilee of Phosphate Discovery at Ocean Is. Inscr "1900 1960".

76 **19** 2d. green and red 70 85
77 – 2½d. black and olive 70 85
78 – 1s. black and turquoise . . . 70 85

DESIGNS: 2½d. Phosphate rock; 1s. Phosphate mining.

1963. Freedom from Hunger. As T **20a** of Gambia.

79 10d. blue . . . . 1·25 30

1963. Red Cross Cent. As T **20b** of Gambia.

80 2d. red and black . . . . . . 1·00 50
81 10d. red and blue . . . . . . 2·00 2·75

23 Eastern Reef Heron in Flight

1964. First Air Service.

82 – 3d. blue, black & lt blue . . . 70 30
83 **23** 1s. lt blue, black and blue . . 90 30
84 – 3s. 7d. green, black & emer . 1·40 1·50

DESIGNS—VERT: 3d. De Havilland Heron 2 and route map; 3s. 7d. De Havilland Heron 2 over Tarawa lagoon.

1965. Cent of I.T.U. As T **44** of Gibraltar.

87 3d. orange and green 20 10
88 2s. 6d. turquoise and purple . . 80 20

26 Gilbertese Women's Dance

1965. Multicoloured.

89 ½d. Maneaba and Gilbertese man blowing Bu shell 10 10
90 1d. Ellice Islanders Reef fishing by flare 10 10
91 2d. Gilbertese girl weaving head-garland 10 10
92 3d. Gilbertese woman performing Ruoia 10 10
93 4d. Gilbertese man performing Kamei 15 10
94 5d. Gilbertese girl drawing water 20 10
95 6d. Ellice Islander performing a Fatele 20 10
96 7d. Ellice youths performing spear dance 25 10
97 1s. Gilbertese girl tending Ikaroa Babai plant 50 10
98 1s. 6d. Ellice Islanders dancing a Fatele . . . . 1·00 65
99 2s. Ellice Islanders pounding Pulaka . . . . 1·00 1·40
100 3s. 7d. Type **26** . . . . . . 2·25 65
101 5s. Gilbertese boys playing a stick game . . . . 2·25 80
102 10s. Ellice youths beating the box for the Fatele . . . . . . 4·00 1·25
103 £1 Coat of arms . . . . . . 4·50 2·50

Nos. 89/99 are vert.

1965. I.C.Y. As T **45** of Gibraltar.

104 ½d. purple and turquoise . . . 10 10
105 3s. 7d. green and lavender . . 75 20

1966. Churchill Commem. As T **46** of Gibraltar.

106 ½d. blue 10 10
107 3d. green 20 10
108 3s. brown 35 35
109 3s. 7d. violet 40 35

1966. Decimal Currency. Nos. 89/103 surch.

110 1 c. on 1d. 10 10
111 2 c. on 2d. 10 10
112 3 c. on 3d. 10 10
113 4 c. on ½d. 10 10
114 5 c. on 6d. 15 10
115 6 c. on 4d. 15 10
116 8 c. on 5d. 15 10
117 10 c. on 1s. 15 10
118 15 c. on 7d. 80 40
119 20 c. on 1s. 6d. 45 25
120 25 c. on 2s. 45 20
121 35 c. on 3s. 7d. . . . . . . 1·25 20
122 50 c. on 5s. 75 35
123 $1 on 10s. 75 40
124 $2 on £1 . . . . 1·50 2·50

1966. World Cup Football Championship. As T **47** of Gibraltar.

125 3 c. multicoloured 20 10
126 35 c. multicoloured 55 20

1966. Inauguration of W.H.O. Headquarters, Geneva. As T **54** of Gibraltar.

127 3 c. black, green and blue . . . 20 10
128 12 c. black, purple & ochre . . 45 40

1966. 20th Anniv of U.N.E.S.C.O. As T **56a/c** of Gibraltar.

129 5 c. multicoloured 25 20
130 10 c. yellow, violet and olive . . 35 10
131 20 c. black, purple & orange . . 60 45

41 H.M.S. "Royalist"

1967. 75th Anniv of Protectorate.

132 **41** 3 c. red, blue and green . . . 30 50
133 – 10 c. multicoloured 15 15
134 – 35 c. sepia, yellow & green . . 30 50

DESIGNS: 10 c. Trading post; 35 c. Island family.

1968. Decimal Currency. As Nos. 89/103, but with values inscr in decimal currency.

135 – 1 c. multicoloured (as 1d.) . . 10 15
136 – 2 c. multicoloured (as 2d.) . . 15 10
137 – 3 c. multicoloured (as 3d.) . . 15 10
138 – 4 c. multicoloured (as ½d.) . . 15 10
139 – 5 c. multicoloured (as 6d.) . . 15 10
140 – 6 c. multicoloured (as 4d.) . . 20 10
141 – 8 c. multicoloured (as 5d.) . . 20 10
142 – 10 c. multicoloured (as 1s.) . . 20 10
143 – 15 c. multicoloured (as 7d.) . . 50 20
144 – 20 c. multicoloured (as 1s. 6d.) 65 15
145 – 25 c. multicoloured (as 2s.) . . 1·25 20
146 **26** 35 c. multicoloured . . . . 1·50 20
147 – 50 c. multicoloured (as 5s.) . . 1·50 2·50
148 – $1 multicoloured (as 10s.) . . 1·50 3·75
149 – $2 multicoloured (as £1) . . 4·00 3·75

45 Map of Tarawa Atoll

1968. 25th Anniversary of Battle of Tarawa.

150 3 c. Type **45** 20 30
151 10 c. Marines landing 20 20
152 15 c. Beach-head assault . . . 30 35
153 35 c. Raising U.S. and British flags 40 50

46 Young Pupil against Outline of Abemama Island

1969. End of Inaugural Year of South Pacific University.

154 **46** 3 c. multicoloured 10 25
155 – 10 c. multicoloured 10 10
156 – 35 c. black, brown & grn . . 15 30

DESIGNS: 10 c. Boy and girl students and Tarawa atoll; 35 c. University graduate and South Pacific islands.

47 "Virgin and Child" in Pacific Setting

1969. Christmas

157 – 2 c. multicoloured 15 20
158 **47** 10 c. multicoloured 15 10

DESIGN: 2 c. as Type **47**. but with grass foreground instead of sand.

48 "Kiss of Life"

1970. Centenary of British Red Cross.

159 **48** 10 c. multicoloured 20 10
160 – 15 c. multicoloured 30 45
161 – 35 c. multicoloured 60 90

Nos. 160/1 are as Type **48**, but arranged differently.

49 Foetus and Patients

1970. 25th Anniversary of U.N.

162 **49** 5 c. multicoloured 15 30
163 – 10 c. black, grey and red . . 15 15
164 – 15 c. multicoloured 20 30
165 – 35 c. blue, green, & black . . 30 45

DESIGNS: 10 c. Nurse and surgical instruments; 15 c. X-ray plate and technician; 35 c. U.N. emblem and map.

53 Map of Gilbert Islands

57 "Child with Halo" (T. Collis)

1970. Centenary of Landing in Gilbert islands by London Missionary Society.

166 **53** 2 c. multicoloured 15 90
167 – 10 c. black and green . . . 25 15
168 – 25 c. brown and blue . . . 20 20
169 – 35 c. blue, black and red . . 50 70

DESIGNS—VERT: 10 c. Sailing-ship "John Williams III"; 25 c. Rev. S. J. Whitmee. HORIZ: 35 c. M.V. "John Williams VII".

1970. Christmas. Sketches. Multicoloured.

170 2 c. Type **57** 10 30
171 10 c. "Sanctuary, Tarawa Cathedral" (Mrs A. Burroughs) 10 10
172 35 c. "Three Ships inside Star" (Mrs. C. Barnett) 20 20

60 Casting Nets

1971. Multicoloured.

173 1 c. Cutting toddy (vert) . . . 10 10
174 2 c. Lagoon fishing 15 30
175 3 c. Cleaning pandanus leaves . 15 15
176 4 c. Type **60** 20 25
177 5 c. Gilbertese canoe 45 15
178 6 c. De-husking coconuts (vert) 30 45
179 8 c. Weaving pandanus fronds (vert) 35 15
180 10 c. Weaving a basket (vert) . . 40 15
181 15 c. Tiger shark and fishermen (vert) . . . . 2·50 1·50
182 20 c. Beating rolled pandanus leaf . . . . 1·50 90
183 25 c. Loading copra . . . . . 2·00 1·00
184 35 c. Fishing at night . . . . 2·25 50
185 50 c. Local handicrafts (vert) . . 1·25 1·50
186 $1 Weaving coconut screens (vert) . . . . 1·75 2·25
187 $2 Coat of arms (vert) . . . . 5·00 11·00

61 House of Representatives

1971. New Constitution. Multicoloured.
188 3 c. Type **61** 10 20
189 10 c. Maneaba Betio (Assembly hut) 20 10

62 Pacific Nativity Scene

1971. Christmas.
190 **62** 3 c. black, yellow and blue . 10 20
191 – 10 c. black, gold and blue . 10 10
192 – 35 c. black, gold and red . . 25 35
DESIGNS: 10 c. Star and palm leaves; 35 c. Outrigger canoe and star.

63 Emblem and Young Boys

1971. 25th Anniv of U.N.I.C.E.F. Multicoloured.
193 3 c. Type **63** 10 60
194 10 c. Young boy 15 15
195 35 c. Young boy's face 45 60
Nos. 193/5 include the UNICEF emblem within each design.

64 Flag and Map of South Pacific

1972. 25th Anniv of South Pacific Commission. Multicoloured.
196 3 c. Type **64** 10 65
197 10 c. Flag and native boats . . 15 20
198 35 c. Flags of member nations . 15 95

65 "Alveopora"

1972. Coral. Multicoloured.
199 3 c. Type **65** 25 45
200 10 c. "Euphyllia" 30 15
201 15 c. "Melithea" 40 35
202 35 c. "Spongodes" 80 60

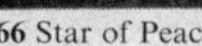

66 Star of Peace

69 Dancer

68 Funafuti ("The Land of Bananas")

1972. Christmas. Multicoloured.
208 3 c. Type **66** 10 10
209 10 c. "The Nativity" 10 10
210 35 c. Baby in "manger" (horiz) 30 30

1972. Royal Silver Wedding. As T **98** of Gibraltar, but with Floral Headdresses in background
211 3 c. brown 10 15
212 35 c. brown 25 15

1973. Legends of Island Names (1st series). Mult.
213 3 c. Type **68** 15 50
214 10 c. Butaritari ("The Smell of the Sea") 25 20
215 25 c. Tarawa ("The Centre of the World") 40 50
216 35 c. Abemama ("The Land of the Moon") 45 60
See also Nos. 252/5.

1973. Christmas. Multicoloured.
217 3 c. Type **69** 10 15
218 10 c. Canoe and lagoon 10 10
219 35 c. Lagoon at evening . . . 30 15
220 50 c. Map of Christmas Island 40 1·25

1973. Royal Wedding. As T **101a** of Gibraltar. Multicoloured, background colours given.
221 3 c. green 10 15
222 35 c. blue 20 15

70 Meteorological Observation

1973. Centenary of I.M.O./W.M.O. Mult.
223 3 c. Type **70** 50 30
224 10 c. Island observing-station . 50 20
225 35 c. Wind-finding radar . . . 70 25
226 50 c. World weather watch stations . . . . 1·10 1·25

71 Te Mataaua Crest

1974. Canoe Crests. Multicoloured.
227 3 c. Type **71** 10 10
228 10 c. "Te Nimta-wawa" . . . 15 10
229 35 c. "Tara-tara-venei-na" . . 25 10
230 50 c. "Te Bou-uoua" 35 60

72 £1 Stamp of 1924 and Te Koroba (canoe)

1974. Centenary of U.P.U.
232 **72** 4 c. multicoloured 20 20
233 – 10 c. multicoloured 20 10
234 – 25 c. multicoloured 25 30
235 – 35 c. multicoloured 30 30
DESIGNS: 10 c. 5s. stamp of 1939 and sailing vessel "Kiakia"; 25 c. $2 stamp of 1971 and B.A.C. One Eleven airplane; 35 c. U.P.U. emblem.

73 Toy Canoe

1974. Christmas. Multicoloured.
236 4 c. Type **73** 10 20
237 10 c. Toy windmill 15 10
238 25 c. Coconut "ball" 20 35
239 35 c. Canoes and constellation Pleiades 25 45

74 North Front Entrance, Blenheim Palace

1974. Birth Cent of Sir Winston Churchill. Mult.
240 4 c. Type **74** 10 35
241 10 c. Churchill painting . . . 10 10
242 35 c. Churchill's statue, London 25 40

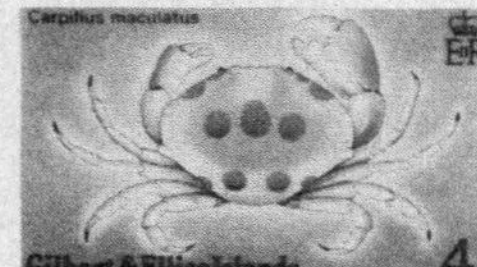

75 Barometer Crab

1975. Crabs. Multicoloured.
243 4 c. Type **75** 40 70
244 10 c. "Ranina ranina" 50 20
245 25 c. Pelagic swimmming crab . 90 70
246 35 c. Ghost crab . . . . . . 1·00 1·25

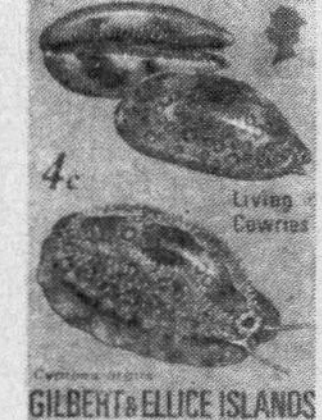

76 Eyed Cowrie

77 "Christ is Born"

1975. Cowrie Shells. Multicoloured.
247 4 c. Type **76** 55 60
248 10 c. Sieve cowrie 80 20
249 25 c. Mole cowrie . . . . . 1·75 1·10
250 35 c. All-red map cowrie . . . 2·00 2·00

1975. Legends of Island Names (2nd series). As T **68**. Multicoloured.
252 4 c. Beru ("The Bud") 10 30
253 10 c. Onotoa ("Six Giants") . . 10 15
254 25 c. Abaiang ("Land to the North") 20 35
255 35 c. Marakei ("Fish-trap floating on eaves") 30 50

1975. Christmas. Multicoloured.
256 4 c. Type **77** 20 50
257 10 c. Protestant Chapel, Tarawa 20 30
258 25 c. Catholic Church, Ocean Island 35 90
259 35 c. Fishermen and star . . . 40 1·50

POSTAGE DUE STAMPS

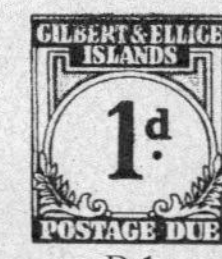

D 1

1940
D1 **D 1** 1d. green . . . . 8·50 22·00
D2 2d. red . . . . 9·50 22·00
D3 3d. brown . . . . 14·00 23·00
D4 4d. blue . . . . 16·00 29·00
D5 4d. olive . . . . 21·00 29·00
D6 6d. purple . . . . 21·00 29·00
D7 1s. violet . . . . 23·00 40·00
D8 1s. 6d. green . . . . . . 45·00 85·00

GILBERT ISLANDS Pt. 1

On 1 January, 1976 the Gilbert Islands and Tuvalu (Ellice) Islands became separate Crown Colonies. The Islands became independent on 12 July 1979, under the name of Kiribati.

100 cents = $1

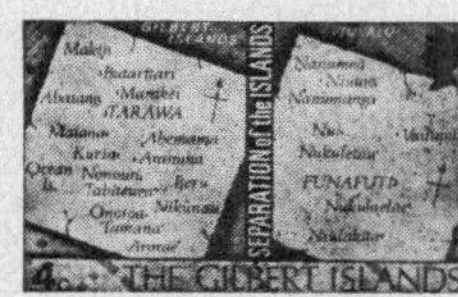

1 Charts of Gilbert Islands and Tuvalu (formerly Ellice) Islands

1976. Separation of the Islands. Multicoloured.
1 4 c. Type **1** 40 75
2 35 c. Maps of Tarawa and Funafuti 70 1·50

1976. Nos. 173/87 of Gilbert and Ellice Islands optd THE GILBERT ISLANDS.
3 1 c. Cutting toddy 25 30
5 2 c. Lagoon fishing 50 30
12 3 c. Cleaning pandanus leaves . 40 1·00
7 4 c. Type **60** 30 80
13 5 c. Gilbertese canoe 50 80
14 6 c. De-husking coconuts . . . 50 80
15 8 c. Weaving pandanus fronds . 50 80
16 10 c. Weaving a basket 50 80
17 15 c. Tiger shark . . . . . . 2·25 1·25
18 20 c. Beating a pandanus leaf . 1·25 1·50
19 25 c. Loading copra . . . . . 2·00 1·25
20 35 c. Fishing at night . . . . 2·00 1·75
21 50 c. Local handicrafts . . . . 2·00 2·75
22 $1 Weaving coconut screens . . 4·00 9·00

3 "Teraaka" (training ship)

1978. Multicoloured.
23 1 c. Type **3** 40 70
24 3 c. "Tautunu" (inter-island freighter) 60 80
25 4 c. Moorish idol (fish) . . . 30 70
26 5 c. Hibiscus 30 30
27 6 c. Eastern reef heron . . . 1·50 90
28 7 c. Catholic Cathedral, Tarawa 30 30
29 8 c. Frangipani 30 30
30 10 c. Maneaba, Bikenibeu . . . 30 30
31 12 c. Betio Harbour 45 45
32 15 c. Evening scene 55 45
33 20 c. Marakei Atoll 35 35
34 35 c. G.I.P.C. Chapel, Tangintebu 35 40
35 40 c. Flamboyant tree 40 45
36 50 c. "Hypolimnas bolina", (butterfly) . . . . 2·25 1·75
37 $1 "Tabakea" (Tarawa Lagoon ferry) . . . . 1·60 2·50
38 $2 National flag . . . . . . 1·60 2·50

4 Church

1976. Christmas. Children's Drawings. Mult.
39 5 c. Type **4** 25 15
40 15 c. Feasting (vert) 35 15
41 20 c. Maneaba (vert) 40 30
42 35 c. Dancing 55 45

5 Porcupine Fish Helmet

6 The Queen in Coronation Robes

1976. Artefacts. Multicoloured.
43 5 c. Type **5** 20 15
44 15 c. Shark's teeth dagger . . . 30 35
45 20 c. Fighting gauntlet 30 40
46 35 c. Coconut body armour . . 45 55

1977. Silver Jubilee. Multicoloured.
48 8 c. Prince Charles' visit, 1970 . 10 10
49 20 c. Prince Philip's visit, 1959 . 15 15
50 40 c. Type **6** 20 35

7 Commodore Bryon and H.M.S. "Dolphin"

1977. Explorers. Multicoloured.
51 5 c. Type **7** . . . . 55 1·50
52 15 c. Capt. Fanning and "Betsey" 65 2·75
53 20 c. Admiral Bellingshausen and "Vostok" . . . . 65 2·75
54 35 c. Capt. Wilkes and U.S.S. "Vincennes" . . . . 80 4·00

8 H.M.S. "Resolution" and H.M.S. "Discovery"

9 Scout Emblem and Island Scene

1977. Christmas and Bicentenary of Capt. Cook's Discovery of Christmas Is. Mult.
55 8 c. Type **8** 30 10
56 15 c. Logbook entry (horiz) . . 30 15
57 20 c. Captain Cook 40 20
58 40 c. Landing party (horiz) . . 40 60

1977. 50th Anniv of Scouting in the Gilbert Is. Multicoloured.
60 8 c. Type **9** 30 10
61 15 c. Patrol meeting (horiz) . . 35 20

62	20 c. Scout making mat (horiz)	40	20
63	40 c. Canoeing	50	55

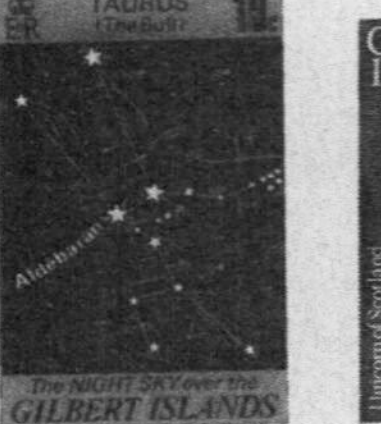

10 Taurus (The Bull) 11 Unicorn of Scotland

1978. The Night Sky over the Gilbert Islands.

64	10	10 c. black and blue	35	20
65	–	20 c. black and red	40	35
66	–	25 c. black and green	40	40
67	–	45 c. black and orange	60	70

DESIGNS: 20 c. Canis Major (the Great Dog); 25 c. Scorpio (the Scorpion); 45 c. Orion (the Giant Warrior).

1978. 25th Anniv of Coronation.

68	11	45 c. green, violet and silver	25	40
69	–	45 c. multicoloured	25	40
70	–	45 c. green, violet and silver	25	40

DESIGNS: No. 69, Queen Elizabeth II. No. 70, Great Frigate Bird.

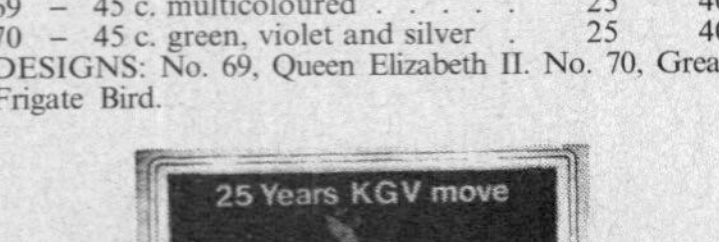

12 Birds in Flight to Tarawa

1978. 25th Anniv of Return of George V School to Tarawa. Multicoloured.

71	10 c. Type **12**	10	10
72	20 c. Tarawa, Abemama and school badge	20	20
73	25 c. Rejoicing islanders	20	20
74	45 c. King George V School on Tarawa and Abemama	35	35

13 "Te Kaue ni Maie"

1978. Christmas. Kaue (traditional head decorations). Multicoloured.

75	10 c. Type **13**	10	10
76	20 c. "Te Itera"	15	15
77	25 c. "Te Bau"	20	20
78	45 c. "Te Tai"	25	30

14 H.M.S. "Endeavour"

1979. Bicentenary of Captain Cook's Voyages. 1768–79.

80	14	10 c. multicoloured	20	15
81	–	20 c. multicoloured	25	30
82	–	25 c. black, lilac and green	25	45
83	–	45 c. multicoloured	25	80

DESIGNS: 20 c. Green Turtle; 25 c. Quadrant; 45 c. Flaxman/Wedgwood medallion.

For later issues see **KIRIBATI**.

GOLD COAST Pt. 1

A British colony on the W. coast of Africa. For later issues after independence in 1957 see under Ghana.

12 pence = 1 shilling
20 shillings = 1 pound

1

4

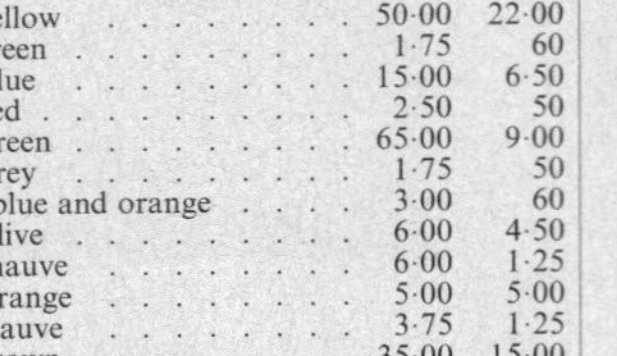

1875.

4	1	½d. yellow	50·00	22·00
11a		½d. green	1·75	60
5		1d. blue	15·00	6·50
12		1d. red	2·50	50
6		2d. green	65·00	9·00
13b		2d. grey	1·75	50
14		2½d. blue and orange	3·00	60
15		3d. olive	6·00	4·50
16		4d. mauve	6·00	1·25
17		6d. orange	5·00	5·00
18a		1s. mauve	3·75	1·25
19a		2s. brown	35·00	15·00

1889. Surch **ONE PENNY.** and bar.

20	1	1d. on 6d. orange	£100	48·00

1889.

26	4	½d. mauve and green	2·00	1·00
27		1d. mauve and red	2·00	50
27b		2d. mauve and red	38·00	£100
28		2½d. mauve and blue	4·50	4·25
29		3d. mauve and orange	4·75	1·50
30		6d. mauve and violet	5·50	1·50
31		1s. green and black	9·00	11·00
32		2s. green and red	9·00	17·00
22		5s. mauve and blue	65·00	12·00
33		5s. green and mauve	50·00	26·00
23		10s. mauve and red	75·00	15·00
34		10s. green and brown	£130	50·00
24		20s. green and red	£3250	
25		20s. mauve & black on red	£150	35·00

1901. Surch **ONE PENNY.** and bar.

35	4	1d. on 2½d. mauve and blue	2·00	3·00
36		1d. on 6d. mauve and violet	2·00	3·00

1902. As T **4**, but with portrait of King Edward VII.

38	½d. purple and green	1·00	40
39	1d. purple and red	1·25	15
51	2d. purple and orange	4·50	50
41	2½d. purple and blue	4·50	9·00
42	3d. purple and orange	2·75	1·50
43	6d. purple and violet	3·00	1·50
44	1s. green and black	10·00	3·25
45	2s. green and red	13·00	16·00
57	2s. 6d. green and yellow	28·00	£100
46	5s. green and mauve	35·00	80·00
47	10s. green and brown	50·00	£130
48	20s. purple and black on red	£130	£180

1907. As last.

59	½d. green	2·50	30
60	1d. red	5·00	40
61	2d. grey	2·25	40
62	2½d. blue	4·00	1·75
63	3d. purple on yellow	7·00	55
64a	6d. purple	3·75	3·50
65	1s. black and green	7·50	50
66	2s. purple and blue on blue	6·50	16·00
67	2s. 6d. black and red on blue	26·00	70·00
68	5s. green and red on yellow	55·00	£140

8

13 King George V and Christiansborg Castle

1908.

69	8	1d. red	2·75	10

1913. As T **4** and **8** (1d.) but portraits of King George V.

86	½d. green	40	30
72	1d. red	70	10
87	1d. brown	40	10
88	1½d. red	1·25	10
89	2d. grey	1·25	30
76	2½d. blue	4·75	1·00
90	2½d. orange	50	8·50
77b	3d. purple on yellow	40	40
91	3d. blue	1·25	60
94	6d. purple	1·40	3·00
79	1s. black on green	1·50	1·25
96	2s. purple and blue on blue	2·50	3·25
97	2s. 6d. black and red on blue	6·00	17·00
98	5s. green and red on yellow	9·50	42·00
83a	10s. green and red on green	18·00	65·00
100a	15s. purple and green	£110	£275
84	20s. purple and black on red	£120	80·00
102	£2 green and orange	£350	£850

1918. Surch **WAR TAX ONE PENNY**.

85	1d. on red (No. 72)	40	40

1928.

103	13	½d. green	60	40
104		1d. brown	60	10
105		1½d. red	60	1·50
106		2d. grey	60	20
107		2½d. orange	1·25	3·50
108		3d. blue	60	40
109		6d. black and purple	85	40
110		1s. black and orange	2·00	75
111		2s. black and violet	15·00	4·50
112		3s. red and olive	48·00	40·00

1935. Silver Jubilee. As T **10a** of Gambia.

113	1d. blue and black	60	50
114	3d. brown and blue	3·00	6·00
115	6d. green and blue	5·00	11·00
116	1s. grey and purple	3·75	11·00

1937. Coronation. As T **10b** of Gambia.

117	1d. brown	1·00	1·50
118	2d. grey	1·10	3·00
119	3d. blue	1·25	1·25

14

15 King George VI and Christiansborg Castle, Accra

1938.

120a	14	½d. green	40	50
121a		1d. brown	40	10
122a		1½d. red	40	50
123a		2d. black	40	10
124a		3d. blue	40	35
125a		4d. mauve	70	1·25
126a		6d. purple	70	20
127a		9d. orange	90	55
128a	15	1s. black and olive	1·00	50
129		1s. 3d. brown and blue	2·00	40
130a		2s. blue and violet	4·50	9·00
131a		5s. olive and red	8·00	12·00
132		10s. black and violet	7·00	17·00

1946. Victory. As T **11a** of Gambia.

133a	2d. grey	10	10
134a	4d. mauve	75	2·75

16 Northern Territories Mounted Constabulary

1948.

135	16	½d. green	20	30
136	–	1d. blue	15	15
137	–	1½d. red	1·25	70
138	–	2d. brown	55	10
139	–	2½d. brown and red	2·00	2·75
140	–	3d. blue	4·00	45
141	–	4d. mauve	3·50	1·25
142	–	6d. black and orange	30	30
143	–	1s. black and red	60	30
144	–	2s. olive and red	3·00	2·00
145	–	5s. purple and black	20·00	4·50
146	–	10s. black and olive	8·00	4·50

DESIGNS—HORIZ: 1d. Christiansborg Castle; 1½d. Emblem of Joint Provincial Council; 2½d. Map showing position of Gold Coast; 3d. Nsuba manganese mine; 4d. Lake Bosumtwi; 1s. Breaking cocoa pods; 2s. Gold Coast Regt. trooping the Colour; 5s. Surfboats. VERT: 2d. Talking drums; 6d. Cocoa farmer; 10s. Forest.

1948. Silver Wedding. As T **11b/c** of Gambia.

147	1½d. red	30	30
148	10s. olive	13·00	18·00

1949. U.P.U. As T **11d/g** of Gambia.

149	2d. brown	30	30
150	2½d. orange	2·00	2·00
151	3d. blue	50	70
152	1s. green	50	50

1952. As 1948 but portrait of Queen Elizabeth II. Designs as for corresponding values except where stated.

153	½d. brown and red (as 2½d.)	10	10
154	1d. blue	30	10
155	1½d. green	30	1·25
156	2d. brown	30	10
157	2½d. red (as ½d.)	35	35
158	3d. mauve	50	10
159	4d. blue	30	30
160	6d. black and orange	30	15
161	1s. black and red	30	15
162	2s. olive and red	11·00	85
163	5s. purple and black	17·00	5·00
164	10s. black and olive	15·00	12·00

1953. Coronation. As T **11h** of Gambia.

165	2d. black and brown	60	10

POSTAGE DUE STAMPS

D 1

1923.

D1	D 1	½d. black	14·00	£110
D2		1d. black	75	1·25
D5		2d. black	3·00	18·00
D6		3d. black	1·50	16·00
D7		6d. black	1·75	8·00
D8		1s. black	1·75	60·00

For later issues see **GHANA**.

GREAT BRITAIN Pt. 1

Consisting of England, Wales, Scotland and Northern Ireland, lying to the N.W. of the European continent.

1840. 12 pence = 1 shilling;
20 shillings = 1 pound sterling.
1971. 100 (new) pence = 1 pound sterling.

1

3

1840. Letters in lower corners. Imperf.

2	1	1d. black	£3500	£190
5		2d. blue	£6500	£400

1841. Imperf.

8	1	1d. brown	£175	10·00
14	3	2d. blue	£1500	60·00

In T **3** there are white lines below "POSTAGE" and above "TWO PENCE".

12

10

1847. Imperf.

59	12	6d. purple	£3250	£550
57	10	10d. brown	£3000	£725
54		1s. green	£3500	£500

1854. Perf.

29	1	1d. brown	£175	10·00
40		1d. red	50·00	9·00
34	3	2d. blue	£1500	50·00

14

18

19

1855. No letters in corners.

66a	14	4d. red	£900	75·00
70	18	6d. lilac	£675	80·00
72	19	1s. green	£800	£225

7

5

8

6

1858. Letters in four corners.

48	7	½d. red	70·00	15·00
43	5	1d. red	10·00	2·00
51	8	1½d. red	£250	40·00
45	6	2d. blue	£225	9·00

21

22

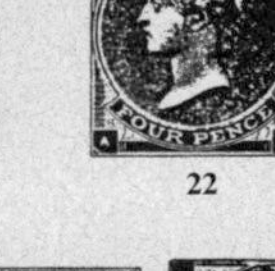

23

24

25

1862. Small white letters in corners.

76	21	3d. red	£1000	£200
80	22	4d. red	£900	70·00
84	23	6d. lilac	£1000	75·00
87	24	9d. bistre	£1900	£225
90	25	1s. green	£1100	£140

30

32

1865. Designs as 1862 and T **30** and **32**, but large white letters in corners.

103	**21**	3d. red	£325	40·00
95	**22**	4d. red	£375	45·00
97	**23**	6d. lilac (with hyphen)	£500	70·00
109		6d. lilac (without hyphen)	£400	65·00
110	**24**	9d. straw	£800	£175
112	**30**	10d. brown	£1500	£250
117	**25**	1s. green	£550	28·00
118	**32**	2s. blue	£1500	£110
121		2s. brown	£8000	£1700

35

38

1867.

126	**35**	5s. red	£3750	£400
128	–	10s. green	£28000	£1300
129	–	£1 brown	£32000	£1900
137	**38**	£5 orange	£6000	£1800

The 10s. and £1 are as Type **35**, but have different frames.

34

1872. Large white letters in corners.

122b	**34**	6d. brown	£475	40·00
125		6d. grey	£1000	£190

41

46

1873. Large coloured letters in corners.

141	**41**	2½d. mauve	£325	35·00
157		2½d. blue	£275	20·00
143	**21**	3d. red	£275	30·00
152	**22**	4d. red	£1000	£275
153		4d. green	£550	£175
160		4d. brown	£275	45·00
161	**34**	6d. grey	£250	50·00
156	**46**	8d. orange	£750	£225
150	**25**	1s. green	£375	50·00
163		1s. brown	£350	£100

The 3d, 4d. and 1s. are as 1862, and the 6d. as Type **34**, but all with large coloured letters.

52

53

1880. Various frames.

164	**52**	½d. green	40·00	10·00
187		½d. blue	17·00	7·00
166	**53**	1d. brown	15·00	10·00
167	–	1½d. brown	£140	35·00
168	–	2d. red	£175	70·00
169	–	5d. blue	£475	90·00

57

58

61

1881.

174	**57**	1d. lilac	2·50	1·50

1883. Types, as 1873, surch **3d**. or **6d**.

159	**21**	3d. on 3d. lilac	£325	£110
162	**34**	6d. on 6d. lilac	£275	£110

1883.

178	**58**	2s. 6d. lilac	£350	£110
180	–	5s. red	£550	£140
183	–	10s. blue	£1250	£375
185	**61**	£1 brown	£15000	£1400
212		£1 green	£2500	£425

The 5s. and 10s. are similar to Type **58**, but have different frames.

62

63

1883. Various frames.

188	**62**	1½d. purple	85·00	35·00
189	**63**	2d. purple	£140	65·00
190		2½d. purple	70·00	12·00
191	**62**	3d. purple	£175	85·00
192		4d. green	£400	£175
193		5d. green	£400	£175
194	**63**	6d. green	£425	£200
195		9d. green	£750	£375
196	**62**	1s. green	£550	£200

71

72

73

74

75

76

77

78

79

80

81

82

1887.

197	**71**	½d. red	1·50	1·00
213		½d. green*	1·75	2·00
198	**72**	1½d. purple and green	15·00	7·00
200	**73**	2d. green and red	28·00	12·00
201	**74**	2½d. purple on blue	22·00	3·00
202	**75**	3d. purple on yellow	22·00	3·25
205a	**76**	4d. green and brown	30·00	13·00
206	**77**	4½d. green and red	10·00	40·00
207a	**78**	5d. purple and blue	35·00	11·00
208	**79**	6d. purple on red	30·00	10·00
209	**80**	9d. purple and blue	60·00	40·00
210	**81**	10d. purple and red	45·00	38·00
211	**82**	1s. green	£200	60·00
214		1s. green and red	50·00	£125

*No. 213, in blue, has had the colour changed after issue.

83

90

1902. Designs not shown are as 1887 (2s. 6d. to £1 as 1883) but with portrait of King Edward VII.

217	**83**	½d. green	2·00	1·50
219		1d. red	2·00	1·50
221	–	1½d. purple and green	30·00	13·00
291	–	2d. green and red	25·00	15·00
231	**83**	2½d. blue	18·00	6·50
234	–	3d. purple on yellow	30·00	12·00
238	–	4d. green and brown	40·00	13·00
240	–	4d. orange	20·00	13·00
294	–	5d. purple and blue	28·00	15·00
246	**83**	6d. purple	30·00	12·00
249	**90**	7d. grey	10·00	12·00
307	–	9d. purple and blue	40·00	32·00
311	–	10d. purple and red	50·00	32·00
314	–	1s. green and red	38·00	22·00
316	–	2s. 6d. purple	£140	85·00
318	–	5s. red	£190	85·00
319	–	10s. blue	£450	£325
320	–	£1 green	£1000	£450

98 (Hair heavy)

99 (Lion unshaded)

1911.

325	**98**	½d. green	4·50	1·50
327	**99**	1d. red	4·50	2·50

101 (Hair light)

102 (Lion shaded)

1912.

344	**101**	½d. green	7·00	3·00
341	**102**	1d. red	4·00	2·00

104

105

106

107

108

109

1912. Lined background.

418	**105**	½d. green	1·00	1·00
419	**104**	1d. red	1·00	1·00
420	**105**	1½d. brown	1·00	1·00
421	**106**	2d. orange	2·50	2·50
422	**104**	2½d. blue	5·00	3·00
376	**106**	3d. violet	7·00	2·00
379		4d. green	12·00	2·00
381	**107**	5d. brown	10·00	5·00
426a		6d. purple	3·00	1·50
387		7d. green	20·00	10·00
390		8d. black on yellow	32·00	11·00
392	**108**	9d. black	18·00	6·00
427		9d. green	12·00	3·50
394		10d. blue	22·00	20·00
395		1s. brown	20·00	4·00
450	**109**	2s. 6d. brown	65·00	35·00
451		5s. red	£150	80·00
452		10s. blue	£325	75·00
403		£1 green	£1300	£800

112

1924. British Empire Exn. Dated "1924".

430	**112**	1d. red	10·00	11·00
431		1½d. brown	15·00	15·00

1925. Dated "1925".

432	**112**	1d. red	15·00	25·00
433		1½d. brown	40·00	65·00

113

114

115

116 St. George and the Dragon

1929. 9th U.P.U. Congress, London.

434	**113**	½d. green	2·25	2·25
435	**114**	1d. red	2·25	2·25
436		1½d. brown	2·25	1·75
437	**115**	2½d. blue	10·00	10·00
438	**116**	£1 black	£750	£550

118

119

120

121

122

123

1934. Solid background.

439	**118**	½d. green	30	40
440	**119**	1d. red	30	40
441	**118**	1½d. brown	30	40
442	**120**	2d. orange	50	75
443	**119**	2½d. blue	1·50	1·25
444	**120**	3d. violet	1·50	1·25
445		4d. green	2·00	1·25
446	**121**	5d. brown	6·00	2·75
447	**122**	9d. olive	12·00	2·25
448		10d. blue	15·00	10·00
449		1s. brown	15·00	1·25

1935. Silver Jubilee.

453	**123**	½d. green	75	50
454		1d. red	1·25	1·50
455		1½d. brown	75	50
456		2½d. blue	4·50	5·50

Emblems at right differ.

124 King Edward VIII

126 King George VI and Queen Elizabeth

1936.

457	**124**	½d. green	30	30
458		1d. red	60	40
459		1½d. brown	30	30
460		2½d. blue	30	75

1937. Coronation.

461	**126**	1½d. brown	50	40

128

129

130

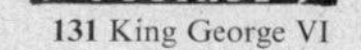
131 King George VI

1937.

462 128 ½d. green 10 25
503 ½d orange 30 30
463 1d. red 10 25
504 1d. blue 50 50
464 1½d. brown 20 25
505 1½d. green 50 60
465 2d. orange 75 50
506 2d. brown 50 40
466 2½d. blue 25 15
507 2½d. red 50 40
490 3d. violet 2·00 1·00
468 129 4d. green 60 60
508 4d. blue 2·50 1·75
469 5d. brown 2·50 75
470 6d. purple 1·25 60
471 130 7d. green 3·25 60
472 8d. red 3·50 70
473 9d. green 5·50 80
474 10d. blue 5·00 80
474a 11d. purple 2·00 2·00
475 1s. brown 5·75 75

1939.

476 131 2s. 6d. brown 38·00 7·00
476a 2s. 6d. green 7·00 1·50
477 5s. red 14·00 2·00
478a – 10s. blue 30·00 6·00
478b – £1 brown 10·00 24·00

The 10s. and £1 values have the portrait in the centre in an ornamental frame.

134 Queen Victoria and King George VI

1940. Centenary of First Adhesive Postage Stamps.

479 134 ½d. green 30 30
480 1d. red 1·00 50
481 1½d. brown 50 50
482 2d. orange 50 50
483 2½d. blue 2·25 1·00
484 3d. violet 3·00 3·25

135

1946. Victory Commemoration.

491 135 2½d. blue 30 30
492 – 3d. violet 30 30

DESIGN—HORIZ: 3d. Symbols of Peace and Reconstruction.

137

138 King George VI and Queen Elizabeth

1948. Royal Silver Wedding.

493 137 2½d. blue 30 30
494 138 £1 blue 38·00 38·00

139 Globe and Laurel Wreath

140 "Speed"

1948. Olympic Games. Inscr "OLYMPIC GAMES 1948".

495 139 2½d. blue 30 30
496 140 3d. violet 30 30
497 – 6d. purple 60 30
498 – 1s. brown 1·25 1·50

DESIGNS: 6d. Olympic symbol; 1s. Winged Victory.

143 Two Hemispheres

144 U.P.U. Monument, Berne

1949. 75th Anniv of U.P.U. Inscr as in T **143/4**.

499 143 2½d. blue 30 30
500 144 3d. violet 30 40
501 – 6d. purple 60 75
502 – 1s. brown 1·25 1·50

DESIGNS: 6d. Goddess Concordia, globe and points of compass; 1s. Posthorn and globe.

147 H.M.S. "Victory"

1951.

509 147 2s. 6d. green 6·00 1·00
510 – 5s. red 32·00 1·50
511 – 10s. blue 21·00 8·50
512 – £1 brown 32·00 20·00

DESIGNS: 5s. White Cliffs of Dover; 10s. St. George and dragon; £1 Royal Coat of Arms.

152 Festival Symbol

1951. Festival of Britain.

513 – 2½d. red 30 30
514 152 4d. blue 50 55

DESIGN: 2½d. Britannia, cornucopia and Mercury.

154 155

157 158

159 Queen Elizabeth II and National Emblems

1952.

570 154 ½d. orange 10 10
571 1d. blue 10 10
517 1½d. green 10 15
573 2d. brown 10 10
574 155 2½d. red 10 10
575 3d. lilac 10 20
576a 4d. blue 15 10
577 4½d. brown 10 30
616c 157 5d brown 30 30
579 6d. purple 40 30
617a 7d. green 60 40
617b 158 8d. mauve 50 40
617c 9d. green 60 40
617d 10d. blue 80 50
553 11d. plum 50 1·75
617e 159 1s. brown 40 50
585 1s. 3d. green 40 40
618a 1s. 6d. blue 2·00 1·75

The 4d., 4½d. and 1s. 3d. values are printed with colour tones reversed.

Stamps with either one or two vertical black lines on the back were issued in 1957 in connection with the Post Office automatic facing machine experiments in the Southampton area. Later the lines were replaced by almost invisible phosphor bands on the face, in the above and later issues. They are listed in the Stanley Gibbons British Commonwealth Catalogue.

For stamps as T 157, but with face values in decimal currency, see Nos. 2031/3.

161

163

1953. Coronation. Portraits of Queen Elizabeth II.

532 161 2½d. red 10 50
533 – 4d. blue 50 2·00
534 163 1s. 3d. green 3·50 3·50
535 – 1s. 6d. blue 7·00 4·50

DESIGNS: 4d. Coronation and National Emblems; 1s. 6d. Crowns and Sceptres dated "2 JUNE 1953".

166 Carrickfergus Castle

1955.

595a 166 2s. 6d. brown 50 30
596a – 5s. red 1·00 60
597a – 10s. blue 3·00 3·50
762 – £1 black 4·50 6·50

CASTLES: 5s. Caernarvon; 10s. Edinburgh; £1 Windsor.

170 Scout Badge and "Rolling Hitch"

171 "Scouts coming to Britain"

1957. World Scout Jubilee Jamboree.

557 170 2½d. red 15 25
558 171 4d. blue 50 1·25
559 – 1s. 3d. green 5·00 4·75

DESIGN: 1s. 3d. Globe within a compass.

1957. Inter-Parliamentary Union Conference. As No. 576a but inscr "46th PARLIAMENTARY CONFERENCE".

560 4d. blue 1·00 1·75

176 Welsh Dragon

1958. 6th British Empire and Commonwealth Games, Cardiff. Inscr as in T **176**.

567 176 3d. lilac 15 10
568 – 6d. mauve 25 45
569 – 1s. 3d. green 3·00 3·00

DESIGNS: 6d. Flag and Games emblem; 1s. 3d. Welsh Dragon.

180 Postboy of 1660 181 Posthorn of 1660

1960. Tercentenary of Establishment of General Letter Office.

619 180 3d. lilac 20 10
620 181 1s. 3d. green 4·00 4·00

182 Conference Emblem

1960. 1st Anniv of European Postal and Telecommunications Conference.

621 182 6d. green and purple 50 60
622 1s. 6d. brown and blue 7·00 5·50

184 "Growth of Savings"

1961. Centenary of Post Office Savings Bank. Inscr "POST OFFICE SAVINGS BANK".

623 – 2½d. black and red 20 20
624 184 3d. brown and violet 20 20
625 – 1s. 6d. red and blue 3·00 2·50

DESIGNS—VERT: 2½d. Thrift plant. HORIZ: 1s. 6d. Thrift plant.

186 C.E.P.T. Emblem

187 Doves and Emblem

1961. Europa.

626 186 2d. orange, pink & brown 25 20
627 187 4d. buff, mauve and blue 25 20
628 – 10d. turquoise, green & bl 60 75

DESIGN: 10d. As 4d. but arranged differently.

189 Hammer Beam Roof, Westminster Hall

1961. 7th Commonwealth Parliamentary Conference.

629 189 6d. purple and gold 25 25
630 – 1s. 3d. green & blue 3·00 3·00

DESIGN—VERT: 1s. 3d. Palace of Westminster.

191 "Units of Productivity"

1962. National Productivity Year.

631 191 2½d. green and red 20 10
632 – 3d. blue and violet 25 10
633 – 1s. 3d. red, blue & green 2·25 2·25

DESIGNS: 3d. Arrows over map; 1s. 3d. Arrows in formation.

194 Campaign Emblem and Family

1963. Freedom from Hunger.

634 194 2½d. red and pink 10 10
635 – 1s. 3d. brown and yellow 2·50 2·50

DESIGN: 1s. 3d. Children of three races.

196 "Paris Conference"

1963. Centenary of Paris Postal Conference.

636 196 6d. green and mauve 50 50

197 Posy of Flowers

1963. National Nature Week. Multicoloured.
637 3d. Type **197** 25 20
638 4½d. Woodland life 40 50

199 Rescue at Sea

1963. 9th International Lifeboat Conference, Edinburgh. Multicoloured.
639 2½d. Type **199** 10 10
640 4d. 19th-century lifeboat . . . 40 40
641 1s. 6d. Lifeboatmen . . . . . 3·00 3·00

202 Red Cross

1963. Red Cross Centenary Congress.
642 **202** 3d. red and lilac 10 10
643 – 1s. 3d. red, blue and grey . 3·25 3·00
644 – 1s. 6d. red, blue and bistre . 3·00 3·00
DESIGNS: Nos. 643/4 are as Type **202** but differently arranged.

205 Commonwealth Cable

1963. COMPAC (Trans-Pacific Telephone Cable) Opening.
645 **205** 1s. 6d. blue and black . . . 2·50 2·50

206 Puck and Bottom
("A Midsummer Night's Dream")

210 Hamlet contemplating Yorick's Skull ("Hamlet") and Queen Elizabeth II

1964. Shakespeare Festival.
646 **206** 3d. multicoloured 10 10
647 – 6d. multicoloured 20 30
648 – 1s. 3d. multicoloured . . . 90 1·00
649 – 1s. 6d. multicoloured . . . 1·25 1·00
650 **210** 2s. 6d. slate-purple . . . 2·25 2·25
DESIGNS—As Type **206**: 6d. Feste ("Twelfth Night"); 1s. 3d. Balcony scene ("Romeo and Juliet"); 1s. 6d. "Eve of Agincourt" ("Henry V").

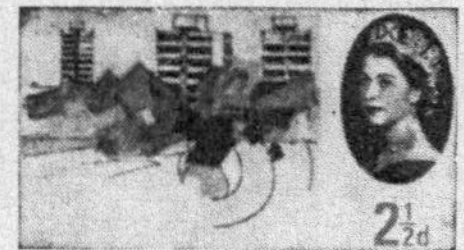

211 Flats near Richmond Park

1964. 20th Int. Geographical Congress, London. Multicoloured.
651 2½d. Type **211** 10 10
652 4d. Shipbuilding yards, Belfast 25 25
653 8d. Beddgelert Forest Park, Snowdonia 60 50
654 1s. 6d. Nuclear reactor, Dounreay . . . . 3·25 3·25
The designs represent "Urban development", "Industrial activity", "Forestry" and "Technological development" respectively.

215 Spring Gentian

1964. 10th Int Botanical Congress, Edinburgh. Multicoloured.
655 3d. Type **215** 10 10
656 6d. Dog rose 20 20
657 9d. Honeysuckle . . . . 1·60 2·50
658 1s. 3d. Fringed water lily . . . 2·50 1·90

219 Forth Road Bridge

1964. Opening of Forth Road Bridge.
659 **219** 3d. black, blue and violet . 15 10
660 – 6d. lilac, blue and red . . 45 40
DESIGN: 6d. Forth Road and Railway Bridges.

221 Sir Winston Churchill

1965. Churchill Commemoration.
661 **221** 4d. black and drab 15 10
662 – 1s. 3d. black and grey . . . 45 40
The 1s. 3d. shows a closer view of Churchill's head.

222 Simon de Montfort's Seal

1965. 700th Anniv of Simon de Montfort's Parliament.
663 **222** 6d. olive 10 10
664 – 2s. 6d. blk, grey & drab . . 1·25 1·25
DESIGN—(58½ × 21½ mm): 2s. 6d. Parliament buildings (after engraving by Hollar, 1647).

224 Bandsmen and Banner

1965. Centenary of Salvation Army. Mult.
665 3d. Type **224** 10 10
666 1s. 6d. Three Salvationists . . . 1·00 1·00

226 Lister's Carbolic Spray

1965. Centenary of Joseph Lister's Discovery of Antiseptic Surgery.
667 **226** 4d. blue, brown & grey . . 10 10
668 – 1s. black, purple & blue . . 1·00 1·50
DESIGN: 1s. Lister and chemical symbols.

228 Trinidad Carnival Dancers

1965. Commonwealth Arts Festival.
669 **228** 6d. black and orange . . . 10 10
670 – 1s. 6d. black and violet . . 1·25 1·50
DESIGN: 1s. 6d. Canadian folk-dancers.

230 Flight of Supermarine Spitfires

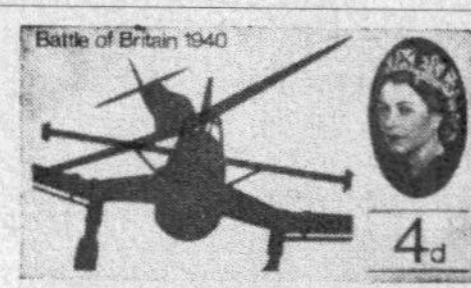

234 Supermarine Spitfire attacking Junkers Ju 878 "Stuka"

1965. 25th Anniv of Battle of Britain. Inscr "Battle of Britain 1940".
671 **230** 4d. olive and black . . . 30 35
672 – 4d. olive and black . . . 30 35
673 – 4d. multicoloured 30 35
674 – 4d. olive and black . . . 30 35
675 **234** 4d. olive and black . . . 30 35
676 – 4d. multicoloured 30 35
677p – 9d. violet, orange and purple . . . . 1·25 80
678p – 1s. 3d. grey, black & bl . . 1·25 80
DESIGNS: No. 672, Pilot in Hawker Hurricane Mk I; 673, Wing-tips of Supermarine Spitfire and Messerschmitt BF 109; 674, Supermarine Spitfires attacking Heinkel HE 111H bomber; 676, Hawker Hurricanes Mk 1 over wreck of Dornier DO-17Z bomber; 9d. Anti-aircraft artillery in action; 1s. 3d. Air battle over St. Paul's Cathedral.

239 Tower and "Nash" Terrace, Regent's Park

1965. Opening of Post Office Tower.
679 – 3d. yellow, blue & green . 10 10
680p **239** 1s. 3d. green and blue . . 70 70
DESIGN—VERT: 3d. Tower and Georgian buildings.

240 U.N. Emblem

1965. 20th Anniv of U.N.O. and International Co-operation Year.
681 **240** 3d. black, orange & blue . 15 20
682 – 1s. 6d. black, purple & bl . 1·10 1·25
DESIGN: 1s. 6d. I.C.Y. Emblem.

242 Telecommunications Network

1965. Centenary of I.T.U. Multicoloured.
683 9d. Type **242** 25 25
684 1s. 6d. Radio waves and switchboard . . . . 1·60 1·75

244 Robert Burns (after Skirving chalk drawing)

1966. Burns Commemoration.
685 **244** 4d. black, indigo and blue . 15 15
686 – 1s. 3d. black, blue and orge . 70 85
DESIGN: 1s. 3d. Robert Burns (after Nasmyth portrait).

246 Westminster Abbey

1966. 900th Anniv of Westminster Abbey.
687 **246** 3d. black, brown and blue 15 20
688 – 2s. 6d. black . . . . . . 85 1·25
DESIGN: 2s. 6d. Fan vaulting, Henry VII Chapel.

248 View near Hassocks, Sussex

1966. Landscapes.
689 **248** 4d. black, green and blue . 15 15
690 – 6d. black, green and blue . 25 25
691 – 1s. 3d. black, yellow & blue . 40 45
692 – 1s. 6d. black, orange & blue 60 60
VIEWS: 6d. Antrim, Northern Ireland; 1s. 3d. Harlech Castle, Wales; 1s. 6d. Cairngorm Mountains, Scotland.

253 Goalmouth Melee

1966. World Cup Football Championship. Multicoloured.
693 4d. Players with ball (vert) . . 15 10
694 6d. Type **253** 20 30
695 1s. 3d. Goalkeeper saving goal 75 90

255 Black-headed Gull

1966. British Birds. Multicoloured.
696 4d. Type **255** 10 15
697 4d. Blue tit 10 15
698 4d. European robin 10 15
699 4d. Blackbird 10 15

1966. England's World Cup Football Victory. As No. 693 but inscr "ENGLAND WINNERS".
700 – 4d. multicoloured 30 30

260 Jodrell Bank Radio Telescope

1966. British Technology.
701 **260** 4d. black and lemon . . . 15 15
702 – 6d. red, blue and orange . . 15 20
703 – 1s. 3d. multicoloured . . . 30 50
704 – 1s. 6d. multicoloured . . . 50 55
DESIGN: 6d. British motor-cars; 1s. 3d. SRN 6 hovercraft; 1s. 6d. Windscale reactor.

264

265

1966. 900th Anniv of Battle of Hastings. Mult.
705 4d. Type **264** 10 15
706 4d. Type **265** 10 15
707 4d. "Yellow" horse 10 15
708 4d. "Blue" horse 10 15
709 4d. "Purple" horse 10 15
710 4d. "Grey" horse 10 15
711 6d. Norman horsemen 10 10
712 1s. 3d. Norman horsemen attacking Harold's troops (59 × 22½ mm). 20 20

272 King of the Orient

274 Sea Freight

1966. Christmas. Multicoloured.
713 3d. Type **272** 10 10
714 1s. 6d. Snowman 40 70

1967. European Free Trade Assn (EFTA).
715 9d. Type **274** 30 30
716 1s. 6d. Air freight 50 50

276 Hawthorn and Bramble

282

1967. British Wild Flowers. Multicoloured.

717p 4d. Type **276** 10 10
718p 4d. Larger bindweed and viper's bugloss 10 10
719p 4d. Ox-eye daisy, coltsfoot and buttercup 10 10
720p 4d. Bluebell, red campion and wood anemone 10 10
721p 9d. Dog violet 10 10
722 1s. 9d. Primroses 20 20

1967.

723 **282** ½d. brown 10 20
724 1d. olive 10 10
726 2d. brown 10 15
729 3d. violet 10 10
731 4d. sepia 10 10
733 4d. red 10 10
735 5d. blue 10 10
736 6d. purple 20 20
737 7d. green 50 30
738 8d. red 20 30
739 8d. turquoise 75 75
740 9d. green 60 30
741 10d. drab 55 50
742 1s. violet 50 30
743 1s. 6d. blue and indigo . . . 60 30
744 1s. 9d. orange and black . . 50 30

For decimal issue, see Nos. X841 etc.

284 "Mares and Foals in a Landscape" (George Stubbs)

1967. British Paintings.

748 – 4d. multicoloured 10 10
749 **284** 9d. multicoloured 20 20
750 – 1s. 6d. multicoloured. . . . 60 60

PAINTINGS—VERT: 4d. "Master Lambton" (Sir Thomas Lawrence). HORIZ: 1s. 6d. "Children Coming Out of School" (L. S. Lowry).

286 "Gipsy Moth IV"

1967. Sir Francis Chichester's World Voyage.

751 **286** 1s. 9d. multicoloured . . . 25 25

287 Radar Screen

1967. British Discovery and Invention. Mult.

752 4d. Type **287** 10 10
753 1s. "Penicillium notatum" . . . 15 15
754 1s. 6d. Vickers VC-10 jet engines 35 35
755 1s. 9d. Television equipment . . 50 50

292 "Madonna and Child" (Murillo)

1967. Christmas.

756 – 3d. multicoloured 10 20
757 **292** 4d. multicoloured 10 20
758 – 1s. 6d. multicoloured . . . 60 60

PAINTINGS—VERT: 3d. "The Adoration of the Shepherds" (School of Seville). HORIZ: 1s. 6d. "The Adoration of the Shepherds" (Louis le Nain).

294 Tarr Steps, Exmoor

1968. British Bridges. Multicoloured.

763 4d. Type **294** 10 10
764 9d. Aberfeldy Bridge 10 10
765 1s. 6d. Menai Bridge 40 40
766 1s. 9d. M4 viaduct 50 50

298 "T U C" and Trades Unionists

1968. British Annivs. Events described on stamps.

767 **298** 4d. multicoloured 10 10
768 – 9d. violet, grey and black . 10 15
769 – 1s. multicoloured 40 35
770 – 1s. 9d. ochre and brown . . 50 50

DESIGNS: 9d. Mrs. Emmeline Pankhurst (statue); 1s. Sopwith Camel and English Electric Lightning fighters; 1s. 9d. Captain Cook's "Endeavour" and signature.

302 "Queen Elizabeth I" (unknown artist)

1968. British Paintings.

771 **302** 4d. multicoloured 10 10
772 – 1s. multicoloured 20 20
773 – 1s. 6d. multicoloured . . . 30 30
774 – 1s. 9d. multicoloured . . . 50 50

PAINTINGS—VERT: 1s. "Pinkie" (Lawrence); 1s. 6d. "Ruins of St. Mary Le Port" (Piper). HORIZ: 1s. 9d. "The Hay Wain" (Constable).

306 Boy and Girl with Rocking Horse

1968. Christmas. Multicoloured.

775 4d. Type **306** 10 10
776 9d. Girl with doll's house . . . 30 30
777 1s. 6d. Boy with train set . . . 45 45

Nos. 776/7 are vert.

310 Elizabethan Galleon

1969. British Ships. Multicoloured.

778 5d. "Queen Elizabeth 2" . . . 10 10
779 9d. Type **310** 10 15
780 9d. East Indiaman 10 15
781 9d. "Cutty Sark" 10 15
782 1s. "Great Britain" 40 30
783 1s. "Mauretania I" 40 30

Nos. 778 and 782/3 are 58 × 23 mm.

315 Concorde in Flight

1969. 1st Flight of Concorde.

784 **315** 4d. multicoloured 10 10
785 – 9d. multicoloured 35 35
786 – 1s. 6d. indigo, grey and blue 50 50

DESIGNS: 9d. Plan and elevation views; 1s. 6d. Concorde's nose and tail.

318 Queen Elizabeth II

1969.

787 **318** 2s. 6d. brown 50 30
788 5s. lake . . . . 2·25 60
789 10s. blue . . . . 7·00 6·50
790 £1 black . . . . 3·00 2·00

For decimal issues see Nos. 829/31b.

No. 790 has an italic "£". For later version with roman "£" see No. 831b.

319 Page from "Daily Mail", and Vickers Vimy Biplane

1969. Anniversary Events described on stamps.

791 **319** 5d. multicoloured 10 10
792 – 9d. multicoloured 20 25
793 – 1s. claret, red and blue . . 25 25
794 – 1s. 6d. multicoloured . . . 25 30
795 – 1s. 9d. turquoise, yell & sepia 30 35

DESIGNS: 9d. Europa and C.E.P.T. emblems; 1s. I.L.O. emblem; 1s. 6d. Flags of N.A.T.O. countries; 1s. 9d. Vickers Vimy biplane and globe showing flight route.

324 Durham Cathedral

1969. British Architecture (Cathedrals). Mult.

796 5d. Type **324** 10 10
797 5d. York Minster 10 10
798 5d. St. Giles' Cathedral, Edinburgh 10 10
799 5d. Canterbury Cathedral . . . 10 10
800 9d. St. Paul's Cathedral 15 15
801 1s. 6d. Liverpool Metropolitan Cathedral 15 15

332 Queen Eleanor's Gate, Caernarvon Castle

1969. Investiture of H.R.H. The Prince of Wales.

802 – 5d. multicoloured 10 10
803 – 5d. multicoloured 10 10
804 **332** 5d. multicoloured 10 10
805 – 9d. multicoloured 20 10
806 – 1s. black and gold 20 10

DESIGNS: No. 802, The King's Gate, Caernarvon Castle; No. 803, The Eagle Tower, Caernarvon Castle; No. 805, Celtic Cross, Margam Abbey; No. 806, H.R.H. The Prince of Wales.

335 Mahatma Gandhi

1969. Gandhi Centenary Year.

807 **335** 1s. 6d. multicoloured . . . 30 30

336 National Giro "G" Symbol

1969. Post Office Technology Commemoration.

808 **336** 5d. multicoloured 10 10
809 – 9d. green, blue and black . 25 25
810 – 1s. green, lavender & black . 25 25
811 – 1s. 6d. purple, blue & black . 50 50

DESIGNS: 9d. International subscriber dialling (Telecommunications); 1s. Pulse code modulations (Telecommunications); 1s 6d. Automatic sorting (Postal Mechanisation).

340 Herald Angel

1969. Christmas. Multicoloured.

812 4d. Type **340** 10 15
813 5d. The Three Shepherds . . . 25 20
814 1s. 6d. The Three Kings . . . 50 50

343 Fife Harling

1970. British Rural Architecture. Multicoloured.

815 5d. Type **343** 10 15
816 9d. Cotswold limestone 30 25
817 1s. Welsh stucco 30 25
818 1s. 6d. Ulster thatch 40 45

The 1s. and 1s. 6d. are larger (38 × 27 mm).

347 Signing the Declaration of Arbroath

1970. Anniversaries. Events described on stamps. Multicoloured.

819 5d. Type **347** 10 10
820 9d. Florence Nightingale attending patients 15 15
821 1s. Signing of International Co-operative Alliance 25 35
822 1s. 6d. Pilgrims and "Mayflower" 30 40
823 1s. 9d. Sir William and Sir John Herschel, Francis Baily and Telescope 30 40

352 Mr Pickwick and Sam ("Pickwick Papers")

357 Queen Elizabeth II

1970. Literary Annivs. Death Cent of Charles Dickens (novelist) (824/7) and Birth Bicent of William Wordsworth (poet) (828). Mult.

824 5d. Type **352** 10 10
825 5d. Mr. and Mrs. Micawber ("David Copperfield") . . . 10 10
826 5d. David Copperfield and Betsy Trotwood ("David Copperfield") 10 10
827 5d. "Oliver asking for more" ("Oliver Twist") 10 10
828 1s. 6d. "Grasmere" (from engraving by J. Farrington, R.A.) 20 20

1970. Decimal Currency. Designs as T **318** but inscr in decimal currency as T **357**.

829 **357** 10p red . . . . 1·00 85
830 20p. green . . . . 1·00 30
831 50p. blue . . . . 2·00 60
831b £1 black . . . . 5·00 1·00

On No. 831b the "£" is in roman type.

360 Cyclists

1970. 9th British Commonwealth Games. Mult.

832 5d. Runners 10 10
833 1s. 6d. Swimmers 50 55
834 1s. 9d. Type **360** 50 55

361 1d. Black (1840)

364 Shepherds and Apparition of the Angel

1970. "Philympia 70" Stamp Exhibition. Mult.

835 5d. Type **361** 10 10
836 9d. 1s. green (1847) 50 50
837 1s. 6d. 4d. red (1855) 50 60

1970. Christmas. Multicoloured.

838 4d. Type **364** 30 30
839 5d. Mary, Joseph, and Christ in the manger 30 30
840 1s. 6d. The Wise Men bearing gifts 50 50

367

1971. Decimal currency. As Nos. 723, etc. but new colours and with decimal figures of value as in T **367**.

X841	½p. blue	10	10
X844	1p. red	10	10
X848	1½p. black	30	15
Y1668	2p. green	10	10
X1001	2p. light green and green	1·25	70
X851	2½p. mauve	25	10
X929	2½p. red	30	30
X855	3p. blue	30	10
X930	3p. mauve	30	30
X859	3½p. grey	50	15
X931	3½p. brown	60	60
X861	4p. brown	30	30
Y1669	4p. blue	10	10
X865	4½p. blue	30	25
X866	5p. violet	30	10
Y1670	5p. brown	10	10
X869	5½p. violet	40	20
Y1671	6p. green	10	15
X872	6½p. blue	50	15
X875	7p. brown	40	30
X937	7p. red	2·00	2·00
Y1672	7p. grey	10	15
X877	7½p. brown	40	30
X879	8p. red	30	30
X881	8½p green	40	30
X882	9p. yellow and black	70	40
X883	9p. violet	50	30
X884	9½p. purple	50	40
X885	10p. brown and light brown	50	40
X888	10p. brown	40	30
Y1673	10p. orange	15	20
X890	10½p. yellow	60	40
X891	10½p. blue	90	50
X892	11p. red	80	40
X893	11½p. drab	60	40
X942	11½p. brown	60	50
X943	12p. green	60	60
X898	12½p. green	50	30
X900	13p. brown	50	40
X944	13p. grey	70	50
X945	13½p. brown	70	70
X903	14p. blue	70	50
X947	15p. blue	85	50
X948	15½p. violet	85	50
X949	16p. brown	70	40
X950	16½p. brown	1·00	1·00
X951	17p. green	90	60
X952	17p. blue	80	60
X953	17½p. brown	1·00	1·00
X954	18p. violet	1·00	1·00
X955	18p. grey	1·00	85
X913	18p. green	75	50
X956	19p. red	1·00	90
Y1674	19p. bistre	30	35
X957	19½p. grey	1·50	1·50
X958	20p. purple	1·00	40
Y1677	20p. green	30	35
X960	20p. black	1·25	75
X961	20½p. blue	1·60	1·40
X962	22p. blue	1·10	70
X963	22p. green	1·10	80
X964	22p. orange	1·00	70
X965	23p. red	1·25	80
X966	23p. green	1·25	70
X967	24p. violet	1·60	1·25
X968	24p. red	2·00	1·25
X969	24p. brown	1·00	60
X970	25p. purple	1·25	1·25
Y1681	25p. red	1·00	1·00
X971	26p. red	1·25	50
Y1682	26p. brown	40	45
X973	27p. brown	1·40	1·40
X974	27p. violet	1·25	1·25
X975	28p. violet	1·40	1·40
X976	28p. ochre	1·40	1·40
X977	28p. grey	1·25	1·25
X978	29p. brown	2·25	1·50
X979	29p. mauve	2·25	1·50
Y1683	29p. grey	1·25	1·25
Y1684	30p. grey	45	50
X981	31p. purple	1·50	1·50
X982	31p. blue	1·50	1·50
Y1685	31p. mauve	50	55
X983	32p. blue	1·75	1·75
X1020	33p. green	1·50	1·50
X985	34p. brown	1·75	1·75
X986	34p. grey	2·00	1·75
X987	34p. mauve	1·50	1·50
X988	35p. brown	1·75	1·50
X989	35p. yellow	1·50	1·25
Y1688	36p. blue	1·40	1·40
X990	37p. red	2·00	2·00
Y1689	37p. mauve	55	60
Y1690	38p. red	1·50	1·50
Y1691	38p. blue	55	60
Y1692	39p. mauve	60	65
Y1757	41p. drab	1·50	1·50
Y1696	43p. brown	65	70
Y1697	44p. brown	65	70
Y1698	50p. brown	75	80
Y1758	60p. grey	2·75	2·75
Y1699	63p. green	95	1·00
Y1700	64p. green	95	1·00
X993	75p. black	3·00	3·00
X1024	75p. grey and black	10·00	9·00
Y1701	£1 violet	1·50	1·60
Y1800	£1.50 red	2·25	2·40
Y1801	£2 blue	3·00	3·25
Y1802	£3 violet	4·50	4·75
Y1803	£5 brown	7·50	7·75

For 26p. in gold see No. 1978.

For stamps in this design but with face values expressed as 2nd, 1st or E see Nos. 1663a etc. (1989) and 1979.

368 "A Mountain Road" (T. P. Flanagan)

1971. "Ulster '71" Festival. Paintings. Mult.

881	3p. Type **368**	10	10
882	7½p. "Deer's Meadow" (Tom Carr)	60	60
883	9p. "Slieve na brock" (Colin Middleton)	70	70

371 John Keats (150th Death Anniv)

1971. Literary Anniversaries.

884	**371**	3p. black, gold and blue	10	10
885	–	5p. black, gold and green	60	60
886	–	7½p. black, gold and brown	70	70

DESIGNS AND ANNIVERSARIES: 5p. Thomas Gray (death bicentenary); 7½p. Sir Walter Scott (birth bicentenary).

374 Servicemen and Nurse of 1921

1971. British Anniversaries Events described on stamps. Multicoloured.

887	3p. Type **374**	10	10
888	7½p. Roman centurion	60	60
889	9p. Rugby football, 1871	70	70

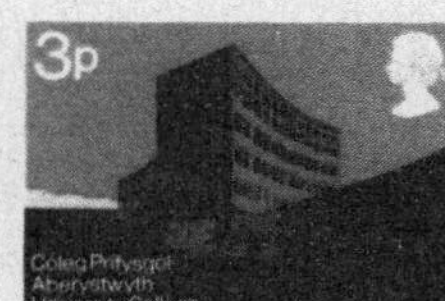

377 Physical Sciences Building, University College of Wales, Aberystwyth

1971. British Architecture. Modern University Buildings.

890	**377**	3p. multicoloured	10	10
891	–	5p. multicoloured	20	20
892	–	7½p. ochre, black & brown	65	65
893	–	9p. multicoloured	1·00	1·00

DESIGNS: 5p. Faraday Building, Southampton University; 7½p. Engineering Department, Leicester University; 9p. Hexagon Restaurant, Essex University.

381 "Dream of the Wise Men"

1971. Christmas. Multicoloured.

894	2½p. Type **381**	20	10
895	3p. "Adoration of the Magi"	20	10
896	7½p. "Ride of the Magi"	1·00	1·00

384 Sir James Clark Ross

391 St. Andrew's Greensted-juxta-Ongar, Essex

388 Statuette of Tutankhamun

1972. British Polar Explorers. Multicoloured.

897	3p. Type **384**	10	10
898	5p. Sir Martin Frobisher	20	20
899	7½p. Henry Hudson	65	65
900	9p. Capt. Robert Scott	1·00	1·00

See also Nos. 923/7.

1972. General Anniveraries. Multicoloured.

901	3p. Type **388**	10	10
902	7½p. 19th-century Coastguard	60	60
903	9p. Ralph Vaughan Williams (composer) and score	70	70

ANNIVERSARIES: 3p. 50th anniversary of discovery of Tutankhamun's tomb; 7½p. 150th anniversary of Formation of H.M. Coastguard; 9p. Birth centenary.

1972. British Architecture. Village Churches. Multicoloured.

904	3p. Type **391**	10	10
905	4p. All Saints, Earls Barton, Northants	20	20
906	5p. St. Andrew's, Letheringsett, Norfolk	30	25
907	7½p. St. Andrew's, Helpringham, Lincs.	90	90
908	9p. St. Mary the Virgin, Huish Episcopi, Somerset	1·00	1·00

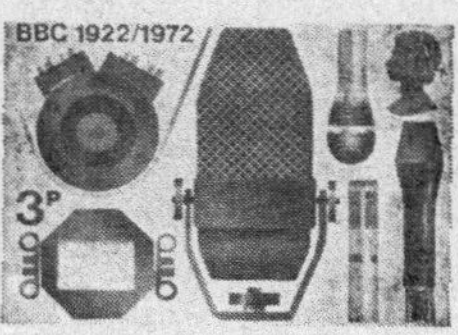

396 Microphones, 1924-69

1972. Broadcasting Anniversaries Multicoloured.

909	3p. Type **396**	10	10
910	5p. Horn loudspeaker	15	20
911	7½p. T.V. camera, 1972	85	85
912	9p. Oscillator and spark transmitter, 1897	85	85

ANNIVERSARIES: Nos. 909/11, 50th anniversary of daily broadcasting by the B.B.C.; No. 912, 75th anniversary of Marconi and Kemp's radio experiments.

400 Angel holding Trumpet

403 Queen Elizabeth and Duke of Edinburgh

1972. Christmas. Multicoloured.

913	2½p. Type **400**	10	15
914	3p. Angel playing lute	10	15
915	7½p. Angel playing harp	1·25	1·10

1972. Royal Silver Wedding.

916	**403**	3p. black, blue and silver	25	25
917		20p. black, purple & silver	1·00	1·00

404 "Europe"

411 W. G. Grace

405 Oak Tree

1973. Britain's Entry into European Communities.

919	**404**	3p. multicoloured	10	10
920		5p. mult (blue jig-saw)	25	50
921		5p. mult (green jig-saw)	25	50

1973. Tree Planting Year. British Trees (1st issue).

922	**405**	9p. multicoloured	50	50

See also No. 949.

1973. British Explorers. As T **384**. Mult.

923	3p. David Livingstone	25	20
924	3p. H. M. Stanley	25	20
925	5p. Sir Francis Drake	20	30
926	7½p. Sir Walter Raleigh	20	30
927	9p. Charles Sturt	25	40

1973. County Cricket 1873–1973. Designs as T **411** showing caricatures of W. G. Grace by Harry Furniss.

928	**411**	3p. black, brown & gold	10	10
929	–	7½p. black, green & gold	80	80
930	–	9p. black, blue and gold	1·00	1·00

414 "Self-portrait" (Reynolds)

INIGO JONES 1573-1652 architect/designer COURT MASQUE COSTUMES 3p

418 Court Masque Costumes

1973. British Paintings. 250th Birth Anniv of Sir Joshua Reynolds, and 150th Death Anniv of Sir Henry Raeburn. Multicoloured.

931	3p. Type **414**	10	10
932	5p. "Self-portrait" (Raeburn)	20	25
933	7½p. "Nelly O' Brien" (Reynolds)	55	50
934	9p. "Rev. R. Walker (The Skater)" (Raeburn)	60	60

1973. 400th Birth Anniv of Inigo Jones (architect and designer). Multicoloured.

935	3p. Type **418**	10	15
936	3p. St. Paul's Church, Covent Garden	10	15
937	5p. Prince's Lodging, Newmarket	50	45
938	5p. Court Masque stage scene	50	45

422 Palace of Westminster, seen from Whitehall

1973. 19th Commonwealth Parliamentary Conf.

939	**422**	8p. stone, grey & black	50	60
940	–	10p. gold and black	50	40

DESIGN: 10p. Palace of Westminster, seen from Millbank.

424 Princess Anne and Capt. Mark Phillips

1973. Royal Wedding.

941	**424**	3½p. violet and silver	10	10
942		20p. brown and silver	90	90

425 "Good King Wenceslas looked out."

1973. Christmas. Multicoloured.

943	Type **425**	15	15
944	3p. King and page at window	15	15
945	3p. Leaving the palace	15	15
946	3p. Struggling against the wind	15	15
947	3p. Delivering gifts	15	15
948	3½p. King, page and peasant	15	15

431 Horse Chestnut

1974. British Trees (2nd issue).

949	**431**	10p. multicoloured	50	50

432 First Motor Fire-engine, 1904

1974. Bicentenary of Fire Prevention (Metropolis) Act. Multicoloured.

950	3½p. Type **432**	10	10
951	5½p. Prize-winning fire-engine, 1863	35	35
952	8p. First steam fire-engine, 1830	45	45
953	10p. Fire-engine. 1766	50	50

436 P. & O. Packet "Peninsular", 1888

1974. Cent of Universal Postal Union. Mult.

954 3½p. Type **436** 10 10
955 5½p. Farman H.F.III biplane, 1911 . . . 30 35
956 8p. Airmail-blue van and postbox, 1930 . . . . . . 40 45
957 10p. Short S.21 flying boat "Maia", 1937 . . . . . . 60 50

440 Robert the Bruce

1974. Medieval Warriors. Multicoloured.

958 4½p. Type **440** 10 10
959 5½p. Owain Glyndwr 20 30
960 8p. Henry the Fifth 50 50
961 10p. The Black Prince 55 50

444 Churchill in Royal Yacht Squadron Uniform

1974. Birth Centenary of Sir Winston Churchill.

962 **444** 4½p. silver, blue & green . . 15 15
963 – 5½p. silver, brown & grey . . 30 25
964 – 8p. silver, red & pink . . . 60 50
965 – 10p. silver, brown & stone . . 65 50

DESIGNS: 5½p. Prime Minister, 1940; 8p. Secretary for War and Air, 1919; 10p. War correspondent, South Africa, 1899.

448 "Adoration of the Magi" (York Minster, c. 1355)

1974. Christmas. Church Roof Bosses. Multicoloured.

966 3½p. Type **448** 10 10
967 4½p. "The Nativity" (St. Helen's Church, Norwich, c. 1480) . . 10 10
968 8p. "Virgin and Child" (Ottery St. Mary Church, c. 1350) . . 55 55
969 10p. "Virgin and Child" (Worcester Cathedral, c. 1224) 65 65

452 Invalid in Wheelchair

1975. Health and Handicap Funds.

970 **452** 4½p. + 1½p. blue and azure . 35 35

453 "Peace—Burial at Sea"

1975. Birth Bicentenary of J. M. W. Turner (painter). Multicoloured.

971 4½p. Type **453** 10 10
972 5½p. "Snowstorm—Steamer off a Harbour's Mouth" . . . 20 20
973 8p. "The Arsenal, Venice" . . . 50 50
974 10p. "St. Laurent" 60 60

457 Charlotte Square, Edinburgh

1975. European Architectural Heritage Year. Multicoloured.

975 7p. Type **457** 50 55
976 7p. The Rows, Chester 50 55
977 8p. Royal Observatory, Greenwich 25 25
978 10p. St. George's Chapel, Windsor 25 25
979 12p. National Theatre, London 25 35

462 Sailing Dinghies

1975. Sailing. Multicoloured.

980 7p. Type **462** 20 20
981 8p. Racing keel yachts 35 35
982 10p. Cruising Yachts 40 40
983 12p. Multihulls 45 45

466 Stephenson's "Locomotion", 1825

1975. 150th Anniv of Public Railways. Mult.

984 7p. Type **466** 30 30
985 8p. "Abbotsford", 1876 . . . . 50 50
986 10p. "Caerphilly Castle", 1923 55 55
987 12p. High Speed Train, 1975 . . 60 60

470 Palace of Westminster

1975. 62nd Inter-Parliamentary Union Conference.

988 **470** 12p. multicoloured 50 50

471 Emma and Mr. Woodhouse ("Emma")

1975. Birth Bicentenary of Jane Austen (novelist). Multicoloured.

989 8½p. Type **471** 20 20
990 10p. Catherine Morland ("Northanger Abbey") . . . 35 35
991 11p. Mr. Darcy ("Pride and Prejudice") 40 40
992 13p. Mary and Henry Crawford ("Mansfield Park") 45 45

475 Angels with Harp and Lute

1975. Christmas. Multicoloured.

993 6½p. Type **475** 20 15
994 8½p. Angel with mandolin . . . 30 30
995 11p. Angel with horn 40 45
996 13p. Angel with trumpet . . . 50 50

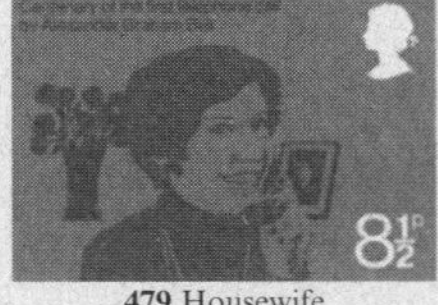

479 Housewife

1976. Centenary of Telephone. Multicoloured.

997 8½p. Type **479** 20 20
998 10p. Policeman 35 35
999 11p. District Nurse 40 40
1000 13p. Industrialist 45 45

483 Hewing Coal (Thomas Hepburn)

1976. Industrial and Social Reformers. Mult.

1001 8½p. Type **483** 20 20
1002 10p. Machinery (Robert Owen) 35 35
1003 11p. Chimney cleaning (Lord Shaftesbury) 40 40
1004 13p. Hands clutching prison bars (Elizabeth Fry) 45 45

487 Benjamin Franklin (bust by Jean-Jacques Caffieri)

488 "Elizabeth of Glamis"

1976. Bicentenary of American Revolution.

1005 **487** 11p. multicoloured . . . 50 50

1976. Centenary of Royal National Rose Society. Multicoloured.

1006 8½p. Type **488** 20 20
1007 10p. "Grandpa Dickson" . . 35 35
1008 11p. "Rosa Mundi" 65 65
1009 13p. "Sweet Briar" 75 75

492 Archdruid

496 Woodcut from "The Canterbury Tales"

1976. British Cultural Traditions. Multicoloured.

1010 8½p. Type **492** 20 20
1011 10p. Morris dancing 35 35
1012 11p. Scots piper 40 40
1013 13p. Welsh harpist 45 45

The 8½p. and 13p. commemorate the 800th Anniv of the Royal National Eisteddfod.

1976. 500th Anniv of British Printing. Multicoloured.

1014 8½p. Type **496** 20 20
1015 10p. Extract from "The Tretyse of Love" 35 35
1016 11p. Woodcut from "The Game and Playe of Chesse" by William Caxton 40 40
1017 13p. Early printing press . . . 45 45

500 Virgin and Child

1976. Christmas. English Medieval Embroidery. Multicoloured.

1018 6½p. Type **500** 15 15
1019 8½p. Angel with crown 30 30
1020 11p. Angel appearing to Shepherds 45 45
1021 13p. The Three Kings 50 50

504 Lawn Tennis

1977. Racket Sports. Multicoloured.

1022 8½p. Type **504** 20 20
1023 10p. Table tennis 35 35
1024 11p. Squash 40 40
1025 13p. Badminton 45 45

508

1977.

1026 **508** £1 green and olive . . . 3·75 40
1026b £1.30 brown and blue . . 6·00 6·00
1026c £1.33 mauve and black . 6·50 6·50
1026d £1.41 brown and blue . . 7·50 7·50
1026e £1.50 olive and black . . 6·00 6·00
1026f £1.60 brown and blue . . 6·50 6·50
1027 £2 green and brown . . 6·50 1·25
1028 £5 pink and blue . . . . 16·00 3·00

509 Steroids — Conformational Analysis

1977. Centenary of Royal Insitute of Chemistry. Multicoloured.

1029 8½p. Type **509** 20 20
1030 10p. Vitamin C — synthesis . 40 40
1031 11p. Starch — chromatography 40 40
1032 13p. Salt — crystallography . 40 40

513

1977. Silver Jubilee. Multicoloured.

1033 8½p. Type **513** 20 20
1034 9p. Type **513** 30 30
1035 10p. "Leaf" initials 30 30
1036 11p. "Star" initials 40 40
1037 13p. "Oak" initials 50 50

517 "Gathering of Nations"

518 West European Hedgehog

1977. Commonwealth Heads of Government Meeting, London.

1038 **517** 13p. multicoloured . . . 50 50

1977. British Wildlife. Multicoloured.

1039 9p. Type **518** 40 20
1040 9p. Brown hare 40 20
1041 9p. Eurasian red squirrel . . . 40 20
1042 9p. European otter 40 20
1043 9p. Eurasian badger 40 20

523 "Three French Hens, Two Turtle Doves and a Partridge in a Pear Tree"

1977. Christmas. "The Twelve Days of Christmas". Multicoloured.

1044 7p. Type **523** 25 15
1045 7p. "Six Geese a-laying, Five Gold Rings, Four Colly Birds" 25 15
1046 7p. "Eight Maids a-milking, Seven Swans a-Swimming" . 25 15
1047 7p. "Ten Pipers piping, Nine Drummers drumming" . . 25 15
1048 7p. "Twelve Lords a leaping, Eleven Ladies dancing" . . 25 15
1049 9p. "A Partridge in a Pear Tree" 25 15

529 Oil — North Sea Production Platform

537 State Coach

533 The Tower of London

1978. Energy Resources. Multicoloured.
1050 9p. Type **529** 25 20
1051 10½p. Coal—modern pithead . 25 30
1052 11p. Natural gas—flame rising from sea 30 30
1053 13p. Electricity—nuclear power station and uranium atom . . . 40 40

1978. British Architecture. Historic Buildings. Multicoloured.
1054 9p. Type **533** 25 20
1055 10½p. Holyroodhouse 25 30
1056 11p. Caernarvon Castle . . . 30 30
1057 13p. Hampton Court Palace . . 40 40

1978. 25th Anniv of Queen's Coronation.
1059 **537** 9p. gold and blue 20 20
1060 – 10½p. gold and red 25 30
1061 – 11p. gold and green . . . 30 30
1062 – 13p. gold and violet . . . 45 40
DESIGNS: 10½p. St. Edward's Crown; 11p. The Sovereign's Orb; 13p. Imperial State Crown.

541 Shire Horse

1978. Horses. Multicoloured.
1063 9p. Type **541** 20 20
1064 10½p. Shetland pony 35 35
1065 11p. Welsh pony 40 40
1066 13p. Thoroughbred 45 45

545 "Penny-farthing" and 1884 Safety Bicycle

1978. Centenaries of Cyclists' Touring Club and British Cycling Federation. Multicoloured.
1067 9p. Type **545** 20 20
1068 10½p. 1920 Touring bicycles . . 25 25
1069 11p. Modern small-wheeled bicycles 30 30
1070 13p. 1978 Road-racers 45 45

549 Singing Carols round the Christmas Tree

1978. Christmas. Carol-singing. Mult.
1071 7p. Type **549** 20 20
1072 9p. The Waits 25 25
1073 11p. 18th-century carol singers 30 30
1074 13p. "The Boar's Head Carol" 35 35

553 Old English Sheepdog

1979. Dogs. Multicoloured.
1075 9p. Type **553** 20 20
1076 10½p. Welsh springer spaniel . 40 40
1077 11p. West Highland terrier . . 40 40
1078 13p. Irish setter 40 40

557 Primrose

1979. Spring Wild Flowers. Multicoloured.
1079 9p. Type **557** 20 20
1080 10½p. Daffodil 40 40
1081 11p. Bluebell 40 40
1082 13p. Snowdrop 40 40

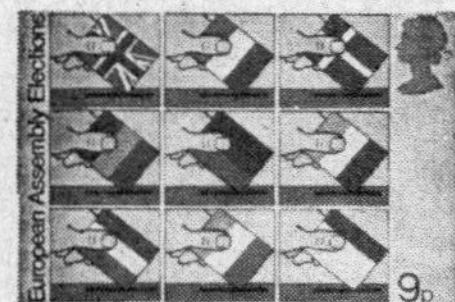

561 Hands placing National Flags into Ballot Boxes

1979. First Direct Elections to European Assembly.
1083 **561** 9p. multicoloured 20 20
1084 – 10½p. multicoloured . . . 30 30
1085 – 11p. multicoloured . . . 30 30
1086 – 13p. multicoloured . . . 40 40
DESIGNS: Nos. 1084/6 differ from Type **561** in the position of the hands and flags.

565 "Saddling 'Mahmoud' for the Derby, 1936" (Sir Alfred Munnings)

1979. Horseracing Paintings. Bicentenary of the Derby (9p). Multicoloured.
1087 9p. Type **565** 25 25
1088 10½p. "The Liverpool Great National Steeple Chase, 1839" (aquatint, F. C. Turner). 30 30
1089 11p. "The First Spring Meeting, Newmarket, 1793" (J. N. Sartorius) 30 30
1090 13p. "Racing at Dorsett Ferry, Windsor, 1684" (Francis Barlow) 30 30

569 "The Tale of Peter Rabbit" (Beatrix Potter)

573 Sir Rowland Hill

1979. International Year of the Child. Multicoloured.
1091 9p. Type **569** 25 20
1092 10½p. "The Wind in the Willows" (Kenneth Grahame) 30 35
1093 11p. "Winnie-the-Pooh" (A. A. Milne). 35 40
1094 13p. "Alice's Adventures in Wonderland" (Lewis Carroll) 65 65

1979. Death Cent of Sir Rowland Hill. Mult.
1095 10p. Type **573** 25 25
1096 11½p. Postman, c. 1839 . . . 30 35
1097 13p. London postman, c. 1839 . 35 40
1098 15p. Woman and young girl with letters, 1840 . . . . . 50 40

577 Policeman on the Beat

1979. 150th Anniv of Metropolitan Police. Mult.
1100 10p. Type **577** 25 25
1101 11½p. Policeman directing traffic 30 35
1102 13p. Mounted policewoman . . 35 40
1103 15p. River patrol boat 50 40

581 The Three Kings

1979. Christmas. Multicoloured.
1104 8p. Type **581** 20 20
1105 10p. Angel appearing to the Shepherds 25 25
1106 11½p. The Nativity 30 35
1107 13p. Mary and Joseph travelling to Bethlehem 40 40
1108 15p. The Annunciation . . . 50 45

586 Common Kingfisher

1980. Cent of Wild Bird Protection Act. Mult.
1109 10p. Type **586** 25 25
1110 11½p. Dipper 45 40
1111 13p. Moorhen 60 50
1112 15p. Yellow wagtails 65 55

590 "Rocket" approaching Moorish Arch, Liverpool

1980. 150th Anniv of Liverpool and Manchester Railway. Multicoloured.
1113 12p. Type **590** 35 25
1114 12p. First and Second Class carriages passing through Olive Mount cutting . . . 35 25
1115 12p. Third Class carriage and sheep truck crosssing Chat Moss 35 25
1116 12p. Horsebox and carriage truck near Bridgewater Canal 35 25
1117 12p. Truck and mail coach at Manchester 35 25

595 Montage of London Buildings

1980. "London 1980" International Stamp Exn.
1118 **595** 50p. brown . . . . . . 1·50 1·50

596 Buckingham Palace

605 Queen Elizabeth the Queen Mother

601 Charlotte Bronte ("Jane Eyre")

1980. London Landmarks. Multicoloured.
1120 10½p. Type **596** 25 25
1121 12p. The Albert Memorial . . 30 30
1122 13½p. Royal Opera House . . 40 40
1123 15p. Hampton Court 50 50
1124 17½p. Kensington Palace . . . 50 50

1980. Famous Authoresses. Multicoloured.
1125 12p. Type **601** 30 30
1126 13½p. George Eliot ("The Mill on the Floss") 45 45
1127 15p. Emily Bronte ("Wuthering Heights") 50 55
1128 17½p. Elizabeth Gaskell ("North and South") 70 70

1980. 80th Birthday of The Queen Mother.
1129 **605** 12p. multicoloured . . . 1·00 1·00

606 Sir Henry Wood

610 Running

1980. British Conductors. Multicoloured.
1130 12p. Type **606** 30 30
1131 13½p. Sir Thomas Beecham . . 45 50
1132 15p. Sir Malcolm Sargent . . 55 55
1133 17½p. Sir John Barbirolli . . . 65 60

1980. Sport Centenaries. Multicoloured.
1134 12p. Type **610** 30 30
1135 13½p. Rugby 50 50
1136 15p. Boxing 50 50
1137 17½p. Cricket 70 70
CENTENARIES: 12p. Amateur Athletics Association; 13½p. Welsh Rugby Union; 15p. Amateur Boxing Association; 17½p. First England–Australia Test Match.

614 Christmas Tree

1980. Christmas. Multicoloured.
1138 10p. Type **614** 25 25
1139 12p. Candles 35 35
1140 13½p. Mistletoe and apples . . 40 40
1141 15p. Crown, chains and bell . 50 50
1142 17½p. Holly wreath 60 60

619 St. Valentine's Day

1981. Folklore. Multicoloured.
1143 14p. Type **619** 35 35
1144 18p. Morris dancers 60 60
1145 22p. Lammastide 70 70
1146 25p. Medieval mummers . . . 85 85

623 Blind Man with Guide Dog

1981. Int Year of Disabled Persons. Mult.
1147 14p. Type **623** 35 35
1148 18p. Hands spelling "Deaf" in sign language 60 60
1149 22p. Disabled man in wheelchair 70 70
1150 25p. Disabled artist painting with foot 85 85

627 "Aglais urticae"

636 Prince Charles and Lady Diana Spencer

631 Glenfinnan, Scotland

1981. Butterflies. Multicoloured.

1151 14p. Type **627** 35 35
1152 18p. "Maculinea arion" . . . 80 80
1153 22p. "Inachis io" 90 90
1154 25p. "Carterocephalus palaemon" . . . . 1·00 1·00

1981. 50th Anniv of National Trust for Scotland. British Landscapes. Multicoloured.

1155 14p. Type **631** 30 30
1156 18p. Derwentwater, England . 40 40
1157 20p. Stackpole Head, Wales . 70 70
1158 22p. Giant's Causeway, Northern Ireland 80 80
1159 25p. St. Kilda, Scotland . . . 90 90

1981. Royal Wedding.

1160 **636** 14p. multicoloured . . . 1·50 1·75
1161 25p. multicoloured . . . 2·50 2·25

637 "Expeditions"

1981. 25th Anniv of Duke of Edinburgh Award Scheme. Multicoloured.

1162 14p. Type **637** 35 35
1163 18p. "Skills" 60 60
1164 22p. "Service" 70 70
1165 25p. "Recreation" 80 80

641 Cockle-dredging from "Linsey II"

1981. Fishing Industry. Multicoloured.

1166 14p. Type **641** 40 40
1167 18p. Hauling in trawl net . . . 60 60
1168 22p. Lobster potting 70 70
1169 25p. Hoisting seine net . . . 80 80

645 Father Christmas

1981. Christmas. Children's Pictures. Mult.

1170 11½p. Type **645** 30 30
1171 14p. Jesus Christ 40 40
1172 18p. Flying Angel 60 60
1173 22p. Joseph and Mary arriving at Bethlehem 70 70
1174 25p. Three Kings approaching Bethlehem 80 80

650 Charles Darwin and Giant Tortoises

1982. Death Cent of Charles Darwin. Mult.

1175 15½p. Type **650** 35 35
1176 19½p. Darwin and Marine iguanas 60 60
1177 26p. Darwin and cactus ground finch and large ground fish 80 80
1178 29p. Darwin and prehistoric skulls 85 85

654 Boys' Brigade **658** Ballerina

1982. Youth Organizations. Multicoloured.

1179 15½p. Type **654** 35 35
1180 19½p. Girls' Brigade 70 70
1181 26p. Boy Scout Movement . . 95 95
1182 29p. Girl Guides Movement . 1·10 1·10

1982. Europa. British Theatre. Multicoloured.

1183 15½p. Type **658** 35 35
1184 19½p. Harlequin 60 60
1185 26p. Hamlet 90 85
1186 29p. Opera singer . . . . . . 1·25 1·25

662 Henry VIII and "Mary Rose"

1982. Maritime Heritage. Multicoloured.

1187 15½p. Type **662** 35 35
1188 19½p. Admiral Blake and "Triumph" 60 60
1189 24p. Lord Nelson and H.M.S. "Victory" 80 80
1190 26p. Lord Fisher and H.M.S. "Dreadnought" 90 90
1191 29p. Viscount Cunningham and H.M.S. "Warspite" . . . . 1·00 1·00

667 "Strawberry Thief" (William Morris)

1982. British Textiles. Multicoloured.

1192 15½p. Type **667** 35 35
1193 19½p. Untitled (Steiner and Co.) 75 75
1194 26p. "Cherry Orchard" (Paul Nash) 90 90
1195 29p. "Chevron" (Andrew Foster) . . . . 1·10 1·10

671 Development of Communications. (⅔-size illustration)

1982. Information Technology. Multicoloured.

1196 15½p. Type **671** 45 50
1197 26p. Modern technological aids 80 85

673 Austin "Seven" and "Metro"

1982. British Motor Industry. Multicoloured.

1198 15½p. Type **673** 50 50
1199 19½p. Ford "Model T" and "Escort" 70 70
1200 26p. Jaguar "SS1" and "XJ6" 90 90
1201 29p. Rolls-Royce "Silver Ghost" and "Silver Spirit" . 1·25 1·25

677 "While Shepherds Watched"

1982. Christmas. Carols. Multicoloured.

1202 12½p. Type **677** 30 30
1203 15½p. "The Holly and the Ivy" 40 40
1204 19½p. "I saw Three Ships" . . 80 80
1205 26p. "We Three Kings" . . . 90 90
1206 29p. "Good King Wenceslas" 1·00 1·00

682 Atlantic Salmon

1983. British River Fishes. Multicoloured.

1207 15½p. Type **682** 35 35
1208 19½p. Northern pike 75 75
1209 26p. Brown trout 90 90
1210 29p. Eurasian perch . . . . . 1·10 1·10

686 Tropical Island

1983. Commonwealth Day. Geographical Regions. Multicoloured.

1211 15½p. Type **686** 35 35
1212 19½p. Desert 75 75
1213 26p. Temperate farmland . . 90 90
1214 29p. Mountain range . . . . 1·10 1·10

690 Humber Bridge

1983. Europa. Engineering Achievements. Multicoloured.

1215 16p. Type **690** 45 45
1216 20½p. Thames Flood Barrier . 1·10 1·10
1217 28p. "Iolair" (oilfield emergency support vessel) . . . . . . 1·25 1·25

693 Musketeer and Pikeman, The Royal Scots (1633) **698** 20th-century Garden, Sissinghurst

1983. British Army Uniforms. Multicoloured.

1218 16p. Type **693** 40 40
1219 20½p. Fusilier and Ensign, The Royal Welsh Fusiliers (mid-18th century) 70 70
1220 26p. Riflemen, 95th Rifles (The Royal Green Jackets) (1805) 1·00 1·00
1221 28p. Sergeant (khaki service uniform) and Guardsman (full dress), The Irish Guards (1900) . . . . 1·00 1·00
1222 31p. Paratroopers, The Parachute Regiment (1983) . 1·10 1·10

1983. British Gardens. Multicoloured.

1223 16p. Type **698** 40 40
1224 20½p. 19th-century garden, Biddulph Grange 60 60
1225 28p. 18th-century garden, Blenheim . . . . 1·00 1·00
1226 31p. 17th-century garden, Pitmedden . . . . 1·10 1·10

702 Merry-go-round

1983. British Fairs. Multicoloured.

1227 16p. Type **702** 40 40
1228 20½p. Big wheel, helter-skelter and performing animals . . 75 75
1229 28p. Side shows 95 95
1230 31p. Early produce fair . . . 1·00 1·00

706 "Christmas Post" (pillar-box)

1983. Christmas. Multicoloured.

1231 12½p. Type **706** 30 30
1232 16p. "The Three Kings" (chimney pots) 35 35
1233 20½p. "World at Peace" (dove and blackbird) 70 70
1234 28p. "Light of Christmas" (street lamp) 90 90
1235 31p. "Christmas Dove" (hedge sculpture) . . . . 1·10 1·10

711 Arms of College of Arms

1984. 500th Anniv of College of Arms. Mult.

1236 16p. Type **711** 40 40
1237 20½p. Arms of King Richard III (founder) 60 60
1238 28p. Arms of Earl Marshal of England . . . . 1·00 1·00
1239 31p. Arms of City of London 1·10 1·10

715 Highland Cow

1984. Cattle. Multicoloured.

1240 16p. Type **715** 40 40
1241 20½p. Chillingham wild bull . . 65 65
1242 26p. Hereford bull 85 85
1243 28p. Welsh black bull 90 90
1244 31p. Irish moiled cow . . . . 1·10 1·10

720 Garden Festival Hall, Liverpool

1984. Urban Renewal. Multicoloured.

1245 16p. Type **720** 40 40
1246 20½p. Milburngate Centre, Durham 70 70
1247 28p. Bush House, Bristol . . 1·00 1·00
1248 31p. Commercial Street development, Perth . . . . 1·10 1·10

725 Abduction of Europa

1984. 25th Anniv of C.E.P.T. (Europa) (Nos. 1249, 1251), and Second Election to European Parliament (others).

1249 – 16p. grey, blue & gold . . 90 90
1250 **725** 16p. grey, black, & gold . 90 90
1251 – 20½p. red, purple & gold . 1·60 1·60
1252 **725** 20½p. red, pur, blk, & gold 1·60 1·60

DESIGN: Nos. 1249 and 1251, Bridge (C.E.P.T. 25th anniv logo).

726 Lancaster House **727** View of Earth from "Apollo II"

1984. London Economic Summit Conference.

1253 **726** 31p. multicoloured. . . . 1·00 1·00

1984. Centenary of Greenwich Meridian. Mult.

1254 16p. Type **727** 40 40
1255 20½p. Navigational chart of the English Channel 65 65
1256 28p. Greenwich Observatory . 90 90
1257 31p. Sir George Airey's Transit Telescope . . . . 1·10 1·10

731 Bath Mail Coach leaving London, 1784

1984. Bicentenary of First Mail Coach Run Bath and Bristol to London. Multicoloured.

1258	16p. Type **731**	70	40
1259	16p. Attack on Exeter Mail, 1816	70	40
1260	16p. Norwich Mail in thunderstorm, 1827	70	40
1261	16p. Holyhead and Liverpool Mails leaving London, 1828	70	40
1262	16p. Edinburgh Mail snowbound, 1831	70	40

736 Nigerian Clinic

1984. 50th Anniv of British Council. Mult.

1263	17p. Type **736**	50	50
1264	22p. Violinist and Acropolis, Athens	75	75
1265	31p. Building project, Sri Lanka	1·00	1·00
1266	34p. British Council library, Middle East	1·10	1·10

740 The Holy Family

1984. Christmas. Multicoloured.

1267	13p. Type **740**	30	30
1268	17p. Arrival in Bethlehem	50	50
1269	22p. Shepherd and Lamb	70	70
1270	31p. Virgin and Child	1·00	1·00
1271	34p. Offering of Frankincense	1·10	1·10

745 "Flying Scotsman"

1985. Famous Trains. Multicoloured.

1272	17p. Type **745**	50	50
1273	22p. "Golden Arrow"	85	85
1274	29p. "Cheltenham Flyer"	1·00	1·00
1275	31p. "Royal Scot"	1·25	1·25
1276	34p. "Cornish Riviera"	1·40	1·40

750 "Bombus terrestris" (bee) **755** "Water Music" (George Frideric Handel)

1985. Insects. Multicoloured.

1277	17p. Type **750**	40	40
1278	22p. "Coccinella septempunctata" (ladybird)	60	60
1279	29p. "Decticus verrucivorus" (bush-cricket)	90	90
1280	31p. "Lucanus cervus" (stag beetle)	1·00	1·00
1281	34p. "Anax imperator" (dragonfly)	1·00	1·00

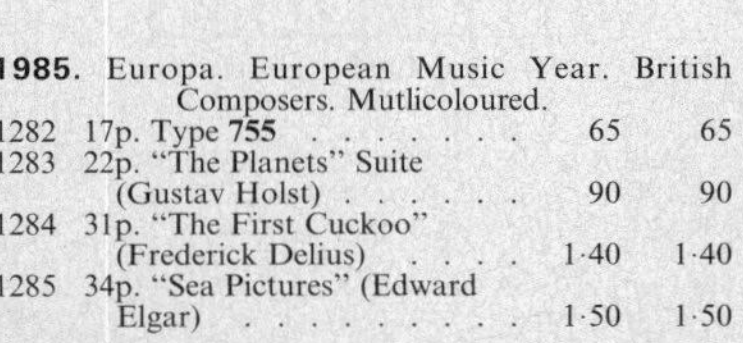

1985. Europa. European Music Year. British Composers. Mutlicoloured.

1282	17p. Type **755**	65	65
1283	22p. "The Planets" Suite (Gustav Holst)	90	90
1284	31p. "The First Cuckoo" (Frederick Delius)	1·40	1·40
1285	34p. "Sea Pictures" (Edward Elgar)	1·50	1·50

759 R.N.L.I. Lifeboat and Signal Flags

1985. Safety at Sea. Multicoloured.

1286	17p. Type **759**	50	50
1287	22p. Beachy Head Lighthouse and chart	75	75
1288	31p. "Marecs A" communications satellite and dish aerials	1·10	1·10
1289	34p. Buoys	1·25	1·25

763 Datapost Motorcyclist, City of London **771** Peter Sellers (from photo by Bill Brandt)

767 King Arthur and Merlin

1985. 350 Years of Royal Mail Public Postal Service. Multicoloured.

1290	17p. Type **763**	50	50
1291	22p. Rural postbus	75	75
1292	31p. Parcel delivery in winter	1·10	1·10
1293	34p. Town letter delivery	1·25	1·25

1985. Arthurian Legends. Multicoloured.

1294	17p. Type **767**	50	50
1295	22p. Lady of the Lake	75	75
1296	31p. Queen Guinevere and Sir Lancelot	1·25	1·25
1297	34p. Sir Galahad	1·40	1·40

1985. British Film Year. Multicoloured.

1298	17p. Type **771**	55	55
1299	22p. David Niven (from photo by Cornell Lucas)	75	75
1300	29p. Charlie Chaplin (from photo by Lord Snowdon)	1·25	1·25
1301	31p. Vivien Leigh (from photo by Angus McBean)	1·40	1·40
1302	34p. Alfred Hitchcock (from photo by Howard Carter)	1·60	1·60

776 Principal Boy

1985. Christmas. Pantomime Characters. Mult.

1303	12p. Type **776**	35	30
1304	17p. Genie	45	40
1305	22p. Dame	70	80
1306	31p. Good fairy	1·00	1·00
1307	34p. Pantomime cat	1·10	1·10

781 Light Bulb and North Sea Oil Drilling Rig (Energy)

1986. Industry Year. Multicoloured.

1308	17p. Type **781**	45	45
1309	22p. Thermometer and pharmaceutical laboratory (Health)	70	70
1310	31p. Garden hoe and steelworks (Steel)	1·10	1·10
1311	34p. Loaf of bread and cornfield (Agriculture)	1·40	1·40

785 Dr. Edmond Halley as Comet

1986. Appearance of Halley's Comet. Multicoloured.

1312	17p. Type **785**	45	45
1313	22p. "Giotto" spacecraft approaching comet	80	80
1314	31p. "Twice in a lifetime"	1·10	1·10
1315	34p. Comet orbiting sun and planets	1·25	1·25

789 Queen Elizabeth II in 1928, 1942 and 1952

1986. 60th Birthday of Queen Elizabeth II. Multicoloured.

1316	17p. Type **789**	70	70
1317	17p. Queen Elizabeth II in 1958, 1973 and 1982	70	70
1318	34p. Type **789**	1·60	1·60
1319	34p. As No. 1317	1·60	1·60

791 Barn Owl

1986. Europa. Nature Conservation. Endangered Species. Multicoloured.

1320	17p. Type **791**	50	50
1321	22p. Pine marten	1·00	1·00
1322	31p. Wild cat	1·50	1·50
1323	34p. Natterjack toad	1·75	1·75

795 Peasants working in Fields

1986. 900th Anniv of Domesday Book. Mult.

1324	17p. Type **795**	50	50
1325	22p. Freemen working at town trades	75	75
1326	31p. Knights and retainers	1·25	1·25
1327	34p. Lord at banquet	1·40	1·40

799 Athletics

1986. 13th Commonwealth Games. Edinburgh, and World Hockey Cup for Men, London. Multicoloured.

1328	17p. Type **799**	50	50
1329	22p. Rowing	70	70
1330	29p. Weightlifting	90	90
1331	31p. Rifle shooting	1·25	1·25
1332	34p. Hockey	1·40	1·40

804 Prince Andrew and Miss Sarah Ferguson (from photo by Gene Nocon) **806** Stylized Cross on Ballot Paper

1986. Royal Wedding.

1333	**804**	12p. multicoloured	60	60
1334	–	17p. multicoloured	90	90

DESIGN: 17p. As Type **804** but with naval motif at foot.

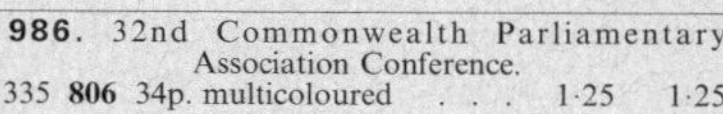

1986. 32nd Commonwealth Parliamentary Association Conference.

1335	**806**	34p. multicoloured	1·25	1·25

807 Lord Dowding and Hawker Hurricane Mk I

1986. History of Royal Air Force. Multicoloured.

1336	17p. Type **807**	50	40
1337	22p. Lord Tedder and Hawker Typhoon IB	75	85
1338	29p. Lord Trenchard and De Havilland D.H.9A	1·00	1·00
1339	31p. Sir Arthur Harris and Avro Type 683 Lancaster	1·25	1·25
1340	34p. Lord Portal and De Havilland D.H.'98 Mosquito	1·50	1·50

Nos. 1336/40 were issued to celebrate 50th anniv of the first R.A.F. Commands.

812 The Glastonbury Thorn

1986. Christmas. Folk Customs. Multicoloured.

1341	12p. Type **812**	50	50
1342	13p. Type **812**	30	30
1343	18p. The Tanad Valley Plygain	45	45
1344	22p. The Hebrides Tribute	75	75
1345	31p. The Dewsbury Church Knell	90	90
1346	34p. The Hereford Boy Bishop	1·00	1·00

817 North American Blanket Flower **821** "Principia Mathematica"

1987. Flower Photographs by Alfred Lammer. Multicoloured.

1347	18p. Type **817**	50	50
1348	22p. Globe thistle	80	80
1349	31p. "Echeveria"	1·25	1·25
1350	34p. Autumn crocus	1·40	1·40

1987. 300th Anniv of "Principia Mathematica" by Sir Isaac Newton. Multicoloured.

1351	18p. Type **821**	50	50
1352	22p. "Motion of Bodies in Ellipses"	80	80
1353	31p. "Optick Treatise"	1·40	1·40
1354	34p. "The System of the World"	1·50	1·50

825 Willis Faber & Dumas Building, Ipswich

1987. Europa. British Architects in Europe.

1355	18p. Type **825**	50	50
1356	22p. Pompidou Centre, Paris	75	75
1357	31p. Staatsgalerie, Stuttgart	1·25	1·25
1358	34p. European Investment Bank, Luxembourg	1·40	1·40

829 Brigade Members with Ashford Litter, 1887 **833** Arms of the Lord Lyon, King of Arms

1987. Centenary of St. John Ambulance Brigade. Multicoloured.
1359 18p. Type **829** 50 50
1360 22p. Bandaging blitz victim, 1940 . . . . 75 75
1361 31p. Volunteer with fainting girl, 1965 . . . . 1·10 1·10
1362 34p. Transport of transplant organ by Air Wing, 1987 . . 1·25 1·25

1987. 300th Anniv of Revival of Order of the Thistle. Multicoloured.
1363 18p. Type **833** 50 50
1364 22p. Scottish heraldic banner of Prince Charles 75 75
1365 31p. Arms of Royal Scottish Academy of Painting, Sculpture and Architecture . 1·25 1·25
1366 34p. Arms of Royal Society of Edinburgh . . . . 1·40 1·40

837 Crystal Palace, "Monarch of the Glen" (Landseer) and Grace Darling

1987. 150th Anniv of Queen Victoria's Accession. Multicoloured.
1367 18p. Type **837** 50 50
1368 22p. "Great Eastern", Beeton's "Book of Household Management" and Prince Albert 75 75
1369 31p. Albert Memorial, ballot box and Disraeli . . . . . 1·25 1·25
1370 34p. Diamond Jubilee emblem, newspaper placard for Relief of Mafeking and morse key 1·40 1·40

841 Pot by Bernard Leach

1987. Studio Pottery. Multicoloured.
1371 18p. Type **841** 50 50
1372 26p. Pot by Elizabeth Fritsch 80 80
1373 31p. Pot by Lucie Rie . . . . 1·25 1·25
1374 34p. Pot by Hans Coper . . . 1·40 1·40

845 Decorating the Christmas Tree

1987. Christmas. Multicoloured.
1375 13p. Type **845** 30 30
1376 18p. Waiting for Father Christmas 50 50
1377 26p. Sleeping child and Father Christmas in sleigh 75 75
1378 31p. Child reading . . . . . 1·10 1·10
1379 34p. Child playing recorder and snowman . . . . 1·25 1·25

850 Short-spined Seascorpion ("Bull-rout") (Jonathan Couch)

1988. Bicentenary of Linnean Society. Archive Illustrations. Multicoloured.
1380 18p. Type **850** 60 60
1381 26p. Yellow Waterlily (Major Joshua Swatkin) 95 95
1382 31p. Whistling ("Bewick's") Swan (Edward Lear) . . . 1·25 1·25
1383 34p. "Morchella esculenta" (James Sowerby) . . . . . 1·40 1·40

INDEX

Countries can be quickly located by referring to the index at the end of this volume.

854 Revd. William Morgan (Bible translator, 1588)

1988. 400th Anniversary of Welsh Bible. Mult.
1384 18p. Type **854** 45 45
1385 26p. William Salesbury (New Testament translator, 1567) 80 80
1386 31p. Bishop Richard Davies (New Testament translator, 1567) . . . . 1·10 1·10
1387 34p. Bishop Richard Parry (editor of Revised Welsh Bible, 1620) . . . . 1·25 1·25

858 Gymnastics (Cent of British Amateur Gymnastics Association)

1988. Sports Organizations. Multicoloured.
1388 18p. Type **858** 45 45
1389 26p. Downhill skiing (Ski Club of Great Britain) 80 80
1390 31p. Tennis (centenary of Lawn Tennis Association) . . . . 1·25 1·25
1391 34p. Football (centenary of Football League) . . . . . 1·40 1·40

862 "Mallard" and Mailbags on Pick-up Arms

1988. Europa. Transport and Mail Services in 1930s. Multicoloured.
1392 18p. Type **862** 50 50
1393 26p. Loading transatlantic mail on liner "Queen Elizabeth" 90 90
1394 31p. Glasgow tram No. 1173 and pillar box . . . . . . 1·10 1·10
1395 34p. Imperial Airways Handley Page "Horatius" and airmail van . . . . 1·40 1·40

866 Early Settler and Sailing Clipper

1988. Bicentenary of Australian Settlement. Mult.
1396 18p. Type **866** 60 30
1397 18p. Queen Elizabeth II with British and Australian Parliament Buildings . . . 60 30
1398 34p. W. G. Grace (cricketer) and tennis racquet . . . . . 1·25 30
1399 34p. Shakespeare, John Lennon (entertainer) and Sydney Opera House . . . . . . 1·50 50

Stamps in similar designs were also issued by Australia.

870 Spanish Galeasse off The Lizard

1988. 400th Anniv of Spanish Armada. Mult.
1400 18p. Type **870** 85 65
1401 18p. English Fleet leaving Plymouth 85 65
1402 18p. Engagement off Isle of Wight 85 65
1403 18p. Attack of English fire-ships, Calais 85 65
1404 18p. Armada in storm, North Sea 85 65

Nos. 1400/4 were printed together, se-tenant, forming a composite design.

875 "The Owl and the Pussy-cat"

1988. Death Centenary of Edward Lear (artist and author).
1405 **875** 19p. black, cream & red . 50 50
1406 – 27p. black, cream & yellow 80 80
1407 – 32p. black, cream & green 1·10 1·10
1408 – 35p. black, cream & blue . 1·25 1·25

DESIGNS: 27p. "Edward Lear as a Bird" (self-portrait); 32p. "Cat" (from alphabet book); 35p. "There was a Young Lady whose Bonnet..." (limerick).

879 Carrickfergus Castle

1988.
1410 **879** £1 green . . . . 4·00 1·00
1411 – £1.50 red . . . . 6·00 1·75
1412 – £2 blue . . . . 8·00 2·50
1413 – £5 brown . . . . 20·00 4·50

DESIGNS: £1.50, Caernarfon Castle; £2, Edinburgh Castle; £5, Windsor Castle.

For similar designs, but with silhouette of Queen's head, see Nos. 1611/14.

883 Journey to Bethlehem

1988. Christmas. Christmas Cards. Multicoloured.
1414 14p. Type **883** 45 45
1415 19p. Shepherds and Star . . . 50 50
1416 27p. Three Wise Men 90 90
1417 32p. Nativity . . . . 1·10 1·10
1418 35p. The Annunciation . . . 1·25 1·25

888 Atlantic Puffin

1989. Centenary of Royal Society for the Protection of Birds. Multicoloured.
1419 19p. Type **888** 45 45
1420 27p. Avocet . . . . 1·25 1·25
1421 32p. Oystercatcher . . . . . 1·25 1·25
1422 35p. Northern gannet . . . . 1·50 1·50

892 Rose

1989. Greetings Stamps. Multicoloured.
1423 19p. Type **892** . . . . 6·25 4·50
1424 19p. Cupid . . . . 6·25 4·50
1425 19p. Yachts . . . . 6·25 4·50
1426 19p. Fruit . . . . 6·25 4·50
1427 19p. Teddy bear . . . . . . 6·25 4·50

897 Fruit and Vegetables

1989. Food and Farming Year. Multicoloured.
1428 19p. Type **897** 50 50
1429 27p. Meat products 80 80
1430 32p. Dairy produce . . . . . 1·25 1·25
1431 35p. Cereal products . . . . 1·40 1·40

901 Mortar Board

905 Toy Train and Airplane

1989. Anniversaries. Multicoloured.
1432 19p. Type **901** (150th anniv of Public Education in England) 1·25 1·25
1433 19p. Cross on Ballot paper (3rd Direct Elections to European Parliament) . . . . 1·25 1·25
1434 35p. Posthorn (26th Postal, Telegraph and Telephone International Congress, Brighton) . . . . 1·75 1·75
1435 35p. Globe (Inter-Parliamentary Union Centenary Conference, London) . . . . 1·75 1·75

1989. Europa. Games and Toys. Multicoloured.
1436 19p. Type **905** 50 50
1437 27p. Building bricks 90 90
1438 32p. Dice and board games . . 1·25 1·25
1439 35p. Toy robot, boat and doll's house . . . . 1·40 1·40

909 Ironbridge, Shropshire

913

1989. Industrial Archaeology. Multicoloured.
1440 19p. Type **909** 60 60
1441 27p. Tin Mine, St. Agnes Head, Cornwall . . . . 1·00 1·00
1442 32p. Cotton Mills, New Lanark, Strathclyde . . . . 1·10 1·10
1443 35p. Ponteysylte Aqueduct, Clwyd . . . . 1·25 1·25

1989.
1663a **913** (2nd) blue 30 35
1447 (1st) black . . . . . . 2·00 2·00
1664a (1st) red 40 45
1664b (E) blue 45 50

The above were sold at the current rate for the day.

No. 1664b was valid for the basic European airmail rate.

The 2nd blue and 1st red exist with ordinary or self-adhesive gum.

For 1st class in gold see No. 1979.

915 Snowflake (× 10)

919 Royal Mail Coach

1989. 150th Anniv of Royal Microscopical Society. Multicoloured.
1453 19p. Type **915** 50 50
1454 27p. "Calliphora erythrocephala" (fly) (× 5) . . 1·00 1·00
1455 32p. Blood cells (× 500) . . . 1·25 1·25
1456 35p. Microchip (× 600) . . . 1·40 1·40

1989. Lord Mayor's Show, London. Multicoloured.
1457 20p. Type **919** 90 90
1458 20p. Escort of Blues and Royals 90 90
1459 20p. Lord Mayor's Coach . . 90 90
1460 20p. Coach team passing St. Paul's 90 90
1461 20p. Blues and Royals drum horse 90 90

This issue commemorates the 800th anniv of the installation of the first Lord Mayor of London.

924 14th-century Peasants from Stained-glass Window

1989. Christmas. 800th Anniv of Ely Cathedral.
1462 **924** 15p. gold, silver & blue . . 40 40
1463 – 15p. + 1p. gold, silver and blue 50 50
1464 – 20p. + 1p. gold, silver and red 60 60

1465 – 34p. + 1p. gold, silver and green . . . . 1·40 1·40
1466 – 37p. + 1p. gold, silver and green . . . . 1·40 1·40
DESIGNS: 15p. + 1p. Arches and roundels, West Front; 20p. + 1p. Octagon Tower; 34p. + 1p. Arcade from West Transept; 37p. + 1p. Triple arch from West Front.

929 Queen Victoria and Queen Elizabeth II 930 Kitten

1990. 150th Anniv of the Penny Black.
1467 **929** 15p. blue 50 50
1469 20p. black and cream . . 75 75
1471 29p. mauve . . . . . . 1·50 1·50
1473 34p. grey . . . . 1·75 1·75
1474 37p. red . . . . 1·75 1·75
For this design with 1st face value see No. 2133.

1990. 150th Anniv of Royal Society for Prevention of Cruelty to Animals. Multicoloured.
1479 20p. Type **930** 65 70
1480 29p. Rabbit . . . . 1·25 1·25
1481 34p. Duckling . . . . 1·50 1·50
1482 37p. Puppy . . . . 1·60 1·60

934 Teddy Bear

1990. Greetings Stamps. "Smiles". Multicoloured (except No. 1492).
1483 20p. Type **934** . . . . . . 3·25 2·50
1484 20p. Dennis the Menace . . . 3·25 2·50
1485 20p. Punch . . . . 3·25 2·50
1486 20p. Cheshire Cat . . . . . 3·25 2·50
1487 20p. The Man in the Moon . . 3·25 2·50
1488 20p. The Laughing Policeman 3·25 2·50
1489 20p. Clown . . . . 3·25 2·50
1490 20p. Mona Lisa . . . . . . 3·25 2·50
1491 20p. Queen of Hearts . . . . 3·25 2·50
1492 20p. Stan Laurel (comedian) (gold and black) . . . . . 3·25 2·50
See also Nos. 1550/9.

944 Alexandra Palace ("Stamp World London 90" Exhibition) 948 Export Achievement Award

1990. Europa. (Nos. 1493 and 1495) and "Glasgow 1990 European City of Culture" (Nos. 1494 and 1496). Multicoloured.
1493 20p. Type **944** 50 50
1494 20p. Glasgow School of Art . 50 50
1495 29p. British Philatelic Bureau, Edinburgh . . . . 1·25 1·25
1496 37p. Templeton Carpet Factory, Glasgow . . . . 1·40 1·40

1990. 25th Anniv of Queen's Awards for Export and Technology. Multicoloured.
1497 20p. Type **948** 75 75
1498 20p. Technological Achievement Award 75 75
1499 37p. Type **948** . . . . . . 1·40 1·40
1500 37p. As No. 1498 . . . . . 1·40 1·40

950 Cycad and Sir Joseph Banks Building 954 Thomas Hardy and Clyffe Clump, Dorset

1990. 150th Anniv of Kew Gardens. Mult.
1502 20p. Type **950** 50 50
1503 29p. Stone pine and Princess of Wales Conservatory 80 80
1504 34p. Willow tree and Palm House . . . . 1·25 1·25
1505 37p. Cedar tree and Pagoda . 1·40 1·40

1990. 150th Anniv of Thomas Hardy (author).
1506 **954** 20p. multicoloured . . . 1·00 1·00

955 Queen Elizabeth the Queen Mother 959 Victoria Cross

1990. 90th Birthday of Queen Elizabeth the Queen Mother. Multicoloured.
1507 20p. Type **955** 70 70
1508 29p. Queen Elizabeth . . . . 1·10 1·10
1509 34p. Elizabeth, Duchess of York 1·75 1·75
1510 37p. Lady Elizabeth Bowes-Lyon . . . . 2·00 2·00

1990. Gallantry Awards. Multicoloured.
1517 20p. Type **959** 90 90
1518 20p. George Cross 90 90
1519 20p. Distinguished Service Cross and Distinguished Service Medal (horiz) 90 90
1520 20p. Military Cross and Military Medal (horiz) 90 90
1521 20p. Distinguished Flying Cross and Distinguished Flying Medal (horiz) 90 90

964 Armagh Observatory, Jodrell Bank Radio Telescope and La Palma Telescope

1990. Astronomy. Multicoloured.
1522 22p. Type **964** 50 40
1523 26p. Newton's moon and tides diagram with early telescopes 80 90
1524 31p. Greenwich Old Observatory and early astronomical equipment . . 1·10 1·10
1525 37p. Stonehenge, gyroscope and navigating by stars . . . . 1·25 1·25
Nos. 1522/5 commemorate the Centenary of the British Astronomical Association and the Bicentenary of the Armagh Observatory.

968 Building a Snowman

1990. Christmas. Multicoloured.
1526 17p. Type **968** 45 35
1527 22p. Fetching the Christmas tree 55 65
1528 26p. Carol singing 80 80
1529 31p. Tobogganing . . . . . 1·10 1·10
1530 37p. Ice-skating . . . . . . 1·25 1·25

973 "King Charles Spaniel" 988 Michael Faraday. (inventor of electric motor) (birth bicentenary)

978 Thrush's Nest

1991. Dogs. Paintings by George Stubbs. Mult.
1531 22p. Type **973** 80 80
1532 26p. "A Pointer" . . . . . . 1·00 1·00
1533 31p. "Two Hounds in a Landscape" . . . . 1·10 1·10
1534 33p. "A Rough Dog" . . . . 1·25 1·25
1535 37p. "Fino and Tiny" . . . . 1·40 1·40

1991. Greetings Stamps. "Good Luck". Mult.
1536 (1st) Type **978** . . . . 1·90 1·90
1537 (1st) Shooting star and rainbow 1·90 1·90
1538 (1st) Magpies and charm bracelet . . . . 1·90 1·90
1539 (1st) Black cat . . . . 1·90 1·90
1540 (1st) Common kingfisher with key . . . . 1·90 1·90
1541 (1st) Mallard and frog . . . . 1·90 1·90
1542 (1st) Four-leaf clover in boot and match box . . . . . . 1·90 1·90
1543 (1st) Pot of gold at end of rainbow . . . . 1·90 1·90
1544 (1st) Heart-shaped butterflies . 1·90 1·90
1545 (1st) Wishing well and sixpence 1·90 1·90
The background of the stamps forms a composite design.
Nos. 1536/45 were sold at the current rate.

1991. Scientific Achievements. Multicoloured.
1546 22p. Type **988** 65 65
1547 22p. Charles Babbage (computer science pioneer) (birth bicentenary) 65 65
1548 31p. Radar sweep of East Anglia (50th anniv of operational radar network) 95 95
1549 37p. Gloster Whittle E28/39 airplane over East Anglia (50th anniv of first flight of Sir Frank Whittle's jet engine) 1·10 1·10

992 Teddy Bear

1991. Greetings Stamps. "Smiles". As Nos. 1483/92, but inscr "1st" as in T **992**. Multicoloured (except No. 1559).
1550 (1st) Type **992** . . . . 1·25 1·25
1551 (1st) Dennis the Menace . . . 1·25 1·25
1552 (1st) Punch . . . . 1·25 1·25
1553 (1st) Cheshire Cat . . . . . 1·25 1·25
1554 (1st) The Man in the Moon . . 1·25 1·25
1555 (1st) The Laughing Policeman 1·25 1·25
1556 (1st) Clown . . . . 1·25 1·25
1557 (1st) Mona Lisa . . . . . . 1·25 1·25
1558 (1st) Queen of Hearts . . . . 1·25 1·25
1559 (1st) Stan Laurel (comedian) (gold and black) . . . . . 1·25 1·25
Nos. 1550/9 were sold at the current rate.

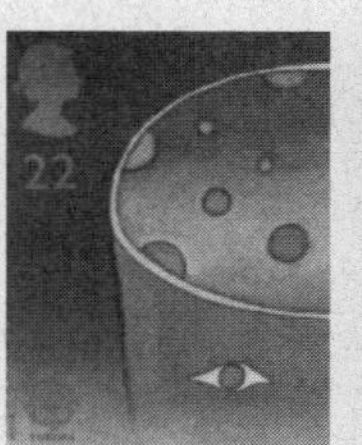

993 Man looking at Space 994

1991. Europa. Europe in Space. Multicoloured.
1560 22p. Type **993** 55 55
1561 22p. Type **994** 55 55
1562 37p. Space looking at Man (Queen's head on left) . . . 1·25 1·25
1563 37p. Similar to No. 1562 (Queen's head on right) . . . 1·25 1·25
Stamps of the same value were printed together in horizontal pairs, each pair forming a composite design.

997 Fencing 1001 "Silver Jubilee"

1991. World Student Games, Sheffield (Nos. 1564/6) and World Cup Rugby Championship (No. 1567).
1564 22p. Type **997** 50 50
1565 26p. Hurdling 80 80
1566 31p. Diving 95 95
1567 37p. Rugby . . . . 1·10 1·10

1991. 9th World Congress of Roses, Belfast. Multicoloured.
1568 22p. Type **1001** 80 80
1569 26p. "Mme Alfred Carriere" . 1·00 1·00
1570 31p. "Rosa moyesii" . . . . 1·10 1·10
1571 33p. "Harvest Fayre" . . . . 1·25 1·25
1572 37p. "Mutabilis" . . . . . . 1·40 1·40

INDEX
Countries can be quickly located by referring to the index at the end of this volume.

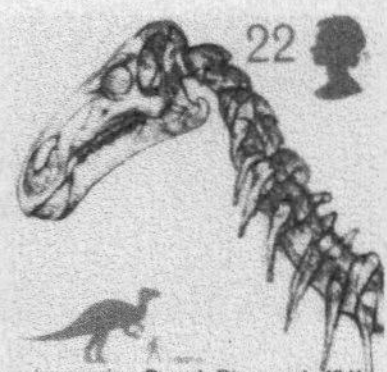

1006 Iguanodon

1991. 150th Anniv of Dinosaurs' Identification by Owen. Multicoloured.
1573 22p. Type **1006** 75 60
1574 26p. Stegosaurus . . . . . . 90 1·10
1575 31p. Tyrannosaurus . . . . . 1·10 1·10
1576 33p. Protoceratops . . . . . 1·40 1·25
1577 37p. Triceratops . . . . . . 1·50 1·50

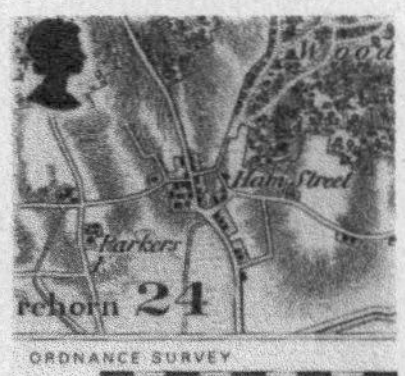

1011 Map of 1816

1991. Bicentenary of Ordnance Survey. Maps of Hamstreet, Kent.
1578 **1011** 24p. black, mauve and cream 50 50
1579 – 28p. multicoloured . . . 85 85
1580 – 33p. multicoloured . . . 1·00 1·00
1581 – 39p. multicoloured . . . 1·25 1·25
DESIGNS: 28p. Map of 1906; 33p. Map of 1959; 39p. Map of 1991.

1015 Adoration of the Magi

1991. Christmas. Illuminated Letters from "Acts of Mary and Jesus" Manuscript in Bodleian Library, Oxford. Multicoloured.
1582 18p. Type **1015** 70 40
1583 24p. Mary and Baby Jesus in the Stable 80 50
1584 28p. The Holy Family and Angel . . . . 85 1·00
1585 33p. The Annunciation . . . 95 1·10
1586 39p. The Flight into Egypt . . 1·10 1·40

1020 Fallow Deer in Scottish Forest

1992. The Four Seasons. Wintertime. Multicoloured.
1587 18p. Type **1020** 50 50
1588 24p. Hare on North Yorkshire moors 70 70
1589 28p. Fox in the Fens 90 90
1590 33p. Redwing and Home Counties village . . . . . 1·10 1·10
1591 39p. Welsh mountain sheep in Snowdonia . . . . 1·25 1·25

1025 Flower Spray

1992. Greetings Stamps. "Memories". Multicoloured.
1592 (1st) Type **1025** . . . . . . 1·10 1·10
1593 (1st) Double locket . . . . . 1·10 1·10
1594 (1st) Key . . . . 1·10 1·10
1595 (1st) Model car and cigarette cards . . . . 1·10 1·10
1596 (1st) Compass and map . . . 1·10 1·10
1597 (1st) Pocket watch . . . . . 1·10 1·10
1598 (1st) 1854 1d. Red stamp and pen . . . . 1·10 1·10
1599 (1st) Pearl necklace . . . . . 1·10 1·10
1600 (1st) Marbles . . . . 1·10 1·10
1601 (1st) Bucket, spade and starfish 1·10 1·10
Nos. 1592/1601 were issued together, se-tenant, the backgrounds forming a composite design.

1035 Queen Elizabeth in Coronation Robes and Parliamentary Emblem

1992. 40th Anniversary of Accession. Multicoloured.
1602 24p. Type **1035** . . . . 1·40 1·40
1603 24p. Queen Elizabeth in Garter robes and archiepiscopal arms 1·40 1·40
1604 24p. Queen Elizabeth with baby Prince Andrew and Royal Arms . . . . 1·40 1·40
1605 24p. Queen Elizabeth at Trooping the Colour . . . 1·40 1·40
1606 24p. Queen Elizabeth and Commonwealth emblem . . 1·40 1·40

1040 Tennyson in 1888 and "The Beguiling of Merlin" (Sir Edward Burne-Jones)

1992. Death Centenary of Alfred, Lord Tennyson (poet). Multicoloured.
1607 24p. Type **1040** 50 50
1608 28p. Tennyson in 1856 and "April Love" (Arthur Hughes) 75 75
1609 33p. Tennyson in 1864 and "I am Sick of the Shadows" (John Waterhouse) . . . . 1·25 1·25
1610 39p. Tennyson as a young man and "Mariana" (Dante Gabriel Rossetti) . . . . . 1·40 1·40

1044 Carrickfergus Castle

1992. Designs as Nos. 1410/13, but showing Queen's head in silhouette as T **1044**.
1611 **1044** £1 green and gold . . . 6·00 2·00
1993 – £1.50 purple & gold . . . 3·50 3·00
1994 – £2 blue and gold . . . . 5·00 4·00
1995 **1044** £3 violet and gold . . . 7·00 9·00
1996 – £5 brown and gold . . . 13·00 8·00

The Queen's head on these stamps is printed in optically variable ink which changes colour from gold to green when viewed from different angles.

1045 British Olympic Association Logo (Olympic Games, Barcelona)

1992. Europa. International Events. Mult.
1615 24p. Type **1045** . . . . 1·00 1·00
1616 24p. British Paralympic Association symbol (Paralympics 92, Barcelona) 1·00 1·00
1617 24p. "Santa Maria" (500th anniv of discovery of America by Columbus) 80 80
1618 39p. "Kaisei" (Japanese cadet brigantine), (Grand Regatta Columbus, 1992) . . . . . 1·10 1·10
1619 39p. British Pavilion, "EXPO '92", Seville . . . . 1·10 1·10

1050 Pikeman

1054 "The Yeomen of the Guard"

1992. 350th Anniversary of the Civil War. Mult.
1620 24p. Type **1050** 55 55
1621 28p. Drummer 70 70
1622 33p. Musketeer . . . . 1·25 1·25
1623 39p. Standard Bearer . . . . 1·40 1·40

1992. 150th Birth Anniv of Sir Arthur Sullivan (composer). Gilbert and Sullivan Operas. Multicoloured.
1624 18p. Type **1054** 45 45
1625 24p. "The Gondoliers" 70 70
1626 28p. "The Mikado" 85 85
1627 33p. "The Pirates of Penzance" 1·40 1·40
1628 39p. "Iolanthe" . . . . . . 1·50 1·50

1059 "Acid Rain Kills"

1992. Protection of the Environment. Children's Paintings. Multicoloured.
1629 24p. Type **1059** 60 60
1630 28p. "Ozone Layer" 90 90
1631 33p. "Greenhouse Effect" . . 1·00 1·00
1632 39p. "Bird of Hope" . . . . 1·10 1·10

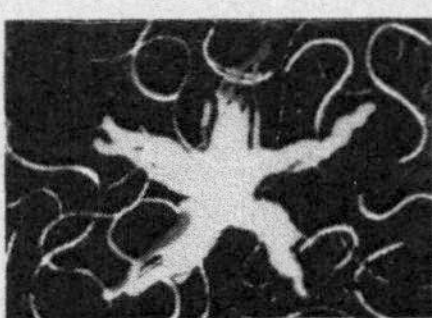
1063 European Star

1992. Single European Market.
1633 **1063** 24p. multicoloured . . . 1·00 1·00

1064 "Angel Gabriel", St. James's, Pangbourne

1992. Christmas. Stained Glass Windows. Multicoloured.
1634 18p. Type **1064** 45 45
1635 24p. "Madonna and Child", St. Mary's, Bibury 75 75
1636 28p. "King with Gold", Our Lady and St. Peter, Leatherhead 90 90
1637 33p. "Shepherds", All Saints, Porthcawl . . . . 1·10 1·10
1638 39p. "Kings with Frankincense and Myrrh", Our Lady and St. Peter, Leatherhead . . . 1·25 1·25

1069 Mute Swan Cob and St. Catherine's Chapel, Abbotsbury

1993. 600th Anniv of Abbotsbury Swannery. Multicoloured.
1639 18p. Type **1069** . . . . 1·50 1·50
1640 24p. Cygnet and decoy . . . . 1·10 1·10
1641 28p. Swans and cygnet . . . . 1·25 1·25
1642 33p. Eggs in nest and tithe barn, Abbotsbury . . . . 2·00 2·00
1643 39p. Young swan and the Fleet 2·25 2·25

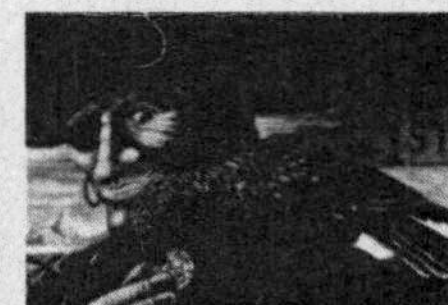
1074 Long John Silver and Parrot ("Treasure Island")

1993. Greetings Stamps. "Gift Giving". Gold, cream and black (No. 1645) or multicoloured (others).
1644 (1st) Type **1074** . . . . 1·10 1·10
1645 (1st) Tweedledum and Tweedledee ("Alice Through the Looking Glass") . . . 1·10 1·10
1646 (1st) William ("William" books) 1·10 1·10
1647 (1st) Mole and Toad ("The Wind in the Willows") . . . 1·10 1·10
1648 (1st) Teacher and Wilfrid ("The Bash Street Kids") . . . . 1·10 1·10
1649 (1st) Peter Rabbit and Mrs. Rabbit ("The Tale of Peter Rabbit") . . . . 1·10 1·10
1650 (1st) Snowman ("The Snowman") and Father Christmas ("Father Christmas") . . . . 1·10 1·10
1651 (1st) The Big Friendly Giant and Sophie ("The BFG") . . . 1·10 1·10
1652 (1st) Bill Badger and Rupert Bear . . . . 1·10 1·10
1653 (1st) Aladdin and the Genie . 1·10 1·10

1084 Decorated Enamel Dial

1993. 300th Birth Anniv of John Harrison (inventor of the marine chronometer). Details of "H4" Clock. Multicoloured.
1654 24p. Type **1084** 50 50
1655 28p. Escapement remontoire and fusee 85 85
1656 33p. Balance, spring and temperature compensator . 1·10 1·10
1657 39p. Back of movement . . . 1·25 1·25

1088 "Britannia"

1993.
1658 **1088** £10 multicoloured . . . 15·00 9·00

1089 "Dendrobium hellwigianum"

1993. 14th World Orchid Conference, Glasgow. Multicoloured.
1659 18p. Type **1089** 40 40
1660 24p. "Paphiopedilum" Maudiae "Magnificum" 65 65
1661 28p. "Cymbidium lowianum" 90 90
1662 33p. "Vanda" Rothschildiana 1·10 1·10
1663 39p. "Dendrobium vexillarius var albiviride" . . . . 1·40 1·40

1094 "Family Group" (bronze sculpture) (Henry Moore)

1993. Europa. Contemporary Art. Multicoloured.
1767 24p. Type **1094** 50 50
1768 28p. "Kew Gardens" (lithograph) (Edward Bawden) 80 80
1769 33p. "St. Francis and the Birds" (Stanley Spencer) . . . . . 1·10 1·10
1770 39p. "Still Life: Odyssey I" (Ben Nicholson) . . . . 1·25 1·25

1098 Emperor Claudius (from gold coin)

1993. Roman Britain. Multicoloured.
1771 24p. Type **1098** 50 50
1772 28p. Emperor Hadrian (bronze head) 80 80
1773 33p. Goddess Roma (from gemstone) . . . . 1·10 1·10
1774 39p. Christ (Hinton St. Mary mosaic) . . . . 1·25 1·25

1102 "Midland Maid" and other Narrow Boats, Grand Junction Canal

1993. Inland Waterways. Multicoloured.
1775 24p. Type **1102** 50 50
1776 28p. "Yorkshire Lass" and other Humber keels, Stainforth and Keadby Canal 80 80
1777 35p. "Valley Princess" and other horse-drawn barges, Brecknock and Abergavenny Canal . . . . 1·10 1·10
1778 39p. Steam barges, including "Pride of Scotland", and fishing boats, Crinan Canal 1·25 1·25

Nos. 1775/8 commemorate the bicentenary of the Acts of Parliament authorising the canals depicted.

1106 Horse Chestnut

1993. The Four Seasons. Autumn. Fruits and Leaves. Multicoloured.
1779 18p. Type **1106** 40 40
1780 24p. Blackberry 65 65
1781 28p. Hazel . . . . 1·00 1·00
1782 33p. Rowan . . . . 1·25 1·25
1783 39p. Pear . . . . 1·40 1·40

1111 "The Reigate Squire"

1116

1993. Sherlock Holmes. Centenary of the Publication of "The Final Problem". Multicoloured.
1784 24p. Type **1111** . . . . 1·00 1·00
1785 24p. "The Hound of the Baskervilles" . . . . 1·00 1·00
1786 24p. "The Six Napoleons" . . 1·00 1·00
1787 24p. "The Greek Interpreter" . 1·00 1·00
1788 24p. "The Final Problem" . . 1·00 1·00

1993. Self-adhesive.
1976 **1116** (2nd) blue . . . . 1·00 1·00
1977 (1st) red . . . . 1·00 1·00

Nos. 1976/7 were sold at the current rates.

1117 Bob Cratchit and Tiny Tim

1993. Christmas. 150th Anniv of Publication of "A Christmas Carol" by Charles Dickens. Multicoloured.
1790 19p. Type **1117** 50 50
1791 25p. Mr. and Mrs. Fezziwig . 80 80
1792 30p. Scrooge . . . . 1·10 1·10
1793 35p. The prize turkey . . . . 1·25 1·25
1794 41p. Mr. Scrooge's nephew . . 1·40 1·40

1122 Class 5 No. 44957 and Class B1 No. 61342 on West Highland Line

1994. The Age of Steam. Railway Photographs by Colin Gifford.
1795 **1122** 19p. green, grey & blk . . 45 45
1796 – 25p. lilac, grey & black . 75 75
1797 – 30p. brown, grey & blk . 1·00 1·00
1798 – 35p. purple, grey & blk . 1·25 1·25
1799 – 41p. blue, grey & black . 1·40 1·40

DESIGNS: 25p. Class A1 No. 60149 "Amadis" at Kings Cross; 30p. Class 4 No. 43000 on turntable at Blyth North; 35p. Class 4 No. 42455 near Wigan Central; 41p. Class "Castle" No. 7002 "Devizes Castle" on bridge crossing Worcester and Birmingham Canal.

1127 Dan Dare and the Mekon

1994. Greetings Stamps. "Messages". Mult.
1800 (1st) Type **1127** . . . . 1·00 1·00
1801 (1st) The Three Bears . . . . 1·00 1·00
1802 (1st) Rupert Bear . . . . . . 1·00 1·00
1803 (1st) Alice ("Alice in Wonderland") . . . . 1·00 1·00
1804 (1st) Noggin and The Ice Dragon . . . . 1·00 1·00
1805 (1st) Peter Rabbit posting a letter . . . . 1·00 1·00
1806 (1st) Red Riding Hood and wolf 1·00 1·00
1807 (1st) Orlando the Marmalade Cat . . . . 1·00 1·00
1808 (1st) Biggles . . . . 1·00 1·00
1809 (1st) Paddington Bear on station . . . . 1·00 1·00

1137 Castell Y Waun (Chirk Castle), Clwyd, Wales

1994. 25th Anniv of Investiture of the Prince of Wales. Paintings by Prince Charles. Multicoloured.
1810 19p. Type **1137** 50 50
1811 25p. Ben Arkle, Sutherland, Scotland 90 90
1812 30p. Mourne Mountains, County Down, Northern Ireland . . . . 1·00 1·00
1813 35p. Dersingham, Norfolk, England . . . . 1·25 1·25
1814 41p. Dolwyddelan, Gwynedd, Wales . . . . 1·40 1·40

1142 Bather at Blackpool

1994. Centenary of Picture Postcards. Mult.
1815 19p. Type **1142** 50 50
1816 25p. "Where's my Little Lad?" 85 85
1817 30p. "Wish You were Here!" . 1·00 1·00
1818 35p. Punch and Judy show . 1·25 1·25
1819 41p. "The Tower Crane" machine . . . . 1·40 1·40

1147 British Lion and French Cockerel over Tunnel

1994. Opening of Channel Tunnel. Multicoloured.
1820 25p. Type **1147** 85 85
1821 25p. Symbolic hands over train 85 85
1822 41p. Type **1147** . . . . 1·60 1·60
1823 41p. As No. 1821 . . . . . . 1·60 1·60

1149 Groundcrew replacing Smoke Canisters on Douglas Boston of 88 Sqn

1994. 50th Anniv of D-Day. Multicoloured.
1824 25p. Type **1149** . . . . . . 1·10 1·10
1825 25p. H.M.S. "Warspite" (battleship) shelling enemy positions . . . . 1·10 1·10
1826 25p. Commandos landing on Gold Beach . . . . 1·10 1·10
1827 25p. Infantry regrouping on Sword Beach . . . . . . 1·10 1·10
1828 25p. Tank and infantry advancing, Ouistreham . . 1·10 1·10

1154 The Old Course, St. Andrews

1994. Scottish Golf Courses. Multicoloured.
1829 19p. Type **1154** 55 55
1830 25p. The 18th Hole, Muirfield . 80 80
1831 30p. The 15th Hole ("Luckyslap"), Carnoustie . 1·00 1·00
1832 35p. The 8th Hole ("The Postage Stamp"), Royal Troon . . . . 1·25 1·25
1833 41p. The 9th Hole, Turnberry . 1·40 1·40
Nos. 1829/33 commemorate the 250th anniversary of golf's first set of rules produced by the Honourable Company of Edinburgh Golfers.

1159 Royal Welsh Show, Llanelwedd

1994. The Four Seasons. Summertime. Multicoloured.
1834 19p. Type **1159** 50 50
1835 25p. All England Tennis Championships, Wimbledon 75 75
1836 30p. Cowes Week . . . . . . 1·10 1·10
1837 35p. Test Match, Lord's . . . 1·25 1·25
1838 41p. Braemar Gathering . . . 1·40 1·40

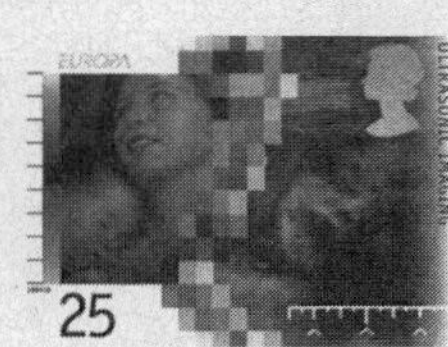

1164 Ultrasonic Imaging

1994. Europa. Medical Discoveries. Multicoloured.
1839 25p. Type **1164** 65 65
1840 30p. Scanning electron microscopy 95 95
1841 35p. Magnetic resonance imaging . . . . 1·00 1·00
1842 41p. Computed tomography . 1·10 1·10

1168 Mary and Joseph

1994. Christmas. Children's Nativity Plays. Multicoloured.
1843 19p. Type **1168** 60 60
1844 25p. Three Wise Men 90 90
1845 30p. Mary with doll . . . . . 1·00 1·00
1846 35p. Shepherds . . . . 1·10 1·10
1847 41p. Angels . . . . 1·40 1·40

1173 Sophie (black cat)

1995. Cats. Multicoloured.
1848 19p. Type **1173** 60 60
1849 25p. Puskas (Siamese) and Tigger (tabby) 75 75
1850 30p. Chloe (ginger cat) . . . 1·00 1·00
1851 35p. Kikko (tortoiseshell) and Rosie (Abyssinian) . . . . 1·10 1·10
1852 41p. Fred (black and white cat) . . . . 1·40 1·40

1178 Dandelions

1995. The Four Seasons. Springtime. Plant Sculptures by Andy Goldsworthy. Multicoloured.
1853 19p. Type **1178** 65 65
1854 25p. Sweet chestnut leaves . . 75 75
1855 30p. Garlic leaves . . . . . . 1·10 1·10
1856 35p. Hazel leaves . . . . . . 1·10 1·10
1857 41p. Spring grass . . . . . . 1·40 1·40

1183 "La Danse a la Campagne" (Renoir)

1995. Greetings Stamps. "Greetings in Art".
1858 **1183** (1st) multicoloured . . . 70 70
1859 – (1st) multicoloured . . . 70 70
1860 – (1st) multicoloured . . . 70 70
1861 – (1st) multicoloured . . . 70 70
1862 – (1st) multicoloured . . . 70 70
1863 – (1st) multicoloured . . . 70 70
1864 – (1st) brown and silver . . . 70 70
1865 – (1st) multicoloured . . . 70 70
1866 – (1st) multicoloured . . . 70 70
1867 – (1st) black, yellow and silver 70 70
DESIGNS: No. 1859, "Troilus and Criseyde" (Peter Brookes); 1860, "The Kiss" (Rodin); 1861, "Girls on the Town" (Beryl Cook); 1862, "Jazz" (Andrew Mockett); 1863, "Girls performing a Kathak Dance" (Aurangzeb period); 1864, "Alice Keppel with her Daughter" (Alice Hughes); 1865, "Children Playing" (L. S. Lowry); 1866, "Circus Clowns" (Emily Firmin and Justin Mitchell); 1867, Decoration from "All the Love Poems of Shakespeare" (Eric Gill).

1193 Fireplace Decoration, Attingham Park, Shropshire

1198 British Troops and French Civilians celebrating

1995. Centenary of The National Trust. Multicoloured.
1868 19p. Type **1193** 55 55
1869 25p. Oak seedling 80 80
1870 30p. Carved table leg, Attingham Park . . . . . 1·00 1·00
1871 35p. St. David's Head, Dyfed, Wales . . . . 1·25 1·25
1872 41p. Elizabethan window, Little Moreton Hall, Cheshire . . . 1·40 1·40

1995. Europa. Peace and Freedom.
1873 **1198** 19p. silver, brown and black 65 65
1874 – 19p. multicoloured . . . 65 65
1875 – 25p. silver, blue and black 95 95
1876 – 25p. multicoloured . . . 95 95
1877 – 30p. multicoloured . . . 1·10 1·10
DESIGNS: No. 1874, Symbolic hands and Red Cross; 1875, St. Paul's Cathedral and searchlights; 1876, Symbolic hand releasing peace dove; 1877, Symbolic hands.
Nos. 1873 and 1875 commemorate the 50th anniversary of the end of the Second World War, No. 1874 the 125th anniversary of the British Red Cross Society and Nos. 1876/7 the 50th anniversary of the United Nations.
Nos. 1876/7 include the "EUROPA" emblem.

1203 "The Time Machine"

1995. Science Fiction. Novels by H. G. Wells. Multicoloured.
1878 25p. Type **1203** 70 70
1879 30p. "The First Men in the Moon" . . . . 1·10 1·10
1880 35p. "The War of the Worlds" . 1·25 1·25
1881 41p. "The Shape of Things to Come" . . . . 1·40 1·40
Nos. 1878/81 commemorate the centenary of publication of Wells's "The Time Machine".

1207 The Swan, 1595

1995. Reconstruction of Shakespeare's Globe Theatre. Multicoloured.
1882 25p. Type **1207** 85 85
1883 25p. The Rose, 1592 . . . . 85 85
1884 25p. The Globe, 1599 . . . . 85 85
1885 25p. The Hope, 1613 . . . . 85 85
1886 25p. The Globe, 1614 . . . . 85 85
Nos. 1882/6 were printed together, se-tenant, forming a composite design.

1212 Sir Rowland Hill and Uniform Penny Postage Petition

1995. Pioneers of Communications.
1887 **1212** 19p. silver, red and black 55 55
1888 – 25p. silver, brown and black 80 80
1889 – 41p. silver, green and black . . . . 1·25 1·25
1890 – 60p. silver, blue and black . . . . 1·60 1·60
DESIGNS: 25p. Hill and Penny Black; 41p. Guglielmo Marconi and early wireless; 60p. Marconi and sinking of "Titanic" (liner).
Nos. 1887/8 mark the birth bicentenary of Sir Rowland Hill and Nos. 1889/90 the centenary of the first radio transmissions.

1216 Harold Wagstaff

1995. Centenary of Rugby League. Multicoloured.
1891 19p. Type **1216** 60 60
1892 25p. Gus Risman 80 80
1893 30p. Jim Sullivan . . . . . . 1·00 1·00
1894 35p. Billy Batten . . . . . . 1·10 1·10
1895 41p. Brian Bevan . . . . . . 1·50 1·50

1221 European Robin in Mouth of Pillar Box

1995. Christmas. Christmas Robins. Multicoloured.
1896 19p. Type **1221** 45 45
1897 25p. European robin on railings and holly 60 60
1898 30p. European robin on snow-covered milk bottles 90 90
1899 41p. European robin on road sign . . . . 1·25 1·25
1900 60p. European robin on door knob and Christmas wreath . 1·60 1·60

1226 Opening Lines of "To a Mouse" and Fieldmouse

1996. Death Bicentenary of Robert Burns (Scottish poet).
1901 **1226** 19p. cream, brown and black 55 55
1902 – 25p. multicoloured . . . 80 80
1903 – 41p. multicoloured . . . 1·25 1·25
1904 – 60p. multicoloured. . . . 1·60 1·60
DESIGNS: 25p. "O my Luve's like a red, red rose" and wild rose; 41p. "Scots, wha hae wi Wallace bled" and Sir William Wallace; 60p. "Auld Lang Syne" and highland dancers.

1230 "MORE! LOVE" (Mel Calman)

1996. Greetings Stamps. Cartoons.
1905 **1230** (1st) black and mauve . . 70 70
1906 – (1st) black and green . . 70 70
1907 – (1st) black and blue . . 70 70
1908 – (1st) black and violet . . 70 70
1909 – (1st) black and red . . . 70 70

1910 – (1st) black and blue . . . 70 70
1911 – (1st) black and red . . . 70 70
1912 – (1st) black and violet . . 70 70
1913 – (1st) black and green . . 70 70
1914 – (1st) black and mauve . . 70 70

DESIGNS: No. 1906, "Sincerely" (Charles Barsotti); 1907, "Do you have something for the HUMAN CONDITION?" (Mel Calman); 1908, "MENTAL FLOSS" (Leo Cullum); 1909, "4.55 P.M." (Charles Barsotti); 1910, "Dear lottery prize winner" (Larry); 1911, "I'm writing to you because...." (Mel Calman); 1912, "FETCH THIS, FETCH THAT" (Charles Barsotti); 1913, "My day starts before I'm ready for it" (Mel Calman); 1914, "THE CHEQUE IN THE POST" (Jack Ziegler).

Nos. 1905/14 were sold at the current rate.

1240 "Muscovy Duck"

1996. 50th Anniv of the Wildfowl and Wetlands Trust. Bird paintings by C. F. Tunnicliffe. Multicoloured.

1915 19p. Type **1240** 50 50
1916 25p. "Lapwing" 70 70
1917 30p. "White-fronted Goose" . 80 80
1918 35p. "Bittern" . . . . 1·25 1·25
1919 41p. "Whooper Swan" . . . 1·60 1·60

1245 The Odeon, Harrogate

1996. Centenary of Cinema.

1920 **1245** 19p. multicoloured . . . 50 50
1921 – 25p. multicoloured . . . 70 70
1922 – 30p. multicoloured . . . 90 90
1923 – 35p. black, red and silver . . . . 1·25 1·25
1924 – 41p. multicoloured . . . 1·60 1·60

DESIGNS: 25p. Laurence Olivier and Vivien Leigh in "Lady Hamilton" (film); 30p. Old cinema ticket; 35p. Pathe News still; 41p. Cinema sign, The Odeon, Manchester.

1250 Dixie Dean

1996. European Football Championship. Multicoloured.

1925 19p. Type **1250** 40 40
1926 25p. Bobby Moore 70 70
1927 35p. Duncan Edwards . . . . 1·25 1·25
1928 41p. Billy Wright . . . . . . 1·40 1·40
1929 60p. Danny Blanchflower . . . 1·75 1·75

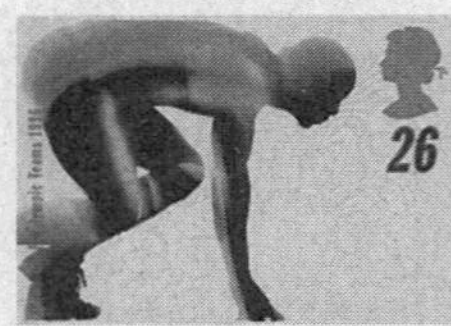

1255 Athlete on Starting Blocks

1996. Olympic and Paralympic Games, Atlanta. Multicoloured.

1930 26p. Type **1255** . . . . 1·00 1·00
1931 26p. Throwing the javelin . . 1·00 1·00
1932 26p. Basketball . . . . 1·00 1·00
1933 26p. Swimming . . . . 1·00 1·00
1934 26p. Athlete celebrating and Olympic Rings . . . . . . 1·00 1·00

1260 Prof. Dorothy Hodgkin (scientist)

1996. Europa. Famous Women.

1935 **1260** 20p. green, grey and black 50 50
1936 – 26p. mauve, grey & black . 70 70
1937 – 31p. bronze, grey and black 90 90
1938 – 37p. silver, grey and black . . . . 1·25 1·25
1939 – 43p. gold, grey and black . . . . 1·40 1·40

DESIGNS: 26p. Dame Margot Fonteyn (ballerina); 31p. Dame Elisabeth Frink (sculptress); 37p. Dame Daphne du Maurier (novelist); 43p. Dame Marea Hartman (sports administrator).

Nos. 1936/7 include the "EUROPA" emblem.

1265 "Muffin the Mule"

1996. 50th Anniv of Children's Television. Multicoloured.

1940 20p. Type **1265** 55 55
1941 26p. "Sooty" 80 80
1942 31p. "Stingray" . . . . . . 1·00 1·00
1943 37p. "The Clangers" . . . . 1·40 1·40
1944 43p. "Dangermouse" . . . . 1·60 1·60

1270 Triumph TR3

1996. Classic Sports Cars. Multicoloured.

1945 20p. Type **1270** 70 70
1946 26p. MG TD 80 80
1947 37p. Austin-Healey 100 . . . 1·10 1·10
1948 43p. Jaguar XK120 . . . . . 1·25 1·25
1949 63p. Morgan Plus 4 . . . . . 1·75 1·75

1275 The Three Kings

1996. Christmas. Multicoloured.

1950 (2nd) Type **1275** 60 60
1951 (1st) The Annunciation . . . 75 75
1952 31p. The Journey to Bethlehem 85 85
1953 43p. The Nativity . . . . . . 1·25 1·25
1954 63p. The Shepherds . . . . 1·60 1·60

1280 "Gentiana acaulis" (Georg Ehret)

1997. Greeting Stamps. 19th-century Flower Paintings. Multicoloured.

1955 (1st) Type **1280** 70 70
1956 (1st) "Magnolia grandiflora" (Ehret) 70 70
1957 (1st) "Camellia japonica" (Alfred Chandler) . . . 70 70
1958 (1st) "Tulipa" (Ehret) 70 70
1959 (1st) "Fuchsia" "Princess of Wales" (Augusta Withers) . 70 70
1960 (1st) "Tulipa gesneriana" (Ehret) 70 70
1961 (1st) "Guzmania splendens" (Charlotte Sowerby) . . . 70 70
1962 (1st) "Iris latifolia" (Ehret) . . 70 70
1963 (1st) "Hippeastrum rutilum" (Pierre-Joseph Redoute) . . 70 70
1964 (1st) "Passiflora coerulea" (Ehret) 70 70

1290 "King Henry VIII"

1997. 450th Death Anniv of King Henry VIII. Multicoloured.

1965 26p. Type **1290** 80 80
1966 26p. "Catherine of Aragon" . . 85 85
1967 26p. "Anne Boleyn" 85 85
1968 26p. "Jane Seymour" 85 85
1969 26p. "Anne of Cleves" . . . 85 85
1970 26p. "Catherine Howard" . . 85 85
1971 26p. "Catherine Parr" 85 85

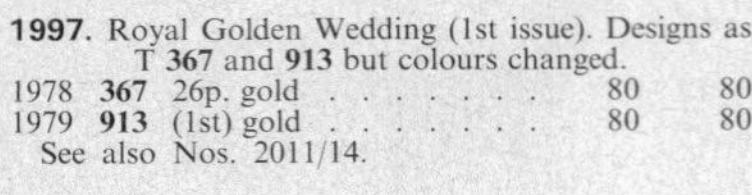

1297 St. Columba in Boat **1303** "Dracula"

1997. Religious Anniversaries. Multicoloured.

1972 26p. Type **1297** 70 70
1973 37p. St. Columba on Iona . . 1·00 1·00
1974 43p. St. Augustine with King Ethelbert . . . . 1·40 1·40
1975 63p. St. Augustine with Model of Cathedral . . . . 1·90 1·90

Nos. 1972/3 commemorate the 1400th death anniversary of St. Columba and Nos. 1974/5 the 1400th anniversary of the arrival of St. Augustine of Canterbury in Kent.

1997. Royal Golden Wedding (1st issue). Designs as T **367** and **913** but colours changed.

1978 **367** 26p. gold 80 80
1979 **913** (1st) gold 80 80

See also Nos. 2011/14.

1997. Europa. Tales and Legends. Horror Stories. Multicoloured.

1980 26p. Type **1303** 90 90
1981 31p. "Frankenstein" . . . . 1·00 1·00
1982 37p. "Dr. Jekyll and Mr. Hyde" . . . . 1·40 1·40
1983 43p. "The Hound of the Baskervilles" . . . . 1·60 1·60

Nos. 1980/3 commemorate the birth bicentenary of Mary Shelley (creator of Frankenstein) with the 26p. and 31p. values incorporating the "EUROPA" emblem.

1307 Reginald Mitchell and Supermarine Spitfire MkIIA

1997. British Aircraft Designers. Multicoloured.

1984 20p. Type **1307** 55 55
1985 26p. Roy Chadwick and Avro Lancaster MkI 95 95
1986 37p. Ronald Bishop and De Havilland Mosquito B MkXVI . . . . 1·10 1·10
1987 43p. George Carter and Gloster Meteor T Mk7 . . . . . . 1·40 1·40
1988 63p. Sir Sidney Camm and Hawker Hunter FGA Mk9 . 1·90 1·90

1312 Carriage Horse and Coachman

1997. "All the Queen's Horses". 50th Anniv of the British Horse Society. Multicoloured.

1989 20p. Type **1312** 70 70
1990 26p. Lifeguards horse and trooper . . . . 1·00 1·00
1991 43p. Blues and Royals drum horse and drummer . . . . 1·40 1·40
1992 63p. Duke of Edinburgh's horse and groom . . . . 1·90 1·90

1316 Haroldswick, Shetland

1997. Sub-Post Offices. Multicoloured.

1997 20p. Type **1316** 65 65
1998 26p. Painswick, Gloucestershire 80 80
1999 43p. Beddgelert, Gwynedd . . 1·40 1·40
2000 63p. Ballyroney, County Down . . . . 1·90 1·90

Nos. 1997/2000 were issued on the occasion of the Centenary of the National Federation of Sub-Postmasters.

1320 "Noddy"

1997. Birth Centenary of Enid Blyton (children's author). Multicoloured.

2001 20p. Type **1320** 55 55
2002 26p. "Famous Five" 95 95
2003 37p. "Secret Seven" . . . . 1·10 1·10
2004 43p. "Faraway Tree" . . . . 1·40 1·40
2005 63p. "Malory Towers" . . . 1·90 1·90

1325 Children and Father Christmas pulling Cracker

1997. Christmas. 150th Anniv of the Christmas Cracker. Multicoloured.

2006 (2nd) Type **1325** 70 70
2007 (1st) Father Christmas with traditional cracker 80 80
2008 31p. Father Christmas riding cracker 90 90
2009 43p. Father Christmas on snowball . . . . 1·40 1·40
2010 63p. Father Christmas and chimney . . . . 1·75 1·75

1330 Wedding Photograph, 1947

1997. Royal Golden Wedding (2nd issue).

2011 **1330** 20p. gold, brown and black 75 75
2012 – 26p. multicoloured . . . 95 95
2013 **1330** 43p. gold, green and black . . . . 1·60 1·60
2014 – 63p. multicoloured . . . 2·25 2·25

DESIGNS: 26p. and 63p. Queen Elizabeth II and Prince Philip, 1997.

1332 Common Dormouse **1338** Diana, Princess of Wales (photo by Lord Snowdon)

1998. Endangered Species. Multicoloured.

2015 20p. Type **1332** 50 50
2016 26p. Lady's slipper orchid . . 60 60
2017 31p. Song thrush 80 80
2018 37p. Shining ram's-horn snail . 1·00 1·00
2019 43p. Mole cricket . . . . . . 1·10 1·10
2020 63p. Devil's bolete . . . . . 1·60 1·60

1998. Diana, Princess of Wales Commemoration. Multicoloured.

2021 26p. Type **1338** 90 90
2022 26p. At British Lung Foundation Function, April 1997 (photo by John Stillwell) 90 90
2023 26p. Wearing tiara, 1991 (photo by Lord Snowdon) . . . 90 90
2024 26p. On visit to Birmingham, October 1995 (photo by Tim Graham) (checked suit) . . 90 90
2025 26p. In evening dress, 1987 (photo by Terence Donovan) 90 90

MINIMUM PRICE

The minimum price quoted is 10p which represents a handling charge rather than a basis for valuing common stamps. For further notes about prices see introductory pages.

1343 Lion of England and Griffin of Edward III **1348**

1998. 650th Anniv of the Order of the Garter. The Queen's Beasts. Multicoloured.

2026 26p. Type **1343** 90 90
2027 26p. Falcon of Plantagenet and Bull of Clarence 90 90
2028 26p. Lion of Mortimer and Yale of Beaufort 90 90
2029 26p. Greyhound of Richmond and Dragon of Wales . . . 90 90
2030 26p. Unicorn of Scotland and Horse of Hanover 90 90

1998. As Type **157** (Wilding definitive of 1952–54) but with face values in decimal currency as Type **1348**.

2031 **1348** 20p. green 75 75
2032 26p. brown 75 75
2033 37p. purple . . . . . . 1·50 1·50

1349 St. John's Point Lighthouse, County Down

1998. 300th Anniv of the 1st Lighthouse and Final Year of Manned Lighthouses. Multicoloured.

2034 20p. Type **1349** 50 50
2035 26p. Smalls Lighthouse, Pembrokeshire 70 70
2036 37p. Needles Rock Lighthouse, Isle of Wight, c.1900 . . . 1·00 1·00
2037 43p. Bell Rock Lighthouse, Arbroath, mid-19th century 1·40 1·40
2038 63p. Eddystone Lighthouse, Plymouth, 1698 . . . . . 1·90 1·90

1354 Tommy Cooper

1998. Comedians. Multicoloured.

2041 20p. Type **1354** 50 50
2042 26p. Eric Morecambe 80 80
2043 37p. Joyce Grenfell . . . . . 1·10 1·10
2044 43p. Les Dawson . . . . . . 1·25 1·25
2045 63p. Peter Cook . . . . . . 1·90 1·90

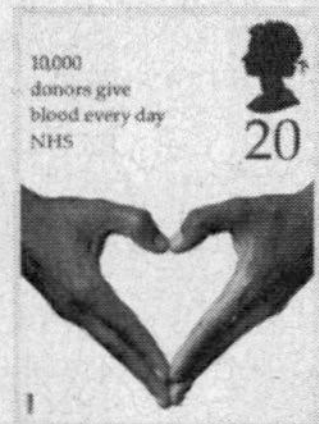

1359 Hands forming Heart

1998. 50th Anniv of the National Health Service. Multicoloured.

2046 20p. Type **1359** 50 50
2047 26p. Adult and child holding hands 70 70
2048 43p. Hands forming cradle . . 1·25 1·25
2049 63p. Hand taking pulse . . . 1·90 1·90

1363 "The Hobbit" (J.R.R. Tolkien)

1998. Famous Children's Fantasy Novels. Multicoloured.

2050 20p. Type **1363** 50 50
2051 26p. "The Lion, The Witch and the Wardrobe" (C.S. Lewis) . 80 80
2052 37p. "The Phoenix and the Carpet" (E. Nesbit) . . . . 1·10 1·10
2053 43p. "The Borrowers" (Mary Norton . . . . 1·25 1·25
2054 63p. "Through the Looking Glass" (Lewis Carroll) . . . 1·90 1·90

Nos. 2050/4 commemorate the birth centenary of C.S. Lewis and the death centenary of Lewis Carroll.

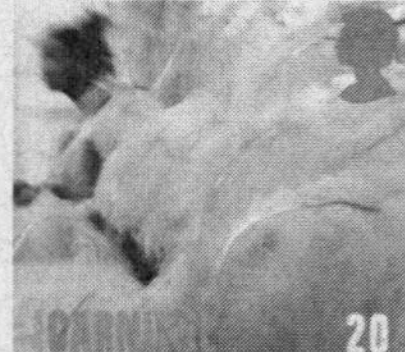

1368 Woman in Yellow Feathered Costume

1998. Europa. Festivals. Notting Hill Carnival. Multicoloured.

2055 20p. Type **1368** 50 50
2056 26p. Woman in blue costume and headdress 70 70
2057 43p. Group of children in white and gold robes . . . . . . 1·10 1·10
2058 63p. Child in "Tree" costume . 1·75 1·75

The 20p. and 26p. incorporate the "EUROPA" emblem.

1372 Sir Malcolm Campbell's "Bluebird", 1925

1998. British Land Speed Record Holders. Multicoloured.

2059 20p. Type **1372** 50 50
2060 26p. Sir Henry Segrave's "Sunbeam", 1926 . . . . . 70 70
2061 30p. John G. Parry Thomas's "Babs", 1926 . . . . . . 1·00 1·00
2062 43p. John R. Cobb's "Railton Mobil Special", 1947 . . . 1·10 1·10
2063 63p. Donald Campbell's "Bluebird CN7", 1964 . . . 1·75 1·75

Nos. 2059/63 commemorate the 50th death anniversary of Sir Malcolm Campbell.

1377 Angel with Hands raised in Blessing

1998. Christmas. Angels. Multicoloured.

2064 20p. Type **1377** 50 50
2065 26p. Angel praying 70 70
2066 30p. Angel plaing flute . . . . 1·00 1·00
2067 43p. Angel playing lute . . . 1·10 1·10
2068 63p. Angel praying (different) . 1·75 1·75

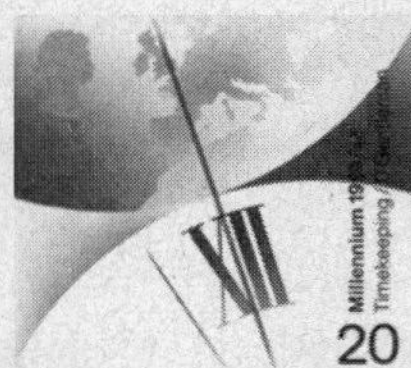

1382 Greenwich Meridian and Clock (John Harrison's chronometer)

1999. Millennium Series. The Inventors' Tale. Multicoloured.

2069 20p. Type **1382** 30 35
2070 26p. Industrial worker and blast furnace (James Watt's discovery of steam power) . 40 45
2071 43p. Early photos of leaves (Henry Fox-Talbot's photographic experiments) . 65 70
2072 63p. Computer inside human head (Alan Turing's work on computers) . . . . 95 1·00

1386 Airliner hugging Globe (International air travel)

1999. Millennium Series. The Travellers' Tale.

2073 **1386** 20p. multicoloured . . 30 35
2074 – 26p. multicoloured . . 40 45
2075 – 43p. black, stone and bronze 65 70
2076 – 63p. multicoloured . . 95 1·00

DESIGNS: 26p. Woman on bicycle (development of the bicycle); 43p. Victorian railway station (growth of public transport); 63p. Captain Cook and Maori (Captain James Cook's voyages).

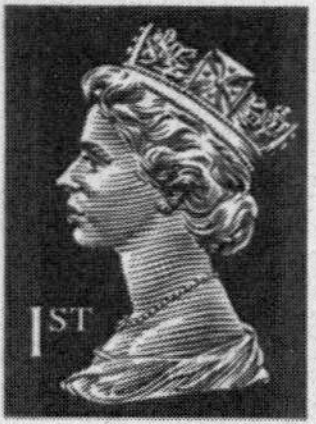

1390

1999. (a) Self-adhesive.

2077 **1390** (1st) grey (face value) (Queen's head in colourless relief) . . 1·00 1·00

(b) Ordinary gum.

2078 **1390** (1st) black . . . . . . 1·00 1·00

1391 Vaccinating Child (pattern in cow markings) (Jenner's development of smallpox vaccine)

1999. Millennium Series. The Patients' Tale. Multicoloured.

2080 20p. Type **1391** 30 35
2081 26p. Patient on trolley (nursing care) 40 45
2082 43p. Penicillin mould (Fleming's discovery of penicillin) . . . 65 70
2083 63p. Sculpture of test-tube baby (development of in vitro fertilization) . . . . 95 1·00

1395 Dove and Norman Settler (medieval migration to Scotland)

1999. Millennium Series. The Settlers' Tale. Multicoloured.

2084 20p. Type **1395** 30 35
2085 26p. Pilgrim Fathers and red indian (17th-century migration to America) . . . 40 45
2086 43p. Sailing ship and aspects of settlement (19th-century migration to Australia) . . 65 70
2087 63p. Hummingbird and superimposed stylised face (20th-century migration to Great Britain) . . . . . . 95 1·00

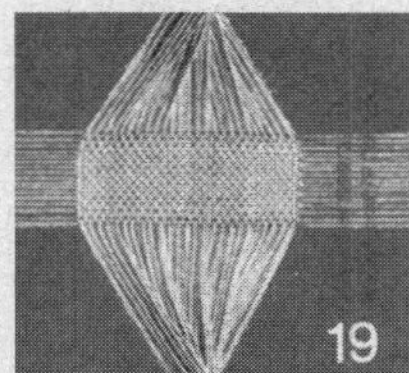

1399 Woven Threads (woollen industry)

1999. Millennium Series. The Workers' Tale. Multicoloured.

2088 19p. Type **1399** 30 35
2089 26p. Salts Mill, Saltaire (cotton industry) 40 45
2090 44p. Hull on slipway (ship-building) 70 75
2091 64p. Lloyd's Building (City of London finance centre) . . 1·00 1·10

1403 Freddie Mercury (lead singer of pop group Queen) ("Popular Music")

1999. Millennium Series. The Entertainers' Tale. Multicoloured.

2092 19p. Type **1403** 30 35
2093 26p. Bobby Moore with World Cup, 1966 ("Sport") . . . 40 45
2094 44p. Dalek from "Dr. Who" (science-fiction series) ("Television") 70 75
2095 64p. Charlie Chaplin (film star) ("Cinema") . . . . 1·00 1·10

1407 Prince Edward and Miss Sophie Rhys-Jones (from photo by John Swannell)

1999. Royal Wedding. Multicoloured.

2096 26p. Type **1407** 60 60
2097 64p. Couple in profile . . . . 1·40 1·40

1409 Suffragette behind Prison Window (Equal Rights for Women)

1999. Millennium Series. The Citizens' Tale. Multicoloured.

2098 19p. Type **1409** 30 35
2099 26p. Water tap (Right to Health) 40 45
2100 44p. Grenerations of school children (Right to Education) 70 75
2101 64p. "MAGNA CARTA" (Human Rights) . . . . . 1·00 1·10

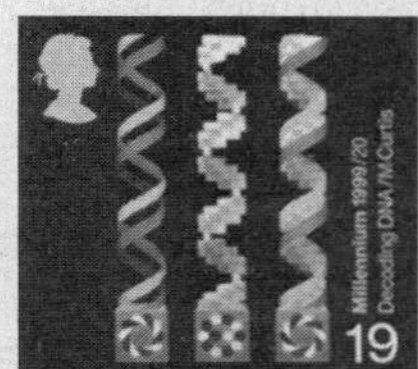

1413 Molecular Structures (DNA Decoding)

1999. Millennium Series. The Scientists' Tale. Multicoloured.

2102 19p. Type **1413** 30 35
2103 26p. Galapagos Finch and Fossilized Skeleton (Darwin's Theory of Evolution) 40 45
2104 44p. Rotation of Polarized Light by Magnetism (Faraday's work on electricity) 70 75
2105 64p. Saturn (development of astronomical telescopes) . . 1·00 1·10

1417 Upland Landscape (Strip Farming)

1999. Millennium Series. The Farmers' Tale. Multicoloured.

2107 19p. Type **1417** 30 35
2108 26p. Horse-drawn plough (Mechanical Farming) . . . 40 45
2109 44p. Man peeling potato (food imports) 70 75
2110 64p. Aerial View of Combine Harvester (Satellite Agriculture) . . . . 1·00 1·10

1421 Robert the Bruce (Battle of Bannockburn, 1314)

1999. The Millennium Series. The Soldiers' Tale.

2111	**1421**	19p. black, stone and silver	30	35
2112	–	26p. multicoloured	40	45
2113	–	44p. grey, black and silver	70	75
2114	–	64p. multicoloured	1·00	1·10

DESIGNS: 26p. Cavalier and horse (English Civil War); 44p. War Graves Cemetery, The Somme (World Wars); 64p. Soldiers with boy (Peace-keeping).

1425 "Hark the herald angels sing" and Hymnbook (John Wesley)

1999. Millennium Series. The Christians' Tale. Multicoloured.

2115	19p. Type **1425**	30	35
2116	26p. King James I and Bible (Authorised version of Bible)	40	45
2117	44p. St. Andrews Cathedral, Fife ("Pilgrimage")	70	75
2118	64p. Nativity ("First Christmas")	1·00	1·10

1429 "World of the Stage" (Allen Jones)

1999. The Millennium Series. The Artists' Tale. Multicoloured.

2119	19p. Type **1429**	30	35
2120	26p. "World of Music" (Bridget Riley)	40	45
2121	44p. "World of Literature" (Lisa Milroy)	70	75
2122	64p. "New Worlds" (Sir Howard Hodgkin)	1·00	1·10

1437 Queen Elizabeth II

1438 Barn Owl (World Owl Trust, Muncaster)

2000. New Millennium.

2124	**1437**	(1st) brown	40	45

2000. Millennium Projects (1st series). "Above and Beyond".

2125	19p. Type **1438**	30	35
2126	26p. Night sky (National Space Science Centre, Leicester)	40	45
2126a	(1st) As No. 2126	40	45
2127	44p. River Goyt and textile mills (Torrs Walkway, New Mills)	70	75
2128	64p. Cape gannets (Seabird Centre, North Berwick)	1·00	1·10

1442 Millennium Beacon (Beacons across The Land)

2000. Millennium Projects (2nd series). "Fire and Light". Multicoloured.

2129	19p. Type **1442**	30	35
2130	26p. Train in Snowdonia (Rheilffordd Eryri, Welsh Highland Railway)	40	45
2131	44p. Lightning (Dynamic Earth Centre, Edinburgh)	70	75
2132	64p. Multicoloured lights (Lighting Croydon's Skyline)	1·00	1·10

2000. As T **929** but with "1st" face value.

2133	(1st) black and cream	75	75

1447 Beach Pebbles (Turning the Tide, Durham Coast)

2000. Millennium Projects (3rd series). "Water and Coast".

2134	19p. Type **1447**	30	35
2135	26p. Frog's legs and water lilies (National Pondlife Centre, Merseyside)	40	45
2136	44p. Cliff Boardwalk (Parc Arfordirol, Llanelli Coast)	70	75
2137	64p. Reflections in water (Portsmouth Harbour Development)	1·00	1·10

1451 Reed Beds, River Braid (ECOS, Ballymena)

2000. Millennium Projects (4th series). "Life and Earth".

2138	(2nd) Type **1451**	30	35
2139	(1st) South American leaf-cutter ants ("Web of Life" Exhibition, London Zoo)	40	45
2140	44p. Solar sensors (Earth Centre, Doncaster)	70	75
2141	64p. Hydroponic leaves (Project SUZY, Teeside)	1·00	1·10

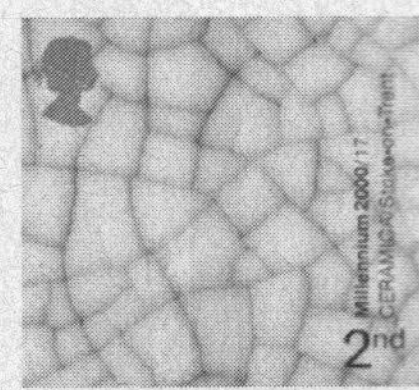

1455 Pottery Glaze (Ceramica Museum, Stoke-on-Trent)

2000. Millennium Projects (5th series). "Art and Craft".

2142	(2nd) Type **1455**	30	35
2143	(1st) Bankside Galleries (Tate Modern, London)	40	45
2144	45p. Cycle lane road marking (Cycle Network Artworks)	70	75
2145	65p. People of Salford (Lowry Centre, Salford)	1·00	1·10

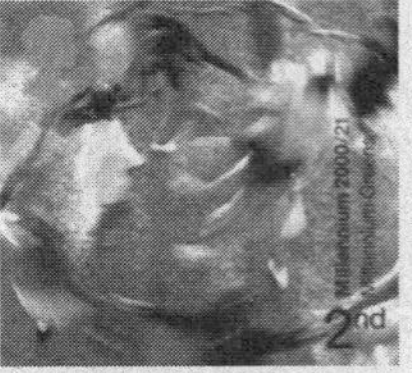

1460 Children playing (Millennium Greens Project)

2000. Millennium Projects (6th series). "People and Places". Multicoloured.

2148	(2nd) Type **1460**	30	35
2149	(1st) Millennium Bridge, Gateshead	40	45
2150	45p. Daisies (Mile End Park, London)	70	75
2151	65p. African Hut and Thatched Cottage ("On the Meridian Line" Project)	1·00	1·10

REGIONAL ISSUES

I. CHANNEL ISLANDS.

Islands in the English Channel off N.W. coast of France. Occupied by German forces from June, 1940 to May, 1945, when separate issues for both islands were made.

C 1 Gathering Vraic (seaweed)

1948. 3rd Anniversary of Liberation.

C1	**C 1**	1d. red	30	30
C2	–	2½d. blue	30	30

DESIGN: 2½d. Islanders gathering vraic.

II. GUERNSEY.

2

3

1958.

6	**2**	2½d. red	35	40
7p	**3**	3d. lilac	20	20
9		4d. blue	10	30
10		4d. sepia	15	20
11		4d. red	15	30
12		5d. blue	15	30

For War Occupation issues and issues of independent postal administration from 1967 see GUERNSEY.

III. ISLE OF MAN.

1

2

3

1958.

1	**1**	2½d. red	50	1·25
2	**2**	3d. lilac	30	20
3p		4d. blue	30	30
5		4d. sepia	25	40
6		4d. red	45	75
7		5d. blue	45	75

1971. Decimal Currency.

8	**3**	2½p. red	20	15
9		3p. blue	20	15
10		5p. violet	40	50
11		7½p. brown	40	65

For issues of independent postal administration from 1973 see ISLE OF MAN.

IV. JERSEY.

8

9

1958.

9	**8**	2½d. red	35	1·00
10p	**9**	3d. lilac	25	25
11p		4d. blue	25	30
12		4d. sepia	25	30
13		4d. red	25	40
14		5d. blue	25	60

For War Occupation issues and issues of independent postal administration from 1969 see JERSEY.

V. NORTHERN IRELAND.

N 1

N 2

N 3

N 4

1958.

NI1	**N 1**	3d. lilac	20	10
NI2		4d. blue	20	15
NI8		4d. sepia	20	15
NI9		4d. red	20	20
NI10		5d. blue	20	20
NI3	**N 2**	6d. purple	20	20
NI4		9d. green	30	70
NI5	**N 3**	1s. 3d. green	30	70
NI6		1s. 6d. blue	30	70

1971.

NI12	**N 4**	2½p. mauve	80	30
NI14		3p. blue	20	15
NI15		3½p. grey	20	20
NI17		4½p. blue	30	30
NI18		5p. violet	1·50	1·50
NI19		5½p. violet	20	20
NI21		6½p. blue	20	20
NI22		7p. brown	35	25
NI23		7½p. brown	2·25	2·25
NI24		8p. red	40	40
NI25		8½p. green	40	40
NI26		9p. violet	40	40
NI27		10p. brown	50	50
NI29		10½p. blue	50	50
NI30		11p. red	50	50
NI34		11½p. drab	85	85
NI31		12p. green	50	50
NI36		12½p. green	75	75
NI37		13p. brown	1·25	90
NI32		13½p. brown	80	80
NI38		14p. blue	90	75
NI33		15p. blue	80	80
NI41		15½p. violet	90	80
NI42		16p. brown	1·00	1·00
NI44		17p. blue	90	90
NI45		18p. violet	1·00	1·00
NI46		18p. grey	90	90
NI47		18p. green	85	85
NI49		19p. red	90	90
NI69		19p. bistre	50	50
NI50		19½p. grey	1·75	2·25
NI51		20p. black	90	90
NI79		20p. green	50	50
NI52		20½p. blue	4·00	4·00
NI53		22p. blue	1·25	1·25
NI54		22p. green	1·25	1·25
NI55		22p. red	1·25	1·00
NI56		23p. green	1·25	1·25
NI57		24p. red	1·25	1·25
NI58		24p. brown	1·00	1·00
NI72		25p. red	1·00	1·00
NI60		26p. red	1·25	1·60
NI61		26p. drab	1·25	1·25
NI81		26p. brown	40	45
NI62		28p. blue	1·25	1·25
NI63		28p. grey	1·25	1·25
NI74		30p. grey	1·25	1·25
NI64		31p. purple	1·75	1·75
NI65		32p. blue	1·50	1·50
NI66		34p. grey	1·75	1·75
NI67		37p. red	1·75	1·75
NI82		37p. mauve	1·00	1·00
NI83		38p blue	60	65
NI68		39p. mauve	1·75	1·75
NI83a		40p. blue	60	65
NI76		41p. brown	1·50	1·50
NI84		63p. green	1·50	1·50
NI85		64p. green	95	1·00
NI86		65p. blue	1·00	1·10

2000. As Type N **4** but with "1st" face value.

NI96	(1st) bright red	40	45

VI. SCOTLAND.

S 1

S 2

S 3 S 4

1958.

S7	**S 1**	3d. lilac	10	15
S8		4d. blue	10	15
S9		4d. sepia	10	10
S10		4d. red	10	10
S11		5d. blue	20	10
S3	**S 2**	6d. purple	20	15
S4		9d. green	50	50
S5	**S 3**	1s. 3d. green	50	50
S6		1s. 6d. blue	35	30

1971. Decimal Currency.

S14	**S 4**	2½p. mauve	30	15
S16		3p. blue	15	15
S17		3½p. grey	20	20
S19		4½p. blue	30	20
S20		5p. violet	1·00	1·00
S21		5½p violet	20	20
S23		6½p. blue	20	20
S24		7p. brown	30	30
S25		7½p. brown	1·25	1·25
S26		8p. red	40	40
S27		8½p. green	40	40
S28		9p. violet	40	40
S29		10p. brown	50	50
S31		10½p. blue	50	50
S32		11p. red	50	50
S36		11½p. drab	90	70
S33		12p. green	50	50

No.	Type	Description	Unused	Used
S38	S 4	12½p. green	80	80
S39		13p. brown	80	80
S34		13½p. brown	80	80
S54		14p. blue	70	70
S35		15p. blue	80	80
S41		15½p. violet	80	80
S42		16p. drab	80	80
S58		17p. blue	80	80
S44		18p. violet	1·00	1·00
S59		18p. grey	90	90
S60		18p. green	80	80
S62		19p. red	90	90
S81		19p. bistre	75	75
S45		19½p. grey	1·75	1·75
S64		20p. black	1·00	1·00
S90		20p. green	50	50
S46		20½p. blue	4·00	4·00
S47		22p. blue	1·25	1·25
S65		22p. green	1·00	1·00
S66		22p. red	1·25	1·00
S67		23p. green	1·25	1·25
S69		24p. red	1·25	1·25
S70		24p. brown	1·00	1·00
S84		25p. red	1·00	1·00
S49		26p. red	1·25	1·25
S73		26p. drab	1·25	1·25
S91		26p. brown	75	75
S74		28p. blue	1·25	1·25
S75		28p. grey	1·25	1·25
S86		30p. grey	1·25	1·25
S76		31p. purple	2·00	2·00
S77		32p. blue	1·50	1·50
S78		34p. grey	1·75	1·75
S79		37p. red	1·75	1·75
S92		37p. mauve	1·00	1·00
S80		39p. mauve	1·50	1·50
S88		41p. brown	1·50	1·50
S93		63p. green	1·50	1·50

S 5 Scottish Flag

1999.

No.	Type	Description	Unused	Used
S94	S 5	(2nd) blue, deep blue and silver	30	35
S95	–	(1st) multicoloured	40	45
S96	–	(E) lilac, deep lilac and silver	45	50
S97	–	64p. multicoloured	1·00	1·10
S98	–	65p. multicoloured	1·00	1·10

DESIGNS: No. S95, Scottish Lion; S96, Thistle; S97, S98, Tartan.

Nos. S94, S95 and S96 were initially sold at 19p., 26p. and 30p., the latter representing the basic European airmail rate.

2000. As Type S 4 but with "1st" face value.

No.	Description	Unused	Used
S108	(1st) bright red	40	45

VII. WALES.

W 1 W 2

W 3 W 4

1958.

No.	Type	Description	Unused	Used
W1	W 1	3d. lilac	20	10
W8		4d. blue	20	10
W9		4d. sepia	20	10
W10		4d. red	20	20
W11		5d. blue	20	10
W3	W 2	6d. purple	50	20
W4		9d. green	50	50
W5	W 3	1s. 3d. green	50	50
W6		1s. 6d. blue	50	50

1971. Decimal Currency.

No.	Type	Description	Unused	Used
W13	W 4	2½p. mauve	20	15
W15		3p. blue	20	20
W16		3½p. grey	20	30
W18		4½p. blue	30	20
W19		5p. violet	1·00	1·00
W20		5½p. violet	20	30
W22		6½p. blue	20	20
W23		7p. brown	30	30
W24		7½p. brown	1·25	1·50
W25		8p. red	40	40
W26		8½p. green	40	40
W27		9p. violet	40	40
W29		10p. brown	40	40
W30		10½p. blue	50	50
W31		11p. red	50	50
W35		11½p. drab	1·00	80
W32		12p. green	50	80
W37		12½p. green	1·00	80
W38		13p. brown	75	75
W33		13½p. brown	80	80
W40		14p. blue	80	80
W41		15p. blue	80	80
W42		15½p. violet	1·00	80
W43		16p. drab	2·00	1·50
W45		17p. blue	1·00	90
W46		18p. violet	1·00	90
W47		18p. grey	1·00	90
W48		18p. green	75	75
W50		19p. red	1·00	80
W70	W 4	19p. bistre	75	75
W51		19½p. grey	2·00	2·00
W52		20p. black	1·00	1·00
W72		20p. green	1·00	1·00
W53		20½p. blue	4·00	4·00
W54		22p. blue	1·25	1·25
W55		22p. green	1·25	1·25
W56		22p. red	1·00	1·00
W57		23p. green	1·25	1·25
W58		24p. red	1·25	1·25
W59		24p. brown	1·25	1·25
W73		25p. red	1·00	1·00
W61		26p. red	1·50	1·50
W62		26p. drab	1·25	1·25
W74		26p. brown	1·00	1·00
W63a		28p. blue	1·25	1·25
W64		28p. grey	1·25	1·25
W75		30p. grey	1·25	1·25
W65		31p. purple	1·50	1·50
W66		32p. blue	1·75	1·75
W67		34p. grey	1·75	1·75
W68		37p. red	1·75	1·75
W76		37p. mauve	1·50	1·50
W69		39p. mauve	1·75	1·75
W77		41p. brown	1·50	1·50
W78		63p. green	2·50	2·50

W 5 Without "p"

1997.

No.	Type	Description	Unused	Used
W79	W 5	20p. green	40	40
W80		26p. brown	75	75
W81		37p. mauve	1·00	1·00
W82		63p. green	1·50	1·50

W 6 Leek

1999.

No.	Type	Description	Unused	Used
W83	W 6	(2nd) brown, orange and black	30	35
W84	–	(1st) multicoloured	40	45
W85	–	(E) multicoloured	45	50
W86	–	64p. multicoloured	1·00	1·10
W87	–	65p. multicoloured	1·00	1·10

DESIGNS: No. W84, Welsh Dragon; W85, Daffodil; W86, W87, Prince of Wales Feathers.

Nos. W83, W84 and W85 were initially sold at 19p., 26p. and 30p., the latter representing the basic European airmail rate.

2000. As Type W 5 but with "1af/st" face value.

No.	Description	Unused	Used
W97	(1st) bright red	40	45

OFFICIAL STAMPS

(for Government Departments)

ADMIRALTY

Overprinted **ADMIRALTY OFFICIAL**.

1903. Stamps of King Edward VII.

No.	Type	Description	Unused	Used
O107	83	½d. turquoise	12·00	7·00
O102	–	1d. red	7·00	4·00
O103	–	1½d. purple and green	70·00	55·00
O104	–	2d. green and red	£140	70·00
O105	83	2½d. blue	£150	55·00
O106	–	3d. purple on yellow	£140	55·00

ARMY

Overprinted **ARMY OFFICIAL**.

1896. Stamps of Queen Victoria.

No.	Type	Description	Unused	Used
O41	71	½d. red	2·50	1·50
O42		½d. green	2·50	4·50
O43	57	1d. lilac	2·50	1·50
O44	74	2½d. purple on blue	6·00	3·50
O45	79	6d. purple on red	18·00	20·00

1902. Stamps of King Edward VII.

No.	Type	Description	Unused	Used
O48	83	½d. turquoise	3·00	1·50
O49		1d. red	3·00	1·50
O50		6d. purple	80·00	35·00

BOARD OF EDUCATION

Overprinted **BOARD OF EDUCATION**.

1902. Stamps of Queen Victoria.

No.	Type	Description	Unused	Used
O81	78	5d. purple on blue	£600	£140
O82	82	1s. green and red	£1100	£450

1902. Stamps of King Edward VII.

No.	Type	Description	Unused	Used
O83	83	½d. turquoise	35·00	10·00
O84		1d. red	35·00	9·00
O85		2½d. blue	£600	70·00
O86	–	5d. purple and blue	£2400	£1100
O87	–	1s. green and red	£40000	£30000

GOVERNMENT PARCELS

Overprinted **GOVT. PARCELS**.

1883. Stamps of Queen Victoria.

No.	Type	Description	Unused	Used
O61	62	1½d. purple	£125	30·00
O62	–	6d. green (No. 194)	£825	£300
O63	–	9d. green (No. 195)	£675	£190
O64	25	1s. brown (No. 163)	£450	80·00

1887. Stamps of Queen Victoria.

No.	Type	Description	Unused	Used
O69	57	1d. lilac	30·00	9·00
O65	72	1½d. purple and green	25·00	3·00
O70	73	2d. green and red	50·00	8·00
O71	77	4½d. green and red	£125	80·00
O66	79	6d. purple on red	60·00	12·00
O67	80	9d. purple and blue	70·00	16·00
O68	82	1s. green	£150	80·00
O72		1s. green and red	£175	55·00

1902. Stamps of King Edward VII.

No.	Type	Description	Unused	Used
O74	83	1d. red	17·00	6·00
O75	–	2d. green and red	70·00	18·00
O76	83	6d. purple	£100	18·00
O77	–	9d. purple and blue	£240	60·00
O78	–	1s. green and red	£375	90·00

INLAND REVENUE

Overprinted **I.R. OFFICIAL**.

1882. Stamps of Queen Victoria.

No.	Type	Description	Unused	Used
O 1	52	½d. green	20·00	2·00
O 5		½d. blue	35·00	22·00
O 3	57	1d. lilac	3·00	2·00
O 6	–	2½d. purple (No.3 190)	£150	55·00
O 4	34	6d. grey (No. 161)	95·00	30·00
O 7	–	1s. green (No. 196)	£2750	£575
O 9	–	5s. red (No. 181)	£1600	£475
O10	–	10s. blue (No. 183)	£3000	£650
O11	61	£1 brown	£22000	

1888.

No.	Type	Description	Unused	Used
O13	71	½d. red	2·50	1·50
O17		½d. green	6·00	4·50
O14	74	2½d. purple on blue	70·00	6·00
O18	79	6d. purple on red	£175	40·00
O15	89	1s. green	£240	40·00
O19		1s. green and red	£850	£250
O16	61	£1 green	£4000	£600

1902. Stamps of King Edward VII.

No.	Type	Description	Unused	Used
O20	83	½d. turquoise	22·00	3·00
O21		1d. red	15·00	2·00
O22		2½d. blue	£475	£100
O23		6d. purple	£90000	£70000
O24	–	1s. green and red	£650	£150
O25	–	5s. red	£4750	£2000
O26	–	10s. blue	£17000	£10000
O27	–	£1 green	£14000	£8000

OFFICE OF WORKS

Overprinted **O.W. OFFICIAL**.

1896. Stamps of Queen Victoria.

No.	Type	Description	Unused	Used
O31	71	½d. red	£110	60·00
O32		½d. green	£190	95·00
O33	57	1d. lilac	£190	60·00
O34	78	5d. purple and blue	£900	£210
O35	81	10d. purple and red	£1500	£300

1902. Stamps of King Edward VII.

No.	Type	Description	Unused	Used
O36	83	½d. turquoise	£425	£110
O37	–	1d red	£425	£110
O38	–	2d. green and red	£750	£110
O39	83	2½d. blue	£850	£300
O40	–	10d. purple and red	£5500	£2000

ROYAL HOUSEHOLD

Overprinted **R.H. OFFICIAL**.

1902. Stamps of King Edward VII.

No.	Type	Description	Unused	Used
O91	83	½d. turquoise	£175	£110
O92		1d. red	£150	£100

POSTAGE DUE STAMPS

D 1 D 4

1914.

No.	Type	Description	Unused	Used
D 1	D 1	½d. green	50	50
D56		½d. orange	20	1·25
D 2		1d. red	50	50
D57		1d. blue	20	75
D 3		1½d. brown	48·00	15·00
D58		1½d. green	1·25	3·50
D69		2d. black	25	75
D60		3d. violet	40	50
D15		4d. green	15·00	3·00
D61		4d. blue	40	30
D62		5d. brown	60	1·00
D63		6d. purple	60	30
D76		8d. red	1·25	1·25
D17		1s. blue	10·00	1·60
D64		1s. brown	1·40	30
D65		2s. 6d. purple on yellow	5·00	45
D66		5s. red on yellow	9·00	1·00
D67		10s. blue on yellow	11·00	6·00
D68		£1 black on yellow	45·00	8·50

On the 2s. 6d. to £1 the inscription reads "TO PAY".

1970. Decimal Currency.

No.	Type	Description	Unused	Used
D77	–	½p. blue	30	30
D78	–	1p. purple	30	30
D79	–	2p. green	30	30
D80	–	3p. blue	30	30
D81	–	4p. brown	30	30
D82	–	5p. violet	30	30
D83	–	7p. brown	35	60
D84	D 4	10p. red	30	60
D85		11p. green	60	75
D86		20p. brown	60	60
D87		50p. blue	1·50	75
D88		£1 black	3·50	1·00
D89		£5 yellow and black	38·00	3·00

DESIGN: ½p. to 7p. similar to Type D 4, but with "TO PAY" reading vertically upwards at the left.

D 5

D 7

1982.

No.	Type	Description	Unused	Used
D 90	D 5	1p. red	15	25
D 91		2p. blue	25	25
D 92		3p. mauve	15	30
D 93		4p. blue	15	30
D 94		5p. brown	25	30
D 95	–	10p. brown	30	40
D 96	–	20p. green	50	40
D 97	–	25p. blue	75	90
D 98	–	50p. black	1·50	1·00
D 99	–	£1 red	3·00	1·00
D100	–	£2 blue	6·00	75
D101	–	£5 orange	14·00	1·00

DESIGNS: 10p. to £5, as Type D 5 but with "TO PAY" horizontal.

1994.

No.	Type	Description	Unused	Used
D102	D 7	1p. red, yellow & blk	10	20
D103		2p. mauve, pur & blk	10	20
D104		5p. yellow, brn & blk	15	20
D105		10p. yellow, grn & blk	30	40
D106		20p. green, vio & blk	50	60
D107		25p. mauve, red & blk	60	70
D108		£1 violet, mve & blk	2·25	2·50
D109		£1.20 blue, grn & blk	2·75	3·00
D110		£5 dp grn, grn & blk	12·00	12·00

GREAT COMORO Pt. 6

A French island north west of Madagascar. From 1914 to 1950 the stamps of Madagascar were used. In 1950 it became part of the Comoro Islands.

100 centimes = 1 franc.

1897. "Tablet" key-type inscr "GRANDE COMORE" in red or blue.

1	D	1 c. black on blue	35	60
2		2 c. brown on buff	45	65
3		4 c. brown on grey	95	90
4		5 c. green on light green	1·25	1·25
5		10 c. black on lilac	2·50	3·00
14		10 c. red	5·50	6·00
6		15 c. blue	7·50	4·00
15		15 c. grey	5·50	5·50
7		20 c. red on green	4·50	6·50
8		25 c. black on pink	4·00	3·50
16		25 c. blue	9·50	5·50
9		30 c. brown on drab	9·00	8·25
17		35 c. black on yellow	9·50	8·00
10		40 c. red on yellow	8·00	7·50
18		45 c. black on green	50·00	40·00
11		50 c. red on pink	19·00	10·00
19		50 c. brown on blue	23·00	20·00
12		75 c. brown on blue	35·00	20·00
13		1 f. green	18·00	15·00

1912. Surch.

20	D	05 on 2 c. brown on buff	20	55
21		05 on 4 c. brown on grey	40	40
22		05 on 15 c. blue	50	50
23		05 on 20 c. red on green	30	70
24		05 on 25 c. black on pink	30	50
25		05 on 30 c. brn on drab	40	40
26		10 on 40 c. red on yellow	40	75
27		10 on 45 c. black on grn	30	55
28		10 on 50 c. red on pink	40	40
29		10 on 75 c. brn on orge	45	80

GREECE Pt. 3

A country in the S.E. of Europe, under Turkish rule till 1830, when it became a kingdom. A republic was established from 1924 to 1935 when the monarchy was restored. The country was under German occupation from April, 1941 to Oct. 1944.

The monarchy was once again abolished during 1973 and a republic set up.

100 lepta = 1 drachma.

1 Hermes 2

1861. Imperf or perf.

62	1	1 l. brown	4·00	4·00
17		2 l. buff	5·00	10·00
55		5 l. green	13·00	1·25
19		10 l. orange on blue	£200	18·00
56		10 l. orange	14·00	1·25
20		20 l. blue	£150	5·00
59a		20 l. red	2·00	1·25
53		30 l. brown	30·00	2·00
60		30 l. blue	£100	6·00
28		40 l. mauve on blue	£200	15·00
37		40 l. orange on green	£400	40·00
43d		40 l. bistre on blue	15·00	22·00
43f		40 l. green on blue	32·00	30·00
50		40 l. buff	15·00	30·00
61		40 l. mauve	35·00	6·00
52		60 l. green	20·00	50·00
22		80 l. red	40·00	9·00

1886. Imperf.

73	2	1 l. brown	1·00	50
86		2 l. buff	1·25	1·25
87b		5 l. green	1·00	50
88		10 l. orange	6·00	50
89c		20 l. red	3·25	25
90d		25 l. blue	25·00	75
91		25 l. purple	3·00	1·50
79		40 l. purple	35·00	12·00
93		40 l. blue	5·00	1·25
80		50 l. green	3·50	80
81		1 d. grey	35·00	1·00

1886. Perf.

100	2	1 l. brown	1·75	1·00
96		2 l. buff	1·25	1·00
102		5 l. green	3·00	75
103		10 l. orange	14·00	75
104		20 l. red	1·75	75
105		25 l. blue	40·00	1·75
106a		25 l. purple	5·00	1·00
107		40 l. purple	50·00	25·00
108		40 l. blue	10·00	1·75
83		50 l. green	10·00	4·50
84		1 d. grey	70·00	4·50

3 Wrestlers

4 Discus thrower

5 Vase depicting Pallas Athene

6 Quadriga of Chariot driving

1896. First Int. Olympic Games. Perf.

110	3	1 l. yellow	50	35
111		2 l. red	50	35
112	4	5 l. mauve	1·25	50
113		10 l. grey	1·75	60
114	5	20 l. brown	8·00	30
115	6	25 l. red	18·00	1·00
116	5	40 l. violet	5·00	3·25
117	6	60 l. black	14·00	9·50
118	–	1 d. blue	40·00	10·00
119	–	2 d. olive	£120	30·00
120	–	5 d. green	£200	£150
121	–	10 d. brown	£250	£180

DESIGNS—As Type 6—HORIZ: 1 d. Acropolis and Stadium; 10 d. Acropolis with Parthenon. VERT: 2 d. "Hermes" (after statue by Praxiteles); 5 d. "Victory" (after statue by Paeonius).

1900. Surch Imperf.

122	2	20 l. on 25 l. blue	1·25	75
130	1	30 l. on 40 l. purple	2·25	1·75
131		40 l. on 2 l. buff	3·00	2·25
132		50 l. on 40 l. buff	4·25	3·25
123	2	1 d. on 40 l. purple	8·00	5·00
124		2 d. on 40 l. purple	£150	
133	1	3 d. on 10 l. orange	30·00	20·00
134		5 d. on 40 l. purple on blue	70·00	70·00

1900. Surch Perf.

125	2	20 l. on 25 l. blue	1·25	1·25
135	1	30 l. on 40 l. purple	3·00	2·75
136		40 l. on 2 l. buff	4·00	4·00
137		50 l. on 40 l. buff	5·00	5·00
126	2	1 d. on 40 l. purple	9·00	7·50
127a		2 d. on 40 l. purple	6·00	6·00
138	1	3 d. on 10 l. orange	40·00	30·00
139		5 d. on 40 l. pur on blue	80·00	80·00

1900. Surch **AM** and value.

140	2	25 l. on 40 l. pur (No. 79)	2·75	2·75
142		25 l. on 40 l. pur (No. 107)	6·50	6·50
141		50 l. on 25 l. blue (No. 90d)	18·00	14·00
143		50 l. on 25 l. blue (No. 105)	28·00	25·00
144	1	1 d. on 40 l. brown on blue (No. 43d)	75·00	70·00
146		1 d. on 40 l. brown on blue (Perf.)	90·00	80·00
145	2	2 d. on 5 l. green (No. 55)	10·00	10·00
147		2 d. on 5 l. green (No. 102)	10·00	10·00

1900. Olympic Games stamps surch **AM** and value.

148	–	5 l. on 1 d. blue	5·00	5·00
149	5	25 l. on 40 l. violet	55·00	45·00
150	–	50 l. on 2 d. olive	40·00	35·00
151	–	1 d. on 5 d. green	£200	£125
152	–	2 d. on 10 d. brown	35·00	28·00

15

16 Hermes after the "Mercury" of Giovanni da Bologna

17

1901.

167	15	1 l. brown	25	25
168		2 l. grey	25	25
169		3 l. orange	35	25
170	16	5 l. green	25	25
171		10 l. red	75	25
172	15	20 l. mauve	1·00	25
173	16	25 l. blue	1·00	25
160	15	30 l. purple	8·50	1·00
175		40 l. brown	1·50	1·10
176		50 l. lake	10·00	75
163	17	1 d. black	25·00	1·00
164		2 d. bronze	7·00	5·00
165		3 d. silver	7·00	7·00
166		5 d. gold	7·00	6·00

19 Head of Hermes

20 Athlete throwing Discus

21 Jumper

23 Atlas offering the Apples of Hesperides to Hercules

1902.

178	19	5 l. orange	1·50	75
179		25 l. green	20·00	1·75
180		50 l. blue	20·00	2·50
181		1 d. red	20·00	7·50
182		2 d. brown	35·00	25·00

1906. Olympic Games. Dated "1906".

183	20	1 l. brown	50	30
184		2 l. black	50	30
185	21	3 l. orange	50	30
186		5 l. green	75	30
187	–	10 l. red	1·50	30
188	23	20 l. red	4·00	30
189	–	25 l. blue	6·00	35
190	–	30 l. purple	3·00	2·50
191	–	40 l. brown	3·00	2·50
192	23	50 l. purple	9·00	2·75
193	–	1 d. black	45·00	8·00
194	–	2 d. red	65·00	23·00
195	–	3 d. yellow	85·00	65·00
196	–	5 d. blue	85·00	65·00

DESIGNS—As Type **20**: 10 l. Victory; 20 l. Wrestlers; 40 l. "Daemon" or God of the Games. As Type **23**: 25 l. Hercules and Antaeus; 1 d., 2 d., 3 d. Race, Ancient Greeks; 5 d. Olympic Offerings.

29 Head of Hermes 30 Iris 31 Hermes

32 Hermes and Arcas

ΕΛΛΗΝΙΚΗ ΔΙΟΙΚΗΣΙΣ

(34) "Greek Administration"

1911. Roul.

213	29	1 l. green	15	10
214	30	2 l. red	15	10
215	29	3 l. red	15	10
216	31	5 l. green	15	10
217	29	10 l. red	15	10
218	30	15 l. blue	25	20
219		20 l. lilac	25	25
220		25 l. blue	2·00	50
221	31	30 l. red	50	25
222	30	40 l. blue	1·25	50
223	31	50 l. purple	2·00	10
224		80 l. purple	3·00	1·00
225	32	1 d. blue	4·00	25
226		2 d. red	4·00	50
227		3 d. red (20 × $26\frac{1}{2}$ mm)	6·50	50
209	–	3 d. red ($20\frac{1}{4}$ × $25\frac{1}{2}$ mm)	16·00	75
228	–	5 d. blue (20 × $26\frac{1}{2}$ mm)	8·00	50
210	–	5 d. blue ($20\frac{1}{4}$ × $25\frac{1}{2}$ mm)	28·00	3·00
229	–	10 b. blue (20 × $26\frac{1}{2}$ mm)	6·50	75
211b	–	10 d. blue ($20\frac{1}{4}$ × $25\frac{1}{2}$ mm)	30·00	20·00
212	–	25 d. blue	35·00	35·00
230	–	25 d. slate	6·50	1·75

The 25 d. is as Type **29** but larger (24 × 31 mm).

1912. Optd with T **34**.

232A	29	1 l. green	50	50
233	30	2 l. red	50	50
234	29	3 l. red	50	50
249B	31	5 l. green	60	25
236A	29	10 l. red	1·00	1·00
237A	30	20 l. lilac	1·25	1·25
231	15	20 l. mauve	2·00	2·00
251A	30	25 l. blue	1·60	80
239A	31	30 l. red	1·75	1·75
240B	30	40 l. blue	2·00	2·00
241A	31	50 l. purple	3·25	2·75
242A	32	1 d. blue	5·00	3·00
243A		2 d. red	32·00	25·00
244B		3 d. red	18·00	18·00
245A		5 d. blue	13·00	13·00
246B		10 d. blue	25·00	30·00
247d	–	25 d. blue (No. 212)	35·00	50·00

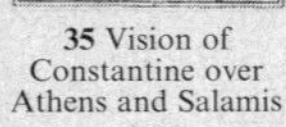

35 Vision of Constantine over Athens and Salamis

36 Victorious Eagle over Mt. Olympus

1913. Occupation of Macedonia, Epirus and the Aegean Is. Rouletted.

252	35	1 l. brown	25	25
253	36	2 l. red	25	25
254		3 l. orange	25	30
255	35	5 l. green	95	25
256		10 l. red	3·50	25
257		20 l. violet	11·50	2·00
258	36	25 l. blue	1·75	50
259	35	30 l. green	40·00	1·50
260	36	40 l. blue	7·00	3·00
261	35	50 l. blue	2·50	1·75
262	36	1 d. purple	4·00	1·75
263	35	2 d. brown	35·00	5·00
264	36	3 d. blue	90·00	14·00
265	35	5 d. grey	80·00	20·00
266	36	10 d. red	80·00	£125
267	35	25 d. black	80·00	£125

37 Hoisting the Greek Flag at Suda Bay, 1 May 1913

(38)

1913. Union of Crete with Greece.

268	37	25 l. black and blue	4·00	2·50

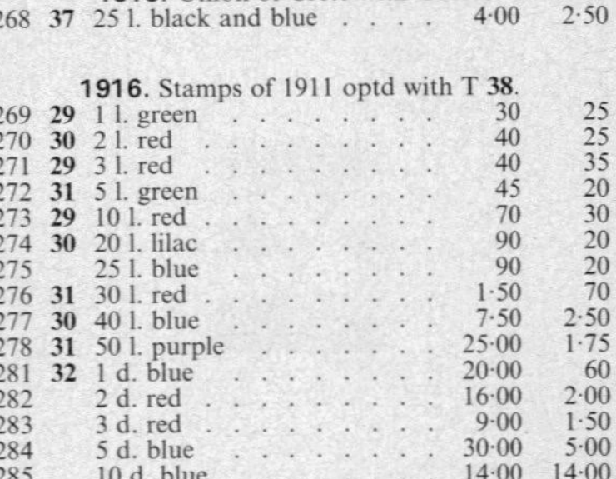

1916. Stamps of 1911 optd with T **38**.

269	29	1 l. green	30	25
270	30	2 l. red	40	25
271	29	3 l. red	40	35
272	31	5 l. green	45	20
273	29	10 l. red	70	30
274	30	20 l. lilac	90	20
275		25 l. blue	90	20
276	31	30 l. red	1·50	70
277	30	40 l. blue	7·50	2·50
278	31	50 l. purple	25·00	1·75
281	32	1 d. blue	20·00	60
282		2 d. red	16·00	2·00
283		3 d. red	9·00	1·50
284		5 d. blue	30·00	5·00
285		10 d. blue	14·00	14·00

39 Iris

ΕΠΑΝΑΣΤΑΣΙΣ
1922
ΛΕΠΤΑ 10

(46) "Revolution, 1922"

1917. Perf or imperf.

286	39	1 l. green	35	25
287		5 l. green	35	25
288		10 l. red	50	25
289		25 l. blue	70	35
290		50 l. purple	5·50	1·75
291		1 d. blue	1·25	50
292		2 d. red	2·75	1·10
293		3 d. red	10·00	4·50
294		5 d. blue	4·00	2·50
295		10 d. blue	40·00	13·00
296		25 d. grey	60·00	60·00

1923. Revolution of 1922. Stamps of 1913, surch as T **46**.

340	36	5 l. on 3 l. orange	15	25
341	35	10 l. on 20 l. violet	1·25	1·50
342	36	10 l. on 25 l. blue	25	30
343	35	10 l. on 30 l. green	25	30
344	36	10 l. on 40 l. blue	1·00	1·25
345	35	50 l. on 50 l. blue	30	40
346		2 d. on 2 d. brown	30·00	45·00
347	36	3 d. on 3 d. blue	2·50	3·00
348	35	5 d. on 5 d. grey	2·50	3·00
349	36	10 d. on 1 d. purple	7·50	10·00
350		10 d. on 10 d. red	£550	

1923. Stamps of 1916 surch as T **46**.

351	39	5 l. on 10 l. red	10	25
352		50 l. on 50 l. purple	15	25
353		1 d. on 1 d. blue	15	25
354		2 d. on 2 d. red	25	25
355		3 d. on 3 d. red	1·00	1·75
356		5 d. on 5 d. blue	1·25	1·50
357		25 d. on 25 d. blue	20·00	23·00

1923. Cretan stamps of 1900 surch as T **46**.

358	1	5 l. on 1 l. brown	25·00	
359	3	10 l. on 10 l. red	25	20
361		10 l. on 25 l. blue	25	25
362	1	50 l. on 50 l. lilac	30	25
363		50 l. on 50 l. blue	4·50	5·00
364	4	50 l. on 1 d. violet	1·50	1·50
365	–	50 l. on 5 d. (No. 19)	25·00	

1923. Cretan stamps of 1905 surch as T **46**.

366	–	10 l. on 20 l. (No. 24)	75·00	75·00
367	–	10 l. on 25 l. (No. 25)	40	40
368	–	50 l. on 50 l. (No. 26)	50	60
369	16	50 l. on 1 d. (No. 27)	1·25	1·50
370	–	3 d. on 3 d. (No. 28)	8·00	10·00
371	–	5 d. on 5 d. (No. 29)	4·00	6·00

1923. Cretan stamps of 1907/8 surch as T **46**.

372	21	10 l. on 10 l. red	30	25
373	19	10 l. on 25 l. blk & blue	1·25	1·50
374		50 l. on 1 d. (No. 31)	3·00	3·50

No. 372 is as Crete No. 36 but without "HELLAS" optd. No. 377 is the optd stamp.

1923. Optd stamps of Crete surch as T **46**.

375	**1**	5 l. on 1 l. brn (No. 32)	25	25
376	–	5 l. on 5 l. grn (No. 34)	25	25
377	**21**	10 l. on 10 l. red (No. 36)	25	25
378	–	10 l. on 20 l. (No. 37)	25	25
379	–	10 l. on 25 l. (No. 30)	30	30
381	–	50 l. on 50 l. (No. 39)	40	30
382	**16**	50 l. on 1 d. (No. 40)	3·00	3·50
384	–	3 d. on 3 d. (No. 42)	7·00	9·00
385	–	5 d. on 5 d. (No. 43)	£100	£125

1923. Postage Due stamps of Crete of 1900 surch as T **38**.

386	D **8**	5 l. on 5 l. red	15	25
387		5 l. on 10 l. red	15	25
388		10 l. on 20 l. red	8·00	10·00
389		10 l. on 40 l. red	25	30
390		50 l. on 50 l. red	25	20
391		50 l. on 1 d. red	65	80
392		50 l. on 1 d. on 1 d. red	6·00	8·00
393		2 d. on 2 d. red	75	85

1923. Postage Due stamps of Crete of 1908 with opt. surch as T **46**.

397	D **8**	5 l. on 5 l. red	25	40
398		5 l. on 10 l. red	25	25
399		10 l. on 20 l. red	25	20
400		50 l. on 50 l. red	50	50
401		50 l. on 1 d. red	1·25	1·50
402		2 d. on 2 d red	4·00	6·00

47 Lord Byron

49 Grave of Marco Botzaris

1924. Byron Centenary.

403	**47**	80 l. blue	40	15
404	–	2 d. black and violet	1·00	50

DESIGN—HORIZ: (45 × 30 mm): 2 d. Byron at Missolonghi.

1926. Cent. of Fall of Missolonghi. Roul.

405	**49**	25 l. mauve	85	35

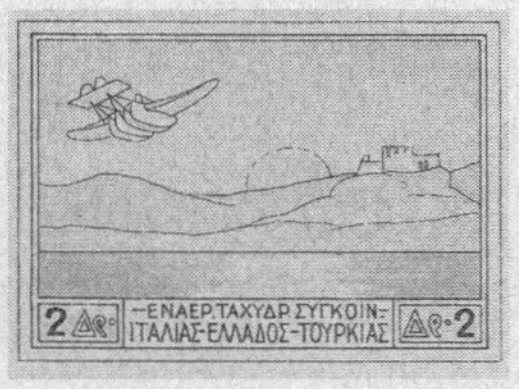

50 Savoia Marchetti S-55C Flying Boat

1926. Air. Each showing Savoia Marchetti S-55C flying boat. Multicoloured.

406	2 d. Type **50**	90	90
407	3 d. Acropolis	11·00	7·50
408	5 d. Map of Greece and Mediterranean	95	1·00
409	10 d. Colonnade	11·50	7·50

51 Corinth Canal

52 Dodecanese Costume

53 Temple of Theseus, Athens

54 Acropolis

1927.

410	**51**	5 l. green	45	10
411	**52**	10 l. red	35	10
412	–	20 l. violet	35	10
413	–	25 l. green	45	10
414	–	40 l. green	50	10
415	**51**	50 l. violet	2·00	10
416		80 l. black and blue	1·40	30
417	**53**	1 d. brown and blue	90	10
418b	–	2 d. black and green	3·25	25
419d	–	3 d. black and violet	3·00	25
419e	–	4 d. brown	13·00	1·25
420	–	5 d. black and orange	10·00	70
421	–	10 d. black and red	30·00	3·00
422	–	15 d. black and green	40·00	10·00
423a	**54**	25 d. black and green	23·00	13·00

DESIGNS—As Type **52**: 20 l. Macedonian costume; 25 l. Monastery of Simon Peter, Athos; 40 l. White Tower, Salonika. As Type **53**: 2 d. Acropolis; 3 d. Cruiser "Averoff"; 4 d. Mistra Cathedral. As Type **54**: 5, 15 d. The Academy of Sciences, Athens; 10 d. Temple of Theseus.

55 General Favier and Acropolis

1927. Centenary of Liberation of Athens.

424	**55**	1 d. red	30	20
425		3 d. blue	1·25	40
426		6 d. green	8·00	7·50

56 Navarino Bay and Pylos

58 Sir Edward Codrington

1927. Centenary of Battle of Navarino.

427	**56**	1 d. 50 green	75	25
428	–	4 d. blue	8·00	1·00
429	**58**	5 d. black & brown (A)	4·00	3·75
430	–	5 d. black & brown (B)	20·00	6·00
431	–	5 d. black and blue	20·00	6·50
432	–	5 d. black and red	11·00	6·75

DESIGNS: 4 d. Battle of Navarino; 5 d. (No. 429) "Sir Codrington" (A); 5 d. (No. 430) "Sir Edward Codrington" (B); 5 d. (No. 431) De Rigny; 5 d. (No. 432) Van der Heyden.

59 Righas Ferreo

64 Monastery of Arkadi, Crete, and Abbott Gabriel

1930. Independence Cent.

433	**59**	10 l. brown	15	10
434	–	20 l. black	15	10
435	–	40 l. green	25	15
436	–	50 l. red	25	15
437	–	50 l. blue	25	15
438	–	1 d. red	25	10
439	–	1 d. orange	25	15
440	–	1 d. 50 blue	35	10
441	–	1 d. 50 red	35	10
442	–	2 d. orange	50	15
443	–	3 d. brown	70	30
444	–	4 d. blue	3·00	50
445	–	5 d. purple	1·25	80
446	–	10 d. black	6·00	3·50
447	–	15 d. green	9·00	7·50
448	–	20 d. blue	11·00	9·00
449	–	25 d. black	9·00	10·00
450	–	50 d. brown	20·00	30·00

DESIGNS as Type **59**: 20 l. Patriarch Gregory V; 40 l. A. Ypsilanti; 50 l. (No. 436) L. Bouboulina; 50 l. (437), Ath. Diakos; 1 d. (438), Th. Colocotroni; 1 d. (439), C. Kanaris; 1 d. 50, (440), Karaiskakes; 1 d. 50 (441), M. Botzaris; 2 d. A. Miaoulis; 3 d. L. Kondouriotis; 5 d. Capo d'Istria; 10 d. P. Mavromichalis; 15 d. Solomos; 20 d. Corais. ($27\frac{1}{2}$ × 40 mm): 4 d. Map of Greece. (27 × 44 mm): 50 d. Sortie from Missolonghi. (43 × $28\frac{1}{2}$ mm): 25 d. Declaration of Independence.

1930.

451	**64**	8 d. violet	12·00	9·00

1932. Stamps of 1927 surch.

452	–	1 d. 50 l. on 5 d. black and blue (No. 431)	1·50	25
453	–	1 d. 50 l. on 5 d. black and red (No. 432)	1·50	25
454	**55**	2 d. on 3 d. blue	1·50	35
455	**58**	2 d. on 5 d. black and brown (No. 429)	1·75	25
456	–	2 d. on 5 d. black and brown (No. 430)	6·00	25
457	**55**	4 d. on 6 d. green	1·50	60

66 "Graf Zeppelin" and Acropolis

1933. Air.

458	**66**	30 d. red	18·00	7·50
459		100 d. blue	90·00	40·00
460		120 d. brown	90·00	40·00

67 Swinging the Propeller

68 "Flight"

1933. Air. Aeroespresso Company issue.

461	**67**	50 l. orange and green	30	50
462	–	1 d. orange and blue	35	50
463	–	3 d. brown and purple	1·00	75
464	**68**	5 d. blue and orange	6·00	6·00
465	–	10 d. black and red	1·75	1·40
466	–	20 d. green and black	10·00	12·00
467	–	50 d. blue and brown	70·00	45·00

DESIGNS—HORIZ: 1 d. Temple of Neptune, Corinth; 3 d. Marina Fiat MF.5 flying boat over Hermoupolis; 10 d. Map of Italy–Greece–Rhodes–Turkey air routes. VERT: 20 d. Hermes and Marina Fiat MF.5 flying boat; 50 d. Woman and Marina Fiat MF.5 flying boat.

71 Greece

1933. Air. Government issue.

468	**71**	50 l. green	55	25
469		1 d. red	1·10	80
470	–	2 d. violet	1·90	1·25
471	–	5 d. blue	9·00	5·25
472	–	10 d. red	16·00	7·75
473	**71**	25 d. blue	45·00	13·50
474	–	50 d. brown	50·00	38·00

DESIGNS—VERT: 2, 10 d. Ikarian Islands. HORIZ: 5, 50 d. Junkers G.24 airplane and Acropolis.

74 Admiral Kondouriotis and Cruiser "Averoff"

75 "Greece"

1933.

475	**74**	50 d. blue and black	60·00	2·00
476	**75**	75 d. purple and black	75·00	£125
477	–	100 d. green and brown	£325	18·00

DESIGN—VERT: 100 d. Statue (Youth of Marathon).

78 Athens Stadium, Entrance

1934.

479	**78**	8 d. blue	48·00	1·25

79 Sun Chariot

83 King Constantine

1935. Air. Mythological designs.

438a	**79**	1 d. red	15	25
488b	–	2 d. blue	15	25
488c	–	5 d. mauve	15	25
488d	–	7 d. blue	15	25
484	–	10 d. brown	1·75	2·50
488e	–	10 d. orange	2·25	4·50
485	–	25 d. red	2·25	3·50
486	–	30 d. green	90	1·50
487	–	50 d. mauve	2·75	4·25
488	–	100 d. brown	1·00	1·25

DESIGNS—HORIZ: 2 d. Iris; 30 d. Triptolemus; 100 d. Phrixus and Helle. VERT: 5 d. Daedalus and Icarus; 7 d. Minerva; 10 d. Hermes; 25 d. Zeus and Ganymede; 50 d. Bellerophon on Pegasus.

(**81**)

(**82**)

1935. Restoration of Greek Monarchy. Surch with T **81** (489/91) or **82** (492/3).

489	D **20**	50 l. on 40 l. blue	30	15
490		3 d. on 3 d. red	65	1·00
492	–	5 d. on 100 d. green & brown (No. 477)	1·25	1·25
493	**75**	15 d. on 75 d. pur & blk	5·00	4·50

1936. Re-interment of King Constantine and Queen Sophia.

494	**83**	3 d. brown and black	40	25
495		8 d. blue and black	75	1·25

85 Pallas Athene (Minerva)

86 Bull-leaping

89 King George II

89a Statue of King Constantine

1937. Cent of Athens University.

496	**85**	3 d. brown	40	40

1937.

497	**86**	5 l. blue and brown	10	10
498	–	10 l. brown and blue	10	10
499	–	20 l. green and black	10	10
500	–	40 l. black and green	10	10
501	–	50 l. black and brown	10	10
502	–	80 l. brown and violet	10	10
503	**89**	1 d. green	20	10
515	**89a**	1 d. 50 green	25	10
504	–	2 d. blue	10	10
505	**89**	3 d. brown	30	25
506	–	5 d. red	10	10
507	–	6 d. olive	10	10
508	–	7 d. brown	30	30
509	**89**	8 d. blue	75	50
510	–	10 d. brown	10	10
511	–	15 d. green	10	10
512	–	25 d. blue	10	10
516	**89a**	30 d. red	1·50	2·75
513	**89**	100 d. red	8·00	9·00

DESIGNS—(Size as Type **89a**). VERT: 10 l. Court Lady of Tiryns; 20 l. Zeus and Thunderbolt; 80 l. Venus of Milo; 25 d. "Glory" of Psara. HORIZ: 40 l. Amphictyonic Coin; 50 l. Chairing Diagoras of Rhodes; 2 d. Battle of Salamis; 5 d. Panathenaic chariot; 6 d. Alexander the Great at Battle of Issus; 7 d. St. Paul on Mt. Areopagus; 10 d. Temple of St. Demetrius, Salonica; 15 d. Leo III (the Isaurian) destroying Saracens.

93 Prince Paul and Princess Frederika Louise

1938. Royal Wedding.

517	**93**	1 d. green	25	15
518		3 d. brown	65	15
519		8 d. blue	1·00	1·00

94 Arms of Greece, Rumania, Turkey and Yugoslavia

1938. Balkan Entente.

520	**94**	6 d. blue	4·00	1·75

1938. Air. Postage Due stamp optd with Junkers G.24 airplane. Perf or rouletted.

521	D **20**	50 l. brown	15	15

96 Arms of Ionian Islands

97 Corfu Bay and Citadel

1939. 75th Anniv of Cession of Ionian Islands.

No.	Type	Description	Unused	Used
523	96	1 d. blue	1·25	50
524	97	4 d. green	2·50	1·25
525	–	20 d. orange	12·00	13·00
526	–	20 d. blue	12·00	13·00
527	–	20 d. red	12·00	13·00

DESIGN—HORIZ: 20 d. As Type **1** of Ionian Is. but with portraits of George I of Greece and Queen Victoria.

99 Javelin Thrower

100 Arms of Greece, Rumania, Turkey and Yugoslavia

1939. 10th Pan-Balkan Games, Athens.

No.	Type	Description	Unused	Used
528	–	50 l. green	20	15
529	99	3 d. red	50	15
530	–	6 d. brown on orange	2·25	1·50
531	–	8 d. blue on grey	2·25	2·00

DESIGNS: 50 l. Runner; 6 d. Discus-thrower; 8 d. Jumper.

1940. Balkan Entente.

No.	Type	Description	Unused	Used
532	100	6 d. blue	4·50	1·50
533		8 d. slate	4·50	2·00

101 Greek Youth Badge

103 Meteora Monasteries

1940. 4th Anniv of Greek Youth Organization.

(a) Postage.

No.	Type	Description	Unused	Used
534	101	3 d. blue, red and silver	1·00	1·00
535	–	5 d. black and blue	2·00	2·00
536	–	10 d. black and orange	3·00	3·00
537	–	15 d. black and green	30·00	30·00
538	–	20 d. black and red	25·00	25·00
539	–	25 d. black and blue	25·00	25·00
540	–	30 d. black and purple	25·00	25·00
541	–	50 d. black and red	32·00	32·00
542	–	75 d. gold, brown & blue	32·00	32·00
543	101	100 d. blue, red & silver	35·00	32·00

DESIGNS—VERT: 5 d. Boy member; 10 d. Girl member; 15 d. Javelin thrower; 20 d. Youths in column formation; 25 d. Standard bearer and buglers; 30 d. Three youths in uniform; 50 d. Youths on parade; 75 d. Coat of arms.

(b) Air.

No.	Type	Description	Unused	Used
544	103	2 d. black and orange	1·00	1·00
545	–	4 d. black and green	2·40	2·00
546	–	6 d. black and red	4·75	3·25
547	–	8 d. black and blue	8·00	7·00
548	–	16 d. black and violet	20·00	14·00
549	–	32 d. black and orange	40·00	35·00
550	–	45 d. black and green	40·00	35·00
551	–	55 d. black and red	45·00	35·00
552	–	65 d. black and blue	40·00	35·00
553	–	100 d. black and violet	48·00	35·00

DESIGNS (views and aircraft): 4 d. Simon Peter Monastery, Mt. Athos; 6, 16 d. Isle of Santorin; 8 d. Church at Pantanassa; 32 d. Ponticonissi, Corfu; 45 d. Acropolis; 55 d. Erechtheum; 65 d. Temple of Nike; 100 d. Temple of Zeus.

1941. Postage Due stamps optd with Junkers G.24 airplane, No. 556 also surch. Perf (558/60), perf or rouletted (556/7).

No.	Type	Description	Unused	Used
556	D 20	1 d. on 2 d. red	10	10
557		5 d. blue	20	20
558		10 d. green	35	35
559		25 d. red	65	70
560		50 d. orange	50	75

105 "Boreas" (North Wind)

1942. Air. Winds. (Symbolic designs).

No.	Type	Description	Unused	Used
561	105	2 d. emerald and green	15	15
562	–	5 d. orange and red	10	15
563	–	10 d. red and brown	10	20
567	–	10 d. red and orange	10	10
564	–	20 d. ultramarine & bl	20	40
565	–	25 d. orange & lt orge	10	15
568	–	25 d. green and grey	10	10
566	–	50 d. black and grey	50	75
569	–	50 d. violet and blue	10	10
570	105	100 d. black and grey	10	10
571	–	200 d. red and pink	10	10
572	–	400 d. green and blue	10	10

DESIGNS: 5 d. "Notos" (South); 10 d. "Apiliotis" (East); 20 d. "Lips" (South-west); 25 d. "Zephyr" (West); 50 d. "Kekias" (North-east); 200 d. "Evros" (South-east); 400 d. "Skiron" (North-west).

106 Windmills on Mykonos Is.

1942.

No.	Type	Description	Unused	Used
573	106	2 d. brown	10	10
574	–	5 d. green	10	10
575	–	10 d. blue	10	10
576	–	15 d. purple	10	10
577	–	25 d. orange	10	10
578	–	50 d. blue	10	10
579	–	75 d. red	10	10
580	–	100 d. black	10	10
581	–	200 d. blue	10	10
582	–	500 d. brown	10	10
583	–	1000 d. brown	10	10
584	–	2000 d. blue	10	10
585	–	5000 d. red	10	10
586	–	15,000 d. purple	10	10
587	–	25,000 d. green	15	15
588	–	500,000 d. blue	20	15
589	106	2,000,000 d. green	20	15
590	–	5,000,000 d. red	20	15

DESIGNS: 5 d., 5,000,000 d. Burzi Fortress, Nauplion; 10 d., 500,000 d. Katokhi on Aspropotamos River; 15 d. Heraklion, Crete; 25 d. Houses on Hydra Is; 50 d., Meteora Monastery; 75 d. Edessa; 100 d., 200 d. Monastery on Mt. Athos; 500 d., 5000 d. Konitza Bridge;. 1000 d., 15,000 d. Ekatontapiliani Church; 2000 d., 25,000 d. Kerkyra (Corfu) Is.

110 Child

1943. Children's Welfare Fund.

No.	Type	Description	Unused	Used
592	110	25 d. + 25 d. green	10	10
593	–	100 d. + 50 d. purple	10	10
594	–	200 d. + 100 d. brown	10	10

DESIGN: 100 d. Mother and child; 200 d. Madonna and child.

(112)

1944. Children's Convalescent Camp Fund. Surch as T **112**. (a) Postage.

No.	Type	Description	Unused	Used
595	106	50,000 d. + 450,000 d. on 2 d. brown	25	50
596	–	50,000 d. + 450,000 d. on 5 d. green (No. 574)	25	50
597	–	50,000 d. + 450,000 d. on 10 d. blue (No. 575)	25	50
598	–	50,000 d. + 450,000 d. on 15 d. purple (No. 576)	25	50
599	–	50,000 d. + 450,000 d. on 25 d. orange (No. 577)	25	50

(b) Air.

No.	Type	Description	Unused	Used
600	–	50,000 d. + 450,000 d. on 10 d. red (No. 567)	25	50
601	–	50,000 d. + 450,000 d. on 25 d. green (No. 568)	25	50
602	–	50,000 d. + 450,000 d. on 50 d. blue (No. 569)	25	50
603	106	50,000 d. + 450,000 d. on 100 d. black	25	50
604	–	50,000 d. + 450,000 d. on 200 d. claret (No. 571)	25	50

ΔΡΑΧΜΑΙ ΝΕΑΙ

(113) (Trans "New drachmas")

1944. Optd as T **113**.

No.	Type	Description	Unused	Used
605	–	50 l. black and brown (No. 501)	10	10
606	–	2 d. blue (No. 504)	10	10
607	–	5 d. red (No. 506)	10	10
608	–	6 d. olive (No. 507)	15	15

92 "Glory" of Psara

114 "OXI" = No

1945.

No.	Type	Description	Unused	Used
609	92	1 d. purple	15	10
610		3 d. red	20	10
611		5 d. blue	20	10
612		10 d. brown	20	10
613		20 d. violet	40	15
614		50 d. green	60	40
615		100 d. blue	4·50	4·50
616		200 d. green	2·00	1·10

For 25 d. in Type **92** but larger, see No. 512.

1945. Resistance to Italian Ultimatum.

No.	Type	Description	Unused	Used
617	114	20 d. orange	10	10
618		40 d. blue	10	10

115 President Roosevelt

117 E. Venizelos

1945. Roosevelt Mourning Issue. Black borders.

No.	Type	Description	Unused	Used
619	115	30 d. purple	10	10
620		60 d. grey	10	10
621		200 d. violet	10	10

(116)

1946. Surch as T **116**.

No.	Type	Description	Unused	Used
622	–	10 d. on 10 d. (No. 567)	25	15
623	–	10 d. on 2000 d. (No. 584)	25	15
624	–	20 d. on 50 d. (No. 569)	25	15
625	–	20 d. on 500 d. (No. 582)	25	15
626	–	20 d. on 1000 d. (No. 583)	25	20
627	–	30 d. on 5 d. (No. 574)	30	15
628	–	50 d. on 50 d. (No. 578)	30	15
629	–	50 d. on 25,000 d. (No. 587)	30	15
630	–	100 d. on 10 d. (No. 575)	85	20
631	106	100 d. on 2,000,000 d.	50	20
632	–	130 d. on 20 l. (No. 499)	50	20
633	–	250 d. on 20 l. (No. 499)	50	20
634	–	300 d. on 80 l. (No. 502)	50	25
635	–	450 d. on 75 d. (No. 579)	1·00	30
636	–	500 d. on 5,000,000 d. (No. 590)	1·75	30
637	–	1000 d. on 500,000 d. (No. 588)	8·00	1·50
638	–	2000 d. on 5,000 d. (No. 585)	20·00	3·50
639	–	5000 d. on 15,000 d. (No. 586)	75·00	20·00

1946. 10th Anniv of Death of Venizelos (statesman).

No.	Type	Description	Unused	Used
640	117	130 d. green	15	10
641		300 d. brown	20	20

1946. Restoration of Monarchy. Surch with value in circle and date **1-9-1946**.

No.	Type	Description	Unused	Used
642	89	50 d. on 1 d. green	30	10
643		250 d. on 3 d. brown	60	15
644		600 d. on 8 d. blue	3·00	1·00
645		3000 d. on 100 d. red	10·50	1·25

119 Women carrying Munitions, Pindos Mountains

121 Panayiotis Tsaldaris

1946. Victory. War Scenes.

No.	Type	Description	Unused	Used
646	–	50 d. green	50	10
647	–	100 d. blue	55	10
648	119	250 d. green	70	10
649	–	500 d. brown	1·00	20
650	–	600 d. brown	1·50	70
651	–	1000 d. violet	2·50	25
682	–	1000 d. green	3·00	30
652	–	2000 d. blue	12·00	2·75
653	–	5000 d. red	22·00	1·50

DESIGNS—HORIZ: 50 d. Convoy; 500 d. Infantry column; 1000 d. (No. 651) Supermarine Spitfire Mk IIB and pilot; 1000 d. (No. 682) Battle of Crete; 2000 d. Torpedo boat "Hyacinth" towing submarine "Perla". VERT: 100 d. Torpedoing of Cruiser "Helle"; 600 d. Badge, Alpine troops and map of Italy; 5000 d. War Memorial at El Alamein.

1946. 10th Death Anniv of P. Tsaldaris (statesman).

No.	Type	Description	Unused	Used
654	121	250 d. brown and pink	1·25	30
655		600 d. blue	1·40	40

1947. King George II Mourning issue. Surch with value in circle in corner and black border.

No.	Type	Description	Unused	Used
656	89	50 d. on 1 d. green	20	10
657		250 d. on 3 d. brown	60	10
658		600 d. on 8 d. blue	1·75	60

124 Castelrosso Fortress

126 Apollo (T **1** of Dodecanese Is.)

1947. Restoration of Dodecanese Is. to Greece.

No.	Type	Description	Unused	Used
659	124	20 d. blue	25	10
660	–	30 d. pink and black	25	10
661	–	50 d. blue	30	10
662	–	100 d. green and olive	30	10
663	–	200 d. orange	55	10
664	–	250 d. grey	80	10
665	–	300 d. orange	80	10
666	–	400 d. blue	1·00	10
667	126	450 d. blue	1·25	10
668	–	450 d. blue	1·10	10
669	126	500 d. red	1·00	10
670	–	600 d. purple	1·00	15
671	–	700 d. mauve	1·10	20
672	–	700 d. green	8·00	50
673	–	800 d. green and violet	1·50	20
674	–	1000 d. olive	1·00	10
675	126	1300 d. red	6·00	35
676	124	1500 d. brown	35·00	1·00
677	–	1600 d. blue	4·50	50
678	–	2000 d. red and brown	22·00	50
679	–	2600 d. green	5·50	85
680	–	5000 d. violet	27·00	50
681	–	10,000 d. blue	35·00	65

DESIGNS—HORIZ: 100, 400 d. St. John's Convent, Patmos. VERT: 30, 1600, 2000 d. Dodecanese vase; 50, 300 d. Woman in national costume; 200, 250 d. E. Xanthos; 450 (No. 668), 800 d. Casos Is. and 19th-century frigate; 600, 700 (2), 5000 d. Statue of Hippocrates; 1000, 2600, 10,000 d. Colossus of Rhodes.

129 Column of Women and Children

1949. Abduction of Greek Children to neighbouring Countries.

No.	Type	Description	Unused	Used
683	129	450 d. violet	1·10	40
684	–	1000 d. brown	3·00	35
685	–	1800 d. red	3·75	40

DESIGNS—VERT: 1000 d. Captive children and map of Greece; 1800 d. Hand menacing woman and child.

130 Maps and Flags

1950. Battle of Crete.

No.	Type	Description	Unused	Used
686	130	1000 d. blue	4·00	25

131 "Youth of Marathon"

1950. 75th Anniv of U.P.U. Inscr "1874–1949" in white figures at top.

No.	Type	Description	Unused	Used
687	131	1000 d. green on buff	1·10	25

133 St. Paul 134

1951. 19th Cent. of St. Paul's Travels in Greece.
688 – 700 d. purple . . . . . . 2·00 50
689 133 1600 d. blue . . . . . . 5·00 1·50
690 134 2600 d. brown . . . . . . 8·00 2·00
691 – 10,000 d. brown . . . . . 85·00 48·00
DESIGNS—As Type 134: 700 d. Sword and altar (horiz); 10,000 d. St. Paul preaching to Athenians (vert).

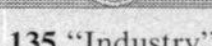

135 "Industry" **136** Blessing before Battle

1951. Reconstruction Issue.
692 135 700 d. orange . . . . . . 3·00 15
693 – 800 d. green . . . . . . 6·50 20
694 – 1300 d. blue . . . . . . 8·00 25
695 – 1600 d. olive . . . . . 22·00 30
696 – 2600 d. violet . . . . . 55·00 1·10
697 – 5000 d. purple . . . . . 55·00 30
DESIGNS—VERT: 800 d. Fish and trident; 1300 d. Workmen and column; 1600 d. Ceres and tractors; 2600 d. Women and loom; 5000 d. Map and stars ("Electrification").

1952. Air. Anti-Communist Campaign.
698 136 1,000 d. blue . . . . . . 20 1·50
699 – 1,700 d. turquoise . . . . 4·50 1·00
700 – 2,700 d. brown . . . . . 9·00 2·75
701 – 7,000 d. green . . . . . 24·00 12·00
DESIGNS—VERT: 1,700 d. "Victory" over mountains; 2,700 d. Infantry attack; 7,000 d. "Victory" and soldiers.

137 King Paul **138** "Spirit of Greece"

1952. 50th Birthday of King Paul.
702 137 200 d. green . . . . . . 1·00 15
703 1,000 d. red . . . . . . 2·50 25
704 138 1,400 d. blue . . . . . 9·00 1·00
705 137 10,000 d. purple . . . . 32·00 9·50

139 "Oranges"

1953. National Products.
706 139 500 d. orange and red . . . 1·25 15
707 – 700 d. yellow and brown . . 1·25 10
708 – 1,000 d. green and blue . . 2·00 15
709 – 1,300 c. buff and purple . . 3·00 15
710 – 2,000 d. green and brown . . 7·50 25
711 – 2,600 d. bistre and violet . 15·00 1·00
712 – 5,000 d. green and brown . 20·00 40
DESIGNS—VERT: 700 d. "Tobacco" (tobacco plant); 1,300 d. "Wine" (wineglass and vase); 2,000 d. "Figs" (basket of figs); 2,600 d. "Dried Fruit" (grapes and currant bread); 5,000 d. "Grapes" (male figure holding grapes). HORIZ: 1,000 d. "Olive Oil" (Pallas Athene and olive branch).

140 Bust of Pericles **141** Alexander the Great **143** Athlete Bearing Torch

1954. Ancient Greek Art. Sculptures, etc.
713 140 100 d. brown 35 10
714 – 200 d. black 45 10
715 – 300 d. violet 60 10
716 – 500 d. green 80 10
717 – 600 d. red . . . . . . 1·25 10
718 141 1,000 d. black and blue . . 1·75 10
719 – 1,200 d. olive . . . . . 1·75 10
720 – 2,000 d. brown . . . . . 5·00 10
721 – 2,400 d. blue . . . . . 5·50 45
722 – 2,500 d. green . . . . . 6·50 35
723 – 4,000 d. red . . . . . 14·00 30
724 – 20,000 d. purple . . . . 95·00 1·00
DESIGNS—As Type 140: VERT: 200 d. Mycenaean oxhead vase; 1,200 d. Head of charioteer of Delphi; 2,000 d. Vase of Dipylon; 2,500 d. Man carrying calf; 20,000 d. Two pitcher bearers. HORIZ: 2,400 d. Hunting wild boar. As Type 141: VERT: 300 d. Bust of Homer; 500 d. Zeus of Istiaca; 600 d. Youth's head; 4,000 d. Dish depicting voyage of Dionysus.
See also Nos. 733a/41.

1954. Air. 5th Anniv of N.A.T.O. Inscr "NATO".
725 143 1,200 d. orange . . . . . 5·00 15
726 – 2,400 d. green . . . . . 30·00 1·50
727 – 4,000 d. blue . . . . . 55·00 2·50
DESIGNS—VERT: 2,400 d. Amphictyonic coin; 4,000 d. Pallas Athene.

Currency revalued. 1000 old drachma = one new drachma.

144 Extracts from "Hansard" (Parliamentary Debates) **145** Samian Coin Depicting Pythagoras

1954. "Enosis" (Union of Cyprus with Greece).
728 144 1.20 d. black and yellow . . 2·50 40
729 2 d. black and salmon . . 8·00 3·50
730 2 d. black and blue . . . . 8·00 3·50
731 2.40 d. black & lavender . . 8·00 1·25
732 2.50 d. black and pink . . 8·50 1·25
733 4 d. black and lemon . . . 20·00 1·90
On No. 728 the text is in Greek, on Nos. 730/1 in French and on the remainder in English.

1955. As Nos. 713/24 but new colours and values.
733a 140 10 l. green 20 10
734 – 20 l. myrtle (No. 714) . . 20 10
734a – 20 l. purple (No. 714) . . 15 25
735 140 30 l. brown 30 10
736 – 50 l. lake (No. 716) . . . 50 10
736a – 50 l. green (No. 716) . . . 50 10
736b – 70 l. orange (No. 719) . . 15 20
737 – 1 d. green (No. 717) . . . 80 10
737a – 1 d. brown (No. 717) . . 1·25 10
737b – 1 d. 50 blue (No. 724) . . 6·50 30
738 141 2 d. black and brown . . 5·00 10
738a 2 d. 50 black and mauve . 6·50 10
739 – 3 d. orange (No. 721) . . 5·50 20
739a – 3 d. blue (No. 722) . . . 1·50 25
740 – 3 d. 50 red (No. 715) . . 6·50 50
741 – 4 d. blue (No. 723) . . . 42·00 35

1955. Pythagorean Congress.
742 145 2 d. green . . . . . . 1·50 25
743 – 3 d. 50 black . . . . . 4·00 1·50
744 145 5 d. purple . . . . . . 27·00 1·25
745 – 6 d. blue . . . . . . 23·00 25·00
DESIGNS—VERT: 3 d. 50, Representation of Pythagoras theorem. HORIZ: 6 d. Map of Samos.

146 Rotary Emblem and Globe **147** King George I

1956. 50th Anniv of Rotary International.
746 146 2 d. blue . . . . . . 6·00 30

1956. Royal Family.
747 – 10 l. violet 20 10
748 – 20 l. purple 20 10
749 147 30 l. brown 25 10
750 – 50 l. brown 25 10
751 – 70 l. blue 25 15
752 – 1 d. blue 40 10
753 – 1 d. 50 grey 45 25
754 – 2 d. black 70 10
755 – 3 d. brown . . . . . . 1·75 15
756 – 3 d. 50 brown . . . . . 5·00 25
757 – 4 d. green . . . . . . 5·00 15
758 – 5 d. red . . . . . . 3·25 10
759 – 7 d. 50 blue . . . . . 5·50 1·25
760 – 10 d. blue . . . . . . 17·00 50
PORTRAITS—HORIZ: 10 l. King Alexander; 5 d. King Paul and Queen Frederika; 10 d. King and Queen and Crown Prince Constantine. VERT: 20 l. Crown Prince Constantine; 50 l. Queen Olga; 70 l. King Otto; 1 d. Queen Amalia; 1 d. 50, King Constantine; 2 d. King Paul; 3 d. King George II; 3 d. 50, Queen Sophia; 4 d. Queen Frederika; 7 d. 50, King Paul.
See also Nos. 764/77.

148 Dionysios Solomos **149** "Argo" (5th Century B.C.)

1957. Death Centenary of D. Solomos (national poet).
761 – 2 d. yellow and brown . . 3·00 20
762 148 3 d. 50 grey and blue . . 3·00 2·25
763 – 5 d. bistre and green . . 4·00 5·50
DESIGNS—HORIZ: 2 d. Solomos and K. Mantzaros (composer); 5 d. Zante landscape and Solomos.

1957. As Nos. 747/60. Colours changed.
764 – 10 l. red 15 10
765 – 20 l. orange 15 10
766 147 30 l. black 15 10
767 – 50 l. green 20 10
768 – 70 l. purple 50 25
769 – 1 d. red 55 10
770 – 1 d. 50 green . . . . . 1·25 10
771 – 2 d. red . . . . . . 1·75 10
772 – 3 d. blue . . . . . . 2·00 10
773 – 3 d. 50 purple . . . . . 5·50 25
774 – 4 d. brown . . . . . . 6·75 15
775 – 5 d. blue . . . . . . 5·50 20
776 – 7 d. 50 yellow . . . . . 1·50 1·00
777 – 10 d. green . . . . . . 30·00 70

1958. Greek Merchant Marine Commemoration. Ship designs.
778 – 50 l. multicoloured 15 10
779 – 1 d. ochre, blk & blue . . . 20 15
780 – 1 d. 50 red, blk & blue . . 1·00 1·00
781 – 2 d. multicoloured 40 25
782 – 3 d. 50 blk, red & bl . . . 1·50 50
783 149 5 d. multicoloured . . . . 9·00 6·00
SHIPS: 50 l. "Michael Carras" (tanker); 1 d. "Queen Frederika" (liner); 1 d. 50, Full-rigged sailing ship, 1821; 2 d. Byzantine galley; 3 d. 50, 6th-century B.C. galley.

150 The Piraeus (Port of Athens) **151** "Narcissus" and Flower

1958. Air. Greek Ports.
784 150 10 d. multicoloured . . . 6·00 25
785 – 15 d. multicoloured . . . 2·00 20
786 – 20 d. multicoloured . . . 7·50 15
787 – 25 d. multicoloured . . . 2·00 55
788 – 30 d. multicoloured . . . 2·00 60
789 – 50 d. blue, black & brn . . 5·00 50
790 – 100 d. blue, blk & brn . . 29·00 2·75
PORTS: 15 d. Salonika; 20 d. Patras; 25 d. Hermoupolis (Syra); 30 d. Volos (Thessaly); 50 d. Kavalla; 100 d. Heraklion (Crete).

1958. Int. Congress for Protection of Nature, Athens. Mythological and Floral designs. Multicoloured.
791 20 l. Type 151 . . . . . . 15 10
792 30 l. "Daphne and Apollo" . . 15 10
793 50 l. "Venus and Adonis" (Venus and hibiscus) 15 10
794 70 l. "Pan and the Nymph" (Pan and pine cones) 35 10
795 1 d. Crocus (21½ × 26 mm) . . 50 15
796 2 d. Iris (22 × 32 mm) . . . 70 10
797 3 d. 50 Tulip (22 × 32 mm) . . 20 25
798 5 d. Cyclamen (22 × 32 mm) . 1·75 1·75

152 Jupiter's Head and Eagle (Olympia 4th-century B.C. coin)

1959. Ancient Greek Coins. Designs as T 152 showing both sides of each coin. Inscriptions in black.
799 152 10 l. green and brown . . . 15 20
800 – 20 l. grey and blue . . . 30 10
801 – 50 l. grey and purple . . . 40 10
802 – 70 l. grey and blue . . . 45 25
803 – 1 d. drab and red 75 10
804 – 1 d. 50 grey and ochre . . 1·25 10
805 – 2 d. 50 drab and mauve . . 1·75 10
806 – 4 d. 50 grey and green . . 5·00 35
807 – 6 d. blue and olive . . . 13·00 10
808 – 8 d. 50 drab and red . . . 2·75 1·25
COINS—HORIZ: 20 l. Athene's head and owl (Athens 5th cent. B.C.); 50 l. Nymph Arethusa and chariot (Syracuse 5th cent. B.C.); 70 l. Hercules and Jupiter (Alexander the Great 4th cent. B.C.); 1 d. 50, Griffin and squares (Abdera, Thrace 5th cent. B.C.); 2 d. 50, Apollo and lyre (Chalcidice, Macedonia 4th cent. B.C.). VERT: 1 d. Helios and rose (Rhodes 4th cent. B.C.); 4 d. 50, Apollo and labyrinth (Crete 3rd cent. B.C.); 6 d. Venus and Apollo (Paphos, Cyprus 4th cent. B.C.); 8 d. 50, Ram's heads and incised squares (Delphi 5th cent. B.C.).
See also Nos. 909/17.

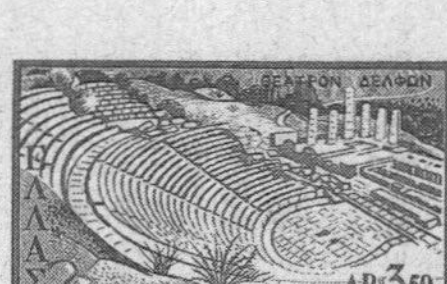

153 Amphitheatre, Delphi **154** "Victory" and Greek Soldiers through the Ages

1959. Ancient Greek Theatre.
809 – 20 l. multicoloured 25 15
810 – 50 l. brown and olive . . . 40 15
811 – 1 d. multicoloured 40 20
812 – 2 d. 50 brown and blue . . 60 15
813 153 3 d. 50 multicoloured . . . 7·50 7·50
814 – 4 d. 50 brown and black . . 1·25 90
815 – 6 d. brown, grey & blk . . 1·25 90
DESIGNS—VERT: 20 l. Ancient theatre audience (after a Pharsala Thessaly vase of 580 B.C.); 50 l. Clay mask of 3rd century B.C.; 1 d. Flute, drum and lyre; 2 d. 50, Actor (3rd century statuette); 6 d. Performance of a satirical play (after a mixing-bowl of 410 B.C.). HORIZ: 4 d. 50, Performance of Euripides' "Andromeda" (after a vase of 4th century B.C.).

1959. 10th Anniv of Greek Anti-Communist Victory.
816 154 2 d. 50 bl, blk & brn . . . 1·75 25

155 "The Good Samaritan" **156** Imre Nagy (formerly Prime Minister of Hungary)

1959. Red Cross Commem. Cross in red.
817 – 20 l. multicoloured 15 15
818 – 50 l. grey, red and blue . . 30 15
819 – 70 l. black, brn, bis & bl . . 50 40
820 – 2 d. 50 blk, brn, grey & red 55 10
821 – 3 d. multicoloured . . . . 4·50 4·50
822 – 4 d. 50 orange and red . . 1·00 1·00
823 155 6 d. multicoloured 70 40
DESIGNS—HORIZ: 20 l. Hippocrates Tree, Cos. VERT: 50 l. Bust of Aesculapius; 70 l. St. Basil (after mosaic in Hosios Loukas Monastery, Boeotia); 2 d. 50, Achilles and Patroclus (from vase of 6th cent B.C.); 3 d. (32 × 47½ mm) Red Cross, globe, infirm people and nurses; 4 d. 50, J. H. Dunant.

1959. 3rd Anniv of Hungarian Revolt.
824 156 4 d. 50 sepia, brn & red . . 75 75
825 6 d. black, blue & ultram . 75 75

157 Kostes Palamas **158** Brig in Storm

159 Scout emulating St. George **160** Sprinting

1960. Birth Cent of Palamas (poet).
826 157 2 d. 50 multicoloured . . . 2·00 25

1960. World Refugee Year. Multicoloured.
827 2 d. 50 Type 158 . . . . . . 50 15
828 4 d. 50 Brig in calm waters . . . 1·25 60

1960. 50th Anniv of Greek Boy Scout Movement. Multicoloured.
829 20 l. Type 159 . . . . . . 15 15
830 30 l. Ephebi Oath and Scout Promise 15 15
831 40 l. Fire rescue work 15 15
832 50 l. Planting tree 35 15
833 70 l. Map reading 15 25

834		1 d. Scouts on beach	30	15
835		2 d. 50 Crown Prince Constantine in uniform	90	15
836		6 d. Greek Scout Flag and Medal	90	60

Nos. 829/30 and 835 are vert and the rest horiz.

1960. Olympic Games.

837	–	20 l. brown, blk & blue	15	10
838	–	50 l. brown and black	15	10
839	–	70 l. brown, blk & green	15	15
840	–	80 l. multicoloured	20	15
841	–	1 d. multicoloured	30	10
842	–	1 d. 50 brown, blk & orge	40	20
843	–	2 d. 50 brown, blk & blue	80	10
844	**160**	4 d. 50 multicoloured	80	40
845	–	5 d. multicoloured	1·50	1·25
846	–	6 d. brown, black & violet	1·50	60
847	–	12 d. 50 multicoloured	5·50	5·50

DESIGNS—VERT: 20 l. "Armistice" (official holding plaque); 70 l. Athlete taking oath; 2 d. 50, Discus-throwing; 5 d. Javelin-throwing. HORIZ: 50 l. Olympic flame; 80 l. Cutting branches from crown-bearing olive tree; 1 d. Entrance of chief judges; 1 d. 50 Long jumping; 6 d. Crowning the victor; 12 d. 50, Quadriga or chariot-driving (entrance of the victor).

1960. 1st Anniv of European Postal and Telecommunications Conference. As T **373** of Belgium.

848		4 d. 50 blue	2·50	1·25

162 Crown Prince Constantine and "Nirefs"

1961. Victory of Crown Prince Constantine in Dragon-class Yacht Race, Olympic Games.

849	**162**	2 d. 50 multicoloured	50	25

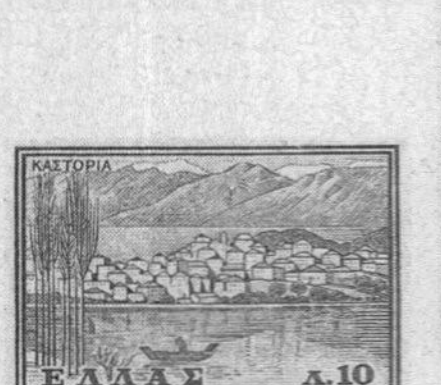

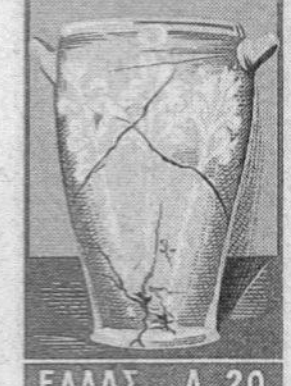

163 Kastoria **164** Lilies Vase of Knossos

1961. Tourist Publicity Issue.

850	**163**	10 l. blue	15	10
851	–	20 l. plum	15	10
852	–	50 l. blue	20	10
853	–	70 l. purple	20	10
854	–	80 l. blue	40	20
855	–	1 d. brown	50	10
856	–	1 d. 50 green	60	10
857	–	2 d. 50 red	1·75	10
858	–	3 d. 50 violet	60	40
859	–	4 d. green	4·25	10
860	–	4 d. 50 blue	85	10
861	–	5 d. lake	4·00	10
862	–	6 d. myrtle	1·40	10
863	–	7 d. 50 black	70	25
864	–	8 d. blue	2·75	15
865	–	8 d. 50 orange	2·75	55
866	–	12 d. 50 sepia	1·10	30

DESIGNS—HORIZ: 20 l. The Meteora (Monasteries); 50 l. Hydra; 70 l. Acropolis, Athens; 80 l. Mykonos. 1 d. Salonika; 1 d. 50, Olympia; 2 d. 50, Knossos; 3 d. 50, Rhodes; 4 d. Epidavros; 4 d. 50, Sounion; 5 d. Temple of Zeus, Athens; 7 d. 50, Yannina; 12 d. 50, Delos, VERT: 6 d. Delphi; 8 d. Mount Athos; 8 d. 50, Santorini (Thira).

1961. Minoan Art.

867	**164**	20 l. multicoloured	20	10
868	–	50 l. multicoloured	40	10
869	–	1 d. multicoloured	45	10
870	–	1 d. 50 multicoloured	75	15
871	–	2 d. 50 multicoloured	3·50	10
872	–	4 d. 50 multicoloured	2·50	1·75
873	–	6 d. multicoloured	4·25	50
874	–	10 d. multicoloured	6·75	5·00

DESIGNS—VERT: 1 d. 50, Knossos rhyton-bearer; 4 d. 50, Part of Hagia trias sarcophagus. HORIZ: 50 l. Partridges and fig-pecker (Knossos frieze); 1 d. Kamares fruit dish; 2 d. 50, Ladies of Knossos Palace (painting); 6 d. Knossos dancer (painting); 10 d. Kamares prochus and pithos with spout.

165 Reactor Building

1961. Inaug. of "Democritus" Nuclear Research Centre, Aghia Paraskevi.

875	**165**	2 d. 50 purple and mauve	25	15
876	–	4 d. 50 blue and grey	60	25

DESIGN: 4 d. 50, Democritus and atomic symbol.

166 Doves **167** Emperor Nicephorus Phocas

1961. Europa.

877	**166**	2 d. 50 red and pink	10	10
878		4 d. 50 ultram & bl	15	15

1961. Millenary of Liberation of Crete from the Saracens.

879	**167**	2 d. 50 multicoloured	45	35

168 "Hermes" 1 l. Stamp of 1861

1961. Cent. of First Greek Postage Stamps. "Hermes" stamps of 1861. Multicoloured.

880	20 l. Type **168**	10	10
881	50 l. "2 l"	10	10
882	1 d. 50 "5 l"	15	10
883	2 d. 50 "10 l"	25	10
884	4 d. 50 "20 l"	30	25
885	6 d. "40 l"	45	40
886	10 d. "80 l"	1·50	1·50

169 Ptolemais Steam Plant

1962. Electrification Project. Multicoloured.

887	20 l. Tauropos dam (vert)	15	10
888	50 l. Ladhon River hydro-electric plant (vert)	20	10
889	1 d. Type **169**	25	25
890	1 d. 50 Louros River dam	30	15
891	2 d. 50 Aliverion steam plant	45	10
892	4 d. 50 Salonika hydro-electric sub-station	90	75
893	6 d. Agra River power station	2·25	1·90

170 Zappion Building

1962. N.A.T.O. Ministers' Conference, Athens.

894	**170**	2 d. 50 multicoloured	20	10
895	–	3 d. sepia, brown & buff	20	10
896	–	4 d. 50 black and blue	30	30
897	–	6 d. black and red	30	30

DESIGNS—VERT: 3 d. Ancient Greek warrior with shield; 4 d. 50, Soldier kneeling (after Marathon tomb); 6 d. (21 × 37 mm), Soldier (statue in Temple of Aphea, Aegina).

171 Europa "Tree"

1962. Europa.

898	**171**	2 d. 50 red and black	25	10
899		4 d. 50 blue and black	65	50

172 "Protection" **173** Demeter, Goddess of Corn

1962. Greek Farmers' Social Insurance Scheme.

900	**172**	1 d. 50 black, brn & red	25	10
901		2 d. 50 black, brn & grn	40	20

1963. Freedom from Hunger. Multicoloured.

902	2 d. 50 Type **173**	25	10
903	4 d. 50 Wheat ears and globe	50	25

174 Kings of the Greek Dynasty

1963. Cent of Greek Royal Dynasty.

904	**174**	50 l. red	30	10
905		1 d. 50 green	35	15
906		2 d. 50 brown	70	10
907		4 d. 50 blue	1·40	70
908		6 d. violet	1·75	20

1963. Ancient Greek Coins. As Nos. 799/808 but colours changed and some designs rearranged. Inscr in black; coins in black and drab or grey; background colours given.

909	50 l. blue (As No. 801)	20	10
910	80 l. purple (As 802)	30	25
911	1 d. green (As 803)	40	10
912	1 d. 50 red (As 804)	50	10
913	3 d. olive (As 799)	25	10
914	3 d. 50 red (As 800)	25	20
915	4 d. 50 brown (As 806)	25	10
916	6 d. turquoise (As 807)	25	10
917	8 d. 50 blue (As 808)	1·25	50

175 "Athens at Dawn" (after watercolour by Lord Baden-Powell) **176** Delphi

1963. 11th World Scout Jamboree, Marathon.

918	**175**	1 d. multicoloured	15	10
919	–	1 d. 50 orge, blk & blue	15	10
920	–	2 d. 50 multicoloured	60	10
921	–	3 d. black, brown & grn	50	15
922	–	4 d. 50 multicoloured	1·00	55

DESIGNS—HORIZ: 3 d. A. Lefkadites (founder of Greek Scout Movement) and Lord Baden-Powell. VERT: 1 d. 50, Jamboree Badge; 2 d. 50, Crown Prince Constantine, Chief Scout of Greece; 4 d. 50, Scout bugling with Atlantic trumpet triton shell.

1963. Red Cross Cent. Multicoloured.

923	1 d. Type **176**	30	15
924	2 d. Centenary emblem	15	10
925	2 d. 50 Queen Olga	15	10
926	4 d. 50 Henri Dunant	45	30

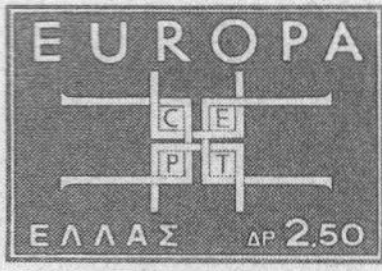

177 "Co-operation"

1963. Europa.

927	**177**	2 d. 50 green	1·75	20
928		4 d. 50 purple	2·25	1·75

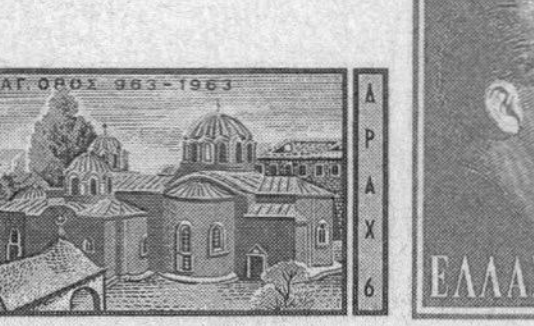

178 Great Lavra Church **179** King Paul

1963. Millenary of Mt. Athos Monastic Community. Multicoloured.

929	30 l. Vatopediou Monastery	10	10
930	80 l. Dionysion Monastery	10	20
931	1 d. Protaton Church, Karyae	15	10
932	2 d. Stavronikita Monastery	40	10
933	2 d. 50 Cover of Nicephorus Phocas Gospel, Great Lavra Church	1·25	10
934	3 d. 50 St. Athanasius the Anthonite (fresco)	50	40
935	4 d. 50 11th-century papyrus, Iviron Monastery	40	30
936	6 d. Type **178**	50	25

The 1 d. and 6 d. are horiz., the rest vert.

1964. Death of Paul I.

937	**179**	30 l. brown	10	10
938		50 l. violet	10	10
939		1 d. green	75	10
940		1 d. 50 orange	15	10
941		2 d. blue	50	10
942		2 d. 50 sepia	60	10
943		3 d. 50 purple	50	10
944		4 d. blue	90	10
945		4 d. 50 blue	1·00	40
946		6 d. red	1·50	10

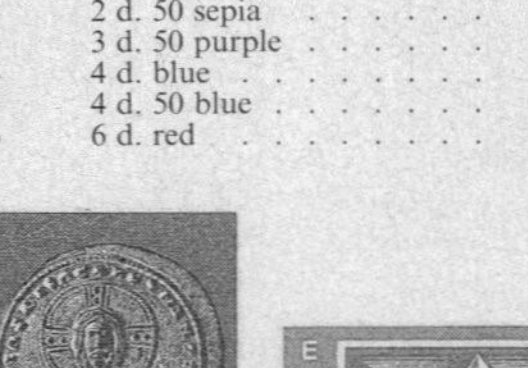

180 Gold Coin **181** Trident of Paxi

1964. Byzantine Art Exn, Athens. Mult.

947	1 d. Type **180**	15	10
948	1 d. 50 "Two Saints"	15	10
949	2 d. "Archangel Michael"	25	10
950	2 d. 50 "Young Lady"	25	10
951	4 d. 50 "Angel"	60	50

DESIGN origins: 1 d. reign of Emperor Basil II (976–1025); 1 d. 50, from Harbaville's 10th cent. ivory triptych (Louvre); 2 d. 14th cent. Constantinople icon (Byzantine Museum, Athens); 2 d. 50, from 14th cent. fresco "The Birth of the Holy Virgin" by Panselinos (Protaton Church, Mt. Athos); 4 d. 50, from 11th cent. mosaic (Daphne Church, Athens).

1964. Centenary of Union of Ionian Islands with Greece. Inscr "1864–1964".

952	**181**	20 l. grey, slate and green	10	10
953	–	30 l. multicoloured	10	10
954	–	1 d. lt brn, brn & red-brn	10	10
955	–	2 d. multicoloured	15	10
956	–	2 d. 50 pale green, deep green and green	25	10
957	–	4 d. 50 multicoloured	75	50
958		6 d. multicoloured	40	35

DESIGNS: 30 l. Venus of Cythera; 1 d. Ulysses of Ithaca; 2 d. St. George of Levkas; 2 d. 50, Zakynthos of Zante; 4 d. 50, Cephalus of Cephalonia; 6 d. War galley emblem of Corfu.

182 Greek Child **183** Europa "Flower"

1964. 50th Anniv of National Institution of Social Welfare (P.I.K.P.A.).

959	**182**	2 d. 50 multicoloured	50	20

1964. Europa.

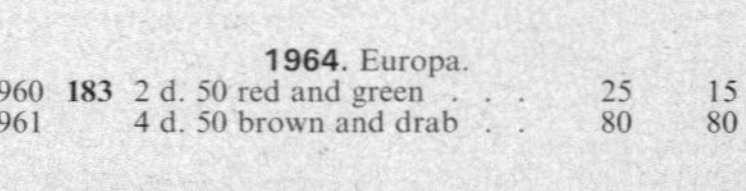

960	**183**	2 d. 50 red and green	25	15
961		4 d. 50 brown and drab	80	80

184 King Constantine II and Queen Anne-Marie **185** Peleus and Atlanta (amphora)

1964. Royal Wedding.

962	**184**	1 d. 50 green	20	15
963		2 d. 50 red	15	10
964		4 d. 50 blue	25	20

1964. Olympic Games, Tokyo. Multicoloured.

965	10 l. Type **185**	10	10
966	1 d. Running (bowl)	10	10
967	2 d. Jumping (pot)	10	10
968	2 d. 50 Throwing the discus	15	10
969	4 d. 50 Chariot-racing (sculpture)	50	25
970	6 d. Boxing (vase)	15	15
971	10 d. Apollo (part of frieze, Zeus Temple, Olympia)	20	20

The 1 d., 2 d., 4 d. 50, and 6 d. are horiz.

186 "Christ stripping off His garments" **187** Aesculapius Theatre, Epidavros

1965. 350th Death Anniv of El Greco. Mult.
972 50 l. Type **186** 15 10
973 1 d. "Angels' Concert" 15 10
974 1 d. 50 El Greco's signature . . 15 10
975 2 d. 50 Self-portrait 15 10
976 4 d. 50 "Storm-lashed Toledo" . 35 30
The 1 d. 50, is horiz.

1965. Greek Artistic Festivals. Mult.
977 1 d. 50 Type **187** 10 10
978 4 d. 50 Herod Atticus Theatre, Athens 25 20

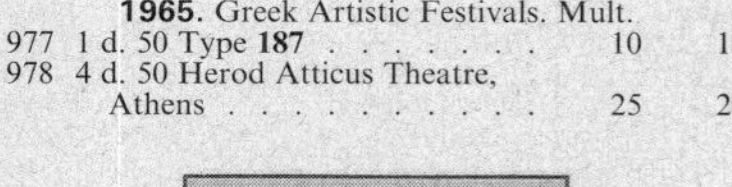

188 ITU Emblem and Symbols

1965. Centenary of I.T.U.
979 **188** 2 d. 50 red, blue and grey . 40 15

189 "New Member making Affirmation" (after Tsokos)

1965. 150th Anniv of "Philiki Hetaeria" ("Friends' Society"). Multicoloured.
980 1 d. 50 Type **189** 10 10
981 4 d. 50 Society flag 25 20

190 AHEPA Emblem **191** Venizelos as Revolutionary

1965. American Hellenic Educational Progressive Assn. (AHEPA) Congress, Athens.
982 **190** 6 d. black, olive & blue . . 30 20

1965. Birth Cent of E. Venizelos (statesman).
983 **191** 1 d. 50 green 25 20
984 – 2 d. blue 20 25
985 – 2 d. 50 brown 15 15
DESIGNS: 2 d. Venizelos signing Treaty of Sevres (1920); 2 d. 50, Venizelos.

192 Games' Flag **193** Symbols of the Planets

1965. Balkan Games, Athens. Multicoloured.
986 1 d. Type **192** 10 10
987 2 d. Victor's medal (vert) . . . 10 10
988 6 d. Karaiskakis Stadium, Athens 20 20

1965. Int Astronautic Conf, Athens. Mult.
989 50 l. Type **193** 15 10
990 2 d. 50 Astronaut in space . . . 15 10
991 6 d. Rocket and space-ship . . . 30 30

194 Europa "Sprig"

1965. Europa.
992 **194** 2 d. 50 blue, black & grey . 25 10
993 4 d. 50 green, blk & ol . . 60 45

195 Hipparchus (astronomer) and Astrolabe

1965. Opening of Evghenides Planetarium, Athens.
994 **195** 2 d. 50 black, red & grn . . 30 10

196 Carpenter Ants **197** St. Andrew's Church, Patras

1965. 50th Anniv of P.O. Savings Bank. Multicoloured.
995 10 l. Type **196** 10 10
996 2 d. 50 Savings Bank and book . 30 15

1965. Restoration of St. Andrew's Head to Greece. Multicoloured.
997 1 d. Type **197** 10 10
998 5 d. St. Andrew, after 11th-cent mosaic, Hosios Loukas Monastry, Boeotia 25 15

198 T. Brysakes **200** Geannares (revolutionary leader)

199 Greek 25 d. Banknote of 1867

1966. Modern Greek Painters. Multicoloured.
999 80 l. Type **198** 10 10
1000 1 d. N. Lytras 10 10
1001 2 d. 50 C. Volonakes 10 10
1002 4 d. N. Gyses 10 10
1003 5 d. G. Jacobides 20 15

1966. 125th Anniv of Greek National Bank.
1004 – 1 d. 50 green 10 10
1005 – 2 d. 50 brown 10 10
1006 – 4 d. blue 15 10
1007 **199** 6 d. black 25 20
DESIGNS—VERT: (23 × 33½ mm): 1 d. 50, J.-G. Eynard; 2 d. 50, G. Stavros (founders). HORIZ: (As Type **199**): 4 d. National Bank Headquarters, Athens.

1966. Centenary of Cretan Revolt. Mult.
1008 2 d. Type **200** 10 10
1009 2 d. 50 Explosion of gun-powder machine, Arkadi Monastery (horiz) 10 10
1010 4 d. 50 Map of Crete (horiz) . . 20 15

201 "Movement of Water" (Decade of World Hydrology) **202** Tragedian's Mask of 4th Century, B.C.

1966. U.N.O. Events.
1011 **201** 1 d. blue, brown & black . 10 10
1012 – 3 d. multicoloured . . . 10 10
1013 – 3 d. black, blue and red . 20 15
DESIGNS—VERT: 3 d. U.N.E.S.C.O. emblem (20th anniv); 5 d. W.H.O. Building (inauguration of H.Q., Geneva).

1966. 2,500th Anniv of Greek Theatre.
1014 **202** 1 d. multicoloured . . . 10 10
1015 – 1 d. 50 black, red & brn . 10 10
1016 – 2 d. 50 blk, grn & lt grn . 10 10
1017 – 4 d. 50 multicoloured . . 25 15
DESIGNS—HORIZ: 1 d. 50, Dionysus in a Thespian ship-chariot (vase painting, 500–480 B.C.); 2 d. 50, Theatre of Dionysus, Athens. VERT: 4 d. 50, Dionysus dancing (after vase painting by Kleophredes, circa 500 B.C.).

203 Boeing 707 Jetliner crossing Atlantic Ocean **204** Tending Plants

1966. Inauguration of Greek Airways Transatlantic Flights.
1018 **203** 6 d. indigo, blue & lt bl . 30 15

1966. Greek Tobacco. Multicoloured.
1019 1 d. Type **204** 15 10
1020 5 d. Sorting leaf 30 25

205 Europa "Ship" **206** Horseman (embroidery)

1966. Europa.
1021 **205** 1 d. 50 black, ol & grn . . 20 10
1022 4 d. 50 deep brown, brown and light brown . . . 45 40

1966. Greek "Popular" Art. Multicoloured.
1023 10 l. Knitting-needle boxes . . 10 10
1024 30 l. Type **206** 10 10
1025 50 l. Cretan lyre 10 10
1026 1 d. "Massa" (Musical instrument) 15 10
1027 1 d. 50 "Cross and Angels" (bas-relief after Melios) . . 15 10
1028 2 d. "Sts. Constantine and Helen" (icon) 75 10
1029 2 d. 50 Carved altar-screen, St. Nicholas' Church, Galaxidion 25 10
1030 3 d. 19th-century ship of Skyros (embroidery) 25 10
1031 4 d. "Psiki" (wedding procession) (embroidery) 60 10
1032 4 d. 50 Distaff 30 10
1033 5 d. Earrings and necklace . . 50 10
1034 20 d. Detail of handwoven cloth 60 25
The 10, 50 l., 1, 1 d. 50, 2, 2 d. 50, 4 d. 50 and 5 d. designs are vert.

207 Princess Alexia **208** "Woodcutter" (after D. Filippotes)

1966. Princess Alexia's First Birthday.
1035 **207** 2 d. green 10 10
1036 – 2 d. 50 brown 20 10
1037 – 3 d. 50 blue 25 20
PORTRAITS: 2 d. 50, Royal Family; 3 d. 50, Queen Anne-Marie with Princess Alexia.

1967. Greek Sculpture. Multicoloured.
1038 20 l. "Night" (I. Cossos) . . . 10 10
1039 50 l. "Penelope" (L. Drossos) . 10 10
1040 80 l. "Shepherd" (G. Phitalis) . 10 10
1041 2 d. "Woman's Torso" (K. Demetriades) 20 10
1042 2 d. 50 "Kolokotronis" (L. Sochos) 10 10
1043 3 d. "Girl Sleeping" (I. Halepas) 30 20
1044 10 d. Type **208** 20 20
Nos. 1038/42 are vert.

MINIMUM PRICE

The minimum price quoted is 10p which represents a handling charge rather than a basis for valuing common stamps. For further notes about prices see introductory pages.

209 Olympic Rings ("Olympic Day") **210** Cogwheels

1967. Sports Events. Multicoloured.
1045 1 d. Type **209** 10 10
1046 1 d. 50 Marathon Cup, first Olympics (1896) 10 10
1047 2 d. 50 Hurdling 15 10
1048 5 d. "The Discus-thrower" after C. Demetriades 30 15
1049 6 d. Ancient Olympic stadium . 35 15
The 2 d. 50, commemorates the European Athletics Cup, 1967. 5 d. (vert), The European Highest Award Championships, 1968. 6 d. The Inaug. of "International Academy" buildings, Olympia.

1967. Europa.
1050 **210** 2 d. 50 multicoloured . . 20 10
1051 4 d. 50 multicoloured . . 60 50

211 "Lonchi" (destroyer) and Sailor **212** The Plaka, Athens

1967. Nautical Week. Multicoloured.
1052 20 l. Type **211** 10 10
1053 1 d. "Eugene Eugenides" (cadet ship) (vert) 10 10
1054 2 d. 50 Merchant Marine Academy, Aspropyrgos, Attica 15 10
1055 3 d. "Averoff" (cruiser) and Naval School, Poros 30 25
1056 6 d. "Australis" (liner) and figurehead 50 15

1967. International Tourist Year. Multicoloured.
1057 2 d. 50 Island of Skopelos (horiz) 15 10
1058 4 d. 50 Apollo's Temple, Bassai, Peleponnese (horiz) 30 25
1059 6 d. Type **212** 40 10

213 Soldier and Phoenix **214** Industrial Skyline

1967. National Revolution of April 21st (1967).
1060 **213** 2 d. 50 multicoloured . . 10 10
1061 3 d. multicoloured . . . 15 10
1062 4 d. 50 multicoloured . . 20 15

1967. 1st Convention of U.N. Industrial Development Organisation, Athens.
1063 **214** 4 d. 50 ultramarine, black and blue 40 30

215 "Seaside Scene" (A. Pelaletos)

1967. Children's Drawings. Multicoloured.
1064 20 l. Type **215** 10 10
1065 1 d. 50 "Steamer and Island" (L. Tsirikas) 10 10
1066 3 d. 50 "Country Cottage" (K. Ambeliotis) 30 25
1067 6 d. "The Church on the Hill" (N. Frangos) 20 15

216 Throwing the Javelin

217 F.I.A. and E.L.P.A. Emblems

1968. Sports Events, 1968. Multicoloured.
1068 50 l. Type **216** 10 10
1069 1 d. Long jumping 10 10
1070 1 d. 50 "Apollo's Head", Temple of Zeus (vert) . . . 10 10
1071 2 d. 50 Olympic scene on Attic vase (vert) 10 10
1072 4 d. Olympic rings (Olympic Day) 25 25
1073 4 d. 50 "Throwing the Discus", sculpture by Demetriades (European Athletic Championships, 1969) (vert) 45 30
1074 6 d. Long-distance running (vert) 20 10
The 50 l., 1 d. and 6 d. represent the Balkan Games, and the 1 d. 50 and 2 d. 50, the Olympic Academy Meeting.

1968. General Assembly of Int Automobile Federation (F.I.A.), Athens.
1075 **217** 5 d. blue and brown . . . 40 15

218 Europa "Key"

1968. Europa.
1076 **218** 2 d. 50 multicoloured . . 25 10
1077 4 d. 50 multicoloured . . 60 45

219 "Athene defeats Alkyoneus" (from frieze, Altar of Zeus, Pergamos)

1968. "Hellenic Fight for Civilization" Exhibition, Athens. Multicoloured.
1078 10 l. Type **219** 10 10
1079 20 l. Athene attired for battle (bronze from Piraeus) . . . 10 10
1080 50 l. Alexander the Great (from sarcophagus of Alexander of Sidon) 10 10
1081 1 d. 50 Emperors Constantine and Justinian making offerings to the Holy Mother (Byzantine mosaic) 15 10
1082 2 d. 50 Emperor Constantine Paleologos (lithograph by D. Tsokos) 15 10
1083 3 d. "Greece in Missolonghi" (painting by Delacroix) . . . 15 10
1084 4 d. 50 "Evzone" (Greek soldier, painting by G. B. Scott) 25 15
1085 6 d. "Victory of Samothrace" (statue) 20 20
The 1 d. 50 is horiz as T **219**, the 20, 50 l. and 2 d. 50 are 24 × 37 mm, and the remainder 28 × 40 mm.

220 "The Unknown Priest and Teacher" (Rhodes monument)

221 Congress Emblem

1968. 20th Anniv of Dodecanese Union with Greece. Multicoloured.
1086 2 d. Type **220** 20 10
1087 5 d. Greek flag on map (vert) . 60 30

1968. 19th Biennial Congress of Greek Orthodox Arch-diocese of North and South America.
1088 **221** 6 d. multicoloured . . . 40 10

222 GAPA Emblem

223 "Hand of Aesculapius" (fragment of bas-relief from Asclepios' Temple, Athens)

1968. Regional Congress of Greek-American Progressive Association (GAPA).
1089 **222** 6 d. multicoloured . . . 40 10

1968. 5th European Cardiological Congress. Athens.
1090 **223** 4 d. 50 black, yell & lake . 80 55

224 Panathenaic Stadium

226 Goddess "Hygeia"

225 Westland Lysander Mk 1 ramming Savoia Marchetti S.M.79–11 Sparviero Bomber

1968. Olympic Games, Mexico. Multicoloured.
1091 2 d. 50 Type **224** 15 10
1092 5 d. Ancient Olympia 35 15
1093 10 d. One of Pindar's odes . . 65 35
The 10 d. is 28 × 40 mm.

1968. Royal Hellenic Air Force. Mult.
1094 2 d. 50 Type **225** 15 10
1095 3 d. 50 Mediterranean Flight in Breguet 19 bomber, 1928 . . 35 15
1096 8 d. Farman H.F.III biplane and Lockheed Super Starfighter (vert) 50 35

1968. 20th Anniv of World Health Organization.
1097 **226** 5 d. multicoloured . . . 40 10

227 St. Zeno, the Letter-carrier

228 "Workers' Festival Parade" (detail from Minoan vase)

1969. Greek Post Office Festival.
1098 **227** 2 d. 50 multicoloured . . 40 10

1969. 50th Anniv of I.L.O. Multicoloured.
1099 1 d. 50 "Hephaestus and Cyclops" (detail from ancient bas-relief 15 10
1100 10 d. Type **228** 80 40

229 Yacht Harbour, Vouliagmeni

230 Ancient Coin of Kamarina

1969. Tourism. Multicoloured.
1101 1 d. Type **229** 15 10
1102 5 d. "Chorus of Elders" (Ancient drama) (vert) . . . 60 35
1103 6 d. View of Astypalia . . . 25 10

1969. 20th Anniv of N.A.T.O. Multicoloured.
1104 2 d. 50 Type **230** 30 10
1105 4 d. 50 "Going into Battle" (from Corinthian vase) (horiz) 55 45

231 Colonnade

232 Gold Medal

1969. Europa.
1106 **231** 2 d. 50 multicoloured . . 55 10
1107 4 d. 50 multicoloured . . 80 70

1969. 9th European Athletic Championships, Athens. Multicoloured.
1108 20 l. Type **232** 15 10
1109 3 d. Pole-vaulting, and ancient pentathlon contest 20 10
1110 5 d. Relay-racing, and Olympic race c. 525 B.C. (horiz) . . . 30 10
1111 8 d. Throwing the discus, modern and c. 480 B.C. . . 50 40

233 "19th-century Brig and Steamship" (I. Poulakas)

234 Raising the Flag on Mt. Grammos

1969. Navy Week and Merchant Marine Year. Multicoloured.
1112 80 l. Type **233** 30 10
1113 2 d. "Olympic Garland" (tanker) (horiz) 30 10
1114 2 d. 50 "Themistodes and Karteria, War of Independence, 1821" (anon) (41 × 29 mm) 70 10
1115 4 d. 50 "Velos" (modern destroyer) (horiz) . . . . . 1·25 40
1116 6 d. "The Battle of Salamis" (K. Volonakis) (41 × 29 mm) . . . . 1·40 65

1969. 20th Anniv of Communists' Defeat on Mounts Grammos and Vitsi.
1117 **234** 2 d. 50 multicoloured . . 60 20

235 Athena Promachos

236 Demetrius Karatasios (statue by G. Demetriades)

1969. 25th Anniv of Liberation. Multicoloured.
1118 4 d. Type **235** 15 10
1119 5 d. "Resistance" (21 × 37 mm) 50 40
1120 6 d. Map of Eastern Mediterranean theatre . . . 15 10

1969. Heroes of Macedonia's Fight for Freedom. Multicoloured.
1121 1 d. 50 Type **236** 10 10
1122 2 d. 50 Emmanuel Pappas (statue by N. Perantinos) . . . 10 10
1123 3 d. 50 Pavlos Melas (from painting by P. Mathiopoulos) 20 10
1124 4 d. 50 Capetan Kotas 45 25

237 Dolphin Mosaic, Delos (110 B.C.)

1970. Greek Mosaics. Multicoloured.
1125 20 l. "Angel of the Annunciation", Daphne (11th-century) 15 10
1126 1 d. Type **237** 20 10
1127 1 d. 50 "The Holy Ghost", Hosios Loukas Monastery (11th-century) 25 10
1128 2 d. "Hunter", Pella (4th-century B.C.) 25 10
1129 5 d. "Bird", St. George's Church, Salonika (5th-century) 30 20
1130 6 d. "Christ", Nea Moni Church, Khios (5th century) 40 40
SIZES—VERT: Nos. 1125, 1127/9, 23 × 34 mm.; No. 1130 as Type **237**.

238 Overwhelming the Cretan Bull (sculpture)

239 "Flaming Sun"

1970. "The Labours of Hercules".
1131 **238** 20 l. multicoloured . . . 10 10
1132 – 30 l. multicoloured . . . 10 10
1133 – 1 d. blk, blue & slate . . 15 10
1134 – 1 d. 50 brn, grn & ochre . 20 10
1135 – 2 d. multicoloured . . . 1·25 10
1136 – 2 d. 50 brn, red & buff . . 25 10
1137 – 3 d. multicoloured . . . 1·25 10
1138 – 4 d. 50 multicoloured . . 25 20
1139 – 5 d. multicoloured . . . 25 10
1140 – 6 d. multicoloured . . . 20 10
1141 – 20 d. multicoloured . . . 50 40
DESIGNS—HORIZ: 30 l. Hercules and Cerberus (from decorated pitcher); 1 d. 50, The Lernean Hydra (from stamnos); 2 d. Hercules and Geryon (from amphora); 4 d. 50, Combat with the River-god Achelous (from pitcher); 5 d. Overwhelming the Nemean Lion (from amphora); 6 d. The Stymphalian Birds (from vase); 20 d. Wrestling with Antaeus (from bowl). VERT: 1 d. Golden Apples of the Hesperides (sculpture); 2 d. 50, The Erymanthine Boar (from amphora); 3 d. The Centaur Nessus (from vase).

1970. Europa.
1142 **239** 2 d. 50 yellow and red . . 1·25 15
1143 – 3 d. blue and light blue . . 50 25
1144 **239** 4 d. 50 yellow and blue . . 1·40 1·25
DESIGN—VERT: 3 d. "Owl" and CEPT emblem.

240 Satellite and Dish Aerial

241 Saints Cyril and Methodius with Emperor Michael III, (from 12th-cent wall-painting)

1970. Satellite Earth Telecommunications Station, Thermopylae.
1145 **240** 2 d. 50 multicoloured . . 15 10
1146 4 d. 50 multicoloured . . 55 45

1970. Saints Cyril and Methodius Commemoration. Multicoloured.
1147 50 l. Saints Demetrius, Cyril and Methodius (mosaic) (21 × 37 mm) 10 10
1148 2 d. St. Cyril (Russian miniature) (25 × 32 mm) 35 25
1149 5 d. Type **241** 45 20
1150 10 d. St. Methodius (Russian miniature) (25 × 32 mm) . . 50 30
Nos. 1148 and 1150 were issued together, se-tenant, forming a composite design.

242 Cephalonian Fir

244 New U.P.U. Headquarters Building, Berne (Opening)

243 "Cultural Links"

1970. Nature Conservation Year. Mult.
1151 80 l. Type **242** 35 30
1152 2 d. 50 "Jankaea heldreichii" (plant) 80 15
1153 6 d. Rock Partridge (horiz) . . 3·50 50
1154 8 d. Wild goat . . . . 1·75 1·75
SIZES: 2 d. 50, is smaller, 23 × 34 mm.

1970. American-Hellenic Education Progressive Association Congress, Athens.
1155 **243** 6 d. multicoloured . . . 55 20

1970. Anniversaries. Multicoloured.
1156 50 l. Type **244** 10 10
1157 2 d. 50 Emblem (Int Education Year) (vert) 25 10
1158 3 d. 50 Mahatma Gandhi (birth cent) (vert) 25 20
1159 4 d. "25" (25th Anniv of United Nations) (vert) 40 15
1160 4 d. 50 Beethoven (birth bicent) (vert) 75 65
Nos. 1157 and 1160 are larger, $28\frac{1}{2}$ × 41 mm.

245 "The Nativity"

1970. Christmas. Scenes from "The Mosaic of the Nativity", Hosios Loukas Monastery. Mult.
1161 2 d. "The Shepherds" (vert) . . 15 10
1162 4 d. 50 "The Magi" (vert) . . 35 25
1163 6 d. Type **245** 40 65

246 "Death of Bishop of Salona in Battle, Alamana" (lithograph)

1971. 150th Anniv of War of Independence. (1st issue). The Church. Multicoloured.
1164 50 l. Warriors taking the oath (medal) (vert) 10 10
1165 2 d. Patriarch Gregory V (statue by Phitalis) (vert) 15 10
1166 4 d. Type **246** 15 10
1167 10 d. "Bishop Germanos blessing the Standard" (Vryzakis) 45 35
See also Nos. 1168/73, 1178/80, 1181/6 and 1187/89.

1971. 150th Anniv of War of Independence (2nd issue). The War at Sea. As T **246**. Multicoloured.
1168 20 l. "Leonidas" (warship) (37 × 24 mm) 15 10
1169 1 d. "Pericles" (warship) (37 × 24 mm) 25 10
1170 1 d. 50 "Terpsichore" (warship) (from painting by Roux) (37 × 24 mm) 30 10
1171 2 d. 50 "Karteria" (warship) (from painting by Hastings) (37 × 24 mm) 40 15
1172 3 d. "Battle of Samos" (contemporary painting) (40 × 28 mm) 80 15
1173 6 d. "Turkish Frigate ablaze, Battle of Yeronda" (Michalis) (40 × 28 mm) . . 1·40 90

247 Spyridon Louis winning Marathon, Athens, 1896

1971. 75th Anniv of Olympic Games Revival. Multicoloured.
1174 3 d. Type **247** 25 10
1175 8 d. P. de Coubertin and Memorial, Olympia (vert) . . 60 35

248 Europa Chain

1971. Europa.
1176 **248** 2 d. 50 yellow, grn & blk . 60 10
1177 5 d. yellow, orge & blk . . 1·50 1·10

1971. 150th Anniv of War of Independence (3rd issue). "Teaching the People". As T **246**. Multicoloured.
1178 50 l. Eugenius Voulgaris (vert) . 15 10
1179 2 d. 50 Dr. Adamantios Korais (vert) 15 10
1180 15 d. "The Secret School" (N. Ghyzis) (horiz) 50 35
SIZES: 50 l., 2 d. 50, 23 × 34 mm. 15 d. as Type **246**.

1971. 150th Anniv of War of Independence (4th issue). The War on Land. As T **246**. Mult.
1181 50 l. "Battle of Corinth" (Krazeisen) (vert) 10 10
1182 1 d. "Sacrifice of Kapsalia" (Vryzakis) (vert) 15 10
1183 2 d. "Suliot Women in Battle" (Deneuville) (horiz) 20 10
1184 5 d. "Battle of Athens" (Zographos) (vert) 30 30
1185 6 d. 50 "Battle of Maniaki" (lithograph) (horiz) 25 15
1186 9 d. "Death of Markos Botsaris at Karpenisi" (Vryzakis) (horiz) 40 35
SIZES: 50 l., 1 d., 5 d. 25 × 40 mm. 2 d. 40 × 25 mm. 6 d. 50, 9 d. as Type **246**.

249 Kaltetsi Monastery and Seal of Peloponnesian Senate

1971. 150th Anniv of War of Independence. (5th issue). Government.
1187 **249** 2 d. black, green & brn . . 15 10
1188 – 2 d. 50 blk, lt bl & bl . . 15 10
1189 – 20 d. black, yell & brn . . 65 35
DESIGNS: 2 d. 50, National Assembly Memorial, Epidavros, and Seal of Provincial Administration; 20 d. Signature and seal of John Capodistria, first President of Greece.

250 Hosios Loukas Monastery, Boeotia

1972. Greek Monasteries and Churches. Mult.
1190 50 l. Type **250** 10 10
1191 1 d. Daphni Church, Attica . . 15 10
1192 2 d. St. John the Divine, Patmos 20 10
1193 2 d. 50 Panaghia Koumbelidiki Church, Kastoria 25 10
1194 4 d. 50 Panaghia ton Chalkeon, Saloniki 25 15
1195 6 d. 50 Panaghia Paregoritissa Church, Arta 30 15
1196 8 d. 50 St. Paul's Monastery, Mount Athos 60 55

251 Cretan Costume

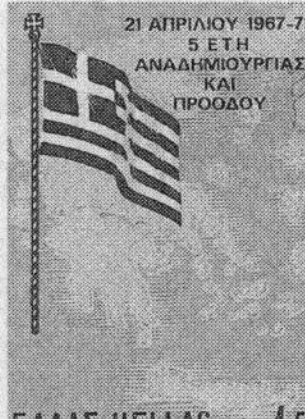

252 Flag and Map

1972. Greek Costumes (1st series). Mult.
1197 50 l. Type **251** 10 10
1198 1 d. Pindus bride 15 10
1199 2 d. Warrior-chief Missolonghi 25 10
1200 2 d. 50 Sarakatsana woman, Attica 10 10
1201 3 d. Nisiros woman 10 10
1202 4 d. 50 Megara woman 15 10
1203 6 d. 50 Trikeri (rural) 20 10
1204 10 d. Pylaia woman, Macedonia . . . . 1·00 50
See also Nos. 1232/48 and 1282/96.

1972. 5th Anniv of 1967 Revolution. Mult.
1205 2 d. 50 Commemorative medal (horiz) 15 10
1206 4 d. 50 Type **252** 20 15
1207 5 d. Facets of modern development 20 15

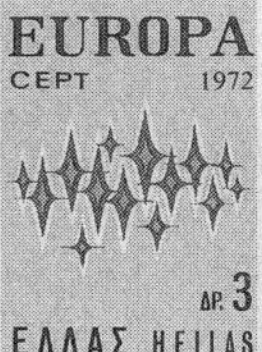

253 "Communications"

254 Acropolis, Athens

1972. Europa.
1208 **253** 3 d. multicoloured . . . 40 10
1209 4 d. 50 multicoloured . . 1·00 90

1972. 20th Anniv of Acropolis Motor Rally. Multicoloured.
1210 4 d. 50 Type **254** 35 35
1211 5 d. Emblem and map 35 35

255 "Gaia delivering Erecthonius to Athene"

1972. Greek Mythology. Museum Pieces (1st series).
1212 **255** 1 d. 50 black and green . . 10 10
1213 – 2 d. black and blue . . . 15 10
1214 – 2 d. 50 black & brown . . 20 10
1215 – 5 d. black and brown . . 30 25
DESIGNS: 2 d. "Uranus" (altar piece); 2 d. 50, "The Gods repulsing the Giants"; 5 d. "Zeus".
See also Nos. 1252/5 and 1271/4.

256 "Young Athlete" (statue)

1972. Olympic Games, Munich. Ancient Olympics. Multicoloured.
1216 50 l. Type **256** 10 10
1217 1 d. 50 "Wrestlers" (bas-relief) (horiz) 10 10
1218 3 d. 50 "Female athlete" (statuette) 15 10
1219 4 d. 50 "Ballgame" (bas-relief) (horiz) 20 15
1220 10 d. "Runners" (amphora) (horiz) 40 35

257 Young Stamp Collector

258 "The Birth of Christ"

1972. Stamp Day.
1221 **257** 2 d. 50 multicoloured . . 15 10

1972. Christmas. Multicoloured.
1222 2 d. 50 "Pilgrimage of the Magi" 10 10
1223 4 d. 50 Type **258** 15 15
Nos. 1222/3 were issued together, se-tenant, forming a composite design.

259 University Buildings

1973. Centenary of Nat. Polytechnic University, Athens.
1224 **259** 2 d. 50 multicoloured . . 15 10

260 "Spring" (wall fresco)

1973. Archaeological Discoveries, Island of Thera. Multicoloured.
1225 10 l. Type **260** 10 10
1226 20 l. "Barley" jug 10 10
1227 30 l. "Blue Apes" fresco (horiz) 10 10
1228 1 d. 50 "Bird" (jug) 10 10
1229 2 d. 50 "Swallows" (detail, "Spring" fresco) (horiz) . . 15 10
1230 5 d. "Wild Goats" fresco (horiz) 20 15
1231 6 d. 50 "Wrestlers" (detail, fresco) (horiz) 40 30

1973. Greek Regional Costumes (2nd series). As Type **251**. Multicoloured.
1232 10 l. Peloponnese 10 10
1233 20 l. Central Greece 10 10
1234 30 l. Locris (Livanates) 10 10
1235 50 l. Skyros (male) 10 10
1236 1 d. Spetsai 10 10
1237 1 d. 50 Almyros 10 10
1238 2 d. 50 Macedonia (Roumlouki) 15 10
1239 3 d. 50 Salamis 15 10
1240 4 d. 50 Epirus (Souli) 15 10
1241 5 d. Lefkas (Santa Maura) . . 20 10
1242 6 d. 50 Skyros (female) 20 10
1243 8 d. 50 Corinth 25 15
1244 10 d. Corfu (Garitsa) 30 10
1245 15 d. Epirus 50 10
1246 20 d. Thessaly (Karagouniko) . . 60 10
1247 30 p. Macedonia (Episkopi) . . 75 10
1248 50 d. Thrace (Makra Gefyra) . 1·40 50

261 Europa "Posthorn"

1973. Europa.
1249 **261** 2 d. 50 blue & light blue . 20 15
1250 3 d. red, orange & lake . . 25 15
1251 4 d. 50 brown, bronze and green 40 30

262 "Olympus" (from photograph by Boissonnas)

1973. Greek Mythology (2nd series).
1252 **262** 1 d. black and grey . . . 10 10
1253 – 2 d. multicoloured . . . 15 15
1254 – 2 d. 50 blk, grey & brn . . 15 10
1255 – 4 d. 50 multicoloured . . 30 30
DESIGNS: 2 d. "Zeus in combat with Typhoeus" (amphora); 2 d. 50, "Zeus at Battle of Giants" (altar relief); 4 d. 50, The "Punishment of Atlas and Prometheus" (vase).

263 Dr. G. Papanicolaou

264 "Our Lady of the Annunciation"

1973. Honouring Dr. George Papanicolaou (cancer specialist).
1256 **263** 2 d. 50 multicoloured . . 10 10
1257 6 d. 50 multicoloured . . 15 15

1973. 150th Anniv of Discovery of Miraculous Icon of our Lady of the Annunciation, Tinos.
1258 **264** 2 d. 50 multicoloured . . 25 15

265 "Triptolemus in a Chariot" (vase)

267 G. Averof

266 Child examining Stamp

1973. European Transport Ministers Conference, Athens.
1259 **265** 4 d. 50 multicoloured . . 20 15

1973. Stamp Day.
1260 **266** 2 d. 50 multicoloured . . 20 15

1973. National Benefactors (1st series).
1261 **267** 1 d. 50 brown 10 10
1262 – 2 d. red 10 10
1263 – 2 d. 50 green 10 10
1264 – 4 d. lilac 10 10
1265 – 6 d. 50 black 15 10
DESIGNS: 2 d. A. Arsakis; 2 d. 50, C. Zappas; 4 d. A. Syngros; 6 d. 50, I. Varvakis.
See also Nos. 1315/18.

268 "Lord Byron in Suliot costume" (by Thomas Phillips)

269 "Harpist of Keros"

1974. 150th Death Anniv of Lord Byron. Multicoloured.
1266 2 d. 50 Type **268** 10 10
1267 4 d. 50 "Byron taking the Oath at Grave of Markos Botsaris" (lithograph) . . . 20 20

1974. Europa. Ancient Greek Sculptures. Multicoloured.
1268 3 d. Type **269** 15 10
1269 4 d. 50 "Athenian Maiden" . . 20 10
1270 6 d. 50 "Charioteer of Delphi" (bronze) 30 35

270 "Theocracy of Zeus" (vase)

271 U.P.U. Emblem within Mycenaean Vase Design

1974. Greek Mythology (3rd series).
1271 **270** 1 d. 50 black & orange . . 10 10
1272 – 2 d. brown, red & orge . . 10 10
1273 – 2 d. 50 black, brn & orge . 10 10
1274 – 10 d. brown, red & orge . 20 15
DESIGNS—HORIZ: 2 d. "Athena's Birth" (vase); 2 d. 50, "Artemis, Apollo and Lito" (vase). VERT: 10 d. "Hermes" (vase).

1974. Centenary of U.P.U. Multicoloured.
1275 2 d. Type **271** 10 10
1276 4 d. 50 Hermes (horiz) 10 10
1277 6 d. 50 Woman reading letter . 20 15

272 Crete 1 d. Stamp of 1905

1974. Stamp Day.
1278 **272** 2 d. 50 black, red & vio . 20 15

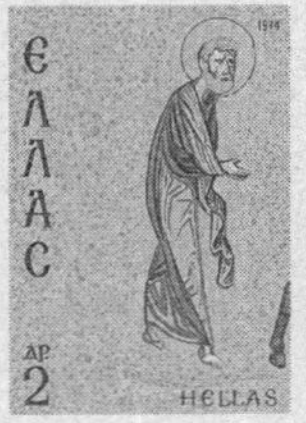

273 Joseph

274 Secret Assembly, Vostitsa

1974. Christmas. Multicoloured.
1279 2 d. Type **273** 10 10
1280 4 d. 50 Virgin and Child on donkey 10 10
1281 8 d. 50 Jacob 15 15
Nos. 1279/81 were issued together, se-tenant, forming a composite design.

1974. Greek Costumes (3rd series). As T **251**. Multicoloured.
1282 20 l. Megara 10 10
1283 30 l. Salamis 10 10
1284 50 l. Edipsos 10 10
1285 1 d. Kymi 10 10
1286 1 d. 50 Sterea Hellas 10 10
1287 2 d. Desfina 10 10
1288 3 d. Epirus 10 10
1289 3 d. 50 Naousa 10 10
1290 4 d. Hasia 10 10
1291 4 d. 50 Thasos 10 10
1292 5 d. Skopelos 10 10
1293 6 d. 50 Epirus 10 10
1294 10 d. Pelion 15 10
1295 25 d. Kerkyra 20 10
1296 30 d. Boeotia (Tanagra) . . . 50 30

1975. 150th Death Anniv of Girgorios Dikeos Papaflessas (Soldier).
1297 **274** 4 d. blk, brn & stone . . 10 10
1298 – 7 d. multicoloured . . . 10 10
1299 – 11 d. multicoloured . . . 20 20
DESIGNS—VERT: 7 d. Papaflessas in uniform. HORIZ: 11 d. Aghioi Apostoli (chapel), Kalamala.

275 Roses in Vase

277 Neolithic Goddess

276 Mansion, Kastoria

1975. Europa. Multicoloured.
1300 4 d. Type **275** 15 10
1301 7 d. Erotokritos and Aretussa . 25 15
1302 11 d. Girl and sheep 40 30

1975. National Architecture.
1303 **276** 10 l. black and blue . . . 10 10
1304 – 40 l. black and red . . . 10 10
1305 – 4 d. black and brown . . 10 10
1306 – 6 d. black and blue . . . 15 10
1307 – 11 d. black and orange . . 25 15
DESIGNS: 40 l. House, Arnea, Halkidiki; 4 d. House, Veria; 6 d. Mansion, Siatista; 11 d. Mansion, Amelakia, Thessaly.

1975. International Women's Year.
1308 **277** 1 d. 50 brown, deep mauve and mauve 10 10
1309 – 8 d. 50 black, red and ochre 10 10
1310 – 11 d. black, dp blue & bl . 15 15
DESIGNS: 8 d. 50, Confrontation between Antigone and Creon; 11 d. Women "Looking to the Future".

278 Alexandros Papanastasiou (founder) and University Buildings

1975. 50th Anniv of Thessaloniki University.
1311 **278** 1 d. 50 sepia & brown . . 10 10
1312 – 4 d. multicoloured . . . 10 10
1313 – 11 d. multicoloured . . . 10 10
DESIGNS: 4 d. Original University building; 11 d. Plan of University city.

279 Greek 100 d. Stamp of 1933

281 Pontos Lyre

280 Evangelos Zappas and Zappeion Building

1975. Stamp Day.
1314 **279** 11 d. brn, cream & grn . . 15 10

1975. National Benefactors (2nd series).
1315 **280** 1 d. black, grey & grn . . 10 10
1316 – 4 d. black, grey & brn . . 10 10
1317 – 6 d. black, brn & orge . . 10 10
1318 – 11 d. black, grey & red . . 20 15
DESIGNS: 4 d. Georgios Rizaris and Rizarios Ecclesiastical School; 6 d. Michael Tositsas and Metsovion Technical University; 11 d. Nicolaos Zosimas and Zosimea Academy.

1975. Musical Instruments. Multicoloured.
1319 10 l. Type **281** 10 10
1320 20 l. Musicians (Byzantine mural) 10 10
1321 1 d. Cretan lyre 10 10
1322 1 d. 50 Tambourine 10 10
1323 4 d. Cithern-player (from amphora) (horiz) 10 10
1324 6 d. Bagpipes 10 10
1325 7 d. Lute 10 10
1326 10 d. Barrel-organ 15 10
1327 11 d. Pipes and zournades . . 15 10
1328 20 d. "Praise God" (Byzantine mural) (horiz) 25 10
1329 25 d. Drums 25 10
1330 30 d. Kanonaki (horiz) 35 20

282 Early telephone

1976. Telephone Centenary. Multicoloured.
1331 7 d. Type **282** 15 10
1332 11 d. Modern telephone and globe 20 15
Nos. 1331/2 were issued together, se-tenant, forming a composite design.

283 Battle of Missolonghi

1976. 150th Anniv of Fall of Missolonghi.
1333 **283** 4 d. multicoloured . . . 10 10

284 Florina Jug

285 Lion attacking Bull

1976. Europa. Multicoloured.
1334 7 d. Type **284** 10 10
1335 8 d. 50 Plate with birds design (25 × 30 mm) 20 10
1336 11 d. Egina pitcher 30 30

1976. Ancient Sealing-stones. Multicoloured.
1337 2 d. Type **285** 10 10
1338 4 d. 50 Water birds 10 10
1339 7 d. Wounded bull 15 10
1340 8 d. 50 Head of Silenus (27 × 40 mm) 20 10
1341 11 d. Cow feeding calf (40 × 27 mm) 25 20

286 Long-jumping

287 Lemnos

1976. Olympic Games, Montreal. Mult.
1342 50 l. Type **286** 10 10
1343 2 d. Handball 10 10
1344 3 d. 50 Wrestling 10 10
1345 4 d. Swimming 10 10
1346 11 d. Athens and Montreal stadiums (52 × 37 mm) . . . 30 15
1347 25 d. The Olympic flame . . . 20 20

1976. Tourist Publicity. Multicoloured.
1348 30 d. Type **287** 30 15
1349 50 d. Lesbos (horiz) 50 20
1350 75 d. Chios (horiz) 75 25
1351 100 d. Samos (horiz) . . . . 1·00 40

288 "The Magi speaking to the Jews"

289 Lascaris Book of Grammar, 1476

1976. Christmas. Illustrations from manuscripts at Esfigmenou Monastery. Multicoloured.
1352 4 d. Type **288** 10 10
1353 7 d. "The Adoration of the Magi" 20 10

1976. 500th Anniv of Printing of First Greek Book.
1354 **289** 4 d. multicoloured . . . 10 10

290 Heinrich Schliemann

291 "Patients visiting Aesculapius" (relief)

1976. Centenary of Schliemann's Excavation of the Royal Graves, Mycenae. Multicoloured.
1355 2 d. Type **290** 10 10
1356 4 d. Gold bracelet (horiz) . . . 10 10
1357 5 d. Silver and gold brooch . . 10 10
1358 7 d. Gold diadem (horiz) . . . 15 10
1359 11 d. Gold mask 20 15

1977. International Rheumatism Year.
1360 **291** 50 l. black, stone & red . . 10 10
1361 – 1 d. black, orge & red . . 10 10
1362 – 1 d. 50 black, stone and red 10 10
1363 – 2 d. black, orge & red . . 10 10
1364 – 20 d. black, stone & red . 15 15
DESIGNS—(22 × 27 mm): 1 d. Ancient clinic; 1 d. 50, "Aesculapius curing a young man" (relief); 2 d. Hercules and nurse. 23 × 34 mm: 20 d. "Cured patient offering model of leg" (relief).

292 Fortresses of Mani

1977. Europa. Multicoloured.
1365 5 d. Type **292** 15 10
1366 7 d. Santorin (vert) 20 10
1367 15 d. Lassithi Plain, Crete . . 35 35

293 Emblem and Transport

1977. 45th European Conference of Ministers of Transport.
1368 **293** 7 d. multicoloured . . . 40 25

294 Alexandria Lighthouse (Roman coin)

1977. "The Civilizing Influence of Alexander the Great". Multicoloured.
1369 50 l. Type **294** 10 10
1370 1 d. "Placing the Works of Homer in Achilles' tomb" (fresco, Raphael) 10 10
1371 1 d. 50 Descending to sea bed in special ship (Flemish miniature) 10 10
1372 3 d. In search of the water of life (Hindu plate) 10 10

1373 7 d. Alexander the Great on horseback (Coptic carpet) . 15 10
1374 11 d. Listening to oracle (Byzantine manuscript) . . . 20 15
1375 30 d. Death of Alexander the Great (Persian miniature) . . 35 25

295 Wreath in Front of University

296 Archbishop Makarios

1977. Restoration of Democracy.
1376 **295** 4 d. blue, green & blk . . 10 10
1377 – 7 d. multicoloured . . . 15 10
1378 – 20 d. multicoloured . . . 30 15
DESIGNS—HORIZ: (26 × 22 mm) 7 d. Demonstrators at University. VERT: (22 × 26 mm) 20 d. Hand with olive branch, University and flags.

1977. Archbishop Makarios Commemoration.
1379 **296** 4 d. black and grey . . . 10 10
1380 – 7 d. blk, brn & stone . . 10 10
DESIGN: 7 d. Makarios and map of Cyprus.

297 Melas Building, Athens (former post office)

1977. 19th-century Hellenic Architecture.
1381 **297** 50 l. black, stone & red . 10 10
1382 – 1 d. black, stone & grn . . 10 10
1383 – 1 d. 50 black, stone & bl . 10 10
1384 – 2 d. black, stone & grn . . 10 10
1385 – 5 d. black, stone & yell . . 10 10
1386 – 50 d. black, stone & orge . 30 15
DESIGNS: 1 d. Institution for the Blind, Thessalonika; 1 d. 50, Town Hall of Hermoupolis, Syros; 2 d. Branch Office of National Bank, Piraeus; 5 d. Ilissia (Palace of Duchess of Plakentia), Athens; 50 d. Municipal Theatre, Patras.

298 The Battle of Navarino

299 Parthenon and Industrial Complex

1977. 150th Anniv of Battle of Navarino.
1387 **298** 4 d. yellow, blk & brn . . 20 10
1388 – 7 d. multicoloured . . . 20 15
DESIGN: 7 d. Admirals Van der Heyden, Sir Edward Codrington and Comte de Rigny.

1977. Environmental Protection. Mult.
1389 3 d. Type **299** 10 10
1390 4 d. Birds and fish (horiz) . . . 15 10
1391 7 d. Living and dead trees (horiz) 15 10
1392 30 d. Head of Erechtheum caryatid and chimneys 25 20

300 Map of Greece and Ships

1977. "Greeks Abroad". Multicoloured.
1393 4 d. Type **300** 10 10
1394 5 d. Globe and Greek flag . . 10 10
1395 7 d. Globe and swallows . . . 10 10
1396 11 d. Envelope with flags . . . 40 20
1397 13 d. Map of the World . . . 20 15

301 "The Port of Kalamata" (C. Parthenis)

1977. Greek Paintings. Multicoloured.
1398 1 d. 50 Type **301** 30 10
1399 2 d. 50 "Arsanas" (S. Papaloucas) (vert) 10 10
1400 4 d. "Santorin" (C. Maleas) . . 15 10
1401 7 d. "The Engagement" (N. Gyzis) 15 10
1402 11 d. "The Straw Hat" (N. Lytras) (vert) 20 10
1403 15 d. "Spring" (G. Iacovidis) . 25 20

302 "Ebenus cretica"

303 Horse Postman and Pre-stamp Cancel

1978. Greek Flora. Multicoloured.
1404 1 d. 50 Type **302** 10 10
1405 2 d. 50 "Fritillaria rhodokanakis" 10 10
1406 3 d. "Campanula oreadum" . . 15 10
1407 4 d. "Lilium heldreichii" . . . 15 10
1408 7 d. "Viola delphinantha" . . 20 10
1409 25 d. "Paeonia rhodia" 30 25

1978. 150th Anniv of Postal Service. Mult.
1410 4 d. Type **303** 15 10
1411 5 d. "Maximilianos" (passenger steamer) and Greek "Hermes" stamp 20 10
1412 7 d. Steam mail train and 1896 Olympic Games stamp . . . 45 25
1413 30 d. Postmen on motor cycles and 1972 "Stamp Day" commemorative 25 25

304 Lighting the Olympic Flame

305 St. Sophia, Salonika

1978. 80th International Olympic Committee Session, Athens. Multicoloured.
1415 7 d. Type **304** 10 10
1416 13 d. Start of 100 m. race . . . 25 20

1978. Europa. Multicoloured.
1417 4 d. Type **305** 15 10
1418 7 d. Lysicrates' Monument, Athens 25 15

306 Bust of Aristotle

307 Rotary Emblem (50th anniv)

1978. 2300th Death Anniv of Aristotle. Multicoloured.
1419 2 d. Type **306** 10 10
1420 4 d. "The School of Athens" (detail Raphael) 10 10
1421 7 d. Map of Chalkidiki and statue plinth 15 10
1422 20 d. "Aristotle the Wise" (Byzantine fresco) (21 × 37 mm) 25 15

1978. Anniversaries and Events. Mult.
1423 1 d. Type **307** 10 10
1424 1 d. 50 Surgery (11th Greek Surgery Congress) (vert) . . 10 10
1425 2 d. 50 Ugo Foscolo (poet, birth bicentenary) 10 10
1426 5 d. Bronze head (25th anniv of European Convention on Human Rights) 10 10
1427 7 d. Hand with reins (Conference of Ministers of Culture of Council of Europe countries) (vert) 15 10
1428 13 d. Wright Flyer I with Daedalus and Icarus (75th anniv of first powered flight) (vert) 35 35

308 The Poor Woman with Five Children

309 Grafted Plant and Circulation Diagram

1978. "The Twelve Months" (Greek fairy tale). Multicoloured.
1429 2 d. Type **308** 10 10
1430 3 d. The poor woman and the twelve months 10 10
1431 4 d. The poor woman and the gold coins 15 10
1432 20 d. The poor woman with her children and the rich woman with the snakes 25 15

1978. Transplants. Multicoloured.
1433 4 d. Type **309** 10 10
1434 10 d. "Miracle of Sts. Cosmas and Damian" (Alonso de Sedano) 20 20

310 "Virgin and Child"

311 First Academy, Nauplion, and Cadet

1978. Christmas. Icons from Stavronikita Monastery, Mount Athos. Multicoloured.
1435 4 d. Type **310** 10 10
1436 7 d. "The Baptism of Christ" . 10 10

1978. 150th Anniv of Military Academy. Multicoloured.
1437 1 d. 50 Type **311** 10 10
1438 2 d. Academy coat of arms (vert) 10 10
1439 10 d. Modern Academy, Athens, and cadet 20 15

312 "Antipliarchos Laskos" (destroyer)

1978. Greek Naval Ships. Multicoloured.
1440 50 l. Type **312** 10 10
1441 1 d. "Andromeda" (motor torpedo-boat) 10 10
1442 2 d. 50 "Papanicolis" (submarine) 10 10
1443 4 d. "Psara" (cruiser) 15 10
1444 5 d. "Madonna of Hydra" (armed sailing caique) . . . 20 10
1445 7 d. Byzantine dromon 25 15
1446 50 d. Athenian trireme . . . . 1·75 1·00

313 Map of Greece

314 Kitsos Tsavellas

1978. The Greek State.
1447 **313** 7 d. multicoloured . . . 20 10
1448 11 d. multicoloured . . . 25 10
1449 13 d. multicoloured . . . 30 20

1979. "The Struggle of the Souliots".
1450 **314** 1 d. 50 lt brn, blk & brn . 10 10
1451 – 3 d. multicoloured . . . 10 10
1452 – 10 d. multicoloured . . . 15 10
1453 – 20 d. ochre, black and brown 25 20
DESIGNS—HORIZ: 3 d. Souli Castle; 10 d. Fighting Souliots. VERT: 20 d. The dance of Zalongo.

315 Figurine found at Amorgos

316 Cretan Postmen

1979. Art of the Aegean.
1454 **315** 20 d. multicoloured . . . 20 15

1979. Europa. Multicoloured.
1455 4 d. Type **316** 10 10
1456 7 d. Mounted postman 15 15
Nos. 1454/5 were issued in se-tenant pairs, forming a composite design.

317 Nicolas Skoufas

318 Flags of Member States forming Ear of Wheat

1979. Anniversaries and Events. Mult.
1457 1 d. 50 Type **317** (founder of Friendly Society, birth bicentenary) 10 10
1458 2 d. Steam and diesel locomotives (75th anniv of railway) (horiz) 35 10
1459 3 d. Basketball (European Basketball Championship) . 10 10
1460 4 d. Fossil moonfish "Mene psarianos" (7th International Congress of Mediterranean Neogene) (horiz) 10 10
1461 10 d. Greek church (Balkan Tourist Year) 15 10
1462 20 d. Victory of Paeonius and flags (50th anniv of Balkan Sports) 25 20

1979. Signing of Treaty, Accession of Greece to European Community. Multicoloured.
1463 7 d. Type **318** 10 10
1464 30 d. European Parliament (horiz) 20 20

319 "Girl with Dove" (classic statue)

320 Head of Philip of Macedonia

1979. International Year of the Child. Multicoloured.
1465 5 d. Type **319** 10 10
1466 8 d. Girl with doves 10 10
1467 20 d. "Mother and Children" (detail, Iacovides) 20 15

1979. Archaeological Discoveries from Vergina. Multicoloured.
1468 6 d. Type **320** 10 10
1469 8 d. Gold Wreath 10 10
1470 10 d. Copper vessel 10 10
1471 14 d. Golden casket (horiz) . . 15 10
1472 18 d. Silver ewer 15 10
1473 20 d. Gold quiver 20 15
1474 30 d. Iron cuirass 30 20

321 Purple Heron

322 Agricultural Bank of Greece (50th anniv)

1979. Endangered Birds. Multicoloured.
1475 6 d. Type **321** 35 10
1476 8 d. Audouin's gull 50 15
1477 10 d. Eleonora's falcon (horiz) . 55 20
1478 14 d. Common kingfisher (horiz) 75 30
1479 20 d. Eastern white pelican . . 1·25 45
1480 25 d. White-tailed sea eagle . . 1·40 90

1979. Anniversaries and Events.

1481 **322** 3 d. black, yell & olive . . 10 10
1482 – 4 d. multicoloured . . . 10 10
1483 – 6 d. multicoloured . . . 10 10
1484 – 8 d. multicoloured . . . 10 10
1485 – 10 d. multicoloured . . . 15 10
1486 – 12 d. multicoloured . . . 15 15
1487 – 14 d. multicoloured . . . 20 15
1488 – 18 d. multicoloured . . . 20 15
1489 – 25 d. multicoloured . . . 30 25

DESIGNS—HORIZ: 10 d. Ionic capital and map of Balkans ("Balkanfila '79" Stamp Exhibition); 25 d. Parliamentary Meeting (104th anniv of Greek Parliament). VERT: 4 d. Cosmas the Aetolian (monk and martyr) (death bicent.); 6 d. Basil the Great (1600th death anniv); 8 d. Magnifying glass and map of Balkan countries ("Balkanfila '79" Stamp Exhibition); 12 d. Aristolelis Valaoritis (poet) (death centenary); 14 d. Golfer (World Golfing Championship); 18 d. Bust of Hippocrates (International Hippocratic Foundation, Kos).

323 Parnassos **324** Gate of Galerius

1979. Landscapes. Multicoloured.

1490 50 l. Type **323** 10 10
1491 1 d. Tempi (horiz) 10 10
1492 2 d. Milos 10 10
1493 4 d. Vikos Gorge 10 10
1494 5 d. Misolonghi (horiz) 10 10
1495 6 d. Louros Aqueduct 10 10
1496 7 d. Samothraki 10 10
1497 8 d. Sithonia, Chalkidike (horiz) 10 10
1498 10 d. Samaria Gorge 10 10
1499 12 d. Sifnos 10 10
1500 14 d. Kymi (horiz) 15 10
1501 18 d. Ios 15 10
1502 20 d. Thasos 15 10
1503 30 d. Paros (horiz) 15 10
1504 50 d. Cephalonia 35 25

1980. 1st Hellenic Nephrology Congress, Thessalonika.

1505 **324** 8 d. blue, black and red . 20 15

325 Aegosthena Castle **326** Aristarchus' Theorem and Temple of Hera

1980. Castles, Caves and Bridges. Mult.

1506 4 d. Type **325** 10 10
1507 6 d. Byzantine castle, Thessalonika (horiz) 10 10
1508 8 d. Perama cave, Ioannina . . 10 10
1509 10 d. Dyros cave, Mani . . . 10 10
1510 14 d. Arta bridge (horiz) . . . 15 10
1511 20 d. Kalogiros bridge, Epirus (horiz) 35 20

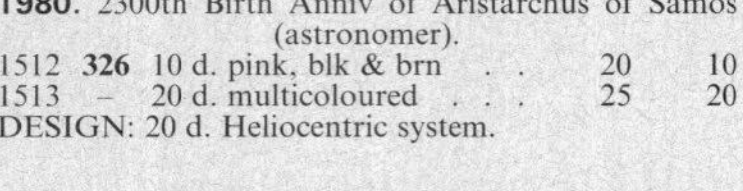

1980. 2300th Birth Anniv of Aristarchus of Samos (astronomer).

1512 **326** 10 d. pink, blk & brn . . 20 10
1513 – 20 d. multicoloured . . . 25 20

DESIGN: 20 d. Heliocentric system.

327 George Seferis (writer)

1980. Europa.

1514 **327** 8 d. brown, blue & black . 15 10
1515 – 14 d. brn, blk and cream . 30 20

DESIGN: 14 d. Maria Callas (opera singer).

328 Open Book

1980. Energy Conservation. Multicoloured.

1516 8 d. Type **328** 10 10
1517 20 d. Lightbulb and candle (vert) 30 20

329 Fire-fighting

1980. Anniversaries and Events. Mult.

1518 4 d. Type **329** (50th anniv of fire brigade) 10 10
1519 6 d. St. Demetrius (mosaic) (1700th birth anniv) (vert) . 10 10
1520 8 d. Revolutionaries (Theriso revolution, 75th anniv) . . . 15 10
1521 10 d. Ancient vase and olive branch (World Olive Oil Year) (vert) 15 10
1522 14 d. International press emblem (15th International Journalists Federation Congress) (vert) 20 10
1523 20 d. Constantinos Ikonomos (cleric and scholar), (birth bicent.) (vert) 25 20

330 Olympia and Coin of Elia

1980. Olympic Games, Moscow. Designs showing Greek stadia. Multicoloured.

1524 8 d. Type **330** 10 10
1525 14 d. Delphi and Delphic coin . 35 20
1526 18 d. Epidaurus and coin of Olympia 20 10
1527 20 d. Rhodes and coin of Kos . 20 10
1528 50 d. Panathenaik stadium and First Olympic Games medal . 50 35

331 Asbestos

1980. Minerals. Multicoloured.

1529 6 d. Type **331** 10 10
1530 8 d. Gypsum (vert) 10 10
1531 10 d. Copper 10 10
1532 14 d. Barite (vert) 20 15
1533 18 d. Chromite 15 10
1534 20 d. Mixed sulphides (vert) . . 15 10
1535 30 d. Bauxite (vert) 35 25

332 Dassault Mirage III Jet Fighter **333** Left Detail of Poulakis' Painting

1980. Anniversaries and Events. Mult.

1536 6 d. Breakdown truck (20th anniv of Automobile and Touring Club of Greece road assistance service) (horiz) . . 10 10
1537 8 d. Type **332** (50th anniv of Air Force) 20 10
1538 12 d. Piper Super Cub light airplane outside hangar (50th anniv of Thessalonika Flying Club) (horiz) 30 15
1539 20 d. Harbour scene (50th anniv of Piraeus Port Organization) 55 20
1540 25 d. Association for Macedonian Studies Headquarters (40th anniv) . 35 25

1980. Christmas. Details from "He is Happy Thanks to You" by T. Poulakis (in St. John's Monastery, Pataros). Multicoloured.

1541 6 d. Type **333** 15 10
1542 14 d. Virgin and Child (centre) 15 10
1543 20 d. Right detail 25 15

Nos. 1541/3 were issued together, se-tenant, forming a composite design.

334 Fresh and Canned Vegetables **335** "Kira Maria" (Alexandrian folk dance)

1981. Exports. Multicoloured.

1544 9 d. Type **334** 10 10
1545 17 d. Fruit 15 10
1546 20 d. Cotton 10 10
1547 25 d. Marble 30 25

1981. Europa. Multicoloured.

1548 12 d. Type **335** 20 10
1549 17 d. "Sousta" (Cretan dance) . 35 30

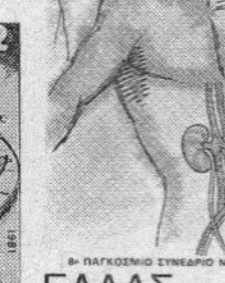

336 Olympic Stadium, Kalogreza **337** Human Figure showing Kidneys

1981. European Athletic Championships, Athens (1982) (1st issue).

1550 **336** 12 d. bl, blk & lt bl . . . 15 10
1551 17 d. multicoloured . . . 30 30

DESIGN: 17 d. Athletes converging on Greece.

See also Nos. 1586/8.

1981. Anniversaries and Events.

1552 **337** 2 d. multicoloured . . . 10 10
1553 – 3 d. multicoloured . . . 20 10
1554 – 6 d. multicoloured . . . 10 10
1555 – 9 d. yellow, blk & brn . . 15 10
1556 – 12 d. multicoloured . . . 50 10
1557 – 21 d. multicoloured . . . 20 15
1558 – 40 d. red, blue & dp blue . 25 20

DESIGNS AND EVENTS—VERT: 2 d. Type **337** (8th World Nephrology Conference, Athens); 3 d. Parachutist, glider, Potez 25 biplane and boy with model glider (50th anniv of Greek National Air Club); 6 d. Meteora Monasteries, Thessaly, and Konitsa Bridge, Epirus (International Historical Symposium, Volos, and centenary of incorporation of Thessaly and Epirus into Greece); 12 d. Oil rig (first Greek oil production); 40 d. Heart (15th World Cardiovascular Surgery Conference Athens). HORIZ: 9 d. Bowl with "eye" decoration (50th anniv of Greek Ophthalmological Society); 21 d. Globes, plant and coin (Foundation in Athens of World Association for International Relations).

338 Variable Scallops **339** Aegean Island Bell Tower

1981. Shells, Fishes and Butterflies. Mult.

1559 4 d. Type **338** 25 10
1560 5 d. Painted comber (fish) . . . 15 10
1561 12 d. Mediterranean parrot-fish 15 10
1562 15 d. Dentex (fish) 20 15
1563 17 d. Apollo (butterfly) 30 25
1564 50 d. Pale clouded yellow (butterfly) 60 30

1981. Bell Towers and Altar Screens. Mult.

1565 4 d. Type **339** 10 10
1566 6 d. Altar gate, St. Paraskevi Church, Metsovo 10 10
1567 9 d. Altar gate, Pelion (horiz) . 15 10
1568 12 d. Bell tower, Saints Constantine and Helen Church, Halkiades, Epirus . 15 10
1569 17 d. Altar screen, St. Nicholas Church, Velvendos (horiz) . 20 15
1570 30 d. Icon of St. Jacob and stand, Alexandroupolis Church Museum 25 15
1571 40 d. Upper section of altar gate, St. Nicholas Church, Makrinitsa 40 25

340 Town Scene

1981. Anniversaries and Events. Mult.

1572 3 d. Type **340** (Council of Europe Urban Renaissance campaign) 10 10
1573 9 d. St. Simeon, Archbishop of Thessalonika (Canonization by Greek Orthodox Church) (vert) 15 10
1574 12 d. Child Jesus (detail from Byzantine icon) (Breast feeding campaign) (vert) . . . 15 10
1575 17 d. Gina Bachauer (pianist, 5th death anniv) (vert) . . . 20 15
1576 21 d. Constantine Broumidis (artist, 175th birth anniv) (vert) 20 20
1577 50 d. "Phoenix" banknotes 1831 (first banknotes, 150th anniv) 45 30

341 Old Parliament Building (museum) **342** "Flight from Missolonghi"

1982. Anniversaries and Events. Mult.

1578 2 d. Type **341** (centenary of Historical and Ethnological Society) 10 10
1579 9 d. Angelos Sikelianos (poet, 31st death anniv) (vert) . . . 20 10
1580 15 d. Harilaos Tricoupis (politician, 150th birth anniv) (vert) 10 10
1581 21 d. Mermaid (History of Aegean Islands Exhibition) (vert) 15 10
1582 30 d. Airbus Industrie A300 jetliner and emblem (25th anniv of Olympic Airways) 35 15
1583 50 d. Skull of Petralona man and Petralona cave (3rd European Congress of Anthropology, Petralona) (vert) 45 30

1982. Europa. Multicoloured.

1584 21 d. Bust of Miltiades and shield (Battle of Marathon) . 25 15
1585 30 d. Type **342** 50 30

343 Pole-vaulter and Wreath

1982. European Athletic Championships (2nd issue). Multicoloured.

1586 21 d. Type **343** 20 15
1587 25 d. Women runners (vert) . . 25 20
1588 40 d. Athletes at start of race, shot putter, high jumper and hurdler 45 25

344 Lectionary Heading **345** "Karaiskakis' Camp in Piraeus" (detail, von Krazeisen)

1982. Byzantine Book Illustrations. Mult.

1589 4 d. Type **344** 10 10
1590 6 d. Initial letter E (vert) . . . 10 10
1591 12 d. Initial letter T (vert) . . . 15 10
1592 15 d. Canon-table of Gospel readings (vert) 25 10
1593 80 d. Heading from zoology book 65 40

1982. Birth Bicent. of Georges Karaiskakis (revolutionary leader).

1594 **345** 12 d. green, black & blue . 15 10
1595 – 50 d. multicoloured . . . 45 30

DESIGN: 50 d. Karaiskakis meditating.

346 Cypriot "Disappearances" Demonstration

1982. Amnesty International Year of the "Disappearances". Multicoloured.

1596 15 d. Type **346** 20 15
1597 75 d. Victims, barbed wire and candle 65 35

INDEX

Countries can be quickly located by referring to the index at the end of this volume.

347 "Demonstration in Athens, 25 March 1942" (P. Zachariou.)

1982. National Resistance, 1941–44. Mult.
1598 1 d. Type **347** 10 10
1599 2 d. "Kalavryta's Sacrifice" (S. Vasillou) 10 10
1600 5 d. "Resistance in Thrace" (A. Tassos) (vert) 10 10
1601 9 d. "The Onset of the Struggle in Crete" (P. Gravalos) (vert) 15 10
1602 12 d. Resistance Fighters (vert) 20 10
1603 21 d. "Gorgopotamos" (A. Tassos) (vert) 40 15
1604 30 d. "Kaisariani, Athens" (G. Sikeliotis) 30 10
1605 50 d. "The Struggle in Northern Greece" (V. Katraki) 50 35

348 Mary and Jesus

1982. Christmas. Early Christians Bas-reliefs. Multicoloured.
1607 9 d. Type **348** 15 10
1608 21 d. Jesus in manger 20 15

349 Figurehead from Tsamados's "Ares" (brig)

1983. 25th Anniv of International Maritime Organization. Ships' Figureheads. Mult.
1609 11 d. Type **349** 30 15
1610 15 d. Miaoulis's "Ares" (full-rigged ship) (vert) 40 20
1611 18 d. Topsail schooner from Sphakia (vert) 45 25
1612 25 d. Bouboulina's "Spetses" (full-rigged ship) (vert) 60 35
1613 40 d. Babas's "Epameinondas" (brig) (vert) 95 50
1614 50 d. "Carteria" (steamer) 1·50 75

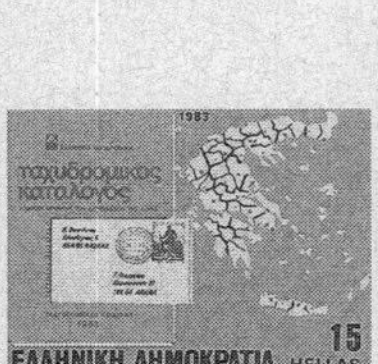

350 Letter and Map of Greece showing Postcode Districts

351 Archimedes

1983. Inauguration of Postcode. Multicoloured.
1615 15 d. Type **350** 20 15
1616 25 d. Hermes' head within post-horn 40 25

1983. Europa. Multicoloured.
1617 25 d. Acropolis, Athens (49 × 34 mm) 45 30
1618 80 d. Type **351** 90 45

352 Rowing

353 Marinos Antypas (farmers' leader)

1983. Sports. Multicoloured.
1619 15 d. Type **352** 15 15
1620 18 d. Water skiing (vert) 40 20
1621 27 d. Windsurfing (vert) 55 40
1622 50 d. Ski lift (vert) 40 15
1623 80 d. Skiing 80 30

1983. Personalities. Multicoloured.
1624 **353** 6 d. multicoloured 10 10
1625 – 9 d. multicoloured 10 10
1626 – 15 d. multicoloured 15 10
1627 – 20 d. multicoloured 20 10
1628 – 27 d. multicoloured 30 15
1629 – 32 d. multicoloured 30 15
1630 – 40 d. yellow, brn & blk 40 10
1631 – 50 d. multicoloured 60 35

DESIGNS: 9 d. Nicholas Plastiras (soldier and statesman); 15 d. George Papandreou (statesman); 20 d. Constantin Cavafy (poet); 27 d. Nikos Kazantzakis (writer); 32 d. Manolis Calomiris (composer); 40 d. George Papanicolaou (medical researcher); 50 d. Despina Achladioti, "Matron of Rho" (patriot).

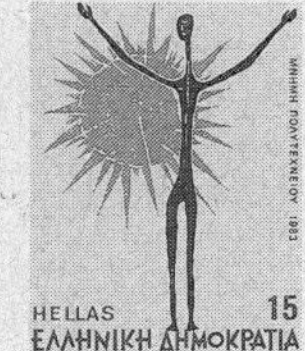

354 Democritus

355 Poster by V. Katraki

1983. 1st Int Democritus Congress, Xanthe.
1632 **354** 50 d. multicoloured 40 20

1983. 10th Anniv of Polytechnic School Uprising. Multicoloured.
1633 15 d. Type **355** 15 10
1634 30 d. Students leaving Polytechnic 35 20

356 The Deification of Homer

357 Horse's Head, Chariot of Seline

1983. Homeric Odes. Multicoloured.
1635 **356** 2 d. sepia and brown 10 10
1636 – 3 d. brn, lt orge & orge 10 10
1637 – 4 d. yell, brn & dp brn 10 10
1638 – 5 d. multicoloured 10 10
1639 – 6 d. orange and brown 10 10
1640 – 10 d. lt orge, brn & orge 10 10
1641 – 14 d. orge, lt orge & brn 15 10
1642 – 15 d. lt orge, orge & brn 15 10
1643 – 20 d. bistre, blk & brn 20 10
1644 – 27 d. brown, pale orange and orange 25 15
1645 – 30 d. brown, pale orange and orange 25 10
1646 – 32 d. orge, brn & lt orge 60 15
1647 – 50 d. brn, lt orge & orge 45 10
1648 – 75 d. brn, orge & red 45 20
1649 – 100 d. sepia, grn & brn 75 40

DESIGN—HORIZ: 3 d. Abduction of Helen by Paris (pot); 4 d. Wooden horse; 5 d. Achilles throwing dice with Ajax (jar); 14 d. Battle between Ajax and Hector (dish); 15 d. Priam requesting body of Hector (pot); 27 d. Ulysses escaping from Polyphemus's cave; 32 d. Ulysses and Sirens; 50 d. Ulysses slaying suitors; 75 d. Heroes of Iliad (cup). VERT: 6 d. Achilles; 10 d. Hector receiving arms from his parents (vase); 20 d. Binding of Polyphemus; 30 d. Ulysses meeting Nausica; 100 d. Homer (bust).

1984. Parthenon Marbles. Multicoloured.
1650 14 d. Type **357** 25 15
1651 15 d. Dionysus 25 10
1652 20 d. Hestia, Dione and Aphrodite 35 10
1653 27 d. Ilissus 40 25
1654 32 d. Lapith and Centaur 80 55

358 Bridge

359 Ancient Stadium, Olympia

1984. Europa. 25th Anniv of C.E.P.T.
1656 **358** 15 d. multicoloured 30 20
1657 27 d. multicoloured 70 60

1984. Olympic Games, Los Angeles. Multicoloured.
1658 14 d. Type **359** 25 15
1659 15 d. Athletes preparing for training 30 15
1660 20 d. Flute player, discus thrower and long jumper 40 20
1661 32 d. Athletes training 45 25
1662 80 d. K. Vikelas and Panathenaic Stadium 1·25 50

360 Tank on Map of Cyprus

361 Pelion Steam Train

1984. 10th Anniv of Turkish Invasion of Cyprus. Multicoloured.
1663 20 d. Type **360** 30 10
1664 32 d. Hand grasping barbed wire and map of Cyprus 45 25

1984. Railway Centenary. Multicoloured.
1665 15 d. Type **361** 45 15
1666 20 d. Steam goods train on Papadia Bridge (vert) 60 30
1667 30 d. Piraeus-Peloponnese steam train 85 55
1668 50 d. Cogwheel railway, Kalavryta (vert) 1·75 80

362 Athens 5th Cent B.C. Silver Coin on Plan of City

363 "10" enclosing Arms

1984. 150th Anniv of Athens as Capital. Multicoloured.
1669 15 d. Type **362** 30 15
1670 100 d. Symbols of ancient Athens and skyline of modern Athens 1·10 40

1984. 10th Anniv of Revolution.
1671 **363** 95 d. multicoloured 90 15

364 "Annunciation"

365 Running

1984. Christmas. Multicoloured.
1672 14 d. Type **364** 30 15
1673 20 d. "Nativity" 40 20
1674 25 d. "Presentation in the Temple" 50 25
1675 32 d. "Baptism of Christ" 55 25

Nos. 1672/5 show scenes from Hagion Panton icon by Athanasios Tountas.

1985. 16th European Indoor Athletics Championships, New Phaleron. Multicoloured.
1676 12 d. Type **365** 20 15
1677 15 d. Putting the shot 25 10
1678 20 d. Sports stadium (37 × 24 mm) 35 15
1679 25 d. Hurdling 40 20
1680 80 d. High jumping 75 40

366 Catacomb Niche

1985. Catacombs of Melos. Multicoloured.
1681 15 d. Type **366** 15 20
1682 20 d. Martyrs' altars and niches central passageway 35 20
1683 100 d. Niches 70 35

367 Apollo and Marsyas

1985. Europa. Multicoloured.
1684 27 d. Type **367** 55 40
1685 80 d. Dimitris Mitropoulos and Nikos Skalkotas (composers) 60 30

368 Coin (315 B.C.) and "Salonika" (relief)

1985. 2300th Anniv of Salonika. Mult.
1686 1 d. Type **368** 10 10
1687 5 d. Saints Demetrius and Methodius (mosaics) (49 × 34 mm) 10 10
1688 15 d. Galerius's Arch (detail) (Roman period) 15 10
1689 20 d. Salonika's eastern walls (Byzantine period) 30 10
1690 32 d. Upper City, Salonika 35 15
1691 50 d. Greek army liberating Salonika, 1912 1·60 40
1692 80 d. Soldier's legs and Salonika (German occupation 1941–44) 60 35
1693 95 d. Contemporary views of Salonika (60th anniv of Aristotelian University and International Trade Fair) (49 × 34 mm) 90 45

369 Urn on Map of Cyprus

370 "Democracy crowning the City" (relief)

1985. 25th Anniv of Republic of Cyprus.
1694 **369** 32 d. multicoloured 35 25

1985. Athens, "Cultural Capital of Europe".
1695 **370** 15 d. multicoloured 15 10
1696 – 20 d. black, grey and blue 25 15
1697 – 32 d. multicoloured 50 20
1698 – 80 d. multicoloured 75 30

DESIGNS—HORIZ: 20 d. Tritons and dolphins (mosaic floor, Roman baths, Hieratis); 80 d. Capodistrian University, Athens. VERT: 32 d. Angel (fresco, Pentelis Cave).

371 Children of different Races

373 Folk Dance

1985. International Youth Year (15, 25 d.) and 40th Anniv of United Nations Organization (27, 100 d.). Multicoloured.
1699 **370** 15 d. multicoloured 15 10
1700 25 d. Doves and youths 25 10
1701 27 d. Interior of U.N. General Assembly 50 15
1702 100 d. U.N. Building, New York, and U.N. emblem 75 45

1985. Pontic Culture. Multicoloured.
1704 12 d. Type **373** 20 10
1705 15 d. Monastery of Our Lady of Soumela 35 10
1706 27 d. Women's costumes (vert) 40 15
1707 32 d. Trapezus High School 45 20
1708 80 d. Sinope Castle 55 45

374 Hestia

375 "Ephebos of Antikythera"

1986. Gods of Olympus.
1709 **374** 5 d. orge, blk & brn 10 10
1710 – 18 d. orge, blk & brn 25 10
1711 – 27 d. orge, blk & bl 35 15
1712 – 32 d. orge, blk & red 40 25
1713 – 35 d. orge, blk & brn 40 20
1714 – 40 d. orge, blk & red 50 10
1715 – 50 d. orange, black and grey 60 20
1716 – 110 d. orge, blk & brn 80 15

1717 – 150 d. orange, black and grey 95 15
1718 – 200 d. orge, blk & bl . . . 1·25 25
1719 – 300 d. orge, blk & bl . . . 1·90 30
1720 – 500 d. orge, blk & bl . . . 3·25 1·60
DESIGNS: 18 d. Hermes; 27 d. Aphrodite; 32 d. Ares; 35 d. Athene; 40 d. Hephaestus; 50 d. Artemis; 110 d. Apollo; 150 d. Demeter; 200 d. Poseidon; 300 d. Hera; 500 d. Zeus.

1986. Sports Events and Anniversaries.
1721 **375** 18 d. grn, blk & grey . . 25 15
1722 – 27 d. yell, blk & red . . 35 15
1723 – 32 d. multicoloured . . . 55 40
1724 – 35 d. grn, blk & bis . . . 60 40
1725 – 40 d. multicoloured . . . 65 30
1726 – 50 d. multicoloured . . . 70 30
1727 – 110 d. multicoloured . . . 1·40 50
DESIGNS—VERT: 18 d. Type **375** (1st World Junior Athletics Championships); 32 d. Footballers (Pan-European Junior Football Finals); 35 d. "Wrestlers" (sculpture) (Pan-European Freestyle and Greco-Roman Wrestling Championships); 50 d. Cyclists (6th International Round Europe Cycling Meet.). HORIZ: 27 d. "Diadoumenos" (sculpture by Polycleitus) (1st World Junior Athletics Championships); 40 d. Volleyball players (Men's World Volleyball Championships); 110 d. "Victory" (unadopted design by Nikephoros Lytras for first Olympic Games commemoratives, 1896) (90th anniv of modern Olympic Games).

376 Fastening Seat Belt

377 Intelpost

1986. European Road Safety Year. Mult.
1728 18 d. Type **376** 25 15
1729 27 d. Motorcyclist in traffic . . 50 40
1730 110 d. Child strapped in back seat of car and speed limit signs . . . . 1·10 30

1986. New Postal Services. Multicoloured.
1731 18 d. Type **377** 25 20
1732 110 d. "Express Mail" banner around globe 80 25

378 Sapling between Hands and burning Forest

379 Victims' Memorial and Workers

1986. Europa.
1733 **378** 35 d. grn, blk & orge . . 1·25 25
1734 – 110 d. bl, blk & grn . . . 2·25 1·10
DESIGN: 110 d. Dalmatian pelicans on Prespa Lake.

1986. Centenary of Chicago May Day Strike.
1735 **379** 40 d. multicoloured . . . 50 25

380 Swearing-in of Venizelos Government

381 Dove and Sun

1986. 50th Death Anniv of Eleftherios Venizelos (politician) (18 d.) and 6th International Crete Conference, Hania (110 d.). Multicoloured.
1736 18 d. Type **380** 25 10
1737 110 d. Hania harbour 85 30

1986. International Peace Year. Multicoloured.
1738 18 d. Type **381** 25 15
1739 35 d. Dove holding olive branch with flags as leaves 45 30
1740 110 d. Dove with olive branch flying out of globe (horiz) . . 65 30

382 "Madonna and Child"

383 "The Fox and the Grapes"

1986. Christmas. Designs showing icons. Multicoloured.
1741 22 d. Type **382** 20 15
1742 46 d. "Adoration of the Magi" (24 × 32 mm) 40 30
1743 130 d. "Christ enthroned with St. John the Evangelist" . . 90 20

1987. Aesop's Fables. Multicoloured.
1744 2 d. Type **383** 10 10
1745 5 d. "The North Wind and the Sun" 10 10
1746 10 d. "The Stag at the Spring and the Lion" 20 10
1747 22 d. "Zeus and the Snake" . . 30 10
1748 32 d. "The Crow and the Fox" . 50 15
1749 40 d. "The Woodcutter and Hermes" 70 50
1750 46 d. "The Ass in a Lion's Skin and the Fox" 75 20
1751 130 d. "The Hare and the Tortoise" . . . . 1·50 25

384 "Composition" (Archilleas Apergis)

385 Player shooting Goal and Indoor Court

1987. Europa. Sculptures. Multicoloured.
1752 40 d. Type **384** . . . . 1·25 40
1753 130 d. "Delphic Light" (Gerassimos Sklavos) . . . 1·60 60

1987. 25th European Men's Basketball Championships, Athens. Multicoloured.
1754 22 d. Type **385** 25 20
1755 25 d. Emblem and spectators (32 × 24 mm) 30 15
1756 130 d. Players . . . . 1·10 30

386 Banner and Students

1987. 150th Annivs. of Athens University (3, 23 d.) and National Metsovio Polytechnic Institute (others). Multicoloured.
1758 3 d. Type **386** 10 10
1759 23 d. Medal and owl 20 10
1760 40 d. Building facade, measuring instruments and computer terminal (vert) 35 20
1761 60 d. Students outside building (vert) 75 50

387 Ionic and Corinthian Capitals, Temple of Apollo, Phigaleia-Bassae

1987. Classical Architecture Capitals. Mult.
1762 2 d. Type **387** 10 10
1763 26 d. Doric capital, Parthenon . 25 10
1764 40 d. Ionic capital, The Erechtheum 35 20
1765 60 d. Corinthian capital, The Tholos, Epidaurus 70 55

388 Hands holding Cup Aloft

389 Diploma Engraving (Yiannis Kephalinos)

1987. Greek Victory in European Basketball Championship.
1766 **388** 40 d. multicoloured . . . 45 20

1987. 150th Anniv of Fine Arts High School (1767) and 60th Anniv of Panteios Political Science High School (1768). Multicoloured.
1767 26 d. Type **389** 25 10
1768 60 d. School campus (horiz) . . 55 40

390 Angel and Christmas Tree (left half)

391 Eleni Papadaki in "Hecuba" (Euripides) and Philippi Amphitheatre

1987. Christmas.
1769 26 d. Type **390** 25 10
1770 26 d. Angel and Christmas tree (right half) 25 10
Nos. 1769/70 were printed together, se-tenant, forming a composite design.

1987. Greek Theatre. Multicoloured.
1771 2 d. Type **391** 10 10
1772 4 d. Christopher Nezer in "The Wasps" (Aristophanes) and Dodona amphitheatre . . . 10 10
1773 7 d. Emilios Veakis in "Oedipus Rex" (Sophocles) and Delphi amphitheatre 10 10
1774 26 d. Marika Kotopouli in "The Shepherdess's Love" (Dimitris Koromilas) . . . 25 10
1775 40 d. Katina Paxinou in "Abraham's Sacrifice" (Vitzentzos Cornaros) . . . 35 15
1776 50 d. Kyveli in "Countess Valeraina's Secret" (Gregory Xenopoulos) 45 20
1777 60 d. Karolos Koun and stage set 55 25
1778 100 d. Dimitris Rontiris teaching National Theatre dancers an ancient dance 90 45

392 "Codonellina sp." (polyzoan)

394 Satellite and Fax Machine

393 Ancient Olympia

1988. Marine Life. Multicoloured.
1779 30 d. Type **392** 40 25
1780 40 d. "Diaperoecia major" (polyzoan (clump-forming animals)) 50 15
1781 50 d. "Artemia" (marine animal) 60 25
1782 60 d. "Posidonia oceanica" (plant) and Marmora seabream 80 50
1783 100 d. "Padina pavonica" (plant) . . . . 1·60 25

1988. Olympic Games, Seoul. Multicoloured.
1784 4 d. Type **393** 20 15
1785 20 d. Ancient athletes in Gymnasium 45 25
1786 30 d. Modern Olympics centenary emblem 90 20
1787 60 d. Ancient athletes training . 1·50 85
1788 170 d. Runner with Olympic flame . . . . 2·50 40

1988. Europa. Transport and Communications. Multicoloured.
1789 60 d. Type **394** . . . . 3·75 1·00
1790 150 d. Modern express and commuter trains . . . . . 4·00 2·00

395 Katarraktis Falls

396 Emblems

1988. European Campaign for Rural Areas. Waterfalls. Multicoloured.
1791 10 d. Type **395** 50 15
1792 60 d. Edessa waterfalls . . . . 1·25 90
1793 100 d. River Edessaios cascades . . . . 2·25 25

1988. 20th European Postal Workers Trade Unions Congress.
1794 **396** 60 d. multicoloured . . . 2·00 75

397 Mytilene Harbour, Lebos (painting by Theophilos)

398 Eleftherios Venizelos, Map and Flag

1988. Prefecture Capitals (1st series). Mult.
1795 2 d. Type **397** 10 10
1796 3 d. Alexandroupolis lighthouse, Evros (vert) 10 10
1797 4 d. St. Nicholas's bell-tower, Kozani (vert) 10 10
1798 5 d. Workmen's centre, Hermoupolis, Cyclades (vert) 10 10
1799 7 d. Sparta Town Hall, Lakonia 10 10
1800 8 d. Pegasus, Leukas 15 15
1801 10 d. Castle of the Knights, Rhodes, Dodecanese (vert) . 10 10
1802 20 d. Acropolis, Athens (vert) . 10 10
1803 25 d. Aqueduct, Kavala . . . 10 10
1804 30 d. Castle and statue of Athanasios Diakos, Lamia, Phthiotis (vert) 15 10
1805 50 d. Preveza Cathedral bell-tower and clock (vert) . . . 25 10
1806 60 d. Esplanade, Corfu 35 40
1807 70 d. Aghios Nicholaos, Lassithi 40 35
1808 100 d. Six Springheads, Poligiros, Khalkidiki 75 15
1809 200 d. Church of Paul the Apostle, Corinth, Corinthia . 1·25 35
See also Nos. 1848/62, 1911/22 and 1955/64.

1988. 75th Annivs. of Union of Crete and Greece (30 d.) and Liberation of Epirus and Macedonia (70 d.). Multicoloured.
1810 30 d. Type **398** 40 15
1811 70 d. Flags, map and "Liberty" 80 40

399 "Adoration of the Magi" (El Greco)

400 Map of EEC and Castle of Knights, Rhodes

1988. Christmas. Multicoloured.
1812 30 d. Type **399** 40 20
1813 70 d. "The Annunciation" (Kostas Parthenis) (horiz) . 80 40

1988. European Economic Community. Meeting of Heads of State, Rhodes. Multicoloured.
1814 60 d. Type **400** 90 80
1815 100 d. Members' flags and coin 1·25 25

401 Ancient Olympia and High Jumper

402 Flags

1989. Centenary (1996) of Modern Olympic Games (1st issue). Multicoloured.
1816 30 d. Type **401** 25 20
1817 60 d. Wrestlers and Delphi . . 90 75
1818 70 d. Acropolis, Athens, and swimmers 90 75
1819 170 d. Stadium and Golden Olympics emblem . . . . . 1·25 40
See also Nos. 1863/7.

1989. International Anniversaries. Mult.
1820 30 d. Type **402** (5th anniv of Six-nation Initiative for Peace and Disarmament) 25 15
1821 50 d. Flag and "Liberty" (bicentenary of French Revolution) 50 15
1822 60 d. Flag and ballot box (third direct European Parliament elections) . . . . 1·00 50
1823 70 d. Coins (cent of Interparliamentary Union) . . . 1·00 60
1824 200 d. Flag (40th anniv of Council of Europe) . . . . 2·25 25

403 Whistling Bird **404** Magnifying Glass and Bird

1989. Europa. Children's Toys. Multicoloured.
1825 60 d. Type **403** 1·75 90
1826 170 d. Butterfly 2·25 40

1989. "Balkanfila XII" International Stamp Exhibition, Salonica. Multicoloured.
1827 60 d. Type **404** 60 25
1828 70 d. Eye looking through magnifying glass 60 25

405 Dog Roses

1989. Wild Flowers. Multicoloured.
1830 8 d. Type **405** 10 10
1831 10 d. Common myrtle 10 10
1832 20 d. Common poppies 15 10
1833 30 d. Anemones 20 10
1834 60 d. Dandelions and chicory 45 15
1835 70 d. Mallow 55 20
1836 200 d. Thistles 1·50 45

406 Brown Bear **407** Gregoris Lambrakis

1990. Endangered Animals. Multicoloured.
1837 40 d. Type **406** 25 10
1838 70 d. Loggerhead turtle 75 30
1839 90 d. Mediterranean monk seal 75 30
1840 100 d. Lynx 1·00 40

1990. Politicians' Death Anniversaries. Mult.
1841 40 d. Type **407** (27th anniv) 35 15
1842 40 d. Pavlos Bakoyiannis (first anniv) 35 15

408 Clasped Hands, Roses and Flag **409** Old Central Post Office Interior

1990. National Reconciliation. Multicoloured.
1843 40 d. Type **408** 25 25
1844 70 d. Dove with banner 40 10
1845 100 d. Map and hands holding roses 75 50

1990. Europa. Post Offices Buildings. Mult.
1846 70 d. Type **409** 1·00 75
1847 210 d. Exterior of modern post office 1·50 50

410 "Animal Fair" (D. Gioldassi) (Karditsa) **411** Yachting

1990. Prefecture Capitals (2nd series). Mult.
1848 2 d. Type **410** 10 10
1849 5 d. Fort, Trikala (horiz) 10 10
1850 8 d. Street, Veroia (Imathia) 10 10
1851 10 d. Monument to Fallen Heroes, Missolonghi (Aetolia) (horiz) 10 10
1852 15 d. Harbour, Chios (horiz) 10 10
1853 20 d. Street, Tripolis (Arcadia) (horiz) 10 10
1854 25 d. "City and Town Hall" (woodcut, A. Tassos) (Volos, Magnesia) (horiz) 45 10
1855 40 d. Town Hall, Kalamata (Messenia) (horiz) 15 25
1856 50 d. Market, Pyrgos (Elia) (horiz) 20 15
1857 70 d. Lake and island, Yannina (horiz) 25 25
1858 80 d. Harhour sculpture, Rethymnon 50 75
1859 90 d. Argostolion (Cephalonia) (horiz) 50 40
1860 100 d. Citadel and islet, Nauplion (Argolis) (horiz) 70 25
1861 200 d. Lighthouse, Patras (Akhaia) 1·00 40
1862 250 d. Street, Florina (horiz) 1·40 35

1990. Centenary (1996) of Modern Olympic Games (2nd issue). Multicoloured.
1863 20 d. Type **411** 20 20
1864 50 d. Wrestling 35 25
1865 80 d. Running 55 65
1866 100 d. Handball 75 25
1867 250 d. Football 2·00 50

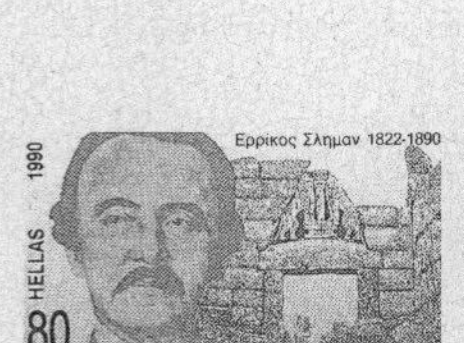

412 Schliemann and Lion Gate, Mycenae **413** "Woman knitting" (lithograph, Vasso Katraki)

1990. Death Cent of Heinrich Schliemann (archaeologist).
1868 **412** 80 d. multicoloured 1·10 65

1990. 50th Anniv of Greek–Italian War. Mult.
1869 50 d. Type **413** 25 20
1870 80 d. "Virgin Mary protecting Army" (lithograph, George Gounaropoulou) 50 40
1871 100 d. "Women's War Work" (lithograph, Kosta Grammatopoulou) 75 35

415 Calliope, Euterpe and Erato

1991. The Nine Muses. Multicoloured.
1873 50 d. Type **415** 50 20
1874 80 d. Terpsichore, Polyhymnia and Melpomene 75 35
1875 250 d. Thalia, Clio and Urania 1·75 40

416 Battle Scene (Ioannis Anousakis)

1991. 50th Anniv of Battle for Crete. Mult.
1876 60 d. Type **416** 80 40
1877 300 d. Map and flags of allied nations (32 × 24 mm) 1·90 65

417 Icarus pushing Satellite **418** Swimming

1991. Europa. Europe in Space. Mult.
1878 80 d. Type **417** 75 25
1879 300 d. Chariot of the Sun 2·25 95

1991. 11th Mediterranean Games, Athens. Multicoloured.
1880 10 d. Type **418** 25 25
1881 60 d. Basketball 35 15
1882 90 d. Gymnastics 65 20
1883 130 d. Weightlifting 85 20
1884 300 d. Throwing the hammer 2·40 1·25

419 Pillar of Democracy **421** Pres Konstantinos Karamanlis signing Treaty of Athens

1991. 2500th Anniv of Birth of Democracy.
1885 **419** 100 d. black, stone & bl 80 40

1991. 10th Anniv of Greek Admission to European Community. Multicoloured.
1887 50 d. Type **421** 30 15
1888 80 d. Map of Europe and Pres. Karamanlis 50 25

422 Emblem and Speed Skaters **423** Throwing the Javelin

1991. Winter Olympic Games, Albertville. Multicoloured.
1889 80 d. Type **422** 85 50
1890 300 d. Slalom skier 1·90 60

1992. Olympic Games, Barcelona. Mult.
1891 10 d. Type **423** 25 10
1892 60 d. Show jumping 55 15
1893 90 d. Runner (37 × 24 mm) 85 25
1894 120 d. Gymnastics 1·10 50
1895 340 d. Runners' heads forming Olympic rings (37 × 24 mm) 2·25 1·00

424 Couple beneath Umbrella **425** "Santa Maria", Map and Columbus

1992. Health. Multicoloured.
1896 60 d. Type **424** (anti-AIDS campaign) 25 15
1897 80 d. Doctor examining child (1st European Gastroenterology Week) 50 25
1898 90 d. Crab killing flower on healthy plant (anti-cancer campaign) 65 25
1899 120 d. Hephaestus's forge (from 6th-century B.C. urn) (European Year of Social Security, Hygiene and Health in the Workplace) 1·00 40
1900 280 d. Alexandros Onassis Cardiosurgical Centre 2·10 70

1992. Europa. 500th Anniv of Discovery of America by Columbus. Multicoloured.
1901 90 d. Type **425** 1·25 60
1902 340 d. Chios in late 15th century 2·25 1·10

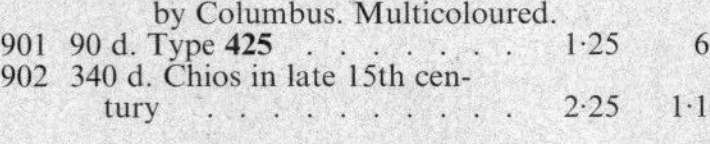

427 Head of Hercules with Lion Skin (relief) **428** Piraeus

1992. Macedonia. Multicoloured.
1904 10 d. Type **427** 15 10
1905 20 d. Map of Macedonia and bust of Aristotle (horiz) 15 10
1906 60 d. Alexander the Great at Battle of Issus (mural) (horiz) 40 15
1907 80 d. Tomb of Philip II at Vergina, and Manolis Andronikos (archaeologist) 60 25
1908 90 d. Deer hunt (mosaic, Pella) 75 35
1909 120 d. Macedonian coin 95 45
1910 340 d. 4th-century Church, Philippi, and Apostle Paul 2·25 1·10

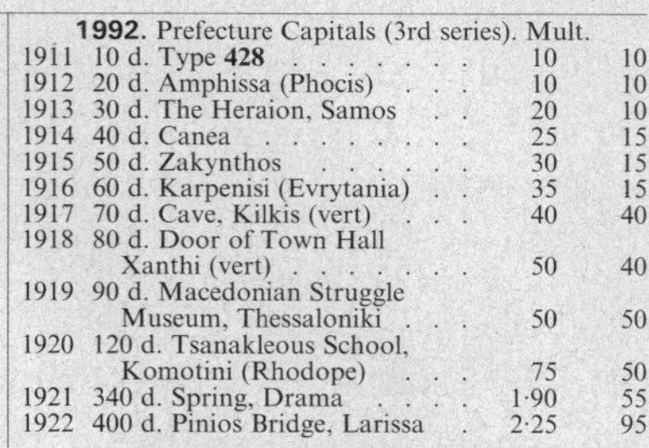

1992. Prefecture Capitals (3rd series). Mult.
1911 10 d. Type **428** 10 10
1912 20 d. Amphissa (Phocis) 10 10
1913 30 d. The Heraion, Samos 20 10
1914 40 d. Canea 25 15
1915 50 d. Zakynthos 30 15
1916 60 d. Karpenisi (Evrytania) 35 15
1917 70 d. Cave, Kilkis (vert) 40 40
1918 80 d. Door of Town Hall Xanthi (vert) 50 40
1919 90 d. Macedonian Struggle Museum, Thessaloniki 50 50
1920 120 d. Tsanakleous School, Komotini (Rhodope) 75 50
1921 340 d. Spring, Drama 1·90 55
1922 400 d. Pinios Bridge, Larissa 2·25 95

429 Column, Map, Flags and European Community Emblem

1992. Single European Market.
1923 **429** 90 d. multicoloured 65 50

430 Headstone (4th century B.C.) **431** Georgakis Olympios at Sekkou Monastery, 1821

1993. 2400th Anniv of Rhodes. Multicoloured.
1924 60 d. Type **430** 40 20
1925 90 d. "Aphrodite bathing" (statue) 75 40
1926 120 d. "St. Irene" (from St. Catherine's church) 1·00 50
1927 250 d. St. Paul's Gate, Naillac Mole 1·75 90

1993. Historical Events. Multicoloured.
1928 10 d. Type **431** (War of Independence) 15 10
1929 30 d. Theodore Kolokotronis (War of Independence) 20 10
1930 60 d. Pavlos Melas (military hero) 35 15
1931 90 d. "Glory crowns the Casualties" (Balkan Wars, 1912–13) 55 30
1932 120 d. Soldiers of Sacred Company, El Alamein, 1942 (horiz) 80 45
1933 150 d. Sacred Company on Aegean Islands, 1943–45 (horiz) 90 50
1934 200 d. Victims' Monument, Kalavryta (destruction of village, 1943) 1·50 80

432 "The Benefits of Transportation" (Konstantinus Parthenis) (left half)

1993. Europa. Contemporary Art. Mult.
1935 90 d. Type **432** 75 50
1936 350 d. "The Benefits of Transportation" (right half) 2·50 1·50

Nos. 1935/6 were issued together, se-tenant, forming a composite design.

433 Athens Concert Hall

1993. Modern Athens. Multicoloured.
1937 30 d. Type **433** 20 15
1938 60 d. Iliou Melathron (former house of Heinrich Schliemann (archaeologist), now Numismatic Museum) 40 20
1939 90 d. National Library 65 30
1940 200 d. Athens Eye Hospital 1·25 75

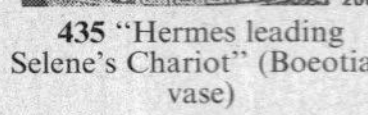

435 "Hermes leading Selene's Chariot" (Boeotian vase)

436 "Last Supper" (icon by Michael Damaskinou, St. Catherine's Church, Heraklion, Crete)

1994. 2nd Pan-European Transport Conf.
1942 **435** 200 d. multicoloured . . . 1·40 30

1994. Easter. Multicoloured.
1943 30 d. Type **436** 15 10
1944 60 d. "Crucifixion" (detail of wall painting, Great Meteoron) 40 20
1945 90 d. "Burial of Christ" (icon, Church of the Presentation of the Lord, Patmos) (horiz) . . 65 30
1946 150 d. "Resurrection" (detail, illuminated manuscript from Mt. Athos) (horiz) . . . . 1·00 50

437 Thales of Miletus (philosopher)

438 Demetrios Vikelas (first president, after G. Roilos)

1994. Europa. Discoveries. Multicoloured.
1947 90 d. Type **437** 75 40
1948 350 d. Konstantinos Karatheodoris (mathematician) and equations . . . . 2·50 1·25

1994. Sports Events and Anniversary. Mult.
1949 60 d. Type **438** (centenary of International Olympic Committee) 35 15
1950 90 d. Modern footballer and ancient relief (World Cup Football Championship, U.S.A.) (horiz) 60 30
1951 120 d. Ball, net and laurel (World Volleyball Championship, Piraeus and Salonika) 90 45

439 "Greece" driving E.U. Chariot

1994. Greek Presidency of European Union. Multicoloured.
1953 90 d. Type **439** 60 40
1954 120 d. Doric columns and E.U. flag 90 60

440 Parigoritissas Byzantine Church, Arta

441 "Declaration of Constitution" (detail, Carl Haupt)

1994. Prefecture Capitals (4th series). Mult.
1955 10 d. Tsalopoulou mansion house, Katerini (Pieria) (vert) 10 10
1956 20 d. Type **440** 10 10
1957 30 d. Bridge and tower, Levadia (Boeotia) (vert) 15 10
1958 40 d. Koumbelidikis church Kastoria 20 10
1959 50 d. Outdoor theatre, Grevena 25 10
1960 60 d. Waterfall, Edessa (Pella) . 30 15
1961 80 d. Red House, Chalkida (Euboea) 45 35
1962 90 d. Government House, Serres 60 35
1963 120 d. Town Hall, Heraklion . . 75 40
1964 150 d. Church of our Lady of the Annunciation, Igoumenitsa (Thesprotia) (vert) 95 40

1994. 150th Anniv of Constitution. Mult.
1965 60 d. Type **441** 40 20
1966 150 d. Ioannis Makrygiannis, Andreas Metaxas and Dimitrios Kallergis (from "Neos Aristophanes" (magazine)) 90 45
1967 200 d. "The Night of 3rd September 1843" (anon) (horiz) . . . . 1·40 75
1968 340 d. Article 107 of 1844 Constitution and Parliament Seal (horiz) . . . . 2·25 1·10

442 Mercouri and Demonstrators (fighter for Democracy)

1995. Melina Mercouri (actress and Minister of Culture) Commemoration. Multicoloured.
1969 60 d. Type **442** 45 25
1970 90 d. Mercouri and Acropolis (politician) 65 40
1971 100 d. Mercouri in three roles (actress) 80 50
1972 340 d. Mercouri with flowers (vert) . . . . 2·25 1·10

443 Prisoners behind Barbed Wire

444 Emblem

1995. Europa. Peace and Freedom. Mult.
1973 90 d. Type **443** 75 50
1974 340 d. Doves flying from crushed barbed wire . . . . 2·00 25
Nos. 1973/4 were issued together, se-tenant, forming a composite design.

1995. Anniversaries and Events. Mult.
1975 10 d. Type **444** (5th World Junior Basketball Championship) 10 10
1976 70 d. Agriculture University, Athens (75th anniv) (horiz) . 40 25
1977 90 d. Delphi (50th anniv of U.N.O.) 50 35
1978 100 d. Greek flag and returning soldier (50th anniv of end of Second World War) 55 35
1979 120 d. "Peace" (statue by Kifissodotos) (50th anniv of U.N.O.) 65 40
1980 150 d. Dolphins (European Nature Conservation Year) (horiz) 90 60
1981 200 d. Old telephone and modern key-pad (cent of telephone in Greece) . . . . 1·25 80
1982 300 d. Owl sitting on ball (29th European Basketball Championship) . . . . 1·75 1·25

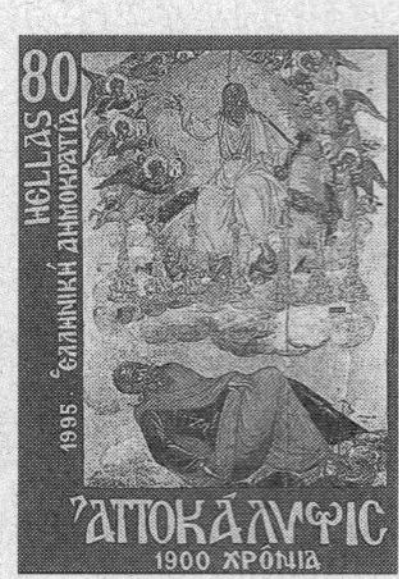

445 "The First Vision of the Apocalypse" (icon, Thomas Bathas)

1995. 1900th Anniv of the Apocalypse of St. John. Multicoloured.
1983 80 d. Type **445** 50 25
1984 110 d. St. John dictating to Prochoros in front of the Cave of the Apocalypse (miniature from the Four Gospels, Code x 81 of library of Patmos Monastery) . . . 65 35
1985 300 d. Trumpet of the First Angel (gilded Gospel cover) (horiz) . . . . 1·60 80

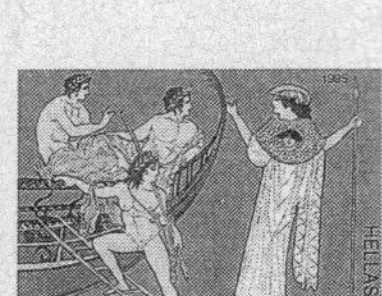

446 Goddess Athene with Argonauts

447 Psyttaleia

1995. Jason and the Argonauts. Mult.
1986 80 d. Type **446** 45 25
1987 120 d. Phineas (blind seer), god Hermes and the Voreadae pursuing Harpies 65 35
1988 150 d. Medea, Nike and Jason taming bull 80 50
1989 200 d. Jason and Medea killing snake and taking the Golden Fleece . . . . 1·10 70
1990 300 d. Jason presenting Golden Fleece to Pelias . . . . . . 1·75 1·00

1995. Lighthouses. Multicoloured.
1991 80 d. Type **447** 45 20
1992 120 d. Sapienza 65 30
1993 150 d. Kastri, Othonoi 80 40
1994 500 d. Zourva, Hydra . . . . 2·75 1·25

449 Sappho (poet)

450 Running

1996. Europa. Famous women.
1996 **449** 120 d. multicoloured 65 50
1997 – 430 d. brown, black & bl . 1·90 1·00
DESIGN: 430 d. Amalia Fleming.

1996. Cent of Modern Olympic Games. Mult.
1998 10 d. Type **450** 20 10
1999 80 d. Throwing the discus . . 40 20
2000 120 d. Weightlifting 60 30
2001 200 d. Wrestling (horiz) . . . 1·00 50

451 Hippocrates

452 Mytilene

1996. 1st Int Medical Olympiad, Athens.
2002 **451** 80 d. brown, pink & blk . 45 20
2003 – 120 d. brown, grn & blk . 65 30
DESIGN: 120 d. Galen.

1996. Castles (1st series). Multicoloured.
2004 10 d. Type **452** 10 10
2005 20 d. Lindos 10 10
2006 30 d. Rethymnon 15 10
2007 70 d. Assos Cephalonia . . . 30 15
2008 80 d. Castle of the Serbs . . . 35 15
2009 120 d. Monemvasia 55 25
2010 200 d. Didimotihon 90 45
2011 430 d. Vonitsas . . . . . . 1·90 95
2012 1000 d. Nikopolis . . . . . . 4·50 2·25
See also Nos. 2069/78.

453 Puppets

1996. Shadow Puppets. Multicoloured.
2013 80 d. Type **453** 35 15
2014 100 d. Men courting woman . 45 20
2015 120 d. Soldiers 55 25
2016 200 d. Men fighting dragon . . 90 45

454 Inscription on Wine Jug (720 B.C.)

456 St Dimitrios (patron saint) (fresco, Aghios Nikolaos Orphanos Church)

455 Papandreou, Cap, Degree and Books

1996. The Greek Language. Multicoloured.
2017 80 d. Type **454** 35 15
2018 120 d. Homer's "Iliad" (papyrus scroll, 436–45 . . . 55 25
2019 150 d. Psalm (6th century) . . 65 30
2020 350 d. Dionysios Solomos (writer) and verse of poem (1824) . . . . 1·60 80

1997. Andreas Papandreou (Prime Minister, 1981–89 and 1993–96) Commemoration. Multicoloured.
2021 80 d. Type **455** (Doctorate in Economics, Harvard University, 1943) 35 15
2022 120 d. Return from exile, 1974, and smoking pipe 55 25
2023 150 d. Parliament building and Papandreou 65 30
2024 500 d. State flag, dove and Papandreou wearing glasses . 2·25 1·10

1997. Thessaloniki, Cultural Capital of Europe. Multicoloured.
2025 80 d. Type **456** 35 15
2026 100 d. Hippocratic Hospital (horiz) 45 20
2027 120 d. Marble statue pedestal (2nd century) and circular relief of woman's head . . . 55 25
2028 150 d. Mosaic (detail) in cupola of Rotunda 65 30
2029 300 d. 14th-century chalice (horiz) . . . . 1·40 70

457 Trikomo

1997. Macedonian Bridges. Multicoloured.
2030 80 d. Type **457** 35 15
2031 120 d. Portitsa 55 25
2032 150 d. Ziakas 65 30
2033 350 d. Kastro . . . . 1·60 80

458 Prometheus the Fire-stealer

1997. Europa. Tales and Legends. Mult.
2034 120 d. Type **458** 55 25
2035 430 d. Knights (Digenes Akritas) . . . . 1·90 95

459 Running

1997. 6th World Athletics Championships, Athens. Multicoloured.
2036 20 d. Type **459** 10 10
2037 100 d. "Nike" (statue) 45 20
2038 140 d. High jumping 60 30
2039 170 d. Hurdling 75 35
2040 500 d. Stadium, Athens . . . 2·25 1·10

460 Alexandros Panagoulis (resistance leader)

461 Vassilis Avlonitis

1997. Anniversaries. Multicoloured.
2041 20 d. Type **460** (20th death anniv (1996)) 10 10
2042 30 d. Grigorios Xenopoulos (writer, 130th birth anniv) . 15 10
2043 40 d. Odysseas Elytis (poet, first death anniv) (horiz) 15 10
2044 50 d. Panayiotis Kanellopoulos (Prime Minister, 1945 and 1967, tenth death anniv (1996)) 20 10

2045 100 d. Harilaos Trikoupis (Prime Minister 1881–85, death centenary (1996)) (horiz) 45 20
2046 170 d. Maria Callas (opera singer, 20th death anniv) (horiz) 75 35
2047 200 d. Rigas Velestinlis-Feraios (revolutionary writer, death bicent (1998)) 85 40

1997. Greek Actors. Multicoloured.
2048 20 d. Type **461** 10 10
2049 30 d. Vassilis Argyropoulos . . 15 10
2050 50 d. Georgia Vassileiadou . . 20 10
2051 70 d. Lambros Constantaras . 30 15
2052 100 d. Vassilis Logothetidis . . 45 20
2053 140 d. Dionysis Papagiannopoulos 60 30
2054 170 d. Nikos Stavrides 75 35
2055 200 d. Mimis Fotopoulos . . . 85 40

462 "Greece", Greek Flag and Colossus of Rhodes

463 Aghia Sofia Hospital, Athens

1998. 50th Anniv of Incorporation of Dodecanese Islands into Greece. Multicoloured.
2056 100 d. German commander signing surrender to British and Greek military authorities at Simi, 1945 . . . . . 45 20
2057 140 d. Type **462** 60 30
2058 170 d. Greek and British military representatives at transfer ceremony, Rhodes, 1947 . 75 35
2059 500 d. Raising Greek flag, Kasos, 1947 . . . . 2·10 1·00

1998. Anniversaries and Events. Mult.
2060 20 d. Type **463** (cent of Aghia Sofia Children's Hospital) . 10 10
2061 100 d. St. Xenophon's Monastery (millenary) (vert) 45 20
2062 140 d. Woman in traditional costume (4th International Thracian Congress, Nea Orestiada) (vert) 60 30
2063 150 d. Parthenon and congress emblem (International Cardiography Research Congress, Rhodes) 65 30
2064 170 d. Sculpture of man and young boy (Cardiography Congress) (vert) 75 35
2065 500 d. Emblem (50th anniv of Council of Europe) (vert) . . 2·10 1·00

464 Ancient Theatre, Epidavros

1998. Europa. National Festivals. Mult.
2066 140 d. Type **464** 60 30
2067 500 d. Festival in Herod Atticus Theatre, Athens . . . . . . 2·10 1·00

466 Ierapetra, Crete

1998. Castles (2nd series). Multicoloured.
2069 30 d. Type **466** 15 10
2070 50 d. Corfu 20 10
2071 70 d. Limnos 30 15
2072 100 d. Argolis 45 20
2073 150 d. Iraklion, Crete 65 30
2074 170 d. Naupaktos (vert) . . . 75 35
2075 200 d. Ioannina (vert) 85 40
2076 400 d. Platamona . . . . . . 1·75 85
2077 550 d. Karitainas (vert) . . . . 2·40 1·10
2078 600 d. Fragkokastello, Crete . 2·50 1·25

467 "Church of St. George of the Greeks" (18th-century copperplate)

1998. 500th Anniv of Greek Orthodox Community in Venice. Multicoloured.
2079 30 d. Type **467** 15 10
2080 40 d. "Christ Pantocrator" (icon) (vert) 15 10
2081 140 d. Illuminated script of hymn "Epi Soi hairei" by Georgios Klontzas (vert) . . 60 30
2082 230 d. "St. George of the Greeks" (illuminated manuscript, 1640) . . . . 1·00 50

468 Homer (poet)

1998. Ancient Greek Writers.
2083 **468** 20 d. brown and gold . . 10 10
2084 – 100 d. brown and gold . . 45 20
2085 – 140 d. red and gold . . . 60 30
2086 – 200 d. black and gold . . 85 40
2087 – 250 d. brown and gold . . 1·10 55
DESIGNS: No. 2084, Sophocles (poet); 2085, Thucydides (historian); 2086, Plato (philosopher); 2087, Demosthenes (orator).

469 Ancient Trireme and Circulation of Mediterranean Sea Currents

1999. International Year of the Ocean. Multicoloured.
2088 40 d. Type **469** 15 10
2089 100 d. Galleon (detail of icon "Thou art Great, O Lord" by I. Kornaros) 40 20
2090 200 d. "Aigaio" (oceanographic vessel), astrolabe and seismic sounding of seabed 80 40
2091 500 d. Apollo on ship (3rd-century B.C. silver tetradrachmon coin of Antigonus Dosonos) . . . . 1·90 95

470 Karamanlis

1999. 1st Death Anniv of Konstantinos Karamanlis (Prime Minister 1955–63 and 1974; President 1980–85 and 1990–95). Multicoloured.
2092 100 d. Type **470** 40 20
2093 170 d. Karamanlis and jubilant crowd, 1974 . . . . 65 30
2094 200 d. Karamanlis and Council of Europe emblem, 1979 . . 80 40
2095 500 d. Karamanlis and Greek flag (vert) . . . . 1·90 95

471 Mt. Olympus and Flowers

1999. Europa. Parks and Gardens. Multicoloured.
2096 170 d. Type **471** 65 30
2097 550 d. Mt. Olympus and flowers (different) . . . . 2·10 1·00
Nos. 2096/7 were issued together, se-tenant, forming a composite design.

472 Ancient Greek and Japanese Noh Theatre Masks

1999. Centenary of Diplomatic Relations between Greece and Japan.
2098 **472** 120 d. multicoloured . . . 45 20

473 Temple of Hylates Apollo, Kourion

1999. Cyprus–Greece Joint Issue. 4000 Years of Greek Culture. Multicoloured.
2099 120 d. Type **473** 45 20
2100 120 d. Mycenaean pot depicting warriors (Athens) 45 20
2101 120 d. Mycenaean crater depicting horse (Nicosia) 45 20
2102 120 d. Temple of Apollo, Delphi 45 20

474 Trains

1999. Fifth Anniv of Community Support Programme. Multicoloured.
2103 20 d. Type **474** (modernization of railways) 10 10
2104 120 d. Bridge over River Antirrio 45 20
2105 140 d. Compact disk, delivery lorries and conveyor belt (modernization of Post Office) 55 25
2106 250 d. Athens underground train 95 45
2107 500 d. Control tower, Eleftherios Venizelos airport, Athens . . . . 1·90 95

475 Helicopter and Commandos in Inflatable Boat

1999. Armed Forces. Multicoloured.
2108 20 d. Type **475** 10 10
2109 30 d. Missile corvette 10 10
2110 40 d. Two F-16 aircraft . . . 15 10
2111 50 d. CL-215 aircraft dispersing water on forest fire 20 10
2112 70 d. Destroyer 25 15
2113 120 d. Forces distributing aid in Bosnia 45 25
2114 170 d. Dassault Mirage 2000 jet fighter above Aegean . . . 65 35
2115 250 d. Helicopters, tanks and soldiers on joint exercise . . 95 50
2116 600 d. Submarine "Okeanos" . 2·40 1·25

CHARITY TAX STAMPS

C 38 Dying Soldier, Widow and Child

C 39 Red Cross, Nurses, Wounded and Bearers

1914. Roul.

C269 C 38 2 l. red 25 25
C270 5 l. blue 40 40

1915. Red Cross. Roul.

C271 C 39 (5 l.) red and blue 10·00 1·50

C 40 Greek Women's Patriotic League Badge

1915. Greek Women's Patriotic League.

C272 C 40 (5 l.) red and blue 50 75

Κ. Π.
λεπτοῦ
1
(C 42)

C 43

Κ. Π.
λεπτοῦ
1
(C 44)

Κ.Π.
10 ΛΕΠΤΑ 10
(C 46)

1917. Surch as Type C 42.

C297 15 1 on 1 l. brown 85 1·75
C303 1 on 3 l. orange 30 30
C299 5 on 1 l. brown 1·00 1·25
C300 5 on 20 l. mauve 50 50
C307 36 5 on 25 l. blue 15 25
C304 15 5 on 40 l. brown 1·00 1·00
C308 36 5 on 40 l. blue 15 25
C305 15 5 on 50 l. lake 55 55
C309 35 5 on 50 l. blue 15 25
C306 17 5 on 1 d. black 1·25 1·25
C301 15 10 on 30 l. purple 50 50
C302 30 on 30 l. purple 90 1·50

1917. Fiscal stamps surch as Type C 44. Roul.

C310 C 43 1 l. on 10 l. blue 75 75
C328 1 l. on 50 l. purple 1·00 1·00
C311 1 l. on 80 l. blue 75 75
C330 5 l. on 10 l. purple 1·00 1·00
C329 5 l. on 10 l. blue 1·00 1·00
C312 5 l. on 60 l. blue 3·75 2·50
C313 5 l. on 80 l. blue 2·50 2·50
C331 10 l. on 50 l. purple 1·00 1·00
C326 10 l. on 70 l. blue 5·00 5·00
C315 10 l. on 90 l. blue 5·00 6·50
C316 20 l. on 20 l. blue £1500 £750
C317 20 l. on 30 l. blue 3·75 3·75
C318 20 l. on 40 l. blue 12·00 9·00
C319 20 l. on 50 l. blue 5·00 4·50
C320 20 l. on 60 l. blue £225 £180
C321 20 l. on 80 l. blue 50·00 30·00
C322 20 l. on 90 l. blue 2·75 2·50
C333 20 l. on 2 d. blue 6·50 3·75

1917. Fiscal stamps surch as Type C 46. Roul.

C334 C 43 1 l. on 10 l. blue 75 75
C341 5 l. on 10 l. pur & red 6·50 1·75
C335 5 l. on 50 l. blue 25·00 25·00
C338 10 l. on 50 l. blue 6·50 5·00
C339 20 l. on 50 l. blue 15·00 13·00
C340 30 l. on 50 l. blue 10·00 7·50

C 48 Wounded Soldier

C 77 St. Demetrius

C 49

1918. Red Cross. Roul.

C342 C 48 5 l. red, blue & yellow 3·75 1·25

1918. Optd P.I.P. in Greek.

C343 C 48 5 l. red, blue & yellow 5·00 1·25

1922. Greek Women's Patriotic League. Surch as in Type C 49.

C344 C 49 5 l. on 10 l. red & blue £125 6·50
C345 5 l. on 20 l. red & blue 25·00 25·00
C346 5 l. on 50 l. red & blue £100 80·00
C347 5 l. on 1 d. red & blue 1·50 35·00

Nos. C344/7 were not issued without surcharge.

1924. Red Cross. As Type C 48 but wounded soldier and family.

C406 10 l. red, blue and yellow 30 25

1934. Salonika Int Exn Fund.

C478 C 77 20 l. brown 10 10

C 78 Allegory of Health

ΠΡΟΝΟΙΑ
(C 85)

1934. Postal Staff Anti-Tuberculosis Fund.

C480 C 78 10 l. orange & green 10 10
C481 20 l. orange & blue 15 25
C482 50 l. orange & green 75 40

1935. As Type C 78 but with country inscription at top.

C494 10 l. orange & green 10 10
C495 20 l. orange & blue 30 10
C496 50 l. orange & green 25 25
C497 50 l. orange & brown 40 20

1937. Nos. D 273 and 415 optd with Type C 85.

C498 D 20 10 l. red 25 25
C500 51 50 l. violet 40 10

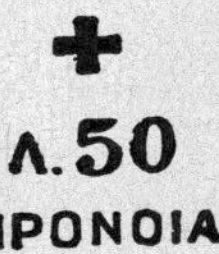

Λ.50
ΠΡΟΝΟΙΑ
(C 95)

C 96 Queens Olga and Sophia

1938. Surch with Type C 95.

C521 D 20 50 l. on 5 l. green 50 50
C522 50 l. on 20 l. slate 1·50 1·75
C523 52 50 l. on 20 l. violet 25 15

1939.

C524 C 96 10 l. red 10 10
C525 50 l. green 10 10
C526 1 d. blue 15 25

ΠΡΟΣΤΑΣΙΑ ΦΥΜΑΤΙΚΩΝ ΤΤΤ
(C 104)

1940. Postal staff Anti-Tuberculosis Fund. Optd with Type C 104.

C554 C 96 50 l. green 15 25

Κ.Π.
λεπτῶν
50
(C 105)

(C 113)

1941. Social Funds. No. 410 surch with Type C 105.

C561 51 50 l. on 5 l. green 20 25

1941. Postal Staff Anti-Tuberculosis Fund. Surch 50 and bars.

C562 C 78 50 l. on 10 l. 50 90
C563 – 50 l. on 10 l. (No. C494) 20 15

ΔΡ.1
(C 107)

ΦΥΜ· Τ.Τ.Τ.
10 ΔΡ.
(C 109)

1942. Sample Fair, Salonika. No. C478 surch with Type C 107.

C573 C 77 1 d. on 20 l. brown. 15 15

1942. Postal Staff Anti-Tuberculosis Fund. Nos. 410 and 413 surch with Type C 109.

C591 51 10 d. on 5 l. green 20 10
C592 10 l. on 25 l. green 10 10

ΦΥΜ · Τ.Τ.Τ.
(C 111)

1944. Postal Staff Anti-Tuberculosis Fund. No. 580 optd with Type C 111.

C599 100 d. black 10 10

ΦΥΜ · Τ.Τ.Τ.
ΔΡ. 5000
(C 112)

1944. Postal Staff Anti-Tuberculosis Fund. No. 579 surch with Type C 112.

C600 5000 d. on 75 d. red 10 10

1944. Postal Staff Anti-Tuberculosis Fund. Surch as Type C 113.

C619 – 1 d. on 40 l. (No. 500) 10 10
C620 – 2 d. on 40 l. (No. 500) 10 10
C605 106 25,000 d. on 2 d. 25 25

(C 117) (C 136)

1946. Postal Staff Anti-Tuberculosis Fund. Surch as Type C 117.

C640 C 117 20 d. on 5 l. 1·00 20
C641 20 d. on 40 l. (No. 500) 50 10

1946. Red Cross. Surch as Type C 117.

C642 C 96 50 d. on 50 l. (No. C525) 50 40

1946. Social Funds. Surch as Type C 117.

C643 C 96 50 d. on 1 d. (No. C526) 25 15

1947. Postal Staff Anti-Tuberculosis Fund. Surch.

C659 C 96 50 d. on 50 l. (C525) 38·00
C660 50 l. on 50 d. (C554) 1·40 15

C 127 St. Demetrius

ΠΡΟΣΘΕΤΟΝ
ΔΡ. 100
(C 139)

1948. Church Restoration Fund.

C682 C 127 50 d. brown 25 10

1950. Postal Staff Anti-Tuberculosis Fund. Surch with Type C 117.

C686 50 d. on 10 l. (No. 498) 75 10

1951. Postal Staff Welfare Fund. Surch with Type C 136.

C698 86 50 d. on 5 l. blue & brn 1·50 15

1951. Postal Staff Anti-Tuberculosis Fund. Surch with Cross of Lorraine and 50.

C699 89 50 d. on 3 d. brown 1·40 15

1952. State Welfare Fund. No. 509 surch with Type C 139.

C706 89 100 d. on 8 d. blue 60 15

C 140 Argostoli, Cephalonia

1953. Ionian Is. Earthquake Fund.

C713 – 300 d. slate 75 15
C714 C 140 500 d. brown & yell 2·25 50

DESIGN: 300 d. Church of Faneromeni, Zante.

C 148 Zeus (Macedonian Coin of Philip II)

1956. Macedonian Cultural Fund.

C761 C 148 50 l. red 1·00 15
C762 – 1 d. blue (Aristotle) 3·50 1·50

POSTAGE DUE STAMPS

D 2

D 20

1875.

D73 D 2 1 l. green and black 75 75
D74 2 l. green and black 75 75
D75 5 l. green and black 1·00 1·00
D88 10 l. green and black 1·00 1·00
D89 20 l. green and black 1·00 1·00
D78 40 l. green and black 5·00 5·00
D91 60 l. green and black 5·00 5·00
D80 70 l. green and black 6·00 5·00
D81 80 l. green and black 9·00 9·00
D82 90 l. green and black 8·00 6·50
D95 100 l. green and black 6·50 6·50
D96 200 l. green and black 9·00 6·50
D83 1 d. green and black 9·00 6·50
D84 2 d. green and black 9·00 7·50

1902.

D183 D 20 1 l. brown 25 25
D184 2 l. grey 25 25
D185 3 l. orange 25 25
D186 5 l. green 25 25
D273 10 l. red 25 25
D188 20 l. mauve 25 25
D275 25 l. blue 15 15
D190 30 l. purple 25 20
D191 40 l. brown 25 30
D451 50 l. brown 15 15
D193 1 d. black 50 50
D194 2 d. bronze 75 75
D195 3 d. silver 1·25 1·00
D196 5 d. gold 4·00 3·00

1912 Optd with T 34.

D252A D 20 1 l. brown 50 50
D253A 2 l. grey 50 50
D254A 3 l. orange 30 30
D255A 5 l. green 45 45
D256A 10 l. red 1·00 1·00
D257D 20 l. mauve 65 65
D258 30 l. purple 2·00 2·00
D259D 40 l. brown 75 75
D260 50 l. brown 65 65
D261D 1 d. black 5·00 5·00
D262D 2 d. bronze 6·00 6·00
D263D 3 d. silver 9·00 10·00
D264D 5 d. gold 20·00 21·00

1913. Perf or roul.

D269 D 20 1 l. green 15 15
D270 2 l. red 15 15
D271 3 l. red 15 15
D274 20 l. slate 15 15
D276 30 l. red 15 15
D277 40 l. blue 20 20
D279 80 l. purple 50 40
D452 1 d. blue 30 25
D453 2 d. red 15 15
D282 3 d. red 3·00 1·50
D455 5 d. blue 15 15
D456 10 d. green 15 10
D595 10 d. orange 10 15
D457 15 d. brown 25 15
D458 25 d. red 45 75
D596 25 d. blue 10 15
D480 50 d. orange 25 40
D481 100 d. green 25 40
D597 100 d. brown 15 15
D598 200 d. violet 15 15

1942. Surch 50.

D564 D 20 50 l. on 30 l. red 40 60

GREEK WAR ISSUES, 1912–1913

For provisional issues used in territories occupied by Greece during the Balkan War, see Stanley Gibbons Part 3 (Balkans) Catalogue.

GREEK OCCUPATION OF ALBANIA Pt. 3

100 lepta = 1 drachma.

Stamps of Greece optd with T 1.

ΕΛΛΗΝΙΚΗ
ΔΙΟΙΚΗϹΙϹ
(1)

1940. Stamps of 1937.

1 **86** 5 l. blue and brown 15 15
2 – 10 l. brn & blue (No. 498) 15 15
3 – 20 l. grn & blk (No. 499) 15 15
4 – 40 l. blk & grn (No. 500) 15 15
5 – 50 l. blk & brn (No. 501) 20 20
6 – 80 l. brn & vio (No. 502) 20 25
7 **89** 1 d. green 20 25
8 – 2 d. blue (No. 504) 20 25
9 **89** 3 d. brown 20 40
10 – 5 d. red (No. 506) 40 45
11 – 6 d. olive (No. 507) 40 45
12 – 7 d. brown (No. 508) 50 60
13 **89** 8 d. blue 40 60
14 – 10 d. brown (No. 510) 70 1·00
15 – 15 d. green (No. 511) 80 1·25
16 – 25 d. blue (No. 512) 1·40 2·00
17 **89a** 30 d. red 1·90 4·25

1940. Charity Tax Stamps of 1939.

18 C **96** 10 l. red on rose 15 15
19 50 l. green on green 15 15
20 1 d. blue on blue 30 35

1940. Nos. 534/53 (Youth Organization).

26 **101** 3 d. bl, red & sil. (postage) 1·10 1·10
27 – 5 d. black and blue 3·25 3·50
28 – 10 d. black and orange 3·50 3·75
29 – 15 d. black and green 20·00 25·00
30 – 20 d. black and red 4·00 6·00
31 – 25 d. black and blue 4·00 6·00
32 – 30 d. black and violet 4·00 6·00
33 – 50 d. black and red 4·50 6·00
34 – 75 d. gold, blue & brown 5·50 7·00
35 **101** 100 d. blue, red and silver 6·00 10·00
36 **103** 2 d. black & orange (air) 1·10 2·25
37 – 4 d. black and green 2·50 5·00
38 – 6 d. black and red 2·50 5·00
39 – 8 d. black and blue 2·50 5·00
40 – 16 d. black and violet 3·00 5·00
41 – 32 d. black and orange 5·00 7·00
42 – 45 d. black and green 5·50 7·00
43 – 55 d. black and red 5·50 7·50
44 – 65 d. black and blue 5·50 9·00
45 – 100 d. black and violet 7·50 10·00

POSTAGE DUE STAMPS

1940. Postage Due stamps of 1913.

D21 D **20** 2 d. red 40 40
D22 5 d. blue 40 45
D23 10 d. green 40 55
D24 15 d. brown 85 75

1940. Postage Due stamp surch also.

D25 D **20** 50 l. on 25 d. red 35 30

GREENLAND Pt. 11

A Danish possession N.E. of Canada. On 5 June 1963, Greenland became an integral part of the Danish Kingdom.

100 ore = 1 krone.

1 Christian X **2** Polar Bear

1938.

1 **1** 1 ore green 10 20
2 5 ore red 1·50 1·00
3 7 ore green 2·50 2·40
4 10 ore violet 60 55
5 15 ore red 60 60
5a 20 ore red 1·50 85
6 **2** 30 ore blue 5·50 6·00
6a 40 ore blue 32·00 6·50
7 1 k. brown 7·00 6·00

3 Harp Seal **4** King Christian X

5 Eskimo Kayak

1945.

8 **3** 1 ore violet and black 35·00 27·00
9 5 ore buff and violet 35·00 27·00
10 7 ore black and green 35·00 27·00
11 **4** 10 ore olive and purple 30·00 27·00
12 15 ore blue and red 30·00 27·00
13 – 30 ore brown and blue 30·00 27·00
14 – 1 k. grey and brown 35·00 27·00
15 **5** 2 k. green and brown 50·00 35·00
16 – 5 k. brown and purple 60·00 35·00

DESIGNS—HORIZ: As Type **5**: 30 ore Dog team; 1 k. Polar bear; 5 k. Eider.

1945. Liberation of Denmark. Nos. 8/16 optd **DANMARK BEFRIET 5 MAJ 1945**.

17 **3** 1 ore violet and black 60·00 38·00
18 5 ore buff and violet 60·00 38·00
19 7 ore black and green 60·00 38·00
20 **4** 10 ore olive and purple 70·00 50·00
21 15 ore blue and red 70·00 50·00
22 – 30 ore brown and blue 70·00 50·00
23 – 1 k. grey and brown 70·00 50·00
24 **5** 2 k. green and brown 70·00 50·00
25 – 5 k. brown and purple 85·00 55·00

7 King Frederik IX **8** Polar Ship "Gustav Holm"

1950.

26 **7** 1 ore green 10 10
27 5 ore red 30 20
28 10 ore green 45 20
29 15 ore violet 80 40
30 25 ore red 2·00 90
31 30 ore blue 24·00 1·50
32 30 ore red 40 30
33 **8** 50 ore blue 48·00 10·00
34 1 k. brown 15·00 2·25
35 2 k. red 8·00 2·25
36 5 k. grey 4·00 1·00

1956. Nos. 6a and 7 surch **60 ore**.

37 **2** 60 ore on 40 ore blue 8·00 1·00
38 60 ore on 1 k. brown 65·00 6·25

10 "Mother of the Sea" **12** Hans Egede (after J. Horner) **14** Knud Rasmussen (founder of Thule)

1957. Greenland Legends.

39 **10** 60 ore blue 3·00 85

1958. Royal Tuberculosis Relief Fund. No. 33 surch with Cross of Lorraine and **30 + 10**.

40 **8** 30 ore + 10 ore on 50 ore bl 3·50 1·75

1958. Death Bicent of Hans Egede (missionary).

41 **12** 30 ore red 7·25 1·00

1959. Greenland Fund. Surch **Gronlandsfonden 30+10** and bars.

42 **7** 30 ore+10 ore on 25 ore red 3·50 3·50

The note below No. 413 of Denmark also applies here.

1960. 50th Anniv of Thule Settlement.

43 **14** 30 ore red 1·40 50

15 Drum Dance **16** Northern Lights

17 Frederik IX **18** Polar Bear

1961. Greenland Legends.

44 **15** 35 ore green 1·00 60

1963.

45 **16** 1 ore green 10 10
46 5 ore red 10 10
47 10 ore green 40 30
48 12 ore green 80 25
49 15 ore purple 80 65
50 **17** 20 ore blue 2·75 2·50
51 25 ore brown 45 20
51a 30 ore green 30 15
52 35 ore red 35 10
53 40 ore grey 40 25
54 50 ore blue 5·75 5·25
54a 50 ore red 40 20
54b 60 ore red 40 20
55 **17** 80 ore orange 80 60
56 **18** 1 k. brown 60 20
57 2 k. red 3·00 60
58 5 k. blue 2·50 85
59 10 k. green 3·00 70

18a Prof. Niels Bohr **19** S. Kleinschmidt

1963. 50th Anniv of Bohr's Atomic Theory.

60 **18a** 35 ore red 50 30
61 60 ore blue 3·50 3·50

1964. 150th Birth Anniv of S. Kleinschmidt (philologist).

62 **19** 35 ore brown 60 60

20 "The Boy and the Fox" **20a** Princess Margrethe and Prince Henri de Monpezat

1966. Greenland Legends.

63 **20** 50 ore red 1·10 80

1967. Royal Wedding.

64 **20a** 50 ore red 3·25 3·00

21 "Great Northern Diver and Raven" **21a** "The Children in the Round Tower" (legend)

1967. Greenland Legends.

65 **21** 90 ore blue 3·50 3·25

1968. Child Welfare.

66 **21a** 60 ore+10 ore red 60 60

22 King Frederik IX and Map of Greenland **23** "The Girl and the Eagle"

1969. King Frederik's 70th Birthday.

67 **22** 60 ore red 1·50 1·10

1969. Greenland Legends.

68 **23** 80 ore brown 1·25 1·00

24 Musk Ox **25** Celebrations at Jakobshavn

1969.

69 – 1 k. blue 55 20
70 – 2 k. green 70 45
71 – 5 k. blue 1·40 70
72 – 10 k. brown 2·50 1·00
73 **24** 25 k. olive 7·00 2·00

DESIGN—HORIZ: 1 k. Bowhead whale and coastline; 2 k. Narwhal; 5 k. Polar bear; 10 k. Walruses.

1970. 25th Anniv of Denmark's Liberation.

74 **25** 60 ore red 1·50 1·50

26 Hans Egede and Gertrud Rask aboard the "Haabet" **27** Mail Kayaks

1971. 250th Anniv of Hans Egede's Arrival in Greenland.

75 **26** 60 ore red 1·25 1·00
76 – 60 ore+10 ore red 1·50 1·50

DESIGN: No. 76, Hans Egede and Gertrud Rask meeting Greenlanders.

The premium on No. 76 was for the Greenland Church Building Fund.

1971. Greenland Mail Transport.

77 **27** 50 ore green 25 20
78 – 70 ore red 50 25
79 – 80 ore black 50 25
80 – 90 ore blue 40 20
81 – 1 k. red 70 60
82 – 1 k. 30 blue 40 40
83 – 1 k. 50 green 50 40
84 – 2 k. deep blue 60 45

DESIGNS: 70 ore Umiak (women's boat); 80 ore Consolidated Catalina amphibian; 90 ore Mail dog-sledge; 1 k. Coaster "Kununguak" and tug "Dlik"; 1 k. 30, Schooner "Sokongen"; 1 k. 50, Sailing longboat "Karen"; 2 k. Sikorsky S-61N helicopter.

28 King Frederik IX and Royal Yacht "Dannebrog" **29** Queen Margrethe

1972. King Frederik IX's and Queen Ingrid's Fund.

85 **28** 60 ore +10 ore red 1·25 1·25

1973.

86 **29** 10 ore green 10 10
87 60 ore brown 30 20
88 90 ore brown 70 35
88a 100 ore red 30 15
89 120 ore blue 80 60
89a 130 ore blue 50 50

For values inscribed "KALAALLIT NUNAAT" at top, see Nos. 99/104.

30 Heimaey Eruption

1973. Aid for Victims of Heimaey (Iceland) Eruption.

90 **30** 70 ore+20 ore blue and red 1·25 1·25

31 "Carl Egede" (trawler) and Kayaks **32** Gyrfalcon and Radio Aerial

1974. Bicentenary of Royal Greenland Trade Department.

91 **31** 1 k. brown 70 45
92 – 2 k. brown 70 45

DESIGN—VERT: 2 k. Trade Department Headquarters, Trangraven, Copenhagen.

1975. 50th Anniv of Greenland's Telecommunications Service.

93 **32** 90 ore red 65 40

33 Sirius Sledge Patrol

1975. 25th Anniv of Sirius Sledge Patrol.

94 **33** 1 k. 20 brown 50 35

34 Arm-wrestling (after H. Egede) **35** Inuit Carved Mask

1976. Greenland Sports Publicity.

95 **34** 100 ore+20 ore brown and green on cream 55 70

1977. Eskimo Mask.

96 **35** 9 k. grey 2·40 2·00

36 Bronlund and Disko Bay, Jakobshavn **37** Cape York Meteorite and "Ulo" (woman's knife)

1977. Birth Centenary of Jorgen Bronlund (explorer).

97 **36** 1 k. brown 30 25

1978. Centenary of Commission for Scientific Researches in Greenland.

98 **37** 1 k. 20 brown . . . 40 25

38 Queen Margrethe

1978.

99 **38** 5 ore red 10 10

100 80 ore brown 20 20

101 120 ore brown 30 20

102 130 ore red 30 20

103 160 ore blue 45 40

104 180 ore green 50 45

39 Sun rising over Mountains

1978. 25th Anniv of Constitution.

105 **39** 1 k. 50 blue 40 35

40 Foundation Ceremony

41 Tupilak (imaginary animal)

1978. 250th Anniv of Godthab.

106 **40** 2 k. 50 brown 50 40

1978. Folk Art.

107 **41** 6 k. red . . . . 1·50 1·25

42 Helmsman

43 Rasmussen with Eskimos

1979. Internal Autonomy.

108 **42** 1 k. 10 brown 30 30

1979. Birth Centenary of Knud Rasmussen (polar explorer).

109 **43** 1 k. 30 + 20 ore red 30 45

44 Soapstone Figure (Simon Kristoffersen)

45 Eskimo Child

1979. Folk Art.

110 **44** 7 k. green . . . . 1·75 1·50

1979. International Year of the Child.

111 **45** 2 k. green 55 30

46 "Eskimo Family" (driftwood sculpture)

47 Queen Margrethe and Map of Greenland

1980. Folk Art.

112 **46** 8 k. blue . . . . 2·10 1·90

1980.

113 **47** 50 ore violet 20 15

114 80 ore brown 40 30

115 1 k. 30 red 40 30

116 1 k. 50 blue 65 55

117 1 k. 60 blue 70 55

118 1 k. 80 red 85 75

119 2 k. 30 green 60 50

120 2 k. 50 red 60 40

121 2 k. 80 brown . . . . . . 1·25 50

122 3 k. red . . . . 1·40 60

122a 3 k. 20 red . . . . 1·50 65

123 3 k. 80 black . . . . . . 1·40 1·40

124 4 k. 10 blue . . . . 1·75 1·75

124a 4 k. 40 blue . . . . 1·90 1·90

48 Eskimos and Rasmus Berthelsen in Library

49 "Foot Race between Quloqutsuk and Aqigssiaq"

1980. 150th Anniv of Greenland Public Libraries.

125 **48** 2 k. brown on yellow 50 40

1980. Woodcut by Aron from Kangeq.

126 **49** 3 k. black 70 60

50 Mikkelsen and Eskimo

51 "Reindeer Sledge and the Larva" (engraving, Jons Kreutzmann)

1980. Birth Centenary of Ejnar Mikkelsen (Inspector of East Greenland).

127 **50** 4 k. green . . . . 1·25 80

1981. Greenland Legends.

128 **51** 1 k. 60 red 50 30

52 Atlantic Cod

53 Stone Tent Ring, Wolf and King Eiders

1981.

129 **52** 25 k. brown and blue . . . 6·75 2·25

1981. Peary Land Expeditions.

130 **53** 1 k. 60 + 20 ore brown . . . 1·00 1·00

54 Reindeer and Hunter (Saqqaq culture, 2000 B.C.)

55 Shrimps

1981. Greenland History.

131 **54** 3 k. 50 blue . . . . 1·00 1·00

132 – 5 k. brown . . . . 1·40 1·40

DESIGN: 5 k. Hunters dragging walrus (Tunit-Dorset culture, 50 B.C.).

1982.

133 **55** 10 k. blue and red . . . . . 2·75 1·40

56 "Harpooning a Walrus" (Jakob Danielsen)

57 Eric the Red discovering Greenland, 982

1982.

134 **56** 2 k. 70 violet 80 60

1982. Greenland History.

135 **57** 2 k. + 40 ore, brown . . . . 1·50 1·50

58 Eskimos hunting Bowhead Whale

1982. Greenland History.

136 **58** 2 k. red 40 40

137 – 2 k. 70 blue 60 45

DESIGN: 2 k. 70, Bishop Joen Smyrill's staff and house at Gardar (1100–1200).

59 Atlantic Salmon

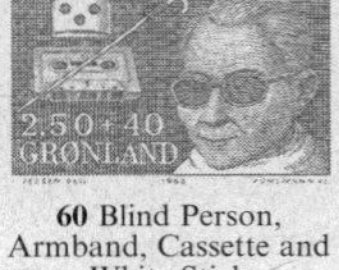

60 Blind Person, Armband, Cassette and White Stick

1983.

138 **59** 50 k. black and blue . . . . 13·00 7·00

1983. Welfare of the Blind.

139 **60** 2 k. 50 + 40 ore red 75 60

61 Eskimos and Northerners bartering (1200–1300)

62 Herrnhut Bandsmen

1983. Greenland History.

140 **61** 2 k. 50 brown 65 65

141 – 3 k. 50 brown 95 95

142 – 4 k. 50 blue . . . . 1·10 1·10

DESIGNS: 3 k. 50, Mummy of Eskimo boy (1300–1400); 4 k. 50, Hans Pothorst's expedition to America (1400–1500).

1983. 250th Anniv of Herrnhut Moravian Brethren Settlement.

143 **62** 2 k. 50 brown 60 70

63 "Polar Bear killing Seal Hunter"

64 Bowhead Whales and Glass Beads (trading goods) (1500–1600)

1984. 50th Death Anniv of Karale Andreassen (writer and artist).

144 **63** 3 k. 70 black . . . . 1·40 90

1984. Greenland History.

145 **64** 2 k. 70 brown . . . . . . 1·25 75

146 – 3 k. 70 blue 90 90

147 – 5 k. 50 brown . . . . . . 1·50 1·50

DESIGNS: 3 k. 70 Greenlanders in European dress and apostle spoons (1600–1700); 5 k. 50, Hans Egede's mission station, Godthab, and key (1700–1800).

65 Prince Henrik of Denmark

66 Danish Grenadier, 1734

1984. Prince Henrik's 50th Birthday.

148 **65** 2 k. 70 brown . . . . . . 1·50 1·40

1984. 250th Anniv of Christianshab.

149 **66** 3 k. 70 brown . . . . . . 1·40 1·25

67 Lund

68 Spotted Wolffish

1984. 36th Death Anniv of Henrik Lund (composer).

150 **67** 5 k. green . . . . 2·40 2·00

1984.

151 **68** 10 k. black and blue . . . . 5·00 3·00

69 "Hvalfisken" (brig) (1800–1900)

70 Queen Ingrid and "Chrysanthemum frutescens" "Sofiero"

1985. Greenland History.

152 **69** 2 k. 80 purple . . . . . . 1·50 1·10

153 – 6 k. black . . . . 2·25 2·00

DESIGN: 6 k. Communications satellite and globe (1900–2000).

1985. 50th Anniv of Queen Ingrid's Arrival in Denmark.

154 **70** 2 k. 80 multicoloured . . . 60 70

71 Nesting Birds and I.Y.Y. Emblem

72 "Hare Hunt"

1985. International Youth Year.

155 **71** 3 k. 80 multicoloured . . . 75 85

1985. 130th Birth Anniv of Gerhard Kleist (artist).

156 **72** 9 k. green . . . . 2·75 2·25

73 Greenland Halibut

74 Post Office Flags

1985.

157 **73** 10 k. brown and blue . . . 3·25 2·75

1986. Postal Independence.

158 **74** 2 k. 80 red 65 65

75 Towing Man on Bladder

76 Ulos (knives for working sealskin)

1986. Traditional Sport.

159 **75** 2 k. 80 + 50 ore mult . . . . 1·40 1·25

1986.

160 **76** 3 k. black and blue . . . . 1·00 1·00

161 – 6 k. 50 brown and green . . 1·50 1·50

DESIGN: 6 k. 50, Lard lamps.

77 "Daily Life in Thule" (Aninaaq)

78 Capelin

1986.

162 **77** 2 k. 80 brown 70 80

1986.

163 **78** 10 k. brown and green . . . 3·50 3·50

80 "Ammassalik Fjord" (Peter Rosing)

81 Father and Son on Ice-floe

1987.

165 **80** 2 k. 80 brown 95 65

1987. Fishing, Sealing and Whaling Industries Year.

166 **81** 3 k. 80 multicoloured . . . 1·40 1·00

82 Needle Case and Combs

83 Rock Ptarmigans

1987. Craftwork.

167 **82** 2 k. 80 brown and red . . . 95 95

168 – 3 k. 80 purple and blue . . 1·40 1·40

DESIGN: 3 k. 80, Eye masks.

1988. Birds. Multicoloured.

169 3 k. Gyrfalcons . . . . 1·75 1·00

170 3 k. 20 Long-tailed ducks . . . 1·50 1·00

171 4 k. Snow geese . . . . 1·50 80

172 4 k. 10 Ravens . . . . 2·25 2·25

173 4 k. 40 Snow buntings . . . . 1·75 1·75

174 5 k. Type **83** . . . . 2·00 1·00

175 5 k. 50 White-tailed sea eagles . 2·40 1·75

176 5 k. 50 Black guillemots . . . 3·25 2·75

177 6 k. 50 Brunnich's guillemots . . 2·75 2·00

178 7 k. Great northern divers . . 3·25 2·75

179 7 k. 50 Long-tailed skuas . . . 2·40 2·40

180 10 k. Snowy owl . . . . 3·75 2·25

85 Telefax, Sledge and De Havilland Dash Seven

1988. 50 Years of Post Office Communication.

191 **85** 3 k. + 50 ore multicoloured . 2·10 2·10

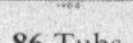

86 Tubs **87** National Flag

1988. Craftwork.

192 **86** 3 k. violet and red 60 60
193 – 5 k. brown and green . . . 1·50 1·50
194 – 10 k. brown and purple . . 3·00 2·40
DESIGNS: 5 k. Harpoon heads; 10 k. Masks.

1989. 10th Anniv of Internal Autonomy. Mult.

195 3 k. 20 Type **87** 90 65
196 4 k. 40 National arms . . . . . 1·40 1·40

88 Cotton Grass **89** Queen Margrethe

1989. Flowers. Multicoloured.

197 4 k. Bellflower (vert) . . . . . 1·10 80
198 4 k. Hairy lousewort (vert) . . . 1·40 80
199 5 k. Type **88** . . . . 1·40 1·40
200 5 k. 50 Labrador tea . . . . . 1·50 1·50
201 6 k. 50 Arctic white heather . . 2·40 2·40
202 7 k. 25 Purple saxifrage . . . . 2·75 2·75
203 10 k. Arctic poppy (vert) . . . 3·00 2·50

1990.

210 **89** 25 ore green 10 10
213 1 k. brown 20 20
218 4 k. red . . . . 1·10 80
219 4 k. 25 red . . . . 1·25 1·25
221 6 k. 50 blue . . . . 2·10 1·60
222 7 k. violet . . . . 1·90 1·90

90 Chained Sledge Dog and nesting Eiders **91** Frederik Lynge

1990. Greenland Environmental Foundation.

225 **90** 400 ore + 50 ore mult . . . 3·00 3·00

1990. Augo and Frederik Lynge (Greenland Members of Danish Folketing).

226 **91** 10 k. red and blue . . . . . 3·50 2·75
227 – 25 k. purple and blue . . . 5·25 4·75
DESIGN: 25 k. Augo Lynge.

92 Ringed Seal ("Phoca hispida") **93** Dogs and Fisherman

1991. Marine Mammals. Multicoloured.

228 4 k. Type **92** . . . . 1·40 1·40
229 4 k. Harp seals ("Pagophilus groenlandicus") . . . . 1·40 1·40
230 7 k. 25 Hooded seals ("Cystophora cristata") . . . 2·40 2·40
231 7 k. 25 Walrus ("Odobenus rosmarus") . . . . 2·40 2·40
232 8 k. 50 Bearded seal ("Erignatus barbatus") . . . . 3·00 3·00
233 8 k. 50 Common seal ("Phoca vitulina") . . . . 3·00 3·00

1991. 250th Anniv of Ilulissat (Jakobshavn).

235 **93** 4 k. multicoloured . . . . 1·50 1·50

94 Iceberg and Summer Flowers

1991. Nordic Countries' Postal Co-operation. Tourism. Multicoloured.

236 4 k. Type **94** . . . . 1·40 80
237 8 k. 50 Ski party and dog sled in winter . . . . 3·00 3·00

95 Birds **96** Jonathan Petersen (composer, 110th anniv)

1991. 75th Anniv of Blue Cross (health education organization)

238 **95** 4 k. + 50 ore mult . . . . . 7·50 7·50

1991. Birth Anniversaries.

239 **96** 10 k. black and blue . . . . 2·40 2·00
240 – 50 k. brown and blue . . . 10·50 10·00
DESIGN: 50 k. Hans Lynge (writer and artist, 85th anniv).

97 Arms and Paamiut

1992. Bicentenary of Paamiut.

241 **97** 7 k. 25 brown and blue . . 2·75 2·40

98 Royal Couple in 1992 and in Official Wedding Photograph

1992. Silver Wedding of Queen Margrethe and Prince Henrik.

242 **98** 4 k. multicoloured . . . . 2·25 1·40

99 Moller and Drawing of Godthab Church **100** Rainbow and Landscape

1992. 150th Birth Anniv of Lars Moller (editor and printer).

243 **99** 100 k. red and blue . . . . 20·00 20·00

1992. Neriuffik Cancer Research Organization.

244 **100** 4 k. + 50 ore mult . . . . 3·75 3·75

101 Mother and Child with Father Christmas **102** Flame and Laurel Wreath framed by Dance Drum

1992. Christmas.

245 **101** 4 k. multicoloured . . . . 2·25 1·90

1993. Int Year of Indigenous Peoples.

246 **102** 4 k. multicoloured . . . . 1·90 1·75

103 Flat Crab

1993. Crabs.

247 **103** 4 k. red, yellow & green . . 80 80
248 – 7 k. 25 brown and blue . . 3·25 3·25
249 – 8 k. 50 multicoloured . . . 3·50 3·50
DESIGNS: 7 k. 25, Sand crab; 8 k. 50, Stone crabs.

104 Ummannaq Church

1993. Nordic Countries' Postal Co-operation. Churches. Multicoloured.

250 4 k. Type **104** 80 80
251 8 k. 50 Hvalso church ruins . . 2·10 2·10

105 Children in Tent

1993. Anniversaries.

252 **105** 4 k. + 50 ore multicoloured 2·40 2·40
253 – 4 k. + 50 ore red & violet . 2·40 2·40
DESIGNS: No. 252 Type **105** (50th anniv of scouts in Greenland); 253, Birds, crosses and landscape (70th anniv of Red Cross in Greenland).

106 Corpuscles and "AIDS"

1993. Anti-AIDS Campaign.

255 **106** 4 k. multicoloured . . . . 1·10 1·10

107 Wolf **108** Dog Sled

1993. Animals. Multicoloured.

255a 4 k. Polar bear . . . . 1·40 1·40
256 5 k. Type **107** . . . . 1·40 1·40
257 5 k. 50 Ermine . . . . 1·40 1·40
258 7 k. 25 Arctic lemmings . . . 2·40 2·40
258a 7 k. 25 Wolverine . . . . . . 2·00 2·00
258b 7 k. 50 Musk ox . . . . . . 2·00 2·00
259 8 k. 50 Arctic fox . . . . . . 2·50 2·50
260 9 k. Mountain hare . . . . . 3·00 3·00
261 10 k. Reindeer . . . . 3·25 3·25

1993. Christmas.

265 **108** 4 k. multicoloured . . . . 1·75 1·75

109 Skiers **111** First Church

110 Transmission Line

1994. Winter Olympic Games, Lillehammer, Norway.

266 **109** 4 k. + 50 ore multicoloured 2·25 2·25

1994. Inauguration of Buksefjorden Hydroelectric Power Station.

268 **110** 4 k. multicoloured . . . . 1·10 1·10

1994. Centenary of Ammassalik.

269 **111** 7 k. 25 blue, brown & grn . 1·90 1·90

112 "Danmark" (steam barque)

1994. Europa. Discoveries. "Danmark" Expedition to North-east Coast, 1906–08. Multicoloured.

270 4 k. Type **112** 85 85
271 7 k. 25 "Danmark" and dogs following ELG Mobil car . . 2·25 2·25

113 "Ceres" (William Moen)

1994. Figureheads from Greenlandic Ships (1st series). Multicoloured.

272 4 k. Type **113** . . . . 1·10 1·10
273 8 k. 50 "Nordlyset" (carved Johan Heldt) . . . . 2·75 2·75
See also Nos. 290/1 and 309/10.

114 Visiting

1994. Christmas. Multicoloured.

274 4 k. Type **114** . . . . 1·10 1·10
275 5 k. Santa Claus outside igloo . 1·75 1·75

115 "Listera cordata" **116** Teacher and Student

1995. Orchids. Multicoloured.

276 4 k. Type **115** . . . . 1·10 1·10
277 7 k. 25 "Leucorchis albida" . . 1·90 1·90

1995. 150th Anniv of Ilinniarfissuaq (teacher training college) (4 k.) and 50th Anniv of United Nations Organization (7 k. 25).

278 **116** 4 k. multicoloured . . . . 1·10 1·10
279 – 7 k. 25 blue, green & red . 1·90 1·90
DESIGN—VERT: 7 k. 25, U.N. emblem and "50".

117 Iceberg and Meadow

1995. Nordic Countries' Postal Co-operation. Tourism.

280 4 k. Type **117** . . . . 1·50 1·50
281 8 k. 50 Mountains and valleys . 3·00 3·00

118 Airmail Envelope

1995. Europa. Peace and Freedom. Multicoloured.

282 4 k. Type **118** 95 95
283 8 k. 50 Doves and seascape . . 2·25 2·25

120 Children with Flag **121** Boy running with Lamps

1995. 10th Anniv of National Flag.

285 **120** 4 k. + 50 ore multicoloured 2·25 2·25
The premium was for the benefit of the Greenland Flag Society.

1995. Figureheads from Greenlandic Ships (2nd series). As T **113**. Multicoloured.
290 4 k. "Hvalfisken" (H. J. Moen) (vert) . . . . 1·00 1·00
291 8 k. 50 "Tjalfe" . . . . 2·50 2·50

1995. Christmas. Multicoloured.
292 4 k. Type **121** 95 95
293 5 k. Boy running with lamp and moon . . . . 1·40 1·40

1995. Nos. 210 and 213 surch.
294 **89** 4 k. 25 on 25 ore green . . . 90 90
295 4 k. 50 on 1 k. brown . . . 95 95

123 Early Coral-root

124 Killer Whale

1996. Arctic Orchids. Multicoloured.
296 4 k. 25 Type **123** 90 90
297 4 k. 50 Round-leaved orchid . . 95 95
298 7 k. 50 Northern green orchid . 1·60 1·60

1996. Whales (1st series). Each black, red and blue.
299 25 ore Type **124** 10 10
300 50 ore Humpback whale 10 10
301 1 k. Beluga 20 20
302 4 k. 50 Sperm whale 95 95
303 6 k. 50 Bowhead whale . . . . 1·40 1·40
304 9 k. 50 Minke whale . . . . . 2·00 2·00
See also Nos. 321/4.

125 Arnarulunnguaq (Eskimo traveller)

1996. Europa. Famous Women.
306 **125** 4 k. 50 blue 95 95

126 Man in Wheelchair at Sea Shore

1996. Regional Society of Handicapped and Disabled in Greenland.
307 **126** 4 k. 25+50 ore mult . . . 1·40 1·40

1996. Figureheads from Greenlandic Ships (3rd series). As T **113**. Multicoloured.
309 15 k. "Blaa Hejren" . . . . . 3·25 3·25
310 20 k. "Gertrud Rask" (horiz) . . 4·25 4·25

127 Child and Angels

1996. Christmas. Multicoloured.
311 4 k. 25 Type **127** 90 90
312 4 k. 50 Star and children . . . 95 95

128 Arctic Fritillary

129 Queen Margrethe in Greenlandic Costume

1997. Butterflies. Multicoloured.
313 2 k. Type **128** 40 40
314 3 k. Northern clouded yellow . . 60 60
315 4 k. 75 Arctic blue 95 95
316 8 k. Small copper . . . . . . 1·60 1·60

1997. Silver Jubilee of Queen Margrethe.
317 **129** 4 k. 50 multicoloured . . . 90 90

130 Globe and Musicians

1997. Katuaq Cultural Centre, Nuuk.
318 **130** 4 k. 50+50 ore mult . . . 1·00 1·00

131 Bear of the Sea inhaling Umiak (boat)

1997. Europa. Tales and Legends.
320 **131** 4 k. 75 blue 85 85

1997. Whales (2nd series). As T **124**. Mult.
321 5 k. Blue whale 95 95
322 5 k. 75 Fin whale . . . . . . 1·10 1·10
323 6 k. Sei whale . . . . 1·10 1·10
324 8 k. Narwhal . . . . 1·50 1·50

132 Dancing Children and Church

1997. Bicentenary of Nanortalik.
326 **132** 4 k. 50 multicoloured . . . 80 80

133 "Trommedanser"

1997. Art. 20th Death Anniv of Aage Gitz-Johansen. Multicoloured.
327 10 k. Type **133** . . . . 2·00 2·00
328 16 k. "Ammassalikkvinde" . . 3·00 3·00

134 Boy with Huskies

1997. Christmas. Multicoloured.
329 4 k. 50 Type **134** 85 85
330 4 k. 75 Family on sledge and father disentangling traces . . 90 90

135 Common Porpoise

1998. International Year of the Ocean. Cetaceans. Multicoloured.
331 2 k. Type **135** 40 40
332 3 k. White-beaked dolphin . . . 55 55
333 4 k. 50 Long-finned pilot whale ("Globicephala melaena") . . 85 85
334 4 k. 50 Northern bottle-nosed whale ("Hyperoodon ampullatus") 85 85
335 4 k. 75 Atlantic white-sided dolphin ("Lagenorhynchus acutus") 90 90
336 4 k. 75 Black right whale ("Eubalaena glacialis") . . . 90 90

136 Augo and Frederik Lynge (first Greenland members of Danish Folketing)

137 Kathrine Chemnitz

1998. New Order, 1950 (redefinition of Greenland's status).
338 **136** 4 k. 50 blue, lilac and red . 85 85

1998. 20th Death Anniv of Kathrine Chemnitz (founder) and 50th Anniv of Women's Society of Greenland.
339 **137** 4 k. 50+50 ore mult . . . 95 95

138 "Children's Faces" (Class 4B, Atuarfik Ukaliusaq School)

139 "Gertrud Rask" (sailing coaster)

1998. Europa. National Festivals. Children's Day. Multicoloured.
341 4 k. 75 Type **138** 90 90
342 10 k. Children playing (Class 5A, Edvard Kruse-p Atuarfia School) . . . . 1·90 1·90

1998. Nordic Countries' Postal Co-operation. Shipping. Multicoloured.
343 4 k. 50 Type **139** 85 85
344 4 k. 75 "Hans Egede" (sailing coaster) 90 90

140 "Breastfeeding Older Brother"

1998. 10th Death Anniv of Hans Lynge (artist). Multicoloured.
345 11 k. Type **140** . . . . 2·10 2·10
346 25 k. "Refuelling" . . . . . . 4·75 4·75

141 Jacket and Slippers on Line

142 Owl with Chicks

1998. Christmas. Multicoloured.
347 4 k. 50 Type **141** 85 85
348 4 k. 75 Hat and slippers on line . 90 90

1999. Endangered Species. The Snowy Owl. Multicoloured.
349 1 k. Type **142** 20 20
350 4 k. 75 Owl in flight 90 90
351 5 k. 50 Male and female owls . . 1·00 1·00
352 5 k. 75 Owl on rock . . . . . 1·10 1·10

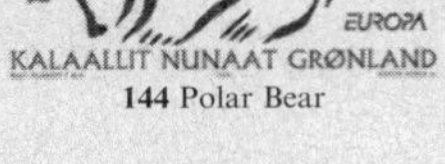

143 Ammassalik Pincushion

144 Polar Bear

1999. Greenland National Museum and Archives.
353 **143** 4 k. 50 + 50 ore black, blue and red 85 85

1999. Europa. Parks and Gardens.
355 **144** 6 k. multicoloured . . . . 1·00 1·00

145 "The Man from Aluk"

1999. Paintings by Peter Rosing. Multicoloured.
356 7 k. Type **145** . . . . 1·25 1·25
357 20 k. "Homecoming" . . . . . 3·50 3·50

146 Viking Longship

1999. Greenland Vikings (1st series).
358 **146** 4 k. 50 green and blue . . 75 75
359 – 4 k. 75 green and blue . . 80 80
360 – 5 k. 75 brown and blue . . 1·00 1·00
361 – 8 k. brown and blue . . . 1·40 1·40
DESIGNS—4 k. 75, Man collecting driftwood; 5 k. 75, Arrowhead and coins; 8 k. Tjodhilde's Church.
See also Nos. 366/9.

147 Writing Letter

1999 Christmas. Multicoloured.
363 4 k. 50 Type **147** 75 75
364 4 k. 75 Candles and clasped hands 80 80

148 Ice Cap

1999. Year 2000.
365 **148** 5 k. 75 multicoloured . . . 1·00 1·00

2000. Greenland Vikings (2nd series). Horiz designs as T **146**.
366 25 o. brown and blue 10 10
367 3 k. brown and blue 50 25
368 5 k. 50 blue 95 50
369 21 k. blue . . . . 3·50 1·75
DESIGNS—25 o., Walruses; 3 k. Story teller and model of great northern diver; 5 k. 50, Dog chasing reindeer; 21 k. Viking with gyrfalcon, polar bear, walrus tusks and straps and bag of ship's tar (trading goods).

PARCEL POST STAMPS

P 1 Arms of Greenland

1905.
P 4 **P 1** 1 ore green . . . . 24·00 29·00
P 5 2 ore yellow . . . . £150 60·00
P 6 5 ore brown . . . . 60·00 70·00
P 7 10 ore blue . . . . 26·00 35·00
P 8 15 ore violet . . . . . . 95·00 £110
P 9 20 ore red . . . . 4·75 5·75
P13 70 ore violet . . . . . . 24·00 90·00
P14 1 k. yellow . . . . 24·00 38·00
P12 3 k. brown . . . . 65·00 £110

Prices for used stamps are for rubber stamp cancellations applied in Copenhagen, the various Greenland cancellations being worth much more. Stamps with numeral cancellations have been used as saving stamps.

GRENADA Pt. 1

One of the Windward Is., Br. W. Indies. Ministerial Government was introduced on 1 January 1960. Achieved Associated Statehood on 3 March 1967 and Independence on 7 February 1974.

1861. 12 pence = 1 shilling;
20 shillings = 1 pound.
1949. 100 cents = 1 West Indian dollar.

1 5

1861.
14 1 1d green . . . 60·00 6·50
6 6d. red . . . £600 12·00

1875. Surch **POSTAGE** and value in words.
21 5 ¼d. mauve . . . 11·00 5·50
22 2½d. lake . . . 50·00 5·50
23 4d. blue . . . 95·00 8·00
13 1s. mauve . . . £650 9·50

1883. Revenue stamp surch crown and value (in green) optd **POSTAGE**.
27 5 1d. orange . . . £275 48·00

1883. Revenue stamp as last but optd **POSTAGE** diagonally on each half.
29 5 Half of 1d. orange . . . £225 £110

13 21

1883.
30 13 ½d. green . . . 1·00 1·00
31 1d. red . . . 65·00 3·25
32 2½d. blue . . . 6·50 1·00
33 4d. grey . . . 4·50 1·75
34 6d. mauve . . . 3·00 4·00
35 8d. brown . . . 8·50 12·00
36 1s. violet . . . £110 55·00

1886. Revenue stamps as No. 27 but surch **POSTAGE** and value in words or figures.
43 5 ½d. on 2s. orange . . . 12·00 17·00
37 1d. on 1½d. orange . . . 38·00 29·00
39 1d. on 4d. orange . . . £140 90·00
38 1d. on 1s. orange . . . 32·00 30·00
41 4d. on 2s. orange . . . 38·00 17·00

1887. As T **13**, but inscr "GRENADA POSTAGE & REVENUE" at top.
40 13 1d. red . . . 60 60

1890. Revenue stamp as No. 27 but surch **POSTAGE AND REVENUE 1d.**
45 5 1d. on 2s. orange . . . 50·00 50·00

1891. Surch **POSTAGE AND REVENUE 1d.**
46 13 1d. on 8d. brown . . . 9·00 11·00

1891. Surch **2½d.**
47 13 2½d. on 8d. brown . . . 8·00 11·00

1895.
48 21 ½d. mauve and green . . . 2·50 1·50
49 1d. mauve and red . . . 4·50 70
50 2d. mauve and brown . . . 40·00 32·00
51 2½d. mauve and blue . . . 5·00 1·50
52 3d. mauve and orange . . . 6·50 16·00
53 6d. mauve and green . . . 10·00 21·00
54 8d. mauve and black . . . 12·00 38·00
55 1s. green and orange . . . 17·00 32·00

23 Flagship of Columbus (Columbus named Grenada "La Concepcion")

1898. 400th Anniv of Discovery of Grenada by Columbus.
56 23 2½d. blue . . . 13·00 6·00

1902. As T **21**, but portrait of King Edward VII.
57 ½d. purple and green . . . 3·00 65
58 1d. purple and red . . . 4·00 20
59 2d. purple and brown . . . 3·00 9·00
60 2½d. purple and blue . . . 3·50 2·50
61 3d. purple and orange . . . 3·50 8·00
72 6d. purple and green . . . 4·50 9·00
63 1s. green and orange . . . 3·25 23·00
64 2s. green and blue . . . 20·00 55·00
65 5s. green and red . . . 38·00 55·00
66 10s. green and purple . . . £110 £200

26 Badge of the Colony 28

1906.
77 26 ½d. green . . . 3·00 30
78 1d. red . . . 4·00 10
79 2d. orange . . . 2·00 3·00
80 2½d. blue . . . 4·50 1·50
84 3d. purple on yellow . . . 3·75 1·75
85 6d. purple . . . 18·00 23·00
86 1s. black on green . . . 5·50 4·25
87 2s. blue and purple on blue . . . 18·00 12·00
88 5s. green and red on yellow . . . 50·00 65·00
83 10s. green and red on green . . . 80·00 £160

1913.
112 28 ½d. green . . . 1·25 15
113 1d red . . . 80 50
114 1d. brown . . . 1·50 20
115 1½d. red . . . 1·50 1·50
116 2d. orange . . . 1·25 15
117 2d. grey . . . 2·50 2·25
94 2½d. blue . . . 1·60 3·25
118 2½d. grey . . . 75 8·50
96 3d. purple on yellow . . . 65 85
121 3d. blue . . . 1·25 10·00
123 4d. black & red on yell . . . 1·00 3·75
124 5d. purple and green . . . 1·50 4·00
97 6d. purple . . . 1·25 8·50
126 6d. black and red . . . 2·25 2·50
127 9d. purple and black . . . 2·25 8·50
98a 1s. black on green . . . 1·00 6·00
129 1s. brown . . . 3·00 10·00
99 2s. purple & blue on blue . . . 5·50 12·00
131 2s. 6d. black & red on bl . . . 6·50 17·00
132 3s. green and violet . . . 6·00 27·00
133 5s. green & red on yellow . . . 12·00 35·00
101 10s. green & red on green . . . 48·00 80·00

1916. Optd **WAR TAX.**
111 28 1d. red . . . 30 20

31 Grand Anse Beach

32 Badge of the Colony

1934.
135 31 ½d. green . . . 15 1·00
136a 32 1d. black and brown . . . 65 35
137a – 1½d. black and red . . . 1·00 55
138 32 2d. black and orange . . . 90 40
139 – 2½d. blue . . . 50 30
140 32 3d. black and olive . . . 70 2·25
141 6d. black and purple . . . 1·60 1·25
142 1s. black and brown . . . 1·25 3·00
143 2s. 6d. black and blue . . . 7·00 27·00
144 5s. black and violet . . . 32·00 50·00
DESIGNS—VERT: 1½d. Grand Etang; 2½d. St. George's.

1935. Silver Jubilee. As T **10a** of Gambia.
145 ½d. black and green . . . 60 1·50
146 1d. blue and grey . . . 60 1·50
147 1½d. blue and red . . . 60 1·50
148 1s. grey and purple . . . 6·00 16·00

1937. Coronation. As T **10b** of Gambia.
149 1d. violet . . . 40 20
150 1½d. red . . . 40 20
151 2½d. blue . . . 80 30

35 King George VI

40 Badge of the Colony

1937.
152b 35 ¼d brown . . . 20 60

1938. As 1934, but with portrait of King George VI.
153b 31 ½d. green . . . 60 1·25
154a 32 1d. black and brown . . . 50 50
155 – 1½d. black and red . . . 50 70
156 32 2d. black and orange . . . 30 50
157 – 2½d. blue . . . 30 30
158ab 32 3d. black and olive . . . 30 80
159 6d. black and purple . . . 1·25 40
160 1s. black and brown . . . 2·25 40
161 2s. black and blue . . . 16·00 1·50
162 5s. black and violet . . . 3·50 1·50
163e 40 10s. blue and red . . . 27·00 8·50

1946. Victory. As T **11a** of Gambia.
164 1½d. red . . . 10 10
165 3½d. blue . . . 10 20

1948. Silver Wedding. As T **11b/c** of Gambia.
166 1½d. red . . . 15 10
167 10s. grey . . . 8·00 16·00

1949. U.P.U. As T **11d/g** of Gambia.
168 5 c. blue . . . 20 10
169 6 c. olive . . . 90 1·25
170 12 c. mauve . . . 35 30
171 24 c. brown . . . 35 30

41 King George VI

42 Badge of the Colony

1951.
172 41 ½ c. black and brown . . . 15 1·00
173 1 c. black and green . . . 15 25
174 2 c. black and brown . . . 15 30
175 3 c. black and red . . . 15 10
176 4 c. black and orange . . . 35 40
177 5 c. black and violet . . . 20 10
178 6 c. black and olive . . . 30 60
179 7 c. black and blue . . . 1·75 10
180 12 c. black and purple . . . 2·25 30
181 42 25 c. black and brown . . . 2·25 50
182 50 c. black and blue . . . 6·50 40
183 $1.50 black and orange . . . 7·50 6·50
184 $2.50 slate and red . . . 5·50 5·50
No. 184 is larger 24½×30½ mm.

43a Arms of University

43b Princess Alice

1951. Inauguration of B.W.I. University College.
185 43a 3 c. black and red . . . 45 20
186 43b 6 c. black and olive . . . 45 20

1951. New Constitution. Nos. 175/7 and 180 optd **NEW CONSTITUTION 1951.**
187 41 3 c. black and red . . . 10 10
188 4 c. black and orange . . . 10 10
189 5 c. black and violet . . . 10 10
190 12 c. black and purple . . . 10 15

1953. Coronation. As T **11h** of Gambia.
191 3 c. black and red . . . 20 10

1953. As T **41**, but with portrait of Queen Elizabeth II, and T **42**, but Royal Cypher changed.
192 41 ½ c. black and brown . . . 10 10
193 1 c. black and green . . . 10 10
214 2 c. black and brown . . . 10 10
195 3 c. black and red . . . 10 10
196 4 c. black and orange . . . 10 10
197 5 c. black and violet . . . 10 10
198 6 c. black and olive . . . 45 1·25
199 7 c. black and blue . . . 1·25 10
219 12 c. black and purple . . . 20 10
201 42 25 c. black and brown . . . 1·25 20
202 50 c. black and blue . . . 5·50 40
203 $1.50 black and orange . . . 11·00 13·00
204 $2.50 slate and red . . . 18·00 10·00
No. 204 is larger 24½×30½ mm.

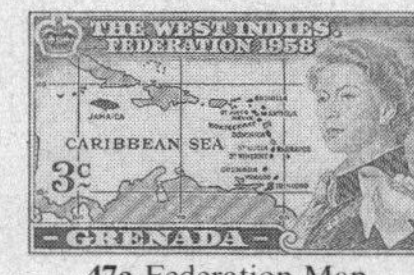

47a Federation Map

1958. British Caribbean Federation.
205 47a 3 c. green . . . 35 10
206 6 c. blue . . . 45 60
207 12 c. red . . . 55 10

48 Queen Victoria, Queen Elizabeth II, Mail Van and Post Office, St. George's

1961. Grenada Stamp Centenary.
208 48 3 c. red and black . . . 25 10
209 – 8 c. blue and orange . . . 55 25
210 – 25 c. lake and blue . . . 55 25
DESIGNS (incorporating Queen Victoria and Queen Elizabeth II): 8 c. Flagship of Columbus; 25 c. "Solent I" (paddle-steamer) and Douglas DC-3 aircraft.

1963. Freedom from Hunger. As T **20a** of Gambia.
211 8 c. green . . . 30 15

1963. Centenary of Red Cross. As T **20b** of Gambia.
212 3 c. red and black . . . 20 15
213 25 c. red and blue . . . 40 15

1965. Centenary of I.T.U. As T **44** of Gibraltar.
221 2 c. orange and olive . . . 10 10
222 50 c. yellow and red . . . 25 20

1965. I.C.Y. As T **45** of Gibraltar.
223 1 c. purple and turquoise . . . 10 15
224 25 c. green and lavender . . . 20 15

1966. Churchill Commen. As T **46** of Gibraltar.
225 1 c. blue . . . 10 15
226 3 c. green . . . 10 15
227 25 c. brown . . . 15 10
228 35 c. violet . . . 25 15

49 Queen Elizabeth II and Duke of Edinburgh

1966. Royal Visit.
229 49 3 c. black and blue . . . 25 15
230 35 c. black and mauve . . . 65 15

52 Hillsborough, Carriacou

1966. Multicoloured.
231 1 c. Type **52** . . . 20 55
232 2 c. Bougainvillea . . . 20 10
233 3 c. Flamboyant plant . . . 30 30
234 5 c. Levera Beach . . . 60 10
235 6 c. Carenage, St. George's . . . 60 10
236 8 c. Annandale Falls . . . 60 10
237 10 c. Cocoa pods . . . 30 10
238 12 c. Inner Harbour . . . 30 60
239 15 c. Nutmeg . . . 30 60
240 25 c. St. George's . . . 30 10
241 35 c. Grand Anse beach . . . 30 10
242 50 c. Bananas . . . 1·00 1·50
243 $1 Badge of the Colony . . . 7·00 3·00
244 $2 Queen Elizabeth II . . . 5·00 6·00
245 $3 Map of Grenada . . . 4·50 12·00
Nos. 243/5 are vert and larger, 25×39 mm.

1966. World Cup Football Championship. As T **47** of Gibraltar.
246 5 c. multicoloured . . . 10 10
247 50 c. multicoloured . . . 40 75

1966. Inauguration of W.H.O. Headquarters, Geneva. As T **54** of Gibraltar.
248 8 c. black, green and blue . . . 15 10
249 25 c. black, purple & ochre . . . 30 20

1966. 20th Anniv of U.N.E.S.C.O. As T **56a/c** of Gibraltar.
250 2 c. multicoloured . . . 10 10
251 15 c. yellow, violet & orange . . . 15 10
252 50 c. black, purple & orange . . . 30 80

1967. Statehood. Nos. 232/3, 236 and 240 optd **ASSOCIATED STATEHOOD 1967.**
253 2 c. multicoloured . . . 10 15
254 3 c. multicoloured . . . 10 15
255 8 c. multicoloured . . . 15 10
256 25 c. multicoloured . . . 15 15

1967. World Fair, Montreal. Nos. 232, 237, 239 and 243/4 surch or optd **expo67 MONTREAL CANADA** and emblem.
257 1 c. on 15 c. multicoloured . . . 10 20
258 2 c. multicoloured . . . 15 20
259 3 c. on 10 c. multicoloured . . . 10 20
260 $1 multicoloured . . . 30 25
261 $2 multicoloured . . . 45 30

1967. Nos. 231/45 optd **ASSOCIATED STATEHOOD.**
262 52 1 c. multicoloured . . . 10 10
263 – 2 c. multicoloured . . . 10 10
264 – 3 c. multicoloured . . . 10 10
265 – 5 c. multicoloured . . . 10 10
266 – 6 c. multicoloured . . . 10 10
267 – 8 c. multicoloured . . . 10 10
268 – 10 c. multicoloured . . . 10 10
269 – 12 c. multicoloured . . . 10 10
270 – 15 c. multicoloured . . . 15 10
271 – 25 c. multicoloured . . . 20 10
272 – 35 c. multicoloured . . . 55 10
273 – 50 c. multicoloured . . . 70 20
274 – $1 multicoloured . . . 80 60
275 – $2 multicoloured . . . 1·25 3·50
276 – $3 multicoloured . . . 2·25 3·50

70 Kennedy and Local Flower

1968. 50th Birth Anniv of Pres. Kennedy. Multicoloured.
277 1 c. Type **70** . . . 10 15
278 15 c. Type **70** . . . 10 10
279 25 c. Kennedy and strelitzia . . . 10 10
280 35 c. Kennedy and roses . . . 10 10
281 50 c. As 25 c. . . . 15 20
282 $1 As 35 c. . . . 25 60

73 Scout Bugler

1968. World Scout Jamboree, Idaho. Mult.
283 1 c. Type **73** 10 10
284 2 c. Scouts camping 10 10
285 3 c. Lord Baden-Powell 10 10
286 35 c. Type **73** 25 10
287 50 c. As 2 c. 35 20
288 $1 As 3 c. 50 55

76 "Near Antibes"

1968. Paintings by Sir Winston Churchill. Multicoloured.
289 10 c. Type **76** 10 10
290 12 c. "The Mediterranean" . . 15 10
291 15 c. "St. Jean, Cap Ferratt" . . 15 10
292 25 c. Type **76** 20 10
293 35 c. As No. 291 . . . . . . 25 10
294 50 c. Sir Winston painting . . . 35 25

1968. No. 275 surch **$5**.
295 $5 on $2 multicoloured . . . . 1·50 2·25

1968. "Children Need Milk". Surch **CHILDREN NEED MILK** and value. (a) Nos. 244/5.
296 2 c. + 3 c. on $2 multicoloured 10 10
297 3 c. + 3 c. on $3 multicoloured 10 10

(b) Nos. 243/4.
298 1 c. + 3 c. on $1 multicoloured 10 40
299 2 c. + 3 c. on $2 multicoloured 13·00 45·00

83 Edith McGuire (U.S.A.)

1968. Olympic Games, Mexico.
300 **83** 1 c. brown, black & blue . . 10 20
301 – 2 c. multicoloured 10 20
302 – 3 c. scarlet, brown & green . . 10 20
303 **83** 10 c. multicoloured 15 20
304 – 50 c. multicoloured 55 75
305 – 60 c. red, brown & orange . . 60 80
DESIGNS: 2 c., 50 c. Arthur Wint (Jamaica); 3 c., 60 c. Ferreira da Silva (Brazil).

86 Hibiscus

102 Kidney Transplant

1968. Multicoloured.
306 1 c. Type **86** 10 10
307 2 c. Strelitzia 10 10
308 3 c. Bougainvillea 10 10
309 5 c. Rock hind 10 10
310 6 c. Sailfish 10 10
311 8 c. Red snapper 10 30
312 10 c. Marine toad 10 10
313 12 c. Turtle 15 10
314 15 c. Tree boa 90 60
314a 15 c. Thunbergia . . . . . . 4·00 2·50
315 25 c. Greater Trinidadian murine opossum 30 10
316 35 c. Nine-banded armadillo . . 35 10
317 50 c. Mona monkey 45 25
317a 75 c. Yacht in St. George's Harbour . . . . 12·00 8·50
318 $1 Bananaquit . . . . 3·00 1·50
319 $2 Brown pelican . . . . . 6·00 9·00
320 $3 Magnificent frigate bird . . 4·50 5·00
321 $5 Bare-eyed thrush . . . . 8·00 16·00
Nos. 309, 311/12, 314, 316 and 317a are horiz. Nos. 318/21 are larger $25\frac{1}{2} \times 48$ mm.

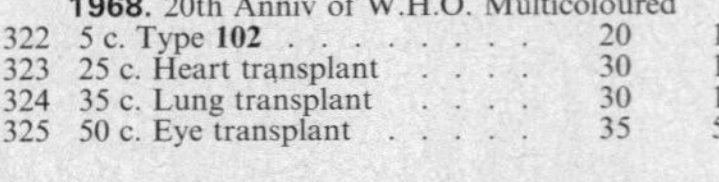
1968. 20th Anniv of W.H.O. Multicoloured.
322 5 c. Type **102** 20 10
323 25 c. Heart transplant 30 10
324 35 c. Lung transplant 30 10
325 50 c. Eye transplant 35 50

106 "The Adoration of the Kings" (Veronese)

114 Dame Hylda Bynoe

111 Dame Hylda Bynoe (Governor) and Island Scene

1968. Christmas.
326 **106** 5 c. multicoloured 10 10
327 – 15 c. multicoloured 10 10
328 – 35 c. multicoloured 10 10
329 – $1 multicoloured 30 40
DESIGNS: 15 c. "Madonna and Child with Saints John and Catherine" (Titian); 35 c. "The Adoration of the Kings" (Botticelli); $1 "A Warrior Adoring" (Catena).

1969. Caribbean Free Trade Area Exhibition. Nos. 300/5 surch **VISIT CARIFTA EXPO '69 April 5-30** and value.
330 **83** 5 c. on 1 c. 10 10
331 – 8 c. on 2 c. 10 10
332 – 25 c. on 3 c. 10 10
333 **83** 35 c. on 10 c. 10 10
334 – $1 on 50 c. 20 30
335 – $2 on 60 c. 35 60

1969. Carifta Expo '69. Multicoloured.
336 5 c. Type **111** 10 10
337 15 c. Premier E. M. Gairy and island scene 10 10
338 50 c. Type **111** 10 25
339 60 c. Emblems of 1958 and 1967 World's Fairs 10 40

1969. Human Rights Year. Multicoloured.
340 5 c. Type **114** 10 10
341 25 c. Dr. Martin Luther King . 15 10
342 35 c. As 5 c. 15 10
343 $1 "Balshazzar's Feast" (Rembrandt) (horiz) 30 45

117 Batsman and Wicket-keeper

1969. Cricket.
344 **117** 3 c. yellow, brown & bl . . 25 1·00
345 – 10 c. multicoloured 30 40
346 – 25 c. brown., ochre & grn . . 60 85
347 – 35 c. multicoloured 80 90
DESIGNS: 10 c. Batsman playing defensive stroke; 25 c. Batsman sweeping ball; 35 c. Batsman playing on-drive.

129 Astronaut handling Moon Rock

1969. First Man on the Moon. Multicoloured.
348 $\frac{1}{2}$ c. As Type **129** but larger (56 x 35 mm) 10 10
349 1 c. Moon rocket and moon . . 10 10
350 2 c. Module landing 10 10
351 3 c. Declaration left on the moon 10 10
352 8 c. Module leaving rocket . . 10 10
353 25 c. Rocket lifting-off . . . 20 10
354 35 c. Spacecraft in orbit . . . 20 10
355 50 c. Capsule with parachutes . 30 30
356 $1 Type **129** . . . . 45 1·00
The 25, 35 and 50 c. are vert.

130 Gandhi

1969. Birth Cent of Mahatma Gandhi. Mult.
358 6 c. Type **130** 15 10
359 15 c. Gandhi standing 20 10
360 25 c. Gandhi walking 25 10
361 $1 Head of Gandhi 50 60

1969. Christmas. Nos. 326/9 optd **1969** and surch (No. 363).
363 – 2 c. on 15 c. multicoloured . 10 30
364 **106** 5 c. multicoloured 10 10
365 – 35 c. multicoloured 20 10
366 – $1 multicoloured . . . . . 80 1·75

135 "Blackbeard" (Edward Teach)

1970. Pirates.
367 **135** 15 c. black 35 10
368 – 25 c. green 50 10
369 – 50 c. lilac 90 20
370 – $1 carmine . . . . 1·50 75
DESIGNS: 25 c. Anne Bonney; 50 c. Jean Lafitte; $1 Mary Read.

1970. No. 348 surch **5c**.
371 5 c. on $\frac{1}{2}$ c. multicoloured . . . 10 10

141/2 "The Last Supper" (detail, Del Sarto)

1970. Easter. Paintings.
372 **141** 5 c. multicoloured 10 15
373 **142** 5 c. multicoloured 10 15
374 – 15 c. multicoloured 15 20
375 – 15 c. multicoloured 15 25
376 – 25 c. multicoloured 20 30
377 – 25 c. multicoloured 20 30
378 – 60 c. multicoloured 30 55
379 – 60 c. multicoloured 30 55
DESIGNS: 15 c. "Christ crowned with Thorns" (detail, Van Dyck); 25 c. "The Passion of Christ" (detail, Memling); 60 c. "Christ in the Tomb" (detail, Rubens).
Each value was issued in sheets containing the two stamps se-tenant. Each design is spread over two stamps as in Type **141/2**.

149 Girl with Kittens in Pram

1970. Birth Bicentenary of Wordsworth. "Children and Pets". Multicoloured.
381 5 c. Type **149** 15 15
382 15 c. Girl with puppy and kitten 20 15
383 30 c. Boy with fishing-rod and cat 25 30
384 60 c. Boys and girls with cats and dogs . . . . 40 1·25

153 Parliament of India

1970. 7th Regional Conference of Commonwealth Parliamentary Association. Parliament Buildings. Multicoloured.
386 5 c. Type **153** 10 10
387 25 c. Great Britain 10 10
388 50 c. Canada 20 15
389 60 c. Grenada 20 15

157 Tower of the Sun

1970. World Fair, Osaka. Multicoloured.
391 1 c. Type **157** 10 10
392 2 c. Livelihood and Industry Pavilion (horiz) 10 10
393 3 c. Flower painting, 1634 . . . 10 10
394 10 c. "Adam and Eve" (Tintoretto) (horiz) 15 10
395 25 c. Organization For Economic Co-operation and Development (O.E.C.D.) Pavilion (horiz) 20 10
396 50 c. San Francisco Pavilion . . 45 1·25

164 Roosevelt and "Raising U.S. Flag on Iwo Jima"

1970. 25th Anniv of Ending of World War II. Multicoloured.
398 $\frac{1}{2}$ c. Type **164** 10 40
399 5 c. Zhukov and "Fall of Berlin" 70 30
400 15 c. Churchill and "Evacuation at Dunkirk" . . . . 1·50 45
401 25 c. De Gaulle and "Liberation of Paris" . . . . 1·50 45
402 50 c. Eisenhower and "D-Day Landing" . . . . 2·00 1·50
403 60 c. Montgomery and "Battle of Alamein" . . . . 2·00 3·00

1970. "Philympia 1970" Stamp Exhibition, London. Nos. 353/6 optd **PHILYMPIA LONDON 1970**.
405 – 25 c. multicoloured 10 10
406 – 35 c. multicoloured 10 10
407 – 50 c. multicoloured 15 15
408 **129** $1 multicoloured 20 30

170 U.P.U. Headquarters Building and Transport

1970. New U.P.U. Headquarters Building. Multicoloured.
409 15 c. Type **170** 35 10
410 25 c. As Type **170**, but modern transport 35 10
411 50 c. Sir Rowland Hill and U.P.U. Building 35 30
412 $1 Abraham Lincoln and U.P.U. Building . . . . 40 1·50
The 50 c. and $1 are both vert.

171 "The Madonna of the Goldfinch" (Tiepolo)

1970. Christmas. Multicoloured.

414 ½ c. Type **171** 10 10
415 ½ c. "The Virgin and Child with St. Peter and St. Paul" (Bouts) 10 10
416 ½ c. "The Virgin and Child" (Bellini) 10 10
417 2 c. "The Madonna of the Basket" (Correggio) 10 10
418 3 c. Type **171** 10 10
419 35 c. As No. 415 . . . . . . 20 10
420 50 c. As 2 c. 30 35
421 $1 As No. 416 . . . . 50 1·50

172 19th-Century Nursing

1970. Cent of British Red Cross. Multicoloured.

423 5 c. Type **172** 20 10
424 15 c. Military ambulance, 1918 25 10
425 25 c. First-Aid post, 1941 . . . 35 10
426 60 c. Red Cross transport, 1970 90 80

173 John Dewey and Art Lesson

1971. Int. Education Year. Multicoloured.

428 5 c. Type **173** 10 10
429 10 c. Jean-Jacques Rousseau and "Alphabetisation" 15 10
430 50 c. Maimonides and laboratory 50 15
431 $1 Bertrand Russell and mathematics class 95 40

174 Jennifer Hosten and Outline of Grenada

1971. Winner of "Miss World" Competition (1970).

433 **174** 5 c. multicoloured 10 10
434 10 c. multicoloured 10 10
435 15 c. multicoloured 15 10
436 25 c. multicoloured 15 10
437 35 c. multicoloured 15 10
438 50 c. multicoloured 35 55

175 French and Canadian Scouts

1971. 13th World Scout Jamboree, Asagiri, Japan. Multicoloured.

440 5 c. Type **175** 10 10
441 35 c. German and American scouts 30 25
442 50 c. Australian and Japanese scouts 40 50
443 75 c. Grenada and British scouts 50 75

176 "Napoleon reviewing the Guard" (E. Detaille)

1971. 150th Death Anniv of Napoleon Bonaparte. Paintings. Multicoloured.

445 5 c. Type **176** 15 15
446 15 c. "Napoleon before Madrid" (Vernet) 25 15
447 35 c. "Napoleon crossing Mt. St. Bernard" (David) 30 15
448 $2 "Napoleon in his Study" (David) . . . . 75 1·50

177 1d. Stamp of 1861 and Badge of Grenada

1971. 110th Anniv of the Postal Service. Mult.

450 5 c. Type **177** 20 20
451 15 c. 6d. stamp of 1861 and Queen Elizabeth II 25 15
452 35 c. 1d. and 6d. stamps of 1861 and badge of Grenada . . . 50 20
453 50 c. Scroll and 1d. stamp of 1861 65 1·75

178 Apollo Splashdown

1971. Apollo Moon Exploration Series. Mult.

455 1 c. Type **178** 10 10
456 2 c. Recovery of "Apollo 13" . 10 10
457 3 c. Separation of Lunar Module from "Apollo 14" 10 10
458 10 c. Shepard and Mitchell taking samples of moon rock 25 10
459 25 c. Moon Buggy 75 20
460 $1 "Apollo 15" blast-off (vert) 2·00 3·25

179 67th Regt of Foot, 1787

1971. Military Uniforms. Multicoloured.

462 ½ c. Type **179** 10 10
463 1 c. 45th Regt of Foot, 1792 . . 10 10
464 2 c. 29th Regt of Foot, 1794 . . 10 10
465 10 c. 9th Regt of Foot, 1801 . . 45 10
466 25 c. 2nd Regt of Foot, 1815 . . 85 20
467 $1 70th Regt of Foot, 1764 . . 2·50 2·00

180 "The Adoration of the Kings" (Memling)

1972. Christmas (1971). Multicoloured.

469 15 c. Type **180** 15 10
470 25 c. "Madonna and Child" (Michelangelo) 20 10
471 35 c. "Madonna and Child" (Murillo) 25 10
472 50 c. "The Virgin with the Apple" (Memling) . . . . 30 1·25

1972. Winter Olympic Games, Sapporo, Japan. Nos. 462/4 surch **WINTER OLYMPICS FEB. 3-13, 1972 SAPPORO, JAPAN**, Olympic rings and premium. Nos. 476/7 additionally optd **AIR MAIL**.

474 $2 on 2 c. mult (postage) . . . 50 90
476 35 c. on ½ c. multicoloured (air) 15 25
477 50 c. on 1 c. multicoloured . . 15 35

1972. General Election. Nos. 307/8, 310 and 315 optd **VOTE FEB. 28 1972**.

478 2 c. multicoloured 10 10
479 3 c. multicoloured 10 10
480 6 c. multicoloured 10 15
481 25 c. multicoloured 15 30

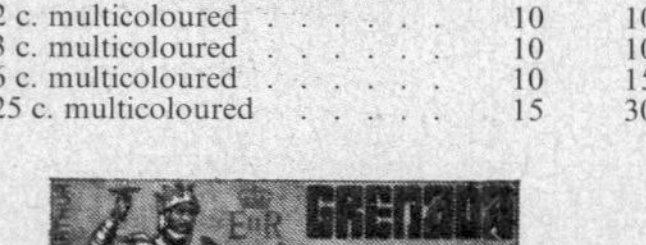

183 King Arthur

1972. U.N.I.C.E.F. Multicoloured.

482 ½ c. Type **183** 10 10
483 1 c. Robin Hood 10 10
484 2 c. Robinson Crusoe (vert) . . 10 10
485 25 c. Type **183** 10 10
486 50 c. As 1 c. 25 40
487 75 c. As 2 c. . . . . 30 1·00
488 $1 Mary and her little lamb (vert) 45 1·25

1972. "Interpex" Stamp Exhib., New York. Nos. 433/8 optd **INTERPEX 1972**.

490 **174** 5 c. multicoloured 10 10
491 10 c. multicoloured 10 10
492 15 c. multicoloured 10 10
493 25 c. multicoloured 10 10
494 35 c. multicoloured 15 15
495 50 c. multicoloured 25 30

1972. Nos. 306/8 and 433 surch **12c**.

497 – 12 c. on 1 c. multicoloured 40 55
498 – 12 c. on 2 c. multicoloured 40 55
499 – 12 c. on 3 c. multicoloured 40 55
500 **174** 12 c. on 5 c. multicoloured 40 55

1972. Air. Optd **AIR MAIL** or surch in addition.

501 – 5 c. mult (No. 309) 10 10
518 **175** 5 c. multicoloured 75 10
502 – 8 c. mult (No. 311) 15 10
503 – 10 c. mult (No. 312) 15 10
504 – 15 c. mult (No. 314a) . . . 30 10
505 – 25 c. mult (No. 315) 35 20
506 – 30 c. on 1 c. mult (No. 306) 40 25
507 – 35 c. mult (No. 316) 40 25
519 – 35 c. mult (No. 441). . . . 2·00 30
508 – 40 c. on 2 c. mult (No. 307) 50 25
509 – 45 c. on 3 c. mult (No. 308) 55 35
510 – 50 c. mult (No. 317) 55 35
520 – 50 c. mult (No. 442) . . . 2·25 45
511 – 60 c. on 5 c. mult (No. 309) 60 40
512 – 70 c. on 6 c. mult (No. 310) 70 50
521 – 75 c. mult (No. 443) . . . 3·00 1·00
513 – $1 mult (No. 318) . . . . 4·50 60
514 – $1.35 on 8 c. mult (No. 311) 3·25 1·75
515 – $2 mult (No. 319) . . . . 6·50 5·00
516 – $3 mult (No. 320) . . . . 7·00 5·00
517 – $5 mult (No. 321) . . . . 8·50 11·00

187 Yachting

1972. Olympic Games, Munich. Multicoloured.

522 ½ c. Type **187** (postage) 10 10
523 1 c. Show-jumping 10 10
524 2 c. Running (vert) 10 10
525 35 c. As 2 c. 30 10
526 50 c. As 1 c. 40 40
527 25 c. Boxing (air) 25 10
528 $1 As 25 c. 65 85

1972. Royal Silver Wedding. As T **98** of Gibraltar, but with Badge of Grenada and Nutmegs in background.

530 8 c. brown 10 10
531 $1 blue 45 55

189 Boy Scout Saluting

1972. 65th Anniv of Boy Scouts. Multicoloured.

532 ½ c. Type **189** (postage) 10 10
533 1 c. Scouts knotting ropes . . . 10 10
534 2 c. Scouts shaking hands . . . 10 10
535 3 c. Lord Baden-Powell 10 10
536 75 c. As 2 c. . . . . 85 2·75
537 $1 As 3 c. . . . . 90 2·75
538 25 c. Type **189** (air) 50 20
539 25 c. As 1 c 70 20

190 Madonna and Child

1972. Christmas. Multicoloured.

541 1 c. Type **190** 10 10
542 3 c. The Three Kings 10 10
543 5 c. The Nativity 10 10
544 25 c. Type **190** 15 10
545 35 c. As 3 c. 15 10
546 $1 As 5 c. 40 75

191 Greater Flamingoes

1973. National Zoo. Multicoloured.

548 25 c. Type **191** 80 35
549 35 c. Brazilian tapir 80 35
550 60 c. Blue and yellow macaws . 1·50 1·50
551 70 c. Ocelot . . . . 1·50 1·75

192 Class II Racing Yacht

1973. Yachting. Multicoloured.

552 25 c. Type **192** 25 10
553 35 c. Harbour, St. George's . . 30 10
554 60 c. Yacht "Bloodhound" . . 45 65
555 70 c. St. George's 50 75

193 Helios (Greek god) and Earth orbiting the Sun

1973. Centenary of I.M.O./W.M.O. Greek Gods. Multicoloured.

556 ½ c. Type **193** 10 10
557 1 c. Poseidon and "Normad" storm detector 10 10
558 2 c. Zeus and radarscope . . . 10 10
559 3 c. Iris and weather ballon . . 10 10
560 35 c. Hermes and "ATS-3" satellite 30 10
561 50 c. Zephyrus and diagram of pressure zones 40 30
562 75 c. Demeter and space photo 50 60
563 $1 Selene and rainfall diagram 50 1·00

194 Racing Class Yachts

1973. Carriacou Regatta. Multicoloured.

565 ½ c. Type **194** 10 10
566 1 c. Cruising Class yacht . . . 10 10
567 2 c. Open-decked sloops . . . 10 10
568 35 c. "Mermaid" (sloop) . . . 30 10
569 50 c. St. George's Harbour . . 35 25
570 75 c. Map of Carriacou 40 55
571 $1 Boat-building 55 70

195 Ignatius Semmelweis (obstetrician)

197 "Virgin and Child" (Maratti)

196 Princess Anne and Capt. Mark Phillips

1973. 25th Anniv of W.H.O. Multicoloured.

573 ½ c. Type **195** 10 10
574 1 c. Louis Pasteur 10 10
575 2 c. Edward Jenner 10 10
576 3 c. Sigmund Freud 10 10
577 25 c. Emil von Behring (bacteriologist) 65 10
578 35 c. Carl Jung 75 20
579 50 c. Charles Calmette (bacteriologist) 1·10 80
580 $1 William Harvey 1·40 2·25

1973. Royal Wedding.

582 **196** 25 c. multicoloured 10 10
583 $2 multicoloured 30 45

1973. Christmas. Multicoloured.

585 ½ c. Type **197** 10 10
586 1 c. "Madonna and Child" (Crivelli) 10 10
587 2 c. "Virgin and Child with two Angels" (Verrocchio) 10 10
588 3 c. "Adoration of the Shepherds" (Roberti) 10 10
589 25 c. "The Holy Family with the Infant Baptist" (Baroccio) 15 10
590 35 c. "The Holy Family" (Bronzino) 15 10
591 77 c. "Mystic Nativity" (Botticelli) 20 20
592 $1 "Adoration of the Kings" (Geertgen) 25 30

1974. Independence. Nos. 306/9, 311/13, 315/16 and 317a/21 optd **INDEPENDENCE 7TH FEB. 1974.**

594 **86** 1 c. multicoloured 10 10
595 – 2 c. multicoloured 10 10
596 – 3 c. multicoloured 10 10
597 – 5 c. multicoloured 10 10
598 – 8 c. multicoloured 15 10
599 – 10 c. multicoloured 20 15
600 – 12 c. multicoloured 20 15
601 – 25 c. multicoloured 45 35
602 – 35 c. multicoloured 75 50
603 – 75 c. multicoloured 2·00 1·25
604 – $1 multicoloured 3·75 1·50
605 – $2 multicoloured 6·00 6·00
606 – $3 multicoloured 8·00 7·50
607 – $5 multicoloured 12·00 15·00

199 Creative Arts Theatre, Jamaica Campus

1974. 25th Anniv of University of West Indies. Multicoloured.

608 10 c. Type **199** 10 10
609 25 c. Marryshow House 10 10
610 50 c. Chapel, Jamaica Campus (vert) 20 10
611 $1 University arms (vert) 30 30

200 Nutmeg Pods and Scarlet Mace

201 Footballers (West Germany v. Chile)

1974. Independence. Multicoloured.

613 3 c. Type **200** 10 10
614 8 c. Map of Grenada 10 10
615 25 c. Prime Minister Eric Gairy 15 10
616 35 c. Grand Anse Beach and flag 15 10
617 $1 Coat of arms 35 40

1974. World Cup Football Championships, West Germany. Multicoloured.

619 ½ c. Type **201** 10 10
620 1 c. East Germany v. Australia 10 10
621 2 c. Yugoslavia v. Brazil 10 10
622 10 c. Scotland v. Zaire 10 10
623 25 c. Netherlands v. Uruguay 15 10
624 50 c. Sweden v. Bulgaria 20 10
625 75 c. Italy v. Haiti 35 15
626 $1 Poland v. Argentina 50 25

202 Early U.S. Mail-trains and Concorde

1974. Centenary of U.P.U. Multicoloured.

628 ½ c. Type **202** 10 10
629 1 c. "Caesar" (snow) (1839) and Westland Wessex HU Mk 5 helicopter 10 10
630 2 c. Airmail transport 10 10
631 8 c. Pigeon post (1480) and telephone dial 15 10
632 15 c. 18th-century bellman and tracking antenna 30 10
633 25 c. Messenger (1450) and satellite 35 10
634 35 c. French pillar-box (1850) and mail-boat 50 10
635 $1 18th-century German postman and British Advanced Passenger train 1·50 85

203 Sir Winston Churchill

1974. Birth Centenary of Sir Winston Churchill.

637 **203** 35 c. multicoloured 15 10
638 $2 multicoloured 45 50

204 "Madonna and Child of the Eucharist" (Botticelli)

1974. Christmas. "Madonna and Child" paintings by named artists. Multicoloured.

640 ½ c. Type **204** 10 10
641 1 c. Niccolo di Pietro 10 10
642 2 c. Van der Weyden 10 10
643 3 c. Bastiani 10 10
644 10 c. Giovanni 10 10
645 25 c. Van der Weyden 20 10
646 50 c. Botticelli 25 20
647 $1 Mantegna 35 50

205 Yachts, Point Saline

1975. Multicoloured.

649 ½ c. Type **205** 10 55
650 1 c. Yacht Club race 10 10
651 2 c. Carenage taxi 10 10
652 3 c. Large working boats 10 10
653a 5 c. Deep-water dock 10 15
654 6 c. Cocoa beans in drying trays 10 10
655 8 c. Nutmegs 75 10
656 10 c. Rum distillery, River Antoine Estate, c. 1785 10 10
657 12 c. Cocoa tree 30 10
658 15 c. Fishermen at Fontenoy 10 10
659 20 c. Parliament Building 15 15
660 25 c. Fort George cannons 20 15
661 35 c. Pearls Airport 20 15
662 50 c. General Post Office 25 30
663 75 c. Carib's Leap, Sauteurs Bay 45 50
664 $1 Carenage, St. George's 50 70
665 $2 St. George's Harbour by night 65 1·50
666 $3 Grand Anse Beach 75 2·00
667 $5 Canoe Bay and Black Bay 90 3·00
668 $10 Sugar-loaf Island 2·50 6·50

Nos. 663/8 are size 45 × 28 mm.

206 Sailfish

1975. Big Game Fishing. Multicoloured.

669 ½ c. Type **206** 10 10
670 1 c. Blue marlin 10 10
671 2 c. White marlin 10 10
672 10 c. Yellow-finned tuna 10 10
673 25 c. Wahoo 25 10
674 50 c. Dolphin (fish) 40 15
675 70 c. Giant grouper 60 20
676 $1 Great barracuda 80 35

207 Granadilla Barbadine

1975. Flowers. Multicoloured.

678 ½ c. Type **207** 10 10
679 1 c. Bleeding Heart (Easter Lily) 10 10
680 2 c. Poinsettia 10 10
681 3 c. Cocoa flower 10 10
682 10 c. Gladioli 10 10
683 25 c. Redhead/Yellowhead 25 10
684 50 c. Plumbago 45 15
685 $1 Orange flower 70 25

208 Dove, Grenada Flag and U.N. Emblem

210 "Blood of the Redeemer" (G. Bellini)

209 Paul Revere's Midnight Ride

1975. Grenada's Admission to the U.N. (1974). Multicoloured.

687 ½ c. Type **208** 10 10
688 1 c. Grenada and U.N. flags 10 10
689 2 c. Grenada coat of arms 10 10
690 35 c. U.N. emblem over map of Grenada 15 10
691 50 c. U.N. buildings and flags 20 15
692 $2 U.N. emblem and scroll 45 45

CANCELLED REMAINDERS*. Some of the following issues have been remaindered, cancelled to order, at a fraction of their face value. For all practical purposes these are indistinguishable from genuine postally used copies. Our used quotations which are indicated by an asterisk are the same for cancelled-to-order or postally used copies.

1975. Bicentenary of American Revolution (1st issue). Multicoloured.

694 ½ c. Type **209** (postage) 10 10*
695 1 c. Crispus Attucks 10 10*
696 2 c. Patrick Henry 10 10*
697 3 c. Franklin visits Washington 10 10*
698 5 c. Rebel troops 10 10*
699 10 c. John Paul Jones 10 10*
700 40 c. "John Hancock" (Copley) (air) 25 10*
701 50 c. "Benjamin Franklin" (Roslin) 40 15*
702 75 c. "John Adams" (Copley) 55 15*
703 $1 "Lafayette" (Casanova) 60 20*

Nos. 700/3 are vert.
See also Nos. 785/91.

1975. Easter. Multicoloured.

705 ½ c. Type **210** 10 10*
706 1 c. "Pieta" (Bellini) 10 10*
707 2 c. "The Entombment" (Van der Weyden) 10 10*
708 3 c. "Pieta" (Bellini) 10 10*
709 35 c. "Pieta" (Bellini) 20 10*
710 75 c. "The Dead Christ" (Bellini) 25 10*
711 $1 "The Dead Christ supported by Angels" (Procaccini) 30 10*

211 Wildlife Study

1975. 14th World Scout Jamboree, Norway. Multicoloured.

713 ½ c. Type **211** 10 10*
714 1 c. Sailing 10 10*
715 2 c. Map-reading 10 10*
716 35 c. First-aid 40 10*
717 40 c. Physical training 45 10*
718 75 c. Mountaineering 60 10*
719 $2 Sing-song 1·25 20*

212 Leafy Jewel Box

213 "Lycorea ceres"

1975. Sea Shells. Multicoloured.

721 ½ c. Type **212** 10 10*
722 1 c. Emerald nerite 10 10*
723 2 c. Yellow American cockle 10 10*
724 25 c. Common purple janthina 85 10*
725 50 c. Atlantic turkey wing 1·75 15*
726 75 c. West Indian fighting conch 2·25 20*
727 $1 Noble wentletrap 2·25 20*

1975. Butterflies. Multicoloured.

729 ½ c. Type **213** 10 10*
730 1 c. "Adelpha cytherea" 10 10*
731 2 c. "Atlides polybe" 10 10*
732 35 c. "Anteos maerula" 80 10*
733 45 c. "Parides neophilus" 85 10*
734 75 c. "Nymula orestes" 1·25 15*
735 $2 "Euptychia cephus" 1·75 20*

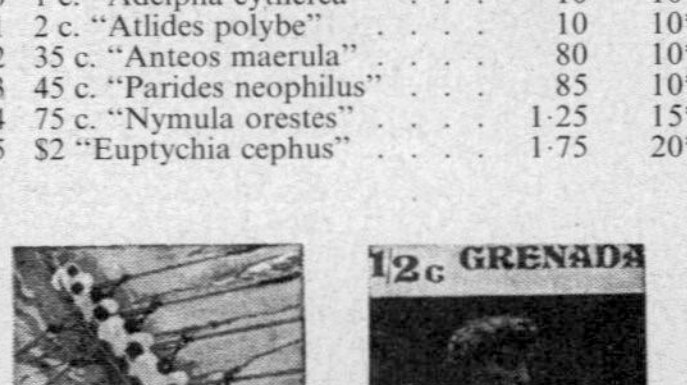

214 Rowing

215 "The Boy David" (Michelangelo)

1975. Pan-American Games, Mexico City. Multicoloured.

737 ½ c. Type **214** 10 10*
738 1 c. Swimming 10 10*
739 2 c. Show-jumping 10 10*
740 35 c. Gymnastics 15 10*
741 45 c. Football 15 10*
742 75 c. Boxing 25 15*
743 $2 Cycling 65 20*

1975. 500th Birth Anniv of Michelangelo. Multicoloured.

745 ½ c. Type **215** 10 10*
746 1 c. "Young Man" (detail) 10 10*
747 2 c. "Moses" 10 10*
748 40 c. "Prophet Zachariah" 40 10*
749 50 c. "St. John the Baptist" 40 15*
750 75 c. "Judith and Holofernes" 55 20*
751 $2 "Doni Madonna" (detail from "Holy Family") 90 25*

216 "Madonna and Child" (Filippino Lippi)

217 Bananaquit

1975. Christmas. "Virgin and Child" paintings by artists named. Multicoloured.

753 ½ c. Type **216** 10 10*
754 1 c. Mantegna 10 10*
755 2 c. Luis de Morales 10 10*
756 35 c. G. M. Morandi 15 10*
757 50 c. Antonello da Messina 15 10*
758 75 c. Durer 20 10*
759 $1 Velasquez 25 10*

1976. Flora and Fauna. Multicoloured.

761 ½ c. Type **217** 10 10*
762 1 c. Brazilian agouti 10 10*
763 2 c. Hawksbill turtle (horiz) 10 10*
764 5 c. Dwarf poinciana 10 10*
765 35 c. Black-finned tuna ("Albacore") (horiz) 90 10*
766 40 c. Cardinal's guard 95 10*
767 $2 Nine-banded armadillo (horiz) 2·50 30*

218 Carnival Time

1976. Tourism. Multicoloured.
769 ½ c. Type **218** 10 10*
770 1 c. Scuba diving 10 10*
771 2 c. Liner "Southward" at St. George's 10 10*
772 35 c. Game fishing 65 10*
773 50 c. St. George's Golf Course . 2·25 20*
774 75 c. Tennis . . . . 2·50 25*
775 $1 Ancient rock carvings at Mount Rich . . . . 2·75 25*

219 "Pieta" (Master of Okolicsno) 220 Sharpshooters

1976. Easter. Paintings by artists named. Multicoloured.
777 ½ c. Type **219** 10 10*
778 1 c. Correggio 10 10*
779 2 c. Van der Weyden 10 10*
780 3 c. Durer 10 10*
781 35 c. Master of the Holy Spirit 15 10*
782 75 c. Raphael 30 15*
783 $1 Raphael 35 20*

1976. Bicentenary of American Revolution (2nd issue). Multicoloured.
785 ½ c. Type **220** 10 10*
786 1 c. Defending the Liberty Pole 10 10*
787 2 c. Loading muskets 10 10*
788 35 c. The Fight for Liberty . . 30 10*
789 50 c. Peace Treaty, 1783 . . . 35 10*
790 $1 Drummers 50 20*
791 $3 Gunboat 90 30*

221 Nature Study 222 Volleyball

1976. 50th Anniv of Girl Guides in Grenada. Multicoloured.
793 ½ c. Type **221** 10 10*
794 1 c. Campfire cooking 10 10*
795 2 c. First aid 10 10*
796 50 c. Camping 65 10*
797 75 c. Home economics 90 15*
798 $2 First aid . . . . 1·25 25*

1976. Olympic Games, Montreal. Multicoloured.
800 ½ c Type **222** 10 10*
801 1 c. Cycling 10 10*
802 2 c. Rowing 10 10*
803 35 c. Judo 30 10*
804 45 c. Hockey 60 10*
805 75 c. Gymnastics 60 20*
806 $1 High jump 60 20*

223 "Cha-U-Kao at the Moulin Rouge" 225 Satellite Assembly

224 Piper Apache 235

1976. 75th Death Anniv of Toulouse-Lautrec. Multicoloured.
808 ½ c. Type **223** 10 10*
809 1 c. "Quadrille of the Moulin Rouge" 10 10*
810 2 c. "Profile of a Woman" . . 10 10*
811 3 c. "Salon in the Rue des Moulins" 10 10*
812 40 c. "The Laundryman" . . . 55 10*
813 50 c. "Marcelle Lender dancing the Bolero" 65 10*
814 $2 "Signor Boileau at the Cafe" 1·75 25*

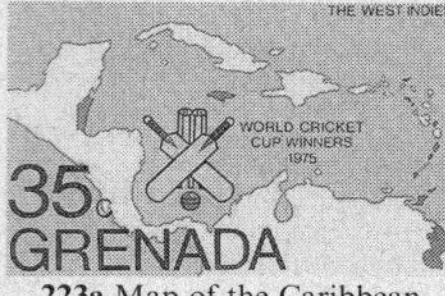

223a Map of the Caribbean

1976. West Indian Victory in World Cricket Cup.
816 35 c. Type **223a** . . . . . . 1·25 35
817 $1 The Prudential Cup . . . . 2·25 5·00

1976. Airplanes. Multicoloured.
818 ½ c. Type **224** 10 10*
819 1 c. Beech 50 Twin Bonanza . . 10 10*
820 2 c. De Havilland Twin Otter 100 10 10*
821 40 c. Britten Norman Islander 70 10*
822 50 c. De Havilland Heron 2 . . 75 10*
823 $2 Hawker Siddeley H.S.748 . . 2·50 50*

1976. Viking and Helios Space Missions. Multicoloured.
825 ½ c Type **225** 10 10*
826 1 c. Helios satellite 10 10*
827 2 c. Helios encapsulation . . . 10 10*
828 15 c. Systems test 10 10*
829 45 c. Viking lander (horiz) . . 20 10*
830 75 c. Lander on Mars 30 15*
831 $2 Viking encapsulation . . . 60 25*

226 S.S. "Geestland"

1976. Ships. Multicoloured.
833 ½ c. Type **226** 10 10*
834 1 c. M.V. "Federal Palm" . . . 10 10*
835 2 c. H.M.S "Blake" 10 10*
836 25 c. M.V. "Vistafjord" 45 10*
837 75 c. S.S. "Canberra" 90 15*
838 $1 S.S. "Regina" . . . . . . 1·10 20*
839 $5 S.S. "Arandora Star" . . . 2·25 40*

227 "San Barnaba Altarpiece" (Botticelli)

1976. Christmas. Multicoloured.
841 ½ c. Type **227** 10 10*
842 1 c. "Annunciation" (Botticelli) 10 10*
843 2 c. "Madonna of Chancellor Rolin" (Jan van Eyck) . . . 10 10*
844 35 c. "Annunciation" (Fra Filippo Lippi) 15 10*
845 50 c. "Madonna of the Magnificat" (Botticelli) . . . 20 10*
846 75 c. "Madonna of the Pomegranate" (Botticelli) . . 30 15*
847 $3 "Madonna with St. Cosmas and other Saints" (Botticelli) 70 25*

228 Alexander Graham Bell and Telephones

1976. Centenary of First Telephone. Multicoloured.
849 ½ c. Type **228** 10 10*
850 1 c. Telephone users within globe 10 10*
851 2 c. Telephone satellite 10 10*
852 18 c. Telephone viewer and console 20 10*
853 40 c. Satellite and tracking stations 25 10*
854 $1 Satellite transmitting to ships 35 15*
855 $2 Dish aerial and modern telephone 55 25*

MINIMUM PRICE

The minimum price quoted is 10p which represents a handling charge rather than a basis for valuing common stamps. For further notes about prices see introductory pages.

229 Coronation Scene

1977. Silver Jubilee. Multicoloured. (a) Perf.
857 ½ c. Type **229** 10 10*
858 1 c. Sceptre and orb 10 10*
859 35 c. The Queen on horseback 10 10*
860 $2 Spoon and ampulla 25 15*
861 $2.50 The Queen and Prince Philip 25 15*

(b) Roul. Self-adhesive.
863 35 c. As $2.50 . . . . 15 25
864 50 c. As $2 . . . . 25 1·00
865 $1 As 1 c. . . . . 50 1·40
866 $3 As 35 c. . . . . 1·25 2·75

230 Water Skiing

1977. Easter Water Parade. Multicoloured.
867 ½ c. Type **230** 10 10*
868 1 c. Speedboat race 10 10*
869 2 c. Row boat race 10 10*
870 22 c. Swimming 20 10*
871 35 c. Work boat race 30 10*
872 75 c. Water polo 50 15*
873 $2 Game fishing . . . . 1·00 25*

231 Meeting Place, Grand Anse Beach

1977. 7th Meeting of Organization of American States.
875 **231** 35 c. multicoloured 10 10
876 $1 multicoloured 25 60
877 $2 multicoloured . . . . . 40 1·75

232 Rafting

1977. Caribbean Scout Jamboree, Jamaica. Multicoloured.
878 ½ c. Type **232** 10 10*
879 1 c. Tug-of-war 10 10*
880 2 c. Sea Scouts regatta 10 10*
881 18 c. Camp fire 25 10*
882 40 c. Field kitchen 35 10*
883 $1 Scouts and sea scouts . . . 75 15*
884 $2 Hiking and map reading . . 1·00 25*

233 Angel and Shepherd

1977. Christmas. Ceiling Panels from Church of St. Martin, Zillis. Multicoloured.
886 ½ c. Type **233** 10 10*
887 1 c. St. Joseph 10 10*
888 2 c. Virgin and Child fleeing to Egypt 10 10*
889 22 c. Angel 10 10*
890 35 c. Magus on horseback . . . 15 10*
891 75 c. Three horses 20 15*
892 $2 Virgin and Child 50 25*

1977. Royal Visit. Nos. 857/61 optd **Royal Visit W. I. 1977.**
894 ½ c. Type **229** 10 10
895 1 c. Sceptre and Orb 10 10
896 35 c. Queen on horseback . . . 10 10
897 $2 Spoon and ampulla 30 40
898 $2.50 The Queen and Prince Philip 35 45

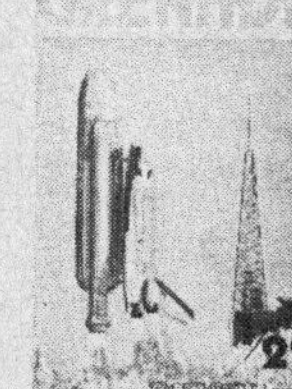

235 Christjaan Eijkman (Medicine) 237 Rocket Launching

236 Count von Zeppelin and First Zeppelin Airship LZ-1

1978. Nobel Prize Winners. Multicoloured.
900 ½ c. Type **235** 10 10*
901 1 c. Sir Winston Churchill (Literature) 30 10*
902 2 c. Woodrow Wilson (Peace) . 10 10*
903 35 c. Frederic Passy (Peace) . . 15 10*
904 $1 Albert Einstein (Physics) . . 1·00 15*
905 $3 Carl Bosch (Chemistry) . . 1·75 25*

1978. 75th Anniv of First Zeppelin Flight and 50th Anniv of Lindbergh's Transatlantic Flight. Multicoloured.
907 ½ c. Type **236** 10 10*
908 1 c. Lindbergh with "Spirit of St. Louis" 10 10*
909 2 c. Airship "Deutschland" . . 10 10*
910 22 c. Lindbergh's arrival in France 30 10*
911 75 c. Lindbergh and "Spirit of St. Louis" in flight 60 10*
912 $1 "Graf Zeppelin" over Alps . 65 15*
913 $3 "Graf Zeppelin" over White House . . . . 1·40 25*

1978. Space Shuttle. Multicoloured.
915 ½ c. Type **237** 10 10*
916 1 c. Booster jettison 10 10*
917 2 c. External tank jettison . . . 10 10*
918 18 c. Space Shuttle in orbit . . 30 10*
919 75 c. Satellite placement . . . 65 10*
920 $2 Landing approach . . . . . 1·40 20*

238 Black-headed Gull 239 "The Landing of Marie de Medici at Marseilles"

1978. Wild Birds of Grenada. Multicoloured.
922 ½ c. Type **238** 10 10*
923 1 c. Wilson's petrel 10 10*
924 2 c. Killdeer 10 10*
925 50 c. White-necked jacobin . . 1·75 10*
926 75 c. Blue-faced booby . . . . 2·00 15*
927 $1 Broad-winged hawk . . . . 3·25 20*
928 $2 Red-necked pigeon . . . . 4·00 30*

1978. 400th Birth Anniv of Peter Paul Rubens. Multicoloured.
930 5 c. Type **239** 10 10*
931 15 c. "Rubens and Isabella Brandt" 10 10*
932 18 c. "Marchesa Brigida Spindola-Doria" 10 10*
933 25 c. "Ludovicus Nonninus" . . 10 10*
934 45 c. "Helene Fourment and her Children" 15 10*
935 75 c. "Clara Serena Rubens" . 25 10*
936 $3 "Le Chapeau de Paille" . . 60 20*

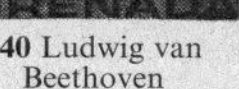

240 Ludwig van Beethoven 241 King Edward's Chair

1978. 150th Death Anniv of Beethoven. Mult.

938 5 c. Type **240** 10 10*
939 15 c. Woman violinist (horiz) . . 15 10*
940 18 c. Musical instruments (horiz) 20 10*
941 22 c. Piano (horiz) 20 10*
942 50 c. Violins 40 10*
943 75 c. Piano and sonata score . . 60 15*
944 $3 Beethoven's portrait and home (horiz) . . . . 1·75 25*

1978. 25th Anniv of Coronation. Mult. (a) Perf.

946 35 c. Type **241** 10 10
947 $2 Queen with regalia 30 35
948 $2.50 St. Edward's Crown . . . 30 40

(b) Roul × imperf. Self-adhesive.

950 25 c. Queen Elizabeth II taking salute, Trooping the Colour . . 15 15
951 35 c. Queen at Maundy Thursday ceremony 15 25
952 $5 Queen and Prince Philip at Opening of Parliament . . . 1·50 2·50

243 Goalkeeper reaching for Ball

244 Aerial Phenomena, Germany, 1561 and U.S.A., 1952

1978. World Cup Football Championships, Argentina.

953 **243** 40 c. multicoloured 10 10
954 – 60 c. multicoloured 15 20
955 – 90 c. multicoloured 25 30
956 – $2 multicoloured 60 60

DESIGNS: 60 c. to $2. Designs similar to Type **243** with goalkeeper reaching for ball.

1978. U.F.O. Research. Multicoloured.

958 5 c. Type **244** 15 10
959 35 c. Various aerial phenomena, 1950 . . . . 35 25
960 $3 U.F.O.s, 1965 . . . . . . 2·00 1·75

245 Wright Flyer III, 1902

1978. 75th Anniv of Powered Flight. Mult.

962 5 c. Type **245** 10 10
963 15 c. Wright Flyer I, 1903 . . . 10 10
964 18 c. Wright Type **A** 10 10
965 22 c. Wright Flyer I from above 15 10
966 50 c. Orville Wright and Wright Type **A** 20 20
967 75 c. Wright Type A, Pau, France, 1908 . . . . 25 25
968 $3 Wilbur Wright and Wright glider No. IV 80 70

246 Cook and Hawaiian Feast

1978. 250th Birth Anniv of Captain James Cook and Bicentenary of Discovery of Hawaii. Multicoloured.

970 18 c. Type **246** 60 20
971 35 c. Cook and Hawaiian dance 75 25
972 75 c. Cook and Honolulu harbour . . . . 1·50 1·00
973 $3 Cook's statue and H.M.S. "Resolution" . . . . 2·50 5·50

247 "Paumgartner Altarpiece" (detail)

248 National Convention and Cultural Centre (interior)

1978. Christmas. Paintings by Durer. Multicoloured.

975 40 c. Type **247** 20 15
976 60 c. "The Adoration of the Magi" 25 20
977 90 c. "Virgin and Child" . . . 30 20
978 $2 "Virgin and Child with St. Anne" (detail) 55 55

1979. 5th Anniv of Independence.

980 5 c. Type **248** 10 10
981 18 c. National Convention and Cultural Centre (exterior) . . 10 10
982 22 c. Easter Water Parade, 1978 10 10
983 35 c. Sir Eric M. Gairy (Prime Minister) 15 10
984 $3 The Cross, Fort Frederick . 60 80

249 "Acalypha hispida"

250 Birds in Flight

1979. Flowers. Multicoloured.

985 18 c. Type **249** 10 10
986 50 c. "Hibiscus rosa sinensis" . 20 15
987 $1 "Thunbergia grandiflora" . 30 25
988 $3 "Nerium oleander" . . . . 80 1·10

1979. 30th Anniv of Declaration of Human Rights. Multicoloured.

990 15 c. Type **250** 10 10
991 $2 Bird in Flight 55 65

251 Children playing Cricket

1979. Int Year of the Child (1st issue). Mult.

992 18 c. Type **251** 40 30
993 22 c. Children playing baseball 40 30
994 $5 Children playing in a tree . . 3·25 6·00

See also Nos. 1006/7 and 1025/33.

252 "Around the World in 80 Days"

1979. 150th Birth Anniv of Jules Verne. Mult.

996 18 c. Type **252** 25 10
997 35 c. "20,000 Leagues under the Sea" 35 15
998 75 c. "From the Earth to the Moon" 50 50
999 $3 "Master of the World" . . . 1·40 1·60

253 Mail Runner, Africa (early 19th-century)

1979. Death Cent of Sir Rowland Hill. Mult.

1001 20 c. Type **253** 10 10
1002 40 c. Pony Express, America (mid 19th-century) 10 10
1003 $1 Pigeon post 20 25
1004 $3 Mail coach, Europe (18–19th century) 50 80

254 "The Pistol of Peace" (vaccination gun), Map of Grenada and Children

1979. International Year of the Child (2nd issue). "Grenada—First Nation 100% Immunized"

1006 **254** 5 c. multicoloured . . . 25 20
1007 $1 multicoloured . . . 75 2·00

255 Reef Shark

1979. Marine Wildlife. Multicoloured.

1008 40 c. Type **255** 40 30
1009 45 c. Spotted eagle ray 40 30
1010 50 c. Many-toothed conger . . 45 40
1011 60 c. Golden olive (shell) . . . 70 75
1012 70 c. West Indian murex (shell) 85 90
1013 75 c. Giant tun (shell) . . . . 90 1·00
1014 90 c. Brown booby . . . . . 2·25 2·00
1015 $1 Magnificent frigate bird . . 2·25 2·00

256 The Flight into Egypt

1979. Christmas. Tapestries. Multicoloured.

1017 6 c. Type **256** 10 10
1018 25 c. The Flight into Egypt (detail) 10 10
1019 30 c. Angel (vert) 10 10
1020 40 c. (Doge Marino Grimani (detail) (vert) 10 10
1021 90 c. The Annunciation to the Shepherds (vert) 20 15
1022 $1 The Flight into Egypt (Rome) (vert) 20 15
1023 $2 The Virgin in Glory (vert) . 35 40

257 Mickey Mouse playing Baseball

258 Paul Harris (founder)

1979. International Year of the Child (3rd issue). Disney Characters. Multicoloured.

1025 $\frac{1}{2}$ c. Type **257** 10 10
1026 1 c. Donald Duck high-jumping 10 10
1027 2 c. Goofy playing basketbal . 10 10
1028 3 c. Goofy hurdling 10 10
1029 4 c. Donald Duck playing golf 10 10
1030 5 c. Mickey Mouse playing cricket 10 10
1031 10 c. Mickey Mouse playing football 10 10
1032 $2 Mickey Mouse playing tennis 2·75 3·25
1033 $2.50 Minnie Mouse riding horse . . . . 2·75 3·25

1980. 75th Anniv of Rotary International. Mult.

1035 6 c. Type **258** 10 10
1036 30 c. "Health" 10 15
1037 90 c. "Hunger" 25 30
1038 $2 "Humanity" 55 80

1980. 1st Anniv of Revolution (1st issue). Nos. 651/2, 654/7, 659/60 and 662/8 optd **PEOPLE'S REVOLUTION 13 MARCH 1979.**

1040 2 c. Carenage taxi 10 10
1041 3 c. Large working boats . . . 10 10
1042 6 c. Cocoa beans in drying trays 10 10
1043 8 c. Nutmegs 10 10
1044 10 c. Rum distillery, River Antoine Estate, c. 1785 . . 10 10
1045 12 c. Cocoa tree 10 10
1046 20 c. Parliament Building . . 10 15
1047 25 c. Fort George cannons . . 30 30
1048 50 c. General Post Office . . . 30 30
1049 75 c. Carib's Leap, Sauteurs Bay 50 40
1050 $1 Carenage, St. George's . . 60 60
1051 $2 St. George's Harbour by night . . . . 1·25 2·00
1052 $3 Grand Anse Beach . . . . 1·50 3·25
1053 $5 Canoe Bay and Black Bay 2·00 5·00
1054 $10 Sugar-loaf Island . . . . 3·25 7·50

See also Nos. 1069/72.

260 Boxing

1980. Olympic Games, Moscow. Multicoloured.

1055 25 c. Type **260** 10 10
1056 40 c. Cycling 15 10
1057 90 c. Show-jumping 20 30
1058 $2 Running . . . . 40 1·00

261 Tropical Kingbird

1980. Wild Birds. Multicoloured.

1060 20 c. Type **261** 85 15
1061 40 c. Rufous-breasted hermit . 1·25 25
1062 $1 Troupial . . . . 1·75 1·75
1063 $2 Ruddy quail dove . . . . 2·25 3·50

1980. "London 1980". International Stamp Exhibition. Nos. 1001/4 optd **LONDON 1980**.

1065 **253** 20 c. Mail runner, Africa . 15 15
1066 – 40 c. Pony Express, America 20 20
1067 – $1 Pigeon post 40 40
1068 – $3 Mail coach, Europe . . 1·25 1·25

263 Free Hot Lunch at Schools

1980. 1st Anniv of Revolution (2nd issue). Multicoloured.

1069 10 c. Type **263** 10 10
1070 40 c. "From tree to can" (agro-industry) 15 15
1071 $1 National Health care . . . 30 30
1072 $2 New housing projects . . . 50 70

264 Jamb Statues, West Portal, Chartres Cathedral

1980. Famous Works of Art. Multicoloured.

1074 8 c. Type **264** 10 10
1075 10 c. "Les Demoiselles d' Avignon" (painting, Picasso) 10 10
1076 40 c. Winged Victory of Samothrace (statue) 15 15
1077 50 c. "The Night Watch" (painting, Rembrandt) . . . 15 15
1078 $1 "Portrait of Edward VI as a Child" (painting, Holbein the Younger) 25 25
1079 $3 Portrait head of Queen Nefertiti (carving) 70 70

265 Carib Canoes

1980. Shipping. Multicoloured.

1081A $\frac{1}{2}$ c. Type **265** 10 10
1082A 1 c. Boat building 10 10
1083A 2 c. Small working boat . . 15 10
1084A 4 c. Columbus's "Santa Maria" 40 10
1085A 5 c. West Indiaman barque, c. 1840 . . . . 40 10
1086A 6 c. "Orinoco" (paddle-steamer), c. 1851 . . . . 40 10
1087A 10 c. Working schooner . . 50 10
1088A 12 c. Trimaran at Grand Anse anchorage 50 10
1089A 15 c. Spice Island cruising yacht "Petite Amie" . . . 50 10
1090A 20 c. Fishing pirogue . . . 1·00 10
1091A 25 c. Harbour police launch . 1·75 20
1092A 30 c. Grand Anse speedboat . 1·50 20
1093A 40 c. "Seimstrand" (freighter) 1·50 25
1094B 50 c. "Ariadne" (cadet schooner) 50 50
1095A 90 c. "Geestide" (freighter) . 1·75 50
1096A $1 "Cunard Countess" (liner) 2·00 70
1097A $3 Rum-runner . . . . . . 2·50 4·00
1098A $5 "Statendam" (liner) off St. George's . . . . 3·50 7·00
1099B $10 Coastguard patrol boat . 6·00 8·50

Nos. 1081/99 come with and without date imprint.

1980. Christmas. Scenes from Walt Disney's "Snow White and the Seven Dwarfs". As T **257**. Multicoloured.

1100 ½ c. Snow White at well . . . 10 10
1101 1 c. The Wicked Queen . . . 10 10
1102 2 c. Snow White singing to animals 10 10
1103 3 c. Snow White doing housework for Dwarfs . . . 10 10
1104 4 c. The Seven Dwarfs 10 10
1105 5 c. Snow White with Dwarfs 10 10
1106 10 c. Witch offering Snow White apple 10 10
1107 $2.50 Snow White with Prince and Dwarfs . . . . 3·00 1·75
1108 $3 Snow White and Prince . . 3·50 2·00

1981. 50th Anniv of Walt Disney's Pluto (cartoon character). As T **257**. Multicoloured.

1110 $2 Pluto with birthday cake . 1·25 1·00

266 Revolution and Grenada Flags

1981. Festival of the Revolution. Multicoloured.

1112 5 c. Type **266** 10 10
1113 10 c. Teacher, pupil, book and pencil ("education") . . . 10 10
1114 15 c. Food processing plant ("industry") 10 10
1115 25 c. Selection of fruits and farm scene ("agriculture") . . . 15 10
1116 40 c. Crawfish and boat ("fishing") 20 15
1117 90 c. "Cunard Countess" arriving at St. George's Harbour ("shipping") . . . 50 30
1118 $1 Straw-work ("native handicrafts") 60 40
1119 $3 Map of Caribbean with expanded view of Grenada . 1·75 1·75

1981. Easter. Walt Disney Cartoon Characters. As T **257**. Multicoloured.

1120 35 c. Mickey Mouse and Goofy 40 15
1121 40 c. Donald Duck, Chip and Daisy Duck 40 15
1122 $2 Minnie Mouse . . . . . . 1·40 1·25
1123 $2.50 Pluto and Mickey Mouse 1·60 1·40

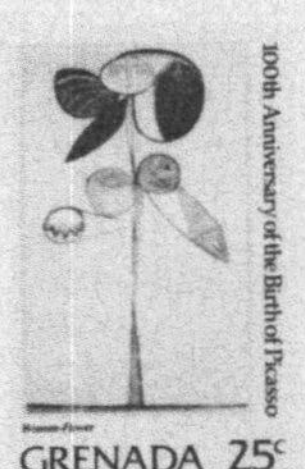

267 "Woman-Flower"

268 Prince Charles playing Polo

1981. Birth Centenary of Picasso. Multicoloured.

1125 25 c. Type **267** 15 10
1126 30 c. "Portrait of Madame" . 20 10
1127 90 c. "Cavalier with Pipe" . 30 30
1128 $4 "Large Heads" . . . . . 1·00 1·25

1991. Royal Wedding (1st issue). Multicoloured.

1134 30 c. Prince Charles and Lady Diana Spencer 20 20
1135 40 c. Holyrood House 30 30
1130 50 c. As 30 c. 10 10
1131 $2 As 40 c. 35 50
1132 $4 Type **268** 50 75

269 Lady Diana Spencer

270 "The Bath" (Mary Cassatt)

1981. Royal Wedding (2nd issue). Multicoloured. Self-adhesive.

1136 $1 Type **269** 30 65
1137 $2 Prince Charles 30 65
1138 $5 Prince Charles and Lady Diana Spencer . . . . . 1·00 1·75

1981. "Decade for Women". Paintings. Mult.

1139 15 c. Type **270** 10 10
1140 40 c. "Mademoiselle Charlotte du Val d'Ognes" (Constance Marie Charpentier) . . . 20 10
1141 60 c. "Self-portrait" (Mary Beale) 30 20
1142 $3 "Woman in White Stockings" (Suzanne Valadon) . . . . 1·25 1·00

1981. Christmas. As T **257** showing scenes from Walt Disney's cartoon film "Cinderella".

1144 ½ c. multicoloured 10 10
1145 1 c. multicoloured 10 10
1146 2 c. multicoloured 10 10
1147 3 c. multicoloured 10 10
1148 4 c. multicoloured 10 10
1149 5 c. multicoloured 10 10
1150 10 c. multicoloured 15 10
1151 $2.50 multicoloured . . . . 3·50 2·25
1152 $3 multicoloured . . . . . 3·50 2·50

271 Landing

273 General Post Office, St. George's

272 West German Footballer and Flag

1981. Space Shuttle Project. Multicoloured.

1154 30 c. Type **271** 20 15
1155 60 c. Working in space . . . 40 30
1156 70 c. Lift off 45 35
1157 $3 Separation . . . . . . 1·10 1·25

1981. World Cup Football Championship, Spain (1982). Multicoloured.

1159 25 c. + 10 c. Type **272** . . . 55 30
1160 40 c. + 20 c. Argentinian footballer and flag 70 40
1161 50 c. + 25 c. Brazilian footballer and flag 80 50
1162 $1 + 50 c. English footballer and flag . . . . 1·25 95

1981. Cent of U.P.U. Membership. Mult.

1164 25 c. Type **273** 20 15
1165 30 c. 1861 1d. stamp 25 20
1166 90 c. New U.P.U. Headquarters Building 25 c. commemorative 55 50
1167 $4 1961 Stamp Centenary 25 c. commemorative . . . . . 1·25 2·00

274 Artist without Hands

276 "Dryas julia"

275 Tending Vegetable Patch

1982. International Year for the Disabled (1981). Multicoloured.

1169 30 c. Type **274** 30 10
1170 40 c. Computer operator without hands 30 10
1171 70 c. Blind schoolteacher teaching braille 60 15
1172 $3 Midget playing drums . . . 1·25 80

1982. 75th Anniv of Boy Scout Movement and 125th Birth Anniv of Lord Baden-Powell. Multicoloured.

1174 70 c. Type **275** 50 45
1175 90 c. Map-reading 55 55
1176 $1 Bee-keeping 65 65
1177 $4 Hospital reading . . . . 2·25 2·75

1982. Butterflies. Multicoloured.

1179 10 c. Type **276** 75 30
1180 60 c. "Phoebis agarithe" . . . 2·50 1·50
1181 $1 "Anartia amathea" . . . 3·00 2·00
1182 $3 "Battus polydamas" . . . 4·25 7·00

277 "Saying Grace"

278 Kensington Palace

1982. Norman Rockwell (painter) Commemoration. Multicoloured.

1184 15 c. Type **277** 40 10
1185 30 c. "Nothing Up His Sleeve" (inscr "Card Tricks") . . . 65 15
1186 60 c. "Pharmacist" 85 25
1187 70 c. "Hobo" (inscr "Pals") . . 90 35

1982. 21st Birthday of Princess of Wales. Multicoloured.

1188 50 c. Type **278** 40 45
1189 60 c. Type **278** 80 45
1190 $1 Prince and Princess of Wales 90 1·00
1191 $2 As $1 . . . . 1·75 1·25
1192 $3 Princess of Wales . . . . 2·00 2·25
1193 $4 As $3 . . . . 2·25 2·25

279 Mary McLeod Bethune appointed Director of Negro Affairs, 1942

1982. Birth Centenary of Franklin D. Roosevelt. Multicoloured.

1195 10 c. Type **279** 10 10
1196 60 c. Huddie Ledbetter "Leadbelly" in concert (Works Progress administration) 35 20
1197 $1.10 Signing bill No. 8802, 1941 (Fair Employment committee) 50 40
1198 $3 Farm Security administration 75 80

1982. Birth of Prince William of Wales. Nos. 1188/93 optd **ROYAL BABY 21.6.82.**

1200 50 c. Type **278** 30 60
1201 60 c. Type **278** 35 35
1202 $1 Prince and Princess of Wales 55 85
1203 $2 As $1 . . . . 1·00 1·00
1204 $3 Princess of Wales . . . . 1·75 1·90
1205 $4 As $3 . . . . 1·90 1·90

280 Apostle and Tormentor

1982. Easter. Details from Painting "The Way to Calvary" by Raphael. Multicoloured.

1207 40 c. Type **280** 30 10
1208 70 c. Captain of the guards (vert) 40 15
1209 $1.10 Christ and apostle (vert) 50 25
1210 $4 Mourners (vert) . . . . . 1·00 1·25

281 "Orient Express"

1982. Famous Trains of the World. Mult.

1212 30 c. Type **281** 50 35
1213 60 c. "Trans-Siberian Express" 60 70
1214 70 c. "Fleche d'Or" 70 80
1215 90 c. "Flying Scotsman" . . . 85 1·00
1216 $1 German Federal Railways steam locomotive . . . . 1·00 1·25
1217 $3 German National Railways Class 05 steam locomotive 2·25 4·00

282 Footballers

1982. World Cup Football Championship Winners.

1219 **282** 60 c. multicoloured . . . 35 35
1220 $4 multicoloured . . . 2·00 2·00

1982. Christmas. Scenes from Walt Disney's cartoon film "Robin Hood". As T **257**, but horiz.

1222 ½ c. multicoloured 10 10
1223 1 c. multicoloured 10 10
1224 2 c. multicoloured 10 10
1225 3 c. multicoloured 10 10
1226 4 c. multicoloured 10 10
1227 5 c. multicoloured 10 10
1228 10 c. multicoloured 10 10
1229 $2.50 multicoloured . . . . 2·75 2·75
1230 $3 multicoloured . . . . . 2·75 2·75

283 Killer Whale

285 Dentistry at Health Centre

284 "Construction of Ark"

1983. Save the Whales. Multicoloured.

1232 15 c. Type **283** . . . . . . 1·00 30
1233 40 c. Sperm whale . . . . . 2·25 90
1234 70 c. Blue whale . . . . . . 2·75 2·75
1235 $3 Common dolphin . . . . 3·50 6·50

1983. 500th Birth Anniv of Raphael. Mult.

1237 25 c. Type **284** 20 10
1238 30 c. "Jacob's Vision" 20 10
1239 90 c. "Joseph interprets the Dreams of his Brothers" . . 40 30
1240 $4 "Joseph interprets Pharaoh's dreams" . . . . 1·10 1·40

1983. Commonwealth Day. Multicoloured.

1242 10 c. Type **285** 10 10
1243 70 c. Airport runway construction 35 35
1244 $1.10 Tourism 40 55
1245 $3 Boat-building . . . . . . 80 1·40

286 Maritime Communications via Satellite

1983. World Communications Year. Multicoloured.

1246 30 c. Type **286** 15 15
1247 40 c. Rural telephone installation 20 15
1248 $2.50 Satellite weather map . . 1·00 1·00
1249 $4 Airport control room . . . 1·10 1·10

287 Franklin Sport Sedan, 1928

1983. 75th Anniv of Model "T" Ford Car. Multicoloured.

1251 6 c. Type **287** 15 10
1252 10 c. Delage "D8", 1933 . . . 20 10
1253 40 c. Alvis, 1938 . . . . . . 35 25
1254 60 c. Invicta "S-type" tourer, 1931 . . . . 45 45
1255 70 c. Alfa-Romeo "1750 Gran Sport", 1930 . . . . . . 55 55
1256 90 c. Isotta Fraschini, 1930 . . 60 65
1257 $1 Bugatti "Royale Type 41" 70 65
1258 $2 BMW "328", 1938 . . . . 1·40 1·50
1259 $3 Marmon "V16", 1931 . . . 1·60 2·25
1260 $4 Lincoln "K8" saloon, 1932 1·90 2·75

288 Airship N.1 "Norge"

1983. Bicentenary of Manned Flight. Multicoloured.

1262 30 c. Type **288** 60 30
1263 60 c. Gloster VI seaplane . . . 1·00 1·00
1264 $1.10 Curtiss NC-4 flying boat . 1·60 1·75
1265 $4 Dornier Do 18 flying boat "Aeolus" . . . . 3·50 4·50

289 Morty

291 William I

290 Daisy Duck on Pommel Horse

1983. Christmas. Multicoloured.

1267 ½ c. Type **289** 10 10
1268 1 c. Ludwig von Drake 10 10
1269 2 c. Gyro Gearloose 10 10
1270 3 c. Pluto and Figaro 10 10
1271 4 c. Morty and Ferdie 10 10
1272 5 c. Mickey Mouse and Goofy 10 10
1273 10 c. Chip n'Dale 10 10
1274 $2.50 Mickey and Minnie Mouse 2·75 3·50
1275 $3 Donald and Grandma Duck 3·00 3·50

Nos. 1267/75 show Disney cartoon characters in scenes from "It's beginning to look a lot like Christmas" (song).

1984. Olympic Games. Los Angeles. Multicoloured.
A. Inscr "1984 LOS ANGELES"
B. Inscr "1984 OLYMPICS LOS ANGELES" and Olympic Emblem

		A		B	
1277	½ c. Type **290**	10	10	10	10
1278	1 c. Mickey Mouse boxing	10	10	10	10
1279	2 c. Daisy Duck in archery event	10	10	10	10
1280	3 c. Clarabelle Cow on uneven bars	10	10	10	10
1281	4 c. Mickey and Minnie Mouse in hurdles race	10	10	10	10
1282	5 c. Donald Duck with Chip'n'Dale weightlifting	10	10	10	10
1283	$1 Little Hiawatha in single kayak	1·75	2·00	1·75	2·00
1284	$2 The Tortoise and the Hare in marathon	2·25	3·00	2·25	3·00
1285	$3 Mickey Mouse polevaulting	2·75	3·25	2·75	3·25

1984. English Monarchs. Multicoloured.

1287 $4 Type **291** 2·50 3·25
1288 $4 William II 2·50 3·25
1289 $4 Henry I 2·50 3·25
1290 $4 Stephen 2·50 3·25
1291 $4 Henry II 2·50 3·25
1292 $4 Richard I 2·50 3·25
1293 $4 John 2·50 3·25
1294 $4 "Henry III" 2·50 3·25
1295 $4 Edward I 2·50 3·25
1296 $4 Edward II 2·50 3·25
1297 $4 Edward III 2·50 3·25
1298 $4 Richard II 2·50 3·25
1299 $4 Henry IV 2·50 3·25
1300 $4 Henry V 2·50 3·25
1301 $4 Henry VI 2·50 3·25
1302 $4 Edward IV 2·50 3·25
1303 $4 Edward V 2·50 3·25
1304 $4 Richard III 2·50 3·25
1305 $4 Henry VII 2·50 3·25
1306 $4 Henry VIII 2·50 3·25
1307 $4 Edward VI 2·50 3·25
1308 $4 Jane Grey 2·50 3·25
1309 $4 Mary I 2·50 3·25
1310 $4 Elizabeth I 2·50 3·25
1311 $4 James I 2·50 3·25
1312 $4 Charles I 2·50 3·25
1313 $4 Charles II 2·50 3·25
1314 $4 James II 2·50 3·25
1315 $4 William III 2·50 3·25
1316 $4 Mary II 2·50 3·25
1317 $4 Anne 2·50 3·25
1318 $4 George I 2·50 3·25
1319 $4 George II 2·50 3·25
1320 $4 George III 2·50 3·25
1321 $4 George IV 2·50 3·25
1322 $4 William IV 2·50 3·25
1323 $4 Victoria 2·50 3·25
1324 $4 Edward VII 2·50 3·25
1325 $4 George V 2·50 3·25
1326 $4 Edward VIII 2·50 3·25
1327 $4 George VI 2·50 3·25
1328 $4 Elizabeth II 2·50 3·25

Although inscribed "Henry III" the portrait on No. 1294 is actually of Edward II.

292 Lantana

1984. Flowers. Multicoloured.

1329 25 c. Type **292** 20 15
1330 30 c. Plumbago 25 20
1331 90 c. Spider lily 70 60
1332 $4 Giant alocasia 2·00 3·00

293 Blue Parrotfish

1984. Coral Reef Fishes. Multicoloured.

1334 10 c. Type **293** 1·40 45
1335 30 c. Flame-backed angelfish 2·75 1·10
1336 70 c. Painted wrasse 4·00 3·25
1337 90 c. Rosy razorfish 4·75 3·50

1984. Universal Postal Union Congress, Hamburg. Nos. 1331/2 optd **19th U.P.U. CONGRESS – HAMBURG**.

1339 90 c. Spider lily 60 65
1340 $4 Giant alocasia 2·00 2·50

295 Freighter

296 "The Night" (detail) (Correggio)

1984. Ships. Multicoloured.

1342 40 c. Type **295** 1·25 55
1343 70 c. "Queen Elizabeth 2" 1·50 1·50
1344 90 c. Sailing boats 1·60 2·00
1345 $4 "Amerikanis" 3·50 8·00

1984. 450th Death Anniv of Correggio (painter). Multicoloured.

1347 10 c. Type **296** 45 15
1348 30 c. "The Virgin adoring the Child" 80 50
1349 40 c. "The Mystical Marriage of St. Catherine with St. Sebastian" 2·00 1·75
1350 $4 "The Madonna and the Fruit Basket" 4·50 5·50

297 "L'Absinthe" (Degas)

298 Train on Puffing Billy Line, Victoria

1984. 150th Birth Anniv of Edgar Degas (painter). Multicoloured.

1352 25 c. Type **297** 80 30
1353 70 c. "Pouting" (horiz) 1·50 1·25
1354 $1.10 "The Millinery Shop" 2·00 2·00
1355 $3 "The Bellelli Family" (horiz) 3·75 4·25

1984. "Ausipex" International Stamp Exhibition, Melbourne. Multicoloured.

1357 $1.10 Type **298** 2·25 1·75
1358 $4 Yacht "Australia II" (winner of America's Cup) 4·75 5·25

299 George Stephenson's "Locomotion" (1825)

1984. Railway Locomotives. Multicoloured.

1360 30 c. Type **299** 80 35
1361 40 c. Braithwaite and Ericsson's "Novelty" (1829) 95 40
1362 60 c. William Norris's "Washington Farmer" (1836) 1·00 75
1363 70 c. French Crampton type (1859) 1·00 1·00
1364 90 c. Dutch State Railways (1873) 1·10 1·50
1365 $1.10 "Champion", U.S.A. (1882) 1·25 2·00
1366 $2 Webb Compound type (1893) 1·75 3·25
1367 $4 Berlin "No. 74" (1900) 2·75 5·50

1984. Opening of Point Saline International Airport (1st issue). Nos. 1247 and 1249 optd **OPENING OF POINT SALINE INT'L AIRPORT**.

1369 40 c. Rural telephone installation 30 30
1370 $3 Airport control room 2·00 2·00

See Nos. 1399/5.

301 Donald Duck as Father Christmas looking into Mirror

1984. Christmas. Walt Disney Cartoon Characters. Multicoloured.

1372 45 c. Type **301** 1·25 40
1373 60 c. Donald Duck filling stocking with presents 1·50 55
1374 90 c. As Father Christmas pulling a sleigh 2·00 1·10
1375 $2 As Father Christmas decorating Christmas tree 3·50 3·50
1376 $4 Donald Duck and nephews singing carols 5·00 5·50

1985. Birth Bicentenary of John J. Audubon (ornithologist) (1st issue). As T **418** of Ghana. Multicoloured.

1378 50 c. Clapper rail (vert) 2·00 75
1379 70 c. Hooded warbler (vert) 2·25 1·50
1380 90 c. Common flicker (vert) 2·75 1·75
1381 $4 Bohemian waxwing (vert) 5·50 8·00

See also Nos. 1480/3.

302 Honda "XL500R"

1985. Centenary of the Motor Cycle. Multicoloured.

1383 25 c. Type **302** 90 50
1384 50 c. Suzuki "GS1100ES" 1·40 1·00
1385 90 c. Kawasaki "KZ700" 2·00 2·00
1386 $4 BMW "K100" 5·50 6·50

303 "Explorer"

1985. 75th Anniv of Girl Guide Movement. Designs showing work for Guide badges. Multicoloured.

1388 25 c. Type **303** 55 30
1389 60 c. "Cook" 90 65
1390 90 c. "Musician" 1·50 1·10
1391 $3 "Home nurse" 3·00 4·50

304 Hawker Siddeley H.S.748 on Inaugural Flight from Barbados

1985. Opening of Point Saline International Airport (1984) (2nd issue). Multicoloured.

1393 70 c. Type **304** 2·50 1·00
1394 $1 Lockheed TriStar 500 on inaugural flight from New York 3·25 1·50
1395 $4 Lockheed TriStar 500 on inaugural flight to Miami 6·50 8·00

305 Douglas DC-8-61

1985. 40th Anniv of International Civil Aviation Organization. Multicoloured.

1397 10 c. Type **305** 40 20
1398 50 c. Lockheed Starliner (inscr "Super Constellation") 1·00 75
1399 60 c. Vickers 952 Cargoliner 1·25 85
1400 $4 De Havilland Twin Otter 200/300 4·50 6·00

306 Model Boat Racing

1985. Water Sports. Multicoloured.

1402 10 c. Type **306** 20 10
1403 50 c. Scuba diving, Carriacou 45 35
1404 $1.10 Windsurfers on Grand Anse Beach 75 1·25
1405 $4 Windsurfing 2·00 4·00

307 Bird of Paradise (flower)

1985. Native Flowers. Multicoloured.

1407 ½ c. Type **307** 50 60
1408 1 c. Passion flower 50 60
1409 2 c. Oleander 50 60
1410a 4 c. Bromeliad 70 60
1411a 5 c. Anthurium 70 40
1412a 6 c. Bougainvillea 70 50
1413a 10 c. Hibiscus 70 30
1414a 15 c. Ginger 1·00 30
1415a 25 c. Poinsettia 1·00 30
1425d 30 c. Mexican creeper 20 60
1417a 40 c. Angel's trumpet 75 50
1425e 50 c. Amaryllis 30 75
1425f 60 c. Prickly pear 30 1·00
1420a 70 c. Chenille plant 1·00 1·00
1420b 75 c. Cordia 1·25 1·75
1425g $1 Periwinkle 35 1·25
1422a $1.10 Ixora 2·25 2·50
1423a $3 Shrimp plant 2·75 6·00
1424a $5 Plumbago 2·50 7·00
1425a $10 "Lantana camara" 4·00 10·00
1425b $20 Peregrina 8·50 16·00

308 The Queen Mother at Royal Opera House, London

309 Youth Gardening (Horticulture)

1985. Life and Times of Queen Elizabeth the Queen Mother. Multicoloured.

1426 $1 Type **308** 40 60
1427 $1.50 The Queen Mother playing snooker at London Press Club (horiz) 55 85
1428 $2.50 At Epsom Races, 1960 95 1·50

Stamps as Nos. 1426/8 but with face values of 90 c., $1 and $3 exist from additional sheetlets with changed background colours.

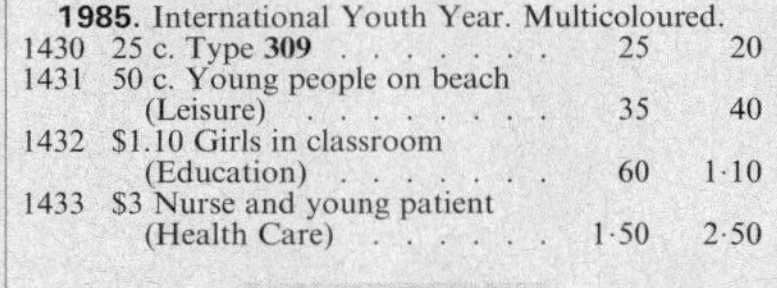

1985. International Youth Year. Multicoloured.

1430 25 c. Type **309** 25 20
1431 50 c. Young people on beach (Leisure) 35 40
1432 $1.10 Girls in classroom (Education) 60 1·10
1433 $3 Nurse and young patient (Health Care) 1·50 2·50

309a Crumhorn

1985. 300th Birth Anniv of Johann Sebastian Bach (composer). Multicoloured.

1435 25 c. Type **309a** 80 20
1436 70 c. Oboe d'amore 1·50 85
1437 $1 Violin 2·00 1·25
1438 $3 Harpsichord 3·00 5·00

310 Cub Scouts Camping

1985. 4th Caribbean Cuboree. Multicoloured.
1440 10 c. Type **310** 30 15
1441 50 c. Cub scouts swimming ("Physical Fitness") 65 40
1442 $1 Stamp collecting . . . . . 1·50 80
1443 $4 Birdwatching . . . . . . 3·50 3·00

310a Flags of Great Britain and Grenada

1985. Royal Visit. Multicoloured.
1445 50 c. Type **310a** 75 40
1446 $1 Queen Elizabeth II (vert) . 1·00 1·25
1447 $4 Royal Yacht "Britannia" . 2·50 5·00

1985. 150th Birth Anniv of Mark Twain (author). As T **145a** of Gambia. Design showing Walt Disney cartoon characters in scenes from "The Prince and the Pauper". Multicoloured.
1449 25 c. Mortie as Tom meeting the Prince (Ferdie) 60 20
1450 50 c. Tom and the Prince exchanging clothes 80 50
1451 $1.10 The Prince with John Cantry . . . . 1·75 1·75
1452 $1.50 The Prince knights Mike Hendon (Goofy) . . . . . 2·25 2·75
1453 $2 Tom and the Whipping Boy 2·50 3·00

1985. Birth Bicentenaries of Grimm Brothers (folklorists). As T **145b** of Gambia, showing Walt Disney cartoon characters in scenes from "The Fisherman and his Wife". Multicoloured.
1455 30 c. The Fisherman (Goofy) catching enchanted fish . . 65 30
1456 60 c. The Fisherman scolded by his Wife (Clarabelle) . . . 90 80
1457 70 c. The Fisherman's Wife with dream cottage . . . . . . 1·10 95
1458 $1 The Fisherman's Wife as King . . . . 1·75 1·50
1459 $3 The Fisherman and Wife in their original shack . . . . 3·25 4·50

311 Red-spotted Hawkfish

1985. Marine Life. Multicoloured.
1461 25 c. Type **311** . . . . 1·25 55
1462 50 c. Spot-finned butterflyfish . 2·00 1·10
1463 $1.10 Fire coral and orange sponges . . . . 3·25 3·25
1464 $3 Pillar coral . . . . 6·00 7·50

311a Mary McLeod Bethune (educationist) and 1975 International Women's Year 10 c.

1985. 40th Anniv of U.N.O. Designs showing United Nations (New York) stamps. Multicoloured.
1466 50 c. Type **311a** 30 30
1467 $2 Maimonides (physician) and 1966 W.H.O. 5 c. . . . . . 2·50 3·50
1468 $2.50 Alexander Graham Bell (telephone inventor) and 1956 I.T.U. 3 c. . . . . 2·00 4·00

312 "Adoration of the Shepherds" (Mantegna)

1985. Christmas. Religious Paintings. Multicoloured.
1470 25 c. Type **312** 20 15
1471 60 c. "Journey of the Magi" (Sassetta) 30 40
1472 90 c. "Madonna and Child enthroned with Saints" (Raphael) 35 70
1473 $4 "Nativity" (Monaco) . . . 1·00 3·50

312a Columbus Monument, 1893

1986. Centenary of Statue of Liberty (1st issue). Multicoloured.
1475 5 c. Type **312a** 15 20
1476 25 c. Columbus Monument, 1986 . . . . 30 20
1477 40 c. Mounted police, Central Park, 1895 (horiz) . . . . 1·75 1·10
1478 $4 Mounted police, 1986 (horiz) . . . . 5·00 8·00
See also Nos. 1644/52.

312b Snowy Egret

1986. Birth Bicentenary of John J. Audubon (ornithologist) (2nd issue). Multicoloured.
1480 50 c. Type **312b** . . . . . . 2·00 80
1481 90 c. Greater flamingo . . . . 2·75 2·00
1482 $1.10 Canada goose . . . . . 2·75 2·50
1483 $3 Smew . . . . 4·50 6·00

1986. Visit of President Reagan. Nos. 1418 and 1424 optd **VISIT OF PRES REAGAN 20 FEB. 1986.**
1485 50 c. Amaryllis 50 50
1486 $5 Plumbago . . . . 3·00 5·00

314 Methodist Church, St. George's

1986. Bicentenary of Methodist Church in Grenada.
1487 **314** 60 c. multicoloured . . . 70 1·00

315 Player with Ball **316** Brown-lined Latirus

1986. World Cup Football Championship, Mexico. Multicoloured.
1489 50 c. Type **315** 80 55
1490 70 c. Player heading ball . . . 1·00 1·00
1491 90 c. Player controlling ball . . 1·50 1·50
1492 $4 Player controlling ball with right foot . . . . 5·50 7·00

1986. Appearance of Halley's Comet (1st issue). As T **151a** of Gambia. Multicoloured.
1494 5 c. Clyde Tombaugh (astronomer) and Dudley Observatory, New York . . 40 40
1495 20 c. N.A.S.A — U.S.A.F. "X-24B" Space Shuttle prototype, 1973 . . . . 50 30
1496 40 c. German comet medal, 1618 . . . . 70 45
1497 $4 Destruction of Sodom and Gomorrah, 1949 B.C. . . . 3·50 4·50
See also Nos. 1533/6 and 1980/3.

1986. 60th Birthday of Queen Elizabeth II. As T **151b** of Gambia.
1499 2 c. black and yellow 10 15
1500 $1.50 multicoloured 60 80
1501 $4 multicoloured . . . . . 1·50 2·50
DESIGNS: 2 c. Princess Elizabeth in 1951, $1.50, Queen presenting trophy at polo match, Windsor, 1965. $4 at Epsom, Derby Day 1977.

315a Goofy as Pitcher

1986. "Ameripex" International Stamp Exhibition, Chicago. Designs showing Walt Disney cartoon characters playing baseball. Multicoloured.
1503 1 c. Type **315a** 10 10
1504 2 c. Goofy as catcher 10 10
1505 5 c. Mickey Mouse striking ball and Donald Duck as catcher 10 10
1506 4 c. Huey forcing out Dewey . 10 10
1507 5 c. Chip n'Dale chasing flyball 10 10
1508 6 c. Mickey Mouse, Donald Duck and Clarabelle in argument 10 10
1509 $2 Minnie Mouse and Donald Duck reading baseball rules 1·75 2·75
1510 $3 Ludwig von Drake as umpire with Goofy and Pete colliding 2·25 3·25

1986. Royal Wedding. As T **153b** of Gambia. Multicoloured.
1512 2 c. Prince Andrew and Miss Sarah Ferguson 10 20
1513 $1.10 Prince Andrew 70 80
1514 $4 Prince Andrew with H.M.S. "Brazen's" Westland Lynx helicopter . . . . 2·75 3·25

1986. Sea Shells. Multicoloured.
1516 25 c. Type **316** 45 25
1517 60 c. Lamellose wentletrap . . 75 90
1518 70 c. Turkey wing . . . . . 85 1·00
1519 $4 Rooster tail conch . . . . 2·75 5·00

317 "Lepiota roseolamellata" **318** Dove on Rifles and Mahatma Gandhi (Disarmament Week)

1986. Mushrooms. Multicoloured.
1521 10 c. Type **317** 60 40
1522 60 c. "Lentinus bertieri" . . . 1·75 1·75
1523 $1 "Lentinus retinervis" . . . 2·50 2·50
1524 $4 "Eccilia cystiophorus" . . 5·75 7·50

1986. World Cup Football Championship Winners, Mexico. Nos. 1489/92 optd **WINNERS Argentina 3 W. Germany 2.**
1526 50 c. Type **315** 85 85
1527 70 c. Player heading ball . . . 1·00 1·00
1528 90 c. Player controlling ball . . 1·40 1·60
1529 $4 Player controlling ball with right foot . . . . 4·50 5·00

1986. International Events. Multicoloured.
1531 60 c. Type **318** 50 50
1532 $4 Hands passing olive branch and Martin Luther King (International Peace Year) (horiz) . . . . 1·50 3·00

1986. Appearance of Halley's Comet (2nd issue). Nos. 1494/7 optd with T **447a** of Ghana.
1533 5 c. Clyde Tombaugh (astronomer) and Dudley Observatory, New York . . 60 60
1534 20 c. N.A.S.A — U.S.A.F. "X-24B" Space Shuttle prototype, 1973 . . . . 85 60
1535 40 c. German comet medal, 1618 . . . . 1·25 70
1536 $4 Destruction of Sodom and Gomorrah, 1949 B.C. . . . 5·00 7·00

318a Mickey Mouse asleep in Armchair

1986. Christmas. Multicoloured.
1538 30 c. Type **318a** 35 25
1539 45 c. Young Mickey Mouse with Father Christmas 45 30
1540 60 c. Donald Duck with toy telephone (horiz) 60 50
1541 70 c. Pluto with pushcart (horiz) 70 70
1542 $1.10 Daisy Duck with doll (horiz) . . . . 1·00 1·25
1543 $2 Goofy as Father Christmas . 1·75 2·00
1544 $2.50 Goofy singing carols at piano . . . . 2·00 2·50
1545 $3 Mickey Mouse, Donald Duck and nephew riding toy train (horiz) . . . . 2·25 3·00

319 Cockerel and Hen

1986. Fauna and Flora. Multicoloured.
1547 10 c. Type **319** 20 10
1548 30 c. Fish-eating bat 35 20
1549 60 c. Goat 55 45
1550 70 c. Cow 60 50
1551 $1 Anthurium . . . . 1·50 1·25
1552 $1.10 Royal poinciana . . . . 1·50 1·25
1553 $2 Frangipani . . . . 2·50 3·25
1554 $4 Orchid . . . . 8·50 9·50

320 Maserati "Biturbo" (1984) **321** Pole Vaulting

1986. Centenary of Motoring. Multicoloured.
1556 10 c. Type **320** 25 25
1557 30 c. AC "Cobra" (1960) . . 40 40
1558 60 c. Corvette (1963) 60 60
1559 70 c. Dusenberg "SJ7" (1932) 70 70
1560 90 c. Porsche (1957) . . . . . 85 1·00
1561 $1 Stoewer (1930) . . . . . 1·00 1·25
1562 $2 Volkswagen "Beetle" (1957) 1·60 2·00
1563 $3 Mercedes "600 Limo" (1963) 1·90 2·50

1986. Olympic Games, Seoul, South Korea (1988). Multicoloured.
1565 10 c. + 5 c. Type **321** 10 30
1566 50 c. + 20 c. Gymnastics . . . 35 60
1567 70 c. + 30 c. Putting the shot 50 85
1568 $2 + $1 High jumping . . . 1·00 2·25
The premiums on Nos. 1565/9 were to support the participation of the Grenada team.

321a Painting by Chagall

1986. Birth Centenary of Marc Chagall (artist). Designs showing various paintings.
1570/1609 $1 × 40 multicoloured Set of 40 . . . . . . 24·00 26·00

321b "Columbia", 1958

1987. America's Cup Yachting Championship. Multicoloured.
1611 10 c. Type **321b** 25 20
1612 60 c. "Resolute", 1920 . . . 55 60
1613 $1.10 "Endeavor", 1934 . . . 85 1·25
1614 $4 "Rainbow", 1934 . . . . 1·75 3·50

322 Virgin Mary and Outline Map of Grenada

323 Black Grouper

1987. 500th Anniv (1992) of Discovery of America by Christopher Columbus (1st issue). Multicoloured.

1616 10 c. Type **322** . . . 20 20
1617 30 c. "Santa Maria", "Pinta" and "Nina" (horiz) . . . 60 35
1618 50 c. Columbus and outline map of Grenada . . . 70 45
1619 60 c. Christopher Columbus . . 70 55
1620 90 c. King Ferdinand and Queen Isabella of Spain (horiz) . . 70 80
1621 $1.10 Map of Antilles by Columbus . . . 90 1·00
1622 $2 Caribs with sailing raft (horiz) . . . 1·10 2·25
1623 $3 Columbus in the New World, 1493 (contemporary drawing) . . . 1·25 2·25

See also Nos. 2051/4, 2091/8, 2222/9, 2389/94 and 2423/4.

322a Cornu's First Helicopter, 1907

1987. Milestones of Transportation. Multicoloured.

1625 10 c. Type **322a** . . . 70 55
1626 15 c. "Monitor" and "Merrimack" (first battle between ironclad warships), 1862 . . . 70 60
1627 30 c. LZ1 (first Zeppelin), 1900 . . . 90 80
1628 50 c. "Sirius" (first transatlantic paddle-steamer crossing), 1838 . . . 1·00 85
1629 60 c. Steam locomotive on Trans-Siberian Railway (longest line) . . . 1·25 1·00
1630 70 c. U.S.S "Enterprise" (largest aircraft carrier), 1960 . . . 1·25 1·25
1631 90 c. Blanchard and Jeffries' balloon (first balloon across English Channel), 1785 . . 1·40 1·40
1632 $1.50 U.S.S. "Holland I" (first steam-powered submarine), 1900 . . . 2·00 2·25
1633 $2 "Oceanic I" (first luxury liner), 1871 . . . 2·50 2·75
1634 $3 Lamborghini "Countach" (fastest commercial car), 1984 2·75 3·25

1987. "Capex '87" International Stamp Exhibition, Toronto. Game Fishes. Multicoloured.

1635 10 c. Type **323** . . . 30 15
1636 30 c. Blue marlin (horiz) . . . 40 15
1637 60 c. White marlin . . . 60 55
1638 70 c. Bigeye threshershark (horiz) . . . 70 70
1639 $1 Bonefish (horiz) . . . 90 1·00
1640 $1.10 Wahoo (horiz) . . . 1·00 1·25
1641 $2 Sailfish (horiz) . . . 1·75 2·25
1642 $4 Albacore (horiz) . . . 2·75 3·50

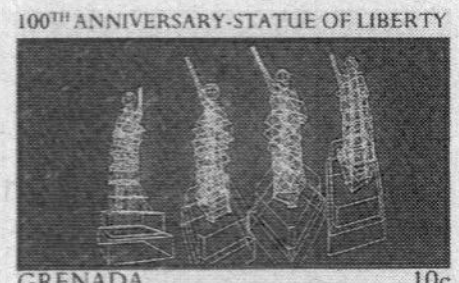

323a Computer Projections on Statue and Base

1987. Centenary of Statue of Liberty (2nd issue). Multicoloured.

1644 10 c. Type **323a** . . . 15 15
1645 25 c. Statue and fireworks . . 20 15
1646 50 c. Statue and fireworks (different) . . . 35 35
1647 60 c. Statue and boats (vert) . 45 45
1648 70 c. Computer projection of top of Statue . . . 50 50
1649 $1 Rear view of Statue and fireworks (vert) . . . 80 80
1650 $1.10 Aerial view of Statue (vert) . . . 95 1·25
1651 $2 Statue and flotilla (vert) . . 2·00 2·25
1652 $4 "Queen Elizabeth 2" in New York Harbour (vert) . . . 3·50 4·00

324 Alice and the Rabbit Hole

1987. 50th Anniv of First Full-Length Disney Cartoon Film. Scenes from various films.

1653/1706 30 c. × 54 multicoloured
Set of 54 . . . 16·00 17·00

325 Isaac Newton holding Apple (Law of Gravity)

1987. Great Scientific Discoveries. Multicoloured.

1708 50 c. Type **325** . . . 85 85
1709 $1.10 John Jacob Berzelius and symbols of chemical elements 1·75 1·75
1710 $2 Robert Boyle (law of Pressure and Volume) . . . 2·50 3·25
1711 $3 James Watt and drawing of steam engine . . . 4·25 4·50

No. 1711 is inscribed "RUDOLF DIESEL" in error.

1987. 60th Anniv of International Social Security Association. Nos. 1413, 1418 and 1423 optd **INTERNATIONAL SOCIAL SECURITY ASSOCIATION** and emblem.

1714 10 c. Hibiscus . . . 10 15
1715 50 c. Amaryllis . . . 25 35
1716 $3 Shrimp plant . . . 1·40 2·25

327a Independance Hall, Philadelphia

1987. Bicentenary of U.S. Constitution. Mult.

1717 15 c. Type **327a** . . . 10 10
1718 50 c. Benjamin Franklin (Pennsylvania delegate) . . 25 35
1719 60 c. State Seal, Massachusetts (horiz) . . . 25 35
1720 $4 Robert Morris (Pennsylvania delegate) . . . 1·75 2·75

328 Goofy in "The Shadow"

329 "The Annunciation" (Fra Angelico)

1987. "Hafnia '87" International Stamp Exhibition. Walt Disney cartoon characters in scenes from Hans Christian Andersen's fairy tales. Mult.

1722 25 c. Type **328** . . . 50 30
1723 30 c. Mother Stork and brood in "The Storks" . . . 50 30
1724 50 c. King Richard, Robin Hood and Little John (from Robin Hood) in "The Emperor's New Clothes" . . . 75 55
1725 60 c. Goofy and Pluto in "The Tinderbox" . . . 75 55
1726 70 c. Daisy and Donald Duck in "The Shepherdess and the Chimney Sweep" . . . 80 70
1727 $1.50 Mickey and Minnie Mouse in "The Little Mermaid" . . . 1·60 1·75
1728 $3 Clarabelle and Goofy in "The Princess and the Pea" 2·50 3·50
1729 $4 Minnie Mouse and Pegleg Pete in "The Marsh King's Daughter" . . . 2·50 3·50

1987. Christmas. Religious Paintings. Multicoloured.

1731 15 c. Type **329** . . . 55 10
1732 30 c. "The Annunciation" (attr. Hubert van Eyck) . . . 90 30
1733 60 c. "The Adoration of the Magi" (Januarius Zick) . . 1·75 1·40
1734 $4 "The Flight into Egypt" (Gerard David) . . . 5·50 7·00

330 T. Albert Marryshow

1988. Birth Centenary of T. Albert Marryshow (nationalist).

1736 **330** 25 c. brown, light brown and red . . . 30 30

330a Wedding Photograph, 1947

1988. Royal Ruby Wedding. Multicoloured.

1737 **330b** 15 c. brown, black and blue . . . 35 10
1738 – 50 c. multicoloured . . . 70 50
1739 – $1 brown and black . . . 1·25 1·00
1740 – $4 multicoloured . . . 3·00 4·00

DESIGNS: 50 c. Queen Elizabeth II with Prince Charles and Princess Anne, c. 1955; $1 Queen with Princess Anne, c. 1957; $4 Queen Elizabeth (from photo by Tim Graham), 1980.

331 Goofy and Daisy Duck lighting Olympic Torch, Olympia

332 Scout fishing from Boat

1988. Olympic Games, Seoul. Designs showing Walt Disney cartoon characters. Multicoloured.

1742 1 c. Type **331** . . . 10 10
1743 2 c. Donald and Daisy Duck carrying Olympic torch . . 10 10
1744 3 c. Donald Duck, Goofy and Mickey Mouse carrying flags of U.S., Korea and Spain . 10 10
1745 4 c. Donald Duck releasing doves . . . 10 10
1746 5 c. Mickey Mouse flying with rocket belt . . . 10 10
1747 10 c. Morty and Ferdie carrying banner with Olympic motto 10 10
1748 $6 Donald Duck, Minnie Mouse and Hodori the Tiger (mascot of Seoul Games) . . . 5·50 5·50
1749 $7 Pluto. Hodori and old post office, Seoul . . . 5·50 5·50

1988. Stamp Exhibitions. Nos. 1631/4 optd.

1751 90 c. Blanchard and Jeffries' balloon, 1785 (optd **OLYMPHILEX '88**, Seoul) . 85 85
1752 $1.50 U.S.S "Holland I", 1900 (optd **INDEPENDENCE 40**, Israel) . . . 1·10 1·25
1753 $2 "Oceanic I", 1871 (optd **FINLANDIA 88**, Helsinki) . 1·60 2·00
1754 $3 Lamborghini "Countach", 1984 (optd **PRAGA 88**, Prague) . . . 2·00 2·50

1988. World Scout Jamboree, Australia. Mult.

1755 20 c. Type **332** . . . 40 15
1756 70 c. Scouts hiking through forest (horiz) . . . 1·00 1·00
1757 90 c. Practising first aid (horiz) 1·40 1·40
1758 $3 Shooting rapids in inflatable canoe . . . 3·00 3·75

333 "Santa Maria de Guia" (Columbus), 1498 and Map of Rotary District

334 Roseate Tern

1988. Rotary District 405 Conference, St. George's.

1760 **333** $2 multicoloured . . . 80 1·00

1988. Birds. Multicoloured.

1762 10 c. Type **334** . . . 60 30
1763 25 c. Laughing gull . . . 80 30
1764 50 c. Osprey . . . 1·25 70
1765 60 c. Rose-breasted grosbeak . 1·25 70
1766 90 c. Purple gallinule . . . 1·25 90
1767 $1.10 White-tailed tropic bird 1·25 1·00
1768 $3 Blue-faced booby . . . 1·75 2·75
1769 $4 Common shoveler . . . 1·90 3·00

335 Vauxhall Type "OE 30/98", 1925

1988. Cars. Multicoloured.

1771 $2 Type **335** . . . 1·10 1·25
1772 $2 Wills "Sainte Claire", 1926 1·10 1·25
1773 $2 Bucciali, 1928 . . . 1·10 1·25
1774 $2 Irving Napier "Golden Arrow", 1929 . . . 1·10 1·25
1775 $2 Studebaker "President", 1930 . . . 1·10 1·25
1776 $2 Thomas "Flyer", 1907 . . 1·10 1·25
1777 $2 Isotta-Franschini "Tipo J", 1908 . . . 1·10 1·25
1778 $2 Fiat 10/14HP, 1910 . . . 1·10 1·25
1779 $2 Mercer "Type 35 Raceabout", 1911 . . . 1·10 1·25
1780 $2 Marmon "Model 34 Cloverleaf", 1917 . . . 1·10 1·25
1781 $2 Tatra "Type 77", 1934 . . 1·10 1·25
1782 $2 Rolls-Royce "Phantom III", 1938 . . . 1·10 1·25
1783 $2 Studebaker "Champion Starlight", 1947 . . . 1·10 1·25
1784 $2 Porsche "Gmund", 1948 . . 1·10 1·25
1785 $2 Tucker, 1948 . . . 1·10 1·25
1786 $2 Peerless "V-16", 1931 . . 1·10 1·25
1787 $2 Minerva "AL", 1931 . . . 1·10 1·25
1788 $2 Reo "Royale", 1953 . . . 1·10 1·25
1789 $2 Pierce Arrow "Silver Arrow", 1933 . . . 1·10 1·25
1790 $2 Hupmobile "Aerodynamic", 1934 . . . 1·10 1·25
1791 $2 Peugeot "404", 1965 . . . 1·10 1·25
1792 $2 Ford "Capri", 1969 . . . 1·10 1·25
1793 $2 Ferrari "312T", 1975 . . . 1·10 1·25
1794 $2 Lotus "T-79", 1978 . . . 1·10 1·25
1795 $2 Williams-Cosworth "FW07", 1979 . . . 1·10 1·25
1796 $2 H.R.G. "1500 Sports", 1948 1·10 1·25
1797 $2 Crosley "Hotshot", 1949 . . 1·10 1·25
1798 $2 Volvo "PV444", 1955 . . . 1·10 1·25
1799 $2 Maserati "Tipo 61", 1960 . 1·10 1·25
1800 $2 Saab "96", 1963 . . . 1·10 1·25

1988. 500th Birth Anniv of Titian (artist). As T **166a** of Gambia. Multicoloured.

1801 10 c. "Lavinia Vecellio" . . . 10 10
1802 20 c. "Portrait of a Man" . . 10 10
1803 25 c. "Andrea de Franceschi" . 10 15
1804 90 c. "Head of a Soldier" . . 40 45
1805 $1 "Man with a Flute" . . . 45 50
1806 $2 "Lucrezia and Tarquinius" . 80 1·00
1807 $3 "Duke of Mantua with Dog" 1·25 1·60
1808 $4 "La Bella di Tiziano" . . . 1·60 2·00

336 "Graf Zeppelin" over Chicago World's Fair, 1933

338 Pineapple

337 Tasmanian Wolf, Mickey Mouse and Pluto

1988. Airships. Multicoloured.

1810	10 c. Type **336**	20	20
1811	15 c. LZ-1 over Lake Constance, 1901 (horiz)	25	25
1812	25 c. "Washington" (balloon) and "George Washington Curtis" (balloon barge), 1862	30	30
1813	45 c. "Hindenburg" and Maybach "Zeppelin" car (horiz)	40	40
1814	50 c. Goodyear Aerospace airship in Statue of Liberty Centenary Race, 1986	40	40
1815	60 c. "Hindenburg" over Statue of Liberty, 1937 (horiz)	50	50
1816	90 c. Heinkel biplane docking experiment with "Hindenburg", 1936 (horiz)	80	80
1817	$2 "Hindenburg" over Olympic Stadium, Berlin, 1936	1·60	1·60
1818	$3 "Hindenburg" over Christ of the Andes Monument, 1937	2·00	2·00
1819	$4 "Hindenburg" and "Bremen" (liner), 1936 (horiz)	2·25	2·25

1988. "Sydpex '88". National Stamp Exhibition, Sydney and 60th Birthday of Mickey Mouse. Multicoloured.

1821	1 c. Type **337**	10	10
1822	2 c. Mickey Mouse feeding wallabies	10	10
1823	3 c. Mickey Mouse and Goofy with kangaroo	10	10
1824	4 c. Mickey and Minnie Mouse riding emus	10	10
1825	5 c. Mickey and Minnie Mouse with wombat	10	10
1826	10 c. Mickey Mouse and Donald Duck watching platypus	10	10
1827	$5 Mickey Mouse and Goofy photographing blue-winged kookaburra	4·50	5·00
1828	$6 Mickey Mouse and Koala on map of Australia	4·50	5·00

1988. 10th Anniv of International Fund for Agricultural Development. Multicoloured.

1830	25 c. Type **338**	25	15
1831	75 c. Bananas	60	60
1832	$3 Mace and nutmeg (horiz)	2·00	2·75

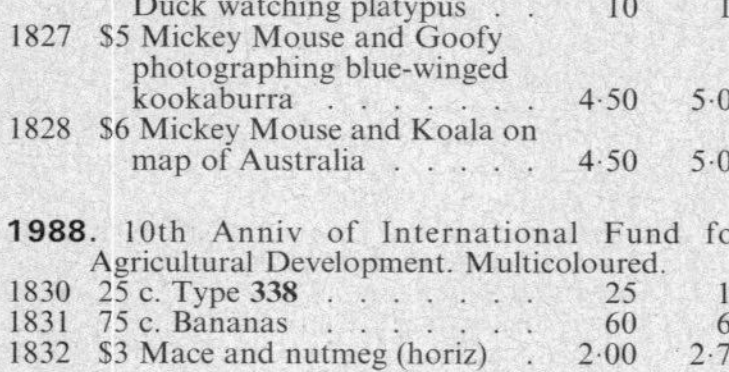

339 Lignum Vitae

1988. Flowering Trees and Shrubs. Mult.

1833	15 c. Type **339**	15	15
1834	25 c. Saman	20	15
1835	35 c. Red frangipani	25	20
1836	45 c. Flowering maple	30	25
1837	60 c. Yellow poui	40	40
1838	$1 Wild chestnut	60	70
1839	$3 Mountain immortelle	1·50	2·25
1840	$4 Queen of flowers	1·75	2·50

340 Mickey Mantle (New York Yankees)

1988. Major League Baseball Players (1st series). Designs showing portraits or league emblems.

1842/1922 30 c. × 81 multicoloured Set of 81 . . . . . . 9·50 11·00

340a Donald Duck's Nephew on Mantelpiece

1988. Christmas. "Mickey's Christmas Eve". Designs showing Walt Disney cartoon characters. Multicoloured.

1923	$1 Type **340a**	65	65
1924	$1 Goofy with string of popcorn	65	65
1925	$1 Chip'n'Dale decorating Christmas tree	65	65
1926	$1 Father Christmas in sleigh	65	65
1927	$1 Donald's nephew with stocking	65	65
1928	$1 Donald's nephew unpacking decorations	65	65
1929	$1 Donald Duck with present	65	65
1930	$1 Mickey Mouse with present	65	65

341 Tina Turner — 342 Atlantic Railway No. 2, 1889, Canada

1988. Entertainers. Multicoloured.

1932	10 c. Type **341**	25	20
1933	25 c. Lionel Ritchie	25	20
1934	45 c. Whitney Houston	35	30
1935	60 c. Joan Armatrading	50	45
1936	75 c. Madonna	70	60
1937	$1 Elton John	1·00	80
1938	$3 Bruce Springsteen	2·00	2·75
1939	$4 Bob Marley	3·00	3·50

No. 1935 is incorrectly inscribed "JOAN AMMERTRADING".

1989. North American Railway Locomotives. Mult.

1941	$2 Type **342**	1·25	1·25
1942	$2 Virginia & Truckee Railroad "J. W Bowker" type, 1875, U.S.A.	1·25	1·25
1943	$2 Philadelphia & Reading Railway "Ariel", 1872, U.S.A.	1·25	1·25
1944	$2 Chicago & Rock Island Railroad "America" type, 1867, U.S.A.	1·25	1·25
1945	$2 Lehigh Valley Railroad Consolidation No. 63, 1866, U.S.A.	1·25	1·25
1946	$2 Great Western Railway "Scotia", 1860, Canada	1·25	1·25
1947	$2 Grand Trunk Railway Class "Birkenhead", 1854, Canada	1·25	1·25
1948	$2 Camden & Amboy Railroad "Monster", 1837, U.S.A.	1·25	1·25
1949	$2 Baltimore & Ohio Railroad Class "Grasshopper", 1834, U.S.A.	1·25	1·25
1950	$2 Peter Cooper's "Tom Thumb", 1829, Baltimore & Ohio Railroad, U.S.A.	1·25	1·25
1951	$2 United Railways of Yucatan "Yucatan", 1925, Mexico	1·25	1·25
1952	$2 Canadian National Railways Class T2, 1924	1·25	1·25
1953	$2 St. Louis–San Francisco Railroad Class "Light Mikado", 1919, U.S.A.	1·25	1·25
1954	$2 Atlantic Coast Line Railroad Class "Light Pacific", 1919, U.S.A.	1·25	1·25
1955	$2 Edaville Railroad No. 7, 1913, U.S.A.	1·25	1·25
1956	$2 Denver & Rio Grande Western Railroad Class K 27, 1903, U.S.A.	1·25	1·25
1957	$2 Pennsylvania Railroad Class E-2 No. 7002, 1902, U.S.A.	1·25	1·25
1958	$2 Pennsylvania Railroad Class H6, 1899, U.S.A.	1·25	1·25
1959	$2 John Jarvis's "De Witt Clinton", 1831, Mohawk & Hudson Railroad, U.S.A.	1·25	1·25
1960	$2 St. Clair Tunnel Company No. 598, 1891, Canada	1·25	1·25
1961	$2 Chesapeake & Ohio Railroad Class M-1 steam turbine electric locomotive No. 500, 1947, U.S.A.	1·25	1·25
1962	$2 Rutland Railroad steam locomotive No. 93, 1946, U.S.A.	1·25	1·25
1963	$2 Pennsylvania Railroad Class T1, 1942, U.S.A.	1·25	1·25
1964	$2 Chesapeake & Ohio Railroad Class H-8, 1942, U.S.A.	1·25	1·25
1965	$2 Atchison, Topeka & Santa Fe Railway Model FT diesel, 1941, U.S.A.	1·25	1·25
1966	$2 Gulf, Mobile & Ohio Railroad Models S-1 & S-2 diesels, 1940, U.S.A.	1·25	1·25
1967	$2 New York, New Haven & Hartford Railroad Class 15, 1937, U.S.A.	1·25	1·25
1968	$2 Seaboard Air Line Railroad Class R, 1936, U.S.A.	1·25	1·25
1969	$2 Newfoundland Railway Class R-2, 1930	1·25	1·25
1970	$2 Canadian National Railway diesel No. 9000, 1928	1·25	1·25

343 Women's Long Jump (Jackie Joyner-Kersee, U.S.A.)

1989. Olympic Gold Medal Winners, Seoul (1988). Multicoloured.

1971	10 c. Type **343**	20	20
1972	25 c. Women's Singles Tennis (Steffi Graf, West Germany)	50	35
1973	45 c. Men's 1500 metres (Peter Rono, Kenya)	60	40
1974	75 c. Men's 1000 metres single kayak (Greg Barton, U.S.A.)	70	60
1975	$1 Women's team foil (Italy)	85	75
1976	$2 Women's 100 metres freestyle swimming (Kristin Otto, East Germany)	1·75	2·00
1977	$3 Men's still rings gymnastics (Holger Behrendt, East Germany)	2·10	2·25
1978	$4 Synchronized swimming pair (Japan)	2·40	2·50

344 Nebulae

1989. Appearance of Halley's Comet (1986) (3rd issue).

1980	**344** 25 c. + 5 c. multicoloured	40	50
1981	– 75 c. + 5 c. black & grn	75	95
1982	– 90 c. + 5 c. multicoloured	85	1·10
1983	– $2 + 5 c. multicoloured	1·25	1·75

DESIGNS: 75 c. + 5 c. Marine astronomical experiments; 90 c. + 5 c. Moon's surface; $2 + 5 c. Edmond Halley, Sir Isaac Newton and his book "Principia". (102 × 69 mm); $5 + 5 c. 17th-century warships and astrological signs.

1989. Japanese Art. Paintings by Hiroshige. As T **177a** of Gambia. Multicoloured.

1985	10 c. "Shinagawa on Edo Bay"	30	20
1986	25 c. "Pine Trees on the Road to Totsuka"	40	30
1987	60 c. "Kanagawa on Edo Bay"	60	50
1988	75 c. "Crossing Banyu River to Hiratsuka"	65	55
1989	$1 "Windy Shore at Odawara"	80	70
1990	$2 "Snow-Covered Post Station of Mishima"	1·40	1·75
1991	$3 "Full Moon at Fuchu"	1·60	2·00
1992	$4 "Crossing the Stream at Okitsu"	2·25	2·50

345 Great Blue Heron

1989. Birds. Multicoloured.

1994	5 c. Type **345**	40	50
1995a	10 c. Green heron	40	40
1996a	15 c. Turnstone	45	45
1997a	25 c. Blue-winged teal	50	20
1998a	35 c. Little ringed plover (vert)	55	20
1999a	45 c. Green-throated carib ("Emerald-throated hummingbird") (vert)	60	30
2000a	50 c. Rufous-breasted hermit (vert)	65	35
2001a	60 c. Lesser Antillean bullfinch (vert)	70	50
2002a	75 c. Brown pelican (vert)	80	60
2003a	$1 Black-crowned night heron (vert)	1·00	80
2004a	$3 American kestrel ("Sparrow hawk") (vert)	1·75	2·50
2005a	$5 Barn swallow (vert)	2·50	3·50
2006	$10 Red-billed tropic bird (vert)	6·00	8·00
2007	$20 Barn owl (vert)	12·00	14·00

345a Scotland Player

1989. World Cup Football Championship, Italy (1990) (1st issue). Multicoloured.

2008	10 c. Type **345a**	40	20
2009	25 c. England and Brazil players	50	30
2010	60 c. Paolo Rossi (Italy)	75	55
2011	75 c. Jairzinho (Brazil)	90	70
2012	$1 Sweden striker	1·10	90
2013	$2 Pele (Brazil)	2·25	2·00
2014	$3 Mario Kempes (Argentina)	3·00	2·75
2015	$4 Pat Jennings (Northern Ireland)	3·25	3·00

See also Nos. 2174/7.

346 Xebec and Sugar Cane

1989. "Philexfrance '89" International Stamp Exhibition, Paris. Designs showing French sailing vessels and plantation crops. Mult.

2017	25 c. Type **346**	80	30
2018	75 c. Lugger and cotton	1·40	85
2019	$1 Full-rigged ship and cocoa	1·60	1·10
2020	$4 Ketch and coffee	3·50	5·50

347 Alan Shepard and "Freedom 7" Spacecraft, 1961 (first American in Space)

1989. 20th Anniv of First Manned Landing on Moon. Multicoloured.

2022	15 c. Type **347**	50	40
2023	35 c. "Friendship 7" spacecraft, 1962 (first manned earth orbit)	65	55
2024	45 c. "Apollo 8" orbiting Moon, 1968 (first manned lunar orbit)	75	65
2025	70 c. "Apollo 15" lunar rover, 1972	1·00	85
2026	$1 "Apollo 11" emblem and lunar module "Eagle" on Moon, 1969	1·25	1·10
2027	$2 "Gemini 8" and "Agena" rocket, 1966 (first space docking)	2·25	2·00
2028	$3 Edward White in space, 1965 (first U.S. space walk)	3·00	2·75
2029	$4 "Apollo 7" emblem	3·50	3·25

348 "Hygrocybe occidentalis" — 349 Y.W.C.A. Logo and Grenada Scenery

1989. Fungi. Multicoloured.

2031	15 c. Type **348**	50	40
2032	40 c. "Marasmius haematocephalus"	65	55
2033	50 c. "Hygrocybe hypohaemacta"	75	65
2034	70 c. "Lepiota pseudoignicolor"	1·00	90
2035	90 c. "Cookeina tricholoma"	1·25	1·25
2036	$1.10 "Leucopaxillus gracillimus"	1·50	1·50
2037	$2.25 "Hygrocybe nigrescens"	2·75	3·00
2038	$4 "Clathrus crispus"	3·75	4·00

1989. Centenary of Young Women's Christian Association. Multicoloured.

2040	50 c. Type **349**	45	45
2041	75 c. Y.W.C.A. logo and town (horiz)	80	80

350 "Historis odius"

1989. Butterflies. Multicoloured.

2042	6 c. Type **350**	30	30
2043	30 c. "Marpesia petreus"	55	55
2044	40 c. "Danaus gilippus"	60	60
2045	60 c. "Dione juno"	80	80
2046	$1.10 "Agraulis vanillae"	1·25	1·25
2047	$1.25 "Danaus plexippus"	1·50	1·50
2048	$4 "Papilio androgeus"	3·25	3·25
2049	$5 "Dryas julia"	3·25	3·25

351 Amerindian Hieroglyph

1989. 500th Anniv (1992) of Discovery of America by Columbus (2nd issue). Designs showing different hieroglyphs.

2051 **351** 45 c. brown, black & bl . . 70 50
2052 – 60 c. brown, black & grn . 80 60
2053 – $1 black, black & vio . . 1·25 1·00
2054 – $4 dp brown, blk & brn . 3·75 4·00

352 Amos leaving Home

1989. "World Stamp Expo '89" International Stamp Exhibition, Washington. Designs showing Walt Disney cartoon characters in scenes from "Ben and Me". Multicoloured.

2056 1 c. Type **352** 10 10
2057 2 c. Meeting of Benjamin Franklin and Amos 10 10
2058 3 c. The Franklin stove . . . 10 10
2059 4 c. Ben and Amos with bi-focals 10 10
2060 5 c. Amos on page of "Pennsylvania Gazette" . . 10 10
2061 6 c. Ben working printing press 10 10
2062 10 c. Conducting experiment with electricity 10 10
2063 $5 Ben disembarking in England . . . . 5·00 5·50
2064 $6 Ben with Document of Agreement . . . . 5·50 6·00

352a "Christ in the House of Mary and Martha"

1990. Christmas. Paintings by Rubens. Multicoloured.

2066 20 c. Type **352a** 30 25
2067 35 c. "The Circumcision" . . 45 40
2068 60 c. "Trinity adored by Duke of Mantua and Family" . . . 75 65
2069 $2 "Holy Family with St. Francis" . . . . 2·25 2·50
2070 $3 "The Ildefonso Altarpiece" 2·75 3·00
2071 $4 "Madonna and Child with Garland and Putti" . . . . 3·25 3·50

353 Alexander Graham Bell and Early Telephone System (150th anniv of invention)

1990. Anniversaries. Multicoloured.

2073 10 c. Type **353** 30 20
2074 25 c. George Washington and Capitol (bicentenary of presidential inauguration) . 30 20
2075 35 c. Shakespeare and birthplace, Stratford (425th birth anniv) 75 30
2076 75 c. Nehru and Gandhi (birth cent of Nehru) . . . . . . 2·00 1·25
2077 $1 Dr. Hugo Eckener, Ferdinand von Zeppelin and airship "Graf Zeppelin" (80th anniv of first passenger Zeppelin) . . . . 1·50 1·25
2078 $2 Charlie Chaplin (birth cent) 3·00 2·75
2079 $3 Container ship in Hamburg Harbour (800th anniv) . . . 2·50 3·25
2080 $4 Friedrich Ebert (first President) and Heidelberg gate (70th anniv of German Republic) . . . . 2·50 3·25

No. 2080 is inscribed "40th Anniversary of German Republic" in error.

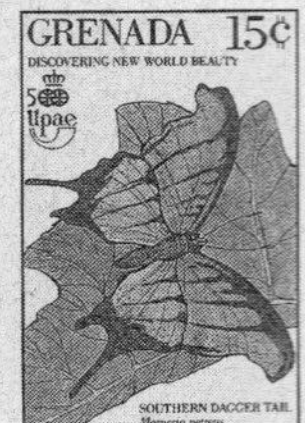

354 "Odontoglossum triumphans" **354a** "Marpesia petreus"

1990. "EXPO '90" International Garden and Greenery Exhibition, Osaka. Caribbean Orchids. Multicoloured.

2082 1 c. Type **354** 10 10
2083 25 c. "Oncidium splendidum" . 30 20
2084 60 c. "Laelia anceps" 60 60
2085 75 c. "Cattleya trianaei" . . . 75 75
2086 $1 "Odontoglossum rossii" . . 1·00 1·00
2087 $2 "Brassia gireoudiana" . . 1·75 1·75
2088 $3 "Cattleya dowiana" . . . 2·25 2·25
2089 $4 "Sobralia macrantha" . . 2·50 2·50

1990. 500th Anniv (1992) of Discovery of America by Columbus (3rd issue). New World Natural History — Butterflies. Multicoloured.

2091 15 c. Type **354a** 45 20
2092 25 c. "Junonia evarete" . . . 60 25
2093 75 c. "Siproeta stelenes" . . . 1·10 70
2094 90 c. "Historis odius" . . . . 1·25 85
2095 $1 "Mestra cana" . . . . . . 1·25 90
2096 $2 "Biblis hyperia" . . . . . 2·00 2·25
2097 $3 "Dryas julia" . . . . . . 2·50 3·00
2098 $4 "Anartia amathea" . . . . 2·50 3·00

354b Caribbean Monk Seal

1990. Local Fauna. Multicoloured.

2100 10 c. Type **354b** 20 20
2101 15 c. Little brown bat 25 25
2102 45 c. Brown rat 50 50
2103 60 c. Common rabbit 60 60
2104 $1 Water opossum 95 95
2105 $2 White-nosed ichneumon . . 1·75 1·75
2106 $3 Little big-eared bat (vert) . 2·25 2·25
2107 $4 Mouse opossum . . . . . 2·25 2·25

354c British Tanks during Operation Battleaxe, 1941

1990. 50th Anniv of Second World War. Mult.

2109 25 c. Type **354c** 30 30
2110 35 c. Allied tank in southern France, 1944 . . . . 40 40
2111 45 c. U.S. forces landing on Guadalcanal, 1942 . . . . . 45 45
2112 50 c. U.S. attack in New Guinea, 1943 . . . . 50 50
2113 60 c. Hoisting U.S. flag on Leyte, Phillippines, 1944 . . 60 60
2114 75 c. U.S. tanks entering Cologne, 1945 . . . . . . 75 75
2115 $1 Anzio offensive, 1944 . . . 95 95
2116 $2 Battle of the Bismarck Sea, 1943 . . . . 1·75 1·75
2117 $3 U.S.S. "Langley" and U.S.S. "Ticonderoga" (aircraft carriers), 1944 . . . . 2·25 2·25
2118 $4 Focke Wulf Fw 190A fighter attacking Salerno landing, 1943 . . . . 2·50 2·50

1990. "Stamp World London '90" International Stamp Exhibition (1st issue). As T **193** of Gambia, but horiz showing Walt Disney cartoon characters and British trains.

2120 5 c. Mickey Mouse driving S.R. "King Arthur" class locomotive, 1925 . . . . . 30 10
2121 10 c. Mickey and Minnie Mouse with "Puffing Billy", 1813 . 30 10
2122 20 c. Mickey Mouse with Pluto pulling Durham colliery wagon, 1765 . . . . 50 15
2123 45 c. Mickey Mouse timing L.N.E.R. locomotive No. 2509 "Silver Link", 1935 . . 80 25
2124 $1 Mickey Mouse and Donald Duck with locomotive No. 60149 "Amadis", 1948 . . 1·75 1·00
2125 $2 Goofy and Mickey Mouse with Liverpool & Manchester Railway locomotive, 1830 . 2·50 2·75
2126 $4 Goofy and Donald Duck with Great Northern locomotive No. 1, 1870 . . 3·25 4·00
2127 $5 Mickey Mouse and Gyro the Mechanic with Advanced Passenger Train, 1972 . . . 3·25 4·00

No. 2126 is inscribed "Flying Scotsman" in error.

355 U.S. Paratroop Drop over Grenada

1990. 50th Anniv of United States Airborne Forces.

2129 **355** 75 c. multicoloured . . . 1·00 1·00

1990. 90th Birthday of Queen Elizabeth the Queen Mother. As T **194** of Gambia showing photographs from the 1960s. Multicoloured.

2131 $2 Queen Mother in coat and hat . . . . 1·75 1·75
2132 $2 Queen Mother in evening dress . . . . 1·75 1·75
2133 $2 Queen Mother in Garter robes . . . . 1·75 1·75

1990. Olympic Games, Barcelona (1992) (1st issue). As T **195a** of Gambia. Multicoloured.

2135 10 c. Men's steeplechase . . . 20 20
2136 15 c. Dressage 30 30
2137 45 c. Men's 200 m. butterfly swimming 45 45
2138 50 c. Men's hockey 80 60
2139 65 c. Women's beam gymnastics 60 60
2140 75 c. "Flying Dutchman" class sailing 80 80
2141 $2 Freestyle wrestling . . . . 1·75 1·75
2142 $3 Men's springboard diving . 2·25 2·50
2143 $4 Women's 1000 m. sprint cycling . . . . 3·00 3·00
2144 $5 Men's basketball . . . . . 3·75 3·75

See also Nos. 2414/21.

357 Yellow Goatfish

1990. Coral Reef Fishes. Multicoloured.

2147 10 c. Type **357** 30 30
2148 25 c. Black margate 45 35
2149 65 c. Blue-headed wrasse . . . 85 75
2150 75 c. Puddingwife 95 85
2151 $1 Four-eyed butterflyfish . . 1·10 95
2152 $2 Honey damselfish . . . . 2·00 2·00
2153 $3 Queen angelfish . . . . . 2·50 2·50
2154 $5 Cherub angelfish . . . . . 3·00 3·50

358 Tropical Mockingbird

1990. Birds. Multicoloured.

2156 15 c. Type **358** 30 30
2157 25 c. Grey kingbird 35 35
2158 65 c. Bare-eyed thrush 75 75
2159 75 c. Antillean crested hummingbird 85 85
2160 $1 House wren . . . . 1·00 1·00
2161 $2 Purple martin . . . . . . 1·75 1·75
2162 $4 Hooded tanager . . . . . 2·50 2·50
2163 $5 Scaly-breasted ground dove . 3·00 3·00

359 Coral Crab

1990. Crustaceans. Multicoloured.

2165 5 c. Type **359** 10 10
2166 10 c. Smoothtail spiny lobster . 15 15
2167 15 c. Flamestreaked box crab . 15 15
2168 25 c. Spotted swimming crab . 25 25
2169 75 c. Sally lightfoot rock crab . 60 60
2170 $1 Spotted spiny lobster . . . 80 80
2171 $3 Longarm spiny lobster . . 2·00 2·50
2172 $20 Caribbean spiny lobster . 13·00 18·00

360 Cameroon Player

1990. World Cup Football Championship, Italy (2nd issue). Multicoloured.

2174 10 c. Type **360** 20 15
2175 25 c. Michel (Spain) 25 15
2176 $1 Brehme (West Germany) . 85 85
2177 $5 Nevin (Scotland) . . . . . 3·00 4·00

1990. Christmas. Paintings by Raphael. As T **195b** of Gambia. Multicoloured.

2180 10 c. "The Ansidei Madonna" . 20 10
2181 15 c. "The Sistine Madonna" . 20 10
2182 $1 "The Madonna of the Baldacchino" . . . . . . 1·50 70
2183 $2 "The Large Holy Family" (detail) . . . . 2·25 2·50
2184 $5 "Madonna in the Meadow" . . . . 3·75 5·50

1991. 350th Death Anniv of Rubens. As T **195c** of Gambia. Multicoloured.

2186 5 c. "The Brazen Serpent" (detail) 15 10
2187 10 c. "The Garden of Love" . 15 10
2188 25 c. "Head of Cyrus" (detail) 30 20
2189 75 c. "Tournament in Front of a Castle" 70 60
2190 $1 "The Brazen Serpent" (different detail) 85 75
2191 $2 "Judgement of Paris" (detail) 1·75 2·00
2192 $4 "The Brazen Serpent" . . 2·50 3·50
2193 $5 "The Karmesse" (detail) . . 3·00 3·50

362 "The Sorcerer's Apprentice"

1991. 50th Anniv of "Fantasia" (cartoon film). Multicoloured.

2195 5 c. Type **362** 30 15
2196 10 c. Dancing mushrooms ("The Nutcracker Suite") 30 15
2197 20 c. Pterodactyls ("The Rite of Spring") 55 15
2198 45 c. Centaurs ("The Pastoral Symphony") . . . . 1·00 40
2199 $1 Bacchus and Jacchus ("The Pastoral Symphony") . . . 1·75 1·00
2200 $2 Dancing ostrich ("Dance of the Hours") . . . . 2·50 3·00
2201 $4 Elephant ballet ("Dance of the Hours") . . . . 3·50 4·25
2202 $5 Diana ("The Pastoral Symphony") . . . . 3·50 4·25

363 "Adelpha iphicla"

1991. Butterflies. Multicoloured.

2205 5 c. Type **363** 30 15
2206 10 c. "Nymphalidae claudina" . 30 20
2207 15 c. "Brassolidae polyxena" . 35 20
2208 20 c. "Zebra Longwing" . . . 40 20
2209 25 c. "Marpesia corinna" . . 40 25
2210 30 c. "Morpho hecuba" . . . 40 30
2211 45 c. "Morpho rhetenor" . . . 55 45
2212 50 c. "Dismorphia spio" . . . 65 55
2213 60 c. "Prepona omphale" . . 75 65
2214 70 c. "Morpho anaxibia" . . 85 75
2215 75 c. "Marpesia iole" 90 80
2216 $1 "Amarynthis meneria" . . 1·00 90
2217 $2 "Morpho cisseis" . . . . 1·75 2·25
2218 $3 "Danaidae plexippus" . . 2·25 2·75
2219 $4 "Morpho achilleana" . . . 2·75 3·50
2220 $5 "Calliona argenissa" . . . 3·25 4·00

363a Vitus Bering in Bering Sea, 1728–9

1991. 500th Anniv (1992) of Discovery of America by Columbus. History of Exploration. Mult.

2222 5 c. Type **363a** 30 30
2223 10 c. De Bougainville off Pacific island, 1766–69 . . . . . 30 30
2224 25 c. Polynesian canoe 30 30
2225 50 c. De Mendana off Solomon Islands, 1567–69 . . . . . 75 40
2226 $1 Darwin's H.M.S. "Beagle", 1831–35 . . . . 1·50 1·00
2227 $2 Cook's H.M.S. "Endeavour", 1768–71 . . 3·00 3·00

2228 $4 William Schouten in LeMaire Strait, 1615–17 . . . . . . 3·25 3·50
2229 $5 Tasman off New Zealand, 1642–44 . . . . 3·25 3·50

1991. "Phila Nippon '91" International Stamp Exhibition, Tokyo. Horiz designs as T **198c** of Gambia showing Walt Disney cartoon characters at Japanese festivals. Multicoloured.

2231 5 c. Minnie Mouse and Daisy Duck at Dolls festival . . . 20 20
2232 10 c. Morty and Ferdie with Boys' Day display 25 20
2233 20 c. Mickey and Minnie Mouse at Star festival 45 20
2234 45 c. Minnie and Daisy folk-dancing 80 35
2235 $1 Huey, Dewey and Louie wearing Eboshi headdresses 1·40 85
2236 $2 Mickey and Goofy pulling decorated car at Gion festival 2·75 3·00
2237 $4 Minnie and Daisy preparing rice broth, Seven Plants festival . . . . 3·50 4·00
2238 $5 Huey and Dewey with straw boat at Lanterns festival . . 3·50 4·00

1991. Death Centenary (1990) of Vincent van Gogh (artist). As T **200b** of Gambia. Multicoloured.

2240 20 c. "Blossoming Almond Branch in Glass" (vert) . . 15 15
2241 25 c. "La Mousme sitting" (vert) 15 15
2242 30 c. "Still Life with Red Cabbages and Onions" . . 20 20
2243 40 c. "Japonaiserie: Flowering Plum Tree" (vert) 30 30
2244 45 c. "Japonaiserie: Bridge in the Rain" (vert) 30 30
2245 60 c. "Still Life with Basket of Apples" 50 50
2246 75 c. "Italian Woman" (vert) . 60 60
2247 $1 "The Painter on his Way to Work" (vert) 80 80
2248 $2 "Portrait of Pere Tanguy" (vert) . . . . 1·50 1·50
2249 $3 "Still Life with Plaster Statuette, a Rose and Two Novels" (vert) . . . . . 2·25 2·25
2250 $4 "Still Life: Bottle, Lemons and Oranges" . . . . . 2·50 2·50
2251 $5 "Orchard with Blossoming Apricot Trees" . . . . . . 2·75 2·75

364 "Psilocybe cubensis"

1991. Fungi. Multicoloured.

2253 15 c. Type **364** 50 30
2254 25 c. "Leptonia caeruleocapitata" 60 30
2255 65 c. "Cystolepiota eriophora" 1·10 75
2256 75 c. "Chlorophyllum molybdites" . . . . 1·25 85
2257 $1 "Xerocomus hypoxanthus" 1·40 1·10
2258 $2 "Volvariella cubensis" . . 2·25 2·50
2259 $4 "Xerocomus coccolobae" . 3·25 3·75
2260 $5 "Pluteus chrysophlebius" . 3·25 3·75

365 Johannes Kepler (astronomer)

1991. Exploration of Mars. Designs showing astronomers, spacecraft and Martian landscapes. Multicoloured.

2262/97 75 c. × 9, $1.25 × 9, $2 × 9, $7 x 9
Set of 36 . . . . . . 48·00 48·00

1991. 65th Birthday of Queen Elizabeth II. As T **198a** of Gambia. Multicoloured.

2299 15 c. Royal Family on balcony after Trooping the Colour, 1985 . . . . 15 15
2300 40 c. Queen and Prince Philip at Peterborough, 1988 . . . 35 35
2301 $2 Queen and Queen Mother at Windsor, 1986 . . . . . 1·75 1·75
2302 $4 Queen and Prince Philip on visit to United Arab Emirates 2·50 3·00

1991. 10th Wedding Anniv of the Prince and Princess of Wales. As T **198b** of Gambia. Multicoloured.

2304 10 c. Prince and Princess in July 1985 . . . . 30 10
2305 50 c. Separate photographs of Prince, Princess and sons . . 75 45
2306 $1 Prince Henry at Trooping the Colour and Prince William in Majorca . . . . 1·00 1·00
2307 $5 Separate photographs of Prince Charles and Princess Diana . . . . 3·75 4·50

366 Anglican High School Pupils

1991. 75th Anniv of Anglican High School (10, 25 c.) and 40th Anniv of University of the West Indies (45, 50 c.). Multicoloured.

2309 10 c. Type **366** 20 20
2310 25 c. Artist's impression of new Anglican High School . . . 30 20
2311 45 c. Marryshow House, Grenada 55 55
2312 50 c. University Administrative Building, Barbados 65 75

367 George Stephenson's First Locomotive, 1814 (Great Britain)

1991. Great Railways of the World. Mult.

2313 75 c. Type **367** 60 60
2314 75 c. George Stephenson . . . 60 60
2315 75 c. Killingworth locomotive, 1816 (Great Britain) 60 60
2316 75 c. George Stephenson's "Locomotion", 1825 (Great Britain) 60 60
2317 75 c. "Locomotion" in Darlington, 1825 (Great Britain) 60 60
2318 75 c. Opening of Stockton & Darlington Railway, 1825 . 60 60
2319 75 c. Timothy Hackworth's "Royal George", 1827 (Great Britain) 60 60
2320 75 c. Northumbrian T831 (Great Britain) 60 60
2321 75 c. "Planet", 1830 (Great Britain) 60 60
2322 $1 "Old Ironsides", 1832 (U.S.A.) 80 80
2323 $1 "Wilberforce", 1832 (Great Britain) 80 80
2324 $1 "Adler", 1835 (Germany) . 80 80
2325 $1 "North Star", 1837 (Great Britain) 80 80
2326 $1 London & Birmingham Railway No. 1, 1838 (Great Britain) 80 80
2327 $1 Stephenson's "Austria", 1838 (Austria) 80 80
2328 $1 Baltimore & Ohio Railroad No. 378 "Muddigger", 1840 (U.S.A.) 80 80
2329 $1 Baltimore & Ohio Railroad Norris, 1840 (U.S.A.) . . . 80 80
2330 $1 "Centaur", 1840 (Great Britain) 80 80
2331 $2 "Lion", 1841 (Great Britain) 1·50 1·50
2332 $2 "Beuth", 1843 (Germany) . 1·50 1·50
2333 $2 "Derwent", 1845 (Great Britain) . . . . 1·50 1·50
2334 $2 "Bets", 1846 (Hungary) . . 1·50 1·50
2335 $2 Opening of Budapest to Vac railway, 1846 (Hungary) . . 1·50 1·50
2336 $2 Carriages, Stockton & Darlington Railway, 1846 (Great Britain) . . . . . 1·50 1·50
2337 $2 "Long Boiler" type, 1847 (France) . . . . 1·50 1·50
2338 $2 Baldwin locomotive, 1850 (U.S.A.) . . . . 1·50 1·50
2339 $2 Steam locomotive, 1850 (Germany) . . . . 1·50 1·50

368 Barbu

1991. Marine Life of the Sandflats. Mult.

2341 50 c. Type **368** 65 65
2342 50 c. Beau Gregory 65 65
2343 50 c. Porcupinefish 65 65
2344 50 c. Queen or pink conch and conchfish 65 65
2345 50 c. Hermit crab 65 65
2346 50 c. Bluestripe lizardfish . . . 65 65
2347 50 c. Spot-finned mojarra . . . 65 65
2348 50 c. Southern stingray . . . 65 65
2349 50 c. Long-spined sea urchin and slippery dick 65 65
2350 50 c. Peacock flounder 65 65
2351 50 c. West Indian sea star . . . 65 65
2352 50 c. Spotted goatfish 65 65
2353 50 c. Netted olive and West Indian sea egg 65 65
2354 50 c. Pearly razorfish 65 65
2355 50 c. Spotted jawfish and yellow-headed jawfish 65 65

Nos. 2341/55 were printed together, are se-tenant, forming a composite design.

1991. Christmas. Religious Paintings by Albrecht Durer. As T **200c** of Gambia. Mult.

2357 10 c. "Adoration of the Magi" (detail) 30 10
2358 35 c. "Madonna with the Siskin" (detail) 60 25
2359 50 c. "Feast of the Rose Garlands" (detail) 80 45
2360 75 c. "Virgin with the Pear" (detail) . . . . 1·25 70
2361 $1 "Virgin in Half-length" (detail) . . . . 1·50 90
2362 $2 "Madonna and Child" (detail) . . . . 2·50 2·75
2363 $4 "Virgin and Child with St. Anne" (detail) . . . . . 3·00 4·00
2364 $5 "Virgin and Child" (detail) 3·00 4·00

369 Goofy windsurfing

1992. Thrill Sports. Walt Disney cartoon characters. Multicoloured.

2366 5 c. Type **369** 25 20
2367 10 c. Mickey Mouse skateboarding 30 20
2368 20 c. Daisy Duck gliding . . . 50 20
2369 45 c. Mickey's nephews stunt kite flying 85 25
2370 $1 Donald Duck mountain biking . . . . 1·50 85
2371 $2 Donald and Chipmunk parachuting . . . . . . 2·25 2·50
2372 $4 Mickey go-karting . . . 3·50 4·25
2373 $5 Minnie water skiing . . . 3·50 4·25

1992. 40th Anniv of Queen Elizabeth II's Accession. As T **202a** of Gambia. Mult.

2375 10 c. Waterfall 35 20
2376 50 c. Street in St. George's . . 55 40
2377 $1 Colonial-style houses, St. George's 90 80
2378 $5 St. George's from the sea . 3·50 4·00

1992. "Granada '92" International Stamp Exhibition, Spain. Spanish Paintings. As T **481a** of Ghana. Multicoloured.

2380 10 c. "The Corpus Christi Procession in Seville" (Manuel Cabral y Aguado) (horiz) 20 20
2381 35 c. "The Mancorbo Channel" (Carlos de Haes) 35 20
2382 50 c. "Amalia de Llano y Dotres, Countess of Vilches" (Federico de Madrazo y Kuntz) 50 40
2383 75 c. "Conchita Serrano y Dominguez, Countess of Santovenia" (Eduardo Rosales Gallina) 70 60
2384 $1 "Queen Maria Isabel de Braganza" (Bernardo Lopez Piquer) 85 75
2385 $2 "The Presentation of Don John of Austria to Charles V" (detail) (Gallina) . . . . . 1·60 1·90
2386 $4 "The Presentation of Don John of Austria to Charles V" (different detail) (Gallina) . 3·00 3·75
2387 $5 "The Testament of Isabella the Catholic" (Gallina) (horiz) . . . . 3·00 3·75

370 Green-winged Macaw

370a Ruby-throated Hummingbird

1992. 500th Anniv of Discovery of America by Columbus (5th issue). World Columbian Stamp "Expo '92", Chicago. Multicoloured.

2389 10 c. Type **370** 25 15
2390 25 c. "Santa Maria" 35 20
2391 35 c. Christopher Columbus . . 40 30
2392 50 c. 15th-century sandglass . . 55 55
2393 75 c. Queen Isabella 70 80
2394 $4 Cantino map of 1502 (detail) . . . . 3·50 4·75

1992. "Genova '92" International Thematic Stamp Exhibition. Hummingbirds. Multicoloured.

2396 10 c. Type **370a** 20 15
2397 25 c. Vervain hummingbird . . 30 20
2398 35 c. Blue-headed hummingbird 35 25
2399 50 c. Cuban emerald 55 55
2400 75 c. Antillean mango 75 75
2401 $2 Purple-throated carib . . . 1·50 1·75
2402 $4 Puerto Rican emerald . . . 2·75 3·25
2403 $5 Green-throated carib . . . 2·75 3·25

371 Gracie Fields

372 Badminton

1992. 50th Anniv of United Service Organization (forces' entertainment programme). Multicoloured.

2405 15 c. Type **371** 30 20
2406 25 c. Jack Benny 30 20
2407 35 c. Jinx Falkenburg 30 25
2408 50 c. Francis Langford 45 40
2409 75 c. Joe E. Brown 80 70
2410 $1 Phil Silvers 90 80
2411 $2 Danny Kaye . . . . . . 1·75 2·00
2412 $5 Frank Sinatra . . . . . . 4·00 4·25

1992. Olympic Games, Barcelona (2nd issue). Multicoloured.

2414 10 c. Type **372** 15 15
2415 25 c. Women's long jump . . . 20 20
2416 35 c. Women's 100 metres . . 30 30
2417 50 c. 1000 metres cycling sprint 50 50
2418 75 c. Decathlon (horiz) . . . 70 70
2419 $2 Judo (horiz) . . . . 1·60 1·75
2420 $4 Women's gymnastics—asymmetrical bars . . . . 2·75 3·25
2421 $5 Men's javelin . . . . . . 2·75 3·25

372a Columbus meeting Amerindians

1992. 500th Anniv of Discovery of America by Columbus (6th issue). Organization of East Caribbean States. Multicoloured.

2423 $1 Type **372a** 70 70
2424 $2 Ships approaching island . 1·40 1·60

372b "The Blue Comet" Locomotive, Boucher (1933)

1992. Toy Trains from American Manufacturers. Mult.

2425 10 c. Type **372b** 15 15
2426 35 c. No. 2220 switching locomotive, Voltamp (1906) 25 25
2427 40 c. No. 221 tunnel locomotive, Knapp (1905) 30 30
2428 75 c. "Grand Canyon" locomotive, American Flyer (1931) 55 55
2429 $1 "Streamliner" tin locomotive, Hafner (1930s) . 70 70
2430 $2 No. 237 switching locomotive, Elektoy (1911) . 1·40 1·75
2431 $4 Parlor car, Ives (1928) . . 2·75 3·25
2432 $5 "Improved President's Special" locomotive, American Flyer (1927) . . . 2·75 3·25

373 "Matador" (yacht), Newport News Regatta

1992. World Regattas. Multicoloured.

2435 15 c. Type **373** 20 20
2436 25 c. "Awesome", Antigua . . 25 25
2437 35 c. "Mistress Quickly", Bermuda 30 30
2438 50 c. "Emeraude", St. Tropez . 50 50
2439 $1 "Diva G", German Admirals Cup 80 80
2440 $2 "Lady Be", French Admirals Cup . . . . 1·50 1·75
2441 $4 "Midnight Sun", Admirals Cup . . . . 2·75 3·25
2442 $5 "CARAT", Sardinia Cup . 2·75 3·25

1992. Christmas. Religious Paintings. As T **207b** of Gambia. Multicoloured.

2444 10 c. "Adoration of the Magi" (detail) (Fra Filippo Lippi) . 25 15
2445 15 c. "Madonna adoring Child in a Wood" (Lippi) . . . 30 20
2446 25 c. "Adoration of the Magi" (detail) (Botticelli) 40 20
2447 35 c. "The Epiphany—Adoration of the Magi" (detail) (Hieronymus Bosch) 45 20
2448 50 c. "Adoration of the Magi" (detail) (Giovanni de Paolo) 70 45
2449 75 c. "Adoration of the Magi" (Gentile da Fabriano) . . . 90 60
2450 90 c. "Adoration of the Magi" (detail) (Juan Batista Maino) . . . . 1·10 70
2451 $1 "Adoration of the Child" (Master of Liesborn) . . . 1·25 80
2452 $2 "Adoration of the Kings" (Master of Liesborn) . . . 2·00 2·25
2453 $3 "Adoration of the Three Wise Men" (Pedro Berruguete) . . . . 2·25 3·00
2454 $4 "Adoration of the Child" (Lippi) . . . . 3·00 3·50
2455 $5 "Adoration of the Child" (Correggio) . . . . 3·00 3·50

No. 2447 is inscribed "Hieronymous" in error.

374 Cher

375 Grenada Dove

1992. Gold Record Award Winners. Mult.

2457 90 c. Type **374** . . . . 1·25 1·25
2458 90 c. Michael Jackson . . . . 1·25 1·25
2459 90 c. Elvis Presley . . . . . 1·25 1·25
2460 90 c. Dolly Parton . . . . . 1·25 1·25
2461 90 c. Johnny Mathis . . . . 1·25 1·25
2462 90 c. Madonna . . . . . . 1·25 1·25
2463 90 c. Nat King Cole . . . . 1·25 1·25
2464 90 c. Janice Joplin . . . . . 1·25 1·25

Nos. 2457/64 were printed together, se-tenant, with a composite background design.

1992. Anniversaries and Events. Mult.

2466 10 c. Type **375** 50 40
2467 25 c. Airship LZ-1 on maiden flight, 1900 (horiz) 70 30
2468 50 c. ENDOSAT (robot plane) project (horiz) 75 55
2469 75 c. Konrad Adenauer (German statesman) and industrial skyline (horiz) . . 80 70
2470 $1.50 Golden lion tamarin (horiz) . . . . 2·00 2·00
2471 $2 Mountain gorilla (horiz) . . 2·50 2·50
2472 $2 Outline of man and heart (horiz) . . . . 2·50 2·50
2473 $3 Wolfgang Amadeus Mozart . . . . 3·25 3·25
2474 $4 "Voyager 2" and Neptune (horiz) . . . . 3·50 3·50
2475 $4 Adenauer with flag and map of West Germany (horiz) . . 3·50 3·50
2476 $5 Count von Zeppelin and "Graf Zeppelin" (horiz) . . 3·50 3·50
2477 $6 Admiral Richard Byrd (polar explorer) (horiz) . . . . 3·50 3·50

ANNIVERSARIES AND EVENTS: No. 2466, National bird; Nos. 2467, 2476, 75th death anniv of Count Ferdinand von Zeppelin; Nos. 2468, 2475, International Space Year; Nos. 2469, 2475, 25th death anniv of Konrad Adenauer; Nos. 2470/1, Earth Summit '92, Rio; No. 2472, United Nations World Health Organization Projects; No. 2473, Death bicentenary of Mozart; No. 2477, 75th anniv of International Association of Lions Clubs.

376 Care Bear on Beach

1992. Ecology.

2479 **376** 75 c. multicoloured . . . 45 45

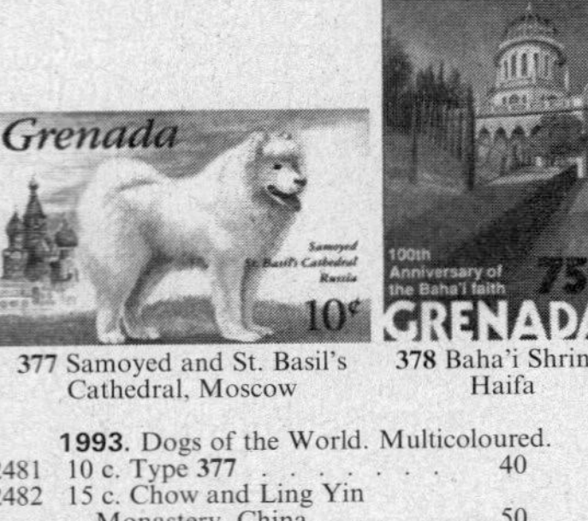

377 Samoyed and St. Basil's Cathedral, Moscow

378 Baha'i Shrine, Haifa

1993. Dogs of the World. Multicoloured.

2481 10 c. Type **377** 40 30
2482 15 c. Chow and Ling Yin Monastery, China 50 30
2483 25 c. Boxer and Tower of London 55 30
2484 90 c. Basenji and Yamma Mosque, Niger . . . . . 1·00 75
2485 $1 Golden labrador and Parliament Building, Ottawa . . . . 1·00 80
2486 $3 St. Bernard and Parsenn, Switzerland . . . . . . 2·25 2·75
2487 $4 Rhodesian ridgeback and Melrose House, South Africa . . . . 2·50 3·00
2488 $5 Afghan hound and Mazar-i-Sharif, Afghanistan . . . . 2·50 3·00

1993. Bicentenary of the Louvre, Paris. Paintings by Jean-Antoine Watteau. As T **209b** of Gambia. Multicoloured.

2490 $1 "The Faux-pas" 70 80
2491 $1 "Portrait of a Gentleman" . 70 80
2492 $1 "Young Lady with Archlute" 70 80
2493 $1 "Young Man Dancing" . . 70 80
2494 $1 "Autumn, Pamona and a Cherub" 70 80
2495 $1 "Judgement of Paris" . . . 70 80
2496 $1 "Pierrot" (detail) 70 80
2497 $1 "Pierrot" (different detail) . 70 80

1993. Centenary of Baha'i Faith.

2499 **378** 75 c. multicoloured . . . 75 75

379 "Citheronia magnifica"

1993. Moths. Multicoloured.

2500 10 c. Type **379** 25 25
2501 35 c. "Automeris metali" . . . 40 25
2502 45 c. "Thysania zenobia" . . . 50 30
2503 75 c. "Agrius cingulatus" . . . 70 55
2504 $1 "Composia fidelissima" . . 80 65
2505 $2 "Synchlora xysteraria" . . 1·50 1·75
2506 $4 "Eumorpha labruscae" . . 2·50 2·75
2507 $5 "Ascalapha odorata" . . . 2·50 2·75

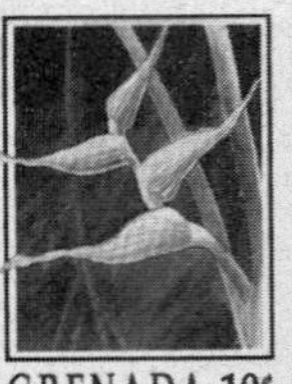

380 Heliconia

381 "Woman with Loaves" (Picasso)

1993. Flowers. Multicoloured.

2509 10 c. Type **380** 25 25
2510 35 c. Pansy 40 25
2511 45 c. Water lily 50 30
2512 75 c. Bougainvillea 70 55
2513 $1 Calla lily 80 65
2514 $2 California poppy . . . . 1·50 1·75
2515 $4 Red ginger . . . . 2·50 3·00
2516 $5 Anthurium . . . . 2·50 3·00

1993. 40th Anniv of Coronation. As T **215a** of Gambia.

2518 35 c. multicoloured 70 75
2519 70 c. multicoloured 80 85
2520 $1 brown and black 85 90
2521 $5 multicoloured . . . . . . 2·25 2·50

DESIGNS: 35 c. Queen Elizabeth II at Coronation (photograph by Cecil Beaton); 70 c. Sceptres; $1 Queen Elizabeth receiving sceptre from Archbishop of Canterbury; $5 Queen and Prince Philip with their children, 1960s.

1993. Anniversaries and Events. Each brown, deep brown and black (Nos. 2527, 2535) or multicoloured (others).

2523 25 c. Type **381** 30 20
2524 35 c. 16th-century telescope . . 35 20
2525 35 c. Public Library building . 35 20
2526 35 c. Gaetan Boucher (speed skating, 1984) 35 20
2527 50 c. Willy Brandt with Senator Edward Kennedy (horiz) . . 40 30
2528 75 c. Carnival float (horiz) . . 50 40
2529 90 c. "Weeping Woman" (Picasso) 65 45
2530 $1 "Marii Prohaska" (Tyrus Czyzewski) 70 50
2531 $3 "Marysia et Burek a Geylan" (S. Wirkiewicz) . . . . . . 2·25 2·25
2532 $4 "Woman seated in Airchair" (Picasso) . . . . 2·75 2·75
2533 $4 Astronaut on Moon . . . 2·75 2·75
2534 $5 Norbert Schramm (figure skating, 1984) . . . . . . 2·75 2·75
2535 $5 Willy Brandt and Kurt Waldheim (horiz) . . . . . 2·75 2·75

ANNIVERSARIES AND EVENTS: Nos. 2523, 2529, 2532, 20th death anniv of Picasso (artist); Nos. 2524, 2533, 450th death anniv of Copernicus (astronomer); No. 2525, Centenary (1992) of Grenada Public Library; Nos. 2526, 2534, Winter Olympic Games '94, Lillehammer; Nos. 2527, 2535, 80th birth anniv (1992) of Willy Brandt (German politician); No. 2528, Grenada Carnival; Nos. 2530/1, "Polska '93" International Stamp Exhibition, Poznan.

382 Red-eyed Vireo

1993. Songbirds. Multicoloured.

2537 15 c. Type **382** 50 50
2538 25 c. Fork-tailed flycatcher ("Scissor-tailed flycatcher") . . 55 55
2539 35 c. Palm chat 60 60
2540 35 c. Chaffinch 60 60
2541 45 c. Yellow wagtail 70 70
2542 45 c. Painted bunting 70 70
2543 50 c. Short-tailed pygmy tyrant ("Short-tailed pygmy flycatcher") 70 70
2544 65 c. Orange-breasted bunting ("Rainbow Bunting") . . . 80 80
2545 75 c. Red crossbill 80 80
2546 75 c. Kauai akialoa 80 80
2547 $1 Yellow-throated longclaw ("Yellow-throated wagtail") 90 90
2548 $4 Barn swallow . . . . . . 2·50 2·50

Nos. 2537/48 were printed together, se-tenant, with the backgrounds forming a composite design.

383 Atlantic Grey Cowrie and Atlantic Yellow Cowrie

1993. Seashells. Multicoloured.

2550 15 c. Type **383** 45 45
2551 15 c. Candy-stick tellin and sunrise tellin 45 45
2552 25 c. Caribbean vase 50 50
2553 35 c. Lightning venus and royal comb venus 55 55
2554 35 c. Crown cone 55 55
2555 45 c. Reticulated cowrie-helmet 65 65
2556 50 c. Barbados mitre and variegated turret shell . . . 65 65
2557 50 c. Common egg cockle and Atlantic strawberry cockle . 65 65
2558 75 c. Measled cowrie 75 75
2559 75 c. Rooster-tail conch . . . 75 75
2560 $1 Lion's-paw scallop and Antillean scallop 85 85
2561 $4 Dog-head triton . . . . . 2·25 2·25

Nos. 2550/61 were printed together, se-tenant, with the backgrounds forming a composite design.

1993. Asian International Stamp Exhibitions. As T **219a** of Gambia. Mult. (a) "Indopex '93", Surabaya, Indonesia.

2563 35 c. Megalithic carving, Sumba Island 35 25
2564 45 c. Entrance to Gao Gajah, Bali 45 30
2565 $1.50 Statue of kris holder . 1·00 1·00
2566 $1.50 Hanuman protecting Sita . . . . 1·00 1·00
2567 $1.50 Sendi of Visu mounted on Garuda . . . . 1·00 1·00
2568 $1.50 Wahana (votif figure) . . 1·00 1·00
2569 $1.50 Hanuman (different) . . 1·00 1·00
2570 $1.50 Singa (symbolic lion) . . 1·00 1·00
2571 $2 Loving-mother Bridge, Taroko Gorge National Park . . . . 1·40 1·50
2572 $4 Head of Kala over temple gateway, Northern Bali . . 2·50 2·75

(b) "Taipei '93", Taiwan.

2574 35 c. Fire-breathing dragon, New Year's Fair, Chongqing 35 25
2575 45 c. Stone elephant, Ming Tomb, Nanjing 45 30
2576 $1.50 "Ornamental Cock" (Han Meilin) . . . . 1·00 1·00
2577 $1.50 "He's even afraid of Cows" (Meilin) . . . . . 1·00 1·00
2578 $1.50 "On a Moonlit Night" (Meilin) . . . . 1·00 1·00
2579 $1.50 "Eyes that see in the Dark" (Meilin) . . . . . . 1·00 1·00
2580 $1.50 "He's well behaved" (Meilin) . . . . 1·00 1·00
2581 $1.50 "He doesn't Bite" (Meilin) . . . . 1·00 1·00
2582 $2 Marble peifang, Ming 13 Tombs, Beijing . . . . . . 1·40 1·50
2583 $4 Stone pillar, Nanjing . . . 2·50 2·75

(c) "Bangkok 1993", Thailand.

2585 35 c. Nora Nair, Prasad Phra Thepidon, Wat Phra Kaew . 35 25
2586 45 c. Stucco deities at Library of Wat Phra Singh 45 30
2587 $1.50 Wooden carved horses . . 1·00 1·00
2588 $1.50 Wheel of the law . . . 1·00 1·00
2589 $1.50 Lanna bronze elephant . 1·00 1·00
2590 $1.50 Kendi in the form of elephant . . . . 1·00 1·00
2591 $1.50 Bronze duck . . . . . 1·00 1·00
2592 $1.50 Horseman . . . . . . 1·00 1·00
2593 $2 Naga snake, Chiang Mai's Temple . . . . 1·40 1·50
2594 $4 Stucco figures, Wat Chang Lom . . . . 2·50 2·75

No. 2590 is incorrectly inscribed "Kendi in the form of an Elphant".

1993. World Cup Football Championship, U.S.A. (1994) (1st issue). As T **221a** of Gambia. Mult.

2596 10 c. Nikolai Larionov (Russia) 20 20
2597 25 c. Andrea Carnevale (Italy) . 40 25
2598 35 c. Enzo Schifo (Belgium) and Soon-Ho Choi (South Korea 50 25
2599 45 c. Gary Lineker (England) . 70 30
2600 $1 Diego Maradona (Argentina) . . . . 1·25 80
2601 $2 Lothar Mattaeus (Germany) . . . . 1·60 2·00
2602 $4 Jan Karas (Poland) and Julio Cesar Silva (Brazil) . . . 2·25 3·25
2603 $5 Claudio Caniggia (Argentina) . . . . 2·50 3·25

See also Nos. 2743/8.

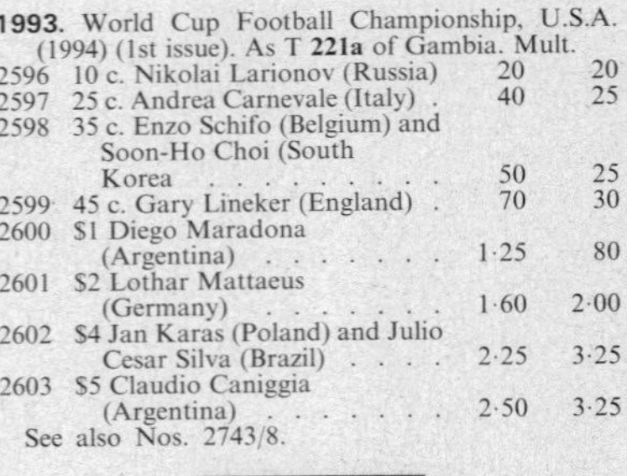

384 James K. Spensley

1993. Centenary of Italian Football. Past and present Genoa players. Each blue, red and black.

2605 $3 Type **384** . . . . 2·25 2·25
2606 $3 Renzo de Vecchi . . . . . 2·25 2·25
2607 $3 Giovanni de Pra' . . . . . 2·25 2·25
2608 $3 Luigi Burlando . . . . . 2·25 2·25
2609 $3 Felice Levratto . . . . . 2·25 2·25
2610 $3 Guglielmo Stabile . . . . 2·25 2·25
2611 $3 Vittorio Sardelli . . . . . 2·25 2·25
2612 $3 Juan Carlos Verdeal . . . 2·25 2·25
2613 $3 Fosco Becattini . . . . . 2·25 2·25
2614 $3 Julio Cesar Abadie . . . . 2·25 2·25
2615 $3 Luigi Meroni . . . . . . 2·25 2·25
2616 $3 Roberto Pruzzo . . . . . 2·25 2·25

385 "The Band Concert", 1935

1993. 65th Anniv of Mickey Mouse. Scenes from Walt Disney cartoon films. Multicoloured.

2618 25 c. Type **385** 55 20
2619 35 c. "Mickey's Circus", 1936 . 60 20
2620 50 c. "Magician Mickey", 1937 . . . . 75 35
2621 75 c. "Moose Hunters", 1937 . 1·00 60
2622 $1 "Mickey's Amateurs", 1937 . . . . 1·25 80
2623 $2 "Tugboat Mickey", 1940 . 1·75 1·75
2624 $4 "Orphan's Benefit", 1941 . 2·75 3·25
2625 $5 "Mickey's Christmas Carol", 1983 . . . . 2·75 3·25

No. 2624 is inscribed "Oprhan's Benefit" in error.

1993. Christmas. Religious Paintings. As T **221b** of Gambia. Black, yellow and red (Nos. 2627/8, 2632 and 2634) or multicoloured (others).

2627 10 c. "The Nativity" (Durer) . 25 15
2628 25 c. "The Annunciation" (Durer) 35 15
2629 35 c. "The Litta Madonna" (Da Vinci) 40 20
2630 60 c. "The Virgin and Child with St. John the Baptist and St. Anne" (Da Vinci) 50 40
2631 90 c. "The Madonna with the Carnation" (Da Vinci) . . . 65 65
2632 $1 "Adoration of the Magi" (Durer) 75 75
2633 $4 "The Benois Madonna" (Da Vinci) . . . . 2·50 3·25
2634 $5 "The Virgin Mary in the Sun" (Durer) . . . . . . 2·50 3·25

Nos. 2629/31 and 2633 are inscribed "LEONARDO DI VINCI".

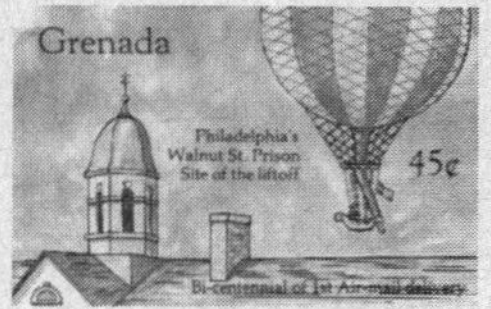

386 Blanchard's Balloon over Walnut St. Prison

1993. Aviation Anniversaries. Multicoloured.

2636 35 c. Airship "Graf Zeppelin" over Vienna at night 35 20
2637 45 c. Type **386** 20 25
2638 50 c. Lysander 50 35
2639 75 c. "Graf Zeppelin" over Pyramids 75 55
2640 $2 Blanchard waving hat from balloon (vert) 90 95
2641 $3 Hawker Typhoon 2·00 2·50
2642 $5 "Graf Zeppelin" over Rio de Janeiro 3·25 3·75

ANNIVERSARIES: Nos. 2636, 2639, 2642, 125th birth anniv of Hugo Eckener (airship commander); Nos. 2637, 2640, Bicentenary of first airmail flight; Nos. 2638, 2641, 75th anniv of Royal Air Force.

387 Mercedes Benz "370 S" Cabriolet, 1932

1993. Centenaries of Henry Ford's First Petrol Engine (Nos. 2645/6)) and Karl Benz's First Four-wheeled Car (others). Multicoloured.

2644 35 c. Type **387** 40 20
2645 45 c. Ford "Mustang", 1966 50 30
2646 $3 Ford "Model A" Phaeton, 1930 3·00 3·50
2647 $4 Mercedes Benz "300 Sl" Gullwing 3·50 4·00

1993. Famous Paintings by Rembrandt and Matisse. As T **221c** of Gambia. Multicoloured.

2649 15 c. "Self-portrait", 1900 (Matisse) 30 20
2650 35 c. "Self-portrait", 1629 (Rembrandt) 35 20
2651 45 c. "Self-portrait", 1918 (Matisse) 40 25
2652 50 c. "Self-portrait", 1640 (Rembrandt) 50 35
2653 75 c. "Self-portrait", 1652 (Rembrandt) 65 55
2654 $2 "Self-portrait", 1906 (Matisse) 1·40 1·75
2655 $4 "Self-portrait", 1900 (different) (Matisse) 2·50 3·25
2656 $5 "Self-portrait", 1625–31 (Rembrandt) 2·75 3·25

388 Fishermen with Blue Marlin

389 National Flag and Ketch in Bay

1994. 25th Anniv of Spice Island Billfish Tournament. Multicoloured.

2658 15 c. Type **388** 40 30
2659 25 c. Sailfish with angler 45 30
2660 35 c. Yellow-finned tuna with angler 55 30
2661 50 c. White marlin with angler 60 50
2662 75 c. Catching a sailfish 75 80

1994. 25th Anniv of Independence.

2663 **389** 35 c. multicoloured 30 30

1994. "Hong Kong '94" International Stamp Exhibition (1st issue). As T **222a** of Gambia. Multicoloured.

2665 40 c. Hong Kong 1971 Scouting 50 c. stamp and "Hong Kong Post Office, 1846" (left detail) (M. Bruce) 35 50
2666 40 c. Grenada 1988 Rotary $2 and "Hong Kong Post Office, 1846" (right detail) (M. Bruce) 35 50

Nos. 2665/6 were printed together, se-tenant, with the centre part of each pair forming the complete painting.

See also Nos. 2667/72.

1994. "Hong Kong '94" International Stamp Exhibition (2nd issue). Qing Dynasty Porcelain. As T **222b** of Gambia. Multicoloured.

2667 45 c. Vase with dragon decoration 35 40
2668 45 c. Hat stand with brown base 35 40
2669 45 c. Gourd-shaped vase 35 40
2670 45 c. Rotating vase with openwork 35 40
2671 45 c. Candlestick with dogs 35 40
2672 45 c. Hat stand with orange base 35 40

390 "Hygrocybe acutoconica"

1994. Fungi. Multicoloured.

2673 35 c. Type **390** 50 30
2674 45 c. "Leucopaxillus gracillimus" 55 30
2675 50 c. "Leptonia caeruleocapitata" 55 30
2676 75 c. "Leucocoprinus birnbaumii" 70 50
2677 $1 "Marasmius atrorubens" 85 75
2678 $2 "Boletellus cubensis" 1·40 1·50
2679 $4 "Chlorophyllum molybdites" 2·25 2·75
2680 $5 "Psilocybe cubensis" 2·25 2·75

391 Quetzalcoatlus

1994. Prehistoric Animals. Multicoloured.

2682 75 c. Type **391** 55 55
2683 75 c. Pteranodon ingens 55 55
2684 75 c. Tropeognathus 55 55
2685 75 c. Phobetor 55 55
2686 75 c. Alamosaurus 55 55
2687 75 c. Triceratops 55 55
2688 75 c. Tyrannosaurus rex 55 55
2689 75 c. Head of Tyrannosaurus rex 55 55
2690 75 c. Lambeosaurus 55 55
2691 75 c. Spinosaurus 55 55
2692 75 c. Parasaurolophus 55 55
2693 75 c. Hadrosaurus 55 55
2694 75 c. Germanodactylus 55 55
2695 75 c. Dimorphodon 55 55
2696 75 c. Ramphorynchus 55 55
2697 75 c. Apatosaurus 55 55
2698 75 c. Pterodactylus 55 55
2699 75 c. Stegosaurus 55 55
2700 75 c. Brathiosaurus 55 55
2701 75 c. Allosaurus 55 55
2702 75 c. Plesiosaurus 55 55
2703 75 c. Ceratosaurus 55 55
2704 75 c. Compsognathus 55 55
2705 75 c. Elaphosaurus 55 55

Nos. 2682/93 and 2694/2705 respectively were printed together, se-tenant, forming composite designs.

1994. 25th Anniv of First Manned Moon Landing. Space Shuttle "Challenger". As T **227a** of Gambia. Multicoloured

2707 $2 Space shuttle "Challenger" 1·10 1·40
2708 $2 Judith Resnick (astronaut) 1·10 1·40
2709 $2 Aircraft in memorial fly past 1·10 1·40
2710 $2 Dick Scobee (astronaut) 1·10 1·40
2711 $2 Mission logo 1·10 1·40
2712 $2 Michael Smith (astronaut) 1·10 1·40

1994. Centenary of International Olympic Committee. Gold Medal Winners. As T **227b** of Gambia. Multicoloured.

2714 50 c. Heike Dreschler (Germany) (long jump), 1992 40 30
2715 $1.50 Nadia Comaneci (Rumania) (gymnastics), 1976 and 1980 1·40 1·40

391a Grenadian Family

1994. International Year of the Family. Mult.

2717 $1 Type **391a** 70 70

1994. 50th Anniv of D-Day. As T **227c** of Gambia. Multicoloured.

2718 40 c. Sherman amphibious tank leaving landing craft 50 30
2719 $2 Tank on Churchill "Ark" bridging vehicle 1·75 1·75
2720 $3 Churchill "Bobbin" tank laying roadway 2·00 2·25

1994. "Philakorea '94" International Stamp Exhibition, Seoul. As T **227d** of Gambia. Multicoloured.

2722 40 c. Wonson Park (horiz) 20 25
2723 $1 Pusan (horiz) 45 50
2724 $1 "Lady in a Hooded Cloak" (left detail) (Sin Yunbok) 45 50
2725 $1 "Lady in a Hooded Cloak" (right detail) 45 50
2726 $1 "Kiaseng House" (left detail) (Sin Yunbok) 45 50
2727 $1 "Kiaseng House" (right detail) 45 50
2728 $1 "Amorous Youth on a Picnic" (left detail) (Sin Yunbok) 45 50
2729 $1 "Amorous Youth on a Picnic" (right detail) 45 50
2730 $1 "Chasing a Cat" (left detail) (Sin Yunbok) 45 50
2731 $1 "Chasing a Cat" (right detail) 45 50
2732 $4 Korean orchestra, National Theatre, Seoul (horiz) 1·90 2·00

Nos. 2724/31 were printed together, se-tenant, forming composite designs of each painting.

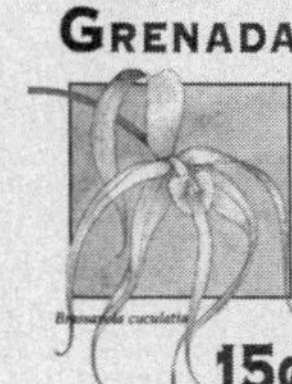

392 "Brassavola cuculatta"

393 Tony Meola (U.S.A.)

1994. Orchids. Multicoloured.

2734 15 c. Type **392** 30 20
2735 25 c. "Comparettia falcata" 40 20
2736 45 c. "Epidendrum ciliare" 50 30
2737 75 c. "Epidendrum cochleatum" 70 50
2738 $1 "Ionopsis utricularioides" 80 70
2739 $2 "Onicidium ceboletta" 1·25 1·40
2740 $4 "Onicidium luridium" 2·25 2·50
2741 $5 "Rodriquezia secunda" 2·25 2·50

1994. World Cup Football Championship, U.S.A. (2nd issue). Multicoloured.

2743 75 c. Type **393** 50 55
2744 75 c. Steve Mark (Grenada) 50 55
2745 75 c. Gianluigi Lentini (Italy) 50 55
2746 75 c. Belloumi (Algeria) 50 55
2747 75 c. Nunoz (Spain) 50 55
2748 75 c. Lothar Matthaus (Germany) 50 55

393a Sir Shridath Ramphal

1994. 1st Recipients of Order of the Caribbean Community. Multicoloured.

2750 15 c. Type **393a** 10 10
2751 65 c. William Demas 40 40
2752 $2 Derek Walcott 1·40 1·60

394 Yellow-tailed Snapper

1994. Fishes. Multicoloured.

2753 15 c. Type **394** 30 20
2754 20 c. Blue tang 30 20
2755 25 c. Porkfish (vert) 30 20
2756 75 c. Four-eyed butterflyfish 65 50
2757 $1 Reid's seahorse (vert) 75 70
2758 $2 Spotted moray (vert) 1·25 1·50
2759 $4 Royal gramma ("Fairy basslet") 2·25 2·50
2760 $5 Queen triggerfish (vert) 2·25 2·50

395 Mickey Mouse bathing Pluto

1994. Chinese New Year ("Year of the Dog"). Walt Disney Cartoon Characters. Multicoloured.

2762 2 c. Type **395** 10 10
2763 3 c. Dog taking mouthwash 10 10
2764 4 c. Dog with curlers in tail 10 10
2765 5 c. Brushing dog's eyelashes 10 10
2766 10 c. Giving dog manicure 20 10
2767 15 c. Mickey spraying Pluto with flea powder 30 15
2768 20 c. Dogs on display 30 20
2769 $4 Judge checking Pluto's teeth 3·00 3·50
2770 $5 Pluto wearing "1st Prize" rosette 3·00 3·50

396 "Anartia amathea"

1994. Butterflies. Multicoloured.

2772A 10 c. Type **396** 10 10
2773A 15 c. "Marpesia petreus" 10 10
2774B 25 c. "Hylephila phylaeus" 10 10
2775B 35 c. "Junonia evarete" 15 20
2776A 45 c. "Pseudolycaena marsyas" 20 25
2777A 50 c. "Heliconius charitonius" 20 25
2778A 75 c. "Hypolimnas misippus" 35 40
2778cB 90 c. "Purgus oilcus" 40 45
2779A $1 "Cepheuptychia cephus" 45 50
2779cB $1.50 "Allosmaitia piplea" 70 75
2780A $2 "Historis odius" 85 90
2781A $3 "Phoebis philea" 1·25 1·40
2782A $4 "Urbanus proteus" 1·75 1·90
2783A $5 "Battus polydamas" 2·10 2·25
2784A $10 "Philaethria dido" 4·25 4·50
2785A $20 "Hamadryas arethusa" 8·75 9·00

1994. Christmas. Religious Paintings by Francisco de Zurbaran. As T **231a** of Gambia. Multicoloured.

2786 10 c. "The Virgin and Child with St. John" (1658) 20 15
2787 15 c. "The Circumcision" 30 20
2788 25 c. "Adoration of St. Joseph" 30 20
2789 35 c. "Adoration of the Magi" 30 20
2790 75 c. "The Portiuncula" 60 45
2791 $1 "The Virgin and Child with St. John" (1662) 75 60
2792 $2 "The Virgin and Child with St. John" (1658/64) 1·25 1·50
2793 $4 "The Flight into Egypt" 2·25 3·00

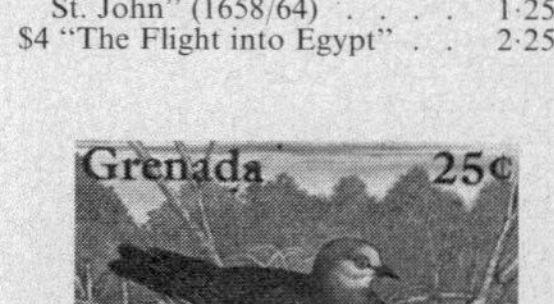

397 Grenada Dove on Nest

1995. Birds. Multicoloured.

2795 25 c. Type **397** 55 30
2796 35 c. Pair of Grenada doves at nest 60 30
2797 45 c. Cuban tody (vert) 65 30
2798 75 c. Grenada dove on branch (vert) 80 80
2799 75 c. Painted bunting 80 80
2800 $1 Grenada dove in flight (vert) 90 90
2801 $1 Red-legged honeycreeper 90 90
2802 $5 Green jay 2·75 3·50

Nos. 2795/6, 2798 and 2800 also show the W.W.F. Panda emblem.

397a Junior Murray (West Indies)

1995. Centenary of First English Cricket Tour to the West Indies. Multicoloured.

2804 25 c. Type **397a** 30 20
2805 35 c. Richie Richardson (West Indies) 35 25
2806 $2 Alec Stewart (England) and Wisden Trophy (horiz) 1·40 1·60

398 Hooded Merganser

1995. Water Birds of the World. Multicoloured.

2808 25 c. Type **398** 30 30
2809 35 c. Green-winged teal 35 30
2810 75 c. King eider 70 75
2811 75 c. Common shoveler 70 75
2812 75 c. Long-tailed duck 70 75
2813 75 c. Chiloe wigeon 70 75
2814 75 c. Red-breasted merganser 70 75
2815 75 c. Falcated teal 70 75

2816 75 c. Vericolor teal 70 75
2817 75 c. Smew 70 75
2818 75 c. Red-crested pochard . . 70 75
2819 75 c. Pintail 70 75
2820 75 c. Barrow's goldeneye . . . 70 75
2821 75 c. Stellar's eider 70 75
2822 $1 Harlequin duck 75 75
2823 $3 European wigeon . . . . 1·75 2·00

Nos. 2810/21 were printed together, se-tenant, forming a composite design.

No. 2811 is inscribed "Shobeler" in error.

399 Pig Priest, China

1995. Chinese New Year ("Year of the Pig"). Ornaments. Multicoloured.

2825 50 c. Type **399** 35 45
2826 75 c. Porcelain pig, Scotland . 45 55
2827 $1 Seated porcelain pig, Italy . 50 60

400 Yellow-tailed Damselfish

1995. Marine Life. Multicoloured.

2829 $1 Type **400** 65 65
2830 $1 Blue-headed wrasse 65 65
2831 $1 Balloonfish 65 65
2832 $1 Shy hamlet 65 65
2833 $1 Orange tube coral 65 65
2834 $1 Rock beauty 65 65
2835 $1 Creole wrasse 65 65
2836 $1 Queen angelfish 65 65
2837 $1 Trumpetfish 65 65
2838 $1 Barred hamlet 65 65
2839 $1 Tube sponge 65 65
2840 $1 Porcupine fish 65 65
2841 $1 Firecoral 65 65
2842 $1 Royal gramma ("Fairy basslet") 65 65
2843 $1 Sea anemone 65 65

Nos. 2829/34 and 2835/43 respectively were printed together, se-tenant, forming composite designs.

401 National Flags

1995. Grenada–Taiwan (Republic of China) Friendship. Multicoloured.

2845 75 c. Type **401** 35 45
2846 $1 Prime Minister Brathwaite and President Lee Teng-hui . 45 55

402 Cocker Spaniel

404 "Swords into Plougshares"

403 Grenadian Scout

1995. Domestic Animals. Multicoloured.

2848 10 c. Type **402** 20 20
2849 15 c. Pinto (horse) 30 20
2850 25 c. Rottweiler 30 20
2851 35 c. German shepherd . . . 40 20
2852 45 c. Persian (cat) 50 25
2853 50 c. Snowshoe (cat) 50 25
2854 75 c. Percheron (horse) . . . 70 50
2855 $1 Scottish fold (cat 75 60
2856 $2 Arabian (horse) . . . . 1·40 1·40
2857 $3 Andalusian (horse) . . . 1·75 2·00
2858 $4 C.P. Shorthair (cat) . . . 2·00 2·50
2859 $5 Chihuahua . . . . . . 2·40 2·75

1995. Centenary (1992) of Sierra Club (environmental protection society). Endangered Species. As T **224a** of Gambia. Multicoloured.

2861 $1 Head of margay at night . 70 70
2862 $1 Margay sitting 70 70
2863 $1 Head of margay in daylight . 70 70
2864 $1 Head of Andean condor . . 70 70
2865 $1 Andean condor facing right 70 70
2866 $1 Andean condor facing left . 70 70
2867 $1 White-faced saki on branch . 70 70
2868 $1 White-faced saki showing mane 70 70
2869 $1 Patagonia landscape . . . 70 70
2870 $1 Lesser rheas feeding (horiz) . 70 70
2871 $1 Pair of lesser rheas (horiz) . 70 70
2872 $1 Lesser rhea (horiz) 70 70
2873 $1 Sunset over snow-covered mountains, Patagonia (horiz) 70 70
2874 $1 Volcanic eruption, Patagonia (horiz) 70 70
2875 $1 White-faced Saki (horiz) . . 70 70
2876 $1 Common caracara on branch (horiz) 70 70
2877 $1 Pair of common caracaras at nest (horiz) 70 70
2878 $1 Common caracara facing left (horiz) 70 70

1995. 18th World Scout Jamboree, Netherlands. Multicoloured.

2879 75 c. Type **403** 45 50
2880 $1 Scout abseiling 55 60
2881 $2 Scout saluting and national flag . . . . 85 1·00

1995. 50th Anniv of End of Second World War in Europe. Fighter Aircraft. As T **237a** of Gambia. Multicoloured.

2883 $2 Lavochkin La-7 (fighter) . 1·25 1·25
2884 $2 Hawker Hurricane . . . . 1·25 1·25
2885 $2 North American P-51D Mustang . . . . 1·25 1·25
2886 $2 Messerschmitt Bf 109 . . . 1·25 1·25
2887 $2 Bristol Type 152 Beaufighter . . . . 1·25 1·25
2888 $2 Messerschmitt Me 262 . . 1·25 1·25
2889 $2 Republic P-47 Thunderbolt . 1·25 1·25
2890 $2 Hawker Tempest . . . . . 1·25 1·25

1995. 50th Anniv of United Nations. Multicoloured.

2892 75 c. Type **404** 40 50
2893 $1 Globe and dove 50 60
2894 $2 U.N. Building, New York . . 85 90

405 Woman with Baskets

406 National Flag and Rotary Logo

1995. 50th Anniv of F.A.O. Multicoloured.

2896 75 c. Type **405** 40 50
2897 $1 Boy with basket on head . . 50 60
2898 $2 Men harvesting bananas . . 85 90

1995. 90th Anniv of Rotary International.

2900 **406** $5 multicoloured . . . . 2·10 2·25

1995. 95th Birthday of Queen Elizabeth the Queen Mother. As T **239a** of Gambia.

2902 $1.50 brown, light brown and black . . . . 1·10 1·10
2903 $1.50 multicoloured . . . . 1·10 1·10
2904 $1.50 multicoloured . . . . 1·10 1·10
2905 $1.50 multicoloured . . . . 1·10 1·10

DESIGNS: No. 2902, Queen Elizabeth the Queen Mother (pastel drawing); 2903, Holding rose; 2904, At desk (oil painting); 2905, In blue hat and white coat.

1995. 50th Anniv of End of Second World War in the Pacific. As T **239b** of Gambia. Multicoloured.

2907 $2 Dogfight over the Marianas . . . . 1·25 1·25
2908 $2 U.S. dive-bomber and burning aircraft carrier, Battle of Midway . . . . 1·25 1·25
2909 $2 U.S. aircraft attacking Japanese transport, Battle of the Bismarck Sea . . . . . 1·25 1·25
2910 $2 "Mushashi" (Japanese battleship) on fire in Leyte Gulf . . . . 1·25 1·25
2911 $2 U.S. aircraft taking off from Henderson Field . . . . . 1·25 1·25
2912 $2 Battleships at Guadalcanal . . . . 1·25 1·25

407 Tian Bingyi (China) (badminton)

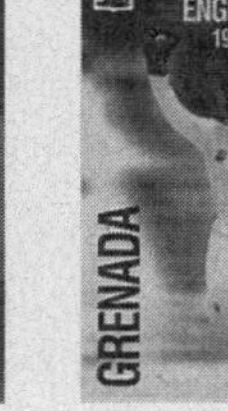

408 Junior Murray (West Indies)

1995. Olympic Games, Atlanta (1996) (1st issue). Multicoloured.

2914 75 c. Type **407** 70 70
2915 75 c. Waldemar Leigien (Poland) and Frank Wieneke (West Germany) (judo) . . 70 70
2916 75 c. Nelli Kim (U.S.S.R.) (gymnastics) 70 70
2917 75 c. Alessandro Andri (Italy) (shot put) 70 70
2918 $2 Jackie Joyner (U.S.A.) (heptathlon) . . . . . . 1·25 1·25
2919 $2 Mitsuo Tsukahara (Japan) (gymnastics) . . . . . . 1·25 1·25
2920 $2 Flo Hyman (U.S.A.) and Zhang Rung Fang (China) (volleyball) . . . . . . 1·25 1·25
2921 $2 Steffi Graf (West Germany) (tennis) . . . . 1·25 1·25

See also Nos. 3102/23.

1995. Anniversaries and Events. Multicoloured.

2923 25 c. Type **408** (centenary of first English cricket tour to the West Indies) 30 20
2924 75 c. Nutmeg (opening of Grenada Spice Factory) . . 50 50
2925 $1 Sendall Tunnel (centenary (1994)) 60 65
2926 $1 Caribbean Development Bank building (25th anniv) . 60 65

409 Ajamu

410 Elvis Presley and Signature

1995. Local Entertainers. Multicoloured.

2927 35 c. Type **409** 30 30
2928 35 c. Mighty Sparrow 30 30
2929 50 c. Mighty Sparrow in evening dress 40 40
2930 75 c. Ajamu (different) 55 65

1995. Entertainment Legends. Multicoloured.

2931 75 c. Type **410** 50 50
2932 75 c. Marilyn Monroe 50 50

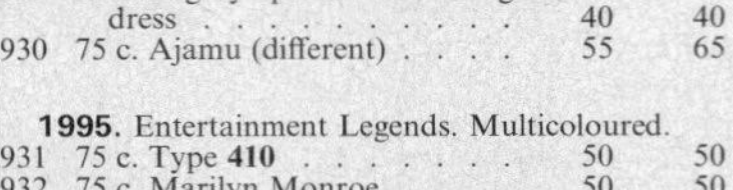

411 Elvis Presley

1995. 60th Birth Anniv of Elvis Presley (singer). Multicoloured.

2933 $1 Type **411** 65 65
2934 $1 With beard 65 65
2935 $1 With long hair and microphone 65 65
2936 $1 Wearing white shirt 65 65
2937 $1 Wearing pink shirt and purple jacket 65 65
2938 $1 With short hair and microphone 65 65
2939 $1 Wearing magenta shirt . . . 65 65
2940 $1 Wearing orange shirt . . . 65 65
2941 $1 Wearing purple shirt . . . 65 65

412 Film Reel and Oscar Statuette

1995. Centenary of Cinema. Multicoloured.

2942 $1 Type **412** 65 65
2943 $1 "HOLLYWOOD" sign . . . 65 65
2944 $1 Charlie Chaplin 65 65
2945 $1 Shirley Temple 65 65
2946 $1 Spencer Tracy and Katherine Hepburn 65 65
2947 $1 Marilyn Monroe 65 65
2948 $1 John Wayne 65 65
2949 $1 Marlon Brando 65 65
2950 $1 Tom Cruise 65 65

Nos. 2942/50 were printed together, se-tenant, forming a composite design.

413 "B1 Level Vista Dome" Electric Locomotive, Japan

1995. Trains of the World (1st series). Multicoloured.

2952 $1 Type **413** 70 70
2953 $1 Rolios Rail Class 25NC steam locomotive, South Africa 70 70
2954 $1 Class 460 electric locomotive, Switzerland 70 70
2955 $1 Central Railway diesel locomotive No. 605, Peru . 70 70
2956 $1 X2000 tilt body train, Sweden 70 70
2957 $1 Via Rail Toronto to Vancouver observation car, Canada 70 70
2958 $1 Intercity 125 diesel locomotive, Great Britain . 70 70
2959 $1 "The Flying Scotsman" steam locomotive, Great Britain 70 70
2960 $1 "Indian Pacific" diesel locomotive, Australia . . . 70 70
2961 $1 ETR 450 electric train, Italy 70 70
2962 $1 Isparta to Bozanonu Line steam locomotive, Turkey . 70 70
2963 $1 TGV train, France 70 70
2964 $1 ICE train, Germany . . . 70 70
2965 $1 Nishi Line electric locomotive, Japan 70 70
2966 $1 "Hikari" train, Japan . . . 70 70
2967 $1 Central Pacific Jupiter steam locomotive, U.S.A. 70 70
2968 $1 Amtrak Type 900 electric locomotive, U.S.A. 70 70
2969 $1 "Sir Nigel Gresley" steam locomotive, Great Britain . 70 70

See also Nos. 3167/82.

414 Teresa Teng

1995. Teresa Teng (Chinese actress) Commem. Different portraits. Multicoloured unless otherwise indicated.

2971 35 c. Type **414** 30 30
2972 35 c. As a child (brown, ochre and yellow) 30 30
2973 35 c. Wearing feather boa (black, grey and yellow) . . 30 30
2974 35 c. With motor scooter . . . 30 30
2975 35 c. Holding microphone . . 30 30
2976 35 c. In white sweater 30 30
2977 35 c. Playing flute 30 30
2978 35 c. With hand to hair (black, grey and yellow) 30 30
2979 35 c. Wearing gold decorated dress 30 30
2980 35 c. With fan 30 30
2981 35 c. As South-sea islander . . 30 30
2982 35 c. With hands clasped . . 30 30
2983 35 c. In kimono 30 30
2984 35 c. Holding bow tie 30 30
2985 35 c. Wearing black blouse . . 30 30
2986 35 c. Resting on chair arm . . 30 30
2987 75 c. In army uniform 55 55
2988 75 c. In navy uniform 55 55
2989 75 c. In air force uniform . . 55 55
2990 75 c. Singing with hand out stretched (black, grey and yellow) 55 55
2991 75 c. Singing with flowers in hair 55 55
2992 75 c. Singing in blue floral dress 55 55
2993 75 c. With pink scarf 55 55
2994 75 c. In fringed dress 55 55
2995 75 c. In pale green sweater . . 55 55
2996 75 c. With hands to face . . . 55 55

Nos. 2987/96 are larger, 34 × 46 mm.

415 Mickey Mouse fighting Big Pete

1995. Mickey's Pirate Adventure. Walt Disney Cartoon Characters. Multicoloured.

2997 15 c. Type **415** 30 20
2998 25 c. Mickey with treasure chest 30 20
2999 35 c. Minnie Mouse trying on plunder 30 20
3000 75 c. Goofy with telescope and Mickey swimming with barrel 55 40
3001 $3 Big Pete . . . . 2·00 2·25
3002 $5 Mickey with monkey, seagull and handkerchief . . . . . 2·50 3·00

416 Albert Michelson (1907 Physics)

1995. Centenary of Nobel Trust Fund. Multicoloured.

3004 $1 Type **416** 70 70
3005 $1 Ralph Bunche (1950 Peace) . 70 70
3006 $1 Edwin Neher (1991 Medicine) 70 70
3007 $1 Klaus Vonklitzing (1985 Physics) 70 70
3008 $1 Johann Deisenhofer (1988 Chemistry) 70 70
3009 $1 Max Delbruck (1969 Medicine) 70 70
3010 $1 J. Georg Bednorz (1987 Physics) 70 70
3011 $1 Feodor Lynen (1964 Medicine) 70 70
3012 $1 Walther Bothe (1954 Physics) 70 70
3013 $1 James Franck (1925 Physics) 70 70
3014 $1 Gustav Hertz (1925 Physics) 70 70
3015 $1 Friedrich Bergius (1931 Chemistry) 70 70
3016 $1 Otto Loewi (1936 Medicine) 70 70
3017 $1 Fritz Lipmann (1953 Medicine) 70 70
3018 $1 Otto Meyerhof (1922 Medicine) 70 70
3019 $1 Paul Heyse (1910 Literature) 70 70
3020 $1 Jane Addams (1931 Peace) . 70 70
3021 $1 Carl Braun (1909 Physics) . 70 70
3022 $1 Hans Dehmelt (1989 Physics) 70 70
3023 $1 Heinrich Boll (1972 Literature) 70 70
3024 $1 Georges Kohler (1984 Medicine) 70 70
3025 $1 Wolfgang Pauli (1945 Physics) 70 70
3026 $1 Sir Bernard Katz (1970 Medicine) 70 70
3027 $1 Ernest Ruska (1986 Physics) 70 70
3028 $1 William Golding (1983 Literature) 70 70
3029 $1 Hartmut Michel (1988 Chemistry) 70 70
3030 $1 Hans Bethe (1967 Physics) . 70 70

Nos. 3004/12, 3013/21 and 3022/30 respectively were printed together, se-tenant, forming composite designs.

No. 3015 is inscribed "Friedrich" in error.

1995. Christmas. Religious Paintings. As T **245a** of Gambia. Multicoloured.

3032 15 c. "The Madonna" (Bartolommeo Montagna) . 20 10
3033 25 c. "Sacred Conversation Piece" (Bonifacio dei Pitati) . 20 10
3034 35 c. "Nativity" (Van Loo) . . 25 10
3035 75 c. "Madonna of the Fountain" (Van Eyck) . . . 45 40
3036 $2 "The Apparition of the Virgin to St. Philip Neri" (Giovanni Tiepolo) . . . . 1·25 1·40
3037 $5 "The Holy Family" (Ribera) . . . . 2·50 3·00

417 Pres. Ronald Reagan at Fort George

1995. 12th Anniv of Liberation of Grenada (1st issue). Multicoloured.

3039 75 c. Type **417** 50 55
3040 75 c. Pres. Reagan with U.S. and Grenadian flags 50 55
3041 75 c. St. George's 50 55

Nos. 3039/41 were printed together, se-tenant, forming a composite design.

See also Nos. 3043/51.

418 Pres. Ronald Reagan

419 Pope John Paul II and Statue of Liberty

1995. 12th Anniv of Liberation of Grenada (2nd issue). Designs showing Pres. Ronald Reagan. Multicoloured.

3043 $1 With wife 55 60
3044 $1 Type **418** 55 60
3045 $1 With microphones 55 60
3046 $1 Wearing stetson 55 60
3047 $1 In front of U.S. flag . . . 55 60
3048 $1 In front of Brandenburg Gate, Berlin 55 60
3049 $1 Saluting by helicopter . . . 55 60
3050 $1 On horseback 55 60
3051 $1 Addressing troops 55 60

1995. Papal Visit to New York. Multicoloured.

3052 $1 Type **419** 65 65
3053 $1 Pope John Paul II and cathedral 65 65

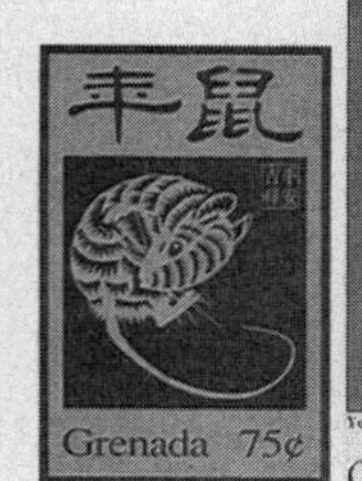

420 Rat asleep

421 "Young Woman" (Durer)

1996. Chinese New Year ("Year of the Rat").

3055 **420** 75 c. buff, green and brown 35 40
3056 – 75 c. orange, red and violet 35 40
3057 – 75 c. buff, red and green . 35 40

DESIGNS: No. 3056, Rat eating; 3057, Rat asleep (T **420** reversed).

1996. Famous Drawings and Paintings by Durer and Rubens. Multicoloured.

3060 15 c. Type **421** 20 10
3061 25 c. "Four Horsemen of the Apocalypse" (Durer) . . . 20 15
3062 35 c. "Assumption and Coronation of the Virgin" (Durer) 20 20
3063 75 c. "Mulay Ahmed" (Rubens) 45 40
3064 $1 "Anthony van Dyck aged 15" (Rubens) 60 50
3065 $2 "Head of a Young Monk" (Rubens) . . . . 1·25 1·40
3066 $3 "A Scholar inspired by Nature" (Rubens) . . . . 1·60 1·75
3067 $5 "Hanns Durer" (Durer) . . 2·40 2·75

422 Goofy Tap-dancing

1996. Famous Dances. Walt Disney Cartoon Characters Dancing. Multicoloured.

3069 35 c. Type **422** 25 20
3070 45 c. Donald Duck doing Mexican hat dance (horiz) . 30 25
3071 75 c. Daisy Duck as hula dancer 55 50
3072 90 c. Mickey and Minnie Mouse doing the tango (horiz) . . 60 55
3073 $1 Donald and Daisy doing the jitterbug 70 60
3074 $2 Mickey and Minnie performing Ukrainian folk dance (horiz) . . . . . . 1·40 1·50
3075 $3 Goofy and Pluto as ballet dancers (horiz) . . . . . 1·75 2·00
3076 $4 Mickey and Minnie line-dancing . . . . 1·90 2·25

1996. 70th Birthday of Queen Elizabeth II. As T **255a** of Gambia showing different photographs. Multicoloured.

3078 35 c. As Type **255a** of Gambia . 15 20
3079 75 c. Wearing white hat . . . 35 40
3080 $4 With bouquet . . . . . . 1·75 1·90

423 Ferrari "125 F1"

1996. Ferrari Racing Cars. Multicoloured.

3082 $1.50 Type **423** 65 70
3083 $1.50 "Tipo 625" 65 70
3084 $1.50 "P4" 65 70
3085 $1.50 "312P" 65 70
3086 $1.50 "312" Formula 1 . . . 65 70
3087 $1.50 "312B" 65 70

1996. 50th Anniv of U.N.I.C.E.F. As T **258a** of Gambia. Multicoloured.

3089 35 c. Child writing in book (horiz) 15 20
3090 $2 Child planting seedling (horiz) 85 90
3091 $3 Children and U.N.I.C.E.F. emblem (horiz) . . . . . . 1·25 1·40

424 Lions' Gate, Jerusalem

1996. 3000th Anniv of Jerusalem. Multicoloured.

3093 75 c. Type **424** 35 40
3094 $2 New Gate 85 90
3095 $3 Dung Gate . . . . 1·25 1·40

1996. Centenary of Radio. Entertainers. As T **259a** of Gambia. Multicoloured.

3097 35 c. Jack Benny 15 20
3098 75 c. Gertrude Berg 35 40
3099 $1 Eddie Cantor 45 50
3100 $2 Groucho Marx 85 90

425 Olympic Stadium, Athens, 1896

1996. Olympic Games, Atlanta (2nd issue). Previous Medal Winners. Multicoloured.

3102 35 c. Gold medal of 1896 (vert) 15 20
3103 75 c. Type **425** 35 40
3104 $1 Boughera el Quafi (France) (Gold, 1928) 45 50
3105 $1 Gustav Jansson (Sweden) (Bronze, 1952) 45 50
3106 $1 Spiridon Louis (Greece) (Gold, 1896) 45 50
3107 $1 Basil Heatley (Great Britain) (Silver, 1964) 45 50
3108 $1 Emil Zatopek (Czechoslovakia) (Gold, 1952) 45 50
3109 $1 Frank Shorter (U.S.A.) (Gold, 1972) 45 50
3110 $1 Alain Minoun O'Kacha (France) (Gold, 1956) . . . 45 50
3111 $1 Kokichi Tsu Uraya (Japan) (Bronze, 1964) 45 50
3112 $1 Delfo Cabrera (Argentina) (Gold, 1948) 45 50
3113 $1 Harald Sakata (U.S.A.) (Silver – light heavyweight, 1948) 45 50
3114 $1 Tom Kono (U.S.A.) (Gold – middleweight, 1952 and 1956) 45 50
3115 $1 Naim Suleymanoglu (Turkey) (Gold – featherweight, 1988) 45 50
3116 $1 Lee Hyung Kun (South Korea) (Gold – light heavyweight, 1988) 45 50
3117 $1 Vassily Alexeyev (U.S.S.R.) (Gold – super heavyweight, 1972 and 1976) 45 50
3118 $1 Chen Weiqiang (China) (Gold – featherweight, 1984) 45 50
3119 $1 Ye Huanming (China) (Gold – featherweight, 1988) . . . 45 50
3120 $1 Manfred Nerlinger (Germany) (Silver – super heavyweight, 1988) 45 50
3121 $1 Joseph Depietro (U.S.A.) (Gold – bantamweight, 1948) 45 50
3122 $2 Ancient Greek runners . . 85 90
3123 $3 Spiridon Louis (Greece) (Gold – marathon, 1896) . . 1·25 1·40

Nos. 3104/12 (marathon runners) and 3113/21 (weightlifters) respectively were printed together, se-tenant, with the backgrounds forming composite designs.

426 Mercedes-Benz, 1929

1996. Classic Cars. Multicoloured.

3125 35 c. Type **426** 15 20
3126 50 c. Bugatti Type 35, 1927 . . 25 30
3127 75 c. J. Dusenberg, 1935 . . . 35 40
3128 $1 Mercer, 1914 . . . . . . 45 50
3129 $1 Type 57C Atalante, 1939 . 45 50
3130 $1 Cannstatt-Daimler, 1900 . 45 50
3131 $1 Delage, 1925 . . . . . . 45 50
3132 $1 Coventry Daimler, 1899 . . 45 50
3133 $1 Vauxhall, 1900 . . . . . 45 50
3134 $1 T-15 Hispano-Suza, 1912 . 45 50
3135 $2 Alfa Romeo, 1929 . . . . 85 90
3136 $3 Rolls Royce, 1910 . . . . 1·25 1·40

427 "Gorch Fock" (cadet barque), Germany, 1916

1996. Ships. Multicoloured.

3138 $1 Type **427** 45 50
3139 $1 "Henry B. Hyde", U.S.A., 1886 . . . . 45 50
3140 $1 "Resolution" (galleon), Great Britain, 1652 . . . . 45 50
3141 $1 Type **427** 45 50
3142 $1 "Henry B. Hyde", U.S.A., 1886 . . . . 45 50
3143 $1 "Resolution" (galleon), Great Britain, 1652 . . . . 45 50
3144 $1 Type **427** 45 50
3145 $1 "Henry B. Hyde" (clipper), U.S.A., 1886 . . . . . . 45 50
3146 $1 "Resolution" (galleon), Great Britain, 1652 . . . . 45 50
3147 $1 H.M.S. "Bounty" 45 50
3148 $1 "Bismark" (German battleship) 45 50
3149 $1 "Chuii Apoo" and two junks 45 50
3150 $1 "Lubeck" (German frigate) 45 50
3151 $1 Dutch galleon 45 50
3152 $1 "Augsburg" (German frigate) 45 50
3153 $1 "Henri Grace a Dieu" (British galleon) 45 50
3154 $1 H.M.S. "Prince of Wales" (battleship) 45 50
3155 $1 "Santa Anna" Spanish carrack) 45 50

428 Jacqueline Kennedy

1996. Jacqueline Kennedy Onassis Commemoration. Multicoloured.

3157 $1 Type **428** 45 50
3158 $1 Wearing mauve blouse . . 45 50
3159 $1 In evening dress (inscr at right) 45 50
3160 $1 In evening dress (inscr at left) 45 50
3161 $1 Wearing pink dress 45 50
3162 $1 Wearing blue dress with collar embroidered 45 50
3163 $1 Wearing white jacket and brooch 45 50
3164 $1 In yellow jacket and green shirt 45 50
3165 $1 Wearing black jacket . . . 45 50

429 Class C51 Locomotive of Imperial Train, Japan

1996. Trains of the World (2nd series). Multicoloured.

3167 35 c. Type **429** 15 20
3168 75 c. "Rheingold" express, Germany 35 40
3169 $1 Atlantic Coast Line locomotive No. 153, 1894, U.S.A. 45 50
3170 $1 Smith Compound No.1619, Great Britain 45 50
3171 $1 Trans-Siberian Soviet Railways 45 50
3172 $1 Palatinate Railway Krauss locomotive, 1898, Germany . 45 50

3173 $1 Paris, Lyons and Mediterranean line, France . 45 50
3174 $1 Diesel-electric 0341 locomotive, Italy 45 50
3175 $1 Class C62 locomotive, Japan 45 50
3176 $1 Shantung Railways locomotive, China 45 50
3177 $1 Class C57 locomotive, Japan 45 50
3178 $1 Diesel express train, Japan 45 50
3179 $1 Shanghai–Nanking Railway locomotive, China 45 50
3180 $1 Class D51 locomotive, Japan 45 90
3181 $2 "Pioneer", 1851, U.S.A. . . 85 90
3182 $3 "France", France . . . . 1·25 1·40

430 Winter Jasmine

1996. Flowers. Multicoloured.
3184 $1 Type **430** 45 50
3185 $1 Chrysanthemum 45 50
3186 $1 Lilac 45 50
3187 $1 Japanese iris 45 50
3188 $1 Hibiscus 45 50
3189 $1 Sacred lotus 45 50
3190 $1 Apple blossom 45 50
3191 $1 Gladiolus 45 50
3192 $1 Japanese quince 45 50
3193 $1 Canterbury bell (vert) . . . 45 50
3194 $1 Rose (vert) 45 50
3195 $1 Nasturtium (vert) 45 50
3196 $1 Daffodil (vert) 45 50
3197 $1 Tulip (vert) 45 50
3198 $1 Snapdragon (vert) 45 50
3199 $1 Zinnia (vert) 45 50
3200 $1 Sweetpea (vert) 45 50
3201 $1 Pansy (vert) 45 50
Nos. 3184/92 and 3193/3201 respectively were printed together, se-tenant, with the backgrounds forming a composite design.

431 Zeppelin L-31 (Germany)

1996. Airships. Multicoloured.
3203 30 c. Type **431** 15 20
3204 30 c. Zeppelin L-35 (Germany) 15 20
3205 50 c. Zeppelin L-30 (Germany) 25 30
3206 75 c. Zeppelin L-2 10 (Germany) 35 40
3207 $1.50 Zeppelin L-21 (Germany) 65 70
3208 $1.50 Zodiac Type 13 Spiess (France) 65 70
3209 $1.50 N1 "Norge" (Roald Amundsen) 65 70
3210 $1.50 LZ-127 "Graf Zeppelin" (Germany) 65 70
3211 $1.50 LZ-129 "Hindenburg" (Germany) 65 70
3212 $1.50 Zeppelin NT (Germany) . 65 70
3213 $3 Zeppelin L-3 (Germany) . . 1·25 1·40
3214 $3 Beardmore No. 24 (Great Britain) . . . . 1·25 1·40

432 Horned Guan

1996. West Indian Birds. Multicoloured.
3216 $1.50 Type **432** 65 70
3217 $1.50 St. Lucia parrot 65 70
3218 $1.50 Black penelopina . . . 65 70
3219 $1.50 Grenada dove 65 70
3220 $1.50 St. Vincent parrot . . . 65 70
3221 $1.50 White-breasted trembler . 65 70
Nos. 3216/21 were printed together, se-tenant, with the backgrounds forming a composite design.

433 Blue Whale

1996. Whales and Turtles. Multicoloured.
3223 $1.50 Type **433** 65 70
3224 $1.50 Humpback whale . . . 65 70
3225 $1.50 Right whale 65 70
3226 $1.50 Hawksbill turtle . . . 65 70
3227 $1.50 Leatherback turtle . . . 65 70
3228 $1.50 Green turtle 65 70

434 Killer Whale **437** Devon Rex

436 Mickey at Tram Stop

1996. Marine Life. Multicoloured.
3229 $1 Type **434** 45 50
3230 $1 Dolphin 45 50
3231 $1 Two dolphins 45 50
3232 $1 Sea lion and regal angelfish . 45 50
3233 $1 Dolphins and hawksbill turtle 45 50
3234 $1 Three hawksbill turtles . . 45 50
3235 $1 Regal angelfish and pennant coralfish 45 50
3236 $1 Pennant coralfish 45 50
3237 $1 Sea lion and squirrelfish . . 45 50
3238 $1 Brown pelican 45 50
3239 $1 Killer whale (different) . . 45 50
3240 $1 Whale 45 50
3241 $1 Dolphins and sea lion . . . 45 50
3242 $1 Shortfin pilot whale, blue-ringed octopus and sea lion . 45 50
3243 $1 Hammerhead sharks and sea lion 45 50
3244 $1 Blue-striped grunts 45 50
3245 $1 Stingray and Van Gogh fusilier 45 50
3246 $1 Van Gogh fusilier, ribbon moray and percoid fish 45 50
Nos. 3229/37 and 3238/46 respectively were printed together, se-tenant, with the backgrounds forming a composite design.

1996. Christmas. Religious Paintings. As T **245a** of Gambia. Multicoloured.
3248 25 c. "The Visitation" (Tintoretto) 10 15
3249 35 c. "Virgin with the Child" (Palma Vecchio) 15 20
3250 50 c. "The Adoration of the Magi" (Botticelli) 25 30
3251 75 c. "The Annunciation" (Titian) 35 40
3252 $1 "The Flight into Egypt" (Tintoretto) 45 50
3253 $3 "The Holy Family with the Infant Saint John" (Andrea del Sarto) . . . . 1·25 1·40
No. 3250 is inscr "Botticceli" in error.

1997. "HONG KONG '97" International Stamp Exhibition. Mickey in Hong Kong. Disney Cartoon Characters. Multicoloured.
3257 35 c. Type **436** 40 50
3258 50 c. Mickey and Donald fishing at Victoria Harbour 40 50
3259 75 c. Donald and Mickey parachuting 50 60
3260 90 c. Mickey and Minnie visiting Bank of China 50 60
3261 $1 Mickey with pet parrot . . 70 75
3262 $1 Mickey drinking Kung-fu Tea 70 75
3263 $1 Mickey, Minnie and Goofy shopping at Chinese Wet Market 70 75
3264 $1 Mickey, Minnie and Goofy with grasshoppers 70 75
3265 $1 Mickey and Goofy with lanterns 70 75
3266 $1 Mickey and Minnie practising Tai-chi 70 75
3267 $2 Goofy delivering bottled gas . . . . 1·10 1·25
3268 $3 Mickey, Minnie and Donald at "Jumbo" floating restaurant . . . . 1·40 1·50

1997. 50th Anniv of U.N.E.S.C.O. As T **273a** of Gambia. Multicoloured.
3270 35 c. Temple, Kyoto, Japan . 15 20
3271 75 c. Timbered houses, Quedlinburg, Germany . . 35 40
3272 90 c. View from walls, Dubrovnik, Croatia 40 45
3273 $1 Ruins at Delphi, Greece . . 45 50
3274 $1 Bryggen Wharf, Bergen, Norway (vert) 45 50
3275 $1 Old city, Berne, Switzerland (vert) 45 50
3276 $1 Warsaw, Poland (vert) . . 45 50
3277 $1 Fortress walls, Luxembourg (vert) 45 50
3278 $1 Interior of Drottningholm Palace, Sweden (vert) . . 45 50
3279 $1 Petajavesi Church, Finland (vert) 45 50
3280 $1 Vilnius, Lithuania (vert) . . 45 50
3281 $1 Jelling Church, Denmark (vert) 45 50
3282 $1 Entrance to caves, Desert of Taklamakan, China (vert) . 45 50
3283 $1 House, Desert of Taklamakan, China (vert) . 45 50
3284 $1 Monument, Desert of Taklamakan, China (vert) . 45 50
3285 $1 Palace of Cielos Purpuras, Wudang, China (vert) . . . 45 50
3286 $1 House, Wudang, China (vert) 45 50
3287 $1 Stone Guardian, The Great Wall, China (vert) . . . 45 50
3288 $1 Ming Dynasty statue, Wudang, China (vert) . . . 45 50
3289 $1 The Great Wall, China (vert) 45 50
3290 $1.50 Segovia Cathedral, Spain 65 70
3291 $1.50 Wurtzburg, Germany . . 65 70
3292 $1.50 Plitvice Lakes, Croatia . 65 70
3293 $1.50 Batalha Monastery, Portugal 65 70
3294 $1.50 River Seine, Paris, France 65 70
3295 $2 Tomar, Portugal 85 90
3296 $3 Palace of Chaillot, Paris, France . . . . 1·25 1·40

1997. Cats and Dogs. Multicoloured.
3298 35 c. Type **437** 15 20
3299 75 c. King Charles spaniel . . 35 40
3300 90 c. Japanese bobtail 40 45
3301 $1 Afghan hound 45 50
3302 $1 Turkish van 45 50
3303 $1 Ragdoll 45 50
3304 $1 Siberian 45 50
3305 $1 Egyptian mau 45 50
3306 $1 American shorthair 45 50
3307 $1 Benegal 45 50
3308 $1 Asian longhair 45 50
3309 $1 Somali 45 50
3310 $1 Turkish angora 45 50
3311 $1 Lhasa apso 45 50
3312 $1 Rough collie 45 50
3313 $1 Norwich terrier 45 50
3314 $1 American cocker spaniel . . 45 50
3315 $1 Chinese crested dog . . . 45 50
3316 $1 Old English sheepdog . . . 45 50
3317 $1 Standard poodle 45 50
3318 $1 German shepherd 45 50
3319 $1 German shorthair pointer . 45 50
3320 $2 Cornish rex 85 90
3321 $3 Pekingese . . . . 1·25 1·40

438 Dunkleosteus

1997. Dinosaurs. Multicoloured.
3323 35 c. Type **438** 15 20
3324 75 c. Tyrannosaurus rex . . . 35 40
3325 $1.50 Sordes 65 70
3326 $1.50 Dimorphodon 65 70
3327 $1.50 Diplodocus 65 70
3328 $1.50 Allosaurus 65 70
3329 $1.50 Pentaceratops 65 70
3330 $1.50 Protoceratops 65 70
3331 $2 Askeptosaurus (vert) . . . 85 90
3332 $3 Triceratops (vert) . . . . 1·25 1·40
Nos. 3325/30 were printed together, se-tenant, with the backgrounds forming a composite design.

439 Porcelain Crab

1997. Marine Life. Multicoloured.
3334 45 c. Type **439** 20 25
3335 75 c. Humpback whale . . . 35 40
3336 90 c. Hermit crab 40 45
3337 $1 Great white shark 45 50
3338 $1.50 Octopus (vert) 65 70
3339 $1.50 Lei triggerfish (vert) . . 65 70
3340 $1.50 Lionfish (vert) 65 70
3341 $1.50 Harlequin wrasse (vert) . 65 70
3342 $1.50 Clown fish (vert) 65 70
3343 $1.50 Moray eel (vert) 65 70
3344 $3 Green sea turtle . . . . 1·25 1·40
3345 $4 Whale shark . . . . . . 1·75 1·90
Nos. 3338/43 were printed together, se-tenant, with the backgrounds forming a composite design.

1997. 10th Anniv of Chernobyl Nuclear Disaster. As T **276a** of Gambia. Multicoloured.
3348 $2 As Type **276a** of Gambia . 85 90
3349 $2 As No. 3348, but inscribed "CHABAD'S CHILDREN OF CHERNOBYL" at foot 85 90

1997. 50th Death Anniv of Paul Harris (founder of Rotary International). As T **276b** of Gambia. Multicoloured.
3350 $3 Paul Harris and vocational training programme, Philippines . . . . 1·25 1·40

1997. Golden Wedding of Queen Elizabeth and Prince Philip. As T **276c** of Gambia. Multicoloured.
3352 $1 Queen Elizabeth and Prince Philip waving 45 50
3353 $1 Royal coat of arms 45 50
3354 $1 Queen Elizabeth with Prince Philip in naval uniform . . 45 50
3355 $1 Queen Elizabeth and Prince Philip at Buckingham Palace 45 50
3356 $1 Windsor Castle 45 50
3357 $1 Prince Philip 45 50

1997. "Pacific '97" International Stamp Exhibition, San Francisco (1st issue). Death Centenary of Heinrich von Stephan (founder of the U.P.U). As T **276d** of Gambia.
3359 $2 green and black 85 90
3360 $2 brown 85 90
3361 $2 blue 85 90
DESIGNS: No. 3359, Postman on motorcycle; 3360, Von Stephan and Mercury; 3361, Postman on skis, Rocky Mountains, 1900s.
See also Nos. 3392/3408.

1997. Birth Bicentenary of Hiroshige (Japanese painter). As T **541a** of Ghana. Multicoloured.
3363 $1.50 "Nihon Embankment, Yoshiwara" 65 70
3364 $1.50 "Asakusa Ricefields and Torinomachi Festival" . . . 65 70
3365 $1.50 "Senju Great Bridge" . 65 70
3366 $1.50 "Dawn inside the Yoshiwara" 65 70
3367 $1.50 "Tile Kilns and Hasiba Ferry, Sumida River" . . . 65 70
3368 $1.50 "View from Massaki of Suijin Shrine, Uchigawa Inlet and Sekiya" 65 70

1997. 175th Anniv of Brothers Grimm's Third Collection of Fairy Tales. Snow White. As T **277a** of Gambia. Multicoloured.
3370 $2 Queen looking in mirror . . 85 90
3371 $2 Snow White and the Seven Dwarfs 85 90
3372 $2 Snow White and Prince . . 85 90

440 One-man Luge

1997. Winter Olympic Games, Nagano, Japan. Multicoloured.
3374 45 c. Type **440** 20 25
3375 75 c. Men's speed skating . . 35 40
3376 $1 One-man luge (different) . . 45 50
3377 $1 Ski jumping (blue ski suit) . 45 50
3378 $1 Downhill skiing 45 50
3379 $1 Speed skating 45 50
3380 $1 Two-man bobsleigh . . . 45 50
3381 $1 Women's figure skating . . 45 50
3382 $1 Alpine combined 45 50
3383 $1 Ice hockey 45 50
3384 $1 Ski jumping (yellow ski suit) 45 50
3385 $2 Men's figure skating . . . 90 95
3386 $3 Slalom . . . . 1·40 1·50

441 Bank of China

1997. Return of Hong Kong to China. Multicoloured.
3388 90 c. Type **441** 40 45
3389 $1 Skyscrapers 45 50
3390 $1.75 "Hong Kong '97" on modern buildings (63 × 32 mm) 70 75
3391 $2 Deng Xiaoping and Hong Kong (63 × 32 mm) 85 90

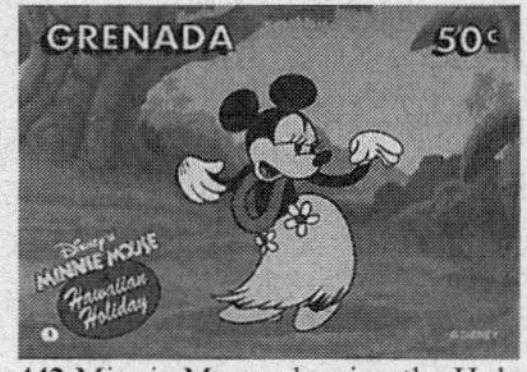

442 Minnie Mouse dancing the Hula

1997. "Pacific '97" International Stamp Exhibition, San Francisco (2nd issue). Centenary of the Cinema. Minnie Mouse in "Hawaiian Holiday". Multicoloured.
3392 50 c. Type **442** (Frame 1) . . . 40 40
3393 50 c. Frame 2 . . . . 40 40
3394 50 c. Frame 3 . . . . 40 40
3395 50 c. Frame 4 . . . . 40 40
3396 50 c. Frame 5 . . . . 40 40
3397 50 c. Frame 6 . . . . 40 40
3398 50 c. Frame 7 . . . . 40 40
3399 50 c. Frame 8 . . . . 40 40
3400 50 c. Frame 9 . . . . 40 40
3401 50 c. Frame 10 . . . . . . 40 40
3402 50 c. Frame 11 . . . . . . 40 40
3403 50 c. Frame 12 . . . . . . 40 40
3404 50 c. Frame 13 . . . . . . 40 40
3405 50 c. Frame 14 . . . . . . 40 40
3406 50 c. Frame 15 . . . . . . 40 40
3407 50 c. Frame 16 . . . . . . 40 40
3408 50 c. Frame 17 . . . . . . 40 40

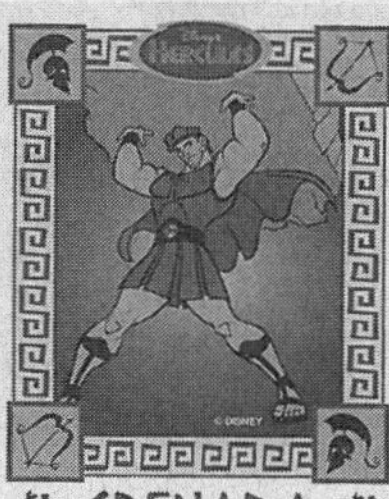

443 Hercules lifting Rock

1997. "Hercules" (cartoon film) (1st series). Multicoloured.
3410 $1 Type **443** 70 70
3411 $1 Pegasus 70 70
3412 $1 Megara 70 70
3413 $1 Philoktetes 70 70
3414 $1 Nessus 70 70
3415 $1 Hydra 70 70
3416 $1 Pain and Panic 70 70
3417 $1 Hades 70 70
See also Nos. 3561/84.

1997. World Cup Football Championship, France (1998). As T **283a** of Gambia. Multicoloured (except Nos. 3422/3 and 3428).
3419 15 c. West German and Italian Players, 1982 (vert) 10 10
3420 75 c. Italian player holding World Cup, 1982 (vert) . . 35 40
3421 90 c. West German and Italian players wearing "20" shirts, 1982 (vert) 40 45
3422 $1 Uruquay team, 1950 (brown) 45 50
3423 $1 Brazilian team, 1958 (brown) 45 50
3424 $1 West German team, 1974 . 45 50
3425 $1 Argentine team, 1986 . . . 45 50
3426 $1 Italian team, 1982 . . . . 45 50
3427 $1 West German team, 1990 . 45 50
3428 $1 Italian team, 1934 (brown) . 45 50
3429 $1 Brazilian team, 1970 . . . 45 50
3430 $1 Seaman, England 45 50
3431 $1 Klinsmann, Germany . . . 45 50
3432 $1 Berger, Czech Republic . . 45 50
3433 $1 McCoist, Scotland 45 50
3434 $1 Gascoigne, England . . . 45 50
3435 $1 Djorkaeff, France 45 50
3436 $1 Sammer, Germany 45 50
3437 $1 Futre, Portugal 45 50
3438 $2 Italian player beating goal keeper, 1982 (vert) 85 90
3439 $3 Goal-mouth melee, 1982 (vert) . . . . 1·25 1·40
3440 $4 Two West German players tackling Italian player (vert) . . . . 1·75 1·90

444 Peacock

1997. Butterflies and Moths. Multicoloured.
3442 45 c. Type **444** 20 25
3443 75 c. Orange flambeau 35 40
3444 90 c. Eastern tailed blue . . . 45 50
3445 $1 Brimstone 45 50
3446 $1 Mocker swallowtail 45 50
3447 $1 American painted lady . . . 45 50
3448 $1 Tiger swallowtail 45 50
3449 $1 Long wing 45 50
3450 $1 Sunset moth 45 50
3451 $1 Australian Blue Mountain swallowtail 45 50
3452 $1 Bird wing 45 50
3453 $2 Black and red 85 90
3454 $3 Large white . . . . . . 1·25 1·40
3455 $4 Oriental swallowtail . . . 1·75 1·90

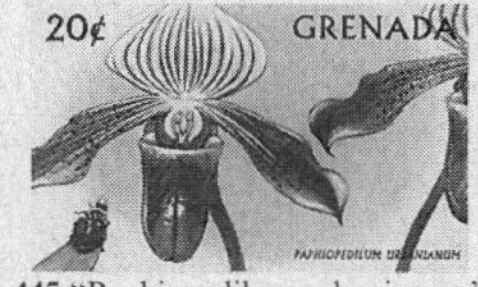

445 "Paphiopedilum urbanianum"

1997. Orchids of the World. Multicoloured.
3457 20 c. Type **445** 10 10
3458 35 c. "Trichoceros parviflorus" 15 20
3459 45 c. "Euanthe sanderiana" (vert) 20 25
3460 75 c. "Oncidium macranthum" (vert) 35 40
3461 90 c. "Psychopsis kramerianum" (vert) . . . 40 45
3462 $1 "Oncidium hastatum" (vert) 45 50
3463 $2 "Broughtonia sanguinea" (vert) 90 95
3464 $2 "Anguloa virginalis" (vert) . 90 95
3465 $2 "Dendrobium bigibbum" (vert) 90 95
3466 $2 "Lucasiana" (vert) . . . 90 95
3467 $2 "Cymbidium" (vert) . . . 90 95
3468 $2 "Cymbidium" and vase (vert) 90 95
3469 $2 "Odontoglossum crispum" (vert) 90 95
3470 $2 "Cattleya brabantiae" (vert) 90 95
3471 $2 "Cattleya bicolor" (vert) . 90 95
3472 $2 "Trichopilia suavia" (vert) . 90 95
3473 $2 "Encyclia mariae" (vert) . . 90 95
3474 $2 "Angraecum leonis" (vert) . 90 95
3475 $3 "Masdevallia saltatix" (vert) . . . . 1·40 1·50
3476 $4 "Cattleya luteola" . . . . 1·90 2·00
Nos. 3463/8 and 3469/74 respectively were printed together, se-tenant, with the backgrounds forming composite designs.

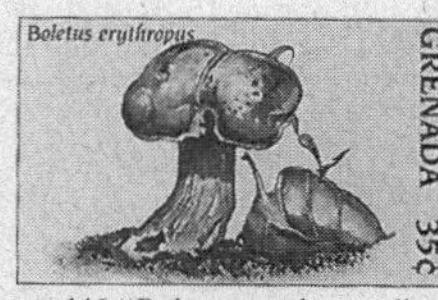

446 "Boletus erythropus"

1997. Fungi of the World. Multicoloured.
3478 35 c. Type **446** 15 20
3479 75 c. "Armillariella mellea" . . 35 40
3480 90 c. "Amanita flavorubens" . 40 45
3481 $1 Indigo milky 45 50
3482 $1.50 "Agaricus solidipes" . . 65 70
3483 $1.50 Salmon waxy cap . . . 65 70
3484 $1.50 Fused maramius 65 70
3485 $1.50 Shellfish-scented russula . 65 70
3486 $1.50 Red-capped scaber stalk . 65 70
3487 $1.50 "Calocybe gambosum" . 65 70
3488 $1.50 "Boletus parasiticus" . . 65 70
3489 $1.50 "Frostis bolete" 65 70
3490 $1.50 "Amanita myscara flavilolvata" 65 70
3491 $1.50 "Volvariella volvacea" . 65 70
3492 $1.50 Stuntz's blue legs . . . 65 70
3493 $1.50 Orange-latex milky . . . 65 70
3494 $2 "Tylopilus balloui" 85 90
3495 $4 "Boletus parasiticus" . . . 1·75 1·90

447 Princess Diana with Landmine Victims

1997. Diana, Princess of Wales Commemoration. Multicoloured.
3497 $1.50 Type **447** 60 65
3498 $1.50 With sick child 60 65
3499 $1.50 With young boy on crutches 60 65
3500 $1.50 With leper 60 65
3501 $1.50 Holding baby 60 65
3502 $1.50 Walking through minefield 60 65

448 "Angel" (Matthias Grunewald)

1997. Christmas. Religious Paintings. Multicoloured.
3504 35 c. Type **448** 15 20
3505 50 c. "St. Demetrius" (icon) . 20 25
3506 75 c. Three-panelled reliquary . 35 40
3507 $1 "Angel of the Annunciation" (Jan van Eyck) 45 50
3508 $3 "The Annunciation" (Simone Martini) . . . . 1·25 1·40
3509 $4 "St. Michael" (icon) . . . 1·75 1·90

449 Black-tailed Damselfish

1998. Fishes. Multicoloured.
3512 65 c. Type **449** 30 35
3513 90 c. Yellow sweetlips 40 45
3514 $1 Common squirrelfish . . . 45 50
3515 $1.50 Blue tang 65 70
3516 $1.50 Porkfish 65 70
3517 $1.50 Banded butterflyfish . . 65 70
3518 $1.50 Thread-finned butterflyfish 65 70
3519 $1.50 Hooded butterflyfish ("Red-headed") 65 70
3520 $1.50 Emperor angelfish . . . 65 70
3521 $1.50 Duboulay's angelfish ("Scribbled Anglefish") . . 65 70
3522 $1.50 Lemon-peel angelfish . . 65 70
3523 $1.50 Bandit angelfish 65 70
3524 $1.50 Bicoloured angelfish ("Biclor Cherub") 65 70
3525 $1.50 Palette surgeonfish ("Regal Tang") 65 70
3526 $1.50 Yellow tang 65 70
3527 $2 Powder-blue surgeonfish . . 85 90
Nos. 3515/20 and 3521/6 respectively were printed together, se-tenant, with the backgrounds forming composite designs.

450 "Sophronitis grandiflora"

1998. Flowers of the World. Multicoloured.
3529 $1.50 Type **450** 65 70
3530 $1.50 "Phalaenopsis amboinensis" 65 70
3531 $1.50 "Zygopetalum intermedium" 65 70
3532 $1.50 "Paphiopedilum purpuratum" 65 70
3533 $1.50 "Miltonia regnellii" . . 65 70
3534 $1.50 "Dendrobium parishii" . 65 70
3535 $1.50 "Arachnis clarkei" . . . 65 70
3536 $1.50 "Cymbidium eburneum" 65 70
3537 $1.50 "Dendrobium chrysotoxum" 65 70
3538 $1.50 "Paphiopedilum insigne" 65 70
3539 $1.50 "Paphiopedilum venustum" 65 70
3540 $1.50 "Renanthera imschootiana" 65 70

451 Dhow

1998. Famous Ships. Multicoloured.
3542 $1 Type **451** 45 50
3543 $1 Galleon 45 50
3544 $1 Felucca 45 50
3545 $1 Schooner 45 50
3546 $1 Aircraft carrier 45 50
3547 $1 Knau 45 50
3548 $1 Destroyer 45 50
3549 $1 Viking longship 45 50
3550 $1 "Queen Elizabeth 2" (liner) . 45 50
3551 $1 Brig 45 50
3552 $1 Clipper 45 50
3553 $1 Caique 45 50
3554 $1 Mississippi riverboat . . . 45 50
3555 $1 Luxury liner 45 50
3556 $1 "Mayflower" (Pilgrim Fathers) 45 50
3557 $1 Frigate 45 50
3558 $1 Janggolan 45 50
3559 $1 Junk 45 50
Nos. 3542/50 and 3551/9 respectively were printed together, se-tenant, forming composite background designs.

1998. "Hercules" (cartoon film) (2nd series). As T **443** showing Disney cartoon characters. Multicoloured.
3561/8 10 c. × 8 Hercules and giant statue; Hercules, Pegasus and Philoktetes; Hercules and Philoktetes with shield and arrows; Hercules swinging from blades; Nessus carrying off Megara; Hercules fighting Nessus; Hercules fighting giant lion; Hercules and Pegasus leaving prints on pavement
3569/76 $1 × 8 Baby Hercules with Zeus and Alcmene; Baby Hercules with Hades; Hades in the Underworld; Baby Hercules and young Pegasus; Baby Hercules with Pain and Panic; Baby Hercules with mortal parents; Hercules towing hay waggon; Hercules receiving gold medallion
3577/84 $1 × 8 Hercules and Megara; Megara and Hades; Hercules training with Philoktetes; Hercules confronting Hades; Giant destroying city; Zeus; Hercules saving Megara by lifting pillar; Hercules diving into sea
3561/84 Set of 24 10·00 11·00

452 Arctic Skua

1998. Seabirds. Multicoloured.
3586 90 c. Type **452** 40 45
3587 $1 Northern fulmar (horiz) . . 45 50
3588 $1 Black-legged kittiwake (horiz) 45 50
3589 $1 Cape petrel (horiz) 45 50
3590 $1 Mediterranean gull (horiz) . 45 50
3591 $1 Brandt's cormorant (horiz) . 45 50
3592 $1 Greater shearwater (horiz) . 45 50
3593 $1 Black-footed albatross (horiz) 45 50
3594 $1 Red-necked phalarope (horiz) 45 50
3595 $1 Black skimmer (horiz) . . . 45 50
3596 $1.10 Humboldt penguin . . . 50 55
3597 $2 Herring gull 85 90
3598 $3 Red knot . . . . 1·25 1·40
Nos. 3587/95 were printed together, se-tenant, with the backgrounds forming a composite design.

453 Supermarine Spitfire Mk I

1998. History of the Supermarine Spitfire (aircraft). Designs showing different versions. Multicoloured.
3600 $1.50 Type **453** 65 70
3601 $1.50 Mark VIII 65 70
3602 $1.50 Mark III 65 70
3603 $1.50 Mark XVI 65 70
3604 $1.50 Mark V 65 70
3605 $1.50 Mark XIX 65 70
3606 $1.50 Mark IX 65 70
3607 $1.50 Mark XIV 65 70
3608 $1.50 Mark XII 65 70
3609 $1.50 Mark XI 65 70
3610 $1.50 H.F. Mark VIII 65 70
3611 $1.50 Mark VB 65 70

454 Walrus

1998. International Year of the Ocean. Multicoloured.
3613 75 c. Type **454** 35 40
3614 75 c. African black-footed penguins 35 40
3615 75 c. African black-footed penguin 35 40
3616 75 c. California sealion . . . 35 40
3617 75 c. Green turtle 35 40
3618 75 c. Redfin anthias 35 40
3619 75 c. Sperm whale 35 40
3620 75 c. French angelfish and Australian sealion 35 40
3621 75 c. Jellyfish 35 40
3622 75 c. Sawfish 35 40
3623 75 c. Cuckoo wrasse 35 40
3624 75 c. Garibaldi 35 40
3625 75 c. Spinecheek anemonefish . 35 40
3626 75 c. Leafy seadragon 35 40
3627 75 c. Blue-spotted goatfish . . 35 40
3628 75 c. Two-spot gobies 35 40
Nos. 3613/28 were printed together, se-tenant, with the backgrounds forming a composite design.

454a Flags of Grenada and CARICOM

1998. 25th Anniv of Caribbean Community.
3630 **454a** $1 multicoloured 45 50

454b Stylized Americas

1998. 50th Anniv of Organization of American States.
3631 **454b** $1 multicoloured 45 50

1998. 25th Death Anniv of Pablo Picasso (painter). As T **291a** of Gambia. Multicoloured.
3632 45 c. "The Bathers" (vert) 20 25
3633 $2 "Luncheon on the Grass" 85 90
3634 $3 "The Swimmer" 1·25 1·40

1998. Birth Centenary of Enzo Ferrari (car manufacturer). As T **564a** of Ghana. Multicoloured.
3636 $2 250 GT Berlinetta Lusso 85 90
3637 $2 250 GTO 85 90
3638 $2 250 GT Boano/Ellena cabriolet 85 90

454c Scout Saluting **454d** Mahatma Gandhi

1998. 19th World Scout Jamboree, Chile. Multicoloured.
3640 $2 Type **454c** 85 90
3641 $3 International scout flag 1·25 1·40
3642 $4 Applying first aid 1·75 1·90

1998. 50th Death Anniv of Mahatma Gandhi.
3644 **454d** $1 black, grey and mauve 45 50

1998. 80th Anniv of Royal Air Force. As T **292a** of Gambia. Multicoloured.
3646 $2 Supermarine Spitfire Mk IIa 85 90
3647 $2 Supermarine Spitfire Mk IXb from above 85 90
3648 $2 Supermarine Spitfire Mk IXb from side 85 90
3649 $2 Hawker Hurricane Mk IIC of Battle of Britain Memorial Flight 85 90
3650 $2 EF-2000 Eurofighter above clouds 85 90
3651 $2 Nimrod MR2P (maritime reconnaissance) 85 90
3652 $2 EF-2000 Eurofighter at low level 85 90
3653 $2 C-47 Dakota (transport) 85 90

455 "Knights in Combat"

1998. Birth Bicentenary of Eugene Delacroix (painter). Multicoloured.
3655 $1 Type **455** 45 50
3656 $1 "Murder of Bishop of Liege" 45 50
3657 $1 "Still Life" 45 50
3658 $1 "Battle of Nancy" 45 50
3659 $1 "Shipwreck of Don Juan" 45 50
3660 $1 "The Death of Ophelia" 45 50
3661 $1 "Attila the Hun" 45 50
3662 $1 "Arab Entertainers" 45 50

1998. 1st Death Anniv of Diana, Princess of Wales. As T **293a** of Gambia. Multicoloured.
3664 $1 Diana, Princess of Wales 45 50

456 Arthur Ashe

1998. Famous Tennis Players. Multicoloured.
3665 45 c. Type **456** 20 25
3666 75 c. Martina Hingis 35 40
3667 90 c. Chris Evert 40 45
3668 $1 Steffi Graf 45 50
3669 $1.50 A. Sanchez Vicario 65 70
3670 $2 Monica Seles 85 90
3671 $3 Martina Navratilova 1·25 1·40

457 Dove of Peace with Stars and Streamers

458 "The Angel's parting from Tobias" (Jean Bilevelt)

1998. Grenada's Participation in U.N. Peacekeeping Operations, Beirut, 1982–4.
3673 **457** $1 multicoloured 45 50

1998. Christmas. Religious Paintings. Multicoloured.
3674 35 c. Type **458** 15 20
3675 45 c. "Allegory of Faith" (Moretto Da Brescia) 20 25
3676 90 c. "Crucifixion" (Ugolino Di Tedice) 40 45
3677 $1 "The Triumphal Entry into Jerusalem" (Master of the Thuison Altarpiece) 45 50

459 Blue-hooded Euphonia

1998. Christmas. Birds. Multicoloured.
3678 45 c. Type **459** 20 25
3679 75 c. Red-billed whistling duck ("Black-bellied Whistling Duck") 35 40
3680 90 c. Purple martin 40 45
3681 $1 Imperial amazon ("Imperial Parrot") 45 50
3682 $2 Adelaide's warbler 85 90
3683 $3 Greater flamingo ("Roseate Flamingo") 1·25 1·40

1999. Millennium Series. Famous People of the Twentieth Century. Great Thinkers of the Past and Present. Designs as T **289a** of Gambia. Mult.
3686 $1 Martin Luther King Jr (civil rights leader) 45 50
3687 $1 Socrates (Greek philosopher) (56×41 mm) 45 50
3688 $1 Sir Thomas More (English scholar) (56×41 mm) 45 50
3689 $1 Chaim Weizmann (first President of Israel) 45 50
3690 $1 Alexander Solzhenitsyn (Russian writer) 45 50
3691 $1 Galileo Galilei (Italian astronomer) (56×41 mm) 45 50
3692 $1 Michael Servetus (Spanish theologian) (56×41 mm) 45 50
3693 $1 Salman Rushdie (British novelist) 45 50
No. 3692 is inscribed "MICHAEL SERVENTUS" in error.

460 Robert H. Goddard (rocket scientist)

1999. Space Exploration. Multicoloured.
3695 $1.50 Type **460** 65 70
3696 $1.50 Wernher von Braun (rocket scientist) 65 70
3697 $1.50 Yuri A. Gagarin (first cosmonaut to orbit Earth, 1961) 65 70
3698 $1.50 "Freedom 7" (first American manned Space flight, 1961) 65 70
3699 $1.50 Aleksei Leonov (first Russian to walk in Space, 1965) 65 70
3700 $1.50 Neil Armstrong and Edwin Aldrin (first astronauts on Moon, 1969) 65 70
3701 $1.50 "Mariner 9" (first spacecraft to orbit Mars, 1971) 65 70
3702 $1.50 "Voyager 1" (Jupiter probe, 1979) 65 70
3703 $1.50 Bruce McCandless (first astronaut to work in Space unattached, 1984) 65 70
3704 $1.50 "Giotto" probe (study of Halley's Comet, 1986) 65 70
3705 $1.50 Space Shuttle "Atlantis" (launch of "Galileo" probe, 1989) 65 70
3706 $1.50 "Magellan" (Venus probe, 1990) 65 70
Nos. 3695/3700 and 3701/6 were respectively printed together, se-tenant, with the backgrounds forming composite designs.

461 Goofy as Best Man

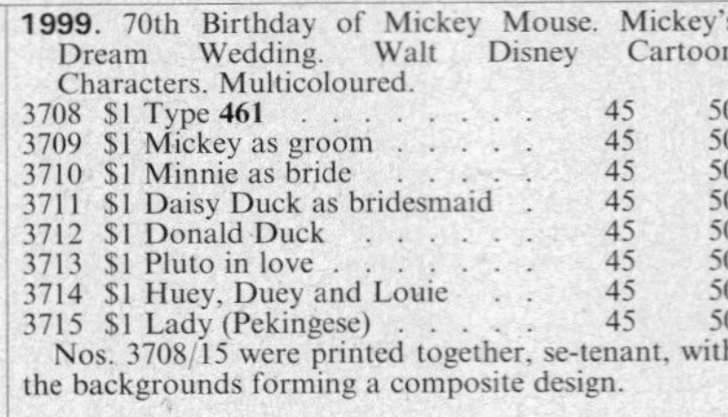

1999. 70th Birthday of Mickey Mouse. Mickey's Dream Wedding. Walt Disney Cartoon Characters. Multicoloured.
3708 $1 Type **461** 45 50
3709 $1 Mickey as groom 45 50
3710 $1 Minnie as bride 45 50
3711 $1 Daisy Duck as bridesmaid 45 50
3712 $1 Donald Duck 45 50
3713 $1 Pluto in love 45 50
3714 $1 Huey, Duey and Louie 45 50
3715 $1 Lady (Pekingese) 45 50
Nos. 3708/15 were printed together, se-tenant, with the backgrounds forming a composite design.

462 Grand Trunk Western, U.S.A.

1999. Trains of the World. Multicoloured.
3717 25 c. Type **462** 10 15
3718 35 c. Louisville & Nashville, U.S.A. 15 20
3719 45 c. Gulf, Mobile and Ohio, U.S.A. 20 25
3720 75 c. Missouri Pacific, U.S.A. 35 40
3721 90 c. "RTG" National Railway, France 40 45
3722 $1 Florida East Coast, U.S.A. 45 50
3723 $1.50 Rio Grande, U.S.A. 65 70
3724 $1.50 Erie Lackawanna, U.S.A. 65 70
3725 $1.50 New York Central, U.S.A. 65 70
3726 $1.50 Pennsylvania, U.S.A. 65 70
3727 $1.50 Milwaukee Road, U.S.A. 65 70
3728 $1.50 Illinois Central, U.S.A. 65 70
3729 $1.50 Burlington Route, U.S.A. 65 70
3730 $1.50 "Texas Special", Missouri, Kansas and Texas, U.S.A. 65 70
3731 $1.50 City of Los Angeles, U.S.A. 65 70
3732 $1.50 Northwestern, U.S.A. 65 70
3733 $1.50 Canadian National 65 70
3734 $1.50 Rock Island, U.S.A. 65 70
3735 $1.50 TGV, French National Railways 65 70
3736 $1.50 HST, British Railways 65 70
3737 $1.50 TEE, Trans Europe Express 65 70
3738 $1.50 Ancona Express, Italy 65 70
3739 $1.50 XPT, Australia 65 70
3740 $1.50 APT-P, British Railways 65 70
3741 $1.50 Western Pacific, U.S.A. 65 70
3742 $1.50 Union Pacific, U.S.A. 65 70
3743 $1.50 Chesapeake and Ohio, U.S.A. 65 70
3744 $1.50 Southern Pacific, U.S.A. 65 70
3745 $1.50 Baltimore and Ohio, U.S.A. 65 70
3746 $1.50 Wabash, U.S.A. 65 70
3747 $3 Kansas City Southern, U.S.A. 1·25 1·40
3748 $4 New Haven, U.S.A. 1·75 1·90
Nos. 3723/8, 3729/34, 3735/40 and 3741/6 respectively were printed together, se-tenant, with the backgrounds forming composite designs.

463 "Papilio blumei" (butterfly)

1999. "Australia '99" World Stamp Exhibition, Melbourne. Wildlife. Multicoloured.
3750 75 c. Type **463** 35 40
3751 75 c. Egret 35 40
3752 75 c. Kumarahou (flower) 35 40
3753 75 c. Javan rhinoceros 35 40
3754 75 c. Silver-eye (bird) 35 40
3755 75 c. Kiore (rodent) 35 40
3756 75 c. "Cyclorana novaehollandiae" (frog) 35 40
3757 75 c. Caterpillar 35 40
3758 75 c. Grey duck 35 40
3759 75 c. Honey blue-eye (fish) 35 40
3760 75 c. Krefft's turtle 35 40
3761 75 c. Archer fish 35 40
3762 75 c. Binturong (vert) 35 40
3763 75 c. Two Indian elephants (vert) 35 40
3764 75 c. Indian elephant (vert) 35 40
3765 75 c. Chestnut-capped laughing thrush (vert) 35 40
3766 75 c. "Vanda hookeriana" (orchid) (vert) 35 40
3767 75 c. Heron (vert) 35 40
3768 75 c. Fur seal (vert) 35 40
3769 75 c. Shag (bird) (vert) 35 40
3770 75 c. Round batfish (vert) 35 40
3771 75 c. Loggerhead turtle (vert) 35 40
3772 75 c. Three harlequin sweetlips (vert) 35 40
3773 75 c. Two harlequin sweetlips (vert) 35 40
3774 $1 Orang-utan 45 50
3775 $2 Douroucouli (monkey) 85 90
3776 $3 Black caiman (alligator) 1·25 1·40
3777 $4 Panther ("Black Leopard") (vert) 1·75 1·90
Nos. 3750/61 and 3762/73 respectively were printed together, se-tenant, with the backgrounds forming composite designs.
Nos. 3753 and 3775 were inscribed "JAUAN RHINOCEROS" and "DOUROCOULI" in error.

1999. "iBRA '99" International Stamp Exhibition, Nuremberg. Horiz designs as T **298a** of Gambia. Multicoloured.
3779 75 c. Railway locomotive, 1893, and Prussia 1860 ½ sgr. stamp 35 40
3780 90 c. "Humboldt" (sailing ship) and Mecklenburg-Schwerin 1856 4 × ¼ s. 40 45
3781 $1 Railway locomotive, 1893, and Saxony 1850 3 pf. 45 50
3782 $2 "Humboldt" (sailing ship) and Mecklenburg-Strelitz 1864 ½ sgr. 85 90

1999. 150th Death Anniv of Katsushika Hokusai (Japanese artist). As T **298b** of Gambia. Multicoloured.
3784 $1.50 "The Actor Ichikawa Danjuro Danjuro as Tomoe Gozen" 65 70
3785 $1.50 "Washing Clothes" (drawing) 65 70
3786 $1.50 "The Prostitute of Eguchi" 65 70
3787 $1.50 "Sudden Shower from a Fine Sky" 65 70
3788 $1.50 "Hanging Clothes out to dry" (drawing) 65 70
3789 $1.50 "Shimada" 65 70
3790 $1.50 "Head of Old Man" 65 70
3791 $1.50 "Piebald Horse" (drawing) 65 70
3792 $1.50 "Girl making Cord for binding Hats" 65 70
3793 $1.50 "Li Po admiring Waterfall of Lo-shan" 65 70
3794 $1.50 "Bay Horse" (drawing) 65 70
3795 $1.50 "Potted Dwarf Pine with Basin" 65 70
No. 3788 is inscribed "DRAWINFS" in error.

1999. 10th Anniv of United Nations Rights of the Child Convention. As T **298c** of Gambia. Multicoloured.
3797 $3 Eskimo girl and Russian boy 1·25 1·40
3798 $3 American girl 1·25 1·40
3799 $3 African boy and Indian girl 1·25 1·40
Nos. 3797/9 were printed together, se-tenant, forming a composite design.

1999. 250th Birth Anniv of Johann von Goethe (German poet and dramatist). Multicoloured designs as T **298d** of Gambia.
3802 $3 mauve, purple and black 1·25 1·40
3803 $3 blue, lilac and black 1·25 1·40
3804 $3 violet, deep violet and black 1·25 1·40
DESIGNS: No. 3802, Faust contemplating Moon; 3803, Goethe and Friedrich von Schiller (dramatist); 3804, Faust talking with Wagner.

1999. 30th Anniv of First Manned Landing on Moon. Horiz designs as T **298e** of Gambia. Multicoloured.
3806 $1.50 The Moon 65 70
3807 $1.50 Edward White on first space walk 65 70
3808 $1.50 Edwin "Buzz" Aldrin 65 70
3809 $1.50 The Earth 65 70
3810 $1.50 Michael Collins 65 70
3811 $1.50 Neil Armstrong 65 70
3812 $1.50 Footprint on the Moon 65 70
3813 $1.50 V2 rocket 65 70
3814 $1.50 Command module "Columbia" 65 70
3815 $1.50 Lunar Rover 65 70
3816 $1.50 Lunar module "Eagle" 65 70
3817 $1.50 Command module re-entering Earth's atmosphere 65 70

464 Astronaut with Letter

1999. 125th Anniv of Universal Postal Union. Space Mail. Multicoloured.
3819 $2 Type **464** 85 90
3820 $2 Supply spaceship "Progress" 85 90
3821 $2 Postmark of space station "MIR" 85 90
3822 $2 Buran shuttle and "MIR" 85 90

465 "Carry On Doctor"

1999. 50th Anniv of the Variety Club of Great Britain. Scenes from "Carry On" Films. Multicoloured.
3824 $1 "Carry On Dick" 45 50
3825 $1 Type **465** 45 50
3826 $1 "Carry On England" . . . 45 50
3827 $1 "Carry On Matron" . . . 45 50
3828 $1 "Carry On Round The Bend" 45 50
3829 $1 "Carry On Up The Jungle" . 45 50
3830 $1 "Carry On Loving" 45 50
3831 $1 "Carry On Up The Khyber" 45 50

1999. Royal Wedding. As T **298** of Gambia. Multicoloured.
3833 $3 Prince Edward . . . . . . 1·25 1·40
3834 $3 Sophie and Prince Edward . 1·25 1·40
3835 $3 Sophie Rhys-Jones . . . . 1·25 1·40

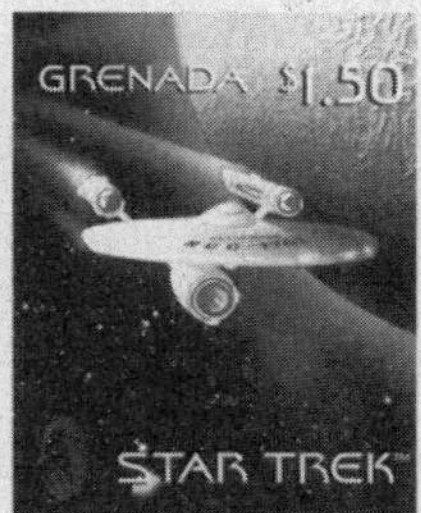

466 "U.S.S. Enterprise NCC" 1701 (from original series)

1999. Spacecraft of "Star Trek". Multicoloured.
3837 $1.50 Type **466** 65 70
3838 $1.50 Kazon warship (blue and orange planets in background) (Voyager series) . . 65 70
3839 $1.50 "U.S.S. Enterprise" 1701 (green planet in background) (Next Generation series) . . 65 70
3840 $1.50 "Voyager" (below blue planet) 65 70
3941 $1.50 "Romulan" (in front of orange planet) (original series) 65 70
3942 $1.50 "U.S.S. Enterprise" 1701 (pink planet in background) (original series) 65 70
3943 $1.50 "Borg Cube" (Next Generation series) 65 70
3944 $1.50 "U.S.S. Enterprise NCC" 1701 (in front of multicoloured flames) 65 70
3945 $1.50 Klingon "Bird of Prey" (original series) 65 70

1999. "Queen Elizabeth the Queen Mother's Century". As T **304a** of Gambia.
3846 $2 black and gold 85 90
3847 $2 multicoloured 85 90
3848 $2 black and gold 85 90
3849 $2 multicoloured 85 90
DESIGNS: No. 3846, Queen Mother with Prince Charles, 1948; 3847, Queen Mother in pink outfit, 1970; 3848, Queen Mother in Australia, 1958; 3849, Queen Mother waving.

467 George Gershwin

1999. American Entertainers. Multicoloured.
3851 $1 Type **467** 45 50
3852 $1 Florence Mills 45 50
3853 $1 Sam Beckett 45 50
3854 $1 Bessie Smith 45 50
3855 $1 Billie Holiday 45 50
3856 $1 Bert Williams 45 50
3857 $1 Cole Porter 45 50
3858 $1 Sofie Tucker 45 50
3859 $1 Lon Chaney 45 50
3860 $1 Buster Keaton 45 50
3861 $1 Norma Shearer 45 50
3862 $1 James Cagney 45 50
3863 $1 Hedda Hopper 45 50
3864 $1 Jean Harlow 45 50
3865 $1 Marlene Dietrich 45 50
3866 $1 Ramon Novarro 45 50
Nos. 3885/8 and 3859/66 respectively were printed together, se-tenant, with the backgrounds forming composite designs.

468 Ouranosaurus

1999. Prehistoric Animals. Multicoloured.
3868 35 c. Type **468** 15 20
3869 45 c. Struthiomimus (vert) . . . 20 25
3870 75 c. Parasaurolophus (vert) . . 35 40
3871 $1 Archaeopteryx 45 50
3872 $1 Brachiosaurus 45 50
3873 $1 Dilophosaurus 45 50
3874 $1 Dimetrodon 45 50
3875 $1 Psittacosaurus 45 50
3876 $1 Acrocanthosaurus 45 50
3877 $1 Stenonychosaurus 45 50
3878 $1 Dryosaurus 45 50
3879 $1 Campsognathus 45 50
3880 $1 Agathaumus 45 50
3881 $1 Camarosaurus 45 50
3882 $1 Quetzalcoatlus 45 50
3883 $1 Alioramus 45 50
3884 $1 Camptosaurus 45 50
3885 $1 Albertosaurus 45 50
3886 $1 Anatosaurus 45 50
3887 $1 Spinosaurus 45 50
3888 $1 Centrosaurus 45 50
3889 $2 Triceratops 85 90
3890 $3 Stegoceras . . . . 1·25 1·40
3891 $4 Stegosaurus . . . . 1·75 1·90
Nos. 3871/9 and 3880/8 were printed together, se-tenant, with the backgrounds forming a composite design.
No. 3871 is inscribed "ARCHEOPTERYX" in error.

469 Christmas Rose

1999. Christmas. Multicoloured.
3893 20 c. Type **469** 10 10
3894 75 c. Tulip 35 40
3895 90 c. Pear 40 45
3896 $1 Hibiscus 45 50
3897 $4 Lily . . . . 1·75 1·90

1999. Faces of the Millennium: Diana, Princess of Wales. Vert designs as T **307** of Gambia showing collage of miniature flower photographs. Multicoloured.
3899 $1 Top of head (face value at left) 45 50
3900 $1 Top of head (face value at right) 45 50
3901 $1 Ear (face value at left) . . . 45 50
3902 $1 Eye and temple (face value at right) 45 50
3903 $1 Cheek (face value at left) . . 45 50
3904 $1 Cheek (face value at right) . 45 50
3905 $1 Blue background (face value at left) 45 50
3906 $1 Chin (face value at right) . . 45 50
Nos. 3899/906 were printed together, se-tenant, and when viewed as a whole, form a portrait of Diana, Princess of Wales.

OFFICIAL STAMPS

1992. Optd **P.R.G.** (a) Nos. 1085/97 and 1099.
O 1 5 c. West Indiaman barque, c. 1840 . . . . 30 20
O 2 6 c. R.M.S.P. "Orinoco", c. 1851 . . . . 30 20
O 3 10 c. Working schooner . . . 30 20
O 4 12 c. Trimaran at Grand Anse anchorage 30 20
O 5 15 c. Spice Island cruising yacht "Petite Amie" 30 20
O 6 20 c. Fishing pirogue 35 20
O 7 25 c. Harbour police launch . 40 30
O 8 30 c. Grand Anse speedboat . 40 30
O 9 40 c. M.V. "Seimstrand" . . . 50 30
O10 50 c. Three-masted schooner "Ariadne" 60 40
O11 90 c. M.V. "Geestide" 90 80
O12 $! M.V "Cunard Countess" . 90 80
O13 $3 Rum-runner . . . . . . 2·25 3·75
O14 $10 Coast-guard patrol boat . 6·00 12·00

(b) Nos. 1130/2 and 113/4.
O15 30 c. Prince Charles and Lady Diana Spencer . . . . . 1·50 2·25
O16 40 c. Holyrood House . . . . 2·25 2·75
O17 50 c. Prince Charles and Lady Diana Spencer . . . . . 1·25 2·00
O18 $2 Holyrood House . . . . . 2·25 3·50
O19 $4 Type **268** . . . . 5·00 8·00

POSTAGE DUE STAMPS

D 1

1892.
D 8 D **1** 1d. black . . . . 3·00 7·00
D 9 2d. black . . . . 10·00 1·75
D10 3d. black . . . . 12·00 6·00

1892. Surch **SURCHARGE POSTAGE** and value.
D4 **13** 1d. on 6d. mauve . . . . . 75·00 1·25
D5 1d. on 8d. brown . . . . . £600 3·25
D6 2d. on 6d. mauve . . . . . £140 2·50
D7 2d. on 8d. brown . . . . . £1100 9·50

1921. As Type D **1** but inscr "POSTAGE DUE" instead of "SURCHARGE POSTAGE".
D11 D **1** 1d. black . . . . 90 1·00
D12 1½d. black . . . . 8·50 17·00
D13 2d. black . . . . 2·00 1·75
D14 3d. black . . . . 2·00 4·25

1952. As last but currency changed.
D15 D **1** 3 c. black . . . . 30 5·50
D16 4 c. black . . . . 30 11·00
D17 6 c. black . . . . 45 11·00
D18 8 c. black . . . . 75 11·00

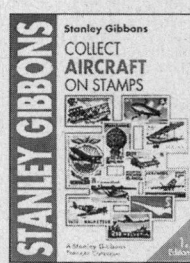

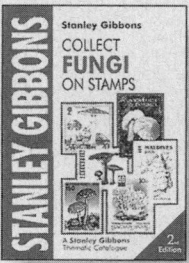

GRENADINES OF GRENADA (CARRIACOU AND PETITE MARTINIQUE) Pt. 1

The southern part of the group, attached to Grenada. Main islands Petit Martinique and Carriacou. From 1999 stamps were inscribed "Grenada Carriacou and Petite Martinique".

100 cents = 1 dollar

1973. Royal Wedding. Nos. 582/3 of Grenada optd **GRENADINES**.

1 **196** 25 c. multicoloured 20 10
2 $2 multicoloured 70 50

1974. Stamps of Grenada optd **GRENADINES**.

4 1 c. multicoloured (No. 306) . . 10 10
5 2 c. multicoloured (No. 307) . . 10 10
6 3 c. multicoloured (No. 308) . . 10 10
7 5 c. multicoloured (No. 309) . . 15 10
8 8 c. multicoloured (No. 311) . . 15 10
9 10 c. multicoloured (No. 312) . . 15 10
10 12 c. multicoloured (No. 313) . . 20 10
11 25 c. multicoloured (No. 315) . . 45 10
12 $1 multicoloured (No. 318) . . . 2·50 45
13 $2 multicoloured (No. 319) . . . 3·00 1·25
14 $3 multicoloured (No. 320) . . . 3·00 1·75
15 $5 multicoloured (No. 321) . . . 3·75 2·25

1974. World Cup Football Championships. As Nos. 619/26 of Grenada, but inscr "GRENADA GRENADINES".

16 ½ c. multicoloured 10 10
17 1 c. multicoloured 10 10
18 2 c. multicoloured 10 10
19 10 c. multicoloured 20 10
20 25 c. multicoloured 25 10
21 50 c. multicoloured 30 15
22 75 c. multicoloured 30 20
23 $1 multicoloured 35 25

1974. Cent. of U.P.U. As Nos. 628/30 and 633 of Grenada, but inscr "GRENADA GRENADINES".

25 8 c. multicoloured 10 10
26 25 c. multicoloured 15 10
27 35 c. multicoloured 15 10
28 $1 multicoloured 70 40

174. Birth Cent. of Sir Winston Churchill. As Nos. 637/8 of Grenada, but inscr "GRENADA GRENADINES".

30 35 c. multicoloured 15 10
31 $2 multicoloured 40 45

1974. Christmas. As Nos. 640/7 of Grenada but inscr "GRENADA GRENADINES" and background colours changed.

33 **204** ½ c. multicoloured 10 10
34 – 1 c. multicoloured 10 10
35 – 2 c. multicoloured 10 10
36 – 3 c. multicoloured 10 10
37 – 10 c. multicoloured 10 10
38 – 25 c. multicoloured 10 10
39 – 50 c. multicoloured 15 15
40 – $1 multicoloured 30 25

1975. Big Game Fishing. As Nos. 669/76 of Grenada inscr "GRENADA GRENADINES" and background colours changed.

42 ½ c. multicoloured 10 10
43 1 c. multicoloured 10 10
44 2 c. multicoloured 10 10
45 10 c. multicoloured 10 10
46 25 c. multicoloured 15 10
47 50 c. multicoloured 20 15
48 70 c. multicoloured 25 20
49 $1 multicoloured 35 35

1975. Flowers. As Nos. 678/85 of Grenada inscr "GRENADINES".

51 ½ c. multicoloured 10 10
52 1 c. multicoloured 10 10
53 2 c. multicoloured 10 10
54 3 c. multicoloured 10 10
55 10 c. multicoloured 10 10
56 25 c. multicoloured 10 10
57 50 c. multicoloured 20 15
58 $1 multicoloured 30 20

CANCELLED REMAINDERS*. Some of the following issues have been remaindered, cancelled-to-order, at a fraction of their face value. For all practical purposes these are indistinguishable from genuine postally used copies. Our used quotations which are indicated by an asterisk are the same for cancelled-to-order or postally used copies.

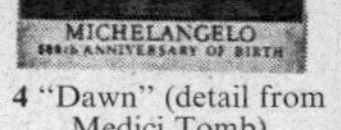

3 "Christ Crowned with Thorns" (Titian)   4 "Dawn" (detail from Medici Tomb)

1975. Easter. Paintings showing Crucifixion and Deposition by artists listed. Multicoloured.

60 ½ c. Type **3** 10 10*
61 1 c. Giotto 10 10*
62 2 c. Tintoretto 10 10*
63 3 c. Cranach 10 10*
64 35 c. Caravaggio 15 10*
65 75 c. Tiepolo 20 10*
66 $2 Velasquez 40 15*

1975. 500th Anniv of Michelangelo. Multicoloured.

68 ½ c. Type **4** 10 10*
69 1 c. "Delphic Sibyl" 10 10*
70 2 c. "Giuliano de Medici" 10 10*
71 40 c. "The Creation" (detail) . . 15 10*
72 50 c. "Lorenzo de Medici" . . . 15 10*
73 75 c. "Persian Sibyl" 20 10*
74 $2 "Head of Christ" 30 15*

1975. Butterflies. As T **213** of Grenada but inscr "GRENADINES". Multicoloured.

76 ½ c. "Morpho peleides" 10 10*
77 1 c. "Danaus eresimus" ("Danaus gilippus") 10 10*
78 2 c. "Dismorphia amphione" . . 10 10*
79 35 c. "Hamadryas feronia" . . . 35 10*
80 45 c. "Philaethria dido" 45 10*
81 75 c. "Phoebis argante" 70 15*
82 $2 "Prepona laertes" . . . . . 1·40 30*

5 Progress "Standard" Badge

1975. 14th World Scout Jamboree, Norway. Multicoloured.

84 ½ c. Type **5** 10 10*
85 1 c. Boatman's badge 10 10*
86 2 c. Coxswain's badge 10 10*
87 35 c. Interpreter's badge 15 10*
88 45 c. Ambulance badge 20 10*
89 75 c. Chief Scout's award 25 10*
90 $2 Queen's Scout award 35 15*

6 The Surrender of Lord Cornwallis

1975. Bicentenary of America Revolution (1976) (1st issue). Multicoloured.

92 ½ c. Type **6** 10 10*
93 1 c. Minute-men 10 10*
94 2 c. Paul Revere's ride 10 10*
95 3 c. Battle of Bunker Hill . . . 10 10*
96 5 c. Fifer and drummers 10 10*
97 45 c. Backwoodsman 20 10*
98 75 c. Boston Tea Party 30 10*
99 $2 Naval engagement 60 10*
100 $2 George Washington 60 35
101 $2 White House and flags . . . 60 35

Nos. 100/1 are larger, 35 × 60 mm.

7 Fencing

1975. Pan-American Games, Mexico City. Multicoloured.

103 ½ c. Type **7** 10 10*
104 1 c. Hurdling 10 10*
105 2 c. Pole-vaulting 10 10*
106 35 c. Weightlifting 15 10*
107 45 c. Throwing the javelin . . . 15 10*
108 75 c. Throwing the discus . . . 15 10*
109 $2 Diving 35 15*

1975. Nos. 649/68 of Grenada additionally inscr "GRENADINES".

111 ½ c. Yachts, Point Saline . . . 10 30
112 1 c. Yacht Club race, St. George's 10 15
113 2 c. Carenage taxi 10 15
114 3 c. Large working boats . . . 10 15
115 5 c. Deep-water dock, St. George's 10 15
116 6 c. Cocoa beans in drying trays 10 15
117 8 c. Nutmegs 10 15
118 10 c. Rum distillery, River Antoine Estate, c. 1785 . . . 10 15
119 12 c. Cocoa tree 10 15
120 15 c. Fishermen at Fontenoy . . 10 15
121 20 c. Parliament Building . . . 10 40
122 25 c. Fort George cannons . . . 10 15
123 35 c. Pearls Airport 50 15
124 50 c. General Post Office . . . 20 75
125 75 c. Carib's Leap, Sauteurs Bay 40 60
126 $1 Carenage, St. George's . . . 60 85
127 $2 St. George's Harbour by night 90 2·00
128 $3 Grand Anse beach . . . . 1·10 2·50
129 $5 Canoe Bay and Black Bay . 1·50 5·00
130 $10 Sugar-loaf Island . . . . . 2·25 5·50

8 Virgin and Child" (Durer)   9 Bleeding Tooth

1975. Christmas. "Virgin and Child" paintings by Artists named.

131 ½ c. Type **8** 10 10*
132 1 c. Durer 10 10*
133 2 c. Correggio 10 10*
134 40 c. Botticelli 15 10*
135 50 c. Niccolo da Cremona . . . 15 10*
136 75 c. Correggio 15 10*
137 $2 Correggio 30 15*

1976. Shells. Multicoloured.

139 ½ c. Type **9** 10 10*
140 1 c. Toothed donax 10 10*
141 2 c. Hawk-wing conch 10 10*
142 3 c. Atlantic distorsio 10 10*
143 25 c. Scotch bonnet 40 10*
144 50 c. King helmet 70 10*
145 75 c. Queen or pink conch . . 1·00 15*

10 Cocoa Thrush

1976. Flora and Fauna. Multicoloured.

147 ½ c. "Lignum vitae" 10 10*
148 1 c. Type **10** 10 10*
149 2 c. "Eurypelma sp." (spider) . 10 10*
150 35 c. Hooded tanager . . . . . 1·25 10*
151 50 c. "Nyctaginaceae" . . . . 1·00 15*
152 75 c. Grenada dove . . . . . 2·50 25*
153 $1 Marine toad . . . . 2·50 25*

11 Hooked Sailfish

1976. Tourism. Multicoloured.

155 ½ c. Type **11** 10 10*
156 1 c. Careened schooner, Carriacou 10 10*
157 2 c. Carriacou Annual Regatta . 10 10*
158 18 c. Boat building on Carriacou 20 10*
159 22 c. Workboat race, Carriacou Regatta 20 10*
160 75 c. Cruising off Petit Martinique 30 20*
161 $1 Water skiing 40 20*

12 Making a Camp Fire

1976. 50th Anniv of Girl Guides in Grenada. Multicoloured.

163 ½ c. Type **12** 10 10*
164 1 c. First aid 10 10*
165 2 c. Nature study 10 10*
166 50 c. Cookery 65 15*
167 $1 Sketching . . . . 1·00 25*

13 "Christ Mocked" (Bosch)   15 Piper Apache

14 "South Carolina" (frigate)

1976. Easter. Multicoloured.

169 ½ c. Type **13** 10 10*
170 1 c. "Christ Crucified" (Antonello da Messina) . . . 10 10*
171 2 c. "Adoration of the Trinity" (Durer) 10 10*
172 3 c. "Lamentation of Christ" (Durer) 10 10*
173 35 c. "The Entombment" (Van der Weyden) 20 10*
174 $3 "The Entombment" (Raphael) 75 30*

1976. Bicentenary of American Revolution (2nd issue). Multicoloured.

176 ½ c. Type **14** 10 10*
177 1 c. "Lee" (schooner) 10 10*
178 2 c. H.M.S. "Roebuck" (frigate) 10 10*
179 35 c. "Andrew Doria" (brig) . . 50 10*
180 50 c. "Providence" (sloop) . . . 60 15*
181 $1 "Alfred" (frigate) . . . . . 1·00 20*
182 $2 "Confederacy" (frigate) . . 1·50 30*

1976. Aircraft. Multicoloured.

184 ½ c. Type **15** 10 10*
185 1 c. Beech 50 Twin Bonanza . . 10 10*
186 2 c. De Havilland Twin Otter . . 10 10*
187 40 c. Britten Norman Islander . 30 10*
188 50 c. De Havilland Heron 2 . . 40 10*
189 $2 Hawker Siddeley H.S.748 . . 1·25 25*

16 Cycling

1976. Olympic Games, Montreal. Multicoloured.

191 ½ c. Type **16** 10 10*
192 1 c. Pommel horse 10 10*
193 2 c. Hurdling 10 10*
194 35 c. Shot putting 10 10*
195 45 c. Diving 15 10*
196 75 c. Sprinting 15 10*
197 $2 Rowing 35 25*

17 "Virgin and Child" (Cima)

1976. Christmas. Multicoloured.

199 ½ c. Type **17** 10 10*
200 1 c. "The Nativity" (Romanino) 10 10*
201 2 c. "The Nativity" (Romanino) (different) 10 10*
202 35 c. "Adoration of the Kings" (Bruegel) 15 10*
203 50 c. "Madonna and Child" (Girolamo) 20 10*
204 75 c. "Adoration of the Magi" (Giorgione) (horiz) 20 15*
205 $2 "Adoration of the Kings" (School of Fra Angelico) (horiz) 40 25*

18 Alexander Graham Bell and First Telephone

1977. Centenary of First Telephone Transmission. Designs showing Alexander Graham Bell and telephone. Multicoloured.

207 ½ c. Type **18** 10 10*
208 1 c. 1895 telephone 10 10*
209 2 c. 1900 telephone 10 10*
210 35 c. 1915 telephone 15 10*
211 75 c. 1920 telephone 20 10*
212 $1 1929 telephone 25 15*
213 $2 1963 telephone 35 25*

19 Coronation Coach

1977. Silver Jubilee. Multicoloured. (a) Perf.

215 35 c. Type **19** 10 10*
216 $2 Queen entering Abbey . . . 20 10*
217 $4 Queen crowned 35 25*

(b) Imperf × roul. Self-adhesive.

219 35 c. Royal visit 15 20
220 50 c. Crown of St. Edward . . . 30 80
221 $2 The Queen and Prince Charles 50 1·60
222 $5 Royal Standard . . . . . . 60 1·75

Nos. 219/22 come from booklets.

21 "Disrobing of Christ" (Fra Angelico)
22 "The Virgin adoring the Child" (Correggio)

1977. Easter. Paintings by artists named. Mult.

223 ½ c. Type **21** 10 10*
224 1 c. Fra Angelico 10 10*
225 2 c. El Greco 10 10*
226 18 c. El Greco 10 10*
227 35 c. Fra Angelico 15 10*
228 50 c. Giottino 20 10*
229 $2 Antonello da Messina . . . 50 25*

1977. Christmas. Multicoloured.

231 ½ c. Type **22** 10 10*
232 1 c. "Virgin and Child" (Giorgione) 10 10*
233 2 c. "Virgin and Child" (Morales) 10 10*
234 18 c. "Madonna della Tenda" (Raphael) 10 10*
235 35 c. "Rest on the Flight into Egypt" (Van Dyck) 15 10*
236 50 c. "Madonna and Child" (Lippi) 20 10*
237 $2 "Virgin and Child" (Lippi) (different) 60 25*

1977. Royal Visit. Nos. 215/17 optd **ROYAL VISIT W.I. 1977.**

239 35 c. Type **19** 10 10
240 $2 Queen entering Abbey . . . 25 20
241 $4 Queen crowned 40 30

24 Life-saving

1977. Caribbean Scout Jamboree, Jamaica. Multicoloured.

243 ½ c. Type **24** 10 10*
244 1 c. Overnight hike 10 10*
245 2 c. Cubs tying knots 10 10*
246 22 c. Erecting a tent 15 10*
247 35 c. Gang show limbo dance . . . 25 10*
248 75 c. Campfire cooking 40 15*
249 $3 Sea Scouts in "Mirror" dinghies 80 30*

25 Blast-off

1977. Space Shuttle. Multicoloured.

251 ½ c. Type **25** 10 10*
252 1 c. Booster jettison 10 10*
253 2 c. External tank jettison . . . 10 10*
254 22 c. Working in orbit 15 10*
255 50 c. Shuttle re-entry 25 10*
256 $3 Shuttle landing 85 30*

26 Alfred Nobel and Physiology/Medicine Medal

1978. Nobel Prize Awards. Multicoloured.

258 ½ c. Type **26** 10 10*
259 1 c. Physics and Chemistry medal . 10 10*
260 2 c. Peace medal (reverse) . . . 10 10*
261 22 c. Nobel Institute, Oslo . . . 25 10*
262 75 c. Peace Prize committee . . 50 15*
263 $3 Literature medal . . . . 1·50 30*

27 German Zeppelin Stamp, 1930

1978. 75th Anniv of First Zeppelin Flight and 50th Anniv of Lindbergh's Transatlantic Flight. Multicoloured.

265 5 c. Type **27** 20 10*
266 15 c. French Concorde stamp, 1970 . . . . 60 10*
267 25 c. Liechtenstein Zeppelin stamp, 1931 . . . . 20 10*
268 35 c. Panama Lindbergh stamp, 1928 . . . . 20 10*
269 50 c. Russia Airship stamp, 1931 . 25 10*
270 $3 Spanish Lindbergh stamp, 1930 . . . . 75 30*

28 Coronation Ring

1978. 25th Anniv of Coronation. Multicoloured. (a) Horiz designs. Perf.

272 50 c. Type **28** 10 10
273 $2 The Orb 25 30
274 $2.50 Imperial State Crown . . 30 35

(b) Vert designs. Roul × imperf. Self-adhesive.

276 18 c. Drummer, Royal Regiment of Fusiliers 15 35
277 50 c. Drummer, Royal Anglian Regiment 15 45
278 $5 Drum Major, Queen's Regiment . . . . 1·00 3·00

30 "Le Chapeau de Paille"
32 Audubon's Shearwater

31 Wright Flyer I

1978. 400th Birth Anniv of Rubens. Mult.

279 5 c. Type **30** 10 10
280 15 c. "Archilles slaying Hector" . 15 10
281 18 c. "Helene Fourment and her Children" 15 10
282 22 c. "Rubens and Isabella Brandt" 20 10
283 35 c. "The Ildefonso Altarpiece" . 20 10
284 $3 "Heads of Negroes" (detail) . 1·10 1·00

1978. 75th Anniv of Powered Flight.

286 **31** 5 c. black, blue & brown . . 10 10
287 – 15 c. black, brown & red . . 10 10
288 – 18 c. black, brown & red . . 10 10
289 – 25 c. black, yell. & green . . 10 10
290 – 35 c. black, pink & purple . 15 10
291 – 75 c. black, lilac & yellow . 25 25
292 – $3 black, violet & mve. . . 75 75

DESIGNS—HORIZ: 25 c. Wright Flyer III, 1905; 35 c. Wright glider No. 1; 75 c. Wright Flyer I (different); $3 Wright Type A. VERT: 15 c. Orville Wright; 18 c. Wilbur Wright.

1978. Birds. Multicoloured.

294 5 c. Type **32** 50 10
295 10 c. Semipalmated plover . . 70 10
296 18 c. Purple-throated carib (horiz) . . . . 1·00 15
297 22 c. Red-billed whistling duck (horiz) . . . . 1·00 20
298 40 c. Caribbean martin (horiz) . 1·50 35
299 $1 Yellow-tailed tropic bird . . 2·25 75
300 $2 Long-billed curlew . . . 3·25 1·25

33 Players with Ball
34 Captain Cook and Kalaniopu (King of Hawaii), 1778

1978. World Cup Football Championship, Argentina. Multicoloured.

302 15 c. Type **33** 10 10
303 35 c. Running with ball . . . 20 10
304 50 c. Player with ball . . . 25 20
305 $3 Heading 80 80

1978. 250th Birth Anniv of Captain James Cook. Multicoloured.

307 18 c. Type **34** 45 10
308 22 c. Cook and native of Hawaii . 60 15
309 50 c. Cook and death scene, 1779 1·00 30
310 $3 Cook and offering ceremony 2·25 1·75

35 "Virgin at Prayer"
36 "Strelitzia reginae"

1978. Christmas. Paintings by Durer. Multicoloured.

312 40 c. Type **35** 20 10
313 60 c. "The Dresden Altarpiece" . 25 15
314 90 c. "Madonna and Child with St. Anne" 30 15
315 $2 "Madonna and Child with Pear" 60 50

1979. Flowers. Multicoloured.

317 22 c. Type **36** 15 10
318 40 c. "Euphorbia pulcherrima" . 25 15
319 $1 "Heliconia humilis" . . . 45 30
320 $3 "Thunbergia alata" . . . 80 80

37 Children with Pig

1979. International Year of the Child. Multicoloured.

322 18 c. Type **37** 10 10
323 50 c. Children with donkey . . 20 25
324 $1 Children with goats . . . 25 30
325 $3 Children fishing 65 80

38 "20,000 Leagues under the Sea"

1979. 150th Birth Anniv of Jules Verne (author). Multicoloured.

327 18 c. Type **38** 30 10
328 38 c. "From the Earth to the Moon" 35 20
329 75 c. "From the Earth to the Moon" (different) . . . 45 35
330 $3 "Five Weeks in a Balloon" . 85 1·00

39 Sir Rowland Hill and Mail Van

1979. Death Centenary of Sir Rowland Hill. Multicoloured.

332 15 c. Type **39** 10 10
333 $1 "Britanis" (cargo liner) . . 20 20
334 $2 Diesel mail train . . . 30 30
335 $3 Concorde 90 70

40 "Virgin and Child Enthroned" (11th-century Byzantine)
42 Doctor Goofy

41 Great Hammerhead

1979. Christmas. Sculptures. Multicoloured.

337 6 c. Type **40** 10 10
338 25 c. "Presentation in the Temple" (Andre Beauneveu) . 10 10
339 30 c. "Flight to Egypt" (Utrecht, c. 1510) 10 10
340 40 c. "Madonna and Child" (Jacopo della Quercia) . . 10 10
341 90 c. "Madonna della Mela" (Luca della Robbia) . . . 15 15
342 $1 "Madonna and Child" (Antonio Rossellino) . . . 20 20
343 $2 "Madonna and Child" (Antwerp, 1700) 35 35

1979. Marine Wildlife. Multicoloured.

345 40 c. Type **41** 40 30
346 45 c. Spot-finned butterflyfish . 45 30
347 50 c. Permit (fish) 45 40
348 60 c. Threaded turban (shell) . 65 55
349 70 c. Milk conch 75 75
350 75 c. Great blue heron . . . 1·25 90
351 90 c. Colourful Atlantic moon (shell) . . . . 95 1·00
352 $1 Red-footed booby . . . . 1·75 1·75

1979. International Year of the Child. Walt Disney Cartoon Characters. Multicoloured.

354 ½ c. Type **42** 10 10
355 1 c. Admiral Mickey Mouse . . 10 10
356 2 c. Fireman Goofy 10 10
357 3 c. Nurse Minnie Mouse . . . 10 10
358 4 c. Drum Major Mickey Mouse . 10 10
359 5 c. Policeman Donald Duck . . 10 10
360 10 c. Pilot Donald Duck . . . 10 10
361 $2 Postman Goofy (horiz) . . . 2·25 2·25
362 $2.50 Train driver Donald Duck (horiz) . . . . 2·25 2·25

See also Nos. 434/7.

1980. 1st Anniv of Revolution. Nos. 116 and 119/30 optd **PEOPLE'S REVOLUTION 13 MARCH 1979.**

364 6 c. Cocoa beans in drying trays . 10 10
365 12 c. Cocoa tree 10 10
366 15 c. Fishermen at Fontenoy . . 10 10
367 20 c. Parliament Building, St. George's 10 10
368 25 c. Fort George cannons . . 15 10
369 35 c. Pearls Airport 20 10
370 50 c. General Post Office . . . 35 15
371 75 c. Carib's Leap, Sauteurs Bay . 40 20
372 $1 Carenage, St. George's . . . 55 30
373 $2 St. George's Harbour by night 85 70
374 $3 Grand Anse Beach . . . . 1·60 1·60
375 $5 Canoe Bay and Black Bay . 2·25 2·50
376 $10 Sugar-loaf Island . . . . 3·75 4·25

43 Classroom

1980. 75th Anniv of Rotary International. Multicoloured.

377 6 c. Type **43** 10 10
378 30 c. Different races encircling Rotary emblem 20 10
379 60 c. Rotary executive presenting doctor with cheque . . . 35 20
380 $3 Nurses with young patients . 1·60 75

44 Yellow-bellied Seedeater
45 Running

1980. Wild Birds. Multicoloured.

382 25 c. Type **44** 50 15
383 40 c. Blue-hooded euphonia . . 55 20
384 90 c. Yellow warbler . . . . 1·25 65
385 $2 Tropical mockingbird . . . 1·75 1·25

1980. Olympic Games, Moscow. Multicoloured.

387 30 c. Type **45** 20 15
388 40 c. Football 15 20
389 90 c. Boxing 35 35
390 $2 Wrestling 70 75

1980. "London 1980" International Stamp Exhibition. Nos. 332/5 optd **LONDON 1980**.

392 15 c. Mail van 15 15
393 $1 "Britanis" (cargo liner) . . . 75 35
394 $2 Diesel mail train . . . . 1·50 1·00
395 $3 Concorde . . . . 2·25 2·00

47 Long-jawed Squirrelfish

1980. Fishes. Multicoloured.

396 ½ c. Type **47** 10 10
397 1 c. Blue chromis 10 10
398 2 c. Four-eyed butterflyfish . . 10 10
399 4 c. Sergeant major 10 10

400 5 c. Yellow-tailed snapper 10 10
401 6 c. Mutton snapper 10 10
402 10 c. Cocoa damselfish 10 10
403 12 c. Royal gramma 10 10
404 15 c. Cherub angelfish 10 10
405 20 c. Black-barred soldierfish 15 10
406 25 c. Mottled grouper 15 15
407 30 c. Caribbean long-nosed butterflyfish 15 20
408 40 c. Puddingwife 20 25
409 50 c. Midnight parrotfish 25 35
410 90 c. Red-spotted hawkfish 40 55
411 $1 Hogfish 45 60
412 $3 Beau Gregory 1·25 1·50
413 $5 Rock beauty 2·00 2·50
414 $10 Barred hamlet 3·50 5·00

1980. Christmas. Scenes from Walt Disney's "Bambi". As T **42**. Multicoloured.
415 ½ c. Bambi with Mother 10 10
416 1 c. Bambi with quails 10 10
417 2 c. Bambi meets Thumper the rabbit 10 10
418 3 c. Bambi meets Flower the skunk 10 10
419 4 c. Bambi and Faline 10 10
420 5 c. Bambi with his father 10 10
421 10 c. Bambi on ice 10 10
422 $2.50 Faline with foals 1·75 1·25
423 $3 Bambi and Faline 1·75 1·25

48 "The Unicorn in Captivity" (15th century unknown artist)

49 "Bust of a Woman"

1981. Art Masterpieces. Multicoloured.
425 6 c. Type **48** 10 10
426 10 c. "The Fighting 'Temeraire'" (Turner) (horiz) 10 10
427 25 c. "Sunday Afternoon on the Ile de la Grande Jatte" (Seurat) (horiz) 15 15
428 90 c. "Max Schmitt in a Single Scull" (Eakins) (horiz.) 45 45
429 $2 "The Burial of the Count of Orgaz" (El Greco) 85 85
430 $3 "Portrait of George Washington" (Stuart) 1·10 1·10

1981. 50th Anniv of Walt Disney's Pluto (cartoon character). As T **42**.
432 $2 Mickey Mouse serving birthday cake to Pluto 90 80

1981. Easter. Walt Disney Cartoon Characters. As T **42**. Multicoloured.
434 35 c. Chip 20 20
435 40 c. Dewey 20 20
436 $2 Huey 60 60
437 $2.50 Mickey Mouse 75 75

1981. Birth Centenary of Picasso. Mult.
439 6 c. Type **49** 10 10
440 40 c. Woman (study for "Les Demoiselles d'Avignon") 25 15
441 90 c. "Nude with raised Arms (The Dancer of Avignon)" 40 30
442 $4 "The Dryad" 1·25 1·25

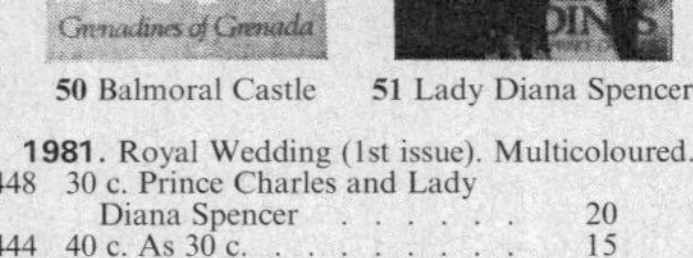

50 Balmoral Castle **51** Lady Diana Spencer

1981. Royal Wedding (1st issue). Multicoloured.
448 30 c. Prince Charles and Lady Diana Spencer 20 20
444 40 c. As 30 c. 15 15
449 40 c. Type **50** 35 35
445 $2 Type **50** 50 50
446 $4 Prince Charles as parachutist 90 90

1981. Royal Wedding (2nd issue). Multicoloured. Self-adhesive.
450 $1 Type **51** 20 35
451 $2 Prince Charles 25 50
452 $5 Prince Charles and Lady Diana Spencer (horiz) 1·25 2·00

INDEX

Countries can be quickly located by referring to the index at the end of this volume.

52 Amy Johnson (1st solo flight, Britain to Australia by Woman, May 1930)

54 Footballer

53 Boeing 747 SCA Carrier

1981. "Decade for Women". Famous Female Aviators. Multicoloured.
453 30 c. Type **52** 45 15
454 70 c. Mme. La Baronne de Laroche (1st qualified woman pilot, March 1910) 70 30
455 $1.10 Ruth Nichols (solo Atlantic flight attempt, June 1931) 80 40
456 $3 Amelia Earhart (1st North Atlantic solo flight by woman, May 1932) 1·75 1·10

1981. Christmas. Designs as T **42** showing scenes from Walt Disney's cartoon film "Lady and the Tramp".
458 ½ c. multicoloured 10 10
459 1 c. multicoloured 10 10
460 2 c. multicoloured 10 10
461 3 c. multicoloured 10 10
462 4 c. multicoloured 10 10
463 5 c. multicoloured 10 10
464 10 c. multicoloured 10 10
465 $2.50 multicoloured 3·00 1·25
466 $3 multicoloured 3·00 1·25

1981. Space Shuttle Project. Multicoloured.
468 10 c. Type **53** 30 10
469 40 c. Re-entry 65 15
470 $1.10 External tank separation 1·25 45
471 $3 Touchdown 1·75 1·00

1981. World Cup Football Championship, Spain (1982).
473 **54** 20 c. multicoloured 15 10
474 – 40 c. multicoloured 20 15
475 – $1 multicoloured 35 30
476 – $2 multicoloured 65 55
DESIGNS: 40 c. to $2 various designs showing footballers.

55 Mail Van and Stage-coach

1982. Cent of U.P.U. Membership. Multicoloured.
478 30 c. Type **55** 30 15
479 40 c. U.P.U. emblem 30 15
480 $2.50 "Queen Elizabeth 2" (liner) and sailing ship 1·50 70
481 $4 Concorde and De Havilland D.H.9 biplane 2·25 1·25

56 National Sports Meeting

1982. 75th Anniv of Boy Scout Movement and 125th Birth Anniv of Lord Baden-Powell. Multicoloured.
483 6 c. Type **56** 15 10
484 90 c. Sea scouts sailing 50 30
485 $1.10 Handicraft 65 60
486 $3 Animal tending 1·40 1·40

57 "Anartia jatrophae"

1982. Butterflies. Multicoloured.
488 30 c. Type **57** 75 30
489 40 c. "Chioides vintra" 80 35
490 $1.10 "Cynthia cardui" 1·75 75
491 $3 "Historis odius" 2·75 1·60

58 Prince and Princess of Wales

60 "Presentation of Christ in the Temple"

59 "New Deal" — Soil Conservation

1982. 21st Birthday of Princess of Wales. Multicoloured.
493 50 c. Blenheim Palace 50 90
494 60 c. As 50 c. 60 75
495 $1 Type **58** 70 1·60
496 $2 Type **58** 1·50 1·75
497 $3 Princess of Wales 2·00 2·25
498 $4 As $3 2·25 2·50

1982. Birth Centenary of Franklin D. Roosevelt. Multicoloured.
500 30 c. Type **59** 25 15
501 40 c. Roosevelt and George Washington Carver (scientist) 25 15
502 70 c. Civilian conservation corps (reafforestation) 40 30
503 $3 Roosevelt with Pres. Barclay of Liberia, Cassblanca Conference, 1943 1·00 90

1982. Birth of Prince William of Wales. Nos. 493/8 optd **ROYAL BABY 21.6.82**.
505 50 c. Blenheim Palace 50 50
506 60 c. As 50 c. 55 60
507 $1 Type **58** 70 75
508 $2 Type **58** 1·00 1·25
509 $3 Princess of Wales 1·25 1·75
510 $4 As $3 1·50 1·75

1982. Easter. Easter Paintings by Rembrandt. Multicoloured.
512 30 c. Type **60** 35 15
513 60 c. "Descent from the Cross" 45 20
514 $2 "Raising of the Cross" 85 75
515 $4 "Resurrection of Christ" 1·40 1·50

61 "Santa Fe", U.S.A.

1982. Famous Trains of the World. Mult.
517 10 c. Type **61** 50 15
518 40 c. "Mistral", France 70 20
519 70 c. "Rheingold", Germany 80 45
520 $1 "ET 403", France 1·00 50
521 $1.10 Steam locomotive "Mallard", Great Britain 1·25 60
522 $2 Tokaido Shinkansen "Hikari", Japan 1·40 90

62 Footballers

1982. World Cup Football Championship Winners.
524 **62** 60 c. multicoloured 75 35
525 $4 multicoloured 2·00 1·25

1982. Christmas. Scenes from Walt Disney's cartoon film "The Rescuers". As T **42**, but horiz.
527 ½ c. multicoloured 10 10
528 1 c. multicoloured 10 10
529 2 c. multicoloured 10 10
530 3 c. multicoloured 10 10
531 4 c. multicoloured 10 10
532 5 c. multicoloured 10 10
533 10 c. multicoloured 10 10
534 $2.50 multicoloured 2·75 1·75
535 $3 multicoloured 2·75 1·75

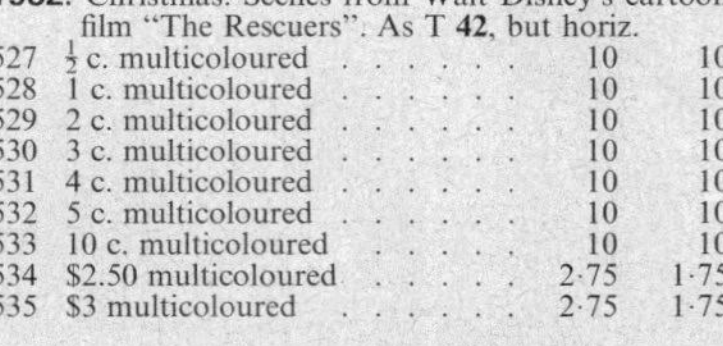

63 Short-finned Pilot Whale

1982. Save the Whale. Multicoloured.
537 10 c. Type **63** 85 55
538 60 c. Dall's porpoise 2·00 1·75
539 $1.10 Humpback whale 3·50 2·75
540 $3 Bowhead whale 6·00 7·00

64 "David and Goliath"

1983. 500th Anniv of Raphael. Multicoloured.
542 25 c. Type **64** 15 15
543 30 c. "David sees Bathsheba" 15 15
544 90 c. "Triumph of David" 30 35
545 $4 "Anointing of Solomon" 70 90

65 Voice and Visual Communication

1983. World Communications Year. Mult.
547 30 c. Type **65** 10 10
548 60 c. Ambulance 25 20
549 $1.10 Westland Whirlwind helicopters 45 45
550 $3 Satellite 1·00 1·00

66 Chrysler "Imperial Roadster", 1931

1983. 75th Anniv of Model "T" Ford Car. Multicoloured.
552 10 c. Type **66** 15 15
553 30 c. Doble steam car, 1925 25 25
554 40 c. Ford "Mustang", 1965 25 30
555 60 c. Packard tourer, 1930 35 40
556 70 c. Mercer "Raceabout", 1913 35 40
557 90 c. Corvette "Stingray", 1963 35 40
558 $1.10 Auburn "851 Supercharger Speedster", 1935 40 45
559 $2.50 Pierce-Arrow "Silver Arrow", 1933 65 95
560 $3 Duesenberg dual cowl phaeton, 1929 75 1·25
561 $4 Mercedes-Benz "SSK", 1928 75 1·50

67 Short Solent 2 Flying Boat

1983. Bicentenary of Manned Flight. Mult.
563 40 c. Type **67** 75 20
564 70 c. Curtiss R3C-2 seaplane 90 35
565 90 c. Hawker Nimrod biplane 1·10 40
566 $4 Montgolfier balloon 3·25 2·75

68 Goofy

69 Weightlifting

1983. Christmas Disney cartoon characters in scenes from "Jingle Bells" (Christmas carol). Multicoloured.
568 ½ c. Type **68** 10 10
569 1 c. Clarabelle Cow 10 10
570 2 c. Donald Duck 10 10
571 3 c. Pluto 10 10
572 4 c. Morty and Ferdie 10 10
573 5 c. Huey, Dewey and Louie 10 10
574 10 c. Daisy and Chip n'Dale 10 10
575 $2.50 Big Bad Wolf 4·75 5·00
576 $5 Mickey Mouse 5·00 5·50

1984. Olympic Games, Los Angeles. Mult.
578 30 c. Type **69** 20 15
579 60 c. Gymnastics 45 35
580 70 c. Archery 50 40
581 $4 Sailing 1·90 1·90

70 Frangipani **71** Goofy

1984. Flowers. Multicoloured.
583 15 c. Type **70** . . . 15 10
584 40 c. Dwarf poinciana . . . 30 25
585 70 c. Walking iris . . . 55 45
586 $4 Lady's slipper . . . 1·75 2·50

1984. Easter. Multicoloured.
588 ½ c. Type **71** . . . 10 10
589 1 c. Chip and Dale . . . 10 10
590 2 c. Daisy Duck and Huey . . 10 10
591 3 c. Daisy Duck . . . 10 10
592 4 c. Donald Duck . . . 10 10
593 5 c. Merlin and Madam Mim . . 10 10
594 10 c. Flower . . . 10 10
595 $2 Minnie and Mickey Mouse . 1·50 2·00
596 $4 Minnie Mouse . . . 2·25 2·75

72 Bobolink

1984. Songbirds. Multicoloured.
598 40 c. Type **72** . . . 1·75 1·50
599 50 c. Eastern kingbird . . . 2·00 1·60
600 60 c. Barn swallow . . . 2·25 2·00
601 70 c. Yellow warbler . . . 2·25 2·00
602 $1 Rose-breasted grosbeak . . 2·50 2·50
603 $1.10 Yellowthroat . . . 2·75 2·75
604 $2 Catbird . . . 3·50 4·50

1984. Universal Postal Union Congress, Hamburg. Nos. 585/6 optd **19th U.P.U. CONGRESS HAMBURG**.
606 70 c. Walking iris . . . 1·00 1·00
607 $4 Lady's slipper . . . 4·50 5·00

74 "Geeststar" (freighter)

1984. Ships. Multicoloured.
609 30 c. Type **74** . . . 75 75
610 60 c. "Daphne" (liner) . . . 1·00 1·25
611 $1.10 "Southwind" (schooner) . 1·25 2·00
612 $4 "Oceanic" (liner) . . . 2·00 5·50

1984. 450th Death Anniv of Correggio (painter). As T **296** of Grenada. Multicoloured.
614 10 c. "The Hunt — Blowing the Horn" . . . 10 10
615 30 c. "St. John the Evangelist" (horiz) . . . 15 15
616 90 c. "The Hunt — The Deer's Head" . . . 50 50
617 $4 "The Virgin crowned by Christ" (horiz) . . . 2·00 2·00

1984. 150th Birth Anniv of Edgar Degas (painter). As T **297** of Grenada. Multicoloured.
619 25 c. "The Song of the Dog" . 40 15
620 70 c. "Cafe-concert" . . . 70 50
621 $1.10 "The Orchestra of the Opera" . . . 1·50 1·25
622 $3 "The Dance Lesson" . . . 2·75 2·75

1984. "Ausipex" International Stamp Exhibition, Melbourne. As T **298** of Grenada. Multicoloured.
624 $1.10 Queen Victoria Gardens, Melbourne . . . 50 50
625 $4 Ayers Rock . . . 2·00 2·00

75 Col. Steven's Model (1825) **76** Kawasaki "750" (1972)

1984. Railway Locomotives. Multicoloured.
627 20 c. Type **75** . . . 55 25
628 50 c. "Royal George" (1827) . 70 50
629 60 c. "Stourbridge Lion" (1829) 75 65
630 70 c. "Liverpool" (1830) . . . 80 85
631 90 c. "South Carolina" (1832) . 90 1·25
632 $1.10 "Monster" (1836) . . . 90 1·50
633 $2 "Lafayette" (1837) . . . 1·10 2·25
634 $4 "Lion" (1838) . . . 1·40 3·75

1984. Opening of Point Saline International Airport. Nos. 547 and 549 optd **OPENING OF POINT SALINE INT'L AIRPORT**.
636 30 c. Type **65** . . . 30 25
637 $1.10 Westland Whirlwind helicopters . . . 95 75

1984. Christmas. Walt Disney Cartoon Characters. As T **301** of Grenada. Multicoloured.
639 45 c. Donald Duck and nephews knitting Christmas stockings . 70 40
640 60 c. Donald Duck and nephews sitting on sofa . . . 80 65
641 90 c. Donald Duck getting out of bed . . . 1·25 1·00
642 $2 Donald Duck putting presents in wardrobe . . . 2·00 2·50
643 $4 Nephews singing carols outside Donald Duck's window . . . 3·25 4·25

1985. Birth Bicentenary of John J. Audubon (ornithologist). As T **418** of Ghana. Mult.
645 50 c. Blue-winged teal . . . 2·00 60
646 90 c. White ibis . . . 2·50 1·25
647 $1.10 Swallow-tailed kite . . 3·50 2·00
648 $3 Moorhen . . . 4·50 4·75
See also Nos. 736/9.

1985. Centenary of the Motor Cycle. Mult.
650 30 c. Type **76** . . . 65 45
651 60 c. Honda "Goldwing GL1000" (1974) (horiz) . . 90 1·00
652 70 c. Kawasaki "Z650" (1976) (horiz) . . . 1·00 1·10
653 $4 Honda "CBX" (1977) . . 4·00 6·50

77 Nursing Cadets folding Bandages (Health)

1985. International Youth Year. Mult.
655 50 c. Type **77** . . . 70 45
656 70 c. Scuba diver and turtle (Environment) . . . 1·00 80
657 $1.10 Yachting (Leisure) . . 1·60 1·50
658 $3 Boys playing chess (Education) . . . 6·00 7·00

1985. 40th Anniv of International Civil Aviation Organization. As T **305** of Grenada. Multicoloured.
660 5 c. Lockheed Lodestar . . . 40 20
661 70 c. Hawker Siddeley H.S.748 . 1·75 55
662 $1.10 Boeing 727-200 . . . 2·25 90
663 $4 Boeing 707 . . . 3·50 2·50

78 Lady Baden-Powell (founder) and Grenadian Guide Leaders

1985. 75th Anniv of Girl Guide Movement. Multicoloured.
665 30 c. Type **78** . . . 50 20
666 50 c. Guide leader and guides on botany field trip . . . 80 30
667 70 c. Guide leader and guides camping (vert) . . . 1·00 45
668 $4 Guides sailing (vert) . . 3·50 2·25

79 "Chiomara asychis"

1985. Butterflies. Multicoloured.
670 ½ c. Type **79** . . . 10 20
671 1 c. "Anartia amathea" . . . 10 20
672 2 c. "Pseudolycaena marsyas" . 10 20
673 4 c. "Urbanus proteus" . . . 10 20
674 5 c. "Polygonus manueli" . . 15 20
675a 6 c. "Battus polydamas" . . 20 15
676 10 c. "Eurema daira" . . . 30 15
677 12 c. "Phoebis agarithe" . . 45 20
678 15 c. "Aphrissa statira" . . 45 20
679 20 c. "Strymon simaethis" . . 60 20
680 25 c. "Mestra cana" . . . 60 25
681 30 c. "Agraulis vanillae" . . 60 30
682 40 c. "Junonia evarete" . . . 75 45
683 60 c. "Dryas julia" . . . 1·00 65
684 70 c. "Philaethria dido" . . 1·10 75
685 $1.10 "Hamadryas feronia" . 1·75 1·25
686 $2.50 "Strymon rufofusca" . . 3·25 3·00
687 $5 "Appias drusilla" . . . 5·00 4·75
688 $10 "Polites dictynna" . . . 8·00 9·00
688b $20 "Euptychia cephus" . . . 12·00 16·00

80 The Queen Mother before Prince William's Christening **81** Scuba Diving

1985. Life and Times of Queen Elizabeth the Queen Mother. Multicoloured.
689 $1 Type **80** . . . 45 60
690 $1.50 In winner's enclosure at Ascot (horiz) . . . 60 75
691 $2.50 With Prince Charles at Garter ceremony, Windsor Castle . . . 85 1·10
Stamps as Nos. 689/91 but with face values of 70 c., $1.10 and $3 exist from additional sheetlets with changed background colours.

1985. Water Sports. Multicoloured.
693 15 c. Type **81** . . . 30 10
694 70 c. Boys playing in waterfall . 60 45
695 90 c. Water skiing . . . 70 55
696 $4 Swimming . . . 2·75 2·25

82 Queen or Pink Conch

1985. Marine Life. Multicoloured.
698 60 c. Type **82** . . . 65 40
699 90 c. Porcupinefish and fire coral 85 55
700 $1.10 Ghost crab . . . 1·00 80
701 $4 West Indies spiny lobster . . 2·50 3·00

1985. 300th Birth Anniv of Johann Sebastian Bach (composer). As T **309a** of Grenada. Multicoloured.
703 15 c. Natural trumpet . . . 50 10
704 60 c. Bass viol . . . 85 40
705 $1.10 Flute . . . 1·50 70
706 $3 Double flageolet . . . 2·25 1·75

1985. Royal Visit. As T **310a** of Grenada. Mult.
708 10 c. Arms of Great Britain and Grenada . . . 20 20
709 $1 Queen Elizabeth II (vert) . . 1·00 1·75
710 $4 Royal Yacht "Britannia" . . 3·50 4·75

1985. 40th Anniv of United Nations Organization. Designs as T **311a** of Grenada showing United Nations (New York) stamps. Multicoloured.
712 $1 Neil Armstrong (first man on Moon) and 1982 Peaceful Uses of Outer Space 20 c. . . . 1·10 1·10
713 $2 Gandhi and 1971 Racial Equality Year 13 c. . . . 3·25 3·75
714 $2.50 Maimonides (physician) and 1956 World Health Organization 3 c. . . . 4·50 5·50

1985. 150th Birth Anniv of Mark Twain (author). As T **145a** of Gambia showing Walt Disney cartoon characters illustrating scenes from "Letters from Hawaii". Multicoloured.
716 25 c. Minnie Mouse dancing the hula . . . 60 30
717 50 c. Donald Duck surfing . . 90 65
718 $1.50 Donald Duck roasting marshmallow in volcano . . 2·25 2·25
719 $3 Mickey Mouse and Chip n'Dale canoeing . . . 3·75 4·00

1985. Birth Bicentenaries of Grimm Brothers (folklorists). As T **145b** of Gambia, but vert, showing Walt Disney cartoon characters in scenes from "The Elves and the Shoemaker". Multicoloured.
721 30 c. Mickey Mouse as the unsuccessful Shoemaker . . 70 40
722 60 c. Two elves making shoes . 1·10 85
723 70 c. The Shoemaker discovering the new shoes . . . 1·40 1·00
724 $4 The Shoemaker's wife (Minnie Mouse) making clothes for the elves . . . 4·25 5·00

83 "Madonna and Child" (Titian) **85** Two Footballers

1985. Christmas. Religious Paintings. Mult.
726 50 c. Type **83** . . . 45 35
727 70 c. "Madonna and Child with St. Mary and John the Baptist" (Bugiardini) . . . 55 50
728 $1.10 "Adoration of the Magi" (Di Fredi) . . . 80 1·40
729 $3 "Madonna and Child with Young St. John the Baptist" (Bartolomeo) . . . 1·25 3·75

1986. Centenary of Statue of Liberty (1st issue). As T **312a** of Grenada. Multicoloured.
731 5 c. Croton Reservoir, New York (1875) . . . 10 10
732 10 c. New York Public Library (1986) . . . 10 10
733 70 c. Old Boathouse, Central Park (1894) . . . 25 40
734 $4 Boating in Central Park (1986) . . . 1·40 2·25
See also Nos. 892/903.

1986. Birth Bicentenary of John J. Audubon (ornithologist) (2nd issue). As T **312b** of Grenada. Multicoloured.
736 50 c. Louisiana heron . . . 2·00 1·00
737 70 c. Black-crowned night heron 2·50 1·50
738 90 c. American bittern . . . 2·75 2·00
739 $4 Glossy ibis . . . 5·00 6·50

1986. Visit of President Reagan of U.S.A. Nos. 684 and 687, optd **VISIT OF PRES. REAGAN 20 FEBRUARY 1986**.
741 70 c. "Philaethria dido" . . 1·50 1·25
742 $5 "Appias drusilla" . . . 6·50 8·00

1986. World Cup Football Championship, Mexico. Designs showing footballers.
743 **85** 10 c. multicoloured . . . 60 40
744 – 70 c. multicoloured . . . 1·75 1·25
745 – $1 multicoloured . . . 2·00 1·75
746 – $4 multicoloured . . . 5·00 6·50

1986. Appearance of Halley's Comet (1st issue). As T **151a** of Gambia. Multicoloured.
748 5 c. Nicholas Copernicus (astronomer) and Earl of Rosse's six foot reflector telescope . . . 40 40
749 20 c. "Sputnik I" (first satellite) orbiting Earth, 1957 . . . 60 40
750 40 c. Tycho Brahe's notes and sketch of 1577 Comet . . 80 60
751 $4 Edmond Halley and 1682 Comet . . . 3·75 4·50
See also Nos. 790/3.
The captions of Nos. 750/1 are transposed.

1986. 60th Birthday of Queen Elizabeth II. As T **151b** of Gambia.
753 2 c. black and yellow . . . 10 15
754 $1.50 multicoloured . . . 80 1·00
755 $4 multicoloured . . . 2·00 2·75
DESIGNS: 2 c. Princesses Elizabeth and Margaret, Windsor Park, 1933; $1.50, Queen Elizabeth; $4 In Sydney, Australia, 1970.

1986. "Ameripex '86" International stamp Exhibition, Chicago. As T **315a** of Grenada. Multicoloured.
757 30 c. Donald Duck riding mule in Grand Canyon . . . 60 45
758 60 c. Daisy Duck, Timothy Mouse and Dumbo on Golden Gate Bridge, San Francisco . 85 1·00
759 $1 Mickey Mouse and Goofy in fire engine and Chicago Watertower . . . 1·50 1·75
760 $3 Mickey Mouse as airmail pilot and White House . . . 3·00 4·00

1986. Royal Wedding. As T **153b** of Gambia. Multicoloured.
762 60 c. Prince Andrew and Miss Sarah Ferguson . . . 55 45
763 70 c. Prince Andrew in car . . 65 55
764 $4 Prince Andrew with Westland Lynx naval helicopter . . 2·75 3·50

86 "Hygrocybe firma" **87** Giant Atlantic or Dolobrate Pyram

1986. Mushrooms of the Lesser Antilles. Mult.
766 15 c. Type **86** . . . 80 40
767 50 c. "Xerocomus coccolobae" . 1·75 1·25
768 $2 "Volvariella cubensis" . . 3·50 4·00
769 $3 "Lactarius putidus" . . . 4·50 5·00

1986. Sea Shells. Multicoloured.
771 15 c. Type **87** . . . 90 50
772 50 c. Beau's murex . . . 2·00 1·25
773 $1.10 West Indian fighting conch 2·50 2·75
774 $4 Alphabet conch . . . 4·75 7·00

1986. World Cup Football Championship Winners, Mexico. Nos. 743/6 optd **WINNERS Argentina 3 W.Germany 2**.
776 **85** 10 c. multicoloured . . . 55 40
777 – 70 c. multicoloured . . . 1·25 1·10
778 – $1 multicoloured . . . 1·50 1·40
779 – $4 multicoloured . . . 4·00 5·50

88 Common Opossum 89 Cycling

1986. Wildlife. Multicoloured.
781 10 c. Type **88** 20 20
782 30 c. Giant toad 40 40
783 60 c. Land tortoise 80 80
784 70 c. Murine opossum (vert) . . 85 85
785 90 c. Burmese mongoose (vert) 90 1·00
786 $1.10 Nine-banded armadillo . 1·00 1·25
787 $2 Agouti . . . . 1·75 2·25
788 $3 Humpback whale . . . . . 4·00 4·25

1986. Appearance of Halley's Comet (2nd issue). Nos. 748/51 optd with T **447a** of Ghana.
790 5 c. Nicholas Copernicus (astronomer) and Earl of Rosse's six foot reflector telescope 60 60
791 20 c. "Sputnik I" orbiting Earth, 1957 . . . . 80 50
792 40 c. Tycho Brahe's notes and sketch of 1577 Comet . . . 1·00 60
793 $4 Edmond Halley and 1682 Comet . . . . 5·00 6·00

1986. Christmas. As T **318a** of Grenada showing Walt Disney cartoon characters. Multicoloured.
795 25 c. Chip n'Dale with hummingbird 25 15
796 30 c. Robin delivering card to Mickey Mouse (vert) 25 20
797 50 c. Piglet, Pooh and Jose Carioca on beach 40 30
798 60 c. Grandma Duck feeding birds (vert) 50 40
799 70 c. Cinderella and birds with mistletoe (vert) 55 50
800 $1.50 Huey, Dewey and Louie windsurfing . . . . 1·25 2·00
801 $3 Mickey Mouse and Morty on beach with turtle . . . . . 1·50 3·00
802 $4 Kittens playing on piano (vert) . . . . 2·00 3·50

1986. Olympic Games, Seoul, South Korea (1988). Multicoloured.
804 10 c. + 5 c. Type **89** 50 40
805 50 c + 20 c. Sailing 60 90
806 70 c. + 30 c. Gymnastics . . . 75 1·10
807 $2 + $1 Horse trials . . . . . 2·00 3·00

90 Aston-Martin "Volante" (1984)

1986. Centenary of Motoring. Multicoloured.
809 10 c. Type **90** 25 25
810 30 c. Jaguar "MK V" (1948) . . 45 45
811 60 c. Nash "Ambassador" (1956) 60 65
812 70 c. Toyota "Supra" (1984) . . 60 70
813 90 c. Ferrari "Testarosa" (1985) 70 90
814 $1 BMW "501B" (1955) . . . 70 95
815 $2 Mercedes-Benz "280 SL" (1968) . . . . 1·00 2·00
816 $3 Austro-Daimler "ADR8" (1932) . . . . 1·25 2·50

1986. Birth Centenary of Marc Chagall (artist). As T **321a** of Grenada, showing various paintings.
818/57 $1.10 × 40 multicoloured. Set of 40 . . . . 28·00 28·00

1987. America's Cup Yachting Championship. As T **321b** of Grenada. Multicoloured.
859 25 c. "Defender", 1895 . . . . 60 40
860 45 c. "Galatea", 1886 . . . . 80 60
861 70 c. "Azzurra", 1981 . . . . 1·00 1·00
862 $4 "Australia II", 1983 . . . . 2·00 3·50

1987. 500th Anniv (1992) of Discovery of America by Christopher Columbus (1st issue). As T **322** of Grenada. Multicoloured.
864 15 c. Christopher Columbus . . 25 25
865 30 c. Queen Isabella of Castile 30 30
866 50 c. "Santa Maria" 45 50
867 60 c. Claiming the New World for Spain 50 60
868 90 c. Early Spanish map of Lesser Antilles 65 75
869 $1 King Ferdinand of Aragon . 70 80
870 $2 Fort La Navidad (drawing by Columbus) . . . . 1·40 2·00
871 $3 Galley and Caribs, Hispaniola (drawing by Columbus) . . . 1·90 2·50
See also Nos. 1191/4, 1224/32, 1366/73, 1494/1500 and 1519/20.

1987. Milestones of Transportation. As T **322a** of Grenada. Multicoloured.
873 10 c. Saunders Roe "SRN1" (first hovercraft), 1959 . . . . . 40 30
874 15 c. Bugatti "Royale" (largest car), 1931 . . . . 50 35
875 30 c. Aleksei Leonov and "Voskhod II" (first spacewalk), 1965 . . . . . 65 55
876 50 c. C.S.S "Hunley" (first submarine to sink enemy ship), 1864 . . . . 85 75
877 60 c. Rolls Royce "Flying Bedstead" (first VTOL aircraft), 1954 . . . . . . 95 85
878 70 c. "Jenny Lind" (first mass produced locomotive class), 1847 . . . . 1·10 1·00
879 90 c. Duryea "Buggvaut" (first U.S petrol-driven car), 1893 . 1·25 1·25
880 $1.50 Steam locomotive, Metropolitan Railway, London (first underground line), 1863 . . . . 2·00 2·25
881 $2 S.S. "Great Britain" (first transatlantic crossing by screw-steamship), 1843 . . . . . 2·50 2·75
882 $3 "Budweiser Rocket" (fastest car), 1979 . . . . 3·00 3·25

1987. "Capex '87" International Stamp Exhibition, Toronto. Game Fishes. As T **323** of Grenada but horiz. Multicoloured.
883 6 c. Yellow chub 15 15
884 30 c. King mackerel 40 30
885 50 c. Short-finned mako . . . 55 55
886 60 c. Dolphin (fish) 60 60
887 90 c. Skipjack tuna ("Bonito") . 75 75
888 $1.10 Cobia . . . . 1·00 1·25
889 $3 Tarpon . . . . 2·25 2·75
890 $4 Swordfish . . . . 2·50 3·25

1987. Centenary of Statue of Liberty (1986) (2nd issue). As T **323a** of Grenada. Multicoloured.
892 10 c. Cleaning face of statue . . 20 20
893 15 c. Commemorative lapel badges 30 30
894 25 c. Band playing and statue . 40 40
895 30 c. Band on parade and statue 45 45
896 45 c. Face of statue 50 50
897 50 c. Cleaning head of statue (horiz) 55 55
898 60 c. Models of statue (horiz) . 65 65
899 70 c. Small boat flotilla (horiz) 75 85
900 $1 Unveiling ceremony 85 90
901 $1.10 Statue and Manhattan skyline . . . . 90 1·00
902 $2 Parade of warships . . . . 1·75 2·00
903 $3 Making commemorative flags 1·90 2·25

1987. Great Scientific Discoveries. As T **325** of Grenada. Multicoloured.
904 60 c. Newton medal 85 80
905 $1 Louis Daguerre (inventor of daguerreotype) . . . . . . 1·25 1·00
906 $3 Antoine Lavoisier and apparatus . . . . 2·25 2·75
907 $3 Rudolf Diesel and first oil engine . . . . 4·50 4·75
No. 907 is inscribed "JAMES WATT" in error.

1987. Bicentenary of U.S. Constitution. As T **327a** of Grenada. Multicoloured.
909 10 c. Washington addressing delegates, Constitutional Convention 25 20
910 50 c. Flag and State Seal, Georgia 85 75
911 60 c. Capitol, Washington (vert) 85 80
912 $4 Thomas Jefferson (statesman) (vert) . . . . 3·75 5·50

1987. "Hafnia '87" International Stamp Exhibition, Copenhagen. Designs as T **328** of Grenada, but horiz, illustrating Hans Christian Andersen's fairy tales. Multicoloured.
914 25 c. Donald and Daisy Duck in "The Swineherd" 50 30
915 30 c. Mickey Mouse, Donald and Daisy Duck in "What the Good Man Does is Always Right" 55 35
916 50 c. Mickey and Minnie Mouse in "Little Tuk" 75 75
917 60 c. Minnie Mouse and Ferdie in "The World's Fairest Rose" 75 75
918 70 c. Mickey Mouse in "The Garden of Paradise" 80 80
919 $1.50 Goofy and Mickey Mouse in "The Naughty Boy" . . . 2·00 2·25
920 $3 Goofy in "What the Moon Saw" . . . . 2·75 3·00
921 $4 Alice as "Thumbelina" . . . 3·25 3·50

91 "The Virgin and Child with Saints Martin and Agnes"

92 Scout signalling with Semaphore Flags

1987. Christmas. Religious Paintings by El Greco. Multicoloured.
923 10 c. Type **91** 40 15
924 50 c. "St. Agnes" (detail from "The Virgin and Child with Saints Martin and Agnes") . 1·25 75
925 60 c. "The Annunciation" . . . 1·25 75
926 $4 "The Holy Family with St. Anne" . . . . 4·75 7·25

1988. Royal Ruby Wedding. As T **330a** of Grenada. Multicoloured.
928 20 c. brown, black & grn . . . 35 15
929 30 c. brown and black 40 20
930 $2 multicoloured . . . . . . 2·00 2·50
931 $3 multicoloured . . . . . . 2·50 3·25
DESIGNS: 20 c. Queen Elizabeth II with Princess Anne, c. 1957; 30 c. Wedding photograph, 1947; $2 Queen with Prince Charles and Princess Anne, c. 1955; $3 Queen Elizabeth (from photo by Tim Graham), 1980.

1988. Olympic Games, Seoul. As T **331** of Grenada showing Walt Disney cartoon characters as Olympic competitors. Multicoloured.
933 1 c. Minnie Mouse as rhythmic gymnast (horiz) 10 10
934 2 c. Pete and Goofy as pankration wrestlers (horiz) 10 10
935 3 c. Huey and Dewey as synchronized swimmers (horiz) 10 10
936 4 c. Huey, Dewey and Louey in hoplite race (horiz) 10 10
937 5 c. Clarabelle and Daisy Duck playing baseball (horiz) . . . 10 10
938 10 c. Goofy and Donald Duck in horse race (horiz) 10 10
939 $6 Donald Duck and Uncle Scrooge McDuck windsurfing (horiz) . . . . 4·50 5·50
940 $7 Mickey Mouse in chariot race (horiz) . . . . 4·75 5·50

1988. World Scout Jamboree, Australia. Mult.
942 50 c. Type **92** 50 35
943 70 c. Canoeing 60 50
944 $1 Cooking over campfire (horiz) 70 65
945 $3 Scouts around campfire (horiz) . . . . 2·00 3·00

1988. Birds. As T **334** of Grenada. Mult.
947 20 c. Yellow-crowned night heron 30 25
948 25 c. Brown pelican 30 25
949 45 c. Audubon's shearwater . . 40 35
950 60 c. Red-footed booby 50 45
951 70 c. Bridled tern 55 50
952 90 c. Red-billed tropic bird . . 70 70
953 $3 Blue-winged teal . . . . . 1·75 2·25
954 $4 Sora . . . . 2·00 2·75

1988. 500th Birth Anniv of Titian (artist). As T **166a** of Gambia. Multicoloured.
956 15 c. "Man with Blue Eyes" . . . 15 15
957 30 c. "The Three Ages of Man" (detail) 20 20
958 60 c. "Don Diego Mendoza" . . 35 35
959 75 c. "Emperor Charles V seated" 50 50
960 $1 "A Young Man in a Fur" . . 60 60
961 $2 "Tobias and the Angel" . . 1·10 1·40
962 $3 "Pietro Bembo" . . . . . 1·60 1·90
963 $4 "Pier Luigi Farnese" . . . 1·75 2·25

1988. Airships. As T **336** of Grenada. Multicoloured.
965 10 c. "Hindenburg" over Sugarloaf Mountain, Rio de Janeiro, 1937 (horiz) 35 20
966 20 c. "Hindenburg" over New York, 1937 (horiz) 45 30
967 30 c. U.S. Navy "K" Class airships on Atlantic escort duty, 1944 (horiz) 50 35
968 40 c. "Hindenburg" approaching Lakehurst, 1937 . . . . . . 60 45
969 60 c. "Graf Zeppelin" and "Hindenburg" over Germany, 1936 . . . . 75 60
970 70 c. "Hindenburg" and "Los Angeles" moored at Lakehurst, 1936 (horiz) . . . 75 70
971 $1 "Graf Zeppelin II" over Dover, 1939 . . . . 80 85
972 $2 "Ersatz Deutschland" on scheduled passenger flight, 1912 (horiz) . . . . 1·40 1·60
973 $3 "Graf Zeppelin" over Dome of the Rock, Jerusalem, 1931 (horiz) . . . . 1·90 2·25
974 $4 "Hindenburg" over Olympic stadium, Berlin, 1936 (horiz) 2·00 2·25

93 Bambi and his Mother

1988. Disney Animal Cartoon Films.
976/1029 30 c. × 54 multicoloured Set of 54 . . . . 15·00 15·00
DESIGNS: Scenes from "Bambi", "Dumbo", "Lady and the Tramp", "The Aristocats", "The Fox and the Hound" and "101 Dalmatians".

1988. "Sydpex '88" National Stamp Exhibition, Sydney and 60th Birthday of Mickey Mouse. As T **337** of Grenada. Multicoloured.
1031 1 c. Mickey Mouse conducting at Sydney Opera House . . 10 10
1032 2 c. Mickey Mouse and Donald Duck at Ayers Rock 10 10
1033 3 c. Goofy and Mickey Mouse on sheep station 10 10
1034 4 c. Goofy and Mickey Mouse at Lone Pine Koala Sanctuary 10 10
1035 5 c. Mickey Mouse, Donald Duck and Goofy playing Australian football 10 10
1036 10 c. Mickey Mouse and Goofy camel racing 10 10
1037 $5 Donald Duck and his nephews bowling . . . . . 4·50 5·00
1038 $6 Mickey Mouse with America's Cup trophy and "Australia II" (yacht) . . . 5·50 6·00

1988. Flowering Trees and Shrubs. As T **339** of Grenada. Multicoloured.
1040 10 c. Potato tree (vert) 15 15
1041 20 c. Wild cotton 15 15
1042 30 c. Shower of gold (vert) . . 20 20
1043 60 c. Napoleon's button (vert) 35 30
1044 90 c. Geiger tree 60 70
1045 $1 Fern tree 70 80
1046 $2 French cashew . . . . . . 1·25 2·00
1047 $4 Amherstia (vert) . . . . . 2·00 3·00

1988. Cars. As T **335** of Grenada. Mult.
1049 $2 Doble "Series E", 1925 . . 1·25 1·25
1050 $2 Alvis "12/50", 1926 . . . . 1·25 1·25
1051 $2 Sunbeam 3-litre, 1927 . . . 1·25 1·25
1052 $2 Franklin "Airman", 1928 . 1·25 1·25
1053 $2 Delage "D8S", 1929 . . . 1·25 1·25
1054 $2 Mors, 1897 . . . . 1·25 1·25
1055 $2 Peerless "Green Dragon", 1904 . . . . 1·25 1·25
1056 $2 Pope-Hartford, 1909 . . . 1·25 1·25
1057 $2 Daniels "Submarine Speedstar", 1920 . . . . . 1·25 1·25
1058 $2 McFarlan 9.3 litre, 1922 . . 1·25 1·25
1059 $2 Frazer Nash "Lemans" replica, 1949 . . . . 1·25 1·25
1060 $2 Pegaso "Z102", 1953 . . . 1·25 1·25
1061 $2 Siata "Spyder V-8", 1953 . 1·25 1·25
1062 $2 Kurtis-Offenhauser, 1953 . 1·25 1·25
1063 $2 Kaiser-Darrin, 1954 . . . 1·25 1·25
1064 $2 Tracta, 1930 . . . . . . 1·25 1·25
1065 $2 Maybach "Zeppelin", 1932 . 1·25 1·25
1066 $2 Railton "Light Sports", 1934 1·25 1·25
1067 $2 Hotchkiss, 1936 . . . . . 1·25 1·25
1068 $2 Mercedes-Benz "W163", 1939 . . . . 1·25 1·25
1069 $2 Aston-Martin "Vantage V8", 1982 . . . . 1·25 1·25
1070 $2 Porsche "956", 1982 . . . 1·25 1·25
1071 $2 Lotus "Esprit Turbo", 1983 1·25 1·25
1072 $2 McLaren "MP4/2", 1984 . 1·25 1·25
1073 $2 Mercedes-Benz "190E 2.3-16", 1985 . . . . . . 1·25 1·25
1074 $2 Ferrari "250 GT Lusso", 1963 . . . . 1·25 1·25
1075 $2 Porsche "904", 1964 . . . 1·25 1·25
1076 $2 Volvo "P1800", 1967 . . . 1·25 1·25
1077 $2 McLaren-Chevrolet "M8D", 1970 . . . . 1·25 1·25
1078 $2 Jaguar "XJ6", 1981 . . . 1·25 1·25

1988. "Mickey's Christmas Parade". As T **340a** of Grenada showing Walt Disney cartoon characters. Multicoloured.
1079 $1 Dumbo 65 65
1080 $1 Goofy as Father Christmas 65 65
1081 $1 Minnie Mouse waving from window 65 65
1082 $1 Clarabelle, Mordie and Ferdie watching parade . . 65 65
1083 $1 Donald Duck's nephews . . 65 65
1084 $1 Donald Duck as drummer . 65 65
1085 $1 Toy soldiers 65 65
1086 $1 Mickey Mouse on wooden horse 65 65

94 Middleweight Boxing (Gold, Henry Maske, East Germany)

1989. Olympic Medal Winners, Seoul (1988). Multicoloured.
1088 15 c. Type **94** 30 20
1089 50 c. Freestyle wrestling (130 kg) (Bronze, Andreas Schroeder, East Germany) 50 40
1090 60 c. Women's team gymnastics (Bronze, East Germany) . . 60 50
1091 75 c. Platform diving (Gold, Greg Louganis, U.S.A.) . . 70 60
1092 $1 Freestyle wrestling (52 kg) (Gold, Mitsuru Sato, Japan) 80 80
1093 $2 Men's freestyle 4 × 200 metres relay swimming (Bronze, West Germany) . . . . . 1·25 1·25
1094 $3 Men's 5000 metres (Silver, Dieter Baumann, West Germany) . . . . 1·60 2·00
1095 $4 Women's heptathlon (Gold, Jackie Joyner-Kersee, U.S.A.) 2·00 2·50

1989. Japanese Art. Paintings by Hiroshige. As T **177a** of Gambia. Multicoloured.
1097 15 c. "Crossing the Oi at Shimada by Ferry" 25 25
1098 20 c. "Daimyo and Entourage at Arai" 30 30
1099 45 c. "Cargo Portage through Goyu" 50 50
1100 75 c. "Snowfall at Fujigawa" . 75 75
1101 $1 "Horses for the Emperor at Chirifu" 85 85
1102 $2 "Rainfall at Tsuchiyama" . 1·60 1·60
1103 $3 "An Inn at Ishibe" . . . . 2·25 2·25
1104 $4 "On the Shore of Lake Biwa at Otsu" . . . . 2·75 2·75

1989. World Cup Football Championship, Italy (1990) (1st issue). As T **345a** of Grenada. Mult.
1106 15 c. World Cup trophy . . . 50 20
1107 20 c. Flags of Argentina (winners 1986) and International Federation of Football Associations (FIFA) (horiz) 50 20

1108 45 c. Franz Beckenbauer (West Germany) with World Cup, 1974 . . . 70 35
1109 75 c. Flags of Italy (winners 1982) and FIFA (horiz) . . 85 55
1110 $1 Pele (Brazil) with Jules Rimet trophy . . . 1·00 85
1111 $2 Flags of West Germany (winners 1974) and FIFA (horiz) . . . 1·60 2·00
1112 $3 Flags of Brazil (winners 1970) and FIFA (horiz) . . . 1·90 2·75
1113 $4 Jules Rimet trophy and Brazil players . . . 2·00 2·75
See also Nos. 1285/8.

1989. North American Railway Locomotives. As T **342** of Grenada. Multicoloured.
1115 $2 Morris & Essex Railroad "Dover", 1841, U.S.A. 1·50 1·50
1116 $2 Baltimore & Ohio Railroad No. 57 "Memnon", 1848, U.S.A. . . . 1·50 1·50
1117 $2 Camden & Amboy Railroad "John Stevens", 1849, U.S.A. 1·50 1·50
1118 $2 Lawrence Machine Shop "Lawrence", 1853, U.S.A. . 1·50 1·50
1119 $2 South Carolina Railroad "James S. Corry", 1859, U.S.A. . . . 1·50 1·50
1120 $2 Mine Hill & Schuylkill Haven Railroad flexible beam No. 3, 1860, U.S.A. . . . 1·50 1·50
1121 $2 Delaware, Lackawanna & Western Railroad "Montrose", 1861, U.S.A. . 1·50 1·50
1122 $2 Central Pacific Railroad No. 68 "Pequop", 1868, U.S.A. . 1·50 1·50
1123 $2 Boston & Providence Railroad "Daniel Nason", 1863, U.S.A. . . . 1·50 1·50
1124 $2 Morris & Essex Railroad "Joe Scranton", 1870, U.S.A. 1·50 1·50
1125 $2 Central Railroad of New Jersey No. 124, 1871, U.S.A. . . . 1·50 1·50
1126 $2 Baldwin tramway steam locomotive, 1876, U.S.A. . 1·50 1·50
1127 $2 Lackawanna & Bloomsburg Railroad "Luzerne", 1878, U.S.A. . . . 1·50 1·50
1128 $2 Central Mexican Railroad No. 150, 1892 . . . 1·50 1·50
1129 $2 Denver South Park & Pacific Railroad No. 15 "Breckenridge", 1879, U.S.A. 1·50 1·50
1130 $2 Miles Planting & Manufacturing Company plantation locomotive "Daisy", 1894, U.S.A. . . . 1·50 1·50
1131 $2 Central of Georgia Railroad Baldwin 854 No. 1136, 1895, U.S.A. . . . 1·50 1·50
1132 $2 Savannah, Florida & Western Railroad No. 111, 1900, U.S.A. . . . 1·50 1·50
1133 $2 Douglas, Gilmore & Company contractors locomotive No. 3, 1902, U.S.A. . . . 1·50 1·50
1134 $2 Lehigh Valley Coal Company compressed air locomotive No. 900, 1903, U.S.A. . . . 1·50 1·50
1135 $2 Louisiana & Texas Railroad McKeen motor locomotive, 1908, U.S.A. . . . 1·50 1·50
1136 $2 Clear Lake Lumber Company Type B Climax locomotive No. 6, 1910, U.S.A. . . . 1·50 1·50
1137 $2 Blue Jay Lumber Company Heisler locomotive No. 10, 1912, U.S.A. . . . 1·50 1·50
1138 $2 Stewartstown Railroad petrol locomotive No. 6, 1920s, U.S.A. . . . 1·50 1·50
1139 $2 Bangor & Aroostook Railroad Class G No. 186, 1921, U.S.A. . . . 1·50 1·50
1140 $2 Hammond Lumber Company Mallet locomotive, No. 6, 1923, U.S.A. . . . 1·50 1·50
1141 $2 Central Railway of New Jersey diesel locomotive No. 1000, 1925, U.S.A. . . . 1·50 1·50
1142 $2 Atchison Topeka & Santa Fe Railroad "Super Chief" diesel express, 1935, U.S.A. . 1·50 1·50
1143 $2 Norfolk & Western Railroad Class Y-6, 1948, U.S.A. . . 1·50 1·50
1144 $2 Boston & Maine Railroad Budd diesel railcar, 1949, U.S.A. . . . 1·50 1·50

94a Mickey Mouse and Donald Duck at Ecole Militaire Inflating Balloon

1989. "Philexfrance '89" International Stamp Exn, Paris. Designs showing Walt Disney cartoon characters in Paris. Multicoloured.
1145 1 c. Type **94a** . . . 10 10
1146 2 c. Mickey and Minnie Mouse on river boat passing Conciergerie . . . 10 10
1147 3 c. Mickey Mouse at Hotel de Ville (vert) . . . 10 10
1148 4 c. Mickey Mouse at Genie of the Bastille monument (vert) 10 10
1149 5 c. Mickey and Minnie Mouse arriving at Opera House . . 10 10
1150 10 c. Mickey and Minnie Mouse on tandem in Luxembourg Gardens . . . 10 10
1151 $5 Mickey Mouse in aeroplane over L'Arch de La Defense (vert) . . . 5·50 6·50
1152 $6 Mickey Mouse at Place Vendome (vert) . . . 5·50 6·50

95 Launch of "Apollo II"

97 Buddy Holly

96 Ethel Barrymore

1989. 20th Anniv of First Manned Landing on Moon. Multicoloured.
1154 25 c. Type **95** . . . 30 30
1155 50 c. Splashdown (horiz) . . . 50 50
1156 60 c. Modules in space . . . 60 60
1157 75 c. Aldrin setting up experiment (horiz) . . . 70 70
1158 $1 "Apollo 11" leaving Earth orbit (horiz) . . . 80 80
1159 $2 Moving "Apollo 11" to launch site . . . 1·60 1·90
1160 $3 Lunar module "Eagle" leaving Moon (horiz) . . . 2·00 2·50
1161 $4 "Eagle" landing on Moon 2·25 2·75

1989. Fungi. As T **348** of Grenada. Mult.
1163 6 c. "Agaricus purpurellus" (incorrectly inscr "Collybia aurea") . . . 35 25
1164 10 c. "Podaxis pistillaris" . . 35 25
1165 20 c. "Hygrocybe firma" . . . 55 45
1166 30 c. "Agaricus rufoaurantiacus" . . . 65 55
1167 75 c. "Leptonia howellii" . . 1·40 1·40
1168 $2 "Marasmiellus purpureus" 2·50 2·75
1169 $3 "Marasmius trinitatis" . . 3·00 3·25
1170 $4 "Collybia aurea" (incorrectly inscr "Hygrocybe martinicensis") . . . 3·25 3·50

1989. Butterflies. As T **350** of Grenada. Mult.
1172 25 c. "Battus polydamas" (inscr "Papilio androgeus") . . . 40 40
1173 35 c. "Phoebis sennae" . . . 45 45
1174 45 c. "Hamadryas feronia" . . 55 55
1175 50 c. "Cynthia cardui" . . . 55 55
1176 75 c. "Ascia monuste" . . . 80 80
1177 90 c. "Eurema lisa" . . . 90 90
1178 $2 "Aphrissa statira" . . . 2·00 2·00
1179 $3 "Hypolimnas misippus" . . 2·50 2·50

1989. 425th Birth Anniv of Shakespeare. Shakespearean Actors. Multicoloured.
1181 15 c. Type **96** . . . 35 25
1182 $1.10 Richard Burton . . . 1·50 1·25
1183 $2 John Barrymore . . . 2·25 2·25
1184 $3 Paul Robeson . . . 2·50 2·75

1989. Musicians. Multicoloured.
1186 10 c. Type **97** . . . 35 25
1187 25 c. Jimmy Hendrix . . . 55 40
1188 75 c. Mighty Sparrow . . . 70 70
1189 $4 Katsutoji Kineya . . . 3·00 4·00

97a Arawaks canoeing

1989. 500th Anniv (1992) of Discovery of America by Columbus (2nd issue). Pre-Columbian Arawak Society. As T **247** of Antigua. Multicoloured.
1191 15 c. Type **97a** . . . 25 25
1192 75 c. Family and campfire . . 75 75
1193 90 c. Using stone tools . . . 95 95
1194 $3 Eating and drinking . . . 2·50 3·00

1989. "World Stamp Expo '89" International Stamp Exhibition, Washington. Designs showing Walt Disney cartoon characters illustrating proverbs from "Poor Richard's Almanack". As T **352** of Grenada. Multicoloured.
1196 1 c. Uncle Scrooge McDuck with gold coins in sinking boat . . . 10 10
1197 2 c. Robin Hood shooting apple off Friar Tuck . . . 10 10
1198 3 c. Winnie the Pooh with honey 10 10
1199 4 c. Goofy, Minnie Mouse and Donald Duck exercising . . 10 10
1200 5 c. Pinnochio holding Jimminy Cricket . . . 10 10
1201 6 c. Huey and Dewey putting up wallpaper . . . 10 10
1202 8 c. Mickey Mouse asleep in storm . . . 15 10
1203 10 c. Mickey Mouse as Benjamin Franklin selling "Pennsylvania Gazette" . . 15 10
1204 $5 Mickey Mouse with chicken, recipe book and egg . . . 4·00 5·00
1205 $6 Mickey Mouse missing carriage . . . 4·50 5·00

1990. Christmas. Paintings by Rubens. As T **352a** of Grenada. Multicoloured.
1207 10 c. "The Annunciation" . . 35 15
1208 15 c. "The Flight of the Holy Family into Egypt" . . . 40 15
1209 25 c. "The Presentation in the Temple" . . . 55 15
1210 45 c. "The Holy Family under the Apple Tree" . . . 70 25
1211 $2 "Madonna and Child with Saints" . . . 2·00 2·50
1212 $4 "The Virgin and Child enthroned with Saints" . . 3·00 4·00
1213 $5 "The Holy Family" . . . 3·00 4·00

1990. "EXPO '90" International Garden and Greenery Exhibition, Osaka. Caribbean Orchids. As T **354** of Grenada. Multicoloured.
1215 15 c. "Brassocattleya" Thalie . 30 30
1216 20 c. "Odontocidium" Tigersun 35 35
1217 50 c. "Odontioda" Hambuhren 55 55
1218 75 c. "Paphiopedium" Delrosi 75 75
1219 $1 "Vuylstekeara" Yokara . . 95 95
1220 $2 "Paphiopedilum" Geelong 1·75 2·00
1221 $3 "Wilsonara" Tigerwood . . 2·00 2·25
1222 $4 "Cymbidium" Ormoulu . . 2·50 2·75

1990. 500th Anniv (1992) of Discovery of America by Columbus (3rd issue). New World Natural History—Insects. As T **354a** of Grenada. Mult.
1224 35 c. "Dynastes hercules" (beetle) . . . 35 35
1225 40 c. "Chalcolepidius porcatus" (beetle) . . . 35 35
1226 50 c. "Acrocinus longimanus" (beetle) . . . 40 40
1227 60 c. "Battus polydamas" (butterfly) . . . 75 75
1228 $1 "Orthemis ferruginea" (skimmer) . . . 95 95
1229 $2 "Psiloptera variolosa" (beetle) . . . 1·60 1·75
1230 $3 "Hypolimnas misippus" (butterfly) . . . 2·50 2·75
1231 $4 Scarab beetle . . . 2·50 2·75

1990. Wildlife. As T **254** of Antigua. Mult.
1233 5 c. West Indies giant rice rat 20 20
1234 25 c. Agouti . . . 35 35
1235 30 c. Humpback whale . . . 70 65
1236 40 c. Pilot whale . . . 70 65
1237 $1 Spotted dolphin . . . 95 95
1238 $2 Egyptian mongoose . . 1·75 2·00
1239 $3 Brazilian tree porcupine . . 2·25 2·75
1240 $4 American manatee . . . 2·50 3·00

1990. 50th Anniv of Second World War. As T **354b** of Grenada. Multicoloured.
1242 6 c. British tanks in France, 1939 . . . 30 30
1243 10 c. Operation "Crusader", North Africa, 1941 . . . 30 30
1244 20 c. Retreat of the Afrika Corps, 1942 . . . 40 40
1245 45 c. American landing on Aleutian Islands, 1943 . . . 50 50
1246 50 c. U.S marines landing on Tarawa, 1943 . . . 55 55
1247 60 c. U.S army entering Rome, 1944 . . . 60 60
1248 75 c. U.S tanks crossing River Seine, 1944 . . . 70 70
1249 $1 Battle of the Bulge, 1944 . 95 95
1250 $5 American infantry in Italy, 1945 . . . 3·00 3·50
1251 $6 B-29 "Enola Gay" dropping atomic bomb on Hiroshima, 1945 . . . 3·50 3·50

1990. "Stamp World London '90" International Stamp Exhibition. As T **193** of Gambia showing Walt Disney cartoon characters at Shakespeare sites. Multicoloured.
1253 15 c. Daisy Duck at Ann Hathaway's Cottage (horiz) 40 20
1254 30 c. Minnie and Bill Mouse at Shakespeare's birthplace, Stratford . . . 55 35
1255 50 c. Minnie Mouse in front of Mary Arden's house, Wilmcote . . . 75 70
1256 60 c. Mickey Mouse leaning on hedge in New Place gardens, Stratford (horiz) . . . 90 90
1257 $1 Mickey Mouse walking in New Place gardens, Stratford (horiz) . . . 1·25 1·25
1258 $2 Mickey Mouse carrying books in Scholars Lane, Stratford . . . 2·25 2·50
1259 $4 Mickey Mouse and Royal Shakespeare Theatre, Stratford . . . 3·25 4·00
1260 $5 Ludwig von Drake teaching Mickey Mouse at the Stratford Grammar School (horiz) . . . 3·25 4·00

1990. 90th Birthday of Queen Elizabeth the Queen Mother. As T **194** of Gambia, showing photographs 1970–79.
1262 $2 Queen Mother wearing pink hat and coat . . . 1·10 1·40
1263 $2 Prince Charles and Queen Mother at Garter ceremony 1·10 1·40
1264 $2 Queen Mother in blue floral outfit . . . 1·10 1·40

1990. Birds. As T **358** of Grenada, but vert Multicoloured.
1267 25 c. Yellow-bellied seedeater 30 30
1268 45 c. Carib grackle . . . 50 50
1269 50 c. Black-whiskered vireo . . 55 55
1270 75 c. Bananaquit . . . 70 70
1271 $1 White-collared swift . . . 95 95
1272 $2 Yellow-bellied elaenia . . 1·50 1·50
1273 $3 Blue-hooded euphonia . . 2·00 2·00
1274 $5 Eared dove . . . 3·25 3·25

1990. Crustaceans. As T **359** of Grenada. Mult.
1276 10 c. Slipper lobster . . . 20 20
1277 25 c. Green reef crab . . . 30 30
1278 65 c. Caribbean lobsterette . . 60 60
1279 75 c. Blind deep sea lobster . . 70 70
1280 $1 Flattened crab . . . 95 95
1281 $2 Ridged slipper lobster . . 1·75 2·00
1282 $3 Land crab . . . 2·25 2·75
1283 $4 Mountain crab . . . 2·50 2·75

98 Lineker, England

1990. World Cup Football Championship, Italy (2nd issue). Multicoloured.
1285 15 c. Type **98** . . . 25 25
1286 45 c. Burruchaga, Argentina . 45 45
1287 $2 Hysen, Sweden . . . 1·75 2·25
1288 $4 Sang Ho, South Korea . . 2·75 3·75

1990. Olympic Games, Barcelona (1992). As T **195a** of Gambia. Multicoloured.
1290 10 c. Boxing . . . 10 10
1291 25 c. Olympic flame . . . 20 20
1292 50 c. Football . . . 40 40
1293 75 c. Discus throwing . . . 60 60
1294 $1 Pole vaulting . . . 85 85
1295 $2 Show jumping . . . 1·75 2·00
1296 $4 Women's basketball . . . 3·50 3·75
1297 $5 Men's gymnastics . . . 3·00 3·75

1991. 350th Death Anniv of Rubens. As T **195c** of Gambia. Multicoloured.
1299 5 c. "Adam and Eve" (Eve detail) (vert) . . . 20 20
1300 15 c. "Esther before Ahasuerus" (detail) . . . 30 20
1301 25 c. "Adam and Eve" (Adam detail) (vert) . . . 40 25
1302 50 c. "Expulsion from Eden" 70 60
1303 $1 "Cain slaying Abel" (detail) (vert) . . . 1·10 1·10
1304 $2 "Lot's Flight" . . . 1·75 2·25
1305 $4 "Samson and Delilah" (detail) . . . 2·75 3·75
1306 $5 "Abraham and Melchizedek" . . . 3·25 3·75

1991. Coral Reef Fishes. As T **357** of Grenada. Multicoloured.
1308 15 c. Barred hamlet . . . 50 25
1309 35 c. Long-spined squirrelfish . 80 50
1310 45 c. Red-spotted hawkfish . . 85 60
1311 75 c. Bigeye . . . 1·25 1·00
1312 $1 Balloonfish ("Spiny puffer") . . . 1·50 1·25
1313 $2 Small-mouth grunt . . . 2·25 2·50
1314 $3 Harlequin bass . . . 2·75 3·25
1315 $4 Creole fish . . . 3·00 3·50

99 Angel with Star and Lantern

100 "Brassia maculata"

1991. Christmas (1990). Hummel Figurines. Multicoloured.
1317 10 c. Type **99** . . . 15 10
1318 15 c. Christ Child and Angel playing mandolin . . . 25 15
1319 25 c. Shepherd . . . 35 25
1320 50 c. Angel with trumpet and lantern . . . 65 50
1321 $1 Nativity scene . . . 1·10 95
1322 $2 Christ Child and Angel holding candle . . . 1·75 2·50
1323 $4 Angel with baskets . . . 2·75 4·00
1324 $5 Angels singing . . . 3·25 4·00

1991. Orchids. Multicoloured.

1326 5 c. Type **100** 30 30
1327 10 c. "Oncidium lanceanum" 30 30
1328 15 c. "Broughtonia sanguinea" 35 20
1329 25 c. "Diacrium bicornutum" 40 20
1330 35 c. "Cattleya labiata" 40 20
1331 45 c. "Epidendrum fragrans" 50 25
1332 50 c. "Oncidium papilio" 55 30
1333 75 c. "Neocogniauxia monophylla" 70 50
1334 $1 "Epidendrum polybulbon" 80 70
1335 $2 "Spiranthes speciosa" 1·40 1·40
1336 $4 "Epidendrum ciliare" 2·25 2·75
1337 $5 "Phais tankervilliae" 2·50 3·00
1338 $10 "Brassia caudata" 4·50 5·00
1339 $20 "Brassavola cordata" 9·25 11·00

1991. Butterflies. As T **363** of Grenada. Mult.

1340 5 c. Crimson-patched longwing 40 30
1341 10 c. "Morpho helena" 40 30
1342 15 c. "Morpho sulkowskyi" 55 35
1343 20 c. "Dynastor napoleon" 60 40
1344 25 c. "Pieridae callinira" 60 45
1345 30 c. "Anartia amathea" 65 50
1346 35 c. "Heliconiidae dido" 65 50
1347 45 c. "Papilionidae columbus" 75 65
1348 50 c. "Nymphalidae praeneste" 85 70
1349 60 c. "Panacea prola" 1·00 80
1350 75 c. "Dryas julia" 1·00 90
1351 $1 "Papilionidae orthosilaus" 1·25 1·10
1352 $2 "Pyrrhopyge cometes" 1·75 2·00
1353 $3 "Papilionidae paeon" 2·00 2·50
1354 $4 "Morpho cypris" 2·50 3·00
1355 $5 Choringa 3·00 3·25

101 Donald and Daisy Duck with Solar-powered Car

1991. Ecology Conservation. Walt Disney cartoon characters. Multicoloured.

1357 10 c. Type **101** 30 20
1358 15 c. Goofy saving water 40 20
1359 25 c. Donald and Daisy on nature hike 55 35
1360 45 c. Donald Duck returning chick to nest 75 55
1361 $1 Donald Duck and balloons 1·40 1·25
1362 $2 Minnie Mouse and Daisy Duck on hot day 2·25 2·50
1363 $4 Mickey's nephews cleaning beach 3·25 3·75
1364 $5 Donald Duck on pedal generator 3·25 3·75

1991. 500th Anniv (1992) of Discovery of America by Columbus (4th issue). History of Exploration. As T **363a** of Grenada. Multicoloured.

1366 15 c. Magellan's "Vitoria" rounding Cape Horn, 1519–21 50 40
1367 20 c. Drake's Golden Hind, 1577-80 60 45
1368 50 c. Cook's H.M.S "Resolution", 1768-71 90 80
1369 60 c. Douglas World Cruiser seaplane, 1924 90 80
1370 $1 "Sputnik I" satellite, 1957 1·00 1·00
1371 $2 Gagarin's space flight, 1961 1·75 2·00
1372 $4 Glenn's space flight, 1962 2·50 3·25
1373 $5 Space shuttle, 1981 3·00 3·50

1991. "Phila Nippon '91" International Stamp Exhibition, Tokyo. As T **198c** of Gambia but horiz showing Walt Disney cartoon characters in Japanese scenes. Multicoloured.

1375 15 c. Minnie Mouse with silkworms 30 20
1376 30 c. Mickey, Minnie, Morty and Ferdie at Torii Gate 45 35
1377 50 c. Donald Duck and Mickey Mouse trying origami 70 60
1378 60 c. Mickey and Minnie diving for pearls 80 70
1379 $1 Minnie Mouse in kimono 1·25 1·10
1380 $2 Mickey making masks 2·25 2·50
1381 $4 Donald and Mickey making paper 3·00 3·25
1382 $5 Minnie and Pluto making pottery 3·25 3·50

1991. Fungi. As T **364** of Grenada. Multicoloured.

1384 5 c. "Pyrrhoglossum pyrrhum" 35 25
1385 45 c. "Agaricus purpurellus" 85 50
1386 50 c. "Amanita craseoderma" 85 55
1387 90 c. "Hygrocybe acutoconica" 1·50 1·25
1388 $1 "Limacella guttata" 1·50 1·25
1389 $2 "Lactarius hygrophoroides" 2·00 2·00
1390 $4 "Boletellus cubensis" 3·25 3·50
1391 $5 "Psilocybe caerulescens" 3·25 3·50

1991. 65th Birthday of Queen Elizabeth II. As T **198a** of Gambia. Multicoloured.

1393 20 c. Queen, Prince Philip, Prince Charles and Prince William at Trooping the Colour, 1990 30 20
1394 25 c. Queen and Prince Charles at polo match, 1985 30 20
1395 $2 Queen and Prince Philip at Maundy service, 1989 2·00 2·50
1396 $4 Queen with Queen Mother on her 87th birthday, 1987 3·25 3·75

1991. 10th Wedding Anniv of Prince and Princess of Wales. As T **198b** of Gambia. Multicoloured.

1398 5 c. Prince and Princess of Wales kissing, 1987 30 15
1399 60 c. Portraits of Prince, Princess and sons 80 70
1400 $1 Prince Henry in 1988 and Prince William in 1987 1·10 1·10
1401 $5 Princess Diana in 1990 and Prince Charles in 1988 4·25 4·75

1991. Death Centenary (1990) of Vincent van Gogh (artist). As T **200b** of Gambia. Multicoloured.

1403 5 c. "Two Thistles" 20 20
1404 10 c. "Baby Marcelle Roulin" 25 20
1405 15 c. "Still Life: Basket with Six Oranges" (horiz) 30 15
1406 25 c. "Orchard in Blossom" 35 20
1407 45 c. "Armand Roulin" 50 35
1408 50 c. "Wood Gatherers in Snow" (detail) (horiz) 60 40
1409 60 c. "Almond Tree in Blossom" 70 50
1410 $1 "An Old Man" 1·00 1·00
1411 $2 "The Seine Bridge at Asnieres" (horiz) 1·75 2·00
1412 $3 "Vase with Lilacs, Daises and Anemones" 2·25 2·50
1413 $4 "Self Portrait" 2·40 2·75
1414 $5 "Patience Escalier" 2·50 2·75

102 Sargassum Triggerfish

1991. Reef Fishes. Multicoloured.

1416 50 c. Type **102** 75 75
1417 50 c. Tobaccofish 75 75
1418 50 c. Caribbean long-nosed butterflyfish 75 75
1419 50 c. Cherub angelfish 75 75
1420 50 c. Black jack 75 75
1421 50 c. Masked goby and black jack 75 75
1422 50 c. Spot-finned hogfish 75 75
1423 50 c. Royal gramma ("Fairy basslet") 75 75
1424 50 c. Orange-backed bass 75 75
1425 50 c. Candy basslet 75 75
1426 50 c. Black-capped basslet 75 75
1427 50 c. Long-jawed squirrelfish 75 75
1428 50 c. Jackknife-fish 75 75
1429 50 c. Bigeye 75 75
1430 50 c. Short bigeye 75 75

Nos. 1416/30 were printed together, se-tenant, forming a composite design.

1991. Christmas. Religious Paintings by Martin Schongauer. As T **200c** of Gambia.

1432 10 c. black and brown 30 15
1433 35 c. multicoloured 85 30
1434 50 c. multicoloured 75 50
1435 75 c. multicoloured 1·00 80
1436 $1 multicoloured 1·40 1·25
1437 $2 multicoloured 2·25 2·50
1438 $4 black and brown 3·25 3·75
1439 $5 black, grey and red 3·50 4·00

DESIGNS: 10 c. "Angel of the Annunciation"; 35 c. "Madonna of the Rose Hedge" (detail); 50 c. "Madonna of the Rose Hedge" (different detail); 75 c. "Nativity" (detail); $1 "Adoration of the Shepherds" (detail); $2 "The Nativity"; $4 "Nativity" (different); $5 "Symbol of St. Matthew".

1992. Great Railways of the World. As T **367** of Grenada. Multicoloured.

1441 75 c. Medoc locomotive No. J-S 58, 1857 (Switzerland) 80 80
1442 75 c. Stirling single locomotive No. 1, 1870 (Great Britain) 80 80
1443 75 c. Paris-Lyon-Mediterranee locomotive No. 90, 1877 (France) 80 80
1444 75 c. Standard type, 1880 (U.S.A.) 80 80
1445 75 c. Class 650 "Vittorio Emanuel II", 1884 (Italy) 80 80
1446 75 c. Johnson single, 1887 (Great Britain) 80 80
1447 75 c. Locomotive No. 999, 1893 (U.S.A.) 80 80
1448 75 c. Class Q1, 1896 (Great Britain) 80 80
1449 75 c. "Claud Hamilton", 1900 (Great Britain) 80 80
1450 $1 Class P8, 1906 (Germany) 80 80
1451 $1 Class P, 1910 (Denmark) 80 80
1452 $1 Southern Railway Ps4, 1926 (U.S.A.) 80 80
1453 $1 "Kestrel", 1932 (Ireland) 80 80
1454 $1 Southern Pacific Class GS2, 1937 (U.S.A.) 80 80
1455 $1 Class 12, 1938 (Belgium) 80 80
1456 $1 Norfolk and Western Railroad Class J No. 600, 1941 (U.S.A.) 80 80
1457 $1 Alco PA series diesel, 1946 (U.S.A.) 80 80
1458 $1 Class 4E electric, 1954 (South Africa) 80 80
1459 $2 Trans Europe Express train, 1957 1·40 1·40
1460 $2 New Haven Railroad Type FL9 diesel, 1960 (U.S.A.) 1·40 1·40
1461 $2 "Hikari" train, 1964 (Japan) 1·40 1·40
1462 $2 Class 103.1 electric, 1970 (Germany) 1·40 1·40
1463 $2 RTG diesel, 1972 (France) 1·40 1·40
1464 $2 ETR 401 Pendolino train, 1976 (Italy) 1·40 1·40
1465 $2 Advanced Passenger Train Class 370, 1981 (Great Britain) 1·40 1·40
1466 $2 Via Rail LRC diesel, 1982 (Canada) 1·40 1·40
1467 $2 MAV BZMOT 601, 1983 (Hungary) 1·40 1·40

1992. 40th Anniv of Queen Elizabeth II's Accession. As T **202a** of Gambia. Multicoloured.

1469 60 c. Swimming jetty on beach 50 40
1470 75 c. View of Grenadines 55 45
1471 $2 Surf on beach 1·60 1·60
1472 $4 Secluded bay 2·75 3·00

1992. Olympic Games, Barcelona. As T **372** of Grenada. Multicoloured.

1474 10 c. Women's backstroke swimming 40 30
1475 15 c. Women's handball 45 30
1476 25 c. Men's 4 × 100 m relay 55 30
1477 35 c. Men's hammer throw 60 35
1478 50 c. Men's 110 m hurdles 70 60
1479 75 c. Men's pole vault 90 80
1480 $1 Men's volleyball 1·10 1·00
1481 $2 Men's weightlifting 2·00 2·25
1482 $5 Men's gymnastics 3·00 3·75
1483 $6 Football 3·25 3·75

1992. Granada '92 Int Stamp Exn, Spain. Spanish Paintings. As T **481a** of Ghana. Mult.

1485 10 c. "The Surrender of Seville" (Zurbaran) 15 15
1486 35 c. "The Liberation of St. Peter by an Angel" (Antonio de Pereda) 25 25
1487 50 c. "Joseph explains the Dreams of the Pharaoh" (Antonio del Castillo Saavedra) (horiz) 55 55
1488 75 c. "The Flower Vase" (Juan de Arellano) 70 70
1489 $1 "The Duke of Pastrana" (Juan Carreno de Miranda) 80 80
1490 $2 "The Annunciation" (detail) (Francisco Rizi) 1·60 1·75
1491 $4 "The Annunciation" (different detail) (Rizi) 2·50 2·75
1492 $5 "Old Women Seated" (attr Antonio Puga) 2·50 2·75

103 Don Isaac Abarbanel, Minister of Finance

1992. 500th Anniv of Discovery of America by Columbus (5th issue). World Columbian Stamp Expo '92, Chicago. Multicoloured.

1494 10 c. Type **103** 15 15
1495 25 c. Columbus on voyage 25 25
1496 35 c. Look-out sighting land 30 30
1497 50 c. King Ferdinand and Queen Isabella of Spain 50 50
1498 60 c. Columbus showing map to Queen Isabella 55 55
1499 $5 "Santa Maria" and bird 4·00 5·50

1992. "Genova '92" International Thematic Stamp Exhibition. Hummingbirds. As T **370a** of Grenada. Multicoloured.

1501 5 c. Male blue-headed hummingbird 10 10
1502 10 c. Female rufous-breasted hermit 10 10
1503 20 c. Female blue-headed hummingbird 15 15
1504 45 c. Male green-throated carib 30 30
1505 90 c. Male Antillean crested hummingbird 60 70
1506 $2 Male purple-throated carib 1·40 1·60
1507 $4 Female purple-throated carib 2·40 2·75
1508 $5 Female Antillean crested hummingbird 2·50 2·75

1992. 50th Anniv of United Service Organization (forces' entertainment programme). As T **371** of Grenada. Multicoloured.

1510 10 c. James Cagney 15 15
1511 15 c. Anne Sheridan 15 15
1512 35 c. Jerry Colonna 25 25
1513 50 c. Spike Jones 40 40
1514 75 c. Edgar Bergen 55 55
1515 $1 The Andrews Sisters 70 70
1516 $2 Dinah Shore 1·40 1·75
1517 $5 Bing Crosby 3·25 3·75

No. 1515 is incorrectly inscribed "THE ANDREW SISTERS".

1992. 500th Anniv of Discovery of America by Columbus (6th issue). Organization of East Caribbean States. As Nos. 2423/4 of Grenada.

1519 $1 Columbus meeting Amerindians 65 65
1520 $2 Ships approaching island 1·25 1·50

1992. Toy Trains from American Manufacturers. As T **372b** of Grenada. Multicoloured.

1521 15 c. No. 2220 switcher locomotive, Voltamp (1910) 25 15
1522 25 c. Clockwork locomotive of Bridge Port Line, American Miniature Railroad (1907) 35 20
1523 50 c. First electric toy locomotive, Ives (1910) 60 40
1524 75 c. "J.C. Penney Special" locomotive, American Flyer (1920s) 80 60
1525 $1 Clockwork cast-metal locomotive, Hafner (1916) 90 80
1526 $2 Pull toy copper-plated locomotive, probably Hubley (1900) 1·75 2·00
1527 $4 "Mayflower" locomotive, American Flyer (1928) 3·00 3·25
1528 $5 "Olympian" locomotive, Ives (1929) 3·00 3·25

1992. Christmas. Religious Paintings. "The Annunciation" by various artists. As T **207b** of Gambia. Multicoloured.

1531 5 c. Robert Campin 10 10
1532 5 c. Melchior Broederlam 15 10
1533 25 c. Fra Filippo Lippi (two-panel diptych) 20 15
1534 35 c. Simone Martini 30 20
1535 50 c. Lippi (detail from left panel) 45 45
1536 75 c. Lippi (detail from right panel) 60 60
1537 90 c. Albert Bouts 70 80
1538 $1 D. di Michelino 80 90
1539 $2 Rogier van der Weyden 1·50 1·75
1540 $3 Sandro Botticelli (detail of angel) 1·90 2·25
1541 $4 Botticelli (detail of Virgin Mary) 2·75 3·00
1542 $5 Bernardo Daddi (horiz) 2·75 3·00

1992. Gold Record Award Winners. As T **374** of Grenada. Multicoloured.

1544 90 c. Leonard Bernstein 1·10 1·10
1545 90 c. Ray Charles 1·10 1·10
1546 90 c. Bob Dylan 1·10 1·10
1547 90 c. Barbra Streisand 1·10 1·10
1548 90 c. Frank Sinatra 1·10 1·10
1549 90 c. Harry Belafonte 1·10 1·10
1550 90 c. Aretha Franklin 1·10 1·10
1551 90 c. Garth Brooks 1·10 1·10

Nos. 1544/51 were printed together, se-tenant, with a composite background design.

1992. 60th Anniv of Goofy (Disney cartoon character). Scenes from various cartoon films. As T **207c** of Gambia. Multicoloured.

1553 5 c. "Father's Day Off", 1953 20 20
1554 10 c. "Cold War", 1951 25 20
1555 15 c. "Home Made Home", 1951 30 20
1556 25 c. "Get Rich Quick", 1951 35 25
1557 50 c. "Man's Best Friend", 1952 55 40
1558 75 c. "Aquamania", 1961 75 55
1559 90 c. "Tomorrow We Diet", 1951 85 65
1560 $1 "Teachers Are People", 1952 90 75
1561 $2 "The Goofy Success Story", 1955 1·60 1·60
1562 $3 "Double Dribble", 1946 2·00 2·25
1563 $4 "Hello Aloha", 1952 2·25 2·50
1564 $5 "Father's Lion", 1952 2·40 2·75

1992. Anniversaries and Events. As T **375** of Grenada. Multicoloured, except No. 1571.

1566 25 c. Zeppelin "Viktoria Luise" over Kiel Harbour (horiz) 55 30
1567 50 c. Space shuttle "Columbia" landing (horiz) 65 35
1568 75 c. German Federal Republic flag and arms (horiz) 65 50
1569 $1.50 Giant anteater (horiz) 1·00 1·00
1570 $2 Scarlet macaw 2·00 1·75
1571 $2 W.H.O. emblem (black and blue) (horiz) 1·25 1·25
1572 $3 Wolfgang Amadeus Mozart 3·00 2·50
1573 $4 The Berlin Airlift (horiz) 2·75 2·50
1574 $4 Repairing "Intelsat VI" satellite in space (horiz) 2·75 2·50
1575 $5 Zeppelin "Hindenburg" on fire (horiz) 2·75 2·75
1576 $5 Admiral Richard Byrd's Ford Trimotor aircraft (horiz) 2·75 2·75

ANNIVERSARIES AND EVENTS: Nos. 1566, 1575, 75th death anniv of Count Ferdinand von Zeppelin; Nos. 1567, 1574, International Space Year; Nos. 1568, 1573, 25th death anniv of Konrad Adenauer (German statesman); Nos. 1569/70, Earth Summit '92, Rio; No. 1571, United Nations World Health Organization Projects; No. 1572, Death bicentenary of Mozart; No. 1576, 75th anniv of International Association of Lions Clubs.

104 "Atalanta" and "Mischief" (yachts), 1881

105 "Battus polydamus"

1992. History of The Americas Cup Challenge Trophy. Multicoloured.

1578 15 c. Type **104** 20 20
1579 25 c. "Valkyrie III" and "Defender", 1895 30 30
1580 35 c. "Shamrock IV" and "Resolute", 1920 45 45
1581 75 c. "Endeavour II" and "Ranger", 1937 70 70

1582 $1 "Sceptre" and "Columbia", 1958 85 85
1583 $2 "Australia II" and "Liberty", 1983 1·50 1·75
1584 $4 "Stars & Stripes" and "Kookaburra III", 1987 2·40 3·00
1585 $5 "New Zealand" and "Stars & Stripes", 1988 2·50 3·00

1993. Dogs of the World. As T **377** of Grenada, but vert. Multicoloured.
1587 35 c. Irish setter and Glendalough, Ireland 50 25
1588 50 c. Boston terrier and Boston State House, U.S.A. 70 50
1589 75 c. Beagle and Temple to Athena, Greece 1·00 60
1590 $1 Weimaraner and Nesselwang, Germany 1·25 85
1591 $3 Norwegian elkhound and Urnes Stave Church, Norway 2·50 3·00
1592 $4 Mastiff and Sphinx, Egypt 2·75 3·00
1593 $5 Akita and Torii Temple, Kyoto, Japan 2·75 3·00
1594 $5 Saluki and Rub'al Khali, Saudi Arabia 2·75 3·00

1993. Bicentenary of the Louvre, Paris. As T **209b** of Gambia. Multicoloured (except No. 1599).
1596 $1 "Madonna and Child with the young John the Baptist" (Botticelli) 90 90
1597 $1 "The Buffet" (Chardin) 90 90
1598 $1 "Return from Market" (Chardin) 90 90
1599 $1 "Erasmus" (Durer) (black and grey) 90 90
1600 $1 "Self-portrait with Eryngium" (Durer) 90 90
1601 $1 "Jeanne of Aragon" (Raphael) 90 90
1602 $1 "La Belle Jardiniere" (detail) (Raphael) 90 90
1603 $1 "La Belle Jardiniere" (different detail) (Raphael) 90 90

1993. Butterflies. Multicoloured.
1605 15 c. Type **105** 40 20
1606 35 c. "Astraptes talus" 55 20
1607 45 c. "Pseudolycaena marsyas" 55 25
1608 75 c. "Siproeta stelenes" 70 50
1609 $1 "Phoebis sennae" 80 60
1610 $2 "Dione juno" 1·40 1·40
1611 $4 "Chlorostrymon simaethis" 2·25 2·75
1612 $5 "Urbanus proteus" 2·50 2·75

1993. Flowers. As T **380** of Grenada. Mult.
1614 35 c. Hibiscus 50 20
1615 35 c. Columbine 50 20
1616 45 c. Red ginger 50 25
1617 75 c. Bougainvillea 70 50
1618 $1 Crown imperial 80 60
1619 $2 Fairy orchid 1·40 1·40
1620 $4 Heliconia 2·25 2·75
1621 $5 Tulip 2·50 2·75

1993. 40th Anniv of Coronation. As T **215a** of Gambia.
1623 35 c. multicoloured 15 40
1624 50 c. multicoloured 25 50
1625 $2 green and black 90 1·10
1626 $4 multicoloured 1·90 2·00
DESIGNS 35 c. Queen Elizabeth II at Coronation (photograph by Cecil Beaton); 50 c. Ampulla and spoon; $2 Queen Elizabeth II leaving for Coronation; $4 Prince Henry's christening.

1993. Anniversaries and Events. As T **381** of Grenada. Multicoloured.
1628 15 c. "Painter and Model" (Picasso) (horiz) 55 30
1629 35 c. Keith Tkachuk and Dmitri Mironov (ice hockey, 1992) (horiz) 80 40
1630 50 c. Early telescope 85 50
1631 75 c. "Gra w Gudziki" (Ludomir Slerdinski) (horiz) 90 70
1632 75 c. Willy Brandt and Lyndon Johnson, 1961 (horiz) 90 70
1633 $1 "Artist and his Model" (Picasso) (horiz) 1·00 80
1634 $2 "Pocalunek Mongolskiego Ksiecia" (S. Wirkiewicz) (horiz) 1·40 1·40
1635 $4 "The Drawing Lesson" (Picasso) (horiz) 2·25 2·25
1636 $4 Radio telescope 2·25 2·25
1637 $5 Alberto Tomba (Giant Slalom, 1984) (horiz) 2·25 2·40
1638 $5 Willy Brandt and Eleanor Hulles, 1957 (horiz) 2·25 2·40
ANNIVERSARIES AND EVENTS: Nos. 1628, 1633, 1635, 20th death anniv of Picasso (artist); Nos. 1629, 1637, Winter Olympic Games '94, Lillehammer; Nos. 1630, 1636, 450th death anniv of Copernicus (astronomer); Nos. 1631, 1634, Polska '93 International Stamp Exhibition, Poznan; Nos. 1632, 1638, 80th birth anniv of Willy Brandt (German politician).

MINIMUM PRICE

The minimum price quoted is 10p which represents a handling charge rather than a basis for valuing common stamps. For further notes about prices see introductory pages.

1993. Songbirds. As T **382** of Grenada. Multicoloured.
1640 15 c. Painted bunting 50 50
1641 15 c. White-throated sparrow 50 50
1642 25 c. Common grackle 60 60
1643 25 c. Amazonian royal flycatcher 60 60
1644 35 c. Swallow tanager 65 65
1645 35 c. Vermilion flycatcher 65 65
1646 45 c. Black-headed bunting 70 70
1647 50 c. Rose-breasted grosbeak 70 70
1648 75 c. Corn bunting 80 80
1649 75 c. Rose-breasted thrush tanager 80 80
1650 $1 Buff-throated saltator 90 90
1651 $4 Plush-capped finch 2·25 2·25
Nos. 1640/51 were printed together, se-tenant, with the backgrounds forming a composite design.
Nos. 1645/6 show the scientific inscriptions transposed between the designs.

1993. Shells. As T **383** of Grenada. Mult.
1653 15 c. Hawk-wing conch 25 25
1654 15 c. Music volute 25 25
1655 25 c. Globe vase and deltoid rock shell 30 30
1656 35 c. Spiny Caribbean vase 30 30
1657 35 c. American common sundial and common purple janthina 30 30
1658 45 c. Toothed donax and gaudy asaphis 35 35
1659 45 c. Mouse cone 35 35
1660 50 c. Gold-mouthed triton 40 40
1661 75 c. Tulip mussel and trigonal tivela 50 50
1662 75 c. Common dove shell and chestnut latirus 50 50
1663 $1 Wide-mouthed purpura 60 60
1664 $4 American thorny oyster and Atlantic wing oyster 1·90 2·00
Nos. 1653/64 were printed together, se-tenant, with the backgrounds forming a composite design.

1993 Asian International Stamp Exhibitions. As T **219a** of Gambia. Multicoloured. (a) "Indopex '93", Surabaya, Indonesia.
1666 35 c. National Museum, Central Jakarta (horiz) 40 20
1667 45 c. Sacred wheel and deer (horiz) 45 25
1668 $1 Ramayana relief, Panataran Temple (horiz) 70 60
1669 $1.50 "Bullock Carts" (Batara Lubis) (horiz) 1·25 1·25
1670 $1.50 "Surat Irsa II" (A. D. Pirous) (horiz) 1·25 1·25
1671 $1.50 "Self-portrait with Goat" (Kartika) (horiz) 1·25 1·25
1672 $1.50 "The Cow-est Cow" (Ivan Sagito) (horiz) 1·25 1·25
1673 $1.50 "Rain Storm" (Sudjana Kerton) (horiz) 1·25 1·25
1674 $1.50 "Story of Pucuk Flower" (Effendi) (horiz) 1·25 1·25
1675 $5 Candi Tikus, Trawulan, East Java (horiz) 2·50 3·00

(b) "Taipei '93", Taiwan.
1677 35 c. Macau Palace Casino, Hong Kong (horiz) 40 20
1678 45 c. Stone lion, Ming Tomb, Nanjing (horiz) 45 25
1679 $1 Stone camels, Ming Tomb, Nanjing (horiz) 70 60
1680 $1.50 Nesting quail incense burner (horiz) 1·25 1·25
1681 $1.50 Standing quail incense burner (horiz) 1·25 1·25
1682 $1.50 Seated qilin incense burner (horiz) 1·25 1·25
1683 $1.50 Pottery horse, Han period (horiz) 1·25 1·25
1684 $1.50 Seated caparisoned elephant (horiz) 1·25 1·25
1685 $1.50 Cow in imitation of Delft faience (horiz) 1·25 1·25
1686 $5 Stone lion and elephant, Ming Tomb, Nanjing (horiz) 2·50 3·00

(c) "Bangkok 1993", Thailand.
1688 35 c. Three Naga snakes, Chiang Mai's Temple (horiz) 40 20
1689 45 c. Sri Mariamman Temple, Singapore (horiz) 45 25
1690 $1 Topiary, Hua Hin Resort (horiz) 70 60
1691 $1.50 "Buddha's Victory over Mara" (horiz) 1·25 1·25
1692 $1.50 "Mythological Elephant" (horiz) 1·25 1·25
1693 $1.50 "Battle with Mara" (Thon Buri) (horiz) 1·25 1·25
1694 $1.50 "Untitled" (Panya Wijinthanasarn) (horiz) 1·25 1·25
1695 $1.50 "Temple Mural" (horiz) 1·25 1·25
1696 $1.50 "Elephants in Pahcekha Buddha's Heaven" (horiz) 1·25 1·25
1697 $5 Pak Tai Temple, Cheung Chau Island (horiz) 2·50 3·00

1993. World Cup Football Championship, U.S.A. (1994) (1st issue). As T **221a** of Gambia. Mult.
1699 15 c. McCall (Scotland) and Verri (Brazil) (horiz) 40 20
1700 25 c. Verri (Brazil) and Maradona (Argentina) (horiz) 50 20
1701 35 c. Schillaci (Italy) and Saldana (Uruguay) (horiz) 55 25
1702 45 c. Gullit (Holland) and Wright (England) (horiz) 60 35
1703 $1 Verri (Brazil) and Maradona (Argentina) (different) (horiz) 80 70
1704 $2 Zubizarreta and Fernandez (Spain) with Albert (Belgium) (horiz) 1·50 1·50
1705 $4 Hagi (Rumania) and McGrath (Ireland) (horiz) 2·50 3·00
1706 $5 Gorriz (Spain) and Scifo (Belgium) (horiz) 2·50 3·00
See also Nos. 1810/15.

1993. 65th Anniv of Mickey Mouse. Scenes from Walt Disney cartoon films. As T **385** of Grenada.
1708 15 c. "Mickey's Rival", 1936 40 25
1709 35 c. "The Worm Turns", 1937 55 25
1710 50 c. "The Pointer", 1939 70 55
1711 75 c. "Society Dog Show", 1939 90 90
1712 $1 "A Gentleman's Gentleman", 1941 1·00 1·00
1713 $2 "The Little Whirlwind", 1941 1·75 2·00
1714 $4 "Mickey Down Under", 1948 2·75 3·00
1715 $5 "R'coon Dawg", 1951 2·75 3·00

1993. Christmas. Religious Paintings. As T **211b** of Gambia. Black, yellow and red (Nos. 1717 and 1721/3) or multicoloured (others).
1717 10 c. "Adoration of the Shepherds" (detail) (Durer) 30 20
1718 25 c. "Adoration of the Magi" (detail) (Raphael) 40 20
1719 35 c. "Presentation in the Temple" (detail) (Raphael) 45 20
1720 50 c. "Adoration of the Magi" (different detail) (Raphael) 55 35
1721 75 c. "Adoration of the Shepherds" (different detail) (Durer) 90 60
1722 $1 "Adoration of the Shepherds" (different detail) (Durer) 1·00 75
1723 $4 "Adoration of the Shepherds" (different detail) (Durer) 2·50 3·00
1724 $5 "Presentation at the Temple" (different detail) (Raphael) 2·50 3·00

1993. Aviation Anniversaries. As T **386** of Grenada. Multicoloured.
1726 15 c. Avro Lancaster 30 20
1727 35 c. Blanchard's balloon crossing the River Delaware 15 20
1728 50 c. Airship "Graf Zeppelin" over Rio de Janeiro 50 35
1729 75 c. Hugo Eckener 65 50
1730 $3 Pres. Washington handing passport to Blanchard 1·40 1·50
1731 $5 Short Sunderland flying boat 2·50 2·75
1732 $5 Eckener in "Graf Zeppelin" 2·50 2·75
ANNIVERSARIES: Nos. 1726, 1731, 75th anniv of Royal Air Force; Nos. 1727, 1730, Bicentenary of first airmail flight; Nos. 1728/9, 1732, 125th birth anniv of Hugo Eckener (airship commander).

1993. Centenaries of Henry Ford's First Petrol Engine (Nos. 1735/6) and Karl Benz's First Four-wheeled Car (others). As T **387** of Grenada. Multicoloured.
1734 25 c. Mercedes Benz "300 SLR", 1955 40 20
1735 45 c. Ford "Thunderbird", 1957 60 25
1736 $4 Ford "150-A" station wagon, 1929 2·75 3·25
1737 $5 Mercedes Benz "540 K" 2·75 3·25

1993. Famous Paintings by Rembrandt and Matisse. As T **221c** of Gambia. Multicoloured.
1739 15 c. "Hendrickje Stoffels as Flora" (Rembrandt) 40 25
1740 35 c. "Lady and Gentleman in Black" (Rembrandt) 50 25
1741 50 c. "Aristotle with the Bust of Homer" (Rembrandt) 60 40
1742 75 c. "Interior: Flowers and Parakeets" (Matisse) 85 60
1743 $1 "Goldfish" (Matisse) 1·00 85
1744 $2 "The Girl with Green Eyes" (Matisse) 1·75 2·00
1745 $3 "Still Life with a Plaster Figure" (Matisse) 2·00 2·50
1746 $5 "Christ and the Woman of Samaria" (Rembrandt) 2·50 2·75

1994. "Hong Kong '94" International Stamp Exhibition (1st issue). As T **222a** of Gambia. Multicoloured.
1748 40 c. Hong Kong 1984 $5 aviation stamp and airliner at Kai Tak Airport 50 65
1749 40 c. Grenada Grenadines 1988 20 c. airships stamp and junk in Kowloon Bay 50 65
Nos. 1748/9 were printed together, se-tenant, forming a composite design.
See also Nos. 1750/5.

1994. "Hong Kong '94" International Stamp Exhibition (2nd issue). Jade Sculptures. As T **222b** of Gambia, but horiz. Multicoloured.
1750 45 c. White jade brush washer 35 40
1751 45 c. Archaic jade brush washer 35 40
1752 45 c. Dark green jade brush washer 35 40
1753 45 c. Green jade almsbowl 35 40
1754 45 c. Archaic jade dog 35 40
1755 45 c. Yellow jade brush washer 35 40

1994. Fungi. As T **390** of Grenada, but with white backgrounds. Multicoloured.
1756 35 c. "Hygrocybe hypohaemacta" 45 30
1757 45 c. "Cantharellus cinnabarinus" 55 35
1758 50 c. "Marasmius haematocephalus" 60 40
1759 75 c. "Mycena pura" 80 60
1760 $1 "Gymnopilus russipes" 90 80
1761 $2 "Calocybe cyanocephala" 1·40 1·50
1762 $4 "Pluteus chrysophlebius" 2·50 2·75
1763 $5 "Chlorophyllum molybdites" 2·50 2·75
No. 1757 is inscribed "Cantherellus cinnabarinus" and No. 1762 "Pleuteus chrysophlebius", both in error.

1994. Prehistoric Animals. As T **391** of Grenada. Multicoloured.
1765 15 c. Spinosaurus 30 25
1766 35 c. Apatosaurus (Brontosaurus) 45 30
1767 45 c. Tyrannosaurus rex 50 35
1768 55 c. Triceratops 55 40
1769 $1 Pachycephalosaurus 85 75
1770 $2 Pteranodon 1·40 1·50
1771 $4 Parasaurolophus 2·50 2·75
1772 $5 Brachiosaurus 2·50 2·75

1994. 25th Anniv of First Manned Moon Landing. Space Shuttle "Challenger". As T **227a** of Gambia. Multicoloured.
1774 $1.10 "Challenger" crew in training 1·00 1·10
1775 $1.10 Christa McAuliffe (astronaut) 1·00 1·10
1776 $1.10 "Challenger" on launch pad 1·00 1·10
1777 $1.10 Gregory Jarvis (astronaut) 1·00 1·10
1778 $1.10 Ellison Onizuka (astronaut) 1·00 1·10
1779 $1.10 Ronald McNair (astronaut) 1·00 1·10

1994. Centenary of International Olympic Committee. Gold Medal Winners. As T **227b** of Gambia. Multicoloured.
1781 50 c. Silke Renk (Germany) (javelin), 1992 35 30
1782 $1.50 Mark Spitz (U.S.A.) (swimming), 1972 90 1·10

1994. International Year of the Family. As T **391a** of Grenada. Multicoloured.
1784 $1 Grenadines family 60 60

1994. 50th Anniv of D-Day. As T **227c** of Gambia. Multicoloured.
1785 40 c. Churchill bridge-laying tank 35 30
1786 $2 Sherman "Firefly" tank leaving landing craft 1·00 1·25
1787 $3 Churchill "Crocodile" flame-thrower 1·60 1·75

1994. "Philakorea '94" International Stamp Exhibition, Seoul (1st issue). As T **227d** of Gambia. Multicoloured.
1789 40 c. Onung Tomb (horiz) 30 30
1790 $1 Stone pagoda, Mt Namsam (horiz) 55 55
1791 $1 "Admiring Spring in the Country" (left detail) (Sin Yunbok) 55 55
1792 $1 "Admiring Spring in the Country" (right detail) 55 55
1793 $1 "Woman on Dano Day" (left detail) (Sin Yunbok) 55 55
1794 $1 "Woman on Dano Day" (right detail) 55 55
1795 $1 "Enjoying Lotuses while Listening to Music" (left detail) (Sin Yunbok) 55 55
1796 $1 "Enjoying Lotuses while Listening to Music" (right detail) 55 55
1797 $1 "Women by a Crystal Stream" (left detail) (Sin Yunbok) 55 55
1798 $1 "Women by a Crystal Stream" (right detail) 55 55
1799 $4 Pusan (horiz) 2·25 2·25
The two details of each painting on Nos. 1791/8 were printed together, se-tenant, each pair forming a composite design.
See also Nos. 1817/30.

1994. Orchids. As T **392** of Grenada. Multicoloured.
1801 15 c. "Cattleya aurantiaca" 35 25
1802 25 c. "Blettia patula" 40 25
1803 45 c. "Sobralia macrantha" 50 30
1804 75 c. "Encyclia belizensis" 70 55
1805 $1 "Sophrolaeliocattleya" 85 75
1806 $2 "Encyclia fragrans" 1·40 1·50
1807 $4 "Schombocattleya" 2·50 2·75
1808 $5 "Brassolaeliocattleya" 2·50 2·75

1994. World Cup Football Championship, U.S.A. (2nd issue). As T **393** of Grenada. Multicoloured.
1810 75 c. Steve Mark (Grenada) 50 50
1811 75 c. Jurgen Kohler (Germany) 50 50
1812 75 c. Almir (Brazil) 50 50
1813 75 c. Michael Windiscmann (U.S.A.) 50 50
1814 75 c. Guiseppe Giannini (Italy) 50 50
1815 75 c. Rashidi Yekini (Nigeria) 50 50

106 Mickey Mouse and Unjin Miruk Window from Kwanch Ok Temple

1994. "Philakorea '94" International Stamp Exhibition, Seoul (2nd issue). Walt Disney cartoon characters. Multicoloured.

1817 3 c. Type **106** 15 15
1818 4 c. Goofy imitating statue of Admiral Yi, Chonju 15 15
1819 5 c. Cousin Gus and Donald Duck eating dinner 15 15
1820 10 c. Mickey playing flute . . 20 15
1821 15 c. Goofy with Tolharubang (statue) 30 20
1822 15 c. Type **106** 30 20
1823 20 c. Mickey and Minnie at Hyang-Wonjong 30 20
1824 35 c. As 4 c. 40 25
1825 50 c. As 5 c. 50 35
1826 75 c. As 10 c. 70 55
1827 $1 As 15 c. 85 75
1828 $2 As 20 c. . . . . 1·40 1·50
1829 $4 Mickey as Somori-Kut shaman . . . . 2·50 2·75
1830 $5 Minnie holding ceremonial fan . . . . 2·50 2·75

1994. 1st Recipients of Order of the Caribbean Community. As Nos. 2750/2 of Grenada. Multicoloured.

1832 25 c. Sir Shridath Ramphal . . 10 10
1833 50 c. William Demas 25 30
1834 $2 Derek Walcott . . . . . . 1·40 1·60

1994. Fishes. As T **394** of Grenada. Multicoloured.

1835 75 c. Porkfish 55 55
1836 75 c. Blue chromis 55 55
1837 75 c. Caribbean reef shark (facing left) 55 55
1838 75 c. Long-spined squirrelfish . 55 55
1839 75 c. Four-eyed butterflyfish . 55 55
1840 75 c. Blue head 55 55
1841 75 c. Royal gramma 55 55
1842 75 c. Sharp-nosed puffer . . . 55 55
1843 75 c. Reid's seahorse 55 55
1844 75 c. Black-barred soldierfish . . 55 55
1845 75 c. Red-lipped blenny . . . 55 55
1846 75 c. Painted wrasse 55 55
1847 75 c. Yellow-tailed snapper . . 55 55
1848 75 c. Caribbean reef shark (facing right) 55 55
1849 75 c. Great barracuda 55 55
1850 75 c. Red-tailed parrotfish . . 55 55
1851 75 c. Blue tang 55 55
1852 75 c. Queen angelfish 55 55
1853 75 c. Red hind 55 55
1854 75 c. Rock beauty 55 55
1855 75 c. Queen parrotfish 55 55
1856 75 c. Spanish hogfish 55 55
1857 75 c. Spotted moray 55 55
1858 75 c. Queen triggerfish 55 55

Nos. 1835/46 and 1847/58 respectively were printed together, se-tenant, forming composite designs.

1994 Christmas. Religious Paintings by Bartolome Murillo. As T **231a** of Gambia. Multicoloured.

1860 15 c. "The Annunciation" . . 30 20
1861 35 c. "The Adoration of the Shepherds" 40 20
1862 50 c. "Virgin and Child with St. Rose" 50 30
1863 50 c. "Flight into Egypt" . . 50 30
1864 75 c. "Virgin and Child" . . 70 45
1865 $1 "Virgin of the Rosary" . . 85 70
1866 $4 "The Holy Family" . . . 2·50 3·25

1995. Birds. As T **397** of Grenada. Multicoloured.

1868 25 c. Scaly-breasted ground dove (vert) 45 35
1869 50 c. White-winged dove . . . 75 55
1870 $2 Inca dove (vert) . . . . 1·75 1·75
1871 $4 Mourning dove . . . . . 3·00 3·75

1995. Centenary of First English Cricket Tour to the West Indies. As T **397a** of Grenada. Multicoloured.

1872 50 c. Mike Atherton (England) and Wisden Trophy 55 45
1873 75 c. Curtly Ambrose (West Indies) (vert) 75 75
1874 $1 Brian Lara (West Indies) (vert) . . . . 90 1·10

107 Aspects of London, National Flag and Map

108 Pig

1995. Capitals of the World. Aspects of various cities, national flags and maps. Multicoloured.

1876 $1 Type **107** 65 70
1877 $1 Cairo 65 70
1878 $1 Vienna 65 70
1879 $1 Paris 65 70
1880 $1 Rome 65 70
1881 $1 Budapest 65 70
1882 $1 Moscow 65 70
1883 $1 Peking ("Beijing") 65 70
1884 $1 Tokyo 65 70
1885 $1 Washington 65 70

1995. Chinese New Year ("Year of the Pig"). Multicoloured designs showing "GRENADA GRENADINES" in colours indicated.

1886 75 c. Type **108** (violet) 45 50
1887 75 c. Pig (carmine) 45 50
1888 75 c. Pig (brown) 45 50
1889 75 c. Pig (vermilion) 45 50

109 Bull Shark and Diver

1995. Marine Life of the Caribbean. Multicoloured.

1891 $1 Type **109** 65 70
1892 $1 Great white shark 65 70
1893 $1 Octopus and shoal of fish . 65 70
1894 $1 Great barracuda 65 70
1895 $1 Green moray 65 70
1896 $1 Spotted eagle ray 65 70
1897 $1 Sea snake 65 70
1898 $1 Stingray 65 70
1899 $1 Grouper 65 70
1900 $1 Dolphins 65 70
1901 $1 Lionfish 65 70
1902 $1 Sea turtle and rock beauty (fish) 65 70
1903 $1 Blue-cheeked butterflyfish and nurse shark 65 70
1904 $1 Queen angelfish 65 70
1905 $1 Grouper and coney 65 70
1906 $1 Rainbow eel and spotted moray 65 70
1907 $1 Sun flower-star and coral crab 65 70
1908 $1 Octopus on sea bed 65 70

110 Suffolk Punch

1995. Domestic Animals. Multicoloured.

1910 15 c. Type **110** 40 30
1911 25 c. Shetland pony 50 30
1912 75 c. Blue persian (cat) . . . 50 55
1913 75 c. Sorrel abyssinian (cat) . . 50 55
1914 75 c. White angora (cat) . . . 50 55
1915 75 c. Brown Burmese (cat) . . 50 55
1916 75 c. Red tabby exotic shorthair (cat) 50 55
1917 75 c. Seal-point birman (cat) . . 50 55
1918 75 c. Korat (cat) 50 55
1919 75 c. Norwegian forest cat . . 50 55
1920 75 c. Lilac-point Balinese (cat) . 50 55
1921 75 c. British shorthair (cat) . . 50 55
1922 75 c. Red self longhair (cat) . . 50 55
1923 75 c. Calico Manx (cat) . . . 50 55
1924 75 c. Shetland sheepdog . . . 50 55
1925 75 c. Bull terrier 50 55
1926 75 c. Afghan hound 50 55
1927 75 c. Scottish terrier 50 55
1928 75 c. Labrador retriever . . . 50 55
1929 75 c. English springer spaniel . 50 55
1930 75 c. Samoyed (dog) 50 55
1931 75 c. Irish setter 50 55
1932 75 c. Border collie 50 55
1933 75 c. Pekingese 50 55
1934 75 c. Dachshund 50 55
1935 75 c. Weimaraner (dog) 50 55
1936 $1 Arab 70 70
1937 $3 Shire horse . . . . 1·75 2·00

1995. Centenary (1992) of Sierra Club (environmental protection society). Endangered Species. As T **224a** of Gambia. Multicoloured.

1939 $1 Spotted owl 65 70
1940 $1 Brown pelican on perch . . 65 70
1941 $1 Head of brown pelican . . 65 70
1942 $1 Head of jaguarundi 65 70
1943 $1 Jaguarundi looking over shoulder 65 70
1944 $1 Maned wolf in undergrowth 65 70
1945 $1 American wood stork standing on two legs . . . 65 70
1946 $1 American wood stork standing on one leg 65 70
1947 $1 Close-up of maned wolf . . 65 70
1948 $1 Brown pelican (horiz) . . . 65 70
1949 $1 Close-up of spotted owl (horiz) 65 70
1950 $1 Spotted owl chick (horiz) . 65 70
1951 $1 Jaguarundi (horiz) 65 70
1952 $1 Central American spider monkey sitting with young (horiz) 65 70
1953 $1 Central American spider monkey carrying young (horiz) 65 70
1954 $1 Central American spider monkey swinging from branch (horiz) 65 70
1955 $1 American wood stork (horiz) 65 70
1956 $1 Pair of maned wolfs (horiz) . 65 70

1995. 18th World Scout Jamboree, Netherlands. As T **403** of Grenada. Multicoloured.

1957 75 c. Grenadian scout on beach 60 70
1958 $1 Scout with staff on hill . . 80 90
1959 $2 Scout saluting and national flag . . . . 1·10 1·25

INDEX

Countries can be quickly located by referring to the index at the end of this volume.

1995. 50th Anniv of End of Second World War in Europe. Bombers. As T **237a** of Gambia. Mult.

1961 $2 Avro Type **683** Lancaster . 1·25 1·25
1962 $2 Junkers Ju 88 . . . . . . 1·25 1·25
1963 $2 North American B-25 Mitchell . . . . 1·25 1·25
1964 $2 Boeing B-17 Flying Fortress 1·25 1·25
1965 $2 Petlyakov Pe-2 . . . . . 1·25 1·25
1966 $2 Martin B-26 Marauder . . 1·25 1·25
1967 $2 Heinkel He 111H . . . . 1·25 1·25
1968 $2 Consolidated B-24 Liberator 1·25 1·25

1995. 50th Anniv of United Nations. As T **404** of Grenada. Multicoloured.

1970 75 c. U.N. Headquarters, New York, and flag 60 70
1971 $1 Trygve Lie (first Secretary-General) 80 90
1972 $2 U.N. soldier . . . . . . 1·10 1·25

Nos. 1970/2 were printed together, se-tenant, forming a composite design.

1995. 50th Anniv of F.A.O. As T **405** of Grenada. Multicoloured.

1974 75 c. Man hoeing 60 70
1975 $1 Woman hoeing 80 90
1976 $2 Man and woman hoeing . . 1·10 1·25

Nos. 1974/6 were printed together, se-tenant, forming a composite design.

1995. 90th Anniv of Rotary International. As T **406** of Grenada. Multicoloured.

1978 $5 Paul Harris (founder) and logo (horiz) . . . . 2·50 3·00

1995. 95th Birthday of Queen Elizabeth the Queen Mother. As T **239a** of Gambia.

1980 $1.50 brown, light brown and black . . . . 1·10 1·10
1981 $1.50 multicoloured . . . . . 1·10 1·10
1982 $1.50 multicoloured . . . . . 1·10 1·10
1983 $1.50 multicoloured . . . . . 1·10 1·10

DESIGNS: No. 1980, Queen Elizabeth the Queen Mother (pastel drawing); 1981, At Remembrance Day service; 1982, At desk (oil painting); 1983, Wearing green hat.

1995. 50th Anniv of End of Second World War in the Pacific. As T **239b** of Gambia. Multicoloured.

1985 $2 Mitsubishi G4M1 "Betty" (bomber) . . . . 1·40 1·50
1986 $2 Japanese submarine "I 14" with seaplane on catapault . 1·40 1·50
1987 $2 Mitsubishi GM31 "Nell" (bomber) . . . . 1·40 1·50
1988 $2 "Akizuki" (Japanese destroyer) . . . . 1·40 1·50
1989 $2 "Kirishima" (Japanese battleship) . . . . 1·40 1·50
1990 $2 "Asigari" (Japanese cruiser) 1·40 1·50

1995. Olympic Games, Atlanta (1996). As T **407** of Grenada. Multicoloured.

1992 15 c. Rosemary Ackerman (East Germany) (high jump) (horiz) 30 30
1993 15 c. Li Ning (China) (gymnastics) (horiz) . . . 30 30
1994 15 c. Denise Parker (U.S.A.) (archery) (horiz) 30 30
1995 $3 Terry Carlisle (U.S.A.) (skeet shooting) (horiz) . . . . 1·75 2·00
1996 $3 Kathleen Nord (East Germany) (swimming) (horiz) . . . . 1·75 2·00
1997 $3 Brigit Schmidt (East Germany) (canoeing) (horiz) 1·75 2·00

111 Brown Pelican

1995. Birds of the Caribbean. Multicoloured.

1999 10 c. Type **111** 30 40
2000 15 c. Black-necked stilt . . . 30 40
2001 25 c. Cuban trogon 30 30
2002 35 c. Greater flamingo 40 30
2003 75 c. Imperial amazon 60 45
2004 $1 Pintail 80 85
2005 $1 Great blue heron 80 85
2006 $1 Jamaican tody 80 85
2007 $1 Laughing gull 80 85
2008 $1 Purple-throated carib . . . 80 85
2009 $1 Red-legged thrush 80 85
2010 $1 Ruddy duck 80 85
2011 $1 Common shoveler 80 85
2012 $1 West Indian red-bellied woodpecker 80 85
2013 $2 Ringed kingfisher . . . . 1·40 1·60
2014 $3 Strip-headed tanager . . . 1·75 2·00

No. 2001 is inscr "Cuban Trogan", No. 2008 "Purple-throated Carb" and No. 2013 Ringed King Fisher, all in error.

1995. Mickey's Pirate Adventure. Walt Disney Cartoon Characters. As T **415** of Grenada. Multicoloured.

2016 10 c. Goofy and Donald Duck with treasure chests (horiz) . 20 20
2017 35 c. Mickey and Minnie Mouse at ship's wheel (horiz) . . . 30 20
2018 75 c. Mickey, Donald and Goofy opening chest (horiz) 55 40
2019 $1 Big Pete and rats confronting Mickey (horiz) 70 60
2020 $2 Mickey, Goofy and Donald in boat (horiz) . . . . . 1·40 1·75
2021 $5 Goofy fighting rat pirate with mop (horiz) . . . . . . 3·25 3·75

1995. Centenary of Nobel Trust Fund. As T **416** of Grenada. Multicoloured.

2023/51 75 c. × 2, $1 × 27 Set of 29 . . . . 15·50 17·00

DESIGNS: 75 c. W. Arthur Lewis (1979 Economics); Derek Walcott (1992 Literature); $1 Jules Border (1919 Medicine); Rene Cassin (1968 Peace); Verner von Heidenstam (1916 Literature); Jose Echegaray (1904 Literature); Otto Wallach (1910 Chemistry); Corneille Heymans (1938 Medicine); Ivar Giaever (1973 Physics); Sir William Cremer (1903 Peace); John Strutt (1904 Physics); James Franck (1925 Physics); Tobias Asser (1911 Peace); Carl Spitteler (1919 Literature); Christiaan Eijkman (1929 Medicine); Ragnar Granit (1967 Medicine); Frederic Passy (1901 Peace); Louis Neel (1970 Physics); Sir William Ramsay (1904 Chemistry); Philip Noel-Baker (1959 Peace); Heike Onnes (1913 Physics); Fridtjof Nansen (1922 Peace); Sir Ronald Ross (1902 Medicine); Paul Muller (1948 Medicine); Allvar Gullstrand (1911 Medicine); Gerhart Hauptmann (1912 Literature); Hans Spemann (1935 Medicine); Cecil Powell (1950 Physics); Walther Bothe (1954 Physics).

Nos. 2025/33, 2034/42 and 2043/51 respectively were printed together, se-tenant, forming composite designs.

No. 2027 (Von Heidenstam) is inscribed "1906" and No. 2044 "Fridtjof Nanser", both in error.

112 Nita Naldi and Rudolph Valentino

114 Symbolic Rat and Candle

113 Man on Donkey

1995. Centenary of Cinema. Multicoloured.

2053 $1 Type **112** 65 70
2054 $1 Ramon Novaro and Alice Terry 65 70
2055 $1 Frederic March and Joan Crawford 65 70
2056 $1 Clark Gable and Vivien Leigh 65 70
2057 $1 Barbara Stanwyck and Burt Lancaster 65 70
2058 $1 Warren Beatty and Natalie Wood 65 70
2059 $1 Spencer Tracy and Katharine Hepburn 65 70
2060 $1 Humphrey Bogart and Lauren Bacall 65 70
2061 $1 Omar Sharif and Julie Christie 65 70
2062 $1 Marion Davies 65 70
2063 $1 Marlene Dietrich 65 70
2064 $1 Lillian Gish 65 70
2065 $1 Bette Davis 65 70
2066 $1 Elizabeth Taylor 65 70
2067 $1 Veronica Lake 65 70
2068 $1 Ava Gardner 65 70
2069 $1 Grace Kelly 65 70
2070 $1 Kim Novak 65 70

Nos. 2053/61 and 2062/70 respectively were printed together, se-tenant, forming composite designs.

1995. Racing Cars. As T **423** of Grenada. Multicoloured.

2072 10 c. Williams-Renault Formula 1, 1990s 20 20
2073 25 c. Porsche "956", Le Mans, 1980s 30 20
2074 35 c. Lotus "John Player Special", 1970s 40 20
2075 75 c. Ford "GT-40", 1960s . . 65 45
2076 $2 Mercedes-Benz "W196", 1950s . . . . 1·50 1·75
2077 $3 Mercedes "SSK", 1920s . . 2·00 2·25

1995. Local Transport. Multicoloured.

2079 35 c. Type **113** 25 20
2080 75 c. Local bus 40 50

1995. Evolution of Sailing Ships. As T **427** of Grenada. Multicoloured.

2081 $1 "Preussen" (full-rigged ship) 65 70
2082 $1 Japanese junk 65 70
2083 $1 Caribbean pirate ship . . . 65 70
2084 $1 "Mayflower" (Pilgrim Fathers) 65 70
2085 $1 Chinese junk 65 70
2086 $1 "Santa Maria" (Columbus) 65 70

1995. Christmas. Religious Paintings. As T **245a** of Gambia. Multicoloured.
2088 10 c. "Immaculate Conception" (Piero di Cosimo) 15 10
2089 15 c. "St. Michael dedicating Arms to the Madonna" (Le Nain) 20 10
2090 35 c. "Annunciation" (Lorenzo di Credi) 25 20
2091 50 c. "The Holy Family" (Jacob Jordaens) 40 30
2092 $3 "Madonna and Child" (Lippi) . . . . 1·75 2·00
2093 $5 "Madonna and Child with Ten Saints" (Fiorentino) . . 3·00 3·50

1996. Chinese New Year ("Year of the Rat"). Multicoloured, background colours given.
2095 **114** 75 c. blue 35 40
2096 75 c. lilac 35 40
2097 75 c. brown 35 40
2098 75 c. green 35 40
The four designs show different Chinese characters.

1996. Works of Art by Durer and Rubens. As T **421** of Grenada. Multicoloured.
2101 15 c. "The Centaur Family" (Durer) 15 10
2102 35 c. "Oriental Ruler Seated" (Durer) 25 20
2103 50 c. "The Entombment" (Durer) 40 30
2104 75 c. "Man in Armour" (Rubens) 55 40
2105 $1 "Peace embracing Plenty" (Rubens) 65 60
2106 $2 "Departure of Lot" (Rubens) . . . . 1·25 1·50
2107 $3 "The Four Evangelists" (Rubens) . . . . 1·75 2·00
2108 $5 "Knight, Death and Devil" (Durer) . . . . 3·00 3·50

115 Mickey and Minnie at New Year's Day "Hopping John" Tradition

1996. Traditional Holidays. Walt Disney Cartoon Characters. Multicoloured.
2110 25 c. Type **115** 20 15
2111 50 c. Disney characters dancing around maypole 35 30
2112 75 c. Mickey, Minnie and Pluto watching Independence Day fireworks 55 40
2113 90 c. Gyro Gearloose and Donald's nephews in Halloween costumes . . . 65 55
2114 $3 Donald Duck as Puritan and nephews as Indians on Thanksgiving Day . . . . 2·00 2·25
2115 $4 Huey and Dewey with Hanukkah dreidle . . . . 2·25 2·50

116 Gateway in Imperial Palace, Peking (½-size illustration)

1996. "CHINA '96" 9th Asian International Stamp Exhibition, Peking. Multicoloured.
2117 $1 Type **116** 45 50
2118 $1 Eastern end of Great Wall at Shanhaiguan 45 50
2119 $1 Great Wall fortress, Shanhaiguan 45 50
2120 $1 Gate of Heavenly Peace, Peking 45 50
2121 $1 Sun Yat-sen's Mausoleum, Nanjing 45 50
2122 $1 Summer Palace, Peking . . 45 50
2123 $1 Temple of Heaven, Peking 45 50
2124 $1 Hall of Supreme Harmony, Forbidden City, Peking . . 45 50

1996. 70th Birthday of Queen Elizabeth II. As T **255a** of Gambia. Multicoloured.
2126 35 c. As Type **255a** of Gambia . 15 20
2127 $2 Queen wearing tiara and green dress 85 90
2128 $4 Windsor Castle . . . . . 1·75 1·90

1996. Flowers. As T **430** of Grenada. Multicoloured.
2130 35 c. "Camellia" "Apple Blossom" 15 20
2131 75 c. "Odontoglossum" . . . 35 40
2132 75 c. "Cattleya" 35 40
2133 75 c. "Paphiopedilum" "Venus's Slipper" 35 40
2134 75 c. "Laeliocattleya" "Marysville" 35 40
2135 75 c. Fuchsia "Citation" . . . 35 40
2136 75 c. Fuchsia "Amy Lye" . . 35 40
2137 75 c. "Clysonimus" (butterfly) and temple 35 40
2138 75 c. Foxglove ("Digitalis purpurea") 35 40
2139 75 c. Martagon lily ("Lilium martagon") 35 40
2140 75 c. "Tulipa" "Couleur Cardinal" 35 40
2141 75 c. Snowdrop ("Galanthus nivalis") 35 40
2142 75 c. "Rosa" "Superstar" . . 35 40
2143 75 c. Crocus "Dutch Yellow Mammoth" 35 40
2144 75 c. Japanese lily ("Lilium speciosum") 35 40
2145 75 c. "Lilium" "Joan Evans" . 35 40
2146 75 c. "Rosa" "Rosemary Harkness" 35 40
2147 90 c. "Camellia japonica" "Extravaganza" 40 45
2148 $1 Chrysanthemum "Primrose Dorothy Else" 45 50
2149 $2 Dahlia "Brandaris" 85 90
Nos. 2135/46 were printed together, se-tenant, with the backgrounds forming a composite design.
No. 2135 is inscribed "Fuschcia" and No. 2133 "Mammouth" in error.

1996. 50th Anniv of U.N.I.C.E.F. As T **258a** of Gambia. Multicoloured.
2151 75 c. Child's face (horiz) . . . 35 40
2152 $2 Child with spoon (horiz) . 85 90
2153 $3 Girl sewing (horiz) . . . . 1·25 1·40

1996. Centenary of Radio. Entertainers. As T **259a** of Gambia. Multicoloured.
2157 35 c. Ed Wynn 15 20
2158 75 c. Red Skelton 35 40
2159 $1 Joe Penner 45 50
2160 $3 Jerry Colonna . . . . . . 1·25 1·40

1996. Olympic Games, Atlanta. Previous Medal Winners. As T **425** of Grenada. Multicoloured.
2162 35 c. Los Angeles Memorial Coliseum 15 20
2163 75 c. Connie Carpenter-Phinney (U.S.A.) (Cycling) 35 40
2164 $1 Josef Neckermann (Germany) (vert) 45 50
2165 $1 Harry Boldt (Germany) (vert) 45 50
2166 $1 Elena Petouchkova (Russia) (vert) 45 50
2167 $1 Alwin Schockemoehle (Germany) (vert) 45 50
2168 $1 Hans Winkler (Germany) (vert) 45 50
2169 $1 Joe Fargis (U.S.A.) (vert) . 45 50
2170 $1 David Broome (Great Britain) (vert) 45 50
2171 $1 Reiner Klimke (Germany) (vert) 45 50
2172 $1 Richard Meade (Great Britain) (vert) 45 50
2173 $1 Julianne McNamara (U.S.A.) (vert) 45 50
2174 $1 Takuti Hayata (Japan) (vert) 45 50
2175 $1 Nikolai Adriana (Russia) (vert) 45 50
2176 $1 Mitch Gaylord (U.S.A.) (vert) 45 50
2177 $1 Ludmilla Tourischeva (Russia) (vert) 45 50
2178 $1 Karin Janz (Germany) (vert) 45 50
2179 $1 Peter Kormann (U.S.A.) (vert) 45 50
2180 $1 Sawoo Kato (Japan) (vert) . 45 50
2181 $1 Nadia Comaneci (Rumania) (vert) 45 50
2182 $2 Mohamed Bouchighe (Algeria) (Boxing) (vert) . . 85 90
2183 $3 Jackie Joyner Kersee (U.S.A.) (Javelin) . . . . . 1·25 1·40
Nos. 2164/72 (equestrians) and 2173/81 (gymnasts) respectively were printed together, se-tenant, with the backgrounds forming composite designs.

1996. Classic Cars. As T **426** of Grenada. Multicoloured.
2185 35 c. Chevrolet Belair convertible 15 20
2186 50 c. V.I.P. car 25 30
2187 75 c. Rolls-Royce Torpedo . . 35 40
2188 $1 Nissan "Cepric" type . . . 45 50
2189 $1 Delaunay-Belleville HB6 . . 45 50
2190 $1 Bugatti Type-15 . . . . . 45 50
2191 $1 Mazda Type 800 . . . . . 45 50
2192 $1 Mercedes 24/100/140 Sport . 45 50
2193 $1 MG K3 Rover 45 50
2194 $1 Plymouth Fury 45 50
2195 $2 Mercedes-Benz 500K . . . 85 90
2196 $3 Bugatti Type-13 . . . . . 1·25 1·40

1996. Ships. As T **427** of Grenada. Multicoloured.
2198 35 c. Grenada schooner . . . 15 20
2199 75 c. Grenada schooner (different) 35 40
2200 $1 Athenian triremes, 1000 B.C. 45 50
2201 $1 Egyptian Nile galley, 30 B.C. 45 50
2202 $1 Bangladesh dinghi, 310 B.C. 45 50
2203 $1 Warship of Queen Hatshepsut, 476 B.C. . . . 45 50
2204 $1 Chinese Junk, 200 B.C. . . 45 50
2205 $1 Polynesian ocean-going canoe, 600 B.C. 45 50
2206 $1 "Europa" (liner), 1957 . . . 45 50
2207 $1 "Lusitania" (liner), 1906 . . 45 50
2208 $1 "Queen Mary" (liner), 1936 . . . . 45 50
2209 $1 "Bianca C" (liner) 45 50
2210 $1 "France" (liner), 1952 . . . 45 50
2211 $1 "Orion" (liner), 1915 . . . 45 50

117 Felix Mendelssohn

120 Hong Kong

119 Springer Spaniel

1996. Composers. Multicoloured.
2213 $1 Type **117** 45 50
2214 $1 Franz Schubert 45 50
2215 $1 Franz Joseph Haydn . . . 45 50
2216 $1 Robert Schumann 45 50
2217 $1 Ludwig van Beethoven . . . 45 50
2218 $1 Gioacchino Rossini 45 50
2219 $1 George Frederick Handel . . 45 50
2220 $1 Pyotr Tchaikovsky 45 50
2221 $1 Frederic Chopin 45 50
2222 $1 Bela Bartok 45 50
2223 $1 Giacomo Puccini 45 50
2224 $1 George Gershwin 45 50
2225 $1 Leonard Bernstein 45 50
2226 $1 Kurt Weill 45 50
2227 $1 John Cage 45 50
2228 $1 Aaron Copland 45 50
2229 $1 Sergei Prokofiev 45 50
2230 $1 Igor Stravinsky 45 50
Nos. 2213/21 and 2222/30 respectively were printed together, se-tenant, with the backgrounds forming composite designs.

1996. Railway Steam Locomotives. As T **429** of Grenada. Multicoloured.
2232 $1.50 Class 38 No. 382, Germany 65 70
2233 $1.50 "Duchess of Hamilton", Great Britain 65 70
2234 $1.50 Class W.P., India . . . 65 70
2235 $1.50 Class 141R "Americaine", France 65 70
2236 $1.50 Class A4 "Mallard", Great Britain 65 70
2237 $1.50 Class 18 No. 201, Germany 65 70
2238 $1.50 Class A2 "Blue Peter", Great Britain 65 70
2239 $1.50 Class P36, Russia . . . 65 70
2240 $1.50 Class QJ, China 65 70
2241 $1.50 Class 12, Belgium . . . 65 70
2242 $1.50 Class "Challenger", U.S.A. 65 70
2243 $1.50 Class 25, South Africa . 65 70

1996. Christmas. Religious Paintings. As T **245a** of Gambia. Showing different details from "Suffer Little Children to Come Unto Me" by Van Dyck.
2245 15 c. multicoloured 10 10
2246 25 c. multicoloured 10 15
2247 $1 multicoloured 45 50
2248 $1.50 multicoloured 65 70
2249 $2 multicoloured 85 90
2250 $4 multicoloured . . . . . . 1·75 1·90

1997. 50th Anniv of U.N.E.S.C.O. As T **273a** of Gambia. Multicoloured.
2253 15 c. Temple, Kyoto, Japan . . 10 10
2254 25 c. Roman ruins, Trier, Germany 10 15
2255 $1 Gateway, Mount Taishan, China 45 50
2256 $1 Temple guardian, Kyoto, Japan (vert) 45 50
2257 $1 Temple deity, Kyoto, Japan (vert) 45 50
2258 $1 Temple lamp, Kyoto, Japan (vert) 45 50
2259 $1 Ayutthaya, Thailand (vert) . 45 50
2260 $1 Statue, Borobudur Temple, Indonesia (vert) 45 50
2261 $1 Monuments at Pattadakal, India (vert) 45 50
2262 $1 Sleeping buddha, Polonnaruwa, Sri Lanka (vert) 45 50
2263 $1 Sagarmatha National Park, Nepal (vert) 45 50
2264 $1 Congonhas Sanctuary, Brazil (vert) 45 50
2265 $1 Cartagena, Colombia (vert) 45 50
2266 $1 Pueblo, Guatemala (vert) . . 45 50
2267 $1 Maya statue, Honduras (vert) 45 50
2268 $1 Popocatepetl Monastery, Mexico (vert) 45 50
2269 $1 Galapagos Islands, Ecuador (vert) 45 50
2270 $1 Waterfall, Costa Rica (vert) 45 50
2271 $1 Glaciares National Park, Argentina (vert) 45 50
2272 $1.50 Notre Dame Cathedral, Paris, France 65 70
2273 $1.50 Timbered house, Maulbronn, Germany . . . 65 70
2274 $1.50 Gateway, Himeji-jo, Japan 65 70
2275 $1.50 Lion statues, Delphi, Greece 65 70
2276 $1.50 Palace of Fontainebleau, France 65 70
2277 $1.50 Scandola Nature Reserve, France 65 70
2278 $2 Citadel, Dubrovnik, Croatia 85 90
2279 $4 Angra do Heroismo, Portugal . . . . 1·75 1·90

1997. Cats and Dogs. Multicoloured.
2281 35 c. Type **119** 15 20
2282 45 c. Abyssinian blue 20 25
2283 50 c. Burmese cream (vert) . . 25 30
2284 75 c. Doberman pinscher . . . 35 40
2285 90 c. Persian tortoiseshell and white 40 45
2286 $1 Italian spinone (vert) . . . 45 50
2287 $1.50 Siamese chocolate point . 65 70
2288 $1.50 Oriental shorthair white . 65 70
2289 $1.50 Burmese sable 65 70
2290 $1.50 Abyssinian tabby . . . 65 70
2291 $1.50 Persian shaded silver . . 65 70
2292 $1.50 Tonkinese natural mink . 65 70
2293 $1.50 Leonberger 65 70
2294 $1.50 Newfoundland 65 70
2295 $1.50 Boxer 65 70
2296 $1.50 St. Bernard 65 70
2297 $1.50 Silky terrier 65 70
2298 $1.50 Miniature schnauzer . . 65 70
2299 $2 Cocker spaniel (vert) . . . 85 90
2300 $3 Oriental shorthair agouti (vert) . . . . 1·25 1·40
Nos. 2287/92 (cats) and Nos. 2293/8 (dogs) respectively were printed together, se-tenant, with the backgrounds forming composite designs.

1997. Dinosaurs. As T **438** of Grenada. Mult.
2302 45 c. Stegosaurus 20 25
2303 90 c. Diplodocus 40 45
2304 $1 Pteranodon (vert) 45 50
2305 $1.50 Rhamphorhynchus and head of Brachiosaurus . . . 65 70
2306 $1.50 Archaeopteryx 65 70
2307 $1.50 Anurognathus and body of Brachiosaurus 65 70
2308 $1.50 Head of Albertosaurus . 65 70
2309 $1.50 Herrerasaurus and legs of Brachiosaurus 65 70
2310 $1.50 Platyhystrix and body of Albertosaurus 65 70
2311 $2 Deinonychus and Ankylasaurus (vert) 85 90
Nos. 2305/10 were printed together, se-tenant, with the backgrounds forming a composite design.

1997. 50th Death Anniv of Paul Harris (founder of Rotary International). As T **276b** of Gambia. Multicoloured.
2314 $3 Paul Harris and village women with water pump, Burkina Faso . . . . . . 1·25 1·40

1997. Golden Wedding of Queen Elizabeth and Prince Philip. As T **276c** of Gambia. Multicoloured (except Nos. 2318/19).
2316 $1 Engagement photograph, 1947 . . . . 45 50
2317 $1 Royal coat of arms 45 50
2318 $1 Queen Elizabeth and Duke of Edinburgh, 1953 (brown) . 45 50
2319 $1 Formal portrait of Queen Elizabeth with Prince Philip in uniform (brown) 45 50
2320 $1 Sandringham House . . . 45 50
2321 $1 Queen Elizabeth and Prince Philip in carriage 45 50

1997. "Pacific '97" International Stamp Exhibition, San Francisco. Death Centenary of Heinrich von Stephan (founder of the U.P.U.). As T **276d** of Gambia.
2323 $1.50 green 65 70
2324 $1.50 brown 65 70
2325 $1.50 violet 65 70
DESIGNS: No. 2323, Pony Express, 1860; 2324, Von Stephan and Mercury; 2325, American steam locomotive.

1997. Birth Bicentenary of Hiroshige (Japanese painter). "100 Famous Views of Edo". As T **541a** of Ghana but horiz. Multicoloured.
2327 $1.50 "Koume Embankment" . . 65 70
2328 $1.50 "Azuma Shrine and the Entwined Camphor" 65 70
2329 $1.50 "Yanagishima" 65 70
2330 $1.50 "Inside Akiba Shrine, Ukeji" 65 70
2331 $1.50 "Distant View of Kinryuzan Temple and Azuma Bridge" 65 70
2332 $1.50 "Night View of Matsuchiyama and the San'ya Canal" 65 70

1997. 175th Anniv of Brothers Grimm's Third Collection of Fairy Tales. "The Fox and the Geese". As T **277a** of Gambia. Multicoloured.
2334 $2 Fox and geese 85 90
2335 $2 Fox with knife and fork and geese 85 90
2336 $2 Fox asleep and singing geese 85 90

1997. Winter Olympic Games, Nagano, Japan. As T **440** of Grenada. Multicoloured.
2338 90 c. Slalom 40 45
2339 $1 Downhill skiing 45 50
2340 $1 Freestyle ski-jumping (blue and green ski suit) 45 50
2341 $1 Curling 45 50
2342 $1 Ski-jumping (pink ski suit) . 45 50
2343 $1 Four-man bobsleigh . . . 45 50
2344 $1 Nordic combined 45 50
2345 $1 Speed skating 45 50
2346 $1 Ice hockey 45 50
2347 $1 Cross-country skiing . . . 45 50
2348 $2 One-man luge 85 90
2349 $3 Men's figure-skating . . . 1·25 1·40
2350 $5 Speed skating (different) . . 2·10 2·25

1997. Return of Hong Kong to China. Multicoloured.
2352 **120** $1 multicoloured 45 50
2353 – $1.25 multicoloured . . . 50 55
2354 – $1.50 multicoloured (63 × 32 mm) 65 70
2355 – $2 multicoloured (63 × 2 mm) 85 90
DESIGNS: $1.25 to $2 Modern Hong Kong shown through inscriptions.

1997. Marine Life. As T **439** of Grenada. Mult.
2356 10 c. Wimplefish 10 10
2357 15 c. Clown triggerfish 10 10
2358 25 c. Ringed emperor angelfish 10 15
2359 35 c. Hooded butterflyfish . . 15 20
2360 45 c. Semicircle angelfish . . . 20 25
2361 75 c. Scribbled angelfish . . . 35 40
2362 90 c. Threadfin butterflyfish . . 40 45
2363 $1.10 Clown surgeonfish . . . 50 55
2364 $2 Bottle-nosed dolphin . . . 85 90
2365 $5 Triggerfish . . . . 2·10 2·25
2366 $10 Lionfish . . . . 4·25 4·50
2367 $20 Jackknifefish . . . . . . 8·75 9·00

121 Winnie the Pooh as Monday's Child

1997. "Monday's Child" (poem). Disney Cartoon Characters from Winnie the Pooh illustrating various verses. Multicoloured.
2368 $1 Type **121** 65 70
2369 $1 Kanga as Tuesday's child . 65 70
2370 $1 Eeyore as Wednesday's child 65 70
2371 $1 Tigger as Thursday's child . 65 70
2372 $1 Piglet as Friday's child . . 65 70
2373 $1 Rabbit as Saturday's child . 65 70

122 Snow White kissing Grumpy

1997. Disney Sweethearts. Disney Cartoon Characters kissing. Multicoloured.
2375 $1 Type **122** 65 70
2376 $1 Figaro the Cat and Cleo the Fish 65 70
2377 $1 Peter Pan and Wendy . . . 65 70
2378 $1 Cinderella and the Prince . 65 70
2379 $1 Ariel and Eric 65 70
2380 $1 Beauty and the Prince . . . 65 70
2381 $1 Aladdin and Jasmine . . . 65 70
2382 $1 Pocahontas and Captain John Smith 65 70
2383 $1 Phoebus and Esmeralda . . 65 70

1997. World Football Championship, France (1998). As T **283a** of Gambia.
2385 10 c. blue 10 10
2386 20 c. multicoloured 10 10
2387 45 c. brown 20 25
2388 $1 black 45 50
2389 $1 brown 45 50
2390 $1 black 45 50
2391 $1 brown 45 50
2392 $1 multicoloured 45 50
2393 $1 multicoloured 45 50
2394 $1 black 45 50
2395 $1 brown 45 50
2396 $1 multicoloured 45 50
2397 $1 black 45 50
2398 $1 black 45 50
2399 $1 black 45 50
2400 $1 black 45 50
2401 $1 black 45 50
2402 $1 black 45 50
2403 $1 black 45 50
2404 $1 black 45 50
2405 $1.50 multicoloured 65 70
2406 $5 black . . . . 2·10 2·25
DESIGNS—HORIZ: No. 2385, Italian team, 1934; 2386, Angolan team; 2387, Brazilian team, 1958; 2388, Uruguay team, 1950; 2389, Winning England team, 1966; 2390, West German team, 1954; 2391, Uruguyan officials with Jules Rimet trophy, 1930; 2392, West German players celebrating, 1990; 2393, Maradona (Argentine player), 1986; 2394, Brazilian players, 1994; 2395, Argentine players, 1978; 2396, West German player holding World Cup, 1974; 2405, West German team, 1974; 2406, Italian team, 1938. VERT: No. 2397, Ademir, Brazil; 2398, Kocsis, Hungary; 2399, Leonidas, Brazil; 2400, Nejedly, Czechoslavakia; 2401, Schiavio, Italy; 2402, Stabile, Uruguay; 2403, Pele, Brazil; 2404, Fritzwalter, West Germany.

1997. Butterflies. As T **444** of Grenada. Mult.
2408 75 c. "Polyura dehaani" . . . 35 40
2409 90 c. "Polyura dolon" 40 45
2410 $1 "Charaxes candiope" . . . 45 50
2411 $1.50 "Pantaporia punctata" . . 65 70
2412 $1.50 "Euthalia confucius" . . 65 70
2413 $1.50 "Euthalia kardama" . . 65 70
2414 $1.50 "Limenitis albomaculata" 65 70
2415 $1.50 "Hestina assimilis" . . . 65 70
2416 $1.50 "Kallima inachus" . . . 65 70
2417 $1.50 "Euthalia teutoides" . . 65 70
2418 $1.50 "Euphaedra francina" . . 65 70
2419 $1.50 "Euphaedra eleus" . . . 65 70
2420 $1.50 "Euphaedra harpalyce" . 65 70
2421 $1.50 "Euphaedra cyparissa" . 65 70
2422 $1.50 "Euphaedra gausape" . . 65 70
2423 $1.50 "Euphaedra imperialis" . 65 70
2424 $2 "Charaxes etesippe" . . . 85 90
2425 $3 "Charaxes castor" . . . . 1·25 1·40
Nos. 2412/17 and 2418/23 respectively were printed together, se-tenant, with the backgrounds forming composite designs.

123 James Dean

124 "Symphyglossum sanguineum"

1997. James Dean (actor) Commemoration. Different portaits. Multicoloured.
2427 $1 Type **123** 45 50
2428 $1 Wearing purple jumper . . 45 50
2429 $1 Wearing stetson and smoking 45 50
2430 $1 Wearing dinner jacket and tie 45 50
2431 $1 Full-face portrait 45 50
2432 $1 Grimacing 45 50
2433 $1 Wearing stetson 45 50
2434 $1 Leaning on arms 45 50
2435 $1 Smoking 45 50

1997. Orchids of the World. Multicoloured.
2436 35 c. Type **124** 15 20
2437 45 c. "Doritaenopsis" "Mythic Beauty" 20 25
2438 75 c. "Odontoglossum cervantesii" 35 40
2439 90 c. "Cattleya" "Pumpernickel" 40 45
2440 $1 "Vanda" "Patricia Low" . 45 50
2441/9 $1 × 9 ("Lycaste" "Aquila"; "Brassolaeliocattleya" "Dorothy Bertsch"; "Phalaenopsis" "Zuma Urchin"; "Promenaea xanthina"; "Amesiella philippinensis"; "Brassocattleya" "Angel Lace"; "Brassoepidendrum" "Peggy Ann"; "Miltonia seine"; "Sophralaeliocattleya" "Precious Stones") . . . 4·25
2450/8 $1 × 9 ("Cymbidium" "Showgirl"; "Disa blackii"; "Phalaenopsis aphrodite"; "Iwanagaara" "Apple Blossom"; "Masdevallia" "Copper Angel"; "Paphiopedilum micranthum"; "Paphiopedilum" "Clare de Lune"; "Cattleya forbesii"; "Dendrobium" "Dawn Maree") . . . . 4·25
2459 $1.50 "Odontonia" "Debutante" 65 70
2460/5 $1.50 × 6 ("Miltoniopsis" "Jean Sabourin"; "Cymbidium" "Red Beauty"; "Brassocattleya" "Green Dragon"; "Phalaenopsis" hybrid; "Laeliocattleya" "Mary Ellen Carter"; "Disa" hybrid) . . . . . . 4·25
2466/71 $1.50 × 6 ("Lycaste macrobulbon"; "Cochleanthes discolor"; "Cymbidium" "Nang Carpenter"; "Paphiopedilum" "Claire de Lune"; "Masdevallia caudata"; "Cymbidium" "Showgirl") . . . . . . 4·25
2472 $2 "Laeliocattleya" "Mini Purple" 85 90
2473 $3 "Phragmipedium dominiarum" . . . . . 1·25 1·40
2436/73 Set of 38 20·00 21·00
Nos. 2460/5 and 2466/71 respectively were printed together, se-tenant, with the backgrounds forming composite designs.

125 "Clitocybe metachroa"

1997. Fungi. Multicoloured.
2475 75 c. Type **125** 35 40
2476 90 c. "Clavulinopsis helvola" . 40 45
2477 $1 "Lycoperdon pyriforme" . 45 50
2478 $1.50 "Auricularia auricula-judae" 65 70
2479 $1.50 "Entoloma incanum" . . 65 70
2480 $1.50 "Coprinus atramentarius" 65 70
2481 $1.50 "Mycena polygramma" . 65 70
2482 $1.50 "Lepista nuda" 65 70
2483 $1.50 "Pleurotis cornucopiae" . 65 70
2484 $1.50 "Laccaria amethystina" . 65 70
2485 $2 "Clathrus archeri" 85 90
2486 $3 "Lactarius trivialis" . . . 1·25 1·40

126 Ludwig van Beethoven

1997. Classical Composers. Multicoloured.
2488 $1 Type **126** 45 50
2489 $1 Pyotr Tchaikovsky 45 50
2490 $1 Johann Christian Bach . . 45 50
2491 $1 Frederic Chopin 45 50
2492 $1 Igor Stravinsky 45 50
2493 $1 Franz Joseph Haydn . . . 45 50
2494 $1 Gustav Mahler 45 50
2495 $1 Gioacchino Antonio Rossini 45 50

127 Diana, Princess of Wales and Buckingham Palace

1997. Diana, Princess of Wales Commemoration. Multicoloured.
2497 $1.50 Type **127** 65 70
2498 $1.50 Princess Diana and lake at Althorp 65 70
2499 $1.50 Princess Diana and Westminster Abbey 65 70
2500 $1.50 Princess Diana and gates to Althorp 65 70
2501 $1.50 Princess Diana in pink hat and gates to Kensington Palace 65 70
2502 $1.50 Princess Diana and Althorp House 65 70

1997. Christmas. Religious Paintings. As T **448** of Grenada. Multicoloured.
2504 20 c. "Choir of Angels (Simon Marmion) 10 15
2505 75 c. "The Annunciation" (Giotto) 35 40
2506 90 c. "Festival of the Rose Garlands" (Albrecht Durer) 40 45
2507 $1.50 "Madonna with Two Angels" (Hans Memling) . . 65 70
2508 $2 "The Ognissanti Madonna" (Giotto) 85 90
2509 $3 "Angel with Candlestick" (Michelangelo) . . . . . 1·25 1·40
No. 2506 is inscribed "DUER" in error.

1998. Fishes. As T **449** of Grenada. Multicoloured.
2511 Queen angelfish 45 50
2512 $1 Clown triggerfish 45 50
2513 $1 Four-spot butterflyfish . . . 45 50
2514 $1 Yellow-tailed damselfish . . 45 50
2515 $1 Yellow-headed wrasse . . . 45 50
2516 $1 Royal gramma 45 50
2517 $1 Candy basslet 45 50
2518 $1 Smooth trunkfish 45 50
2519 $1 Coral hind 45 50
Nos. 2511/19 were printed together, se-tenant, with the backgrounds forming a composite design.

128 Tiger (hologram)

1998. Chinese New Year ("Year of the Tiger").
2521 **128** $1.50 black on silver foil . 65 70

129 "Alabama" (Confederate warship)

1998. Famous Ships. Multicoloured. (a) Ships of the 1860s.
2523 75 c. Type **129** 35 40
2524 75 c. "Persia" (paddle-steamer) 35 40
2525 75 c. "Ariel" (clipper) 35 40
2526 75 c. "Florida" (Confederate warship) 35 40
2527 75 c. "Great-Eastern" (paddle-steamer) 35 40
2528 75 c. "Jacob Bell" on fire . . 35 40
2529 75 c. "Star of India" (clipper) . 35 40
2530 75 c. "Robert E. Lee" (Mississippi paddle-steamer) 35 40
2531 75 c. U.S.S. "Passaic" (monitor) 35 40
2532 75 c. "Madagascar" (clipper) . 35 40
2533 75 c. H.M.S. "Devastation" (battleship) 35 40
2534 75 c. "General Grant" (clipper) 35 40

(b) Ships of the American Civil War.
2535 $1 Clark Gable as Rhett Butler in "Gone with the Wind" (vert) 45 50
2536 $1 Crew abandoning blockade runner wrecked on Sullivan's Island (vert) 45 50
2537 $1 Margaret Mitchell (author of "Gone with the Wind") (vert) 45 50
2538 $1 George Alfred Trenholm (ship owner) (vert) 45 50
2539 $1 Dock Street Theatre, Charleston (vert) 45 50
2540 $1 "Howlett" (paddle-steamer) sinking (vert) 45 50
2541 $1 U.S.S. "Tecumseh" on fire (vert) 45 50
2542 $1 City Jail, Charleston (vert) . 45 50

130 Concept Strike Fighter

1998. Aircraft Designs of the Future. Multicoloured.
2544 70 c. Type **130** 30 35
2545 90 c. Concept space shuttle . . 40 45
2546 $1 Velocity 173 RG Elite . . . 45 50
2547 $1 Davis DA-9 . . . . 45 50
2548 $1 Concorde 45 50
2549 $1 Voyager 45 50
2550 $1 Factimobile 45 50
2551 $1 RAF 2000 . . . . 45 50
2552 $1 Boomerang 45 50
2553 $1 N1M Flying Wing 45 50
2554 $2 Concept air and space jet . 85 90
2555 $3 V Jet II . . . . 1·25 1·40

131 "Lycaste deppei"

1998. Orchids of the World. Multicoloured.
2557 $1 Type **131** 45 50
2558 $1 "Dendrobium victoriae" . . 45 50
2559 $1 "Dendrobium nobile" . . . 45 50
2560 $1 "Cymbidium dayanum" . . 45 50
2561 $1 "Cymbidium" "Starbright" 45 50
2562 $1 "Cymbidium giganteum" . . 45 50
2563 $1 "Chysis aurea" 45 50
2564 $1 "Broughtonia sanguinea" . 45 50
2565 $1 "Cattleya guttata" 45 50
2566 $1 "Calanthe vestita" 45 50
2567 $1 "Cattleya bicolor" 45 50
2568 $1 "Laelia anceps" 45 50
2569 $1 "Epidendrum prismatocarpum" 45 50

2570 $1 "Coelogyne ochracea" . . 45 50
2571 $1 "Doritaenopsis eclantant" . 45 50
2572 $1 "Laelia gouldiana" 45 50
2573 $1 "Encyclia vitellina" 45 50
2574 $1 "Maxillaria praestans" . . 45 50
2575 $1 "Laelia tenebrosa" 45 50
2576 $1.50 "Phragmipedium besseae" 65 70
2577 $2 "Pschopsis papilio" 85 90
2578 $3 "Masdevallia coccinea" . . 1·25 1·40

1998. Seabirds. As T **452** of Grenada. Multicoloured.
2580 75 c. Bonaparte's gull (horiz) . 35 40
2581 90 c. Western sandpiper (horiz) 40 45
2582 $1.50 Common tern (horiz) . . 65 70
2583 $1.50 Brown pelican (horiz) . . 65 70
2584 $1.50 Black-legged kittiwake and white tern (horiz) . . . 65 70
2585 $1.50 Herring gull (horiz) . . 65 70
2586 $1.50 Lesser noddy (horiz) . . 65 70
2587 $1.50 Black-legged kittiwake (horiz) 65 70
2588 $1.50 Whimbrel (horiz) . . . 65 70
2589 $1.50 Golden white-tailed tropic bird (horiz) 65 70
2590 $1.50 Arctic tern (horiz) . . . 65 70
2591 $1.50 Ruddy turnstone (horiz) . 65 70
2592 $1.50 Imperial shag (horiz) . . 65 70
2593 $1.50 Magellan gull (horiz) 65 70
2594 $2 Great black-backed gull (horiz) 85 90
2595 $3 Dotterell (horiz) . . . . . 1·25 1·40

1998. International Year of the Ocean. As T **454** of Grenada. Multicoloured.
2597 75 c. Great black-backed gull . 35 40
2598 75 c. Common dolphin . . . 35 40
2599 75 c. Seal 35 40
2600 75 c. Amazonian catfish . . . 35 40
2601 75 c. Shark 35 40
2602 75 c. Goldfish 35 40
2603 75 c. Cyathopharynx 35 40
2604 75 c. Killer whale 35 40
2605 75 c. Telmatochromis 35 40
2606 75 c. Crab 35 40
2607 75 c. Octopus 35 40
2608 75 c. Turtle 35 40
2609 90 c. Two dolphins 40 45
2610 90 c. Seal 40 45
2611 90 c. Turtle on rock 40 45
2612 90 c. Leopard shark 40 45
2613 90 c. Flame angelfish 40 45
2614 90 c. Syndontis 40 45
2615 90 c. Lamprologus 40 45
2616 90 c. "Krptopterus bicirrhus" . 40 45
2617 90 c. "Pterophyllum scalare" . 40 45
2618 90 c. Swimming pancake . . . 40 45
2619 90 c. Cowfish 40 45
2620 90 c. Seahorse 40 45

Nos. 2597/2608 and 2609/20 respectively were printed together, se-tenant, with the backgrounds forming composite designs.

1998. 50th Anniv of Organization of American States. As T **454a** of Grenada.
2622 $1 violet, orange and black 45 50

1998. 25th Death Anniv of Pablo Picasso (painter). As T **291a** of Gambia. Multicoloured.
2623 45 c. "Bust of a Woman" (vert) 20 25
2624 $2 "Three Musicians" 85 90
2625 $3 "Studio at La Californie" . 1·25 1·40

1998. Birth Centenary of Enzo Ferrari (car manufacturer). As T **454b** of Grenada. Multicoloured.
2627 $2 275 GTB 85 90
2628 $2 340 MM 85 90
2629 $2 250 GT SWB Berlinetta "Hot Rod" 85 90

1998. 19th World Scout Jamboree, Chile. As T **455** of Grenada. Multicoloured.
2631 90 c. Scout greeting 40 45
2632 $1.50 Lord Baden-Powell . . 65 70
2633 $5 Scout salute . . . . 2·10 2·25

1998. 50th Death Anniv of Mahatma Gandhi. As T **455a** of Grenada.
2635 $1 grey, brown and black . . 45 50

1998. 80th Anniv of Royal Air Force. As T **292a** of Gambia. Multicoloured.
2637 $2 Tornado GR1 . . . . . . 85 90
2638 $2 BAe Hawk T1A 85 90
2639 $2 Sepecat Jaguar GR1 . . . 85 90
2640 $2 Harrier GR7 . . . . . . 85 90
2641 $2 Chinook helicopter carrying three loads 85 90
2642 $2 Silhouette of BAe Harrier GR5 . . . . 85 90
2643 $2 Panavia Tornado F3 ADV at sunset 85 90
2644 $2 Chinook HC2 carrying 105 mm light gun 85 90

1998. Birth Bicentenary of Eugene Delacroix (painter). As T **294** of Gambia. Multicoloured.
2646 $1 "The Natchez" 45 50
2647 $1 "Christ and His Disciples Crossing the Sea of Galilee" 45 50
2648 $1 "Sunset" 45 50
2649 $1 "Moroccans outside the Walls of Tangier" 45 50
2650 $1 "The Fireplace" 45 50
2651 $1 "Forest View with an Oak Tree" 45 50
2652 $1 "View of the Harbour at Dieppe" 45 50
2653 $1 "Arab Tax Collectors" . . . 45 50

1998. 1st Death Anniv of Diana, Princess of Wales. As T **293a** of Gambia.
2655 $1.50 multicoloured 65 70

132 Father Christmas and Hare

1998. Disney's Christmas Trains. Walt Disney cartoon characters in train carriages. Multicoloured.
2656 $1 Type **132** 45 50
2657 $1 Giraffe, elephant and tiger . 45 50
2658 $1 Three Pigs and Wolf . . . 45 50
2659 $1 Pied Piper, Jiminy Cricket, penguins and children . . . 45 50
2660 $1 Swans, Little Hiawatha and tortoise 45 50
2661 $1 Mickey Mouse as train driver 45 50
2662 $1 Pluto, Chip and Dale . . . 45 50
2663 $1 Donald and Daisy Duck . . 45 50
2664 $1 Goofy, Huey, Dewey and Louie 45 50
2665 $1 Minnie Mouse and presents 45 50
2666 $1 Piglet as train driver . . . 45 50
2667 $1 Winnie the Pooh and honey 45 50
2668 $1 Rabbit and Owl 45 50
2669 $1 Kanga, Roo and Christopher Robin 45 50
2670 $1 Eeyore and Tigger 45 50

133 Troodon

1999. "Australia '99" World Stamp Exhibition, Melbourne. Prehistoric Animals. Multicoloured.
2673 $1 Type **133** 45 50
2674 $1 Camptosaurus 45 50
2675 $1 Parasaurolophus 45 50
2676 $1 Dryosaurus 45 50
2677 $1 Gallimimus 45 50
2678 $1 Camarasaurus 45 50
2679 $1.50 Duckbill (horiz) 65 70
2680 $1.50 Lambeosaurus (horiz) . . 65 70
2681 $1.50 Igaunodon (horiz) . . . 65 70
2682 $1.50 Euoplocephalus (horiz) . 65 70
2683 $1.50 Triceratops (horiz) . . . 65 70
2684 $1.50 Brachiosaurus (horiz) . . 65 70
2685 $1.50 Ponoptosaurus (horiz) . . 65 70
2686 $1.50 Stegosaurus (horiz) . . . 65 70

134 Great Indian Peninsula Passenger and Mail Locomotive

1999. Steam Trains of the World. Multicoloured.
2688 15 c. Type **134** 10 10
2689 75 c. Midland Great Western passenger locomotive (Ireland) 35 40
2690 90 c. Canada Pacific express locomotive 40 45
2691 $1.50 East Indian Railway express locomotive 65 70
2692 $2 Victorian Railways suburban tank locomotive (Australia) . 85 90
2693 $2 Eastern Railways compound locomotive (France) 85 90
2694 $2 Govt Railways Class WF tank locomotive (New Zealand) 85 90
2695 $2 Burma Railways oil-burning tank locomotive, 1899 . . . 85 90
2696 $2 Federated Malay States Railway Class G steam locomotive, 1899 . . . . . 85 90
2697 $2 Belfast and Northern Counties Railway narrow-gauge tank locomotive . . . 85 90
2698 $2 Shunting tank locomotive (Russia) 85 90
2699 $2 G.N.R. Ivatt large-boilered "Atlantic" type 85 90
2700 $2 Palatine Railway "Atlantic" type express locomotive (Germany) 85 90
2701 $2 Belgian State Railways "Dunalastair" type locomotive 85 90
2702 $2 Swedish State Railways Class Cc locomotive 85 90
2703 $2 Antofagasta and Bolivian Railway tank locomotive (Chile) 85 90
2704 $2 Bolivian State Fairlie type locomotive 85 90
2705 $2 Belgian State Railways express locomotive 85 90
2706 $2 London and South Western Railway Drummond's mixed traffic locomotive 85 90
2707 $2 Belfast and Northern Counties Railways Compound locomotive . . . 85 90
2708 $2 Dutch State Railway express passenger locomotive . . . 85 90
2709 $2 Gothard Railway heavy freight locomotive (Switzerland) 85 90
2710 $2 Waterford, Limerick and Western railway goods locomotive (Ireland) 85 90
2711 $2 Atchison, Topeka and Santa Fe railway tandem compound express locomotive (U.S.A.) . 85 90
2712 $2 Midland Railway Class "Princess of Wales" locomotive (Great Britain) 85 90
2713 $3 Glasgow and South Western Railway Stirling type locomotive . . . . 1·25 1·40

No. 2701 is inscribed "Dunalastiar" in error.

135 Porkfish

1999. Fauna and Flora. Multicoloured.
2715 75 c. Type **135** 35 40
2716 90 c. Leatherback turtle . . . 40 45
2717 $1 White-tailed tropic bird (vert) 45 50
2718 $1 Laughing gull (vert) 45 50
2719 $1 Palm tree (vert) 45 50
2720 $1 Humpback whale (vert) . . 45 50
2721 $1 Painted bunting (vert) . . . 45 50
2722 $1 Common grackle (vert) . . 45 50
2723 $1 Green anole (lizard) (vert) . 45 50
2724 $1 "Morpho peleides" (butterfly) (vert) 45 50
2725 $1 "Prepona meander" (butterfly) (vert) 45 50
2726 $1 Common dolphin (vert) . . 45 50
2727 $1 "Catonephele numilia" (butterfly) (vert) 45 50
2728 $1 Sooty tern (vert) 45 50
2729 $1 Vermilion flycatcher (vert) . 45 50
2730 $1 Blue grosbeak (vert) 45 50
2731 $1 Great egret (vert) 45 50
2732 $1 "Actinate pellenea" (butterfly) (vert) 45 50
2733 $1 "Anteos clorinde" (butterfly) (vert) 45 50
2734 $1 Common iguana (vert) . . 45 50
2735 $1.50 Ruby-throated hummingbird 65 70
2736 $2 "Theope eudocia" (butterfly) 85 90

Nos. 2717/25 and 2726/34 respectively were printed together, se-tenant, with the backgrounds forming composite designs.

No. 2727 is inscribed "numili" in error.

136 John H. Glenn (astronaut), 1998

1999. John Glenn's (first American to orbit Earth) Return to Space. Multicoloured, except Nos. 2716, 2718 and 2720/1.
2738 $1 Type **136** 45 50
2739 $1 Glenn and Pres. John F. Kennedy (brown and red) . . 45 50
2740 $1 Inside "Discovery", 1998 . . 45 50
2741 $1 Climbing from "Friendship 7" capsule, 1962 (brown and red) 45 50
2742 $1 Medical checkup 45 50
2743 $1 Climbing into space capsule, 1962 (brown and red) . . . 45 50
2744 $1 As Democratic Senator for Ohio, 1974 (vert) (brown and red) 45 50
2745 $1 In space suit, 1962 (vert) . . 45 50
2746 $1 Smiling during suit up test, 1998 (vert) 45 50
2747 $1 Preparing for "Discovery" flight (vert) 45 50
2748 $1 At press conference (with microphone) (vert) 45 50
2749 $1 Smiling at camera (wearing glasses) (vert) 45 50
2750 $1 Participating in medical research (vert) 45 50
2751 $1 Posing in space suit, 1998 (vert) 45 50

No. 2744 was inscribed "Junior Senator form Ohio (1974)" in error.

1999. "iBRA '99" International Stamp Exhibition, Nuremberg. As T **298a** of Gambia. Multicoloured.
2752 35 c. "Luckenbach" (full-rigged ship) and Thurn and Taxis Northern District 1852 $\frac{1}{4}$ sgr. stamp 15 20
2753 45 c. Leipzig-Dresden Railway carriage and Schleswig-Holstein 1850 1 s. 20 25
2754 $1.50 Leipzig-Dresden Railway carriage and Oldenburg 1852 $\frac{1}{3}$ sgr. 65 75
2755 $3 "Luckenbach" (full-rigged ship) and North German Confederation 1868 $\frac{1}{4}$ g. . . 1·25 1·40

1999. 150th Death Anniv of Katsushika Hokusai (Japanese artist). As T **298b** of Gambia. Multicoloured.
2757 $1.50 "Fuchu" 65 70
2758 $1.50 "Doll Fair at Fikkendana" 65 70
2759 $1.50 "Sumo Wrestlers" (in arm hold) 65 70
2760 $1.50 "Sumo Wrestlers" (in head lock) 65 70
2761 $1.50 "Sojo Henjo" 65 70
2762 $1.50 "Twin Gardens Gateway of Asakusa Kannon Temple" 65 70
2763 $1.50 "A Breeze on a Fine Day" 65 70
2764 $1.50 "Ejiri" 65 70
2765 $1.50 "Horse Drawings" (galloping) 65 70
2766 $1.50 "Horse Drawings" (stationary) 65 70
2767 $1.50 "View along Bank of Sumida River" 65 70
2768 $1.50 "Thunderstorm Below the Mountain" 65 70

No. 2762 is inscribed "TWIN GARDAINS GATEWAY" in error.

1999. 10th Anniv of United Nations Rights of the Child Convention. As T **298c** of Gambia. Multicoloured.
2770 $3 African boy . . . . 1·25 1·40
2771 $3 Liv Ullman (U.N.I.C.E.F.'s first female ambassador) . . 1·25 1·40
2772 $3 African woman in head scarf . . . . 1·25 1·40

Nos. 2770/2 were printed together, se-tenant, forming a composite design.

1999. 250th Birth Anniv of Johann von Goethe (German writer). As T **298d** of Gambia.
2775 $3 multicoloured . . . . . . 1·25 1·40
2776 $3 blue, and black . . . . . 1·25 1·40
2777 $3 blue, violet and black . . . 1·25 1·40

DESIGNS: No. 2775, Peasants dancing under linden-tree; 2776, Von Goethe and Von Schiller; 2777, Faust dreams of soaring above the mortal.

1999. Royal Wedding. As T **298** of Gambia. Multicoloured.
2779 $3 Sophie Rhys-Jones . . . . 1·25 1·40
2780 $3 Sophie and Prince Edward . 1·25 1·40
2781 $3 Prince Edward . . . . . . 1·25 1·40

1999. "Queen Elizabeth the Queen Mother's Century". As T **304a** of Gambia.
2783 $2 black and gold 85 90
2784 $2 multicoloured 85 90
2785 $2 black and gold 85 90
2786 $2 multicoloured 85 90

DESIGNS: No. 2783, Lady Elizabeth Bowes-Lyon as a child; 2784, Queen Mother in Rhodesia, 1957; 2785, Queen Mother with Princesses Elizabeth and Anne, 1950; 2786, Queen Mother, 1988.

OFFICIAL STAMPS

1982. Optd **P.R.G.** (a) Nos. 400/12 and 414.
O 1 5 c. Yellow-tailed snapper . . 10 15
O 2 6 c. Mutton snapper 10 15
O 3 10 c. Cocoa damselfish 10 15
O 4 12 c. Royal gramma 10 15
O 5 15 c. Cherub angelfish 10 15
O 6 20 c. Black-barred soldierfish . . 10 20
O 7 25 c. Mottled grouper 10 20
O 8 30 c. Long-snouted butterflyfish 15 20
O 9 40 c. Puddingwife 15 25
O10 50 c. Midnight parrotfish . . . 20 30
O11 90 c. Redspotted hawkfish . . . 40 55
O12 $1 Hogfish 40 60
O13 $3 Beau Gregory . . . . . . 1·25 2·25
O14 $10. Barred hamlet . . . . . 4·25 6·00

(b) Nos. 444/6 and 448/9.
O15 30 c. Prince Charles and Lady Diana Spencer . . . . . . 2·00 2·00
O16 40 c. Prince Charles and Lady Diana Spencer . . . . . . 1·60 1·60
O17 40 c. Type **50** . . . . 2·00 2·75
O18 $2 Type **50** . . . . 2·50 3·50
O19 $4 Prince Charles as parachutist 6·50 8·50

(c) Nos. 473/6.
O20 **54** 20 c. multicoloured 10 20
O21 – 40 c. multicoloured 15 25
O22 – $1 multicoloured 35 70
O23 – $2 multicoloured . . . . . 70 1·40

GRENADINES OF ST. VINCENT Pt. 1

Part of a group of Islands south of St. Vincent which include Bequia, Mustique, Canouan and Union.

100 cents = 1 dollar

1973. Royal Wedding. As T **101a** of Gibraltar. Multicoloured. Background colours given.

1 25 c. green 10 10
2 $1 brown 15 15

1974. Nos. 286/300 of St. Vincent optd **GRENADINES OF.**

3 1 c. Green heron 10 10
4 2 c. Lesser Antillean bullfinches 15 15
25 3 c. St. Vincent amazon 25 30
6 4 c. Rufous-thoated solitaire (vert) 10 10
7 5 c. Red-necked pigeon (vert) . . 10 10
8 6 c. Bananaquits 15 10
9 8 c. Purple-throated carib . . . 15 10
10 10 c. Mangrove cuckoo (vert) . . 15 10
11 12 c. Common black hawk (vert) 20 15
12 20 c. Bare-eyed thrush 30 20
13 25 c. Hooded tanager 30 20
14 50 c. Blue hooded euphonia . . 60 40
15 $1 Barn owl (vert) . . . . . . 1·00 75
16 $2.50 Yellow-bellied elaenia (vert) 1·00 1·00
17 $5 Ruddy quail dove . . . . . 1·25 1·75

2 Map of Bequia

1974. Maps (1st series).

18 **2** 5 c. black, green & dp green . 10 10
19 – 15 c. multicoloured 10 10
20 – 20 c. multicoloured 10 10
21 – 30 c. black, pink and red . . . 10 10
22 – 40 c. black., violet & purple . . 10 10
23 – $1 black, ultramarine & blue . 20 20

MAPS: 15 c. Prune Island; 20 c. Mayreau Island and Tobago Cays; 30 c. Mustique Island; 40 c. Union Island; $1 Canouan Island.

See also Nos. 85/8.

3a U.P.U. Emblem

1974. Centenary of U.P.U. Multicoloured.

26 2 c. Type **3a** 10 10
27 15 c. Globe within posthorn . . 10 10
28 40 c. Map of St. Vincent and hand-cancelling 10 10
29 $1 Map of the World 25 15

4 Boat-building

1974. Bequia Island (1st series). Multicoloured.

34 5 c. Type **4** 10 15
31 30 c. Careening at Port Elizabeth 10 15
32 35 c. Admiralty Bay 10 15
33 $1 Fishing-boat race 15 25

See also Nos. 185/88.

5 Music Volute

1974. Shells and Molluscs. Multicoloured.

35A 1 c. American thorny oyster . 10 10
36A 2 c. Zigzag scallop 10 10
37A 3 c. Reticulated cowrie-helmet 10 10
38A 4 c. Type **5** 10 10
39A 5 c. Amber pen shell 10 10
40A 6 c. Angular triton 10 10
41A 8 c. Flame helmet 10 10
42A 10 c. Caribbean olive 10 10
43A 12 c. American or common sundial 10 10
44A 15 c. Glory of the Atlantic cone 25 20
45B 20 c. Flame auger 30 20
46A 25 c. King venus 50 20
47A 35 c. Long-spined star shell . 35 25
48A 45 c. Speckled tellin 35 30
49A 50 c. Rooster-tail conch . . . 40 25
50B $1 Green star shell 60 60
51A $2.50 Antillean or incomparable cone 60 75
52A $5 Rough file clam 75 80
52cA $10 Measled cowrie . . . . 3·50 1·00

Nos. 38/42, 45, 47 and 49/50 come with and without an imprint below the design.

1974. Birth Centenary of Sir Winston Churchill. As Nos. 403/6 of St. Vincent, but inscr "GRENADINES OF ST. VINCENT" and values (Nos. 53/5) and colours changed.

53 **75** 5 c. multicoloured 10 10
54 – 40 c. multicoloured 10 15
55 – 50 c. multicoloured 10 15
56 – $1 multicoloured 20 30

6 Cotton House, Mustique

1975. Mustique Island. Multicoloured.

57 5 c. Type **6** 10 10
58 35 c. "Blue Waters", Endeavour Bay 10 10
59 45 c. Endeavour Bay 10 10
60 $1 "Les Jolies Eaux", Gelliceaux Bay 25 20

7 "Danaus plexippus"

1975. Butterflies. Multicoloured.

61 3 c. Type **7** 20 10
62 5 c. "Agraulis vanillae" 25 10
63 35 c. "Battus polydamas" . . . 50 10
64 45 c. "Evenus dindymus" and "Junonia evarete" 60 10
65 $1 "Anartia jatrophae" 90 45

8 Resort Pavilion

1975. Petit St. Vincent. Multicoloured.

66 5 c. Type **8** 10 10
67 35 c. The Harbour 10 10
68 45 c. The Jetty 15 15
69 $1 Sailing in coral lagoon . . . 50 80

9 Ecumenical Church, Mustique

1975. Christmas. Multicoloured.

70 5 c. Type **9** 10 10
71 25 c. Catholic Church, Union Island 10 10
72 50 c. Catholic Church, Bequia . 10 10
73 $1 Anglican Church, Bequia . . 25 15

10 Sunset Scene

1976. Union Island (1st series). Multicoloured.

74 5 c. Type **10** 10 10
75 35 c. Customs and Post Office, Clifton 10 10
76 45 c. Anglican Church, Ashton . 10 10
77 $1 Mail schooner, Clifton Harbour 25 20

See also Nos. 242/5.

11 Staghorn Coral

1976. Corals. Multicoloured.

78 5 c. Type **11** 10 10
79 35 c. Elkhorn coral 20 10
80 45 c. Pillar coral 20 10
81 $1 Brain coral 40 20

12 25 c. Bicentennial Coin

1976. Bicentenary of American Revolution.

82 **12** 25 c. silver, black and blue . . 10 10
83 – 50 c. silver, black and red . . 20 10
84 – $1 silver, black and mauve . . 25 20

DESIGNS: 50 c. Half-dollar coin. $1 One dollar coin.

1976. Maps (2nd series). As T **2**.

85 5 c. black, dp green & green . . 10 10
86 10 c. black, green and blue . . . 10 10
87 35 c. black, brown and red . . . 20 20
88 45 c. black, red and orange . . . 25 25

Nos. 85/8 exist in 7 different designs to each value as follows: A, Bequia, B, Canouan, C, Mayreau, D, Mustique, E, Petit St. Vincent, F, Prune, G, Union. To indicate any particular design use the appropriate catalogue No. together with the suffix for the island concerned.

13 Station Hill School and Post Office

1977. Mayreau Island. Multicoloured.

89 5 c. Type **13** 10 10
90 35 c. Church at Old Wall . . . 10 10
91 45 c. La Sourciere Anchorage . . 10 10
92 $1 Saline Bay 25 15

14 Coronation Crown Coin

1977. Silver Jubilee. Multicoloured.

93 25 c. Type **14** 15 10
94 50 c. Silver Wedding crown . . 20 10
95 $1 Silver Jubilee crown 20 15

15 Fiddler Crab

1977. Crustaceans. Multicoloured.

96 5 c. Type **15** 10 10
97 35 c. Ghost crab 20 10
98 50 c. Blue crab 25 10
99 $1.25 Spiny lobster 55 40

16 Snorkel Diving

1977. Prune Island. Multicoloured.

100 5 c. Type **16** 10 10
101 35 c. Palm Island Resort . . . 10 10
102 45 c. Casuarina Beach 10 15
103 $1 Palm Island Beach Club . . 30 95

17 Mustique Island

1977. Royal Visit. Surch as in T **17**.

104 **17** 40 c. turquoise and green . . 15 10
105 $2 ochre and brown 40 25

18 The Clinic, Charlestown

1977. Canouan Island (1st series). Mult.

106 5 c. Type **18** 10 10
107 35 c. Town jetty, Charlestown . 15 10
108 45 c. Mail schooner arriving at Charlestown 15 10
109 $1 Grand Bay 35 90

See also Nos. 307/10.

19 Tropical Mockingbird

1978. Birds and their Eggs. Multicoloured.

110 1 c. Type **19** 10 50
111 2 c. Mangrove cuckoo 15 50
112 3 c. Osprey 20 50
113 4 c. Smooth-billed ani 20 50
114 5 c. House wren 20 40
115 6 c. Bananaquit 20 40
116 8 c. Carib grackle 20 45
117 10 c. Yellow-bellied elaenia . . 20 45
118 12 c. Collared plover . . . . . 30 1·00
119 15 c. Cattle egret 30 45
120 20 c. Red-footed booby 30 45
121 25 c. Red-billed tropic bird . . 30 45
122 40 c. Royal tern 45 90
123 50 c. Grenada flycatcher . . . 45 90
124 80 c. Purple gallinule 70 90
125 $1 Broad-winged hawk 75 90
126 $2 Scaly-breasted ground dove 90 1·60
127 $3 Laughing gull . . . . . . 1·25 1·75
128 $5 Common noddy . . . . . 2·75 2·00
129 $10 Grey kingbird . . . . . 3·00 3·00

19a Worcester Cathedral

1978. 25th Anniv of Coronation. British Cathedrals. Multicoloured.

130 5 c. Type **19a** 10 10
131 40 c. Coventry Cathedral . . . 10 10
132 $1 Winchester Cathedral . . . 15 20
133 $3 Chester Cathedral 25 45

20 Green Turtle

1978. Turtles. Multicoloured.

135 5 c. Type **20** 10 10
136 40 c. Hawksbill turtle 15 10
137 50 c. Leatherback turtle 15 10
138 $1.25 Loggerhead turtle 40 40

21 Three Kings following Star

22 Sailing Yachts

1978. Christmas. Scenes and Verses from the Carol "We Three Kings". Multicoloured.

139 5 c. Type **21** 10 10
140 10 c. King presenting gold . . 10 10
141 25 c. King presenting frankincense 10 10
142 50 c. King presenting myrrh . . 10 10
143 $2 Kings paying homage to infant Jesus 30 20

1979. National Regatta.

145 **22** 5 c. multicoloured 10 10
146 – 40 c. multicoloured 20 10
147 – 50 c. multicoloured 25 10
148 – $2 multicoloured 75 60

DESIGNS: 40 c. to $2, Various sailing yachts.

22a Green Iguana

1979. Wildlife. Multicoloured.
149 20 c. Type **22a** 10 10
150 40 c. Common opossum ("Manicou") 15 10
151 $2 Red-legged tortoise 60 65

22b Sir Rowland Hill

1979. Death Centenary of Sir Rowland Hill. Multicoloured.
152 80 c. Type **22b** 15 15
153 $1 Great Britain 1d. and 4d. stamps of 1858 with "A10" (Kingstown, St. Vincent) postmark 15 25
154 $2 St. Vincent ½d and 1d. stamps of 1894 with Bequia postmark 25 40

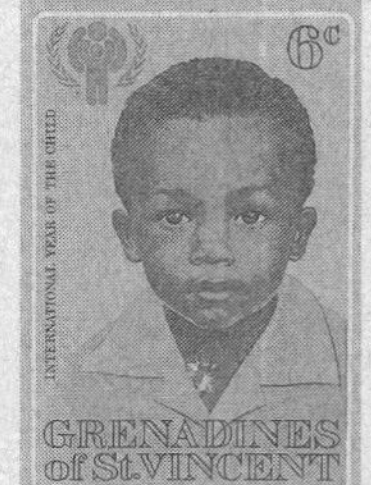

22c Young Child

1979. International Year of the Child. Designs showing portraits of young children.
156 **22c** 6 c. black, silver and blue . 10 10
157 – 40 c. black, silver & salmon . 10 10
158 – $1 black, silver and buff . . 20 10
159 – $3 black, silver and lilac . . 45 30

22d National Flag and "Ixora salicifolia" (flower)

1979. Independence. Multicoloured.
160 5 c. Type **22d** 10 10
161 40 c. House of Assembly and "Ixora odorata" (flower) . . 10 10
162 $1 Prime Minister R. Milton Cato and "Ixora javanica" (flower) 20 20

23 False Killer Whale

1980. Whales and Dolphins. Multicoloured.
163 10 c. Type **23** 60 10
164 50 c. Spinner dolphin 60 35
165 90 c. Bottle-nosed dolphin . . . 70 80
166 $2 Short-finned Pilot whale ("Blackfish") . . . . 2·00 1·50

23a Queen Elizabeth II

1980. "London 1980" International Stamp Exhibition. Multicoloured.
167 40 c. Type **23a** 10 10
168 50 c. St. Vincent 2 c. stamp of 1965 . . . . 15 10
169 $3 First Grenadines stamps . . 40 1·00

23b Running

1980. Sport. Multicoloured.
171 25 c. Type **23b** 10 10
172 50 c. Sailing 10 10
173 $1 Long-jumping 20 20
174 $2 Swimming 30 30

1980. Hurricane Relief. Nos. 171/4 optd **HURRICANE RELIEF 50c**.
175 **22** 25 c. + 50 c. multicoloured 10 30
176 – 50 c. + 50 c. multicoloured 15 40
177 – $1 + 50 c. multicoloured . . 20 50
178 – $2 + 50 c. multicoloured . . 30 70

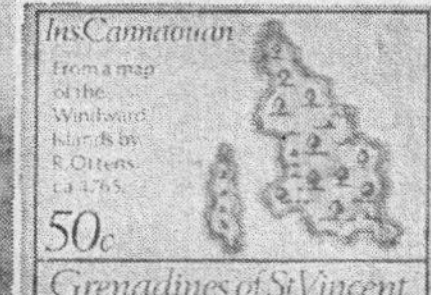

24 Scene and Verse from the Carol "De Borning Day"
26 Ins. Cannaouan (from map of Windward Islands by R. Ottens, c. 1765)

25 Post Office, Port Elizabeth

1980. Christmas. Multicoloured.
179 5 c. Type **24** 10 10
180 50 c. "Mary and de Baby lonely" 10 10
181 60 c. "Mary and de Baby weary" 10 10
182 $1 "Mary and de Baby rest easy" 15 15
183 $2 "Star above shine in de sky" 25 25

1981. Bequia Island (2nd series). Mult.
185 50 c. Type **25** 15 15
186 60 c. Moonhole 15 20
187 $1.50 Fishing boats, Admiralty Bay 30 40
188 $2 "The Friendship Rose" (yacht) at jetty 40 55

1981. Details from Early Maps. Multicoloured.
189 50 c. Type **26** 30 30
190 50 c. Cannouan Is. (from chart by J. Parsons, 1861) 30 30
191 60 c. Ins. Moustiques (from map of Windward Islands by R. Ottens, c. 1765) 30 35
192 60 c. Mustique Is, (from chart by J. Parsons, 1861) 30 35
193 $2 Ins. Bequia (from map of Windward Islands by R. Ottens, c.1765) 50 75
194 $2 Bequia Is. (from map surveyed in 1763 by T. Jefferys) . . . 50 75

26a "Mary"

1981. Royal Wedding. Royal Yachts. Multicoloured.
195 50 c. Type **26a** 10 15
196 50 c. Prince Charles and Lady Diana Spencer 35 40
197 $3 "Alexandra" 20 30
198 $3 As No. 196 . . . . 60 90
199 $3.50 "Britannia" 25 35
200 $3.50 As No. 196 . . . . . . 65 90

27 Bar Jack

1981. Game Fish. Multicoloured.
204 10 c. Type **27** 15 10
205 50 c. Tarpon 30 10
206 60 c. Cobia 35 10
207 $2 Blue marlin . . . . . . 1·00 70

28 H.M.S. "Experiment" (frigate)

1982. Ships. Multicoloured.
208 1 c. Type **28** 10 20
209 3 c. "Lady Nelson" (cargo liner) 15 20
210 5 c. "Daisy" (brig) 20 20
211 6 c. Carib canoe 20 20
212 10 c. "Hairoun Star" (freighter) 30 10
213 15 c. "Jupiter" (liner) 40 10
214 20 c. "Christina" (steam yacht) 40 10
215 25 c. "Orinoco" (mail paddle-steamer) 55 15
216 30 c. "H.M.S. Lively" (frigate) 55 15
217 50 c. "Alabama" (Confederate warship) 70 30
218 60 c. "Denmark" (freighter) . . 80 30
219 75 c. "Santa Maria" . . . . . 1·10 50
220 $1 "Baffin" (research vessel) . . 1·10 55
221 $2 "Queen Elizabeth 2" (liner) 1·50 1·25
222 $3 R.Y. "Britannia" . . . . 1·50 1·75
223 $5 "Geeststar" (freighter) . . . 1·50 2·00
224 $10 "Grenadines Star" (ferry) . 2·50 5·00

29 Prickly Pear Fruit
30 Anne Neville. Princess of Wales, 1470

1982. Prickly Pear Cactus. Multicoloured.
225 10 c. Type **29** 15 15
226 50 c. Prickly pear flower buds 35 35
227 $1 Flower of prickly pear cactus 60 60
228 $2 Prickly pear cactus . . . . 1·25 1·25

1982. 21st Birthday of Princess of Wales. Multicoloured.
229 50 c. Type **30** 10 15
230 60 c. Coat of arms of Anne Neville 10 15
231 $6 Diana, Princess of Wales . . 60 80

31 Old and New Uniforms

1982. 75th Anniv of Boy Scout Movement. Multicoloured.
232 $1.50 Type **31** 60 75
233 $2.50 Lord Baden-Powell . . . 90 1·00

1982. Birth of Prince William of Wales. Nos. 224/6 optd **ROYAL BABY** and Island name.
234 50 c. Type **30** 10 15
235 60 c. Coat of arms of Anne Neville 10 15
236 $6 Diana, Princess of Wales . . 60 80

Nos. 229/32 exist optd with 5 different island names as follows: A, Bequia, B, Canouan, C, Mayreau, D, Mustique, E, Union Island. To indicate any particular overprint use the appropriate catalogue No. together with the suffix for the island concerned.

33 Silhouette Figures of Mary and Joseph

1982. Christmas. Silhouette of figures. Multicoloured.
237 10 c. Type **33** 10 10
238 $1.50 Animals in stable 45 45
239 $2.50 Mary and Joseph with baby Jesus 60 60

1983. No. 123 surch **45c**.
241 45 c. on 50 c. Grenada flycatcher 30 30

35 Power Station, Clifton

1983. Union Island (2nd issue). Multicoloured.
242 50 c. Type **35** 25 15
243 60 c. Sunrise, Clifton harbour 25 15
244 $1.50 Junior Secondary School, Ashton 60 40
245 $2 Frigate Rock and Conch Shell Beach 85 55

36 British Man-of-war
37 Montgolfier Balloon, 1783

1983. Bicentenary of Treaty of Versailles. Mult.
246 45 c. Type **36** 35 15
247 60 c. American man-of-war . . 35 15
248 $1.50 Soldiers carrying U.S flags 75 45
249 $2 British troops in battle . . . 80 55

1983. Bicentenary of Manned Flight. Mult.
250 45 c. Type **37** 10 15
251 60 c. Ayres Turbo Thrush Commander (horiz) 15 15
252 $1.50 Lebaudy-Juillot airship No. 1 "La Jaune" (horiz) 35 45
253 $2 Space shuttle "Columbia" (horiz) 40 55

38 Coat of Arms of Henry VIII
39 Quarter Dollar and Half Dollar, 1797

1983. Leaders of the World. British Monarchs. Multicoloured.
255 60 c. Type **38** 15 25
256 60 c. Henry VIII 15 25
257 60 c. Coat of Arms of James I 15 25
258 60 c. James I 15 25
259 75 c. Henry VIII at Hampton Court 15 25
260 75 c. Hampton Court 15 25
261 75 c. James I at Edinburgh Castle 15 25
262 75 c. Edinburgh Castle 15 25
263 $2.50 The "Mary Rose" . . . 25 35
264 $2.50 Henry VIII and Portsmouth harbour 25 35
265 $2.50 Gunpowder Plot 25 35
266 $2.50 James I and Gunpowder Plot 25 35

1983. Old Coinage. Multicoloured.
267 20 c. Type **39** 10 10
268 45 c. Nine Bitts, 1811–14 . . . 15 15
269 75 c. Twelve Bitts and Six Bitts, 1811–14 . . . . 25 25
270 $3 Sixty-six Shillings, 1798 . . 80 80

40 Class D13

1984. Leaders of the World. Railway Locomotives (1st series). The first design in each pair shows technical drawings and the second the locomotive at work.
271 5 c. multicoloured 10 10
272 5 c. multicoloured 10 10
273 10 c. multicoloured 10 10
274 10 c. multicoloured 10 10
275 15 c. multicoloured 10 15
276 15 c. multicoloured 10 15
277 35 c. multicoloured 15 20
278 35 c. multicoloured 15 20
279 45 c. multicoloured 15 20
280 45 c. multicoloured 15 20

281 60 c. multicoloured 15 20
282 60 c. multicoloured 15 20
283 $1 multicoloured 20 25
284 $1 multicoloured 20 25
285 $2.50 multicoloured 25 35
286 $2.50 multicoloured 25 35

DESIGNS: Nos. 271/2, Class D13, U.S.A., 1892 (Type **40**); 273/4, High Speed Train 125, Great Britain (1980); 275/6, Class T9, Great Britain (1899); 277/8, "Claud Hamilton", Great Britain (1900); 279/80, Class J, U.S.A. (1941); 281/2, Class D16, U.S.A (1895); 283/4, "Lode Star", Great Britain (1907); 285/6, "Blue Peter". Great Britain (1948).

See also Nos. 321/26, 351/8, 390/7, 412/9, 443/58, 504/19 and 520/35.

41 Spotted Eagle Ray

1984. Reef Fishes. Multicoloured.

287 45 c. Type **41** 25 20
288 60 c. Queen triggerfish 25 35
289 $1.50 White spotted filefish . . 40 1·25
290 $2 Schoolmaster . . . . 40 1·50

42 R. A. Woolmer **44** Lady of the Night

43 Junior Secondary School

1984. Leaders of the World. Cricketers (1st series). The first design in each pair shows a portrait and the second the cricketer in action.

291 1 c. multicoloured 10 10
292 1 c. multicoloured 10 10
293 3 c. multicoloured 10 10
294 3 c. multicoloured 10 10
295 5 c. multicoloured 10 10
296 5 c. multicoloured 10 10
297 30 c. multicoloured 30 30
298 30 c. multicoloured 30 30
299 60 c. multicoloured 40 40
300 60 c. multicoloured 40 40
301 $1 multicoloured 40 40
302 $1 multicoloured 40 40
303 $2 multicoloured 45 70
304 $2 multicoloured 45 70
305 $3 multicoloured 55 80
306 $3 multicoloured 55 80

DESIGNS: Nos. 291/2, R. A. Woolmer (Type **42**); K. S Ranjitsinhji; 295/6, W. R Hammond; 297/8, D. L Underwood; 299/300, W. G Grace; 301/2, E. A. E. Baptiste; 303/4, A. P. E. Knott; 305/6, L. E. G. Ames.

See also Nos. 331/8 and 364/9.

1984. Canouan Island (2nd series). Multicoloured.

307 35 c. Type **43** 20 20
308 45 c. Police Station 25 25
309 $1 Post Office 50 50
310 $3 Anglican Church . . . . . 1·25 1·50

1984. Leaders of the World. Railway Locomotives (2nd issue). As T **40**. The first design in each pair shows technical drawings and the second the locomotive at work.

311 1 c. multicoloured 10 10
312 1 c. multicoloured 10 10
313 5 c. multicoloured 10 10
314 5 c. multicoloured 10 10
315 20 c. multicoloured 15 15
316 20 c. multicoloured 15 15
317 35 c. multicoloured 15 15
318 35 c. multicoloured 15 15
319 60 c. multicoloured 20 20
320 60 c. multicoloured 20 20
321 $1 multicoloured 20 25
322 $1 multicoloured 20 25
323 $1.50 multicoloured 25 30
324 $1.50 multicoloured 25 30
325 $3 multicoloured 35 55
326 $3 multicoloured 35 55

DESIGNS: Nos. 311/12, Class C62, Japan (1948); 313/14, Class V, Great Britain (1903); 315/16, Richard Trevithick's "Catch-Me-Who-Can", Great Britain (1808); 317/18, Class E10, Japan (1948); 319/20, "J. B. Earle", Great Britain (1904); 321/2, No. 762 "Lyn", Great Britain (1898); 323/4, "Talyllyn", Great Britain (1865); 325/6, "Cardean", Great Britain (1906).

1984. Night-blooming Flowers. Mult.

327 35 c. Type **44** 35 30
328 45 c. Four o'clock 40 35
329 75 c. Mother-in-law's tongue . . 60 60
330 $3 Queen of the night . . . . 1·50 2·75

1984. Leaders of the World. Cricketers (2nd series). As T **42**. The first in each pair listed shows a head portrait and the second the cricketer in action.

331 5 c. multicoloured 10 10
332 5 c. multicoloured 10 10
333 30 c. multicoloured 25 20
334 30 c. multicoloured 25 20
335 $1 multicoloured 30 40
336 $1 multicoloured 30 40
337 $2.50 multicoloured 45 80
338 $2.50 multicoloured 45 80

DESIGNS: Nos. 331/2, S. F. Barnes; 333/4, R. Peel; 335/6, H. Larwood; 337/8, Sir John Hobbs.

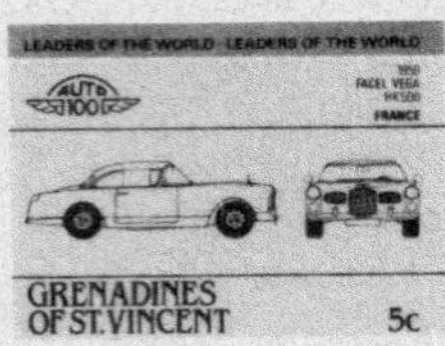

45 Facel "Vega HK500"

1984. Leaders of the World. Automobiles (1st series). The first design in each pair shows technical drawings and the second paintings.

339 5 c. black, blue and green . . . 10 10
340 5 c. multicoloured 10 10
341 25 c. black, lilac and pink . . . 10 10
342 25 c. multicoloured 10 10
343 50 c. black, blue and orange . . 15 15
344 50 c. multicoloured 15 15
345 $3 black, stone and brown . . . 30 45
346 $3 multicoloured 30 45

DESIGNS: Nos. 339/40, Facel "Vega HK500" (Type **45**); 341/2, BMW "328"; 343/4, Frazer-Nash "TT Replica 1.5L"; 345/6, Buick "Roadmaster Riviera".

See also Nos. 378/85 and 431/42.

46 Three Wise Men and Star

1984. Christmas. Multicoloured.

347 20 c. Type **46** 10 10
348 45 c. Journeying to Bethlehem . 15 25
349 $3 Presenting gifts . . . . . . 70 1·40

1985. Leaders of the World. Railway Locomotives (3rd series). As T **40**. The first in each pair shows technical drawings and the second the locomotive at work.

351 1 c. multicoloured 10 10
352 1 c. multicoloured 10 10
353 15 c. multicoloured 10 10
354 15 c. multicoloured 10 10
355 75 c. multicoloured 20 25
356 75 c. multicoloured 20 25
357 $3 multicoloured 50 70
358 $3 multicoloured 50 70

DESIGNS: Nos. 351/2, P.L.M "Grosse C", France (1898); 353/4, Class C12, Japan (1932); 355/6, Class D50, Japan (1923); 357/8, "Fire Fly", Great Britain (1840).

47 Caribbean King Crab

1985. Shell Fish. Multicoloured.

360 25 c. Type **47** 20 15
361 60 c. Queen or pink conch . . . 30 35
362 $1 White sea urchin 35 55
363 $3 West Indian top shell or wilk . 75 1·75

1985. Leaders of the World. Cricketers (3rd series). As T **42** (55, 60 c.) the first in each pair showing a head portrait and the second the cricketer in action, or horiz designs showing teams ($2).

364 55 c. multicoloured 25 35
365 55 c. multicoloured 25 35
366 60 c. multicoloured 25 40
367 60 c. multicoloured 25 40
368 $2 multicoloured 40 85
369 $2 multicoloured 40 85

DESIGNS—VERT (As T **42**): Nos. 364/5, M. D. Moxon; 366/7, L. Potter. HORIZ (59 × 42 mm): No. 368, Kent team; 369, Yorkshire team.

HAVE YOU READ THE NOTES AT THE BEGINNING OF THIS CATALOGUE?

These often provide answers to the enquiries we receive.

48 "Cypripedium calceolus"

1985. Leaders of the World. Flowers. Multicoloured.

370 5 c. Type **48** 10 10
371 5 c. "Gentiana asclepiadea" . . 10 10
372 55 c. "Clianthus formosus" . . 15 20
373 55 c. "Clemisia coriacea" . . . 15 20
374 60 c. "Erythronium americanum" 15 20
375 60 c. "Laelia anceps" 15 20
376 $2 "Leucadendron discolor" . . 35 50
377 $2 "Meconopsis horridula" . . 35 50

1985. Leaders of the World. Automobiles (2nd series). As T **45**. The first in each pair shows technical drawings and the second paintings.

378 5 c. black, yellow and blue . . 10 10
379 5 c. multicoloured 10 10
380 60 c. black, yellow and orange . 15 15
381 60 c. multicoloured 15 15
382 $1 black, green and blue . . . 15 20
383 $1 multicoloured 15 20
384 $1.50 black, blue and green . . 15 25
385 $1.50 multicoloured 15 25

DESIGNS: Nos. 378/9, Winton (1903); 380/1, Invicta 4½ litre (1932); 382/3, Daimler "SP250 Dart" (1959); 384/5, Brabham "Repco BT19" (1966).

49 Windsurfing

1985. Tourism. Watersports. Multicoloured.

386 35 c. Type **49** 20 15
387 45 c. Water-skiing 20 15
388 75 c. Scuba-diving 20 25
389 $3 Deep-sea game fishing . . . 40 1·40

1985. Leaders of the World. Railway Locomotives (4th series). As T **40**. The first design in each pair shows technical drawings and the second the locomotive at work.

390 10 c. mutlicoloured 10 10
391 10 c. multicoloured 10 10
392 40 c. multicoloured 20 20
393 40 c. multicoloured 20 20
394 50 c. multicoloured 20 20
395 50 c. multicoloured 20 20
396 $2.50 multicoloured 70 80
397 $2.50 multicoloured 70 80

DESIGNS: Nos. 390/1, Class 581 electric train, Japan (1968); 392/3, 231-132BT, Algeria (1936); 394/5, "Slieve Gullion", Ireland (1913); 396/7, Class "Beattie" well tank, Great Britain (1874).

50 Passion Fruits and Blossom

1985. Fruits and Blossoms. Multicoloured.

398 30 c. Type **50** 15 20
399 75 c. Guava 25 40
400 $1 Sapodilla 35 55
401 $2 Mango . . . . 50 1·10

51 Queen Elizabeth the Queen Mother

1985. Leaders of the World. Life and Times of Queen Elizabeth the Queen Mother. Various vertical portraits.

403 **51** 40 c. multicoloured 10 20
404 – 40 c. multicoloured 10 20
405 – 75 c. multicoloured 10 20
406 – 75 c. multicoloured 10 20
407 – $1.10 multicoloured 15 20
408 – $1.10 multicoloured 15 20
409 – $1.75 multicoloured 15 30
410 – $1.75 multicoloured 15 30

Each value, issued in pairs, shows a floral pattern across the bottom of the portraits which stops short of the left-hand edge on the first stamp and of the right-hand edge on the second.

1985. Leaders of the World. Railway Locomotives (5th series). As T **40**. The first design in each pair shows technical drawings and the second the locomotive at work.

412 35 c. multicoloured 15 20
413 35 c. multicoloured 15 20
414 70 c. multicoloured 20 30
415 70 c. multicoloured 20 30
416 $1.20 multicoloured 30 40
417 $1.20 multicoloured 30 40
418 $2 multicoloured 40 65
419 $2 multicoloured 40 65

DESIGNS: Nos. 412/13, "Coronation", Great Britain (1937); 414/15, Class E18, Germany (1935); 416/17, Hayes type, U.S.A. (1854); 418/19, Class 2120, Japan (1890).

1985. Royal Visit. Nos. 199/200, 222, 287, 398 and 407/8 optd **CARIBBEAN ROYAL VISIT 1985** or surch also.

420 **50** 30 c. multicoloured . . . . 80 1·25
421 **41** 45 c. multicoloured . . . . 1·00 1·75
422 – $1.10 multicoloured (No. 407) 1·75 3·75
423 – $1.10 multicoloured (No. 408) 1·75 3·75
424 – $1.50 on $3.50 multicoloured (No. 199) . . . . 2·00 2·25
425 – $1.50 on $3.50 multicoloured (No. 200) . . . . 15·00 17·00
426 – $3 multicoloured (No. 222) . 2·25 3·25

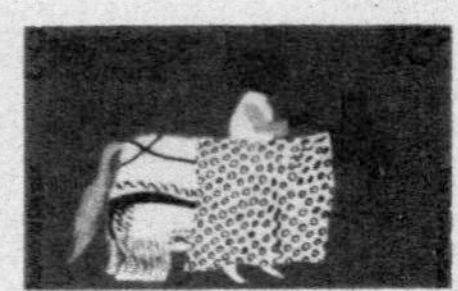

52 Donkey Man

1985. Traditional Dances. Multicoloured.

427 45 c. Type **52** 15 30
428 75 c. Cake dance (vert) 20 40
429 $1 Bois-Bois man (vert) . . . 25 55
430 $2 Maypole dance . . . . . . 45 1·10

1986. Leaders of the World. Automobiles (3rd series). As T **45**. The first in each pair shows technical drawings and the second paintings.

431 15 c. black, lilac and mauve. . . 10 10
432 15 c. multicoloured 10 10
433 45 c. black, yellow & brown . . 10 20
434 45 c. multicoloured 10 20
435 60 c. black, green and blue . . 10 25
436 60 c. multicoloured 10 25
437 $1 black, brown and green . . 15 25
438 $1 multicoloured 15 25
439 $1.75 black, yellow & orange . 15 35
440 $1.75 multicoloured 15 35
441 $3 multicoloured 25 45
442 $3 multicoloured 25 45

DESIGNS: Nos. 431/2, Mercedes-Benz 4.5 litre (1914); 433/4, Rolls Royce "Silver Wraith" (1954); 435/6, Lamborghini "Countach" (1974); 437/8, Marmon "V-16" (1932); 439/40, Lotus-Ford "49 B" (1968); 441/2, Delage 1.5 litre (1927).

1986. Leaders of the World. Railway Locomotives (6th series). As T **40**. The first in each pair shows technical drawings and the second the locomotive at work.

443 15 c. multicoloured 15 10
444 15 c. multicoloured 15 10
445 45 c. multicoloured 20 20
446 45 c. multicoloured 20 20
447 60 c. multicoloured 20 30
448 60 c. multicoloured 20 30
449 75 c. multicoloured 20 35
450 75 c. multicoloured 20 35
451 $1 multicoloured 25 40
452 $1 multicoloured 25 40
453 $1.50 multicoloured 25 50
454 $1.50 multicoloured 25 50
455 $2 multicoloured 30 65
456 $2 multicoloured 30 65
457 $3 multicoloured 30 80
458 $3 multicoloured 30 80

DESIGNS: Nos. 443/4, Class T15, Germany (1897); 445/6, Class 13, Great Britain (1900); 447/8, "Halesworth", Great Britain (1879); 449/50, Class "Problem", Great Britain (1859); 451/2, Class "Western" diesel, Great Britain (1961); 453/4, Drummond's "Bug", Great Britain (1899); 455/6, Class "Clan", Great Britain (1951); 457/8, Class 1800, Japan (1884).

52a Queen Elizabeth II

1986. 60th Birthday of Queen Elizabeth II. Mult.

459 5 c. Type **52a** 15 15
460 $1 At Princess Anne's christening, 1950 . . . . . 30 35
461 $4 Princess Elizabeth 60 90
462 $6 In Canberra, 1982 (vert) . . 75 1·50

53 Handmade Dolls

1986. Handicrafts. Multicoloured.
464 10 c. Type **53** 10 10
465 60 c. Basketwork 20 35
466 $1 Scrimshaw work 30 50
467 $3 Model sailing dinghy 80 1·90

54 Uruguayan Team

1986. World Cup Football Championship, Mexico. Multicoloured.
468 1 c. Type **54** 10 10
469 10 c. Polish team 10 10
470 45 c. Bulgarian player (28 × 42 mm) 25 30
471 75 c. Iraqi player (28 × 42 mm) 35 40
472 $1.50 South Korean player (28 × 42 mm) 75 90
473 $2 Northern Irish player (28 × 42 mm) 80 1·10
474 $4 Portuguese team 1·25 1·50
475 $5 Canadian team 1·25 1·50

55 "Marasmius pallescens"

1986. Fungi. Multicoloured.
477 45 c. Type **55** 2·25 75
478 60 c. "Leucocoprinus fragilissimus" 2·50 1·10
479 75 c. "Hygrocybe occidentalis" 2·75 1·60
480 $3 "Xerocomus hypoxanthus" 8·00 7·00

55a Miss Sarah Ferguson and Princess Diana applauding

1986. Royal Wedding (1st issue). Multicoloured.
481 60 c. Type **55a** 15 25
482 60 c. Prince Andrew at shooting match 15 25
483 $2 Prince Andrew and Miss Sarah Ferguson (horiz) 50 80
484 $2 Prince Charles with Prince Andrew, Princess Anne and Princess Margaret on balcony (horiz) 50 80

1986. Royal Wedding (2nd issue). Nos. 481/4 optd **Congratulations to T.R.H. The Duke and Duchess of York.**
486 60 c. Miss Sarah Ferguson and Princess Diana applauding 30 50
487 60 c. Prince Andrew at shooting match 30 50
488 $2 Prince Andrew and Miss Sarah Ferguson (horiz) 1·00 1·25
489 $2 Prince Charles, Prince Andrew, Princess Anne and Princess Margaret on balcony (horiz) 1·00 1·25

INDEX
Countries can be quickly located by referring to the index at the end of this volume.

56 "Brachymesia furcata"

1986. Dragonflies. Multicoloured.
490 45 c. Type **56** 25 20
491 60 c. "Lepthemis vesiculosa" 30 40
492 75 c. "Perithemis domitta" 30 45
493 $2.50 "Tramea abdominalis (vert) 45 1·40

57 American Kestrel

58 Santa playing Steel Band Drums

1986. Birds of Prey. Multicoloured.
495 10 c. Type **57** 75 45
496 45 c. Common black hawk 1·90 50
497 60 c. Peregrine falcon 2·25 1·25
498 $4 Osprey 5·00 6·50

1986. Christmas. Multicoloured.
499 45 c. Type **58** 30 30
500 60 c. Santa windsurfing 35 35
501 $1.25 Santa skiing 60 85
502 $2 Santa limbo dancing 1·10 1·60

1987. Railway Locomotives (7th series). As T **40**. The first in each pair shows technical drawings and the second the locomotive at work.
504 10 c. multicoloured 15 10
505 10 c. multicoloured 15 10
506 40 c. multicoloured 25 25
507 40 c. multicoloured 25 25
508 50 c. multicoloured 30 30
509 50 c. multicoloured 30 30
510 60 c. multicoloured 30 30
511 60 c. multicoloured 30 30
512 75 c. multicoloured 30 40
513 75 c. multicoloured 30 40
514 $1 multicoloured 30 50
515 $1 multicoloured 30 50
516 $1.25 multicoloured 30 60
517 $1.25 multicoloured 30 60
518 $1.50 multicoloured 40 75
519 $1.50 multicoloured 40 75

DESIGNS: Nos. 504/5, Class 1001, No. 1275, Great Britain (1874); 506/7, Class 4P Garratt, Great Britain (1927); 508/9, "Papyrus", Great Britain (1929); 510/11, Class VI, Great Britain (1930); 512/13, Class 40 diesel, No. D200, Great Britain (1958); 514/15, Class 42 "Warship" diesel, Great Britain (1958); 516/17, Class P-69, U.S.A. (1902); 518/19, Class 60-3 Shay, No. 15, U.S.A. (1913).

1987. Railway Locomotives (8th series). As T **40**. The first in each pair shows technical drawings and the second the locomotive at work.
520 10 c. multicoloured 15 15
521 10 c. multicoloured 15 15
522 40 c. multicoloured 25 30
523 40 c. multicoloured 25 30
524 50 c. multicoloured 30 35
525 50 c. multicoloured 30 35
526 60 c. multicoloured 30 40
527 60 c. multicoloured 30 40
528 75 c. multicoloured 30 45
529 75 c. multicoloured 30 45
530 $1 multicoloured 30 45
531 $1 multicoloured 30 45
532 $1.50 multicoloured 40 55
533 $1.50 multicoloured 40 55
534 $2 multicoloured 45 70
535 $2 multicoloured 45 70

DESIGNS: Nos. 520/1, Class 142, East Germany (1977); 522/3, Class 120, West Germany (1979); 524/5, Class X, Australia (1954); 526/7, Class 59, Great Britain (1986); 528/9, New York Elevated Railroad "Spuyten Duyvel", U.S.A. (1875); 530/1, Camden & Amboy Railroad "Stevens" and rebuilt "John Bull", U.S.A. (1832); 532/3, Class HI-d, No. 2850, Canada (1938); 534/5, "Pioneer Zephyr" 3-car diesel set, U.S.A. (1934).

59 Queen Elizabeth with Prince Andrew

61 "Australia IV"

60 Banded Coral Shrimp

1987. Royal Ruby Wedding and 150th Anniv of Queen Victoria's Accession.
536 **59** 15 c. multicoloured 20 15
537 – 45 c. brown, black and yellow 25 20
538 – $1.50 multicoloured 30 50
539 – $3 multicoloured 45 80
540 – $4 multicoloured 50 1·10

DESIGNS: 45 c. Queen Victoria and Prince Albert, c. 1855; $1.50, Queen and Prince Philip after Trooping the Colour, 1977; $3 Queen and Duke of Edinburgh, 1953; $4 Queen in her study, c. 1980.

1987. Marine Life. Multicoloured.
542 45 c. Type **60** 55 35
543 50 c. Arrow crab and flamingo tongue 60 50
544 65 c. Cardinal fish 70 90
545 $5 Moray eel 2·00 3·75

1988. Ocean Racing Yachts. Multicoloured.
547 50 c. Type **61** 30 35
548 65 c. "Crusader II" 35 50
549 75 c. "New Zealand II" 40 60
550 $2 "Italia" 60 1·25
551 $4 "White Crusader" 70 2·00
552 $5 "Stars and Stripes" 70 2·25

62 Seine-fishing Boats racing

1988. Bequia Regatta. Multicoloured.
554 5 c. Type **62** 10 15
555 50 c. "Friendship Rose" (cruising yacht) 15 30
556 75 c. Fishing boats racing 20 45
557 $3.50 Yachts racing 75 2·25

63 Britten Norman Islander making Night Approach

1988. Mustique Airways. Multicoloured.
559 15 c. Type **63** 10 15
560 65 c. Beech Baron aircraft in flight 15 35
561 75 c. Britten Norman Islander over forest 15 35
562 $5 Beech Baron on airstrip 1·00 2·25

64 "Sv. Pyotr" in Arctic (Bering)

65 Asif Iqbal Razvi

1988. Explorers. Multicoloured.
564 15 c. Type **64** 35 20
565 75 c. Bering's ships in pack ice 40 30
566 $1 Livingstone's steam launch "Ma-Robert" on Zambesi 40 40
567 $2 Meeting of Livingstone and H. M Stanley at Ujiji 50 75
568 $3 Speke and Burton at Tabori 50 90
569 $3.50 Speke and Burton in canoe on Lake Victoria 50 1·10
570 $4 Sighting the New World, 1492 60 1·25
571 $4.50 Columbus trading with Indians 60 1·40

1988. Cricketers of 1988 International Season. Multicoloured.
573 20 c. Type **65** 30 30
574 45 c. R. J. Hadlee 50 50
575 75 c. M. D. Crowe 70 80
576 $1.25 C. H. Lloyd 80 1·25
577 $1.50 A. R. Boarder 90 1·50
578 $2 M. D. Marshall 1·10 2·00
579 $2.50 G. A. Hick 1·10 2·25
580 £3.50 C. G. Greenidge (horiz) 1·25 2·75

66 Pam Shriver

1988. International Tennis Players. Mult.
582 15 c. Type **66** 20 20
583 50 c. Kevin Curran (vert) 20 30
584 75 c. Wendy Turnbull (vert) 25 35
585 $1 Evonne Cawley (vert) 30 50
586 $1.50 Ilie Nastase 35 65
587 $2 Billie Jean King (vert) 40 75
588 $3 Bjorn Borg (vert) 45 1·25
589 $3.50 Virginia Wade with Wimbledon trophy (vert) 50 1·50

No. 584 is inscribed "WENDY TURNBALL" in error.

67 Mickey and Minnie Mouse visiting Fatehpur Sikri

1989. "India-'89" International Stamp Exhibition. Designs showing Walt Disney cartoon characters in India. Multicoloured.
591 1 c. Type **67** 10 10
592 2 c. Mickey and Minnie Mouse aboard "Palace on Wheels" train 10 10
593 3 c. Mickey and Minnie Mouse passing Old Fort, Delhi 10 10
594 5 c. Mickey and Minnie Mouse on camel, Pinjore Gardens, Haryana 10 10
595 10 c. Mickey and Minnie Mouse at Taj Mahal, Agra 15 10
596 25 c. Mickey and Minnie Mouse in Chandni Chowk, Old Delhi 20 10
597 $4 Goofy on elephant with Mickey and Minnie Mouse at Agra Fort, Jaipur 3·00 3·50
598 $5 Goofy, Mickey and Minnie Mouse at Gandhi Memorial Cape Comorin 3·00 3·50

1989. Japanese Art. As T **177a** of Gambia but horiz. Multicoloured.
600 5 c. "The View at Yotsuya" (Hokusai) 20 20
601 30 c. "Landscape at Ochanomizu" (Hokuju) 50 50
602 45 c. "Itabashi" (Eisen) 60 60
603 65 c. "Early Summer Rain" (Kunisada) 75 75
604 75 c. "High Noon at Kasumigaseki" (Kuniyoshi) 80 80
605 $1 "The Yoshiwara Embankment by Moonlight" (Kuniyoshi) 1·00 1·00
606 $4 "The Bridge of Boats at Sano" (Hokusai) 2·75 3·00
607 $5 "Lingering Snow on Mount Hira" (Kunitora) 2·75 3·00

68 Player with Ball and Mt Vesuvius

71 "Marpesia petreus"

70 Command Module "Columbia"

1989. World Cup Football Championship, Italy (1st issue). Designs showing players and Italian landmarks. Multicoloured.
609 $1.50 Type **68** 1·40 1·40
610 $1.50 Fallen player, opponent kicking ball and Coliseum 1·40 1·40
611 $1.50 Player blocking ball and Venice 1·40 1·40
612 $1.50 Player tackling and Forum, Rome 1·40 1·40
613 $1.50 Two players competing for ball and Leaning Tower, Pisa 1·40 1·40

614 $1.50 Goalkeeper and Florence 1·40 1·40
615 $1.50 Two players competing for ball and St. Peter's, Vatican 1·40 1·40
616 $1.50 Player kicking ball and Pantheon 1·40 1·40
Nos 609/16 were printed together, se-tenant, forming a composite foreground design.
See also Nos. 680/3.

1989. 500th Anniv (1992) of Discovery of America by Columbus (1st issue). Pre-Columbian Arawak Society. As T **97a** of Grenadines of Grenada. Multicoloured.
617 25 c. Arawak smoking tobacco 35 25
618 75 c. Arawak rolling cigar 65 65
619 $1 Applying body paint 80 80
620 $1.50 Making fire 1·10 1·40
621 $1.50 Cassava production 1·10 1·40
622 $1.50 Woman baking bread 1·10 1·40
623 $1.50 Using stone implement 1·10 1·40
624 $4 Arawak priest 2·50 2·75
Nos. 620/3 were printed together, se-tenant, forming a composite design.
See also Nos. 818/23 and 864/5.

1989. 20th Anniv of First Manned Landing on Moon. Multicoloured.
626 5 c. Type **70** 30 30
627 40 c. Astronaut Neil Armstrong saluting U.S. flag 1·00 85
628 55 c. "Columbia" above lunar surface 1·25 90
629 65 c. Lunar module "Eagle" leaving moon 1·25 1·10
630 70 c. "Eagle" on Moon 1·25 1·10
631 $1 "Columbia" re-entering Earth's atmosphere 1·40 1·40
632 $3 "Apollo II" emblem 2·75 3·00
633 $5 Armstrong and Aldrin on Moon 3·00 3·50

1989. Butterflies. Multicoloured.
635 5 c. Type **71** 40 40
636 30 c. "Papilio androgeus" 1·00 60
637 45 c. "Strymon maesites" 1·25 65
638 65 c. "Junonia coenia" 1·60 1·40
639 75 c. "Eurema gratiosa" 1·75 1·50
640 $1 "Hypolimnas misippus" 2·00 1·75
641 $4 "Urbanus proteus" 3·75 4·00
642 $5 "Junonia evarete" 3·75 4·00

72 "Solanum urens"

74 Exhibition Emblem

1989. Flowers from St. Vincent Botanical Gardens. Multicoloured.
644 80 c. Type **72** 1·25 1·25
645 $1.25 "Passiflora andersonii" 1·60 1·60
646 $1.65 "Miconia andersonii" 2·00 2·00
647 $1.85 "Pitcairnia sulphurea" 2·25 2·25

1989. Christmas. As T **183** of Gambia. Mult.
648 5 c. Goofy and Mickey Mouse in Rolls Royce "Silver Ghost", 1907 20 15
649 10 c. Daisy Duck driving first Stanley Steamer, 1897 20 15
650 15 c. Horace Horsecollar and Clarabelle Cow in Darracq "Genevieve", 1904 25 20
651 45 c. Donald Duck driving Detroit electric coupe, 1914 55 40
652 55 c. Mickey and Minnie Mouse in first Ford, 1896 55 40
653 $2 Mickey Mouse driving Reo "Runabout", 1904 2·00 2·00
654 $3 Goofy driving Winton mail truck, 1899 2·75 2·75
655 $5 Mickey and Minnie Mouse in Duryea car, 1893 3·50 4·00

1990. 50th Anniv of Second World War. As T **354c** of Grenada. Multicoloured.
657 10 c. Destroyer in action, First Battle of Narvik, 1940 25 25
658 15 c. Allied tank at Anzio, 1944 35 35
659 20 c. U.S. carrier under attack, Battle of Midway, 1942 40 40
660 45 c. North American B-25 Mitchell bombers over Gustav Line, 1944 70 70
661 55 c. Map showing Allied zones of Berlin, 1945 75 75
662 65 c. German U-boat pursuing convoy, Battle of the Atlantic, 1943 80 80
663 90 c. Allied tank, North Africa, 1943 1·00 1·00
664 $3 U.S. forces landing on Guam, 1944 2·50 2·50
665 $5 Crossing the Rhine, 1945 3·50 3·50
666 $6 Japanese battleships under attack, Lete Gulf, 1944 4·00 4·00

1990. "Stamp World London 90" International Stamp Exhibition (1st issue). Mickey's Shakespeare Company. As T **193** of Gambia showing Walt Disney cartoon characters. Multicoloured.
668 20 c. Goofy as Mark Anthony ("Julius Caesar") 30 20
669 30 c. Clarabelle Cow as the Nurse ("Romeo and Juliet") 35 25
670 45 c. Pete as Falstaff ("Henry IV") 50 40
671 50 c. Minnie Mouse as Portia ("The Merchant of Venice") 55 40
672 $1 Donald Duck as Hamlet ("Hamlet") 1·00 85
673 $2 Daisy Duck as Ophelia ("Hamlet") 1·75 2·00
674 $4 Donald and Daisy Duck as Benedick and Beatrice ("Much Ado About Nothing") 3·00 3·25
675 $5 Minnie Mouse and Donald Duck as Katherine and Petruchio ("The Taming of the Shrew") 3·00 3·25

1990. "Stamp World London 90" International Stamp Exhibition (2nd issue). 150th Anniv of the Penny Black.
677 **74** $1 black, pink and mauve 1·50 1·25
678 – $5 black, lilac and blue 3·75 4·25
DESIGNS: $5 Negative image of Penny Black.

74a McCleish, Scotland

1990. World Cup Football Championship, Italy (2nd issue). Multicoloured.
680 25 c. Type **74a** 80 40
681 50 c. Rasul, Egypt 1·10 80
682 $2 Lindenberger, Austria 2·75 2·75
683 $4 Murray, U.S.A. 3·75 4·25

74b "Paphiopedilum"

1990. "EXPO 90" International Garden and Greenery Exposition, Osaka. Orchids. Mult.
685 5 c. Type **74b** 50 40
686 25 c. "Dendrobium phalaenopsis" and "Cymbidium hybrid" 1·00 90
687 30 c. "Miltonia candida hybrid" 1·00 90
688 50 c. "Epidendrum ibaguense" and "Cymbidium" Elliot Rogers 1·50 1·25
689 $1 "Rossioglossum grande" 2·00 1·75
690 $2 "Phalaenopsis" Elisa Chang Lou and "Masdevallia coccinea" 2·50 2·25
691 $4 "Cypripedium acaule" and "Cypripedium calceolus" 3·00 3·50
692 $5 "Orchis spectabilis" 3·00 3·50

75 Scaly-breasted Ground Dove

1990. Birds of the Caribbean. Multicoloured.
694 5 c. Type **75** 20 20
695 25 c. Purple martin 40 40
696 45 c. Painted bunting 70 70
697 55 c. Blue-hooded euphonia 80 80
698 75 c. Blue-grey tanager 1·00 1·00
699 $1 Red-eyed vireo 1·25 1·25
700 $2 Palm chat 2·00 2·00
701 $3 Northern jacana 2·50 2·50
702 $4 Green-throated carib 2·75 2·75
703 $5 St. Vincent amazon 3·00 3·00

1991. 90th Birthday of Queen Elizabeth the Queen Mother. As T **194** of Gambia.
705 $2 multicoloured 1·40 1·25
706 $2 multicoloured 1·40 1·25
707 $2 multicoloured 1·40 1·25
708 $2 multicoloured 1·40 1·25
709 $2 multicoloured 1·40 1·25
710 $2 multicoloured 1·40 1·25
711 $2 multicoloured 1·40 1·25
712 $2 multicoloured 1·40 1·25
713 $2 multicoloured 1·40 1·25
714 $2 multicoloured 1·40 1·25
715 $2 multicoloured 1·40 1·25
716 $2 multicoloured 1·40 1·25
717 $2 multicoloured 1·40 1·25
718 $2 multicoloured 1·40 1·25
719 $2 multicoloured 1·40 1·25
720 $2 multicoloured 1·40 1·25
721 $2 multicoloured 1·40 1·25
722 $2 multicoloured 1·40 1·25
723 $2 multicoloured 1·40 1·25
724 $2 multicoloured 1·40 1·25
725 $2 multicoloured 1·40 1·25
726 $2 multicoloured 1·40 1·25
727 $2 multicoloured 1·40 1·25
728 $2 multicoloured 1·40 1·25
729 $2 multicoloured 1·40 1·25
730 $2 multicoloured 1·40 1·25
731 $2 multicoloured 1·40 1·25
DESIGNS: No. 705, Lady Elizabeth Bowes-Lyon with sister; 706, Young Lady Elizabeth in long dress; 707, Young Lady Elizabeth wearing a hat; 708, Lady Elizabeth leaning on wall; 709, Lady Elizabeth on pony; 710, Studio portrait; 711, Lady Elizabeth in evening dress; 712, Duchess of York in fur-lined cloak; 713, Duchess of York holding rose; 714, Coronation, 1937; 715, King and Queen with Princess Elizabeth at Royal Lodge, Windsor; 716, Queen Elizabeth in blue hat; 717, King George VI and Queen Elizabeth; 718, Queen Elizabeth with Princess Elizabeth; 719, Queen Elizabeth watching sporting fixture; 720, Queen Elizabeth in white evening dress; 721, Princess Anne's christening, 1950; 722, Queen Mother with yellow bouquet; 723, Queen Mother and policewoman; 724, Queen Mother at ceremonial function; 725, Queen Mother in pink coat; 726, Queen Mother in academic robes; 727, Queen Mother in carriage with Princess Margaret; 728, Queen Mother in blue coat and hat; 729, Queen Mother with bouquet; 730, Queen Mother outside Clarence House on her birthday; 731, Queen Mother in turquoise coat and hat.

1991. Death Centenary (1990) of Vincent van Gogh (artist). As T **200b** of Gambia. Mult.
733 5 c. "View of Arles with Irises" 20 20
734 10 c. "Saintes-Maries" (vert) 20 20
735 15 c. "Old Woman of Arles" (vert) 25 25
736 20 c. "Orchard in Blossom, bordered by Cypresses" 30 30
737 25 c. "Three White Cottages in Saintes-Maries" 30 30
738 35 c. "Boats at Saintes-Maries" 40 40
739 40 c. "Interior of a Restaurant in Arles" 45 45
740 45 c. "Peasant Women" (vert) 50 50
741 55 c. "Self-portrait" (vert) 60 60
742 60 c. "Pork Butcher's Shop from a Window" (vert) 70 70
743 75 c. "The Night Cafe in Arles" 80 80
744 $1 "2nd Lieut. Millet of the Zouaves" 95 95
745 $2 "The Cafe Terrace, Place du Forum, Arles at Night" (vert) 1·50 1·50
746 $3 "The Zouave" (vert) 2·00 2·00
747 $4 "The Two Lovers" (detail) (vert) 2·75 2·75
748 $5 "Still Life" 3·00 3·00

1991. 65th Birthday of Queen Elizabeth II. As T **198a** of Gambia. Multicoloured.
750 15 c. Inspecting the Yeomen of the Guard 30 20
751 40 c. Queen Elizabeth II with the Queen Mother at the Derby, 1988 55 30
752 $2 The Queen and Prince Philip leaving Euston, 1986 2·00 2·00
753 $4 The Queen at the Commonwealth Institute, 1987 2·75 3·00

1991. 10th Wedding Anniv of Prince and Princess of Wales. As T **198b** of Gambia. Multicoloured.
755 10 c. Prince and Princess at polo match, 1987 50 20
756 50 c. Separate family portraits 90 40
757 $1 Prince William and Prince Henry at Kensington Palace, 1991 1·00 1·00
758 $5 Portraits of Prince Charles and Princess Diana 3·75 4·00

76 Class 150 Steam Locomotive and Map

1991. "Phila Nippon '91" International Stamp Exhibition, Toyko. Japanese Railway Locomotives. Each in black, red and green.
760 10 c. Type **76** 60 50
761 25 c. Class 7100 locomotive, "Benkei", 1880 90 80
762 35 c. Class 8620 steam locomotive, 1914 1·00 90
763 50 c. Class C53 steamlined steam locomotive, 1928 1·50 1·25
764 $1 Class DD51 diesel-hydraulic locomotive, 1962 2·00 1·75
765 $2 Class KTR001 electric railcar Tango Explorer (inscr "RF 22327") 2·50 2·50
766 $4 Class EF55 electric locomotive, 1936 3·00 3·50
767 $5 Class EF58 electric locomotive, 1946 3·00 3·50

77 President Gorbachev and Brandenburg Gate

1991. Anniversaries and Events. Multicoloured.
769 45 c. Type **77** 40 40
770 60 c. General de Gaulle in Djibouti, 1959 90 55
771 65 c. "DIE MAUER MUSS WEG!" slogan 65 65
772 80 c. East German border guard escaping to West 80 80
773 $1 "Abduction from the Seraglio" 1·75 1·50
774 $1.50 Lilienthal and glider 1·75 1·75
775 $1.75 Trans-Siberian identity plate 2·25 2·00
776 $1.75 Trans-Siberian steam locomotive (vert) 2·25 2·00
777 $2 Czechoslovakia 1918 20 h. stamp and scout delivering mail 2·25 2·25
778 $2 Zurich couple maypole dancing 2·25 2·25
779 $2 Man and woman in Vaud traditional costumes 2·25 2·25
780 $2 Georg Laves (architect) and Hoftheater 2·25 2·25
781 $3 Dresden, 1749 3·00 2·50
782 $4 Scouts and cog train on Snowdon (vert) 3·00 2·75
ANNIVERSARIES AND EVENTS: Nos. 769, 771/2, Bicentenary of Brandenburg Gate; 770, Birth centenary of Charles de Gaulle (French statesman); 773, 781, Death bicentenary of Mozart; 774, Centenary of Otto Lilienthal's gliding experiments; 775/6, Centenary of Trans-Siberian Railway; 777, 782, 50th death anniv of Lord Baden-Powell and World Scout Jamboree, Korea; 778/9, 700th anniv of Swiss Confederation; 780, 750th anniv of Hanover.

78 Japanese Aircraft and Submarines leaving Truk

1991. 50th Anniv of Japanese Attack on Pearl Harbor. Multicoloured.
784 $1 Type **78** 1·60 1·60
785 $1 "Akagi" (Japanese aircraft carrier) 1·60 1·60
786 $1 Nakajima B5N2 "Kate" bombers 1·60 1·60
787 $1 Nakajima B5N2 "Kate" bombers attacking Battleship Row 1·60 1·60
788 $1 Burning aircraft, Ford Island airfield 1·60 1·60
789 $1 Doris Miller winning Navy Cross 1·60 1·60
790 $1 U.S.S. "West Virginia" and "Tennessee" (battleships) ablaze 1·60 1·60
791 $1 U.S.S. "Arizona" (battleship) sinking 1·60 1·60
792 $1 U.S.S. "New Orleans" (cruiser) 1·60 1·60
793 $1 President Roosevelt declaring war 1·60 1·60

78a Pluto pulling Mickey Mouse in Sledge, 1974

1991. Christmas. Walt Disney Company Christmas Cards. Multicoloured.
794 10 c. Type **78a** 35 30
795 55 c. Mickey, Pluto and Donald Duck watching toy band, 1961 80 70
796 65 c. "The Same Old Wish", 1942 85 85
797 75 c. Mickey, Peter Pan, Donald and Nephews with Merlin the magician, 1963 95 95
798 $1.50 Mickey and Donald with leprechauns, 1958 1·75 2·00
799 $2 Mickey and friends with book "Old Yeller", 1957 2·00 2·25
800 $4 Mickey controlling Pinocchio, 1953 3·25 3·50
801 $5 Cinderella and Prince dancing, 1987 3·25 3·50

1992. 40th Anniv of Queen Elizabeth II's Accession. As T **202a** of Gambia. Multicoloured.
803 15 c. View across bay 40 20
804 45 c. Schooner at anchor, Mayreau 75 25
805 $2 Hotel on hillside 1·50 1·75
806 $4 Tourist craft at anchor 3·00 3·25

78b Big Pete as Hernando Cortes in Mexico

1992. International Stamp Exhibitions. Walt Disney cartoon characters. Multicoloured. (a) "Grenada '92", Spain. Spanish Explorers.

808 15 c. Type **78b** 30 15
809 40 c. Mickey Mouse as Hernando de Soto at Mississippi River . 50 30
810 $2 Goofy as Vasco Nunez de Balboa sights Pacific . . . . 1·75 1·75
811 $4 Donald Duck as Francisco Coronado on Rio Grande . . 2·75 3·00

(b) "World Columbian Stamp Expo '92", Chicago. Local Personalities.

813 10 c. Mickey Mouse and Pluto outside Walt Disney's birthplace 30 20
814 50 c. Donald Duck and nephews in George Pullman's railway sleeping car 70 55
815 $1 Daisy Duck as Jane Addams (social reformer) and Hull House . . . . 1·00 85
816 $5 Mickey as Carl Sandburg (novelist, poet and historian) . 3·25 3·75

79 King Ferdinand and Queen Isabella of Spain

1992. 500th Anniv of Discovery of America by Columbus (2nd issue). Multicoloured.

818 10 c. Type **79** 25 25
819 45 c. "Santa Maria" and "Nina" in Acul Bay, Haiti 50 50
820 55 c. "Santa Maria" (vert) . . 55 55
821 $2 Ships of Columbus (vert) . . 1·40 1·40
822 $4 Wreck of "Santa Maria" . . 2·50 2·50
823 $5 "Pinta" and "Nina" . . . . 2·75 2·75

79a "Paulogramma spa"

1992. "Genova '92" International Thematic Stamp Exhibition (1st issue). Butterflies. Multicoloured.

825 15 c. Type **79a** 65 65
826 20 c. "Heliconius cydno" . . . 70 70
827 30 c. "Eutresis hypereia" . . . 75 75
828 45 c. "Eurytides columbus" (vert) 90 90
829 55 c. "Papilio ascolius" . . . . 1·00 1·00
830 75 c. "Anaea pasibula" . . . . 1·25 1·25
831 80 c. "Heliconius doris" . . . 1·25 1·25
832 $1 "Perisama pitheas" . . . . 1·25 1·25
833 $2 "Batesia hypochlora" . . . 1·75 1·75
834 $3 "Heliconius erato" . . . . 2·25 2·25
835 $4 "Elzunia cassandrina" . . . 2·50 2·50
836 $5 "Sais ivcidice" . . . . . . 2·50 2·50

See also Nos. 851/62.

79b "Entoloma bakeri"

1992. Fungi. Multicoloured

838 10 c. Type **79b** 50 50
839 15 c. "Hydropus paraensis" . . 55 55
840 20 c. "Leucopaxillus gracillimus" 60 60
841 45c. "Hygrotrama dennisianum" 80 80
842 50 c. "Leucoagaricus hortensis" 80 80
843 65 c. "Pyrrhoglossum pyrrhum" 1·00 1·00
844 75 c. "Amanita craeoderma" . 1·00 1·00
845 $1 "Lentinus bertieri" . . . 1·25 1·25
846 $2 "Dennisiomyces griseus" . 2·00 2·00
847 $3 "Xerulina asprata" . . . 2·50 2·50
848 $4 "Hygrocybe acutoconica" . 3·00 3·00
849 $5 "Lepiota spiculata" . . . . 3·00 3·00

1992. "Genova '92" International Thematic Stamp Exhibition (2nd issue). Hummingbirds. As T **370a** of Grenada. Multicoloured.

851 5 c. Antillean crested hummingbird (female) (horiz) 30 30
852 10 c. Blue-tailed emerald (female) 30 30
853 35 c. Antillean mango (male) (horiz) 45 45
854 45 c. Antillean mango (female) (horiz) 45 45
855 55 c. Green-throated carib (horiz) 55 55
856 65 c. Green violetear (male) . . 70 70
857 75 c. Blue-tailed emerald (male) (horiz) 80 80
858 $1 Purple-throated carib . . . 1·00 1·00
859 $2 Copper-rumped hummingbird (horiz) . . . . 2·00 2·00
860 $3 Rufous-breasted hermit . . 2·75 2·75
861 $4 Antillean crested hummingbird (male) . . . . 3·50 3·50
862 $5 Green-breasted mango (male) 3·75 3·75

1992. 500th Anniv of Discovery of America by Columbus (3rd issue). Organization of East Caribbean States. As T **372a** of Grenada. Multicoloured.

864 $1 Columbus meeting Amerindians 75 75
865 $2 Ships approaching island . . 1·75 2·25

1992. Olympic Games, Albertville and Barcelona. As T **372** of Grenada. Multicoloured.

866 10 c. Men's volleyball 40 40
867 15 c. Men's gymnastics (horiz) 50 50
868 25 c. Men's cross-country skiing 60 60
869 30 c. Men's 110 metres hurdles (horiz) 60 60
870 45 c. Men's 120 metre ski-jumping (horiz) 70 70
871 55 c. Women's 4 × 100 metre relay 80 80
872 75 c. Men's triple jump . . . . 1·00 1·00
873 80 c. Men's mogul skiing . . . 1·00 1·00
874 $1 Men's 110 metre butterfly swimming (horiz) . . . . . 1·25 1·25
875 $2 "Tornado" Class yachting (horiz) . . . . 1·75 1·75
876 $3 Men's decathlon (horiz) . . 1·90 1·90
877 $5 Show jumping (horiz) . . . 2·75 2·75

1992. Christmas. Religious Paintings. As T **207b** of Gambia. Multicoloured.

879 10 c. "Our Lady with St. Roch and St. Anthony of Padua" (Giorgione) 30 30
880 40 c. "Anthony of Padua" (Master of the Embroidered Leaf) 55 55
881 45 c. "Madonna and Child" (detail) (Orazio Gentileschi) . 60 60
882 50 c. "Madonna and Child with St. Anne (detail) (Da Vinci) . 65 65
883 55 c. "The Holy Family" (Crespi) 70 70
884 65 c. "Madonna and Child" (Del Sarto) 80 80
885 75 c. "Madonna and Child with Sts. Lawrence and Julian" (Gentile da Fabriano) . . . 90 90
886 $1 "Virgin and Child" (detail) (School of Parma) . . . . 1·10 1·10
887 $2 "Madonna with the Iris" (detail) (style of Durer) . . 1·75 1·75
888 $3 "Virgin and Child with St. Jerome and St. Dominic" (Lippi) . . . . 2·25 2·25
889 $4 "Rapolano Madonna" (Ambrogio Lorenzetti) . . . 2·75 2·75
890 $5 "The Virgin and Child with Angels in a Garden with a Rose Hedge" (Stefano da Verona) . . . . 2·75 2·75

80 "Nina" in Baracoa Harbour

1992. Anniversaries and Events. Multicoloured.

892 10 c. Type **80** 70 70
893 75 c. Airship LZ-3 . . . . . . 1·75 1·75
894 75 c. Blind man with guide dog 1·75 1·75
895 75 c. Training guide dog . . . 1·75 1·75
896 $1 Ships of Columbus . . . . 1·75 1·75
897 $1 Adenauer, state arms and German flag . . . . 1·75 1·75
898 $1 "America III" and "Il Moro" (yachts) with trophy . . . 1·75 1·75
899 $1 Hands breaking bread and emblem (vert) . . . . . . 1·50 1·50
900 $2 "Voyager 2" and planet . . 2·75 2·50
901 $3 Adenauer and children watching Berlin Airlift . . . 2·50 2·50
902 $4 Airship LZ-37 in flames . . 2·75 3·00
903 $4 Adenauer and ruins in Cologne . . . . 2·75 3·00
904 $4 Mozart with his wife Constanze (vert) . . . . . . 3·00 3·00
905 $5 Adenauer and modern office blocks . . . . 2·75 3·00

ANNIVERSARIES AND EVENTS: Nos. 892, 896, 500th anniv of discovery of America by Columbus; Nos. 893, 902, 75th death anniv of Count Ferdinand von Zeppelin (airship pioneer); Nos. 894/5, 75th anniv of International Association of Lions Clubs; Nos. 897, 901, 903, 905, 25th death anniv of Konrad Adenauer (German statesman); No. 898, Americas Cup yachting championship; No. 899, International Conference on Nutrition, Rome; No. 900, International Space Year; No. 904, Death bicentenary of Mozart.

81 Olivia and Flaversham

1992. Walt Disney Cartoon Films.

907/50 60 c. × 44 mult
Set of 44 . . . . 19·00 21·00

Nos. 907/50 were printed as five se-tenant sheetlets, each of nine different designs except for that for "Darkwing Duck" which contains eight vertical designs (Nos. 943/50). The other four sheetlets depict scenes from "The Great Mouse Detective", "Oliver and Company", "The Legend of Sleepy Hollow" and "Ducktales the Movie".

1992. 15th Death Anniv of Elvis Presley (singer). As T **260** of Dominica. Mult.

952 $1 Elvis Presley . . . . 2·50 2·25
953 $1 Elvis with guitar . . . . . 2·50 2·25
954 $1 Elvis with microphone . . . 2·50 2·25

82 Prince Mickey searching for Bride

1992. "Tales of Uncle Scrooge" (fairy stories). Walt Disney cartoon characters.

955/1008 60 c. × 54 mult
Set of 54 . . . . 21·00 22·00

Nos. 955/1008 (issued as six sheetlets each of nine different designs) depict scenes from "The Princess and the Pea", "Little Red Riding Hood", "Goldilocks and the Three Bears", "The Pied Piper of Hamelin", "Hop O'-My-Thumb" and "Puss in Boots".

83 Oleander

1994. Medicinal Plants. Multicoloured.

1010 5 c. Type **83** 20 30
1011 10 c. Beach morning glory . . 30 20
1012 30 c. Calabash 40 30
1013 45 c. Portia tree 50 30
1014 55 c. Cashew 60 40
1015 75 c. Prickly pear 70 70
1016 $1 Shell ginger 80 80
1017 $1.50 Avocado pear . . . . . 1·40 1·60
1018 $2 Mango . . . . 1·75 2·00
1019 $3 Blood flower . . . . . . 2·25 2·50
1020 $4 Sugar apple . . . . 2·50 2·75
1021 $5 Barbados lily . . . . . . 2·50 2·75

OFFICIAL STAMPS

1982. Nos. 195/200 optd **OFFICIAL**.

O1 50 c. "Mary" 10 15
O2 50 c. Prince Charles and Lady Diana Spencer 30 35
O3 $3 "Alexandra" 20 20
O4 $3 Prince Charles and Lady Diana Spencer 65 70
O5 $3.50 "Britannia" 20 20
O6 $3.50 Prince Charles and Lady Diana Spencer 65 70

APPENDIX

The following stamps have either been issued in excess of postal needs, or have not been made available to the public in reasonable quantities at face value.

BEQUIA

1984.

Leaders of the World. Railway Locomotives (1st series). Two designs for each value, the first showing technical drawings and the second the locomotive at work. 1, 5, 10, 25, 35, 45 c, $1.50, $2, each × 2.

Grenadines of St. Vincent 1982 Ships definitives (Nos. 208/24) optd **BEQUIA**. 1, 3, 5, 6, 10, 15, 20, 25, 30, 50, 60, 75c., $1, $2, $3, $5, $10.

Leaders of the World. Automobiles (1st series). Two designs for each value, the first showing technical drawings and the second the car in action. 5, 40 c., $1, $1.50, each × 2.

Leaders of the World. Olympic Games, Los Angeles. 1, 10, 60 c., $3, each × 2.

Leaders of the World. Railway Locomotives (2nd series). Two designs for each value, the first showing technical drawings and the second the locomotive at work. 1, 10, 20, 25, 75 c., $1, $2.50, $3, each × 2.

Leaders of the World. Automobiles (2nd series). Two designs for each value, the first showing technical drawings and the second the car in action. 5, 10, 20, 25, 75 c., $1.50, $3, each × 2.

1985.

Leaders of the World. Railway Locomotives (3rd series). Two designs for each value, the first showing technical drawings and the second the locomotive at work. 25, 55, 60c., $2, each × 2.

Leaders of the World. Dogs. 25, 35, 55 c., $2, each × 2.

Leaders of the World. Warships of the Second World War. Two designs for each value, the first showing technical drawings and the second the ship at sea. 15, 50 c., $1, $1.50, each × 2.

Leaders of the World. Flowers. 10, 20, 70 c., $2.50, each × 2.

Leaders of the World. Automobiles (3rd series). Two designs for each value, the first showing technical drawings and the second the car in action. 5, 25, 50 c., $1, $1.25, $2, each × 2.

Leaders of the World. Railway Locomotives (4th series). Two designs for each value, the first showing technical drawings and the second the locomotive at work. 25, 55, 60, 75 c., $1, $2.50, each × 2.

Leaders of the World. Life and Times of Queen Elizabeth the Queen Mother. Two designs for each value showing different portraits. 20, 65 c., $1.35, $1.80, each × 2.

Leaders of the World. Automobiles (4th series). Two designs for each value, the first showing technical drawings and the second the car in action. 10, 35, 75 c., $1.15, $1.50, $2, each × 2.

1986.

Leaders of the World. Automobiles (5th series). Two designs for each value, the first showing technical drawings and the second the car in action. 25, 50, 65, 75c., $1, $3, each × 2.

60th Birthday of Queen Elizabeth II. 5, 75 c., $2, $8.

World Cup Football Championship, Mexico. 1, 2, 5, 10, 45, 60, 75 c., $1.50, $1.50, $2, $3.50, $6.

Royal Wedding (1st issue). 60 c., $2, each × 2.

Railway Engineers and Locomotives. $1, $2.50, $3, $4.

Royal Wedding (2nd issue). Previous issue optd "**Congratulations T.R.H. The Duke & Duchess of York**". 60 c., $2, each × 2.

Automobiles (6th series). Two designs for each value, the first showing technical drawings and the second the car in action. 20, 60, 75, 90 c., $1, $3, each × 2.

1987.

Automobiles (7th series). Two designs for each value, the first showing technical drawings and the second the car in action. 5, 20, 35, 60, 75, 80 c., $1.25, $1.75, each × 2.

Royal Ruby Wedding. 15, 75 c., $1, $2.50, $5.

Railway Locomotives (5th series). Two designs for each value, the first showing technical drawings and the second the locomotive at work. 15, 25, 40, 50, 60, 75 c., $1, $2, each × 2.

1988.

Explorers. 15, 50 c., $1.75, $2, $2.50, $3, $3.50, $4.

International Lawn Tennis Players. 15, 45, 80 c., $1.25, $1.75, $2, $2.50, $3.

1989.

"Philexfrance '89" International Stamp Exhibition, Paris. Walt Disney Cartoon Characters. 1, 2, 3, 4, 5, 10 c., $5, $6.

1991.

Centenary of Otto Lilienthal's Gliding Experiments. $5.

50th Anniv of Japanese Attack on Pearl Harbor. 50 c., $1.

Death Anniv of Mozart. 10, 75 c., $4.

50th Death Anniv of Lord Baden-Powell and World Jamboree, Korea. 50 c., $1, $2, $3.

1997.

Diana, Princess of Wales Commemoration. $1.

CANOUAN

1997.

Diana, Princess of Wales Commemoration. $1.

MUSTIQUE

1997.

Diana, Princess of Wales Commemoration. $1.

UNION ISLAND

1984.

Leaders of the World. British Monarchs. Two designs for each value forming a composite picture. 1, 5, 10, 20, 60 c., $3, each × 2.

Leaders of the World. Railway Locomotives (1st series). Two designs for each value, the first showing technical drawings and the second the locomotive at work. 5, 60 c., $1, $2.

Grenadines of St. Vincent 1982 Ships definitives (Nos. 208/24) optd **UNION ISLAND**. 1, 3, 5, 6, 10, 15, 20, 25, 30, 50, 60, 75 c., $1, $2, $3, $5, $10.

Leaders of the World. Cricketers. Two designs for each value, the first showing a portrait and the second the cricketer in action. 1, 10, 15, 55, 60, 75 c., $1.50, $3, each × 2.

Leaders of the World. Railway Locomotives (2nd series). Two designs for each value, the first showing technical drawings and the second the locomotive at work. 5, 10, 20, 25, 75 c., $1, $2.50, $3, each × 2.

1985.

Leaders of the World. Automobiles (1st series). Two designs for each value, the first showing technical drawings and the second the car in action. 1, 50, 75 c., $2.50, each × 2.

Leaders of the World. Birth Bicentenary of John J. Audubon (ornithologist). Birds. 15, 50 c., $1.50, each × 2.

Leaders of the World. Railway Locomotives (3rd series). Two designs for each value, the first showing technical drawings and the second the locomotive at work. 5, 50, 60 c., $2, each × 2.

Leaders of the World. Butterflies. 15, 25, 75 c., $2, each × 2.

Leaders of the World. Automobiles (2nd series). Two designs for each value, the first showing technical drawings and the second the car in action. 5, 60 c., $1, $1.50, each × 2.

Leaders of the World. Automobiles (3rd series). Two designs for each value, the first showing technical drawings and the second the car in action. 10, 55, 60, 75, 90 c., $1, $1.50, $2, each × 2.

Leaders of the World. Life and Times of Queen Elizabeth the Queen Mother. Two designs for each value showing different portraits. 55, 70 c., $1.05, $1.70, each × 2.

1986.

Leaders of the World. Railway Locomotives (4th series). Two designs for each value, the first showing technical drawings and the second the locomotive at work. 15, 30, 45, 60, 75 c., $1.50, $2.50, $3, each × 2.

60th Birthday of Queen Elizabeth II. 10, 60 c., $2, $8.

World Cup Football Championship, Mexico. 1, 10, 30, 75 c., $1, $2.50, $3, $6.

Royal Wedding (1st issue). 60 c., $2, each × 2.

Automobiles (4th series). Two designs for each value, the first showing technical drawings and the second the car in action. 10, 60, 75 c., $1, $1.50, $3, each × 2.

Royal Wedding (2nd issue). Previous issue optd as Bequia. 60 c., $2, each × 2.

Railway Locomotive (5th series). Two designs for each value, the first showing technical drawings and the second the locomotive at work. 15, 45, 60, 75 c., $1, $2, $3, each × 2.

1987.

Railway Locomotives (6th series). Two designs for each value, the first showing technical drawings and the second the locomotives at work. 15, 25, 40, 50, 60, 75 c., $1, $2, each × 2.

Royal Ruby Wedding. 15, 45 c., $1.50, $3, $4.

Railway Locomotives (7th series). Two designs for each value, the first showing technical drawings and the second the locomotive at work. 15, 20, 30, 45, 50, 75 c., $1, $1.50, each × 2.

1989.

"Philexfrance 89" International Stamp Exhibition, Paris. Walt Disney Cartoon Characters. 1, 2, 3, 4, 5, 10 c., $5, $6.

1997.

Diana, Princess of Wales Commemoration. $1.

GRIQUALAND WEST Pt. 1

A British colony, later annexed to the Cape of Good Hope and now part of South Africa, whose stamps it uses.

12 pence = 1 shilling;
20 shillings = 1 pound

1874. Stamp of Cape of Good Hope ("Hope" seated) with pen-and-ink surch.

1	4	1d. on 4d. blue	£750	£1300

1877. Stamps of Cape of Good Hope ("Hope" seated) optd **G. W.**

2	6	1d. red	£425	75·00
3		4d. blue	£325	65·00

1877. Stamps of Cape of Good Hope ("Hope" seated) optd **G.**

14	6	½d. grey	5·00	7·00
16		1d. red	6·50	4·50
6a	4	4d. blue	£150	26·00
26	6	4d. blue	20·00	3·50
27	4	6d. violet	95·00	6·00
28		1s. green	80·00	3·50
29	6	5s. orange	£300	6·00

GUADELOUPE Pt. 6

An overseas department of France, formerly a Fr. colony in the W. Indies, consisting of a group of islands between Antigua and Dominica. Now uses the stamps of France.

100 centimes = 1 franc.

1884. French Colonies, "Peace and Commerce" type, surch **G. P. E.** and new value in frame.

6	H	20 on 30 c. brown	38·00	30·00
7		25 on 35 c. black on orange	35·00	30·00

1889. French Colonies, "Commerce" type, surch **GUADELOUPE** and value in figures and words in plain frame.

8	J	3 c. on 20 c. red on green	2·25	2·25
9		15 c. on 20 c. red on green	19·00	17·00
10		25 c. on 20 c. red on green	18·00	17·00

1889. French Colonies, "Commerce" type, surch **GUADELOUPE** and value in figures and words in ornamental frame.

11	J	5 c. on 1 c. black on blue	7·50	7·25
12		10 c. on 40 c. red on yellow	19·00	17·00
13		15 c. on 20 c. red on green	18·00	13·50
14		25 c. on 30 c. brown on drab	27·00	23·00

1890. French Colonies, "Commerce" type, surch **5 C. GPE.**

15	J	5 c. on 10 c. black on lilac	8·25	6·75
16		5 c. on 1 f. olive on green	8·75	6·75

1891. French Colonies, "Ceres" and "Commerce" types, optd **GUADELOUPE**.

21	J	1 c. black on blue	75	75
22		2 c. brown on buff	1·25	80
23		4 c. brown on grey	2·75	2·50
24		5 c. green on light green	3·75	3·50
25		10 c. black on lilac	8·00	6·75
26		15 c. blue on light blue	20·00	2·25
27		20 c. red on green	23·00	16·00
28		25 c. black on pink	22·50	2·50
19	F	30 c. brown	£225	£225
29	J	30 c. brown on drab	24·00	19·00
30		35 c. black on orange	48·00	40·00
31		40 c. red on yellow	29·00	26·00
32		75 c. red on pink	90·00	80·00
20	F	80 c. red	£550	£550
33	J	1 f. green	50·00	48·00

1892. "Tablet" key-type inscr "GUADELOUPE ET DEPENDANCES" in red (1, 5, 15, 25, 50 (No. 52), 75 c., 1 f.) or blue (others).

34	D	1 c. black on blue	75	65
36		2 c. brown on buff	65	60
37		4 c. brown on grey	65	70
38		5 c. green on light green	1·75	50
39		10 c. black on lilac	6·25	1·60
49		10 c. red	3·75	1·25
40		15 c. blue	5·75	45
50		15 c. grey	5·50	80
41		20 c. red on green	4·50	2·00
42		25 c. black on pink	4·75	75
51		25 c. blue	65·00	60·00
43		30 c. brown on drab	11·50	7·25
44		40 c. red on yellow	11·50	6·25
45		50 c. red on pink	21·00	10·00
52		50 c. brown on blue	24·00	17·00
46		75 c. brown on yellow	16·00	12·50
47		1 f. green	22·00	20·00

1903. "Tablet" key-type surch **G & D** (5, 15 c., 1 f.) or **G et D** (10, 40 c.) and new value.

53b	D	5 on 30 c. brown on buff	2·50	2·25
54b		10 on 40 c. red on yellow	3·50	3·75
55		15 on 50 c. red	4·75	4·75
56		40 on 1 f. green	5·75	5·75
57		1 f. on 75 c. brown on yellow	23·00	23·00

1904. Nos. 56/7 further optd **1903** in frame.

59c	D	40 on 1 f. green	23·00	25·00
60		1 f. on 75 c. brown on yell	40·00	40·00

49 Mt. Houllemont, Basse-Terre

50 La Soufriere

51 Pointe-a-Pitre, Grande Terre

1905.

61	49	1 c. black on blue	10	10
62		2 c. brown on yellow	15	15
63		4 c. brown on grey	20	20
64		5 c. green	60	25
83		5 c. blue	15	20
65		10 c. red	60	15
84		10 c. green	30	35
85		10 c. red on blue	15	25
66		15 c. lilac	25	15
67	50	20 c. red on green	15	15
86		20 c. green	15	25
68		25 c. blue	25	25
87		25 c. green	15	15
69		30 c. black	2·25	1·75
88		30 c. red	25	30
89		30 c. olive on lilac	25	30
70		35 c. black on yellow	30	25
71		40 c. red on yellow	40	50
72		45 c. brown on lilac	35	40
90		45 c. red	40	55
73		50 c. green on yellow	3·00	1·50
91		50 c. blue	45	60
92		50 c. mauve	30	25
93		65 c. blue	45	55
74		75 c. red on blue	50	45
75	51	1 f. black on green	80	85
94		1 f. blue	60	75
76		2 f. red on orange	90	90
77		5 f. blue on orange	3·75	4·25

1912. Nos. 37 and 43/4 surch in figures.

78	D	05 on 4 c. brown on grey	25	45
79		05 on 30 c. brown on drab	40	60
80		10 on 40 c. red on yellow	70	1·00

1915. Surch **5c** and red cross.

81	49	10 c. + 5 c. red	2·00	1·75
82		15 c. + 5 c. lilac	1·25	1·75

1924. Surch in figures and bars.

95	51	25 c. on 5 f. blue on orange	35	45
96		65 on 1 f. green	60	60
97		85 on 1 f. green	60	65
98	50	90 c. on 75 c. red	60	60
99	51	1 f. 05 on 2 f. red	30	45
100		1 f. 25 on 1 f. blue	15	30
101		1 f. 50 on 1 f. blue	45	60
102		3 f. on 5 f. brown	55	70
103		10 f. on 5 f. red on yellow	5·25	5·75
104		20 f. on 5 f. mauve on red	6·00	6·50

53 Sugar Refinery

54 Saints Harbour

55 Pointe-a-Pitre Harbour

1928.

105	53	1 c. mauve and yellow	10	25
106		2 c. red and black	10	20
107		3 c. mauve and yellow	10	25
108		4 c. brown and green	10	25
109		5 c. green and red	15	20
110		10 c. blue and brown	15	25
111		15 c. black and red	15	25
112		20 c. brown and mauve	15	20
113	54	25 c. olive and blue	15	15
114		30 c. green & deep green	15	15
115		35 c. green	30	40
116		40 c. mauve and yellow	20	20
117		45 c. grey and purple	40	50
118		45 c. deep green & green	50	65
119		50 c. red and green	20	20
120		55 c. red and blue	40	50
121		60 c. red and blue	35	50
122		65 c. red and black	20	30
123		70 c. red and black	25	35
124		75 c. green and red	30	35
125		80 c. brown and red	30	45
126	54	90 c. red	85	1·25
127		90 c. blue and red	50	60
128	55	1 f. blue and red	2·75	1·75
129		1 f. orange and red	75	75
130		1 f. brown and blue	30	45
131		1 f. 05 red and blue	70	80
132		1 f. 10 green and orange	1·75	1·90
133		1 f. 25 brown and blue	35	50
134		1 f. 25 orange and red	45	60
135		1 f. 40 mauve and blue	45	60
136		1 f. 50 light blue & blue	20	25
137		1 f. 60 orange & mauve	40	60
138		1 f. 75 brown and mauve	2·25	1·75
139		1 f. 75 blue	3·50	3·00
140		2 f. brown and green	25	25
141		2 f. 25 blue	45	55
142		2 f. 50 green and orange	60	75
143		3 f. black and brown	25	30
144		5 f. red and blue	40	40
145		10 f. brown and mauve	50	60
146		20 f. red and green	65	65

1931. "Colonial Exhibition" key-types inscr "GUADELOUPE".

147	E	40 c. black and green	1·50	1·60
148	F	50 c. black and mauve	1·60	1·75
149	G	90 c. black and red	3·25	3·50
150	H	1 f. 50 black and blue	2·50	2·50

57 Richelieu founding W. India Co., 1635

58 Victor Hughes and Corsairs 1793

1935. West Indies Tercentenary.

151	57	40 c. brown	5·25	5·50
152		50 c. red	5·25	5·00
153		1 f. 50 blue	5·25	5·00
154	58	1 f. 75 mauve	5·25	5·00
155		5 f. brown	5·25	5·25
156		10 f. green	5·25	5·25

58a Sailing Ships

1937. International Exhibition, Paris.

157	–	20 c. violet	65	70
158	58a	30 c. green	65	65
159	–	40 c. red	95	1·00
160	–	50 c. brown	95	1·00
161	–	90 c. red	95	1·00
162	–	1 f. 50 blue	95	1·00

DESIGNS—VERT: 20 c. Allegory of Commerce; 50 c. Allegory of Agriculture. HORIZ: 40 c. Berber Negress and Annamite; 90 c. France with torch of Civilization; 1 f. 50, Diane de Poitiers.

58b Pierre and Marie Curie

1938. International Anti-Cancer Fund.

163	58b	1 f. 75 + 50 c. blue	5·25	6·75

58c

1939. New York World's Fair.

164	58c	1 f. 25 red	60	60
165		2 f. 25 blue	60	60

58d Storming the Bastille

1939. 150th Anniv of French Revolution.

166	58d	45 c. + 25 c. green & black	4·75	4·75
167		70 c. + 30 c. brown & black	5·00	5·00
168		90 c. + 35 c. orange & blk	5·00	5·00
169		1 f. 25 + 1 f. red & black	5·00	5·00
170		2 f. 25 + 2 f. blue & black	5·00	5·00

1944. Surch **Un franc** (No. 177) or in figures (others).

(a) On Nos. 164/5.

178		40 c. on 1 f. 25 red	45	40
179		40 c. on 2 f. 25 blue	90	80

(b) On Issue of 1928.

172	54	40 c. on 35 c. green	40	45
173		50 c. on 25 c. olive & blue	20	30
174		50 c. on 65 c. red & black	60	60
175		1 f. on 90 c. red	85	90
176		1 f. on 90 c. blue and red	55	55
177		1 f. on 65 c. red & black	60	55

(c) On No. 99.

171	51	4 f. on 1 f. 05 on 2 f. red	1·25	1·10

58e

58f Felix Eboue

1944. Mutual Aid and Red Cross Funds.

180	58e	5 f. + 20 f. blue	60	70

1945.

181	58f	2 f. black	25	30
182		25 f. green	65	70

63

1945.

183	63	10 c. blue and orange	15	30
184		30 c. green and orange	15	30
185		40 c. blue and red	35	35
186		50 c. orange and green	15	20
187		60 c. grey and blue	15	30
188		70 c. grey and green	35	45
189		80 c. green and yellow	40	40
190		1 f. purple and green	20	20
191		1 f. 20 mauve and green	20	25
192		1 f. 50 brown and red	35	25
193		2 f. red and blue	35	35
194		2 f. 40 red and green	70	80
195		3 f. brown and blue	25	25
196		4 f. blue and orange	20	20
197		4 f. 50 orange and green	25	15
198		5 f. violet and green	30	25
199		10 f. green and mauve	30	25
200		15 f. grey and orange	60	50
201		20 f. grey and orange	1·00	75

63a Fairey FC-1

1945. Air.

202	63a	50 f. green	65	65
203		100 f. red	90	90

63b "Victory"

1946. Air. Victory.

204	63b	8 f. brown	65	75

63c Chad

1946. Air. From Chad to the Rhine.

205	63c	5 f. olive	85	95
206	–	10 f. blue	85	95
207	–	15 f. purple	85	85
208	–	20 f. red	90	95
209	–	25 f. black	85	85
210	–	50 f. brown	85	85

DESIGNS: 10 f. Koufra; 15 f. Mareth; 20 f. Normandy; 25 f. Paris; 50 f. Strasbourg.

64 Woman and Port Basse Terre

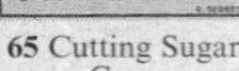
65 Cutting Sugar Cane

66 Guadeloupe Woman

67 Sud Ouest Bretagne over Guadeloupe, Woman and Fishing Boats

1947.

211	64	10 c. lake (postage)	15	25
212		30 c. brown	15	25
213		50 c. green	15	30
214	65	60 c. brown	15	25
215		1 f. red	25	40
216		1 f. 50 blue	55	55
217	–	2 f. green	65	70
218	–	2 f. 50 red	65	65
219	–	3 f. blue	70	75
220	–	4 f. violet	70	75
221	–	5 f. green	70	75
222	–	6 f. red	70	75
223	–	10 f. blue	70	75
224	–	15 f. purple	1·10	1·00
225	–	20 f. red	1·40	1·25
226	66	25 f. green	2·00	1·75
227		40 f. orange	2·25	1·75
228	–	50 f. purple (air)	4·00	3·25
229	–	100 f. blue	4·50	3·50
230	67	200 f. red	7·50	4·75

DESIGNS—As Type **66**: 2 f. to 3 f. Women carrying pineapples; 4 f. to 6 f. Woman in kerchief facing left; 10 f. to 20 f. Picking coffee. As Type **67**: 50 f. Latecoere 631 flying boat over village; 100 f. Short Hythe flying boat landing in bay.

POSTAGE DUE STAMPS.

D 1

D 3

1876.

D1	D 1	15 c. black on blue	25·00	20·00
D2		25 c. black on white	£575	£500
D3		30 c. black on white	60·00	40·00
D4		40 c. black on blue	—	£18000
D5		40 c. black on white	£575	£575

1884. Imperf.

D 8	D 3	5 c. black on white	13·50	13·50
D 9		10 c. black on blue	35·00	20·00
D10		15 c. black on lilac	60·00	38·00
D11		20 c. black on red	90·00	60·00
D12		30 c. black on yellow	85·00	80·00
D13		35 c. black on grey	26·00	23·00
D14		50 c. black on green	13·00	11·50

1903. Postage Due stamps of French Colonies surch **G & D 30** in frame.

D59b	U	30 on 60 c. brn on buff	£150	£150
D61c		30 on 1 f. red on yellow	£200	£200

D 48 Gustavia Bay, Island of St Bartholomew — D 56 Allee Dumanoir, Capesterre — D 68 Palms and Houses

1905.

D63	D 48	5 c. blue	15	20
D64		10 c. brown	20	20
D65		15 c. green	20	40
D66		20 c. brown on yellow	35	40
D67		30 c. red	30	45
D68		50 c. black	1·00	1·75
D69		60 c. orange	70	85
D70		1 f. lilac	1·75	1·90

1926. Surch in figures and words and **a percevoir**.

D105	D 48	2 f. on 1 f. grey	90	1·00
D106		3 f. on 1 f. blue	1·25	1·40

1928.

D147	D 56	2 c. mauve & brown	15	25
D148		4 c. brown and blue	15	25
D149		5 c. brown and green	15	25
D150		10 c. yellow & mauve	15	25
D151		15 c. olive and red	15	30
D152		20 c. olive and orange	15	30
D153		25 c. green and red	25	35
D154	D 56	30 c. yellow and blue	25	35
D155		50 c. red and brown	30	45
D156		60 c. black and blue	50	60
D157		1 f. red and green	1·00	1·75
D158		2 f. red and brown	1·00	1·25
D159		3 f. blue and mauve	55	60

1947.

D231	D 68	10 c. black	15	25
D232		30 c. green	15	25
D233		50 c. blue	15	30
D234		1 f. green	20	30
D235		2 f. blue	40	30
D236		3 f. brown	55	60
D237		4 f. purple	65	70
D238		5 f. violet	85	90
D239		10 f. red	1·00	1·25
D240		20 f. purple	1·25	1·40

GUAM — Pt. 22

An island in the Pacific Ocean belonging to the United States. Now uses U.S. stamps.

100 cents = 1 dollar.

1899. Stamps of United States optd **GUAM**.

1	1 c. green (No. 283)	16·00	20·00
2	2 c. red (No. 270)	14·00	20·00
3	3 c. violet (No. 271)	£100	£140
5	4 c. brown (No. 285)	£110	£140
6	5 c. blue (No. 286)	23·00	35·00
7	6 c. purple (No. 287a)	£100	£150
8	8 c. brown (No. 275)	95·00	£140
9	10 c. brown (No. 289)	35·00	45·00
11	15 c. green (No. 290)	£120	£130
12	50 c. orange (No. 278)	£225	£275
13	$1 black (No. 279)	£275	£300

SPECIAL DELIVERY STAMP

1899. Special Delivery stamp of United States optd **GUAM**.

E15	E 46	10 c. blue (No. E283)	£120	£150

GUANACASTE — Pt. 15

A province of Costa Rica whose stamps it now uses.

100 centavos = 1 peso.

Stamps of Costa Rica optd.

1885. Stamps of 1883 optd **Guanacaste** or **GUANACASTE**.

G 1	8	1 c. green	2·00	2·00
G36		2 c. red	2·00	2·00
G 3		5 c. violet	8·00	3·00
G 4		10 c. orange	8·00	8·00
G 5		40 c. blue	15·00	15·00

1887. Stamps of 1887 optd **Guanacaste**.

G37	14	5 c. violet	10·00	4·00
G39		10 c. orange	2·00	2·00

1887. Fiscal stamps optd **Guanacaste** or **GUANACASTE**.

G44	1 c. red	£150	£150
G41	2 c. blue	25·00	25·00

1889. Stamps of 1889 optd **GUANACASTE**.

G62	17	1 c. brown	75	75
G63		2 c. blue	75	75
G64		5 c. orange	75	75
G65		10 c. lake	75	75
G56		20 c. green	80	70
G57		50 c. red	2·00	2·00
G59		1 p. blue	4·00	4·00
G60		2 p. violet	6·00	6·00
G61		5 p. olive	20·00	20·00

GUATEMALA — Pt. 15

A republic of Central America; independent since 1847.

1871. 100 centavos = 8 reales = 1 peso.
1927. 100 centavos de quetzal = 1 quetzal.

1 Arms 2 — 3 Liberty

1871.

1	1	1 c. bistre	50	6·50
2		5 c. brown	3·00	5·00
3		10 c. blue	3·50	5·75
4		20 c. red	2·75	5·00

1873.

5	2	4 r. mauve	£200	5·00
6		1 p. yellow	£100	70·00

1875. Various frames

7	3	$\frac{1}{4}$ r. black	90	2·25
8		$\frac{1}{2}$ r. green	90	2·00
9		1 r. blue	90	2·00
10		2 r. red	90	2·00

4 Native Indian

5 Resplendent Quetzal

1878.

11	4	$\frac{1}{2}$ r. green	50	2·00
12		2 r. red	85	2·75
13		4 r. mauve	85	3·00
14		1 p. yellow	1·40	6·00

1879.

15	5	$\frac{1}{4}$ r. green and brown	6·00	8·00
16		1 r. green and black	9·00	12·00

For similar stamps, but inscr differently, see Nos. 21/25.

1881. Surch.

17	5	1 c. on $\frac{1}{4}$ r. green and brown	11·00	16·00
18	4	5 c. on $\frac{1}{2}$ r. green	3·50	5·00
19	5	10 c. on 1 r. green and black	15·00	22·00
20	4	20 c. on 2 r. red	24·00	27·00

1881. As T **5** inscr "UNION POSTAL UNIVERSAL—GUATEMALA". Centres in green.

21	5	1 c. black	3·50	2·00
22		2 c. brown	3·50	2·00
23		5 c. red	6·50	2·50
24		10 c. lilac	3·25	2·00
25		20 c. yellow	3·25	2·40

7 President J. Rufino Barios

Correos Nacionales
150 c. 150 c.
Guatemala.
150 c. 150 c.
150 Ctavos.
(8)

1886. Railway stamp variously surch as T **8**.

26	7	25 c. on 1 p. red	85	70
27		50 c. on 1 p. red	85	70
28		75 c. on 1 p. red	85	70
29		100 c. on 1 p. red	1·40	1·40
30		150 c. on 1 p. red	1·40	1·25

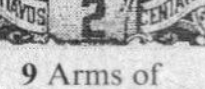
9 Arms of Guatemala

16 Steamship, arms, portrait of Pres. J. M. Reyna Barrios and locomotive in centre. Arms of El Salvador, Honduras, Nicaragua and Costa Rica in corners

1886.

43a	9	1 c. blue	2·75	30
44		2 c. brown	3·75	35
46		5 c. violet	4·50	25
47		6 c. mauve	5·75	40
48		10 c. red	4·75	25
49		20 c. green	11·00	75
50		25 c. orange	35·00	2·75
37		50 c. olive	28·00	7·50
38		75 c. red	20·00	6·00
39		100 c. brown	28·00	14·00
40		150 c. blue	35·00	24·00
41		200 c. yellow	30·00	18·00

See also Nos. 101/9.

1886. Surch **PROVISIONAL. 1886. 1 UN CENTAVO**.

42h	9	1 c. on 2 c. brown	4·25	10·00

1894. Surch **1894**, bar and value.

55	9	1 c. on 2 c. brown	1·75	1·60
51		2 c. on 100 c. brown	9·50	7·50
57		6 c. on 150 c. blue	15·00	8·75
53		10 c. on 75 c. red	13·00	9·50
54		10 c. on 200 c. yellow	9·50	5·75

1895. Surch **1895 1 CENTAVO** and bar.

59	9	1 c. on 5 c. violet	90	60

1897. Central American Exhibition.

62	16	1 c. black on grey	60	45
63		2 c. black on green	60	45
64		6 c. black on orange	60	45
65		10 c. black on blue	60	45
66		12 c. black on red	95	80
67		18 c. black on white	8·50	7·00
68		20 c. black on red	1·40	1·00
69		25 c. black on brown	1·40	1·00
70		50 c. black on brown	1·40	1·00
71		75 c. black on blue	70·00	60·00
72		100 c. black on green	1·40	1·00
73		150 c. black on pink	£120	£100
74		200 c. black on mauve	1·40	1·00
75		500 c. black on green	1·40	1·00

1897. Surch **UN CENTAVO 1898**.

76	16	1 c. on 12 c. black on red	1·10	1·10

1898. Surch **1898**, bar and value.

77	9	1 c. on 5 c. violet	2·75	15
78		1 c. on 25 c. orange	6·25	4·00
79		1 c. on 50 c. olive	5·50	3·25
80		1 c. on 75 c. red	5·50	3·25
81		6 c. on 5 c. violet	6·25	1·00
82		6 c. on 10 c. red	24·00	17·00
83		6 c. on 20 c. green	10·00	6·50
84		6 c. on 100 c. brown	10·00	6·50
85		6 c. on 150 c. blue	10·00	6·50
86		6 c. on 200 c. yellow	10·00	6·50
87		10 c. on 20 c. green	10·00	6·50

20

22

1898. Fiscal stamps as T **20** optd **CORREOS NACIONALES** or surch **2 CENTAVOS** also.

88	20	1 c. blue	1·50	1·50
89		2 c. on 1 c. blue	2·50	2·50

1898. Fiscal stamps dated "1898" as T **22** surch **CORREOS NACIONALES** and value.

90	22	1 c. on 10 c. blue	50	50
91		2 c. on 1 c. red	2·40	1·75
92		2 c. on 5 c. violet	85	70
93		2 c. on 10 c. blue	4·50	4·75
94		2 c. on 25 c. red	5·00	5·50
95		2 c. on 50 c. blue	5·50	6·00
96		6 c. on 1 p. violet	2·75	3·00
97		6 c. on 5 p. blue	5·00	5·00
98		6 c. on 10 p. green	5·00	5·00

1899. Surch **Un 1 Centavo 1899**.

99	9	1 c. on 5 c. violet	80	50

1900. Surch **1900 1 CENTAVO**.

100	9	1 c. on 10 c. red	85	70

1900.

101	9	1 c. green	1·00	30
102		2 c. red	1·00	30
103		5 c. blue	3·75	1·00
104		6 c. green	1·10	30
105		10 c. brown	3·75	40
106		20 c. mauve	11·00	11·00
107		20 c. brown	17·00	24·00
108		25 c. yellow	11·00	11·00
109		25 c. green	17·00	24·00

1901. Surch **1901** and value.

110	9	1 c. on 20 c. green	1·25	85
111		1 c. on 25 c. orange	1·25	85
112		2 c. on 20 c. green	3·50	2·25

1902. Fiscal stamp surch **CORREOS NACIONALES 1902** and value in figures and words.

113	20	1 c. on 1 c. blue	2·40	1·50
114		2 c. on 1 c. blue	2·40	1·25

1902. Fiscal stamp, dated "1898", surch **CORREOS 1902 Seis 6 Cts**.

115	22	6 c. on 25 c. red	40	1·75

30 Arms

31 J. Rufino Barrios Statue

35 Statesmen discussing Independence (after painting by E. Bravo)

47 President Manuel Estrada Cabrera

1902. Inscr "U.P.U. 1902".

116	30	1 c. purple and green	15	15
117	31	2 c. black and red	15	15
118a	–	5 c. black and blue	20	15
119	–	6 c. green and yellow	20	15
120	–	10 c. blue and orange	20	15
121	35	$12\frac{1}{2}$ c. black and blue	15	15
122	–	20 c. black and red	45	20
141	–	25 c. black and blue	55	20
123a	–	50 c. blue and brown	30	15
124	–	75 c. black and lilac	35	20
125	–	1 p. black and brown	45	20
126	–	2 p. black and orange	55	35
142	47	5 p. black and red	70	70

DESIGNS—HORIZ: 5 c. La Reforma Palace; 6 c. Temple of Minerva; 10 c. Lake Amatitlan; 20 c. Cathedral; 25 c. G.P.O.; 50 c. Columbus Theatre; 75 c. Artillery Barracks; 1 p. Columbus Monument; 2 p. Indian Institute.

1903. Surch **1903 25 CENTAVOS**.
127 **9** 25 c. on 1 c. green 2·00 65
128 25 c. on 2 c. red 2·60 65
129 25 c. on 6 c. green 4·00 2·40
130 25 c. on 10 c. brown 17·00 5·25
131 25 c. on 75 c. red 22·00 13·00
132 25 c. on 150 c. blue 22·00 13·00
133 25 c. on 200 c. yellow 25·00 15·00

1908. Surch **1908** and value in figures and words.
134 – 1 c. on 10 c. blue and orange (No. 120) 35 35
135 **35** 2 c. on 12½ c. black & blue 35 35
136 – 6 c. on 20 c. black and red (No. 122) 30 30

1909. Surch **1909** and value in figures and words.
137 2 c. on 75 c. blk & lil (No. 124) 55 55
138 6 c. on 50 c. bl & brn (No. 123) 30 30
139 12½ c. on 2 p. black and orange (No. 126) 45 45

45 M. Garcia Granados

1910. Granados Centenary.
140 **45** 6 c. black and bistre 55 35

1911. Surch **1911 Un Centavo**.
143 **45** 1 c. on 6 c. black & bistre 13·00 5·00

1911. Surch **Correos de Guatemala 1911** and value.
144 2 c. on 5 c. (No. 118a) 1·00 50
145 6 c. on 10 c. (No. 120) 85 85

1912. Surch **1912** and value.
146 1 c. on 20 c. (No. 122) 35 35
147 2 c. on 50 c. (No. 123a) 35 35
148 5 c. on 75 c. (No. 124) 90 90

1913. Surch **1913** and value.
149 1 c. on 50 c. (No. 123a) 30 30
150 6 c. on 1 p. (No. 125) 45 45
151 12½ c. on 2 p. (No. 126) 45 45

1916. Surch with value only.
156 **30** 2 c. on 1 c. purple & grn 30 30
152 6 c. on 1 c. purple & grn 30 30
153 12½ c. on 1 c. pur & grn 30 30
154 **31** 25 c. on 2 c. black & red 20 20

59 Pres. Manuel Estrada Cabrera
60

1917. Re-election of President Cabrera.
155 **59** 25 c. brown and blue 35 20

1918.
157 **60** 1 p. 50 c. blue 90 25

61 Arms
64 Technical School

1919. Buildings and Obligatory Tax G.P.O. Rebuilding Fund (No. 158).
158 **61** 12½ c. red (obligatory tax) 20 15
159 – 30 c. black & red (postage) 4·00 75
160 – 60 c. black and olive 90 45
161 **64** 90 c. black and brown 70 70
169 – 1 p. 50 orange and blue 50 30
162 – 3 p. black and green 1·75 45
170 – 5 p. green and sepia 1·25 40
171 – 15 p. red and black 45·00 17·00
DESIGNS—Dated 1918: 30 c. Radio station; 60 c. Maternity hospital; 3 p. Arms. Dated 1921; 1 p. 50, Monolith at Quirigua; 5 p. Garcia Granados Monument; 15 p. La Penitenciaria railway bridge, Guatemala City.

1920. Nos. 159/60 surch **1920 2 centavos**.
163 2 c. on 30 c. black and red 65 65
164 2 c. on 60 c. black and olive 25 25

1920. No. 126 surch **25 Centavos** and bars.
165 25 c. on 2 p. black and orange 35 30

68

1920. Telegraph stamp as T **68** optd **CORREOS**.
166 **68** 25 c. green 25 15

1921. Surch **1921** and value in words.
167 12½ c. on 20 c. black and red (No. 122) 35 20
168 50 c. on 75 c. black and lilac (No. 124) 45 35

1921. Optd **1921 CORREOS**.
173 **63** 25 c. green 35 20

1921. Surch **1921 CORREOS DOCE Y MEDIO**.
172 **68** 12½ c. on 25 c. green 30 20

1922. Surch **1922** and value in words.
174 – 12½ c. on 20 c. (No. 122) 30 30
175 – 12½ c. on 60 c. (No. 160) 70 70
176 **64** 12½ c. on 90 c. (No. 161) 70 70
179 – 12½ c. on 3 p. (No. 162) 30 25
180 – 12½ c. on 5 p. (No. 170) 70 65
181 – 12½ c. on 15 p. (No. 171) 1·60 1·10
185 – 25 c. on 30 c. (No. 159) 1·40 1·40
186 – 25 c. on 60 c. (No. 160) 1·40 1·40
187 – 25 c. on 75 c. (No. 124) 45 45
188 **64** 25 c. on 90 c. (No. 161) 1·40 1·40
189 – 25 c. on 1 p. (No. 125) 35 35
190 – 25 c. on 1 p. 50 (No. 169) 35 35
191 – 25 c. on 2 p. (No. 126) 55 55
192 – 25 c. on 3 p. (No. 162) 45 45
193 – 25 c. on 5 p. (No. 170) 1·10 1·10
184 – 25 c. on 15 p. (No. 171) 2·00 2·00

80 Independence Centenary Palace
81 National Palace, Antigua

1922.
195 **80** 12½ c. green 20 15
196 **81** 25 c. brown 20 15

82 Columbus Theatre
83 Resplendent Quetzal
84 Garcia Granados Monument

1923.
197 **82** 50 c. red 45 30
198 **83** 1 p. green 90 30
199 **84** 5 p. orange 1·40 55

1924. Surch **1924** and value.
200 – 1 p. on 1 p. 50 (No. 169) 35 30
201 **84** 1 p. 25 on 5 p. orange 55 45

87 Pres. J. R. Barrios
88 Dr. L. Montufar

1924.
202 – 6 c. olive (as No. 119) 20 15
203 **81** 25 c. brown 20 15
204 – 50 c. red (as No. 123a) 20 15
205 – 1 p. brown (as No. 125) 20 15
206 **87** 1 p. 25 blue 50 15
207 – 2 p. orange (as No. 126) 35 25
208 **88** 2 p. 50 purple 55 30
209 – 3 p. green (as No. 162) 2·40 55
210 – 15 p. black (as No. 171) 5·50 3·50
These all have imprint "PERKINS BACON & CO. LD. LONDRES" at foot.

1925. No. 201 further surch with two bars.
211 **84** 1 p. on 5 p. orange 55 45

89 Aurora Park
90 General Post Office

91 National Observatory
92 Proposed new G.P.O

1926. Dated "1926".
212 – 6 c. bistre (as No. 119) 15 15
213 **89** 12½ c. green 15 15
214 **81** 25 c. brown 15 15
215 **90** 50 c. red 20 15
216 – 1 p. brown (as No. 125) 20 20
217 **87** 1 p. 50 blue 20 20
218 **91** 2 p. orange 85 70
219 **88** 2 p. 50 purple 1·75 70
220 – 3 p. green (as No. 162) 55 30
221 – 5 p. lilac (as No. 170) 70 45
222 – 15 p. black (as No. 171) 7·25 3·50
These all have imprint "WATERLOW & SONS LIMITED, LONDRES" at foot.

1927. Obligatory Tax. G.P.O. Rebuilding Fund.
223 **92** 1 c. olive 15 15

1928. Surch **1928** and value.
224 **91** ½ c. de q. on 2 p. orange 70 55
225 – ½ c. de q. on 5 p. lilac (No. 221) 35 30
226 **88** 1 c. de q. on 2 p. 50 purple (No. 219) 35 30

95 Pres. J. R. Barrios
96 Dr. L. Montufar

97 Garcia Granados
98 General Orellana

99 City Arms, Guatemala

1929.
227 **91** ½ c. green 70 15
228 **81** 1 c. sepia 20 15
229 **95** 2 c. blue 20 15
230 **96** 3 c. lilac 20 15
231 **97** 4 c. yellow 20 20
232 **98** 5 c. red 30 15
233 – 10 c. brown (as No. 119) 45 15
234 – 15 c. blue (as No. 125) 55 15
235 **31** 25 c. brown 90 20
236 **89** 30 c. green 1·10 35
237 – 50 c. red (as No. 120) 1·75 45
238 **99** 1 q. black 3·00 55
These all have imprint "T. DE LA RUE & CO. LD. LONDRES" at foot.

1929. Air. Nos. 210 and 222 surch **SERVICIO POSTAL AEREO ANO DE 1928** and new value.
239 3 c. on 15 p. black (222) 2·25 2·25
240 5 c. on 15 p. black (222) 1·00 1·00
240a 5 c. on 15 p. black (210) 4·50 4·50
241 15 c. on 15 p. black (222) 2·75 2·75
242 20 c. on 15 p. black (222) 4·50 4·50

1929. Air. Surch **SERVICIO POSTAL AEREO ANO DE 1929 Q0.03**.
243 **88** Q 0.03 on 2 p. 50 purple (No. 208) 1·00 1·00

1929. Opening of Guatemala–El Salvador Railway. No. 220 surch **FERROCARRIL ORIENTAL 1929** and new value.
244 Q 0·03 on 3 p. green 3·00 3·00
245 Q 0·05 on 3 p. green 3·00 3·00

1930. Opening of Los Altos Railway. No. 222 surch **FERROCARRIL DE LOS ALTOS Inaugurado en 1929** and new value.
246 1 c. on 15 p. black 1·75 2·25
247 2 c. on 15 p. black 1·75 2·25
248 3 c. on 15 p. black 1·75 2·25
249 5 c. on 15 p. black 1·75 2·25
250 15 c. on 15 p. black 1·75 2·25

104 Bridge and Permanent Way

1930. Opening of Los Altos Railway.
251 – 2 c. black and purple 2·00 1·25
252 **104** 3 c. black and red 4·25 3·25
253 – 5 c. blue and orange 4·25 3·25
DESIGNS: 2 c. Quetzaltenango Dam; 5 c. Quetzaltenango railway station.

105 Fokker Super Trimotor over Mt. Agua

1930. Air.
254 **105** 6 c. red 75 55

1930. Air. Surch **SERVICIO AEREO INTERIOR 1930** and value.
255 1 c. on 3 p. green (No. 220) 20 20
256 2 c. on 3 p. green 50 90
257 3 c. on 3 p. green 50 90
258 4 c. on 3 p. green 70 70
259 10 c. on 15 p. black (No. 222) 5·50 3·75

1931. Air. Optd **EXTERIOR - 1931**.
260 **105** 6 c. red 70 70

1931. Air. Optd **AEREO EXTERIOR 1931**.
261 **97** 4 c. yellow 35 30

1931. Air. Optd **AEREO INTERNACIONAL 1931**.
262 – 15 c. blue (No. 234) 1·00 35
263 **89** 30 c. green (No. 236) 1·75 60

1931. Air. Optd **Primer Vuelo Posta BARRIOS-MIAMI 1931**.
264 **95** 2 c. blue 1·75 2·00
265 **96** 3 c. lilac 1·75 2·00
266 – 15 c. blue (No. 234) 1·75 2·00

1932. Air. Surch **SERVICIO AEREO INTERIOR 1932** and value.
267 **87** 2 c. on 1 p. 50 blue (217) 75 60
268 – 3 c. on 3 p. green (220) 70 20
270 – 10 c. on 15 p. blk (222) 19·00 12·50
271 – 15 c. on 15 p. blk (222) 24·00 19·00

114 Monolith of Quirigua
116 Flag of the Race, Columbus and Tecum Uman

1932.
272 **114** 3 c. red 50 15
See also Nos. 416a/b.

1933. Air. Optd **AEREO INTERIOR 1933**.
273 **97** 4 c. yellow 35 20

1933. 441st Anniv of Departure of Columbus from Palos.
274 **116** ½ c. green 35 70
275 1 c. brown 70 85
276 2 c. blue 70 85
277 3 c. mauve 70 50
278 5 c. red 70 70

1934. Air. (a) Optd **AERO EXTERIOR 1934**.
280 **98** 5 c. red 1·75 15
281 – 15 c. blue (No. 234) 1·75 35
(b) Optd **AEREO INTERIOR 1934**.
279 **95** 2 c. blue 55 20

117 Barrios' Birthplace

118 Barrios and "Agamemnon" (freighter)

1935. Birth Centenary of J. R. Barrios.
282 **117** ½ c. pink & grn (postage) 35 40
283 – 1 c. blue and orange 35 40
284 – 2 c. black and orange 35 45
285 – 3 c. blue and red 3·50 2·00
286 – 4 c. red and blue 3·50 9·00
287 – 5 c. brown and green 2·75 3·50
288 – 10 c. red and green 4·00 4·50
289 – 15 c. brown and green 3·50 4·00
290 – 25 c. black and red 3·50 4·00
291 **118** 10 c. blue & brown (air) 4·75 4·00
292 – 15 c. brown and grey 1·40 1·50
293 – 30 c. violet and red 1·40 1·00
DESIGNS—POSTAGE—HORIZ: 1 c. San Lorenzo; 2 c. Barrios and Official Decree; 3 c. Arms and locomotive; 5 c. Telegraph office and Barrios; 10 c. Polytechnic School; 15 c. Police H.Q.; 25 c. Pres. Ubico, arms and Barrios. VERT: 4 c. G.P.O. AIR—HORIZ: Barrios and (15 c.) tomb, (30 c.) statue.

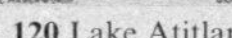

120 Lake Atitlan **121** Resplendent Quetzal

122 Arms and Map of Guatemala

1935.
293a – ½ c. blue and green . . . 15 15
294 **120** 1 c. red and brown . . . 20 15
295 **121** 3 c. green and orange . . 1·10 25
296 3 c. green and red . . . 1·10 25
297 – 4 c. red and blue . . . 45 20
297a **122** 5 c. brown and blue . . . 55 20
DESIGNS—As Type **120**: ½ c. Govt. Printing Works; 4 c. National Assembly.

123 Lake Amatitlan

1935. Air. (a) Inscr "INTERIOR" (37 × 17 mm).
298 **123** 2 c. brown 15 15
299 – 3 c. blue 40 20
300 – 4 c. black 35 10
300a – 4 c. blue 30 10
301 **123** 6 c. green 35 15
301a 6 c. violet . . . . 2·75 10
302 – 10 c. red 35 35
303 – 15 c. orange 45 55
303a – 15 c. green 45 65
304 – 30 c. olive . . . . 4·00 4·50
304a – 30 c. brown 50 35
305 – 50 c. purple . . . . 12·00 10·00
305a – 50 c. blue . . . . 2·75 2·00
306 **123** 1 q. orange . . . . 12·00 13·00
306a 1 q. red . . . . 3·00 2·00
DESIGNS: 3 c. Puerto Barrios; 4 c. San Felipe; 10 c. Livingston; 15 c. San Jose; 30 c. Atitlan; 50 c. La Aurora Airport.

(b) Inscr "EXTERIOR" (34 × 15 mm) (except Nos. 319/20 which are 46 × 20 mm).
307 1 c. brown 10 10
308 2 c. red 20 20
309 3 c. mauve 35 35
309a 4 c. yellow . . . . 1·25 1·00
309b 4 c. red 70 50
310 5 c. blue . . . . 1·75 40
310a 5 c. orange . . . . 1·50 25
311 10 c. brown 35 25
311a 10 c. green 35 25
312 15 c. red 35 10
312a 15 c. orange 30 10
313 20 c. blue . . . . 1·60 2·00
313a 20 c. red 35 25
314 25 c. black . . . . 2·00 2·40
314a 25 c. green 65 35
315 30 c. green . . . . 9·50 6·00
315a 30 c. red . . . . 3·75 30
316 50 c. red . . . . 22·00 19·00
316a 50 c. violet . . . . 17·00 8·75
317 1 q. blue . . . . 15·00 17·00
318 1 q. green . . . . 5·00 5·00
319 2 q. 50 olive and red . . . . 3·50 2·00
320 5 q. blue and orange . . . . 4·75 2·75
DESIGNS: 1 c. Guatemala City; 2 c., 15 c. (No. 312) Views of Central Park; 3 c. Cerrito del Carmen; 4 c. Estuary of R. Dulce; 5 c. Plaza J. R. Barrios; 10 c. National Liberators' Monument; 15 c. (No. 312a) R. Dulce; 20 c. Quezaltenango; 25 c. Antigua; 30 c. Puerto Barrios; 50 c. San Jose; 1 q. Aurora Airport; 2 q. 50, Islet; 5 q. Rocks on Atlantic Coast.

1936. Obligatory Tax. 65th Anniv of Liberal Revolution. Optd **1871 30 DE JUNIO 1936**.
321 **92** 1 c. green 35 35

1936. Obligatory Tax. 115th Anniv of Independence. Optd **1821 15 de SEPTIEMBRE 1936**.
322 **92** 1 c. green 45 25

1936. Obligatory Tax. National Fair. Optd **FERIA NACIONAL 1936**.
323 **92** 1 c. olive 55 55

1937. Philatelic Exhibition Fund. Optd **EXPOSICION FILATELICA 1937** or surch **+ 1** also.
325 **120** 1 c. + 1 c. red & brown . . 90 70
326 **121** 3 c. + 1 c. green & orge . . 90 70
327 3 c. + 1 c. green & red . . 90 70
329 – 4 c. + 1 c. (No. 300a) . . 75 75
328 **122** 5 c. + 1 c. brown & blue . . 90 70
330 – 6 c. + 1 c. (No. 301a) . . 75 75
331 – 10 c. + 1 c. (No. 311a) . . 75 75
332 – 15 c. + 1 c. (No. 312a) . . 75 75
324 **92** 1 c. olive 40 40

128 Resplendent Quetzal **129** General Ubico on horseback

130 Quezaltenango

1937. Second Term of Pres. Ubico. (a) Postage.
333 **128** ½ c. red and blue 80 50
334 – 1 c. brown and grey . . . 45 45
335 – 2 c. red and violet . . . 45 45
336 – 3 c. blue and purple . . . 35 35
337 – 4 c. olive and yellow . . . 1·40 1·25
338 – 5 c. purple and red . . . 1·40 1·25
339 – 10 c. black and purple . . 2·00 2·40
340 – 15 c. red and blue . . . 1·60 2·40
341 – 25 c. violet and orange . . 2·00 2·50
342 – 50 c. orange and green . . 3·00 3·75
343 **129** 1 q. purple and brown . . 15·00 17·00
344 – 1 q. 50 brown and olive . . 15·00 17·00
DESIGNS: As Type **128**—VERT: 1. c. Tower of the Reformer; 5 c. National Congress entrance; 10 c. Customs House. HORIZ: 2 c. Union Park, Quezaltenango; 3 c. G.P.O; 4 c. Government Building, Retalhuleu; 15 c. Aurora Airport; 25 c. National Fair; 50 c. Presidential Guards' Barracks. As Type **129**: 1 q. 50, Gen. Ubico.

(b) Air. As T **130**, inscr "INTERIOR" and optd with aeroplane.
345 **130** 2 c. black and red 20 15
346 – 3 c. black and blue 70 85
347 – 4 c. black and yellow . . . 20 15
348 – 6 c. black and green . . . 50 35
349 – 10 c. black, and purple . . 1·40 1·50
350 – 15 c. black and orange . . 1·00 70
351 – 30 c. black and olive . . . 2·50 2·00
352 – 50 c. black and blue . . . 3·50 3·00
353 – 75 c. black and violet . . . 7·00 7·50
354 – 1 q. black and red . . . 7·50 8·00
DESIGNS: 3 c. Lake Atitlan; 4 c. Progressive colony on Lake Amatitlan; 6 c. Carmen Hill; 10 c. Relief map; 15 c. National University; 30 c. Plaza Espana; 50 c. Aurora Police Station; 75 c. Aurora Amphitheatre; 1 q. Aurora Airport.

(c) Air. As T **130** inscr "EXTERIOR" and optd with aeroplane.
355 – 1 c. blue and orange 15 15
356 – 2 c. violet and red 25 20
357 – 3 c. brown and purple . . . 70 70
358 – 5 c. red and green . . . . 2·75 2·00
359 – 10 c. green and red 85 70
360 – 15 c. olive and pink 55 35
361 – 20 c. black and blue . . . 1·75 1·10
362 – 25 c. red and grey . . . . 1·75 1·75
363 – 30 c. violet and green . . . 85 85
364 – 50 c. blue and purple . . . 30·00 30·00
365 – 1 q. purple and olive . . . 7·00 8·00
366 – 1 q. 50 c. brown and red . . 7·00 8·00
DESIGNS: 1 c. Seventh Avenue; 2 c. Liberators' Monument; 3 c. National Printing Offices; 5 c. National Museum; 10 c. Central Park; 15 c. Escuintla Park; 20 c. Mobile Police; 25 c. Slaughter-house, Escuintla; 30 c. Campo de Marte Stadium; 50 c. Plaza Barrios; 1 q. Polytechnic; 1 q. 50 c. Aurora Airport.

1938. 150th Anniv of U.S. Constitution. Optd **1787–1789 CL ANIVERSARIO DE LA CONSTITUCION EE. UU. 1937-1939**.
367 **92** 1 c. olive 25 20

1938. Obligatory Tax. No. 223 optd **1938**.
368a **92** 1 c. olive 25 15

134

1938. 1st Central American Philatelic Exn.
(a) Air. As T **134** inscr "PRIMERA EXPOSICION FILATELICA CENTRO AMERICANA".
369 **134** 1 c. brown and orange . . 25 25
370 – 2 c. brown and red 25 25
371 – 3 c. brown, buff & green . . 40 40
372 – 4 c. brown and purple . . 55 55
373 – 5 c. brown and grey . . . 35 40
374 – 10 c. brown and blue . . . 70 1·00
DESIGNS: 2 c. to 10 c. Various portraits as Type **134**.

(b) Postage. No. 223 optd **Primera Exposicion Filatelica Centroamericana 1938**.
375 **92** 1 c. olive 25 15

137 La Merced Church

1939. Optd with flying quetzal.
(a) Inland Air Mail. As T **137** inscr "CORREO AEREO INTERIOR".
376 **137** 1 c. brown and olive . . . 15 10
377 – 2 c. green and red 20 15
378 – 3 c. olive and blue 20 20
379 – 4 c. green and pink 20 10
380 – 5 c. blue and purple 25 20
381 – 6 c. grey and orange . . . 35 25
382 – 10 c. grey and brown . . . 55 30
383 – 15 c. black and purple . . 70 20
384 – 30 c. red and blue 75 35
385 – 50 c. violet and orange . . 1·00 55
386 – 1 q. blue and green . . . . 1·40 1·00
DESIGNS: 2 c. Christ's Church Ruins, Antigua; 3 c. Aurora Airport; 4 c. Campo de Marte Stadium; 5 c. Cavalry Barracks; 6 c. Palace of Justice; 10 c. Customs House, San Jose; 15 c. Post Office, Retalhuleu; 30 c. Municipal Theatre, Quezaltenango; 50 c. Customs House, Retalhuleu; 1 q. Departmental Palace, Retalhuleu.

(b) Foreign Air Mail. As T **137** inscr "AEREO EXTERIOR" (10 c. and 25 c.) or "AEREO INTERNACIONAL".
387 – 1 c. brown and sepia 15 10
388 – 2 c. black and green 25 25
389 – 3 c. green and blue 20 15
390 – 4 c. green and brown 20 15
391 – 5 c. red and green 35 10
392 – 10 c. slate and red . . . . 1·10 10
393 – 15 c. red and blue . . . . 1·40 10
394 – 20 c. yellow and green . . . 55 25
395 – 25 c. olive and purple . . . 2·25 20
396 – 30 c. grey and red 70 15
397 – 50 c. orange and red . . . 1·00 20
398 – 1 q. green and orange . . . 1·60 35
DESIGNS: 1 c. Mayan Altar, Aurora Park; 2 c. Ministry of Health; 3 c. Lake Amatitlan; 4 c. Lake Atitlan; 5 c. Bridge over Tamazulapa; 10 c. National Liberators' Monument; 15 c. Palace of the Captains General; 20 c. Carmen Hill; 25 c. Barrios Square; 30 c. Mayan Altar, Archaeological Museum; 50 c. Carlos III Fountain; 1 q. Antigua.

1939. Obligatory Tax. No. 223 optd **1939**.
399 **92** 1 c. olive 25 15

140 National Flower (White Nun) **142** Arms and Map of Guatemala

1939.
400 ½ c. brown and green . . . 20 20
401 **140** 2 c. black and blue . . . . 1·00 35
402 – 3 c. green and brown . . . 1·50 75
403 – 3 c. green and red . . . . 1·50 75
404 **142** 5 c. red and blue . . . . 1·25 1·25
DESIGNS—As Type **142**: ½ c. Mayan Calendar; 3 c. Resplendent Quetzal.

1939. No. 229 surch **UN CENTAVO**.
405 **95** 1 c. on 2 c. blue 30 20

1940. Obligatory Tax. No. 223 optd **1940**.
406 **92** 1 c. olive 25 15

1940. 50th Anniv of Pan-American Union.
(a) Optd **Conmemorativo Union Panamericana 1890-1940**.
407 **92** 1 c. olive 25 15

(b) Air. Optd **UNION PANAMERICANA 1890-1940 CORREO AEREO**.
408 – 15 c. blue (No. 234) 35 20

1940. Surch with new values.
409 **31** 1 c. on 25 c. brown 25 15
410 – 5 c. on 50 c. red (No. 237) . . 35 30

1941. Obligatory Tax. Optd **1941**.
411 **92** 1 c. olive 25 15

1941. Obligatory Tax. Surch **CONSTRUCCION** (twice) and **UN CENTAVO**.
412 **95** 1 c. on 2 c. blue 25 15

1941. Air. 2nd Pan-American Health Day. Optd **DICIEMBRE 2 1941 SEGUNDO DIA PAN-AMERICANO DE LA SALUD**.
414 – 2 c. blk & grn (No. 388) . . . 55 30

1941. Surch **½ MEDIO CENTAVO ½**.
415 **31** ½ c. on 25 c. brown 20 20

1942. Obligatory Tax. Surch **CONSTRUCCION 1942 UN CENTAVO**.
416 **95** 1 c. on 2 c. blue 25 15

1942. As T **114**, but tablet dated "1942".
416a – 3 c. green 35 20
416b – 3 c. blue 35 20

153 Archway between wings of new G.P.O. **154** Guastatoya Vase

1942. Obligatory Tax.
417a **153** 1 c. brown 25 15

1942.
418 **154** ½ c. brown 20 15
419 – 1 c. red 25 15
DESIGN—HORIZ: 1 c. Old people's home.

156 Ruins of Zakuleu **157** National Printing Works

158 National Police H.Q.

159 San Carlos Borromeo University, Antigua, Guatemala

1943.
420 **156** ½ c. brown (postage) . . . 15 10
421 **157** 2 c. red 20 15
422 **158** 10 c. mauve (air) 50 15
423 **159** 15 c. brown 55 15

160 Don Pedro de Alvarado **161** Archway between wings of G.P.O.

1943. Air. 400th Anniv of Founding of Antigua.
424 **160** 15 c. blue 55 15

1943. Obligatory Tax.
425 **161** 1 c. orange 25 15

162 Rafael Maria Landivar

1943. 150th Death Anniv of R. M. Landivar (poet).
426 **162** 5 c. blue 35 20

163 National Palace

1944. Inauguration of National Palace.
427 **163** 3 c. green (postage) 20 15
444 5 c. red (air) 35 15
445 10 c. lilac 35 15
446 15 c. blue 35 30

1945. Optd **25 de junio de 1944 PALACIO NACIONAL** and bar.
428 **163** 3 c. blue 35 15

1945. Air. Optd **PALACIO NACIONAL** and bar.
429 **163** 5 c. red 30 20

165 Archway between Wings of G.P.O. **166** Allegory of the Revolution

1945. Obligatory Tax.

430	**165**	1 c. orange	25	15
479		1 c. blue	25	15

1945. Revolution of 20 October 1944.

431	**166**	3 c. blue (postage)	15	15
432		5 c. red (air)	45	30
433		6 c. green	45	30
434		10 c. violet	45	30
435		15 c. blue	45	30

1945. Air. Book Fair. No. 389 surch **1945 FERIA DEL LIBRO 2½ CENTAVOS**.

436	2½ c. on 3 c. green and blue	1·40	1·40

168 Jose Milla y Vidaurre (author) **169** Archbishop Pavo Enriquez de Rivera **170** Torch

1945.

437	**168**	1 c. green (postage)	15	15
438	**169**	2 c. violet	15	15
439		5 c. red (air)	35	20
678		5 c. olive	20	10
679		5 c. blue	20	10
680		5 c. green	20	10
681		5 c. orange	20	10
682		5 c. violet	20	10
683		5 c. grey	20	10
440	**168**	7½ c. purple	50	90
441		7½ c. blue	30	30

For stamps as Type **169** but dated "1660 1951" see Nos. 523/27.

1945. 1st Anniv of Revolution of 20 October 1944.

442	**170**	3 c. blue (postage)	20	15
443		5 c. mauve (air)	45	30

171 Jose Batres y Montufar (military leader and writer) **174** Rowland Hill

1945.

447	**171**	½ c. brown (postage)	20	15
448		3 c. blue	25	15
449		3 c. green	30	25
450		10 c. green (air)	45	20

DESIGN—HORIZ: 10 c. Montufar.

1946. Centenary of First Postage Stamps.

451	–	1 c. olive & vio (postage)	30	25
452	**174**	5 c. brown and grey (air)	25	20
453	–	15 c. blue, green and red	35	35

DESIGNS: 1 c. U.P.U. Monument, Berne; 15 c. Hemispheres and quetzal.

175 Signing the Declaration of Independence **176** Franklin D. Roosevelt

1946. Air. 125th Anniv of Independence.

454	**175**	5 c. red	15	10
455		6 c. brown	20	15
456		10 c. violet	25	20
457		20 c. blue	50	45

1947. Air. 2nd Anniv of Revolution of 20 October 1944. As T **170** but inscr "1944 1946" instead of "1944 1945" and "II" for "I".

458	1 c. green	20	15
459	2 c. red	20	15
460	3 c. violet	20	15
461	5 c. blue	25	15

1947. Air.

462	**176**	5 c. red	20	15
463		6 c. blue	25	15
464		10 c. blue	55	20
465		30 c. black	1·75	1·40
466		50 c. violet	1·75	1·75
467		1 q. green	2·75	2·75

177 "Labour" **180** Football Match

1948. Labour Day and 1st Anniv of Adoption of Labour Code.

468	**177**	1 c. green	20	15
469		2 c. purple	20	15
470		3 c. blue	20	15
471		5 c. red	20	15

1948. Optd **1948**.

472	**142**	5 c. red and blue	20	15

1948. Air. Optd **1948 AEREO**.

473	**142**	5 c. red and blue	25	20

1948. Air. 4th Central American and Caribbean Football Championship Games.

474	**180**	3 c. black and red	40	20
475		5 c. black and green	50	30
476		10 c. black and mauve	60	70
477		30 c. black and blue	2·00	2·40
478		50 c. black and yellow	2·75	2·75

181 Fray Bartolomede Las Casas and Indian **182** Seal of University of Guatemala

1949. Fray Bartolome de Las Casas ("Apostle of the Indians").

480	**181**	½ c. red	20	15
661		½ c. blue	15	10
481		1 c. brown	20	15
662		1 c. violet	15	10
663		2 c. green	15	10
664		3 c. red	15	10
484		4 c. blue	30	20
665a		4 c. brown	10	10

1949. Air. Latin-American Universities' Congress.

485	**182**	3 c. blue and red	35	35
486		10 c. blue and green	75	55
487		50 c. blue and yellow	1·90	2·10

183 Gathering Coffee **184** Tecum Uman Monument

1950. Tourist Propaganda. (a) Postage.

488	**183**	½ c. olive, blue and pink	30	15
489	–	½ c. blue and brown	20	15
490	–	1 c. olive, brown & yell	30	15
491	–	1 c. green and orange	20	15
492	–	2 c. blue, green and red	30	15
493	–	2 c. brown and red	20	15
494	–	3 c. brown, blue and violet	30	15
495	–	6 c. violet, orange & grn	55	15

DESIGNS—As Type **183**: ½ c. (No. 489); 3 c. Cutting sugar canes; 1 c. (No. 490); 2 c. (No. 493); Agricultural colony; 1 c. (No. 491); 2 c. (No. 492); Banana trees; 6 c. International Bridge.

(b) Air. Multicoloured centres.

496	–	3 c. red	55	15
497	**184**	5 c. lake	55	15
498	–	8 c. black	30	20
499	–	13 c. brown	60	35
500	–	35 c. violet	1·50	1·75

DESIGNS—As Type **184**—HORIZ: 3 c. Lake Atitlan; 8 c. San Cristobal Church; 35 c. Momostenango Cliffs. VERT: 13 c. Weaver.

185 Footballers **186** Ministry of Health Badge

187 Nursing School

1950. Air. 6th Central American and Caribbean Games. Inscr "VI JUEGOS DEPORTIVOS 1950".

501	**185**	1 c. black and violet	35	15
502	–	3 c. black and red	40	15
503	–	4 c. black and brown	50	20
504	–	8 c. black and purple	60	20
505	–	35 c. black and blue	1·40	1·90
506	–	65 c. green	3·00	3·00

DESIGNS—HORIZ: 4 c. Pole vaulting; 35 c. Diving; 65 c. Stadium. VERT: 3 c. Runners; 8 c. Tennis.

1950. Social Assistance and Public Health Fund.

507	**186**	1 c. blue & red (postage)	20	15
508	–	3 c. red & grn (Nurse)	35	20
509	–	5 c. brn & blue (Map)	55	35
511	–	5 c. red, grn & vio (air)	25	20
512	**187**	10 c. green and brown	40	35
513	–	50 c. purple, green & red	1·40	1·60
514	–	1 q. olive, grn & yellow	1·60	1·75

DESIGNS—As Type **187**: 5 c. Nurse; 50 c., 1 q. Zacapa and Roosevelt Hospitals.

1951. No. E479 without surcharge for use as ordinary postage.

517	E **181**	4 c. black and green	35	30

188 School **189** Ceremonial Axe-head

1951. Aerial views of schools as T **188**.

519	**188**	½ c. brown and violet	20	15
520	–	1 c. green and lake	20	15
521	**188**	2 c. brown and blue	20	20
522	–	4 c. purple and black	30	20

1952. As No. 438 but dated "1660 1951" below portrait.

523	**169**	½ c. violet	15	10
524		1 c. red	15	10
525		2 c. green	15	10
526		4 c. orange	20	15
527		4 c. blue	15	10

1953. Air.

528	**189**	3 c. drab and blue	20	20
529		5 c. brown and slate	20	20
530		10 c. slate and violet	45	35

190 Flag and Constitution **191** R. Alvarez Ovalle (music), J. J. Palma (words)

1953. Air. Presidential Succession, 1951.

531	**190**	1 c. multicoloured	30	20
532		2 c. multicoloured	35	30
533		4 c. multicoloured	45	35

1953. National Anthem.

534	**191**	½ c. grey and violet	35	20
535		1 c. brown and grey	45	20
536		2 c. olive and brown	45	25
537		3 c. olive and blue	45	25

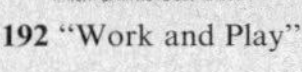

192 "Work and Play" **193** Horse Racing

1953. Air. National Fair. Inscr "FERIA NACIONAL".

538	–	1 c. red and blue	20	15
539	–	4 c. green and orange	90	25
540	**192**	5 c. brown and green	55	30
541	**193**	15 c. lilac and brown	85	75
542	–	20 c. blue and red	75	70
543	–	30 c. blue and sepia	85	1·00
544	–	50 c. black and violet	1·00	1·00
545	–	65 c. green and blue	1·75	1·90
546	–	1 q. green and red	17·00	11·00

DESIGNS—VERT: 1 c. National dance; 4 c. National flower (white nun); 30 c. Picture and corn cob; 1 q. Resplendent quetzal. HORIZ: 20 c. Ruins of Zakuleu; 50 c. Champion bull; 65 c. Cycle-racing.

194 Indian Warrior **196** Flags of Guatemala and O.D.E.C.A.

1954. Air. National Revolutionary Army Commemoration.

547	**194**	1 c. red	35	35
548		2 c. blue	35	35
549		4 c. green	35	35
550		5 c. turquoise	55	45
551		6 c. orange	55	45
552		10 c. violet	70	55
553		20 c. sepia	1·90	2·00

1954. As T **5** but inscr "UNION POSTAL UNIVERSAL GUATEMALA" around oval.

554	1 c. blue	90	25
1222	1 c. green	25	10
555	2 c. violet	45	20
556	2 c. brown	60	20
1222a	2 c. blue	25	10
557	3 c. red	60	20
558	3 c. blue	60	20
1225	3 c. brown	25	10
1226	3 c. green	25	10
1227	3 c. orange	25	10
559	4 c. orange	1·00	20
560	4 c. violet	90	20
1228	4 c. brown	25	10
561	5 c. brown	1·40	25
562	5 c. red	1·40	25
563	5 c. green	1·00	25
564	5 c. grey	1·75	25
1228a	5 c. mauve	25	10
565	6 c. green	1·40	45
1229	6 c. blue	25	10

1954. Air. 3rd Anniv of Organization of Central American States.

566	**196**	1 c. multicoloured	20	15
567		2 c. multicoloured	20	15
568		4 c. multicoloured	30	20

197 Goal-keeper **198** Red Cross and Globe

1955. Golden Jubilee of Football in Guatemala. Inscr "1902–1952".

569	–	4 c. violet (Camposeco)	70	45
570	–	4 c. red (Camposeco)	70	45
571	–	4 c. green (Camposeco)	70	45
572	–	10 c. green (Matheu)	2·00	55
573	**197**	15 c. blue	2·00	1·50

1956. Red Cross. Inscr "CONMEMORATIVAS CRUZ ROJA".

574	**198**	1 c. red & brn (postage)	20	20
575	–	3 c. red and green	20	20
576	–	4 c. red and black	25	20
577	–	5 c. + 15 c. red & blue	60	90
578	–	15 c. + 50 c. red & lilac	1·40	1·75
579	**198**	25 c. + 50 c. red and blue	1·40	1·75
580	–	35 c. + 1 q. grn & red (air)	3·50	3·75
581	–	50 c. + 1 q. red & blue	3·50	3·75
582	–	1 q. + 1 q. red & green	3·50	3·75

DESIGNS: 3 c., 15 c., Telephone and red cross; 4 c., 5 c. Nurse, patient and red cross; 35 c. Red Cross ambulance; 50 c. Nurse and hospital; 1 q. Red Cross nurse.

199 Road Map of Guatemala **200** Maya Warrior

1956. Revolution of 1954–55. Inscr "LIBERACION 1954–55".
583 – ½ c. violet (postage) 15 10
584 **199** 1 c. green 15 10
585 – 3 c. sepia 15 10
586 **200** 2 c. multicoloured (air) 20 15
587 – 4 c. black and red 20 15
588 – 5 c. brown and blue 30 30
589 – 6 c. blue and sepia 20 20
590 – 20 c. brn, blue & violet 1·00 1·00
591 – 30 c. olive and blue 1·75 1·00
592 – 65 c. green and brown 1·50 1·75
593 – 1 q. multicoloured 2·25 2·40
594 – 5 q. brown, blue & green 9·00 9·50
DESIGNS: ½ c. Liberation dagger symbol; 3 c. Oil production; 4 c. Family; 5 c. Sword smashing Communist emblems; 6 c. Hands holding map and cogwheel; 20 c. Martyrs' Monument; 30 c. Champerico Port; 65 c. Telecommunications symbols; 1 q. Flags of ODECA countries; 5 q. Pres. Armas.

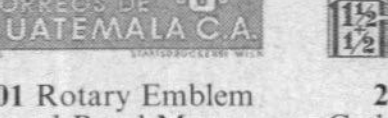

201 Rotary Emblem and Road Map
203 Esquipulas Cathedral and "Black Christ"

1956. Air. 50th Anniv of Rotary International.
595 **201** 4 c. bistre and blue 35 30
596 6 c. bistre and green 35 30
597 35 c. bistre and violet 1·00 1·40

1957. Air. Red Cross Fund. Nos. 577/9 optd **AEREO-1957** and ornaments.
598 – 5 c. + 15 c. red & blue 4·00 4·50
599 – 15 c. + 50 c. red & lilac 4·00 4·50
600 **198** 25 c. + 50 c. red & blue 4·00 4·50

1957. Esquipulas Highway Fund. Inscr "PRO-CARRETERA ESQUIPULAS JUNIO 1957".
601 **203** 1½ c. + ½ c. violet and brown (postage) 70 45
602 – 10 c. + 1 q. brown and green (air) 4·00 4·50
603 – 15 c. + 1 q. grn & sepia 4·00 4·50
604 – 20 c. + 1 q. slate & brn 4·00 4·50
605 – 25 c. + 1 q. red & lilac 4·00 4·50
DESIGNS—HORIZ: 10 c. Esquipulas Cathedral. VERT: 15 c. Cathedral and "Black Christ"; 20 c. Map of Guatemala and "Black Christ"; 25 c. Bishop of Esquipulas.

204 Red Cross, Map and Resplendent Quetzal
207 Caravel of 1532 and freighter "Quetzaltenango"

1958. Air. Red Cross.
606 **204** 1 c. multicoloured 50 25
607 – 2 c. red, brown & blue 35 15
608 – 3 c. brown, red & blue 35 15
609 – 4 c. red, green & brown 35 15
DESIGNS—VERT: 2 c. J. R. Angulo; Mother and Child. HORIZ: 3 c. P. de Bethancourt and Invalid; 4 c. R. Ayau and Red Cross.

1959. Birth Centenary of R. A. Ovalle (composer of National Anthem). Optd **1858 1958 CENTENARIO**.
610 **191** ½ c. grey and violet 30 30

1959. Air. Pres. Castillo Armas Commem. As No. 594 but inscr "LIBERACION 3 DE JULIO DE 1954", etc. Centre in blue and yellow. Frame colours given.
615 1 c. black 15 15
616 2 c. red 15 15
617 4 c. brown 15 15
618 6 c. green 20 15
619 10 c. violet 35 25
620 20 c. green 1·00 65
621 35 c. grey 1·75 95

1959. Air United Nations. Optd **HOMENAJE A LAS NACIONES UNIDAS**.
622 **168** 7½ c. blue 1·10 1·10

1959. Air. Central American Merchant Marine Commemoration.
623 **207** 6 c. blue and red 80 15

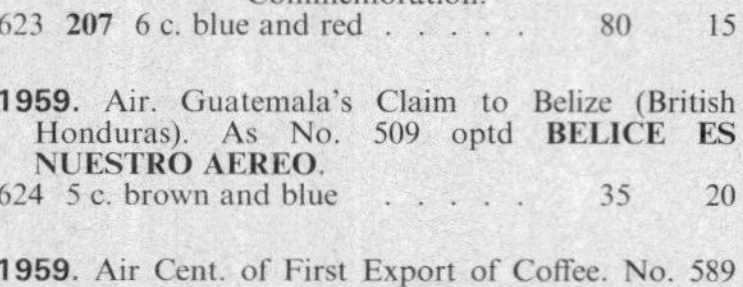

1959. Air. Guatemala's Claim to Belize (British Honduras). As No. 509 optd **BELICE ES NUESTRO AEREO**.
624 5 c. brown and blue 35 20

1959. Air Cent. of First Export of Coffee. No. 589 optd **1859 CENTENARIO PRIMERA EXPORTACION DE CAFE 1959**.
625 6 c. blue and sepia 55 20

210 Pres. and Senora Morales

1959. Air. Visit of President of Honduras.
626 **210** 6 c. brown 20 15

211 Red Cross Shield
213 Abraham Lincoln

1960. Red Cross Commem. Cross in red.
627 **211** 1 c. + 1 c. blue and brown (postage) 30 20
628 – 3 c. + 3 c. blue and lilac 30 20
629 **211** 4 c. + 4 c. blue & black 30 25
630 – 5 c. + 5 c. blue, pink and red (air) 1·40 1·50
631 – 6 c. + 6 c. green and red 1·40 1·50
632 – 10 c. + 10 c. pink, blue and deep blue 1·40 1·50
633 – 15 c. + 15 c. red, blue and brown 1·40 1·50
634 – 20 c. + 20 c. green, pink and purple 1·40 1·50
635 – 25 c. + 25 c. pink, blue and grey 1·40 1·50
636 – 30 c. + 30 c. multicoloured 1·40 1·50
DESIGNS—3 c., 5 c. Wounded soldier at Solferino; 6 c., 20 c. Houses and debris afloat on flood waters; 10 c., 25 c. Earth, Moon and planets; 15 c., 30 c. Red Cross H.Q., Guatemala City.

1960. Air. World Refugee Year. Nos. 606/9 optd **ANO MUNDIAL DE REFUGIADOS** or surch also.
637 1 c. multicoloured 1·75 1·00
638 2 c. red, brown and blue 90 70
639 3 c. brown, red and blue 90 70
640 4 c. red, green and brown 90 70
641 6 c on 1 c. multicoloured 3·50 2·10
642 7 c. on 2 c. red, brown & blue 1·50 1·25
643 10 c., on 3 c. brown, red & bl 2·50 2·75
644 20 c. on 4 c. red, green & brn 2·75 2·75

1960. Air. Founding of City of Melchor de Mencos. No. 589 optd **Fundacion de la cuidad Melchor de Mencos 30-IV-1960**.
645 6 c. blue and sepia 1·10 1·10

1980. Air. 150th Birth Anniv of Abraham Lincoln.
646 **213** 5 c. blue 30 20
647 30 c. violet 70 1·00
648 50 c. slate 3·50 4·00

214 U.N.E.S.C.O. Headquarters, Paris

1960. Air. Inaug of U.N.E.S.C.O. Headquarters Building, Paris (1958).
649 **214** 5 c. violet and mauve 15 15
650 6 c. sepia and blue 20 15
651 8 c. red and green 35 20
652 20 c. blue and brown 85 90

1961. Air. Red Cross. Nos. 606/9 optd **MAYO DE 1960**.
653 1 c. multicoloured 75 40
654 2 c. red, brown and blue 45 40
655 3 c. brown, red and blue 45 40
656 4 c. red, green and brown 45 40

216 Romulus, Remus and Wolf
217 Independence Ceremony

1961. Plaza Italia Inauguration.
657 **216** 3 c. blue 15 15

1962. Air. 140th Anniv of Independence.
658 **217** 4 c. sepia 15 15
659 5 c. blue 20 15
660 15 c. violet 70 35

1962. Air. Malaria Eradication. Optd **1962 EL MUNDO UNIDO CONTRA LA MALARIA**.
666 **214** 6 c. sepia and blue 55 85

219 Dr. Jose Luna

1962. Air. Guatemalan Doctors.
667 **219** 1 c. violet and olive 35 15
668 – 4 c. green and yellow 35 15
669 – 5 c. brown and blue 35 15
670 – 6 c. black and salmon 35 15
671 – 10 c. brown and green 55 20
672 – 20 c. blue and mauve 70 45
DOCTORS: 4 c. R. Robles; 5 c. N. Esparragoza; 6 c. J. Ortega; 10 c. D. Gonzalez; 20 c. J. Flores.

1962. Air. Pres. Ydigoras's Tour of Central America. No. 589 optd **PRESIDENTE YDIGORAS FUENTES RECORRE POR TIERRA CENTRO AMERICA 14 A 20 DIC. 1962**.
673 6 c. blue and sepia 60 55

1963. Air. New ODECA Charter Commem. Optd **CONMEMORACION FIRMA NUEVA CARTA ODECA.—1962**.
674 **214** 6 c. sepia and blue 30 15
675 8 c. red and green 35 15

222 Girl with Basket of Fruit on head
224 Arms

1963. Air. National Fair, 1960.
676 **222** 1 c. multicoloured 15 10

1963. Air. Presidential Meeting. No. 589 with 11-line opt starting **"REUNION PRESIDENTES: KENNEDY"**.
677 6 c. blue and sepia 2·40 1·60

1963.
684 **224** 10 c. red 35 15
685 10 c. black 30 15
686 10 c. brown 30 15
687 20 c. violet 55 20
688 20 c. blue 55 20

225 Harvester (after "The Reaper", Mathieson)
226 Ceiba (national tree)

1963. Air. Freedom from Hunger.
689 **225** 5 c. turquoise 20 15
690 10 c. blue 35 20

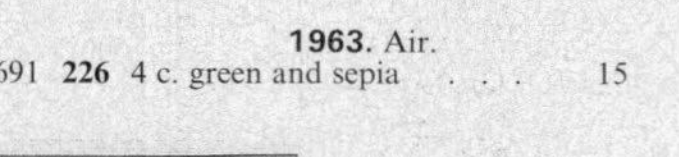

1963. Air.
691 **226** 4 c. green and sepia 15 15

227 Pedro Bethancourt, tending sick man
228 Patzun Palace

1964. Campaign for Canonization of Pedro Bethancourt.
692 **227** 2½ c. brown (postage) 15 10
693 2½ c. blue (air) 10 10
694 3 c. orange 10 10
695 4 c. violet 15 10
696 5 c. green 20 10

1964. Air. Guatemalan Palaces.
697 **228** 1 c. brown and red 15 10
698 – 3 c. green and mauve 20 10
699 – 4 c. lake and blue 20 15
700 – 5 c. blue and brown 25 15
701 – 6 c. blue and green 25 15
PALACES: 3 c. Coban; 4 c. Retalhuleu; 5 c. San Marcos; 6 c. Los Capitanes Generales.

229 Municipal Building

1964. Air. New Buildings. (a) As T **229**.
702 **229** 3 c. brown and blue 15 15
703 – 4 c. blue and brown 20 15
DESIGN: 4 c. Social Security Building.

(b) Designs as Nos. 702/3 but different style frame and inscr, and new designs.
704 – 3 c. green (As No. 703) 20 10
705 – 4 c. slate 20 10
706 **229** 7 c. blue 25 15
707 – 7 c. bistre 25 15
DESIGNS: 4 c. University Rectory; 7 c. (No. 707), Engineering Faculty.

1964. Air. Olympic Games, Tokyo. Optd with Olympic rings and **OLIMPIADAS TOKIO-1964**.
708 **204** 1 c. 1·25 1·00
709 – 2 c. (No. 607) 75 75
710 – 3 c. (No. 608) 75 75
711 – 4 c. (No. 609) 75 75

1964. Air. New York World's Fair. Optd **FERIA MUNDIAL DE NEW YORK**.
712 **204** 1 c. 1·25 90
713 – 2 c. (No. 607) 50 50
714 – 3 c. (No. 608) 50 50
715 – 4 c. (No. 609) 50 50

1964. Air. Surch **HABILITADA 1964** and value.
716 **204** 7 c. on 1 c. 40 25
717 – 9 c. on 2 c. (No. 607) 40 35
718 – 13 c. on 3 c. (No. 608) 45 45
719 – 21 c. on 4 c. (No. 609) 75 75

1964. Air. 8th Cycle Race. Optd **VIII VUELTA CICLISTICA**.
720 **204** 1 c. 2·50 1·40
721 – 2 c. (No. 607) 70 70
722 – 3 c. (No. 608) 70 70
723 – 4 c. (No. 609) 70 1·00

234 Pres. Kennedy

1964. Air. Pres. Kennedy Commem.
724 **234** 1 c. violet 70 55
725 2 c. green 70 55
726 3 c. brown 70 55
727 7 c. blue 70 55
728 50 c. green 4·00 4·25

235 Centenary Emblem
237 Bishop F. Marroquin

1964. Air. Red Cross Centenary. Emblem in silver and red.
730 **235** 7 c. blue 55 35
731 9 c. orange 55 35
732 13 c. violet 85 35
733 21 c. green 50 70
734 35 c. brown 1·00 1·00
735 1 q. bistre 1·60 2·00

1964. 15th Anniv (1963) of International Society of Guatemala Collectors. No. 559 optd **HOMENAJE A LA "I.S.G.C." 1948–1963**.
736 4 c. orange 50 25

1985. Air. 400th Death Anniv of Bishop Maroquin.
737 **237** 4 c. brown and purple 15 10
738 7 c. sepia and grey 25 15
739 9 c. black and blue 30 15

1965. Air. Optd **AYUDENOS MAYO 1965**. Emblem in silver and red.
740 **235** 7 c. blue 35 30
741 9 c. orange 45 35
742 13 c. violet 55 45
743 21 c. green 70 60
744 35 c. brown 70 95

239 Scout Badge

240 Flags

1966. Air. 5th Regional Scout Training Conference, Guatemala City. Multicoloured.

745	5 c. Type **239**	35	15
746	9 c. Scouts by campfire	45	25
747	10 c. Scout carrying torch and flag	55	35
748	15 c. Scout saluting	70	55
749	20 c. Lord Baden-Powell	90	90

1966. Air. "Centro America". 145th Anniv of Central American Independence.

No.	Type	Description		
750	**240**	6 c. multicoloured	25	15

241 Nefertari's Temple, Abu Simbel

242 Arms

1966. Air. Nubian Monuments Preservation.

No.	Type	Description		
751	**241**	21 c. violet and bistre	55	35

1966. Air.

No.	Type	Description		
752	**242**	5 c. orange	20	10
753		5 c. green	20	10
754		5 c. grey	20	10
755		5 c. violet	20	10
756		5 c. blue	20	10
757		5 c. deep blue	20	10
758		5 c. violet	20	10
759		5 c. green	15	10
760		5 c. lake	15	10
761		5 c. green on yellow	15	10

243 Mgr. M. Rossell y Arellano

244 Mario M. Montenegro (revolutionary)

1966. Air. Monseigneur Rossell Commem.

No.	Type	Description		
765	**243**	1 c. violet	20	15
766		2 c. green	25	10
767		3 c. sepia	25	15
768		7 c. blue	35	25
769		50 c. slate	95	1·10

1966. Air. Montenegro Commemoration.

No.	Type	Description		
770	**244**	2 c. red	15	10
771		3 c. orange	20	15
772		4 c. red	25	15
773		5 c. grey	35	15
774		5 c. blue	35	15
775		5 c. green	35	15
776		5 c. black	35	15

245 Morning Glory

1967. Air. Flowers. Multicoloured.

777	4 c. Type **245**	25	15
778	8 c. "Bird of Paradise"	25	15
779	10 c. "White Nun" orchid (national flower)	35	25
780	20 c. "Nymphs of Amatitlan"	60	35

Nos. 778/9 are horiz.

246 Institute Emblem

1967. Air. 8th General Assembly of Pan-American Geographical and Historical Institute (1965).

No.	Type	Description		
781	**246**	4 c. purple, black & brown	20	15
782		5 c. blue, black & bistre	35	15
783		7 c. blue, black & yellow	55	15

247 Map of Guatemala and British Honduras

1967. Guatemala's Claim to British Honduras.

No.	Type	Description		
784	**247**	4 c. blue, red and green	15	10
785		5 c. blue, red & yellow	20	10
786		6 c. blue, grey & orange	20	15

1967. Air. Guatemalan Victory in "Norceca" Football Games. No. 704 optd **GUATEMALA CAMPEON III Norceca Foot-Ball** and football motif.

787	3 c. green	35	30

1967. Air. American Heads of State Meeting, Punta del Este. No. 705 optd **REUNION JEFES DE ESTADO AMERICANO, PUNTA DEL ESTE,** etc.

788	4 c. slate	70	55

250 "Peace and Progress"

1967. Air. International Co-operation.

No.	Type	Description		
789	**250**	7 c. multicoloured	35	15
790		21 c. multicoloured	55	35

251 Yurrita Church

1967. Air. Religion in Guatemala.

No.	Type	Description		
791	**251**	1 c. brown, grn & blue	20	10
792	–	2 c. brn, pur & salmon	25	10
793	–	3 c. indigo, red & blue	25	10
794	–	4 c. grn, pur & salmon	25	10
795	–	5 c. brn, pur and grn	25	10
796	–	7 c. black, blue & mauve	35	15
797	–	10 c. blue, violet & yell	55	20

DESIGNS—HORIZ: 2 c. Santo Domingo Church; 3 c. San Francisco Church; 7 c. Mercy Church, Antigua; 10 c. Metropolitan Cathedral. VERT: 4 c. Antonio Jose de Irisarri; 5 c. Church of the Recollection.

252 Lincoln

1967. Air. Death Centenary (1965) of Abraham Lincoln.

No.	Type	Description		
798	**252**	7 c. red and blue	35	20
799		9 c. black and green	45	25
800		11 c. black and brown	45	25
801		15 c. red and blue	45	35
802		30 c. green and purple	1·00	1·10

1967. Air. 8th Central American Scout Camporee. Nos. 745/9 optd **VIII Camporee Scout Centroamericano Diciembre 1–8/1967**.

803	5 c. Type **239**	35	35
804	9 c. Scouts by campfire	55	55
805	10 c. Scout carrying torch and flag	70	70
806	15 c. Scout saluting	70	70
807	20 c. Lord Baden-Powell	90	90

1967. Air. Award of Nobel Prize for Literature to Miguel Angel Asturias (1st issue). Nos. 694/5 optd **"Premio Nobel de Literatura – 10 diciembre 1967 – Miguel Angel Asturias"**.

No.	Type	Description		
808	**227**	3 c. orange	35	30
809	–	4 c. violet	35	30

See also No. 838.

255 U.N.E.S.C.O. Emblem and Children

1967. Air. 20th Anniv (1966) of U.N.E.S.C.O.

No.	Type	Description		
810	**255**	4 c. green	15	10
811		5 c. blue	20	15
812		7 c. grey	25	15
813		21 c. purple	60	60

256 Institute Emblem

1967. Air. 25th Anniv of Inter-American Institute of Agricultural Sciences.

No.	Type	Description		
814	**256**	9 c. black and green	45	45
815		25 c. red and brown	95	95
816		1 q. ultramarine & blue	2·40	2·40

1968. Air. 3rd Meeting of Central American Presidents. Optd **III REUNION DE PRESIDENTES Nov. 15–18, 1967.**

No.	Type	Description		
817	**204**	1 c. (No. 606)	1·25	90
819	–	2 c. (No. 607)	70	70
821	–	3 c. (No. 608)	70	70
823	**235**	7 c. (No. 730)	70	70
824		9 c. (No. 731)	70	90
825		13 c. (No. 732)	95	90
826		21 c. (No. 733)	1·40	70
827		35 c. (No. 734)	1·10	1·10

258 "Madonna of the Choir"

260 Miguel Angel Asturias

1968. Air. 400th Anniv of "Madonna of the Choir".

No.	Type	Description		
828a	**258**	4 c. blue	10	10
829		7 c. slate	35	15
830		9 c. green	55	15
830a		9 c. lilac	25	10
831		10 c. red	70	15
832		10 c. grey	45	15
832a		10 c. blue	25	10
833		1 q. purple	2·40	2·00
834		1 q. yellow	2·40	2·00

1968. Air. 11th Cycle Race. Nos. 784/6 optd **AEREO XI VUELTA CICLISTICA 1967**.

No.	Type	Description		
835	**247**	4 c. blue, red and green	55	55
836		5 c. blue, red & yellow	55	55
837		6 c. blue, grey & orange	45	45

1968. Air. Award of Nobel Prize for Literature to Miguel Angel Asturias.

No.	Type	Description		
838	**260**	20 c. blue	70	35

1968. Air. Campaign for Conservation of the Forests. No. 789 optd **AYUDA A CONSERVAR LOS BOSQUES.—1968.**

No.	Type	Description		
839	**250**	7 c. multicoloured	35	15

1968. Air. Human Rights Year. No. 626 optd **1968.—ANO INTERNACIONAL DERECHOS HUMANOS.—ONU.**

No.	Type	Description		
840	**210**	6 c. brown	55	30

1968. Air. Nahakin Scientific Expedition. No. 589 optd **Expedicion Cientifica** etc.

841	6 c. blue and sepia	30	20

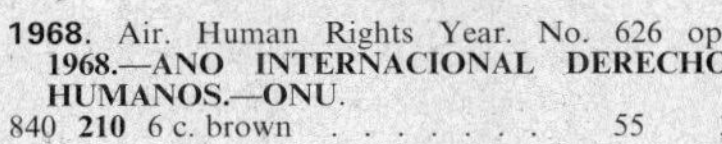

264 "Visit Guatemala"

265 Mayan Ball Game Ring and Resplendent Quetzal

1968. Air. Tourism.

No.	Type	Description		
842	**264**	10 c. red and green	30	15
843		20 c. red and black	55	35
844		50 c. blue and red	85	85

1968. Olympic Games, Mexico. Quetzal in green and red.

No.	Type	Description		
845	**265**	1 c. black	50	10
850		1 c. slate	50	10
846		5 c. yellow	65	15
851		5 c. pink	40	15
852		5 c. brown	40	15
853		5 c. blue	40	15
847		8 c. orange	80	20
848		15 c. blue	1·40	30
849		30 c. violet	2·40	85

1968. Air. 20th Anniv of Federation of Central American Universities. No. 705 optd **CONFEDERACION DE UNIVERSIDADES CENTROAMERICANAS 1948 1968.**

854	4 c. slate	30	15

267 Presidents Gustavo Diaz Ordaz and Julio Cesar Mendez Montenegro

1968. Air. Exchange Visits of Mexican and Guatemalan Presidents.

No.	Type	Description		
855	**267**	5 c. multicoloured	15	15
856		10 c. blue and ochre	35	20
857		25 c. blue and ochre	55	50

268 I.T.U. Emblem and Symbols

269 Young Girl and Poinsettia

1968. Air. Centenary (1965) of I.T.U.

No.	Type	Description		
858	**268**	7 c. blue	20	15
859		15 c. black and green	35	15
859a		15 c. brown and orange	55	15
860		21 c. purple	55	35
861		35 c. red and green	70	35
862		75 c. green and red	1·40	1·40
863		3 q. brown and red	4·50	4·50

1969. Help for Abandoned Children.

No.	Type	Description		
864	**269**	2½ c. ochre, red & green	20	10
865		2½ c. orange, red & green	20	10
866		5 c. black, red & green	30	10
867		21 c. violet, red & green	65	55

1969. Air. Nos. 845/9 optd **AEREO** and motifs. Quetzal in green and red.

No.	Type	Description		
868	**265**	1 c. black	75	25
869		5 c. yellow	95	35
870		8 c. orange	80	60
871		15 c. blue	95	70
872		30 c. violet	1·25	70

271 Dante

273 "Apollo II" and Moon Landing

272 Map of Central and South America

1969. Air. 700th Birth Anniv (1965) of Dante.

No.	Type	Description		
873	**271**	7 c. blue and plum	20	10
874		10 c. blue	25	10
875		20 c. green	35	15
876		21 c. slate and brown	70	25
877		35 c. violet and green	1·00	55

1969. Air. 20th Anniv of Latin-American Universities Union.

No.	Type	Description		
878	**272**	2 c. mauve and black	15	10
879	–	9 c. black and grey	25	15

DESIGN: (26 × 27 mm) 9 c. University seal.

1969. Air. 1st Man on the Moon.

No.	Type	Description		
881	**273**	50 c. black and purple	1·40	1·40
882		1 q. black and blue	2·40	2·50

1970. 50th Anniv of Int. Labour Organization. Nos. 847/8 optd **Cincuentenario O.I.T.** and ornaments.
884 **265** 8 c. orange, grn & red . . 50 15
886 15 c. blue, green & red . . 75 20

275 Lake Atitlan

1970. Air. Conservation of Atitlan Grebes. Multicoloured.
888 4 c. Type **275** 15 15
889 9 c. Family of Atitlan Grebes . 2·50 50
890 20 c. Young grebe in nest (vert) . 4·50 1·25

276 Dr. V. M. Calderon

1970. Air. 1st Death Anniv of Dr. Victor M. Calderon (medical scientist).
892 **276** 1 c. black and blue 15 10
893 2 c. black and green . . . 15 10
894 9 c. black and yellow . . . 30 15

277 Hand holding Bible **280** Maya Indians and C.A.R.E. Package

279 Arms and Newspaper

1970. Air. 400th Anniv of Spanish Bible.
895 **277** 5 c. multicoloured 15 10

1971. Air. Surch **VALE Q0.50**.
896 **268** 50 c. on 3 q. brn & red . . 1·25 1·25

1971. Air. Stamp Centenary (1st issue) and Centenary of Newspaper "Gaceta de Guatemala".
897 **279** 2 c. blue and red . . . 10 10
899b 5 c. brown and red . . . 10 10
899 25 c. blue and red . . . 55 35
899c 50 c. mauve and brown . . 90 35
See also Nos. 988/9d.

1971. 25th Anniv of C.A.R.E. (Co-operative for American Relief Everywhere). Mult.
900 1 c. Type **280** (black inscr) (postage) 15 10
901 1 c. Type **280** (brown inscr) . . 15 10
902 1 c. Type **280** (violet inscr) . . 15 10
903 2 c. Maya porter and C.A.R.E. parcel (air) 15 15
904 5 c. Two Maya warriors and parcel 20 20
905 10 c. C.A.R.E. parcel within Maya border 35 20
SIZES: 2 c. (36 × 30 mm); 50 c. (46 × 27 mm); 10 c. (28 × 31 mm).

282 J. Rufino Barrios, M. Garcia Granados and Emblems

1971. Air. Centenary of Liberal Reforms.
909 **282** 2 c. multicoloured . . . 95 15
910 10 c. multicoloured . . . 2·00 30
911 50 c. multicoloured . . . 7·50 3·50
912 1 q. multicoloured . . . 14·50 7·25

283 J. A. Chavarry Arrue (stamp engraver) and Leon Bilak (philatelist)

1971. Air. "Homage to Philately".
913 **283** 1 c. black and green . . . 10 10
914 2 c. black and brown . . . 15 10
915 5 c. black and orange . . . 15 15

1971. Air. "INTERFER 71" Int. Fair, Guatemala. Optd **FERIA INTERNACIONAL "INTERFER—71" 30 Oct. al 21 Nov.**
916 **207** 6 c. blue and red 20 15

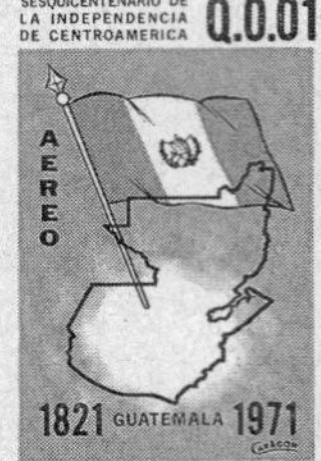

285 Flag and Map **286** Maya Statue and U.N.I.C.E.F. Emblem

1971. Air. 150th Anniv of Central American Independence.
917 **285** 1 c. blue, black & lilac . . 10 10
918 3 c. bl, brown & pink . . 10 10
919 5 c. bl, brown & orange . . 15 10
920 9 c. bl, black & green . . 25 15

1971. Air. 25th Anniv of U.N.I.C.E.F.
921 **286** 1 c. green 10 10
921a 2 c. purple 15 10
922 50 c. purple . . . . . . 1·10 1·10
923 1 q. blue . . . . 2·00 2·00

287 Boeing "Peashooter" and North American P-51 Mustang

1972. Air. 50th Anniv of Guatemala Air Force.
924 **287** 5 c. blue and brown . . . 20 10
925 – 10 c. blue 50 20
DESIGN—56 × 32 mm: 10 c. Bleriot XI airplane.

289 Ruins of Capuchin Monastery

1972. Air. Tourism. Ruins of Antigua.
927 **289** 1 c. blue and light blue . . 20 10
928 A 1 c. blue and light blue . . 20 10
929 B 1 c. blue and light blue . . 20 10
930 C 1 c. blue and light blue . . 20 10
931 D 1 c. blue and light blue . . 20 10
932 E 1 c. blue and light blue . . 20 10
933 **289** 2 c. black and brown . . . 15 10
934 A 2 c. black and brown . . . 15 10
935 B 2 c. black and brown . . . 15 10
936 C 2 c. black and brown . . . 15 10
937 D 2 c. black and brown . . . 15 10
938 E 2 c. black and brown . . . 15 10
939 **289** 2½ c. black, mve & silver . 35 10
940 A 2½ c. black, mve & silver . 35 10
941 B 2½ c. black, mve & silver . 35 10
942 C 2½ c. black, mve & silver . 35 10
943 D 2½ c. black, mve & silver . 35 10
944 E 2½ c. black, mve & silver . 35 10
945 **289** 5 c. black, blue & orange . 70 15
946 A 5 c. black, blue & orange . 70 15
947 B 5 c. black, blue & orange . 70 15
948 C 5 c. black, blue & orange . 70 15
949 D 5 c. black, blue & orange . 70 15
950 E 5 c. black, blue & orange . 70 15
951 **289** 20 c. black and yellow . . 55 35
952 A 20 c. black and yellow . . 55 35
953 B 20 c. black and yellow . . 55 35
954 C 20 c. black and yellow . . 55 35
955 D 20 c. black and yellow . . 55 35
956 E 20 c. black and yellow . . 55 35
957 **289** 1 q. lt blue, red & blue . . 2·40 1·75
958 A 1 q. lt blue, red & blue . . 2·40 1·75
959 B 1 q. lt blue, red & blue . . 2·40 1·75
960 C 1 q. lt blue, red & blue . . 2·40 1·75
961 D 1 q. lt blue, red & blue . . 2·40 1·75
962 E 1 q. lt blue, red & blue . . 2·40 1·75
DESIGNS: A, "La Recoleccion" archways; B, Cathedral ruins; C, Santa Clara courtyard; D, San Francisco gateway; E, Fountain, Central Park.
See also Nos. 1230/41.

290 Pres. Carlos Arana Osorio

1973. National Census.
963 **290** 2 c. black and blue 10 10
964 – 3 c. brown, pink & orge . . 15 10
965 **290** 5 c. purple, mve & blk . . 20 10
966 – 8 c. green, blk & emer . . 35 10
DESIGNS—VERT: 3 c. Pres. Osorio seated; 8 c. Pres. Osorio standing.

291 Francisco Ximenez

1973. International Book Year (1972).
967 **291** 2 c. black and green . . . 10 10
968 3 c. brown and orange . . 10 10
969a 3 c. black and yellow . . 10 10
969 6 c. black and blue . . . 20 10

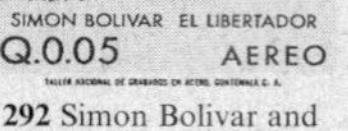

292 Simon Bolivar and Map **293** Eleanor Roosevelt

1973. Air. Simon Bolivar "The Liberator".
970 **292** 3 c. black and red 10 10
971 3 c. blue and orange . . . 10 10
972 5 c. black and yellow . . . 15 10
973 5 c. black and green . . . 15 10

1973. Air. 90th Birth Anniv (1974) of Eleanor Roosevelt (sociologist).
974 **293** 7 c. blue 15 10

294 Star Emblem

1973. Air. Cent. of Polytechnic School.
975 **294** 5 c. yellow, brown & blue . 10 10
See also Nos. 1000/1.

1973. Air. Nos. 927/32 optd **"II Feria Internacional" INTERFER/73 31 Octubre-Noviembre 18 1973 GUATEMALA.**
976 **289** 1 c. blue and light blue . . 20 10
977 A 1 c. blue and light blue . . 20 10
978 B 1 c. blue and light blue . . 20 10
979 C 1 c. blue and light blue . . 20 10
980 D 1 c. blue and light blue . . 20 10
981 E 1 c. blue and light blue . . 20 10

296 1 c. Stamp of 1871

1973. Air. Stamp Centenary (1971). (2nd issue).
988 **296** 1 c. brown 15 10
988a 6 c. orange 15 10
988b 6 c. green 15 10
988c 6 c. blue 15 10
988d 6 c. grey 15 10
989 1 q. red . . . . 1·75 1·75

297 School Building

1973. Air. Centenary of Instituto Varones. Chiquimula.
990 **297** 3 c. multicoloured 10 10
991 5 c. red and black 15 10

1974. No. 863 surch **Desvalorizadas a Q0.50** and leaves.
992 **268** 50 c. on 3 q. brn & red . . 85 70

1974. Air. Centenary of Universal Postal Union Nos. 927/32 optd **UPU HOMENAJE CENTENARIO 1874 1974** and U.P.U. emblem.
993 **289** 1 c. blue and light blue . . 25 20
994 A 1 c. blue and light blue . . 25 20
995 B 1 c. blue and light blue . . 25 20
996 C 1 c. blue and light blue . . 25 20
997 D 1 c. blue and light blue . . 25 20
998 E 1 c. blue and light blue . . 25 20

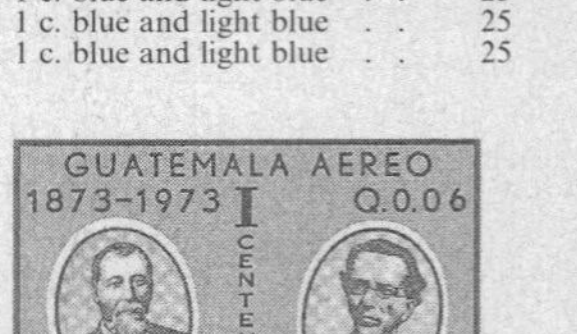

300 Barrios and Granados

1974. Air. Centenary (1973) of Polytechnic School (2nd issue).
1000 **300** 6 c. red, grey and blue . . 15 10
1001 – 25 c. multicoloured . . . 45 20
DESIGN—VERT: 25 c. School building.

1974. Air. Protection of the Resplendent Quetzal (Guatemala's national bird). No. 800 surch with bars, **VALE 10c. Proteccion del Ave Nacional el Quetzal** and bird.
1002 **252** 10 c. on 11 c. blk & brn . 75 25

302 Costume of San Martin Sacatepequez

1974. Air. Guatemalan Costumes. Mult.
1003 2 c. Solola costume 10 10
1004 2½ c. Type **302** 10 10
1005 9 c. Coban costume 20 10
1006 20 c. Chichicastenango costume 35 15

303 Mayan Girl and Resplendent Quetzals

1975. Air. International Women's Year.
1007 **303** 8 c. multicoloured 25 10
1008 20 c. multicoloured . . . 65 25

304 Rotary Emblem

1975. Air. 50th Anniv of Guatemala City Rotary Club.
1009 **304** 10 c. multicoloured . . . 15 10
1010 15 c. multicoloured . . . 30 15

305 I.W.Y. Emblem and Orchid

1975. Air. International Women's Year (2nd series).

1011 305 1 c. multicoloured 10 10
1012 8 c. multicoloured 15 10
1013 26 c. multicoloured . . . 45 20

306 Ruined Village

1976. Air. Earthquake of 4 February 1976. Multicoloured.

1014 1 c. Type **306** 10 10
1015 3 c. Food queue 10 10
1016 5 c. Jaguar Temple, Tikal . . . 15 10
1017 10 c. Broken bridge 20 10
1018 15 c. Open-air casualty station . 35 15
1019 20 c. Harvesting sugarcane . . 35 15
1020 25 c. Ruined house 55 20
1021 30 c. Reconstruction, Tecpan . 70 20
1022 50 c. Ruined church, Cerrodel Carmen 90 35
1023 75 c. Clearing debris . . . . . 1·40 55
1024 1 q. Military aid . . . . . 1·75 70
1025 2 q. Lake Atitlan . . . . . . 3·50 1·40

Text in panels expresses gratitude for foreign aid.

307 Eagle and Resplendent Quetzal Emblems

1976. Air. Bicentenary of American Revolution. Multicoloured.

1029 1 c. Type **307** 25 10
1030 2 c. Boston Tea Party 10 10
1031 3 c. Thomas Jefferson (after G. Stuart) (vert) 10 10
1032 4 c. Eagle & Resplendent Quetzal emblems (vert) . . . 25 10
1033 5 c. "Death of Gen. Warren at Bunker Hill" (detail, Trumbull) 10 10
1034 10 c. "Washington reviewing his Ragged Army" (detail, Trego) 20 10
1035 15 c. "Washington rallying the Troops at Monmouth" (detail, Leutze) 20 15
1036 20 c. Eagle & Resplendent Quetzal emblems (diff.) . . . 40 20
1037 25 c. "Meeting of Generals at Yorktown after the Surrender" (detail, Peale) . . 55 20
1038 30 c. "Washington crossing the Delaware" (detail, Leutze) . . 70 20
1039 35 c. Eagle & Resplendent Quetzal emblems (diff.) . . . 75 30
1040 40 c. "Declaration of Independence" (detail, Trimbull) 60 30
1041 45 c. "Patrick Henry before Virginia House of Burgesses" (detail, Rothermel) (vert) . . 90 35
1042 50 c. "Congress voting Independence" (detail, Savage) . . . . 1·00 35
1043 1 q. George Washington (after G. Stuart) (vert) . . . . . 1·75 1·50
1044 2 q. Abraham Lincoln (after D. D. Eisenhower). (vert) . . . 2·75 2·75
1045 3 q. Benjamin Franklin (after C. W. Peale). (vert) . . . . 4·00 4·00
1046 5 q. John F. Kennedy (35 × 55 mm) . . . . 7·00 2·50

308 Quetzal Coin

1976. Air. 50th Anniv of Quetzal Currency.

1051 308 8 c. black, orge & blue . . 20 10
1052 20 c. black, mve & blue . . 45 20

309 "The Engineers" (sculpture)

1976. Air. Centenary of Engineering School, Guatemala City.

1053 309 9 c. blue 20 10
1054 10 c. green 20 10

310 Sculpture of Christ (Pedro de Mendoza)

1977. Holy Week. Multicoloured.

1055 6 c. Type **310** (postage) 10 10
1056 8 c. Sculpture of Christ (Lanuza Brothers) 15 10
1057 3 c. Statue of Christ (air) . . . 10 10
1058 4 c. Statue of Christ (vert) . . 10 10
1059 7 c. Statue of Christ (vert) . . 20 10
1060 9 c. Statue of Christ (vert) . . 25 10
1061 20 c. Statue of Christ and Virgin (vert) 55 15
1062 26 c. Statue of Christ 70 55

311 Deed to Site of Guatemala City

312 Arms of Quetzaltenango

1977. Air. Bicentenary of Nueva Guatemala de la Asuncion (Guatemala City). Mult.

1064 6 c. Type **311** 10 10
1065 7 c. City Hall and Bank of Guatemala (horiz) 10 10
1066 8 c. Site of first legislative assembly (horiz) 10 10
1067 9 c. Archbishop's arms (horiz) . 10 10
1068 22 c. Arms of Guatemala City . 30 15

1977. Air. 150th Anniv of Founding of Quetzaltenango.

1071 312 7 c. black and silver . . . 15 10
1072 – 30 c. orange and blue . . 55 20

DESIGN: 30 c. City Hall and torch.

313 "Interfer 77" Emblem

315 "The Holy Family"

XIV CONGRESO INTERNACIONAL DEL NOTARIADO LATINO
GUATEMALA AEREO Q.0.10 1977

314 Mayan Bas-relief

1977. 4th International Fair, Guatemala City.

1073 313 7 c. multicoloured 10 10

1977. Air. 14th Congress of Latin Notaries.

1074 314 10 c. black and red . . . 20 10

1977. Air. Christmas. Multicoloured.

1075 1 c. Type **315** 10 10
1076 2 c. Boy and girl with animals, and Jesus in crib 10 10
1077 4 c. Boy and girl with Mary and Jesus 15 10

316 Man from Almolongo

317 Virgin of Sorrows, Antigua

1978. Air. Guatemalan Costumes. Mult.

1078 1 c. Type **316** 10 10
1079 2 c. Woman from Nebaj . . . 10 10
1080 5 c. Couple from San Juan Cotzal 15 10
1081 6 c. Couple from Todos Santos . 20 10
1082 20 c. Couple from Regidores . 70 15
1083 30 c. Woman from San Cristobal 70 20

1978. Air. Holy Week. Multicoloured.

1085 2 c. Type **317** 10 10
1086 4 c. Virgin of Mercy, Antigua . 15 10
1087 5 c. Virgin of Anguish, Yurrita 15 10
1088 6 c. Virgin of the Rosary, Santo Domingo 15 10
1089 8 c. Virgin of Sorrows, Santo Domingo 20 10
1090 9 c. Virgin of the Rosary, Quetzaltenango 20 15
1091 10 c. Virgin of the Immaculate Conception, Church of St. Francis 25 15
1092 20 c. Virgin of the Immaculate Conception, Cathedral Church 55 20

318 Footballer

319 Gymnastics

1978. Air. World Cup Football Championship, Argentina.

1094 318 10 c. multicoloured . . . 20 15

1978. Air. 13th Central American and Caribbean Games, Medellin, Colombia.

1095 319 6 c. mauve, blue & blk . . 10 10
1096 – 6 c. brt blue, bl & blk . . 15 10
1097 – 6 c. blue, brt blue & blk . . 15 10
1098 – 6 c. blue, mauve & blk . . 15 10
1099 – 8 c. mauve, blue & blk . . 15 10

DESIGNS: No 1096, Volleyball; No. 1097, Target Shooting; No. 1098, Weightlifing; No. 1099, Running.

320 "Cattleya pachecoi"

321 University Seal

1978. Air. Orchids. Multicoloured.

1100 1 c. Type **320** 10 10
1101 1 c. "Sobralia xantholeuca" . . 10 10
1102 1 c. "Cypripedium irapeanum" 10 10
1103 1 c. "Oncidium splendidum" . 10 10
1104 3 c. "Cattleya bowringiana" . . 10 10
1105 3 c. "Encyclia cordigera" . . . 10 10
1106 3 c. "Epidendrum imatophyllum" 10 10
1107 3 c. "Barkeria skinneri" . . . 10 10
1108 8 c. "Spiranthes speciosa" . . 20 10
1109 20 c. "Lycaste skinneri" . . . 55 15

1978. Air. 300th Anniv of San Carlos University of Guatemala. Multicoloured.

1110 6 c. Type **321** 15 10
1111 7 c. Students from different faculties (26 × 46 mm) . . . 15 10
1112 12 c. 17th-century student . . 20 10
1113 14 c. Student and molecular model 30 10

322 Brown and White Children

323 Planting Seedling

1978. Air. Guatemalan Children's Year (1977). Multicoloured.

1114 6 c. Type **322** 15 10
1115 7 c. Child skipping 15 10
1116 12 c. "Helping Hand" 20 10
1117 14 c. Hands protecting Indian girl 30 10

1979. Air. Forestry. Multicoloured.

1118 6 c. Type **323** 10 10
1119 8 c. Burnt forest 15 10
1120 9 c. Woodland scene 15 10
1121 10 c. Sawmill 15 10
1122 26 c. Forest conservation . . . 35 15

324 Ocellated Turkey

325 Clay Jar

1979. Air. Wildlife Conservation. Mult.

1124 1 c. Type **324** 40 15
1125 3 c. White-tailed deer (horiz) . 25 10
1126 5 c. King Vulture . . . . . . 1·25 15
1127 7 c. Great Horned Owl . . . . 2·50 55
1128 9 c. Ocelot 55 10

1979. Air. Archaeological Treasures from Tikal. Multicoloured.

1130 2 c. Type **325** 10 10
1131 3 c. Ceramic head of Mayan woman 10 10
1132 4 c. Earring 10 10
1133 5 c. Vase 10 10
1134 6 c. Ceramic figure 10 10
1135 7 c. Carved bone 10 10
1136 8 c. Striped vase 15 10
1137 10 c. Tripod vase with lid . . . 15 10

326 Presidential Guard Headquarters

GUATEMALA
AEREO 0.08 1978

327 National Coat of Arms

1979. 30th Anniv of Presidential Guard. Multicoloured.

1138 10 c. Type **326** (postage) . . . 15 10
1139 8 c. Presidential Guard insignia (air) 15 10

1979. Air. Municipal Arms. Multicoloured.

1140 8 c. Type **327** 15 10
1141 8 c. Alta Verapaz 15 10
1142 8 c. Baja Verapaz 15 10
1143 8 c. Chimal Tenango 15 10
1144 8 c. Chiquimula 15 10
1145 8 c. Escuintla 15 10
1146 8 c. Flores (Peten) 15 10
1147 8 c. Guatemala 15 10
1148 8 c. Huehuetenango 15 10
1149 8 c. Izabal . . . . 2·50 75
1150 8 c. Jalapa 15 10
1151 8 c. Jutiapa 15 10
1152 8 c. Mazatenango 15 10
1153 8 c. El Progreso 15 10
1154 8 c. Quezaltenango 15 10
1155 8 c. Quiche 15 10
1156 8 c. Retalhuleu 15 10
1157 8 c. Sacatepequez 15 10
1158 8 c. San Marcos 15 10
1159 8 c. Santa Rosa 15 10
1160 8 c. Solola 15 10
1161 8 c. Totonicapan 15 10
1162 8 c. Zacapa 15 10

328 Rotary Emblem and Girl with Flowers

329 The Creation of the World

1980. 75th Anniv of Rotary International. Multicoloured.

1164 4 c. Type **328** 10 10
1165 6 c. Diamond, emblem and Resplendent Quetzal 50 10
1166 10 c. Paul P. Harris (founder), emblem and Resplendent Quetzal 90 40

1981. Air. "Popol Vuh". Designs showing medallic illustrations of Guatemalan history and legends from the Sacred Book of the Ancient Quiches of Guatemala. (a) The Creation.
1167 **329** 1 c. black and mauve . . . 10 10
1168 – 2 c. black and green . . . 10 10
1169 – 4 c. black and blue . . . 10 10
1170 – 8 c. black and yellow . . 15 10
1171 – 10 c. black and pink . . . 15 10
1172 – 22 c. black and brown . . 30 10

(b) The Adventures of Hun Ahpu and Xbalanque.
1173 – 1 c. black and mauve . . . 10 10
1174 – 4 c. black and violet . . . 10 10
1175 – 6 c. black and brown . . . 10 10
1176 – 8 c. black and green . . . 15 10
1177 – 10 c. black and yellow . . 15 10
1178 – 26 c. black and green . . 35 10

(c) The Founding of the Quiche Race.
1179 – 2 c. black and mauve . . . 10 10
1180 – 4 c. black and blue . . . 10 10
1181 – 6 c. black and pink . . . 10 10
1182 – 8 c. black and yellow . . 15 10
1183 – 10 c. black and green . . 15 10
1184 – 30 c. black and green . . 45 15

(d) The Territorial Expansion of the Quiches.
1185 – 3 c. black and blue . . . 10 10
1186 – 4 c. black and violet . . . 10 10
1187 – 6 c. black and pink . . . 10 10
1188 – 8 c. black and grey . . . 15 10
1189 – 10 c. black and green . . 15 10
1190 – 50 c. black and mauve . . 70 20

DESIGNS: No. 1168, Populating the earth; No. 1169, Birth of the stick-men; No. 1170, Destruction of the stick-men; No. 1171, Creation of the men of corn; No. 1172, "Thanks to the creator"; No. 1173, Origin of the twin semi-gods; No. 1174, Punishment of the Princess Xquic; No. 1175, Odyssey of Hun Ahpu and Xbalanque; No. 1176, The test in Xibalba; No. 1177, Multiplication of the prodigies; No. 1178, The deification of Hun Ahpu and Xbalanque; No. 1179, Balam Quitze, father of Caviquib; No. 1180, Caha Paluma, wife of Balam Quitze; No 1181, Balam Acab, father of Nihaibab; No. 1182, Chomiia, wife of Balam Acab; No. 1183, Mahucutah, father of Ahau Quiche; No. 1184, Tzununiha, wife of Mahucutah; No. 1185, Cotuha, Quiche monarch; No. 1186, The invincible Cotuha and Iztayul; No. 1187, Cucumatz, the prodigious king; No. 1188, Warrior with captive; No. 1189, "None can conquer or kill the king"; No. 1190, "This was the greatness of the Quiches".

330 Early and Modern Telephones (cent)

331 Roderico Toledo and German Chupina (first and present Police Chiefs)

1981. Air. Anniversaries.
1191 – 3 c. red and black 10 10
1192 – 5 c. blue and black . . . 10 10
1193 **330** 6 c. multicoloured . . . 10 10
1194 – 7 c. multicoloured . . . 10 10
1195 – 12 c. multicoloured . . . 15 10
1196 – 25 c. multicoloured . . . 35 10

DESIGNS—26 × 46 mm: 3 c. Thomas Edison (centenary of gramophone); 29 × 39 mm: 7 c. Charles Lindbergh (50th anniv of solo Atlantic flight); 12 c. Jose Cecilio del Valle (patriot, birth bicentenary); 25 c. Jesues Castillo (composer, birth centenary); 46 × 26 mm: 5 c. Spool of film (50th anniv of sound film).

1981. Air. Centenary of National Police. Multicoloured.
1197 2 c. Type **331** 10 10
1198 4 c. Police Headquarters . . . 10 10

332 Mayan Sun Calendar

1981. Air. Seventh Latin American Aviculture Congress.
1199 **332** 1 c. green, yell & blk . . . 10 10

333 Bernardo O'Higgins (Chile)

1982. Air. Liberators of the Americas.
1200 **333** 2 c. multicoloured 10 10
1201 – 3 c. multicoloured 10 10
1202 – 4 c. multicoloured 10 10
1203 – 10 c. grey and black . . . 15 10

DESIGNS—(31 × 45 mm): 4 c. Jose de San Martin (Argentine); 10 c. Miguel Garcia Granados (Guatemala). (26 × 35 mm): 3 c. Jose Artigas (Uruguay).

334 General Barrios and Bank

1982. Air. Centenary of Banco de Occidente.
1204 **334** 1 c. multicoloured 10 10
1205 – 2 c. black, red & blue . . 10 10
1206 – 3 c. multicoloured 10 10
1207 – 4 c. multicoloured 10 10

DESIGNS—HORIZ: 2 c. Bank building. VERT: 3 c. Centenary emblem; 4 c. Centenary medals.

335 Old and New Bank Buildings, Guatemala City

1982. Air. 50th Anniv of National Mortgage Bank.
1208 **335** 1 c. multicoloured 10 10
1209 – 2 c. black, yell & grn . . 10 10
1210 – 5 c. multicoloured 10 10
1211 – 10 c. black, yell & grn . . 15 10

DESIGNS—HORIZ: 2 c. Bank emblem; 10 c. Bank and Anniversary emblems. VERT: 5 c. Bronze anniversary medallion.

336 Brother Pedro

337 I.T.U. and W.H.O. Emblems with Ribbons forming Caduceus

1983. Air. Blessed Brother Pedro. Mult.
1212 1 c. Type **336** 10 10
1213 20 c. Apparition of Virgin Mary 30 10

1983. Air. World Communications and Health Day.
1214 **337** 10 c. yellow, red & blk . . 15 10

338 Hands holding Bible

340 F.A.O. Emblem and Starving Children

339 Train crossing Las Vacas Bridge

1983. Air. Centenary (1982) of Evangelical Church in Guatemala. Multicoloured.
1215 3 c. Type **338** 10 10
1216 5 c. Central Evangelical Church 10 10

1983. Air. Centenary (1980) of Guatemalan Railways. Multicoloured.
1217 10 c. Type **339** 75 65
1218 25 c. General Barrios and trains at station . . . . 2·00 1·50
1219 30 c. Train crossing Lake Amatitlan Dam . . . . . . 2·25 1·75

1983. Air. World Food Day (1981). Mult.
1220 8 c. Maize and Globe 10 10
1221 1 q. Type **340** 95 70

1984. Air. As Nos. 927/32 and 945/50 but colours changed. Values inscribed in black.
1230 **289** 1 c. black and green . . . 10 10
1231 A 1 c. black and green . . . 10 10
1232 B 1 c. black and green . . . 10 10
1233 C 1 c. black and green . . . 10 10
1234 D 1 c. black and green . . . 10 10
1235 E 1 c. black and green . . . 10 10
1236 **289** 5 c. black and orange . . 10 10
1237 A 5 c. black and orange . . 10 10
1238 B 5 c. black and orange . . 10 10
1239 C 5 c. black and orange . . 10 10
1240 D 5 c. black and orange . . 10 10
1241 E 5 c. black and orange . . 10 10

341 Pope John Paul II

1984. Air. Papal Visit. Multicoloured.
1242 4 c. Type **341** 10 10
1243 8 c. Woman kneeling before Pope 15 10

342 Rafael Landivar

1984. Air. 250th Birth Anniv of Rafael Landivar (poet). Multicoloured.
1244 2 c. Type **342** 10 10
1245 4 c. Landivar's tomb, Antigua Guatemala (horiz) 10 10

343 Casariego y Acevedo

344 Bank's Emblem

1984. Air. 1st Death Anniv of Cardinal Mario Casariego y Acevedo, Archbishop of Guatemala.
1246 **343** 10 c. multicoloured . . . 15 10

1984. Air. 20th Anniv of Central American Bank for Economic Integration.
1247 **344** 30 c. multicoloured . . . 50 15

345 Planting Coffee, 1870

346 "Beaver" Cub and Tikal Pyramid

1984. Air. Coffee.
1248 **345** 1 c. black and brown . . 10 10
1249 – 2 c. black and flesh . . . 10 10
1250 – 3 c. black and stone . . . 10 10
1251 – 4 c. black and buff . . . 30 10
1252 – 5 c. multicoloured 10 10
1253 – 10 c. multicoloured . . . 15 10
1254 – 12 c. multicoloured . . . 15 10
1255 – 25 c. multicoloured . . . 1·40 30
1256 – 25 c. black & brown . . . 35 10
1257 – 30 c. multicoloured . . . 40 10

DESIGNS: As T **345**: 2 c. Harvesting coffee, 1870; 3 c. Drying coffee beans, 1870; 4 c. Exporting coffee, 1870; 5 c. Grafting seedlings; 10 c. Instant coffee; 12 c. Harvesting and processing coffee; 25 c. (1255), Exporting coffee (different). (81 × 108 mm): 25 c. (1256) Women picking coffee. (100 × 81 mm): 30 c. Globe and coffee beans.

1985. Air. 75th Anniv of Boy Scout Movement. Multicoloured.
1258 5 c. Type **346** 10 10
1259 6 c. "Wolf" cub and Captains Palace, Old Guatemala . . . 10 10
1260 8 c. Scout, xylophone player and countryside 15 10
1261 10 c. Rover scout and dancers . 15 10
1262 20 c. Lord Baden-Powell (founder) and Carlos Cipriani (founder of Guatemalan scouts) 30 10

347 Family

348 Emblem

1985. Air. Inter-American Family Year.
1263 **347** 10 c. multicoloured . . . 15 10

1985. Air. 25th Anniv of Central American Air Navigation Services Association.
1264 **348** 10 c. multicoloured . . . 15 10

349 Morse Key, Samuel Morse, J. Rufino Barrios and Telegraph Aerial

1985. Air. National Telegraph Service.
1265 **349** 4 c. black and brown . . 10 10

350 Olympic Rings and Maya Pelota Player

351 Rescue Team with Person in Cradle

1986. Air. 90th Anniv of First Modern Olympic Games and Foundation of International Olympic Committee. Multicoloured.
1266 8 c. Type **350** 15 10
1267 10 c. Rings and Baron Pierre de Coubertin 15 10

1986. Air. Volunteer Fireman (1st series).
1268 **351** 6 c. multicoloured 10 10
See also Nos. 1271/2.

352 Temple of Minerva, Quetzaltenango

1986. Air. Centenary (1984) of Independence Fair, Quetzaltenango. Multicoloured.
1269 8 c. Type **352** 15 10
1270 10 c. City arms in courtyard of Quetzaltenango Municipal Palace 15 10

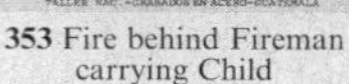

353 Fire behind Fireman carrying Child

354 Arms

1986. Air. Volunteer Firemen (2nd series). Multicoloured.
1271 8 c. Type **353** 15 10
1272 10 c. Searching rubble after explosion (33 × 24 mm) . . 15 10

1986. Air. 25th Anniv (1976) of Association of Telegraphists and Radio-Telegraph Operators.
1273 **354** 6 c. multicoloured 25 10

355 Architect with Plans looking at Building

1987. Air. 25th Anniv of San Carlos University Architecture Faculty.

1274	**355**	10 c. multicoloured	15	10

356 Emblem and Boeing 727

1987. Air. 40th Anniv of I.C.A.O. Mult.

1275	8 c Type **356**	15	10
1276	10 c. Boeing 727 airplane on runway (vert)	15	10

357 Aerial View of Site

1987. Air. Chixoy Hydro-electric Plant.

1277	**357**	2 c. multicoloured	10	10

358 Dr. Cayetano Francos y Monroy, Archbishop of Guatemala (founder)

360 Girls in Traditional Costumes

359 Column beside Man studying Book

1987. Air. Bicentenary (1981) of St. Joseph Children's College. Multicoloured.

1278	8 c. Type **358**	10	10
1279	10 c. College emblem	15	10

1987. Air. Regional Book Promotion Centre for Latin America and Caribbean.

1280	**359**	12 c. multicoloured	15	10

1987. Coban Folklore Festival. Mult.

1281	50 c. Girl weaving	55	15
1282	1 q. Type **360**	1·25	30

361 Cesar Branas

1987. Air. Writers (1st series).

1283	**361**	6 c. orange and black	10	10
1284	–	8 c. red and black	10	10
1285	–	9 c. purple and black	15	10

DESIGNS: 8 c. Rafael Arevalo Martinez; 9 c. Jose Milla y Vidaurre.

See also Nos. 1297/8 and 1307/11.

362 Footballer

1987. Air. Pan-American Games National Football Selection.

1286	**362**	10 c. blue and black	15	10

363 Miguel Angel Asturias Cultural Centre

364 Stylized Dove

1987.

1287	**363**	1 c. blue	10	10
1287a		2 c. brown	10	10
1288		3 c. blue	10	10
1289		4 c. mauve	10	10
1290		5 c. orange	10	10
1291		6 c. green	10	10
1292		7 c. red	10	10
1293		8 c. mauve	10	10
1294		9 c. black	10	10
1295		10 c. green	15	10

1988. Air. Writers (2nd series). As T **361**.

1297	4 c. red and black	10	10
1298	5 c. brown and black	10	10

DESIGNS: 4 c. Enrique A. Hidalgo; 5 c. Enrique Gomez Carrillo.

1988. Air. "Esquipulas II—A Firm Step towards Peace".

1299	**364**	10 c. green	15	10
1300	–	40 c. red	45	10
1301	–	60 c. blue	65	20

DESIGNS—HORIZ: 40 c. Three stylized doves. VERT: 60 c. Stylized dove.

366 St. John and Boys

1989. Death Centenary of St. John Bosco (founder of Salesian Brothers).

1303	**366**	40 c. black and gold	55	15

367 Birds

368 Madrid Codex (detail)

1989. Air. Bicentenary of French Revolution.

1304	**367**	1 q. red, blue & black	90	35

1990. Air. America. Pre-Columbian Culture. Multicoloured.

1305	10 c. Type **368**	10	10
1306	20 c. Tikal Pyramid	10	10

1990. Air. Writers (3rd series). As T **361**.

1307	1 c. mauve and black	10	10
1308	2 c. orange and black	10	10
1309	3 c. blue and black	10	10
1310	7 c. black and green	10	10
1311	10 c. black and yellow	10	10

DESIGNS: 1 c. Flavio Herrera; 2 c. Rosendo Santa Cruz; 3 c. Werner Ovalle Lopez; 7 c. Clemente Marroquin Rojas; 10 c. Miguel Angel Asturias.

369 Games Emblem

1990. 6th Central American and Caribbean University Games. Multicoloured.

1312	15 c. Type **369**	10	10
1313	20 c. Mascot holding flame (vert)	10	10
1314	25 c. Mascot playing volleyball	10	10
1315	30 c. Mascot playing football	10	10
1316	45 c. Mascot performing judo movement	10	10
1317	1 q. Mascot playing baseball	25	10
1318	2 q. Mascot playing basketball	45	10
1319	3 q. Mascot hurdling	70	20

370 Family, Cereal and Emblem

1990. Air. 40th Anniv of Central America and Panama Nutrition Institute.

1320	**370**	20 c. multicoloured	10	10

371 Palais de l'Athenee, Geneva (venue of founding meeting)

1990. Air. 125th Anniv (1988) of International Red Cross.

1321	**371**	50 c. multicoloured	15	10

372 Arms

1991. Air. Centenary of National Defence Staff.

1322	**372**	20 c. multicoloured	10	10

373 Atitlan Lake

1991. America. Natural World. Multicoloured.

1323	10 c. Pacaya Volcano in eruption	10	10
1324	60 c. Type **373**	15	10

374 Martin and Vicente Pinzon

375 Crops

1992. Air. America. 500th Anniv of Discovery of America by Columbus. Each black and green.

1325	40 c. Type **374**	35	15
1326	60 c. Christopher Columbus and "Santa Maria" (vert)	40	15

1992. Air. 50th Anniv of International Institute for Agricultural Co-operation.

1327	**375**	10 c. multicoloured	10	10

376 Emblem

377 "Encyclia cochleata"

1992. International Anti-AIDS Campaign.

1328	**376**	1 q. multicoloured	25	10

1994. Air. Orchids (1st series). Multicoloured.

1329	50 c. Type **377**	10	10
1330	1 q. "Encyclia vitellina"	20	10
1331	2 q. "Odontoglossum uroskinneri"	45	10

See also Nos. 1355/6.

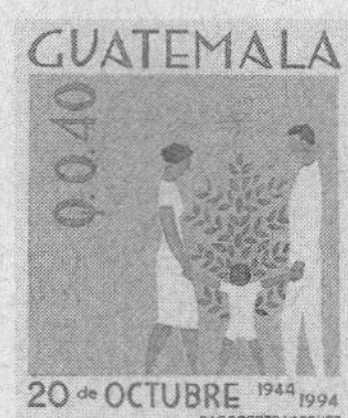

378 Family around Tree

1994. 50th Anniv of 20 October Revolution. Multicoloured.

1332	40 c. Type **378**	10	10
1333	60 c. Dove on hand (horiz)	15	10
1334	1 q. Man holding book and rifle	20	10
1335	2 q. Representations of social developments since 1944	45	10
1336	3 q. Three youths supporting torch ("Revolution, Liberty, Justice and Peace")	65	15

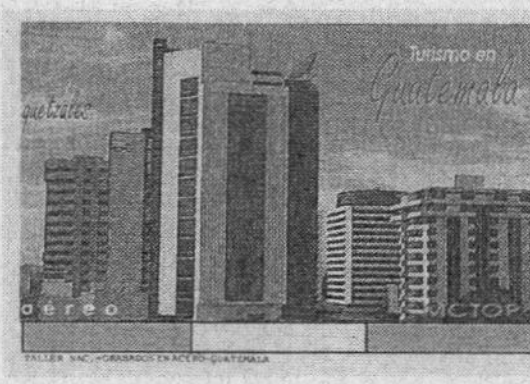

379 City Buildings

1995. Air. Tourism. Multicoloured.

1337	20 c. White water rafting	10	10
1338	40 c. Windsurfing	10	10
1339	60 c. Pleasure boat on Lake Atitlan	15	10
1340	80 c. Tourist launch "Crucero"	15	10
1341	1 q. Erupting volcano	20	10
1342	2 q. Type **379**	45	10
1343	3 q. Parrots on perch (vert)	65	15
1344	4 q. Mayan ruins (vert)	90	20
1345	5 q. Ceremony (vert)	1·10	25

380 Greeting Crowd

1996. Air. Papal Visit. Pope John Paul II. Multicoloured.

1350	10 c. Type **380**	10	10
1351	1 q. Holding child	20	10
1352	1 q. 75 Holding crucifix and wearing mitre	35	10
1353	1 q. 90 Wearing cross and red cloak	40	10
1354	2 q. 90 Wearing red hat	60	15

1996. Air. Orchids (2nd series). As T **377**. Mult.

1355	20 c. "Phragmipedium caudatum"	10	10
1356	1 q. 50 "Odontoglossum laeve"	30	10

381 Carlos Merida

1996. Air. Personalities.

1357	**381**	40 c. lt blue, blue & blk	10	10
1358	–	50 c. brown, blue & blk	10	10
1359	–	60 c. brown, blue & blk	10	10

DESIGNS: 50 c. Jose Eulalio Samayoa; 60 c. Manuel Montufar y Coronado.

382 University Hall

1997. Buildings. Multicoloured.

1360		50 c. Type **382**	10	10
1361		1 q. Brewery	20	10

383 Breastfeeding

1997. Air. Breastfeeding Campaign.

1362	**383**	1 q. multicoloured	20	10

384 Parent and Child (Marion Contreras Castanaza)

1997. 50th Anniv (1996) of U.N.I.C.E.F. "Children and Peace". Multicoloured.

1363		10 c. Type **384**	10	10
1364		20 c. Child riding birds (Marvin Sac Coyoy) (horiz)	10	10

385 Child writing (Education)

1997. Air. Public Finance Projects. Mult.

1365		20 c. Type **385**	10	10
1366		60 c. Child receiving medication (health)	10	10
1367		80 c. Road (infrastructure)	15	10
1368		1 q. Family (security)	20	10

EXPRESS LETTER STAMPS.

1940. No. 231 optd **EXPRESO**.

E411	**97**	4 c. yellow	85	35

E **181** Motor cyclist

1948. Surch.

E479	E **181**	10 c. on 4 c. blk & grn	1·00	60

OFFICIAL STAMPS

Franqueo Oficial
Guatemala.
1902
2
CENTAVOS

O **41** O **100**

1902.

O127	O **41**	1 c. green	2·50	1·25
O128		2 c. red	2·50	1·25
O129		5 c. blue	3·00	1·00
O130		10 c. purple	3·50	1·00
O131		25 c. orange	3·50	1·00

1929.

O239	O **100**	1 c. blue	30	30
O240		2 c. sepia	30	30
O241		3 c. green	30	30
O242		4 c. purple	35	35
O243		5 c. lake	35	35
O244		10 c. brown	40	40
O245		25 c. blue	85	70

1939. Air. Nos. 369/74 optd **OFICIAL OFICIAL**.

O400	**134**	1 c. brown and orange	50	75
O401	–	2 c. brown and red	50	75
O402	–	3 c. brown, buff & green	50	75
O403	–	4 c. brn and purple	50	75
O404	–	5 c. brown and grey	50	75
O405	–	10 c. brown and blue	50	75

GUERNSEY Pt. 1

An island in the English Channel off N.W. coast of France. Occupied by German Forces from June, 1940, to May, 1945. "Regional" issues were introduced from 1958 (see after GREAT BRITAIN). The island's postal service was organised as a separate postal administration in 1969.

(a) War Occupation Issues.

1

1941.

No.	Type	Description	Unused	Used
1	1	½d. green	3·25	2·50
2		1d. red	2·75	1·50
3a		2½d. blue	4·50	4·50

(b) Independent Postal Administration.

4 Castle Cornet and Edward the Confessor

5 View of Sark

1969.

No.	Type	Description	Unused	Used
13	4	½d. mauve and black	10	10
14	–	1d. blue and black*	10	10
14b	–	1d. blue and black*	30	30
15	–	1½d. brown and black	10	10
16	–	2d. multicoloured	10	10
17	–	3d. multicoloured	15	15
18	–	4d. multicoloured	25	25
19	–	5d. multicoloured	25	15
20	–	6d. multicoloured	30	30
21	–	9d. multicoloured	40	30
22	–	1s. multicoloured	30	30
23	–	1s. 6d. green and black*	30	30
23b	–	1s. 6d. green and black*	2·25	1·75
24	–	1s. 9d. multicoloured	1·25	1·50
25	–	2s. 6d. violet and black	5·00	4·25
26	5	5s. multicoloured	3·25	3·25
27	–	10s. multicoloured	26·00	22·00
28a	–	£1 multicoloured	2·00	1·75

DESIGNS—As Type **4**: 1d. Map and William I; 1½d. Martello tower and Henry II; 2d. Arms of Sark and King John; 3d. Arms of Alderney and Edward III; 4d. Guernsey lily and Henry V; 5d. Arms of Guernsey and Elizabeth I; 6d. Arms of Alderney and Charles II; 9d. Arms of Sark and George III; 1s. Arms of Guernsey and Queen Victoria; 1s. 6d, As 1d; 1s. 9d. Guernsey lily and Elizabeth I; 2s. 6d. Martello tower and King John. As Type **5**: 10s. View of Alderney; 20s. View of Guernsey.

*On Nos. 14 and 23 the degree of latitude is inscr (incorrectly) as 40° 30′ N. On Nos. 14b and 23b it has been corrected to 49° 30.

19 Isaac Brock as Colonel

1969. Birth Bicent of Sir Isaac Brock. Mult.

No.	Type	Description	Unused	Used
29		4d. Type **19**	20	20
30		5d. Sir Isaac Brock as Major-General	20	20
31		1s. 9d. Isaac Brock as Ensign	1·40	1·25
32		2s. 6d. Arms and flags	1·40	1·25

The 2s. 6d., is horiz.

23 H.M.S. "L103" (landing craft) entering St. Peter's Harbour

1970. 25th Anniv of Liberation.

No.	Type	Description	Unused	Used
33	23	4d. blue	40	40
34	–	5d. brown, lake and grey	40	40
35	–	1s. 6d. brown and buff	2·50	2·50

DESIGNS—HORIZ: 5d. H.M.S. "Bulldog" and H.M.S. "Beagle" (destroyers) entering St. Peter Port. VERT: 1s. 6d. Brigadier Snow reading Proclamation.

26 Guernsey "Toms"

32 St. Peter's Church, Sark

1970. Agriculture and Horticulture. Mult.

No.	Type	Description	Unused	Used
36		4d. Type **26**	80	20
37		5d. Guernsey cow	90	20
38		9d. Guernsey bull	4·50	2·75
39		1s. 6d. Freesias	5·50	3·00

1970. Christmas. Churches (1st series). Mult.

No.	Type	Description	Unused	Used
40		4d. St. Anne's Church, Alderney (horiz)	35	20
41		5d. St. Peter's Church (horiz)	45	25
42		9d. Type **32**	1·75	1·10
43		1s. 6d. St. Tugual Chapel, Herm	2·00	1·50

See also Nos. 63/6.

34 Martello Tower and King John

1971. Decimal Currency. Nos. 13, etc., but with new colours and decimal values as T **34**.

No.	Type	Description	Unused	Used
44		½p. mauve & black (as No. 13)	10	15
45		1p. blue & black (as No. 14b)	10	10
46		1½p. brown & blk (as No. 15)	15	15
47		2p. multicoloured (as No. 18)	15	15
48		2½p. multicoloured (as No. 19)	15	10
49		3p. multicoloured (as No. 17)	20	20
50		3½p. multicoloured (as No. 24)	25	25
51		4p. multicoloured (as No. 16)	35	25
52		5p. green & black (as No. 14b)	30	25
53		6p. multicoloured (as No. 20)	30	35
54		7½p. multicoloured (as No. 22)	40	45
55		9p. multicoloured (as No. 21)	50	75
56a		10p. violet & blk (as No. 25)	1·75	1·75
57a		20p. multicoloured (as No. 26)	1·00	1·00
58		50p. multicoloured (as No. 27)	2·00	2·00

35 Hong Kong 2 c. of 1862

1971. Thomas De La Rue Commemoration.

No.	Type	Description	Unused	Used
59	35	2p. purple	50	30
60	–	2½p. red	50	30
61	–	4p. green	2·50	2·25
62	–	7½p. blue	2·75	2·25

DESIGNS (Each showing portraits of Queen Elizabeth and Thomas De La Rue): 2½p. Great Britain 4d. of 1855–7; 4p. Italy 5 c. of 1862; 7½p. Confederate States 5 c. of 1862.

1971. Christmas. Churches (2nd series). As T **32**. Multicoloured.

No.	Type	Description	Unused	Used
63		2p. Ebenezer Church, St. Peter Port (horiz)	25	25
64		2½p. Church of St. Pierre du Bois (horiz)	25	25
65		5p. St. Joseph's Church, St. Peter Port	2·25	1·75
66		7½p. Church of St. Philippe de Torteval	2·25	1·75

37 "Earl of Chesterfield" (1794)

1972. Mail Packet Ships (1st series). Mult.

No.	Type	Description	Unused	Used
67		2p. Type **37**	15	15
68		2½p. "Dasher" (1827)	20	20
69		7½p. "Ibex" (1891)	90	1·00
70		9p. "Alberta" (1900)	1·50	1·40

See also Nos. 80/3.

1972. World Conference of Guernsey Breeders, Guernsey. As No. 38 but size 48 × 29 mm, and additional inscription with face value changed.

No.	Type	Description	Unused	Used
71		5p. multicoloured	75	60

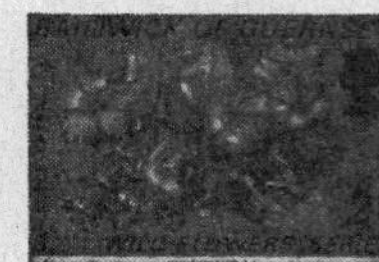
39 Bermuda Buttercup

1972. Wild Flowers. Multicoloured.

No.	Type	Description	Unused	Used
72		2p. Type **39**	15	20
73		2½p. Heath spotted orchid (vert)	15	20
74		7½p. Kaffir fig	1·00	90
75		9p. Scarlet pimpernel (vert)	1·40	1·25

40 Angels adoring Christ

42 "The Good Shepherd"

41 Supermarine Sea Eagle

1972. Royal Silver Wedding and Christmas. Stained-glass Windows from Guernsey Churches. Multicoloured.

No.	Type	Description	Unused	Used
76		2p. Type **40**	10	10
77		2½p. The Epiphany	15	15
78		7½p. The Virgin Mary	60	55
79		9p. Christ	75	60

See also Nos. 89/92.

1973. Mail Packet Boats (2nd series). As T **37**. Multicoloured.

No.	Type	Description	Unused	Used
80		2½p. "St. Julien" (1925)	20	10
81		3p. "Isle of Guernsey" (1930)	30	20
82		7½p. "St. Patrick" (1947)	1·10	60
83		9p. "Sarnia" (1961)	1·25	75

1973. 50th Anniv of Air Service. Mult.

No.	Type	Description	Unused	Used
84		2½p. Type **41**	10	10
85		3p. Westland Wessex trimotor	15	15
86		5p. De Havilland Dragon Rapide	30	25
87		7½p. Douglas DC-3	90	50
88		9p. Vickers Viscount 800 "Anne Marie"	1·00	55

1973. Christmas. Stained-glass Windows from Guernsey Churches. Multicoloured.

No.	Type	Description	Unused	Used
89		2½p. Type **42**	10	10
90		3p. Christ at the well of Samaria	10	10
91		7½p. St. Dominic	30	30
92		20p. Mary and the Child Jesus	60	60

43 Princess Anne and Capt. Mark Phillips

1973. Royal Wedding.

No.	Type	Description	Unused	Used
93	43	25p. multicoloured	1·00	75

44 "John Lockett", 1875

1974. 150th Anniv of Royal National Lifeboat Institution. Multicoloured.

No.	Type	Description	Unused	Used
94		2½p. Type **44**	10	10
95		3p. "Arthur Lionel", 1912	10	10
96		8p. "Euphrosyne Kendal", 1954	45	45
97		10p. "Arun", 1972	45	45

45 Private, East Regt, 1815

46 Driver, Field Battery, Royal Guernsey Artillery, 1848

1974. Guernsey Militia. Multicoloured. (a) As T **45**.

No.	Type	Description	Unused	Used
98		½p. Type **45**	10	10
99		1p. Officer, 2nd North Regt, 1825	10	10
100		1½p. Gunner, Guernsey Artillery, 1787	10	10
101		2p. Gunner, Guernsey Artillery, 1815	10	10
102		2½p. Corporal, Royal Guernsey Artillery, 1868	10	10
103		3p. Field Officer, Royal Guernsey Artillery, 1895	10	10
104		3½p. Sergeant, 3rd Regt, 1867	10	10
105		4p. Officer, East Regt, 1822	15	15
105a		5p. Field Officer, Royal Guernsey Artillery, (1895	15	15
106		5½p. Colour-Sergeant of Grenadiers, East Regt, 1833	20	25
107		6p. Officer, North Regt, 1834	20	25
107a		7p. Officer, East Regt, 1822	25	25
108		8p. Field Officer, Rifle Company, 1868	25	30
109		9p. Private, 4th West Regt, 1785	30	30
110		10p. Field Officer, 4th West Regt, 1824	30	30

(b) As T **46**.

No.	Type	Description	Unused	Used
111		20p. Type **46**	55	40
112		50p. Officer, Field Battery, Royal Guernsey Artillery, 1868	1·50	1·25
113		£1 Cavalry Trooper, Light Dragoons, 1814 (horiz)	3·25	2·50

47 Badge of Guernsey and U.P.U. Emblem

1974. Centenary of U.P.U. Multicoloured.

No.	Type	Description	Unused	Used
114		2½p. Type **47**	10	10
115		3p. Map of Guernsey	10	10
116		8p. U.P.U. Building, Berne, and Guernsey flag	45	45
117		10p. "Salle des Etats"	45	45

48 "Cradle Rock"

1974. Renoir Paintings. Multicoloured.

No.	Type	Description	Unused	Used
118		3p. Type **48**	10	10
119		5½p. "Moulin Huet Bay"	15	15
120		8p. "Au Bord de la Mer" (vert)	40	40
121		10p. Self-portrait (vert)	45	45

49 Guernsey Spleenwort

50 Victor Hugo House

1975. Guernsey Ferns. Multicoloured.

No.	Type	Description	Unused	Used
122		3½p. Type **49**	15	10
123		4p. Sand quillwort	15	10
124		8p. Guernsey quillwort	50	40
125		10p. Least adder's tongue	60	50

1975. Victor Hugo's Exile in Guernsey. Mult.

No.	Type	Description	Unused	Used
126		3½p. Type **50**	10	10
127		4p. Candie Gardens (vert)	20	10
128		8p. United Europe Oak, Hauteville (vert)	40	40
129		10p. Tapestry Room, Hauteville	50	50

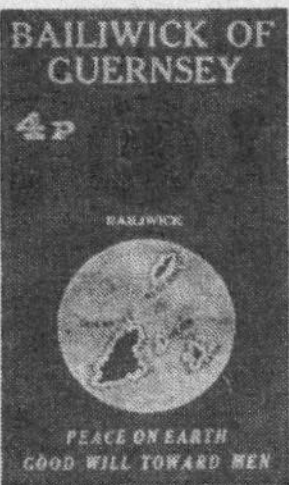

51 Globe and Seal of Bailiwick

1975. Christmas. Multicoloured.

No.	Type	Description	Unused	Used
131		4p. Type **51**	10	10
132		6p. Guernsey flag	15	15
133		10p. Guernsey flag and Alderney shield (horiz)	45	35
134		12p. Guernsey flag and Sark shield (horiz)	50	50

52 Les Hanois

1976. Bailiwick Lighthouses. Multicoloured.

135	4p. Type **52**	10	10
136	6p. Les Casquets	20	20
137	11p. Quesnard	50	45
138	13p. Point Robert	55	60

53 Milk Can

1976. Europa.

139	**53** 10p. brown and green	40	40
140	– 25p. grey and blue	85	85

DESIGN: 25p. Christening cup.

54 Pine Forest, Guernsey

1976. Bailiwick Views. Multicoloured.

141	5p. Type **54**	15	10
142	7p. Herm and Jethou	15	20
143	11p. Grand Greve Bay, Sark (vert)	55	45
144	13p. Trois Vaux Bay, Alderney (vert)	55	65

55 Royal Court House, Guernsey

1976. Christmas. Buildings. Multicoloured.

145	5p. Type **55**	15	10
146	7p. Elizabeth College, Guernsey	15	15
147	11p. La Seigneurie, Sark	55	50
148	13p. Island Hall, Alderney	55	65

56 Queen Elizabeth II 58 Statue-menhir, Castel

57 Woodland, Talbot's Valley

1977. Silver Jubilee. Multicoloured.

149	7p. Type **56**	25	25
150	35p. Queen Elizabeth (half-length portrait)	1·00	1·00

1977. Europa. Multicoloured.

151	7 p. Type **57**	35	35
152	25p. Pastureland, Talbot's Valley	90	90

1977. Prehistoric Monuments. Multicoloured.

153	5p. Type **58**	10	10
154	7p. Megalithic tomb, St. Saviour (horiz)	15	15
155	11p. Cist, Tourgis (horiz)	55	55
156	13p. Statue-menhir, St. Martin	60	60

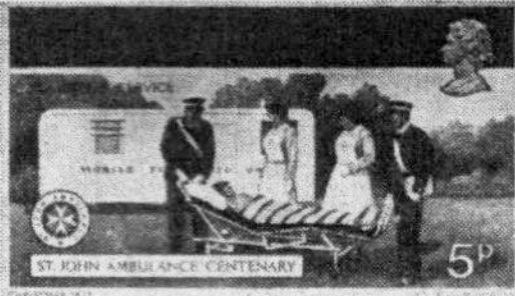

59 Mobile First Aid Unit

1977. Christmas and St. John Ambulance Centenary. Multicoloured.

157	5p. Type **59**	10	10
158	7p. Mobile radar unit	15	15
159	11p. Marine ambulance "Flying Christine II" (vert)	55	55
160	13p. Cliff rescue (vert)	60	60

60 View from Clifton, c. 1830

1978. Old Guernsey Prints (1st series).

161	**60** 5p. black and green	10	10
162	– 7p. black and stone	15	15
163	– 11p. black and pink	55	55
164	– 13p. black and blue	60	60

DESIGNS: 7p. Market Square, St. Peter Port, c. 1838; 11p. Petit-Bo Bay, c. 1839; 13p. The Quay, St. Peter Port, c. 1830.

See also Nos. 249/52.

61 "Prosperity" Memorial 62 Queen Elizabeth II

1978. Europa. Multicoloured.

165	5p. Type **61**	35	35
166	7p. Victoria Monument (vert)	40	40

1978. 25th Anniversary of Coronation.

167	**62** 20p. black, grey and blue	75	75

1978. Royal Visit. As T **62**, but inscr "VISIT OF H.M THE QUEEN AND H.R.H THE DUKE OF EDINBURGH JUNE 28-29, 1978 TO THE BAILIWICK OF GUERNSEY".

168	7p. black, grey and green	50	50

63 Northern Gannet

1978. Birds. Multicoloured.

169	5p. Type **63**	15	15
170	7p. Firecrest	25	25
171	11p. Dartford warbler	60	45
172	13p. Spotted redshank	70	55

64 Solanum

1978. Christmas. Multicoloured.

173	5p. Type **64**	10	10
174	7p. Christmas rose	20	20
175	11p. Holly (vert)	40	40
176	13p. Mistletoe (vert)	50	50

65 One Double Coin, 1830 67 Pillar-box and Postmark, 1853, and Mail Van and Postmark, 1979

1979. Coins.

177	**65** $\frac{1}{2}$p. multicoloured	10	10
178	– 1p. multicoloured	10	10
179	– 2p. multicoloured	10	10
180	– 4p. multicoloured	10	10
181	– 5p. black, silver and brown	15	10
182	– 6p. black, silver and red	15	15
183	– 7p. black, silver and green	15	20
184	– 8p. black, silver and brown	20	20
185	– 9p. multicoloured	25	20
186	– 10p. multicoloured (green background)	50	50
187	– 10p. multicoloured (orange background)	35	30
188	– 11p. multicoloured	25	30
189	– 11$\frac{1}{2}$p. multicoloured	25	30
190	– 12p. multicoloured	30	30
191	– 13p. multicoloured	30	30
192	– 14p. black, silver and blue	30	30
193	– 15p. black, silver and brown	35	35
194	– 20p. black, silver and brown	50	45
195	– 50p. black, silver and red	1·00	75
196	– £1 black, silver and green	2·00	1·50
197	– £2 black, silver and blue	4·00	2·50
198	– £5 multicoloured	10·00	8·50

DESIGNS—VERT (As Type **65**): 1p. Two doubles, 1899; 2p. Four doubles, 1902; 4p. Eight doubles, 1959; 5p. Three pence, 1956; 6p. Five new pence, 1968; 7p. Fifty new pence, 1969; 8p. Ten new pence, 1970; 9p. Half new penny, 1971; 10p. (both) One new penny, 1971; 11p. Two new pence, 1971; 11$\frac{1}{2}$p. Half penny, 1979; 12p. One penny, 1977; 13p. Two pence, 1977; 14p. Five pence, 1977; 15p. Ten pence, 1977; 20p. Twenty-five pence, 1972; (26×45 mm): 50p. William I commemorative 10s., 1966; £5 Seal of the Bailiwick. HORIZ (45×26 mm): £1 Silver Jubilee crown, 1977; £2 Royal Silver Wedding crown, 1972.

1979. Europa. Communications. Multicoloured.

201	6p. Type **67**	30	30
202	8p. Telephone, 1897 and telex machine, 1979	30	30

68 Steam Train, 1879

1979. History of Public Transport. Multicoloured.

203	6p. Type **68**	15	15
204	8p. Electric tram, 1896	20	20
205	11p. Motor bus, 1911	55	55
206	13p. Motor bus, 1979	60	60

69 Bureau and Postal Headquarters

1979. 10th Anniv of Guernsey Postal Administration. Multicoloured.

207	6p. Type **69**	15	15
208	8p. "Mails and telegrams"	25	15
209	13p. "Parcels"	50	55
210	15p. "Philately"	60	60

70 Major-General Le Marchant

1980. Europa Personalities. Multicoloured.

212	10p. Type **70**	45	45
213	13$\frac{1}{2}$p. Admiral Lord de Saumarez	50	50

71 Policewoman with Lost Child

1980. 60th Anniv of Guernsey Police Force. Mult.

214	7p. Type **71**	20	20
215	15p. Motorcycle escort	55	55
216	17$\frac{1}{2}$p. Dog-handler	65	65

72 Golden Guernsey Goat

1980. Golden Guernsey Goats. Multicoloured.

217	7p. Type **72**	20	20
218	10p. Head of goat	30	35
219	15p. Goat	55	45
220	17$\frac{1}{2}$p. Goat and kids	65	60

73 "Sark Cottage"

1980. Peter Le Lievre Paintings. Multicoloured.

221	7p. Type **73**	25	20
222	10p. "Moulin Huet"	35	25
223	13$\frac{1}{2}$p. "Boats at Sea"	40	30
224	15p. "Cow Lane" (vert)	50	40
225	17$\frac{1}{2}$p. "Peter Le Lievre" (vert)	65	50

74 "Polyommatus icarus"

1981. Butterflies. Multicoloured.

226	8p. Type **74**	25	25
227	12p. "Vanessa atalanta"	40	40
228	22p. "Aglais urticae"	90	70
229	25p. "Lasiommata megera"	1·00	90

75 Sailors paying respect to "Le Petit Bonhomme Andriou" (rock resembling head of a man) 76 Prince Charles

1981. Europa. Folklore.

230	**75** 12p. gold, brown and light brown	45	45
231	– 18p. gold, blue and light blue	55	55

DESIGN: 18p. Fairies and Guernsey lily.

1981. Royal Wedding. Multicoloured.

232	8p. Type **76**	50	50
233	8p. Prince Charles and Lady Diana Spencer	50	50
234	8p. Lady Diana	50	50
235	12p. Type **76**	90	90
236	12p. As No. 233	90	90
237	12p. As No. 234	90	90
238	25p. Royal Family (49×32 mm)	1·50	1·50

77 Sark Launch

1981. Inter-island Transport. Multicoloured.

240	8p. Type **77**	20	20
241	12p. Britten Norman "short nose" Trislander airplane	40	40
242	18p. Hydrofoil	60	50
243	22p. Herm catamaran	75	65
244	25p. "Sea Trent" (coaster)	90	75

78 Rifle Shooting

1981. Int Year for Disabled Persons. Mult.

245	8p. Type **78**	20	20
246	12p. Riding	35	35
247	22p. Swimming	65	55
248	25p. "Work"	75	60

1982. Old Guernsey Prints (2nd series). Prints from Sketches by T. Compton. As T **60**.

249	8p. black and blue	20	20
250	12p. black and green	35	35
251	22p. black and brown	65	65
252	25p. black and lilac	75	75

DESIGNS: 8p. Jethou; 12p. Fermain Bay; 22p. The Terres; 25p. St. Peter Port.

79 Sir Edgar MacCulloch (founder-president) and Guille-Alles Library, St. Peter Port

1982. Cent of La Societe Guernesiaise. Mult.
253 8p. Type **79** . . . 20 20
254 13p. French invasion fleet crossing English Channel, 1066 ("history") . . . 35 35
255 20p. H.M.S "Crescent", 1793 ("history") . . . 45 45
256 24p. Dragonfly ("entomology") . . . 70 70
257 26p. Common snipe caught for ringing ("ornithology") . . . 80 80
258 29p. Samian bowl, 160-200 A.D. ("archaeology") . . . 85 85

The 13p. and 20p. designs also include the Europa C.E.P.T. emblem.

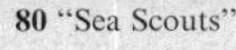

80 "Sea Scouts" **82** Flute Player and Boats

81 Midnight Mass

1982. 75th Anniv of Boy Scout Movement. Mult.
259 8p. Type **80** . . . 20 25
260 13p. "Scouts" . . . 50 50
261 26p. "Cub Scouts" . . . 70 70
262 29p. "Air Scouts" . . . 85 80

1982. Christmas. Multicoloured.
263 8p. Type **81** . . . 20 20
264 13p. Exchanging gifts . . . 30 30
265 24p. Christmas meal . . . 75 75
266 26p. Exchanging cards . . . 75 75
267 29p. Queen's Christmas message . . . 80 80

1982. Centenary of Boys' Brigade. Multicoloured.
268 8p. Type **82** . . . 25 25
269 13p. Cymbal player and tug o' war . . . 40 40
270 24p. Trumpet player and bible class . . . 85 85
271 26p. Drummer and cadets marching . . . 90 90
272 29p. Boys' Brigade band . . . 95 95

83 Building Albert Pier Extension, 1850s

1983. Europa. Development of St. Peter Port Harbour. Multicoloured.
273 13p. Type **83** . . . 35 35
274 13p. St. Peter Port harbour, 1983 . . . 35 35
275 20p. St. Peter Port, 1680 . . . 75 75
276 20p. Artist's impression of future development scheme . . . 75 75

84 "View at Guernsey" (Renoir)

1983. Cent of Renoir's Visit to Guernsey. Mult.
277 9p. Type **84** . . . 25 25
278 13p. "Children on the Seashore" (25 × 39 mm) . . . 45 45
279 26p. "Marine, Guernesey" . . . 80 80
280 28p. "La Bale du Moulin Huet a travers les Arbres" . . . 1·10 1·10
281 31p. "Brouillard a Guernesey" . . . 1·25 1·25

85 Launching "Star of the West", 1869, and Capt. J. Lenfestey

1983. Guernsey Shipping (1st series). Mult.
282 9p. Type **85** . . . 25 25
283 13p. Leaving St. Peter Port . . . 40 40
284 26p. Off Rio Grande Bar . . . 80 80
285 28p. Off St. Lucia . . . 1·10 1·10
286 31p. Map of 1879–80 voyage . . . 1·25 1·25

See also Nos. 415/19.

86 Dame of Sark as Young Woman

1984. Birth Centenary of Sibyl Hathaway, Dame of Sark. Multicoloured.
287 9p. Type **86** . . . 25 25
288 13p. German occupation, 1940–45 . . . 40 45
289 26p. Royal visit, 1957 . . . 90 90
290 28p. Chief Pleas . . . 95 95
291 31p. The Dame of Sark rose . . . 1·10 1·10

87 C.E.P.T. 25th Anniversary Logo

1984. Europa.
292 **87** 13p. lt blue, blue & black . . . 65 65
293 20½p. green, dp green & blk . . . 85 85

88 The Royal Court and St. George's Flag **89** St. Apolline Chapel

1984. Links with the Commonwealth. Mult.
294 9p. Type **88** . . . 40 40
295 31p. Castle Cornet and Union flag . . . 1·10 1·10

1984. Views. Multicoloured.
296 1p. Little Chapel . . . 20 10
297 2p. Fort Grey (horiz) . . . 20 10
298 3p. Type **89** . . . 20 10
299 4p. Petit Port (horiz) . . . 20 10
300 5p. Little Russel (horiz) . . . 20 10
301 6p. The Harbour, Herm (horiz) . . . 20 15
302 7p. Saints (horiz) . . . 20 20
303 8p. St. Saviour . . . 20 20
304 9p. New Jetty (inscr "Cambridge Berth") (horiz) . . . 20 25
305 10p. Belvoir, Herm (horiz) . . . 25 25
306 11p. La Seigneurie, Sark (horiz) . . . 25 25
306b 12p. Petit Bot . . . 40 30
307 13p. St. Saviours reservoir (horiz) . . . 30 30
308 14p. St. Peter Port . . . 30 35
309 15p. Havelet . . . 30 35
309c 16p. Hostel of St. John (horiz) . . . 30 35
309d 18p. Le Variouf . . . 35 40
310 20p. La Coupee, Sark (horiz) . . . 50 45
310b 21p. King's Mills (horiz) . . . 45 45
310c 26p. Town Church . . . 70 55
311 30p. Grandes Rocques (horiz) . . . 60 65
312 40p. Torteval Church . . . 80 85
313 50p. Bordeaux (horiz) . . . 1·00 1·10
314 £1 Albecq (horiz) . . . 2·00 2·10
315 £2 L 'Ancresse (horiz) . . . 4·25 4·25

See also Nos. 398/9a.

90 "A Partridge in a Pear Tree" **91** Sir John Doyle and Coat of Arms

1984. Christmas. "The Twelve Days of Christmas". Multicoloured.
316 5p. Type **90** . . . 20 20
317 5p. "Two turtle doves" . . . 20 20
318 5p. "Three French hens" . . . 20 20
319 5p. "Four colly birds" . . . 20 20
320 5p. "Five gold rings" . . . 20 20
321 5p. "Six geese a-laying" . . . 20 20
322 5p. "Seven swans a-swimming" . . . 20 20
323 5p. "Eight maids a-milking" . . . 20 20
324 5p. "Nine drummers drumming" . . . 20 20
325 5p. "Ten pipers piping" . . . 20 20
326 5p. "Eleven ladies dancing" . . . 20 20
327 5p. "Twelve lords a-leaping" . . . 20 20

1984. 150th Death Anniv of Lieut-General Sir John Doyle. Multicoloured.
328 13p. Type **91** . . . 40 40
329 29p. Battle of Germantown, 1777 (horiz) . . . 1·00 1·00
330 31p. Reclamation of Braye du Valle, 1806 (horiz) . . . 1·25 1·25
331 34p. Mail for Alderney, 1812 (horiz) . . . 1·25 1·25

92 Cuckoo Wrasse

1985. Fishes. Multicoloured.
332 9p. Type **92** . . . 40 40
333 13p. Red gurnard . . . 60 60
334 29p. Red mullet . . . 1·50 1·10
335 31p. Mackerel . . . 1·50 1·10
336 34p. Oceanic sunfish . . . 1·60 1·25

93 Dove

1985. 40th Anniv of Peace in Europe.
337 **93** 22p. multicoloured . . . 1·10 1·10

94 I.Y.Y. Emblem and Young People of Different Races

1985. International Youth Year. Multicoloured.
338 9p. Type **94** . . . 40 40
339 31p. Girl Guides cooking over campfire . . . 1·00 1·00

95 Stave of Music enclosing Flags

1985. Europa. European Music Year. Multicoloured.
340 14p. Type **95** . . . 45 40
341 22p. Stave of music and musical instruments . . . 95 1·00

96 Guide Leader, Girl Guide and Brownie **97** Santa Claus

1985. 75th Anniv of Girl Guide Movement.
342 **96** 34p. multicoloured . . . 1·50 1·50

1985. Christmas. Gift-bearers. Multicoloured.
343 5p. Type **97** . . . 40 35
344 5p. Lussibruden (Sweden) . . . 40 35
345 5p. King Balthazar . . . 40 35
346 5p. Saint Nicholas (Netherlands) . . . 40 35
347 5p. La Befana (Italy) . . . 40 35
348 5p. Julenisse (Denmark) . . . 40 35
349 5p. Christkind (Germany) . . . 40 35
350 5p. King Wenceslas (Czechoslovakia) . . . 40 35
351 5p. Shepherd of Les Baux (France) . . . 40 35
352 5p. King Caspar . . . 40 35
353 5p. Baboushka (Russia) . . . 40 35
354 5p. King Melchior . . . 40 35

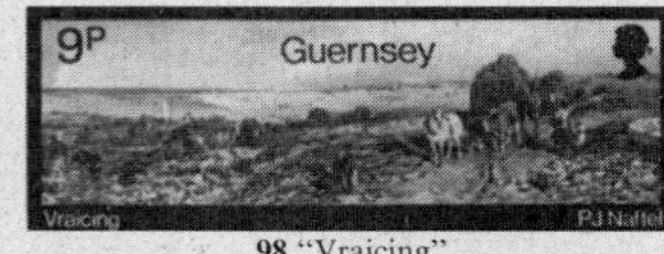

98 "Vraicing"

1985. Paintings by Paul Jacob Naftel. Multicoloured.
355 9p. Type **98** . . . 30 30
356 14p. "Castle Cornet" . . . 40 40
357 22p. "Rocquaine Bay" . . . 90 90
358 31p. "Little Russel" . . . 1·40 1·40
359 34p. "Seaweedgatherers" . . . 1·50 1·50

99 Squadrom off Nargue Island, 1809 **100** Profile of Queen Elizabeth II (after R. Maklouf)

1986. 150th Death Anniv of Admiral Lord De Saumarez. Multicoloured.
360 9p. Type **99** . . . 40 40
361 14p. Battle of the Nile, 1798 . . . 50 50
362 29p. Battle of St. Vincent, 1797 . . . 1·25 1·25
363 31p. H.M.S "Crescent" off Cherbourg, 1793 . . . 1·40 1·40
364 34p. Battle of the Saints, 1782 . . . 1·40 1·40

1986. 60th Birthday of Queen Elizabeth II.
365 **100** 60p. multicoloured . . . 2·50 2·50

101 Northern Gannet and Nylon Net ("Operation Gannet") **102** Prince Andrew and Miss Sarah Ferguson

1986. Europa. Nature and Environmental Protection. Multicoloured.
366 10p. Type **101** . . . 45 45
367 14p. Loose-flowered orchid . . . 75 75
368 22p. Guernsey elm . . . 1·00 1·00

1986. Royal Wedding. Multicoloured.
369 14p. Type **102** . . . 75 75
370 34p. Prince Andrew and Miss Sarah Ferguson (different) (47 × 30 mm) . . . 1·50 1·50

103 Bowls **105** "While Shepherds Watched their Flocks by Night"

104 Guernsey Museum and Art Gallery, Candie Gardens

1986. Sport in Guernsey. Multicoloured.
371 10p. Type **103** . . . 30 30
372 14p. Cricket . . . 50 50
373 22p. Squash . . . 75 75
374 29p. Hockey . . . 1·25 1·25
375 31p. Swimming (horiz) . . . 1·40 1·40
376 34p. Rifle shooting (horiz) . . . 1·50 1·50

1986. Cent of Guernsey Museums. Mult.
377 14p. Type **104** 60 60
378 29p. Fort Grey Maritime Museum . . . . 1·10 1·10
379 31p. Castle Cornet . . . . 1·10 1·10
380 34p. National Trust of Guernsey Folk Museum . . . . 1·40 1·40

1986. Christmas. Carols. Multicoloured.
381 6p. Type **105** 40 40
382 6p. "In The Bleak Midwinter" 40 40
383 6p. "O Little Town of Bethlehem" 40 40
384 6p. "The Holly and the Ivy" . . 40 40
385 6p. "O Little Christmas Tree" . . 40 40
386 6p. "Away in a Manger" . . . 40 40
387 6p. "Good King Wenceslas" . . 40 40
388 6p. "We Three Kings of Orient Are" 40 40
389 6p. "Hark the Herald Angels Sing" 40 40
390 6p. "I Saw Three Ships" . . . 40 40
391 6p. "Little Donkey" 40 40
392 6p. "Jingle Bells" 40 40

107 Post Office Headquarters **108** Sir Edmund Andros and La Plaiderie, Guernsey

1987. Europa. Modern Architecture. Mult.
394 15p. Type **107** 55 55
395 15p. Architect's elevation of Post Office Headquarters 55 55
396 22p. Guernsey Grammar School 80 80
397 22p. Architect's elevation of Grammar School 80 80

1987. Designs as Nos. 306, 306b, 309 and 309c but smaller.
398 11p. La Seigneurie, Sark (22 × 18 mm) 30 40
398a 12p. Petit Bot (18 × 22 mm) . . 25 25
399 15p. Havelet (18 × 22 mm) . . 45 55
399a 16p. Hostel of St. John (22 × 18 mm) 35 35

1987. 350th Birth Anniv of Sir Edmund Andros (colonial administrator). Multicoloured.
400 15p. Type **108** 45 45
401 29p. Governor's Palace, Virginia 1·00 1·00
402 31p. Governor Andros in Boston 1·10 1·10
403 34p. Map of New Amsterdam (New York), 1661 . . . . 1·40 1·40

109 The Jester's Warning to Young William **110** John Wesley preaching on the Quay, Alderney

1987. 900th Death Anniv of William the Conqueror. Multicoloured.
404 11p. Type **109** 45 35
405 15p. Hastings battlefield . . . 50 50
406 15p. Norman soldier with pennant 50 50
407 22p. William the Conqueror . . 80 75
408 22p. Queen Matilda and Abbaye aux Dames, Caen 80 80
409 34p. William's coronation regalia and Halley's Comet . . . . 1·25 1·25

1987. Bicentenary of John Wesley's Visit to Guernsey. Multicoloured.
410 7p. Type **110** 30 30
411 15p. Wesley preaching at Mon Plaisir, St. Peter Port 45 45
412 29p. Preaching at Assembly Rooms . . . . 1·25 1·25
413 31p. Wesley and La Ville Baudu (early Methodist meeting place) . . . . 1·25 1·25
414 34p. Wesley and first Methodist Chapel, St. Peter Port . . . 1·25 1·25

111 "Golden Spur" off St. Sampson Harbour

1988. Guernsey Shipping (2nd series). "Golden Spur". Multicoloured.
415 11p. Type **111** 35 35
416 15p. "Golden Spur" entering Hong Kong harbour 50 50
417 29p. Anchored off Macao . . . 1·25 1·25
418 31p. In China Tea Race . . . 1·25 1·25
419 34p. "Golden Spur" and map showing voyage of 1872–74 . 1·25 1·25

112 Rowing Boat and Bedford "Rascal" Mail Van

1988. Europa. Transport and Communications. Multicoloured.
420 16p. Type **112** 60 60
421 16p. Rowing boat and Vickers Viscount mail plane 60 60
422 22p. Postman on bicycle and horse-drawn carriages, Sark . 95 95
423 22p. Postmen on bicycles and carriage 95 95
Nos. 420/1 and 422/3 were each printed together, se-tenant, the two stamps of each value forming a composite design.

113 Frederick Corbin Lukis and Lukis House, St. Peter Port

1988. Birth Bicentenary of Frederick Corbin Lukis (archaeologist). Multicoloured.
424 12p. Type **113** 40 40
425 16p. Natural history books and reconstructed pot 50 50
426 29p. Lukis directing excavation of Le Creux es Faies and prehistoric beaker . . . . . 1·10 1·10
427 31p. Lukis House Observatory and garden . . . . 1·25 1·25
428 34p. Prehistoric artifacts . . . 1·25 1·25

114 "Cougar", "Rocky" and "Annabella" (powerboats) and Westland Wessex Rescue Helicopter off Jethou

1988. World Off-shore Powerboat Championships. Multicoloured.
429 16p. Type **114** 60 60
430 30p. "Poul Pilot" (powerboats) in Gouliot Passage . . . . . . 1·10 1·10
431 32p. Start of race at St. Peter Port (vert) . . . . 1·25 1·25
432 35p. Admiralty chart showing course (vert) . . . . 1·50 1·50

115 Joshua Gosselin and Herbarium

116 Coutances Cathedral, France

1988. Bicentenary of Joshua Gosselin's "Flora Sarniensis". Multicoloured.
433 12p. Type **115** 40 40
434 16p. Hares-tail grass 55 55
435 16p. Dried hares-tail grass . . . 55 55
436 23p. Variegated catchfly . . . 80 80
437 23p. Dried variegated catchfly . 80 80
438 35p. Rock sea lavender . . . . 1·40 1·40

1988. Christmas. Ecclesiastical Links. Mult.
439 8p. Type **116** 35 35
440 8p. Interior of Notre Dame du Rosaire Church, Guernsey . . 35 35
441 8p. Stained glass, St. Sampson's Church, Guernsey 35 35
442 8p. Dol-de-Bretagne Cathedral, France 35 35
443 8p. Bishop's throne, Town Church, Guernsey 35 35
444 8p. Winchester Cathedral . . . 35 35
445 8p. St. John's Cathedral, Portsmouth 35 35
446 8p. High altar, St. Joseph's Church, Guernsey 35 35
447 8p. Mont Saint-Michel, France 35 35
448 8p. Chancel, Vale Church, Guernsey 35 35
449 8p. Lychgate, Forest Church, Guernsey 35 35
450 8p. Marmoutier Abbey, France 35 35

117 Le Cat (Tip Cat)

118 Outline Map of Guernsey

1989. Europa. Children's Toys and Games. Multicoloured.
451 12p. Type **117** 40 40
452 16p. Girl with Cobo Alice doll . 60 60
453 23p. Le Colimachaon (hopscotch) . . . . 1·25 1·25

1989. Coil Stamp. No value expressed.
454 **118** (–) blue 40 40
455 (–) green 60 60
No. 454 is inscribed "MINIMUM BAILIWICK POSTAGE PAID" and No. 455 "MINIMUM FIRST CLASS POSTAGE TO UK PAID". They were initally sold at 14p. and 18p. but this was changed in line with postage rate rises.

119 Guernsey Airways De Havilland Dragon Express and Mail Van

1989. 50th Anniv of Guernsey Airport (Nos. 456, 458 and 460) and 201 Squadron's Affiliation with Guernsey (Nos. 457, 459 and 461). Mult.
456 12p. Type **119** 50 40
457 12p. Supermarine Southampton II flying boat at mooring . . 50 40
458 18p. B.E.A. De Havilland Rapide 75 75
459 18p. Short S.25 Sunderland Mk V flying boat taking off . . . 75 75
460 35p. Air U.K. British Aerospace BAe 146 . . . . 1·25 1·25
461 35p. Avro Shackleton M.R.3 . 1·25 1·25

120 "Queen Elizabeth II" (June Mendoza)

122 Two-toed Sloth

121 "Ibex" at G.W.R. Terminal, St. Peter Port

1989. Royal Visit.
462 **120** 30p. multicoloured . . . . . 1·25 1·25

1989. Centenary of Great Western Railway Steamer Service to Channel Islands. Multicoloured.
463 12p. Type **121** 30 30
464 18p. "Great Western" (paddle-steamer) in Little Russel . . 65 65
465 29p. "St. Julien" passing Casquets Light 90 90
466 34p. "Roebuck" off Portland . 1·25 1·25
467 37p. "Antelope" and boat train on Weymouth Quay . . . . 1·40 1·40

1989. 10th Anniv of Guernsey Zoological Trust. Animals of the Rainforest. Multicoloured.
469 18p. Type **122** . . . . 1·10 90
470 29p. Capuchin monkey . . . . 1·10 90
471 32p. White-lipped tamarin . . 1·10 90
472 34p. Common squirrel-monkey 1·10 90
473 37p. Common gibbon . . . . . 1·10 90

MINIMUM PRICE

The minimum price quoted is 10p which represents a handling charge rather than a basis for valuing common stamps. For further notes about prices see introductory pages.

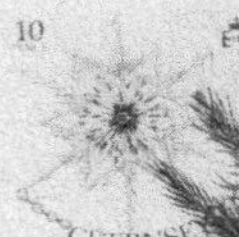
123 Star

125 Penny Black and Mail Steamer off St. Peter Port, 1840

124 Sark Post Office, c. 1890

1989. Christmas. Christmas Tree Decorations. Multicoloured.
474 10p. Type **123** 35 35
475 10p. Fairy 35 35
476 10p. Candles 35 35
477 10p. Bird 35 35
478 10p. Present 35 35
479 10p. Carol-singer 35 35
480 10p. Christmas cracker 35 35
481 10p. Bauble 35 35
482 10p. Christmas stocking . . . 35 35
483 10p. Bell 35 35
484 10p. Fawn 35 35
485 10p. Church 35 35

1990. Europa. Post Office Buildings.
486 **124** 20p. deep brown, sepia and light brown 60 60
487 – 20p. multicoloured 60 60
488 – 24p. deep brown, sepia and light brown 75 75
489 – 24p. multicoloured 75 75
DESIGNS: No. 487, Sark Post Office, 1990; 488, Arcade Post Office counter, St. Peter Port, c. 1840; 489, Arcade Post Office counter, St. Peter Port, 1990

1990. 150th Anniv of the Penny Black. Mult.
490 14p. Type **125** 45 45
491 20p. Penny Red, 1841 and pillar box of 1853 . . . . 60 60
492 32p. Bisected 2d., 1940 and German Army band . . . . 1·00 90
493 34p. Regional 3d., 1958 and Guernsey emblems . . . . . 1·10 95
494 37p. Independent postal administration 1½d., 1969 and queue outside Main Post Office . . . . 1·10 1·00

126 Lt. Philip Saumarez writing Log Book

1990. 250th Anniv of Anson's Circumnavigation. Multicoloured.
496 14p. Type **126** 45 45
497 20p. Anson's squadron leaving Portsmouth, 1740 . . . . . 60 60
498 29p. Ships at St. Catherine's Island, Brazil . . . . . . 1·00 90
499 34p. H.M.S "Tryal" (sloop) dismasted, Cape Horn, 1741 1·10 95
500 37p. Crew of H.M.S "Centurion" on Juan Fernandez . . . . 1·10 1·00

127 Grey Seal and Pup

1990. Marine Life. Multicoloured.
501 20p. Type **127** 60 60
502 26p. Bottle-nosed dolphin . . . 1·00 80
503 31p. Basking shark . . . . . . 1·25 1·25
504 37p. Common porpoise . . . . 1·50 1·50

128 Blue Tit and Great Tit

129 Air Raid and 1941 ½d. Stamp

1990. Christmas. Winter Birds. Multicoloured.

505 10p. Type **128** 40 40
506 10p. Snow bunting 40 40
507 10p. Common kestrel 40 40
508 10p. Common starling 40 40
509 10p. Greenfinch 40 40
510 10p. European robin 40 40
511 10p. Winter wren 40 40
512 10p. Barn owl 40 40
513 10p. Mistle thrush 40 40
514 10p. Grey heron 40 40
515 10p. Chaffinch 40 40
516 10p. Common kingfisher 40 40

1991. 50th Anniv of First Guernsey Stamps. Multicoloured.

517 37p. Type **129** 1·25 1·25
518 53p. 1941 1d. stamp 1·60 1·60
519 57p. 1944 2½d. stamp 1·60 1·60

130 Visit of Queen Victoria to Guernsey, and Discovery of Neptune, 1846

1991. Europa. Europe in Space. Multicoloured.

520 21p. Type **130** 65 65
521 21p. Visit of Queen Elizabeth II and Prince Philip to Sark, and "Sputnik" (first artificial satellite), 1957 65 65
522 26p. Maiden voyage of "Sarnia" (ferry) and "Vostok I" (first manned space flight), 1961 90 75
523 26p. Cancelling Guernsey stamps, and first manned landing on Moon, 1969 90 75

131 Children in Guernsey Sailing Trust "GP14" Dinghy

132 Pair of Oystercatchers

1991. Centenary of Guernsey Yacht Club. Mult.

524 15p. Type **131** 50 50
525 21p. Guernsey Regatta 80 80
526 26p. Lombard Channel Islands' Challenge race 90 90
527 31p. Rolex Swan Regatta 1·00 1·00
528 37p. Old Gaffers' Association gaff-rigged yacht 1·25 1·25

1991. Nature Conservation. L'Eree Shingle Bank Reserve. Multicoloured.

530 15p. Type **132** 60 40
531 15p. Three turnstones 60 40
532 15p. Dunlins and turnstones 60 40
533 15p. Curlew and turnstones 60 40
534 15p. Ringed plover with chicks 60 40
535 21p. Gull, sea campion and sea radish 60 50
536 21p. Yellow horned poppy 60 50
537 21p. Pair of stonechats, hare's foot clover and fennel 60 50
538 21p. Hares's foot clover, fennel and slender oat 60 50
539 21p. Sea kale on shore 60 50

Nos. 530/4 and 535/9 were each printed together, se-tenant, with the backgrounds forming composite designs.

133 "Rudolph the Red-nosed Reindeer" (Melanie Sharpe)

134 Queen Elizabeth II in 1952

1991. Christmas. Children's Paintings. Mult.

540 12p. Type **133** 35 35
541 12p. "Christmas Pudding" (James Quinn) 35 35
542 12p. "Snowman" (Lisa Guille) 35 35
543 12p. "Snowman in Top Hat" (Jessica Ede-Golightly) 35 35
544 12p. "Robins and Christmas Tree" (Sharon Le Page) 35 35
545 12p. "Shepherds and Angels" (Anna Coquelin) 35 35
546 12p. "Nativity" (Claudine Lihou) 35 35
547 12p. "Three Wise Men" (Jonathan Le Noury) 35 35
548 12p. "Star of Bethlehem and Angels" (Marcia Mahy) 35 35
549 12p. "Christmas Tree" (Laurel Garfield) 35 35
550 12p. "Santa Claus" (Rebecca Driscoll) 35 35
551 12p. "Snowman and Star" (Ian Lowe) 35 35

1992. 40th Anniv of Accession. Multicoloured.

552 23p. Type **134** 70 70
553 28p. Queen Elizabeth in 1977 75 75
554 33p. Queen Elizabeth in 1986 85 85
555 39p. Queen Elizabeth in 1991 1·10 1·10

135 Christopher Columbus

1992. 500th Anniv of Discovery of America by Columbus. Multicoloured.

556 23p. Type **135** 60 60
557 23p. Examples of Columbus's signature 60 60
558 28p. "Santa Maria" 1·10 1·10
559 28p. Map of first voyage 1·10 1·10

137 Stock

138 Building the Ship

1992. Horticultural Exports. Multicoloured.

562 1p. "Stephanotis floribunda" 10 10
563 2p. Potted hydrangea 10 10
564 3p. Type **137** 10 10
565 4p. Anemones 10 10
566 5p. Gladiolus 15 15
567 6p. "Asparagus plumosus" and "Gypsophila paniculata" 15 15
568 7p. Guernsey lily 20 20
569 8p. Enchantment lily 20 25
570 9p. Clematis "Freckles" 20 25
571 10p. Alstroemeria 25 25
572 16p. Standard carnation (horiz) 35 35
572b 18p. Standard rose 45 45
573 20p. Spray rose 50 50
574 23p. Mixed freesia (horiz) 55 55
575 24p. Standard rose (horiz) 60 60
576 25p. Iris "Ideal" (horiz) 60 60
576b 26p. Freesia "Pink Glow" 60 60
577 28p. Lisianthus (horiz) 65 65
578 30p. Spray chrysanthemum (horiz) 70 70
579 40p. Spray carnation 1·00 1·00
580 50p. Single freesia (horiz) 1·25 1·25
581 £1 Floral arrangement (35 × 26½ mm) 2·50 2·50
582 £2 Chelsea Flower Show exhibit (35 × 26½ mm) 4·50 4·50
582a £3 "Floral Fantasia" (exhibit) (35 × 28 mm) 6·00 6·25

1992. "Operation Asterix" (excavation of Roman ship). Multicoloured.

583 16p. Type **138** 45 45
584 23p. Loading the cargo 60 60
585 28p. Ship at sea 80 80
586 33p. Ship under attack 95 95
587 39p. Crew swimming ashore 1·10 1·10

139 Tram No. 10 decorated for Battle of Flowers

1992. Guernsey Trams. Multicoloured.

588 16p. Type **139** 45 45
589 23p. Tram No. 10 passing Hougue a la Perre 60 60
590 28p. Tram No. 1 at St. Sampsons 80 80
591 33p. First steam tram at St. Peter Port 95 95
592 39p. Last electric tram, 1934 1·10 1·10

140 Man in Party Hat

141 Rupert Bear, Bingo and Dog

1992. Christmas. Seasonal Fayre. Multicoloured.

593 13p. Type **140** 35 35
594 13p. Girl and Christmas tree 35 35
595 13p. Woman and balloons 35 35
596 13p. Mince pies and champagne 35 35
597 13p. Roast turkey 35 35
598 13p. Christmas pudding 35 35
599 13p. Christmas cake 35 35
600 13p. Fancy cakes 35 35
601 13p. Cheese 35 35
602 13p. Nuts 35 35
603 13p. Ham 35 35
604 13p. Chocolate log 35 35

Nos. 593/604 were printed together, se-tenant, forming a composite design.

1993. Rupert Bear and Friends (cartoon characters created by Mary and Herbert Tourtel).

605 **141** 24p. multicoloured 1·00 1·00

142 Tapestry by Kelly Fletcher

1993. Europa. Contemporary Art. Multicoloured.

607 24p. Type **142** 80 80
608 24p. "Le Marchi a Paissaon" (etching and aquatint, Sally Reed) (48 × 33½ mm) 80 80
609 28p. "Red Abstract" (painting Molly Harris) 90 90
610 28p. "Dress Shop, King's Road" (painting, Damon Bell) (48 × 33½ mm) 90 90

143 Arrest of Guernsey Parliamentarians, Fermain Bay

1993. 350th Anniv of Siege of Castle Cornet. Multicoloured.

611 16p. Type **143** 40 40
612 24p. Parliamentary ships attacking Castle Cornet 65 65
613 28p. Parliamentary captives escaping 85 85
614 33p. Castle cannon firing at St. Peter Port 95 95
615 39p. Surrender of Castle Cornet, 19 December 1651 1·10 1·10

144 Playing Cards

145 "The Twelve Pearls"

1993. Birth Bicentenary of Thomas de la Rue (printer).

617 **144** 16p. multicoloured 40 40
618 – 24p. multicoloured 65 65
619 – 28p. multicoloured 80 80
620 – 33p. red 95 95
621 – 39p. green 1·10 1·10

DESIGNS: 24p. Fountain pens; 28p. Envelope-folding machine; 33p. Great Britain 1855 4d. stamp; 39p. Thomas de la Rue and Mauritius £1 banknote.

1993. Christmas. Stained Glass Windows by Mary-Eily de Putron from the Chapel of Christ the Healer. Multicoloured.

622 13p. Type **145** 45 45
623 13p. "Healing rays" 45 45
624 13p. "Hand of God over the Holy City" 45 45
625 13p. "Wing and Seabirds" (facing left) 45 45
626 13p. "Christ the Healer" 45 45
627 13p. "Wing and Seabirds" (facing right) 45 45
628 13p. "The Young Jesus in the Temple" 45 45
629 13p. "The Raising of Jairus' Daughter" 45 45
630 13p. "Suffer little Children to come unto Me" 45 45
631 13p. "Pilgrim's Progress" 45 45
632 13p. "The Light of the World" 45 45
633 13p. "Raphael, the Archangel of Healing, with Tobias" 45 45

146 Les Fouaillages (ancient burial ground)

1994. Europa. Archaeological Discoveries. Multicoloured.

634 24p. Type **146** 60 60
635 24p. Mounted Celtic warrior 60 60
636 30p. Jars, arrow heads and stone axe from Les Fouaillages 80 80
637 30p. Sword, spear head and torque from King's Road burial 80 80

148 Peugeot "Type 3", 1894

1994. Cent of First Car in Guernsey. Mult.

639 16p. Type **148** 45 45
640 24p. Mercedes "Simplex", 1903 70 70
641 35p. Humber tourer, 1906 1·00 1·00
642 41p. Bentley sports tourer, 1936 1·10 1·10
643 60p. MG TC Midget, 1948 1·75 1·75

149 "Trident" (Herm ferry)

1994. 25th Anniv of Guernsey Postal Administration. Multicoloured.

645 16p. Type **149** 35 35
646 24p. Handley Page Super Dart Herald of Channel Express 55 55
647 35p. Britten Norman Trislander of Aurigny Air Services 75 75
648 41p. "Bon Marin de Serk" (Sark ferry) 85 85
649 60p. Map of Bailiwick 1·40 1·40

150 Dolls' House

151 Seafood "Face"

1994. Christmas. Bygone Toys. Multicoloured.

651 13p. Type **150** 40 40
652 13p. Doll 40 40
653 13p. Teddy in bassinette 40 40
654 13p. Sweets in pillar box and playing cards 40 40
655 13p. Spinning top 40 40
656 13p. Building blocks 40 40
657 24p. Rocking horse 75 75
658 24p. Teddy bear 75 75
659 24p. Tricycle 75 75
660 24p. Wooden duck 75 75
661 24p. Hornby toy locomotive 75 75
662 24p. Ludo game 75 75

Nos. 651/6 and 657/62 respectively were printed together, se-tenant, forming composite designs.

1995. Greetings Stamps. "The Welcoming Face of Guernsey". Multicoloured.

663 24p. Type **151** 65 65
664 24p. Buckets and spade "face" 65 65
665 24p. Flowers "face" 65 65
666 24p. Fruit and vegetables "face" 65 65
667 24p. Sea shells and seaweed "face" 65 65
668 24p. Anchor and life belts "face" 65 65
669 24p. Glasses, cork and cutlery "face" 65 65
670 24p. Butterflies and caterpillars "face" 65 65

152 Winston Churchill and Wireless

1995. 50th Anniv of Liberation. Multicoloured.

672 16p. Type **152** 50 50
673 24p. Union Jack and Royal Navy ships off St. Peter Port 75 75
674 35p. Royal Arms and military band 1·00 1·00
675 41p. "Vega" (Red Cross supply ship) 1·00 1·00
676 60p. Rejoicing crowd 1·75 1·75

153 Silhouette of Doves on Ground (½-size illustration)

1995. Europa. Peace and Freedom. Multicoloured.

678 25p. Type **153** 65 65
679 30p. Silhouette of doves in flight 85 85

The designs of Nos. 678/9 each provide a stereogram or hidden three-dimensional image of a single dove.

154 Prince Charles, Castle Cornet and Bailiwick Arms

1995. Royal Visit.

680 **154** £1.50 multicoloured 4·00 4·00

155 Part of United Nations Emblem (face value at top left)

1995. 50th Anniv of United Nations. Designs showing different segments of the United Nations Emblem. Each blue and gold.

682 50p. Type **155** 1·25 1·25
683 50p. Face value at top right 1·25 1·25
684 50p. Face value at bottom left 1·25 1·25
685 50p. Face value at bottom right 1·25 1·25

156 "Christmas Trees for Sale in Bern" (Cornelia Huisboum-Weibel)

1995. Christmas. 50th Anniv of U.N.I.C.E.F. Multicoloured.

686 13p. Type **156** (face value at left) 40 40
687 13p. "Christmas Trees for Sale in Bern" (face value at right) 40 40
688 13p. + 1p. "Evening Snowfall" (Katerina Mertikas) (face value at left) 40 40
689 13p. + 1p. "Evening Snowfall" (face value at right) 40 40
690 24p. "It came upon a Midnight Clear" (Georgia Guback) (face value at left) 70 70
691 24p. "It came upon a Midnight Clear" (Georgia Guback) (face value at right) 70 70
692 24p. + 2p. "Children of the World" (face value at left) 70 70
693 24p. + 2p. "Children of the World" (face value at right) 70 70

Nos. 686/7, 688/9, 690/1 and 692/3 were printed together, se-tenant, each pair forming a composite design.

157 Princess Anne (President, Save the Children Fund) and Children

1996. Europa. Famous Women. Multicoloured.

694 25p. Type **157** 65 65
695 30p. Queen Elizabeth II and people of the Commonwealth 85 85

158 England v. U.S.S.R., 1968 (value at right)

1996. European Football Championship. Multicoloured.

696 16p. Type **158** 55 55
697 16p. England v. U.S.S.R., 1968 (value at left) 55 55
698 24p. Italy v. Belgium, 1972 (value at right) 75 75
699 24p. Italy v. Belgium, 1972 (value at left) 75 75
700 35p. Ireland v. Netherlands, 1988 (value at right) 80 80
701 35p. Ireland v. Netherlands, 1988 (value at left) 80 80
702 41p. Denmark v. Germany, 1992 final (value at right) 95 95
703 41p. Denmark v. Germany, 1992 final (value at left) 95 95

160 Ancient Greek Runner

162 The Annunciation

161 Humphrey Bogart as Philip Marlowe

1996. Centenary of Modern Olympic Games. Ancient Greek Athletes. Each black, yellow and orange.

705 16p. Type **160** 50 50
706 24p. Throwing the javelin 95 95
707 41p. Throwing the discus 1·10 1·10
708 55p. Wrestling (53 × 31 mm) 1·40 1·40
709 60p. Jumping 1·60 1·60

No. 708 also includes the "OLYMPHILEX '96" International Stamp Exhibition, Atlanta, logo.

1996. Centenary of Cinema. Screen Detectives. Multicoloured.

711 16p. Type **161** 40 40
712 24p. Peter Sellers as Inspector Clouseau 60 60
713 35p. Basil Rathbone as Sherlock Holmes 85 85
714 41p. Margaret Rutherford as Miss Marple 90 90
715 60p. Warner Oland as Charlie Chan 1·40 1·40

1996. Christmas. Multicoloured.

716 13p. Type **162** 30 30
717 13p. Journey to Bethlehem 30 30
718 13p. Arrival at the inn 30 30
719 13p. Angel and shepherds 30 30
720 13p. Mary, Joseph and Jesus in stable 30 30
721 13p. Shepherds worshipping Jesus 30 30
722 13p. Three Kings following star 30 30
723 13p. Three Kings with gifts 30 30
724 13p. The Presentation in the Temple 30 30
725 13p. Mary and Jesus 30 30
726 13p. Joseph warned by angel 30 30
727 13p. The Flight into Egypt 30 30
728 24p. Mary cradling Jesus (horiz) 60 60
729 25p. The Nativity (horiz) 60 60

163 Holly Blue

1997. Endangered Species. Butterflies and Moths. Multicoloured.

730 18p. Type **163** 60 60
731 25p. Hummingbird hawk-moth 75 75
732 26p. Emperor moth 90 90
733 37p. Brimstone 1·10 1·10

164 Gilliatt fighting Octopus

1997. Europa. Tales and Legends. Scenes from "Les Travailleurs de la Mer" by Victor Hugo. Multicoloured.

735 26p. Type **164** 65 65
736 31p. Gilliatt grieving on rock 75 75

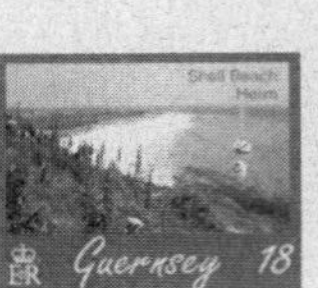

165 Shell Beach, Herm

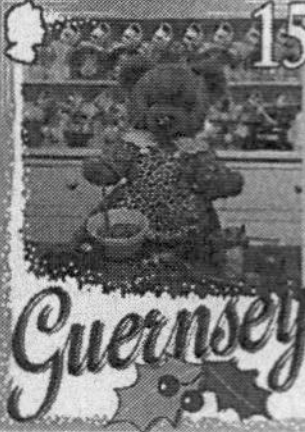

168 Teddy Bear making Cake

167 Transistor Radio, Microphone and Radio Logos

1997. Guernsey Scenes (1st series). Multicoloured. Self-adhesive.

737 18p. Type **165** 50 50
738 25p. La Seigneurie, Sark (vert) 70 70
739 26p. Castle Cornet, Guernsey 70 70

See also Nos. 770/3.

1997. Methods of Communication. Multicoloured.

741 18p. Type **167** 45 45
742 25p. Television, video camera and satellite dish 70 70
743 26p. Fax machine, telephones and mobile phone 70 70
744 37p. Printing press, newspaper and type 1·00 1·00
745 43p. Stamp, coding machine and postbox 1·10 1·10
746 63p. C.D., computer and disk 1·60 1·60

1997. Christmas. Teddy Bears. Multicoloured.

747 15p. Type **168** 45 45
748 25p. Teddy bears decorating Christmas tree 70 70
749 26p. Two teddy bears in armchair 70 70
750 37p. Teddy bear as Father Christmas 1·00 1·00
751 43p. Teddy bears unwrapping presents 1·10 1·10
752 63p. Teddy bears eating Christmas dinner 1·60 1·60

169 Visiting Guernsey, 1957

1997. Golden Wedding of Queen Elizabeth and Prince Philip. Multicoloured.

754 18p. Type **169** 45 45
755 25p. Coronation Day, 1953 70 70
756 26p. Royal family, 1957 70 70
757 37p. On royal yacht, 1972 1·00 1·00
758 43p. Queen Elizabeth and Prince Philip at Trooping the Colour, 1987 1·10 1·10
759 63p. Queen Elizabeth and Prince Philip, 1997 1·60 1·60

No. 755 is inscribed "1947" in error.

170 Tapestry of 11th-century Guernsey (St. Martin)

171 Fort Grey

1998. The Millennium Tapestries Project. Each showing a different century contributed by individual parishes. Multicoloured.

760 25p. Type **170** 60 60
761 25p. 12th-century (St. Saviour) 60 60
762 25p. 13th-century (Vale) 60 60
763 25p. 14th-century (St. Sampson) 60 60
764 25p. 15th-century (Torteval) 60 60
765 25p. 16th-century (Castel) 60 60
766 25p. 17th-century (St. Andrew) 60 60
767 25p. 18th-century (Forest) 60 60
768 25p. 19th-century (St. Pierre du Bois) 60 60
769 25p. 20th-century (St. Peter Port) 60 60

1998. Guernsey Scenes (2nd series). Multicoloured. Self-adhesive.

770 (20p.) Type **171** 40 45
771 (20p.) Grand Havre 40 45
772 (25p.) Little Chapel 50 55
773 (25p.) Guernsey cow 50 55

Nos. 770/1 are inscribed "Bailiwick Minimum Postage Paid" and were intially sold at 20p. Nos. 772/3 are inscribed "UK Minimum Postage Paid" and were initially sold at 25p.

172 Fairey IIIC, Balloon, Sopwith Camel and Avro 504

1998. 80th Anniv of the Royal Air Force. Multicoloured.

774 20p. Type **172** 50 50
775 25p. Fairey Swordfish, Tiger Moth, Supermarine Walrus and Gloster Gladiator 60 60
776 30p. Hawker Hurricane, Supermarine Spitfire, Vickers Wellington, Short Sunderland (flying boat), Westland Lysander and Bristol Blenheim 70 70
777 37p. De Havilland Mosquito, Avro Lancaster, Auster III, Gloster Meteor and Horsa glider 85 85
778 43p. Canberra, Hawker Sea Fury, Bristol Sycamore, Hawker Hunter, Handley Page Victor and BAe Lightning 95 95
779 63p. Pavania Tornado GRI, BAe Hawk, BAe Sea Harrier, Westland Lynx (helicopter) and Hawker Siddeley Nimrod 1·40 1·40

174 Girls in Traditional Costume watching Sheep Display, West Show

1998. Europa. Festivals. Multicoloured.

781 20p. Type **174** 50 50
782 25p. Marching band and "Battle of Flowers" exhibit, North Show 60 60
783 30p. Prince Charles, monument and tank, Liberation Day 70 70
784 37p. Goat, dahlias and show-jumping, South Show 90 90

The 25p. and 30p. incorporate the "EUROPA" emblem.

175 Outboard Motorboat

176 Royal Yacht "Britannia"

1998. Maritime Heritage. Multicoloured.

785 1p. Type **175** 10 10
786 2p. St. John Ambulance inshore rescue dinghy 10 10
787 3p. Pilot boat, St. Peter Port 10 10
788 4p. "Flying Christine III" (St. John Ambulance launch) 10 10
789 5p. Crab fishing boat 10 10
790 6p. Herm Island ferry 10 10
791 7p. "Sarnia" (St. Peter Port Harbour Authority launch) 15 20
792 8p. "Leopardess" (States' fisheries protection launch) 15 20
793 9p. Trawler 20 25
794 10p. Powerboat (30 × 30 mm) 20 25
797 40p. Motor cruiser (30 × 30 mm) 80 85
798 50p. Ocean-going sailing yacht (30 × 30 mm) 1·00 1·10
799 75p. Motor yacht, "Beaucette Marina" (30 × 30 mm) 1·50 1·75
800 £1 "Queen Elizabeth 2" (liner) (32 × 28 mm) 2·00 2·10
802 £5 Type **176** 10·00 10·50

177 Modern Tree, Teletubby and Playstation

1998. 150th Anniv of the Introduction of the Christmas Tree. Multicoloured.

810 17p. Type **177** 40 40
811 25p. 1960s tinsel tree, toy bus and doll 60 60
812 30p. 1930s gold foil tree, panda and toy tank 70 70
813 37p. 1920s tree, model of "Bluebird" and doll 90 90
814 43p. 1900 tree, teddy bear and toy train 1·00 1·00
815 63p. 1850s tree, wooden doll and spinning top 1·50 1·50

178 Elizabeth Bowes Lyon, 1907

180 Burnet Rose and Local Carriage Label

179 "Spirit of Guernsey", 1995

1999. Life and Times of Queen Elizabeth the Queen Mother. Multicoloured.

817 25p. Type **178** 60 60
818 25p. On wedding day, 1923 60 60
819 25p. Holding Princess Elizabeth, 1926 60 60
820 25p. At Coronation, 1937 60 60
821 25p. Visiting bombed areas of London, 1940 (wearing green hat) 60 60
822 25p. Fishing near Auckland, New Zealand, 1966 60 60
823 25p. At Guernsey function, 1963 (wearing tiara) 60 60
824 25p. Receiving flowers on her birthday, 1992 60 60
825 25p. Presenting trophy, Sandown Park races, 1989 60 60
826 25p. Opening Royal Norfolk Regimental Museum, Norwich, 1990 (wearing blue hat) 60 60

1999. 175th Anniv of Royal National Lifeboat Institution. Multicoloured.

827 20p. Type **179** 50 50
828 25p. "Sir William Arnold", 1973 60 60
829 30p. "Euphrosyne Kendal", 1954 70 70
830 38p. "Queen Victoria", 1929 90 90
831 44p. "Arthur Lionel", 1912 1·10 1·10
832 64p. "Vincent Kirk Ella", 1888 1·40 1·40

1999. Europa. Parks and Gardens. Herm Island. Designs each showing a different local carriage label. Multicoloured.

833 20p. Type **180** 40 45
834 25p. Puffin 60 60
835 30p. Small heath butterfly 60 65
836 38p. Shells on Shell Beach 75 80

182 Major-General Le Marchant (founder) and Cadet at Sword Drill

183 The Nativity

1999. Bicentenary of The Royal Military Academy, Sandhurst. Multicoloured.

838 20p. Type **182** 40 45
839 25p. The Duke of York (official sponsor) and cadet on horseback 50 55
840 30p. Field-Marshal Earl Haig and cadets on parade 60 65
841 38p. Field-Marshal Viscount Montgomery and bridging exercise 75 80
842 44p. David Niven (actor) and rifle practice 90 95
843 64p. Sir Winston Churchill and tank 1·25 1·40

1999. Christmas. Wood Carvings by Denis Brehaut from Notre Dame Church. Multicoloured.

844 17p. Type **183** 35 40
845 25p. Virgin Mary and Child 50 55
846 30p. Holy Family 60 65
847 38p. Cattle around manger 75 80
848 44p. Adoration of the Shepherds 90 95
849 64p. Adoration of the Magi 1·25 1·40

184 "Space Bus" (Fallon Ephgrave)

2000. New Millennium. "Stampin' the Future" (children's stamp design competition). Multicoloured.

851 20p. Type **184** 40 45
852 25p. "Children holding hands" (Abigail Downing) 50 55
853 30p. "No Captivity" (Laura Martin) 60 65
854 38p. "Post Office of the Future" (Sarah Haddow) 75 80
855 44p. "Solar-powered car" (Sophie Medland) 90 95
856 64p. "Woman flying" (Danielle McIver) 1·25 1·40

POSTAGE DUE STAMPS

D 1 Castle Cornet

1969. Face values in black.

D1 **D 1** 1d. plum 2·25 1·25
D2 2d. green 2·25 1·25
D3 3d. red 3·75 4·00
D4 4d. blue 5·00 5·00
D5 5d. ochre 5·50 5·50
D6 6d. turquoise 6·50 6·00
D7 1s. brown 17·00 17·00

1971. Decimal Currency. Face values in black.

D 8 **D 1** ½p. plum 10 10
D 9 1p. green 10 10
D10 2p. red 10 10
D11 3p. blue 15 15
D12 4p. ochre 15 15
D13 5p. blue 15 15
D14 6p. violet 20 20
D15 8p. orange 30 30
D16 10p. brown 35 35
D17 15p. grey 60 60

D 2 St. Peter Port

1977. Face values in black.

D18 **D 2** ½p. brown 10 10
D19 1p. purple 10 10
D20 2p. orange 10 10
D21 3p. red 10 10
D22 4p. blue 10 10
D23 5p. green 15 15
D24 6p. green 20 20
D25 8p. brown 25 25
D26 10p. blue 40 40
D27 14p. green 45 45
D28 15p. violet 45 45
D29 16p. red 55 55

D 3 Milking Cow

1982. Guernsey Scenes, c. 1900.

D30 **D 3** 1p. blue and green 10 10
D31 – 2p. brown, lt brown & blue 10 10
D32 – 3p. green and lilac 10 10
D33 – 4p. green and orange 10 10
D34 – 5p. blue and green 10 10
D35 – 16p. blue and light blue 30 35
D36 – 18p. blue and green 35 40
D37 – 20p. green and blue 40 45
D38 – 25p. blue and pink 50 55
D39 – 30p. green and yellow 60 65
D40 – 50p. brown and blue 1·00 1·10
D41 – £1 lt brown and brown 2·00 2·10

DESIGNS: 2p. Vale Mill; 3p. Sark cottage; 4p. Quay-side, St. Peter Port; 5p. Well, Water Lane, Moulin Huet; 16p. Seaweed gathering; 18p. Upper Walk, White Rock; 20p. Cobo Bay; 25p. Saint's Bay; 30p. La Coupee, Sark; 50p. Old Harbour, St. Peter Port; £1 Greenhouses, Doyle Road, St. Peter Port.

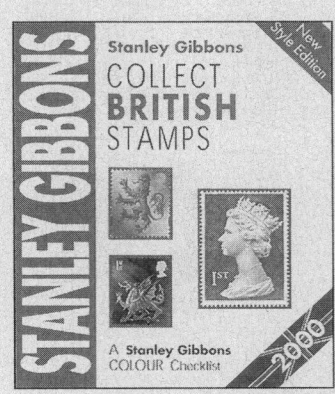

ALDERNEY

The following issues are provided by the Guernsey Post Office for use on Alderney. They are also valid for postal purposes throughout the rest of the Bailiwick of Guernsey.

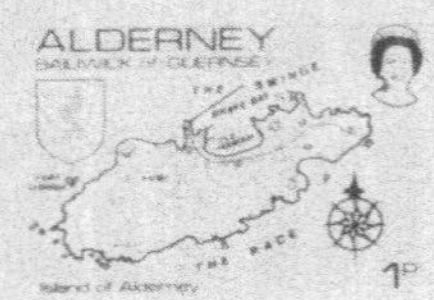

A 1 Island Map

1983. Island Scenes. Multicoloured.

A 1 1p. Type A **1** 10 10
A 2 4p. Hanging Rock 10 10
A 3 9p. States' Building, St. Anne 25 25
A 4 10p. St. Anne's Church . . . 25 25
A 5 11p. Yachts in Braye Bay . . 25 25
A 6 12p. Victoria St., St. Anne . . 30 30
A 7 13p. Map of Channel 30 25
A 8 14p. Fort Clonque 35 35
A 9 15p. Corblets Bay and Fort . 40 40
A10 16p. Old Tower, St. Anne . . 40 40
A11 17p. Golf course and Essex Castle 45 45
A12 18p. Old Harbour 45 45
A12a 20p. Quesnard Lighthouse . . 1·00 1·00
A12b 21p. Braye Harbour . . . . 1·00 1·00
A12c 23p. Island Hall 90 90
A12d 24p. "J.T. Daly" (steam locomotive) . . . . . . 2·00 2·00
A12e 28p. "Louis Marchesi of the Round Table" (lifeboat) . . 2·25 2·25

Nos. A12a/e are larger, 38×27 mm.

A 2 Oystercatcher

1984. Birds. Multicoloured.

A13 9p. Type A **2** . . . . 1·50 1·50
A14 13p. Turnstone . . . . 1·50 2·00
A15 26p. Ringed plover . . . . . 5·00 4·00
A16 28p. Dunlin . . . . 5·00 4·00
A17 31p. Curlew . . . . 5·00 4·00

A 3 Westland Wessex HU MK 5 Helicopter of the Queen's Flight

1985. 50th Anniv of Alderney Airport. Mult.

A18 9p. Type A **3** . . . . 2·50 2·25
A19 13p. Britten Norman "Longnose" Trislander . . 2·50 3·00
A20 29p. De Havilland Heron 1B . 6·00 5·00
A21 31p. De Havilland Dragon Rapide "Sir Henry Lawrence" 6·50 6·00
A22 34p. Saro Windhover flying boat "City of Portsmouth . . . 7·00 6·00

A 4 Royal Engineers, 1890

A 5 Fort Grosnez

1985. Regiments of the Alderney Garrison. Multicoloured.

A23 9p. Type A **4** 45 45
A24 14p. Duke of Albany's Own Highlanders, 1856 . . . . . 1·00 1·00
A25 29p. Royal Artillery, 1855 . . 1·50 1·50
A26 31p. South Hampshire Regiment, 1810 . . . . . . 1·75 1·75
A27 34p. Royal Irish Regiment, 1782 2·00 2·00

1986. Alderney Forts. Multicoloured.

A28 10p. Type A **5** . . . . 1·10 1·10
A29 14p. Fort Tourgis . . . . . . 1·75 1·75
A30 31p. Fort Clonque . . . . . 4·00 4·00
A31 34p. Fort Albert . . . . . . 4·25 4·25

INDEX

Countries can be quickly located by referring to the index at the end of this volume.

A 6 "Liverpool" (full-rigged ship), 1902

1987. Alderney Shipwrecks. Multicoloured.

A32 11p. Type A **6** . . . . 2·00 1·75
A33 15p. "Petit Raymond" (schooner), 1906 . . . . . 2·25 2·00
A34 29p. "Maina" (yacht), 1910 . . 5·50 5·25
A35 31p. "Burton" (steamer), 1911 6·00 5·75
A36 34p. "Point Law" (oil tanker), 1975 . . . . 6·50 6·25

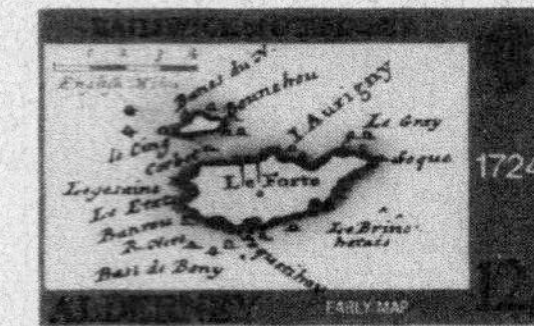

A 7 Moll's Map of 1724

1989. 250th Anniv of Bastide's Survey of Alderney.

A37 A **7** 12p. multicoloured. . . . 45 45
A38 – 18p. black, blue & brown . 60 60
A39 – 27p. black, blue & green . 1·25 1·25
A40 – 32p. black, blue & red . . 1·40 1·40
A41 – 35p. multicoloured . . . 1·60 1·60

DESIGNS: 18p. Bastide's survey of 1739; 27p. Goodwin's map of 1831; 32p. General Staff map of 1943; 35p. Ordnance Survey map, 1988.

A 8 H.M.S. "Alderney" (bomb ketch), 1738

1990. Royal Navy Ships named after Alderney.

A42 A **8** 14p. black and bistre . . 45 45
A43 – 20p. black and brown . . 65 65
A44 – 29p. black and brown . . 1·25 1·25
A45 – 34p. black and blue . . 1·25 1·25
A46 – 37p. black and blue . . . 1·40 1·40

DESIGNS: 20p. H.M.S. "Alderney" (sixth rate), 1742; 29p. H.M.S. "Alderney" (sloop), 1755; 34p. H.M.S. "Alderney" (submarine), 1945; 37p. H.M.S. "Alderney" (patrol vessel), 1979.

A 9 Wreck of H.M.S. "Victory", 1744

1991. Automation of The Casquets Lighthouse. Multicoloured.

A47 21p. Type A **9** . . . . 1·60 2·00
A48 26p. Lighthouse keeper's daughter rowing back to the Casquets . . . . 2·00 2·25
A49 31p. MBB-Bolkow Bo 105D helicopter leaving pad on St. Thomas Tower . . . . . 2·50 2·75
A50 37p. Migrating birds over lighthouse . . . . 3·50 3·75
A51 50p. Trinity House vessel "Patricia" and arms . . . . 6·00 5·00

A 10 Two French Warships on Fire

A 11 Spiny Lobster

1992. 300th Anniv of the Battle of La Hogue. Multicoloured.

A52 23p. Type A **10** . . . . . . 2·00 2·00
A53 28p. Crews leaving burning ships . . . . 2·75 2·75
A54 33p. French warship sinking . 3·00 3·00
A55 50p. "The Battle of La Hogue" (47×32 mm) . . . . . . 4·50 4·50

Nos. A52/4 show details of the painting on the 50p. value.

1993. Endangered Species. Marine Life. Mult.

A56 24p. Type A **11** 90 90
A57 28p. Plumose anemone . . . . 1·00 1·00
A58 33p. Starfish . . . . 1·25 1·25
A59 39p. Sea urchin . . . . . . 1·60 1·60

Nos. A56/9 were printed together, se-tenant, the backgrounds forming a composite design.

A 12 Blue-tailed Damselfly, Dark Hair Water Crowfoot and Branched Bur-reed

1994. Flora and Fauna. Multicoloured.

A60 1p. Type A **12** 10 10
A61 2p. White-toothed shrew and flax-leaved St. John's wort . 10 10
A62 3p. Fulmar and kaffir fig . . . 10 10
A63 4p. Clouded yellow (butterfly) and red clover 10 10
A64 5p. Bumble bee, prostrate broom and giant broom-rape 10 10
A65 6p. Dartford warbler and lesser dodder 15 20
A66 7p. Peacock (butterfly) and stemless thistle 15 20
A67 8p. Mole and bluebell 15 20
A68 9p. Great green grasshopper and common gorse 20 25
A69 10p. Six-spot burnet (moth) and viper's bugloss 20 25
A70 16p. Common blue (butterfly) and pyramidal orchid . . . 30 35
A70b 18p. Small tortoiseshell (butterfly) and buddleia . . 35 40
A71 20p. Common rabbit and creeping buttercup 40 45
A72 24p. Great black-backed gull and sand crocus 50 55
A72b 25p. Rock pipit and sea stock 50 55
A72c 26p. Sand digger wasp and sea bindweed (horiz) 50 55
A73 30p. Atlantic puffin and English stonecrop 60 65
A74 40p. Emperor (moth) and bramble 80 85
A75 50p. Pale-spined hedgehog and pink oxalis . . . . . . 1·00 1·10
A76 £1 Common tern and Bermuda grass (horiz) . . . . . . 2·00 2·10
A77 £2 Northern gannet and "Fucus vesiculosus" (seaweed) (horiz) . . . . 4·00 4·25

A 13 Royal Aircraft Factory SE5A

1995. Birth Cent of Tommy Rose (aviator). Mult.

A78 35p. Type A **13** 85 85
A79 35p. Miles Master II and other Miles aircraft 85 85
A80 35p. Miles Aerovan and Miles Monitor 85 85
A81 41p. Miles Falcon Six winning King's Cup air race, 1935 . 1·00 1·00
A82 41p. Miles Hawk Speed Six winning Manx Air Derby, 1947 . . . . 1·00 1·00
A83 41p. Miles Falcon Six breaking U.K.–Cape record, 1936 . . 1·00 1·00

A 15 Signallers training on Alderney

1996. 25th Anniv of Adoption of 30th Signal Regiment by Alderney. Multicoloured.

A85 24p. Type A **15** 65 65
A86 41p. Communications station, Falkland Islands . . . . . 1·10 1·10
A87 60p. Dish aerial and land rover, Gulf War . . . . 1·50 1·50
A88 75p. Service with United Nations . . . . 1·75 1·75

Nos. A85/8 were printed together, se-tenant, forming a composite design.

A 16 Cat with Butterfly

A 17 Harold Larwood

1996. Cats. Multicoloured.

A89 16p. Type A **16** 45 45
A90 24p. Blue and white on table . 65 65
A91 25p. Tabby kitten grooming blue and white persian kitten . . 65 65
A92 35p. Red persian under table . 95 95
A93 41p. White cat with tortoiseshell and white in toy cart . . . 1·10 1·10
A94 60p. Siamese playing with wool . . . . 1·75 1·75

1997. 150th Anniv of Cricket on Alderney. Multicoloured.

A96 18p. Type A **17** 50 50
A97 25p. John Arlott 65 65
A98 37p. Pelham J. Warner . . . 1·00 1·00
A99 43p. W. G. Grace . . . . . 1·25 1·25
A100 63p. John Wisden . . . . . 1·60 1·60

A 18 Railway under Construction

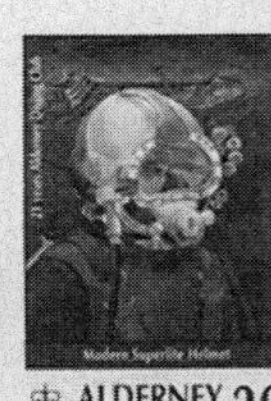

A 19 Modern Superlite Helmet and Wreck of "Point Law" (oil tanker)

1997. Garrison Island (1st series). 150th Anniv of Harbour. Multicoloured.

A102 18p. Type A **18** 45 45
A103 18p. "Ariadne" (paddle steamer) at anchor 45 45
A104 25p. Quarrying stone 65 65
A105 25p. Quarry railway 65 65
A106 26p. Queen Victoria and Prince Albert on Alderney . . . 70 70
A107 26p. Royal Yacht "Victoria and Albert" and guard of honour 70 70
A108 31p. Railway workers greet Queen Victoria 80 80
A109 31p. Royal party in railway wagons 80 80

See also Nos. A116/23 and A132/9.

1998. 21st Anniv of Alderney Diving Club. Multicoloured.

A110 20p. Type A **19** 50 50
A111 30p. Cousteau-Gagnan demand valve and wreck of "Stella" (steamer) 75 75
A112 37p. Heinke closed helmet and "Liverpool" (full-rigged ship) 90 90
A113 43p. Siebe closed helmet . . 1·00 1·00
A114 63p. Deane open helmet . . 1·50 1·50

1998. Garrison Island (2nd series). As Type A **18**. Multicoloured.

A116 20p. Alderney Post Office . . 50 50
A117 20p. Traders in Victoria Street 50 50
A118 25p. Court House 60 60
A119 25p. Police Station and fire engine 60 60
A120 30p. St. Anne's Church . . . 70 70
A121 30p. Wedding party at Albert Gate 70 70
A122 37p. "Courier" (ferry) at Braye Bay 85 85
A123 37p. Fishermen at quay . . . 85 85

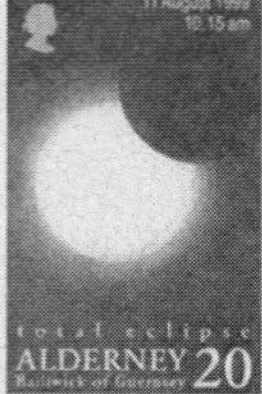

A 21 Solar Eclipse at 10.15 am

A 22 Peregrine Falcon attacking Turnstone

1999. Total Eclipse of the Sun (11 August). Designs showing stages of the eclipse. Multicoloured.

A125 20p. Type A **21** 50 50
A126 25p. At 10.51 am 60 60
A127 30p. At 11.14 am 70 70
A128 38p. At 11.16 am 90 90
A129 44p. At 11.17 am . . . . . 1·00 1·00
A130 64p. At 11.36 am . . . . . 1·50 1·50

1999. Garrison Island (3rd series). Forts. As Type A **18**. Multicoloured.

A132 20p. Field gun and crew, Fort Grosnez, c. 1855 . . . . . 40 45
A133 20p. Parade of 9th Bn, Royal Garrison Artillery 40 45
A134 25p. The Arsenal, Fort Albert, c. 1862 . . . . 50 55
A135 25p. Royal Engineers loading wagons 50 55
A136 30p. 2nd Bn, Royal Scots on parade 60 65
A137 30p. Garrison at work, Fort Tourgis, c. 1865 . . . . . 60 65
A138 38p. Gun emplacement, Fort Houmet Herbe, c. 1870 . . 75 80
A139 38p. Royal Alderney Artillery Militia loading cannon . . 75 80

Nos. A132/3, A134/5, A136/7 and A138/9 respectively were printed together, se-tenant, forming composite designs.

2000. Endangered Species. Peregrine Falcon. Multicoloured.

A140 21p. Type A **22** 40 45
A141 26p. Two falcons and prey . . 50 55
A142 34p. Falcon guarding eggs . . 70 75
A143 38p. Falcon feeding young . . 75 80
A144 44p. Falcon and prey 90 95
A145 64p. Two young falcons . . . 1·25 1·40

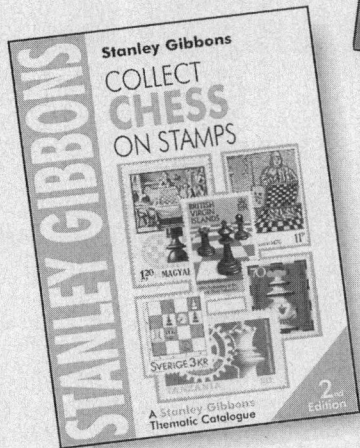

GUINEA Pt. 13

The former French Colony on the W. coast of Africa which became fully independent in 1958.

1959. 100 centimes = 1 franc.
1973. 100 caury = 1 syli.
1986. 100 centimes = 1 franc.

1959. Stamps of Fr. West Africa optd **REPUBLIQUE DE GUINEE** or surch also.
188 – 10 f. mult (No. 118) . . . . 2·00 2·50
189 **20** 45 f. on 20 f. pur, grn & ol . . 2·00 2·50

10 Pres. Sekou Toure

1959. Proclamation of Independence.
190 **10** 5 f. red 20 10
191 10 f. blue 30 20
192 20 f. orange 50 35
193 65 f. green . . . . 1·60 1·00
194 100 f. violet . . . . . . 2·50 1·90

12 Tamara Lighthouse and Fishing Boats

13 Flying Doves

1959.
201 **12** 1 f. red (postage) 10 10
202 2 f. green 10 10
203 3 f. brown 10 10
204 – 5 f. blue 15 15
205 – 10 f. purple 15 10
206 – 15 f. brown 85 25
207 – 20 f. purple 60 30
208 – 25 f. brown . . . . 1·50 30
209 **13** 40 f. blue (air) 35 25
210 50 f. green 55 40
211 100 f. lake . . . . 1·25 65
212 200 f. red . . . . 2·25 1·25
213 500 f. red . . . . 6·00 3·25
DESIGNS—VERT: 5 f. Palms and dhow; 20 f. Pres. Sekou Toure. HORIZ: 10 f. Pirogue being launched; 15 f. African Elephant (front view); 25 f. African Elephant (side view).

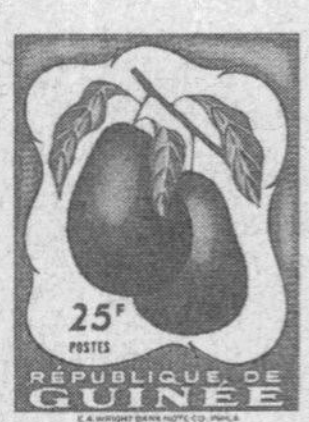

14 Mangoes

16 "Raising the Flag"

15 Lockheed Super Constellation Airliner

1959. Fruits in natural colours. Frame colours given.
214 – 10 f. red (Bananas) 15 15
215 – 15 f. green (Grapefruit) . . . 25 15
216 – 20 f. brown (Lemons) 45 20
217 **14** 25 f. blue 55 30
218 – 50 f. violet (Pineapple) . . . 1·00 35

1959. Air.
219 **15** 100 f. blue, brn & mauve . . 1·75 95
220 200 f. mauve, brn & grn . . 5·00 1·25
221 – 500 f. multicoloured . . . 8·00 2·50
DESIGN: 500 f. Lockheed Super Constellation airliner on ground.

1959. 1st Anniv of Independence.
222 **16** 50 f. multicoloured 55 25
223 100 f. multicoloured . . . . 1·25 65

18 Africans acclaiming U.N. Headquarters Building

1959. U.N.O.
230 **18** 1 f. blue & orange (postage) . 15 10
231 2 f. purple and green . . . 15 10
232 3 f. brown and red 15 10
233 5 f. brown and turquoise . . 15 10
234 50 f. grn, blue and brn (air) . 65 50
235 100 f. green, red and blue . . 90 70
Nos. 234/5 are larger (45 × 26 mm).

19 Eye-testing

20 "Uprooted Tree"

1960. National Health. Inscr "POUR NOTRE SANTE NATIONALE".
236 **19** 20 f. + 10 f. red and blue . . 75 70
237 – 30 f. + 20 f. violet & orge . . 75 70
238 – 40 f. + 20 f. blue and red . . 1·10 95
239 – 50 f. + 50 f. brown & green . 2·00 1·60
240 – 100 f. + 100 f. green & pur . 2·75 2·10
DESIGNS—HORIZ: 30 f. Laboratory assistant; 40 f. Spraying trees. VERT: (28½ × 40 mm): 50 f. Research with microscope; 100 f. Operating theatre.

1960. World Refugee Year.
241 **20** 25 f. multicoloured 50 35
242 50 f. multicoloured 70 45

21 U.P.U. Monument, Berne

23 Flag and Map

1960. 1st Anniv of Admission to U.P.U. Background differs for each value.
243 **21** 10 f. black and brown . . . 15 10
244 15 f. lilac and mauve . . . 25 15
245 20 f. indigo and blue . . . 40 15
246 – 25 f. myrtle and green . . . 55 15
247 – 50 f. sepia and orange . . . 65 25
DESIGN: 25 f., 50 f. As Type **10** but vert.

1960. Olympic Games. Optd **Jeux Olympiques Rome 1960** and Olympic rings.
248 **16** 50 f. multicoloured (post.) . 5·00 5·00
249 100 f. multicoloured . . . 7·50 7·50
250 **15** 100 f. blue, green and mauve (air) . . . . 6·50 4·50
251 200 f. mauve, brn & grn . . 13·00 6·50
252 – 500 f. multicoloured (No. 221) . . . . 32·00 32·00

1960. 2nd Anniv of Independence.
253 **23** 25 f. multicoloured 30 25
254 30 f. multicoloured 40 35

1960. 15th Anniv of U.N.O. Optd **XVEME ANNIVERSAIRE DES NATIONS UNIES**.
(a) Nos. 214/18. Fruits in natural colours.
255 – 10 f. red 20 20
256 – 15 f. green 30 25
257 – 20 f. brown 35 30
258 **14** 25 f. blue 45 35
259 – 50 f. violet 75 60

(b) Nos. 230/35.
260 **18** 1 f. blue & orange (postage) . 10 10
261 2 f. purple and green . . . 10 10
262 3 f. brown and red 10 10
263 5 f. brown and turquoise . . 10 10
264 50 f. green, bl & brn (air) . . 65 70
265 100 f. green, red and blue . . 90 70

1961. Surch **1961** and value.
266 **20** 25 f. + 10 f. multicoloured . 4·75 4·75
267 50 f. + 20 f. multicoloured . 4·75 4·75

27 Bohar Reedbuck

1961. Centres in brown, green and blue. Inscriptions and value tablets in colours given.
268 **27** 5 f. turquoise 15 10
269 10 f. green 15 10
270 25 f. violet 40 15
271 40 f. orange 55 20
272 50 f. red . . . . 1·25 25
273 75 f. blue . . . . 1·75 45

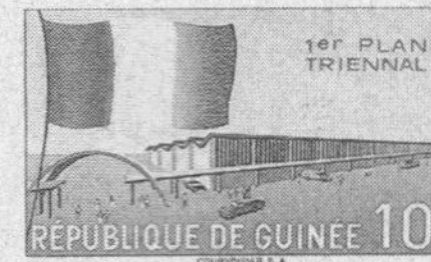

28 Guinea Flag and Exhibition Hall, Conakry

1961. First Three-Year Plan. Flag in red, yellow and green.
274 **28** 5 f. blue and red 15 15
275 10 f. brown and red 15 15
276 25 f. green and red 25 25

29 Helmet Guineafowl

1961. Guineafowl in purple and blue.
277 **29** 5 f. mauve and blue 70 30
278 10 f. red and blue 75 30
279 25 f. red and blue 75 45
280 40 f. brown and blue . . . 1·10 50
281 50 f. bistre and blue . . . 1·25 70
282 75 f. olive and blue . . . . 3·25 85

1961. Protection of Animals. Surch **POUR LA PROTECTION DE NOS ANIMAUX +5 FRS**.
283 **27** 5 f. + 5 f. turquoise 15 15
284 10 f. + 5 f. green 25 15
285 25 f. + 5 f. violet 55 30
286 40 f. + 5 f. orange 70 40
287 50 f. + 5 f. red 95 55
288 75 f. + 5 f. blue . . . . . 1·50 70

31 Patrice Lumumba

1962. 1st Death Anniv of Lumumba (Congo leader).
289 **31** 10 f. multicoloured 30 25
290 25 f. multicoloured 40 25
291 50 f. multicoloured 60 30

1962. Malaria Eradication (1st issue). Nos. 236/40 optd with Malaria Eradication emblem and **ERADICATION DE LA MALARIA**.
292 **19** 20 f. + 10 f. red and blue . . 35 35
293 – 30 f. + 20 f. violet & orge . . 50 50
294 – 40 f. + 20 f. blue and red . . 60 60
295 – 50 f. + 50 f. brown & green . 1·25 1·25
296 – 100 f. + 100 f. grn & pur . . 2·50 2·50

33 King Mohammed V and Map

34a Posthorn on North Africa

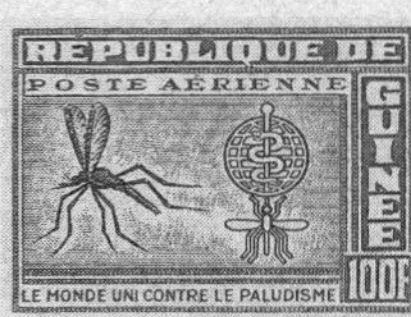

34 Mosquito and Emblem

1962. 1st Anniv of Casablanca Conference.
297 **33** 25 f. multicoloured 95 25
298 75 f. multicoloured . . . . 1·90 45

1962. Air. Malaria Eradication (2nd issue).
299 **34** 25 f. black and orange . . . 40 20
300 50 f. black and red 50 35
301 100 f. black and green . . . 1·00 60

1962. African Postal Union Commemoration.
303 **34a** 25 f. green, brown & orge . 65 15
304 100 f. orange and brown . . 1·60 40

1962. Guinea-fowl stamps surch **POUR LA PROTECTION DE NOS OISEAUX +5 FRS**.
305 **29** 5 f. + 5 f. 60 35
306 10 f. + 5 f. 60 45
307 25 f. + 5 f. 80 55
308 40 f. + 5 f. 95 70
309 50 f. + 5 f. . . . . 2·10 90
310 75 f. + 5 f. . . . . 3·75 1·90

36 Bote-player

37 Hippopotamus

1962. Native Musicians.
311 **36** 30 c. red, grn & bl (postage) 15 10
312 A 50 c. green, brn & salmon . 15 10
313 B 1 f. purple and green . . . 15 10
314 C 1 f. 50 turq, red & yell . . . 15 10
315 D 2 f. green, red and mauve . . 15 10
316 C 3 f. violet, green & turq . . 15 10
317 B 10 f. blue, brown & orge . . 25 10
318 D 20 f. red, sepia and olive . . 30 20
319 **36** 25 f. violet, sepia & olive . . 45 25
320 A 40 f. mauve, green & bl . . 45 35
321 **36** 50 f. blue, red and rose . . . 60 40
322 A 75 f. blue, brown & ochre . 2·50 55
323 D 100 f. blue, red & pink (air) . 1·10 50
324 D 200 f. red and blue . . . . 2·50 75
325 E 500 f. blue, violet & brown . 6·50 2·50
DESIGNS—(Musicians playing). HORIZ: A, Bolon; C, Koni; D, Kora; E, Balafon. VERT: B, Flute.

1962. Wild Game.
326 **37** 10 f. sepia, green & orge . . 30 10
327 – 25 f. brown, sepia & grn . . 60 20
328 – 30 f. sepia, yellow & olive . 70 20
329 **37** 50 f. sepia, green & blue . . 1·00 35
330 – 75 f. brown, pur & lilac . . 1·50 60
331 – 100 f. sepia, yellow & turq . 2·00 80
DESIGNS: 25 f., 75 f. Lion; 30 f., 100 f. Leopard.

38 Boy at Blackboard

43 Crowned Crane

39 Alfa Yaya

1962. Campaign Against Illiteracy.
332 **38** 5 f. sepia, yellow & red . . . 10 10
333 – 10 f. sepia, orge & purple . . 10 10
334 **38** 15 f. sepia, green & red . . . 20 10
335 – 20 f. sepia, turq & pur . . . 30 20
DESIGN: 10 f., 20 f. Teacher at blackboard.

1962. African Heroes and Martyrs.
336 **39** 25 f. sepia, turq & gold . . 30 15
337 – 30 f. sepia, ochre & gold . . 40 20
338 – 50 f. sepia, purple & gold . . 55 25
339 – 75 f. sepia, green & gold . . 1·10 40
340 – 100 f. sepia, red & gold . . 1·40 60
PORTRAITS: 30 f. King Behanzin; 50 f. King Ba Bemba of Sikasso; 75 f. Almamy Samory; 100 f. Chief Tierno Aliou of the Goumba.

1962. Algerian Refugees Fund. Surch **Aide aux Refugies Algeriens** and premium.
341 **33** 25 f. + 15 f. multicoloured . 65 65
342 75 f. + 25 f. multicoloured . 1·25 1·25

1962. Air. "The Conquest of Space". Optd with capsule and **La Conquete De L'Espace**.
343 **13** 40 f. blue 50 25
344 50 f. green 60 30
345 100 f. lake . . . . 1·00 50
348 200 f. red . . . . 1·75 95

1962. Birds. Multicoloured.
349 30 c. Type **43** (postage) . . . . 1·10 25
350 50 c. Grey Parrot . . . . . 1·10 25
351 1 f. Abyssinian Ground Hornbill . . . . 1·25 25
352 1 f. 50 White Spoonbill . . . 1·25 45
353 2 f. Bateleur . . . . 1·25 45
354 3 f. Type **43** . . . . 1·50 45
355 10 f. As 50 d. . . . . . . 1·50 45
356 20 f. As 1 f. . . . . 2·00 95
357 25 f. As 1 f. 50 . . . . . . 2·50 1·10
358 40 f. As 2 f. . . . . 2·50 1·10

359 50 f. Type **43** . . . . 2·75 1·40
360 75 f. As 50 c. . . . . 5·75 1·50

361 100 f. As 1 f. (air) . . . . . . 6·75 1·90
362 200 f. As 1 f. 50 . . . . 11·50 3·50
363 500 f. As 2 f. . . . . 24·00 9·00
All except T **43** are horiz.

44 Handball

1963. Sports.

364 **44** 30 c. purple, red & green (postage) 10 10
365 A 50 c. violet, lilac & blue . . 10 10
366 B 1 f. sepia, orange & green . 10 10
367 C 1 f. 50 bl, orge & pur . . . 10 10
368 D 2 f. blue, turq & purple . . 10 10
369 **44** 3 f. purple, olive & blue . . 10 10
370 A 4 f. violet, mauve & blue . . 10 10
371 B 5 f. sepia, green & purple . . 15 10
372 C 10 f. blue & bright purple . 20 10
373 D 20 f. blue, orge & red . . . 30 15
374 **44** 25 f. pur, grn & blk 40 15
375 A 30 f. violet, black & blue . . 45 25

376 B 100 f. sepia, lake & green (air) . . . . 1·10 40
377 C 200 f. blue, brown & pur . . 2·25 90
378 D 500 f. blue, brn & purple . . 5·00 2·25
DESIGNS: A, Boxing; B, Running; C, Cycling; D, Canoeing.

45 Campaign Emblem **47** "African Unity"

48 Capsule encircling Globe

1963. Centenary of Red Cross.

404 **48** 5 f. red & green (postage) . . 10 10
405 10 f. red and blue 15 10
406 15 f. red and yellow . . . 20 15

407 25 f. red & black (air) . . . 45 20

1963. Air. 1st Pan-American Conakry–New York Direct Air Service. Optd **PREMIER SERVICE DIRECT CONAKRY-NEW YORK PAN AMERICAN 30 JUILLET 1963**.

409 **15** 10 f. blue, grn & mauve . . 1·90 75
410 200 f. mauve, brn & grn . . 3·25 1·25

1963. Olympic Games Preparatory Commission, Conakry. Nos. 364/6 surch **COMMISSION PREPARATOIRE AUX JEUX OLYMPIQUES A CONAKRY**, rings and new value.

411 40 f. on 30 c. purple, red and green . . . . 1·00 80
412 50 f. on 50 c. violet, lilac and blue . . . . 1·40 1·10
413 75 f. on 1 f. sep, orge & grn . . 2·40 1·90

51 Jewel Cichlid

1964. Guinea Fishes. Multicoloured.

414 30 c. Type **51** (postage) 10 10
415 40 c. Golden pheasant panchax . 10 10
416 50 c. Blue gularis 10 10
417 1 f. Banded jewelfish and jewel cichlid 10 10
418 1 f. 50 Yellow gularis 10 10
419 2 f. Six-banded lyretail 25 10
420 5 f. Type **51** 25 10
421 30 f. As 40 c. 65 20
422 40 f. As 50 c. . . . . 1·25 35
423 75 f. As 1 f. . . . . 2·25 55

424 100 f. As 1 f. 50 (air) . . . . 2·25 55
425 300 f. As 2 f. . . . . 7·00 1·75

52 President Kennedy **53** Pipeline under Construction

1964. Pres. Kennedy Memorial Issue. Flag in red and blue.

426 **52** 5 f. violet & black (postage) . 10 10
427 25 f. violet and green . . . 25 20
428 50 f. violet and brown . . . 60 30

429 100 f. black & violet (air) . . 1·00 85

1964. Inaug. of Piped Water Supply, Conakry.

430 **53** 5 f. red 10 10
431 – 10 f. violet 10 10
432 – 20 f. brown 15 10
433 – 30 f. blue 30 15
434 – 50 f. green 55 30
DESIGNS—HORIZ: 10 f. Reservoir; 20 f. Joining pipes; 30 f. Transporting pipes; 50 f. Laying pipes.

56 Eleanor Roosevelt with Children

1964. 15th Anniv of Declaration of Human Rights.

442 **56** 5 f. green (postage) 10 10
443 10 f. orange 10 10
444 15 f. blue 15 10
445 25 f. red 30 15

446 50 f. violet (air) 70 30

57 Striped Hyena

1964. Animals.

447 **57** 5 f. sepia and yellow 20 10
448 30 f. sepia and blue 40 20
449 – 40 f. black and mauve . . . 55 25
450 – 75 f. sepia and green . . . 1·50 30
451 – 100 f. sepia and ochre . . . 2·00 50
452 – 300 f. dp violet & orge . . . 4·00 1·75
ANIMALS: 40 f., 300 f. African Buffalo; 75 f., 100 f. African Elephant.

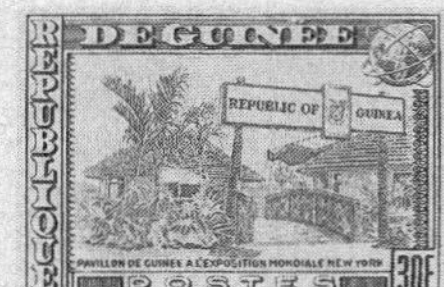

58 Guinea Pavilion

1964. New York World's Fair.

453 **58** 30 f. green and lilac 25 15
454 40 f. green and purple . . . 40 15
455 50 f. green and brown . . . 50 15
456 75 f. blue and red 75 25
See also Nos. 484/87.

60 Nefertari, Isis and Hathor

1964. Nubian Monuments Preservation. Multicoloured.

458 10 f. Type **60** (postage) 20 15
459 25 f. Pharaoh in battle 25 15
460 50 f. The Nile—partly submerged sphinxes 45 20
461 100 f. Rameses II, entrance hall of Great Temple, Abu Simbel 1·10 45
462 200 f. Lower part of Colossi, Abu Simbel . . . . 2·00 80

463 300 f. Nefertari (air) . . . . . 3·75 1·60

61 Athlete with Torch **62** Doudou (Boke) Mask

1965. Olympic Games, Tokyo (2nd issue). Multicoloured.

464 5 f. Weightlifter and children (postage) 15 10
465 10 f. Type **61** 15 10
466 25 f. Pole vaulting 25 20
467 40 f. Running 30 20
468 50 f. Judo 50 30
469 75 f. Japanese hostess . . . . 1·00 45

470 100 f. Air hostess and Convair Coronado airliner (horiz) (air) . . . . 1·50 55

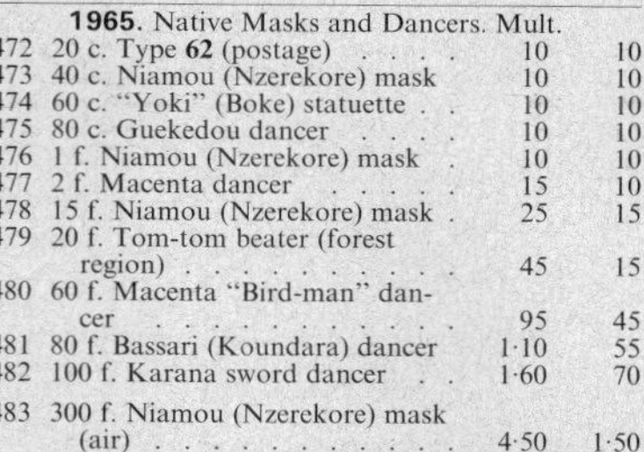

63 Metal-work

54 Ice hockey

1964. Winter Olympic Games, Innsbruck. Rings, frame and tablet in gold.

435 **54** 10 f. olive & green (postage) 15 10
436 – 25 f. slate and violet . . . 40 20
437 – 50 f. black and blue . . . 75 40

438 – 100 f. black & brn (air) . . 1·10 55
DESIGNS: 25 f. Ski-jumping; 50 f. Skiing; 100 f. Figure-skating.

1964. Air. Olympic Games, Tokyo (1st issue). Nos. 376/8 optd **JEUX OLYMPIQUES TOKYO 1964** and Olympic rings.

439 100 f. sepia, lake and green . . 1·50 1·00
440 200 f. blue, brown & purple . . 2·25 1·50
441 500 f. blue, brown & purple . . 5·00 3·50

46 "Amauris niavius"

1963. Freedom from Hunger.

379 **45** 5 f. yellow and red 10 10
380 10 f. yellow and green . . . 10 10
381 15 f. yellow and brown . . . 15 10
382 25 f. yellow and olive . . . 25 15

1963. Butterflies. Multicoloured.

383 10 c. Type **46** (postage) 10 10
384 30 c. "Papilio demodocus" . . . 10 10
385 40 c. As 30 c. 10 10
386 50 c. "Graphum policenes" . . . 10 10
387 1 f. "Papilio nireus" 15 10
388 1 f. 50 Type **46** 20 10
389 2 f. "Papilio menestheus" . . . 20 10
390 3 f. As 30 c. 20 10
391 10 f. As 50 c. 35 10
392 20 f. As 1 f. 60 15
393 25 f. Type **46** . . . . 1·00 20
394 40 f. As 2 f. . . . . 1·40 30
395 50 f. As 30 c. . . . . 1·90 35
396 75 f. As 1 f. . . . . 2·75 60

397 100 f. Type **46** (air) . . . . . 1·75 35
398 200 f. As 50 c. . . . . 4·00 80
399 500 f. As 2 f. . . . . 8·00 2·50

1963. Conference of African Heads of State, Addis Ababa.

400 **47** 5 f. sep, blk & turq on grn . 10 10
401 10 f. sepia, black and yellow on yellow 10 10
402 15 f. sep, blk & ol on ol . . 15 10
403 25 f. sepia, black and brown on cinnamon 25 15

1965. Native Masks and Dancers. Mult.

472 20 c. Type **62** (postage) 10 10
473 40 c. Niamou (Nzerekore) mask 10 10
474 60 c. "Yoki" (Boke) statuette . . 10 10
475 80 c. Guekedou dancer 10 10
476 1 f. Niamou (Nzerekore) mask . 10 10
477 2 f. Macenta dancer 15 10
478 15 f. Niamou (Nzerekore) mask . 25 15
479 20 f. Tom-tom beater (forest region) 45 15
480 60 f. Macenta "Bird-man" dancer 95 45
481 80 f. Bassari (Koundara) dancer 1·10 55
482 100 f. Karana sword dancer . . 1·60 70

483 300 f. Niamou (Nzerekore) mask (air) . . . . 4·50 1·50
The 40 c., 1 f., 15 f. and 300 f. each show different masks.

1965. New York World's Fair. As Nos. 453/6 but additionally inscr "1965".

484 **58** 30 f. orange and green . . . 20 15
485 40 f. green and red 30 15
486 50 f. violet and blue 45 25
487 75 f. violet and brown . . . 65 35

1965. Native Handicrafts. Multicoloured.

489 15 f. Type **63** (postage) 15 10
490 20 f. Pottery 20 15
491 60 f. Dyeing 60 35
492 80 f. Basket-making 85 45

493 100 f. Ebony-work (air) . . . . 1·25 45
494 300 f. Ivory-work . . . . . . 4·50 1·25

64 I.T.U. Emblem and Symbols

1965. I.T.U. Centenary.

495 **64** 25 f. mult (postage) 30 15
496 50 f. multicoloured 60 25

497 100 f. multicoloured (air) . . 1·10 40
498 200 f. multicoloured . . . . 2·00 65

67 U.N. Headquarters and I.C.Y. Emblem

1965. I.C.Y.

501 **67** 25 f. red & green (postage) . 25 15
502 45 f. red and violet 35 20
503 75 f. red and brown 70 30

504 100 f. orange & blue (air) . . 1·25 45

68 Polytechnic Institute, Conakry

1965. 7th Anniv of Independence. Mult.

505 25 f. Type **68** (postage) 15 15
506 30 f. Camayenne Hotel 20 15
507 40 f. Gbessia Airport 60 30
508 75 f. "28 Septembre" Stadium . 55 35

509 200 f. Polytechnic Institute, North facade (air) . . . . . 1·40 1·00
510 500 f. Ditto, West facade . . . 4·25 2·50
Nos. 509/10 are larger, 53 × 23 mm.

69 Moon, Globe and Satellite **70** Sabre Dance, Karana

1965. "To the Moon". Multicoloured.

No.	Description	Unused	Used
511	5 f. Type **69** (postage)	15	10
512	10 f. Trajectory of "Ranger 7"	20	10
513	25 f. "Relay" satellite	30	20
514	45 f. "Vostok 1, 2" and Globe	55	25
515	100 f. "Ranger 7" approaching Moon (air)	85	40
516	200 f. Launching of "Ranger 7"	2·00	75

Nos. 512/9 are larger, 36×25½ mm.; Nos. 515/6 are vert., 25×36 mm.

1966. Guinean Dances. Multicoloured.

No.	Description	Unused	Used
519	10 c. Type **70** (postage)	10	10
520	30 c. Young girls' dance, Lower Guinea	10	10
521	50 c. Tiekere musicians, "Eyora" (bamboo) dance Bandjinguene	10	10
522	5 f. Doundouba dance, Kouroussa	10	10
523	40 f. Bird-man's dance, Macenta	85	30
524	100 f. Kouyate Kandia, national singer (air)	1·25	45

The 50 c. and 100 f. are horiz, 36×29 mm.
See also Nos. 561/6.

1966. Stamp Cent. Exn., Cairo. Nos. 460 and 463 optd **CENTENAIRE DU TIMBRE CAIRE 1966**.

No.	Description	Unused	Used
525	50 f. multicoloured (postage)	55	40
526	300 f. multicoloured (air)	2·25	1·50

1966. Pan Arab Games, Cairo (1965). Nos. 464/5, 467/9 optd **JEUX PANARABES CAIRE 1965** and pyramid motif.

No.	Type	Description	Unused	Used
527	–	5 f. multicoloured (postage)	20	15
528	**61**	10 f. multicoloured	20	15
529	–	40 f. multicoloured	55	35
530	–	50 f. multicoloured	70	45
531	–	75 f. multicoloured	1·25	75
532	–	100 f. multicoloured (air)	1·25	40

73 Vonkou Rocks, Telimele

74 U.N.E.S.C.O. Emblem

1966. Landscapes (1st series). Multicoloured.

No.	Description	Unused	Used
534	20 f. Type **73** (postage)	15	10
535	25 f. Artificial lake, Coyah	20	10
536	40 f. Waterfalls, Kate	35	15
537	50 f. Bridge, Forecariah	45	20
538	75 f. Liana bridge	70	35
539	100 f. Lighthouse and bay, Boulbinet (air)	1·50	45

See also Nos. 603/608.

1966. 20th Anniv of U.N.E.S.C.O. (a) Postage.

No.	Type	Description	Unused	Used
540	**74**	25 f. multicoloured	40	20

(b) Air. Nos. 509/10 optd **vingt ans 1946 1966** and U.N.E.S.C.O. Emblem.

No.	Description	Unused	Used
541	200 f. multicoloured	2·00	1·25
542	500 f. multicoloured	4·50	2·75

76

78 Decade and U.N.E.S.C.O. Symbols

1966. Guinean Flora and Female Head-dresses. Similar designs.

No.	Type	Description	Unused	Used
543	**76**	10 c. mult (postage)	10	10
544	–	20 c. multicoloured	10	10
545	–	30 c. multicoloured	10	10
546	–	40 c. multicoloured	10	10
547	–	3 f. multicoloured	10	10
548	–	4 f. multicoloured	10	10
549	–	10 f. multicoloured	15	10
550	–	25 f. multicoloured	55	10
551	–	30 f. multicoloured	70	15
552	–	50 f. multicoloured	1·10	30
553	**76**	80 f. multicoloured	1·40	40
554	–	200 f. multicoloured (air)	2·75	75
555	–	300 f. multicoloured	4·50	1·50

Nos. 551/555 are 29×42 mm.

1966. Int. Hydrological Decade.

No.	Type	Description	Unused	Used
558	**78**	5 f. red and blue	10	10
559		25 f. red and green	20	10
560		100 f. red and purple	1·00	50

1966. Guinean National Ballet. Designs show various dances as T **70**.

No.	Description	Unused	Used
561	60 c. multicoloured	10	10
562	1 f. multicoloured	10	10
563	1 f. 50 multicoloured	15	10
564	25 f. multicoloured	35	20
565	50 f. multicoloured	85	30
566	75 f. multicoloured	1·40	50

SIZES—VERT: (26×36 mm): 60 c., 1 f., 1 f. 50, 50 f. HORIZ: (36×29 mm): 25 f., 75 f.

79 "Village"

1966. 20th Anniv of U.N.I.C.E.F. Multicoloured designs showing children's drawings.

No.	Description	Unused	Used
567	2 f. "Elephant"	10	10
568	3 f. "Doll"	10	10
569	10 f. "Girl"	10	10
570	20 f. Type **79**	15	10
571	25 f. "Footballer"	35	15
572	40 f. "Still Life"	55	20
573	50 f. "Bird in Tree"	70	25

80 Dispensing Medicine

1967. Inauguration of W.H.O. Headquarters, Geneva. Multicoloured.

No.	Description	Unused	Used
574	30 f. Type **80**	25	10
575	50 f. Doctor examining child	35	20
576	75 f. Nurse weighing baby	60	30
577	80 f. W.H.O. Building & flag	75	45

81 Niamou Mask

1967. Guinean Masks. Multicoloured.

No.	Description	Unused	Used
578	10 c. Banda-di (Kanfarade Boke region)	10	10
579	30 c. Niamou (N'zerekore region) (different)	10	10
580	50 c. Type **81**	10	10
581	60 c. Yinadjinkele (Kankan region)	10	10
582	1 f. As 10 c.	10	10
583	1 f. 50, As 30 c.	10	10
584	5 f. Type **81**	15	10
585	25 f. As 60 c.	20	10
586	30 f. As 10 c.	30	10
587	50 f. As 30 c.	55	20
588	75 f. As Type **81**	1·10	35
589	100 f. As 60 c.	1·50	50

82 Research Institute

1967. Pastoria Research Institute. Mult.

No.	Description	Unused	Used
590	20 c. Type **82** (postage)	10	10
591	30 c. "Python regius" (snake)	10	10
592	50 c. Extracting snake's venom	10	10
593	1 f. "Python sebae"	10	10
594	2 f. Attendants handling viper	10	10
595	5 f. Gabon viper	10	10
596	20 f. "Dendroaspis viridis"	35	10
597	30 f. As 5 f.	65	10
598	50 f. As 1 f.	1·10	20
599	75 f. As 50 c.	1·60	30
600	200 f. As 20 c. (air)	2·25	80
601	300 f. As 2 f.	4·00	1·50

Nos. 596/601 are 56×26 mm.

1967. Landscapes (2nd series). As T **73**. Mult.

No.	Description	Unused	Used
603	5 f. Loos Islands (postage)	10	10
604	30 f. Tinkisso waterfalls	20	10
605	70 f. The "Elephant's Trunk", Kakoulima	45	10
606	80 f. Seashore, Ratoma	70	20
607	100 f. House of explorer Olivier de Sanderval (air)	1·10	35
608	200 f. Aerial view of Conakry	1·60	75

83 People's Palace, Conakry

1967. 20th Anniv of Guinean Democratic Party and Inaug. of People's Palace. Multicoloured.

No.	Description	Unused	Used
609	5 f. Type **83** (postage)	10	10
610	30 f. African elephant's head	50	50
611	55 f. Type **83**	40	25
612	200 f. As 30 f. (air)	1·75	1·00

1967. 50th Anniv of Lions Int. Landscape series optd **AMITE DES PEUPLES GRACE AU TOURISME 1917–1967** and Lions Emblem.

No.	Description	Unused	Used
613	5 f. (No. 603) (postage)	15	10
614	30 f. (No. 604)	30	20
615	40 f. (No. 536)	35	20
616	50 f. (No. 537)	45	25
617	70 f. (No. 605)	60	35
618	75 f. (No. 538)	85	45
619	80 f. (No. 606)	1·00	45
620	100 f. (No. 539) (air)	1·10	60
621	100 f. (No. 607)	1·10	60
622	200 f. (No. 608)	2·00	1·10

85 Section of Mural

86 W.H.O. Building, Brazzaville

1967. Air. "World of Tomorrow". Jose Vanetti's Mural, Conf. Building, U.N. Headquarters. Designs showing various sections of mural.

No.	Type	Description	Unused	Used
623	–	30 f. multicoloured	20	15
624	–	50 f. multicoloured	30	20
625	**85**	100 f. multicoloured	80	40
626	–	200 f. multicoloured	1·60	60

1967. Inaug of W.H.O. Building, Brazzaville.

No.	Type	Description	Unused	Used
628	**86**	30 f. olive, ochre & blue	30	15
629		75 f. red, ochre and blue	60	25

87 Human Rights Emblem

88 Coyah, Oubreka Region

1968. Human Rights Year.

No.	Type	Description	Unused	Used
630	**87**	30 f. red, green & ochre	25	15
631		40 f. red, blue & violet	30	15

1968. Regional Costumes and Habitations. Multicoloured.

No.	Description	Unused	Used
632	20 c. Type **88** (postage)	10	10
633	30 c. Kankan Region	10	10
634	40 c. Kankan, Upper Guinea	10	10
635	50 c. Forest region	10	10
636	60 c. Foulamory, Gaoual Region	10	10
637	5 f. Cognagui, Koundara Region	10	10
638	15 f. As 50 c.	10	10
639	20 f. As 20 c.	30	15
640	30 f. As 30 c.	45	20
641	40 f. Fouta-Djallon, Middle Guinea	70	25
642	100 f. Labe, Middle Guinea	1·50	40
643	300 f. Bassari, Koundara Region (air)	3·25	1·00

The 60 c. to 300 f. are larger (60×39 mm).

89 "The Village Story-teller"

1968. Paintings of African Legends (1st series). Multicoloured.

No.	Description	Unused	Used
644	25 f. Type **89** (postage)	15	10
645	30 f. "The Moon and the Stars"	15	10
646	75 f. "Leuk the Hare sells his Sister"	60	35
647	80 f. "The Hunter and the Female Antelope"	1·00	35
648	100 f. "Old Faya's Inheritance" (air)	1·00	30
649	200 f. "Soumangourou Kante killed by Djegue"	2·00	45

The 75 f. and 100 f are vert. designs.

1968. Paintings of African Legends (2nd series). As T **89**. Multicoloured.

No.	Description	Unused	Used
651	15 f. "Little Demons of Mount Nimba" (postage)	10	10
652	30 f. "Lan, the Baby Buffalo"	20	10
653	40 f. "The Nianablas and the Crocodiles"	30	20
654	50 f. "Leuk the Hare and the Drum"	50	20
655	70 f. "Malissadio—the Young Girl and the Hippopotamus" (air)	75	20
656	300 f. "Little Goune, Son of the Lion"	3·25	1·10

The 30, 50 and 300 f. are vert.

90 Olive Baboon

1968. African Fauna. Multicoloured.

No.	Description	Unused	Used
658	5 f. Type **90** (postage)	15	10
659	10 f. Leopards	20	10
660	15 f. Hippopotami	30	15
661	20 f. Crocodile	55	20
662	30 f. Warthog	70	20
663	50 f. Kob	85	25
664	75 f. African buffalo	1·60	45
665	100 f. Lions (air)	1·75	40
666	200 f. African elephant	4·00	1·00

Nos 665/6 are 50×35 mm.

91 Robert F. Kennedy

1968. "Martyrs of Liberty". Multicoloured.

No.	Description	Unused	Used
668	30 f. Type **91** (postage)	20	10
669	75 f. Martin Luther King	50	20
670	100 f. John F. Kennedy	65	35
671	50 f. Type **91** (air)	45	15
672	100 f. Martin Luther King	80	25
673	200 f. John F. Kennedy	1·75	60

92 Running

1969. Olympic Games, Mexico (1968). Multicoloured.

No.	Description	Unused	Used
674	5 f. Type **92** (postage)	10	10
675	10 f. Boxing	10	10
676	15 f. Throwing the javelin	15	10
677	25 f. Football	25	10
678	30 f. Hurdling	30	10
679	50 f. Throwing the hammer	50	25
680	75 f. Cycling	70	25
681	100 f. Gymnastics (air)	70	30
682	200 f. Exercising on rings	1·25	50
683	300 f. Pole-vaulting	2·50	95

The 25, 100, 200 and 300 f. are larger, 57×30 mm. Each design also shows one of three different sculptured figures.

1969. Moon Flight of "Apollo 8". Nos. 514/16 optd **APOLLO 8 DEC. 1968** and earth and moon motifs or surch also.

No.	Description	Unused	Used
684	30 f. on 45 f. mult (postage)	35	35
685	45 f. multicoloured	35	35
686	25 f. on 200 f. mult (air)	35	15
687	100 f. multicoloured	1·10	65
688	200 f. multicoloured	2·00	1·00

95 "Tarzan"

1969. "Tarzan" (famous Guinea Chimpanzee). Multicoloured.

No.	Description	Unused	Used
689	25 f. Type **95**	25	15
690	30 f. "Tarzan" in front of Pastoria Institute	30	20
691	75 f. "Tarzan" and family	65	25
692	100 f. "Tarzan" squatting on branch	1·25	40

96 Pioneers lighting Fire

1969. Guinean Pioneer Youth Organization. Multicoloured.
693 5 f. Type **96** 10 10
694 25 f. Pioneer and village 20 10
695 30 f. Pioneers squad 25 10
696 40 f. Playing basketball 35 20
697 45 f. Two pioneers 40 20
698 50 f. Pioneers emblem 50 25

97 "Apollo" Launch

1969. 1st Man on the Moon. Multicoloured.
700 25 f. Type **97** 15 10
701 30 f. View of Earth 20 10
702 50 f. Modules descent to the Moon 35 10
703 60 f. Astronauts on Moon . . . 45 20
704 75 f. Landing module on Moon . 50 25
705 100 f. Take-off from Moon . . 1·00 40
706 200 f. "Splashdown" . . . . . 2·00 1·00
No. 705 is size 35 × 71 mm.
The above stamps were issued with English and French inscriptions.

98 Pylon and Heavy Industry

1969. 50th Anniv of I.L.O. Multicoloured.
707 25 f. Type **98** 20 10
708 30 f. Broadcasting studio . . . 20 10
709 75 f. Harvesting 50 20
710 200 f. Making pottery . . . . . 1·40 65

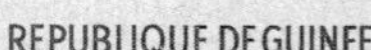

99 Child suffering from Smallpox
100 O.E.R.S. Countries on Map of Africa

1970. Campaign Against Measles and Smallpox. Multicoloured.
711 25 f. Type **99** 15 10
712 30 f. Mother and child with measles 20 15
713 40 f. Inoculating girl 30 15
714 50 f. Inoculating boy 50 25
715 60 f. Inoculating family 60 25
716 200 f. Dr. Edward Jenner . . . 2·25 1·00

1970. Meeting of Senegal River Riparian States Organization (Organisation des Etats Riverains du fleuve Senegal).
717 **100** 30 f. multicoloured . . . 20 15
718 200 f. multicoloured . . . 1·50 95
NOTE: The Riparian States are Guinea, Mali, Mauritania and Senegal.

101 Dish Aerial and Open book

1970. World Telecommunications Day.
719 **101** 5 f. black and blue 15 15
720 10 f. black and red 15 15
721 50 f. black and yellow . . 45 15
722 200 f. black and lilac . . . 2·00 95

102 Lenin

1970. Birth Centenary of Lenin. Multicoloured.
723 5 f. Type **102** 10 10
724 20 f. "Lenin in the Smolny" (Serov) 20 10
725 30 f. "Lenin addressing Workers" (Serov) 25 15
726 40 f. "Lenin speaking to Servicemen" (Vasiliev) . . . 40 15
727 100 f. "Lenin with Crowd" (Vasilev) . . . . 1·00 35
728 200 f. Type **102** . . . . 1·75 1·00

103 Congo Tetra

1971. Fishes. Multicoloured.
729 5 f. Type **103** 15 10
730 10 f. Red-spotted gularis . . . 20 10
731 15 f. Red-chinned panchax . . . 20 10
732 20 f. Six-barred distichodus . . 35 15
733 25 f. Jewel cichlid 40 25
734 30 f. Rainbow krib 65 25
735 40 f. Two-striped lyretail . . . 75 25
736 45 f. Banded jewelfish . . . . 1·10 35
737 50 f. Red-tailed notho . . . . 1·25 50
738 75 f. Freshweater butterfly-fish . 2·25 55
739 100 f. Golden trevally . . . . . 2·75 65
740 200 f. African mouth-brooder . 5·50 1·75

104 Violet-crested Turaco

1971. Wild Birds. Multicoloured.
741 5 f. Type **104** (postage) . . . . 1·10 55
742 20 f. Golden Oriole . . . . . . 1·50 75
743 30 f. Blue headed Coucal . . . 1·75 90
744 40 f. Great Grey Shrike . . . . 1·90 1·00
745 75 f. Vulturine Guineafowl . . . 3·75 1·25
746 100 f. Southern Ground Hornbill . . . . 5·50 1·60
747 50 f. Type **104** (air) . . . . . . 2·25 1·10
748 100 f. As 20 f. . . . . 2·75 1·40
749 200 f. As 75 f. . . . . 8·25 2·00

105 U.N.I.C.E.F. Emblem on Map of Africa

1971. 25th Anniv of U.N.I.C.E.F.
750 **105** 25 f. multicoloured 15 10
751 30 f. multicoloured 20 10
752 50 f. multicoloured 35 15
753 60 f. multicoloured 50 20
754 100 f. multicoloured . . . 80 35

106 John and Robert Kennedy and Martin Luther King

1972. Air. Martyrs for Peace. Embossed on silver or gold foil.
755 **106** 300 f. silver . . . . 3·25
756 1500 f. gold, cream and green . . . . 16·00

107 Jules Verne and Moon Rocket

1972. Air. Moon Exploration. Embossed on silver or gold foil.
757 **107** 300 f. silver . . . . 3·25
758 1200 f. gold . . . . 13·00

108 Pres. Richard Nixon

1972. Air. Pres. Nixon's Visit to Peking. Embossed on gold or silver foil.
759 **108** 90 f. silver 75
760 – 90 f. silver 75
761 – 90 f. silver 75
762 – 90 f. silver 75
763 **108** 290 f. gold . . . . 2·50
764 – 290 f. gold . . . . 2·50
765 – 290 f. gold . . . . 2·50
766 – 290 f. gold . . . . 2·50
767 – 1200 f. gold and red . . . 13·00
DESIGNS—VERT: Nos. 760, 764 Chinese table-tennis player; Nos. 761, 765, American table-tennis player; Nos. 762, 766, Mao Tse-tung. HORIZ: (45 × 35 mm); No. 767, Pres. Nixon and Mao Tse-tung.

109 "Flying Flatfish"

1972. Imaginary Space Creatures. Mult.
768 5 f. Type **109** 10 10
769 20 f. "Radioactive crab" . . . 20 10
770 30 f. "Space octopus" 25 10
771 40 f. "Rocket-powered serpent" . 45 10
772 100 f. "Winged eel" . . . . . 1·10 40
773 200 f. "Flying dragon" . . . . 2·00 70

110 African Child

1972. Racial Equality Year. Multicoloured.
774 15 f. Type **110** (postage) 10 10
775 20 f. Asiatic child 15 10
776 30 f. Indian youth 20 10
777 50 f. European girl 45 20
778 100 f. Heads of four races . . . 85 35
779 100 f. As No. 778 (air) 90 40

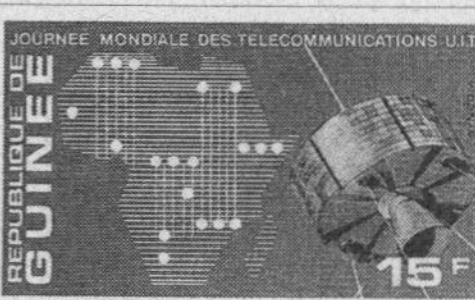

111 "Syncom" and African Map

1972. World Telecommunications Day. Mult.
780 15 f. Type **111** (postage) 15 10
781 30 f. "Relay" 25 10
782 75 f. "Early Bird" 60 30
783 80 f. "Telstar" . . . . 1·00 40
784 100 f. As 30 f. (air) . . . . . 1·00 35
785 200 f. As 75 f. . . . . 1·90 65

112 APU Emblem and Dove with Letter

1972. 10th Anniv of African Postal Union.
786 **112** 15 f. mult (postage) . . . 10 10
787 30 f. multicoloured 20 10
788 75 f. multicoloured 50 25
789 80 f. multicoloured 65 40
790 – 100 f. multicoloured (air) . . 85 40
791 – 200 f. multicoloured . . . 1·75 75
DESIGNS: 100 f. to 200 f. APU emblem and airmail envelope.

113 Child reading Book
114 Throwing the Javelin

1972. International Book Year. Multicoloured.
792 5 f. Type **113** 10 10
793 15 f. Book with sails 15 10
794 40 f. Girl with book and plant . 30 15
795 50 f. "Key of Knowledge" and open book 50 20
796 75 f. "Man" reading book and globe 75 40
797 200 f. Open book and laurel sprigs . . . . 1·75 70

1972. Olympic Games, Munich. Mult.
798 5 f. Type **114** (postage) 10 10
799 10 f. Pole-vaulting 10 10
800 25 f. Hurdling 25 10
801 30 f. Throwing the hammer . . 35 10
802 40 f. Boxing 50 15
803 50 f. Gymnastics (horse) 65 25
804 75 f. Running 90 35
805 100 f. Gymnastics (rings) (air) . 1·50 45
806 200 f. Cycling . . . . 2·75 85

1972. U.N. Environmental Conservation Conf., Stockholm. Nos. 750/4 optd **UNE SEULE TERRE** and emblem.
808 **105** 25 f. multicoloured 20 10
809 30 f. multicoloured 20 10
810 50 f. multicoloured 45 15
811 60 f. multicoloured 70 25
812 100 f. multicoloured . . . 1·00 50

116 Dimitrov addressing "Reichstag Fire" Court

1972. 90th Birth Anniv of George Dimitrov (Bulgarian statesman).
813 **116** 5 f. blue, gold and green . . 10 10
814 – 25 f. blue, gold & green . . 15 10
815 – 40 f. blue, gold and green . 30 20
816 – 100 f. blue, gold & green . 80 35
DESIGNS: 25 f. In Moabit Prison, Berlin, 1933; 40 f. Writing memoirs; 100 f. G. Dimitrov.

117 Emperor Haile Selassie

118 "Syntomeida epilais"

1972. Emperor Haile Selassie of Ethiopia's 80th Birthday. Multicoloured.

817 40 f. Type **117** 35 20
818 200 f. Emperor Haile Selassie in military uniform 1·60 80

1973. Guinean Insects. Multicoloured.

819 5 f. Type **118** 10 10
820 15 f. "Hippodamia californica" 25 10
821 30 f. "Tettigonia viridissima" 50 15
822 40 f. "Apis mellifica" 60 25
823 50 f. "Photinus pyralis" 85 30
824 200 f. "Ancyluris formosissima" 3·50 1·25

119 Dr. Kwame Nkrumah

1973. 10th Anniv of Organization of African Unity.

825 **119** 1 s. 50 blk, gold & green 15 10
826 – 2 s. 50 blk, gold & green 25 10
827 – 5 s. black, gold & green 50 25
828 – 10 s. violet and gold 1·00 45

DESIGNS: Nos. 826/8, different portraits of Dr. Kwame Nkrumah similar to Type **119**.

120 Institute of Applied Biology, Kindia

1973. 25th Anniv of W.H.O. Multicoloured.

829 1 s. Type **120** 10 10
830 2 s. 50 Preparing vaccine from an egg 25 10
831 3 s. Filling ampoules with vaccine 30 20
832 4 s. Sterilization of vaccine 40 20
833 5 s. Packing vaccines 60 25
834 10 s. Preparation of vaccine base 1·25 40
835 20 s. Inoculating patient 2·50 75

Nos. 833/35 are size 48 × 31 mm.

121 Volcanic Landscape

1973. 500th Birth Anniv of Copernicus. Mult.

836 50 c. Type **121** 10 10
837 2 s. Sun over desert 20 10
838 4 s. Earth and Moon 35 10
839 5 s. Lunar landscape 60 15
840 10 s. Jupiter 1·25 35
841 20 s. Saturn 2·25 70

122 Loading Bauxite at Quayside

1974. Air. Bauxite Industry, Bok. Mult.

843 4 s. Type **122** 50 15
844 6 s. Bauxite train 2·50 40
845 10 s. Bauxite mining 2·75 50

123 "Clappertonia ficifolia"

125 Pioneers testing Rope-bridge

124 Drummers and Pigeon

1974. Flowers of Guinea. Multicoloured.

846 50 c. Type **123** (postage) 10 10
847 1 s. "Rothmannia longiflora" 10 10
848 2 s. "Oncoba spinosa" 20 10
849 3 s. "Venidium fastuosum" 30 15
850 4 s. "Bombax costatum" 50 15
851 5 s. "Clerodendrum splendens" 75 20
852 7 s. 50 "Combretuni grandiflorum" 1·25 25
853 10 s. "Mussaendra erythrophylla" 1·50 40
854 12 s. "Argemone mexicana" 1·75 60
855 20 s. "Thunbergia alata" (air) 2·50 80
856 25 s. "Diascia barberae" 3·50 80
857 50 s. "Kigelia africana" 7·00 1·90

SIZES—VERT: Nos. 847/9, As Type **123**: Nos. 850/3, 36 × 47 mm. DIAMOND: Nos. 854/7, 61 × 61 mm.

No. 855 is wrongly inscribed "Thunbegia alata".

1974. Centenary of U.P.U. Multicoloured.

858 5 s. Type **124** 40 20
859 6 s. Runner and pigeon 55 25
860 7 s. Monorail train, lorry and pigeon 1·40 35
861 10 s. Boeing 707, "United States" (liner) and pigeon 1·50 60

1974. National Pioneers (Scouting) Movement. Multicoloured.

863 50 c. Type **125** 15 10
864 2 s. "On safari" 25 10
865 4 s. Using field-telephone 35 15
866 5 s. Cooking on camp-fire 60 15
867 7 s. 50 Saluting 85 35
868 10 s. Playing basketball 1·75 55

127 Chimpanzee

1975. Wild Animals. Multicoloured.

871 1 s. Type **127** 10 10
872 2 s. Impala 20 10
873 3 s. Warthog 35 10
874 4 s. Waterbuck 40 20
875 5 s. Leopard 60 20
876 6 s. Greater kudu 60 25
877 6 s. 50 Common zebra 75 35
878 7 s. 50 African buffalo 75 35
879 8 s. Hippopotamus 1·25 35
880 10 s. Lion 1·50 40
881 12 s. Black rhinoceros 1·90 45
882 15 s. African elephant 2·75 80

128 Lion and Lioness beside Pipeline

1975. 10th Anniv of African Development Bank.

884 5 s. Type **128** 70 20
885 7 s. African elephants beside pipeline 1·00 30
886 10 s. Lions beside pipeline (horiz) 1·25 35
887 20 s. African elephant and calf beside pipeline (horiz) 2·25 80

129 Women playing Saxophones

1976. Int Women's Year (1975). Mult.

888 5 s. Type **129** 40 20
889 7 s. Women playing guitars 60 30
890 9 s. Woman railway shunter 3·75 50
891 15 s. Woman doctor 1·75 65
892 20 s. Genetics emblems 2·25 90

130 Gymnastics

1976. Olympic Games, Montreal. Mult.

894 3 s. Type **130** 25 10
895 4 s. Long jump 35 15
896 5 s. Throwing the hammer 40 20
897 6 s. Throwing the discus 45 25
898 6 s. 50 Hurdling 50 25
899 7 s. Throwing the javelin 50 30
900 8 s. Running 60 30
901 8 s. 50 Cycling 95 35
902 10 s. High-jumping 1·10 35
903 15 s. Putting the shot 1·60 60
904 20 s. Pole vaulting 2·25 65
905 25 s. Football 2·75 90

131 Bell and Early Telephone

1976. Telephone Centenary. Multicoloured.

907 5 s. Type **131** 50 20
908 7 s. Bell and wall telephone 75 25
909 12 s. Bell and satellite "Syncom" 1·40 50
910 15 s. Bell and satellite "Telstar" 1·75 60

132 "Collybia fusipes"

1977. Mushrooms. Multicoloured.

912 5 s. Type **132** (postage) 1·50 20
913 7 s. "Lycoperdon perlatum" 2·25 25
914 9 s. "Boletus edulis" 3·00 35
915 9 s. 50 "Lactarius deliciosus" 3·00 45
916 11 s. 50 "Agaricus campestris" 4·75 80
917 10 s. "Morchella esculenta" (air) 3·50 40
918 12 s. "Lepiota procera" 4·50 60
919 15 s. "Cantharellus cibarius" 6·50 1·10

133 Duplex Murex

1977. Sea Shells. Multicoloured.

921 1 s. Type **133** 10 10
922 2 s. Wavy-leaved turrid 25 10
923 4 s. Queen marginella 60 15
924 5 s. "Tympanotonos radula" 90 20
925 7 s. Striped marginella 1·00 25
926 8 s. Doris harp 1·40 30
927 10 s. Obtuse demoulia 1·75 45
928 20 s. Pitted frog shell 3·25 80
929 25 s. Adanson's marginella 4·00 1·00

Nos. 927/9 are 50 × 34 mm in size.

134 President Sekou Toure

1977. 30th Anniv of Guinean Democratic Party (PDG). Multicoloured.

930 5 s. Type **134** 35 25
931 10 s. Labourers and oxen 95 45
932 20 s. Soldier driving tractor 2·10 95
933 25 s. Pres. Toure addressing U.N. General Assembly 2·50 1·25
934 30 s. Pres. Toure (vert) 3·00 1·50
935 40 s. As 30 s. 3·75 1·60

135 "Varanus niloticus"

1977. Reptiles. Multicoloured.

937 3 s. Type **135** (postage) 35 10
938 4 s. "Hyperolius quinquevittatus" 40 15
939 5 s. "Uromastix" 50 15
940 6 s. "Scincus scincus" 75 15
941 6 s. 50 "Agama agama" 95 20
942 7 s. "Naja melanoleuca" 1·10 20
943 8 s. 50 "Python regius" 1·40 25
944 20 s. "Bufo mauritanicus" 3·00 60
945 10 s. "Chamaeleo diepis" (air) 2·00 30
946 15 s. "Crocodylus niloticus" 2·75 50
947 25 s. "Testudo elegans" 4·25 75

136 Eland (male)

1977. Endangered Animals. Multicoloured.

948 1 s. Type **136** (postage) 15 10
949 1 s. Eland (female) 15 10
950 1 s. Eland (young) 15 10
951 2 s. Chimpanzee (young) 20 10
952 2 s. Chimpanzee 20 10
953 2 s. Chimpanzee sitting 20 10
954 2 s. 50 African elephant 30 10
955 2 s. 50 African elephant 30 10
956 2 s. 50 African elephant 30 10
957 3 s. Lion 50 10
958 3 s. Lioness 50 10
959 3 s. Lion Cub 50 10
960 4 s. Indian Palm squirrel 60 15
961 4 s. Indian Palm squirrel 60 15
962 4 s. Indian Palm squirrel 60 15
963 5 s. Hippopotamus 80 20
964 5 s. Hippopotamus 80 20
965 5 s. Hippopotamus 80 20
966 5 s. Type **136** (air) 60 20
967 5 s. As No. 949 60 20
968 5 s. As No. 950 60 20
969 8 s. As No. 954 1·50 25
970 8 s. As No. 955 1·50 25
971 8 s. As No. 956 1·50 25
972 9 s. As No. 963 1·50 25
973 9 s. As No. 964 1·50 25
974 9 s. As No. 965 1·50 25
975 10 s. As No. 951 1·75 30
976 10 s. As No. 952 1·75 30
977 10 s. As No. 953 1·75 30
978 12 s. As No. 960 1·75 40
979 12 s. As No. 961 1·75 40
980 12 s. As No. 962 1·75 40
981 13 s. As No. 957 2·00 50
982 13 s. As No. 958 2·00 50
983 13 s. As No. 959 2·00 50

Issued se-tenant in strips of three within the sheet, each strip showing different views of the same animal.

137 Lenin taking Parade in Red Square, Moscow

1976. 60th Anniv of Russian Revolution. Multicoloured.
984 2 s. 50 Lenin's first speach in Moscow (postage) 25 10
985 5 s. Lenin addressing revolutionary crowd 45 15
986 7 s. 50 Lenin with militia-men . 85 20
987 8 s. Type **137** . . . . 1·10 20
988 10 s. Russian ballet (air) . . . . 2·00 30
989 30 s. Pushkin Monument . . . 3·75 75

138 Pres. Giscard d'Estaing at Microphones

1979. Visit of President Giscard d'Estaing of France.
990 **138** 3 s. brown and yellow-brown (postage) 30 10
991 – 5 s. brown, pale green and deep green 55 15
992 – 6 s. 50 brown, pale mauve and deep mauve 80 20
993 – 7 s. brown, pale blue and blue 85 20
994 – 8 s. 50 brn, rose & carm . . 1·25 30
995 – 10 s. brown, pale violet and violet . . . . 1·60 40
996 – 20 s. brown, pale green and deep green . . . . . . 3·50 65
997 – 25 s. multicoloured (air) . . 4·00 1·25

DESIGNS—HORIZ: 5 s. President Giscard d'Estaing and Sekou Toure in conference; 6 s. 50, Presidents signing agreement; 7 s. Presidents at official meeting; 8 s. 50, Presidents with their wives; 10 s. Presidents in conference; 20 s. Toasting the agreement. VERT: 25 s. President Giscard d'Estaing.

139 "20,000 Leagues Under the Sea"

1979. 150th Birth Anniv (1978) of Jules Verne. Multicoloured.
998 1 s. Type **139** (postage) 10 10
999 3 s. "The Children of Captain Grant" 30 10
1000 5 s. "The Mysterious Island" . 60 15
1001 7 s. "A Captain of Fifteen Years" . . . . 1·25 35
1002 10 s. "The Amazing Adventure of Barsac" . . . . 1·75 50
1003 20 s. "Five Weeks in a Balloon" (air) . . . . 2·25 40
1004 25 s. "Robur the Conqueror" . 3·00 60

140 William Henson's "Aerial Steam Carriage", 1842

1979. Aviation History. Multicoloured.
1005 3 s. Type **140** 30 10
1006 5 s. Wright Type A (inscr "Flyer I"), 1903 . . . . . . 55 15
1007 6 s. 50 Caudron C-46O, 1934 . 75 20
1008 7 s. Charles Lindbergh's "Spirit of St. Louis", 1927 . . . . 95 20
1009 8 s. 50 Bristol Beaufighter, 1940 . . . . 1·25 20
1010 10 s. Bleriot XI, 1909 . . . . 1·50 25
1011 20 s. Boeing 727-100, 1963 . 2·75 55
1012 20 s. Concorde . . . . 3·50 70

141 Hafla Football Team

1979. Hafla Football Club's Victories. Mult.
1013 1 s. Type **141** 10 10
1014 2 s. Team members with cup (vert) 20 20
1015 5 s. President Toure presenting medals 60 15
1016 7 s. President Toure presenting cup (vert) 85 20
1017 8 s. Ahmed Sekou Toure Cup (vert) 95 25
1018 10 s. Team captains shaking hands (vert) . . . . 1·25 30
1019 20 s. The winning goal . . . . 2·40 75

142 Children dancing round Tree

1980. International Year of the Child. Mult.
1020 2 s. Type **142** 15 10
1021 4 s. "Heureuse Enfance" . . . 40 15
1022 5 s. Steam train (horiz) . . . . 1·60 15
1023 7 s. Village (horiz) 85 20
1024 10 s. Boy climbing tree (horiz) . 1·25 25
1025 25 s. Children of different races (horiz) . . . . 3·00 70

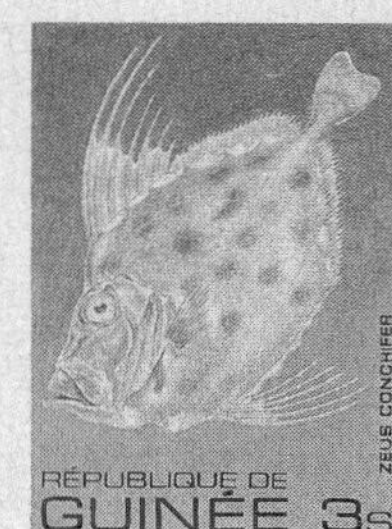

143 Buckler Dory

1980. Fishes, Multicoloured.
1026 1 s. Robust butterflyfish (horiz) 10 10
1027 2 s. Blue-pointed porgy (horiz) 20 15
1028 3 s. Type **143** 35 15
1029 4 s. African hind (horiz) . . . 45 25
1030 5 s. Spotted seahorse 55 25
1031 6 s. Marine hatchetfish (horiz) . 90 30
1032 7 s. Half-banded snake-eel (horiz) . . . . 1·40 30
1033 8 s. Flying gurnard . . . . . . 1·60 40
1034 9 s. West African squirrel-fish (horiz) . . . . 1·75 40
1035 10 s. Guinean fingerfish . . . 1·90 40
1036 12 s. African sergeant major (horiz) . . . . 2·25 75
1037 15 s. West African trigger-fish (horiz) . . . . 3·00 1·00

144 Rocket on Launch Pad

1980. 10th Anniv of 1st Moon Landing. Multicoloured.
1038 1 s. Type **144** 10 10
1039 2 s. Earth from the Moon . . . 20 10
1040 4 s. Armstrong descending from lunar module 35 15
1041 5 s. Armstrong on the Moon . 50 15
1042 7 s. Astronaut collecting samples 75 20
1043 8 s. Parachute descent 95 25
1044 12 s. Winching capsule aboard recovery vessel . . . . . . 1·60 35
1045 20 s. Astronauts . . . . 3·00 70

145 Dome of the Rock

1981. Palestinian Solidarity.
1046 **145** 8 s. multicoloured . . . . 1·40 55
1047 11 s. multicoloured . . . 1·90 70

146 Map of Member States and Agricultural Produce

1982. 5th Anniv of Economic Community of West African States. Multicoloured.
1048 6 s. Type **146** 85 30
1049 7 s. Transport . . . . 4·50 75
1050 9 s. Heavy Industry . . . . . 1·40 45

147 Ataturk as Soldier

1982. Birth Centenary of Kemal Ataturk (Turkish statesman). Multicoloured.
1051 7 s. Type **147** (postage) 95 40
1052 10 s. Ataturk as statesman . . 1·25 50
1053 25 s. Equestrian statue (horiz) . 3·50 85
1054 25 s. As No. 1053 (air) . . . . 4·00 85

148 Football

1982. Olympic Games, Moscow. Multicoloured.
1055 1 s. Type **148** (postage) 10 10
1056 2 s. Basketball 20 15
1057 3 s. Diving 25 15
1058 4 s. Gymnastics 30 15
1059 5 s. Boxing 55 20
1060 6 s. High jumping 75 25
1061 7 s. Running 95 35
1062 8 s. Long jumping . . . . . . 1·10 40
1063 9 s. Fencing (air) . . . . . . 1·10 20
1064 10 s. Football (vert) . . . . . 1·25 30
1065 11 s. Basketball (vert) . . . . 1·40 45
1066 20 s. Diving (vert) . . . . . . 3·00 55
1067 25 s. Boxing (vert) . . . . . . 3·50 65

149 Balaidos Stadium, Vigo

1982. World Cup Football Championship. Spain. Football Stadia. Multicoloured.
1068 6 s. Type **149** (postage) 90 15
1069 8 s. El Molinon, Gijon . . . . 1·10 25
1070 9 s. San Mames, Bilbao . . . 1·60 30
1071 10 s. Sanchez Pizjuan, Seville . 1·75 35
1072 10 s. Luis Casanova, Valencia (air) . . . . 1·75 35
1073 20 s. Nou Camps, Barcelona . 3·50 45
1074 25 s. Santiago Bernabeu, Madrid . . . . 4·50 65

150 Wrestling

151 Marquis d'Arlandes, Pilatre de Rozier and Montgolfier Balloon, 1783

1983. Olympic Games, Los Angeles (1st issue). Multicoloured.
1075 5 s. Type **150** (postage) 40 15
1076 7 s. Weightlifting 50 25
1077 10 s. Gymnastics. 95 35
1078 15 s. Discus . . . . 1·60 60
1079 20 s. Kayak (air) . . . . . . 1·60 50
1080 25 s. Equestrian . . . . 2·25 80
See also Nos. 843/9.

1983. Bicentenary of Manned Flight. Mult.
1082 5 s. Type **151** (postage) 55 15
1083 7 s. Jean-Francois Pilatre de Rozier and Montgolfier balloon "Marie Antoinette", 1784 . . . . 65 25
1084 10 s. Henri Dupuy de Lome and airship, 1872 (horiz) . . 95 35
1085 15 s. Major A. Parseval and "Airship No. 1", 1906 (horiz) . . . . 1·60 60
1086 20 s. Count Zeppelin and airship "Bodensee", 1919 (horiz) (air) . . . . 1·60 50
1087 25 s. Balloon "Double Eagle II" and crew, 1978 . . . . . . 2·25 80

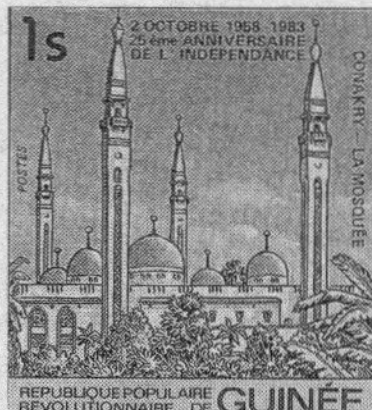

152 Lungs and Monkey

1983. Cent of Discovery of Tubercle Bacillus. Multicoloured.
1089 6 s. Type **152** 75 20
1090 10 s. Cow . . . . 1·25 30
1091 11 s. Robert Koch and microscope . . . . 1·50 35
1092 12 s. Koch using microscope . 1·75 50
1093 15 s. Laboratory . . . . 2·25 55
1094 20 s. Scientist with test tube and monkey . . . . 3·00 70
1095 25 s. Doctor examining young boy . . . . 3·50 95

153 Disabled and Emblem

1983. International Year of Disabled Persons.
1096 **153** 10 s. multicoloured . . . 1·25 55
1097 20 s. multicoloured . . . 2·50 1·00

154 Mosque, Conakry

1983. 25th Anniv of Independence.
1098 **154** 1 s. multicoloured 10 10
1099 2 s. multicoloured 20 10
1100 5 s. multicoloured 40 15
1101 10 s. multicoloured . . . 90 40

155 Citizens with Scrolls

1983. 10th Anniv of Mano River Union. Multicoloured.

1103	2 s. Type **155**	20	10
1104	7 s. Union emblem	50	25
1105	8 s. Map and presidents of Guinea, Sierra Leone and Liberia	60	25
1106	10 s. Signing the Declaration of Union	85	35

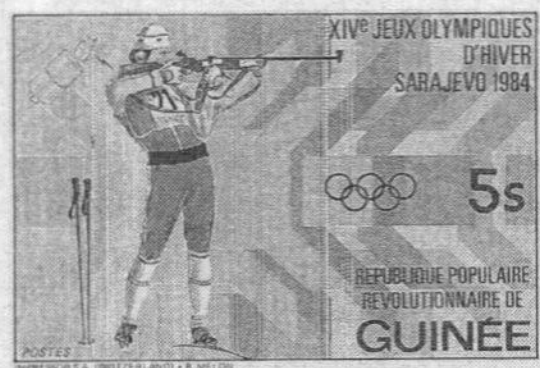

156 Biathlon

1983. Winter Olympic Games, Sarajevo. Multicoloured.

1108	5 s. Type **156** (postage)	50	15
1109	7 s. Luge	60	25
1110	10 s. Slalom	1·25	40
1111	15 s. Speed skating	1·60	60
1112	20 s. Ski jump (air)	1·90	55
1113	25 s. Ice dancing	2·50	80

157 Raphael and "Virgin with the Blue Diadem"

1984. Anniversaries (1983). Multicoloured.

1115	5 s. Type **157**	40	20
1116	7 s. Rubens and "Holy Family"	60	25
1117	10 s. Rembrandt and "Portrait of Saskia"	95	40
1118	15 s. Goethe and scene from "The Young Werther"	1·40	60
1119	20 s. Lord Baden-Powell and scout camp	1·75	55
1120	25 s. P.P. Harris and speaker at Rotary meeting	2·50	80

158 Abraham Lincoln

1984. Personalities. Multicoloured.

1122	5 s. Type **158** (postage)	40	20
1123	7 s. Jean-Henri Dunant (founder of Red Cross)	65	25
1124	10 s. Gottlieb Daimler (automobile designer)	1·25	40
1125	15 s. Louis Bleriot (pilot)	1·75	55
1126	20 s. Paul P. Harris (founder of Rotary Club) (air)	1·75	65
1127	25 s. Auguste Piccard (ocean explorer)	2·50	85

159 "The Mystic Marriage of Sts. Catherine and Sebastian" (detail, Correggio)

1984. Paintings. Multicoloured.

1129	5 s. Type **159** (postage)	40	20
1130	7 s. "The Holy Family" (A. Durer)	60	25
1131	10 s. "The Veiled Lady" (Raphael)	1·00	40
1132	15 s. "Portrait of a Young Man" (A. Durer)	1·25	55
1133	20 s. "Portrait of Soutine" (A. Modigliani) (air)	1·75	65
1134	25 s. "The Esterhazy Madonna" (Raphael)	2·50	85

160 Congo River Steamer and Canoe

1984. Transport. Multicoloured.

1136	5 s. Type **160** (postage)	60	20
1137	7 s. Airship "Graf Zeppelin"	70	25
1138	10 s. Daimler car, 1886	1·50	40
1139	15 s. Beyer-Garratt steam locomotive	2·40	1·25
1140	20 s. Latecoere seaplane "Comte de la Vaulx" (air)	1·75	55
1141	25 s. Savoia Marchetti S-73 airplane	2·50	80

161 W. Hoppe and D. Schauerhammer (bobsleigh)

1984. Winter Olympic Gold Medal Winners. Multicoloured.

1143	5 s. Type **161** (postage)	40	20
1144	7 s. T. L. Wassberg (cross-country skiing)	60	25
1145	10 s. G. Boucher (speed skating)	1·00	40
1146	15 s. K. Witt (ladies figure skating)	1·50	65
1147	20 s. W. D. Johnson (downhill skiing) (air)	2·00	85
1148	25 s. U.S.S.R. (ice hockey)	2·75	90

162 T. Ruiz and C. Costie (Synchronized Swimming Duet)

1985. Olympic Games Gold Medal Winners. Multicoloured.

1150	5 s. Type **162** (postage)	40	20
1151	7 s. R. Klimke, H. Krug and U. Sauer, West Germany (team dressage)	85	25
1152	10 s. McKee and Buchan, U.S.A. (sailing, "Flying Dutchman" class)	95	40
1153	15 s. Mark Todd (equestrian three-day event)	1·25	65
1154	20 s. Daley Thompson (decathlon) (air)	2·00	75
1155	25 s. M. Smith, C. Homfeld, L. Burr and J. Fargis, U.S.A. (equestrian team jumping)	2·25	85

163 "Rhodophyllus callidermus"

1985. Fungi. Multicoloured.

1157	5 s. Type **163** (postage)	80	35
1158	7 s. "Agaricus niger"	1·00	45
1159	10 s. "Thermitomyces globulus"	1·90	70
1160	15 s. "Amanita robusta"	2·50	1·10
1161	20 s. "Lepiota subradicans" (air)	3·50	1·00
1162	25 s. "Cantharellus rhodophylus"	3·75	1·10

164 Hermann Oberth and 2-Stage Conical Motor Rocket

1985. Space Achievements. Multicoloured.

1164	7 s. Type **164** (postage)	50	25
1165	10 s. "Lunik 1"	95	40
1166	15 s. "Lunik 2" on Moon, 1959	1·25	55
1167	20 s. "Lunik 3" photographing hidden face of Moon	1·90	75
1168	30 s. Armstrong, Aldrin and Collins (first manned landing on Moon) (air)	2·50	75
1169	35 s. Sally Ride (first American woman in space)	3·25	80

165 Maimonides in Jewish Quarter (850th Birth Anniv)

1985. Anniversaries and Events. Multicoloured.

1171	7 s. Type **165** (postage)	80	35
1172	10 s. Christopher Columbus departing from Palos, 1492	1·75	50
1173	15 s. Frederic Bartholdi and Statue of Liberty (centenary)	1·50	55
1174	20 s. Queen Mother with Duke of York and Princess Elizabeth (85th birthday)	1·75	75
1175	30 s. Ulf Merbold and space shuttle "Columbia" (air)	2·50	75
1176	35 s. Prince Charles and Lady Diana Spencer (Royal Wedding)	3·00	85

166 Black-billed Cuckoo

1995. Birth Bicentenary of John J. Audubon (ornithologist). Multicoloured.

1178	7 s. Type **166** (postage)	65	50
1179	10 s. Carolina parakeet	1·00	75
1180	15 s. American anhinga (vert)	1·50	1·10
1181	20 s. Red-shouldered hawk	3·25	1·60
1182	30 s. Screech owl (air)	4·00	1·90
1183	35 s. Brown thrasher (vert)	5·00	2·40

167 Blue-point Siamese

1985. Cats and Dogs. Multicoloured.

1185	7 s. Type **167** (postage)	60	25
1186	10 s. Cocker spaniel	1·25	40
1187	15 s. Poodles	1·50	55
1188	20 s. Persian blue cat	2·00	70
1189	25 s. European tortoise-shell cat	2·40	85
1190	30 s. German shepherd dog (air)	2·75	85
1191	35 s. Abyssinian cats	3·25	95
1192	40 s. Boxer dog	3·75	1·25

168 Bebeto and Footballers

1985. World Cup Football Championship, Mexico (1986) (1st issue). Multicoloured.

1194	7 s. Type **168** (postage)	60	25
1195	10 s. Rinat Dassaev	1·25	40
1196	15 s. Phil Neal	1·50	55
1197	20 s. Jean Tigana	2·40	70
1198	30 s. Fernando Chalana (air)	3·00	75
1199	35 s. Michel Platini	3·50	85

See also Nos. 1268/71.

1985. Air. Nos. 1126 and 1119/20 optd.

1201	20 s. **80e ANNIVERSAIRE 1905 1985** (1126)	1·60	90
1202	20 s. **Rassemblement Jambville—1985** (1119)	1·60	90
1203	25 s. **80e ANNIVERSAIRE 1905 1985** (1120)	2·25	1·25

1985. Nos. 1157/62 surch.

1205	1 s. on 5 s. Type **163** (postage)	20	10
1206	2 s. on 7 s. "Agaricus niger"	50	10
1207	8 s. on 10 s. "Thermitomyces globulus"	1·50	40
1208	30 s. on 15 s. "Amanita robusta"	4·50	1·25
1209	35 s. on 20 s. "Lepiota subradicans" (air)	4·75	1·40
1210	40 s. on 25 s. "Cantharellus rhodophyllus"	5·25	1·90

171 Class 8 F Locomotive

1985. Trains (1st series). Multicoloured.

1212	7 s. Type **171** (postage)	1·10	40
1213	15 s. Class III electric locomotive, Germany	3·00	1·00
1214	25 s. Pacific steam locomotive No. 270	5·00	1·50
1215	35 s. German electric commuter train Series 420 (air)	6·50	2·40

Nos. 1213 and 1215 commemorate 150th anniv of German railways.

See also Nos. 1252/5.

172 Columbus and "Pinta"

1985. 480th Death Anniv of Christopher Columbus (explorer) (1st issue). Multicoloured.

1217	10 s. Type **172** (postage)	1·75	70
1218	20 s. "Santa Maria"	3·00	1·10
1219	30 s. "Nina" (air)	3·50	1·25
1220	40 s. "Santa Maria" and crow's nest	4·50	1·75

See also Nos. 1257/60.

173 Chopin, aged Eight, playing Piano

1986. International Youth Year. Multicoloured.

1222	10 s. Type **173** (postage)	1·10	45
1223	20 s. Sandro Botticelli and "Birth of Venus"	1·75	65
1224	35 s. Gioachino Antonio Rossini, aged 15, conducting orchestra	3·50	90
1225	25 s. Pablo Picasso and "Paul as Harlequin" (air)	2·25	85

174 Bayeux Tapestry

1986. Appearance of Halley's Comet. Multicoloured.

1227	5 f. Type **174** (postage)	10	10
1228	30 f. Comet as seen by the Arabs	20	10
1229	40 f. Comet as seen by Montezuma II	30	15
1230	50 f. Edmond Halley and trajectory diagram	40	15
1231	300 f. Halley and Sir Isaac Newton (air)	2·25	55
1232	500 f. Comet, Earth, sun, "Giotto", Soviet and N.A.S.A. space probes	4·00	1·10

175 "Challenger" Space Shuttle Memorial Roll

1986. Air. "Challenger" Astronauts Comm. Multicoloured.

1234 100 f. Type **175** 70 30
1235 170 f. Shuttle diagram and Christa McAuliffe holding model . . . . 1·25 55

1986. Various stamps surch.

(a) Nos. 1212/5 (Trains).

1237 2 f. on 7 s. multicoloured . . . 50 10
1238 25 f. on 15 s. mult 70 15
1239 50 f. on 25 s. mult . . . . . . 1·25 25
1240 90 f. on 35 s. mult . . . . . . 2·60 50

(b) Nos. 1217/20 (Columbus).

1242 5 f. on 10 s. multicoloured . . 30 15
1243 35 f. on 20 s. multicoloured . . 45 15
1244 70 f. on 30 s. multicoloured . . 75 30
1245 200 f. on 40 s. mult . . . . . 1·75 80

(c) Nos. 1222/5 (International Youth Year).

1247 5 f. on 10 s. mult (postage) . . 15 10
1248 35 f. on 20 s. multicoloured . . 25 15
1249 90 f. on 35 s. multicoloured . . 60 25
1250 50 f. on 25 s. mult (air) 30 15

177 Dietrich Autorail Diesel Railcar

1986. Trains (2nd series). Multicoloured.

1252 20 f. Type **177** (postage) . . . 25 10
1253 100 f. Class T.13 steam locomotive No. 7906, Prussia . . . 1·25 25
1254 300 f. German steam locomotive No. 01220 . . . . . . 3·50 80
1255 400 f. Autorail ABH-3 type 5020 diesel train (air) . . . 4·75 95

Nos. 1253/4 commemorate 150th anniv of German Railways.

178 Building Fort Navidad and Map of First Voyage, 1492–93

1986. 480th. Death Anniv of Christopher Columbus (explorer) (2nd issue). Multicoloured.

1257 40 f. Type **178** (postage) . . . 30 15
1258 70 f. Disembarking at Hispaniola and map of second voyage, 1493–96 . . 55 20
1259 200 f. Columbus on deck with natives and map of third voyage, 1498–1500 . . . . 1·50 50
1260 500 f. Columbus and crew with natives and map of fourth voyage, 1502–04 (air) . . . 3·50 1·40

179 Prince and Princess of Wales and Prince William

1986. Celebrities. Multicoloured.

1262 30 f. Type **179** (postage) . . . 20 10
1263 40 f. Alain Prost (1985 Formula I world champion) 25 10
1264 100 f. Duke and Duchess of York 60 20
1265 300 f. Elvis Presley (entertainer) . . . . 2·75 75
1266 500 f. Michael Jackson (entertainer) (air) . . . . . . 3·50 1·00

180 Pfaff, Trophy and Satellite

1986. World Cup Football Championship. Mexico (2nd issue). Multicoloured.

1268 100 f. Type **180** (postage) . . . 75 20
1269 300 f. Michel Platini . . . . . 2·25 60
1270 400 f. Matthaus . . . . 3·00 80
1271 500 f. Diego Maradona (air) . 3·75 1·00

181 Judo

1987. Olympic Games, Seoul (1988). Mult.

1273 20 f. Type **181** (postage) . . . 15 10
1274 30 f. High jumping 20 10
1275 40 f. Handball 25 10
1276 100 f. Gymnastics 60 20
1277 300 f. Javelin throwing (air) . . 1·75 55
1278 500 f. Showjumping . . . . . 3·00 80

182 Rifle shooting

1987. Winter Olympic Games, Calgary (1988) (1st issue). Multicoloured.

1280 50 f. on 40 f. Type **182** (postage) 30 10
1281 100 f. Cross-country skiing . . 65 20
1282 400 f. Ski jumping (air) . . . . 2·75 75
1283 500 f. Two-man bobsleigh . . 3·25 85

183 Skiing

1987. Winter Olympic Games, Calgary (1988) (2nd issue). Multicoloured.

1285 25 f. Type **183** (postage) . . . 20 10
1286 50 f. Ice hockey 40 15
1287 100 f. Men's figure skating . . 70 20
1288 150 f. Slalom . . . . 1·25 35
1289 300 f. Speed skating (air) . . . 2·00 70
1290 500 f. Four-man bobsleigh . . 3·25 1·10

184 S. K. Doe, Gen. Lansana Conte, Gen. J. Momoh and National Flags

185 Dimetrodon

1987. 10th Anniv of River Mano Reconciliation.

1292 **184** 40 f. multicoloured . . . 25 15
1293 50 f. multicoloured . . . 30 15
1294 75 f. multicoloured . . . 50 25
1295 100 f. multicoloured . . . 70 35
1296 150 f. multicoloured . . . 90 45

1987. Pre-historic Animals. Multicoloured.

1297 50 f. Type **185** (postage) . . . 45 15
1298 100 f. Iguanodon 80 25
1299 200 f. Tylosaurus . . . . . . 1·50 55
1300 300 f. Cave bear . . . . . . 2·50 75
1301 400 f. Sabre-tooth tiger (air) . . 3·25 85
1302 500 f. Stegosaurus . . . . . . 4·25 1·10

186 Statue and Portrait of Marquis de Lafayette (revolutionary)

1987. Celebrities. Multicoloured.

1304 50 f. Type **186** (230th birth anniv) (postage) 35 15
1305 100 f. Ettore Bugatti (motor manufacturer) (40th death anniv) and "White Elephant" 70 25
1306 200 f. Gary Kasparov (world chess champion) and game diagram of Kasparov v. Karpov, 1986 . . . . 2·00 65
1307 300 f. Flag and George Washington (first U.S. President) (bicentenary of American constitution) . . . 2·00 75
1308 400 f. Boris Becker (tennis player) (air) . . . . 3·50 85
1309 500 f. Winston Churchill (statesman) . . . . 4·00 1·10

188 Tennis Player and Emblem

1987. Olympic Games, Seoul (1988). Tennis.

1311 **188** 50 f. mult (postage) . . . 40 10
1312 – 100 f. multicoloured . . . 70 25
1313 – 150 f. multicoloured . . . 1·10 35
1314 – 200 f. multicoloured . . . 1·50 55
1315 – 300 f. mult (air) . . . . . 2·00 75
1316 – 500 f. multicoloured . . . 3·50 1·10

DESIGNS: 100 f. to 500 f. Various tennis players.

189 Discus thrower and Courtyard of Hospital of the Holy Cross and St. Paul

1987. Olympic Games, Barcelona (1992). Multicoloured.

1318 50 f. Type **189** (postage) . . . 30 10
1319 100 f. Statue of Pablo Casals (cellist) and pole vaulter . . 60 25
1320 150 f. Long jumper and Labyrinth of Horta 90 35
1321 170 f. Lizard in Guell Park and javelin thrower . . . . . . 1·00 40
1322 400 f. Gymnast and Church of Mercy (air) . . . . 2·50 75
1323 500 f. Tennis player and Picasso Museum . . . . 3·00 95

190 African Wild Dogs

1987. Endangered Wildlife. Multicoloured.

1325 50 f. Type **190** (postage) . . . 35 10
1326 70 f. African wild dog 55 20
1327 100 f. African wild dogs stalking prey 75 25
1328 170 f. African wild dog chasing prey . . . . 1·25 40
1329 400 f. South African crowned cranes (air) . . . . 4·00 2·25
1330 500 f. Giant eland . . . . . 3·50 1·40

191 "Galaxy"-"Grasp"

1988. Space Exploration. Multicoloured.

1332 50 f. Type **191** (postage) . . . 30 10
1333 150 f. "Energia"-"Mir" link-up 1·00 25
1334 200 f. NASA space station. . . 1·40 40
1335 300 f. "Ariane-5" rocket depositing satellite pay-load . . . . 2·00 70
1336 400 f. Mars "Rover" space vehicle (air) . . . . 2·75 85
1337 450 f. Venus "Vega" space probe . . . . 3·00 95

192 Red-headed Bluebill

193 Queen Elizabeth II and Prince Philip

1988. Scouts, Birds and Butterflies. Designs showing scouts studying featured animals. Multicoloured.

1339 50 f. Type **192** (postage) . . . 75 20
1340 100 f. "Medon nymphalidae" (butterfly) 65 25
1341 150 f. Red bishop . . . . . . 1·50 45
1342 300 f. Beautiful sunbird . . . . 2·75 1·50
1343 400 f. "Sophia nymphalidae" (butterfly) (air) . . . . . 3·00 1·00
1344 450 f. "Rumia nymphalidae" (butterfly) . . . . 3·00 1·10

1988. Celebrities. Multicoloured.

1346 200 f. Type **193** (40th wedding anniv (1987)) (postage) . . 1·25 40
1347 250 f. Fritz von Opel (car designer) and "Rak 2 Opel", 1928 . . . . 1·75 55
1348 300 f. Wolfgang Amadeus Mozart (composer) . . . . 2·25 55
1349 400 f. Steffi Graf (tennis player) . . . . 3·00 70
1350 450 f. Edwin "Buzz" Aldrin (astronaut) (air) . . . . . . 3·25 80
1351 500 f. Paul Harris (founder of Rotary International) . . . 3·50 95

194 Vreni Schneider (Women's Slalom and Giant Slalom)

195 Scientist using Microscope

1988. Calgary Winter Olympic Games Gold Medal Winners. Multicoloured.

1353 50 f. Type **194** (postage) . . . 30 10
1354 150 f. Matti Nykaenen (Ski jumping) . . . . 1·10 25
1355 250 f. Marina Kiehl (Women's downhill) . . . . 1·75 40
1356 400 f. Frank Piccard (Men's super giant slalom) . . . . 2·50 75
1357 100 f. Frank-Peter Roetsch (Biathlon) (air) 70 25
1358 450 f. Katarina Witt (Women's figure skating) . . . . . . 2·75 95

1988. World Health Day. Multicoloured.

1360 50 f. Type **195** 20 10
1361 150 f. Nurse vaccinating boy . 55 15
1362 500 f. Dental check . . . . . 1·90 50

196 Baron Pierre de Coubertin (founder of modern Olympics)

1988. International Olympic Committee.
1363 **196** 50 f. multicoloured . . . 20 10
1364 100 f. multicoloured . . . 40 10
1365 150 f. multicoloured . . . 55 15
1366 500 f. multicoloured . . . 1·90 50

197 Hands exchanging Letter
198 Earth Communications Station

1988. 25th Anniv of Pan-African Postal Union.
1367 **197** 50 f. multicoloured . . . 20 10
1368 75 f. multicoloured . . . 30 10
1369 100 f. multicoloured . . . 40 10
1370 150 f. multicoloured . . . 55 15

1988. Inauguration of MT 20 International Transmission Centre.
1371 **198** 50 f. multicoloured . . . 20 10
1372 100 f. multicoloured . . . 40 10
1373 150 f. multicoloured . . . 55 15

199 "Helix Nebular"

1989. Appearance of Halley's Comet. Nebulae. Multicoloured.
1374 100 f. + 25 f. Type **199** (postage) 50 15
1375 150 f. + 25 f. Orion 70 20
1376 200 f. + 25 f. "The Eagle" . . . 90 25
1377 250 f. + 25 f. "Triffid" . . . . 1·10 30
1378 300 f. + 25 f. Eta-Carinae (air) . 1·25 30
1379 500 f. + 25 f. NGC 2264 . . . 2·00 50

200 Diving

1989. Olympic Games, Barcelona (1992) (1st issue). Multicoloured.
1381 50 f. Type **200** (postage) . . . 20 10
1382 100 f. Running (vert) 40 10
1383 150 f. Shooting 60 15
1384 250 f. Tennis (vert) . . . . . 1·00 25
1385 400 f. Football (air) . . . . . 1·60 40
1386 500 f. Equestrian (dressage) (vert) . . . . 2·00 50

201 Oath of the Tennis Court and Jean Sylvain Bailly (President of National Assembly)

1989. "Philexfrance 89" Stamp Exhibition and Bicentenary of French Revolution. Mult.
1388 250 f. Type **201** (postage) . . . 1·00 25
1389 300 f. King addressing the Three Estates and Comte de Mirabeau . . . . 1·25 30
1390 400 f. 18th July 1790 celebrations and Marquis de La Fayette . . . . 1·60 40
1391 450 f. The King's arrest at Varennes and Jerome Petion (first President of the Convention) (air) . . . . . 1·75 45

202 Girl carrying Plants

1989. 10th Anniv (1987) of International Fund for Agricultural Development. Campaign for Self-sufficiency. Multicoloured.
1393 25 f. Type **202** 10 10
1394 50 f. Men irrigating crops . . . 20 10
1395 75 f. Family with cattle 30 10
1396 100 f. Fishermen 70 20
1397 150 f. Harvesting crops 60 15
1398 300 f. Pumping water . . . . 1·25 30

203 Buildings, Vehicles and Envelopes on Map

1989. 15th Anniv of Mano River Union. Mult.
1399 150 f. Map **203** 60 15
1400 300 f. Map and Presidents of member countries . . . . . 1·25 30

204 Emblem, Banknotes and Produce

1989. 25th Anniv of African Development Bank.
1401 **204** 300 f. multicoloured . . . 1·25 30

205 Skiing and Super-Tignes

1990. Winter Olympic Games, Albertville (1992). Multicoloured.
1402 150 f. Type **205** (postage) . . . 55 15
1403 250 f. Cross-country skiing and Le Lavachet 90 25
1404 400 f. Bobsleighing and Val-Claret . . . . 1·40 35
1405 500 f. Speed skating and Meribel (air) . . . . 1·75 45

206 Presidents Bush and Gorbachev (1989 Summit, Malta)

1990. Multicoloured.
1407 200 f. Type **206** (postage) . . . 70 20
1408 250 f. De Gaulle's appeal to resist, June 1940 . . . . . 90 25
1409 300 f. Pope Jean-Paul II, President Gorbachev and dove (1989 meeting) . . . . 1·10 30
1410 400 f. Concorde and TGV Atlantique express train, France . . . . 3·25 1·00
1411 450 f. Robin Yount (cent of Baseball) (air) . . . . . . 1·60 40
1412 500 f. "Galileo" space probe . 1·75 45

207 St. Dominic's, Naples
208 View of Exhibition

1990. World Cup Football Championship, Italy. Multicoloured.
1414 200 f. Type **207** (postage) . . . 70 20
1415 250 f. Piazza San Carlo, Turin . 90 25
1416 300 f. San Cataldo church . . 1·10 30
1417 450 f. St. Francis's Church, Udine (air) . . . . 1·60 40

1991. "Telecom 91" International Telecommunications Exhibition. Multicoloured.
1419 150 f. Type **208** 55 10
1420 300 f. Emblem (horiz) . . . . 1·10 30

209 Health Centre

1991. Medecins sans Frontieres.
1421 **209** 300 f. multicoloured . . . 1·10 30

210 "Madonna della Tenda"

1991. Christmas (1990). Paintings by Raphael. Multicoloured.
1422 50 f. Type **210** (postage) . . . 20 10
1423 100 f. Small Cowper Madonna 40 10
1424 150 f. Tempi Madonna 55 15
1425 250 f. Niccolini Madonna . . . 95 25
1426 300 f. Orleans Madonna (air) . 1·10 30
1427 500 f. Solly Madonna . . . . 1·90 50

211 Rudi Voller

1991. West Germany, 1990 World Cup Football Champion. West German Players and Goals Scored. Multicoloured.
1429 200 f. Type **211** (postage) . . . 75 20
1430 250 f. Uwe Bein 95 25
1431 300 f. Pierre Littbarski . . . . 1·10 30
1432 400 f. Jurgen Klinsmann . . . 1·50 35
1433 450 f. Lothar Matthaus (air) . 1·75 45
1434 500 f. Andreas Brehme . . . . 1·90 50

212 Fairey Swordfish sinking "Bismarck" (German battleship) and Admirals Raeder and Tovey

1991. Battles of Second World War. Mult.
1436 100 f. Type **212** (postage) . . . 55 10
1437 150 f. Aichi D3A "Val" bombers sinking U.S.S. "Yorktown" (aircraft carrier) and Admirals Yamamoto and Nimitz (Battle of Midway) 70 15
1438 200 f. American torpedo boat and Admirals Kondo and Halsey (Guadalcanal) . . . 85 20
1439 250 f. "Crusader III" tanks, Hawker Hurricane Mk II aircraft, Rommel and Montgomery (El Alamein) . 95 25
1440 300 f. "Tiger II" tanks and Generals Guderian and Patton (Ardennes) (air) . . . 1·10 30
1441 450 f. Grumman TBF Avenger aircraft sinking "Yamato" (Japanese battleship) and Admiral Kogo and General MacArthur . . . . 2·00 45

1991. Various stamps surch.
1443 100 f. on 170 f. mult (No. 1321) (postage) 15 10
1444 100 f. on 170 f. mult (No. 1328) 15 10
1445 100 f. on 250 f. mult (No. 1388) 15 10
1446 100 f. on 400 f. mult (No. 1270) 15 10
1447 100 f. on 400 f. mult (No. 1349) 15 10
1448 100 f. on 400 f. mult (No. 1356) 15 10
1449 100 f. on 400 f. mult (No. 1404) 15 10
1450 100 f. on 400 f. mult (No. 1410) 2·25 1·00
1451 100 f. on 500 f. mult (No. 1362) 15 10
1452 100 f. on 500 f. mult (No. 1366) 15 10
1453 100 f. on 400 f. mult (No. 1301) (air) 15 10
1454 100 f. on 400 f. mult (No. 1308) 15 10
1455 100 f. on 400 f. mult (No. 1322) 15 10
1456 100 f. on 400 f. mult (No. 1329) 15 10
1457 100 f. on 400 f. mult (No. 1343) 15 10
1458 100 f. on 400 f. mult (No. 1385) 15 10
1459 300 f. on 450 f. mult (No. 1350) 50 15
1460 300 f. on 450 f. mult (No. 1411) 50 15

214 Nat King Cole Trio

1991. Music and Films. Multicoloured.
1461 100 f. Type **214** (postage) . . . 15 10
1462 150 f. Yul Brynner and scene from "The Magnificent Seven" 25 10
1463 250 f. Judy Garland and scene from "The Wizard of Oz" . 40 10
1464 300 f. Steve McQueen and scene from "Papillon" 50 15
1465 500 f. Gary Cooper and scene from "Sergeant York" (air) . 80 20
1466 600 f. Bing Crosby and scene from "High Society" . . . . 1·00 25

215 Dancer
216 Doves, Map and Pope John Paul II

1991. African Tourism Year. Multicoloured.
1468 100 f. Type **215** 15 10
1469 150 f. Baskets (horiz) 25 10
1470 250 f. Drum (horiz) 40 10
1471 300 f. Flautist 50 15

1991. Papal Visit. Litho.
1472 **216** 150 f. multicoloured . . . 25 10

217 "ERS-1" Observation Satellite and Earth

1991. Anniversaries and Events. Mult.
1473 100 f. Type **217** (postage) . . . 15 10
1474 150 f. "Sunflowers" (Vincent van Gogh, 1888) 25 10
1475 200 f. Napoleon I (170th death anniv) 35 15
1476 250 f. Henri Dunant (founder of Red Cross) and Red Cross volunteers 40 10
1477 300 f. Bicentenary of Brandenburg Gate and second anniversary of fall of Berlin Wall 50 15

1478 400 f. Pope John Paul II's tour of Africa, 1989 . . . . . . 65 15
1479 450 f. Garry Kasparov and Anatoli Karpov (World Chess Championship, 1990) (air) 75 20
1480 500 f. Boy feeding dove and Rotary International and Lions International emblems 80 20

218 Care-a-Lot and Care Bears around Globe

1991. Ecology. Care Bear cartoon characters. Multicoloured.
1481 50 f. Type **218** 10 10
1482 100 f. Care Bears around sink ("Save Water!") 15 10
1483 200 f. Care Bears in tree ("Recycle!") 35 15
1484 300 f. Traffic jam and Care Bear ("Control Noise") 50 15
1485 400 f. Elephant and Care Bear ("Protect Our Wild Life") (horiz) 65 15

219 Player, Trophy and Little Five Points

220 Emblem

1992. World Cup Football Championship, U.S.A. (1994) (1st issue). Multicoloured.
1487 100 f. Type **219** (postage) . . . 15 10
1488 300 f. Germany player and Fulton Stadium, Atlanta . . 40 10
1489 400 f. Player and Inman Park 50 15
1490 500 f. Player and Museum of Fine Art (air) 65 15
See also Nos. 1565/8.

1992. 75th Anniv of Lions International.
1492 **220** 150 f. multicoloured . . . 25 10
1493 400 f. multicoloured . . . 65 15

221 Emblem

1992. International Nutrition Conference, Rome.
1494 **221** 150 f. mult (postage) . . . 25 10
1495 400 f. multicoloured . . . 65 15
1496 500 f. multicoloured (air) . 80 20

222 Scene from "The Devil and Catherine" and Antonin Dvorak (composer)

1992. Anniversaries and Events. Multicoloured.
1497 200 f. Type **222** (150th birth (1991)) (postage) 25 10
1498 300 f. Antonio Vivaldi (composer) (250th death (1991)) and as choirmaster to the Hospital of the Pieta, Venice 40 10
1499 350 f. Meeting of airship "Graf Zeppelin" and Santos-Dumont's flying boat and Count Ferdinand von Zeppelin (airship pioneer) . . 45 10
1500 400 f. Projected locomotive emerging from Channel Tunnel (construction) . . . 2·75 75
1501 450 f. Konrad Adenauer (German statesman) and Brandenburg Gate, Berlin (bicentenary of Gate) (air) . 60 15
1502 500 f. Emperor Hirohito of Japan (third death anniv) . . . 65 15

223 Charlie Chaplin (actor) and Scene from "Modern Times"

1992. Anniversaries and Events. Multicoloured.
1504 50 f. Type **223** (15th death anniv) (postage) 10 10
1505 100 f. Pavilion and Christopher Columbus ("Expo '92" World's Fair, Seville) . . . 30 10
1506 150 f. St. Peter's Square, Rome 20 10
1507 200 f. Marlene Dietrich (actress, death) in scene from "Shanghai Express" 25 10
1508 250 f. Michael Schumacher and Formula 1 racing car . . . 35 10
1509 300 f. Rocket launch and John Glenn (30th anniv of Glenn's three-orbit flight in "Mercury" space capsule) . 40 10
1510 400 f. Bill Koch (skipper) and "America 3" (yacht) (winner of Americas Cup) (air) . . . 50 15
1511 450 f. Victory of Washington Redskins in 26th American Superbowl baseball championships 60 15
1512 500 f. Recovery of "Intelsat VI" satellite by "Endeavour" space shuttle 65 15

1993. 50th Death Anniv (1991) of Robert Baden-Powell (founder of Scouting Movement). Nos. 1339/44 optd **50eme ANNIVERSAIRE DE LA MORT DE BADEN POWEL**.
1515 **192** 50 f. mult (postage) . . . 10 10
1516 – 100 f. multicoloured . . . 15 10
1517 – 150 f. multicoloured . . . 20 10
1518 – 300 f. multicoloured . . . 40 10
1519 – 400 f. mult (air) 50 15
1520 – 450 f. multicoloured . . . 60 15

1993. Bicentenary of Year One of First Republic of France. Nos. 1388/91 optd **BICENTENAIRE DE L'AN I DE LA REPUBLIQUE FRANCAISE**.
1522 **201** 250 f. mult (postage) . . . 35 10
1523 – 300 f. multicoloured . . . 40 10
1524 – 400 f. multicoloured . . . 50 15
1525 – 450 f. mult (air) 60 15

1993. Winter Olympic Games, Albertville, Gold Medal Winners. Nos. 1402/5 variously optd.
1527 150 f. **SLALOM GEANT Alberto Tomba, Italie** (postage) 20 10
1528 250 f. **SKI NORDIQUE Vegard Ulvang, Norvege** 35 15
1529 400 f. **BOB A DEUX G. Weder/ D. Acklin, Suisse** 50 15
1530 500 f. **PATINAGE DE VITESSE Olaf Zinke 1000 m., Allemagne** (air) 65 15

1993. World Cup Football Championship, Italy, Results. Nos. 1414/17 optd **1. ALLEMAGNE 2. ARGENTINE 3. ITALIE**.
1532 **207** 200 f. mult (postage) . . . 25 10
1533 – 250 f. multicoloured . . . 35 15
1534 – 300 f. multicoloured . . . 40 15
1535 – 450 f. mult (air) 60 15

1993. Air. Bobby Fischer–Boris Spassky Chess Match (1537) and 75th Anniv of Lions International (1538). Nos. 1479/80 optd.
1537 450 f. **RENCONTRE FISCHER - SPASSKY 3 SEPT au 5 NOV 1992 AU MONTENEGRO** 60 15
1538 500 f. **75eme ANNIVERSAIRE LIONS** 65 15

230 West Germany Footballer and Little White House

1993. Olympic Games, Atlanta (1996) (1st issue). Multicoloured.
1539 150 f. Type **230** (postage) . . . 20 10
1540 250 f. Cyclist and Georgia World Congress Center . . 35 10
1541 400 f. Basketball player and underground station 50 15
1542 500 f. Baseball player and steam train, New Georgia Railroad (air) . . . . 4·50 75
See also Nos. 1623/7.

231 Ice Hockey and "Whale Hunt" (sculpture)

232 "Luna 3" and Dark Side of Moon

1993. Winter Olympic Games, Lillehammer, Norway (1994). Multicoloured.
1544 150 f. Type **231** (postage) . . . 20 10
1545 250 f. Two-man bobsleigh and Edvard Grieg's house . . . 35 10
1546 400 f. Biathlon and Fredrikstad Park (air) 50 15
1547 450 f. Ski jumping and Eidsvoll Manor 60 15

1993. 25th Anniv (1994) of First Manned Moon Landing. Multicoloured.
1549 150 f. Type **232** 20 10
1550 150 f. "Ranger 7" 10 10
1551 150 f. "Luna 9" 20 10
1552 150 f. "Surveyor 1" (first lunar probe) 20 10
1553 150 f. Lunar "Orbiter 1" and moon 20 10
1554 150 f. Launch of "Saturn 5" (rocket) carrying "Apollo 11" 20 10
1555 150 f. "Apollo 11" command module in lunar orbit . . . 20 10
1556 150 f. Astronaut climbing from "Apollo 11" 20 10
1557 150 f. "Apollo 12" astronaut recovering "Surveyor 1" camera 20 10
1558 150 f. Explosion of "Apollo 13" 20 10
1559 150 f. "Luna 16" probe (first collection of lunar samples by automatic probe) 20 10
1560 150 f. Lunokhod of "Luna 17" (first lunar vehicle) 20 10
1561 150 f. Alan Sheppard playing golf on moon 20 10
1562 150 f. First lunar jeep from "Apollo 15" mission 20 10
1563 150 f. First lunar telescope from "Apollo 16" mission 20 10
1564 150 f. Astronaut from "Apollo 17" (last "Apollo" mission) . 20 10

233 San Francisco

1993. World Cup Football Championship, U.S.A. (1994) (2nd issue). Multicoloured.
1565 100 f. Type **233** (postage) . . . 15 10
1566 300 f. Washington D.C. . . . 40 10
1567 400 f. Renaissance Center, Detroit 50 15
1568 500 f. Dallas (air) 65 15

234 Euparkeria

1993. Prehistoric Animals. Multicoloured.
1570 50 f. Type **234** 10 10
1571 50 f. Plateosaurus 10 10
1572 50 f. Anchisaurus 10 10
1573 50 f. Ornithosuchus 10 10
1574 100 f. Megalosaurus 15 10
1575 100 f. Scelidosaurus 15 10
1576 100 f. Camptosaurus 15 10
1577 100 f. Ceratosaurus 15 10
1578 250 f. Ouranosaurus 35 10
1579 250 f. Dicraeosaurus 35 10
1580 250 f. Tarbosaurus 35 10
1581 250 f. Gorgosaurus 35 10
1582 250 f. Polacanthus 35 10
1583 250 f. Deinonychus 35 10
1584 250 f. Corythosaurus 35 10
1585 250 f. Spinosaurus 35 10

235 Prince Johann I of Liechtenstein

236 Johann Kepler and "Pluto" Space Probe

1994. Mult. (a) Battle of Austerlitz, 1805.
1587 150 f. Type **235** 20 10
1588 150 f. Marshal Joachim Murat 20 10
1589 600 f. Napoleon (59 × 47 mm) 80 20
Nos. 1587/9 were issued together, se-tenant, forming a composite design of a battle scene.

(b) Battle of the Moskva, 1912.
1590 150 f. Marshal Michel Ney . . 20 10
1591 150 f. Prince Pyotr Ivanovich Bagration 20 10
1592 600 f. Napoleon on horseback (59 × 47 mm) 80 20
Nos. 1590/2 were issued together, se-tenant, forming a composite design of a battle scene.

(c) Normandy Landings, 1944.
1593 150 f. Field-Marshal Erwin Rommel (wrongly inscr "Romel") 20 10
1594 150 f. Gen. George Patton . . 20 10
1595 600 f. Gen. Dwight David Eisenhower (59 × 47 mm) . 80 20
Nos. 1593/5 were issued together, se-tenant, forming a composite design of a battle scene.

(d) Battle of the Ardennes, 1944.
1596 150 f. Lt-Gen. William H. Simpson 20 10
1597 150 f. Gen. Heinz Guderian . . 20 10
1598 600 f. Tank battle scene (59 × 47 mm) 80 20
Nos. 1596/8 were issued together, se-tenant, forming a composite design of a battle scene.

1994. Astronomers. Multicoloured.
1599 300 f. Type **236** 40 10
1600 300 f. Sir Isaac Newton and "Voyager" space probe . . . 40 10
1601 500 f. Nicolas Copernicus and "Galileo" space probe (59 × 47 mm) 65 15
Nos. 1599/1601 were issued together, se-tenant, forming a composite design.

1994. Winter Olympic Games, Lillehammer. Gold Medal Winners. Nos. 1544/7 variously optd.
1602 150 f. **MEDAILLE D'OR SUEDE** (postage) 20 10
1603 250 f. **G. WEDER D. ACKLIN SUISSE** 35 10
1604 400 f. **F.B. LUNDBERG NORVEGE** (air) 50 15
1605 450 f. **J. WEISSFLOG ALLEMAGNE** 60 15

1994. World Cup Football Championship, U.S.A., Winners. Nos. 1565/8 optd **1. BRESIL 2. ITALIE 3. SUEDE**.
1607 **233** 100 f. mult (postage) . . . 15 10
1608 – 300 f. multicoloured . . . 40 10
1609 – 400 f. multicoloured . . . 50 15
1610 – 500 f. mult (air) 65 15

239 Banea Dam

1995. Garafiri Water Management. Mult.
1612 100 f. Type **239** 10 10
1613 150 f. Donkea 20 10
1614 200 f. Tinkisso overflow (vert) . 25 10
1615 250 f. Waterfalls 30 10
1616 500 f. Water works, Kinkon . . 60 15

240 Red and White Persian

1995. Cats. Multicoloured.

1617 150 f. Type **240** (inscr "Tortoiseshell") 20 10
1618 250 f. Tabby and white 30 10
1619 500 f. Black smoke persian ("Smoke long-haired") 60 15
1620 500 f. Red tabby 60 15
1621 500 f. Tortoiseshell and white persian ("longhair") 60 15

241 Throwing the Javelin **242** Goldfinch

1995. Olympic Games, Atlanta (1996) (2nd issue). Multicoloured.

1623 150 f. Type **241** 20 10
1624 250 f. Boxing 30 10
1625 500 f. Football 60 15
1626 500 f. Basketball 60 15
1627 500 f. Weightlifting 60 15

1995. Birds. Multicoloured.

1629 150 f. Type **242** 20 10
1630 250 f. Nightingale ("Luscinia megarhynchos") 30 10
1631 500 f. Canary ("Serinus canaria") 60 15
1632 500 f. Chaffinch ("Fringilla coelebs") 60 15
1633 500 f. Greenfinch ("Carduelis chloris") 60 15

243 Mona Monkey

1995. Mammals. Multicoloured.

1635 150 f. Type **243** 20 10
1636 250 f. Savanna monkey 35 10
1637 500 f. Demidoff's galago ("Galagoides demidovi") 65 15
1638 500 f. Hare ("Lepus crawshayi") (horiz) 65 15
1639 500 f. Giant ground pangolin ("Manis gigantea") (horiz) 65 15

244 Pup-150 (Great Britain)

1995. Aircraft. Multicoloured.

1641 100 f. Type **244** 15 10
1642 150 f. Gardan GY-80 "Horizon" (France) 20 10
1643 250 f. Piper J-3 Cub (U.S.A.) 35 10
1644 500 f. Piper PA-28 Cherokee Arrow (U.S.A.) 65 15
1645 500 f. Pilatus PC-6 Porter (Switzerland) 65 15
1646 500 f. Valmet L-90TP Redigo (Finland) 65 15

245 Yoked Oxen

1995. 50th Anniv of F.A.O. Multicoloured.

1648 200 f. Type **245** 25 10
1649 750 f. Nutrition lesson 1·00 25

246 Jacobean Lily **247** Players

1995. Flowers. Multicoloured.

1650 100 f. Type **246** 15 10
1651 150 f. "Rudbeckia purpurea" 20 10
1652 250 f. Himalayan blue poppy 35 10
1653 500 f. Iris "Starshine" 65 15
1654 500 f. Rose "Gail Borden" 65 15
1655 500 f. Sweet pea ("Lathyrus odoratus") 65 15

1995. World Cup Football Championship, France (1998) (1st issue). Multicoloured.

1657 150 f. Type **247** 20 10
1658 250 f. Player challenging player No. 2 35 10
1659 500 f. Players in blue and white shirt and red shirt in tackle 65 15
1660 500 f. Players Nos. 3 and 10 running after ball 65 15
1661 500 f. Player No. 2 high-kicking ball 65 15

See also Nos. 1719/24.

248 Arab Horse **249** "Leccinum nigrescens"

1995. Arab Horses. Multicoloured.

1663 100 f. Type **248** 15 10
1664 150 f. Dark brown horse with white star 20 10
1665 250 f. Chestnut 35 10
1666 500 f. Grey 65 15
1667 500 f. Bay 65 15
1668 500 f. Bay with harness and rein (horiz) 65 15

1995. Fungi. Multicoloured.

1670 150 f. Type **249** 20 10
1671 250 f. "Boletus rhodoxanthus" 35 10
1672 500 f. "Cantharellus lutescens" 65 15
1673 500 f. Brown roll-rim ("Paxillus involutus") 65 15
1674 500 f. "Xerocomus rubellus" 65 15

250 Enterprise, 1832

1995. Veteran Omnibuses. Multicoloured.

1676 250 f. Type **250** 35 10
1677 300 f. Daimler, 1898 40 10
1678 400 f. V.H. Bussing, 1904 50 15
1679 450 f. M.A.N. autobus, 1906 60 15
1680 500 f. M.A.N. autocar, 1934 65 15

251 Locomotive "Tom Thumb", 1829, U.S.A.

1996. Rail Transport. Multicoloured.

1681 200 f. Type **251** 25 10
1682 250 f. Locomotive "Genf", 1858, Switzerland (68 × 27 mm) 30 10
1683 300 f. Canterbury Frozen Meat Company Dubs locomotive, 1873, New Zealand 35 10
1684 400 f. Bagnall fireless steam accumulator locomotive No. 2, Great Britain 50 15
1685 450 f. Werner von Siemen's first electric locomotive, 1879, and passenger carriage (68 × 27 mm) 60 15
1686 500 f. North London Tramways Company tram, 1885–89, Great Britain 65 15

252 Rock Formation **253** Red Siskin

1996. Multicoloured.

1688 200 f. Type **252** 25 10
1689 750 f. Child 95 25
1690 1000 f. Women carrying faggots 1·25 30

1996. Birds. Multicoloured.

1691 200 f. Type **253** 25 10
1692 250 f. Red-cheeked cordon-bleu 30 10
1693 300 f. Chestnut-breasted mannikin 35 10
1694 400 f. Paradise sparrow 50 10
1695 450 f. Gouldian finch 55 15
1696 500 f. Red bishop 60 15

254 Bull Terrier **256** Chestnut

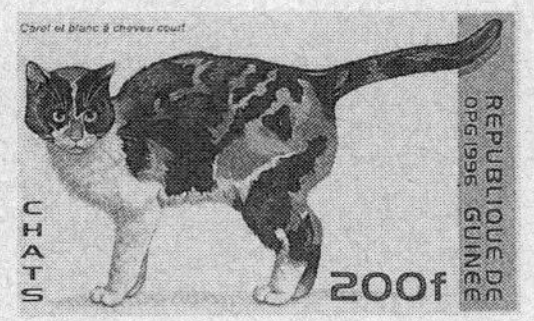

255 Tortoiseshell and White Shorthair

1996. Dogs. Multicoloured.

1698 200 f. Type **254** 25 10
1699 250 f. Elkhound 30 10
1700 300 f. Akita 35 10
1701 400 f. Collie 50 10
1702 450 f. Rottweiler 55 15
1703 500 f. Boxer 60 15

1996. Cats. Multicoloured.

1705 200 f. Type **255** 25 10
1706 250 f. Bicolour shorthair 30 10
1707 300 f. Tortoiseshell and white Japanese bobtail 35 10
1708 400 f. Chocolate point Himalayan 50 10
1709 450 f. Red longhair 55 15
1710 500 f. Blue Persian 60 15

1996. Fungi. Multicoloured.

1712 200 f. Type **256** 25 10
1713 250 f. Granular 30 10
1714 300 f. Destroying angel 35 10
1715 400 f. Milky blue 50 10
1716 450 f. Violet cortinarius 55 15
1717 500 f. Rough-stemmed 60 15

257 Players **258** "Paphiopedilum millmoore"

1997. World Cup Football Championship, France (1998) (2nd issue). Multicoloured.

1719 200 f. Type **257** 25 10
1720 250 f. Player No. 5 30 10
1721 300 f. Three players 35 10
1722 400 f. Player dribbling ball past opposition (horiz) 45 10
1723 450 f. Player No. 12 with opposing player on ground (horiz) 50 15
1724 500 f. Ball passing lunging goalkeeper (horiz) 55 15

1997. Orchids. Multicoloured.

1726 200 f. Type **258** 25 10
1727 250 f. "Paphiopedilum ernest read" 30 10
1728 300 f. "Paphiopedilum harrisianum" 35 10
1729 400 f. "Paphiopedilum gaudianum" 45 10
1730 450 f. "Paphiopedilum papa rohl" 50 15
1731 500 f. "Paphiopedilum sea cliff" 55 15

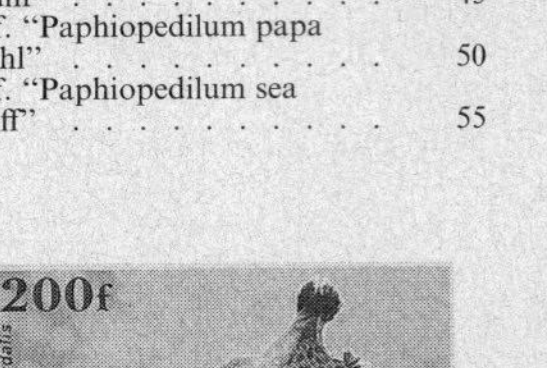

259 Giraffe

1997. Mammals. Multicoloured.

1733 200 f. Type **259** 25 10
1734 250 f. White rhinoceros (vert) 30 10
1735 300 f. Warthog 35 10
1736 400 f. Cheetah 45 10
1737 450 f. African elephant (vert) 50 15
1738 500 f. Pygmy hippopotamus 55 10

260 H.M.S. "Captain" (turret ship, Great Britain, 1870)

1997. 19th-Century Warships. Multicoloured.

1740 200 f. Type **260** 30 15
1741 250 f. "Kaiser Wilhelm" (ironclad, Germany, 1869) 35 15
1742 300 f. H.M.S. "Temeraire" (turret ship, Great Britain, 1871) 40 15
1743 400 f. "Mouillage" (turret ship, Italy, 1866) 50 15
1744 450 f. H.M.S. "Inflexible" (battleship, Great Britain, 1881) 55 20
1745 500 f. "Magenta" (ironclad, France, 1862) 60 20

261 "Siganus trispilos"

1997. Fishes. Multicoloured.

1747 200 f. Type **261** 25 10
1748 250 f. Dusky parrotfish 30 10
1749 300 f. Harlequin tuskfish 35 10
1750 400 f. Masked unicornfish 45 10
1751 450 f. "Hypoplectrus gemma" 50 15
1752 500 f. Red-tailed surgeon-fish 55 15

262 Officer, Von Witerfeldt's Regiment **264** 14th-century Thai Knight, Rook and King

263 Baldwin Steam Locomotive

1997. Prussian Infantry Uniforms. Mult.

No.	Description	Unused	Used
1754	200 f. Type **262**	25	10
1755	250 f. Non-commissioned officer, Von Kanitz's Regiment	30	10
1756	300 f. Private, Prince Franz von Anhalt-Dessau's Regiment	35	10
1757	400 f. Private, Von Kalnein's Regiment	45	10
1758	450 f. Grenadier, Duke Ferdinand of Brunswick's Regiment	50	15
1759	500 f. Grenadier musician, Rekow's Guards Battalion	55	15

1997. Steam Locomotives. Multicoloured.

No.	Description	Unused	Used
1761	200 f. Type **263**	25	10
1762	250 f. Steam locomotive No. 1	30	10
1763	300 f. Vulcan steam locomotive	35	10
1764	400 f. Commonwealth Edison Company Baldwin steam locomotive No. 2	50	15
1765	450 f. TCID Railroad steam locomotive No. 108	60	15
1766	500 f. Pittsburgh–Hanover Coal Company steam locomotive No. 3	65	15

1997. Chess Pieces. Multicoloured.

No.	Description	Unused	Used
1768	200 f. Type **264**	25	10
1769	250 f. Chinese pawn, king and knight, 1930	30	10
1770	300 f. Portuguese ivory "sea-horse" pawn, queen and king, 1920	35	10
1771	400 f. German pewter "military" knight, king and pawn	45	10
1772	450 f. Russian amber queen, king, bishop and knight from reign of Catherine II	50	15
1773	500 f. Max Ernst's designs for queen, king, bishop and knight	55	15

265 Siberian Husky

1997. Dogs. Multicoloured.

No.	Description	Unused	Used
1775	200 f. Type **265**	25	10
1776	250 f. Teckel	30	10
1777	300 f. Boston terrier	35	10
1778	400 f. Basset hound	45	10
1779	450 f. Dalmatian	50	15
1780	500 f. Rottweiler	55	15

POSTAGE DUE STAMPS

D **11**

D **17**

1959.

No.	Type	Description	Unused	Used
D195	D **11**	1 f. green	15	15
D196		2 f. red	15	15
D197		3 f. brown	30	20
D198		5 f. blue	90	45
D199		10 f. orange	1·60	70
D200		20 f. mauve	3·25	1·60

1959.

No.	Type	Description	Unused	Used
D224	D **17**	1 f. red	10	15
D225		2 f. orange	15	15
D226		3 f. lake	15	15
D227		5 f. green	40	30
D228		10 f. sepia	1·00	90
D229		20 f. blue	1·90	1·60

APPENDIX

The following stamps have either been issued in excess of postal needs or have not been available to the public in reasonable quantities at face value. Such stamps may later be given full listing if there is evidence of regular postal use.

1982.

World Cup Winners. Nos. 1068/74 optd.

1983.

Olympic Games, Los Angeles. 100 s.

Bicentenary of Manned Flight. 100 s.

Winter Olympic Games, Sarajevo. 100 s.

1984.

Winter Olympic Gold Medal Winners. 100 s.

1985.

Space Achievements. 200 s.

Anniversaries and Events. 85th Birthday of Queen Elizabeth the Queen Mother. 100 s.

1986.

Appearance of Halley's Comet. 1500 f.

1987.

Winter Olympic Games, Seoul. 1500 f.

1989. Embossed on gold foil.

Scout and Butterfly. Air 1500 f.

Bicentenary of French Revolution. Air 1500 f.

1990. Embossed on gold foil.

World Cup Football Championship, Italy. Air 1500 f.

Winter Olympic Games, Albertville (1992). Air 1500 f.

De Gaulle and Free French Forces. Air 1500 f.

1992. Embossed on gold foil.

Olympic Games, Barcelona. Air 1500 f.

World Cup Football Championship, U.S.A. (1994) (1st issue). Air 1500 f. (vert design).

Elvis Presley. Air 1500 f.

Pope John Paul II's African Tour. Air 1500 f.

1993. Embossed on gold foil.

Bicentenary of Year One of First Republic of France. Air. Optd on 1989 French Revolution issue. 1500 f.

Olympic Games, Atlanta. Air 1500 f.

Winter Olympic Games, Lillehammer, Norway. Air 1500 f.

World Cup Football Championship, U.S.A. (1994) (2nd issue). Air 1500 f. (square design).

1995. Embossed on gold foil.

Normandy Landing, 1944. Air. Optd on 1990 De Gaulle Appendix. 1500 f.

GUINEA-BISSAU Pt. 13

Following an armed rebellion against Colonial rule, the independence of former Portuguese Guinea was recognised on September 10th 1974.

1974. 100 centavos = 1 escudo.
1976. 100 centavos = 1 peso.

77 Amilcar Cabral, Map and Flag

1974. 1st Anniv of Proclamation of Republic. Country name inscr in white.
426 **77** 1 p. multicoloured 50 40
427 2.5 p. multicoloured 75 65
428 5 p. multicoloured . . . . 15·00 8·50
429 10 p. multicoloured . . . . 2·50 2·00

1975. No. 425 of Port. Guinea optd **REP. DA BISSAU.**
430 2 e. multicoloured 60 60

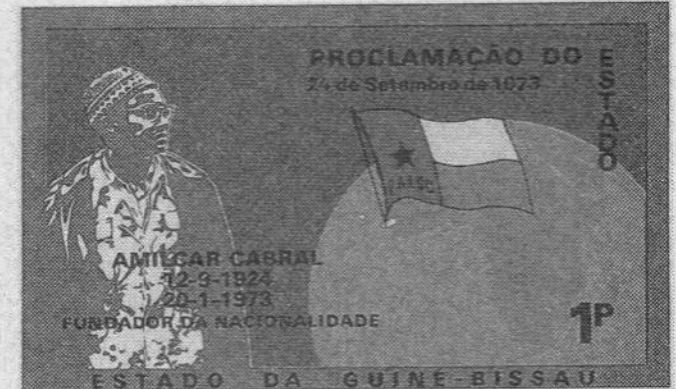

79 Amilcar Cabral, Map and Flag

1975. 2nd Anniv of Proclamation of Republic (1st issue). Country name inscr in black.
431 **79** 1 p. multicoloured 45 30
432 2.5 p. multicoloured 60 45
433 5 p. multicoloured . . . . 2·50 1·40
434 10 p. multicoloured . . . . 2·50 2·25
See also Nos. 439/440.

80 Amilcar Cabral, Arms and Flag

1975. 51st Birth Anniv of Amilcar Cabral (founder of P.A.I.G.C.).
435 **80** 1 e. multicoloured 20 10
436 10 e. multicoloured 80 40

81 Family, Arms and Flag

1975. 19th Anniv of P.A.I.G.C. (Partido Africano da Independencia da Guine e do Cabo Verde).
437 **81** 2 e. multicoloured 50 20
438 10 e. multicoloured . . . . 2·00 75

82 Pres. Luis Cabral, Arms and Flag

1975. 2nd Anniv of Proclamation of Republic (2nd issue).
439 **82** 3 e. multicoloured 40 20
440 5 e. multicoloured 85 30

83 General Henry Knox (after Stuart) and Cannons of Ticonderoga (after Lovell)

1976. Bicent of American Independence (1st issue). Multicoloured.
441 5 e. Type **83** (postage) 25 15
442 10 e. General Putnam and Battle of Bunker Hill 55 30
443 15 e. Washington and Crossing of the Delaware 80 35
444 20 e. General Kosciuszko and Battle of Saratoga . . . . . . 1·25 50
445 30 e. General von Steuben and Valley Forge (air) . . . . . 1·75 90
446 40 e. Lafayette and Monmouth Court House . . . . 2·00 1·00
See also Nos. 503/6.

84 Masked Dancer

1976. Dancers. Multicoloured
448 2 p. Type **84** (postage) 30 10
449 3 p. Dancer and drummer . . . 35 15
450 5 p. Dancers on stilts . . . . . 60 20#
451 10 p. Dancers with spears and bows (air) 65 40
452 15 p. Masked dancer . . . . . 1·00 50
453 20 p. "Devil" dancer . . . . . 1·50 65

1976. Cent. of Universal Postal Union (1st issue). Nos. 1448/53 optd **CENTENARIO DA U.P.U. 1874. MEMBRO DA U.P.U. 1974** and emblem.
455 **84** 2 p. multicoloured (post) . . 10 10
456 – 3 p. multicoloured 20 10
457 – 5 p. multicoloured 25 15
458 – 10 p. multicoloured (air) . . 50 25
459 – 15 p. multicoloured 65 40
460 – 20 p. multicoloured 90 50
See also Nos. 518/23.

1976. Nos. 435/40 surch in new currency.
462 1 p. on 1 e. multicoloured . . . 10 10
463 2 p. on 2 e. multicoloured . . . 10 10
464 3 p. on 3 e. multicoloured . . . 15 10
465 5 p. on 5 e. multicoloured . . . 25 15
466 10 p. on 10 e. multicoloured . . 50 30
467 10 p, on 10 e. multicoloured . . 50 30

87 Amilcar Cabral and Funeral

1976. 3rd Anniv of Amilcar Cabral's Assassination.
468 **87** 3 p. multicoloured 15 10
469 5 p. multicoloured 20 15
470 6 p. multicoloured 25 20
471 10 p. multicoloured 40 25

88 Party Emblem

89 Launch of "Soyuz" Spacecraft

1976. 20th Anniv of P.A.I.G.C.
472 **88** 3 p. multicoloured 15 15
473 15 p. multicoloured 65 50
474 50 p. multicoloured . . . . 1·60 1·25

1976. Air. "Apollo-Soyuz" Space Link. Multicoloured.
475 5 p. Type **89** 25 15
476 10 p. Launch of "Apollo" spacecraft 45 30
477 15 p. Leonov, Stafford and meeting in Space 80 45
478 20 p. Eclipse of the Sun . . . . . 1·25 55
479 30 p. Infra-red photograph of Earth . . . . 1·75 85
480 40 p. Return of Spacecraft to Earth . . . . 2·25 95

90 Bell Telephone of 1876 and Laying First Atlantic Cable

1976. Telephone Centenary. Multicoloured.
482 2 p. Type **90** (postage) 15 10
483 3 p. French telephone of 1890 and first telephone box, 1893 . 20 10
484 5 p. German automatic telephone of 1908 and automatic telephone, 1898 . . . . 25 15
485 10 p. English telephone of 1910 and trans-horizon link, 1963 (air) 55 25
486 15 p. French telephone of 1924 and communications satellite . 85 45
487 20 p. Modern telephone and "Molnya" satellite . . . . . 1·25 50

91 Women's Figure Skating

1976. Winter Olympic Games, Innsbruck. Multicoloured.
489 1 p. Type **91** (postage) 15 10
490 3 p. Ice-hockey 30 10
491 5 p. Bobsleighing 30 15
492 10 p. Pairs figure-skating (air) . . 55 30
493 20 p. Cross-country skiing . . . 1·25 45
494 30 p. Speed skating . . . . . . 1·75 85

92 Footballers and Montreal Skyline

1976. Olympic Games, Montreal. Mult.
496 1 p. Type **92** 10 10
497 3 p. Pole vaulting 15 10
498 5 p. Hurdling 25 15
499 10 p. Discus throwing 45 25
500 20 p. Running 90 50
501 30 p. Wrestling . . . . 1·40 75

93 "Viking" orbiting Mars

1976. Bicentenary of American Revolution (2nd issue). Multicoloured.
(a) Postage. Horiz designs as T **83**.
503 3 p. 50 Crispus Attuck and Boston Massacre 30 10
504 5 p. Martin Luther King and Capitol 40 20
(b) Air. Success of "Viking" Mission. Vert.
505 25 p. Type **93** . . . . 1·25 65
506 35 p. Lander scooping samples from surface of Mars . . . . 1·75 90

94 Amilcar Cabral

1977. 4th Death Anniv of Amilcar Cabral. Multicoloured.
507 50 c. Type **94** (postage) 15 10
508 3 p. 50 Luis Cabral addressing U.N. Assembly 35 10
509 15 p. Type **94** (air) 55 30
510 30 p. As No. 508 . . . . 1·25 50

95 Henri Dunant (Peace, 1901)

1977. 75th Anniv of 1st Nobel Prizes. Mult.
511 3 p. 50 Type **95** (postage) . . . 30 10
512 5 p. Albert Einstein (Physics, 1921) 35 20
513 6 p. Irene and Jean-Frederic Joliot-Curie (Chemistry, 1935) 75 20
514 30 p. Alexander Fleming (Medicine, 1945) . . . . . . 1·75 90
515 35 p. Ernest Hemingway (Literature, 1954) (air) . . . 2·00 90
516 40 p. J. Tinbergen (Economic Sciences, 1969) . . . . . . 2·25 1·00

96 Postal Runner and "Telstar" Satellite

1977. Cent. (1974) of Universal Postal Union (2nd issue). Multicoloured.
518 3 p. 50 Type **96** (postage) . . . 25 15
519 5 p. A.E.G. J-II biplane, and satellites circling globe . . . 35 15
520 6 p. Mail van and satellite control room 55 15
521 30 p. Stage-coach and astronaut cancelling letters on Moon . . 1·75 50
522 35 p. French locomotive (1844) and "Intelsat 4" satellite (air) . 6·50 2·75
523 40 p. Aircraft and "Apollo"–"Soyuz" link . . . . . . 2·50 90

97 Coronation Coach

1977. Silver Jubliee of Queen Elizabeth II. Multicoloured.
525 3 p. 50 Type **97** (postage) . . . 20 10
526 5 p. Coronation ceremony . . . 25 15
527 10 p. Yeoman of the Guard and Crown Jewels 45 25
528 20 p. Trumpeter sounding fanfare 90 45
529 25 p. Royal Horse Guard (air) . . 1·25 50
530 30 p. Royal Family on balcony . 1·50 70

98 Congress Emblem

99 "Massacre of the Innocents" (detail)

1977. Third P.A.I.G.C. Congress, Bissau.
532 **98** 3 p. 50 multicoloured . . . 25 15

1977. 400th Birth Anniv of Peter Paul Rubens (artist). Multicoloured.
533 3 p. 50 Type **99** (postage) . . . 20 10
534 5 p. "Rape of the Daughters of Leukippos" 25 15
535 6 p. "Lamentation of Christ" (horiz) 35 15
536 30 p. "Francisco IV Gonzaga, Prince of Mantua" . . . . 1·60 50
537 35 p. "The Four Continents" (detail) (horiz) (air) . . . 1·75 50
538 40 p. "Marquise Brigida Spinola Doria" . . . . 2·25 60

100 Santos-Dumont's Airship "Ballon No. 6"

1978. Airships. Multicoloured.

540 3 p. 50 Type **100** (postage) . . . 25 15
541 5 p. Beardmore airship R-34 crossing Atlantic 35 15
542 10 p. "Norge" over North Pole . 55 20
543 20 p. "Graf Zeppelin" over Abu Simbel . . . . 1·40 50
544 25 p. "Hindenburg" over New York (air) . . . . 1·75 70
545 30 p. "Graf Zeppelin" Concorde airliner and space shuttle . . 2·25 75

101 Footballers, Cup and Poster (Uruguay, 1930)

1978. World Cup Football Championship, Argentina. Multicoloured.

547 3 p. 50 Type **101** (postage) . . . 20 10
548 5 p. "Coupe du Monde, 1938" . 25 15
549 10 p. Brazil, 1950 . . . . . . 55 25
550 20 p. Chile, 1962 . . . . 1·10 45
551 25 p. Mexico, 1970 (air) . . . . 1·40 50
552 30 p. "FIFA World Cup 1974" (Germany) . . . . 1·60 65

DESIGNS: showing match scenes and posters from previous championships.

102 Black Antelope

1978. Endangered Animals. Multicoloured.

554 3 p. 50 Type **102** (postage) . . . 30 10
555 5 p. Fennec . . . . 1·75 55
556 6 p. Secretary bird . . . . . . 2·00 70
557 30 p. Hippopotamuses . . . . 2·00 65
558 35 p. Cheetahs (air) . . . . . 2·25 65
559 40 p. Gorillas . . . . 2·50 75

103 Microwave-antenna **104** Child

1978. Telecommunications Day.

561 **103** 3 p. 50 multicoloured . . . 20 15
562 10 p. multicoloured . . . 55 30

1978. Children's Day.

563 **104** 50 c. blue and green . . . 10 10
564 – 3 p. bright red and red . . 15 10
565 – 5 p. light brown and brn . 25 15
566 – 30 p. brown and red . . . 1·40 1·00

DESIGNS: 3 p. Amilcar Cabral and child; 5 p. Children; 30 p. Two children playing.

105 Reading the Proclamation

1978. 25th Anniv of Coronation of Queen Elizabeth II. Multicoloured.

567 3 p. Type **105** (postage) 20 10
568 5 p. Queen and Prince Philip in Coronation Coach 25 15
569 10 p. Queen and Prince Philip . 45 25
570 20 p. Mounted drummer . . . 90 45
571 25 p. Imperial State Crown and St. Edward's Crown (air) . . 1·25 50
572 30 p. Queen holding orb and sceptre . . . . 1·25 65
573 100 p. Queen, stained glass window and Imperial State Crown (55 × 38 mm) . . . . 4·50 1·50

106 Wright Brothers and Wright Flyer I

1978. History of Aviation. Multicoloured.

575 3 p. 50 Type **106** (postage) . . . 20 10
576 10 p. Alberto Santos-Dumont . 45 20
577 15 p. Louis Bleriot 75 35
578 20 p. Charles Lindbergh (air) . . 90 40
579 25 p. Moon landing . . . . . 1·25 50
580 30 p. Space shuttle . . . . . . 1·50 65

1978. World Cup Football Championship Results. Nos. 547/52 optd **10 ARGENTINA 20 HOLANDA 30 BRAZIL**.

582 3 p. 50 mult (postage) 20 10
583 5 p. multicoloured 25 15
584 10 p. multicoloured 45 25
585 20 p. multicoloured . . . . . . 1·10 55
586 25 p. multicoloured (air) . . . 1·25 55
587 30 p. multicoloured . . . . . . 1·50 70

108 "Virgin and Child", 1497

1978. 450th Death Anniv of Albrecht Durer (artist). Multicoloured.

589 3 p. 50 Type **108** (postage) . . . 20 10
590 5 p. "Virgin and Child", 1507 . 25 15
591 6 p. "Virgin and Child", 1512 . 30 15
592 30 p. "Virgin", 1518 . . . . . 1·40 70
593 35 p. "Virgin and Child with St. Anne", 1519 (air) . . . . . 1·75 50
594 40 p. "Virgin of the Pear", 1526 2·00 75

109 Rowland Hill and Wurttemberg 70 k. Stamp, 1873

1978. Death Centenary of Rowland Hill.

596 3 p. 50 Type **109** (postage) . . . 15 10
597 5 p. Belgian 10 c. stamp, 1849 . 25 15
598 6 p. Monaco 5 f. stamp, 1885 . 30 20
599 30 p. Spanish 10 r. stamp, 1851 . 1·50 70
600 35 p. Swiss 5 r. stamp, 1851 (air) . . . . 1·75 50
601 40 p. Naples ½ t. stamp, 1860 . . 2·00 75

DESIGNS: 5 p. to 40 p. show Rowland Hill and stamp.

110 Nurse immunising Child

1979. International Year of the Child (1st issue). Multicoloured.

603 3 p. 50 Type **110** (postage) . . . 20 10
604 10 p. Children drinking 55 25
605 15 p. Children with book . . . 1·00 35
606 20 p. Space shuttle (air) . . . . 1·00 40
607 25 p. "Skylab" space station . . 1·40 50
608 30 p. Children playing chess . . 2·00 75

See also Nos. 616/19.

111 Family

1979. National Census.

610 **111** 50 c. brown, bl & pink . . 10 10
611 2 p. brown, bl & lt blue . . 15 10
612 4 p. brown, bl & yellow . . 25 15

112 Wave Pattern and Human Figures **113** Monument

1979. World Telecommunications Day. Mult.

613 50 c. Type **112** 10 10
614 4 p. Wave pattern and human figures (different) 20 15

1979. 20th Anniv of Pindjiuouiti Massacre.

615 **113** 4 p. 50 multicoloured . . . 30 15

114 Classroom Scene

1980. International Year of the Child (2nd issue). Multicoloured.

616 6 p. Type **114** (postage) 30 25
617 10 p. Jules Verne and child reading novel (vert) 45 30
618 25 p. Locomotive "Northumbrian" (1831), Japanese "Hikari" express train and child with toy steam locomotive (vert) . . . . . 9·00 1·25
619 35 p. Man and child with bows and arrows (vert) . . . . . 1·60 75

115 Amilcar Cabral, Workers and Children reading Books

1980. Literacy Campaign. Multicoloured.

621 3 p. 50 Type **115** (postage) . . . 20 10
622 5 p. Luis Cabral displaying school textbooks 30 15
623 15 p. Type **115** (air) 80 50
624 25 p. As No. 622 . . . . 1·40 75

116 Globe and Cogwheel

1980. Technical Co-operation among Developing Countries.

625 **116** 3 p. 50 multicoloured . . . 20 10
626 6 p. multicoloured 30 20
627 10 p. multicoloured . . . 45 30

117 Wood Carvings **118** Ernst Udet

1980. Handicrafts. Multicoloured.

628 3 p. Type **117** 20 10
629 6 p. Weaving (horiz) 30 20
630 20 p. Bust and statuette (horiz) . 1·00 50

1980. History of Aviation. Air Aces of 1st World War. Multicoloured.

631 3 p. 50 Type **118** (postage) . . . 25 15
632 5 p. Charles Nungesser 35 25
633 6 p. Manfred von Richthofen . . 55 25
634 30 p. Francesco Baracca . . . . 1·75 70
635 35 p. Willy Coppens de Houthulst (air) . . . . . . 2·10 75
636 40 p. Charles Guynemer . . . . 2·50 90

119 Speed Skating

1980. Winter Olympic Games, Lake Placid. Multicoloured.

638 3 p. Type **119** (postage) 20 10
639 5 p. Ski jumping 30 20
640 6 p. Luge 40 25
641 30 p. Cross country skiing . . . 1·75 70
642 35 p. Downhill skiing (air) . . . 2·00 75
643 40 p. Figure skating . . . . . 2·40 90

120 Putting the Shot

1980. Olympic Games, Moscow. Multicoloured.

645 3 p. 50 Type **120** (postage) . . . 20 15
646 5 p. Gymnastics (ring exercise) . 25 20
647 6 p. Long jump 35 25
648 30 p. Fencing . . . . 1·50 70
649 35 p. Gymnastics (backward somersault) (air) . . . . . . 1·75 75
650 40 p. Running . . . . 2·00 90

121 Congress Meeting

1980. 16th Anniv of Cassaca Congress.
652 **121** 3 p. 50 multicoloured . . . 15 10
653 6 p. 50 multicoloured . . . 30 20
654 10 p. multicoloured . . . 40 30

122 Satellites

1981. Space Achievements. Multicoloured.
655 3 p. 50 Type **122** (postage) . . . 20 10
656 5 p. Satellite . . . 25 15
657 6 p. Rocket . . . 30 15
658 30 p. Space Shuttle "Columbia" 1·75 95
659 35 p. "Viking I" (air) . . . 1·75 75
660 40 p. U.S.–Soviet space link . . 2·00 90

123 Platini (France) and Football Scene

1981. World Cup Football Championship, Spain. Multicoloured.
662 3 p. 50 Type **123** (postage) . . . 30 10
663 5 p. Bettega (Italy) . . . 35 15
664 6 p. Rensenbrink (Netherlands) . 40 15
665 30 p. Rivelino (Brazil) . . . 1·90 80
666 35 p. Rummenigge (West Germany) (air) . . . 1·90 80
667 40 p. Kempes (Argentina) . . . 2·00 90

124 Lady Diana Spencer with Horse

1981. Wedding of Prince of Wales. Multicoloured.
669 3 p. 50 Type **124** (postage) . . . 20 15
670 5 p. Investiture of Prince of Wales . . . 25 15
671 6 p. Lady Diana Spencer with Children . . . 30 15
672 30 p. St. Paul's Cathedral . . 1·25 95
673 35 p. Althorp House (air) . . . 1·40 1·00
674 40 p. Arms of Prince of Wales . 1·50 1·25

125 Eric the Red and Viking Ship

1981. Navigators. Multicoloured.
676 3 p. 50 Type **125** (postage) . . . 25 15
677 5 p. Vasco da Gama and "Sao Gabriel" . . . 30 15
678 6 p. Magellan and "Vitoria" . . 35 20
679 30 p. Cartier and "Emerillon" . . 2·00 1·00
680 35 p. Drake and "Golden Hind" (air) . . . 2·50 1·25
681 40 p. Cook and H.M.S. "Endeavour" . . . 2·75 1·60

MINIMUM PRICE

The minimum price quoted is 10p which represents a handling charge rather than a basis for valuing common stamps. For further notes about prices see introductory pages.

126 "Girl with Bare Feet"

1981. Birth Centenary of Pablo Picasso. Multicoloured.
683 3 p. 50 Type **126** (postage) . . . 20 15
684 5 p. "Acrobat on Ball" . . . 25 15
685 6 p. "Pierrot" . . . 30 15
686 30 p. "Girl in front of a Mirror" . . . 1·50 95
687 35 p. "The First Steps" (air) . . 2·00 1·00
688 40 p. "Woman in Turkish Dress" . . . 2·25 1·25

1s27 "Retable of St. Zeno" (Mantegna)

1981. Christmas. Multicoloured.
690 3 p. 50 Type **127** (postage) . . . 20 15
691 5 p. "Virgin with Child" (Bellini) . . . 25 15
692 6 p. "Virgin and Child with Cherubs" (Mantegna) . . . 30 15
693 25 p. "Madonna Campori" (Correggio) . . . 1·50 1·00
694 30 p. "Virgin and Child" (Memling) (air) . . . 2·00 1·10
695 35 p. "Virgin and Child" (Bellini) . . . 2·25 1·25

128 Archery

1982. 75th Anniv of Boy Scout Movement. Multicoloured.
697 3 p. 50 Type **128** (postage) . . . 15 10
698 5 p. First aid . . . 20 15
699 6 p. Bugler . . . 25 15
700 30 p. Cub scouts . . . 1·60 80
701 35 p. Girl scout in canoe (air) . 2·25 90
702 40 p. Scouts with model aircraft 2·40 1·25

129 Keegan

1982. World Cup Football Championship, Spain. Multicoloured.
704 3 p. 50 Type **129** (postage) . . . 20 10
705 5 p. Rossi . . . 20 15
706 6 p. Zico . . . 25 15
707 30 p. Arconada . . . 1·60 80
708 35 p. Kempes (air) . . . 2·25 1·00
709 40 p. Kaltz . . . 2·50 1·10

130 Lady Diana Spencer

1982. 21st Birthday of Princess of Wales. Multicoloured.
711 3 p. 50 Type **130** (postage) . . . 15 10
712 5 p. Playing croquet . . . 25 15
713 6 p. Lady Diana with pony . . 30 15
714 30 p. Fishing . . . 1·75 80
715 35 p. Engagement picture (air) . 1·90 90
716 40 p. Honeymoon picture . . . 2·00 1·10

1982. Birth of Prince William of Wales, Nos. 711/16 optd **21 DE JULHO 1982. GUILHERMO ARTHUR FILIPE LUIS PRINCIPE DE GALES.**
718 3 p. 50 multicoloured (postage) . 20 10
719 5 p. multicoloured . . . 25 15
720 6 p. multicoloured . . . 30 15
721 30 p. multicoloured . . . 1·60 95
722 35 p. multicoloured (air) . . . 1·90 1·10
723 40 p. multicoloured . . . 2·00 1·25

132 National Colours

1982. Visit of President Eanes of Portugal. Multicoloured.
725 4 p. 50 Type **132** . . . 10 10
726 20 p. Doves on national colours 20 10

133 Montgolfier Balloon

1983. Bicent of Manned Flight. Mult.
727 50 c. Type **133** . . . 10 10
728 2 p. 50 Charles's hydrogen balloon . . . 15 10
729 3 p. 50 Charles Green's balloon "Royal Vauxhall" . . . 20 10
730 5 p. Gaston Tissandier's balloon "Zenith" . . . 30 10
731 10 p. Salomon Andree's balloon "Ornen" over Arctic . . . 60 20
732 20 p. Stratosphere balloon "Explorer II" . . . 1·25 40
733 30 p. Modern hot-air balloons . 2·00 60

134 Hamadryas Baboon

136 Satellite

1983. African Primates. Multicoloured.
735 1 p. Type **134** . . . 10 10
736 1 p. 50 Gorilla . . . 20 10
737 3 p. 50 Gelada . . . 30 10
738 5 p. Mandrill . . . 40 15
739 8 p. Chimpanzee . . . 80 20
740 20 p. Eastern black-and-white colobus . . . 1·50 50
741 30 p. Diana monkey . . . 2·40 85

1983. Cosmonautics Day. Multicoloured.
743 1 p. Type **136** . . . 10 10
744 1 p. 50 Satellite (different) . . . 15 10
745 3 p. 50 Rocket carrying space shuttle . . . 20 10
746 5 p. Satellite (different) . . . 30 15
747 8 p. Satellite (different) . . . 60 20
748 20 p. Satellite (different) . . . 1·25 45
749 30 p. "Soyuz" docking with "Salyut" . . . 2·00 70

137 Woodcut from Caxton's "Game and Playe of Chesse", Arabian Pawn and Rook

1983. Chess. Multicoloured.
751 1 p. Type **137** . . . 15 10
752 1 p. 50 12th-century European king and knight . . . 15 10
753 3 p. 50 Mid 18th-century German rook, queen and king . . . 25 10
754 5 p. Late 12th/early 13th-century Danish bishop and knight . . 40 10
755 10 p. 18th-century French king and queen . . . 80 25
756 20 p. 18th-century Venetian king, knight and queen . . . 1·75 55
757 40 p. 19th-century faience knight, queen and rook . . . 3·00 1·10

138 "Vision of Ezekiel"

1983. 500th Birth Anniv of Raphael (artist). Multicoloured.
759 1 p. Type **138** . . . 10 10
760 1 p. 50 "Tempi Madonna" . . . 10 10
761 3 p. 50 "Della Tenda Madonna" . . . 20 10
762 5 p. "Orleans Madonna" . . . 25 10
763 8 p. "La Belle Jardiniere" . . . 45 20
764 15 p. "Small Cowper Madonna" . . . 90 35
765 30 p. "St. George and the Dragon" . . . 2·00 60

139 Swimming

1983. Olympic Games, Los Angeles (1932 and 1984) (1st issue). Multicoloured.
767 1 p. Type **139** . . . 10 10
768 1 p. 50 Hurdling . . . 15 10
769 3 p. 50 Fencing . . . 20 10
770 5 p. Weightlifting . . . 30 10
771 10 p. Marathon . . . 60 15
772 20 p. Show jumping . . . 1·10 35
773 40 p. Cycling . . . 2·40 65
See also Nos. 843/9.

141 Rowland Hill and Penny Black

1983. World Communications Year. Mult.
776 50 c. Type **141** . . . 10 10
777 2 p. 50 Samuel Morse and morse machine . . . 15 10
778 3 p. 50 Heinrich Rudolf Hertz and electromagnetic wave diagrams . . . 20 10
779 5 p. Lord Kelvin and "Agamemnon" (cable ship) . 50 10
780 10 p. Alexander Graham Bell and telephones . . . 60 15
781 20 p. Guglielmo Marconi and wireless apparatus . . . 1·40 40
782 30 p. Vladimir Kosma Zworykin and television . . . 1·60 55

142 JAAC Emblem

1983. First JAAC Congress. Multicoloured.
784 4 p. Crowd and emblem 25 15
785 5 p. Type **142** 30 15

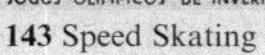
143 Speed Skating 145 U.D.E.M.U. Emblem

144 Hoeing Vegetable Patch

1983. Winter Olympic Games, Sarajevo (1st issue). Multicoloured.
786 1 p. Type **143** 10 10
787 1 p. 50 Ski jumping 15 10
788 3 p. Cross-country skiing 20 10
789 5 p. Bobsleigh 25 10
790 10 p. Ice hockey 70 25
791 15 p. Ice skating 1·10 30
792 20 p. Luge 1·25 35
See also Nos. 816/22.

1983. World Food Day.
794 **144** 1 p. 50 multicoloured 10 10
795 2 p. multicoloured 15 10
796 4 p. multicoloured 30 15

1983. Democratic Union of Women. Multicoloured.
798 4 p. 50 Type **145** 30 15
799 7 p. 50 Flag and woman 50 20
800 9 p. Woman sewing 70 30
801 12 p. Women working on plantation 1·00 45

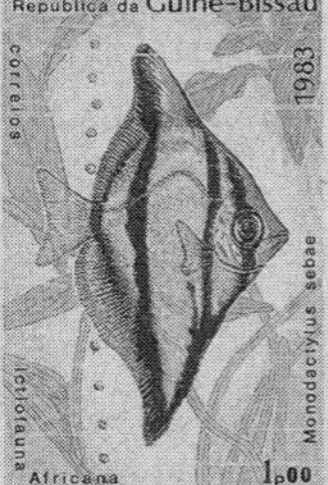

146 "Canna coccinea" 147 Guinean Fingerfish

1983. Flowers. Multicoloured.
802 1 p. Type **146** 15 10
803 1 p. 50 "Bouganville litoralis" 20 10
804 3 p. 50 "Euphorbia milii" 25 10
805 5 p. "Delonix regia" 30 10
806 8 p. "Bauhinia variegata" 50 15
807 10 p. "Spathodea campanulata" 70 20
808 30 p. "Hibiscus rosa sinensis" 2·00 60

1983. Fishes. Multicoloured.
809 1 p. Type **147** 20 15
810 1 p. 50 Clown loach 25 15
811 3 p. 50 Spotted climbing-perch 35 20
812 5 p. Berthold's panchax 50 20
813 8 p. Red-barred lyretail 75 30
814 10 p. Two-striped lyretail 1·10 40
815 30 p. Lyre-tailed panchax 3·50 1·40

148 Ski Jumping

1984. Winter Olympic Games, Sarajevo (2nd issue). Multicoloured.
816 50 c. Type **148** 10 10
817 2 p. 50 Speed skating 15 10
818 3 p. 50 Ice hockey 30 10
819 5 p. Cross-country skiing 35 10
820 6 p. Downhill skiing 60 15
821 20 p. Ice skating 1·25 40
822 30 p. Two-man bobsleigh 2·00 60

149 Duesenberg, 1928

1984. 150th Birth Anniv of Gottlieb Daimler (automobile designer). Multicoloured.
824 5 p. Type **149** 15 10
825 8 p. MG "Midget" 1932 25 10
826 15 p. Mercedes, 1928 50 20
827 20 p. Bentley, 1928 60 30
828 24 p. Alfa Romeo, 1929 85 30
829 30 p. Datsun, 1932 1·25 35
830 35 p. Lincoln, 1932 1·75 40

150 Sud Aviation Caravelle

1984. 40th Anniv of I.C.A.O. Mult.
832 8 p. Type **150** 25 10
833 22 p. Douglas DC-6B 80 30
834 80 p. Ilyushin Il-76 2·25 90

151 "Dona Tadea Arias de Enriquez" (Goya) 153 Fabric Headdress

152 Football

1984. "Espana 84" International Stamp Exhibition, Madrid. Multicoloured.
835 3 p. "Virgin and Child" (Morales) 15 10
836 6 p. Type **151** 20 10
837 10 p. "Saint Cassilda" (Zurbaran) 30 10
838 12 p. "Saints Andrew and Francis" (El Greco) 35 15
839 15 p. "Infanta Isabel Clara Eugenia" (Coello) 55 15
840 35 p. "Queen Maria of Austria" (Velazquez) 1·40 45
841 40 p. "The Trinity" (El Greco) 1·75 55

1984. Olympic Games, Los Angeles (2nd issue). Multicoloured.
843 6 p. Type **152** 15 10
844 8 p. Show jumping 25 10
845 15 p. Sailing 50 15
846 20 p. Hockey 70 20
847 22 p. Handball 75 20
848 30 p. Canoeing 1·10 35
849 40 p. Boxing 1·75 60

1984. "Lubrapex 84" Portuguese–Brazilian Stamp Exhibition, Lisbon. Multicoloured.
851 7 p. 50 Type **153** 25 15
852 7 p. 50 Headdress 25 15
853 7 p. 50 Carved bird headdress 25 15
854 7 p. 50 Wooden mask 25 15
855 7 p. 50 Carving of horse 25 15
856 7 p. 50 Statuette 25 15

154 Tiger

1984. Wild Cats. Multicoloured.
857 3 p. Type **154** 15 10
858 6 p. Lions 25 10
859 10 p. Clouded leopard 35 15
860 12 p. Cheetahs 45 20
861 15 p. Lynx 60 25
862 35 p. Leopard 1·40 55
863 40 p. Snow leopard 1·75 65

155 Pearl Throne, Cameroun 156 Amilcar Cabral making Speech

1984. World Heritage. Multicoloured.
864 3 p. Type **155** 10 10
865 6 p. Antelope (carving), West Sudan 20 10
866 10 p. Setial, East Africa 30 15
867 12 p. Mask, West African coast 40 20
868 15 p. Leopard (statuette), Guinea coast 60 25
869 35 p. Carved statuette of woman, Zaire 1·25 50
870 40 p. Funeral figures, South-east Africa and Madagascar 1·25 55

1984. 60th Birth Anniv of Amilcar Cabral. Multicoloured.
871 5 p. Type **156** 15 10
872 12 p. Amilcar Cabral in combat dress 35 15
873 20 p. Amilcar Cabral memorial 60 25
874 50 p. Amilcar Cabral mausoleum 1·50 60

157 Mechanic working on Engine

1984. 11th Anniv of Independence. Mult.
875 3 p. Type **157** 10 10
876 6 p. Children in school 20 10
877 10 p. Laying bricks 30 10
878 12 p. Doctor tending child (vert) 35 20
879 15 p. Sewing (vert) 40 20
880 35 p. Telephonist and switchboard 1·25 50
881 40 p. P.A.I.G.C. headquarters 1·25 55

158 Grey Whales

1984. Whales. Multicoloured.
882 5 p. Type **158** 25 10
883 8 p. Blue whales 30 15
884 15 p. Bottle-nosed dolphins 60 25
885 20 p. Sperm whale 70 25
886 24 p. Killer whale 85 35
887 30 p. Bowhead whale 1·50 40
888 35 p. Sei whale 1·75 45

159 "Hypolimnas dexithea"

1984. Butterflies and Moths. Multicoloured.
889 3 p. Type **159** 15 15
890 6 p. "Papilio arcturus" 20 15
891 10 p. "Morpho menelaus terrestris" 35 15
892 12 p. "Apaturina erminea" 45 20
893 15 p. "Prepona praeneste" 70 25
894 35 p. "Ornithoptera paradisea" 1·60 55
895 40 p. "Morpho hecuba obidona" 1·60 60

160 Carl Lewis (400 metres relay)

1984. Olympic Gold Medallists, Los Angeles. Multicoloured.
896 6 p. Type **160** 15 10
897 8 p. Koji Gushiken (men's gymnastics) 15 10
898 15 p. Dr. Reiner Klimke (individual dressage) 45 20
899 20 p. Tracie Ruiz (synchronized swimming) 55 20
900 22 p. May Lou Retton (women's gymnastics) 65 25
901 30 p. Michael Gross (100 m. freestyle and 100 m. butterfly) 90 35
902 40 p. Edwin Moses (400 metres hurdles) 1·25 50

161 White Mountain Central Railway locomotive, 1926, U.S.A.

1984. Locomotives. Multicoloured.
904 5 p. Type **161** 20 15
905 8 p. Talyllyn Mountain Railway locomotive No. 86, 1886, Great Britain 25 15
906 15 p. Wuppetal Overhead Railway, 1901, Germany 50 20
907 20 p. Peruvian mountain rack railway locomotive 60 25
908 24 p. Steam locomotive, Achensee rack railway, Austria 80 30
909 30 p. Vitznau–Rigi rack railway locomotive, Switzerland 1·10 40
910 35 p. Vitznau–Rigi rack railway locomotive No. 7, Switzerland 1·60 60

162 Harley Davidson Motor Cycle

1985. Centenary of Motor Cycle. Mult.
912 5 p. Type **162** 20 15
913 8 p. Kawasaki 25 15
914 15 p. Honda 45 20
915 20 p. Yamaha 70 30
916 25 p. Suzuki 1·00 35
917 30 p. BMW 1·40 45
918 35 p. Moto Guzzi 1·50 50

163 Brown Pelican 164 "Clitocybe gibba"

1985. Air. Birth Bicentenary of John J. Audubon (ornithologist). Multicoloured.
920 5 p. Type **163** 35 15
921 10 p. American white pelican 65 25
922 20 p. Great blue heron 1·00 30
923 40 p. Greater flamingo 2·40 65

1985. Fungi. Multicoloured.
924 7 p. Type **164** 35 15
925 9 p. "Morchella elata" 50 20
926 12 p. "Lepista nuda" 75 25
927 20 p. "Lactarius deliciosus" 90 30
928 30 p. "Russula virescens" 1·25 35
929 35 p. "Chroogomphus rutilus" 1·75 50

165 Dunant, Piper Twin Commanche and Volunteers attending Patient

1985. 75th Death Anniv of Henri Dunant (Red Cross founder). Multicoloured.

930 20 p. Type **165** . . . 40 15
931 25 p. Doctor and volunteer putting patient in ambulance . . 50 15
932 40 p. Helicopter team attending wounded soldier . . . 75 35
933 80 p. Volunteers in boat rescuing man from water . . . 1·40 55

166 Long-haired White Cat

167 Vincenzo Bellini, 1820 Harp and 16th-century Descant Viol

1985. Cats. Multicoloured.

934 7 p. Type **166** . . . 20 15
935 10 p. Siamese cat . . . 25 15
936 12 p. Grey cat . . . 30 15
937 15 p. Tortoiseshell cat . . . 40 15
938 20 p. Ginger cat . . . 55 20
939 40 p. Tabby cat . . . 1·00 35
940 45 p. Short-haired white cat . . 1·40 35

1985. International Music Year. Composers. Multicoloured.

942 4 p. Type **167** (150th death anniv of Bellini) . . . 15 15
943 5 p. Robert Schumann (175th birth anniv) and pyramid piano, 1829 . . . 15 15
944 7 p. Frederic Chopin (175th birth anniv) and piano, 1817 . . . 15 15
945 12 p. Luigi Cherubini (225th birth anniv), 1720 baryton and 18th-century quinton . . . 20 15
946 20 p. Giovanni Battista Pergolesi (275th birth anniv) and harpsichord, 1734 . . . 45 15
947 30 p. Georg Friedrich Handel (300th birth anniv), 1825 valve trumpet and 18th-century timpani . . . 65 20
948 50 p. Heinrich Schutz (400th birth anniv), 17th-century bass viol and 1680 oboe . . . 1·00 45

168 "Santa Maria"

169 U.N. Emblem, Rainbow and Peace Doves

1985. Sailing Ships. Multicoloured.

950 8 p. Type **168** . . . 30 15
951 15 p. 16th-century Dutch carrack . . . 40 15
952 20 p. "Mayflower" . . . 50 15
953 30 p. "St. Louis" (French galleon) . . . 75 20
954 35 p. "Royal Sovereign" (galleon), 1660 . . . 85 20
955 45 p. "Soleil Royal" (17th-century French warship) . . . 1·25 35
956 80 p. 18th-century British naval brig . . . 1·90 60

1985. 40th Anniv of U.N.O.

957 **169** 10 p. multicoloured . . . 25 15
958 – 20 p. blue and brown . . . 50 35

DESIGN: 20 p. U.N. emblem in "40".

170 "Madonna of the Rose Garden" (detail)

1985. "Italia '85" International Stamp Exhibition, Rome. Paintings by Botticelli. Multicoloured.

959 7 p. Type **170** . . . 15 10
960 10 p. "Venus and Mars" (detail) . . 15 10
961 12 p. "St. Augustine in his Study" (detail) . . . 20 15
962 15 p. "Spring" (detail) . . . 25 15
963 20 p. "Virgin and Child" (detail) . . . 35 15
964 40 p. "Virgin and Child with St. John" (detail) . . . 1·00 30
965 45 p. "Birth of Venus" (detail) . 1·10 35

171 Youths dancing

1985. International Youth Year. Mult.

967 7 p. Type **171** . . . 10 10
968 13 p. Windsurfing . . . 20 15
969 15 p. Roller skating . . . 20 15
970 25 p. Hang-gliding . . . 35 15
971 40 p. Surfing . . . 55 25
972 50 p. Skateboarding . . . 75 40
973 80 p. Free-falling from airplane . 1·50 60

172 Alfa Touring Car

1986. Anniversaries and Events. Mult.

975 15 p. Tail of comet . . . 1·25 50
976 15 p. Head of comet . . . 1·25 50
977 15 p. Type **172** . . . 1·25 50
978 15 p. Frankfurt-on-Main railway station, 1914 . . . 2·25 75
979 15 p. Top of trophy . . . 2·50 1·00
980 15 p. Base of trophy . . . 2·50 1·00
981 15 p. Olympic rings . . . 3·00 1·00
982 15 p. View of Barcelona . . . 3·00 1·00
983 15 p. Part of space station . . . 1·25 50
984 15 p. Deflectors . . . 1·25 50
985 15 p. Space station and Shuttle . 1·25 50
986 15 p. Part of space station and Earth . . . 1·25 50
987 15 p. Boris Becker's head and arm . . . 1·50 75
988 15 p. Becker's body . . . 1·50 75
989 15 p. Javier's head and arms . 1·50 75
990 15 p. Javier's body and legs . . 1·50 75

ANNIVERSARIES: Nos. 975/6, Appearance of Halley's Comet; 977, Centenary of motor car; 978, 150th anniv of German railways; 979/80, World Cup Football Championship, Mexico; 981, Olympic Games, Seoul (1988); 982, "500th anniv of discovery of America by Columbus" Exhibition and Olympic Games, Barcelona (1992); 983/6, 25 years of manned space flights; 987/8, Wimbledon Men's Singles champion, 1986; 989/90, Ivan Lendl, winner of U.S. Masters Tournament, 1986.

Nos. 975/90 were printed together in se-tenant sheetlets of 16 stamps, stamps for the same event forming a composite design.

173 "Santa Maria"

1987. 500th Anniv (1992) of Discovery of America by Columbus. Multicoloured.

992 50 p. Type **173** . . . 2·25 80
993 50 p. View of Seville . . . 2·25 80
994 50 p. Pedro Alvares Cabral disembarking at Bahia . . . 2·00 60
995 50 p. View of Seville (different) 2·25 80

1987. Nos. 352/5, 359 and 362/3 of Portuguese Guinea surch **DA BISSAU** and new value.

997 100 p. on 20 c. Type **51** . . . 35 15
998 200 p. on 35 c. African rock python . . . 70 25
999 300 p. on 70 c. Boomslang . 1·10 35
1000 400 p. on 80 c. West African mamba . . . 1·25 40
1001 500 p. on 3 e. 50 Brown house snake . . . 1·50 50
1002 1000 p. on 15 e. Striped beauty snake . . . 3·00 1·00
1003 2000 p. on 20 e. African egg-eating snake (horiz) . . . 6·00 3·00

1987. No. 430 surch **2500,00.**

1004 **76** 2500 p. on 2 e. mult . . . 7·00 3·25

176 Ice Dancing

1988. Winter Olympic Games, Calgary. Mult.

1005 5 p. Type **176** . . . 10 10
1006 10 p. Luge . . . 10 10
1007 50 p. Skiing . . . 30 15
1008 200 p. Downhill skiing . . . 75 30
1009 300 p. Slalom . . . 1·25 40
1010 500 p. Ski jumping (vert) . . . 2·00 55
1011 800 p. Speed skating (vert) . . 3·00 1·10

177 Yachting

178 Football

1988. Olympic Games, Seoul. Multicoloured.

1013 5 p. Type **177** . . . 10 10
1014 10 p. Equestrian events (horiz) . 10 10
1015 50 p. High jumping (horiz) . . 15 10
1016 200 p. Rifle shooting (horiz) . . 70 30
1017 300 p. Triple jumping . . . 1·10 40
1018 500 p. Tennis . . . 2·00 50
1019 800 p. Archery . . . 2·75 1·00

1988. "Essen 88" Stamp Fair and European Football Championship, Germany.

1021 **178** 5 p. multicoloured . . . 10 10
1022 – 10 p. multicoloured . . . 10 10
1023 – 50 p. multicoloured . . . 15 10
1024 – 200 p. multicoloured . . . 70 30
1025 – 300 p. multicoloured . . . 1·10 40
1026 – 500 p. multicoloured . . . 2·00 50
1027 – 800 p. multicoloured . . . 2·75 1·10

DESIGNS: 10 to 800 p. Various footballing scenes.

179 Lioness

1988. Animals. Multicoloured.

1029 5 p. Type **179** . . . 10 10
1030 10 p. Ferruginous pygmy owl . 10 10
1031 50 p. Hoopoe (horiz) . . . 10 10
1032 200 p. Common zebra (horiz) . 30 10
1033 300 p. African elephant . . . 50 20
1034 500 p. Vulturine guineafowl . . 80 30
1035 800 p. Black rhinoceros . . . 1·25 50

180 Machel

1988. 2nd Death Anniv of Pres. Samora Machel of Mozambique. Multicoloured.

1036 10 p. Type **180** . . . 10 10
1037 50 p. With arm raised . . . 10 10
1038 200 p. With soldier . . . 30 10
1039 300 p. Wearing suit . . . 50 20

181 Henry Dunant (founder)

1988. 125th Anniv of Int Red Cross. Mult.

1040 10 p. Type **181** . . . 10 10
1041 50 p. Dr T. Maunoir . . . 10 10
1042 200 p. Dr Louis Appia . . . 30 10
1043 800 p. Gustave Moynier . . . 1·25 50

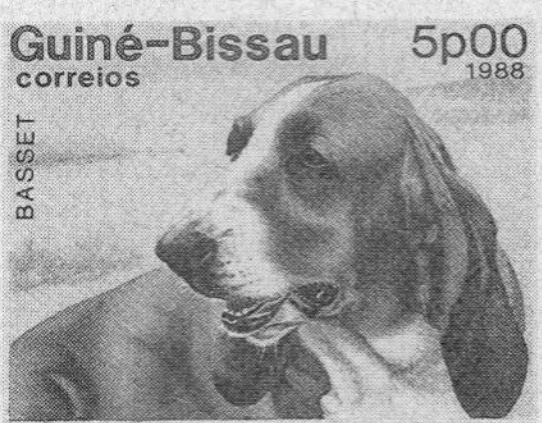

182 Basset Hound

1988. Dogs. Multicoloured.

1044 5 p. Type **182** . . . 10 10
1045 10 p. Grand bleu de Gascogne . 10 10
1046 50 p. Italian spinone . . . 10 10
1047 200 p. Yorkshire terrier . . . 30 10
1048 300 p. Munsterlander . . . 50 20
1049 500 p. Pointer . . . 80 30
1050 800 p. German shorthaired pointer . . . 1·25 50

183 Egyptian Ship, 3300 B.C.

1988. Sailing Ships. Multicoloured.

1052 5 p. Type **183** . . . 10 10
1053 10 p. Ship of Sahu Re, 2500 B.C. (wrongly inscr "2700 B.C.") . . . 10 10
1054 50 p. Ship of Hatshepshut, 1500 B.C. . . . 10 10
1055 200 p. Ship of Rameses III, 1200 B.C. . . . 35 10
1056 300 p. Greek trireme, 480 B.C. . 60 25
1057 500 p. Etruscan bireme, 600 B.C. . . . 1·00 40
1058 800 p. 12th-century Venetian galley . . . 1·50 65

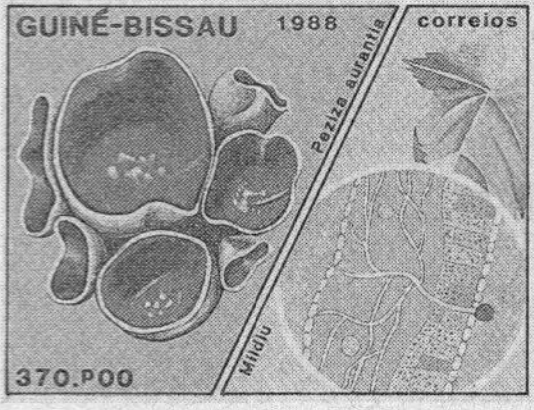

184 "Peziza aurantia"

1988. Fungi. Multicoloured.

1059 370 p. Type **184** . . . 75 30
1060 470 p. Morel . . . 1·00 35
1061 600 p. Caesar's mushroom . . 1·25 45
1062 780 p. Fly agaric . . . 1·60 55
1063 800 p. Deadly amanite . . . 1·60 55
1064 900 p. Cultivated mushroom . . 1·90 70
1065 945 p. Pixie stool . . . 2·10 75

185 Francois-Andre Philidor and Rook

186 Trumpeter, Flag Bearer and Drummer

1988. "Finlandia 88" International Stamp Exhibition, Helsinki. Chess. Multicoloured.

1066 5 p. Type **185** . . . 10 10
1067 10 p. Howard Staunton and chessmen . . . 10 10
1068 50 p. Adolf Anderssen and queen . . . 10 10
1069 200 p. Paul Morphy and pawn . 30 10
1070 300 p. Wilhelm Steinitz and knight . . . 50 20
1071 500 p. Emanuel Lasker and bishop . . . 80 30
1072 800 p. Jose Capablanca and king . . . 1·25 50

1988. Abel Djassi Pioneers Organisation. Multicoloured.

1074 10 p. Type **186** . . . 10 10
1075 50 p. Girls saluting . . . 10 10
1076 200 p. Drawing on floor (horiz) . . . 30 10
1077 300 p. Playing ball (horiz) . . 50 20

187 Monument **188** Woman with Long Hair

1988. 400th Anniv of Cacheu. Multicoloured.

1078 10 p. Type **187** 10 10
1079 50 p. Fort (horiz) 10 10
1080 200 p. Early building (horiz) 35 10
1081 300 p. Church (horiz) 50 20

1989. Traditional Hairstyles.

1082 **188** 50 p. multicoloured 10 10
1083 – 100 p. multicoloured 15 10
1084 – 200 p. multicoloured 30 10
1085 – 350 p. multicoloured 60 25
1086 – 500 p. multicoloured 80 30
1087 – 800 p. multicoloured 1·25 50
1088 – 1000 p. multicoloured 1·60 65

DESIGNS: 100 p. to 1000 p. Different hairstyles.

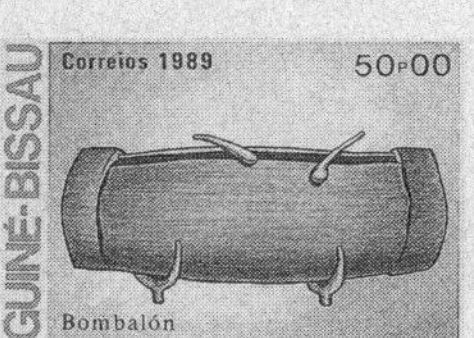

189 Bombalon

1989. Traditional Musical Instruments. Mult.

1089 50 p. Type **189** 10 10
1090 100 p. Flute 15 10
1091 200 p. Tambor 35 15
1092 350 p. Dondon 65 25
1093 500 p. Balafon 90 35
1094 800 p. Kora 1·50 60
1095 1000 p. Nhanhero 1·75 70

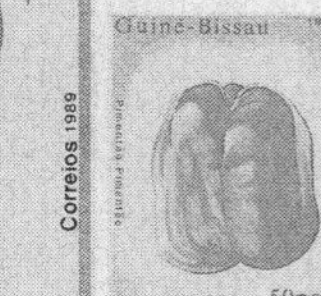

190 Seychelles Blue Pigeon **191** Pimento

1989. Birds. Multicoloured.

1096 50 p. Type **190** 10 10
1097 100 p. Laughing dove 15 10
1098 200 p. Namaqua dove 35 15
1099 350 p. Purple-breasted ground dove 65 25
1100 500 p. African collared dove 90 35
1101 800 p. Pheasant pigeon 1·50 60
1102 1000 p. Emerald dove 1·75 70

1989. Plants.

1104 **191** 50 p. blue 10 10
1105 – 100 p. violet 15 10
1106 – 200 p. green 35 15
1107 – 350 p. red 65 25
1108 – 500 p. brown 90 35
1109 – 800 p. brown 1·50 60
1110 – 1000 p. green 1·75 70

DESIGNS: 100 p. Solanum; 200 p. "Curcumis peco"; 350 p. Tomato; 500 p. "Solanum itiopium"; 800 p. "Hibiscus esculentus"; 1000 p. Baguiche.

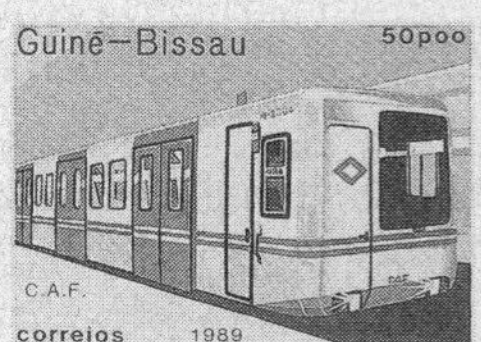

192 Madrid Rapid Transit Train No. M-2004, Spain

1989. Trains. Multicoloured.

1111 50 p. Type **192** 15 10
1112 100 p. Class TEM-2 diesel locomotive, Russia 20 10
1113 200 p. Diesel locomotive, Brazil 50 15
1114 350 p. Diesel railcar, Spain 95 25
1115 500 p. Type 55E electric locomotive, Czechoslovakia 1·40 35
1116 800 p. Class Tu-7E diesel shunting locomotive, Russia 2·25 60
1117 1000 p. Electric multiple unit, Spain (68 × 27 mm) 2·60 70

193 Hurdling

1989. Olympic Games, Barcelona (1992) (1st issue). Multicoloured.

1119 50 p. Type **193** 10 10
1120 100 p. Boxing 20 10
1121 200 p. High jumping 35 15
1122 350 p. Sprinters in starting blocks 60 25
1123 500 p. Runner leaving starting block 90 35
1124 800 p. Gymnastics 1·50 60
1125 1000 p. Pole vaulting 1·75 70

See also Nos. 1245/8.

194 "Limelight" **196** Teotihuacan Pot

195 "La Marseillaise" (relief by Rude from Arc de Triomphe)

1989. Lilies. Multicoloured.

1127 50 p. Type **194** 10 10
1128 100 p. "Lilium candidum" 20 10
1129 200 p. "Lilium pardalinum" 35 15
1130 350 p. "Lilium auratum" 65 25
1131 500 p. "Lilium canadense" 90 35
1132 800 p. "Enchantment" 1·50 60
1133 1000 p. "Black Dragon" 1·75 70

1989. "Philex France 89" International Stamp Exhibition, Paris. Multicoloured.

1135 50 p. Type **195** 10 10
1136 100 p. Champ de Mars 20 10
1137 200 p. Storming of the Bastille 35 15
1138 350 p. Fete (27 × 44 mm) 65 25
1139 500 p. Dancing round Tree of Liberty 90 35
1140 800 p. Rouget de Lisle singing "The Marseillaise" 1·50 60
1141 1000 p. Storming of the Bastille (different) 1·75 70

1989. "Brasiliana 89" International Stamp Exhibition, Rio de Janeiro. Multicoloured.

1143 50 p. Type **196** 10 10
1144 100 p. Mochica jar 20 10
1145 200 p. Jaina statuette 35 15
1146 350 p. Nayarit anthro-zoomorphic jug 65 25
1147 500 p. Inca vase 90 35
1148 800 p. Hopewell statuette of mother and child 1·50 60
1149 1000 p. Taina mask 1·75 70

197 Players Tackling

1989. World Cup Football Championship, Italy (1990). Multicoloured.

1151 50 p. Type **197** 10 10
1152 100 p. Players and ball 20 10
1153 200 p. Players and ball (different) 35 15
1154 350 p. "Scissors" kick 65 25
1155 500 p. Goalkeeper 90 35
1156 800 p. Foul 1·50 60
1157 1000 p. Player scoring goal 1·75 70

198 Trachodon

1989. Prehistoric Animals. Multicoloured.

1159 50 p. Type **198** 10 10
1160 100 p. Edaphosaurus (68 × 22 mm) 20 10
1161 200 p. Mesosaurus 35 15
1162 350 p. "Elephius primigenius" 65 25
1163 500 p. Tyrannosaurus (horiz) 90 35
1164 800 p. Stegosaurus (horiz) 1·50 60
1165 1000 p. "Cervus megaceros" 1·75 70

199 Speed Skating

1989. Winter Olympic Games, Albertville (1992). Multicoloured.

1166 50 p. Type **199** 10 10
1167 100 p. Figure skating 20 10
1168 200 p. Ski jumping 35 15
1169 350 p. Skiing 65 25
1170 500 p. Skiing (different) 90 35
1171 800 p. Bobsleighing 1·50 60
1172 1000 p. Ice hockey 1·75 70

200 African Buffalo **201** "Adoration of Baby Jesus" (Fra Filippo Lippi)

1989. Animals

1174 **200** 50 p. brown and red 10 10
1175 – 100 p. ultram & blue 20 10
1176 – 200 p. green & lt green 35 15
1177 – 350 p. purple and lilac 65 25
1178 – 500 p. chestnut & brn 90 35
1179 – 800 p. violet & dp vio 1·50 60
1180 – 1000 p. deep red & red 1·75 70
1181 – 1500 p. red and yellow 2·75 1·10

DESIGNS: 100 p. Steppe zebra; 200 p. Black rhinoceros; 350 p. Okapi; 500 p. Rhesus macacque; 800 p. Hippopotamus; 1000 p. Cheetah; 1500 p. Lion.

1989. Christmas. Multicoloured.

1182 50 p. Type **201** 10 10
1183 100 p. "Adoration of the Kings" (Pieter Brueghel) 20 10
1184 200 p. "Adoration of the Kings" (Jan Mostaert) 35 15
1185 350 p. "Nativity" (Albert Durer) 65 25
1186 500 p. "Adoration of the Kings" (Peter Paul Rubens) 90 35
1187 800 p. "Adoration of the Kings" (Roger van der Weyden) 1·50 60
1188 1000 p. "Adoration of the Kings" (Francesco Francia) (horiz) 1·75 70

202 Pope John-Paul II and Map **204** Cockerel and Hen

1990. Papal Visit. Multicoloured.

1189 500 p. Type **202** 80 20
1190 1000 p. Pope and couple 1·60 40

1990. "Lubrapex 90" Brazilian–Portuguese Stamp Exhibition, Brasilia. Coop Fowls. Multicoloured.

1193 500 p. Type **204** 80 30
1194 800 p. Turkey 1·25 50
1195 1000 p. Duck and ducklings 1·60 65

205 Radar Rainfall Map

1990. World Meteorology Day. Multicoloured.

1197 1000 p. Type **205** 1·60 65
1198 3000 p. Campbell-Stokes heliograph 5·00 2·00

206 Crying Man and Baby in Womb **207** Cotton Plant

1990. 40th Anniv of United Nations Development Programme.

1199 **206** 1000 p. multicoloured 1·60 65

1991. Traditional Cotton Weaving. Mult.

1200 400 p. Type **207** 60 25
1201 500 p. Weaver 75 30
1202 600 p. Traditional cloth pattern 95 40

208 Mickey Mouse

1991. Carnival Masks. Multicoloured.

1204 200 p. Type **208** 30 10
1205 300 p. Hippopotamus 45 20
1206 600 p. Buffalo 75 30
1207 1200 p. Buffalo (different) 95 40

209 Royal Threadfin

1991. Fishes. Multicoloured.

1208 300 p. Type **209** 45 20
1209 400 p. Guinean fingerfish 95 55
1210 500 p. Goree spadefish 1·60 85
1211 600 p. Long-finned pompano 2·00 90

210 Fire Engine with Water Cannons **211** Lizard Buzzard

1991. Fire and First Aid Service. Mult.

1212 200 p. Type **210** 30 10
1213 500 p. Fire engine with ladders 75 30
1214 800 p. Emergency vehicle with ladders 1·25 50
1215 1500 p. Ambulance 2·25 90

1991. Birds. Multicoloured.

1216 100 p. Type **211** 15 10
1217 250 p. Crowned crane 40 10
1218 350 p. Abyssinian ground hornbill 55 20
1219 500 p. Saddle-bill stork 75 30

212 "Best Wishes" **213** Fula

1991. Greetings Stamps. Multicoloured.
1221 250 p. Type **212** 40 10
1222 400 p. Couple embracing ("With love") 65 25
1223 800 p. Horn-blower and map of Africa ("Congratulations") . 1·25 50
1224 1000 p. Doves ("Season's greetings") . . . . 1·50 60

1992. Traditional Costume. Multicoloured.
1225 400 p. Type **213** 10 10
1226 600 p. Balanta 15 10
1227 1000 p. Fula (different) 25 10
1228 1500 p. Manjaco 40 15

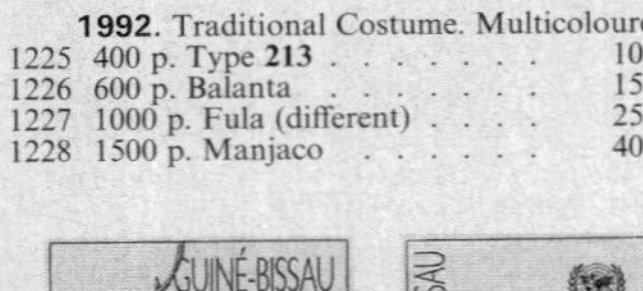

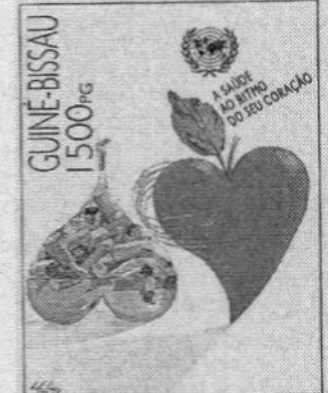

214 "Landolfia owariensis" **215** Cigarette and Fruit "Hearts"

1992. Fruits. Multicoloured.
1229 500 p. Type **214** 15 10
1230 1500 p. "Dialium guineensis" . 40 15
1231 2000 p. "Adansonia digitata" . 50 20
1232 3000 p. "Parkia biglobosa" . . 75 30

1992. World Health Day. "Health in Rhythm with the Heart". Multicoloured.
1233 1500 p. Type **215** 40 15
1234 4000 p. "Heart" running over food . . . . 1·00 40

216 "Cassia alata"

1992. "Lubrapex 92" Brazilian–Portuguese Stamp Exhibition, Lisbon. Plants. Multicoloured.
1235 100 p. Type **216** 10 10
1236 400 p. "Perlebia purpurea" . . 10 10
1237 1000 p. "Caesalpinia pulcherrima" 25 15
1238 1500 p. "Adenanthera pavonina" 40 15
Nos. 1235/8 were issued together, se-tenant, forming a composite design.

217 Canoe

1992. Canoes. Multicoloured.
1240 750 p. Type **217** 35 10
1241 800 p. Pirogue 35 10
1242 1000 p. Pirogue (different) . . 45 10
1243 1300 p. Skiff 60 20

218 Volleyball

1992. Olympic Games, Barcelona (2nd issue). Multicoloured.
1245 600 p. Basketball 15 10
1246 1000 p. Type **218** 25 10
1247 1500 p. Handball 40 15
1248 2000 p. Football 50 20

219 "Afzelia africana" **221** Colobus

1992. Forest Preservation. Multicoloured.
1249 1000 p. Type **219** 25 10
1250 1500 p. African mahogany . . 40 15
1251 2000 p. Iroko 50 20
1252 3000 p. Ambila 75 30

1992. The Red Colobus. Multicoloured.
1254 2000 p. Type **221** 50 20
1255 2000 p. Colobus sitting in tree fork 50 20
1256 2000 p. Mother and young . . 50 20
1257 2000 p. Two colobus on tree branch 50 20

222 Puff Adder

1993. Reptiles. Multicoloured.
1258 1500 p. Type **222** 40 15
1259 3000 p. African dwarf crocodile 80 30
1260 4000 p. Nile monitor . . . . . 1·10 45
1261 5000 p. Rainbow lizard . . . . 1·40 55

224 Waterside Village

1993. Tourism. Multicoloured.
1264 1000 p. Type **224** 25 10
1265 2000 p. Masked villagers on shore and crops 55 20
1266 4000 p. Villages on offshore islands . . . . 1·10 45
1267 5000 p. Crops on island . . . 1·40 55
Nos. 1264/7 were issued together, se-tenant, forming a composite design.

225 Bracelet

1994. Jewellery. Multicoloured.
1268 1500 p. Type **225** 40 15
1269 3000 p. Tribal mask pendant . 80 30
1270 4000 p. Circles pendant . . . 1·10 45
1271 5000 p. Filigree pendant . . . 1·40 55

226 "Erythrina senegalensis"

1994. Medicinal Plants. Multicoloured.
1273 2000 p. Type **226** 20 10
1274 3000 p. "Cassia occidentalis" . 30 10
1275 4000 p. "Gardenia ternifolia" . 45 20
1276 6000 p. "Cochlospermum tinctorium" 65 25

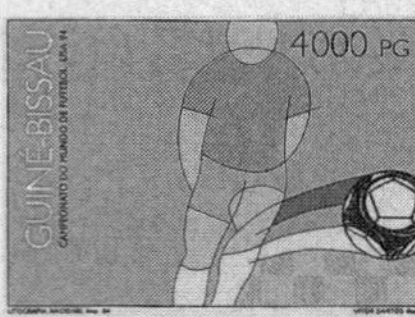

227 Player kicking Ball

1994. World Cup Football Championship, U.S.A. Multicoloured.
1277 4000 p. Type **227** 40 15
1278 5000 p. Goalkeeper making save 55 20
1279 5500 p. Heading the ball . . . 60 25
1280 6500 p. Dribbling the ball . . . 70 30

228 Common Egg-eater (Dasypeltis scabra)

1994. "Philakorea 1994" International and "Singpex '94" Stamp Exhibitions. Snakes. Multicoloured.
1281 5000 p. Type **228** 45 20
1282 5000 p. Green snake ("Philothamnus sp.") . . . 45 20
1283 5000 p. Black-lipped cobra ("Naja melanoleuca") . . . 45 20
1284 5000 p. African python ("Python sebae") 45 20

229 Collecting Fruits

1995. Palm Oil. Multicoloured.
1286 3000 p. Type **229** 20 10
1287 6500 p. Crushing fruit 45 20
1288 7500 p. Palm oil production . . 55 20
1289 8000 p. Animals and pot of palm oil 80 35

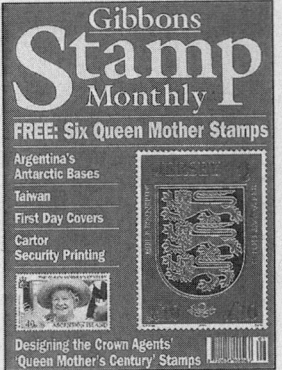

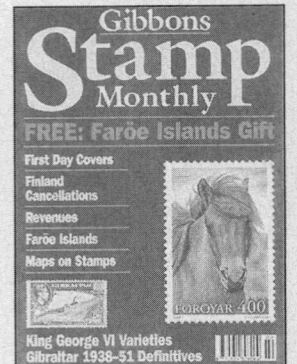

GUYANA Pt. 1

Formerly British Guiana. Attained independence on 26 May, 1966, and changed its name to Guyana.

100 cents = 1 dollar

CANCELLED REMAINDERS. In 1969 remainders of some issues were put on the market cancelled-to-order in such a way as to be indistinguishable from genuine postally used copies for all practical purposes. Our quotations which are indicated by an asterisk are the same for cancelled-to-order or postally used copies.

1966. Nos. 331 etc of British Guiana optd **GUYANA INDEPENDENCE 1966**.

No.	Type	Description	Unused	Used
399	55	1 c. black	10	10
421	–	2 c. green	10	10
422	–	3 c. green and brown	30	10
400	–	4 c. violet	10	10
388	–	5 c. red and black	20	10
424	–	6 c. green	10	10
401	–	8 c. blue	10	10
391	–	12 c. black and brown	10	10
435	–	24 c. black and orange	3·00	10
393	–	36 c. red and black	30	30
405	–	48 c. blue and red	30	30
395	–	72 c. red and green	50	50
396	–	$1 multicoloured	1·75	35
397	–	$2 mauve	1·50	75
398	–	$5 blue and black	1·00	1·75

74 Flag and Map

1966. Independence. Multicoloured.

No.	Type	Description	Unused	Used
408		5 c. Type **74**	15	10
409		15 c. Type **74**	20	10
410		25 c. Arms of Guyana	20	10
411		$1 Arms of Guyana	65	1·25

76 Bank Building

1966. Opening of Bank of Guyana.

No.	Type	Description	Unused	Used
412	76	5 c. multicoloured	10	10
413		25 c. multicoloured	10	10

77 British Guiana One Cent Stamp of 1856

1967. World's Rarest Stamp Commemoration.

No.	Type	Description	Unused	Used
414	77	5 c. multicoloured	10	10*
415		25 c. multicoloured	10	10*

78 Chateau Margot

1967. 1st Anniv of Independence. Multicoloured.

No.	Type	Description	Unused	Used
416		6 c. Type **78**	10	10*
417		15 c. Independence Arch	10	10*
418		25 c. Fort Island	10	10*
419		$1 National Assembly	20	15

Nos. 418/9 are horiz.

MINIMUM PRICE

The minimum price quoted is 10p which represents a handling charge rather than a basis for valuing common stamps. For further notes about prices see introductory pages.

83 "Millie" (Blue and Yellow Macaw)

84 Wicket-keeping

1967. Christmas.

No.	Type	Description	Unused	Used
441	83	5 c. yell, bl, black & green	10	10*
443		5 c. yell, blue, black & red	10	10*
442		25 c. yell, blue, blk, & violet	15	10*
444		25 c. yell, blue, blk, & green	15	10*

1968. M.C.C.'s West Indies Tour. Multicoloured.

No.	Type	Description	Unused	Used
445		5 c. Type **84**	10	10*
446		6 c. Batting	10	10*
447		25 c. Bowling	30	10*

87 Pike Cichlid

102 "Christ of St. John of the Cross" (Salvador Dali)

1968. Multicoloured.

No.	Type	Description	Unused	Used
448		1 c. Type **87**	10	10
449		2 c. Red paranha ("Pirai")	10	10
450		3 c. Peacock cichlid ("Lukunani")	10	10
451		5 c. Armoured catfish ("Hassar")	10	10
489		6 c. Black acara ("Patua")	10	50
490		10 c. Spix's guan (vert)	30	40
491		15 c. Harpy eagle (vert)	30	10
455		20 c. Hoatzin (vert)	60	10
493		25 c. Guianan cock of the rock (vert)	30	10
457		40 c. Great kiskadee (vert)	1·00	50
495		50 c. Brazilian agouti ("Accouri")	35	15
459		60 c. White-lipped peccary	80	10
460		$1 Paca ("Labba")	80	10
461		$2 Nine-banded armadillo	1·25	2·00
462		$5 Ocelot	1·50	3·00

1968. Easter.

No.	Type	Description	Unused	Used
463	102	5 c. multicoloured	10	10*
464		25 c. multicoloured	20	10*

103 "Efficiency Year"

1968. "Savings Bonds and Efficiency". Multicoloured.

No.	Type	Description	Unused	Used
465		6 c. Type **103**	10	10*
466		25 c. Type **103**	10	10*
467		30 c. "Savings Bonds"	10	10*
468		40 c. "Savings Bonds"	10	10*

105 Open Book, Star and Crescent

1968. 1400th Anniv of Holy Quran.

No.	Type	Description	Unused	Used
469	105	6 c. black, gold & flesh	10	10*
470		25 c. black, gold & lilac	10	10*
471		30 c. black, gold & green	10	10*
472		40 c. black, gold & blue	10	10*

107 Broadcasting Greetings

1968. Christmas.

No.	Type	Description	Unused	Used
473	107	6 c. brown, black & green	10	10*
474		25 c. brown, violet & green	10	10*
475	–	30 c. green & turquoise	10	10*
476	–	40 c. red and turquoise	10	10*

DESIGNS: 30 c. and 40 c. Map showing radio link, Guyana—Trinidad.

109 Festival Ceremony

1969. Hindu Festival of Phagwah. Multicoloured.

No.	Type	Description	Unused	Used
477		6 c. Type **109**	10	10
478		25 c. Ladies spraying scent	10	10
479		30 c. Type **109**	10	10
480		40 c. As No. 478	10	10

111 "Sacrament of the Last Supper" (Dali)

1969. Easter.

No.	Type	Description	Unused	Used
481	111	6 c. multicoloured	10	10
482		25 c. multicoloured	10	10
483		30 c. multicoloured	10	10
484		40 c. multicoloured	10	10

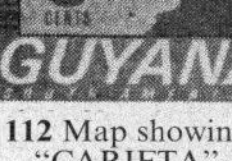

112 Map showing "CARIFTA" Countries

114 Building "Independence" (first aluminium ship)

1969. 1st Anniv of "CARIFTA".

No.	Type	Description	Unused	Used
500	112	6 c. red, blue & turquoise	15	15
501	–	25 c. lemon, brown & red	15	15

DESIGN—HORIZ: 25 c. "Strength in Unity".

1969. 50th Anniv of I.L.O.

No.	Type	Description	Unused	Used
502	114	30 c. blue, black & silver	40	25
503	–	40 c. multicoloured	50	25

DESIGN—HORIZ: 40 c. Bauxite processing plant.

116 Scouts raising Flag

1969. 3rd Caribbean Scout Jamboree and Diamond Jubilee of Scouting in Guyana. Multicoloured.

No.	Type	Description	Unused	Used
504		6 c. Type **116**	10	10
505		8 c. Camp-fire cooking	10	10
506		25 c. Type **116**	10	10
507		30 c. As 8 c.	10	10
508		50 c. Type **116**	15	15

118 Gandhi and Spinning-wheel

1969. Birth Centenary of Mahatma Gandhi.

No.	Type	Description	Unused	Used
509	118	6 c. black, brown & olive	20	50
510		15 c. black, brown & lilac	25	50

119 "Mother Sally" Dance Troupe

121 Forbes Burnham and Map

1969. Christmas. Unissued stamps optd as in T **119**. Multicoloured.

No.	Type	Description	Unused	Used
511		5 c. Type **119**	10	10
512		6 c. City Hall, Georgetown	10	10
513		25 c. Type **119**	10	10
514		60 c. As 6 c.	20	25

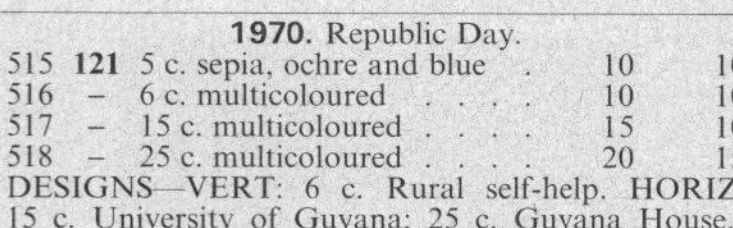

1970. Republic Day.

No.	Type	Description	Unused	Used
515	121	5 c. sepia, ochre and blue	10	10
516	–	6 c. multicoloured	10	10
517	–	15 c. multicoloured	15	10
518	–	25 c. multicoloured	20	15

DESIGNS—VERT: 6 c. Rural self-help. HORIZ: 15 c. University of Guyana; 25 c. Guyana House.

125 "The Descent from the Cross"

128 "Mother and Child" (Philip Moore)

127 "Peace" and U.N. Emblem

1970. Easter. Paintings by Rubens. Multicoloured.

No.	Type	Description	Unused	Used
519		5 c. Type **125**	10	10
520		6 c. "Christ on the Cross"	10	10
521		15 c. Type **125**	20	15
522		25 c. As 6 c.	20	15

1970. 25th Anniv of United Nations. Mult.

No.	Type	Description	Unused	Used
523		5 c. Type **127**	10	10
524		6 c. U.N. emblem, gold-panning and drilling	10	10
525		15 c. Type **127**	10	10
526		25 c. As 6 c.	10	15

1970. Christmas.

No.	Type	Description	Unused	Used
527	128	5 c. multicoloured	10	10
528		6 c. multicoloured	10	10
529		15 c. multicoloured	15	15
530		25 c. multicoloured	15	15

129 National Co-operative Bank

1971. Republic Day.

No.	Type	Description	Unused	Used
531	129	6 c. multicoloured	10	10
532		15 c. multicoloured	15	15
533		25 c. multicoloured	15	15

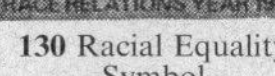

130 Racial Equality Symbol

131 Young Volunteer felling Tree (from painting by J. Criswick)

1971. Racial Equality Year.

No.	Type	Description	Unused	Used
534	130	5 c. multicoloured	10	10
535		6 c. multicoloured	10	10
536		15 c. multicoloured	15	15
537		25 c. multicoloured	15	15

1971. 1st Anniv of Self-help Road Project.

No.	Type	Description	Unused	Used
538	131	5 c. multicoloured	10	10
539		20 c. multicoloured	20	10
540		25 c. multicoloured	20	10
541		50 c. multicoloured	30	1·75

132 Yellow Allamanda

134 Obverse and Reverse of Guyana $1 Coin

133 Child praying at Bedside

1971. Flowering Plants. Multicoloured.

542	1 c. Pitcher Plant of Mt. Roraima	10	10
543	2 c. Type **132**	10	10
544	3 c. Hanging heliconia	10	10
545	5 c. Annatto tree	10	10
546	6 c. Cannon-ball tree	10	10
547	10 c. Cattleya	3·25	10
548a	15 c. Christmas orchid	65	10
549	20 c. "Paphinia cristata"	3·00	20
550	25 c. Marabunta	4·00	4·50
550ab	25 c. Marabunta	45	10
551	40 c. Tiger beard	3·50	10
552	50 c. "Guzmania lingulata"	40	85
553	60 c. Soldier's cap	30	65
554	$1 "Chelonanthus uliginoides"	30	55
555	$2 "Norantea guianensis"	35	55
556	$5 "Odontadenia grandiflora"	55	55

No. 550 shows the flowers facing upwards and has the value in the centre. No. 550ab has the flowers facing downwards with the value to the right.

1971. Christmas. Multicoloured.

557	5 c. Type **133**	10	10
558	20 c. Type **133**	10	10
559	25 c. Carnival masquerader (vert)	10	10
560	50 c. As 25 c.	20	60

1972. Republic Day.

561	**134** 5 c. silver, black and red	10	10
562	– 20 c. silver, black and red	15	10
563	**134** 25 c. silver, black & blue	15	15
564	– 50 c. silver, black & grn	25	45

DESIGN: 20 c., 50 c. Reverse and obverse of Guyana $1 coin.

135 Hands and Irrigation Canal

136 Map and Emblem

1972. Youman Nabi (Mohammed's Birthday).

565	**135** 5 c. multicoloured	10	10
566	25 c. multicoloured	10	10
567	30 c. multicoloured	10	10
568	60 c. multicoloured	20	20

1972. Conference of Foreign Ministers of Non-aligned Countries.

569	**136** 8 c. multicoloured	10	10
570	25 c. multicoloured	10	10
571	40 c. multicoloured	15	15
572	50 c. multicoloured	20	20

137 Hand reaching for Sun

138 Joseph, Mary and the Infant Jesus

1972. 1st Caribbean Festival of Arts.

573	**137** 8 c. multicoloured	10	10
574	25 c. multicoloured	10	10
575	40 c. multicoloured	15	20
576	50 c. multicoloured	20	25

1972. Christmas.

577	**138** 8 c. multicoloured	10	10
578	25 c. multicoloured	10	10
579	40 c. multicoloured	15	25
580	50 c. multicoloured	15	25

139 Umana Yana (Meeting-house)

141 Stylized Blood Cell

140 Pomegranate

1973. Republic Day. Multicoloured.

581	8 c. Type **139**	10	10
582	25 c. Bethel Chapel	10	10
583	40 c. As 25 c.	20	20
584	50 c. Type **139**	25	20

1973. Easter. Multicoloured.

585	8 c. Type **140**	10	10
586	25 c. Cross and map (34 × 17 mm)	10	10
587	40 c. As 25 c.	10	10
588	50 c. Type **140**	15	15

1973. 25th Anniv of Guyana Red Cross.

589	**141** 8 c. red and black	10	10
590	25 c. red and purple	25	15
591	40 c. red and blue	35	50
592	50 c. red and green	50	1·00

142 Steel-Band Players

143 Symbol of Progress

1973. Christmas. Multicoloured.

593	8 c. Type **142**	10	10
594	25 c. Type **142**	20	10
595	40 c. "Virgin and Child" stained-glass window (34 × 47mm)	50	75
596	50 c. As 40 c.	55	75

1974. Republic Day. Multicoloured.

597	8 c. Type **143**	10	10
598	25 c. Wai-Wai Indian	10	10
599	40 c. Type **143**	15	30
600	50 c. As 25 c.	15	40

1974. No. 546 surch **8c**.

601	8 c. on 6 c. multicoloured	10	10

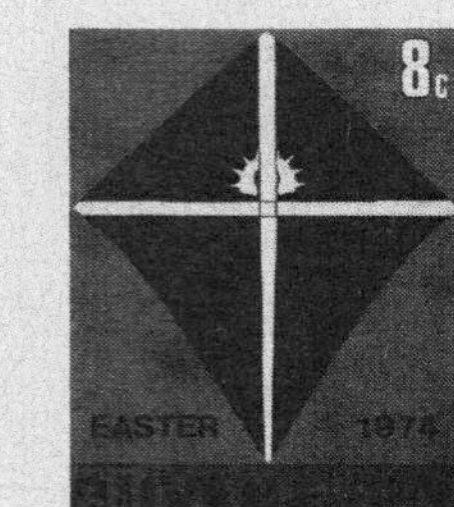

145 Kite with Crucifixion Motif

1974. Easter.

602	**145** 8 c. multicoloured	10	10
603	– 25 c. black and green	10	10
604	– 40 c. black and mauve	10	15
605	**145** 50 c. multicoloured	15	25

DESIGN: Nos. 603/4, "Crucifixion" in pre-Columbian style.

146 British Guiana 24 c. Stamp of 1874

148 Buck Toyeau

147 Guides with Banner

1974. Centenary of Universal Postal Union.

606	**146** 8 c. multicoloured	25	10
607	– 25 c. lt green, green & blk	35	10
608	**146** 40 c. multicoloured	35	20
609	– 50 c. green, brn and blk	45	45

DESIGN—VERT (42 × 25 mm): 25, 50 c. U.P.U. emblem and Guyana postman.

1974. Golden Jubilee of Girl Guides. Mult.

610	8 c. Type **147**	20	10
611	25 c. Guides in camp	30	15
612	40 c. As 25 c.	45	40
613	50 c. Type **147**	45	45

1974. Christmas. Multicoloured.

615	8 c. Type **148**	10	10
616	35 c. Five-fingers and awaras	10	10
617	50 c. Pawpaw and tangerine	15	10
618	$1 Pineapple and sapodilla	30	60

1975. No. 544 surch **8c**.

620	8 c. on 3 c. multicoloured	10	10

149 Golden Arrow of Courage

150 Old Sluice Gate

1975. Republic Day. Guyana Orders and Decorations. Multicoloured.

621	10 c. Type **149**	10	10
622	35 c. Cacique's Crown of Honour	10	15
623	50 c. Cacique's Crown of Valour	15	20
624	$1 Order of Excellence	35	60

1975. Silver Jubilee of International Commission on Irrigation and Drainage. Multicoloured.

625	10 c. Type **150**	10	10
626	35 c. Modern sluice gate (horiz)	10	15
627	50 c. Type **150**	15	30
628	$1 As 35 c.	35	60

151 I.W.Y. Emblem and Rock Drawing

1975. International Women's Year. Designs showing different rock drawings.

630	**151** 10 c. green and yellow	10	10
631	– 35 c. violet and blue	15	10
632	– 50 c. blue and orange	20	15
633	– $1 brown and blue	30	45

152 Freedom Monument

153 G.N.S. Emblem

1975. Namibia Day. Multicoloured.

635	10 c. Type **152**	10	10
636	35 c. Unveiling of Monument	15	10
637	50 c. Type **152**	25	10
638	$1 As 35 c.	35	35

1975. 1st Anniv of National Service.

639	**153** 10 c. yellow, green & vio	10	10
640	– 35 c. orange, green & vio	10	10
641	– 50 c. blue, green & brown	15	15
642	– $1 mauve, green & lt grn	40	40

Nos. 640/2 are as Type **153** but have different symbols within the circle.

154 Court Building, 1875, and Forester's Badge

1975. Centenary of Guyanese Ancient Order of Foresters. Multicoloured.

644	10 c. Type **154**	10	10
645	35 c. Rock drawing of hunter and quarry	10	10
646	50 c. Crossed axes and bugle-horn	15	10
647	$1 Bow and arrow	40	40

1976. No. 553 surch **35c**.

649	35 c. on 60 c. Soldier's cap	20	15

156 Shoulder Flash

157 Triumphal Arch

1976. 50th Anniv of St. John Ambulance in Guyana.

650	**156** 8 c. silver, black & mauve	10	10
651	– 15 c. silver, black & orge	10	10
652	– 35 c. silver, black & grn	20	20
653	– 40 c. silver, black & blue	25	25

Nos. 651/3 are as Type **156** but show different shoulder flashes.

1976. 10th Anniv of Independence. Multicoloured.

654	8 c. Type **157**	10	10
655	15 c. Stylised Victoria Regia lily	10	10
656	35 c. "Onward to Socialism"	15	15
657	40 c. Worker pointing the way	15	15

1976. West Indies Victory in World Cricket Cup. As T **223a** of Grenada.

659	15 c. Map of the Caribbean	1·25	1·75
660	15 c. Prudential Cup	1·25	1·75

158 Flame in Archway

159 Festival Emblem and "Musical Instrument"

1976. Deepavali Festival. Multicoloured.

661	8 c. Type **158**	10	10
662	15 c. Flame in hand	10	10
663	35 c. Flame in bowl	15	20
664	40 c. Goddess Latchmi	15	25

1977. Second World Black and African Festival of Arts and Culture, Nigeria.

666	**159** 10 c. red, black and gold	10	10
667	25 c. violet, black & gold	15	10
668	50 c. blue, black & gold	20	25
669	$1 green, black & gold	35	75

160 1 c. and 5 c. Coins

1977. New Coinage.

671	**160** 8 c. multicoloured	20	10
672	– 15 c. brown, grey & black	25	10
673	– 35 c. green, grey & black	45	30
674	– 40 c. red, grey and black	50	35
675	– $1 multicoloured	1·00	1·25
676	– $2 multicoloured	1·50	2·75

DESIGNS: 15 c. 10 and 25 c. coins; 35 c., 50 c. and $1 coins; 40 c. $5 and $10 coins; $1 $50 and $100 coins; $2 Reverse of $1 coin.

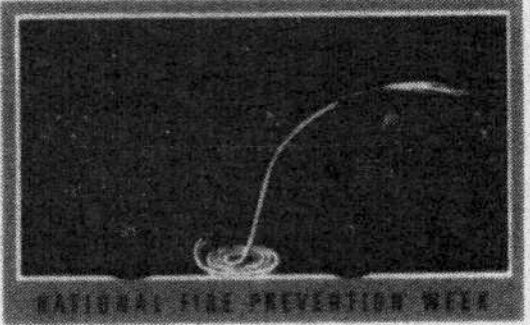

161 Hand Pump, circa 1850

1977. National Fire Prevention Week. Mult.

677	8 c. Type **161**	50	10
678	15 c. Steam engine, circa 1860	85	10
679	35 c. Fire engine, circa 1930	1·00	60
680	40 c. Fire engine, 1977	1·10	85

162 Cuffy Monument

1977. Cuffy Monument (commemorating 1763 Slave Revolt). Multicoloured.

681 8 c. Type **162** 10 10
682 15 c. Cuffy Monument (different view) 10 10
683 35 c. Type **162** 15 20
684 40 c. As 15 c. 15 30

163 American Manatee

1978. Wildlife Conservation. Multicoloured.

685 8 c. Type **163** 65 10
686 15 c. Giant sea turtle 85 20
687 35 c. Harpy eagle (vert) . . . . 3·25 1·50
688 40 c. Iguana (vert) . . . . . . 3·25 1·50

164 L.F.S. Burnham (Prime Minister) and Parliament Buildings, Georgetown

1978. 25th Anniv of Prime Minister's Entry into Parliament.

689 **164** 8 c. black, violet & grey . . 10 10
690 – 15 c. black, blue & grey . . 10 10
691 – 35 c. black, red and grey . 15 20
692 – 40 c. black, orange & grey 15 20

DESIGNS: 15 c. Burnham, graduate and children ("Free Education"); 35 c. Burnham and industrial works (Nationalization of Bauxite Industry); 40 c. Burnham and village scene ("The Co-operative Village").

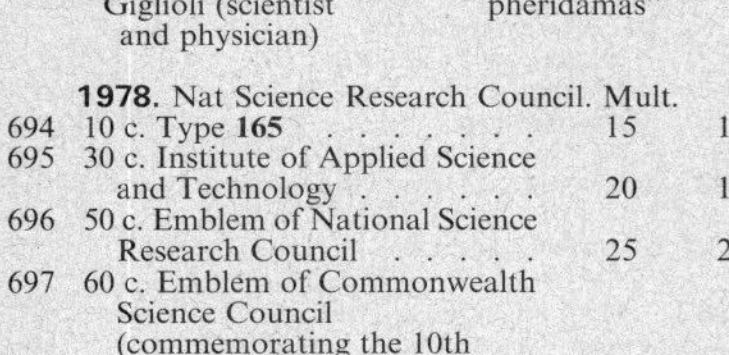

165 Dr. George Giglioli (scientist and physician)

166 "Prepona pheridamas"

1978. Nat Science Research Council. Mult.

694 10 c. Type **165** 15 10
695 30 c. Institute of Applied Science and Technology 20 15
696 50 c. Emblem of National Science Research Council 25 25
697 60 c. Emblem of Commonwealth Science Council (commemorating the 10th meeting) (horiz) 25 25

1978. Butterflies. Multicoloured.

698 5 c. Type **166** . . . . 1·50 10
699 10 c. "Archonias bellona" . . . 1·50 10
700 15 c. "Eryphanis polyxena" . . 1·50 10
701 20 c. "Helicopis cupido" . . . 1·50 10
702 25 c. "Nessaea batesii" . . . 1·50 10
702a 30 c. "Nymphidium mantus" . 1·25 1·75
703 35 c. "Anaea galanthis" . . . 1·50 10
704 40 c. "Morpho rhetenor" (male) 1·50 10
705 50 c. "Hamadryas amphinome" 1·50 20
705a 60 c. "Papilio androgeus" . . 1·25 1·00
706 $1 "Agrias claudina" . . . . 3·75 20
707 $2 "Morpho rhetenor" (female) 5·50 35
708 $5 "Morpho deidamia" . . . 6·50 90
708a $10 "Elbella patrobas" . . . 6·50 4·25

Nos. 706/8 are vertical, 25 × 39 mm.

168 Amerindian Stone-chip Grater in Preparation

169 Dish Aerial by Night

1978. National/International Heritage Year. Multicoloured.

709 10 c. Type **168** 10 10
710 30 c. Cassiri and decorated Amerindian jars 15 10
711 50 c. Fort, Kyk-over-al 20 15
712 60 c. Fort Island 20 20

1979. Satellite Earth Station. Multicoloured.

713 10 c. Type **169** 10 10
714 30 c. Dish aerial by day 20 15
715 50 c. Satellite with solar veins . 30 15
716 $3 Cylinder satellite . . . . . 1·00 90

170 Sir Rowland Hill and British Guiana 1850 12 c. "Cottonreel" Stamp

1979. Death Cent of Sir Rowland Hill. Mult.

717 10 c. Type **170** 15 10
718 30 c. British Guiana 1856 1 c. black on magenta stamp (vert) 25 15
719 50 c. British Guiana 1898 1 c. Mount Roraima stamp . . . 35 25
720 $3 Printing press used for early British Guiana stamps (vert) 70 1·10

171 "Me and my Sister" 172 "An 8 Hour Day"

1979. International Year of the Child. Children's Paintings. Multicoloured.

721 10 c. Type **171** 10 10
722 30 c. "Fun with the Fowls" (horiz) 15 15
723 50 c. "Two Boys catching Ducks" (horiz) 20 20
724 $3 "Mango Season" (horiz) . . 65 1·25

1979. 60th Anniv of Guyana Labour Union. Multicoloured.

725 10 c. Type **172** 10 10
726 30 c. "Abolition of Night Baking" (horiz) 10 10
727 50 c. "Introduction of the Workmen's Compensation Ordinance" 15 15
728 $3 H. N. Critchlow (founder) . 55 90

173 Guyana Flag

1980. 10th Anniv of Republic.

729 **173** 10 c. multicoloured 10 10
730 – 35 c. black and orange . . 30 10
731 – 60 c. multicoloured 50 20
732 – $3 multicoloured 80 90

DESIGNS: 35 c. Demerara River Bridge; 60 c. Kaieteur Falls; $3 "Makanaima, the Great Ancestral Spirit of the Amerindians".

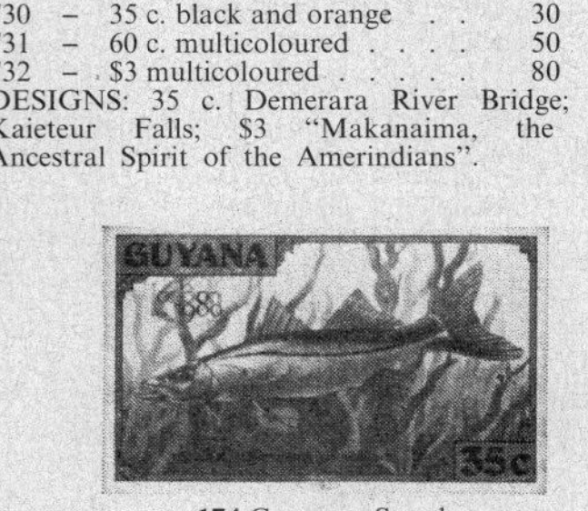

174 Common Snook

1980. "London 1980" International Stamp Exhibition. Fishes. Multicoloured.

733 35 c. Type **174** 25 20
734 35 c. Trahira ("Haimara") . . 25 20
735 35 c. Electric eel 25 20
736 35 c. Golden rivulus 25 20
737 35 c. Golden pencilfish 25 20
738 35 c. Four-eyed fish 25 20
739 35 c. Red piranha ("Pirai") . . 25 20
740 35 c. Smoking hassar 25 20
741 35 c. Manta 25 20
742 35 c. Festival cichlid ("Flying patwa") 25 20
743 35 c. Arapaima 25 20
744 35 c. Peacock cichlid ("Lukanani") 25 20

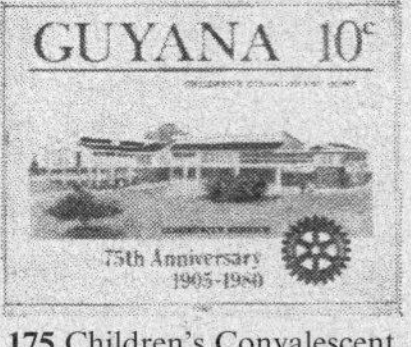

175 Children's Convalescent Home (Community Service)

1980. 75th Anniv of Rotary International. Multicoloured.

745 10 c. Type **175** 10 10
746 30 c. Georgetown Rotary Club and Rotary International emblems 10 10
747 50 c. District 404 emblem (vert) 20 20
748 $3 Rotary anniversary emblem (vert) 80 80

176 "C" encircling Globe, Caduceus Emblem and Sea

1980. 25th Anniv of Commonwealth Caribbean Medical Research Council. Multicoloured.

749 10 c. Type **176** 10 10
750 60 c. Researcher with microscope, Caduceus emblem, stethoscope and beach scene 40 20
751 $3 Caduceus emblem, "C" encircling researcher and island silhouettes . . . . 1·10 1·00

177 "Virola surinamensis"

1980. Christmas. Trees and Foliage. Multicoloured.

752 10 c. Type **177** 10 10
753 30 c. "Hymenaea courbaril" . . 20 10
754 50 c. "Mora excelsa" 30 15
755 $3 "Peltogyne venosa" . . . . 1·25 1·10

178 Brazilian Tree Porcupine 181 Map of Guyana

1981. Wildlife. Multicoloured.

756 30 c. Type **178** 40 45
757 30 c. Red howler 40 45
758 30 c. Common squirrel-monkey 40 45
759 30 c. Two-toed sloth 40 45
760 30 c. Brazilian tapir 40 45
761 30 c. Collared peccary 40 45
762a 30 c. Six-banded armadillo . . 40 45
763 30 c. Tamandua 40 45
764 30 c. Giant anteater 40 45
765 30 c. Murine opossum 40 45
766 30 c. Brown four-eyed opossum 40 45
767 30 c. Brazilian agouti 40 45

1981. Liberation of Southern Africa Conference. No. 635 surch **1981 CONFERENCE $1.05**.

768 $1.05 on 10 c. Type **152** 40 30

1981. Royal Wedding (1st issue). Nos. 554 and 556 surch **ROYAL WEDDING 1981** and value.

769c $3.60 on $5 "Odontadenia grandiflora" 60 65
770 $7.20 in $1 "Chelonanthus uliginoides" 60 60

See also Nos. 841/3 and 930/6.

1981. Fiscal stamps surch for postal use.

771 **181** 10 c. on 3 c. black, blue and red 30 10
940 15 c. on 2 c. black, blue and grey 50 15
941 20 c. on 2 c. black, blue and grey . . . . 3·50 30
1029 25 c. on 2 c. black, blue and grey 35 10
772 30 c. on 2 c. black, blue and grey 45 15
989 40 c. on 2 c. black, blue and grey . . . . 1·00 15
945 45 c. on 2 c. black, blue and grey . . . . 1·75 45
773 50 c. on 2 c. black, blue and grey 40 15
774 60 c. on 2 c. black, blue and grey 45 15
948 75 c. on 2 c. black, blue and grey . . . . 6·00 25
775 75 c. on 3 c. black, blue and red 45 20
949 80 c. on 2 c. black, blue and grey . . . . 5·00 20
950 85 c. on 2 c. black, blue and grey 75 25
951 100 c. on 3 c. black, blue and red . . . . 1·00 35
952 110 c. on 3 c. black, blue and red 80 30

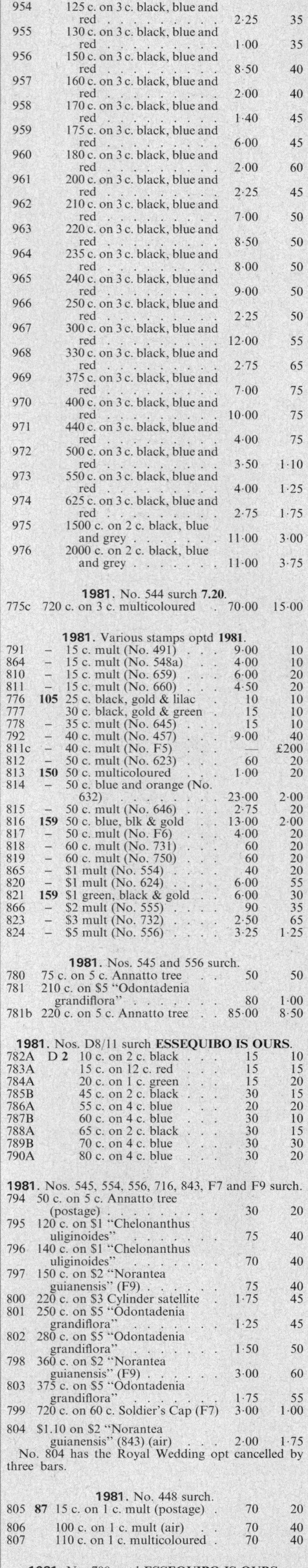

953 **181** 120 c. on 3 c. black, blue and red . . . . 8·00 35
954 125 c. on 3 c. black, blue and red . . . . 2·25 35
955 130 c. on 3 c. black, blue and red . . . . 1·00 35
956 150 c. on 3 c. black, blue and red . . . . 8·50 40
957 160 c. on 3 c. black, blue and red . . . . 2·00 40
958 170 c. on 3 c. black, blue and red . . . . 1·40 45
959 175 c. on 3 c. black, blue and red . . . . 6·00 45
960 180 c. on 3 c. black, blue and red . . . . 2·00 60
961 200 c. on 3 c. black, blue and red . . . . 2·25 45
962 210 c. on 3 c. black, blue and red . . . . 7·00 50
963 220 c. on 3 c. black, blue and red . . . . 8·50 50
964 235 c. on 3 c. black, blue and red . . . . 8·00 50
965 240 c. on 3 c. black, blue and red . . . . 9·00 50
966 250 c. on 3 c. black, blue and red . . . . 2·25 50
967 300 c. on 3 c. black, blue and red . . . . 12·00 55
968 330 c. on 3 c. black, blue and red . . . . 2·75 65
969 375 c. on 3 c. black, blue and red . . . . 7·00 75
970 400 c. on 3 c. black, blue and red . . . . 10·00 75
971 440 c. on 3 c. black, blue and red . . . . 4·00 75
972 500 c. on 3 c. black, blue and red . . . . 3·50 1·10
973 550 c. on 3 c. black, blue and red . . . . 4·00 1·25
974 625 c. on 3 c. black, blue and red . . . . 2·75 1·75
975 1500 c. on 2 c. black, blue and grey . . . . 11·00 3·00
976 2000 c. on 2 c. black, blue and grey . . . . 11·00 3·75

1981. No. 544 surch **7.20**.

775c 720 c. on 3 c. multicoloured . 70·00 15·00

1981. Various stamps optd **1981**.

791 – 15 c. mult (No. 491) . . . 9·00 10
864 – 15 c. mult (No. 548a) . . . 4·00 10
810 – 15 c. mult (No. 659) . . . 6·00 20
811 – 15 c. mult (No. 660) . . . 4·50 20
776 **105** 25 c. black, gold & lilac . 10 10
777 30 c. black, gold & green . 15 10
778 – 35 c. mult (No. 645) . . . 15 10
792 – 40 c. mult (No. 457) . . . 9·00 40
811c – 40 c. mult (No. F5) . . . — £200
812 – 50 c. mult (No. 623) . . . 60 20
813 **150** 50 c. multicoloured . . . 1·00 20
814 – 50 c. blue and orange (No. 632) . . . . 23·00 2·00
815 – 50 c. mult (No. 646) . . . 2·75 20
816 **159** 50 c. blue, blk & gold . . 13·00 2·00
817 – 50 c. mult (No. F6) . . . 4·00 20
818 – 60 c. mult (No. 731) . . . 60 20
819 – 60 c. mult (No. 750) . . . 60 20
865 – $1 mult (No. 554) 40 20
820 – $1 mult (No. 624) . . . . 6·00 55
821 **159** $1 green, black & gold . . 6·00 30
866 – $2 mult (No. 555) 90 35
823 – $3 mult (No. 732) . . . . 2·50 65
824 – $5 mult (No. 556) . . . . 3·25 1·25

1981. Nos. 545 and 556 surch.

780 75 c. on 5 c. Annatto tree . . 50 50
781 210 c. on $5 "Odontadenia grandiflora" . . . . 80 1·00
781b 220 c. on 5 c. Annatto tree . . 85·00 8·50

1981. Nos. D8/11 surch **ESSEQUIBO IS OURS**.

782A D 2 10 c. on 2 c. black . . . 15 10
783A 15 c. on 12 c. red . . . 15 15
784A 20 c. on 1 c. green . . . 15 20
785B 45 c. on 2 c. black . . . 30 15
786A 55 c. on 4 c. blue . . . 20 20
787B 60 c. on 4 c. blue . . . 30 10
788A 65 c. on 2 c. black . . . 30 15
789B 70 c. on 4 c. blue . . . 30 30
790A 80 c. on 4 c. blue . . . 30 20

1981. Nos. 545, 554, 556, 716, 843, F7 and F9 surch.

794 50 c. on 5 c. Annatto tree (postage) 30 20
795 120 c. on $1 "Chelonanthus uliginoides" 75 40
796 140 c. on $1 "Chelonanthus uliginoides" 70 40
797 150 c. on $2 "Norantea guianensis" (F9) 75 40
800 220 c. on $3 Cylinder satellite . 1·75 45
801 250 c. on $5 "Odontadenia grandiflora" . . . . 1·25 45
802 280 c. on $5 "Odontadenia grandiflora" . . . . 1·50 50
798 360 c. on $2 "Norantea guianensis" (F9) . . . . . 3·00 60
803 375 c. on $5 "Odontadenia grandiflora" . . . . 1·75 55
799 720 c. on 60 c. Soldier's Cap (F7) 3·00 1·00
804 $1.10 on $2 "Norantea guianensis" (843) (air) . . . 2·00 1·75

No. 804 has the Royal Wedding opt cancelled by three bars.

1981. No. 448 surch.

805 **87** 15 c. on 1 c. mult (postage) . 70 20
806 100 c. on 1 c. mult (air) . . 70 40
807 110 c. on 1 c. multicoloured . 70 40

1981. No. 700 optd **ESSEQUIBO IS OURS**.

808 15 c. "Eryphanis polyxena" . . 2·25 10

1981. Various stamps surch.
825 **116** 55 c. on 6 c mult 3·50 80
826 **111** 70 c. on 6 c. mult 1·00 20
827 100 c. on 6 c. mult 1·25 20
828 – 100 c. on 8 c. multicoloured (No. 505) 3·00 20
829 **152** 100 c. on $1.05 on 10 c. mult (No. 768) 32·00 4·00
830 **116** 110 c. on 6 c. mult 2·00 30
831 **149** 110 c. on 10 c. mult 2·50 30
832 **151** 110 c. on 10 c. green and yellow 6·00 45
834 – 125 c. on $2 multicoloured (No. 555) 12·00 80
835 **116** 180 c. on 6 c. mult 2·25 45
840 – 240 c. on $3 multicoloured (No. 728) 8·00 75
836 **116** 400 c. on 6 c. mult 3·50 80
837a 440 c. on 6 c. mult 1·50 55
838 – 550 c. on $10 multicoloured (No. O21) 5·50 1·00
839 – 625 c. on 40 c. mult (No. F5) 14·00 1·75

1981. Royal Wedding (2nd issue). Nos. 544 and 555/6 surch **Royal Wedding 1981** (No. 843 **Air Mail** also) and value.
841 60 c. on 3 c. Hanging heliconia (postage) 30 35
842 75 c. on $5 "Odontadenia grandiflora" 30 35
843 $1.10 on $2 "Norantea guianensis" (air) 30 35

1981. World Cup Football Championship, Spain (1982) (1st issue). No. 781a optd **Espana 82**.
844 220 c. on 5 c. Annatto tree 1·25 40
See also Nos. 937/9 and 1218.

1981. 150th Birth Anniv of Heinrich von Stephan (founder of U.P.U.) No. 720 surch **1831—1981 Von Stephan. 330**
845 330 c. on $3 Printing press used for early British Guiana stamps 1·10 55

1981. No. 489 surch with large figure over smaller figure.
847 12 c. on 12 c. on 6 c. Black acara ("Patua") 20 25
848 15 c. on 10 c. on 6 c. Black acara ("Patua") 15 10
849 15 c. on 30 c. on 6 c. Black acara ("Patua") 15 10
850 15 c. on 50 c. on 6 c. Black acara ("Patua") 15 10
851 15 c. on 60 c. on 6 c. Black acara ("Patua") 15 10
Nos. 847/51 are further surcharges on previously unissued stamps.

214 Coromantyn Free Negro Armed Ranger, c. 1772. and Cuffy Monument

1981. 16th Anniv of Guyana Defence Force. Multicoloured.
853 15 c. on 10 c. Type **214** 30 10
854 50 c. Private, 27th Foot Regiment, c. 1825 45 30
855 $1 on 30 c. Private, Col. Fourgeoud's Marines, c. 1775 55 45
856 $1.10 on $3 W.O. and N.C.O., Guyana Defence Force, 1966 60 70
The 15 c., $1 and $1.10 values are surcharged on previously unissued stamps.

215 Louis Braille

1981. International Year for Disabled Persons. Famous Disabled People. Multicoloured.
857 15 c. on 10 c. Type **215** 25 10
858 50 c. Helen Keller and Rajkumari Singh 50 40
859 $1 on 60 c. Beethoven and Sonny Thomas 55 50
860 $1.10 on $3 Renoir 55 55
The 15 c., $1 and $1.10 values are surcharged on previously unissued stamps.

1981. No. 489 surch (Nos. 862/3 optd **AIR** also).
861 12 c. on 6 c. Black acara ("Patua") (postage) 15 10
862b 50 c. on 6 c. Black acara ("Patua") (air) 20 15
863 $1 on 6 c. Black acara ("Patua") 50 30

1981. Nos. 601, 620, 644, O13, 717, 720, 728, 749, 751 and 755 surch (Nos. 868/9 twice).
867 110 c. on 10 c. Type **154** 3·00 30
868 110 c. on 110 c. on 8 c. on 3 c. Hanging heliconia 3·00 40
869 110 c. on 110 c. on 8 c. on 6 c. Cannon-ball tree 3·00 40
869b 110 c. on 10 c. on 25 c. Marabunta 2·25 40
870 110 c. on 10 c. Type **170** 2·00 30
871 110 c. on 10 c. Type **176** 8·00 50
872 110 c. on $3 Printing press used for early British Guiana stamps 1·75 30
873 110 c. on $3 H. N. Critchlow 6·50 45
874 110 c. on $3 Caduceus emblem, "C" encircling researcher and island silhouettes 2·00 30
875 110 c. on $3 "Peltogyne venosa" 4·00 50

1981. No. 698 surch **Nov 81 50c.**
876 50 c. on 5 c. Type **166** 5·00 20

222 Yellow Allamanda ("Allamanda cathartica")

225 Tape Measure and Guyana Metrication Board Van

1981. Flowers.
877 **222** 15 c. on 2 c. lilac, blue and green 15 15
878 – 15 c. on 8 c. lilac, blue and mauve 15 15
DESIGN: 15 c. on 8 c. Mazaruni pride ("Sipanea prolensis").
Nos. 877/8 are surcharges on previously unissued stamps.

1981. Air. Human Rights Day. No. 748 surch **Human Rights Day 1981 110 AIR**.
879 110 c. on $3 Rotary anniversary emblem 1·25 60

1981. 35th Anniv of U.N.I.C.E.F. No. 724 surch **U.N.I.C.E.F. 1946-1981 125**.
880 125 c. on $2 "Mango Season" 1·00 40

1981. "Cancun 81" International Conference. No. 698 surch **Cancun 81 50c.**
880a 50 c. on 5 c. Type **166** 4·00 55

1982. Metrication. Multicoloured.
881 15 c. Type **225** 25 25
882 15 c. "Metric man" 25 25
883 15 c. "Postal service goes metric" 25 25
884 15 c. Weighing child on metric scales 25 25
885 15 c. Canje Bridge 25 25
886 15 c. Tap filling litre bucket 25 25

1982. Various stamps optd **1982**.
887 – 20 c. multicoloured (No. 549) 1·50 20
888 **105** 25 c. black, gold and lilac 60 15
889 – 25 c. mult (No. 550ab) 2·00 20
See also Nos. 914/17, 919/21, 923/4, 977, 992/8, 1001, 1004, 1006/8, 1015, 1017, 1059, 1117 and OP3/4.

1982. No. 506 optd **POSTAGE** and Nos. 546 and 601 surch.
890 20 c. on 6 c. Cannon-ball tree 35 10
892 25 c. Type **116** 1·00 10
893 125 c. on 8 c. on 6 c. Cannon-ball tree 35 20

230 Guyana Soldier and Flag

1982. Savings Campaign.
894 **230** $1 multicoloured 30 20
No. 894 is a fiscal stamp optd for postal use. See also Nos. 913 and 990.

1982. 125th Birth Anniv of Lord Baden-Powell and 75th Anniv of Boy Scout Movement. Nos. 543, 545 and 601 surch as given in brackets.
895 15 c. on 2 c. Type **132** (**BADEN POWELL 1857-1982**) 10 30
896 15 c. on 2 c. Type **132** (**Scout Movement 1907-1982**) 10 30
897 15 c. on 2 c. Type **132** (**1907-1982**) 15 40
898 15 c. on 2 c. Type **132** (**1857-1982**) 15 15
899 15 c. on 2 c. Type **132** (**1982**) 10 10
900 110 c. on 5 c. Annatto tree (**BADEN POWELL 1857-1982**) 1·00 20
901 110 c. on 5 c. Annatto tree (**Scout Movement 1907-1982**) 60 20
902 110 c. on 5 c. Annatto tree (**1907-1982**) 1·50 1·00
903 110 c. on 5 c. Annatto tree (**1857-1982**) 1·50 1·00
904 110 c. on 5 c. Annatto tree (**1982**) 60 20
905 125 c. on 8 c. on 6 c. Cannon-ball tree (**BADEN POWELL 1857-1982**) 1·00 20
906 125 c. on 8 c. on 6 c. Cannon-ball tree (**Scout Movement 1907-1982**) 1·00 20
907 125 c. on 8 c. on 6 c. Cannon-ball tree (**1907-1982**) 1·50 1·00
908 125 c. on 8 c. on 6 c. Cannon-ball tree (**1857-1982**) 1·50 1·00
909 125 c. on 8 c. on 6 c. Cannon-ball tree (**1982**) 75 20

1982. 250th Birth Anniv of George Washington. Nos. 718 and 720 surch **Geo Washington 1732 . . . 1982** and value and No. 708 optd **GEORGE WASHINGTON 1732-1982**.
910 100 c. on $3 Printing press used for early British Guiana stamps 45 30
911 400 c. on 30 c. British Guiana 1856 1 c. black on purple 1·60 1·25
912 $5 "Morpho deidamia" 7·50 5·50

1982. Savings Campaign. As T **230**. Mult.
913 110 c. on $5 Guyana male and female soldiers with flag 50 20
No. 913 is a fiscal stamp surch for postal use. See also No. 990.

1982. Easter. Optd **1982** or surch also.
914 **111** 25 c. multicoloured 20 15
915 30 c. multicoloured 20 15
916 45 c. on 6 c. mult 20 25
917 75 c. on 40 c. mult 35 25

1982. No. 703 surch **20**.
918 20 c. on 35 c. "Anaea galanthis" 3·50 10

1982. No. F5 optd **1982 180**.
919 180 c. on 40 c. Tiger beard 3·50 40

1982. Nos. 555/6 optd **1982**.
920 $2 "Norantea guianensis" 80 30
921 $5 "Odontadenia grandiflora" 1·40 70

1982. No. 542 surch **220**.
922 220 c. on 1 c. Pitcher Plant of Mt. Roraima 1·25 40

1982. Nos. 472 and 684 optd **1982**.
923 **105** 40 c. black, gold & blue 35 15
924 – 40 c. multicoloured 50 25

1982. Nos. 469, 751 and 842/3 surch.
925 **105** 80 c. on 6 c. black, gold and flesh 30 20
926 85 c. on 6 c. black, gold and flesh 50 20
927 – 160 c. on $1.10 on $2 mult (No. 843) 80 30
928 – 210 c. on $3 mult (No. 751) 2·50 40
929 – 235 c. on 75 c. on 85 mult (No. 842) 2·50 60

1982. Royal Wedding (3rd issue). Nos. 841/3 surch.
930 85 c. on 60 c. on 3 c. Hanging heliconia 2·50 50
931 130 c. on 60 c. on 3 c. Hanging heliconia 1·75 45
932 160 c. on. $1.10 on $2 "Norantea guianensis" 2·25 1·00
933 170 c. on $1.10 on $2 "Norantea guianensis" 6·00 4·50
934 210 c. on 75 c. on $5 "Odontadenia grandiflora" 1·25 40
935 235 c. on 75 c. on $5 "Odontadenia grandiflora" 2·00 1·40
936 330 c. on $1.10 on $2 "Norantea guianensis" 1·75 40

1982. World Cup Football Championship, Spain (2nd issue). Nos. 544, 546 and 554 optd **ESPANA 1982** or surch also.
937 $1 "Chelonanthus uliginoides" 75 40
938 110 c. on 3 c. Hanging heliconia 75 25
939 250 c. on 6 c. Cannon-ball tree 1·00 60
See also No. 1218.

1982. No. 548a optd **1982**.
977 15 c. Christmas orchid 7·00 10

1982. No. O26 optd **POSTAGE**.
978 110 c. on 6 c. Type **116** 3·50 35

1982. Air. 21st Birthday of Princess of Wales. Nos. 542, 545 and 555 surch **AIR Princess of Wales 1961–1982**
979 110 c. on 5 c. Annatto tree 50 30
980 220 c. on 1 c. Pitcher Plant of Mt. Roraima 80 60
981 330 c. on $2 "Norantea guianensis" 90 90

1982. Birth of Prince William of Wales. Surch **H.R.H Prince William 21st June 1982**. (a) On stamps of British Guiana with additional opt **GUYANA**.
982 50 c. on 2 c. green (No. 332) 40 30
983 $1.10 on 3 c. green and brown (No. 333) 80 50

(b) On stamps of Guyana previously optd **GUYANA INDEPENDENCE 1966.**
984 50 c. on 2 c. green (No. 421) 10·00 3·25
985 $1.10 on 3 c. green and brown (No. 422) 18·00 3·25
986 $1.25 on 6 c. green (No. 424) 60 60
987 $2.20 on 24 c. black and orange (No. 435) 1·50 1·50

1982. Savings Campaign. As No. 913 but showing inverted comma before "OURS" in opt.
990 110 c. on $5 Guyana male and female soldiers with flag 5·50 75

1982. Italy's Victory in World Cup Football Championship. No. F7 surch **ESPANA 1982 ITALY $2.35**.
991 $2.35 on 180 c. on 60 c. Soldier's cap 3·50 55

1982. Wildlife Protection. Nos. 687 and 733/8 optd **1982**.
992 35 c. Harpy eagle 2·00 40
993 35 c. Type **174** 2·00 40
994 35 c. Trahira ("Haimara") 2·00 40
995 35 c. Electric eel 2·00 40
996 35 c. Golden rivulus 2·00 40
997 35 c. Golden pencilfish 2·00 40
998 35 c. Four-eyed fish 2·00 40

1982. Central America and Caribbean Games, Havana. Nos. 542/3 surch **C.A. & CARIB GAMES 1982**.
999 50 c. on 2 c. Type **132** 1·00 25
1000 60 c. on 1 c. Pitcher plant of Mt. Roraima 1·25 15

1982. No. 730 optd **1982**.
1001 35 c. black and orange 30 20

1982. Nos. 841 and 979 further surch.
1002 130 c. on 60 c. on 3 c. Hanging heliconia 40 30
1003 170 c. on 110 c. on 5 c. Annatto tree 70 45

1982. No. 841 surch **1982 440**.
1004 440 c. on 60 c. on 3 c. Hanging heliconia 75 45

1982. Commonwealth Games, Brisbane, Australia. No. 546 surch **Commonwealth GAMES AUSTRALIA 1982 1.25**
1005 $1.25 on 6 c. Cannon-ball tree 1·00 30

1982. Nos. 552, 641 and 719 optd **1982**.
1006 50 c. multicoloured (No. 552) 2·00 25
1007 50 c. blue, green and brown (No. 641) 1·50 25
1008 50 c. multicoloured (No. 719) 60 25

1982. Various Official stamps additionally optd **POSTAGE.**
1009 15 c. Christmas Orchid (No. O 23) 8·00 30
1010 50 c. "Guzmania lingulata" (No. O14) 90 15
1011 100 c. on $3 Cylinder satellite (No. O19) 1·25 35

1982. International Food Day. No. 617 optd **INT. FOOD DAY 1982**.
1012 50 c. Pawpaw and tangerine 11·00 65

1982. International Year of the Elderly. No. 747 optd **INT. YEAR OF THE ELDERLY.**
1013 50 c. District 404 emblem 7·00 50

1982. Centenary of Robert Koch's Discovery of Tubercle Bacillus. No. 750 optd **Dr. R. KOCH CENTENARY TBC BACILLUS DISCOVERY.**
1014 60 c. Researcher with microscope, Caduceus emblem, stethoscope and beach scene 2·00 30

1982. International Decade for Women. No. 633 optd **1982**.
1015 $1 brown and blue 2·50 60

1982. Birth Centenary of F. D. Roosevelt (American statesman). No. 706 optd **F. D. ROOSEVELT 1882-1982.**
1016 $1 "Agrias claudina" 3·25 50

1982. 1st Anniv of G.A.C. Inaugural Flight Georgetown to Boa Vista, Brazil. No. 842 optd **1982 GAC Inaug. Flight Georgetown—Boa Vista, Brasil 200.**
1017 200 c. on 75 c. on $5 "Odontadenia grandiflora" 8·00 1·40

1982. CARICOM Heads of Government Conference, Kingston, Jamaica. Nos. 881/6 surch **50 CARICOM Heads of Gov't Conference July 1982.**
1018 50 c. on 15 c. Type **225** 1·25 30
1019 50 c. on 15 c. "Metric man" 1·25 30
1020 50 c. on 15 c. "Postal service goes metric" 1·25 30
1021 50 c. on 15 c. Weighing child on metric scales 1·25 30
1022 50 c. on 15 c. Canje Bridge 1·25 30
1023 50 c. on 15 c. Tap filling litre bucket 1·25 30

1982. Christmas. Nos. 895/9 optd **CHRISTMAS 1982.**
1024 15 c. on 2 c. Type **132** (surch **BADEN POWELL 1857–1982**) 25 15
1025 15 c. on 2 c. Type **132** (surch **Scout Movement 1907–1982**) 25 15
1026 15 c. on 2 c. Type **132** (surch **1907–1982**) 65 50
1027 15 c. on 2 c. Type **132** (surch **1857–1982**) 65 50
1028 15 c. on 2 c. Type **132** (surch **1982**) 6·50 7·00

1982. Nos. 543 and 546 surch in figures (no "c" after face value).
1034 15 c. on 2 c. Type **132** 10 10
1035 20 c. on 6 c. Cannon-ball tree 10 10
See also No. 1086.

1982. No. 489 surch.
1032 50 c. on 6 c. Black acara ("Patua") 20 15
1033 100 c. on 6 c. Black acara ("Patua") 40 30

1983. Optd **1983**.
1036 – 15 c. mult (No. 655) . . . 3·50 1·50
1037 – 15 c. brown, grey and black (No. 672) 60 10
1038 – 15 c. mult (No. 682) . . . 40 10
1039 **214** 15 c. on 10 c. mult . . . 35 10
1040 **215** 15 c. on 10 c. mult . . . 15 10
1041 – 50 c. mult (No. 646) . . . 4·00 25
1042 – 50 c. mult (No. 696) . . . 4·00 25
1043 – 50 c. mult (No. 719) . . . 1·50 25
See also Nos. 1060/1, 1069/70, 1072/9c, 1096, 1101 and 1110/16.

1983. No. O17 optd **POSTAGE**.
1044 15 c. Harpy Eagle . . . . . 13·00 10

1983. National Heritage. Nos. 710/12 and 778 surch.
1045 90 c. on 30 c. Cassiri and decorated Amerindian jars . 1·25 50
1046 90 c. on 35 c. Rock drawing of hunter and quarry 35 20
1047 90 c. on 50 c. Fort Kyk-over-al 1·25 50
1048 90 c. on 60 c. Fort Island . . 1·75 20

258 Guyana Flag (inscr. "60TH BIRTHDAY ANNIVERSARY")

262

1983. 60th Birthday of President Burnham and 30 Years in Parliament. Multicoloured.
1049 25 c. Type **258** 15 20
1050 25 c. As T **258** but position of flag reversed and inscr. "30th ANNIVERSARY IN PARLIAMENT" 15 20
1051 $1.30 Youth display (41 × 25 mm) 40 65
1052 $6 Presidential standard (43½ × 25 mm) . . . . . . 1·00 2·75

1983. Surch in words.
1053 **170** 50 c on 10 c. mult (No. 717) . . . . 2·00 30
1054 – 50 c. on 400 c. on 30 c. mult (No. 911) . . . . . . 2·50 30
1055 **152** $1 on 10 c. mult (No. 635) 7·50 45
1056 $1 on $1.05 on 10 c. mult (No. 768) . . . . . . 6·50 45
1056a – $1 on $1.10 on $2 mult (No. 843) . . . . . . 1·00 2·50
1057 – $1 on 220 c. on 5 c. mult (No. 844) . . . . . . 7·50 75
1058 – $1 on 330 c. on $2 mult (as No. 981) 60 45
1059 – $1 on $12 on $1.10 on $2 mult (No. P3) . . . . 2·50 2·00
See also Nos. 1080/4.

1983. No. 859 optd **1983**.
1060 $1 on 60 c. Beethoven and Sonny Thomas . . . . . . 6·00 45

1983. Conference of Foreign Ministers of Non-aligned Countries, New Delhi. No. 569 surch **FIFTY CENTS** and No. 570 optd **1983**.
1061 **136** 25 c. multicoloured . . . 75 25
1062 50 c. on 8 c. multicoloured 1·50 25

1983. No. 771 further surch **20**.
1064 **181** 20 c. on 10 c. on 3 c. black, blue and red 55 10

1983. Commonwealth Day. Nos. 424 and 435 surch **Commonwealth Day 14 March 1983**, emblem and value.
1065 **60** 25 c. on 6 c. green . . . . 1·00 20
1066 $1.20 on 6 c. green 50 50
1067 **63** $1.30 on 24 c. black and orange . . . . 1·75 55
1068 $2.40 on 24 c. black and orange . . . . 2·25 1·25

1983. Easter. Nos. 482/3 optd **1983**.
1069 **111** 25 c. multicoloured . . . 15 10
1070 30 c. multicoloured . . . 30 15

1983. 25th Anniv of International Maritime Organization. British Guiana fiscal stamp optd.
1071 **262** $4.80 blue and green . . . 2·00 4·00

1983. Optd **1983**.
1072 **152** 50 c. mult (No. 637) . . 1·50 25
1073 **159** 50 c. blue, black and yellow (No. 668) . . . . . . 2·00 25
1073a – 50 c. mult (No. 723) . .
1074 – 50 c. mult (No. 854) . . 60 25
1075 – 50 c. mult (No. 858) . . 1·75 25
1076 – $1 mult (No. 628) . . . 4·00 45
1077 – $1 mult (No. 638) . . . 4·75 45
1078 – $1 mult (No. 675) . . . 4·00 45
1079 – $1 on 30 c. mult (No. 855) 1·25 45
1079a – $3 mult (No. 720) . . . 17·00 90
1079b – $3 mult (No. 724) . . . 22·00 1·50
1079c – $3 mult (No. 748) . . . 65·00 7·00

1983. Surch **FIFTY CENTS**.
1080 **148** 50 c. on 8 c. mult (No. 615) 1·75 25
1081 **162** 50 c. on 8 c. mult (No. 681) 6·00 25
1082 **171** 50 c. on 10 c. mult (No. 721) 3·00 25
1083 – 50 c. on 10 c. on 25 c. mult (No. O13) . . . . . . 5·00 25
1084 – 50 c. on 330 c. on $3 mult (No. 845) . . . . . . 4·00 25

1983. Surch in figures with **c** after new face value.
1098 **105** 15 c. on 6 c. black, gold & pink (No. 469) 10 10
1100 – 20 c. on 6 c. multicoloured (No. 546) 15 10

1087 **111** 50 c. on 6 c. multicoloured (No. 481) 40 30
1099 – 50 c. on 6 c. multicoloured (No. 489) 30 30

1983 No. 489 surch **$1**.
1088 $1 on 6 c. Black acara ("Patua") . . . . 1·25 30

1983. No. 639 surch **110**.
1089 **153** 110 c. on 10 c. yellow, green and violet . . . . . . 1·75 50

1983. Nos. 551 and 556 surch.
1090 250 c. on 40 c. Tiger beard . . 7·50 55
1091 400 c. on $5 "Odontadenia grandiflora" . . . . 5·50 70

1983. World Telecommunications and Health Day. Nos. 842 and 980 further surch.
1092 25 c. on 220 c. on 1 c. Pitcher plant of Mt. Roraima (surch **ITU 1983 25**) 30 30
1093 25 c. on 220 c. on 1 c. Pitcher plant of Mt. Roraima (surch **WHO 1983 25**) 30 30
1094 25 c. on 220 c. on 1 c. Pitcher plant of Mt. Roraima (surch **17 MAY '83 ITU/WHO 25**) 30 30
1095 $4.50 on 75 c. on $5 "Odontadenia grandiflora" (surch **ITU/WHO 17 MAY 1983**) . . . . 13·00 1·50

1983. 30th Anniv of President's Entry into Parliament. Nos. 690 and 692 surch in words, No. 1096 additionally optd **1983**.
1096 $1 on 15 c. black, blue and grey 6·00 50
1097 $1 on 40 c. black, orange and grey . . . . 9·00 50

1983. No. 611 optd **1983**.
1101 25 c. Guides in camp . . . . 48·00 4·00

1983. 15th World Scout Jamboree, Alberta. Nos. 835/6 and O25 optd **CANADA 1983**, Nos. 1103 and 1105 additionally surch.
1103 – $1.30 on 100 c. on 8 c. multicoloured . . . . 2·50 1·25
1104 **116** 180 c. on 6 c. mult . . . 2·50 2·00
1105 $3.90 on 400 c. on 6 c. multicoloured . . . . 2·75 4·00

1983. Nos. 659/60 surch.
1106 60 c. on 15 c. Map of the Caribbean . . . . 9·00 40
1107 $1.50 on 15 c. Prudential Cup 10·00 1·25

1983. As Nos. 1049/50, but without commemorative inscr above flag.
1108 25 c. As Type **258** 15 15
1109 25 c. As No. 1050 . . . . . 15 15

1983. Optd **1983**.
1110 **105** 30 c. black, gold and green (No. 471) 75 20
1111 – 30 c. multicoloured (No. 695) . . . . 9·50 30
1112 – 30 c. multicoloured (No. 718) . . . . 4·50 20
1113 – 30 c. multicoloured (No. 722) . . . . 8·00 20
1114 – 30 c. multicoloured (No. 746) . . . . 14·00 20
1115 – 60 c. multicoloured (No. 697) . . . . 4·50 20
1116 – 60 c. multicoloured (No. 731) . . . . 5·50 20

1983. No. 553 optd **1982**.
1117 60 c. Soldier's cap . . . . . 4·00 35

1983. Surch.
1118 **157** 120 c. on 8 c. mult (No. 654) 2·75 40
1119 – 120 c. on 10 c. red, black and gold (No. 666) . . . 3·00 40
1120 – 120 c. on 35 c. mult (No. 622) . . . . 3·00 40
1121 – 120 c. on 35 c. orange, grn & vio (No. 640) . . . . 3·00 40

1983. Nos. 716 and 729 surch.
1122 120 c. on 10 c. Type **173** . . . 2·75 40
1123 120 c. on 375 c. on $3 Cylinder satellite . . . . 2·50 40
No. 1123 also carries an otherwise unissued surcharge in red reading **INTERNATIONAL SCIENCE YEAR 1982 375**. As issued much of this is obliterated by two heavy bars.

1983. British Guiana No. D1a and Guyana. No. D8 surch **120 GUYANA**.
1124 **D 1** 120 c. on 1 c. green . . . 2·00 45
1125 **D 2** 120 c. on 1 c. olive . . . 2·00 45

1983. CARICOM Day. No. 823 additionally surch **CARICOM DAY 1983 60**.
1126 60 c. on $3 "Makanaima the Great Ancestral Spirit of the Amerindians" . . . . . . 1·25 35

271 "Kurupukari"

1983. Riverboats.
1127 **271** 30 c. black and red . . . 20 20
1128 – 60 c. black and violet . . 25 35
1129 – 120 c. black and yellow . . 30 60
1130 – 130 c. black 30 65
1131 – 150 c. black and green . . 30 80
DESIGNS: 60 c. "Makouria"; 120 c. "Powis"; 130 c. "Pomeroon"; 150 c. "Lukanani".

1983. Unissued Royal Wedding surch similar to No. 843 additionally surch.
1132 $2.30 on $1.10 on $2 "Norantea guianensis" 60 40
1133 $3.20 on $1.10 on $2 "Norantea guianensis" 60 40

1983. Bicentenary of Manned Flight and 20th Anniv of Guyana Airways. Nos. 701/2a optd as indicated in brackets.
1134 20 c. multicoloured (**BW**) . . 40 35
1135 20 c. multicoloured (**LM**) . . 40 35
1136 20 c. multicoloured (**GY 1963 1983**) 40 35
1137 20 c. multicoloured (**JW**) . . . 40 35
1138 20 c. multicoloured (**CU**) . . . 40 35
1139 20 c. multicoloured (**Mont Golfier 1783–1983**) 40 35
1140 25 c. multicoloured (**BGI**) . . 70 25
1141 25 c. multicoloured (**GEO**) . . 25 10
1142 25 c. multicoloured (**MIA**) . . 70 25
1143 25 c. multicoloured (**BVB**) . . 70 25
1144 25 c. multicoloured (**PBM**) . . 70 25
1145 25 c. multicoloured (**Mont Golfier 1783–1983**) 30 15
1146 25 c. multicoloured (**POS**) . . 70 25
1147 25 c. multicoloured (**JFK**) . . 70 25
1148 30 c. multicoloured (**AHL**) . . 50 30
1149 30 c. multicoloured (**BCG**) . . 50 30
1150 30 c. multicoloured (**BMJ**) . . 50 30
1151 30 c. multicoloured (**EKE**) . . 50 30
1152 30 c. multicoloured (**GEO**) . . 50 30
1153 30 c. multicoloured (**GFO**) . . 50 30
1154 30 c. multicoloured (**IBM**) . . 50 30
1155 30 c. multicoloured (**Mont Golfier 1783–1983**) 25 15
1156 30 c. multicoloured (**KAI**) . . 50 30
1157 30 c. multicoloured (**KAR**) . . 50 30
1158 30 c. multicoloured (**KPG**) . . 50 30
1159 30 c. multicoloured (**KRG**) . . 50 30
1160 30 c. multicoloured (**KTO**) . . 50 30
1161 30 c. multicoloured (**LTM**) . . 50 30
1162 30 c. multicoloured (**MHA**) . . 50 30
1163 30 c. multicoloured (**MWJ**) . . 50 30
1164 30 c. multicoloured (**MYM**) . . 50 30
1165 30 c. multicoloured (**NAI**) . . 50 30
1166 30 c. multicoloured (**ORJ**) . . 50 30
1167 30 c. multicoloured (**USI**) . . 50 30
1168 30 c. multicoloured (**VEG**) . . 50 30

1983. No. 649 further surch **240**.
1169 240 c. on 35 c. on 60 c. Soldier's cap . . . . 1·25 1·00

1983. F.A.O. Fisheries Project. Nos. 448 and 450 surch **FAO 1983** and value.
1170 30 c. on 1 c. Type **87** 15 15
1171 $2.60 on 3 c. Peacock cichild ("Lukunani") . . . . . . 1·50 2·25

277 G.B. 1857 1d. with Georgetown "AO3" Postmark

1983. 125th Anniv of Use of Great Britain Stamps in Guyana. (a) Inscriptions in black.
1172 **277** 25 c. brown and black . . 15 10
1173 – 30 c. red and black . . . 15 15
1174 – 60 c. violet and black . . 25 30
1175 – 120 c. green and black . . 50 55

(b) Inscriptions in blue.
1176 **277** 25 c. brown and black . . 15 10
1177 – 25 c. red and black . . . 15 10
1178 – 25 c. violet and black . . 15 10
1179 – 25 c. green and black . . 15 10
1180 **277** 30 c. brown and black . . 15 15
1181 – 30 c. red and black . . . 15 15
1182 – 30 c. violet and black . . 15 15
1183 – 30 c. green and black . . 15 15
1184 **277** 45 c. brown and black . . 30 25
1185 – 45 c. red and black . . . 30 25
1186 – 45 c. violet and black . . 30 25
1187 – 45 c. green and black . . 30 25
1188 **277** 120 c. brown and black . . 30 55
1189 – 130 c. red and black . . 30 60
1190 – 150 c. violet and black . . 30 70
1191 – 200 c. green and black . . 30 95
DESIGNS: Nos. 1173, 1177, 1181, 1185, 1189, G.B. 1857 4d. red; Nos. 1174, 1178, 1182, 1186, 1190, G.B. 1856 6d. lilac; Nos. 1175, 1179, 1183, 1187, 1191, G.B. 1856 1s. green.
Each design incorporates the "AO3" postmark except Nos. 1189/91 which show mythical postmarks of the Crowned-circle type inscribed "DEMERARA", "BERBICE" or "ESSEQUIBO".

1983. International Communications Year. No. 716 surch **INT. COMMUNICATIONS YEAR 50**.
1192 50 c. on 375 c. on $3 Cylinder satellite . . . . 4·50 30
No. 1192 also carries an otherwise unissued "375" surcharge. As issued much of this surcharge is obliterated by two groups of six horizontal lines.

1983. St. Johns Ambulance Commemoration. Nos. 650 and 653 surch.
1193 **156** 75 c. on 8 c. silver, black and mauve . . . . . . 4·50 50
1194 – $1.20 on 40 c. silver, black and blue . . . . . . 6·50 75

1983. International Food Day. No. 616 surch **$1.20 Int. Food Day 1983**.
1195 $1.20 on 35 c. Five-fingers and awaras . . . . 1·00 50

1983. 65th Anniv of I.L.O. and 25th Death Anniv of H. N. Critchlow (founder of Guyana Labour Union). No. 840 further optd **1918-1983 I.L.O.**
1196 240 c. on $3 H. N. Critchlow . 1·50 1·50

1983. Deepavali Festival. Nos. 661 and 663/4 surch.
1197 25 c. on 8 c. Type **158** 20 10
1198 $1.50 on 35 c. Flame in bowl . 1·25 60
1199 $1.50 on 40 c. Goddess Latchmi 80 60

1983. No. 732 optd **1982** and No. 798 further optd **1983**.
1200 $3 "Makanaima the Great Ancestral Spirit of the Amerindians" . . . . . 1·25 70
1201 360 c. on $2 "Norantea guianensis" . . . . 1·25 80

1983. Wildlife Protection. Nos. 686 and 688 surch and No. 852 optd **1983**.
1202 30 c. Six-banded armadillo . . 50 15
1203 60 c. on 15 c. Giant sea turtle 75 30
1204 $1.20 on 40 c. Iguana . . . . 1·25 50

1983. Human Rights Day. No. 1079c optd **Human Rights Day**.
1205 $3 Rotary anniversary emblem 2·00 1·25

1983. Olympic Games, Los Angeles (1984) (1st issue). Nos. 733/44 surch **LOS ANGELES 1984 125**, Nos. 1206/17 further surch **55**.
1206 55 c. on 125 c. on 35 c. Type **174** 25 25
1207 55 c. on 125 c. on 35 c. Trahira ("Haimara") 25 25
1208 55 c. on 125 c. on 35 c. Electric eel 25 25
1209 55 c. on 125 c. on 35 c. Golden rivulus 25 25
1210 55 c. on 125 c. on 35 c. Golden pencilfish 25 25
1211 55 c. on 125 c. on 35 c. Four-eyed fish 25 25
1212 55 c. on 125 c. on 35 c. Red piranha ("Pirai") 25 25
1213 55 c. on 125 c. on 35 c. Smoking hassar 25 25
1214 55 c. on 125 c. on 35 c. Manta 25 25
1215 55 c. on 125 c. on 35 c. Festive cichlid ("Flying patwa") . 25 25
1216 55 c. on 125 c. on 35 c. Arapaima 25 25
1217 55 c. on 125 c. on 35 c. Peacock cichlid ("Lukanani") . . . 25 25
1217a 125 c. on 35 c. Type **174** . . 6·00
1217b 125 c. on 35 c. Trahira ("Haimara") . . . . . . 6·00
1217c 125 c. on 35 c. Electric eel . . 6·00
1217d 125 c. on 35 c. Golden rivulus 6·00
1217e 125 c. on 35 c. Golden pencilfish . . . . 6·00
1217f 125 c. on 35 c. Four-eyed fish 6·00
1217g 125 c. on 35 c. Red piranha ("Pirai") . . . . 6·00
1217h 125 c. on 35 c. Smoking hassar 6·00
1217i 125 c. on 35 c. Manta . . . 6·00
1217j 125 c. on 35 c. Festive cichlid ("Flying patwa") . . . . 6·00
1217k 125 c. on 35 c. Arapaima . . 6·00
1217l 125 c. on 35 c. Peacock cichlid ("Lukanani") . . . . . . 6·00
See also Nos. 1308/17 and 1420.

1983. No. F7 with unissued **ESPANA 1982** surch further optd **1983**.
1218 180 c. on 60 c. Soldier's cap . 2·50 65

1983. Commonwealth Heads of Government Meeting, New Delhi. No. 542 surch **COMMONWEALTH HEADS OF GOV'T MEETING—INDIA 1983 150**.
1219 150 c. on 1 c. Pitcher plant of Mt. Roraima . . . . . . 3·00 60

1983. Christmas. No. 861 further surch **CHRISTMAS 1983 20c**.
1220 20 c. on 12 c. on 6 c. Black acara ("Patua") . . . . 2·00 10

1984. Nos. 838 and F9 optd **POSTAGE**.
1221 $2 "Norantea guianensis" . . 3·50 70
1221b 550 c. on $10 "Elbella patrobas" . . . . 13·00 7·50

1984. Flowers. Unissued stamps as T **222** surch.
1222 17 c. on 2 c. lilac, blue and green 1·50 1·25
1223 17 c. on 8 c. lilac, blue and mauve . . . . 1·50 1·25

1984. Republic Day. No. 703 and 705a variously optd or surch..
1224 25 c. on 35 c. mult (surch **ALL OUR HERITAGE 25**) . . . 35 20
1225 25 c. on 35 c. mult (surch **1984 25**) 50 30
1226 25 c. on 35 c. mult (surch **REPUBLIC DAY 25**) . . . 50 30
1227 25 c. on 35 c. mult (surch **25**) 50 30
1228 25 c. on 35 c. mult (surch **BERBICE 25**) . . . . . 2·00 2·00
1229 25 c. on 35 c. mult (surch **DEMERARA 25**) . . . . . 2·00 2·00
1230 25 c. on 35 c. mult (surch **ESSEQUIBO 25**) . . . . . 2·00 2·00
1232 60 c. mult (optd **ALL OUR HERITAGE**) 70 40
1233 60 c. mult (optd **REPUBLIC DAY**) 70 40
1234 60 c. mult (optd **1984**) . . . 70 40

1984. Guyana Olympic Committee Appeal. Nos. 841/3 surch **OLYMPIC GAMES 84 25c POSTAGE** (+**2.25 SURTAX**) and rings, the whole surch inverted.
1235 25 c. + $2.25 on 60 c. on 3 c. Hanging heliconia . . . . 2·00 4·50
1236 25 c. + $2.25 on 75 c. on $5 "Odontadenia grandiflora" 2·00 4·50
1237 25 c. + $2.25 on $1.10 on $2 "Norantea guianensis" . . 2·00 4·50

1984. Nature Protection. Various stamps optd **Protecting our Heritage**, some additionally surch.
1238 20 c. on 15 c. mult (No. 491) 8·50 10
1239 20 c. on 15 c. mult (No. 791) 8·50 10
1240a 20 c. on 15 c. mult (No. 1044) 17·00 1·25
1241 25 c. mult (No. 550ab) 13·00 10
1242 30 c. on 15 c. mult (No. 548a) 20·00 30
1243 40 c. mult (No. 457) 12·00 20
1244 50 c. mult (No. 552) 1·50 25
1245 50 c. mult (No. F6) 1·50 25
1246 60 c. mult (No. 459) 9·50 30
1247 90 c. on 40 c. mult (No. 551) 16·00 50
1248 180 c. on 40 c. mult (No. 919) 16·00 90
1249 $2 multicoloured (No. 461) 50·00 1·50
1250 225 c. on 10 c. mult (No. 490) 23·00 1·00
1251 260 c. on $1 mult (No. 460) 11·00 1·00
1252 320 c. on 40 c. mult (No. 551) 12·00 2·25
1253 350 c. on 40 c. mult (No. 551) 20·00 2·50
1254 380 c. on 50 c. mult (No. 495) 6·00 2·50
1255 450 c. on $5 mult (No. 462) 7·00 2·50

1984. Easter. Nos. 483 and 916/17 optd **1984** and No. 481 surch **130**.
1256 **111** 30 c. multicoloured 20 20
1257 45 c. on 6 c. multicoloured 25 25
1258 75 c. on 40 c. multicoloured 35 35
1259 130 c. on 6 c. multicoloured 65 60

1984. Nos. 937/9 and 991 surch.
1260 75 c. on $1 "Chelonanthus uliginoides" 9·50 35
1261 75 c. on 110 c. on 3 c. Hanging heliconia 9·50 35
1262 225 c. on 250 c. on 6 c. Cannon-ball tree 3·00 1·25
1263 230 c. on $2.35 on 180 c. on 60 c. Soldier's cap 3·00 1·00

1984. Nos. 899/901, 904/6 and 909 surch.
1264 20 c. on 15 c. on 2 c. Type **132** (No. 899) 1·50 30
1265 75 c. on 110 c. on 5 c. Annatto tree (No. 904) 9·00 70
1266 90 c. on 110 c. on 5 c. Annatto tree (No. 900) 5·50 85
1267 90 c. on 110 c. on 5 c. Annatto tree (No. 901) 7·00 85
1268 120 c. on 125 c. on 8 c. on 6 c. Cannon-ball tree (No. 905) 7·00 1·00
1269 120 c. on 125 c. on 8 c. on 6 c. Cannon-ball tree (No. 906) 7·00 1·00
1270 120 c. on 125 c. on 8 c. on 6 c. Cannon-ball tree (No. 909) 2·75 1·00

1984. World Telecommunications and Health Day. Nos. 802 and 980 surch.
1271 25 c. on 220 c. on 1 c. Pitcher plant of Mt. Roraima (surch **ITU DAY 1984 25**) 20 20
1272 25 c. on 220 c. on 1 c. Pitcher plant of Mt. Roraima (surch **WHO DAY 1984 25**) 20 20
1273 25 c. on 220 c. on 1 c. Pitcher plant of Mt. Roraima (surch **ITU/WHO DAY 1984 25**) 20 20
1274 $4.50 on 280 c. on $5 "Odontadenia grandiflora" (surch **ITU/WHO DAY 1984 $4.50**) 1·75 1·25

1984. No. 1005 surch **120**.
1275 120 c. on $1.25 on 6 c. Cannon-ball tree 7·00 55

1984. World Forestry Conference. No. 755 optd **1984** and Nos. 752/4 and 875 surch.
1276 55 c. on 30 c. "Hymenaea courbaril" 2·75 30
1277 75 c. on 110 c. on $3 "Peltogyne venosa" 40 35
1278 160 c. on 50 c. "Mora excelsa" 75 70
1279 260 c. on 10 c. Type **177** 1·25 1·25
1280 $3 "Peltogyne venosa" 1·40 1·40

1984. No. 625 surch.
1281 55 c. on 110 c. on 10 c. Type **150** 1·00 30
1282 90 c. on 110 c. on 10 c. Type **150** 1·25 45
Nos. 1281/2 also carry an otherwise unissued 110 c. surch

1984. U.P.U. Congress, Hamburg. Nos. 1188/91 optd **UPU Congress 1984 Hamburg**.
1283 120 c. brown and black 50 60
1284 130 c. red and black 55 70
1285 150 c. violet and black 60 75
1286 200 c. green and black 80 90

1984. Nos. 982/3 and 986/7 surch.
1287 45 c. on 50 c. on 2 c. green 60 25
1288 60 c. on $1.10 on 3 c. olive and brown 2·25 40
1289 120 c. on $1.25 on 6 c. green 75 55
1290 200 c. on $2.20 on 24 c. black and orange 6·00 1·10

1984. Nos. 979/80 and 1003 surch and No. 981 optd **1984**.
1291 75 c. on 110 c. on 5 c. Annatto tree 60 35
1292 120 c. on 170 c. on 110 c. on 5 c. Annatto tree 80 55
1293 200 c. on 220 c. on 1 c. Pitcher plant of Mt. Roraima 12·00 85
1294 330 c. on $2 "Norantea guianensis" 1·75 1·75

1984. CARICOM Day. No. 1200 additionally surch **CARICOM DAY 1984 60**.
1295 60 c. on $3 "Makanaima the Great Ancestral Spirit of the Amerindians" 40 30

1984. No. 544 surch **150**.
1296 150 c. on 3 c. Hanging heliconia 1·25 65

1984. CARICOM Heads of Government Conference. No. 544 surch **60 CARICOM HEADS OF GOV'T CONFERENCE JULY 1984**.
1297 60 c. on 3 c. Hanging heliconia 40 30

301 Children and Thatched School

1984. Cent of Guyana Teachers' Association. Mult.
1298 25 c. Type **301** 10 15
1299 25 c. Torch and graduates 10 15
1300 25 c. Torch and target emblem 10 15
1301 25 c. Teachers of 1884 and 1984 in front of school 10 15

1984. 60th Anniv of International Chess Federation. No. 1048 optd or surch also.
1302 25 c. on 90 c. on 60 c. Fort Island (surch **INT. CHESS FED. 1924–1984 25**) 1·25 25
1303 25 c. on 90 c. on 60 c. Fort Island (surch **1984 25**) 2·25 45
1304 75 c. on 90 c. on 60 c. Fort Island (surch **INT. CHESS FED. 1924–1984 75**) 1·25 40
1305 75 c. on 90 c. on 60 c. Fort Island (surch **1984 75**) 2·25 70
1306 90 c. on 60 c. Fort Island (optd **INT. CHESS FED. 1924–1984**) 1·25 50
1307 90 c. on 60 c. Fort Island (optd **1984**) 2·25 90

1984. Olympic Games, Los Angeles (2nd issue). No. 1051 surch.
1308 25 c. on $1.30 mult (surch **TRACK AND FIELD 25**) 20 25
1309 25 c. on $1.30 mult (surch **BOXING 25**) 20 30
1310 25 c. on $1.30 mult (surch **OLYMPIC GAMES 1984 LOS ANGELES 25**) 20 30
1311 25 c. on $1.30 mult (surch **CYCLING 25**) 1·00 50
1312 25 c. on $1.30 mult (surch **OLYMPIC GAMES 1984 25**) 3·00 1·25
1313 $1.20 on $1.30 mult (surch **TRACK AND FIELD $1.20**) 1·00 1·10
1314 $1.20 on $1.30 mult (surch **BOXING $1.20**) 1·00 1·10
1315 $1.20 on $1.30 mult (surch **OLYMPIC GAMES 1984 LOS ANGELES $1.20**) 1·00 1·25
1316 $1.20 on $1.30 mult (surch **CYCLING $1.20**) 1·75 1·50
1317 $1.20 on $1.30 mult (surch **OLYMPIC GAMES 1984 $1.20**) 3·50 3·00

1984. 60th Anniv of Girl Guide Movement in Guyana. Nos. 900/9 surch **25 GIRL GUIDES 1924-1984**.
1318 25 c. on 110 c. on 5 c. Annatto tree (No. 900) 20 20
1319 25 c. on 110 c. on 5 c. Annatto tree (No. 901) 20 20
1320 25 c. on 110 c. on 5 c. Annatto tree (No. 902) 70 60
1321 25 c. on 110 c. on 5 c. Annatto tree (No. 903) 70 60
1322 25 c. on 110 c. on 5 c. Annatto tree (No. 904) 5·50 6·00
1323 25 c. on 125 c. on 8 c. on 6 c. Cannon-ball tree (No. 905) 20 20
1324 25 c. on 125 c. on 8 c. on 6 c. Cannon-ball tree (No. 906) 20 20
1325 25 c. on 125 c. on 8 c. on 6 c. Cannon-ball tree (No. 907) 70 60
1326 25 c. on 125 c. on 8 c. on 6 c. Cannon-ball tree (No. 908) 70 60
1327 25 c. on 125 c. on 8 c. on 6 c. Cannon-ball tree (No. 909) 5·50 6·00

1984. Various stamps surch.
1328 20 c. on 15 c. on 2 c. Type **132** (No. 1034) 30 10
1341 25 c. on 10 c. Cattleya (No. 547) 35·00 2·00
1343 25 c. on 15 c. Christmas orchid (No. 548a) £120 5·00
1342 25 c. on 15 c. Christmas orchid (No. 864) 14·00 15
1346 25 c. on 15 c. Christmas orchid (No. 977) 13·00 10
1347 25 c. on 15 c. Christmas orchid (No. 1009) 13·00 10
1348 25 c. on 15 c. Christmas orchid (No. O23) 13·00 10
1342a 25 c. on 35 c. on 60 c. Soldier's cap (No. 649) 90·00 4·50
1331 60 c. on 110 c. on 8 c. on 3 c. Hanging heliconia (As No. 868 but with only one **110**) 29·00 4·50
1332 120 c. on 125 c. on 8 c. on 6 c. Cannon-ball tree (No. 893) 5·00 50
1333 120 c. on 125 c. on $2 "Norantea guianensis" (No. 834) 40·00 5·50
1334 120 c. on 125 c. on $2 "Norantea guianensis" (No. O20) 2·75 50
1335 120 c. on 140 c. on $1 "Chelonanthus uliginoides" (No. 796) 5·50 50
1349 130 c. on 110 c. on $2 "Norantea guianensis" (No. 804) 70·00 4·00
1350 130 c. on 110 c. on $2 "Norantea guianensis" (No. O22) 1·75 1·25
1336 200 c. on 220 c. on 1 c. Pitcher plant of Mt. Roraima (No. 922) 10·00 75
1337 320 c. on $1.10 on $2 "Norantea guianensis" (No. 804) 1·25 75
1338 350 c. on 375 c. on $5 "Odontadenia grandiflora" (No. 803) 3·25 80
1339 390 c. on 400 c. on $5 "Odontadenia grandiflora" (No. 1091) 4·00 90
1340 450 c. on $5 "Odontadenia grandiflora" (No. O16) 7·00 2·75
1351a 600 c. on $7.20 on $1 "Chelonanthus uliginoides" (No. 770) 75 75

1984. Various stamps optd **1984**.
1352 20 c. "Paphinia cristata" (No. 549) 22·00 10
1358 25 c. Marabunta (No. 550) 85·00 4·50
1359 25 c. Marabunta (No. F4) 4·25 50
1359a 25 c. Marabunta (No. F4a) 2·00 30
1354 50 c. on 8 c. Type **136** (No. 1062) 10·00 25
1355 60 c. on 1 c. Pitcher plant of Mt. Roraima (No. 1000) 65 25
1356 $2 "Norantea guianensis" (No. O33) 1·50 60
1360 $3.60 on $5 "Odontadenia grandiflora" (No. 769) 85 1·10

1984. No. 899 optd with fleur-de-lis.
1358a 25 c. Marabunta 85·00 4·50

1984. 40th Anniv of I.C.A.O. Nos. 981, 1017 and 1148/68 optd **ICAO** or as indicated.
1361 30 c. multicoloured (No. 1148) 60 60
1362 30 c. multicoloured (No. 1149) 60 60
1363 30 c. multicoloured (No. 1150) 60 60
1364 30 c. multicoloured (No. 1151) 60 60
1365 30 c. multicoloured (No. 1152) 60 60
1366 30 c. multicoloured (No. 1153) 60 60
1367 30 c. multicoloured (No. 1154) (optd **IMB/ICAO**) 60 60
1368 30 c. multicoloured (No. 1155) (optd **KCV/ICAO**) 60 60
1369 30 c. multicoloured (No. 1156) (optd **KAI/ICAO**) 60 60
1370 30 c. multicoloured (No. 1157) 60 60
1371 30 c. multicoloured (No. 1158) 60 60
1372 30 c. multicoloured (No. 1155) (optd **1984**) 60 60
1373 30 c. multicoloured (No. 1155) (optd **KPM/ICA**) 60 60
1374 30 c. multicoloured (No. 1159) 60 60
1375 30 c. multicoloured (No. 1160) 60 60
1376 30 c. multicoloured (No. 1161) 60 60
1377 30 c. multicoloured (No. 1155) (optd **PMT/ICAO**) 60 60
1378 30 c. multicoloured (No. 1162) 60 60
1379 30 c. multicoloured (No. 1163) 60 60
1380 30 c. multicoloured (No. 1164) 60 60
1381 30 c. multicoloured (No. 1165) 60 60
1382 30 c. multicoloured (No. 1166) 60 60
1383 30 c. multicoloured (No. 1167) 60 60
1384 30 c. multicoloured (No. 1168) 60 60
1385 200 c. on 330 c. on $2 multicoloured (No. 981) 65 70
1386 200 c. on 75 c. on $5 multicoloured (No. 1017) 2·25 1·75
No. 1385 also carries an otherwise unissued surch **G.A.C. Inaug. Flight Georgetown—Toronto 200**.

1984. Wildlife Protection. Nos. 756/67 optd **1984**.
1387 30 c. Type **178** 30 25
1388 30 c. Red howler 30 25
1389 30 c. Common squirrel-monkey 30 25
1390 30 c. Two-toed sloth 30 25
1391 30 c. Brazilian tapir 30 25
1392 30 c. Collared peccary 30 25
1393 30 c. Six-banded armadillo 30 25
1394 30 c. Tamandua ("Ant Eater") 30 25
1395 30 c. Giant anteater 30 25
1396 30 c. Murine opossum 30 25
1397 30 c. Brown four-eyed opossum 30 25
1398 30 c. Brazilian agouti 30 25

1984. Nos. D10/11 surch **120 GUYANA**.
1399 D **2** 120 c. on 4 c. blue 3·25 45
1402 120 c. on 12 c. red 3·25 45

1984. 175th Birth Anniv of Louis Braille (inventor of alphabet for the blind). No. 1040 surch **$1.50**.
1403 $1.50 on 15 c. on 10 c. Type **215** 6·50 55

1984. International Food Day. No. 1012 surch **1**.
1404 150 c. on 50 c. Pawpaw and tangerine 1·75 55
The surcharge places a "1" alongside the original face value and obliterates the "1982" date on the previous overprint.

1984. Birth Centenary of H. N. Critchlow (founder of Guyana Labour Union). No. 873 surch **240** and No. 1196, both optd **1984**.
1405 240 c. on 110 c. on $3 H. N. Critchlow (No. 873) 1·00 65
1406 240 c. on $3 H. N. Critchlow (No. 1196) 6·50 70

1984. Nos. 910/12 and 1184/7 surch.
1407 **277** 25 c. on 45 c. brown and black 15 15
1408 – 25 c. on 45 c. red and black (No. 1185) 15 15
1409 – 25 c. on 45 c. violet and black (No. 1186) 15 15
1410 – 25 c. on 45 c. green and black (No. 1187) 15 15
1411 – 120 c. on 100 c. on $3 mult (No. 910) 9·50 45
1412 – 120 c. on 400 c. on 30 c. mult (No. 911) 90 45
1413 – 320 c. on $5 multicoloured (No. 912) 17·00 1·75

1984. Deepavali Festival. Nos. 544/5 surch **MAHA SABHA 1934-1984** and new value.
1414 25 c. on 5 c. Annatto tree 30 10
1415 $1.50 on 3 c. Hanging heliconia 1·75 55

1984. A.S.D.A. Philatelic Exhibition, New York. Nos. 1188/91 optd **Philatelic Exhibition New York 1984**.
1416 **277** 120 c. brown and black 40 45
1417 – 130 c. red and black 45 50
1418 – 150 c. violet and black 50 55
1419 – 200 c. green and black 70 75

1984. Olympic Games, Los Angeles (3nd issue). Design as No. 1051, but with Olympic rings and inscr "OLYMPIC GAMES 1984 LOS ANGELES".
1420 $1.20 Youth display (41 × 25 mm) 1·50 45

1984. Nos. 847, 861, 1099 and 1088 surch.
1421 20 c. on 12 c. on 12 c. on 6 c. mult (No. 847) 60 10
1422 20 c. on 12 c. on 6 c. mult (No. 861) 65·00
1423 25 c. on 50 c. on 6 c. mult (No. 1099) 30 10
1424 60 c. on $1 on 6 c. mult (No. 1088) 45 25

318 Pair of Swallow-tailed Kites on Tree

1984. Christmas. Swallow-tailed Kites. Mult.
1425 60 c. Type **318** 3·00 1·75
1426 60 c. Swallow-tailed kite on branch 3·00 1·75
1427 60 c. Kite in flight with wings raised 3·00 1·75
1428 60 c. Kite in flight with wings lowered 3·00 1·75
1429 60 c. Kite gliding 3·00 1·75
Nos. 1425/9 were printed together, se-tenant, with the backgrounds forming a composite design. Each stamp is inscribed "CHRISTMAS 1982".

319 St. George's Cathedral, Georgetown

1985. Georgetown Buildings. Each black and stone.
1430 25 c. Type **319** 10 10
1431 60 c. Demerara Mutual Life Assurance Building 15 25
1432 120 c. As No. 1431 20 45
1433 120 c. Town Hall 20 45
1434 120 c. Victoria Law Courts 20 45
1435 200 c. As No. 1433 20 75
1436 300 c. As No. 1434 20 1·10
Nos. 1432/4 were printed together, se-tenant, forming a composite design.

1985. International Youth Year. No. 1420 optd **International Youth Year 1985**.
1437 $1.20 Youth display 2·00 45
Examples of No. 1420 used for this overprint all show the second line of the original inscription as "LOS ANGELLES".

1985. Republic Day. Nos. 1049/50 and 1052 optd or surch **Republic Day 1970–1985**.
1438 25 c. Type **238** 30 30
1439 25 c. Flag (inscr "30th ANNIVERSARY IN PARLIAMENT") 30 30
1440 120 c. on $6 Presidential standard 80 80
1441 130 c. on $6 Presidential standard 90 90

322 Young Ocelot on Branch

1985. Wildlife Protection. Multicoloured.
1442A 25 c. Type **322** (green background) 1·50 10
1443A 60 c. Young ocelot (different) (brown background) 30 25
1444B 120 c. As No. 1443 15 20
1445B 120 c. Type **322** 15 20
1446B 120 c. Young ocelot (different) (brown background) 15 20
1447A 130 c. As No. 1446 45 60
1448A 320 c. Scarlet macaw (28 × 46 mm) 3·00 1·50
1449A 330 c. Young ocelot reaching for branch (28 × 46 mm) 90 1·50

1985. Revenue stamp as T **181**, and Nos. 912, 940, 1016 and No. O24 surch.
1450 30 c. on 50 c. mult (No. O24) 50 10
1451 55 c. on 2 c. black, blue and grey 65 20
1452 55 c. on 15 c. on 2 c. black, blue and grey (940) 65 20
1453 90 c. on $1 mult (No. 1016) 5·00 30
1454 225 c. on $5 mult (No. 912) 8·50 90
1455 230 c. on $5 mult (No. 912) 8·50 95
1456 260 c. on $5 mult (No. 912) 8·50 1·00

1985. International Youth Year Save the Children Fund Campaign. Nos. 880, 1073a, 1079b and 1082 optd **International Youth Year 1985** or surch also.

1457 50 c. "Two Boys catching Ducks" (No. 1073a) . . . . 2·25 20
1458 50 c. on 10 c. Type **171** (No. 1082) . . . . 7·00 20
1459 120 c. on 125 c. on $3 "Mango Season" (No. 880) . . . 2·25 45
1460 $3 "Mango Season" (No. 1079b) . . . . 2·25 1·10

1985. 125th Anniv of British Guiana Post Office (1st issue). No. 699 surch **25** and names of post offices and postal agencies open in 1860.

1461 25 c. on 10 c. mult (**Airy Hall**) . 65 65
1462 25 c. on 10 c. multicoloured (**Belfield Arab Coast**) . . . 65 65
1463 25 c. on 10 c. multicoloured (**Belfield E. C. Dem.**) . . . 65 65
1464 25 c. on 10 c. mult (**Belladrum**) 65 65
1465 25 c. on 10 c. multicoloured (**Beterver-wagting**) 65 65
1466 25 c. on 10 c. multicoloured (**Blairmont Ferry**) 65 65
1467 25 c. on 10 c. mult (**Boeraserie**) 65 65
1468 25 c. on 10 c. mult (**Brahm**) . . 65 65
1469 25 c. on 10 c. mult (**Bushlot**) . 65 65
1470 25 c. on 10 c. mult (**De Kinderen**) 65 65
1471 25 c. on 10 c. multicoloured (**Fort Wellington**) 65 65
1472 25 c. on 10 c. mult (**Georgetown**) 65 65
1473 25 c. on 10 c. mult (**Hague**) . . 65 65
1474 25 c. on 10 c. mult (**Leguan**) . 65 65
1475 25 c. on 10 c. mult (**Mahaica**) . 65 65
1476 25 c. on 10 c. mult (**Mahaicony**) 65 65
1477 25 c. on 10 c. multicoloured (**New Amsterdam**) 65 65
1478 25 c. on 10 c. mult (**Plaisance**) 65 65
1479 25 c. on 10 c. multicoloured (**No. 6 Police Station**) 65 65
1480 25 c. on 10 c. mult (**Queenstown**) 65 65
1481 25 c. on 10 c. multicoloured (**Vergenoegen**) 65 65
1482 25 c. on 10 c. mult (**Vigilance**) 65 65
1483 25 c. on 10 c. multicoloured (**Vreed-en-Hoop**) 65 65
1484 25 c. on 10 c. mult (**Wakenaam**) 65 65
1485 25 c. on 10 c. multicoloured (**Windsor Castle**) 65 65

See also Nos. 1694/1717, 2140/64 and 2278/2301.

1985. I.T.U./W.H.O. Day. Nos. 1148/68 optd **1985** or with single capital letter.

1486 30 c. multicoloured (1148) . . 65 65
1487 30 c. multicoloured (1149) . . 65 65
1488 30 c. multicoloured (1150) . . 65 65
1489 30 c. multicoloured (1151) . . 65 65
1490 30 c. multicoloured (1152) . . 65 65
1491 30 c. multicoloured (1153) . . 65 65
1492 30 c. multicoloured (1154) (**I**) . 65 65
1493 30 c. multicoloured (1155) (**T**) . 65 65
1494 30 c. multicoloured (1156) (**U**) . 65 65
1495 30 c. multicoloured (1157) . . 65 65
1496 30 c. multicoloured (1158) . . 65 65
1497 30 c. multicoloured (1155) (**W**) . 65 65
1498 30 c. multicoloured (1155) (**H**) . 65 65
1499 30 c. multicoloured (1155) (**O**) . 65 65
1500 30 c. multicoloured (1159) . . 65 65
1501 30 c. multicoloured (1160) . . 65 65
1502 30 c. multicoloured (1161) (**D**) . 65 65
1503 30 c. multicoloured (1155) (**A**) . 65 65
1504 30 c. multicoloured (1162) (**Y**) . 65 65
1505 30 c. multicoloured (1163) . . 65 65
1506 30 c. multicoloured (1164) . . 65 65
1507 30 c. multicoloured (1165) . . 65 65
1508 30 c. multicoloured (1166) . . 65 65
1509 30 c. multicoloured (1167) . . 65 65
1510 30 c. multicoloured (1168) . . 65 65

1985. No. 861 surch **20**.

1511 20 c. on 12 c. on 6 c. Patua . . 3·00 10

1985. 10th Anniv of Caribbean Agricultural Research Development Institute. No. 544 surch **60 CARDI 1975-1985**.

1512 60 c. on 3 c. Hanging heliconia 1·75 25

1985. No. 839 surch **600**.

1513 600 c. on 625 c. on 40 c. Tiger beard . . . . 20·00 2·75

1985. 80th Anniv of Rotary International. Nos. 707 and 879 surch **ROTARY INTERNATIONAL 1905-1985**.

1514 120 c. on 110 c. on $3 Rotary anniversary emblem . . . . 11·00 45
1515 300 c. on $2 "Morpho rhetenor" . . . . 7·00 2·50

1985. CARICOM Day. No. 1200 surch **CARICOM DAY 1985 60**.

1516 60 c. on $3 "Makanaima the Great Ancestral Spirit of the Amerindians" 60 30

1985. 135th Anniv of First British Guiana Stamps. No. 870 surch **135th Anniversary Cotton Reel 1850-1985 120**.

1517 120 c. on 110 c. on 10 c. Type **170** 65 55

"REICHENBACHIA" ISSUES. Due to the proliferation of these designs the catalogue uses the book plate numbers as description for each design. The following index gives the species on each plate.

Series 1

Plate No. 1 (Series 1) "Odontoglossum crispum"
Plate No. 2 (Series 1) "Cattleya percivaliana"
Plate No. 3 (Series 1) "Cypripedium sanderianum"
Plate No. 4 (Series 1) "Odontoglossum rossi"
Plate No. 5 (Series 1) "Cattleya dowiana aurea"
Plate No. 6 (Series 1) "Coelogyne cristata maxima"
Plate No. 7 (Series 1) "Odontoglossum insleayi splendens"
Plate No. 8 (Series 1) "Laelia euspatha"
Plate No. 9 (Series 1) "Dendrobium wardianum"
Plate No. 10 (Series 1) "Laelia autumnalis xanthotropis"
Plate No. 11 (Series 1) "Phalaenopsis grandiflora aurea"
Plate No. 12 (Series 1) "Cattleya lawrenceana"
Plate No. 13 (Series 1) "Masdevallia shuttleworthii" and "M. xanthocorys"
Plate No. 14 (Series 1) "Aeranthus sesquipedalis"
Plate No. 15 (Series 1) "Cattleya mendelii Duke of Marlborough"
Plate No. 16 (Series 1) "Zygopetalum intermedium"
Plate No. 17 (Series 1) "Phaius humblotii"
Plate No. 18 (Series 1) "Chysis bractescens"
Plate No. 19 (Series 1) "Masdevallia backhousiana"
Plate No. 20 (Series 1) "Cattleya citrina"
Plate No. 21 (Series 1) "Oncidium jonesianum" and "Oncidium jonesianum phaeanthum"
Plate No. 22 (Series 1) "Saccolabium giganteum"
Plate No. 23 (Series 1) "Cypripedium io"
Plate No. 24 (Series 1) "Odontoglossum blandum"
Plate No. 25 (Series 1) "Maxillaria sanderiana"
Plate No. 26 (Series 1) "Odontoglossum Edward II"
Plate No. 27 (Series 1) "Vanda teres"
Plate No. 28 (Series 1) "Odontoglossum hallii xanthoglossum"
Plate No. 29 (Series 1) "Odontoglossum crispum hrubyanum"
Plate No. 30 (Series 1) "Oncidium concolor"
Plate No. 31 (Series 1) "Trichopilia suavis alba"
Plate No. 32 (Series 1) "Cattleya superba splendens"
Plate No. 33 (Series 1) "Odontoglossum luteo-purpureum"
Plate No. 34 (Series 1) "Cypripedium niveum"
Plate No. 35 (Series 1) "Stanhopea shuttleworthii"
Plate No. 36 (Series 1) "Laelia anceps percivaliana"
Plate No. 37 (Series 1) "Odontoglossum hebraicum"
Plate No. 38 (Series 1) "Cypripedium oenanthum superbum"
Plate No. 39 (Series 1) "Dendrobium superbiens"
Plate No. 40 (Series 1) "Laelia harpophylla"
Plate No. 41 (Series 1) "Lycaste skinneri" and "alba"
Plate No. 42 (Series 1) "Phalaenopsis stuartiana"
Plate No. 43 (Series 1) "Cattleya trianaei ernesti"
Plate No. 44 (Series 1) "Sobralia xantholeuca"
Plate No. 45 (Series 1) "Odontoglossum crispum kinlesideanum"
Plate No. 46 (Series 1) "Cattleya trianaei schroederiana"
Plate No. 47 (Series 1) "Epidendrum vitellinum"
Plate No. 48 (Series 1) "Laelia anceps stella" and "barkeriana"
Plate No. 49 (Series 1) "Odontoglossum harryanum"
Plate No. 50 (Series 1) "Dendrobium leechianum"
Plate No. 51 (Series 1) "Phalaenopsis speciosa"
Plate No. 52 (Series 1) "Laelia elegans schilleriana"
Plate No. 53 (Series 1) "Zygopetalum wendlandi"
Plate No. 54 (Series 1) "Cypripedium selligerum majus"
Plate No. 55 (Series 1) "Angraecum articulatum"
Plate No. 56 (Series 1) "Laelia anceps sanderiana"
Plate No. 57 (Series 1) "Vanda coerulea"
Plate No. 58 (Series 1) "Dendrobium nobile sanderianum"
Plate No. 59 (Series 1) "Laelia gouldiana"
Plate No. 60 (Series 1) "Odontoglossum grande"
Plate No. 61 (Series 1) "Cypripedium rothschildianum"
Plate No. 62 (Series 1) "Vanda sanderiana"
Plate No. 63 (Series 1) "Dendrobium aureum"
Plate No. 64 (Series 1) "Oncidium macranthum"
Plate No. 65 (Series 1) "Cypripedium tautzianum"
Plate No. 66 (Series 1) "Cymbidium mastersi"
Plate No. 67 (Series 1) "Angraecum caudatum"
Plate No. 68 (Series 1) "Laelia albida"
Plate No. 69 (Series 1) "Odontoglossum roezlii"
Plate No. 70 (Series 1) "Oncidium ampliatum majus"
Plate No. 71 (Series 1) "Renanthera lowii"
Plate No. 72 (Series 1) "Cattleya warscewiczii"
Plate No. 73 (Series 1) "Oncidium lanceanum"
Plate No. 74 (Series 1) "Vanda hookeriana"
Plate No. 75 (Series 1) "Cattleya labiata gaskelliana"
Plate No. 76 (Series 1) "Epidendrum prismatocarpum"
Plate No. 77 (Series 1) "Cattleya guttata leopoldi"
Plate No. 78 (Series 1) "Oncidium splendidum"
Plate No. 79 (Series 1) "Odontoglossum hebraicum aspersum"
Plate No. 80 (Series 1) "Cattleya dowiana var chrysotoxa"
Plate No. 81 (Series 1) "Cattleya trianae alba"
Plate No. 82 (Series 1) "Odontoglossum humeanum"
Plate No. 83 (Series 1) "Cypripedium argus"
Plate No. 84 (Series 1) "Odontoglossum luteo-purpureum prionopetalum"
Plate No. 85 (Series 1) "Cattleya rochellensis"
Plate No. 86 (Series 1) "Odontoglossum triumphans"
Plate No. 87 (Series 1) "Phalaenopsis casta"
Plate No. 88 (Series 1) "Oncidium tigrinum"
Plate No. 89 (Series 1) "Cypripedium lemoinierianum"
Plate No. 90 (Series 1) "Catasetum bungerothii"
Plate No. 91 (Series 1) "Cattleya ballantiniana"
Plate No. 92 (Series 1) "Dendrobium brymerianum"
Plate No. 93 (Series 1) "Cattleya eldorado crocata"
Plate No. 94 (Series 1) "Odontoglossum sanderianum"
Plate No. 95 (Series 1) "Cattleya labiata warneri"
Plate No. 96 (Series 1) "Odontoglossum schroderianum"

Series 2

Plate No. 1 (Series 2) "Cypripedium morganiae burfordiense"
Plate No. 2 (Series 2) "Cattleya bowringiana"
Plate No. 3 (Series 2) "Dendrobium formosum"
Plate No. 4 (Series 2) "Phaius tuberculosus"
Plate No. 5 (Series 2) "Odontoglossum crispum mundyanum"
Plate No. 6 (Series 2) "Laelia praestans"
Plate No. 7 (Series 2) "Dendrobium phalaenopsis var statterianum"
Plate No. 8 (Series 2) "Cypripedium boxalli atratum"
Plate No. 9 (Series 2) "Odontoglossum wattianum"
Plate No. 10 (Series 2) "Cypripedium lathamianum inversum"
Plate No. 11 (Series 2) "Paphinia rugosa" and "Zygopetalum xanthinum"
Plate No. 12 (Series 2) "Dendrobium melanodiscus"
Plate No. 13 (Series 2) "Laelia anceps schroderiana"
Plate No. 14 (Series 2) "Phaius hybridus cooksonii"
Plate No. 15 (Series 2) "Disa grandiflora"
Plate No. 16 (Series 2) "Selenipedium hybridum grande"
Plate No. 17 (Series 2) "Cattleya schroederae alba"
Plate No. 18 (Series 2) "Lycaste skinnerii armeniaca"
Plate No. 19 (Series 2) "Odontoglossum excellens"
Plate No. 20 (Series 2) "Laelio-cattleya elegans var blenheimensis"
Plate No. 21 (Series 2) "Odontoglossum coradinei"
Plate No. 22 (Series 2) "Odontoglossum wilckeanum var rothschildianum"
Plate No. 23 (Series 2) "Cypripedium lawrenceanum hyeanum"
Plate No. 24 (Series 2) "Cattleya intermedia punctatissima"
Plate No. 25 (Series 2) "Laelia purpurata"
Plate No. 26 (Series 2) "Masdevallia harryana splendens"
Plate No. 27 (Series 2) "Selenipedium hybridum nitidissimum"
Plate No. 28 (Series 2) "Cattleya mendelii var measuresiana"
Plate No. 29 (Series 20 "Odontoglossum vexillarium" ("miltonia vexillaria")
Plate No. 30 (Series 2) "Saccolabium coeleste"
Plate No. 31 (Series 2) "Cypripedium hybridum youngianum"
Plate No. 32 (Series 2) "Miltonia (hybrida) bleuana"
Plate No. 33 (Series 2) "Laelia grandis"
Plate No. 34 (Series 2) "Cattleya labiata var lueddemanniana"
Plate No. 35 (Series 2) "Odontoglossum coronarium"
Plate No. 36 (Series 2) "Cattleya granulosa var schofieldiana"
Plate No. 37 (Series 2) "Odontoglossum (hybridum) leroyanum"
Plate No. 38 (Series 2) "Cypripedium (hybridum) laucheanum" and "eyermanianum"
Plate No. 39 (Series 2) "Cychnoches chlorochilon"
Plate No. 40 (Series 2) "Cattleya O'Brieniana"
Plate No. 41 (Series 2) "Odontoglossum ramosissimum"
Plate No. 42 (Series 2) "Dendrobium phalaenopsis var"
Plate No. 43 (Series 2) "Cypripedium (hybridum) pollettianum" and "maynardii"
Plate No. 44 (Series 2) "Odontoglossum naevium"
Plate No. 45 (Series 2) "Cypripedium (hybridum) castleanum"
Plate No. 47 (Series 2) "Cattleya amethystoglossa"
Plate No. 48 (Series 2) "Cattleya (hybrida) arnoldiana"
Plate No. 49 (Series 2) "Cattleya labiata"
Plate No. 50 (Series 2) "Dendrobium (hybridum) venus" and "cassiope"
Plate No. 51 (Series 2) "Selenipedium (hybridum) weidlichianum"
Plate No. 52 (Series 2) "Cattleya mossiae var reineckiana"
Plate No. 53 (Series 2) "Cymbidium lowianum"
Plate No. 54 (Series 2) "Oncidium loxense"
Plate No. 56 (Series 2) "Coelogyne sanderae"
Plate No. 58 (Series 2) "Coelogyne pandurata"
Plate No. 59 (Series 2) "Schomburgkia sanderiana"
Plate No. 60 (Series 2) "Oncidium superbiens"
Plate No. 61 (Series 2) "Dendrobium johnsoniae"
Plate No. 62 (Series 2) "Laelia hybrida behrensiana"
Plate No. 63 (Series 2) Hybrid "Calanthes Victoria Regina", "Bella" and "Burfordiense"
Plate No. 64 (Series 2) "Cattleya mendelii Quorndon House var"
Plate No. 65 (Series 2) "Arachnanthe clarkei"
Plate No. 66 (Series 2) "Zygopetalum burtii"
Plate No. 67 (Series 2) "Cattleya (hybrida) parthenia"
Plate No. 68 (Series 2) "Phalaenopsis sanderiana" and "intermedia portei"
Plate No. 69 (Series 2) "Phaius blumei var assamicus"
Plate No. 70 (Series 2) "Angraecum humblotii"
Plate No. 71 (Series 2) "Odontoglossum pescatorei"
Plate No. 72 (Series 2) "Cattleya rex"
Plate No. 73 (Series 2) "Zygopetalum crinitum"
Plate No. 74 (Series 2) "Cattleya lueddemanniana alba"
Plate No. 75 (Series 2) "Cymbidium (hybridum) winnianum"
Plate No. 76 (Series 2) Hybrid "Masdevallias courtauldiana", "geleniana" and "measuresiana"
Plate No. 77 (Series 2) "Cypripedium (hybridum) calypso"
Plate No. 78 (Series 2) "Masdevallia chimaera var mooreana"
Plate No. 79 (Series 2) "Miltonia phalaenopsis"
Plate No. 80 (Series 2) "Lissochilus giganteus"
Plate No. 82 (Series 2) "Thunia brymeriana"
Plate No. 83 (Series 2) "Miltonia moreliana"
Plate No. 84 (Series 2) "Oncidium kramerianum"
Plate No. 85 (Series 2) "Cattleya Victoria Regina"
Plate No. 86 (Series 2) "Zygopetalum klabochorum"
Plate No. 87 (Series 2) "Laelia autumnalis alba"
Plate No. 88 (Series 2) "Spathoglottis kimballiana"
Plate No. 89 (Series 2) "Laelio-cattleya" ("The Hon. Mrs. Astor")
Plate No. 90 (Series 2) "Phaius hybridus amabilis" and "marthiae"
Plate No. 91 (Series 2) "Zygopetalum rostratum"
Plate No. 92 (Series 2) "Coelogyne swaniana"
Plate No. 93 (Series 2) "Laelio-cattleya (hybrida) phoebe"
Plate No. 94 (Series 2) "Epidendrum atro-purpureum var randianum"
Plate No. 95 (Series 2) "Dendrobium imperatrix"
Plate No. 96 (Series 2) "Vanda parishii var marriottiana"

331 "Cattleya lawrenceana" (Plate No. 12 (Series 1))

1985. Centenary of Publication of Sanders' "Reichenbachia" (1st issue). Orchids. Mult.

1518 25 c. Type **331** 50 30
1519 60 c. Plate No. 2 (Series 1) . . 60 35
1520 60 c. Plate No. 7 (Series 1) . . 60 35
1521 60 c. Plate No. 10 (Series 1) . . 60 35
1522 60 c. Plate No. 19 (Series 1) . . 60 35
1523 60 c. Plate No. 31 (Series 1) . . 60 35
1524 120 c. Plate No. 27 (Series 1) . 75 55
1525 130 c. Plate No. 3 (Series 1) . 75 55
1759 130 c. Plate No. 6 (Series 1) . 75 20
1760 130 c. Plate No. 13 (Series 1) . 75 20
1528 130 c. Plate No. 18 (Series 1) . 2·50 55
1761 130 c. Plate No. 20 (Series 1) . 75 20
1762 130 c. Plate No. 25 (Series 1) . 75 20
1531 130 c. Plate No. 29 (Series 1) . 1·75 55
1532 130 c. Plate No. 30 (Series 1) . 1·75 55
1533 200 c. Plate No. 4 (Series 1) . 1·75 85

See also Nos. 1551/66, 1571/1806, 1597, 1620/1863, 1663/73, 1679/83, 1731/8, 1747/54, 1809/19, 1822, 1868/9, 1872/81, 1884/7, 1907, 1912/15, 1916/24, 1925/9, 2066/73, 2171/8, 2180/2, 2190/3, 2216/18, 2219/20, 2225/7, 2235/42, 2314/18, 2322/5, 2328, 2314/18, 2322/5, 2329/31, 2468/71, 2498/2511 and 2605/8.

332 Arms of Guyana

337 Leaders of the 1763 Rebellion

1985.

1535b **332** 25 c. multicoloured . . 15 20

For Type **332** within frame, see No. 2183.

1985. 85th Birthday of Queen Elizabeth the Queen Mother (1st issue). Nos. 1528 and 1531/2 optd **QUEEN MOTHER 1900-1985**.

1536 130 c. Plate No. 18 (Series 1) . 75 80
1537 130 c. Plate No. 29 (Series 1) . 75 80
1538 130 c. Plate No. 30 (Series 1) . 75 80

1985. International Youth Year. Nos. 900/4 surch **25 International Youth Year 1985**.

1540 25 c. on 110 c. on 5 c. multicoloured (900) 15 15
1541 25 c. on 110 c. on 5 c. multicoloured (901) 15 15
1542 25 c. on 110 c. on 5 c. multicoloured (902) 50 50
1543 25 c. on 110 c. on 5 c. multicoloured (903) 50 50
1544 25 c. on 100 c. on 5 c. multicoloured (904) . . . . 3·50 3·50

1985. 75th Anniv of Girl Guide Movement. No. 612 surch **225 1910-1985**.

1545 225 c. on 350 c. on 225 c. on 40 c. Guides in camp . . . 28·00 2·00

No. 1545 also carries two otherwise unissued surcharges at top right.

1985. Birth Bicentenary of John J. Audubon (ornithologist). No. 992 surch **J. J. Audubon 1785-1985 240**.

1546 240 c. on 35 c. Harpy eagle . . 21·00 2·25

1985. 150th Anniv (1984) of Abolition of Slavery (1st issue).

1547 **337** 25 c. black and grey . . . 25 10
1548 – 60 c. black and mauve . . 20 25
1549 – 130 c. black and blue . . 25 50
1550 – 150 c. black and lilac . . 60 55

DESIGNS: 60 c. Damon and Parliament Buildings, Georgetown; 130 c. Quamina and Demerara, 1823; 150 c. "Den Arendt" (slave ship), 1627.

For these designs in changed colours see Nos. 2552/5.

1985. Centenary of Publication of Sanders' "Reichenbachia" (2nd issue). As T **331** showing orchids. Multicoloured.
1551 25 c. Plate No. 52 (Series 1) . 80 25
1763 55 c. Plate No. 9 (Series 1) . . 55 10
1764 55 c. Plate No. 22 (Series 1) . 55 10
1765 55 c. Plate No. 49 (Series 1) . 55 10
1766 55 c. Plate No. 64 (Series 1) . 55 10
1556 60 c. Plate No. 44 (Series 1) . 70 35
1557 60 c. Plate No. 47 (Series 1) . 70 35
1558 120 c. Plate No. 36 (Series 1) . 1·25 55
1559 130 c. Plate No. 16 (Series 1) . 1·25 55
1560 130 c. Plate No. 38 (Series 1) . 1·25 55
1561 150 c. Plate No. 32 (Series 1) . 1·25 55
1562 150 c. Plate No. 34 (Series 1) . 1·25 55
1563 150 c. Plate No. 35 (Series 1) . 1·25 55
1564 150 c. Plate No. 41 (Series 1) . 1·25 55
1565 150 c. Plate No. 48 (Series 1) . 1·25 55
1566 150 c. Plate No. 62 (Series 1) . 1·25 55

1985. Signing of Guyana—Libya Friendship Treaty. No. 621 surch **Guyana/Libya Friendship 1985 150.**
1567 **149** 150 c. on 10 c. multi . . . 9·00 2·75

1985. Namibia Day. No. 636 surch **150**.
1568 150 c. on 35 c. Unveiling of monument . . . . 2·75 55

1985. World Cup Football Championship, Mexico (1986) (1st issue). No. F2 surch **Mexico 1986 275**.
1569 275 c. on 3 c. Hanging heliconia 6·50 1·10
See also No. 1727.

1985. Centenary of Publication of Sanders' "Reichenbachia" (3rd issue). As T **331** showing orchids. Multicoloured.
1571 25 c. Plate No. 8 (Series 1) . . 1·00 20
1572 25 c. Plate No. 23 (Series 1) . 1·00 20
1573 25 c. Plate No. 51 (Series 1) . 1·00 20
1574 25 c. Plate No. 61 (Series 1) . 1·00 20
1575 25 c. Plate No. 63 (Series 1) . 1·00 20
1576 25 c. Plate No. 70 (Series 1) . 1·00 20
1577 25 c. Plate No. 72 (Series 1) . 1·00 20
1578 120 c. Plate No. 1 (Series 1) (horiz) . . . . 1·25 55
1579 120 c. Plate No. 11 (Series 1) (horiz) . . . . 1·25 55
1580 120 c. Plate No. 28 (Series 1) (horiz) . . . . 1·25 55
1767 150 c. Plate No. 40 (Series 1) (horiz) 45 20
1768 150 c. Plate No. 42 (Series 1) (horiz) 45 20
1769 150 c. Plate No. 45 (Series 1) (horiz) 45 20
1584 200 c. Plate No. 14 (Series 1) . 1·50 80
1585 200 c. Plate No. 21 (Series 1) (horiz) . . . . 1·50 80
1770 200 c. Plate No. 43 (Series 1) (horiz) 55 30

1985. 30th Anniv of Commonwealth Caribbean Medical Research Council. Nos. 819, 871, 874, 928 and 1014 optd **1955–1985** or surch also.
1587 – 60 c. mult (No. 819) . . . 20 25
1588 – 60 c. multi (No. 1014) . . 20 25
1589 **176** 120 c. on 110 c. on 10 c. multicoloured (No. 871) 40 45
1590 – 120 c. on 110 c. on $3 mult (No. 874) 40 45
1592 – 120 c. on 210 c. on $3 mult (No. 928) 40 45

1985. 20th Anniv of Guyana Defence Force. No. 856 surch **1965–1985**.
1593 25 c. on $1.10 on $3 W.O. and N.C.O; Guyana Defence Force, 1966 . . . . 1·00 10
1594 225 c. on $1.10 on $3 W.O. and N.C.O; Guyana Defence Force, 1966 . . . . 2·50 1·25

1985. Fire Prevention. Nos. 678 and 680 optd **1985** and surch.
1595 25 c. on 40 c. Fire engine, 1977 8·00 20
1596 320 c. on 15 c. Steam engine, circa 1860 . . . . 15·00 3·75

1985. Centenary of Publication of Sanders' "Reichenbachia" (4th issue). As T **331**. Mult.
1597 60 c. Plate No. 55 (Series 1) . 1·00 30

1985. Columbus Day. Unissued value as T **331** surch **350 CRISTOBAL COLON 1492–1992.** Mult.
1598 350 c. on 120 c. Plate No. 65 (Series 1) . . . . 4·50 2·50

1985. 20th Death Anniv of Sir Winston Churchill. No. 707 optd **SIR WINSTON CHURCHILL 1965–1985.**
1599 $2 "Morpho rhetenor" (female) . . . . 8·00 1·60

1985. 35th Anniv of International Commission of Irrigation and Drainage. No. 625 with unissued surcharge further surch **1950–1985**.
1600 **150** 25 c. on 110 c. on 10 c. multicoloured 30 10
1601 200 c. on 110 c. on 10 c. multicoloured . . . . 1·25 85

1985. 40th Anniv of U.N.O. Nos. 714/16, 800 and O19 optd **United Nations 1945–1985.**
1602 30 c. mult (No. 714) . . . . 1·75 10
1603 50 c. mult (No. 715) . . . . 1·75 20
1604 100 c. on $3 mult (No. O19) . 1·50 40
1605 225 c. on 220 c. on $3 mult (No. 800) . . . . 8·00 75
1606 $3 mult (No. 716) . . . . . . 3·50 1·75

1985. Nos. 551/3, O14/15, O18, O21, OP1/2 and F7 optd **POSTAGE**.
1607 30 c. on $2 "Norantea guianensis" (No. O18) . . . 40 10
1608 40 c. Tiger beard (No. 551) . . 32·00 40
1609 50 c. "Guzmania lingulata" (No. 552) 40 20
1610 50 c. "Guzmania lingulata" (No. O14) 40 20
1611 60 c. Soldier's cap (No. 553) . 3·00 25
1612 60 c. Soldier's cap (No. O15) . 2·75 25
1613 60 c. Soldier's cap (No. F7) . . 1·50 25
1614 $10 "Elbella patrobas" (No. O21) . . . . 17·00 5·50
1615 $15 on $1 "Chelonanthus uliginoides" (No. OP1) . . 8·00 9·00
1616 $20 on $1 "Chelonanthus uliginoides" (No. OP2) . . 9·00 11·00

1985. Deepavali Festival. Nos. 542/3 surch **Deepavali 1985**.
1617 25 c. on 2 c. Type **132** 20 10
1618 150 c. on 1 c. Pitcher plant of Mt. Roraima . . . . . . 1·40 55

1985. Centenary of Publication of Sanders' "Reichenbachia" (5th issue). As T **331** showing orchids. Multicoloured.
1620 25 c. Plate No. 59 (Series 1) . 75 20
1771 30 c. Plate No. 53 (Series 1) . 30 10
1622 60 c. Plate No. 57 (Series 1) (horiz) 90 35
1623 60 c. Plate No. 73 (Series 1) (horiz) 90 35
1624 60 c. Plate No. 75 (Series 1) (horiz) 90 35
1772 75 c. Plate No. 55 (Series 1) . 35 15
1773 100 c. Plate No. 65 (Series 1) . 35 15
1627 120 c. Plate No. 37 (Series 1) . 1·50 55
1628 120 c. Plate No. 46 (Series 1) . 1·50 55
1629 120 c. Plate No. 56 (Series 1) . 1·50 55
1630 120 c. Plate No. 58 (Series 1) . 1·50 55
1631 120 c. Plate No. 67 (Series 1) . 1·50 55
1632 130 c. Plate No. 66 (Series 1) . 1·60 65
1633 150 c. Plate No. 26 (Series 1) . 1·75 75
1634 200 c. Plate No. 33 (Series 1) (horiz) . . . . 2·00 85
1774 225 c. Plate No. 24 (Series 1) . 45 35
The 30, 75, 100 and 225 c. values have "GUYANA" in blue.

351 Clive Lloyd (cricketer)

1985. Clive Lloyd's Testimonial Year. Multicoloured.
1636 25 c. Type **351** 40 60
1637 25 c. Clive Lloyd, bat and wicket 40 60
1638 25 c. Cricket equipment . . . 40 60
1639 60 c. As No. 1638 (25 × 33 mm) 45 40
1640 $1.30 As No. 1637 (25 × 33 mm) 50 85
1641 $2.25 Type **351** (25 × 33 mm) . 60 1·25
1642 $3.50 Clive Lloyd with the Prudential Cup (36 × 56 mm) 65 1·75

1985. Wildlife Protection. Nos. 756/67 optd **1985**.
1643 30 c. Type **178** 75 75
1644 30 c. Red howler 75 75
1645 30 c. Common squirrel-monkey 75 75
1646 30 c. Two-toed sloth 75 75
1647 30 c. Brazilian tapir 75 75
1648 30 c. Collared peccary 75 75
1649 30 c. Six-banded armadillo . . 75 75
1650 30 c. Tamandua 75 75
1651 30 c. Giant anteater 75 75
1652 30 c. Murine opossum 75 75
1653 30 c. Brown four-eyed opossum 75 75
1654 30 c. Brazilian agouti 75 75

1985. No. 847 surch **20**.
1655 20 c. on 12 c. on 12 c. on 6 c. Black acara ("Patua") . . . 1·75 15

1986. Centenary of the Appearance of "Reichenbachia" Volume 1. Nos. 1768 and 1770 optd **REICHENBACHIA 1886–1986.**
1657 150 c. Plate No. 42 (Series 1) . 2·50 60
1658 200 c. Plate No. 43 (Series 1) . 2·50 75

1986. Republic Day. Nos. 1108/9 and 1052 optd **Republic Day 1986** or surch also.
1659 25 c. As Type **258** 10 10
1660 25 c. As No. 1050 . . . . . 10 10
1661 120 c. on $6 Presidential standard 40 45
1662 225 c. on $6 Presidential standard 70 75

1986. Centenary of Publication of Sanders' "Reichenbachia" (6th issue). As T **331**. Mult.
1663 40 c. Plate No. 77 (Series 1) . 55 20
1664 45 c. Plate No. 54 (Series 1) . 55 25
1665 50 c. Plate No. 92 (Series 1) . 55 25
1666 60 c. Plate No. 95 (Series 1) . 60 30
1667 75 c. Plate No. 5 (Series 1) . 65 35
1668 90 c. Plate No. 84 (Series 1) . 75 40
1669 150 c. Plate No. 78 (Series 1) . 95 60
1670 200 c. Plate No. 79 (Series 1) . 1·25 80
1671 300 c. Plate No. 83 (Series 1) . 1·75 1·25
1672 320 c. Plate No. 50 (Series 1) . 1·75 1·40
1673 360 c. Plate No. 85 (Series 1) . 1·90 1·50

1986. Easter. No. 481 optd **1986** and surch also.
1674 **111** 25 c. on 6 c. mult . . . 35 10
1675 50 c. on 6 c. mult . . . 50 20
1676 100 c. on 6 c. mult . . . 75 40
1677 200 c. on 6 c. mult . . . 1·50 70

1986. 60th Anniv of St. John's Ambulance in Guyana. No. 652 surch **1926 1986 150**.
1678 150 c. on 35 c. silver, black and green . . . . 3·00 55

1986. Centenary of Publication of Sanders' "Reichenbachia" (7th issue). As T **331**. Mult.
1679 25 c. Plate No. 71 (Series 1) (horiz) 60 20
1680 120 c. Plate No. 69 (Series 1) (horiz) . . . . 1·50 55
1681 150 c. Plate No. 87 (Series 1) (horiz) . . . . 1·75 65
1682 225 c. Plate No. 60 (Series 1) . 1·75 90
1683 350 c. Plate No. 94 (Series 1) (horiz) . . . . 2·25 1·50

1986. 60th Birthday of Queen Elizabeth II. No. 1760 optd **1926 1986 QUEEN ELIZABETH**.
1684 130 c. Plate No. 13 (Series 1) . 1·50 50

1986. Wildlife Protection. Nos. 685, 739/44 and 993/8 surch **Protect the** and value.
1686 60 c. on 35 c. Type **174** . . . 35 35
1687 60 c. on 35 c. Trahira ("Haimara") 35 35
1688 60 c. on 35 c. Electric eel . . 35 35
1689 60 c. on 35 c. Golden rivulus 35 35
1690 60 c. on 35 c. Golden pencilfish 35 35
1691 60 c. on 35 c. Four-eyed fish 35 35
1691a 60 c. on 35 c. Red piranha ("Pirai") . . . . 5·50 2·00
1691b 60 c. on 35 c. Smoking hassar 5·50 2·00
1691c 60 c. on 35 c. Manta . . . . 5·50 2·00
1691d 60 c. on 35 c. Festive cichlid ("Flying patwa") . . . . 5·50 2·00
1691e 60 c. on 35 c. Arapaima . . . 5·50 2·00
1691f 60 c. on 35 c. Peacock cichlid ("Lukanani") . . . . . . 5·50 2·00
1692 $6 on 8 c. Type **163** . . . . 3·00 2·50

1986. No. 799 surch **600**.
1693 600 c. on 720 c. on 60 c. Soldier's cap . . . . 10·00 75

1986. 125th Anniv of British Guiana Post Office (2nd issue). No. 702a surch **25** and names of postal agencies opened between 1860 and 1880.
1694 25 c. on 30 c. mult (surch **Abary**) 60 60
1695 25 c. on 30 c. multicoloured (surch **Anna Regina**) 60 60
1696 25 c. on 30 c. multicoloured (surch **Aurora**) 60 60
1697 25 c. on 30 c. multicoloured (surch **Bartica Grove**) . . . 60 60
1698 25 c. on 30 c. multicoloured (surch **Bel Air**) 60 60
1699 25 c. on 30 c. multicoloured (surch **Belle Plaine**) 60 60
1700 25 c. on 30 c. multicoloured (surch **Clonbrook**) 60 60
1701 25 c. on 30 c. multicoloured (surch **T.P.O. Dem. Railway**) 60 60
1702 25 c. on 30 c. multicoloured (surch **Enmore**) 60 60
1703 25 c. on 30 c. multicoloured (surch **Fredericksburg**) . . . 60 60
1704 25 c. on 30 c. multicoloured (surch **Good Success**) . . . 60 60
1705 25 c. on 30 c. mult (surch **1986**) 60 60
1706 25 c. on 30 c. multicoloured (surch **Mariabba**) 60 60
1707 25 c. on 30 c. multicoloured (surch **Massaruni**) 60 60
1708 25 c. on 30 c. mult (surch **Nigg**) 60 60
1709 25 c. on 30 c. multicoloured (surch **No. 50**) 60 60
1710 25 c. on 30 c. multicoloured (surch **No. 63 Benab**) . . . 60 60
1711 25 c. on 30 c. multicoloured (surch **Philadelphia**) 60 60
1712 25 c. on 30 c. multicoloured (surch **Sisters**) 60 60
1713 25 c. on 30 c. multicoloured (surch **Skeldon**) 60 60
1714 25 c. on 30 c. multicoloured (surch **Suddie**) 60 60
1715 25 c. on 30 c. multicoloured (surch **Taymouth Manor**) . . 60 60
1716 25 c. on 30 c. mult (surch **Wales**) 60 60
1717 25 c. on 30 c. mult (surch **Whim**) 60 60

1986. 20th Anniv of Independence. (a) No. 332 of British Guiana surch **GUYANA INDEPENDENCE 1966–1986**, Nos. 424 and 435 of Guyana surch **1986** and No. 656 surch **25**.
1718 25 c. on 2 c. green (No. 332) . 15 10
1719 25 c. on 35 c. mult (No. 656) . 15 10
1720 60 c. on 2 c. green (No. 332) . 25 10
1721 120 c. on 6 c. green (No. 424) 40 20
1722 130 c. on 24 c. black and orange (No. 435) . . . . 4·75 30

(b) Nos. 1188/91 surch **INDEPENDENCE 1966–1986.**
1723 **277** 25 c. on 120 c. brown, black and blue (No. 1188) . . 25 20
1724 – 25 c. on 130 c. red, black and blue (No. 1189) . . 25 20
1725 – 25 c. on 150 c. violet and blue (No. 1190) 25 20
1726 – 225 c. on 200 c. green, black and blue (No. 1191) . . 65 60

1986. World Cup Football Championship, Mexico (2nd issue). No. 544 surch **MEXICO 1986 225**.
1727 225 c. on 3 c. Hanging heliconia 8·50 70

1986. CARICOM Day. No. 705a optd **CARICOM DAY 1986**.
1728 60 c. "Papilio androgeus" . . 6·00 30

1986. CARICOM Heads of Government Conference, Georgetown. Nos. 544 and 601 surch **CARICOM HEADS OF GOV'T CONFERENCE JULY 1986** and value.
1729 25 c. on 8 c. on 6 c. Cannon-ball tree . . . . 1·25 10
1730 60 c. on 3 c. Hanging heliconia 1·75 25

1986. Centenary of Publication of Sanders' "Reichenbachia" (8th issue). As T **331**. Mult.
1731 30 c. Plate No. 86 (Series 1) . 50 15
1732 55 c. Plate No. 17 (Series 1) . 50 20
1733 60 c. Plate No. 93 (Series 1) . 50 20
1734 100 c. Plate No. 68 (Series 1) . 1·00 20
1735 130 c. Plate No. 91 (Series 1) . 1·10 30
1736 250 c. Plate No. 74 (Series 1) . 75 60
1737 260 c. Plate No. 39 (Series 1) . 75 60
1738 375 c. Plate No. 90 (Series 1) . 2·25 85

1986. International Peace Year. Nos. 542 and 546 surch **INT. YEAR OF PEACE** and value.
1739 25 c. on 1 c. Pitcher plant of Mt. Roraima 20 20
1740 60 c. on 6 c. Cannon-ball tree 50 50
1741 120 c. on 6 c. Cannon-ball tree 50 50
1742 130 c. on 6 c. Cannon-ball tree 50 50
1743 150 c. on 6 c. Cannon-ball tree 50 50

363 Halley's Comet and British Guiana 1907 2 c. Stamp

1986. Appearance of Halley's Comet.
1744 **363** 320 c. red, black and lilac 30 50
1745 – 320 c. multicoloured . . . 30 50
DESIGN: No. 1745, Guyana 1985 320 c. scarlet macaw stamp.

1986. Centenary of Publication of Sanders' "Reichenbachia" (9th issue). As T **331**. Mult.
1747 40 c. Plate No. 96 (Series 1) . 90 15
1748 45 c. Plate No. 81 (Series 1) . 30 15
1749 90 c. Plate No. 89 (Series 1) . 50 20
1750 100 c. Plate No. 88 (Series 1) . 1·50 20
1751 150 c. Plate No. 76 (Series 1) . 1·75 35
1752 180 c. Plate No. 15 (Series 1) . 50 40
1753 320 c. Plate No. 82 (Series 1) . 60 70
1754 330 c. Plate No. 80 (Series 1) . 1·75 90

1986. No. 489 surch **20**.
1755 20 c. on 6 c. Patua . . . . . 3·75 15

1986. 50th Anniv of Guyana United Sadr Islamic Association. Nos. 469/70 optd **GUSIA 1936–1986**, No. 1757 surch also.
1756 **105** 25 c. black, gold and lilac 1·50 10
1757 $1.50 on 6 c. black, gold and flesh . . . . 3·00 80

1986. Regional Pharmacy Conference. No. 545 surch **REGIONAL PHARMACY CONFERENCE 1986 130**.
1758 130 c. on 5 c. Annatto tree . . 4·50 30

1986. Centenary of Publication of Sanders' "Reichenbachia" (10th issue). As T **331**. Mult.
1809 30 c. Plate No. 30 (Series 2) . 50 15
1810 45 c. Plate No. 21 (Series 2) (horiz) 50 15
1811 75 c. Plate No. 8 (Series 2) . . 50 15
1812 80 c. Plate No. 42 (Series 2) (horiz) 50 15
1813 90 c. Plate No. 4 (Series 2) . . 55 25
1814 130 c. Plate No. 38 (Series 2) . 1·50 35
1815 160 c. Plate No. 5 (Series 2) (horiz) . . . . 1·75 40
1816 200 c. Plate No. 9 (Series 2) . 75 50
1817 320 c. Plate No. 12 (Series 2) . 1·50 70
1818 350 c. Plate No. 29 (Series 2) (horiz) . . . . 1·75 70
1819 360 c. Plate No. 34 (Series 2) 3·00 70

1986. 20th Anniv of Independence (2nd issue). As T **332** but additionally inscr "1966–1986" at foot.
1820 25 c. multicoloured 20 25

1986. Centenary of Publication of Sanders' "Reichenbachia" (11th issue). Design as No. 1735, but with different face value. Mult.
1822 40 c. Plate No. 91 (Series 1) . 75 15

1986. Nos. 1361/84 surch **120**.
1823 120 c. on 30 c. mult (No. 1361) 90 90
1824 120 c. on 30 c. mult (No. 1362) 90 90
1825 120 c. on 30 c. mult (No. 1363) 90 90
1826 120 c. on 30 c. mult (No. 1364) 90 90
1827 120 c. on 30 c. mult (No. 1365) 90 90
1828 120 c. on 30 c. mult (No. 1366) 90 90
1829 120 c. on 30 c. mult (No. 1367) 90 90
1830 120 c. on 30 c. mult (No. 1368) 90 90
1831 120 c. on 30 c. mult (No. 1369) 90 90
1832 120 c. on 30 c. mult (No. 1370) 90 90
1833 120 c. on 30 c. mult (No. 1371) 90 90
1834 120 c. on 30 c. mult (No. 1372) 90 90
1835 120 c. on 30 c. mult (No. 1373) 90 90
1836 120 c. on 30 c. mult (No. 1374) 90 90
1837 120 c. on 30 c. mult (No. 1375) 90 90
1838 120 c. on 30 c. mult (No. 1376) 90 90
1839 120 c. on 30 c. mult (No. 1377) 90 90
1840 120 c. on 30 c. mult (No. 1378) 90 90
1841 120 c. on 30 c. mult (No. 1379) 90 90
1842 120 c. on 30 c. mult (No. 1380) 90 90
1843 120 c. on 30 c. mult (No. 1381) 90 90
1844 120 c. on 30 c. mult (No. 1382) 90 90
1845 120 c. on 30 c. mult (No. 1383) 90 90
1846 120 c. on 30 c. mult (No. 1384) 90 90

1986. 12th World Orchid Conference, Tokyo (1st issue). Unissued design as No. 1731, but with different face value, surch **12th World Orchid Conference TOKYO JAPAN MARCH 1987 650**.
1847 650 c. on 40 c. Plate No. 86 (Series 1) . . . . 8·50 3·75
No. 1847 is inscribed "ONTOGLOSSUM TRIUMPHANS" in error.
See also No. 2138.

1986. Columbus Day. Unissued design as No. 1774, but with different face value, surch **1492-1992 CHRISTOPHER COLUMBUS 320**.
1864 320 c. on 150 c. Plate No. 24 (Series 1) . . . . 2·50 90

1986. International Food Day. Nos. 1170/1 further surch **1986** and value.
1866 50 c. on 30 c. on 1 c. Type **87** . 1·50 15
1867 225 c. on $2.60 on 3 c. Peacock cichlid ("Lukunani") . . . 4·50 75

1986. Centenary of Publication of Sanders' "Reichenbachia" (12th issue). As T **331**, one as No. 1731 with different face value. Mult.
1868 40 c. Plate No. 86 (Series 1) . 50 15
1869 90 c. Plate No. 10 (Series 2) . 75 30

1986. Air. 40th Annivs of U.N.I.C.E.F. and U.N.E.S.C.O. No. 706 surch.
1870 120 c. on $1 "Agrias claudina" (surch **UNICEF 1946–1986 AIR 120**) . . . . 3·75 3·75
1871 120 c. on $1 "Agrias claudina" (surch **UNESCO 1946–1986 AIR 120**) . . . . 7·50 7·50

1986. Centenary of Publication of Sanders' "Reichenbachia" (13th issue). As T **331**. Mult.
1872 45 c. Plate No. 17 (Series 2) . 30 15
1873 50 c. Plate No. 33 (Series 2) . 30 15
1874 60 c. Plate No. 27 (Series 2) . 45 15
1875 75 c. Plate No. 56 (Series 2) . 55 20
1876 85 c. Plate No. 45 (Series 2) . 2·00 20
1877 90 c. Plate No. 13 (Series 2) . 70 20
1878 200 c. Plate No. 44 (Series 2) . 1·00 45
1879 300 c. Plate No. 50 (Series 2) . 1·50 60
1880 320 c. Plate No. 10 (Series 2) . 1·50 70
1881 390 c. Plate No. 6 (Series 2) . 1·50 95

1986. Deepavali Festival. Nos. 543 and 601 surch **Deepavali 1986** and value.
1882 25 c. on 2 c. Type **132** 75 10
1883 200 c. on 8 c. on 6 c. Cannon-ball tree . . . . 2·25 40

1986. Centenary of Publication of Sanders' "Reichenbachia" (14th issue). As T **331**, two as Nos. 1732 and 1734 with different face values. Multicoloured.
1884 40 c. Plate No. 68 (Series 1) . 1·25 15
1885 80 c. Plate No. 17 (Series 1) . 2·00 25
1886 200 c. Plate No. 2 (Series 2) . 1·40 60
1887 225 c. Plate No. 24 (Series 2) . 1·40 70

1986. Christmas. No. 489 surch **CHRISTMAS 1986 20**.
1888 20 c. on 6 c. Black acara ("Patua") . . . . 1·25 10

1986. Wildlife Protection. Nos. 756/67 optd **1986.**
1894 30 c. Type **178** 90 90
1895 30 c. Red howler 90 90
1896 30 c. Common squirrel-monkey 90 90
1897 30 c. Two-toed sloth 90 90
1898 30 c. Brazilian tapir 90 90
1899 30 c. Collared peccary 90 90
1900 30 c. Six-banded armadillo . . . 90 90
1901 30 c. Tamandua 90 90
1902 30 c. Giant anteater 90 90
1903 30 c. Murine opossum 90 90
1904 30 c. Brown four-eyed opossum 90 90
1905 30 c. Brazilian agouti 90 90

1986. No. 1642 surch **$15.**
1906 $15 on $3.50 Clive Lloyd with Prudential Cup . . . . . . 22·00 13·00

1986. Centenary of Publication of Sanders' "Reichenbachia" (15th issue). Design as No. 1877, but with different face value. Mult.
1907 50 c. Plate No. 13 (Series 2) . 65 15

375 Memorial

1986. President Burnham Commemoration. Multicoloured.
1908 25 c. Type **375** 10 10
1909 120 c. Map of Guyana and flags 20 20
1910 130 c. Parliament Buildings and mace 20 20
1911 $6 L. F. Burnham and Georgetown mayoral chain (vert) . 60 1·25

1986. Centenary of Publication of Sanders' "Reichenbachia" (16th issue). As Nos. 1765/6, 1874 and 1887 but with different face values. Multicoloured.
1912 50 c. Plate No. 49 (Series 1) . 75 20
1913 50 c. Plate No. 64 (Series 1) . 75 20
1914 85 c. Plate No. 24 (Series 2) . 75 35
1915 90 c. Plate No. 27 (Series 2) . 1·50 35

1986. Centenary of Publication of Sanders' "Reichenbachia" (17th issue). As T **331**. Mult.
1916 25 c. Plate No. 20 (Series 2) . 35 15
1917 40 c. Plate No. 7 (Series 2) . . 35 15
1918 85 c. Plate No. 15 (Series 2) . 50 20
1919 90 c. Plate No. 3 (Series 2) . . 50 20
1920 120 c. Plate No. 14 (Series 2) . 50 30
1921 130 c. Plate No. 32 (Series 2) . 50 30
1922 150 c. Plate No. 22 (Series 2) . 60 35
1923 320 c. Plate No. 18 (Series 2) . 80 55
1924 330 c. Plate No. 28 (Series 2) . 80 70

1987. Centenary of Publication of Sanders' "Reichenbachia" (18th issue). As Nos. 1772, 1876, 1886, 1918 and 1923 but with different face values. Multicoloured.
1925 35 c. Plate No. 45 (Series 2) . 40 15
1926 50 c. Plate No. 15 (Series 2) . 40 15
1927 50 c. Plate No. 55 (Series 1) . 40 15
1928 85 c. Plate No. 18 (Series 2) . 1·25 25
1929 90 c. Plate No. 2 (Series 2) . . . 50 25

1987. 10th Anniv of Guyana Post Office Corporation (1st issue). Unissued designs as Nos. 1771 and 1774, but with different face values, surch or optd **G P O C 1977 – 1987.**
1930 $2.25 Plate No. 53 (Series 1) . 1·50 35
1931 $10 on 150 c. Plate No. 24 (Series 1) . . . . 4·00 4·50
See also Nos. 2074/80.

1987. Various "Reichenbachia" issues surch.
2375 120 c. on 40 c. Plate No. 91 (Series 1) (No. 1822) . . . 60 40
2380 120 c. on 40 c. Plate No. 90 (Series 1) 60 40
2387 120 c. on 50 c. Plate No. 9 (Series 1) 60 40
1994 120 c. on 50 c. Plate No. 49 (Series 1) (No. 1912) . . . 50 40
1995 120 c. on 50 c. Plate No. 64 (Series 1) (No. 1913) . . . 50 40
2388 120 c. on 50 c. Plate No. 22 (Series 1) 60 40
2389 120 c. on 50 c. Plate No. 3 (Series 2) 60 40
2390 120 c. on 50 c. Plate No. 6 (Series 2) 60 40
2391 120 c. on 50 c. Plate No. 20 (Series 2) 60 40
2392 120 c. on 50 c. Plate No. 32 (Series 2) 60 40
2019 120 c. on 50 c. Plate No. 24 (Series 1) 50 40
2020 120 c. on 50 c. Plate No. 53 (Series 1) 50 40
2021 120 c. on 50 c. Plate No. 65 (Series 1) 50 40
1980 120 c. on 55 c. Plate No. 9 (Series 1) (No. 1763) . . . 50 40
2003 120 c. on 55 c. Plate No. 49 (Series 1) (No. 1765) . . . 50 40
1981 120 c. on 55 c. Plate No. 64 (Series 1) (No. 1766) . . . 50 30
2006 120 c. on 55 c. Plate No. 22 (Series 1) (No. 1764) . . . 50 40
2009 120 c. on 55 c. Plate No. 15 (Series 1) 50 40
2010 120 c. on 55 c. Plate No. 81 (Series 1) 50 40
2011 120 c. on 55 c. Plate No. 82 (Series 1) 50 40
2012 120 c. on 55 c. Plate No. 89 (Series 1) 50 40
2394 120 c. on 60 c. Plate No. 2 (Series 1) (No. 1519) . . . 60 30
2027 120 c. on 60 c. Plate No. 10 (Series 1) (No. 1521) . . . 50 40
2028 120 c. on 60 c. Plate No. 19 (Series 1) (No. 1522) . . . 50 40
2029 120 c. on 60 c. Plate No. 31 (Series 1) (No. 1523) . . . 50 40
2030 120 c. on 60 c. Plate No. 5 (Series 1) 50 40
2403 120 c. on 60 c. Plate No. 50 (Series 1) 60 40
2404 120 c. on 60 c. Plate No. 54 (Series 1) 60 40
2405 120 c. on 60 c. Plate No. 69 (Series 1) 60 40
2034 120 c. on 60 c. Plate No. 71 (Series 1) 50 40
2406 120 c. on 60 c. Plate No. 79 (Series 1) 60 40
2036 120 c. on 60 c. Plate No. 87 (Series 1) 50 40
2407 120 c. on 60 c. Plate No. 94 (Series 1) 60 40
2038 120 c. on 75 c. Plate No. 60 (Series 1) 50 40
2039 120 c. on 75 c. Plate No. 83 (Series 1) 50 40
2040 120 c. on 75 c. Plate No. 92 (Series 1) 50 40
2041 120 c. on 75 c. Plate No. 95 (Series 1) 50 40
1933 200 c. on 25 c. Plate No. 8 (Series 1) (No. 1571) . . . 60 50
1934 200 c. on 25 c. Plate No. 51 (Series 1) (No. 1573) . . . 60 50
1949 200 c. on 25 c. Plate No. 52 (Series 1) (No. 1551) . . . 60 50
1951 200 c. on 25 c. Plate No. 72 (Series 1) (No. 1577) . . . 60 50
1952 200 c. on 25 c. Plate No. 71 (Series 1) (No. 1679) . . . 60 50
1953 200 c. on 30 c. Plate No. 86 (Series 1) (No. 1731) . . . 60 50
1954 200 c. on 30 c. Plate No. 53 (Series 1) (No. 1771) . . . 60 50
1932 200 c. on 40 c. Plate No. 90 (Series 1) 60 50
1937 200 c. on 40 c. Plate No. 68 (Series 1) (No. 1884) . . . 60 50
1955 200 c. on 40 c. Plate No. 77 (Series 1) (No. 1663) . . . 60 50
1956 200 c. on 40 c. Plate No. 86 (Series 1) (No. 1868) . . . 60 50
1957 200 c. on 45 c. Plate No. 81 (Series 1) (No. 1748) . . . 60 50
1958 200 c. on 45 c. Plate No. 77 (Series 1) 60 50
1959 200 c. on 45 c. Plate No. 78 (Series 1) 60 50
1960 200 c. on 45 c. Plate No. 85 (Series 1) 60 50
2044 200 c. on 45 c. Plate No. 84 (Series 1) 50 40
1939 200 c. on 50 c. Plate No. 92 (Series 1) (No. 1665) . . . 60 50
1940 200 c. on 50 c. Plate No. 22 (Series 1) 60 50
1961 200 c. on 50 c. Plate No. 24 (Series 1) 60 50
1962 200 c. on 50 c. Plate No. 53 (Series 1) 60 50
1963 200 c. on 50 c. Plate No. 65 (Series 1) 60 50
2046 200 c. on 50 c. Plate No. 55 (Series 1) (No. 1927) . . . 90 50
1941 200 c. on 55 c. Plate No. 22 (Series 1) (No. 1764) . . . 60 50
1964 200 c. on 55 c. Plate No. 49 (Series 1) (No. 1765) . . . 60 50
1965 200 c. on 55 c. Plate No. 17 (Series 1) (No. 1732) . . . 60 50
2050 200 c. on 55 c. Plate No. 15 (Series 1) . . . . 2·00 50
2051 200 c. on 55 c. Plate No. 81 (Series 1) . . . . 2·00 50
2052 200 c. on 55 c. Plate No. 82 (Series 1) . . . . 5·00 50
2053 200 c. on 55 c. Plate No. 89 (Series 1) . . . . 2·00 50
1942 200 c. on 60 c. Plate No. 5 (Series 1) 60 50
1967 200 c. on 60 c. Plate No. 7 (Series 1) (No. 1520) . . . 60 50
1968 200 c. on 60 c. Plate No. 10 (Series 1) (No. 1521) . . . 60 50
1969 200 c. on 60 c. Plate No. 19 (Series 1) (No. 1522) . . . 60 50
1970 200 c. on 60 c. Plate No. 31 (Series 1) (No. 1523) . . . 60 50
1971 200 c. on 60 c. Plate No. 44 (Series 1) (No. 1556) . . . 60 50
1972 200 c. on 60 c. Plate No. 47 (Series 1) (No. 1557) . . . 60 50
1973 200 c. on 60 c. Plate No. 57 (Series 1) (No. 1622) . . . 60 50
1974 200 c. on 60 c. Plate No. 73 (Series 1) (No. 1623) . . . 60 50
1975 200 c. on 60 c. Plate No. 75 (Series 1) (No. 1624) . . . 60 50
1976 200 c. on 60 c. Plate No. 71 (Series 1) 60 50
1977 200 c. on 60 c. Plate No. 87 (Series 1) 60 50
1943 200 c. on 75 c. Plate No. 5 (Series 1) (No. 1667) . . . 60 50
1944 200 c. on 75 c. Plate No. 60 (Series 1) 60 50
1945 200 c. on 75 c. Plate No. 92 (Series 1) 60 50
1946 200 c. on 85 c. Plate No. 18 (Series 2) (No. 1928) . . . 60 50
1947 200 c. on 375 c. Plate No. 90 (Series 1) (No. 1738) . . . 60 50
1987 225 c. on 40 c. Plate No. 91 (Series 1) (No. 1822) . . . 70 60
1988 225 c. on 40 c. Plate No. 90 (Series 1) 70 60
2055 225 c. on 40 c. Plate No. 86 (Series 1) (No. 1868) . . . 1·25 60
2056 225 c. on 40 c. Plate No. 68 (Series 1) (No. 1884) . . . 90 60
1988a 225 c. on 50 c. Plate No. 92 (Series 1) (No. 1665) . . . 10·00 3·00
1989 225 c. on 50 c. Plate No. 22 (Series 1) 70 60
1990 225 c. on 60 c. Plate No. 55 (Series 1) (No. 1597) . . . 70 60
1990a 225 c. on 60 c. Plate No. 95 (Series 1) (No. 1666) . . . 10·00 3·00
1991 225 c. on 60 c. Plate No. 93 (Series 1) (No. 1733) . . . 70 60
2058 225 c. on 65 c. Plate No. 76 (Series 1) 90 60
2059 225 c. on 65 c. Plate No. 80 (Series 1) 90 60
2060 225 c. on 65 c. Plate No. 88 (Series 1) 90 60
2061 225 c. on 65 c. Plate No. 96 (Series 1) 90 60
1992 225 c. on 80 c. Plate No. 93 (Series 1) 70 60
1978 225 c. on 90 c. Plate No. 89 (Series 1) (No. 1749) . . . 65 55
1993 225 c. on 150 c. Plate No. 42 (Series 1) (No. 1657) . . . 70 60
2062 600 c. on 80 c. Plate No. 17 (Series 1) (No. 1885) . . . 1·50 1·50
2063 600 c. on 80 c. Plate No. 39 (Series 1) . . . . 1·50 1·50
2064 600 c. on 80 c. Plate No. 74 (Series 1) . . . . 1·50 1·50
2065 600 c. on 80 c. Plate No. 93 (Series 1) . . . . 1·50 1·50

1987. Nos. 1518 and 1572 surch **TWO DOLLARS**.
1935 $2 on 25 c. Plate No. 12 (Series 1) (No. 1518) . . . 60 50
1936 $2 on 25 c. Plate No. 23 (Series 1) (No. 1572) . . . 60 50

1987. Various "Reichenbachia" issues surch. **1987**.
1983 $10 on 25 c. Plate No. 53 (Series 1) . . . . 2·00 2·25
1984 $12 on 80 c. Plate No. 74 (Series 1) . . . . 2·25 2·50
1985 $15 on 80 c. Plate No. 39 (Series 1) . . . . 2·75 3·00
1986 $25 on 25 c. Plate No. 53 (Series 1) . . . . 4·50 5·00

1987. Centenary of Publication of Sanders' "Reichenbachia" (19th issue). Multicoloured.
2066 180 c. Plate 41 (Series 2) . . . 75 40
2067 230 c. Plate 25 (Series 2) . . . 80 50
2068 300 c. Plate 85 (Series 2) . . . 3·00 65
2069 330 c. Plate 82 (Series 2) . . . 3·25 70
2070 425 c. Plate 87 (Series 2) . . . 3·25 85
2071 440 c. Plate 88 (Series 2) . . . 3·25 85
2072 590 c. Plate 52 (Series 2) . . . 1·50 1·25
2073 650 c. Plate 65 (Series 2) . . . 1·75 1·50

1987. 10th Anniv of Guyana Post Office Corporation (2nd issue). Nos. 543, 545, 548a and 601 surch **Post Office Corp. 1977-1987**.
2074 25 c. on 2 c. Type **132** 15 10
2075 25 c. on 5 c. Annatto tree . . . 15 10
2076 25 c. on 8 c. on 6 c. Cannon-ball tree 15 10
2077 25 c. on 15 c. Christmas orchid 1·75 10
2078 60 c. on 15 c. Christmas orchid 3·25 15
2079 $1.20 on 2 c. Type **132** 75 75
2080 $1.30 on 15 c. Christmas orchid 3·50 1·25

1987. No. 1535b surch **1987 200.**
2081 **332** 200 c. on 25 c. mult . . . 1·00 1·00

1987. Various "Reichenbachia" issues optd **1987**.
2112 120 c. Plate No. 1 (Series 1) (No. 1578) . . . . 2·00 60
2113 120 c. Plate No. 11 (Series 1) (No. 1579) . . . . 1·50 60
2114 120 c. Plate No. 28 (Series 1) (No. 1580) . . . . 2·00 60
2115 120 c. Plate No. 37 (Series 1) (No. 1627) . . . . 1·00 60
2116 120 c. Plate No. 46 (Series 1) (No. 1628) . . . . 4·50 60
2117 120 c. Plate No. 56 (Series 1) (No. 1629) . . . . 1·50 60
2118 120 c. Plate No. 58 (Series 1) (No. 1630) . . . . 1·50 60
2132 120 c. Plate No. 67 (Series 1) (No. 1631) 50 40
2084 130 c. Plate No. 3 (Series 1) (No. 1525) 50 40
2093 130 c. Plate No. 6 (Series 1) (No. 1759) 50 40
2094 130 c. Plate No. 20 (Series 1) (No. 1761) 50 40
2087 130 c. Plate No. 18 (Series 1) (No. 1536) 50 40
2088 130 c. Plate No. 29 (Series 1) (No. 1537) 50 40
2089 130 c. Plate No. 30 (Series 1) (No. 1538) 50 40
2090 130 c. Plate No. 16 (Series 1) (No. 1559) 50 40
2091 130 c. Plate No. 66 (Series 1) (No. 1632) 50 40
2092 130 c. Plate No. 13 (Series 1) (No. 1684) 50 40
2109 130 c. Plate No. 91 (Series 1) (No. 1735) 50 40
2111 130 c. Plate No. 25 (Series 1) (No. 1762) 50 40
2123 150 c. Plate No. 40 (Series 1) (No. 1767) . . . . 1·25 70
2124 150 c. Plate No. 45 (Series 1) (No. 1769) . . . . 1·00 70
2125 150 c. Plate No. 42 (Series 1) (No. 1657) . . . . 3·00 70
2137 150 c. Plate No. 26 (Series 1) (No. 1633) 50 50
2095 200 c. Plate No. 4 (Series 1) (No. 1533) 60 50
2096 200 c. Plate No. 14 (Series 1) (No. 1584) 60 50
2097 200 c. Plate No. 21 (Series 1) (No. 1585) 60 50
2098 200 c. Plate No. 33 (Series 1) (No. 1634) 60 50
2099 200 c. Plate No. 43 (Series 1) (No. 1658) 60 50
2100 200 c. Plate No. 79 (Series 1) (No. 1670) 60 50
2101 200 c. Plate No. 9 (Series 2) (No. 1816) 60 50
2102 200 c. Plate No. 2 (Series 2) (No. 1886) 60 50
2103 250 c. Plate No. 74 (Series 1) (No. 1736) 70 60
2104 260 c. Plate No. 39 (Series 1) (No. 1737) 70 60

1987. 12th World Orchid Conference, Tokyo (2nd issue). Nos. 1763 surch **12th World Orchid Conference 650**.
2138 650 c. on 55 c. Plate No. 9 (Series 1) . . . . 4·25 2·75

1987. 125th Anniv of British Guiana Post Office (3rd issue). No. 699 surch **25** and names of postal agencies opened by 1885.
2140 25 c. on 10 c. multicoloured (surch **AGRICOLA**) . . . 70 40
2141 25 c. on 10 c. multicoloured (surch **BAGOTVILLE**) . . 70 40
2142 25 c. on 10 c. multicoloured (surch **BOURDA**) 70 40
2143 25 c. on 10 c. multicoloured (surch **BUXTON**) 70 40
2144 25 c. on 10 c. multicoloured (surch **CABACABURI**) . . 70 40
2145 25 c. on 10 c. mult (surch **CARMICHAEL STREET**) 70 40
2146 25 c. on 10 c. mult (surch **COTTON TREE**) 70 40
2147 25 c. on 10 c. multicoloured (surch **DUNOON**) 70 40
2148 25 c. on 10 c. multicoloured (surch **FELLOWSHIP**) . . 70 40
2149 25 c. on 10 c. multicoloured (surch **GROVE**) 70 40
2150 25 c. on 10 c. multicoloured (surch **HACKNEY**) 70 40
2151 25 c. on 10 c. multicoloured (surch **LEONORA**) 70 40
2152 25 c. on 10 c. mult (surch **1987**) 70 40
2153 25 c. on 10 c. multicoloured (surch **MALLALI**) 70 40
2154 25 c. on 10 c. multicoloured (surch **PROVIDENCE**) . . 70 40
2155 25 c. on 10 c. multicoloured (surch **RELIANCE**) 70 40
2156 25 c. on 10 c. multicoloured (surch **SPARTA**) 70 40
2157 25 c. on 10 c. multicoloured (surch **STEWARTVILLE**) . 70 40
2158 25 c. on 10 c. multicoloured (surch **TARLOGY**) 70 40
2159 25 c. on 10 c. mult (surch **T.P.O. BERBICE RIV.**) 70 40
2160 25 c. on 10 c. multicoloured (surch **T.P.O. DEM. RIV.**) . 70 40
2161 25 c. on 10 c. multicoloured (surch **T.P.O. ESSEO. RIV.**) 70 40
2162 25 c. on 10 c. mult (surch **T.P.O. MASSARUNI RIV.**) . . . 70 40

2163 25 c. on 10 c. multicoloured (surch **TUSCHEN (De VRIENDEN)**) 70 40
2164 25 c. on 10 c. multicoloured (surch **ZORG**) 70 40

1987. 50th Anniv of First Georgetown to Port-of-Spain Flight by P.A.A. No. 708a optd **28 MARCH 1927 PAA GEO-POS**.
2165 $10 "Elbella patrobas" . . . 10·00 5·50

1987. No. 704 surch **25**.
2166 25 c. on 40 c. "Morpho rhetenor" (male) . . . . . 5·00 10

1987. Easter. Nos. 481/2 and 484 optd **1987** or surch also.
2167 **111** 25 c. multicoloured . . . 40 10
2168 120 c. on 6 c. mult . . . 60 20
2169 320 c. on 6 c. mult . . . 90 55
2170 500 c. on 40 c. mult . . . 1·50 90

1987. Centenary of Publication of Sanders' "Reichenbachia" (20th issue). As T **331**. Mult.
2171 240 c. Plate No. 47 (Series 2) . 80 45
2172 260 c. Plate No. 39 (Series 2) . 90 55
2173 275 c. Plate No. 58 (Series 2) (horiz) 90 55
2174 390 c. Plate No. 37 (Series 2) (horiz) . . . . 1·10 70
2175 450 c. Plate No. 19 (Series 2) (horiz) . . . . 1·50 90
2176 460 c. Plate No. 54 (Series 2) (horiz) . . . . 1·50 90
2177 500 c. Plate No. 51 (Series 2) . 1·75 1·10
2178 560 c. Plate No. 1 (Series 2) . 2·00 1·50

1987. No. 706 optd **1987**.
2179 **167** $1 multicoloured . . . . 4·00 15

1987. Centenary of Publication of Sanders' "Reichenbachia" (21st issue). As T **331**. Mult.
2180 500 c. Plate No. 86 (Series 2) . 1·50 1·10
2181 520 c. Plate No. 89 (Series 2) . 1·50 1·25
2182 $20 Plate No. 83 (Series 2) . . 4·50 7·00

1987. As T **332** but within frame.
2183 25 c. multicoloured 30 30
2184 25 c. multicoloured 30 30
No. 2183 has a bird with a short tail (as in Type **332**) in the lower part of the arms; No. 2184 has a bird with crest and long tail.

1987. "Capex '87" International Stamp Exhibition, Toronto. Nos. 1744/5 optd **CAPEX '87**.
2185 **363** 320 c. red, black & lilac . 1·00 1·25
2186 – 320 c. multicoloured . . . 1·00 1·25

1987. Commonwealth Heads of Government Meeting, Vancouver. Nos. 1066/8 further optd **1987**.
2187 $1.20 on 6 c. green 45 20
2188 $1.30 on 24 c. black & orange 3·25 30
2189 $2.40 on 24 c. black & orange 4·75 1·25

1987. Centenary of Publication of Sanders' "Reichenbachia" (22nd issue). As T **331**. Mult.
2190 400 c. Plate No. 80 (Series 2) . 1·25 80
2191 480 c. Plate No. 77 (Series 2) . 1·50 1·00
2192 600 c. Plate No. 94 (Series 2) . 1·50 1·50
2193 $25 Plate No. 72 (Series 2) . . 4·50 8·00

396 Steam Locomotive No. 4 "Alexandra"

1987. Guyana Railways.
2194 **396** $1.20 green 25 30
2195 – $1.20 green 25 30
2196 – $1.20 green 25 30
2197 – $1.20 green 25 30
2198 **396** $1.20 purple 25 30
2199 – $1.20 purple 25 30
2200 – $1.20 purple 25 30
2201 – $1.20 purple 25 30
2202 **396** $3.20 blue 80 90
2203 – $3.20 blue 80 90
2204 – $3.20 blue 80 90
2205 – $3.20 blue 80 90
2206 – $3.20 blue 80 90
2207 – $3.30 black 80 90
2208 **396** $3.30 black 80 90
2209 – $3.30 black 80 90
2210 – $3.30 black 80 90
2211 – $3.30 black 80 90
2212 – $10 multicoloured . . . 60 1·50
2213 – $12 multicoloured . . . 60 1·75
DESIGNS:—As T **396**: Nos. 2195, 2199, 2203, 2207, Front view of diesel locomotive; Nos. 2196, 2200, 2204, 2210, Steam locomotive with searchlight; Nos. 2197, 2201, 2205, 2209, Side view of diesel locomotive No. 21. (82 × 55 mm): No. 2206, Molasses warehouses and early locomotive; No. 2211, Diesel locomotive and passenger train. (88 × 39 mm): No. 2212, Cattle train and Parika–Rosignol Railway route map; No. 2213, Molasses train and Parika–Rosignol Railway route map.

1987. 50th Anniv of First Flights from Georgetown to Massaruni and Mabaruma. No. 706 optd.
2214 $1 multicoloured (optd **FAIREY NICHOLL 8 AUG 1927 GEO-MAZ**) . . . . . . 5·00 5·00
2215 $1 multicoloured (optd **FAIREY NICHOLL 15 AUG 1927 GEO-MAB**) . . . . . . 5·00 5·00

1987. Centenary of Publication of Sanders' "Reichenbachia" (23rd issue). As T **331**. Mult.
2216 200 c. Plate No. 43 (Series 2) . 2·50 80
2217 200 c. Plate No. 48 (Series 2) . 2·50 80
2218 200 c. Plate No. 92 (Series 2) . 2·50 80

1987. Centenary of Publication of Sanders' "Reichenbachia" (24th issue). No. 2219 surch **600**. Multicoloured.
2219 600 c. on 900 c. Plate No. 74 (Series 2) . . . . 2·25 2·50
2220 900 c. Plate No. 74 (Series 2) . 2·25 2·50

1987. Columbus Day.
2221 225 c. on 350 c on 120 c. Plate No. 65 (Series 1) (No. 1598 further surch **225**) 75 40
2222 950 c. on 900 c. Plate No. 74 (Series 2) (No. 2220 surch **950 CRISTOVAO COLOMBO 1492 – 1992**) . . . . . . 1·75 2·25
2223 950 c. on 900 c. Plate No. 74 (Series 2) (No. 2220 surch **950 CHRISTOPHE COLOMB 1492 – 1992**) . . . . 1·75 2·25

1987. Centenary of Publication of Sanders' "Reichenbachia" (25th issue). As T **331**. Mult.
2225 325 c. Plate No. 68 (Series 2) (horiz) . . . . 1·50 90
2226 420 c. Plate No. 95 (Series 2) (horiz) . . . . 1·75 1·25
2227 575 c. Plate No. 60 (Series 2) . 4·50 2·25

1987. Deepavali Festival. Nos. 544/5 surch **DEEPAVALI 1987** and new value.
2228 25 c. on 3 c. Hanging heliconia 50 10
2229 $3 on 5 c. Annatto tree . . . 2·00 85

1987. Christmas. No. 489 surch **CHRISTMAS 1987 20**.
2230 20 c. on 6 c. Black acara ("Patua") . . . . 1·00 10

1987. Royal Ruby Wedding. No. 1684 optd **1987**.
2233 130 c. Plate No. 13 (Series 1) . 1·75 30

1987. Centenary of Publication of Sanders' "Reichenbachia" (26th issue). As T **331**. Mult.
2235 255 c. Plate No. 61 (Series 2) . 2·75 1·25
2236 290 c. Plate No. 53 (Series 2) . 2·75 1·50
2237 375 c. Plate No. 96 (Series 2) . 2·00 1·60
2238 680 c. Plate No. 64 (Series 2) . 6·00 2·50
2239 720 c. Plate No. 49 (Series 2) . 7·00 4·00
2240 750 c. Plate No. 66 (Series 2) . 3·00 4·00
2241 800 c. Plate No. 79 (Series 2) . 3·00 4·50
2242 850 c. Plate No. 76 (Series 2) . 3·00 4·50

1987. Air. No. 1620 surch **AIR 75**.
2243 75 c. on 25 c. Plate No. 59 (Series 1) . . . . 3·75 50

1987. Wildlife Protection. Nos. 756/67 optd **1987**, Nos. 1432/4 surch **Protect our Heritage '87 320** and Nos. 1631/3, 1752/3 and 1847 optd **PROTECT OUR HERITAGE '87**.
2244 30 c. Type **178** 20 15
2245 30 c. Red howler 20 15
2246 30 c. Common squirrel-monkey 20 15
2247 30 c. Two-toed sloth 20 15
2248 30 c. Brazilian tapir 20 15
2249 30 c. Collared peccary 20 15
2250 30 c. Six-banded armadillo . . 20 15
2251 30 c. Tamandua 20 15
2252 30 c. Giant anteater 20 15
2253 30 c. Murine opossum 20 15
2254 30 c. Brown four-eyed opossum 20 15
2255 30 c. Brazilian agouti 20 15
2256 120 c. Plate No. 67 (Series 1) . 50 30
2257 130 c. Plate No. 66 (Series 1) . 50 30
2258 150 c. Plate No. 26 (Series 1) . 55 35
2259 180 c. Plate No. 15 (Series 1) . 60 40
2260 320 c. Plate No. 82 (Series 1) . 80 60
2261 320 c. on 120 c. Demerara Mutual Life Assurance Building 80 80
2262 320 c. on 120 c. Town Hall . . 80 80
2263 320 c. on 120 c. Victoria Law Courts 80 80
2264 650 c. on 40 c. Plate No. 86 (Series 1) . . . . 2·00 2·00

1987. Air. Various "Reichenbachia" issues optd **AIR**.
2265 60 c. Plate No. 55 (Series 1) (No. 1597) . . . . 3·50 4·00
2463 75 c. Plate No. 55 (Series 1) (No. 1772) 90 55
2464 75 c. Plate No. 5 (Series 1) (No. 1667) 90 55
2466 75 c. Plate No. 83 (Series 1) . 90 55
2467 75 c. Plate No. 95 (Series 1) . 90 55

1988. World Scout Jamboree, Australia. No. 837a optd **AUSTRALIA 1987 JAMBOREE 1988** and Nos. 830, 837a and 1104 surch **$10 AUSTRALIA 1987 JAMBOREE 1988**.
2266 **116** 440 c. on 6 c. mult (No. 837a) . . . . 3·75 30
2267 $10 on 110 c. on 6 c. mult (No. 830) 75 70
2268 $10 on 180 c. on 6 c. mult (No. 1104) 75 70
2269a $10 on 440 c. on 6 c. mult (No. 837a) 75 70

1988. 10th Anniv of International Fund for Agricultural Development. Nos. 448 and 450 surch **IFAD For a World Without Hunger**.
2270 25 c. on 1 c. Type **87** 50 10
2271 $5 on 3 c. Lukunani . . . . . 2·25 1·00

1988 Republic Day. Nos. 545, 548a and 555 surch **Republic Day 1988**.
2272 25 c. on 5 c. Annatto tree . . 10 10
2273 120 c. on 15 c. Christmas orchid 2·25 50
2274 $10 on $2 "Noranthea guianensis" . . . . . . 2·50 2·50

1988. Centenary of Publication of Sanders' "Reichenbachia" (28th series). As T **331**. Multicoloured.
2276 $10 Plate No. 40 (Series 2) . . 1·50 2·00
2277 $12 Plate No. 91 (Series 2) . . 1·50 2·00

1988. 125th Anniv of British Guiana Post Office (4th issue). No. 702a surch **25** and names of postal agencies opened between 1886 and 1900.
2278 25 c. on 30 c. multicoloured (surch **Albouystown**) 70 50
2279 25 c. on 30 c. multicoloured (surch **Anns Grove**) 70 50
2280 25 c. on 30 c. multicoloured (surch **Amacura**) 70 50
2281 25 c. on 30 c. multicoloured (surch **Arakaka**) 70 50
2282 25 c. on 30 c. multicoloured (surch **Baramanni**) 70 50
2283 25 c. on 30 c. multicoloured (surch **Cuyuni**) 70 50
2284 25 c. on 30 c. multicoloured (surch **Hope Placer**) 70 50
2285 25 c. on 30 c. multicoloured (surch **H M P S**) 70 50
2286 25 c. on 30 c. mult (surch **Kitty**) 70 50
2287 25 c. on 30 c. multicoloured (surch **M'M'Zorg**) 70 50
2288 25 c. on 30 c. multicoloured (surch **Maccaseema**) 70 50
2289 25 c. on 30 c. mult (surch **1988**) 70 50
2290 25 c. on 30 c. multicoloured (surch **Morawhanna**) . . . 70 50
2291 25 c. on 30 c. multicoloured (surch **Naamryck**) 70 50
2292 25 c. on 30 c. mult (surch **Purini**) 70 50
2293 25 c. on 30 c. multicoloured (surch **Potaro Landing**) . . 70 50
2294 25 c. on 30 c. multicoloured (surch **Rockstone**) 70 50
2295 25 c. on 30 c. multicoloured (surch **Rosignol**) 70 50
2296 25 c. on 30 c. multicoloured (surch **Stanleytown**) 70 50
2297 25 c. on 30 c. multicoloured (surch **Santa Rosa**) 70 50
2298 25 c. on 30 c. multicoloured (surch **Tumatumari**) 70 50
2299 25 c. on 30 c. multicoloured (surch **Weldaad**) 70 50
2300 25 c. on 30 c. multicoloured (surch **Wismar**) 70 50
2301 25 c. on 30 c. mult (surch **TPO Berbice Railway**) 70 50

1988. Olympic Games, Seoul (1st issue). Nos. 1206/17 further surch **120 Olympic Games 1988**.
2302 120 c. on 55 c. on 125 c. on 35 c. Type **174** . . . . 1·00 1·00
2303 120 c. on 35 c. on 125 c. on 35 c. Trahira ("Haimara") . . . 1·00 1·00
2304 120 c. on 55 c. on 125 c. on 35 c. Electric eel . . . . 1·00 1·00
2305 120 c. on 55 c. on 125 c. on 35 c. Golden rivulus . . . . . . 1·00 1·00
2306 120 c. on 55 c. on 125 c. on 35 c. Golden pencilfish . . . . . 1·00 1·00
2307 120 c. on 55 c. on 125 c. on 35 c. Four-eyed fish . . . . . . 1·00 1·00
2308 120 c. on 55 c. on 125 c. on 35 c. Red piranha ("Pirai") . . . 1·00 1·00
2309 120 c. on 55 c. on 125 c. on 35 c. Smoking hassar . . . . . 1·00 1·00
2310 120 c. on 55 c. on 125 c. on 35 c. Manta . . . . 1·00 1·00
2311 120 c. on 55 c. on 125 c. on 35 c. Festive cichlid ("Flying patwa") . . . . 1·00 1·00
2312 120 c. on 55 c. on 125 c. on 35 c. Arapaima . . . . 1·00 1·00
2313 120 c. on 55 c. on 125 c. on 35 c. Peacock cichlid ("Lukanani") . . . . . . 1·00 1·00
See also Nos. 2476/95.

1988. Centenary of Publication of Sanders' "Reichenbachia" (29th issue). As T **331**. Mult.
2314 320 c. Plate No. 62 (Series 2) . 1·25 40
2315 475 c. Plate No. 73 (Series 2) . 1·50 70
2316 525 c. Plate No. 36 (Series 2) . 2·00 90
2317 530 c. Plate No. 69 (Series 2) . 1·00 90
2318 $15 Plate No. 67 (Series 2) . 2·00 4·00

1988. CARICOM Day. Nos. 545/6 and 555 surch **Caricom Day 1988** and new value.
2319 25 c. on 5 c. Annatto tree . . 15 10
2320 $1.20 on 6 c. Cannon-ball tree 40 10
2321 $10 on $2 "Norantea guianensis" . . . . 2·25 2·50

1988. Centenary of Publication of Sanders' "Reichenbachia" (30th issue). As T **331**. Mult.
2322 700 c. Plate No. 62 (Series 2) . 1·00 1·25
2323 775 c. Plate No. 59 (Series 2) . 1·25 1·40
2324 875 c. Plate No. 31 (Series 2) . 3·50 1·50
2325 950 c. Plate No. 78 (Series 2) . 1·75 1·75

1988. 40th Anniv of World Health Day. No. 705a optd.
2326 60 c. "Papilio androgeus" (optd **WHO 1948–1988**) . . . . 8·50 9·50
2327 60 c. "Papilio androgeus" (optd **1988**) 15 10

1988. Centenary of Publication of Sanders' "Reichenbachia" (31st issue). As T **331**. Mult.
2328 350 c. Plate No. 74 (Series 2) . 90 40

1988. Centenary of Publication of Sanders' "Reichenbachia" (32nd issue). As T **331**, but additionally inscr "1985–1988". Multicoloured.
2329 130 c. Plate No. 73 (Series 2) . 85 25
2330 200 c. Plate No. 96 (Series 2) . 50 30
2331 260 c. Plate No. 16 (Series 2) . 1·50 45

1988. Conservation of Resources. (a) Nos. 1444/6 optd.
2333 120 c. Young Ocelot (No. 1444) (optd **CONSERVE TREES**) 50 40
2334 120 c. Young Ocelot (No. 1444) (optd **CONSERVE ELECTRICITY**) 50 40
2335 120 c. Young Ocelot (No. 1444) (optd **CONSERVE WATER**) 50 40
2336 120 c. Type **322** (optd **CONSERVE ELECTRICITY**) 50 40
2337 120 c. Type **322** (optd **CONSERVE WATER**) . . 50 40
2338 120 c. Type **322** (optd **CONSERVE TREES**) . . . 50 40
2339 120 c. Young Ocelot (No. 1446) (optd **CONSERVE WATER**) 50 40
2340 120 c. Young Ocelot (No. 1446) (optd **CONSERVE TREES**) 50 40
2341 120 c. Young Ocelot (No. 1446) (optd **CONSERVE ELECTRICITY**) 50 40
(b) Nos. 1634, 1670, 1683 and 1774 optd **CONSERVE WATER**.
2342 200 c. Plate No. 33 (Series 1) . 50 40
2343 200 c. Plate No. 79 (Series 1) . 50 40
2344 225 c. Plate No. 24 (Series 1) . 50 40
2345 350 c. Plate No. 94 (Series 1) . 50 40

1988. Road Safety Campaign. Nos. 2194/2201 optd.
2346 **396** $1.20 green (optd **BEWARE OF ANIMALS**) . . . 1·10 1·10
2347 – $1.20 green (No. 2195) (optd **BEWARE OF CHILDREN**) . . . . . 1·10 1·10
2348 – $1.20 green (No. 2196) (optd **DRIVE SAFELY**) 1·10 1·10
2349 – $1.20 green (No. 2197) (optd **DO NOT DRINK AND DRIVE**) . . . . 1·10 1·10
2350 **396** $1.20 purple (optd **BEWARE OF ANIMALS**) . . . . . 1·10 1·10
2351 – $1.20 purple (No. 2199) (optd **BEWARE OF CHILDREN**) . . . . . 1·10 1·10
2352 – $1.20 purple (No. 2200) (optd **DRIVE SAFELY**) 1·10 1·10
2353 – $1.20 purple (No. 2201) (optd **DO NOT DRINK AND DRIVE**) . . . . 1·10 1·10

1988. No. 706 optd **1988** or surch **120**.
2354 $1 "Agrias claudina" . . . . 3·00 70
2355 120 c. on $1 "Agrias claudina" 3·00 70

1988. Various "Reichenbachia" issues surch.
2356 120 c. on 25 c. Plate No. 61 (Series 1) (No. 1574) . . . 60 40
2357 120 c. on 25 c. Plate No. 63 (Series 1) (No. 1575) . . . 60 40
2358 120 c. on 25 c. Plate No. 70 (Series 1) (No. 1576) . . . 60 40
2359 120 c. on 25 c. Plate No. 59 (Series 1) (No. 1620) . . . 60 40
2360 120 c. on 25 c. Plate No. 71 (Series 1) (No. 1679) . . . 60 40
2429 120 c. on 25 c. Plate No. 72 (Series 1) (No. 1577) . . . 60 40
2361 120 c. on 30 c. Plate No. 53 (Series 1) (No. 1771) . . . 60 40
2362 120 c. on 30 c. Plate No. 86 (Series 1) (No. 1731) . . . 60 40
2363 120 c. on 30 c. Plate No. 30 (Series 2) (No. 1809) . . . 60 40
2365 120 c. on 30 c. Plate No. 7 (Series 2) 60 40
2366 120 c. on 30 c. Plate No. 14 (Series 2) 60 40
2368 120 c. on 30 c. Plate No. 22 (Series 2) 60 40
2369 120 c. on 30 c. Plate No. 28 (Series 2) 60 40
2371 120 c. on 35 c. Plate No. 45 (Series 2) (No. 1925) . . . 60 40
2372 120 c. on 40 c. Plate No. 77 (Series 1) (No. 1663) . . . 60 40
2374 120 c. on 40 c. Plate No. 96 (Series 1) (No. 1747) . . . 60 40
2377 120 c. on 40 c. Plate No. 86 (Series 1) (No. 1868) . . . 60 40
2378 120 c. on 40 c. Plate No. 68 (Series 1) (No. 1884) . . . 60 40
2381 120 c. on 45 c. Plate No. 54 (Series 1) (No. 1664) . . . 60 40
2382 120 c. on 45 c. Plate No. 81 (Series 1) (No. 1748) . . . 60 40
2383 120 c. on 45 c. Plate No. 21 (Series 2) (No. 1810) . . . 60 40
2384 120 c. on 50 c. Plate No. 92 (Series 1) (No. 1665) . . . 60 40
2385 120 c. on 50 c. Plate No. 13 (Series 2) (No. 1907) . . . 60 40
2386 120 c. on 50 c. Plate No. 15 (Series 2) (No. 1926) . . . 60 40
2393 120 c. on 55 c. Plate No. 17 (Series 1) (No. 1732) . . . 60 40
2395 120 c. on 60 c. Plate No. 57 (Series 1) (No. 1622) . . . 60 40
2397 120 c. on 60 c. Plate No. 73 (Series 1) (No. 1623) . . . 60 40
2398 120 c. on 60 c. Plate No. 75 (Series 1) (No. 1624) . . . 60 40
2400 120 c. on 60 c. Plate No. 95 (Series 1) (No. 1666) . . . 60 40
2401 120 c. on 60 c. Plate No. 93 (Series 1) (No. 1733) . . . 60 40
2402 120 c. on 60 c. Plate No. 27 (Series 2) (No. 1874) . . . 60 40
2408 120 c. on 70 c. Plate No. 8 (Series 2) 60 40
2409 120 c. on 70 c. Plate No. 9 (Series 2) 60 40
2411 120 c. on 70 c. Plate No. 12 (Series 2) 60 40
2413 120 c. on 70 c. Plate No. 17 (Series 2) 60 40
2414 120 c. on 80 c. Plate No. 39 (Series 1) 60 40
2415 120 c. on 80 c. Plate No. 74 (Series 1) 60 40

2416 120 c. on 80 c. Plate No. 93 (Series 1) 60 40
2417 120 c. on 85 c. Plate No. 45 (Series 2) (No. 1876) . . . 60 40
2418 120 c. on 85 c. Plate No. 24 (Series 2) (No. 1914) . . . 60 40
2419 120 c. on 85 c. Plate No. 15 (Series 2) (No. 1918) . . . 60 40
2420 120 c. on 85 c. Plate No. 18 (Series 2) (No. 1928) . . . 60 40
2421 120 c. on 90 c. Plate No. 84 (Series 1) (No. 1668) . . . 60 40
2422 120 c. on 90 c. Plate No. 89 (Series 1) (No. 1749) . . . 60 40
2423 120 c. on 90 c. Plate No. 10 (Series 2) (No. 1869) . . . 60 40
2424 120 c. on 90 c. Plate No. 13 (Series 2) (No. 1877) . . . 60 40
2425 120 c. on 90 c. Plate No. 27 (Series 2) (No. 1915) . . . 60 40
2426 120 c. on 90 c. Plate No. 2 (Series 2) (No. 1929) 60 40
2427 200 c. on 80 c. Plate No. 42 (Series 2) (No. 1812) . . . 60 40
2428 200 c. on 90 c. Plate No. 4 (Series 2) (No. 1813) 60 40
2430 240 c. on 140 c. Plate No. 30 (Series 2) 60 40
2431 240 c. on 140 c. Plate No. 34 (Series 2) 60 40
2432 240 c. on 425 c. Plate No. 87 (Series 2) (No. 2070) . . . 60 40
2433 260 c. on 375 c. Plate No. 90 (Series 1) (No. 1378) . . . 60 40

1988. Conservation of Resources. Various "Reichenbachia" issues optd **CONSERVE OUR RESOURCES**.

2434 100 c. Plate No. 65 (Series 1) (No. 1773) 60 40
2435 100 c. Plate No. 68 (Series 1) (No. 1734) 60 40
2436 100 c. Plate No. 88 (Series 1) (No. 1750) 60 40
2438 120 c. Plate No. 27 (Series 1) (No. 1524) 60 40
2439 120 c. Plate No. 36 (Series 1) (No. 1558) 60 40
2440 120 c. Plate No. 37 (Series 1) (No. 1627) 60 40
2441 120 c. Plate No. 56 (Series 1) (No. 1629) 60 40
2442 120 c. Plate No. 58 (Series 1) (No. 1630) 60 40
2443 120 c. Plate No. 67 (Series 1) (No. 1631) 60 40
2444 120 c. Plate No. 69 (Series 1) (No. 1680) 60 40
2445 130 c. Plate No. 38 (Series 1) (No. 1560) 60 40
2446 130 c. Plate No. 66 (Series 1) (No. 1632) 60 40
2447 130 c. Plate No. 91 (Series 1) (No. 1735) 60 40
2448 130 c. Plate No. 13 (Series 1) (No. 1760) 60 40
2249 130 c. Plate No. 20 (Series 1) (No. 1761) 60 40
2450 150 c. Plate No. 26 (Series 1) (No. 1633) 60 40
2451 150 c. Plate No. 78 (Series 1) (No. 1669) 60 40
2452 150 c. Plate No. 87 (Series 1) (No. 1681) 60 40
2453 150 c. Plate No. 76 (Series 1) (No. 1751) 60 40
2454 250 c. Plate No. 74 (Series 1) (No. 1736) 60 40

1988. 125th Anniv of International Red Cross. Nos. 2202/5 and 2207/10 optd with cross.

2455 **396** $3.20 blue 90 90
2456 – $3.20 blue (No. 2203) . . 90 90
2457 – $3.20 blue (No. 2204) . . 90 90
2458 – $3.20 blue (No. 2205) . . 90 90
2459 – $3.30 black (No. 2207) . . 90 90
2460 **396** $3.30 black 90 90
2461 – $3.30 black (No. 2209) . . 90 90
2462 – $3.30 black (No. 2210) . . 90 90

1988. Centenary of Publication of Sanders' "Reichenbachia" (33rd issue). As T **331**. Mult.

2468 270 c. Plate No. 90 (Series 2) . 1·10 60
2469 360 c. Plate No. 84 (Series 2) . 75 75
2470 550 c. Plate No. 70 (Series 2) (horiz) . . . . 1·25 1·00
2471 670 c. Plate No. 71 (Series 2) (horiz) . . . . 1·50 1·75

1988. 60th Anniv of Cricket in Guyana. Nos. 1584, 1670, 1681 and 1815 optd **1928-1988 CRICKET JUBILEE** or surch also.

2472 200 c. Plate No. 14 (Series 1) . 12·00 14·00
2473 200 c. Plate No. 79 (Series 1) . 1·00 40
2474 800 c. on 150 c. Plate No. 87 (Series 1) . . . . 6·50 8·00
2475 800 c. on 160 c. Plate No. 5 (Series 2) . . . . 3·25 3·25

1988. Olympic Games, Seoul. (a) Nos. 1628, 1634, 1671, 1681, 1683, 1814, 1818/19, 1880 and 2069 optd **OLYMPIC GAMES 1988** or surch also.

2476 120 c. Plate No. 46 (Series 1) . 20 20
2477 130 c. Plate No. 38 (Series 2) . 20 20
2478 150 c. Plate No. 87 (Series 1) . 20 20
2479 200 c. Plate No. 33 (Series 1) . 20 20
2480 300 c. Plate No. 83 (Series 1) . 20 20
2481 300 c. on 360 c. Plate No. 34 (Series 2) 30 30
2482 320 c. Plate No. 10 (Series 2) . 30 30
2483 330 c. Plate No. 82 (Series 2) . 30 30
2484 350 c. Plate No. 94 (Series 1) . 30 30
2485 350 c. Plate No. 29 (Series 2) . 30 30

(b) Design as No. 1420 but incorrectly inscr "LOS ANGELLES" optd or surch **OLYMPICS 1988** (A) or **KOREA 1988** (B).

2486 $1.20 multicoloured (A) . . . 20 20
2487 $1.20 multicoloured (B) . . . 20 20
2488 130 c. on $1.20 mult (A) . . . 20 20
2489 130 c. on $1.20 mult (B) . . . 20 20
2490 150 c. on $1.20 mult (A) . . . 20 20
2491 150 c. on $1.20 mult (B) . . . 20 20
2492 200 c. on $1.20 mult (A) . . . 25 25
2493 200 c. on $1.20 mult (B) . . . 25 25
2594 350 c. on $1.20 mult (A) . . . 35 35
2495 350 c. on $1.20 mult (B) . . . 35 35

1988. Columbus Day. Nos. 1672/3 optd or surch **V CENTENARY OF THE LANDING OF CHRISTOPHER COLUMBUS IN THE AMERICAS**.

2496 320 c. Plate No. 50 (Series 1) . 1·25 30
2497 $15 on 360 c. Plate No. 85 (Series 1) . . . . 2·75 3·50

1988. Centenary of Publication of Sanders' "Reichenbachia" (34th issue). As T **331**. Mult.

2498 100 c. Plate No. 44 (Series 2) . 60 55
2499 130 c. Plate No. 42 (Series 2) (horiz) 60 55
2500 140 c. Plate No. 4 (Series 2) . 75 65
2501 160 c. Plate No. 50 (Series 2) . 75 65
2502 175 c. Plate No. 51 (Series 2) . 90 75
2503 200 c. Plate No. 11 (Series 2) . 2·00 75
2504 200 c. Plate No. 23 (Series 2) . 2·00 75
2505 200 c. Plate No. 26 (Series 2) . 2·00 75
2506 200 c. Plate No. 75 (Series 2) . 2·00 75
2507 200 c. Plate No. 93 (Series 2) . 2·00 75
2508 250 c. Plate No. 79 (Series 2) . 1·00 90
2509 280 c. Plate No. 62 (Series 2) . 1·25 1·00
2510 285 c. Plate No. 63 (Series 2) . 2·50 1·00
2511 380 c. Plate No. 35 (Series 2) . 2·75 1·25

1988. Christmas (1st issue). Various "Reichenbachia" issues optd or surch. (a) Optd or surch **SEASON'S GREETINGS**.

2519 120 c. on 100 c. Plate No. 6 (Series 1) 50 50
2520 120 c. on 100 c. Plate No. 13 (Series 1) 50 50
2521 120 c. on 100 c. Plate No. 20 (Series 1) 50 50
2522 120 c. on 100 c. Plate No. 25 (Series 1) 50 50
2523 120 c. on 100 c. Plate No. 40 (Series 1) (horiz) 20 20
2524 120 c. on 100 c. Plate No. 42 (Series 1) (horiz) 20 20
2525 120 c. on 100 c. Plate No. 43 (Series 1) (horiz) 20 20
2526 120 c. on 100 c. Plate No. 45 (Series 1) (horiz) 20 20
2512 150 c. Plate No. 32 (Series 1) (No. 1561) 50 50
2513 150 c. Plate No. 62 (Series 1) (No. 1566) 50 50
2514 225 c. Plate No. 60 (Series 1) (No. 1682) 50 50
2532 240 c. on 180 c. Plate No. 15 (Series 1) (No. 1752) . . . 50 50
2515 260 c. Plate No. 39 (Series 1) (No. 1737) 50 50
2516 320 c. Plate No. 82 (Series 1) (No. 1753) 50 50
2517 330 c. Plate No. 80 (Series 1) (No. 1754) 50 50
2518 360 c. Plate No. 85 (Series 1) (No. 1673) 50 50

(b) Optd **SEASON'S GREETINGS 1988**.

2527 225 c. Plate No. 24 (Series 1) (No. 1774) 75 75
2528 225 c. Plate No. 60 (Series 1) (No. 1682) 75 75
2530 225 c. on 350 c. on 120 c. Plate No. 65 (Series 1) (No. 2221) 75 75

1988. Christmas (2nd issue). Nos. 489, 1188/91 and 1449 surch or optd **CHRISTMAS 1988**.

2533 – 20 c. on 6 c. mult (No. 489) 15 10
2534 **277** 120 c. brown, blk & bl . . 25 35
2535 – 120 c. on 130 c. red, black and blue (No. 1189) . . 25 35
2536 – 120 c. on 150 c. violet, black and blue (No. 1190) . . 25 35
2537 – 120 c. on 200 c. green, black and blue (No. 1191) . . 25 35
2538 – 500 c. on 330 c. mult (No. 1449) . . . . 1·50 1·75

1988. AIDS Information Campaign. Nos. 707/8a optd or surch with various slogans.

2539 120 c. on $5 "Morpho deidamia" (A) . . . . . . 2·00 2·00
2540 120 c. on $5 "Morpho deidamia" (B) . . . . . . 2·00 2·00
2541 120 c. on $5 "Morpho deidamia" (C) . . . . . . 2·00 2·00
2542 120 c. on $5 "Morpho deidamia" (D) . . . . . . 2·00 2·00
2543 120 c. on $5 "Morpho deidamia" (E) . . . . . . 2·00 2·00
2544 120 c. on $10 "Elbella patrobas" (A) . . . . 2·00 2·00
2545 120 c. on $10 "Elbella patrobas" (B) . . . . 2·00 2·00
2546 120 c. on $10 "Elbella patrobas" (C) . . . . 2·00 2·00
2547 120 c. on $10 "Elbella patrobas" (D) . . . . 2·00 2·00
2548 120 c. on $10 "Elbella patrobas" (E) . . . . 2·00 2·00
2549 $2 "Morpho rhetenor" (female) (E) . . . . 5·50 2·00
2550 $5 "Morpho deidamia" (E) . . 8·00 4·50
2551 $10 "Elbella patrobas" (E) . . 9·50 7·00

OVERPRINTS: (A) **Be compassionate towards AIDS victims**; (B) **Get information on AIDS. it may save your life.**; (C) **Get the facts. Education helps to prevent AIDS.**; (D) **Say no to Drugs and limit the spread of AIDS.**; (E) **Protect yourself from AIDS. Better safe than sorry.**

1988. 150th Anniv of Abolition of Slavery (1984) (2nd issue). Designs as Nos. 1547/50, but colours changed.

2552 **337** 25 c. black and brown . . 15 10
2553 – 60 c. black and lilac . . 20 15
2254 – 130 c. black and green . . 25 40
2555 – 150 c. black and blue . . 30 45

1989. Olympic Medal Winners, Seoul. Nos. 1672, 1923 and 2178 surch **SALUTING WINNERS OLYMPIC GAMES 1988**.

2556 550 c. on 560 c. Plate No. 1 (Series 2) . . . . 1·25 1·00
2557 900 c. on 320 c. Plate No. 18 (Series 2) . . . . 1·75 2·00
2558 1050 c. on 320 c. Plate No. 50 (Series 1) . . . . 2·25 2·75

1989. Republic Day. Nos. 2194/2201 and 2212 optd **REPUBLIC DAY 1989**.

2559 **396** $1.20 green 30 40
2560 – $1.20 green (No. 2195) . . 30 40
2561 – $1.20 green (No. 2196) . . 30 40
2562 – $1.20 green (No. 2197) . . 30 40
2563 **396** $1.20 purple 30 40
2564 – $1.20 purple (No. 2199) . . 30 40
2565 – $1.20 purple (No. 2200) . . 30 40
2566 – $1.20 purple (No. 2201) . . 30 40
2567 – $10 multicoloured . . . . 2·00 2·50

1989. Nos. 2202/5 and 2207/10 surch **$5.00**.

2568 **396** $5 on $3.20 blue . . . . 1·25 1·50
2569 – $5 on $3.20 blue (No. 2203) 1·25 1·50
2570 – $5 on $3.20 blue (No. 2204) 1·25 1·50
2571 – $5 on $3.20 blue (No. 2205) 1·25 1·50
2572 – $5 on $3.30 black (No. 2207) . . . . 1·25 1·50
2573 **396** $5 on $3.30 black . . . . 1·25 1·50
2574 – $5 on $3.30 black (No. 2209) . . . . 1·25 1·50
2575 – $5 on $3.30 black (No. 2210) . . . . 1·25 1·50

1989. Various "Reichenbachia" issues surch.

2576 120 c. on 140 c. Plate No. 25 (Series 2) . . . . 1·00 1·00
2577 120 c. on 140 c. Plate No. 52 (Series 2) . . . . 1·00 1·00
2578 120 c. on 140 c. Plate No. 65 (Series 2) . . . . 1·00 1·00
2580 120 c. on 140 c. Plate No. 38 (Series 2) . . . . 1·00 1·00
2581 120 c. on 140 c. Plate No. 41 (Series 2) . . . . 1·00 1·00
2579 120 c. on 175 c. Plate No. 54 (Series 2) . . . . 1·00 1·00
2582 170 c. on 175 c. Plate No. 58 (Series 2) . . . . 1·00 1·00
2583 250 c. on 280 c. Plate No. 66 (Series 2) . . . . 1·50 1·50
2584 250 c. on 280 c. Plate No. 67 (Series 2) . . . . 1·50 1·50
2585 300 c. on 290 c. Plate No. 53 (Series 2) (No. 2236) . . . 1·60 1·60

1989. Nos. 1744/5 and 2185/6 surch **TEN DOLLARS $10.00** (Nos. 2586, 2588) or **TEN DOLLARS** (Nos. 2587, 2589).

2586 **363** $10 on 320 c. red, black and lilac (No. 1744) . . . . 1·75 2·25
2587 – $10 on 320 c. mult (No. 1745) . . . . 1·75 2·25
2588 **363** $10 on 320 c. red, black and lilac (No. 2185) . . . . 1·75 2·25
2589 – $10 on 320 c. mult (No. 2186) . . . . 1·75 2·25

1989. Nos. O54/7, O59/63 and O65/9 optd **POSTAGE** or surch also.

2591 125 c. on 130 c. Plate No. 92 (Series 2) 80 80
2592 125 c. on 140 c. Plate No. 36 (Series 2) 80 80
2593 150 c. Plate No. 43 (Series 2) 80 80
2594 150 c. on 175 c. Plate No. 31 (Series 2) 80 80
2595 250 c. Plate No. 59 (Series 2) . 1·00 1·00
2596 250 c. on 225 c. Plate No. 26 (Series 2) . . . . 1·00 1·00
2597 250 c. on 230 c. Plate No. 68 (Series 2) . . . . 1·00 1·00
2598 250 c. on 275 c. Plate No. 69 (Series 2) . . . . 1·00 1·00
2599 300 c. on 275 c. Plate No. 90 (Series 2) . . . . 1·00 1·00
2750 350 c. Plate No. 95 (Series 2) . 1·00 1·00
2601 350 c. on 330 c. Plate No. 23 (Series 2) . . . . 1·00 1·00
2602 600 c. Plate No. 70 (Series 2) . 1·25 1·25
2603 $12 Plate No. 71 (Series 2) . . 2·25 2·75
2604 $15 Plate No. 84 (Series 2) . . 2·50 3·00

1989. Centenary of Publication of Sanders' "Reichenbachia" (35th issue). As T **331**. Mult.

2605 200 c. Plate No. 49 (Series 2) . 75 75
2606 200 c. Plate No. 53 (Series 2) . 75 75
2607 200 c. Plate No. 60 (Series 2) . 75 75
2608 200 c. Plate No. 64 (Series 2) . 75 75

1989. No. 1442 surch **250**.

2609 **322** 250 c. on 25 c. mult . . . 1·60 15

1989. 40th Anniv of Guyana Red Cross. No. 1872 surch **RED CROSS 1948 1988** and new value.

2610 375 c. on 45 c. Plate No. 17 (Series 2) . . . . 1·50 80
2611 425 c. on 45 c. Plate No. 17 (Series 2) . . . . 1·50 80

1989. World Health Day. Nos. 1875 and 2239 surch with new value and inscr as indicated.

2612 250 c. on 75 c. Plate No. 56 (Series 2) surch **HEALTH FOR ALL** 90 90
2613 250 c. on 75 c. Plate No. 56 (Series 2) surch **ALL FOR HEALTH** 90 90
2614 675 c. on 720 c. Plate No. 49 (Series 2) surch **ALL FOR HEALTH** . . . . 1·75 1·75
2615 675 c. on 720 c. Plate No. 49 (Series 2) surch **HEALTH FOR ALL** . . . . 1·75 1·75

1989. Scouting Anniversaries. Nos. 1873, 1879, 2322, 2509 and unissued value as No. 1873 optd or surch also.

2616 250 c. on 50 c. Plate No. 33 (Series 2) (surch **BOY SCOUTS 1909 1989**) . . . 75 75
2617 250 c. on 50 c. Plate No. 33 (Series 2) (surch **GIRL GUIDES 1924 1989**) . . . 75 75
2618 250 c. on 100 c. Plate No. 33 (Series 2) (surch **BOY SCOUTS 1909 1989**) . . . 75 75
2619 250 c. on 100 c. Plate No. 33 (Series 2) (surch **GIRL GUIDES 1924 1989**) . . . 75 75
2620 300 c. Plate No. 50 (Series 2) (optd **BOY SCOUTS 1909 1989**) 90 90
2621 300 c. Plate No. 50 (Series 2) (optd **GIRL GUIDES 1924 1989**) 90 90
2622 $25 on 280 c. Plate No. 62 (Series 2) (surch **LADY BADEN POWELL 1889 - 1989**) . . . . 4·50 5·50
2623 $25 on 700 c. Plate No. 62 (Series 2) (surch **LADY BADEN POWELL 1889 - 1989**) . . . . 4·50 5·50

The events commemorated are the 80th anniv of Boy Scout Movement in Guyana, 65th anniv of Girl Guide Movement in Guyana and birth centenary of Lady Baden-Powell.

1989. 150 Years of Photography. No. 1881 surch **PHOTOGRAPHY 1839-1989** and new value.

2624 550 c. on 390 c. Plate No. 6 (Series 2) . . . . 1·00 1·00
2625 650 c. on 390 c. Plate No. 6 (Series 2) . . . . 1·00 1·00

1989. 70th Anniv of International Labour Organization. No. 1875 surch **I.L.O. 1919-1989 300**.

2627 300 c. on 75 c. Plate No. 56 (Series 2) . . . . 3·50 40

1989. Various stamps surch.

2628 80 c. on 6 c. Patua (No. 489) . 40 20
2629 $1 on 2 c. Type **132** 40 20
2630 $2.05 on 3 c. Hanging heliconia (No. 544) 40 25
2641 $2.55 on 5 c. Annatto tree (No. 545) 40 25
2642 $3.25 on 6 c. Cannon-ball tree (No. 546) 40 25
2633 $5 on 6 c. Type **111** 40 30
2634 $6.40 on 10 c. "Archonias bellona" (No. 699) . . . 3·25 75
2648 $6.40 on $3.30 black (No. 2207) . . . . 3·00 2·00
2649 $6.40 on $3.30 black (No. 2208) . . . . 3·00 2·00
2650 $6.40 on $3.30 black (No. 2209) . . . . 3·00 2·00
2651 $6.40 on $3.30 black (No. 2210) . . . . 3·00 2·00
2646 640 c. on 675 c. on 720 c. Plate No. 49 (Series 2) (No. 2614) 1·25 1·25
2647 640 c. on 675 c. on 720 c. Plate No. 49 (Series 2) (No. 2615) 1·25 1·25
2637a $7.65 on 35 c. "Anaea galanthus" (No. 703) . . . 3·75 80
2638 $7.65 on 40 c. "Morpho retenor" (male) (No. 704) . 3·75 80
2652 $7.65 on $3.20 blue (No. 2202) 3·00 2·00
2653 $7.65 on $3.20 blue (No. 2203) 3·00 2·00
2654 $7.65 on $3.20 blue (No. 2204) 3·00 2·00
2655 $7.65 on $3.20 blue (No. 2205) 3·00 2·00
2635 $8.90 on 60 c. "Papilio androgeus" (No. 705a) . . 4·25 85
2643 $50 on $2 "Morpho rhetenor" (female) (No. 707) . . . . 12·00 4·50
2644 $100 on $2 "Morpho rhetenor" (female) (No. 707) 17·00 11·00

1989. CARICOM Day. No. 1878 surch **CARICOM DAY 125**.

2656 125 c. on 200 c. Plate No. 44 (Series 2) . . . . 1·75 30

454 "Stalachtis calliope"

455 Kathryn Sullivan (first U.S. woman to walk in space)

1989. Butterflies (1st series). Multicoloured.

2657 80 c. Type **454** 50 10
2658 $2.25 "Morpho rhetenor" . . 60 15
2659 $5 "Agrias claudia" 70 15
2660 $6.40 "Marpesia marcella" . . 75 20
2661 $7.65 "Papilio zagreus" . . . 80 30
2662 $8.90 "Chorinea faunus" . . . 90 30
2663 $25 "Euptychia cephus" . . . 2·50 2·50
2664 $100 "Nessaea regina" . . . . 6·50 7·50

See also Nos. 2789/2860.

1989. 25 Years of Women in Space. Mult.

2665 $6.40 Type **455** 50 20
2666 $12.80 Svetlana Savitskaya (first Soviet woman to walk in space) 80 45
2667 $15.30 Judy Resnik and Christa McAuliffe and "Challenger" logo 80 45
2668 $100 Sally Ride (first U.S. woman astronaut) . . . . 5·00 6·00

1989. Centenary of Ahmadiyya (Moslem organization). Nos. 543/5 surch **AHMADIYYA CENTENARY 1899-1989**.
2669 80 c. on 2 c. Type **132** . . . . 1·75 40
2670 $6.40 on 3 c. Hanging heliconia 6·00 3·25
2671 $8.90 on 5 c. Annatto tree . . 6·50 4·00

457 Head of Harpy Eagle

458 Channel-billed Toucan

1990. Endangered Species. Harpy Eagle. Multicoloured.
2672 $2.25 Type **457** 75 25
2673 $5 Harpy eagle with monkey prey . . . . 1·00 30
2674 $8.90 Eagle on branch (facing right) . . . . 1·25 50
2675 $30 Eagle on branch (facing left) 3·00 3·50

1990. Birds of Guyana. Multicoloured.
2676 $15 Type **458** 90 70
2677 $25 Blue and yellow macaw . 1·40 50
2678 $50 Wattled jacana (horiz) . . 2·75 2·25
2679 $60 Hoatzin . . . . 3·00 2·50

1990. 85th Anniv of Rotary International. Optd **Rotary International 1905–1990** and emblem.
(a) On Nos. 2657/64.
2681 80 c. Type **454** 60 20
2682 $2.25 "Morpho rhetenor" . . 90 30
2683 $5 "Agrias claudia" . . . . 1·25 30
2684 $6.40 "Marpesia marcella" . . 1·40 35
2685 $7.65 "Papilio zagreus" . . . 1·50 50
2686 $8.90 "Chorinea faunus" . . . 1·60 55
2687 $25 "Euptychia cephus" . . . 2·75 3·25
2688 $100 "Nessaea regina" . . . . 8·00 9·00

(b) On Nos. 2665/8.
2689 $6.40 Type **455** 85 40
2690 $12.80 Svetlana Savitskaya (first Soviet woman to walk in space) . . . . 1·50 80
2691 $15.30 Judy Resnik and Christa McAuliffe with "Challenger" logo . . . . 1·60 90
2692 $100 Sally Ride (first U.S. woman astronaut) . . . . 6·00 7·00

460 Indian Post Runner, 1837

1990. 150th Anniv of the Penny Black and 500th Anniv of Thurn and Taxis Postal Service. Multicoloured.
2693/2746 $15.30 × 27, $17.80 × 9, $20 × 18
Set of 54 . . . . . . 28·00 29·00
Nos. 2693/2746 depict various forms of mail transport.

1990. 9th Conference of Rotary District 405, Georgetown. Nos. 1759, 1762/3 and 1765/6 surch **ROTARY DISTRICT 405 9th CONFERENCE MAY 1990 GEORGETOWN** and new value.
2748 80 c. on 55 c. Plate No. 9 (Series 1)
2749 80 c. on 55 c. Plate No. 49 (Series 1)
2750 80 c. on 55 c. Plate No. 64 (Series 1)
2751 $6.40 on 130 c. Plate No. 6 (Series 1)
2752 $6.40 on 130 c. Plate No. 25 (Series 1)
2753 $7.65 on 130 c. Plate No. 25 (Series 1)

1990. 90th Birthday of Queen Elizabeth the Queen Mother. Nos. 2657/64 surch **90th Birthday H.M. The Queen Mother**.
2754 80 c. Type **454** 50 20
2755 $2.25 "Morpho rhetenor" . . 75 30
2756 $5 "Agrias claudia" 90 30
2757 $6.40 "Marpesia marcella" . . 1·00 40
2758 $7.65 "Papilio zagreus" . . . 1·25 50
2759 $8.90 "Chorinea faunus" . . . 1·50 55
2760 $25 "Euptychia cephus" . . . 3·00 3·25
2761 $100 "Nessaea regina" . . . . 8·00 9·00

463 Collared Trogon

464 "Melinaea idae"

1990. Birds. Multicoloured.
2762 80 c. Guiana partridge (horiz) . 30 10
2763 $2.55 Type **463** 40 15
2764 $3.25 Derby aracari 40 15
2765 $5 Black-necked aracari . . . 50 20
2766 $5.10 Green aracari 50 30
2767 $5.80 Ivory-billed aracari . . 50 30
2768 $6.40 Guiana toucanet 50 30
2769 $6.50 Sulphur-breasted toucan 50 30
2770 $7.55 Red-billed toucan . . . 65 30
2771 $7.65 Toco toucan 65 30
2772 $8.25 Natterers toucanet . . . 65 30
2773 $8.90 Welcome trogon 65 30
2774 $9.75 Doubtful trogon 65 30
2775 $11.40 Banded aracari 75 40
2776 $12.65 Golden-headed train bearer 75 40
2777 $12.80 Rufous-breasted hermit 75 40
2778 $13.90 Band tail barbthroat . 75 40
2779 $15.30 White-tipped sickle bill . 80 50
2780 $17.80 Black jacobin 90 60
2781 $19.20 Fiery topaz 90 60
2782 $22.95 Tufted coquette . . . 1·00 70
2783 $26.70 Ecuadorian pied-tail . 1·00 70
2784 $30 Quetzal . . . . 1·00 70
2785 $50 Green-crowned brilliant . 1·75 1·25
2786 $100 Emerald-chinned hummingbird . . . . . . 2·75 2·75
2787 $190 Lazuline sabre-wing . . 4·50 5·00
2788 $225 Beryline hummingbird . 4·50 5·50

1990. Butterfiles (2nd series). Multicoloured.
2789/2860 80 c., $2.55, $5, $6.40, $7.65, $8.90, $10 × 64, $50 and $100
Set of 72 . . . . . . 12·00 13·00
DESIGNS—VERT: $2.55, "Rhetus dysonii"; $5 "Actinote anteas"; $6.40, "Heliconius tales"; $7.65, "Thecla telemus"; $8.90, "Theope eudocia"; $10 (2795), "Heleconius vetustus"; 2796, "Mesosemia eumene"; 2797, "Parides phosphorus"; 2798, "Polystichtis emylius"; 2799, "Xanthocleis aedesia"; 2800, "Doxocopa agathina"; 2801, "Adelpha plesaure"; 2802, "Heliconius wallacei"; 2803, "Notheme eumeus"; 2804, "Melinaea mediatrix"; 2805, "Theritas coronata"; 2806, "Dismorphia orise"; 2807, "Phyciodes ianthe"; 2808, "Morpho aega"; 2809, "Zaretis isidora"; 2810, "Pierella lena"; 2811, "Heliconius silvana"; 2812, "Eunica alcmena"; 2813, "Mechanitis polymnia"; 2814, "Mesosemia ephyne"; 2815, "Thecla erema"; 2816, "Callizona acesta"; 2817, "Stalachtis phaedusa"; 2818, "Battus belus"; 2819, "Nymula phliasus"; 2820, "Parides childrenae"; 2821, "Stalachtis euterpe"; 2822, "Dysmathia portia"; 2823, "Tithorea hermias"; 2824, "Prepona pheridamas"; 2825, "Dismorphia fortunata"; 2826, "Hamadryas amphinome"; $50 "Heliconius vicini"; $100 "Amarynthis meneria". HORIZ: $10 (2827), "Thecla falerina"; 2828, "Pheles heliconides"; 2829, "Echenias leucocyana"; 2830, "Heliconius xanthocles"; 2831, "Mesopthalma idotea"; 2832, "Parides aeneas"; 2833, "Heliconius numata"; 2834, "Thecla critola"; 2835, "Themone pais"; 2836, "Nymula agle"; 2837, "Adelpha cocala"; 2838, "Anaea eribotes"; 2839, "Prepona demophon"; 2840, "Selenophanes cassiope"; 2841, "Consul hippona"; 2842, "Antirrhaea avernus"; 2843, "Thecla telemus"; 2844, "Thyridia confusa"; 2845, "Heliconius burneyi"; 2846, "Parides lysander"; 2847, "Eunica orphise"; 2848, "Adelpha melona"; 2849, "Morpho menelaus"; 2850, "Nymula phylleus"; 2851, "Stalachtis phlegia"; 2852, "Theope barea"; 2853, "Morpho perseus"; 2854, "Lycorea ceres"; 2855, "Archonias bellona"; 2856; "Caeronis chorinaeus"; 2857, "Vila azeca"; 2858, "Nessaea batesii".
Nos. 2795/2810, 2811/26, 2827/42 and 2843/58 respectively were printed together, se-tenant, forming composite designs.

465 "Vanilla inodora"

466 Ivory-billed Woodpecker

1990. Flowers. Multicoloured.
2862/2965 $7.65, $8.90, $10 × 32, $12.80 × 65, $15.30, $17.80, $20, $25 and $100
Set of 104 . . . . . . 14·00 15·00
DESIGNS—VERT: $8.90, "Epidendrum ibaguense"; $10 (2864), "Dichea muricata"; 2865, "Octomeria erosilabia"; 2866, "Spiranthes orchioides"; 2867, "Brassavola nodosa"; 2868, "Epidendrum rigidum"; 2869, "Brassia caudata"; 2870, "Pleurothallis diffusa"; 2871, "Aspasia variegata"; 2872, "Stenia pallida"; 2873, "Cyrtopodium punctatum"; 2874, "Cattleya deckeri"; 2875, "Cryptarrhena lunata"; 2876, "Cattleya violacea"; 2877, "Caularthron bicornutum"; 2878, "Oncidium carthagenense"; 2879, "Galeandra devoniana"; 2880, "Bifrenaria aurantiaca"; 2881, "Epidendrum ciliare"; 2882, "Dichaea picta"; 2883, "Scaphyglottis violacea"; 2884, "Cattleya percivaliana"; 2885, Map and national flag; 2886, "Epidendrum difforme"; 2887, "Eulophia maculata"; 2888, "Spiranthes tenuis"; 2889, "Peristoria guttata"; 2890, "Pleurothallis pruinosa"; 2891, "Cleistes rosea"; 2892, "Maxillaria variabilis"; 2893, "Brassavola cucullata"; 2894,"Epidendrum moyobambae"; 2895, "Oncidium orthostate"; $12.80, "Maxillaria parkeri"; $12.80 (2897), "Brassavola martiana"; 2898, "Paphinia cristata"; 2899, "Aganisia pulchella"; 2900, "Oncidium lanceanum"; 2901, "Lockhartia imbricata"; 2902, "Caularthron bilamellatum"; 2903, "Oncidium nanum"; 2904, "Pleurothallis ovalifolia"; 2905, "Galeandra dives"; 2906, "Cycnoches loddigesii"; 2907, "Ada aurantiaca"; 2908, "Catasetum barbatum"; 2909, "Palmorchis pubescens"; 2910, "Epidendrum anceps"; 2911, "Huntleya meleagris"; 2912, "Sobralia sessilis"; $15.30, "Epidendrum nocturnum"; $17.80, "Catasetum discolor"; $20 "Scuticaria hadwenii"; $25 "Epidendrum fragrans"; $100 "Epistephium parviflorum". HORIZ: $12.80 (2913), "Cochlospermum vitifolium"; 2914, "Eugenia malaccensis"; 2915, "Plumiera rubra"; 2916, "Erythrina glauca"; 2917, "Spathodea campanulata"; 2918, "Jacaranda filicifolia"; 2919, "Samanea saman"; 2920, "Cassia fistula"; 2921, "Abutilon integerrimum"; 2922, "Lagerstroemia speciosa"; 2923, "Tabebuia serratifolia"; 2924, "Guaiacum officinale"; 2925, "Solanum macranthum"; 2926, "Peltophorum roxburghii"; 2927, "Bauhinia variegata"; 2928, "Plumiera alba"; 2929, "Maxillaria camaridii"; 2930, "Vanilla pompona"; 2931, "Stanhopea grandiflora"; 2932, "Oncidium pusillum"; 2933, "Polycycnis vittata"; 2934, "Cattleya lawrenceana"; 2935, "Menadenium labiosum"; 2936, "Rodriguezia secunda"; 2937, "Mormodes buccinator"; 2938, "Otostylis brachystalix"; 2939, "Maxillaria discolor"; 2940, "Liparis elata"; 2941, "Gongora maculata"; 2942, "Koellensteinia graminea"; 2943, "Rudolfiella aurantiaca"; 2944, "Scuticaria steelei"; 2945, "Gloriosa rothschildiana"; 2946, "Pseudocalymma alliaceum"; 2947, "Callichlamys latifolia"; 2948, "Distictis riversii"; 2949, "Maurandya barclaiana"; 2950, "Beaumontia fragrans"; 2951, "Phaseolus caracalla"; 2952, "Mandevilla splendens"; 2953, "Solandra longiflora"; 2954, "Passiflora coccinea"; 2955, "Allamanda cathartica"; 2956, "Bauhinia galpini"; 2957, "Verbena maritima"; 2958, "Mandevilla sauveolens"; 2959, "Phryganocydia corymbosa"; 2960, "Jasminum sambac".
Nos. 2864/79, 2880/95, 2897/2912, 2913/28, 2929/44 and 2945/60 respectively were printed together, se-tenant, forming composite designs.

1990. Fauna. Multicoloured.
2967/86 $12.80 × 20 (vert designs showing endangered birds)
2987/3006 $12.80 × 20 (vert designs showing tropical birds)
3007/26 $12.80 × 20 (vert designs showing prehistoric animals)
3027/46 $12.80 × 20 (horiz designs showing endangered wildlife)
Set of 80 . . . . . . 32·00 32·00
DESIGNS—VERT: No. 2968, Cauca guan; 2969, Sun conure; 2970, Quetzal; 2971, Long-wattled umbrellabird; 2972, Banded cotinga; 2973, Blue-chested parakeet; 2974, Rufous-bellied chachalaca; 2975, Yellow-faced amazon; 2976, Toucan barbet; 2977, Red siskin; 2978, Cock-of-the-rock; 2979, Hyacinth macaw; 2980, Yellow cardinal; 2981, Bare-necked umbrellabird; 2982, Saffron toucanet; 2983, Red-billed curassow; 2984, Spectacled parrotlet; 2985, Lovely cotinga; 2986, Black-breasted gnateater; 2987, Swallow-tailed kite; 2988, Hoatzin; 2989, Ruby-topaz hummingbird; 2990, American black vulture; 2991, Rufous-tailed jacamar; 2992, Scarlet macaw; 2993, Rose-breasted thrush tanager; 2994, Toco toucan; 2995, Bearded bellbird; 2996, Blue-crowned motmot; 2997, Green oropendola; 2998, Pompadour cotinga; 2999; Vermilion flycatcher; 3000, Blue and yellow macaw; 3001, White-barred piculet; 3002, Great razor-billed curassow; 3003, Ruddy quail dove; 3004, Paradise tanager; 3005, American darter ("Anhinga"); 3006, Greater flamingo; 3007, Palaelodus; 3008, Archaeotrogon; 3009, Vulture; 3010, Bradypus tridactylus; 3011, Natalus stramineus bat; 3012, Cebidae; 3013, Cuvieronius; 3014, Phororhacos; 3015, Smilodectes; 3016, Megatherium; 3017, Titanotylopus; 3018, Teleoceras; 3019, Macrauchenia; 3020, Mylodon; 3021, Smilodon; 3022, Glyptodon; 3023, Protohydrocherus; 3024, Archaeohyrax; 3025, Pyrotherium; 3026, Platypittamys. HORIZ: $12.80 (3027), Harpy eagle and hyacinth macaw; 3028, Andean condor; 3029, Amazonian umbrellabird; 3030, Spider monkeys; 3031, Hyacinth macaws; 3032, Red siskin; 3033, Toucan barbet; 3034, Three-toed sloth; 3035, Guanacos; 3036, Spectacled bear; 3037, White-lipped peccary; 3038, Maned wolf; 3039, Jaguar; 3040, Spectacled cayman; 3041, Giant armadillo; 3042, Giant anteater; 3043, South American river otter; 3044, Yapok; 3045, Central American river turtle; 3046, Cauca guan.
Nos. 2967/86, 2987/3006, 3007/26 and 3027/46 respectively were printed together, se-tenant, forming composite designs.
No. 2982 is inscribed "Toucanette" and No. 2995 "Bellbird", both in error.

468 Ramon Folist (Cuba) (fencing, 1900)

1991. Winter Olympic Games, Albertville (1st issue), and Olympic Games, Barcelona. Previous Gold Medal Winners. Multicoloured.
3048/3119 $15.30 × 9, $17.80 × 9, $20 × 18, $25 × 18 and $30 × 18
Set of 72 . . . . . . 30·00 32·00
DESIGNS: $15.30 (3049), Lucien Gaudin (France) (fencing, 1924); 3050, Ole Lilloe-Olsen (Norway) (shooting, 1924); 3051, Morris Fisher (U.S.A.) (rifle shooting, 1924); 3052, Ray Ewry (U.S.A.) (long jump, 1900); 3053, Hubert van Innes (Belgium) (archery, 1900); 3054, Alvin Kraenzlein (U.S.A.) (hurdles, 1900); 3055, Johnny Weissmuller (U.S.A.) (swimming, 1924); 3056, Hans Winkler (West Germany) (show jumping, 1956); $17.80 (3057), Viktor Chukarin (Russia) (gymnastics, 1952); 3058, Agnes Keleti (Hungary) (gymnastics, 1952); 3059, Barbel Wochel (East Germany) (200 metres, 1980); 3060, Eric Heiden (U.S.A.) (speed skating, 1980); 3061, Alvodar Gerevich (Hungary) (fencing, 1932); 3062, Giuseppe Delfino (Italy) (fencing, 1952); 3063, Alexander Tikhonov (Russia) (skiing, 1980); 3064, Pahud de Mortanges (Netherlands) (equestrian, 1932); 3065, Patricia McCormick (U.S.A.) (diving, 1952); $20 (3066), Olga Korbut (Russia) (gymnastics, 1972); 3067, Lyudmila Turischeva (Russia) (gymnastics, 1972); 3068, Lasse Viren (Finland) (10,000 metres, 1972); 3069, George Miez (Switzerland) (gymnastics, 1936); 3070, Roland Matthes (East Germany) (swimming, 1972); 3071, Pal Kovaks (Hungary) (fencing, 1936); 3072, Jesse Owens (U.S.A.) (200 metres, 1936); 3073, Mark Spitz (U.S.A.) (swimming, 1972); 3074, Eduardo Mangiarotti (Italy) (fencing, 1936); 3075, Nelli Kim (Russia) (gymnastics, 1976); 3076, Viktor Krovopuskov (Russia) (fencing, 1976); 3077, Viktor Sidiak (Russia) (fencing, 1976); 3078, Nikolai Andrianov (Russia) (gymnastics, 1976); 3079, Nadia Comaneci (Rumania) (gymnastics, 1976); 3080, Mitsuo Tsukahara (Japan) (gymnastics, 1976); 3081, Yelena Novikova-Belova (Russia) (fencing, 1976); 3082, John Naber (U.S.A.) (swimming, 1976); 3083, Kornella Ender (Rumania) (swimming, 1976); $25 (3084), Lydia Skoblikova (Russia) (speed skating, 1964); 3085, Ivar Ballangrud (Norway) (speed skating, 1936); 3086, Clas Thunberg (Finland) (speed skating, 1928); 3087, Anton Heida (U.S.A.) (gymnastics, 1904); 3088, Akinori Nakayama (Japan) (gymnastics, 1968); 3089, Sixten Jernberg (Sweden) (skiing, 1964); 3090, Yevgeniy Grischin (Russia) (speed skating, 1956); 3091, Paul Radmilovic (East Germany) (waterpolo, 1920); 3092, Charles Daniels (U.S.A.) (swimming, 1904); 3093, Sawao Kato (Japan) (gymnastics, 1968); 3094, Rudolf Karpati (Hungary) (fencing, 1948); 3095, Jeno Fuchs (Hungary) (fencing, 1908); 3096, Emil Zatopek (Czechoslovakia) (10,000 metres, 1948); 3097, Fanny Blankers-Koen (Netherlands) (hurdles, 1948); 3098, Melvin Sheppard (U.S.A.) (4 x 400 metres relay, 1908); 3099, Gert Fredriksson (Sweden) (kayak, 1948); 3100, Paul Elvstrom (Denmark) (sailing, 1948); 3101, Harrison Dillard (U.S.A.) (100 metres, 1948); $30 (3102), Al Oerter (U.S.A.) (discus, 1956); 3103, Polina Atsakhova (Russia) (gymnastics, 1956); 3104, Takashi Ono (Japan) (gymnastics, 1956); 3105, Valentin Muratov (Russia) (gymnastics, 1956); 3106, Henri St. Cyr (Sweden) (equestrian, 1956); 3107, Iain Murray Rose (Australia) (swimming, 1956); 3108, Larisa Latynina (Russia) (gymnastics, 1956); 3109, Carlo Pavesi (Italy) (fencing, 1956); 3110, Dawn Fraser (Australia) (swimming, 1956); 3111, Betty Cuthbert (Australia) (400 metres, 1964); 3112, Vera Caslavska (Czechoslovakia) (gymnastics, 1964); 3113, Galin Kulakova (Russia) (skiing, 1972); 3114, Yukio Endo (Japan) (gymnastics, 1972); 3115, Vladimir Morozov (Russia) (kayak, 1972); 3116, Boris Shaklin (Russia) (gymnastics, 1964); 3117, Don Schollander (U.S.A.) (swimming, 1964); 3118, Gyozo Kulscar (Hungary) (fencing, 1964); 3119, Christian D'Oriloa (France) (fencing, 1956).
Nos. 3048/56, 3057/65, 3066/74, 3075/83, 3084/92, 3093/3101, 3102/10 and 3111/19 respectively were printed together, se-tenant, forming composite designs.
Sheetlets containing Nos. 3057/65, 3084/92 and 3111/19 were subsequently re-issued with Nos. 3063, 3086 and 3113 overprinted "ALBERTVILLE '92".
See also Nos. 3186/94 and 3246/53.

1991. 85th Anniv of Rotary International (1990).
(a) Nos. 2789/94 and 2859/60 optd or surch **Paul Percy Harris Founder 1868–1947** and emblem (A) or with Rotary emblem and **1905–1990** (B).
3121 80 c. Type **464** (B) 10 10
3122 $2.55 "Rhetus dysonii" (A) . . 10 10
3123 $5 "Actinote anteas" (A) . . . 10 10
3124 $6.40 "Heliconius tales" (A) . 10 10
3125 $7.65 "Thecla telemus" (A) . . 10 10
3126 $100 on $8.90 "Theope eudocia" (A) . . . . 1·25 1·40
3127 $190 on $50 "Heliconius vicini" (B) . . . . 2·25 2·50
3128 $225 on $100 "Amarynthis meneria" (B) . . . . 2·50 2·75

(b) Nos. 2795/2810 optd or surch as Nos. 3121/8 or with emblems and inscriptions of other international organizations.
3129 $10 "Heliconius vetustus" (B) . 15 15
3130 $10 "Mesosemia eumene" (optd Boy Scout emblem and **1907–1992**) 15 15
3131 $10 "Parides phosphorus" (optd Lions Club emblem and **1917–1992**) 15 15
3132 $10 "Polystichtis emylius" (A) . 15 15
3133 $10 "Xanthocleis aedesia" (optd **125 Years Red Cross** and cross) 15 15
3134 $10 "Doxocopa agathina" (optd with part Rotary emblem) . 15 15
3135 $10 "Adelpha plesaure" (optd with part Rotary emblem) . 15 15
3136 $10 "Heliconius wallacei" (optd **125 Years Red Cross** and cross) 15 15
3137 $10 "Notheme eumeus" (optd Lions Club emblem and **1917–1992**) 15 15
3138 $10 "Melinaea mediatrix" (optd with part Rotary emblem) . 15 15
3139 $10 "Theritas coronata" (optd with part Rotary emblem) . 15 15
3140 $10 "Dismorphia orise" (optd Boy Scout emblem and **1907–1992**) 15 15
3141 $50 on $10 "Phyciodes ianthe" (A) 65 65
3142 $75 on $10 "Morpho aega" (surch Boy Scout emblem and **1907–1992**) . . . . . . 1·00 1·10
3143 $100 on $10 "Zaretis isidora" (surch Lions Club emblem and **1917–1992**) . . . . . 1·25 1·40
3144 $190 on $10 "Pierella lena" (B) . . . . 2·25 2·50

1991. 65th Birthday of Queen Elizabeth II and 70th Birthday of Prince Philip. As T **198a** of Gambia. Multicoloured.

3146 $12.80 Queen and Prince Philip in evening dress 15 20
3147 $15.30 Queen Elizabeth II . . 15 20
3148 $100 Queen and Prince Philip . 1·00 1·10
3149 $130 Prince Philip . . . . . 1·25 1·40
3150 $150 Prince Philip in R.A.F. uniform . . . . 1·50 1·60
3151 $200 The Queen with Queen Elizabeth the Queen Mother . . . . 2·25 2·40

1991. 10th Wedding Anniv of Prince and Princess of Wales. As T **198b** of Gambia. Multicoloured.

3153 $8.90 Prince and Princess of Wales 20 20
3154 $50 Separate portraits of Princess and sons 80 80
3155 $75 Prince Charles with Prince William . . . . 1·25 1·25
3156 $190 Princess Diana with Prince Henry . . . . 2·75 3·00

1991. 75th Anniv of Lions International (1992). (a) Nos. 2789/94 and 2859/60 optd or surch **Melvin Jones Founder 1880–1961** (A) or with Lions Club emblem and **Lions International 1917–1992** (B).

3158 80 c. Type **464** (B) 15 10
3159 $2.55 "Rhetus dysonii" (B) . . 20 15
3160 $5 "Actinote anteas" (A) . . . 30 20
3161 $6.40 "Heliconius tales" (A) . . 30 25
3162 $7.65 "Thecla telemus" (A) . . 30 25
3163 $100 on $8.90 "Theope eudocia" (A) . . . . 1·50 1·50
3164 $190 on $50 "Heliconius vicini" (B) . . . . 2·50 2·75
3165 $225 on $100 "Amarynthis meneria" (B) . . . . 2·50 2·75

(b) Nos. 2843/58 optd or surch as Nos. 3158/65 or with emblems and inscriptions of other international organizations.

3166 $10 "Thecla telemus" (optd Lions Club emblem and **1917–1992**) 15 15
3167 $10 "Thyridia confusa" (optd Rotary emblem and **1905–1990**) 15 15
3168 $10 "Heliconius burneyi" (optd Boy Scout emblem and **1907–1992**) 15 15
3169 $10 "Parides lysander" (A) . . 15 15
3170 $10 "Eunica orphise" (optd **125 Years Red Cross** and cross) 15 15
3171 $10 "Adelpha melona" (optd with part Lions Club emblem) 15 15
3172 $10 "Morpho menelaus" (optd with part Lions Club emblem) 15 15
3173 $10 "Nymula phylleus" (optd **125 Years Red Cross** and cross) 15 15
3174 $10 "Stalachtis phlegia" (optd Rotary emblem and **1905–1990**) 15 15
3175 $10 "Theope barea" (optd with part Lions Club emblem) . 15 15
3176 $10 "Morpho perseus" (optd with part Lions Club emblem) 15 15
3177 $10 "Lycorea ceres" (optd Boy Scout emblem and **1907–1992**) 15 15
3178 $50 on $10 "Archonias bellona" (A) 65 65
3179 $75 on $10 "Caerois chorinaeus" (surch Boy Scout emblem and **1907–1992**) . . 1·00 1·10
3180 $100 on $10 "Vila azeca" (surch Rotary emblem and **1905–1990**) . . . . 1·25 1·40
3181 $190 on $10 "Nessaea batesii" (surch Lions Club emblem and **1917–1992**) . . . . . 2·25 2·50

1991. Winter Olympic Games, Albertville (1992) (2nd issue). Nos. 2738/46 optd or surch **ALBERTVILLE 92** or **XVIth Olympic Winter Games in Albertville** (No. 3190).

3186/94 $20 x 6, $70 on $20, $100 on $20, $190 on $20
Set of 9 . . . . 8·50 9·00

474 "Akagi" (Japanese aircraft carrier)

1991. 50th Anniv of Japanese Attack on Pearl Harbor. Each blue, red and black.

3197 $50 Type **474** 85 85
3198 $50 Beached Japanese midget submarine 85 85
3199 $50 Mitsubishi A6M Zero-Sen fighter 85 85
3200 $50 U.S.S. "Arizona" (battleship) under attack . . 85 85
3201 $50 Aichi D3A1 "Val" dive bomber 85 85
3202 $50 U.S.S. "California" (battleship) sinking 85 85
3203 $50 Curtiss P-40 fighters taking off 85 85
3204 $50 U.S.S. "Cassin" and U.S.S. "Downes" damaged in dry dock 85 85
3205 $50 Boeing B-17 Flying Fortress crash landing at Bellows Field 85 85
3206 $50 U.S.S. "Nevada" (battleship) on fire 85 85

475 Brandenburg Gate and Location Plan

1991. Anniversaries and Events. Multicoloured.

3207 $10 Type **475** 20 20
3208 $25 President Bush, President Lech Walesa of Poland and Brandenburg Gate 50 50
3209 $25 Scout handshake 50 50
3210 $30 Scouts hiking at Philmont Scout Ranch 60 60
3211 $40 Jamboree and Scout Movement emblems 70 70
3212 $60 General de Gaulle at Venice, 1944 . . . . 90 90
3213 $75 De Gaulle with Khrushchev, 1960 . . . . 1·25 1·25
3214 $75 Mozart and Castle of Laxenburg . . . . 1·25 1·25
3215 $75 Caroline Herschel (astronomer) and Old Town Hall, Hanover . . . . . . 1·25 1·25
3216 $75 Map of Switzerland and woman in Valais costume . 1·25 1·25
3217 $80 De Gaulle at Algiers, 1958 . 1·40 1·40
3218 $80 Mozart and death of Leopold II . . . . 1·40 1·40
3219 $80 Otto Lilienthal and "Flugzeug Nr. 3" . . . . . 1·40 1·40
3220 $100 Chancellor Kohl, Foreign Minister Genscher and Brandenburg Gate . . . . 1·50 1·50
3221 $100 Lord Baden-Powell (vert) 1·50 1·50
3222 $100 De Gaulle with Pope Paul VI, 1967 . . . . 1·50 1·50
3223 $100 Mozart and birthplace, Salzburg . . . . 1·50 1·50
3224 $100 Class P36 steam locomotive . . . . 1·50 1·50

ANNIVERSARIES and EVENTS: Nos. 3207/8, 3220, Bicentenary of Brandenburg Gate, Berlin; 3209/11, 3221, 17th World Scout Jamboree, Korea; 3212/13, 3217, 3222, Birth centenary (1990) of Charles de Gaulle (French statesman); 3214, 3218, 3223, Death bicentenary of Mozart; 3215, 750th anniv of Hanover; 3216, 700th anniv of Swiss Confederation; 3219, Centenary of Otto Lilienthal's first gliding experiments; 3224, Centenary of Trans-Siberian Railway.

No. 3222 is inscribed "Pope John VI" in error.

476 Disney Characters Carol Singing, 1989

1991. Christmas. Walt Disney Christmas Cards. Multicoloured.

3226 80 c. Type **476** 10 10
3227 $2.55 Disney characters and carol singers in tram, 1962 . 15 15
3228 $5 Donald Duck and Pluto with parcel, 1971 . . . . 20 20
3229 $6.40 "SEASON'S GREETINGS" and Mickey Mouse with candle, 1948 . . 20 20
3230 $7.65 Mickey Mouse as Father Christmas, 1947 . . . . . 20 20
3231 $8.90 Shadow of Pinocchio with candle, 1939 . . . . 20 20
3232 $50 Three Little Pigs dancing on wolf rug, 1933 . . . . . . 90 90
3233 $50 Conductor and Donald Duck, 1940 (vert) 90 90
3234 $50 Elephant and ostrich carol singing, 1940 (vert) 90 90
3235 $50 Hippo, centaurs, Pinocchio and Goofy, 1940 (vert) . . 90 90
3236 $50 Snow White, Dopey, Mickey and Minnie, 1940 (vert) 90 90
3237 $50 Dino, Pluto and Walt Disney, 1940 (vert) 90 90
3238 $50 Mickey Mouse in sleigh, 1974 (vert) 90 90
3239 $50 Three Little Pigs, Winnie the Pooh, Bambi and Thumper, 1974 (vert) 90 90
3240 $50 Baloo, King Louis, Lady and the Tramp, 1974 (vert) . 90 90
3241 $50 Alice, Robin Hood, the Cheshire Cat and Goofy, 1974 (vert) 90 90
3242 $50 Dumbo, Pinocchio, Peter Pan, Tinkerbelle, Seven Dwarfs and Donald Duck, 1974 (vert) 90 90
3243 $50 Pluto pulling sleigh, 1974 (vert) 90 90
3244 $200 Mickey and mice carol singing, 1949 . . . . 3·50 4·00

477 Gus Gander playing Ice Hockey

1991. Winter Olympic Games, Albertville (1992) (3rd issue). Walt Disney Cartoon Characters. Multicoloured.

3246 $6.40 Type **477** 20 10
3247 $7.65 Mickey and Minnie Mouse in bobsleigh 20 10
3248 $8.90 Donald's Nephews on luge and skis 25 10
3249 $12.80 Goofy freestyle skiing . 40 20
3250 $50 Goofy ski jumping . . . . 1·00 1·00
3251 $100 Donald and Daisy Duck speed skating . . . . . . 1·75 1·75
3252 $130 Pluto cross-country skiing 2·00 2·25
3253 $190 Mickey and Minnie Mouse ice dancing . . . . 3·00 3·50

478 Columbus landing on Trinidad

1992. 500th Anniv of Discovery of America by Columbus. Multicoloured.

3255 $6.40 Type **478** 40 40
3256 $7.65 Columbus the map-maker 45 45
3257 $8.90 Fleet blown off course . 45 45
3258 $12.80 Map of third voyage and Columbus in chains 55 55
3259 $15.30 Sighting land 55 55
3260 $50 "Nina" and "Pinta" . . . 90 90
3261 $75 "Santa Maria" . . . . . 1·25 1·25
3262 $100 Columbus trading with Amerindians . . . . 1·75 1·75
3263 $125 Crew and sea monster . . 2·00 2·00
3264 $130 Columbus landing on San Salvador and map of first voyage . . . . 2·00 2·00
3265 $140 Priest and Amerindians . 2·00 2·00
3266 $150 Columbus before King Ferdinand and Queen Isabella of Spain . . . . . 2·00 2·00

479 Tom Mix in "The Great K&A Train Robbery", 1926

1992. Classic Movie Posters. Multicoloured.

3268 $8.90 Type **479** 40 40
3269 $12.80 Richard Dix and Irene Dunne in "Cimarron", 1931 50 50
3270 $15.30 Fatty Arbuckle in "Buzzin' Around", 1934 . . 50 50
3271 $25 Tom Tyler in "The Adventures of Captain Marvel", 1941 . . . . . . 70 70
3272 $30 Boris Karloff in "The Mummy", 1932 . . . . . . 85 85
3273 $50 Rudolph Valentino in "A Sainted Devil", 1924 . . . 1·10 1·10
3274 $75 Seven posters for "A Tale of Two Cities", 1935 . . . . 1·40 1·40
3275 $100 Chester Conklin in "A Tugboat Romeo", 1916 . . 1·90 1·90
3276 $130 Douglas Fairbanks in "The Thief of Bagdad", 1924 . . . . 2·25 2·25
3277 $150 Laurel and Hardy in "Bacon Grabbers", 1929 . . 2·75 2·75
3278 $190 Marx Brothers in "A Night at the Opera", 1935 . 3·50 3·50
3279 $200 Orson Welles in "Citizen Kane", 1941 . . . . 3·50 3·50

1992. Easter. Paintings by Durer. As T **204a** of Gambia. Multicoloured.

3281 $6.40 "The Martyrdom of Ten Thousand" (detail) 25 10
3282 $7.65 "Adoration of the Trinity" (detail of Virgin Mary) 25 10
3283 $12.80 "The Martyrdom of Ten Thousand" (execution detail) 40 20
3284 $15.30 "Adoration of the Trinity" (different detail) . . 45 25
3285 $50 "The Martyrdom of Ten Thousand" (detail of bishop) 1·00 75
3286 $100 "Adoration of the Trinity" (different detail) . . . . . 1·50 1·50
3287 $130 "The Martyrdom of Ten Thousand" (different detail) . . . . 1·75 2·00
3288 $190 "Adoration of the Trinity" (different detail) . . . . . 3·25 4·00

1992. Baha'i Holy Year. Surch **BAHA'I HOLY YEAR 1992** and value.

3290 $6.40 on 60 c. Plate No. 10 (Series 1) (No. 1521)
3291 $7.65 on 60 c. Plate No. 31 (Series 1) (No. 1523)
3292 $8.90 on 60 c. Plate No. 19 (Series 1) (No. 1522)
3293 $50 on 60 c. Plate No. 2 (Series 1) (No. 1519)

481 Queen Elizabeth II and Duke of Edinburgh

1992. 40th Anniv of Queen Elizabeth II's Accession. Multicoloured.

3294 $8.90 Type **481** 35 25
3295 $12.80 Queen at Trooping the Colour 40 30
3296 $100 Queen at Coronation . . 2·25 2·25
3297 $130 Queen in Garter robes . 2·50 2·50

482 Holy Cross Church, Annai Rupununi

1992. 150th Anniv of Diocese of Guyana. Multicoloured.

3299 $6.40 Type **482** 15 10
3300 $50 St. Peter's Church 80 65
3301 $100 Interior of St. George's Cathedral (vert) . . . . . 1·50 1·60
3302 $190 Map of Guyana (vert) . . 2·75 3·25

483 Burmese

1992. Cats. Multicoloured.

3304 $5 Type **483** 10 10
3305 $6.40 Turkish van 10 10
3306 $12.80 American shorthair . . 15 20
3307 $15.30 Sphynx 15 20
3308 $50 Egyptian mau 50 55
3309 $50 Russian blue 50 55
3310 $50 Havana brown 50 55
3311 $50 Himalayan 50 55
3312 $50 Manx 50 55
3313 $50 Cornish rex 50 55
3314 $50 Black Persian 50 55
3315 $50 Scottish fold 50 55
3316 $50 Siamese 50 55
3317 $100 Japanese bobtail . . . . 1·00 1·10
3318 $130 Abyssinian . . . . . . 1·25 1·40
3319 $225 Oriental shorthair . . . 2·25 2·40

484 Red Howler

1992. Animals of Guyana. Multicoloured.

3321 $8.90 Type **484** 20 10
3322 $12.80 Ring-tailed coati . . . 25 20
3323 $15.30 Jaguar 30 20
3324 $25 Two-toed sloth 50 30
3325 $50 Giant armadillo . . . . . 1·00 80
3326 $75 Giant anteater . . . . . 1·50 1·75
3327 $100 Capybara . . . . 1·75 1·90
3328 $130 Ocelot . . . . 2·00 2·25

485 Oligocene Mammoth

1992. Elephants. Multicoloured.

3330 $50 Type **485** . . . . 1·25 1·25
3331 $50 Mid-Miocene stegodon . . 1·25 1·25
3332 $50 Pliocene mammoth . . . 1·25 1·25
3333 $50 Carthaginian elephant crossing Alps, 219 B.C. . . . 1·25 1·25
3334 $50 Ceremonial elephant of Maharaja of Mysore, India . 1·25 1·25

3335 $50 Elephant pulling teak trunks, Burma 1·25 1·25
3336 $50 Tiger-hunting by elephant, India 1·25 1·25
3337 $50 Elephant towing raft on River Kwai, Thailand 1·25 1·25

486 Palomino

1992. Horses. Multicoloured.

3339 $190 Type **486** 3·00 3·00
3340 $190 Appaloosa 3·00 3·00
3341 $190 Clydesdale 3·00 3·00
3342 $190 Arab 3·00 3·00
3343 $190 Morgan 3·00 3·00
3344 $190 Friesian 3·00 3·00
3345 $190 Pinto 3·00 3·00
3346 $190 Thoroughbred 3·00 3·00

No. 3340 is inscribed "APALOOSA" in error.

1992. International Conference on Nutrition, Rome. Surch **INT. CONFERENCE ON NUTRITION 1992** and value.

3348 $6.40 on 150 c. Plate No. 45 (Series 1) (No. 1769)
3349 $7.65 on 150 c. Plate No. 42 (Series 1) (No. 1768)
3350 $8.90 on 150 c. Plate No. 40 (Series 1) (No. 1767)
3351 $10 on 200 c. Plate No. 43 (Series 1) (No. 1658)
3352 $50 on 200 c. Plate No. 43 (Series 1) (No. 1658)

488 Marklin Swiss "Crocodile" Locomotive, 1933

1992. "Genova '92" International Thematic Stamp Exhibition. Toy Trains from German Manufacturers. Multicoloured.

3353/61 $45 × 9 (Made by Marklin: Type **488**; French tramcar, 1902; British "Flatiron" tank engine, 1913; German switching engine, 1970; Third class carriage, 1909; American style locomotive, 1904; Zurich tramcar, 1928; Central London Railway locomotive in Paris–Orleans livery, 1904; British GWR "Great Bear" locomotive, 1909
3362/70 $45 × 9 (Made by Marklin: LMS "Precursor" tank engine, 1923; American "Congressional Limited" passenger carriage, 1908; Swiss Type "Ae 3/6" locomotive, 1934; German Class 80, 1975; British Southern Railways third class carriage, 1926; LNWR Bowen-Cooke tank engine, 1913; London Underground "Two Penny Tube", 1901; French Paris–Orsay steeplecab, 1920; Passenger locomotive, 1895
3371/9 $45 × 9 (Made by Marklin: American style locomotive, 1907; German passenger carriage, 1908; British Great Eastern Railway locomotive, 1908; London Underground steeplecab, 1904; Santa Fe Railroad diesel locomotive, 1962; British GNR locomotive, 1903; Caledonian Railway "Cardean", 1906; British LNWR passenger carriage, 1903; Swiss St. Gotthard Railway locomotive, 1920
3380/8 $45 × 9 (Made by Marklin: British LB & SCR tank engine No. 22, 1920; Central London Railway steeplecab locomotive, 1904; German "Borsig" streamlined, 1935; French Paris–Lyon–Mediterranee first class carriage, 1929; American style locomotive No. 1021, 1904; French Paris–Orsay long-nose steeplecab, 1920; British LNER "Cock o' the North", 1936; Prussian State Railways Class P8, 1975; German diesel railcar set, 1937
3389/97 $45×9 (Marklin North British Railway "Atlantic", 1913; Bing British LNWR "Precursor", 1916; Marklin British GWR "King George V", 1937; Marklin "Kaiser Train" passenger carriage, 1901; Bing side tank locomotive No. 88, 1904; Marklin steeplecab, 1912; Marklin "Adler", 1935; Bing British GWR "County of Northampton", 1909; Bing British Midland Railway "Black Prince", 1908
3398/3406 $45 × 9 (Made by Bing: Midland Railway "Deeley Type" No. 483, 1909; British Midland Railway No. 2631, 1903; German Pacific, 1927; British GWR third class coach, 1926; British LSWR "M7" No. 109, 1909; Side tank engine "Pilot", 1901; British LNWR Webb "Cauliflower", 1912; Side tank locomotive No. 112, 1910; British GNR "Stirling Single", 1904
3407/15 $45 × 9 (Carette tin "Penny Bazaar" train, 1904; Winteringham locomotive, 1917; Carette British Northeastern Railway Smith Compound, 1905; Carette S.E. & C.R. steam railcar, 1908; Carette British Great Northern Railway Stirling Single No. 776, 1903; Carette British Midland Railways locomotive No. 1132M, 1911; Carette London Metropolitan Railway Co. "Westinghouse" locomotive No. 5, 1908; Carette Clestory carriage, 1907; Carette steam railcar No. 1, 1906
3416/24 $45 × 9 (Made by Bing: Engine and tender, 1895; British Midland Railway "Single" No. 650, 1913; No. 524/510 reversible locomotive, 1916; "Kaiser Train" passenger carriage, 1902; British rural station, 1915; British LSWR M7 tank locomotive, 1909; "Windcutter", 1912; British Great Central Railway "Sir Sam Fay", 1914; Scottish Caledonian Railway "Dunalastair" locomotive, 1910)
3353/3424 Set of 72 40·00 45·00

489 Aquarius

1992. Signs of the Zodiac. Multicoloured.

3427 $30 Type **489** 80 80
3428 $30 Pisces 80 80
3429 $30 Aries 80 80
3430 $30 Taurus 80 80
3431 $30 Gemini 80 80
3432 $30 Cancer 80 80
3433 $30 Leo 80 80
3434 $30 Virgo 80 80
3435 $30 Libra 80 80
3436 $30 Scorpio 80 80
3437 $30 Sagittarius 80 80
3438 $30 Capricorn 80 80

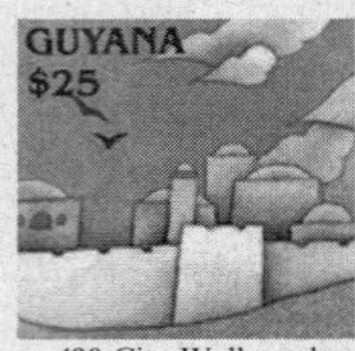

490 City Walls and Two Birds

1992. Bible Stories (1st series). David and Goliath. Multicoloured.

3439 $25 Type **490** 50 50
3440 $25 City walls and one bird at right 50 50
3441 $25 Sun over city gateway 50 50
3442 $25 City walls and one bird at left 50 50
3443 $25 City walls and no birds 50 50
3444 $25 Philistine army and edge of shield 50 50
3445 $25 Goliath's head and torso 50 50
3446 $25 Goliath's arm and spear 50 50
3447 $25 Philistine army and spearhead 50 50
3448 $25 Philistine infantry 50 50
3449 $25 Philistine cavalry and infantry 50 50
3450 $25 Goliath's shield 50 50
3451 $25 Goliath's waist and thigh 50 50
3452 $25 David with sling 50 50
3453 $25 Israelite soldier with spear 50 50
3454 $25 Two Israelite soldiers with spears and shields 50 50
3455 $25 Goliath's right leg 50 50
3456 $25 Goliath's left leg (face value at foot) 50 50
3457 $25 David's legs and Israelite standard 50 50
3458 $25 Three Israelite soldiers 50 50
3459 $25 Israelite soldier and parts of two shields 50 50
3460 $25 Israelite soldier with sword 50 50
3461 $25 Back of Israelite soldier 50 50
3462 $25 Israelite soldier leaning on rock 50 50
3463 $25 Israelite soldier looking left 50 50

Nos. 3439/63 were printed together, se-tenant, forming a composite design.

See also Nos. 4020/4116.

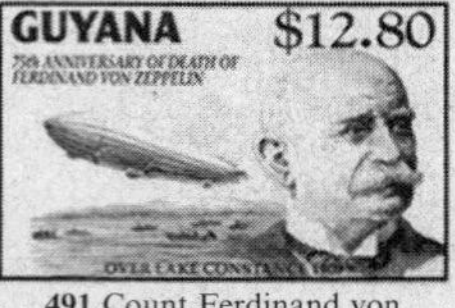

491 Count Ferdinand von Zeppelin and Airship over Lake Constance, 1909

1992. Anniversaries and Events. Multicoloured.

3464 $12.80 Type **491** 50 35
3465 $50 "Voyager I" and Jupiter 1·50 1·00
3466 $50 Chancellor Adenauer with President Kennedy, 1961 1·00 1·00
3467 $100 Aeromedical airlift 2·00 2·00
3468 $100 Boutu ("Amazon Dolphin") 2·00 2·00
3469 $130 Baby gorilla 2·50 2·50
3470 $130 Mobile eye screening unit and doctor with child 2·50 2·50
3471 $130 "Stars and Stripes" (winning yacht, 1987) 2·50 2·50
3472 $130 Lift-off of "Voyager I", 1977 2·50 2·50
3473 $190 Adenauer with President De Gaulle of France, 1962 3·25 3·25
3474 $225 Von Zeppelin and airship preparing for take-off, 1905 3·50 3·50

ANNIVERSARIES and EVENTS: Nos. 3464, 3474, 75th death anniv of Count Ferdinand von Zeppelin; 3465, 3472, International Space Year; 3466, 3473, 75th death anniv of Konrad Adenauer (German statesman); 3467, United Nations World Health Organization projects; 3468/9, Earth Summit '92, Rio; 3470, 75th anniv of International Association of Lions Clubs; 3471, Americas Cup Yachting Championship.

492 Hyacinth Macaw

1993. South American Parrots. Multicoloured.

3476 80 c. Type **492** 30 15
3477 $6.40 Scarlet macaw (preening) 50 25
3478 $7.65 Buffon's macaw ("Green Macaw") (vert) 50 25
3479 $15.30 Orange-chinned parakeet ("Tovi Parakeet") 70 50
3480 $50 Blue and yellow macaw 1·00 80
3481 $100 Military macaw (vert) 1·50 1·25
3482 $130 Green-winged macaw ("Red and Green Macaw") (vert) 1·75 1·75
3483 $190 Chestnut-fronted macaw ("Severa Macaw") 2·50 3·00

493 Crimson Topaz

1993. Birds of Guyana. Multicoloured.

3485 $50 Type **493** 75 75
3486 $50 Bearded bellbird 75 75
3487 $50 Amazonian umbrellabird 75 75
3488 $50 Paradise jacamar 75 75
3489 $50 Paradise tanager 75 75
3490 $50 White-tailed trogon 75 75
3491 $50 Scarlet macaw 75 75
3492 $50 Hawk-headed parrot ("Red-fan Parrot") 75 75
3493 $50 Cuvier's toucan ("Red-billed Toucan") 75 75
3494 $50 White-faced antcatcher ("White-plumed Antbird") 75 75
3495 $50 Crimson-hooded manakin 75 75
3496 $50 Guianan cock of the rock 75 75

Nos. 3485/96 were printed together, se-tenant, with the backgrounds forming a composite design.

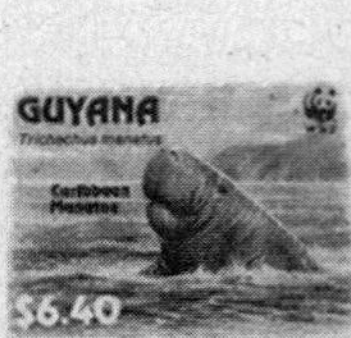

494 Manatee surfacing

495 Tamandua

1993. Endangered Species. American Manatee ("Caribbean Manatee"). Multicoloured.

3498 $6.40 Type **494** 50 30
3499 $7.60 Cow and calf feeding 50 30
3500 $8.90 Manatee underwater 50 30
3501 $50 Two manatees 2·00 2·00

1993. Animals of Guyana. Multicoloured.

3502 $50 Type **495** 75 75
3503 $50 Pale-throated sloth ("Three-toed Sloth") 75 75
3504 $50 Red howler 75 75
3505 $50 Four-eyed opossum 75 75
3506 $50 Black spider monkey 75 75
3507 $50 Giant otter 75 75
3508 $50 Red brocket 75 75
3509 $50 Brazilian tree porcupine 75 75
3510 $50 Tayra 75 75
3511 $50 Brazilian tapir 75 75
3512 $50 Ocelot 75 75
3513 $50 Giant armadillo 75 75

Nos. 3502/13 were printed together, se-tenant, the backgrounds forming a composite design.

496 Pteranodon

1993. Prehistoric Animals. Multicoloured.

3515/26 $30 × 12 (Type **496**; Cearadactylus; Eudimorphodon; Pterodactylus; Staurikosaurus; Euoplocephalus; Tuojiangosaurus; Oviraptor; Protoceratops; Panaoplosaurus; Psittacosaurus; Corythosaurus)
3527/38 $30 × 12 (Sordes; Quetzalcoatlus; Archaeopteryx in flight; Rhamphorynchus; Spinosaurus; Anchisaurus; Stegosaurus; Leaellynosaurs; Minmi; Heterdontosaurus; esothosaurus; Deninonychus)
3539/50 $30 × 12 (Archaeopteryx on branch; Pteranodon (different); Quetzalcoatlus (three); Protoavis; Dicraeosaurus; Moschops; Lystrosaurus; Dimetrondon; Staurikosaurus; Cacops; Diarthrognathus; Estemmenosuchus)
3515/50 Set of 36 13·50 15·00

Nos. 3515/26, 3527/38 and 3539/50 respectively were printed together, se-tenant, with the backgrounds forming composite designs.

1993. 40th Anniv of Coronation. As T **215a** of Gambia. Multicoloured.

3551 $25 Queen Elizabeth II in Coronation robes (photograph by Cecil Beaton) 85 85
3552 $50 Royal gems 1·25 1·25
3553 $75 Queen Elizabeth and Prince Philip 1·40 1·40
3554 $130 Queen opening Parliament 1·75 2·00

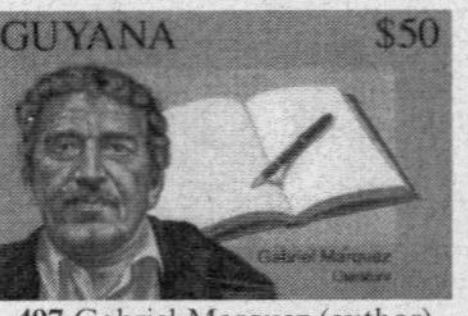

497 Gabriel Marquez (author)

1993. Famous People of the Twentieth Century. Multicoloured. (a) Arts and Literature.

3556 $50 Type **497** 75 75
3557 $50 Pablo Picasso (artist) 75 75
3558 $50 Cecil De Mille (film director) 75 75
3559 $50 Martha Graham (dancer) 75 75
3560 $50 Peace dove (inscr "20th Century Arts and Literature") 75 75
3561 $50 Charlie Chaplin (actor) 75 75
3562 $50 Paul Robeson (actor) 75 75
3563 $50 Rudolph Dunbar (musician) 75 75
3564 $50 Louis Armstrong (musician) 75 75

(b) Science and Medicine.

3566 $50 Louis Leakey (archaeologist and anthropologist) 75 75
3567 $50 Jonas Salk (discoverer of polio vaccine) 75 75
3568 $50 Hideyo Noguchi (bacteriologist) 75 75
3569 $50 Karl Landsteiner (pathologist) 75 75
3570 $50 As No. 3550, but inscr "20th Century Science and Medicine" 75 75
3571 $50 Sigmund Freud (founder of psychoanalysis) 75 75
3572 $50 Louis Pasteur (chemist) 75 75
3573 $50 Madame Curie (physicist) 75 75
3574 $50 Jean Baptiste Perrin (physicist) 75 75

(c) Sports Personalities.

3576 $50 O. J. Simpson (American football) 75 75
3577 $50 Rohan Kanhai (cricket) 75 75
3578 $50 Gabriela Sabatini (tennis) 75 75
3579 $50 Severiano Ballesteros (golf) 75 75
3580 $50 As No. 3550, but inscr "20th Century Sports" 75 75
3581 $50 Franz Beckenbauer (football) 75 75
3582 $50 Pele (football) 75 75
3583 $50 Wilt Chamberlain (basketball) 75 75
3584 $50 Nadia Comaneci (gymnastics) 75 75

(d) Peace and Humanity.

3586 $100 Mahatma Gandhi (India) 1·10 1·10
3587 $100 Dalai Lama (Tibet) 1·10 1·10
3588 $100 Michael Manley (Jamaica) 1·10 1·10
3589 $100 Perez de Cuellar (U.N. Secretary-General) 1·10 1·10
3590 $100 Peace dove and globe 1·10 1·10
3591 $100 Mother Teresa (India) 1·10 1·10
3592 $100 Martin Luther King (U.S.A.) 1·10 1·10
3593 $100 Pres. Nelson Mandela (South Africa) 1·10 1·10
3594 $100 Raoul Wallenberg (Sweden) 1·10 1·10

(e) Politics.

3596 $100 Nehru (India) 1·10 1·10
3597 $100 Dr. Eric Williams (Trinidad and Tobago) 1·10 1·10

3598 $100 Pres. John F. Kennedy (U.S.A.) . . . . 1·10 1·10
3599 $100 Pres. Hugh Desmond Hoyte (Guyana) . . . . . 1·10 1·10
3600 $100 Peace dove and map of the Americas . . . . 1·10 1·10
3601 $100 Friedrich Ebert (Germany) . . . . 1·10 1·10
3602 $100 Pres. F. D. Roosevelt (U.S.A.) . . . . 1·10 1·10
3603 $100 Mikhail Gorbachev (Russia) . . . . 1·10 1·10
3604 $100 Sir Winston Churchill (Great Britain) . . . . . . 1·10 1·10

(f) Transportation and Technology.

3606 $100 Douglas DC-3 cargo plane . . . . 1·10 1·10
3607 $100 Space shuttle . . . . . 1·10 1·10
3608 $100 Concord . . . . 1·10 1·10
3609 $100 Count Ferdinand von Zeppelin and "Graf Zeppelin" . . . . 1·10 1·10
3610 $100 Peace dove and rocket trails . . . . 1·10 1·10
3611 $100 Marconi and aerial tower . . . . 1·10 1·10
3612 $100 Adrian Thompson (mountaineer) and Mt. Roraima . . . . 1·10 1·10
3613 $100 "Hikari" express train, Japan . . . . 1·10 1·10
3614 $100 Johann von Neumann and computer . . . . 1·10 1·10

Nos. 3556/64, 3566/74, 3576/84, 3586/94, 3596/3604 and 3606/14 respectively were printed together, se-tenant, with composite background designs on Nos. 3586/94, 3596/3604 and 3606/14.

No. 3562 is inscribed "Paul Roebeson" in error.

498 "Bather, Paris" (Picasso)

1993. Anniversaries and Events. Multicoloured.

3616 $15.30 Type **498** 15 20
3617 $25 Willy Brandt with Prime Minister of Israel Golda Meir, 1969 (horiz) 40 40
3618 $50 "Pantaloons" (left half) (Tadeusz Brzozowski) . . . 50 55
3619 $50 Georg Hackl (men's single luge, 1992) 70 70
3620 $50 Astrolabe 70 70
3621 $75 Miedzyrecz Castle 75 80
3622 $100 "Two Nudes" (Picasso) . 1·00 1·10
3623 $130 "Pantaloons" (right half) (Tadeusz Brzozowski) . . . 1·25 1·40
3624 $130 Karen Magnussen (women's figure skating, 1972) . . . . 1·50 1·50
3625 $190 "Nude seated on a Rock" (Picasso) . . . . 1·90 2·00
3626 $190 Willy Brandt at Georgsmarienhutten Steel Mill, 1969 (horiz) . . . . . 2·25 2·25
3627 $190 Dish aerial . . . . . . 2·25 2·25

ANNIVERSARIES and EVENTS: Nos. 3616, 3622, 3625, 20th death anniv of Picasso (artist); 3617, 3626, 80th birth anniv (1992) of Willy Brandt (German politician); 3618, 3621, 3623, "Polska '93" International Stamp Exhibition, Poznan; 3619, 3624, Winter Olympic Games '94, Lillehammer; 3620, 3627, 450th death anniv of Copernicus (astronomer).

Nos. 3618 and 3623 were printed together, se-tenant, forming a composite design showing the complete painting.

499 Audie Murphy (most decorated U.S. serviceman)

1993. 50th Anniv of Second World War (1st issue). Multicoloured.

3629 $6.40 Type **499** 40 20
3630 $7.65 Allied troops in Normandy (8 June 1944) . . 40 25
3631 $8.90 American howitzer crew, Battle of Montecassino (18 May 1944) 45 30
3632 $12.80 American aircraft attacking "Yamato" (Japanese battleship), Battle of East China Sea (7 April 1945) 60 50
3633 $15.30 St. Basil's Cathedral, Moscow (Foreign Ministers' Conference, 19 October 1943) 60 50
3634 $50 American troops crossing Rhine at Remagen (7 March 1945) . . . . 1·00 75
3635 $100 Boeing B-29 Super-fortresses raiding Japan from China (15 June 1944) . . . 1·75 1·60
3636 $130 General Patton and map of Sicily (17 August 1943) . . 1·90 2·00
3637 $190 Destruction of "Tirpitz" (German battleship) (12 November 1944) . . . . . 2·75 3·00
3638 $200 American forces in Brittany (1 August 1944) . . 2·75 3·00
3639 $225 American half-track (ceasefire in Italy, 2 May 1945) . . . . 3·00 3·50

No. 3631 is inscribed "Monte Casino" in error.

See also Nos. 3641/60 and 3942/61.

500 R.A.A.F. Bristol Type 156 Beaufighter, Battle of the Bismarck Sea (2–4 March 1943)

1993. 50th Anniv of Second World War (2nd issue). Multicoloured.

3641 $50 Type **500** 80 80
3642 $50 Lockheed P-38 Lightning attacking Admiral Yamamoto's plane, Bougainville (7 April 1943) . 80 80
3643 $50 Consolidated B-24 Liberator bombers, Tarawa (17–19 September 1943) . . 80 80
3644 $50 North American B-25 Mitchell bomber, Rabaul (12 October 1943) 80 80
3645 $50 U.S. Navy aircraft attacking Makin (19 November 1943) . 80 80
3646 $50 U.S.A.A.F. bombers on first daylight raid over Germany (27 January 1943) 80 80
3647 $50 R.A.F. De Havilland D.H.98 Mosquito bombers on first daylight raid over Berlin (30 January 1943) . . 80 80
3648 $50 Allied aircraft over Hamburg (24–30 July 1943) . 80 80
3649 $50 Consolidated B-24 Liberators bombing Ploesti oil refineries, Rumania (1 August 1943) 80 80
3650 $50 German nightfighter attacking Allied bombers over Berlin (18 November 1943) . 80 80
3651 $50 Japanese aircraft carriers during Operation 1 (7 April 1943) 80 80
3652 $50 Lt. John F. Kennedy's motor torpedo boat U.S.S. "PT109" in Blackett Strait (1 August 1943) 80 80
3653 $50 U.S.S. "Enterprise" (aircraft carrier) 80 80
3654 $50 American battleships bombarding Rabaul (12 October 1943) 80 80
3655 $50 American landing craft at Cape Gloucester (26 December 1943) 80 80
3656 $50 Commissioning of U.S.S. "Bogue" (first anti-submarine escort carrier) (February 1943) 80 80
3657 $50 Grumman FM-2 Wildcat fighters from U.S.S. "Bogue" sinking "U-118" 80 80
3658 $50 U-boat launching torpedo during peak of Battle of the Atlantic (March 1943) . . . 80 80
3659 $50 Surrender of Italian fleet at Malta (10 September 1943) . 80 80
3660 $50 H.M.S. "Duke of York" (battleship) sinking "Scharnhorst" (26 December 1943) 80 80

501 Stuart Pearce (England)

502 Sir Shridath Ramphal

1993. World Cup Football Championship, U.S.A. (1994) (1st issue). Multicoloured.

3661 $5 Type **501** 15 10
3662 $6.40 Ronald Koeman (Netherlands) 15 10
3663 $7.65 Gianluca Vialli (Italy) . 20 10
3664 $12.80 McStay (Scotland) and Alemao (Brazil) 30 20
3665 $15.30 Ceulemans (Belgium) and Butcher (England) . . 30 20
3666 $50 Dragan Stojkovic (Yugoslavia) 75 65
3667 $100 Ruud Gullit (Netherlands) . . . . . . 1·25 1·25
3668 $130 Miloslav Kadlec (Czechoslovakia) . . . . . 1·40 1·50
3669 $150 Ramos (Uruguay) and Berthold (Germany) . . . . 1·75 2·00
3670 $190 Baggio (Italy) and Wright (England) . . . . 2·25 2·50
3671 $200 Yarentchuck (Russia) and Renquin (Belgium) . . . . 2·40 2·75
3672 $225 Timofte (Rumania) and Aleinikov (Russia) . . . . 2·50 3·00

See also Nos. 4142/58.

1993. 1st Recipients of Order of the Caribbean Community. Multicoloured.

3674 $7.65 Type **502** 60 50
3675 $7.65 William Demas 60 50
3676 $7.65 Derek Walcott . . . . 1·00 65

1993. Christmas. Paintings by Rubens and Durer. As T **270** of Dominica. Each black, yellow and red (Nos. 3678, 3680/1, 3684) or multicoloured (others).

3677 $6.40 "The Holy Family under the Apple Tree" (detail) (Rubens) 10 10
3678 $7.65 "The Virgin in Glory" (detail) (Durer) 10 10
3679 $12.80 "The Holy Family under the Apple Tree" (different detail) (Rubens) 10 15
3680 $15.30 "The Virgin in Glory" (different detail) (Durer) . . 15 20
3681 $50 "The Virgin in Glory" (different detail) (Durer) . . 50 55
3682 $130 "The Holy Family under the Apple Tree" (different detail) (Rubens) . . . . . 1·25 1·40
3683 $190 "The Holy Family under the Apple Tree" (different detail) (Rubens) . . . . . 1·90 2·00
3684 $250 "The Virgin in Glory" (different detail) (Durer) . . 2·50 2·75

1993. Bicentenary of the Louvre, Paris. As T **209b** of Gambia. Multicoloured.

3686 $50 "Mona Lisa" (Leonardo da Vinci)
3687/94 $50 × 8 "Self-portrait with Spectacles" (Chardin), "Infanta Maria Theresa" (Velazquez); "Spring" (Arcimboldo); "The Virgin of Sorrows" (Bouts); "The Student" (Fragonard); "Francois I" (Clouet); "Le Condottiere" (Antonello da Messina); "La Bohemienne" (Hals)
3695/3702 $50 × 8 "The Village Bride" (left detail) (Greuze); "The Village Bride" (centre detail); "The Village Bride" (right detail); "Self-portrait" (Melendez); "The Knight, the Girl and the Mountain" (Baldung-Grien); "The Young Beggar" (Murillo); "The Pilgrims of Emmaus" (left detail) (Le Nain); "The Pilgrims of Emmaus" (right detail)
3703/10 $50 × 8 "Woman with a Flea" (detail) (Crespi); "The Woman with Dropsy" (detail) (Dou); "Portrait of a Couple" (Ittenbach); "Cleopatra" (Moreau); "Riches" (Vouet); "Old Man and Young Boy" (Ghirlandaio); "Louis XIV" (Rigaud); "The Drinker" (Pieter de Hooch)
3711/18 $50 × 8 "Woman with a Flea" (Crespi); "Self-portrait at Easel" (Rembrandt); "Algerian Women" (detail) (Delacroix); "Head of a Young Man" (Raphael); "Venus and The Graces" (detail) (Botticelli); "Still Life with Chessboard" (detail) (Lubin Baugin); "Lady Macbeth" (Fussli); "The Smoke-filled Room" (detail) (Chardin)
3719/26 $50 × 8 "The Virgin with the Rabbit" (Titian); "The Virgin with the Rabbit" (detail of head) (Titian); "The Beautiful Gardener" (detail) (Raphael); "The Lace-maker" (Vermeer); "Jeanne d'Aragon" (detail) (Raphael); "The Astronomer" (Vermeer); "The Rialto Bridge" (detail) (Canaletto); "Sigismond Malatesta" (Piero della Francesca)
3686/3726 Set of 41 . . . . 23·00 24·00

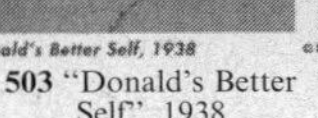

503 "Donald's Better Self", 1938

505 President Dr. Cheddi Jagan

504 Aladdin

1993. Donald Duck Film Posters. Multicoloured.

3728/35 $60 × 8 Type **503**; "Donald's Golf Game", 1938; "Sea Scouts", 1939; "Donald's Penguin", 1939; "A Good Time for a Dime", 1941; "Truant Officer Donald"; "Orphan's Benefit", 1941; "Chef Donald", 1941
3736/43 $60 × 8 "The Village Smithy"; "Donald's Snow Fight"; "Donald's Garden"; "Donald's Gold Mine"; "The Vanishing Private"; "Sky Trooper"; "Bellboy Donald"; "The New Spirit", all 1942
3744/51 $60 × 8 "Saludos Amigos", 1943; "The Eyes Have It", 1945; "Donald's Crime", 1945; "Straight Shooters", 1947; "Donald's Dilemma", 1947; "Bootle Beetle", 1947; "Daddy Duck", 1948; "Soup's On", 1948
3752/9 $80 × 8 "Donald's Happy Birthday", 1949; "Sea Salts", 1949; "Honey Harvester", 1949; "All in a Nutshell", 1949; "The Greener Yard", 1949; "Slide, Donald, Slide", 1949; "Lion Around", 1950; "Trailer Horn", 1950
3760/7 $80 × 8 "Bee at the Beach", 1950; "Out on a Limb", 1950; "Corn Chips", 1951; "Test Pilot Donald", 1951; "Lucky Number", 1951; "Out of Scale", 1951; "Bee on Guard", 1951; "Let's Stick Together", 1952
3768/75 $80 × 8 "Trick or Treat", 1952; "Don's Fountain of Youth", 1953; "Rugged Bear", 1953; "Canvas Back Duck", 1953; "Dragon Around", 1954; "Grin and Bear It", 1954; "The Flying Squirrel", 1954; "Up a Tree", 1955
3776/81 $80 × 8 Scenes from "Pirate Gold": In the crow's nest; Aracuan Bird carrying treasure chest; Donald with treasure map; Donald at souvenir stall; Aracuan Bird with Donald; Donald on jetty (all horiz)
3728/81 Set of 56 . . . . 40·00 45·00

1993. "Aladdin" (film). Disney Cartoon Characters. Multicoloured.

3783/90 $7.65 × 8 Type **504**; Abu the monkey; Jasmine; Rajah the tiger; Jafar; Iago the parrot; The Sultan; The Genie
3791/9 $50 × 9 Jafar and magic scarab; Tiger Head entrance, Cave of Wonders; Jafar; Aladdin and Abu at breakfast; Aladdin rescuing Jasmine; Aladdin, Jasmine and Abu; Rajah comforts Jasmine; Jafar disguised as an old man; Aladdin and Abu in treasure chamber (all horiz)
3800/8 $65 × 9 Aladdin with lamp and magic carpet; The Genie measuring Aladdin; Abu turned into an elephant; Aladdin in disguise at palace; Aladdin and Jasmine on magic carpet; Aladdin in disguise, Jasmine and Sultan; Aladdin fighting Jafar; Aladdin and Jasmine; The Genie with suitcase and golf clubs (all horiz)
3783/3808 Set of 26 . . . . 10·50 11·00

1993. 1st Anniv of Election of President Jagan.

3810 **505** $6.40 multicoloured . . . 30 30

1994. "Hong Kong '94" International Stamp Exhibition (1st issue). As T **222a** of Gambia. Multicoloured.

3812 $50 Hong Kong 1984 Royal Hong Kong Jockey Club $1.30 stamp and Happy Valley Racecourse 70 80
3813 $50 Guyana 1992 Movie Posters $190 stamp and Happy Valley Racecourse 70 80

Nos. 3812/13 were printed together, se-tenant, with the centre part of each pair forming a composite design.

1994. "Hong Kong '94" International Stamp Exhibition (2nd issue). Ch'ing Dynasty Snuff Boxes (Nos. 3814/19) or Porcelain (Nos. 3820/5). As T **222b** of Gambia. Multicoloured.

3814 $20 Painted enamel in shape of bamboo 30 30
3815 $20 Painted enamel showing woman 30 30
3816 $20 Amber with lions playing ball 30 30
3817 $20 Agate in shape of two gourds 30 30
3818 $20 Glass overlay with dog design 30 30
3819 $20 Glass with foliage design . 30 30
3820 $20 Covered jar with dragon design 30 30
3821 $20 Rotating brush-holder . . 30 30
3822 $20 Covered jar with horses design 30 30
3823 $20 Amphora vase with bats and peaches 30 30
3824 $20 Tea caddy with Fo dogs . . 30 30
3825 $20 Vase with camellias and peaches design 30 30

1994. Centenary of the Sign for the Mahdi. Nos. 1622/4 and 1634 surch **CENTENARY Sign For The MAHDI 1894-1994** and new value.

3826 $6 on 60 c. Plate No. 73 (Series 1) (horiz) . . . .
3827 $20 on 200 c. Plate No. 33 (Series 1) (horiz) . . . .
3828 $30 on 60 c. Plate No. 57 (Series 1) (horiz) . . . .
3829 $35 on 60 c. Plate No. 75 (Series 1) (horiz) . . . .

The surcharges on Nos. 3826 and 3828 show the third line as "MADHI".

1994. Hummel Figurines. As T **501a** of Ghana. Multicoloured.

3830 $20 Girl holding inscribed heart 20 25
3831 $25 Boy with heart under arm 25 30
3832 $35 Baker 35 40

3833 $50 Girl with pot of flowers 50 55
3834 $60 Girl with trumpet, pot plant and bird 60 65
3835 $130 Four girls 1·25 1·40
3836 $190 Boy and two girls with dog 1·90 2·00
3837 $250 Boy with cake and dog 2·50 2·75

1994. 75th Anniv of I.L.O. Nos. 1760 and 1629/30 surch **I L O 75th Anniversary 1919-1994** and new value.
3839 $6 on 130 c. Plate No. 13 (Series 1)
3840 $30 on 120 c. Plate No. 58 (Series 1)
3841 $35 on 120 c. Plate No. 56 (Series 1)

1994. Centenary (1992) of Sierra Club (environmental protection society). Endangered Species. As T **224a** of Gambia. Multicoloured.
3842 $70 Red Kangaroo with young 90 90
3843 $70 Head of American alligator 90 90
3844 $70 Head of bald eagle 90 90
3845 $70 Giant panda eating bamboo 90 90
3846 $70 Head of red kangaroo 90 90
3847 $70 Alaskan brown bear sitting 90 90
3848 $70 Bald eagle 90 90
3849 $70 Head of giant panda 90 90
3850 $70 Red kangaroo (horiz) 90 90
3851 $70 Whooping crane facing left (horiz) 90 90
3852 $70 Male whooping crane in courtship display (horiz) 90 90
3853 $70 Whooping crane looking right (horiz) 90 90
3854 $70 Alaskan brown bear and cub (horiz) 90 90
3855 $70 Alaskan brown bear fishing (horiz) 90 90
3856 $70 Bald eagle on branch (horiz) 90 90
3857 $70 Giant panda (horiz) 90 90
3858 $70 American alligator (logo at left) (horiz) 90 90
3859 $70 American alligator (logo at right) (horiz) 90 90
3860 $70 Italian Alps at sunrise (horiz) 90 90
3861 $70 Italian Alps and meadow (horiz) 90 90
3862 $70 Mono Lake at sunset (horiz) 90 90
3863 $70 Rock pinnacles, Mono Lake (horiz) 90 90
3864 $70 Sea lion 90 90
3865 $70 Head of sea lion 90 90
3866 $70 Sea lions on rocks 90 90
3867 $70 Rock pinnacles, Mono Lake 90 90
3868 $70 Sierra Club Centennial emblem (black, brown and green) 90 90
3869 $70 Lake, Italian Alps 90 90
3870 $70 Summit of Matterhorn 90 90
3871 $70 Matterhorn and village 90 90
3872 $70 Clouds over Matterhorn 90 90

1994. Royal Visit. Nos. 3551/4 optd **ROYAL VISIT FEB 19-22, 1994**.
3873 $25 Queen Elizabeth II in Coronation robes (photograph by Cecil Beaton) 55 60
3874 $50 Royal gems 90 1·00
3875 $75 Queen Elizabeth and Prince Philip 1·25 1·40
3876 $130 Queen opening Parliament 1·50 1·75

509 "Cestrum parqui"

1994. Flowers. Multicoloured.
3878 $6.40 Type **509** 10 10
3879 $7.65 "Brunfelsia calycina" 10 10
3880 $12.80 "Datura rosei" 10 15
3881 $15.30 "Ruellia macrantha" 15 20
3882 $50 "Portlandia albiflora" 50 55
3883 $50 "Clusia grandiflora" 50 55
3884 $50 "Begonia haageana" 50 55
3885 $50 "Fuchsia simplicicaulis" 50 55
3886 $50 "Guaiacum officinale" 50 55
3887 $50 "Pithecoctenium cynanchoides" 50 55
3888 $50 "Sphaeralcea umbellata" 50 55
3889 $50 "Erythrina poeppigiana" 50 55
3890 $50 "Steriphoma paradoxa" 50 55
3891 $50 "Allemanda violacea" 50 55
3892 $50 "Centropogon cornutus" 50 55
3893 $50 "Passiflora quadrangularis" 50 55
3894 $50 "Victoria amazonica" 50 55
3895 $50 "Cobaea scandens" 50 55
3896 $50 "Pyrostegia venusta" 50 55
3897 $50 "Petrea kohautiana" 50 55
3898 $50 "Hippobroma longiflora" 50 55
3899 $50 "Cleome hassleriana" 50 55
3900 $50 "Verbena peruviana" 50 55
3901 $50 "Tropaeolum peregrinum" 50 55
3902 $50 "Plumeria rubra" 50 55
3903 $50 "Selenicereus grandiflorus" 50 55
3904 $50 "Mandevilla splendens" 50 55
3905 $50 "Pereskia aculeata" 50 55
3906 $50 "Ipomoea learii" 50 55
3907 $130 "Pachystachys coccinea" 1·25 1·40
3908 $190 "Beloperone guttata" 1·90 2·00
3909 $250 "Ferdinandusa speciosa" 2·50 2·75

Nos. 3883/94 and 3895/3906 respectively were printed together, se-tenant, forming composite background designs.

1994. 25th Anniv of First Moon Landing (1st issue). As T **326** of Antigua. Multicoloured.
3911 $60 Walter Dornberger and launch of first A-4 rocket 90 90
3912 $60 Rudolph Nebel and "Surveyor 1" 90 90
3913 $60 Robert H. Goddard and "Apollo 7" 90 90
3914 $60 Kurt Debus and view of Earth from Moon ("Apollo 8") 90 90
3915 $60 James T. Webb and "Apollo 9" 90 90
3916 $60 George E. Mueller and "Apollo 10" lunar module 90 90
3917 $60 Wernher von Braun and launch of "Apollo 11" 90 90
3918 $60 Rocco A. Petrone and "Apollo 11" astronaut on Moon 90 90
3919 $60 Eberhard Rees and "Apollo 12" astronaut on Moon 90 90
3920 $60 Charles A. Berry and damaged "Apollo 13" 90 90
3921 $60 Thomas O. Paine and "Apollo 14" before splashdown 90 90
3922 $60 A. F. Staats and "Apollo 15" on Moon 90 90
3923 $60 Robert R. Gilruth and "Apollo 16" astronaut on Moon 90 90
3924 $60 Ernst Stuhlinger and "Apollo 17" crew on Moon 90 90
3925 $60 Christopher C. Kraft and X-30 National Aero-Space Plane 90 90
3926 $60 Rudolf Opitz and Messerschmitt Me 163B Komet (rocket engine), 1943 90 90
3927 $60 Clyde W. Tombaugh and "face" on Mars 90 90
3928 $60 Hermann Oberth and scene from "The Girl in the Moon" 90 90

See also Nos. 4169/86.

1994. Centenary of International Olympic Committee. Medal Winners. As T **227b** of Gambia. Multicoloured.
3930 $20 Nancy Kerrigan (U.S.A.) (1994 figure skating silver) 30 30
3931 $35 Sawao Kato (Japan) (1976 gymnastics gold) 50 50
3932 $130 Florence Griffith Joyner (U.S.A.) (1988 100 and 200 metres gold) 1·75 2·00

1994. Centenary of First English Cricket Tour to the West Indies (1995). As T **397a** of Grenada. Multicoloured.
3934 $20 Clive Lloyd (Guyana and West Indies) (vert) 40 30
3935 $35 Carl Hooper (Guyana and West Indies) and Wisden Trophy 55 50
3936 $60 Graham Hick (England) and Wisden Trophy 90 1·00

1994. 50th Anniv of D-Day. Aircraft. As T **227c** of Gambia. Multicoloured.
3938 $6 Supermarine Spitfire Mk XI fighter on photo reconnaissance 20 15
3939 $35 North American B-25 Mitchell bomber 60 50
3940 $190 Republic P-47 Thunderbolt fighters 2·50 3·00

1994. 50th Anniv of Second World War (3rd issue). As T **500**. Multicoloured.
3942 $60 Paratroops drop, D-Day 80 80
3943 $60 Glider assault, D-Day 80 80
3944 $60 U.S.S. "Arkansas" (battleship) bombarding Omaha Beach, D-Day 80 80
3945 $60 U.S. fighters attacking train 80 80
3946 $60 Allied landing craft approaching beaches 80 80
3947 $60 Troops in beach obstacles 80 80
3948 $60 Commandos leaving landing craft 80 80
3949 $60 U.S. flail tank destroying mines 80 80
3950 $60 U.S. tank breaking through sea wall 80 80
3951 $60 Tanks and infantry advancing 80 80
3952 $60 Landings at Anzio (22 January 1944) 80 80
3953 $60 R.A.F. attacking Amiens Prison (18 February 1944) 80 80
3954 $60 Soviet Army tank in Sevastopol (9 May 1944) 80 80
3955 $60 British bren-gun carriers at the Gustav Line (19 May 1944) 80 80
3956 $60 D-Day landings (6 June 1944) 80 80
3957 $60 "V-1" over London (13 June 1944) 80 80
3958 $60 Allies entering Paris (19 August 1944) 80 80
3959 $60 German "V-2" rocket ready for launch (8 September 1944) 80 80
3960 $60 Sinking of "Tirpitz" (German battleship) (12 November 1944) 80 80
3961 $60 U.S. tanks at Bastogne (29 December 1944) 80 80

1994. "Philakorea '94" International Stamp Exhibition, Seoul (1st issue). As T **227d** of Gambia. Multicoloured.
3962 $6 Socialist ideals statue, Pyongyang (vert) 10 10
3963 $25 Statue of Admiral Yi Sun-sin (vert) 25 30
3964 $60 Fruits and mountain peaks 60 65
3965 $60 Manchurian crane, bamboo and peaks 60 65
3966 $60 Rising sun and two cranes on pine 60 65
3967 $60 Five cranes on pine and peak 60 65
3968 $60 Three cranes in flight 60 65
3969 $60 Sea, rocky shore and fungi 60 65
3970 $60 Sea, rocky shore and fruit 60 65
3971 $60 Hind at seashore and fruit 60 65
3972 $60 Stag in pine forest 60 65
3973 $60 Deer and fungi by waterfall 60 65
3974 $60 Tops of pines and mountain peaks 60 65
3975 $60 Manchurian crane in flight 60 65
3976 $60 Three cranes on pine tree 60 65
3977 $60 Crane on pine tree 60 65
3978 $60 Top of fruit tree 60 65
3979 $60 Stag and two hinds on mountainside 60 65
3980 $60 Deer and fungi 60 65
3981 $60 Stag by waterfall and hind drinking 60 65
3982 $60 Pine tree, fruit and fungi 60 65
3983 $60 Fungi on mountainside 60 65
3984 $120 Sokkat'ap Pagoda, Pulguksa 1·25 1·40
3985 $130 Village Guardian (statue), Chejudo Island 1·25 1·40

Nos. 3964/73 and 3974/83, all 23×49 mm, were printed together, se-tenant, in sheetlets of 10, each sheetlet forming a composite design showing panels from a screen painting of longevity symbols from the late Chosun dynasty.

See also Nos. 4117/40.

510 Miki Maya

1994. 80th Anniv of Takarazuka Revue of Japan. Multicoloured.
3987 $20 Type **510** 55 60
3988 $20 Fubuki Takane 55 60
3989 $20 Seika Kuze 55 60
3990 $20 Saki Asaji 55 60
3991 $60 Mira Anju (34×47 mm) 75 80
3992 $60 Yuki Amami (34×47 mm) 75 80
3993 $60 Maki Ichiro (34×47 mm) 75 80
3994 $60 Yu Shion (34×47 mm) 75 80

511 "Heliconius melpomene"

1994. Butterflies. Multicoloured.
3995 $6 Type **511** 20 20
3996 $20 "Helicopis cupido" 45 45
3997 $25 "Agrias claudina" 50 50
3998 $30 "Parides coelus" 60 60
3999 $50 "Heliconius hecale" 75 75
4000 $50 "Anaea marthesia" 75 75
4001 $50 "Brassolis astyra" 75 75
4002 $50 "Heliconius melpomene" 75 75
4003 $50 "Haetera piera" 75 75
4004 $50 "Morpho diana" 75 75
4005 $50 "Parides coelus" 75 75
4006 $50 "Catagramma pitheas" 75 75
4007 $50 "Nessaea obrinus" 75 75
4008 $50 "Automeris janus" 75 75
4009 $50 "Papilio torquatus" 75 75
4010 $50 "Eunica sophonisba" 75 75
4011 $50 "Ceratinia nise" 75 75
4012 $50 "Panacea procilla" 75 75
4013 $50 "Pyrrhogyra neaerea" 75 75
4014 $50 "Morpho deidamia" 75 75
4015 $50 "Dismorphia orise" 75 75
4016 $60 "Morpho diana" 85 85
4017 $190 "Dismorphia orise" 2·50 3·00
4018 $250 "Morpho deidamia" 3·00 3·50

512 Jacob **513** Peregrine Falcon

1994. Bible Stories (2nd series). Multicoloured. (a) Joseph.
4020/43 $20×24 arranged as blocks of 4 depicting Jacob giving Joseph a coat of many colours (Type **512** at top left); Joseph thrown into a pit; Joseph sold as a slave; Joseph accused by Potiphar's wife; Joseph interprets Pharoah's dreams; Joseph reunited with his brothers

(b) The Parting of the Red Sea.
4044/67 $20×24 Palm trees on shore; Pyramids; Palm trees on shore and black cloud; Three palm trees; Blue and white dove; Red and white bird; Egyptian army engulfed by sea; Yellow and white dove; Red and green fishes; Egyptian chariot with wall of water at left; Chariots between walls of water; Dolphins; Two doves; Israelites and water to left; Israelites and water to right; Turquoise and purple fishes; Israelites with tree at left; Iraelites with goats; Moses; Israelites with tree at right; Israelites with woman on horse; Israelites with old man and woman carrying pack; Israelites with woman carrying young child; Israelites with cart

(c) Ruth.
4068/91 $20×24 arranged as blocks of 6 depicting Ruth and Naomi; Ruth gleaning in cornfield; Boaz establishing kinsman's rights; Naomi with Ruth, Boaz and Obed

(d) Daniel in the Lions' Den.
4092/4116 $20×25 Palm fronds and hibiscus flower; Frigate bird and palm fronds; Frigate birds and tops of stone pillars; Frigate bird, pillars and sail at bottom right; Hibiscus, sails of ship and top of pillar; Yellow arum lilies and palm trees; Heads of adult and immature frigate birds and palm trees; Palm trees, butterfly and stone pillars; Two butterflies and stone pillars; Stone pillar and sailing ship; Standing heron; Purple irises and palm trees; Daniel; Angel; Donkey foal; Orchids; Lioness and two cubs; Daniel's legs and lions; Lion; Three crowns; Goat and kid; Kid; Cub and head of lion; Lioness; Heron in flight
4020/4116 Set of 97 22·00 24·00

Nos. 4020/43, 4044/67, 4068/91 and 4092/4116 respectively were printed together, se-tenant, forming composite designs.

1994. "Philakorea '94" International Stamp Exhibition, Seoul (2nd issue). Birds of the World. Multicoloured.
4117 $35 Type **513** 45 50
4118 $35 Great spotted woodpecker 45 50
4119 $35 White-throated kingfisher 45 50
4120 $35 Peruvian cock of the rock 45 50
4121 $35 Yellow-headed amazon 45 50
4122 $35 Victoria crowned pigeon 45 50
4123 $35 Little owl 45 50
4124 $35 Ring-necked pheasant 45 50
4125 $35 Goldfinch 45 50
4126 $35 Jay 45 50
4127 $35 Sulphur-breasted toucan 45 50
4128 $35 Japanese blue flycatcher 45 50
4129 $35 Northern goshawk 45 50
4130 $35 Lapwing 45 50
4131 $35 Ornate umbrellabird 45 50
4132 $35 Slaty-headed parakeet 45 50
4133 $35 Regent bowerbird 45 50
4134 $35 Egyptian goose 45 50
4135 $35 White-winged crossbill 45 50
4136 $35 Waxwing 45 50
4137 $35 Ruff 45 50
4138 $35 Hoopoe 45 50
4139 $35 Superb starling 45 50
4140 $35 Great jacamar 45 50

514 Paulo Futre (Portugal)

1994. World Cup Football Championship, U.S.A. (2nd issue). Multicoloured.
4142 $6 Type **514** 10 10
4143 $35 Lyndon Hooper (Canada) 35 40
4144 $60 Enzo Francescoli (Uruguay) 60 65
4145 $60 Paolo Maldini (Italy) 60 65
4146 $60 Guyana player 60 65
4147 $60 Bwalya Kalusha (Zambia) 60 65
4148 $60 Diego Maradona (Argentina) 60 65
4149 $60 Andreas Brehme (Germany) 60 65
4150 $60 Eric Wynalda (U.S.A.) (pursuing ball) 60 65
4151 $60 John Doyle (U.S.A.) 60 65
4152 $60 Eric Wynalda (U.S.A.) (kicking ball) 60 65
4153 $60 Thomas Dooley (U.S.A.) 60 65
4154 $60 Ernie Stewart (U.S.A.) 60 65
4155 $60 Marcelo Balboa (U.S.A.) 60 65
4156 $60 Bora Milutinovic (U.S.A. coach) 60 65
4157 $190 Freddy Rincon (Colombia) 1·90 2·00

Nos. 4145/50 and 4151/6 respectively were printed together, se-tenant, forming composite background designs.

515 Anja Fichtel (individual foil, 1988)

1994. Olympic Games, Atlanta (1996) (1st issue). Previous German Gold Medal Winners. Mult.

4159 $6 Type **515** 10 10
4160 $25 Annegret Richter (100 metres, 1976) (vert) 25 30
4161 $30 Heike Henkel (high jump, 1992) (vert) 30 35
4162 $35 Armin Hary (100 metres, 1960) (vert) 35 40
4163 $50 Heide Rosendahl (long jump, 1972) (vert) 75 75
4164 $60 Josef Neckermann (dressage, 1968) (vert) . . . 60 65
4165 $130 Heike Drechsler (long jump, 1988) (vert) . . . 1·25 1·40
4166 $190 Ulrike Mayfarth (high jump, 1984) (vert) . . . . 1·90 2·00
4167 $250 Michael Gross (200 metres freestyle and 100 metres butterfly, 1984) . . . . . 2·50 2·75

See also Nos. 4492/4507 and 4739/87.

516 Dog Laika and Rocket, 1957

1994. 25th Anniv of First Moon Landing (2nd issue). Multicoloured.

4169 $60 Type **516** 80 80
4170 $60 Yury Gagarin (first man in space), 1961 . . . . . . 80 80
4171 $60 John Glenn (first American to orbit Earth), 1962 . . . 80 80
4172 $60 Edward White walking in space, 1965 . . . . 80 80
4173 $60 Neil Armstrong, walking on Moon and "Apollo 11" logo 80 80
4174 $60 "Luna 16" leaving Moon, 1970 . . . . 80 80
4175 $60 Lunar Module 1 on Moon, 1970 . . . . 80 80
4176 $60 Skylab 1, 1973 . . . . 80 80
4177 $60 Astronauts and Apollo–Soyuz link-up, 1975 . . . 80 80
4178 $60 "Mars 3" 80 80
4179 $60 "Mariner 10" 80 80
4180 $60 "Voyager" 80 80
4181 $60 "Pioneer" 80 80
4182 $60 "Giotto" 80 80
4183 $60 "Magellan" 80 80
4184 $60 "Galileo" 80 80
4185 $60 "Ulysses" 80 80
4186 $60 "Cassini" 80 80

Nos. 4178/86 were printed together, se-tenant, with the backgrounds forming a composite design of Space.

517 South Caroline Railroad "Best Friend of Charleston", 1830, U.S.A.

1994. History of Trains. Steam Locomotives. Multicoloured.

4188 $25 Type **517** 40 40
4189 $25 South Eastern Railway No. 285, 1882 . . . . 40 40
4190 $30 Camden & Amboy Railway No. 1 "John Bull", 1831, U.S.A. 45 45
4191 $30 Stephenson "Patentee" type locomotive, 1837 . . . . . 45 45
4192 $30 "Atlantic", 1832 . . . . 45 45
4193 $30 "Stourbridge Lion", 1829, U.S.A. 45 45
4194 $30 Polonceau locomotive, 1854 . . . . 45 45
4195 $30 "Thomas Rogers", 1855, U.S.A. 45 45
4196 $30 "Vulcan", 1858 . . . . 45 45
4197 $30 "Namur", 1846 . . . . 45 45
4198 $30 John Jarvis's "De Witt Clinton", 1831, U.S.A. . . 45 45
4199 $30 Seguin locomotive, 1829 . 45 45
4200 $30 Stephenson's "Planet", 1830 . . . . 45 45
4201 $30 Norris locomotive, 1840 . 45 45
4202 $30 "Sampson", 1867, U.S.A. . 45 45
4203 $30 "Andrew Jackson", 1832 . 45 45
4204 $30 "Herald", 1831 . . . . . 45 45
4205 $30 "Cumberland", 1845, U.S.A. 45 45
4206 $30 Pennsylvania Railroad Class K, 1880 . . . . . . 45 45
4207 $30 Cooke locomotive No. 11, 1885 . . . . 45 45
4208 $30 "John B. Turner", 1867, U.S.A. 45 45
4209 $30 Baldwin locomotive, 1871 45 45
4210 $30 Richard Trevithick's locomotive, 1803 . . . . . 45 45
4211 $30 John Stephens's locomotive, 1825 . . . . 45 45
4212 $30 John Blenkinsop's locomotive, 1814 . . . . . 45 45
4213 $30 "Pennsylvania," 1803 . . 45 45
4214 $300 Mount Washington Cog Railway locomotive No. 6, 1886 . . . . 3·00 3·00
4215 $300 Stroudley locomotive "Brighton", 1872 . . . . 3·00 3·00

No. 4198 is inscribed "West Point Foundry 1832 Locomotive" and No. 4202 "Union Iron Works os San Francisco", both error.

1994. Christmas. Religious Paintings. As T **231a** of Gambia. Multicoloured.

4217 $6 "Joseph with the Christ Child" (Guido Reni) . . . 15 10
4218 $20 "Adoration of the Christ Child" (Girolamo Romanino) 25 25
4219 $25 "Adoration of the Christ Child with St. Barbara and St. Martin" (Raffaello Botticini) 30 30
4220 $30 "Holy Family" (Pompeo Batoni) 35 35
4221 $35 "Flight into Egypt" (Bartolommeo Carducci) . 40 40
4222 $60 "Holy Family and the Baptist" (Andrea del Sarto) 70 70
4223 $120 "Sacred Conversation" (Cesare de Sesto) . . . . 1·75 2·00
4224 $190 "Madonna and Child with Saints Joseph and John the Baptist" (Pontormo) . . . 2·75 3·25

518 Riker and Dr. Crusher

1994. "Star Trek Generations" (film). Designs showing "Enterprise" crew in 19th-century naval uniforms (Nos. 4226/34) or in 23rd-century (Nos. 4235/43). Multicoloured.

4226 $100 Type **518** . . . . 1·50 1·50
4227 $100 Geordi, Dr. Crusher with Lt. Worf in chains . . . . 1·50 1·50
4228 $100 Captain Picard . . . . 1·50 1·50
4229 $100 Data and Geordi . . . 1·50 1·50
4230 $100 "U.S.S. Enterprise" (sailing ship) . . . . . . 1·50 1·50
4231 $100 Captain Picard and Riker on quarterdeck . . . . . 1·50 1·50
4232 $100 Data . . . . 1·50 1·50
4233 $100 Lt. Worf . . . . 1·50 1·50
4234 $100 Dr. Crusher . . . . . . 1·50 1·50
4235 $100 Captain Picard . . . . 1·50 1·50
4236 $100 Riker . . . . 1·50 1·50
4237 $100 Captain Kirk . . . . . 1·50 1·50
4238 $100 Soron with phaser . . . 1·50 1·50
4239 $100 Captains Kirk and Picard on horseback . . . . . 1·50 1·50
4240 $100 Klingon women . . . . 1·50 1·50
4241 $100 Captains Kirk and Picard . . . . 1·50 1·50
4242 $100 Troi . . . . 1·50 1·50
4243 $100 Captain Picard and Data 1·50 1·50
4244 $100 "BOLDLY GO" film poster . . . . 1·50 1·50

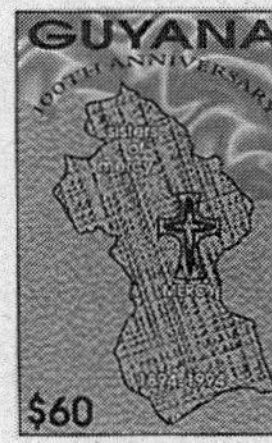

519 Cross and Map of Guyana

1994. Centenary of Sisters of Mercy in Guyana.

4246 **519** $60 multicoloured 80 80

1994. 1st Recipients of Order of the Caribbean Community. As T **393a** of Grenada. Mult.

4247 $60 Sir Shridath Ramphal . . 65 75
4248 $60 William Demas 65 75
4249 $60 Derek Walcott 65 75

520 Garfield Sobers congratulating Brian Lara

1995. Brian Lara's Achievements in Cricket. Multicoloured.

4250 $20 Type **520** 35 25
4251 $30 Brian Lara setting world record for highest Test Match score (vert) 45 35
4252 $375 Lara and Chanderpaul . 4·25 4·75

521 Babe Ruth

1995. Birth Centenary of Babe Ruth (baseball player). Each brown and black.

4254 $65 Type **521** 70 80
4255 $65 Preparing to bat (full-length photo) 70 80
4256 $65 Head and shoulders portrait (cap with limp brim) . . . 70 80
4257 $65 In retirement (bare-headed) 70 80
4258 $65 Running (in plain shirt) . 70 80
4259 $65 Head and shoulders portrait (cap with emblem and stiff brim) 70 80
4260 $65 Wearing "NEW YORK" shirt 70 80
4261 $65 Preparing to hit (in "NEW YORK" shirt) 70 80
4262 $65 Wearing "YANKEES" shirt 70 80
4263 $65 At base with bat on shoulder (in striped shirt) 70 80
4264 $65 Watching the ball (in striped shirt) 70 80
4265 $65 In cap and coat at Old Timer's Day, Yankee Stadium, 1948 . . . . . . 70 80

522 Mickey Mouse as Family Doctor

1995. Disney Characters at Work. Multicoloured.

4267/75 $30 × 9 Type **522**; Goofy and optometrist; Daisy Duck as nurse; Scrooge McDuck as psychiatrist; Daisy Duck as physiotherapist; Horace Horsecollar and dentist; Goofy and radiologist; Goofy as pharmacist; Big Pete as chiropractor
4276/84 $30 × 9 Mickey Mouse as vet; Donald Duck training seals; Ludwig von Duck as animal psychiatrist; Goofy as ornithologist; Daisy Duck grooming Old English sheepdog; Minnie Mouse as herpetologist; Mickey Mouse as pet shop keeper with Pluto; J. Audubon Woodlore as park ranger; Donald Duck as aquarist
4285/93 $30 × 9 Mickey Mouse as animator with Pluto; Goofy the tailor with Mickey Mouse; Pete the glassblower with Morty; Minnie Mouse painting Clarabelle; Daisy Duck sculpting Donald; Donald Duck as potter; Chip and Dale the watchmakers; Donald Duck the locksmith; Grandma Duck making quilt
4294/4301 $35 × 8 Mickey Mouse as policeman; Donald Duck as fireman; Uncle Scrooge as ambulance driver; Grandma Duck as crossing patrol; Daisy Duck as museum attendant and Donald as visitor; Goofy as census taker and family of rabbits; Horace Horsecollar and Big Pete as street maintenance workers; Donald Duck as sanitation worker at recycling bin (all vert)
4302/9 $35 × 8 Mickey Mouse with Pluto driving lorry; Mickey Mouse as carpenter sawing; Goofy riding road drill; Minnie Mouse with electric drill; Donald Duck driving forklift; Minnie Mouse and Goofy as construction contractors; Mickey Mouse with Pluto as carpenter making table; Pluto driving bulldozer (all vert)
4310/17 $35 × 8 Mickey Mouse as plumber; Mickey Mouse the paperboy; Huey, Dewey and Louie moving furniture; Big Pete as handyman; Donald Duck and nephews house painting; Goofy as washing machine repairman; Minnie Mouse as babysitter; Daisy Duck as carer (all vert)
4267/4317 Set of 51 . . . . 18·00 20·00

No. 4271 is inscribed "PHYSICAL THEREPIST" in error.

1995. Centenary of Salvation Army. Nos. 1519 and 1521/3 surch **SALVATION ARMY 1895 — 1995** and new value.

4319 $6 on 60 c. Plate No. 10 (Series 1)
4320 $20 on 60 c. Plate No. 19 (Series 1)
4321 $30 on 60 c. Plate No. 2 (Series 1)
4322 $35 on 60 c. Plate No. 31 (Series 1)

524 Pig

525 Goshawk

1995. Chinese New Year ("Year of the Pig"). Symbolic pigs. Multicoloured.

4323 $20 Type **524** 30 40
4324 $30 Pig facing left 40 50
4325 $50 Pig facing front (face value bottom right) 50 55
4326 $100 Pig facing front (face value bottom left) . . . . 1·00 1·10

1995. Birds. Multicoloured.

4329 $5 Type **525** 10 10
4330 $6 Lapwing 10 10
4331 $8 Ornate umbrellabird . . . 10 10
4332 $15 Slaty-headed parakeet . . 10 10
4333 $19 Regent bowerbird . . . 20 25
4334 $20 Egyptian goose 20 25
4335 $25 White-winged crossbill . . 25 30
4336 $30 Waxwing 30 35
4337 $35 Ruff 35 40
4338 $60 Hoopoe 60 65
4339 $100 Superb starling . . . . 1·00 1·10
4340 $500 Great jacamar . . . . 5·00 5·25

526 Norwegian Forest Cat

1995. "Singapore '95" International Stamp Exhibition. Multicoloured.

4341/52 $35 × 12 Cats (Type **526**; Scottish fold; Red Burmese; British blue-hair; Abyssinian; Siamese; Exotic shorthair; Turkish van cat; Black Persian; Black-tipped burmilla; Singapura; Calico shorthair)
4353/64 $35 × 12 Dogs (Gordon setter; Long-haired chihuahua; Dalmatian; Afghan hound; Old English bulldog; Miniature schnauzer; Clumber spaniel; Pekingese; St. Bernard; English cocker spaniel; Alaskan malamute; Rottweiler)
4365/76 $35 × 12 Horses (chestnut thoroughbred colt; liver chestnut quarter horse; black Friesian; chestnut Belgian; Appaloosa; Lippizaner; chestnut hunter; British shire; Palomino; pinto ("Seal Brown Point"); Arab; Afghanistan kabardin)
4341/76 Set of 36 . . . . 13·00 15·00

No. 4355 is inscribed "Dalmation", No. 4367 "Freisian" and No. 4370 "Lipizzanas", all in error.

527 Captain John Smith leaving for New World, 1607

1995. "Pocahontas". Characters and scenes from Disney cartoon film. Multicoloured. (a) Vert designs showing characters.

4378/85 $50 × 8 Pocahontas and Meeko; John Smith; Chief Powhatan; Kocoum; Ratcliffe; Wiggins; Nakoma; Thomas

(b) Horiz designs showing film scenes.

4386/94 $8 × 9 Type **527**; Ratcliffe; Chief Powhatan greeted by his people; Pocahontas standing on cliff; Pocahontas, Nakoma and Meeko in canoe; Powhatan asking Pocahontas to marry Kocoum; Pocahontas receiving her mother's necklace; Pocahontas seeking guidance from Grandmother Willow; Pocahontas watching arrival of "Susan Constant"

4395/4403	$30×9 Ratcliffe claiming land for English Crown; Kekata having vision; Meeting of John Smith and Pocahontas; Namantack watching settlers; Powhatan and wounded Namantack; Pocahontas showing John Smith the colours of the wind; Nakoma finds Pocahontas with John Smith; Pocahontas offering John "Indian gold" (corn); Pocahontas, John Smith and Grandmother Willow		
4404/12	$35×9 Kocoum telling Pocahontas about the war council; Nakoma telling Kocoum to find Pocahontas; John Smith and Kocoum wrestling over knife; Powhatan sentencing John to death; Pocahontas and Grandmother Willow; Pocahontas saving John Smith; Ratcliffe under arrest; Powhatan draping his cloak over wounded John Smith; Pocahontas and John Smith saying goodbye		
4378/4412	Set of 35	26·00	27·00

1995. 95th Birthday of Queen Elizabeth the Queen Mother. As T **239a** of Gambia.

4414	$100 brown, light brown and black	1·25	1·25
4415	$100 multicoloured	1·25	1·25
4416	$100 multicoloured	1·25	1·25
4417	$100 multicoloured	1·25	1·25

DESIGNS: No. 4414, Queen Elizabeth the Queen Mother (pastel drawing); 4415, Wearing purple hat; 4416, Wearing turquoise hat; 4417, At desk (oil painting).

528 Paul Harris (founder) and Rotary Emblem

1995. 90th Anniv of Rotary International. Multicoloured.

4419	**528**	$200 multicoloured	2·00	2·10

529 Girl carrying Sack on Head

1995. 50th Anniv of F.A.O. Multicoloured.

4421	$35 Type **529**	50	55
4422	$60 Man and woman carrying sacks of food aid	80	85
4423	$200 Woman holding sack	2·00	2·10

Nos. 4421/3 were printed together, se-tenant, forming a composite design.

530 Scouts around Campfire

1995. 18th World Scout Jamboree, Netherlands. Multicoloured.

4425	$20 Type **530**	30	25
4426	$25 Scout on beach	35	30
4427	$30 Scouts hiking	40	35
4428	$35 Scout snorkelling	45	40
4429	$60 Scout saluting and flag of Guyana	70	65
4430	$200 Scout fishing from boat	2·00	2·50

1995. 50th Anniv of End of World War II in Europe. As T **237a** of Gambia. Multicoloured.

4432	$60 American tank during Battle of the Bulge	65	75
4433	$60 Allied tanks crossing Siegfried Line	65	75
4434	$60 Liberated concentration camp prisoners	65	75
4435	$60 Allied plane dropping food to Dutch	65	75
4436	$60 U.S. infantry patrol, North Italy	65	75
4437	$60 "Daily Mail" headline announcing Hitler's death	65	75
4438	$60 Soviet tanks entering Berlin	65	75
4439	$60 Surrender of "U858" in U.S. waters	65	75

No. 4433 was incorrectly inscribed "SIGFRIED LINE".

1995. 50th Anniv of End of Second World War in the Pacific. As T **239b** of Gambia. Multicoloured.

4441	$60 P61 Black Widow	65	75
4442	$60 PT boat	65	75
4443	$60 Martin B-26 Marauder bomber	65	75
4444	$60 U.S.S. "San Juan" (cruiser)	65	75
4445	$60 "Gato" class submarine	65	75
4446	$60 Destroyer	65	75

531 Thanksgiving (U.S.A.)

1995. Holidays of the World. Multicoloured.

4448	$60 Type **531**	65	75
4449	$60 Christmas (Germany)	65	75
4450	$60 Hanukkah (Israel)	65	75
4451	$60 Easter (Spain)	65	75
4452	$60 Carnivale (Brazil)	65	75
4453	$60 Bastille Day (France)	65	75
4454	$60 Independence Day (India)	65	75
4455	$60 St. Patrick's Day (Ireland)	65	75

532 Map of the Americas and U.N. Soldier

1995. 50th Anniv of United Nations. Multicoloured.

4457	$35 Type **532**	35	40
4458	$60 Map of Africa and Western Asia	60	65
4459	$200 Map of Eastern Asia and Australasia with refugees	2·00	2·10

Nos. 4457/9 were printed together, se-tenant, forming a composite design.

533 Four-eyed Butterflyfish

1995. Marine Life. Multicoloured.

4461	$30 Type **533**	30	35
4462	$30 Lemon shark	30	35
4463	$35 Blue-headed wrasse	35	40
4464	$35 Green turtle	35	40
4465	$60 Three-spotted damselfish	60	65
4466	$60 Sawfish	60	65
4467	$60 Sei whales	60	65
4468	$60 Great barracuda	60	65
4469	$60 Mutton snapper	60	65
4470	$60 Hawksbill turtle	60	65
4471	$60 Spanish hogfish	60	65
4472	$60 Queen angelfish	60	65
4473	$60 Porkfish	60	65
4474	$60 Trumpetfish	60	65
4475	$60 Lesser electric ray	60	65
4476	$60 Tiger shark	60	65
4477	$60 Needlefish	60	65
4478	$60 Horse-eyed jack	60	65
4479	$60 Princess parrotfish	60	65
4480	$60 Yellow-tailed snapper	60	65
4481	$60 Spotted snake eel	60	65
4482	$60 Buffalo trunkfish	60	65
4483	$60 Cherubfish angelfish	60	65
4484	$60 French angelfish	60	65
4485	$80 Cocoa damselfish (vert)	80	85
4486	$80 Sergeant major (vert)	80	85
4487	$80 Beaugregory (vert)	80	85
4488	$80 Yellow-tailed damselfish (vert)	80	85
4489	$200 Fin-spot wrasse	2·00	2·10
4490	$200 Stingray	2·00	2·10

Nos. 4461, 4463, 4465 and 4489; Nos. 4462, 4464, 4466 and 4490; Nos. 4467/75; Nos. 4476/84 and Nos. 4485/8 respectively were printed together, se-tenant, the backgrounds forming composite designs.

534 Pole Vaulting

535 Sand Martin

1995. Olympic Games, Atlanta (1996) (2nd issue). Multicoloured.

4492	$60 Type **534**	60	65
4493	$60 Long jumping	60	65
4494	$60 Woman with relay baton	60	65
4495	$60 Wrestling	60	65
4496	$60 Discus (side view)	60	65
4497	$60 Basketball	60	65
4498	$60 Boxing	60	65
4499	$60 Weightlifting	60	65
4500	$60 Shot put	60	65
4501	$60 Man in relay race	60	65
4502	$60 Female gymnast on beam	60	65
4503	$60 Cycling	60	65
4504	$60 Synchronized swimming	60	65
4505	$60 Hurdling	60	65
4506	$60 Male gymnast on pommel horse	60	65
4507	$60 Discus (front view)	60	65

Nos. 4492/9 and 4500/7 respectively were printed together, se-tenant, the backgrounds forming composite designs.

1995. Wildlife. Multicoloured.

4509	$20 Type **535**	20	25
4510	$35 House martin	35	40
4511	$60 Hobby	60	65
4512	$60 Olive colobus	60	65
4513	$60 Violet-backed starling	60	65
4514	$60 Diana monkey	60	65
4515	$60 African palm civet	60	65
4516	$60 Giraffe and zebras	60	65
4517	$60 African linsang	60	65
4518	$60 Royal antelope	00	00
4519	$60 Duikers	60	65
4520	$60 Palm squirrel	60	65
4521	$200 Long-tailed skua	60	65

Nos. 4509/11 and 4521; and 4512/20 respectively were printed together, se-tenant, forming composite background designs.

536 Queenstown Jama Masjid

1995. Centenary of Queenstown Jama Masjid (mosque), Georgetown.

4523	**536**	$60 multicoloured	40	45

537 Woman Soldier with Sub-machine Gun

1995. 30th Anniv of Guyana Defence Force. Multicoloured.

4524	$6 Type **537**	10	10
4525	$60 Soldier with rifle	40	45

538 Bank Logo and Headquarters

1995. 25th Anniv of Caribbean Development Bank.

4526	**538**	$60 multicoloured	40	45

1995. Christmas. Religious Paintings. As T **245a** of Gambia. Multicoloured.

4527	$25 "Angel of the Annunciation" (Carracci)	30	30
4528	$30 "Virgin of the Annunciation" (Carracci)	35	35
4529	$35 "Assumption of the Madonna" (Carracci)	40	40
4530	$60 "Baptism of Christ" (Carracci)	70	70
4531	$100 "Madonna and Child with Saints" (detail) (Carracci)	1·25	1·50
4532	$300 "Birth of the Virgin" (Carracci)	3·00	3·50

539 John Lennon

540 Albrecht Kossel (1910 Medicine)

1995. 15th Death Anniv of John Lennon (musician).

4534	**539**	$35 multicoloured	65	65

1995. Centenary of Nobel Trust Fund. Multicoloured.

4535/43	$35×9 Type **540**; Arthur H. Compton (1927 Physics); N. M. Butler (1931 Peace); Charles Laveran (1907 Medicine); George R. Minot (1934 Medicine); Henry H. Dale (1936 Medicine); Jacques Monod (1965 Medicine); Alfred Hershey (1969 Medicine); Par Lagerkvist (1951 Literature)		
4544/52	$35×9 Norman F. Ramsey (1989 Physics); Chen Ning Yang (1957 Physics); Earl W. Sutherland Jr. (1971 Medicine); Paul Karrer (1937 Chemistry); Harmut Michel (1988 Chemistry); Richard Kuhn (1938 Chemistry); P. A. M. Dirac (1933 Physics); Victor Grignard (1912 Chemistry); Richard Willstatter (1915 Chemistry)		
4553/61	$35×9 Adolf von Baeyer (1905 Chemistry); Hideki Yukawa (1949 Physics); George W. Beadle (1958 Medicine); Edwin M. McMillan (1951 Chemistry); Samuel C. C. Ting (1976 Physics); Saint-John Perse (1960 Literature); John F. Enders (1954 Medicine); Felix Bloch (1952 Physics); P. B. Medawar (1960 Medicine)		
4562/70	$35×9 Nikolai Basov (1964 Physics); Klas Arnoldson (1908 Peace); Rene Sully-Prudhomme (1901 Literature); Robert W. Wilson (1978 Physics); Hugo Theorell (1955 Medicine); Nelly Sachs (1966 Literature); Hans von Euler-Chelpin (1929 Chemistry); Mairead Corrigan (1976 Peace); Willis E. Lamb Jr. (1955 Physics)		
4571/9	$35×9 Francis Crick (1962 Medicine); Manne Siegbahn (1924 Physics); Eisaku Sato (1974 Peace); Robert Koch (1905 Medicine); Edgar D. Adrian (1932 Medicine); Erwin Neher (1991 Medicine); Henry Taube (1983 Chemistry); Norman Angell (1933 Peace); Robert Robinson (1947 Chemistry)		
4580/8	$35×9 Henri Becquerel (1903 Physics); Igor Tamm (1958 Physics); Georges Kohler (1984 Medicine); Gerhard Domagk (1939 Medicine); Yasunari Kawabata (1968 Literature); Maurice Allais (1988 Economic Sciences); Aristide Briand (1926 Peace); Pavel Cherenkov (1958 Physics); Feodor Lynen (1964 Medicine)		
4535/88	Set of 54	13·00	14·50

Nos. 4535/43, 4544/52, 4553/61, 4562/70, 4571/9 and 4580/8 respectively were printed together, se-tenant, with the backgrounds forming composite designs.

541 David Copperfield

1995. David Copperfield (magician). Multicoloured.

4590	$60 Type **541**	40	45
4591	$60 David Copperfield in cloak and top hat	40	45
4592	$60 With flaming torch	40	45
4593	$60 David Copperfield in close up	40	45
4594	$60 Head of Statue of Liberty	40	45
4595	$60 David Copperfield climbing rope	40	45
4596	$60 With handcuffs	40	45
4597	$60 With woman dancer	40	45
4598	$60 David Copperfield wearing white shirt	40	45

Nos. 4590/8 were printed together, se-tenant, forming a composite background design.

542 Marilyn Monroe

1995. 70th Birth Anniv of Marilyn Monroe (entertainer). Multicoloured.

4600	$60 Type **542**	40	45
4601	$60 Marilyn Monroe with circular earrings	40	45
4602	$60 Marilyn Monroe (red top right corner)	40	45
4603	$60 Marilyn Monroe (signature at bottom right)	40	45
4604	$60 With hair over left eye	40	45

4605 $60 With pink satin at left . . 40 45
4606 $60 With arm raised . . . 40 45
4607 $60 With pink satin at bottom right 40 45
4608 $60 With square earring . . . 40 45

Nos. 4600/8 were printed together, se-tenant, with the background forming a composite design.

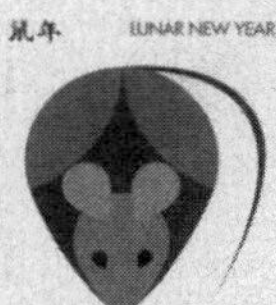

543 Rat

1995. Chinese New Year ("Year of the Rat").

4610 543 $20 multicoloured 15 20
4611 – $30 multicoloured (face value bottom left) . . . 20 25
4612 – $50 multicoloured (face value top right) 35 40
4613 – $100 multicoloured (face value top left) . . . . 1·40 1·50

DESIGNS: $30 to $100 Symbolic rats.

1996. Paintings by Rubens. As T **421** of Grenada. Multicoloured.

4617 $6 "The Garden of Love" (detail) 10 10
4618 $10 "Two Sleeping Children" . 10 10
4619 $20 "All Saints Day" 15 20
4620 $25 "Sacrifice of Abraham" . 20 25
4621 $30 "The Last Supper" . . . 20 25
4622 $35 "The Birth of Henry of Navarre" 25 30
4623 $40 "Study of standing female saint 30 35
4624 $50 "The Garden of Love" (different detail) 35 40
4625 $60 "The Garden of Love" (different detail) 40 45
4626 $200 "The Martyrdom of St. Livinus" . . . . 1·40 1·50
4627 $200 "St. Francis of Paola" . 1·40 1·50
4628 $300 "The Union of Maria de Medici and Henry IV" . . 2·00 2·10

545 Apatosaurus

1996. Prehistoric Animals. Multicoloured.

4630/41 $35 × 12 Type **545**; Archaeopteryx; Dimorphodon; Deinonychus; Coelophysis; Tyrannosaurus; Triceratops; Anatosaurus; Saltasaurus; Allosaurus; Oviraptor; Stegosaurus
4642/53 $35 × 12 Ornithomimus; Pteranodon; Rhamphorynchus; Ornitholestes; Brachiosaurus; Parasaurolophus; Ceratosaurus; Camarasaurus; Euoplocephalus; Scutellosaurus; Compsognathus; Stegoceras
4654/65 $35 × 12 Eudimorphodon; Criorhynchus; Elasmosaurus; Rhomaleosaurus; Ceresiosaurus; Mesosaurus; Grendelius; Nothosaurus; Mixosaurus; Placodus; Coelacanth; Mosasaurus
4666/77 $35 × 12 Tarbosaurus; Hadrosaurus; Polacanthus; Psittacosaurus; Ornitholestes; Yangchuanosaurus; Scelidosaurus; Kentrosaurus; Coelophysis; Lesothosaurus; Plateosaurus; Staurikosaurus (all vert)
4630/77 Set of 48 . . . . 12·00 13·00

Nos. 4630/41, 4642/53, 4654/65 and 4666/77 respectively were printed together, se-tenant, with the backgrounds forming composite designs.

546a Deng Xiaoping writing Inscription

1996. Deng Xiaoping (Chinese leader) Commemoration. Multicoloured.

4681c $30 Type **546a** 20 25
4681d $30 Deng Xiaoping addressing meeting (value in red) . . . 20 25
4681e $30 Signing first day cover for army officer (value in yellow) 20 25
4681f $30 Waving 20 25
4681g $30 As No. 4681d (value in yellow) 20 25
4681h $30 As No. 4681e (value in red) 20 25

547 "Morchella esculenta" and "Doryphorella princeps" (leaf beetle)

549 Hulda Gates

1996. Fungi of Guyana. Multicoloured.

4682 $20 Type **547** 15 20
4683 $25 Green-spored mushroom . 20 25
4684 $30 Common mushroom and leaf beetle 20 25
4685 $35 Pine cone mushroom and "Danaus plexippus" caterpillar 25 30
4686 $60 "Armillaria mellea" . . . 40 45
4687 $60 "Gomphus floccosus" . . 40 45
4688 $60 "Pholiota astragalina" . . 40 45
4689 $60 "Helvellaa crispa" 40 45
4690 $60 "Hygrophorus miniatus" . 40 45
4691 $60 "Omphalotus olearius" . . 40 45
4692 $60 "Hygrocybe acutoconica" . 40 45
4693 $60 "Mycena viscosa" 40 45
4694 $60 Cockle-shell lentinus . . . 40 45
4695 $60 "Volvariella surrecta" . . 40 45
4696 $60 "Lepiota josserandii" . . 40 45
4697 $60 "Boletellus betula" . . . 40 45
4698 $60 "Amanita muscaria" . . . 40 45
4699 $60 "Russula claroflava" and "Semiotus angulatus" (click beetle) 40 45
4700 $60 "Dictyophora duplicata" and "Musca domestica" (house fly) 40 45
4701 $60 "Stropharia" and "Editha magnifica" (butterfly hunter) 40 45
4702 $60 "Leotia viscosa" 40 45
4703 $60 "Calostoma cinnabarina" . 40 45
4704 $60 Stalkless paxillus 40 45
4705 $60 "Amanita spissa" 40 45

Nos. 4686 and 4692 are inscribed "Armillauella mellea" and "Hygzocybe acutoconica", both in error.

1996. 70th Birthday of Queen Elizabeth II. As T **255a** of Gambia. Multicoloured.

4707 $100 Queen Elizabeth II . . . 70 75
4708 $100 Queen wearing green and blue jacket and hat . . . 70 75
4709 $100 Queen at State Opening of Parliament 70 75

1996. Commonwealth Pharmacy Week. Unissued values in designs of Nos. 1810 and 1873 surch **COMMONWEALTH PHARMACY WEEK JUNE 16th 22nd 1996.**

4711 $6 on 130 c. Plate No. 21 (Series 2) . . . .
4712 $60 on 100 c. Plate No. 33 (Series 2) . . . .

1996. Centenary of Radio. Entertainers. As T **259a** of Gambia. Multicoloured.

4713 $20 Frank Sinatra 15 20
4714 $35 Gene Autry 25 30
4715 $60 Groucho Marx 40 45
4716 $200 Red Skelton . . . . . 1·40 1·50

1996. 3000th Anniv of Jerusalem. Multicoloured.

4718 $30 Type **549** 20 25
4719 $35 Church of St. Mary Magdalene 25 30
4720 $200 Absalom's Tomb, Kidron Valley . . . . 1·40 1·50

550 Long-billed Starthroat

1996. Birds of the World. Multicoloured.

4722 $60 Type **550** 40 45
4723 $60 Velvet-purple coronet . . 40 45
4724 $60 Racquet-tailed coquette . 40 45
4725 $60 Violet-tailed sylph . . . 40 45
4726 $60 Broad-tailed hummingbird 40 45
4727 $60 Blue-tufted starthroat . . 40 45
4728 $60 White-necked jacobin . . 40 45
4729 $60 Ruby-throated hummingbird 40 45
4730 $60 Blue and yellow macaw . 40 45
4731 $60 Andean condor 40 45
4732 $60 Guiana crested eagle . . . 40 45
4733 $60 White-tailed trogon . . . 40 45
4734 $60 Toco toucan 40 45
4735 $60 Great horned owl 40 45
4736 $60 Andean cock-of-the-rock . 40 45
4737 $60 Great curassow 40 45

Nos. 4722/9 and 4730/7 respectively were printed together, se-tenant, the backgrounds forming composite designs.

551 Pancratium (ancient Olympic event)

1996. Olympic Games, Atlanta (3rd issue). Multicoloured.

4739 $20 Type **551** 15 20
4740 $30 Olympic Stadium, Melbourne, 1956 . . . . 20 25
4741/9 $50 × 9 Volleyball; Basketball; Tennis; Table tennis; Baseball; Handball; Hockey; Water polo; Football
4750/8 $50 × 9 Cycling; Hurdling; High jumping; Diving; Weight- lifting; Canoeing; Wrestling; Gymnastics; Running (all vert)
4759/67 $50 × 9 Florence Griffith-Joyner (track and field) (U.S.A.); Ines Geissler (swimming) (Germany); Nadia Comaneci (gymnastics) (Rumania); Tatiana Gutsu (gymnastics) (Unified team); Ogla Korbut (gymnastics) (Russia); Barbara Krause (swimming) (Germany); Olga Bryzgina (track and field) (Russia); Fanny Blankers-Koen (track and field) (Holland); Irena Szewinska (track and field) (Poland) (all vert)
4768/76 $50 × 9 Gerd Wessig (Germany); Jim Thorpe (U.S.A.); Norman Read (New Zealand); Lasse Viren (Finland); Milt Campbell (U.S.A.); Abebe Bikila (Ethiopia); Jesse Owens (U.S.A.); Viktor Saneev (Russia); Waldemer Cierpinski (Germany) (all track and field) (all vert)
4777/85 $50 × 9 Ditmar Schmidt (handball) (Germany); Pam Shriver (tennis doubles) (U.S.A.); Zina Garrison (tennis doubles) (U.S.A); Hyun Jung-Hua (table tennis doubles) (Korea); Steffi Graf (tennis) (Germany); Michael Jordan (basketball) (U.S.A.); Karch Kiraly (volleyball) (U.S.A.); "Magic" Johnson (basketball) (U.S.A.); Ingolf Weigert (handball) (Germany) (all vert)
4786 $60 Leonid Spirin winning 20 kilometre walk, 1956 (vert) 40 45
4787 $200 Lars Hall, Gold medal winner, Modern Pentathalon, 1952 and 1956 (Sweden) (vert) . . 1·40 1·50
4739/87 Set of 49 . . . . 18·00 19·00

Nos. 4741/9, 4750/8, 4759/67, 4768/76 and 4777/85 (the last three showing Gold medal winners) respectively were printed together, se-tenant, forming composite background designs.

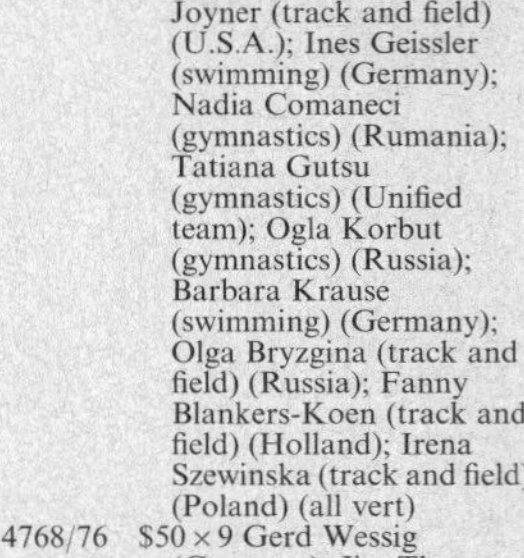

552 Mickey's Bait Shop

1996. Mickey Mouse and Friends Outdoors. Multicoloured.

4789 $60 Type **552** 85 85
4790 $60 Mickey and Pluto as lumberjacks 85 85
4791 $60 Mickey fishing 85 85
4792 $80 Donald Duck in BMX bike championships (vert) . . . 1·00 1·00
4793 $80 Goofy as ice hockey superstar (vert) . . . . . 1·00 1·00
4794 $80 Donald Duck at Malibu Surf City (vert) . . . . . 1·00 1·00
4795 $100 Mickey as naval captain (vert) . . . . 1·25 1·25
4796 $100 Captain Mickey's Seamanship School (vert) . 1·25 1·25
4797 $100 Mickey as sailor with ship's wheel and full-rigged sailing ship (vert) . . . . 1·25 1·25

INDEX
Countries can be quickly located by referring to the index at the end of this volume.

553 Two Gun Mickey

1996. Disney Antique Toys. Multicoloured.

4799 $6 Type **553** 20 20
4800 $6 Wood-jointed Mickey figure 20 20
4801 $6 Donald jack-in-the-box . . 20 20
4802 $6 Rocking Minnie 20 20
4803 $6 Fireman Donald Duck . . 20 20
4804 $6 Long-billed Donald Duck . 20 20
4805 $6 Painted-wood Mickey figure 20 20
4806 $6 Wind-up Jiminy Cricket . . 20 20

554 Elvis Presley

1996. 60th Birth Anniv (1995) of Elvis Presley. Multicoloured, background colours given.

4808 554 $100 red 70 75
4809 – $100 mauve 70 75
4810 – $100 brown 70 75
4811 – $100 blue 70 75
4812 – $100 purple 70 75
4813 – $100 blue 70 75

DESIGNS: Nos. 4809/13, Various portraits.

556 Birman

1996. Cats of the World. Multicoloured.

4815 $60 Type **556** 40 45
4816 $60 American curl 40 45
4817 $60 Turkish angora 40 45
4818 $60 European shorthair (Italy) 40 45
4819 $60 Persian (Great Britain) . . 40 45
4820 $60 Scottish fold 40 45
4821 $60 Sphynx (Canada) 40 45
4822 $60 Malayan (Thailand) . . . 40 45
4823 $60 Cornish rex (Great Britain) 40 45
4824 $60 Norwegian forest (vert) . . 40 45
4825 $60 Russian shorthair (vert) . 40 45
4826 $60 European shorthair (Italy) (vert) 40 45
4827 $60 Birman (vert) 40 45
4828 $60 Ragdoll (U.S.A.) (vert) . . 40 45
4829 $60 Egyptian mau (vert) . . . 40 45
4830 $60 Persian (Great Britain) (vert) 40 45
4831 $60 Turkish angora (vert) . . 40 45
4832 $60 Siamese (vert) 40 45

Nos. 4815/23 and 4824/32 respectively were printed together, se-tenant, with the backgrounds forming composite designs.

557 Hyed Snapper

1996. Marine Life. Multicoloured.

4834 $6 Type **557** 10 10
4835 $6 Angelfish 10 10
4836 $20 Boxfish 15 20
4837 $25 Golden damselfish 20 25
4838 $30 Goblin shark and coelacanth 20 25
4839 $30 "Jason" (American remote-controlled submersible) . . 20 25
4840 $30 Deep-water invertebrates . 20 25
4841 $30 Submarine NR-1 . . . . 20 25
4842 $30 Giant squid 20 25
4843 $30 Sperm whale 20 25
4844 $30 Volcanic vents and "Alvin" (submersible) 20 25
4845 $30 Air-recycling pressure suits and shipwreck 20 25

4846 $30 "Shinkai" 6500 (submersible) 20 25
4847 $30 Giant tube worms 20 25
4848 $30 Anglerfish 20 25
4849 $30 Six-gill shark 20 25
4850 $30 Autonomous underwater vehicle ABE 20 25
4851 $30 Octopus and viperfish . . 20 25
4852 $30 Swallower and hatchetfish . 20 25
4853 $35 Clown triggerfish 25 30
4854 $60 Red gorgonians 40 45
4855 $60 Soft coral and butterflyfish 40 45
4856 $60 Soft coral and slender snapper 40 45
4857 $60 Common clownfish, anemone and mushroom coral 40 45
4858 $60 Anemone and horse-eyed jack 40 45
4859 $60 Splendid coral trout . . . 40 45
4860 $60 Anemones 40 45
4861 $60 Brain coral 40 45
4862 $60 Cup coral 40 45
4863 $200 Harlequin tuskfish . . . 1·40 1·50

Nos. 4838/52 and 4854/62 respectively were printed together, se-tenant, with the backgrounds forming composite designs.

No. 4853 is inscribed "CLOWN TUGGERFISH" in error.

558 Snow White and Reindeer

1996. Christmas. Disney's "Snow White and the Seven Dwarfs". Multicoloured.

4865 $6 Type **558** 15 10
4866 $20 Doc with presents . . . 35 25
4867 $25 Dopey and Sneezy 35 30
4868 $30 Sleepy, Happy and Bashful 40 35
4869 $35 Dopey and Santa Claus . 40 40
4870 $60 Dopey with socks at fireplace 75 65
4871 $100 Dopey and Grumpy . . 1·40 1·50
4872 $200 Dopey dressed as Santa Claus . . . . 2·75 3·00

559 Hotel Tower

1996. 50th Anniv of Hotel Tower, Georgetown.

4874 **559** $30 multicoloured 20 25

561 Ox

1997. Chinese New Year. "Year of the Ox".

4882 **561** $20 multicoloured 15 20
4883 – $30 multicoloured 20 25
4884 – $35 multicoloured 25 30
4885 – $50 multicoloured 35 40

DESIGNS: Nos. 4883/5 depict symbolic oxen.

562 Mickey with Traditional Box of Sweets

1997. Mickey Mouse and Friends celebrate Chinese New Year. Multicoloured.

4888 $6 Type **562** 10 10
4889 $20 Mickey and Minnie at home with friends 15 20
4890 $25 Mickey and Minnie hanging fortune lantern 20 25
4891 $30 Minnie and Daisy with paper silhouette 20 25
4892 $30 Mickey and friends receiving traditional red money . . 20 25
4893 $30 Mickey in lion dance . . . 20 25
4894 $30 Mickey preparing Chinese calligraphy wall hangings . . 20 25
4895 $30 Mickey with symbols of surplus 20 25
4896 $30 Donald Duck playing with fireworks 20 25
4897 $30 Donald, Mickey and Minnie on ox 20 25
4898 $35 Donald Duck and friends at New Year flower market . . 25 30
4899 $60 Mickey and Minnie as "harmonious man and woman" 40 45

563 Burgess Meredith as Ernie Pyle in "The Story of G.I. Joe"

1997. Centenary of Cinema. Second World War Films. Multicoloured.

4901 $50 Type **563** 35 40
4902 $50 M. E. Clifton-James as General Montgomery in "I was Monty's Double" . . . 35 40
4903 $50 Audie Murphy as himself in "To Hell and Back" 35 40
4904 $50 Gary Cooper as Dr. Wassell in "The Story of Dr. Wassell" 35 40
4905 $50 James Mason as Erwin Rommel in "The Desert Fox" 35 40
4906 $50 Manart Kippen as Stalin in "Mission to Moscow" . . . 35 40
4907 $50 Robert Taylor as Col. Paul Tibbets in "Above and Beyond" 35 40
4908 $50 James Cagney as Admiral Bill Halsey in "The Gallant Hours" 35 40
4909 $50 John Garfield as Al Schmid in "Pride of the Marines" . . 35 40

564 "Washington in Battle"

1997. Bicentenary of George Washington's Retirement from U.S. Presidency. Multicoloured.

4911 $60 Type **564** 40 45
4912 $60 "Washington taking Presidential Oath" 40 45
4913 $60 "Washington seated in Armchair" (engraving after Chappel) 40 45
4914 $60 "Col. Washington of the Virginia Militia" (Charles W. Peale) 40 45
4915 $60 "George Washington" (Rembrandt Peale) 40 45
4916 $60 "Washington addressing Constitutional Convention" (Junius B. Stearns) 40 45
4917 $60 "Washington on his way to Continental Congress" . . . 40 45
4918 $60 "Washington on a White Charger" (John Faed) . . . 40 45
4919 $60 "Washington surveying" (engraving by G. R. Hall) . . 40 45
4920 $60 "Washington praying at Valley Forge" (bas-relief) . . 40 45
4921 $60 "Death of Gen. Mercer at Battle of Princeton" (John Trumbull) 40 45
4922 $60 "Washington taking Command at Cambridge" . . 40 45
4923 $60 "Washington before Battle of Trenton" (John Trumbull) 40 45
4924 $60 "Washington and his Family at Mount Vernon" (Alonzo Chappel) 40 45
4925 $60 "Washington's Inauguration" (Chappel) . . 40 45
4926 $60 "Washington" (Adolph Ulrich Wertmuller) 40 45
4927 $60 "Washington accepts Commission as Commander-in-Chief" (Currier & Ives lithograph) 40 45
4928 $60 "Washington" (mezzotint by Sartain) 40 45
4929 $60 "Mount Vernon" 40 45
4930 $60 "Washington with Farm Workers" (print by Junius B. Stearns) 40 45
4931 $60 "Wedding of Nellie Custis" (Ogden) 40 45
4932 $60 "Washington crossing the Delaware" (Leutze) 40 45
4933 $60 "Washington and Gen. Braddock" 40 45
4934 $60 "Washington's Birthplace" (Currier & Ives lithograph) . 40 45
4935 $300 "George Washington" (Gilbert Stuart) (66 × 91 mm) . . . . 2·00 2·10
4936 $300 "Washington at Yorktown" (James Peale) (66 × 91 mm) . . . . 2·00 2·10

EXPRESS LETTER STAMPS

1986. Various stamps surch **EXPRESS** and new values.

E1 $12 on 350 c. on 120 c. multicoloured (No. 1598) . . 6·50 6·50
E2 $15 on 40 c. multicoloured (No. 1868) . . . . 8·50 8·50
E3 $20 on $6.40 multicoloured . . 6·50 6·50
E4 $25 on 25 c. multicoloured (as No. 1771, but value changed) . . 12·00 12·00

No. E3 was previously a miniature sheet for Halley's Comet containing two 320 c. stamps. As surch the original values on both designs have been cancelled and replaced by a single $20 face value.

1987. No. E3 additionally optd with small Maltese cross above surch.

E5 $20 on $6.40 multicoloured . . 7·00 7·00

1987. Centenary of Publication of Sanders' "Reichenbachia". As T **331** additionally inscr "EXPRESS". Multicoloured.

E6 $15 Plate No. 11 (Series 2) . . . 4·00 4·00
E7 $20 Plate No. 93 (Series 2) . . . 3·50 4·00
E8 $25 Plate No. 63 (Series 2) . . . 3·75 4·25
E9 $45 Plate No. 35 (Series 2) . . . 7·00 8·00

1987. Nos. 1744/5 imperf between surch **EXPRESS FORTY DOLLARS** and star.

E10 $40 on $6.40 multicoloured . . 11·00 11·00

1987. No. E2 additionally optd **1987**.

E11 $15 on 40 c. multicoloured . . 9·50 5·00

1988. Nos. 2206 and 2211 surch **SPECIAL DELIVERY** and new value.

E12 $40 on $3.20 blue . . . . . . 10·00 10·00
E13 $45 on $3.30 black . . . . . 10·00 10·00

1989. Imperf between pairs of Nos. 1744/5 and 2185/6 surch **EXPRESS FORTY DOLLARS** (without stars).

E14 $40 on $6.40 multicoloured (Nos. 1744/5) . . . . 5·50 5·50
E15 $40 on $6.40 multicoloured (Nos. 2185/6) . . . . 5·50 5·50

1989. Nos. 2206 and 2211 surch **SPECIAL DELIVERY** and new value.

E16 $190 on $3.30 black . . . . . 14·00 16·00
E17 $225 on $3.20 blue . . . . . 15·00 17·00

OFFICIAL STAMPS

1981. Nos. 556, F4a and F6/7 optd **OPS** or surch also.

O13 10 c. on 25 c. Marabunta . . . 1·50 2·00
O14 50 c. "Guzmania lingulata" . . 1·25 30
O15 60 c. Soldier's cap . . . . . . 1·25 20
O16 $5 "Odontadenia grandiflora" . 2·25 1·75

1981. Nos. 491, 708a, 716, 804, 834 and F9 optd **OPS** or surch also.

O17 15 c. Harpy eagle (postage) . . 9·00 65
O18 30 c. on $2 "Norantea guianensis" (F9) 45 30
O19 100 c. on $3 Cylinder satellite 3·00 40
O20 125 c. on $2 "Norantea guianensis" . . . . 1·25 60
O21 $10 "Elbella patrobas" . . . . 7·50 8·50
O22 $1.10 on $2 "Norantea guianensis" (804) (air) . . . 75 2·00

1981. Nos. 548a, 719, 828 and 830 optd **OPS** or surch also.

O23 15 c. Christmas orchid . . . . 8·00 1·50
O24 50 c. British Guiana 1898 1 c. stamp . . . . 1·25 35
O25 100 c. on 8 c. Camp-fire cooking 1·25 50
O26 110 c. on 6 c. Type **116** . . . 2·50 1·25

1982. Various stamps optd **OPS**.

O27 – 20 c. multicoloured (No. 701) . . . . 4·25 60
O28 **136** 40 c. multicoloured . . . 75 15
O29 – 40 c. red, grey and black (No. 674) . . . . 1·00 15
O30 – $2 multicoloured (No. 676) 7·00 75

1982. Nos. 911 and 980 optd or surch **OPS**.

O31 250 c. on 400 c. on 30 c. multicoloured (postage) . . 80 60
O32 220 c. on 1 c. multicoloured (air) 1·00 60

1982. No. F9 optd **OPS**.

O33 $2 "Norantea guianensis" . . . 8·00 2·00

1982. Air. No. 979 optd **OPS**.

O34 110 c. on 5 c. Annatto tree . . 1·25 40

1984. No. 912 surch **OPS**.

O35 150 c. on $5 multicoloured . . 5·50 2·75
O36 200 c. on $5 multicoloured . . 6·00 3·00
O37 225 c. on $5 multicoloured . . 6·00 3·25
O38 230 c. on $5 multicoloured . . 6·00 3·25
O39 260 c. on $5 multicoloured . . 6·00 3·50
O40 320 c. on $5 multicoloured . . 7·50 4·00
O41 350 c. on $5 multicoloured . . 8·00 4·50
O42 600 c. on $5 multicoloured . . 9·50 5·50

1984. Nos. O32 and O34 surch and No. 981 optd **OPS**.

O43 25 c. on 110 c. on 5 c. Annatto tree 90 30
O44 30 c. on 110 c. on 5 c. Annatto tree . . . . 1·00 35
O45 45 c. on 220 c. on 1 c. Pitcher plant of Mt. Roraima . . . 1·10 40
O46 55 c. on 110 c. on 5 c. Annatto tree . . . . 1·40 50
O47 60 c. on 220 c. on 1 c. Pitcher plant of Mt. Roraima . . . 1·40 50
O48 75 c. on 220 c. on 1 c. Pitcher plant of Mt. Roraima . . . 1·50 60
O49 90 c. on 220 c. on 1 c. Pitcher plant of Mt. Roraima . . . 1·50 70
O50 120 c. on 220 c. on 1 c. Pitcher plant of Mt. Roraima . . . 1·75 85
O51 130 c. on 220 c. on 1 c. Pitcher plant of Mt. Roraima . . . 2·00 90
O52 330 c. on $2 "Norantea guianensis" . . . . 3·50 2·75

1987. Centenary of Publication of Sanders' "Reichenbachia". As T **331** additionally inscr "OFFICIAL". Multicoloured.

O53 120 c. Plate No. 48 (Series 2) . 90 25
O54 130 c. Plate No. 92 (Series 2) . 90 25
O55 140 c. Plate No. 36 (Series 2) . 60 25
O56 150 c. Plate No. 43 (Series 2) . 90 25
O57 175 c. Plate No. 31 (Series 2) . 70 30
O58 200 c. Plate No. 61 (Series 2) . 1·00 35
O59 225 c. Plate No. 26 (Series 2) . 1·00 35
O60 230 c. Plate No. 68 (Series 2) (horiz) 50 35
O61 250 c. Plate No. 59 (Series 2) . 50 40
O62 260 c. Plate No. 69 (Series 2) . 50 40
O63 275 c. Plate No. 90 (Series 2) . 1·00 40
O64 320 c. Plate No. 75 (Series 2) . 1·00 50
O65 330 c. Plate No. 23 (Series 2) . 1·75 60
O66 350 c. Plate No. 95 (Series 2) (horiz) 50 60
O67 600 c. Plate No. 70 (Series 2) (horiz) . . . . 75 1·25
O68 $12 Plate No. 71 (Series 2) (horiz) . . . . 1·40 2·00
O69 $15 Plate No. 84 (Series 2) . . 1·50 2·25

OFFICIAL PARCEL POST STAMPS

1981. Nos. P1/2 optd **OPS**.

OP1 $15 on $1 "Chelonanthus uliginoides" . . . . 7·50 2·25
OP2 $20 on $1 "Chelonanthus uliginoides" . . . . 10·00 2·75

1983. No. 843 surch **OPS Parcel Post $12.00** and additionally optd **1982**.

OP3 $12 on $1.10 on $2 "Norantea guianensis" . . . . 65·00 17·00

1983. No. OP3 with additional **OPS** opt.

OP4 $12 on $1.10 on $2 "Norantea guianensis" . . . . 20·00 4·00

1983. No. P4 optd **OPS**.

OP5 $12 on $1.10 on $2 "Norantea guianensis" . . . . 6·00 4·00

PARCEL POST STAMPS

1981. No. 554 surch **PARCEL POST** and new value.

P1 $15 on $1 "Chelonanthus uliginoides" . . . . 10·00 3·00
P2 $20 on $1 "Chelonanthus uliginoides" . . . . 10·00 6·00

1983. No. 843 surch **PARCEL POST $12.00**.

P3 $12 on $1.10 on $2 "Norantea guianensis" . . . . 3·25 2·50

1983. Unissued Royal Wedding surch, similar to No. 843, further surch **Parcel Post $12.00**.

P4 $12 on $1.10 on $2 "Norantea guianensis" . . . . 1·00 1·75

1985. No. 673 surch **TWENTY FIVE DOLLARS PARCEL POST 25.00**.

P5 $25 on 35 c. green, grey and black 22·00 18·00

POSTAGE DUE STAMPS

D 2

1987.

D 8 **D 2** 1 c. green . . . . 20 3·00
D 9 2 c. black . . . . 20 3·00
D10 4 c. blue . . . . 20 3·00
D11 12 c. red . . . . 30 3·00

POSTAL FISCAL STAMPS

1975. Nos. 543/5 and 550ab/6 optd **REVENUE ONLY**.

F 1 2 c. Type **132** 40 40
F 2 3 c. Hanging heliconia . . . 40 40
F 3 5 c. Annatto tree 65 30
F 4 25 c. Marabunta . . . . . . 2·50 30
F 4a 25 c. Marabunta (No. 550) . . 15·00 13·00
F 5 40 c. Tiger beard . . . . . . 5·00 30
F 6 50 c. "Guzmania lingulata" . 60 40
F 7 60 c. Soldier's cap 75 50
F 8 $1 "Chelonanthus uliginoides" 75 1·25
F 9 $2 "Norantea guianensis" . 1·00 2·75
F10 $5 "Odontadenia grandiflora" 1·75 9·00

Although intended for fiscal use Nos. F1/F10 were allowed by the postal authorities as an "act of grace" to do duty as postage stamps until 30 June 1976.

GWALIOR Pt. 1

A "convention" state of Central India.

12 pies = 1 anna; 16 annas = 1 rupee

1885. Queen Victoria stamps of India optd **GWALIOR** at foot and native opt at top.

1 **23** ½ a. turquoise 90·00 18·00
2 – 1 a. purple 65·00 24·00
6 – 1½ a. brown 55·00
3 – 2 a. blue 55·00 12·00
8 – 4 a. green (No. 69) 65·00
9 – 6 a. brown (No. 80) 65·00
10 – 8 a. mauve 55·00
11 – 1 r. grey (No. 101) 55·00

Stamps of India overprinted **GWALIOR** above native overprint unless otherwise stated.

1885. Queen Victoria.

16c **23** ½ a. turquoise 20 10
17 – 9 p. red 28·00 50·00
18 – 1 a. purple 40 15
20c – 1 a. 6 p. brown 70 40
21c – 2 a. blue 50 10
23 – 2 a. 6 p. green 5·00 14·00
25c – 3 a. orange 65 15
14 – 4 a. green (No. 69) 17·00 9·00
27c – 4 a. green (No. 96) 1·75 45
29 – 6 a. brown (No. 80) 1·40 5·00
30c – 8 a. mauve 2·00 60
32c – 12 a. purple on red 3·00 65
33c – 1 r. grey (No. 101) 2·00 85
34 **37** 1 r. green and red 2·50 2·75
35 **38** 2 r. red and orange 5·50 3·00
36 3 r. brown and green 7·50 3·50
37 5 r. blue and violet 13·00 6·50

1899. Queen Victoria.

38 **40** 3 p. red 10 20
39 3 p. grey 6·00 60·00
40 **23** ½ a. green 20 1·00
41 – 1 a. red 50 35
42 – 2 a. lilac 75 3·50
43 – 2½ a. blue 90 4·00

1903. King Edward VII.

46A **41** 3 p. grey 50 20
48A – ½ a. green (No. 122) 10 10
49A – 1 a. red (No. 123) 10 10
50A – 2 a. lilac 60 60
52B – 2 a. 6 p. blue 75 6·00
53A – 3 a. orange 1·10 30
54A – 4 a. olive 1·10 40
56B – 6 a. bistre 3·75 1·00
57A – 8 a. mauve 2·75 1·25
59B – 12 a. purple on red 3·50 3·25
60A – 1 r. green and red 1·75 1·75
61B **52** 2 r. red and orange 8·50 11·00
62B 3 r. brown and green 25·00 40·00
63B 5 r. blue and violet 18·00 26·00

1907. King Edward VII inscr "INDIA POSTAGE AND REVENUE".

65 ½ a. green (No. 149) 45 15
66 1 a. red (No. 150) 90 10

1912. King George V.

67 **55** 3 p. grey 10 10
68 **58** ½ a. green 20 10
102 **79** ½ a. green 40 10
88 **80** 9 p. green 1·50 20
69 **57** 1 a. red 25 10
80 1 a. brown 30 10
103 **81** 1 a. brown 10 10
90 **82** 1 a. 3 p. mauve 30 10
81 **58** 1½ a. brown (No. 165) 1·00 50
82 1½ a. red 15 20
70 **59** 2 a. lilac 40 10
91 **70** 2 a. lilac 50 20
104 **59** 2 a. red 60 1·60
83 **61** 2½ a. blue 1·25 1·75
84 2½ a. orange 25 50
71 **62** 3 a. orange 50 15
92 3 a. blue 75 40
72 **63** 4 a. olive 50 60
93 **71** 4 a. green 85 90
73 **64** 6 a. bistre 80 80
74 **65** 8 a. mauve 90 30
75 **66** 12 a. red 1·00 2·25
76 **67** 1 r. brown and green 3·00 40
77 2 r. red and orange 4·50 4·25
78 5 r. blue and violet 20·00 6·50

1922. No. 192 (King George V) optd **GWALIOR** only.

79 **57** 9 p. on 1a. red 10 40

1928. King George V. Optd in larger type (19 mm long).

96 **67** 1 r. brown and green 1·60 2·75
97 2 r. red and orange 4·00 3·50
98 5 r. blue and violet 15·00 20·00
99 10 r. green and red 42·00 30·00
100 15 r. blue and olive 65·00 48·00
101 25 r. orange and blue £140 £110

1938. King George V.

105 **91** 3 p. slate 4·00 10
106 ½ a. brown 4·00 10
107 9 p. green 32·00 2·75
108 1 a. red 4·00 15
109 3 a. green (No. 253) 10·00 2·75
110 4 a. brown (No. 255) 38·00 1·75
111 6 a. green (No. 256) 2·50 6·00
112 **93** 1 r. slate and brown 6·00 1·50
113 2 r. purple and brown 28·00 7·00
114 5 r. green and blue 38·00 32·00
115 10 r. purple and red 38·00 40·00
116 15 r. brown and green £120 £160
117 25 r. slate and purple £110 £120

1942. King George VI.

118 **100a** 3 p. slate 45 10
119 ½ a. mauve 45 10
120 9 p. green 45 10
121 1 a. red 40 10
122 **101** 1½ a. violet 3·50 20
123 2 a. red 55 20
124 3 a. violet 6·50 30
125 **102** 4 a. brown 1·25 20
126 6 a. green 20·00 18·00
127 8 a. violet 2·75 2·75
128 12 a. purple 4·50 16·00

OFFICIAL STAMPS

Stamps of India overprinted with native inscription at top and bottom, unless otherwise stated.

1895. Queen Victoria.

O 1 **23** ½ a. turquoise 10 10
O 3 – 1 a. purple 65 10
O 4 – 2 a. blue 1·25 35
O 7 – 4 a. green (No. 96) 1·25 1·00
O 9 – 8 a. mauve 1·25 90
O10 **37** 1 r. green and red 3·75 3·00

1901. Queen Victoria.

O23 **40** 3 p. red 30 30
O24 3 p. grey 1·00 1·75
O26 **23** ½ a. green 20 10
O27 – 1 a. red 3·25 10
O28 – 2 a. lilac 55 1·50

1903. King Edward VII.

O29 **41** 3 p. grey 30 10
O41 – ½ a. green (No. 122) 1·60 15
O32 – 1 a. red (No. 123) 40 10
O33a – 2 a. lilac 1·00 20
O44 – 4 a. olive 2·50 85
O36 – 8 a. mauve 3·25 70
O38 – 1 r. green and red 2·75 1·40

1907. King Edward VII inscr "POSTAGE & REVENUE".

O49 – ½ a. green (No. 149) 70 15
O48 – 1 a. red (No. 150) 4·00 15

1913. King George V.

O51 **55** 3 p. grey 20 10
O62 **56** ½ a. green 10 15
O73 **79** ½ a. green 15 15
O63 **80** 9 p. green 10 15
O53a **57** 1 a. red 20 10
O64 1 a. brown 10 10
O74 **81** 1 a. brown 15 15
O65 **82** 1 a. 3 p. mauve 50 15
O55 **59** 2 a. lilac 45 20
O66 **70** 2 a. lilac 20 15
O75 **59** 2 a. red 20 40
O77 **63** 4 a. olive 50 75
O67 **71** 4 a. green 50 30
O68 **65** 8 a. mauve 50 70
O58 **67** 1 r. brown and green 15·00 14·00

1922. No. O97 (King George V Official) optd **GWALIOR** only.

O59 **57** 9 p. on 1a. red 10 30

1927. King George V. Optd in large type (21 mm long).

O69 **67** 1 r. brown and green 80 1·75
O70 2 r. red and orange 7·00 8·50
O71 5 r. blue and violet 12·00 £130
O72 10 r. green and red 90·00 £275

1938. King George VI.

O78 **91** ½ a. brown 6·50 30
O79 1 a. red 1·10 20
O91 **93** 1 r. slate and brown 8·00 13·00
O92 2 r. purple and brown 21·00 70·00
O93 5 r. green and blue 38·00 £375
O94 10 r. purple and red £110 £750

1940. King George VI. Optd at bottom only.

O80 **O 20** 3 p. slate 50 10
O81 ½ a. brown 3·00 25
O82 ½ a. purple 50 10
O83 9 p. green 70 50
O84 1 a. red 2·25 10
O85 1 a. 3 p. brown 30·00 1·60
O86 1 a. 6 p. violet 1·00 30
O87 2 a. orange 1·00 30
O88 4 a. brown 1·25 1·60
O89 8 a. violet 2·50 6·00

1942. No. O65 surch **1A 1A** and bar.

O90 **82** 1 a. on 1¼a. mauve 16·00 2·50

HAITI Pt. 15

The W. portion of the island of San Domingo in the West Indies. A republic, independent from 1804.

100 centimes = 1 gourde or piastre.

1 Liberty 2 Pres. Salomon

1881. Imperf.

1 **1** 1 c. red 5·00 3·00
2 2 c. purple 6·50 3·25
3 3 c. bistre 11·00 4·00
4 5 c. green 18·00 7·00
5 7 c. blue 12·50 2·50
6 20 c. brown 45·00 16·00

1882. Perf.

7 **1** 1 c. red 3·25 1·00
9 2 c. purple 5·00 1·50
12 3 c. bistre 6·50 2·25
15 **1** 5 c. green 3·75 75
17 7 c. blue 5·00 1·25
20 20 c. brown 4·50 1·00

1887.

24 **2** 1 c. lake 30 30
25 2 c. mauve 55 50
26 3 c. blue 50 40
27 5 c. green 2·10 40

1890. Surch **DEUX 2 CENT.**

28 **2** 2 c. on 3 c. blue 40 35

4 Tree with Leaves Upright 5 Tree with Leaves Drooping 6

1891. Tree with leaves upright.

29 **4** 1 c. mauve 40 15
30 2 c. blue 60 20
31 3 c. lilac 60 40
31a 3 c. grey 80 50
32 5 c. orange 2·25 40
33 7 c. red 4·75 1·75

1892. Surch **DEUX 2 CENT.**

34 **4** 2 c. on 3 c. lilac 85 70
34a 2 c. on 3 c. grey 85 70

1893. Tree with leaves drooping.

35a **5** 1 c. purple 15 10
41 1 c. blue 20 20
36 2 c. blue 20 10
42 2 c. red 40 25
37 3 c. lilac 60 40
43 3 c. brown 20 15
38 5 c. orange 2·25 20
44 5 c. green 20 15
39 7 c. red 40 35
45 7 c. grey 30 20
40 20 c. brown 80 60
46 20 c. orange 40 40

1898. Surch **DEUX 2 CENT.**

47 **5** 2 c. on 20 c. brown 85 25
48 2 c. on 20 c. orange 35 25

1898.

49a **6** 2 c. red 20 15
50a 5 c. green 20 15

8 Pres. Simon Sam 9

1898.

51 **8** 1 c. blue 10 10
67 **9** 1 c. green 10 10
52 **8** 2 c. orange 15 15
68 **9** 2 c. red 15 15
53 **8** 3 c. green 15 15
54 **9** 4 c. red 15 15
55 **8** 5 c. brown 15 15
69 **9** 5 c. blue 15 10
56 **8** 7 c. grey 15 15
57 **9** 8 c. red 20 15
58 10 c. orange 15 15
59 15 c. olive 35 25
60 **8** 20 c. black 30 25
61 50 c. lake 35 25
62 1 g. mauve 1·40 1·25

1902. Optd **MAI Gt Pre 1902** in frame.

70 **8** 1 c. blue 45 45
71 **9** 1 c. green 35 15
72 **8** 2 c. orange 45 45
73 **9** 2 c. red 35 15
74 **8** 3 c. green 35 35
75 **9** 4 c. red 45 45
76 **8** 5 c. brown 90 90
77 **9** 5 c. blue 35 35
78 **8** 7 c. grey 45 45
79 **9** 8 c. red 45 45
80 10 c. orange 45 45
81 15 c. olive 2·10 1·50
82 **8** 20 c. black 3·25 1·75
83 50 c. lake 7·50 3·75
84 1 g. mauve 9·50 7·75

12 Arms 13 J.-J. Dessalines

1904. Cent. of Independence. Optd **1804 POSTE PAYE 1904** in frame. T **12** and portraits as T **13**.

89 **12** 1 c. green 25 25
90 – 2 c. black and red 30 30
91 – 5 c. black and blue 30 30
92 **13** 7 c. black and red 30 30
93 – 10 c. black and yellow 30 30
94 – 20 c. black and grey 30 30
95 – 50 c. black and olive 30 30

DESIGNS: 2 c., 5 c. Toussaint l'Ouverture; 20, 50 c. Petion.

1904. Nos. 89/95 but without opt.

96 1 c. green 20 15
97 2 c. black and red 20 15
98 5 c. black and blue 20 15
99 7 c. black and red 20 15
100 10 c. black and yellow 20 15
101 20 c. black and grey 20 15
102 50 c. black and olive 20 15

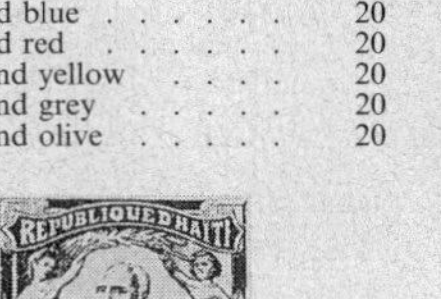

15 Pres. Nord Alexis

1904. External Mail. Optd **1804 POSTE PAYE 1904** in frame.

103 **15** 1 c. green 45 35
104 2 c. red 45 35
105 5 c. blue 45 35
106 10 c. brown 45 35
107 20 c. orange 45 35
108 50 c. plum 45 35

1904. Nos. 103/108, but without opt.

109 **15** 1 c. green 10 10
110 2 c. red 10 10
111 5 c. blue 10 10
112 10 c. brown 10 10
113 20 c. orange 10 10
114 50 c. plum 10 10

1906. Optd **SERVICE EXTERIEUR PROVISOIRE EN PIASTRES FORTES** in oval.

117 **8** 1 c. blue 55 45
118 **9** 1 c. green 55 55
119 **8** 2 c. orange 1·10 1·10
120 **9** 2 c. red 90 90
121 **8** 3 c. green 90 90
122 **9** 4 c. red 3·75 3·00
123 **8** 5 c. brown 3·75 3·00
124 **9** 5 c. blue 45 45
125 **8** 7 c. grey 3·00 3·00
126 **9** 8 c. red 45 45
127 10 c. orange 85 55
128 15 c. olive 1·10 60
129 **8** 20 c. black 3·75 3·00
130 50 c. lake 3·75 1·75
131 1 g. mauve 6·25 4·75

19 Pres. Nord Alexis

20 Arms

1906.

132 **19** 1 c. de g. blue 20 10
133 **20** 2 c. de g. orange 35 15
134 2 c. de g. yellow 55 15
135 **19** 3 c. de g. grey 30 10
136 **20** 7 c. de g. green 55 35

21 Iron Market, Port-au-Prince

24 Pres. A. T. Simon

1906. Currency changed from "gourdes" to "piastres".

137 **20** 1 c. de p. green 20 15
138 **19** 2 c. de p. red 35 20
139 **21** 3 c. de p. sepia 1·75 40
140 3 c. de p. orange 4·25 4·50
141 – 4 c. de p. red 55 30
167 – 4 c. de p. olive 5·50 4·25
142 **19** 5 c. de p. blue 1·10 20
143 – 7 c. de p. grey 85 45
168 – 7 c. de p. red 12·50 8·25
144 – 8 c. de p. red 4·00 1·25
169 – 8 c. de p. olive 17·00 11·00
145 – 10 c. de p. orange 55 20
170 – 10 c. de p. brown 7·25 7·50
146 – 15 c. de p. olive 1·10 45
171 – 15 c. de p. yellow 3·25 1·75
147 **19** 20 c. de p. blue 1·10 45
148 **20** 50 c. de p. red 1·75 1·25
172 50 c. de p. yellow 3·75 2·50
149 – 1 pi. red 3·25 2·10
173 – 1 pi. red 3·75 3·00

DESIGNS—As Type **21**: 4 c. Palace of Sans Souci-Milot; 7 c. Independence Palace, Gonaives; 8 c. Entrance to Catholic College, Port-au-Prince; 10 c. Catholic Monastery and Church, Port-au-Prince; 15 c. Government Offices, Port-au-Prince; 1 p. President's Palace, Port-au-Prince.

1906. Surch with value in double-lined frame Without opt.

154 **15** 1 c. on 5 c. blue 30 20
155 1 c. on 10 c. brown 25 10
156 1 c. on 20 c. orange 30 20
157 2 c. on 10 c. brown 25 20
158 2 c. on 20 c. orange 25 20
159 2 c. on 50 c. plum 35 20

1910.
160 **24** 1 c. de g. black and lake 15 15
161 2 c. de p. black and red 55 35
162 5 c. de p. black & blue 7·75 55
163 20 c. de p. black & green 6·25 4·75

25 Pres. C. Leconte
38

1912. Various frames.
164 **25** 1 c. de g. lake 20 20
165 2 c. de g. orange 25 20
166 5 c. de p. blue 55 20

1914. Optd **GL O.Z. 7 FEV. 1914** in frame.
A. On 1898 issue.
174 **9** 8 c. red 7·75 6·25
B. On 1904 issue, without opt.
175 **15** 1 c. green (No. 109) 22·00 19·00
176 2 c. red 22·00 19·00
177 5 c. blue 45 15
178 10 c. brown 45 15
179 20 c. orange 45 35
180 50 c. plum 1·75 55
C. On pictorial stamps of 1906.
181 **20** 2 c. de g. yellow 35 15
182 **19** 3 c. de g. grey 35 20
D. On pictorial stamps of 1906.
183 **20** 1 c. de p. green (No. 137) 35 25
184 **19** 2 c. de p. red (No. 138) 55 25
185 **21** 3 c. de p. sepia (No. 139) 4·25 75
186 3 c. de p. orge (No. 140) 3·25 3·25
187 – 4 c. de p. red (No. 141) 45 60
198 – 4 c. de p. olive (No. 167) 75 40
188 – 7 c. de p. grey (No. 143) 1·75 1·75
200 – 7 c. de p. red (No. 168) 1·75 1·75
189 – 8 c. de p. red (No. 144) 5·25 2·50
201 – 8 c. de p. olive (No. 169) 6·50 6·50
190 – 10 c. de p. orge (No. 145) 55 55
202 – 10 c. de p. brn (No. 170) 85 55
191 – 15 c. de p. ol (No. 146) 1·75 1·75
203 – 15 c. de p. yell (No. 171) 75 45
192 **19** 20 c. de p. bl (No. 147) 2·25 55
194 **20** 50 c. de p. red (No. 148) 3·75 3·75
204 50 c. de p. yell (No. 172) 3·75 3·75
195 – 1 pi. red (No. 149) 3·75 3·75
205 – 1 pi. red (No. 173) 3·75 3·75
E. On stamp of 1910.
193 **24** 20 c. de p. black & grn 2·40 2·40
F. On stamps of 1912.
196 **25** 1 c. de g. lake 25 20
197 2 c. de g. orange 45 30
199 5 c. de p. blue 70 20

1914. Stamps of 1904, without the opt., surch **GL O.Z 7 FEV 1914 7 CENT** in diamond frame.
213 **15** 7 c. on 20 c. orange (No. 113) 45 20
214 7 c. on 50 c. plum (No. 114) 35 20

1914. Pictorial stamps of 1906 (Nos. 148/73), surch **GL OZ 1 CENT DE PIASTRE 7 FEV. 1914** in frame.
215 **20** 1 c. de p. on 50 c. red 30 20
216 1 c. de p. on 50 c. yellow 45 35
217 – 1 c. de p. on 1 p. red 45 35
218 – 1 c. de p. on 1 p. red 55 45

1915.
219 – 2 c. de g. black & yellow 45
220 **38** 5 c. de g. black & green 45
221 – 7 c. de g. black and red 45
PORTRAIT: 2 c.; 7 c. O. Zamor.

1915. As T **24**, inscr "EMISSION 1914".
222 1 c. de p. black & green 85
223 3 c. de p. black and olive 15
224 5 c. de p. black and blue 25
225 7 c. de p. black and orge 60
226 10 c. de p. black & brown 20
227 15 c. de p. black & olive 25
228 20 c. de p. black & brown 55
DESIGNS: 1 c., 5 c., 10 c., 15 c. O. Zamor; 3 c., 20 c. Arms; 7 c. T. Auguste.

1915. Surch with figure in frame.
229 1 on 5 c. blue (No. 111) 85 85
230 1 on 7 c. grey (No. 143) 10 10
231 1 on 10 c. brown (No. 112) 15 15
232 1 on 20 c. orange (No. 107) 45 35
233 1 on 20 c. orange (No. 113) 55 70
234 1 on 50 c. plum (No. 108) 1·10 55
235 1 on 50 c. plum (No. 114) 15 10
236 2 on 1 pi. red (No. 172) 20 15

1917. Surch **GOURDE** and value in frame.
A. On provisional stamps of 1906.
237 **8** 1 c. on 50 c. lake (No. 130) 16·00 11·00
238 1 c. on 1 g. mauve (No. 131) 19·00 14·00
B. On pictorial stamps of 1906.
239 – 1 c. on 4 c. de p. red (No. 141) 15 15
240 – 1 c. on 4 c. de p. olive (No. 167) 30 30
241 – 1 c. on 7 c. de p. red (No. 168) 45 45
242 – 1 c. on 10 c. de p. orange (No. 145) 10 10
243 – 1 c. on 15 c. de p. yellow (No. 171) 45 30
244 **19** 1 c. on 20 c. de p. blue (No. 147) 20 15
246 **24** 1 c. on 20 c. de p. black and green (No. 163) 2·50 2·50
247 **20** 1 c. on 50 c. de p. red (No. 148) 20 15
249 – 1 c. on 50 c. de p. yellow (No. 172) 85 85
250 – 1 c. on 1 p. red (No. 173) 85 85
251 **21** 2 c. on 3 c. de p. sepia (No. 139) 2·75 1·50
252 2 c. on 3 c. de p. orange (No. 140) 3·50 1·50
253 – 2 c. on 8 c. de p. red (No. 144) 2·25 75
255 – 2 c. on 8 c. de p. olive (No. 169) 3·25 2·50
256 – 2 c. de p. on 10 c. brown (No. 170) 35 45
257 – 2 c. on 15 c. de p. olive (No. 146) 20 10
258 – 2 c. on 15 c. de p. yellow (No. 171) 45 45
259 **19** 2 c. on 20 c. de p. blue (No. 147) 25 15
260 – 5 c. on 10 c. de p. brown (No. 170) 45 45
261 – 5 c. on 15 c. de p. yellow (No. 171) 3·25 3·25

1919. For inland use. Provisionals of 1914.
(a) Surch with new value without frame.
262 – 1 c. on 15 c. de p. olive (No. 191) 20 20
263 **19** 1 c. on 20 c. de p. blue (No. 192) 20 20
264 **24** 1 c. on 20 c. de p. black and green (No. 193) 35 35
265 – 1 c. on 1 p. red (No. 195) 20 15
267 – 1 c. on 1 p. red (No. 205) 35 35
(b) Surch with new value in frame.
268 – 2 c. on 4 c. de p. red (No. 187) 35 35
269 – 2 c. on 8 c. de p. red (No. 189) 2·75 1·50
270 – 2 c. on 8 c. de p. olive (No. 201) 3·75 1·75
271 **24** 2 c. on 20 c. de p. black and green 30 15
272 **20** 2 c. on 50 c. de p. red (No. 194) 15 10
274 2 c. on 50 c. de p. yellow (No. 204) 15 35
275 – 2 c. on 1 p. red (No. 195) 1·75 1·75
276 – 2 c. on 1 p. red (No. 205) 90 90
277 **21** 3 c. on 3 c. de p. sepia (No. 185) 3·00 1·25
278 – 3 c. on 7 c. de p. red (No. 200) 35 20
279 **21** 5 c. on 3 c. de p. sepia (No. 185) 4·50 1·75
280 5 c. on 3 c. de p. orange (No. 186) 6·00 7·00
281 – 5 c. on 4 c. de p. red (No. 187) 45 45
282 – 5 c. on 4 c. de p. olive (No. 198) 25 25
283 – 5 c. on 7 c. de p. grey (No. 188) 30 30
284 – 5 c. on 7 c. de p. red (No. 200) 35 35
285 **15** 5 c. on 7 c. on 20 c. orange (No. 213) 35 35
286 5 c. on 7 c. on 50 c. plum (No. 214) 2·40 2·40
287 **19** 5 c. on 10 c. de p. orange (No. 190) 25 25
289 – 5 c. on 10 c. de p. orange (No. 190) 45 45
288 – 5 c. on 15 c. de p. yellow (No. 203) 35 35
No. 289 has the word "PIASTRE" in the surcharge.

1919. Postage Due stamps surch **POSTES** and new value in frame.
290 D **23** 5 c. de g. on 10 c. de p. purple (No. D211) 35 35
291 5 c. de g. on 50 c. de p. olive (No. D153) 9·25 7·75
292 5 c. de g. on 50 c. de p. olive (No. D212) 45 45

48 "Agriculture"

1920.
294 **48** 3 c. de g. orange 2·50 3·50
295 5 c. de g. green 5·00 25
296 – 10 c. de g. red 55 30
297 – 15 c. de g. violet 45 15
298 – 25 c. de g. blue 55 15
DESIGN: 10 c., 15 c., 25 c. "Commerce".

50 Pres. L. J. Borno
51 Christophe's Citadel

54 Coffee

1924.
299 **50** 5 c. green 20 10
300 **51** 10 c. red 35 10
301 – 20 c. blue 40 15
304 **54** 35 c. green 1·75 25
302 **50** 50 c. black and orange 40 20
303 – 1 g. olive 1·10 25
DESIGNS—VERT: 20 c. Map of W. Indies. HORIZ: 1 g. National Palace.

55 Pres. Borno

1929. Frontier Agreement between Haiti and Dominican Republic.
305 **55** 10 c. red 30 20

56 Fokker Super Trimotor over Port-au-Prince

1929. Air.
306 **56** 25 c. green 35 30
307 50 c. violet 55 20
308 75 c. red 1·10 90
309 1 g. blue 1·50 1·10

57 Salomon and S. Vincent

1931. 50th Anniv of U.P.U. Membership.
310 **57** 5 c. green 85 45
311 – 10 c. red (S. Vincent) 85 45

1933. Air. "Columbia" New York–Haiti Flight. Surch **COLUMBIA VOL-DIRECT N.-Y.-P.AU-P. BOYD-LYON 60 CTS.**
311a 60 c. on 20 c. blue (No. 301) 42·00 42·00

59 Pres. S. Vincent
60 Prince's Aqueduct

1933. T **59** and designs as T **60**.
312 **59** 3 c. orange 10 10
313 3 c. green 15 10
316 **60** 5 c. green 15 10
317 5 c. olive 45 10
318 – 10 c. red 35 10
320 – 10 c. brown 35 10
321 – 25 c. blue 40 20
322 – 50 c. brown 1·75 20
323 – 1 g. green 1·75 20
324 – 2 g. 50 olive 2·75 35
DESIGNS: 10 c. Fort National; 25 c. Palace of Sans Souci; 50 c. Christophe's Chapel, Milot; 1 g. King's Gallery, Citadel; 2 g. 50, Vallieres Battery.

62 Fokker Super Trimotor over Christophe's Citadel

1933. Air.
325 **62** 50 c. orange 3·25 40
326 50 c. olive 3·00 40
327 50 c. red 1·75 1·10
328 50 c. black 1·40 40
329 60 c. brown 40 10
330 1 g. blue 1·10 35

63 Alexandre Dumas and his Father and Son

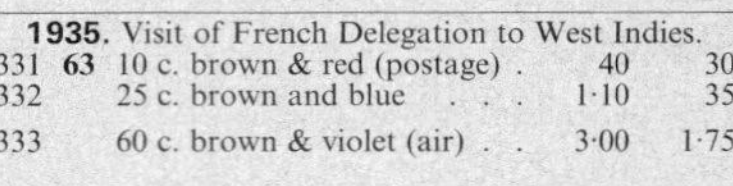
1935. Visit of French Delegation to West Indies.
331 **63** 10 c. brown & red (postage) 40 30
332 25 c. brown and blue 1·10 35
333 60 c. brown & violet (air) 3·00 1·75

64 Arms of Haiti, and George Washington

1938. Air. 150th Anniv of U.S. Constitution.
334 **64** 60 c. blue 25 25

1939. Surch **25c** between bars.
335 **54** 25 c. on 35 c. green 45 30

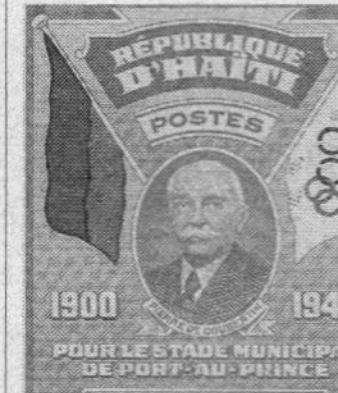

66 Pierre de Coubertin
67

1939. Port-au-Prince Athletic Stadium Fund.
336 **66** 10 c. + 10 c. red (postage) 18·00 18·00
337 60 c. + 40 c. violet (air) 12·00 12·00
338 1 g. 25 + 60 c. black 12·00 12·00

1941. 3rd Caribbean Conference.
339 **67** 10 c. red (postage) 65 35
340 25 c. blue 40 25
341 60 c. olive (air) 2·25 40
342 1 g. 25 violet 2·10 25

68 Our Lady of Perpetual Succour

1942. Our Lady of Perpetual Succour (National Patroness).
343 **68** 3 c. purple (postage) 35 30
344 5 c. green 35 30
345 10 c. red 35 30
346 15 c. orange 40 30
347 20 c. brown 40 30
348 25 c. blue 1·10 30
349 50 c. red 1·60 65
350 2 g. 50 brown 5·50 1·45
351 5 g. violet 11·50 2·75
The 5 g. is larger ($32\frac{1}{2} \times 47$ mm).
352 **68** 10 c. olive (air) 35 15
353 25 c. blue 35 35
354 50 c. green 45 30
355 60 c. red 90 25
356 1 g. 25 black 1·90 25

69 Admiral Killick and Flagship "Crete-a-Pierrot"

1943. 41st Death Anniv of Admiral Killick.
358 **69** 3 c. orange (postage) 15 50
359 5 c. green 55 25
360 10 c. red 55 15
361 25 c. blue 70 25
362 50 c. olive 1·40 35
363 5 g. brown 5·50 3·75
364 60 c. violet (air) 95 35
365 1 g. 25 black 3·75 1·90

1944. Surch (a) Postage.
366 **59** 0.02 on 3 c. green 15 15
367 0.05 on 3 c. green 20 20
368 **68** 0.10 on 15 c. orange 35 30
369 **69** 0.10 on 25 c. blue 35 30
370 – 0.10 on 1 g. olive (No. 303) 35 15
371 – 0.20 on 2 g. 50 olive (No. 324) 35 30
(b) Air.
372 **62** 0.10 on 60 c. brown 55 30

71

1944. Obligatory Tax. United Nations Relief Fund.

No.	Type	Description		
373	71	5 c. blue	90	35
374		5 c. black	90	35
375		5 c. olive	90	35
376		5 c. violet	90	35
377		5 c. brown	90	35
378		5 c. green	90	35
379		5 c. red	90	35

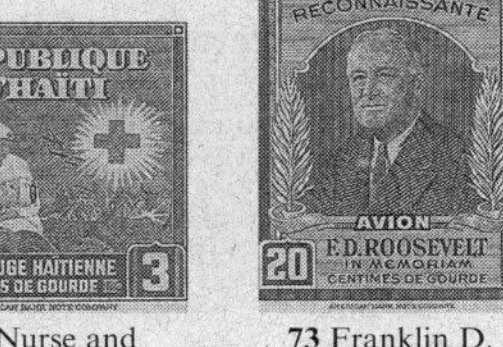

72 Nurse and Wounded Soldier

73 Franklin D. Roosevelt

1945. Red Cross stamps. Cross in red.

No.	Type	Description		
381	72	3 c. black (postage)	10	10
382		5 c. green	15	10
383		10 c. orange	20	10
384		20 c. brown	15	10
385		25 c. blue	30	10
386		35 c. orange	30	20
387		50 c. red	35	25
388		1 g. olive	40	30
389		2½ g. violet	1·75	25
390		20 c. orange (air)	15	10
391		25 c. blue	15	10
392		50 c. brown	20	10
393		60 c. purple	25	10
394		1 g. yellow	90	15
395		1 g. 25 c. red	70	30
396		1 g. 35 c. green	70	30
397		5 g. black	4·50	1·75

1946. Air.

No.	Type	Description		
398	73	20 c. black	15	15
399		60 c. black	20	10

74 Capois-la-Mort

75 J.-J. Dessalines

1946.

No.	Type	Description		
400	74	3 c. orange (postage)	10	10
401		5 c. green	10	10
402		10 c. red	10	10
403		20 c. black	10	10
404		25 c. blue	10	10
405		35 c. orange	20	15
406		50 c. brown	25	20
407		1 g. olive	35	10
408		2 g. 50 grey	90	35
409		20 c. red (air)	10	10
410		25 c. green	10	10
411		50 c. orange	15	10
412		60 c. purple	20	10
413		1 g. slate	35	10
414		1 g. 25 violet	40	35
415		1 g. 35 black	45	30
416		5 g. red	1·40	90

1947. 141st Death Anniv of Emperor Jean-Jacques Dessalines, founder of National Independence.

No.	Type	Description		
417	75	3 c. orange (postage)	10	10
418		5 c. green	10	10
419		5 c. violet	45	10
420		10 c. red	10	10
421		25 c. blue	20	10
422		20 c. brown (air)	20	10

1947. Surch.

No.	Type	Description		
423	74	10 c. on 35 c. orge (post.)	20	10
424		5 c. on 1 g. 35 black (air)	55	20
425		30 c. on 50 c. orange	45	30
426		30 c. on 1 g. 35 black	45	40

77 Sanatorium and Mosquito

1949. Air. Anti-T.B. and Malaria Fund. Cross in red.

No.	Type	Description		
427	77	20 c. + 20 c. sepia	6·25	4·50
428		30 c. + 30 c. green	6·25	4·50
429		45 c. + 45 c. brown	6·25	4·50
430		80 c. + 80 c. violet	6·25	4·50
431		1 g. 25 + 1 g. 25 red	6·25	4·50
432		1 g. 75 + 1 g. 75 blue	6·25	4·50

78 Washington, Dessalines and Bolivar

1949. Obligatory Tax. Bicent of Port-au-Prince.

No.	Type	Description		
434	78	5 c. red	20	15
435		5 c. brown	20	15
436		5 c. orange	20	15
437		5 c. grey	20	15
438		5 c. violet	20	15
439		5 c. blue	20	15
440		5 c. green	20	15
441		5 c. black	20	15

79 Arms of Port-au-Prince

80 Columbus and "Santa Maria"

83 Cocoa

1950. Bicentenary of Port-au-Prince Exn.

(a) Postage. Multicoloured arms.

No.	Type	Description		
442	79	10 c. red	15	10

(b) Air.

No.	Type	Description		
443	80	30 c. blue and grey	3·25	70
444	–	1 g. black (Pres. D. Estime)	45	30

1950. 75th Anniv of U.P.U. Optd **U P U 1874 1949** or surch also.

No.	Type	Description		
445	78	3 on 5 c. grey (postage)	10	10
446		5 c. green	25	20
447		10 on 5 c. red	25	20
448		20 on 5 c. blue	35	35
449	74	30 on 25 c. green (air)	30	30
450		1 g. slate	35	30
451		1.50 on 1 g. 35 black	60	40

1951. National Products.

No.	Type	Description		
456	83	5 c. green (postage)	25	10
457	–	30 c. orange (Bananas) (air)	30	20
458	–	80 c. pink and green (Coffee)	85	35
459	–	5 g. grey (Sisal)	3·00	2·50

84 Isabella the Catholic

85 Pres. Magloire and Nursery, La Saline

1951. Air. 5th Birth Cent of Isabella the Catholic.

No.	Type	Description		
460	84	15 c. brown	25	15
461		30 c. blue	45	45

1953. Projects realized by Pres. Magloire. Designs with medallion of president.

No.	Type	Description		
462	85	5 c. green (postage)	10	10
463	–	10 c. red	15	10
464	–	20 c. blue (air)	15	10
465	–	30 c. brown	30	15
466	–	1.50 g. black	45	45
467	–	2.50 g. violet	90	65

DESIGNS—HORIZ: 10 c. Road-making; 20 c. Anchorage, Cap-Haitien; 30 c. Workers' estate, St. Martin; 1.50 g. Old Cathedral restoration; 2.50 g. School canteen.

1953. 150th Death Anniv of Toussaint l'Ouverture. No. 405 surch **7 AVRIL 1803 - 1953 50**.

No.	Type	Description		
469	74	50 c. on 35 c. orange	35	20

1953. Air. 150th Anniv of National Flag. Surch **18 MAI 1803 - 1953 50**.

No.	Type	Description		
470	74	50 c. on 60 c. purple	35	15
471		50 c. on 1 g. 35 black	35	15

87 J.-J. Dessalines and Pres. Magloire

88 Toussaint l'Ouverture

89 Marie-Jeanne and Lamartiniere on La Crete-a-Pierrot

1954. 150th Anniv of Independence. (a) As T **87/8**.

No.	Type	Description		
472	87	3 c. blk & blue (postage)	10	10
473	88	5 c. black and green	20	10
474	–	5 c. black and green	15	10
475	–	5 c. black and green	20	10
476	–	5 c. black and green	15	10
477	87	10 c. black and red	15	10
478	–	15 c. black and lilac	20	10
479	88	50 c. black and green (air)	35	20
480	–	50 c. black and green	35	20
481	–	50 c. black and red	35	20
482	–	50 c. black and brown	35	20
483	–	50 c. black and blue	35	20
484	–	1 g. black and grey	45	25
485	–	1 g. 50 black and mauve	90	60
486	87	7 g. 50 black and orange	3·00	3·00

PORTRAITS—As Type **88**. Nos. 474, 482, Lamartiniere; Nos. 475, 482, Boisrond-Tonnerre; Nos. 476, 483, 485, A. Petion; No. 478, Capois-La-Mort; No. 480, J. J. Dessalines; No. 481, H. Christophe.

For stamps as No. 480 without dates see Nos. 533/4.

(b) As T **89**.

No.	Type	Description		
487	89	25 c. orange (postage)	20	10
488	–	25 c. slate	20	10
489	89	50 c. red (air)	25	10
490		50 c. black	25	10
491	–	50 c. pink	25	15
492	–	50 c. blue	25	15

DESIGN—HORIZ: Nos. 488, 491, 492, Battle of Vertieres; Nos. 489/92 are larger (31½ × 26 mm).

90 Mme. Magloire

1954.

No.	Type	Description		
493	90	10 c. orange (postage)	15	10
494		10 c. blue	15	10
495		20 c. red (air)	10	10
496		50 c. brown	20	20
497		1 g. green	45	35
498		1 g. 50 red	45	40
499		2 g. 50 green	65	60
500		5 g. blue	1·90	1·40

91 Tomb and Arms of King Henri Christophe

92 Christophe, Citadel and Pres. Magloire

1954. Restoration of Christophe's Citadel.

(a) T **91**. Flag in black and red.

No.	Type	Description		
501	91	10 c. red (postage)	15	10
502		50 c. orange (air)	35	15
503		1 g. blue	40	30
504		1 g. 50 green	60	50
505		2 g. 50 grey	1·10	65
506		5 g. red	1·75	1·25

(b) T **92**.

No.	Type	Description		
507	92	10 c. red (postage)	15	10
508		50 c. black & orge (air)	35	15
509		1 g. black and blue	40	30
510		1 g. 50 black and green	60	50
511		2 g. 50 black and grey	1·10	65
512		5 g. black and red	1·75	1·25

93 Columbus's Drawing of Fort de la Nativite

1954. Air.

No.	Type	Description		
513	93	50 c. red	35	30
514		50 c. slate	35	30

94 Sikorsky S-55 Helicopter over Ruins

95 Sikorsky S-55 Helicopter

1955. Obligatory Tax. Cyclone "Hazel" Relief Fund (1st issue).

No.	Type	Description		
515	94	10 c. blue	10	10
516		10 c. green	10	10
517		10 c. orange	10	10
518		10 c. black	15	10
519		20 c. red	10	10
520		20 c. green	15	10

1955. Obligatory Tax. Cyclone "Hazel" Relief Fund (2nd issue).

No.	Type	Description		
521	95	10 c. black & grey (postage)	10	10
522		20 c. deep blue and blue	15	10
523		10 c. red and brown (air)	15	10
524		20 c. red and pink	15	10

96 J.-J. Dessalines

97 Pres. Magloire and Monument

1955. Dessalines Commemoration.

No.	Type	Description		
525	96	3 c. black & brn (postage)	10	10
526		5 c. black and lilac	10	10
527		10 c. black and red	10	10
528		10 c. black and pink	10	10
529		25 c. black and blue	20	10
530		25 c. black and light blue	20	10
531		20 c. black & green (air)	10	10
532		20 c. black and orange	10	10

1955. Air. As No. 480 but without dates and colours changed.

No.	Type	Description		
533		50 c. black and blue	30	10
534		50 c. black and grey	30	15

1955. 21st Anniv of Haitian Army.

No.	Type	Description		
535	97	10 c. blue & black (postage)	30	25
536		10 c. red and black	30	25
537		1 g. 50 green & blk (air)	35	20
538		1 g. 50 blue and black	45	20

98 Mallard

99 Douglas DC-4, Liner and Map

1955.

No.	Type	Description		
539	–	10 c. blue (postage)	3·00	40
540	98	25 c. green & turquoise	4·00	65
541	99	50 c. black & grey (air)	1·00	20
542	–	50 c. red and grey	30	15
543	99	75 c. green & turquoise	1·25	45
544	–	1 g. olive and blue	55	30
545	–	2 g. 50 orange	16·00	3·00
546	98	5 g. red and buff	26·00	5·50

DESIGNS—VERT: 10 c., 2 g. 50, Greater Flamingo. HORIZ: 50 c. (No. 542), 1 g. Car on coast road.

100 Immanuel Kant

101 Zim Basin and Waterfall

1956. 10th Anniv of 1st Int. Philosophical Congress.

No.	Type	Description		
547	100	10 c. blue (postage)	15	10
548		50 c. brown (air)	25	15
549		75 c. green	35	20
550		1 g. 50 mauve	85	45

1957.

No.	Type	Description		
552	101	10 c. orge & bl (postage)	15	10
553		50 c. green & turq (air)	20	15
554		1 g. 50 olive and blue	35	30
555		2 g. 50 blue & light blue	60	45
556		5 g. violet and blue	1·40	1·10

102 J.-J. Dessalines and Monument

103 The "Atomium"

1958. Birth Bicentenary of J. J. Dessalines.
557 102 5 c. green & blk (postage) . 10 10
558 10 c. red and black . . . 10 10
559 25 c. blue and black . . . 20 10
560 20 c. grey and black (air) . 10 10
561 50 c. orange and black . . 25 15

1958. Brussels International Exhibition.
562 103 50 c. brown (postage) . . . 30 15
563 – 75 c. green 30 20
564 103 1 g. violet 35 25
565 – 1 g. 50 orange 30 25
566 103 2 g. 50 red (air) 60 35
567 – 5 g. blue 85 60
DESIGN—HORIZ: 75 c., 1 g. 50, 5 g. Exhibition view.

104 Sylvio Cator making Long Jump

106 Head of U.S. Satellite

1958. Sylvio Cator (athlete) Commem.
569 104 5 c. green (postage) 10 10
570 10 c. brown 10 10
571 20 c. purple and mauve . . 15 10
572 – 50 c. black (air) 20 10
573 – 50 c. green 20 10
574 – 1 g. brown 35 15
575 – 5 g. black and grey . . . 1·40 70
DESIGN—HORIZ: Nos. 572/75, Sylvio Cator making long jump (head-on view).

1958. Red Cross. Nos. 564/66 surch with red cross and **+50 CENTIMES**.
576 103 1 g. + 50 c. violet (postage) 2·50 2·50
577 – 1 g. 50 + 50 c. orange . . . 2·50 2·50
578 103 2 g. 50 + 50 c. red (air) . . 2·75 2·75

1958. I.G.Y. Inscr as in T **106**.
579 106 10 c. lake & turq (postage) . 15 10
580 – 20 c. black and orange . . 3·25 90
581 – 50 c. red and green . . . 35 25
582 – 1 g. black and blue . . . 80 20
583 106 50 c. lake and blue (air) . . 20 20
584 – 1 g. 50 brown and red . . 7·00 1·50
585 – 2 g. red and blue . . . . 1·10 35
DESIGNS: 20 c., 1 g. 50, King Penguins on icefloe; 50 c., 2 g. Giant radio telescope; 1 g. Ocean-bed exploration.

107 Duvalier

108 Map of Haiti

1958. 1st Anniv of Installation of President Francois Duvalier. Commemorative inscr in blue.
587 107 10 c. blk & pink (postage) . 10 10
588 50 c. black and green . . . 35 15
589 1 g. black and red . . . 55 30
590 5 g. black and salmon . . 1·60 1·10
591 – 50 c. black and red (air) . . 60 20
592 – 2 g. 50 black and orange . . 80 55
593 – 5 g. black and mauve . . 1·10 90
594 – 7 g. 50 black and green . . 1·60 1·25
DESIGN: Nos. 591/94 as Type **107** but horiz.

1958. As T **107** but without commem. inscr.
(a) Postage. Vert. portrait.
596 5 c. black and blue 10 10
597 10 c. black and pink 10 10
598 20 c. black and yellow . . . 10 10
599 50 c. black and green 20 15
600 1 g. black and red 30 20
601 1 g. 50 c. black and pink . . . 45 35
602 2 g. 50 c. black & lavender . . 70 60
603 5 g. black and salmon . . . . 1·10 85
(b) Air. Horiz. portrait.
604 50 c. black and red 25 15
605 1 g. black and violet 30 25
606 1 g. 50 c. black and brown . . . 35 30
607 2 g. black and pink 60 35
608 2 g. 50 c. black and orange . . 60 35
609 5 g. black and mauve . . . . 1·10 85
610 7 g. 50 c. black and green . . . 1·90 1·10

1958. United Nations.
611 108 10 c. red (postage) 10 10
612 25 c. green 15 10
613 – 50 c. red and blue (air) . . 20 10
614 108 75 c. blue 30 15
615 1 g. brown 45 20
DESIGN: 50 c. Flags of Haiti and U.N.

1959. 10th Anniv of Declaration of Human Rights. Nos. 611/5 optd **10TH ANNIVERSARY OF THE UNIVERSAL DECLARATION OF HUMAN RIGHTS**. (E), In English. (F), In French. (P), In Portuguese. (S), In Spanish. (a) Postage.

			E		F	
617 108	10 c. red . . .	10	10	10	10
618	25 c. green . . .	25	15	25	15
		P		S	
617 108	10 c. red . . .	10	10	10	10
618	25 c. green . . .	25	15	25	15

(b) Air.

		E		F	
619 –	50 c. red & blue	30	30	30	30
620 108	75 c. blue . . .	40	40	40	40
621	1 g. brown . . .	90	90	90	90
		P		S	
619 –	50 c. red & blue	30	30	30	30
620 108	75 c. blue . . .	40	40	40	40
621	1 g. brown . . .	90	90	90	90

Overprinted alternately in different languages through the sheet of 25.

110 Pope Pius XII with Children

1959. Pope Pius XII Commem. Inscr "PIE XII PAPE DE LA PAIX".
622 110 10 c. olive & blue (postage) 10 10
623 – 50 c. brown and green . . 25 15
624 – 2 g. sepia and lake 40 35
625 110 50 c. violet & green (air) . . 20 10
626 – 1 g. 50 brown and olive . . 35 15
627 – 2 g. 50 blue and purple . . 60 30
DESIGNS: 50 c. (No. 623), 1 g. 50, Pope at prayer; 2 g., 2 g. 50, Pope giving blessing.

1959. Red Cross.
(a) United Nations stamps surch with red cross and **+25 CENTIMES**.
628 108 10 c. + 25 c. (postage) . . 25 20
629 25 c. + 25 c. 35 30
630 – 50 c. + 25 c. (air) 35 35
631 108 75 c. + 25 c. 45 35
632 1 g. + 25 c. 65 70
(b) Pope Pius XII stamps surch with red cross and **+50 CENTIMES**.
633 110 10 c. + 50 c. (postage) . . 45 20
634 – 50 c. + 50 c. 45 30
635 – 2 g. + 50 c. 65 90
636 110 50 c. + 50 c. (air) 60 60
637 – 1 g. 50 + 50 c. 60 60
638 – 2 g. 50 + 50 c. 65 65

111 Abraham Lincoln when a young man

1959. 150th Birth Anniv of Abraham Lincoln.
639 111 50 c. pur & blue (postage) . 30 15
640 – 1 g. brown & green (air) . . 30 20
641 – 2 g. myrtle and green . . . 35 20
642 – 2 g. 50 c. blue and buff . . 40 35
PORTRAITS of Lincoln (bearded): 1 g. Looking right; 2 g., 2 g. 50, Looking left. The designs include various buildings associated with Lincoln.

1959. World Refugee Year (1st issue). Nos. 639/42 surch **Nations Unies ANNEE DES REFUGIES 1959–1960 + 20 Centimes**.
644 111 50 c. + 20 c. purple & blue (postage) 45 45
645 – 1 g. + 20 c. brown and green (air) 60 60
646 – 2 g. + 20 c. myrtle and green 60 60
647 – 2 g. 50 + 20 c. bl & buff . . 70 70

113 Chicago's First House and Modern Skyline

1959. 3rd Pan-American Games, Chicago.
649 113 25 c. sepia & blue (postage) 30 15
650 – 50 c. multicoloured 30 20
651 – 75 c. sepia and blue 45 25
652 – 50 c. brown & turq (air) . . 35 20
653 113 1 g. turquoise & purple . . 60 35
654 – 1 g. 50 multicoloured . . . 65 45
DESIGNS—HORIZ: 50 c., 1 g. 50, Discus-thrower and Haitian flag. VERT: 50 c. (air), 75 c. J. B. Paul Dessables (founder of Chicago) and map.

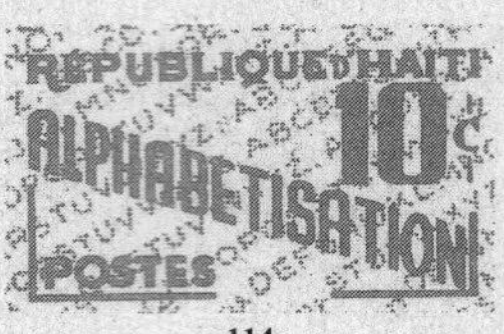

114

1959. Obligatory Tax. Literacy Fund.
(a) Postage. (i) Size 40 × 23 mm.
655 114 5 c. green 10 10
656 10 c. black 10 10
657 10 c. red 10 10
(ii) Size 29 × 17 mm.
658 114 5 c. green 10 10
659 5 c. red 10 10
660 10 c. blue 10 10
(b) Air. Size 29 × 17 mm.
661 114 5 c. yellow 10 10
662 10 c. blue 10 10
663 10 c. orange 10 10

1959. Sports Fund. Nos. 649/54 surch **POUR LE SPORT + 0.75 CENTIMES**.
664 25 c. + 75 c. sepia and blue (postage) 45 45
665 50 c. + 75 c. multicoloured . . 60 45
666 75 c. + 75 c. sepia and blue . . 60 45
667 50 c. + 75 c. brn & turq (air) . 60 45
668 1 g. + 75 c. turq & purple . . 60 45
669 1 g. 50 + 75 c. multicoloured . 60 60

1960. UNICEF Commem. Nos. 600 and 607/8 surch **Hommage a l'UNICEF +G.0,50**.
670 1 g. + 50 c. blk & red (post.) . . 60 60
671 2 g. + 50 c. blk & pink (air) . . 65 65
672 2 g. 50 + 50 c. black & orge . . 1·10 1·10

1960. Winter Olympic Games. Nos. 650 and 652/4 optd with Olympic rings and **VIIIEME JEUX OLYMPIQUES D'HIVER CALIFORNIE USA 1960**.
673 50 c. multicoloured (postage) . . 1·10 90
674 50 c. brown & turquoise (air) . . 70 70
675 1 g. turquoise and purple . . . 1·10 1·10
676 1 g. 50 multicoloured . . . . 1·25 1·25

118 "Uprooted Tree"

1960. World Refugee Year (2nd issue).
677 118 10 c. green & orge (post.) . 10 10
678 50 c. purple and violet . . 20 15
679 50 c. brn and bl (air) . . . 20 15
680 1 g. red and green . . . 45 30

1960. Surch in figures.
682 96 5 c. on 3 c. blk & brown . . 10 10
683 10 c. on 3 c. black & brn . . 15 10

1960. 28th Anniv of Haitian Red Cross. 1945 Red Cross stamps optd **"28eme ANNIVERSAIRE"** or surch also.
684 72 1 g. on $2\frac{1}{2}$ g. vio (postage) . 45 35
685 $2\frac{1}{2}$ g. violet 85 65
686 20 c. on 1 g. 35 grn (air) . . 20 10
687 50 c. on 60 c. purple 25 15
688 50 c. on 1 g. 35 green . . . 25 20
689 50 c. on $2\frac{1}{2}$ g. violet . . . 25 20
690 60 c. purple 30 20
691 1 g. on 1 g. 35 green 35 35
692 1 g. 35 green 60 55
693 2 g. on 1 g. 35 green 95 85
No. 689 is also optd **Avion**.

121 "Sugar Queen, 1960" and Beach

1960. Election of Miss Claudinette Fouchard ("Miss Haiti") as World "Sugar Queen, 1960".
694 – 10 c. vio & brn (postage) . . 15 10
695 – 20 c. black and brown . . . 20 10
696 121 50 c. brown and blue . . . 45 10
697 – 1 g. brown and green . . . 45 20
698 – 50 c. brown & mve (air) . . 35 15
699 121 2 g. 50 brown and blue . . 55 35
DESIGNS: Sugar Queen and—10 c., 1 g. Plantation (different views); 20 c., 50 c. Harvesting.

1960. Education Campaign. Surch **ALPHABETISATION** and premium.
700 118 10 c. + 20 c. green and orange (postage) 25 15
701 10 c. + 30 c. grn & orge . . 30 25
702 50 c. + 20 c. pur & vio . . 30 35
703 50 c. + 30 c. pur & vio . . 40 35
704 50 c. + 20 c. black and blue (air) 25 15
705 50 c. + 30 c. black & bl . . 35 25
706 1 g. + 20 c. red & green . 60 45
707 1 g. + 30 c. red & green . 60 45

123 Olympic Torch, Victory Parade at Athens, 1896, and Melbourne Stadium

1960. Olympic Games, Rome.
708 123 10 c. blk & orge (postage) . 10 10
709 – 20 c. blue and red 10 10
710 – 50 c. green and brown . . 20 10
711 – 1 g. blue and black 45 15
712 – 50 c. pur & bistre (air) . . 15 15
713 – 1 g. 50 mauve & green . . 35 25
714 – 2 g. 50 slate, pur & blk . . 60 35
DESIGNS: 20 c. and 1 g. 50, "The Discus-thrower" and Rome Stadium; 50 c. (No. 710), Pierre de Coubertin (founder) and Athletes Parade, Melbourne; 50 c. (No. 712), As Type **123** but P. de Coubertin inset; 1 g. Athens Stadium, 1896; 2 g. 50, Victory Parade, Athens, 1896, and Athletes' Parade, Melbourne.

1960. Nos. 710/3 surch **+25 CENTIMES**.
716 50 c. + 25 c. grn & brn (post.) . 35 25
717 1 g. + 25 c. blue and black . . 45 30
718 50 c. + 25 c. pur & bis (air) . . 25 20
719 1 g. 50 + 25 c. mve & green . . 30 25

125 Occide Jeanty

1960. Birth Cent of Occide Jeanty (composer).
720 125 10 c. pur & orge (postage) . 15 10
721 – 20 c. purple and blue . . . 30 10
722 125 50 c. sepia and green . . . 40 20
723 50 c. blue & yellow (air) . . 20 10
724 – 1 g. 50 slate and mauve . . 45 25
DESIGN: 20 c., 1 g. 50, Jeanty and Capitol, Port-au-Prince.

126 U.N., New York

1960. 15th Anniv of U.N.O.
731 126 1 g. black & grn (postage) . 35 20
732 50 c. black and red (air) . . 20 10
733 1 g. 50 black and blue . . 45 25

127 Sud Aviation Caravelle

1960. Air. Aviation Week.
735 127 20 c. blue and red 10 10
736 – 50 c. brown and green . . . 30 20
737 – 50 c. blue and green . . . 30 20
738 – 50 c. black and green . . . 30 20
739 127 1 g. green and red 45 25
740 – 1 g. 50 pink and blue . . . 50 35
DESIGNS: 50 c. (3) Boeing 707 airliner and Wright Flyer I; 1 g. 50, Boeing 707 and 60 c. "Columbia" stamp of 1933.

1961. U.N.I.C.E.F. Child Welfare Fund. Surch **UNICEF + 25 centimes**.
748 126 1 g. + 25 c. black and green (postage) 45 30
749 50 c. + 25 c. black and red (air) 30 25
750 1 g. 50 + 25 c. black & bl . 55 35

129 Alexandre Dumas (father and son)

1961. Alexandre Dumas Commemoration.
751 – 5 c. brown & bl (postage) 10 10
752 – 10 c. black, purple & red 10 10
753 **129** 50 c. blue and red 30 20
754 – 50 c. black & blue (air) 30 15
755 – 1 g. red and black 35 20
756 – 1 g. 50 black and green 55 35
DESIGNS—HORIZ: 5 c. Dumas' House; 50 c. (No. 754), A. Dumas and "The Three Musketeers". VERT: 10 c. A. Dumas and horseman in "Twenty Years After"; 1 g. A. Dumas (son) and "The Lady of the Camellias" (Marguerite Gauthier); 1 g. 50, A. Dumas, and "The Count of Monte Cristo".

130 Pirates

1961. Tourist Publicity.
761 – 5 c. yellow & bl (postage) 10 10
762 **130** 10 c. yellow and mauve 10 10
763 – 15 c. orange and green 10 10
764 – 20 c. orange and brown 40 10
765 – 50 c. yellow and blue 80 20
766 – 20 c. yell and blue (air) 40 10
767 – 50 c. orange and violet 80 20
768 – 1 g. yellow and green 35 25
DESIGNS: Nos. 761, 768, Map of Tortuga; No. 763, Two pirates on beach; Nos. 764, 766, Pirate ships attacking galleon; Nos. 765, 767, Pirate in rigging.

1961. Re-election of Pres. Duvalier. Optd **Dr. F. Duvalier President 22 Mai 1961**.
769 **102** 5 c. grn & black (postage) 10 10
770 10 c. red and black 10 10
771 25 c. blue and black 20 15
772 **74** 2 g. 50 grey 65 45
773 **102** 20 c. grey & black (air) 10 10
774 50 c. orange and black 20 15
775 **99** 75 c. green & turquoise 35 30

1961. Air. 18th World Scout Conference, Lisbon. Nos. 735 and 739/40 surch **18e CONFERENCE INTERNATIONALE DU SCOUTISME MONDIAL LISBONNE SEPTEMBRE 1961 + 0,25** and Scout emblem.
776 20 c. + 25 c. blue and red 30 20
777 1 g. + 25 c. green and red 45 35
778 1 g. 50 + 25 c. pink & blue 55 55

1961. U.N. and Haitian Malaria Eradication Campaign. Surch **OMS SNEM + 20 CENTIMES**.
780 **126** 1 g. + 20 c. black and green (postage) 45 35
781 **126** 50 c. + 20 c. black & red (air) 85 85
782 1 g. 50 + 20 c. blk & bl 1·10 1·10

1961. Duvalier-Ville Reconstruction Fund Nos. 598, 600, 602, 604/5 and 608/10 surch with U.N.I.C.E.F. emblem, **Duvalier-Ville** and premium.
783 20 c. + 25 c. black and yellow (postage) 30 25
787 1 g. + 50 c. black and red 60 45
788 2 g. 50 + 50 c. black and blue 65 50
784 50 c. + 25 c. black & red (air) 25 25
785 1 g. + 50 c. black and violet 25 25
789 2 g. 50 + 50 c. black & orge 40 30
786 5 g. + 50 c. black and mauve 85 60
790 7 g. 50 + 50 c. black & green 90 85

1962. Colonel Glenn's Space Flight. Nos. 761, 768 optd **EXPLORATION SPATIALE JOHN GLENN** and outline of capsule or surch also.
795 50 c. on 5 c. yell & bl (postage) 45 30
796 1 g. 50 on 5 c. yellow & blue 90 65
797 1 g. yellow and green (air) 30 30
798 2 g. on 1 g. yellow and green 85 70

136 Campaign Emblem

1962. Malaria Eradication.
799 **136** 5 c. blue & red (postage) 10 10
800 – 10 c. green and brown 10 10
801 **136** 50 c. red and blue 30 15
802 – 20 c. red and violet (air) 10 10
803 **136** 50 c. red and green 20 15
804 – 1 g. blue and orange 35 25
DESIGN: 10 c., 20 c., 1 g. As Type **136** but with long side of triangle at top.

1962. World Refugee Year (3rd issue). As T **118** but additionally inscr "1962" and colours changed.
806 **118** 10 c. orange & bl (postage) 10 10
807 50 c. green and mauve 25 20
808 50 c. brown & blue (air) 15 15
809 1 g. black and buff 25 25

137 Scout Badge

1962. 22nd Anniv of Haitian Boy Scout Movement.
811 **137** 3 c. orange, black and violet (postage) 10 10
812 – 5 c. brown, olive & black 10 10
813 – 10 c. brown, black & grn 10 10
814 **137** 25 c. black, lake & olive 15 10
815 – 50 c. green, violet & red 30 15
816 – 20 c. slate, green and purple (air) 10 10
817 **137** 50 c. brown, green & red 25 15
818 – 1 g. 50 turq, sepia & brn 45 35
DESIGNS—VERT: 5 c., 20 c., 50, c. (post) Scout and camp. HORIZ: 10 c., 1 g. 50, Lord and Lady Baden-Powell.

1962. Surch with premium. (a) Nos. 799/804.
820 **136** 5 c. + 25 c. (postage) 20 15
821 – 10 c. + 25 c. 25 20
822 **136** 50 c. + 25 c. 30 20
823 – 20 c. + 25 c. (air) 20 20
824 **136** 50 c. + 25 c. 25 25
825 – 1 g. + 25 c. 35 30

(b) Nos. 806/9.
827 **118** 10 c. + 20 c. (postage) 15 15
828 50 c. + 20 c. 25 15
829 50 c. + 20 c. (air) 25 15
830 1 g. + 20 c. 35 30

1962. Air. Port-au-Prince Airport Construction Fund. Optd **AEROPORT INTERNATIONAL 1962** with No. 848 additionally optd **Poste Aerienne**.
831 – 20 c. No. 816 15 10
832 – 50 c. No. 815 25 15
833 **137** 50 c. No. 817 25 15
834 – 1 g. 50 No. 818 45 35

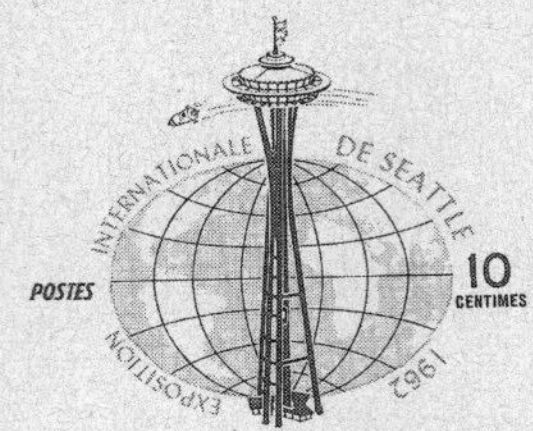

140 Tower, World's Fair

1962. "Century 21" Exn (World's Fair), Seattle.
835 **140** 10 c. purple & bl (postage) 10 10
836 20 c. blue and red 10 10
837 50 c. green and yellow 35 10
838 1 g. red and green 55 20
839 50 c. black & lilac (air) 25 10
840 1 g. red and grey 45 15
841 1 g. 50 purple & orange 55 20

141 Town plan and 1904 10 c. stamp

1963. Duvalier-ville Commemoration.
843 **141** 5 c. black, yellow and violet (postage) 10 10
844 10 c. black, yellow & red 10 10
845 25 c. blk, yellow & grey 20 15
846 – 50 c. brn and orge (air) 20 15
847 – 1 g. brown and blue 35 30
848 – 1 g. 50 brown and green 55 45
DESIGN: Nos. 846/8 Houses and 1881 2 c. stamp.

1963. "Peaceful Uses of Outer Space". Nos. 837/38 and 841/2 optd **UTILISATIONS PACIFIQUES DE L'ESPACE** and space capsule.
853 **140** 50 c. green and yellow (postage) 20 15
854 1 g. red and green 45 30
855 1 g. red and grey (air) 45 35
856 1 g. 50 purple and orge 65 65

1963. Literacy Campaign. Surch **ALPHABETISATION + 0,10**.
857 **141** 25 c. + 10 c. (postage) 15 10
858 – 50 c. + 10 c. (No. 846) (air) 25 15
859 – 1 g. 50 + 10 c. (No. 848) 35 35

143 Harvesting

145 Dessalines Statue

144 Dag Hammarskjold and U.N. Emblem

146 "Alphabetisation"

1963. Freedom from Hunger.
860 **143** 10 c. orange and black (postage) 10 10
861 20 c. turquoise & black 10 10
862 50 c. mauve & blk (air) 15 10
863 1 g. green and black 30 20

1963. Air. Dag Hammarskjold Commemoration. Portrait in blue.
864 **144** 20 c. brown and bistre 10 10
865 50 c. red and blue 20 20
866 1 g. blue and mauve 30 30
867 1 g. 50 green and grey 55 45
Nos. 864/67 were printed in sheets of 25 (5 × 5) with a map of Sweden in the background covering most stamps in the second and third vertical rows.

1963. Dessalines Commemoration.
869 **145** 5 c. red & brown (postage) 10 10
870 10 c. blue, grn & ochre 10 10
871 50 c. grn & brown (air) 20 10
872 50 c. pur, violet & blue 20 10

1963. Obligatory Tax. Education Fund.
873 **146** 10 c. red (postage) 10 10
874 10 c. blue 10 10
875 10 c. olive 10 10
876 10 c. brown (air) 10 10
877 10 c. violet 10 10
878 10 c. violet 10 10
See also Nos. 974/78, 1157/63 and 1260/1.

1964. Mothers' Festival. Optd **FETE DES MERES 1964** or surch also.
879 **145** 10 c. blue, green and ochre (postage) 10 10
880 50 c. grn & brown (air) 25 15
881 50 c. purple, vio & blue 25 15
882 1 g. 50 on 80 c. pink and green (No. 458) 35 25

1964. Winter Olympic Games, Innsbruck. Surch **JEUX OLYMPIQUES D'HIVER INNSBRUCK 1964 0.50 + 0.10**, Olympic rings and games emblem.
883 **137** 50 c. + 10 c. on 3 c. (postage) 45 30
884 50 c. + 10 c. on 5 c. (No. 812) 45 30
885 – 50 c. + 10 c. on 10 c. (No. 813) 45 30
886 **137** 50 c. + 10 c. on 25 c. 45 30
887 **101** 50 c. + 10 c. on 2 g. 50 (air) 70 65

1964. Air. Red Cross Cent (1963). Optd **1863 1963** and Centenary Emblem, on surch also. Portrait in blue.
888 **144** 20 c. brown and bistre 30 10
889 50 c. red and blue 30 15
890 1 g. blue and mauve 45 30
891 1 g. 50 green and grey 55 35
892 2 g. 50 + 1 g. 25 on 1 g. 50 green and grey 85 60

150 Weightlifting

151 Our Lady of Perpetual Succour and Airport

1964. Olympic Games, Tokyo (1st issue).
893 **150** 10 c. sepia & bl (postage) 10 10
894 25 c. sepia and salmon 10 10
895 – 50 c. sepia and mauve 20 15
896 **150** 50 c. sepia & purple (air) 15 15
897 – 50 c. sepia and green 15 15
898 – 75 c. sepia and yellow 20 20
899 – 1 g. 50 sepia and grey 35 35
DESIGN: Nos. 895, 897/99, Hurdling; Nos. 893/09 were printed in sheets of 50 (10 × 5) with a large map of Japan in the background.

1964. International Airport.
901 **151** 10 c. blk & ochre (postage) 15 10
902 25 c. black & turquoise 25 10
903 50 c. black and green 35 15
904 1 g. black and red 55 35
905 50 c. blk & orange (air) 30 15
906 1 g. 50 black & mauve 40 20
907 2 g. 50 black and violet 1·10 55

1965. Int Airport Opening. Optd **1965**.
908 **151** 10 c. blk & ochre (postage) 10 10
909 25 c. black & turquoise 25 15
910 50 c. black and green 35 15
911 1 g. black and red 55 30
912 50 c. black & orge (air) 30 10
913 1 g. 50 black and mauve 50 25
914 2 g. 50 black and violet 75 40

1965. Olympic Games. Tokyo (2nd issue). Nos. 893/9 surch **+ 5 c.**
915 **150** 10 c. + 5 c. (postage) 10 10
916 – 25 c. + 5 c. 15 15
917 – 50 c. + 5 c. 30 25
918 **150** 50 c. + 5 c. (air) 25 25
919 – 50 c. + 5 c. 25 25
920 – 75 c. + 5 c. 35 35
921 – 1 g. 50 + 5 c. 45 45

154 Unisphere

157 I.T.U. Emblem and Symbols

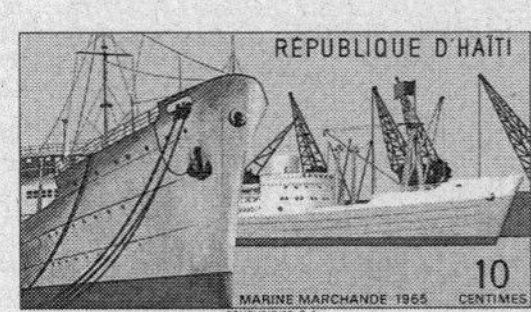

155 "Likala" (freighter) in Port

1965. New York World's Fair.
923 **154** 10 c. mult (postage) 10 10
924 – 20 c. purple and yellow 15 10
925 **154** 50 c. multicoloured 30 20
926 – 50 c. blue & yellow (air) 25 10
927 – 1 g. 50 black and yellow 45 30
928 **154** 5 g. multicoloured 1·60 1·40
DESIGN: 20 c., 50 c. (No. 926), 1 g. 50, "Reaching for the Stars" (statue).

1965. Haitian Merchant Marine Commem.
929 **155** 10 c. mult (postage) 50 15
930 50 c. multicoloured 80 20
931 50 c. multicoloured (air) 70 15
932 1 g. 50 multicoloured 1·40 55

1965. Air 20th Anniv of U.N. Optd **O.N.U. 1945–1965**. Portrait in blue.
933 **144** 20 c. brown and bistre 10 10
934 50 c. red and blue 15 10
935 1 g. blue and mauve 25 20
936 1 g. 50 green and grey 20 30

1965. Cent of I.T.U.
937 **157** 10 c. mult (postage) 10 10
938 25 c. multicoloured 15 10
939 50 c. multicoloured 20 15
940 50 c. multicoloured (air) 15 10
941 1 g. multicoloured 30 25
942 1 g. 50 multicoloured 45 35
943 2 g. multicoloured 65 50

1965. 25th Anniv of U.N.E.S.C.O. Nos. 937/41 optd **20e Anniversaire UNESCO**.
945 **157** 10 c. mult (postage) 20 20
946 25 c. multicoloured 55 55
947 50 c. multicoloured 75 75
948 50 c. multicoloured (air) 90 35
949 1 g. multicoloured 1·75 70

158 Cathedral Facade

159 "Passiflora quadrangularis"

1965. Bicentenary of Cathedral of Our Lady of the Assumption, Port-au-Prince. Mult.

951 5 c. Type **158** (postage) 10 10
952 10 c. High Altar (vert) 10 10
953 25 c. "Our Lady of the Assumption" (painting) (vert) 10 10

954 50 c. Type **158** (air) 20 10
955 1 g. High Altar (vert) 30 20
956 7 g. 50, as 25 c., but larger 38 × 51 mm 1·75 1·25

1965. Haitian Flowers. Multicoloured.

957 3 c. Type **159** (postage) 10 10
958 5 c. "Sambucus canadensis" 10 10
959 10 c. "Hibiscus esculentus" 10 10
960 15 c. As 5 c. 10 10
961 50 c. Type **159** 30 15

962 50 c. Type **159** (air) 15 10
963 50 c. As 5 c. 15 10
964 50 c. As 10 c. 15 10
965 1 g. 50, As 5 c. 45 35
966 1 g. 50, As 10 c. 45 35
967 5 g. Type **159** 1·10 75

160 Amulet

162 Astronauts and "Gemini" Capsules

1966. "Culture". Multicoloured.

968 5 c. Type **160** (postage) 10 10
969 10 c. Carved stool and Veve decoration (horiz) 10 10
970 50 c. Type **160** 20 15

971 50 c. Carved stool and Veve decoration (horiz) (air) 20 15
972 1 g. 50 Type **160** 55 45
973 2 g. 50 Modern abstract painting (52 × 37 mm) 60 50

1966. Obligatory Tax. Education Fund. As T **146** but larger (17 × $25\frac{1}{2}$ mm).

974 **146** 10 c. green (postage) 10 10
975 10 c. violet 10 10

977 10 c. orange (air) 10 10
978 10 c. blue 10 10

1966. State Visit of Emperor Haile Selassie of Ethiopia. Nos. 969 and 971/3 optd **Hommage Haile Selassie 1er 24–25 Avril 1966**.

979 – 10 c. mult (postage) 15 15

980 – 50 c. multicoloured (air) 20 15
981 **160** 1 g. 50 multicoloured 55 45
982 – 2 g. 50 multicoloured 60 50

1966. Space Rendezvous. Astronauts and capsules in brown.

983 **162** 5 c. indigo & bl (postage) 10 10
984 10 c. violet and blue 10 10
985 25 c. green and blue 15 10
986 50 c. red and blue 25 15

987 – 50 c. indigo & blue (air) 20 15
988 – 1 g. green and blue 35 30
989 – 1 g. 50 red and blue 55 45

DESIGN: Nos. 987/9, Astronauts and "Gemini" capsules (different arrangement).

163 Football and Pres. Duvalier

1966. Caribbean Football Championships. Portrait in black.

(i) Inscr "CHAMPIONNAT DE FOOTBALL DES CARAIBES".

990 **163** 5 c. grn & flesh (postage) 10 10
991 – 10 c. green and blue 10 10
992 **163** 15 c. green and apple 10 10
993 – 50 c. green and lilac 25 15

994 **163** 50 c. purple & sage (air) 15 15
995 – 1 g. 50 purple and pink 55 45

(ii) As Nos. 990/5 but additionally inscr "COUPE DR. FRANCOIS DUVALIER 22 JUIN".

996 **163** 5 c. grn & flesh (postage) 10 10
997 – 10 c. green and blue 10 10
998 **163** 15 c. green and apple 10 10
999 – 50 c. green and lilac 25 15

1000 **163** 50 c. pur & sage (air) 15 15
1001 – 1 g. 50 purple & pink 55 45

DESIGN: 10 c., 50 c. (No. 991, 993), 1 g. 50, Footballer and Pres. Duvalier.

164 Audio-visual Aids

1966. National Education.

1002 – 5 c. purple, green and pink (postage) 10 10
1003 – 10 c. sepia, lake & brn 10 10
1004 **164** 25 c. violet, blue & grn 10 10

1005 – 50 c. pur, grn & yell (air) 15 15
1006 – 1 g. sepia, brn & orge 30 30
1007 **164** 1 g. 50 blue, turq & grn 45 45

DESIGNS—VERT: 5 c., 50 c. Young Haitians walking towards ABC "sun"; 10 c., 1 g. Scouting—hat, knot and saluting hand.

165 Dr. Albert Schweitzer and Maps of Alsace and Gabon

1967. Schweitzer Commem. Multicoloured.

1008 5 c. Type **165** (postage) 10 10
1009 10 c. Dr. Schweitzer and organ pipes 10 10
1010 20 c. Dr. Schweitzer and Hospital Deschapelles, Haiti 15 10

1011 50 c. As 20 c. (air) 20 15
1012 1 g. As 20 c. 35 30
1013 1 g. 50 Type **165** 50 45
1014 2 g. As 10 c. 65 55

166 J.-J. Dessalines and Melon

1967. Dessalines Commem. With Portrait of Dessalines. Multicoloured.

1015 5 c. Type **166** (postage) 10 10
1016 10 c. Chou (cabbage) 10 10
1017 20 c. Mandarine (orange) 10 10
1018 50 c. Mirliton (gourd) 15 15

1019 50 c. Type **166** (air) 15 10
1020 1 g. As 20 c. 30 20
1021 1 g. 50 As 20 c. 45 35

1967. World Scout Jamboree, Idaho. Nos. 957/8, 960/1, 963 and 965 surch **12e Jamboree Mondial 1967.** or with additional premium only.

1022 10 c. + 10 c. on 5 c. (postage) 10 10
1023 15 c. + 10 c. 10 10
1024 50 c. on 3 c. 20 15
1025 50 c. + 10 c. 20 20

1026 50 c. + 10 c. (air) 20 20
1027 1 g. 50 + 50 c. 60 50

1967. World Fair, Montreal. Nos. 968/70 and 972 optd **EXPO CANADA 1967** and emblem, also surch with new values (1 g. and 2 g.).

1028 **160** 5 c. mult (postage) 10 10
1029 – 10 c. multicoloured 10 10
1030 **160** 50 c. multicoloured 15 15
1031 1 g. on 5 c. mult 35 30

1032 1 g. 50 mult (air) 55 45
1033 2 g. on 1 g. 50 mult 70 55

169 Head of Duvalier and Guineafowl Emblem

1967. 10th Anniv of Duvalierists Revolution.

1034 **169** 5 c. gold & red (postage) 10 10
1035 10 c. gold and blue 10 10
1036 25 c. gold and brown 15 10
1037 50 c. gold and purple 25 15

1038 1 g. gold & green (air) 45 30
1039 1 g. 50 gold and violet 70 45
1040 2 g. gold and red 90 55

170 "Literacy"

1967. National Education. Multicoloured.

1041 5 c. Type **170** (postage) 10 10
1042 10 c. "Scouting" (Scout badge) (vert) 10 10
1043 25 c. "Visual Aids" (slide projection) 15 10

1044 50 c. Type **170** (air) 15 10
1045 1 g. As 10 c. (vert) 30 25
1046 1 g. 50 As 25 c. 45 35

1968. Olympic Games, Mexico. Nos. 990, 992 and 995 surch **MEXICO 1968.** with Olympic rings and value or optd only (1 g. 50).

1047 **163** 50 c. on 15 c. (postage) 20 15
1048 1 g. on 5 c. 30 25

1049 – 1 g. 50 (air) 55 45
1050 – 2 g. 50 + 1 g. 25 on 1 g. 50 1·25 1·00

1968. Winter Olympic Games, Grenoble. Nos. 986/9 optd **Xeme JEUX OLYMPIQUES D'HIVER-GRENOBLE 1968** and Games' emblem.

1051 **162** 50 c. red & blue (postage) 60 60

1052 – 50 c. indigo & blue (air) 45 30
1053 – 1 g. green and blue 60 35
1054 – 1 g. 50 red and blue 1·10 75

173 Bois Caiman Ceremony

174 "The Unknown Slave"

1968. Slaves' Revolt Commem.

1055 **173** 5 c. mult (postage) 10 10
1056 10 c. multicoloured 10 10
1057 25 c. multicoloured 10 10
1058 50 c. multicoloured 20 15

1059 50 c. multicoloured (air) 15 10
1060 50 c. multicoloured 15 10
1061 1 g. multicoloured 30 30
1062 1 g. multicoloured 30 25
1063 1 g. 50 multicoloured 45 45
1064 2 g. multicoloured 45 55
1065 5 g. multicoloured 85 60

Nos. 1060 and 1062/4 are in a larger size—$49\frac{1}{2}$ × 36 mm.

1968. Inaug. of Slavery Freedom Monument.

1066 **174** 5 c. black & bl (postage) 10 10
1067 10 c. black and brown 10 10
1068 20 c. black and violet 15 10
1069 25 c. black and blue 15 10
1070 50 c. black and green 30 15

1071 50 c. black & ochre (air) 20 15
1072 1 g. black and red 35 25
1073 1 g. 50 black & orange 55 35

1968. Air. Nos. 1044/6 surch **CULTURE + 0.10.**

1074 **170** 50 c. + 10 c. mult 20 20
1075 – 1 g. + 10 c. mult 30 30
1076 – 1 g. 50 + 10 c. mult 45 45

176 Various Arms and Palm

1968. Consecration of Haitian Bishopric.

1077 **176** 5 c. mult (postage) 10 10
1078 – 10 c. multicoloured 10 10
1079 – 25 c. multicoloured 20 10

1080 **176** 50 c. mult (air) 15 10
1081 – 1 g. multicoloured 30 25
1082 – 1 g. 50 multicoloured 45 35
1083 – 2 g. 50 multicoloured 70 65

DESIGNS—HORIZ: (50 × 30 mm): 10 c., 1 g., 2 g. 50, Virgin Mary; 25 c., 1 g. 50, Cathedral, Port-au-Prince.

177 Boeing 727-100 over Control Tower

1968. Inauguration of Duvalier Airport, Port-au-Prince. Portrait in black.

1084 **177** 5 c. brown & bl (postage) 10 10
1085 10 c. brown and blue 10 10
1086 25 c. brown and lilac 10 10

1087 – 50 c. pur & violet (air) 20 15
1088 – 1 g. 50 purple & blue 55 35
1089 – 2 g. 50 purple & turq 70 45

DESIGN: 50 c., 1 g. 50, 2 g. 50, Boeing 727-100 over airport entrance.

INDEX
Countries can be quickly located by referring to the index at the end of this volume.

178 President Duvalier, Emblems and Map

1968. Air. 4th Anniv of Francois Duvalier's "Life Presidency". Die-stamped in gold.

1090 **178** 30 g. gold, black & red 16·00

179 Slave breaking Chains

1968. "Revolt of the Slaves" (1791).

1091 **179** 5 c. purple, purple and blue (postage) 10 10
1092 10 c. mve, pur & orge 10 10
1093 25 c. mve, pur & ochre 10 10

1094 50 c. mve, pur & lil (air) 15 10
1095 1 g. mauve, pur & grn 35 25
1096 1 g. 50 mve, pur & bl 50 35
1097 2 g. mauve, pur & turq 60 45

180 "Learning the Alphabet"

1968. "National Education". Multicoloured.

1098 5 c. Type **180** (postage) 10 10
1099 10 c. Children watching TV screen ("Education by Audio-visual Methods") 10 10
1100 50 c. Hands with ball ("Education Through Sport") 15 10

1101 50 c. As No. 1099 (air) 15 10
1102 1 g. As No. 1100 30 25
1103 1 g. 50 As No. 1099 55 35

181 Boesman and Balloon

182 Airmail Cachet of 1925

1968. Air. Boesman's Balloon Flight.

1104 **181** 70 c. brown and green 40 30
1105 1 g. 75 brown and blue 1·00 70

1968. Air. Galiffet's Balloon Flight of 1784. Each black and purple on mauve.

1106 70 c. Airplane and "AVION" ("2 May 1925") 35 35
1107 70 c. Type **182** 35 35
1108 70 c. "AVION" and airplane ("28 March 1927") 35 35
1109 70 c. "HAITI POSTE AVION" and airplane ("12 July 1927") 35 35
1110 70 c. Airplane and "AVION" within ring ("13 Sept. 1927") 35 35
1111 70 c. "LINDBERGH" and airplane ("6th February 1928") 35 35

Nos. 1106/11 were issued together se-tenant within a small sheet containing two blocks of six (3 × 2) with an overall background design representing Galiffet's balloon.

183 Churchill as Elder Brother of Trinity House

185 Blue-hooded Euphonia

1968. Churchill Commemoration. Mult.

1112 3 c. Type **183** (postage) 10 10
1113 5 c. Churchill painting 10 10
1114 10 c. As Knight of the Garter . 10 10
1115 15 c. 79th birthday portrait and troops 10 10
1116 20 c. Churchill and Farman M.F.7 floatplane 10 10
1117 25 c. Karsh portrait and taking leave of the Queen 10 10
1118 50 c. Giving "V"-sign and Houses of Parliament . . . 15 10
1119 50 c. As No. 1116 (air) 15 10
1120 75 c. As No. 1115 . . . . . . 25 15
1121 1 g. As No. 1117 . . . . . . 30 25
1122 1 g. 50 As No. 1118 . . . . . 45 35

1969. Nos. 1070/2 surch.

1124 **174** 70 c. on 50 c. (postage) . . 45 20
1125 70 c. on 50 c. (air) 35 25
1126 1 g. 75 on 1 g. 85 55

1969. Birds. Multicoloured.

1127 5 c. Type **185** (postage) . . . . 1·40 30
1128 10 c. Hispaniolan trogon . . . 1·40 30
1129 20 c. Palm chat . . . . 1·60 30
1130 25 c. Stripe-headed tanager . . 1·90 40
1131 50 c. Type **185** . . . . 2·40 45
1132 50 c. As 10 c. (air) . . . . . . 2·25 60
1133 1 g. Black-cowled oriole . . . 2·50 1·10
1134 1 g. 50 As 25 c. . . . . 3·00 1·40
1135 2 g. Hispaniolan woodpecker . 3·50 1·75

186 "Theato, Paris-1900"

1969. Winners of Olympic Marathon showing commemorative inscr and stamp of "host" country. Multicoloured.

1136 5 c. "Louis, Athens-1896" (postage) 10 10
1137 10 c. Type **186** 15 15
1138 15 c. "Hicks, St. Louis-1904" . 15 15
1139 20 c. "Hayes, London-1908" . 25 25
1140 20 c. "McArthur, Stockholm-1912" 25 25
1141 25 c. "Kolehmainen, Antwerp-1920" 40 40
1142 25 c. "Steenroos, Paris-1924" . 40 40
1143 25 c. "El Quafi, Amsterdam-1928" 40 40
1144 30 c. "Zabala, Los Angeles-1932" (air) 45 45
1145 50 c. "Son, Berlin-1936" . . . 70 70
1146 60 c. "Cabrera, London-1948" . 90 90
1147 75 c. "Zatopek, Helsinki-1952" 1·25 1·25
1148 75 c. "Mimoun, Melbourne-1956" . . . . 1·25 1·25
1149 90 c. "Bikila, Rome-1960" . . 1·50 1·50
1150 1 g. "Bikila, Tokyo-1964" . . 1·75 1·75
1151 1 g. 25 "Wolde, Mexico-1968" . 2·50 2·50

Nos. 1136, 1139, 1142 and 1149 are larger, size 66 × 36 mm.

187 Pylons and Electric Light Bulb

189 Practising the Alphabet

1969. Construction of Duvalier Hydro-electric Scheme.

1153 **187** 20 c. violet & bl (postage) 10 10
1154 20 c. blue and violet (air) . 10 10
1155 25 c. green and red . . . 10 10
1156 25 c. red and green . . . 15 10

1969. Obligatory Tax. Education Fund. As Nos. 974/8.

1157 **146** 10 c. brown (postage) . . 10 10
1158 10 c. blue 10 10
1159 10 c. purple (air) 10 10
1160 10 c. red 10 10
1161 10 c. yellow 10 10
1162 10 c. green 10 10
1163 10 c. maroon 10 10

1969. League of Red Cross Societies. 50th Anniv Various stamps surch **50 eme. Anniversaire de la Ligue des Societes de la Croix Rouge**.

1164 10 c. + 10 c. (No. 1099) (postage) 10 10
1165 50 c. + 20 c. (No. 1100) . . . 20 20
1166 50 c. + 20 c. (No. 1101) (air) . 30 20
1167 1 g. 50 + 25 c. (No. 1103) . . 70 50

1969. "National Education". Multicoloured.

1168 5 c. Type **189** (postage) 10 10
1169 10 c. Children at play 10 10
1170 50 c. Audio-visual education . 15 10
1171 50 c. As No. 1170 (air) 15 10
1172 1 g. Type **189** 35 20
1173 1 g. 50 As No. 1169 . . . . . 55 35

Nos. 1169/71 and 1173 are vert.

190 I.L.O. Emblem

1969. 50th Anniv of I.L.O.

1174 **190** 5 c. grn & blk (postage) . 10 10
1175 10 c. brown and black . . 10 10
1176 20 c. blue and black . . . 10 10
1177 25 c. red & black (air) . . 15 10
1178 70 c. orange and black . . 25 15
1179 1 g. 75 violet & black . . 40 45

191 "Papilio zonaria"

1969. Haitian Butterflies. Multicoloured.

1180 10 c. Type **191** (postage) . . . 15 10
1181 20 c. "Zerene cesonia" 30 10
1182 25 c. "Papilio machaonides" . 35 10
1183 50 c. "Danaus eresimus" (air) . 45 10
1184 1 g. 50 "Anaea marthesia" . . 1·40 60
1185 2 g. "Prepona antimache" . . 1·75 85

192 Dr. Martin Luther King

1970. Dr. Martin Luther King (American Civil Rights leader). Commemoration.

1186 **192** 10 c. brown, red and ochre (postage) 10 10
1187 20 c. blk, red & new bl . . 10 10
1188 25 c. black, red & pink . . 10 10
1189 50 c. black, red and green (air) 20 10
1190 1 g. black, red & orange . 35 25
1191 1 g. 50 black, red & blue . 55 35

193 "Laeliopsis dominguensis"

194 U.P.U. Monument Berne, and Map of Haiti

1970. Haitian Orchids. Multicoloured.

1192 10 c. Type **193** (postage) . . . 10 10
1193 20 c. "Oncidium haitiense" . . 15 10
1194 25 c. "Oncidium calochilum" . 25 15
1195 50 c. "Tetramicra elegans" (air) 15 10
1196 1 g. 50 "Epidendrum truncatum" 45 35
1197 2 g. "Oncidium desertorum" . 65 50

1970. 16th U.P.U. Congress, Tokyo.

1198 **194** 10 c. brown, black and green (postage) 10 10
1199 – 25 c. yellow, blk & red . . 15 10
1200 – 50 c. grn, blk & blue . . . 35 25
1201 – 50 c. brn, blk & vio (air) . 15 10
1202 – 1 g. 50, yell, blk & red . . 55 35
1203 **194** 2 g. brown, blk & green . . 70 50

DESIGNS—VERT: 25 c., 1 g. 50, Stylised "propeller". HORIZ: 50 c. (both), Doves and globe.

195 Map, Dam and Generator

1970. Construction of Duvalier Central Hydro-electric Power Station. Multicoloured.

1205 20 c. Type **195** 15 10
1206 25 c. Map, dam and pylon . . 20 10

1970. 25th Anniv of United Nations. Nos. 1200/203 optd **XXVe ANNIVERSAIRE O.N.U.** and emblem.

1207 – 50 c. green, black and blue (postage) 20 15
1208 – 50 c. brn, blk & blue (air) . 20 10
1209 – 1 g. 50 yellow, blk & red . 55 35
1210 **194** 2 g. brown, blk & grn . . 70 50

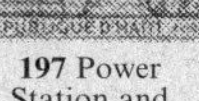

197 Power Station and Pylon

198 Fort Nativity, 1492

1970. Obligatory Tax. Duvalier Hydro-electric Project.

1212 **197** 20 c. brn & lil (postage) . 15 10
1213 20 c. grey & brn (air) . . 15 10
1214 20 c. violet and blue . . . 15 10

See also No. 1268.

1970. Christmas.

1215 **198** 3 c. brn & yell (postage) . 10 10
1216 5 c. black and green . . . 20 15
1217 – 1 g. 50 mult (sepia panel) (air) 55 35
1218 – 1 g. 50 mult (blue panel) . 55 35
1219 – 2 g. multicoloured 60 50

DESIGN—SQUARE (33 × 33 mm): Nos. 1217/19, "Haitian Nativity" (Toussaint Auguste).

199 "The Oriental" (Rembrandt)

200 Football

1971. Paintings. Multicoloured.

1220 5 c. Type **199** (postage) 10 10
1221 10 c. "The Ascension" (C. Bazile) 10 10
1222 20 c. "Irises in a vase" (Van Gogh) 15 10
1223 50 c. "The Baptism of Christ" (C. Bazile) 30 15
1224 50 c. "The Nativity" (R. Benoit) (air) 20 15
1225 1 g. "Head of a Negro" (Rubens) 35 30
1226 1 g. 50 As 10 c. 55 45

1971. World Cup Football Championships, Mexico (1970).

1228 **200** 5 c. black & orange . . . 10 10
1229 50 c. black & brown . . . 25 15
1230 – 50 c. blk, yell & pink . . 25 15
1231 – 1 g. black, yell & lilac . . 40 25
1232 **200** 1 g. 50 black & drab . . 55 45
1233 – 5 g. black, yell & grey . . 1·10 1·00

DESIGNS: Nos. 1230/31, 1233, Jules Rimet Cup.

1971. Inauguration of Duvalier Central Power Station. Surch **INAUGURATION 22-7-71** and premium.

1235 **195** 20 c. + 50 c. mult 30 25
1236 – 25 c. + 1 g. 50 mult (No. 1206) 70 55

202 Balloon and Airmail Stamp of 1929

1971. Air. 40th Anniv of Airmail Service (1969).

1237 **202** 20 c. black, red & blue . . 25 10
1238 50 c. black, red & blue . . 45 20
1239 – 1 g. black and orange . . 1·00 50
1240 – 1 g. 50 black & mauve . . 1·60 60

DESIGN: 1 g., 1 g. 50, Concorde and 1929 air stamp.

1971. Obligatory Tax. Education Fund. Nos. 1205/6 surch **ALPHABETISATION** and value.

1242 **195** 20 c. + 10 c. mult 15 10
1243 – 25 c. + 10 c. mult 15 10

1972. Air. "INTERPEX" Int. Stamp Exhib., New York Nos. 1237/40 optd **INTERPEX 72** and emblem.

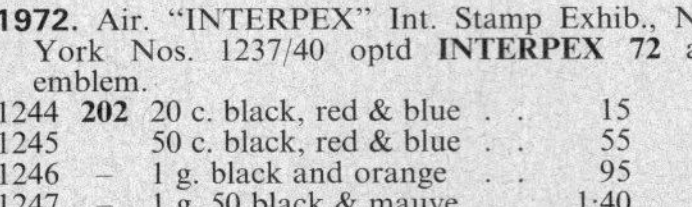

1244 **202** 20 c. black, red & blue . . 15 10
1245 50 c. black, red & blue . . 55 20
1246 – 1 g. black and orange . . 95 50
1247 – 1 g. 50 black & mauve . . 1·40 75

205 J.-J. Dessalines and Emblem

208 "Sun" and "EXPO" Emblem

1972. Jean-Jacques Dessalines ("founder of Haiti") (1st issue). Commemoration.

1248 **205** 5 c. black & grn (postage) 10 10
1249 10 c. black and blue . . . 10 10
1250 25 c. black and orange . . 10 10
1251 50 c. black & grn (air) . . 20 10
1252 2 g. 50 black and lilac . . 55 20

See also Nos. 1304/10, 1343/52, 1357/60, 1413/17 and 1451/2.

1972. Air. Fifth "Haipex" Congress. Nos. 1237/40 optd **HAIPEX 5eme. CONGRES** and emblem.

1253 **202** 20 c. black, red & blue . . 15 10
1254 – 50 c. blk, red and blue . . 55 20
1255 – 1 g. black & orange . . . 95 45
1256 – 1 g. 50 black & mauve . . 1·40 65

1972. Air. "Belgica 72" Stamp Exhibition, Brussels. Nos. 1238/40 optd **BELGICA 72** and emblem.

1257 50 c. black, red & blue 55 20
1258 1 g. black and orange 90 55
1259 1 g. 50 black & mauve . . . . 1·60 65

1972. Obligatory Tax. As Nos. 974/8.

1260 **146** 5 c. red 10 10
1261 5 c. blue 10 10

1972. "EXPO 70" World Fair, Osaka, Japan (1970).

1262 **208** 10 c. mult (postage) . . . 10 10
1263 – 25 c. multicoloured . . . 10 10
1264 – 50 c. multicoloured (air) . . 15 10
1265 – 1 g. multicoloured 35 25
1266 – 1 g. 50 multicoloured . . 45 30
1267 – 2 g. 50 multicoloured . . 90 55

DESIGNS—HORIZ: Nos. 1264/7, Sun Tower and emblem.

1972. Obligatory Tax. Duvalier Hydro-electric Project. As Nos. 1212/14.

1268 **197** 20 c. brown and blue . . 10 10

209 Basket Vendors

210 Headquarters and Map

1973. 20th Anniv of Caribbean Travel Assn. Multicoloured.

1269 50 c. Type **209** 20 10
1270 80 c. Postal bus service 30 20
1271 1 g. 50 Type **209** 55 30
1272 2 g. 50 As 80 c. 75 55

1973. Air. Education Fund. As Nos. 977/8 but larger size 17 × 25 mm.

1273 **146** 10 c. brown and blue . . 10 10
1274 10 c. brown and green . . 10 10
1275 10 c. brown and orange . 10 10

1973. Air. 70th Anniv of Pan-American Health Organization. Multicoloured.

1276 **210** 50 c. multicoloured . . . 15 10
1277 80 c. multicoloured . . . 25 20
1278 1 g. 50 multicoloured . . 45 30
1279 2 g. multicoloured 55 45

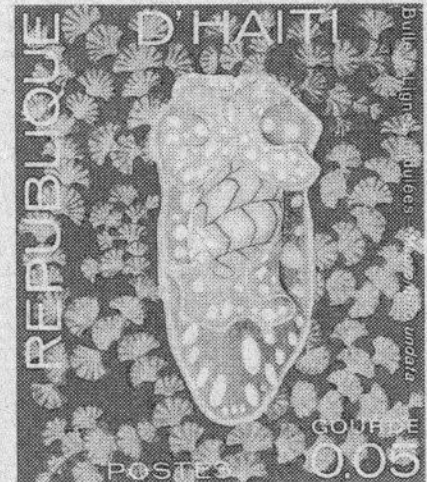

211 Miniature Melo

1973. Marine Life. Multicoloured.

1280 5 c. Type **211** (postage) . . . 15 10
1281 10 c. "Nemaster rubiginosa" . 10 10
1282 25 c. "Cyerce cristallina" . . . 30 10
1283 50 c. "Desmophyllum riisei" . 15 10
1284 50 c. "Platypodia spectabilis" (air) 15 10
1285 85 c. "Goniaster tessellatus" . 25 20
1286 1 g. 50 "Stephanocyathus diadema" 45 30
1287 2 g. "Phyllangia americana" . 55 35

211a Royal Gramma

1973. Fishes. Multicoloured.
1288 10 c. Type **211a** (postage) . . . 20 10
1289 50 c. Blue tang 35 15
1290 50 c. Black-capped basslet (air) 35 15
1291 85 c. Rock beauty 55 30
1292 1 g. 50 Peppermint basslet . . 1·00 55
1293 5 g. Creole wrasse . . . . . . 2·00 1·00

212 Haitian Flag

1973. Air.
1294 **212** 80 c. black and red . . . 25 20
1295 – 80 c. black and red . . . 25 20
1296 – 1 g. 85 black and red . . 55 30
1297 – 1 g. 85 black and red . . 55 30
DESIGNS—As Type **212**: No. 1295, Flag and arms (framed). (47 × 29 mm): No. 1296, Flag and arms; No. 1297, Flag and Pres. Jean-Claude Duvalier.

213 Football Stadium **214** J.-J. Dessalines

1973. World Cup Football Championships. Preliminary Games between Caribbean Countries.
1298 **213** 10 c. green, black and brown (postage) . . . 10 10
1299 – 20 c. mve, blk & brn . . . 10 10
1300 **213** 50 c. grn, blk & red (air) . 15 10
1301 – 80 c. grn, blk & blue . . 25 20
1302 – 1 g. 75 grn, blk & brn . . 50 35
1303 – 10 g. green, blk & brn . . 1·75 1·25
DESIGNS: 20 c., 1 g. 75, 10 g. World Cup stamp of 1971.

1974. Jean-Jacques Dessalines Commemoration (2nd issue).
1304 **214** 10 c. green & bl (postage) . 10 10
1305 20 c. black and red . . . 10 10
1306 25 c. violet and brown . . 10 10
1307 50 c. blue & brn (air) . . 15 10
1308 80 c. brown and grey . . 20 20
1309 1 g. purple and green . . 30 20
1310 1 g. 75 green & mauve . . 50 35

215 Symbol of Solar System **216** Pres. Jean-Claude Duvalier

1974. 500th Birth Anniv (1973) of Nicolas Copernicus (astronomer). Multicoloured.
1311 10 c. Type **215** (postage) . . . 10 10
1312 25 c. Copernicus 10 10
1313 50 c. Type **215** (air) 15 10
1314 50 c. As 25 c. 15 10
1315 80 c. Type **215** 25 20
1316 1 g. As 25 c. 30 20
1317 1 g. 75 Type **215** 50 35

1974.
1319 **216** 10 c. grn & gold (postage) 10 10
1320 20 c. purple and gold . . 10 10
1321 50 c. blue and gold . . . 15 10
1322 50 c. pur & gold (air) . . 15 15
1323 80 c. red and gold . . . 25 20
1324 1 g. purple and gold . . . 30 20
1325 1 g. 50 blue and gold . . 45 30
1326 1 g. 75 violet and gold . . 55 35
1327 5 g. grey and gold 85 60

1975. Air. Nos. 1296/7 surch.
1328 80 c. on 1 g. 85 black & red . . 25 20
1329 80 c. on 1 g. 85 black & red . . 25 20

1975. Air. Centenary of U.P.U. Nos. 1296/7 optd **1874 UPU 1974 100 ANS.**
1330 1 g. 85 black and red . . . 55 30
1331 1 g. 85 black and red . . . 55 30

219 Haiti 60 c. Stamp of 1937

1976. Bicentenary of American Revolution.
1332 **219** 10 c. mult (postage) . . . 10 10
1333 – 50 c. multicoloured (air) . 15 10
1334 – 80 c. multicoloured . . . 25 15
1335 – 1 g. 50 multicoloured . . 45 30
1336 – 7 g. 50 multicoloured . . 1·75 1·25
DESIGN: 50 c. to 7 g. 50, text with names of Haitians at Siege of Savannah.

1976. Surch.
1337 **205** 80 c. on 25 c. black and pink (postage) 35 20
1338 – 80 c. on 10 c. multicoloured (No. 1288) . . 35 20
1339 **214** 80 c. on 25 c. vio & brn . 35 20
1340 **215** 80 c. on 10 c. mult . . . 35 20
1341 – 80 c. on 85 c. multicoloured (No. 1285) (air) 25 20
1342 – 80 c. on 85 c. multicoloured (No. 1291) . . 25 20

1977. Jean-Jacques Dessalines Commem (3rd issue).
1343 **205** 20 c. black and brown (postage) 10 10
1344 50 c. black and mauve . . 15 10
1345 75 c. black & yell (air) . . 20 20
1346 1 g. black and blue . . . 30 15
1347 1 g. 25 black & olive . . . 35 30
1348 1 g. 50 black & grey . . . 45 30
1349 1 g. 75 black & red . . . 50 35
1350 2 g. black and yellow . . 55 45
1351 5 g. black and blue . . . 85 60
1352 10 g. black and brown . . 1·75 1·25

1977. Air. Lindbergh's Transatlantic Flight Nos. 1313/14 and 1316/17 optd or surch **C. LINDBERGH. N.Y.-PARIS 1927–1977.**
1353 1 g. Copernicus 30 20
1354 1 g. 25 on 50 c. Type **215** . . . 35 30
1355 1 g. 25 on 50 c. Copernicus . . 35 30
1356 1 g. 25 on 1 g. 75 Type **215** . . 35 30

1977. Jean-Jacques Dessalines Commem. (4th issue).
1357 **205** 10 c. black and mauve (postage) 10 10
1358 50 c. black and brown . . 15 10
1359 80 c. black & grn (air) . . 25 15
1360 1 g. black and brown . . 30 20

1977. Air. Various stamps surch with **G. O.80.**
1361 – 80 c. on 1 g. 50 multicoloured (No. 1266) . . 20 20
1366 – 80 c. on 1 g. 50 multicoloured (No. 1335) . . 20 20
1364 **215** 80 c. on 1 g. 75 mult . . 20 20
1365 **216** 80 c. on 1 g. 75 violet and gold 20 20
1363 – 80 c. on 1 g. 85 black and red (No. 1296) . . . 20 20
1362 – 80 c. on 2 g. 50 multicoloured (No. 1267) . . 20 20

1978. Surch with **1.00.**
1367 **205** 1 g. on 20 c. blk & brn . . 30 20
1368 1 g. on 1 g. 75 black and red 30 20
1369 1 g. 25 on 75 c. black and yellow 35 25
1370 1 g. 25 on 1 g. 50 black and green 35 25
Nos. 1368/70 have the inscription "AVION" obliterated by the surcharge.

224 J.-C. Duvalier Telecommunications Stations **225** Flag-raising Ceremony

1978. Telephone Centenary (1976). Mult.
1372 10 c. Type **224** (postage) . . . 10 10
1373 20 c. Video telephone 10 10
1374 50 c. Alexander Graham Bell (vert) 15 10
1375 1 g. Satellite over Earth (air) . . 30 15
1376 1 g. 25 Type **224** 35 25
1377 2 g. Wall telephone, 1890 (vert) 55 45

1978. Olympic Games, Montreal (1976). Multicoloured.
1378 5 c. Type **225** (postage) 10 10
1379 25 c. Cycling 10 10
1380 50 c. High jump 15 10
1381 1 g. 25 Horse jumping (air) . . 35 25
1382 2 g. 50 Basketball 70 55
1383 5 g. Yachting . . . . 1·40 1·10

226 Mother feeding Baby **227** Mother feeding Child

1979. 50th Anniv of Inter-American Child Institute. Multicoloured.
1384 25 c. Type **226** (postage) . . . 10 10
1385 1 g. 25 Type **226** (air) 35 25
1386 2 g. Nurse vaccinating child . . 55 45

1979. 30th Anniv of Co-operative for American Relief Everywhere (CARE). Multicoloured.
1387 25 c. Type **227** (postage) . . . 10 10
1388 50 c. Type **227** 15 15
1389 1 g. Spinning cotton (air) . . . 30 20
1390 1 g. 25 As No. 1389 . . . . . 35 25
1391 2 g. As No. 1389 . . . . . . 55 45

228 Human Rights Emblem **229** Anteor Firmin and Book

1979. 30th Anniv of Declaration of Human Rights.
1392 **228** 25 c. mult (postage) . . . 10 10
1393 1 g. multicoloured (air) . . 30 20
1394 1 g. 25 multicoloured . . 35 25
1395 2 g. multicoloured 55 45

1979. International Anti-Apartheid Year.
1396 **229** 50 c. pink and brown (postage) 15 15
1397 1 g. green & brown (air) . 30 20
1398 1 g. 25 blue and brown . . 35 25
1399 2 g. olive and brown . . . 55 45

230 Children playing

1979. International Year of the Child.
1400 **230** 10 c. mult (postage) . . . 10 10
1401 25 c. multicoloured . . . 10 10
1402 50 c. multicoloured . . . 15 10
1403 1 g. multicoloured (air) . . 30 20
1404 1 g. 25 multicoloured . . 35 25
1405 2 g. 50 multicoloured . . 45 55
1406 5 g. multicoloured 85 60

1980. Air. Wedding of President Duvalier. Nos. 1322 and 1325/6 optd **27 5 80 JOUR FASTE.**
1407 **216** 50 c. purple and gold . . 15 10
1408 1 g. 50 blue and gold . . 45 30
1409 1 g. 75 violet and gold . . 50 40

1980. Nos. 1252, 1357 and 1359 surch **TIMBRE POSTE** with value changed.
1410 **205** 1 g. on 2 g. 50 blk & lil . . 30 20
1411 **205** 1 g. 25 on 10 c. blk & mve 35 35
1412 1 g. 25 on 80 c. blk & grn . 35 55

1980. Jean-Jacques Dessalines Commemoration (5th issue).
1413 **205** 25 c. black and orange (postage) 10 10
1414 1 g. black and grey (air) . 30 20
1415 1 g. 25 black and pink . . 35 25
1416 2 g. black and green . . . 55 45
1417 5 g. black and blue . . . 85 60

233 Henri Christophe Citadel

1981. World Tourism Conference, Manila. Multicoloured.
1418 5 c. Type **233** (postage) 10 10
1419 25 c. Sans-Souci Palace 10 10
1420 50 c. Vallieres market 15 10
1421 1 g. Type **233** (air) 30 20
1422 1 g. 25 As No. 1419 . . . . . 35 25
1423 1 g. 50 Carnival dancers . . . 45 30
1424 2 g. Women with flowers . . . 55 45
1425 2 g. 50 As No. 1424 . . . . . 70 50

234 Players and Flag of Uruguay (1930)

1981. 50th Anniv of First World Cup Football Championship. Multicoloured.
1426 10 c. Type **234** (postage) . . . 10 10
1427 20 c. Italy (1934) 10 10
1428 25 c. Italy (1938) 10 10
1429 50 c. Uruguay (air) 15 10
1430 75 c. West Germany (1954) . . 20 20
1431 1 g. Brazil (1958) 30 20
1432 1 g. 25 Brazil (1962) 35 25
1433 1 g. 50 England (1966) 45 30
1434 1 g. 75 Brazil (1970) 50 40
1435 2 g. West Germany (1974) . . . 55 45
1436 5 g. Argentina (1978) 85 60

235 "Woman with Birds and Flowers" (Hector Hyppolite) **237** President Duvalier, Dish Aerial and Freighter at Quayside

1981. Paintings. Multicoloured.
1437 5 c. Type **235** (postage) 10 10
1438 10 c. "Going to Church" (Gregoire Etienne) 10 10
1439 20 c. "Street Market" (Petion Savain) 10 10
1440 25 c. "Market Sellers" (Michele Manual) 10 10
1441 50 c. Type **235** (air) 15 10
1442 1 g. 25 As No. 1438 . . . . . 35 25
1443 2 g. As No. 1439 . . . . . . 55 45
1444 5 g. As No. 1440 . . . . . . 85 60

1981. Various stamps surch **1.25.**
1445 **233** 1 g. 25 on 5 c. multicoloured (postage) . . 35 30
1446 **235** 1 g. 25 on 5 c. multicoloured 35 30
1447 – 1 g. 25 on 10 c. multicoloured (No. 1438) . . 35 30
1448 – 1 g. 25 on 20 c. multicoloured (No. 1427) . . 35 30
1449 – 1 g. 25 on 1 g. 50 multicoloured (No. 1423) (air) 35 30
1450 **205** 2 g. on 5 g. black and blue (No. 1417) 55 45
The surcharge on No. 1446 is inverted.

1982. Jean-Jacques Dessalines ("founder of Haiti"). Commemoration (6th issue).
1451 **205** 1 g. 25 black & brown . . 35 30
1452 2 g. black and violet . . . 55 45

1982. 10th Anniv of Duvalier Reforms ("Jean-Claudisme").
1453 **237** 25 c. green and black . . 15 10
1454 50 c. green and black . . 25 10
1455 1 g. purple and black . . 50 20
1456 1 g. 25 blue and black . . 55 30
1457 2 g. orange and black . . 75 45
1458 5 g. orange and black . . 2·25 1·10

1982. Nos. 1453 and 1455/7 optd **1957–1982 25 ANS DE REVOLUTION.**
1459 **237** 25 c. green and black . . 10 10
1460 1 g. purple and black . . 35 30
1461 1 g. 25 blue and black . . 45 40
1462 2 g. orange and black . . 65 60

239 Scouts planting Trees

1983. 75th Anniv of Boy Scout Movement. Multicoloured.
1463 5 c. Type **239** (postage) 10 10
1464 10 c. Lord Baden-Powell (vert) . 10 10
1465 25 c. Scout teaching villagers to read 25 10
1466 50 c. As No. 1464 . . . . . . 15 10
1467 75 c. As No. 1465 (air) 65 20
1468 1 g. Type **239** 30 20
1469 1 g. 25 As No. 1465 . . . . . 90 30
1470 2 g. As No. 1464 . . . . . . 55 45

240 Our Lady of Perpetual Succour

1983. Centenary of Miracle of Our Lady of Perpetual Succour.

1471 **240** 10 c. mult (postage) . . . 10 10
1472 20 c. multicoloured . . . 10 10
1473 25 c. multicoloured . . . 10 10
1474 50 c. multicoloured . . . 15 10

1475 **240** 75 c. multicoloured (air) . 20 20
1476 1 g. multicoloured 30 20
1477 1 g. 25 multicoloured . . 35 30
1478 1 g. 50 multicoloured . . 45 30
1479 1 g. 75 multicoloured . . 50 45
1480 – 2 g. multicoloured 55 45
1481 – 5 g. multicoloured 85 60

Nos. 1480/1 differ slightly in design of the frame.

241 Arms of Haiti and U.P.U. Monument, Berne

1983. Centenary (1981) of U.P.U. Membership.

1483 **241** 5 c. brown, red and black (postage) 10 10
1484 – 10 c. brown, black & bl . . 10 10
1485 – 25 c. green, blk & red . . 10 10
1486 – 50 c. grn, red & blk . . . 15 10

1487 – 75 c. lilac, black and blue (air) 20 20
1488 – 1 g. blue, red & black . . 30 20
1489 – 1 g. 25 blue, blk & red . . 35 30
1490 – 2 g. blue, black and red . 55 45

DESIGNS: 50 c., 1 g. Type **241**; 10, 75 c. L. F. Salomon and J. C. Duvalier; 25 c., 1 g. 25, 2 g. First Haitian stamp and U.P.U. Monument, Berne.

242 Argentine and Belgian Footballers

1983. World Cup Football Championship, Spain.

1491 **242** 5 c. blk & bl (postage) . . 10 10
1492 – 10 c. black & brown . . . 10 10
1493 – 20 c. black & green . . . 10 10
1494 – 25 c. black & green . . . 10 10
1495 – 50 c. black & yellow . . . 15 10

1496 – 1 g. mult (air) 30 20
1497 – 1 g. 25 multicoloured . . 35 30
1498 – 1 g. 50 multicoloured . . 45 30
1499 – 2 g. multicoloured 55 45
1500 – 2 g. 50 multicoloured . . 65 55

DESIGNS—VERT: 10 c. Northern Ireland and Yugoslavia; 20 c. England and France; 25 c. Spain and Northern Ireland; 50 c. Italian player with Cup. HORIZ: 1 g. Brazil and Scotland; 1 g. 25, Northern Ireland and France; 1 g. 50, Poland and Cameroun; 2 g. Italy and West Germany; 2 g. 50, Argentine and Brazil.

243 1 c. Stamp of 1881

1984. Stamp Centenary (1981).

1501 **243** 5 c. mult (postage) . . . 10 10
1502 – 10 c. multicoloured . . . 10 10
1503 – 25 c. multicoloured . . . 10 10
1504 – 50 c. multicoloured . . . 20 15

1505 – 75 c. yellow, brown and silver (air) 25 20
1506 – 1 g. blue, red and gold . . 35 30
1507 – 1 g. 25 multicoloured . . 45 40
1508 – 2 g. gold, brown and green 70 60

DESIGNS: 10 c. 1881 2 c. stamp; 25 c., 1881 3 c. stamp; 50 c. 1881 7 c. stamp; 75 c., 1 g. Pres. Salomon; 1 g. 25, 2 g. Pres. Duvalier.

244 Modern Communications Equipment

1984. World Communications Year.

1509 **244** 25 c. blue and purple . . 10 10
1510 50 c. blue and olive . . . 20 15
1511 – 1 g. orge, brn & grn . . . 35 30
1512 – 1 g. 25 orge, brn & bl . . 45 40
1513 – 2 g. bl, orge & blk 70 60
1514 – 2 g. 50 bl, bis & blk . . . 1·00 80

DESIGNS—VERT: 1 g., 1 g. 25, Pres. Petion's drum; 2 g., 2 g. 50, W.C.Y. emblem as satellite over globe.

245 Javelin-thrower, Runner and Polevaulter

1984. Olympic Games, Los Angeles.

1515 **245** 5 c. black, green and red . 10 10
1516 10 c. black, olive and red . 10 10
1517 – 25 c. black, green and red 10 10
1518 – 50 c. black, ochre and red 20 15
1519 – 1 g. black, blue and red . 35 30
1520 – 1 g. 25 blk, bl & orge . 45 40
1521 – 2 g. black, violet and red . 70 60

DESIGNS—HORIZ: 25 c., 50 c. Hurdler. VERT: 1 g. to 2 g. 50, Long jumper.

246 Head of "The Unknown Indian", Toussaint Square, Louverture

1984. 500th Anniv of Arrival of Europeans in America (1st issue).

1523 **246** 5 c. mult (postage) . . . 10 10
1524 10 c. multicoloured . . . 10 10
1525 25 c. multicoloured . . . 10 10
1526 50 c. multicoloured . . . 15 10

1527 – 1 g. mult (air) 25 20
1528 – 1 g. 25 multicoloured . . 35 30
1529 – 2 g. multicoloured 55 50

DESIGN: 1 to 2 g. "The Unknown Indian".
See also Nos. 1539/44.

247 Simon Bolivar and Alexandre Petion

1985. Birth Bicentenary of Simon Bolivar. Mult.

1531 5 c. Type **247** (postage) 10 10
1532 25 c. Bolivar and Alexandre Petion (different) 10 10
1533 50 c. Bolivar and flags of members of Grand Colombian Confederation 15 10

1534 1 g. Type **247** (air) 25 20
1535 1 g. 25, As No. 1532 . . . . . 30 25
1536 2 g. Type **247** 50 45
1537 7 g. 50, As No. 1532 . . . . . 1·60 1·25

248 Chief Henri **250** Planting Saplings

1986. 500th Anniv of Arrival of Europeans in America (2nd issue).

1539 **248** 10 c. mult (postage) . . . 10 10
1540 25 c. multicoloured . . . 10 10
1541 50 c. multicoloured . . . 15 10

1542 – 1 g. mult (air) 25 15
1543 – 1 g. 25 multicoloured . . 30 20
1544 – 2 g. multicoloured 35 25

DESIGN: 1 to 2 g. Chief Henri hunting.

1986. Various stamps surch.

1546 **241** 25 c. on 5 c. brown, red and black (postage) . . 10 10
1547 **242** 25 c. on 5 c. blk & bl . . 10 10
1548 **243** 25 c. on 5 c. mult . . . 10 10
1549 – 25 c. on 75 c. mult (1430) (air) 10 10
1550 – 25 c. on 75 c. mult (1467) . 10 10
1551 – 25 c. on 1 g. 50 mult (1122) 10 10

1986. International Youth Year (1985). Multicoloured.

1552 10 c. Type **250** (postage) . . . 10 10
1553 25 c. I.Y.Y. emblem 10 10
1554 50 c. Boy and girl scouts and flag 15 10

1555 1 g. Type **250** (air) 25 15
1556 1 g. 25 As No. 1553 . . . . . 30 20
1557 2 g. As No. 1554 . . . . . . 50 40

251 Dove above Peace Year Emblem on Globe

1987. International Peace Year (1986) and 40th Anniv of United Nations Educational, Scientific and Cultural Organization.

1559 **251** 10 c. mult (postage) . . . 10 10
1560 25 c. multicoloured . . . 10 10
1561 50 c. multicoloured . . . 15 10

1562 1 g. mult (air) 25 15
1563 1 g. 25 multicoloured . . 30 25
1564 2 g. 50 multicoloured . . 60 50

252 Peralte and Flag

1989. Charlemagne Peralte Commemoration.

1566 **252** 25 c. mult (postage) . . . 10 10
1567 50 c. multicoloured . . . 15 10

1568 1 g. mult (air) 25 15
1569 2 g. multicoloured 50 40
1570 3 g. multicoloured 80 70

253 Slaves and Tree forming Fist

1991. Bicentenary of Uprising of Slaves. Mult.

1572 25 c. Type **253** (postage) . . . 10 10
1573 50 c. Type **253** 10 10

1574 1 g. Gathering of slaves around fire (air) 10 10
1575 2 g. As No. 1574 . . . . . . 25 20
1576 3 g. As No. 1574 . . . . . . 35 30

254 Amerindian watching Europeans landing

1993. America. 500th Anniv (1992) of Discovery of America by Columbus. Multicoloured.

1578 25 c. Type **254** (postage) . . . 20 10
1579 50 c. Type **254** 20 10

1580 1 g. Columbus's fleet at anchor and rowing boats on shore (vert) (air) 20 10
1581 2 g. As No. 1580 . . . . . . 30 15
1582 3 g. As No. 1580 . . . . . . 50 30

255 Map of Haiti and Emblem

1995. 25th General Assembly of Organization of American States. Multicoloured.

1584 50 c. Type **255** 10 10
1585 75 c. Type **255** 10 10
1586 1 g. Map of Americas and emblems (vert) 10 10
1587 2 g. As No. 1586 . . . . . . 15 10
1588 3 g. As No. 1586 . . . . . . 25 20
1589 5 g. As No. 1586 . . . . . . 40 35

256 Dove holding Flags in Beak

1995. 50th Anniv of U.N.O. Multicoloured.

1591 50 c. Type **256** (postage) . . . 10 10
1592 75 c. Type **256** 10 10

1593 1 g. Dove with olive branch flying over flags (air) 10 10
1594 2 g. As No. 1593 . . . . . . 15 10
1595 3 g. As No. 1593 . . . . . . 25 20
1596 5 g. As No. 1593 . . . . . . 40 35

1996. Various stamps surch **XXIIIES JEUX OLYMPIQUES LOS ANGELES 1984**.

1598 2 g. on 1 g. 25 black, blue and orange (1520) (postage) . . 15 10

1599 1 g. on 1 g. 25 mult (1556) (air) 10 10
1600 3 g. on 1 g. 25 mult (1535) . . 20 15
1601 3 g. on 1 g. 25 mult (1477) . . 20 15

259 Players **260** "Virgin and Child" (Jacopo Bellini)

1996. Olympic Games, Atlanta. Mult

(a) Centenary of Volleyball.

1605 50 c. Type **259** 10 10
1606 75 c. Umpire and players . . . 10 10
1607 1 g. Players holding Olympic Flame 10 10
1608 2 g. Players jumping for ball . 15 10

(b) 1984 Medal Winners.

1609 3 g. 400 metre hurdles (U.S.A.) 20 15
1610 10 g. Decathlon (gold, Great Britain) 70 60

Nos. 1605/6 were issued together, se-tenant, forming a composite design of a match scene and Nos. 1607/8 a composite design of a map.

1996. Christmas. Multicoloured.

1612 2 g. Type **260** 15 10
1613 3 g. "Adoration of the Shepherds" (Bernardo Strozzi) 20 15
1614 6 g. "Virgin and Child" (Giovanni Bellini) 45 35
1615 10 g. "Virgin and Child" (Francesco Mazzola) 70 60
1616 25 g. "Adoration of the Magi" (Gentile da Fabriano) . . . 1·75 1·40

50-me ANNIVERSAIRE DE L'UNICEF
261 Children in Street

1997. 50th Anniv (1996) of U.N.I.C.E.F.

1618 **261** 4 g. multicoloured 30 25
1619 5 g. multicoloured 35 30
1620 6 g. multicoloured 45 35
1621 10 g. multicoloured . . . 70 60
1622 20 g. multicoloured . . . 1·40 1·25

262 Sleeping Beauty

1998. 175th Anniv (1997) of Third Collection of Fairy Tales by Brothers Grimm. Multicoloured.

1623 2 g. Type **262** 15 10
1624 3 g. Snow White 20 15
1625 4 g. Sleeping Beauty and Prince 30 25
1626 6 g. Man in bed (Water of Life) 45 35
1627 10 g. Cinderella 70 60
1628 20 g. Serving patient with the Water of Life . . . . 1·40 1·25

OFFICIAL STAMPS

1960. Nos. 736/40 optd **OFFICIEL.**

O742 – 50 c. brown and grn . . 25
O743 – 50 c. blue and green . . 25
O744 – 50 c. black and green . . 25
O745 **127** 1 g. green and red . . 35
O746 – 1 g. 50 pink and blue . . 55

The above were only issued precancelled.

O **135** Dessalines' Statue

1962. Air. (a) Size 20½ × 37½ mm.

O791 O **135** 50 c. sepia & blue . . 20 15
O792 1 g. red and blue . . . 35 30
O793 1 g. 50 blue and bistre . 55 45

(b) Size 30½ × 40 mm.

O794 O **135** 5 g. green and red . . 1·10 1·00

PARCEL POST STAMPS

1960. Optd **COLIS POSTAUX.**

P725 **102** 5 c. green & blk (postage) 10 10
P726 10 c. red and black . . . 10 10
P727 25 c. blue and black . . . 15 15
P728 **74** 2 g. 50 grey . . . . . . 1·10 1·10
P729 **102** 50 c. orge & blk (air) . . 25 20
P730 **101** 5 g. violet and blue . . . 2·10 1·75

P **130** Arms

1961.

P757 P **130** 50 c. violet and bistre (postage) 35 15
P758 1 g. blue and red . . . 55 30
P759 2 g. 50 lake & grn (air) . 90 70
P760 5 g. green & orge . . . 1·50 1·10

POSTAGE DUE STAMPS

D **10** D **23**

1898.

D63 D **10** 2 c. blue 20 25
D64 5 c. brown 35 40
D65 10 c. orange 50 50
D66 50 c. grey . . . . . . 1·00 1·00

1902. Optd **MAI Gt Pre 1902** in frame.

D85 D **10** 2 c. blue 45 50
D86 5 c. brown 45 50
D87 10 c. orange 50 50
D88 50 c. grey . . . . . . 3·75 2·10

1906.

D150 D **23** 2 c. red 45 35
D151 5 c. blue . . . . . . 1·50 1·50
D152 10 c. purple . . . . . 1·50 1·50
D153 50 c. olive . . . . . 6·75 3·75

1914. Optd **GL O. Z. 7 FEV. 1914** in frame.

D206 D **10** 5 c. brown 45 35
D207 10 c. orange 40 40
D208 50 c. grey . . . . . . 3·25 2·25

1914. optd **GL O. Z 7 FEV. 1914** in frame.

D209 D **23** 2 c. red 55 35
D210 5 c. blue 90 55
D211 10 c. purple . . . . . 2·60 2·25
D212 50 c. olive . . . . . 4·75 3·00

D **83**

1951.

D452 D **83** 10 c. red 10 10
D453 20 c. brown 15 15
D454 40 c. green 20 20
D455 50 c. yellow 30 30

SPECIAL DELIVERY STAMP

S **86** G.P.O.

1953.

E468 S **86** 25 c. red 30 30

APPENDIX

The following stamps have either been issued in excess of postal needs or have not been available to the public in reasonable quantities at face value. Such stamps may later be given full listing if there is evidence of regular postal use.

1968.

Medal Winners, Winter Olympic Games, Grenoble. Postage 5, 10, 20, 25, 50 c., 1 g. 50; Air 2 g.

1969.

Moon Landing of "Apollo 11". Optd on 1969 Birds issue. Nos. 1132/5. Air 50 c., 1 g. 50, 2 g.

Space Flights of "Apollo 7" and "Apollo 8". Postage 10, 15, 20, 25 c.; Air 70 c., 1 g. 25, 1 g. 50.

1970.

Moon Mission of "Apollo 12". Postage 5, 10, 15, 20, 25, 30, 40, 50 c.; Air 25, 30, 40, 50, 75 c., 1 g., 1 g., 1 g. 25, 1 g. 50.

1971.

Safe Return of "Apollo 13". Optd on 1970 "Apollo 12" issue. Postage 5, 10, 15, 20, 25, 30, 40, 50 c.; Air 25, 30, 40, 50, 75 c., 1 g., 1 g. 25, 1 g. 50.

1972.

Gold Medal Winners Olympic Games, Munich. Air 50, 75 c., 1 g. 50, 2 g. 50, 5 g.

1973.

American and Russian Space Exploration. Postage 5, 10, 20, 25, 50 c., 2 g. 50, 5 g.; Air 50, 75 c., 1 g. 50, 2 g. 50, 5 g.

Moon Mission of "Apollo 17". Optd on 1973 Space Exploration issue. 50 c., 2 g. 50, 5 g.

HAMBURG Pt. 7

A port in north-west Germany, formerly a Free City. In 1867 it joined the North German Confederation.

16 schillinge = 1 mark.

1 3 4

1859. Imperf.

1 **1** ½ s. black . . . . 90·00 £700
2 1 s. brown . . . . 90·00 75·00
3 2 s. red . . . . 90·00 £100
4 3 s. blue . . . . 95·00 £120
6 4 s. green £100 £1100
7 7 s. orange . . . . 70·00 27·00
10 9 s. yellow £200 £1800

1864. Imperf.

11 **3** 1¼ s. lilac . . . . £120 70·00
15 1¼ s. grey . . . . 80·00 65·00
17 1¼ s. blue £325 £800
18 **4** 2½ s. green £120 £120

1864. Perf.

19 **1** ½ s. black . . . . 5·00 12·00
20 1 s. brown . . . . 12·00 16·00
21 **3** 1¼ s. mauve . . . . 70·00 7·50
25 **1** 2 s. red . . . . 13·00 22·00
27 **4** 2½ s. green . . . . £120 28·00
30 **1** 3 s. blue . . . . 35·00 32·00
33 4 s. green . . . . 7·50 18·00
34 7 s. orange £140 £120
37 7 s. mauve . . . . 9·00 20·00
38 9 s. yellow . . . . 30·00 £1800

5

1866. Roul.

44 **5** 1¼ s. mauve . . . . 32·00 35·00
45 1½ s. pink . . . . 6·50 £130

1867. Perf.

46 **1** 2½ s. green . . . . 7·50 65·00

HANOVER Pt. 7

In north-east Germany. An independent kingdom until 1866, when it was annexed by Prussia.

1850. 12 pfennige = 1 gutegroschen.
24 gutengroschen = 1 thaler.
1858. 10 (new) pfennige = 1 (new) groschen.
30 (new) groschen = 1 thaler.

2 4

1850. On coloured paper. Imperf.

1 **2** 1 ggr. black on blue . . . . . £2500 42·00
2 1 ggr. black on green . . . . . 20·00 5·00
3 $\frac{1}{30}$ th. black on orange . . . . 60·00 40·00
4 $\frac{1}{30}$ th. black on red . . . . . 60·00 40·00
5 $\frac{1}{15}$ th. black on blue . . . . 85·00 60·00
6 $\frac{1}{10}$ th. black on orange . . . . 95·00 50·00

1853. Imperf.

18 **4** 3 pf. pink . . . . 50·00 85·00

1855. With coloured network. Imperf.

12 **4** 3 pf. pink and black £200 £300
14 **2** 1 ggr. black and green . . . . 24·00 7·50
15 $\frac{1}{30}$ th. black and pink . . . . 80·00 30·00
16 $\frac{1}{15}$ th. black and blue . . . . . 55·00 70·00
10 $\frac{1}{10}$ th. black and orange . . . £150 £140

5 King George V 6

1859. Imperf.

23 **5** 1 gr. pink . . . . 2·50 1·40
25a 2 gr. blue . . . . 14·00 30·00
28 3 gr. yellow . . . . £140 55·00
29 3 gr. brown . . . . 20·00 50·00
31 10 gr. green £250 £750

1860. Imperf.

33 **6** ½ gr. black . . . . 60·00 £200

1863. Imperf.

34 **4** 3 pf. green £275 £900

1864. Roul.

35 **4** 3 pf. green . . . . 22·00 55·00
36 **6** ½ gr. black £160 £225
37 **5** 1 gr. pink . . . . 5·00 1·75
38 2 gr. blue . . . . 65·00 45·00
39 3 gr. brown . . . . 65·00 65·00

HATAY Pt. 16

The territory of Alexandretta. Autonomous under French control from 1923 to Sept. 1938. Hatay was returned to Turkey in June 1939.

1938. 100 centiemes = 1 piastre.
1939. 100 santims = 40 paras = 1 kurus.

1938. Stamps of Syria of 1930/31 optd **Sandjak d'Alexandrette** (Nos. 1, 4, 7 and 11) or **SANDJAK D'ALEXANDRETTE** (others), Nos. 7 and 11 surch also.

1 0p. 10 purple 30 30
2 0p. 20 red 30 30
3 0p. 50 violet 30 30
4 0p. 75 red 35 35
5 1 p. brown 35 35
6 2 p. violet 40 40
7 2 p. 50 on 4 p. orange 65 65
8 3 p. green 90 90
9 4 p. orange . . . . 1·00 1·00
10 6 p. black . . . . 1·50 1·50
11 12 p. 50 on 15 p. red (No. 267) . 2·25 2·25
12 25 p. purple . . . . 5·50 5·50

1938. Air. Stamps of Syria of 1937 (Nos. 322 etc) optd **SANDJAK D'ALEXANDRETTE.**

13 ½ p. violet 35 35
14 1 p. black 35 35
15 2 p. green . . . . 1·10 1·10
16 3 p. blue . . . . 1·60 1·60
17 5 p. mauve . . . . 3·25 3·25
18 10 p. brown . . . . 4·50 4·50
19 15 p. brown . . . . 5·50 5·50
20 25 p. blue . . . . 6·50 6·50

1938. Death of Kemal Ataturk. Nos. 4, 5, 7, 9 and 11 optd **10-11-1938** in frame.

27 0p. 75 red . . . . 19·00 17·00
28 1 p. brown . . . . 14·00 12·00
29 2 p. 50 on 4 p. orange . . . . . 8·00 7·00
30 4 p. orange . . . . 12·00 8·50
31 12 p. 50 on 15 p. red . . . . . 20·00 19·00

1939. Stamps of Turkey surch **HATAY DEVLETI** and value.

32 **112** 10 s. on 20 pa. orange . . . 20 20
33 25 s. on 1 k. green 20 20
34 50 s. on 2 k. violet 20 20
35 75 s. on 2½ k. green 20 20
36 1 k. on 4 k. grey 20 20
37 1 k. on 5 k. red 25 25
38 1½ k. on 3 k. brown 40 40
39 2½ k. on 4 k. grey 40 40
40 5 k. on 8 k. blue . . . . . 1·25 1·25
41 12½ k. on 20 k. green . . . 2·00 2·25
42 20 k. on 25 k. blue . . . . 2·25 2·50

9 Map of Hatay **10** Flag of Hatay

1939.

48 **9** 10 pa. orange and blue . . . 65 75
49 30 pa. violet and blue 80 90
50 1½ k. olive and blue . . . . . 1·00 1·10
51 – 2½ k. green 25 25
52 – 3 k. blue 35 35
53 – 5 k. red 35 35
54 **10** 6 k. red and blue 40 40
55 7½ k. red and green 35 35
56 12 k. red and violet 50 50
57 12½ k. red and blue 55 55
58 – 17½ k. red . . . . 1·25 1·25
59 – 25 k. olive . . . . 1·60 1·60
60 – 50 k. blue . . . . 3·50 3·50

DESIGNS—HORIZ: 2½ k., 3 k., 5 k. Lions of Antioch. 17½ k., 25 k., 50 k. Parliament House, Antioch.

1939. Commemorating Turkish Annexation. Optd **T. C. ilhak tarihi 30-6-1939.**

65 **9** 10 pa. orange and blue . . . 85 1·10
66 30 pa. violet and blue . . . . 1·25 1·40
67 1½ k. olive and blue . . . . . 1·40 1·50
68 – 2½ k. green (No. 51) 25 25
69 – 3 k. blue (No. 52) 35 35
70 – 5 k. red (No. 53) 35 35
71 **10** 6 k. red and blue 40 40
72 7½ k. red and green 40 40
73 12 k. red and violet 45 45
74 12½ k. red and blue 60 60
75 – 17½ k. red (No. 58) . . . . . 1·25 1·25
76 – 25 k. olive (No. 59) . . . . 1·90 1·90
77 – 50 k. blue (No. 60) . . . . . 3·75 3·75

POSTAGE DUE STAMPS

1938. Postage Due stamps of Syria of 1925 optd **SANDJAK D'ALEXANDRETTE.**

D21 D **20** 0p. 50 brown on yellow . 75 75
D22 – 1 p. purple on pink . . . 1·00 1·00
D23 – 2 p. black on blue . . . 1·50 1·50
D24 – 3 p. black on red . . . . 2·00 2·00
D25 – 5 p. black on green . . . 5·00 5·00
D26 – 8 p. black on blue . . . 5·00 5·00

1939. Postage Due stamps of Turkey optd **HATAY DEVLETI** or surch also.

D43 D **121** 1 k. on 2 k. blue 30 30
D44 3 k. violet 45 45
D45 4 k. on 5 k. green . . . 60 60
D46 5 k. on 12 k. red . . . . 90 1·10
D47 12 k. red . . . . 7·50 6·50

D **11** Castle at Antioch

1939.

D61 D **11** 1 k. red 30 30
D62 3 k. brown 45 45
D63 4 k. green 50 50
D64 5 k. grey 70 70

1939. Nos. D61/4 optd **T. C. ilhak tarihi 30-6-1939.**

D73 D **11** 1 k. red 75 75
D74 3 k. brown 85 85
D75 4 k. green . . . . 1·00 1·00
D76 5 k. grey . . . . 1·10 1·10

HAWAII Pt. 22

A group of islands in the central Pacific, an independent kingdom till 1893 when a provisional government was set up. Annexed in 1898 by the United States. Now a State of the U.S.A.

100 cents = 1 dollar.

1 3 Kamehameha III

1851. Inscr "Hawaiian Postage". Imperf.

1 **1** 2 c. blue £450000 £225000
2 5 c. blue £28000 £16000
3 13 c. blue £14000 £11000

On Nos. 1/2 the value is expressed in words.

1852. Inscr "H.L. & US. Postage". Imperf.

4 **1** 13 c. blue £35000 £17000

1853. Imperf.

18	3	5 c. blue	16·00	
19		13 c. red	£160	

5

6 Kamehameha IV

1859. Inter-island post.

9	5	1 c. blue	£4750	£3500
12		1 c. black	£275	£625
10		2 c. blue	£3750	£2250
14d		2 c. black	£425	£350

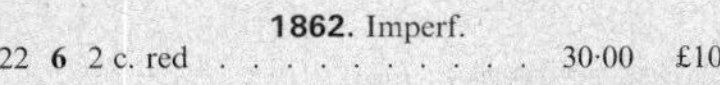

1862. Imperf.

22	6	2 c. red	30·00	£100

7 Princess Victoria Kamamalu

12

1864. Perf.

27	7	1 c. mauve	7·00	5·75
41	–	2 c. red	11·50	7·00
42	–	5 c. blue	11·50	2·50
30	–	6 c. green	19·00	6·50
31	–	18 c. red	65·00	27·00

DESIGNS: 2 c. Kamehameha IV; 5 c., 6 c. Portraits of Kamehameha V; 18 c. H.E. Mataio Kekuanaoa.

1865. Inter-island post.

32	12	1 c. blue	£190	
33		2 c. blue	£190	
34		5 c. blue on blue	£600	£425
35	–	5 c. blue on blue	£500	£350

DESIGN: No. 35. As Type 12 but inscr "HAWAIIAN POSTAGE" on left side of frame.

16 Princess Likelike

22 Princess (later Queen) Liliuokalani

1875.

38	16	1 c. blue	4·50	7·75
39		1 c. green	2·10	1·40
36	–	2 c. brown	5·75	2·25
40b	–	2 c. red	3·00	75
44	–	10 c. black	27·00	15·00
45	–	10 c. red	25·00	9·75
46	–	10 c. brown	23·00	7·75
37	–	12 c. black	42·00	21·00
47	–	12 c. lilac	55·00	25·00
48	–	15 c. brown	42·00	19·00
49	–	25 c. purple	95·00	42·00
50	–	50 c. red	£120	60·00
51	–	$1 red	£170	£100

DESIGNS: 2 c. King Kalakaua; 10 c. Same in uniform; 12 c. Prince Leleiohoku; 15 c. Queen Kapiolani; 25 c. Statute of Kamehameha I; 50 c. King Lunalilo; $1, Queen Emma Kaleleonalani.

1890.

53	22	2 c. violet	3·50	1·10

1893. Stamps of 1864, 1875 and 1889, optd **Provisional GOVT. 1893**.

54	7	1 c. mauve	5·50	9·50
55	16	1 c. blue	4·50	9·50
56		1 c. green	1·25	2·25
57	–	2 c. brown	7·50	15·00
58	22	2 c. violet	1·25	95
67	–	2 c. red (No. 41)	50·00	55·00
68	–	2 c. red (No. 40b)	1·00	1·75
60	–	5 c. blue	4·50	2·00
61	–	6 c. green	11·50	20·00
62	–	10 c. black	7·00	11·00
70	–	10 c. red	11·50	23·00
71	–	10 c. brown	5·75	9·75
64	–	12 c. black	7·00	13·50
65	–	12 c. lilac	£120	£160
73	–	15 c. brown	15·00	23·00
74	–	18 c. red	19·00	27·00
66	–	25 c. purple	19·00	30·00
75	–	50 c. red	45·00	70·00
76	–	$1 red	85·00	£130

24 Arms

26 Statue of King Kamehameha I

1894.

77	24	1 c. orange	1·75	1·00
89		1 c. green	1·25	90
78	–	2 c. brown	1·75	40
90a	–	2 c. pink	1·10	60
79	26	5 c. red	3·50	1·25
91		5 c. blue	4·00	2·25
80	–	10 c. green	4·50	3·25
81	–	12 c. blue	9·50	10·00
82	–	25 c. blue	9·50	10·00

DESIGNS—HORIZ: 2 c. Honolulu; 12 c. "Arawa" (steamer). VERT: 10 c. Star and palms; 25 c. President S. B. Dole.

OFFICIAL STAMPS

O 30 Secretary L. A. Thurston

1896.

O83	O 30	2 c. green	28·00	13·00
O84		5 c. brown	28·00	13·00
O85		6 c. blue	32·00	13·00
O86		10 c. red	28·00	13·00
O87		12 c. orange	40·00	13·00
O88		25 c. violet	45·00	13·00

HELIGOLAND Pt. 1

An island off the N. coast of Germany, ceded to that country by Great Britain in 1890.

1867. 16 schillings = 1 mark.
1875. 100 pfennig = 1 mark.

Many of the Heligoland stamps found in old collections and the majority of those offered at a small fraction of catalogue prices today, are reprints which have very little value.

1

1867. Perf (½, 1, 2 and 6 sch. also roul).

5	1	¼ sch. green and red	26·00	£1500
6b		½ sch. green and red	95·00	£150
7		¾ sch. red and green	29·00	£1100
8a		1 sch. red and green	£120	£180
9		1½ sch. green and red	65·00	£250
3		2 sch. red and green	10·00	55·00
4		6 sch. green and red	12·00	£250

2

3

4

5

1875.

10	2	1 pf. (¼d.) green and red	10·00	£500
11		2 pf. (½d.) red and green	10·00	£600
12a	3	3 pf. (⅝d.) green, red & yell	£160	£850
13	2	5 pf. (¾d.) green and red	10·00	18·00
14a		10 pf. (1½d.) red and green	10·00	20·00
15b	3	20 pf. (2½d.) green, red and yellow	12·00	28·00
16	2	25 pf. (3d.) green and red	12·00	26·00
17		50 pf. (6d.) red and green	18·00	32·00
18	4	1 m. (1s.) green, red & black	£140	£200
19	5	5 m. (5s.) green, red & black	£150	£950

HOI-HAO (HOIHOW) Pt. 17

An Indo-Chinese post office in China, closed in 1922.

1901. 100 centimes = 1 franc.
1918. 100 cents = 1 piastre.

HOI HAO
州 瓊
(1)

1902. Stamps of Indo-China "Tablet" key-type, optd with T 1. Chinese characters read "HOI-HAO" and are the same on every value.

1	D	1 c. black on blue	1·50	1·60
2		2 c. brown on yellow	1·90	1·75
3		4 c. red on grey	1·75	1·75
4	D	5 c. green	1·75	1·75
5		10 c. black on lilac	3·25	3·00
6		15 c. blue	£1100	£550
7		15 c. grey	1·40	1·40
8		20 c. red on green	10·00	9·50
9		25 c. black on red	5·50	3·25
10		30 c. brown	18·00	17·00
11		40 c. red on yellow	18·00	13·50
12		50 c. red on rose	24·00	19·00
13		75 c. brown on orange	£150	£140
14		1 f. olive	£525	£450
15		5 f. mauve on lilac	£425	£375

1903. Stamps of Indo-China, "Tablet" key-type, surch as T 1. Chinese characters indicate the value and differ for each denomination.

16	D	1 c. black on blue	60	60
17		2 c. brown on yellow	60	60
18		4 c. red on grey	1·40	1·40
19		5 c. green	1·40	1·40
20		10 c. red	1·40	1·40
21		15 c. grey	1·40	1·40
22		20 c. red on green	3·75	3·75
23		25 c. blue	1·50	1·50
24		25 c. black on red	1·60	1·60
25		30 c. brown	1·90	1·90
26		40 c. red on yellow	20·00	21·00
27		50 c. red on rose	20·00	21·00
28		50 c. brown on blue	70·00	70·00
29		75 c. brown on orange	27·00	27·00
30		1 f. olive	30·00	30·00
31		5 f. mauve on lilac	£140	£140

1906. Stamps of Indo-China surch **HOI-HAO** and with value in Chinese.

32	8	1 c. olive	1·10	1·10
33		2 c. red on yellow	1·10	1·10
34		4 c. mauve on blue	1·60	1·60
35		5 c. green	2·00	2·00
36		10 c red	2·00	2·00
37		15 c. brown on blue	2·25	2·25
38		20 c. red on green	3·25	3·00
39		25 c. blue	4·50	4·50
40		30 c. brown on cream	4·50	4·50
41		35 c. black on yellow	7·25	7·50
42		40 c. black on grey	8·00	8·00
43		50 c. brown	8·25	8·25
44	D	75 c. brown on orange	21·00	21·00
45	8	1 f. green	21·00	21·00
46		2 f. brown on yellow	21·00	21·00
47	D	5 f. mauve on lilac	80·00	80·00
48	8	10 f. red on green	£100	£100

1908. Native types of Indo-China surch **HOIHAO** (1 to 50 c.) or **HOI-HAO** (others) and with value in Chinese.

49	10	1 c. black and olive	45	45
50		2 c. black and brown	50	50
51		4 c. black and blue	80	75
52		5 c. black and green	1·00	1·00
53		10 c. black and red	1·40	1·40
54		15 c. black and violet	2·50	2·75
55	11	20 c. black and violet	3·00	3·25
56		25 c. black and blue	3·25	3·00
57		30 c. black & brown	3·25	3·25
58		35 c. black and green	3·25	3·00
59		40 c. black and brown	2·75	3·00
60		50 c. black and red	4·00	4·00
61	12	75 c. black and orange	4·50	4·50
62		1 f. black and red	9·50	9·50
63		2 f. black and green	23·00	23·00
64		5 f. black and blue	40·00	40·00
65		10 f. black and violet	60·00	60·00

1919. Stamps as last surch in addition with value in figures and words.

66	10	⅖ c. on 1 c. black & olive	55	55
67		⅘ c. on 2 c. black & brn	55	55
68		1⅗ c. on 4 c. black & blue	75	70
69		2 c. on 5 c. black & grn	55	55
70		4 c. on 10 c. black & red	75	75
71		6 c. on 15 c. black & violet	75	70
72	11	8 c. on 20 c. black & violet	1·10	1·10
73		10 c. on 25 c. black & blue	2·75	2·75
74		12 c. on 30 c. black & brn	85	85
75		14 c. on 35 c. black & grn	85	90
76		16 c. on 40 c. black & brn	1·00	1·00
77		20 c. on 50 c. black & red	1·10	1·10
78	12	30 c. on 75 c. black & orge	1·60	1·60
79	–	40 c. on 1 f. black & red	4·25	4·25
80	–	80 c. on 2 f. black & grn	11·00	11·00
81	–	2 p. on 5 f. black & blue	35·00	35·00
82	–	4 p. on 10 f. black & violet	£110	£120

HONDURAS Pt. 15

A republic of C. America, independent since 1838.

1866. 8 reales = 1 peso.
1878. 100 centavos = 1 peso.
1933. 100 centavos = 1 lempira.

1 Seal of Honduras

5 Pres. F. Morazan

6

1866. Imperf.

1	1	2 r. black on green	60	
2		2 r. black on red	60	

1878. Perf.

31	5	1 c. violet	40	60
32		2 c. brown	40	70
33		½ r. black	40	70
34		1 r. green	1·25	1·25
35		2 r. blue	1·75	1·75
36		4 r. red	2·75	2·00
37		1 p. orange	3·00	3·00

1890.

45	6	1 c. green	25	30
46		2 c. red	25	30
47		5 c. blue	25	30
48		10 c. orange	25	30
49		20 c. bistre	25	30
50		25 c. red	25	35
51		30 c. violet	25	70
52		40 c. blue	25	60
53		50 c. brown	25	60
54		75 c. green	25	1·50
55		1 p. lake	25	1·75

8 President Bogran

10

1891.

56	8	1 c. blue	15	20
57		2 c. brown	15	20
58		5 c. green	15	20
59		10 c. red	15	20
60		20 c. lake	15	25
61		25 c. red	20	30
62		30 c. grey	20	60
63		40 c. green	15	60
64		50 c. sepia	15	60
65		75 c. violet	15	90
66		1 p. brown	15	1·25
67	–	2 p. black and brown	60	3·50
68	–	5 p. black and violet	60	4·00
69	–	10 p. black and green	60	4·00

DESIGN (LARGER): 2, 5, 10 p. Pres. Bogran facing left.

1892. 400th Anniv of Discovery of America.

70	10	1 c. grey	20	25
71		2 c. blue	20	25
72		5 c. green	20	25
73		10 c. green	20	30
74		20 c. red	20	30
75		25 c. brown	20	50
76		30 c. blue	20	50
77		40 c. orange	20	80
78		50 c. brown	20	65
79		75 c. lake	20	1·00
80		1 p. violet	20	1·25

11 Gen. Cabanas

12

1893.

81	11	1 c. green	20	30
82		2 c. red	20	30
83		5 c. blue	20	30
84		10 c. brown	20	30
85		20 c. brown	20	40
86		25 c. blue	20	50
87		30 c. orange	20	70
88		40 c. black	20	90
89		50 c. sepia	20	1·00
90		75 c. violet	20	1·40
91		1 p. brown	20	1·60

1895.

92	12	1 c. red	20	20
93		2 c. blue	20	20
94		5 c. grey	20	30
95		10 c. lake	20	30
96		20 c. lilac	20	60
97		30 c. lilac	20	90
98		50 c. brown	20	1·25
99		1 p. green	20	1·60

13 President Arias

14 Steam Train

1896.

100	13	1 c. blue	30	30
101		2 c. brown	30	30
102		5 c. purple	90	30
103		10 c. red	30	30
104		20 c. green	75	40
105		30 c. blue	50	60
106		50 c. lake	70	1·00
107		1 p. sepia	1·25	1·75

1898.

108	14	1 c. brown	20	10
109		2 c. red	30	15
110		5 c. blue	30	15
111		6 c. purple	40	20
112		10 c. blue	40	35
113		20 c. bistre	1·00	95
114		50 c. orange	2·10	3·50
115		1 p. green	2·50	4·00

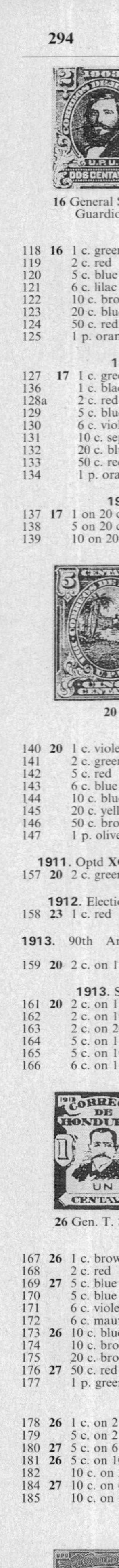

16 General Santos Guardiola

17 President Medina

1903.
118 **16** 1 c. green 25 20
119 2 c. red 25 25
120 5 c. blue 25 25
121 6 c. lilac 30 25
122 10 c. brown 30 30
123 20 c. blue 35 35
124 50 c. red 70 70
125 1 p. orange 70 70

1907. Perf or imperf.
127 **17** 1 c. green 25 25
136 1 c. black . . . . 10·00 7·50
128a 2 c. red 30 25
129 5 c. blue 35 30
130 6 c. violet 35 30
131 10 c. sepia 35 35
132 20 c. blue 60 55
133 50 c. red 70 70
134 1 p. orange 90 65

1910. Surch in figures.
137 **17** 1 on 20 c. blue . . . . . . 4·00 3·50
138 5 on 20 c. blue . . . . . . 4·00 3·50
139 10 on 20 c. blue . . . . . 4·00 3·50

20

23

1911.
140 **20** 1 c. violet 15 15
141 2 c. green 15 15
142 5 c. red 15 15
143 6 c. blue 30 30
144 10 c. blue 35 35
145 20 c. yellow 45 45
146 50 c. brown . . . . 1·10 1·10
147 1 p. olive . . . . 1·60 1·25

1911. Optd **XC Aniversario de la Independencia.**
157 **20** 2 c. green . . . . 8·00 7·50

1912. Election of President Manuel Bonilla.
158 **23** 1 c. red . . . . 9·25 9·25

1913. 90th Anniv of Independence. Surch **2 CENTAVOS.**
159 **20** 2 c. on 1 c. violet 65 50

1913. Surch in figures and words.
161 **20** 2 c. on 1 c. violet . . . . . 4·50 4·00
162 2 c. on 10 c. blue . . . . . 1·10 90
163 2 c. on 20 c. yellow . . . . 3·00 3·00
164 5 c. on 1 c. violet . . . . . 1·10 50
165 5 c. on 10 c. blue . . . . . 1·40 90
166 6 c. on 1 c. violet . . . . . 1·40 90

26 Gen. T. Sierra

27 Gen. M. Bonilla

1913.
167 **26** 1 c. brown 20 15
168 2 c. red 25 20
169 **27** 5 c. blue 30 20
170 5 c. blue 30 20
171 6 c. violet 40 30
172 6 c. mauve 45 35
173 **26** 10 c. blue 50 50
174 10 c. brown . . . . 1·10 50
175 20 c. brown 70 55
176 **27** 50 c. red . . . . 1·40 1·25
177 1 p. green . . . . 1·60 1·25

1914. Surch.
178 **26** 1 c. on 2 c. red 50 50
179 5 c. on 2 c. red 90 90
180 **27** 5 c. on 6 c. violet . . . . . 1·60 1·60
181 **26** 5 c. on 10 c. brown . . . . 1·75 1·25
182 10 c. on 2 c. red . . . . . 1·60 1·60
184 **27** 10 c. on 6 c. violet . . . . 1·60 1·60
185 10 c. on 50 c. red . . . . . 4·00 3·00

32 Railway Bridge over River Ulua at Pimienta

34 Pres. Francisco Bertrand

1915. Dated "1915".
186 **32** 1 c. brown . . . . 2·50 35
187 2 c. red . . . . 2·75 35
188 – 5 c. blue 25 10
189 – 6 c. violet 25 20
190 **32** 10 c. blue . . . . 6·75 50
191 20 c. brown . . . . 9·00 4·50
192 – 50 c. red 70 70
193 – 1 p. green . . . . 1·40 1·25
DESIGN: 5 c., 6 c., 50 c., 1 p. Bonilla Theatre.

1916.
194 **34** 1 c. orange . . . . 1·75 1·90

1918. No. O206 optd **CORRIENTE** and bar.
195 5 c. blue . . . . 1·75 1·40

36 Statue of Francisco Morazan

36a

1919. Dated "1919" at top.
196 **36** 1 c. brown 10 10
197 2 c. red 20 10
198 5 c. red 20 10
199 6 c. mauve 25 10
200 10 c. blue 25 20
201 15 c. blue 55 25
202 15 c. violet 45 25
203 20 c. brown 50 25
204 50 c. brown . . . . 1·10 70
205 1 p. green . . . . 2·75 1·50

1920. Assumption of Power by Gen. R. L. Gutierrez.
206 **36a** 2 c. red . . . . 1·90 1·75
207 2 c. gold . . . . 5·75 5·25
208 2 c. silver . . . . 5·75 5·25
209 2 c. red . . . . 5·25 4·75
Nos. 207/9 are larger (51 × 40 mm).

1921. As T **36**, but dated "1920" at top.
210 **36** 6 c. purple . . . . 3·00 1·75

1922. Surch **VALE SEIS CTS.**
211 **36** 6 c. on 2 c. red 30 25

1923. Surch **HABILITADO VALE** and value in words and figures.
212 **36** $0.10 on 1 c. brown . . . . 1·10 75
213 $0.50 on 2 c. red . . . . . 1·10 1·10
214 1 p. on 5 c. red . . . . . . 2·00 2·00

39 Dionisio de Herrera

40 M. Paz Baraona

1923.
215 **39** 1 c. olive 20 10
216 2 c. red 20 10
217 6 c. purple 30 10
218 10 c. blue 30 15
219 20 c. brown 60 25
220 50 c. red . . . . 1·25 55
221 1 p. green . . . . 2·25 70

1925. Inauguration of President Baraona. Imperf or perf.
222 **40** 1 c. blue . . . . 1·75 1·75
224 1 c. red . . . . 4·50 4·50
225 1 c. brown . . . . 7·25 7·25

1925. Air. Nos. 186/93 optd **AERO CORREO** or surch also.
227 5 c. blue . . . . 65·00 65·00
229 10 c. blue £225 £225
231 20 c. brown £160 £160
235 25 c. on 1 c. brown £110 £110
236 25 c. on 5 c. blue £200 £200
236c 25 c. on 10 c. blue £50000
237 25 c. on 20 c. brown £225 £225
233 50 c. red £300 £300
234 1 p. green £900 £900

1926. Optd **Acuerdo Mayo 3 de 1926 HABILITADO.**
238 **36** 6 c. mauve 95 70

1926. Optd **HABILITADO 1926.**
242 **32** 2 c. red . . . . 3·75 3·25
243 **36** 2 c. red 20 20

1926. Optd **1926.**
239 – 6 c. violet (No. 189) . . . . 1·75 1·75
240 **36** 6 c. violet . . . . 2·10 2·10

1926. Surch **Vale 6 Cts. 1926** and bar.
243d **36** 6 c. on 10 c. blue 35 20

1927. Surch **vale 6 cts. 1927** and bar.
244 **36** 6 c. on 15 c. violet 70 70
245 **32** 6 c. on 20 c. brown . . . . 3·75 3·25
246 **36** 6 c. on 20 c. brown 65 55

47 Copan Ruins

50 President Colindres and Vice-President Chavez

1927. Various designs as T **47**.
247 – 1 c. blue (Road) 20 15
248 **47** 2 c. red 20 10
249 – 5 c. purple (Pine Tree) . . . 20 10
250 – 5 c. blue (Pine Tree) . . . . 2·75 1·60
251 – 6 c. black (Palace) 60 55
252 – 6 c. blue (Palace) 25 15
253 – 10 c. blue (P. Leiva) 45 20
254 – 15 c. blue (Pres. Soto) . . . 60 25
255 – 20 c. blue (Lempira) 75 35
256 – 30 c. brown (Map) . . . . . 1·25 70
257 – 50 c. green (Pres. Lindo) . . 1·60 90
258 – 1 p. red (Columbus) . . . . 3·25 1·40

1929. Installation of President Colindres.
259 **50** 1 c. lake . . . . 2·40 2·40
260 – 2 c. green . . . . 2·40 2·40
DESIGN—VERT: 2 c. Pres. Colindres.

1929. Air.
(a) Surch **Servicio aereo Vale**, value and **1929**.
262 **39** 5 c. on 20 c. brown . . . . 1·40 1·40
263 10 c. on 50 c. red . . . . . 1·90 1·60
264 15 c. on 1 p. green . . . . 3·25 3·25
261 25 c. on 50 c. red . . . . . 3·75 3·75
(b) Surch **Servicio Aereo Internacional 1929** and value.
265 **39** 5 c. on 10 c. blue 50 50
266 20 c. on 50 c. red 95 95

1929. Herrera Monument type, dated 1924–1928. Surch **Vale 1 cts. XI 1929.**
267 – 1 c. on 6 c. mauve 70 70

1929. Nos. 247/58 optd **1929 a 1930.**
268 – 1 c. blue 15 10
269 **47** 2 c. red 20 20
270 – 5 c. purple 30 20
271 – 5 c. blue 70 55
272 – 6 c. black . . . . 1·75 1·40
273 – 6 c. blue 30 15
274 – 10 c. blue 30 15
275 – 15 c. blue 30 15
276 – 20 c. blue 30 20
277 – 30 c. brown 55 45
278 – 50 c. green 70 70
279 – 1 p. red . . . . 1·90 1·90

1930. Air. No. O264 optd **HABILITADO Servicio Aereo Internacional 1930.**
281 – 50 c. green and yellow . . . 1·40 1·40

1930. Air. Surch **Servicio Aereo Internacional Vale**, value and **1930.**
282 **39** 5 c. on 10 c. blue 55 55
284 5 c. on 20 c. brown £100 £100
285 10 c. on 20 c. brown 70 70
287 – 25 c. on 50 c. red (No. 192) . 95 95

1930. Air. Surch **Vale** and value in addition in large letters and figures.
290 **39** 10 c. on 5 c. on 20 c. brown (No. 284) 90 90
291 10 c. on 10 c. on 20 c. brown (No. 285) . . . . 75·00 75·00
292 – 50 c. on 25 c. on 1 p. green (No. 193) . . . . 3·50 3·50

1930. Air. Surch **Servicio aereo Vale**, value and **Marzo—1930.**
293 **39** 5 c. on 10 c. blue 50 50
294 15 c. on 20 c. brown 55 55
295 – 20 c. on 50 c. red (No. 192) . 95 95

1930. Surch **Vale**, value and **1930.**
297 **39** 1 c. on 10 c. blue 35 30
298 2 c. on 10 c. blue 35 30

1930. Nos. O259/60 optd **Habilitado para el servicio publico 1930.**
299 – 1 c. blue 50 50
300 O **50** 2 c. red 90 90

1930. Air. Surch **Servicio aereo Vale 5 centavos oro Mayo.**
301 **39** 5 c. on 20 c. brown . . . . 1·10 1·10

1930. Air. Nos. O264/5 ptd. **HABILITADO Servicio Aereo MAYO 1930.**
302 20 c. blue . . . . 1·10 1·10
303 50 c. green and yellow . . . . 1·10 90
304 1 p. red . . . . 1·25 1·25

1930. Optd **Habilitado julio—1930.**
305 **32** 1 c. brown . . . . 1·75 1·90
306 **36** 1 c. brown . . . . 8·50 8·50
309 **39** 1 c. olive 20 15
310 2 c. red 25 25
307 **36** 20 c. brown . . . . 8·50 8·50
308 $0.50 on 2 c. red (No. 213) . 60·00 60·00

66 Title Page, First Issue Government Gazette

1930. Newspaper Centenary.
311 **66** 2 c. blue 45 45
312 2 c. orange 45 45
313 2 c. red 45 45

67 National Palace, Tegucigalpa

1930. Air.
314 **67** 5 c. yellow 55 30
315 10 c. red 75 55
316 15 c. green . . . . 1·10 70
317 20 c. violet . . . . 1·40 70
318 1 p. brown . . . . 3·50 2·75

68 Pres. Baraona

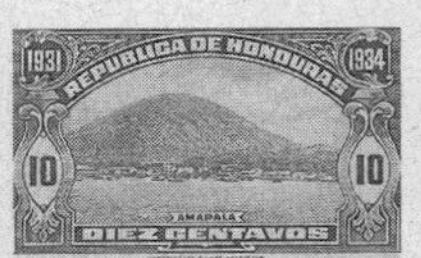

69 Amapala

1931.
319 **68** 1 c. sepia 15 10
320 – 2 c. red 15 10
321 – 5 c. violet 55 10
322 – 6 c. green 25 10
323 **69** 10 c. brown 35 15
324 – 15 c. blue 35 15
325 – 20 c. black 55 20
326 – 50 c. olive . . . . 1·40 60
327 – 1 p. slate . . . . 2·40 1·10
DESIGNS—As Type **68**: 2 c. Bonilla 15 c. Copan Ruins; 20 c. Columbia. As Type **69**: 5 c. Lake Yojoa; 6 c. Tegucigalpa Palace; 50 c. Discovery of America; 1 p. Loarq Bridge at Loarq.

1931. Nos. 319/27 and 314/18 opt. **T.S.de.C.**
328 **68** 1 c. sepia (postage) 20 15
329 – 2 c. red 25 15
330 – 5 c. violet 50 25
331 – 6 c. green 25 15
332 **69** 10 c. brown 35 30
333 – 15 c. blue 35 25
334 – 20 c. black 45 25
335 – 50 c. olive . . . . 2·75 2·50
336 – 1 p. slate . . . . 3·50 3·25
337 **67** 5 c. yellow (air) . . . . . 1·10 1·10
338 10 c. red . . . . 2·50 2·50
339 15 c. green . . . . 3·50 3·50
339a 20 c. violet . . . . 4·25 4·25
339b 1 p. brown . . . . 9·25 9·25

1931 Air. Surch **Servicio aereo interior Vale 15 cts Octubre 1931.**
340 **39** 15 c. on 20 c. . . . . . . 3·50 3·50
344a **32** 15 c. on 20 c. (No. O209) . 22·00 22·00
342 **36** 15 c. on 20 c. (No. O218) . 4·25 4·25
344c **39** 15 c. on 20 c. (No. O226) . 1·00 1·00
343 – 15 c. on 50 c. (No. O210) . 4·25 4·25
346 **36** 15 c. on 50 c. (No. O219) . 3·25 3·25
341 – 15 c. on 1 p. (No. O265) . 4·25 4·25
Nos. 342/3 come with or without the original OFICIAL overprint obliterated.

1932. Air. Surch **S.—Aereo VI. 15 cts. XI 1931.**
347 **39** 15 c. on 20 c. brown . . . . 3·00 3·00
348 **36** 15 c. on 50 c. (No. O219) . 3·00 3·00
349 – 15 c. on 50 c. (No. O264) . 3·00 3·00
350 – 15 c. on 1 p. (No. O265) . 2·40 2·40

1932. Air. Nos. O 328/36 optd **Servicio Aereo Exterior. Habilitado X. 1931.**
350c O **70** 1 c. blue 35 35
350d 2 c. purple 90 90
350e 5 c. olive . . . . 1·10 1·10
350f 6 c. red . . . . 1·10 1·10
350g 10 c. green . . . . 1·25 1·25
350h 15 c. brown . . . . 1·75 1·75
350i 20 c. brown . . . . 1·75 1·75
350j 50 c. violet . . . . 1·40 1·40
350k 1 p. orange . . . . 1·75 1·75

1932. Nos. O223/25 surch **Aereo interior VALE 15 Cts. 1932.**
351 **39** 15 c. on 2 c. red 45 45
352 15 c. on 6 c. purple 45 45
353 15 c. on 10 c. blue 45 45

78 Pres. Carias and Vice-Pres. Williams

1933. Inauguration of Pres. Carias.
355 **78** 2 c. red 30 25
356 6 c. green 35 25
357 10 c. blue 45 30
358 15 c. orange 55 35

79 Flag of the Race

1933. 441st Anniv of Departure of Columbus from Palos.

359 **79** 2 c. blue 35 30
360 6 c. yellow 45 35
361 10 c. yellow 55 45
362 15 c. violet 70 60
363 50 c. red . . . . 3·00 2·40
364 1 l. green . . . . 4·75 4·75

80 Pres. T. Carias

1935. Inscr as in T **80**.

365 – 1 c. green 20 15
366 **80** 2 c. red 20 20
367 – 5 c. blue 25 25
368 – 6 c. brown 35 35

DESIGNS: 1 c. Masonic Temple, Tegucigalpa; 5 c. National Flag; 6 c. Pres. T. E. Palma.

82 Tegucigalpa

1935. Air. Inscr as in T **82**.

369 – 8 c. blue 10 10
370 **82** 10 c. grey 20 10
371 – 15 c. olive 30 15
372 – 20 c. green . . . . 3·75 60
373 – 40 c. brown 55 20
374 – 50 c. yellow . . . . 18·00 4·50
375 – 1 l. green . . . . 1·75 1·40

DESIGNS: 8 c. G.P.O. and Congress Building; 15 c. Map of Honduras; 20 c. Presidential Palace and Mayol Railway Bridge; 40 c. Different view of Tegucigalpa; 50 c. Great Horned Owl; 1 l. National Arms.

84 President Carias and Carias Bridge

1937. Re-election of President Carias.

376 **84** 6 c. red and olive . . . . . 1·40 55
377 21 c. green and violet . . . 1·60 70
378 46 c. orange and brown . . 2·75 85
379 55 c. blue and black . . . . 3·75 1·75

85 Book of the Constitution and Flags of U.S. and Honduras

1937. Air. 150th Anniv of U.S. Constitution.

380 **85** 46 c. multicoloured . . . . 1·40 1·25

86 Comayagua Cathedral

1937. Air. 400th Anniv of Comayagua.

381 **86** 2 c. red 20 10
382 – 8 c. blue 25 15
383 – 15 c. black 45 35
384 – 50 c. brown . . . . 1·75 1·10

DESIGNS: 8 c. Founding of Comayagua; 15 c. Portraits of Caceres and Carias; 50 c. Lintel of Royal Palace.

90 Arms of Honduras **91** Copan Ruins

1939. Dated "1939 1942".

385 **90** 1 c. yellow (postage) 10 10
386 – 2 c. red 10 10
387 – 3 c. red 15 10
388 – 5 c. orange 20 15
389 – 8 c. blue 25 20

DESIGNS: 2 c. Central District Palace; 3 c. Map of Honduras; 5 c. Choluteca Bridge; 8 c. National flag.

390 **91** 10 c. brown (air) 15 10
391 – 15 c. blue 20 10
392 – 21 c. slate 35 10
393 – 30 c. green 45 10
394 – 40 c. violet 70 15
395 – 46 c. brown 70 45
396 – 55 c. green 90 60
397 – 66 c. black . . . . 1·40 80
398 – 1 l. olive . . . . 2·10 55
399 – 2 l. red . . . . 3·00 1·75

DESIGNS: 15 c. Pres. Carias; 21 c. Mayan Temple; 30 c. J. C. del Valle; 40 c. The Presidency; 46 c. Statue of Lempira; 55 c. Suyapa Church; 66 c. J. T. Reyes; 1 l. Choluteca Hospital; 2 l. R. Rosa.

1940. Air. Dedication of Columbus Memorial Lighthouse. Type O **4** optd **Correo Aereo Habilitado para Servicio Publico Pro-Faro-Colon-1940**.

400 O **92** 2 c. blue and green . . . 20 15
401 5 c. blue and orange . . . 25 25
402 8 c. blue and brown . . . 25 25
403 15 c. blue and red . . . 35 35
404 46 c. blue and olive . . . 70 70
405 50 c. blue and violet . . . 70 70
406 1 l. blue and brown . . . 3·00 2·00
407 2 l. blue and red . . . . 5·75 4·50

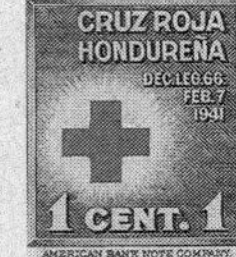

97 Francisco Morazan **98** Red Cross

1941. Obligatory Tax. Death Centenary of Gen. Morazan.

408 **97** 1 c. brown 15 10

1941. Obligatory Tax. Red Cross.

409 **98** 1 c. blue and red 15 10

1941. Air. Official stamps optd **Habilitada para el Servicio Publico 1941**.

410 O **92** 5 c. blue and orange . . . 2·50 25
411 8 c. blue and brown . . . 4·00 25

1941. Air. Official stamps surch **Rehabilitada para el Servicio Publico 1941 Vale** and value in words.

412 O **92** 3 c. on 2 c. blue & green . 30 20
413 8 c. on 2 c. blue & green . 35 30
414 8 c. on 15 c. blue & red . 35 25
415 8 c. on 46 c. blue & olive . 55 45
416 8 c. on 50 c. blue & violet . 70 55
417 8 c. on 1 l. blue & brown . 1·10 70
418 8 c. on 2 l. blue and red . 1·40 1·10

1942. Air. Surch **Correo Aereo** and value.

419 8 c. on 15 c. blue (No. 391) . . 60 20
420 16 c. on 46 c. brown (No. 395) . 60 20

102 Morazan's Birthplace **103** Tomb

1942. Air. Death Centenary of Gen. Morazan.

421 – 2 c. orange 10 10
422 – 5 c. blue 10 10
423 **102** 8 c. purple 15 10
424 **103** 14 c. black 30 30
425 – 16 c. olive 20 20
426 – 21 c. blue 90 70
427 – 1 l. blue . . . . 2·75 1·75
428 – 2 l. brown . . . . 7·25 5·75

DESIGNS—HORIZ: 2 c. Commemoration plate; 5 c. Battle of La Trinidad; 16 c. Morazan's monument (as in Type **36**); 21 c. Church where Morazan was baptised; 1 l. Arms of C. American Federation. VERT: 2 l. Morazan.

105 Coat of Arms **106** Western Hemisphere

1943. Air.

429 **105** 1 c. green 10 10
430 – 2 c. blue 10 10
431 – 5 c. green 20 10
432 – 6 c. green 20 10
433 – 8 c. purple 25 10
434 – 10 c. brown 25 10
435 – 15 c. red 25 10
436 – 16 c. red 30 10
437 – 21 c. blue 40 10
438 – 30 c. brown 45 10
439 – 40 c. red 45 10
440 – 55 c. black 70 55
441 – 1 l. green . . . . 1·25 1·10
442 **106** 2 l. lake . . . . 3·50 3·00
443 – 5 l. orange . . . . 8·75 8·75

DESIGNS—HORIZ: 2 c. National flag; 5 c. Cattle; 8 c. Rosario; 15 c. Tobacco plant; 21 c. Orchid; 30 c. Oranges; 40 c. Wheat; 5 l. Map of Honduras. VERT: 6 c. Banana Tree; 10 c. Pine tree; 16 c. Sugar cane; 55 c. Coconut palms; 1 l. Maize.

114 Agricultural College **117** Flag, Mother and Child

1944. Air. Inauguration of Pan-American Agricultural College.

444 **114** 21 c. green 30 20

1944. Optd **HABILITADO 1944-45**.

445 **90** 1 c. yellow 30 30
446 – 2 c. red (No. 386) 45 45

1945. Air. Surch **Correo Aereo HABILITADO Acd. No. 798-1945** and value.

447 – 1 c. on 50 c. (No. 384) . . . 10 10
448 **86** 2 c. on 2 c. red 15 10
449 – 8 c. on 15 c. (No. 383) . . . 20 20
450 **91** 10 c. on 10 c. brown 35 30
451 – 15 c. on 15 c. (No. 391) . . . 20 20
452 – 30 c. on 21 c. (No. 392) . . 3·00 3·00
453 – 40 c. on 40 c. (No. 394) . . 1·75 1·40
454 – 1 l. on 46 c. (No. 395) . . 1·75 1·40
455 – 2 l. on 66 c. (No. 397) . . 3·00 3·00

1945. Obligatory Tax. Red Cross.

456 **117** 1 c. brown and red . . . 15 10
456a – 1 c. red and brown . . . 15 10

DESIGN: No. 456a, Red Cross.

118 Arms of Honduras **119** Broken Column and F. D. Roosevelt

1946. Air. Coats of Arms.

457 **118** 1 c. red 10 10
458 – 2 c. orange 10 10
459 – 5 c. violet 20 10
461 – 15 c. purple 35 20
462 – 21 c. blue 35 30
463 – 1 l. green . . . . 1·40 90
464 – 2 l. grey . . . . 2·10 1·60

ARMS: 2 c. Von Gracias and Trujillo; 5 c. Comayagua and S. J. de Olancho; 15 c. Honduras Province and S. J. de Puerto Caballos; 21 c. Comayagua and Tencoa; 1 l. Jerez de la Frontera de Choluteca and San Pedro de Zula; 2 l. San Miguel de Heredia de Tegucigalpa.

1946. Air. Allied Victory over Japan and Death of Pres. Roosevelt. (a) Inscribed "F.D.R.".

460 **119** 8 c. brown 70 55

(b) "FRANKLIN D. ROOSEVELT".

465 **119** 8 c. brown 45 30

120 Honduras and Copan Antiquities

1947. Air. 1st International Conference of Caribbean Archaeologists. Various frames.

466 **120** 16 c. green 35 15
467 22 c. yellow 25 15
468 40 c. orange 55 35
469 1 l. blue 90 90
470 2 l. mauve . . . . 3·00 3·00
471 5 l. brown . . . . 7·25 6·50

121 Flag and Arms of Honduras **122** Galvez, Carias and Lozano

123 National Stadium **124** President Galvez

1949. Air. Inauguration of President Juan Manuel Galvez. Inscr "CONMEMORATIVA DE LA SUCESION PRESIDENCIAL", etc.

472 **121** 1 c. blue 10 10
473 **124** 2 c. red 10 10
474 – 5 c. blue 10 10
475 – 9 c. brown 10 10
476 – 15 c. brown 20 10
477 **122** 21 c. black 35 10
478 **123** 30 c. olive 45 15
479 – 40 c. grey 70 20
480 – 1 l. brown . . . . 1·10 35
481 – 2 l. violet . . . . 2·00 1·75
482 – 5 l. red . . . . 5·75 5·25

DESIGNS—HORIZ: 40 c. Toncontin Customs House; 5 l. Galvez and Lozano. VERT: 5 c., 15 c. Lozano (different frames); 9 c. Galvez; 1 l. Palace of Tegucigalpa; 2 l. Carias.

1951. Air. 75th Anniv of U.P.U. Optd **U.P.U. 75 Aniversario 1874–1949**.

483 **120** 16 c. green 55 55
484 – 22 c. yellow 70 70
485 – 40 c. orange 70 70
486 – 1 l. blue . . . . 2·40 2·40
487 – 2 l. mauve . . . . 3·50 3·50
488 – 5 l. brown . . . . 26·00 26·00

1951. Air. Founding of Central Bank. Nos. 472/81 optd **Conmemorativa Fundacion Banco Central Administracion Galvez-Lozano Julio 1o. de 1950**.

489 1 c. blue 10 10
490 2 c. red 10 10
491 5 c. blue 10 10
492 9 c. brown 15 10
493 15 c. brown 15 10
494 21 c. black 25 25
495 30 c. olive 45 35
496 40 c. grey 70 65
497 1 l. brown . . . . 1·75 1·25
498 2 l. violet . . . . 4·50 3·25

127 Discovery of America **128** Isabella the Catholic

1952. Air. 500th Anniv of Birth of Isabella the Catholic.

499 **127** 1 c. slate and orange . . . 10 10
500 – 2 c. brown and blue . . . 10 10
501 – 8 c. sepia and green . . . 20 10
502 **128** 16 c. black and blue . . . 30 20
503 – 30 c. green and violet . . . 55 55
504 – 1 l. black and red . . . . 1·40 1·10
505 **127** 2 l. violet and brown . . . 2·75 2·75
506 **128** 5 l. olive and purple . . . 7·00 7·00

DESIGNS—HORIZ: 2 c. 1 l. King Ferdinand and Queen Isabella receive Columbus; 8 c. Surrender of Granada; 30 c. Queen Isabella pledging her jewels.

1953. Air. Surch **HABILITADO 1953** and value.

507 **122** 5 c. on 21 c. black 10 10
508 8 c. on 21 c. black 20 10
509 16 c. on 21 c. black 35 20

1953. Air. Nos. O507/509 and O512/14 surch **HABILITADO 1953** and value or optd only.
510 **127** 10 c. on 1 c. olive & pur . . 10 10
511 12 c. on 1 c. olive & pur . . 10 10
512 – 15 c. on 2 c. vio & brn . . 15 15
513 – 20 c. on 2 c. vio & brn . . 25 25
514 – 24 c. on 2 c. vio & brn . . 25 25
515 – 25 c. on 2 c. vio & brn . . 25 25
516 – 30 c. on 8 c. black & red . . 25 25
517 – 35 c. on 8 c. black & red . . 30 30
518 – 50 c. on 8 c. black & red . . 45 45
519 – 60 c. on 8 c. black & red . . 55 55
520 – 1 l. sepia and green . . . . 1·40 1·25
521 **127** 2 l. brown and blue . . . 3·50 2·75
522 **128** 5 l. slate and orange . . . 9·00 9·00

130 U.N. Emblem

1953. Air. United Nations. Inscr as in T **130**.
523 – 1 c. blue and black 10 10
524 **130** 2 c. blue and black 15 10
525 – 3 c. violet and black . . . 20 15
526 – 5 c. green and black . . . 15 15
527 – 15 c. brown and black . . . 35 30
528 – 30 c. brown and black . . 90 75
529 – 1 l. red and black . . . . 6·00 5·25
530 – 2 l. orange and black . . . 7·25 6·00
531 – 5 l. green and black . . . 18·00 16·00
DESIGNS: 1 c. U.N. and Honduras flags; 3 c. U.N. Building, New York; 5 c. Arms of U.S.A.; 15 c. Pres. J. M. Galvez; 30 c. Indian girl (U.N.I.C.E.F.); 1 l. Refugee mother and child (U.N.R.R.A.); 2 l. Torch and open book (U.N.E.S.C.O.); 5 l. Cornucopia (F.A.O.).

1955. Air. 50th Anniv of Rotary International. Nos. O532/38 optd with rotary emblem, **1905 1955**, clasped hands and laurel sprigs or surch also.
532 1 c. blue and black 15 15
533 2 c. green and black 15 15
534 3 c. orange and black 20 20
535 5 c. red and black 25 25
536 8 c. on 1 c. blue and black . . . 15 15
537 10 c. on 2 c. green and black . . 20 20
538 12 c. on 3 c. orange & black . . 25 25
539 15 c. sepia and black 35 35
540 30 c. purple and black . . . . 1·10 1·10
541 1 l. olive and black . . . . . 18·00 18·00

1956. Air. 10th Anniv of U.N.O. Nos. O523/5 and 527/31 optd **O N U X ANIVERSARIO 1945–1955**.
542 1 c. blue and black 20 20
543 2 c. green and black 20 20
544 3 c. orange and black 25 25
545 5 c. red and black 30 30
546 15 c. brown and black 35 35
547 30 c. brown and black 55 55
548 1 l. red and black . . . . . 3·50 3·00
549 2 l. orange and black . . . . 5·25 4·00
550 5 l. green and black . . . . 13·00 11·00

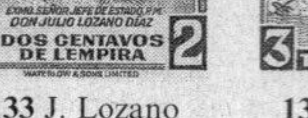

133 J. Lozano Diaz **134** Southern Highway

1956. Air.
551 – 1 c. blue and black . . . 10 10
552 **133** 2 c. blue and black . . . 10 10
553 **134** 3 c. sepia and black . . . 10 10
554 – 4 c. purple and black . . . 10 10
555 – 5 c. red and black . . . 10 10
556 – 8 c. multicoloured . . . 10 10
557 – 10 c. green and black . . . 15 10
558 – 12 c. green and black . . . 15 10
559 – 15 c. black and red . . . 20 10
560 – 20 c. blue and black . . . 20 15
561 **133** 24 c. purple and black . . . 25 20
562 – 25 c. green and black . . . 30 25
563 – 30 c. red and black . . . 30 25
564 – 40 c. brown and black . . . 35 30
565 – 50 c. turquoise and black . . 45 35
566 – 60 c. orange and black . . . 55 45
567 – 1 l. purple and black . . . 1·40 1·10
568 – 2 l. red and black . . . 2·75 1·75
569 – 5 l. lake and black . . . 5·25 3·50
DESIGNS—HORIZ: 1 c. Suyapa Basilica; 8 c. Landscape and cornucopia; 10 c. National Stadium; 12 c. United States School; 15 c. Projected Central Bank of Honduras; 20 c. Legislative Building; 25 c. Projected Development Bank; 30 c. Toncontin Airport; 40 c. J. R. Molina Bridge; 60 c. Treasury Building; 1 l. Blood Bank. VERT: 4 c. Dona de Estrada Palma; 5 c. Dona de Morazan; 50 c. Peace Memorial; 2 l. Electrical Communications Building; 5 l. Presidential Palace.

135 Revolutionary Flag **136** Flags of Honduras and the U.S.A. and Book

1957. Air. Revolution of October 21, 1956. Frames in black.
570 **135** 1 c. blue and yellow . . . 10 10
571 – 2 c. purple, green & orge . . 10 10
572 **135** 5 c. blue and pink 15 10
573 – 8 c. violet, olive & orge . . 20 10
574 – 10 c. brown and violet . . 20 15
575 **135** 12 c. blue and turquoise . . 25 20
576 – 15 c. brown and green . . 30 25
577 – 30 c. grey and pink . . . 45 25
578 – 1 l. brown and blue . . . 1·40 1·25
579 – 2 l. grey and green . . . 2·75 1·75
DESIGNS: 2 c., 8 c. Obelisk and mountains; 10 c., 15 c., 1 l. Indian with bow and arrow; 30 c., 2 l. Arms of 1821.

NOTE. In July 1958 after stocks of current issues had been looted, eighteen different facsimile signatures validated the remaining stamps for use.

1958. Air. Bi-national Centre Commem. (Institute of American Culture). Flags in national colours.
580 **136** 1 c. blue 10 10
581 2 c. red 10 10
582 5 c. green 10 10
583 10 c. brown 20 20
584 20 c. orange 35 20
585 30 c. red 35 30
586 50 c. grey 45 35
587 1 l. yellow . . . . . . 1·10 95
588 2 l. olive . . . . 3·00 1·90
589 5 l. blue . . . . 4·50 4·50

137 Abraham Lincoln **138** Henri Dunant

1959. Air. 150th Birth Anniv of Abraham Lincoln. Flags in blue and red
590 **137** 1 c. green 15 15
591 – 2 c. blue 15 15
592 – 3 c. violet 20 20
593 – 5 c. red 20 20
594 – 10 c. slate 25 20
595 – 12 c. sepia 25 20
596 **137** 15 c. orange 35 20
597 – 25 c. purple 55 30
598 – 50 c. blue 70 55
599 – 1 l. brown . . . . . . 1·40 1·25
600 – 2 l. olive . . . . 1·90 1·40
601 – 5 l. yellow . . . . . . 4·00 3·25
DESIGNS—HORIZ: 2 c., 25 c. Lincoln's birthplace; 3 c., 50 c. Gettysburg Address; 5 c., 1 l. Lincoln at conference to free slaves; 10 c., 2 l. Assassination of Lincoln; 12 c., 5 l. Lincoln Memorial, Washington.

1959. Obligatory Tax. Red Cross.
602 **138** 1 c. red and blue 15 10
647 1 c. red and green 20 10
648 1 c. red and brown 20 10
Nos. 647/8 have no frame around portrait and values are at left.

139 Constitution of 21 December 1957 **140** King Alfonso XIII of Spain and Map

1959. Air. 2nd Anniv of New Constitution. Inscr "21 DE DICIEMBRE DE 1957".
603 **139** 1 c. red, blue and brown . . 10 10
604 – 2 c. brown 10 10
605 – 3 c. blue 10 10
606 – 5 c. orange 20 10
607 **139** 10 c. red, blue and green . . 25 10
608 – 12 c. red 35 20
609 – 25 c. violet 70 25
610 – 50 c. grey blue . . . . . 1·10 35
DESIGNS—HORIZ: 2 c., 12 c. Inaug. of Pres. R. V. Morales. VERT: 3 c., 25 c. Pres. R. V. Morales; 5 c., 50 c. Flaming torch.

1961. Air. Settlement of Boundary Dispute with Nicaragua.
611 **140** 1 c. blue 10 10
612 – 2 c. pink 10 10
613 – 5 c. green 10 10
614 – 10 c. brown 15 10
615 – 20 c. red 30 20
616 – 50 c. brown 70 55
617 – 1 l. slate . . . . 1·10 90
DESIGNS: 2 c. 1906 award (document); 5 c. Arbitration commission, 1907; 10 c. International Court of Justice, The Hague; 20 c. 1960 award (document); 50 c. Pres. Morales Foreign Minister Puerto and map; 1 l. Presidents Davila and Morales.

1964. Air. Freedom from Hunger. Flags in National colours. Optd **F A O Lucha Contra el Hambre**.
621 **136** 1 c. blue 20 20
622 2 c. red 20 20
623 5 c. green 25 25
624 30 c. red . . . . 1·10 70
625 2 l. olive . . . . 5·25 4·00

1964. Air. Olympic Games, Tokyo. Optd with Olympic Rings and **1964**.
626 – 1 c. blue & black (No. 523) 15 15
627 **130** 2 c. blue and black . . . 25 25
628 – 3 c. violet & blk (No. 525) . 30 30
629 – 15 c. brn & blk (No. 527) . 55 55
See also No. O646.

144 Ancient Stadium

1964. Air. "Homage to Sport" and Olympic Games, Tokyo.
630 **144** 1 c. black and green . . . 10 10
631 – 2 c. black and mauve . . . 10 10
632 – 5 c. black and blue 15 15
633 – 8 c. black & grey green . . 25 25
634 **144** 10 c. black & bistre 35 30
635 – 12 c. black and yellow . . 55 35
636 – 1 l. black and buff . . . 1·40 90
637 – 2 l. black and olive . . . 3·00 1·75
638 **144** 3 l. black and red . . . . 4·50 2·75
DESIGNS: 2 c., 12 c. Boundary stones; 5 c., 1 l. Mayan ball player; 8 c., 2 l. Olympic Stadium, Tokyo.

1964. Air. Surch.
639 – 4 c. on 5 c. (No. 593) . . . 15 10
618 **137** 6 c. on 15 c. 20 10
619 – 8 c. on 25 c. (No. 597) . . 20 10
640 – 10 c. on 15 c. (No. 476) . . 15 10
620 – 10 c. on 50 c. (No. 598) . . 30 20
641 – 12 c. on 16 c. (No. 425) . . 15 10
642 – 12 c. on 21 c. (No. 426) . . 25 10
643 **120** 12 c. on 22 c. 25 10
644 30 c. on 1 l. 45 25
645 – 40 c. on 1 l. (No. 480) . . 65 30
646 **120** 40 c. on 2 l. 65 30
See also Nos. 716/8 and O647/9.

1965. Air. Presidential Investiture of General Lopez. Optd **Toma de Posesion General Oswaldo Lopez A. Junio 6, 1965**. Flags in blue and red.
649 **137** 1 c. green 10 10
650 – 2 c. green 10 10
651 – 3 c. violet (No. 592) . . . 10 10
652 – 5 c. red (No. 593) 10 10
653 **137** 15 c. orange 20 15
654 – 25 c. purple (No. 597) . . . 30 20
655 – 50 c. red 50 35
656 – 2 l. olive (No. 600) . . . . 1·75 1·40
657 – 5 l. yellow (No. 601) . . . 5·25 3·50

147 Ambulance and Clinic

1965. Air. Order of Malta Campaign Against Leprosy.
658 **147** 1 c. blue 25 25
659 – 5 c. green 35 35
660 – 12 c. black 55 55
661 – 1 l. brown . . . . . . 1·75 1·75
DESIGNS: 5 c. Hospital; 12 c. Patients receiving treatment; 1 l. Map of Honduras.

148 Father Subirana **151** 2 r. Stamp of 1866

1965. Air. Death Cent. of Father Manuel de Jesus Subirana. Centres in black and gold; inscr in black.
662 – 1 c. violet 10 10
663 – 2 c. flesh 10 10
664 **148** 8 c. pink 10 10
665 – 10 c. purple 10 10
666 – 12 c. brown 20 15
667 – 20 c. green 35 30
668 – 1 l. sage . . . . 1·75 70
669 – 2 l. blue . . . . 3·00 1·75
DESIGNS: 1 c. Abraham, Jicaque Indian; 2 c. Allegory of Catechism; 10 c. Msgr. Juan de Jesus Zepeda; 12 c. Pope Pius IX; 20 c. Subirana's Tomb, Yoro; 1 l. Hermitage; 2 l. Jicaque Indian woman and child.

1965. Air. Churchill Commem. Nos. 499/500 and 470 optd **IN MEMORIAM Sir Winston Churchill 1874–1965**.
671 **127** 1 c. black and orange . . . 35 35
672 – 2 c. brown and blue . . . 70 70
673 – 2 l. mauve . . . . 5·75 5·00
See also No. O674.

1966. Air. Pope Paul's Visit to U.N. Organisation. Nos. 662/68 optd **CONMEMORATIVA Visita S. S. Pablo VI a la ONU. 4-X-1965**.
675 – 1 c. violet 15 10
676 – 2 c. flesh 15 10
677 **148** 8 c. pink 25 15
678 – 10 c. purple 25 15
679 – 12 c. brown 30 15
680 – 20 c. green 35 20
681 – 1 l. sage . . . . 2·40 90

1966. Air. Stamp Cent. Inscriptions in black (1 c., 2 c.) or in gold (others).
682 **151** 1 c. black, green & gold . . 10 10
683 – 2 c. blue, black & orge . . 10 10
684 – 3 c. purple and red . . . 10 10
685 – 4 c. indigo and blue . . . 10 10
686 – 5 c. purple and mauve . . 5·00 2·00
687 – 6 c. violet and lilac . . . 10 10
688 – 7 c. slate and turquoise . . 10 10
689 – 8 c. indigo and blue . . . 15 15
690 – 9 c. blue and cobalt . . . 15 15
691 – 10 c. black and olive . . . 15 15
692 – 12 c. yellow, black & grn . . 15 15
693 – 15 c. purple and mauve . . 25 25
694 – 20 c. black and orange . . 30 30
695 – 30 c. blue and yellow . . . 35 35
696 – 40 c. multicoloured . . . 55 55
697 – 1 l. green and emerald . . 1·25 1·10
698 – 2 l. black and grey . . . 2·25 1·75
DESIGNS—VERT: 2 c. Honduras; 5 c. air stamp of 1925; 3 c. T. Estrada Palma, 1st Director of Posts; 8 c. Sir Rowland Hill; 10 c. Pres. Arellano; 12 c. Postal emblem; 15 c. H. von Stephan; 30 c. Honduras flag; 40 c. Honduras arms; 1 l. U.P.U. Monument, Berne; 2 l. J. M. Medina (statesman). HORIZ: 4 c. Post Office, Tegucigalpa; 5 c. Steam locomotive No. 59; 6 c. 19th-century mule transport; 7 c. 19th-century sorting office; 9 c. Mail van; 20 c. Curtiss C-46 Commando mail plane.
See also No. E700.

1966. Air. World Cup Football Championships, Final Match between England and Germany. Optd **CAMPEONATO DE FOOTBALL Copa Mundial 1966 Inglaterra-Alemania Wembley, Julio 30**.
701 – 2 c. violet and brown (No. O508) 20 20
702 **128** 16 c. black and blue . . . 35 35
703 **127** 2 l. violet and brown . . . 7·25 5·75

1967. Air. 20th Anniv of U.N.O. Nos. 662/4 and 666/9 optd **CONMEMORATIVA del XX Aniversario ONU 1966**.
704 – 1 c. violet 20 20
705 – 2 c. flesh 25 25
706 **148** 8 c. pink 35 35
707 – 12 c. brown 55 45
708 – 20 c. green 70 60
709 – 1 l. sage . . . . 1·75 1·40
710 – 2 l. blue . . . . 3·00 2·75

1967. Birth Bicent. of Simeon Canas y Villacorta (slave liberator). Nos. 551, 553, 559, 552 and 568. Optd **Simeon Canas y Villacorta Libertador de los esclavos en Centro America 1767–1967**.
711 1 c. blue and black 15 15
712 3 c. sepia and black 25 25
713 15 c. black and red 35 35
714 25 c. green and black 70 55
715 2 l. red and black . . . . . 2·00 1·75

1967. Air. Nos. E570 and 480/1 surch.
716 E **135** 10 c. on 20 c. grey, black and red 20 10
717 – 10 c. on 1 l. brown . . . 20 10
718 – 10 c. on 2 l. violet . . . 20 10

156 J. C. del Valle (Honduras)

1967. Air. Founding of Central-American Journalists' Federation.
719 **156** 11 c. black, blue & gold . . 10 10
720 – 12 c. black, yellow & blue . 10 10
721 – 14 c. black, green & silver . 15 10
722 – 20 c. black, green & mve . 20 15
723 – 30 c. black, yell & lilac . . 25 25
724 – 40 c. gold, blue & violet . . 70 70
725 – 50 c. green, red & olive . . 70 70
DESIGNS: 12 c. Ruben Dario (Nicaragua); 14 c. J. B. Montufar (Guatemala); 20 c. F. Gavidia (El Salvador); 30 c. J. M. Fernandez (Costa Rica); 40 c. Federation emblem; 50 c. Central American map.

157 Olympic Rings and Flags of Mexico and Honduras

1968. Air. Olympic Games, Mexico. Mult.
726 1 c. Type **157** 15 15
727 2 c. Type **157** 25 25
728 5 c. Italian flag and boxing 30 30
729 10 c. French flag and skiing 35 35
730 12 c. West German flag and show-jumping 55 55
731 50 c. British flag and athletics 1·75 1·75
732 1 l. U.S. flag and running 5·75 5·75

158 J. F. Kennedy and Rocket Launch

1968. Air. International Telecommunications Union Centenary. Multicoloured.
734 1 c. Type **158** 15 15
735 2 c. Dish aerial and telephone 20 20
736 3 c. Dish aerial and television 20 20
737 5 c. Dish aerial, globe and I.T.U. emblem as satellite 35 35
738 8 c. "Early Bird" satellite 50 50
739 10 c. Type **158** 55 55
740 20 c. Type **158** 75 75

1969. Air. Robert F. Kennedy Commemoration. Nos. 734 and 739/40 optd **In-Memoriam Robert F. Kennedy 1925–1968**.
741 1 c. multicoloured 40 40
742 10 c. multicoloured 40 40
743 20 c. multicoloured 40 40

1969. Air. Gold Medal Winners, Olympic Games. Nos. 735/8 optd **Medallas de Oro Mexico 1968**.
744 2 c. multicoloured 25 25
745 3 c. multicoloured 25 25
746 5 c. multicoloured 40 40
747 8 c. multicoloured 75 75

161 Patient and Nurse

1968. Obligatory Tax. Red Cross.
748 **161** 1 c. red and blue 15 10

162 Rocket Launch

1969. Air. First Man on the Moon. Mult.
749 5 c. Type **162** 10 10
750 10 c. Moon 10 10
751 12 c. Lunar landing module leaving space-ship (horiz) 15 10
752 20 c. Astronaut on Moon (horiz) 15 15
753 24 c. Lunar landing module taking off from Moon 20 15
754 30 c. Capsule re-entering Earth's atmosphere (horiz) 30 20

1970. No. E700 optd with **"HABILITADO"** for use as ordinary postage stamp.
755 20 c. brown, orange & gold 35 25

1970. Air. Various stamps surch in figures.
756 **151** 4 c. + 1 c. (No. 682) 10 10
757 – 4 c. + 3 c. (No. 525) 10 10
758 – 5 c. + 1 c. (No. 662) 10 10
759 – 5 c. + 7 c. (No. 688) 10 10
760 – 8 c. + 2 c. (No. 663) 20 20
761 – 10 c. + 2 c. (No. 500) 25 25
762 **133** 10 c. + 2 c. (No. 552) 25 25
763 – 10 c. + 3 c. (No. 525) 25 25
764 **134** 10 c. + 3 c. (No. 553) 25 25
765 – 10 c. + 3 c. (No. 684) 25 25
766 – 10 c. + 9 c. (No. 690) 10 10
767 **156** 10 c. + 11 c. (No. 719) 10 10
768 – 12 c. + 14 c. (No. 721) 15 15
769 E **135** 12 c. + 20 c. (No. E570) 15 15
770 – 12 c. + 1 l. (No. 480) 15 15
771 – 15 c. + 12 c. (No. 783) 35 35
772 – 30 c. + 12 c. (No. 783) 70 70
773 – 40 c. + 24 c. (No. 753) 90 90
774 – 40 c. + 50 c. (No. 731) 90 90

1970. Air. Safe Return of "Apollo 13". Nos. 749/54 optd **Admiracion al Rescate del Apolo XIII, James A. Lovell, Fred W. Haise Jr., John L. Swigert Jr.**
775 5 c. multicoloured 10 10
776 10 c. multicoloured 15 15
777 12 c. multicoloured 20 20
778 20 c. multicoloured 30 30
779 24 c. multicoloured 35 35
780 30 c. multicoloured 45 45

165 J. A. Sanhueza (firefighter)

166 Hotel Honduras Maya

1970. Air. Campaign Against Forest Fires. Multicoloured.
781 5 c. Type **165** 10 10
782 8 c. R. Ordonez Rodriguez (fire-fighter) 15 10
783 12 c. Fire Brigade emblems (horiz) 15 15
784 20 c. Flag, map and emblems 30 25
785 1 l. Emblems, and flags of Honduras, U.N. and U.S.A. 70 65

1970. Air. Opening of Hotel Honduras Maya, Tegucigalpa.
787 **166** 12 c. black and blue 25 25

1972. Air. 50th Anniv of Honduras Masonic Grand Lodge. Nos. 749 and 751/3. optd **Anniversario Gran Logia de Honduras 1922–1972.** or surch also.
791 5 c. multicoloured 25 30
792 12 c. multicoloured 55 45
793 1 l. on 20 c. multicoloured 1·10 70
794 2 l. on 24 c. multicoloured 1·75 1·40

168 Soldiers' Bay, Guanaja

1972. Air. 150th Anniv of Independence (1970). Multicoloured.
795 4 c. Type **168** 10 10
796 5 c. Bugler sounding "Last Post" (vert) 10 10
797 6 c. Lake Yojoa 10 10
798 7 c. "The Banana Carrier" (R. Aguilar) (vert) 10 10
799 8 c. Soldiers marching and fly-past 15 10
800 9 c. "Brassavola digbyana" (national flower) (vert) 15 10
801 10 c. As 9 c. 20 10
802 12 c. Machine-gunner 20 10
803 15 c. Tela beach at sunset 25 10
804 20 c. Stretcher-bearers 25 10
805 30 c. "San Antonio de Oriente" (A. Velasquez) 35 25
806 40 c. Ruins of Copan 55 30
807 50 c. "Woman from Huacal" (P. Zelaya Sierra) 55 35
808 1 l. Trujillo Bay 1·75 90
809 2 l. As 9 c. 1·75 1·40

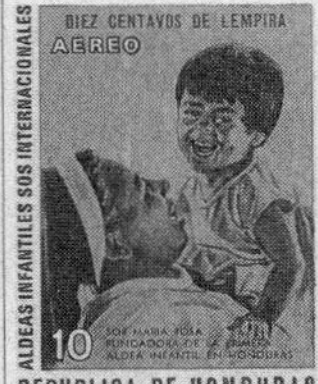

169 Sister Maria Rosa and Child

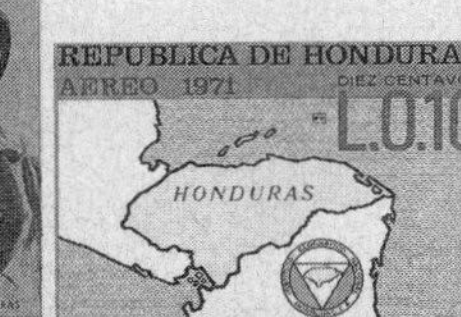

170 Map of Honduras

1972. Air. "S.O.S." Children's Villages in Honduras, each brown, green and gold.
812 10 c. Type **169** 20 10
813 15 c. "S.O.S. Villages" emblem (horiz) 25 10
814 30 c. Father J. T. Reyes (educationalist) 45 15
815 40 c. First Central American "S.O.S." village (horiz) 45 20
816 1 l. "Future Citizen" (boy) 1·40 70

1973. Air. 25th Annivs of Nat. Cartographic Service (10 c.) and Joint Cartographic Work (12 c.).
817 **170** 10 c. multicoloured 35 25
818 – 12 c. multicoloured 45 25
DESIGN: 12 c. Similar to Type **170** but with two badges and inscr "25 Anos de Labor Cartografica Conjunta".

171 Illustration from "Habitante de la Osa"

1973. Air. 25th Anniv of U.N.E.S.C.O. and Juan Ramon Molina (poet) Commem. Multicoloured.
819 8 c. Type **171** 20 10
820 20 c. Juan Ramon Molina 70 30
821 1 l. Illustration from "Tierras Mares y Cielos" 1·40 70
822 2 l. U.N.E.S.C.O. emblem 2·40 1·60

1973. Air. Census and World Population Year. Various stamps optd **Censos de Poblacion y Vivienda, marzo 1974. 1974 Ano Mundial de Poblacion**.
824 **169** 10 c. brown, grn & gold 10 10
828 **170** 10 c. multicoloured 10 10
829 – 12 c. mult (No. 818) 30 15
825 – 15 c. brown, green and gold (No. 813) 35 20
826 – 30 c. brown, green and gold (No. 814) 10 10
827 – 40 c. brown, green and gold (No. 815) 10 10

1974. Air. Various stamps surch.
830 – 2 c. on 1 c. blue and black (No. 551) 10 10
831 **137** 2 c. on 1 c. green 10 10
832 – 3 c. on 1 c. blue and black (No. 551) 10 10
833 **137** 3 c. on 1 c. green 10 10
834 – 16 c. on 1 c. bl & blk (551) 15 15
835 **135** 16 c. on 1 c. bl, yell & blk 15 15
836 **137** 16 c. on 1 c. green 15 15
837 – 16 c. on 1 c. mult (O602) 15 15
838 – 16 c. on 1 c. violet (662) 15 15
839 **170** 18 c. on 10 c. mult 20 15
840 – 18 c. on 12 c. mult (818) 20 15
841 **171** 18 c. on 8 c. mult 20 15
842 **169** 18 c. on 10 c. mult 20 15
843 – 50 c. on 30 c. mult (814) 55 45
844 **137** 1 l. on 2 l. mauve 1·40 1·00
845 – 1 l. on 2 l. violet (No. 481) 1·40 1·00
846 – 1 l. on 50 c. blue (610) 1·40 1·00
847 – 1 l. on 30 c. mult (814) 90 70

1974. Air. Honduras' Children's Villages. 25th Anniv. Nos. 786/9 optd **1949–1974 SOS Kinderdorfer International Honduras-Austria**.
851 **169** 10 c. multicoloured 15 10
852 – 15 c. multicoloured 20 15
853 – 30 c. multicoloured 25 15
854 – 40 c. multicoloured 35 25

175 Flags of West Germany and Austria

1975. Air. Centenary (1974) of U.P.U. Mult.
855 1 c. Type **175** 10 10
856 2 c. Belgium and Denmark 10 10
857 3 c. Spain and France 10 10
858 4 c. Hungary and Russia 10 10
859 5 c. Great Britain and Italy 10 10
860 10 c. Norway and Sweden 20 10
861 12 c. Honduras 25 15
862 15 c. United States and Switzerland 35 20
863 20 c. Greece and Portugal 35 20
864 30 c. Rumania and Yugoslavia 55 25
865 1 l. Egypt and Netherlands 1·75 1·50
866 2 l. Luxembourg and Turkey 3·00 3·00

176 Jalteva Youth Centre

1976. Air. International Women's Year (1975). Multicoloured.
868 8 c. Humuya Youth Centre 10 10
869 16 c. Type **176** 20 10
870 18 c. Sra Arellano and I.W.Y. emblem 20 15
871 30 c. El Carmen Youth Centre, San Pedro Sula 35 20
872 55 c. Flag of National Social Welfare Organization (vert) 55 35
873 1 l. Sports and recreation grounds, La Isla 1·10 65
874 2 l. Women's Social Centre 1·75 1·75

177 "CARE" Package

1976. Air. 20th Anniv of "CARE" (Co-operative for American Relief Everywhere) in Honduras.
875 **177** 1 c. blue and black 10 10
876 5 c. mauve and black 10 10
877 **177** 16 c. red and black 20 10
878 18 c. green and black 25 10
879 **177** 30 c. blue and black 35 20
880 50 c. green and black 55 30
881 **177** 55 c. brown and black 55 30
882 70 c. purple and black 70 45
883 **177** 1 l. blue and black 1·10 65
884 2 l. orange and black 1·75 1·75
DESIGN—HORIZ: 5 c., 18 c., 50 c., 70 c., 2 l. "CARE" on globe.

Each of the above stamps has a different inscription detailing "CARE's" various fields of activities in Honduras.

178 White-tailed Deer in Burnt Forest

179 Boston Tea Party and "Liberty" Flag

1976. Air. Forest Protection. Multicoloured.
885 10 c. Type **178** 15 10
886 16 c. COHDEFOR emblem 15 10
887 18 c. Forest stream (horiz) 15 15
888 30 c. Live and burning trees 35 20
889 50 c. Type **178** 80 30
890 70 c. Protection emblem 70 45
891 1 l. Forest of young trees (horiz) 1·10 65
892 2 l. As 30 c. 1·75 1·75
COHDEFOR = Corporation Hondurena de Desarollo Forestal.

1976. Air. Bicentenary of American Revolution. Multicoloured.
894 1 c. Type **179** 10 10
895 2 c. Hoisting the "Liberty and Union" flag 10 10
896 3 c. Battle of Bunker Hill and Pine Tree flag 10 10
897 4 c. Loading stores aboard "Washington" and "An Appeal to Heaven" flag 10 10
898 5 c. First naval ensign and navy warship 30 15
899 6 c. Presidential Palace, Tegucigalpa, and Honduras flag 10 10
900 18 c. Capitol, Washington and U.S. flag 35 30
901 55 c. Washington at Valley Forge and Grand Union flag 70 40
902 2 l. Battle scene and Bennington flag 1·75 1·50
903 3 l. Betsy Ross flag 3·00 3·00

180 Queen Sophia of Spain

181 Mayan Stelae

1977. Air. Visit of King and Queen of Spain. Multicoloured.
905 16 c. Type **180** 15 10
906 18 c. King Juan Carlos 15 10
907 30 c. Queen Sophia and King Juan Carlos 25 20
908 2 l. Arms of Honduras and Spain (horiz) 1·40 1·40

1978. Air. "Honduras 78". Stamp Exhibition. Multicoloured.
909 15 c. Type **181** 20 10
910 18 c. Giant head 25 15
911 30 c. Kneeling figure 35 20
912 55 c. Sun God 70 60

182 Del Valle's Birthplace

1978. Air. Birth Bicentenary of Jose Cecelio del Valle. Multicoloured.
914 8 c. Type **182** 10 10
915 14 c. La Merced Church, Choluteca 15 10
916 15 c. Baptismal font (vert) . . . 15 10
917 20 c. Reading Independence Act 25 15
918 25 c. Portrait, documents and map of Central America . . . 30 15
919 40 c. Portrait (vert) 45 35
920 1 l. Monument, Choluteca (vert) . . . . 1·10 90
921 3 l. Bust (vert) . . . . 3·00 3·00

183 Rural Heath Centre

1978. Air. 75th Anniv (1977) of Panamerican Health Organization. Multicoloured.
922 5 c. Type **183** 10 10
923 6 c. Child at water tap 10 10
924 10 c. Los Laureles Dam, Tegucigalpa 10 10
925 20 c. Rural aqueduct 25 10
926 40 c. Teaching hospital, Tegucigalpa 55 30
927 2 l. Parents and child . . . . . 1·75 1·75
928 3 l. Vaccination of child . . . . 3·00 3·00
929 5 l. Panamerican Health Organization Building, Washington . . . . 4·50 4·50

184 Luis Landa and "Botanica"

1978. Air. Birth Centenary of Professor Luis Landa (botanist). Multicoloured.
930 14 c. Type **184** 20 15
931 16 c. Map of Honduras 20 15
932 18 c. Medals received by Landa . 20 15
933 30 c. Birthplace, San Ignacio . . 20 15
934 2 l. "Brassavola" (national flower) . . . . 2·00 1·75
935 3 l. Women's normal school . . 3·00 3·00

1978. Air. Argentina's Victory in World Cup Football Championship. Nos. 909/12 optd with **Argentina Campeon Holanda sub-Campeon XI Campeonato Mundial de Football** and emblem.
936 **181** 15 c. multicoloured 10 10
937 – 18 c. multicoloured 15 15
938 – 30 c. multicoloured 30 20
939 – 55 c. multicoloured 55 30

186 Central University

1978. Air. 400th Anniv of Founding of Tegucigalpa.
941 **186** 6 c. brown and black . . . 10 10
942 – 6 c. multicoloured 10 10
943 – 8 c. brown and black . . . 10 10
944 – 8 c. multicoloured 10 10
945 – 10 c. brown and black . . . 10 10
946 – 10 c. multicoloured 10 10
947 – 16 c. brown and black . . . 20 10
948 – 16 c. multicoloured 20 10
949 – 20 c. brown and black . . . 20 15
950 – 20 c. multicoloured 20 15
951 – 40 c. brown and black . . . 45 25
952 – 40 c. multicoloured 45 25
953 – 50 c. brown and black . . . 55 35
954 – 50 c. multicoloured 55 35
955 – 5 l. brown and black . . . 4·50 4·50
956 – 5 l. multicoloured . . . . 4·50 4·50
DESIGNS—HORIZ: No. 942, University City; No. 943, Manuel Bonilla Theatre; No. 944, Present Manuel Bonilla Theatre; No. 947, National Palace; No. 948, Presidential House; No. 949, General San Felipe Hospital; No. 950, Teaching Hospital; No. 951, Parish Church and Convent of San Francisco; No. 952, Metropolitan Cathedral; No. 953, Old view of Tegucigalpa; No. 954, Modern view of Tegucigalpa. VERT: No. 945, Court House; No. 946, North Boulevard highway intersection; No. 955, Arms of San Miguel de Tegucigalpa; No. 956, President Marco Aurelio Soto.

187 Footballers jumping for Ball

1978. Air. 7th Youth Football Championship of Central American Football League. Multicoloured.
958 15 c. Type **187** 20 10
959 30 c. Goalkeeper (horiz) 35 15
960 55 c. Tackling 55 30
961 1 l. Goalkeeper and players (horiz) . . . . 1·10 90
962 2 l. Players at goalmouth (horiz) 1·75 1·75

188 National Postal Emblem

1979. Air. Centenary of Honduras's U.P.U. Membership (1st issue). Multicoloured.
963 2 c. Type **188** 10 10
964 15 c. U.P.U. emblem 15 10
965 25 c. Roman Rosa (vert) 20 15
966 50 c. Marco Aurelio Soto (vert) . 35 30
See also Nos. 975/6.

189 Rotary Emblem and "50"

1979. Air. 50th Anniv of Tegucigalpa Rotary Club.
967 **189** 3 c. orge, turq & bistre . . 10 10
968 5 c. grn, emer & bistre . . 10 10
969 50 c. ochre, mauve & bis . . 35 30
970 2 l. blue, violet & bistre . . 1·40 1·00

190 Map of Caratasca Lagoon

1979. Air. 50th Anniv of Pan-American Institute of History and Geography. Multicoloured.
971 5 c. Type **190** 10 10
972 10 c. Aerial view of Fort San Fernando de Omoa 10 10
973 24 c. Institute anniversary emblem (vert) 20 15
974 5 l. Map of Santanilla Islands . 3·00 3·00

191 Model of New General Post Office Building

1980. Air. Centenary (1979) of U.P.U. Membership (2nd issue).
975 **191** 24 c. multicoloured 20 15
976 – 3 l. brown, yell and blk . . 1·75 1·75
DESIGN: 3 l. 19th century Post Office.

192 "Landscape" (Roman E. Cooper)

1980. Air. International Year of the Child (1979). Multicoloured.
977 1 c. "Workers in a Field (J. E. Mejia) (horiz) 10 10
978 5 c. Type **192** 10 10
979 15 c. "Sitting boy" (D. M. Zavala) 20 10
980 20 c. I.Y.C. emblem 35 15
981 30 c. "Beach scene" (M. A. Hernandez) (horiz) 45 20

193 Hill and "Maltese Cross" Cancellations

1980. Air. Death Centenary (1979) of Sir Rowland Hill. Multicoloured.
983 1 c. Type **193** 10 10
984 2 c. Great Britain "Penny Black" 10 10
985 5 c. 1866 Honduras 2 r. green . 15 10
986 10 c. 1866. Honduras 2 r. rose . 20 15
987 15 c. Honduras postal emblem . 35 15
988 20 c. Flags of Honduras and United Kingdom 75 40
Nos. 987/8 are 46 × 34 mm.

194 Visitacion Padilla (founder of Honduras section)
195 "O'Higgins during the Liberation of Chile" (Cosmo San Martin)

1981. Air. 50th Anniv of Inter-American Women's Commission. Multicoloured.
990 2 c. Type **194** 10 10
991 10 c. Maria Trinidad del Cid (founder of Honduras section) 15 10
992 40 c. Intubucana Indian mother and child 50 30
993 1 l. Emblem (horiz) 65 65

1981. Air. Bernardo O'Higgins Commemoration. Multicoloured.
994 16 c. Type **195** 15 10
995 20 c. Don Ambrosio O'Higgins (father) (vert) 20 15
996 30 c. "Bernardo O'Higgins" (Jose Gil de Castro) (vert) . . 35 20
997 1 l. "Bernardo O'Higgins laying-down Office" (M. Antonio Caro) 70 70

196 National Sports Emblem

1981. Air. World Cup Football Championship Preliminary Round. Multicoloured.
998 20 c. Type **196** 15 15
999 50 c. Footballer and map of Honduras 30 30
1000 70 c. Flags of Honduras, CONCACAF and FIFA . . 40 40
1001 1 l. National stadium 60 60

197 Curtiss Condor II Biplane

1983. Air. 50th Anniv of Honduras Air Force. Multicoloured.
1003 3 c. Type **197** 10 10
1004 15 c. North America Texan . . 35 15
1005 25 c. Chance Vought F4U-5 Corsair 40 25
1006 65 c. Douglas C-47 Skytrain . . 85 65
1007 1 l. Cessna Dragonfly 90 65
1008 2 l. Dassault Super Mystere SMB-11 . . . . 1·90 1·25

198 U.P.U. Monument, Berne

1983. Air. Election to U.P.U. Executive Council (1979). Multicoloured.
1010 16 c. Type **198** 20 15
1011 18 c. 18th U.P.U. Congress emblem 25 15
1012 30 c. Honduras's postal emblem 20 20
1013 55 c. View of Rio de Janeiro . 45 45
1014 2 l. "Stamp" showing pigeon on globe (vert) . . . . 1·25 1·25

199 I.Y.D.P. Emblem

1983. Air. International Year of Disabled Persons.
1016 **199** 25 c. multicoloured . . . 40 25

200 National Library, Tegucigalpa

1983. Air. Centenary (1980) of National Library and Archives. Multicoloured.
1017 9 c. Type **200** 10 10
1018 1 l. Books 60 60

1983. Air. Papal Visit. Nos. 951/2 optd **CONMEMORATIVA DE LA VISITA DE SS. JUAN PABLO II 8 de marzo de 1983.**
1019 40 c. brown and black 35 35
1020 40 c. multicoloured 35 35

202 Agricultural Produce
203 Hands reaching for Open Book

1983. Air. World Food Day (1981).
1021 **202** 65 c. multicoloured . . . 40 40

1983. Air. Literacy Campaign (1980). Mult.
1022 40 c. Type **203** 25 20
1023 1 l. 50 Family with books . . . 90 90

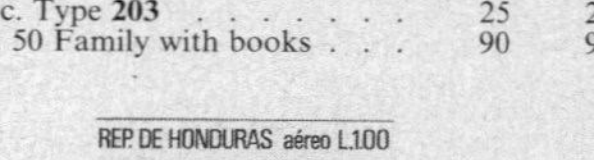

204 Motorway Bridge over River Comayagua

1983. 20th Anniv of Inter-American Development Bank. Multicoloured.
1024 1 l. Type **204** 60 55
1025 2 l. Luis Borgran Technical Institute . . . . 1·25 1·00

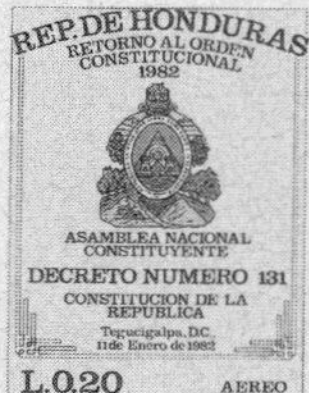

205 Arms
206 Hand, Dove and Map on Globe

1984. Air. 2nd Anniv of Return of Constitutional Government. Multicoloured.
1026 20 c. Type **205** 40 20
1027 20 c. President Roberto Suazo Cordova 40 20

1984. "Internationalization of Peace".
1028 **206** 78 c. black, bl & green . . 75 45
1029 85 c. blk, orge & grn . . . 80 50
1030 95 c. blk, orge & grn . . . 90 55
1031 1 l. 50 blk, red & grn . . 1·25 75
1032 2 l. blk, lt grn & grn . . . 1·50 1·00
1033 5 l. black, pur & grn . . . 3·25 2·40

207 Front Page of "La Gaceta"

1984. Air. 150th Anniv of "La Gaceta".
1034 **207** 10 c. brn, blk & grn . . . 10 10
1035 20 c. brn, blk & sepia . . 20 15

1986. Various stamps surch.
1036 **184** 60 c. on 14 c. mult (postage) 40 25
1037 **177** 5 c. on 1 c. blue and black (air) 10 10
1038 – 10 c. on 8 c. mult (No. 868) 10 10
1039 **176** 20 c. on 16 c. mult . . . 15 10
1040 – 50 c. on 14 c. mult (No. 915) 35 15
1041 – 85 c. on 6 c. mult (No. 942) 50 30
1042 **186** 85 c. on 6 c. brn & blk . . 50 30
1043 – 95 c. on 6 c. brn & blk . . 70 40
1044 – 95 c. on 6 c. mult (No. 942) 70 40
1045 **177** 1 l. on 1 c. blue and black 70 40

1986. Air. "Exfilhon '86" Stamp Exhibition and World Cup Winners. Nos. 951/2 optd.
1046 40 c. **"EXFILHON '86"/ ARGENTINA CAMPEON/ MEXICO'86** (951) 25 15
1047 40 c. **"EXFILHON '86"/ ALEMANIA FEDERAL Sub Campeon/ MEXICO'86** (952) 25 15
1048 40 c. **"EXFILHON '86"/ "FRANCIA TERCER LUGAR"/ MEXICO'86** (952) 25 15
1049 40 c. **"EXFILHON '86"/ "BELGICA— CUARTO LUGAR"/ MEXICO'86** (951) 25 15

210 Phulapanzak

REPUBLICA DE HONDURAS, C.A.
"PRIMER ANIVERSARIO GOBIERNO DEMOCRATICO, ING. JOSE AZCONA"
AEREO L.0.20

211 Pres. Jose Azcona and Flag

1986. Air. Tourism. Multicoloured.
1050 20 c. Type **210** 15 10
1051 78 c. Aerial view of Bahia Island beach and jetty (horiz) 45 25
1052 85 c. Yacht off Bahia Islands (horiz) . . . . 1·50 60
1053 95 c. Yojoa lake 60 35
1054 1 l. Woman painting pottery . 60 35

1987. Air. 1st Anniv of Democratic Government.
1056 **211** 20 c. multicoloured . . . 15 10
1057 85 c. multicoloured . . . 50 30

212 Edward Warner Award Medal

213 "Eupatorium cyrilli-nelsonii"

1987. 25th Anniv (1985) of Central American Air Navigation Services Association. Mult.
1058 2 c. Type **212** 10 10
1059 5 c. Flags of member countries (horiz) 10 10
1060 60 c. Transmission mast, arrows and airplane (horiz) 50 20
1061 75 c. Emblem 45 25
1062 1 l. Members' flags and emblem (horiz) 60 35

1987. Air. Flowering Plants. Multicoloured.
1064 10 c. Type **213** 10 10
1065 20 c. "Salvia ernestivargasii" . 15 10
1066 95 c. "Robinsonella erasmi-sosae" 60 35

214 Turquoise-browed Motmot

216 Emblem

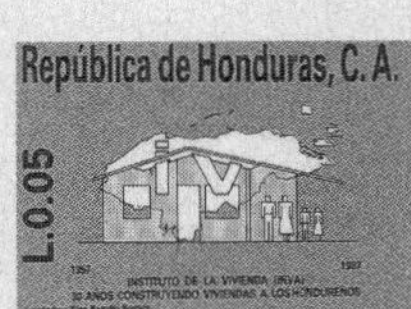

215 Family and House on Emblem

1987. Air. Birds. Multicoloured.
1067 50 c. Type **214** . . . . 1·25 50
1068 60 c. Keel-billed toucan . . . 1·50 55
1069 85 c. Red-crowned amazon . . 2·25 85

1987. 30th Anniv of Housing Institute.
1070 **215** 5 c. multicoloured 10 10
1071 – 95 c. blk, brn & bl . . . 60 35
DESIGN: 95 c. Emblem.

1987. Air. 30th Anniv of Honduras National Autonomous University.
1072 **216** 1 l. red, black and yellow . 60 35

217 Emblem

218 Emblem of President

1987. Air. 50th Anniv of Honduras Red Cross.
1073 **217** 20 c. red and blue 15 10

1988. Air. 17th Lions International Latin-American and Caribbean Forum, Honduras.
1074 **218** 95 c. blue and yellow . . 60 35

219 1913 Headquarters Building, La Ceiba

1988. Air. 75th Anniv of Banco Atlantida.
1075 10 c. Type **219** 10 10
1076 85 c. Present headquarters building, Tegucigalpa . . . 50 30

1988. Nos. 941/4 surch.
1078 5 c. on 6 c. brown & black . . 10 10
1079 5 c. on 6 c. multicoloured . . . 10 10
1080 20 c. on 8 c. brown & black . . 10 10
1081 20 c. on 8 c. multicoloured . . 10 10

221 Postal Messenger

222 Athletes

1988. Air. "Exfilhon 88" Stamp Exhibition, Honduras.
1082 **221** 85 c. brown 50 30
1083 – 2 l. brown and red . . . 1·10 60
DESIGN: 2 l. Handstamp on cover.

1988. Air. Olympic Games, Seoul.
1085 **222** 85 c. blk, yell & mve . . . 50 30
1086 – 1 l. yell, blk & orge . . . 60 35
DESIGN: 1 l. Ball games equipment.

223 Three-legged Tub

228 Monkey swinging through Trees

1988. Air. 500th Anniv (1992) of Discovery of America by Christopher Columbus. Mult.
1088 10 c. Type **223** 10 10
1089 25 c. Bowl (horiz) 15 10
1090 30 c. Dish with legs shaped as animal heads (horiz) 20 15
1091 50 c. Jug 35 20

1989. Air. Various stamps surch.
1093 – 10 c. on 16 c. brown and black (No. 947) 10 10
1094 – 10 c. on 16 c. mult (No. 948) 10 10
1095 – 15 c. on 6 c. mult (No. 923) 10 10
1096 **195** 20 c. on 16 c. mult . . . 10 10
1097 **176** 50 c. on 16 c. mult . . . 10 10
1098 – 95 c. on 18 c. mult (No. 910) 20 15
1099 – 1 l. on 16 c. mult (No. 836) 20 15

1990. Air. 4th Central American Games. Nos. 887 and 878 surch **IV Juegos Olimpicos Centroamericanos** and value.
1101 75 c. on 18 c. multicoloured . . 15 10
1102 85 c. on 18 c. green & blk . . . 20 15

1990. Air. Nos. 915 and 870 surch **L. 0.20.**
1103 20 c. on 14 c. multicoloured . . 10 10
1104 20 c. on 18 c. multicoloured . . 10 10

1990. Air. 50th Anniv (1989) of I.H.C.I. Nos. 930 and 915 surch **"50 Aniversario IHCI" 1939–1989** and new value.
1105 **184** 20 c. on 14 c. mult . . . 10 10
1106 – 1 l. on 14 c. mult 20 15

1990. Air. The Black-handed Spider Monkey. Multicoloured.
1107 10 c. Type **228** 10 10
1108 10 c. Mother and baby 10 10
1109 20 c. Monkey swinging through trees (different) 10 10
1110 20 c. Mother and baby (different) 10 10

1990. Air. World Cup Football Championship, Italy. No. 960 surch **ITALIA '90 L.1.00.**
1111 **1** l. on 55 c. multicoloured . . 20 15

230 Institute Building

1990. Air Centenary of Luis Bogran Technical Institute, Tegucigalpa.
1113 **230** 20 c. red, black & green . 10 10
1114 – 85 c. multicoloured . . . 20 15
DESIGN: 85 c. Cogwheel, globe and Institute emblem.

231 Emblem

232 "Santa Maria", Shoreline, Fish and Fruit

1990. Air. 45th Anniv of F.A.O.
1116 **231** 95 c. multicoloured . . . 20 15

1990. America. The Natural World. Mult.
1117 20 c. Type **232** 30 10
1118 1 l. Maize, fish, fruit and palm (horiz) 20 15

233 Congress Emblem

1990. Air. 30th Anniv and 17th Congress of Inter-American Construction Industry Federation.
1119 **233** 20 c. black and green . . 10 10
1120 – 1 l. black and blue . . . 20 15
DESIGN—HORIZ: 1 l. Jose Cecilio del Valle Palace, Tegucigalpa (Ministry of Foreign Relations).

REPUBLICA DE HONDURAS
CORREO AEREO L 0.20
NAVIDAD 1990

234 Virgin and Child with Apostles

1990. Air. Christmas. Multicoloured.
1121 20 c. Type **234** 10 10
1122 95 c. Virgin and Child (vert) . 20 15

235 St. John Bosco (founder) (after Mario Caffaro Roke)

1990. Air. 80th Anniv of Salesian Brothers in Honduras. Multicoloured.
1124 75 c. Type **235** 15 10
1125 1 l. Bosco and National Youth Sanctuary, Tegucigalpa . . . 20 15

L0.30 AEREO
HONDURAS
Primer Año de Gobierno
Lic Rafael Leonardo Callejas

236 Pres. Callejas

1991. Air. 1st Anniv of Presidency of Rafael Leonardo Callejas. Multicoloured.
1126 30 c. Type **236** 10 10
1127 2 l. Pres. Callejas wearing sash . 45 25

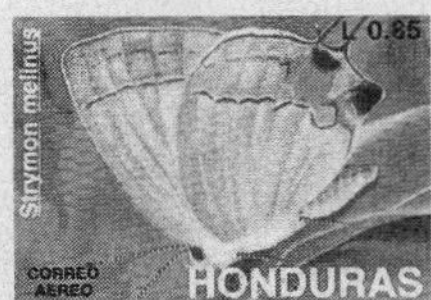

237 "Strymon melinus"

1991. Air. Butterflies. Multicoloured.
1128 85 c. Type **237** 15 10
1129 90 c. "Diorina sp." 20 15
1130 1 l. 50 "Hyalophora cecropia" . 30 20

238 "Rhyncholaelia glauca"

1991. Air. Orchids. Multicoloured.
1132 30 c. Type **238** 10 10
1133 50 c. "Oncidium splendidum" (vert) 10 10
1134 95 c. "Laelia anceps (vert) . . 20 10
1135 1 l. 50 "Cattleya skinneri" . . 30 20

239 International Latin Lawyers Union Emblem and Flags

1991. Air. 6th Caribbean and North and Central American Lawyers' Day.
1136 **239** 50 c. multicoloured . . . 10 10

241 Emblem, Flags and Carving

1991. Air. 25th Anniv of Italian–Latin American Institute.
1138 **241** 1 l. multicoloured 20 10

242 Meeting of Old and New Worlds

1991. Air. "Espamer '91" Spain–Latin America Stamp Exhibition, Buenos Aires.
1139 **242** 2 l. multicoloured 45 30

243 Valle

1991. Air. Birth Centenary of Rafael Heliodoro Valle.
1141 **243** 2 l. black and red 45 30

244 Show Jumping

1991. Air. 11th Pan-American Games, Havana. Multicoloured.
1142 30 c. Type **244** 10 10
1143 85 c. Judo 20 10
1144 95 c. Swimming 20 10

245 St Manuel de Colohete's Church, Gracias, Lempira

1991. Air. Churches. Multicoloured.
1146 30 c. Type **245** 10 10
1147 95 c. Church of Mercy, Gracias, Lempira 20 10
1148 1 l. Comayagua Cathedral . . 20 10

246 Stone Carving and Cobs of Corn

1991. Air. America. Pre-Columbian Civilisations. Multicoloured.
1149 25 c. Type **246** 10 10
1150 40 c. Stone carving, dried corn and map 10 10
1151 1 l. 50 Stone carving and map of Honduras 30 20

247 Means of Control

248 Poinsettias in Basket

1991. Air. 4th International Congress on Pest Control. Multicoloured.
1152 30 c. Type **247** 10 10
1153 75 c. Hoeing crop (scientific co-operation) 15 10
1154 1 l. Co-operation of scientists and producers 20 10

1991. Christmas. Multicoloured.
1156 1 l. Type **248** 20 10
1157 2 l. Poinsettia in chicken-shaped pot 45 30

249 "Taking Possession of the New Continent" (Enrique Escher)

1992. Air. 75th Anniv of Savings Bank of Honduras. Multicoloured.
1158 85 c. Type **249** 25 15
1159 1 l. "First Celebration of Mass in the Americas" (Maury Flores) 45 15

250 Presidents Callejas and Cossiga of Italy

1992. Air. 2nd Year in Office of President Rafael Leonardo Callejas. Multicoloured.
1161 20 c. Type **250** 10 10
1162 2 l. Callejas with Pope 40 25

251 View From Crow's Nest

252 Skiing

1992. Air. America 1991. 500th Anniv of Discovery of America. Multicoloured.
1163 90 c. Type **251** 15 10
1164 1 l. Fleet 30 10
1165 2 l. Ship approaching island . . 50 25

1992. Winter Olympic Games, Albertville. Multicoloured.
1166 50 c. Type **252** 10 10
1167 3 l. Jenny Palacios de Stillo (cross-country skier) 60 40

253 Athletics

254 "Seller" (Manuel Rodriguez)

1992. Olympic Games, Barcelona. Mult.
1168 20 c. Type **253** 10 10
1169 50 c. Tennis 10 10
1170 85 c. Football 15 10

1992. Mother's Day. Paintings. Multicoloured.
1171 20 c. Type **254** 10 10
1172 50 c. "Grandmother and Baby" (Manuel Rodriguez) 10 10
1173 5 l. "Sellers" (Maury Flores) . 95 60

255 "Chlosyne janais"

1992. Butterflies. Multicoloured.
1174 25 c. Type **255** 10 10
1175 85 c. "Agrilus vanillae" . . . 15 10
1176 3 l. "Morpho granadensis" . . 60 40

256 "Bougainvillea glabra" "Napoleon"

1992. Air. Flowers. Multicoloured.
1178 20 c. Type **256** 10 10
1179 30 c. "Canna indica" 10 10
1180 75 c. "Epiphyllum sp." 15 10
1181 95 c. "Sobralia macrantha" . . 20 10

257 Dam

258 Crops

1992. Air. General Francisco Morazan Hydroelectric Project. Multicoloured.
1182 85 c. Type **257** 15 10
1183 4 l. Inner view of dam (horiz) . 75 45

1992. Air. 50th Anniv of Inter-American Institute for Agricultural Co-operation.
1184 **258** 95 c. multicoloured (white background) 20 10
1185 95 c. multicoloured (black background) 20 10

259 "Huancasco" (Arturo Lopez Rodezno)

260 Morazan on Horseback (after Francisco Cisneros)

1992. Air. Children's Day. Multicoloured.
1186 25 c. Type **259** 10 10
1187 95 c. "Bougainvillea" (Enrique Escher) 20 10
1188 2 l. "Melissa" (Cesar Ordonez) 40 25

1992. Air. Birth Bicentenary of General Francisco Morazan. Multicoloured.
1189 5 c. Type **260** 10 10
1190 10 c. Statue of Morazan, Ampala 10 10
1191 50 c. Morazan's watch and sword (horiz) 10 10
1192 95 c. Josefa Lastiri de Morazan (wife) 20 10

261 Globe as Pot filled with Food

1992. Air. International Nutrition Conference, Rome.
1194 **261** 1 l. 05 multicoloured . . . 20 10

262 Cinnamon Hummingbird

1992. Air. "Exfilhon '92" National Stamp Exhibition, Tegucigalpa. Multicoloured.
1195 1 l. 50 Type **262** 30 20
1196 2 l. 45 Scarlet macaw 50 30

263 Bee-keeping

1992. Air. 50th Anniv of Pan-American School of Agriculture. Multicoloured.
1198 20 c. Type **263** 10 10
1199 85 c. Tending goats 15 10
1200 1 l. Ploughing with oxen . . . 20 10
1201 2 l. Hoeing (vert) 40 25

264 Fruit, Locomotive, Clock and Bridge

1992. Air. Centenary of El Progreso (City).
1202 **264** 1 l. 55 multicoloured . . . 2·75 90

265 Amerindian Village

266 Columbus's Fleet and Landing Craft

1992. Air. America. 500th Anniv of Discovery of America by Columbus. Multicoloured.
1203 35 c. Type **265** 10 10
1204 5 l. Columbus's landing party meeting Amerindians . . . 1·25 60

1992. Air. 500th Anniv of Discovery of America by Columbus. Details of "The First Mass" by Roque Zelaya. Multicoloured.
1205 95 c. Type **266** 20 10
1206 1 l. Mass (horiz) 20 10
1207 2 l. View of village (horiz) . . 40 25

267 Road and Bridge

1992. Air. 1st Central America–Panama Highway Maintenance Congress, San Pedro Sula. Multicoloured.
1208 20 c. Type **267** 10 10
1209 85 c. Bulldozer 15 10

268 The Greasy Pole

1992. Air. Christmas. Multicoloured.
1210 20 c. Type **268** 10 10
1211 85 c. Crib, San Antonio de Flores (horiz) 15 10

269 Globes, Children and Emblem

1992. Air. 90th Anniv of Pan-American Health Organization.
1212 **269** 3 l. 95 multicoloured . . . 75 45

1992. Air. Nos. 894 and 899/900 surch.
1213 **179** 20 c. on 1 c. mult 10 10
1214 – 20 c. on 6 c. mult 10 10
1215 – 85 c. on 18 c. mult . . . 15 10

271 Pres. Callejas at Ceremony

272 Mother and Child

1993. Air. 3rd Year of Rafael L. Callejas's Presidential Term and International Court of Justice's Decision on Border with El Salvador. Multicoloured.

1216 90 c. Type **271** 15 10
1217 1 l. 05 Map (horiz) 20 10

1993. Air. Mother's Day. Multicoloured.

1218 50 c. Type **272** 10 10
1219 95 c. Mother and child (different) 20 10

273 American Manatee

1993. Air. Endangered Mammals. Mult.

1220 85 c. Type **273** 15 10
1221 2 l. 45 Puma 50 30
1222 10 l. Jaguar (vert) . . . . . . 1·90 1·25

274 Scarlet Macaws

276 30 r "Bull's Eye" Stamp

1993. Air. National Symbols. Multicoloured.

1223 25 c. Type **274** 10 10
1224 95 c. White-tailed deer 15 10

1993. Air. Various stamps surch.

1225 – 20 c. on 3 c. mult (No. 896) 10 10
1226 **189** 20 c. on 3 c. orange, blue and bistre 10 10
1227 **197** 20 c. on 3 c. mult 10 10
1228 – 20 c. on 8 c. mult (No. 868) 10 10
1229 **182** 20 c. on 8 c. mult 10 10
1230 **176** 50 c. on 16 c. mult 10 10
1231 **177** 50 c. on 16 c. red and black 10 10
1232 – 50 c. on 16 c. mult (No. 886) 10 10
1233 **180** 50 c. on 16 c. mult 10 10
1234 – 50 c. on 16 c. mult (No. 931) 10 10

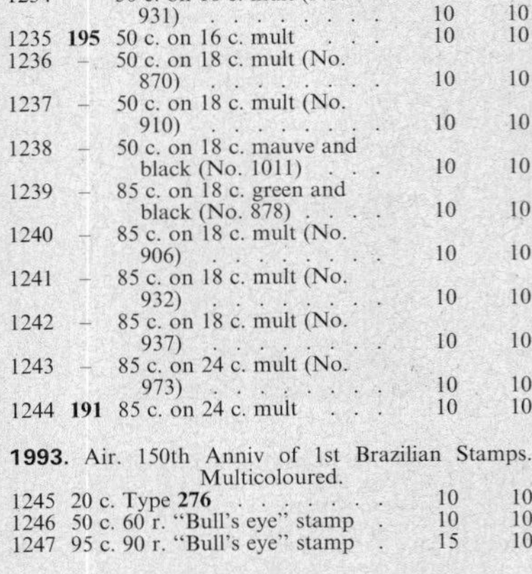

1235 **195** 50 c. on 16 c. mult 10 10
1236 – 50 c. on 18 c. mult (No. 870) 10 10
1237 – 50 c. on 18 c. mult (No. 910) 10 10
1238 – 50 c. on 18 c. mauve and black (No. 1011) 10 10
1239 – 85 c. on 18 c. green and black (No. 878) 10 10
1240 – 85 c. on 18 c. mult (No. 906) 10 10
1241 – 85 c. on 18 c. mult (No. 932) 10 10
1242 – 85 c. on 18 c. mult (No. 937) 10 10
1243 – 85 c. on 24 c. mult (No. 973) 10 10
1244 **191** 85 c. on 24 c. mult 10 10

1993. Air. 150th Anniv of 1st Brazilian Stamps. Multicoloured.

1245 20 c. Type **276** 10 10
1246 50 c. 60 r. "Bull's eye" stamp . . 10 10
1247 95 c. 90 r. "Bull's eye" stamp . . 15 10

277 Atlantida

1993. Air. Departments. Multicoloured.

1248 20 c. Type **277** 10 10
1249 20 c. Colon 10 10
1250 20 c. Cortes 10 10
1251 20 c. Choluteca 10 10
1252 20 c. El Paraiso 10 10
1253 20 c. Francisco Morazan 10 10
1254 50 c. Comayagua (vert) 10 10
1255 50 c. Copan (vert) 10 10
1256 50 c. Intibuca (vert) 10 10
1257 50 c. Bahia Islands (vert) . . . 10 10
1258 50 c. Lempira (vert) 10 10
1259 50 c. Ocotepeque (vert) 10 10
1260 1 l. 50 La Paz 20 10
1261 1 l. 50 Olancho 20 10
1262 1 l. 50 Santa Barbara 20 10
1263 1 l. 50 Valle 20 10
1264 1 l. 50 Yoro 20 10
1265 1 l. 50 Gracias a Dios 20 10

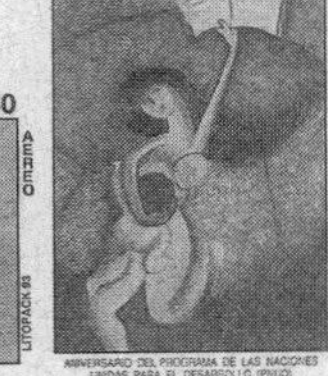

278 Muscovy Duck

279 Painting by Julia Padilla

1993. Air. America. Endangered Birds. Mult.

1266 20 c. Ornate hawk eagle (vert) . 10 10
1267 80 c. Type **278** 10 10
1268 2 l. Harpy eagle 25 15

1993. Air. 40th Anniv of United Nations Development Programme.

1269 **279** 95 c. multicoloured . . . 15 10

280 Church

281 Ramon Rosa

1993. Air. Christmas. Paintings by Aida Lara de Pedemonte. Multicoloured.

1270 20 c. Type **280** 10 10
1271 85 c. Flower vendor 10 10

1993. Air. Personalities. Multicoloured.

1272 25 c. Type **281** 10 10
1273 65 c. Jesus Aguilar Paz 10 10
1274 85 c. Augusto Coello 10 10

282 Grey Angelfish

1993. Air. Fishes. Multicoloured.

1275 20 c. Type **282** 15 10
1276 85 c. Queen angelfish 20 10
1277 3 l. Banded butterflyfish . . . 65 45

283 Norma Callejas planting Tree

284 Family with Rushes (Aida Lara de Pedemonte)

1994. Air. 4th Year of Rafael L. Callejas's Presidential Term. Multicoloured.

1278 95 c. Type **283** 15 10
1279 1 l. Pres. Callejas and Government House (horiz) . 15 10

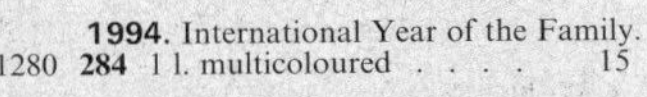

1994. International Year of the Family.

1280 **284** 1 l. multicoloured 15 10

285 Dove and Maps on Globe

286 "Madonna and Child"

1994. Air. Int Peace and Development in Central America Conference, Tegucigalpa.

1281 **285** 1 l. multicoloured 15 10

1994. Air. Christmas. Paintings by Gelasio Gimenez. Multicoloured.

1282 95 c. Type **286** 10 10
1283 1 l. "Holy Family" 15 10

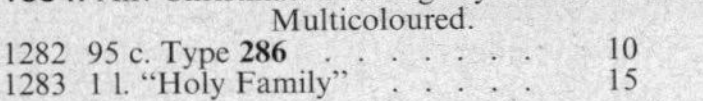

287 "Family Scene" (Delmer Mejia)

288 Pres. Reina

1995. Air. 50th Anniv of U.N.O. Mult.

1284 1 l. "The Sowing: Ecological Family" (Elisa Dulcey) . . . 15 10
1285 2 l. Type **287** 25 15
1286 3 l. Anniversary emblem . . . 40 25

1995. Air. 1st Anniv of Presidency of Carlos Roberto Reina. Multicoloured.

1287 80 c. Type **288** 10 10
1288 95 c. Pres. Reina with arms raised (horiz) 10 10
1289 1 l. Pres. Reina at summit conference (horiz) 15 10

289 Postman loading Mail Van

1995. Air. America. Postal Transport. Paintings by Ramiro Rodriguez Zelaya. Multicoloured.

1290 1 l. 50 Type **289** 20 10
1291 2 l. Postman on motor cycle . . 25 15

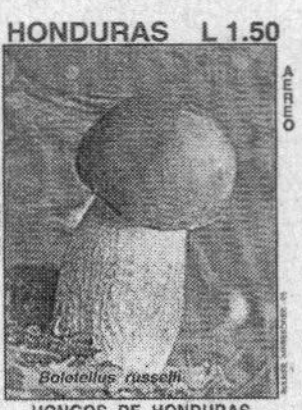

290 "Boletellus russelli"

1995. Air. Fungi. Multicoloured.

1292 1 l. "Marasmius cohaerens" (horiz) 45 15
1293 1 l. Blue leg ("Lepista nuda") (horiz) 45 15
1294 1 l. "Polyporus pargamenus" (horiz) 45 15
1295 1 l. "Fomes sp." (horiz) . . . 45 15
1296 1 l. "Paneolus sphinctrinus" (horiz) 45 15
1297 1 l. "Hygrophorus aurantiaca" (horiz) 45 15
1298 1 l. 50 The blusher ("Amanita rubescens") 65 20
1299 1 l. 50 "Boletus frostii" . . . 65 20
1300 1 l. 50 "Fomes annosus" . . . 65 20
1301 1 l. 50 "Psathyrella sp." . . . 65 20
1302 1 l. 50 Type **290** 65 20
1303 1 l. 50 "Marasmius spegazzinii" 65 20
1304 2 l. "Amanita sp." 80 25
1305 2 l. Golden tops ("Psilocybe cubensis") 80 25
1306 2 l. Royal boletus ("Boletus regius") 80 25
1307 2 l. Black trumpet ("Craterellus cornucopioides") 80 25
1308 2 l. "Auricularia delicata" . . 80 25
1309 2 l. "Clavariadelphus pistilaris" 80 25
1310 2 l. 50 "Scleroderma aurantium" (horiz) 95 35
1311 2 l. 50 "Amanita praegraveolens" (horiz) 95 35
1312 2 l. 50 Chanterelle ("Cantharellus cibarius") (horiz) 95 35
1313 2 l. 50 "Geastrum triplex" (horiz) 95 35
1314 2 l. 50 "Russula emetica" (horiz) 95 35
1315 2 l. 50 "Boletus pinicola" (horiz) 95 35
1316 3 l. "Fomes versicolor" (horiz) 1·25 40
1317 3 l. "Cantharellus purpurascens" (horiz) . . . . . 1·25 40
1318 3 l. "Lyophyllum decastes" (horiz) . . . . 1·25 40
1319 3 l. Oyster fungus ("Pleurotus ostreatus") (horiz) . . . . 1·25 40
1320 3 l. "Boletus ananas" (horiz) . 1·25 40
1321 3 l. Caesar's mushroom ("Amanita caesarea") (horiz) . . . . 1·25 40

291 "Food for All"

1995. Air. 50th Anniv of F.A.O.

1322 **291** 3 l. multicoloured 25 15

292 Family and Farm over Globe

1995. Air. 50th Anniv of CARE (Co-operative for Assistance and Remittances Overseas). Multicoloured.

1323 1 l. 40 Type **292** 15 10
1324 5 l. 40 Crop farming 55 35
1325 5 l. 40 Toucan, orchid, planting tree and animals at waterfall 55 35

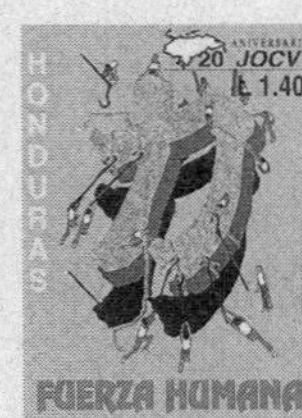

294 People around Japanese Character

1995. 20th Anniv of Japanese Overseas Co-operation Voluntary Workers in Honduras. Multicoloured.

1327 1 l. 40 Type **294** (postage) . . 15 10
1328 4 l. 30 Amerindian-style figures on pages of leaflet (horiz) (air) 40 25
1329 5 l. 40 Volunteer and people in traditional costumes (horiz) . 55 35

295 Scorpion Mud Turtle

1995. Air. America. Environmental Protection. Multicoloured.

1330 1 l. 40 Type **295** 15 10
1331 4 l. 54 Alpinia purpurata (flower) (vert) 45 30
1332 10 l. Common caracara (vert) . 1·00 65

296 "Agalychnis sp"

1995. Air. Reptiles and Amphibians. Mult.

1333 5 l. 40 Type **296** 55 35
1334 5 l. 40 Iguana 55 35

297 Bell

1995. Air. Christmas. Multicoloured.

1335 1 l. 40 Type **297** 15 10
1336 5 l. 40 Crib figures (horiz) . . 55 35
1337 6 l. 90 Deer (carving) 70 45

298 "SICA" over Map

1996. Air. 3rd Anniv of Central American Integration System. Multicoloured.

1338 1 l. 40 Type **298** (signing of Protocol, 1991) 15 10
1339 4 l. 30 Emblem 40 25
1340 5 l. 40 Presidents of Central American countries at 17th Summit 55 35

299 Allegorical Design

1996. Air. United Nations Decade against Drug Abuse and Drug Trafficking. Multicoloured.
1341 1 l. 40 Type **299** 15 10
1342 5 l. 40 Woman's head with butterfly as hat (vert) 55 35
1343 10 l. Guitar and bar of music . 1·00 65

300 Traditional Headdress

1996. Air. Bicentenary of Arrival of Garifunas Tribe in Honduras. Multicoloured.
1344 1 l. 40 Type **300** 15 10
1345 5 l. 40 Tribesmen dancing to music (horiz) 55 35
1346 10 l. Drums (horiz) . . . . . 1·00 60

301 Steam Locomotive "San Jose"

1996. Air. "Exfilhon 96" National Stamp Exn, Tegucigalpa. Railway Locomotives. Mult.
1347 5 l. 40 Type **301** 95 55
1348 5 l. 40 Diesel railcar No. 203 . 95 55

302 Football

1996. Air. 6th Central American Games, San Pedro Sula (1997). Multicoloured.
1350 4 l. 30 Type **302** 40 25
1351 4 l. 54 Volleyball and games emblem 45 30
1352 5 l. 40 Games mascot (vert) . . 55 35

303 Honduran and International Badges

1996. Air. 75th Anniv of Honduran Scouts' Association. Multicoloured.
1353 2 l. 15 Type **303** 20 10
1354 5 l. 40 Anniversary emblem (vert) 50 30
1355 6 l. 90 Scout feeding deer (vert) 65 40

304 Poinsettia and Candles

1996. Air. Christmas. Multicoloured.
1356 1 l. 40 Type **304** 15 10
1357 3 l. Poinsettia 25 15
1358 5 l. 40 As Type **304** but vert . . 50 30

305 Opatoro Man

306 Children playing in River (Oscar Moncada)

1997. Air. America (1996). Traditional Costumes. Multicoloured.
1359 4 l. 55 Type **305** 40 25
1360 5 l. 40 Jocomico woman . . . 50 30
1361 10 l. Intibuca couple 90 60

1997. Air. 20th Anniv of Honduran Plan and 60th Anniv of International Plan. Multicoloured.
1362 1 l. 40 Type **306** 15 10
1363 5 l. 40 Girl beside river (Nataly Alexandra Reyes) (horiz) . . 50 30
1364 9 l. 70 Street (Walter Enrique Martinez) (horiz) 90 60

307 Red-tailed Hawk

308 Von Stephan

1997. Birds. Multicoloured.
1365 1 l. 40 Type **307** (postage) . . 15 10
1366 1 l. 50 Keel-billed toucan . . . 15 10
1367 2 l. Red-billed whistling duck . 20 10
1368 2 l. 15 Collared forest falcon . 20 10
1369 3 l. Common caracara 25 15
1370 5 l. 40 King vulture (air) . . . 50 30

1997. Air. Death Centenary of Dr. Heinrich von Stephan (founder of U.P.U.).
1372 **308** 5 l. 40 multicoloured . . . 50 30

309 Children and Adults in Room (Yorvin Ramon Toro)

1997. Air. World Population Day. Mult.
1373 1 l. 40 Type **309** 15 10
1374 6 l. 90 Family group and house (Marvin Lamberth Harry) . 65 40

310 "Rothschildia forbesi"

1997. Air. Butterflies and Moths. Mult.
1375 1 l. Type **310** 10 10
1376 1 l. 40 "Parides photinus" . . 15 10
1377 2 l. 15 Emperor 20 10
1378 3 l. Jamaican kite swallowtail . 25 15
1379 4 l. 30 "Parides iphidamas" . . 40 25
1380 5 l. 40 Monarch 50 30

311 St. Theresa

312 Observatory

1997. Air. Death Centenary of St. Theresa of Lisieux. Multicoloured.
1382 1 l. 40 Type **311** 10 10
1383 5 l. 40 St. Theresa (different) . 45 30

1997. Air. 150th Anniv of National University and 40th Anniv of Free University. Multicoloured.
1384 1 l. 40 Type **312** 10 10
1385 5 l. 40 Statue of Fr. Jose Trinidad Reyes (founder) . . 45 30
1386 10 l. Woman with book guiding boy 90 60

313 Diana, Princess of Wales

314 Children around Statue (Nelson Leonel Rodriguez)

1997. Air. Diana, Princess of Wales Commemoration. Multicoloured.
1387 1 l. 40 Type **313** 10 10
1388 5 l. 40 Visiting minefield (horiz) 45 30

1997. Air. 37th Anniv of Alcoholics Anonymous (rehabilitation organization).
1390 **314** 5 l. 40 multicoloured . . . 45 30

315 "Christ of Picacho" (statue)

316 Basketball

1997. Air. Christmas. Multicoloured.
1391 1 l. 40 Type **315** 10 10
1392 5 l. 50 "Virgin of Suyapa" . . 50 30

1997. Air. 6th Central American Games, San Pedro Sula. Multicoloured.
1393 1 l. 40 Type **316** 10 10
1394 1 l. 40 Baseball (batting) . . . 10 10
1395 1 l. 40 Football 10 10
1396 1 l. 40 Squash 10 10
1397 1 l. 40 Volleyball 10 10
1398 1 l. 40 Handball 10 10
1399 1 l. 40 Bowls 10 10
1400 1 l. 40 Table tennis 10 10
1401 1 l. 40 Rings on map of Honduras 10 10
1402 1 l. 40 Baseball (bowling) . . . 10 10
1403 1 l. 50 Taekwondo (kicking) . . 15 10
1404 1 l. 50 Karate (one hand raised) 15 10
1405 1 l. 50 Judo (bowing) 15 10
1406 1 l. 50 Wrestling 15 10
1407 1 l. 50 Weightlifting 15 10
1408 1 l. 50 Boxing 15 10
1409 1 l. 50 Body-building 15 10
1410 1 l. 50 Fencing 15 10
1411 1 l. 50 Games emblem 15 10
1412 1 l. 50 Shooting 15 10
1413 2 l. 15 Cycling (on bicycle) . . 20 10
1414 2 l. 15 Road cycle racing (running beside bicycle) 20 10
1415 2 l. 15 Swimming 20 10
1416 2 l. 15 Water polo 20 10
1417 2 l. 15 Hurdling 20 10
1418 2 l. 15 Gymnastics (ring exercise) 20 10
1419 2 l. 15 Horse riding 20 10
1420 2 l. 15 Tennis 20 10
1421 2 l. 15 Pedrito Pichete (Games mascot) 20 10
1422 2 l. 15 Chess 20 10

317 "Cichlasoma dovii"

1997. Air. Fishes. Multicoloured.
1423 1 l. 40 Type **317** 10 10
1424 2 l. "Cichlasoma spilurum" (facing left) 20 10
1425 3 l. "Cichlasoma spilurum" (facing right) 25 15
1426 5 l. 40 "Astyanay fasciatus" . . 45 30

318 Queen Triggerfish

320 Sculpted Skull from Temple 16

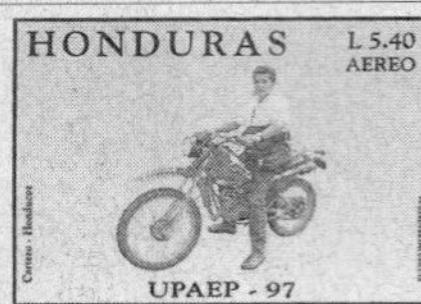

319 Postman on Motor Cycle

1998. Air. 50th Anniv of Bancahsa. Marine Life of Bahia Coral Reef. Multicoloured.
1427 2 l. 50 Type **318** 20 10
1428 2 l. 50 White grunt ("Haemulon plumieri") 20 10
1429 2 l. 50 French angelfish ("Pomacanthus paru") . . . 20 10
1430 2 l. 50 Wrasse (juvenile) ("Halichoeres garnoti") . . 20 10
1431 2 l. 50 Grey angelfish (complete fish) ("Pomacanthus arcuatus") 20 10
1432 2 l. 50 Queen angelfish ("Holacanthus ciliaris") . . 20 10
1433 2 l. 50 Diver and "Pseud opterogorgia" (coral) 20 10
1434 2 l. 50 Diver's oxygen tank and "Pseud opterogorgia" . . . 20 10
1435 2 l. 50 Six fingers of pillar coral ("Dendrogyra cylindrus") (inscr in Latin) 20 10
1436 2 l. 50 Squirrelfish facing right ("Holocentrus adscensionis") 20 10
1437 2 l. 50 Three fingers of pillar coral ("Dendrogyra cylindrus") (inscr in Latin) . . . 20 10
1438 2 l. 50 "Stegastes fuscus" (fish) 20 10
1439 2 l. 50 "Gorgonia mariae" (coral) 20 10
1440 2 l. 50 Three fingers of pillar coral (inscr in English) . . . 20 10
1441 2 l. 50 Head of grey angelfish ("Pomacanthus arcuatus") . 20 10
1442 2 l. 50 Squirrelfish facing left ("Holocentrus adscensionis") 20 10
1443 2 l. 50 "Eusmilia fastigiata" (coral) 20 10
1444 2 l. 50 Midnight parrotfish ("Scarus coelestinus") . . . 20 10
1445 2 l. 50 One finger of pillar coral (inscr in English) 20 10
1446 2 l. 50 Hogfish ("Lachnolaimus maximus") 20 10

Nos. 1427/46 were issued together, se-tenant, forming a composite design.

1998. Air. America (1997). Postal Service. Multicoloured.
1447 5 l. 40 Type **319** 45 30
1448 5 l. 40 Post Office 45 30

1998. Air. Maya Culture. Multicoloured.
1449 1 l. Type **320** 10 10
1450 1 l. 40 Stone carving 10 10
1451 2 l. 15 Steles H and F 20 10
1452 5 l. 40 Carved water vessel . . 45 30

321 Players and Trophy

1998. Air. World Cup Football Championship, France. Multicoloured.
1454 5 l. 40 Type **321** 45 30
1455 10 l. Players in tackle and trophy (vert) 90 60

322 Green Iguana

1998. Air. Reptiles. Multicoloured.
1457 1 l. 40 Type **322** 10 10
1458 2 l. Eyelash viper 20 10
1459 3 l. Green lizards 25 15
1460 5 l. 40 Coral snake 45 30

323 Robin giving Gift to Girl

1998. Air. Christmas. Multicoloured.
1462 3 l. Type **323** 25 15
1463 5 l. 40 Child Jesus in crib (horiz) 45 30
1464 10 l. Child leading donkey . . 85 55

324 Flores and his Wife greeting Pope

1999. Air. First Anniv of Inauguration of President Carlos Roberto Flores.

1465	5 l. 40 Type **324**	45	30
1466	10 l. President and Mary Flores (vert)	85	55

325 Floods, Central Zone

1999. Air. Hurricane Mitch Victims' Fund. Multicoloured.

1467	5 l. 40 Type **325**	45	30
1468	5 l. 40 Man carrying boy on back through flood and trogon	45	30
1469	5 l. 40 Prince Felipe of Spain and Mary Flores (President's wife)	45	30
1470	5 l. 40 Child crying and orchid	45	30
1471	5 l. 40 People clearing timber in Comayaguela and orchid	45	30
1472	5 l. 40 People wading through flood in North Zone and owl	45	30
1473	5 l. 40 Destruction of La Hoya quarter, Tegucigalpa, and orchid	45	30
1474	5 l. 40 Soldier helping woman and child in North Zone and manakin	45	30
1475	5 l. 40 Collapsed houses in rural zone and orchids	45	30
1476	5 l. 40 Collapsed bridge and damaged motor cars ("Red Vial") and tanager	45	30
1477	5 l. 40 Damaged houses, motor cars and uprooted trees ("Red Vial") and orchids	45	30
1478	5 l. 40 Mexican soldiers with dogs and airplane	45	30
1479	5 l. 40 Two children swimming in North Zone and blue bird	45	30
1480	5 l. 40 Mary and President Flores with Hillary Clinton (wfe of U.S. President)	45	30
1481	5 l. 40 Crowd before collapsed building in South Zone and motmot	45	30
1482	5 l. 40 President Flores and George Bush (U.S. President, 1988–92)	45	30
1483	5 l. 40 Three men digging out rubble and jay	45	30
1484	5 l. 40 Helicopter on beach and orchid	45	30
1485	5 l. 40 Car submerged under flood water in North Zone and bird with crest	45	30
1486	5 l. 40 Tipper Gore (U.S. Vice-president's wife) and Mary Flores in flooded building	45	30
1487	5 l. 40 Flooded banana plantation and orchid	45	30
1488	5 l. 40 Tegucigalpa submerged under flood water and red and green bird	45	30
1489	5 l. 40 Traffic jam behind rocks from landslide ("Red Vial")	45	30
1490	5 l. 40 Comayaguela and blue bird with purple chest	45	30
1491	5 l. 40 Destruction of Comayaguela street and orchid	45	30
1492	5 l. 40 People carrying plank in Eastern Zone and parrot	45	30
1493	5 l. 40 Mexican truck being filled with debris and orchid	45	30
1494	5 l. 40 Bulldozer clearing street and bird with long curved beak	45	30
1495	5 l. 40 President Flores and President Chirac of France	45	30
1496	5 l. 40 Comayaguela commercial zone flooded and green bird	45	30
1497	5 l. 40 People looking at flood water in Tegucigalpa and woodpecker	45	30
1498	5 l. 40 Stranded BMW motor car in Comayaguela street and parakeet	45	30

326 Pilar Salinas

1999. Air. America (1998). Famous Women. Multicoloured.

1499	2 l. 60 Type **326**	20	10
1500	7 l. 30 Clementina Suarerz (poet)	65	40
1501	10 l. 65 Mary Flores (President's wife)	90	60

EXPRESS LETTER STAMPS

1953. No. O507 surch **ENTREGA INMEDIATA 1953 L O.20**.

E523	**127**	20 c. on 1 c. olive & pur	1·60	1·60

E **135** Lockheed Constellation

1956. Air. Optd **ENTREGA INMEDIATA** as in Type E **135**.

E570	E **135**	20 c. grey and black	60	50

1966. Stamp Cent. Design similar to T **144**.

E700	20 c. brn, gold and lt brn	45	45

DESIGN—HORIZ: 20 c. Motor cyclist.

1972. As T **168**, but inscr "ENTREGA INMEDIATA". Multicoloured.

E811	20 c. Chance Vought F4U-5 Corsair fighter aircraft	45	25

1975. No. E811 surch.

E848	60 c. on 20 c. multicoloured	75	55

1976. As T **178**.

E893	60 c. Deer in forest	70	40

OFFICIAL STAMPS

Various stamps overprinted **OFICIAL**.

1890. Stamps of 1890.

O56	**6**	1 c. yellow	15
O57		2 c. yellow	15
O58		5 c. yellow	15
O59		10 c. yellow	15
O60		20 c. yellow	15
O61		25 c. yellow	15
O62		30 c. yellow	15
O63		40 c. yellow	15
O64		50 c. yellow	15
O65		75 c. yellow	15
O66		1 p. yellow	15

1891. Stamps of 1891.

O70	**8**	1 c. yellow	15
O71		2 c. yellow	15
O72		5 c. yellow	15
O73		10 c. yellow	15
O74		20 c. yellow	15
O75		25 c. yellow	15
O76		30 c. yellow	15
O77		40 c. yellow	15
O78		50 c. yellow	15
O79		75 c. yellow	15
O80		1 p. yellow	15

1898. Stamps of 1898.

O116	**14**	5 c. blue	70
O117		10 c. blue	70
O118		20 c. bistre	75
O119		50 c. orange	1·50
O120		1 p. green	3·00

1911. Stamps of 1911.

O148	**20**	1 c. violet	90	35
O149		2 c. green	55	55
O150		5 c. red	90	90
O151		6 c. blue	1·60	1·25
O152		10 c. blue	90	70
O153		20 c. yellow	90	90
O154		50 c. brown	3·25	2·50
O155		1 p. olive	7·00	5·75

1914. No. O150 and O148 surch.

O186	**20**	1 c. on 5 c. red	1·10	90
O187		2 c. on 5 c. red	1·25	90
O188		10 c. on 1 c. violet	2·25	2·25
O189		10 c. on 5 c. red	8·75	8·75
O190		20 c. on 1 c. violet	1·60	1·60

1914. No. O190 and O146 surch **OFICIAL** and value.

O191	**20**	10 c. on 20 c. on 1 c. vio	3·50	3·50
O193		20 c. on 50 c. brown	3·25	3·25

1915. Stamps of 1913.

O194	**26**	1 c. brown	25	25
O195		2 c. red	25	25
O197	**27**	5 c. blue	25	25
O198		6 c. violet	85	85
O199	**26**	10 c. brown	70	70
O200		20 c. brown	1·75	1·75
O202	**27**	50 c. red	3·50	3·50

1915. No. 168 surch **OFICIAL $0.01**.

O203	**26**	1 c. on 2 c. red	1·75	1·75

1915. Stamps of 1915.

O204	**32**	1 c. brown	2·00	2·25
O205		2 c. red	2·00	2·25
O206	–	5 c. blue	20	20
O207	–	6 c. violet	30	30
O208	**32**	10 c. blue	8·00	8·00
O209		20 c. brown	4·50	6·00
O210	–	50 c. red	1·25	1·25
O211	–	1 p. green	2·25	2·25

1921. Stamps of 1919.

O212	**36**	1 c. brown	1·60	1·60
O213		2 c. red	3·75	3·75
O214		5 c. red	3·75	3·75
O215		6 c. mauve	35	35
O216		10 c. blue	45	45
O217		15 c. blue	50	50
O218		20 c. brown	70	70
O219		50 c. brown	1·10	1·10
O220		1 p. green	1·60	1·60

1925. Stamps of 1923.

O222	**39**	1 c. olive	10	10
O223		2 c. red	15	15
O224	**39**	6 c. purple	25	25
O225		10 c. blue	35	35
O226		20 c. brown	45	45
O227		50 c. red	95	95
O228		1 p. green	1·40	1·40

O **50** J. R. Molina

1929.

O259	–	1 c. blue	15	15
O260	O **50**	2 c. red	20	20
O261	–	5 c. violet	30	30
O262	–	10 c. green	35	35
O263	–	20 c. blue	45	45
O264	–	50 c. green & yellow	90	90
O265	–	1 p. brown	1·60	1·60

DESIGNS: J. C. Valle; 5 c. Coffee Tree; 10 c. J. T. Reyes; 20 c. Tegucigalpa Cathedral; 50 c. Lake Yojoa; 1 p. Wireless Station.

1930. Air. Nos. O224/8 surch **Servicio aereo Vale 5 centavos VI—1930** or optd **Servicio aereo Habilitado VI—1930**.

O319	**39**	5 c. on 6 c. purple	1·10	1·10
O320		6 c. purple	50·00	50·00
O321		10 c. blue	1·00	1·00
O322		20 c. brown	1·00	1·00
O323		50 c. red	1·50	1·50
O324		1 p. green	1·00	1·00

O **70** Tegucigalpa

1931.

O328	O **70**	1 c. blue	20	20
O329		2 c. purple	75	75
O330		5 c. olive	90	90
O331		6 c. red	90	90
O332		10 c. green	1·00	1·00
O333		15 c. brown	1·75	1·75
O334		20 c. brown	1·75	1·75
O335		50 c. violet	1·25	1·25
O336		1 p. orange	1·75	1·75

1933. Air. Various stamps surch **Aereo Oficial Vale 1933** and new value.

O354	**66**	20 c. on 2 c. blue	3·50	3·50
O355		20 c. on 2 c. orange	3·50	3·50
O356		20 c. on 2 c. red	3·50	3·50
O357		40 c. on 2 c. orange	2·10	2·10
O358		40 c. on 2 c. red	4·25	4·25
O360	–	40 c. on 5 c. purple (249)	4·25	4·25
O361	–	40 c. on 5 c. blue (250)	7·00	7·00
O362	–	40 c. on 5 c. purple (270)	4·25	4·25
O363	–	40 c. on 5 c. blue (271)	9·50	9·50
O370	–	40 c. on 5 c. vio (O261)	95	95
O372	**39**	60 c. on 6 c. pur (O224)	70	70
O365	–	70 c. on 5 c. blue (188)	3·00	3·00
O374	–	70 c. on 5 c. bl (O206)	5·50	5·50
O366	**39**	70 c. on 10 c. blue	3·50	3·50
O375	**32**	70 c. on 10 c. bl (O208)	28·00	28·00
O377	**36**	70 c. on 10 c. bl (O216)	4·75	4·75
O378	**39**	70 c. on 10 c. bl (O225)	3·50	3·50
O380	**36**	70 c. on 15 c. bl (O217)	90·00	90·00
O381		90 c. on 10 c. bl (O216)	5·50	5·50
O382		90 c. on 15 c. bl (O217)	4·00	4·00
O383	**39**	1 l. on 2 c. red	1·40	1·40
O367	**36**	1 l. on 20 c. brown	3·50	3·50
O384		1 l. on 20 c. brn (O218)	2·50	2·50
O385	**39**	1 l. on 20 c. brn (O226)	4·00	4·00
O368		1 l. on 50 c. red	14·00	14·00
O386	**36**	1 l. on 50 c. brn (O219)	1·90	1·90
O387	**39**	1 l. on 50 c. red (O227)	4·25	4·25
O369	**36**	1.20 l. on 1 p. green	1·10	1·10
O388	–	1.20 l. on 1 p. grn (O211)	9·50	9·50
O389	**39**	1.20 l. on 1 p. grn (O288)	1·60	1·60

1935. Stamps of 1931 optd **HABILITADO 1935–1938** between thick lines.

O390	O **70**	1 c. blue	20	20
O391		2 c. purple	20	20
O392		5 c. olive	25	25
O393		6 c. red	35	35
O394		10 c. green	40	40
O395		15 c. brown	45	45
O396		20 c. brown	55	55
O397		50 c. violet	1·25	1·25

O **92** Coat of Arms and National Flag

1939. Air.

O400	O **92**	2 c. blue and green	10	10
O401		5 c. blue and orange	10	10
O402		8 c. blue and brown	15	15
O403		15 c. blue and red	35	30
O404		46 c. blue and olive	45	45
O405		50 c. blue and violet	60	45
O406		1 l. blue and brown	1·75	1·75
O407		2 l. blue and red	3·00	3·00

1952. Air. 500th Birth Anniv of Isabella the Catholic. As Nos. 499/506 but colours changed, optd **OFICIAL**.

O507	**127**	1 c. olive and purple	10	10
O508	–	2 c. violet and brown	10	10
O509	–	8 c. black and red	15	15
O510	**128**	16 c. green and violet	25	25
O511	–	30 c. black and blue	30	30
O512	–	1 l. sepia and green	1·50	1·25
O513	**127**	2 l. brown and blue	3·00	3·00
O514	**128**	5 l. slate and orange	7·00	7·00

1953. Air. United Nations. As Nos. 523/31 but colours changed (except 1 c.), optd **OFICIAL**.

O532	–	1 c. blue and black	10	10
O533	**130**	2 c. green and black	10	10
O534	–	3 c. orange and black	20	20
O535	–	5 c. red and black	20	20
O536	–	15 c. sepia and black	30	30
O537	–	30 c. purple and black	55	55
O538	–	1 l. olive and black	4·00	2·75
O539	–	2 l. purple and black	5·00	3·25
O540	–	5 l. blue and black	11·50	11·00

1956. Air. As Nos. 551/69 but colours changed, optd **OFICIAL**.

O570	1 c. lake and black	10	10
O571	2 c. red and black	10	10
O572	3 c. purple and black	10	10
O573	4 c. orange and black	10	10
O574	5 c. turquoise and black	10	10
O575	8 c. multicoloured	15	15
O576	10 c. brown and black	15	15
O577	12 c. red and black	15	15
O578	15 c. black and red	15	15
O579	20 c. olive and black	15	15
O580	24 c. blue and black	20	20
O581	25 c. purple and black	25	25
O582	30 c. green and black	25	25
O583	40 c. orange and black	35	35
O584	50 c. red and black	35	35
O585	60 c. purple and black	45	45
O586	1 l. sepia and black	1·75	1·40
O587	2 l. blue and black	3·00	2·40
O588	5 f. blue and black	5·75	5·25

1957. Air. Revolution of October 21, 1956. Nos. 570/9 optd **OFICIAL**. Frames in black.

O589	1 c. blue and yellow	10	10
O590	2 c. purple, green & orange	10	10
O591	5 c. blue and pink	10	10
O592	8 c. violet, olive & orange	10	10
O593	10 c. brown and violet	15	15
O594	12 c. blue and turquoise	15	15
O595	15 c. brown and green	20	15
O596	30 c. grey and pink	35	35
O597	1 l. brown and blue	1·75	1·40
O598	2 l. grey and green	3·00	2·40

1959. Air. Abraham Lincoln. 150th Birth Anniv No. 590/601 but colours changed and optd **OFICIAL**. Flags in blue and red.

O602	1 c. yellow	10	10
O603	2 c. olive	10	10
O604	3 c. brown	10	10
O605	5 c. blue	10	10
O606	10 c. purple	15	15
O607	12 c. orange	15	15
O608	15 c. sepia	20	20
O609	25 c. slate	30	30
O610	50 c. red	45	45
O611	1 l. violet	1·10	1·10
O612	2 l. blue	1·75	1·75
O613	5 l. green	5·25	5·25

1964. Air. Pres. Kennedy Memorial Issue. Optd **IN MEMORIAM JOHN F. KENNEDY 22 NOVIEMBRE 1963**.

O626	1 c. yellow (No. O602)	15	15
O627	2 c. olive (No. O603)	20	20
O628	3 c. brown (No. O604)	25	25
O629	5 c. blue (No. O605)	30	30
O630	15 c. sepia (No. O608)	1·40	1·10
O631	50 c. red (No. O610)	5·75	4·75

1964. Air. Nos. O611/4 surch.

O647	10 c. on 50 c. red	15	10
O648	12 c. on 15 c. sepia	25	10
O649	12 c. on 25 c. slate	25	10
O621	20 c. on 25 c. slate	45	35

1964. Air. Olympic Games, Tokyo. Optd with Olympic Rings and **1964**.

O632	2 l. purple & blk (No. O539)	5·75	4·75

1965. Air. Nos. 630/38 optd **OFICIAL**.

O650	**144**	1 c. black and green	10	10
O651	–	2 c. black and mauve	10	10
O652	–	5 c. black and blue	15	15
O653	–	8 c. black and green	15	15
O654	**144**	10 c. black and bistre	25	25
O655	–	12 c. black and yellow	30	30
O656	–	1 l. black and buff	3·00	2·75
O657	–	2 l. black and olive	6·50	5·75
O658	**144**	3 l. black and red	7·50	7·00

1965. Air. Churchill Commem. Optd **IN MEMORIAM Sir Winston Churchill 1874–1965**.

O674	**128**	16 c. green and violet	70	70

1971. Air. Various official stamps surch in figures.

O788	**134**	10 c. on 3 c. (O572)	25	10
O789	–	10 c. on 2 c. (O603)	25	10
O790	–	10 c. on 3 c. (O604)	25	10

1974. Air. Nos. O570 and O602 surch.

O849	2 c. on 1 c. lake & black	10	10
O850	2 c. on 1 c. yellow	10	10

HONG KONG Pt. 1, Pt. 17

Former British colony at the mouth of the Canton R., consisting of the island of Hong Kong and peninsula of Kowloon. Under Japanese Occupation from 25 December, 1941, until liberated by British forces on 16 September, 1945.

Hong Kong became a Special Administrative Region of the People's Republic of China on 1 July 1997.

100 cents = 1 Hong Kong dollar

1

1862.

8a	**1**	2 c. brown	£110	7·00
34		4 c. grey	9·00	85
10		6 c. lilac	£350	9·50
11b		8 c. yellow	£350	11·00
12a		12 c. blue	25·00	5·50
22		16 c. yellow	£1200	65·00
4		18 c. lilac	£500	45·00
14		24 c. green	£500	8·50
15a		30 c. red	£650	15·00
16		30 c. mauve	£180	5·50
17a		48 c. red	£800	23·00
18		96 c. olive	£25000	£550
19		96 c. grey	£1000	42·00

1877. Surch in figures and words, thus **5 cents.**

23	**1**	5 c. on 8 c. yellow	£700	90·00
24		5 c. on 18 c. lilac	£700	60·00
25		10 c. on 12 c. blue	£800	55·00
26		10 c. on 16 c. yellow	£3750	£150
27		10 c. on 24 c. green	£1200	85·00
20		16 c. on 18 c. lilac	£1900	£150
21		28 c. on 30 c. mauve	£1100	48·00

1880.

33	**1**	2 c. red	26·00	85
56		2 c. green	25·00	85
57		4 c. red	14·00	85
35		5 c. blue	21·00	85
58		5 c. yellow	17·00	6·50
30		10 c. mauve	£450	13·00
37a		10 c. green	£110	1·00
38		10 c. purple on red	19·00	1·00
59		10 c. blue	45·00	1·75
39a		30 c. green	60·00	16·00
61		30 c. brown	30·00	20·00
31		48 c. brown	£1000	90·00

1885. Surch in figures and words, thus **20 CENTS**.

54	**1**	10 c. on 30 c. green	£450	£750
40		20 c. on 30 c. red	90·00	5·00
45a		20 c. on 30 c. green	£100	£130
41		50 c. on 48 c. brown	£325	26·00
46		50 c. on 48 c. purple	£225	£250
42		$1 on 96 c. olive	£600	50·00
47		$1 on 96 c. purple on red	£650	£350
53a		$1 on 96 c. black	£2750	£3500

1891. Surch in figures and words, thus **7 cents.**

43	**1**	7 c. on 10 c. green	60·00	7·50
44		14 c. on 30 c. mauve	£120	50·00

13 (20 c.) **14** (50 c.) **15** ($1)

1891. T **1** surch with figures and words and with Chinese surch also.

55	–	10 c. on 30 c. green	38·00	70·00
48a	**13**	20 c. on 30 c. green	26·00	5·00
49	**14**	50 c. on 48 c. purple	70·00	5·50
50	**15**	$1 on 96 c. purple on red	£400	22·00
52		$1 on 96 c. black	£130	27·00

The Chinese surch on No. 55 is larger than Type **13**.

1891. 50th Anniv of Colony. Optd **1841 Hong Kong JUBILEE 1891**.

51	**1**	2 c. red	£375	95·00

20 24

1903.

62	**20**	1 c. purple and brown	2·00	50
91		1 c. brown	3·00	90
77		2 c. green	4·25	1·25
78a		4 c. purple on red	5·50	60
93		4 c. red	4·75	40
79a		5 c. green and orange	10·00	5·00
94		6 c. brown and purple	16·00	3·50
66		8 c. grey and violet	7·50	1·25
81		10 c. purple & blue on blue	14·00	90
95		10 c. blue	17·00	40
68		12 c. green & purple on yell	7·00	4·25
83a		20 c. grey and brown	22·00	2·25
96		20 c. purple and green	35·00	38·00
84		30 c. green and black	27·00	14·00
97		30 c. purple and yellow	48·00	19·00
85		50 c. green and purple	48·00	7·00
98		50 c. black on green	38·00	14·00
86a		$1 purple and olive	85·00	18·00
87a		$2 grey and red	£150	80·00

99 **20** $2 red and black £250 £225
88 $3 grey and blue £160 £180
89 $5 purple and green £350 £300
76 $10 grey & orange on blue £850 £400

1912.

117 **24** 1 c. brown 1·00 40
118 2 c. green 2·25 30
118c 2 c. grey 13·00 5·00
119 3 c. grey 4·00 1·00
120a 4 c. red 2·25 30
121 5 c. violet 4·75 30
103 6 c. orange 3·75 85
104 8 c. grey 23·00 4·50
123 8 c. orange 3·50 1·00
124 10 c. blue 2·75 30
106 12 c. purple on yellow 3·75 5·50
125 20 c. purple and olive 3·50 30
126 25 c. purple 3·25 40
127 30 c. purple and orange 10·00 1·50
128 50 c. black on green 8·50 30
129 $1 purple & blue on blue 22·00 50
130 $2 red and black 85·00 6·00
131 $3 green and purple £150 48·00
132 $5 green and red on green £400 65·00
116 $10 purple & black on red £500 80·00

1935. Silver Jubilee. As T **10a** of Gambia.
133 3 c. blue and black 4·00 3·25
134 5 c. green and blue 8·00 3·25
135 10 c. brown and blue 20·00 1·60
136 20 c. grey and purple 38·00 7·50

1937. Coronation. As T **10b** of Gambia.
137 4 c. green 4·50 2·50
138 15 c. red 10·00 3·25
139 25 c. blue 13·00 2·50

29 King George VI

30 Street Scene

1938.

140 **29** 1 c. brown 1·75 80
141 2 c. grey 2·00 30
142 4 c. orange 3·25 1·25
143 5 c. green 1·25 20
144 8 c. brown 1·75 2·25
145b 10 c. violet 6·00 70
146 15 c. red 1·75 30
147 20 c. black 1·25 30
148 20 c. red 7·00 40
149 25 c. blue 26·00 80
150 25 c. olive 4·75 1·25
151a 30 c. olive 22·00 8·00
152 30 c. blue 7·00 20
153b 50 c. lilac 9·00 20
154 80 c. red 5·00 95
155 $1 purple and blue 8·00 2·50
156 $1 orange and green 17·00 30
157 $2 orange and green 70·00 14·00
158 $2 violet and red 26·00 95
159 $5 purple and red 55·00 48·00
160 $5 green and violet 80·00 5·00
161 $10 green and violet £400 85·00
162 $10 violet and blue £140 23·00

1941. Centenary of British Occupation. Dated "1841 1941".
163 **30** 2 c. orange and brown 4·50 1·75
164 – 4 c. purple and mauve 4·50 1·75
165 – 5 c. black and green 2·50 50
166 – 15 c. black and red 5·50 1·00
167 – 25 c. brown and blue 12·00 3·50
168 – $1 blue and orange 45·00 7·00
DESIGNS—HORIZ: 4 c. "Empress of Japan" (liner) and junk; 5 c. University; 15 c. Harbour; $1 "Falcon" (clipper) and Short S.23 Empire "C" Class flying boat. VERT: 25 c. Hong Kong Bank.

For Japanese issues see "Japanese Occupation of Hong Kong".

36

1946. Victory.
169 **36** 30 c. blue and red 2·00 1·25
170 $1 brown and red 3·50 75

1948. Silver Wedding. As T **11b/c** of Gambia.
171 10 c. violet 2·75 80
172 $10 red £250 75·00

1949. U.P.U. As T **11d/g** of Gambia.
173 10 c. violet 3·75 50
174 20 c. red 15·00 3·00
175 30 c. blue 12·00 1·75
176 80 c. mauve 35·00 9·50

1953. Coronation. As T **11h** of Gambia.
177 10 c. black and purple 5·00 30

1954. As T **29** but portrait of Queen Elizabeth, facing left.
178 5 c. orange 1·50 20
179 10 c. lilac 2·50 10
180a 15 c. green 4·00 45
181 20 c. brown 5·00 30
182a 25 c. red 3·00 70
183 30 c. grey 4·50 20
184 40 c. blue 4·50 40
185 50 c. purple 4·75 20
186 65 c. grey 19·00 7·50
187 $1 orange and green 7·50 20
188 $1.30 blue and red 23·00 1·00
189 $2 violet and red 12·00 40
190 $5 green and purple 75·00 1·50
191 $10 violet and blue 60·00 8·50

38 University Arms

1961. Golden Jubilee of Hong Kong University.
192 **38** $1 multicoloured 7·00 2·00

39 Statue of Queen Victoria

40 Queen Elizabeth II (after Annigoni)

1962. Stamp Centenary.
193 **39** 10 c. black and mauve 60 10
194 20 c. black and blue 1·75 2·00
195 50 c. black and bistre 4·00 40

1962.

196 **40** 5 c. orange 60 60
223 10 c. violet 70 40
198 15 c. green 2·50 85
199 20 c. brown 1·75 85
200 25 c. mauve 2·50 1·75
201 30 c. blue 2·50 10
202 40 c. turquoise 2·00 40
203 50 c. red 1·75 30
230a 65 c. blue 6·00 6·50
231 $1 sepia 12·00 1·50
206 – $1.30 multicoloured 5·00 20
207 – $2 multicoloured 7·00 50
208 – $5 multicoloured 17·00 1·25
209 – $10 multicoloured 30·00 2·50
210 – $20 multicoloured £140 23·00
Nos. 206/10 are as T **40** but larger 26 × 40½ mm.

1963. Freedom from Hunger. As T **20a** of Gambia.
211 $1.30 green 55·00 8·00

1963. Cent of Red Cross. As T **20b** of Gambia.
212 10 c. red and black 5·00 30
213 $1.30 red and blue 35·00 8·00

1965. Cent of I.T.U. As T **44** of Gibraltar.
214 10 c. purple and yellow 4·00 25
215 $1.30 olive and green 25·00 5·50

1965. I.C.Y. As T **45** of Gibraltar.
216 10 c. purple and turquoise 3·00 25
217 $1.30 green and lavender 20·00 5·50

1966. Churchill Commen. As T **46** of Gibraltar.
218 10 c. blue 3·00 15
219 50 c. green 3·50 30
220 $1.30 brown 24·00 3·00
221 $2 violet 38·00 10·00

1966. Inauguration of W.H.O. Headquarters, Geneva. As T **54** of Gibraltar.
237 10 c. black, green and blue 3·00 30
238 50 c. black, purple & ochre 10·00 1·75

1966. 20th Anniv of U.N.E.S.C.O. As T **56a/c** of Gibraltar.
239 10 c. multicoloured 3·50 20
240 50 c. yellow, violet and olive 13·00 90
241 $2 black, purple & orange 55·00 20·00

42 Rams' Heads on Chinese Lanterns

1967. Chinese New Year ("Year of the Ram").
242 **42** 10 c. red, olive and yellow 4·00 50
243 – $1.30 green, red & yellow 32·00 11·00
DESIGN: $1.30, Three rams.

44 Cable Route Map

1967. Completion of Malaysia–Hong Kong Link of SEACOM Telephone Cable.
244 **44** $1.30 blue and red 17·00 4·50

45 Rhesus Macaques in Tree

1968. Chinese New Year ("Year of the Monkey").
245 **45** 10 c. gold, black and red 4·50 50
246 – $1.30 gold, black and red 30·00 10·00
DESIGN: $1.30, Family of rhesus macaques.

47 "Iberia" (liner) at Ocean Terminal

53 "Bauhinia blakeana"

1968. Sea Craft.
247 **47** 10 c. multicoloured 2·00 15
248 – 20 c. blue, black and brown 3·25 1·00
249 – 40 c. orange, black & mve 11·00 9·00
250 – 50 c. red, black and green 7·50 75
251 – $1 yellow, black & red 16·00 4·50
252 – $1.30 blue, black and pink 45·00 4·25
DESIGNS: 20 c. Pleasure launch; 40 c. Car ferry; 50 c. Passenger ferry; $1 Sampan; $1.30, Junk.

1968. Multicoloured.
253 65 c. Type **53** 9·00 50
254 $1 Arms of Hong Kong 9·00 40

55 "Aladdin's Lamp" and Human Rights Emblem

1968. Human Rights Year.
255 **55** 10 c. orange, black & grn 1·50 75
256 50 c. yellow, black & pur 4·50 2·25

56 Cockerel

1969. Chinese New Year ("Year of the Cock"). Multicoloured.
257 10 c. Type **56** 5·00 1·00
258 $1.30 Cockerel (vert) 65·00 14·00

58 Arms of Chinese University

1969. Establishment of Chinese University of Hong Kong.
259 **58** 40 c. violet, gold and blue 7·00 3·50

59 Earth Station and Satellite

1969. Opening of Communications Satellite Tracking Station.
260 **59** $1 multicoloured 24·00 4·50

60 Chow's Head

62 "Expo '70" Emblem

1970. Chinese New Year ("Year of the Dog"). Multicoloured.
261 10 c. Type **60** 5·50 1·25
262 $1.30 Chow standing (horiz) 65·00 14·00

1970. World Fair, Osaka. Multicoloured.
263 15 c. Type **62** 65 85
264 25 c. "Expo '70" emblem and junks (horiz) 1·40 1·50

64 Plaque in Tung Wah Hospital

1970. Centenary of Tung Wah Hospital.
265 **64** 10 c. multicoloured 75 25
266 50 c. multicoloured 3·25 1·50

65 Symbol

1970. Asian Productivity Year.
267 **65** 10 c. multicoloured 1·00 60

66 Pig

1971. Chinese New Year ("Year of the Pig").
268 **66** 10 c. multicoloured 5·00 90
269 $1.30 multicoloured 30·00 11·00

67 "60" and Scout Badge

68 Festival Emblem

1971. Diamond Jubilee of Scouting in Hong Kong.
270 **67** 10 c. black, red & yellow 75 10
271 50 c. black, green and blue 3·50 1·00
272 $2 black, mauve & violet 20·00 11·00

1971. Hong Kong Festival.
273 **68** 10 c. orange and purple 1·25 20
274 – 50 c. multicoloured 2·75 90
275 – $1 multicoloured 8·50 6·50
DESIGNS—39 × 23 mm: 50 c. Coloured streamers. 23 × 39 mm: $1 "Orchid".

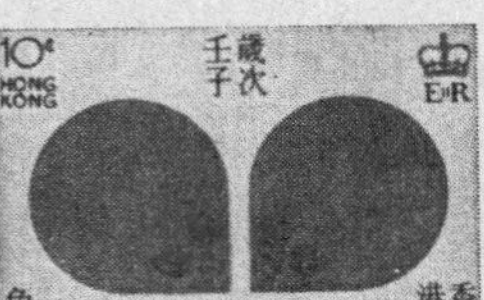

69 Stylised Rats

1972. Chinese New Year. ("Year of the Rat").
276 **69** 10 c. red, black and gold 3·50 50
277 $1.30 red, black and gold 32·00 11·00

70 Tunnel Entrance

1972. Opening of Cross-Harbour Tunnel.
278 **70** $1 multicoloured 5·00 2·25

1972. Royal Silver Wedding. As T **98** of Gibraltar, but with Phoenix and Dragon in background.
279 10 c. multicoloured 30 15
280 50 c. multicoloured 1·10 1·40

72 Ox

73 Queen Elizabeth II

1973 Chinese New Year ("Year of the Ox").
281 **72** 10 c. orange, brown & blk . 2·00 50
282 – $1.30 yellow, orange & blk . 6·50 6·50
DESIGN—HORIZ: $1.30, Ox.

1973.
311 **73** 10 c. orange 55 30
284 15 c. green . . . . 7·00 6·00
313 20 c. violet 50 10
286 25 c. brown . . . . 11·00 6·50
315 30 c. blue 70 30
316 40 c. blue . . . . 1·25 1·50
289 50 c. red . . . . 1·25 60
318 60 c. lavender . . . . . . 1·75 2·00
290 65 c. brown . . . . 12·00 11·00
320 70 c. yellow . . . . 1·75 30
321 80 c. red . . . . 2·25 2·75
321c 90 c. brown . . . . 7·50 1·40
291 $1 green . . . . 2·25 80
323 – $1.30 yellow and violet . . 2·50 30
324 – $2 green and brown . . . 3·00 1·25
324c – $5 pink and blue . . . 4·75 1·75
324d – $10 pink and green . . . 8·00 5·50
324e – $20 pink and black . . . 13·00 11·00
Values of $1.30 and above are size 27 × 32 mm.

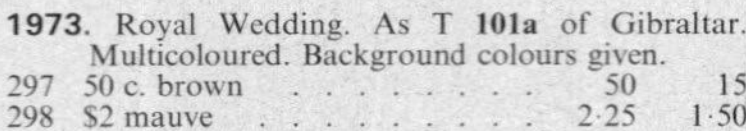

1973. Royal Wedding. As T **101a** of Gibraltar. Multicoloured. Background colours given.
297 50 c. brown 50 15
298 $2 mauve . . . . 2·25 1·50

75 Festival Symbols forming Chinese Character

1973. Hong Kong Festival.
299 **75** 10 c. red and green . . . 40 10
300 – 50 c. mauve and orange . . 2·00 95
301 – $1 green and mauve . . 4·75 4·75
DESIGNS—Festival symbols arranged to form a Chinese character: 10 c. "Hong"; 50 c. "Kong"; $1 "Festival".

76 Tiger

1974. Chinese New Year ("Year of the Tiger").
302 **76** 10 c. multicoloured . . . 3·50 50
303 – $1.30 multicoloured . . . 11·00 12·00
DESIGN—VERT: $1.30, similar to Type **76**.

77 Chinese Mask

1974. Arts Festival.
304 **77** 10 c. multicoloured . . . 75 10
305 – $1 multicoloured . . . 6·00 4·25
306 – $2 multicoloured . . . 9·00 8·50
DESIGNS: $1, $2, Chinese masks similar to T **77**.

78 Pigeons with Letters

1974. Centenary of U.P.U.
308 **78** 10 c. blue, green & black . . 40 10
309 – 50 c. mauve, orange & blk . 1·00 40
310 – $2 multicoloured . . . . 5·25 4·25
DESIGNS: 50 c. Globe within letters; $2 Hands holding letters.

79 Stylized Hare

1975. Chinese New Year ("Year of the Hare").
327 **79** 10 c. silver and red . . . 1·00 60
328 – $1.30 gold and green . . 8·00 8·00
DESIGN: $1.30, Pair of hares.

80 Queen Elizabeth II, the Duke of Edinburgh and Hong Kong Arms

1975. Royal Visit.
329 **80** $1.30 multicoloured . . . 2·75 2·00
330 $2 multicoloured . . . 3·75 4·25

81 Mid-Autumn Festival

82 Hwamei

1975. Hong Kong Festivals of 1975. Mult.
331 50 c. Type **81** . . . . . 2·00 50
332 $1 Dragon-boat Festival . . 8·00 2·50
333 $2 Tin Hau Festival . . . 28·00 8·50

1975. Birds. Multicoloured.
335 50 c. Type **82** . . . . . 2·50 50
336 $1.30 Chinese bulbul . . . 8·50 5·00
337 $2 Black-capped kingfisher . . 16·00 12·00

83 Dragon

1976. Chinese New Year ("Year of the Dragon").
338 **83** 20 c. mauve, purple & gold . 75 10
339 – $1.30 green, red and gold . 6·50 3·25
DESIGN: $1.30, As Type **83** but dragon reversed.

84 "60" and Girl Guides Badge

1976. Diamond Jubilee of Girl Guides. Multicoloured.
354 20 c. Type **84** 50 10
355 $1.30 Badge, stylised diamond and "60" . . . . . 5·50 4·00

85 "Postal Services" in Chinese Characters

1976. Opening of New G.P.O.
356 **85** 20 c. green, grey and black . 75 10
357 – $1.30 orange, grey and blk . 3·75 2·00
358 – $2 yellow, grey and black . 6·50 4·50
DESIGNS: $1.30, Old G.P.O.; $2 New G.P.O.

86 Tree Snake on Branch

1977. Chinese New Year ("Year of the Snake"). Multicoloured.
359 20 c. Type **86** 50 15
360 $1.30 Snake facing left . . . 4·00 4·75

87 Presentation of the Orb

1977. Silver Jubilee. Multicoloured.
361 20 c. Type **87** 40 10
362 $1.30 The Queen's visit, 1975 . 1·25 1·25
363 $2 The Orb (vert) . . . . 1·50 1·50

88 Tram Cars

89 Buttercup Orchid

1977. Tourism. Multicoloured.
364 20 c. Type **88** 55 10
365 60 c. Star ferryboat . . . . 1·50 2·25
366 $1.30 The Peak Railway . . 2·75 2·25
367 $2 Junk and sampan . . . 3·50 3·75

1977. Orchids. Multicoloured.
368 20 c. Type **89** . . . . . 1·25 20
369 $1.30 Lady's slipper orchid . . 4·00 2·25
370 $2 Susan orchid . . . . . 6·00 4·75

90 Horse

1978. Chinese New Year ("Year of the Horse").
371 **90** 20 c. mauve, olive and bistre . 50 10
372 $1.30 orange, brn & lt brn . 3·75 4·25

91 Queen Elizabeth II

1978. 25th Anniv of Coronation.
373 **91** 20 c. mauve and blue . . 40 10
374 $1.30 blue and mauve . . 1·50 2·25

92 Girl and Boy holding Hands

1978. Centenary of Po Leung Kuk (children's charity). Multicoloured.
375 20 c. Type **92** 30 15
376 $1.30 Ring of children . . . 1·75 2·25

93 Electronics Industry

1979. Hong Kong Industries.
377 **93** 20 c. yellow, olive & orge . . 30 10
378 – $1.30 multicoloured . . . 1·10 1·75
379 – $2 multicoloured . . . 1·10 2·25
DESIGNS: $1.30, Toy industry; $2 Garment industry.

94 "Precis orithya"   96 Tsui Shing Lau Pagoda

95 Diagrammatic View of Railway Station

1979. Butterflies. Multicoloured.
380 20 c. Type **94** . . . . . 1·00 10
381 $1 "Graphium sarpedon" . . 1·75 80
382 $1.30 "Heliophorus epicles" . 2·50 1·60
383 $2 "Danaus genutia" . . . 2·75 3·50

1979. Mass Transit Railway. Multicoloured.
384 20 c. Type **95** 80 10
385 $1.30 Diagrammatic view of car 2·25 80
386 $2 Plan showing route of railway 2·50 2·25

1980. Rural Architecture.
387 **96** 20 c. black, mauve & yellow 40 20
388 – $1.30 multicoloured . . . 1·10 1·25
389 – $2 multicoloured . . . 1·60 2·50
DESIGNS—HORIZ: $1.30, Village house, Sai O; $2 Ching Chung Koon Temple.

97 Queen Elizabeth the Queen Mother

1980. 80th Birthday of The Queen Mother.
390 **97** $1.30 multicoloured . . . 1·25 1·50

98 Botanical Gardens

1980. Parks. Multicoloured.
391 20 c. Type **98** 50 15
392 $1 Ocean Park 85 60
393 $1.30 Kowloon Park . . . 90 95
394 $2 Country parks . . . . 2·00 2·75

99 Red-spotted Grouper

1981. Fishes. Multicoloured.
395 20 c. Type **99** 40 15
396 $1 Golden thread-finned bream . 1·10 70
397 $1.30 Scar-breasted tuskfish . . 1·25 95
398 $2 Blue-barred orange parrotfish . . . . . 2·00 3·25

100 Wedding Bouquet from Hong Kong

101 Suburban Development

1981. Royal Wedding. Multicoloured.
399 20 c. Type **100** 30 10
400 $1.30 Prince Charles in Hong Kong 70 50
401 $5 Prince Charles and Lady Diana Spencer . . . . . 2·25 3·00

1981. Public Housing.
402 **101** 20 c. multicoloured 25 10
403 – $1 multicoloured 90 70
404 – $1.30 multicoloured . . . 1·25 1·25
405 – $2 multicoloured . . . . . 1·40 2·25
DESIGNS: $1 to $2, Various suburban developments.

102 "Victoria from the Harbour, c. 1855"

1982. Hong Kong Port, Past and Present. Multicoloured.
407 20 c. Type **102** 60 15
408 $1 "West Point, Hong Kong, 1847" . . . . 1·75 90
409 $1.30 Fleet of junks . . . . . 2·25 1·10
410 $2 Liner "Queen Elizabeth 2" at Hong Kong . . . . 3·00 2·75

103 Large Indian Civet

1982. Wild Animals.
411 **103** 20 c. black, pink & brown . 60 15
412 – $1 multicoloured . . . . . 1·25 90
413 – $1.30 black, green & orge . 1·50 1·10
414 – $5 black, brown & yellow . 3·00 4·50
DESIGNS: $1 Chinese pangolin; $1.30, Chinese porcupine; $5 Indian muntjac.

104 Queen Elizabeth II

107 Dancing

106 Table Tennis

1982.
415 **104** 10 c. lt red, red & yellow . 80 60
416 20 c. blue, violet & lavender 90 70
417 30 c. lt violet, vio & pink . 1·50 30
418 40 c. red and blue . . . . 1·50 30
419 50 c. chestnut, brn & grn . 90 40
476 60 c. purple and grey . . 1·50 1·10
477 70 c. green, myrtle & yell . 2·25 40
478 80 c. bistre, brown & green . 2·50 1·75
479 90 c. dp green, grn & turq . 2·50 50
480 $1 dp orange, orge & red . 1·75 40
481 $1.30 blue and mauve . . 2·50 45
482 $1.70 dp blue, bl & grn . . 4·00 1·50
483 $2 blue and pink . . . . . 3·75 1·50
484 – $5 red, purple & yellow . 7·00 3·25
485 – $10 brown & lt brown . . 8·00 4·00
486 – $20 red and blue . . . . 10·00 7·50
487 – $50 red and grey . . . . 30·00 25·00
Nos. 484/7 are as Type **104** but larger, 26×30 mm.

1982. Sport for the Disabled. Multicoloured.
431 30 c. Type **106** 50 10
432 $1 Racing 75 80
433 $1.30 Basketball . . . . 2·75 1·50
434 $5 Archery . . . . 5·00 6·50

1983. Performing Arts.
435 **107** 30 c. light blue and blue . . 50 10
436 – $1.30 red and purple . . . 2·00 1·25
437 – $5 green and deep green 6·50 5·50
DESIGNS: $1.30, "Theatre"; $5 "Music".

108 Aerial View of Hong Kong

1983. Commonwealth Day. Multicoloured.
438 30 c. Type **108** 70 10
439 $1 "Liverpool Bay" (container ship) . . . . 1·75 1·25
440 $1.30 Hong Kong flag . . . . 1·75 1·25
441 $5 Queen Elizabeth II and Hong Kong . . . . 3·50 5·00

109 Victoria Harbour

1983. Hong Kong by Night. Multicoloured.
442 30 c. Type **109** . . . . 1·25 15
443 $1 Space Museum, Tsim Sha Tsui Cultural Centre . . . . . . 3·75 1·50
444 $1.30 Fireworks display . . . . 4·75 2·00
445 $5 "Jumbo", floating restaurant 15·00 8·50

110 Old and new Observatory Buildings

1983. Centenary of Hong Kong Observatory.
446 **110** 40 c. orange, brown & black 75 10
447 – $1 mauve, dp mve & blk . 2·00 1·75
448 – $1.30 blue, dp blue & blk . 2·75 1·75
449 – $5 yellow, green & black . 8·00 9·00
DESIGNS: $1 Wind measuring equipment; $1.30, Thermometer; $5 Ancient and modern seismometers.

111 De Havilland D.H.86 Dragon Express "Dorado" (Hong Kong–Penang Service, 1936)

1984. Aviation in Hong Kong. Multicoloured.
450 40 c. Type **111** . . . . 1·00 15
451 $1 Sikorsky S-42B flying boat (San Francisco–Hong Kong Service, 1937) . . . . 2·25 1·75
452 $1.30 Cathay-Pacific Boeing 747 jet leaving Kai Tak Airport . 3·25 1·75
453 $5 Baldwin brothers' balloon, 1891 (vert) . . . . 9·00 10·00

112 Map by Capt. E. Belcher, 1836

1984. Maps of Hong Kong.
454 40 c. Type **112** . . . . 1·00 20
455 $1 Bartholomew map of 1929 . 1·75 1·25
456 $1.30 Early map of Hong Kong waters . . . . 3·00 1·75
457 $5 Chinese-style map of 1819 . 11·00 10·00

113 Cockerel

1984. Chinese Lanterns. Multicoloured.
458 40 c. Type **113** 80 15
459 $1 Dog . . . . 1·75 1·25
460 $1.30 Butterfly . . . . 3·00 1·75
461 $5 Fish . . . . 9·00 8·50

114 Jockey on Horse and Nurse with Baby ("Health Care")

1984. Centenary of Royal Hong Kong Jockey Club. Designs showing aspects of Club's charity work. Multicoloured.
462 40 c. Type **114** . . . . 1·25 20
463 $1 Disabled man playing handball ("Support for Disabled") . . . . 2·00 1·75
464 $1.30 Ballerina ("The Arts") . . 3·00 2·00
465 $5 Humboldt penguins ("Ocean Park") . . . . 9·00 11·00

115 Hung Sing Temple

1985. Historic Buildings. Multicoloured.
467 40 c. Type **115** 60 20
468 $1 St. John's Cathedral . . . . 1·75 1·60
469 $1.30 The Old Supreme Court Building . . . . 2·25 1·75
470 $5 Wan Chai Post Office . . . 9·50 8·50

116 Prow of Dragon Boat

1985. 10th International Dragon Boat Festival. Designs showing different parts of dragon boat. Multicoloured.
488 40 c. Type **116** 50 15
489 $1 Drummer and rowers . . . 1·75 1·25
490 $1.30 Rowers . . . . 3·00 1·60
491 $5 Stern of boat . . . . 9·25 8·00

117 The Queen Mother with Prince Charles and Prince William, 1984

1985. Life and Times of Queen Elizabeth the Queen Mother. Multicoloured.
493 40 c. At Glamis Castle, aged 7 . 60 10
494 $1 Type **117** . . . . 1·75 1·25
495 $1.30 The Queen Mother, 1970 (from photo by Cecil Beaton) 2·00 1·40
496 $5 With Prince Henry at his christening (from photo by Lord Snowdon) . . . . . . 3·25 4·00

118 Melastoma

1985. Native Flowers. Multicoloured.
497 40 c. Type **118** . . . . 1·50 20
498 50 c. Chinese lily . . . . . . 1·75 40
499 60 c. Grantham's camellia . . . 2·00 90
500 $1.30 Narcissus . . . . 3·25 1·25
501 $1.70 Bauhinia . . . . 3·75 1·50
502 $5 Chinese New Year flower . 7·00 9·00

119 Hong Kong Academy for Performing Arts

1985. New Buildings. Multicoloured.
503 50 c. Type **119** 80 15
504 $1.30 Exchange Square (vert) . 1·75 1·50
505 $1.70 Hong Kong Bank Headquarters (vert) . . . . 2·50 1·75
506 $5 Hong Kong Coliseum . . . . 8·00 11·00

120 Halley's Comet in the Solar System

1986. Appearance of Halley's Comet. Mult.
507 50 c. Type **120** . . . . 1·25 20
508 $1.30 Edmond Halley and Comet 2·00 1·40
509 $1.70 Comet over Hong Kong . 2·75 1·50
510 $5 Comet passing the Earth . . 11·00 8·00

120a At Wedding of Miss Celia Bowes-Lyon, 1931

1986. 60th Birthday of Queen Elizabeth II. Multicoloured.
512 50 c. Type **120a** 50 10
513 $1 Queen in Garter procession, Windsor Castle, 1977 . . . . 85 60
514 $1.30 In Hong Kong, 1975 . . . 1·10 70
515 $1.70 At Royal Lodge, Windsor, 1980 (from photo by Norman Parkinson) . . . . 1·25 75
516 $5 At Crown Agents Head Office, London, 1983 . . . . 4·00 5·00

121 Mass Transit Train, Boeing 747 Airliner and Map of World

1986. "Expo '86" World Fair, Vancouver. Multicoloured.
517 50 c. Type **121** 80 30
518 $1.30 Hong Kong Bank Headquarters and map of world . . . . 1·50 1·00
519 $1.70 Container ship and map of world . . . . 2·25 1·40
520 $5 Dish aerial and map of world 6·50 7·00

122 Hand-liner Sampan

1986. Fishing Vessels. Designs showing fishing boat and outline of fish. Multicoloured.
521 50 c. Type **122** 80 15
522 $1.30 Stern trawler . . . . . . 1·50 1·10
523 $1.70 Long liner junk . . . . . 2·25 1·40
524 $5 Junk trawler . . . . 7·00 7·50

123 "The Second Puan Khequa" (attr Spoilum)

1986. 19th-century Hong Kong Portraits. Multicoloured.
525 50 c. Type **123** 55 15
526 $1.30 "Chinese Lady" (19th-century copy) . . . . 1·50 1·10
527 $1.70 "Lamqua" (self-portrait) . 1·75 1·40
528 $5 "Wife of Wo Hing Qua" (attr G. Chinnery) . . . . 5·50 5·50

124 Rabbit

1987. Chinese New Year ("Year of the Rabbit"). Designs showing stylized rabbits.
529 124 50 c. multicoloured 65 15
530 – $1.30 multicoloured . . . 1·50 1·25
531 – $1.70 multicoloured . . . 1·75 1·40
532 – $5 multicoloured . . . . 6·50 6·00
Nos. 530/1 have the "0" omitted from their face values.

125 "Village Square, Hong Kong Island, 1838" (Auguste Borget)

1987. 19th-century Hong Kong Scenes. Mult.
534 50 c. Type 125 . . . . . . 60 15
535 $1.30 "Boat Dwellers, Kowloon Bay, 1838 (Auguste Borget) 1·75 1·10
536 $1.70 "Flagstaff House, 1846" (Murdoch Bruce) . . . . 2·25 1·40
537 $5 "Wellington Street, late 19th-century" (C. Andrasi) . . . 7·00 7·50

126 Queen Elizabeth II and Central Victoria
127 Hong Kong Flag

1987.
600 126 10 c. multicoloured . . . 60 75
639A 40 c. multicoloured . . . 1·50 1·40
602 50 c. multicoloured . . . 90 30
603 60 c. multicoloured . . . 90 30
604 70 c. multicoloured . . . 90 60
605 80 c. multicoloured . . . 90 40
606 90 c. multicoloured . . . 90 40
607 $1 multicoloured 90 30
607a $1.20 multicoloured . . . 2·75 2·50
608 $1.30 multicoloured . . . 1·75 50
609 $1.40 multicoloured . . . 1·75 70
547A $1.70 multicoloured . . . 3·00 80
610 $1.80 multicoloured . . . 1·25 60
611 $2 multicoloured . . . . 1·25 50
611a $2.30 multicoloured . . . 2·75 2·75
612 – $5 multicoloured . . . . 4·50 1·50
613 – $10 multicoloured . . . . 6·00 5·25
614 – $20 multicoloured . . . . 8·00 8·00
615 – $50 multicoloured . . . . 19·00 17·00
DESIGNS—25 × 31 mm: Queen Elizabeth II and $5 Kowloon; $10 Victoria Harbour; $20 Legislative Council Building; $50 Government House.
With the exception of Nos. 607a and 611a which are dated, all the above exist with or without a date in the design.

1987.
554a 127 10 c. multicoloured . . . 50 50
554b – 50 c. brown, red & black . 1·25 1·50
554c – 80 c. mauve, green & blk . 70 1·50
554d – 90 c. blue, brown & black . 70 90
554e – $1.30 green, blue & black . 1·40 1·75
554f – $2.30 brown, violet & blk . 1·60 2·25
DESIGN: 50 c. to $2.30, Map of Hong Kong.

128 Alice Ho Miu Ling Nethersole Hospital, 1887

1987. Hong Kong Medical Centenaries. Mult.
555 50 c. Type 128 . . . . 1·00 20
556 $1.30 Matron and nurses, Nethersole Hospital, 1891 . . 2·25 1·40
557 $1.70 Scanning equipment, Faculty of Medicine . . . . 2·75 1·40
558 $5 Nurse and patient, Faculty of Medicine . . . . 8·50 8·00

129 Casual Dress with Fringed Hem, 220–589

1987. Historical Chinese Costumes. Multicoloured.
559 50 c. Type 129 . . . . . . 55 10
560 $1.30 Two-piece dress and wrap, 581–960 . . . . 1·40 1·25
561 $1.70 Formal dress, Song Dynasty, 960–1279 . . . . 1·75 1·50
562 $5 Manchu empress costume, 1644–1911 . . . . 5·75 6·50

130 Dragon

1988. Chinese New Year ("Year of the Dragon"). Designs showing dragons.
563 130 50 c. multicoloured 75 15
564 – $1.30 multicoloured . . . 1·75 1·25
565 – $1.70 multicoloured . . . 2·00 1·40
566 – $5 multicoloured . . . . . 4·00 5·00

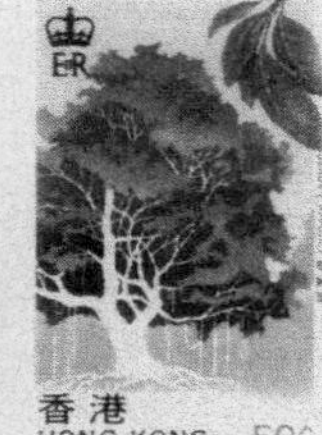

131 White-breasted Kingfisher
132 Chinese Banyan

1988. Hong Kong Birds. Multicoloured.
568 50 c. Type 131 . . . . 1·25 30
569 $1.30 Fukien niltava . . . . . 2·50 1·40
570 $1.70 Black kite . . . . 3·00 1·50
571 $5 Lesser pied kingfisher . . . 5·50 6·00

1988. Trees of Hong Kong. Multicoloured.
572 50 c. Type 132 . . . . 40 10
573 $1.30 Hong Kong orchid tree . 85 65
574 $1.70 Cotton tree . . . . . . 1·25 85
575 $5 Schima . . . . 3·50 4·50

133 Lower Terminal, Peak Tramway
134 Hong Kong Catholic Cathedral

1988. Centenary of The Peak Tramway. Mult.
577 50 c. Type 133 . . . . 60 10
578 $1.30 Tram on incline . . . . 1·00 1·00
579 $1.70 Peak Tower Upper Terminal . . . . 1·10 1·00
580 $5 Tram . . . . 3·50 4·50

1988. Centenary of Hong Kong Catholic Cathedral.
582 134 60 c. multicoloured . . . . 1·25 75

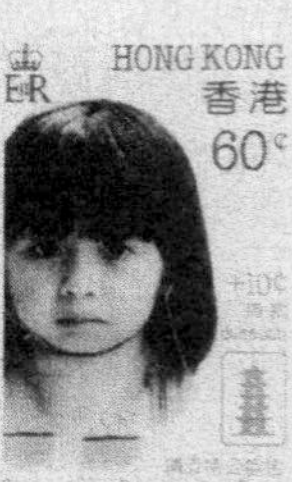

135 Deaf Girl
137 Girl and Doll

136 Snake

1988. Community Chest Charity.
583 135 60 c. + 10 c. blk, red & blue 60 75
584 – $1.40 + 20 c. black, red and green . . . . 80 1·00
585 – $1.80 + 30 c. black, red and orange . . . . 1·50 1·60
586 – $5 + $1 black, red & brn 4·25 5·50
DESIGNS: $1.40, Elderly woman; $1.80, Blind boy using braille typewriter; $5 Mother and baby.

1989. Chinese New Year ("Year of the Snake"). Multicoloured.
587 60 c. Type 136 . . . . 30 15
588 $1.40 Snake and fish . . . . 1·25 70
589 $1.80 Snake on branch . . . 1·75 85
590 $5 Coiled snake . . . . . . 5·50 5·50

1989. Cheung Chau Bun Festival. Multicoloured.
592 60 c. Type 137 . . . . 55 15
593 $1.40 Girl in festival costume 1·25 70
594 $1.80 Paper effigy of god Taai Si Wong . . . . 1·40 80
595 $5 Floral gateway . . . . . . 3·50 4·25

138 "Twins" (wood carving, Cheung Yee)
139 Lunar New Year Festivities

1989. Modern Art. Multicoloured.
596 60 c. Type 138 . . . . 50 15
597 $1.40 "Figures" (acrylic on paper, Chan Luis) . . . . . 1·25 70
598 $1.80 "Lotus" (copper sculpture, Van Lau) . . . . 1·40 80
599 $5 "Zen Painting" (ink and colour on paper, Lui Shou-kwan) . . . . 3·00 4·25

1989. Hong Kong People. Multicoloured.
616 60 c. Type 139 . . . . 50 10
617 $1.40 Shadow boxing and horse racing . . . . 1·25 80
618 $1.80 Foreign-exchange dealer and traditional builder . . . 1·60 90
619 $5 Multi-racial society . . . . 4·00 5·50

140 University of Science and Technology
141 Prince and Princess of Wales and Hong Kong Skyline

1989. Building for the Future.
620 140 60 c. black, yellow & brn . 35 15
621 – 70 c. blk, pale pink & pink . 40 30
622 – $1.30 black, lt green & grn . 90 70
623 – $1.40 black, lt blue & bl . 90 70
624 – $1.80 black, turquoise & bl . 1·10 1·00
625 – $5 brown, orange & red . 3·75 4·00
DESIGNS: 70 c. Cultural Centre; $1.30, Eastern Harbour motorway interchange; $1.40, New Bank of China Building; $1.80, Convention and Exhibition Centre; $5 Mass Transit electric train.

1989. Royal Visit. Multicoloured.
626 60 c. Type 141 . . . . 75 15
627 $1.40 Princess of Wales . . . 1·25 80
628 $1.80 Prince of Wales . . . . 1·40 1·10
629 $5 Prince and Princess of Wales in evening dress . . . . . . 5·50 6·00

143 Horse

1990. Chinese New Year ("Year of the Horse").
631 143 60 c. multicoloured 60 20
632 – $1.40 multicoloured . . . 1·40 1·00
633 – $1.80 multicoloured . . . 1·50 1·25
634 – $5 multicoloured . . . . . 4·75 5·50
DESIGNS: $1.40 to $5, Different horse designs.

144 Chinese Lobster Dish
145 Air Pollution and Clean Air

1990. International Cuisine. Designs showing various dishes. Multicoloured.
636 60 c. Type 144 . . . . 50 15
637 70 c. Indian 50 30
638 $1.30 Chinese vegetables . . . 90 65
639 $1.40 Thai 90 65
640 $1.80 Japanese . . . . 1·25 80
641 $5 French . . . . 4·25 5·50

1990. U.N. World Environment Day. Mult.
642 60 c. Type 145 . . . . 40 15
643 $1.40 Noise pollution and music 85 70
644 $1.80 Polluted and clean water 1·00 80
645 $5 Litter on ground and in bin 2·75 3·50

146 Street Lamp and Des Voeux Road, 1890

1990. Centenary of Electricity Supply.
647 146 60 c. black, bistre & brn . . 50 10
648 – $1.40 multicoloured . . . 1·10 90
649 – $1.80 black, bistre & blue . 1·25 1·00
650 – $5 multicoloured . . . . . 2·50 4·00
DESIGNS: $1.40, Street Lamp and "Jumbo" (floating restaurant), 1940; $1.80, Street lamp and pylon, 1960; $5 Street lamp and Hong Kong from harbour, 1980.

147 Christmas Tree and Skyscrapers

1990. Christmas. Multicoloured.
652 50 c. Type 147 . . . . 25 10
653 60 c. Dove with holly 25 15
654 $1.40 Firework display 80 40
655 $1.80 Father Christmas hat on skyscraper . . . . 1·00 50
656 $2 Children with Father Christmas . . . . 1·40 1·25
657 $5 Candy stick with bow and Hong Kong skyline . . . . 3·00 4·50

148 Ram

1991. Chinese New Year ("Year of the Ram").
658 148 60 c. multicoloured 25 15
659 – $1.40 multicoloured . . . 65 45
660 – $1.80 multicoloured . . . 80 60
661 – $5 multicoloured . . . . . 2·75 3·75
DESIGNS: $1.40 to $5, Different ram designs.

149 Letter "A", Clock, Teddy Bear and Building Bricks (Kindergarten)
150 Rickshaw

1991. Education. Multicoloured.
663 80 c. Type 149 . . . . 50 20
664 $1.80 Globe, laboratory flask and mathematical symbols (Primary and Secondary) . . 1·25 70
665 $2.30 Machinery (Vocational) . 1·40 1·25
666 $5 Mortar board, computer and books (Tertiary) . . . . . . 3·50 4·50

1991. 100 Years of Public Transport. Mult.
667 80 c. Type 150 . . . . 30 15
668 90 c. Double-decker bus . . . 70 40
669 $1.70 Harbour ferry . . . . . 1·10 75
670 $1.80 Double-deck tram . . . 1·40 75
671 $2.30 Mass Transit electric train 2·00 1·75
672 $5 Jetfoil . . . . 3·50 5·00

151 Victorian Pillar Box and Cover of 1888
152 Bronze Buddha, Lantau Island

1991. 150th Anniv of Hong Kong Post Office. Multicoloured.

673 80 c. Type **151** 40 15
674 $1.70 Edwardian pillar box and cover 90 75
675 $1.80 King George V pillar box and cover of 1935 . . . . . 1·00 75
676 $2.30 King George VI pillar box and cover of 1938 . . . . . 1·40 1·75
677 $5 Queen Elizabeth II pillar box and cover of 1989 . . . . . 3·75 5·50

1991. Landmarks.

679 **152** 80 c. red and black 50 15
680 – $1.70 green and black . . . 1·00 80
681 – $1.80 violet and black . . . 1·25 80
682 – $2.30 blue and black . . . 1·25 1·75
683 – $5 orange and black . . . 3·50 5·00

DESIGNS: $1.70, Peak Pavilion; $1.80, Clocktower of Kowloon–Canton Railway Station; $2.30, Catholic Cathedral; $5 Wong Tai Sin Temple.

153 Monkey

1992. Chinese New Year ("Year of the Monkey").

686 **153** 80 c. multicoloured 40 15
687 – $1.80 multicoloured . . . 70 55
688 – $2.30 multicoloured . . . 1·25 1·40
689 – $5 multicoloured . . . . . 2·75 4·50

DESIGNS: $1.80 to $5, Different monkey designs.

1992. 40th Anniv of Queen Elizabeth II's Accession. As T **179a** of Gibraltar. Multicoloured.

691 80 c. Royal barge in Hong Kong harbour 30 15
692 $1.70 Queen watching dancing display 60 35
693 $1.80 Fireworks display 60 35
694 $2.30 Three portraits of Queen Elizabeth 90 85
695 $5 Queen Elizabeth II . . . . 2·00 2·75

154 Running

1992. Olympic Games, Barcelona. Multicoloured.

696 80 c. Type **154** 40 20
697 $1.80 Swimming and javelin . . 80 80
698 $2.30 Cycling . . . . 1·60 1·75
699 $5 High jump . . . . 2·25 3·75

155 Queen Elizabeth II

157 Principal Male Character

156 Stamps and Perforation Gauge

1992.

702 **155** 10 c. mauve, blk & cerise 30 40
702bp 20 c. black, indigo & bl . 70 80
703 50 c. red, black and yellow 30 30
704 60 c. blue, black and light blue 65 45
705 70 c. mauve, black and lilac 65 65
706 80 c. mauve, black and pink 30 20
707 90 c. grn, blk & grey . . 30 20
708 $1 brown, black and yellow 35 20
708b $1.10 red, black & orge . 55 50
709 $1.20 violet, blk & lilac . 35 25
757c $1.30 blue, black and orange 50 65
709c $1.40 green, black and yellow 35 30
709d $1.50 brown, black and blue 80 60
709e $1.60 green, black and lilac 45 50
710 $1.70 ultram, blk & bl . 80 75
711 $1.80 mauve, black and grey . . . . 1·25 55
711a $1.90 green, black and stone 80 75
764 $2 blue, black & green . 60 75
712b **155** $2.10 red, black & grn . 1·25 75
713 $2.30 brown, black and pink . . . . 1·25 75
759 $2.40 bl, blk & grey . . 95 1·40
713b $2.50 green, black and yellow 55 70
713c $2.60 choc, blk & brn . 1·25 1·25
713d $3.10 brown, black and blue 65 80
759e $5 green, black & lt grn . 1·00 1·75
715 – $10 brown, black and cinnamon . . . . . 3·25 2·75
716 – $20 red, black & orange . 4·25 4·50
717 – $50 dp grey, blk & grey . 8·50 11·00

Nos. 715/17 are as Type **155**, but larger, 26 × 30 mm.

1992. Stamp Collecting. Multicoloured.

718 80 c. Type **156** 30 20
719 $1.80 Handstamp of 1841, 1891 Jubilee overprint and tweezers 60 65
720 $2.30 Stamps of 1946 and 1949 under magnifying glass . . . 85 1·00
721 $5 2 c. of 1862 and watermark detector . . . . 2·00 3·25

1992. Chinese Opera. Multicoloured.

724 80 c. Type **157** 50 25
725 $1.80 Martial character . . . . 1·00 1·00
726 $2.30 Principal female character 1·40 1·50
727 $5 Comic character . . . . . 2·50 4·50

158 Hearts

1992. Greetings Stamps. Multicoloured.

728 80 c. Type **158** 30 20
729 $1.80 Stars 55 60
730 $2.30 Presents 75 95
731 $5 Balloons . . . . 1·60 2·50

159 Cockerel

1993. Chinese New Year ("Year of the Cock").

732 **159** 80 c. multicoloured 30 20
733 – $1.80 multicoloured . . . 70 80
734 – $2.30 multicoloured . . . 95 1·10
735 – $5 multicoloured . . . . . 2·25 3·50

DESIGNS: $1.80 to $5, Different cock designs.

160 Pipa

161 Central Waterfront, Hong Kong in 1954

1993. Chinese String Musical Instruments. Multicoloured.

737 80 c. Type **160** 40 20
738 $1.80 Erhu 70 70
739 $2.30 Ruan . . . . 95 1·00
740 $5 Gehu . . . . 2·00 3·25

1993. 40th Anniv of Coronation. Multicoloured.

741 80 c. Type **161** 40 20
742 $1.80 Hong Kong in 1963 . . . 70 65
743 $2.30 Hong Kong in 1975 . . . 90 1·10
744 $5 Hong Kong in 1992 . . . 2·25 3·00

162 University of Science and Technology Building and Student

1993. Hong Kong's Contribution to Science and Technology. Multicoloured.

747 80 c. Type **162** 30 20
748 $1.80 Science Museum building and energy machine exhibit . 50 40
749 $2.30 Governor's Award and circuit board 60 90
750 $5 Dish aerials and world map . 1·40 3·00

163 Red Calico Egg-fish

1993. Goldfish. Multicoloured.

752 $1 Type **163** 35 20
753 $1.90 Red cap oranda 60 50
754 $2.40 Red and white fringetail . 90 1·00
755 $5 Black and gold dragon-eye . 2·25 3·50

164 Dog

1994. Chinese New Year ("Year of the Dog").

766 **164** $1 multicoloured 30 20
767 – $1.90 multicoloured . . . 50 55
768 – $2.40 multicoloured . . . 70 90
769 – $5 multicoloured . . . . . 1·75 3·00

DESIGNS: $1.90 to $5, Different dog designs.

165 Modern Police Constables on Traffic Duty

1994. 150th Anniv of Royal Hong Kong Police Force. Multicoloured.

772 $1 Type **165** 30 20
773 $1.20 Marine policeman with binoculars 40 35
774 $1.90 Police uniforms of 1950 . . 55 45
775 $2 Tactical firearms unit officer with sub-machine gun . . 75 65
776 $2.40 Early 20th-century police uniforms . . . . 90 1·00
777 $5 Sikh and Chinese constables of 1900 . . . . 2·75 3·75

166 Dragon Boat Festival

1994. Traditional Chinese Festivals. Multicoloured.

778 $1 Type **166** 35 20
779 $1.90 Lunar New Year 60 60
780 $2.40 Seven Sisters Festival . . 85 1·10
781 $5 Mid-Autumn Festival . . . 1·75 3·00

167 Swimming

1994. 15th Commonwealth Games, Victoria, Canada. Multicoloured.

783 $1 Type **167** 25 20
784 $1.90 Bowls 40 50
785 $2.40 Gymnastics 60 85
786 $5 Weightlifting . . . . . . 1·25 2·50

168 Dr. James Legge and Students

1994. Dr. James Legge (Chinese scholar) Commemoration.

787 **168** $1 multicoloured 55 60

169 Alcyonium Coral

1994. Corals. Multicoloured.

788 $1 Type **169** 35 20
789 $1.90 Zoanthus 45 55
790 $2.40 Tubastrea . . . . 65 1·00
791 $5 Platygyra . . . . 1·25 2·50

170 Pig

1995. Chinese New Year ("Year of the Pig").

793 **170** $1 multicoloured 30 30
794 – $1.90 multicoloured . . . 50 70
795 – $2.40 multicoloured . . . 60 95
796 – $5 multicoloured . . . . . 1·00 2·00

DESIGNS: $1.90 to $5, Different pig designs.

171 Hong Kong Rugby Sevens

1995. International Sporting Events in Hong Kong. Multicoloured.

798 $1 Type **171** 45 20
799 $1.90 The China Sea Yacht Race 60 65
800 $2.40 International Dragon Boat Races . . . . 85 1·00
801 $5 Hong Kong International Horse Races . . . . 1·75 2·75

172 Tsui Shing Lau Pagoda

1995. Hong Kong Traditional Rural Buildings. Multicoloured.

802 $1 Type **172** 30 20
803 $1.90 Sam Tung Uk village . . 45 55
804 $2.40 Lo Wai village . . . . . 60 1·00
805 $5 Man Shek Tong house . . . 1·10 2·50

173 Regimental Badge

1995. Disbandment of the Royal Hong Kong Regiment. Multicoloured.

806 $1.20 Type **173** 40 25
807 $2.10 Regimental guidon (horiz) 50 55
808 $2.60 Colour of Hong Kong Volunteer Defence Corps, 1928 (horiz) 60 85
809 $5 Cap badge of Royal Hong Kong Defence Force, 1951 . 1·00 2·00

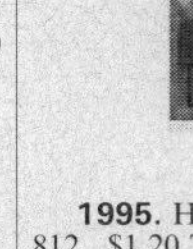

174 Bruce Lee

1995. Hong Kong Film Stars. Multicoloured.

812 $1.20 Type **174** . . . . 1·50 55
813 $2.10 Leung Sing-por . . . . 1·75 1·40
814 $2.60 Yam Kim-fai . . . . . 2·75 1·60
815 $5 Lin Dai . . . . 2·75 3·25

175 Rat

1996. Chinese New Year ("Year of the Rat").

816 **175** $1.20 multicoloured . . . 25 30
817 – $2.10 multicoloured . . . 45 55
818 – $2.60 multicoloured . . . 50 65
819 – $5 multicoloured . . . . . 1·25 1·75

DESIGNS: $2.10 to $5, Rats (different).

176 Rhythmic Gymnastics

1996. Olympic Games, Atlanta. Multicoloured with Royal cypher and face values in black and Olympic rings multicoloured.
822 $1.20 Type **176** 25 25
823 $2.10 Diving 45 55
824 $2.60 Athletics 55 75
825 $5 Basketball . . . . 1·50 2·50
See also Nos. 832/5.

177 Painted Pottery Basin, c. 4500–3700 B.C.

1996. Archaeological Discoveries. Multicoloured.
828 $1.20 Type **177** 35 25
829 $2.10 Stone "yue" (ceremonial axe), c. 2900–2200 B.C. . . . 40 65
830 $2.60 Stone "ge" (halberd), c. 2200–1500 B.C. . . . . . 45 1·00
831 $5 Pottery tripod, c. 25–220 A.D. . . . . 1·00 2·50

1996. Opening of Centennial Olympic Games, Atlanta. Designs as Nos. 822/5, but with Royal Cypher and Olympic Rings in gold and face values in colours quoted.
832 $1.20 Type **176** (mauve) . . . 35 25
833 $2.10 As No. 823 (blue) 40 60
834 $2.60 As No. 824 (green) . . . 45 90
835 $5 As No. 825 (red) . . . . 1·00 2·75

178 Pat Sin Leng Mountain

1996. Mountains. Multicoloured.
837 $1.30 Type **178** 40 35
838 $2.50 Ma On Shan (40 × 35 mm) . . . . 60 1·00
839 $3.10 Lion Rock (35 × 40 mm) . 80 1·00
840 $5 Lantau Peak (25 × 46½ mm) . . . . 1·00 2·25

179 Main Building, University of Hong Kong, 1912

1996. Urban Heritage. Multicoloured.
843 $1.30 Type **179** 40 70
844 $2.50 Western Market, 1906 . . 60 85
845 $3.10 Old Pathological Institute, 1905 . . . . 65 1·00
846 $5 Flagstaff House, 1846 . . . 80 2·25

180 Part of Hong Kong Skyline

1997.
848 **180** 10 c. purple and pink . . . 15 20
849 – 20 c. brown and red . . . 30 30
850 – 50 c. green and orange . . 20 20
851 – $1 blue and yellow . . . 30 20
852 – $1.20 green and yellow . . 30 25
853 – $1.30 violet and green . . 30 25
854 – $1.40 purple and green . . 30 25
855 – $1.60 purple and green . . 30 30
856 – $2 green and blue . . . 40 35
857 – $2.10 turquoise and blue . . 40 35
858 – $2.50 violet and mauve . . 50 55
859 – $3.10 purple and mauve . . 60 70
860 – $5 mauve and orange . . . 1·25 1·00
861 – $10 multicoloured (28 × 32 mm) . . . . 2·00 2·00
862 – $20 multicoloured (28 × 32 mm) . . . . 3·50 4·00
863 – $50 multicoloured (28 × 32 mm) . . . . 8·00 9·00
DESIGNS: 20 c. to $50 Different sections of Hong Kong skyline.

181 Ox

1997. Chinese New Year ("Year of the Ox").
874 **181** $1.30 multicoloured . . . 25 25
875 $2.50 multicoloured . . . 50 55
876 $3.10 multicoloured . . . 75 90
877 $5 multicoloured . . . . . 1·25 2·00

182 Yellow-breasted Bunting

1997. Migratory Birds. Multicoloured.
884 $1.30 Type **182** 30 35
885 $2.50 Great knot 50 55
886 $3.10 Falcated teal 75 90
887 $5 Black-faced spoonbill . . . 1·25 2·00

183 Hong Kong Stadium

1997. Modern Landmarks. Multicoloured.
888 $1.30 Type **183** 25 25
889 $2.50 Peak Tower 50 55
890 $3.10 Hong Kong Convention and Exhibition Centre . . . 75 1·00
891 $5 Lantau bridge . . . . . . 1·10 2·00

184 House of Sam Tung Uk
186 Clam

185 Graphs and Hong Kong Bank (Finance and Banking)

1997. Establishment of Hong Kong as Special Administrative Region of People's Republic of China. Multicoloured.
900 $1.30 Type **184** 20 20
901 $1.60 Hong Kong Bank and vehicles 25 25
902 $2.50 Buildings and Hong Kong Convention and Exhibition Centre 40 40
903 $2.60 Container Terminal . . . 40 40
904 $3.10 Junks and dolphins . . . 50 50
905 $5 Bauhinia flower and clouds . 80 80

1997. World Bank Group and International Monetary Fund Annual Meetings. Multicoloured.
907 $1.30 Type **185** 20 20
908 $2.50 Share prices (Investment) and Stock Exchange 40 40
909 $3.10 Map on printed circuit and dish aerial (Trade and Telecommunications) 50 50
910 $5 Satellite image and road junctions (Infrastructure and Transport) 80 80

1997. Sea Shells. Multicoloured.
911 $1.30 Type **186** 20 20
912 $2.50 Cowrie 40 40
913 $3.10 Cone 50 50
914 $5 Murex 80 80

187 Tiger

1998. Chinese New Year ("Year of the Tiger").
915 **187** $1.30 multicoloured . . . 20 20
916 $2.50 multicoloured . . . 40 40
917 $3.10 multicoloured . . . 50 50
918 $5 multicoloured 80 80

188 "Star", 1900s

1998. Centenary of Star Ferry. Multicoloured.
920 $1.30 Type **188** 20 20
921 $2.50 "Star", 1910s–20s 40 40
922 $3.10 "Star", 1920s–1950s . . . 50 50
923 $5 "Star", 1950s onwards . . . 80 80

189 Observation Lounge

1998. Inauguration of Hong Kong International Airport, Chek Lap Kok. Multicoloured.
924 $1.30 Type **189** 20 20
925 $1.60 Couple boarding train . . 25 25
926 $2.50 Train and suspension bridge 40 40
927 $2.60 Concourse and mail vans at Airmail Centre 40 40
928 $3.10 Aircraft in bays 50 50
929 $5 Airplane taking off 80 80

191 Grasshopper and Cub Scouts and Knot
192 Graphic Design

1998. 85th Anniv of Hong Kong Scout Association. Multicoloured.
932 $1.30 Type **191** 20 20
933 $2.50 Two scouts, knot, watch-tower and tents 40 40
934 $3.10 Two venture scouts, knot, sailing dinghies and helicopter . . 50 50
935 $5 Rover scout and adult leader, knot and buildings 80 80

1998. Hong Kong Design. Multicoloured.
936 $1.30 Type **192** 20 20
937 $2.50 Product design 40 40
938 $3.10 Interior design 50 50
939 $5 Fashion design 80 80

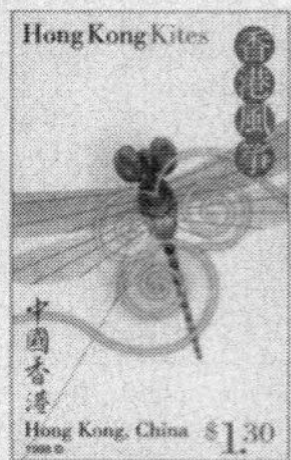

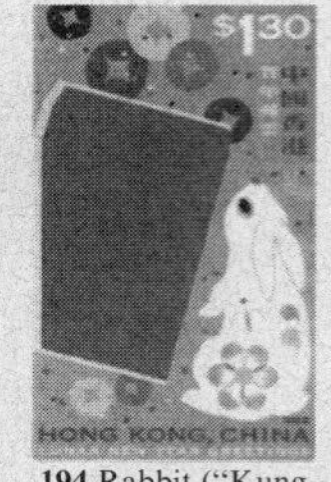

193 Dragonfly Kite
194 Rabbit ("Kung Hei Fat Choi")

1998. Kites. Multicoloured.
940 $1.30 Type **193** 20 20
941 $2.50 Dragon kite 40 40
942 $3.10 Butterfly kite 50 50
943 $5 Goldfish kite 80 80

1999. Chinese New Year ("Year of the Rabbit"). Multicoloured.
945 $1.30 Type **194** 20 20
946 $2.50 Rabbit and scroll ("Good Health") 40 40
947 $3.10 Rabbit and tangerine ("Good Luck") 50 50
948 $5 Rabbit and sweet tray ("May all your wishes come true") . 80 80
The gold panels of the designs can be scratched off to reveal a greeting in Chinese characters as given in brackets. Prices for Nos. 945/8 are for examples with the gold panels intact.

196 Calligraphy

1999. International Year of the Elderly. Mult.
950 $1.30 Type **196** 20 20
951 $2.50 Holding bird cage 40 40
952 $3.10 Playing chess 50 50
953 $5 Holding walking stick (voluntary services) 80 80

198 Bus

1999. Public Transport. Multicoloured.
956 $1.30 Type **198** 20 20
957 $2.40 Minibus 40 40
958 $2.50 Tram 40 40
959 $2.60 Taxi 40 40
960 $3.10 "Airport Express" train . . 50 50

199 Hong Kong Harbour

1999. Hong Kong–Singapore Joint Issue. Mult.
961 $1.20 Type **199** 20 20
962 $1.30 Singapore skyline 20 20
963 $2.50 Giant Buddha, Lantau Island, Hong Kong 40 40
964 $2.60 Merlion statue, Sentosa Island, Singapore 40 40
965 $3.10 Street scene, Hong Kong . 50 50
966 $5 Bugis Junction, Singapore . . 80 80

200 Flags of Hong Kong and People's Republic, and Hong Kong

1999. 50th Anniv of People's Republic of China. Multicoloured.
969 $1.30 Type **200** 20 20
970 $2.50 "Bauhinia blakeana" and Hong Kong harbour 40 40
971 $3.10 Chinese dragon dance . . 50 50
972 $5 Firework display over Hong Kong 80 80

201 Museum of Tea Ware
202 Dolphins

1999. Hong Kong Landmarks and Tourist Attractions. Multicoloured.

973	10 c. Type **201**	10	10
974	20 c. St. John's Cathedral	10	10
975	50 c. Legislative Council building	10	10
976	$1 Tai Fu Tai	15	15
977	$1.20 Wong Tai Sin Temple	20	20
978	$1.30 Victoria Harbour	20	20
979	$1.40 Hong Kong Railway Museum	20	20
980	$1.60, Tsim Sha Tsui clock-tower	25	25
981	$2 Happy Valley racecourse	30	30
982	$2.10 Kowloon–Canton Railway	35	35
983	$2.50 Chi Lin Nunnery, Kowloon	40	40
984	$3.10 Giant Buddha, Po Lin Monastery, Lantau Island	50	50
985	$5 Pagoda, Aw Boon Haw Gardens	80	80
986	$10 Tsing Ma bridge (26 × 31 mm)	1·00	1·00
987	$20 Hong Kong Convention and Exhibition Centre (26 × 31 mm)	3·25	3·25
988	$50 Hong Kong International Airport (26 × 31 mm)	8·00	8·00

1999. Endangered Species. Indo-Pacific Hump-backed Dolphin ("Chinese White Dolphin").

995	**202**	$1.30 multicoloured	20	20
996	–	$2.50 multicoloured	40	40
997	–	$3.10 multicoloured	50	50
998	–	$5 multicoloured	80	80

DESIGNS: $2.50 to $5 Various designs showing dolphins as Type **202**.

POSTAGE DUE STAMPS

D **1** Post-office Scales

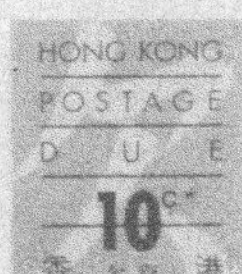

D **2**

1923.

D 1ab	D **1**	1 c. brown	30	1·00
D 2a		2 c. green	10·00	5·00
D 6a		2 c. grey	1·10	10·00
D 3a		4 c. red	27·00	7·00
D 7a		4 c. orange	2·50	9·50
D18		5 c. red (21 × 18 mm)	2·25	5·00
D 4		6 c. yellow	26·00	13·00
D 8		6 c. red	9·50	5·50
D 9		8 c. brown	5·50	32·00
D 5		10 c. blue	23·00	8·00
D15		10 c. violet	3·50	4·25
D16		20 c. black	6·00	4·25
D22		50 c. blue	4·50	10·00

1976. As Type D **1** but smaller design 21 × 17 mm with redrawn value.

D25a	D **1**	10 c. violet	80	2·00
D26a		20 c. grey	90	2·25
D27a		50 c. blue	90	2·75
D28a		$1 yellow	1·40	4·00

1987.

D31	D **2**	10 c. green	10	10
D32		20 c. brown	10	10
D33		50 c. violet	10	10
D34		$1 orange	15	20
D35		$5 blue	80	1·10
D36		$10 red	1·60	2·25

JAPANESE OCCUPATION OF HONG KONG

100 sen = 1 yen

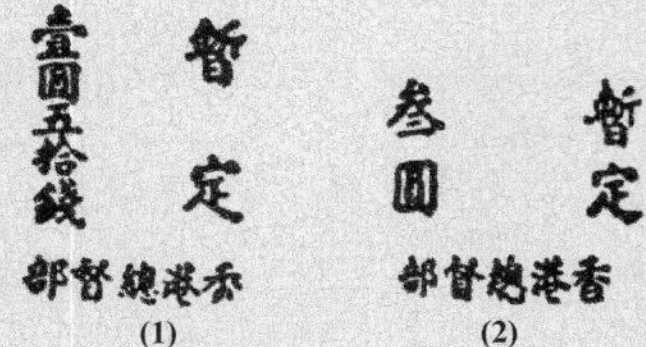

(1) (2)

1945. Stamps of Japan surch as T **1** (No. J1) or T **2**.

J1	**126**	1.50 yen on 1 s. brown	26·00	21·00
J2	**84**	3 yen on 2 s. red	12·00	18·00
J3		5 yen on 5 s. red (No. 396)	£850	£130

HORTA Pt. 9

A district of the Azores for which separate issues were used from 1892 to 1905.

1865. 1000 reis = 1 milreis.

1892. As T **4** of Funchal, but inscr "HORTA".
4 5 r. yellow 2·25 1·60
5 10 r. mauve 2·25 2·00
6 15 r. brown 2·25 2·10
7 20 r. lilac 2·50 2·50
2 25 r. green 4·00 1·00
8 50 r. blue 6·25 3·00
22 75 r. red 7·00 4·50
10 80 r. green 9·25 8·75
23 100 r. brown on yellow 40·00 19·00
24 150 r. red on rose 45·00 40·00
25 200 r. blue on blue 45·00 40·00
26 300 r. blue on brown 45·00 40·00

1897. "King Carlos" key-type inscr "HORTA". Name and value in red (Nos. 46 and 41) or black (others).
28 S 2½ r. grey 45 30
29 5 r. orange 45 30
30 10 r. green 45 30
31 15 r. brown 6·25 4·75
42 15 r. green 1·25 1·00
32 20 r. lilac 1·25 1·00
33 25 r. green 2·10 90
43 25 r. red 1·25 60
34 50 r. blue 2·40 80
45 65 r. blue 90 65
35 75 r. red 2·25 1·00
46 75 r. brown on yellow 9·50 8·25
36 80 r. mauve 1·25 85
37 100 r. blue on blue 2·40 85
47 115 r. red on pink 1·60 1·25
48 130 r. brown on yellow 1·60 1·25
38 150 r. brown on yellow 1·60 1·10
49 180 r. black on pink 1·60 1·25
39 200 r. purple on pink 4·50 3·75
40 300 r. blue on pink 8·00 6·00
41 500 r. black on blue 10·00 9·50

HUNGARY Pt. 2

A country in central Europe. A Kingdom ruled by the Emperor of Austria until 1918. A Republic was then proclaimed, and later a Soviet style constitution was adopted. In 1919 parts of the country were occupied by France, Serbia and Rumania, including Budapest. Following the withdrawal of the Rumanians a National Republic was instituted, and in 1920 Hungary was declared a Monarchy with Admiral Nicholas Horthy as Regent. In 1946 Hungary became a Republic again.

1858. 100 krajczar = 1 forint
1900. 100 filler (heller) = 1 korona (krone).
1926. 100 filler = 1 pengo.
1946. 100 filler = 1 forint.

1 2

1871.
8 1 2 k. yellow 55·00 14·50
9 3 k. green £125 50·00
10 5 k. red 70·00 1·75
11 10 k. blue £275 27·00
12 15 k. brown £325 45·00
13 25 k. lilac £225 £100

1874.
26 2 2 k. mauve 1·40 25
28 3 k. green 1·00 25
29 5 k. red 5·00 50
31 10 k. blue 4·25 55
32a 20 k. grey 6·00 70

1888. Numerals in black on the krajczar values, in red on the forint values.
39a 2 1 k. black 40 15
40 2 k. mauve and light mauve 60 25
41 3 k. green and light green 1·00 30
42 5 k. red and pink 1·25 35
43 8 k. orange and yellow 5·25 45
57 10 k. blue 3·00 20
45 12 k. brown and green 10·00 90
59 15 k. red and blue 3·00 25
47 20 k. grey 6·50 1·25
61 24 k. purple and red 4·25 1·40
62 30 k. olive and brown 5·75 3·50
63 50 k. red and orange 14·50 12·50
51 1 fo. grey and silver £125 2·50
38i 3 fo. brown and gold 21·00 9·00

7 "Turul" (mythical bird of the Magyars)
8 King Francis Joseph wearing Hungarian Crown
12

1900. Figures of value in black.
99 7 1 f. grey 15 10
100 2 f. yellow 15 10
118 3 f. orange 10 10
67 4 f. mauve 50 10
102 5 f. green 10 10
69a 6 f. purple 45 10
103 6 f. drab 25 10
120 6 f. green 10 10
121 10 f. red 10 10
105 12 f. lilac 35 10
122 12 f. lilac on yellow 15 10
123 16 f. green 15 15
124 20 f. brown 15 10
125 25 f. blue 15 10
126 30 f. brown 15 10
127 35 f. purple 15 10
111 50 f. red 65 10
128 50 f. red on blue 15 10
129 60 f. green 2·10 1·60
130 60 f. green on pink 50 10
131 70 f. brown and green 25 10
132 80 f. violet 25 10
133 8 1 k. red 2·75 10
134 2 k. blue 7·25 65
81 3 k. blue 70·00 3·50
135 5 k. red 14·50 3·50

1913. Flood Charity stamps. As T **7/8**, but with label as T **12**.
136 12 1 f. + 2 f. grey 65 60
137 2 f. + 2 f. yellow 35 35
138 3 f. + 2 f. orange 35 35
139 5 f. + 2 f. green 30 30
140 6 f. + 2 f. drab 65 60
141 10 f. + 2 f. red 20 15
142 12 f. + 2 f. lilac on yellow 1·25 1·10
143 16 f. + 2 f. green 70 70
144 20 f. + 2 f. brown 2·75 1·50
145 25 f. + 2 f. blue 1·10 50
146 30 f. + 2 f. brown 1·25 65
147 35 f. + 2 f. purple 90 40
148 50 f. + 2 f. lake on blue 6·50 2·50
149 60 f. + 2 f. green on red 7·75 1·25
150 8 1 k. + 2 f. red 27·00 10·50
151 2 k. + 2 f. blue 70·00 42·00
152 5 k. + 2 f. red 25·00 18·00

1914. War Charity. Nos. 136/52 (with labels) surch **Hadi segely Ozvegyeknek es arvaknak ket (2) filler**.
153 12 1 f. + 2 f. grey 80 40
154 2 f. + 2 f. yellow 80 50
155 3 f. + 2 f. orange 80 50
156 5 f. + 2 f. green 30 15
157 6 f. + 2 f. drab 90 50
158 10 f. + 2 f. red 30 15
159 12 f. + 2 f. lilac on yellow 95 35
160 16 f. + 2 f. green 95 25
161 20 f. + 2 f. brown 1·10 65
162 25 f. + 2 f. blue 1·25 70
163 30 f. + 2 f. brown 1·50 70
164 35 f. + 2 f. purple 4·00 1·50
165 50 f. + 2 f. lake on blue 2·50 90
166 60 f. + 2 f. green on red 6·50 1·50
167 8 1 k. + 2 f. red (No. 150) 70·00 35·00
168 2 k. + 2 f. blue (No. 151) 28·00 18·00
169 5 k. + 2 f. red (No. 153) 28·00 16·00

1915. War Charity. Stamps of 1900 (without labels) surch as last round the stamp.
170 7 1 f. + 2 f. grey 10 10
171 2 f. + 2 f. yellow 10 10
172 3 f. + 2 f. orange 10 10
173 5 f. + 2 f. green 10 10
174 6 f. + 2 f. drab 10 10
175 10 f. + 2 f. red 10 10
176 12 f. + 2 f. lilac on yellow 10 10
177 16 f. + 2 f. green 30 30
178 20 f. + 2 f. brown 30 30
179 25 f. + 2 f. blue 10 10
180 30 f. + 2 f. brown 10 10
181 35 f. + 2 f. purple 15 10
182 50 f. + 2 f. lake on blue 30 15
183 60 f. + 2 f. green on red 80 80
185 8 1 k. + 2 f. red (No. 133) 1·75 1·40
186 2 k. + 2 f. blue (No. 134) 4·25 3·50
187 5 k. + 2 f. red (No. 135) 10·50 10·00

18 Harvesters
19 Parliament Buildings, Budapest

1916. As T **18** but with white figures in top corners.
243 18 10 f. red 70 10
244 15 f. purple 60 10

1916. Inscr "MAGYAR KIR POSTA".
245 18 2 f. brown 10 10
246 3 f. red 10 10
247 4 f. slate 10 10
248 5 f. green 10 10
249 6 f. blue 10 10
250 10 f. red 70 10
251 15 f. violet 10 10
252 20 f. brown 10 10
253 25 f. blue 10 10
254 35 f. brown 10 10
255 40 f. olive 10 10
256 19 50 f. purple 10 10
257 75 f. blue 10 10
258 80 f. green 20 10
259 1 k. lake 10 10
260 2 k. brown 20 10
261 3 k. grey and violet 50 10
262 5 k. brown 70 15
263 10 k. lilac and brown 1·00 65

In Type **19** the colours of the centres differ slightly from those of the frames.

For later issues in Types **18** and **19**, see Nos. 372/86 and 404/11.

20 In Trenches
22 "Turul" at bay
23 Queen Zita

1916. War Charity.
264 20 10 f. + 2 f. red 15 15
265 – 15 f. + 2 f. violet 40 40
266 22 40 f. + 2 f. lake 55 55
DESIGN: 15 f. Hand to hand combat.

1916. Coronation.
267 23 10 f. mauve 70 70
268 – 15 f. red (Emperor Charles IV) 70 70

1917. War Charity Exhibition. Nos. 243/4 surch **Jozsef foherczeg vezerezredes hadi kiallitasa 1 korona** (= "Archduke Joseph Colonel General War Exhibition").
269 18 10 f. + 1 k. red 70 70
270 15 f. + 1 k. violet 70 70

1918. Air. Surch **REPULO POSTA** and value.
271 19 1 k. 50 on 75 f. blue 18·00 18·00
272 4 k. 50 on 2 k. brown 16·00 16·00

27 Charles IV
28 Zita

1918.
273 27 10 f. red 10 10
274 15 f. violet 15 15
275 20 f. brown 10 10
276 25 f. blue 10 10
277 28 40 f. olive 10 10
278 50 f. purple 10 10

1918. Optd **KOZTARSASAG**.

(a) War Charity Stamps (Nos. 264/6).
279 20 10 + 2 f. red 15 15
280 – 15 + 2 f. violet 15 15
281 22 40 + 2 f. red 15 15

(b) Harvesters and Parliament.
282 18 2 f. brown 10 10
283 3 f. red 10 10
284 4 f. grey 10 10
285 5 f. green 10 10
286 6 f. blue 10 10
287 10 f. red 10 10
288 20 f. brown 20 20
289 40 f. green 10 10
290 19 1 k. red 10 10
291 2 k. brown 10 10
292 3 k. grey and violet 70 70
293 5 k. brown 2·10 2·10
294 10 k. mauve and brown 2·50 2·50

(c) Charles and Zita.
295 27 10 f. pink 10 10
296 15 f. purple 10 10
297 20 f. brown 10 10
298 25 f. blue 15 15
299 28 40 f. green 15 15
300 50 f. purple 15 15

1919. As T **18/19**, but inscr "MAGYAR POSTA".
301 18 2 f. brown 10 10
302 4 f. grey 10 10
303 5 f. green 10 10
304 6 f. blue 10 10
305 10 f. red 10 10
306 15 f. violet 10 10
307 20 f. brown 10 10
308 20 f. green 10 10
309 25 f. blue 10 10
310 40 f. green 10 10
311 40 f. red 10 10
312 45 f. orange 10 10
313 19 50 f. purple 10 10
314 60 f. blue and brown 10 10
315 95 f. blue 10 10
316 1 k. red 10 10
317 1 k. blue and indigo 10 10
318 1 k. 20 green 10 10
319 1 k. 40 green 10 10
320 2 k. brown 10 10
321 3 k. grey and violet 10 10
322 5 k. brown 10 10
323 10 k. mauve and brown 60 25

32 Karl Marx

1919.
324 32 20 f. red and brown 30 30
325 – 45 f. green and orange 35 35
326 – 60 f. brown and grey 4·00 4·00
327 – 75 f. brown and red 4·00 4·00
328 – 80 f. brown and olive 4·00 4·00
PORTRAITS: 45 f. S. Petofi; 60 f. Ignacs Martinovics; 75 f. G. Dozsa; 80 f. F. Engels.

1919. Nos. 301 etc optd **MAGYAR TANACSKOZTARSASAG.** (second word hyphenated on 2 to 45 f.) (= "Hungarian Soviet Republic").
329 18 2 f. brown 15 15
330 3 f. purple 15 15
331 4 f. grey 15 15
332 5 f. green 15 15
333 6 f. blue 15 15
334 10 f. red 15 15
335 15 f. violet 15 15
336 20 f. brown 15 15
337 25 f. blue 15 15
338 40 f. green 15 15
339 45 f. orange 15 15
340 19 50 f. purple 15 15
341 95 f. blue 15 15
342 1 k. red 15 15
343 1 k. 20 green 70 70
344 1 k. 40 green 70 70
345 2 k. brown 1·10 1·10
346 3 k. grey and violet 1·10 1·10
347 5 k. brown 1·10 1·10
348 10 k. mauve and brown 1·40 1·40

1919. Entry of National Army into Budapest. Nos. 303 etc optd **A nemzeti hadsereg bevonulasa. 1919. XI/16.**
348a 18 5 f. green 90 90
348b 10 f. red 90 90
348c 15 f. violet 90 90
348d 20 f. brown 90 90
348e 25 f. blue 90 90

(36) (37)

1920. Nos. 329/48 optd with T **36** (2 to 45 f.) or **37** (others).
349 18 2 f. brown 40 40
350 3 f. purple 10 10
351 4 f. grey 40 40
352 5 f. green 10 10
353 6 f. blue 10 10
354 10 f. red 10 10
355 15 f. violet 10 10
356 20 f. brown 10 10
357 25 f. blue 10 10
358 40 f. green 75 75
359 45 f. orange 75 75
360 19 50 f. purple 75 75
361 95 f. blue 75 75
362 1 k. red 80 80
363 1 k. 20 green 1·75 1·75
364 1 k. 40 green 1·75 1·75
365 2 k. brown 2·00 2·00
366 3 k. grey and violet 2·00 2·00
367 5 k. brown 30 30
368 10 k. mauve and brown 5·00 5·00

38 Returning P.O.W.
42 Madonna and Child

1920. Returned Prisoners-of-War Fund.
369 38 40 f. + 1 k. lake 1·75 1·75
370 – 60 f. + 2 k. brown 70 70
371 – 1 k. + 5 k. blue 70 70
DESIGNS—HORIZ: 60 f. Prison Camp. VERT: 1 k. Family Reunion.

1920. Re-issue of T **18** inscr "MAGYAR KIR. POSTA".
372 18 5 f. brown 10 10
373 10 f. purple 10 10
374 40 f. red 10 10
375 50 f. green 10 10
376 50 f. blue 10 10
377 60 f. black 10 10
378 1 k. green 10 10
379 1½ k. purple 10 10
380 2 k. blue 10 10
381 2½ k. green 10 10
382 3 k. brown 10 10
383 4 k. red 10 10
384 4½ k. violet 15 10
385 5 k. brown 15 10
386 6 k. blue 15 10
387 10 k. brown 15 10
388 15 k. black 15 10
389 20 k. red 15 10
390 25 k. orange 15 10
391 40 k. green 15 10
392 50 k. blue 15 10
393 100 k. purple 15 10
394 150 k. green 15 10
395 200 k. green 15 10
442 300 k. red 15 10
397 350 k. violet 20 20
443 400 k. blue 15 10
444 500 k. black 15 10
445 600 k. bistre 15 10
446 800 k. yellow 25 15

1920. Air. No. 263 surch **LEGI POSTA** and value.
401 19 3 k. on 10 k. lilac & brn 1·25 2·50
402 8 k. on 10 k. lilac & brn 1·25 2·50
403 12 k. on 10 k. lilac & brn 1·25 2·50

1920. Re-issue of T **19** inscr "MAGYAR KIR. POSTA".
404 **19** 2 k. 50 blue 10 10
405 3 k. 50 grey 10 10
406 10 k. brown 10 10
407 15 k. grey 10 10
408 20 k. red 10 10
409 25 k. orange 10 10
410 30 k. lake 15 10
411 40 k. green 15 10
412 50 k. blue 15 10
413 100 k. brown 15 10
414 400 k. green 20 15
415 500 k. violet 15 10
416 1000 k. red 30 10
448 2000 k. red 45 15

1921.
418 **42** 50 k. blue and brown 25 10
419 100 k. brown and bistre 40 10
420 200 k. ultramarine & blue 40 10
421 500 k. mauve and purple 40 15
422 1000 k. purple & mauve 40 15
423 2000 k. mauve and green 50 25
424 2500 k. brown and bistre 40 10
425 3000 k. mauve and red 70 10
426 5000 k. lt green & green 70 10
427 10000 k. blue and violet 1·40 45

44 Statue of Petofi in National Dress
45 John, the hero, on flying dragon

47 Death of Petofi

1923. Birth Centenary of Petofi (poet).
428 **44** 10 k. (+ 10 k.) blue 55 70
429 **45** 15 k. (+ 15 k.) blue 1·25 1·60
430 – 25 k. (+ 25 k.) brown 55 70
431 **47** 40 k. (+ 40 k.) red 1·75 2·25
432 – 50 k. (+ 50 k.) purple 1·75 2·25
DESIGNS—VERT: As Type **45**: 25 k. Petofi; 50 k. Petofi addressing the people.

49 Icarus over Budapest
50

1924. Air.
433 **49** 100 k. pink and brown 1·25 1·60
434 500 k. lt green & green 1·25 1·60
435 1000 k. brown & bistre 1·25 1·60
436 2000 k. blue & dp blue 1·25 1·60
436a 5000 k. mauve & purple 1·75 2·25
436b 10000 k. purple and red 1·75 2·25

1924. Tuberculosis Relief Fund.
437 **50** 300 k. (+ 300 k.) blue 2·40 3·00
438 – 500 k. (+ 500 k.) brown 2·40 3·00
439 – 1000 k. (+ 1000 k.) green 2·40 3·00
DESIGNS: 500 k. Mother and child; 1000 k. Bowman.

53 M. Jokai
55

1925. Birth Cent of Maurus Jokai (novelist).
449 **53** 1000 k. brown and green 2·75 3·50
450 2000 k. brown 1·00 50
451 2500 k. brown and blue 2·75 3·50

1925. Sports Association Fund.
452 – 100 k. (+ 100 k.) brn & grn 2·50 2·50
453 – 200 k. (+ 200 k.) grn & brn 2·50 3·25
454 – 300 k. (+ 300 k.) blue 4·00 4·25
455 – 400 k. (+ 400 k.) grn & bl 4·00 5·00
456 – 500 k. (+ 500 k.) purple 5·00 5·50
457 – 1000 k. (+ 1000 k.) red 6·50 6·00
458 **55** 2000 k. (+ 2000 k.) purple 8·50 7·00
459 – 2500 k. (+ 2500 k.) sepia 10·00 8·00
DESIGNS—HORIZ: 100 k. Athletes; 500 k. Fencing. VERT: 200 k. Skiing; 300 k. Skating; 400 k. Diving; 1000 k. Scouts; 2500 k. Hurdles.

56 Crown of St. Stephen
57 Matthias Church and Fisher's Bastion
60 Madonna and Child

58 Royal Palace, Budapest **59**

1926. T **59** is without boat.
460 **56** 1 f. black 20 10
461 2 f. blue 20 10
462 3 f. orange 20 10
463 4 f. mauve 20 10
464 6 f. green 25 10
465 8 f. mauve 60 10
466 **57** 10 f. blue 60 10
467 16 f. violet 60 10
468 20 f. red 60 10
469 25 f. brown 60 10
470 **59** 30 f. green 1·75 10
471 **58** 32 f. violet 1·75 15
472 40 f. blue and deep blue 2·75 15
473 **59** 46 f. blue 2·50 10
474 50 f. black 2·50 10
475 70 f. red 2·75 10
476 **60** 1 p. violet 35·00 1·00
477 2 p. red 18·00 1·60
478 5 p. blue 30·00 7·00
See also Nos. 502/6.

61 The fabulous "Turul"
62 Mercury astride a "Turul"

1927. Air.
478a **61** 4 f. orange 60 25
479 12 f. green 55 20
480 16 f. brown 65 25
481 20 f. red 65 35
482 32 f. purple 1·75 1·50
483 40 f. blue 1·50 75
484 **62** 50 f. red 1·50 1·00
485 72 f. olive 1·75 1·10
486 80 f. violet 2·00 1·50
487 1 p. green 2·50 1·60
488 2 p. red 5·00 4·75
489 5 p. blue 17·50 22·00

66 Royal Palace, Budapest
67 St. Stephen

1928. T **66** has the boat in a different place and a redrawn frame.
502 **66** 30 f. green 1·90 15
503 32 f. purple 2·40 15
504 40 f. blue 2·50 15
505 46 f. green 2·50 15
506 50 f. brown 2·40 15

1928. 890th Death Anniv of St. Stephen of Hungary.
507 **67** 8 f. green 30 20
508 16 f. red 40 20
509 32 f. blue 2·50 2·00

1929. Colours changed.
510 **67** 8 f. red 30 15
511 16 f. violet 40 20
512 32 f. bistre 1·75 1·40

68 Admiral Horthy
69 St. Emeric

1930. 10th Anniv of Regency.
513 **68** 8 f. green 80 15
514 16 f. violet 80 20
515 20 f. red 3·50 1·00
516 32 f. brown 4·25 6·25
517 40 f. blue 5·50 2·50

1930. 900th Death Anniv of St. Emeric.
518 **69** 8 f. + 2 f. green 70 60
519 – 16 f. + 4 f. purple 90 80
520 – 20 f. + 4 f. red 2·00 2·00
521 – 32 f. + 8 f. blue 3·50 3·50
DESIGNS—VERT: 16 f. St. Stephen and Queen Gisela; 20 f. St. Ladislas. HORIZ: 32 f. Sts. Gellert and Emeric.

1931. Surch.
526 **56** 2 on 3 f. orange 90 15
527 6 on 8 f. mauve 90 10
528 **57** 10 on 16 f. violet 90 10
525 20 on 25 f. brown 1·10 1·00

1931. Air. Optd **Zeppelin 1931**.
529 **62** 1 p. orange 45·00 75·00
530 2 p. purple 45·00 75·00

73 St. Elizabeth
75 Madonna and Child
77

1932. 700th Death Anniv of St. Elizabeth of Hungary.
531 **73** 10 f. blue 55 10
532 20 f. red 55 10
533 – 32 f. purple 2·50 1·50
534 – 40 f. blue 1·75 1·10
DESIGN—18 × 28 mm: 32, 40 f. St. Elizabeth giving cloak to the poor.

1932.
535 **75** 1 p. green 21·00 70
536 2 p. red 21·00 1·75
537 5 p. blue 80·00 8·75
538 10 p. brown £110 60·00

1932. No. 527 further surch **2**.
540 **56** 2 on 6 on 8 f. mauve 1·25 10

1932. Famous Hungarians.
541 – 1 f. grey 15 10
542 – 2 f. orange 15 10
543 – 4 f. blue 15 10
543a **77** 5 f. brown 15 10
544 – 6 f. green 15 10
545 – 10 f. green 15 10
546 – 16 f. violet 15 10
547 – 20 f. red 45 10
547a – 25 f. green 70 10
548 – 30 f. brown 60 10
549 – 32 f. purple 90 15
550 – 40 f. blue 90 10
551 – 50 f. green 1·25 90
552 – 70 f. red 1·75 60
DESIGNS: 1 f. I. Madach (poet); 2 f. J Arany (poet); 4 f. I. Semmelweis (physician); 5 f. F. Kolcsey (poet); 6 f. L. Eotvos (physicist); 10 f. I. Szechenyi (statesman); 16 f. F. Deak (statesman); 20 f. F. Liszt (composer); 25 f. M. Vorosmarty (poet); 30 f. L. Kossuth (statesman); 32 f. I. Tisza (statesman); 40 f. M. Munkacsy (painter); 50 f. S. Korosi Csoma (explorer); 70 f. F. Bolyai (mathematician).

1933. Surch **10**.
553 **59** 10 on 70 f. red 1·25 20

79 "Justice for Hungary" over Danube
80 Gift Plane from Mussolini
83 "The Stag of Hungary"

1933. Air.
554 **79** 10 f. green 2·00 25
555 16 f. violet 2·00 40
556 **80** 20 f. red 3·25 90
557 40 f. blue 3·75 90
558 – 48 f. black 17·00 2·00
559 – 72 f. brown 42·00 3·00
560 – 1 p. green 22·00 2·75
561 – 2 p. red 35·00 16·00
562 – 5 p. grey £110 £170
DESIGNS—VERT: As Type **80**: 48, 72 f. "Spirit of Flight" on wing of Lockheed Model 8A Sirius; 1, 2, 5 p. Mercury and propeller.

1933. International Scout Jamboree, Godollo.
563 **83** 10 f. green 90 90
564 16 f. red 2·50 2·50
565 20 f. red 1·75 1·40
566 32 f. yellow 5·25 5·25
567 40 f. blue 4·75 3·50

84 Ferenc Rakoczi II
85 Cardinal Peter Pazmany

1935. Death Bicentenary of Prince Rakoczi.
569 **84** 10 f. green 75 70
570 16 f. violet 3·50 3·50
571 20 f. red 1·00 90
572 32 f. red 6·25 6·00
573 40 f. blue 8·00 6·50

1935. Tercentenary of Budapest University.
574 **85** 6 f. green 1·10 70
575 – 10 f. green 30 15
576 **85** 16 f. violet 1·40 1·25
577 20 f. mauve 30 15
578 – 32 f. red 2·75 2·50
579 – 40 f. blue 2·25 2·25
DESIGN—HORIZ: (35 × 25 mm): 10 f., 32 f., 40 f. Pazmany signing deed.

87 Fokker F.VIIb/3m

1936. Air.
580 **87** 10 f. green 30 10
581 20 f. red 30 10
582 36 f. brown 45 15
583 – 40 f. blue 50 15
584 – 52 f. orange 80 65
585 – 60 f. violet 22·00 2·25
586 – 80 f. green 3·00 60
587 – 1 p. green 3·00 50
588 – 2 p. lake 7·00 2·25
589 – 5 p. blue 29·00 32·00
DESIGNS: 40 f. to 80 f. Fokker F.VIIb/3m over Parliament Buildings; 1 p. to 5 p. Fokker F.VIIb/3m (different).

88 Ancient Buda

1936. 250th Anniv of Recapture of Buda from Turks.
590 **88** 10 f. green 35 15
591 – 16 f. mauve 2·25 2·00
592 – 20 f. red 35 15
593 – 32 f. brown 2·50 2·00
594 **88** 40 f. blue 2·50 2·00
DESIGNS: 16 f. Angel of Peace over Buda; 20 f. Arms of Buda; 32 f. Colour bearer and bugler.

89 "Commerce", "May Fair, 1937" and R. Danube
90 St. Stephen, the Church Builder

1937. Budapest International Fair.
595 **89** 2 f. orange 10 10
596 6 f. green 20 10
597 10 f. green 20 10
598 20 f. red 50 35
599 32 f. violet 90 55
600 40 f. blue 70 60

1938. 900th Death Anniv of St. Stephen. (1st issue).
601 – 1 f. violet 15 10
602 **90** 2 f. sepia 15 10
603 – 4 f. blue 20 10
604 – 5 f. mauve 50 10
605 – 6 f. green 70 10
606 – 10 f. red 55 10
607 **90** 16 f. violet 90 50
608 – 20 f. red 40 10
609 – 25 f. green 70 50
610 – 30 f. bistre 1·00 10
611 – 32 f. red on yellow 1·25 1·50
612 – 40 f. blue 1·00 10
613 – 50 f. purple on green 1·25 10
614 – 70 f. green on blue 2·75 40
DESIGNS: 1 f., 10 f. Abbot Astrik receiving Crown from Pope; 4 f., 20 f. St. Stephen enthroned; 5 f., 25, St. Gellert, St. Emeric and St. Stephen; 6 f., 30 f. St. Stephen offering Crown to Virgin Mary; 32 f., 50 f. St. Stephen; 40 f. Madonna and Child; 70 f. Crown of St. Stephen.
See also Nos. 620/1.

92 Admiral Horthy
93 Eucharistic Symbols

1938.

615 **92** 1 p. green 75 10
616 2 p. sepia . . . . 1·50 10
617 5 p. blue . . . . 4·50 1·50

1938. 34th International Eucharistic Congress.

618 – 16 f. + 16 f. blue . . . . . 2·75 4·50
619 **93** 20 f. + 20 f. red . . . . . 2·75 4·50

DESIGN: 16 f. St. Ladislas.

94 St. Stephen the Victorious

1938. 900th Death Anniv of St. Stephen. (2nd issue).

620 **94** 10 f. + 10 f. purple . . . . 2·75 5·25
621 – 20 f. + 20 f. red . . . . 2·75 5·25

DESIGN: 20 f. Differing crown to Virgin Mary.

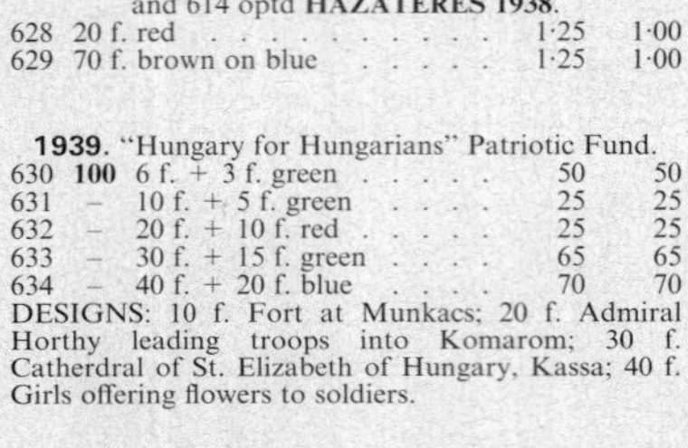

95 Debrecen College **100** Statue representing Northern Provinces

1938. 400th Anniv of Debrecen College.

622 **95** 6 f. green 15 10
623 – 10 f. brown 10 10
624 – 16 f. red 15 10
625 – 20 f. red 10 10
626 – 32 f. green 30 20
627 – 40 f. blue 30 15

DESIGNS—HORIZ: 10 f., 20 f. 18th and 19th-cent. views of College. VERT: 16 f., 18th-century students as firemen; 32 f. Prof. Marothi; 40 f. Dr. Hatvani.

1938. Acquisition of Czech Territory. As Nos. 608 and 614 optd **HAZATERES 1938.**

628 20 f. red . . . . 1·25 1·00
629 70 f. brown on blue . . . . . 1·25 1·00

1939. "Hungary for Hungarians" Patriotic Fund.

630 **100** 6 f. + 3 f. green 50 50
631 – 10 f. + 5 f. green 25 25
632 – 20 f. + 10 f. red 25 25
633 – 30 f. + 15 f. green 65 65
634 – 40 f. + 20 f. blue 70 70

DESIGNS: 10 f. Fort at Munkacs; 20 f. Admiral Horthy leading troops into Komarom; 30 f. Catherdral of St. Elizabeth of Hungary, Kassa; 40 f. Girls offering flowers to soldiers.

101 Crown of St. Stephen **102** Esztergom Basilica

1939.

635 **101** 1 f. purple 10 10
636 2 f. green 10 10
690 3 f. brown 10 10
637 4 f. brown 10 10
638 5 f. violet 10 10
639 6 f. green 10 10
693 8 f. green 10 10
640 10 f. brown 10 10
695 12 f. red 10 10
641 16 f. violet 10 10
642 – 20 f. red 10 10
697 – 24 f. red 10 10
643 – 25 f. blue 10 10
699 – 30 f. mauve 10 10
645 – 32 f. brown 20 10
700 **102** 40 f. green 10 10
701 – 50 f. green 10 10
702 – 70 f. red 15 10
698 – 80 f. brown 15 10

DESIGNS—As T **101**: 20, 24 f. St. Stephen; 25, 80 f. Madonna and Child. As T **102**: 30 f. Buda Cathedral; 32 f. Debrecen Reformed Church; 50 f. Budapest Evangelical Church; 70 f. Kassa Cathedral.

For further issues in these designs, see Nos. 751/5.

103 Guides' Salute **104** Memorial Tablets

1939. Girl Guides' Rally, Godollo. Inscr "I. PAX-TING".

649 **103** 2 f. orange 20 15
650 – 6 f. green 35 15
651 – 10 f. brown 35 35
652 – 20 f. pink . . . . 1·00 70

DESIGNS: 6 f. Lily symbol and Hungarian arms; 10 f. Guide and girl in national costume; 20 f. Dove of peace.

1939. National Protestant Day and Int. Protestant Cultural Fund.

653 **104** 6 f. + 3 f. green 40 20
654 – 10 f. + 5 f. purple 40 20
655 – 20 f. + 10 f. red 70 60
656 – 32 f. + 16 f. brown 80 80
657 – 40 f. + 20 f. blue 90 90

DESIGNS—HORIZ: 10 f., 20 f. G. Karoli and A. Molnar di Szenci (translators of the Bible and the Psalms). VERT: 32 f. Prince Gabriel Bethlen; 40 f. Zsuzsanna Lorantffy.

106 Boy Scout with Kite **107** Regent and Szeged Cathedral

1940. Admiral Horthy Aviation Fund.

658 **106** 6 f. + 6 f. green 55 55
659 – 10 f. + 10 f. brown 85 85
660 – 20 f. + 20 f. red . . . . 1·25 1·25

DESIGNS: 10 f. "Spirit of Flight"; 20 f. St. Elizabeth carrying Crown and Cross of St. Stephen.

1940. 20th Anniv of Regency.

661 **107** 6 f. green 10 10
662 – 10 f. brown and olive . . . 10 10
663 – 20 f. red 20 10

DESIGNS: 10 f. Admiral Horthy; 20 f. Kassa Cathedral and Angelic bellringer.

108 Stemming the Flood

1940. Flood Relief Fund.

664 **108** 10 f. + 2 f. purple 15 10
665 20 f. + 4 f. orange 15 10
666 20 f. + 50 f. brown 45 40

109 Hunyadi Family Arms **110** Hunyadi Castle

1940. 500th Birth Anniv of King Matthias Hunyadi and Cultural Institutes Fund.

667 **109** 6 f. + 3 f. green 20 20
668 **110** 10 f. + 5 f. brown 20 20
669 – 16 f. + 8 f. olive 25 25
670 – 20 f. + 10 f. red 30 30
671 – 32 f. + 16 f. grey 30 30

DESIGNS—VERT: 16 f. Bust of King Matthias (dated "1440–1490"); 32 f. Corvin Codex (dated "1473"). HORIZ: 20 f. Equestrian Statue of King Matthias.

111 Crown of St. Stephen **112** Madonna and Martyr

1940. Recovery from Rumania of North-Eastern Transylvania.

672 **111** 10 f. green and yellow . . 15 10

1940. Transylvanian Relief Fund. Various designs dated "1940".

673 – 10 f. + 50 f. green 40 40
674 **112** 20 f. + 50 f. red 40 40
675 – 32 f. + 50 f. brown 50 50

DESIGNS: 10 f. Prince Csaba and soldier; 32 f. Mother offering child to Fatherland.

113 Spirit of Music

1940. Artists' Relief Fund. Inscr "MAGYAR MUVESZETERT".

676 **113** 6 f. + 6 f. green 35 35
677 – 10 f. + 10 f. brown . . . 35 35
678 – 16 f. + 16 f. violet 35 35
679 – 20 f. + 20 f. red 35 35

DESIGNS—VERT: 10 f. Sculpture; 16 f. Painting. HORIZ: 20 f. Poetry (Pegasus).

114 Pilot

1941. Air stamps. Horthy Aviation Fund. Various allegorical designs inscribed "HORTHY MIKLOS NEMZETI REPULO ALAP".

680 **114** 6 f. + 6 f. olive 30 40
681 – 10 f. + 10 f. brown . . . 60 40
682 – 20 f. + 20 f. red 60 40
683 – 32 f. + 32 f. blue 60 85

DESIGNS: 10 f. Youth releasing model glider; 20 f. Glider; 32 f. Madonna.

1941. Acquisition of Yugoslav Territory Overprinted **DEL-UISSZATER** ("The South comes home").

684 **101** 10 f. brown 15 10
685 – 20 f. red (No. 642) 15 10

116 Admiral Horthy

1941.

686 **116** 1 p. green and yellow . . . 15 10
687 2 p. brown and yellow . . 15 10
688 5 p. purple and yellow . . 80 70

118 Szechenyi

119 Giant opening Straits of Kazan

1941. 150th Birth Anniv of Count Istvan Szechenyi.

703 **118** 10 f. olive 10 10
704 – 16 f. brown 15 10
705 **119** 20 f. red 15 10
706 – 32 f. orange 25 15
707 – 40 f. blue 45 15

DESIGNS: 16 f. Count Szechenyi and Academy of Science; 32 f. Budapest Chain Bridge; 40 f. Mercury, Locomotive and "Szent Istvan" (river steamer).

120 Infantry in Action **121** Pilot and Airplane

1941. Soldiers' Gifts Fund. Inscr "HONVEDEINK KARACSONYARA 1941". (a) First issue.

708 **120** 8 f. + 12 f. green 25 15
709 – 12 f. + 18 f. brown . . . 25 15
710 – 20 f. + 30 f. blue 30 25
711 – 40 f. + 60 f. brown . . . 30 25

DESIGNS: 12 f. Artillery; 20 f. Tanks; 40 f. Cavalryman and cyclist.

(b) 2nd Issue (for Christmas Gifts).

712 – 20 f. + 40 f. red . . . . . . 1·00 85

DESIGN: Soldier in helmet; cross and sword.

1942. Air. Horthy Aviation Fund. Inscr "HORTHY MIKLOS NEMZETI REPULO ALAP".

713 **121** 8 f. + 8 f. green 35 30
714 – 12 f. + 12 f. blue 70 50
715 – 20 f. + 20 f. brown . . . 70 50
716 – 30 f. + 30 f. red 35 30

DESIGNS—VERT: 30 f. Airmen and Turul. HORIZ: 12 f. Aircraft and horsemen; 20 f. Airplane and archer.

122 Blood Transfusion **123** Vice-regent Stephen Horthy

1942. Red Cross Fund. Cross in red.

717 **122** 3 f. + 18 f. green 65 60
718 – 8 f. + 32 f. brown 65 60
719 – 12 f. + 50 f. purple . . . 65 60
720 – 20 f. + 1 p. blue 65 60

DESIGNS: 8 f. First Aid ("APOLAS"); 12 f. Wireless and carrier-pigeon service ("GONDOZAS"); 20 f. Bereaved parents and orphans ("GYAMOLITAS").

1942. Air. Mourning for Stephen Horthy and Horthy Aviation Fund.

721 – 20 f. black 25 10
722 **123** 30 f. + 20 f. violet 30 15

No. 721 is squarer in shape than No. 722 and is dated "1904–1942".

124 Stephen Horthy's Widow **125** King Ladislas

1942. Red Cross Fund. Cross and Crown in red.

723 **124** 6 f. + 1 p. blue . . . . . 1·75 2·25
724 – 8 f. + 1 p. green . . . . . 1·75 2·25
725 – 20 f. + 1 p. brown . . . . 1·75 2·25

DESIGNS—HORIZ: 8 f. Nurse and wounded soldier. VERT: 20 f. Stephen Horthy's mother.

1942. Cultural Funds.

726 **125** 6 f. + 6 f. brown 30 40
727 – 8 f. + 8 f. green 30 40
728 – 12 f. + 12 f. brown . . . 30 40
729 – 20 f. + 20 f. green 30 40
730 – 24 f. + 24 f. brown . . . 30 40
731 – 30 f. + 30 f. red 30 40

DESIGNS—Statuettes: 8 f. Ladislas on horseback; 20 f. Bela IV with architect; 30 f. Lajos the Great enthroned. King's heads; 12 f. Bela IV; 24 f. Lajos the Great.

126 Prince Arpad **127** St. Stephen's Crown

1943.

732 **126** 1 f. grey 10 10
733 – 2 f. orange 10 10
734 – 3 f. blue 10 10
735 – 4 f. brown 10 10
736 – 5 f. red 10 10
737 – 6 f. blue 10 10
738 – 8 f. green 10 10
739 – 10 f. brown 10 10
740 – 12 f. green 10 10
741 – 18 f. black 10 10
742 **127** 20 f. brown 10 10
743 – 24 f. purple 10 10
744 **127** 30 f. red 10 10
745 – 30 f. red 10 10
746 **127** 50 f. blue 10 10
747 80 f. brown 10 10
748 1 p. green 10 10
749 2 p. brown 20 10
750 5 p. purple 30 15

DESIGNS: 2 f. King Ladislas; 3 f. Miklos Toldi; 4 f. Janos Hunyadi; 5 f. Pal Kinizsi; 6 f. Miklos Zrinyi; 8 f. Ferenc Rakoczi II; 10 f. Andre Hadik; 12 f. Artur Gorgey; 18 f. and 24 f. Madonna; 30 f. (No. 745), St. Margaret.

1943. As T **102** (designs and colours changed).

751 – 30 f. red 10 10
752 – 40 f. grey 10 10
753 **102** 50 f. blue 10 10
754 – 70 f. green 10 10
755 – 80 f. brown 10 10

DESIGNS: 30 f. Kassa Cathedral; 40 f. Debrecen Reformed Church; 70 f. Budapest Evangelical Church; 80 f. Buda Cathedral.

128 Mounted Archer

129 Model Glider

1943. Wounded Soldiers' Relief Fund. Inscr as in T **128**.
756 **128** 1 f. + 1 f. grey 10 10
757 – 3 f. + 1 f. lilac 20 30
758 – 4 f. + 1 f. brown 15 10
759 – 8 f. + 2 f. green 15 10
760 – 12 f. + 2 f. brown 15 10
761 – 20 f. + 2 f. brown 15 10
762 – 40 f. + 4 f. grey 15 10
763 – 50 f. + 6 f. brown 15 10
764 – 70 f. + 8 f. blue 15 10
DESIGNS—VERT: 3 f., 4 f. Magyar soldier with battle-axe and buckler; 8 f. Warrior with shield and sword; 20 f. Musketeer; 50 f. Artilleryman; 70 f. Magyar Arms. HORIZ: 12 f. Lancer; 40 f. Hussar.

1943. Air. Horthy Aviation Fund. Inscr "HORTHY MIKLOS NEMZETI REPULO ALAP".
765 **129** 8 f. + 8 f. green 50 45
766 – 12 f. + 12 f. blue 50 45
767 – 20 f. + 20 f. brown . . . 1·50 55
768 – 30 f. + 30 f. red 50 45
DESIGNS: 12 f. Gliders in flight; 20 f. White-tailed sea eagle and aircraft; 30 f. Cant Z.1007 bis Alcione bomber and gliders.

130 Shepherds and Angels

1943. Christmas.
769 **130** 4 f. green 15 10
770 – 20 f. blue 15 10
771 – 30 f. red 15 10
DESIGNS: 20 f. Nativity; 30 f. Adoration of the Wise Men.

131 Nurse and Soldier

1944. Red Cross Fund. Cross and Crown in red.
772 **131** 20 f. + 20 f. brown . . . 30 25
773 – 30 f. + 30 f. brown . . . 30 25
774 – 50 f. + 50 f. purple . . . 30 25
775 – 70 f. + 70 f. blue 30 25
DESIGNS: 30 f. Soldier, nurse, mother and child; 50 f. Nurse shielding a lamp over the Fallen; 70 f. Soldier with crutches, nurse and sapling.

132 Drummer and Flags

133 St. Elizabeth

1944. 50th Death Anniv of Kossuth (statesman).
776 – 4 f. brown 10 10
777 **132** 20 f. green 10 10
778 – 30 f. red 10 10
779 – 50 f. blue 10 10
DESIGNS—VERT: 4 f. Kossuth and family group; 50 f. Portrait. HORIZ: 30 f. Kossuth speaking before an assembly.

1944. Famous Women.
780 **133** 20 f. bistre 10 10
781 – 24 f. purple 10 10
782 – 30 f. red 10 10
783 – 50 f. blue 10 10
784 – 70 f. red 10 10
785 – 80 f. brown 10 10
PORTRAITS: 24 f. St. Margaret; 30 f. Elizabeth Szilagyi; 50 f. Dorothy Kanizsai; 70 f. Zsuzsanna Lorantffy; 80 f. Ilona Zrinyi.

1945. Stamps as Nos. 732/48, surch **FELSZABADULAS** (= Liberation) **1945 apr 4** and value. On yellow or blue surface-tinted paper (same price).
786 10 f. on 1 f. grey . . . . . 1·75 1·75
787 20 f. on 3 f. blue . . . . . 1·75 1·75
788 30 f. on 4 f. brown . . . . 1·75 1·75
789 40 f. on 6 f. blue . . . . . 1·75 1·75
790 50 f. on 8 f. green . . . . 1·75 1·75
791 1 p. on 10 f. brown . . . . 1·75 1·75
792 150 f. on 12 f. green . . . . 1·75 1·75
793 2 p. on 18 f. black . . . . 1·75 1·75
794 3 p. on 20 f. brown . . . . 1·75 1·75
795 5 p. on 24 f. purple . . . . 1·75 1·75
796 6 p. on 50 f. blue . . . . . 1·75 1·75
797 10 p. on 80 f. brown . . . . 1·75 1·75
798 20 p. on 1 p. green . . . . 1·75 1·75

135 Bajcsy-Zsilinszky

1945. Bajcsy-Zsilinszky (patriot).
799 **135** 1 p. + 1 p. purple 70 70

1945. Provisionals. 1st issue. Surch **1945** and value. (a) On stamps of 1943, Nos. 732/50, surface-tinted paper.
800 10 f. on 4 f. brown on blue . . . 10 10
801 10 f. on 10 f. brown on blue . . 20 20
802 10 f. on 12 f. green on yellow . . 10 10
803 20 f. on 1 f. grey on yellow . . . 10 10
804 20 f. on 18 f. black on yellow . . 10 10
805 28 f. on 5 f. red on blue . . . 10 10
806 30 f. on 30 f. red on blue (No. 745) 10 10
807 30 f. on 30 f. red on blue (No. 744) 10 10
808 40 f. on 24 f. purple on yellow . 10 10
809 42 f. on 20 f. brown on yellow . 10 10
810 50 f. on 50 f. blue on yellow . . 10 10
811 60 f. on 8 f. green on yellow . . 10 10
812 1 p. on 80 f. brown on blue . . 10 10
813 1 p. on 1 p. green on yellow . . 10 10
814 150 f. on 6 f. blue on yellow . . 90 90
815 2 p. on 2 p. brown on blue . . . 10 10
816 3 p. on 3 f. blue on yellow . . . 15 15
817 5 p. on 5 p. purple on yellow . . 15 15
818 10 p. on 2 f. orange on blue . . 5·75 5·75
(b) On Famous Women Series of 1944 (Nos. 780/5), surface-tinted paper.
819 20 f. on 20 f. bistre on blue . . 10 10
820 30 f. on 30 f. red on blue . . . 10 10
821 40 f. on 24 f. purple on yell . . 10 10
822 50 f. on 50 f. blue on yellow . . 10 10
823 80 f. on 80 f. brown on yell . . 10 10
824 1 p. on 70 f. red on blue 10 10

1945. Provisionals. 2nd issue. Surch **1945** and value. (a) On stamps of 1943, Nos. 732/48, surface-tinted paper.
825 40 f. on 10 f. brown on blue . . 10 10
826 1 p. on 20 f. brown on yell . . . 10 10
827 1.60 p. on 12 f. grn on yell . . . 10 10
828 2 p. on 4 f. brown on blue . . . 10 10
829 4 p. on 30 f. red on blue (No. 744) 10 10
830 5 p. on 8 f. green on yellow . . 10 10
831 6 p. on 50 f. blue on yellow . . 10 10
832 7 p. on 1 p. green on yellow . . 10 10
833 9 p. on 1 f. grey on yellow . . . 10 10
834 10 p. on 80 f. brown on blue . . 10 10
(b) On Famous Women Series of 1944. (Nos. 780/3), surface-tinted paper.
835 80 f. on 24 f. purple on yell . . 10 10
836 3 p. on 50 f. blue on yellow . . 10 10
837 8 p. on 20 f. bistre on blue . . 10 10
838 20 p. on 30 f. red on blue . . . 10 10

1945. National High School Fund. Nos. 776/9, with coloured surfaces, surch **BEKE A NEPFOISKOLAKERT**, new value and premium.
839 **132** 3 p. + 9 p. on 20 f. green on yellow 20 20
840 – 4 p. + 12 p. on 4 f. brown on blue 20 20
841 – 8 p. + 24 p. on 50 f. blue on yellow 20 20
842 – 10 p. + 30 p. on 30 f. red on blue 20 20

138 Mining

1945. Int Trade Union Conference, Paris.
843 **138** 40 f. grey . . . . 7·25 7·25
844 – 1 p. 60 brown . . . . . . 7·25 7·25
845 – 2 p. green . . . . 7·25 7·25
846 – 3 p. purple . . . . 7·25 7·25
847 – 5 p. red . . . . 7·25 7·25
848 – 8 p. brown . . . . 7·25 7·25
849 – 10 p. red . . . . 7·25 7·25
850 – 20 p. blue . . . . 7·25 7·25
DESIGNS: Trade Symbols—1 p. 60, Hammer and anvil (ironworking); 2 p. Winged wheel (railway workers); 3 p. Trowel and bricks (building); 5 p. Plough (agriculture); 8 p. Carrier pigeon (communications); 10 p. Compasses (engineering); 20 p. Winged pen and book (clerks).

139 I. Sallai and S. Furst

1945. National Relief Fund.
851 **139** 2 p. + 2 p. brown . . . . 1·50 1·50
852 – 3 p. + 3 p. red . . . . . 1·50 1·50
853 – 4 p. + 4 p. violet . . . . 1·50 1·50
854 – 6 p. + 6 p. green . . . . 1·50 1·50
855 – 10 p. + 10 p. red . . . . 1·50 1·50
856 – 15 p. + 15 p. olive . . . . 1·50 1·50
857 – 20 p. + 20 p. brown . . . 1·50 1·50
858 – 40 p. + 40 p. blue . . . . 1·50 1·50
PORTRAITS: 3 p. L. Kabok and I. Monus; 4 p. F. Rozsa and Z. Schonherz; 6 p. A. Koltoi and P. Knurr; 10 p. G. Sarkozi and I. Nagy; 15 p. V. Tartsay and J. Nagy; 20 p. J. Kiss and E. Bajcsy-Zsilinszky; 40 p. E. Sagvari and O. Hoffmann.

1945. Provisionals. 3rd issue. Nos. 738, 740/1 and 745 (coloured surfaces) surch **1945** and new value.
859 40 p. on 8 f. green on yell . . . 10 10
860 60 p. on 18 f. black on yell . . . 10 10
861 100 p. on 12 f. green on yell . . 10 10
862 300 p. on 30 f. red on blue . . . 10 10

140 Reconstruction

1945.
863 **140** 12 p. olive 25 25
864 20 p. green 10 10
865 24 p. brown 25 25
866 30 p. black 10 10
867 40 p. green 10 10
868 60 p. red 10 10
869 100 p. orange 10 10
870 120 p. blue 10 10
871 140 p. red 30 30
872 200 p. brown 10 10
873 240 p. blue 10 10
874 300 p. red 10 10
875 500 p. green 10 10
876 1000 p. purple 10 10
877 3000 p. red 10 10

Owing to the collapse of the pengo, the following stamps were overprinted to show the postage rate for which they were valid, and they were sold at the appropriate rate for the day. **Any.** or **Nyomtatv** = Sample Post or Printed Matter. **Hlp** or **Helyi lev. lap** = Local Postcard. **Hl** or **Helyi level** = Local Letter. **Tlp** or **Tavolsagi lev.-lap** = Inland Postcard. **Tl** or **Tavolsagi level** = Inland Letter. **Ajl** or **Ajanlas** = Registered Letter. **Cs.** or **Csomag** = Parcel.

1946. Optd as above. (a) First Issue.
878 **126** "Any. 1" on 1 f. grey . . 10 10
879 – "Hlp. 1" on 8 p. on 20 f. bistre on blue (No. 837) 10 10
880 – "Hl. 1" on 50 f. blue (No. 783) 10 10
881 – "Tlp. 1" on 4 f. brown (No. 735) 10 10
882 – "Tl. 1" on 10 f. brown (No. 739) 10 10
883 **133** "Ajl. 1" on 20 f. bistre . . 10 10
883b **127** "Cs. 5–1" on 30 f. red (No. 744) . . . . . . 14·50 14·50
884 – "Cs. 5–1" on 70 f. red (No. 784) 10 10
885 – "Cs. 10–1" on 70 f. red (No. 784) 10 10
885a **127** "Cs. 10–1" on 80 f. brown (No.747) . . . . . . 14·50 14·50
(b) Second Issue.
886 **126** "Any. 2" on 1 f. grey . . . 10 10
887 – "Hlp. 2" on 8 p. on 20 f. bistre on blue (No. 837) . 10 10
888 – "Hl. 2" on 40 f. on 10 f. brn on blue (No. 825) . . . 10 10
889 – "Tlp. 2" on 4 f. brown (No. 735) 10 10
890 – "Tl. 2" on 10 f. on 4 f. brn on blue (No. 800) . . . 10 10
891 – "Ajl. 2" on 12 f. green (No. 740) 10 10
892 – "Cs. 5–2" on 24 f. purple (No. 743) 10 10
893 – "Cs. 10–2" on 80 f. brown (No. 785) 10 10
(c) Third Issue.
894 – "Nyomtatv. 20 gr." on 60 f. on 8 f. green on yellow (No. 811) 10 10
895 – "Helyi lev.-lap" on 2 f. bistre on blue (as No. 780) . . 10 10
896 – "Helyi level" on 10 f. brown on blue (as No. 739) . . . 10 10
897 – "Tavolsagi lev.-lap" on 4 f. brown (No. 735) 10 10
898 – "Tavolsagi level" on 18 f. black (No. 741) 10 10
899 – "Ajanlas" on 24 f. purple (No. 781) 10 10
900 – "Csomag 5 kg" on 2 p. on 4 f. brown on blue (No. 828) . 10 10
901 – "Csomag 10 kg." on 30 f. red on blue (as No. 782) . . . 10 10

Abbreviations used in the following issues:
ez(er) p. = thousand pengos.
m(illio) p. = million pengos.
m.p. (milpengo) = million pengos.
md.p. (milliard. p) = thousand million pengos.
b.p. (billio. p) = million million pengos.
ez. ap (ezer adopengo) = thousand "tax" pengos.
m. ap. (millio adopengo) = million "tax" pengos.

143

144

1946. Foundation of Republic.
902 **143** 3 ez. p. brown 10 10
903 15 ez. p. blue 10 10

1946.
904 **144** 4 ez. p. brown 10 10
905 10 ez. p. red 10 10
906 15 ez. p. blue 10 10
907 20 ez. p. brown 10 10
908 30 ez. p. purple 10 10
909 50 ez. p. grey 10 10
910 80 ez. p. blue 10 10
911 100 ez. p. red 10 10
912 160 ez. p. green 10 10
913 200 ez. p. green 10 10
914 500 ez. p. red 10 10
915 640 ez. p. olive 10 10
916 800 ez. p. violet 10 10

145

146

1946. 75th Anniv of First Hungarian Stamps.
917 **145** 500 + 500 ez. p. green . . 1·75 1·75
918 1 + 1 m. p. brown . . . . 1·75 1·75
919 1.5 + 1.5 m. p. red . . . 1·75 1·75
920 2 + 2 m. p. blue . . . . 1·75 1·75

1946.
921 **146** 1 m. p. red 10 10
922 2 m. p. blue 10 10
923 3 m. p. brown 10 10
924 4 m. p. grey 10 10
925 5 m. p. violet 10 10
926 10 m. p. green 10 10
927 20 m. p. red 10 10
928 50 m. p. green 10 10

147 Posthorn and Arms

148 Posthorn

149 Dove and Letter

1946.
929 **147** 100 m.p. red 10 10
930 200 m.p. red 10 10
931 500 m.p. red 10 10
932 1000 m.p. red 10 10
933 2000 m.p. red 10 10
934 3000 m.p. red 10 10
935 5000 m.p. red 10 10
936 10,000 m.p. red 10 10
937 20,000 m.p. red 10 10
938 30,000 m.p. red 10 10
939 50,000 m.p. red 10 10

1946.
940 **148** 100 md.p. green and red . . 10 10
941 200 md.p. green and red . . 10 10
942 500 md.p. green and red . . 10 10

1946.
943 **149** 1 b.p. black and red . . . 10 10
944 2 b.p. black and red . . . 10 10
945 5 b.p. black and red . . . 10 10
946 10 b.p. black and red . . 10 10
947 20 b.p. black and red . . 10 10
948 50 b.p. black and red . . 10 10
949 100 b.p. black and red . . 10 10
950 200 b.p. black and red . . 10 10
951 500 b.p. black and red . . 10 10
952 1000 b.p. black and red . . 10 10
953 10,000 b.p. black & red . . 10 10
954 50,000 b.p. black & red . . 15 15
955 100,000 b.p. black & red . 15 15
956 500,000 b.p. black & red . 15 15

150 Locomotive "Heves", 1846

151 Posthorn

1946. Centenary of Hungarian Railways.
957 **150** 10000 ap. brown . . . . 4·50 4·00
958 – 20000 ap. blue . . . . . 4·50 4·00
959 – 30000 ap. green . . . . 4·50 4·00
960 – 40000 ap. red . . . . . 4·50 4·00
DESIGNS: 20000 ap. Class 424 steam locomotive; 30000 ap. Class V44 electric locomotive; 40000 ap. "Arpad" diesel railcar, 1935.

1946.

961 **151** 5 ez. ap. green and black . 10 10
962 10 ez. ap. green & black . . 10 10
963 20 ez. ap. green & black . . 10 10
964 50 ez. ap. green & black . . 10 10
965 80 ez. ap. green & black . . 10 10
966 100 ez. ap. green & black . 10 10
967 200 ez. ap. green & black . 10 10
968 500 ez. ap. green & black . 10 10
969 1 m. ap. red and black . . 10 10
970 5 m. ap. red and black . . 10 10

152 Industry **153** Agriculture

1946. Currency Reform.

971 **152** 8 fi. brown 15 10
972 10 fi. brown 15 10
973 12 fi. brown 15 10
974 20 fi. brown 15 10
975 30 fi. brown 15 10
976 40 fi. brown 15 10
977 60 fi. brown 20 10
978 **153** 1 fo. green 60 10
979 1 fo. 40 green 60 10
980 2 fo. green 65 10
981 3 fo. green . . . . 5·00 10
982 5 fo. green . . . . 1·50 10
983 10 fo. green . . . . 2·50 20

154 Ceres **155** Liberty Bridge

1946. Agricultural Fair.

984 **154** 30 fi. + 60 fi. green . . . 7·25 7·25
985 60 fi. + 1 fo. 20 red . . . 7·25 7·25
986 1 fo. + 2 fo. blue . . . . 7·25 7·25

1947. Air. Views.

987 – 10 fi. red 15 10
988 – 20 fi. grey 15 10
989 **155** 50 fi. brown 65 10
990 – 70 fi. green 40 10
991 – 1 fo. blue . . . . 1·50 10
992 – 1 fo. 40 brown . . . . . . 1·50 10
993 – 3 fo. green . . . . 3·00 25
994 – 5 fo. lilac . . . . 7·25 1·50

DESIGNS: 10 fi. Loyalty Tower, Sopron; 20 fi. Esztergom Cathedral; 70 fi. Palace Hotel, Lillafured; 1 fo. Vajdahunyad Castle, Budapest; 1 fo. 40, Visegrad Fortress; 3 fo. "Falcone" (racing yacht) on Lake Balaton; 5 fo. Parliament Buildings and Kossuth Bridge.

156 Gyorgy Dozsa **157** Doctor Examining X-Ray Photograph

1947. Liberty issue.

995 **156** 8 fi. red 15 10
996 – 10 fi. blue 15 10
997 – 12 fi. brown 15 10
998 – 20 fi. green 30 10
999 – 30 fi. brown 30 10
1000 – 40 fi. purple 40 10
1001 – 60 fi. red 70 10
1002 – 1 fo. blue 75 10
1003 – 2 fo. violet . . . . . . 1·50 35
1004 – 4 fo. green . . . . 2·25 55

PORTRAITS: 10 fi. A. Budai Nagy; 12 fi. T. Esze; 20 fi. I. Martinovics; 30 fi. J. Batsanyi; 40 fi. L. Kossuth; 60 fi. M. Tancsics; 1 fo. S. Petofi; 2 fo. E. Ady; 4 fo. A. Jozsef.

1947. Welfare Organizations. Inscr "SIESS! ADJ! SEGITS!" (trans. "Come! Give! Help!").

1005 – 8 fi. + 50 fi. blue . . . 5·00 5·00
1006 **157** 12 fi. + 50 fi. brown . . . 5·00 5·00
1007 – 20 fi. + 50 fi. green . . . 5·00 5·00
1008 – 60 fi. + 50 fi. red . . . . 2·75 2·75

DESIGNS: 8 fi. Doctor testing syringe; 20 fi. Nurse and child; 60 fi. Released prisoner-of-war.

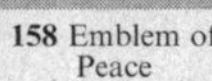

158 Emblem of Peace **159** Liberty Statue

1947. Peace Treaty.

1009 **158** 60 fi. red 20 10

1947. 30th Anniv of Soviet Union and Hungarian–Soviet Cultural Society Fund.

1010 – 40 fi. + 40 fi. brn & grn . 5·25 5·25
1011 **159** 60 fi. + 60 fi. grey & red . 3·50 3·50
1012 – 1 fo. + 1 fo. blk & blue . 5·25 5·25

PORTRAITS: 40 fi. Lenin; 1 fo. Stalin.

161 Savings Bank **162** XVIth Century Mail Coach

1947. Savings Day. Type **161** and design inscr "TAKAREKOS JELENBOLDOG JOVO".

1013 – 40 fi. red (beehive) . . . 40 10
1014 **161** 60 fi. red 40 10

1947. Stamp Day.

1015 **162** 30 fi. (+ 50 fi.) brown . . 10·50 10·50

165 Arms of Hungary . **167** Johann Gutenberg

1948. Centenary of Insurrection.

1016 – 8 fi. red 15 10
1017 – 10 fi. blue 15 10
1018 – 12 fi. brown 15 10
1019 – 20 fi. green 50 10
1020 – 30 fi. brown 20 10
1021 – 40 fi. purple 20 10
1022 – 60 fi. red 90 10
1023 **165** 1 fo. blue 90 10
1024 2 fo. brown . . . . 2·50 10
1025 3 fo. green . . . . 3·00 45
1026 4 fo. red . . . . 5·25 70

DESIGNS—HORIZ: 8 fi., 40 fi. Hungarian independence flag; 10 fi. Printing press; 12 fi. Latticed window; 20 fi. Shako, trumpet and sword; 30 fi., 60 fi. Slogan.

1948. Air. Explorers and Inventors.

1027 **167** 1 fi. red 15 15
1028 – 2 fi. mauve 20 15
1029 – 4 fi. blue 20 15
1030 – 5 fi. brown 40 20
1031 – 6 fi. green 25 20
1032 – 8 fi. purple 25 20
1033 – 10 fi. brown 45 25
1034 – 12 fi. green . . . . 1·00 30
1035 – 30 fi. red . . . . 1·50 60
1036 – 40 fi. violet . . . . . . 1·40 1·40

PORTRAITS: 2 fi. Christopher Columbus; 4 fi. Robert Fulton; 5 fi. George Stephenson; 6 fi. David Schwarz and Count Ferdinand von Zeppelin; 8 fi. Thomas Edison; 10 fi. Louis Bleriot; 12 fi. Roald Amundsen; 30 fi. Kalman Kando; 40 fi. Alexander Popov.

169 Lorand Eotvos

1948. Birth Centenary of L. Eotvos (physicist).

1037 **169** 60 fi. red . . . . 1·10 35

170 William Shakespeare

1948. Air. Writers.

1038 **170** 1 fi. blue 15 15
1039 – 2 fi. red 20 15
1040 – 4 fi. green 20 15
1041 – 5 fi. mauve 25 20
1042 – 6 fi. blue 25 20
1043 – 8 fi. brown 25 20
1044 – 10 fi. red 30 25
1045 – 12 fi. violet 35 30
1046 – 30 fi. brown . . . . 1·25 1·25
1047 – 40 fi. brown . . . . 1·40 1·40

PORTRAITS: 2 fi. Voltaire; 4 fi. Goethe; 5 fi. Byron; 6 fi. Victor Hugo; 8 fi. Edgar Allan Poe; 10 fi. Petofi; 12 fi. Mark Twain; 30 fi. Tolstoy; 40 fi. Gorki.

171 Globe and Pigeon **172** Symbolizing Industry, Agriculture and Culture

1948. 5th National Philatelic Exhibition.

1048 **171** 30 fi. blue . . . . 4·50 4·50

Sold at 1 fo. 30 (incl 1 fo. entrance fee).

1948. 17th Trades' Union Congress.

1049 **172** 30 fi. red 70 70

173 Agricultural Worker **174** Reproduction of T **32**

1949. International Women's Day.

1050 **173** 60 fi. + 60 fi. mauve . . 1·40 1·40

1949. 30th Anniv of Bolshevist Regime.

1051 **174** 40 fi. brown and red . . . 25 15
1052 – 60 fi. olive and red . . . 30 15

DESIGN: 60 fi. Reproduction of No. 325.

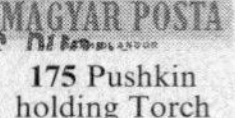

175 Pushkin holding Torch and Scroll **176** Symbolising Workers of Five Continents

1949. 150th Birth Anniv of A. S. Pushkin (poet).

1053 **175** 1 fo. + 1 fo. red . . . . 9·00 9·00

1949. 2nd World Federation of Trade Unions Congress, Milan. Flag in red.

1054 **176** 30 fi. brown . . . . . . 3·50 3·50
1055 40 fi. purple . . . . . . 3·50 3·50
1056 60 fi. red . . . . 3·50 3·50
1057 1 fo. blue . . . . 3·50 3·50

177 Sandor Petofi **178** Heads and Globe

1949. Death Centenary of Petofi (poet).

1058 **177** 40 fi. purple 55 15
1096 40 fi. brown 55 15
1059 60 fi. red 20 10
1060 1 fo. blue 55 10
1098 1 fo. green 45 10

1949. World Youth Festival, Budapest.

1061 **178** 20 fi. brown 90 90
1062 – 30 fi. green . . . . 1·10 1·10
1063 – 40 fi. bistre . . . . . . 1·40 1·40
1064 – 60 fi. red . . . . 1·10 1·10
1065 – 1 fo. blue . . . . 2·00 2·00

DESIGNS: 30 fi. Three clenched fists; 40 fi. Man breaking chains; 60 fi. Young people and banner; 1 fo. Workers and tractor.

179 Hungarian Coat-of-Arms

1949. Ratification of Constitution. Arms in blue, brown, red and green.

1066 **179** 20 fi. green . . . . . . 1·10 30
1067 60 fi. red 50 10
1068 1 fo. blue 90 40

181 Globes and Posthorn **182** Chain Bridge

1949. 75th Anniv of U.P.U.

1069 **181** 60 fi. red (postage) . . . 55 55
1070 1 fo. blue 55 55
1071 – 2 fo. brown (air) . . . . 1·10 1·10

DESIGN: 2 fo. Lisunov Li-2 airplane replaces posthorn.

1949. Centenary of Budapest Chain Bridge.

1073 **182** 40 fi. green (postage) . . 60 55
1074 60 fi. brown 60 35
1075 1 fo. blue 60 35
1076 1 fo. 60 red (air) . . . . 1·10 70
1077 2 fo. olive . . . . 1·10 70

183 Postman and Forms of Transport **184** Joseph Stalin

1949. Air. Stamp Day.

1078 **183** 50 fi. grey . . . . 5·00 5·00

1949. Stalin's 70th Birthday.

1079 **184** 60 fi. red 70 10
1080 1 fo. blue . . . . 1·10 40
1081 2 fo. brown . . . . 1·40 85

185 Miners

1950. Five Year Plan.

1082 **185** 8 fi. grey 60 15
1083 – 10 fi. purple 40 10
1084 – 12 fi. red 60 10
1085 – 20 fi. green 40 10
1086 – 30 fi. purple 60 10
1087 – 40 fi. brown 60 10
1088 – 60 fi. red 70 10
1089 – 1 fo. violet and yellow . . 1·25 10
1090 – 1 fo. 70 green & yellow . . 1·75 10
1091 – 2 fo. red and orange . . . 2·75 10
1092 – 3 fo. blue and buff . . . 3·00 10
1093 – 4 fo. green & orange . . . 3·00 45
1094 – 5 fo. purple & yellow . . 5·00 1·00
1095 – 10 fo. brown & yellow . . 9·00 2·25

DESIGNS: 10 fi. Iron foundry; 12 fi. Power station; 20 fi. Textiles; 30 fi. Factory workers' entertainment; 40 fi. Mechanical farming; 60 fi. Village co-operative office; 1 fo. Class 303 steam locomotive on bridge; 1 fo. 70, Family at health resort; 2 fo. Soldier and tank; 3 fo. Freighter and Lisunov Li-2 airplane; 4 fo. Cattle; 5 fo. Draughtsman and factory; 10 fo. Sportsman, woman and football match.

186 Philatelic Museum

1950. 20th Anniv of P.O. Philatelic Museum.

1099 **186** 60 fi. brown and black (postage) . . . . . 7·25 7·25
1100 – 2 fo. red and yellow (air) . 10·50 9·00

DESIGN—HORIZ: 2 fo. Globe, coach, Douglas DC-4 airliner and stamps.

188 Family Greeting Soviet Troops

1950. 5th Anniv of Liberation.

1101 **188** 40 fi. black . . . . 1·10 45
1102 60 fi. lake 75 10
1103 1 fo. blue 75 15
1104 2 fo. brown . . . . 1·10 60

189 Chess Match

1950. 1st International Candidates Chess Tournament, Budapest. Designs incorporate rook and chessboard.
1105 **189** 60 fi. mauve (postage) . . 1·75 40
1106 – 1 fo. blue . . . . 3·50 1·00
1107 – 1 fo. 60 brown (air) . . . 5·25 2·00
DESIGNS: 1 fo. Trade Union Building; 1 fo. 60, Map.

190 Workers and Star

1950. May Day. Inscr as in T **190**.
1108 **190** 40 fi. brown . . . . . . 2·00 70
1109 – 60 fi. red 90 10
1110 **190** 1 fo. blue . . . . 1·50 45
DESIGN: 60 fi. Two workers.

191 Workers and Flag

1950. World Federation of Trade Unions Congress, Budapest.
1111 – 40 fi. green (postage) . . . 1·40 55
1112 **191** 60 fi. red 70 35
1113 – 1 fo. brown (air) . . . . 1·40 40
DESIGNS: 40 fi. Statue, dove and globes; 1 fo. Globes, Chain Bridge and Parliament Bldgs.

192 Baby and Nursery

1950. Children's Day.
1114 **192** 20 fi. brown and grey . . 1·50 1·25
1115 – 30 fi. mauve & brown . . 65 10
1116 – 40 fi. green and blue . . 65 10
1117 – 60 fi. red and brown . . £1800 £1800
1117a – 60 fi. red and brown . . 65 10
1118 – 1 fo. 70 blue & green . . 1·40 85
DESIGNS: 30 fi. Baby boy and holiday scene; 40 fi. Schoolgirl and classroom; 60 fi. Pioneer boy and camp; 1 fo. 70, Pioneer boy and girl and model glider class.
No. 1117 is inscr "UTANPOTLASUNK A JOVO HARCAIHOZ" and No. 1117a is inscr. "SZABAD HAZABAN BOLDOG IFJUSAG".

193 Workers and Globe

1950. 1st Congress of Young Workers, Budapest.
1119 **193** 20 fi. green 90 30
1120 – 30 fi. orange 15 10
1121 – 40 fi. brown 15 10
1122 – 60 fi. mauve 65 10
1123 – 1 fo. 70 green . . . . . 1·50 55
DESIGNS:—HORIZ: 30 fi. Foundry worker and cauldron. VERT: 40 fi. Man, woman and banner; 60 fi. Workers, banner and Liberty Statue; 1 fo. 70, Three workers and banner.

194 Peonies 195 Miner

1950. Flowers.
1124 **194** 30 fi. purple and green . . 1·25 35
1125 – 40 fi. green, yell & mve . . 1·25 45
1126 – 60 fi. brown, yell & grn . 2·50 60
1127 – 1 fo. violet, red & green . 3·50 1·40
1128 – 1 fo. 70 vio, grn & lilac . 4·25 2·50
DESIGNS: 40 fi. Pasque flowers; 60 fi. Yellow pheasant's-eye; 1 fo. Geranium; 1 fo. 70, Campanulas.

1950. 2nd National Inventions Exhibition.
1129 **195** 40 fi. brown . . . . . . 1·40 45
1130 – 60 fi. red . . . . 1·25 35
1131 – 1 fo. blue . . . . 1·75 75
DESIGNS: 60 fi. Turner; 1 fo. Building factory.

196 Liberty Statue

1950. Air.
1132 **196** 20 fi. red 15 10
1133 – 30 fi. violet 15 10
1134 – 70 fi. purple 20 10
1135 – 1 fo. brown 25 10
1136 – 1 fo. 60 blue 75 10
1137 – 2 fo. red 90 10
1138 – 3 fo. black . . . . . . 2·50 40
1139 – 5 fo. blue . . . . 1·60 45
1140 – 10 fo. brown . . . . . 7·25 80
1140a – 20 fo. green . . . . . . 11·00 4·00
DESIGNS—VERT: 30 fi. Crane and buildings; 70 fi. Diosgyor steelworks; 1 fo. "Stalinyec" tractor; 1 fo. 60, "Szeged" (freighter); 2 fo. Combine harvester; 3 fo. Class 303 steam locomotive; 5 fo. Matyas Rakosi steel-mill; 10, 20 fo. Lisunov Li-2 airplane at Budaors airport.
For No. 1139 but on silver paper see No. 1437.

198 Worker signing Peace Petition

1950. Peace Propaganda.
1141 **198** 40 fi. brown and blue . . 12·50 12·50
1142 – 60 fi. green & orange . . 3·50 3·50
1143 – 1 fo. brown and green . . 12·50 12·50
DESIGNS—VERT: 60 fi. Girl holding dove. HORIZ: 1 fo. Soldier mother and children.

199 Swimmers

1950.
1144 **199** 10 fi. blue and light blue (postage) 10 10
1145 – 20 fi. brown & orange . . 15 10
1146 – 1 fo. green and olive . . 60 55
1147 – 1 fo. 70 red & verm . . 1·10 90
1148 – 2 fo. violet and brown . . 2·25 1·25
1149 – 30 fi. mve & vio (air) . . 35 10
1150 – 40 fi. blue and green . . 60 10
1151 – 60 fi. orge, brn & grn . . 1·25 35
1152 – 70 fi. brown and grey . . 1·50 60
1153 – 3 fo. chestnut & brown . . 3·50 1·25
DESIGNS—POSTAGE: 20 fi. Vaulting; 1 fo. Mountaineering; 1 fo. 70, Basketball; 2 fo. Motor cycling. AIR: 30 fi. Volleyball; 40 fi. Throwing the javelin; 60 fi. Emblem of "Ready for work and action" movement; 70 fi. Football; 3 fo. Gliding.

200 Jozef Bem and Battle of Piski 201 Workers and Soldier

1950. Death Centenary of Gen. Bem.
1154 **200** 40 fi. brown . . . . . . 1·10 35
1155 60 fi. red . . . . 1·10 45
1156 1 fo. blue . . . . 2·10 70

1951. 2nd Hungarian Communist Party Congress.
1157 **201** 10 fi. green 20 10
1158 – 30 fi. brown 30 40
1159 – 60 fi. red 70 55
1160 – 1 fo. blue . . . . 1·25 70
DESIGNS—HORIZ: 30 fi. Workers, soldier and banner; 60 fi. Portrait and four workers with flags. VERT: 1 fo. Procession with banner.

202 Flags 203 Mare and Foal

1951. Hungarian-Soviet Amity. Inscr "MAGYAR SZOVJET BARATSAG HONAPJA 1951".
1161 **202** 60 fi. red 25 10
1162 – 1 fo. violet 60 20
DESIGN: 1 fo. Hungarian and Russian workers.

1951. Livestock Expansion Plan.
1163 **203** 10 fi. brown and ochre (postage) 15 10
1164 – 30 fi. brown and red . . . 40 25
1165 – 40 fi. brown and green . . 45 25
1166 – 60 fi. brown & orange . . 60 10
1167 **203** 20 fi. brn & grn (air) . . . 30 10
1168 70 fi. ochre and brown . . 60 60
1169 1 fo. brown and blue . . 2·75 1·25
1170 1 fo. 60 chest & brn . . . 5·00 1·75
DESIGNS: 30, 70 fi. Sow and litter; 40 fi., 1 fo. Ewe and lamb; 60 fi., 1 fo. 60, Cow and calf.

204 Worker

1951. May Day. Inscr "1951 MAJUS".
1171 **204** 40 fi. brown 90 90
1172 – 60 fi. red 60 10
1173 – 1 fo. blue 90 45
DESIGNS—VERT: 60 fi. People with banners. HORIZ: 1 fo. Labour Day rally.

205 Leo Frankel 206 Street-fighting

1951. 80th Anniv of Paris Commune.
1174 **205** 60 fi. brown 70 10
1175 **206** 1 fo. blue and red . . . . 1·10 20

207 Children's Heads 208 Ganz Wagon Works

1951. Int. Children's Day. Inscr "NEMZETKOZI GYERMEKNAP 1951".
1176 **207** 30 fi. brown 30 10
1177 – 40 fi. green 40 10
1178 – 50 fi. brown 65 20
1179 – 60 fi. mauve 65 35
1180 – 1 fo. 70 fi. blue 90 80
DESIGNS: 40 fi. Flying model airplane; 50 fi. Diesel train on Budapest Pioneer Railway; 60 fi. Chemistry experiment; 1 fo. 70, Blowing bugle.

1951. Rebuilding Plan (1st series).
1180a – 8 fi. green 50 10
1180b – 10 fi. violet 80 10
1180c – 12 fi. red 50 10
1181 **208** 20 fi. green 80 10
1182 – 30 fi. orange 65 10
1183 – 40 fi. brown 95 10
1183a – 50 fi. blue 65 10
1184 – 60 fi. red 90 10
1184a – 70 fi. brown . . . . . . 1·75 10
1184b – 80 fi. purple . . . . . . 1·40 10
1185 – 1 fo. blue . . . . 1·25 10
1185a – 1 fo. 20 red . . . . . . 1·75 10
1185b – 1 fo. 70 blue . . . . . . 1·75 10
1185c – 2 fo. green . . . . . . 2·00 10
1186 – 3 fo. purple . . . . . . 2·25 10
1186a – 4 fo. olive . . . . . . 2·50 10
1186b – 5 fo. black . . . . . . 3·75 15
BUILDINGS: 8 fi. Stalin School; 10 fi. Szekesfehervar railway station; 12 fi. Ujpest medical dispensary; 30 fi. Flats; 40 fi. Central Railway Station, Budapest; 50 fi. Inota power station; 60 fi. Matyas Rakosi Cultural Institute; 70 fi. Hajdunanas grain elevator; 80 fi. Tiszalok dam; 1 fo. Kilian Road School; 1 fo. 20, Mining Apprentices Institute, Ajkacsingervolgy; 1 fo. 70, Iron and Steel Apprentices Institute, Csepel; 2 fo. Cultural Centre, Hungarian Optical Works; 3 fo. Building Workers' Union Headquarters; 4 fo. Miners' Union Headquarters; 5 fo. Flats.
See also Nos. 1296/1304.

209 Gorky 210 Engineers and Tractors

1951. 15th Death Anniv of Maksim Gorky (Russian writer).
1187 **209** 60 fi. red 15 10
1188 1 fo. blue 45 10
1189 2 fo. purple . . . . . . 1·40 70

1951. 1st Anniv of Five Year Plan.
1190 **210** 20 fi. sepia (postage) . . . 15 10
1191 – 30 fi. blue 20 10
1192 – 40 fi. red 55 10
1193 – 60 fi. brown 60 10
1194 – 70 fi. brown (air) 75 30
1195 – 1 fo. green 90 50
1196 – 2 fo. purple . . . . . . 1·60 50
DESIGNS: 30 fi. Doctor X-raying patient; 40 fi. Workman instructing apprentices; 60 fi. Girl driving tractor; 70 fi. Electrical engineers constructing pylon; 1 fo. Young people and recreation home; 2 fo. Lisunov Li-2 airplane over Stalin (later Arpad) Bridge.

211 1871 Stamp without portrait and Hungarian Arms 212 Soldiers Parading

1951. 80th Anniv of 1st Hungarian Postage Stamp.
1197 **211** 60 fi. green . . . . 5·25 3·50
1198 1 fo. + 1 fo. red . . . . 18·00 14·00
1199 2 fo. + 2 fo. blue . . . . 21·00 18·00

1951. Army Day.
1200 **212** 1 fo. brown (postage) . . 1·25 15
1201 – 60 fi. blue (air) 70 15
DESIGN—VERT: 60 fi. Tanks and Liberty Statue.

213 Lily of the Valley 214 Revolutionaries and Flags

1951. Flowers.
1202 – 30 fi. violet, blue & grn . . 35 10
1203 **213** 40 fi. myrtle & green . . . 1·25 45
1204 – 60 fi. red, pink & green . . 90 35
1205 – 1 fo. blue, red & green . . 1·50 70
1206 – 1 fo. 70 brn, yell & grn . . 3·25 2·10
FLOWERS: 30 fi. Cornflowers; 60 fi. Tulips; 1 fo. Poppies; 1 fo. 70, Cowslips.

1951. 34th Anniv of Russian Revolution.
1207 **214** 40 fi. green 90 20
1208 – 60 fi. blue 70 35
1209 – 1 fo. red 90 45
DESIGNS: 60 fi. Lenin addressing revolutionaries; 1 fo. Lenin and Stalin.

215 Parade before Stalin Statue

1951. Stalin's 72nd Birthday.
1210 **215** 60 fi. red . . . . 1·40 60
1211 1 fo. blue . . . . 1·40 60

216 Bolshoi State Theatre, Moscow

1952. Views of Moscow.
1212 **216** 60 fi. lake and green . . . 25 10
1213 – 1 fo. brown and red . . . 65 35
1214 – 1 fo. 60 olive and lake . . 1·10 55
DESIGNS: 1 fo. Lenin Mausoleum; 1 fo. 60, Kremlin.

217 Rakosi and Peasants

218 Rakosi

1952. 60th Birth Anniv of Rakosi.
1215 **217** 60 fi. purple 70 35
1216 **218** 1 fo. brown 70 40
1217 – 2 fo. blue . . . . 1·75 70
DESIGN: 2 fo. Rakosi and foundry workers.

219 L. Kossuth

1952. Heroes of 1848 Revolution.
1218 **219** 20 fi. green 10 10
1219 – 30 fi. purple (Petofi) . . . 15 10
1220 – 50 fi. black (Bem) 30 15
1221 – 60 fi. lake (Tancsics) . . . 55 10
1222 – 1 fo. bl (Damjanich) . . . 65 10
1223 – 1 fo. 50 brn (Nagy) . . . 70 55

220 Avocet

1952. Air. Birds.
1224 **220** 20 fi. black and green . . 15 10
1225 – 30 fi. black and green . . 25 10
1226 – 40 fi. black, yell & brn . . 35 15
1227 – 50 fi. black and orange . . 35 15
1228 – 60 fi. black and red . . . 40 15
1229 – 70 fi. black, orge & red . . 55 20
1230 – 80 fi. black, yell & grn . . 80 30
1231 – 1 fo. black, red & blue . . 1·10 35
1232 – 1 fo. 40 multicoloured . . 1·25 40
1233 – 1 fo. 60 blk, grn & brn . . 1·50 60
1234 – 2 fo. 50 black & purple . . 3·00 1·00
DESIGNS: 30 fi. White stork; 40 fi. Golden oriole; 50 fi. Kentish plover; 60 fi. Black-winged stilt; 70 fi. Lesser grey strike; 80 fi. Great bustard; 1 fo. Red-footed falcon; 1 fo. 40, European bee eater; 1 fo. 60, Glossy ibis; 2 fo. 50, Great egret.

1952. Budapest Philatelic Exn. No. 1050 with bars obliterating inscription and premium.
1235 **173** 60 fi. mauve . . . . . . 60·00 60·00

222 Drummer and Flags

1952. May Day. Inscr "1952 MAJUS I".
1236 **222** 40 fi. red and green . . . 1·40 60
1237 – 60 fi. red and brown . . . 1·25 60
1238 – 1 fo. red and brown . . . 1·25 60
DESIGNS: 60 fi. Workers; 1 fo. Workman and globe.

223 Running

1952. 15th Olympic Games, Helsinki.
1239 **223** 30 fi. brown (postage) . . 60 10
1240 – 40 fi. green 60 10
1241 – 60 fi. red 90 10
1242 – 1 fo. blue . . . . 1·40 60

1243 – 1 fo. 70 orange (air) . . . 1·75 1·25
1244 – 2 fo. brown . . . . . . 2·10 1·75
DESIGNS: 40 fi. Swimming; 60 fi. Fencing; 1 fo. Gymnastics; 1 fo. 70, Throwing the hammer; 2 fo. Stadium.

224 Leonardo da Vinci

225 Train and Railwayman

1952. Air. 500th Birth Anniv of Leonardo da Vinci and 150th Birth Anniv of Victor Hugo.
1245 **224** 1 fo. 60 blue . . . . . . 1·10 70
1246 – 2 fo. purple (Victor Hugo) . . . . 1·40 1·10

1952. Railway Day. Inscr "1952 VIII 10".
1247 **225** 60 fi. brown . . . . . . 1·00 20
1248 – 1 fo. green . . . . . . 1·75 30
DESIGN: 1 fo. Railway tracks.

226 Mechanical Coal-cutter

227 L. Kossuth

1952. Miners' Day. Inscr as in T **226**.
1249 **226** 60 fi. brown 90 15
1250 – 1 fo. green . . . . 1·25 45
DESIGN: 1 fo. Miners operating machinery.

1952. 150th Birth Anniv of Kossuth (statesman).
1251 **227** 40 fi. olive on pink . . . 90 15
1252 – 60 fi. black on blue . . . 20 10
1253 **227** 1 fo. lilac on yellow . . . 90 50
DESIGN: 60 fi. Statue of Kossuth.

228 Gy Dozsa

229 Boy, Girl and Stamp Exhibition

1952. Army Day. Inscr as T **228**.
1254 20 fi. lilac (J. Hunyadi) 15 10
1255 30 fi. green (T **228**) 15 10
1256 40 fi. blue (M. Zrinyi) 15 10
1257 60 fi. purple (I. Zrinyi) 45 10
1258 1 fo. turquoise (B. Vak) . . . 70 30
1259 1 fo. 50, brn (A. Stromfeld) . . 1·40 55

1952. Air. Stamp Day. Inscr "XXV. BELYEGNAP 1952".
1260 – 1 fo. + 1 fo. blue . . . . 9·00 9·00
1261 **229** 2 fo. + 2 fo. red . . . . 9·00 9·00
DESIGN: 1 fo. Children examining stamps.

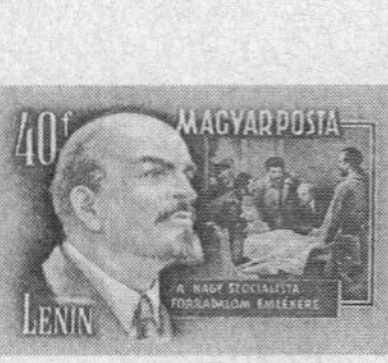
230 Lenin and Revolutionary Council

231 Harvester

1952. 35th Anniv of Russian Revolution.
1262 **230** 40 fi. olive and purple . . 1·40 30
1263 – 60 fi. olive and black . . 70 10
1264 – 1 fo. olive and red . . . 1·40 15
DESIGNS: 60 fi. Stalin and Cossacks; 1 fo. Marx, Engels, Lenin, Stalin and Spassky Tower.

1952. 3rd Hungarian Peace Congress. Inscr as in T **231**.
1265 **231** 60 fi. red on yellow . . . 70 10
1266 – 1 fo. brown on green . . . 70 20
DESIGN—HORIZ: 1 fo. Workers' discussion group.

232 Tunnel Construction

1953. Budapest Underground Railway. Inscr "BUDAPESTI FOLDALATTI GYORSVASUT".
1267 **232** 60 fi. green . . . . . . 1·25 15
1268 – 1 fo. lake . . . . 1·75 60
DESIGN—HORIZ: 1 fo. Underground map and station.

233 Russian Flag and Tank

234 Eurasian Red Squirrel

1953. 10th Anniv of Battle of Stalingrad.
1269 **233** 40 fi. red . . . . 1·25 15
1270 – 60 fi. brown . . . . . . 1·25 60
DESIGN: 60 fi. Soldier, map and flags.

1953. Air. Forest Animals.
1271 **234** 20 fi. brown and olive . . 25 10
1272 – 30 fi. sepia and brown . . 30 10
1273 – 40 fi. sepia and green . . 35 10
1274 – 50 fi. sepia and brown . . 45 40
1275 – 60 fi. brown & turquoise . . 65 40
1276 – 70 fi. brown and olive . . 60 45
1277 – 80 fi. brown and green . . 90 70
1278 – 1 fo. brown and green . . 1·10 90
1279 – 1 fo. 50, black & bistre . . 2·50 1·25
1280 – 2 fo. sepia and brown . . 2·75 1·50
DESIGNS—HORIZ: 30 fi. West European hedgehog; 40 fi. Brown hare; 60 fi. European otter; 70 fi. Red fox; 1 fo. Roe deer; 1 fo. 50, Wild boar. VERT: 50 fi. Beech marten; 80 fi. Fallow deer; 2 fo. Red deer.

235 Stalin

236 Rest Home, Galyateto

1953. Death of Stalin.
1281 **235** 60 fi. black 15 10

1953. Workers' Rest Homes.
1282 **236** 30 fi. brown (postage) . . 15 10
1283 – 40 fi. blue 20 10
1284 – 50 fi. ochre 20 10
1285 – 60 fi. green 20 10
1286 – 70 fi. red 25 10

1287 – 1 fo. turquoise (air) . . . 35 15
1288 – 1 fo. 50 purple 70 35
DESIGNS: 40 fi. Terrace, Mecsek; 50 fi. Parad Spa; 60 fi. Sports field, Kekes; 70 fi. Balaton-fured Spa; 1 fo. Children paddling at Balaton; 1 fo. 50, Lillafured Rest Home.

237 Young People and Banners

238 Karl Marx

1953. May Day.
1289 **237** 60 fi. brn & red on yell . . 70 10

1953. 70th Death Anniv of Karl Marx.
1290 **238** 1 fo. black on pink . . . 70 15
See also No. 2354.

239 Peasants and Flag

1953. 250th Anniv of Rakoczi Rebellion.
1291 **239** 20 fi. orge & grn on grn . 70 40
1292 – 30 fi. orange & purple . . 90 90
1293 – 40 fi. orge & bl on pk . 1·10 1·10
1294 – 60 fi. orge & grn on yell . 1·75 1·40
1295 – 1 fo. red & brn on yell . . 2·50 1·75
DESIGNS: 30 fi. Drummer and insurgents; 40 fi. Battle scene; 60 fi. Cavalryman attacking soldier; 1 fo. Ferenc Rakoczi II.

INDEX
Countries can be quickly located by referring to the index at the end of this volume.

1953. Rebuilding Plan (2nd series). As T **208**.
1296 8 fi. green 25 10
1297 10 fi. lilac 35 10
1298 12 fi. red 75 10
1299a 20 fi. green 65 10
1300 30 fi. orange . . . . 1·25 10
1301 40 fi. brown . . . . 1·40 10
1302 50 fi. blue . . . . 1·25 10
1303a 60 fi. red . . . . 1·10 10
1304 70 fi. brown . . . . 3·25 10
BUILDINGS: 8 fi. Day nursery, Ozd; 10 fi. Nursing school, Szombathely; 12 fi. Workers houses, Komlo; 20 fi. Department store, Ujpest; 30 fi. Factory, Maly; 40 fi. General Hospital, Fovaros; 50 fi. Gymnasium, Sztalinvaros; 60 fi. Post Office, Csepel; 70 fi. Blast-furnace, Diosgyor.

240 Cycling

1953. Opening of People's Stadium. Budapest. Inscr "1953 NEPSTADION".
1313 **240** 20 fi. brown and orange (postage) 30 10
1314 – 30 fi. brown and green . . 15 10
1315 – 40 fi. brown and blue . . 20 10
1316 – 50 fi. brown and olive . . 30 10
1317 – 60 fi. brown and yellow . 30 10

1318 – 80 fi. brn & turq (air) . . 45 10
1319 – 1 fo. brown & purple . . 65 10
1320 – 2 fo. brown & green . . . 1·50 70
1321 – 3 fo. brown & red . . . . 2·00 85
1322 – 5 fo. turquoise & brn . . 3·00 2·40
DESIGNS: 30 fi. Swimming; 40 fi. Gymnastics; 50 fi. Throwing the discus; 60 fi. Wrestling; 80 fi. Water polo; 1 fo. Boxing; 2 fo. Football; 3 fo. Running; 5 fo. Stadium.

241 Kazar

242 Postwoman Delivering Letters

1953. Provincial Costumes.
1323 **241** 20 fi. green . . . . 1·00 60
1324 – 30 fi. brown . . . . . . 1·75 90
1325 – 40 fi. blue . . . . 2·40 1·25
1326 – 60 fi. red . . . . 2·75 1·50
1327 – 1 fo. turquoise . . . . . 4·25 2·25
1328 – 1 fo. 70 green . . . . . 6·00 3·25
1329 – 2 fo. red . . . . 9·00 3·75
1330 – 2 fo. 50 purple . . . . . 13·00 7·00
PROVINCES: 30 fi. Ersekcsanad; 40 fi. Kalocsa; 60 fi. Sioagard; 1 fo. Sarkoz; 1 fo. 70, Boldog; 2 fo. Orhalom; 2 fo. 50, Hosszuheteny.

1953. Stamp Day.
1331 **242** 1 fo. + 1 fo. turquoise . . 4·50 4·50
1332 2 fo. + 2 fo. lilac . . . . 4·50 4·50

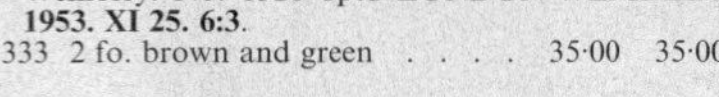

1953. Air. Hungarian Football Team's Victory at Wembley. No. 1320 optd **LONDON-WEMBLEY 1953. XI 25. 6:3.**
1333 2 fo. brown and green . . . . 35·00 35·00

244 Bihari

245 Lenin

1953. Air. Hungarian Composers.
1334 **244** 30 fi. grey and brown . . 30 10
1335 – 40 fi. orange and brown (Erkel) 35 10
1336 – 60 fi. grn & brn (Liszt) . . 40 10
1337 – 70 fi. red and brown (Mosonyi) 55 10
1338 – 80 fi. blue and brown (Goldmark) 65 15
1339 – 1 fo. bistre and brown (Bartok) 85 40
1340 – 2 fo. lilac and brown (Kodaly) . . . . . . 1·50 70

1954. 30th Death Anniv of Lenin.
1341 **245** 40 fi. green . . . . 1·10 60
1342 – 60 fi. brown . . . . 1·50 35
1343 – 1 fo. lake . . . . 2·75 1·10
DESIGNS: 60 fi. Lenin addressing meeting; 1 fo. Profile portrait of Lenin.

246 Turnip Beetle

247 Mother and Baby

1954. Air. Insects.
1344 **246** 30 fi. brown & orange . . 30 15
1345 – 40 fi. brown and green . . 35 15
1346 – 50 fi. black and red . . . 45 25
1347 – 60 fi. brn, yell & lilac . . 55 25
1348 – 80 fi. claret, pur & grn . . 75 45
1349 – 1 fo. black and brown . . 85 70
1350 – 1 fo. 20 brown & green . 1·00 85
1351 – 1 fo. 50 dp brn & brn . . 1·40 1·10
1352 – 2 fo. brown & chestnut . . 1·75 1·40
1353 – 3 fo. brown and green . . 2·50 1·75
INSECTS—HORIZ: 40 fi. Crawling cockchafer; 50 fi. Longhorn beetle; 60 fi. Hornet; 1 fo. 20, European field cricket; 1 fo. 50, European rhinoceros beetle; 2 fo. Stag beetle. VERT: 80 fi. Apple beetle; 1 fo. Corn beetle; 3 fo. Great silver water beetle.

1954. Child Welfare.
1354 – 30 fi. blue (postage) . . . 15 10
1355 **247** 40 fi. bistre 20 10
1356 – 60 fi. lilac 55 10
1357 – 1 fo. green (air) 90 35
1358 – 1 fo. 50 red . . . . . . 1·25 40
1359 – 2 fo. turquoise . . . . . 2·10 1·10
DESIGNS: 30 fi. Woman having blood-test; 60 fi. Doctor examining child; 1 fo. Children in creche; 1 fo. 50, Doctor, mother and child; 2 fo. Children in nursery school.

248 Worker and Flag

249 Maypole

1954. 35th Anniv of Proclamation of Hungarian Soviet Republic.
1360 – 40 fi. blue and red . . . . 1·75 1·40
1361 **248** 60 fi. brown and red . . . 3·50 2·10
1362 – 1 fo. black and red . . . 5·25 3·50
DESIGNS—HORIZ: 40 fi. Worker reading book; 1 fo. Soldier with rifle.

1954. May Day. Inscr "1954-MAJUS I".
1363 **249** 40 fi. olive 15 10
1364 – 60 fi. red 20 10
DESIGN: 60 fi. Worker and flag.

250 Agricultural Worker

1954. 3rd Hungarian Communist Party Congress, Budapest.
1365 **250** 60 fi. red on yellow . . . 60 10

251 Boy Building Model Glider

1954. Air.
1366 **251** 40 fi. grey and brown . . 20 10
1367 – 50 fi. brown and grey . . 30 10
1368 – 60 fi. grey and brown . . 25 10
1369 – 80 fi. brown and violet . . 30 10
1370 – 1 fo. grey and brown . . 30 10
1371 – 1 fo. 20 brown & green . . 45 30
1372 – 1 f. 50 grey and purple . 1·40 50
1373 – 2 fo. brown and blue . . 1·75 1·10
DESIGNS—As Type **251**: 60 fi. Gliders; 1 fo. Parachutists; 1 fo. 50, Lisunov Li-2 airplane; 43 × 43 mm; 50 fi. Boy flying model airplane; 80 fi. Libis KB-6T Matajur aircraft and hangar; 1 fo. 20, Letov C-4 biplane; 2 fo. Mikoyan Gurevich MiG-15 jet fighters.

252 Hungarian National Museum

253 Paprika

1954. 5th Anniv of Constitution.
1374 **252** 40 fi. blue . . . . 1·25 70
1375 – 60 fi. brown . . . . . . 1·10 40
1376 – 1 fo. brown . . . . . . 1·25 55
DESIGNS: 60 fi. Hungarian Coat of Arms; 1 fo. Dome of Parliament Buildings, Budapest.

1954. Fruits. Multicoloured.
1377 40 fi. Type **253** 60 10
1378 50 fi. Tomatoes 60 10
1379 60 fi. Grapes 60 10
1380 80 fi. Apricots 60 60
1381 1 fo. Apples 90 60
1382 1 fo. 20 Plums . . . . . . 1·25 90
1383 1 fo. 50 Cherries . . . . . 2·50 1·40
1384 2 fo. Peaches . . . . 3·50 1·75

254 M. Jokai

255 C. J. Apacai

1954. 50th Death Anniv of Jokai (novelist).
1385 **254** 60 fi. green 70 35
1386 1 fo. purple . . . . 1·40 1·10

1954. Hungarian Scientists.
1387 **255** 8 fi. black on yellow . . . 10 10
1388 – 10 fi. lake on pink 10 10
1389 – 12 fi. black on blue . . . 10 10
1390 – 20 fi. brown on yellow . . 10 10
1391 – 30 fi. blue on pink . . . 15 10
1392 – 40 fi. green on yellow . . 20 10
1393 – 50 fi. brown on green . . 20 10
1394 – 60 fi. blue on pink . . . 30 10
1395 – 1 fo. olive 40 10
1396 – 1 fo. 70 red on yellow . . 70 20
1397 – 2 fo. turquoise . . . . . 1·10 30
PORTRAITS: 10 fi. S. Korosi Csoma; 12 fi. A. Jedlik; 20 fi. I. Semmelweis; 30 fi. J. Irinyi; 40 fi. F. Koranyi; 50 fi. A. Vambery; 60 fi. K. Than; 1 fo. O. Herman; 1 fo. 70, T. Puskas; 2 fo. E. Hogyes.

256 Speed Skaters

1955. Air. Winter Sports.
1398 – 40 fi. brown, blue & blk . 60 15
1399 – 50 fi. red, green & brn . . 60 15
1400 – 60 fi. red, blue & brn . . 80 40
1401 – 80 fi. green, brn & blk . . 1·00 50
1402 – 1 fo. red, blue & brown . 1·25 70
1403 **256** 1 fo. 20 red, grn & blk . . 1·50 1·10
1404 – 1 fo. 50 red, grn & brn . . 2·00 1·25
1405 – 2 fo. red, green & brn . . 2·50 1·50
DESIGNS—VERT: 40 fi. Boys on toboggan; 60 fi. Ice-yacht; 1 fo. Ski jumper; 1 fo. 50, Skier turning. HORIZ: 50 fi. Cross-country skier; 80 fi. Ice-hockey players; 2 fo. Figure skaters.

257 Blast Furnace

1955. 10th Anniv of Liberation.
1406 – 40 fi. brown and red . . . 40 15
1407 **257** 60 fi. red and green . . . 40 10
1408 – 1 fo. green and brown . . 80 60
1409 – 2 fo. brown and green . . 1·00 75
DESIGNS—VERT: 40 fi. Reading room; 2 fo. Liberty statue. HORIZ: 1 fo. Combine harvester.

258 "1st May"

1955. May Day.
1410 **258** 1 fo. red 40 10

259 State Printing Works

1955. Cent of Hungarian State Printing Office.
1411 **259** 60 fi. brown and green . . 15 10

260 Young Workers and Flag

1955. 2nd Congress of Young Workers' Federation.
1412 **260** 1 fo. brown 40 10

261 Postilion

262 Radio Mechanic

1955. Opening of P.O. Museum.
1413 **261** 1 fo. purple 30 10

1955. Workers.
1414 – 8 fi. brown 10 10
1415 – 10 fi. turquoise 10 10
1416 – 12 fi. orange 10 10
1417 **262** 20 fi. olive 10 10
1418 – 30 fi. red 10 10
1419 – 40 fi. brown 90 10
1420 – 50 fi. blue 15 10
1421 – 60 fi. red 15 10
1422 – 70 fi. olive 20 10
1423 – 80 fi. purple 25 10
1424 – 1 fo. blue 30 10
1425 – 1 fo. 20 bistre 40 10
1426 – 1 fo. 40 green 85 10
1427 – 1 fo. 70 lilac 60 10
1428 – 2 fo. lake 70 10
1429 – 2 fo. 60 red 90 10
1430 – 3 fo. green . . . . . . 1·40 10
1431 – 4 fo. blue . . . . 3·00 15
1432 – 5 fo. brown . . . . . . 2·00 15
1433 – 10 fo. violet . . . . . . 3·75 20
DESIGNS: 8 fi. Market gardener; 10 fi. Fisherman; 12 fi. Bricklayer; 30 fi. Potter; 40 fi. Railway guard; 50 fi. Shop assistant; 60 fi. Post Office worker; 70 fi. Herdsman; 80 fi. Mill-girl; 1 fo. Boat-builder; 1 fo. 20, Carpenter; 1 fo. 40, Tram conductor; 1 fo. 70, Swineherd; 2 fo. Welder; 2 fo. 60, Tractor-driver; 3 fo. Horse and groom; 4 fo. Bus driver; 5 fo. Telegraph lineman; 10 fo. Miner.

263 M. Csokonai Vitez

1955. Hungarian Poets.
1434 **263** 60 fi. black 90 15
1435 – 1 fo. blue 70 45
1436 – 2 fo. red 90 60
PORTRAITS: 1 fo. M. Vorosmarty; 2 fo. A. Jozsef.

1955. Air. Light Metal Industries Int Congress, Budapest. As No. 1139.
1437 5 fo. blue on silver . . . . . 16·00 16·00

HAVE YOU READ THE NOTES AT THE BEGINNING OF THIS CATALOGUE?
These often provide answers to the enquiries we receive.

264 Bela Bartok

1955. 10th Death Anniv of Bartok (composer).
1438 **264** 60 fi. brown (postage) . . 70 20
1439 1 fo. green (air) . . . . . 1·75 1·50
1440 1 fo. brown . . . . . . 3·50 2·00

265 "Hargita" Diesel Multiple Unit

1955. Transport.
1441 **265** 40 fi. brown and green . . 65 10
1442 – 60 fi. bistre and green . . 35 10
1443 – 80 fi. brown and green . . 40 10
1444 – 1 fo. green and brown . . 55 35
1445 – 1 fo. 20 black & brown . 1·40 50
1446 – 1 fo. 50 brown & black . . 85 25
1447 – 2 fo. brown and green . . 1·75 65
DESIGNS: 60 fi. Motor coach; 80 fi. Motor cyclist; 1 fo. Lorry; 1 fo. 20, Class 303 steam locomotive; 1 fo. 50, Tipper; 2 fo. "Beke" (freighter).

266 Puli Sheepdog

1956. Hungarian Dogs.
1448 **266** 40 fi. black, red & yell . . 30 10
1449 – 50 fi. black, buff & bl . . 30 10
1450 – 60 fi. black, red & grn . . 40 15
1451 – 80 fi. blk, orge & grey . . 50 15
1452 – 1 fo. blk, orge & turq . . 70 25
1453 – 1 fo. 20 blk, brn & orge . 75 30
1454 – 1 fo. 50 blk, buff & bl . 1·25 45
1455 – 2 fo. black, brn & mve . . 1·75 80
DESIGNS—RECTANGULAR (36 × 26 mm): 50 fi. Puli and cattle; 1 fo. 50, Kuvasz sheepdog and cottage. (27 × 35 mm): 80 fi. Hungarian retriever. (27 × 38 mm): 1 fo. Hungarian retriever carrying mallard. As Type **266**: 60 fi. Pumi; 1 fo. 20, Kuvasz sheepdog; 2 fo. Komondor sheepdog.

268 Pioneers' Badge

269 Hunyadi on Horseback

1956. 10th Anniv of Pioneers Movement.
1456 **268** 1 fo. red 20 10
1457 1 fo. grey 20 10

1956. 500th Death Anniv of Janos Hunyadi.
1458 **269** 1 fo. brown on yellow . . 55 45

270 Miner

271 Horse-jumping

1956. Miners' Day.
1459 **270** 1 fo. blue 40 10

1956. Olympic Games. Inscr "1956". Centres in brown.
1460 – 20 fi. blue (Canoeing) . . 15 10
1461 **271** 30 fi. olive 15 10
1462 – 40 fi. brown (Fencing) . . 20 10
1463 – 60 fi. turq (Hurdling) . . 20 10
1464 – 1 fo. red (Football) . . . 25 10
1465 – 1 fo. 50 violet (Weight-lifting) 40 20
1466 – 2 fo. grn (Gymnastics) . . 1·00 20
1467 – 3 fo. mauve (Basketball) . . 1·75 65

272 Chopin **274** Dr. L. Zamenhof

1956. Hungarian–Polish Philatelic Exn., Budapest.
1468 – 1 fo. blue (Liszt) . . . . 1·75 1·75
1469 **272** 1 fo. mauve . . . . . . 1·75 1·75

1957. Hungarian Red Cross Fund Nos. 1417 etc., surch with shield, cross and premium.
1470 **262** 20 fi. + 20 fi. olive . . . 15 15
1471 – 30 fi. + 30 fi. red 25 15
1472 – 40 fi. + 40 fi. brown . . . 55 20
1473 – 60 fi. + 60 fi. red 50 15
1474 – 1 fo. + 1 fo. blue . . . . 1·10 70
1475 – 2 fo. + 2 fo. lake . . . . 1·90 1·25

1957. Air. 70th Anniv of Esperanto.
1476 – 60 fi. brown 30 10
1477 **274** 1 fo. green 35 15
DESIGN—HORIZ: 60 fi. Esperanto Star.

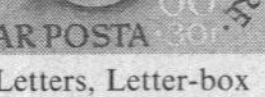

275 Letters, Letter-box and Globe **276** Janos Arany

1957. Air. Hungarian Red Cross Fund. Cross in red.
1478 **275** 60 fi. + 30 fi. brown . . . 40 15
1479 – 1 fo. + 50 fi. lilac 55 15
1480 – 2 fo. + 1 fo. red . . . . 1·40 20
1481 – 3 fo. + 1 fo. 50 blue . . . 1·90 90
1482 – 5 fo. + 2 fo. 50 grey . . . 3·50 2·50
1483 – 10 fo. + 5 fo. green . . . 6·00 3·75
DESIGNS: 1 fo. Postal coach; 2 fo. Top of telegraph pole; 3 fo. Radio aerial mast; 5 fo. Desk telephone; 10 fo. (46 × 31 mm) Posthorn.

1957. 75th Death Anniv of Janos Arany (poet).
1484 **276** 2 fo. blue 60 10

277 Arms **278** Congress Emblem

1957. Inaug. of National Emblem.
1485 **277** 60 fi. red 20 10
1486 1 fo. green 70 10

1957. 4th W.F.T.U. Congress, Leipzig.
1487 **278** 1 fo. red 15 10

279 Courier

1957. Air. Stamp Day.
1488 **279** 1 fo. (+ 4 fo.) brown and bistre on cream 70 70
1489 – 1 fo. (+ 4 fo.) brown and bistre on cream 70 70
DESIGN: No. 1489, Tupolev Tu-104A airplane over Budapest.

280 Dove of Peace and Flags

1957. 40th Anniv of Russian Revolution. Flags multicoloured.
1490 **280** 60 fi. black and grey . . . 15 10
1491 – 1 fo. black and drab . . . 45 10
DESIGN: 1 fo. Lenin.

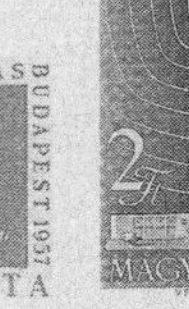

281 Komarom Tumbler Pigeons **282** Television Building

1957. Int Pigeon-fanciers' Exn, Budapest.
1492 **281** 30 fi. brown, yell and green (postage) 10 10
1493 – 40 fi. black and brown . . 15 10
1494 – 60 fi. grey and blue . . . 20 10
1495 – 1 fo. brown and grey . . . 40 10
1496 – 2 fo. grey and mauve . . . 75 40
1497 – 3 fo. green, grey and red (air) 85 40
DESIGNS: 40 fi. Two short-beaked Budapest pigeons; 60 fi. Giant domestic pigeon; 1 fo. Three Szeged pigeons; 2 fo. Two Hungarian fantail pigeons; 3 fo. Two carrier pigeons.

IMPERFORATE STAMPS. Most modern Hungarian stamps issued up to the end of 1991 also exist imperforate.

1958. Inaug of Hungarian Television Service.
1498 **282** 2 fo. purple . . . . . . 1·10 25

283 Mother and Child

1958. Savings Campaign.
1499 **283** 20 fi. dp green & green . . 10 10
1500 – 30 fi. purple and green . . 10 10
1501 – 40 fi. brown and bistre . . 45 10
1502 – 60 fi. myrtle and red . . . 70 10
1503 – 1 fo. brown and green . . 1·10 10
1504 – 2 fo. green and orange . . 1·40 1·00
DESIGNS: 30 fi. Old man feeding pigeons; 40 fi. Schoolboys with savings stamps; 60 fi. "The Cricket and the Ant."; 1 fo. Bees on honeycomb; 2 fo. Hands holding banknotes.

284 Hungarian Pavilion

1958. Air. Brussels Int Exn. Inscr "BRUXELLES 1958".
1505 **284** 20 fi. brown and red . . . 10 10
1506 – 40 fi. sepia and blue . . . 15 10
1507 – 60 fi. sepia and red . . . 15 10
1508 – 1 fo. brown and ochre . . 45 10
1509 – 1 fo. 40 multicoloured . . 70 10
1510 – 2 fo. sepia and brown . . 90 10
1511 – 3 fo. sepia and green . . 1·50 60
1512 – 5 fo. multicoloured . . . 2·50 1·00
DESIGNS—HORIZ: 40 fi. Map of Hungary and exhibits; 60 fi. Parliament Buildings, Budapest; 1 fo. Chain Bridge, Budapest; 1 fo. 40, Arms of Belgium and Hungary and Exhibition emblem; 5 fo. Exhibition emblem. VERT: 2 fo. "Mannekin Pis" statue, Brussels; 3 fo. Town Hall, Brussels.

285 Arms of Hungary **286** Youth with Book

1958. 1st Anniv of Amended Constitution. Arms multicoloured.
1513 **285** 60 fi. red 10 10
1514 1 fo. green 15 10
1515 2 fo. drab 55 10

1958. 5th Youth Festival, Keszthely.
1516 **286** 1 fo. brown 55 40

287 Town Hall, Prague and Posthorn

1958. Organization of Socialist Countries' Postal Administrations Conference, Prague.
1517 **287** 60 fi. green (postage) . . 45 35
1518 – 1 fo. lake (air) 45 35
DESIGN: 1 fo. Prague Castle, telegraph pole and wires.

288 "Linum dolomiticum"

1958. Flowers.
1519 **288** 20 fi. yellow and purple . 35 10
1520 – 30 fi. brown and blue . . 20 10
1521 – 40 fi. brn, buff & sepia . . 40 10
1522 – 60 fi. mauve and green . . 55 10
1523 – 1 fo. green and red . . . 80 10
1524 – 2 fo. yellow and green . . 1·50 35
1525 – 2 fo. 50 pink and blue . . 1·75 60
1526 – 3 fo. pink, lt green & grn . 2·25 80
FLOWERS—TRIANGULAR: 30 fi. "Kitaibelia vitifolia"; 2 fo. 50, "Dianthus collinus"; 3 fo. "Rosa sancti andreae". VERT: ($20\frac{1}{2}$ × 31 mm): 40 fi. "Doronicum hungaricum"; 60 fi. "Colchicum arenarium"; 1 fo. "Helleborus purpuracens"; 2 fo. "Hemerocallis lilio-asphodelus".

289 Table-tennis Bat and Ball

1958. European Table-tennis and Swimming Championships, and World Wrestling Championships, Budapest.
1527 **289** 20 fi. red on pink 10 10
1528 – 30 fi. olive on green . . . 15 10
1529 – 40 fi. purple on yellow . . 25 10
1530 – 60 fi. brown on blue . . . 30 10
1531 – 1 fo. blue on blue 50 10
1532 – 2 fo. 50 red on yellow . . 95 65
1533 – 3 fo. blue on turquoise . . 1·75 90
DESIGNS—VERT: 30 fi. Table-tennis player; 40 fi. Wrestlers; 1 fo. Water-polo player; 2 fo. 50, High-diver. HORIZ: 60 fi. Wrestlers; 3 fo. Swimmer.

290 **291** Airliner over Millennium Monument Budapest

1958. Air. (a) Int Correspondence Week.
1534 **290** 60 fi. bistre and purple . . 40 10
1535 – 1 fo. bistre and blue . . . 60 20

(b) National Stamp Exhibition, Budapest.
1536 – 1 fo. (+ 2 fo.) bistre and red 90 90
1537 **290** 1 fo. (+ 2 fo.) bistre and green 90 90
DESIGNS: No. 1535, Posthorn, envelope and transport; No. 1536, Stamp and magnifier.

1958. Air. 40th Anniv of 1st Hungarian Air Mail Stamp.
1538 **291** 3 fo. pur, red & drab . . 1·00 45
1539 – 5 fo. blue, red & drab . . 1·50 60
DESIGN: 5 fo. Airliner over Sopron Tower.
For similar stamps but without commemorative inscription see Nos. 1542/51.

292 Red Flag

1958. 40th Anniv of Hungarian Communist Party and Founding of the "Red Journal".
1540 **292** 1 fo. red and brown . . . 40 10
1541 – 2 fo. red and blue 60 10
DESIGN: 2 fo. Hand holding up the newspaper "Voros Ujsag" (Red Journal).

1958. Air. As T **291** but with "LEGIPOSTA" at top in place of commem. inscription. On cream paper.
1542 – 20 fi. green and red . . . 10 10
1543 – 30 fi. violet and red . . . 10 10
1544 – 70 fi. purple and red . . . 15 10
1545 – 1 fo. blue and red 20 10
1546 – 1 fo. 60 pur and red . . . 30 10
1547 – 2 fo. green and red . . . 50 10
1548 – 3 fo. brown and red (No. 1539) 50 10
1549 **291** 5 fo. green and red . . . 85 20
1550 – 10 fo. blue and red . . . 2·75 55
1551 – 20 fo. sepia and red . . . 5·50 1·50
DESIGNS: Airliner over: 20 fi. Town Hall, Szeged; 30 fi. Sarospatak Castle; 70 fi. Town Hall, Gyor; 1 fo. Opera House, Budapest; 1 fo. 60, Old City of Veszprem; 2 fo. Chain Bridge, Budapest; 10 fo. Danube Embankment, Budapest; 20 fo. Budapest Cathedral.

293 Rocket approaching the Moon

1959. I.G.Y. Achievements.
1552 – 10 fi. brown and red . . . 15 10
1553 – 20 fi. black and blue . . . 55 10
1554 – 30 fi. buff and green . . . 60 15
1555 – 40 fi. light blue & blue . . 1·40 25
1556 **293** 60 fi. green and blue . . . 75 25
1557 – 1 fo. brown and red . . . 1·25 35
1558 – 5 fo. brown & dp brown . 2·25 50
DESIGNS—($31\frac{1}{2}$ × 21 mm): 10 fi. Eotvos torsion balance (gravimetry); 20 fi. Ship using echo-sounder (oceanography); 30 fi. "Northern Lights" and polar scene. ($35\frac{1}{2}$ × $26\frac{1}{2}$ mm): 40 fi. Russian polar camp and Antarctic route map; 1 fo. Observatory and the sun; 5 fo. Russian "Sputnik" and American "Vanguard" (artificial satellites).
See also No. 1605.

294 Revolutionary **296** Nagy Model of Locomotive "Deru", 1847

295 Rose

1959. 40th Anniv of Proclamation of Hungarian Soviet Republic.
1559 **294** 20 fi. red and purple . . . 10 10
1560 60 fi. red and blue 35 10
1561 1 fo. red and brown . . . 60 10

1959. May Day.
1562 **295** 60 fi. red, green & lilac . . 30 10
1563 1 fo. red, green & brn . . 40 10

1959. Transport Museum issue.
1564 **296** 20 fi. mult (postage) . . . 35 10
1565 – 30 fi. green, blk & buff . . 35 10
1566 – 40 fi. multicoloured . . . 60 10
1567 – 60 fi. multicoloured . . . 35 10
1568 – 1 fo. multicoloured . . . 45 10
1569 – 2 fo. multicoloured . . . 70 15
1570 – 2 fo. 50 multicoloured (blue background) . . 85 40
1571 – 3 fo. mult (air) . . . . . 2·00 1·25
DESIGNS—HORIZ: 30 fi. Ganz diesel railcar; 60 fi. Csonka motor car; 1 fo. Ikarusz rear-engine motor coach; 2 fo. First Lake Balaton steamer "Kisfaludy"; 2 fo. 50, Stagecoach; 3 fo. Aladar Zselyi's monoplane. VERT: 40 fi. Early railway semaphore signal.
See also No. 1572.

1959. Int Philatelic Federation Congress, Hamburg. As No. 1570 but colours changed.
1572 2 fo. 50 multicoloured (yellow background) . . . . 1·75 1·75

297 Posthorn 298 Common Cormorant

1959. Organization of Socialist Countries' Postal Administration Conference, Berlin.
1573 **297** 1 fo. red 70 70

1959. Water Birds. Inscr "1959".
1574 **298** 10 fi. black and green . . 20 10
1575 – 20 fi. green and blue . . . 30 10
1576 – 30 fi. vio, myrtle & orge . 45 15
1577 – 40 fi. grey and green . . . 60 30
1578 – 60 fi. brown & purple . . 65 30
1579 – 1 fo. black & turquoise . . 90 45
1580 – 2 fo. black and red . . . 1·25 45
1581 – 3 fo. brown and bistre . . 2·25 1·00
DESIGNS: 20 fi. Little Egret; 30 fi. Purple Heron; 40 fi. Great Egret; 60 fi. White Spoon-bill; 1 fo. Grey Heron; 2 fo. Squacco Heron; 3 fo. Glossy Ibis.

299 10th-century Man-at-Arms 300 Bathers at Lake Balaton

1959. 24th World Fencing Championships, Budapest. Inscr as in T **299**.
1582 **299** 10 fi. black and blue . . . 10 10
1583 – 20 fi. black and lemon . . 10 10
1584 – 30 fi. black and violet . . 15 10
1585 – 40 fi. black and red . . . 20 10
1586 – 60 fi. black and purple . . 25 10
1587 – 1 fo. black & turquoise . . 35 10
1588 – 1 fo. 40, black & orange . 70 10
1589 – 3 fo. black and green . . 1·40 25
DESIGNS (Evolution of Hungarian swordsmanship): 20 fi. 15th-century man-at-arms; 30 fi. 18th-century soldier; 40 fi. 19th-century soldier; 60 fi. 19th-century cavalryman. Fencer: at the assault (1 fo.); on guard (1 fo. 40); saluting (3 fo.).

1959. Lake Balaton Summer Courses.
1590 – 30 fi. bl on yell (postage) . 20 10
1591 – 40 fi. red on green . . . 10 10
1592 **300** 60 fi. brown on pink . . . 20 10
1593 – 1 fo. 20 violet on pink . . 50 10
1594 – 2 fo. red on yellow . . . 75 20
1595 – 20 fi. green (air) 10 10
1596 – 70 fi. blue 20 10
1597 – 1 fo. red and blue . . . 30 10
1598 – 1 fo. 70 brown on yell . . 70 30
DESIGNS—VERT: 20 fi. Tihany (view); 30 fi. "Kek Madar" (yacht); 70 fi. "Tihany" (waterbus); 1 fo. Waterlily and view of Heviz; 1 fo. 20, Anglers; 1 fo. 70, "Saturnus" (yacht) and statue of fisherman (Balaton pier); 2 fo. Holiday-makers and "Beloiannis" (lake steamer). HORIZ: 40 fi. Vintner with grapes.

301 302 Shepherd with Letter

1959. 150th Death Anniv of Haydn (composer).
1599 **301** 40 fi. yellow and purple . . 40 10
1600 – 60 fi. buff and slate . . . 75 20
1601 – 1 fo. orange and violet . . 1·25 20
DESIGNS—HORIZ: 60 fi. Fertod Chateau. VERT: 1 fo. Haydn.

1959. Birth Bicentenary of Schiller (poet). As T **301** but inscr "F. SCHILLER" etc.
1602 40 fi. yellow and olive 35 10
1603 60 fi. pink and blue 65 10
1604 1 fo. yellow and purple . . . . 1·00 10
DESIGNS—VERT: 40 fi. Stylized initials "F" and "Sch" and Schiller's birthplace; 1 fo. Schiller. HORIZ: 60 fi. Pegasus.

1959. Landing of Russian Rocket on the Moon. As T **293** with addition of Russian Flag and "22 h 02' 34" on Moon in red.
1605 **293** 60 fi. green and blue . . . 35 10

1959. Stamp Day and National Stamp Exn.
1606 **302** 2 fo. purple . . . . . . 2·10 2·10

303 "Taking delivery"

1959. International Correspondence Week.
1607 **303** 60 fi. multicoloured . . . 55 10

304 Lenin and Szamuely

1959. Russian Stamp Exhibition, Budapest.
1608 **304** 20 fi. brown and red . . . 10 10
1609 – 40 fi. lake & brn on blue . 10 10
1610 – 60 fi. buff and blue . . . 35 35
1611 – 1 fo. multicoloured . . . 55 50
DESIGNS: 40 fi. Pushkin; 60 fi. Mayakovsky; 1 fo. Arms with hands clasping flag.

305 Swallowtail 306

1959. Butterflies and Moths. Butterflies in natural colours, background colours given.
1612 **305** 20 fi. black and green (postage) 45 10
1613 – 30 fi. black and blue . . . 45 10
1614 – 40 fi. black and brown . . 65 10
1615 – 60 fi. black and bistre . . 85 15
1616 – 1 fo. black & grn (air) . . 1·25 25
1617 – 2 fo. black and lilac . . 2·50 85
1618 – 3 fo. black and green . . 3·75 1·40
DESIGNS—HORIZ: 30 fi. Hebe tiger moth; 40 fi. Adonis blue; 2 fo. Death's-head hawk moth. VERT: 60 fi. Purple emperor; 1 fo. Scarce copper; 3 fo. Red emperor.

1959. 7th Socialist Workers' Party Congress. Flag in red and green.
1619 **306** 60 fi. brown 10 10
1620 – 1 fo. red 10 10
DESIGN: 1 fo. Flag inscr "MSZMP VII. KONGRESSZUSA".

307 "Fairy Tales" 308 Sumeg Castle

1959. Fairy Tales (1st series). Centres and inscr in black.
1621 **307** 20 fi. multicoloured . . . 20 10
1622 – 30 fi. pink 20 10
1623 – 40 fi. turquoise 30 10
1624 – 60 fi. blue 50 10
1625 – 1 fo. yellow 65 35
1626 – 2 fo. green 85 35
1627 – 2 fo. 50 salmon . . . . 1·10 40
1628 – 3 fo. red . . . . . . 1·50 50
FAIRY TALE SCENES: 30 fi. "The Sleeping Beauty"; 40 fi. "Mat the Goose"; 60 fi. "The Cricket and the Ant"; 1 fo. "Mashenka and the Bears"; 2 fo. "The Babes in the Wood"; 2 fo. 50, "The Pied Piper of Hamelin"; 3 fo. "Little Red Riding Hood".
See also Nos. 1702/9 and 2133/41.

1960. Hungarian Castles. On white paper.
1629 **308** 8 fi. purple 10 10
1630 – 10 fi. brown 10 10
1631 – 12 fi. blue 10 10
1632 – 20 fi. green 10 10
1633 – 30 fi. brown 10 10
1634 – 40 fi. turquoise 10 10
1635 – 50 fi. brown 10 10
1636 – 60 fi. red 25 10
1637 – 70 fi. green 25 10
1638 – 80 fi. purple 15 10
1639 – 1 fo. blue 20 10
1640 – 1 fo. 20 purple 30 10
1641 – 1 fo. 40 blue 30 10
1642 – 1 fo. 70 lilac ("SOMLO") 35 10
1642a – 1 fo. 70 lilac ("SOMLYO") 70 10
1643 – 2 fo. bistre 60 10
1644 – 2 fo. 60 blue 75 10
1645 – 3 fo. brown 80 10
1646 – 4 fo. violet . . . . . . 1·00 10
1647 – 5 fo. green . . . . . . 1·50 35
1648 – 10 fo. red . . . . . . 2·50 40
CASTLES—As Type **308**: 10 fi. Kisvarda; 12 fi. Szigliget; 20 fi. Tata; 30 fi. Diosgyor; 40 fi. Simon Tornya; 50 fi. Fuzer; 60 fi. Sarospatak; 70 fi. Nagyvazsony; 80 fi. Egervar. $28\frac{1}{2} \times 21\frac{1}{2}$ mm: 1 fo. Vitany; 1 fo. 20, Sirok; 1 fo. 40, Siklos; 1 fo. 70, Somlyo; 2 fo. Boldogko; 2 fo. 60, Holloko; 4 fo. Eger. $21\frac{1}{2} \times 28\frac{1}{2}$ mm: 3 fo. Csesznek; 5 fo. Koszeg; 10 fo. Sarvar.
See also Nos. 1694/700.

309 Halas Lace 310 Cross-country Skiing

1960. Halas Lace (1st series). Designs showing lace as T **309**. Inscriptions and values in orange.
1649 20 fi. sepia 20 10
1650 30 fi. violet 20 10
1651 40 fi. turquoise 30 10
1652 60 fi. brown 40 10
1653 1 fo. green 75 35
1654 1 fo. 50 green 90 40
1655 2 fo. blue . . . . 1·50 60
1656 3 fo. red . . . . 2·75 80
Nos. 1650/1, 1654/5 are larger 38 × 44 mm.
See also Nos. 1971/8.

1960. Winter Olympic Games.
1657 **310** 30 fi. bistre and blue . . . 10 10
1658 – 40 fi. bistre and green . . 15 10
1659 – 60 fi. bistre and red . . . 25 10
1660 – 80 fi. bistre and violet . . 30 10
1661 – 1 fo. bistre & turquoise . . 75 10
1662 – 1 fo. 20 bistre & lake . . 85 25
1663 – 2 fo. + 1 fo. mult . . . . 2·25 60
DESIGNS: 40 fi. Ice hockey; 60 fi. Ski jumping; 80 fi. Speed skating; 1 fo. Skiing; 1 fo. 20, Figure skating; 2 fo. Games emblem.

311 Kato Haman 312 Yellow Pheasant's-eye and Quill

1960. Celebrities and Anniversaries. Portrait as T **311**.
1664 60 fi. purple (T **311**) 20 10
1665 60 fi. brown (Clara Zetkin) . . 20 10
1666 60 fi. violet (Garibaldi) . . . 20 10
1667 60 fi. green (I. Turr) 20 10
1668 60 fi. red (I. Tukory) 20 10
1669 60 fi. deep blue and blue (O. Herman) 20 10
1670 60 fi. brown (Beethoven) . . . 45 10
1671 60 fi. red (F. Mora) 20 10
1672 60 fi. black and grey (B. I. Toth) 20 10
1673 60 fi. purple and mauve (D. Banki) 20 10
1674 60 fi. deep green & green (A. G. Pattantyus) 20 10
1675 60 fi. blue and cobalt (I. P. Semmelweis) 25 10
1676 60 fi. brown (Joliot-Curie) . . 40 10
1677 60 fi. red (F. Erkel) 20 10
1678 60 fi. blue and light blue (J. Bolyai) 20 10
1679 60 fi. red (V. I. Lenin) 25 10
COMMEMORATIVE EVENTS: Nos. 1664/5, Int Women's Day: 1666, Centenary of Sicilian Expedition; 1669, 125th Birth Anniv; 1670, Martonvasar Beethoven Concerts: 1671, Szeged Festival: 1672, Miners' Day: 1677, 150th Birth Anniv; 1678, Birth Centenary; 1679, 90th Birth Anniv.

1960. Stamp Exhibition Budapest.
1680 **312** 2 fo. (+ 4 fo.) yellow, green and brown . . . 1·25 1·25

313 Soldier 314 Rowing

1960. 15th Anniv of Liberation.
1681 **313** 40 fi. brown and red . . . 35 10
1682 – 60 fi. red, green & brn . . 70 10
DESIGN—HORIZ: 60 fi. Student with flag (inscr "1945 FELSZABADULASUNK... 1960").

1960. Summer Olympic Games. Centres and inscr in black (3 fo. multicoloured). Circular frames in bistre. Background colours given.
1683 10 fi. blue (T **314**) 10 10
1684 20 fi. brown (Boxing) 10 10
1685 30 fi. lilac (Archery) 10 10
1686 40 fi. ochre (Discus) 10 10
1687 50 fi. red (Ball game) 10 10
1688 60 fi. green (Javelin) 15 10
1689 1 fo. purple (Horse-riding) . . 55 10
1690 1 fo. 40 blue (Wrestling) . . . 60 10
1691 1 fo. 70 brown (Swordplay) . . 70 10
1692 2 fo. + 1 fo. red (Romulus, Remus and Wolf) . . . . 1·00 35
1693 3 fo. grey (Olympic Rings and Arms of Hungary) . . . . 2·50 1·25

1960. Hungarian Castles. As Nos. 1629, 1632/3, 1636/7 and 1641/2 but printed on coloured paper.
1694 8 fi. purple on blue 10 10
1695 20 fi. bronze on green 25 10
1696 30 fi. brown on yellow 25 10
1697 60 fi. red on pink 30 10
1698 70 fi. green on blue 40 10
1699 1 fo. 40 blue on blue 65 10
1700 1 fo. 70 lilac on blue ("SOMLO") . . . . . . 1·50 15

315 Girl in Mezokovesd Provincial Costume 316 "The Turnip"

1960. Stamp Day.
1701 **315** 2 fo. (+ 4 fo.) mult . . . 1·75 1·75

1960. Fairy Tales (2nd series). Multicoloured.
1702 20 fi. Type **316** 10 10
1703 30 fi. "Snow White and the Seven Dwarfs" 15 10
1704 40 fi. "The Miller, Son and Donkey" 15 10
1705 60 fi. "Puss in Boots" 20 10
1706 80 fi. "The Fox and the Raven" 45 10
1707 1 fo. "The Maple-wood Pipe" . 70 10
1708 1 fo. 70 "The Stork and the Fox" 85 40
1709 2 fo. "Momotaro" (Japanese tale) . . . . 1·75 55

317 F. Rozsa 318 Eastern Grey Kangaroo with Young

1961. Celebrities and Anniversaries. Portraits as T **317**.
1710 1 fo. brown (T **317**) 15 10
1711 1 fo. turq (G. Kilian) 15 10
1712 1 fo. red (J. Rippi-Ronai) . . . 15 10
1713 1 fo. olive (S. Latinka) 15 10
1714 1 fo. green (M. Zalka) 15 10
1715 1 fo. lake (J. Katona) 15 10
COMMEMORATIVE EVENTS: No. 1710, Press Day; No. 1711, Gyorgy Kilian Sports Movement; No. 1712, Birth Cent; No. 1713, 75th Birth Anniv; No. 1714, 65th Birth Anniv.

1961. Budapest Zoo Animals. Inscr "ZOO 1961".
1716 **318** 20 fi. black and orange . . 20 10
1717 – 30 fi. sepia and green . . 25 10
1718 – 40 fi. brown & chestnut . 30 10
1719 – 60 fi. grey and mauve . . 50 10
1720 – 80 fi. yellow and black . . 65 10
1721 – 1 fo. brown and green . . 70 10
1722 – 1 fo. 40 sepia & turquoise . 90 10
1723 – 2 fo. black and red . . 1·75 50
1724 – 2 fo. 60 brown & violet . 1·75 80
1725 – 3 fo. multicoloured . . . 2·25 1·25
DESIGNS—HORIZ: 30 fi. American bison; 60 fi. Indian elephant and calf; 80 fi. Tiger and cubs; 1 fo. 40, Polar bear; 2 fo. Common zebra and foal; 2 fo. 60, European bison cow with calf. VERT: 40 fi. Brown bear; 1 fo. Ibex; 3 fo. Main entrance, Budapest Zoo.

319 Child chasing Butterfly 320 Launching of Rocket "Vostok"

1961. Health. Inscr "1961". Cross in red.

1726	319	30 fi. black, pur & brn	20	10
1727	–	40 fi. sepia, blue & turq	30	10
1728	–	60 fi. yellow, grey & vio	35	10
1729	–	1 fo. multicoloured	40	10
1730	–	1 fo. 70 yell, bl & grn	65	10
1731	–	4 fo. green and grey	1·25	45

DESIGNS—As Type **319**: 40 fi. Patient on operating table. LARGE (29½ × 35 mm): 60 fi. Ambulance and stretcher; 1 fo. Traffic lights and scooter; 1 fo. 70, Syringe and jars; 4 fo. Emblem of Health Department.

1961. World's First Manned Space Flight. Inscr "1961.IV.12".

1732	320	1 fo. brown and blue	1·00	1·00
1733	–	2 fo. brown and blue	3·50	3·50

DESIGN: 2 fo. Gagarin and "Vostok" in flight.

321 Roses **322** "Venus" Rocket

1961. May Day.

1734	321	1 fo. red and green	20	10
1735	–	2 fo. red and green	70	35

DESIGN: 2 fo. As Type **321** but roses and inscr reversed.

1961. Launching of Soviet "Venus" Rocket. Inscr "VENUSZ RAKETA 1961 11.12".

1736	40 fi. black, bistre & blue	55	55
1737	60 fi. black, bistre & blue	95	95
1738	80 fi. black and blue	1·00	1·00
1739	2 fo. bistre & violet-blue	2·50	2·50

DESIGNS: 40 fi. Type **322**; 60 fi. Separation of rocket capsule in flight; 80 fi. Capsule and orbit diagram; 2 fo. Allegory of flying woman and crescent moon.

323 Conference Emblem, Letter and Transport

1961. Organization of Socialist Countries' Postal Administrations Conference.

1740	40 fi. black & orge (T **323**)	25	10
1741	60 fi. black and mauve	15	10
1742	1 fo. black and blue	50	35

DESIGNS: 60 fi. Television aerial; 1 fo. Radar receiving equipment.

324 Hungarian Flag **325** George Stephenson

1961. Int. Stamp Exhibition, Budapest.
(a) 1st issue. Background in silver.

1743	1 fo. red, green and black	25	25
1744	1 fo. 70 multicoloured	70	70
1745	2 fo. 60 multicoloured	1·00	1·00
1746	3 fo. multicoloured	1·50	1·50

(b) 2nd issue. Background in gold. Inscriptions at left altered on 1 fo. and 3 fo.

1747	1 fo. red, green and black	25	25
1748	1 fo. 70 multicoloured	70	70
1749	2 fo. 60 multicoloured	1·00	1·00
1750	3 fo. multicoloured	1·25	1·25

DESIGNS: 1 fo. Type **324**; 1 fo. 70, Late spider orchids; 2 fo. 60, Small tortoiseshell; 3 fo. Goldfinch.
See also Nos. 1765/8.

1961. Communications Ministers' Conference, Budapest. Inscr "KOZLEKEDESUGYI", etc.

1751	325	60 fi. olive	15	10
1752	–	1 fo. bistre, blk & blue	20	10
1753	–	2 fo. brown	45	10

DESIGNS: 1 fo. Communications emblems; 2 fo. J. Landler (Minister of Communications).

326 Football and Club Badge

1961. 50th Anniv of VASAS Sports Club. Badge in gold, red and blue.

1754	40 fi. orange, black & gold	10	10
1755	60 fi. green, black & gold	10	10
1756	1 fo. bistre, black & gold	10	10
1757	2 fo. + 1 fo. bl, blk & gold	90	60

DESIGNS: 40 fi. Type **326**; 60 fi. Wrestling; 1 fo. Vaulting; 2 fo. Sailing.

327 Three Racehorses

1961. Racehorses.

1758	30 fi. multicoloured	15	10
1759	40 fi. multicoloured	25	10
1760	60 fi. multicoloured	35	10
1761	1 fo. black, green & orange	40	35
1762	1 fo. 70 sepia, black and green	85	40
1763	2 fo. black, blue and brn	1·00	70
1764	3 fo. multicoloured	1·75	1·00

DESIGNS: 30 fi. Type **327**; 40 fi. Three hurdlers; 60 fi. Trotting race (two horses); 1 fo. Trotting race (three horses); 1 fo. 70, Two racehorses and two foals; 2 fo. Hungarian trotter "Baka"; 3 fo. 19th century champion mare, "Kincsem".

328 Budapest

1961. Stamp Day and Int. Stamp Exhibition, Budapest (3rd issue). Designs as T **328**.

1765	2 fo. + 1 fo. blue, brn & ol	1·40	1·40
1766	2 fo. + 1 fo. blue, brn & ol	1·40	1·40
1767	2 fo. + 1 fo. blue, brn & ol	1·40	1·40
1768	2 fo. + 1 fo. blue, brn & ol	1·40	1·40

Nos. 1765/8 are printed together in sheets of 40 (4 × 10) with one vertical row of each design. Horizontal strips of four form a composite panorama of Budapest.

329 Music, Keyboard and Silhouette **330** Lenin

1961. 150th Birth and 75th Death Anniv of Liszt (composer).

1769	329	60 fi. black and gold	40	10
1770	–	1 fo. black	60	15
1771	–	2 fo. green and blue	1·40	60

DESIGNS—VERT: 1 fo. Statue. HORIZ: 2 fo. Music Academy.

1961. 22nd Soviet Communist Party Congress, Moscow.

1772	330	1 fo. brown	35	10

331 Monk's Hood **332** Nightingale

1961. Medicinal Plants. Multicoloured.

1773	20 fi. Type **331**	10	10
1774	30 fi. Centaury	15	10
1775	40 fi. Blue iris	20	10
1776	60 fi. Thorn-apple	25	10
1777	1 fo. Purple hollyhock	50	10
1778	1 fo. 70 Hop	65	10
1779	2 fo. Poppy	1·00	15
1780	3 fo. Mullein	1·40	40

1961. Birds of Woods and Fields. Multicoloured. Inscr "1961".

1781	30 fi. Type **332**	10	10
1782	40 fi. Great tit	15	10
1783	60 fi. Chaffinch (horiz)	25	10
1784	1 fo. Jay	35	10
1785	1 fo. 20 Golden oriole (horiz)	50	10
1786	1 fo. 50 Blackbird (horiz)	75	15
1787	2 fo. Yellowhammer	90	20
1788	3 fo. Lapwing (horiz)	1·50	35

333 M. Karolyi **334** Railway Signals

1962. Celebrities and Anniversaries. Inscr "1962".

1789	333	1 fo. sepia	15	10
1790	–	1 fo. brn (F. Berkes)	15	10
1791	–	1 fo. blue (J. Pech)	15	10
1792	–	1 fo. violet (A. Chazar)	15	10
1793	–	1 fo. blue (Dr. F. Hutyra)	15	10
1794	–	1 fo. red (G. Egressy)	15	10

ANNIVERSARIES: No. 1790, 5th Co-operative Movement Congress; 1791, 75th anniv of Hydrographic Institute; 1792, 50th anniv of Sports Club for the Deaf; 1793, 175th anniv of Hungarian Veterinary Service; 1794, 125th anniv of National Theatre.

1962. 14th Int Railwaymen's Esperanto Congress.

1795	334	1 fo. green	30	10

335 Green Swordtail

1962. Ornamental Fishes. Inscr "1962". Mult.

1796	20 fi. Type **335**	10	10
1797	30 fi. Paradise fish	15	10
1798	40 fi. Fan-tailed guppy	15	10
1799	60 fi. Siamese fighting fish	20	10
1800	80 fi. Tiger barb	25	10
1801	1 fo. Freshwater angelfish	40	10
1802	1 fo. 20 Sunfish	45	15
1803	1 fo. 50 Lyretail panchax	75	15
1804	2 fo. Neon tetra	85	20
1805	3 fo. Blue discus	1·10	75

336 Flags of Argentina and Bulgaria

1962. World Football Championships, 1962. Inscr "CHILE 1962". Flags in national colours: ball, flagpole, value, etc., in bistre.

1806	–	30 fi. mauve	10	10
1807	–	40 fi. green	15	10
1808	–	60 fi. lilac	20	10
1809	–	1 fo. blue	30	10
1810	336	1 fo. 70 orange	90	35
1811	–	2 fo. turquoise	1·00	40
1812	–	3 fo. red	1·40	50
1813	–	4 fo. + 1 fo. green	2·50	1·00

FLAGS: 30 fi. Colombia and Uruguay; 40 fi. U.S.S.R. and Yugoslavia; 60 fi. Switzerland and Chile; 1 fo. German Federal Republic and Italy; 2 fo. Hungary and Great Britain; 3 fo. Brazil and Mexico; 4 fo. Spain and Czechoslovakia. The two flags on each stamp represent the football teams playing against each other in the first round.

337 Gutenberg **338** Campaign Emblem

1962. Centenary of Hungarian Printing Union.

1814	337	1 fo. blue	15	10
1815	–	1 fo. brown	15	10

PORTRAIT: No. 1815, Miklos Kis (first Hungarian printer).

1962. Malaria Eradication.

1816	338	2 fo. 50 bistre & black	1·25	45

339 "Beating Swords into Ploughshares" **340** Festival Emblem

1962. World Peace Congress, Moscow.

1817	339	1 fo. brown	15	10

1962. World Youth Festival, Helsinki.

1818	340	3 fo. multicoloured	70	10

341 Icarus **342** Hybrid Tea

1962. Air. Development of Flight.

1819	341	30 fi. bistre and blue	15	10
1820	–	40 fi. blue and green	20	10
1821	–	60 fi. red and blue	30	10
1822	–	80 fi. silver, blue & turq	35	10
1823	–	1 fo. silver, blue & pur	40	10
1824	–	1 fo. 40 orange & blue	45	15
1825	–	2 fo. brown & turquoise	65	20
1826	–	3 fo. blue, silver & violet	75	25
1827	–	4 fo. silver, black & grn	1·00	30

DESIGNS: 40 fi. Modern glider and Lilienthal monoplane glider; 60 fi. Zlin Trener 6 and Rakos's monoplane; 80 fi. Airship "Graf Zeppelin" and Montgolfier balloon; 1 fo. Ilyushin Il-18B and Wright Flyer I; 1 fo. 40, Nord 3202 sports airplane and Peter Nesterov's Nieuport biplane; 2 fo. Mil Mi-6 helicopter and Asboth's helicopter; 3 fo. Myasichev Mya-4 airliner and Zhukovsky's wind tunnel; 4 fo. Space rocket and Tsiolkovsky's rocket.

1962. Rose Culture. Roses in natural colours. Background colours given.

1828	–	20 fi. brown	20	10
1829	342	40 fi. myrtle	30	10
1830	–	60 fi. violet	35	10
1831	–	80 fi. red	50	10
1832	–	1 fo. myrtle	60	35
1833	–	1 fo. 20 orange	80	50
1834	–	2 fo. turquoise	1·75	55

ROSES: 20 fi. Floribunda; 60 fi. to 2 fo. Various hybrid teas.

343 Globe, "Vostok 3" and "Vostok 4"

1962. Air. 1st "Team" Manned Space Flight.

1835	343	1 fo. brown and blue	40	25
1836	–	2 fo. brown and blue	1·00	70

DESIGN: 2 fo. Cosmonauts Nikolaev and Popovich.

344 Weightlifting **345** Austrian 2 kr. stamp of 1850

1962. European Weightlifting Championships, Budapest.

1837	344	1 fo. brown	45	10

1962. 35th Stamp Day.

1838	345	2 fo. + 1 fo. brn & yell	1·00	1·00
1839	–	2 fo. + 1 fo. brn & pk	1·00	1·00
1840	–	2 fo. + 1 fo. brn & bl	1·00	1·00
1841	–	2 fo. + 1 fo. brn & grn	1·00	1·00

DESIGNS: Hungarian stamps of: No. 1839, 1919 (75 fi. Dozsa); No. 1840, 1955 (1 fo. 50 Skiing); No. 1841, 1959 (3 fo. "Vanessa atalanta").

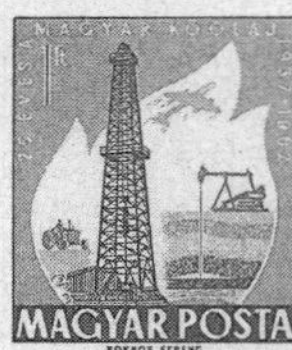

346 Primitive and Modern Oilwells **347** Gagarin

1962. 25th Anniv of Hungarian Oil Industry.

1842	346	1 fo. green	30	10

1962. Air. Astronautical Congress, Paris.

1843	347	40 fi. ochre and purple	20	10
1844	–	60 fi. ochre and green	25	10
1845	–	1 fo. ochre & turquoise	40	10
1846	–	1 fo. 40 ochre & brown	60	10
1847	–	1 fo 70 ochre and blue	1·00	35
1848	–	2 fo. 60 ochre and violet	1·40	50
1849	–	3 fo. ochre and brown	2·00	75

ASTRONAUTS: 60 fi. Titov; 1 fo. Glenn; 1 fo. 40, Scott Carpenter; 1 fo. 70, Nikolaev; 2 fo. 60, Popovich; 3 fo. Schirra.

INDEX

Countries can be quickly located by referring to the index at the end of this volume.

348 Cup and Football

349 Osprey

1962. "Budapest Vasas" Football Team's Victory in Central European Cup Competition.

No.	Description	Unused	Used
1850	348 2 fo. + 1 fo. mult	75	75

1962. Air. Birds of Prey. Multicoloured.

No.	Description	Unused	Used
1851	30 fi. Eagle owl	35	10
1852	40 fi. Type 349	40	15
1853	60 fi. Marsh harrier	45	15
1854	80 fi. Booted eagle	65	25
1855	1 fo. African fish eagle	75	30
1856	2 fo. Lammergeier	1·10	50
1857	3 fo. Golden eagle	1·60	65
1858	4 fo. Common kestrel	1·90	80

350 Racing Motor Cyclist

1962. Motor Cycle and Car Sports. Mult.

No.	Description	Unused	Used
1859	20 fi. Type 350	10	10
1860	30 fi. Sidecar racing	10	10
1861	40 fi. "Scrambling" (hill climb)	15	10
1862	60 fi. Dirt-track racing	20	10
1863	1 fo. Wearing "garland"	40	10
1864	1 fo. 20 Speed trials	45	15
1865	1 fo. 70 Sidecar trials	70	15
1866	2 fo. "Go-kart" racing	80	15
1867	3 fo. Car racing	1·25	65

351 Ice Skater

1963. European Figure Skating and Ice Dancing Championships, Budapest.

No.	Description	Unused	Used
1868	351 20 fi. green, brn & lilac	10	10
1869	– 40 fi. blk, brn & salmon	15	10
1870	– 60 fi. multicoloured	30	10
1871	– 1 fo. multicoloured	45	10
1872	– 1 fo. 40 multicoloured	65	40
1873	– 2 fo. red, brown & grn	1·00	50
1874	– 3 fo. multicoloured	2·00	70

DESIGNS—VERT: 40 fi., 2 fo. Skater leaping; 60 fi., 1 fo. Pairs dancing; 1 fo. 40, Skater turning. HORIZ: 3 fo. Pair dancing.

352 J. Batsanyi

1963. Celebrities and Anniversaries.

No.	Description	Unused	Used
1875	40 fi. lake (Type 352)	10	10
1876	40 fi. green (F. Entz)	15	10
1877	40 fi. blue (I. Markovits)	15	10
1878	40 fi. olive (L. Weiner)	35	10
1879	60 fi. purple (Dr. F. Koranyi)	35	10
1880	60 fi. bronze (G. Gardonyi)	15	10
1881	60 fi. brown (P. de Coubertin)	25	10
1882	60 fi. violet (J. Eotvos)	15	10

ANNIVERSARIES: No. 1875, Revolutionary, Birth Bicent; No. 1876. Horticulture College founder, Horticulture Cent; No. 1877, Inventor, Hungarian Shorthand, Cent; No. 1878, Composer, Budapest Music Competitions; No. 1879, Tuberculosis researcher, 50th Death Anniv; No. 1880, Novelist, Birth Cent; No. 1881, Olympic Games reviver, Birth Cent; No. 1882, Author, 150th Birth Anniv.

353 Bulgarian 2 l. Rocket Stamp of 1959

1963. Organization of Socialist Countries Postal Administrations Conference, Budapest.

No.	Description	Unused	Used
1883	– 20 fi. red, yellow & grn	10	10
1884	353 30 fi. red, brown & pur	10	10
1885	– 40 fi. purple and blue	10	10
1886	– 50 fi. violet and blue	10	10
1887	– 60 fi. multicoloured	15	10
1888	– 80 fi. turq, blk & blue	15	10
1889	– 1 fo. multicoloured	20	10
1890	– 1 fo. 20 yell, vio & bl	95	10
1891	– 1 fo. 40 blue, red & brn	35	10
1892	– 1 fo. 70 brn, grn & lt brn	50	15
1893	– 2 fo. orge, blue & pur	55	15
1894	– 2 fo. 60 vio, red & grn	80	70

DESIGNS: Various "space" stamps—HORIZ: 20 fi. Albania 1 l. 50 (1962); 40 fi. Czechoslovakia 80 h. (1962); 50 fi. China 8 f. (1958); 60 fi. N. Korea 10 ch. (1961); 80 fi. Poland 40 g. (1959); 1 fo. Hungary 60 fi. (1961); 1 fo. 40, East Germany 25 pf. (1961); 1 fo. 70, Rumania 1 l. 20 (1957); 2 fo. 60, N. Vietnam 6 x. (1961). VERT: 1 fo. 20, Mongolia 30 m. (1959); 2 fo. Russia 6 k. (1961).

354 Fair Emblem

1963. International Fair, Budapest.

No.	Description	Unused	Used
1895	354 1 fo. violet	20	10

355 Erkel (composer)

1963. Students' Erkel Memorial Festival, Gyula.

No.	Description	Unused	Used
1896	355 60 fi. brown	40	10

356 Roses

1963. 5th National Rose Show, Budapest.

No.	Description	Unused	Used
1897	356 2 fo. red, green & brown	55	10

357 Helicon Monument

1963. 10th Youth Festival, Keszthely.

No.	Description	Unused	Used
1898	357 40 fi. blue	10	10

358 Chain Bridge and "Snow White" (Danube steamer)

1963. Transport and Communications.

No.	Description	Unused	Used
1899	358 10 fi. blue	10	10
1900	– 20 fi. green	15	10
1901	– 30 fi. blue	10	10
1902	– 40 fi. orange	25	10
1902b	– 40 fi. grey	25	25
1903	– 50 fi. brown	20	10
1904	– 60 fi. red	10	10
1905	– 70 fi. olive	25	10
1906	– 80 fi. brown	20	10
1906a	– 1 fo. brown	15	10
1907	– 1 fo. purple	20	10
1908	– 1 fo. 20 brown	1·50	70
1909	– 1 fo. 20 violet	20	10
1910	– 1 fo. 40 green	30	10
1911	– 1 fo. 70 brown	65	10
1912	– 2 fo. turquoise	40	10
1913	– 2 fo. 50 purple	60	10
1914	– 2 fo. 60 olive	1·25	10
1915	– 3 fo. blue	40	10
1916	– 4 fo. blue	60	10
1917	– 5 fo. brown	85	10
1918	– 6 fo. ochre	90	10
1919	– 8 fo. mauve	1·50	20
1920	– 10 fo. green	1·50	75

DESIGNS—As Type 358: HORIZ: 20 fi. Tramcar; 30 fi. Open-deck bus; 40 fi. (No. 1902), Articulated bus; 40 fi. (No. 1902b), Budapest 100 Post Office; 50 fi. Railway truck with gas cylinders; 60 fi. Trolley bus; 70 fi. Railway T.P.O. coach; 80 fi. Motor cyclist. VERT: 1 fo. (No. 1906a), Hotel Budapest. 28½ × 21 mm: 1 fo. (No. 1907) Articulated trolley bus; 1 fo. 40, Postal coach; 1 fo. 70, Diesel-electric multiple unit train; 2 fo. T.V. broadcast coach; 2 fo. 50, Tourist coach; 2 fo. 60, Signalbox and train; 3 fo. Parcels conveyor; 5 fo. Railway fork-lift truck; 6 fo. Telex operator; 8 fo. Telephonist and map; 10 fo. Postwoman. 21 × 28½ mm: 1 fo. 20, (No. 1908), Mail plane and trolley on tarmac; 1 fo. 20, (No. 1909), Control tower, Miskolc; 4 fo. Pylon, Pecs.

See also Nos. 2767/70.

359 Holidaymaker and "Beloiannis" (lake steamer)

1963. Cent of Siofok Resort, Lake Balaton.

No.	Description	Unused	Used
1921	– 20 fi. black, grn & red	50	10
1922	359 40 fi. multicoloured	50	15
1923	– 60 fi. orange, brown & bl	90	20

DESIGNS—TRIANGULAR: 20 fi. "Tihany" (water bus); 60 fi. Yacht.

360 Mail Coach and Arc de Triomphe, Paris

1963. Centenary of Paris Postal Conf.

No.	Description	Unused	Used
1924	360 1 fo. red	20	10

361 Performance in front of Szeged Cathedral

1963. Summer Drama Festival, Szeged.

No.	Description	Unused	Used
1925	361 40 fi. blue	15	10

362 Child with towel

364 Karancssag

363 Pylon and Map

1963. Red Cross Cent. Inscr "1863–1963". Mult.

No.	Description	Unused	Used
1926	30 fi. Type 362	10	10
1927	40 fi. Girl with medicine bottle and tablets	10	10
1928	60 fi. Girls of three races	20	10
1929	1 fo. Girl and "heart"	25	10
1930	1 fo. 40 Boys of three races	35	10
1931	2 fo. Child being medically examined	45	10
1932	3 fo. Hands tending plants	1·10	25

1963. Village Electrification.

No.	Description	Unused	Used
1933	363 1 fo. black and grey	25	10

1963. Provincial Costumes.

No.	Description	Unused	Used
1934	364 20 fi. lake	20	10
1935	– 30 fi. green (Kapuvar)	25	10
1936	– 40 fi. brown (Debrecen)	25	10
1937	– 60 fi. blue (Hortobagy)	35	10
1938	– 1 fo. red (Csokoly)	50	35
1939	– 1 fo. 70 violet (Dunantul)	60	40
1940	– 2 fo. turquoise (Bujak)	70	50
1941	– 2 fo. 50 red (Alfold)	85	55
1942	– 3 fo. blue (Mezokovesd)	2·00	60

365 Hyacinth

367 Calendar

366 Skiing (slalom)

1963. Stamp Day. Flowers. Multicoloured.

No.	Description	Unused	Used
1943	2 fo. + 1 fo. Type 365	80	80
1944	2 fo. + 1 fo. Narcissus	80	80
1945	2 fo. + 1 fo. Chrysanthemum	80	80
1946	2 fo. + 1 fo. Tiger lily	80	80

1963. Winter Olympic Games, Innsbruck, 1964. "MAGYAR" and emblems red and black; centres brown: background colours given.

1947	**366**	40 fi. green	10	10
1948	–	60 fi. violet	10	10
1949	–	70 fi. blue	15	10
1950	–	80 fi. green	15	10
1951	–	1 fo. orange	20	10
1952	–	2 fo. blue	40	10
1953	–	2 fo. 60 purple	1·00	40
1954	–	4 fo. + 1 fo. blue	1·50	50

DESIGNS: 60 fi. Skiing (biathlon); 70 fi. Ski jumping; 80 fi. Rifle-shooting on skis; 1 fo. Figure skating (pairs); 2 fo. Ice hockey; 2 fo. 60 Speed skating; 4 fo. Bobsleighing.

1963. New Year Issue. Hungarian Postal and Philatelic Museum Fund. Multicoloured.

1955	20 fi. Type **367**	10	10
1956	30 fi. Young chimney-sweep with glass of wine	10	10
1957	40 fi. Four-leafed clover	15	10
1958	60 fi. Piglet in top-hat	15	10
1959	1 fo. Young pierrot	20	10
1960	2 fo. Chinese lanterns and mask	30	10
1961	2 fo. 50 + 1 fo. 20 Holly, mistletoe, clover and horse-shoe	50	20
1962	3 fo. + 1 fo. 50 Piglets with balloon	1·25	60

SIZES: As Type **367**—HORIZ: 20 fi., 1 fo., 3 fo. VERT: 40 fi. LARGER (28 × 38 mm.): 30 fi., 60 fi., 2 fo., 2 fo. 50.

368 Moon Rocket

1964. Space Research. Multicoloured.

1963	30 fi. Type **368**	15	10
1964	40 fi. Venus rocket	20	10
1965	60 fi. "Vostok 1"	20	10
1966	1 fo. U.S. spaceship	25	10
1967	1 fo. 70 Soviet team space flights	45	10
1968	2 fo. "Telstar"	50	10
1969	2 fo. 60 Mars rocket	1·00	50
1970	3 fo. "Space Research" (rockets and tracking equipment)	1·40	65

The 60 fi., 2 fo. and 3 fo. are horiz., the rest vert.

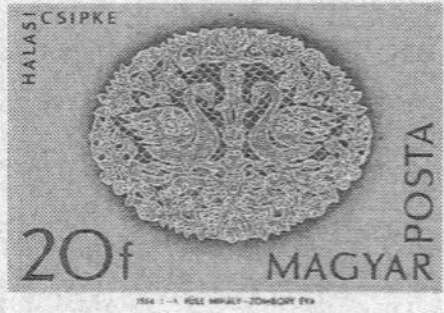

369 Swans

1964. Halas Lace (2nd series). Lace patterns die-stamped in white on black; inscriptions black.

1971	**369**	20 fi. green	30	10
1972	–	30 fi. yellow	45	10
1973	–	40 fi. red	65	10
1974	–	60 fi. olive	85	10
1975	–	1 fo. orange	1·00	10
1976	–	1 fo. 40 blue	1·25	15
1977	–	2 fo. turquoise	1·40	15
1978	–	2 fo. 60 violet	1·75	40

LACE PATTERNS—VERT: (38½ × 45 mm.): 30 fi. Peacocks; 40 fi. Pigeons; 60 fi. Peacock; 1 fo. Deer; 1 fo. 40, Fisherman; 2 fo. Pigeons. As Type **369**: 2 fo. 60, Butterfly.

370 Armour and Swords

371 Basketball

372 Dozsa and Kossuth

373 Fair and Emblem

374 "Breasting the Tape"

1964. Anniversaries and Events of 1964. Designs as T **370/4**, some showing portraits.

(a) As T **370**.

1979	60 fi. purple (I. Madach)	15	10
1980	60 fi. olive (E. Szabo)	15	10
1981	60 fi. olive (A. Fay)	15	10
1982	1 fo. red (Skittles)	40	10
1983	2 fo. brown (T **370**)	35	10

ANNIV OR EVENT: No. 1979, (author, death cent.); No. 1980, (founder of Municipal Libraries, 60th anniv); No. 1981, (death cent.); No. 1982, (1st European Skittles Championships, Budapest); No. 1983, (50th anniv of Hungarian Fencing Assn.).

(b) As T **371**.

1984	60 fi. turquoise (Stalactites and stalagmites)	50	10
1985	60 fi. blue (Bauxite excavator)	75	10
1990	60 fi. red (K. Marx)	15	10
1986	1 fo. green (Forest and water-fall)	45	10
1987	2 fo. brown (Galileo)	55	10
1988	2 fo. lake (Shakespeare)	50	10
1989	2 fo. blue (T **371**)	1·40	10

ANNIV OR EVENT—VERT: No. 1984, (Aggteleki Cave); No. 1985, (30th anniv or Hungarian Aluminium Production); No. 1986, (National Forestry Federation Congress); No. 1987, (400th birth anniv); No. 1988 (400th birth anniv); No. 1989, (European Women's Basketball Championships). HORIZ: No. 1990, (cent of "First International").

(c) As T **372**.

1991	1 fo. blue (T **372**)	25	10
1992	3 fo. + 1 fo. 50, black, grey and orange (Sports Museum, Budapest)	70	30

ANNIV OR EVENT: No. 1991, (60th Anniv of City of Cegled); No. 1992, (Lawn Tennis Historical Exn, Budapest).

(d) T **373**.

1993	1 fo. green (Budapest Int Fair)	25	10

(e) As T **374**.

1994	60 fi. slate ("Alba Regia" statue)	15	10
1995	1 fo. brown (M. Ybl)	25	10
1996	2 fo. brown (T **374**)	40	10
1997	2 fo. dull pur (Michelangelo)	50	10

ANNIV OR EVENT: No. 1994, (Szekesfehervar Days); No. 1995, (architect, 150th birth anniv); No. 1996, (50th anniv of Hungarian-Swedish Athletic Meeting); No. 1997, (400th death anniv).

375 Eleanor Roosevelt

377 Peaches ("Magyar Kajszi")

376 Fencing

1964. Eleanor Roosevelt Commemoration.

1998	**375**	2 fo. ochre, deep brown and brown	50	35

1964. Olympic Games, Tokyo. Multicoloured.

1999	30 fi. Type **376**	10	10
2000	40 fi. Gymnastics	10	10
2001	60 fi. Football	10	10
2002	80 fi. Horse-jumping	15	10
2003	1 fo. Running	20	10
2004	1 fo. 40 Weightlifting	25	10
2005	1 fo. 70 Gymnastics (trapeze)	30	10
2006	2 fo. Throwing the hammer, and javelin	40	10
2007	2 fo. 50 Boxing	1·00	15
2008	3 fo. + 1 fo. Water-polo	1·10	60

1964. National Peaches and Apricots Exn, Budapest. Designs of peaches or apricots. Multicoloured.

2009	40 fi. "J. H. Hale"	15	10
2010	60 fi. Type **377**	15	10
2011	1 fo. "Mandula Kajszi"	30	10
2012	1 fo. 50 "Borsi Rozsa"	40	10
2013	1 fo. 70 "Alexander"	60	35
2014	2 fo. "Champion"	80	35
2015	2 fo. 60 "Elberta"	1·00	50
2016	3 fo. "Mayflower"	1·40	65

378 Lilac

1964. Stamp Day. Multicoloured.

2017	2 fo. + 1 fo. Type **378**	1·00	1·00
2018	2 fo. + 1 fo. Mallard	1·50	1·50
2019	2 fo. + 1 fo. Gymnast	1·00	1·00
2020	2 fo. + 1 fo. Rocket and globe	1·00	1·00

379 Pedestrian Road Crossing

1964. Road Safety. Multicoloured.

2021	20 fi. Type **379**	30	10
2022	60 fi. Child with ball running into road	45	10
2023	1 fo. Woman and child waiting to cross road	70	20

380 Arpad Bridge, Budapest

1964. Opening of Reconstructed Elizabeth Bridge, Budapest.

2024	**380**	20 fi. grey, green and blue	10	10
2025	–	30 fi. grn, bl & brn	10	10
2026	–	60 fi. brn, grn & dp brn	30	10
2027	–	1 fo. brn, bl & dp brn	70	10
2028	–	1 fo. 50 grey, bl & brn	85	15
2029	–	2 fo. grey, grn & brn	1·00	25
2030	–	2 fo. 50 grey, bl & brn	2·25	1·00

BUDAPEST BRIDGES: 30 fi. Margaret; 60 fi. Chain; 1 fo. Elizabeth; 1 fo. 50, Liberty; 2 fo. Petofi; 2 fo. 50, South.

381 Ring-necked Pheasant

1964. "Hunting". Multicoloured.

2034	20 fi. Type **381**	40	10
2035	30 fi. Wild boar	15	10
2036	40 fi. Grey partridges	60	10
2037	60 fi. Brown hare	25	10
2038	80 fi. Fallow deer	40	10
2039	1 fo. Mouflon	60	10
2040	1 fo. 70 Red deer	1·00	10
2041	2 fo. Great bustard	3·00	40
2042	2 fo. 50 Roe deer	1·25	30
2043	3 fo. Emblem of Hunters' Federation	1·40	75

382 Horse-riding and Medals

1965. Olympic Games, Tokyo—Hungarian Winners' Medals. Medals: Gold and brown (G); Silver and black (S); Bronze and brown (B).

2044	20 fi. brn & olive (G)	10	10
2045	30 fi. brown and violet (S)	10	10
2046	50 fi. brown and olive (G)	15	10
2047	60 fi. brown & lt blue (G)	15	10
2048	70 fi. brn, slate & stone (B)	20	10
2049	80 fi. brown & green (G)	25	10
2050	1 fo. brown, vio & mve (S)	30	10
2051	1 fo. 20 brown & blue (S)	60	35
2052	1 fo. 40 brn and grey (S)	80	35
2053	1 fo. 50 brown & bistre (G)	95	40
2054	1 fo. 70 brown & red (S)	1·25	55
2055	3 fo. brown & turquoise (G)	1·75	1·10

DESIGNS: 20 fi. Type **382**; 30 fi. Gymnastics; 50 fi. Rifle-shooting; 60 fi. Water-polo; 70 fi. Putting the shot; 80 fi. Football; 1 fo. Weightlifting; 1 fo. 20, Canoeing; 1 fo. 40, Throwing the hammer; 1 fo. 50, Wrestling; 1 fo. 70, Throwing the javelin; 3 fo. Fencing.

383 Mil Mi-4 Helicopter and Polar Station

384 Asters

1965. International Quiet Sun Year.

2056	**383**	20 fi. orge, blk & blue	10	10
2057	–	30 fi. grn, blk & grey	10	10
2058	–	60 fi. yell, blk & mve	15	10
2059	–	80 fi. yellow, blk & grn	20	10
2060	–	1 fo. 50 multicoloured	25	10
2061	–	1 fo. 70 blk, mve & bl	30	10
2062	–	2 fo. red, black & blue	1·40	30
2063	–	2 fo. 50 yell, blk & brn	60	40
2064	–	3 fo. blk, blue & yell	1·10	90

DESIGNS: 30 fi. Rocket and radar aerials; 60 fi. Rocket and diagram; 80 fi. Radio telescope; 1 fo. 50, Compass needle on Globe; 1 fo. 70, Weather balloon; 2 fo. Northern Lights and Adelie Penguins; 2 fo. 50, Space satellite; 3 fo. I.Q.S.Y. emblem and world map.

1965. 20th Anniv of Liberation. Multicoloured.

2066	20 fi. Type **384**	10	10
2067	30 fi. Peonies	10	10
2068	50 fi. Carnations	10	10
2069	60 fi. Roses	15	10
2070	1 fo. 40 Lilies	30	10
2071	1 fo. 70 Godetia	40	10
2072	2 fo. Gladiolus	45	10
2073	2 fo. 50 Parrot tulips	60	50
2074	3 fo. Mixed bouquet	1·25	80

385 Leonov in Space

386 "Red Head" (after Leonardo da Vinci)

1965. Air. "Voskhod 2" Space Flight.

2075	**385**	1 fo. grey and violet	40	10
2076	–	2 fo. brown & purple	1·10	70

DESIGN: 2 fo. Belyaev and Leonov.

1965. Int Renaissance Conference, Budapest.

2077	**386**	60 fi. brown and ochre	20	10

387 Nikolaev, Tereshkova and View of Budapest

1965. Visit of Astronauts Nikolaev and Tereshkova.

2078	**387**	1 fo. brown and blue	25	10

388 I.T.U. Emblem and Symbols

1965. Centenary of I.T.U.
2079 **388** 60 fi. blue 20 10

390 French 13th-cent Tennis **391** Marx and Lenin

1965. "History of Tennis".
2081 **390** 30 fi. + 10 fi. lake on buff 20 10
2082 – 40 fi. + 10 fi. blk on lilac . 25 10
2083 – 60 fi. + 10 fi. grn on bis . 30 10
2084 – 70 fi. + 30 fi. pur on turq 35 10
2085 – 80 fi. + 40 fi. bl on lav . . 40 15
2086 – 1 fo. + 50 fi. grn on yell . 70 15
2087 – 1 fo. 50 + 50 fi. brown on green 75 35
2088 – 1 fo. 70 + 50 fi. blk on bl 80 65
2089 – 2 fo. + 1 fo. red on green 95 75
DESIGNS: 40 fi. Hungarian 16th-cent. game; 60 fi. French 18th-cent. "long court"; 70 fi. 16th-cent. "tennys courte"; 80 fi. 16th-cent. court at Fontainebleau; 1 fo. 17th-cent. game; 1 fo. 50, W. C. Wingfield and Wimbledon Cup, 1877; 1 fo. 70, Davis Cup, 1900. 2 fo. Bela Kehrling in play.

1965. Organization of Socialist Countries' Postal Administrations Congress, Peking.
2090 **391** 60 fi. multicoloured . . . 10 10

392 I.C.Y. Emblem and Pulleys **393** Equestrian Act

1965. International Co-operation Year.
2091 **392** 2 fo. red 30 10

1965. "Circus 1965". Multicoloured.
2093 20 fi. Type **393** 15 10
2094 30 fi. Musical clown 15 10
2095 40 fi. Performing elephant . . 20 10
2096 50 fi. Performing seal 25 10
2097 60 fi. Lions 35 10
2098 1 fo. Wild cat leaping through burning hoops 40 10
2099 1 fo. 50 Black panthers 65 15
2100 2 fo. 50 Acrobat with hoops . . 80 40
2101 3 fo. Performing panther and dogs . . . . 1·10 50
2102 4 fo. Bear on bicycle . . . . . 1·75 1·00

394 Rescue Boat

1965. Danube Flood Relief.
2103 **394** 1 fo. + 50 fi. brn & bl . . 1·00 1·00

395 Dr. I. Semmelweis

1965. Death Centenary of Ignac Semmelweis (physician).
2105 **395** 60 fi. brown 30 10

396 Running

1965. University Games, Budapest. Mult.
2106 20 fi. Type **396** 10 10
2107 30 fi. Start of swimming race . 10 10
2108 50 fi. Diving 10 10
2109 60 fi. Gymnastics 15 10
2110 80 fi. Tennis 20 10
2111 1 fo. 70 Fencing 30 10
2112 2 fo. Volleyball 45 10
2113 2 fo. 50 Basketball 65 35
2114 4 fo. Water-polo 90 70

397 Congress Emblem

1965. 6th W.F.T.U. Congress, Warsaw.
2116 **397** 60 fi. blue 10 10

398 "Phyllocactus hybridum"

1965. Cacti and Orchids. Multicoloured.
2117 20 fi. Type **398** 15 10
2118 30 fi. "Cattleya warszewiczii" . 20 10
2119 60 fi. "Rebutia calliantha" . . 25 10
2120 70 fi. "Paphiopedilum hybridum" 35 10
2121 80 fi. "Opuntia rhodantha" . . 35 10
2122 1 fo. "Laelia elegans" 60 10
2123 1 fo. 50 "Zygocactus truncatus" 50 10
2124 2 fo. "Strelitzia reginae" . . . 75 10
2125 2 fo. 50 "Lithops weberi" . . 80 50
2126 3 fo. "Victoria amazonica" . . 1·60 70

399 Reproduction of No. 1127

1965. Stamp Day. Designs show reproductions of Hungarian stamps. Multicoloured.
2127 2 fo. + 1 fo. Type **399** . . . . 1·00 1·00
2128 2 fo. + 1 fo. No. 1280 . . . . 1·40 1·40
2129 2 fo. + 1 fo. No. 1873 . . . . 1·00 1·00
2130 2 fo. + 1 fo. No. 1733 . . . . 1·00 1·00

400 F.I.R. Emblem

1965. 5th International Federation of Resistance Fighters Congress, Budapest.
2132 **400** 2 fo. blue 50 10

401 The Magic Horse **402** "Mariner 4"

1965. Fairy Tales (3rd series). Scenes from "The Arabian Nights Entertainments". Multicoloured.
2133 20 fi. Type **401** 10 10
2134 30 fi. Sultan Schahriah and Scheherazade 10 10
2135 50 fi. Sinbad's 5th Voyage (ship) 10 10
2136 60 fi. Aladdin and Genie of the Lamp 20 10
2137 80 fi. Haroun al Rashid 30 10
2138 1 fo. The Magic Carpet . . . 50 10
2139 1 fo. 70 The Fisherman and the Genie 70 35
2140 2 fo. Ali Baba 85 45
2141 3 fo. Sinbad's 2nd Voyage (roc—legendary bird) . . . 1·40 60

1965. Air. Space Research.
2142 **402** 20 fi. black, yell & blue . . 20 10
2143 – 30 fi. violet, yell & brn . . 25 10
2144 – 40 fi. brn, mve & blue . . 30 10
2145 – 60 fi. multicoloured . . . 45 10
2146 – 1 fo. multicoloured . . . 65 10
2147 – 2 fo. 50 black, grey & pur 1·10 35
2148 – 3 fo. black, grn & brn . . 1·25 35
DESIGNS: 30 fi. "San Marco" (Italian satellite); 40 fi. "Molnyija 1" (Polish satellite); 60 fi. Moon rocket; 1 fo. "Shapir" rocket; 2 fo. 50, "Szonda 3" satellite; 3 fo. "Syncom 3" satellite.

403 Scarlet Tiger Moth

1966. Butterflies and Moths. Multicoloured.
2150 20 fi. Type **403** 15 10
2151 60 fi. Orange tip 30 10
2152 70 fi. Meleager's blue 45 10
2153 80 fi. Scarce swallowtail . . . 55 10
2154 1 fo. Common burnet 65 10
2155 1 fo. 50 Southern festoon . . . 75 20
2156 2 fo. Camberwell beauty . . . 85 20
2157 2 fo. 50 Nettle-tree butterfly . . 1·00 25
2158 3 fo. Clouded yellow . . . . . 1·40 65

404 Bela Kun

1966. Anniversaries of 1966.
2159 60 fi. black and red (T **404**) . . 15 10
2160 60 fi. black & blue (T. Esze) . . 15 10
2161 1 fo. violet (Shastri) 50 10
2162 2 fo. brown and ochre (I. Szechenyi) 30 10
2163 2 fo. sepia and bistre (M. Zrinyi) 20 10
2164 2 fo. sepia and green (S. Koranyi) 20 10
EVENTS: No. 2159, 80th Birth Anniv (workers' leader); No. 2160, (after statue by M. Nemeth) 300th Birth Anniv (war hero); No. 2161, Death commem (Indian Prime Minister); No. 2162, 175th Birth Anniv (statesman); No. 2163, 400th Death Anniv (military commander); No. 2164, Birth Cent (scientist).

MINIMUM PRICE

The minimum price quoted is 10p which represents a handling charge rather than a basis for valuing common stamps. For further notes about prices see introductory pages.

405 "Luna 9" in Space **406** Crocus

1966. Moon Landing of "Luna 9".
2165 **405** 2 fo. black, yell & violet . 45 10
2166 – 3 fo. black, yellow & bl . 1·10 65
DESIGN—HORIZ: 3 fo. "Luna 9" on Moon.

1966. Flower Protection. Multicoloured.
2167 20 fi. Type **406** 20 10
2168 30 fi. European cyclamen . . . 25 10
2169 60 fi. Ligularia 40 10
2170 1 fo. 40 Orange lily 60 35
2171 1 fo. 50 Fritillary 70 45
2172 3 fo. "Dracocephalum ruyschiana" . . . . 1·75 65

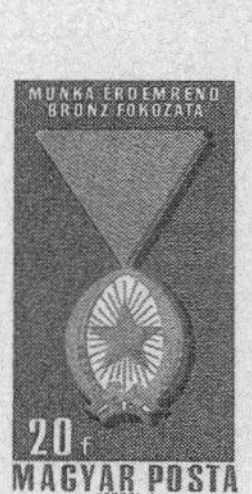

407 Order of Labour (bronze) **409** Barn Swallows

408 Early Transport and Budapest Railway Station, 1846

1966. Hungarian Medals and Orders. Mult.
2173 20 fi. Type **407** 10 10
2174 30 fi. Order of Labour (silver) . 10 10
2175 50 fi. Banner Order of Republic, 3rd class ($21\frac{1}{2} \times 28\frac{1}{2}$ mm.) . 10 10
2176 60 fi. Order of Labour (gold) . 10 10
2177 70 fi. Banner Order of Republic, 2nd class ($25 \times 30\frac{1}{2}$ mm.) . . 10 10
2178 1 fo. Red Banner Order of Labour 20 10
2179 1 fo. 20 Banner Order of Republic, 1st class ($28\frac{1}{2} \times 38$ mm.) 25 10
2180 2 fo. Order of Merit of Republic 55 35
2181 2 fo. 50 Hero of Socialist Labour 75 55

1966. Re-opening of Transport Museum, Budapest.
2182 **408** 1 fo. brown, grn & yell . . 50 15
2183 – 2 fo. blue, brown & grn . 1·25 35
DESIGN: 2 fo. Modern transport and South Station, Budapest.

1966. Protection of Birds. Multicoloured.
2184 20 fi. Type **409** 45 10
2185 30 fi. Long-tailed tits 55 10
2186 60 fi. Red crossbill 70 10
2187 1 fo. 40 Middle spotted woodpecker . . . . 1·40 30
2188 1 fo. 50 Hoopoe . . . . . . 1·50 50
2189 3 fo. Forest and emblem of National Forestry Association . . . . . . 1·50 90

410 W.H.O. Building

1966. Inaug of W.H.O. Headquarters, Geneva.
2190 **410** 2 fo. black and blue . . . 50 10

412 Nuclear Research Institute

1966. 10th Anniv of United Nuclear Research Institute, Dubna (U.S.S.R.).
2192 **412** 60 fi. black and green . . 50 10

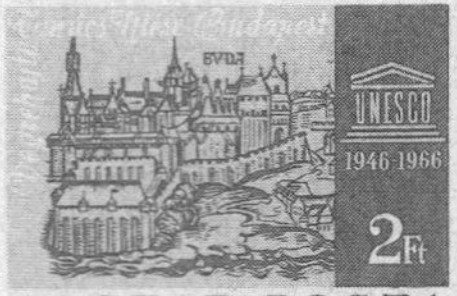

413 Buda Fortress, after Schedel's "Chronicle" (1493)

1966. 20th Anniv of UNESCO and 72nd Executive Board Session, Budapest.
2193 **413** 2 fo. violet and blue . . . 65 10

414 Jules Rimet, Football and Cup

1966. World Cup Football Championships. Multicoloured.
2194 20 fi. Type **414** 10 10
2195 30 fi. Montevideo, 1930 . . . 10 10
2196 60 fi. Rome, 1934 . . . . . . 15 10
2197 1 fo. Paris, 1938 . . . . . 25 10
2198 1 fo. 40 Rio de Janeiro, 1950 . 30 10
2199 1 fo. 70 Berne, 1954 . . . . . 65 10
2200 2 fo. Stockholm, 1958 . . . . 85 35
2201 2 fo. 50 Santiago de Chile, 1962 . . . . 1·25 55
2202 3 fo. + 1 fo. World Cup emblem on Union Jack, and map of England . . . . . 1·75 1·25

415 Girl Pioneer and Emblem

1966. 20th Anniv of Hungarian Pioneers Movement.
2203 **415** 60 fi. red and violet . . . 50 10

416 Fire Engine

1966. Cent. of Voluntary Fire Brigades.
2204 **416** 2 fo. black & orange . . . 65 20

417 Red Fox 418 Throwing the Discus

1966. Hunting Trophies. Multicoloured.
2205 20 fi. Type **417** 10 10
2206 60 fi. Wild boar 15 10
2207 70 fi. Wild cat 25 10
2208 80 fi. Roe deer 25 10
2209 1 fo. 50 Red deer 55 10
2210 2 fo. 50 Fallow deer . . . . . 1·25 35
2211 3 fo. Mouflon . . . . 1·40 55

1966. 8th European Athletic Championships, Budapest. Multicoloured.
2212 20 fi. Type **418** 10 10
2213 30 fi. High-jumping 10 10
2214 40 fi. Throwing the javelin . . 15 10
2215 50 fi. Throwing the hammer . . 35 10
2216 60 fi. Long-jumping 55 10
2217 1 fo. Putting the shot 75 10
2218 2 fo. Pole-vaulting . . . . . . 1·25 65
2219 3 fo. Running . . . . 1·75 75

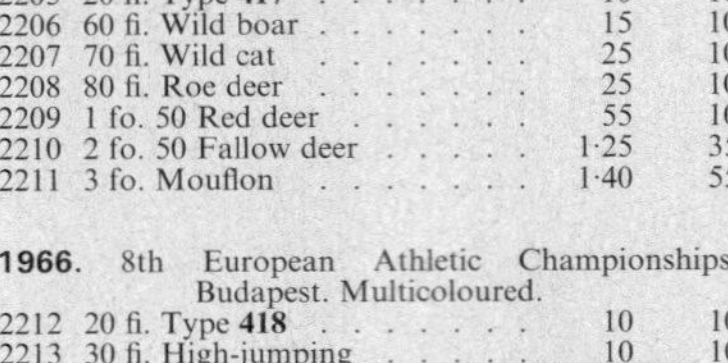

419 Archery 420 Helsinki

1966. Stamp Day. Multicoloured.
2221 2 fo. + 50 fi Types **419** . . . . 90 1·00
2222 2 fo. + 50 fi. Grapes . . . . 90 1·00
2223 2 fo. + 50 fi. Poppies . . . . 90 1·00
2224 2 fo. + 50 fi. Space dogs . . . 90 1·00

1966. Air.
2226 **420** 20 fi. red 10 10
2227 – 50 fi. brown 10 10
2228 – 1 fo. blue 15 10
2229 – 1 fo. 10 black 20 10
2230 – 1 fo. 20 orange 20 10
2231 – 1 fo. 50 green 30 10
2232 – 2 fo. blue 40 10
2233 – 2 fo. 50 red 45 10
2234 – 3 fo. green 60 15
2235 – 4 fo. brown . . . . 2·00 1·25
2236 – 5 fo. violet 75 20
2237 – 10 fo. blue . . . . 1·90 40
2238 – 20 fo. green . . . . 3·00 60

DESIGNS—Ilyushin Il-18 over: 50 fi. Athens; 1 fo. Beirut; 1 fo. 10, Frankfurt; 1 fo. 20, Cairo; 1 fo. 50, Copenhagen; 2 fo. London; 2 fo. 50, Moscow; 3 fo. Paris; 4 fo. Prague; 5 fo. Rome; 10 fo. Damascus; 20 fo. Budapest.

For 2 fo. 60 in similar design see No. 2369.

421 "Girl in the Woods" (after Barabas)

1966. Paintings in Hungarian National Gallery (1st series). Multicoloured.
2239 60 fi. Type **421** 20 15
2240 1 fo. "Mrs. Istvan Bitto" (Barabas) 50 15
2241 1 fo. 50 "Laszlo Hunyadi Farewell" (Benczur) 90 40
2242 1 fo. 70 "Woman Reading" (Benczur) . . . . 1·25 55
2243 2 fo. "The Faggot-carrier" (Munkacsy) . . . . . . 1·40 60
2244 2 fo. 50 "The Yawning Apprentice" (Munkacsy) . . 1·60 65
2245 3 fo. "Woman in Lilac" (Szinyei) . . . . 2·10 75

The 1 fo. 70 is horiz.

See also Nos. 2282/8, 2318/24, 2357/63, 2411/17, 2449/55 and 2525/2531.

422 "Vostok 3" and "Vostok 4" (Nikolaev and Popovich)

1966. Twin Space Flights. Multicoloured.
2247 20 fi. Type **422** 10 10
2248 60 fi. Borman and Lovell, Schirra and Stafford . . . 15 10
2249 80 fi. Bykovsky and Tereshkova 15 10
2250 1 fo. Stafford and Cernan . . . 25 10
2251 1 fo. 50 Belyaev and Leonov (Leonov in space) 40 10
2252 2 fo. McDivitt and White (White in space) 50 10
2253 2 fo. 50 Komarov, Feoktistov and Yegorov 85 15
2254 3 fo. Conrad and Gordon . . 1·40 35

423 Kitaibel and "Kitaibelia vitifolia" 424 Militiaman

1967. 150th Death Anniv of Pal Kitaibel (botanist). Carpathian Flowers. Multicoloured.
2255 20 fi. Type **423** 10 10
2256 60 fi. "Dentaria glandulosa" . . 20 10
2257 1 fo. "Edraianthus tenuifolius" . 30 10
2258 1 fo. 50 "Althaea pallida" . . 45 10
2259 2 fo. "Centaurea mollis" . . . 60 10
2260 2 fo. 50 "Sternbergia colchiciflora" . . . . 1·10 15
2261 3 fo. "Iris hungarica" . . . . 1·25 65

1967. 10th Anniv of Workers' Militia.
2262 **424** 2 fo. blue 25 10

425 Faustus Verancsics' Parachute Descent, 1617

1967. Air. "Aerofila 67". Airmail Stamp Exn, Budapest.
2263 2 fo. + 1 fo. sepia & yellow . . 1·00 1·00
2264 2 fo. + 1 fo. sepia & blue . . 1·00 1·00
2265 2 fo. + 1 fo. sepia & green . . 1·00 1·00
2266 2 fo. + 1 fo. sepia & pink . . 1·00 1·00
2268 2 fo. + 1 fo. blue & green . . 1·00 1·00
2269 2 fo. + 1 fo. blue & orange . . 1·00 1·00
2270 2 fo. + 1 fo. blue & yellow . . 1·00 1·00
2271 2 fo. + 1 fo. blue & pink . . . 1·00 1·00

DESIGNS: No. 2263, Type **425**; No. 2264, David Schwartz's aluminium airship, 1897; No. 2265, Erno Horvath's monoplane, 1911; No. 2266, PKZ-2 helicopter, 1918; No. 2268, Parachutist; No. 2269, Mil Mi-1 helicopter; No. 2270, Tupolev Tu-154 airliner; No. 2271, "Luna 12".

426 I.T.Y. Emblem and Transport

1967. International Tourist Year.
2273 **426** 1 fo. black and blue . . . 25 10

428 "Ferenc Deak" (paddle-steamer), Schonbuchel Castle and Austrian Flag

1967. 25th Session of Danube Commission. Vessels of Mahart Shipping Company.
2275 **428** 30 fi. multicoloured . . . 1·60 30
2276 – 60 fi. multicoloured . . . 2·10 45
2277 – 1 fo. multicoloured . . . 3·00 50
2278 – 1 fo. 50 multicoloured . . 4·50 75
2279 – 1 fo. 70 multicoloured . . 5·50 1·10
2280 – 2 fo. multicoloured . . . 5·75 2·10
2281 – 2 fo. 50 multicoloured . . 6·25 3·00

DESIGNS (Vessels, backgrounds and flags): 60 fi. River-bus "Revfulop" Bratislava Castle, Czechoslovakia; 1 fo. Diesel passenger boat "Hunyadi", Buda Castle, Hungary; 1 fo. 50, Diesel tug "Szekszard", Golubac Castle, Yugoslavia; 1 fo. 70, Tug "Miscolc", Vidin Castle, Bulgaria; 2 fo. Motor-freighter "Tihany", Galati shipyard, Rumania; 2 fo. 50, Hydrofoil "Siraly I", port of Izmail, U.S.S.R.

429 "Szidonia Deak" (A. Gyorgyi)

1967. Paintings in National Gallery, Budapest (2nd series). Multicoloured.
2282 60 fi. "Liszt" (M. Munkacsy) . 20 15
2283 1 fo. "Self-portrait" (S. Lanyi) . 30 15
2284 1 fo. 50 "Portrait of a Lady" (J. Borsos) 40 15
2285 1 fo. 70 "The Lovers" (after P. Szinyei Merse) 85 15
2286 2 fo. Type **429** 90 15
2287 2 fo. 50 "National Guardsman" (J. Borsos) . . . . 1·00 45
2288 3 fo. "Louis XV and Madame Dubarry" (G. Benczur) . . . 1·10 60

The 1 fo. 70 is horiz.

430 Poodle

1967. Dogs. Multicoloured.
2289 30 fi. Type **430** 15 10
2290 60 fi. Collie 25 10
2291 1 fo. Pointer 35 10
2292 1 fo. 40 Fox terriers 50 10
2293 2 fo. Pumi 70 15
2294 3 fo. Alsatian 85 45
2295 4 fo. Puli . . . . 1·40 80

The 60 fi., 1 fo. 40 and 3 fo. are vert, size $23\frac{1}{2} \times 35$ mm.

431 Sterlet

1967. 14th International Anglers' Federation Congress, and World Angling Championships, Dunaujvaros. Multicoloured.
2296 20 fi. Type **431** 10 15
2297 60 fi. Zander 20 15
2298 1 fo. Common carp 25 15
2299 1 fo. 70 Wels 70 15
2300 2 fo. Northern pike 75 15
2301 2 fo. 50 Asp 90 60
2302 3 fo. + 1 fo. Anglers' and C.I.P.S. (Federation) emblem . . . . 1·50 70

432 "Prince Igor" (Borodin)

1967. Popular Operas. Designs showing scenes from various operas. Multicoloured.
2303 20 fi. Type **432** 20 10
2304 30 fi. "Der Freischutz" (Weber) 20 10
2305 40 fi. "The Magic Flute" (Mozart) 35 10
2306 60 fi. "Bluebeard's Castle" (Bartok) 50 10
2307 80 fi. "Carmen" (Bizet) 65 10
2308 1 fo. "Don Carlos" (Verdi) . . 85 45
2309 1 fo. 70 "Tannhauser" (Wagner) . . . . 1·00 80
2310 3 fo. "Laszlo Hunyadi" (Erkel) 1·40 1·25

Nos. 2307/10 are vert.

433 "Teaching" (14th-cent class)

1967. 600th Anniv of Higher Education in Hungary.
2311 **433** 2 fo. green and gold . . . 85 10

INDEX

Countries can be quickly located by referring to the index at the end of this volume.

434 Faculty Building

1967. 300th Anniv of Political Law and Science Faculty, Lorand Eotvos University, Budapest.
2312 434 2 fo. green 85 10

435 "Lenin as Teacher"

1967. 50th Anniv of October Revolution. Multicoloured.
2313 60 fi. Type 435 . . . . 10 10
2314 1 fo. "Lenin" 10 10
2315 3 fo. "Lenin aboard the Aurora" 75 40

436 "Venus 4"

1967. Landing of "Venus 4" on planet Venus.
2316 436 5 fo. multicoloured . . . 1·40 1·00

437a "Brother and Sister" (A. Fenyes)

1967. Paintings in National Gallery, Budapest (3rd series). As T 437a. Multicoloured.
2318 60 fi. Type 437a 20 10
2319 1 fo. "Boys Wrestling on Beach" (O. Glatz) 30 10
2320 1 fo. 50 "October" (K. Ferenczy) 60 10
2321 1 fo. 70 "Women by the River" (I. Szonyi) 75 15
2322 2 fo. "Godfather's Breakfast" (I. Csok) 75 15
2323 2 fo. 50 "The Eviction Order" (G. Derkovits) 80 45
2324 3 fo. "Self-Portrait" (T. Csontvary) 90 65
The 1 fo. 70 is horiz.
"The Women by the River" (1 fo. 70) is in a private collection in Budapest.

438 Rifle-shooting on Skis

1967. Winter Olympic Games, Grenoble. Multicoloured.
2326 30 fi. Type 438 . . . . 10 10
2327 60 fi. Figure skating (pairs) . . 15 10
2328 1 fo. Bobsleighing 15 10
2329 1 fo. 40 Downhill skiing . . . 25 10
2330 1 fo. 70 Figure skating 35 10
2331 2 fo. Speed skating 45 10
2332 3 fo. Ski jumping 80 50
2333 4 fo. + 1 fo. Ice stadium, Grenoble . . . . 1·25 70

439 Kalman Kando, Class V43 Electric Locomotive and Map

1968. Kando Commemoration.
2335 439 2 fo. blue 60 10

440 Cat

1968. Cats. Multicoloured.
2336 20 fi. Type 440 . . . . 25 10
2337 60 fi. Cream angora 30 10
2338 1 fo. Smoky angora 40 10
2339 1 fo. 20 Domestic kitten . . . 50 10
2340 1 fo. 50 White angora 70 35
2341 2 fo. Striped angora 85 50
2342 2 fo. 50 Siamese . . . . . . 1·25 50
2343 5 fo. Blue angora . . . . . . 2·00 80

441 Zoltan Kodaly (composer) 442 City Hall, Arms, Grapes and Apricot

1968. Kodaly Commemoration.
2344 441 5 fo. multicoloured . . . 1·40 75

1968. 600th Anniv of Kecskemet.
2345 442 2 fo. brown 45 10

443 White Stork 444 Karl Marx

1968. Int Council for Bird Preservation Congress, Budapest. Protected Birds. Multicoloured.
2346 20 fi. Type 443 . . . . 20 10
2347 50 fi. Golden orioles 35 10
2348 60 fi. Imperial eagle 40 15
2349 1 fo. Red-footed falcons . . . 45 15
2350 1 fo. 20 Scops owl 60 20
2351 1 fo. 50 Great bustard 75 25
2352 2 fo. European bee eaters . . 1·60 30
2353 2 fo. 50 Greylag goose . . . . 2·00 75

1968. 150th Birth Anniv of Karl Marx.
2354 444 1 fo. purple 15 10
See also No. 1290.

446 Student

1968. 150th Anniv of Mosonmagyarovar Agricultural College.
2356 446 2 fo. green 45 10

1968. Paintings in National Gallery, Budapest (4th series). As T 437a. Multicoloured.
2357 40 fi. "Girl with a Pitcher" (Goya) 10 10
2358 60 fi. "Head of an Apostle" (El Greco) 15 10
2359 1 fo. "Boy with Apples" (Nunez) 20 10
2360 1 fo. 50 "The Repentant Magdalen" (El Greco) . . . 55 10
2361 2 fo. 50 "The Breakfast" (Velasquez) 85 10
2362 4 fo. "St. Elizabeth" (detail from "The Holy Family"; El Greco) . . . . 1·00 50
2363 5 fo. "The Knife-grinder" (Goya) . . . . 1·25 65
The 1 fo. and 2 fo. 50 are horiz.

447 Lake Steamer, Flags and Badacsony Hills 448 Ilyushin Il-18 over St. Stephen's Cathedral, Vienna

1968. Lake Balaton Resorts. Multicoloured.
2365 20 fi. Type 447 . . . . 15 10
2365a 40 fi. Type 447 . . . . 15 10
2366 60 fi. Tihany peninsula, tower and feather 15 10
2367 1 fo. Yachts and buoy, Balatonalmadi 20 10
2368 2 fo. Szigliget bay, vineyard, wine and fish 40 15

1968. Air. 50th Anniv of Budapest–Vienna Airmail Service.
2369 448 2 fo. 60 violet 50 15

449 Class 424 Steam Locomotive No. 176 451 M. Tompa

450 Grazing Stud

1968. Centenary of Hungarian State Railways.
2370 449 2 fo. multicoloured . . . 1·40 25

1968. Horse-breeding on the Hortobagy "puszta" (Hungarian steppe). Multicoloured.
2371 30 fi. Type 450 . . . . 15 10
2372 40 fi. Horses in storm 15 10
2373 60 fi. Grooms horse-racing . . 20 10
2374 80 fi. Horse-drawn sleigh . . . 30 10
2375 1 fo. Four-in-hand 40 10
2376 1 fo. 40 Seven-in-hand 55 10
2377 2 fo. Driving five horses . . . 60 10
2378 2 fo. 50 Groom preparing evening meal 70 20
2379 4 fo. Five-in-hand . . . . . . 1·75 45

1968. Death Centenary of Mihaly Tompa (poet).
2380 451 60 fi. violet 15 10

452 Festival Emblem, Bulgarian and Hungarian Couples in National Costume

1968. 9th World Youth Festival, Sofia.
2381 452 60 fi. multicoloured . . . 20 10

454 Swimming

1968. Air. Olympic Games, Mexico. Mult.
2383 20 fi. Type 454 . . . . 10 10
2384 60 fi. Football 10 10
2385 80 fi. Wrestling 10 10
2386 1 fo. Canoeing 10 10
2387 1 fo. 40 Gymnastics 25 10
2388 2 fo. + 1 fo. Horse-jumping . 80 30
2389 3 fo. Fencing . . . . 1·00 45
2390 4 fo. Throwing the Javelin . . 1·40 65

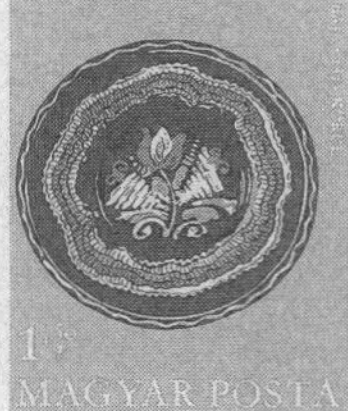

455 Baja Plate, 1870 456 Society Emblem

1968. Stamp Day. Hungarian Ceramics. Mult.
2391 1 fo. + 50 fi. Type 455 . . . . 80 90
2392 1 fo. + 50 fi. West Hungarian jug, 1618 . . . . 80 90
2393 1 fo. + 50 fi. Tiszafured flagon, 1847 . . . . 80 90
2394 1 fo. + 50 fi. Mezocsat flask, 1848 . . . . 80 90

1968. "Hungarian Society for Popularisation of Scientific Knowledge".
2396 456 2 fo. black and blue . . . 45 10

457 Rocket Hesperus 458 Two Girls waving Flags

1968. Garden Flowers. Multicoloured.
2397 20 fi. Type 457 . . . . 15 10
2398 60 fi. Pansy 30 10
2399 80 fi. Zinnias 45 10
2400 1 fo. Morning Glory 65 35
2401 1 fo. 40 Petunia 85 35
2402 1 fo. 50 Purslane 90 40
2403 2 fo. Michaelmas daisies . . . 1·10 40
2404 2 fo. 50 Dahlia . . . . 1·25 85

1968. Children's Stamp Designs for 50th Anniv of Hungarian Communist Party. Multicoloured.
2405 40 fi. Type 458 . . . . 20 10
2406 60 fi. Children with flags and banner 60 10
2407 1 fo. Pioneer bugler in camp . 90 10

459 "Workers of the World Unite" (Bertalan Por's 1918 poster) 460 Human Rights Emblem

1968. 50th Anniv of Hungarian Communist Party.
2408 459 1 fo. black, red & gold . . 10 10
2409 – 2 fo. multicoloured . . . 10 10
DESIGN—HORIZ: 2 fo. "Martyrs" (statue by Zoltan Kiss).

1968. Human Rights Year.
2410 **460** 1 fo. brown 45 10

1968. Paintings in National Gallery, Budapest (5th series). Italian Masters. Designs as T **437a**. Multicoloured.
2411 40 fi. "Esterhazy Madonna" (Raphael) 10 10
2412 60 fi. "The Annunciation" (Strozzi) 10 10
2413 1 fo. "Portrait of a Young Man" (Raphael) 15 10
2414 1 fo. 50 "The Three Graces" (Naldini) 30 10
2415 2 fo. 50 "Portrait of a Man" (Sebastian del Piombo) . . . 50 10
2416 4 fo. "The Doge Marcantonio Trevisani" (Titian) . . . . 1·10 45
2417 5 fo. "Venus, Cupid and Jealousy" (Bronzino) . . . 1·50 75
Nos. 2411/17 are vert.

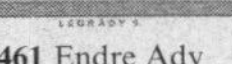
461 Endre Ady **462** Press Emblem

1969. 50th Death Anniv of Endre Ady (poet).
2419 **461** 1 fo. black, pur & gold . . 35 10

1969. Centenary of Athenaeum Press.
2420 **462** 2 fo. multicoloured . . . 40 10

464 Throwing the Javelin

1969. Olympic Gold Medal Winners. Mult.
2422 40 fi. Type **464** 10 10
2423 60 fi. Canoeing 10 10
2424 1 fo. Football 15 10
2425 1 fo. 20 Throwing the Hammer 15 10
2426 2 fo. Fencing 30 10
2427 3 fo. Wrestling 75 10
2428 4 fo. Kayak-canoeing . . . . 1·00 35
2429 5 fo. Horse-jumping . . . . . 1·40 65

465 Poster by O. Danko

1969. 50th Anniv of Proclamation of Hungarian Soviet Republic.
2431 **465** 40 fi. black, red & gold . . 10 10
2432 – 60 fi. black, red & gold . . 10 10
2433 – 1 fo. black, red & gold . . 10 10
2434 – 2 fo. multicoloured . . . 40 10
2435 – 3 fo. multicoloured . . . 65 35
DESIGNS: 60 fi. "Lenin" by unknown artist; 1 fo. "Young Man Breaking Chains" (R. Steiner); 2 fo. "Worker" (I. Foldes and G. Vegh); 3 fo. "Soldier" (unknown artist).

466 Space Link-up of "Soyuz 4" and "Soyuz 5"

1969. Air. Space Flights of "Soyuz 4" and "Soyuz 5". Multicoloured.
2437 2 fo. Type **466** 35 40
2438 2 fo. Link-up and astronauts "walking" in Space 35 40

467 Jersey Tiger Moth

1969. Butterflies and Moths. Multicoloured.
2439 40 fi. Type **467** 30 10
2440 60 fi. Eyed hawk moth 30 10
2441 80 fi. Painted lady 35 10
2442 1 fo. Foxy charaxes 40 10
2443 1 fo. 20 Lesser fiery copper . . 55 10
2444 2 fo. Large blue . . . . . . 1·00 15
2445 3 fo. Dark crimson underwing . 1·40 40
2446 4 fo. Peacock . . . . 1·60 70

468 I.L.O. Emblem

1969. 50th Anniv of Int Labour Organisation.
2447 **468** 1 fo. brown and red . . . 35 10

469 Chain Bridge, Budapest

1969. "Budapest 71" Stamp Exhibition.
2448 **469** 5 fo + 2 fo. mult . . . . 1·50 1·75

470 "Black Pigs" (Gauguin)

1969. Paintings in National Gallery, Budapest (6th series). French Masters. Multicoloured.
2449 40 fi. Type **470** 10 10
2450 60 fi. "The Ladies" (Toulouse-Lautrec) (horiz.) 10 10
2451 1 fo. "Venus on Clouds" (Vouet) 15 10
2452 2 fo. "Lady with Fan" (Manet) (horiz.) 35 10
2453 3 fo. "Petra Camara" (Chasseriau) . . . . . . 1·00 10
2454 4 fo. "The Cowherd" (Troyon) (horiz.) . . . . 1·40 40
2455 5 fo. "The Wrestlers" (Courbet) . . . . 1·90 70

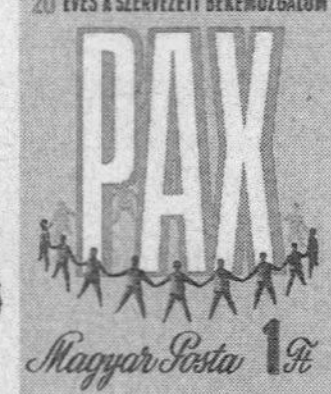

471 Vac **472** "PAX"

1969. Danube Towns. Multicoloured.
2457 40 fi. Type **471** 10 10
2458 1 fo. Szentendre 20 10
2459 1 fo. 20 Visegrad 25 10
2460 3 fo. Esztergom 50 10

1969. 20th Anniv of Int Peace Movement.
2461 **472** 1 fo. gold, dp bl & bl . . 35 10

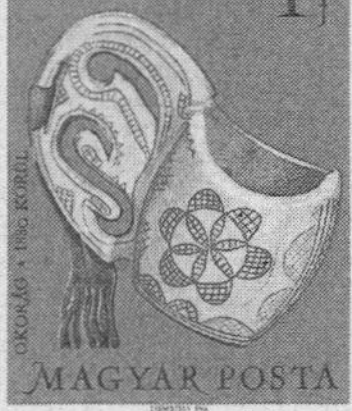

474 Zelkova Leaf (fossil) **475** Okorag Stirrupcup, 1880

1969. Cent of Hungarian Geological Institute. Minerals and Fossils. Multicoloured.
2463 40 fi. Type **474** 20 10
2464 60 fi. Greenockite calcite sphalerite crystals 25 10
2465 1 fo. Hungarian herring (fossilized fish) 30 10
2466 1 fo. 20 Quartz crystals . . . 30 10
2467 2 fo. "Reineckia crassicostata" (ammonite) 45 10
2468 3 fo. Copper ore 70 15
2469 4 fo. "Placochelys placodonta" (fossilized turtle) . . . . 1·50 50
2470 5 fo. Cuprite crystals . . . . 2·00 75

1969. Stamp Day. Hungarian Folk Art. Wood-carvings. Multicoloured.
2471 1 fo. + 50 fi. Type **475** . . . 75 90
2472 1 fo. + 50 fi. Felsotizavidek jar, 1898 . . . . 75 90
2473 1 fo. + 50 fi. Somogyharsagy pot, 1935 . . . . 75 90
2474 1 fo. + 50 fi. Alfold smoking-pipe, 1740 . . . . 75 90

476 "The Scientist at his Table" (Rembrandt)

1969. Int "History of Art" Congress, Budapest.
2476 **476** 1 fo. sepia 20 10

477 Horse-jumping

1969. World Pentathlon Championships, Budapest. Multicoloured.
2477 40 fi. Type **477** 20 10
2478 60 fi. Fencing 25 10
2479 1 fo. Pistol-shooting 40 35
2480 2 fo. Swimming 80 40
2481 3 fo. Running . . . . 1·10 55
2482 5 fo. All five sports . . . . . 1·75 80

478 Postcard and Letterbox **479** Mahatma Gandhi

1969. Centenary of 1st Hungarian Postcard.
2483 **478** 60 fi. ochre and red . . . 10 10

1969. Birth Centenary of Mahatma Gandhi.
2484 **479** 5 fo. multicoloured . . . 1·40 55

480 Hemispheres **481** "Janos Nagy" (self-portrait)

1969. World Trade Unions Federations Congress, Budapest.
2485 **480** 2 fo. blue and brown . . 45 10

1969. 50th Death Anniv of Janos Nagy (painter).
2486 **481** 5 fo. multicoloured . . . 1·25 70

482 "Flight to the Moon" (after Jules Verne)

1969. Air. 1st Man on the Moon. Mult.
2487 40 fi. Type **482** 10 10
2488 60 fi. Tsiolkovsky's "space station" 10 10
2489 1 fo. "Luna 1" 20 10
2490 1 fo. 50 "Ranger 7" 35 10
2491 2 fo. "Luna 9" 45 10
2492 2 fo. 50 "Apollo 8" 50 10
2493 3 fo. "Soyuz 4" and "5" . . . 90 35
2494 4 fo. "Apollo 10" . . . . . . 1·40 60

483 "St John the Evangelist" (Van Dyck)

1969. Dutch Paintings in Hungarian Museums. Multicoloured.
2495 40 fi. Type **483** 10 10
2496 60 fi. "Peasants" (P. de Molyn) 10 10
2497 1 fo. "Boy lighting Pipe" (H. Terbruggen) 25 10
2498 2 fo. "The Musicians" (detail, Jan Steen) 40 10
2499 3 fo. "Woman reading Letter" (P. de Hooch) 70 10
2500 4 fo. "The Fiddler" (Dirk Hals) . . . . 1·10 45
2501 5 fo. "J. Asselyn" (Frans Hals) 1·50 65

484 Kiskunfelegyhaza Pigeon

1969. International Pigeon Exn, Budapest.
2503 **484** 1 fo. multicoloured . . . 30 10

485 Daimler (1886)

1970. Air. Old Motor Cars. Multicoloured.
2504 40 fi. Type **485** 20 10
2505 60 fi. Peugeot (1894) 25 10
2506 1 fo. Benz (1901) 30 10
2507 1 fo. 50 Cudell (1902) 40 10
2508 2 fo. Rolls-Royce (1908) . . . 60 35
2509 2 fo. 50 Ford "T" (1908) . . . 80 50
2510 3 fo. Vermorel (1912) . . . . 1·10 60
2511 4 fo. Csonka (1912) . . . . . 1·40 75

486 View of Budapest **487** "Soyuz 6, 7, 8"

1970. Budapest 71 Stamp Exn and Cent of Hungarian Stamps (1st series). Multicoloured. Background colours given.
2512 **486** 2 fo. + 1 fo. brown . . . 40 55
2513 – 2 fo. + 1 fo. lilac 40 55
2514 – 2 fo. + 1 fo. blue 40 55
DESIGNS: Nos. 2513/4 show different views of Budapest, in style as Type **486**.
See also Nos. 2572/5 and 2604/7.

1970. Air. Space Exploration. Multicoloured.
2515 3 fo. (× 4) Type **487** . . . . 2·50 3·00
2516 3 fo. (× 4) Astronauts on Moon (Apollo 12) . . . . . 2·50 3·00
Nos. 2515/6 were only available each in small sheets of four, and are priced thus.

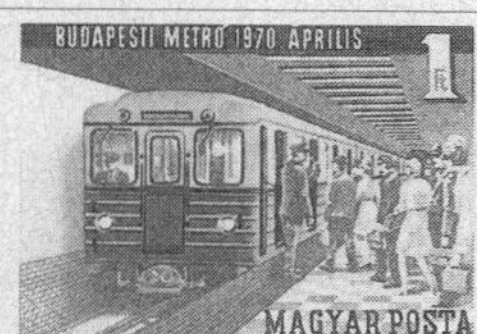

488 Underground Train at Station

1970. Opening of Budapest Underground Railway.
2517 **488** 1 fo. blue, turquoise & blk 40 10

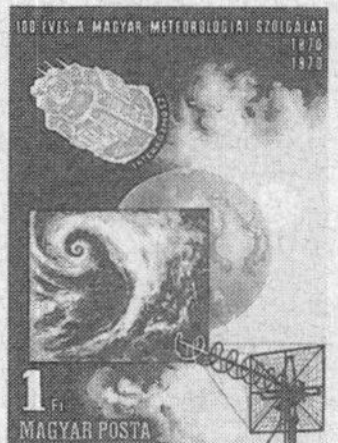
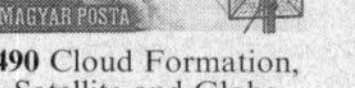

490 Cloud Formation, Satellite and Globe

491 Lenin

1970. Cent of Hungarian Meteorological Service.
2519 **490** 1 fo. multicoloured . . . 30 10

1970. Birth Centenary of Lenin. Mult.
2520 1 fo. Lenin Statue, Budapest . 10 10
2521 2 fo. Type **491** 35 10

492 Lehar and Music

1970. Birth Cent of Franz Lehar (composer).
2522 **492** 2 fo. multicoloured . . . 60 20

493 Fujiyama and Hungarian Pavilion

1970. Air. Expo 70. Multicoloured.
2523 2 fo. Type **493** 70 70
2524 3 fo. Tower of the Sun and Peace Bell . . . . 1·00 1·00

494 "Samson and Delilah" (M. Rocca)

1970. Paintings in National Gallery, Budapest (7th series). Multicoloured.
2525 40 fi. Type **494** 10 10
2526 60 fi. "Joseph's Dream" (G. B. Langetti) 15 10
2527 1 fo. "Clio" (P. Mignard) . . . 20 10
2528 1 fo. 50 "Venus and Satyr" (S. Ricci) (horiz.) 25 10
2529 2 fo. 50 "Andromeda" (F. Furini) 50 10
2530 4 fo. "Venus, Adonis and Cupid" (L. Giordano) . . . 80 45
2531 5 fo. "Allegory" (woman) (C. Giaquinto) . . . . . . 1·25 65

496 Beethoven (from statue at Martonvasar)

497 Foundryman

1970. Birth Bicentenary of Beethoven.
2534 **496** 1 fo. green, lilac & yell . . 1·00 25

1970. Bicent of Diosgyor Foundry, Miskolc.
2535 **497** 1 fo. multicoloured . . . 15 10

498 St. Stephen

500 Illuminated Initial

499 Rowing Four

1970. 1,000th Birth Anniv of St. Stephen (King Stephen I of Hungary).
2536 **498** 3 fo. multicoloured . . . 40 15

1970. 17th European Women's Rowing Championships, Lake Tata.
2537 **499** 1 fo. multicoloured . . . 30 10

1970. Stamp Day. Paintings and Illuminated Initials from Codices of King Matthias.
2538 1 fo. + 50 fi. Type **500** 75 85
2539 1 fo. + 50 fi. "N" and flowers . 75 85
2540 1 fo. + 50 fi. "O" and ornamentation 75 85
2541 1 fo. + 50 fi. "King Matthias" 75 85

502 "Bread" (sculpture by I. Szabo) and F.A.O. Emblem

1970. 7th F.A.O. European Regional Conference, Budapest.
2544 **502** 1 fo. multicoloured . . . 35 10

503 Boxing

1970. 75th Anniv of Hungarian Olympic Committee. Multicoloured.
2545 40 fi. Type **503** 10 10
2546 60 fi. Canoeing 10 10
2547 1 fo. Fencing 10 10
2548 1 fo. 50 Water-polo 20 10
2549 2 fo. Gymnastics 40 10
2550 2 fo. 50 Throwing the Hammer 45 10
2551 3 fo. Wrestling 50 15
2552 5 fo. Swimming . . . . 1·10 35

504 Family and "Flame of Knowledge"

1970. 5th Education Congress, Budapest.
2553 **504** 1 fo. blue, green & orge . 35 10

505 Chalice of Benedek Suky, c. 1400

1970. Goldsmiths' Craft. Treasures from Budapest National Museum and Esztergom Treasury. Multicoloured.
2554 40 fi. Type **505** 10 10
2555 60 fi. Altar-cruet, c. 1500 . . . 10 10
2556 1 fo. "Nadasdy" goblet, 16th-century 20 10
2557 1 fo. 50 Coconut goblet with gold case, c. 1600 . . . . . 25 10
2558 2 fo. Silver tankard of M. Toldalaghy, c. 1623 . . . . 40 10
2559 2 fo. 50 Communion-cup of G.I. Rakoczi, c. 1670 . . . 60 10
2560 3 fo. Tankard, c. 1690 . . . . 80 40
2561 4 fo. "Bell-flower" cup, c. 1710 1·25 70

506 "The Virgin and Child" ("Giampietrino", G. Pedrini)

1970. Paintings. Religious Art from Christian Museum, Esztergom. Multicoloured.
2562 40 fi. Type **506** 10 10
2563 60 fi. "Love" (G. Lazzarini) . . 10 10
2564 1 fo. "Legend of St. Catherine of Alexandria" ("Master of Bat") 15 10
2565 1 fo. 50 "Adoration of the Shepherds" (F. Fontebasso) (horiz.) 30 10
2566 2 fo. 50 "Adoration of the Magi" ("Master of Aranyosmarot") 60 10
2567 4 fo. "Temptation of St. Anthony the Hermit" (J. de Cock) . . . . 1·25 45
2568 5 fo. "St. Sebastian" (Palmezzano) . . . . 1·40 60

507 Mauthausen Camp Memorial (A. Makrisz)

1970. 25th Anniv of Liberation of Concentration Camps.
2570 **507** 1 fo. brown and blue . . 25 10

509 Budapest, 1470

1971. "Budapest 71" Stamp Exn, and Cent of Hungarian Stamp (2nd series). "Budapest Through the Ages".
2572 **509** 2 fo. + 1 fo. blk & yell . 70 80
2573 – 2 fo. + 1 fo. blk & mve . 70 80
2574 – 2 fo. + 1 fo. blk & grn . 70 80
2575 – 2 fo. + 1 fo. blk & orge . 70 80
DESIGNS: Budapest in: No. 2573, 1600; No. 2574, 1638; No. 2575, 1770.

511 "The Marseillaise" (sculpture by Rude)

512 Bela Bartok

1971. Centenary of Paris Commune.
2578 **511** 3 fo. brown & green . . . 75 35

1971. 90th Birth Anniv of Bela Bartok (composer).
2579 **512** 1 fo. black, grey & red . . 90 15

513 Gyor in 1594

1971. 700th Anniv of Gyor.
2580 **513** 2 fo. multicoloured . . . 30 10

1971. Birth Cent of Andras L. Achim (peasant leader). Portrait in similar style to T **512.**
2582 1 fo. black, grey & green . . . 35 10

516 Hunting European Bison

1971. World Hunting Exhibition, Budapest. Multicoloured.
2583 40 fi. Type **516** 15 10
2584 60 fi. Hunting wild boar . . . 15 10
2585 80 fi. Deer-stalking 30 15
2586 1 fo. Falconry . . . . 1·50 20
2587 1 fo. 20 Stag-hunting 65 25
2588 2 fo. Great Bustards with young . . . . 2·00 45
2589 3 fo. Netting fish . . . . . . 1·25 50
2590 4 fo. Angling . . . . 1·75 65

518 Emblem on Flower

1971. 25th Anniv of Hungarian Young Pioneers.
2593 **518** 1 fo. multicoloured . . . 60 10

519 F.I.R. Emblem

1971. 20th Anniv of International Federation of Resistance Fighters.
2594 **519** 1 fo. multicoloured . . . 20 10

520 "Walking in the Garden" (Toyokuni School)

1971. Japanese Colour Prints from Ferenc Hopp Collection, Budapest. Multicoloured.

2595	40 fi. Type **520**	10	10
2596	60 fi. "Geisha in boat" (Yeishi)	30	10
2597	1 fo. "Woman with scroll-painting" (Yeishi)	20	10
2598	1 fo. 50 "Oirans" (Kiyonaga)	35	10
2599	2 fo. "Awabi Fishers" (Utamaro)	45	10
2600	2 fo. 50 "Scated Oiran" (Harunobu)	60	10
2601	3 fo. "Peasant Girl carrying Faggots" (Hokusai)	80	45
2602	4 fo. "Women and Girls Walking" (Yeishi)	1·25	70

521 Locomotive "Bets" and Route Map (1846)

1971. 125th Anniv of Hungarian Railways.

No.	Type	Description		
2603	**521**	1 fo. multicoloured	55	10

522 Hungarian Newspaper Stamp of 1871

1971. "Budapest 71" Stamp Exn and Cent of Hungarian Stamp (3rd series). Multicoloured.

2604	2 fo. + 1 fo. Type **522**	70	85
2605	2 fo. + 1 fo. 45 f. "Petofi" stamp of 1919	70	85
2606	2 fo. + 1 fo. 400 k. "Harvesters" stamp of 1920	70	85
2607	2 fo. + 1 fo. 16 f. + 16 f. "Art" stamp of 1940	70	85

523 Griffin with Inking Balls

1971. Cent of State Printing Office, Budapest.

No.	Type	Description		
2609	**523**	1 fo. multicoloured	55	55

524 O.I.J. Emblem and Page of "Magyar Sajto"

1971. 25th Anniv of Int Organisation of Journalists.

No.	Type	Description		
2610	**524**	1 fo. gold and blue	15	10

526 J. Winterl (founder) and "Waldsteinia geoides"

1971. Bicentenary of Botanical Gardens, Budapest. Multicoloured.

2612	40 fi. Type **526**	10	10
2613	60 fi. "Bromeliaceae"	15	10
2614	80 fi. "Titanopsis calcarea"	20	10
2615	1 fo. "Vinca herbacea"	25	10
2616	1 fo. 20 "Gymnocalycium mihanovichii"	25	10
2617	2 fo. "Nymphaea gigantea"	50	10
2618	3 fo. "Iris arenaria"	80	20
2619	5 fo. "Paeonia banatica"	1·40	45

527 Horse-racing

1971. Equestrian Sport. Multicoloured.

2620	40 fi. Type **527**	15	10
2621	60 fi. Trotting	20	10
2622	80 fi. Cross-country riding	20	10
2623	1 fo. Show-jumping	25	10
2624	1 fo. 20 Start of race	30	10
2625	2 fo. Polo	55	10
2626	3 fo. Steeplechasing	85	40
2627	5 fo. Dressage	1·40	70

528 "Execution of Koppany"

529 Racial Equality Year Emblem

1971. Miniatures from the "Illuminated Chronicle" of King Lajos I of Hungary. Multicoloured.

2628	40 fi. Type **528**	15	10
2629	60 fi. "The Pursuit of King Peter"	15	10
2630	1 fo. "Bazarad's Victory over King Karoly I"	20	10
2631	1 fo. 50 "The Strife between King Salamon and Prince Geza"	35	10
2632	2 fo. 50 "The Founding of Obuda Monastery by King Stephen and Queen Gisela"	55	10
2633	4 fo. "Reconciliation of King Kalman and his brother, Almos"	75	45
2634	5 fo. "King Ladislas I supervising the construction of Nagyvarad Church"	1·40	65

1971. Racial Equality Year.

No.	Type	Description		
2636	**529**	1 fo. multicoloured	15	10

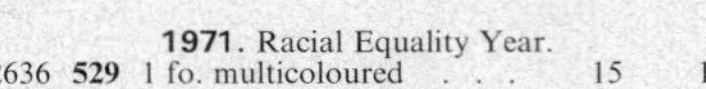

530 Ice Hockey

1971. Winter Olympic Games, Sapporo, Japan (1972). Multicoloured.

2637	40 fi. Type **530**	10	10
2638	60 fi. Downhill skiing	15	10
2639	80 fi. Figure skating (female)	15	10
2640	1 fo. Ski jumping	20	10
2641	1 fo. 20 Cross-country skiing	30	10
2642	2 fo. Figure skating (male)	40	10
2643	3 fo. Bobsleighing	50	20
2644	4 fo. Rifle-shooting (Biathlon)	85	45

532 Class 303, 1950

1972. Railway Steam Locomotives. Mult.

2647	40 fi. Type **532**	30	10
2648	60 fi. Class P6, 1902, Prussia	30	10
2649	80 fi. Class 380, 1894, Italy	40	15
2650	1 fo. Class P36, 1950, Russia	60	15
2651	1 fo. 20 Heisler locomotive, Japan	70	30
2652	2 fo. Scottish Caledonian tank locomotive, 1837	90	35
2653	4 fo. Class 166, 1882, Austria	1·25	70
2654	5 fo. Locomotive "Continent", 1854	1·60	85

533 "J. Pannonius" (A. Mantegna)

535 Doorway of Csempeszkopacs Church

534 "Mariner 9"

1972. 500th Death Anniv of Janus Pannonius (poet).

No.	Type	Description		
2655	**533**	1 fo. multicoloured	15	10

1972. Exploration of Mars. Multicoloured.

2656	2 fo. Type **534**	50	50
2657	2 fo. "Mars 2 and 3"	50	50

1972. Protection of Monuments.

No.	Type	Description		
2658	**535**	3 fo. green	1·00	35

536 Hungarian Greyhound

1972. Dogs. Multicoloured.

2659	40 fi. Type **536**	20	10
2660	60 fi. Afghan hound (head)	25	10
2661	80 fi. Irish wolfhound	25	10
2662	1 fo. 20 Borzoi (head)	30	10
2663	2 fo. Greyhound	65	20
2664	4 fo. Whippet (head)	1·50	30
2665	6 fo. Afghan hound	2·00	75

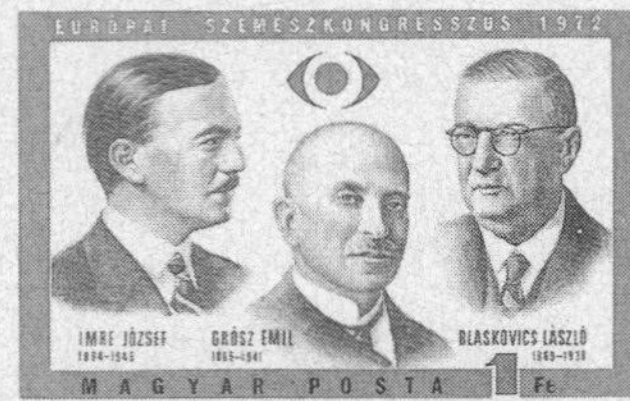

537 J. Imre, E. Grosz and L. Blaskovics

1972. 1st. European Oculists' Congress, Budapest. Famous Oculists.

No.	Type	Description		
2666	**537**	1 fo. brown and red	85	10
2667	–	2 fo. brown and blue	1·25	50

DESIGN: 2 fo. A. Gullstrand, V. P. Filatov and J. Gonin.

538 Footballers and Flag of Hungary

1972. Air. European Football Championships. Footballers and Flags of participating countries. Multicoloured.

2668	40 fi. Type **538**	10	10
2669	60 fi. Rumania	15	10
2670	80 fi. West Germany	20	10
2671	1 fo. England	25	10
2672	1 fo. 20 Yugoslavia	35	35
2673	2 fo. Russia	80	40
2674	4 fo. Italy	1·25	65
2675	5 fo. Belgium	1·75	85

539 "V. Miskolcz" postmark, 1818–43

1972. Stamp Day.

No.	Type	Description		
2676	**539**	2 fo. + 1 fo. black & bl	70	85
2677	–	2 fo. + 1 fo. blk & yell	70	85
2678	–	2 fo. + 1 fo. blk & grn	70	85
2679	–	2 fo. + 1 fo. mult	70	85

DESIGNS: No. 2677, "Szegedin" postmark, 1827–48; No. 2678, "Esztergom" postmark, 1848–51; No. 2679, "Budapest 71" stamp cent., cancellation, 1971.

540 Girl reading Book

541 Roses

1972. International Book Year.

No.	Type	Description		
2681	**540**	1 fo. multicoloured	40	10

1972. National Rose Exhibition.

No.	Type	Description		
2682	**541**	1 fo. multicoloured	45	10

543 G. Dimitrov

545 Gy. Dozsa

1972. 90th Birth Anniv of Georgi Dimitrov (Bulgarian leader).

No.	Type	Description		
2684	**543**	3 fo. multicoloured	40	10

1972. 500th Birth Anniv of Gyorgy Dozsa (revolutionary).

No.	Type	Description		
2686	**545**	1 fo. multicoloured	40	10

546 Football

1972. Olympic Games, Munich. Multicoloured.

2687	40 fi. Type **546**	10	10
2688	60 fi. Water-polo	10	10
2689	80 fi. Javelin-throwing	15	10
2690	1 fo. Kayak-canoeing	20	10
2691	1 fo. 20 Boxing	25	10
2692	2 fo. Gymnastics	45	10
2693	3 fo. + 1 fo. Wrestling	65	25
2694	5 fo. Fencing	1·25	65

547 Prince Geza indicating Site of Szekesfehervar

1972. Millenary of Szekesfehervar and 750th Anniv of "Aranybulla" (legislative document). Multicoloured.

2696 40 fi. Type **547** 10 10
2697 60 fi. King Stephen and shield . 10 10
2698 80 fi. Soldiers and cavalry . . 15 10
2699 1 fo. 20 King Stephen drawing up legislation 30 10
2700 2 fo. Mason sculpting column . 40 10
2701 4 fo. Merchant displaying wares to King Stephen . . . . . 1·00 15
2702 6 fo. Views of Szekesfehervar and Palace . . . . 1·40 55

548 Parliament Building, Budapest

1972. Constitution Day. Multicoloured.

2704 5 fo. Type **548** 80 10
2705 6 fo. Parliament in session . . 1·10 40

549 Eger and "Bulls Blood"

1972. World Wines Competition, Budapest Multicoloured.

2706 1 fo. Type **549** 25 10
2707 2 fo. Tokay and "Tokay Aszu" . . . . 1·00 40

550 Ear of Wheat and Emblems on Open Book

1972. 175th Anniv of Georgikon Agricultural Academy, Keszthely.

2708 **550** 1 fo. multicoloured . . . 15 10

551 "Rothschild" Vase

553 Commemorative Emblem

552 Class M62 Diesel Train and U.I.C. Emblem

1972. Herendi Porcelain. Multicoloured.

2709 40 fi. Type **551** 15 10
2710 60 fi. "Poisson" bonboniere . . 15 10
2711 80 fi. "Victoria" vase 20 10
2712 1 fo. "Miramare" dish 20 10
2713 1 fo. 20 "Godollo" pot 25 10
2714 2 fo. "Empire" tea-set 40 10
2715 4 fo. "Apponyi" dish 80 45
2716 5 fo. "Baroque" vase . . . . 1·40 70

The 60 fi., 1 fo., 20, and 4 fo. are size 34 × 36 mm.

1972. 50th Anniv of Int Railway Union.

2717 **552** 1 fo. red 50 15

1972. 25th Anniv of National Economy Plan.

2718 **553** 1 fo. yell, sepia & brn . . 15 10

554 River Steamer and Old Obuda

1972. Centenary of Unification of Buda, Obuda and Pest as Budapest.

2719 **554** 1 fo. purple and blue . . 30 10
2720 – 1 fo. blue and purple . . 45 10
2721 – 2 fo. green and brown . . 30 10
2722 – 2 fo. brown and green . . 50 10
2723 – 3 fo. brown and green . . 40 15
2724 – 3 fo. green and brown . . 75 15

DESIGNS: No. 2720, River hydrofoil and modern Obuda; 2721, Buda, 1872; 2722, Budapest, 1972; 2723, Pest, 1872; 2724, Parliament Buildings, Budapest.

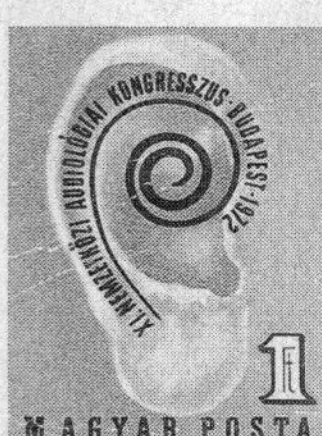

555 Congress Emblem within Ear

558 Miklos Radnoti (poet)

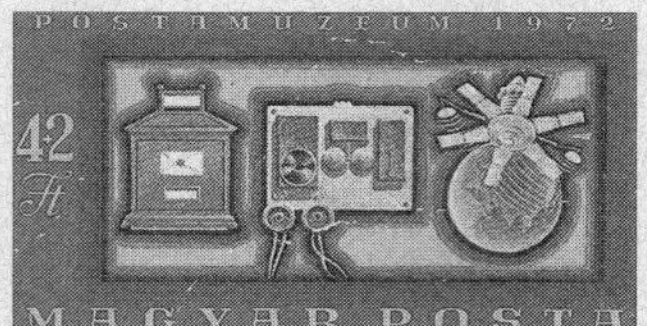

557 Postbox, Bell Telephone and Satellite "Molnya"

1972. Int. Audiological Congress, Budapest.

2725 **555** 1 fo. multicoloured . . . 35 10

1972. Reopening of Postal and Philatelic Museums, Budapest. Multicoloured.

2727 4 fo. + 2 fo. Type **557** . . . . 90 1·10
2728 4 fo. + 2 fo. Globe, posthorn and stamps . . . . 90 1·10

1972. Radnoti Commemoration.

2729 **558** 1 fo. multicoloured . . . 10 10

559 F. Martos

560 "The Muses" (J. Rippl-Ronai)

1972. 75th Birth Anniv of Flora Martos (patriot).

2730 **559** 1 fo. multicoloured . . . 10 10

1972. Stained Glass Windows. Multicoloured.

2731 40 fi. Type **560** 15 10
2732 60 fi. "16th-century Scribe" (F. Sebestenyl) 15 10
2733 1 fo. "Exodus to Egypt" (K. Lotz and B. Szekely) 20 10
2734 1 fo. 50 "Prince Arpad's Messenger" (J. Percz) . . . 35 10
2735 2 fo. 50 "The Nativity" (L. Sztehlo) 55 10
2736 4 fo. "Prince Arpad and Leaders" (K. Kernstock) . . 1·00 40
2737 5 fo. "King Matthias reprimands the Rich Aristocrats" (J. Haranghy) . . . . . . 1·50 65

561 "Textiles"

1972. Opening of Textiles Technical Museum, Budapest.

2738 **561** 1 fo. multicoloured . . . 45 10

562 Main Square, Szarvas

563 S. Petofi

1972. Views.

2739 **562** 40 fi. brown & orange . . 15 10
2739a – 40 fi. black and green . . 10 10
2740 – 1 fo. blue & light blue . . 20 10
2741 – 1 fo. brown & yellow . . 15 10
2742 – 3 fo. green and blue . . 50 10
2743 – 4 fo. red and orange . . 80 10
2743a – 4 fo. brown and pink . . 70 10
2744 – 5 fo. blue and cobalt . . 1·00 10
2745 – 6 fo. brown and red . . 1·25 10
2746 – 7 fo. violet and lilac . . 85 10
2747 – 8 fo. dp green & grn . . 1·25 10
2748 – 10 fo. brown & yellow . . 1·50 10
2749 – 20 fo. multicoloured . . 3·75 60
2750 – 50 fo. multicoloured . . 7·00 1·50

DESIGNS: 21 × 18 mm: 40 fi. (No. 2739a) Rotunda (public health centre), Vasvar; 1 fo. (No. 2740) Salgotarjan; 1 fo. (No. 2741) Nyirbator. 28 × 22 mm: 3 fo. Tokay; 4 fo. (No. 2743) Esztergom; 4 fo. (No. 2743a) Szentendre; 5 fo. Szolnok; 6 fo. Dunaujvaros; 7 fo. Kaposvar; 8 fo. Vac; 10 fo. Kiskunfelegyhaza; 20 fo. Veszprem; 50 ra. Pecs.

1972. 150th Birth Anniv of Sandor Petofi (poet and patriot).

2762 – 1 fo. red 10 10
2763 **563** 2 fo. lilac 15 10
2764 – 3 fo. green 30 15

DESIGNS: 1 fo. Petofi making speech in Cafe Pilvax; 3 fo. Petofi on horseback during War of Independence, 1848–49.

564 Arms of U.S.S.R.

1972. 50th Anniv of U.S.S.R.

2765 **564** 1 fo. multicoloured . . . 10 10

565 Code Map and Crow Symbol

1973. Introduction of Postal Codes.

2766 **565** 1 fo. black and red . . . 15 10

1973. As Nos. 1912, 1915/16 and 1918 but smaller.

2767 2 fo. blue 40 25
2768 3 fo. blue 60 35
2769 4 fo. green 80 50
2770 6 fo. ochre . . . . 1·25 85

SIZES: Nos. 2767/8 and 2770, 22 × 19 mm. No. 2769 19 × 22 mm.

567 I. Madach

568 Carnival Mask

1973. 150th Birth Anniv of Imre Madach (writer).

2772 **567** 1 fo. multicoloured . . . 35 10

1973. Busho-Walking Ceremony, Mohacs. Carnival Masks.

2773 **568** 40 fi. multicoloured . . . 10 10
2774 – 60 fi. multicoloured . . . 10 10
2775 – 80 fi. multicoloured . . . 15 10
2776 – 1 fo. 20 multicoloured . . 25 10
2777 – 2 fo. multicoloured . . . 40 10
2778 – 4 fo. multicoloured . . . 1·00 15
2779 – 6 fo. multicoloured . . . 1·75 65

569 Copernicus

571 Show-jumping (Pentathlon) and Gold Medal

1973. 500th Birth Anniv of Copernicus.

2780 **569** 3 fo. blue . . . . 1·10 40

1973. Hungarian Medal Winners, Olympic Games, Munich. Multicoloured.

2782 40 fi. Type **571** 15 10
2783 60 fi. Weightlifting (Gold) . . 15 10
2784 1 fo. Canoeing (Silver) 25 10
2785 1 fo. 20 Swimming (Silver) . . 30 10
2786 1 fo. 80 Boxing (Gold) 35 10
2787 4 fo. Wrestling (Gold) 75 60
2788 6 fo. Fencing (Gold) . . . . . 1·10 80

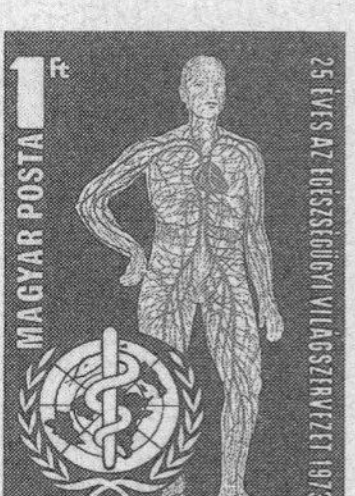

572 Biological Man

573 Winter Wrens

1973. 25th Anniv of W.H.O.

2790 **572** 1 fo. brown and green . . 20 10

1973. Air. Hungarian Birds. Multicoloured.

2791 40 fi. Type **573** 35 10
2792 60 fi. Rock Thrush 40 10
2793 80 fi. European Robins 45 10
2794 1 fo. Firecrests 55 15
2795 1 fo. 20 Linnets 80 15
2796 2 fo. Blue Tits 85 25
2797 4 fo. Bluethroat . . . . . . 1·40 40
2798 5 fo. Grey Wagtails . . . . . 1·90 45

574 Soldier and Weapons

1973. Military Stamp Collectors' Exhibition, Budapest.

2799 **574** 3 fo. multicoloured . . . 40 20

575 "Budapest 61" 1 fo. Stamp

1973. "IBRA 73" Stamp Exn, Munich, and "POLSKA '73", Poznan. Repoductions of Hungary Exhibition stamps. Multicoloured.

2800 40 fi. Type **575** 10 10
2801 60 fi. "Budapest 61" 1 fo. 70 stamp 10 10
2802 80 fi. "Budapest 61" 2 fo. 60 stamp 15 10
2803 1 fo. "Budapest 61" 3 fo. stamp 30 10
2804 1 fo. 20 "Budapest 71" 2 fo. stamp 20 10
2805 2 fo. "Budapest 71" 2 fo. stamp 30 10
2806 4 fo. "Budapest 71" 2 fo. stamp 95 35
2807 5 fo. "Budapest 71" 2 fo. stamp . . . . 1·25 40

Nos. 2804/7 depict stamps from miniature sheets.

576 Setting Type and Preparing Ink

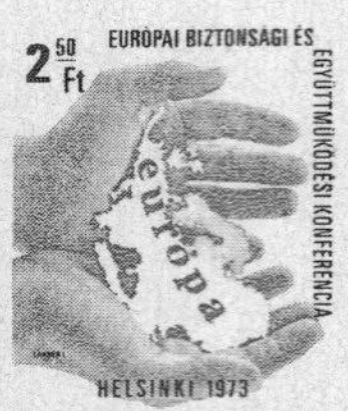

578 "Europa" Poster

577 "Storm over Hortobagy Puszta"

1973. 500th Anniv of Bookprinting in Hungary.

2809 **576** 1 fo. black and gold . . . 10 10
2810 – 3 fo. black and gold . . . 65 10

DESIGN: 3 fo. Printer operating press.

1973. Paintings by Csontvary Kosztka. Multicoloured.

2811 40 fi. Type **577** 10 10
2812 60 fi. "Mary's Well, Nazareth" 15 10
2813 1 fo. "Carriage drive by Moonlight" 25 10
2814 1 fo. 50 "Pilgrimage to the Lebanese Cedars" 30 10
2815 2 fo. 50 "The Lone Cedar" . . 40 10
2816 4 fo. "Waterfall at Jajce" . . . 90 45
2817 5 fo. "Ruins of Greek Theatre at Taormina" . . . . . . 1·40 80

Nos. 2813/14 are vert.

1973. European Security and Co-operation Conference, Helsinki.

2819 **578** 2 fo. 50 brown & blk . . 2·50 2·50

579 "Rosa gallica"

580 "Let's be friends...!"

1973. Wild Flowers. Multicoloured.

2820 40 fi. Type **579** 15 10
2821 60 fi. "Cyclamen europaeum" . 20 10
2822 80 fi. "Pulmonaria mollissima" 25 10
2823 1 fo. 20 "Bellis perennis" . . 35 10
2824 2 fo. "Adonis vernalis" . . . 50 10
2825 4 fo. "Viola cyanea" 85 40
2826 6 fo. "Papaver rhoeas" . . . . 1·10 70

1973. Road Safety.

2827 **580** 40 fi. green and red . . . 15 10
2828 – 60 fi. violet & orange . . 20 10
2829 – 1 fo. blue and red . . . 45 10

DESIGNS: 60 fi. "Not even a glass!" (hand reaching for tumbler); 1 fo. "Cyclist - use a lamp" (car running down cyclist).

581 Silver "Eagle" Disc

584 Csokonai's Statue, Debrecen

583 "The Three Kings" (Master of the High Altar, Szmrecsany)

1973. Jewelled Treasures, National Museum. Multicoloured.

2830 2 fo. + 50 fi. Type **581** . . . . 90 1·00
2831 2 fo. + 50 fi. Serpent's head ring . . . . 90 1·00
2832 2 fo. + 50 fi. "Loving couple" buckle . . . . 90 1·00
2833 2 fo. + 50 fi. Silver "floral" buckle . . . . 90 1·00

1973. Esztergom Millennium. "Old Master" Paintings in the Christian Museum. Mult.

2836 40 fi. Type **583** 10 10
2837 60 fi. "Angels making Music" (Master "B.E.") 10 10
2838 1 fo. "The Adoration of the Magi" (anon.) 15 10
2839 1 fo. 50 "The Annunciation" (Szmrecsany Master) 30 10
2840 2 fo. 50 "Angels making Music" (different Master "B.E.") 45 10
2841 4 fo. "The Visitation of Mary and Elizabeth" (Szmrecsany Master) 70 40
2842 5 fo. "The Legend of St. Catharine of Alexandria" (Master Bati) . . . . . . 1·25 70

1973. Birth Bicentenary of M. Csokonai Vitez (poet).

2844 **584** 2 fo. multicoloured . . . 55 10

585 J. Marti

586 B. Pesti

1973. 120th Birth Anniv of Jose Marti (Cuban patriot).

2845 **585** 1 fo. brown, red & blue . 10 10

1973. 30th Death Anniv of Barnabas Pesti (patriot).

2846 **586** 1 fo. lt brn, brn & bl . . . 10 10

588 Kayak-canoeing

1973. World Aquatic Sports Championships, Belgrade and Tampere. Multicoloured.

2855 40 fi. Type **588** 15 10
2856 60 fi. Water polo 15 10
2857 80 fi. Men's solo kayak 20 10
2858 1 fo. 20 Swimming 30 10
2859 2 fo. Men's kayak fours . . . 45 10
2860 4 fo. Men's solo canoe 75 50
2861 6 fo. Men's double canoe . . . 1·25 70

590 Lenin

1974. 50th Death Anniv of Lenin.

2863 **590** 2 fo. brown, blue & gold . 60 10

591 J. Boczor, I. Bekes and T. Elek

1974. Hungarian Heroes of the French Resistance.

2864 **591** 3 fo. multicoloured . . . 60 10

592 "Comecon" Building, Moscow, and Flags

1974. 25th Anniv of Council for Mutual Economic Aid.

2865 **592** 1 fo. multicoloured . . . 20 10

593 Savings Bank Emblem, Note and Coins

595 Pres. Salvador Allende

594 "Mariner 4" on course for Mars

1974. 25th Anniv of National Savings Bank.

2866 **593** 1 fo. multicoloured . . . 10 10

1974. Mars Research Projects. Multicoloured.

2867 40 fi. Type **594** (postage) . . . 10 10
2868 60 fi. "Mars 2" approaching Mars 15 10
2869 80 fi. "Mariner 4" space probe 20 10
2870 1 fo. Mt. Palomar telescope and Mars photo 35 10
2871 1 fo. 20 "Mars 3" on planet's surface 45 10
2872 5 fo. "Mariner 9" approaching Mars and satellites . . . . 1·25 15
2873 6 fo. G. Schiaparelli and Martian "canals" map (air) . 1·50 75

1974. Pres. Allende of Chile Commemoration.

2875 **595** 1 fo. multicoloured . . . 20 10

596 "Mona Lisa" (Leonardo da Vinci)

1974. Exhibition of "Mona Lisa" in Japan.

2876 **596** 4 fo. multicoloured . . . 14·00 14·00

598 Dove with Letter

1974. Centenary of U.P.U. Multicoloured.

2878 40 fi. Type **598** 10 10
2879 60 fi. Mail coach 10 10
2880 80 fi. Early mail van and post-box 15 10
2881 1 fo. 20 Balloon post 20 10
2882 2 fo. Diesel mail train 80 10
2883 4 fo. Post-bus . . . . 1·00 40
2884 6 fo. Tupolev Tu-154 mail plane . . . . 1·25 70

599 Swiss $2\frac{1}{2}$ r. "Basle Dove" Stamp of 1845

1974. "Internaba 1974" Stamp Exn, Basle.

2886 **599** 3 fo. multicoloured . . . 1·25 1·50

600 13th-century miniature from King Alfonso X's "Book of Chess, Dice and Tablings" and Pawn

1974. 50th Anniv of International Chess Federation and 21st Chess Olympiad, Nice.

2887 **600** 40 fi. black, green & bl . . 30 10
2888 – 60 fi. black, brn & lilac . . 50 10
2889 – 80 fi. black, yell & grn . . 75 10
2890 – 1 fo. 20 black, yellow and lilac 85 15
2891 – 2 fo. black, stone & blue . 1·25 15
2892 – 4 fo. black, yell & pink . . 1·75 65
2893 – 6 fo. black, brn & grn . . 1·90 85

DESIGNS: 60 fi. 15th-century woodcut from "The Game and Playe of Chesse" by William Caxton and knight; 80 fi. 15th-century illustration from Italian chess book and bishop; 1 fo. 20, "The Chess Players" (17th-century engraving by Jacob van der Heyden) and rock; 2 fo. Kempelen's chess playing machine (1769) and king; 4 fo. Geza Maroczy (Hungarian master) and queen; 6 fo. View of Nice and tournament emblem.

602 Congress Emblem

1974. 4th International Economists' Congress, Budapest.

2895 **602** 2 fo. black, blue & silver . 60 10

603 "Woman Bathing" (K Lotz)

1974. Nudes, Paintings. Multicoloured.

2896 40 fi. Type **603** 15 10
2897 60 fi. "Awakening" (K. Brocky) 15 10
2898 1 fo. "Venus and Cupid" (K. Brocky) (horiz) 25 10
2899 1 f. 50 "After Bathing" (K. Lotz) 40 10
2900 2 f. 50 "Honi soit qui mal y pense" (reclining nude) (I. Csok) (horiz) 60 35
2901 4 fo. "After Bathing" (B. Szekely) . . . . 1·10 50
2902 5 fo. "Devotion" (E. Korb) . . 1·40 65

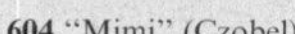

604 "Mimi" (Czobel) **605** "Inter-sputnik" Satellite Tracking Radar

1974. 91st Birth Anniv of Bela Czobel (painter).
2904 **604** 1 fo. multicoloured . . . 90 15

1974. 25th Anniv of Technical and Scientific Co-operation between Hungary and Soviet Union.
2905 **605** 1 fo. violet and blue . . . 15 10
2906 – 3 fo. mauve & green . . . 75 10
DESIGN—HORIZ: 3 fo. Power installations.

606 Neruda **607** Swedish 3 s. Stamp, 1855, and "Swedish Lion"

1974. Pablo Neruda (Chilean poet) Commemoration.
2907 **606** 1 fo. brown, deep brown and blue 15 10

1974. "Stockholmia 74" International Stamp Exhibition.
2908 **607** 3 fo. green blue and gold . 1·10 1·40

608 Tanks, and Infantry

1974. Military Day.
2909 **608** 1 fo. black, red and gold (postage) 30 10
2910 – 2 fo. blk, grn & gold (air) . 50 10
2911 – 3 fo. black, bl & gold . . 75 15
DESIGNS—VERT: 2 fo. Guided missile and radar. HORIZ: 3 fo. Parachutist, helicopter and jet fighter.

609 J. A. Segner and Moon

1974. 270th Birth Anniv of Janos Segner (scientist).
2912 **609** 3 fo. multicoloured . . . 75 15

610 Hansa Brandenburg C-1 Biplane, 1918

1974. Air. "Aerofila 1974" International Airmail Exhibition, Budapest. Multicoloured.
2913 2 fo. + 1 fo. Type **610** . . . 1·25 1·10
2914 2 fo. + 1 fo. Airship "Graf Zeppelin" . . . . 1·25 1·10
2915 2 fo. + 1 fo. Hot air balloon . . 1·25 1·10
2916 2 fo. + 1 fo. Mil Mi-1 helicopter . . . . 1·25 1·10

611 Purple Tiger Moth

1974. Butterflies and Moths. Multicoloured.
2918 40 fi. Type **611** 40 10
2919 60 fi. Marbled white 50 10
2920 80 fi. Apollo 60 15
2921 1 fo. Spurge hawk moth . . . 70 15
2922 1 fo. 20 Clifden's nonpareil . . 85 30
2923 5 fo. Purple emperor . . . . 1·60 45
2924 6 fo. Purple-edged copper . . . 2·00 95

612 Istvan Pataki **613** Mother and Child

1974. Hungarian Antifascist Martyrs. Mult.
2925 1 fo. Type **612** 10 10
2926 1 fo. Robert Kreutz 10 10

1974. "Mothers".
2927 **613** 1 fo. black, yellow & blue . 15 10

614 Puppy **616** F. Bolyai

615 Lambarene Hospital

1974. Young Animals. (1st series). Mult.
2928 40 fi. Type **614** 10 10
2929 60 fi. Kittens (horiz.) 15 10
2930 80 fi. Rabbit 20 10
2931 1 fo. 20 Foal (horiz.) 30 10
2932 2 fo. Lamb 55 10
2933 4 fo. Calf (horiz.) 85 15
2934 6 fo. Piglet . . . . 1·40 90
See also Nos. 3014/20.

1975. Birth Cent of Dr. Albert Schweitzer (Nobel Peace Prize Winner). Multicoloured.
2935 40 fi. Type **615** 10 10
2936 60 fi. Casualty being treated . . 15 10
2937 80 fi. Casualty being transported by canoe 20 10
2938 1 fo. 20 Charitable goods arriving by freighter 30 10
2939 2 fo. View of Lambarene, doves, globe and Red Cross emblem 55 10
2940 4 fo. Schweitzer's Nobel Peace Prize medal and inscription . 90 15
2941 6 fo. Schweitzer and organ-pipes . . . . 1·25 35

1975. Birth Bicentenary of Farkas Bolyai (mathematician).
2942 **616** 1 fo. grey and red 35 10

617 Carrier-pigeon **618** Karolyi

1975. Air. Pigeon-racing Olympics, Budapest.
2943 **617** 3 fo. multicoloured . . . 1·60 95

1975. Birth Centenary of Count Mihaly Karolyi (politician).
2944 **618** 1 fo. brown and blue . . 15 10

619 Woman's Head

1975. International Woman's Year.
2945 **619** 1 fo. black and blue . . . 15 10

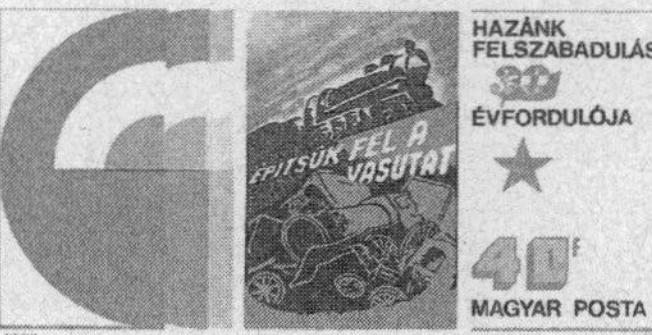

620 "Railway Rebuilding"

1975. 30th Anniv of Liberation. Mult.
2946 40 fi. Type **620** 40 10
2947 60 fi. Hammer and sickle representing agriculture 10 10
2948 2 fo. Blacksmith's hammer representing Communist party action 35 10
2949 4 fo. Power hammer as "3" representing the "Three Year Heavy Industry Plan" . . . 1·50 30
2950 5 fo. Blocks of Flats representing "developed socialist society" . . . . 1·00 15

621 1915 "Arrow"

1975. 75th Anniv of Hungarian Automobile Club. Vintage Motor Cars. Multicoloured.
2951 40 fi. Type **621** 20 10
2952 60 fi. 1911 "Swift" 20 10
2953 80 fi. 1908 Ford "T" 25 10
2954 1 fo. 1901 Mercedes 30 10
2955 1 fo. 20 1912 Panhard Levassor 40 35
2956 5 fo. 1906 Csonka . . . . . . 1·25 50
2957 6 fo. Hungarian Automobile Club and international motoring organisations emblems . . . . 2·25 70

623 Academy Building

1975. 150th Anniv of National Academy of Sciences. Multicoloured.
2959 1 fo. Type **623** 10 10
2960 2 fo. Dates "1825" and "1975" . 60 35
2961 3 fo. Count Istvan Szechenyi (statesman) 90 50

624 Olympic Stadium, Moscow

1975. "Socphilex V" International Stamp Exhibition, Moscow.
2962 **624** 5 fo. multicoloured . . . 1·50 1·75

625 French 1 f. Stamp, 1964

1975. "Arphila 75" International Stamp Exhibition, Paris.
2963 **625** 5 fo. multicoloured . . . 1·25 1·40

626 Electric Railway Locomotive and Transformer

1975. 75th Anniv of Hungarian Electro-technical Association.
2964 **626** 1 fo. multicoloured . . . 70 10

627 "Sputnik 2"

1975. Air. "Apollo-Soyuz" Space Link. Mult.
2965 40 fi. Type **627** 10 10
2966 60 fi. "Mercury Atlas 5" . . . 10 10
2967 80 fi. "Lunokhod 1" (moon vehicle) 15 10
2968 1 fo. 20 "Apollo 15" (moon vehicle) 25 10
2969 2 fo. Launch of "Soyuz" from Baikonur 40 10
2970 4 fo. Launch of "Apollo" . . . 1·10 15
2971 6 fo. "Apollo-Soyuz" link-up . 1·40 70

628 Sword, Epee, Rapier, and Globe **631** A. Zimmermann

1975. World Fencing Championships, Budapest.
2973 **628** 1 fo. multicoloured 25 10

1975. Birth Centenary of Dr. Agoston Zimmermann (veterinary surgeon).
2976 **631** 1 fo. dp brown, brn & bl . 20 10

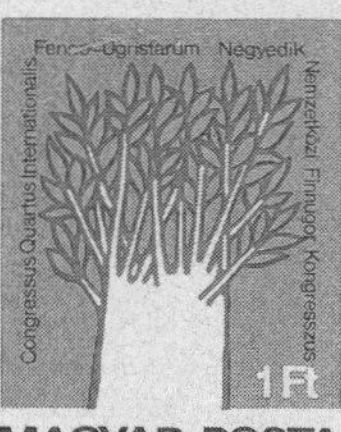

632 Branches of Tree symbolizing 14 Languages **634** Anjou Wall Fountain

1975. International Finno-Ugrian Congress, Budapest.
2977 **632** 1 fo. multicoloured . . . 15 10

1975. Stamp Day. Preservation of Monuments. Monuments in Visegrad Palace. Multicoloured.

2979	2 fo. + 1 fo. Type **634**	2·00	2·50
2980	2 fo. + 1 fo. Anjou well house	2·00	2·50
2981	2 fo. + 1 fo. Hunyadi wall fountain	2·00	2·50
2982	2 fo. + 1 fo. Hercules fountain	2·00	2·50

635 Hungarian Arms and Map **636** Ocean Pollution

1975. 25th Anniv of Hungarian Council System. Multicoloured.

2984	1 fo. Type **635**	15	10
2985	1 fo. Voters participating in council election	15	10

1975. International Exposition, Okinawa. Environmental Protection. Multicoloured.

2986	40 fi. Type **636**	10	10
2987	60 fi. Strangled rose (water pollution)	15	10
2988	80 fi. Clown anemonefish struggling for uncontaminated water (river pollution)	20	10
2989	1 fo. Dead carnation (soil pollution)	30	10
2990	1 fo. 20 Falling bird (air pollution)	40	10
2991	5 fo. Infected lung (smoke pollution)	1·00	20
2992	6 fo. Healthy and skeletal hands (life and death)	1·25	65

637 Mariska Gardos (writer) (1885–1973)

1975. Birth Annivs of Celebrities. Each black and red.

2993	1 fo. Type **637**	15	10
2994	1 fo. Imre Tarr (soldier) (1900–1937)	15	10
2995	1 fo. Imre Meso (Communist martyr) (1905–1956)	15	10

638 Treble Clef, Organ and Orchestra

1975. Centenary of Ferenc Liszt Music Academy, Budapest.

2996	**638**	1 fo. multicoloured	40	10

639 18th-century Icon of Szigetcsep

1975. Hungarian Icons depicting the Virgin and Child. Multicoloured.

2997	40 fi. Type **639**	10	10
2998	60 fi. 18th-century Icon of Graboc	15	10
2999	1 fo. 18th-century Icon of Esztergom	20	10
3000	1 fo. 50 18th-century Icon of Vatoped	35	10
3001	2 fo. 50 17th-century Icon of Tottos	50	10
3002	4 fo. 17th-century Icon of Gyor	1·10	15
3003	5 fo. 18th-century Icon of Kazan	1·40	45

640 Mother and Child, Flags and Radar Equipment

1975. 20th Anniv of Warsaw Treaty.

3004	**640**	1 fo. multicoloured	15	10

641 Ice Hockey

1975. Winter Olympic Games, Innsbruck. Multicoloured.

3005	40 fi. Type **641**	25	10
3006	60 fi. Slalom skiing	25	10
3007	80 fi. Slalom skiing (different)	25	10
3008	1 fo. 20 Ski jumping	35	10
3009	2 fo. Speed skating	40	10
3010	4 fo. Cross country skiing	80	15
3011	6 fo. Bobsleighing	1·00	70

642 Banknotes of 1925 and 1975

1976. 50th Anniv of State Banknote Printing Office, Budapest.

3013	**642**	1 fo. multicoloured	35	10

1976. Young Animals (2nd series). As T **614**. Multicoloured.

3014	40 fi. Wild boars (horiz)	10	10
3015	60 fi. Eurasian red squirrels	10	10
3016	80 fi. Lynx (horiz)	25	10
3017	1 fo. 20 Wolf cubs	40	10
3018	2 fo. Red fox cubs (horiz)	55	10
3019	4 fo. Brown bear cubs	95	15
3020	6 fo. Lion cubs (horiz)	1·40	45

643 Alexander Graham Bell, Telecommunications Satellite and Dish Aerial

1976. Telephone Centenary.

3021	**643**	3 fo. multicoloured	85	85

645 "Clash between Rakoczi's Kuruts and Hapsburg Soldiers"

1976. 300th Birth Anniv of Prince Ferenc Rakoczi II (soldier). Paintings. Multicoloured.

3023	40 fi. Type **645**	10	10
3024	60 fi. "Meeting of Rakoczi and Tamas Esze"	15	10
3025	1 fo. "The Parliament of Onod" (Mor Than)	30	10
3026	2 fo. "Kuruts' Encampment"	65	10
3027	3 fo. "Ilona Zrinyi" (Rakoczi's mother) (vert.)	1·40	20
3028	4 fo. "Kuruts Officers" (vert.)	2·00	60
3029	5 fo. "Prince Rakoczi II" (A. Manyoki) (vert.)	2·75	90

646 Metric System Act, 1876 **647** Knight

1976. Centenary of Introduction of Metric System into Hungary. Multicoloured.

3030	1 fo. Type **646**	10	10
3031	2 fo. Istvan Krusper (scientist) and vacuum balance	45	10
3032	3 fo. Interferometer, space rocket and emblem	75	35

1976. Stamp Day. Gothic Statues from Buda Castle.

3033	2 fo. 50 + 1 fo. Type **647**	70	80
3034	2 fo. 50 + 1 fo. Armour bearer	70	80
3035	2 fo. 50 + 1 fo. Apostle	70	80
3036	2 fo. 50 + 1 fo. Bishop	70	80

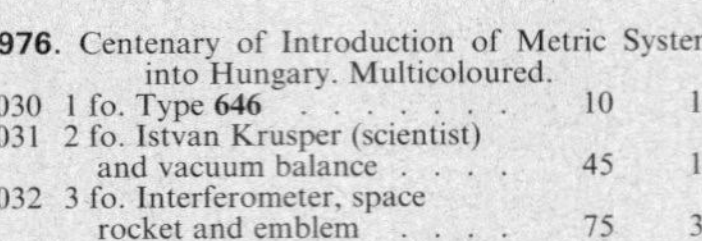

648 U.S. 6 c. Stamp, 1968

1976. "Interphil '76". Int Stamp Exn, Philadelphia.

3038	**648**	5 fo. multicoloured	1·50	1·75

649 "Children Playing" (E. Gebora) within "30"

1976. 30th Anniv of Hungarian Pioneers Movement.

3039	**649**	1 fo. multicoloured	25	10

650 Truck, Tractor and Safety Headgear with Emblem

1976. Industrial Safety.

3040	**650**	1 fo. multicoloured	25	10

651 "Intelstar IV" Telecommunications Satellite

1976. Olympic Games, Montreal. Mult.

3041	40 fi. Type **651**	10	10
3042	60 fi. Horse-jumping	10	10
3043	1 fo. Swimming	15	10
3044	2 fo. Canoeing	30	10
3045	3 fo. Fencing	50	10
3046	4 fo. Javelin-throwing	85	10
3047	5 fo. Gymnastics	1·00	30

652 Danish 1851 4 R.B.S. Stamp and "Little Mermaid" Statue

1976. "Hafnia '76" International Stamp Exhibition, Copenhagen.

3049	**652**	3 fo. multicoloured	1·00	1·25

653 "Flora" (Titian)

1976. 400th Death Anniv of Titian (painter).

3050	**653**	4 fo. multicoloured	75	15

655 Pal Gyulai (1826–1909) **656** "Hussar" (Zs. Kisfaludy-Strobl)

1976. Writers' Anniversaries.

3052	**655**	2 fo. black and red	20	10
3053	–	2 fo. black, yell & gold	20	10

DESIGN: No. 3053, Daniel Berzsenyi (1776–1836).

1976. 150th Anniv of Herend China Factory.

3054	**656**	4 fo. multicoloured	75	15

657 Tuscany 1 q. Stamp, 1851 and Arms of Milan

1976. "Italia '76" International Stamp Exhibition, Milan.

3055	**657**	5 fo. multicoloured	3·00	3·50

658 Russian Dancer, Flags and Building

1976. 2nd Anniv of House of Soviet Culture and Science, Budapest.

3056	**658**	1 fo. multicoloured	20	10

659 Ignac Bogar

1976. Hungarian Labour Movement Celebrities.

3057	**659**	1 fo. brown and red	15	10
3058	–	1 fo. brown and red	15	10
3059	–	1 fo. brown and red	15	10

PORTRAITS: No. 3058, Rudolf Golub; No. 3059, Jozsef Madzsar.

660 Dr. F. Koranyi and Dispensary

1976. 75th Anniv of Koranyi T.B. Dispensary.
3060 **660** 2 fo. multicoloured . . . 50 10

661 Launch of "Viking" Mission

1976. Air. Space Probes to Mars and Venus. Multicoloured.
3061 40 fi. Type **661** 10 10
3062 60 fi. "Viking" in flight 15 10
3063 1 fo. "Viking" on Mars 20 10
3064 2 fo. Launch of "Venera" . . . 30 10
3065 3 fo. "Venera 9" in flight . . . 55 10
3066 4 fo. "Venera 10" descending to Venus 85 10
3067 5 fo. "Venera" on Venus . . . 95 60

662 Locomotive No. 4, 1875

1976. Cent of Gyor–Sopron Railway. Mult.
3069 40 fi. Type **662** 20 10
3070 60 fi. Locomotive No. 17, 1885 25 10
3071 1 fo. Rail-bus, 1925 . . . . . 30 10
3072 2 fo. Steam locomotive, 1920 . 55 10
3073 3 fo. Diesel railcar, 1926 . . . 75 10
3074 4 fo. Diesel railcar, 1934 . . . 1·25 40
3075 5 fo. Diesel railcar, 1971 . . . 2·00 60

663 Tree Foliage and Map

1976. "Afforestation of 1,000,000th Hectare".
3076 **663** 1 fo. multicoloured . . . 20 10

664 Weightlifting and Wrestling (silver medals)

1976. Olympic Games, Montreal. Hungarian Medal-winners. Multicoloured.
3077 40 fi. Type **664** 10 10
3078 60 fi. Men's solo kayak and Women's pairs kayak (silver medals) 15 10
3079 1 fo. Men's gymnastics (horse) (gold medal) 20 10
3080 4 fo. Women's rapier (gold medal) 85 15
3081 6 fo. Men's javelin (gold medal) . . . . 1·75 70

665 White Spoonbill

1977. Birds of Hortabagy National Park. Multicoloured.
3083 40 fi. Type **665** 25 10
3084 60 fi. White stork 35 10
3085 1 fo. Purple heron 40 15
3086 2 fo. Great bustard 50 20
3087 3 fo. Common crane 80 30
3088 4 fo. Pied wagtail . . . . . . 1·40 50
3089 5 fo. Garganey . . . . 1·75 65

666 Imre Abonyi (champion driver) and Carriage, 1976

1977. Historic Horse-drawn Vehicles. Mult.
3090 40 fi. Type **666** 20 10
3091 60 fi. Omnibus, 1870 . . . . . 25 10
3092 1 fo. Hackney-carriage, 1890 . 60 10
3093 2 fo. 19th-century mail coach . 45 10
3094 3 fo. 18th-century covered wagon 80 15
3095 4 fo. Coach, 1568 . . . . . . 1·00 30
3096 5 fo. Saint Elizabeth's carriage, 1430 . . . . 1·25 65

667 Common Peafowl

1977. Peafowl and Pheasants. Multicoloured.
3097 40 fi. Type **667** 25 10
3098 60 fi. Green peafowl 30 10
3099 1 fo. Congo peafowl 35 10
3100 3 fo. Great Argus pheasant . . 1·00 15
3101 4 fo. Himalayan monal pheasant . . . . 1·50 25
3102 6 fo. Burmese peacock-pheasant . . . . 1·50 95

668 Front Page of "Nepszava" and Printing Works

670 Isaac Newton and Lens

669 Flower painting (Mihaly Munkacsy)

1977. Cent. of Newspaper "Nepszava".
3103 **668** 1 fo. black, red and gold . 10 10

1977. Flower Paintings by Hungarian Artists. Multicoloured.
3104 40 fi. Type **669** 10 10
3105 60 fi. Jakab Bogdany 10 10
3106 1 fo. Istvan Csok (horiz.) . . . 15 10
3107 2 fo. Janos Halapy 30 10
3108 3 fo. Jozsef Rippl-Ronai (horiz) 65 10
3109 4 fo. Janos Tornyai 85 25
3110 5 fo. Jozsef Koszta . . . . . 1·00 80

1977. 250th Death Anniv of Isaac Newton (mathematician).
3111 **670** 3 fo. black, brn & red . . 85 85

671 Children Running

673 Janos Vajda

672 "Acrofila 74" 2 fo. + 1 fo. Stamp

1977. Youth Sports.
3112 **671** 3 fo. + 1 fo. 50 mult . . 1·00 85

1977. Stamp Exhibitions.
3113 **672** 3 fo. multicoloured . . . 1·40 50

1977. 150th Birth Anniv of Janos Vajda (poet).
3114 **673** 1 fo. stone, black & grn . 10 10

674 Netherlands 5 c. Stamp, 1852

1977. "Amphilex 77" International Stamp Exhibition, Amsterdam.
3115 **674** 3 fo. multicoloured . . . 1·00 1·25

675 "Wedding at Nagyrede" Dance

1977. 25th Anniv of State Folk Ensemble.
3116 **675** 3 fo. multicoloured . . . 95 15

677 View of Sopron (from medieval engraving), Arms and Fidelity Tower

679 East German 10 pf. Stamp, 1957

678 Kincsem (champion racehorse)

1977. 700th Anniv of Sopron.
3118 **677** 1 fo. multicoloured . . . 1·60 1·75

1977. 150th Anniv of Horse Racing in Hungary.
3119 **678** 1 fo. multicoloured . . . 1·25 1·25

1977. "Sozphilex 77" Stamp Exhibition, East Berlin.
3120 **679** 3 fo. multicoloured . . . 1·10 1·25

680 Scythian Iron Bell (6th century B.C.)

681 "Sputnik 1"

1977. Stamp Day and 175th Anniv of Hungarian National Museum. Art Treasures.
3121 **680** 2 fo. brown and blue . . 90 1·00
3122 – 2 fo. brown & violet . . . 90 1·00
3123 – 2 fo. brown & dp brn . . 90 1·00
3124 – 2 fo. gold & mauve . . . 90 1·00
DESIGNS: No. 3122, Bronze candlestick, 12–13th century; 3123, Copper aquamanile, 13th century; 3124, Cast gold Christ (from crucifix), 11th century.

1977. Space Research. Multicoloured.
3126 40 fi. Type **681** 10 10
3127 60 fi. "Skylab" 15 10
3128 1 fo. "Soyuz-Salyut 5" space station 20 10
3129 3 fo. "Luna 24" 60 10
3130 4 fo. "Mars 3" . . . . 1·25 15
3131 6 fo. "Viking" . . . . 1·75 70

683 Tupolev Tu-154

1977. Air.
3134 **683** 60 fi. black & orange . . 15 10
3135 – 1 fo. 20 black & lilac . . 20 10
3136 – 2 fo. black and orange . . 30 10
3137 – 2 fo. 40 black & turq . . 35 10
3138 – 4 fo. black and blue . . 50 10
3139 – 5 fo. black and mauve . . 70 10
3140 – 10 fo. black and blue . . 2·00 30
3141 – 20 fo. black and green . 3·00 80
DESIGNS—As T **683**: 1 fo. 20, Douglas DC-8-62; 2 fo. Ilyushin Il-62M; 2 fo. 40, Airbus Industrie A300B4; 4 fo. Boeing 747; 5 fo. Tupolev Tu-144; 10 fo. Concorde. 38 × 28 mm: 20 fo. Ilyushin Il-86.

684 Montgolfier Brothers and Balloon

1977. Air. Airships. Multicoloured.
3142 40 fi. Type **684** 10 10
3143 60 fi. David Schwarz and his aluminium airship 20 10
3144 1 fo. Alberto Santos-Dumont and airship "Ballon No. 5" over Paris 30 10
3145 2 fo. K. E. Tsiolkovsky and airship "Lebedi" over Kremlin . 50 10
3146 3 fo. Roald Amundsen and airship "Norge" over North Pole 75 20
3147 4 fo. Hugo Eckener and airship "Graf Zeppelin" over Mount Fuji . . . . 1·10 30
3148 5 fo. Ferdinand Zeppelin and "Graf Zeppelin" over Chicago World Exhibition . 1·60 55

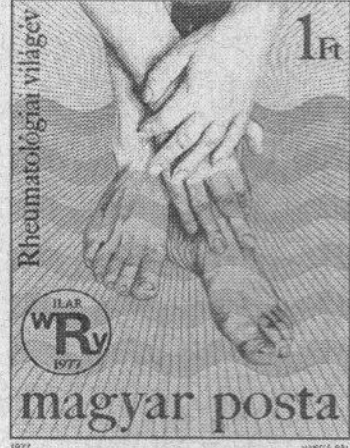

685 Feet Immersed in Water

686 Ervin Szabo

1977. World Rheumatism Year.
3150 **685** 1 fo. multicoloured . . . 35 10

1977. Anniversaries.
3151 – 1 fo. black and red . . . 10 10
3152 **686** 1 fo. grey, black and red . 10 10
DESIGNS: No 3151, Jamos Szanto Kovacs (agrarian socialist movement leader, 125th birth anniv); 3152, Type **686** (director of Municipal Libraries, journalist and labour movement leader, birth centenary).

687 Monument to Hungarian Participants, Omsk

1977. 60th Anniv of Russian Revolution.
3153 **687** 1 fo. black and red . . . 10 10

688 Endre Ady **689** Lesser Panda

1977. Birth Centenary of Endre Ady (poet).
3154 **688** 1 fo. blue 20 20

1977. Bears. Multicoloured.
3155 40 fi. Type **689** 15 10
3156 60 fi. Giant Panda 25 10
3157 1 fo. Asiatic black bear 40 10
3158 4 fo. Polar bear . . . . 1·75 15
3159 6 fo. Brown bear . . . . . . 2·50 50

691 Border-country Lancer, 17th-cent

1978. Hussars. Multicoloured.
3161 40 fi. Type **691** 15 10
3162 60 fi. Kuruts horseman, 1710 . . 20 10
3163 1 fo. Baranya hussar, 1762 . . 30 10
3164 2 fo. Palatine Hussars officer, 1809 . . . . 50 10
3165 4 fo. Alexander Hussar, 1848 . . 95 20
3166 6 fo. Trumpeter, 5th Honved Regiment, 1900 . . . . . . 1·75 70

692 Moon Station

1978. Air. Science Fiction in Space Research. Multicoloured.
3167 40 fi. Type **692** 10 10
3168 60 fi. Moon settlement 15 10
3169 1 fo. Phobos 25 10
3170 2 fo. Exploring an asteroid . . 45 10
3171 3 fo. Spacecraft in gravitational field of Mars 65 10
3172 4 fo. One of Saturn's rings . . 95 15
3173 5 fo. "Jupiter 3" . . . . . . 1·25 45

693 School of Arts and Crafts

1978. Bicent of School of Art and Crafts.
3174 **693** 1 fo. multicoloured . . . 10 10

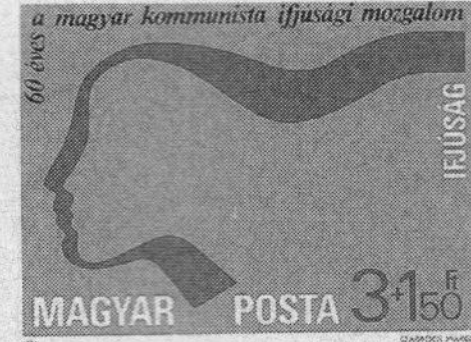

694 Profile Heads

1978. Youth Stamp Exhibition, Hatvan.
3175 **694** 3 fo. + 1 fo. 50 silver, red and black . . . . . . 2·00 2·50

695 "Generations" (Gyula Derkovits)

1978. "Socphilex 78" Stamp Exhibition, Szombathely.
3176 **695** 3 fo. + 1 fo. 50 mult . . 1·00 1·25

696 Louis Bleriot

1978. Air. Famous Aviators and their Airplanes. Multicoloured.
3177 40 fi. Type **696** 15 10
3178 60 fi. John Alcock and Arthur Whitten Brown 20 10
3179 1 fo. Albert C. Read 25 10
3180 2 fo. Hermann Kohl, Gunther Hunefeld and James Fitzmaurice 55 10
3181 3 fo. Amy Johnson and Jim Mollison 75 15
3182 4 fo. Georgy Endresz and Sandor Magyar 95 20
3183 5 fo. Wolfgang von Gronau . . 1·00 70

697 Glass Vase and Glass-blowing Tube

1978. Cent. of Ajka Glass Works.
3185 **697** 1 fo. multicoloured . . . 20 10

698 West Germany and Poland

1978. World Cup Football Championship, Argentina, Multicoloured.
3186 2 fo. Type **698** 75 20
3187 2 fo. Hungary and Argentina . 75 20
3188 2 fo. France and Italy 75 20
3189 2 fo. Tunisia and Mexico . . . 75 20
3190 2 fo. Sweden and Brazil . . . 75 20
3191 2 fo. Spain and Austria . . . 75 20
3192 2 fo. Peru and Scotland . . . 75 45
3193 2 fo. Iran and Netherlands . . 75 60

699 Canadian 3d. Stamp, 1851

1978. "Capex 78" International Stamp Exhibition, Toronto.
3195 **699** 3 fo. multicoloured . . . 1·00 1·25

700 Diesel MK 45 Locomotive **702** Festival Emblem

1978. 30th Anniv of Budapest Pioneer Railway.
3196 **700** 1 fo. multicoloured . . . 30 10

1978. 11th World Youth and Students' Festival, Havana. Multicoloured.
3198 1 fo. Type **702** 10 10
3199 1 fo. Map of Cuba and emblem 10 10

703 Human Torso and Heart **705** Dove and Fist holding Olive Branch

1978. World Hypertension Year.
3200 **703** 1 fo. red, black & blue . . 25 10

1978. 20th Anniv of Communist Party Review "Peace and Socialism".
3202 **705** 1 fo. red and black . . . 10 10

706 Vladimir Remek cancelling Letters, "Salyut 6" and "Soyuz 28"

1978. Air. "Praga 1978" International Stamp Exhibition, Prague.
3203 **706** 3 fo. multicoloured . . . 1·00 1·00

707 Toshiba Automatic Letter Sorting Equipment

1978. Automation of Letter Sorting.
3204 **707** 1 fo. multicoloured . . . 20 20

708 Putto offering Grapes **710** Imre Thokoly

709 Methods of Communication

1978. Stamp Day. Mosaics. Multicoloured.
3205 2 fo. Type **708** . . . . 2·00 2·50
3206 2 fo. Tiger . . . . 2·00 2·50
3207 2 fo. Bird . . . . 2·00 2·50
3208 2 fo. Dolphin . . . . 2·00 2·50

1978. Organization of Socialist Countries' Postal Administrations Conference, Tbilisi.
3210 **709** 1 fo. multicoloured . . . 35 10

1978. 300th Anniv of Thokoly's Revolt.
3211 **710** 1 fo. black and yellow . . 35 10

712 "The Red Coach" (novel)

1978. Birth Cent of Gyula Krudy (novelist).
3213 **712** 3 fo. red and black . . . 50 10

713 St. Ladislas (bust, Gyor Cathedral)

1978. 900th Anniv of Accession of St. Ladislas.
3214 **713** 1 fo. multicoloured . . . 20 10

714 Buildings and Arms of Koszeg

1978. 650th Anniv of Koszeg.
3215 **714** 1 fo. multicoloured . . . 20 10

715 Samu Czaban and Gizella Berzeviczy

1978. Birth Centenaries of Samu Czaban and Gizella Berzeviczy (teachers).
3216 **715** 1 fo. multicoloured . . . 20 10

716 Communist Party Emblem

1978. 60th Anniv of Hungarian Communist Party.
3217 **716** 1 fo. red, grey and black . 10 10

717 "Girl cutting Bread"

1978. Ceramics by Margit Kovacs. Mult.
3218 1 fo. Type **717** 25 10
3219 2 fo. "Girl with Pitcher" . . . 40 20
3220 3 fo. "Boy Potter" 70 25

718 "Self-portrait in Fur Coat"

1978. 450th Death Anniv of Albrecht Durer (artist). Multicoloured.

3221	40 fi. "Madonna with Child"	10	10
3222	60 fi. "Adoration of the Magi" (horiz.)	10	10
3223	1 fo. Type **718**	20	10
3224	2 fo. "St. George"	35	10
3225	3 fo. "Nativity" (horiz.)	85	10
3226	4 fo. "St. Eustace"	1·00	40
3227	5 fo. "The Four Apostles"	1·25	70

719 Human Rights Emblem
720 Child with Dog

1979. 30th Anniv of Declaration of Human Rights.

3229	**719**	1 fo. blue & light blue	1·50	1·75

1979. International Year of the Child (1st issue). Multicoloured.

3230	1 fo. Type **720**	1·00	75
3231	1 fo. Family group	1·00	75
3232	1 fo. Children of different races	6·00	6·00

See also Nos. 3287/93.

721 "Soldiers of the Red Army, Forward!" (poster by Bela Uitz)

1979. 60th Anniv of First Hungarian Soviet Republic.

3233	**721**	1 fo. black, red & grey	10	10

722 "Girl Reading" (Ferenc Kovacs)

1979. Youth Stamp Exhibition, Bekescsaba.

3234	**722**	3 fo. + 1 fo. 50 grey, blue and black	70	75

723 Chessmen and Cup

1979. 23rd Chess Olympiad, Buenos Aires (1978).

3235	**723**	3 fo. multicoloured	1·60	1·00

724 Alexander Nevski Cathedral, Sofia, and First Bulgarian Stamp

1979. "Philaserdica 79" International Stamp Exhibition, Sofia.

3236	**724**	3 fo. multicoloured	90	1·00

725 Stephenson's "Rocket", 1829

1979. International Transport Exhibition, Hamburg. Multicoloured designs depicting development of the railway.

3237	40 fi. Type **725**	25	10
3238	60 fi. Siemens's electric locomotive, 1879	30	10
3239	1 fo. Locomotive "Pioneer", 1851 (wrongly dated "1936")	40	10
3240	2 fo. Hungarian Class MAV I.e pulling "Orient Express", 1883	60	15
3241	3 fo. "Trans-Siberian Express", 1898	95	30
3242	4 fo. Japanese "Hikari" express train, 1964	1·25	40
3243	5 fo. German "Transrapid 05" Maglev train, 1979	1·50	85

726 Soyuz Gas Pipeline and Compressor Station
727 Zsigmond Moricz (after J. Rippl-Ronai)

1979. 30th Anniv of Council of Mutual Economic Aid. Multicoloured.

3245	1 fo. Type **726**	10	10
3246	2 fo. Pylon and dam, Lenin hydro-electric power station, Dnepropetrovsk	45	10
3247	3 fo. Council building, Moscow	50	10

1979. Birth Centenary of Zsigmond Moricz (writer).

3248	**727**	1 fo. multicoloured	10	10

728 City Hall, Helsinki (1952 Games)

1979. Olympic Games, Moscow (1980) (1st issue). Multicoloured.

3249	40 fi. Type **728**	10	10
3250	60 fi. Colosseum, Rome (1960)	35	10
3251	1 fo. Asakusa Temple, Tokyo (1964)	50	10
3252	2 fo. Cathedral, Mexico City (1968)	65	10
3253	3 fo. Frauenkirche, Munich (1972)	75	35
3254	4 fo. Modern quarter, Montreal (1976)	1·00	40
3255	5 fo. Lomonosov University, Moscow, and Misha the bear (mascot) (1980)	1·25	60

See also Nos. 3323/29.

729 "Child with Horse and Greyhounds" (Janos Vaszary)

1979. Animal Paintings. Multicoloured.

3256	40 fi. Type **729**	20	10
3257	60 fi. "Coach and Five" (Karoly Lotz)	25	10
3258	1 fo. "Lads on Horseback" (Celesztin Pallya)	30	10
3259	2 fo. "Farewell" (Karoly Lotz)	40	35
3260	3 fo. "Horse Market" (Celeztin Pallya)	55	40
3261	4 fo. "Wandering" (Bela Ivanyi-Grunwald)	90	60
3262	5 fo. "Ready for Hunting" (Karoly Sterio)	1·40	70

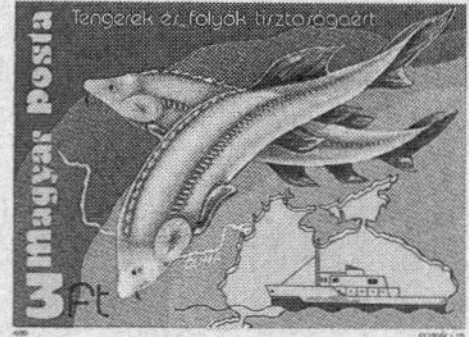

730 Sturgeon, Cousteau's Ship "Calypso" and Black Sea

1979. Sea and River Purity.

3263	**730**	3 fo. multicoloured	80	15

731 Globe and Five Pentathlon Sports

1979. Pentathlon World Championship, Budapest.

3264	**731**	2 fo. multicoloured	55	10

732 Stephen I Denarius (reverse)
735 Flags and Globe filled with Coins

1979. Ninth International Numismatic Congress, Berne. Designs showing old Hungarian coins. Multicoloured.

3265	1 fo. Type **732**	25	10
3266	2 fo. Bela III copper coin (obverse)	40	10
3267	3 fo. Louis the Great groat (reverse)	50	15
3268	4 fo. Matthias I gold forint (obverse)	65	40
3269	5 fo. Wladislaw II gulden (reverse)	1·25	70

1979. World Savings Day.

3272	**735**	1 fo. multicoloured	15	10

736 "Vega-Chess" (Victor Vasarely)
737 European Otter

1979. Modern Art.

3273	**736**	1 fo. multicoloured	20	10

1979. Protected Animals. Multicoloured.

3274	40 fi. Type **737**	20	10
3275	60 fi. Wild cat	25	10
3276	1 fo. Pine marten	45	10
3277	2 fo. Eurasian badger	65	15
3278	4 fo. Steppe polecat	1·40	15
3279	6 fo. Beech marten	2·00	50

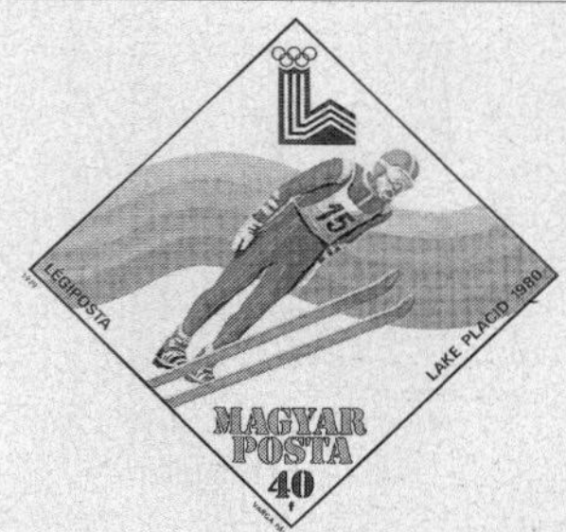

738 Ski Jumping

1979. Air. Winter Olympic Games, Lake Placid (1980). Multicoloured.

3280	40 fi. Type **738**	25	10
3281	60 fi. Figure skating	55	10
3282	1 fo. Slalom	70	35
3283	2 fo. Ice hockey	85	40
3284	4 fo. Bobsleigh	1·40	50
3285	6 fo. Cross-country skiing	1·60	80

739 "Tom Thumb"

1979. International Year of the Child (2nd issue). Designs depicting children's stories. Multicoloured.

3287	40 fi. Type **739**	15	10
3288	60 fi. "The Ugly Duckling" (Andersen)	25	10
3289	1 fo. "The Fisher and the Goldfish"	35	10
3290	2 fo. "Cinderella"	60	10
3291	3 fo. "Gulliver's Travels" (Swift)	80	10
3292	4 fo. "The Little Pig and the Wolves"	85	15
3293	5 fo. "Gallant John"	1·50	85

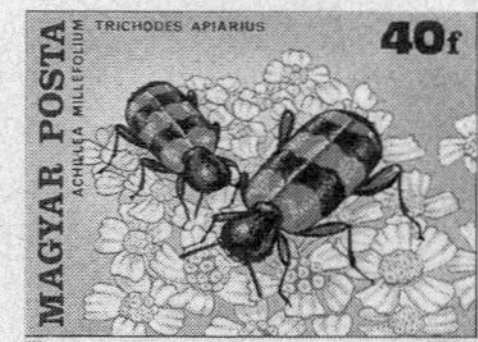

740 Achillea and Bee-eating Beetles

1980. Pollination. Multicoloured.

3295	40 fi. Type **740**	15	10
3296	60 fi. Gaillardia and bee	15	10
3297	1 fo. Rudbeckia and red admiral	20	10
3298	2 fo. Dog rose and rose chafer	40	10
3299	4 fo. "Petroselinum hortense" and striped bug	85	20
3300	6 fo. Achillea and longhorn beetle	1·25	50

741 Hanging Gardens of Babylon

1980. Seven Wonders of the Ancient World. Multicoloured.

3301	40 fi. Type **741**	15	10
3302	60 fi. Temple of Artemis, Ephesus	15	10
3303	1 fo. Statue of Zeus, Olympia	20	10
3304	2 fo. Mausoleum of Halicarnassus	40	10
3305	3 fo. Colossus of Rhodes	55	15
3306	4 fo. Pharos, Alexandria	75	20
3307	5 fo. Pyramids of Egypt	1·75	60

MINIMUM PRICE

The minimum price quoted is 10p which represents a handling charge rather than a basis for valuing common stamps. For further notes about prices see introductory pages.

742 Gabor Bethlen (copperplate)

1980. 400th Birth Anniv of Gabor Bethlen (Prince of Transylvania).

3308	742	1 fo. multicoloured	20	10

743 Tihany Abbey

1980. 925th Anniv of Foundation of Tihany Abbey.

3309	743	1 fo. multicoloured	10	10

744 Easter Sepulchre 745 Bunch of Wild Flowers

1980. Easter Sepulchre of Garamszentbenedek. Designs showing details of sepulchre. Mult.

3310		1 fo. Type **744**	15	10
3311		2 fo. Three Marys	25	10
3312		3 fo. Apostle Jacob	55	40
3313		4 fo. Apostle Thaddeus	70	50
3314		5 fo. Apostle Andrew	90	75

1980. 35th Anniv of Liberation.

3315	745	1 fo. multicoloured	20	10

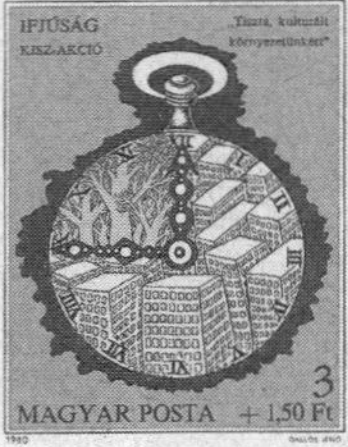

746 Watch symbolising Environmental Protection 747 Attila Jozsef

1980. Youth Stamp Exhibition, Dunaujvaros.

3316	746	3 fo. + 1 fo. 50 mult	70	80

1980. 75th Birth Anniv of Attila Jozsef (poet).

3317	747	1 fo. green and red	10	10

748 "Madonna and Child" Stamp of 1921 with Inverted Centre

1980. 50th Anniv of Hungarian Stamp Museum.

3318	748	1 fo. multicoloured	1·00	1·00

749 Great Britain 2d. Blue and Life Guard

1980. "London 1980" International Stamp Exhibition.

3319	749	3 fo. multicoloured	1·25	1·40

750 Soviet and Hungarian Cosmonauts 751 Margit Kaffka

1980. Air. Soviet–Hungarian Space Flight.

3320	750	5 fo. multicoloured	1·60	20

1980. Birth Centenary of Margit Kaffka (writer).

3321	751	1 fo. yellow, blk & violet	10	10

752 Norwegian 1951 Olympic Stamp and Statue "Mother and Child" (Gustav Vigeland)

1980. "Norwex 80" International Stamp Exhibition, Oslo.

3322	752	3 fo. multicoloured	60	75

753 Handball

1980. Air. Olympic Games, Moscow (2nd issue). Multicoloured.

3323		40 fi. Type **753**	10	10
3324		60 fi. Double kayak	10	10
3325		1 fo. Running	15	10
3326		2 fo. Gymnastics	30	10
3327		3 fo. Show-jumping (modern pentathlon)	50	10
3328		4 fo. Wrestling	85	40
3329		5 fo. Water polo	1·10	75

754 Endre Hogyes (physician) and Congress Emblem 756 Zoltan Schonherz

1980. 28th International Congress of Physiological Sciences, Budapest.

3331	754	1 fo. multicoloured	15	10

1980. 75th Birth Anniv of Zoltan Schonherz (Workers' Movement member).

3333	756	1 fo. multicoloured	10	10

757 Decanter 759 Bertalan Por (self portrait)

1980. Stamp Day. Glassware. Multicoloured.

3334		1 fo. Type **757**	20	10
3335		2 fo. Wine glass, Budapest	40	35
3336		3 fo. Drinking glass, Zay-Ugrocz	60	50

1980. Birth Centenary of Bertalan Por (artist).

3339	759	1 fo. multicoloured	10	10

760 Greylag Goose

1980. Protected Birds. Multicoloured.

3340		40 fi. Type **760**	20	10
3341		60 fi. Black-crowned night herons	30	10
3342		1 fo. Common shovelers	30	15
3343		2 fo. White-winged black tern	70	25
3344		4 fo. Great crested grebes	1·50	65
3345		6 fo. Black-winged stilts	2·25	1·10

762 Johannes Kepler

1980. 350th Death Anniv of Johannes Kepler (astronomer).

3348	762	1 fo. multicoloured	30	15

763 Karoly Kisfaludy

1980. 150th Death Anniv of Karoly Kisfaludy (dramatist and poet).

3349	763	1 fo. multicoloured	10	10

764 U.N. Building, New York

1980. 25th Anniv of United Nations Membership. Multicoloured.

3350		40 fi. Type **764**	15	10
3351		60 fi. U.N. building, Geneva	10	10
3352		1 fo. International Centre, Vienna	20	10
3353		2 fo. U.N. and Hungarian flags	35	10
3354		4 fo. U.N. emblem and Hungarian arms	75	10
3355		6 fo. World map	2·00	1·25

765 Ferenc Erdei 766 Bela Szanto

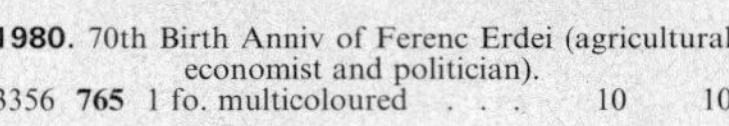

1980. 70th Birth Anniv of Ferenc Erdei (agricultural economist and politician).

3356	765	1 fo. multicoloured	10	10

1981. Birth Cent. of Bela Szanto (founder member of Hungarian Communist Party).

3357	766	1 fo. multicoloured	10	10

767 Lajos Batthyany (after Miklos Barabas)

1981. 175th Birth Anniv of Lajos Batthyany (politician).

3358	767	1 fo. multicoloured	10	10

768 Cheetah 769 "Graf Zeppelin" over Tokyo

1981. Air. Birth Centenary of Kalman Kittenberger (explorer and zoologist). Multicoloured.

3359		40 fi. Type **768**	20	10
3360		60 fi. Lion	20	10
3361		1 fo. Leopard	30	10
3362		2 fo. Black rhinoceros	60	15
3363		3 fo. Greater kudu	65	20
3364		4 fo. African elephant	1·10	25
3365		5 fo. Kittenberger and Hungarian National Museum	2·50	1·10

1981. Air. "Luraba" International Exhibition of Aero- and Astro-philately, Lucerne. "Graf Zeppelin" Flights. Multicoloured.

3366		1 fo. Type **769** (first round-the-world flight, 1929)	15	10
3367		2 fo. Franz Josef Land and ice-breaker "Malygin" (Polar flight, 1931)	45	10
3368		3 fo. Nine-arch Bridge, Hortobagy (Hungary flight, 1931)	45	15
3369		4 fo. Hostentor, Lubeck (Baltic flight, 1931)	60	15
3370		5 fo. Tower Bridge (England flight, 1931)	70	20
3371		6 fo. Federal Palace, Chicago (World Exhibition flight, 1933)	75	25
3372		7 fo. Lucerne (1st Swiss flight, 1929)	1·10	75

771 Flag of House of Arpad (11th century)

1981. Historical Hungarian Flags. Mult.

3374		40 fi. Type **771**	20	10
3375		60 fi. Hunyadi Family flag (15th century)	30	10
3376		1 fo. Flag of Gabor Bethlen (1600)	45	10
3377		2 fo. Flag of Ferenc Rakoczi II (1706)	65	10
3378		4 fo. "Honved" (1848–49)	95	40
3379		6 fo. Troop Flag (1919)	1·25	70

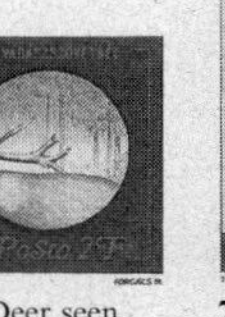

772 Red Deer seen through Binoculars 773 First Hungarian Telephone Exchange

1981. Centenary of Association of Hungarian Huntsmen.

3380	772	2 fo. multicoloured	35	10

1981. Centenary of First Hungarian Telephone Exchange, Budapest.

3381	773	2 fo. multicoloured	65	10

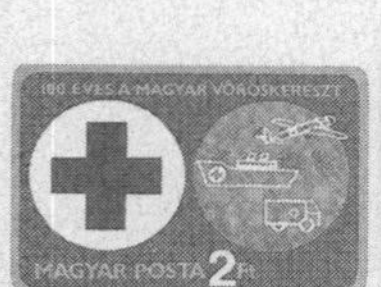

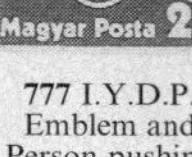

775 Red Cross, Transport and Globe

777 I.Y.D.P. Emblem and Person pushing Wheelchair

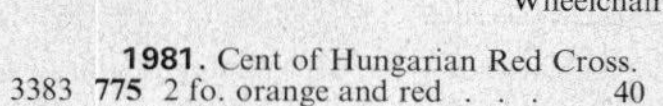

1981. Cent of Hungarian Red Cross.
3383 **775** 2 fo. orange and red . . . 40 10

1981. International Year of Disabled Persons.
3385 **777** 2 fo. + 1 fo. grn & yell . 1·10 70

778 Young People and Factory

779 Stephenson and "Locomotion"

1981. 10th Young Communist League Congress, Budapest.
3386 **778** 4 fo. + 2 fo. mult . . . . 1·25 1·00

1981. Birth Bicentenary of George Stephenson (railway pioneer).
3387 **779** 2 fo. yellow, grey & brn . 60 25

780 Bela Vago

1981. Birth Centenary of Bela Vago (founder member of Hungarian Communist Party).
3388 **780** 2 fo. green and brown . . 45 10

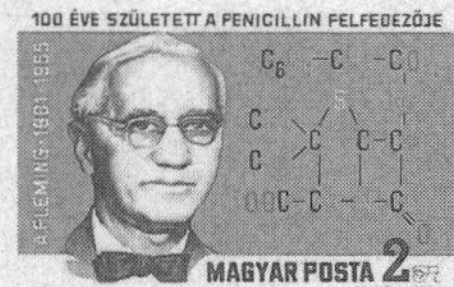

781 Alexander Fleming

1981. Birth Centenary of Alexander Fleming (discoverer of penicillin).
3389 **781** 2 fo. multicoloured . . . 65 15

782 Bridal Chest from Szentgal

1981. Stamp Day. Bridal Chests. Mult.
3390 1 fo. Type **782** 40 35
3391 2 fo. Chest from Hodmezovasarhely 70 60

783 Calvinist College

784 Hands holding F.A.O. Emblem

1981. 450th Anniv of Calvinist College, Papa.
3393 **783** 2 fo. multicoloured . . . 20 10

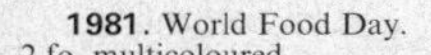

1981. World Food Day.
3394 **784** 2 fo. multicoloured . . . 85 10

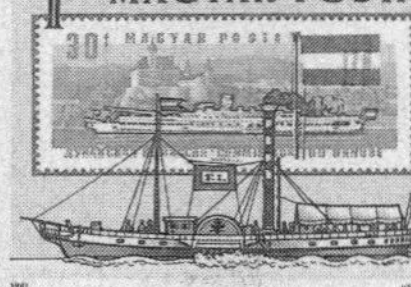

785 German Costume

786 "Franz I" (1830) and "Ferene Deak" on 30 fi. Stamp

1981. National Costumes of Hungarian Ethnic Minorities. Multicoloured.
3395 1 fo. Slovakian costume . . . 1·50 1·75
3396 2 fo. Type **785** . . . . 1·50 1·75
3397 3 fo. Croatian costume . . . . 1·50 1·75
3398 4 fo. Rumanian costume . . . 1·50 1·75

1981. 125th Anniv of Danube Commission. Paddle-steamers and Danube Commission stamps issued in 1967. Multicoloured.
3399 1 fo. Type **786** 35 20
3400 1 fo. "Arpad" (1834) and "Revfulop" on 60 fi. stamp . 35 20
3401 2 fo. "Szechenyi" (1853) and "Hunyadi" on 1 fo. stamp . 50 35
3402 2 fo. "Grof Szechenyi Istvan" (1896) and "Szekszard" on 1 fo. 50 stamp 50 35
3403 4 fo. "Zsofia" (1914) and "Miscolc" on 1 fo. 70 stamp 85 60
3404 6 fo. "Felszabadulas" (1917) and "Tihany" on 2 fo. stamp . . . . 1·50 1·25
3405 8 fo. "Rakoczi" (1964) and "Siraly I" on 2 fo. 50 stamp . 2·00 2·00

787 "Mother Breast-feeding" (pottery, Margit Kovacs)

788 "Pen Pals" (Rockwell)

1981. Christmas. Multicoloured.
3407 1 fo. Type **787** 35 10
3408 2 fo. "Madonna of Csurgo" (bronze Amerigo Tot) . . . 60 10

1981. Illustrations by Norman Rockwell and Anna Lesznai. Multicoloured.
3409 1 fo. Type **788** 15 10
3410 2 fo. "Courting under the Clock at Midnight" (Rockwell) . . 30 10
3411 2 fo. "Maiden Voyage" (Rockwell) 30 10
3412 4 fo. "Threading the Needle" (Rockwell) 70 40
3413 4 fo. "At the End of the Village" (detail) (Lesznai) . . 70 40
3414 5 fo. "Dance" (detail) (Lesznai) . . . . 1·00 55
3415 6 fo. "Sunday" (detail) (Lesznai) . . . . 1·25 90

790 Militiaman at Shooting Practice

791 Congress Emblem and Havana

1982. 25th Anniv of Workers' Militia. Mult.
3417 1 fo. Type **790** 15 10
3418 4 fo. Three generations of militiamen 60 10

1982. 10th World Trade Unions Federation Congress, Havana.
3419 **791** 2 fo. multicoloured . . . 20 10

792 Gyula Alpari

793 Dr. Robert Koch

1982. Birth Centenary of Gyula Alpari (journalist).
3420 **792** 2 fo. yellow, purple & brn 20 10

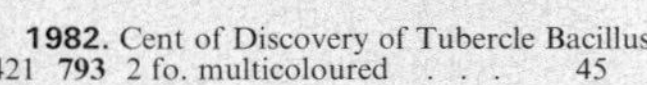

1982. Cent of Discovery of Tubercle Bacillus.
3421 **793** 2 fo. multicoloured . . . 45 15

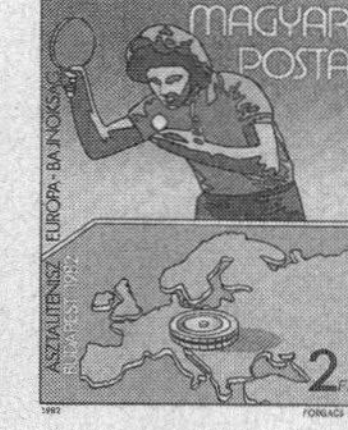

794 Tennis Racket and Ball

796 Table Tennis Player and Map of Europe

795 Hungary v Egypt, 1934

1982. Youth Stamp. European Junior Tennis Cup.
3422 **794** 4 fo. + 2 fo. mult . . . . 1·10 1·10

1982. World Cup Football Championship, Spain. Multicoloured.
3423 1 fo. Type **795** 20 10
3424 1 fo. Italy v Hungary, 1938 . . 20 10
3425 2 fo. West Germany v Hungary, 1954 . . . . 40 10
3426 2 fo. Hungary v Mexico, 1958 . 40 10
3427 4 fo. Hungary v England, 1962 80 10
3428 6 fo. Hungary v Brazil, 1966 . 1·25 15
3429 8 fo. Argentine v Hungary, 1978 . . . . 1·60 80

1982. European Table Tennis Championship, Budapest.
3431 **796** 2 fo. multicoloured . . . 45 10

797 "Pascali"

798 Georgi Dimitrov

1982. Roses. Multicoloured.
3432 1 fo. Type **797** 25 10
3433 1 fo. "Michele Meilland" . . . 25 10
3434 2 fo. "Diorama" 45 10
3435 2 fo. "Wendy Cussons" . . . 45 10
3436 3 fo. "Blue Moon" 75 15
3437 3 fo. "Invitation" 75 15
3438 4 fo. "Tropicana" . . . . . 1·25 65

1982. Birth Centenary of Georgi Dimitrov (Bulgarian statesman).
3440 **798** 2 fo. grey, green & brn . . 25 25

799 "Columbia" Space Shuttle

800 Watermark

1982. Space Research. Multicoloured.
3441 1 fo. Type **799** 20 10
3442 1 fo. Neil Armstrong (first man on Moon) 20 10
3443 2 fo. A. Leonov (first space-walker) 35 10
3444 2 fo. Yuri Gagarin (first man in space) 35 10
3445 4 fo. Laika (first dog in space) . 75 20
3446 4 fo. "Sputnik I" (first artificial satellite) 75 20
3447 6 fo. K. E. Tsiolkovsky (Russian scientist) . . . . . 1·25 40

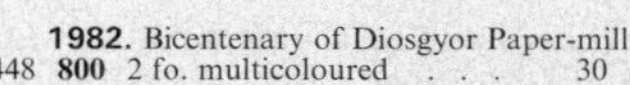

1982. Bicentenary of Diosgyor Paper-mill.
3448 **800** 2 fo. multicoloured . . . 30 10

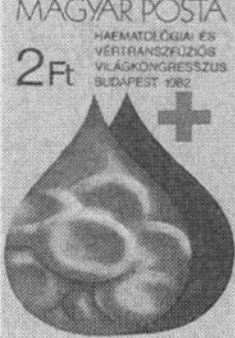

801 Rubik Cube

804 Blood Drop

1982. World Rubik Cube Championship, Budapest.
3449 **801** 2 fo. multicoloured . . . 40 10

1982. World Haematology Congress, Budapest.
3452 **804** 2 fo. multicoloured . . . 40 10

805 Zirc Abbey and Seal of King Bela III

806 Fishermen's Bastion, Budapest

1982. 800th Anniv of Zirc Abbey.
3453 **805** 2 fo. multicoloured . . . 30 10

1982. Stamp Day. Multicoloured.
3454 4 fo. + 2 fo. Type **806** . . . . 1·00 1·25
3455 4 fo. + 2 fo. Cupola of Parliament, Budapest . . . 1·00 1·25

808 Kner Emblem

1982. Cent of Kner Printing Office, Gyoma.
3457 **808** 2 fo. yell, blk and red . . 30 10

809 Agricultural Symbols on Map of Hungary

1982. "Agrofila '82" Stamp Exhibition, Godollo.
3458 **809** 5 fo. multicoloured . . . 1·00 1·00

810 Horse-drawn Bus and Underground Train

1982. 150th Anniv of Public Transport in Budapest.
3459 **810** 2 fo. multicoloured . . . 60 20

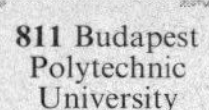

811 Budapest Polytechnic University

812 Gyorgy Boloni

1982. Bicentenary of University Engineering Education.
3460 **811** 2 fo. brown, stone & blue . 30 10

1982. Birth Centenary of Gyorgy Boloni (journalist).
3461 **812** 2 fo. yellow, brown and deep brown 30 10

813 Lenin

1982. 65th Anniv of Russian Revolution.
3462 **813** 5 fo. multicoloured . . . 70 10

814 Vuk and Bird

1982. Vuk the Fox Cub (cartoon character). Multicoloured.

3463	1 fo. Type **814**	20	10
3464	1 fo. Two dogs	20	10
3465	2 fo. Vuk and cock	40	10
3466	2 fo. Vuk and owl	40	10
3467	4 fo. Vuk and geese	75	10
3468	6 fo. Vuk and frog	1·25	35
3469	8 fo. Vuk, old fox and butterflies	1·60	85

815 St. Stephen (sculpture, Imre Varga)

816 Dog and Cat crossing road

1982. Works of Art in Hungarian Chapel, Vatican. Multicoloured.

3470	2 fo. Type **815**	35	40
3471	2 fo. "Pope Silvester II making donation to St. Stephen" (37 × 18 mm.)	35	40
3472	2 fo. "St. John of Capistrano ringing Angelus to commemorate Hungarian victory over Turks" (37 × 18 mm.)	35	40
3473	2 fo. "Pope Paul VI showing Cardinal Lekai site of Hungarian Chapel" (37 × 18 mm.)	35	40
3474	2 fo. "Pope John Paul II consecrating chapel" (37 × 18 mm.)	35	40
3475	2 fo. "Madonna" (sculpture, Imre Varga)	35	40

Nos. 3470/5 were printed together, se-tenant, Nos. 3471/4 forming a composite design of a relief by Amerigo Tot.

1982. New Year.
3476 **816** 2 fo. multicoloured . . . 50 10

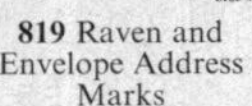

819 Raven and Envelope Address Marks

821 Student at School Door

820 "Ship of Peace" (Endre Szasz)

1983. 10th Anniv of Postal Codes.
3479 **819** 2 fo. black, grey & red . . 30 10

1983. Budapest Spring Festival.
3480 **820** 2 fo. grey, gold & black . 30 10

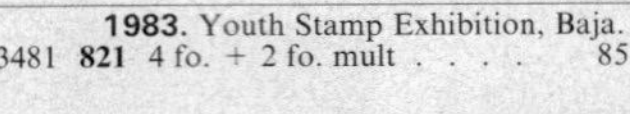

1983. Youth Stamp Exhibition, Baja.
3481 **821** 4 fo. + 2 fo. mult 85 85

822 Gyula Juhasz

823 Menner's Balloon, 1811

1983. Birth Cent of Gyula Juhasz (writer).
3482 **822** 2 fo. dp brn, brn & blk . . 30 10

1983. Air. Bicent of Manned Flight. Mult.

3483	1 fo. Type **823** (1st manned flight in Hungary)	20	10
3484	1 fo. Captive observation balloon at Budapest Exhibition, 1896	20	10
3485	2 fo. Pursuit race, 1904	50	25
3486	2 fo. Hot-air balloon "Pannonia", 1977	50	25
3487	4 fo. Hot-air balloon "Malev", 1981	90	50
3488	4 fo. Hungarian National Defence Union balloon, 1982	90	50
3489	5 fo. Non-rigid airship over Mecsek television tower, 1981	1·25	75

824 Szentgotthard Monastery and Seal

1983. 800th Anniv of Szentgotthard.
3491 **824** 2 fo. multicoloured . . . 30 10

825 Watermill, Tapolca

1983. "Tembal 83" Thematic Stamps Exhibition, Basel.
3492 **825** 5 fo. multicoloured . . . 90 90

827 Jeno Hamburger

828 "Giovanna d'Aragona"

1983. Birth Centenary of Jeno Hamburger (doctor and revolutionary).
3494 **827** 2 fo. brown, bl and red . . 30 10

1983. 500th Birth Anniv of Raphael (artist). Multicoloured.

3495	1 fo. Type **828**	15	10
3496	1 fo. "Lady with Unicorn"	15	10
3497	2 fo. "Madonna of the Chair"	30	10
3498	2 fo. "Madonna of the Grand Duke"	30	10
3499	4 fo. "La Muta"	60	10
3500	6 fo. "Lady with a Veil"	1·00	30
3501	8 fo. "La Fornaria"	1·25	45

829 Vagi and Newspapers

830 Bolivar and Map of Americas

1983. Birth Cent of Istvan Vagi (secretary of Socialist Workers' Party).
3503 **829** 2 fo. multicoloured . . . 30 10

1983. Birth Bicent of Simon Bolivar.
3504 **830** 2 fo. multicoloured . . . 30 10

831 Globe and Congress Emblem

833 Lesser Spotted Eagle

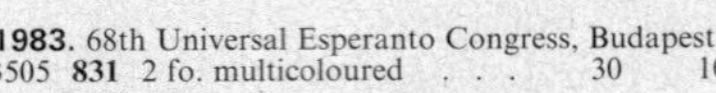

1983. 68th Universal Esperanto Congress, Budapest.
3505 **831** 2 fo. multicoloured . . . 30 10

1983. Birds of Prey. Multicoloured.

3507	1 fo. Type **833**	25	15
3508	1 fo. Imperial eagle	25	15
3509	2 fo. White-tailed sea eagle	50	20
3510	2 fo. Red-footed falcon	50	20
3511	4 fo. Saker falcon	80	45
3512	6 fo. Rough-legged buzzard	1·50	65
3513	8 fo. Common buzzard	2·00	1·00

834 Bee collecting Pollen

835 Old National Theatre (after R Alt)

1983. 29th Apimondia (Bee Keeping) Congress, Budapest.
3514 **834** 1 fo. multicoloured . . . 25 10

1983. Stamp Day. Engravings of Budapest Buildings.

3515	**835**	4 fo. + 2 fo. yellow, brown and black	1·25	1·25
3516	–	4 fo. + 2 fo. yellow, brown and black	1·25	1·25

DESIGN—HORIZ: No. 3516, Municipal concert hall, Pest (after H. Luders).

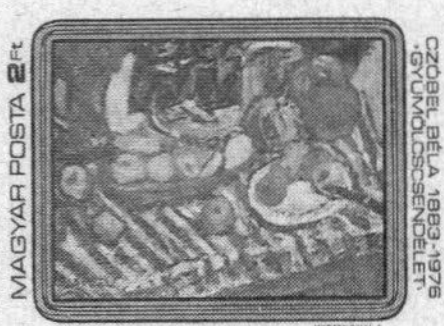

836 "Fruit-piece"

1983. Birth Centenary of Bela Czobel (artist).
3518 **836** 2 fo. multicoloured . . . 30 10

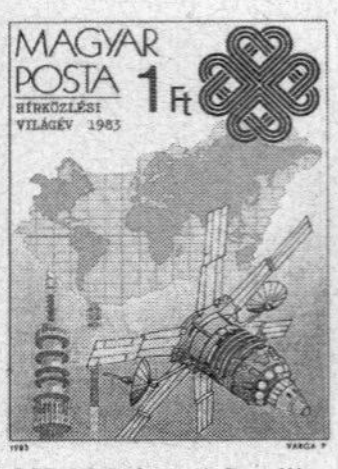

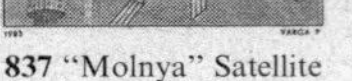

837 "Molnya" Satellite and Kekes TV Tower

838 Flags encircling Globe

1983. World Communications Year. Mult.

3519	1 fo. Type **837**	15	10
3520	1 fo. Dish aerials and rockets	15	10
3521	2 fo. Manual telephone exchange and modern "TMM-81" telephone	35	10
3522	3 fo. Computer terminal	50	10
3523	5 fo. Automatic letter-storing equipment	85	15
3524	8 fo. Teletext and newspaper mastheads	1·50	35

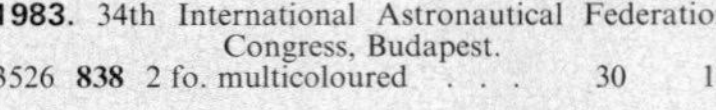

1983. 34th International Astronautical Federation Congress, Budapest.
3526 **838** 2 fo. multicoloured . . . 30 10

839 Kremlin, Moscow

1983. "Sozphilex '83" Stamp Exhibition, Moscow.
3527 **839** 2 fo. multicoloured . . . 35 35

841 Babits (after Jozsef Rippl-Ronai)

842 "Madonna with Rose"

1983. Birth Cent of Mihaly Babits (writer).
3529 **841** 2 fo. multicoloured . . . 30 10

1983. Christmas. Multicoloured.

3530	1 fo. Type **842**	10	10
3531	2 fo. Altar painting, Csikmenasag	20	10

843 Zanka

844 Ice Dancing

1983. Hungarian Resorts. Multicoloured.

3532	1 fo. Type **843**	30	10
3533	2 fo. Hajduszoboszlo	30	10
3534	5 fo. Heviz	70	10

1983. Winter Olympic Games, Sarajevo.

3535	**844**	1 fo. multicoloured	25	10
3536	–	1 fo. multicoloured	25	10
3537	–	2 fo. multicoloured (man lifting girl)	45	10
3538	–	2 fo. multicoloured	45	10
3539	–	4 fo. multicoloured (man with both arms bent)	75	15
3540	–	4 fo. multicoloured (man with one arm outstretched)	75	15
3541	–	6 fo. multicoloured	1·00	45

DESIGNS: Nos. 3536/41, Different ice dancing designs.

846 Csoma (statue) and Sepulchre, Darjeeling

847 "Energy" and Sun

1984. Birth Bicentenary of Sandor Korosi Csoma (traveller and philologist).
3544 **846** 2 fo. multicoloured . . . 30 10

1984. Save Energy Campaign.
3545 **847** 1 fo. red and black . . . 10 10

848 Parent and Child

850 Hair Ornaments from Rakamaz

1984. Youth Stamp.
3546 **848** 4 fo. + 2 fo. mult . . . . 1·10 1·25

1984. Archaeological Finds.

3548	**850**	1 fo. stone and brown	20	10
3549	–	1 fo. stone and brown	20	10
3550	–	2 fo. stone and brown	35	10
3551	–	2 fo. stone and brown	35	10
3552	–	4 fo. stone and brown	60	10
3553	–	6 fo. stone and brown	95	15
3554	–	8 fo. stone and brown	1·40	40

DESIGNS: No. 3549, Purse plates from Szolnok-Strazsahalom and Galgocz; 3550, Hair ornaments from Sarospatak; 3551, St. Stephen's sword (Prague) and Attila's sword (Aachen); 3552, Bowl from Ketpo; 3553, Stick handles from Hajdudorog and Szabadattyan; 3554, Saddle-bow from Izsak and bit and stirrups from Muszka.

INDEX

Countries can be quickly located by referring to the index at the end of this volume.

851 Cracow and Emblem

852 "Epiphile dilecta"

1984. 25th Session of Permanent Committee of Posts and Telecommunications, Cracow, Poland.
3555 **851** 2 fo. multicoloured . . . 30 10

1984. Butterflies. Multicoloured.
3556 1 fo. Type **852** 40 10
3557 1 fo. "Agrias sara" 40 10
3558 2 fo. Blue morpho ("Morpho cypris") 65 20
3559 2 fo. "Ancyluris formosissima" 65 20
3560 4 fo. African monarch . . . 1·00 30
3561 6 fo. "Catagramma cynosura" . 1·50 70
3562 8 fo. Paradise birdwing . . . . 1·90 85
No. 3557 is inscribed "Agra sara".

853 "Archer"

854 Hevesi

1984. Birth Centenary of Zsigmond Kisfaludy Strobl (sculptor).
3563 **853** 2 fo. brown and yellow . . 30 10

1984. Birth Cent of Akos Hevesi (activist in working-class movement).
3564 **854** 2 fo. multicoloured . . . 30 10

855 Doves around Map of Hungary

856 World Map and Airplane

1984. Peace Festival, Pusztavacs.
3565 **855** 2 fo. multicoloured . . . 30 10

1984. World Aerobatics Championship, Bekescsaba.
3566 **856** 2 fo. multicoloured . . . 50 20

857 Four-in-hand

858 Conference Emblem

1984. World Team-driving Championships, Szilvasvarad.
3567 **857** 2 fo. multicoloured . . . 50 15

1984. 14th Organization of Socialist Countries' Postal Administrations Conference, Budapest.
3568 **858** 2 fo. multicoloured . . . 30 10

859 Four-handled Vase

1984. Stamp Day. Multicoloured.
3569 1 fo. Type **859** 25 10
3570 2 fo. Platter with flower decoration 40 20

860 "Music crowned by Fame" (fresco, Mor Than)

1984. Reopening of Budapest Opera House. Multicoloured.
3572 1 fo. Type **860** 25 10
3573 2 fo. Central staircase 50 20
3574 5 fo. Auditorium . . . . . . 1·00 55

861 Atrium Hyatt Hotel

1984. Budapest Hotels along the Danube. Multicoloured.
3576 1 fo. Type **861** 35 10
3577 2 fo. Duna Intercontinental . . 40 20
3578 4 fo. Forum 95 30
3579 4 fo. Thermal Hotel, Margaret Island 60 30
3580 5 fo. Hilton 75 35
3581 8 fo. Gellert . . . . 1·25 50

862 Cep ("Boletus edulis")

863 Kato Haman (Labour Movement leader)

1984. Edible Mushrooms. Multicoloured.
3583 1 fo. Type **862** 50 15
3584 1 fo. Scotch bonnet ("Marasmius orcades") . . 50 15
3585 2 fo. Common morel ("Morchella esculenta") . . 75 15
3586 2 fo. Field mushroom ("Agaricus campester") . . 75 15
3587 3 fo. Chanterelle ("Cantharellus cibarius") 90 25
3588 3 fo. Parasol mushroom ("Macrolepiota procera") . . 90 25
3589 4 fo. Boot-lace fungus . . . . 1·25 60

1984. Birth Centenaries.
3590 **863** 2 fo. brown, gold and black 30 10
3591 – 2 fo. brown, gold and black 30 10
DESIGN: No. 3591, Bela Balazs (writer).

864 "Virgin and Child" (small altar, Trencseny)

865 Torah Crown (Buda)

1984. Christmas
3592 **864** 1 fo. multicoloured . . . 20 10

1984. Reopening of Jewish Museum, Budapest. Multicoloured.
3593 1 fo. Type **865** 25 10
3594 1 fo. Chalice (Moscow) 25 10
3595 2 fo. Torah shield (Vienna) . . . 40 10
3596 2 fo. Elias chalice (Warsaw) . . 40 10
3597 4 fo. Esrog holder (Augsburg) . 70 10
3598 6 fo. Candle holder (Warsaw) . 95 20
3599 8 fo. Urn (Pest) . . . . . . 1·25 45

866 Barn Owl

868 Novi Sad Bridge, Yugoslavia

1984. Owls. Multicoloured.
3600 1 fo. Type **866** 65 20
3601 1 fo. Little owl 65 20
3602 2 fo. Tawny owl . . . . . . 1·10 20
3603 2 fo. Long-eared owl . . . . 1·10 20
3604 4 fo. Snowy owl . . . . . . 1·75 45
3605 6 fo. Ural owl . . . . . . 2·25 75
3606 8 fo. Eagle owl . . . . . . 2·50 1·00

1985. Danube Bridges. Multicoloured.
3608 1 fo. Type **868** 20 10
3609 1 fo. Baja, Hungary 45 10
3610 2 fo. Arpad bridge, Budapest . . 75 15
3611 2 fo. Bratislava, Czechoslovakia 40 15
3612 4 fo. Reichsbrucke bridge, Vienna . . . . 1·25 30
3613 6 fo. Linz, Austria 95 50
3614 8 fo. Regensburg, West Germany . . . . 1·25 70

869 Laszlo Rudas

870 Woman and Flowers

1985. Birth Centenary of Laszlo Rudas (philosopher and socialist).
3616 **869** 2 fo. brn, gold & blk . . . 30 10

1985. International Women's Day.
3617 **870** 2 fo. multicoloured . . . 30 10

871 1925 200 k. Skiing Stamp

873 "Little Red Riding Hood"

1985. "Olymphilex '85" International Olympic Stamps Exhibition, Lausanne.
3618 **871** 4 fo. green, gold and blue . 70 15
3619 – 5 fo. bl, brn & gold . . . 90 15
DESIGN: 5 fo. 1925 300 k. Skating stamp.

1985. Birth Centenary of Jacob Grimm (folklorist).
3621 **873** 4 fo. + 2 fo. mult . . . . 1·25 85

874 Gyorgy Lukacs

875 Title Page

1985. Birth Centenary of Gyorgy Lukacs (philosopher).
3622 **874** 2 fo. multicoloured . . . 30 10

1985. 300th Anniv of Totfalusi Bible.
3623 **875** 2 fo. black and gold . . . 30 10

876 Peter Pazmany (founder)

877 Boxing

1985. 350th Anniv of Lorand Eotvos University.
3624 **876** 2 fo. grey and red 30 30

1985. 26th European Boxing Championships, Budapest.
3625 **877** 2 fo. multicoloured . . . 30 10

878 Women Footballers

1985. International Youth Year. Mult.
3626 1 fo. Type **878** 20 10
3627 2 fo. Windsurfing 40 10
3628 2 fo. Women exercising . . . 40 10
3629 4 fo. Karate 70 10
3630 4 fo. Go-karting 70 10
3631 5 fo. Hang gliding . . . . . . 1·00 35
3632 6 fo. Skate-boarding 95 40

879 Monorail Train

1985. "Expo '85" World's Fair, Tsukuba. Multicoloured.
3633 2 fo. Type **879** 75 20
3634 4 fo. Fuyo Theatre 70 20

880 Common Flicker

1985. Birth Bicentenary of John J. Audubon (ornithologist). Multicoloured.
3635 2 fo. Type **880** (postage) . . . 50 20
3636 2 fo. Bohemian waxwing . . . 50 20
3637 2 fo. Pileated woodpecker . . 50 20
3638 4 fo. Northern oriole 95 35

3639 4 fo. Common flicker (air) . . 95 35
3640 6 fo. Common cardinal . . . . 1·60 65

881 Nonius XXXVI

1985. Bicentenary of Horsebreeding at Mezohegyes. Multicoloured.
3641 1 fo. Type **881** 30 10
3642 2 fo. Furioso XXIII 50 10
3643 4 fo. Gidran I 90 15
3644 4 fo. Ramses III 90 15
3645 6 fo. Krozus I . . . . 1·40 40

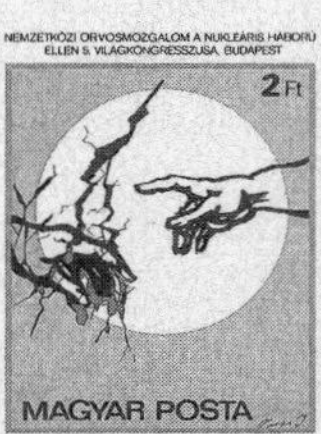

882 Hand pointing to Cracked Earth (Imre Varga)

883 Handel, Kettledrum and Horn

1985. Fifth Congress of International Association of Physicians against Nuclear War, Budapest.
3646 **882** 2 fo. multicoloured . . . 30 10

1985. Music Year. Multicoloured.
3647 1 fo. Type **883** (300th birth anniv) 30 10
3648 2 fo. Bach and Thomas Church organ, Leipzig (300th birth anniv) 55 10
3649 4 fo. Luigi Cherubini, harp, bass violin and baryton (225th anniv) 90 10
3650 4 fo. Chopin and piano (175th birth anniv) 90 10
3651 5 fo. Mahler, viola, double horn and kettledrum (125th birth anniv) . . . . 1·25 25
3652 6 fo. Ferenc Erkel, viola and bass tuba (175th birth anniv) . . . . 1·40 45

886 Key with Globe as Head **887** Flags on Computer Keyboards

1985. World Tourism Day.
3655 **886** 2 fo. multicoloured . . . 30 10

1985. "COMNET '85" Computer Networks Conference, Budapest.
3656 **887** 4 fo. multicoloured . . . 30 10

889 Water Holder **890** Italian 1960 5 l. Stamp

1985. Stamp Day. Haban Ceramics. Mult.
3658 1 fo. Type **889** 15 10
3659 2 fo. Tankard with cover . . . 40 30

1985. "Italia '85" International Stamp Exhibition, Rome.
3661 **890** 5 fo. multicoloured . . . 1·25 1·25

891 Dove and U.N. Emblem **892** Red Lily

1985. 40th Anniv of United Nations Organization.
3662 **891** 4 fo. turq, bl & dp bl . . 35 10

1985. Lily Family. Multicoloured.
3663 1 fo. Type **892** 25 10
3664 2 fo. Turk's-cap lily 35 10
3665 2 fo. Dog's tooth violet . . . 35 10
3666 4 fo. Tiger lily 65 10
3667 4 fo. Snake's-head fritillary . . 65 10
3668 5 fo. Day lily 85 30
3669 6 fo. "Bulbocodium vernum" . 1·10 40

893 Carol Singers

1985. Christmas.
3670 **893** 2 fo. multicoloured . . . 30 10

894 Istvan Ries **895** Three Houses under One Roof

1985. Birth Centenary of Istvan Ries (Minister of Justice).
3671 **894** 2 fo. multicoloured . . . 30 10

1985. SOS Childrens' Village.
3672 **895** 4 fo. + 2 fo. mult . . . . 1·40 1·40

896 Fantic "Sprinter", 1984

1985. Centenary of Motor Cycle.
3673 **896** 1 fo. black, orge & bl . . 25 10
3674 – 2 fo. black, yell & bl . . . 40 10
3675 – 2 fo. black, grn & grey . . 40 10
3676 – 4 fo. multicoloured . . . 65 10
3677 – 4 fo. black, grn & grey . . 65 10
3678 – 5 fo. multicoloured . . . 90 20
3679 – 6 fo. multicoloured . . . 1·10 45
DESIGNS: No. 3674, Harley-Davidson "Duo-Glide", 1960; 3675, Suzuki "Katana GSX", 1983; 3676, BMW "R47", 1927; 3677, Rudge-Whitworth, 1935; 3678, NSU, 1910; 3679, Daimler, 1885.

897 "Ice" Satellite and Dinosaurs **898** Bela Kun

1986. Air. Appearance of Halley's Comet. Multicoloured.
3680 2 fo. Type **897** 45 10
3681 2 fo. "Vega" satellite and detail of Bayeux Tapestry showing comet 45 10
3682 2 fo. "Suisei" satellite and German engraving of 1507 . 45 10
3683 4 fo. "Giotto" satellite and "The Magi" (tapestry after Giotto) 75 10
3684 4 fo. "Astron" satellite and Virgo, Leo, Corvus, Crater and Hydra constellations . . 75 10
3685 6 fo. Space shuttle and Edmond Halley (wrongly inscr "Edmund") . . . . 1·25 40

1986. Birth Centenary of Bela Kun (Communist Party leader).
3686 **898** 4 fo. multicoloured . . . 35 10

900 Guide Dog **901** Running for Ball

1986. The Blind.
3688 **900** 4 fo. multicoloured . . . 75 10

1986. World Cup Football Championship, Mexico. Multicoloured.
3689 2 fo. Type **901** 45 10
3690 2 fo. Heading ball 45 10
3691 4 fo. Tackling . . . . 1·00 10
3692 4 fo. Goalkeeper diving for ball . . . . 1·00 10
3693 4 fo. Goalkeeper catching ball . 1·00 10
3694 6 fo. Tackling (different) . . . 1·40 45

902 Cable Railway **904** Japanese and Hungarian Dolls

1986. Re-opening of Buda Castle Cable Railway.
3696 **902** 2 fo. brn, yell & orge . . 65 25

1986. Hungarian Days in Tokyo.
3698 **904** 4 fo. multicoloured . . . 75 10

905 Fay **906** Flag and "40"

1986. Birth Bicentenary of Andras Fay (writer, politician and founder of First Hungarian Savings Bank Union).
3699 **905** 4 fo. brown & pale brown 60 20

1986. Youth Stamp. 40th Anniv of Young Pioneers Movement.
3700 **906** 4 fo. + 2 fo. mult . . . . 1·00 1·00

907 Ferrari Racing Cars, 1961 and 1985

1986. Centenary of Motor Car. Multicoloured.
3701 2 fo. Type **907** 50 10
3702 2 fo. Alfa Romeo racing cars, 1932 and 1984 . . . . . . 50 10
3703 2 fo. Volkswagen "Beetle", 1936, and Porsche "959", 1986 . . . . 50 10
3704 4 fo. Renault "14 CV", 1902, and "5 GT Turbo", 1985 . . 1·00 15
3705 4 fo. Fiat "3 1/2", 1899, and "Ritmo", 1985 . . . . . 1·00 15
3706 6 fo. Daimler, 1886, and Mercedes-Benz "230 SE", 1986 . . . . 1·50 50

908 "Wasa" (Swedish ship of the line), 1628

1986. "Stockholmia '86" International Stamp Exhibition.
3707 **908** 2 fo. multicoloured . . . 2·00 1·50

909 Moritz Kaposi (cancer specialist) **911** "Tranquillity"

910 "Recapture of Buda Castle" (Gyula Benczur) (Illustration half-size)

1986. 14th International Cancer Congress, Budapest.
3708 **909** 4 fo. multicoloured . . . 75 10

1986. 300th Anniv of Recapture of Buda from Turks.
3709 **910** 4 fo. multicoloured . . . 60 10

1986. Stamp Day. Multicoloured.
3710 2 fo. Type **911** 40 30
3711 2 fo. "Confidence" 40 30

912 Fragment of 15th-cent Carpet from Anatolia

1986. 5th International Oriental Carpets and Tapestry Conference, Vienna and Budapest.
3713 **912** 4 fo. multicoloured . . . 60 10

914 Piano and Liszt **915** Dove

1986. 175th Birth Anniv of Franz Liszt (pianist and composer).
3715 **914** 4 fo. dp grn & grn . . . 75 15

1986. International Peace Year.
3716 **915** 4 fo. multicoloured . . . 80 70

917 Pogany **918** Munnich

1986. Birth Centenary of Jozsef Pogany (writer and journalist).
3718 **917** 4 fo. multicoloured . . . 50 10

1986. Birth Centenary of Ferenc Munnich (former Prime Minister).
3719 **918** 4 fo. multicoloured . . . 50 10

919 Heads

1986. 12th General Assembly of World Federation of Democratic Youth, Budapest.
3720 **919** 4 fo. multicoloured . . . 50 10

920 Apricots ("Kajszi" C.235)

1986. Fruits. Multicoloured.
3721 2 fo. Type **920** 50 10
3722 2 fo. Cherries ("Good bearer of Erd") 50 10
3723 4 fo. Apples ("Jonathan" M.14) . . . . 1·00 15
3724 4 fo. Raspberries ("Nagymaros") . . . . . 1·00 15
3725 4 fo. Peaches ("Piroska") . . . 1·00 15
3726 6 fo. Grapes ("Zalagyongye") . 1·25 40

921 Forgach Castle, Szecseny **922** Wild Cat

1986. Castles. Inscr "MAGYAR POSTA".
3727 **921** 2 fo. bistre and yellow . . 15 10
3728 – 3 fo. green & lt green . . 15 10
3729 – 4 fo. blue and light blue . 20 10
3730 – 5 fo. red and pink . . . 25 10
3731 – 6 fo. brown & orange . . 30 10
3732 – 8 fo. red and orange . . . 60 10
3733 – 10 fo. brown & ochre . . 60 10
3734 – 20 fo. green and yellow . 1·10 35
3735 – 30 fo. lt green & green . 1·50 50
3736 – 40 fo. blue & lt blue . . 1·90 70
3737 – 50 fo. deep red & red . . 2·50 90
3738 – 70 fo. dp grey & grey . . 3·50 1·25
3739 – 100 fo. violet and lilac . . 4·75 1·75

DESIGNS: 3 fo. Savoya Castle, Rackeve; 4 fo. Batthyany Castle, Kormend; 5 fo. Szechenyi Castle, Nagycenk; 6 fo. Rudnyanszky Castle, Nagyteteny; 8 fo. Szapary Castle, Buk; 10 fo. Festetics Castle, Keszthely; 20 fo. Brunswick Castle, Martonvasar; 30 fo. De La Motte Castle, Noszvaj; 40 fo. L'Huillier-Coburg Castle, Edeleny; 50 fo. Teleki-Degenfeld Castle, Szirak; 70 fo. Magochy Castle, Pacin; 100 fo. Esterhazy Castle, Fertod.
See also Nos. 3888 and 4045/9.

1986. Protected Animals. Multicoloured.
3740 2 fo. Type **922** 50 10
3741 2 fo. European otter 50 10
3742 2 fo. Stoat 50 10
3743 4 fo. Eurasian red squirrel . . 1·00 15
3744 4 fo. East European hedgehog . 1·00 15
3745 6 fo. European pond turtle . . 1·50 40

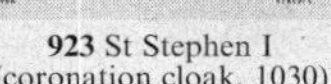

923 St Stephen I (coronation cloak, 1030)
924 Death Cap ("Amanita phalloides")

1986. Kings (1st series).
3746 **923** 2 fo. brown, bl & red . . 40 10
3747 – 2 fo. brown, grey & red . 40 10
3748 – 4 fo. brown, grn & red . . 75 10
3749 – 4 fo. brown, grey & red . 75 10
3750 – 6 fo. brown, bl & red . . 1·25 35
DESIGNS: No. 3747, Geza I (enamel portrait on Hungarian crown, 1070); 3748, St. Ladislas I (Gyor Cathedral, 1400); 3749, Bela III (Kalocsa Cathedral statue, 1200); 3750, Bela IV (Jak church statue, 1230).
See also Nos. 3835/7.

1986. Fungi. Multicoloured.
3751 2 fo. Type **924** 70 25
3752 2 fo. Fly agaric ("Amanita muscaria") 70 25
3753 2 fo. Red-staining inocybe ("Inocybe patouillardi") . . 70 25
3754 4 fo. Olive-wood pleurotus ("Omphalotus olearius") . . 1·50 60
3755 4 fo. Panther cap ("Amanita pantherina") . . . . . . 1·50 60
3756 6 fo. Beefsteak morel . . . . 2·10 1·00

925 Banded Gourami
926 "Sitting Woman"

1987. Fishes. Multicoloured.
3757 2 fo. Type **925** 60 10
3758 2 fo. Thread-finned rainbowfish ("Iriathorina werneri") . . . 60 10
3759 2 fo. Zebra mbuna ("Pseudotropheus zebra") . 60 10
3760 4 fo. Ramirez dwarf cichlid ("Papiliochromis ramirezi") . 1·25 25
3761 4 fo. Multicoloured lyretail ("Aphyosemion multicolor") . . . . 1·25 25
3762 6 fo. Bleeding-heart tetra ("Hyphessobrycon erythrostigma") . . . . 1·90 75

1987. Birth Centenary of Bela Uitz (painter).
3763 **926** 4 fo. multicoloured 50 10

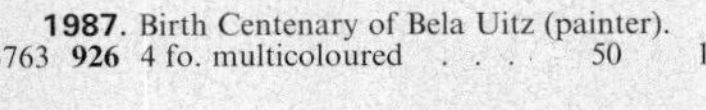

927 Abstract
928 Flag, Books, Torch and Dove

1987. Birth Centenary of Lajos Kassak (writer and painter).
3764 **927** 4 fo. black and red . . . 50 10

1987. 30th Anniv of Young Communist League.
3765 **928** 4 fo. + 2 fo. mult . . . . 1·00 1·10

929 Hippocrates (medical oath)
930 Food Jar, Hodmezovasarhely

1987. Pioneers of Medicine (1st series).
3766 **929** 2 fo. brown and blue . . 50 10
3767 – 4 fo. green and black . . 1·00 10
3768 – 4 fo. blue and black . . . 1·00 10
3769 – 4 fo. brown and black . . 1·00 10
3770 – 6 fo. brown and black . . 1·50 35
DESIGNS: No. 3767, Avicenna ("Kanun" book of medical rules); 3768, Ambroise Pare (improved treatment of wounds); 3769, William Harvey (circulation of blood); 3770, Ignac Semmelweis (aseptic treatment of wounds).
See also Nos. 3939/43.

1987. Neolithic and Copper Age Art. Multicoloured.
3771 **930** 2 fo. brown and green . . 60 10
3772 – 4 fo. brown and flesh . . 1·00 10
3773 – 4 fo. brown and pink . . 1·00 10
3774 – 5 fo. brown and green . . 1·40 25
DESIGNS: No. 3772, Altar, Szeged; 3773, Statue with sickle, Szegvar-Tuzkoves; 3774, Vase with face, Center.

932 Old and Modern Ambulances

1987. Centenary of Hungarian First Aid Association.
3776 **932** 4 fo. multicoloured . . . 65 10

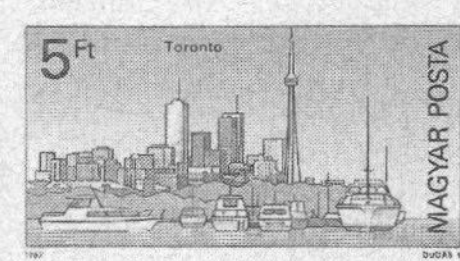

933 Toronto ("Capex '87")

1987. International Stamp Exhibitions. Mult.
3777 5 fo. Type **933** . . . . 1·25 1·00
3778 5 fo. "Olymphilex 87" building, Rome . . . . 1·00 85
3779 5 fo. "Hafnia 87" building, Copenhagen . . . . 1·00 85

934 Jozsef Marek

1987. Bicentenary of University of Veterinary Sciences, Budapest.
3780 **934** 4 fo. silver, blue & blk . . 50 10

935 Teleki, Route Map and Porters

1987. Centenary of Samuel Teleki's African Expedition.
3781 **935** 4 fo. multicoloured . . . 50 10

936 Printing Shop (17th-century wood-print, Abraham von Werdt)
937 James Cook and H.M.S. "Resolution"

1987. 125th Anniv of Hungarian Printing, Paper and Press Workers' Union.
3782 **936** 4 fo. brown and stone . . 50 10

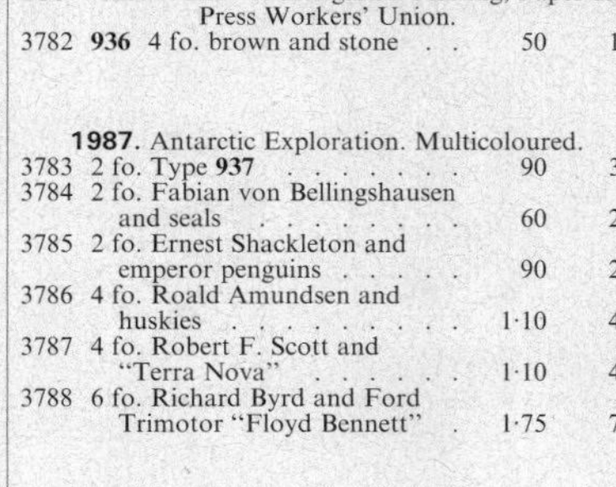

1987. Antarctic Exploration. Multicoloured.
3783 2 fo. Type **937** 90 30
3784 2 fo. Fabian von Bellingshausen and seals 60 20
3785 2 fo. Ernest Shackleton and emperor penguins 90 20
3786 4 fo. Roald Amundsen and huskies . . . . 1·10 45
3787 4 fo. Robert F. Scott and "Terra Nova" . . . . . . 1·10 45
3788 6 fo. Richard Byrd and Ford Trimotor "Floyd Bennett" . 1·75 70

938 Old and New Railway Emblems and Institute
939 Flowers and Dolphin

1987. Centenary of Railway Officers' Training Institute.
3790 **938** 4 fo. black and blue . . . 60 25

1987. Stamp Day. Carvings from Buda Castle.
3791 **939** 2 fo. ind, bl & azure . . . 30 10
3792 – 4 fo. ol, grn & turq . . . 60 40
DESIGN: 4 fo. King Matthias's arms.

940 Jesse Altar
941 "Orchis purpurea"

1987. Gyongyospata Church.
3794 **940** 4 fo. multicoloured . . . 75 85

1987. Orchids. Multicoloured.
3795 2 fo. Type **941** 50 10
3796 2 fo. "Cypripedium calceolus" . 50 10
3797 4 fo. "Ophrys scolopax" . . . 90 10
3798 4 fo. "Himantoglossum hircinum" 90 10
3799 5 fo. "Cephalanthera rubra" . 1·25 20
3800 6 fo. "Epipactis atrorubens" . 1·50 40

942 Speed Skating
945 "The White Crane" (Japanese folk tale)

1987. Winter Olympic Games, Calgary. Mult.
3802 2 fo. Type **942** 40 10
3803 2 fo. Cross-country skiing . . 40 10
3804 4 fo. Biathlon 80 10
3805 4 fo. Ice hockey 80 10
3806 4 fo. Four-man bobsleigh . . . 80 10
3807 6 fo. Ski jumping . . . . . . 1·25 30

1987. Fairy Tales. Multicoloured.
3816 2 fo. Type **945** 45 10
3817 2 fo. "The Fox and the Raven" (Aesop) 45 10
3818 4 fo. "The Hare and The Tortoise" (Aesop) 90 20
3819 4 fo. "The Ugly Duckling" (Hans Christian Andersen) . 90 20
3820 6 fo. "The Brave Little Lead Soldier" (Hans Christian Andersen) . . . . 1·40 40

946 Zeppelin and Airship LZ-2

1988. 150th Birth Anniv of Ferdinand von Zeppelin (airship pioneer).
3821 **946** 2 fo. black and blue . . . 50 20
3822 – 4 fo. dp brown & brn . . 90 50
3823 – 4 fo. purple and lilac . . 90 50
3824 – 8 fo. olive and green . . 1·60 80
DESIGNS: No. 3822, LZ-4; 3823, "Schwaben"; 3824, "Graf Zeppelin".

947 Skater
949 Monus

1988. World Figure Skating Championships, Budapest. Skaters from 19th-century to date. Multicoloured.
3825 2 fo. Type **947** 40 10
3826 2 fo. Man wearing hat 40 10
3827 4 fo. Woman 80 10
3828 4 fo. Man in hat and coat . . 80 10
3829 5 fo. Woman in modern skating dress . . . . 1·00 10
3830 6 fo. Pair . . . . 1·25 35

1988. Birth Centenary of Illes Monus (newspaper editor).
3833 **949** 4 fo. blue, red & black . . 40 10

1988. Kings (2nd series). As T **923**.
3835 2 fo. brown, green & red . . . 30 10
3836 4 fo. brown, blue and red . . . 55 10
3837 6 fo. brown, violet & red . . . 90 10
DESIGNS: 2 fo. Karoly I (Charles Robert) (detail of decorated initial from "Illuminated Chronicle", 1358); 4 fo. Lajos the Great (relief, St. Simeon's reliquary, Zara, 1380); 6 fo. Zsigmond (Sigismund of Luxembourg) (after great seal, 1433).

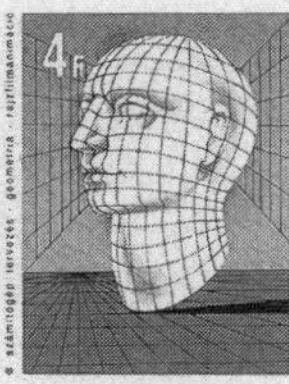

951 Rowing
952 Computer Drawing of Head

1988. Olympic Games, Seoul. Multicoloured.
3838 2 fo. Type **951** 30 10
3839 4 fo. Hurdling 50 10
3840 4 fo. Fencing 50 10
3841 6 fo. Boxing 80 30

1988. 6th Anniv of "Dilemma" (first computer-animated film).
3843 **952** 4 fo. multicoloured . . . 50 10

953 Card and Emblem

1988. Eurocheque Congress, Budapest.
3844 **953** 4 fo. multicoloured . . . 50 10

954 "Santa Maria", 1492 **955** Damaged Head

1988. Ships. Multicoloured.
3845 2 fo. Type **954** 60 40
3846 2 fo. "Mayflower", 1620 . . . 60 40
3847 2 fo. "Sovereign of the Seas", 1637 . . . . 60 40
3848 4 fo. "Jylland" (steam warship), 1860 . . . . 1·25 55
3849 6 fo. "St. Jupat" (yacht), 1985 . 1·90 75

1988. Anti-Drugs Campaign.
3850 **955** 4 fo. multicoloured . . . 50 10

956 Green-winged Teal ("Anas crecca") **957** Steam Train

1988. Wild Ducks. Multicoloured.
3851 2 fo. Type **956** 75 40
3852 2 fo. Goldeneye ("Bucephula clangula") 75 40
3853 4 fo. European wigeon ("Anas penelope") . . . . 1·40 60
3854 4 fo. Red-crested pochard ("Netta rufina") . . . . . . 1·40 60
3855 6 fo. Gadwell . . . . 1·75 80

1988. Exhibits in Toy Museum, Kecskemet. Multicoloured.
3857 2 fo. Type **957** . . . . 1·40 30
3858 2 fo. See-saw 35 10
3859 4 fo. + 2 fo. Pecking chicks . . 1·00 20
3860 5 fo. Johnny Hussar 85 15

958 Facade **959** Congress Emblem

1988. 450th Anniv of Debrecen Calvinist College.
3861 **958** 4 fo. multicoloured . . . 50 10

1988. 58th American Society of Travel Agents Congress, Budapest.
3862 **959** 4 fo. multicoloured . . . 50 10

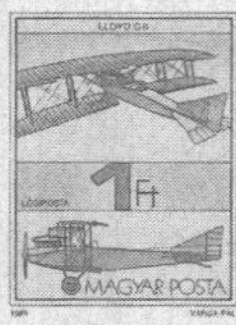

960 Lloyd C.II Biplane **961** Post Official's Collar and Badge

1988. Air. Hungarian Biplanes.
3863 **960** 1 fo. green 15 10
3864 – 2 fo. purple 35 10
3865 – 4 fo. bistre 60 25
3866 – 10 fo. blue . . . . 1·50 75
3867 – 12 fo. red . . . . 1·90 75
DESIGNS: 2 fo. Hansa Brandenburg C-1; 4 fo. UFAG C-1; 10 fo. Gerte 13 scout plane; 12 fo. WM 13 trainer.

1988. Centenary of Post Office Training School.
3868 **961** 4 fo. red, blue & brn . . . 50 10

962 Baross and Postal Savings Bank, Budapest

1988. Stamp Day. 140th Birth Anniv of Gabor Baross (politician). Multicoloured.
3869 2 fo. Type **962** 40 40
3870 4 fo. Baross with telephone and telegraph equipment 75 75

963 Lengyel **964** Christmas Tree

1988. Birth Centenary of Gyula Lengyel (labour movement activist).
3872 **963** 4 fo. multicoloured 50 10

1988. Christmas.
3873 **964** 2 fo. multicoloured . . . 35 10

965 Richard Adolf Zsigmondy (chemistry, 1925) **966** Szakasits

1988. Noble Prize Winners.
3874 **965** 2 fo. dp brown & brown . 35 10
3875 – 2 fo. dp green & green . . 35 10
3876 – 2 fo. dp brown & brown . 35 10
3877 – 4 fo. dp mauve & mauve . 70 10
3878 – 4 fo. green and grey . . . 70 10
3879 – 6 fo. brown & lt brown . 1·10 20
DESIGNS: No. 3875, Robert Barany (medicine, 1914,); 3876, Gyorgy Hevesy (chemistry, 1943); 3877, Albert Szent-Gyorgyi (chemistry, 1937); 3878, Gyorgy Bekesy (medicine, 1961); 3879, Denes Gabor (physics, 1971).

1988. Birth Centenary of Arpad Szakasits (President, 1948–50).
3880 **966** 4 fo. multicoloured . . . 50 10

968 Silver Teapot from Pest, 1846

1988. Metal Work.
3882 **968** 2 fo. blue and brown . . 40 10
3883 – 2 fo. deep brown & brn . 40 10
3884 – 4 fo. lilac and brown . . 80 15
3885 – 5 fo. green and brown . . 1·00 20
DESIGNS: No. 3883, 18th-century silver pot, Buda; 3884, Silver sugar basin from Pest, 1822; 3885, Pierced cast iron plate from Resicabanya, 1850.

969 Emblem **970** Wallisch

1989. Foundation of Post and Savings Bank Company.
3886 **969** 5 fo. blue, silver & black . 50 10

1989. Birth Centenary of Kalman Wallisch (workers' movement activist).
3887 **970** 3 fo. blue and red 35 10

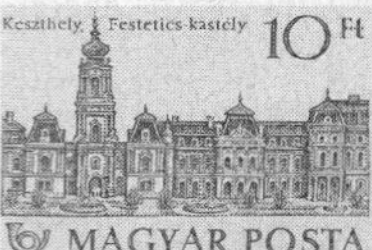

971 Festetics Castle, Keszthely

1989.
3888 **971** 10 fo. brown & bistre . . 60 10

972 Athletes **974** Gyetvai

1989. 2nd International Indoor Athletics Championships, Budapest.
3889 **972** 3 fo. multicoloured . . . 35 10

1989. Birth Centenary of Janos Gyetvai (journalist).
3891 **974** 3 fo. green and red . . . 35 10

975 "Sky-high Tree" (detail, carpet)

1989. 27th National Youth Stamp Exhibition, Veszprem.
3892 **975** 5 fo. + 2 fo. mult . . . . 1·10 1·10

976 O Bajan

1989. Bicentenary of Babolina Stud Farm. Mult.
3893 3 fo. Type **976** 50 50
3894 3 fo. Stud officer 50 50
3895 3 fo. Gazal II 50 50

977 Disabled People and "ART '89" **978** Arrangement of Narcissi, Crocuses and Violets

1989. "Art '89" International Festival of Disabled People and their Artist Friends.
3896 **977** 5 fo. multicoloured . . . 50 10

1989. Flower Arrangements. Multicoloured.
3897 2 fo. Type **978** 30 10
3898 3 fo. Irises, tulips and lilies (horiz) 45 10
3899 3 fo. Roses and chrysanthemums 45 10
3900 5 fo. Dahlias and lilies (horiz) . 75 15
3901 10 fo. Roses, Chinese lanterns and holly . . . . 1·40 30

979 Birds

1989. Bicentenary of French Revolution.
3902 **979** 5 fo. black, red & blue . . 50 10

980 Model of Veszto Church **981** Photographer with Camera

1989. Veszto Church Excavation.
3904 **980** 3 fo. multicoloured . . . 35 10

1989. 150th Anniv of Photography.
3905 **981** 5 fo. lt brown, blk & brn . 50 10

982 Turistvandi Water-mill

1989. Mills. Multicoloured.
3906 2 fo. Type **982** 25 10
3907 3 fo. Szarvas horse-driven mill . 40 10
3908 5 fo. Kiskunhalas windmill . . 65 15
3909 10 fo. Shipmill, River Drava . 1·25 25

984 Messenger Glider

1989. "Old Timer" Rally, Budakeszi Airport, and 60th Anniv of Gliding in Hungary. Multicoloured.
3911 3 fo. Type **984** 65 35
3912 5 fo. Pal glider . . . . 1·10 50

985 Sand Lizard

1989. Endangered Reptiles. Multicoloured.
3913 2 fo. Type **985** 25 10
3914 3 fo. Green lizard 40 10
3915 5 fo. Grass snake ("Natrix natrix") 65 15
3916 5 fo. Orsinis's viper ("Vipera rakosiensis") 65 15
3917 10 fo. European pond terrapin . 1·40 25

986 Competitors

1989. 31st World Modern Pentathlon Championships, Budapest.
3918 **986** 5 fo. multicoloured . . . 50 10

1989. Nos. 3851 and 3853 surch.
3919 3 fo. on 2 fo. mult 55 30
3920 5 fo. on 4 fo. mult 85 50

988 Baradla Cave, Aggtelek **989** Carriage

1989. 10th World Speleology Congress, Budapest. Multicoloured.
3921 3 fo. Type **988** 30 10
3922 5 fo. Szemlohegy cave, Budapest 50 10
3923 10 fo. Anna Cave, Lillafured . 1·10 20
3924 12 fo. Tapolca cave lake, Miskolctapolca . . . . . . 1·25 25

1989. World Two-in-Hand Carriage Driving Championship, Balatonfenyves.
3925 **989** 5 fo. multicoloured . . . 75 10

990 Zsuzsa Kossuth (War of Independence nurse) **993** Flowers and Broken Barbed Wire

1989. Stamp Day. 125th Anniv of Red Cross Movement.
3926 **990** 5 fo. black, blue & red . . 50 50
3927 – 10 fo. multicoloured . . . 1·10 1·10
DESIGN: 10 fo. Florence Nightingale (nursing pioneer) and decoration.

1989. Dismantling of Electrified Fence on Western Border.
3931 **993** 5 fo. multicoloured . . . 50 10

994 "Conquest of Hungary" (Mor Than)

1989. 1100th Anniv of Arpad as Prince of the Magyars.
3932 **994** 5 fo. multicoloured . . . 75 10

995 Flight into Egypt **996** Nehru

1989. Christmas.
3933 **995** 3 fo. multicoloured . . . 60 10

1989. Birth Centenary of Jawaharlal Nehru (Indian statesman).
3934 **996** 3 fo. brown and stone . . 70 10

997 "Miska" (Dezso Korniss)

1990. Modern Hungarian Paintings. Mult.
3935 3 fo. Type **997** 40 10
3936 5 fo. "Sunrise" (Lajos Kassak) 65 10
3937 10 fo. "Grotesque Burial" (Endre Balint) . . . . . . 1·40 20
3938 12 fo. "Remembered Toys" (Tihamer Gyarmathy) . . . 1·60 25

1989. Pioneers of Medicine (2nd series). As T **929**.
3939 3 fo. green 40 10
3940 3 fo. brown 40 10
3941 4 fo. black 55 10
3942 6 fo. grey 80 15
3943 10 fo. purple . . . . 1·40 30
DESIGNS: No. 3939, Claudius Galenus (anatomist and physiologist); 3940, Paracelsus (pharmacy); 3941, Andreas Vesalius (dissection); 3942, Rudolf Virchow (pathology of cells); 3943, Ivan Petrovich Pavlov (blood circulation, digestion and nervous system).

998 Hands holding Coin

1990. 150th Anniv of Savings Banks in Hungary.
3944 **998** 5 fo. multicoloured . . . 50 10

999 Sewing Machine **1000** Wall Telephone and Jozsefvaros Telephone Exchange

1990. 125th Anniv of Singer Sewing Machine.
3945 **999** 5 fo. brn & cinnamon . . 50 10

1990. Posts and Telecommunications. Mult.
3946 3 fo. Type **1000** 25 10
3947 5 fo. Pillar box and Head Post Office, Budapest 40 10

1001 Bullfinch ("Pyrrhula pyrrhula") **1002** "Protea compacta"

1990. Birds. Multicoloured.
3960 3 fo. Type **1001** 65 35
3961 3 fo. Common kingfisher ("Alcedo atthis") 65 35
3962 3 fo. Syrian woodpecker ("Dendrocopos syriacus") . 65 35
3963 5 fo. Hoopoe ("Upupa epops") . . . . 1·25 65
3964 5 fo. European bee eater ("Merops apiaster") . . . . 1·25 65
3965 10 fo. Common roller . . . . 2·25 1·25

1990. African Flowers. Multicoloured.
3966 3 fo. Type **1002** 40 10
3967 3 fo. "Leucadendron spissifolium" 40 10
3968 3 fo. "Leucadendron tinctum pubibracteolatum" 40 10
3969 5 fo. "Protea barbigera" . . . 70 15
3970 5 fo. "Protea lepidocarpodendron neriifolia" 70 15
3971 10 fo. "Protea cynaroides" . . 1·40 30

1003 Sarospatak Teachers' Training School

1990. 28th National Youth Stamp Exhibition, Sarospatak.
3973 **1003** 8 fo. + 4 fo. mult . . . . 1·40 1·40

1004 Janos Hunyadi (regent) **1006** Gaspar Karoli (statue)

1990. The Hunyadis. Multicoloured.
3974 5 fo. Type **1004** 50 15
3975 5 fo. King Matthias I Corvinus 50 15

1990. 400th Anniv of Publication of Karoli Bible (first Hungarian translation).
3977 **1006** 8 fo. cream, grn & red . . 1·00 1·00

1007 Footballers

1990. World Cup Football Championship, Italy.
3978 **1007** 3 fo. multicoloured . . . 35 10
3979 – 5 fo. multicoloured (ball on ground) 60 10
3980 – 5 fo. multicoloured (ball in air) 60 10
3981 – 8 fo. multicoloured (dribbling) 95 15
3982 – 8 fo. mult (heading ball into goal) 95 15
3983 – 10 fo. multicoloured . . 1·25 20
DESIGNS: Nos. 3979/83, Various footballing scenes.

1008 Hand writing with Quill Pen

1990. 300th Birth Anniv of Kelemen Mikes (writer).
3985 **1008** 8 fo. black and gold . . 90 10

1009 "Weaver" (Noemi Ferenczy) **1010** Kazinczy

1990. Birth Centenaries of Noemi and Beni Ferenczy (artists).
3986 **1009** 3 fo. multicoloured . . . 60 10
3987 – 5 fo. black & brown . . 85 10
DESIGN: 5 fo. Bronze figure (Beni Ferenczy).

1990. 159th Death Anniv of Ferenc Kazinczy (writer and language reformer).
3988 **1010** 8 fo. multicoloured . . . 65 10

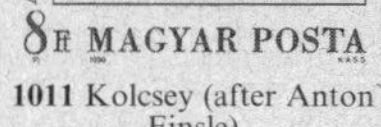

1011 Kolcsey (after Anton Einsle) **1013** Cabernet Franc Grapes, Hajos

1012 "St. Stephen" (carving in Parliament Hall) and Arms

1990. Birth Bicentenary of Ferenc Kolcsey (composer of national anthem).
3989 **1011** 8 fo. multicoloured . . . 65 10

1990. New State Arms.
3990 **1012** 8 fo. multicoloured . . . 65 10

1990. Wine Grapes and Regions (1st series). Multicoloured.
3992 3 fo. Type **1013** 30 10
3993 5 fo. Cabernet Sauvignon, Villany 45 10
3994 8 fo. Riesling, Badacsony . . . 75 15
3995 8 fo. Kadarka, Szekszard . . . 75 15
3996 8 fo. Leanyka, Eger 75 15
3997 10 fo. Furmint, Tokaj-Hegyalja . . . . 1·00 15
See also Nos. 4363/5 and 4436/7.

1014 "Feast"

1990. Stamp Day. Paintings by Ender Szasz. Multicoloured.
3998 8 fo. Type **1014** 80 80
3999 12 fo. "Message" . . . . . . 1·25 1·25

1015 Tarbosaurus

1990. Prehistoric Animals. Multicoloured.
4001 3 fo. Type **1015** 30 10
4002 5 fo. Brontosaurus 45 10
4003 5 fo. Dimorphodon 45 10
4004 5 fo. Stegosaurus 45 10
4005 8 fo. Platybelodon 75 15
4006 10 fo. Mammoth . . . . . . 1·00 20

1016 Dinosaurs reading

1990. International Literacy Year.
4007 **1016** 10 fo. multicoloured . . 90 10

1017 Bird holding Letter

1990. 60th Anniv of Stamp Museum, Budapest.
4008 **1017** 5 fo. red and green . . . 50 10

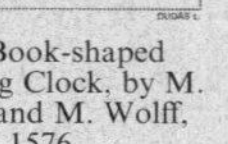

1019 Book-shaped Travelling Clock, by M. Fenich and M. Wolff, 1576 **1020** "Madonna and Child" (Sandro Botticelli)

1990. Clocks. Multicoloured.
4010 3 fo. Type **1019** 40 10
4011 5 fo. Clock by Hans Schmidt, 1643 . . . . 65 10
4012 5 fo. Rococo style clock by J. M. Welz, 1790 . . . . . . 65 10
4013 10 fo. Clock by Johann Hillrich, 1814 . . . . 1·40 25

1990. Christmas.
4014 **1020** 5 fo. multicoloured . . . 50 10

1021 Lorand Eotvos (inventor) and Torsion Pendulum **1022** "Mandevilla splendens"

1991. Centenary of Torsion Pendulum.
4015 **1021** 12 fo. multicoloured . . 85 10

1991. Flowers of the Americas. Mult.
4016 5 fo. Type **1022** 25 10
4017 7 fo. "Lobelia cardinalis" . . . 35 10
4018 7 fo. Cup and saucer flower . . 35 10
4019 12 fo. "Steriphoma paradoxa" . 60 15
4020 15 fo. Shrimp plant 75 20

1023 Post Office, Budapest **1024** "Ulysses" Jupiter Probe

1991. Hungarian Full Membership of Council of Europe and Entry into C.E.P.T. (European Posts and Telecommunications Conference). Mult.
4022 5 fo. Type **1023** . . . . . . 2·50 1·75
4023 7 fo. Post Office, Pecs . . . . 3·50 2·50

1991. Europa. Europe in Space. Multicoloured.
4024 12 fo. Type **1024** 85 70
4025 30 fo. "Cassini" and "Huygens" (wrongly inscr "Hughes") Saturn probes . . 1·90 1·50

1025 "Peter and the Wolf" (tapestry, Gabriella Hajnal)

1991. Youth Stamp.

4026 **1025** 12 fo. + 6 fo. mult . . . 85 85

1026 Gorilla

1991. 125th Anniv of Budapest Zoological and Botanic Gardens. Multicoloured.

4027 7 fo. Type **1026** 35 20
4028 12 fo. Polar bear 75 40
4029 12 fo. Rhinoceros 75 40
4030 12 fo. Keel-billed toucan . . . 75 40
4031 20 fo. Orchid and glasshouse . 95 55

1027 Teleki **1028** Map, Emblem and Fencers

1991. 50th Death Anniv of Count Pal Teleki (Prime Minister, 1920–21 and 1939–41).

4032 **1027** 12 fo. brown, cinnamon and black 80 30

1991. 44th World Fencing Championships, Budapest.

4033 **1028** 12 fo. multicoloured . . 80 30

1029 Mariapocs

1991. Visit of Pope John Paul II (1st issue). Shrines to Virgin Mary. Multicoloured.

4034 7 fo. Type **1029** 35 20
4035 12 fo. Mariagyud 55 30
4036 12 fo. Celldomolk 55 30
4037 12 fo. Mariaremete 55 30
4038 20 fo. Esztergom 95 55

1030 "Appeggi Landscape" and Marko

1991. Birth Bicent of Karoly Marko (painter).

4039 **1030** 12 fo. multicoloured . . 80 30

1031 Lilienthal and Monoplane Gliders, 1891

1991. Centenary of First Heavier-than-Air Manned Flight by Otto Lilienthal.

4040 **1031** 7 fo. blk, ochre & brn . . 55 30
4041 – 12 fo. blk, drab & bis . . 1·00 50
4042 – 20 fo. dp bl, azure & bl . 1·60 80
4043 – 30 fo. blk, lilac & vio . . 2·40 1·25

DESIGNS: 12 fo. Wright brothers' Flyer 1, 1903; 20 fo. Santos-Dumont's "14 bis", 1906; 30 fo. Aladar Zselyi's monoplane, 1910.

1032 Players **1034** Map of Europe and Congress Emblem

1991. Centenary of Basketball.

4044 **1032** 12 fo. multicoloured . . 80 30

1991. Castles. Inscr "MAGYARORSZAG". As T **921**.

4045 7 fo. brown and sepia 35 20
4047 12 fo. ultramarine and blue . . 55 30
4049 15 fo. brown and green . . . 55 30

DESIGNS—32 × 25 mm; 7 fo. Esterhazy Castle, Papa; 12 fo. Dory Castle, Mihaly. 35 × 26 mm; 15 fo. Festetics Castle, Keszthely.

1991. 3rd International Hungarian Philological Society Congress, Szeged.

4056 **1034** 12 fo. multicoloured . . 55 30

1035 Szechenyi **1036** Mozart as Child

1991. Birth Bicentenary of Count Istvan Szechenyi (social reformer).

4057 **1035** 12 fo. red 75 30

1991. Stamp Day. Death Bicentenary of Wolfgang Amadeus Mozart (composer). Multicoloured.

4058 12 fo. Type **1036** 55 30
4059 20 fo. Mozart as youth 95 50

1037 "Telecom 91"

1991. "Telecom 91" International Telecommunications Exhibition, Geneva.

4061 **1037** 12 fo. multicoloured . . 80 55

1991. 35th Anniv of 1956 Uprising. No. 4047 optd **A FORRADALOM EMLEKERE 1956 1991**.

4062 12 fo. ultramarine and blue . . 80 30

1039 Sebastian Cabot **1040** Arms of Order

1991. 500th Anniv (1992) of Discovery of America by Columbus. Multicoloured.

4063 7 fo. Type **1039** 60 30
4064 12 fo. Amerigo Vespucci . . 90 45
4065 12 fo. Hernan Cortes 90 45
4066 15 fo. Ferdinand Magellan . . 1·25 65
4067 20 f. Francisco Pizarro . . . . 1·60 80

1991. Postal Convention with Sovereign Military Order of Malta.

4069 **1040** 12 fo. multicoloured . . 80 30

1041 "Virgin of Mariapocs" **1042** Flower

1991. Christmas. Multicoloured.

4070 7 fo. Type **1041** 55 30
4071 12 fo. "Virgin of Mariaremete" 70 35

1991. Human Rights.

4072 **1042** 12 fo. multicoloured . . 80 30

1043 Biathlon **1045** Arms

1991. Winter Olympic Games, Albertville (1992). Multicoloured.

4073 7 fo. Type **1043** 35 20
4074 12 fo. Slalom 55 30
4075 15 fo. Four-man bobsleigh . . 70 35
4076 20 fo. Ski jumping 95 40
4077 30 fo. Ice hockey . . . . . 1·40 70

1992. 350th Anniv of Piarist Order in Hungary.

4080 **1045** 10 fo. gold, blue and ultramarine 40 20

1046 Holloko

1992. U.N.E.S.C.O. World Heritage Site.

4081 **1046** 15 fo. multicoloured . . 1·00 70

1047 Swimming

1992. Olympic Games, Barcelona. Mult.

4082 7 fo. Type **1047** 70 20
4083 9 fo. Cycling . . . . 1·00 50
4084 10 fo. Gymnastics . . . . . 1·00 50
4085 15 fo. Running . . . . 1·75 70

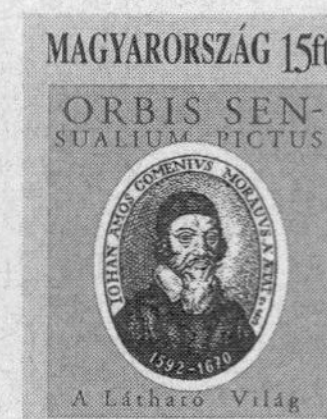

1048 "Indian's Head" Map **1049** Comenius

1992. "Expo '92" World's Fair, Seville. Fantasy Maps. Multicoloured.

4086 10 fo. Type **1048** 75 30
4087 10 fo. Islands, sea monsters and "Santa Maria" forming face 75 30
4088 15 fo. "Conquistador's head" map . . . . 1·25 55
4089 15 fo. Navigation instruments and map forming face . . . 1·25 55

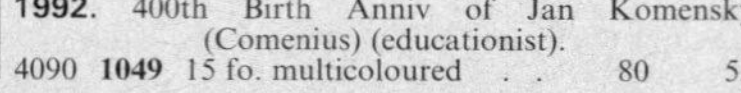

1992. 400th Birth Anniv of Jan Komensky (Comenius) (educationist).

4090 **1049** 15 fo. multicoloured . . 80 55

1050 Mindszenty

1992. Birth Centenary of Cardinal Jozsef Mindszenty, Archbishop of Esztergom.

4091 **1050** 15 fo. brn, cream & red . 80 55

1051 Statue of Mayan Man **1052** "Self-portrait" (Renata Toth)

1992. Europa. 500th Anniv of Discovery of America by Columbus. Multicoloured.

4092 15 fo. Type **1051** 80 55
4093 40 fo. Statue of Mayan woman 2·00 1·75

1992. Youth Stamps. Children's Drawings. Multicoloured.

4094 9 fo. + 4 fo. Type **1052** . . . 50 50
4095 10 fo. + 4 fo. "The Sun Shines for Me" (Sandor Pusoma) (horiz) 50 50
4096 15 fo. + 4 fo. "I will be a Beauty King" (Endre Knipf) 70 70

1053 Gymnasts and Emblem

1992. European Gymnastics Championships, Budapest.

4097 **1053** 15 fo. multicoloured . . 80 30

1054 St. Margaret (after J. S. Scott) **1055** Saker Falcon

1992. 750th Birth Anniv of St. Margaret.

4098 **1054** 15 fo. turq, lt bl & bl . . 80 60

1992. Birds of Prey. Multicoloured.

4099 9 fo. Type **1055** 35 20
4100 10 fo. Booted eagle 35 20
4101 15 fo. Short-toed eagle 55 30
4102 40 fo. Red kite . . . . 1·40 70

1056 Wallenberg **1057** Millennium Monument, Budapest

1992. 80th Birth Anniv of Raoul Wallenberg (Swedish diplomat).

4103 **1056** 15 fo. grey, red & grn . . 55 30

1992. 3rd World Federation of Hungarians Congress, Budapest.

4104 **1057** 15 fo. multicoloured . . 55 30

1058 Theodore von Karman (space pioneer, birth centenary (1991))

1992. Anniversaries.
4105 **1058** 15 fo. grey, black and deep grey 55 30
4106 – 40 fo. grey, blk & brn . . 1·40 1·00
DESIGN: 40 fo. Neumann Janos (mathematician, 35th death anniv).

1059 Current Hungarian Post Emblem

1061 Entwined Cables

1992. Stamp Day. "Eurofilex '92" International Postal History Exhibition, Budapest. Mult.
4107 10 fo. + 5 fo. Hungarian Royal Post emblem, 1867 (vert) . . 80 80
4108 15 fo. + 5 fo. Type **1059** . . . 1·25 1·25

1992. As No. 4108 but without premium and commemorative inscription.
4111 15 fo. multicoloured 50 25

1992. "Europa Telecom '92" Telecommunications Exhibition, Budapest.
4112 **1061** 15 fo. multicoloured . . 50 25

1062 Istvan Bathory (King Stefan I of Poland)

1063 Pieces on Board

1992. Princes of Transylvania. Multicoloured.
4113 10 fo. Type **1062** 35 20
4114 15 fo. Istvan Bocskai 50 25
4115 40 fo. Gabor Bethlen . . . . 1·40 70

1992. 10th European Chess Team Championship, Debrecen.
4116 **1063** 15 fo. multicoloured . . 80 50

1064 "Clianthus formosus"

1065 Postal Rider of Prince Ferenc Rakoczi II, 1703–11

1992. Australian Flowers. Multicoloured.
4117 9 fo. Type **1064** 35 20
4118 10 fo. "Leschenaultia biloba" . 35 20
4119 15 fo. "Anigosanthos manglesii" 55 30
4120 40 fo. "Comesperma ericinum" . . . . 1·40 1·00

1992. Post Office Uniforms. Multicoloured.
4122 10 fo. Type **1065** 45 35
4123 15 fo. Postmen, 1874 . . . . . 70 50

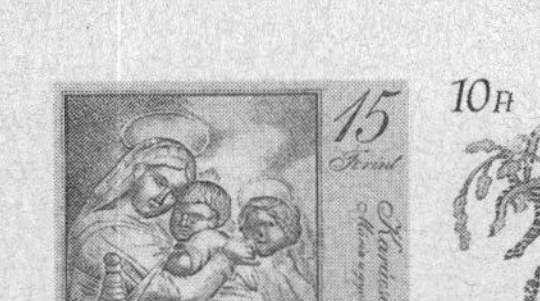

1066 "Holy Family" (iron relief, 1850)

1067 "Arachnis flos-aeris"

1992. Christmas.
4124 **1066** 15 fo. black and blue . . 35 20

1993. Asian Flowers. Multicoloured.
4125 10 fo. Type **1067** 35 20
4126 10 fo. "Dendrobium densiflorium" 35 20
4127 15 fo. "Lilium speciosum" . . 50 25
4128 15 fo. "Meconopsis aculeata" . 50 25

1068 Shield Decoration of Deer

1993. Scythian Remains in Hungary. Mult.
4130 10 fo. Type **1068** 35 20
4131 17 fo. Gilt-silver embossed deer 60 30

1069 Single Sculls

1993. Centenary of Rowing Association.
4132 **1069** 17 fo. multicoloured . . 85 55

1070 Queen Beatrix and King Matthias I Corvinus (detail of Missal) (⅔ size illustration)

1993. King Matthias I Corvinus's "Missale Romanum".
4133 **1070** 15 fo. multicoloured . . 80 50

1071 Animals in Wood

1072 Competitors and Globe

1993. Youth Stamps. Tapestries by Erzsebet Szekeres. Multicoloured.
4135 10 fo. + 5 fo. Type **1071** . . . 80 75
4136 17 fo. + 8 fo. Animals in tree hiding from dragons . . . . 1·40 1·25

1993. World Motocross Championships, Cserenfa.
4137 **1072** 17 fo. multicoloured . . 55 30

1073 Diagram of Solar System and Copernicus

1993. "Polska'93" International Stamp Exn.
4138 **1073** 17 fo. multicoloured . . 55 30

1074 Paks Catholic Church

1075 Cauliflower Clavaria

1993. Europa. Contemporary Art. Architecture by Imre Makovecz. Multicoloured.
4139 17 fo. Type **1074** 55 30
4140 45 fo. Hungarian pavilion at "Expo '92" World's Fair, Seville . . . . 1·00 50

1993. Fungi. Multicoloured.
4141 10 fo. Type **1075** 35 15
4142 17 fo. Death trumpet 70 30
4143 45 fo. Caesar's mushroom . . 1·40 55

1076 "St. Christopher" (Albrecht Durer)

1993. European Year of the Aged.
4144 **1076** 17 fo. black, cream and silver 55 30

1077 Class 326 and 424 Steam Locomotives

1078 Rowing Boat approaching Town

1993. 125th Anniv of Hungarian Railways.
4145 **1077** 17 fo. blue and cobalt . . 80 20

1993. 900th Anniv of Mohacs.
4146 **1078** 17 fo. brown, cinnamon and red 55 30

1079 Poplar Admiral

1080 Kalman Latabar

1993. Butterflies. Multicoloured.
4147 10 fo. Type **1079** 25 15
4148 17 fo. "Aricia artaxerxes" . . 55 30
4149 30 fo. "Plebejides pylaon" . . 75 40

1993. Great Humourists. Multicoloured.
4150 17 fo. Type **1080** 55 30
4151 30 fo. Charlie Chaplin 75 40

1082 Solar Panel absorbing Sun's Rays

1083 Laszlo Nemeth

1993. International Solar Energy Society Congress, Budapest.
4153 **1082** 17 fo. multicoloured . . 55 30

1993. Writers. Each blue and azure.
4154 17 fo. Type **1083** 55 30
4155 17 fo. Dezso Szabo 55 30
4156 17 fo. Antal Szerb 55 30

1084 Zoltan Nagy and 1953 20 fi. Stamp

1085 Arms

1993. Stamp Day. Designers. Multicoloured.
4157 10 fo. + 5 fo. Type **1084** . . . 50 50
4158 17 fo. + 5 fo. Sandor Legrady and 1938 50 f. stamp 75 75

1993. 175th Anniv of Faculty of Agronomics, Pannon Agricultural University, Magyarovar.
4160 **1085** 17 fo. multicoloured . . 55 30

1086 "Szent Istvan", 1892

1087 Prehistoric Man and Skull (Vertesszolos)

1993. Hungarian Ships. Multicoloured.
4161 10 fo. Type **1086** 40 15
4162 30 fo. "Szent Istvan" (battleship), 1915 . . . . 1·00 45

1993. Palaeolithic Remains in Hungary. Mult.
4163 17 fo. Type **1087** 55 30
4164 30 fo. Men round fire and stone tool (Szeleta Cave, Lillafured) 85 45

1089 "Madonna and Child" (altarpiece by F. A. Hillebrant, Szekestehervar Cathedral)

1091 Antall

1090 Szechenyi Chain Bridge (½-size illustration)

1993. Christmas.
4166 **1089** 10 fo. multicoloured . . 35 20

1993. "Expo '96" World's Fair, Budapest (1st issue).
4167 **1090** 17 fo. dp green & green . 55 30
4168 – 30 fo. purple and claret . 75 40
4169 – 45 fo. dp brown & brn . 1·10 55
DESIGNS—HORIZ: 30 fo. Opera House. VERT: 45 fo. Matthias Church.
See also Nos. 4236/8 and 4268/9.

1993. Jozsef Antall (Prime Minister since 1990) Commemoration.
4170 **1091** 19 fo. multicoloured . . 55 30

1092 Skiing

1994. Winter Olympic Games, Lillehammer, Norway. Multicoloured.
4172 12 fo. Type **1092** 30 15
4173 19 fo. Ice hockey 55 30

1093 Douglas DC-3

1994. 50th Anniv of I.C.A.O.
4174 **1093** 56 fo. multicoloured . . 1·40 1·00

1094 "Golgotha" (detail, Mihaly Munkacsy)

1095 Mihaly Munkacsy (self-portrait)

1994. Easter.

4175 **1094** 12 fo. multicoloured . . 35 20

1994. Artists' 150th Birth Anniversaries. Multicoloured.

4176 12 fo. Gyula Benczur (self-portrait) 35 20
4177 19 fo. Type **1095** 60 30

1096 Kossuth

1097 Hen with Chicks

1994. Death Centenary of Lajos Kossuth (Governor of 1849 Republic).

4178 **1096** 19 fo. multicoloured . . 60 30

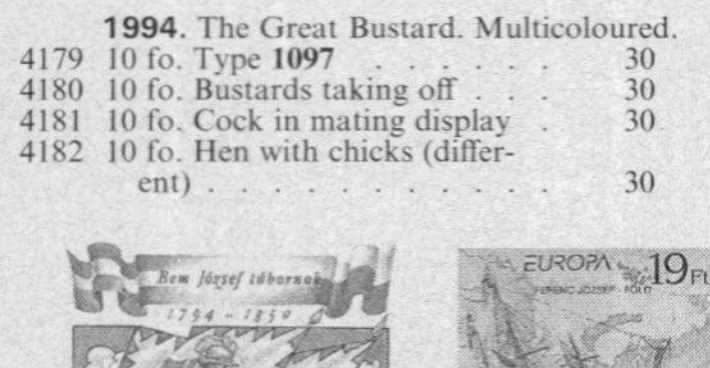

1994. The Great Bustard. Multicoloured.

4179 10 fo. Type **1097** 30 15
4180 10 fo. Bustards taking off . . . 30 15
4181 10 fo. Cock in mating display . . 30 15
4182 10 fo. Hen with chicks (different) 30 15

1098 Bem

1099 Discovery of Franz Josef Land (120th anniv)

1994. Birth Bicentenary of Jozsef Bem (revolutionary).

4183 **1098** 19 fo. multicoloured . . 60 30

1994. Europa. Discoveries. Multicoloured.

4184 19 fo. Type **1099** 85 30
4185 50 fo. Mark Aurel Stein and Buddha (expeditions in Asia) . . . . 1·40 1·00

1100 "The Little Prince"

1101 Balint Balassi (poet, 400th death)

1994. Youth Stamp. 50th Anniv of Disappearance of Antoine de Saint-Exupery (writer and pilot).

4186 **1100** 19 fo. + 5 fo. mult . . . 70 70

1994. Writers' Anniversaries.

4187 **1101** 19 ft. pink and brown . . 50 25
4188 – 19 ft. stone and grey . . 50 25

DESIGN: No. 4188, Miklos Josika (novelist, birth bicentenary).

1102 Horsemen

1104 Elvis Presley and Players

1103 Athens Stadium, 1896

1994. 1100th Anniv (1996) of Magyar Conquest (1st issue). Multicoloured.

4189 19 ft. Type **1102** 45 20
4190 19 ft. Arpad and standard bearers (58 × 39 mm) . . . 45 20
4191 19 ft. Mounted archer 45 20

Nos. 4189/91 were issued together, se-tenant, forming a composite design of a detail of the painting "in the round" commissioned to celebrate the millenary of the Conquest.

See also Nos. 4240/2 and 4275/7.

1994. Centenary of International Olympic Committee. Multicoloured.

4192 12 ft. Olympic medals of 1896 and 1992 . . . . 25 10
4193 19 ft. Type **1103** 40 20
4194 19 ft. Ancient Greek athletes, Olympic flag and flame . . . 40 20
4195 35 ft. Pierre de Coubertin (founder) 75 35

1994. World Cup Football Championship, U.S.A. American Entertainers. Multicoloured.

4196 19 ft. Type **1104** 55 25
4197 19 ft. Marilyn Monroe and players 55 25
4198 35 ft. John Wayne and players . 1·10 55

1105 Family

1994. International Year of the Family.

4199 **1105** 19 fo. multicoloured . . 60 30

1106 Summer Snowflake

1994. European Flowers. Multicoloured.

4200 12 fo. Type **1106** 25 10
4201 19 fo. Common rock-rose . . . 30 15
4202 35 fo. "Eryngium alpinum" . . 40 20
4203 50 fo. Pennycress 85 40

1107 Heinrich von Stephan (founder) and Emblem

1108 Csik Megye

1994. 120th Anniv of Universal Postal Union.

4205 **1107** 19 fo. grey, brown & blk 30 15
4206 – 35 fo. blue, brown & blk 55 25

DESIGN: 35 fo. Gervay Mihaly (first Director General of Posts) and U.P.U. emblem.

1994. Traditional Patterns.

4208 – 1 fo. violet and black . . 10 10
4209 – 2 fo. multicoloured . . 10 10
4210 – 3 fo. multicoloured . . 10 10
4210a – 5 fo. multicoloured . . 10 10
4211 – 9 fo. multicoloured . . 15 10
4212 **1108** 11 fo. multicoloured . . 20 10
4213 – 12 fo. multicoloured . . 25 10
4214 – 13 fo. multicoloured . . 25 10
4215 – 14 fo. multicoloured . . 25 10
4216 – 16 fo. multicoloured . . 30 15
4217 – 17 fo. blk, grey & red . 30 15
4218 – 19 fo. multicoloured . . 35 15
4219 – 22 fo. multicoloured . . 40 30
4220 – 24 fo. multicoloured . . 60 30
4220a – 24 fo. multicoloured . . 10 10
4220b – 27 fo. multicoloured . . 65 35
4221 – 32 fo. multicoloured . . 70 35
4222 – 35 fo. multicoloured . . 75 30
4223 – 38 fo. multicoloured . . 80 40
4224 – 40 fo. multicoloured . . 85 55
4225 – 50 fo. multicoloured . . 90 60
4225a – 65 fo. black, red and grey 30 15
4226 – 75 fo. multicoloured . . 1·00 70
4226a – 79 fo. multicoloured . . 40 20
4227 – 80 fo. multicoloured . . 1·10 75
4228 – 90 fo. multicoloured . . 45 20
4229 – 100 fo. multicoloured . . 50 25
4229a – 200 fo. multicoloured . 1·00 50
4230 – 300 fo. multicoloured . 3·50 2·50
4231 – 500 fo. multicoloured . 5·50 3·00

DESIGNS: 1 fo. Torocko; 2 fo. Buzsak; 3 fo. Vas megye (flowers); 5 fo. Rabakoz; 9, 24 fo. (4220) Felfold; 12, 27 fo. Vas megye (birds); 13, 32 fo. Debrecen; 14, 80 fo. Sarkoz; 16 fo. Csiki-Medence; 17, 35, 65 fo. Dunantul; 19, 24 fo. (4220a) Kalocsa; 22, 90 fo. Heves megye; 300 fo. Kalocsa (different); 38, 75 fo. Oroshaza; 40 fo. Kalotaszeg; 50 fo. Szentgal; 79 fo. Moldvai csango; 100 fo. Szecseny videke; 200 fo. Mezokovesd; 500 fo. Szolnok megye.

1110 Hebrew Tombstone

1111 "Nativity"

1994. Holocaust Victims' Commemoration.

4233 **1110** 19 fo. multicoloured . . 40 20

1994. Christmas. Paintings by Pal Molnar. Multicoloured.

4234 12 fo. Type **1111** 35 15
4235 35 fo. "Flight into Egypt" (31 × 29 mm) 95 45

1112 National Museum

1994. "Expo '96" World's Fair, Budapest (2nd issue). Budapest landmarks.

4236 **1112** 19 fo. green 40 20
4237 – 19 fo. brown 40 20
4238 – 19 fo. violet 40 20

DESIGNS: No. 4237, University of Technical Sciences; 4238, Vajdahunyad Castle.

1113 "Ferencz Jozsef I" (paddle-steamer) and "Baross" (container ship)

1995. Cent of Hungarian Shipping Company.

4239 **1113** 22 fo. multicoloured . . 60 20

1995. 1100th Anniv (1996) of Magyar Conquest (2nd issue). As T **1102**. Multicoloured.

4240 22 fo. Ox cart 40 20
4241 22 fo. Arpad's consort in ox cart (59 × 39 mm) 40 20
4242 22 fo. Men and pack ox . . . 40 20

Nos. 4240/2 were issued together, se-tenant, forming a composite design of a detail of the painting "in the round" commissioned to celebrate the millenary of the Conquest.

1114 Lamb of God

1116 Weather Map and Barometer

1115 Paddle-steamer

1995. Easter.

4243 **1114** 14 fo. purple and black . . 25 10

1995. 150th Anniv of Steamer Service on River Tisza (14 fo.) and Birth Bicentenary of Pal Vasarhelyi (engineer) (60 fo.). Multicoloured.

4244 14 fo. Type **1115** 25 10
4245 60 fo. Vasarhelyi (after Miklos Barabas) and survey ship . . 1·25 85

1995. Anniversaries. Multicoloured.

4246 22 fo. Type **1116** (125th anniv of Hungarian Meteorological Service) 45 20
4247 22 fo. Emblem (50th anniv of F.A.O.) (25 × 41 mm) . . . 45 20
4248 22 fo. + 10 fo. John the Hero (150th anniv of poem by Petofi) (37 × 45mm) 65 65

No. 4248 is the 1995 Youth Stamp.

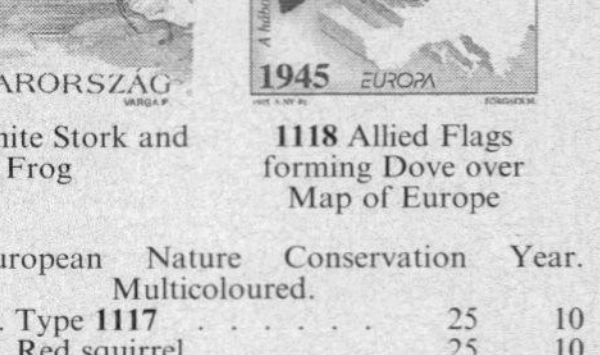

1117 White Stork and Frog

1118 Allied Flags forming Dove over Map of Europe

1995. European Nature Conservation Year. Multicoloured.

4249 14 fo. Type **1117** 25 10
4250 14 fo. Red squirrel 25 10
4251 14 fo. Blue tit 25 10
4252 14 fo. Butterfly and hedgehog . 25 10

Nos. 4249/52 were issued together, se-tenant, forming a composite design.

1995. Europa. Peace and Freedom.

4253 **1118** 22 fo. multicoloured . . 35 15

1119 Gymnastics and Ferenc Kemeny (founder)

1995. Centenary of Hungarian Olympic Committee. Multicoloured.

4254 22 fo. Type **1119** 35 15
4255 60 fo. Throwing the javelin . . 1·00 75
4256 100 fo. Fencing . . . . 1·60 1·25

1120 Exhibition Emblem

1995. "Olympiafila '95" International Olympic and Sports Stamps Exhibition, Budapest.

4257 **1120** 22 fo. + 11 fo. mult (rings in yellow) 55 55
4258 22 fo. + 11 fo. mult (rings in purple) 55 55

1121 Saint Ladislas (detail of fresco, Szekelyderzs Castle Chapel)

1122 Almasy

1995. 900th Death Anniv of St. Ladislas, King of Hungary.

4259 **1121** 22 fo. multicoloured . . 35 15

1995. Birth Centenary of Laszlo Almasy (explorer).

4260 **1122** 22 fo. multicoloured . . 35 15

1123 Museum of Applied Arts, Budapest, and Lechner

1995. 150th Birth Anniv of Odon Lechner (architect).

4261 **1123** 22 fo. multicoloured . . 45 20

INDEX

Countries can be quickly located by referring to the index at the end of this volume.

1124 "K XVIII 1923" (Laszlo Moholy-Nagy)

1125 College Building and Jozsef Eotvos (founder)

1995. Artists' Birth Centenaries. Multicoloured.

4262 22 fo. Type **1124** 45 20
4263 22 fo. "The Fiddler" (Aurel Bernath) 45 20

1995. Centenary of Eotvos College.

4264 **1125** 60 fo. multicoloured . . 1·25 60

1126 Postal Carriage and Map of Postal Routes

1995. Stamp Day. Multicoloured.

4265 22 fo. Type **1126** 40 20
4266 40 fo. Airplane and route map . 85 40

1995. "Expo '96" World's Fair, Budapest (3rd issue). As T **1112** showing Budapest landmarks.

4268 22 fo. grey 60 20
4269 22 fo. purple 45 20

DESIGNS: No. 4268, West Railway Station; 4269, Music Hall.

1127 Anniversary Emblem

1128 Sparklers

1995. 50th Anniv of U.N.O.

4270 **1127** 60 fo. multicoloured . . 1·25 60

1995. Christmas. Multicoloured.

4271 14 fo. Type **1128** 30 15
4272 60 fo. Three wise men in stable 1·25 60

1129 St Elizabeth bathing Leper

1995. Saint Elizabeth of Hungary.

4273 **1129** 22 fo. multicoloured . . 45 20

1130 Nobel Medals

1995. Centenary of Nobel Trust Fund.

4274 **1130** 100 fo. multicoloured . . 2·00 1·00

1996. 1100th Anniv of Magyar Conquest (3rd issue). As T **1102**. Multicoloured.

4275 24 fo. Rejoicing crowd 35 15
4276 24 fo. Shaman presenting sacrificial white horse (59 × 39 mm) 35 15
4277 24 fo. Bards 35 15

Nos. 4275/7 were issued together, se-tenant, forming a composite design.

1131 Leather Purse

1133 Headquarters

1996. 9th-century Relics from Kares Cemeteries. Multicoloured.

4278 24 fo. Type **1131** 35 15
4279 24 fo. Gold and silver sabre hilt 35 15

1996. Centenary of Journalists' Association.

4281 **1133** 50 fo. multicoloured . . 65 30

1134 Emblem

1135 Swimming

1996. Promotion of Hungarian Production.

4282 **1134** 24 fo. black, red & grn . 35 15

1996. Centenary of Modern Olympic Games and Olympic Games, Atlanta. Multicoloured.

4283 24 fo. Type **1135** 35 15
4284 50 fo. Tennis (Csilla Orosz) . . 65 30
4285 75 fo. Canoeing 95 45

1136 First Carriage

1996. Centenary of Budapest Underground Railway.

4287 **1136** 24 fo. multicoloured . . 35 15

1137 Queen Gizella (wife of St. Stephen)

1996. Europa. Famous Women. Hungarian Queens. Multicoloured.

4288 24 fo. Type **1137** 40 20
4289 75 fo. Queen Elisabeth (wife of Francis Joseph I) 85 40

1138 Triumphal Arch (entrance to Cathedral)

1139 Bird and "DRUG"

1996. Millenary of Pannonhalma Monastery.

4290 **1138** 17 fo. brown 20 10
4291 – 24 fo. blue 35 15

DESIGN: 24 fo. Monks gathered in cloisters.

See also Nos. 4305/6.

1996. International Day against Drug Abuse.

4292 **1139** 24 fo. multicoloured . . 35 15

1140 Denes Mihaly (television pioneer)

1996. Inventors. Multicoloured.

4293 24 fo. Type **1140** 35 15
4294 50 fo. Laszlo Biro and ballpoint pen 65 30
4295 75 fo. Zoltan Bay and Moon radar 95 45

1141 Laszlo Vitez (puppet)

1143 Pyramid

1142 "Heves", 1846

1996. Youth Stamp. Puppet Festival, Budapest.

4296 **1141** 24 fo. + 10 fo. mult . . . 45 45

1996. 150th Anniv of Hungarian Railways. Steam Locomotives. Multicoloured.

4297 17 fo. Class 303 . . . . 20 10
4298 24 fo. Class 325 . . . . 40 20
4299 24 fo. Type **1142** 40 20

On No. 4299 the nameplate is inscribed "PEST".

1996. 2nd European Mathematics Congress, Budapest.

4300 **1143** 24 fo. multicoloured . . 35 15

1144 Hungarian Long-horned Wood Beetle ("Ropalopus ungaricus")

1996. "NATUREXPO '96" international Nature Conservation Exhibition, Budapest, Mult.

4301 13 fo. Type **1144** 15 10
4302 13 fo. Lynx ("Lynx lynx") . . 15 10
4303 13 fo. Siberian iris ("Iris sibirica") 15 10
4304 13 fo. Great egret ("Egretta alba") 15 10

1996. Millenary of Pannonhalma Monastery. As T **1138**.

4305 17 fo. brown 20 10
4306 24 fo. green 35 15

DESIGNS: 17 fo. Refectory; 24 fo. Main library.

1145 Homage to Prince Arpad (from "Vienna Picture Chronicle")

1146 1871 10 k. Engraved Stamp

1996. Stamp Day. "Budapest '96" International Stamp Exhibition, Budapest. Mult.

4307 17 fo. Type **1145** 20 10
4308 24 fo. Prince Arpad on horseback and soldiers (from "Vienna Picture Chronicle") . . 35 15

1996. World Convention of Hungarian Stamps and Postal History.

4310 **1146** 24 fo. multicoloured . . 35 15

1147 Map and Paddle-steamer "Kisfaludy"

1996. 150th Anniv of Steamer Service on Lake Balaton.

4311 **1147** 17 fo. multicoloured . . 30 10

1148 Mastheads and Demonstration

1996. 40th Anniv of 23rd October Uprising. Multicoloured.

4312 13 fo. Type **1148** 15 10
4313 16 fo. Newspaper, burning flag and motor vehicle 20 10
4314 17 fo. Men with rifles and newspaper 20 10
4315 24 fo. Newspaper and Imre Nagy (Prime Minister, Oct—Nov 1956) 35 15

1150 "Madonna and Child with Two Angels" (Matteo di Giovanni)

1996. Christmas. Multicoloured.

4318 17 fo. Type **1150** 10 10
4319 24 fo. "Adoration of the Wise Men" (Salzburg Master) . . 15 10

1151 List of Years

1152 Bust, Book, Quill and Shield

1996. 50th Anniv of U.N.I.C.E.F.

4320 **1151** 24 fo. multicoloured . . 15 10

1996. Birth Bicentenary of Miklos Wesselenyi (writer).

4321 **1152** 24 fo. multicoloured . . 15 10

1153 Kalman Mikszath and Characters

1997. Writers' Birth Anniversaries. Mult.

4322 27 fo. Type **1153** (150th anniv) 15 10
4323 27 fo. Aron Tamasi (cent) . . 15 10

1154 Baranya

1997. Arms. Multicoloured. (a) As T **1154**.

4324 27 fo. Type **1154** 15 10
4325 27 fo. Bacs-Kiskun 15 10
4326 27 fo. Bekes 15 10
4327 27 fo. Borsod-Abauj-Zemplen . 15 10
4328 27 fo. Fejer 10 10
4329 27 fo. Gyor-Moson-Sopron . . 15 10
4330 27 fo. Heves 15 10
4331 27 fo. Jasz-Nagykun-Szolnok . 15 10
4332 27 fo. Komarom-Esztergom . . 15 10
4333 27 fo. Nograd 15 10
4334 27 fo. Pest 15 10
4335 27 fo. Somogy 15 10
4336 27 fo. Tolna 15 10
4337 27 fo. Vas 15 10
4338 27 fo. Veszprem 15 10
4339 27 fo. Zala 15 10

(b) Size 50 × 32 mm.

4340 27 fo. Hajku-Bihar 15 10
4341 27 fo. Budapest 15 10
4342 27 fo. Csongrad 15 10
4343 27 fo. Szabolcs-Szatmar-Bereg . 15 10

1155 Badge, Camp and Sailing

1997. 90th Anniv of Scout Movement.
4345 1155 20 fo. multicoloured . . 10 10

1156 Book, Knight and Arany

1997. 150th Anniv of Composition of "Miklos Toldi" by Janos Arany (winning entry in poetry competition).
4346 1156 27 fo. + 10 fo. mult . . . 20 20

1157 St. Adalbert 1158 Emblem and City

1997. Death Millenary of St. Adalbert (Bishop of Prague).
4347 1157 80 fo. lilac 50 25

1997. World Customs' Union Conference, Budapest.
4348 1158 90 fo. multicoloured . . 55 25

1159 Gemsboks

1997. African Animals. Multicoloured.
4349 16 fo. Type 1159 . . . . . . 10 10
4350 20 fo. Common zebras 10 10
4351 20 fo. Black rhinoceroses . . . 10 10
4352 27 fo. Lions 15 10

1160 "The Enchanted Hart"

1997. Europa. Tales and Legends. Mult.
4354 27 fo. Type 1160 . . . . . . 15 10
4355 90 fo. King St. Stephen overseeing burial of Prince Geza (death millenary) 55 25

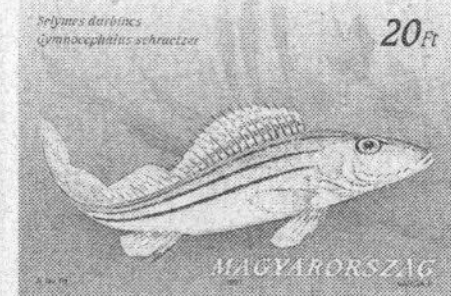

1161 Schraetzer ("Gymnocephalus schraetzer")

1997. Fishes. Multicoloured.
4356 20 fo. Type 1161 . . . . . . 10 10
4357 20 fo. Bullhead "Cottus gobio" 10 10
4358 20 fo. Schneider "Alburnoides bipunctatus" 10 10
4359 20 fo. Spiny loach ("Cobitis taenia") 10 10
Nos. 4356/9 were issued together, se-tenant, forming a composite design.

1162 St. Jadwiga (after Peter Prokop) 1163 Janos Selye

1997. Canonization of Queen Jadwiga of Poland.
4360 1162 90 fo. multicoloured . . 55 25

1997. Int Congress on Stress. Budapest.
4361 1163 90 fo. multicoloured . . 55 25

1997. No. 4220 surch **60 f.**
4362 60 fo. on 24 fo. multicoloured . 35 15

1997. Wine Grapes and Regions (2nd series). As T 1013. Multicoloured.
4363 27 fo. Harslevelu, Gyongyos . 15 10
4364 27 fo. Nemes Kadarka, Kiskoros 15 10
4365 27 fo. Teltfurtu Ezerjo, Mor . 15 10

1165 Flower surrounded by Flood Waters

1997. Flood Relief Funds.
4366 1165 27 fo. + 100 fo. mult . . 75 75

1166 Postman and Csonka Tricycle, 1900

1997. Stamp Day. Multicoloured.
4367 27 fo. + 5 fo. Type 1166 . . . 20 20
4368 55 fo. + 5 fo. Registered letter receiving-machine, 1906 (vert) 35 35

1167 Nativity

1997. Christmas. Multicoloured.
4370 20 fo. Type 1167 . . . . . . 10 10
4371 27 fo. Adoration of the Wise Men 15 10

1168 Weightlifter 1169 Skiing

1997. 68th World Weightlifting Championships, Thailand.
4372 1168 90 fo. multicoloured . . 50 25

1998. Winter Olympic Games, Nagano, Japan. Multicoloured.
4373 30 fo. Type 1169 . . . . . . 15 10
4374 100 fo. Snowboarding 55 25

1170 Szechenyi with Camera

1998. Birth Centenary of Zsigmond Szechenyi (travel writer).
4375 1170 60 fo. multicoloured . . 35 15

1171 Leaf and Lyrics

1998. 175th Anniv of National Hymn by Ferenc Kolcsey.
4376 1171 75 fo. multicoloured . . 40 20

1172 Balint Postas holding Envelope 1173 Hearts and Post Box

1998. Introduction of Balint Postas (post mascot). Multicoloured.
4377 23 fo. Type 1172 . . . . . . 10 10
4378 24 fo. Balint Postas bowing . . 15 10
4379 30 fo. Balint Postas with arms outstretched 15 10
4380 65 fo. Balint Postas flying . . . 35 15

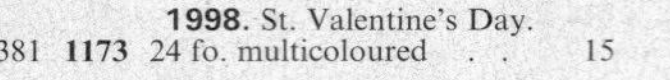
1998. St. Valentine's Day.
4381 1173 24 fo. multicoloured . . 15 10

1174 Szilard 1175 Sandor Petofi (poet)

1998. Birth Cent of Leo Szilard (scientist).
4382 1174 50 fo. multicoloured . . 30 15

1998. 150th Anniv of March Revolution, 1848. Multicoloured.
4383 23 fo. Type 1175 . . . . . . 15 10
4384 24 fo. Mihaly Tancsics (politician and workers' newspaper editor) and inkwell 15 10
4385 30 fo. Lajos Kossuth (Governor of 1849 Republic) and coin . 15 10

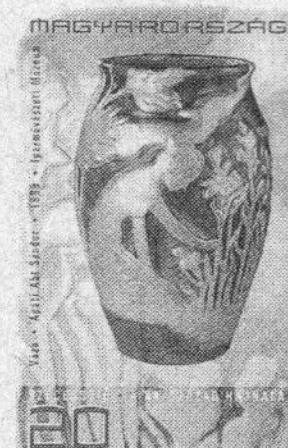

1176 "The Resurrection of Christ" (El Greco) 1177 Vase

1998. Easter.
4387 – 24 fo. red and black . . 15 10
4388 1176 30 fo. multicoloured . . 15 10
DESIGN: 27 × 39 mm—24 fo. Dots forming outline of egg.

1998. Ceramics. Multicoloured.
4389 20 fo. Type 1177 . . . . . . 10 10
4390 24 fo. Bowl decorated with butterflies (horiz) 15 10
4391 30 fo. Spiral vase 15 10
4392 95 fo. Bowl with lid (horiz) . . 55 25

1178 Postman

1998. Stamp Day. 250th Anniv of Inauguration of Postal Service by Empress Maria Theresa. Multicoloured.
4393 24 fo. + 10 fo. Type 1178 . . 20 20
4394 30 fo. + 10 fo. Mounted courier 20 20

1179 American Bison

1998. American Animals. Multicoloured.
4396 23 fo. Type 1179 . . . . . . 15 10
4397 24 fo. Brown bear 15 10
4398 24 fo. Mississippi alligator . . 15 10
4399 30 fo. Ocelot 15 10

1180 Jendrassik 1181 Hurdling

1998. Birth Centenary of Gyorgy Jendrassik (engineer).
4401 1180 100 fo. blue 55 25

1998. European Light Athletics Championships, Budapest. Multicoloured.
4402 24 fo. Type 1181 . . . . . . 15 10
4403 65 fo. High jumping 35 15
4404 80 fo. Throwing the hammer . 45 20

1182 Canoe

1998. World White-water Canoeing Championships, Szeged.
4405 1182 30 fo. multicoloured . . 15 10

1183 Players

1998. World Cup Football Championship, France. Multicoloured.
4406 30 fo. Type 1183 . . . . . . 15 10
4407 110 fo. Players with ball on ground 60 30
Nos. 4406/7 were issued together, se-tenant, forming a composite design.

1184 Baross (after Miklos Barabos) 1185 Signalman and Pioneers in Railway Carriage

1998. 150th Birth Anniv of Gabor Baross (politician).
4408 1184 60 fo. multicoloured . . 35 15

1998. 50th Anniv of Budapest Pioneer Railway.
4409 1185 24 fo. multicoloured . . 15 10

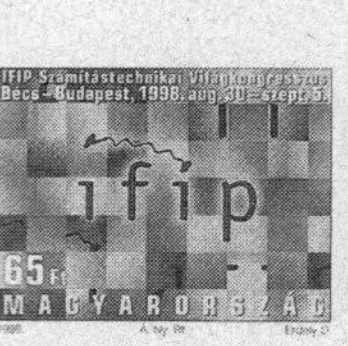

1186 Congress Emblem 1187 Carved Poles

1998. World Congress of Computer Technology, Vienna and Budapest.
4410 1186 65 fo. multicoloured . . 35 15

1998. Europa. National Festivals. Mult.
4411 50 fo. Type 1187 (Republic Day) 30 15
4412 60 fo. Carved shield and corn (National Day) 35 15

1188 Emblem

1998. 60th Anniv of Hungarians Abroad Organization.

4413 **1188** 100 fo. multicoloured . . 55 25

1189 Hortobagyi National Park

1998. National Parks (1st series). Multicoloured.

4414 24 fo. Type **1189** 15 10
4415 70 fo. Kiskunsagi National Park 40 20

See also Nos. 4438/9.

1190 "Adoration of the Shepherds" (Agnolo Bronzino)

1998. Christmas. Multicoloured.

4416 20 fo. Type **1190** 10 10
4417 24 fo. "Madonna and Child Enthroned" (Carlo Crivelli) (vert) 10 10

For 24 fo. as Type **1190** see No. 4485.

1191 Easter Eggs

1999. Easter. Multicoloured.

4418 27 fo. Type **1191** 15 10
4419 32 fo. Head of Christ (Ferenc Svindt) (37 × 52 mm) 15 10

1192 "Self-portrait" (wood carving, Jeno Szervatiusz)

1999. International Year of the Elderly.

4420 **1192** 32 fo. multicoloured . . 15 10

1193 "Novara" (full-rigged ship)

1999. Sailing Ships. Multicoloured.

4421 32 fo. Type **1193** 15 10
4422 79 fo. "Phoenix" (barge) . . . 40 20
4423 110 fo. "Folyami Vitorlas" (galley) 55 25

1195 Artur Gorgey (commander of Upper Danube)

1999. 150th Anniv of 1848–49 Uprising. Multicoloured.

4425 24 fo. Type **1195** 10 10
4426 27 fo. Lajos Batthyany (politician) 15 10
4427 32 fo. General Jozef Bem . . . 15 10

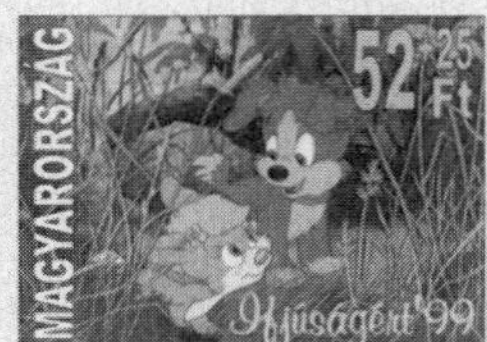

1196 Scene from "Bobo and the Hare" (animated film)

1999. Youth Stamp.

4429 **1196** 52 fo. + 25 fo. mult . . 40 40

1197 Cathedrals within Map and Emblem

1199 Papai

1999. 50th Anniv of North Atlantic Treaty Organization.

4430 **1197** 110 fo. multicoloured . . 55 25

1999. 350th Birth Anniv of Ferenc Pariz Papai (scientist, physician and lexicographer).

4432 **1199** 50 fo. green and orange . 25 10

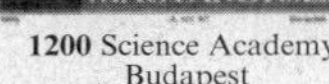

1200 Science Academy, Budapest

1201 Anniversary Badge on Scroll

1999. World Science Congress, Budapest.

4433 **1200** 65 fo. multicoloured . . 30 15

1999. Centenary of Ferencvaros Sports Club.

4434 **1201** 100 fo. multicoloured . . 50 25

1202 Council Flag

1999. 50th Anniv of Council of Europe.

4435 **1202** 50 fo. multicoloured . . 25 10

1203 Juhfark, Somlo

1999. Wine Grapes and Regions (3rd series). Multicoloured.

4436 24 fo. Type **1203** 10 10
4437 27 fo. Kekfrankos, Sopron . . 15 10

1999. Europa. Parks and Gardens. National Parks (2nd series). As T **1189**. Multicoloured.

4438 27 fo. Aggtelek National Park . 15 10
4439 32 fo. Bukk National Park . . 15 10

1204 Bengali Tiger

1999. Asian Animals. Multicoloured.

4440 27 fo. Type **1204** 15 10
4441 32 fo. Giant panda 15 10
4442 52 fo. Black leopard 25 10
4443 79 fo. Orang-utan 40 20

1205 Title Page of Decree

1999. Stamp Day. 250th Anniv of Decree by Empress Maria Theresa establishing Regular Mail Coach Service. Multicoloured.

4445 32 fo. + 15 fo. Type **1205** . . 25 10
4446 52 fo. + 20 fo. Passengers boarding coach and woman with letters 35 15

1206 Common Poppy

1207 Cukor

1999. Greetings Stamps. Flowers. Multicoloured.

4448 27 fo. Type **1206** 15 10
4449 32 fo. Trumpet gentian 15 10

1999. Birth Centenary of George Cukor (film director).

4450 **1207** 50 fo. multicoloured . . 25 10

1208 U.P.U. Emblem

1210 High-backed Chair, Szepesseg (17th century)

1209 Woodcut by Samuel Mikoviny (from "Notitia Hungarie" by Matyas Bel)

1999. 125th Anniv of Universal Postal Union. "China '99" International Stamp Exhibition, Peking.

4451 **1208** 32 fo. multicoloured . . 15 10

1999. International Book Fair, Frankfurt.

4452 **1209** 40 fo. multicoloured . . 20 10

1999. Antique Furniture.

4458 **1210** 10 fo. bistre and black . 10 10
4464 – 20 fo. dull green and black 10 10
4472 – 50 fo. dull blue and black 25 10
4476 – 70 fo. brown-rose and black 35 15
4481 – 100 fo. light brown and black 50 25

DESIGNS—VERT: 20 fo. Armchair by Karoly Lingel, 1915; 50 fo. Prince Pal Esterhazy's armchair (16th century); 70 fo. Chair with umbrella-shaped back, 1820. HORIZ: 100 fo. Couch by Lajos Kozma, 1920.

1211 Three Wise Men (Zsuzsa Demeter)

1212 Wigner

1999. Christmas. Multicoloured

4485 24 fo. Type **1190** 10 10
4486 27 fo. Type **1211** 15 10
4487 32 fo. "Madonna and Child" (stained glass window, Miksa Roth) (vert) 15 10

1999. 97th Birth Anniv of Jeno Wigner (physicist).

4488 **1212** 32 fo. blue 15 10

1214 Coronation Sceptre

2000. New Millenium.

4490 **1214** 28 fo. bistre and purple . 15 10
4491 30 fo. bistre and purple . 15 10
4492 – 34 fo. multicoloured . . 15 10
4493 – 40 fo. multicoloured . . 20 10

DESIGN:—34, 40 fo. Millennium flag.

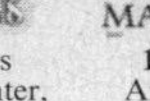

1215 Miklos Kis Misztotfalusi (printer, 350th anniv)

1216 Fekete and Animal Characters

2000. Birth Anniversaries.

4494 **1216** 30 fo. green, stone and brown 15 10
4495 – 40 fo. blue, stone and brown 20 10
4496 – 50 fo. red, stone and brown 25 15
4497 – 80 fo. brown and stone . 40 20

DESIGNS:— 40 fo., Anyos Jedlik (physicist, bicentenary); 50 fo., Jeno Kvassay (engineer, 150th anniv); Jeno Barcsay (artist, centenary).

2000. Youth Stamp. Birth Centenary of Istvon Fekete (writer).

4498 **1216** 60 fo. + 30 fo. mult . . 45 45

1217 Hungarian Cultural Foundation and Exhibition Emblem

2000. "Hunphilex 2000" Stamp Exhibition, Budapest.

4499 **1217** 200 fo. + 100 fo. mult . 1·50 75

EXPRESS LETTER STAMPS

E 36

1916. Inscr "MAGYAR KIR POSTA".
E245 **E 36** 2 f. olive and red . . . 20 20

1916. Optd **KOZTARSASAG**.
E301 **E 36** 2 f. olive and red . . . 20 30

1919. Inscr "MAGYAR POSTA".
E349 **E 36** 2 f. olive and red . . . 15 15

IMPERIAL JOURNAL STAMPS

J 1 J 2

1868. Imperf.
J52 **J 1** 1 k. blue . . . . 1·00 30
J 3 **J 2** 1 k. blue £12000 £7500
J53 2 k. brown . . . . 3·75 4·50
No. J3 has the arms at the foot as in Type **J 2** but the corner designs differ.

NEWSPAPER STAMPS

N 2 St. Stephen's Crown and Posthorn
N 4
N 9

1871. Posthorn turned to left. Imperf.
N8 **N 2** 1 k. red . . . . 70·00 27·00

1872. As Type **N 2** but with posthorn turned to right. Imperf.
N14 1 k. red . . . . 14·00 2·75

1874. Imperf.
N64 **N 4** 1 k. orange . . . . . . 1·00 10

1900. Imperf.
N136 **N 9** (2 f.) orange 10 10
N401 (10 f.) blue 10 10
N402 (20 f.) purple 10 10

OFFICIAL STAMPS

O 44

1921.
O428 **O 44** 10 f. black & purple . . 10 15
O429 20 f. black & brown . . 10 15
O430 60 f. black and grey . . 10 15
O431 100 f. black and red . . 10 15
O432 250 f. black and blue . . 10 15
O433 350 f. black and blue . . 10 15
O434 500 f. black & brown . . 10 15
O435 1000 f. black & brn . . 10 15

1922. Nos. O429/33 surch (No. O439 optd **KORONA** only).
O436 **O 44** 15 k. on 20 f. black and brown 10 15
O437 25 k. on 60 f. black and grey 10 15
O438 150 k. on 100 f. black and pink 70 15
O439 (350) k. on 350 f. black and blue 85 30
O440 2000 k. on 250 f. black and blue . . . . . . 1·00 40

1922.
O441 **O 44** 5 k. brown 10 15
O442 10 k. brown 10 15
O443 15 k. grey 10 15
O444 25 k. orange 10 15
O445 50 k. red and brown . . 10 15
O446 100 k. red and bistre . . 10 15
O447 150 k. red and green . . 10 15
O448 300 k. red 10 15
O449 350 k. red and violet . . 10 15
O450a 500 k. red and orange . 1·25 40
O451 600 k. red and bistre . . 70 75
O452 1000 k. red and blue . 1·25 70
O453 3000 k. red and violet . 80 25
O454 5000 k. red and blue . 1·00 75

PARCEL POST STAMPS

1954. No. 979 surch.
P1398 **153** 1 fo. 70 on 1 fo. 40 grn . 75 35
P1399 2 fo. on 1 fo. 40 green . 1·25 45
P1400 3 fo. on 1 fo. 40 green . 1·75 60

POSTAGE DUE STAMPS

D 9

1903. Inscr "MAGYAR KIR. POSTA". Figures in centre in black.
D170 **D 9** 1 f. green 10 15
D171 2 f. green 10 10
D172 5 f. green 25 20
D119 6 f. green 35 30
D174 10 f. green 40 40
D175 12 f. green 10 10
D176 20 f. green 10 10
D177 50 f. green 20 25
D 91 100 f. green 75 65

1915. Surch **20**.
D188 **D 9** 20 on 100 f. blk & grn . 1·00 80

1915. As Type **D 9**, but figures in red.
D190 **D 9** 1 f. green 10 10
D191 2 f. green 10 10
D192 5 f. green 70 15
D193 6 f. green 15 15
D194 10 f. green 10 10
D195 12 f. green 10 10
D196 15 f. green 15 10
D197 20 f. green 10 10
D198 30 f. green 10 10
D349 40 f. green 15 15
D350 50 f. green 15 15
D351 120 f. green 15 15
D352 200 f. green 15 15
D430 2 k. green 10 15
D431 5 k. green 10 15
D432 50 k. green 10 15

1919. Overprinted **KOZTARSASAG**.
D325 **D 9** 2 f. red and green . . . 10 10
D326 3 f. red and green . . . 10 10
D327 10 f. red and green . . . 10 10
D328 20 f. red and green . . . 10 10
D329 40 f. red and green . . . 10 10
D324 50 f. black and green . . 1·25 1·25
D330 50 f. red and green . . . 10 10

1919. As Type **D 9** but inscr "MAGYAR POSTA" and optd with **T 37** and **MAGYAR TANACS KOZTARSASAG**. Figures in black.
D369 **D 9** 2 f. green 35 35
D370 3 f. green 35 35
D371 10 f. green . . . . . 3·25 3·25
D372 20 f. green 35 35
D373 40 f. green 35 35
D374 50 f. green 35 35

1919. As Type **D 9**, but inscribed. "MAGYAR POSTA". Figures in Black.
D375 **D 9** 2 f. green 10 10
D376 3 f. green 10 10
D377 20 f. green 10 15
D378 40 f. green 10 15
D379 50 f. green 10 15

1921. Surch **PORTO** and value. Inscr "MAGYAR KIR POSTA".
D428 **18** 100 f. on 15 f. purple . . . 10 10
D429 500 f. on 15 f. purple . . . 10 10
D433 $2\frac{1}{2}$ k. on 10 f. purple . . . 10 10
D434 3 k. on 15 f. purple . . . 10 10
D437 6 k. on $1\frac{1}{2}$ k. purple . . . 10 10
D435 9 k. on 40 f. green 10 10
D438 10 k. on $2\frac{1}{2}$ k. green . . . 10 10
D436 12 k. on 60 f. green . . . 10 10
D439 15 k. on $1\frac{1}{2}$ k. purple . . . 10 10
D440 20 k. on $2\frac{1}{2}$ k. green . . . 10 10
D441 25 k. on $1\frac{1}{2}$ k. purple . . . 10 10
D442 30 k. on $1\frac{1}{2}$ k. purple . . . 10 10
D443 40 k. on $2\frac{1}{2}$ k. green . . . 10 10
D444 50 k. on $1\frac{1}{2}$ k. purple . . . 10 10
D445 100 k. on $4\frac{1}{2}$ k. pur . . . 10 10
D446 200 k. on $4\frac{1}{2}$ k. pur . . . 10 10
D447 300 k. on $4\frac{1}{2}$ k. pur . . . 15 10
D448 500 k. on 2 k. blue 15 10
D449 500 k. on 3 k. brown . . . 15 10
D450 1000 k. on 2 k. blue . . . 15 10
D451 1000 k. on 3 k. brn . . . 30 10
D452 2000 k. on 2 k. blue . . . 30 10
D453 2000 k. on 3 k. brn . . . 50 15
D454 5000 k. on 5 k. brn . . . 75 40

D 61 D 84 D 115

1926.
D479 **D 61** 1 f. red 10 10
D480 2 f. red 10 10
D481 3 f. red 10 10
D482 4 f. red 10 10
D483 5 f. red . . . . 1·40 70
D509 8 f. red 10 10
D510 10 f. red 10 10
D486 16 f. red 15 10
D512 20 f. red 20 10
D487 32 f. red 30 15
D513 40 f. red 30 10
D489 50 f. red 50 15
D490 80 f. red . . . . . . 1·25 70

1927. Nos. 434/36b surch **PORTO** and value.
D491 **49** 1 f. on 500 k. light green and green 15 10
D492 2 f. on 1000 k. brown and bistre 15 10
D493 3 f. on 2000 k. blue and deep blue 15 35
D494 5 f. on 5000 k. mauve and purple 60 75
D495 10 f. on 10000 k. purple and red 50 50

1931. Surch.
D529 **D 61** 4 f. on 5 red 15 10
D534 10 f. on 16 f. red . . . 50 70
D531 10 f. on 80 f. red . . . 45 35
D532 12 f. on 50 f. red . . . 55 45
D533 20 f. on 32 f. red . . . 60 60

1934.
D569 **D 84** 2 f. blue 10 10
D570 4 f. blue 10 10
D571 6 f. blue 10 10
D572 8 f. blue 10 10
D573 10 f. blue 10 10
D574 12 f. blue 10 10
D575 16 f. blue 10 10
D576 20 f. blue 15 10
D577 40 f. blue 20 10
D578 80 f. blue 50 20

1941.
D684 **D 115** 2 f. brown 10 10
D685 3 f. brown 10 10
D686 4 f. brown 10 10
D687 6 f. brown 10 10
D688 8 f. brown 10 10
D689 10 f. brown 10 10
D690 12 f. brown 10 10
D691 16 f. brown 10 10
D692 18 f. brown 10 10
D693 20 f. brown 10 10
D694 24 f. brown 10 10
D695 30 f. brown 10 10
D696 36 f. brown 10 10
D697 40 f. brown 10 10
D698 50 f. brown 10 10
D699 60 f. brown 15 10

1945. Surch **1945** and value. Blue surface-tinted paper.
D825 **D 115** 10 f. on 2 f. brown . . 10 10
D826 10 f. on 3 f. brown . . 10 10
D827 20 f. on 4 f. brown . . 10 10
D828 20 f. on 6 f. brown . . 5·00 5·00
D829 20 f. on 8 f. brown . . 10 10
D830 40 f. on 12 f. brown . . 10 10
D831 40 f. on 16 f. brown . . 10 10
D832 40 f. on 18 f. brown . . 10 10
D833 60 f. on 24 f. brown . . 10 10
D834 80 f. on 30 f. brown . . 10 10
D835 90 f. on 36 f. brown . . 10 10
D836 1 p. on 10 f. brown . . 10 10
D837 1 p. on 40 f. brown . . 10 10
D838 2 p. on 20 f. brown . . 10 10
D839 2 p. on 50 f. brown . . 10 10
D840 2 p. on 60 f. brown . . 10 10
D841 10 p. on 3 f. brown . . 10 10
D842 12 p. on 8 f. brown . . 10 10
D843 20 p. on 24 f. brown . . 10 10

D 154 Numeral D 201 D 215

1946.
D984 **D 154** 4 f. red and brown . . 20 10
D985 10 f. red and brown . . 75 10
D986 20 f. red and brown . . 20 10
D987 30 f. red and brown . . 20 10
D988 40 f. red and brown . . 55 10
D989 50 f. red and brown . 1·40 40
D990 60 f. red and brown . . 75 10
D991 1 fo. 20 red & brn . . 1·25 35
D992 2 fo. red and brown . . 2·00 40

1950.
D1114 **D 154** 4 fi. purple 10 10
D1115 10 fi. purple 10 10
D1116 20 fi. purple 10 10
D1117 30 fi. purple 10 10
D1118 40 fi. purple 30 10
D1119 50 fi. purple 65 10
D1120 60 fi. purple 55 10
D1121 1 fo. 20 purple . . . 85 10
D1122 2 fo. purple . . . . 1·75 10

1951. Fiscal stamps surch with Arms. **MAGYAR POSTA PORTO** and value.
D1157 **D 201** 8 fi. brown 15 15
D1158 10 fi. brown 15 15
D1159 12 fi. brown 25 25

1951.
D1210 **D 215** 4 fi. brown 10 10
D1211 6 fi. brown 10 10
D1212 8 fi. brown 10 10
D1213 10 fi. brown 10 10
D1214 14 fi. brown 10 10
D1215 20 fi. brown 10 10
D1216 30 fi. brown 10 10
D1217 40 fi. brown 10 10
D1218 50 fi. brown 20 10
D1219 60 fi. brown 25 10
D1220 1 fo. 20 brown . . . 35 10
D1221 2 fo. brown 60 10

D 240 D 282

1953. 50th Anniv of 1st Hungarian Postage Due Stamps.
D1305 **D 240** 4 fi. black & grn . . 10 10
D1306 6 fi. black & grn . . 10 10
D1307 8 fi. black & grn . . 10 10
D1308 10 fi. black & grn . . 10 10
D1309 12 fi. black & grn . . 10 10
D1310 14 fi. black & grn . . 10 10
D1311 16 fi. black & grn . . 10 10
D1312 20 fi. black & grn . . 10 10
D1313 24 fi. black & grn . . 10 10
D1314 30 fi. black & grn . . 10 10
D1315 36 fi. black & grn . . 10 10
D1316 40 fi. black & grn . . 15 10
D1317 50 fi. black & grn . . 20 10
D1318 60 fi. black & grn . . 20 10
D1319 70 fi. black & grn . . 25 10
D1320 80 fi. black & grn . . 30 10
D1321 1 fo. 20 black & grn . 40 10
D1322 2 fo. black & grn . . 70 10

1958. Forint values are larger (31 × 22 mm.).
D1498 **D 282** 4 fi. black & red . . . 10 10
D1499 6 fi. black & red . . 10 10
D1500 8 fi. black & red . . 10 10
D1501 10 fi. black & red . . 10 10
D1502 12 fi. black & red . . 10 10
D1503 14 fi. black & red . . 10 10
D1504 16 fi. black & red . . 10 10
D1505 20 fi. black & red . . 10 10
D1506 24 fi. black & red . . 10 10
D1507 30 fi. black & red . . 10 10
D1508 36 fi. black & red . . 10 10
D1509 40 fi. black & red . . 10 10
D1510 50 fi. black & red . . 10 10
D1511 60 fi. black & red . . 15 10
D1512 70 fi. black & red . . 20 10
D1513 80 fi. black & red . . 25 10
D1514 – 1 fo. brown 15 10
D1515 – 1 fo. 20 brown . . . 35 10
D1516 – 2 fo. brown 60 10
D1517 – 4 fo. brown 60 10

D 587 Money-order Cancelling Machine
D 944 Foot Messenger

1973. Postal Operations.
D2847 **D 587** 20 fi. brown & red . . 10 10
D2848 – 40 fi. blue and red . . 10 10
D2849 – 80 fi. violet & red . . 20 10
D2850 – 1 fo. green & red . . 25 10
D2851 – 1 fo. 20 grn & red . . 30 10
D2852 – 2 fo. violet & red . . 1·40 10
D2853 – 3 fo. blue and red . . 65 10
D2854 – 4 fo. brown & red . . 70 10
D2855 – 8 fo. purple & red . . 80 10
D2856 – 10 fo. green & red . . 1·00 10
DESIGNS—As Type **D 587**: 40 fi. Parcel scales, self-service post office; 80 fi. Automatic parcels-registration machine; 1 fo. Data-recording machine; 28 × 22 mm: 1 fo. 20, Ilyushin Il-18 mail plane and van; 2 fo. Diesel mail train; 3 fo. Postman on motor cycle; 4 fo. Postman at mailboxes; 8 fo. Toshiba automatic sorting machine; 10 fo. Postman on motor cycle (different).

1987. Postal History. Multicoloured.
D3810 1 fo. Type **D 944** 10 10
D3811 4 fo. Post rider 10 10
D3812 6 fo. Horse-drawn mail coach 40 10
D3813 8 fo. Railway mail carriage . 2·50 65
D3814 10 fo. Mail van 65 10
D3815 20 fo. Mail plane . . . . 1·40 10

SAVINGS BANK STAMP

B 17

1916.

B199 B 17 10 f. purple 15 15

SZEGED

The following issues were made by the Hungarian National Government led by Admiral Horthy, which was set up in Szeged in 1919, then under French occupation, and which later replaced the Communist regime established by Bela Kun.

100 filler = 1 korona.

1919. Stamps of Hungary optd **MAGYAR NEMZETI KORMANY Szeged, 1919.** or surch.

(a) War Charity stamps of 1916.

1 **20** 10 f. (+ 2 f.) red . . . . . . 1·25 1·25
2 – 15 f. (+ 2 f.) violet 50 50
3 **22** 40 f. (+ 2 f.) lake . . . . . 3·00 3·00

(b) Harvesters and Parliament Types.

4 **18** 2 f. brown 15 15
5 3 f. red 15 15
6 5 f. green 15 15
7 6 f. blue . . . . 8·00 8·00
8 15 f. violet 30 30
9 20 f. brown (No. 307) . . . . 20·00 20·00
10 25 f. blue (No. 309) 15 15
11 **19** 50 f. purple . . . . 3·75 3·75
12 75 f. blue 30 30
13 80 f. green . . . . 3·00 3·00
14 1 k. lake 20 20
15 2 k. brown 35 35
16 3 k. grey and violet 45 45
17 5 k. brown . . . . 28·00 28·00
18 10 k. lilac and brown . . . . 28·00 28·00

(c) Nos. 5 and 14 further surch.

19 **18** 45 on 3 f. red 40 40
20 **19** 10 on 1 k. lake . . . . . . 2·50 2·50

(d) Karl and Zita stamps.

21 **27** 10 f. red 20 20
22 20 f. brown 15 15
23 25 f. blue . . . . 11·00 11·00
24 **28** 40 f. olive 70 70

The following (Nos. 25/39) are also optd **KOZTARSASAG.**

(e) War Charity stamp.

25 **22** 40 f. (+ 2 f.) lake . . . . . 3·25 3·25

(f) Harvesters and Parliament Types.

26 **18** 3 f. red . . . . 8·50 8·50
27 4 f. slate 45 45
28 5 f. green . . . . 4·50 4·50
29 6 f. blue . . . . 2·00 2·00
30 10 f. red . . . . 5·00 5·00
31 20 f. brown . . . . 21·00 21·00
32 20 (f) on 2 f. bistre 15 15
33 40 f. olive 20 20
34 **19** 3 k. grey and violet . . . . . 20·00 20·00

(g) Karl and Zita stamps.

35 **27** 10 f. red . . . . 3·00 3·00
36 15 f. violet 70 70
37 20 f. brown . . . . 21·00 21·00
38 25 f. blue . . . . 5·00 5·00
39 **28** 50 f. purple 15 15

EXPRESS LETTER STAMP

1919. No. E245 optd as above.

E41 E 18 2 f. olive and red . . . . 2·00 2·00

NEWSPAPER STAMP

1919. No. N136 optd **MAGYAR NEMZETI KORMANY Szeged, 1919.**

N40 N 9 (2 f.) orange 15 15

POSTAGE DUE STAMPS

1919. Nos. D191, etc. (a) Optd as above, in red.

D42 D 9 2 f. red and green 60 60
D43 6 f. red and green . . . . 1·40 1·40
D44 10 f. red and green . . . . 1·00 1·00
D45 12 f. red and green . . . . 1·00 1·00
D46 20 f. red and green 80 80
D47 30 f. red and green . . . . 1·00 1·00

(b) No. E41 surch **PORTO** and new value in red.

D48 E 18 50 f. on 2 f. olive & red . 60 60
D49 100 f. on 2 f. olive & red . 1·25 1·25

HYDERABAD Pt. 1

A state in India. Now uses Indian stamps.

12 pies = 1 anna; 16 annas = 1 rupee

1

1869.

1 1 1 a. green . . . . 13·00 6·00

2

3

1870.

2 **2** ½ a. brown . . . . 4·00 4·00
3 2 a. green . . . . 42·00 38·00

1871.

13 **3** ½ a. brown . . . . 1·40 10
13d ½ a. red . . . . 1·25 10
14 1 a. purple . . . . 4·00 4·00
14b 1 a. brown 60 15
14c 1 a. black . . . . 1·10 10
15 2 a. green . . . . 2·25 15
16b 3 a. brown . . . . 1·00 85
17b 4 a. grey . . . . 3·25 1·75
17c 4 a. green . . . . 3·00 85
18 8 a. brown . . . . 1·25 2·00
19 12 a. blue . . . . 3·00 4·50
19a 12 a. green . . . . 2·50 2·75

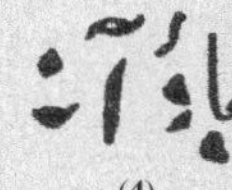

(4)

1898. Surch with T **4**.

20 **3** ½ a. on ½ a. brown 50 85

5

6

1900.

21 **5** ¼ a. blue . . . . 4·00 2·75

1905.

22 **6** ¼ a. blue . . . . 1·25 45
32d ¼ a. grey 30 10
33 ¼ a. purple 50 10
23b ½ a. red . . . . 1·75 25
34 ½ a. green 40 10
26 1 a. red . . . . 1·10 10
27cb 2 a. lilac . . . . 1·10 10
28b 3 a. orange 90 60
29c 4 a. green 90 30
30c 8 a. purple . . . . 1·10 35
31c 12 a. green . . . . 3·00 1·50

8 Symbol

9

1915.

35 **8** ½ a. green 60 10
58 ½ a. red . . . . 1·25 50
36 1 a. red 80 10
37 **9** 1 r. yellow . . . . 9·00 11·00

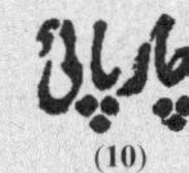

(10)

1930. Surch as T **10**.

38 **6** 4 p. on ¼ a. grey . . . . . 50·00 15·00
39 4 p. on ¼ a. purple 25 10
40 **8** 8 p. on ½ a. green 25 10

12 Symbols

13 The Char Minar

1931.

60 **12** 2 p. brown . . . . 1·00 1·75
41 4 p. black 30 10
59 6 p. red . . . . 6·00 5·00
42 8 p. green 35 10
43 **13** 1 a. brown 35 10
44 – 2 a. violet . . . . 2·00 10
45 – 4 a. blue . . . . 1·25 30
46 – 8 a. orange . . . . . . 4·00 2·50
47 – 12 a. red . . . . 4·00 8·50
48 – 1 r. yellow . . . . 4·00 3·00

In No. 59 "POSTAGE" is at foot.

DESIGNS—HORIZ (32½ × 21 mm): 2 a. High Court of Justice; 4 a. Osman Sagar Reservoir; 12 a. Bidar College. VERT: 8 a. Entrance to Ajanta Caves; 1 r. Victory Tower, Daulatabad.

15 Unani General Hospital

1937. Inscr "H.E.H. THE NIZAM'S SILVER JUBILEE".

49 **15** 4 p. slate and violet 40 80
50 – 8 p. slate and brown 70 85
51 – 1 a. slate and yellow 70 60
52 – 2 a. slate and green . . . . . 90 3·00

DESIGNS: 8 p. Osmania General Hospital; 1 a. Osmania University; 2 a. Osmania Jubilee Hall.

16 Family Reunion

17 Town Hall

1945. Victory Commemoration.

53 **16** 1 a. blue 10 10

1947. Reformed Legislature.

54 **17** 1 a. black . . . . 70 1·00

18 Power House, Hyderabad

1947. Inscr as in T **18**.

55 **18** 1 a. 4 p. green . . . . 75 1·50
56 – 3 a. blue . . . . 85 2·25
57 – 6 a. brown . . . . 3·00 10·00

DESIGNS—HORIZ: 3 a. Kaktyai Arch, Warangal Fort; 6 a. Golkunda Fort.

OFFICIAL STAMPS

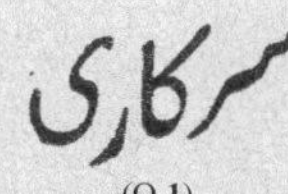

(O 1)

1873. Optd with Type O **1**.

O2 **2** ½ a. brown . . . . — £400
O1 **1** 1 a. green . . . . 60·00 20·00
O3a **2** 2 a. olive . . . . — £130

1873. Optd with Type O **1**.

O 9a **3** ½ a. brown . . . . 6·00 2·50
O11 1 a. brown . . . . 70·00 48·00
O12a 1 a. drab . . . . 1·50 1·60
O19 1 a. black . . . . 55·00 10
O13a 2 a. green . . . . 3·00 4·00
O20d 3 a. brown . . . . 3·00 1·00
O15a 4 a. grey . . . . 11·00 11·00
O20e 4 a. green . . . . £275 3·25
O16b 8 a. brown . . . . 30·00 24·00
O17a 12 a. blue . . . . 35·00 50·00
O20g 12 a. green . . . . — 60·00

1909. Optd as Type O **1**, or similar smaller opt.

O37e **6** ¼ a. grey 70 35
O38 ¼ a. lilac . . . . 1·60 10
O21a ½ a. red £100 15
O39d ½ a. green . . . . 1·25 10
O40 **8** ½ a. green . . . . 1·50 10
O54 ½ a. red . . . . 9·00 5·50
O31d **6** 1 a. red 75 15
O41e **8** 1 a. red 85 10
O32b **6** 2 a. lilac 85 25
O33b 3 a. orange . . . . 9·00 1·75
O34d 4 a. green . . . . 2·25 10
O35 8 a. purple . . . . 3·00 20
O36 12 a. green . . . . 11·00 60

1930. Official stamps surch as T **10**.

O42 **6** 4 p. on ¼ a. grey . . . . . £200 17·00
O43 4 p. on ¼ a. lilac 65 10
O45 8 p. on ½ a. green . . . . . 35·00 45·00
O44 **8** 8 p. on ½ a. green 60 10

1934. Optd as Type O **1** but smaller.

O55 **12** 2 p. brown . . . . 7·00 6·00
O46 4 p. black . . . . 1·00 10
O56 6 p. red . . . . 8·50 17·00
O47 8 p. green 40 10
O48 **13** 1 a. brown 60 10
O49 – 2 a. violet (No. 44) . . . . 4·00 10
O50 – 4 a. blue (No. 45) . . . . 1·75 20
O51 – 8 a. orange (No. 46) . . . 8·00 50
O52 – 12 a. red (No. 47) . . . . 5·50 1·25
O53 – 1 r. yellow (No. 48) . . . 13·00 2·00

ICELAND Pt. 11

An island lying S.E. of Greenland. An independent state formerly under the Danish sovereign, now a republic.

1873. 96 skilling = 1 riksdaler.
1876. 100 aurar (singular: eyrir) = 1 krona.

1

þrír

(6)

1873.

1 **1** 2 s. blue £700 £1500
5 3 s. grey £350 £1000
2 4 s. red £130 £700
3 8 s. brown £225 £750
7 16 s. yellow . . . . 90·00 £475

1876.

42 **1** 3 a. yellow . . . . 2·25 11·00
27 4 a. grey and red . . . . . 13·00 14·00
13 5 a. blue £225 £500
28 5 a. green . . . . 3·00 2·10
29a 6 a. grey . . . . 11·00 13·00
30 10 a. red . . . . 5·50 2·10
31 16 a. brown . . . . 45·00 55·00
18 20 a. mauve £800 £325
32a 20 a. blue . . . . 27·00 21·00
33 25 a. blue and brown . . . . 13·00 16·00
19 40 a. green . . . . 75·00 £160
23b 40 a. mauve . . . . 28·00 30·00
24 50 a. red and blue . . . . . 55·00 70·00
25 100 a. purple and brown . . . 55·00 85·00

1897. Surch as T **6** with figure **3** under word.

38 **1** 3 on 5 a. green £325 £300

1897. Surch as T **6**.

40 **1** 3 on 5 a. green £300 £275

1902. Optd **I GILDI '02—'03**.

54 **1** 3 a. yellow . . . . 85 1·40
55 4 a. grey and red . . . . . 21·00 32·00
56 5 a. green . . . . 75 5·25
58 6 a. grey . . . . 75 5·25
60 10 a. red . . . . 85 7·75
61 16 a. brown . . . . 15·00 32·00
62 20 a. blue . . . . 70 6·75
64 25 a. blue and brown . . . . 75 10·50
66 40 a. mauve . . . . 70 40·00
67 50 a. red and blue . . . . . 3·75 45·00
52 100 a. purple and brown . . . 38·00 55·00

11 King Christian IX

12 Kings Christian IX and Frederik VIII

13 Jon Sigurdsson

1902.

68 **11** 3 a. orange . . . . 4·25 2·50
69 4 a. red and grey . . . . . 2·25 1·10
70 5 a. green . . . . 12·00 1·10
71 6 a. brown . . . . 11·00 7·00
72 10 a. red . . . . 3·25 1·10
73 16 a. brown . . . . 3·75 6·50
74 20 a. blue . . . . 2·10 2·40
75 25 a. green and brown . . . 5·75 5·25
76 40 a. mauve . . . . 3·25 3·25
77 50 a. black and grey . . . . 7·50 16·00
78 1 k. brown and blue . . . . 5·75 7·00
79 2 k. blue and brown . . . . 23·00 55·00
80 5 k. grey and brown £130 £170

1907.

81 **12** 1 e. red and green . . . . . 1·10 95
82 3 a. brown . . . . 3·25 1·10
83 4 a. red and grey . . . . . 1·90 75
84 5 a. green . . . . 45·00 1·10
85 6 a. grey . . . . 19·00 2·10
114 10 a. red . . . . 2·10 1·10
87 15 a. green and red . . . . 5·25 1·25
88 16 a. brown . . . . 5·50 23·00
89 20 a. blue . . . . 6·25 2·75
90 25 a. green and brown . . . 8·50 9·00
91 40 a. red . . . . 4·25 9·50
92 50 a. red and grey . . . . . 5·25 8·50
93 1 k. brown and blue . . . . 26·00 38·00
94 2 k. green and brown . . . 23·00 48·00
95 5 k. blue and brown £150 £225

1911. Birth Cent. of Jon Sigurdsson (historian and Althing member).

96 **13** 1 e. green . . . . 1·75 1·50
97 3 a. brown . . . . 3·25 7·50
98 4 a. blue . . . . 1·25 1·25
99 6 a. grey . . . . 7·50 16·00
100 15 a. violet . . . . 8·50 1·25
101 25 a. orange . . . . 16·00 26·00

1912. As T **13**, but portrait of King Frederik VIII and "JON SIGURDSSON" omitted.

102 5 a. green . . . . 16·00 8·50
103 10 a. red . . . . 16·00 8·50
104 20 a. blue . . . . 32·00 12·00
105 50 a. red . . . . 6·50 21·00
106 1 k. yellow . . . . 21·00 42·00
107 2 k. red . . . . 21·00 38·00
108 5 k. brown £120 £170

15 King Christian X

22 Landing Mails at Vik

1920.
116 **15** 1 e. red and green 65 95
117 3 a. brown 2·75 9·50
184 4 a. red and grey 2·10 1·60
132 5 a. green 1·60 1·60
185 6 a. grey 1·75 2·75
186 7 a. green 70 1·25
121 8 a. brown 7·75 1·60
122 10 a. red 1·75 5·00
133 10 a. green 2·40 1·50
187 10 a. brown 85·00 1·00
123 15 a. violet 24·00 1·10
124 20 a. blue 1·40 9·50
134 20 a. brown 48·00 1·10
125 25 a. green and brown 11·50 1·25
135 25 a. red 10·50 26·00
189 30 a. green and red 19·00 4·25
127 40 a. red 30·00 2·10
136 40 a. blue 60·00 10·50
128 50 a. red and grey £120 7·00
191 1 k. brown and blue 32·00 5·75
130 2 k. green and brown £130 17·00
131 5 k. blue and brown 40·00 10·50
193 10 k. black and green £225 £160

1921. Various types surch.
137 **11** 5 a. on 16 a. brown 2·75 21·00
138 **12** 5 a. on 16 a. brown 1·40 5·25
139 **15** 10 a. on 5 a. green 5·25 2·40
140 **11** 20 a. on 25 a. green & brown 5·50 5·50
141 **12** 20 a. on 25 a. grn & brn 2·75 4·75
142 **11** 20 a. on 40 a. mauve 5·25 15·00
143 **12** 20 a. on 40 a. red 6·50 13·00
144 **11** 30 a. on 50 a. grey 17·00 21·00
145 50 a. on 5 k. grey & brn 42·00 42·00
146 **15** 1 k. on 40 a. blue £100 27·00
147 **13** 2 k. on 25 a. orange 70·00 95·00
148 – 10 k. on 50 a. red (No. 105) £200 £350
149 – 10 k. on 1 k. yell (No. 106) £250 £425
150 **11** 10 k. on 2 k. black & brn 42·00 21·00
150a **12** 10 k. on 5 k. black & brn £325 £450

1925.
151 **22** 7 a. green 30·00 6·25
152 – 10 a. brown and blue 30·00 80
153 – 20 a. red 30·00 1·00
154 – 35 a. blue 45·00 7·50
155 **22** 50 a. brown and green 45·00 2·10
DESIGNS: 10 a., 35 a. Reykjavik and Esjaberg (mountain); 20 a. National Museum, Reykjavik.

1928. Air. Optd with airplane.
156 **15** 10 a. red 1·00 9·00
157 **12** 50 a. purple and grey 45·00 85·00

24 Discovery of Iceland

25 Gyrfalcon

1930. Parliament Millenary Celebration.
158 – 3 a. violet (postage) 1·60 7·25
159 **24** 5 a. blue and grey 2·40 7·25
160 – 7 a. green 1·60 7·25
161 – 10 a. purple 7·75 12·00
162 – 15 a. blue 1·60 7·25
163 – 20 a. red 32·00 55·00
164 – 25 a. brown 5·50 9·50
165 – 30 a. green 4·25 9·00
166 – 35 a. blue 4·75 10·00
167 – 40 a. red, blue and grey 4·25 9·00
168 – 50 a. brown 55·00 85·00
169 – 1 k. green 55·00 85·00
170 – 2 k. blue and green 70·00 £110
171 – 5 k. orange and yellow 32·00 80·00
172 – 10 k. lake 32·00 80·00
173 **25** 10 a. blue (air) 26·00 55·00
DESIGNS—HORIZ: 3 a. Parliament House, Reykjavik; 7 a. Encampment at Thingvellir; 10 a. Arrival of Ingolf Arnarsson; 15 a. Naming the Island; 20 a. The Dash for "Althing" (Parliament); 25 a. Discovery of Arnarsson's pillar; 30 a. Lake Thingvellir; 35 a. Queen Aud; 40 a. National flag; 50 a. First "Althing" (Parliament), A.D. 930; 1 k. Map of Iceland; 2 k. Winter-bound farmstead; 5 k. Woman spinning; 10 k. Viking sacrifice to Thor.

26 Snaefellsjokull

1930. Air. Parliamentary Millenary.
174 **26** 15 a. blue and brown 24·00 48·00
175 – 20 a. blue and brown 21·00 48·00
176 – 35 a. brown and green 38·00 80·00
177 – 50 a. blue and green 38·00 80·00
178 – 1 k. red and green 38·00 80·00
DESIGNS: 20 a. Old Icelandic fishing boat; 35 a. Icelandic Pony; 50 a. The Gullfoss Falls; 1 k. Statue of Arnarsson, Reykjavik.

1931. Air. Optd **Zeppelin 1931**.
179 **15** 30 a. green and red 27·00 £110
180 1 k. brown and blue 8·00 £110
181 2 k. green and brown 42·00 £110

29 Gullfoss Falls

30 Shipwreck and Breeches-buoy

1931.
195 **29** 5 a. grey 10·50 75
196 20 a. red 9·50 10
197 35 a. blue 11·00 11·50
198 60 a. mauve 9·00 1·10
199 65 a. brown 2·75 95
200 75 a. blue 85·00 26·00

1933. Charity.
201 **30** 10 a. + 10 a. brown 1·90 4·75
202 – 20 a. + 20 a. red 1·90 4·75
203 **30** 35 a. + 25 a. blue 1·90 4·75
204 – 50 a. + 25 a. green 1·90 4·75
DESIGNS: 20 a. Children gathering flowers; 50 a. Aged fisherman and rowing boat.

1933. Air. Balbo Transatlantic Mass Formation Flight. Optd **Hopflug Itala 1933**.
205 **15** 1 k. brown and blue £110 £450
206 5 k. blue and brown £275 £1100
207 10 k. black and green £650 £2250

32 Avro 504K Biplane over Thingvellir

1934. Air.
208 **32** 10 a. blue 1·50 1·90
209 20 a. green 3·00 4·00
210a – 25 a. violet 11·00 15·00
211 – 50 a. purple 4·00 6·75
212 – 1 k. brown 20·00 28·00
213 – 2 k. red 10·50 10·00
DESIGNS: 25 a., 50 a. Monoplane and Aurora Borealis; 1 k., 2 k. Monoplane over map of Iceland.

33 Dynjandi Falls

35 Matthias Jochumsson

36 King Christian X

1935.
214 **33** 10 a. blue 19·00 10
215 – 1 k. green 30·00 10
DESIGN—HORIZ: 1 k. Mt. Hekla.

1935. Birth Centenary of Matthias Jochumsson (poet).
216 **35** 3 a. green 50 2·75
217 5 a. grey 10·50 80
218 7 a. green 15·00 1·25
219 35 a. blue 40 1·10

1937. Silver Jubilee of King Christian X.
220 **36** 10 a. green 2·50 17·00
221 30 a. brown 2·50 7·75
222 40 a. red 2·50 7·75

37 The Great Geyser

38 Reykjavik University

1938.
226 **37** 15 a. purple 5·75 8·75
227 20 a. red 19·00 35
228 35 a. blue 65 50
229 – 40 a. brown 9·50 18·00
230 – 45 a. blue 80 75
231 – 50 a. green 17·00 75
232a – 60 a. blue 5·25 1·00
233 – 1 k. blue 1·90 10
The frames of the 40 a. to 1 k. differ from Type **37**.

1938. 20th Anniv of Independence.
234 **38** 25 a. green 5·00 10·00
235 30 a. brown 5·00 10·00
236 40 a. purple 5·00 10·00

1939. Surch **5**.
237 **35** 5 on 35 a. blue 70 90

40 Trylon and Perisphere

41 Atlantic Cod

42 Icelandic Flag

1939. New York World's Fair.
238 **40** 20 a. red 3·00 5·25
239 – 35 a. blue 3·25 7·00
240 – 45 a. green 4·25 7·75
241 – 2 k. black 40·00 £110
DESIGNS: 35 a. Viking longship and route to America; 45 a., 2 k. Statue of Thorfinn Karlsefni, Reykjavik.

1939.
242 **41** 1 e. blue 10 3·00
243 – 3 a. violet 15 40
244 **41** 5 a. brown 15 10
245 – 7 a. green 4·75 7·25
246 **42** 10 a. red and blue 1·60 95
247 – 10 a. green 26·00 10
248 – 10 a. black 40 10
249 – 12 a. green 30 10
250 **41** 25 a. red 24·00 45
251 25 a. brown 35 10
252 – 35 a. red 55 10
253 **41** 50 a. green 45 10
DESIGN: 3, 7, 10 a. (Nos. 247/8); 12, 35 a. Atlantic herring.

43 Statue of Thorfinn Karlsefni

46 Statue of Snorri Sturluson (O. Vigeland)

1939.
254 **43** 2 k. grey 2·40 10
255 5 k. brown 17·00 20
256 10 k. brown 11·50 1·40

1940. New York World's Fair. Optd **1940**.
257 **40** 20 a. red 10·00 24·00
258 – 35 a. blue (No. 239) 11·50 28·00
259 – 45 a. green (No. 240) 10·00 24·00
260 – 2 k. black (No. 241) 85·00 £300

1941. Surch **25**.
261 **35** 25 a. on 3 a. olive 65 1·25

1941. 700th Death Anniv of Snorri Sturluson (historian).
262 **46** 25 a. red 75 1·60
263 50 a. blue 1·40 3·75
264 1 k. olive 1·40 3·75

47 Jon Sigurdsson (historian and Althing member)

48 Grumman Goose Amphibian over Thingvellir

1944. Proclamation of Republic.
265 **47** 10 a. grey 40 75
266 25 a. brown 55 75
267 50 a. green 55 75
268 1 k. black 95 75
269 5 k. brown 2·75 8·75
270 10 k. brown 32·00 80·00

1947. Air.
271 **48** 15 a. orange 60 1·00
272 – 30 a. black 60 1·00
273 – 75 a. red 50 1·00
274 – 1 k. blue 50 1·00
275 – 1 k. 80 blue 12·00 13·00
276 – 2 k. brown 1·40 1·50
277 – 2 k. 50 green 24·00 1·40
278 – 3 k. green 1·40 2·00
279 – 3 k. 30 blue 9·50 6·75
DESIGNS—HORIZ: 30 a. Catalina flying boat over Isafjordur; 75 a. Douglas DC-3 over Eyjafjord; 1 k. 80, Douglas DC-3 over Snaefellsjokull; 2 k. 50, Catalina over Eiriksjokull; 3 k. Douglas DC-3 over Reykjavik; 3 k. 30, Douglas DC-3 over Oraefajokull. VERT: 1 k. Grumman Goose over Sethisfjordur, Strandatindur; 2 k. Catalina over Hvalfjordur, Thyrill.
For stamps as Type **48** but without airplane, see Nos. 346/8.

50 Mt. Hekla in Eruption

53 Hospital and Child

1948. Inscr "HEKLA 1947".
280 **50** 12 a. purple 15 10
281 – 25 a. green 1·50 10
282 – 35 a. red 35 10
283 **50** 50 a. brown 1·75 10
284 – 60 a. blue 6·75 3·75
285 – 1 k. brown 13·50 10
286 – 10 k. violet 38·00 45
DESIGNS—VERT: 35 a., 60 a. Mt. Hekla in Eruption (different view). HORIZ: 25 a., 1 k., 10 k. Mt. Hekla.

1949. Red Cross Fund.
287 **53** 10 a. + 10 a. green 65 80
288 – 35 a. + 15 a. red 65 80
289 – 50 a. + 25 a. brown 90 80
290 – 60 a. + 25 a. blue 90 80
291 – 75 a. + 25 a. blue 90 1·10
DESIGNS: 35 a. Nurse and patient; 50 a. Nurse arranging patient's bed; 60 a. Aged couple; 75 a. Freighter and ship's lifeboat.

54 Pony Pack-train

1949. 75th Anniv of U.P.U.
292 **54** 25 a. green 30 40
293 – 35 a. red 30 40
294 – 60 a. blue 40 80
295 – 2 k. orange 1·50 1·25
DESIGNS: 35 a. Reykjavik; 60 a. Map of Iceland; 2 k. Almannagja Gorge

55 Trawler "Ingolfur Arnarson"

56 Bishop Jon Arason

1950.
296 – 5 a. brown 10 10
297 **55** 10 a. grey 20 10
298 – 20 a. brown 10 10
299 **55** 25 a. red 30 10
300 – 60 a. green 13·00 19·00
301 – 75 a. orange 40 35
302 – 90 a. red 65 45
303 – 1 k. brown 5·75 45
304 **55** 1 k. 25 purple 19·00 35
305 1 k. 50 blue 13·50 45
306 – 2 k. violet 23·00 45
307 – 5 k. green 32·00 1·25
308 – 25 k. black £150 14·50
DESIGNS—As T **55**: 5, 90 a., 2 k. Vestmannaeyjar harbour; 20, 75 a., 1 k. Tractor; 60 a., 5 k. Flock of sheep. 29 × 33 mm: 25 k. Parliament Building, Reykjavik.

1950. 400th Death Anniv of Bishop Arason.
309 **56** 1 k. 80 red 2·75 3·00
310 3 k. 30 green 1·75 2·25

57 Postman, 1776

58 President Bjornsson

1951. 175th Anniv of Icelandic Postal Service.
311 **57** 2 k. blue 2·40 2·40
312 – 3 k. purple 2·75 3·25
DESIGN: 3 k. as 2 k. but aeroplane replaces man.

1952. Death of S. Bjornsson (First President of Iceland).
313 **58** 1 k. 25 blue 2·75 35
314 2 k. 20 green 75 4·75
315 5 k. blue 8·50 2·40
316 10 k. brown 35·00 23·00

1953. Netherlands Flood Relief Fund. Surch **Hollandshjalp 1953 + 25**.
317 – 75 a. + 25 a. orange (No. 301) 1·00 3·75
318 **55** 1 k. 25 + 25 a. purple 1·60 3·75

60 "Reykjabok" (Saga of Burnt Njal)

62 Hannes Hafstein

1953.
319 **60** 10 a. black 10 10
320 – 70 a. green 30 10
321 – 1 k. red 95 10
322 – 1 k. 75 blue . . . . . . 24·00 1·40
323 – 10 k. brown . . . . . . 9·50 95
DESIGNS: 70 a. Hand writing on manuscript; 1 k. "Stjorn" (15th century manuscript); 1 k. 75, Books and candle; 10 k. Page from "Skardsbok" (14th century law manuscript).

1954. No. 282 surch **5 AURAR** and bars.
324 5 a. on 35 a. red 10 45

1954. 50th Anniv of Appointment of Hannes Hafstein as first native Minister of Iceland. Portraits of Hafstein.
325 **62** 1 k. 25 blue . . . . 3·00 45
326 – 2 k. 45 green . . . . 19·00 28·00
327 – 5 k. red . . . . 19·00 4·75

63 Icelandic Wrestling

64 St. Thorlacas

1955. Icelandic National Sports.
328 **63** 75 a. brown 45 15
329 – 1 k. 25 blue (Diving) . . . 55 15
330 **63** 1 k. 50 red 95 10
331 – 1 k. 75 blue (Diving) . . . 55 10

1956. 9th Cent of Consecration of First Icelandic Bishop and Skalholt Rebuilding Fund. Inscr as in T **64**.
332 **64** 75 a. + 25 a. red 45 30
333 – 1 k. 25 + 75 a. brown . . . 45 30
334 – 1 k. 75 + 1 k. 25 black . . . 95 85
DESIGNS—HORIZ: 1 k. 25, Skalholt Cathedral, 1772. VERT: 1 k. 75, J. P. Vidalin, Bishop of Skalholt, 1698–1720.

65 Skogafoss

67 Map of Iceland

1956. Power Plants and Waterfalls.
335 **65** 15 a. blue 40 10
336 – 50 a. green 50 10
337 – 60 a. brown . . . . 2·50 3·75
338 – 1 k. 50 violet . . . . . . 24·00 10
339 – 2 k. brown . . . . 1·90 10
340 – 2 k. 45 black . . . . . . 5·75 8·00
341 – 3 k. blue . . . . 3·75 95
342 – 5 k. green . . . . 11·50 1·90
DESIGNS—HORIZ: 50 a. Ellidaarvirkjun; 60 a. Godafoss; 1 k. 50, Sogsvirkjun; 2 k. Dettifoss; 2 k. 45, Andakilsarvirkjun; 3 k. Laxarvirkjun. VERT: 5 k. Gullfoss.

1956. 50th Anniv of Icelandic Telegraph System.
343 **67** 2 k. 30 blue 30 75

67a Whooper Swans

1956. Northern Countries' Day.
344 **67a** 1 k. 50 red . . . . 1·00 75
345 1 k. 75 blue . . . . 12·00 9·50

1957. Designs as T **48** but airplane omitted.
346 2 k. green . . . . 2·75 45
347 3 k. blue . . . . 3·25 45
348 10 k. brown . . . . 5·75 45
DESIGNS—HORIZ: 2 k. Snaefellsjokull; 3 k. Eiriksjokull; 10 k. Oraefajokull.

68 Presidential Residence, Bessastadir

69 Norwegian Spruce

1957.
349 **68** 25 k. black . . . . 17·00 3·75

1957. Reafforestation Campaign.
350 **69** 35 a. green 20 10
351 – 70 a. green 20 10
DESIGN: 70 a. Icelandic birch and saplings.

70 Jonas Hallgrimsson

71 River Beauty

72 Icelandic Pony

1957. 150th Birth Anniv of Hallgrimsson (poet).
352 **70** 5 k. black and green . . . . 1·40 40

1958. Flowers. Multicoloured.
353 1 k. Type **71** 15 10
354 2 k. 50 Wild pansy 20 15

1958.
355 **72** 10 a. black 15 10
356 1 k. red 35 10
357 2 k. 25 brown 75 10

73 Icelandic Flag

74 Old Government House

1958. 40th Anniv of Icelandic Flag.
358 **73** 3 k. 50, red and blue . . . . 1·40 40
359 50 k. red and blue . . . . . 5·75 4·75
No. 359 is $23\frac{1}{2} \times 26\frac{1}{2}$ mm.

1958.
360 **74** 1 k. 50 blue 40 10
361 2 k. green 50 10
362 3 k. red 40 10
363 4 k. brown 70 15

75 Jon Porkelsson with Children

76 Vickers Viscount and 1919 Avro 504K Biplane

1959. Death Bicent. of Jon Porkelsson (Johannes Thorkillius, Rector of Skalholt).
364 **75** 2 k. turquoise 60 40
365 3 k. purple 60 65

1959. Air. 40th Anniv of Iceland Civil Aviation.
366 **76** 3 k. 50 blue 70 50
367 – 4 k. 05 green 55 75
DESIGN: 4 k. 05, Douglas DC-4 and Avro 504K aircraft.

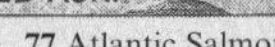

77 Atlantic Salmon

78 "The Outcast" (after Jonsson)

1959.
368 **77** 25 a. blue 15 10
369 – 90 a. black and brown . . . 55 10
370 – 2 k. black and green 70 10
371 **77** 5 k. green . . . . 8·00 95
372 – 25 k. violet and yellow . . . 14·00 11·00
DESIGNS—VERT: 90 a., 2 k. Eiders; 25 k. Gyrfalcon.

1960. World Refugee Year.
373 **78** 2 k. 50 brown 10 10
374 4 k. 50 blue 75 60

78a Conference Emblem

1960. Europa.
375 **78a** 3 k. green 95 30
376 5 k. 50 blue . . . . 95 1·10

79 Dandelions

80 Sigurdsson

1960. Wild Flowers.
377 – 50 a. violet, green and myrtle (Campanulas) 10 10
378 – 1 k. 20 violet, green & brown (Geraniums) 20 10
379 **79** 2 k. 50 yell, green & brn . . 25 10
380 – 3 k. 50 yellow, green and blue (Buttercup) 45 10
See also Nos. 412/5 and 446/7.

1961. 150th Birth Anniv of Jon Sigurdsson (historian and Althing member).
381 **80** 50 a. red 10 15
382 3 k. blue . . . . 1·25 90
383 5 k. purple 75 45

81 Reykjavik Harbour

82 Doves

1961. 175th Anniv of Reykjavik.
384 **81** 2 k. 50 blue and green . . . 50 10
385 4 k. 50 blue and violet . . . 75 15

1961. Europa.
386 **82** 5 k. 50 multicoloured . . . 30 50
387 6 k. multicoloured 30 50

83 B. Sveinsson

84 Productivity Institute

1961. 50th Anniv of Iceland University.
388 **83** 1 k. brown 10 10
389 – 1 k. 40 blue 10 10
390 – 10 k. green . . . . 1·00 75
DESIGNS—VERT: 1 k. 40, B. M. Olsen (first Vice-chancellor). HORIZ: 10 k. University building.

1962. Icelandic Buildings.
392 **84** 2 k. 50 blue 30 10
393 – 4 k. green 40 15
394 – 6 k. brown 50 40
DESIGNS: 4 k. Fishing Research Institute; 6 k. Agricultural Society's Headquarters.

85 Europa "Tree"

86 Cable Map

1962. Europa.
395 **85** 5 k. 50 brown, grn & yell . . 15 15
396 6 k. 50 brown, grn & yell . . 55 45

1962. Opening of North Atlantic Submarine Telephone Communications.
397 **86** 5 k. green, red and lavender . 1·00 25
398 7 k. green, red and blue . . 50 15

87 S. Gudmundsson (scholar and curator)

88 Herring Catch

1963. Centenary of National Museum.
399 **87** 4 k. brown and bistre . . . 50 15
400 – 5 k. 50 brown and olive . . 40 15
DESIGN: 5 k. 50, Detail from carving on church door, Valthjofsstad.

1963. Freedom from Hunger.
401 **88** 5 k. multicoloured 80 20
402 7 k. 50 multicoloured . . . 30 20

89 View of Akureyri

90 "Co-operation"

1963.
403 **89** 3 k. green 20 10

1963. Europa.
404 **90** 6 k. yellow, ochre & brn . . 30 30
405 7 k. yellow, green & blue . . 30 30

91 Ambulance

1963. Red Cross Cent.
406 **91** 3 k. + 50 a. multicoloured . 55 1·75
407 3 k. 50 + 50 a. mult . . . . 55 1·75

92 "Gullfoss" (cargo liner)

93 Scout Emblem

1964. 50th Anniv of Iceland Steamship Co.
408 **92** 10 k. black, purple & blue . 2·10 1·25

1964. Icelandic Boy Scouts Commemoration.
409 **93** 3 k. 50 multicoloured . . . 70 10
410 4 k. 50 multicoloured . . . 70 20

94 Arms of Iceland

95 Europa "Flower"

1964. 20th Anniv of Icelandic Republic.
411 **94** 25 k. multicoloured . . . . 2·75 1·75

1964. Wild Flowers. As T **79**. Multicoloured.
412 50 a. Mountain avens 10 10
413 1 k. Glacier buttercup 15 10
414 1 k. 50 Bogbean 20 10
415 2 k. White clover 25 10

1964. Europa.
416 **95** 4 k. 50 turquoise, cream and brown 65 30
417 9 k. sepia, cream and blue . 75 50

96 Running

97 Rock Ptarmigan (Summer Plumage)

1964. Olympic Games, Tokyo.
418 **96** 10 k. black and green . . . 1·10 45

1965. Charity.
419 **97** 3 k. 50 + 50 a. mult . . . . 1·00 2·00
420 – 4 k. 50 + 50 a. mult . . . . 1·25 2·25
DESIGN: 4 k. 50, Rock Ptarmigan in winter plumage.

98 "Sound Waves"

99 Eruption, Nov., 1963

1965. Centenary of I.T.U.
421 **98** 4 k. 50 green 1·40 40
422 7 k. 50 blue 20 15

1965. Birth of Surtsey Island. Multicoloured.
423 1 k. 50 Type **99** 60 40
424 2 k. Surtsey in April 1964 60 45
425 3 k. 50 Surtsey in Sept. '64 90 95
Nos. 424/5 are horiz.

100 Europa "Sprig"
101 E. Benediktsson

1965. Europa.
426 **100** 5 k. green, brown & ochre 1·40 90
427 8 k. green, brown & turq 90 90

1965. 25th Death Anniv of Einar Benediktsson (poet).
428 **101** 10 k. brown, black & bl 3·75 3·75

102 Girl in National Costume
103 White-tailed Sea Eagle

1965.
429 **102** 100 k. multicoloured 7·50 7·00

1966. Multicoloured.
430 20 k. Great Northern Diver 5·50 4·75
431 50 k. Type **103** 10·50 8·50

104 Londrangar
105 Europa "Ship"

1966. Landscapes (1st series). Multicoloured.
432 2 k. 50 Type **104** 25 20
433 4 k. Myvatn 35 15
434 5 k. Bulandstindur 45 15
435 6 k. 50 Dyrholaey 55 15
See also Nos. 465/8.

1966. Europa.
436 **105** 7 k. turquoise blue & red 1·40 1·40
437 8 k. brown, cream & red 1·40 1·40

106 Society Emblem
107 Cogwheels

1966. 150th Anniv of Icelandic Literary Society.
438 **106** 4 k. blue 20 10
439 10 k. red 75 55

1967. Europa.
440 **107** 7 k. blue, brown & yellow 1·10 85
441 8 k. blue, grey and green 1·10 85

108 Old and New Maps of Iceland

1967. World Fair, Montreal.
442 **108** 10 k. multicoloured 45 25

109 Trade Symbols

1967. 50th Anniv of Icelandic Chamber of Commerce.
443 **109** 5 k. multicoloured 40 15

110 Nest and Eggs of Ringed Plover

1967. Charity.
444 **110** 4 k. + 50 a. multicoloured 65 1·90
445 – 5 k. + 50 a. multicoloured 65 1·90
DESIGN: 5 k. Nest and eggs of Rock Ptarmigan.

1968. Wild Flowers. As T **79**. Multicoloured.
446 50 a. Saxifrage 10 10
447 2 k. 50 Orchid 20 10

111 Europa "Key"
112 Right-hand Traffic

1968. Europa.
448 **111** 9 k. 50 mve, blk & yell 95 95
449 10 k. yellow, sepia & grn 95 95

1968. Adoption of Changed Rule of the Road.
450 **112** 4 k. brown and yellow 15 10
451 5 k. brown 15 10

113 "Fridriksson and Boy" (statue by S. Ólafsson)
114 Library Interior

1968. Birth Cent. of Pastor Fridrik Fridriksson (founder of Icelandic Y.M.C.A. and Y.W.C.A.).
452 **113** 10 k. black and blue 45 20

1968. 150th Anniv of National Library.
453 **114** 5 k. brown and buff 10 10
454 20 k. ultram and blue 95 95

115 Jon Magnusson (former Prime Minister)
116 Viking Ships

1968. 50th Anniv of Independence.
455 **115** 4 k. lake 40 10
456 50 k. sepia 4·75 3·75

1969. 50th Anniv of Northern Countries' Union.
457 **116** 6 k. 50 red 20 30
458 10 k. blue 45 40

117 Colonnade

1969. Europa.
459 **117** 13 k. multicoloured 2·40 1·90
460 14 k. 50 multicoloured 30 40

118 Republican Emblem (after S. Jonsson)
119 Boeing 727 Airliner

1969. 25th Anniv of Republic.
461 **118** 25 k. multicoloured 75 90
462 100 k. multicoloured 6·25 7·00

1969. 50th Anniv of Icelandic Aviation.
463 **119** 9 k. 50 ultram and blue 30 40
464 – 12 k. ultram and blue 30 40
DESIGN: 12 k. Canadair CL-44-D4 (inscr "Rolls-Royce 400").

120 Snaefellsjokull

1970. Landscapes (2nd series). Multicoloured.
465 1 k. Type **120** 10 10
466 4 k. Laxfoss and Baula 10 10
467 5 k. Hattver (vert.) 10 10
468 20 k. Fjardagil (vert.) 95 30

121 First Court Session
122 Part of "Skardsbok" (14th-cent law manuscript)

1970. 50th Anniv of Icelandic Supreme Court.
469 **121** 6 k. 50 multicoloured 15 10

1970. Icelandic Manuscripts. Multicoloured.
470 5 k. Type **122** 10 10
471 15 k. Part of preface to "Flateyjarbok" 35 50
472 30 k. Illuminated initial from "Flateyjarbok" 95 80

123 "Flaming Sun"
124 Nurse tending Patient

1970. Europa.
473 **123** 9 k. yellow and brown 1·90 1·40
474 25 k. brown and green 3·50 2·40

1970. 50th Anniv of Icelandic Nurses Assn.
475 **124** 7 k. ultramarine and blue 30 15

125 G. Thomsen
126 "The Halt" (T. B. Thorlaksson)

1970. 150th Birth Anniv of Grimur Thomsen (poet).
476 **125** 10 k. indigo and blue 75 25

1970. International Arts Festival, Reykjavik.
477 **126** 50 k. multicoloured 1·90 1·25

127 Purple Saxifrage
128 U.N. Emblem and Map

1970. Nature Conservation Year. Mult.
478 3 k. Type **127** 20 25
479 15 k. Lakagigar (view) 75 65

1970. 25th Anniv of United Nations.
480 **128** 12 k. multicoloured 45 30

129 "Flight" (A. Jonsson)

1971. "Help for Refugees".
481 **129** 10 k. multicoloured 95 95

130 Europa Chain

1971. Europa.
482 **130** 7 k. yellow, red & black 2·10 1·90
483 15 k. yellow, blue & blk 2·10 1·60

131 Postgiro Emblem
132 Society Emblem

1971. Inaug of Postal Giro Service.
484 **131** 5 k. blue and light blue 10 10
485 7 k. green & light green 35 15

1971. Centenary of Icelandic Patriotic Society.
486 **132** 30 k. blue and cobalt 1·10 75
487 – 100 k. grey and black 5·75 4·75
DESIGN: 100 k. T. Gunnarsson (President and editor).

133 Freezing Plant and "Melanogrammus aeglefinus"
135 "Communications"

134 Mt. Herdubreid

1971. Icelandic Fishing Industry. Mult.
488 5 k. Type **133** 15 10
489 7 k. Landing catch and "Gadus morhua" 10 10
490 20 k. Canning shrimps and "Pandalus borealis" 1·00 65

1972.
491 **134** 250 k. multicoloured 75 10

1972. Europa.
492 **135** 9 k. multicoloured 1·40 45
493 13 k. multicoloured 1·75 1·75

136 "Municipalities"

1972. Centenary of Icelandic Municipal Laws.
494 **136** 16 k. multicoloured 10 15

137 World Map on Chessboard

1972. World Chess Championship, Reykjavik.
495 **137** 15 k. multicoloured 40 20

138 Tomatoes

1972. Hot-house Plant Cultivation. Mult.
496 8 k. Type **138** 10 10
497 12 k. Steam source and valve 10 10
498 40 k. Rose cultivation 1·10 60

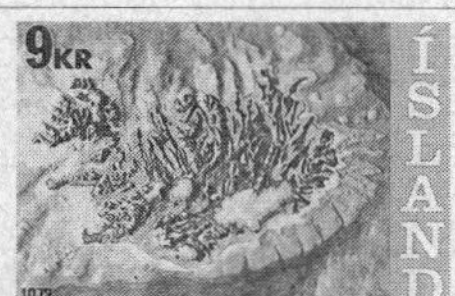
139 Contour Map and Continental Shelf

1972. Iceland's Offshore Claims.
499 **139** 9 k. multicoloured 10 10

140 Arctic Tern feeding Young

141 Europa "Posthorn"

1972. Charity Stamps.
500 **140** 7 k. + 1 k. multicoloured . 60 90
501 9 k. + 1 k. multicoloured . 65 95

1973. Europa.
502 **141** 13 k. multicoloured . . . 2·50 2·00
503 25 k. multicoloured . . . 40 20

142 Postman and 2 s. stamp of 1873

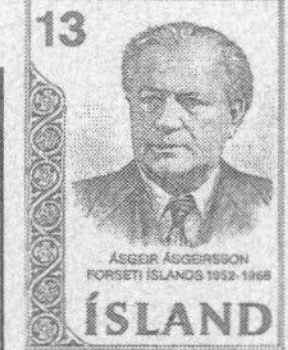
144 Pres. Asgeirsson

143 "The Nordic House", Reykjavik

1973. Stamp Centenary. Multicoloured.
504 10 k. Type **142** 45 20
505 15 k. Pony train 10 10
506 20 k. "Esja" (mail steamer) . . 10 10
507 40 k. Mail van 10 10
508 80 k. Beech Model 18 mail plane . . . . 1·10 70

1973. Nordic Countries' Postal Co-operation.
509 **143** 9 k. multicoloured 20 10
510 10 k. multicoloured . . . 1·10 95

1973. 5th Death Anniv of Asgeir Asgeirsson (politician).
511 **144** 13 k. red 45 15
512 15 k. blue 15 15

145 Exhibition Emblem

146 "The Elements"

1973. "Islandia 73" Stamp Exhibition. Mult.
513 17 k. Type **145** 20 30
514 20 k. Exhibition emblem (different) 20 25

1973. Centenary of I.M.O.
515 **146** 50 k. multicoloured . . . 95 40

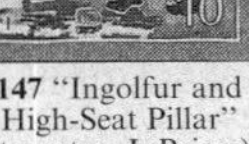
147 "Ingolfur and High-Seat Pillar" (tapestry, J. Briem)

148 "Horseman" (17th-century wood-carving)

1974. 1100th Anniv of Icelandic Settlement. Multicoloured.
516 10 k. Type **147** 15 10
517 13 k. "Grimur Geitskor at Thingvellir" (painting) (horiz.) 15 10
518 15 k. Bishop G. Thorlaksson of Holar 10 10
519 17 k. "Snorri Sturluson slaying the King's messenger" (T. Skulason) 20 15
520 20 k. Stained glass window from Hallgrimskirkja, Saurbaer . . 20 15
521 25 k. Illuminated "I", from "Flateyjarbok" (manuscript) . 10 10
522 30 k. "Christ the King" (mosaic altar-piece, Skalholt Cathedral) 65 25
523 40 k. 18th-century wood-carving 95 25
524 60 k. "Curing the Catch" (concrete relief by S. Olafsson) . . 95 45
525 70 k. "Saemunder smiting the Devil Seal" (bronze) 95 45
526 100 k. Altar-cloth, Church of Stafafell (horiz.) . . . . . . 1·25 75

1974. Europa. Sculptures. Multicoloured.
527 13 k. Type **148** 10 10
528 20 k. "Through the Sound Barrier" (bronze, A. Sveinsson) 95 65

149 Purchasing Stamps

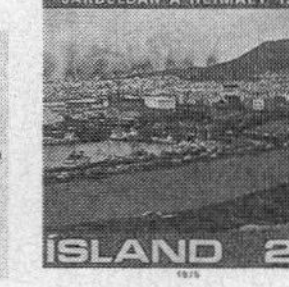
150 Village with Erupting Volcano in distance

1974. Centenary of Universal Postal Union.
529 **149** 17 k. brn, bl & yell 45 20
530 – 20 k. brn, bl & grn 20 25
DESIGN: 20 k. Postman sorting mail.

1975. Volcanic Eruption, Heimaey (1973).
531 **150** 20 k. multicoloured . . . 40 30
532 25 k. multicoloured . . . 20 10

151 "Autumn Bird" (T. Skullason)

152 Stephan G. Stephansson (poet)

1975. Europa. Paintings. Multicoloured.
533 18 k. Type **151** 20 10
534 23 k. "Sun Queen" (J. S. Kjarval) (vert.) 95 30

1975. Centenary of Icelandic Settlements in North America.
535 **152** 27 k. brown and green . . 65 25

153 Hallgrimur Petursson (religious poet)

154 Red Cross Flag on Map of Iceland

1975. Celebrities.
536 **153** 18 k. black and green . . . 10 55
537 – 23 k. blue 10 10
538 – 30 k. red 10 10
539 – 50 k. blue 35 10
PORTRAITS: 23 k. Arni Magnusson (historian); 30 k. Jon Eiriksson (statesman); 50 k. Einar Jonsson (painter and sculptor).

1975. 50th Anniv of Icelandic Red Cross.
540 **154** 23 k. multicoloured . . . 15 15

155 "Abstract" (N. Tryggvadottir)

156 "Bertel Thorvaldsen" (self-statue)

1975. International Women's Year.
541 **155** 100 k. multicoloured . . . 1·40 60

1975. Cent. of Thorvaldsen Society (Charity organization).
542 **156** 27 k. multicoloured . . . 65 15

157 "Forestry"

158 "Landscape" (Asgrimur Jonsson)

1975. Reafforestation.
543 **157** 35 k. multicoloured . . . 75 25

1976. Birth Cent of Asgrimur Jonsson (painter).
544 **158** 150 k. multicoloured . . . 1·75 75

159 Wooden Bowl

1976. Europa. Old Wooden Crafts. Mult.
545 35 k. Type **159** 95 75
546 45 k. Spinning-wheel (vert.) . . 95 95

160 Title page of Postal Services Order

161 Iceland 5 a. Stamp with Reykjavik Postmark, 1876

1976. Bicent of Icelandic Postal Services.
547 **160** 35 k. brown 50 25
548 – 45 k. blue 75 25
DESIGN: 45 k. Signature appended to Postal Services Order.

1976. Cent of Icelandic Aurar-currency Stamps.
549 **161** 30 k. multicoloured . . . 15 10

162 "Workers" and Federation Emblem

1976. 60th Anniv of Icelandic Labour Federation.
550 **162** 100 k. multicoloured . . . 85 40

163 Water-lilies

164 Ofaerufoss, Eldgja

1977. Nordic Countries' Co-operation in Nature Conservation and Environment Protection.
551 **163** 35 k. multicoloured . . . 75 40
552 45 k. multicoloured . . . 75 40

1977. Europa. Multicoloured.
553 45 k. Type **164** . . . . 1·50 50
554 85 k. Kirkufell from Grundarfjord 75 20

165 Harlequin Duck

166 Co-operative Emblem

1977. European Wetlands Campaign.
555 **165** 40 k. multicoloured . . . 50 10

1977. 75th Anniv of Federation of Icelandic Co-operative Societies.
556 **166** 60 k. blue & bright blue . . 75 30

167 Thermal Spring and Rheumatic Treatment

1977. World Rheumatism Year.
557 **167** 90 k. multicoloured . . . 70 30

168 Cairn and Glacier

169 Thorvaldur Thoroddsen (geologist)

1977. 50th Anniv of Icelandic Touring Club.
558 **168** 45 k. blue 80 40

1978. Famous Icelanders.
559 **169** 50 k. green and brown . . 15 10
560 – 60 k. brown and green . . 65 30
DESIGN: 60 k. Briet Bjarnhedinsdottir (suffragette).

170 Videy Mansion

1978. Europa. Multicoloured.
561 80 k. Type **170** 75 45
562 120 k. Husavik Church (vert.) . 95 45

171 Dr. A. Johannesson and Junkers Seaplanes

1978. 50th Anniv of Domestic Flights.
563 **171** 60 k. black and blue . . . 20 15
564 – 100 k. multicoloured . . . 30 15
DESIGN: 100 k. Fokker Friendship.

172 Skeidara Bridge

1978. Skeidara Bridge.
565 **172** 70 k. multicoloured . . . 15 10

173 "Lava Scene near Mt. Hekla" (J. Stefansson)

1978.
566 **173** 1000 k. multicoloured . . . 3·50 1·25

174 Wreck of "Sargon" and Breeches-buoy

1978. 50th Anniv of National Life-Saving Association of Iceland.
567 **174** 60 k. black 40 15

175 "Reykjanesviti" Lighthouse

176 Halldor Hermannsson

1978. Centenary of Lighthouses in Iceland.
568 **175** 90 k. multicoloured . . . 65 20

1978. Birth Centenary of Halldor Hermannsson (scholar and librarian).
569 **176** 150 k. blue 30 25

177 Old Telephone

178 Bjarni Thorsteinsson (clergyman and composer)

1979. Europa. Multicoloured.
570 110 k. Type **177** 65 40
571 190 k. Posthorn and mail-bag . . 75 45

1979. Famous Icelanders.
572 – 80 k. purple 10 10
573 **178** 100 k. black 10 10
574 – 120 k. red 10 10
575 – 130 k. brown 20 20
576 – 170 k. red 30 25
DESIGNS: 80 k. Ingibjorg H. Bjarnason (headmistress and first female member of Althing); 120 k. Petur Gudjohnsen (organist); 130 k. Sveinbjorn Sveinbjornsson (composer); 170 k. Torfhildur Holm (poetess and novelist).

179 Children with Flowers

180 Icelandic Arms to 1904 and 1904–19

1979. International Year of the Child.
577 **179** 140 k. multicoloured . . . 65 30

1979. 75th Anniv of Ministry of Iceland.
578 **180** 500 k. multicoloured . . . 1·40 80

181 Sigurdsson and I. Einarsdottir

1979. Death Centenaries of Jon and Ingibjorg Sigurdsson (historians and Althing members).
579 **181** 150 k. black 30 30

182 Part of Kringla Leaf (MS of Heimskringla)

183 Icelandic Dog

1979. 800th Birth Anniv of Snorri Sturluson (saga writer).
580 **182** 200 k. multicoloured . . . 70 40

1980. Fauna.
581 **183** 10 k. black 10 10
582 – 90 k. brown 20 10
583 – 160 k. purple 70 10
584 – 170 k. black 90 35
585 – 190 k. brown 45 15
DESIGNS: 90 k. Arctic fox; 160 k. Greater red-fish; 170 k. Atlantic puffins; 190 k. Common seal.
See also Nos. 611/13.

184 Jon Sveinsson "alias" Nonni (writer)

185 Rowan Berries

1980. Europa.
586 **184** 140 k. pink and black . . . 35 30
587 – 250 k. pink and black . . . 75 50
DESIGN: 250 k. Gunnar Gunnarsson (writer).

1980. Year of the Tree.
588 **185** 120 k. multicoloured . . . 20 15

186 Sports Complex, Reykjavik

187 Embroidered Cushion

1980. Olympic Games, Moscow.
589 **186** 300 k. turquoise 45 40

1980. Nordic Countries' Postal Co-operation. Multicoloured.
590 150 k. Carved and painted cabinet door 60 30
591 180 k. Type **187** 70 40

188 University Hospital

189 Loudspeaker

1980. 50th Anniv of University Hospital.
592 **188** 200 k. multicoloured . . . 30 25

1980. 50th Anniv of State Broadcasting Service.
593 **189** 400 k. multicoloured . . . 85 30

(New currency. 100 (old) Kronur = 1 (new) Krona).

190 Magnus Stephensen (Chief Justice and publisher)

191 Loftur the Sorcerer

1981. Famous Icelanders.
594 **190** 170 a. blue 40 25
595 – 190 a. green 40 25
DESIGN: 190 a. Finnur Magnusson (writer and Keeper of Privy Archives).

1981. Europa. Multicoloured. Designs showing illustrations of Icelandic legends.
596 180 a. Type **191** . . . . 1·40 50
597 220 a. Witch wading the deeps off Iceland . . . . 1·40 50

192 Winter Wren

193 Human Jigsaw

1981. Birds.
598 **192** 50 a. brown 25 25
599 – 100 a. blue 50 50
600 – 200 a. black . . . . 1·00 1·00
DESIGNS: 100 a. Golden Plover; 200 a. Raven

1981. International Year for Disabled Persons.
601 **193** 200 a. multicoloured . . . 25 20

194 Skyggnir Dish Aerial

195 "Hauling the Line" (Gunnlaugur Scheving)

1981. 75th Anniv of Icelandic Telephone Service.
602 **194** 500 a. multicoloured . . . 1·25 40

1981.
603 **195** 5000 a. multicoloured . . . 5·25 2·75

196 Medieval Driftwood crucifix from Alftamyri

197 Leaf-bread (star pattern)

1981. Millenary of Missionary Work in Iceland.
604 **196** 200 a. lilac 20 15

1981. Christmas. Multicoloured.
605 200 a. Type **197** 95 50
606 250 a. Leaf-bread (tree pattern) . 75 50

198 Common Northern Whelk

199 Casting Dais Post into Sea (first Iceland settlement, 874)

1982. Shells.
607 **198** 20 a. red 10 10
608 – 600 a. brown 75 30
DESIGN: 600 a. Iceland scallop.

1982. Europa. Multicoloured.
609 350 a. Type **199** . . . . 1·50 60
610 450 a. Discovery of Vinland (America), 1000 . . . . 1·50 60

200 Sheep

201 Co-operative Trading House, Husavik

1982. Domestic Animals.
611 **200** 300 a. brown 65 30
612 – 400 a. red 30 15
613 – 500 a. grey 30 15
DESIGNS: 400 a. Cow; 500 a. Cat.

1982. Centenary of Thingeyjar Co-operative Society.
614 **201** 1000 a. black & brown . . 75 40

202 Horseman

1982. Iceland Ponies and Horsemanship.
615 **202** 700 a. multicoloured . . . 45 25

203 Holar

1982. Cent. of Holar Agricultural College.
616 **203** 1500 a. multicoloured . . . 1·10 55

204 "Mount Herdubreid" (Isleifur Konradsson)

205 Thorbjorg Sveinsdottir

1982. Year of the Aged.
617 **204** 800 a. multicoloured . . . 85 25

1982. Famous Icelanders. Thorbjorg Sveinsdottir (midwife and founder of Icelandic Women's Association).
618 **205** 900 a. brown 40 40

207 Doves and Opening of "The Night was such a Splendid One"

1982. Christmas. Multicoloured.
620 300 a. Type **207** 70 30
621 350 a. Bells and close of "The Night was such a Splendid One" (composed by Sigvaldi Kaldalons from poem by E. Sigurdsson) 80 40

208 Marsh Marigold

209 Mount Sulur

1983. Flowers. Multicoloured.
622 7 k. 50 Type **208** 30 30
623 8 k. Alpine catchfly 60 30
624 10 k. Marsh cinquefoil 95 30
625 20 k. Water forgetmenot . . . 1·60 50

1983. Nordic Countries' Postal Co-operation. "Visit the North". Multicoloured.
626 4 k. 50 Type **209** 75 50
627 5 k. Urridafossar Falls 75 50

210 Thermal Area and Heat-exchange Plant

211 Stern Trawler

1983. Europa. Multicoloured.
628 5 k. Type **210** . . . . 3·25 90
629 5 k. 50 Thermal area heating houses . . . . 8·50 1·40

1983. Fishing Industry.
630 **211** 11 k. blue . . . . 1·75 1·50
631 – 13 k. blue . . . . 1·50 60
DESIGN: 13 k. Line fishing.

212 "Laki Craters" (Finnur Jonsson)

1983. Bicentenary of Skafta Eruption.
632 **212** 15 k. multicoloured . . . 75 35

213 Skiing

214 Aircraft and W.C.Y. Emblem

1983. Outdoor Sports. Multicoloured.

633 12 k. Type **213** 80 40

634 14 k. Jogging 80 50

1983. World Communications Year.

635 **214** 30 k. multicoloured . . . 2·00 1·00

216 Virgin Mary and Child

217 Pres. Eldjarn

1983. Christmas. Multicoloured.

637 600 a. Type **216** 50 40

638 650 a. Visitation of the Angel . 50 40

1983. 1st Death Anniv (September) of Kristjan Eldjarn (President, 1968–80).

639 **217** 6 k. 50 red 85 50

640 7 k. blue 40 20

218 Burnet Rose

219 Bridge

1984. Flowers. Multicoloured.

641 6 k. Type **218** 75 35

642 25 k. Silverweed . . . . 1·00 65

See also Nos. 648/9, 657/60 and 717/18.

1984. Europa. 25th Anniv of European Post and Telecommunications Conference.

643 **219** 6 k. 50 dp blue & blue . 1·25 40

644 7 k. 50 dp purple & pur . . 75 30

221 Icelandic Flags

222 I.O.G.T. Lodge, Akureyri

1984. 40th Anniv of Republic.

646 **221** 50 k. multicoloured . . . 4·75 1·00

1984. Centenary of International Order of Good Templars in Iceland.

647 **222** 10 k. green 50 40

1984. Flowers. As T **218**. Multicoloured.

648 6 k. 50 Wild azalea 35 30

649 7 k. 50 Alpine bearberry 75 90

223 Basalt symbolising Industries

224 Bjorn Bjarnarson (founder) (after J. P. Wildenradt)

1984. 50th Anniv of Confederation of Icelandic Employers.

650 **223** 30 k. multicoloured . . . 1·75 55

1984. Centenary of National Gallery.

651 **224** 12 k. black, brown and green 50 40

652 – 40 k. black, green and red . 2·25 50

DESIGN: 40 k. New gallery building.

225 Virgin and Child

226 Text from Bible

1984. Christmas.

653 **225** 600 a. bl, lt bl & gold . . . 40 15

654 – 650 a. red and gold . . . 50 25

DESIGN: 650 a. Angel with Christmas rose.

1984. 400th Anniv of Gudbrand's Bible.

655 **226** 6 k. 50 red 40 25

656 – 7 k. 50 purple 30 75

DESIGN: 7 k. 50, Illustration from Bible.

1985. Flowers. As T **218**. Multicoloured.

657 8 k. Stone bramble 40 25

658 9 k. Rock speedwell 50 25

659 16 k. Sea pea . . . . 1·40 60

660 17 k. Alpine whitlow-grass . . . 70 40

227 Lady playing Langspil

228 Swedish Whitebeam

1985. Europa. Music Year. Multicoloured.

661 6 k. 50 Type **227** 80 40

661 7 k. 50 Man playing Icelandic violin . . . . 1·10 40

1985. Centenary of Iceland Horticultural Society.

663 **228** 20 k. multicoloured . . . 90 50

229 Girl and I.Y.Y. Emblem

230 Common Squid

1985. International Youth Year.

664 **229** 25 k. multicoloured . . . 1·10 45

1985. Marine Life.

665 **230** 7 k. purple 35 15

666 – 8 k. brown 30 10

667 – 9 k. red 40 30

DESIGNS: 8 k. Common spider crab; 9 k. Sea anemone.

231 Rev. Hannes Stephensen (politician)

1985. Famous Icelanders.

668 **231** 13 k. red 50 40

669 – 30 k. violet . . . . . . 1·50 45

DESIGN: 30 k. Jon Gudmundsson (editor and politician).

232 "Flight Yearning"

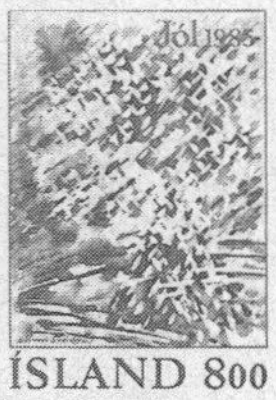

233 Snow Scene

1985. Birth Centenary of Johannes Sveinsson Kjarval (artist).

670 **232** 100 k. multicoloured . . . 4·75 1·00

1985. Christmas. Multicoloured.

671 8 k. Type **233** 50 10

672 9 k. Snow scene (different) . . . 50 30

234 Pied Wagtail

1986. Birds. Multicoloured.

673 6 k. Type **234** 65 35

674 10 k. Pintail . . . . 1·60 95

675 12 k. Merlin . . . . 1·40 95

676 15 k. Razorbill . . . . 1·25 75

See also Nos. 697/700, 720/1, 726/7, 741/2 and 763/4.

235 Skaftafell National Park

1986. Europa. Multicoloured.

677 10 k. Type **235** . . . . 5·25 1·10

678 12 k. Jokulsargljufur National Park . . . . 2·40 60

236 Stykkisholmur

1986. Nordic Countries' Postal Co-operation. Twinned Towns. Multicoloured.

679 10 k. Type **236** . . . . 1·00 60

680 12 k. Seydisfjordur . . . . . . 1·00 40

237 Head Office, Reykjavik

1986. Centenary of National Bank. Mult.

681 **237** 13 k. green 75 40

682 – 250 k. brown . . . . . . 8·00 2·50

DESIGN: 250 k. Reverse of first National Bank; 5 k. note.

238 First Official Seal

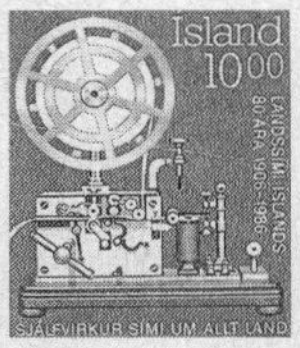

239 Early Telephone Equipment

1986. Bicentenary of Reykjavik.

683 **238** 10 k. red 95 25

684 – 12 k. brown . . . . 1·00 50

685 – 13 k. green 95 45

686 – 40 k. blue . . . . 1·90 65

DESIGNS: 12 k. "Reykjavik pond, 1856" (illustration from "Journey in the Northern Seas" by Charles Edmond); 13 k. Women washing clothes in natural hot water brook, Laugardalur; 40 k. City Theatre.

1986. 80th Anniv of Icelandic Telephone and Telegraph Service. Multicoloured.

687 10 k. Type **239** 50 20

688 20 k. Modern digital telephone system . . . . 1·00 65

241 "Christmas at Peace"

1986. Christmas. Multicoloured.

690 10 k. Type **241** 60 15

691 12 k. "Christmas Night" . . . 40 25

242 "Svanur" (ketch) anchored off Olafsvik

1987. 300th Anniv of Olafsvik Trading Station.

692 **242** 50 k. purple . . . . . . 3·00 1·00

243 Terminal and Boeing 727 Tail

1987. Opening of Leif Eiriksson Terminal, Keflavik Airport.

693 **243** 100 k. multicoloured . . . 4·00 1·00

244 Christ carrying Cross

245 Rask

1987. Europa. Stained Glass Windows by Leifur Breidfoerd, Fossvogur Cemetery Chapel. Multicoloured.

694 12 k. Type **244** . . . . 1·00 25

695 15 k. Soldiers and peace dove . 75 40

1987. Birth Bicentenary of Rasmus Kristjan Rask (philologist).

696 **245** 20 k. black 80 60

1987. Birds. As T **234**. Multicoloured.

697 13 k. Short-eared owl 65 55

698 40 k. Redwing . . . . 1·75 1·50

699 70 k. Oystercatcher . . . . . . 3·00 2·40

700 90 k. Mallard . . . . 4·00 3·25

246 Girl Brushing Teeth

247 Vulture

1987. Dental Protection.

701 **246** 12 k. multicoloured . . . 40 25

1987. National Guardian Spirits. Each red.

702 13 k. Type **247** 95 75

703 13 k. Dragon 95 75

704 13 k. Bull 95 75

705 13 k. Giant 95 75

See also Nos. 713/16, 732 and 743/50.

249 Christmas Tree

250 Steinn Steinarr (poet)

1987. Christmas. Multicoloured.

707 13 k. Type **249** 65 20

708 17 k. "Christmas Light" 65 65

1988. Famous Icelanders. Multicoloured.

709 16 k. Type **250** 55 25

710 21 k. David Stefansson (writer) . 60 60

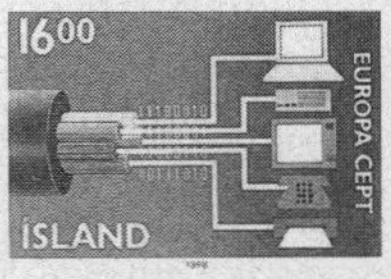

251 Transmission of Messages by Modern Data System

1988. Europa. Communications. Multicoloured.

711 16 k. Type **251** 55 25

712 21 k. Phone pad and globe within envelope (transmission of letters by facsimile machine) . . . . 1·50 1·40

1988. National Guardian Spirit. As Nos. 702/5 but values and colour changed.

713 16 k. black (Type **247**) 95 75

714 16 k. black (Dragon) 95 75

715 16 k. black (Bull) 95 75

716 16 k. black (Giant) 95 75

1988. Flowers. As T **218**. Multicoloured.

717 10 k. Tufted vetch 50 25

718 50 k. Wild thyme . . . . . . 1·10 40

252 Handball

254 Mother and Baby

1988. Olympic Games, Seoul.

719 **252** 18 k. multicoloured . . . 70 45

1988. Birds. As T **234**. Multicoloured.
- 720 5 k. Black-tailed godwit 25 15
- 721 30 k. Long-tailed duck . . . . 1·40 60

1988. 40th Anniv of W.H.O. "Health for All in 2000".
- 723 **254** 19 k. multicoloured . . . 45 35

255 Fisherman with Haul of Fish

1988. Christmas. Multicoloured.
- 724 19 k. Type **255** 60 25
- 725 24 k. Trawler and buoy 90 90

1989. Birds. As T **234**. Multicoloured.
- 726 19 k. Red-necked phalarope . . 75 50
- 727 100 k. Snow buntings . . . . . 3·25 60

256 Peysufot (dress costume)

257 Children at Seaside

1989. Nordic Countries' Postal Co-operation. Traditional Costumes. Multicoloured.
- 728 21 k. Type **256** 70 35
- 729 26 k. Upphlutur (everyday wear) 70 50

1989. Europa. Childrens' Toys and Games. Multicoloured.
- 730 21 k. Type **257** . . . . 2·40 60
- 731 26 k. Girl with hoop and boy with hobby-horse . . . . . 2·40 70

1989. National Guardian Spirits. As No. 703 but colour and value changed.
- 732 500 k. brown (Dragon) . . . . 10·50 5·00

258 Mount Skeggi, Arnarfjord

1989. Landscapes. Multicoloured.
- 733 35 k. Type **258** 75 50
- 734 45 k. Namaskard thermal spring 95 70

See also Nos. 757/8 and 765/6.

259 College

1989. Cent of Hvanneyri Agricultural College.
- 735 **259** 50 k. multicoloured . . . 1·00 85

261 Stefan Stefansson (co-founder) and Flowers

262 "Virgin and Child"

1989. Centenary of Icelandic Natural History Society. Multicoloured.
- 737 21 k. Type **261** 75 45
- 738 26 k. Atlantic cod and Bjarni Saemundsson (first Chairman) 85 45

1989. Christmas. Multicoloured.
- 739 21 k. Type **262** 75 35
- 740 26 k. "Three Wise Men" . . . 85 75

1990. Birds. As T **234**. Multicoloured.
- 741 21 k. European wigeons 60 50
- 742 80 k. Pink-footed goose and goslings . . . . 2·00 1·10

1990. National Guardian Spirits. As Nos. 702/5 but value and colours changed.
- 743 5 k. green (Type **247**) 35 10
- 744 5 k. green (Dragon) 35 10
- 745 5 k. green (Bull) 35 10
- 746 5 k. green (Giant) 35 10
- 747 21 k. blue (Type **247**) 70 70
- 748 21 k. blue (Dragon) 70 70
- 749 21 k. blue (Bull) 70 70
- 750 21 k. blue (Giant) 70 70

263 Gudrun Larusdottir (writer and politician) (after Halldor Petursson)

264 Posthouse Street, Reykjavik, Post Office and Old Scales

1990. 110th Birth Anniversaries. Mult.
- 751 21 k. Type **263** 75 35
- 752 21 k. Ragnhildur Petursdottir (women's educationist) (after Asgrimur Jonsson) . . . 75 35

1990. Europa. Post Office Buildings. Mult.
- 753 21 k. Type **264** . . . . 1·40 75
- 754 40 k. Thoenglabakki 4, Reykjavik, Post Office and modern scales . . . . 1·40 1·40

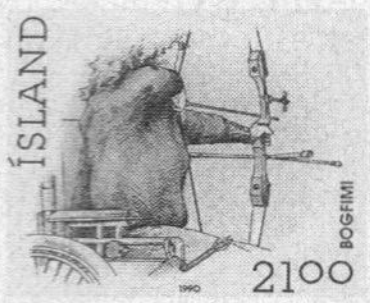

265 Archery

1990. Sport. Multicoloured.
- 755 21 k. Type **265** 50 45
- 756 21 k. Football 50 45

1990. Landscapes. As T **258**. Multicoloured.
- 757 25 k. Hvitserkur, Hunafjord . . 1·10 55
- 758 200 k. Lomagnupur . . . . . 4·25 2·10

266 Bird, Stars and Map

1990. European Tourism Year.
- 759 **266** 30 k. multicoloured . . . 90 65

268 Children around Christmas Tree

1990. Christmas. Multicoloured.
- 761 25 k. Type **268** . . . . 1·25 50
- 762 30 k. Carol singers . . . . . . 1·25 85

1991. Birds. As T **234**. Multicoloured.
- 763 25 k. Slavonian grebes 75 45
- 764 100 k. Northern gannets . . . . 2·75 1·50

1991. Landscapes. As T **258**. Multicoloured.
- 765 10 k. Mt. Vestrahorn 20 10
- 766 300 k. Kverkfjoll range . . . . 6·25 4·25

269 Meteorological Information

1991. Europa. Europe in Space. Mult.
- 767 26 k. Type **269** . . . . 2·10 95
- 768 47 k. Telecommunications satellite . . . . 2·10 1·60

270 Joekulsarlon

1991. Nordic Countries' Postal Co-operation. Tourism. Multicoloured.
- 769 26 k. Type **270** . . . . 1·40 50
- 770 31 k. Strokkur hot spring . . . 95 60

272 Golf

273 Pall Isolfsson (composer) (after Hans Muller)

1991. Sports. Multicoloured.
- 772 26 k. Type **272** 50 45
- 773 26 k. Glima (wrestling) 50 45

1991. Famous Icelanders. Multicoloured.
- 774 60 k. Ragnar Jonsson (founder of Reykjavik College of Music) (after Joannes Kjarval) (horiz) . . . . 1·25 1·00
- 775 70 k. Type **273** . . . . 1·75 1·25

274 College Building

1991. Centenary of College of Navigation, Reykjavik.
- 776 **274** 50 k. multicoloured . . . 1·00 85

275 "Soloven" (mail brigantine)

276 "Light of Christmas"

1991. Stamp Day. Ships. Multicoloured.
- 777 30 k. Type **275** . . . . 2·75 2·00
- 778 30 k. "Arcturus" (cargo liner) . 2·75 2·00
- 779 30 k. "Gullfoss I" (cargo liner) . 2·75 2·00
- 780 30 k. "Esja II" (cargo liner) . . 2·75 2·00

1991. Christmas. Multicoloured.
- 781 30 k. Type **276** 60 50
- 782 35 k. Star 70 60

277 Skiing

1992. Sport. Multicoloured.
- 783 30 k. Type **277** 90 50
- 784 30 k. Volleyball 90 50

278 Map and "Santa Maria"

1992. Europa. 500th Anniv of Discovery of America by Columbus. Multicoloured.
- 785 55 k. Map and Viking ship (Leif Eriksson) . . . . 2·00 1·50
- 786 55 k. Type **278** . . . . 2·00 1·50

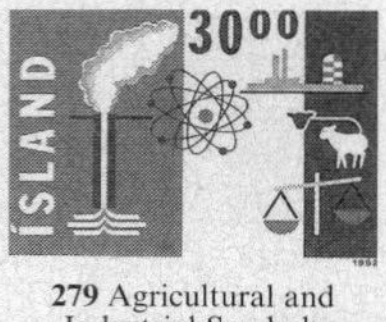

279 Agricultural and Industrial Symbols

1992. 75th Anniv of Iceland Chamber of Commerce (30 k.) and 50th Anniv of Icelandic Freezing Plants Corporation (35 k.). Multicoloured.
- 788 30 k. Type **279** 60 60
- 789 35 k. Trawler and Atlantic cod . 1·10 75

280 River Fnjoska Bridge, Skogar

1992. Bridges. Multicoloured.
- 790 5 k. Type **280** 10 10
- 791 250 k. River Olfusa bridge, Selfoss . . . . 6·25 4·00

See also Nos. 804/5.

281 Ford "TT", 1920–26

282 Face and Candle reflected in Window

1992. Postal Vehicles. Multicoloured.
- 792 30 k. Type **281** . . . . 2·40 90
- 793 30 k. Citroen snowmobile, 1929 . 2·40 90
- 794 30 k. Mail/passenger transport car "RE 231", 1933 . . . . . 2·40 90
- 795 30 k. Ford bus, 1946 . . . . . 2·40 90

1992. Christmas. Multicoloured.
- 796 30 k. Type **282** . . . . 1·00 45
- 797 35 k. Full moon 90 80

283 Gyrfalcon with Chicks

284 Handball

1992. The Gyrfalcon. Multicoloured.
- 798 5 k. Type **283** 75 10
- 799 10 k. Beating wings . . . . . . 1·40 55
- 800 20 k. Eating . . . . 2·40 75
- 801 35 k. On ground . . . . 2·75 1·90

1993. Sport. Multicoloured.
- 802 30 k. Type **284** 80 45
- 803 30 k. Running 80 45

1993. Bridges. As T **280**. Multicoloured.
- 804 90 k. River Hvita bridge, Ferjukot . . . . 1·90 1·40
- 805 150 k. River Jokulsa a Fjollum bridge, Grimsstadir . . . . . 3·25 3·00

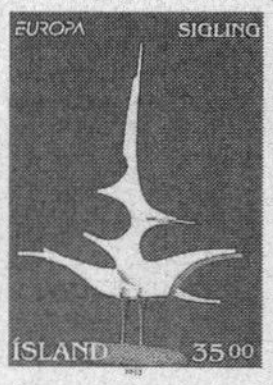

285 The Blue Lagoon, Svartsengi

286 "Sailing" (Jon Gunnar Arnason)

1993. Nordic Countries' Postal Co-operation. Tourism. Multicoloured.
- 806 30 k. Type **285** 95 70
- 807 35 k. Perlan (The Pearl), Reykjavik 95 90

1993. Europa. Contemporary Art. Mult.
- 808 35 k. Type **286** . . . . 1·10 90
- 809 55 k. "Hatching of the Jet" (Magnus Tomasson) . . . . 2·25 1·90

288 Junkers "F-13" Seaplane "Sulan"

1993. 65th Anniv of 1st Icelandic Postal Flight. Multicoloured.
- 811 30 k. Type **288** . . . . 1·40 80
- 812 30 k. Waco YKS-7 seaplane . . 1·40 80
- 813 30 k. Grumman Goose amphibian ("RVK") . . . . 1·40 80
- 814 30 k. Consolidated PBY-5 Catalina flying boat "Old Peter" ("TF-ISP") . . . . . 1·40 80

289 Three Wise Men adoring Child

290 Swimming

1993. Christmas. Multicoloured.

815 30 k. Type **289** 90 45
816 35 k. Madonna and Child . . . 95 90

1994. Sport. Multicoloured.

817 30 k. Type **290** 55 45
818 30 k. Weightlifting 55 45

291 Finger Puppets

1994. International Year of the Family.

819 **291** 40 k. multicoloured . . . 75 65

292 St. Brendan visiting Iceland

1994. Europa. Discoveries. St. Brendan's Voyages. Multicoloured.

820 35 k. Type **292** . . . . 1·25 60
821 55 k. St. Brendan discovering Faroe Islands . . . . 1·50 1·40

293 Conductor and Instruments

1994. 50th Anniv of Independence. Art and Culture. Multicoloured.

823 30 k. Type **293** (44th anniv of Icelandic Symphony Orchestra) 55 45
824 30 k. Pottery (55th anniv of College of Arts and Crafts) . 55 45
825 30 k. Cameraman and actors (16th anniv of National Film Fund) 55 45
826 30 k. Ballerina and modern dancers (21st anniv of Icelandic Dance Company) 55 45
827 30 k. Theatre masks (44th anniv of Icelandic National Theatre) 55 45

294 Gisli Sveinsson (President of United Althing, 1944)

1994. 50th Anniv of New Constitution.

828 **294** 30 k. multicoloured . . . 80 45

297 Woman and Stars

1994. Christmas. Multicoloured.

831 30 k. Type **297** 80 45
832 35 k. Man and stars 90 55

298 Emblem and Airplane

1994. 50th Anniv of I.C.A.O.

833 **298** 100 k. multicoloured . . . 2·40 1·75

299 Flag and Salvation Army Soldiers

300 Geyser

1995. Anniversaries. Multicoloured.

834 35 k. Type **299** (centenary of Salvation Army in Iceland) . 70 60
835 90 k. Map of fjord (centenary of Seydisfjordur) . . . . 2·10 1·90

1995. 14th World Men's Handball Championship. Multicoloured.

836 35 k. Type **300** . . . . 1·40 1·40
837 35 k. Stadium . . . . 1·40 1·40
838 35 k. Volcano . . . . 1·40 1·40
839 35 k. Entrance to fjord . . . . 1·40 1·40

301 Laufas

302 "Spell-broken" (Einar Jonsson)

1995. Nordic Countries' Postal Co-operation. Tourism. Multicoloured.

840 30 k. Type **301** 60 50
841 35 k. Fjallsjokull Glacier . . . 95 60

1995. Europa. Peace and Freedom.

842 **302** 35 k. multicoloured . . . 70 60
843 55 k. multicoloured . . . 1·10 95

303 "Laura"

1995. Post Boats. Multicoloured.

844 30 k. Type **303** 85 50
845 30 k. "Dronning Alexandrine" . 85 50
846 30 k. "Laxfoss" 85 50
847 30 k. "Godafoss III" 85 50

304 Common Redpoll

1995. European Nature Conservation Year. Birds. Multicoloured.

848 25 k. Type **304** 50 45
849 250 k. Common snipe . . . . . 5·25 5·25

305 Boeing 757

1995. 40th Anniv of Iceland–Luxembourg Air Link.

850 **305** 35 k. multicoloured . . . 70 60

307 Snowman and Snowwoman

308 Anniversary Emblem

1995. Christmas. Multicoloured.

852 30 k. Type **307** 60 50
853 35 k. Coloured fir trees 70 60

1995. 50th Anniv of U.N.O.

854 **308** 100 k. multicoloured . . . 2·00 2·00

309 Common Cormorant

1996. Birds. Multicoloured.

855 20 k. Type **309** 35 30
856 40 k. Barrow's goldeneye . . . 1·00 90

310 "Seamen in a Boat" (Gunnlaugur Scheving)

1996. Paintings. Multicoloured.

857 100 k. Type **310** . . . . 1·90 1·60
858 200 k. "At the Washing Springs" (Kristin Jonsdottir) . . . . . 4·25 4·00

311 Halldora Bjarnadottir (founder of women's societies)

1996. Europa. Famous Women. Mult.

859 35 k. Type **311** 65 55
860 55 k. Olafia Johannsdottir (women's rights campaigner and temperance worker) . . . 1·00 85

312 1931 Buick

1996. Post Buses. Multicoloured.

861 35 k. Type **312** 65 55
862 35 k. 1933 Studebaker 65 55
863 35 k. 1937 Ford 65 55
864 35 k. 1946 Reo 65 55

313 Running

1996. Olympic Games, Atlanta. Mult.

865 5 k. Type **313** 10 10
866 25 k. Throwing the javelin . . . 45 40
867 45 k. Long jumping 85 70
868 65 k. Putting the shot . . . . . 1·25 1·10

314 Hospital Ward

1996. Centenary of Order of the Sisters of St. Joseph in Iceland.

869 **314** 65 k. black, stone & pur . . 1·25 1·10

315 School

1996. 150th Anniv of Reykjavik School.

870 **315** 150 k. multicoloured . . . 2·75 2·75

317 Reykjavik Cathedral

318 "Virgin Mary holding Child Jesus" (ivory figurine)

1996. Bicentenary of Reykjavik Cathedral.

872 **317** 45 k. multicoloured . . . 1·10 95

1996. Christmas. Exhibits from National Museum of Iceland. Multicoloured.

873 35 k. Type **318** 65 55
874 45 k. Pax depicting nativity . . 85 70

319 Red-breasted Merganser

1997. Ducks. Multicoloured.

875 10 k. Type **319** 15 10
876 500 k. Green-winged teal . . . 9·50 9·00

320 "Song of Iceland" (Svavar Gudnason)

1997. Paintings. Multicoloured.

877 150 k. Type **320** . . . . 2·75 2·50
878 200 k. "The Harbour" (Thorvaldur Skulason) . . . 3·75 3·50

321 De Havilland D.H.89A Dragon Rapide

1997. Mail Planes. Multicoloured.

879 35 k. Type **321** 85 75
880 35 k. Stinson S.R. 8B Reliant seaplane 85 75
881 35 k. Douglas DC-3 Dakota . . 85 75
882 35 k. De Havilland D.H.C.6 Twin Otter 85 75

322 Hurdling

1997. 7th European Small States' Games. Multicoloured.

883 35 k. Type **322** 60 50
884 45 k. Sailing . . . . 1·00 90

323 The Deacon of Myrka

1997. Europa. Tales and Legends. Paintings by Asgrimur Jonsson. Multicoloured.

885 45 k. Type **323** . . . . 1·00 90
886 65 k. Surtla at Blalandseyjar . . 1·40 1·25

324 Printer's Colour Control and Pieces of Type

1997. Centenary of Formation of Icelandic Printers' Association (now part of Union of Icelandic Graphic Workers).

887 **324** 90 k. multicoloured . . . 2·00 1·75

325 Stefania Gudmundsdottir and Idno Theatre

328 Mounted Mail Carrier

327 Wise Men

1997. Centenary of Reykjavik Theatre.
888 **325** 100 k. multicoloured . . . 2·00 1·75
The actress is shown in the role of the Fairy in "New Year's Night" by Indridi Einarsson.

1997. Christmas. Multicoloured.
890 35 k. Type **327** 60 50
891 45 k. Nativity . . . . 1·00 90

1997. Rural Post.
892 **328** 50 k. multicoloured . . . 1·10 1·00

329 Downhill Skiing

1998. Winter Olympic Games, Nagano, Japan. Multicoloured.
893 35 k. Type **329** 60 50
894 45 k. Cross-country skiing . . . 1·00 90

330 Sailing Dinghies

1998. Nordic Countries' Postal Co-operation. Sailing. Multicoloured.
895 35 k. Type **330** 60 50
896 45 k. Yachts . . . . 1·00 90

331 Lumpsucker

1998. Int Year of the Ocean. Fishes (1st series). Multicoloured.
897 5 k. Type **331** 10 10
898 10 k. Atlantic cod 15 10
899 60 k. Skate . . . . 1·25 1·10
900 300 k. Atlantic wolffish . . . . 6·25 5·50
See also Nos. 913/14.

332 Children waving Flags

333 Scolecite

1998. Europa. National Festivals. National Day. Multicoloured.
902 45 k. Type **332** 75 65
903 65 k. Statue of President Jon Sigurdsson and flags . . . . 1·40 1·25

1998. Minerals (1st series). Multicoloured.
904 35 k. Type **333** 60 50
905 45 k. Stilbite 75 65
See also Nos. 933/4.

334 Hospital

335 Anniversary Emblem

1998. Centenary of Founding of Leprosy Hospital, Laugarnes.
906 **334** 70 k. multicoloured . . . 1·25 1·10

1998. 125th Anniv of First Iceland Stamps.
907 **335** 35 k. multicoloured . . . 60 50

337 Cat and Houses (Thelma Ingolfsdottir)

1998. Christmas. Multicoloured.
909 35 k. Type **337** 60 50
910 45 k. Two angels (Telma Thrastardottir) 75 60

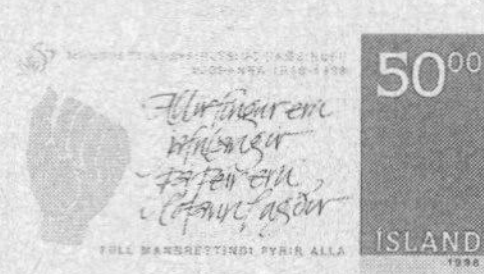

338 Writing and Hand forming Fist

1998. 50th Anniv of Universal Declaration of Human Rights.
911 **338** 50 k. black, green & red . . 85 75

339 Leifs

1999. Birth Centenary of Jon Leifs (composer).
912 **339** 35 k. multicoloured . . . 60 50

1999. Fishes. As T **331**. Multicoloured.
913 35 k. Plaice 60 50
914 55 k. Atlantic herring 95 80

340 Killer Whale

1999. Marine Mammals. Multicoloured.
915 35 k. Type **340** 60 50
916 45 k. Sperm whale 80 70
917 65 k. Blue whale . . . . 1·00 85
918 85 k. Common porpoise . . . . 1·50 1·25

341 Arnold Jung's "Minor", 1892

1999. Transport. Multicoloured.
920 25 k. Type **341** 45 40
921 50 k. Type **341** 85 70
922 75 k. "Sigurfari" (fishing cutter) 1·25 1·10

342 Dates and Doves

1999. 50th Anniv of Council of Europe.
923 **342** 35 k. multicoloured . . . 60 50

343 Larch Boletes

1999. Fungi. Multicoloured.
924 35 k. Type **343** 60 50
925 75 k. Field mushrooms . . . . 1·25 1·10

344 Skutustadagigar, Lake Myvatn

1999. Europa. Parks and Gardens. Multicoloured.
926 50 k. Type **344** 85 75
927 75 k. Arnarstapi Point . . . . 1·25 1·10

345 Wheat ("Land Graedsla")

1999. Nature Conservation. Multicoloured.
928 35 k. Type **345** 60 50
929 35 k. Rainbow and tree within sun ("Loft") 60 50
930 35 k. Nest with eggs ("Vot Lendis") 60 50
931 35 k. Tree stump ("Skog Raekt") 60 50
932 35 k. Fish and birds ("Stlendur") 60 50

1999. Minerals (2nd series). As T **333**. Mult.
933 40 k. Calcite 70 60
934 50 k. Heulandite 85 70

346 "Facescape" (Erro)

1999. Reykjavmk, European Cultural City. Mult.
935 35 k. Type **346** 60 50
936 50 k. Cultural symbols 85 70

OFFICIAL STAMPS

1873. As T **1** but inscr "PJON. FRIM." at foot.
O 8 4 s. green . . . . 65·00 £275
O10 8 s. mauve £325 £375

O 4

1876.
O36 **O 4** 3 a. yellow . . . . . . 6·50 11·00
O37 4 a. grey . . . . 21·00 21·00
O21a 5 a. brown . . . . . . 7·25 13·00
O22a 10 a. blue . . . . . . 32·00 10·50
O23a 16 a. red . . . . 11·00 24·00
O24a 20 a. green . . . . . . 11·50 22·00
O25 50 a. mauve . . . . . . 32·00 38·00

1902. Optd **1 GILDI '02—'03.**
O87 **O 4** 3 a. yellow . . . . 60 1·60
O88 4 a. grey . . . . 65 1·60
O89 5 a. brown . . . . 80 1·60
O90 10 a. blue . . . . 80 1·60
O84 16 a. red . . . . 4·75 35·00
O91 20 a. green . . . . 75 15·00
O86 50 a. mauve . . . . 5·25 45·00

1902. As T **11**, but inscr "PJONUSTA".
O92 3 a. sepia and yellow . . . . 3·25 1·60
O93 4 a. sepia and green . . . . 3·75 1·50
O94 5 a. sepia and brown . . . . 2·10 2·75
O95 10 a. sepia and blue . . . . 2·10 2·75
O96 16 a. sepia and red . . . . 2·75 8·50
O97 20 a. sepia and green . . . . 9·50 6·25
O98 50 a. sepia and mauve . . . 6·25 7·50

1907 As T **12**, but inscr "PJONUSTU".
O 99 3 a. grey and yellow . . . . 3·25 4·25
O100 4 a. grey and green . . . . 2·40 4·75
O101 5 a. grey and brown . . . . 5·25 3·25
O102 10 a. grey and blue . . . . 1·90 2·50
O103 15 a grey and blue . . . . 2·10 5·25
O104 16 a. grey and red . . . . 2·75 12·00
O105 20 a. grey and green . . . . 6·50 2·75
O106 50 a. grey and mauve . . . 3·75 4·75

1920. As T **15**, but inscr "PJONUSTU".
O132 3 a. black and yellow . . . . 3·25 3·25
O133 4 a. black and green . . . . 1·10 2·75
O134 5 a. black and orange . . . . 1·10 1·60
O135 10 a. black and blue . . . . 1·90 1·10
O136 15 a. black and blue . . . . 1·10 1·40
O137 20 a. black and green . . . . 24·00 2·75
O138 50 a. black and violet . . . . 17·00 1·60
O139 1 k. black and red . . . . 17·00 2·10
O140 2 k. black and blue . . . . 4·25 10·50
O141 5 k. black and brown . . . 21·00 35·00

1922. Optd **Pjonusta.**
O153 **15** 20 a. on 10 a. red . . . 10·50 1·60
O151a **13** 2 k. red (No. 107) . . . 21·00 38·00
O152 5 k. brown (No. 108) . . . £130 £160

1930. Parliamentary Commemoratives of 1930 optd **Pjonustumerki**.
O174 **24** 3 a. violet (postage) . . . 7·50 27·00
O175 – 5 a. blue and grey . . . . 9·50 28·00
O176 – 7 a. green . . . . 7·50 27·00
O177 – 10 a. purple . . . . . . 9·50 28·00
O178 – 15 a. blue . . . . 7·50 27·00
O179 – 20 a. red . . . . 7·50 27·00
O180 – 25 a. brown . . . . . . 7·50 27·00
O181 – 30 a. green . . . . . . 7·50 27·00
O182 – 35 a. blue . . . . 7·50 27·00
O183 – 40 a. red, blue & grey . . 7·50 27·00
O184 – 50 a. brown . . . . . . 90·00 £170
O185 – 1 k. green . . . . 90·00 £170
O186 – 2 k. blue and green . . . 90·00 £170
O187 – 5 k. orange & yellow . . . 90·00 £170
O188 – 10 k. lake . . . . 90·00 £170
O189 **25** 10 a. blue (air) . . . . . 32·00 55·00

1936. Optd **Pjonusta.**
O220 **15** 7 a. green . . . . 2·10 27·00
O221 10 a. red . . . . 2·10 1·60
O222 **12** 50 a. red and grey . . . . 16·00 16·00

IDAR Pt. 1

A state in Western India. Now uses Indian stamps.

12 pies = 1 anna; 16 annas = 1 rupee

1 Maharaja Singh Himat **2**

1939.
1b **1** $\frac{1}{2}$ a. green . . . . 12·00 18·00

1944.
3 **2** $\frac{1}{2}$ a. green . . . . 2·00 50·00
4 1 a. violet . . . . 2·25 45·00
5 2 a. blue . . . . 2·50 75·00
6 4 a. red . . . . 2·75 80·00

IFNI Pt. 9

Spanish enclave on the Atlantic coast of Northern Morocco ceded in 1860.

By an agreement, made effective on 30th June, 1969, Ifni was surrendered by Spain to Morocco.

100 centimos = 1 peseta.

1941. Stamps of Spain optd **TERRITORIO DE IFNI**.
1 **181** 1 c. green (imperf.) . . . . 4·75 4·25
2 **182** 2 c. brown . . . . 4·75 4·25
3 **183** 5 c. brown 70 40
4 10 c. red . . . . 2·75 1·50
5 15 c. green 60 40
6 **196** 20 c. violet 60 40
7 25 c. red 60 40
8 30 c. blue 60 60
9 40 c. slate 95 40
10 50 c. slate . . . . 5·50 1·40
11 70 c. blue . . . . 5·50 3·75
12 1 PTA. black . . . . 5·50 3·75
13 2 PTAS. brown . . . . . . 65·00 23·00
14 4 PTAS. red £200 £110
15 10 PTS. brown £650 £275

3 El Santuario

4 Nomad Family

1943.
16 A 1 c. mve & brn (postage) . . 10 10
17 B 2 c. blue and green 10 10
18 C 5 c. blue and purple 10 10
19 A 15 c. green and deep green . . 15 15
20 B 20 c. brown and violet . . . 15 15
21 A 40 c. violet and purple . . . 15 15
22 B 45 c. red and brown 20 20
35 **4** 50 c. black and brown . . . . 6·00 55
23 C 75 c. blue and indigo 20 20
24 A 1 p. brown and red . . . . 1·25 1·10
25 B 3 p. green and blue . . . . 1·40 1·25
26 C 10 p. black and brown . . . 15·00 14·00
27 **3** 5 c. brown & purple (air) . . 15 15
28 D 25 c. brown and green . . . 15 15
29 **3** 50 c. blue and indigo 20 20
30 D 1 p. blue and violet 20 20
31 **3** 1 p. 40 blue and green . . . 20 20
32 D 2 p. brown and purple . . . 85 70
33 **3** 5 p. violet and brown . . . 1·25 1·10
34 D 6 p. green and blue . . . . 17·00 15·00
DESIGNS: A. Nomadic shepherds; B, Arab rifleman; C, La Alcazaba; D, Airplane over oasis.

1947. Air. Autogyro type of Spain optd **IFNI**.
36 **195** 5 c. yellow . . . . 2·00 50
37 10 c. green . . . . 2·00 50

1948. Stamps of Spain optd **Territorio de Ifni**.
45 **182** 2 c. brown (postage) 10 10
46 **183** 5 c. brown 10 10
47 10 c. red 10 10
48 15 c. green 10 10
39 **229** 15 c. green 1·90 45
49 **196** 25 c. purple 15 10
50 30 c. blue 15 15
51 **232** 40 c. brown 15 15
52 45 c. red 20 20
53 **196** 50 c. grey 20 15
54 **232** 75 c. blue 25 20
55 **201** 90 c. green 25 20
41 **196** 1 PTA. black 20 15
56 **201** 1 p. 35 violet 2·50 2·40
57 **196** 2 PTAS. brown 1·90 1·60
58 4 PTAS. pink 7·00 4·25
59 10 PTAS. brown 16·00 13·00

60 **195** 25 c. red (air) 25 10
61 50 c. brown 30 15
62 1 p. blue 30 15
63 2 p. green 1·75 45
64 4 p. blue 5·00 2·75
65 10 p. violet 7·00 6·00

1949. Stamp Day and 75th Anniv of U.P.U. Spanish stamps optd **Territorio de Ifni**.
42 **240** 50 c. brown (postage) 1·50 75
43 75 c. blue 1·50 75
44 4 p. olive (air) 1·60 75

8 General Franco

9 Lope Sancho de Valenzuela

1950. Child Welfare.
66 **8** 50 c. + 10 c. sepia 35 25
67 1 p. + 25 c. blue 13·00 5·00
68 6 p. 50 + 1 p. 65 green 4·50 2·40

1950. Air. Colonial Stamp Day.
69 **9** 5 p. green 1·75 55

10 Woman and Dove

11 General Franco

1951. Air. 500th Birth Anniv of Isabella the Catholic.
70 **10** 5 p. red 19·00 5·50

1951. Gen. Franco's Visit to Ifni.
71 **11** 50 c. orange 25 10
72 1 p. brown 3·50 80
73 5 p. green 27·00 8·00

12 Fennec Fox

13 Mother and Child

1951. Colonial Stamp Day.
74 **12** 5 c. + 5 c. brown 10 10
75 10 c. + 5 c. orange 10 10
76 60 c. + 15 c. olive 20 10

1952. Child Welfare.
77 **13** 5 c. + 5 c. brown 10 10
78 50 c. + 10 c. black 10 10
79 2 p. + 30 c. blue 95 35

14 Ferdinand the Catholic

15 Shag

1952. Air. 500th Birth Anniv of Ferdinand the Catholic.
80 **14** 5 p. brown 25·00 5·50

1952. Colonial Stamp Day.
81 **15** 5 c. + 5 c. brown 15 10
82 10 c. + 5 c. red 25 10
83 60 c. + 15 c. green 1·25 25

16

17 Addra Gazelle and Douglas DC-4 Airliner

1952. 400th Death Anniv of Leo Africanus (geographer).
84 **16** 5 c. orange 10 10
85 35 c. green 10 10
86 60 c. brown 15 10

1953. Air.
87 **17** 60 c. green 10 10
88 1 p. 20 lake 15 10
89 1 p. 60 brown 25 10
90 2 p. blue 1·75 20
91 4 p. myrtle 95 20
92 10 p. purple 5·75 1·25

18 Musician

1953. Child Welfare. Inscr "PROINFANCIA 1953".
93 **18** 5 c. + 5 c. lake 10 10
94 – 10 c. + 5 c. purple 10 10
95 **18** 15 c. olive 10 10
96 – 60 c. brown 10 10
DESIGN: 10 c., 60 c. Two native musicians.

19 Fish and Jellyfish

1953. Colonial Stamp Day. Inscr "DIA DEL SELLO COLONIAL 1953".
97 **19** 5 c. + 5 c. blue 15 10
98 – 10 c. + 5 c. mauve 15 10
99 **19** 15 c. green 15 10
100 – 60 c. brown 25 10
DESIGN: 10, 60 c. Dusky grouper and seaweed.

20 Mediterranean Gull

21 Asclepiad

1954.
101 **20** 5 c. orange 45 10
102 **21** 10 c. green 10 10
103 – 25 c. red 10 10
104 **20** 35 c. green 30 10
105 **21** 40 c. purple 10 10
106 – 60 c. brown 10 10
107 **20** 1 p. brown 14·00 50
108 **21** 1 p. 25 red 10 10
109 – 2 p. blue 10 10
110 **21** 4 p. 50 green 20 40
111 – 5 p. black 32·00 9·75
DESIGN—VERT: 25, 60 c., 2, 5 p. Cactus.

22 Woman and child

23 Lobster

1954. Child Welfare. Inscr "PRO-INFANCIA 1954".
112 **22** 5 c. + 5 c. orange 10 10
113 – 10 c. + 5 c. mauve 10 10
114 **22** 15 c. green 10 10
115 – 60 c. brown 10 10
DESIGN: 10 c., 60 c. Woman and girl.

1954. Colonial Stamp Day. Inscr "DIA DEL SELLO COLONIAL 1954".
116 **23** 5 c. + 5 c. brown 10 10
117 – 10 c. + 5 c. violet 10 10
118 **23** 15 c. green 10 10
119 – 60 c. lake 10 10
DESIGN: 10, 60 c. Smooth hammerhead.

24 Ploughman and "Justice"

1955. Native Welfare. Inscr "PRO-INDIGENAS 1955".
120 **24** 10 c. + 5 c. purple 10 10
121 – 25 c. + 10 c. lilac 10 10
122 **24** 50 c. olive 10 10
DESIGN: 25 c. Camel caravan and "Spain".

25 Eurasian Red Squirrel

26 "Senecio antheuphorbium"

1955. Colonial Stamp Day.
123 **25** 5 c. + 5 c. brown 10 10
124 – 15 c. + 5 c. bistre 10 10
125 **25** 70 c. green 15 10
DESIGN: 15 c. Eurasian red squirrel holding nut.

1956. Child Welfare. Inscr "PRO-INFANCIA 1956".
126 **26** 5 c. + 5 c. green 10 10
127 – 15 c. + 5 c. brown 10 10
128 **26** 20 c. green 10 10
129 – 50 c. sepia 15 10
DESIGN: 15 c., 50 c., "Limoniastrum ifniensis".

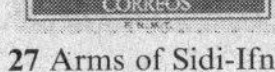
27 Arms of Sidi-Ifni and Drummer

28 Rock Doves

1956. Colonial Stamp Day. Inscr "DIA DEL SELLO 1956".
130 – 5 c. + 5 c. sepia 10 10
131 **27** 15 c. + 5 c. brown 10 10
132 – 70 c. green 10 10
DESIGNS—VERT: 5 c. Arms of Spain and Bohar reedbucks. HORIZ: 70 c. Arms of Sidi-Ifni, shepherd and sheep.

1957. Child Welfare Fund.
133 **28** 5 c. + 5 c. green & brown 15 10
134 – 15 c. + 5 c. brn & ochre 30 10
135 **28** 70 c. brown and green 95 25
DESIGN: 15 c. Stock doves in flight.

29 Golden Jackal

1957. Colonial Stamp Day. Inscr "DIA DEL SELLO 1957".
136 **29** 10 c. + 5 c. brown & pur 10 10
137 – 15 c. + 5 c. green & brn 10 10
138 **29** 20 c. brown and green 10 10
139 – 70 c. brown and green 15 10
DESIGN—VERT: 15 c., 70 c., Head of Golden jackal.

30 Barn Swallows and Arms of Valencia and Sidi-Ifni

31 Basketball

1958. "Aid for Valencia".
140 **30** 10 c. + 5 c. brown 10 10
141 – 15 c. + 10 c. brown 15 10
142 – 50 c. + 10 c. brown 35 25

1958. Child Welfare Fund.
143 **31** 10 c. + 5 c. brown 10 10
144 – 15 c. + 5 c. brown 10 10
145 **31** 20 c. green 10 10
146 – 70 c. green 15 10
DESIGN: 15, 70 c. Cycling.

32 Greater Spotted Dogfish

1958. Colonial Stamp Day.
147 **32** 10 c. + 5 c. red 10 10
148 – 25 c. + 10 c. purple 10 10
149 – 50 c. + 10 c. brown 15 10
DESIGNS—VERT: 25 c. Black-chinned guitar-fish. HORIZ: 50 c. Fishing boats.

33 Ewe and Lamb

34 Footballer

1959. Child Welfare Fund.
150 **33** 10 c. + 5 c. brown 10 10
151 – 15 c. + 5 c. brown 10 10
152 – 20 c. turquoise 10 10
153 **33** 70 c. green 10 10
DESIGNS—VERT: 15 c. Native trader with mule; 20 c. Mountain goat.

1959. Colonial Stamp Day. Inscr "DIA DEL SELLO 1959".
154 **34** 10 c. + 5 c. brown 10 10
155 – 20 c. + 5 c. myrtle 10 10
156 – 50 c. + 20 c. olive 15 10
DESIGNS: 20 c. Footballers; 50 c. Javelin-thrower.

35 Dromedaries

36 White Stork

1960. Child Welfare.
157 **35** 10 c. + 5 c. purple 10 10
158 – 15 c. + 5 c. brown 10 10
159 – 35 c. green 50 10
160 **35** 80 c. green 10 10
DESIGNS: 15 c. Wild boar; 35 c. Red-legged partridges.

1960. Birds.
161 **36** 25 c. violet 10 10
162 – 50 c. brown 20 10
163 – 75 c. purple 25 10
164 **36** 1 p. red 30 10
165 – 1 p. 50 turquoise 35 15
166 – 2 p. purple 40 20
167 **36** 3 p. blue 1·50 25
168 – 5 p. brown 2·50 50
169 – 10 p. green 6·50 1·40
BIRDS—HORIZ: 50 c., 1 p. 50, 5 p. Goldfinches. VERT: 75 c., 2, 10 p. Sky larks.

37 Church of Santa Cruze del Mar **38** High Jump

1960. Stamp Day. Inscr "DIA DEL SELLO 1960".

170	**37**	10 c. + 5 c. brown	10	10
171	–	20 c. + 5 c. green	10	10
172	**37**	30 c. + 10 c. brown	10	10
173	–	50 c. + 50 c. brown	10	10

DESIGN—HORIZ: 20 c., 50 c. School building.

1961. Child Welfare. Inscr "PRO-INFANCIA 1961".

174	**38**	10 c. + 5 c. red	10	10
175	–	25 c. + 10 c. violet	10	10
176	**38**	80 c. + 20 c. turquoise	10	10

DESIGN—VERT: 25 c. Football.

39

1961. 25th Anniv of General Franco as Head of State.

177	–	25 c. grey	10	10
178	**39**	50 c. brown	10	10
179	–	70 c. green	10	10
180	**39**	1 p. red	10	10

DESIGNS—VERT: 25 c. Map. HORIZ: 70 c. Government Building.

40 Camel and Motor Lorry **41** Admiral Jofre Tenorio

1961. Stamp Day. Inscr "DIA DEL SELLO 1961".

181	**40**	10 c. + 5 c. lake	10	10
182	–	25 c. + 10 c. plum	10	10
183	**40**	30 c. + 10 c. brown	10	10
184	–	1 p. + 10 c. orange	15	10

DESIGN: 25 c., 1 p. Freighter at wharf.

1962. Child Welfare. Inscr "PRO-INFANCIA 1962".

185	**41**	25 c. violet	10	10
186	–	50 c. turquoise	10	10
187	**41**	1 p. brown	10	10

DESIGN: 50 c. C. Fernandez-Duro (historian).

42 Desert Postman **43** "Golden Tower", Seville

1962. Stamp Day.

188	**42**	15 c. blue	10	10
189	–	35 c. mauve	10	10
190	**42**	1 p. purple	10	10

DESIGN: 35 c. Winged letter on hands.

1963. Seville Flood Relief.

191	**43**	50 c. green	10	10
192	–	1 p. brown	10	10

44 Moroccan Copper and Flower **45** Child and Flowers

1963. Child Welfare. Inscr "PRO-INFANCIA 1963".

193	–	25 c. blue	20	10
194	**44**	50 c. green	30	10
195	–	1 p. red	50	10

DESIGN: 25 c., 1 p. Moroccan orange-tips.

1963. "For Barcelona".

196	**45**	50 c. green	10	10
197	–	1 p. brown	10	10

46 Beetle ("Steraspis speciosa") **47** Edmi Gazelle

1964. Stamp Day. Inscr "DIA DEL SELLO 1963".

198	**46**	25 c. blue	10	10
199	–	50 c. olive	10	10
200	**46**	1 p. brown	10	10

DESIGN: 50 c. Desert locust.

1964. Child Welfare.

201	**47**	25 c. violet	10	10
202	–	50 c. grey	10	10
203	**47**	1 p. red	10	10

DESIGN: 50 c. Head of roe deer.

48 Cyclists Racing

1964. Stamp Day.

204	**48**	50 c. brown	10	10
205	–	1 p. red	10	10
206	**48**	1 p. 50 green	10	10

DESIGN: 1 p. Motor cycle racing.

49 Port Installation, Sidi Ifni

1965. 25th Anniv of End of Spanish Civil War.

207	–	50 c. green	10	10
208	–	1 p. red	10	10
209	**49**	1 p. 50 blue	10	10

DESIGNS—VERT: 50 c. Ifnian; 1 p. "Education" (children in class).

50 "Eugaster fernandezi"

1965. Child Welfare.

210	**50**	50 c. purple	10	10
211	–	1 p. red ("Halter haltera-tus")	10	10
212	**50**	1 p. 50 blue	15	10

51 Arms of Ifni

1965. Stamp Day.

213	–	50 c. brown	60	20
214	**51**	1 p. red	10	10
215	–	1 p. 50 blue	90	20

DESIGN—VERT: 50 c., 1 p. 50, Golden Eagle.

52 De Havilland D.H.9C Biplanes

1966. Child Welfare.

216	–	1 p. brown	15	10
217	–	1 p. 50 blue	25	15
218	**52**	2 p. 50 violet	1·50	90

DESIGN—VERT: 1 p., 1 p. 50, Douglas DC-8 jet-liner over Sidi Ifni.

53 Maid Alice Moth **54** Coconut Palm

1966. Stamp Day. Insects.

219	**53**	10 c. green and red	10	10
220	–	40 c. brown & dp brown	15	10
221	**53**	1 p. 50 violet and yellow	50	10
222	–	4 p. blue and purple	70	10

DESIGN: 40 c., 4 p. African monarch (butterfly).

1967. Child Welfare.

223	**54**	10 c. green and brown	10	10
224	–	40 c. green and brown	10	10
225	**54**	1 p. 50 turquoise & sepia	15	10
226	–	4 p. sepia and brown	30	20

DESIGN: 40 c., 4 p. Cactus.

55 Bulk Carrier and Floating Crane

1967. Inauguration of Port Ifni.

227	**55**	1 p. 50 brown and green	20	10

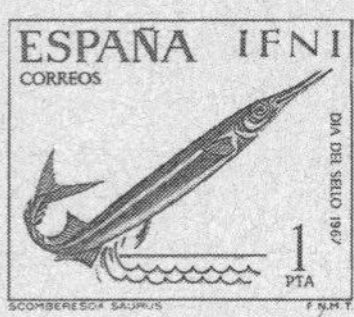

56 Skipper

1967. Stamp Day.

228	**56**	1 p. green and blue	10	10
229	–	1 p. 50 purple & yellow	10	10
230	–	3 p. 50 red and blue	15	10

FISH—VERT: 1 p. 50, John Dory, HORIZ: 3 p. 50, Tub gurnard.

1968. Child Welfare. Signs of the Zodiac. As T **47** of Fernando Poo.

231	1 p. mauve on yellow	10	10
232	1 p. 50 brown on pink	10	10
233	2 p. 50 violet on yellow	20	10

DESIGNS: 1 p., Fishes (Pisces); 1 p. 50, Ram (Aries); 2 p. 50, Archer (Sagittarius).

57 Posting Letter

1968. Stamp Day.

234	**57**	1 p. black and yellow	10	10
235	–	1 p. 50 black, plum & blue	10	10
236	–	2 p. 50 black, blue & grn	15	10

DESIGNS: 1 p. 50, Dove with letter; 2 p. 50, Magnifying-glass and stamp.

EXPRESS LETTER STAMPS

1943. As T **4**, but view of La Alcazaba inscr "URGENTE".

E35	25 c. red and green	90	65

1949. Express Letter stamp of Spain optd **Territorio de Ifni**.

E66	E **198**	25 c. red	15	10

INDIA Pt. 1

A peninsula in the S. of Asia. Formerly consisted of British India and numerous Native States, some of which issued stamps of their own. Divided in 1947 into the Dominion of India and the Dominion of Pakistan. Now a republic within the British Commonwealth.

1852. 12 pies = 1 anna; 16 annas = 1 rupee.
1957. 100 naye paise = 1 rupee.
1964. 100 paisa = 1 rupee.

1 **3**

9 **10**

1852. "Scinde Dawk". Imperf.

S1	**1**	$\frac{1}{2}$ a. white	£4500	£800
S2		$\frac{1}{2}$ a. blue	£12000	£3500
S3		$\frac{1}{2}$ a. red	£65000	£8000

1854. Imperf.

1	**3**	$\frac{1}{2}$ a. red	£800	
2		$\frac{1}{2}$ a. blue	55·00	14·00
14		1 a. red	42·00	35·00
31	**10**	2 a. green	85·00	23·00
23	**9**	4 a. blue and red	£2500	£225

11 **12**

1855. Perf.

75	**11**	$\frac{1}{2}$ a. blue	3·50	50
59		1 a. brown	3·50	40
41		2 a. pink	£375	23·00
63		2 a. orange	21·00	2·00
46		4 a. black	£160	4·75
64		4 a. green	£325	18·00
73		8 a. red	25·00	4·75

1860. Inscr "EAST INDIA POSTAGE". Various frames.

57	**12**	8 p. mauve	9·00	8·00
77	–	9 p. lilac	11·00	11·00
71	–	4 a. green	17·00	1·60
81	–	6 a. brown	5·00	1·50
72	–	6 a. 8 p. grey	32·00	18·00
82	–	12 a. brown	7·00	18·00
79	–	1 r. grey	32·00	22·00

14 **23**

1866. Optd **POSTAGE**.

66	**14**	6 a. purple	£600	£110

1882. Inscr "INDIA POSTAGE". Various frames.

84	**23**	$\frac{1}{2}$ a. turquoise	3·50	10
86	–	9 p. red	70	1·50
88	–	1 a. purple	3·50	30
90	–	1 a. 6 p. brown	70	90
91	–	2 a. blue	3·50	30
94	–	3 a. orange	6·00	60
96	–	4 a. green	12·00	60
97	–	4 a. 6 p. green	15·00	4·00
98	–	8 a. mauve	19·00	2·00
100	–	12 a. purple on red	6·50	2·75
101	–	1 r. grey	12·00	5·00

1891. No. 97 surch **$2\frac{1}{2}$ As.**

102	$2\frac{1}{2}$ a. on $4\frac{1}{2}$ a. green	2·25	60

40 **37**

38

1892. As 1882 and some new designs.

111	**40**	3 p. red	15	10
112		3 p. grey	50	70
113	**23**	$\frac{1}{2}$ a. green	1·40	45
115	–	1 a. red	1·25	15
116	–	2 a. lilac	3·25	1·00
103	–	2 a. 6 p. green	1·50	40
118	–	2 a. 6 p. blue	3·25	3·75
106	**37**	1 r. green and red	8·00	2·00
107	**38**	2 r. red and brown	35·00	11·00
108		3 r. brown and green	25·00	10·00
109		5 r. blue and violet	35·00	23·00

1898. Surch $\frac{1}{4}$.

110	**23**	$\frac{1}{4}$ a. on $\frac{1}{2}$ a. turquoise	10	50

41

52

1902. As 1882 and 1892, but portrait of King Edward VII (inscribed "INDIA POSTAGE").

119	**41**	3 p. grey	1·00	10
121	–	$\frac{1}{2}$ a. green	1·00	20
123	–	1 a. red	1·10	10
124	–	2 a. violet	3·50	40
125	–	2 a. mauve	2·75	10
126	–	2 a. 6 p. blue	4·25	35
127	–	3 a. orange	4·25	40
128	–	4 a. green	3·00	40
132	–	6 a. bistre	10·00	4·50
133	–	8 a. purple	8·50	1·00
135	–	12 a. purple on red	8·00	2·00
136	–	1 r. green and red	6·50	70
139	**52**	2 r. red and brown	38·00	4·00
140		3 r. brown and green	25·00	19·00
142		5 r. blue and violet	50·00	35·00
144		10 r. green and red	£100	26·00
146		15 r. blue and brown	£130	42·00
147		25 r. orange and blue	£750	£800

1905. No. 121 surch $\frac{1}{4}$.

148	$\frac{1}{4}$ a. on $\frac{1}{2}$ a. green	55	10

1906. As Nos. 121 and 123, but inscr "INDIA POSTAGE & REVENUE".

149	$\frac{1}{2}$ a. green	2·50	10
150	1 a. red	1·40	10

55

56

57 58

59 70

60 61

62 63

71 64

65 66

67

1911.

*Two types of $1\frac{1}{2}$ a. brown. Type A as illustrated. Type B inscr "$1\frac{1}{2}$ As. ONE AND A HALF ANNAS".

201	**55**	3 p. grey	30	10
202	**56**	$\frac{1}{2}$ a. green	75	10
161	**57**	1 a. red	2·00	15
203		1 a. brown	50	10
163	**58**	$1\frac{1}{2}$ a. brown (A)*	2·50	30
165		$1\frac{1}{2}$ a. brown (B)*	2·75	3·50
204		$1\frac{1}{2}$ a. red (B)*	1·25	10
166	**59**	2 a. mauve	3·00	30
168		2 a. violet	4·50	40
206	**70**	2 a. purple	1·00	10
170	**60**	2 a. 6 p. blue	2·00	3·00
171	**61**	2 a. 6 p. blue	2·00	20
207		2 a. 6 p. orange	1·25	10
173	**62**	3 a. orange	3·50	20
209		3 a. blue	6·50	10
210	**63**	4 a. olive	1·50	10
211	**71**	4 a. green	6·00	10
176	**64**	6 a. bistre	4·00	1·00
212	**65**	8 a. mauve	4·00	10
213	**66**	12 a. red	5·00	30
214	**67**	1 r. brown and green	5·00	45
215		2 r. red and orange	10·00	80
216		5 r. blue and violet	22·00	1·25
217		10 r. green and red	42·00	3·00
218w		15 r. blue and olive	24·00	28·00
219		25 r. orange and blue	90·00	38·00

See also Nos. 232, etc.

1921. Surch **NINE PIES** and bar.

192	**57**	9 p. on 1 a. red	60	30

1922. Surch $\frac{1}{4}$.

195	**56**	$\frac{1}{4}$ a. on $\frac{1}{2}$ a. green	30	35

72 De Havilland Hercules

1929. Air.

220w	**72**	2 a. green	1·50	60
221		3 a. blue	1·00	1·60
222		4 a. olive	2·25	1·00
223		6 a. bistre	2·25	90
224		8 a. purple	2·50	1·00
225		12 a. red	9·50	5·00

73 Purana Qila

1931. Inauguration of New Delhi.

226	**73**	$\frac{1}{4}$ a. green and orange	1·50	2·50
227	–	$\frac{1}{2}$ a. violet and green	1·25	40
228	–	1 a. mauve and brown	1·25	20
229	–	2 a. green and blue	1·50	1·75
230	–	3 a. brown and red	2·50	2·50
231	–	1 r. violet and green	8·00	22·00

DESIGNS: $\frac{1}{2}$ a. War Memorial Arch; 1 a. Council House; 2 a. Viceroy's House; 3 a. Secretariat; 1 r. Dominion Columns and Secretariat.

79

80

81

82

83

84 Gateway of India, Bombay

1932.

232	**79**	$\frac{1}{2}$ a. green	1·50	10
233	**80**	9 p. green	45	10
234	**81**	1 a. brown	3·50	10
235	**82**	$1\frac{1}{4}$ a. mauve	30	10
236	**70**	2 a. red	9·00	4·00
236b	**59**	2 a. red	3·75	50
237	**62**	3 a. red	3·50	10
238	**83**	$3\frac{1}{2}$ a. blue	3·00	20

1935. Silver Jubilee.

240	**84**	$\frac{1}{2}$ a. black and green	75	20
241	–	9 p. black and green	45	20
242w	–	1 a. black and brown	45	10
243	–	$1\frac{1}{4}$ a. black and violet	45	10
244w	–	$2\frac{1}{2}$ a. black and orange	1·75	95
245	–	$3\frac{1}{2}$ a. black and blue	3·75	3·25
246	–	8 a. black and purple	3·50	3·25

DESIGNS: 9 p. Victoria Memorial, Calcutta; 1 a. Rameswaram Temple, Madras; $1\frac{1}{4}$ a. Jain Temple, Calcutta; $2\frac{1}{2}$ a. Taj Mahal, Agra; $3\frac{1}{2}$ a. Golden Temple, Amritsar; 8 a. Pagoda in Mandalay.

91 King George VI

93 King George VI

92 Dak Runner

1937.

247	**91**	3 p. slate	50	10
248		$\frac{1}{2}$ a. brown	1·75	10
249		9 p. green	5·00	20
250		1 a. red	70	10
251	**92**	2 a. red	3·25	30
252	–	2 a. 6 p. violet	75	20
253	–	3 a. green	4·75	30
254	–	3 a. 6 p. blue	3·25	50
255	–	4 a. brown	13·00	20
256	–	6 a. blue	14·00	80
257	–	8 a. violet	7·50	50
258	–	12 a. red	18·00	1·10
259	**93**	1 r. slate and brown	1·00	15
260		2 r. purple and brown	3·75	30
261		5 r. green and blue	17·00	50
262		10 r. purple and red	15·00	70
263		15 r. brown and green	70·00	60·00
264		25 r. slate and purple	95·00	17·00

DESIGNS—As Type **92**: 2 a. 6 p. Dak bullock cart; 3 a. Dak tonga; 3 a. 6 p. Dak camel; 4 a. Mail train; 6 a. "Strathnaver" (liner); 8 a. Mail lorry; 12 a. Armstrong Whitworth Ensign 1 mail plane (small head).

100a King George VI

101

102 King George VI

1940.

265	**100a**	3 p. slate	30	10
266		$\frac{1}{2}$ a. mauve	60	10
267		9 p. green	60	10
268		1 a. red	60	10
269	**101**	1 a. 3 p. brown	90	10
269a		$1\frac{1}{2}$ a. violet	75	10
270		2 a. red	1·50	10
271		3 a. violet	2·50	10
272		$3\frac{1}{2}$ a. blue	70	10
273	**102**	4 a. brown	45	10
274		6 a. green	3·50	10
275		8 a. violet	1·50	30
276		12 a. purple	3·00	50
277	–	14 a. purple	18·00	1·25

No. 277 is as No. 258, but with large head.

105 "Victory" and King George VI

1946. Victory Commemoration.

278	**105**	9 p. green	30	40
279		$1\frac{1}{2}$ a. purple	30	30
280		$3\frac{1}{2}$ a. blue	75	60
281		12 a. red	1·50	65

1946. Surch **3 PIES** and bars.

282	**101**	3 p. on 1 a. 3 p. brown	10	15

DOMINION OF INDIA

303 Douglas DC-4

1947. Independence. Inscr "15TH AUG 1947".

301	–	$1\frac{1}{2}$ a. green	15	10
302	–	$3\frac{1}{2}$ a. red, blue and green	30	1·10
303	**303**	12 a. blue	1·50	2·00

DESIGNS—VERT: $1\frac{1}{2}$ a. Asokan capital. HORIZ: $3\frac{1}{2}$ a. Indian national flag.

1948. Air. Inauguration of India–U.K. Service. As T **303**, but showing Lockheed Constellation flying in opposite direction and inscr "AIR INDIA INTERNATIONAL FIRST FLIGHT 8TH JUNE 1948".

304	12 a. black and blue	1·00	2·00

305 Mahatma Gandhi

1948. 1st Anniv of Independence.

305	**305**	$1\frac{1}{2}$ a. brown	1·75	30
306		$3\frac{1}{2}$ a. violet	4·25	1·50
307		12 a. green	6·00	60
308	–	10 r. brown and red	55·00	40·00

DESIGN—$22\frac{1}{2} \times 37$ mm: 10 r. Profile portrait of Mahatma Gandhi.

307 Ajanta Panel

308 Konarak Horse

314 Bhuvanesvara **315** Gol Gumbad, Bijapur

319 Red Fort, Delhi

322 Satrunjaya Temple, Palitana

1949.

309	**307**	3 p. violet	15	10
310	**308**	6 p. brown	25	10
311	–	9 p. green	40	10
312	–	1 a. blue (A)	60	10
333	–	1 a. blue (B)	2·50	10
313	–	2 a. red	80	10
333b	–	$2\frac{1}{2}$ a. lake	2·50	2·50
314	–	3 a. salmon	1·50	10
315	–	$3\frac{1}{2}$ a. blue	1·50	2·75
316	**314**	4 a. lake	4·00	20
333c		4 a. blue	6·00	10
317	**315**	6 a. violet	1·50	10
318	–	8 a. green	1·50	10
319	–	12 a. blue	1·50	20
320	–	1 r. violet and green	9·00	10
321	**319**	2 r. red and violet	10·00	20
322	–	5 r. green and brown	28·00	90
323	–	10 r. brown and blue	45·00	5·00
324	**322**	15 r. brown and red	14·00	17·00

1 anna: (A) Left arm of statue outstretched. (B) Reversed—right arm outstretched.

DESIGNS—As Type **307**: 9 p. Trimurti; 1 a. Bodhisattva; 2 a. Nataraja. As Type **314**: $2\frac{1}{2}$ a., $3\frac{1}{2}$ a. Bodh Gaya Temple; 3 a. Sanchi Stupa, East Gate. As Type **315**: 8 a. Kandarya Mahadeva Temple; 12 a. Golden Temple, Amritsar. As Type **319**—VERT: 1 r. Victory Tower, Chittorgarh; 10 r. Qutb Minar, Delhi. HORIZ: 5 r. Taj Mahal, Agra.

323 Globe and Asokan Capital

1949. 75th Anniv of U.P.U.

325	**323**	9 p. green	1·00	2·00
326		2 a. red	1·00	2·00
327		$3\frac{1}{2}$ a. blue	1·75	2·25
328		12 a. red	3·00	2·50

REPUBLIC OF INDIA

324 Rejoicing Crowds

1950. Inauguration of Republic.
329 **324** 2 a. red . . . . 1·00 40
330 – 3½ a. blue . . . . 1·50 2·75
331 – 4 a. violet . . . . 1·50 65
332 – 12 a. purple . . . . 3·25 2·25
DESIGNS—VERT: 3½ a. Quill, ink-well and verse. HORIZ: 4 a. Ear of corn and plough; 12 a. Spinning-wheel and cloth.

329 "Stegodon ganesa"

1951. Centenary of Geological Survey.
334 **329** 2 a. black and red . . . . 2·00 50

330 Torch 331 Kabir

1951. 1st Asian Games, New Delhi.
335 **330** 2 a. purple and orange . . 1·00 30
336 12 a. brown and blue . . . 4·00 90

1952. Indian Saints and Poets.
337 **331** 9 p. green 30 40
338 – 1 a. red (Tulsidas) 30 15
339 – 2 a. orange (Meera) . . . 1·00 20
340 – 4 a. blue (Surdas) . . . . 1·25 40
341 – 4½ a. mauve (Ghalib) . . . 30 80
342 – 12 a. brown (Tagore) . . . 2·25 80

332 Locomotives of 1853 and 1953

1953. Centenary of Indian Railways.
343 **332** 2 a. black 75 10

333 Mount Everest

1953. Conquest of Mount Everest.
344 **333** 2 a. violet 75 10
345 14 a. brown . . . . 3·00 25

334 Telegraph Poles of 1851 and 1951

1953. Centenary of Indian Telegraphs.
346 **334** 2 a. green 30 10
347 12 a. blue . . . . 2·50 40

335 Postal Transport, 1854

1954. Indian Stamp Centenary.
348 **335** 1 a. purple 30 20
349 – 2 a. mauve 30 10
350 – 4 a. brown . . . . 2·75 75
351 – 14 a. blue . . . . 1·50 40
DESIGNS: 2, 14 a. "Airmail"; 4 a. Postal transport, 1954.

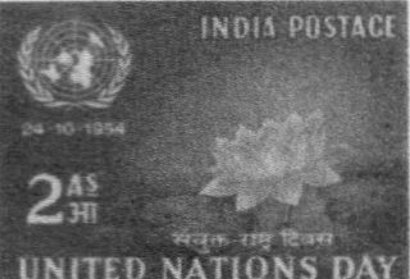

338 U.N. Emblem and Lotus

1954. U.N. Day.
352 **338** 2 a. turquoise 40 30

339 Forest Research Institute

1954. 4th World Forestry Congress, Dehra Dun.
353 **339** 2 a. blue 20 10

340 Tractor 344 Woman Spinning

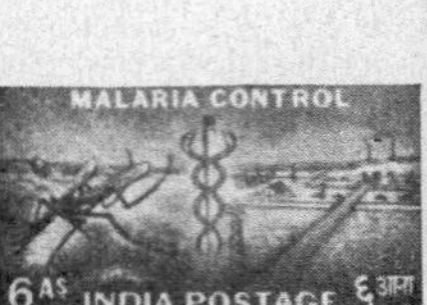

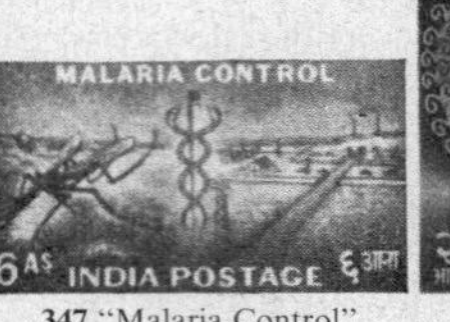
347 "Malaria Control" (Mosquito and Staff of Aesculapius) 358 Bodhi Tree

1955. Five Year Plan.
354 **340** 3 p. mauve 30 10
355 – 6 p. violet 30 10
356 – 9 p. brown 40 10
357 – 1 a. green 45 10
358 **344** 2 a. blue 30 10
359 – 3 a. green 50 10
360 – 4 a. red 50 10
361 **347** 6 a. brown . . . . 1·50 10
362 – 8 a. blue . . . . 6·00 10
363 – 10 a. turquoise . . . . . 2·50 1·75
364 – 12 a. blue . . . . 2·00 10
365 – 14 a. green . . . . 3·75 20
413 – 1 r. myrtle . . . . 3·75 10
367 – 1 r. 2 a. grey . . . . . 2·00 2·75
368 – 1 r. 8 a. purple . . . . . 7·00 4·00
369 – 2 r. mauve . . . . 4·25 10
415 – 5 r. brown . . . . 9·00 30
371 – 10 r. orange . . . . . . 14·00 4·25
DESIGNS—As Type **340**: 6 p. Power loom; 9 p. Bullock-driven well; 1 a. Damodar Valley Dam; 4 a. Bullocks; 8 a. Chittaranjan Locomotive Works; 12 a. Hindustan Aircraft Factory, Bangalore; 1 r. Telephone engineer; 2 r. Rare Earth Factory, Alwaye; 5 r. Sindri Fertiliser Factory; 10 r. Steel plant. As Type **344**: 3 a. Woman hand-weaving. As Type **347**: 10 a. Marine Drive, Bombay; 14 a. Kashmir landscape; 1 r. 2 a. Cape Comorin; 1 r. 8 a. Mt. Kangchenjunga.

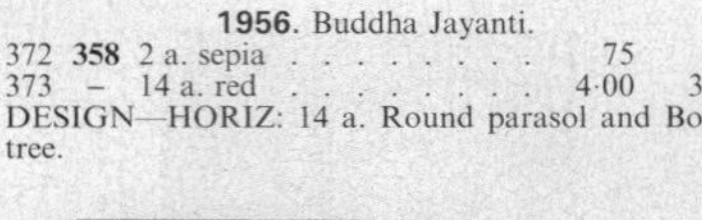

1956. Buddha Jayanti.
372 **358** 2 a. sepia 75 10
373 – 14 a. red . . . . 4·00 3·50
DESIGN—HORIZ: 14 a. Round parasol and Bodhi tree.

360 Lokmanya Bal Gangadhar Tilak 361 Map of India

1956. Birth Centenary of Tilak (journalist).
374 **360** 2 a. brown 10 10

1957. Value in naye paise.
375 **361** 1 n.p. green 10 10
376 2 n.p. brown 10 10
377 3 n.p. brown 10 10
402 5 n.p. green 10 10
379 6 n.p. grey 10 10
404 8 n.p. turquoise 90 10
405 10 n.p. myrtle 15 10
381 13 n.p. red 30 10
407 15 n.p. violet 60 10
408 20 n.p. blue 30 10
409 25 n.p. blue 30 10
410 50 n.p. orange 30 10
411 75 n.p. purple 40 10
385a 90 n.p. purple . . . . . 3·50 1·50

362 The Rani of Jhansi 363 Shrine

1957. Centenary of Indian Mutiny.
386 **362** 15 n.p. brown 15 10
387 **363** 90 n.p. purple . . . . . . 1·50 70

364 Henri Dunant and Conference Emblem

1957. 19th Int Red Cross Conf, New Delhi.
388 **364** 15 n.p. grey and red . . . 10 10

365 "Nutrition" 369 Calcutta University

1957. Children's Day.
389 **365** 8 n.p. purple 10 15
390 – 15 n.p. turquoise 10 10
391 – 90 n.p. brown 25 15
DESIGNS—HORIZ: 15 n.p. "Education". VERT: 90 n.p. "Recreation".

1957. Centenary of Indian Universities.
392 – 10 n.p. violet 15 30
393 **369** 10 n.p. grey 15 30
394 – 10 n.p. brown 30 30
DESIGNS—21½ × 38 mm: No. 392, Bombay University. As Type **369**: No. 394, Madras University.

371 J. N. Tata (founder) and Steel Plant 372 Dr. D. K. Karve

1958. 50th Anniv of Steel Industry.
395 **371** 15 n.p. red 10 10

1958. Birth Centenary of Karve (educationist).
396 **372** 15 n.p. brown 10 10

373 Westland Wapiti Biplane and Hawker Hunter 375 Bipin Chandra Pal

1958. Silver Jubilee of Indian Air Force.
397 **373** 15 n.p. blue . . . . . . 1·00 10
398 90 n.p. blue . . . . . . 1·25 1·25

1958. Birth Centenary of Pal (patriot).
418 **375** 15 n.p. green 10 10

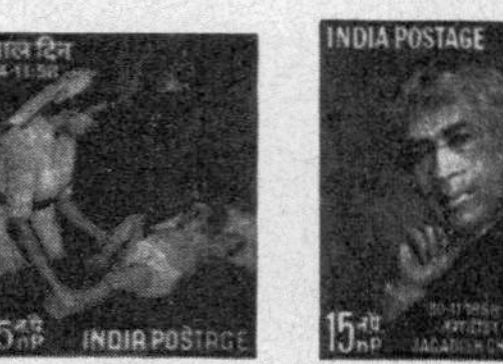

376 Nurse with Child Patient 377 Jagadish Chandra Bose

1958. Children's Day.
419 **376** 15 n.p. violet 10 10

1958. Birth Centenary of Bose (botanist).
420 **377** 15 n.p. turquoise 20 10

378 Exhibition Gate

1958. India 1958 Exhibition, New Delhi.
421 **378** 15 n.p. purple 10 10

379 Sir Jamsetjee Jejeebhoy 381 Boys awaiting admission to Children's Home

380 "The Triumph of Labour" (after Chowdhury)

1959. Death Centenary of Sir Jamsetjee Jejeebhoy (philanthropist).
422 **379** 15 n.p. brown 10 10

1959. 40th Anniv of I.L.O.
423 **380** 5 n.p. green 10 10

1959. Children's Day.
424 **381** 15 n.p. green 10 10

382 "Agriculture" 383 Thiruvalluvar (philosopher)

1959. 1st World Agriculture Fair, New Delhi.
425 **382** 15 n.p. grey 20 10

1960. Thiruvalluvar Commemoration.
426 **383** 15 n.p. purple 10 10

384 Yaksha pleading with the Cloud (from the "Meghaduta") 385 Shakuntala writing a letter to Dushyanta (from the "Shakuntala")

1960. Kalidasa (poet) Commemoration.
427 **384** 15 n.p. grey 30 10
428 **385** 1 r. 3 n.p. yellow & brown 1·40 1·00

386 S. Bharati (poet) 387 Dr. M. Visvesvaraya

1960. Subramania Bharati Commemoration.
429 **386** 15 n.p. blue 10 10

1960. Birth Centenary of Dr. M. Visvesvaraya (engineer).
430 **387** 15 n.p. brown and red . . 10 10

388 "Children's Health"

1960. Children's Day.
431 **388** 15 n.p. green 10 10

389 Children greeting U.N. Emblem

1960. U.N.I.C.E.F. Day.
432 **389** 15 n.p. brown and drab . . 10 10

390 Tyagaraja 391 "First Aerial Post" Cancellation

392 Air India Boeing 707 Airliner and Humber Sommer Biplane

1961. 114th Death Anniv of Tyagaraja (musician).
433 **390** 15 n.p. blue 10 10

1961. 50th Anniv of 1st Official Airmail Flight, Allahabad-Naini.
434 **391** 5 n.p. olive . . . . . . 1·10 30
435 **392** 15 n.p. green and grey . . 1·10 30
436 – 1 r. purple and grey . . . 3·75 1·90
DESIGN—As Type **392**: 1 r. H. Pecquet flying Humber Sommer plane, and "Aerial Post" cancellation.

394 Shivaji on Horseback 395 Motilal Nehru (politician)

1961. Chatrapati Shivaji (Maratha ruler) Commemoration.
437 **394** 15 n.p. brown and green . . 70 30

1961. Birth Centenary of Pandit Motilal Nehru.
438 **395** 15 n.p. brown & orange . . 20 10

396 Tagore (poet) 397 All India Radio Emblem and Transmitting Aerials

1961. Birth Centenary of Rabindranath Tagore.
439 **396** 15 n.p. orange & turq . . . 70 30

1961. Silver Jubilee of All India Radio.
440 **397** 15 n.p. blue 10 10

398 Ray 399 Bhatkande

1961. Birth Centenary of Prafulla Chandra Ray (social reformer).
441 **398** 15 n.p. grey 10 20

1961. Birth Centenary (1960) of V. N Bhatkande (composer).
442 **399** 15 n.p. drab 10 10

400 Child at Lathe 401 Fair Emblem and Main Gate

1961. Children's Day.
443 **400** 15 n.p. brown 10 20

1961. Indian Industries Fair, New Delhi.
444 **401** 15 n.p. blue and red . . . 10 10

402 Indian Forest 403 Pitalkhora: Yaksha

1961. Centenary of Scientific Forestry.
445 **402** 15 n.p. green and brown . . 30 20

1961. Cent of Indian Archaeological Survey.
446 **403** 15 n.p. brown 20 10
447 – 90 n.p. olive and brown . . 40 20
DESIGN—HORIZ: 90 n.p. Kalibangan seal.

405 M. M. Malaviya 406 Gauhati Refinery

1961. Birth Centenary of Malaviya (educationist).
448 **405** 15 n.p. slate 10 20

1962. Inauguration of Gauhati Oil Refinery.
449 **406** 15 n.p. blue 30 20

407 Bhikaiji Cama 408 Village Panchayati and Parliament Building

1962. Birth Centenary of Bhikaiji Cama (patriot).
450 **407** 15 n.p. purple 10 10

1962. Inauguration of Panchayati System of Local Government.
451 **408** 15 n.p. mauve 10 10

409 D. Saraswati (religious reformer) 410 G. S. Vidhyarthi (journalist)

1962. Dayanard Saraswati Commem.
452 **409** 15 n.p. brown 10 10

1962. Ganesh Shankar Vidhyarthi Commem.
453 **410** 15 n.p. brown 10 10

411 Malaria Eradication Emblem 412 Dr. R. Prasad

1962. Malaria Eradication.
454 **411** 15 n.p. yellow and lake . . 10 10

1962. Retirement of President Dr. Rajendra Prasad.
455 **412** 15 n.p. purple 30 20

413 Calcutta High Court 416 Ramabai Ranade

1962. Centenary of Indian High Courts.
456 **413** 15 n.p. green 50 20
457 – 15 n.p. brown (Madras) . . 50 20
458 – 15 n.p. slate (Bombay) . . 50 20

1962. Birth Centenary of Ramabai Ranade (social reformer).
459 **416** 15 n.p. orange 10 20

417 Indian Rhinoceros

1962. Wild Life Week.
460 **417** 15 n.p. brown & turquoise . 40 15

418 "Passing the Flag to Youth"

1962. Children's Day.
461 **418** 15 n.p. red and green . . . 15 20

419 Human Eye within Lotus Blossom 420 S. Ramanujan

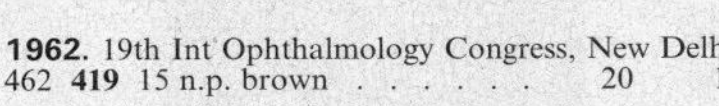

1962. 19th Int Ophthalmology Congress, New Delhi.
462 **419** 15 n.p. brown 20 10

1962. 75th Birth Anniv of Srinivasa Ramanujan (mathematician).
463 **420** 15 n.p. brown 60 40

421 S. Vivekananda 423 Hands reaching for F.A.O. Emblem

1963. Birth Cent of Vivekananda (philosopher).
464 **421** 15 n.p. brown and olive . . 15 20

1963. Surch.
465 **385** 1 r. on 1 r. 3 n.p. yellow and brown 30 10

1963. Freedom from Hunger.
466 **423** 15 n.p. blue . . . . 1·00 30

424 Henri Dunant (founder) and Centenary Emblem 427 D. Naoroji (parliamentarian)

425 Artillery and Mil Mi-4 Helicopter

1963. Centenary of Red Cross.
467 **424** 15 n.p. red and grey . . . 2·50 30

1963. Defence Campaign.
468 **425** 15 n.p. green 40 10
469 – 1 r. brown 70 65
DESIGN: 1 r. Sentry and parachutists.

1963. Dadabhai Naoroji Commemoration.
470 **427** 15 n.p. grey 10 10

428 Annie Besant (patriot and theosophist) 434 "School Meals"

1963. Annie Besant Commemoration.
471 **428** 15 n.p. green 15 10
No. 471 is incorrectly dated "1837". Mrs. Besant was born in 1847.

1963. Wild Life Preservation. Animal designs as T **417**.
472 10 n.p. black and orange . . . 75 1·50
473 15 n.p. brown and green . . . 1·50 60
474 30 n.p. slate and ochre . . . 3·75 1·50
475 50 n.p. orange and green . . . 3·50 80
476 1 r. brown and blue . . . . 2·50 50
ANIMALS—As Type **417**: 10 n.p. Gaur. $25\frac{1}{2} \times 35\frac{1}{2}$ mm: 15 n.p. Lesser panda; 30 n.p. Indian elephant. $35\frac{1}{2} \times 25\frac{1}{2}$ mm: 50 n.p. Tiger; 1 r. Lion.

1963. Children's Day.
477 **434** 15 n.p. bistre 10 10

435 Eleanor Roosevelt at Spinning-wheel

1963. 15th Anniv of Declaration of Human Rights.
478 **435** 15 n.p. purple 10 15

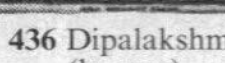

436 Dipalakshmi (bronze) **437** Gopabandhu Das (social reformer)

1964. 26th Int Orientalists Congress, New Delhi.
479 **436** 15 n.p. blue 20 15

1964. Gopabandhu Das Commemoration.
480 **437** 15 n.p. purple 10 10

438 Purandaradasa **439** S. C. Bose and I.N.A. Badge

1964. 400th Death Anniv of Purandaradasa (composer).
481 **438** 15 n.p. brown 15 10

1964. 67th Birth Anniv of Subhas Chandra Bose (nationalist).
482 **439** 15 n.p. olive 40 20
483 – 55 n.p. black, orge & red . 40 45
DESIGN: 35 n.p. Bose and Indian National Army.

441 Sarojini Naidu **442** Kasturba Gandhi

1964. 85th Birth Anniv of Sarojini Naidu (poetess).
484 **441** 15 n.p. green and purple . . 10 10

1964. 20th Death Anniv of Kasturba Gandhi.
485 **442** 15 n.p. brown 10 10

443 Dr. W. M. Haffkine (immunologist) **444** Jawaharlal Nehru (statesman)

1964. Haffkine Commemoration.
486 **443** 15 n.p. brown on buff . . . 10 10

1964. Nehru Mourning Issue.
487 **444** 15 p. slate 10 10

445 Sir Asutosh Mookerjee **446** Sri Aurobindo

1964. Birth Centenary of Sir Asutosh Mookerjee (education reformer).
488 **445** 15 p. brown and olive . . . 10 10

1964. 92nd Birth Anniv of Sri Aurobindo (religious teacher).
489 **446** 15 p. purple 15 10

447 Raja R. Roy (social reformer) **448** I.S.O. Emblem and Globe

1964. Raja Rammohun Roy Commemoration.
490 **447** 15 n.p. brown 10 10

1964. 6th Int Organization for Standardisation General Assembly, Bombay.
491 **448** 15 p. red 15 20

449 Jawaharlal Nehru (from 1 r. commemorative coin) **450** St. Thomas (after statue, Ortona Cathedral, Italy)

1964. Children's Day.
492 **449** 15 p. slate 10 10

1964. St. Thomas Commemoration.
493 **450** 15 p. purple 10 30
No. 493 was issued on the occasion of Pope Paul's visit to India.

451 Globe **452** J. Tata (industrialist)

1964. 22nd International Geological Congress.
494 **451** 15 p. green 30 30

1965. Jamsetji Tata Commemoration.
495 **452** 15 p. dull purple & orange 30 20

453 Lala Lajpat Rai **454** Globe and Congress Emblem

1965. Birth Centenary of Lala Lajpat Rai (social reformer).
496 **453** 15 p. brown 20 10

1965. 20th International Chamber of Commerce Congress, New Delhi.
497 **454** 15 p. green and red 15 15

455 Freighter "Jalausha" and Visakhapatnam **456** Abraham Lincoln

1965. National Maritime Day.
498 **455** 15 p. blue 30 30

1965. Death Centenary of Lincoln.
499 **456** 15 p. brown and ochre . . 15 10

457 I.T.U. Emblem and Symbols

1965. Centenary of I.T.U.
500 **457** 15 p. purple 90 30

458 "Everlasting Flame" **459** I.C.Y. Emblem

1965. 1st Death Anniv of Nehru.
501 **458** 15 p. red and blue 15 10

1965. International Co-operation Year.
502 **459** 15 p. green and brown . . 90 60

460 Climbers on Summit **466** Electric Locomotive

475 Dal Lake, Kashmir

1965. Indian Mount Everest Expedition.
503 **460** 15 p. purple 20 10

1965.

504	–	2 p. brown	10	50
505	–	3 p. olive	10	2·25
505a	–	4 p. brown	10	2·25
506	–	5 p. red	10	10
507	–	6 p. black	10	2·50
508	–	8 p. brown	30	3·75
509	**466**	10 p. blue	40	10
510	–	15 p. green	1·75	10
511	–	20 p. purple	5·00	10
512	–	30 p. sepia	15	10
513	–	40 p. purple	15	10
514	–	50 p. green	20	10
515	–	60 p. grey	35	10
516	–	70 p. blue	60	10
517	–	1 r. brown and plum . . .	60	10
518	**475**	2 r. blue and violet . . .	2·00	10
519	–	5 r. violet and brown . .	2·50	75
520	–	10 r. black and green . .	14·00	80

DESIGNS—VERT (as Type **466**): 2 p. Bidri vase; 3 p. Brass lamp; 5 p. "Family Planning"; 6 p. Konarak elephant; 8 p. Spotted deer ("Chital"); 30 p. Indian dolls; 50 p. Mangoes; 60 p. Somnath Temple. (as Type **475**): 1 r. Woman writing a letter (medieval sculpture). HORIZ (as Type **466**): 4 p. Coffee berries; 15 p. Plucking tea; 20 p. Hindustan Aircraft Industries Ajeet jet fighter; 40 p. Calcutta G.P.O.; 70 p. Hampi Chariot (sculpture). (As Type **475**): 5 r. Bhakra Dam, Punjab; 10 r. Atomic reactor, Trombay.
See also Nos. 721/38c.

479 G. B. Pant (statesman) **480** V. Patel

1965. Govind Ballabh Pant Commemoration.
522 **479** 15 p. brown and green . . 10 20

1965. 90th Birth Anniv of Vallabhbhai Patel (statesman).
523 **480** 15 p. brown 10 30

481 C. Das **482** Vidyapati (poet)

1965. 95th Birth Anniv of Chittaranjan Das (lawyer and patriot).
524 **481** 15 p. brown 10 10

1965. Vidyapati Commemoration.
525 **482** 15 p. brown 10 10

483 Sikandra, Agra **484** Soldier, Hindustan Aircraft Industries Ajeet Jet Fighters and Cruiser "Mysore"

1966. Pacific Area Travel Assn Conf, New Delhi.
526 **483** 15 p. slate 10 10

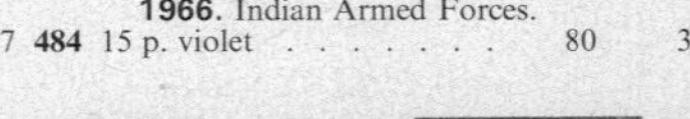

1966. Indian Armed Forces.
527 **484** 15 p. violet 80 30

485 Lal Bahadur Shastri (statesman) **486** Kambar (poet)

1966. Shastri Mourning Issue.
528 **485** 15 p. black 40 10

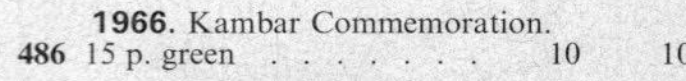

1966. Kambar Commemoration.
529 **486** 15 p. green 10 10

487 B. R. Ambedkar **488** Kunwar Singh (patriot)

1966. 75th Birth Anniv of Dr. Bhim Rao Ambedkar (lawyer).
530 **487** 15 p. purple 10 10

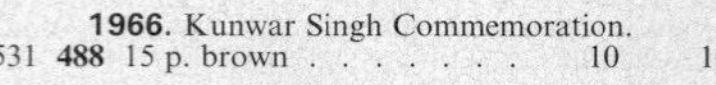

1966. Kunwar Singh Commemoration.
531 **488** 15 p. brown 10 10

489 G. K. Gokhale

1966. Birth Centenary of Gopal Krishna Gokhale (patriot).
532 **489** 15 p. purple and yellow . . 10 10

490 Acharya Dvivedi (poet) **491** Maharaja Ranjit Singh (warrior)

1966. Dvivedi Commemoration.
533 **490** 15 p. drab 10 10

1966. Maharaja Ranjit Singh Commemoration.
534 **491** 15 p. purple 30 15

492 Homi Bhabha (scientist) and Nuclear Reactor

1966. Dr. Homi Bhabha Commemoration.
535 **492** 15 p. purple 15 30

493 A. K. Azad (scholar)

1966. Abul Kalam Azad Commemoration.
536 **493** 15 p. blue 15 15

494 Swami Tirtha

1966. 60th Death Anniv of Swami Rama Tirtha (social reformer).
537 **494** 15 p. blue 20 30

495 Infant and Dove Emblem

496 Allahabad High Court

1966. Children's Day.
538 **495** 15 p. purple 30 20

1966. Centenary of Allahabad High Court.
539 **496** 15 p. purple 30 30

497 Indian Family

1966. Family Planning.
540 **497** 15 p. brown 15 15

498 Hockey Game

1966. India's Hockey Victory in 5th Asian Games.
541 **498** 15 p. blue . . . . 1·00 50

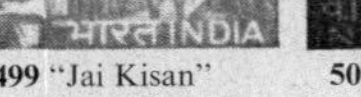
499 "Jai Kisan"

500 Voter and Polling Booth

1967. 1st Death Anniv of Shastri.
542 **499** 15 p. green 15 30

1967. Indian General Election.
543 **500** 15 p. brown 15 15

501 Gurudwara Shrine, Patna

502 Taj Mahal, Agra

1967. 300th Birth Anniv (1966) of Guru Gobind Singh (Sikh religious leader).
544 **501** 15 p. violet 15 15

1967. International Tourist Year.
545 **502** 15 p. brown and orange . . 15 15

503 Nandalal Bose and "Garuda"

504 Survey Emblem and Activities

1967. 1st Death Anniv of Nandalal Bose (painter).
546 **503** 15 p. brown 15 15

1967. Bicentenary of Survey of India.
547 **504** 15 p. lilac 30 30

505 Basaveswara

1967. 800th Anniv of Basaveswara (reformer and statesman).
548 **505** 15 p. red 15 15

506 Narsinha Mehta (poet)

507 Maharana Pratap

1967. Narsinha Mehta Commemoration.
549 **506** 15 p. sepia 15 15

1967. Maharana Pratap (Rajput leader) Commem.
550 **507** 15 p. brown 15 15

508 Narayana Guru

509 Pres. Radhakrishnan

1967. Narayana Guru (philosopher) Commem.
551 **508** 15 p. brown 15 20

1967. 75th Birth Anniv of Sarvepalli Radhakrishnan (former President).
552 **509** 15 p. red 40 15

510 Martyrs' Memorial, Patna

1967. 25th Anniv of "Quit India" Movement.
553 **510** 15 p. lake 15 15

511 Route Map

512 Wrestling

1967. Centenary of Indo-European Telegraph Service.
554 **511** 15 p. black and blue . . . 30 20

1967. World Wrestling Championships, New Delhi.
555 **512** 15 p. purple and brown . . 30 20

513 Nehru leading Naga Tribesmen

514 Rashbehari Basu (nationalist)

1967. 4th Anniv of Nagaland as a State of India.
556 **513** 15 p. blue 15 15

1967. Rashbehari Basu Commemoration.
557 **514** 15 p. purple 15 20

515 Bugle, Badge and Scout Salute

1967. 60th Anniv of Scout Movement in India.
558 **515** 15 p. brown 60 30

516 Men embracing Universe

517 Globe and Book of Tamil

1968. Human Rights Year.
559 **516** 15 p. green 30 30

1968. Int Conf and Seminar of Tamil Studies, Madras.
560 **517** 15 p. lilac 30 15

518 U.N. Emblem and Transport

1968. United Nations Conference on Trade and Development, New Delhi.
561 **518** 15 p. blue 40 15

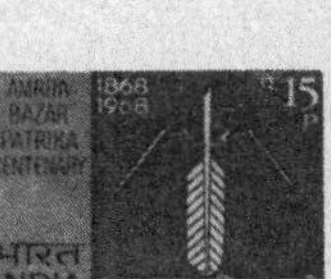

519 Quill and Bow Symbol

520 Maxim Gorky

1968. Centenary of "Amrita Bazar Patrika" (newspaper).
562 **519** 15 p. sepia and yellow . . 15 15

1968. Birth Centenary of Maxim Gorky.
563 **520** 15 p. plum 15 20

521 Emblem and Medal

522 Letter-box and "100,000"

1968. 1st Triennale Art Exhibition, New Delhi.
564 **521** 15 p. orange, blue & lt bl . 30 20

1968. Opening of 100,000th Indian Post Office.
565 **522** 20 p. red, blue and black . 30 15

523 Stalks of Wheat, Agricultural Institute and Production Graph

1968. Wheat Revolution.
566 **523** 20 p. green and brown . . 30 15

524 "Self-portrait"

525 Lakshminath Bezbaruah

1968. 30th Death Anniv of Gaganendranath Tagore (painter).
567 **524** 20 p. purple and ochre . . 30 15

1968. Birth Cent of Lakshminath Bezbaruah (writer).
568 **525** 20 p. brown 20 15

526 Athlete's Legs and Olympic Rings

1968. Olympic Games, Mexico.
569 **526** 20 p. brown and grey . . . 15 15
570 1 r. sepia and olive 40 15

527 Bhagat Singh and Followers

1968. 61st Birth Anniv of Bhagat Singh (patriot).
571 **527** 20 p. brown 20 20

528 Azad Hind Flag, Swords and Chandra Bose (founder)

529 Sister Nivedita

1968. 25th Anniv of Azad Hind Government.
572 **528** 20 p. blue 20 15

1968. Birth Cent of Sister Nivedita (social reformer).
573 **529** 20 p. green 30 30

530 Marie Curie and Radium Treatment

1968. Birth Centenary of Marie Curie.
574 **530** 20 p. lilac . . . . 1·40 50

531 Map of the World

532 Cochin Synagogue

1968. 21st Int Geographical Congress, New Delhi.
575 **531** 20 p. blue 15 15

1968. 400th Anniv of Cochin Synagogue.
576 **532** 20 p. blue and red 55 40

533 I.N.S. "Nilgiri"

1968. Navy Day.
577 **533** 20 p. blue . . . . 1·50 40

534 Red-billed Blue Magpie

1968. Birds.
578 **534** 20 p. multicoloured 55 40
579 – 50 p. red, black & green . . 1·10 1·50
580 – 1 r. blue and brown . . . 1·75 1·00
581 – 2 r. multicoloured . . . . 1·75 1·50
DESIGNS—HORIZ: 50 p. Brown-fronted pied woodpecker; 2 r. Yellow-backed sunbird. VERT: 1 r. Slaty-headed scimitar babbler.

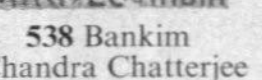

538 Bankim Chandra Chatterjee

539 Dr. Bhagavan Das

1969. 130th Birth Anniv of Chatterjee (writer).
582 **538** 20 p. blue 15 20

1969. Birth Centenary of Das (philosopher).
583 **539** 20 p. brown 15 15

540 Dr. Martin Luther King

1969. Martin Luther King Commemoration.
584 **540** 20 p. brown 40 20

541 Mirza Ghalib and Letter Seal

1969. Death Centenary of Mirza Ghalib (poet).
585 **541** 20 p. sepia, red and flesh . . 15 15

542 Osmania University

1969. 50th Anniv of Osmania University.
586 **542** 20 p. green 15 20

543 Rafi Ahmed Kidwai and Lockheed Constellation Mail Plane

1969. 20th Anniv of "All-up" Airmail Scheme.
587 **543** 20 p. blue 60 30

544 I.L.O. Badge and Emblem

1969. 50th Anniv of Int Labour Organization.
588 **544** 20 p. brown 15 20

545 Memorial, and Hands dropping Flowers

546 K. Nageswara Rao Pantulu (journalist)

1969. 50th Anniv of Jallianwala Bagh Massacre, Amritsar.
589 **545** 20 p. red 15 20

1969. Kasinadhuni Nageswara Rao Pantulu Commemoration.
590 **546** 20 p. brown 15 20

547 Ardaseer Cursetjee Wadia, and Ships

1969. Ardaseer Cursetjee Wadia (ship-builder) Commemoration.
591 **547** 20 p. turquoise 40 30

548 Serampore College

549 Dr. Zakir Husain

1969. 150th Anniv of Serampore College.
592 **548** 20 p. plum 15 20

1969. President Dr. Zakir Husain Commemoration.
593 **549** 20 p. sepia 15 20

550 Laxmanrao Kirloskar

1969. Birth Centenary of Laxmanrao Kirloskar (agriculturist).
594 **550** 20 p. black 15 15

551 Gandhi and his Wife

1969. Birth Centenary of Mahatma Gandhi.
595 **551** 20 p. brown 60 30
596 – 75 p. flesh and drab . . . 1·25 90
597 – 1 r. blue . . . . . . 1·25 65
598 – 5 r. brown and orange . . . 4·50 6·50
DESIGNS AND SIZES—VERT: 75 p. Gandhi's head and shoulders (28 × 38 mm); 1 r. Gandhi walking (woodcut) (20 × 38 mm). HORIZ: 5 r. Gandhi with charkha (36 × 26 mm).

555 "Ajanta" (bulk carrier) and I.M.C.O. Emblem

1969. 10th Anniv of Inter-Governmental Maritime Consulative Organization.
599 **555** 20 p. blue . . . . 1·50 40

556 Outline of Parliament Building and Globe

1969. 57th Inter-Parliamentary Conf, New Delhi.
600 **556** 20 p. blue 15 20

557 Astronaut walking beside Space Module on Moon

558 Gurudwara Nankana Sahib (birthplace)

1969. 1st Man on the Moon.
601 **557** 20 p. brown 40 30

1969. 500th Birth Anniv of Guru Nanak Dev (Sikh religious leader).
602 **558** 20 p. violet 15 20

559 Tiger's Head and Hands holding Globe

1969. Int Union for the Conservation of Nature and Natural Resources Conf, New Delhi.
603 **559** 20 p. brown and green . . 30 30

560 Sadhu Vaswani

561 Thakkar Bapa

1969. 90th Birth Anniv of Sadhu Vaswani (educationist).
604 **560** 20 p. grey 15 15

1969. Birth Centenary of Thakkar Bapa (humanitarian).
605 **561** 20 p. brown 15 20

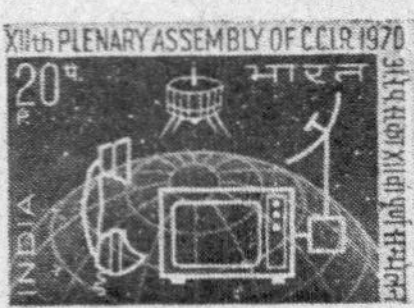

562 Satellite, Television, Telephone and Globe

1970. 12th Plenary Assembly of Int Radio Consultative Committee.
606 **562** 20 p. blue 40 20

563 C. N. Annadurai

564 M. N. Kishore and Printing Press

1970. 1st Death Anniv of Conjeevaram Natrajan Annadurai (statesman).
607 **563** 20 p. purple and blue . . . 15 15

1970. 75th Death Anniv of Munshi Newal Kishore (publisher).
608 **564** 20 p. lake 15 20

565 Nalanda College

1970. Centenary of Nalanda College.
609 **565** 20 p. brown 60 40

566 Swami Shraddhanand (social reformer)

567 Lenin

1970. Swami Shraddhanand Commemoration.
610 **566** 20 p. brown 60 40

1970. Birth Centenary of Lenin.
611 **567** 20 p. brown and sepia . . 30 20

568 New U.P.U. H.Q. Building

569 Sher Shah Suri (15th century ruler)

1970. New U.P.U. Headquarters Building, Berne.
612 **568** 20 p. green, grey & black . . 15 20

1970. Sher Shah Suri Commemoration.
613 **569** 20 p. green 15 20

570 V. D. Savarkar (patriot) and Cellular Jail, Andaman Islands

571 "U N" and Globe

1970. Vinayak Damodar Savarkar Commem.
614 **570** 20 p. brown 15 20

1970. 25th Anniv of United Nations.
615 **571** 20 p. blue 30 20

572 Symbol and Workers

1970. Asian Productivity Year.
616 **572** 20 p. violet 20 20

573 Dr. Montessori and I.E.Y. Emblem

1970. Birth Centenary of Dr. Maria Montessori (educationist).
617 **573** 20 p. purple 30 30

574 J. N. Mukherjee (revolutionary) and Horse

1970. Jatindra Nath Mukherjee Commem.
618 **574** 20 p. brown 75 30

575 V. S. Srinivasa Sastri

576 I. C. Vidyasagar

1970. Srinivasa Sastri (educationist) Commemoration.
619 **575** 20 p. yellow and purple . . 30 30

1970. 150th Birth Anniv of Iswar Chandra Vidyasagar (educationist).
620 **576** 20 p. brown and purple . . 30 30

577 Maharishi Valmiki

1970. Maharishi Valmiki (ancient author) Commem.
621 **577** 20 p. purple 30 30

578 Calcutta Port

1970. Centenary of Calcutta Port Trust.
622 **578** 20 p. blue . . . . 1·00 50

579 University Building

1970. 50th Anniv of Jamia Millia Islamia University.
623 **579** 20 p. green 40 40

580 Jamnalal Bajaj 581 Nurse and Patient

1970. Jamnalal Bajaj (industrialist) Commemoration.
624 **580** 20 p. grey 15 30

1970. 50th Anniv of Indian Red Cross.
625 **581** 20 p. red and blue 60 40

582 Sant Namdeo 583 Beethoven

1970. 700th Birth Anniv of Sant Namdeo (mystic).
626 **582** 20 p. orange 15 30

1970. Birth Bicentenary of Beethoven.
627 **583** 20 p. orange and black . . 1·50 60

584 Children examining Stamps

1970. Indian National Philatelic Exhibition, New Delhi.
628 **584** 20 p. orange and green . . 30 10
629 – 1 r. brown and ochre . . . 2·25 80
DESIGN: 1 r. Gandhi commemorative through magnifier.

585 Girl Guide 586 Hands and Lamp (emblem)

1970. Diamond Jubilee of Girl Guide Movement in India.
630 **585** 20 p. purple 60 30

1971. Centenary of Indian Life Insurance.
631 **586** 20 p. brown and red . . . 20 30

587 Vidyapith Building

1971. 50th Anniv of Kashi Vidyapith University.
632 **587** 20 p. brown 20 30

588 Sant Ravidas

1971. Sant Ravidas (15th-century mystic) Commemoration.
633 **588** 20 p. red 30 30

589 C. F. Andrews 590 Acharya Narendra Deo (scholar)

1971. Birth Centenary of Charles Freer Andrews (missionary).
634 **589** 20 p. brown 35 30

1971. 15th Death Anniv of Acharya Narendra Deo.
635 **590** 20 p. green 15 30

591 Crowd and "100"

1971. Centenary of Decennial Census.
636 **591** 20 p. brown and blue . . . 30 30

592 Sri Ramana Maharishi (mystic) 593 Raja Ravi Varma and "Damayanti and the Swan"

1971. 21st Death Anniv of Ramana Maharishi.
637 **592** 20 p. orange and brown . . 20 30

1971. 65th Death Anniv of Ravi Varma (artist).
638 **593** 20 p. green 40 40

594 Dadasaheb Phalke and Camera

1971. Birth Centenary of Dadasaheb Phalke (cinematographer).
639 **594** 20 p. purple 70 40

595 "Abhisarika" (Tagore) 596 Swami Virjanand (Vedic scholar)

1971. Birth Centenary of Abanindranath Tagore (painter).
640 **595** 20 p. grey, yellow & brn . . 30 30

1971. Swami Virjanand Commemoration.
641 **596** 20 p. brown 30 40

597 Cyrus the Great and Procession

1971. 2500th Anniv of Charter of Cyrus the Great.
642 **597** 20 p. brown 75 55

598 Globe and Money Box

1971. World Thrift Day.
643 **598** 20 p. grey 20 30

599 Ajanta Caves Painting 600 "Women at Work" (Geeta Gupta)

1971. 25th Anniv of U.N.E.S.C.O.
644 **599** 20 p. brown . . . . 1·25 50

1971. Children's Day.
645 **600** 20 p. red 20 40

607 Refugees 608 C. V. Raman (scientist) and Light Graph

1971. Obligatory Tax. Refugee Relief. (a) Optd **REFUGEE RELIEF** in Hindi and English.
646 – 5 p. red (No. 506) 60 10

(b) Optd **Refugee Relief**.
647 – 5 p. red (No. 506) . . . . . 2·50 1·00

(c) Optd **REFUGEE RELIEF**.
649 – 5 p. red (No. 506) . . . . . 3·25 1·50

(d) Optd **Refugee relief**.
650c – 5 p. red (No. 506) . . . . 14·00 3·75

(e) Optd **Refugee Relief** in Hindi and English.
650d – 5 p. red (No. 506) . . . . .

(f) Type **607**.
651 **607** 5 p. red 30 10

From 15 November 1971 until 31 March 1973 the Indian Government levied a 5 p. surcharge on all mail, except postcards and newspapers, for the relief of refugees from the former East Pakistan.

1971. 1st Death Anniv of Chandrasekhara Venkata Raman.
652 **608** 20 p. orange and brown . . 50 30

609 Visva Bharati Building and Rabindranath Tagore (founder)

1971. 50th Anniv of Visva Bharati University.
653 **609** 20 p. sepia and brown . . 20 30

610 Cricketers

1971. Indian Cricket Victories.
654 **610** 20 p. green, myrtle & sage 2·00 65

INDEX

Countries can be quickly located by referring to the index at the end of this volume.

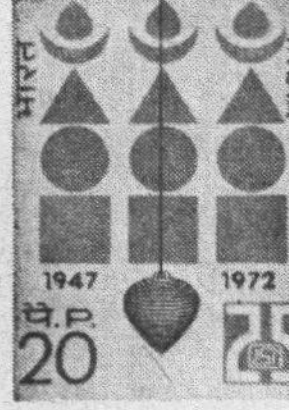

611 Map and Satellite 612 Elemental Symbols and Plumb-line

1972. 1st Anniv of Arvi Satellite Earth Station.
655 **611** 20 p. purple 15 30

1972. 25th Anniv of Indian Standards Institution.
656 **612** 20 p. grey and black . . . 15 40

613 Signal Box Panel 614 Hockey-player

1972. 50th Anniv of Int Railways Union.
657 **613** 20 p. multicoloured 60 40

1972. Olympic Games, Munich.
658 **614** 20 p. violet . . . . 1·50 25
659 – 1 r. 45 green and lake . . . 2·25 2·00
DESIGN: 1 r. 45, Various sports.

615 Symbol of Sri Aurobindo 617 Inter-Services Crest

616 Celebrating Independence Day in front of Parliament

1972. Birth Centenary of Sri Aurobindo (religious teacher).
660 **615** 20 p. yellow and blue . . . 20 30

1972. 25th Anniv of Independence. (1st issue).
661 **616** 20 p. multicoloured 30 30
See also Nos. 673/4.

1972. Defence Services Commemoration.
662 **617** 20 p. multicoloured 30 40

618 V. O. Chidambaran Pillai (trade union leader) and Ship

1972. Birth Cent of V. O. Chidambaran Pillai.
663 **618** 20 p. blue and brown . . . 75 40

619 Bhai Vir Singh 620 T. Prakasam

1972. Birth Centenary of Bhai Vir Singh (poet).
664 **619** 20 p. purple 30 40

1972. Birth Centenary of Tanguturi Prakasam (lawyer).
665 **620** 20 p. brown 20 40

621 Vemana

622 Bertrand Russell

1972. 300th Birth Anniv of Vemana (poet).
666 **621** 20 p. black 20 40

1972. Birth Centenary of Bertrand Russell (philosopher).
667 **622** 1 r. 45 black . . . . 3·25 2·75

623 Symbol of "Asia '72"

1972. "Asia '72" (Third Asian International Trade Fair), New Delhi.
668 **623** 20 p. black and orange . . 10 20
669 – 1 r. 45 orange and black . . 60 1·75
DESIGN: 1 r. 45, Hand of Buddha.

624 V. A. Sarabhai and Rocket

1972. 1st Death Anniv of Dr. Vikram A. Sarabhai (scientist).
670 **624** 20 p. brown and green . . 20 40

625 Flag of U.S.S.R. and Kremlin Tower

1972. 50th Anniv of U.S.S.R.
671 **625** 20 p. red and yellow . . . 20 40

626 Exhibition Symbol

627 "Democracy"

1973. "Indipex '73" Stamp Exhibition (1st issue).
672 **626** 1 r. 45 mauve, gold & blk . 45 1·25
See also No. 701.3.

1973. 25th Anniv of Independence (2nd issue). Multicoloured.
673 20 p. Type **627** 15 15
674 1 r. 45 Hindustan Aircraft Industries Ajeet jet fighters over India Gate (38 × 20 mm) . . . . 1·40 1·60

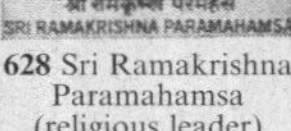

628 Sri Ramakrishna Paramahamsa (religious leader)

629 Postal Corps Emblem

1973. Sri Ramakrishna Paramahamsa Commem.
675 **628** 20 p. brown 20 40

1973. 1st Anniv of Army Postal Service Corps.
676 **629** 20 p. blue and red 40 50

630 Flag and Map of Bangladesh

631 Kumaran Asan

1973. "Jai Bangla" (Inauguration of 1st Bangladesh Parliament).
677 **630** 20 p. multicoloured 15 40

1973. Birth Centenary of Kumaran Asan (writer and poet).
678 **631** 20 p. brown 20 45

632 Flag and Flames

634 "Radha-Kishangarh" (Nihal Chand)

633 Dr. Bhim Rao Ambedkar (lawyer)

1973. Homage to Martyrs for Independence.
679 **632** 20 p. multicoloured 15 40

1973. Ambedkar Commemoration.
680 **633** 20 p. green and purple . . 20 75

1973. Indian Miniature Paintings. Multicoloured.
681 20 p. Type **634** 30 35
682 50 p. "Dance Duet" (Aurangzeb's period) . . . . 60 1·50
683 1 r. "Lovers on a Camel" (Nasir-ud-din) . . . . . . 1·50 2·75
684 2 r. "Chained Elephant" (Zain-al-Abidin) . . . . 2·00 3·25

635 Mount Everest

1973. 15th Anniv of Indian Mountaineering Foundation.
685 **635** 20 p. blue 50 50

636 Tail of Boeing 747

1973. 25th Anniv of Air-India's International Services.
686 **636** 1 r. 45 blue and red . . . . 4·00 4·00

637 Cross, Church of St. Thomas' Mount, Madras

638 Michael Madhusudan Dutt (poet—Death Centenary)

1973. 19th Death Centenary of St. Thomas.
687 **637** 20 p. grey and brown . . . 20 50

1973. Centenaries.
688 **638** 20 p. green and brown . . 1·00 65
689 – 30 p. brown . . . . 1·25 2·50
690 – 50 p. brown . . . . 1·50 2·50
691 – 1 r. violet and red . . . . 1·50 1·50
DESIGNS—HORIZ: 30 p. Vishnu Digambar Paluskar (musician, birth cent); 50 p. Dr. G. A. Hansen (cent of discovery of leprosy bacillus); 1 r. Nicolaus Copernicus (astronomer, 5th birth cent).

639 A. O. Hume

641 R. C. Dutt

640 Gandhi and Nehru

1973. Allan Octavian Hume (founder of Indian National Congress) Commemoration.
692 **639** 20 p. grey 20 40

1973. Gandhi and Nehru Commemoration.
693 **640** 20 p. multicoloured 20 40

1973. Romesh Chandra Dutt (writer) Commem.
694 **641** 20 p. brown 20 40

642 K. S. Ranjitsinhji

643 Vithalbhai Patel

1973. K. S. Ranjitsinhji (cricketer) Commemoration.
695 **642** 30 p. green . . . . 3·50 3·25

1973. Vithalbhai Patel (lawyer) Commemoration.
696 **643** 50 p. brown 20 65

644 Sowar of President's Bodyguard

645 Interpol Emblem

1973. Bicentenary of President's Bodyguard.
697 **644** 20 p. multicoloured 35 40

1973. 50th Anniv of Interpol.
698 **645** 20 p. brown 30 40

646 Syed Ahmad Khan (social reformer)

1973. Syed Ahmad Khan Commemoration.
699 **646** 20 p. brown 20 60

647 "Children at Play" (Bela Raval)

1973. Children's Day.
700 **647** 20 p. multicoloured 20 30

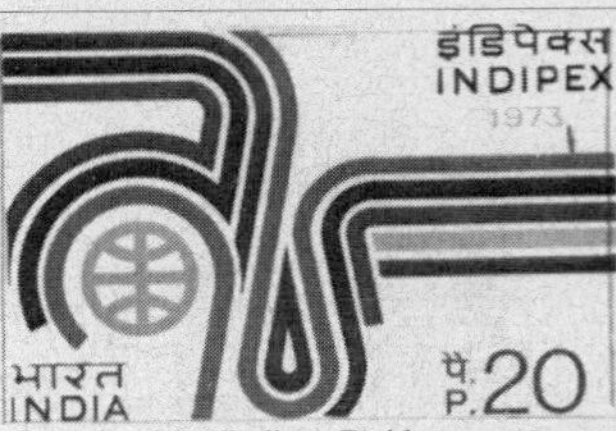

648 Indipex Emblem

1973. "Indipex '73" Philatelic Exhibition, New Delhi (2nd issue). Multicoloured.
701 20 p. Type **648** 20 30
702 1 r. Ceremonial elephant and $1\frac{1}{2}$ a. stamp of 1947 (vert) . . 1·25 2·00
703 2 r. Common peafowl (vert) . . 1·50 3·00

649 Emblem of National Cadet Corps

650 C. Rajagopalachari (statesman)

1973. 25th Anniv of National Cadet Corps.
705 **649** 20 p. multicoloured 20 30

1973. Chakravarti Rajagopalachari Commemoration.
706 **650** 20 p. brown 20 50

651 "Sun" Mask

652 Chhatrapati

1974. Indian Masks. Multicoloured.
707 20 p. Type **651** 15 15
708 50 p. "Moon" mask 30 55
709 1 r. "Narasimha" . . . . . . 70 1·25
710 2 r. "Ravana" (horiz) . . . . 1·00 2·00

1974. 300th Anniv of Coronation of Chhatrapati Shri Shivaji Maharaj (patriot and ruler).
712 **652** 25 p. multicoloured 40 30

653 Maithili Sharan Gupta (poet)

654 Kandukuri Veeresalingam (social reformer)

1974. Indian Personalities (1st series).
713 **653** 25 p. brown 15 45
714 – 25 p. brown 15 45
715 – 25 p. brown 15 45
PORTRAITS: No. 714, Jainarain Vyas (politician and journalist); No. 715, Utkal Gourab Madhusudan Das (social reformer).

1974. Indian Personalities (2nd series).
716 **654** 25 p. brown 25 50
717 – 50 p. purple . . . . 55 1·75
718 – 1 r. brown . . . . 70 1·75
PORTRAITS: 50 p. Tipu Sultan; 1 r. Max Mueller (Sanskrit scholar).

655 Kamala Nehru

1974. Kamala Nehru Commemoration.
719 **655** 25 p. multicoloured 50 50

656 W.P.Y. Emblem

657 Spotted Deer

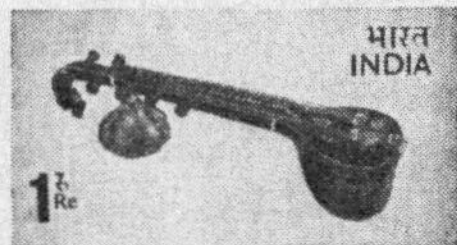

657a Sitar

1974. World Population Year.
720 **656** 25 p. purple and brown . . 20 30

1974. (a) Values expressed with "p" or "Re".
721 – 15 p. brown . . . . . . 3·25 70
722 **657** 25 p. brown . . . . . . 75 1·25
723 **657a** 1 r. brown and black . . 2·50 30
(b) Values expressed as numerals only.
724 – 2 p. brown . . . . . . 70 2·25
725 – 5 p. red 30 10
729 – 10 p. blue 30 15
730 – 15 p. brown . . . . . . 1·50 10
731 – 20 p. green 15 10
732 – 25 p. brown . . . . . . 5·50 2·00
732b – 30 p. brown . . . . . . 3·00 55
733 – 50 p. violet . . . . . . 4·50 10
734 – 60 p. grey . . . . . . 1·00 80
735 **657a** 1 r. brown and black . . 3·25 10
736 – 2 r. violet and brown . . 12·00 40
737 – 5 r. violet and brown . . 1·50 1·00
738d – 10 r. grey and green . . 1·10 1·10
DESIGNS—VERT (as Type **657**): 2 p. Bidri vase; 5 p. "Family Planning"; 15 p. Tiger; 25 p. Gandhi; 30 p. Indian dolls; 60 p. Somnath Temple. HORIZ (as Type **657a**): 10 p. Electric locomotive; 20 p. Handicrafts toy; 50 p. Great egret in flight. (As Type **657a**): 2 r. Himalayas; 5 r. Bhakra Dam, Punjab; 10 r. Atomic reactor, Trombay.
For 30, 35, 50, 60 p. and 1 r. values as No. 732 see Nos. 968, 979, 1073, 1320 and 1436.

658 President V. Giri

660 Woman Flute-player (sculpture)

659 U.P.U. Emblem

1974. Retirement of President Giri.
739 **658** 25 p. multicoloured 15 30

1974. Centenary of U.P.U.
740 **659** 25 p. violet, blue & black . 40 10
741 – 1 r. multicoloured . . . . 75 1·00
742 – 2 r. multicoloured . . . . 1·00 2·00
DESIGNS:—1 r. Birds and nest, "Madhubani" style. VERT: 2 r. Arrows around globe.

1974. Centenary of Mathura Museum.
744 **660** 25 p. chestnut and brown . 50 45
745 – 25 p. chestnut and brown . 50 45
DESIGN: No. 745, Vidyadhara with garland.

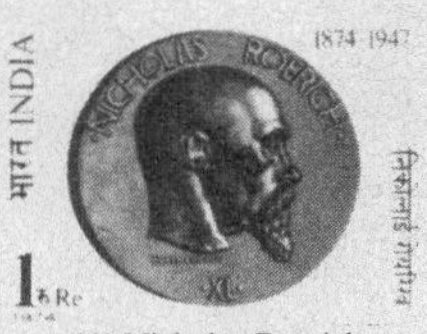

661 Nicholas Roerich (medallion by H. Dropsy)

1974. Birth Centenary of Professor Roerich (humanitarian).
746 **661** 1 r. green and yellow . . . 50 55

662 Pavapuri Temple

1974. 2,500th Anniv of Bhagwan Mahavira's Attainment of Nirvana.
747 **662** 25 p. black 40 20

663 "Cat" (Rajesh Bhatia)

664 "Indian Dancers" (Amita Shah)

1974. Children's Day.
748 **663** 25 p. multicoloured 70 40

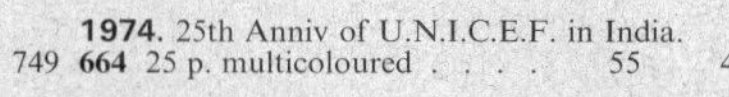

1974. 25th Anniv of U.N.I.C.E.F. in India.
749 **664** 25 p. multicoloured 55 45

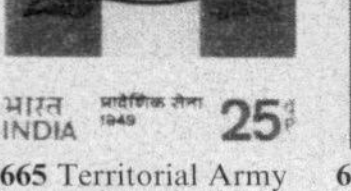

665 Territorial Army Badge

666 Krishna as Gopal Bal with Cows (Rajasthan painting on cloth)

1974. 25th Anniv of Indian Territorial Army.
750 **665** 25 p. black, yellow & grn . 60 40

1974. 19th International Dairy Congress, New Delhi.
751 **666** 25 p. purple and brown . . 40 30

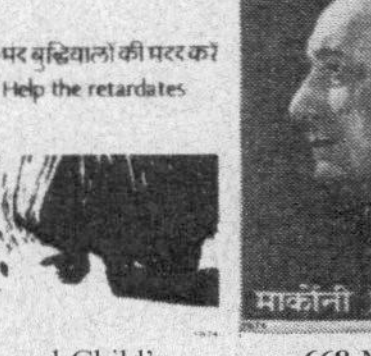

667 Symbols and Child's Face

668 Marconi

1974. Help for Retarded Children.
752 **667** 25 p. red and black 50 50

1974. Birth Centenary of Guglielmo Marconi (radio pioneer).
753 **668** 2 r. blue . . . . 2·00 1·25

669 St. Francis Xavier's Shrine, Goa

670 Saraswati (Deity of Language and Learning)

1974. St. Francis Xavier Celebration.
754 **669** 25 p. multicoloured 15 30

1975. World Hindi Convention, Nagpur.
755 **670** 25 p. grey and red 30 30

671 Parliament House, New Delhi

1975. 25th Anniv of Republic.
756 **671** 25 p. black, silver and blue 30 30

672 Table-tennis Bat

1975. World Table-tennis Championships, Calcutta.
757 **672** 25 p. black, red & green . . 55 30

673 "Equality, Development and Peace"

1975. International Women's Year.
758 **673** 25 p. multicoloured 85 45

674 Stylised Cannon

676 Saraswati

675 Arya Samaj Emblem

1975. Bicent of Indian Army Ordnance Corps.
759 **674** 25 p. multicoloured 65 45

1975. Centenary of Arya Samaj Movement.
760 **675** 25 p. red and brown . . . 30 30

1975. World Telugu Language Conf, Hyderabad.
761 **676** 25 p. black and green . . . 45 30

677 Satellite "Aryabhata"

1975. Launch of First Indian Satellite.
762 **677** 25 p. lt blue, blue & pur . . 50 40

678 Blue-winged Pitta

1975. Indian Birds. Multicoloured.
763 25 p. Type **678** 65 25
764 50 p. Asian black-headed oriole 1·50 2·00
765 1 r. Western tragopan (vert) . . 2·25 2·75
766 2 r. Himalayan monal pheasant (vert) . . . . 3·00 5·00

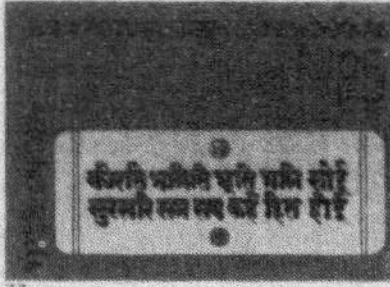

679 Page from "Ramcharitmanas" (manuscript)

1975. 4th Centenary of "Ramcharitmanas" (epic poem by Goswami Tulsidas).
767 **679** 25 p. black, yellow & red . 40 20

680 Young Women within Y.W.C.A. Badge

681 "The Creation"

1975. Centenary of Indian Y.W.C.A.
768 **680** 25 p. multicoloured 30 30

1975. 500th Birth Anniv of Michelangelo. "Creation" Frescoes from Sistine Chapel.
769 **681** 50 p. multicoloured 80 90
770 – 50 p. multicoloured 80 90
771 – 50 p. multicoloured 80 90
772 – 50 p. multicoloured 80 90
Nos. 770 and 772 are size 49 × 34 mm. The four stamps form a composite design.

682 Commission Emblem

683 Stylised Ground Antenna

1975. 25th Anniv of Int Commission on Irrigation and Drainage.
773 **682** 25 p. multicoloured 40 20

1975. Inauguration of Satellite Instructional Television Experiment.
774 **683** 25 p. multicoloured 40 20

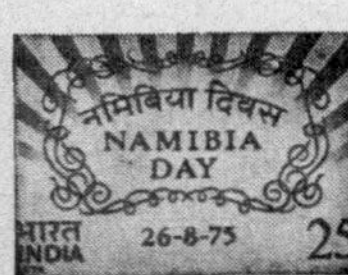

684 St. Arunagirinathar

685 Commemorative Text

1975. 600th Birth Anniv of St. Arunagirinathar.
775 **684** 50 p. purple and black . . 1·00 1·00

1975. Namibia Day.
776 **685** 25 p. black and red 40 40

686 Mir Anees (poet)

687 Memorial Temple to Ahilyabai Holkar (ruler)

1975. Indian Celebrities.
777 **686** 25 p. green 25 65
778 **687** 25 p. brown 25 65

688 Bharata Natyam

689 Ameer Khusrau

1975. Indian Dances. Multicoloured.
779 25 p. Type **688** 65 20
780 50 p. Orissi . . . . 1·00 1·50
781 75 p. Kathak . . . . 1·25 1·75
782 1 r. Kathakali . . . . . . 1·50 1·25
783 1 r. 50 Kuchipudi . . . . . 2·25 3·25
784 2 r. Manipuri . . . . 2·25 3·75

1975. 650th Death Anniv of Ameer Khusrau (poet).
785 **689** 50 p. brown and bistre . . 80 1·50

690 V. K. Krishna Menon

691 Text of Poem

1975. 1st Death Anniv of V. K. Krishna Menon (statesman).
786 **690** 25 p. green 50 60

1975. Birth Bicentenary of Emperor Bahadur Shah Zafar.
787 **691** 1 r. black, buff & brown . . 65 90

692 Sansadiya Soudha, New Delhi

1975. 21st Commonwealth Parliamentary Conference, New Delhi.
788 **692** 2 r. green . . . . 2·00 2·50

693 V. Patel

694 N. C. Bardoloi

1975. Birth Centenary of Vallabhbhai Patel (statesman).
789 **693** 25 p. green 15 40

1975. Birth Centenary of Nabin Chandra Bardoloi (politician).
790 **694** 25 p. brown 30 50

695 "Cow" (Sanjay Nathubhai Patel)

1975. Children's Day.
791 **695** 25 p. multicoloured 60 60

696 Original Printing Works, Nasik Road

697 Gurdwara Sisganj (site of martyrdom)

1975. 50th Anniv of India Security Press.
792 **696** 25 p. multicoloured 40 40

1975. Tercentenary of the Martyrdom of Guru Tegh Bahadur (Sikh leader).
793 **697** 25 p. multicoloured 40 40

698 Theosophical Society Emblem

699 Weather Cock

1975. Centenary of Theosophical Society.
794 **698** 25 p. multicoloured 40 40

1975. Cent of Indian Meteorological Department.
795 **699** 25 p. multicoloured 50 50

700 Early Mail Cart

1975. "Inpex '75" Nat Philatelic Exn, Calcutta.
796 **700** 25 p. black and brown . . 50 30
797 – 2 r. brown, purple & blk . 2·25 3·25
DESIGN: 2 r. Indian bishop mark, 1775.

701 L. N. Mishra

702 Tiger

1976. 1st Death Anniv of Lalit Narayan Mishra (politician).
798 **701** 25 p. brown 40 40

1976. Birth Cent of Jim Corbett (naturalist).
799 **702** 25 p. multicoloured . . . . 1·00 70

703 Painted Storks

1976. Keoladeo Ghana Bird Sanctuary, Bharatpur.
800 **703** 25 p. multicoloured 80 50

704 Vijayanta Tank

1976. Bicent of 16th Light Cavalry Regiment.
801 **704** 25 p. green and brown . . 1·60 30

705 Alexander Graham Bell

706 Muthuswami Dikshitar

1976. Alexander Graham Bell Commem.
802 **705** 25 p. brown and black . . 70 40

1976. Birth Bicentenary of Muthuswami Dikshitar (composer).
803 **706** 25 p. violet 70 40

707 Eye and Red Cross

1976. World Health Day. Prevention of Blindness.
804 **707** 25 p. brown and red . . . 80 50

708 "Industries"

710 Nehru

709 Type WDM Diesel Locomotive, 1963

1976. Industrial Development.
805 **708** 25 p. multicoloured 30 30

1976. Locomotives. Multicoloured.
806 25 p. Type **709** 55 10
807 50 p. Radjustan Malvan Railway Class F/1 steam locomotive, 1895 . . . . 1·50 55
808 1 r. Southern Railway Class WP/1 steam locomotive, 1963 . . . . 2·75 1·25
809 2 r. Great Peninsular Railway Class GIP steam locomotive, 1853 . . . . 3·50 2·50

1976.
810b **710** 25 p. violet . . . . 4·00 80
811 – 25 p. brown . . . . . . 1·00 30
DESIGN: No. 811, Gandhi.
For these designs in a smaller format see Nos. 732, 968/9, 979/80, 1073/4 and 1320.

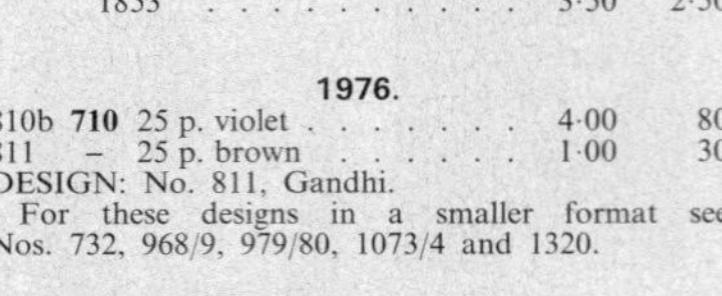

713 "Spirit of '76" (Willard)

714 K. Kamaraj (politician)

1976. Bicentenary of American Revolution.
812 **713** 2 r. 80 multicoloured . . . 1·25 1·25

1976. Kumaraswamy Kamaraj Commemoration.
813 **714** 25 p. brown 15 15

715 "Shooting"

716 Subhadra Kumari Chauhan (poetess)

1976. Olympic Games, Montreal.
814 **715** 25 p. violet and red 30 10
815 – 1 r. multicoloured . . . . 1·00 90
816 – 1 r. 50 mauve and black . . 1·75 2·75
817 – 2 r. 80 multicoloured . . . 1·75 4·00
DESIGNS: 1 r. Shot-put; 1 r. 50, Hockey; 2 r. 80, Sprinting.

1976. S. K. Chauhan Commemoration.
818 **716** 25 p. blue 15 40

717 Param Vir Chakra Medal

718 University Building, Bombay

1976. Param Vir Chakra Commemoration.
819 **717** 25 p. multicoloured 15 50

1976. 60th Anniv of Shreemati Nathibai Damodar Thackersey Women's University.
820 **718** 25 p. violet 30 30

719 Bharatendu Harischandra (writer)

720 S. C. Chatterji

1976. Harischandra Commemoration.
821 **719** 25 p. brown 15 30

1976. Birth Centenary of Sarat Chandra Chatterji (writer).
822 **720** 25 p. black 15 30

721 Planned Family

722 Maharaja Agrasen and Coins

1976. Family Planning.
823 **721** 25 p. multicoloured 15 30

1976. Maharaja Agrasen Commemoration.
824 **722** 25 p. brown 10 30

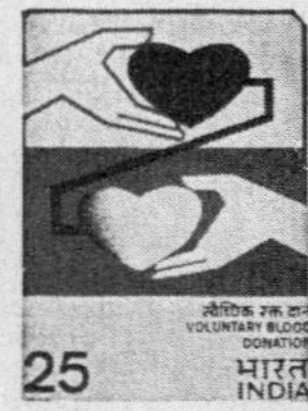

723 Swamp Deer

724 Hands holding Hearts

1976. Indian Wildlife. Multicoloured.
825 25 p. Type **723** 45 40
826 50 p. Lion . . . . 1·25 2·25
827 1 r. Leopard (horiz) . . . . . 1·75 2·25
828 2 r. Caracal (horiz) . . . . . 2·00 3·50

1976. Voluntary Blood Donation.
829 **724** 25 p. yellow, red & black . 60 40

725 Suryakant Tripathi ("Nirala")

726 "Loyal Mongoose" (H. D. Bhatia)

1976. 80th Birth Anniv of "Nirala" (poet and novelist).
830 **725** 25 p. violet 15 30

1976. Children's Day.
831 **726** 25 p. multicoloured 40 40

727 Hiralal Shastri (social reformer)

728 Dr. Hari Singh Gour (lawyer)

1976. Shastri Commemoration.
832 **727** 25 p. brown 20 30

1976. Dr. Hari Singh Gour Commemoration.
833 **728** 25 p. purple 20 30

729 Airbus Industrie A300B4

1976. Inauguration of Indian Airlines' Airbus Service.
834 **729** 2 r. multicoloured . . . . 2·25 2·25

730 Hybrid Coconut Palm

731 First Stanza of "Vande Mataram"

1976. Diamond Jubilee of Coconut Research.
835 **730** 25 p. multicoloured 20 30

1976. Centenary of "Vande Mataram" (patriotic song by B. C. Chatterjee).
836 **731** 25 p. multicoloured 20 30

732 Globe and Film Strip

1977. 6th International Film Festival of India, New Delhi.
837 **732** 2 r. multicoloured . . . . 1·10 2·00

733 Seismograph and Crack in Earth's Crust

734 Tarun Ram Phookun

1977. 6th World Conference on Earthquake Engineering, New Delhi.
838 **733** 2 r. lilac . . . . 1·00 2·00

1977. Birth Cent of Tarun Ram Phookun (politician).
839 **734** 25 p. grey 15 30

735 Paramahansa Yogananda

736 Asian Regional Red Cross Emblem

1977. Paramahansa Yogananda (religious leader) Commem.
840 **735** 25 p. orange 40 30

1977. 1st Asian Regional Red Cross Conference, New Delhi.
841 **736** 2 r. red, pink and blue . . 2·00 2·50

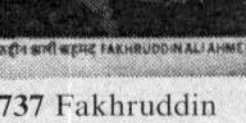

737 Fakhruddin Ali Ahmed

738 Emblem of Asian–Oceanic Postal Union

1977. Death of President Ahmed.
842 **737** 25 p. multicoloured 35 35

1977. 15th Anniv of Asian–Oceanic Postal Union.
843 **738** 2 r. multicoloured . . . . 1·10 1·75

739 Narottam Morarjee and "Loyalty" (liner)

740 Makhanlal Chaturvedi (writer and poet)

1977. Birth Cent of Morarjee (ship owner).
844 **739** 25 p. blue 75 70

1977. Chaturvedi Commemoration.
845 **740** 25 p. brown 15 30

741 Mahaprabhu Vallabhacharya (philosopher)

742 Federation Emblem

1977. Vallabhacharya Commemoration.
846 **741** 1 r. brown 30 40

1977. 50th Anniv of Federation of Indian Chambers of Commerce and Industry.
847 **742** 25 p. purple, brown and yellow 15 40

744 "Environment Protection"

1977. World Environment Day.
848 **744** 2 r. multicoloured . . . . 60 1·25

745 Rajya Sabha Chamber

1977. 25th Anniv of Rajya Sabha (Upper House of Parliament).
849 **745** 25 p. multicoloured 15 30

746 Lotus

1977. Indian Flowers. Multicoloured.
850 25 p. Type **746** 25 15
851 50 p. Rhododendron (vert) . . 45 90
852 1 r. Kadamba (vert) . . . . . 60 1·00
853 2 r. Gloriosa lily . . . . 90 2·25

747 Berliner Gramophone

1977. Centenary of Sound Recording.
854 **747** 2 r. brown and black . . . 1·00 2·00

748 Coomaraswamy and Siva

750 Dr. Samuel Hahnemann (founder of homeopathy)

749 Ganga Ram and Hospital

1977. Birth Centenary of Ananda Kentish Coomaraswamy (art historian).
855 **748** 25 p. multicoloured 40 40

1977. 50th Death Anniv of Sir Ganga Ram (social reformer).
856 **749** 25 p. purple 30 30

1977. 32nd Int Homeopathic Congress, New Delhi.
857 **750** 2 r. black and green . . . 3·50 2·75

751 Ram Manohar Lohia (politician)

752 Early Punjabi Postman

1977. Ram Manohar Lohia Commemoration.
858 **751** 25 p. brown 30 30

1977. "Inpex '77" Philatelic Exn, Bangalore.
859 **752** 25 p. multicoloured 50 30
860 – 2 r. grey and red . . . . . 2·00 2·75
DESIGN: 2 r. "Lion and Palm" essay, 1853.

753 Scarlet "Scinde Dawks" of 1852

1977. "Asiana '77" Philatelic Exn, Bangalore.
861 **753** 1 r. multicoloured . . . . 1·50 1·00
862 – 3 r. blue, orange and black 2·50 3·25
DESIGN: 3 r. Foreign mail arriving at Ballard Pier, Bombay, 1927.

754 "Mother and Child" (Khajuraho sculpture)

756 Symbolic Sun

755 Statue of Kittur Rani Channamma, Belgaum

1977. 15th Int Congress of Pediatrics, New Delhi.
863 **754** 2 r. blue and brown . . . 2·25 2·75

1977. Kittur Rani Channama, (ruler) Commem.
864 **755** 25 p. green 80 40

1977. Union Public Service Commission.
865 **756** 25 p. multicoloured 35 30

757 Ear of Corn

759 Jotirao Phooley (social reformer)

758 "Cats" (Nikur Dilipbhai Mody)

1977. "Agriexpo '77" Agricultural Exhibition, New Delhi.
866 **757** 25 p. green 40 40

1977. Children's Day. Multicoloured.
867 25 p. Type **758** 50 30
868 1 r. "Friends" (Bhavsar Ashish Ramanlal) . . . . 2·25 3·00

1977. Indian Personalities.
869 **759** 25 p. olive 30 45
870 – 25 p. brown 30 45
DESIGN: No. 870, Senapti Bapat (patriot).

760 Diagram of Population Growth

761 Kamta Prasad Guru and Vyakarna (Hindi Grammar)

1977. 41st Session of International Statistical Institute, New Delhi.
871 **760** 2 r. turquoise and red . . . 60 1·00

1977. Kamta Prasad Guru (writer) Commem.
872 **761** 25 p. brown 20 30

762 Kremlin Tower and Soviet Flag

763 Climber crossing a Crevice

1977. 60th Anniv of October Revolution.
873 **762** 1 r. multicoloured 45 75

1978 Conquest of Kanchenjunga (1977). Multicoloured.
874 25 p. Type **763** 10 10
875 1 r. Indian flag near summit (horiz) 45 80

764 "Shikara" on Lake Dal, Kashmir

1978. 27th Pacific Area Travel Association Conference, New Delhi.
876 **764** 1 r. multicoloured . . . . 2·00 1·50

765 Children in Library

1978. 3rd World Book Fair, New Delhi.
877 **765** 1 r. brown and slate . . . 45 80

766 Mother-Pondicherry 767 Wheat and Globe

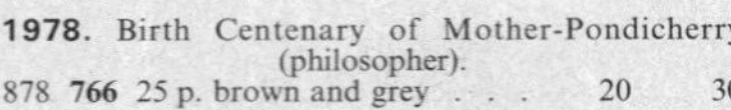

1978. Birth Centenary of Mother-Pondicherry (philosopher).
878 **766** 25 p. brown and grey . . . 20 30

1978. 5th International Wheat Genetics Symposium, New Delhi.
879 **767** 25 p. yellow & turquoise . 20 30

768 Nanalal Dalpatram Kavi (poet) 769 Surjya Sen (revolutionary)

1978. Nanalal Dalpatram Kavi Commemoration.
880 **768** 25 p. brown 20 30

1978. Surjya Sen Commemoration.
881 **769** 25 p. bistre and red 20 30

770 "Two Vaishnavas" (Jamini Roy)

1978. Modern Indian Paintings. Multicoloured.
882 25 p. Type **770** 20 30
883 50 p. "The Mosque" (Sailoz Mookherjea) . . . . 40 1·25
884 1 r. "Head" (Rabindranath Tagore) . . . . 70 1·50
885 2 r. "Hill Women" (Amrita Sher Gil) . . . . 90 2·00

771 "Self-portrait" (Rubens) 772 Charlie Chaplin

1978. 400th Birth Anniv of Peter Paul Rubens.
886 **771** 2 r. multicoloured . . . . 2·00 3·00

1978. Charlie Chaplin Commemoration.
887 **772** 25 p. blue and gold 90 45

773 Deendayal Upadhyaya (politician) 774 Syama Prasad Mookerjee

1978. Deendayal Upadhyaya Commemoration.
888 **773** 25 p. brown and orange . . 20 40

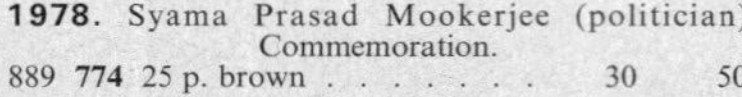

1978. Syama Prasad Mookerjee (politician) Commemoration.
889 **774** 25 p. brown 30 50

775 Airavat (mythological elephant). Jain Temple, Gujerat (Kachchh Museum) 776 Krishna and Arjuna in Battle Chariot

1978. Treasures from Indian Museums. Mult.
890 25 p. Type **775** 30 30
891 50 p. Kalpadruma (magical tree), Besnagar (Indian Museum) . 50 1·25
892 1 r. Obverse and reverse of Kushan gold coin (National Museum) . . . . 70 1·50
893 2 r. Dagger and knife of Emperor Jehangir, Mughal (Salar Jung Museum) . . . . 1·00 2·00

1978. Bhagawadgeeta (Divine Song of India) Commemoration.
894 **776** 25 p. gold and red 20 30

777 Bethune College 778 E. V. Ramasami

1978. Centenary of Bethune College, Calcutta.
895 **777** 25 p. brown and green . . 20 30

1978. E. V. Ramasami (social reformer) Commemoration.
896 **778** 25 p. black 20 20

779 Uday Shankar 780 Leo Tolstoy

1978. Uday Shankar (dancer) Commem.
897 **779** 25 p. brown 20 30

1978. 150th Birth Anniv of Leo Tolstoy (writer).
898 **780** 1 r. multicoloured 30 30

781 Vallathol Narayana Menon 783 Machine Operator

782 "Two Friends" (Dinesh Sharma)

1978. Birth Centenary of Vallathol Narayana Menon (poet).
899 **781** 25 p. purple and brown . . 15 40

1978. Children's Day.
900 **782** 25 p. multicoloured 20 40

1978. National Small Industries Fair, New Delhi.
901 **783** 25 p. green 20 30

784 Sowars of Skinner's Horse 785 Mohammad Ali Jauhar

1978. 175th Anniv of Skinner's Horse (cavalry regiment).
902 **784** 25 p. multicoloured 60 60

1978. Birth Centenary of Mohammad Ali Jauhar (patriot).
903 **785** 25 p. olive 20 30

786 Chakravarti Rajagopalachari 787 Wright Brothers and Flyer I

1978. Birth Centenary of Chakravarti Rajagopalachari (first post-independence Governor-General).
904 **786** 25 p. brown 20 30

1978. 75th Anniv of Powered Flight.
905 **787** 1 r. violet and yellow . . . 65 30

788 Ravenshaw College 789 Schubert

1978. Centenary of Ravenshaw College, Cuttack.
906 **788** 25 p. red and green 20 30

1978. 150th Death Anniv of Franz Schubert (composer).
907 **789** 1 r. multicoloured 80 55

790 Uniforms of 1799, 1901 and 1979 with Badge

1979. 4th Reunion of Punjab Regiment.
908 **790** 25 p. multicoloured 90 70

791 Bhai Parmanand 792 Gandhi with Young Boy

1979. Bhai Parmanand (scholar) Commemoration.
909 **791** 25 p. violet 20 30

1979. International Year of the Child.
910 **792** 25 p. brown and red . . . 40 30
911 – 1 r. brown and orange . . 60 1·50
DESIGN: 1 r. India I.Y.C. emblem.

793 Albert Einstein 794 Rajarshi Shahu Chhatrapati

1979. Birth Centenary of Albert Einstein (physicist).
912 **793** 1 r. blue 40 50

1979. Rajarshi Shahu Chhatrapati (ruler of Kolhapur State, and precursor of social reform in India) Commemoration.
913 **794** 25 p. purple 20 30

795 Exhibition Logo

1979. "India '80" International Stamp Exhibition (1st issue).
914 **795** 30 p. green and orange . . 20 30
See also Nos. 942/5 and 955/8.

796 Postcards under Magnifying Glass 797 Raja Mahendra Pratap

1979. Centenary of Indian Postcards.
915 **796** 50 p. multicoloured 20 40

1979. Raja Mahendra Pratap (patriot) Commemoration.
916 **797** 30 p. green 20 40

798 Hilsa, Pomfret and Prawn 800 Jatindra Nath Das

1979.

920	–	2 p. violet	10	10
921a	**798**	5 p. blue	10	10
922a	–	10 p. green	20	10
923	–	15 p. green	20	10
924a	–	20 p. red	30	10
925a	–	25 p. brown	30	10
925bb	–	25 p. green	30	10
926ab	–	30 p. green	30	10
927	–	35 p. purple	50	10
928c	–	50 p. violet	30	10
929b	–	1 r. brown	10	10
932ab	–	2 r. lilac	10	10
933c	–	2 r. 25 red and green	10	10
934	–	2 r. 80 red and green	70	40
934ca	–	3 r. 25 orange & green	10	10
935c	–	5 r. red and green	60	40
936b	–	10 r. purple and green	30	35

DESIGNS—HORIZ: 2 p. Adult education class; 10 p. Irrigation canal; 25 p. (925a) Chick hatching from egg; 25 p. (925bb) Village, wheat and tractor; 30 p. Harvesting maize; 50 p. Woman dairy farmer, cows and milk bottles. (36 × 19 mm): 10 r. Forest on hillside. VERT (17 × 20 mm): 15 p. Farmer and agricultural symbols; 20 p. Mother feeding child; 35 p. "Family". (17 × 28 mm): 1 r. Cotton plant; 2 r. Weaving. (20 × 38 mm): 2 r. 25, Cashew; 2 r. 80, Apples; 3 r. 25, Oranges; 5 r. Rubber tapping.
For 75 p. in same design as No. 927 see No. 1214.

1979. 50th Death Anniv of Jatindra Nath Das (revolutionary).
941 **800** 30 p. brown 20 30

801 De Havilland Puss Moth 802 Early and Modern Lightbulbs

1979. "Air India 80" International Stamp Exhibition (2nd issue). Mail-carrying Aircraft. Multicoloured.
942 30 p. Type **801** 30 25
943 50 p. Indian Air Force Hindustan Aircraft Industries Chetak helicopter 50 45

944 1 r. Indian Airlines Boeing 737 airliner 65 75

945 2 r. Air India Boeing 747 airliner 75 95

1979. Centenary of Electric Lightbulb.

946 **802** 1 r. purple 20 30

803 Gilgit Record

1979. International Archives Week.

947 **803** 30 p. yellow and brown . . 20 50

804 Hirakud Dam, Orissa

1979. 50th Anniv and 13th Congress of International Commission on Large Dams.

948 **804** 30 p. brown & turquoise . 20 30

805 Fair Emblem

806 Child learning to Read

1979. India International Trade Fair, New Delhi.

949 **805** 1 r. black and red 20 30

1979. International Children's Book Fair, New Delhi.

950 **806** 30 p. multicoloured 20 30

807 Dove with Olive Branch and I.A.E.A. Emblem

1979. 23rd International Atomic Energy Agency Conference, New Delhi.

951 **807** 1 r. multicoloured 20 45

808 Hindustan Aircraft Industries HAL-26 Pushpak Light Plane and Rohini-1 Glider

1979. Flying and Gliding.

952 **808** 30 p. black, brown & bl . . 1·00 80

809 Gurdwara Baoli Sahib Temple, Goindwal, Amritsar District

810 Ring of People encircling U.N. Emblem and Cogwheel

1979. 500th Birth Anniv of Guru Amar Das (Sikh leader).

953 **809** 30 p. multicoloured 20 30

1980. 3rd United Nations Industrial Development Organization General Conference, New Delhi.

954 **810** 1 r. multicoloured 20 30

HAVE YOU READ THE NOTES AT THE BEGINNING OF THIS CATALOGUE?

These often provide answers to the enquiries we receive.

811 Army Post Office and Postmarks

812 Energy Symbols

1980. "India '80" International Stamp Exhibition (3rd issue).

955 **811** 30 p. green 40 30

956 – 50 p. brown & dp brown . 70 1·00

957 – 1 r. red . . . . 80 1·00

958 – 2 r. brown . . . . 80 2·00

DESIGNS: 50 p. Money order transfer document, 1879; 1 r. Copper prepayment ticket, 1774; 2 r. Sir Rowland Hill and birthplace at Kidderminster.

1980. Institution of Engineers (India) Commem.

959 **812** 30 p. gold and blue 20 30

813 Uniforms of 1780 and 1980, Crest and Ribbon

814 Books

1980. Bicentenary of Madras Sappers.

960 **813** 30 p. multicoloured 60 50

1980. 4th World Book Fair, New Delhi.

961 **814** 30 p. blue 30 30

815 Bees and Honey-Comb

816 Welthy Fisher and Saksharta Nicketan (Literacy House), Lucknow

1980. 2nd International Conference on Agriculture.

962 **815** 1 r. bistre and brown . . . 50 45

1980. Welthy Fisher (teacher) Commemoration.

963 **816** 30 p. blue 30 30

817 Darul-Uloom, Deoband

818 Keshub Chunder Sen

1980. Darul-Uloom College Commemoration.

964 **817** 30 p. green 20 30

1980. Keshub Chunder Sen (religious and social reformer) Commemoration.

965 **818** 30 p. brown 20 30

819 Chhatrapati Shivaji Maharaj

820 Table Tennis

1980. 300th Death Anniv of Chhatrapati Shivaji Maharaj (warrior).

966 **819** 30 p. multicoloured 20 30

1980. 5th Asian Table Tennis Championships, Calcutta.

967 **820** 30 p. purple 30 30

1980. As Nos. 732 and 810, but 17 × 20 mm in size.

968 30 p. brown (Gandhi) . . . . 3·75 80

969 30 p. violet (Nehru) . . . . . 1·00 40

821 N. M. Joshi

822 Ulloor S. Parameswara Iyer

1980. Narayan Malhar Joshi (trade unionist) Commemoration.

970 **821** 30 p. mauve 60 40

1980. Ulloor S. Parameswara Iyer (poet) Commemoration.

971 **822** 30 p. purple 60 40

823 S. M. Zamin Ali

824 Helen Keller

1980. Syed Mohammed Zamin Ali (educationist and poet) Commemoration.

972 **823** 30 p. green 20 40

1980. Birth Centenary of Helen Keller (campaigner for the handicapped).

973 **824** 30 p. black and orange . . 50 40

825 High-jumping

826 Prem Chand

1980. Olympic Games, Moscow. Multicoloured.

974 1 r. Type **825** 40 40

975 2 r. 80 Horse-riding . . . . . 1·40 2·50

1980. Birth Cent of Prem Chand (novelist).

976 **826** 30 p. brown 20 40

827 Mother Teresa and Nobel Peace Prize Medallion

828 Lord Mountbatten

1980. Award of 1979 Nobel Peace Prize to Mother Teresa.

977 **827** 30 p. violet 50 30

1980. Lord Mountbatten Commemoration.

978 **828** 2 r. 80 multicoloured . . . 2·00 2·50

1980. As Nos. 968/9, but new face value.

979 35 p. brown . . . . 1·00 30

980 35 p. violet 30 20

DESIGNS: No. 979, Gandhi; No. 980, Nehru.

829 Scottish Church College, Calcutta

830 Rajah Annamalai Chettiar

1980. 150th Anniv of Scottish Church College, Calcutta.

981 **829** 35 p. lilac 20 30

1980. Rajah Annamalai Chettiar (banker and educationist) Commemoration.

982 **830** 35 p. lilac 20 30

831 Gandhi marching to Dandi

832 Jayaprakash Narayan

1980. 50th Anniv of "Dandi March" (Gandhi's defiance of Salt Tax Law).

983 **831** 35 p. black, blue & gold . . 25 70

984 – 35 p. black, mauve & gold . 25 70

DESIGN: No. 984, Gandhi picking up handful of salt at Dandi.

1980. Jayaprakash Narayan (socialist) Commemoration.

985 **832** 35 p. brown 40 40

833 Great Indian Bustard

834 Arabic Commemorative Inscription

1980. International Symposium on Bustards, Juipur.

986 **833** 2 r. 30 multicoloured . . . 1·00 2·00

1980. Moslem Year 1400 A.H. Commemoration.

987 **834** 35 p. multicoloured 15 30

835 "Girls Dancing" (Pampa Paul)

836 Dhyan Chand

1980. Children's Day.

988 **835** 35 p. multicoloured 40 40

1980. Dhyan Chand (hockey player). Commemoration.

989 **836** 35 p. brown 80 75

837 Gold Mining

838 M. A. Ansari

1980. Cent of Kolar Gold Fields, Karnataka.

990 **837** 1 r. multicoloured . . . . 1·10 30

1980. Mukhtayar Ahmad Ansari (medical practitioner and politician) Commemoration.

991 **838** 35 p. green 40 40

839 India Government Mint, Bombay

1980. 150th Anniv of India Government Mint, Bombay.

992 **839** 35 p. black, blue & silver . 20 30

840 Bride from Tamil Nadu

841 Mazharul Haque

1980. Brides in Traditional Costume. Multicoloured.

993 1 r. Type **840** 40 75
994 1 r. Rajasthan 40 75
995 1 r. Kashmir 40 75
996 1 r. Bengal 40 75

1981. Mazharul Haque (journalist) Commem.

997 **841** 35 p. blue 20 40

842 St. Stephen's College

1981. Centenary of St. Stephen's College, Delhi.

998 **842** 35 p. red 20 40

843 Gommateshwara

844 G. V. Mavalankar

1981. Millenium of Gommateshwara (statue at Shravanabelgola).

999 **843** 1 r. multicoloured 20 30

1981. 25th Death Anniv of Ganesh Vasudeo Mavalankar (parliamentarian).

1000 **844** 35 p. red 20 40

845 Flame of Martyrdom

846 Heinrich von Stephan and U.P.U. Emblem

1981. "Homage to Martyrs".

1001 **845** 35 p. multicoloured 20 30

1981. 150th Birth Anniv of Heinrich von Stephan (founder of U.P.U.).

1002 **846** 1 r. brown 20 50

847 Disabled Child being helped by Able-bodied Child

1981. International Year for Disabled Persons.

1003 **847** 1 r. black and blue . . . 20 30

848 Bhil

849 Stylised Trees

1981. Tribes of India. Muticoloured.

1004 1 r. Type **848** 40 35
1005 1 r. Dandami Maria 40 35
1006 1 r. Toda 40 35
1007 1 r. Khlamngam Naga 40 35

1981. Forests Conservation.

1008 **849** 1 r. multicoloured 20 30

850 Nilmoni Phukan

851 Sanjay Gandhi

1981. Nilmoni Phukan (poet) Commemoration.

1009 **850** 35 p. brown 20 40

1981. 1st Death Anniv of Sanjay Gandhi (politician).

1010 **851** 35 p. multicoloured . . . 40 55

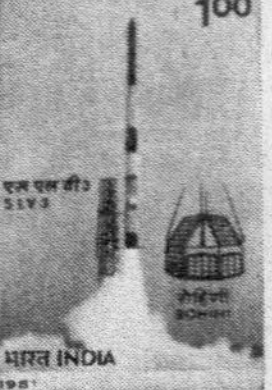

852 Launch of "SLV 3" and Diagram of "Rohini"

853 Games Logo

1981. Launch of "SLV 3" Rocket with "Rohini" Satellite.

1011 **852** 1 r. black, pink and blue . 30 30

1981. Asian Games, New Delhi (1st issue). Multicoloured.

1012 1 r. Type **853** . . . . 1·00 65
1013 1 r. Games emblem and stylised hockey players . . . . . . 1·00 65

See also Nos. 1026, 1033, 1057, 1059 and 1061/6.

854 Flame of the Forest

855 W. F. D. Emblem and Wheat

1981. Flowering Trees. Multicoloured.

1014 35 p. Type **854** 40 15
1015 50 p. Crateva 75 75
1016 1 r. Golden shower . . . . . . 1·00 50
1017 2 r. Bauhinia . . . . 1·40 2·25

1981. World Food Day.

1018 **855** 1 r. yellow and blue . . . 20 20

856 "Stichophthalma camadeva"

1981. Butterflies. Multicoloured.

1019 35 p. Type **856** 90 15
1020 50 p. "Cethosia biblis" . . . 1·75 1·40
1021 1 r. "Cyrestis achates" (vert) . 2·25 70
1022 2 r. "Teinopalpus imperialis" (vert) . . . . 2·75 5·00

857 Bellary Raghava

1981. Bellary Raghava (actor) Commemoration.

1023 **857** 35 p. green 70 30

858 Regimental Colour

859 "Toyseller" (Kumari Ruchita Sharma)

1981. 40th Anniv of Mahar Regiment.

1024 **858** 35 p. multicoloured . . . 90 30

1981. Children's Day.

1025 **859** 35 p. multicoloured . . . 75 30

860 Rajghat Stadium

861 Kashi Prasad Jayasawal and Yaudheya Coin

1981. Asian Games, New Delhi (2nd issue).

1026 **860** 1 r. multicoloured . . . . 1·50 30

1981. Birth Centenary of Kashi Prasad Jayasawal (lawyer and historian).

1027 **861** 35 p. blue 50 30

862 Indian and P.L.O. Flags, and People

1981. Palestinian Solidarity.

1028 **862** 1 r. multicoloured . . . . 2·00 40

863 I.N.S. "Taragiri" (frigate)

1981. Indian Navy Day.

1029 **863** 35 p. multicoloured . . . 2·25 1·25

864 Henry Heras and Indus Valley Seal

1981. Henry Heras (historian) Commemoration.

1030 **864** 35 p. lilac 45 30

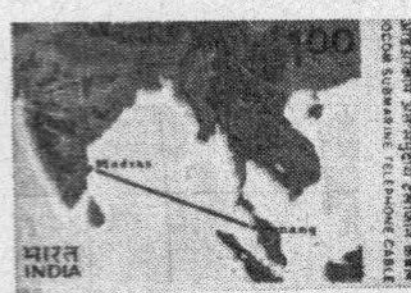

865 Map of South-East Asia showing Cable Route

1981. Inauguration of I.O.C.O.M. (Indian Ocean Commonwealth Cable) Submarine Telephone Cable.

1031 **865** 1 r. multicoloured . . . . 2·00 35

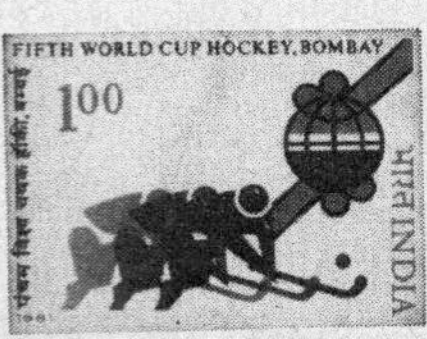

866 Stylised Hockey-players and Championship Emblem

1981. World Cup Hockey Championship, Bombay.

1032 **866** 1 r. multicoloured . . . 95 30

867 Jawaharlal Nehru Stadium

868 Early and Modern Telephones

1981. Asian Games, New Delhi (3rd issue).

1033 **867** 1 r. multicoloured 30 20

1982. Centenary of Telephone Services.

1034 **868** 2 r. black, blue and grey . . 30 30

869 Map of World

870 Sir J. J. School of Art

1982. International Soil Science Congress, New Delhi.

1035 **869** 1 r. multicoloured 30 20

1982. 125th Anniv of Sir J. J. School of Art, Bombay.

1036 **870** 35 p. multicoloured . . . 20 20

871 "Three Musicians"

872 Deer (stone carving), 5th-century A.D.

1982. Birth Centenary (1981) of Picasso.

1037 **871** 2 r. 85 multicoloured . . 1·10 50

1982. Festival of India. Ancient Sculpture. Multicoloured.

1038 2 r. Type **872** 20 40
1039 3 r. 05 Kaliya Mardana (bronze statue), 9th-century A.D. . . . 35 60

873 Radio Telescope, Ooty

1982. Festival of India. Science and Technology.

1040 **873** 3 r. 05 multicoloured . . 35 40

874 Robert Koch and Symbol of Disease

1982. Centenary of Robert Koch's Discovery of Tubercle Bacillus.

1041 **874** 35 p. lilac . . . . 1·40 75

875 Durgabai Deshmukh

1982. 1st Death Anniv of Durgabai Deshmukh (social reformer).

1042 **875** 35 p. blue 60 70

876 Blue Poppy

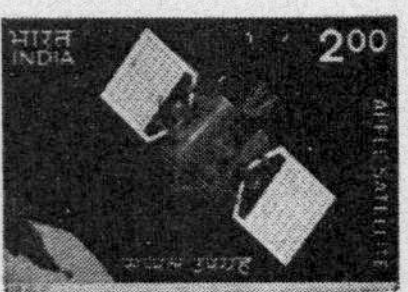

877 "Apple" Satellite

1982. Himalayan Flowers. Multicoloured.

1043 35 p. Type **876** 65 20
1044 1 r. Showy inula . . . . . . 1·50 30
1045 2 r. Cobra lily . . . . 2·00 3·00
1046 2 r. 85 Brahma kamal . . . . 2·50 3·75

1982. 1st Anniv of "Apple" Satellite Launch.
1047 **877** 2 r. multicoloured 50 80

878 Bidhan Chandra Roy

1982. Birth Centenary of Bidhan Chandra Roy (doctor and politician).
1048 **878** 50 p. brown . . . . . . 80 1·25

879 "Sagar Samrat" Oil Rig

1982. 25th Anniv of Oil and Natural Gas Commission.
1049 **879** 1 r. multicoloured . . . . 1·00 60

880 "Bindu" (S. H. Raza)

881 Red Deer Stag, Kashmir

1982. Festival of India. Contemporary Paintings. Multicoloured.
1050 2 r. Type **880** 40 50
1051 3 r. 05 "Between the Spider and the Lamp" (M. F. Hussain) 60 1·25

1982. Wildlife Conservation.
1052 **881** 2 r. 85 multicoloured . . 1·50 1·25

882 Westland Wapiti Biplane and Mikoyan Gurevich MiG-25 Aircraft

1982. 50th Anniv of Indian Air Force.
1053 **882** 1 r. multicoloured . . . . 4·00 1·25

883 J. Tata with De Havilland Puss Moth

1982. 50th Anniv of Civil Aviation in India.
1054 **883** 3 r. 25 multicoloured . . 3·50 1·60

884 Police Patrol

1982. Police Commemoration Day.
1055 **884** 50 p. green 50 30

885 Coins and Economic Symbols

1982. Centenary of Post Office Savings Bank.
1056 **885** 50 p. brown and light brown 20 20

886 Wrestling Bout

888 Arjuna shooting Arrow at Fish

887 Troposcatter Communication Link

1982. Asian Games, New Delhi (4th issue).
1057 **886** 1 r. multicoloured 30 30

1982. 1st Anniv of Troposcatter Communication Link between India and U.S.S.R.
1058 **887** 3 r. 05 multicoloured . . 30 40

1982. Asian Games, New Delhi (5th issue).
1059 **888** 1 r. multicoloured . . . . 1·75 30

889 "Mother and Child" (Deepak Sharma)

890 Stylised Cyclists

1982. Children's Day.
1060 **889** 50 p. multicoloured . . . 30 30

1982. Asian Games, New Delhi (6th issue). Multicoloured.
1061 50 p. Type **890** 10 10
1062 2 r. Javelin-throwing 25 30
1063 2 r. 85 Discus-throwing . . . 30 45
1064 3 r. 25 Football 40 55

891 "Enterprise" Dinghies Race

1982. Asian Games, New Delhi (7th issue). Multicoloured.
1065 2 r. Type **891** 90 30
1066 2 r. 85 Rowing . . . . 1·10 55

892 Chetwode Building

1982. 50th Anniv of Indian Military Academy Dehradun.
1067 **892** 50 p. multicoloured . . . 30 50

893 Purushottamdas Tandon

1982. Birth Cent of Purushottamdas Tandon (politician).
1068 **893** 50 p. brown 30 70

894 Darjeeling Himalayan Railway

1982. Cent of Darjeeling Himalayan Railway.
1069 **894** 2 r. 85 multicoloured . . 4·25 4·25

895 Vintage Rail Coach and Silhouette of Steam Locomotive

1982. "Inpex 82" Stamp Exhibition. Multicoloured.
1070 50 p. Type **895** 75 85
1071 2 r. 1854 $\frac{1}{2}$ anna blue stamp and 1947 3$\frac{1}{2}$ anna Independence commem (33 × 44 mm) . . 2·00 2·25

896 Antarctic Camp

1983. 1st Indian Antarctic Expedition.
1072 **896** 1 r. multicoloured . . . . 3·50 2·25

1983. As Nos. 968/9, but with new face value.
1073a 50 p. brown (Gandhi) . . . 3·00 1·50
1074a 50 p. blue (Nehru) . . . . . 1·50 55

897 Roosevelt with Stamp Collection

1983. Birth Centenary of Franklin D. Roosevelt (American statesman).
1075 **897** 3 r. 25 brown . . . . . . 55 1·25

898 "Siberian Cranes at Bharatpur" (Diane Pierce)

899 Jat Regiment Uniforms Past and Present

1983. International Crane Workshop, Bharatpur.
1076 **898** 2 r. 85 multicoloured . . 2·00 2·50

1983. Presentation of Colours to Battalions of the Jat Regiment.
1077 **899** 50 p. multicoloured . . . 1·50 1·25

900 Non-aligned Summit Logo

1983. 7th Non-aligned Summit Conference, New Delhi.
1078 **900** 1 r. lt brown, brn & blk . 20 30
1079 – 2 r. multicoloured 30 95
DESIGN: 2 r. Nehru.

901 Shore Temple, Mahabalipuram

1983. Commonwealth Day. Multicoloured.
1080 1 r. Type **901** 15 30
1081 2 r. Gomukh, Gangotri Glacier 30 1·25

902 Acropolis and Olympic Emblems

1983. Int Olympic Committee Session, New Delhi.
1082 **902** 1 r. multicoloured 30 50

903 "St. Francis and Brother Falcon" (statue by Giovanni Collina)

904 Karl Marx and "Das Kapital"

1983. 800th Birth Anniv of St. Francis of Assisi.
1083 **903** 1 r. brown 30 30

1983. Death Centenary of Karl Marx.
1084 **904** 1 r. brown 20 30

905 Darwin and Map of Voyage

1983. Death Centenary (1982) of Charles Darwin (naturalist).
1085 **905** 2 r. multicoloured . . . . 2·25 2·75

906 Swamp Deer

907 Globe and Satellite

1983. 50th Anniv of Kanha National Park.
1086 **906** 1 r. multicoloured . . . . 1·50 75

1983. World Communications Year.
1087 **907** 1 r. multicoloured 40 40

908. Simon Bolivar.

908 Simon Bolivar

909 Meera Behn

1983. Birth Bicentenary of Simon Bolivar (South American statesman).
1088 **908** 2 r. multicoloured . . . . 1·75 2·00

1983. India's Struggle for Freedom (1st series).
1089 50 p. red and green . . . . 90 2·00
1090 50 p. brown, green and red . 90 2·00
1091 50 p. multicoloured . . . . . 90 1·50
1092 50 p. brown, green and red . 15 30
1093 50 p. brown, green & orange . 15 30
1094 50 p. green, yellow & orange . 15 30
DESIGNS—VERT: No. 1089, Type **909**; 1090, Mahadev Desai; 1092, Hemu Kalani (revolutionary); 1093, Acharya Vinoba Bhave (social reformer); 1094, Surendranath Banerjee (political reformer). HORIZ (43 × 31 mm): No. 1091, Quit India Resolution.

See also Nos. 1119/24, 1144/9, 1191/4, 1230/5, 1287/96 and 1345/9.

910 Ram Nath Chopra

1983. Ram Nath Chopra (pharmacologist) Commemoration.
1095 **910** 50 p. red 40 80

911 Nanda Devi Mountain

1983. 25th Anniv of Indian Mountaineering Federation.

1096 **911** 2 r. multicoloured . . . . 1·10 90

912 Great Indian Hornbill

913 View of Garden

1983. Centenary of Natural History Society, Bombay.

1097 **912** 1 r. multicoloured . . . . 2·75 90

1983. Rock Garden, Chandigarh.

1098 **913** 1 r. multicoloured . . . . 1·25 85

914 Golden Langur

1983. Indian Wildlife. Monkeys. Multicoloured.

1099 1 r. Type **914** . . . . 1·25 50
1100 2 r. Lion-tailed macaque . . . 2·50 3·25

915 Ghats of Varanasi

1983. 5th General Assembly of World Tourism Organization.

1101 **915** 2 r. multicoloured 50 40

916 Krishna Kanta Handique

918 Woman and Child (from "Festival" by Kashyap Premsawala)

1983. Krishna Kanta Handique (scholar).

1102 **916** 50 p. blue 30 70

1983. Children's Day.

1103 **918** 50 p. multicoloured . . . 30 50

920 "Udan Khatola", First Indian Hot Air Balloon

921 Tiger

1983. Bicentenary of Manned Flight.

1104 1 r. Type **920** 75 20
1105 2 r. Montgolfier balloon . . . 1·00 80

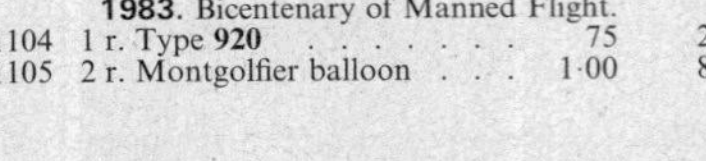

1983. Ten Years of "Project Tiger".

1106 **921** 2 r. multicoloured . . . . 2·50 3·00

922 Commonwealth Logo

923 "Pratiksha"

1983. Commonwealth Heads of Government Meeting, New Delhi. Multicoloured.

1107 1 r. Type **922** 10 15
1108 2 r. Goanese couple, early 19th century 25 30

1983. Birth Centenary of Nanda Lal Bose (artist).

1109 **923** 1 r. multicoloured 30 30

925 Lancer in Ceremonial Uniform

926 Troopers in Ceremonial Uniform and Tank

1984. Bicentenary of 7th Light Cavalry.

1110 **925** 1 r. multicoloured . . . . 3·25 1·40

1984. Presentation of Regimental Guidon to the Deccan Horse.

1111 **926** 1 r. multicoloured . . . . 3·25 1·40

927 Society Building and Sir William Jones (founder)

928 Insurance Logo

1984. Bicentenary of Asiatic Society.

1112 **927** 1 r. green and purple . . . 30 50

1984. Centenary of Postal Life Insurance.

1113 **928** 1 r. multicoloured 30 30

929 Hawker Siddeley Sea Harrier

1984. President's Review of the Fleet. Multicoloured.

1114 1 r. Type **929** . . . . 1·50 1·75
1115 1 r. "Vikrant" (aircraft carrier) . . 1·50 1·75
1116 1 r. "Vela" (submarine) . . . 1·50 1·75
1117 1 r. "Kashin" (destroyer) . . . 1·50 1·75

Nos. 1114/17 were printed together, se-tenant, forming a composite design.

930 I.L.A. Logo and Hemispheres

1984. 12th International Leprosy Congress.

1118 **930** 1 r. multicoloured 30 30

1984. India's Struggle for Freedom (2nd series). As T **909**.

1119 50 p. green, lt green & orge . . 30 40
1120 50 p. brown, green & orge . . 30 40
1121 50 p. multicoloured 50 60
1122 50 p. multicoloured 50 60
1123 50 p. multicoloured 50 60
1124 50 p. multicoloured 50 60

DESIGNS: No. 1119, Vasudeo Balvant Phadke (revolutionary); 1120, Baba Kanshi Ram (revolutionary); 1121, Tatya Tope; 1122, Nana Sahib; 1123, Begum Hazrat Mahal; 1124, Mangal Pandey.

932 "Salyut 7"

1984. Indo-Soviet Manned Space Flight.

1125 **932** 3 r. multicoloured 55 55

935 G. D. Birla

1984. 90th Birth Anniv of G. D. Birla (industrialist).

1126 **935** 50 p. brown 30 70

936 Basketball

937 Gwalior

1984. Olympic Games, Los Angeles. Multicoloured.

1127 50 p. Type **936** 90 65
1128 1 r. High jumping 75 30
1129 2 r. Gymnastics (horiz) . . . 1·00 1·50
1130 2 r. 50 Weightlifting (horiz) . . 1·25 2·50

1984. Forts. Multicoloured.

1131 50 p. Type **937** 70 55
1132 1 r. Vellore (vert) 95 30
1133 1 r. 50 Simhagad (vert) . . . 1·75 2·75
1134 2 r. Jodhpur . . . . 2·00 3·00

938 B. V. Paradkar and Newspaper

939 Dr. D. N. Wadia and Institute of Himalayan Geology, Dehradun

1984. B. V. Paradkar (journalist) Commemoration.

1135 **938** 50 p. brown 30 60

1984. Birth Centenary (1983) of Dr. D. N. Wadia (geologist).

1136 **939** 1 r. multicoloured . . . . 1·25 30

940 "Herdsman and Cattle in Forest" (H. Kassam)

942 Congress Emblem

941 Indira Gandhi

1984. Children's Day.

1137 **940** 50 p. multicoloured . . . 75 95

1984. Prime Minister Indira Gandhi Commemoration (1st issue).

1138 **941** 50 p. black, violet & orange 2·25 2·25

See also Nos. 1151, 1167 and 1170.

1984. 12th World Mining Congress, New Delhi.

1139 **942** 1 r. black and yellow . . . 1·25 30

943 Dr. Rajendra Prasad at Desk

944 Mrinalini (rose)

1984. Birth Centenary of Dr. Rajendra Prasad (former President).

1140 **943** 50 p. multicoloured . . . 1·00 85

1984. Roses. Multicoloured.

1141 1 r. 50 Type **944** . . . . . . 2·00 2·00
1142 2 r. Sugandha . . . . 2·25 2·25

945 "Fergusson College" (Gopal Deuskar)

1985. Centenary of Fergusson College, Pune.

1143 **945** 1 r. multicoloured 55 55

1985. India's Struggle for Freedom (3rd series). As T **909**.

1144 50 p. brown, green & orge . . 50 70
1145 50 p. brown, green & orge . . 50 70
1146 50 p. brown, green & orge . . 50 70
1147 50 p. brown, green & orge . . 50 70
1148 50 p. blue, green & orge . . 50 70
1149 50 p. black, green & orge . . 50 70

DESIGNS—VERT: No. 1144, Narhar Vishnu Gadgil (politician); 1145, Jairamdas Doulatram (journalist); 1147, Kakasaheb Kalelkar (author); 1148, Master Tara Singh (politician); 1149, Ravishankar Maharaj (politician). HORIZ: No. 1146, Jatindra and Nellie Sengupta (politicians).

947 Gunner and Howitzer from Mountain Battery

1985. 50th Anniv of Regiment of Artillery.

1150 **947** 1 r. multicoloured . . . . 3·50 1·50

948 Indira Gandhi making Speech

1985. Indira Gandhi Commemoration (2nd issue).

1151 **948** 2 r. multicoloured . . . . 2·75 3·25

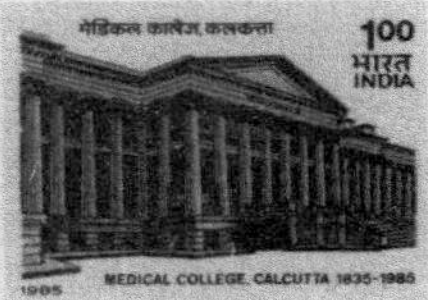

949 Minicoy Lighthouse

950 Medical College Hospital

1985. Centenary of Minicoy Lighthouse.

1152 **949** 1 r. multicoloured . . . . 3·75 85

1985. 150th Anniv of Medical College, Calcutta.

1153 **950** 1 r. yellow, brown & purple 2·50 70

951 Medical College, Madras

1985. 150th Anniv of Medical College, Madras.
1154 **951** 1 r. light brown and brown . . 2·50 70

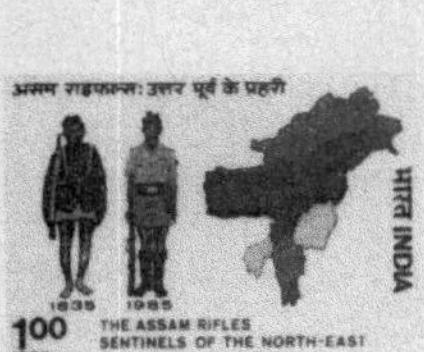
952 Riflemen of 1835 and 1985 and Map of North-East India

953 Potato Plant

1985. 150th Anniv of Assam Rifles.
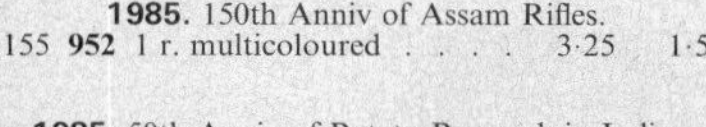
1155 **952** 1 r. multicoloured . . . . 3·25 1·50

1985. 50th Anniv of Potato Research in India.
1156 **953** 50 p. deep brown and brown . . . . 1·50 1·60

954 Baba Jassa Singh Ahluwalia

956 White-winged Wood Duck

955 St. Xavier's College

1985. Death Bicentenary (1983) of Baba Jassa Singh Ahluwalia (Sikh leader).
1157 **954** 50 p. purple . . . . . . 1·50 1·60

1985. 125th Anniv of St. Xavier's College, Calcutta.
1158 **955** 1 r. multicoloured . . . . 1·00 50

1985. Wildlife Conservation. White-winged Wood Duck.
1159 **956** 2 r. multicoloured . . . . 4·50 4·50

957 "Mahara"

958 Yaudheya Copper Coin, c. 200 B.C.

1985. Bougainvillea. Multicoloured.
1160 50 p. Type **957** . . . . 1·25 2·00
1161 1 r. "H. B. Singh" . . . . . 1·50 1·50

1985. Festival of India (1st issue).
1162 **958** 2 r. multicoloured . . . . 2·25 2·25

959 Statue of Didarganj Yakshi (deity)

962 Swami Haridas

1985. Festival of India (2nd issue).
1163 **959** 1 r. multicoloured . . . . 1·25 40

1985. Swami Haridas (philosopher) Commemoration.
1164 **962** 1 r. multicoloured . . . . 1·75 1·50

963 Stylised Mountain Road

1985. 25th Anniv of Border Roads Organization.
1165 **963** 2 r. red, violet and black . 2·00 2·50

964 Nehru addressing General Assembly

1985. 40th Anniv of United Nations Organization.
1166 **964** 2 r. multicoloured . . . . 1·10 90

965 Indira Gandhi with Crowd

1985. Indira Gandhi Commemoration (3rd issue).
1167 **965** 2 r. brown and black . . . 2·50 3·00

966 Girl using Home Computer

1985. Children's Day.
1168 **966** 50 p. multicoloured . . . 90 90

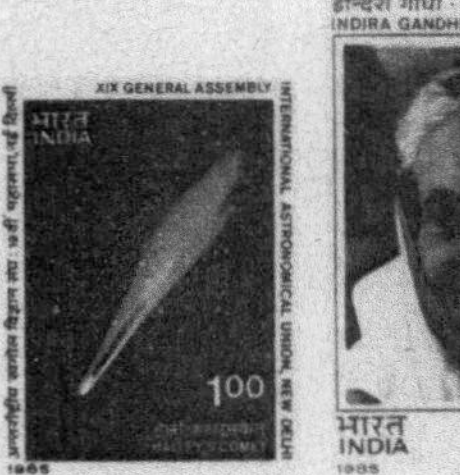
967 Halley's Comet

968 Indira Gandhi

1985. 19th General Assembly of International Astronomical Union, New Delhi.
1169 **967** 1 r. multicoloured . . . . 2·00 1·50

1985. Indira Gandhi Commemoration (4th issue).
1170 **968** 3 r. multicoloured . . . . 2·50 3·00

969 St. Stephen's Hospital

1985. Centenary of St. Stephen's Hospital, Delhi.
1171 **969** 1 r. black and brown . . . 80 40

971 Map showing Member States

1985. 1st Summit Meeting of South Asian Association for Regional Co-operation, Dhaka, Bangladesh. Multicoloured.
1172 1 r. Type **971** . . . . 1·50 40
1173 3 r. Flags of member nations (44 × 32 mm) . . . . 2·50 4·00

972 Shyama Shastri

975 Young Runners and Emblem

1985. Shyama Shastri (composer) Commemoration.
1174 **972** 1 r. multicoloured . . . . 2·25 1·50

1985. International Youth Year.
1175 **975** 2 r. multicoloured . . . . 1·50 75

976 Handel and Bach

1985. 300th Birth Annivs of George Frederick Handel and Johann Sebastian Bach (composers).
1176 **976** 5 r. multicoloured . . . . 3·50 4·00

977 A. O. Hume (founder) and Early Congress Presidents

1985. Centenary of Indian National Congress. Designs showing miniature portraits of Congress Presidents.
1177 **977** 1 r. black, orange, green and grey . . . . 1·50 1·75
1178 – 1 r. black, orange and green 1·50 1·75
1179 – 1 r. black, orange and green 1·50 1·75
1180 – 1 r. black, orange, green and grey . . . . 1·50 1·75

Nos. 1178/80 each show sixteen miniature portraits. The individual stamps can be distinguished by the position of the face value and inscription which are at the top on Nos. 1177/8 and at the foot on Nos. 1179/80. No. 1180 shows a portrait of Prime Minister Rajiv Gandhi in a grey frame at bottom right.

978 Bombay and Duncan Dry Docks, Bombay.

1181 **978** 2 r. 50 multicoloured . . 3·75 4·00

979 Hawa Mahal and Jaipur 1904 2 a. Stamp

1986. "INPEX '86" Philatelic Exhibition, Jaipur. Multicoloured.
1182 50 p. Type **979** . . . . 1·00 1·00
1183 2 r. Mobile camel post office, Thar Desert . . . . 2·25 3·00

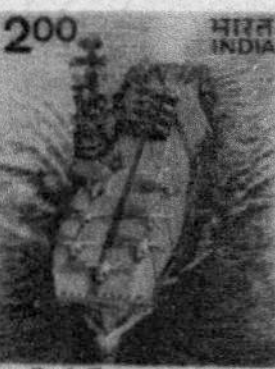
980 I.N.S. "Vikrant" (aircraft carrier)

981 Humber Sommer Biplane and Later Mail Planes

1986. Completion of 25 Years Service by I.N.S. "Vikrant".
1184 **980** 2 r. multicoloured . . . . 4·50 4·50

1986. 75th Anniv of First Official Airmail Flight, Allahabad–Naini. Multicoloured.
1185 50 p. Type **981** . . . . 2·25 1·75
1186 3 r. Modern Air India Airbus Industries A300 mail plane and Humber Sommer biplane (37 × 24 mm) . . . . 4·75 6·50

982 Triennale Emblem

983 Chaitanya Mahaprabhu

1986. 6th Triennale Art Exhibition, New Delhi.
1187 **982** 1 r. purple, yellow & black 1·50 95

1986. 500th Birth Anniv of Chaitanya Mahaprabhu (religious leader).
1188 **983** 2 r. multicoloured . . . . 2·75 3·50

984 Main Building, Mayo College

1986. Mayo College (public school), Ajmer, Commemoration.
1189 **984** 1 r. multicoloured . . . . 1·50 1·00

985 Two Footballers

1986. World Cup Football Championship, Mexico.
1190 **985** 5 r. multicoloured . . . . 4·25 4·25

1986. India's Struggle for Freedom (4th series). As T **909**.
1191 50 p. brown, green and red . . 1·25 1·75
1192 50 p. brown, green and red . . 1·25 1·75
1193 50 p. black, green & orange . 1·25 1·75
1194 50 p. brown, green and red . . 1·25 1·75

DESIGNS: No. 1191, Bhim Sen Sachar; 1192, Alluri Seeta Rama Raju; 1193, Sagarmal Gopa; 1194, Veer Surendra Sai.

987 Swami Sivananda

988 Volleyball

1986. Birth Centenary of Swami Sivananda (spiritual leader).
1195 **987** 2 r. multicoloured . . . . 3·00 3·50

1986. Asian Games, Seoul, South Korea. Multicoloured.
1196 1 r. 50 Type **988** . . . . . . 2·50 2·75
1197 3 r. Hurdling . . . . 3·00 3·75

989 Madras G.P.O.

1986. Bicentenary of Madras G.P.O.
1198 **989** 5 r. black and red . . . . 4·50 5·00

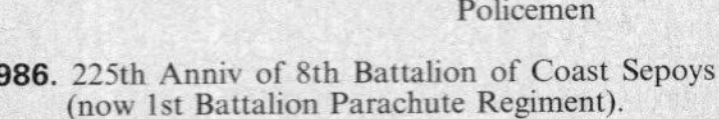

990 Parachutist

991 Early and Modern Policemen

1986. 225th Anniv of 8th Battalion of Coast Sepoys (now 1st Battalion Parachute Regiment).
1199 **990** 3 r. multicoloured . . . . 5·00 5·00

1986. 125th Anniv of Indian Police. Designs showing early and modern police.
1200 **991** 1 r. 50 multicoloured . . 3·50 4·00
1201 – 2 r. multicoloured . . . . 3·50 4·00
Nos. 1200/1 were printed together, se-tenant, forming a composite design.

992 Hand holding Flower and World Map

1986. International Peace Year.
1202 **992** 5 r. multicoloured . . . . 2·50 1·25

993 "Girl Rock Climber" (Sujasha Dasgupta)

994 Windmill

1986. Children's Day.
1203 **993** 50 p. multicoloured . . . 2·25 2·25

1986. Science and Technology.
1211 – 35 p. red 10 10
1212 – 40 p. red 10 10
1213 – 60 p. green and red . . . 10 10
1214a – 75 p. red 30 20
1215 – 1 r. black and red . . . 15 10
1217 – 5 r. brown and orange . . 15 20
1218 – 20 r. brown and blue . . 55 60
1219 **994** 50 r. black, blue and mauve . . . . 1·40 1·50
DESIGNS—20×17 mm: 35 p. Family planning. 37×20 mm: 60 p. Indian family; 20 r. Bio gas. 17×20 mm: 40 p. Television set, dish aerial and transmitter; 75 p. "Family" (as No. 927). 20×37 mm: 1 r. Petrol pump nozzle (Oil conservation); 5 r. Solar energy.

995 Growth Monitoring

1986. 40th Anniv of U.N.I.C.E.F. Multicoloured.
1221 50 p. Type **995** . . . . 2·00 2·00
1222 5 r. Immunization . . . . . 4·25 6·00

996 Tansen

997 Indian Elephant

1986. Tansen (musician and composer) Commem.
1223 **996** 1 r. multicoloured . . . . 2·00 60

1986. 50th Anniv of Corbett National Park. Multicoloured.
1224 1 r. Type **997** . . . . . . 3·50 1·00
1225 2 r. Gharial . . . . 4·00 6·00

998 St. Martha's Hospital

1986. Centenary of St. Martha's Hospital, Bangalore.
1226 **998** 1 r. blue, orange & black . . 2·00 1·40

999 Yacht "Trishna" and Route Map

1987. Indian Army Round the World Yacht Voyage, 1985–7.
1227 **999** 6 r. 50 multicoloured . . 4·50 4·00

1000 Map of Southern Africa and Logo

1001 Emblem

1987. Inauguration of AFRICA Fund.
1228 **1000** 6 r. 50 black . . . . . . 4·50 4·75

1987. 29th Congress of International Chamber of Commerce, New Delhi.
1229 **1001** 5 r. violet, blue and red . 3·00 1·75

1987. India's Struggle for Freedom (5th series). As T **909**.
1230 60 p. brown, green and orge . 2·00 30
1231 60 p. violet, green and red . . 30 30
1232 60 p. brown, green and red . . 30 30
1233 60 p. blue, green & orange . . 30 30
1234 60 p. brown, green and red . . 30 30
1235 60 p. brown, green and red . . 30 30
1236 60 p. red, green & orange . . 30 30
DESIGNS: No. 1230, Hakim Ajmal Khan; No. 1231, Lala Har Dayal; No. 1232, M. N Roy; No. 1233, Tripuraneni Ramaswamy Chowdary; No. 1234, Dr. Kailas Nath Katju; No. 1235, S. Satyamurti; No. 1236, Pandit Hriday Nath Kunzru.

1002 Blast Furnace and Railway Emblem

1003 Kalia Bhomora Bridge, Tezpur, Assam

1987. Cent of South Eastern Railway. Mult.
1237 1 r. Type **1002** 40 15
1238 1 r. 50 Tank locomotive No. 691, 1887 (horiz) 45 35
1239 2 r. Electric train on viaduct, 1987 . . . . 55 60
1240 4 r. Steam locomotive, c. 1900 (horiz) . . . . 80 1·25

1987. Inauguration of Brahmaputra Bridge.
1241 **1003** 2 r. multicoloured . . . 30 30

1004 Madras Christian College

1987. 150th Anniv of Madras Christian College.
1242 **1004** 1 r. 50 black and red . . 20 20

MINIMUM PRICE

The minimum price quoted is 10p which represents a handling charge rather than a basis for valuing common stamps. For further notes about prices see introductory pages.

1005 Shree Shree Ma Anandamayee

1006 "Rabindranath Tagore" (self-portrait)

1987. Shree Shree Ma Anandamayee (Hindu spiritual leader) Commemoration.
1243 **1005** 1 r. brown 30 20

1987. Rabindranath Tagore (poet) Commem.
1244 **1006** 2 r. multicoloured . . . 40 30

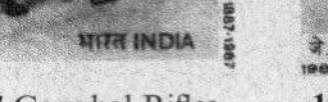

1007 Garwhal Rifles Uniforms of 1887

1008 J. Krishnamurti

1987. Centenary of Garwhal Rifles Regiment.
1245 **1007** 1 r. multicoloured . . . 50 20

1987. J. Krishnamurti (philosopher) Commem.
1246 **1008** 60 p. brown 60 90

1009 Regimental Uniforms of 1887

1987. Centenary of 37th Dogra Regt (now 7th Battalion) (1 Dogra), Mechanised Infantry Regt.
1247 **1009** 1 r. multicoloured . . . 40 20

1010 Hall of Nations, Pragati Maidan, New Delhi

1011 "Sadyah-Snata" Sculpture, Sanghol

1987. "India '89" International Stamp Exhibition, New Delhi (1st issue). Multicoloured.
1248 50 p. Exhibition logo 10 15
1249 5 r. Type **1010** 45 50
See also Nos. 1264/7, 1333/4, 1341/2 and 1358/61.

1987. Festival of India, U.S.S.R.
1251 **1011** 6 r. 50 multicoloured . . 1·00 75

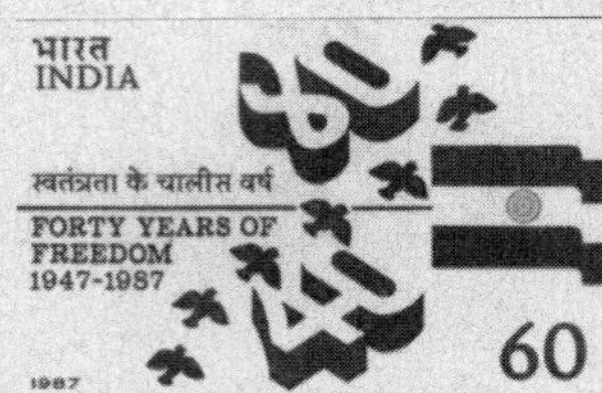

1012 Flag and Stylized Birds with "40" in English and Hindi

1987. 40th Anniv of Independence.
1252 **1012** 60 p. orange, green & bl . 20 20

1013 Sant Harchand Singh Longowal

1014 Guru Ghasidas

1987. Sant Harchand Singh Longowal (Sikh leader) Commemoration.
1253 **1013** 1 r. multicoloured . . . 40 20

1987. Guru Ghasidas (Hindu leader) Commemoration.
1254 **1014** 60 p. red 20 20

1015 Thakur Anukul Chandra

1016 University of Allahabad

1987. Thakur Anukul Chandra (spiritual leader) Commemoration.
1255 **1015** 1 r. multicoloured . . . 40 20

1987. Centenary of Allahabad University.
1256 **1016** 2 r. multicoloured . . . 30 40

1017 Pankha Offering

1018 Chhatrasal on Horseback

1987. Phoolwalon Ki Sair Festival, Delhi.
1257 **1017** 2 r. multicoloured . . . 30 40

1987. Chhatrasal (Bundela ruler) Commemoration.
1258 **1018** 60 p. brown 30 20

1019 Family and Stylized Houses

1987. International Year of Shelter for the Homeless.
1259 **1019** 5 r. multicoloured . . . 45 60

1020 Map of Asia and Logo

1987. Asia Regional Conference of Rotary International.
1260 **1020** 60 p. brown and green . 15 15
1261 – 6 r. 50 multicoloured . . 60 80
DESIGN: 6 r. 50, Oral polio vaccination.

1021 Blind Boy, Braille Books and Computer

1987. Centenary of Service to Blind.
1262 **1021** 1 r. multicoloured . . . 15 15
1263 – 2 r. deep blue & blue . . 35 30
DESIGN: 2 r. Eye donation.

1022 Iron Pillar, Delhi

1987. "India '89" International Stamp Exhibition, New Delhi (2nd issue). Delhi Landmarks. Mult.
1264 60 p. Type **1022** 10 15
1265 1 r. 50 India Gate 15 20
1266 5 r. Dewan-e-Khas, Red Fort . 45 50
1267 6 r. 50 Old Fort 60 65

1023 Tyagmurti Goswami Ganeshdutt **1024** "My Home" (Siddharth Deshprabha)

1987. Tyagmurti Goswami Ganeshdutt (spiritual leader and social reformer) Commemoration.
1269 **1023** 60 p. red 20 20

1987. Children's Day.
1270 **1024** 60 p. multicoloured . . . 30 20

1025 Chinar **1026** Logo (from sculpture "Worker and Woman Peasant" by V. Mukhina)

1987. Indian Trees. Multicoloured.
1271 **1025** 60 p. multicoloured . . . 15 15
1272 – 1 r. 50 multicoloured . . . 20 20
1273 – 5 r. black, green & brown 55 65
1274 – 6 r. 50 brown, red & green 80 80
DESIGNS—HORIZ: 1 r. 50, Pipal; 6 r. 50, Banyan. VERT: 5 r. Sal.

1987. Festival of U.S.S.R., India.
1275 **1026** 5 r. multicoloured . . . 50 50

1027 White Tiger **1028** Execution of Veer Narayan Singh

1987. Wildlife. Multicoloured.
1276 1 r. Type **1027** 50 15
1277 5 r. Snow leopard (horiz) . . . 1·25 85

1987. Veer Narayan Singh (patriot) Commemoration.
1278 **1028** 60 p. brown 20 20

1029 Rameshwari Nehru **1030** Father Kuriakose Elias Chavara

1987. Rameshwari Nehru (women's rights campaigner) Commemoration.
1279 **1029** 60 p. brown 20 20

1987. Father Kuriakose Elias Chavara (founder of Carmelites of Mary Immaculate) Commemoration.
1280 **1030** 60 p. brown 20 20

1031 Dr. Rajah Sir Muthiah Chettiar

1987. Dr. Rajah Sir Muthiah Chettiar (politician) Commemoration.
1281 **1031** 60 p. grey 20 20

1032 Golden Temple, Amritsar **1033** Rukmini Devi and Dancer

1987. 400th Anniv of Golden Temple, Amritsar.
1282 **1032** 60 p. multicoloured . . . 30 20

1987. Rukmini Devi (Bharatanatyam dance pioneer). Commemoration.
1283 **1033** 60 p. red 30 20

1034 Dr. Hiralal **1035** Light Frequency Experiment and Bodhi Tree

1987. Dr. Hiralal (historian) Commemoration.
1284 **1034** 60 p. blue 20 20

1988. 75th Session of Indian Science Congress Association.
1285 **1035** 4 r. multicoloured . . . 50 60

1036 Rural Patient **1037** U Tirot Singh

1988. 13th Asian Pacific Dental Congress.
1286 **1036** 4 r. multicoloured . . . 50 50

1988. India's Struggle for Freedom (6th series). As T **909**.
1287 60 p. black, green and orange 20 40
1288 60 p. brown, green & orange . 20 40
1289 60 p. red, green and orange . . 20 40
1290 60 p. purple, green & orange . 20 40
1291 60 p. purple, green and red . . 20 40
1292 60 p. black, green and orange 20 40
1293 60 p. lilac, green and red . . . 20 40
1294 60 p. deep green, green & red 20 30
1295 60 p. brown, green and green 20 30
1296 60 p. mauve, green & orange . 20 30
DESIGNS: No. 1287, Mohan Lal Sukhadia; 1288, Dr. S. K. Sinha; 1289, Chandra Shekhar Azad; 1290, G. B. Pant; 1291, Dr. Anugrah Narain Singh; 1292, Kuladhor Chaliha; 1293, Shivprasad Gupta; 1294, Sarat Chandra Bose; 1295, Baba Kharak Singh; 1296, Sheikh Mohammad Abdullah.

1988. U Tirot Singh (Khasis leader) Commem.
1297 **1037** 60 p. brown 20 20

1038 Early and Modern Regimental Uniforms **1039** Balgandharva

1988. Bicentenary of 4th Battalion of the Kumaon Regiment.
1298 **1038** 1 r. multicoloured . . . 30 20

1988. Birth Centenary of Balgandharva (actor).
1299 **1039** 60 p. brown 20 20

1040 Soldiers and Infantry Combat Vehicle **1041** B. N. Rau

1988. Presentation of Colours to Mechanised Infantry Regiment.
1300 **1040** 1 r. multicoloured . . . 35 20

1988. B. N. Rau (constitutional lawyer) Commemoration.
1301 **1041** 60 p. black 20 20

1042 Mohindra Government College **1043** Dr. D. V. Gundappa

1988. Mohindra Government College, Patiala.
1302 **1042** 1 r. mauve 20 20

1988. Dr. D. V. Gundappa (scholar) Commem.
1303 **1043** 60 p. grey 20 20

1044 Rani Avantibai **1045** "Malayala Manorama" Office, Kottayam

1988. Rani Avantibai of Ramgarh Commem.
1304 **1044** 60 p. mauve 20 20

1988. Centenary of "Malayala Manorama" (newspaper).
1305 **1045** 1 r. black and blue . . . 20 20

1046 Maharshi Dadhichi **1047** Mohammad Iqbal

1988. Maharshi Dadhichi (Hindu saint) Commemoration.
1306 **1046** 60 p. red 20 20

1988. 50th Death Anniv of Mohammad Iqbal (poet).
1307 **1047** 60 p. gold and red . . . 20 20

1048 Samarth Ramdas **1049** Swati Tirunal Rama Varma

1988. Samarth Ramdas (Hindu spiritual leader) Commemoration.
1308 **1048** 60 p. green 20 20

1988. 175th Birth Anniv of Swati Tirunal Rama Varma (composer).
1309 **1049** 60 p. mauve 20 20

1050 Bhaurao Patil and Class

1988. Bhaurao Patil (educationist) Commem.
1310 **1050** 60 p. brown 20 20

1051 "Rani Lakshmi Bai" (M. F. Husain)

1988. Martyrs from 1st War of Independence.
1311 **1051** 60 p. multicoloured . . . 20 20

1052 Broad Peak

1988. Himalayan Peaks.
1312 **1052** 1 r. 50 lilac, violet and blue 35 30
1313 – 4 r. multicoloured . . . 70 60
1314 – 5 r. multicoloured . . . 80 70
1315 – 6 r. 50 multicoloured . . 95 85
DESIGNS: 4 r. K 2 (Godwin Austen); 5 r. Kanchenjunga; 6 r. 50, Nanda Devi.

1053 Child with Grandparents

1988. "Love and Care for Elders".
1316 **1053** 60 p. multicoloured . . . 20 20

1054 Victoria Terminus, Bombay

1988. Centenary of Victoria Terminus Station, Bombay.
1317 **1054** 1 r. multicoloured . . . 40 20

1055 Lawrence School, Lovedale

1988. 130th Anniv of Lawrence School, Lovedale.
1318 **1055** 1 r. brown and green . . 30 20

1056 Khejri Tree

1988. World Environment Day.
1319 **1056** 60 p. multicoloured . . . 20 15

1988. As No. 732, but new face value.
1320 60 p. black (Gandhi) 55 15

1057 Rani Durgawati **1058** Acharya Shanti Dev

1988. Rani Durgawati (Gondwana ruler) Commemoration.
1322 **1057** 60 p. red 20 20

1988. Acharya Shanti Dev (Buddhist scholar) Commemoration.
1323 **1058** 60 p. brown 20 20

1059 Y. S. Parmar **1061** Durgadas Rathore

1060 Arm pointing at Proclamation in Marathi

1988. Dr. Yashwant Singh Parmar (former Chief Minister of Himachal Pradesh) Commemoration.
1324 **1059** 60 p. violet 20 20

1988. 40th Anniv of Independence. Bal Gangadhar Tilak (patriot) Commemoration. Multicoloured.
1325 60 p. Type **1060** 20 20
1326 60 p. Battle scene 20 20
Nos. 1325/6 were printed together, se-tenant, forming a composite design showing a painting by M. F. Husain.

1988. 150th Birth Anniv of Durgadas Rathore (Regent of Marwar).
1327 **1061** 60 p. brown 20 20

1062 Gopinath Kaviraj **1063** Lotus and Outline Map of India

1988. Gopinath Kaviraj (scholar) Commem.
1328 **1062** 60 p. brown 20 20

1988. Hindi Day.
1329 **1063** 60 p. red, green & brown 20 20

1064 Indian Olympic Association Logo **1065** Jerdon's Courser

1988. "Sports–1988" and Olympic Games, Seoul.
1330 **1064** 60 p. purple 35 15
1331 – 5 r. multicoloured . . . 2·25 75
DESIGN—HORIZ: 5 r. Various sports.

1988. Wildlife Conservation. Jerdon's Courser.
1332 **1065** 1 r. multicoloured . . . 1·00 30

1988. "India '89" International Stamp Exhibition, New Delhi (3rd issue). General Post Offices. As T **1022**. Multicoloured.
1333 4 r. Bangalore G.P.O. 40 35
1334 5 r. Bombay G.P.O. 50 45

1066 "Times of India" Front Page

1988. 150th Anniv of "The Times of India".
1335 **1066** 1 r. 50 black, gold & yell 20 20

1067 "Maulana Abul Kalam Azad" (K. Hebbar)

1988. Birth Centenary of Maulana Abul Kalam Azad (politician).
1336 **1067** 60 p. multicoloured . . . 20 20

1068 Nehru

1988. Birth Centenary (1989) of Jawaharlal Nehru (1st issue).
1337 **1068** 60 p. black, orange and green 30 15
1338 – 1 r. multicoloured . . . 35 15
DESIGN—VERT: 1 r. "Jawaharlal Nehru" (Svetoslav Roerich).
See also No. 1393.

1069 Birsa Munda

1988. Birsa Munda (Munda leader) Commem.
1339 **1069** 60 p. brown 20 20

1070 Bhakra Dam

1988. 25th Anniv of Dedication of Bhakra Dam.
1340 **1070** 60 p. red 35 60

1071 Dead Letter Office Cancellations of 1886

1988. "India '89" International Stamp Exhibition, New Delhi (4th series). Postal Cancellations.
1341 **1071** 60 p. brown, blk & red . 25 15
1342 – 6 r. 50 brown and black 1·00 1·00
DESIGN: 6 r. 50, Allahabad–Cawnpore travelling post office handstamp of 1864.

1072 K. M. Munshi

1988. Birth Centenary (1987) of K. M. Munshi (author and politician).
1343 **1072** 60 p. green 20 20

1073 Mannathu Padmanabhan **1074** Lok Sabha Secretariat

1989. Mannathu Padmanabhan (social reformer) Commemoration.
1344 **1073** 60 p. brown 20 20

1989. India's Struggle for Freedom (7th series). As T **909**.
1345 60 p. black, green & orange . 20 30
1346 60 p. orange, green & lilac . . 20 50
1347 60 p. black, green & orange . 20 50
1348 60 p. brown, green & orange . 20 50
1349 60 p. brown, green & orange . 20 30
DESIGNS: No. 1345, Hare Krishna Mahtab; 1346, Balasaheb Gangadhar Kher; 1347, Raj Kumari Amrit Kaur; 1348, Saifuddin Kitchlew; 1349, Asaf Ali.

1989. 60th Anniv of Lok Sabha Secretariat (formerly Legislative Assembly Department).
1355 **1074** 60 p. green 20 20

1075 Goddess Durga seated on Lion (5th-cent terracotta plaque) **1076** Baldev Ramji Mirdha

1989. 125th Anniv of Lucknow Museum.
1356 **1075** 60 p. deep blue and blue 20 20

1989. Birth Centenary of Baldev Ramji Mirdha (nationalist).
1357 **1076** 60 p. green 20 20

1077 Girl with Stamp Collection

1989. "India'89" International Stamp Exhibition, New Delhi (5th issue). Philately.
1358 **1077** 60 p. yellow, red & blue 15 10
1359 – 1 r. 50 grey, yellow and black 20 15
1360 – 5 r. red and blue 60 50
1361 – 6 r. 50 black, brown & bl 70 60
DESIGNS: 1 r. 50, Dawk gharry, c. 1842; 5 r. Travancore 1888 2 ch. conch shell stamp; 6 r. 50, Early Indian philatelic magazines.

1078 St. John Bosco and Boy **1079** Modern Tank and 19th-century Sowar

1989. St. John Bosco (founder of Salesian Brothers) Commemoration.
1362 **1078** 60 p. red 20 20

1989. 3rd Cavalry Regiment.
1363 **1079** 60 p. multicoloured . . . 30 20

1080 Dargah Sharif, Ajmer

1989. Dargah Sharif (Sufi shrine), Ajmer.
1364 **1080** 1 r. multicoloured . . . 20 20

1081 Task Force and Indian Naval Ensign

1989. President's Review of the Fleet.
1365 **1081** 6 r. 50 multicoloured . . 1·25 1·00

1082 Shaheed Laxman Nayak and Barbed Wire Fence

1989. Shaheed Laxman Nayak Commemoration.
1366 **1082** 60 p. brown, grn & orge 20 20

1083 Rao Gopal Singh **1085** Bishnu Ram Medhi

1084 Sydenham College

1989. Rao Gopal Singh Commemoration.
1367 **1083** 60 p. brown 20 20

1989. 75th Anniv (1988) of Sydenham College, Bombay.
1368 **1084** 60 p. black 30 20

1989. Birth Centenary (1988) of Bishnu Ram Medhi (politician).
1369 **1085** 60 p. grn, dp grn & red . 30 20

1086 Dr. N. S. Hardikar **1087** "Advaita" in Devanagari Script

1989. Birth Centenary of Dr. Narayana Subbarao Hardikar (nationalist).
1370 **1086** 60 p. brown 20 20

1989. Sankaracharya (philosopher) Commem.
1371 **1087** 60 p. multicoloured . . . 20 20

1088 Gandhi Bhavan, Punjab University

1988. Punjab University, Chandigarh.
1372 **1088** 1 r. brown and blue . . . 20 20

1089 Scene from Film "Raja Harischandra" **1090** Cactus and Cogwheels

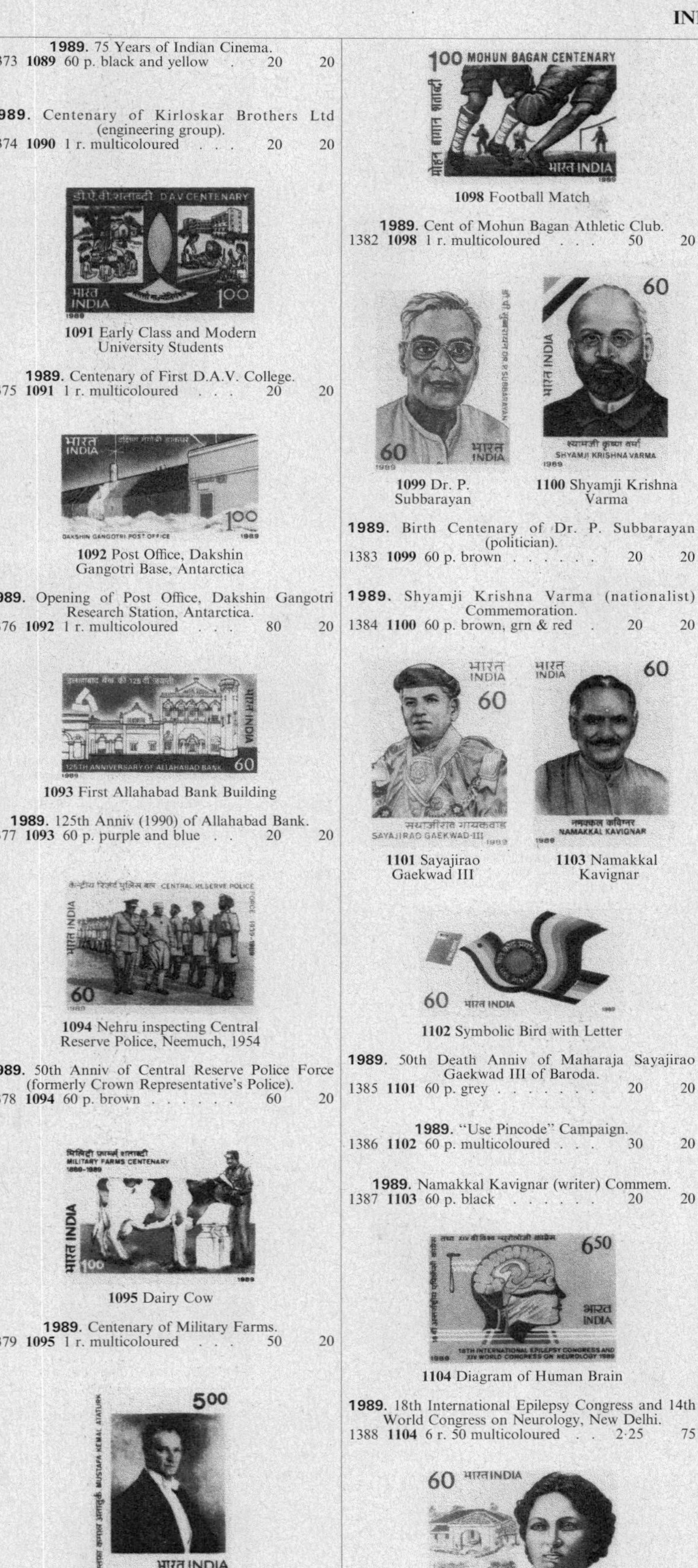

1989. 75 Years of Indian Cinema.
1373 **1089** 60 p. black and yellow . 20 20

1989. Centenary of Kirloskar Brothers Ltd (engineering group).
1374 **1090** 1 r. multicoloured . . . 20 20

1091 Early Class and Modern University Students

1989. Centenary of First D.A.V. College.
1375 **1091** 1 r. multicoloured . . . 20 20

1092 Post Office, Dakshin Gangotri Base, Antarctica

1989. Opening of Post Office, Dakshin Gangotri Research Station, Antarctica.
1376 **1092** 1 r. multicoloured . . . 80 20

1093 First Allahabad Bank Building

1989. 125th Anniv (1990) of Allahabad Bank.
1377 **1093** 60 p. purple and blue . . 20 20

1094 Nehru inspecting Central Reserve Police, Neemuch, 1954

1989. 50th Anniv of Central Reserve Police Force (formerly Crown Representative's Police).
1378 **1094** 60 p. brown 60 20

1095 Dairy Cow

1989. Centenary of Military Farms.
1379 **1095** 1 r. multicoloured . . . 50 20

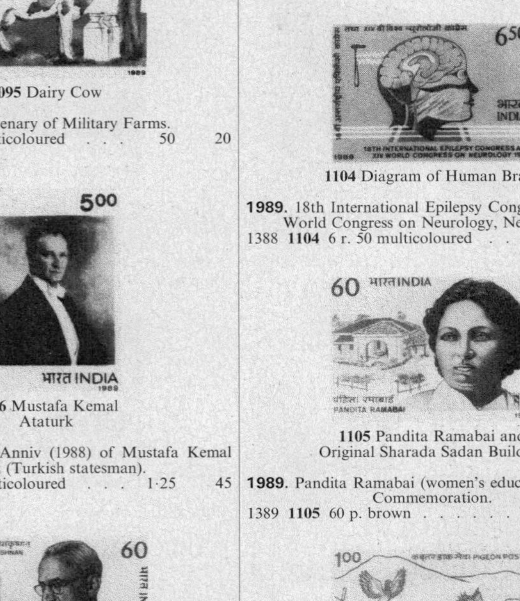

1096 Mustafa Kemal Ataturk

1989. 50th Death Anniv (1988) of Mustafa Kemal Ataturk (Turkish statesman).
1380 **1096** 5 r. multicoloured . . . 1·25 45

1097 Dr. S. Radhakrishnan

1989. Birth Centenary (1988) of Dr. Sarvepalli Radhakrishnan (former President).
1381 **1097** 60 p. black 20 20

1098 Football Match

1989. Cent of Mohun Bagan Athletic Club.
1382 **1098** 1 r. multicoloured . . . 50 20

1099 Dr. P. Subbarayan

1100 Shyamji Krishna Varma

1989. Birth Centenary of Dr. P. Subbarayan (politician).
1383 **1099** 60 p. brown 20 20

1989. Shyamji Krishna Varma (nationalist) Commemoration.
1384 **1100** 60 p. brown, grn & red . 20 20

1101 Sayajirao Gaekwad III

1103 Namakkal Kavignar

1102 Symbolic Bird with Letter

1989. 50th Death Anniv of Maharaja Sayajirao Gaekwad III of Baroda.
1385 **1101** 60 p. grey 20 20

1989. "Use Pincode" Campaign.
1386 **1102** 60 p. multicoloured . . . 30 20

1989. Namakkal Kavignar (writer) Commem.
1387 **1103** 60 p. black 20 20

1104 Diagram of Human Brain

1989. 18th International Epilepsy Congress and 14th World Congress on Neurology, New Delhi.
1388 **1104** 6 r. 50 multicoloured . . 2·25 75

1105 Pandita Ramabai and Original Sharada Sadan Building

1989. Pandita Ramabai (women's education pioneer) Commemoration.
1389 **1105** 60 p. brown 30 20

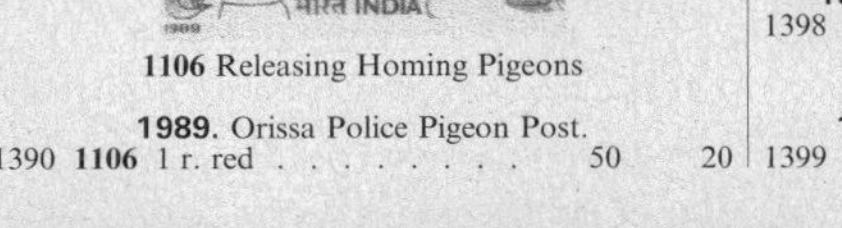

1106 Releasing Homing Pigeons

1989. Orissa Police Pigeon Post.
1390 **1106** 1 r. red 50 20

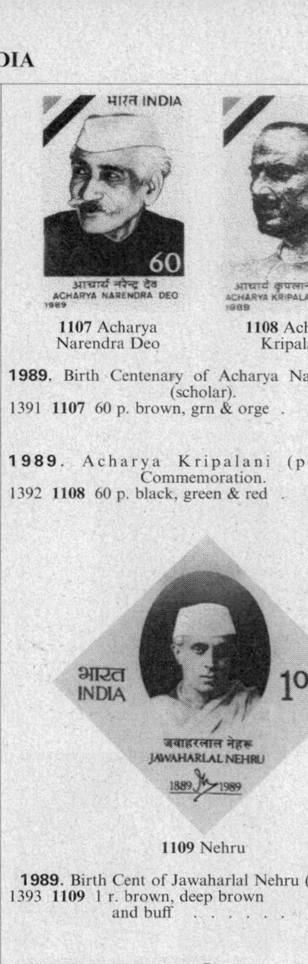

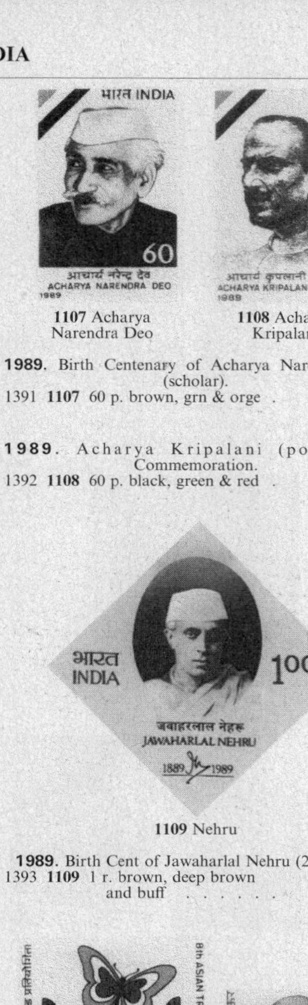

1107 Acharya Narendra Deo

1108 Acharya Kripalani

1989. Birth Centenary of Acharya Narendra Deo (scholar).
1391 **1107** 60 p. brown, grn & orge . 20 20

1989. Acharya Kripalani (politician) Commemoration.
1392 **1108** 60 p. black, green & red . 20 20

1109 Nehru

1989. Birth Cent of Jawaharlal Nehru (2nd issue).
1393 **1109** 1 r. brown, deep brown and buff 65 20

1110 Meeting Logo

1111 Sir Gurunath Bewoor

1989. 8th Asian Track and Field Meeting, New Delhi.
1394 **1110** 1 r. black, orange & grn . 30 20

1989. Sir Gurunath Bewoor (former Director-General, Posts and Telegraphs) Commemoration.
1395 **1111** 60 p. brown 20 20

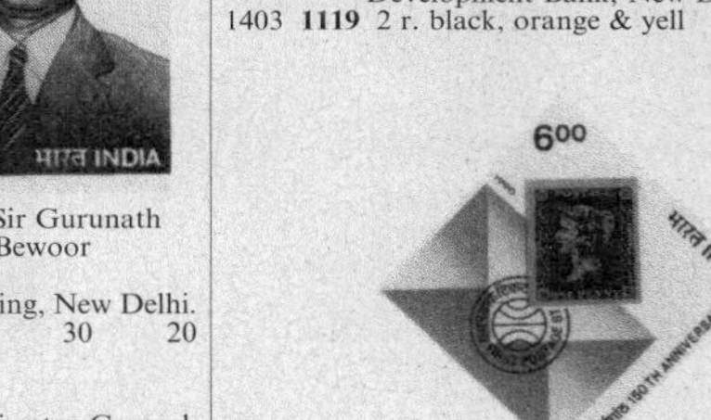

1112 Balkrishna Sharma Navin

1113 Abstract Painting of Houses

1989. Balkrishna Sharma Navin (politician and poet) Commemoration.
1396 **1112** 60 p. black 20 20

1989. Cent of Bombay Art Society (1988).
1397 **1113** 1 r. multicoloured . . . 20 20

1114 Lesser Florican

1115 Centenary Logo

1989. Wildlife Conservation. Lesser Florican.
1398 **1114** 2 r. multicoloured . . . 1·50 55

1989. Centenary of Indian Oil Production.
1399 **1115** 60 p. brown 30 20

1116 Dr. M. G. Ramachandran

1117 Volunteers working at Sukhna Lake, Chandigarh

1990. Dr. M. G. Ramachandran (former Chief Minister of Tamil Nadu) Commemoration.
1400 **1116** 60 p. brown 40 20

1990. Save Sukhna Lake Campaign.
1401 **1117** 1 r. multicoloured . . . 20 20

1118 Gallantry Medals

1990. Presentation of New Colours to Bombay Sappers.
1402 **1118** 60 p. multicoloured . . . 80 1·00

1119 Indian Chank Shell and Logo

1990. 23rd Annual General Meeting of Asian Development Bank, New Delhi.
1403 **1119** 2 r. black, orange & yell 75 30

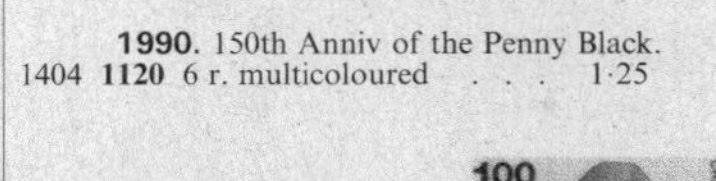

1120 Penny Black and Envelope

1990. 150th Anniv of the Penny Black.
1404 **1120** 6 r. multicoloured . . . 1·25 40

1121 Ho Chi-Minh and Vietnamese House

1122 Chaudhary Charan Singh

1990. Birth Centenary of Ho Chi-Minh (Vietnamese leader).
1405 **1121** 2 r. brown and green . . 30 30

1990. 3rd Death Anniv of Chaudhary Charan Singh (former Prime Minister).
1406 **1122** 1 r. brown 20 20

1123 Armed Forces' Badge and Map of Sri Lanka

1124 Wheat

1990. Indian Peace-keeping Operations in Sri Lanka.
1407 **1123** 2 r. multicoloured . . . 30 30

1990. 60th Anniv of Indian Council of Agricultural Research (1989).
1408 **1124** 2 r. black, grn & dp grn . 30 30

1125 Khudiram Bose **1127** K. Kelappan

1126 "Life in India" (Tanya Vorontsova)

1990. Khudiram Bose (patriot) Commemoration.
1409 **1125** 1 r. orange, green & red 20 20

1990 Indo–Soviet Friendship. Children's Paintings. Multicoloured.
1410 1 r. Type **1126** . . . . 1·50 2·00
1411 6 r. 50 "St. Basil's Cathedral and Kremlin, Moscow" (Sanjay Adhikari) . . . . 1·50 2·00

Stamps in similar designs were also issued by U.S.S.R.

1990. K. Kelappan (social reformer) Commem.
1412 **1127** 1 r. brown 20 20

1128 Girl in Garden **1129** Hand guiding Child's Writing

1990. Year of the Girl Child.
1413 **1128** 1 r. multicoloured . . . 50 30

1990. International Literacy Year.
1414 **1129** 1 r. multicoloured . . . 50 30

1130 Woman using Water Pump **1131** Sunder Lal Sharma

1990. Safe Drinking Water Campaign.
1415 **1130** 4 r. black, red & green . 1·25 1·75

1990. 50th Death Anniv of Sunder Lal Sharma (patriot).
1416 **1131** 60 p. red 50 50

1132 Kabbadi **1133** A. K. Gopalan

1990. 11th Asian Games, Peking. Mult.
1417 1 r. Type **1132** 40 20
1418 4 r. Athletics . . . . 1·50 2·00
1419 4 r. Cycling . . . . 1·50 2·00
1420 6 r. 50 Archery . . . . 1·75 2·50

1990. Ayillyath Kuttiari Gopalan (social reformer) Commemoration.
1421 **1133** 1 r. brown 50 30

1134 Gurkha Soldier **1135** Suryamall Mishran

1990. 50th Anniv of 3rd and 5th Battalions, 5th Gurkha Rifles.
1422 **1134** 2 r. black and brown . . 1·40 1·60

1990. 75th Birth Anniv of Suryamall Mishran (poet).
1423 **1135** 2 r. brown and orange . 50 65

1136 "Doll and Cat" (Subhash Kumar Nagarajan)

1990. Children's Day.
1424 **1136** 1 r. multicoloured . . . 60 30

1137 Security Post and Border Guard on Camel **1138** Hearts and Flowers

1990. 25th Anniv of Border Security Force.
1425 **1137** 5 r. blue, brown & black 1·50 1·75

1990. Greetings Stamps. Multicoloured.
1426 1 r. Type **1138** 20 15
1427 4 r. Ceremonial elephants (horiz) 50 65

1139 Bikaner

1990. Cities of India. Multicoloured.
1428 4 r. Type **1139** 55 60
1429 5 r. Hyderabad 65 75
1430 6 r. 50 Cuttack . . . . 90 1·25

1140 Bhakta Kanakadas and Udipi Temple **1141** Shaheed Minar Monument

1990. Bhakta Kanakadas (mystic and poet) Commemoration.
1431 **1140** 1 r. red 55 30

1990. 300th Anniv of Calcutta.
1432 **1141** 1 r. multicoloured . . . 30 20
1433 – 6 r. black, brown & red 1·25 1·50

DESIGN—HORIZ (44 × 36 mm): 6 r. 18th-century shipping on the Ganges.

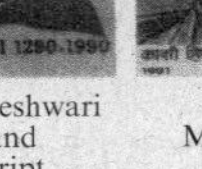

1142 Dnyaneshwari (poet) and Manuscript **1143** Madan Mohan Malaviya (founder) and University

1990. 700th Anniv of Dnyaneshwari (spiritual epic).
1434 **1142** 2 r. multicoloured . . . 30 50

1991. 75th Anniv of Banaras Hindu University.
1435 **1143** 1 r. red 30 20

1991. As No. 732 but new face value.
1436 1 r. brown (Gandhi) 10 10

1144 Road Users **1145** Exhibition Emblem

1991. International Traffic Safety Conference, New Delhi.
1437 **1144** 6 r. 50 black, blue & red 75 1·00

1991. 7th Triennale Art Exhibition, New Delhi.
1438 **1145** 6 r. 50 multicoloured . . 60 75

1146 Jagannath Sunkersett and Central Railways Headquarters **1147** Tata Memorial Centre

1991. 125th Death Anniv (1990) of Jagannath Sunkersett (educationist and railway pioneer).
1439 **1146** 2 r. blue and red 50 60

1991. 50th Anniv of Tata Memorial Medical Centre.
1440 **1147** 2 r. brown and stone . . 30 40

1148 River Dolphin

1991. Endangered Marine Mammals.
1441 **1148** 4 r. brown, blue & green 1·50 1·50
1442 – 6 r. 50 multicoloured . . 2·00 2·00

DESIGN: 6 r. 50, Sea cow.

1149 Drugs **1150** Hand, Bomb Explosion and Dove

1991. International Conference on Drug Abuse, Calcutta.
1443 **1149** 5 r. violet and red . . . 1·60 1·60

1991. World Peace.
1444 **1150** 6 r. 50 blk, lt brn & brn . 75 1·00

1151 Remote Sensing Satellite "IA" **1152** Babu Jagjivan Ram

1991. Launch of Indian Remote Sensing Satellite "IA".
1445 **1151** 6 r. 50 brown and blue 60 85

1991. Babu Jagjivan Ram (politician) Commemoration.
1446 **1152** 1 r. brown 20 20

1153 Dr. B. R. Ambedkar and Demonstration

1991. Birth Centenary of Dr. Bhimrao Ramji Ambedkar (social reformer).
1447 **1153** 1 r. brown and blue . . . 30 20

1154 Valar Dance

1991. Tribal Dances. Multicoloured.
1448 2 r. 50 Type **1154** 50 40
1449 4 r. Kayang 70 80
1450 5 r. Hozagiri 80 90
1451 6 r. 50 Velakali . . . . 1·00 1·40

1155 Ariyakudi Ramanuja Iyengar and Temples **1156** Karpoori Thakur

1991. Ariyakudi Ramanuja Iyengar (singer and composer) Commemoration.
1452 **1155** 2 r. brown and green . . 50 65

1991. Jan Nayak Karpoori Thakur (politician and social reformer) Commemoration.
1453 **1156** 1 r. brown 20 20

1157 Emperor Penguins

1991. 30th Anniv of Antarctic Treaty. Mult.
1454 5 r. Type **1157** . . . . 1·75 2·00
1455 6 r. 50 Antarctic map and pair of Adelie penguins . . . . . 1·75 2·00

Nos. 1454/5 were printed together, se-tenant, forming a composite design.

1158 Rashtrapati Bhavan Building, New Delhi

1991. 60th Anniv of New Delhi. Multicoloured.
1456 5 r. Type **1158** . . . . 1·00 1·40
1457 6 r. 50 New Delhi monuments 1·00 1·40

Nos. 1456/7 were printed together, se-tenant, forming a composite design.

1159 Sri Ram Sharma Acharya

1991. Sri Ram Sharma Acharya (social reformer) Commemoration.
1458 **1159** 1 r. green and red . . . 20 20

1160 "Shankar awarded Padma Vibhushan" (cartoon)

1991. Keshav Shankar Pillai (cartoonist) Commemoration.
1459 **1160** 4 r. brown . . . . . . 1·00 1·40
1460 – 6 r. 50 lilac . . . . . . 1·40 1·75
DESIGN—VERT: 6 r. 50, "The Big Show".

1161 Sriprakash and Kashi Vidyapith University

1162 Gopinath Bardoloi

1991. 20th Death Anniv of Sriprakash (politician).
1461 **1161** 2 r. brown & light brown 30 30

1991. Birth Centenary (1990) of Gopinath Bardoloi (Assamese politician).
1462 **1162** 1 r. lilac 20 20

1163 Rajiv Gandhi

1991. Rajiv Gandhi (Congress Party leader) Commemoration.
1463 **1163** 1 r. multicoloured . . . 40 40

1164 Muni Mishrimalji and Memorial

1991. Birth Centenary of Muni Mishrimalji (Jain religious leader).
1464 **1164** 1 r. brown 30 20

1165 Mahadevi Verma (poetess) and "Varsha"

1991. Hindu Writers.
1465 **1165** 2 r. black and blue . . . 15 25
1466 – 2 r. black and blue . . . 15 25
DESIGN: No. 1466, Jayshankar Prasad (poet and dramatist) and scene from "Kamayani".

1166 Parliament House and C.P.A. Emblem

1991. 37th Commonwealth Parliamentary Association Conference, New Delhi.
1467 **1166** 6 r. 50 blue and brown . 40 60

1167 Frog

1168 "Cymbidium aloifolium"

1991. Greetings Stamps.
1468 **1167** 1 r. green and red . . . 20 40
1469 – 6 r. 50 red and green . . 35 55
DESIGN: 6 r. 50, Symbolic bird carrying flower.

1991. Orchids. Multicoloured.
1470 1 r. Type **1168** 30 15
1471 2 r. 50 "Paphiopedilum venustum" 35 35
1472 3 r. "Aerides crispum" 40 50
1473 4 r. "Cymbidium bicolour" . . 50 65
1474 5 r. "Vanda spathulata" . . . 55 70
1475 6 r. 50 "Cymbidium devonianum" . . . . . . 70 1·00

1169 Gurkha Soldier in Battle Dress

1170 Couple on Horse (embroidery)

1991. 90th Anniv of 2nd Battalion, Third Gurkha Rifles.
1476 **1169** 4 r. multicoloured . . . 1·50 1·50

1991. 3rd Death Anniv of Kamaladevi Chattopadhyaya (founder of All India Handicrafts Board).
1477 **1170** 1 r. lake, red & yellow . . 40 20
1478 – 6 r. 50 multicoloured . . 1·50 1·75
DESIGN: 6 r. 50, Traditional puppet.

1171 Chithira Tirunal and Temple Sculpture

1172 "Children in Traditional Costume" (Arpi Snehalbhai Shah)

1991. Chithira Tirunal Bala Rama Varma (former Maharaja of Travancore) Commemoration.
1479 **1171** 2 r. violet 65 75

1991. Children's Day.
1480 **1172** 1 r. multicoloured . . . 70 30

1173 Mounted Sowar and Tanks

1991. 70th Anniv (1992) of the 18th Cavalry Regiment.
1481 **1173** 6 r. 50 multicoloured . . 2·00 2·50

1174 Kites

1175 Sports on Bricks

1991. India Tourism Year.
1482 **1174** 6 r. 50 multicoloured . . 60 1·00

1991. International Conference on Youth Tourism, New Delhi.
1483 **1175** 6 r. 50 multicoloured . . 1·10 1·50

1176 "Mozart at Piano" (unfinished painting, J. Lange)

1177 Homeless Family

1991. Death Bicentenary of Mozart.
1484 **1176** 6 r. 50 multicoloured . . 1·50 2·00

1991. South Asian Association for Regional Co-operation Year of Shelter.
1485 **1177** 4 r. brown and ochre . . 55 70

1178 People running on Heart

1179 "Sidhartha with an Injured Bird" (Asit Kumar Haldar)

1991. "Run for Your Heart" Marathon, New Delhi.
1486 **1178** 1 r. black, grey and red . 20 20

1991. Birth Centenary (1990) of Asit Kumar Haldar (artist).
1487 **1179** 2 r. yellow, red and black 30 50

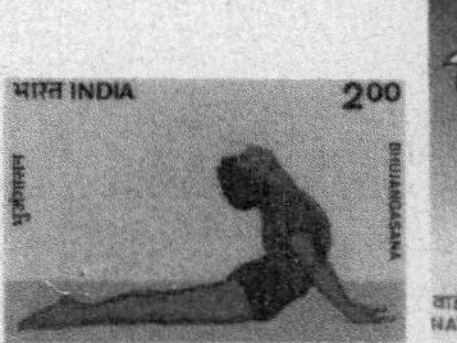

1180 Bhujangasana

1181 Y.M.C.A. Logo

1991. Yoga Exercises. Multicoloured.
1488 2 r. Type **1180** 20 25
1489 5 r. Dhanurasana 40 55
1490 6 r. 50 Ustrasana 50 70
1491 10 r. Utthita trikonasana . . . 85 1·25

1992. Centenary (1991) of National Council of Young Men's Christian Association.
1492 **1181** 1 r. red and blue 20 20

1182 Madurai Temple Tower and Hooghly River Bridge

1183 Goat Seal from Harappa Culture, 2500 to 1500 B.C.

1992. 14th Congress of International Association for Bridge and Structural Engineering, New Delhi.
1493 **1182** 2 r. brown, red and blue 45 65
1494 – 2 r. brown, red and blue 45 65
DESIGN: No. 1494, Gate, Sanchi Stupa and Hall of Nations, New Delhi.

1992. 5th International Goat Conference, New Delhi.
1495 **1183** 6 r. blue and brown . . . 1·75 2·25

1184 Early 19th-century Letter with Mail Pouch and National Archives Building, New Delhi

1185 Krushna Chandra Gajapathi

1992. Centenary (1991) of National Archives.
1496 **1184** 6 r. multicoloured . . . 50 65

1992. Krushna Chandra Gajapathi (former Chief Minister of Orissa) Commemoration.
1497 **1185** 1 r. lilac 15 15

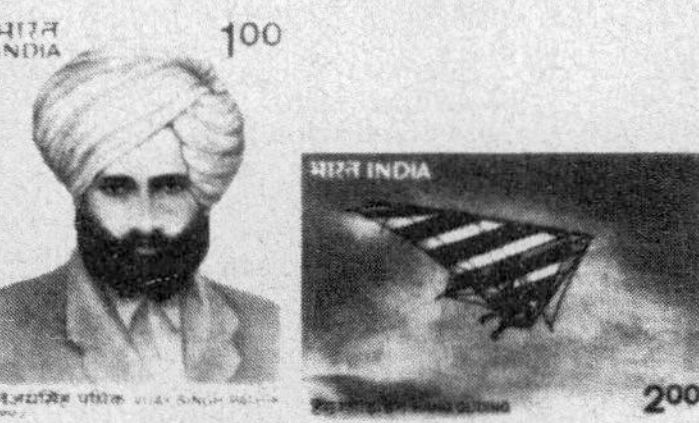

1186 Vijay Singh Pathik

1187 Hang-gliding

1992. Vijay Singh Pathik (writer) Commem.
1498 **1186** 1 r. brown 15 15

1992. Adventure Sports. Multicoloured.
1499 2 r. Type **1187** 25 20
1500 4 r. Windsurfing 50 60
1501 5 r. River rafting 60 70
1502 11 r. Skiing . . . . 1·25 2·00

1188 Henry Gidney and Anglo-Indians

1992. 50th Death Anniv of Sir Henry Gidney (ophthalmologist).
1503 **1188** 1 r. black and blue . . . 30 15

1189 Telecommunications Training Centre, Jabalpur

1190 Sardar Udham Singh

1992. 50th Anniv of Telecommunications Training Centre, Jabalpur.
1504 **1189** 1 r. bistre 20 15

1992. Sardar Udham Singh (patriot) Commemoration.
1505 **1190** 1 r. black and brown . . 20 15

1191 Men's Discus

1192 Spinning Wheel Emblem

1992. Olympic Games, Barcelona. Mult.
1506 1 r. Type **1191** 30 10
1507 6 r. Women's gymnastics . . . 90 1·00
1508 8 r. Men's hockey . . . . . 2·00 2·25
1509 11 r. Boxing . . . . 2·00 2·25

1992. 50th Anniv of "Quit India" Movement.
1510 **1192** 1 r. black and pink . . . 75 30
1511 – 2 r. black, brown & grey 1·50 1·75
DESIGN: 2 r. Mahatma Gandhi and mantra.

1193 Treating Casualty

1992. 50th Anniv of 60th Parachute Field Ambulance.
1512 **1193** 1 r. multicoloured . . . 1·25 40

1194 Dr. S. R. Ranganathan and Madras University

1992. Birth Centenary of Shiyali Ramamrita Ranganathan (librarian).
1513 **1194** 1 r. blue 65 30

1195 "Dev Narayan"

1196 Hanuman Prasad Poddar

1992. Phad Scroll Paintings from Rajasthan.
1514 **1195** 5 r. multicoloured . . . 55 70

1992. Hanuman Prasad Poddar (editor) Commemoration.
1515 **1196** 1 r. green 15 15

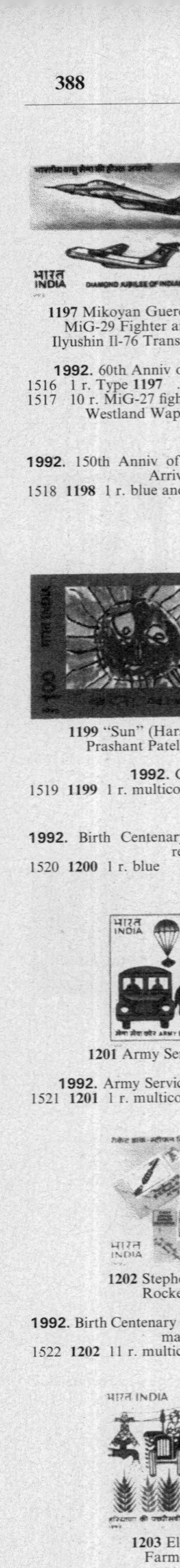

1197 Mikoyan Guerevich MiG-29 Fighter and Ilyushin Il-76 Transport

1198 Lighting Candle

1992. 60th Anniv of Indian Air Force. Mult.
1516 1 r. Type **1197** 60 75
1517 10 r. MiG-27 fighter and Westland Wapiti biplane . . 1·00 1·25

1992. 150th Anniv of Sisters of Jesus and Mary's Arrival in India.
1518 **1198** 1 r. blue and grey . . . 15 15

1199 "Sun" (Harshit Prashant Patel)

1200 Yogiji Maharaj

1992. Children's Day.
1519 **1199** 1 r. multicoloured . . . 20 15

1992. Birth Centenary of Yogiji Maharaj (Hindu reformer).
1520 **1200** 1 r. blue 40 15

1201 Army Service Corps Transport

1992. Army Service Corps Commemoration.
1521 **1201** 1 r. multicoloured . . . 1·25 40

1202 Stephen Smith and Early Rocket Post Covers

1992. Birth Centenary (1991) of Stephen Smith (rocket mail pioneer).
1522 **1202** 11 r. multicoloured . . . 90 1·25

1203 Electricity Pylons, Farmers and Crops

1992. 25th Anniv of Haryana State.
1523 **1203** 2 r. red, dp green & grn 15 15

1204 Madanlal Dhingra

1205 Osprey

1992. Madanlal Dhingra (revolutionary) Commemoration.
1524 **1204** 1 r. brown, red & grn . . 30 15

1992. Birds of Prey. Multicoloured.
1525 2 r. Type **1205** 90 60
1526 6 r. Peregrine falcon . . . . . 1·25 1·10
1527 8 r. Lammergeier . . . . . . 1·40 1·75
1528 11 r. Golden eagle . . . . . 1·60 2·00

1206 Pandit Ravishankar Shukla

1208 Fakirmohan Senapati

1207 William Carey

1992. Pandit Ravishankar Shukla (social reformer) Commemoration.
1529 **1206** 1 r. purple 15 15

1993. Bicent of William Carey's Appointment as Baptist Missionary to India.
1530 **1207** 6 r. multicoloured . . . 1·00 1·00

1993. Fakirmohan Senapati Commemoration.
1531 **1208** 1 r. red 40 15

1209 Workers and C.S.I.R emblem

1993. 50th Anniv of Council of Scientific and Industrial Research.
1532 **1209** 1 r. purple 40 15

1210 Parachute Drop and Field Gun

1993. 50th Anniv of 9th Parachute Field Artillery Regiment.
1533 **1210** 1 r. multicoloured . . . 1·25 30

1211 Westland Wapiti Biplane

1993. 60th Anniv of No. 1 Squadron, Indian Air Force.
1534 **1211** 1 r. multicoloured . . . 1·25 30

1212 Rahul Sankrityayan

1993. Birth Centenary of Rahul Sankrityayan (politician).
1535 **1212** 1 r. black, cinnamon and brown 20 15

1213 Parliament Building and Emblem

1993. 89th Inter-Parliamentary Union Conference, New Delhi.
1536 **1213** 1 r. black 20 15

1214 Neral Matheran Railway Tank Locomotive, 1905

1993. Mountain Locomotives. Multicoloured.
1537 1 r. Type **1214** 60 20
1538 6 r. Darjeeling and Himalayan Railway, 1889 . . . . . . 1·25 1·25
1539 8 r. Nilgiri Mountain Railway, 1914 . . . . 1·40 1·60
1540 11 r. Kalka–Simla Railway, 1934 . . . . 1·90 2·25

1215 Students and College Building

1993. Centenary of Meerut College.
1541 **1215** 1 r. black and brown . . 20 15

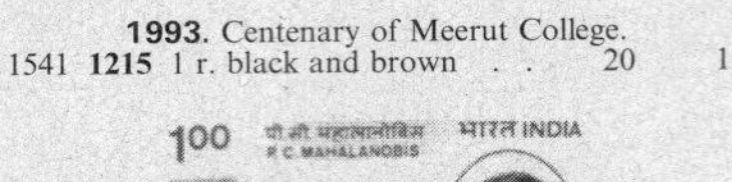

1216 Mahalanobis and Office Block

1993. Prasanta Chandra Mahalanobis Commemoration.
1542 **1216** 1 r. brown 20 15

1217 Bombay Town Hall

1993. Centenary of Bombay Municipal Corporation.
1543 **1217** 2 r. multicoloured . . . 20 30

1218 Abdul Ghaffar Khan and Mountainside

1993. Abdul Ghaffar Khan Commemoration.
1544 **1218** 1 r. multicoloured . . . 15 15

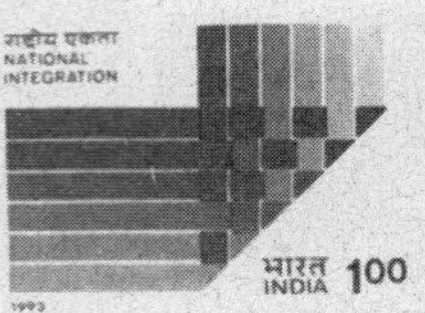

1219 National Integration Emblem

1993. National Integration Campaign.
1545 **1219** 1 r. orange and green . . 15 15

1220 Dadabhai Naoroji and Houses of Parliament, London

1221 Swami Vivekananda and Art Institute, Chicago

1993. Centenary of Dadabhai Naoroji's Election to the House of Commons.
1546 **1220** 6 r. multicoloured . . . 45 60

1993. Centenary of Swami Vivekananda's Chicago Address.
1547 **1221** 2 r. orange and grey . . 40 40

1222 "Lagerstroemia speciosa"

1223 College Building and Emblem

1993. Flowering Trees.
1548 **1222** 1 r. red, green & brn . . 20 15
1549 – 6 r. multicoloured . . . 40 55
1550 – 8 r. multicoloured . . . 55 70
1551 – 11 r. multicoloured . . . 75 1·00
DESIGNS: 6 r. "Cochlospermum religiosum"; 8 r. "Erythrina variegata"; 11 r. "Thespesia populnea".

1993. 50th Anniv of College of Military Engineering, Pune.
1552 **1223** 2 r. multicoloured . . . 20 30

1224 Dr. Dwaram Venkataswamy Naidu playing Violin

1225 Children on Elephant

1993. Birth Centenary of Dwaram Venkataswamy Naidu (violinist).
1553 **1224** 1 r. red 20 20

1993. Children's Day.
1554 **1225** 1 r. multicoloured . . . 20 20

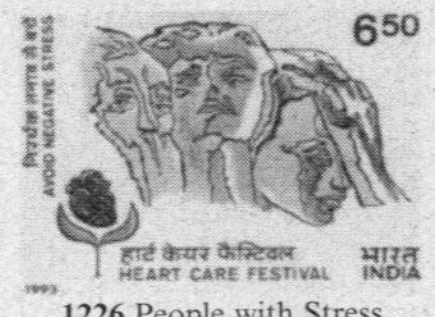

1226 People with Stress

1993. Heart Care Festival.
1555 **1226** 6 r. 50 multicoloured . . 60 70

1227 Dr. Kotnis performing Operation

1993. Dr. Dwarkanath Kotnis (surgeon) Commemoration.
1556 **1227** 1 r. black 20 20

1228 Tea Symbol

1993. Indian Tea Production.
1557 **1228** 6 r. green and red . . . 50 65

1229 Papal Seminary Arms and Building

1993. Centenary of Papal Seminary, Pune.
1558 **1229** 6 r. multicoloured . . . 50 65

1230 Meghnad Saha and Eclipse of the Sun

1993. Meghnad Saha (astronomer) Commem.
1559 **1230** 1 r. blue 30 20

1231 Speedpost Letter and Arrows circling Globe

1993. Inpex '93 National Stamp Exn, Calcutta. Multicoloured.
1560 1 r. Type **1231** 20 15
1561 2 r. "Custom-house Wharf, Calcutta" (Sir Charles D'Oyly) 35 45

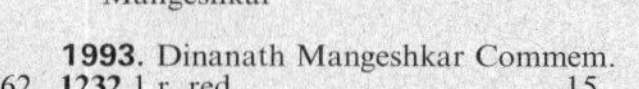

1232 Dinanath Mangeshkar **1233** Nargis Dutt

1993. Dinanath Mangeshkar Commem.
1562 **1232** 1 r. red 15 15

1993. Nargis Dutt Commemoration.
1563 **1233** 1 r. red 15 15

1234 S. C. Bose inspecting Troops

1993. 50th Anniv of Indian National Army.
1564 **1234** 1 r. grn, dp grn & red . . 30 20

1235 Satyendra Nath Bose and Equation

1994. Birth Centenary of Satyendra Nath Bose (scientist).
1565 **1235** 1 r. brown 30 15

1236 Dr. Sampurnanand

1994. Dr. Sampurnanand (politician) Commemoration.
1566 **1236** 1 r. brown, green and red . 15 10

1237 Scene from "Pather Panchali" ($\frac{1}{2}$-size illustration)

1994. Satyajit Ray (film director) Commemoration. Multicoloured.
1567 6 r. Type **1237** . . . . 1·25 1·50
1568 11 r. Satyajit Ray and Oscar (35 × 35 mm) . . . . . . 1·40 1·60

1238 Dr. Bhatnagar and University Building

1994. Dr. Shanti Swarup Bhatnagar (scientist) Commemoration.
1569 **1238** 1 r. blue 15 10

1239 Prajapita Brahma and Memorial

1994. 25th Death Anniv of Prajapita Brahma (social reformer).
1570 **1239** 1 r. lilac and blue . . . 15 10

1240 "Window" (K. Subramanyan) **1241** Agricultural Products and Tea Garden

1994. 8th Triennale Art Exhibition, New Delhi.
1571 **1240** 6 r. orange, red and blue . 40 60

1994. Centenary of United Planters' Association of Southern India.
1572 **1241** 2 r. multicoloured . . . 20 20

1242 Indian Family **1242a** Sanchi Stupa

1994.
1573 **1242** 75 p. brown and red . 10 10
1574 – 1 r. mauve and green . 10 10
1575 – 3 r. purple 15 20
1576 **1242a** 5 r. brown and green . 15 20
DESIGNS (as T **1242**)—HORIZ: 1 r. Family outside home. VERT: 3 r. Baby and drop of polio vaccine.

1243 Rani Rashmoni on River Bank

1994. Birth Bicentenary of Rani Rashmoni.
1589 **1243** 1 r. brown 15 10

1244 Indians releasing Peace Doves

1994. 75th Anniv of Jallianwala Bagh Massacre, Amritsar.
1590 **1244** 1 r. black and red . . . 15 10

1245 Chandra Singh Garhwali

1994. 15th Death Anniv of Chandra Singh Garhwali (nationalist).
1591 **1245** 1 r. green and orange . . 15 10

1246 Emblems and National Flag **1247** Silhouette of Drummer and Logo

1994. 75th Anniv of I.L.O.
1592 **1246** 6 r. multicoloured . . . 40 60

1994. 50th Anniv of Indian People's Theatre Association.
1593 **1247** 2 r. black, green and gold . 15 15

1248 Statue of Sepoy **1249** Institute Building and Emblem

1994. Bicentenary of 4th Battalion, The Madras Regiment.
1594 **1248** 6 r. 50 multicoloured . . 55 65

1994. Bicentenary of Institute of Mental Health, Madras.
1595 **1249** 2 r. red and blue 15 15

1250 Mahatma Gandhi and Indian Flag **1251** Symbols of Cancer

1994. 125th Birth Anniv of Mahatma Gandhi. Multicoloured.
1596 6 r. Type **1250** . . . . 1·00 1·25
1597 11 r. Aspects of Gandhi's life on flag (69 × 34 mm) . . . . 1·25 1·50
Nos. 1596/7 were printed together, se-tenant, forming a composite design.

1994. 16th International Cancer Congress, New Delhi.
1598 **1251** 6 r. multicoloured . . . 55 65

1252 Human Resources Emblem

1994. Human Resource Development World Conference, New Delhi.
1599 **1252** 6 r. blue, red and azure . 55 65

1253 "Me and My Pals" (Namarata Amit Shah) **1254** Family and Emblem

1994. Children's Day.
1600 **1253** 1 r. multicoloured . . . 10 10

1994. International Year of the Family.
1601 **1254** 2 r. multicoloured . . . 20 15

1255 "Taj Mahal" (illustration from Badsha Nama)

1994. Khuda Bakhsh Oriental Public Library, Patna, Commemoration.
1602 **1255** 6 r. multicoloured . . . 4·00 1·00

1256 Andaman Teal

1994. Endangered Water Birds. Multicoloured.
1603 1 r. Type **1256** . . . . 5·00 2·00
1604 6 r. Eastern white stork . . . 8·00 4·00
1605 8 r. Black-necked crane . . . 9·00 4·50
1606 11 r. Pink-headed duck . . . 11·00 6·00
It is reported that Nos. 1603/6 were withdrawn shortly after issue.

1257 J. R. D. Tata and Aspects of Industrial Symbols

1994. J. R. D. Tata (industrialist) Commemoration.
1607 **1257** 2 r. multicoloured . . . 30 30

1258 School Building and Computer Class

1994. Centenary of Calcutta Blind School.
1608 **1258** 2 r. red, brown and cinnamon 20 15

1259 Begum Akhtar **1261** Cavalryman, Infantryman and Dog Handler

1260 College Building

1994. 80th Birth Anniv of Begum Akhtar (singer).
1609 **1259** 2 r. multicoloured . . . 4·25 4·25

1994. 125th Anniv of St. Xavier's College, Bombay.
1610 **1260** 2 r. brown and blue . . . 15 15

1994. 215th Anniv of Remount Veterinary Corps.
1611 **1261** 6 r. multicoloured . . . 75 60

1262 College Building

1994. Bicentenary of College of Engineering, Guindy, Madras.
1612 **1262** 2 r. red, brown and black . 15 10

1263 Righthand Ornament of Bronze Stand **1265** Statue of King Rajaraja Chola

1264 "200" and Aspects of Postal Service ($\frac{1}{2}$-size illustration)

1994. Centenary of Baroda Museum.
1613 **1263** 6 r. yellow and brown . 2·50 75
1614 – 11 r. yellow and brown . 2·50 75
DESIGN: 11 r. Bronze Rishabhanatha statue of Buddha on stand.

1994. Bicentenary of Bombay General Post Office.
1615 **1264** 6 r. multicoloured . . . 5·00 1·50

1995. 8th International Conference-Seminar of Tamil Studies, Thanjavur.
1616 **1265** 2 r. blue, ultramarine and black . . . . 3·50 75

1266 Globe and Emblem

1267 Chhotu Ram

1995. 60th Anniv of National Science Academy.
1617 **1266** 6 r. multicoloured . . . 50 60

1995. Chhotu Ram (social reformer) Commem.
1618 **1267** 1 r. brown . . . . . . 1·00 25

1268 Film Reel and Globe

1995. Centenary of Cinema. Multicoloured.
1619 6 r. Type **1268** 60 70
1620 11 r. Film reel and early equipment 80 90

1269 Symbolic Hands and Children

1270 Prithviraj Kapoor and Mask

1995. South Asian Association for Regional Cooperation Youth Year.
1621 **1269** 2 r. multicoloured . . . 20 20

1995. 50th Anniv of Prithvi Theatre.
1622 **1270** 2 r. multicoloured . . . 3·75 75

1271 Field-Marshal Cariappa

1272 Textile Pattern

1995. Field-Marshal K. Cariappa Commemoration.
1623 **1271** 2 r. multicoloured . . . 30 20

1995. "TEX-STYLES INDIA '95" Fair, Bombay.
1624 **1272** 2 r. brown, buff and red . 20 20

1273 Rafi Ahmed Kidwai

1274 K. L. Saigal, Film Reel and Gramophone

1995. Birth Centenary (1994) of Rafi Ahmed Kidwai (politician).
1625 **1273** 1 r. brown 15 10

1995. 90th Birth Anniv of K. L. Saigal (singer).
1626 **1274** 5 r. brown, grey and black 75 80

1275 R. S. Ruikar

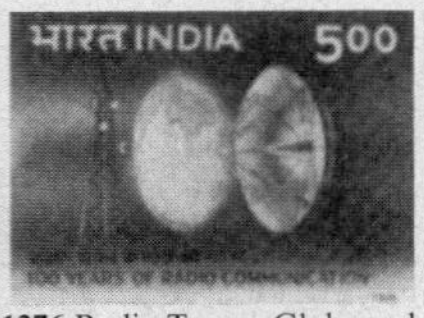

1276 Radio Tower, Globe and Dish Aerial

1995. Birth Centenary of R. S. Ruikar (trade unionist).
1627 **1275** 1 r. brown 15 10

1995. Centenary of Telecommunications.
1628 **1276** 5 r. multicoloured . . . 60 70

1277 Leaves and Symbolic Houses

1995. Delhi Development Authority.
1629 **1277** 2 r. multicoloured . . . 20 20

1278 Handshake

1279 Colonnade on Book Cover

1995. 50th Anniv of United Nations. Multicoloured.
1630 1 r. Type **1278** 10 10
1631 6 r. Work of U.N. Agencies . . 45 55

1995. Centenary of Bharti Bhawan Library, Allahabad.
1632 **1279** 6 r. black, brown and red 55 65

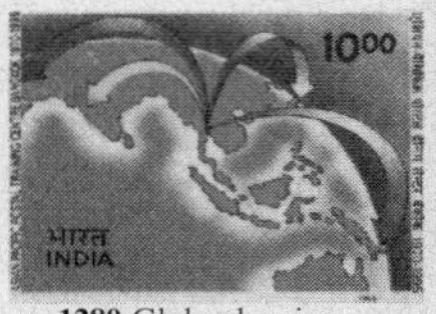

1280 Globe showing South-east Asia

1281 "75" and Taurus Formation Sign

1995. 25th Anniv of Asian-Pacific Postal Training Centre, Bangkok.
1633 **1280** 10 r. multicoloured . . 80 90

1995. 75th Anniv of Area Army Headquarters, Delhi.
1634 **1281** 2 r. multicoloured . . . 30 20

1282 Louis Pasteur in Laboratory (from painting by Edelfelt)

1995. Death Centenary of Louis Pasteur (chemist).
1635 **1282** 5 r. black and stone . . 70 80

1283 La Martiniere College, Lucknow

1284 Gandhi in South Africa

1995. 150th Anniv of La Martiniere College, Lucknow.
1636 **1283** 2 r. multicoloured . . . 20 20

1995. India–South Africa Co-operation. 125th Birth Anniv (1994) of Mahatma Gandhi.
1637 **1284** 1 r. red 25 25
1638 – 2 r. red 30 30
DESIGN: 2 r. Gandhi wearing dhoti.

1285 Ears of Grain, "50" and Emblem on Globe

1286 P. M. Thevar

1995. 50th Anniv of F.A.O.
1640 **1285** 5 r. multicoloured . . . 60 70

1995. Pasumpon Muthuramalingam Thevar (social reformer) Commemoration.
1641 **1286** 1 r. red 15 10

1287 W. C. Rontgen

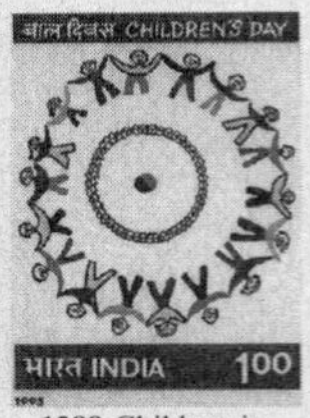

1288 Children in Circle

1995. 150th Birth Anniv of W. C. Rontgen (discoverer of X-rays).
1642 **1287** 6 r. multicoloured . . . 65 75

1995. Children's Day.
1643 **1288** 1 r. multicoloured . . . 20 10

1289 Sitar

1290 Jat War Memorial, Bareilly

1995. Communal Harmony Campaign.
1644 **1289** 2 r. multicoloured . . . 50 30

1995. Bicentenary of Jat Regiments.
1645 **1290** 5 r. multicoloured . . . 80 80

1291 Men of Rajputana Rifles

1995. 175th Anniv of 5th (Napier's) Battalion, Rajputana Rifles.
1646 **1291** 5 r. multicoloured . . . 80 80

1292 Sant Tukdoji Maharaj and Rural Meeting

1293 Dr. Yellapragada Subbarow

1995. Sant Tukdoji Maharaj Commemoration.
1647 **1292** 1 r. brown 15 10
Although dated "1993", No. 1647 was not issued until the date quoted above.

1995. Dr. Yellapragada Subbarow (pharmaceutical scientist) Commemoration.
1648 **1293** 1 r. brown 30 10

1294 Pres. Giani Zail Singh

1295 Dargah of Ala Hazrat Barelvi

1995. 1st Death Anniv of Pres. Giani Zail Singhn.
1649 **1294** 1 r. multicoloured . . . 15 10

1995. 75th Death Anniv of Ala Hazrat Barelvi (Moslem scholar).
1650 **1295** 1 r. multicoloured . . . 15 10

1296 Tata Institute Building

1996. 50th Anniv (1995) of Tata Institute of Fundamental Research.
1651 **1296** 2 r. multicoloured . . . 20 20

1297 Kasturba Gandhi

1298 Sectioned Heart

1996. 50th Anniv of the Kasturba Trust.
1652 **1297** 1 r. grey, green and red . 15 10

1996. 100 Years of Cardiac Surgery.
1653 **1298** 5 r. multicoloured . . . 60 70

1299 C. K. Nayudu

1300 "Vasant" (Spring) (Ragini Basanti)

1996. Cricketers. Multicoloured.
1654 2 r. Type **1299** 25 25
1655 2 r. Vinoo Mankad 25 25
1656 2 r. Deodhar 25 25
1657 2 r. Vijay Merchant 25 25

1996. Miniature Paintings of the Seasons. Multicoloured.
1658 5 r. Type **1300** 60 70
1659 5 r. "Greeshma" (Summer) (Jyestha) 60 70
1660 5 r. "Varsha" (Monsoon) (Rag Megh Malbar) 60 70
1661 5 r. "Hernant" (Winter) (Pausha) 60 70

1301 Kunjilal Dubey

1302 Morarji Desai

1996. Kunjilal Dubey Commemoration.
1662 **1301** 1 r. brown & chocolate . 15 10

1996. Birth Centenary of Morarji Desai (former Prime Minister) (1st issue).
1663 **1302** 1 r. red 20 10
See also No. 1702.

1303 Blood Pheasant

1996. Himalayan Ecology. Multicoloured.
1664 5 r. Type **1303** 60 70
1665 5 r. Markhor (goat) 60 70
1666 5 r. "Meconopsis horridula" (Tsher Gnoin) (plant) . . . 60 70
1667 5 r. "Saussurea simpsoniana" (Sunflower) 60 70

1304 S.K.C.G. College Building
1305 Muhammad Ismail Sahib

1996. Centenary of S.K.C.G. College, Gajapati.
1669 **1304** 1 r. brown and cream . 15 10

1996. Birth Centenary of Muhammad Ismail Sahib (Moslem politician).
1670 **1305** 1 r. purple 15 10

1306 Modern Stadium and Ancient Athens
1307 Sister Alphonsa

1996. Olympic Games, Atlanta. Multicoloured.
1671 5 r. Type **1306** 35 40
1672 5 r. Hand holding Olympic torch 35 40

1996. 50th Death Anniv of Sister Alphonsa.
1673 **1307** 1 r. black and blue . . 15 10

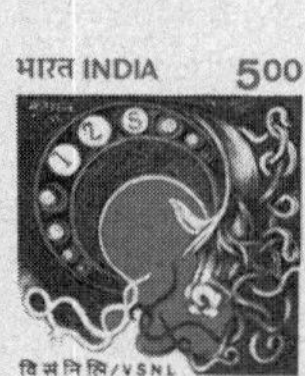

1308 "Communications"
1309 Sir Pherozeshah Mehta

1996. 125th Anniv of Videsh Sanchar Nigam Limited (telecommunications company).
1674 **1308** 5 r. multicoloured . . . 35 40

1996. 150th Birth Anniv of Sir Pherozeshah Mehta (politician).
1675 **1309** 1 r. blue 15 10

1310 Ahilyabai
1311 Chembai Vaidyanatha Bhagavathar

1996. Death Bicentenary (1995) of Ahilyabai (ruler of Holkar).
1676 **1310** 2 r. brown and deep brown 20 20

1996. Birth Centenary of Chembai Vaidanatha Bhagavathar (musician).
1677 **1311** 1 r. brown and green . . 15 10

1312 Red Junglefowl Cockerel

1996. 20th World Poultry Congress, New Delhi.
1678 **1312** 5 r. multicoloured . . . 70 70

1313 Rani Gaidinliu
1314 Nath Pai

1996. Rani Gaidinliu (Naga leader) Commemoration.
1679 **1313** 1 r. blue 15 10

1996. 25th Death Anniv of Nath Pai (politician).
1680 **1314** 1 r. blue 15 10

1315 Exhibition Logo
1317 Jananayak Debeswar Sarmah

1316 Historic Steam Locomotives

1996. INDEPEX '97 International Stamp Exhibition, New Delhi (1st issue).
1681 **1315** 2 r. gold and purple . . 20 20
See also Nos. 1713/16, 1722/5, 1741/4 and 1758/61.

1996. 25th Anniv of National Rail Museum.
1682 **1316** 5 r. multicoloured . . . 70 70

1996. Birth Centenary of Jananayak Debeswar Sarmah (politician).
1683 **1317** 2 r. brown and deep brown 20 20

1318 Monument and Sikh Sentry

1996. 150th Anniv of Sikh Regiment.
1684 **1318** 5 r. multicoloured . . . 50 55

1319 Dr. Salim Ali

1996. Birth Centenary of Salim Ali (ornithologist). Multicoloured.
1685 8 r. Type **1319** . . . . 90 1·00
1686 11 r. Storks at nest . . . . . 1·00 1·25
Nos. 1685/6 were printed together, se-tenant, with the backgrounds forming a composite design.

1320 "Indian Village" (child's painting)

1996. Children's Day.
1687 **1320** 8 r. multicoloured . . . 50 55

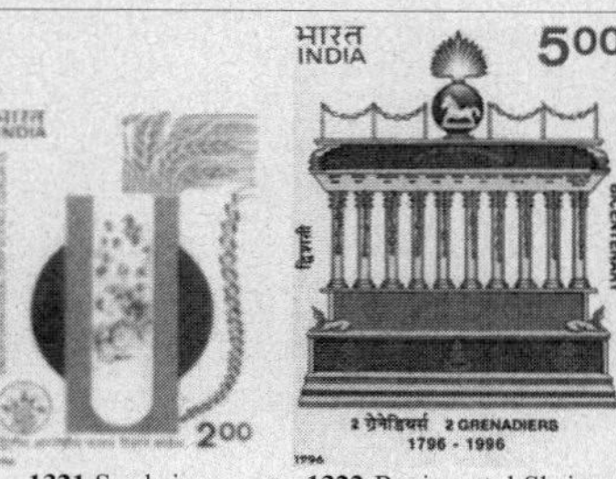

1321 Seeds in a Test-tube
1322 Regimental Shrine

1996. 2nd International Crop Science Congress.
1688 **1321** 2 r. multicoloured . . . 20 20

1996. Bicentenary of 2nd Battalion, Grenadiers.
1689 **1322** 5 r. multicoloured . . . 50 55

1323 Woman writing
1324 Abai Konunbaev

1996. 10th Anniv of South Asian Association for Regional Co-operation (S.A.A.R.C.).
1690 **1323** 11 r. multicoloured . . 65 70

1996. 150th Birth Anniv (1995) of Abai Konunbaev (Kazakh poet).
1691 **1324** 5 r. chestnut, brown and lilac 35 40

1325 Buglers in front of Memorial
1327 Victorian Doctors performing Operation

1326 Vivekananda Rock Memorial (½-size illustration)

1996. 25th Anniv of the Liberation of Bangladesh.
1692 **1325** 2 r. multicoloured . . . 20 20

1996. 25th Anniv of Vivekananda Rock Memorial, Kanyakumari.
1693 **1326** 5 r. multicoloured . . . 65 70

1996. 150th Anniv of Anaesthetics.
1694 **1327** 5 r. multicoloured . . . 50 55

1328 Roorkee University Buildings
1329 Dr. Vrindavanlal Verma

1997. 150th Anniv of Roorkee University.
1695 **1328** 8 r. multicoloured . . . 60 70

1997. Dr. Vrindavanlal Verma (writer) Commemoration.
1696 **1329** 2 r. red 20 20

1330 Field Post Office
1331 Subhas Chandra Bose

1997. 25th Anniv of Army Postal Service Corps.
1697 **1330** 5 r. multicoloured . . 35 40

1997. Birth Centenary of Subhas Chandra Bose (nationalist).
1698 **1331** 1 r. brown 20 10

1332 Jose Marti
1333 Conference Logo

1997. Jose Marti (Cuban writer) Commemoration.
1699 **1332** 11 r. black and pink . . 65 70

1996. "Towards Partnership between Men and Women in Politics" Inter-Parliamentary Conference, New Delhi.
1700 **1333** 5 r. multicoloured . . 35 40

1334 St. Andrew's Church
1335 Morarji Desai

1997. St. Andrew's Church, Egmore, Madras Commemoration.
1701 **1334** 8 r. multicoloured . . 50 55

1997. Birth Centenary of Morarji Desai (former Prime Minister) (2nd issue).
1702 **1335** 1 r. brown and deep brown 10 10

1336 Shyam Lal Gupt
1337 Saint Dnyaneshwar

1997. Birth Centenary (1996) of Shyam Lal Gupt (social reformer).
1703 **1336** 1 r. cinnamon and brown 10 10

1997. 700th Death Anniv (1996) of Saint Dnyaneshwar.
1704 **1337** 5 r. multicoloured . . 30 35

1338 Parijati Tree
1339 Monument, Rashtriya Military College

1997. Parijati Tree. Multicoloured.
1705 5 r. Type **1338** 30 40
1706 6 r. Parijati flower 30 40

1997. 75th Anniv of Rashtriya Military College, Dehra Dun.
1707 **1339** 2 r. multicoloured . . 40 30

1340 Ram Manohar Lohia

1341 Society Centenary Emblem

1997. Ram Manohar Lohia Commemoration.
1708 **1340** 1 r. multicoloured . . 10 10

1997. Centenary of the Philatelic Society of India. Multicoloured.
1709 2 r. Type **1341** 30 35
1710 2 r. Cover of 1st "Philatelic Journal of India", 1897 . . 30 35

1342 Gyandith Award Winners

1343 Madhu Limaye

1997. Gyandith Award Scheme.
1711 **1342** 2 r. multicoloured . . 15 15

1997. Madhu Limaye Commemoration.
1712 **1343** 2 r. green 15 15

1344 Nalanda Monastic University

1997. "INDEPEX '97" International Stamp Exhibition, New Delhi (2nd issue). Buddhist Cultural Sites. Multicoloured.
1713 2 r. Type **1344** 10 10
1714 6 r. The Bodhi Tree, Bodhgaya 25 30
1715 10 r. Stupa and Pillar, Vaishali 40 45
1716 11 r. Stupa, Kushinagar . . . 40 45

1345 Pandit Omkarnath Thakur

1346 Ram Sewak Yadav

1997. Birth Centenary of Pandit Omkarnath Thakur (musician).
1717 **1345** 2 r. black and blue . . 20 20

1997. Ram Sewak Yadav (politician) Commemoration.
1718 **1346** 2 r. brown 20 20

1347 Sibnath Banerjee

1348 Rukmini Lakshmipathi

1997. Birth Centenary of Sibnath Banerjee (trade unionist).
1719 **1347** 2 r. red and purple . . 20 20

1997. Rukmini Lakshmipathi (social reformer) Commemoration.
1720 **1348** 2 r. brown 30 30

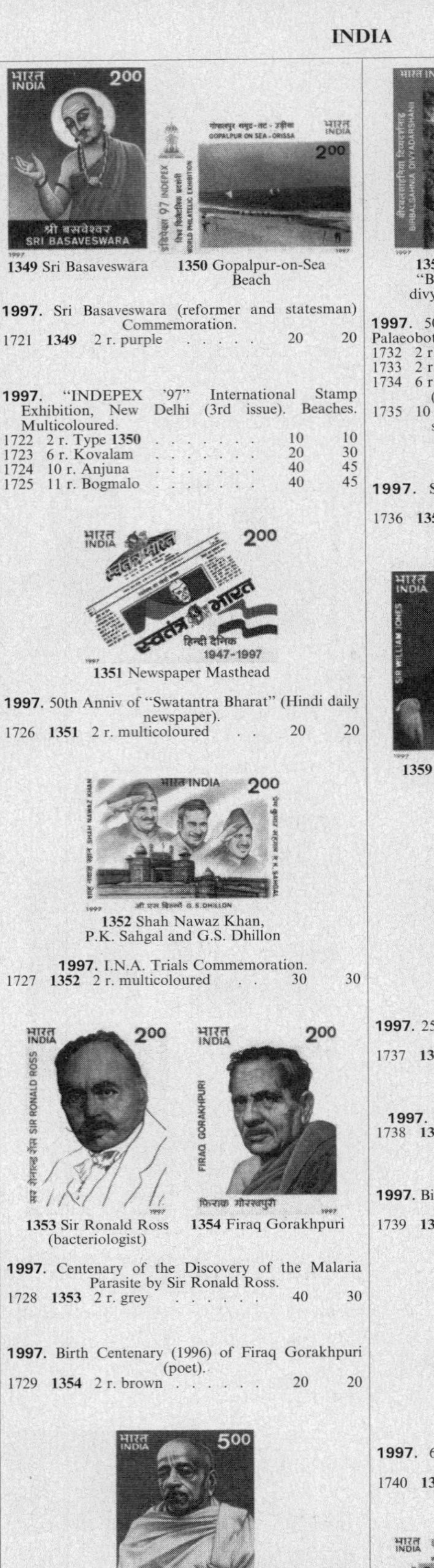

1349 Sri Basaveswara

1350 Gopalpur-on-Sea Beach

1997. Sri Basaveswara (reformer and statesman) Commemoration.
1721 **1349** 2 r. purple 20 20

1997. "INDEPEX '97" International Stamp Exhibition, New Delhi (3rd issue). Beaches. Multicoloured.
1722 2 r. Type **1350** 10 10
1723 6 r. Kovalam 20 30
1724 10 r. Anjuna 40 45
1725 11 r. Bogmalo 40 45

1351 Newspaper Masthead

1997. 50th Anniv of "Swatantra Bharat" (Hindi daily newspaper).
1726 **1351** 2 r. multicoloured . . 20 20

1352 Shah Nawaz Khan, P.K. Sahgal and G.S. Dhillon

1997. I.N.A. Trials Commemoration.
1727 **1352** 2 r. multicoloured . . 30 30

1353 Sir Ronald Ross (bacteriologist)

1354 Firaq Gorakhpuri

1997. Centenary of the Discovery of the Malaria Parasite by Sir Ronald Ross.
1728 **1353** 2 r. grey 40 30

1997. Birth Centenary (1996) of Firaq Gorakhpuri (poet).
1729 **1354** 2 r. brown 20 20

1355 Bhaktivedanta Swami

1997. Birth Centenary (1996) of Bhaktivedanta Swami (philosopher).
1730 **1355** 5 r. brown 50 55

1356 Parachute Regiment Emblem

1997. Bicentenary of 2nd (Maratha) Battalion, Parachute Regiment.
1731 **1356** 2 r. multicoloured . . 30 30

1357 Fossil of "Birbalsahnia divyadarshanii"

1358 Swami Brahmanand

1997. 50th Anniv of Birbal Sahni Institute of Palaeobotany, Lucknow. Plant Fossils. Multicoloured.
1732 2 r. Type **1357** 20 20
1733 2 r. "Glossopteris" 20 20
1734 6 r. "Pentoxylon" (reconstruction) 50 55
1735 10 r. "Williamsonia sewardiana" (model) . . . 75 85

1997. Swami Brahmanand (social reformer) Commemoration.
1736 **1358** 2 r. grey and stone . . 20 20

1359 "Sir William Jones"

1361 V. K. Krishna Menon

1360 Lawrence School Building and Crest

1997. 250th Birth Anniv (1996) of Sir William Jones (Sanskrit scholar).
1737 **1359** 4 r. multicoloured . . 30 30

1997. 150th Anniv of Lawrence School, Sanawar.
1738 **1360** 2 r. multicoloured . . 30 30

1997. Birth Centenary (1996) of V. K. Krishna Menon (politician).
1739 **1361** 2 r. red 30 30

1362 Policemen and Globe

1997. 66th General Assembly Session of ICPO Interpol.
1740 **1362** 4 r. multicoloured . . . 65 65

1363 Woman from Arunachal Pradesh

1364 Students in Meditation, Astachai

1997. "INDEPEX '97" International Stamp Exhibition, New Delhi (4th issue). Women's Costumes. Multicoloured.
1741 2 r. Type **1363** 10 10
1742 6 r. Gujarat costume 25 30
1743 10 r. Ladakh costume 40 45
1744 11 r. Kerala costume 45 50

1997. Centenary of Scindia School, Gwalior. Multicoloured.
1745 5 r. Type **1364** 30 35
1746 5 r. Gwalior Fort 30 35

1365 "Ocimum sanctum"

1997. Medicinal Plants. Multicoloured.
1747 2 r. Type **1365** 10 10
1748 5 r. "Curcuma longa" 20 25
1749 10 r. "Rauvolfia serpentina" . 40 45
1750 11 r. "Aloe barbadensis" . . 45 50

1366 Sant Kavi Sunderdas

1367 K. Rama Rao

1997. 400th Birth Anniv (1996) of Sant Kavi Sunderdas (Hindu theologian).
1751 **1366** 2 r. brown 30 30

1997. Birth Centenary of K. Rama Rao (parliamentarian and journalist).
1752 **1367** 2 r. bistre and brown . 30 30

1368 Jawaharlal Nehru and Child

1997. Children's Day.
1753 **1368** 2 r. multicoloured . . 35 30

1369 Animals on Globe

1370 Hazari Prasad Dwivedi

1997. World Convention on Reverence for All Life, Pune.
1754 **1369** 4 r. multicoloured . . 65 65

1997. 90th Birth Anniv of Hazari Prasad Dwivedi (scholar).
1755 **1370** 2 r. grey 30 30

1372 Vallabhbhai Patel and Marchers

1997. 47th Death Anniv of Vallabhbhai Patel (politician).
1757 **1372** 2 r. brown 35 30

1373 Head Post Office, Pune

1997. "INDEPEX '97" International Stamp Exhibition, New Delhi (5th issue). Post Office Heritage. Multicoloured.
1758 2 r. Type **1373** 20 20
1759 6 r. River mail barge 40 45
1760 10 r. Jal Cooper (philatelist) and cancellations 70 75
1761 11 r. "Hindoostan" (paddle-steamer) 70 75

1374 50th Anniversary Emblem

1997. 50th Anniv of Indian Armed Forces.
1762 **1374** 2 r. multicoloured . . 40 30

1375 Dr. Pattabhi Sitaramayya

1377 Ram Prasad Bismil and Ashfaqullah Khan

1376 Father Jerome d'Souza and Cathedral

1997. Dr. Pattabhi Sitaramayya (politician) Commemoration.
1763 **1375** 2 r. brown 30 30

1997. Birth Centenary of Father Jerome d'Souza (academic).
1764 **1376** 2 r. brown 30 30

1997. 70th Death Anniv of Ram Prasad Bismil and Ashfaqullah Khan (revolutionaries).
1765 **1377** 2 r. brown 30 30

1378 Jail Buildings **1379** Sword and Kukri

1997. Cellular Jail, Port Blair.
1766 **1378** 2 r. multicoloured . . 30 30

1998. 50th Anniv of 11th Gorkha Rifles.
1767 **1379** 4 r. multicoloured . . 65 65

1380 Nahar Singh

1381 Nanak Singh

1998. 140th Death Anniv of Nahar Singh (Sikh leader).
1768 **1380** 2 r. purple 30 30

1998. Birth Centernary (1997) of Nanak Singh (writer).
1769 **1381** 2 r. red 30 30

1382 Rotary International Emblem

1998. Meeting of Rotary International Council on Legislation, Delhi.
1770 **1382** 8 r. yellow and blue . . 50 55

1383 Maharana Pratap **1384** V. S. Khandekar

1998. 400th Death Anniv of Maharana Pratap (Rajput leader).
1771 **1383** 2 r. purple 30 30

1998. Birth Centenary of V. S. Khandekar (writer).
1772 **1384** 2 r. red 30 30

1385 Elephant and Dancers

1998. India Tourism Day.
1773 **1385** 10 r. multicoloured . . 1·00 1·00

1386 Jagdish Chandra Jain

1998. Jagdish Chandra Jain (educationist) Commemoration.
1774 **1386** 2 r. brown 30 30

1387 Gandhi as a Young Man and Peasants in Fields

1388 A. Vedaratnam

1998. 50th Death Anniv of Mahatma Gandhi. Multicoloured.
1775 2 r. Type **1387** 10 10
1776 6 r. Woman weaving and Gandhi distributing food . 25 30
1777 10 r. Gandhi collecting salt . . 40 45
1778 11 r. Gandhi carrying flag . . 45 50
Nos. 1775/8 were printed together, se-tenant, with the backgrounds forming a composite design.

1998. Birth Centenary (1997) of A. Vedaratnam (social reformer).
1779 **1388** 2 r. purple 30 30

1389 Anniversary Emblem

1391 Sir Syed Ahmad Khan

1390 Savitribai Phule

1998. 50th Anniv of Universal Declaration of Human Rights.
1780 **1389** 6 r. multicoloured . . . 50 50

1998. Death Centenary (1997) of Savitribai Phule (educational reformer).
1781 **1390** 2 r. brown 30 30

1998. Death Centenary of Sir Syed Ahmed Khan (social reformer).
1782 **1391** 2 r. brown 30 30

1392 Barren Landscape and Living Forest

1998. 1st Assembly Meeting of Global Environment Facility, Delhi.
1783 **1392** 11 r. multicoloured . . 75 80

1393 Ramana Maharshi

1998. Ramana Maharshi (religious leader) Commemoration.
1784 **1393** 2 r. lilac 30 30

1394 College Arms

1998. 50th Anniv of Defence Services Staff College, Wellington.
1785 **1394** 6 r. red 50 50

1395 Diesel Train on Viaduct (½-size illustration)

1998. Completion of Konkan Railway.
1786 **1395** 8 r. multicoloured . . . 60 70

1396 Narayan Ganesh Goray **1397** Dr. Zakir Husain

1998. Narayan Ganesh Goray (social reformer) Commemoration.
1787 **1396** 2 r. brown 20 20

1998. Birth Centenary (1997) of Dr. Zakir Husain (former President of India).
1788 **1397** 2 r. brown 20 20

1398 Mohammed Abdurahiman Shahib **1399** Lokanayak Omeo Kumar Das

1998. Mohammed Abdurahiman Shahib (nationalist) Commemoration.
1789 **1398** 2 r. brown 20 20

1998. Lokanayak Omeo Kumar Das (writer) Commemoration.
1790 **1399** 2 r. brown 20 20

1400 Vakkom Abdul Khader, Satyendra Chandra Bardhan and Fouja Singh

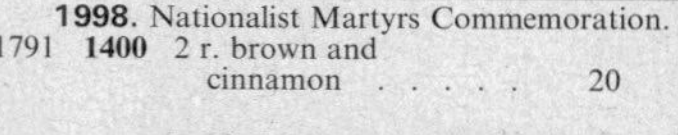

1998. Nationalist Martyrs Commemoration.
1791 **1400** 2 r. brown and cinnamon 20 20

1401 Bishnu Dey, Tarashankar Bandopadhyay and Ashapurna Devi

1402 Big Ben, London

1998. Bangla Jnanpith Literary Award Winners Commemoration.
1792 **1401** 2 r. brown 20 20

1998. 50th Anniv of First Air India International Flight.
1793 5 r. Type **1402** 30 35
1794 6 r. Lockheed Super Constellation airliner, globe and Gateway of India, Bombay (55 × 35 mm) . . 30 35
Nos. 1793/4 were printed together, se-tenant, forming a composite design.

1403 Dr. C. Vijiaraghavachariar

1405 Bhagawan Gopinathji

1404 Anniversary Logo and Savings Stream

1998. Dr. C. Vijiaraghavachariar (lawyer and social reformer) Commemoration.
1795 **1403** 2 r. brown 15 15

1998. 50th Anniv of National Savings Organization. Multicoloured.
1796 5 r. Type **1404** 15 20
1797 6 r. Hand dropping coin into jar 20 25
Nos. 1796/7 were printed together, se-tenant, forming a composite design.

1998. Birth Centenary of Bhagawan Gopinathji (spiritual leader).
1798 **1405** 3 r. brown 15 20

1406 Ardeshir and Pirojsha Godrej

1998. Centenary of Godrej (industrial conglomerate).
1799 **1406** 3 r. green 15 20

1407 Aruna Asaf Ali

1998. Aruna Asaf Ali (nationalist) Commemoration.
1800 **1407** 3 r. brown 15 20

1408 Iswar Chandra Vidyasagar (educationist) and College

1998. 125th Anniv of Vidyasagar College, Calcutta.
1801 **1408** 2 r. black 15 15

1409 Shivpujan Sahai

1998. Shivpujan Sahai (writer) Commemoration.
1802 **1409** 2 r. brown 15 15

1410 Red Fort, Delhi, and Spinning Wheel

1411 Gostha Behari Paul

1998. Homage to Martyrs for Independence. Multicoloured.
1803 3 r. Type **1410** 15 20
1804 8 r. Industrial and scientific development in modern India 25 30

1998. Gostha Paul (footballer) Commemoration.
1805 **1411** 3 r. purple 20 20

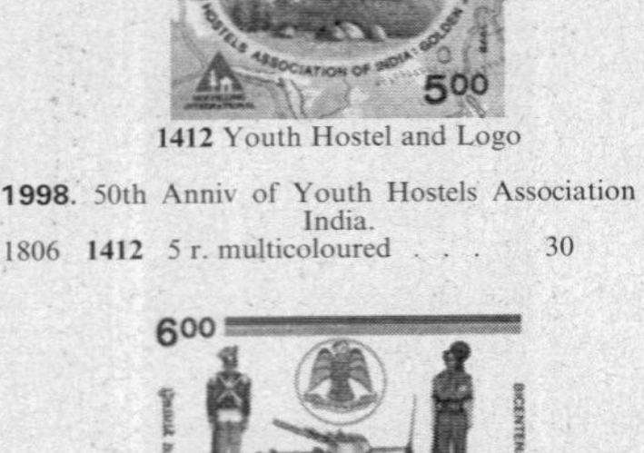

1412 Youth Hostel and Logo

1998. 50th Anniv of Youth Hostels Association of India.
1806 **1412** 5 r. multicoloured . . . 30 30

1413 Uniforms, Badge and Tank

1998. Bicentenary of 4th Battalion, Guards' Brigade (1 Rajput).
1807 **1413** 6 r. multicoloured . . . 30 35

1414 Bhai Kanhaiyaji

1998. Bhai Kanhaiyaji (Sikh social reformer) Commemoration.
1808 **1414** 2 r. red 15 15

1415 Emblem and Diagram of Head

1998. 20th International Congress of Radiology.
1809 **1415** 8 r. multicoloured . . . 30 35

1416 Dove of Peace and Boy reading Book

1417 Dr. Tristao Braganza Cunha

1998. 26th International Books for Young People Congress.
1810 **1416** 11 r. multicoloured . . 30 35

1998. Dr. Tristao Braganza Cunha (nationalist) Commemoration.
1811 **1417** 3 r. brown 15 20

1418 Jananeta Hijam Irawat Singh

1419 Women Aviators and Bi-plane

1998. Jananeta Hijam Irawat Singh (social reformer) Commemoration.
1812 **1418** 3 r. brown 15 20

1998. Indian Women's Participation in Aviation.
1813 **1419** 8 r. blue 30 40

1420 Acharya Tulsi

1998. 1st Death Anniv of Acharya Tulsi (Jain religious leader).
1814 **1420** 3 r. brown and orange . . 15 20

1421 Girl and Bird reading Book

1998. Children's Day.
1815 **1421** 3 r. multicoloured . . . 15 20

1422 I.N.S. "Delhi" (destroyer)

1998. Navy Day.
1816 **1422** 3 r. multicoloured . . . 15 20

1423 Mounted Trumpeter

1424 Sir David Sassoon and Library, Bombay

1998. 225th Anniv of President's Bodyguard.
1817 **1423** 3 r. multicoloured . . . 15 20

1998. David Sassoon Library and Reading Room Commemoration.
1818 **1424** 3 r. ultramarine and blue 15 20

1425 Regimental Arms and Soldier

1998. Bicentenary of 2nd Battalion, Rajput Regiment.
1819 **1425** 3 r. multicoloured . . . 15 20

1426 Army Postal Service Centre, Kamptee

1998. 50th Anniv of Army Postal Service Training Centre.
1820 **1426** 3 r. multicoloured . . . 15 20

1427 Connemara Public Library, Madras

1998. Centenary (1996) of Connemara Public Library.
1821 **1427** 3 r. brown and ochre . 15 20

1428 Neem Tree and Leaves

1429 Baba Raghav Das

1998. 50th Anniv of The Indian Pharmaceutical Congress Association.
1822 **1428** 3 r. multicoloured . . . 15 20

1998. 40th Death Anniv of Baba Raghav Das (social reformer).
1823 **1429** 2 r. violet 10 15

1430 Lt. Indra Lal Roy D.F.C.

1998. Birth Centenary of Indra Lal Roy (First World War pilot).
1824 **1430** 3 r. multicoloured . . . 15 20

1431 Sant Gadge Baba

1998. Sant Gadge Baba (social reformer) Commemoration.
1825 **1431** 3 r. lilac, blue and black . 15 20

1432 Rudra Veena (stringed instrument)

1998. Musical Instruments. Multicoloured.
1826 2 r. Type **1432** 10 15
1827 6 r. Flute 20 25
1828 8 r. Pakhawaj (wooden barrel drum) 25 30
1829 10 r. Sarod (stringed instrument) 30 35

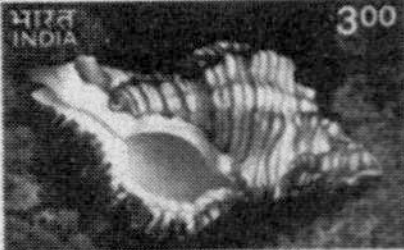

1433 "Chicoreus brunneus" (Murex shell)

1998. Shells. Multicoloured.
1830 3 r. Type **1433** 20 25
1831 3 r. "Cassis cornuta" (horned helmet) 20 25
1832 3 r. "Cypraea staphylaea" (cowrie) 20 25
1833 11 r. "Lambis lambis" (common spider conch) 50 60

1434 Stylised Police Officers

1999. 50th Anniv of Indian Police Service.
1834 **1434** 3 r. multicoloured . . . 20 20

1435 Modern Weapon Systems

1999. 40th Anniv of Defence Research and Development Organization.
1835 **1435** 10 r. multicoloured . . 30 35

1436 Issue of "Orunodoi" (Assamese newspaper) for January, 1846

1999. 150th Anniv of Newspapers in Assam.
1836 **1436** 3 r. black, yellow and orange 15 20

1437 College Building

1999. Centenary of Hindu College, Delhi.
1837 **1437** 3 r. blue 15 15

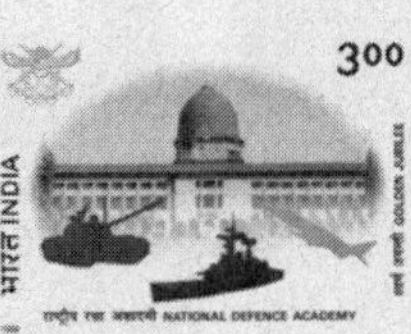

1438 National Defence Academy and Military Equipment

1999. 50th Anniv of National Defence Academy.
1838 **1438** 3 r. multicoloured . . . 15 15

1439 College Building

1999. 175th Anniv of Sanskrit College, Calcutta.
1839 **1439** 3 r. brown and ochre . . 15 15

1440 Patnaik and Tugs

1441 Globe and Satellite Dish

1999. Biju Patnaik Commemoration.
1840 **1440** 3 r. brown and green . . 15 15

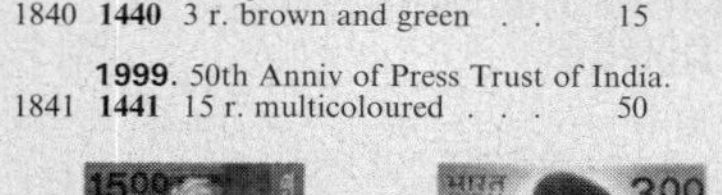

1999. 50th Anniv of Press Trust of India.
1841 **1441** 15 r. multicoloured . . . 50 55

1442 "Apsara removing a Thorn from her Foot" (temple statue)

1443 Dr. K. B. Hedgewar

1999. Millenary of the Khajuraho Temples.
1842 **1442** 15 r. deep brown, light brown and black . . . 50 55

1999. Dr. Keshavrao Hedgewar (founder of Rashtriya Swayamsevak Sangha) Commemoration.
1843 **1443** 3 r. multicoloured . . . 15 15

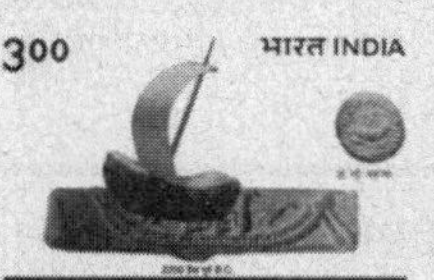

1444 Terracotta Model Boat from Lothal, 2200 B.C., and Seal

1999. Maritime Heritage. Multicoloured.
1844 3 r. Type **1444** 15 15
1845 3 r. Ghurab (sailing ship) of Kanhoji Angre, 1700 . . . 15 15

1445 Golden Temple, Amritsar

1999. 300th Anniv of the Khalsa (Sikh movement).
1846 **1445** 3 r. multicoloured . . . 15 15

1446 Bethune College

1999. 150th Anniv of Bethune Collegiate School, Calcutta.
1847 **1446** 3 r. green 15 15

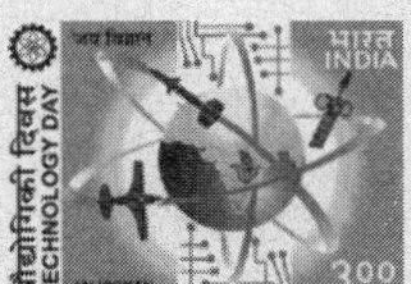

1447 Plane, Satellite and Rocket orbiting Globe

1999. Technology Day.
1848 **1447** 3 r. multicoloured . . . 15 15

1448 Mumbai Port

1449 Handshake and Airliner

1999. 125th Anniv of Mumbai (Bombay) Port Trust.
1849 **1448** 3 r. blue 15 15

1999. Mizoram Accord (peace agreement) Commemoration.
1850 **1449** 3 r. multicoloured . . . 15 15

1450 Gulzarilal Nanda

1451 Jijabai and Chatrapati Shivaji

1999. Birth Centenary of Gulzarilal Nanda (former Prime Minster).
1851 **1450** 3 r. multicoloured . . . 15 15

1999. Jijabai (mother of Chatrapati Shivaji (Maratha leader)) Commemoration.
1852 **1451** 3 r. purple 15 15

1452 P. S. Kumaraswamy Raja

1453 Balai Chand Mukhopadhyay

1999. P. S. Kumaraswamy Raja (politician) Commemoration.
1853 **1452** 3 r. brown and blue . . 15 15

1999. Birth Centenary of Balai Chand Mukhopadhyay ("Banaphool") (Bengali writer).
1854 **1453** 3 r. blue 15 15

1454 River Sindhu, Ladakh

1999. Sindhu Darshan Festival.
1855 **1454** 3 r. multicoloured . . . 15 15

1455 Soldier and Young Girl

1999. 50th Anniv of Geneva Conventions.
1856 **1455** 15 r. black and red . . . 40 45

1456 Sardar Ajit Singh

1457 Kalki Krishnamurthy

1999. Heroes of Struggle for Freedom.
1857 **1456** 3 r. brown and red . . . 15 15
1858 – 3 r. brown and blue . . 15 15
1859 – 3 r. blue and red 15 15
1860 – 3 r. purple and drab . . 15 15

DESIGNS: No. 1858, Swami Ramanand Teerth; No. 1859, Vishwambhar Dayalu Tripathi; No. 1860, Swami Keshawanand.

1999. Kalki Krishnamurthy Commemoration.
1861 **1457** 3 r. grey 15 15

1458 Ramdhari Sinha

1999. Ramdhari Sinha "Dinkar" (writer) Commemoration.
1862 **1458** 3 r. brown and blue . . 15 15

1459 Jhaverchand Kalidas Meghani and Graves

1999. Jhaverchand Kalidas Meghani Commem.
1863 **1459** 3 r. red and green . . . 15 15

1460 Rambrikish Benipuri and Statue of Horse

1999. Rambrikish Benipuri Commemoration.
1864 **1460** 3 r. brown and light brown 15 15

1461 Kazi Nazrul Islam

1999. Birth Centenary of Kazi Nazrul Islam (Bengali poet).
1865 **1461** 3 r. sepia and yellow . . 15 15

1462 Arati Gupta

1999. Arati Gupta (swimmer) Commemoration.
1866 **1462** 3 r. multicoloured . . . 15 15

1463 Lionesses

1999. Endangered Species. Asiatic Lion. Mult.
1867 3 r. Type **1463** 15 15
1868 3 r. Lions and lionesses lying down 15 15
1869 3 r. Lioness with cubs 15 15
1870 15 r. Two lions 40 45

1464 A. D. Shroff

1465 A. B. Walawalkar and Map

1999. A. D. Shroff Commemoration.
1871 **1464** 3 r. green and brown . . 15 15

1999. A. B. Walawalkar Commemoration.
1872 **1465** 3 r. purple 15 15

1466 Chhaganlal K. Parekh and Medical Staff with Child

1999. Chhaganlal K. Parekh (doctor) Commem.
1873 **1466** 3 r. blue and brown . . 15 15

1467 Dr. T. M. A. Pai and Hospital

1999. 20th Death Anniv of Dr. T. M. A. Pai.
1874 **1467** 3 r. chocolate and stone . 15 15

1468 Chhau Dance Masks

1999. 125th Anniv of Universal Postal Union. Multicoloured.
1875 3 r. Type **1468** 15 15
1876 3 r. Elephant and horseman (Rathva wall painting) (vert) 15 15
1877 3 r. Man ploughing (Muria ritual collar) 15 15
1878 15 r. Angami ornament (vert) . 15 15

1469 Veerapandia Kattabomman

1470 Ustad Allauddin Khan Saheb (sarod player)

1999 Death Bicentenary of Veerapandia Kattabomman (ruler of Panchalankuruchi).
1879 **1469** 3 r. green 15 15

1999. Modern Masters of Indian Classical Music. Multicoloured.
1880 3 r. Type **1470** 15 15
1881 3 r. Musiri Subramania Iyer (singer) 15 15

1471 Brigadier Rajinder Singh

1472 Elephant and Rhinoceros

1999. Birth Centenary of Brigadier Rajinder Singh (First recipient of M.V.C. medal).
1882 **1471** 3 r. purple 15 15

1999. Children's Day.
1883 **1472** 3 r. multicoloured . . . 15 15

OFFICIAL STAMPS

1866. Optd **Service**.

O20	**11**	½ a. blue	26·00	40
O 8	**12**	8 p. mauve	18·00	45·00
O23	**11**	1 a. brown	32·00	45
O27		2 a. orange	4·75	2·25
O13		4 a. green	£170	70·00
O29	–	4 a. green (No. 69)	3·00	1·50
O30	**11**	8 a. red	3·25	1·50

1866. Fiscal stamp with head of Queen Victoria surch **SERVICE TWO ANNAS**.

O15	2 a. purple	£275	£225

1866. Fiscal stamps optd **SERVICE POSTAGE**.

O19	½ a. mauve on lilac	£400	85·00
O16	2 a. purple	£800	£400
O17	4 a. purple	£3250	£1100
O18	8 a. purple	£3750	£3500

1874. Optd **On H. M. S.** (Queen Victoria).

O31	**11**	½ a. blue	7·00	20
O32		1 a. brown	11·00	20
O33a		2 a. orange	35·00	13·00
O34	–	4 a. green (No. 69)	12·00	3·00
O35	**11**	8 a. red	5·00	3·75

1883. Queen Victoria stamps of 1882 and 1892 optd **On H. M. S.**

O37a	**40**	3 p. red	20	10
O39	**23**	½ a. turquoise	70	10
O49		½ a. green	1·75	70
O41	–	1 a. purple	30	10
O50	–	1 a. red	2·50	10
O42	–	2 a. blue	4·00	60
O51	–	2 a. lilac	28·00	1·00
O44a	–	4 a. green	12·00	35
O46	–	8 a. mauve	8·00	50
O48	**37**	1 r. green and red	9·50	40

1902. King Edward VII stamps optd **On H. M. S.**

O54	**41**	3 p. grey	2·00	30
O56	–	½ a. green (No. 122)	1·25	30
O57	–	1 a. red (No. 123)	1·00	10
O59	–	2 a. lilac	3·25	10
O60	–	4 a. olive	8·00	30
O62	–	6 a. bistre	1·50	15
O63	–	8 a. mauve	6·00	85
O65	–	1 r. green and red	4·00	70
O68	**52**	2 r. red and orange	8·00	1·10
O69		5 r. blue and violet	14·00	1·50
O70		10 r. green and red	26·00	11·00
O71		15 r. blue and olive	60·00	35·00
O72		25 r. orange and blue	£140	60·00

1906. Nos. 149/50 optd **On H. M. S.**

O66	½ a. green	90	10
O67	1 a. red	1·75	10

1912. King George V stamps optd **SERVICE.**

O109	**55**	3 p. grey	15	10
O 76	**56**	½ a. green	30	10
O 80	**57**	1 a. red	1·00	10
O111		1 a. brown	15	10
O 83	**59**	2 a. lilac	55	10
O112	**70**	2 a. lilac	20	10
O129		2 a. red	1·00	2·25
O132	**63**	4 a. olive	1·00	10
O113	**71**	4 a. green	40	20
O 87	**64**	6 a. bistre	1·50	2·00
O115	**65**	8 a. mauve	60	10
O116	**66**	12 a. red	60	1·60
O117	**67**	1 r. brown and green	2·25	1·00
O 92		2 r. red and orange	3·25	4·00
O 93		5 r. blue and violet	13·00	17·00
O 94		10 r. green and red	42·00	42·00
O 95		15 r. blue and olive	90·00	£100
O 96		25 r. orange and blue	£200	£160

1921. No. O81 surch **NINE PIES.**

O97	**57**	9 p. on 1 a. red	85	75

1925. Nos. O70/2 surch in words.

O 99	**52**	1 r. on 15 r. blue & olive	4·25	3·50
O100		1 r. on 25 r. orange & blue	20·00	65·00
O101		2 r. on 10 r. green & red	3·75	3·75

1925. Nos. O94/6 surch in words.

O102	**67**	1 r. on 15 r. blue & olive	19·00	70·00
O103		1 r. on 25 r. orange & bl	5·00	9·50
O104		2 r. on 10 r. green & red	£750	

1926. No. O62 surch **ONE ANNA.**

O105	1 a. on 6 a. bistre	30	30

1926. Surch **SERVICE ONE ANNA** and two bars.

O106	**58**	1 a. on 1½ a. brown (A)	20	10
O107		1 a. on 1½ a. brown (B)	1·40	3·75
O108	**61**	1 a. on 2 a. 6 p. blue	60	80

1932. Optd **SERVICE.**

O126	**79**	½ a. green	60	10
O127	**80**	9 p. green	30	10
O127a	**81**	1 a. brown	2·25	10
O128	**82**	1 a. 3 p. mauve	30	10
O130a	**59**	2 a. red	1·00	10
O131	**61**	2 a. 6 p. orange	30	10

1937. King George VI stamps optd **SERVICE.**

O135	**91**	½ a. brown	16·00	20
O136		9 p. green	17·00	30
O137		1 a. red	3·00	10
O138	**93**	1 r. slate and brown	50	50
O139		2 r. purple and brown	1·50	2·50
O140		5 r. green and blue	2·50	5·50
O141		10 r. purple and red	14·00	4·75

1939. King George V stamp surch **SERVICE 1A.**

O142	**82**	1 a. on 1¼ a. mauve	11·00	20

O 20 King George VI

O 21 Asokan Capital

1939.

O143	**O 20**	3 p. slate	40	10
O144		½ a. brown	4·00	10
O144a		½ a. purple	30	10
O145		9 p. green	30	10
O146		1 a. red	30	10
O146a		1 a. 3p. brown	3·00	70
O146b		1½ a. violet	65	10
O147		2 a. orange	60	10
O148		2½ a. violet	60	50
O149		4 a. brown	60	10
O150		8 a. violet	90	30

1948. 1st Anniv of Independence. Optd **SERVICE.**

O150a	**305**	1½ a. brown	42·00	30·00
O150b		3½ a. violet	£750	£450
O150c		12 a. green	£2000	£1600
O150d	–	10 r. brown and red (No. 308)	£11000	

1950.

O151	**O 21**	3 p. violet	10	10
O152		6 p. brown	10	10
O153		9 p. green	30	10
O154		1 a. blue	70	10
O155		2 a. red	1·00	10
O156		3 a. red	3·00	1·75
O157		4 a. purple	5·00	20
O158		4 a. blue	50	10
O159		6 a. violet	3·00	40
O160		8 a. brown	1·50	10
O186	–	1 r. violet	15	10
O187	–	2 r. red	25	10
O188	–	5 r. green	40	60
O189	–	10 r. brown	90	80

The rupee values are larger and with a different frame.

1957. Value in naye paise.

O175	**O 21**	1 n.p. slate	10	10
O166		2 n.p. violet	10	10
O167		3 n.p. brown	10	10
O168		5 n.p. green	10	10
O169		6 n.p. turquoise	10	10
O180		10 n.p. green	1·75	1·50
O170		13 n.p. red	10	10
O182		15 n.p. violet	10	10
O183		20 n.p. red	30	10
O184		25 n.p. blue	10	10
O185		50 n.p. brown	15	10

O 23　　O 25　　O 26

1967.

O200	**O 23**	2 p. violet	10	90
O201		3 p. brown	10	1·00
O202		5 p. green	10	10
O203		6 p. blue	65	1·00
O204		10 p. green	10	30
O205		15 p. plum	10	30
O206		20 p. red	10	30
O207		25 p. red	8·00	3·75
O208		30 p. blue	10	60
O209		50 p. brown	10	60
O197		1 r. purple	50	10

1971. Obligatory Tax. Refugee Relief. Optd **REFUGEE RELIEF** in English and Devanagari (No. O210) or in English only (No. O211).

O210	**O 23**	5 p. green	30	30
O211		5 p. green	1·25	40
O213	**O 25**	5 p. green	15	15

See note below Nos. 646/51.

1977. Designs redrawn showing face-value in figures only and smaller Capital with Hindi motto beneath as Type **O 26**.

O214	**O 26**	2 p. blue	20	1·00
O254		5 p. green	10	10
O255		10 p. green	10	10
O256		15 p. purple	10	10
O257		20 p. red	10	10
O258		25 p. red	15	10
O259		30 p. blue	15	10
O260		35 p. violet	20	10
O261		40 p. violet	10	10
O269		50 p. brown	10	10
O263		60 p. brown	20	10
O270		1 r. purple	10	10
O225b	–	2 r. red	40	1·50
O226b	–	5 r. green	60	2·25
O227	–	10 r. red	1·25	3·50

The 2, 5 and 10 r. values are larger.

O 27　　O 28

1981. Redrawn with face value figures in bottom corners.

O271	**O 27**	2 r. red	10	10
O272a		3 r. orange	10	10
O273		5 r. green	15	20
O274		10 r. brown	30	35

1982. As 1977 and 1981 issue but with simulated perforations. Imperf.

O231	**O 28**	5 p. green	55	75
O232		10 p. green	70	80
O233		15 p. purple	70	80
O234		20 p. red	75	85
O235		25 p. red	1·50	1·75
O236		35 p. violet	85	50
O237		50 p. brown	1·50	1·25
O238		1 r. brown	1·75	1·25
O239		2 r. red	1·75	3·75
O240		5 r. green	2·00	4·50
O241		10 r. brown	2·50	6·50

INDIAN CUSTODIAN FORCES IN KOREA　Pt. 1

Stamps used by the Indian Forces on custodian duties in Korea in 1953.

12 pies = 1 anna; 16 annas = 1 rupee

भारतीय
संरक्षा कटक
कोरिया
(1)

1953. Stamps of India (archaeological series) optd with T **1**.

K 1	**307**	3 p. violet	1·75	4·50
K 2	**308**	6 p. brown	1·50	4·50
K 3	–	9 p. green	1·75	4·50
K 4	–	1 a. blue (B)	1·50	4·50
K 5	–	2 a. red	1·50	4·50
K 6	–	2½ a. lake	1·50	4·75
K 7	–	3 a. salmon	1·50	4·75
K 8	**314**	4 a. blue	2·00	4·75
K 9	**315**	6 a. violet	8·50	9·00
K10	–	8 a. green	3·25	9·00
K11	–	12 a. blue	4·50	17·00
K12	–	1 r. violet and green	6·00	17·00

INDIAN EXPEDITIONARY FORCES　Pt. 1

Stamps used by Indian Forces during, and after, the War of 1914-18.

12 pies = 1 anna; 16 annas = 1 rupee

1914. Stamps of India (King George V) optd **I. E. F.**

E 1	**55**	3 p. grey	15	30
E 2	**56**	½ a. green	30	30
E 3	**57**	1 a. red	75	30
E 5	**59**	2 a. lilac	80	30
E 6	**61**	2 a. 6 p. blue	1·50	3·00
E 7	**62**	3 a. orange	80	90
E 8	**63**	4 a. olive	70	90
E 9	**65**	8 a. mauve	1·00	2·00
E12	**66**	12 a. red	2·25	5·50
E13	**67**	1 r. brown and green	2·50	4·00

INDIAN FORCES IN INDO-CHINA　Pt. 1

Stamps used by Indian Forces engaged in the International Commission in Indo-China.

1954. 12 pies = 1 anna; 16 annas = 1 rupee.
1957. 100 naye paise = 1 rupee.
1964. 100 paisa = 1 rupee.

अन्तर्राष्ट्रीय आयोग कम्बोज	अन्तर्राष्ट्रीय आयोग लाओस	अन्तर्राष्ट्रीय आयोग वियत नाम
(N **1**)	(N **2**)	(N **3**)

1954. Stamps of India (archaeological series) overprinted. (a) Optd with Type N **1** for use in Cambodia.

N1	**307**	3 p. violet	1·25	8·00
N2	–	1 a. blue (B)	90	75
N3	–	2 a. red	90	80
N4	–	8 a. green	2·00	3·50
N5	–	12 a. blue	2·00	4·00

(b) Optd with Type N **2** for use in Laos.

N 6	**307**	3 p. violet	1·25	8·00
N 7	–	1 a. blue (B)	90	75
N 8	–	2 a. red	90	80
N 9	–	8 a. green	2·00	3·50
N10	–	12 a. blue	2·00	4·00

(c) Optd with Type N **3** for use in Vietnam.

N11	**307**	3 p. violet	1·25	8·00
N12	–	1 a. blue (B)	90	75
N13	–	2 a. red	90	80
N14	–	8 a. green	2·00	3·50
N15	–	12 a. blue	2·00	4·00

1957. Map type of India overprinted. (a) Optd with Type N **1** for use in Cambodia.

N16	**361**	2 n.p. brown	75	30
N17		6 n.p. grey	50	30
N18		13 n.p. red	70	40
N19		50 n.p. orange	2·25	1·25
N20		75 n.p. purple	2·25	1·25

(b) Optd with Type N **2** for use in Laos.

N21	**361**	2 n.p. brown	75	30
N39		3 n.p. brown	10	20
N40		5 n.p. green	10	15
N22		6 n.p. grey	50	30
N23		13 n.p. red	70	40
N24		50 n.p. orange	2·25	1·25
N25		75 n.p. purple	2·25	1·25

(c) Optd with Type N **3** for use in Vietnam.

N43	**361**	1 n.p. turquoise	10	20
N26		2 n.p. brown	75	30
N45		3 n.p. brown	10	20
N46		5 n.p. green	10	15
N27		6 n.p. grey	50	30
N28		13 n.p. red	70	40
N29		50 n.p. orange	2·25	1·25
N30		75 n.p. purple	2·25	1·25

1965. Children's Day stamp of India optd **ICC** for use in Laos and Vietnam.

N49	**469**	15 p. slate	60	3·25

1968. Nos. 504/6, 509/10, 515 and 517/18, of India optd **ICC** in English and Devanagari, for use in Laos and Vietnam.

N50	–	2 p. brown	10	2·50
N51	–	3 p. olive	10	2·50
N52	–	5 p. red	10	75
N53	–	10 p. blue	1·75	1·75
N54	**467**	15 p. green	60	1·75
N55	–	60 p. grey	35	1·25
N56	–	1 r. brown and plum	50	1·75
N57	–	2 r. blue and violet	1·25	8·00

INDIAN U.N. FORCE IN CONGO　Pt. 1

Stamps used by Indian Forces attached to the United Nations Force in Congo.

100 naye paise = 1 rupee

1962. Map type of India optd **U.N. FORCE (INDIA) CONGO.**

U1	**361**	1 n.p. turquoise	90	2·50
U2		2 n.p. brown	90	80
U3		5 n.p. green	90	55
U4		8 n.p. turquoise	90	30
U5		13 n.p. red	90	40
U6		50 n.p. orange	90	70

INDIAN U.N. FORCE IN GAZA (PALESTINE)　Pt. 1

Stamps used by Indian Forces attached to the United Nations Force in Gaza.

100 paise = 1 rupee

1965. Children's Day stamp of India optd **UNEF.**

G1	**449**	15 p. slate	1·50	6·00

INDO-CHINA　Pt. 6

A French territory in south-east Asia. In 1949 it was split up into the three states of Vietnam, Cambodia and Laos.

1889. 100 centimes = 1 franc.
1918. 100 cents = 1 piastre.

1889. Stamp of French Colonies, "Commerce" type, surch. (a) **INDO-CHINE 1889 5 R-D.**

1	**J 5**	on 35 c. black on orange	60·00	40·00

(b) **INDO-CHINE 89 5 R D.**

2	**J 5**	on 35 c. black on orange	5·25	4·50

1892. "Tablet" key-type inscr "INDO-CHINE" in red (1, 5, 15, 25, 50 (No. 27), 75 c., 1 f.) or blue (others).

6	D	1 c. black on blue	55	40
7		2 c. brown on buff	60	50
8		4 c. brown on grey	60	50
23		5 c. green	55	25
10		10 c. black on lilac	1·75	50
24		10 c. red	1·25	45
11		15 c. blue	20·00	55
25		15 c. grey	3·50	40
12		20 c. red on green	4·25	2·25
13a		25 c. black on pink	6·75	1·40
26		25 c. blue	9·75	85
14		30 c. brown on drab	11·00	3·25
15		40 c. red on yellow	12·00	3·25
16		50 c. red on pink	26·00	7·00
27		50 c. brown on blue	11·00	2·75
17		75 c. brown on orange	16·00	8·50
18		1 f. green	27·00	11·00
19		5 f. mauve on lilac	80·00	55·00

1903. Surch.

28	D	5 on 15 c. grey	45	50
29		15 on 25 c. blue	70	65

8 "Grasset" type

1904.

30	**8**	1 c. green	25	15
31		2 c. purple on yellow	40	15
32		4 c. mauve on blue	25	15
33		5 c. green	30	15
34		10 c. pink	70	15
35		15 c. brown on blue	55	20
36		20 c. red on green	1·40	40
37		25 c. blue	7·25	60
38		30 c. brown on cream	3·25	1·00
39		35 c. black on yellow	9·00	80
40		40 c. black on grey	2·50	65
41		50 c. brown	4·00	1·00
42		75 c. red on orange	29·00	15·00
43		1 f. green	11·50	2·75
44		2 f. brown on yellow	28·00	22·00
45		5 f. violet	£150	£110
46		10 f. red on green	£140	£110

10 Annamite 11 Cambodian 12 Cambodian

1907.

51 **10** 1 c. black and sepia 20 15
52 2 c. black and brown 15 15
53 4 c. black and blue 40 45
54 5 c. black and green 30 20
55 10 c. black and red 30 15
56 15 c. black and violet 70 50
57 **11** 20 c. black and violet 1·25 65
58 25 c. black and blue 3·00 30
59 30 c. black and brown 4·50 3·00
60 35 c. black and green 85 45
61 40 c. black and brown 2·25 1·00
62 45 c. black and orange 5·50 3·25
63 50 c. black and red 7·75 3·00
64 **12** 75 c. black and orange 5·50 3·75
65 – 1 f. black and red 26·00 6·50
66 – 2 f. black and green 7·75 6·50
67 – 5 f. black and blue 29·00 15·50
68 – 10 f. black and violet 55·00 50·00

DESIGNS:—As Type **12**: 1 f. Annamites; 2 f. Muong; 5 f. Laotian; 10 f. Cambodian.

1912. Surch in figures.

69 **8** 05 on 4 c. mauve on blue 3·50 2·75
70 05 on 15 c. brown on blue 40 40
71 05 on 30 c. brn on cream 45 50
72 10 on 40 c. black on grey 50 60
73 10 on 50 c. brown 50 45
74 10 on 75 c. red on orange 2·75 2·75

1914. Red Cross. Surch **5c** and cross.

76 **10** 5 c. + 5 c. black & green 35 60
75 10 c. + 5 c. black and red 50 35
78 15 c. + 5 c. black & violet 80 80

1918. Nos. 75/6 and 78 further surch in figures and words.

79 **10** 4 c. on 5 c. + 5 c. blk & grn 2·25 2·25
80 6 c. on 10 c. + 5 c. black and red 2·25 2·00
81 8 c. on 15 c. + 5 c. blk & vio 8·00 6·50

1919. French stamps of "War Orphans" issue surch **INDOCHINE** and value in figures and words.

82 **23** 10 c. on 15 c. + 10 c. grey 90 95
83 16 c. on 25 c. + 15 c. blue 3·00 3·00
84 – 24 c. on 35 c. + 25 c. violet and grey 4·25 4·75
85 – 40 c. on 50 c. + 50 c. brn 8·75 8·75
86 **26** 80 c. on 1 f. + 1 f. red 17·00 17·00
87 4 p. on 5 f. + 5 f. bl & blk £170 £170

1919. Surch in figures and words.

88 **10** $\frac{2}{5}$ c. on 1 c. black & sepia 30 20
89 $\frac{4}{5}$ c. on 2 c. black & brown 55 45
90 1$\frac{3}{5}$ c. on 4 c. black and blue 95 40
91 2 c. on 5 c. black & green 40 20
92 4 c. on 10 c. black and red 40 15
93 6 c. on 15 c. black & violet 1·10 40
94 **11** 8 c. on 20 c. black & violet 1·25 1·25
95 10 c. on 25 c. black & blue 1·25 30
96 12 c. on 30 c. black & brn 3·25 45
97 14 c. on 35 c. black & grn 70 30
98 16 c. on 40 c. black & brn 3·25 70
99 18 c. on 45 c. black & orge 3·25 1·25
100 20 c. on 50 c. black & red 4·75 50
101 **12** 30 c. on 75 c. blk & orge 5·50 1·10
102 – 40 c. on 1 f. black and red 9·75 1·00
103 – 80 c. on 2 f. black & green 11·50 3·00
104 – 2 p. on 5 f. black and blue 55·00 48·00
105 – 4 p. on 10 f. black & violet 90·00 80·00

1922. As T **10** and **11** but value in cents or piastres.

115 **10** $\frac{1}{10}$ c. red and grey 15 25
116 $\frac{1}{5}$ c. black and blue 15 15
117 $\frac{2}{5}$ c. black and brown 20 20
118 $\frac{4}{5}$ c. black and mauve 25 25
119 1 c. black and brown 20 15
120 2 c. black and green 40 15
121 3 c. black and violet 25 20
122 4 c. black and orange 20 15
123 5 c. black and red 20 15
124 **11** 6 c. black and red 25 20
125 7 c. black and green 25 25
126 8 c. black on lilac 65 50
127 9 c. black and yellow 65 50
128 10 c. black and blue 20 20
129 11 c. black and violet 25 20
130 12 c. black and brown 25 25
131 15 c. black and orange 40 25
132 20 c. black and blue 50 30
133 40 c. black and red 1·10 65
134 1 p. black and green 3·25 3·00
135 2 p. blk & pur on pink 5·75 4·50

INDEX
Countries can be quickly located by referring to the index at the end of this volume.

22 Ploughman and Tower of Confucius 23 Bay of Along

24 Ruins of Angkor

1927.

136 **22** $\frac{1}{10}$ c. olive 15 30
137 $\frac{1}{5}$ c. yellow 15 30
138 $\frac{2}{5}$ c. blue 20 30
139 $\frac{4}{5}$ c. brown 30 30
140 1 c. orange 30 15
141 2 c. green 50 20
142 3 c. blue 40 20
143 4 c. mauve 75 55
144 5 c. violet 35 15
145 **23** 6 c. red 1·10 20
146 7 c. brown 70 40
147 8 c. olive 65 65
148 9 c. purple 75 60
149 10 c. blue 80 45
150 11 c. orange 80 60
151 12 c. grey 55 30
152 **24** 15 c. brown and red 5·00 4·00
153 20 c. grey and violet 2·00 80
154 – 25 c. mauve and brown 4·75 3·50
155 – 30 c. olive and blue 2·50 1·75
156 – 40 c. blue and red 3·50 2·00
157 – 50 c. grey and green 4·75 1·40
158 – 1 p. black, yellow & blue 8·50 6·00
159 – 2 p. blue, orange and red 11·00 8·00

DESIGNS:—As T **24**: 25, 30 c. Wood-carver; 40, 50 c. Temple, Thuat-Luong; 1, 2 p. Founding of Saigon.

1931. "Colonial Exn" key-types inscr "INDOCHINE" and surch with new value.

160 F 4 c. on 50 c. mauve 1·40 1·10
161 G 6 c. on 90 c. red 1·60 1·60
162 H 10 c. on 1 f. 50 blue 2·50 1·40

33 Junk 36 "Apsara", or dancing Nymph

1931.

163 **33** $\frac{1}{10}$ c. blue 15 25
164 $\frac{1}{5}$ c. red 15 20
165 $\frac{2}{5}$ c. orange 15 30
166 $\frac{1}{2}$ c. brown 20 25
167 $\frac{4}{5}$ c. violet 20 30
168 1 c. brown 20 15
169 2 c. green 25 15
170 – 3 c. brown 20 15
171 – 3 c. green 2·75 85
172 – 4 c. blue 25 20
173 – 4 c. green 40 50
174 – 4 c. yellow 30 30
175 – 5 c. purple 30 15
176 – 5 c. green 30 30
177 – 6 c. red 30 20
178 – 7 c. black 25 25
179 – 8 c. red 25 30
180 – 9 c. black on yellow 30 35
181 – 10 c. blue 40 25
182 – 10 c. blue on pink 30 25
183 – 15 c. brown 3·50 60
184 – 15 c. blue 25 15
185 – 18 c. blue 25 30
186 – 20 c. red 20 15
187 – 21 c. green 25 25
188 – 22 c. green 25 30
189 – 25 c. purple 1·50 85
190 – 25 c. blue 30 40
191 – 30 c. brown 30 20
192 **36** 50 c. brown 30 15
193 60 c. purple 30 20
194 70 c. blue 35 30
195 1 p. green 50 35
196 2 p. red 55 35

DESIGNS:—As Type **33**: 3 c. to 9 c. Ruins at Angkor; 10 c. to 30 c. Worker in rice field.

42 Farman F.190 Mail Plane 44 Emperor Bao Dai of Annam

1933. Air.

197 **42** 1 c. brown 20 30
198 2 c. green 15 25
199 5 c. green 30 40
200 10 c. brown 35 20
201 11 c. red 30 35
202 15 c. blue 40 40
203 16 c. mauve 40 40
204 20 c. green 40 35
205 30 c. brown 20 25
206 36 c. red 1·00 30
207 37 c. green 20 25
208 39 c. green 40 50
209 60 c. purple 30 30
210 66 c. green 40 30
211 67 c. blue 65 65
212 69 c. blue 40 40
213 1 p. black 35 15
214 2 p. orange 70 20
215 5 p. violet 1·00 50
216 10 p. red 2·25 80
217 20 p. green 6·75 3·00
218 30 p. brown 7·50 3·00

1936. Issue for Annam.

219 **44** 1 c. brown 50 55
220 2 c. green 50 55
221 4 c. violet 60 65
222 5 c. lake 60 70
223 10 c. red 95 90
224 15 c. blue 1·10 1·00
225 20 c. red 1·25 1·40
226 30 c. purple 1·50 1·60
227 50 c. green 1·90 1·60
228 1 p. mauve 3·00 3·00
229 2 p. black 3·50 3·25

45 King Sisowath Monivong of Cambodia 46 Pres. Doumer

1936. Issue for Cambodia.

230 **45** 1 c. brown 50 55
231 2 c. green 50 50
232 4 c. violet 65 65
233 5 c. lake 65 70
234 10 c. red 1·60 1·60
235 15 c. blue 1·90 1·90
236 20 c. red 1·40 1·40
237 30 c. purple 1·40 1·40
238 50 c. green 1·50 1·50
239 1 p. mauve 1·90 1·60
240 2 p. black 3·00 3·00

1937. Int Exn, Paris. As T **58a** of Guadeloupe.

241 2 c. violet 45 65
242 3 c. green 45 60
243 4 c. red 40 55
244 6 c. brown 40 50
245 9 c. red 45 60
246 15 c. blue 40 55

1938. Opening of Trans-Indo-China Railway.

247 **46** 5 c. red (postage) 1·40 60
248 6 c. brown 1·40 50
249 18 c. blue 1·75 60
250 37 c. orange (air) 2·10 25

1938. Int Anti-Cancer Fund. As T **58b** of Guadeloupe.

251 18 c. + 5 c. blue 5·50 6·75

1939. New York World's Fair. As T **58c** of Guadeloupe.

252 13 c. red 30 35
253 23 c. blue 35 45

47 Mot Cot Pagoda, Hanoi 48 King Sihanouk of Cambodia

1939. San Francisco Exn.

254 **47** 6 c. sepia 50 50
255 9 c. red 50 50
256 23 c. blue 35 40
257 39 c. purple 50 55

1939. 150th Anniv of French Revolution. As T **58d** of Guadeloupe.

258 6 c. + 2 c. green and black (postage) 5·00 5·50
259 7 c. + 3 c. brown and black 5·00 5·50
260 9 c. + 4 c. orange and black 5·00 5·50
261 13 c. + 10 c. red and black 5·00 5·50
262 23 c. + 20 c. blue and black 5·00 5·50
263 39 c. + 40 c. blk & orge (air) 12·00 13·50

1941. Coronation of King of Cambodia. No gum.

264 **48** 1 c. orange 50 50
265 6 c. violet 1·00 1·00
266 25 c. blue 11·50 11·50

49 Processional Elephant 51 Hanoi University

1942. Fetes of Nam-Giao. No gum.

267 **49** 3 c. brown 90 70
268 6 c. red 90 70

1942. No. 189 surch **10 cents** and bars.

269 10 c. on 25 c. purple 40 30

1942. University Fund. No gum.

270 **51** 6 c. + 2 c. red 35 40
271 15 c. + 5 c. purple 55 55

Surch **10c + 2 c.**

272 **51** 10 c. + 2 c. on 6 c. + 2 c. red 30 40

53 Marshal Petain 54 Shield and Sword

1942. No gum.

273 **53** 1 c. brown 15 25
274 3 c. brown 30 25
275 6 c. red 20 30
276 10 c. green 30 30
277 40 c. blue 25 35
278 40 c. grey 65 65

1942. National Relief Fund. No gum.

279 **54** 6 c. + 2 c. red and blue 25 35
280 15 c. + 5 c. blk, red & bl 40 45

Surch **10c + 2 c.**

281 **54** 10 c. + 2 c. on 6 c. + 2 c. red and blue 30 30

55 Emperor Bao Dai of Annam 56 King Sihanouk of Cambodia

57 Empress Nam-Phaong of Annam 58 King Sisavang-Vong of Laos

1942. No gum.

282 **55** $\frac{1}{2}$ c. purple 35 30
283 **56** 1 c. purple 50 40
284 **58** 1 c. brown 25 30
285 **55** 6 c. red 70 40
286 **56** 6 c. red 40 30
287 **57** 6 c. red 55 35
288 **58** 6 c. red 35 30

59 Saigon Fair 60 Alexandre Yersin

1942. Saigon Fair. No gum.

289 **59** 6 c. red 30 35

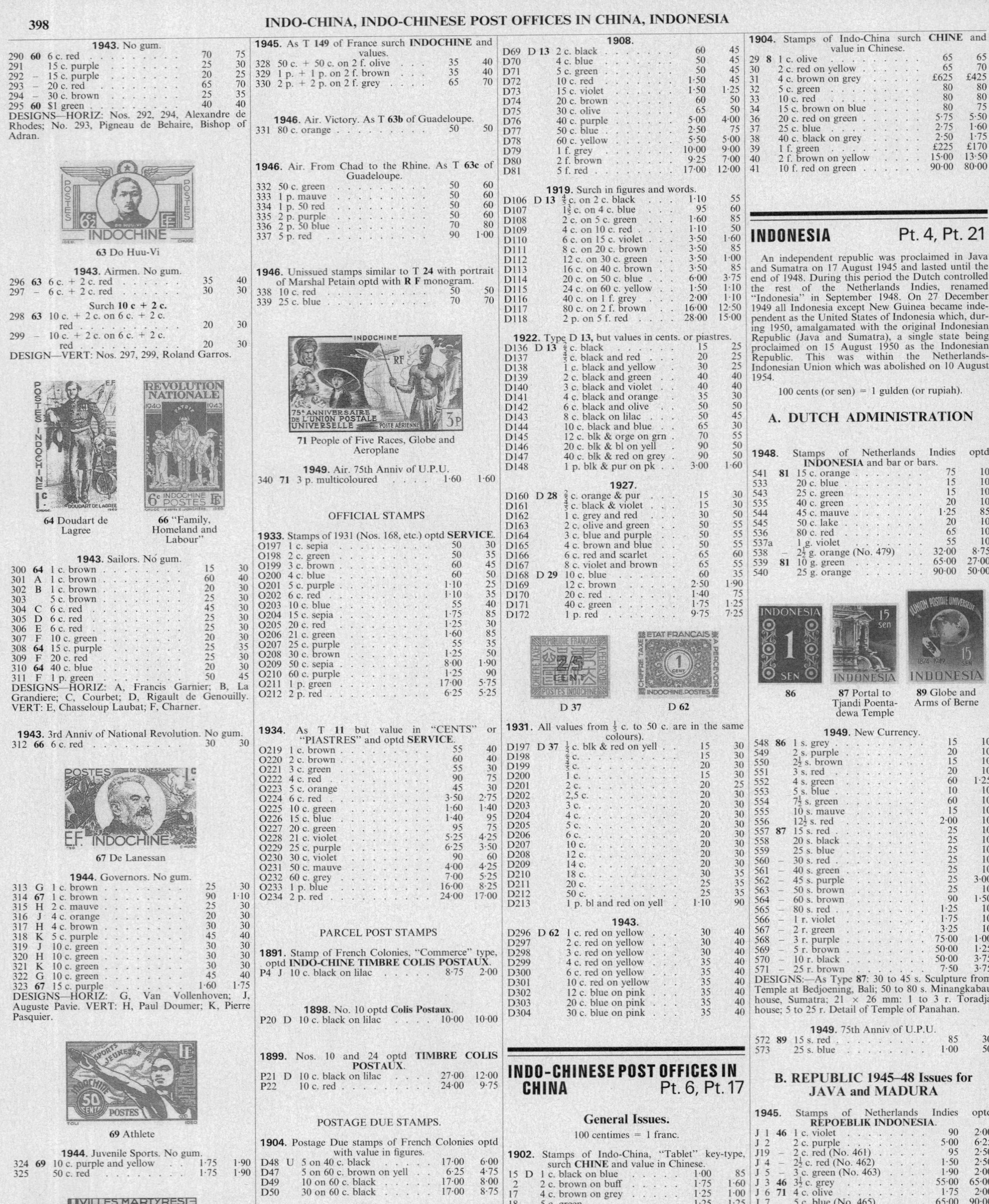

1943. No gum.
290 **60** 6 c. red 70 75
291 15 c. purple 25 30
292 – 15 c. purple 20 25
293 – 20 c. red 65 70
294 – 30 c. brown 25 35
295 **60** $1 green 40 40
DESIGNS—HORIZ: Nos. 292, 294, Alexandre de Rhodes; No. 293, Pigneau de Behaire, Bishop of Adran.

63 Do Huu-Vi

1943. Airmen. No gum.
296 **63** 6 c. + 2 c. red 35 40
297 – 6 c. + 2 c. red 30 30

Surch **10 c + 2 c.**
298 **63** 10 c. + 2 c. on 6 c. + 2 c. red 20 30
299 – 10 c. + 2 c. on 6 c. + 2 c. red 20 30
DESIGN—VERT: Nos. 297, 299, Roland Garros.

64 Doudart de Lagree

66 "Family, Homeland and Labour"

1943. Sailors. No gum.
300 **64** 1 c. brown 15 30
301 A 1 c. brown 60 40
302 B 1 c. brown 20 30
303 5 c. brown 25 30
304 C 6 c. red 45 30
305 D 6 c. red 25 30
306 E 6 c. red 25 30
307 F 10 c. green 20 30
308 **64** 15 c. purple 25 35
309 F 20 c. red 25 30
310 **64** 40 c. blue 20 30
311 F 1 p. green 50 45
DESIGNS—HORIZ: A, Francis Garnier; B, La Grandiere; C, Courbet; D, Rigault de Genouilly. VERT: E, Chasseloup Laubat; F, Charner.

1943. 3rd Anniv of National Revolution. No gum.
312 **66** 6 c. red 30 30

67 De Lanessan

1944. Governors. No gum.
313 G 1 c. brown 25 30
314 **67** 1 c. brown 90 1·10
315 H 2 c. mauve 25 30
316 J 4 c. orange 20 30
317 H 4 c. brown 30 30
318 K 5 c. purple 45 40
319 J 10 c. green 30 30
320 H 10 c. green 30 30
321 K 10 c. green 30 30
322 G 10 c. green 45 40
323 **67** 15 c. purple 1·60 1·75
DESIGNS—HORIZ: G, Van Vollenhoven; J, Auguste Pavie. VERT: H, Paul Doumer; K, Pierre Pasquier.

69 Athlete

1944. Juvenile Sports. No gum.
324 **69** 10 c. purple and yellow 1·75 1·90
325 50 c. red 1·75 1·90

70 Orleans Cathedral

1944. Martyr Cities. No gum.
326 **70** 15 c. + 60 c. purple 70 60
327 40 c. + 1 p. 10 blue 85 75

1945. As T **149** of France surch **INDOCHINE** and values.
328 50 c. + 50 c. on 2 f. olive 35 40
329 1 p. + 1 p. on 2 f. brown 35 40
330 2 p. + 2 p. on 2 f. grey 65 70

1946. Air. Victory. As T **63b** of Guadeloupe.
331 80 c. orange 50 50

1946. Air. From Chad to the Rhine. As T **63c** of Guadeloupe.
332 50 c. green 50 60
333 1 p. mauve 50 60
334 1 p. 50 red 50 60
335 2 p. purple 50 60
336 2 p. 50 blue 70 80
337 5 p. red 90 1·00

1946. Unissued stamps similar to T **24** with portrait of Marshal Petain optd with **R F** monogram.
338 10 c. red 50 50
339 25 c. blue 70 70

71 People of Five Races, Globe and Aeroplane

1949. Air. 75th Anniv of U.P.U.
340 **71** 3 p. multicoloured 1·60 1·60

OFFICIAL STAMPS

1933. Stamps of 1931 (Nos. 168, etc.) optd **SERVICE.**
O197 1 c. sepia 50 30
O198 2 c. green 50 35
O199 3 c. brown 60 45
O200 4 c. blue 60 50
O201 5 c. purple 1·10 25
O202 6 c. red 1·10 35
O203 10 c. blue 55 40
O204 15 c. sepia 1·75 85
O205 20 c. red 1·25 30
O206 21 c. green 1·60 85
O207 25 c. purple 55 35
O208 30 c. brown 1·25 50
O209 50 c. sepia 8·00 1·90
O210 60 c. purple 1·25 90
O211 1 p. green 17·00 5·75
O212 2 p. red 6·25 5·25

1934. As T **11** but value in "CENTS" or "PIASTRES" and optd **SERVICE.**
O219 1 c. brown 55 40
O220 2 c. brown 60 40
O221 3 c. green 55 30
O222 4 c. red 90 75
O223 5 c. orange 45 30
O224 6 c. red 3·50 2·75
O225 10 c. green 1·60 1·40
O226 15 c. blue 1·40 95
O227 20 c. green 95 75
O228 21 c. violet 5·25 4·25
O229 25 c. purple 6·25 3·50
O230 30 c. violet 90 60
O231 50 c. mauve 4·00 4·25
O232 60 c. grey 7·00 5·25
O233 1 p. blue 16·00 8·25
O234 2 p. red 24·00 17·00

PARCEL POST STAMPS

1891. Stamp of French Colonies, "Commerce" type, optd **INDO-CHINE TIMBRE COLIS POSTAUX.**
P4 J 10 c. black on lilac 8·75 2·00

1898. No. 10 optd **Colis Postaux.**
P20 D 10 c. black on lilac 10·00 10·00

1899. Nos. 10 and 24 optd **TIMBRE COLIS POSTAUX.**
P21 D 10 c. black on lilac 27·00 12·00
P22 10 c. red 24·00 9·75

POSTAGE DUE STAMPS.

1904. Postage Due stamps of French Colonies optd with value in figures.
D48 U 5 on 40 c. black 17·00 6·00
D47 5 on 60 c. brown on yell 6·25 4·75
D49 10 on 60 c. black 17·00 8·00
D50 30 on 60 c. black 17·00 8·75

D 13 Annamite Dragon

D 28 Mot Cot Pagoda Hanoi

D 29 Annamite Dragon

1908.
D69 D **13** 2 c. black 60 45
D70 4 c. blue 50 45
D71 5 c. green 50 45
D72 10 c. red 1·50 45
D73 15 c. violet 1·50 1·25
D74 20 c. brown 60 50
D75 30 c. olive 65 50
D76 40 c. purple 5·00 4·00
D77 50 c. blue 2·50 75
D78 60 c. yellow 5·50 5·00
D79 1 f. grey 10·00 9·00
D80 2 f. brown 9·25 7·00
D81 5 f. red 17·00 12·00

1919. Surch in figures and words.
D106 D **13** $\frac{4}{5}$ c. on 2 c. black 1·10 55
D107 $1\frac{3}{5}$ c. on 4 c. blue 95 60
D108 2 c. on 5 c. green 1·60 85
D109 4 c. on 10 c. red 1·10 50
D110 6 c. on 15 c. violet 3·50 1·60
D111 8 c. on 20 c. brown 3·50 85
D112 12 c. on 30 c. green 3·50 1·00
D113 16 c. on 40 c. brown 3·50 85
D114 20 c. on 50 c. blue 6·00 3·75
D115 24 c. on 60 c. yellow 1·50 1·10
D116 40 c. on 1 f. grey 2·00 1·10
D117 80 c. on 2 f. brown 16·00 12·50
D118 2 p. on 5 f. red 28·00 15·00

1922. Type D **13**, but values in cents. or piastres.
D136 D **13** $\frac{2}{5}$ c. black 15 25
D137 $\frac{3}{5}$ c. black and red 20 25
D138 1 c. black and yellow 30 25
D139 2 c. black and green 40 40
D140 3 c. black and violet 40 40
D141 4 c. black and orange 35 30
D142 6 c. black and olive 50 50
D143 8 c. black on lilac 50 45
D144 10 c. black and blue 65 30
D145 12 c. blk & orge on grn 70 55
D146 20 c. blk & bl on yell 90 50
D147 40 c. blk & red on grey 90 50
D148 1 p. blk & pur on pk 3·00 1·60

1927.
D160 D **28** $\frac{2}{5}$ c. orange & pur 15 30
D161 $\frac{3}{5}$ c. black & violet 15 30
D162 1 c. grey and red 30 50
D163 2 c. olive and green 50 55
D164 3 c. blue and purple 50 55
D165 4 c. brown and blue 50 55
D166 6 c. red and scarlet 65 60
D167 8 c. violet and brown 65 55
D168 D **29** 10 c. blue 60 35
D169 12 c. brown 2·50 1·90
D170 20 c. red 1·40 75
D171 40 c. green 1·75 1·25
D172 1 p. red 9·75 7·25

D 37

D 62

1931. All values from $\frac{1}{5}$ c. to 50 c. are in the same colours).
D197 D **37** $\frac{1}{5}$ c. blk & red on yell 15 30
D198 $\frac{2}{5}$ c. 15 30
D199 $\frac{3}{5}$ c. 20 30
D200 1 c. 15 30
D201 2 c. 20 25
D202 2,5 c. 20 30
D203 3 c. 20 30
D204 4 c. 20 30
D205 5 c. 20 30
D206 6 c. 20 30
D207 10 c. 20 30
D208 12 c. 20 30
D209 14 c. 20 30
D210 18 c. 30 35
D211 20 c. 25 35
D212 50 c. 25 35
D213 1 p. bl and red on yell 1·10 90

1943.
D296 D **62** 1 c. red on yellow 30 40
D297 2 c. red on yellow 30 40
D298 3 c. red on yellow 30 40
D299 4 c. red on yellow 35 40
D300 6 c. red on yellow 35 40
D301 10 c. red on yellow 35 40
D302 12 c. blue on pink 35 40
D303 20 c. blue on pink 35 40
D304 30 c. blue on pink 35 40

INDO-CHINESE POST OFFICES IN CHINA Pt. 6, Pt. 17

General Issues.

100 centimes = 1 franc.

1902. Stamps of Indo-China, "Tablet" key-type, surch **CHINE** and value in Chinese.
15 D 1 c. black on blue 1·00 85
2 2 c. brown on buff 1·75 1·60
17 4 c. brown on grey 1·25 1·00
18 5 c. green 1·25 1·25
5 10 c. red 1·75 1·60
6 15 c. grey 2·75 2·75
20 20 c. red on green 3·50 3·00
21 25 c. black on pink 5·00 4·25
22 25 c. blue 4·00 3·50
23 30 c. brown on drab 2·50 2·50
24 40 c. red on yellow 11·50 10·00
11 50 c. red on pink 40·00 35·00
25 50 c. brown on blue 6·25 5·00
26 75 c. brown on orange 18·00 15·00
27 1 f. green 22·00 22·00
28 5 f. mauve on lilac 55·00 48·00

1904. Stamps of Indo-China surch **CHINE** and value in Chinese.
29 **8** 1 c. olive 65 65
30 2 c. red on yellow 65 70
31 4 c. brown on grey £625 £425
32 5 c. green 80 80
33 10 c. red 80 80
34 15 c. brown on blue 80 75
36 20 c. red on green 5·75 5·50
37 25 c. blue 2·75 1·60
38 40 c. black on grey 2·50 1·75
39 1 f. green £225 £170
40 2 f. brown on yellow 15·00 13·50
41 10 f. red on green 90·00 80·00

INDONESIA Pt. 4, Pt. 21

An independent republic was proclaimed in Java and Sumatra on 17 August 1945 and lasted until the end of 1948. During this period the Dutch controlled the rest of the Netherlands Indies, renamed "Indonesia" in September 1948. On 27 December 1949 all Indonesia except New Guinea became independent as the United States of Indonesia which, during 1950, amalgamated with the original Indonesian Republic (Java and Sumatra), a single state being proclaimed on 15 August 1950 as the Indonesian Republic. This was within the Netherlands-Indonesian Union which was abolished on 10 August 1954.

100 cents (or sen) = 1 gulden (or rupiah).

A. DUTCH ADMINISTRATION

1948. Stamps of Netherlands Indies optd **INDONESIA** and bar or bars.
541 **81** 15 c. orange 75 10
533 20 c. blue 15 10
543 25 c. green 15 10
535 40 c. green 20 10
544 45 c. mauve 1·25 85
545 50 c. lake 20 10
536 80 c. red 65 10
537a 1 g. violet 55 10
538 – $2\frac{1}{2}$ g. orange (No. 479) 32·00 8·75
539 **81** 10 g. green 65·00 27·00
540 25 g. orange 90·00 50·00

86

87 Portal to Tjandi Poentadewa Temple

89 Globe and Arms of Berne

1949. New Currency.
548 **86** 1 s. grey 15 10
549 2 s. purple 20 10
550 $2\frac{1}{2}$ s. brown 15 10
551 3 s. red 20 10
552 4 s. green 60 1·25
553 5 s. blue 10 10
554 $7\frac{1}{2}$ s. green 60 10
555 10 s. mauve 15 10
556 $12\frac{1}{2}$ s. red 2·00 10
557 **87** 15 s. red 25 10
558 20 s. black 25 10
559 25 s. blue 25 10
560 – 30 s. red 25 10
561 – 40 s. green 25 10
562 – 45 s. purple 25 3·00
563 – 50 s. brown 25 10
564 – 60 s. brown 90 1·50
565 – 80 s. red 1·25 10
566 – 1 r. violet 1·75 10
567 – 2 r. green 3·25 10
568 – 3 r. purple 75·00 1·00
569 – 5 r. brown 50·00 1·25
570 – 10 r. black 50·00 3·75
571 – 25 r. brown 7·50 3·75
DESIGNS:—As Type **87**: 30 to 45 s. Sculpture from Temple at Bedjoening, Bali; 50 to 80 s. Minangkabau house, Sumatra; 21 × 26 mm: 1 to 3 r. Toradja house; 5 to 25 r. Detail of Temple of Panahan.

1949. 75th Anniv of U.P.U.
572 **89** 15 s. red 85 30
573 25 s. blue 1·00 50

B. REPUBLIC 1945–48 Issues for JAVA and MADURA

1945. Stamps of Netherlands Indies optd **REPOEBLIK INDONESIA.**
J 1 **46** 1 c. violet 90 2·00
J 2 2 c. purple 5·00 6·25
J19 – 2 c. red (No. 461) 95 2·50
J 4 – $2\frac{1}{2}$ c. red (No. 462) 1·50 2·50
J 5 – 3 c. green (No. 463) 1·90 2·00
J 3 **46** $3\frac{1}{2}$ c. grey 55·00 65·00
J 6 **71** 4 c. olive 1·50 2·00
J 7 5 c. blue (No. 465) 65·00 90·00

1945. Stamps of Japanese Occupation of Netherlands Indies optd as above.
J 8 – $3\frac{1}{2}$ s. red (No. 2) £250 £350
J10 – $3\frac{1}{2}$ c. red (No. 5) 17·50 32·00
J 9 – 5 s. green (No. 3) 10·00 8·75
J11 **2** 5 s. green 35 75
J12 – 10 c. blue (No. 7) 35 90
J13 – 20 c. olive (No. 8) 65 90
J14 – 40 c. purple (No. 9) 1·25 1·50
J15 **4** 60 c. orange 1·50 1·90
J16 – 80 s. brown (No. 11) 12·50 19·00

J 5 Bull

1945. Declaration of Independence. Inscr "17 AGOESTOES 1945". Perf or imperf.
J23 **J 5** 10 s. (+ 10 s.) brown . . . 5·00 7·50
J24 – 20 s. (+ 10 s.) brown & red 5·00 7·50
DESIGN—VERT: 20 s. Bull and Indonesian flag.

J 9 Boat in Storm
J 10 Wayang Puppet

1946.
J49 – 5 s. blue . . . . 90 1·10
J50 – 20 s. brown . . . . 1·10 1·40
J51 **J 9** 30 s. red . . . . 1·00 3·75
DESIGNS: 5 s. Road and mountains; 20 s. Soldier on waterfront.

1946.
J52 **J 10** 50 s. blue . . . . 12·50 12·50
J53 – 60 s. red . . . . 5·00 £150
J54 – 80 s. violet . . . . 65·00 £150
DESIGNS: 60 s. Kris and flag; 80 s. Temple.

J 13 Buffalo breaking Chains
J 14 Bandung, March, 1946

1946. Perf or imperf.
J55 **J 13** 3 s. red 10 50
J56 **J 14** 5 s. blue 45 65
J57 – 10 s. black . . . . . . 7·50 10·00
J58 – 15 s. purple 90 90
J59 – 30 s. green . . . . . . 1·25 1·50
J60 – 40 s. blue . . . . 1·00 1·00
J61a **J 13** 50 s. black . . . . . . 1·10 1·00
J62 **J 14** 60 s. lilac . . . . . . 1·50 2·00
J63 – 80 s. red . . . . 1·25 8·75
J64 – 100 s. red . . . . . . 1·00 1·00
J65 – 200 s. lilac . . . . . . 1·10 1·90
J66 – 500 s. red . . . . . . 5·00 7·50
J67 – 1000 s. green . . . . . 5·00 7·50
DESIGNS—HORIZ: 10, 15 s. Soerabaya, November 1945; 30 s. Anti-aircraft gunners; 100 s. Ambarawa, November 1945; 200 s. Wonokromo Dam, Soerabaya; 1000 s. Cavalryman. VERT: 40 s. Quay at Tandjong Priok; 80 s. Airman; 500 s. Mass meeting with flags, Djakarta.

1948. Postage Due Stamps of Netherlands Indies surch **SEGEL 25 sen PORTO**.
J68 **D 7** 25 s. on 7½ c. orange . . . 12·50 30·00
J69 25 s. on 15 c. orange . . . 10·00 25·00
Although surcharged for use as postage due stamps the above were employed for ordinary postal use.

J 16 "Labour and Transport"
J 18 Flag over Waves

1948. 3rd Anniv of Independence. Imperf.
J70 **J 16** 50 s. blue . . . . 6·00 8·00
J71 100 s. red . . . . 9·50 10·00

1949. Government's Return to Jogjakarta. Perf. or Imperf.
J77 **J 18** 100 s. red . . . . 6·25 18·00
J78 150 s. red . . . . 10·00 25·00

POSTAGE DUE STAMPS

1948. Nos. J67 and J70/1 optd **DENDA**, or surch also.
JD72 **J 16** 50 s. blue . . . . . . — 13·50
JD73 – 100 s. red . . . . . . — 13·50
JD74 – 1 r. on 50 s. blue (A) . . — 13·50
JD75 1 r. on 50 s. blue (B) . . — 13·50
JD76 – 1 r. on 1000 s. green . . — 13·50
A. Surcharged "RP 1"; B. Surcharged "1—RP".

ISSUES FOR SUMATRA

1946. Stamps of Netherlands Indies surch **Repoeblik Indonesia** and value.
S1 – 15 s. on 5 c. blue (No. 465) . 2·50 3·75
S2 **46** 20 s. on 3½ c. grey . . . . 12·50 12·50
S3 30 s. on 1 c. violet . . . 12·50 12·50
S4 40 s. on 2 c. purple . . . . 60 1·75
S7 – 50 s. on 17½ c. orange (No. 431) . . . . . . 10·00 10·00
S 9 **46** 60 s. on 2½ c. bistre . . . 17·50 17·50
S10 80 s. on 3 c. green . . . . 12·50 12·50
S11 – 1 r. on 10 c. red (No. 429) . 3·00 3·00

S 9 Ploughing
S 10 Pres. Sukarno
S 12

1946. Freedom Fund.
S17 **S 9** 5 s. (+25 s.) green . . . . 75 7·50
S18 5 s. (+25 s.) blue . . . . 65 5·00
S19 – 15 s. (+35 s.) red . . . . 5·00 12·50
S20 – 15 s. (+35 s.) blue . . . 60 5·00
S21 – 40 s. (+60 s.) orange . . . 1·00 7·50
S22 – 40 s. (+60 s.) red . . . . 2·50 15·00
S23 – 40 s. (+60 s.) purple . . . 9·25 32·00
S24 – 40 s. (+60 s.) brown . . . 19·00 60·00
DESIGNS—VERT: 15 s. Soldier and flag; 40 s. Oil well and factories, Palembang.

1946.
S25 **S 10** 40 s. (+60 s.) red . . . . 1·50 19·00

1946. "FONDS KEMERDEKAAN" obliterated by one or two bars.
S27 **S 9** 5 s. blue . . . . 60·00 85·00
S28 – 40 s. red (No. S22) . . . 60·00 85·00

1946. As Type **S 9** but without "FONDS KEMERDEKAAN". Perf or imperf.
S29 2 s. red . . . . 1·00 15·00
S30 2 s. brown . . . . 6·25 38·00
S31 3 s. green . . . . 1·00 15·00
S32 3 s. red . . . . 7·50 38·00
S33 3 s. blue £180
S34 5 s. blue . . . . 85 8·75
S35 15 s. blue . . . . 60 4·00
S36 15 s. green . . . . 4·00 38·00
S37 40 s. brown . . . . 60 6·25
S38 40 s. blue . . . . 20·00 60·00
DESIGNS: 2, 3, 5 s. As Type **S 9**. 15 s. Soldier and flag; 40 s. Oil well and factories, Palembang.

1947. Fund for Palembang War Victims. Nos. S18, S20 and S23 optd **BPKPP** over triple circle.
S39 **S 9** 5 s. blue . . . . 85·00 £125
S40 – 15 s. blue . . . . 85·00 £125
S41 – 40 s. brown . . . . . . 85·00 £125

1947. Fiscal stamps of Japanese Occupation with blank panels optd in black with **prangko N.R.I** and value as in Type **S 12**.
S42 **S 12** 0 f. 50 orange . . . . . 30·00 50·00
S43 1 f. orange . . . . . 25·00 38·00
S44 2 f. orange . . . . . 38·00 50·00
S45 2 f. 50 orange . . . . . 20·00 25·00

1947. No. S25 surch with new value and bars.
S46 50 s. on 40 s. red . . . . . . 6·25 8·75
S47 1 f. on 40 s. red . . . . . . 10·00 8·75
S48 1 f. 50 on 40 s. red . . . . . 6·25 8·75
S49 2 f. 50 on 40 s. red . . . . . 95 4·25
S50 3 f. 50 on 40 s. red . . . . . 95 4·25
S51 5 f. on 40 s. red . . . . . . 95 4·25

1947. Surch with ornament and new value.
S63 1 s. on 15 s. (No. S35) . . . . 60 6·25
S64 5 s. on 3 s. (No. S33) . . . . 60 6·25
S65 10 s. on 15 s. red (as Nos. S35/6) . . . . 60 6·25
S52 30 s. on 40 s. (No. S28) . . . 1·10 3·75
S66 50 s. on 3 s. (No. S32) . . . 20·00 38·00
S53 50 s. on 5 s. (No. S34) . . . 8·75 8·75
S59 50 s. on 40 s. (No. S28) . . . 19·00 25·00
S54 1 f. on 5 s. (No. S34) . . . 8·75 8·75
S60 1 f. on 40 s. (No. S28) . . . 1·00 3·75
S55 1 f. 50 on 5 s. (No. S34) . . . 8·75 8·75
S61 1 f. 50 on 40 s. (No. S28) . . 2·50 3·75
S62 2 f. 50 on 40 s. (No. S28) . . 1·00 3·75
S56 1 r. on 40 s. (No. S37) . . . 60 6·25
S57 2 r. on 5 s. (No. S34) . . . 1·00 6·25

1947. No. S56 surch **50**.
S58 50(r.) on 1 r. on 40 s. . . . . 60·00 85·00

1947. Air. Surch **Pos Udara** with ornament and new value.
S67 10 r. on 40 s. (No. S22) . . . 5·00 7·50
S68 20 r. on 5 s. (No. S34) . . . 2·50 7·50

1947. Stamps of 1946 (Nos. S 29/37) surch.
S69 10 s. on 15 s. blue . . . . . 15·00 15·00
S70 20 s. on 15 s. blue . . . . . 22·00 22·00
S71 30 s. on 15 s. blue . . . . . 15·00 15·00
S75 50 s. on 5 s. blue £1100 £1100
S76 50 s. on 15 s. blue £500 £500
S77 0 f. 50 on 15 s. blue £1100 £1100
S78 1 f. on 5 s. blue £250 £250
S79 1 f. on 15 s. blue £400 £400
S72 1 r. on 2 s. red . . . . . . 70·00 70·00
S88 2 r. on 3 s. green . . . . . 22·00 38·00
S80 2 f. 50 on 5 s. blue £1100 £1100
S73 2 f. 50 on 15 s. blue . . . . 15·00 15·00
S82 2 f. 50 on 40 s. brown £550 £550
S85 2 r. 50 on 3 s. green . . . . . 22·00 38·00
S83 5 f. on 15 s. blue £1100 £1100
S74 5 f. on 40 s. brown £225 £225
S89 5 r. on 15 s. blue . . . . . 8·75 25·00
S87 10 r. on 3 s. green £140 £140
S91 20 r. on 2 s. red £550 £550
S92 50 r. on 15 s. blue £500 £500
S93 100 r. on 15 s. blue £140 £140
S94 150 r. on 40 s. red £160 £160
No. S94 is surcharged on No. S22 with a pen-stroke through "FONDS KEMERDEKAAN".

(**S 23**) "O.R.I." = "Oeang Repoeblik Indonesia" (Indonesian Republican Money)

1947. Change of Currency. Various stamps optd with Type **S 23**.

(a) On stamps of Netherlands Indies.
S 99 **D 7** 1 c. red (No. D226) . . . 6·50 7·00
S 96 **46** 3 c. green (No. 338) . . . 4·00 5·00
S 97 **71** 4 c. olive (No. 464) . . . 6·00 6·50
S 98 – 5 c. blue (No. 465) . . . 3·00 4·50
S100 **D 7** 15 c. red (No. D448) . . . 5·00 6·00

(b) On stamps of Japanese Occupation of Netherlands Indies.
S101 – 1 c. green (No. 15) . . . . 90 1·25
S102 – 2 c. green (No. 16) . . . . 90 1·25
S103 – 3 c. blue (No. 17) . . . . 90 1·25
S104 – 3½ c. red (No. 18) . . . . 1·25 1·60
S105 – 4 c. blue (No. 19) . . . . 2·00 3·00
S106 – 5 c. orange (No. 20) . . . 1·25 1·60
S107 – 10 c. blue (No. 21) . . . . 5·00 5·50
S111 – 10 c. red (No. 57) 70 90
S108 – 20 c. brown (No. 22) . . . 5·00 5·50
S113 – 25 c. green (No. 62) . . . 8·00 10·00
S109 **6** 30 c. purple (No. 23) . . . 90 90
S114 – 30 c. brown (No. 63) . . . 6·50 7·50
S110 – 50 c. brown (No. 25) . . . 4·50 4·50
S115 – 50 c. red (No. 66) . . . . 8·50 10·50
S116 – 60 c. blue (No. 67) . . . . 4·50 5·00
S117 – 80 c. red (No. 68) . . . . 4·50 6·00
S118 – 1 g. violet (No. 69) . . . . 8·50 10·00

(c) On stamps of Japan.
S119 – 1 s. brown (No. 317) . . . 80 1·25
S120 – 3 s. green (No. 319) . . . 80 1·25
S121 – 4 s. green (No. 320) . . . 4·00 4·50
S122 – 6 s. orange (No. 322) . . . 1·25 1·60
S123 – 25 s. brn & choc (No. 329) . 80 1·25
S124 – 30 s. green (No. 330) . . . 2·00 2·75
S125 – 50 s. grn & bis (No. 331) . . 80 1·25
S126 – 1 y. brown and chocolate (No. 332) . . . . 2·00 2·75

(d) On stamps of Indonesia-Sumatra.
S149 – 1 s. on 15 s. bl (No. S63) . . 15·00 15·00
S136 – 2 s. red (No. S29) . . . . 12·50 12·50
S137 – 3 s. green (No. S31) . . . 15·00 15·00
S138 – 3 s. red (No. S32) . . . . 12·50 12·50
S132 **S 9** 5 s. grn (No. S17) . . . . 13·50 13·50
S133 – 5 s. blue (No. S18) . . . . 5·00 5·00
S139 – 5 s. blue (No. S34) . . . . 7·50 7·50
S150 – 10 s. on 15 s. red (No. S65) . . . . 15·00 15·00
S134 – 15 s. blue (No. S20) . . . . 20·00 20·00
S140 – 15 s. blue (No. S35) . . . . 3·75 3·75
S141 – 15 s. grn (No. S36) . . . . 6·25 6·25
S127 **46** 20 s. on 3½ c. grey (No. S2) . . . . 38·00 38·00
S128 – 30 s. on 1 c. violet (No. S3) . . . . 35·00 35·00
S146 – 30 s. on 40 s. red (No. S52) . . . . 12·50 12·50
S129 **46** 40 s. on 2 c. purple (No. S4) . . . . 12·50 12·50
S135 – 40 s. red (No. S22) . . . . 7·50 7·50
S142 – 40 s. brn (No. S37) . . . . 6·25 6·25
S151 – 50 s. on 5 s. blue (No. S53) . . . . 20·00 20·00
S143 – 1 f. 50 on 40 s. red (No. S48) . . . . 30·00 30·00
S147 – 1 f. 50 on 40 s. red (No. S61) . . . . 12·50 12·50
S152 – 1 f. 50 on 5 s. blue (No. S55) . . . . 30·00 30·00
S153 – 2 r. on 5 s. blue (No. S57) . 20·00 20·00
S144 – 2 f. 50 on 40 s. red (No. S49) . . . . 22·00 22·00
S148 – 2 f. 50 on 40 s. red (No. S62) . . . . 12·50 12·50
S145 – 3 f. 50 on 40 s. red (No. S50) . . . . 10·00 10·00
S154 – 10 r. on 40 s. red (No. S67) . . . . 38·00 38·00

C. UNITED STATES OF INDONESIA

90 Indonesian Flag

1950. Inauguration of United States of Indonesia.
574 **90** 15 s. red (20½ × 26 mm.) . . 1·00 10
575 15 s. red (18 × 23 mm.) . . . 5·25 1·00

1950. Stamps of 1949 optd **RIS.**
579 **86** 1 s. grey 75 65
580 2 s. purple . . . . 1·00 1·75
581 2½ s. brown 75 50
582 3 s. red 75 35
583 4 s. green 75 65
584 5 s. blue 75 65
585 7½ s. green 75 65
586 10 s. mauve 75 65
587 12½ s. red 90 65
588 **87** 20 s. black . . . . 22·00 25·00
589 25 s. blue 75 50
590 – 30 s. red . . . . 7·50 16·00
591 – 40 s. green 75 40
592 – 45 s. purple . . . . . . 1·50 1·00
593 – 50 s. brown . . . . . . 1·25 75
594 – 60 s. brown . . . . . . 6·25 10·00
595 – 80 s. red . . . . 2·50 75
596 – 1 r. violet . . . . 2·00 35
597 – 2 r. green . . . . £300 75·00
598 – 3 r. purple . . . . . . £100 50·00
599 – 5 r. brown . . . . . . 38·00 15·00
600 – 10 r. black . . . . . . 65·00 32·00
601 – 25 r. brown . . . . . . 19·00 12·50

D. INDONESIAN REPUBLIC

94 Indonesian Arms
95 Maps and Torch

1950. 5th Anniv of Proclamation of Independence.
602 **94** 15 s. red . . . . 2·00 10
603 25 s. green . . . . 2·50 1·00
604 1 r. sepia . . . . 8·25 1·25

1951. Asiatic Olympic Games, New Delhi.
605 **95** 5 s. + 3 s. green 15 10
606 10 s. + 5 s. blue 15 10
607 20 s. + 5 s. red 15 10
608 30 s. + 10 s. brown 35 20
609 35 s. + 10 s. blue . . . . 1·40 2·00

96
97 General Post-Office, Bandung

98 "Spirit of Indonesia"
99 President Sukarno

1951.
610 **96** 1 s. grey 35 65
611 2 s. mauve 35 55
612 2½ s. brown . . . . 4·50 15
613 5 s. red 35 15
614 7½ s. green 35 15
615 10 s. blue 35 10
616 15 s. violet 35 10
618 20 s. red 35 10
619 25 s. green 35 10
620 **97** 30 s. red 15 10
621 35 s. violet 65 10
622 40 s. green 15 10
623 45 s. purple 15 10
624 50 s. brown . . . . 2·75 10
625 **98** 60 s. brown 15 10
626 70 s. grey 15 10
627 75 s. blue 15 10
628 80 s. purple 15 10
629 90 s. green 15 10

1951.
630 **99** 1 r. violet 10 10
631 1 r. 25 orange . . . . . . 1·50 10
632 1 r. 50 brown 10 10
633 2 r. green 10 10
634 2 r. 50 brown 10 10
635 3 r. blue 10 10
636 4 r. green 10 10
637 5 r. brown 10 10
638 6 r. mauve 10 10
639 10 r. grey 10 10
640 15 r. stone 10 10
641 20 r. purple 10 10
642 25 r. red 65 10
643 40 r. green . . . . 65 2·00
644 50 r. violet . . . . 1·00 10

101 Sports Emblem
102 Doves

1951. National Sports Festival.

655 **101** 5 s. + 3 s. green 15 40
656 10 s. + 5 s. blue 15 40
657 20 s. + 5 s. orange 15 40
658 30 s. + 10 s. sepia 15 40
659 35 s. + 10 s. blue 15 90

1951. U.N. Day.

660 **102** 7½ s. green . . . . 4·00 75
661 10 s. violet 90 20
662 20 s. orange 90 20
663 30 s. red 90 50
664 35 s. blue . . . . 90 1·00
665 1 r. sepia . . . . 15·00 2·25

1953. Natural Disasters Relief Fund. Surch **1953 BENTJANA ALAM + 10s.**

666 **97** 35 s. + 10 s. violet 25 10

104 Melati Flowers

105 Merapi Volcano in Eruption

1953. Mothers' Day and 25th Anniv of Indonesian Women's Congress.

667 **104** 50 s. green . . . . 10·00 50

1954. Natural Disasters Relief Fund.

668 **105** 15 s. + 10 s. green . . . 1·00 1·25
669 35 s. + 15 s. violet . . . 1·00 1·00
670 50 s. + 25 s. red . . . . 1·00 1·00
671 75 s. + 25 s. blue . . . . 1·00 1·00
672 1 r. + 25 s. red . . . . . 1·00 1·00
673 2 r. + 50 s. brown . . . . 2·50 1·00
674a 3 r. + 1 r. green . . . . 12·50 5·00
675a 5 r. + 2 r. 50 brown . . . 15·00 7·50

106 Girls with Musical Instruments

107 Globe and Doves

1954. Child Welfare.

676 **106** 10 s. + 10 s. purple . . . 10 50
677 – 15 s. + 10 s. green 10 60
678 – 35 s. + 15 s. mauve . . . 10 60
679 – 50 s. + 15 s. purple . . . 50 60
680 – 75 s. + 25 s. blue . . . . 15 2·40
681 – 1 r. + 25 s. red . . . . . 45 4·25

DESIGNS: 15 s. Menangkabau boy and girl performing Umbrella Dance; 35 s. Girls playing "Tjongkak"; 50 s. Boy on bamboo stilts; 75 s. Ambonese boys playing flutes; 1 r. Srimpi dancing girl.

1955. Asian-African Conference, Bandung.

682 **107** 15 s. black 50 50
683 35 s. brown 50 20
684 50 s. red . . . . 1·75 10
685 75 s. turquoise 80 10

108 Semaphore Signaller

109 Proclamation of Independence

1955. National Scout Jamboree.

686 – 15 s. + 10 s. green 20 45
687 **108** 35 s. + 15 s. blue 20 45
688 – 50 s. + 25 s. red 20 45
689 – 75 s. + 25 s. brown 20 45
690 – 1 r. + 50 s. violet 20 45

DESIGNS: 15 s. Indonesian scout badge; 50 s. Scouts round campfire; 75 s. Scout feeding baby sika deer; 1 r. Scout saluting.

1955. 10th Anniv of Independence.

691 **109** 15 s. green 65 60
692 35 s. blue 65 60
693 50 s. brown . . . . 5·00 35
694 75 s. purple 95 35

110 Postmaster Sukarto

111 Electors

1955. 10th Anniv of Indonesian Post Office.

695 **110** 15 s. brown 75 20
696 35 s. red 75 20
697 50 s. blue . . . . 5·00 1·50
698 75 s. green 95 20

1955. First General Indonesian Elections.

699 **111** 15 s. purple 35 20
700 35 s. green 35 20
701 50 s. red . . . . 1·60 20
702 75 s. blue 65 20

112 Memorial Column, Wreath and Helmet

113 Weaving

1955. Heroes' Day.

703 **112** 25 s. green 80 35
704 50 s. blue 80 20
705 1 r. red . . . . 7·00 20

1956. Blind Relief Fund.

706 **113** 15 s. + 10 s. green 40 50
707 – 35 s. + 15 s. brown . . . 40 50
708 – 50 s. + 25 s. red . . . . 1·10 1·00
709 – 75 s. + 50 s. blue 40 50

DESIGNS—VERT: 35 s. Basketwork; 50 s. Map reading; 75 s. Reading.

114 Torch and Book

115 Lesser Malay Chevrotain

1956. Asian and African Students' Conf, Bandung.

710 **114** 25 s. blue 85 60
711 50 s. red . . . . 4·50 20
712 1 r. green 85 20

1956.

713 **115** 5 s. blue 10 10
714 10 s. brown 10 10
715 15 s. purple 10 10
716 – 20 s. green 10 10
717 – 25 s. purple 10 10
718 – 30 s. orange 10 10
719 – 35 s. blue 10 10
720 – 40 s. green 10 10
721 – 45 s. purple . . . . 1·00 10
722 – 50 s. bistre 10 10
723 – 60 s. blue 10 10
724 – 70 s. red . . . . 1·50 10
725 – 75 s. sepia 10 10
726 – 80 s. red 15 15
727 – 90 s. green 15 15

DESIGNS: 20 s. to 30 s. Hairy-nosed otter; 35 s. to 45 s. Malayan pangolin; 50 s. to 70 s. Banteng; 75 s. to 90 s. Sumatran rhinoceros.

116 Red Cross

117

1956. Red Cross Fund.

728 **116** 10 s. + 10 s. red and blue . 20 10
729 15 s. + 10 s. red & carm . 20 10
730 – 35 s. + 15 s. red & brown . 20 10
731 – 50 s. + 15 s. red & green . 20 10
732 – 75 s. + 25 s. red & orge . . 25 45
733 – 1 r. + 25 s. red & violet . . 25 45

DESIGNS: 35 s., 50 s. Blood transfusion bottle; 75 s., 1 r. Hands and drop of blood.

1956. Bicentenary of Djokjakarta.

734 **117** 15 s. green 90 10
735 35 s. brown 90 10
736 50 s. blue . . . . 2·50 1·10
737 75 s. purple . . . . 2·00 45

118 Crippled Child

119 Telegraph Key and Tape

120 Two men with Savings-box

1957. Cripples' Rehabilitation Fund. Inscr "UNTUK PENDERITA TJATJAT".

738 – 10 s. + 10 s. blue 15 10
739 – 15 s. + 10 s. brown . . . 15 10
740 – 35 s. + 15 s. red 15 10
741 **118** 50 s. + 15 s. violet 15 10
742 – 75 s. + 25 s. green 20 25
743 – 1 r. + 25 s. red 20 25

DESIGNS: 10 s. One-legged woman painting cloth; 15 s. One-handed artist; 35 s. One-handed machinist; 75 s. Doctor tending cripple; 1 r. Man writing with artificial arm.

1957. Centenary of Telegraphs in Indonesia.

744 **119** 10 s. red . . . . 1·60 75
745 15 s. blue 50 60
746 25 s. black 50 15
747 50 s. red 60 20
748 75 s. green 65 15

1957. Co-operation Day. Inscr "HARI KOOPERASI".

749 **120** 10 s. blue 25 20
750 – 15 s. red 40 20
751 **120** 50 s. green 65 35
752 – 1 r. violet 80 10

DESIGN: 15 s., 1 r. "Co-operative Prosperity" (hands holding ear of rice and cotton).

121 Kembodja ("Plumeria acuminata")

122 Convair CV 340 Airliner

1957. Various Charity Funds. Floral designs. Multicoloured.

753 10 s. + 10 s. Type **121** . . . . 1·60 40
754 15 s. + 10 s. Tjempakakuning (michelia) . . . . 1·10 40
755 35 s. + 15 s. Matahari (sun-flower) 55 35
756 50 s. + 15 s. Melati (jasmine) . 40 25
757 75 s. + 50 s. Larat (orchid) . . 40 25

1958. National Aviation Day. Inscr "HARI PENERBANGAN NASIONAL 9–4–1958".

758 **122** 10 s. brown 15 15
759 – 15 s. blue 15 15
760 – 35 s. orange 30 20
761 **122** 50 s. turquoise 65 30
762 – 75 s. slate 95 40

DESIGNS: 15 s. Hiller "Skeeter" helicopter; 35 s. Nurtiano Sikumbang trainer; 75 s. De Havilland Vampire jet fighter.

123 "Helping Hands"

124 Thomas Cup

1958. Indonesian Orphans Welfare Fund Inscr "ANAK PIATU".

763 **123** 10 s. + 10 s. blue 10 15
764 – 15 s. + 10 s. red 10 15
765 **123** 35 s. + 15 s. green 10 15
766 – 50 s. + 25 s. drab 10 15
767 **123** 75 s. + 50 s. brown 10 15
768 – 1 r. + 50 s. brown 10 15

DESIGN: 15 s., 50 s., 1 r. Girl and boy orphans.

1958. Indonesian Victory in Thomas Cup World Badminton Championships, Singapore.

769 **124** 25 s. red 15 10
770 50 s. orange 15 10
771 1 r. brown 15 10

125 Satellite encircling Globe

126 Racing Cyclist

1958. International Geophysical Year

785 **125** 10 s. pink, green & blue . . 75 50
786 15 s. drab, violet & grey . . 20 10
787 35 s. blue, sepia & pink . . 20 10
788 50 s. brown, blue & drab . . 20 10
789 75 s. lilac, black & yellow . 20 10

1958. Tour of Java Cycle Race.

790 **126** 25 s. blue 15 15
791 50 s. red 25 15
792 1 r. grey 15 10

127 "Human Rights"

128 Babirusa

129 Indonesian Scout Badge

1958. 10th Anniv of Declaration of Human Rights.

793 **127** 10 s. sepia 10 10
794 – 15 s. brown 10 10
795 – 35 s. blue 10 10
796 – 50 s. bistre 15 10
797 – 75 s. green 15 10

DESIGNS: 15 s. Hands grasping "Flame of Freedom"; 35 s. Native holding candle; 50 s. Family acclaiming "Flame of Freedom"; 75 s. "Flame" superimposed on figure "10".

1959. Animal Protection Campaign.

798 **128** 10 s. sepia and olive . . . 10 10
799 – 15 s. sepia and brown . . . 20 10
800 – 20 s. sepia and green . . . 20 10
801 – 50 s. sepia and brown . . . 25 10
802 – 75 s. sepia and red 25 15
803 – 1 r. black and turquoise . . 30 15

ANIMALS: 15 s. Anoa (buffalo); 20 s. Orang-utan; 50 s. Javan rhinoceros; 75 s. Komodo lizard; 1 r. Malayan tapir.

1959. 10th World Scout Jamboree, Manila. Inscr as in T **129**. Badges in red.

804 **129** 10 s. + 5 s. bistre 10 10
805 – 15 s. + 10 s. green 10 10
806 **129** 20 s. + 10 s. violet 10 10
807 – 50 s. + 25 s. olive 10 10
808 **129** 75 s. + 35 s. brown . . . 10 10
809 – 1 r. + 50 s. slate 15 10

DESIGN: 15 s., 50 s., 1 r. Scout badge within compass.

130

131 Factory and Girder

1959. Re-adoption of 1945 Constitution.

810 **130** 20 s. red and blue 10 10
811 50 s. black and red 10 10
812 75 s. red and brown . . . 10 10
813 1 r. 50 black and green . . 10 10

1959. 11th Colombo Plan Conf, Djakarta.

814 **131** 15 s. black and green . . . 10 10
815 – 20 s. black and orange . . 10 10
816 **131** 50 s. black and red . . . 10 10
817 – 75 s. black and blue . . . 10 10
818 – 1 r. 15 black and purple . . 15 15

DESIGNS: 20, 75 s. Cogwheel and diesel train; 1 r. 15, Forms of transport and communications.

132

133 Refugee Camp

1960. Indonesian Youth Conf, Bandung. Inscr "1960".

819 **132** 15 s. + 5 s. sep & bistre . . 10 10
820 – 20 s. + 10 s. sep & grn . . 10 10
821 **132** 50 s. + 25 s. pur & blue . . 10 10
822 – 75 s. + 35 s. grn & bis . . 10 10
823 – 1 r. 15 + 50 s. blk & red . 25 15

DESIGNS: 20 s., 75 s. Test-tubes in frame; 1 r. 15, Youth wielding manifesto.

1960. World Refugee Year. Centres in black.

824 **133** 10 s. purple 10 10
825 – 15 s. ochre 10 10
826 – 20 s. brown 10 10
827 **133** 50 s. green 10 10
828 – 75 s. blue 15 10
829 – 1 r. 15 red 20 20

DESIGNS: 15 s., 75 s. Outcast family; 20 s., 1 r. 15, "Care of refugees" (refugee with protecting hands).

134 Tea plants

135 Mosquito

1960. Agricultural Products.

830 – 5 s. grey 10 10
831 – 10 s. brown 10 10
832 – 15 s. purple 10 10
833 – 20 s. bistre 10 10
834 **134** 25 s. green 10 10
835 – 50 s. blue 10 10
836 – 75 s. red 10 10
837 – 1 r. 15 red 10 10

DESIGNS: 5 s. Oil palm; 10 s. Sugar cane; 15 s. Coffee plant; 20 s. Tobacco plant; 50 s. Coconut palm; 75 s. Rubber trees; 1 r. 15, Rice plants.

1960. World Health Day.

838 **135** 25 s. red 20 10
839 50 s. brown 20 10
840 75 s. green 20 10
841 3 r. orange 20 10

136 Socialist Emblem

1960. 3rd Socialist Day. Inscr as in T **136**.

842 **136** 10 s. + 10 s. brn & black . 10 10
843 – 15 s. + 15 s. pur & black . 10 10
844 – 20 s. + 20 s. blue & black . 10 10
845 – 50 s. + 25 s. black & brn . 15 15
846 – 75 s. + 25 s. black & grn . 15 20
847 – 3 r. + 50 s. black & red . . 20 20

DESIGNS: 15 s. Emblem similar to Type **136** within plants; 20 s. Lotus flower; 50 s. Boy and girl; 75 s. Ceremonial watering of plant; 3 r. Mother with children.

137 Pres. Sukarno and Workers Hoeing

1961. National Development Plan.

848 **137** 75 s. black 25 10

1961. Flood Relief Fund. Nos. 832/3 and 836 surch **BENTJANA ALAM 1961** and premium.

849 15 s. + 10 s. purple 10 10
850 20 s. + 15 s. brown 10 10
851 75 s. + 25 s. red 10 10

139 Bull Race

1961. Tourist Publicity.

852 – 10 s. purple 30 20
853 – 15 s. grey 30 20
854 **139** 20 s. orange 30 20
855 – 25 s. red 30 20
856 – 50 s. lake 30 20
857 – 75 s. brown 30 20
858 – 1 r. green 75 20
859 – 1 r. 50 bistre 75 20
860 – 2 r. blue . . . . 1·10 20
861 – 3 r. grey . . . . 1·10 20

DESIGNS: 10 s. Ambonese boat; 15 s. Tangkuban Perahu crater; 25 s. Daja dancer; 50 s. Toradja houses; 75 s. Balinese temple; 1 r. Lake Toba; 1 r. 50, Bali dancer; 2 r. "Buffalo Hole" (gorge); 3 r. Borobudur temple.

140 Stadium

1961. Thomas Cup World Badminton Championships.

863 **140** 75 s. lilac and blue 10 10
864 1 r. olive and green 10 10
865 3 r. salmon and blue . . . 15 10

141 "United Efforts"

1961. 16th Anniv of Independence.

866 **141** 75 s. violet and blue . . . 10 10
867 1 r. 50 green and cream . . 10 10
868 3 r. red and salmon . . . 15 10

142 Sultan Hasanuddin

1961. National Independence Heroes. Portraits in sepia; inscriptions in black.

869 – 20 s. olive 10 15
870 **142** 25 s. olive 10 15
871 – 30 s. violet 10 15
872 – 40 s. brown 10 15
873 – 50 s. myrtle 10 15
874 – 60 s. turquoise 10 15
875 – 75 s. brown 10 15
876 – 1 r. blue 60 15
877 – 1 r. 25 green 50 15
878 – 1 r. 50 green 60 15
879 – 2 r. red 40 15
880 – 2 r. 50 red 60 15
881 – 3 r. slate 50 15
882 – 4 r. green 35 15
883 – 4 r. 50 purple 20 15
884 – 5 r. red 50 15
885 – 6 r. ochre 60 15
886 – 7 r. 50 blue 65 15
887 – 10 r. green . . . . 1·40 15
888 – 15 r. orange 45 15

PORTRAITS: 20 s. Abdul Muis; 30 s. Surjopranoto; 40 s. Tengku Tjhik Di Tiro; 50 s. Teuku Umar; 60 s. K. H. Samanhudi; 75 s. Capt. Pattimura; 1 r. Raden Adjeng Kartini; 1 r. 25, K. H. Achmad Dahlan; 1 r. 50, Tuanku Imam Bondjol; 2 r. Si Singamangaradja XII; 2 r. 50, Mohammed Husni Thamrin; 3 r. Ki Hadjar Dewantoro; 4 r. Gen. Sudirman; 4 r. 50, Dr. G. S. S. J. Ratulangie; 5 r. Pangeran Diponegoro; 6 r. Dr. Setyabudi; 7 r. 50, H. O. S. Tjokroaminoto; 10 r. K. H. Agus Salim; 15 r. Dr. Soetomo.

143 Census Emblems **144** Nenas (pineapples)

1961. 1st Indonesian Census.

889 **143** 75 s. purple 20 10

1961. Charity Fruits.

890 **144** 20 s. + 10 s. yellow, red and blue 35 25
891 – 75 s. + 25 s. purple, green and slate 40 25
892 – 3 r. + 1 r. red, yell & grn . 70 50

FRUITS: 75 s. Manggis; 3 r. Rambutan.

145 Djataju

1962. Ramayana Dancers.

893 **145** 30 s. brown and ochre . . . 15 15
894 – 40 s. violet and purple . . 15 15
895 – 1 r. purple and green . . . 25 15
896 – 1 r. 50 green and pink . . 25 15
897 – 3 r. blue and green . . . . 1·40 20
898 – 5 r. brown and buff . . . 1·10 20

DANCERS: 40 s. Hanoman; 1 r. Dasamuka; 1 r. 50, Kidang Kentjana; 3 r. Dewi Sinta; 5 r. Rama.

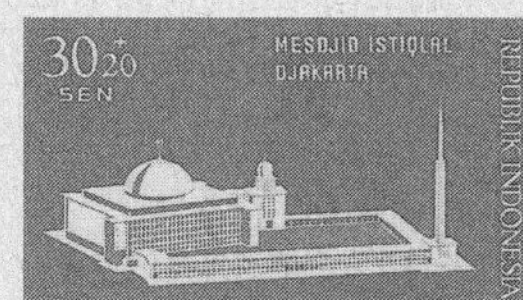

146 Aerial View of Mosque

1962. Construction of Istiqlal Mosque.

899 **146** 30 s. + 20 s. blue & yellow 25 10
900 – 40 s. + 20 s. red & yellow . 25 10
901 **146** 1 r. 50 + 50 s. brn & yell . 25 15
902 – 3 r. + 1 r. green & yellow . 25 20

DESIGN: 40 s., 3 r. Ground-level view of Mosque.

147 Games Emblem **148** Campaign Emblem

1962. 4th Asian Games, Djakarta. Inscr as in T **147**.

903 – 10 s. green and yellow . . 10 10
904 – 15 s. brown and ochre . . 10 10
905 – 20 s. lilac and green . . . 10 10
906 – 25 s. red and green . . . 10 10
907 – 30 s. green and buff . . . 10 10
908 – 40 s. ultramarine & blue . . 10 15
909 – 50 s. brown and drab . . . 10 15
910 – 60 s. mauve and grey . . . 10 15
911 – 70 s. brown and red . . . 10 10
912 – 75 s. brown and orange . . 10 15
913 – 1 r. violet and blue . . . 10 15
914 **147** 1 r. 25 blue and mauve . . 10 15
915 – 1 r. 50 red and mauve . . 1·00 15
916 – 1 r. 75 red and pink . . . 65 15
917 **147** 2 r. brown and green . . . 60 15
918 – 2 r. 50 blue and green . . 60 15
919 **147** 3 r. black and red 60 15
920 – 4 r. 50 green and red . . . 60 15
921 **147** 5 r. green and bistre . . . 50 15
922 – 6 r. red and brown 50 15
923 – 7 r. 50 brown and pink . . 50 15
924 – 10 r. ultramarine & blue . . 85 25
925 – 15 r. violet & lt violet . . 1·00 90
926 – 20 r. green and bistre . . . 2·50 1·10

DESIGNS—VERT: 10 s. Basketball; 20 s. Weightlifting; 40 s. Throwing the discus; 50 s. Diving; 60 s. Football; 70 s. Press building; 75 s. Boxing; 1 r. Volleyball; 1 r. 50, Badminton; 1 r. 75, Wrestling; 2 r. 50, Shooting; 4 r. 50, Hockey; 6 r. Water polo; 7 r. 50, Tennis; 10 r. Table tennis; 15 r. Cycling; 20 r. "Welcome" monument. HORIZ: 15 s. Main stadium; 25 s. Hotel Indonesia; 30 s. Road improvement.

1962. Malaria Eradication.

927 **148** 40 s. blue and violet . . . 15 10
928 1 r. 50 orange and brown . 15 10
929 3 r. green and blue 15 10
930 6 r. violet and black . . . 15 10

On the 1 r. 50 and 6 r. the inscription is at top.

149 National Monument **150** Atomic Symbol

1962. National Monument.

931 **149** 1 r. + 50 c. brown & blk . 20 20
932 – 1 r. 50 + 50 c. grn & blue . 20 20
933 **149** 3 r. + 1 r. mauve & green . 20 15
934 – 6 r. + 1 r. 50 blue & red . 20 15

DESIGN: 1 r. 50, 6 r. Aerial view of Monument.

1962. "Science for Development".

935 **150** 1 r. 50 blue and yellow . . 10 10
936 4 r. 50 red and yellow . . . 10 10
937 6 r. green and yellow . . . 15 10

151 "Phalaenopis amabilis" **152** West Irian Monument, Djakarta

1962. Charity. Orchids. Multicoloured.

938 1 r. + 50 s. "Vanda tricolor" . 25 15
939 1 r. 50 + 50 s. Type **151** . . . 25 15
940 3 r. + 1 r. "Dendrobium phalaenopsis" 25 15
941 6 r. + 1 r. 50 "Paphiopedilum praestans" 25 15

Nos. 938 and 941 are horiz.

1963. Construction of West Irian Monument

942 **152** 1 r. + 50 c. green and red . 10 10
943 1 r. 50 + 50 c. sepia, black and mauve 10 10
944 3 r. + 1 r. brown & blue . 15 10
945 6 r. + 1 r. 50 bistre & grn . 15 10

153 Conference Emblem **154** Rice Sheaves

1963. 12th Pacific Area Travel Association Conference, Djakarta.

946 **153** 1 r. blue and green 15 15
947 – 1 r. 50 blue and olive . . . 15 15
948 **153** 3 r. blue and brown . . . 35 15
949 – 6 r. blue and orange . . . 35 15

DESIGNS: 1 r. 50, Prambanan Temple and Mt. Merapi; 6 r. Balinese Meru in Pura Taman Ajun.

1963. Freedom from Hunger.

950 **154** 1 r. yellow and blue . . . 10 10
951 – 1 r. 50 blue and green . . . 10 10
952 **154** 3 r. yellow and red 10 10
953 – 6 r. orange and black . . . 15 10

DESIGN—HORIZ: 1 r. 50, 6 r. Tractor; Nos. 950/1 are inscr "CONTRE LA FAIM"; Nos. 952/3, "FREEDOM FROM HUNGER".

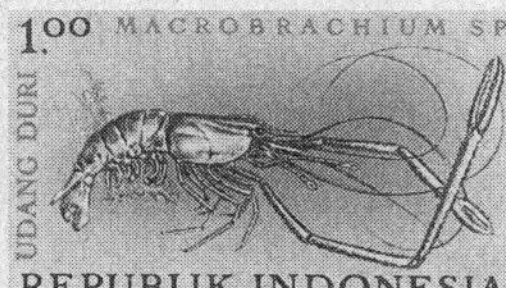

155 Lobster

1963. Marine Life. Multicoloured.

954 1 r. Type **155** 20 10
955 1 r. 50 Kawakawa 35 10
956 3 r. River snapper 60 20
957 6 r. Chinese pomfret 90 25

156 Conference Emblem

1963. Asian-African Journalists' Conference.

958 **156** 1 r. red and blue 10 10
959 – 1 r. 50 brown & lavender . 15 10
960 – 3 r. blue, black & olive . . 25 15
961 – 6 r. salmon and black . . . 35 20

DESIGNS—HORIZ: 1 r. 50, Pen, emblem and map. VERT: 3 r. Pen. Globe and broken chain; 6 r. Pen severing chain around Globe.

157 Indonesia, from Atjeh to Merauke

1963. Acquisition of West Irian (West New Guinea).

962 **157** 1 r. 50 orge, red & blk . . 10 10
963 – 4 r. 50 blue, green & pur . 15 10
964 – 6 r. brown, yell & green . 30 15

DESIGNS: 4 r. 50, Parachutist; 6 r. Greater Bird of Paradise.

158 Centenary Emblem **159** Volcano

1963. Centenary of Red Cross.

965 **158** 1 r. green and red 20 10
966 – 1 r. 50 red and blue . . . 20 10
967 **158** 3 r. grey and red 20 10
968 – 6 r. red and bistre 20 10

DESIGN: 1 r. 50, 6 r. Red Cross (inscribed in English).

1963. Bali Volcano Disaster Fund.

969 **159** 4 r. (+2 r.) red 10 10
970 6 r. (+3 r.) green 10 10

160 Bank of Indonesia, Djakarta

1963. National Banking Day.

971 **160** 1 r. 75 purple and blue . . 10 10
972 – 4 r. green and yellow . . . 10 10
973 **160** 6 r. brown and green . . . 10 10
974 – 12 r. purple and orange . . 10 10

DESIGN—VERT: 4 r., 12 r. Daneswara, God of Prosperity.

161 Athletes with Banners

1963. Games of the New Emerging Forces, Djakarta.

975 **161** 1 r. 25 sepia and violet . . 10 10
976 – 1 r. 75 olive and buff . . . 10 10
977 – 4 r. sepia and green . . . 10 10
978 – 6 r. sepia and brown . . . 15 10
979 – 10 r. sepia and green . . . 15 10
980 – 12 r. olive and red 25 10
981 – 25 r. ultramarine & blue . . 35 20
982 – 50 r. sepia and red 45 25

DESIGNS: 1 r. 75, "Pendet" dance; 4 r. Conference Hall, Djakarta; 6 r. Archery; 10 r. Badminton; 12 r. Throwing the javelin; 25 r. Sailing; 50 r. "Ganefo" torch.

162 "Papilio blumei" **163** Pres. Sukarno

1963. Social Day. Butterflies. Multicoloured.

983 1 r. 75 + 50 s. Type **162** 15 10
984 4 r. + 1 r. "Charaxes dehaani" 15 10
985 6 r. + 1 r. 50 Purple-spotted swallowtail 30 15
986 12 r. + 3 r. "Troides amphrysus" 30 20

1964.

987 **163** 6 r. blue and brown 10 10
988 12 r. purple and bistre 10 10
989 20 r. orange and blue 10 10
990 30 r. blue and orange 10 10
991 40 r. brown and green 10 10
992 50 r. green and red 10 10
993 75 r. red and violet 10 10
994 100 r. brown and grey 10 10
995 250 r. grey and blue 10 10
996 500 r. gold and red 10 10

164 Lorry and Trailer

165 Rameses II, Abu Simbel

1964.

997 – 1 r. purple 10 10
998 **164** 1 r. 25 brown 10 10
999 – 1 r. 75 blue 15 10
1000 – 2 r. red 10 10
1001 – 2 r. 50 blue 15 10
1002 – 4 r. green 20 10
1003 – 5 r. brown 10 10
1004 – 7 r. 50 green 15 10
1005 – 10 r. orange 20 10
1006 – 15 r. blue 25 10
1007 – 25 r. blue 15 10
1008 – 35 r. brown 15 10

DESIGNS—HORIZ: 1 r. Ox-cart; 1 r. 75, "Hadju Agus Salim" (freighter); 2 r. Lockheed Electra airliner; 4 r. Cycle-postman; 5 r. Douglas DC-3 airliner; 7 r. 50, Teletypist; 10 r. Diesel train; 15 r. "Sam Ratulangi" (freighter); 25 r. Convair Coronado airliner; 35 r. Telephone operator. VERT: 2 r. 50, Buginese sailing boat.

1964. Nubian Monuments Preservation. Monuments in brown.

1009 **165** 4 r. drab 15 10
1010 – 6 r. blue 15 10
1011 **165** 12 r. pink 15 10
1012 – 18 r. green 15 10

DESIGN: 6 r., 18 r., Trajan's Kiosk, Philae.

166 Various Stamps of Netherlands Indies and Indonesia

1964. Stamp Centenary.

1013 **166** 10 r. multicoloured 65 10

167 Indonesian Pavilion at Fair

1964. New York World's Fair.

1014 **167** 25 r. red, blue & silver 25 10
1015 50 r. red, turq & gold 85 10

168 Thomas Cup

170 Pied Fantail

169 "Sandjaja" and "Siliwanghi" (destroyers)

1964. Thomas Cup World Badminton Championships.

1016 **168** 25 r. gold, red & green 10 10
1017 50 r. gold, red and blue 15 10
1018 75 r. gold, red & violet 50 75

1964. Indonesian Navy.

1019 **169** 20 r. brown & yellow 20 10
1020 – 30 r. black and red 25 10
1021 – 40 r. blue and green 40 1·10

DESIGNS: 30 r. "Nanggala" (submarine); 40 r. "Matjan Tutul" (torpedo-boat).

1965. Social Day. Birds.

1022 **170** 4 r. + 1 r. black, lilac and yellow 20 10
1023 – 6 r. + 1 r. 50 black, buff and green 20 10
1024 – 12 r. + 3 r. black, blue and olive 25 20
1025 – 20 r. + 5 r. yellow, red and purple 30 20
1026 – 30 r. + 7 r. 50 black, slate and mauve 40 20

BIRDS: 6 r. Zebra Dove; 12 r. Black Drongo; 20 r. Black-naped Oriole; 30 r. Java Sparrow.

171 Map and Mosque

172 Scroll in Hand

1965. Afro-Asian Islamic Conf, Bandung.

1027 **171** 10 r. blue and violet 15 10
1028 – 15 r. brown and orange 15 10
1029 **171** 25 r. green and brown 25 10
1030 – 50 r. purple and red 25 1·00

DESIGN: 15 r., 50 r. Mosque and handclasp.

1965. 10th Anniv of 1st Afro-Asian Conference, Bandung.

1031 **172** 15 r. red and silver 20 10
1032 – 25 r. gold, red & turq 20 10
1033 **172** 50 r. blue and gold 25 10
1034 – 75 r. gold, red and lilac 35 80

DESIGN: 25 r., 75 r. Conference 10th-anniv emblem.

1965. Conf. of "New Emerging Forces", Djakarta. T **163** additionally inscr "Conefo". Value, "Conefo" and frame in red; portrait colour given.

1035 1 r. + 1 r. brown 10 10
1036 1 r. 25 + 1 r. 25 red 10 10
1037 1 r. 75 + 1 r. 75 purple 10 10
1038 2 r. + 2 r. green 10 10
1039 2 r. 50 + 2 r. 50 brown 10 10
1040 4 r. + 3 r. 50 blue 10 10
1041 6 r. + 4 r. green 10 10
1042 10 r. + 5 r. brown 10 10
1043 12 r. + 5 r. 50 orange 10 10
1044 15 r. + 7 r. 50 turquoise 10 10
1045 20 r. + 10 r. brown 10 10
1046 25 r. + 10 r. violet 10 10
1047 40 r. + 15 r. purple 10 1·25
1048 50 r. + 15 r. violet 10 10
1049 100 r. + 25 r. brown 10 10

174 Makara Mask and Rays

175 "Happy Family"

1965. Campaign against Cancer.

1050 **174** 20 r. + 10 r. red and blue 15 10
1051 30 r. + 15 r. blue and red 15 10

1965. The State's Five Principles and 20th Anniv of Republic.

1052 **175** 10 r. + 5 r. yellow, black and brown 20 10
1053 – 20 r. + 10 r. red, black and yellow 15 10
1054 – 25 r. + 10 r. green, black and red 15 10
1055 – 40 r. + 15 r. black, red and blue 20 10
1056 – 50 r. + 15 r. yellow, black and mauve 20 10

DESIGNS: ("State's Principles"): 20 r. "Humanitarianism" (globe and clasped hands); 25 r. "Nationalism" (map and garland); 40 r. "Democracy" (council meeting); 50 r. "Belief in God" (churches and mosques).

177 Samudra Beach Hotel

1965. Tourist Hotels.

1060 **177** 10 r. + 5 r. blue & turq 10 10
1061 – 25 r. + 10 r. violet, black and green 15 10
1062 **177** 40 r. + 15 r. brown, black and blue 20 10
1063 – 80 r. + 20 r. pur & orge 25 10

DESIGN: 25 r., 80 r. Ambarrukmo Palace Hotel.

178 "Gloriosa superba"

180 Pres. Sukarno

1965. Flowers. Multicoloured, Inscr "1965" and with commas and dashes after figures of value.

1064 30 r. + 10 r. Type **178** 35 15
1065 40 r. + 15 r. "Hibiscus tiliaceus" 25 15
1066 80 r. + 20 r. "Impatiens balsamina" 35 15
1067 100 r. + 25 r. "Lagerstroemia Indica" 45 15

See also Nos. 1108/1116.

(Currency revalued. 100 (old) rupiahs = 1 (new) rupiah.)

1965. Revalued Currency. Optd **'65 Sen**.

(a) On Nos. 989/94.

1068 **163** (20) s. on 20 r. 10 10
1069 (30) s. on 30 r. 10 10
1070 (40) s. on 40r. 10 10
1071 (50) s. on 50 r. 10 10
1072 (75) s. on 75r. 10 1·25
1073 (100) s. on 100r. 15 10

(b) On Nos. 1005/7.

1074 – (10) s. on 10 r. 35 10
1075 – (15) s. on 15 r. 25 10
1076 – (25) s. on 25 r. 25 10

1966. Revalued Currency. Inscr "1967" (12 r.) or "1966" (others). Values and frames turquoise (12 r., 25 r.) or chocolate (others); portrait and country name in colour given.

1077 **180** 1 s. blue 75 1·50
1078 3 s. olive 65 1·10
1079 5 s. red 10 20
1080 8 s. turquoise 65 75
1081 10 s. blue 10 10
1082 15 s. black 10 10
1083 20 s. green 10 10
1084 25 s. brown 10 10
1085 30 s. blue 10 10
1086 40 s. brown 10 10
1087 50 s. violet 10 10
1088 80 s. orange 10 10
1089 1 r. green 10 10
1090 1 r. 25 brown 10 10
1091 1 r. 50 green 10 10
1092 2 r. purple 10 10
1093 2 r. 50 slate 10 10
1094 5 r. orange 10 10
1095 10 r. olive 10 10
1096 12 r. orange 10 60
1097 25 r. violet 10 10

1966. Flowers. As T **178** but inscr "1966" and additionally inscr "sen" instead of commas and dashes. Multicoloured.

1108 10 s. + 5 s. "Cassia alata" 25 15
1109 20 s. + 5 s. "Barleria cristata" 35 15
1110 30 s. + 10 s. "Ixora coccinea" 35 15
1111 40 s. + 10 s. "Hibiscus rosa sinensis" 35 15

1966. National Disaster Fund. Floral designs as T **178** additionally inscr "BENT-JANA ALAM NASIONAL 1966". Multicoloured.

1113 15 a. + 5 s. "Gloriosa superba" 25 20
1114 25 a. + 5 s. "Hibiscus tiliaceus" 25 20
1115 30 s. + 10 s. "Impatiens balsamina" 25 20
1116 80 s. + 20 s. "Lagerstroemia Indica" 40 20

MINIMUM PRICE

The minimum price quoted is 10p which represents a handling charge rather than a basis for valuing common stamps. For further notes about prices see introductory pages.

181 Cleaning Ship's Rudder

182 Gen. A. Yani

1966. Maritime Day.

1117 **181** 20 s. green and blue 15 10
1118 – 40 s. blue and pink 15 10
1119 – 50 s. brown and green 15 10
1120 – 1 r. multicoloured 15 10
1121 – 1 r. 50 green and lilac 30 10
1122 – 2 r. red and grey 20 10
1123 – 2 r. 50 red and mauve 20 10
1124 – 3 r. black and green 60 15

DESIGNS: 40 s. Anyer Kidul lighthouse; 50 s. Fisherman; 1 r. Maritime emblem; 1 r. 50, Madurese sailing boat; 2 r. Quayside; 2 r. 50 Pearl-diving; 3 r. Liner in dry-dock.

1966. Victims of Attempted Communist Coup, 1965. Frames and date in blue.

1126 **182** 5 r. brown 20 10
1127 A 5 r. green 20 10
1128 B 5 r. purple 20 10
1129 C 5 r. olive 20 10
1130 D 5 r. grey 20 10
1131 E 5 r. violet 20 10
1132 F 5 r. purple 20 10
1133 G 5 r. green 20 10
1134 H 5 r. purple 20 10
1135 I 5 r. orange 20 10

PORTRAITS: A, Lt-Gen. R. Soeprapto; B, Lt-Gen. M. Harjono; C, Lt-Gen. S. Parman; D, Maj.-Gen. D. Pandjaitan; E, Maj.-Gen. S. Siswomihardjo; F, Brig.-Gen. Katamso; G, Col. Soegijono; H, Capt. P. Tendean; I, Insp. K. S. Tubun.

183 Python

1966. Reptiles.

1136 **183** 2 r. + 25 s. brown, green and flesh 15 10
1137 – 3 r. + 50 s. grn, brn & lil 15 10
1138 – 4 r. + 75 s. purple, buff and green 15 10
1139 – 6 r. + 1 r. blk, brn & bl 15 10

REPTILES: 3 r. Chameleon; 4 r. Crocodile; 6 r. Green turtle.

184 Tjlempung

1967. Musical Instruments.

1140 **184** 50 s. red and black 15 10
1141 – 1 r. sepia and red 15 10
1142 – 1 r. 25 lake and blue 15 10
1143 – 1 r. 50 green and violet 15 10
1144 – 2 r. blue & ochre 15 10
1145 – 2 r. 50 green and red 15 10
1146 – 3 r. green and purple 15 10
1147 – 4 r. blue and orange 25 10
1148 – 5 r. red and blue 25 10
1149 – 6 r. blue and mauve 15 15
1150 – 8 r. lake and green 15 15
1151 – 10 r. violet and red 20 10
1152 – 12 r. green and violet 35 10
1153 – 15 r. violet and olive 20 10
1154 – 20 r. black and sepia 20 10
1155 – 25 r. black and green 20 10

INSTRUMENTS: 1 r. Sasando; 1 r. 25, Foi doa; 1 r. 50, Kultjapi; 2 r. Arababu; 2 r. 50, Genderang; 3 r. Katjapi; 4 r. Hape; 5 r. Gangsa; 6 r. Serunai; 8 r. Rebab; 10 r. Trompet; 12 r. Totobuang; 15 r. Tamburn; 20 r. Kulintang; 25 r. Keledi.

185 Pilot and Mikoyan Gurevich MiG-21 Fighter

186 Thomas Cup and Silhouettes

1967. Aviation Day. Multicoloured.
1156 2 r. 50 Type **185** 20 15
1157 4 r. Convair Coronado airliner and control tower 20 15
1158 5 r. Lockheed C-130 Hercules transport aircraft on tarmac . 25 10

1967. Thomas Cup World Badminton Championships. Multicoloured.
1159 5 r. Type **186** 20 10
1160 12 r. Thomas Cup on Globe . 35 10

187 Balinese Girl

188 Heroes Monument

1967. International Tourist Year.
1161 **187** 12 r. multicoloured . . . 75 65

1967. "Heroes of the Revolution". Monument.
1163 **188** 2 r. 50 brown & green . . 10 10
1164 – 5 r. purple and drab. . . 20 15
1165 – 7 r. 50 green and pink . . 20 15
DESIGNS—HORIZ: 5 r. Monument and shrine. VERT: 7 r. 50, Shrine.

190 "Forest Fire"

1967. Paintings by Raden Saleh.
1175 **190** 25 r. red and green . . . 25 10
1176 – 50 r. purple and red . . . 30 10
PAINTING: 50 r. "A Fight to the Death".

191 Flood Victims

192 Human Rights Emblem

1967. National Disaster Fund.
1178 **191** 1 r. 25 + 10 s. bl & yell . 10 15
1179 – 2 r. 50 + 25 s. bl & yell . 10 15
1180 – 4 r. + 40 s. blk & orge . . 15 15
1181 – 5 r. + 50 s. blk & orge . . 20 15
DESIGNS: 2 r. 50, Landslide; 4 r. Burning house; 5 r. Erupting volcano.

1968. Human Rights Year.
1183 **192** 5 r. red, green and blue . 25 10
1184 12 r. red, green and drab . 25 15

193 Academy Badge

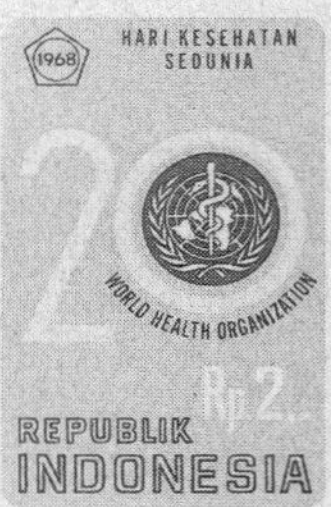

197 W.H.O. Emblem and "20"

194 **195** **196**
"Sudhana and Manohara at Court of Druma" (relief on wall of Borobudur)

1968. Indonesian Military Academy.
1185 **193** 10 r. multicoloured . . . 35 10

1968. "Save Borobudur Monument".
1186 **194** 2 r. 50 + 25 s. deep green and green 25 20
1187 **195** 2 r. 50 + 25 s. deep green and green 25 20
1188 **196** 2 r. 50 + 25 s. deep green and green 25 20
1189 – 7 r. 50 + 75 s. green and orange 35 20
DESIGN—VERT: 7 r. 50, Buddhist and statue of Buddha.

1968. 20th Anniv of W.H.O.
1191 **197** 2 r. purple and yellow . . 25 15
1192 – 20 r. black and green . . 25 15
DESIGN: 20 r. W.H.O. emblem.

198 Diesel Train (1967) and Steam Train (1867)

1968. Centenary (1967) of Indonesian Railways.
1193 **198** 20 r. multicoloured . . . 90 40
1194 30 r. multicoloured . . . 90 40

199 Scout with Pick **200** Butterfly Dancer

1968. "Wirakarya" Scout Camp.
1195 **199** 5 r. + 50 s. brn & orge . 25 20
1196 – 10 r. + 1 r. grey & brn . 35 60
1197 – 30 r. + 3 r. brn & grn . . 40 20
DESIGNS—VERT: 10 r. Bugler on hillside. HORIZ: (69 × 29 mm); 30 r. Scouts in camp.

1968. Tourism.
1198 **200** 30 r. multicoloured. . . . 1·00 60

202 Observatory and Stars

1968. 40th Anniv of Bosscha Observatory.
1207 **202** 15 r. blue, yellow & blk . 30 15
1208 – 30 r. violet & orange . . . 35 15
DESIGN—VERT: 30 r. Observatory on Globe.

203 Yachting **204**

1968. Olympic Games, Mexico.
1209 – 5 r. green, brown & blk . 15 10
1210 **203** 7 r. 50 blue, yell & red . . 10 10
1211 **204** 7 r. 50 blue, yell & red . . 10 10
1212 – 12 r. red, blue & yellow . 20 10
1213 – 30 r. brn, grn & orge . . 35 15
DESIGNS:—$28\frac{1}{2} \times 44\frac{1}{2}$ mm: 5 r. Weightlifting; 12 r. Basketball. $44\frac{1}{2} \times 28\frac{1}{2}$ mm: 30 r. Dove and Olympic flame.

Nos. 1210/11 were issued together, se-tenant, forming the composite design illustrated.

205 "Eugenia aquea"

1968. Fruits. Multicoloured.
1215 7 r. 50 Type **205** 20 10
1216 15 r. "Carica papaya" 35 15
1217 30 r. "Durio zibethinus" (vert.) 45 15

206 I.L.O. Emblem and part of Globe

207 R. Dewi Sartika

1969. 50th Anniv of I.L.O.
1219 **206** 5 r. red and green 15 10
1220 – 7 r. 50 green & orange . . 15 10
1221 **206** 15 r. red and violet . . . 15 10
1222 – 25 r. red and turquoise . . 15 10
DESIGN: 7 r. 50, 25 r. I. L. O. emblem.

1969. National Independence Heroes.
1223 **207** 15 r. green and violet . . 25 15
1224 – 15 r. purple and green . . 25 15
1225 – 15 r. blue and red 25 15
1226 – 15 r. ochre and red . . . 25 15
1227 – 15 r. sepia and blue . . . 25 15
1228 – 15 r. lilac and blue . . . 25 15
PORTRAITS: No. 1224, Tjut Nja Din; No. 1225, Tjut Nja Meuthia; No. 1226, Sutan Sjahrir; No. 1227, Dr. F. L. Tobing; No. 1228, General G. Subroto.

208 Woman with Flower

209 Red Cross "Mosaic"

1969. Women's Emancipation Campaign.
1229 **208** 20 r. + 2 r. red, yellow and green 35 10

1969. 50th Anniv of League of Red Cross Societies.
1230 **209** 15 r. red and green . . . 25 10
1231 – 20 r. red and yellow . . . 25 15
DESIGN: 20 r. Hands encircling Red Cross.

210 "Planned" Family and Factory

1969. South-East Asia and Oceania Family Planning Conference.
1232 **210** 10 r. orange and green . . 20 10
1233 – 20 r. mauve and green . . 30 15
DESIGN: 20 r. "Planned" family and "National Prosperity".

211 Balinese Mask

1969. Tourism in Bali. Multicoloured.
1234 12 r. Type **211** 30 20
1235 15 r. Girl with offerings . . . 40 25
1236 30 r. Cremation rites 60 25

212 "Agriculture"

213 Dish Aerial

1969. Five-year Development Plan.
1238 – 5 r. blue and green . . . 15 10
1239 **212** 7 r. 50 yellow & purple . . 15 10
1240 – 10 r. red and blue 15 10
1241 – 12 r. red and blue . . . . 1·00 35
1242 – 15 r. yellow & green . . . 15 10
1243 – 20 r. yellow and violet . . 15 10
1244 – 25 r. red and black . . . 15 10
1245 – 30 r. black and red . . . 30 10
1246 – 40 r. orange and green . . 45 10
1247 – 50 r. brown and orange . . 75 10
DESIGNS: 5 r. Religious emblems ("Co-existence"); 10 r. Modern family ("Social Welfare"); 12 r. Crane and crate ("Overseas Trade"); 15 r. Bobbins ("Clothing Industry"); 20 r. Children in class ("Education"); 25 r. Research worker ("Scientific Research"); 30 r. Family and hypodermic syringe ("Health Care"); 40 r. Tunas in net ("Fisheries"); 50 r. Graph ("Statistics").

1969. Satellite Communications and Inauguration of Djatiluhur Earth Station. Multicoloured.
1248 15 r. Type **213** 25 15
1249 30 r. Communications satellite . 40 20

214 Vickers Vimy Biplane over Borobudur Temple

1969. 50th Anniv of 1st England–Australia Flight by Ross and Keith Smith.
1253 **214** 75 r. purple and red . . . 40 25
1254 – 100 r. green & yellow . . 50 25
DESIGNS: 100 r. Vickers Vimy and map of Indonesia.

215 Noble Volute

1969. Sea Shells. Multicoloured.
1255 5 r. + 50 c. Type **215** 20 20
1256 7 r. 50 + 50 c. Common hairy triton 20 20
1257 10 r. + 1 r. Common spider conch 35 35
1258 15 r. + 1 r. 50 Bramble murex 35 35

216 Indonesian Pavilion

217 Prisoner's Hands and Scales of Justice

1970. "Expo 70" World Fair, Osaka, Japan.
1259 **216** 5 r. yellow, grn & brn . . 35 15
1260 – 15 r. red, blue & green . . 50 20
1261 **216** 30 r. yellow, blue & red . 1·00 30
DESIGN: 15 r. Indonesian "Garuda" symbol.

1970. "Purification of Justice".
1262 **217** 10 r. purple and red . . . 35 15
1263 15 r. purple and green . . 50 15

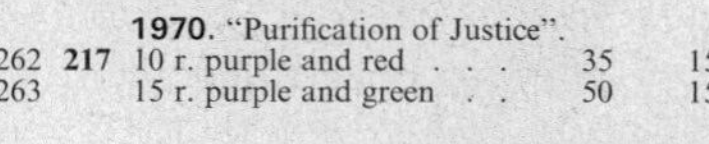

218 U.P.U. Monument, Berne **219** Timor Dancers

1970. Inauguration of New U. P. U. Headquarters Building, Berne.
1264 **218** 15 r. red & green 50 25
1265 – 30 r. blue and ochre . . . 65 30
DESIGN: 30 r. New Headquarters building.

1970. "Visit Indonesia Year". Traditional Dancers. Multicoloured.
1266 20 r. Type **219** 65 25
1267 45 r. Bali dancers . . . . . . 1·25 65

220 "Productivity" Symbol

221 Independence Monument

1970. Asian Productivity Year.
1269 **220** 5 r. red, yellow & green . . 40 10
1270 30 r. red, yell & violet . . 90 50

1970. 25th Anniv of Independence.
1271 **221** 40 r. violet, purple & bl . . 10·00 1·90

222 Emblems of Post and Giro, and of Telecommunications
223 U.N. Emblem and Doves

1970. 25th Anniv of Indonesian Post and Telecommunications Services.
1272 **222** 10 r. brown, yell & grn . . 3·75 1·00
1273 – 25 r. black, yell & pink . . 6·25 50
DESIGN: 25 r. Telephone dial and P.T.T. worker.

1970. 25th Anniv of United Nations.
1274 **223** 40 r. multicoloured . . . 10·00 1·25

224 I.E.Y. Emblem on globe
225 "Chrysocoris javanus" (shieldbug)

1970. International Education Year
1275 **224** 25 r. brn, red & yellow . . 7·50 1·75
1276 – 50 r. red, black and blue . 12·50 3·25
DESIGNS: 50 r. I.E.Y. emblem.

1970. Insects. Multicoloured.
1277 7 r. 50 + 50 c. Type **225** . . . . 5·00 1·25
1278 15 r. + 1 r. 50 "Orthetrum testaceum" (darter) . . . . . . 8·75 5·75
1279 20 r. + 2 r. "Xylocopa flavonigrescens" (carpenter bee) . . 17·50 4·25

226 Batik handicrafts

1971. "Visit ASEAN (South East Asian Nations Association) Year". Multicoloured.
1280 20 r. Type **226** . . . . 2·25 1·00
1281 50 r. Javanese girl playing angklung (musical instrument) (vert.) . . . . . . 3·25 2·75
1282 75 r. Wedding group, Minangkabau . . . . . . 8·25 3·75

227 Restoration of Fatahillah Park

1971. 444th Anniv of Djakarta. Multicoloured.
1284 15 r. Type **227** . . . . . . 1·90 75
1285 65 r. Performance at Lenong Theatre . . . . 3·25 3·00
1286 80 r. Ismail Marzuki Cultural Centre . . . . 7·50 2·50

228 Sita and Rama
229 Pigeon with Letter, and Workers

1971. International Ramayana Festival.
1288 **228** 30 r. multicoloured . . . 2·00 50
1289 – 100 r. black, blue & red . 3·00 1·25
DESIGN: 100 r. Rama.

1971. 5th Asian Regional Telecommunications Conference.
1290 **229** 50 r. chocolate, brown and buff . . . . 1·40 65

230 U.P.U. Monument, Berne, and Hemispheres

1971. U.P.U. Day.
1291 **230** 40 r. purple, blk & blue . 1·50 65

231 Schoolgirl
233 Microwave Tower

232 Clown Surgeonfish

1971. 25th Anniv of U.N.I.C.E.F. Mult.
1292 20 r. Type **231** . . . . 2·00 25
1293 40 r. Boy with rice-stalks . . . 3·00 80

1971. Fishes (1st series). Multicoloured.
1294 15 r. Type **232** . . . . 3·75 1·00
1295 30 r. Moorish idol . . . . . . 7·50 2·75
1296 40 r. Emperor angelfish . . . 11·50 3·75
See also Nos. 1318/20, 1343/5, 1390/2 and 1423/5.

1972. 25th Anniv of E.C.A.F.E.
1297 **233** 40 r. blue and turquoise . 2·50 75
1298 – 75 r. multicoloured . . . 2·50 75
1299 – 100 r. multicoloured . . . 3·75 1·50
DESIGNS—VERT: 40 r. E.C.A.F.E. emblem. HORIZ: 100 r. Irrigation and highways.

234 Human Heart
235 Ancient and Modern Textile Production

1972. World Heart Month.
1300 **234** 50 r. multicoloured . . . 1·60 65

1972. 50th Anniv of Textile Technological Institute.
1301 **235** 35 r. purple, yell & orge . 1·60 65

236 Children reading Books
237 "Essa 8" Weather Satellite

1972. International Book Year.
1302 **236** 75 r. multicoloured . . . 2·10 65

1972. Space Exploration.
1303 **237** 35 r. brown, violet & bl . 1·50 50
1304 – 50 r. blue, blk & pink . . 2·50 2·50
1305 – 60 r. black, grn & brn . . 4·75 75
DESIGNS: 50 r. Astronaut on Moon; 60 r. Indonesian "Kartika I" rocket.

238 Hotel Indonesia

1972. 10th Anniv of Hotel Indonesia.
1306 **238** 50 r. grn, pale grn & red . 1·75 75

239 "Silat" (unarmed combat)
240 Family and Religious Buildings

1972. Olympic Games, Munich.
1307 **239** 20 r. purple, cobalt & bl . 1·00 10
1308 – 35 r. violet, brn & mve . . 1·00 15
1309 – 50 r. emer, dp grn & grn . 2·00 55
1310 – 75 r. rose, purple & pink . 2·00 1·40
1311 – 100 r. brown, blue & grn . 4·00 2·25
DESIGNS: 35 r. Running; 50 r. Diving; 75 r. Badminton; 100 r. Olympic stadium.

1972. Family Planning Campaign. Mult.
1312 30 r. Type **240** . . . . 1·50 50
1313 75 r. "Healthy family" . . . . 3·50 2·00
1314 80 r. "Family of workers" . . 5·00 2·00

241 Moluccas Dancer
242 Thomas Cup and Shuttlecock

1972. "Art and Culture" (1st series).
1315 **241** 30 r. brown, pink & grn . 1·50 50
1316 – 60 r. multicoloured . . . 3·50 2·00
1317 – 100 r. bl, brn & cinnamon 5·00 2·00
DESIGNS—VERT: 60 r. Couple and Toraja traditional house. HORIZ: 100 r. West Irian traditional house.
See also 1336/8, 1373/5 and 1401/3.

1972. Fishes (2nd series). As T **232**. Mult.
1318 30 r. Triangle butterflyfish . . 5·00 1·50
1319 50 r. Royal angelfish . . . . . 8·75 2·25
1320 100 r. Clown triggerfish . . . 11·50 3·75

1972. Thomas Cup Badminton Championships, Djakarta.
1321 **242** 30 r. blue and green . . . 65 15
1322 – 75 r. red and green . . . 1·40 20
1323 – 80 r. brown and red . . . 2·50 70
DESIGNS: 75 r. Thomas Cup and Sports Centre; 80 r. Thomas Cup and player.

243 Emblem, Anemometer and "Gatotkaca"

1973. I.M.O. and W.M.O. Weather Organization Centenary.
1324 **243** 80 r. multicoloured . . . 1·50 65

244 "Health begins at Home"
245 Java Mask

1973. 25th Anniv of W.H.O.
1325 **244** 80 r. blue, orange & grn . 1·25 25

1973. Tourism. Indonesian Folk Masks. Mult.
1326 30 r. Type **245** . . . . 3·75 75
1327 60 r. Kalimantan mask . . . . 6·25 2·75
1328 100 r. Bali mask . . . . . . 10·00 1·50

246 Savings Bank and Thrift Plant
247 Chess

1973. Two-Year National Savings Drive.
1329 **246** 25 r. black, yell & bis . . 75 20
1330 – 30 r. green, gold & yell . . 1·25 30
DESIGN—HORIZ: 30 r. Hand and "City" savings bank.

1973. National Sports Week. Multicoloured.
1331 30 r. Type **247** . . . . 1·25 90
1332 60 r. Karate . . . . 2·25 90
1333 75 r. Hurdling (horiz) . . . . 4·00 75

248 International Policemen

1973. 50th Anniv of Interpol.
1334 **248** 30 r. multicoloured . . . 75 15
1335 – 50 r. yellow, pur & blk . . 1·25 50
DESIGN—VERT: 50 r. Giant temple guard.

1973. "Art and Culture" (2nd series). Weaving and Fabrics. As T **241**. Multicoloured.
1336 60 r. Parang Rusak pattern . . 2·00 1·50
1337 80 r. Pagi Sore pattern . . . . 3·75 1·75
1338 100 r. Merak Ngigel pattern . . 6·75 3·00

249 "Food Cultivation"

1973. 10th Anniv of World Food Programme.
1339 **249** 30 r. multicoloured . . . 1·75 50

250 "Religion"
252 Bengkulu Costume

251 Admiral Sudarso and Naval Battle of Arafuru

1973. Family Planning.
1340 **250** 20 r. blue, lt blue & red . 65 15
1341 – 30 r. black, yell & brn . . 1·40 50
1342 – 60 r. black, yell & grn . . 2·50 45
DESIGNS: 30 r. Teacher and class ("Population Education"); 60 r. Family and house ("Health").

1973. Fishes (3rd series). As T **232**. Mult.
1343 40 r. Powder-blue surgeonfish . 1·25 90
1344 65 r. Melon butterflyfish . . . 5·00 1·60
1345 100 r. Blue-ringed angelfish . . 6·25 2·50

1974. Naval Day.
1346 **251** 40 r. multicoloured . . . 1·40 50

1974. Pacific Area Travel Association Conference, Djakarta. Provincial Costumes. Multicoloured.
1347 5 r. Type **252** . . . . 12·50 90
1348 7 r. 50 Kalimantan. Timor . . 6·25 90
1349 10 r. Kalimantan, Tengah . . 4·25 65
1350 15 r. Jambi . . . . 1·25 65
1351 20 r. Sulawesi, Tenggara . . . 1·25 65
1352 25 r. Nusatenggara, Timor . . 1·25 65
1353 27 r. 50 Maluku . . . . 1·25 3·75
1354 30 r. Lampung . . . . 1·25 1·25
1355 35 r. Sumatera, Barat . . . . 1·25 65
1356 40 r. Aceh . . . . 1·25 65
1357 45 r. Nusatenggara, Barat . . 3·25 65
1358 50 r. Riau . . . . 1·90 3·00
1359 55 r. Kalimantan, Barat . . . 2·50 65
1360 60 r. Sulawesi, Utara . . . . 2·50 65
1361 65 r. Sulawesi, Tengah . . . . 2·50 65
1362 70 r. Sumatera, Selatan . . . 2·75 65
1363 75 r. Java, Barat . . . . . . 2·75 65
1364 80 r. Sumatera, Utara . . . . 2·75 65
1365 90 r. Yogyakarta . . . . . . 2·75 7·50
1366 95 r. Kalimantan, Selatan . . 2·75 65
1367 100 r. Java, Timor . . . . . . 2·75 1·25
1368 120 r. Irian, Jaya . . . . . . 5·00 90
1369 130 r. Java, Tengah . . . . . 5·00 65
1370 135 r. Sulawesi, Selatan . . . 5·75 65
1371 150 r. Bali . . . . 5·75 65
1372 160 r. Djakarta . . . . 5·75 1·25

1974. "Art and Culture" (3rd series). Shadow Plays. As T **241**. Multicoloured.

1373 40 r. Baladewa . . . . 2·25 1·00
1374 80 r. Kresna . . . . 4·00 2·00
1375 100 r. Bima . . . . 5·00 2·00

254 Pres. Suharto

1974.

1376 **254** 40 r. brown, grn & blk . . 65 10
1377 50 r. brown, blue & blk . 1·50 10
1378 65 r. brown, mve & blk . 90 50
1379 75 r. brown, yell & blk . . 1·50 10
1380 100 r. brown, yell & blk . 1·50 10
1381 150 r. brown, grn & blk . 1·50 10

See also Nos. 1444/7.

255 "Improvement of Living Standards"

256 "Welfare"

1974. World Population Year.

1382 **255** 65 r. multicoloured . . . 1·10 20

1974. Family Planning.

1383 **256** 25 r. multicoloured . . . 75 35
1384 – 40 r. blue, black & grn . . 75 35
1385 – 65 r. ochre, brn & yell . 2·25 35

DESIGNS: 40 r. Young couple ("Development"); 65 r. Arrows ("Religion").

257 Bicycle Postmen

1974. Centenary of U.P.U.

1386 **257** 20 r. brown, yell & grn . . 1·60 35
1387 – 40 r. brown, orge & blue . 1·60 60
1388 – 65 r. brown, yell & blk . . 1·60 60
1389 – 100 r. black, blue & red . 1·60 1·50

DESIGNS: 40 r. Mail-cart; 65 r. Mounted postman; 100 r. East Indies galley.

1974. Fishes (4th series). As T **232**. Mult.

1390 40 r. Sail-finned tang . . . . . 2·00 20
1391 80 r. Blue-girdled angelfish . 3·00 1·50
1392 100 r. Mandarin fish . . . . . 5·00 1·90

258 Drilling for Oil

1974. 17th Anniv of Pertamina Oil Complex. Multicoloured.

1393 40 r. Type **258** 30 20
1394 75 r. Oil refinery 30 20
1395 95 r. Control centre (vert) . . 30 20
1396 100 r. Road tanker (vert) . . . 30 20
1397 120 r. Fokker Fellowship airliner over storage tank farm (vert) . . . . 1·40 60
1398 130 r. Pipelines and tanker (vert) . . . . 1·40 60
1399 150 r. Petrochemical storage tanks 45 20
1400 200 r. Offshore oil rig . . . . 2·40 1·10

1975. "Art and Culture" (4th series). As T **241**.

1401 50 r. silver, red & black . . . 1·10 1·00
1402 75 r. silver, green & black . . 1·90 1·00
1403 100 r. yellow, blue & blk . . . 3·25 1·00

DESIGNS: 50 r. Sumatran spittoon; 75 r. Sumatran "sirh" dish; 100 r. Kalimantan "sirh" dish.

260 "Donorship"

261 Measures and Globe

1975. Blood Donors' Campaign.

1404 **260** 40 r. red, yellow & green . . 90 20

1975. Centenary of Metre Convention.

1405 **261** 65 r. blue, red & yellow . 1·50 50

262 Women in Public Service

1975. International Women's Year. Mult.

1406 40 r. Type **262** . . . . 1·25 35
1407 100 r. I.W.Y. emblem (21 × 29 mm.) . . . . 1·75 35

263 "Dendrobium pakarena"

264 Stupas and Damaged Temple

1975. Tourism. Indonesian Orchids. Mult.

1408 40 r. Type **263** . . . . 3·25 65
1409 70 r. "Aeridachnis bogor" . . 3·25 1·50
1410 85 r. "Vanda genta" . . . . . 6·00 2·25

1975. U.N.E.S.C.O. "Save Borobudur Temple" Campaign. Multicoloured.

1411 25 r. Type **264** . . . . 2·50 65
1412 40 r. Buddhist shrines and broken wall . . . . 2·75 90
1413 65 r. Stupas and damaged building (horiz) . . . . . . 5·50 3·50
1414 100 r. Buddha and stupas (horiz) . . . . 8·00 3·50

265 Battle of Banjarmasin

1975. 30th Anniv of Independence.

1415 **265** 25 r. black & yellow . . . 65 20
1416 – 40 r. black and red . . . 90 20
1417 – 75 r. black and red . . . 1·25 1·00
1418 – 100 r. black and orange . 1·25 75

DESIGNS: 40 r. Battle of Batua; 75 r. battle of Margarana; 100 r. Battle of Palembang.

266 "Education"

267 Heroes' Monument, Surabaya

1975. Family Planning. Multicoloured.

1419 20 r. Type **266** 35 10
1420 25 r. "Religion" 75 20
1421 40 r. "Prosperity" . . . . . . 1·25 20

1975. 30th Anniv of Independence War.

1422 **267** 100 r. red and green . . . 1·75 20

1975. Fishes (5th series). As T **232**. Mult.

1423 40 r. Twin-spotted wrasse . . . 1·40 35
1424 75 r. Saddleback butterflyfish . 3·75 1·10
1425 150 r. Dusky batfish (vert) . . 5·00 1·75

269 Thomas Cup

1976. Indonesian Victory in World Badminton Championships. Multicoloured.

1428 20 r. Type **269** 75 20
1429 40 r. Uber cup 75 35
1430 100 r. Thomas and Uber cups . 1·60 35

270 Refugees and New Village

1976. World Human Settlements Day. Multicoloured.

1431 30 r. Type **270** 65 20
1432 50 r. Old and restored villages . 1·10 20
1433 100 r. Derelict and rebuilt houses . . . . 1·25 20

271 Early and Modern Telephones

272 Human Eye

1976. Telephone Centenary.

1434 **271** 100 r. brn, red & yell . . 1·00 45

1976. World Health Day. Multicoloured.

1435 20 r. Type **272** 25 10
1436 40 r. Blind man with stick . . 55 20

273 Main Stadium, Montreal

1976. Olympic Games, Montreal.

1437 **273** 100 r. blue 85 35

274 Lake Tondano, Sulawesi

275 "Light Traffic" Station

1976. Tourism. Multicoloured.

1438 35 r. Type **274** 50 20
1439 40 r. Lake Kelimutu, Flores . . 50 20
1440 75 r. Lake Maninjau, Sumatra . 1·25 20

1976. Inaug of Domestic Satellite System.

1441 **275** 20 r. multicoloured 50 20
1442 – 50 r. black and green . . 50 20
1443 – 100 r. turquoise, bl & vio . 1·10 35

DESIGNS: 50 r. "Master control" station; 100 r. "Palapa" satellite.

1976. Vert designs as T **254** but with background of wavy lines.

1444 200 r. brown, blue & green . . 6·25 10
1445 300 r. brown, red & flesh . . 1·90 10
1446 400 r. brown, green & yell . . 3·00 20
1447 500 r. brown, red and lilac . . 4·00 65

276 "Vanda Putri Serang"

1976. Orchids. Multicoloured.

1448 25 r. "Arachnis flos-aeris" . . 1·75 75
1449 40 r. Type **276** . . . . 1·75 75
1450 100 r. "Coelogyne pandurata" . 2·50 1·50

277 Stylised Tree

279 Open Book

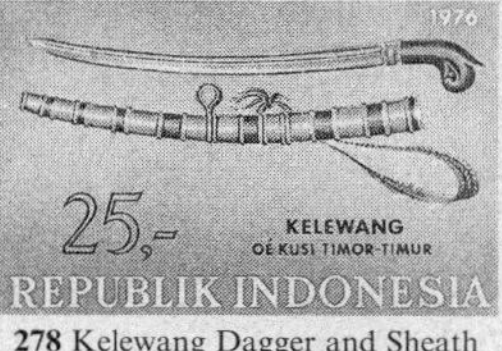

278 Kelewang Dagger and Sheath (Timor)

1976. Reafforestation Week.

1452 **277** 20 r. green, blue & brn . . 65 15

1976. Daggers and Sheaths.

1453 **278** 25 r. green, black & brn . 90 20
1454 – 40 r. brown, yell & orge . 1·40 60
1455 – 100 r. brown, yell & grn . 2·00 1·60

DESIGNS: 40 r. Mandau dagger and sheath (Borneo); 100 r. Rencong dagger and sheath (Aceh).

1976. Books for Children.

1457 **279** 20 r. green, orange & bl . 50 10
1458 – 40 r. violet, red & yell . . 1·00 20

DESIGN: 40 r. Children reading book.

280 UNICEF Emblem

281 Ballot Box

1976. 30th Anniv of UNICEF.

1459 **280** 40 r. blue, turq & vio . . 90 20

1977. Elections.

1460 **281** 40 r. blue, yell & grey . 1·40 20
1461 – 75 r. blue, yell & pink . . 1·75 20
1462 – 100 r. bistre, red & blk . . 2·75 80

DESIGNS: 75 r. Ballot box, factory and produce; 100 r. Indonesian arrow.

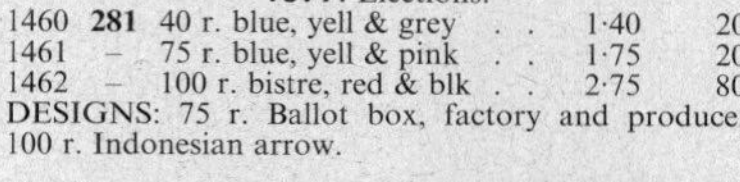

282 Scout Emblems and Camp

283 Letter and A.O.P.U. Emblem

1977. 11th National Scout Jamboree. Mult.

1463 25 r. Type **282** 75 45
1464 30 r. Emblems, tent and trees . 75 45
1465 40 r. Emblems, tent and flags . 1·75 90

1977. 15th Anniv of Asian–Oceanic Postal Union. Multicoloured.

1466 65 r. Type **283** 50 20
1467 100 r. Stylized carrier pigeon . 90 45

284 Anniversary Emblem

285 Rose

1977. 450th Anniv of Jakarta.

1468 **284** 20 r. blue and red 65 25
1469 – 40 r. green and blue . . . 65 25
1470 – 100 r. blue & turquoise . 1·25 60

DESIGNS: 40; 100 r. Similar to Type **284** but with emblem and arms differently arranged.

1977. "Amphilex 77" International Stamp Exhibition, Amsterdam.

1472 **285** 100 r. red, green & blk . . 95 40
1473 – 100 r. red, green & blk . . 95 20

DESIGN: No. 1473, Envelope.

286 Sports Pictograms

287 Trophy

1977. Ninth National Sports Week.

1475 **286** 40 r. silver, grn & red . . 2·00 1·25
1476 – 50 r. silver, blue & red . 2·50 1·25
1477 – 100 r. gold, blk & red . . 4·25 2·50

DESIGNS: 50; 100 r. Similar to Type **286** but with different pictograms.

1977. 10th National Koran Reading Contest.

1478 **287** 40 r. brown, grn & yell . . 1·75 25
1479 – 100 r. black, yell & grn . 2·25 60

DESIGN: 100 r. Emblem.

288 Carrier Pigeon and Map **289** Government Officer, Djakarta Region

1977. 10th Anniv of Association of South East Asian Nations. Multicoloured.
1480 25 r. Type **288** 20 10
1481 35 r. Map of ASEAN members . . . . 1·75 35
1482 50 r. Transport and flags of ASEAN members . . . . . 1·75 60

1977. Economic and Cultural Co-operation with Pakistan.
1483 **289** 25 r. brown, gold & grn . 20 10

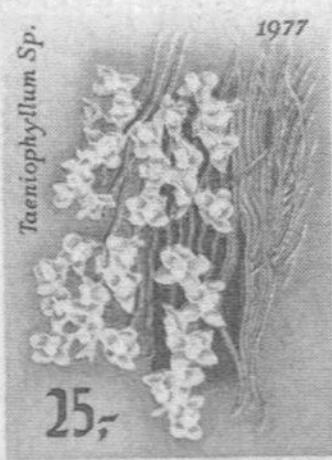

290 "Taeniophyllum sp." **291** Child and Mosquito

1977. Orchids. Multicoloured.
1484 25 r. Type **290** . . . . 1·75 60
1485 40 r. "Phalaenopsis violacea" . 1·75 1·25
1486 100 r. "Dendrobium spectabile" . . . . 3·50 1·90

1977. National Health Campaign.
1488 **291** 40 r. red, green & black . 50 10

292 Proboscis Monkey

1977. Wildlife (1st series). Multicoloured.
1489 20 r. Type **292** . . . . 1·25 50
1490 40 r. Indian elephant . . . . . 1·50 1·00
1491 100 r. Tiger . . . . 3·50 2·25

293 Hands holding U.N. Emblem **294** Mother feeding Baby

1978. U.N. Conference on Technical Co-operation among Developing Countries.
1493 **293** 100 r. blue & ultram . . . 90 15

1978. Campaign for the Promotion of Breast Feeding.
1494 **294** 40 r. green and blue . . . 30 10
1495 – 75 r. brown and red . . . 65 15
DESIGN: 75 r. Stylised mother and child.

295 Dome of the Rock

1978. Palestine Welfare.
1496 **295** 100 r. multicoloured . . . 1·00 25

296 World Cup Emblem **297** Head and Blood Circulation Diagram

1978. World Cup Football Competition, Argentina.
1497 **296** 40 r. green, black & bl . . 35 15
1498 100 r. mauve, blk & bl . . 90 30

1978. World Health Day.
1499 **297** 100 r. blue, black and red . 75 15

298 Leather Puppets

1978. Puppets from Wayang Museum, Djakarta. Multicoloured.
1500 40 r. Type **298** . . . . 1·75 50
1501 75 r. Wooden puppets . . . . 2·00 1·00
1502 100 r. Actors wearing masks . 3·75 1·50

300 Congress Emblem **301** I.A.Y. Emblem

1978. 27th Congress of World Confederation of Organizations of the Teaching Profession, Djakarta.
1509 **300** 100 r. grey 75 15

1978. International Anti-Apartheid Year.
1510 **301** 100 r. blue and red . . . 90 15

302 Couple and Tree **303** Anniversary Emblem

1978. 8th World Forestry Congress, Djakarta.
1511 **302** 40 r. blue and green . . . 20 10
1512 – 100 r. dp grn & lt grn . . 60 10
DESIGN: 100 r. People and trees.

1978. 50th Anniv of Youth Pledge.
1513 **303** 40 r. brown and red . . . 30 10
1514 100 r. brn, red & pk . . . 75 20

1978. Wildlife (2nd series). As T **292**. Mult.
1515 40 r. Long-nosed echidna . . . 1·00 20
1516 75 r. Sambar . . . . 1·90 90
1517 100 r. Clouded leopard . . . . 2·75 1·10

304 "Phalaenopsis sri rejeki" **307** Thomas Cup and Badminton Player

306 Douglas DC-3 over Volcano

1978. Orchids. Multicoloured.
1519 40 r. Type **304** 90 25
1520 75 r. "Dendrobium macrophillum" . . . . 1·25 40
1521 100 r. "Cymbidium fynlaysonianum" . . . . 2·25 50

1979. 30th Anniv of Garuda Indonesian Airways. Multicoloured.
1531 40 r. Type **306** 50 15
1532 75 r. Douglas DC-9-30 over village 60 30
1533 100 r. Douglas DC-10 over temple . . . . 1·40 75

1979. Thomas Cup Badminton Championships, Djakarta.
1534 **307** 40 r. pink & turquoise . . 25 50
1535 – 100 r. brown and pink . . 75 60
1536 – 100 r. brown and pink . . 75 60
DESIGNS: No. 1535, Player on left side of net hitting shuttlecock; 1536, Player on right side of net.
Nos. 1535/6 were issued together, se-tenant, forming a composite design.

308 "Paphiopedilum lowii" **309** Family and Houses

1979. Orchids. Multicoloured.
1537 60 r. Type **308** 75 25
1538 100 r. "Vanda limbata" . . . 1·25 40
1539 125 r. "Phalaenopsis gigantea" 1·75 65

1979. 3rd Five Year Development Plan.
1541 **309** 35 r. drab and green . . . 10 10
1542 – 60 r. green and blue . . . 15 10
1543 – 100 r. brown and blue . . 20 20
1544 – 125 r. brown & green . . 60 10
1545 – 150 r. yell, orge & red . . 75 10
DESIGNS: 60 r. Pylon, dam and fields; 100 r. School and clinic; 125 r. Loading produce at factory; 150 r. Delivering mail.

310/311 Mrs. R. A. Kartini

1979. Birth Cent of Mrs. R. A. Kartini (pioneer of women's rights).
1546 **310** 100 r. brown and green . 35 20
1547 **311** 100 r. green and brown . 35 20

312 Bureau Emblem **313** Self Defence

1979. 50th Anniv of International Bureau of Education.
1549 **312** 150 r. bl, lt bl & lil . . . 90 20

1979. 10th South East Asia Games, Djakarta.
1550 **313** 60 r. yellow, blk & grn . . 25 15
1551 – 125 r. orge, grey & bl . . 70 30
1552 – 150 r. yellow, blk & red . 1·00 35
DESIGNS: 125 r. Games emblem; 150 r. Main stadium, Senayan.

314 Co-operation Emblem **315** National I.Y.C. Emblem

1979. Co-operation Day.
1553 **314** 150 r. multicoloured . . . 50 15

1979. International Year of the Child.
1554 **315** 60 r. black and green . . 25 10
1555 – 150 r. blue and black . . 40 25
DESIGN: 150 r. International I.Y.C. emblem.

316 Exhibition Emblem **317** Drug Addict

1979. 3rd World Telecommunications Exhibition, Geneva
1556 **316** 150 r. grey, blue & orge . 50 15

1979. "End Drug Abuse" Campaign.
1557 **317** 150 r. black and pink . . 50 15

1979. Wildlife (3rd series). As T **292**. Mult.
1558 60 r. Bottle-nosed dolphin . . 75 40
1559 125 r. Irrawaddy dolphin . . . 2·00 50
1560 150 r. Leatherback Turtle . . . 3·00 90

318 Pinisi Sailing Ship

1980. Djakarta–Amsterdam Spice Race.
1562 **318** 60 r. blue 45 20
1563 – 125 r. brown 65 30
1564 – 150 r. purple . . . . . . 1·10 35
DESIGNS—HORIZ: 125 r. Schooner made of cloves. VERT: 150 r. Madurese sailing boat.

319 Riding the Rapids

1980. Adventure Sports. Multicoloured.
1566 60 r. Type **319** 25 10
1567 125 r. Mountaineering (vert.) . 35 25
1568 150 r. Hang gliding 95 45

320 Cigarettes and Heart **321** Artificial Flowers in Vase

1980. Anti-smoking Campaign.
1570 **320** 150 r. flesh, blk & pink . . 75 20

1980. Second Flower Festival, Jakarta. Mult.
1571 125 r. Type **321** 50 25
1572 150 r. Artificial bouquet . . . 90 25

322 Conference Building and Globe **323** Danau Poso Statue

1980. 25th Anniv of First Asian–African Conference, Bandung.
1573 **322** 150 r. mauve and gold . . 65 20

1980. Prehistoric Monuments. Multicoloured.
1575 60 r. Type **323** 35 10
1576 125 r. Elephant stone, Pasemah Village, South Sumatra . . . 40 25
1577 150 r. Taman Bali sarcophagus 90 30

324 Discus Thrower **325** Draughtsman in Wheelchair

1980. Olympics for the Disabled, Arnhem.
1580 **324** 75 r. brown & orange . . 65 10

1980. 30th Anniv of Disabled Veterans Corps.
1581 **325** 100 r. yell, blue & blk . . 65 10

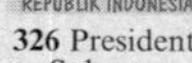

326 President Suharto

327 People and Map of Indonesia

1980.

1581a **326** 10 r. olive and green . . 1·25 10
1582 12 r. 50 grn & lt grn . . 15 10
1582a 25 r. brown & orange . . 20 10
1583 50 r. blue and green . . 15 10
1583a 55 r. red & vermilion . . 20 10
1584 75 r. brown & yellow . . 50 10
1585a 100 r. blue, vio & mve . 1·00 20
1586 200 r. brown & orge . . 1·40 10
1586b 300 r. vio, lil & gold . . 1·40 15
1586c 400 r. grey, pink and gold . . . . 1·40 15

Nos. 1585a and 1586 exist dated "1980" or "1981", and Nos. 1582a, 1583a and 1586b/c are dated "1983".

See also Nos. 1830/4.

1980. Population Census.

1587 **327** 75 r. blue and pink . . . 35 10
1588 200 r. blue and yellow . . 55 20

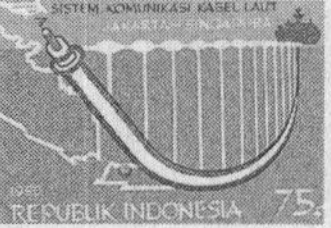

328 Ship laying Cable

329 Immigrants

1980. Inauguration of Singapore-Indonesia Submarine Cable.

1589 **328** 75 r. grn, dp grn & orge . 35 10
1590 200 r. bl, dp bl & orge . . 50 25

1980. Indonesian Immigration.

1591 **329** 12 r. 50 red and green . . 15 10

330 1946 50 s. Stamp

331 Map of A.O.P.U. Members

1980. 35th Anniv of Independence.

1592 **330** 75 r. cream, black & brn . 40 20
1593 – 100 r. cream, pur & gold . 75 30
1594 – 200 r. cream, pink & silver . . . . 1·00 35

DESIGNS—HORIZ: 100 r. 1946; 15 s. stamp. VERT: 200 r. 1946; 15 s. Freedom Fund stamp.

1980. 10th Anniv of Asian-Oceanic Postal Union Training School, Bangkok.

1595 **331** 200 r. blue, lt bl & turq . 90 20

332 O.P.E.C. Emblem on Globe

1980. 20th Anniv of Organization of Petroleum Exporting Countries.

1596 **332** 200 r. turq, blue & red . . 90 20

333 Service Members with Linked Arms

1980. 35th Anniv of Armed Forces. Mult.

1597 75 r. Indonesians hailing flag . 50 10
1598 200 r. Type **333** 75 20

334 Pesquet's Parrot

335 "Dendrobium insigne"

1980. Parrots. Multicoloured.

1599 75 r. Type **334** . . . . 1·75 35
1600 100 r. Chattering Lory . . . . 1·75 1·00
1601 200 r. Rainbow Lory . . . . 2·75 1·50

1980. Orchids. Multicoloured.

1603 75 r. Type **335** 75 20
1604 100 r. "Dendrobium discolor" . 1·25 55
1605 200 r. "Dendrobium lasianthera" . . . . 2·40 40

336 Von Stephan and U.P.U. Emblem

1981. 150th Birth Anniv of Heinrich von Stephan (U.P.U. founder).

1607 **336** 200 r. blue & deep blue . 90 25

337 Jamboree and Scouting Emblems

1981. 6th Asia-Pacific Scout Jamboree, Cibubur. Multicoloured.

1608 75 r. Type **337** 25 15
1609 100 r. Scout and Guide map-reading (vert.) 75 20
1610 200 r. Jamboree emblem and tents 90 30

338 Ship (relief carving)

339 Child holding Blood Drop

1981. 5th Asian-Oceanic Postal Union Congress, Yogyakarta.

1612 **338** 200 r. bl, blk & lt bl . . . 1·00 20

1981. Blood Donors.

1613 **339** 75 r. blue, black & red . . 25 10
1614 – 100 r. red and grey . . . 40 15
1615 – 200 r. red, dp bl & bl . . 50 25

DESIGNS: 100 r. Hands holding blood drop; 200 r. Hands and blood drop.

340 Monuments

1981. International Family Planning Conference.

1616 **340** 200 r. pale bl, brn & bl . . 65 15

341 "Song of Sritanjung"

1981. Traditional Balinese Paintings. Mult.

1617 100 r. Type **341** 80 15
1618 200 r. "Song of Sritanjung" (different) . . . . 1·00 50

Nos. 1617/18 were issued together, se-tenant, forming a composite design.

342 Secretariat Building and Emblem

343 Uber Cup

1981. Inauguration of A.S.E.A.N. Secretariat, Djakarta.

1620 **342** 200 r. yell, orge & pur . . 1·00 20

1981. International Ladies' Badminton Championships, Tokyo

1621 **343** 200 r. brn, yell & orge . . 1·75 25

344 "Tree of Life" (relief from Candi Mendut)

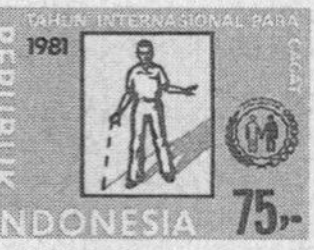

346 Blind Man

345 Students reading Koran, Mosque and Emblem

1981. World Environment Day.

1622 **344** 75 r. bistre, grey & blk . . 35 15
1623 – 200 r. bistre, grey & blk . . 75 15

DESIGN: 200 r. "Yaksha Apacaka".

1981. 12th National Koran Reading Contest, Banda Aceh.

1624 **345** 200 r. black, red & yell . . 75 25

1981. International Year of Disabled Persons.

1625 **346** 75 r. brown, yell & bis . . 25 10
1626 – 200 r. blue, brn & grn . . 65 50

DESIGN: 200 r. Deaf and dumb person.

347 Soekarno-Hatta Monument, Djakarta

1981. Independence Monument.

1627 **347** 200 r. blue, yell & gold . . 1·00 20

348 Parachute Jumping

349 Food Produce

1981. National Sports Week, Djakarta.

1628 **348** 75 r. red, black and blue . 20 15
1629 – 100 r. blk, blue & red . . 35 20
1630 – 200 r. brn, grn & red . . 95 35

DESIGNS—HORIZ: 100 r. Scuba diving. VERT: 200 r. Horse riding.

1981. World Food Day.

1631 **349** 200 r. multicoloured . . . 1·60 50

350 Arms of Aceh Special Territory

351 Salmon-crested Cockatoo

1981. Provincial Arms (1st series).

1632 **350** 100 r. yell, grn & gold . . 1·75 35
1633 – 100 r. multicoloured . . . 1·75 35
1634 – 100 r. multicoloured . . . 1·75 35
1635 – 100 r. multicoloured . . . 2·25 1·10
1636 – 100 r. multicoloured . . . 7·50 50

DESIGNS: No. 1633, Bali; No. 1634, Bengkulu; No. 1635, Irian Jaya; No. 1636, Djakarta.

See also Nos. 1643/62 and 1710.

1981. Cockatoos. Multicoloured.

1637 75 r. Type **351** . . . . . . 2·00 35
1638 100 r. Sulphur-crested Cockatoo . . . . 2·10 35
1639 200 r. Palm Cockatoo . . . . 3·50 1·60

1982. Provincial Arms (2nd series). As T **350**. Multicoloured.

1641 100 r. Jambi 75 10
1642 100 r. Java Barat (West) . . . 75 10
1643 100 r. Java Tengah (Cent) . . 75 10
1644 100 r. Java Timur (East) . . . 75 10
1645 100 r. Kalimantan Barat (West) 75 10
1646 100 r. Kalimantan Selatan (South) 75 10
1647 100 r. Kalimantan Timur (East) 75 10
1648 100 r. Kalimantan Tengah (Central) 75 10
1649 100 r. Lampung 75 10
1650 100 r. Moluccas 50 10
1651 100 r. Nusa Tengarra Barat (West) 50 10
1652 100 r. Nusa Tengarra Timur (East) 50 10
1653 100 r. Riau 75 10
1654 100 r. Sulawesi Tengah (Central Celebes) 50 10
1655 100 r. Sulawesi Tenggara (South-east Celebes) 50 10
1656 100 r. Sulawesi Selatan (South Celebes) 50 10
1657 100 r. Sumatera Utara (North Celebes) 50 10
1658 100 r. Sumatera Barat (West) . 75 10
1659 100 r. Sumatera Selatan (South) 50 10
1660 100 r. Sumatera Utara (North) 50 10
1661 100 r. Yogyakarta . . . . . . 1·25 10
1662 250 r. Republic of Indonesia (45 × 29 mm) . . . . . . 3·25 35

352 Hands enclosing Family

1982. 70th Anniv of Bumiputera Mutual Life Insurance Company.

1663 **352** 75 r. yell, plum & pur . . 20 10
1664 – 100 r. yell, lt grn & grn . . 40 15
1665 – 200 r. multicoloured . . 1·25 40

DESIGNS: 100 r. Family in countryside; 200 r. Hands supporting industrial activities.

353 Helicopter Rescue

354 Houses and Ballot Boxes

1982. 10th Anniv of Search and Rescue Institute.

1666 **353** 250 r. multicoloured . . . 1·75 70

1982. General Election. Multicoloured.

1667 75 r. Type **354** 25 10
1668 100 r. Rural houses and ballot boxes 25 10
1669 200 r. Houses and National arms . . . . 1·00 50

355 Human Figures, Satellite and Dove

357 Footballers

356 Thomas Cup

1982. 2nd U.N. Conference on Exploration and Peaceful Uses of Outer Space, Vienna.

1670 **355** 150 r. blue, violet & blk . . 35 10
1671 – 250 r. green, light green and deep green 75 15

DESIGN: 250 r. Peace dove and text.

1982. Thomas Cup Badminton Championship, London.

1672 **356** 250 r. multicoloured . . . 1·25 20

1982. World Cup Football Championship, Spain.

1674 **357** 250 r. multicoloured . . . 1·25 25

358 Taman Siswa Emblem

1982. 60th Anniv of Taman Siswa (educational organization).

1676 **358** 250 r. yellow, green & red 65 15

359 Flags forming "15"

1982. 15th Anniv of Association of South-East Asian Nations.
1677 **359** 150 r. orge, red & bl 1·25 25

360 President Suharto **362** Rothschild's Mynah

1982.
1678 **360** 110 r. red and orange 15 10
1679 250 r. brown & orange 65 10
1680 275 r. green & yellow 95 10
Nos. 1678 and 1680 are inscribed "1983".

1982. Third World National Parks Congress, Bali. Multicoloured.
1682 100 r. Type **362** 2·00 30
1683 250 r. King Bird of Paradise 3·00 70

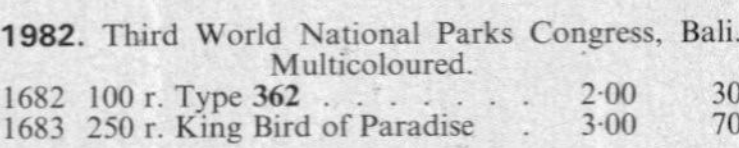

363 River Bridge

1982. Five Year Plan.
1685 **363** 17 r. 50 brown & green 35 10

364 Arfak Parotia **365** Scouts and Anniversary Emblem

1982. Birds of Paradise. Multicoloured.
1686 100 r. Type **364** 1·50 30
1687 150 r. Twelve-wired bird of paradise 2·25 40
1688 250 r. Red bird of paradise 3·75 1·40

1983. 75th Anniv of Boy Scout Movement.
1690 **365** 250 r. blue, green & vio 80 20

366 Temple Restoration and Relief

1983. Borobudur Temple.
1691 **366** 100 r. green, bl & lt bl 1·25 20
1692 – 150 r. lt grn, grn & brn 1·25 20
1693 – 250 r. blk, dp brn & brn 3·75 1·25
DESIGNS—VERT: 150 r. Temple and statue. HORIZ: 250 r. Silhouette of temple and seated Buddha.

367 President Suharto **368** Gas Storage Tanks

1983.
1695 **367** 500 r. brown 1·00 15

1983. Seventh International Liquefied Natural Gas Conference, Djarkarta.
1696 **368** 275 r. multicoloured 1·00 20

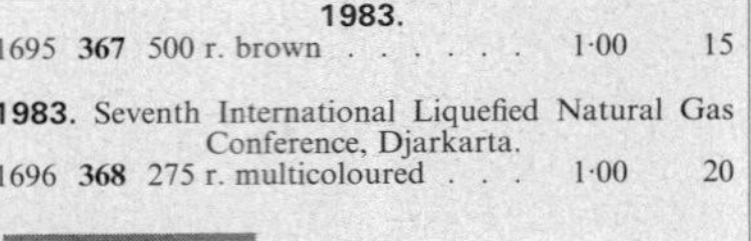

369 Ships and Bird **370** Man and Woman reading Koran

1983. World Communications Year.
1697 **369** 75 r. multicoloured 15 10
1698 – 110 r. multicoloured 25 15
1699 – 175 r. blue and red 30 20
1700 – 275 r. blue, dp bl & red 90 30
DESIGNS: 110 r. Satellite and receiving station; 175 r. Aircraft and dish aerial, 275 r. Globe and letter.

1983. 13th National Koran Reading Competition.
1701 **370** 275 r. yellow, grn & blk 90 10

371 Eclipse and Map of Indonesia

1983. Total Solar Eclipse.
1702 **371** 110 r. brn, dp brn & blk 50 15
1703 – 275 r. blue, vio & pur 1·50 20
DESIGN: 275 r. Map of Indonesia showing path of eclipse.

372 Satellite transmitting to Indonesia **373** Patient receiving Radiation Treatment

1983. Launching of "Palapa B" Communications Satellite.
1705 **372** 275 r. green, blue & silver 90 20

1983. Anti-cancer Campaign.
1706 **373** 55 r.+20 r. mult 50 20
1707 75 r.+25 r. mult 75 20

374 Agricultural Produce

1983. Agricultural Census.
1708 **374** 110 r. grey, grn & blk 65 20
1709 – 275 r. red, black & grn 1·10 50
DESIGN: 275 r. Farmer with produce.

1983. Provincial Arms (3rd series). As T **350**. Multicoloured.
1710 100 r. Timor Timur 1·25 10

375 Traditional Weaving, Pakistan

1983. Indonesia-Pakistan Economic and Cultural Co-operation. Multicoloured.
1711 275 r. Type **375** 1·10 20
1712 275 r. Traditional weaving, Indonesia 1·10 20

376 Eruption of Krakatoa

1983. Centenary of Krakatoa Volcanic Eruption. Multicoloured.
1713 110 r. Type **376** 20 15
1714 275 r. Map showing position of Krakatoa 1·10 20

377 Casa-Nurtanio CN-235 Short-haul Passenger Aircraft

1983. Indonesian Aircraft.
1715 **377** 275 r. multicoloured 1·60 65

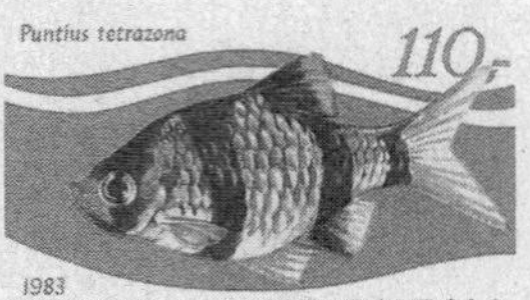

378 Tiger Barb

1983. Tropical Fishes. Multicoloured.
1717 110 r. Type **378** 1·50 50
1718 175 r. Brilliant rasbora 1·50 50
1719 275 r. Archerfish 4·50 1·50

379 Wilson's Bird of Paradise

1983. Birds of Paradise. Multicoloured.
1721 110 r. Type **379** 1·25 20
1722 175 r. Black sicklebill 1·75 25
1723 275 r. Black-billed sicklebill 2·75 80
1724 500 r. As No. 1723 4·25 2·25

380 Emblems of Peace and Co-operation

1983. Palestinian Solidarity.
1726 **380** 275 r. blue, brn & sil 1·00 10

381 "Stop" Emblem **382** Agriculture

1984. Anti-poliomyelitis Campaign.
1732 **381** 110 r. red, pur & bl 10 10
1733 – 275 r. pur, orge & red 1·00 15
DESIGN: 275 r. Emblem of Save the Children Fund.

1984. Fourth Five Year Plan.
1734 **382** 55 r. yellow and blue 10 10
1735 – 75 r. green and brown 30 15
1736 – 110 r. blue and orange 40 20
1737 – 275 r. multicoloured 60 10
DESIGNS: 75 r. Casa-Nurtiano CN-235 airliner (aircraft industry); 110 r. Shipbuilding; 275 r. Telephone (telecommunications).

383 Manufacturing Plywood

1984. Forestry. Multicoloured.
1738 75 r. Type **383** 80 10
1739 110 r. Seedling 80 10
1740 175 r. Measuring tree trunk 80 20
1741 275 r. Transporting trees 80 30

384 Children playing with Toys

1984. Children's Day. Multicoloured.
1743 75 r.+25 r. Type **384** 75 10
1744 110 r.+25 r. Scout camp 50 15
1745 175 r.+25 r. Children on farm 1·25 20
1746 275 r.+25 r. Scouts and guides in camp 1·25 25

385 Flags of Member Nations

1984. Association of South-East Asian Nations Meeting, Djakarta.
1747 **385** 275 r. multicoloured 1·40 25

386 Pole Vaulting **387** Horse Dance

1984. Olympic Games, Los Angeles. Multicoloured.
1748 75 r. Type **386** 20 10
1749 110 r. Archery 20 10
1750 175 r. Boxing 20 10
1751 250 r. Shooting 1·10 25
1752 275 r. Weightlifting 1·50 25
1753 325 r. Swimming 2·50 15

1984. Art and Culture. Multicoloured.
1754 75 r. Type **387** 65 10
1755 110 r. "Reog" mask 90 10
1756 275 r. Lion dance 90 50
1757 325 r. "Barong" mask 2·10 55

388 Thomas Cup (badminton)

1984. National Sports Day. Multicoloured.
1758 110 r. Type **388** 60 10
1759 275 r. Keep-fit exercise 1·10 20

389 Map and Post Code Zones **390** Lauterbach's Bowerbird

1984. Introduction of New Post Code Zones.
1763 **389** 110 r. bl, brn & orge 20 10
1764 275 r. orge, bl & brn 60 15

1984. Birds. Multicoloured.
1765 75 r. Type **390** 2·00 20
1766 110 r. Flamed bowerbird 3·00 50
1767 275 r. Arfak bird of paradise 3·75 1·75
1768 325 r. Superb bird of paradise 3·75 1·10

391 Flag and Fists **392** Boeing 747-200

1984. Youth Pledge.
1770 **391** 275 r. black and red 75 10

1984. 40th Anniv of I.C.A.O.
1771 **392** 275 r. red, black & bl . . 1·50 50

393 "Tyro" and Geological Structure of Seabed
394 Stylised Birds

1985. Indonesia–Belanda Expedition.
1772 **393** 50 r. blue and brown . . 50 10
1773 – 100 r. blue & purple . . . 90 20
1774 – 275 r. blue and green . . 1·00 55
DESIGNS: 100 r. "Tyro" (oceanographic survey ship) and map; 275 r. "Tyro" and coral reef.

1985. International Women's Day.
1775 **394** 100 r. mauve and red . . 1·50 50
1776 – 275 r. red and brown . . 2·25 2·50
DESIGN: 275 r. Profile silhouettes.

395 Jet Airliner and workers
396 Pres. Suharto

1985. 4th Five Year Plan.
1777 **395** 75 r. red and brown . . . 25 15
1778 – 140 r. grey & brown . . . 40 10
1779 – 350 r. green & brown . . 50 10
DESIGNS: 140 r. Children in classroom; 350 r. Industrial equipment and buildings.

1985.
1780 **396** 140 r. brown and red . . 50 10
1781 350 r. mauve and red . . 1·00 10

397 Conference Building

1985. 30th Anniv of First Asian-African Conference, Bandung.
1786 **397** 350 r. multicoloured . . . 1·25 40

398 Globe and Teenagers waving Palm Leaves
399 Profiles

1985. International Youth Year.
1787 **398** 75 r. yell, brn & grn . . . 25 10
1788 – 140 r. bl, grn & mve . . . 1·10 10
DESIGN: 140 r. Flower on globe supported by teenagers.

1985. United Nations Women's Decade.
1789 **399** 55 r. brown & green . . . 40 10
1790 – 140 r. blk, grn & brn . . . 65 10
DESIGN: 140 r. Globe and decade emblems.

400 Housing and Hydro-electricity

401 Sky Diving

1985. 40th Anniv of Indonesian Republic.
1791 **400** 140 r. green and red . . . 50 10
1792 – 350 r. blue, mve & yell . . 1·10 20
DESIGN: 350 r. Tractor and industrial complex.

1985. National Sports Week, Djakarta. Multicoloured.
1793 55 r. Type **401** 15 10
1794 100 r. Unarmed combat . . . 65 10
1795 140 r. High jumping 65 15
1796 350 r. Sailboards (vert) . . . . 1·10 65

402 O.P.E.C. Emblem and Globe
403 Tanker

1985. 25th Anniv of Organization of Petroleum Exporting Countries.
1797 **402** 40 r. blue, mve & orge . . 75 10

1985. Centenary of Indonesian Oil Industry. Multicoloured.
1798 140 r. Type **403** 60 20
1799 250 r. Refinery 80 40
1800 350 r. Derrick and rigs . . . . 1·50 65

404 Doves, "40" and U.N. Emblem

1985. 40th Anniv of U.N.O. Multicoloured.
1801 140 r. Type **404** 40 10
1802 300 r. Bombs and green leaves . 85 15

405 Javan Rhinoceros
406 Emblem

1985. Wildlife.
1803 **405** 75 r. brown, grn & bl . . 75 10
1804 – 150 r. brn, orge & grn . . 1·00 25
1805 – 300 r. brown, bl & red . . 2·00 55
DESIGNS: 150 r. Anoa; 300 r. Komodo dragon.

1986. Economic Census. Each orange and violet.
1806 175 r. Type **406** 50 10
1807 175 r. Symbols of economy . . 50 10

407 Baby feeding, Powdered Milk, Syringe and Graph
408 Industry

1986. 40th Anniv of U.N.I.C.E.F.
1808 **407** 75 r. multicoloured . . . 40 10
1809 – 140 r. flesh, brn & pk . . 70 10
DESIGN: 140 r. Vaccinating baby.

1986. 4th Five Year Plan.
1810 **408** 140 r. multicoloured . . . 10 10
1811 – 500 r. yellow, brown & bl . 30 10
DESIGN: 500 r. Agriculture.

409 Thomas Cup and Racket

410 Pinisi Sailing Ship

1986. Thomas (men's) and Uber (women's) Cup Badminton Championships, Djakarta.
1812 **409** 55 r. blk, yell & bl . . . 50 10
1813 – 150 r. red, brn & gold . . 85 15
DESIGN: 150 r. Thomas and Uber Cups and shuttlecock.

1986. "Expo 86" World's Fair, Vancouver.
1814 **410** 75 r. black, red & yellow . 40 10
1815 – 150 r. multicoloured . . . 75 15
1816 – 300 r. silver, red & purple 1·10 20
DESIGNS: 150 r. Kentongan village drum and "Palapa" satellite; 300 r. Indonesian pavilion emblem.

411 Guides on Parade

1986. National Jamboree. Multicoloured.
1817 100 r. Type **411** 15 10
1818 140 r. Guides cooking over fire 1·00 15
1819 210 r. Scouts consulting map (vert.) . . . . 1·25 25

412 "86"

1986. Indonesia Air Show.
1820 **412** 350 r. multicoloured . . . 1·00 50

413 Tari Legong Kraton

1986. Traditional Dances. Multicoloured.
1821 140 r. Type **413** . . . . . . 1·00 10
1822 350 r. Tari Barong . . . . . 1·75 20
1823 500 r. Tari Kecak . . . . . 2·25 35

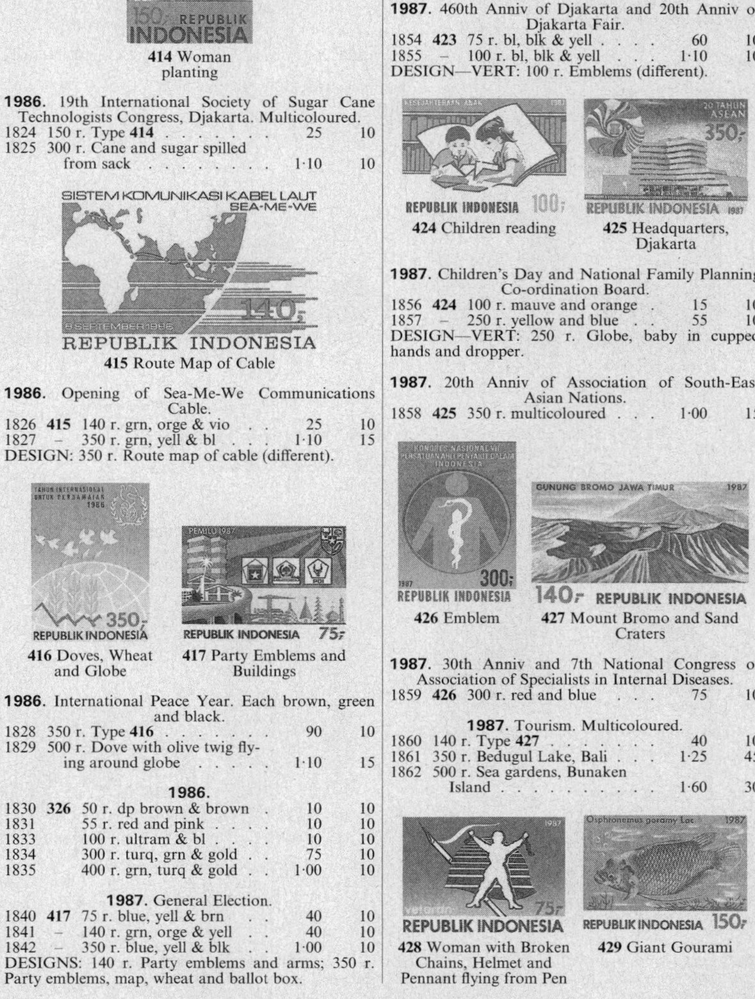

414 Woman planting

1986. 19th International Society of Sugar Cane Technologists Congress, Djakarta. Multicoloured.
1824 150 r. Type **414** 25 10
1825 300 r. Cane and sugar spilled from sack . . . . 1·10 10

415 Route Map of Cable

1986. Opening of Sea-Me-We Communications Cable.
1826 **415** 140 r. grn, orge & vio . . 25 10
1827 – 350 r. grn, yell & bl . . . 1·10 15
DESIGN: 350 r. Route map of cable (different).

416 Doves, Wheat and Globe
417 Party Emblems and Buildings

1986. International Peace Year. Each brown, green and black.
1828 350 r. Type **416** 90 10
1829 500 r. Dove with olive twig flying around globe . . . . . 1·10 15

1986.
1830 **326** 50 r. dp brown & brown . 10 10
1831 55 r. red and pink 10 10
1833 100 r. ultram & bl 10 10
1834 300 r. turq, grn & gold . . 75 10
1835 400 r. grn, turq & gold . . 1·00 10

1987. General Election.
1840 **417** 75 r. blue, yell & brn . . 40 10
1841 – 140 r. grn, orge & yell . . 40 10
1842 – 350 r. blue, yell & blk . . 1·00 10
DESIGNS: 140 r. Party emblems and arms; 350 r. Party emblems, map, wheat and ballot box.

418 Satellite and Globe

419 Boy carving Figures

1987. Launch of "Palapa B2" Satellite.
1843 **418** 350 r. yell, grn & brn . . 75 15
1844 – 500 r. multicoloured . . . 1·10 20
DESIGN—VERT: 500 r. Rocket and satellite.

1987. 4th Five Year Plan.
1845 **419** 140 r. brn, yell & bl . . . 15 10
1846 – 350. r. vio, grn & orge . . 25 10
DESIGN: 350 r. Graph and cattle.

420 Crab and Scanner Unit

421 East Kalimantan Couple

1987. 10th Anniv of Indonesian Cancer Foundation.
1847 **420** 350 r. + 25 r. yellow & bl . 90 15

1987. Wedding Costumes (1st series). Mult.
1848 140 r. Type **421** . . . . . . 1·10 15
1849 350 r. Aceh couple . . . . . 7·50 3·50
1850 400 r. East Timor couple . . . 8·75 1·00
See also Nos. 1891/6, 1955/60, 1992/7 and 2010/15.

422 Weightlifting

423 Emblems

1987. 14th South-East Asia Games, Djakarta. Designs showing pictograms.
1851 **422** 140 r. yellow, red and blue 15 10
1852 – 250 r. blue, yellow and red 60 20
1853 – 350 r. red, blue and brown 90 20
DESIGNS: 250 r. Swimming; 350 r. Running.

1987. 460th Anniv of Djakarta and 20th Anniv of Djakarta Fair.
1854 **423** 75 r. bl, blk & yell 60 10
1855 – 100 r. bl, blk & yell . . . 1·10 10
DESIGN—VERT: 100 r. Emblems (different).

424 Children reading
425 Headquarters, Djakarta

1987. Children's Day and National Family Planning Co-ordination Board.
1856 **424** 100 r. mauve and orange . 15 10
1857 – 250 r. yellow and blue . . 55 10
DESIGN—VERT: 250 r. Globe, baby in cupped hands and dropper.

1987. 20th Anniv of Association of South-East Asian Nations.
1858 **425** 350 r. multicoloured . . . 1·00 15

426 Emblem
427 Mount Bromo and Sand Craters

1987. 30th Anniv and 7th National Congress of Association of Specialists in Internal Diseases.
1859 **426** 300 r. red and blue . . . 75 10

1987. Tourism. Multicoloured.
1860 140 r. Type **427** 40 10
1861 350 r. Bedugul Lake, Bali . . . 1·25 45
1862 500 r. Sea gardens, Bunaken Island . . . . 1·60 30

428 Woman with Broken Chains, Helmet and Pennant flying from Pen

429 Giant Gourami

1987. "Woman's Physical Revolution".
1863 **428** 75 r. green, red & yell . . 10 10
1864 – 100 r. green, yell & red . . 50 10
DESIGN: 100 r. Women with rifles and barbed wire.

1987. Fishes.
1865 **429** 150 r. mauve, yell & bl . . 1·25 50
1866 – 200 r. mauve, yell & bl . . 1·25 30
1867 – 500 r. black, yell & bl . . 3·75 30
DESIGNS: 200 r. Goldfish; 300 r. Walking catfish.

430 Soldiers
432 Carved Snake and Frog
431 Welder

1988. 31st Anniv of Veterans Legion.
1868 **430** 250 r. green and orange . 65 10

1988. National Safety and Occupational Health Day.
1869 **431** 350 r. blue and green . . 90 10

1988. 8th Anniv of National Crafts Council.
1870 **432** 120 r. blue and brown . . 50 10
1871 – 350 r. blue and brown . . 75 20
1872 – 500 r. brown & green . . 1·25 20
DESIGN: 350 r. Cane rocking-chair; 500 r. Bamboo goods.

433 Industrial Symbols
434 Indonesian Girls

1988. 4th Five Year Plan.
1873 **433** 140 r. blue and green . . 15 15
1874 – 400 r. purple and red . . 50 25
DESIGN: 400 r. Fishing industry.

1988. "Expo 88" World's Fair, Brisbane. Multicoloured.
1875 200 r. Type **434** 70 10
1876 300 r. Indonesian girl 70 10
1877 350 r. Indonesian girl and boy . 1·10 15

435 Anniversary Emblem
436 "Dendrobium none betawi"

1988. 125th Anniv of Red Cross.
1879 **435** 350 r. grey, black & red . 75 15

1988. Flowers. Multicoloured.
1880 400 r. Type **436** . . . . . . 1·25 15
1881 500 r. "Dendrobium abang betawi" . . . . 1·25 20

437 Running
438 Figures around Emblem

1988. Olympic Games, Seoul.
1882 **437** 75 r. black, brn & gold . . 40 10
1883 – 100 r. blk, red & gold . . 75 10
1884 – 200 r. blk, mve & gold . . 75 15
1885 – 300 r. blk, grn & gold . . 50 15
1886 – 400 r. black, bl & gold . . 50 15
1887 – 500 r. black, bl & gold . 2·25 35
DESIGNS: 100 r. Weightlifting; 200 r. Archery; 300 r. Table tennis; 400 r. Swimming; 500 r. Tennis.

1988. Centenary of International Women's Council.
1889 **438** 140 r. black and blue . . 50 10

439 Family, Water and Ear of Wheat
440 President Suharto

1988. National Farmers' and Fishermen's Week.
1890 **439** 350 r. stone and red . . . 75 10

1988. Wedding Costumes (2nd series). As T **421**. Multicoloured.
1891 55 r. Sumatera Barat (West) . . 10 10
1892 75 r. Jambi 10 10
1893 100 r. Bengkulu 50 10
1894 120 r. Lampung 65 10
1895 200 r. Moluccas . . . . . . 1·25 10
1896 250 r. Nusa Tenggara Timur (East) . . . . 1·60 75

1988.
1897 **440** 200 r. blue, pink & red . . 15 10
1898 700 r. mve, lt grn & grn . 50 10
1899 1000 r. multicoloured . . 65 15

441 Emblem
442 Doves and Envelopes

1988. 13th Non-Aligned News Agencies Co-ordinating Committee Meeting, Djakarta.
1901 **441** 500 r. blue and red . . . 90 10

1988. International Correspondence Week.
1902 **442** 140 r. blue and red . . . 65 10

443 Means of Transport and Communications

1988. Asian-Pacific Transport and Communications Decade.
1904 **443** 350 r. blue and black . . 75 45

444 Al Mashun Mosque, Medan
445 "Papilio gigon"

1988. Tourism. Multicoloured.
1905 250 r. Type **444** 40 10
1906 300 r. Pagaruyung Palace, Batusangkar 60 20
1907 500 r. Keong Emas Theatre, Djakarta . . . . 1·50 25

1988. Butterflies. Multicoloured.
1909 400 r. Type **445** . . . . . 1·00 20
1910 500 r. "Graphium androcles" . 1·75 25

446 "Rafflesia sp."
447 "40" and Boeing 747

1989. Flowers. Multicoloured.
1916 200 r. Type **446** 50 20
1917 1000 r. "Amorphophallus titanum" . . . . 1·75 65

1989. 40th Anniv of Garuda Airline.
1919 **447** 350 r. blue and green . . 1·25 40

448 Mother and Baby
449 Industrial Site

1989. Endangered Animals. The Orang-Utan. Multicoloured.
1920 75 r. Type **448** . . . . . . 2·50 1·00
1921 100 r. Orang-utan in tree . . . 2·50 50
1922 140 r. Mother and baby in trees . . . . 2·50 50
1923 500 r. Orang-utan . . . . . 7·50 4·25

1989. 5th Five Year Plan.
1925 **449** 55 r. violet and green . . 10 10
1926 – 150 r. blue and brown . . 15 10
1927 – 350 r. green & orange . . 20 15
DESIGNS: 150 r. Cement works; 350 r. Gas plant.

450 Stamp and Map
451 Ki Hadjar Dewantara and Graduate

1989. 125th Anniv of First Netherlands Indies Stamp.
1928 **450** 1000 r. grn, pur & bl . . . 1·25 35

1989. National Education Day.
1929 **451** 140 r. red and purple . . 40 10
1930 – 300 r. violet and green . . 65 10
DESIGN: 300 r. Dewantara (founder of Taman Siswa School), pencil and books.

452 Emblem on Map
453 Flag and Cup

1989. 10th Anniv of Asia-Pacific Telecommunity.
1931 **452** 350 r. purple and green . 65 10

1989. Sudirman Cup.
1932 **453** 100 r. brown and red . . 1·10 10

454 Students
455 Headquarters

1989. Children's Day.
1933 **454** 100 r. brown & orange . . 40 10
1934 – 250 r. blue and green . . 55 10
DESIGN: 250 r. Youths exercising.

1989. 10th Anniv of Asia-Pacific Integrated Rural Development Centre.
1935 **455** 140 r. brown and blue . . 50 10

456 Skull of "Sangiran 17" and Hunters
457 Globe and People

1989. Centenary of Palaeoanthropology in Indonesia.
1936 **456** 100 r. black & brown . . 40 10
1937 150 r. green and red . . 50 10
1938 200 r. blue and brown . . 75 10
1939 250 r. violet & brown . . 90 10
1940 300 r. green and red . . 1·10 15
1941 350 r. blue and brown . . 1·40 15
DESIGNS—HORIZ: 150 r. Skull of "Perning 1" and cavemen; 200 r. Skull of "Sangiran 10" and hunter. VERT: 250 r. Skull of "Wajak 1"; 300 r. Skull of "Sambungmacan 1"; 350 r. Skull of "Ngandong 7".

1989. Cent of Interparliamentary Union.
1942 **457** 350 r. green and blue . . 65 50

458 Kung Fu

1989. 12th National Games, Djakarta. Mult.
1943 75 r. Type **458** 40 10
1944 100 r. Tennis 40 10
1945 140 r. Judo 40 10
1946 350 r. Volleyball . . . . . . 1·00 45
1947 500 r. Boxing . . . . 1·90 15
1948 1000 r. Archery . . . . . . 2·25 35

459 Taman Burung
460 Trophy

1989. Tourism. Multicoloured.
1949 120 r. Type **459** 50 10
1950 350 r. Prangko Museum . . . 75 40
1951 500 r. Istana Anak-Anak (vert) 1·25 15

1989. Film Industry.
1953 **460** 150 r. ochre & brown . . 65 10

1989. Wedding Costumes (3rd series). As T **421**. Multicoloured.
1955 50 r. Sumatera Utara (North) . 15 10
1956 75 r. Sumatera Selatan (South) 15 10
1957 100 r. Djakarta 15 10
1958 140 r. Sulawesi Utara (North Celebes) 35 10
1959 350 r. Sulawesi Tengah (Central Celebes) 75 70
1960 500 r. Sulawesi Selatan (South Celebes) . . . . 1·00 40

461 Worker wearing Safety Belt and Flag

1990. Occupational Safety.
1962 **461** 200 r. brown and green . 50 10

462 Benteng Marlborough, Bengkulu

1990. Tourism. Multicoloured.
1963 200 r. Type **462** 65 10
1964 400 r. National Museum, Djakarta 95 10
1965 500 r. Baiturrahman Mosque, Banda Aceh 95 15

463 "Mammilaria fragilis"

1990. Plants. Multicoloured.
1967 75 r. Type **463** 10 10
1968 1000 r. Bonsai of "Gmelina elliptica" . . . . 1·25 30

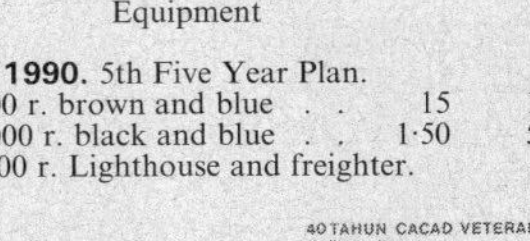

464 Tree-felling Equipment

1990. 5th Five Year Plan.
1970 **464** 200 r. brown and blue . . 15 10
1971 – 1000 r. black and blue . . 1·50 55
DESIGN: 1000 r. Lighthouse and freighter.

465 Arrow pointing to Indonesia

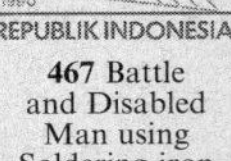

467 Battle and Disabled Man using Soldering-iron

1990. Visit Indonesia Year (1991) (1st issue). Multicoloured.
1972 100 r. Type **465** 15 10
1973 500 r. Temple 80 15
See also Nos. 1998/2000.

1990. 40th Anniv of Disabled Veterans Corp.
1976 **467** 1000 r. orange & green 1·00 25

468 Player and Goalkeeper
469 U.N. Population Award 

1990. World Cup Football Championship, Italy. Multicoloured.
1977 75 r. Type **468** 40 10
1978 150 r. Player tackling 50 10
1979 400 r. Players competing for high ball 1·10 15

1990. 20th Anniv of Family Planning Movement.
1981 **469** 60 r. brown and red 10 10

470 Figure with Pencil and Open Book
471 Children 

1990. Population Census.
1982 **470** 90 r. green & turquoise 40 10

1990. Children's Day.
1983 **471** 500 r. purple and red 75 10

472 Soldier planting Flag
473 Buildings and Cultural Identities 

1990. 45th Anniv of Independence. Mult.
1984 200 r. Type **472** 40 10
1985 500 r. Modern building and roads 70 15

1990. Indonesia–Pakistan Economic and Cultural Co-operation Organization. Multicoloured.
1987 75 r. Type **473** 35 10
1988 400 r. Dancer (vert) 70 10

474 Emblem
475 Anniversary Emblem 

1990. 20th Anniv of Asian-Pacific Postal Training Centre.
1989 **474** 500 r. blue & ultramarine 65 10

1990. 30th Anniv of Organization of Petroleum Exporting Countries.
1990 **475** 200 r. blk, grey & orge 50 10

476 Houses
477 Dancer and House 

1990. Environmental Health.
1991 **476** 1000 r. multicoloured 1·25 15

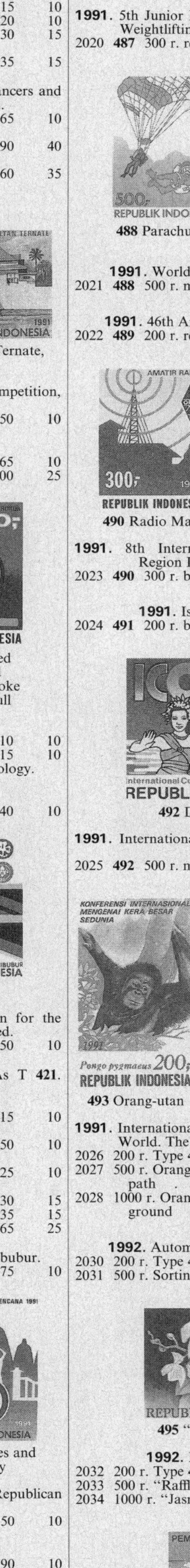

1990. Wedding Costumes (4th series). As T **421**. Multicoloured.
1992 75 r. Java Barat (West) 15 10
1993 100 r. Java Tengah (Central) 15 10
1994 150 r. Yogyakarta 15 10
1995 200 r. Java Timur (East) 20 10
1996 400 r. Bali 30 15
1997 500 r. Nusa Tenggara Barat (West) 35 15

1991. Visit Indonesia Year (2nd issue). Dancers and Traditional Houses. Multicoloured.
1998 200 r. Type **477** 65 10
1999 500 r. House and dancer with saucers 90 40
2000 1000 r. Dancer and house (different) 1·60 35

478 Emblem
479 Palace of Sultan Ternate, Moluccas 

1991. 16th National Koran Reading Competition, Yogyakarta.
2002 **478** 200 r. green and yellow 50 10

1991. Tourism. Multicoloured.
2003 500 r. Type **479** 65 10
2004 1000 r. Bari House, Palembang 1·00 25

480 Steel Mill
481 Damaged Lungs and Cigarette Smoke forming Skull 

1991. 5th Five Year Plan.
2006 **480** 75 r. red and blue 10 10
2007 – 200 r. blue and black 15 10
DESIGN—HORIZ: 200 r. Computer technology.

1991. Anti-smoking Campaign.
2008 **481** 90 r. red and black 40 10

482 Hands
483 Tents 

1991. 24th Anniv of National Federation for the Welfare of the Mentally Handicapped.
2009 **482** 200 r. + 25 r. black & red 50 10

1991. Wedding Costumes (5th series). As T **421**. Multicoloured.
2010 100 r. Kalimantan Barat (West) 15 10
2011 200 r. Kalimantan Tengah (Central) 50 10
2012 300 r. Kalimantan Selatan (South) 25 10
2013 400 r. Sulawesi Tenggara (South-east Celebes) 30 15
2014 500 r. Riau 35 15
2015 1000 r. Irian Jaya 65 25

1991. National Boy Scout Jamboree, Cibubur.
2016 **483** 200 r. blue, black & red 75 10

484 Monument
485 Temples and Family 

1991 42nd Anniv of Return of Republican Government to Djokjakarta.
2017 **484** 200 r. green and brown 50 10

1991. Farmers' Week.
2018 **485** 500 r. yellow and blue 90 10

486 Cells
487 Weightlifters 

1991. "chemindo '91" Chemistry Congress, Surabaya.
2019 **486** 400 r. red and green 65 10

1991. 5th Junior Men's and Fourth Women's Asian Weightlifting Championships, Manado.
2020 **487** 300 r. red and black 65 10

488 Parachutists
489 Red Cross and Hands 

1991. World Parachuting Championships.
2021 **488** 500 r. mauve and blue 65 10

1991. 46th Anniv of Indonesian Red Cross.
2022 **489** 200 r. red and green 50 10

490 Radio Mast
491 Script and Mosque 

1991. 8th International Amateur Radio Union Region III Conference, Bandung.
2023 **490** 300 r. blue and yellow 65 10

1991. Istiqlal Festival, Djakarta.
2024 **491** 200 r. black and red 65 10

492 Dancer and Inspectors

1991. International Convention on Quality Control Circles, Bali.
2025 **492** 500 r. multicoloured 75 10

493 Orang-utan
494 Model of Jakarta Post Office 

1991. International Conference on Great Apes of the World. The Orang-utan. Multicoloured.
2026 200 r. Type **493** 65 10
2027 500 r. Orang-utan on forest path 75 15
2028 1000 r. Orang-utan sitting on ground 1·60 45

1992. Automation of Postal Service. Mult.
2030 200 r. Type **494** 15 10
2031 500 r. Sorting machine 30 10

495 "Phalaenopsis ambilis"

1992. Flowers. Multicoloured.
2032 200 r. Type **495** 15 10
2033 500 r. "Rafflesia arnoldii" 55 10
2034 1000 r. "Jasminum sambac" 1·10 25

496 Buildings, Ballot Boxes and State Arms

1992. Parliamentary Elections. Mult.
2036 75 r. Type **496** 10 10
2037 100 r. Ballot boxes and globe 10 10
2038 500 r. Ballot boxes and hands holding voting slips 65 10

497 Lembah Baliem, Irian Jaya

1992. Visit ASEAN Year. Multicoloured.
2039 300 r. Type **497** 45 10
2040 500 r. Tanah Lot, Bali 65 10
2041 1000 r. Lembah Anai, Sumatra Barat 1·40 20

498 Road-building
499 Emblem and Crab 

1992. 5th Five Year Plan.
2043 **498** 150 r. purple & green 10 10
2044 – 300 r. blue and mauve 20 10
DESIGN: 300 r. Aircraft.

1992. 15th Anniv of Indonesian Cancer Foundation.
2045 **499** 200 r. + 25 r. red & brown 15 15
2046 500 r. + 50 r. red & blue 35 35

500 Weightlifting
501 White-crested Laughing Thrush 

1992. Olympic Games, Barcelona. Mult.
2047 75 r. Type **500** 10 10
2048 200 r. Badminton 15 10
2049 300 r. Sports pictograms 45 10
2050 500 r. Tennis 55 15
2051 1000 r. Archery 1·25 30

1992. Birds. Multicoloured.
2053 100 r. Type **501** 10 10
2054 200 r. Golden-backed three-toed woodpecker 15 10
2055 400 r. Rhinoceros hornbill 50 10
2056 500 r. Amboina king parrot 75 15

502 Busy Street (Tammy Filia)

1992. National Children's Day. Children's paintings. Multicoloured.
2058 75 r. Type **502** 10 10
2059 100 r. Children with balloons (Cynthia Widiyana Halim) 10 10
2060 200 r. Native boats (Dandy Rahmad Adi Kurniawan) 40 10
2061 500 r. Girl and bird (Intan Sari Dewi Saputro) 90 50

503 Anniversary Emblem
504 Earth and "Palapa B-4" (satellite) 

1992. 25th Anniv of Association of South-East Asian Nations. Multicoloured.
2062 200 r. Type **503** 15 10
2063 500 r. Map and flags of member nations 75 10
2064 1000 r. "25" and flags 1·50 20

1992. Communications. Multicoloured.
2065 200 r. Type **504** 15 10
2066 500 r. "Palapa" satellite (16th anniv of launch) 55 10
2067 1000 r. Old and modern telephones (modernization of telephone system) 1·25 20

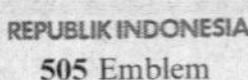

505 Emblem

506 Ngremo Dance, East Java

1992. 10th Non-Aligned Countries Summit, Djakarta. Multicoloured.

2068 200 r. Type **505** 40 10
2069 500 r. Members' flags and emblem 65 15

1992. Traditional Dances (1st series). Mult.

2070 200 r. Type **506** 15 10
2071 500 r. Gending Sriwijaya dance, South Sumatra 70 75

See also Nos. 2122/4, 2168/72, 2211/14, 2292/5, 2366/70 and 2476/80.

507 Anniversary Emblem

508 Antara Building, Djakarta

1992. 40th Anniv of International Planned Parenthood Federation.

2073 **507** 200 r. blue and green . . 50 10

1992. 55th Anniv of Antara News Agency.

2074 **508** 500 r. black and blue . . 65 15

509 Planting Saplings

1992. National Afforestation.

2075 **509** 500 r. multicoloured . . . 65 15

1993. No. 1831 surch **50r**.

2076 **326** 50 r. on 55 r. red and pink 10 10

511 State Arms and Assembly Building

1993. 10th People's Consultative Assembly. Multicoloured.

2077 300 r. Type **511** 20 10
2078 700 r. Assembly hall 45 20

512 Soldiers and Buildings

1993. 5th Five Year Plan. Multicoloured.

2079 300 r. Type **512** 20 10
2080 700 r. Workers and arrow . . . 45 20
2081 1000 r. Runners 65 30

513 Swarm of "Ornithoptera goliath"

1993.

2082 **513** 1000 r. multicoloured . . 1·00 30

514 Peristiwa Hotel, Yamato, and Adipura Kencana Medal

1993. 700th Anniv of Surabaya (300, 700 r.) and "indo tourism 93" (1000 r.). Multicoloured.

2083 300 r. Type **514** 20 10
2084 700 r. Modern city and World Habitat Award, 1992 . . . 45 20
2085 1000 r. Candi Bajang Ratu (temple) 65 30

1993. "indopex'93" Asian Stamp Exhibition. Surabaya. Nos. 2082/5 optd **indopex'93 surabaya**.

2086 **514** 300 r. multicoloured . . . 20 10
2087 – 700 r. multicoloured . . . 45 20
2088 **513** 1000 r. mult (No. 2082) . 65 30
2089 – 1000 r. mult (No. 2085) . 65 30

517 "Jasminum sambac"

518 Scouts making Road

1993. Environmental Protection. Mult.

2091 300 r. Type **517** 45 10
2092 300 r. Moth orchid ("Phalaenopsis amabilis") . 45 10
2093 300 r. "Rafflesia arnoldi" (flower) 45 10
2094 700 r. Komodo dragon 90 20
2095 700 r. Asian bonytongue . . . 90 30
2096 700 r. Java hawk eagle 90 20

Stamps of the same value were issued together, se-tenant, in strips of three stamps, each strip forming a composite design.

1993. 1st World Community Development Camp, Lebakharjo. Multicoloured.

2098 300 r. Type **518** 15 10
2099 700 r. Pres. Suharto greeting girl scout 45 20

519 President Suharto

520 "Papilio blumei"

1993.

2100 **519** 150 r. multicoloured . . . 10 10
2101 300 r. multicoloured . . . 15 10
2102 700 r. multicoloured . . . 45 20

On No. 2102 part of the background is a draped flag.

1993. International Butterfly Conference, Ujungpandang.

2103 **520** 700 r. multicoloured . . . 70 20

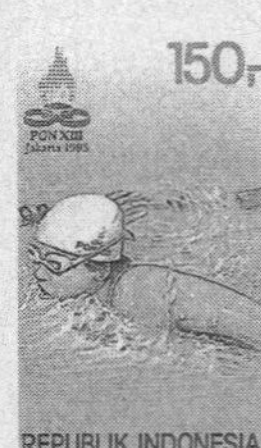

521 Swimming

522 Sigura-Gura Waterfall, North Sumatra

1993. "Pon XIII" Sports Week, Djakarta. Multicoloured.

2105 150 r. Type **521** 10 10
2106 300 r. Cycling 20 10
2107 700 r. Mascot 45 20
2108 1000 r. High jumping 60 30

1993. World Tourism Organization Meeting, Bali. Multicoloured.

2111 300 r. Type **522** 20 10
2112 700 r. Goa Petruk (cave), Central Java 45 20
2113 1000 r. Danau Segara Anak (cove), West Nusa Tenggara (horiz) 60 30

MINIMUM PRICE

The minimum price quoted is 10p which represents a handling charge rather than a basis for valuing common stamps. For further notes about prices see introductory pages.

523 General Soedirman

524 "Michelia champaca"

1993. Armed Forces. Each brown, black and red.

2115 300 r. Type **523** 20 10
2116 300 r. Lt-Gen. Oerip Soemohardjo 20 10

Nos. 2115/16 were issued together, se-tenant, forming a composite design.

1993. Flora and Fauna. Multicoloured.

2117 300 r. Type **524** 45 10
2118 300 r. "Cananga adorata" . . 45 10
2119 300 r. Orange-tailed shama ("Copsychus pyrrhopygus") . 45 10
2120 300 r. Hill myna ("Gracula religiosa") 45 10

525 Plantation

526 South Sumatran Dancer

1993. Resettlement Programme.

2121 **525** 700 r. multicoloured . . . 40 20

1993. Traditional Dances (2nd series). Mult.

2122 300 r. Type **526** 45 10
2123 700 r. West Kalimantan . . . 65 20
2124 1000 r. Irian Jaya 90 30

527 Emblems

528 Working Women

1994. International Year of the Family.

2126 **527** 300 r. multicoloured . . . 20 10

1994. 6th Five Year Plan. Multicoloured.

2127 100 r. Type **528** 10 10
2128 700 r. Graduate and school pupils 40 20
2129 2000 r. Doctor, nurse and children . . . . 1·10 55

529 Netherlands Indies, Japanese Occupation and Indonesia Stamps

1994. 130th Anniv of 1st Netherlands Indies Stamps.

2130 **529** 700 r. multicoloured . . . 40 20

530 Ladige's Rainbowfish

1994. Fishes. Multicoloured.

2131 300 r. Type **530** 25 15
2132 700 r. Boeseman's rainbow fish 65 30

531 Emblem

532 Figure, Globe, and Anniversary Emblem

1994. National Kidney Foundation.

2134 **531** 300 r. + 30 r. mult 20 10

1994. 75th Anniv of International Red Cross Red Crescent Organization.

2135 **532** 300 r. black, red & blue . 20 10

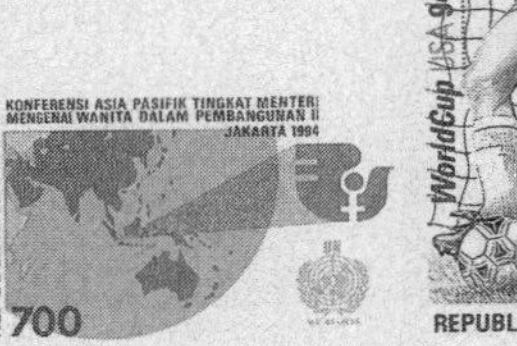

533 Map and Emblem

534 Player

1994. Asia–Pacific Ministerial Conference on Women, Djakarta.

2136 **533** 700 r. multicoloured . . . 40 20

1994. World Cup Football Championship, U.S.A.

2137 **534** 150 r. multicoloured . . . 10 10
2138 – 300 r. multicoloured . . . 20 10
2139 – 700 r. blue, red & blk . . 40 20
2140 – 1000 r. multicoloured . . 60 30

DESIGNS—VERT: 300 r. Striker (mascot). HORIZ: 700 r. Emblem; 1000 r. Ball in net.

535 Player and Uber Cup (Women's)

536 Hand holding Scales

1994. Indonesian Victories in World Team Badminton Championships. Multicoloured.

2142 300 r. Type **535** 20 10
2143 300 r. Thomas Cup (Men's) . . 20 10

Nos. 2142/3 were issued together, se-tenant, forming a composite design.

1994. National Commission on Human Rights.

2145 **536** 700 r. multicoloured . . . 40 20

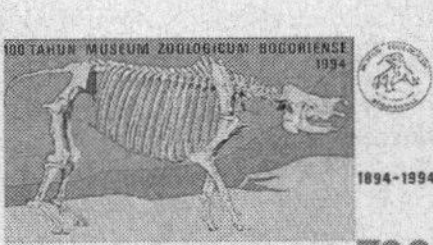

537 Vase with Bead Cover

538 Skeleton of Quadruped

1994. Indonesia–Pakistan Economic and Cultural Co-operation Organization. Multicoloured.

2147 300 r. Type **537** 15 10
2148 700 r. Blue and white vase . . 40 20

1994. Centenary of Bogoriense Zoological Museum. Multicoloured.

2149 700 r. Type **538** 40 20
2150 1000 r. Outline and skeleton of whale (80 × 22 mm) 55 25

539 Mascots

1994. 12th Asian Games, Hiroshima, Japan. Multicoloured.

2152 300 r. Type **539** 15 10
2153 700 r. Hurdling 40 20

540 Communications and Map

541 "Morus macroura"

1994. 25th Anniv of Bakosurtanal.

2154 **540** 700 r. multicoloured . . . 40 20

1994. Flora and Fauna. Multicoloured.

2155 150 r. Type **541** 10 10
2156 150 r. "Oncosperma tiquillaria" 10 10
2157 150 r. "Eucalyptus urophylla" 10 10
2158 150 r. Moth orchid ("Phalaenopsis amabilis") 45 10
2159 150 r. "Pometia pinnata" 10 10
2160 150 r. Great argus pheasant ("Argusianus argus") 10 10
2161 150 r. Blue-crowned hanging parrot ("Loriculus pusillus") 45 10
2162 150 r. Timor helmeted friarbird ("Philemon buceroides") 10 10
2163 150 r. Amboina king parrot ("Alisterus amboinensis") 10 10
2164 150 r. Twelve-wired bird of paradise ("Seleucidis melanoleuca") 10 10

542 Venue

1994. Asia–Pacific Economic Co-operation Summit, Bogor.

2166 **542** 700 r. multicoloured 40 20

543 Airplane

1994. 50th Anniv of I.C.A.O.

2167 **543** 700 r. multicoloured 40 20

1994. Traditional Dances (3rd series). As T **506**. Multicoloured.

2168 150 r. Mengaup, Jambi 10 10
2169 300 r. Topeng, West Java 15 10
2170 700 r. Anging Mamiri, South Sulawesi 40 20
2171 1000 r. Pisok, North Sulawesi 55 25
2172 2000 r. Bidu, East Nusa Tenggara 1·10 55

544 Yogyakarta Palace

1995. 20th Anniv of World Tourism Organization. Multicoloured.

2174 300 r. Type **544** 15 10
2175 700 r. Floating market, Banjarmasin 40 20
2176 1000 r. Pasola (equestrian tradition), Sumba 55 25

545 Children, President Suharto and First Lady

1995. "Dedication to the Nation".

2177 **545** 700 r. multicoloured 40 20

546 Letter from King of Klungkung, Bali

547 "Schizostachyum brachycladum"

1995. 6th Five Year Plan. National Letter Writing Campaign. Multicoloured.

2178 300 r. Type **546** 15 10
2179 700 r. Carrier pigeon (campaign mascot) and letters 40 20

1995. 4th International Bamboo Congress, Ubud, Bali. Multicoloured.

2180 300 r. Type **547** 15 10
2181 700 r. "Dendrocalamus asper" 40 20

INDEX

Countries can be quickly located by referring to the index at the end of this volume.

548 N250 and National Flag

1995. Inaugural Flight of I.P.T.N. N250 Airliner.

2182 **548** 700 r. multicoloured 40 20

549 Anniversary Emblem

1995. 50th Anniv of Indonesian Republic. Multicoloured.

2183 300 r. Type **549** 15 10
2184 700 r. Boy with national flag 40 20

550 Kota Intan Drawbridge

1995. "Jakarta '95" Asian Stamp Exn. Mult.

2186 300 r. Type **550** 15 10
2187 700 r. Fatahillah Jakarta History Museum 40 20

551 "Dewarutji" (cadet barquentine), Pinisi Sailing Ship and Flag

1995. "Sail Indonesia '95" Tall Ship Race and Fleet Review.

2188 **551** 700 r. multicoloured 40 20

552 "Mother Love" (Patricia Saerang)

553 Mushaf Istiqlal (illuminated Islamic text)

1995. 10th Asia and Pacific Regional Conference of Rehabilitation International, Indonesia.

2190 **552** 700 r. + 100 r. mult 45 45

1995. Istiqlal Festival.

2191 **553** 700 r. multicoloured 40 20

554 PTT Monument

1995. 50th Anniv of Take-over of PTT Headquarters by Republicans.

2192 **554** 700 r. multicoloured 40 20

555 Rice

556 Flags and Emblem

1995. 50th Anniv of F.A.O.

2193 **555** 700 r. multicoloured 40 20

1995. 50th Anniv of U.N.O. Multicoloured.

2194 300 r. Type **556** 15 10
2195 700 r. Emblem, Earth and rainbow 40 20

557 "Cyrtostachys renda"

1995. Flora and Fauna. Multicoloured.

2196 150 r. Type **557** 10 10
2197 150 r. Tiger ("Panthera tigris") 10 10
2198 150 r. "Bouea macrophylla" 10 10
2199 150 r. Javan rhinoceros ("Rhinoceros sondaicus") 10 10
2200 150 r. "Santalum album" 10 10
2201 150 r. Komodo dragon ("Varanus komodoensis") 10 10
2202 150 r. "Diospyros celebica" 10 10
2203 150 r. Maleo fowl ("Macrocephalon maleo") 10 10
2204 150 r. "Nephelium rambutan-ake" 10 10
2205 150 r. Malay peacock-pheasant ("Polyplectron schleiermacheri") 10 10

558 Yogyakarta Palace

1995. Award of Aga Khan Prize for Architecture to Indonesia. Multicoloured.

2207 300 r. Type **558** 15 10
2208 700 r. Surakarta Palace 40 20

559 Hill and Postal Carriers

560 Economic Sectors

1995. Birth Bicentenary of Sir Rowland Hill (instigator of postal stamps). Multicoloured.

2209 300 r. Type **559** 15 10
2210 700 r. Hill and Indonesian Postal Service emblem 40 20

1995. Traditional Dances (4th series). As T **506**. Multicoloured.

2211 150 r. Nguri dance, West Nusa Tenggara 10 10
2212 300 r. Muli Betanggai dance, Lampung 15 10
2213 700 r. Mutiara dance, Moluccas 40 20
2214 1000 r. Gantar dance, East Kalimantan 55 25

1996. Economic Census.

2216 **560** 300 r. orange and blue 15 10
2217 – 700 r. turquoise & orge 40 20

DESIGN—HORIZ: 700 r. Graph of economic activity.

561 Satellite orbiting Earth

1996. Launch of "Palapa-C" Satellite. Multicoloured.

2218 300 r. Type **561** 15 10
2219 700 r. Satellite orbiting Earth (triangular) 40 20

562 Mixed Flowers

563 Soemanang Soeriowinoto (Association head, 1946–47 and 1949–50)

1996. Greetings Stamps. "Happy Holiday". Inscr "Selamat Hari Raya". Multicoloured.

2220 150 r. Type **562** 10 10
2221 300 r. Mixed flowers (different) 15 10
2222 700 r. Mixed flowers (different) 40 20

1996. 50th Anniv of Indonesian Journalists' Association. Multicoloured.

2223 300 r. Type **563** 15 10
2224 700 r. Djamaluddin Adinegoro (head of Indonesian Press Bureau Foundation and founder of Academy of Publicity and Publicity Faculty, Padjadjaran University) 40 20

564 Tank firing and Map

1996. 47th Anniv of Return of Republican Government to Djokjakarta. Multicoloured.

2225 700 r. + 100 r. Type **564** 45 45
2226 700 r. + 100 r. Attack on Palace 45 45

Nos. 2225/6 were issued together, se-tenant, forming a composite design.

565 State House, Bandung

1996. "indonesia 96" International Youth Stamp Exhibition, Bandung. Multicoloured.

2227 300 r. Type **565** 15 10
2228 700 r. Painted parasols 40 20

566 Indonesian Bear Cuscus

567 Roses

1996. Cuscuses. Multicoloured.

2230 300 r. Australian spotted cuscus 15 10
2231 300 r. Type **566** 15 10

Nos 2230/1 were issued together, se-tenant, forming a composite design.

1996. Greetings Stamps. "Congratulations and Best Wishes". Inscr "Selamat dan Sukses". Multicoloured.

2233 150 r. Type **567** 10 10
2234 300 r. Orchids 15 20
2235 700 r. Chrysanthemums 40 20

568 Students (Y. Edwin Purwanto)

1996. Compulsory Nine Year Education Programme. Winning Entries in Children's Stamp Design Competition. Multicoloured.

2236 150 r. Type **568** 10 10
2237 300 r. Children in playground (Andi Pradhana) 15 10
2238 700 r. Teacher and pupils (Intan Sari Dewi) 40 20

569 Archery

1996. Olympic Games, Atlanta. Mult.

2239 300 r. Type **569** 15 10
2240 700 r. Weightlifting 40 20
2241 1000 r. Badminton 55 25

571 Pres. Suharto and Procession

1996. National Youth Kirab. Multicoloured.

2244 300 r. Type **571** 15 10
2245 700 r. Pres. Suharto presenting national flag 40 20

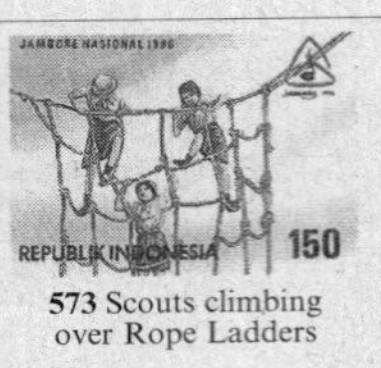

572 Nusantara N-2130 Prototype over Soekarno-Hatta Airport

573 Scouts climbing over Rope Ladders

1996. Aviation and Maritime Year. Mult.

2246 300 r. Type **572** 15 10
2247 700 r. "Palindo Jaya" (inter-island ferry) . . . 40 20

1996. National Scout Jamboree, Djakarta. Multicoloured.

2248 150 r. Type **573** 10 10
2249 150 r. Scouts on ladder and death slide 10 10
2250 150 r. Scouts at base of rope ladders 10 10
2251 150 r. Girl scouts constructing wooden apparatus 10 10
2252 150 r. Scouts on unicycle and climbing frame 10 10
2253 150 r. Girl scouts building frame on campsite 10 10
2254 150 r. Soldering metal 10 10
2255 150 r. Girl at radio taking notes 10 10

Nos. 2248/55 were issued together, se-tenant, Nos. 2248/51 and 2252/5 forming composite designs.

574 Pinisi Prows and Wave

1996. 50th Anniv of Bank BNI. Multicoloured.

2256 300 r. Type **574** 15 10
2257 700 r. Pinisi sailing ship . . . 40 20

575 Mother and Child reading (Salt Iodization Programme)

1996. 50th Anniv of U.N.I.C.E.F. Each brown, green and mauve.

2258 300 r. Type **575** 15 10
2259 700 r. Giving oral vaccine to children (elimination of polio) 40 20
2260 1000 r. Children (Children's Rights Convention) 55 25

576 Ibu Tien Suharto

577 Softball

1996. Ibu Tien Suharto (First Lady) Commemoration.

2261 **576** 700 r. multicoloured . . . 40 20

1996. National Sports Week. Multicoloured.

2263 300 r. Type **577** 15 10
2264 700 r. Hockey 40 20
2265 1000 r. Basketball 55 25

578 Head of Sumatran Rhinoceros

1996. The Sumatran Rhinoceros ("Dicerorhinus sumatrensis") and the Javan Rhinoceros ("Rhinoceros sondaicus"). Multicoloured.

2267 300 r. Type **578** 15 10
2268 300 r. Sumatran rhinoceros . . 15 10
2269 300 r. Javan rhinoceros 15 10
2270 300 r. Adult and baby Javan rhinoceros 15 10

579 Flower Arrangement

581 Celebes Hornbill

580 Coins and Banknotes

1996. Greetings Stamps. "Happy New Year". Inscr "Selamat Tahun Baru". Multicoloured.

2272 150 r. Type **579** 10 10
2273 300 r. Arrangement including red and yellow roses 15 10
2274 700 r. Arrangement including white rose and yellow chrysanthemums 40 20

1996. 50th Anniv of Financial Day.

2275 **580** 700 r. multicoloured . . . 30 15

1996. National Flora and Fauna Day. Multicoloured.

2276 300 r. Type **581** 15 10
2277 300 r. Irrawaddy dolphin ("Orcaella brevirostris") . . 15 10
2278 300 r. Black-naped oriole ("Oriolus chinensis") . . . 15 10
2279 300 r. Sun bear ("Helarctos malayanus") 15 10
2280 300 r. Rothschild's mynah ("Leucopsar rothschildi") . . 15 10
2281 300 r. Lontar palms ("Borassus flabellifer") 15 10
2282 300 r. Black orchid ("Coelogyne pandurata") 15 10
2283 300 r. Michelia ("Michelia alba") 15 10
2284 300 r. Giant aroid lily ("Amorphophallus titanum") 15 10
2285 300 r. Majegau ("Dysoxylum densiflorum") 15 10

582 Somba Opu Fortress

1996. Eastern Region. Multicoloured.

2288 300 r. Divers and sea-bed . . . 15 10
2289 700 r. Type **582** 40 20

583 School-children at Play

585 Children shaking Hands ("Happy Birthday")

584 Dish Aerial and Control Room

1996. National Movement of Foster Parents. Multicoloured.

2290 150 r. Type **583** 10 10
2291 300 r. Poor children and photograph of school-child (horiz) 15 10

1996. Traditional Dances (5th series). As T **506**. Multicoloured.

2292 150 r. Baksa Kembang dance, South Kalimantan 10 10
2293 300 r. Ngarojeng dance, Djakarta 15 10
2294 700 r. Rampai dance, Aceh . . 40 20
2295 1000 r. Boituka dance, East Timor 50 25

1997. Telecommunications Year. Mult.

2297 300 r. Type **584** 15 10
2298 700 r. Key pad, communications satellite orbiting Earth and woman using telephone . 40 20

1997. Greetings Stamps.

2299 **585** 600 r. multicoloured . . . 30 15
2300 – 600 r. black, brn & mve . . 30 15

DESIGN: No. 2300, Heart and ribbons ("Best Wishes").

586 Transport, Ballot Boxes and National Flag

1997. General Election. Multicoloured.

2301 300 r. Type **586** 15 10
2302 700 r. State arms, map, ballot boxes and buildings . . . 40 20
2303 1000 r. State arms, ballot boxes, map and city skyline 55 25

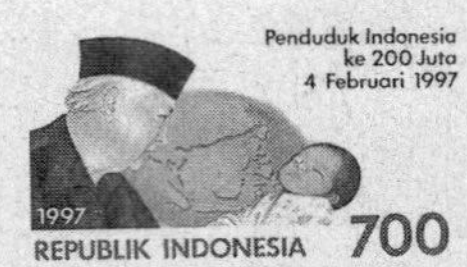

587 Pres. Suharto and Wahyu Nusantaraaji

1997. Indonesia's 200,000,000th Citizen.

2305 **587** 700 r. multicoloured . . . 40 20

588 Children with Stamp Collection

589 Wage Rudolf Soepratman

1997. 75th Anniv of Indonesian Philatelic Association. Multicoloured.

2306 300 r. Type **588** 15 10
2307 700 r. Magnifying glass on 1994 150 r. Flora and Fauna stamp 40 20

1997. Cultural Anniversaries. Multicoloured.

2308 300 r. Type **589** (composer of "Indonesia Raya" (national anthem), 60th death anniv (1998)) 15 10
2309 700 r. Usmar Ismail (film director, 25th death anniv (1996)) 35 15
2310 1000 r. Self-portrait of Affandi (painter, 90th birth anniv) . 50 25

590 Picture Jasper

1997. "Indonesia 2000" International Stamp Exn, Bandung (1st issue). Minerals. Multicoloured.

2312 300 r. Type **590** 15 10
2313 700 r. Chrysocolla 35 15
2314 1000 r. Geode 50 25

See also Nos. 2403/5 and 2529/31.

592 Crowd giving Thumbs Up to "No Smoking" Sign

593 Fishes and Coral Reef

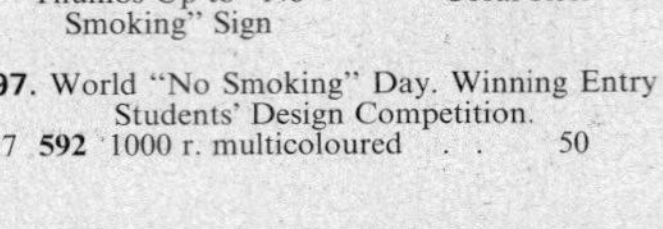

1997. World "No Smoking" Day. Winning Entry in Students' Design Competition.

2317 **592** 1000 r. multicoloured . . 50 25

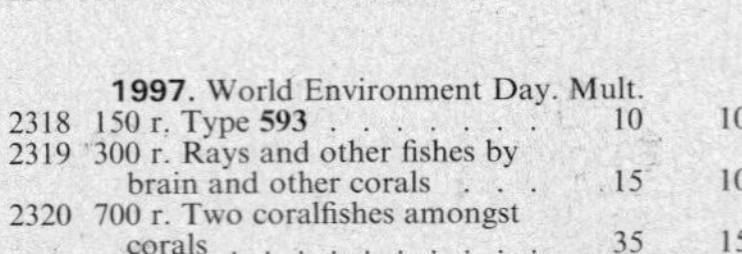

1997. World Environment Day. Mult.

2318 150 r. Type **593** 10 10
2319 300 r. Rays and other fishes by brain and other corals . . . 15 10
2320 700 r. Two coralfishes amongst corals 35 15

594 Paksi Naga Liman Carriage (built by Pangeran Losari)

1997. 2nd Indonesian Royal Palace Festival, Cirebon. Multicoloured.

2322 300 r. Type **594** 15 10
2323 700 r. Singa Barong carriage (built by Ki Nataguna), 1549 . . . . 35 15

595 Venue's Main Gateway

1997. 18th National Koran Reading Contest, Jambi. Multicoloured.

2324 300 r. Type **595** 15 10
2325 700 r. Al Ikhsaniah Mosque, Olak Kemang, Jambi . . . 35 15

596 Co-operatives Monument, Tasikmalaya

597 Pres. Suharto and Dr. Mohammad Hatta (first vice-president)

1997. 50th Anniv of Co-operatives Movement. Multicoloured.

2326 150 r. Type **596** 10 10
2327 150 r. Co-operatives Monument, Djakarta . . . 10 10
2328 300 r. Child's hand clasping adult's hand 15 10
2329 300 r. Figure before globe . . 15 10
2330 700 r. Type **597** 35 15

598 Hands on Globe

1997. 30th Anniv of Association of South-East Asian Nations. Multicoloured.

2331 300 r. Type **598** 15 10
2332 700 r. Ears of cereals forming "30th" and globe 35 15

599 Games Emblem and Mascot

1997. 19th South-East Asian Games, Djakarta. Multicoloured.

2333 300 r. Type **599** 15 10
2334 300 r. Torch carrier, flags and emblem 15 10
2335 700 r. Running and throwing the discus 30 15
2336 700 r. Hurdling and sprinting . 30 15

600 Coach, Bus, Java "International Harvester" Bus and Bullock Cart

1997. National Communications Day. Transport Development. Multicoloured.

2337 300 r. Type **600** 15 10
2338 300 r. Electric, express, diesel and steam railway locomotives 15 10
2339 700 r. Container ship, passenger ship, cargo vessel and lette (Madurese sailing boat) . . 30 15
2340 700 r. Seulawah and IPTN CN-235, CN-250 and N-2130 airliners 30 15

601 U.P.U. Monument and Mas Soeharto (first head of Indonesian P.T.T.)

1997. 50th Anniv of Indonesian Membership of U.P.U. Multicoloured.

2341 300 r. Type **601** 10 10
2342 700 r. Heinrich von Stephan (founder of U.P.U.) and monument 30 15

602 Assembly Emblem and Building

1997. People's Consultative Assembly General Session.

2343 **602** 700 r. multicoloured . . . 25 10

603 Village Programme (Army)

1997. Armed Forces Day. Multicoloured.

2344 300 r. Type **603** 10 10
2345 300 r. Frigates and Jalesveva Jayamahe Monument, Surabaya (Navy) 10 10
2346 300 r. "Blue Falcon" acrobatic team (Air Force) 10 10
2347 300 r. Rapid Reaction Unit (Police Force) 10 10

605 Duku Fruit ("Lansium domesticum")

607 AIDS Ribbon

606 Oil Field

1997. National Flora and Fauna Day. Mult.

2349 300 r. Type **605** 10 10
2350 300 r. Salacca of Condet ("Salacca zalacca") 10 10
2351 300 r. Tengawang tungkul ("Shorea stenoptera") . . . 10 10
2352 300 r. Ebony ("Diospyros macrophylla") 10 10
2353 300 r. Fibre orchid ("Diplocaulobium utile") . . 10 10
2354 300 r. Belida fish ("Chitala lopis") 10 10
2355 300 r. Brahminy kite ("Haliastur indus") 10 10
2356 300 r. Helmeted hornbill ("Rhinoplax vigil") 10 10
2357 300 r. Timor deer ("Cervus timorensis") 10 10
2358 300 r. Anoa ("Bubalus depressicornis") 10 10

1997. Association of South-east Asian Nations Council on Petroleum Conference, Djakarta. Multicoloured.

2360 300 r. Type **606** 10 10
2361 300 r. Oil refinery 10 10
2362 300 r. "Eka Putra" (oil tanker) 10 10
2363 300 r. Petrol tankers 10 10

1997. World AIDS Day.

2364 **607** 700 r. + 100 r. mult . . . 10 10

608 Letter from Foster Son

1997. National Foster Parents Movement.

2365 **608** 700 r. multicoloured . . . 15 10

1997. Traditional Dances (6th series). As T **506**. Multicoloured.

2366 150 r. Mopuputi Cengke dance, Central Sulawesi 10 10
2367 300 r. Mandan Talawang Nyai Balau dance, Central Kalimantan 10 10
2368 600 r. Gambyong dance, Central Java 15 10
2369 700 r. Cawan dance, North Sumatra 15 10
2370 1000 r. Legong Keraton dance, Bali 20 10

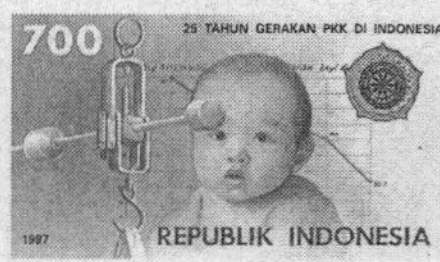

609 Baby and Scales

1997. 25th Anniv of Family Welfare Movement.

2372 **609** 700 r. multicoloured . . . 15 10

610 Erau Festival, East Kalimantan

1998. Year of Art and Culture. Festivals. Multicoloured.

2373 300 r. Type **610** 10 10
2374 700 r. Tabot Festival, Bengkulu 15 10

611 Malin Kundang and his Mother

1998. Folk Tales (1st series). Multicoloured.

(a) "Malin Kundung".

2375 300 r. Type **611** 10 10
2376 300 r. Malin returning home and rejecting Mother . . . 10 10
2377 300 r. Malin's mother praying to God to curse him . . . 10 10
2378 300 r. Malin's ship in storm . . 10 10
2379 300 r. Malin turned to stone . 10 10

(b) "Sangkuriang".

2380 300 r. Dayang Sumbi weaving . 10 10
2381 300 r. Dayang Sumbi expelling her son Sanguriang after he killed their dog 10 10
2382 300 r. Dayang Sumbi discovering her lover is her son . . . 10 10
2383 300 r. Dayang Sumbi creating fake dawn and Sanguriang hurling wooden boat 10 10
2384 300 r. Tangkuban Parahu (upturned boat) Mountain . 10 10

(c) "Roro Jonggrang".

2385 300 r. Pengging people attacking Prambanan people . . . 10 10
2386 300 r. Bandung Bondowoso proposing to Roro Jonggrang 10 10
2387 300 r. Bandung Bondowoso building temples 10 10
2388 300 r. Women banging rice-mothers to prematurely announce dawn 10 10
2389 300 r. Prambanan Temple and petrified Roro Jonggrang . . 10 10

(d) "Tengger".

2390 300 r. Roro Anteng and Joko Seger marrying 10 10
2391 300 r. Roro and Joko praying to gods for a child 10 10
2392 300 r. Volcano erupting . . . 10 10
2393 300 r. Raden Kusuma (youngest son) sacrificing himself . . . 10 10
2394 300 r. Tengger people giving offerings to volcano 10 10

Nos. 2375/94 were issued together, se-tenant, forming a composite design.

See also Nos. 2489/508.

612 Djakarta Palace

1997. Presidential Palaces. Multicoloured.

2396 300 r. Type **612** 10 10
2397 300 r. Bogor Palace 10 10
2398 300 r. Cipanas Palace 10 10
2399 300 r. Yogyakarta Palace . . . 10 10
2400 300 r. Tampak Siring Palace, Bali 10 10

613 Man and Pregnant Woman

1998. 50th Anniv of W.H.O. Multicoloured.

2401 300 r. Type **613** 10 10
2402 700 r. Mother and child (horiz) 10 10

1998. "Indonesia 2000" International Stamp Exhibition. Bandung (2nd issue). Minerals. As T **590**. Multicoloured.

2403 300 r. Chrysopal 10 10
2404 700 r. Tektite 10 10
2405 1000 r. Amethyst 15 10

614 Boys playing Football

1998. World Cup Football Championship. France. Multicoloured.

2408 300 r. Type **614** 10 10
2409 700 r. Boys and goal-posts . . 10 10
2410 1000 r. Boys challenging for ball 15 10

615 Tropical Rainforest

1998. Environmental Protection. Ecophila Stamp Day. Multicoloured.

2412 700 r. Type **615** 10 10
2413 700 r. Tropical rainforest (different) 10 10

Nos. 2412/13 were issued together, se-tenant, forming a composite design.

617 School-children and Drug Addict

1998. International Day Against Drug Abuse and Illicit Trafficking. Multicoloured.

2415 700 r. Type **617** 10 10
2416 700 r. Students campaigning against drugs 10 10

618 Besakih Temple

1998. Tourism. Multicoloured.

2417 700 r. Type **618** 10 10
2418 700 r. Taman Ayun Temple (31 × 23 mm) 10 10

620 Cattle Wagon and Truck

1998. Railway Rolling Stock. Multicoloured.

2421 300 r. Type **620** 10 10
2422 300 r. Truck and goods wagon 10 10
2423 300 r. Green and yellow passenger carriages . . . 10 10
2424 300 r. Passenger carriage and tender 10 10
2425 300 r. Class B50 steam locomotive 10 10
2426 300 r. Front half of Class D52 steam locomotive 10 10
2427 300 r. Back half of Class D52 steam locomotive with tender 10 10
2428 300 r. Passenger carriage with two doors 10 10
2429 300 r. Observation car 10 10
2430 300 r. Goods wagon 10 10

Nos. 2421/30 were issued together, se-tenant, forming a composite design of a train.

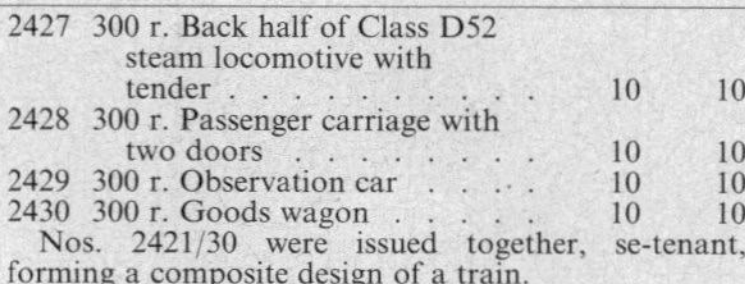

621 Pres. Bacharuddin Habibie

1998.

2432 **621** 300 r. multicoloured . . . 10 10
2433 700 r. multicoloured . . . 10 10
2434 4500 r. multicoloured . . 70 35
2435 5000 r. multicoloured . . 80 40

622 Fencing

1998. 13th Asian Games, Bangkok, Thailand. Multicoloured.

2436 300 r. Type **622** 10 10
2437 700 r. Taekwondo 10 10
2438 4000 r. Kung fu 70 35

623 "Baruna Jaya IV" (research ship)

1998. International Year of the Ocean.

2440 **623** 700 r. multicoloured . . . 10 10

625 1974 20 r. U.P.U. Stamp

1998. World Stamp Day. Multicoloured.

2442 700 r. Type **625** 10 10
2443 700 r. 1955 15 s. Post Office Anniversary stamp 10 10

626 Magpie Goose

1998. Water Fowl (1st series). Multicoloured.

2444 4000 r. Type **626** 70 35
2445 5000 r. Spotted whistling duck . 90 45
2446 10000 r. Salvadori's duck . . . 1·90 95
2447 15000 r. Radjah shelduck . . . 2·75 1·25
2448 20000 r. White-winged wood duck . . . . 3·50 1·75

See also Nos. 2468/74.

628 State Flag and Jayawijaya Peak

1998. "The Red and White Flag". Multicoloured.

2451 700 r. Type **628** 10 10
2452 700 r. State flag and Himalayan peak 10 10

629 State Flag

1998. Political Reforms. Multicoloured.

2453 700 r. Type **629** 10 10
2454 700 r. Dove and State flag 10 10
2455 1000 r. Students in front of Parliament building (82 × 25 mm) 20 10

630 "Stelechocarpus burahol"

631 Monument at Blitar and Museum, Bogor

1998. Flora and Fauna. Multicoloured.

2456 500 r. Type **630** 10 10
2457 500 r. Tuberose ("Polianthes tuberosa") 10 10
2458 500 r. Four o'clock ("Mirabilis jalapa") 10 10
2459 500 r. "Mangifera casturi" 10 10
2460 500 r. "Ficus minahassae" 10 10
2461 500 r. Zebra dove ("Geopelia striata") 10 10
2462 500 r. Red and green junglefowl hybrid ("Gallus varius x G. gallus") 10 10
2463 500 r. Indian elephant ("Elephas maximus") 10 10
2464 500 r. Proboscis monkey ("Nasalis larvatus") 10 10
2465 500 r. Eastern tarsier ("Tarsius spectrum") 10 10

1998. 55th Anniv of Formation of Volunteer National Armed Forces (independence fighters).

2467 **631** 700 r. + 100 r. mult 15 10

632 Australian White-eyed Duck

1998. Water Fowl (2nd series). Multicoloured.

2468 250 r. Type **632** 10 10
2469 500 r. Spotbill duck 10 10
2470 700 r. Grey teal 10 10
2471 1000 r. Cotton pygmy goose 20 10
2472 1500 r. Green pygmy goose 25 10
2473 2500 r. Indian whistling duck 45 20
2474 3500 r. Wandering whistling duck 60 30

1998. Traditional Dances (7th series). As T **506**. Multicoloured.

2476 300 r. Oreng oreng gae dance, Sulawesi Tenggara (South-east Celebes) 10 10
2477 500 r. Persembahan dance, Bengkulu 10 10
2478 700 r. Kipas (fan) dance, Riau 10 10
2479 1000 r. Srimpi dance, Yogyakarta 20 10
2480 2000 r. Pasambahan, Sumatera Barat (West) 35 15

633 Water Wheel and Power Lines

1999. Year of Creation and Engineering. Multicoloured.

2482 500 r. Type **633** 10 10
2483 700 r. Water pipe and pipe network in valley 10 10

634 Throwing the Shot

635 Emblem

1999. 7th Far East and South Pacific Games for Disabled Persons, Bangkok. Multicoloured.

2484 500 r. Type **634** 10 10
2485 500 r. Medal and wheelchair 10 10

1999. 50th Anniv of Garuda Indonesia (state airline). Multicoloured.

2486 500 r. Type **635** 10 10
2487 700 r. Jet engine 10 10
2488 2000 r. Pilot, stewardess and airplane 35 15

1999. Folk Tales (2nd series). As T **611**. Multicoloured. (a) "Lake Toba".

2489 500 r. Man and yellow fish 10 10
2490 500 r. Man proposing to woman 10 10
2491 500 r. Woman giving food for father to son Sam and Sam eating it 10 10
2492 500 r. Wife turning back into a fish 10 10
2493 500 r. Samosir Island and Lake Toba 10 10

(b) "Banjarmasin".

2494 500 r. Rebels and contenders to throne 10 10
2495 500 r. Local governors crown Prince Samudera 10 10
2496 500 r. Tumenggung sends fleet to Samudera's capital, Bandar Masih 10 10
2497 500 r. Samudera and Tumenggung meet on board ship 10 10
2498 500 r. Ships in Banjarmasin Harbour 10 10

(c) "Buleleng".

2499 500 r. I Gusti Gede Paseken leaving with guards for Den Bukit 10 10
2500 500 r. Forest giant appearing to I Gusti Gede Paseken 10 10
2501 500 r. I Gusti Gede Paseken lifting stranded ship 10 10
2502 500 r. I Gusti Gede Paseken arriving before King of Den Bukit 10 10
2503 500 r. Procession in kingdom of Buleleng 10 10

(d) "Woiram".

2504 500 r. Woiram teaching archery to Woiwallytmang and with wife Donadebu 10 10
2505 500 r. Mesan and Mecy looking for shrimps 10 10
2506 500 r. Woiram cursing Demontin village 10 10
2507 500 r. Woiwallytmang and Mecy clinging to tree trunk 10 10
2508 500 r. Woiram's footprints in rock 10 10

Nos. 2489/2508 were issued together, se-tenant, forming a composite design.

638 "Ascosparassis heinricherii"

1999. Fungi. Multicoloured. (a) T **638** and similar diamond-shaped designs.

2512 500 r. Type **638** 10 10
2513 500 r. "Mutinus bambusinus" 10 10
2514 500 r. "Mycena" sp. 10 10
2515 700 r. "Gloephyllum imponens" 10 10
2516 700 r. "Microporus xanthopus" 10 10
2517 700 r. "Termitomyces eurrhizus" 10 10
2518 1000 r. "Boedijnopeziza insititia" 20 10
2519 1000 r. "Aseroe rubra" 20 10
2520 1000 r. "Calostoma orirubra" 20 10

(b) As Nos. 2512/14 but rectangular designs, size 31 × 23 mm.

2521 500 r. As No. 2513 10 10
2522 500 r. As No. 2512 10 10
2523 500 r. As No. 2514 10 10

639 Doctor and Patients outside Surgery

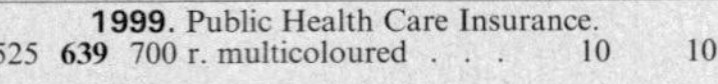
1999. Public Health Care Insurance.

2525 **639** 700 r. multicoloured 10 10

641 Y2K "Bug"

1999. Millennium Bug (computer programming fault). Multicoloured.

2527 500 r. Type **641** 10 10
2528 500 r. Robot exploding 10 10

Nos. 2527/8 were issued together, se-tenant, forming a composite design.

642 Chrysoprase

1999. "Indonesia 2000" International Stamp Exhibition, Bandung (3rd issue). Gemstones. Multicoloured.

2529 500 r. Type **642** 10 10
2530 1000 r. Smoky quartz 20 10
2531 2000 r. Blue opal 35 15

643 People carrying Banner

1999. General Election. Multicoloured.

2534 1000 r. Type **643** 20 10
2535 1000 r. Ballot box and map of Indonesia 20 10

Nos. 2534/5 were issued together, se-tenant, forming a composite design.

EXPRESS LETTER STAMPS

E 189 "Garuda" Bird

1967. Inscr "1967".
E1166 E **189** 10 r. purple & blue 40 20
E1167 15 r. purple & orge 55 20

1968. As Nos. E1166/7 but dated "1968".
E1202 E **189** 10 r. purple & blue 45 10
E1203 15 r. purple & orange 55 10
E1204 20 r. purple & yellow 55 15
E1205 30 r. purple & green 75 25
E1206 40 r. purple & lt pur 55 15

1969. As Nos. E1166/7 but dated "1969".
E1250 E **189** 20 r. purple & yellow 40 10
E1251 30 r. purple & green 40 10
E1252 40 r. pur & lt pur 50 15

POSTAGE DUE STAMPS

1950. Postage Due stamps of Netherlands Indies surch **BAJAR PORTO** and new value.
D576 2½ s. on 50 c. (No. D499) 65 50
D577 5 s. on 100c. (No. D501) 1·90 80
D578 10 s. on 75 c. (No. D500) 3·75 1·10

D 100 D 268 D 333a

1951.
D645 D **100** 2½ s. orange 10 50
D646 5 s. orange 10 10
D647 10 s. orange 10 10
D648 15 s. red 10 10
D773 15 s. orange 10 10
D649 20 s. blue 10 10
D774 20 s. orange 10 10
D650 25 s. olive 25 10
D775 25 s. orange 10 10
D651 30 s. brown 25 10
D776 30 s. orange 10 10
D652 40 s. green 25 20
D777 50 s. orange 1·00 15
D778 50 s. green 10 10
D779 100 s. orange 25 10
D780 100 s. brown 10 10
D781 250 s. blue 10 10
D782 500 s. yellow 10 10
D783 750 s. lilac 10 10
D784 1000 s. salmon 10 10
D654 1 r. green 1·40 1·25

D 176

1965. Provisional issue for use on parcels.
D1057 D **176** 25 r. black on yell 20

1966.
D1058 D **100** 50 r. red 10 10
D1059 100 r. lake 10 10

1966. As Type D **100**, but with coloured network background incorporating "1966".
D1098 5 s. green and yellow 15 20
D1099 10 s. red and blue 15 20
D1100 20 s. blue and pink 15 20
D1101 30 s. sepia and red 15 20
D1102 40 s. violet and bistre 15 20
D1103 50 s. olive and mauve 15 10
D1104 100 s. lake and green 15 10
D1105 200 s. green and pink 15 10
D1106 500 s. yellow and blue 15 10
D1107 1000 s. red and yellow 15 15

1967. As Nos. 1098/1107 but dated "1967".
D1168 50 s. green and lilac 20 15
D1169 100 s. red and green 20 15
D1170 200 s. green and pink 20 15
D1171 500 s. brown and blue 45 30
D1172 1000 s. mauve & yellow 45 30
D1173 15 r. orange & grey 80 40
D1174 25 r. violet and grey 1·40 75

1973. As Type D **100** but inscr "BAYAR PORTO" and dated "1973".
D1320a 25 r. violet and grey 75 10

1974. As Type D **100** but inscr "BAYAR PORTO" and dated "1974".
D1346 65 r. green and yellow 1·25 35
D1347 125 r. purple and pink 2·25 95

1975. As Type D **100** but inscr "BAYAR PORTO" and dated "1975".
D1401 25 r. violet and drab 1·00 20

1976.
D1426 D **268** 25 r. violet & drab 50 25
D1427 65 r. grn & stone 50 25

1978. Various stamps surch **BAYAR PORTO** and value.
D1503 25 r. on 1 r. sepia and red (No. 1141) 25 25
D1504 50 r. on 2 r. blue and ochre (No. 1144) 25 25
D1505 100 r. on 4 r. blue and orange (No. 1147) 50 50
D1506 200 r. on 5 r. red and blue (No. 1148) 1·00 1·00
D1507 300 r. on 10 r. violet and red (No. 1151) 1·40 1·40
D1508 400 r. on 15 r. violet and olive (No. 1153) 1·60 1·60

1978. Nos. 1145 and 1152 surch **BAYAR PORTO** and value.
D1523 40 r. on 2 r. 50 grn & red 65 65
D1524 40 r. on 12 r. grn & vio 65 65
D1525 65 r. on 2 r. 50 grn & red 1·25 1·25
D1526 65 r. on 12 r. grn & vio 2·25 2·25
D1527 125 r. on 2 r. 50 grn & red 65 65
D1528 125 r. on 12 r. grn & vio 65 65
D1529 150 r. on 2 r. 50 grn & red 1·25 1·25
D1530 150 r. on 12 r. grn & vio 2·25 2·25

1980. Dated "1980".
D1599 D **268** 25 r. mve & drab 10 10
D1600 D **333a** 50 r. grn & lilac 20 10
D1601 75 r. pur & pink 25 15
D1062 D **268** 125 r. mve & pk 55 30

1981. Dated "1981".
D1641 D **333a** 25 r. pur & stone 10 10
D1642 50 r. grn & lilac 10 10
D1643 75 r. pur & pink 15 10
D1644 125 r. pur & grn 65 65

1982. Dated "1982".
D1645 D **333a** 125 r. pur & pink 1·25 10

1983. Dated "1983".
D1728 D **333a** 200 r. lilac & blue 15 10
D1729 300 r. grn & yell 25 15
D1730 400 r. grn & buff 30 30
D1731 500 r. brn & pk 65 25

1984. Dated "1984".
D1772 D **333a** 25 r. pur & stone 50 15
D1773 50 r. grn & lilac 50 15
D1774 500 r. deep brown and brown 5·00 65

1988. Dated "1988".
D1912 D **333a** 1000 r. pur & grey 65 45
D1913 2000 r. red & mve 1·00 95
D1914 3000 r. red & yell 1·90 1·10
D1915 5000 r. grn & blue 3·00 1·50

INDORE (HOLKAR STATE) Pt. 1

A state in C. India. Now uses Indian stamps.

12 pies = 1 anna; 16 annas = 1 rupee

1 Maharaja Tukoji Rao Holkar II 2

1886.
2 **1** ½ a. mauve 1·75 1·10

1889. No gum. Imperf.
4 **2** ½ a. black on pink 2·00 2·75

3 Maharaja Shivaji Rao Holkar 5 Maharaja Tukoji Holkar III

1889.
5 **3** ¼ a. orange 65 45
6a ½ a. purple 80 15
7 1 a. green 90 50
8 2 a. red 3·25 1·00

1904.
9 **5** ¼ a. orange 30 10
10 ½ a. red 8·50 10
11 1 a. green 1·60 10
12 2 a. brown 8·00 50
13 3 a. violet 13·00 5·00
14a 4 a. blue 5·00 1·10
The ¼ a. is inscr "HOLKAR".

पाव आना.
(6)

1905. No. 6a. surch as T **6**.
15 **3** ¼ a. on ½ a. purple 3·75 17·00

7 Maharaja Yeshwant Rao Holkar II 9

1928.
16 **7** ¼ a. orange 30 10
17 ½ a. purple 40 10
18 1 a. green 90 10
19 1¼ a. green 1·50 25
20 2 a. brown 3·75 1·00
21 2 a. green 10·00 70
22 3 a. violet 1·50 9·00
23 3 a. blue 15·00
24 3½ a. violet 4·75 9·50
25 4 a. blue 3·25 3·25
26 4 a. yellow 22·00 1·50
27 8 a. grey 5·50 4·50
28 8 a. orange 16·00 19·00
29 12 a. red 5·00 10·00
30 – 1 r. black and blue 8·00 14·00
31 – 2 r. black and red 35·00 35·00
32 – 5 r. black and brown 55·00 60·00
The rupee values are larger 23 × 28 mm.

1940. Surch diagonally in words.
33 – ¼ a. on 5 r. (No. 32) 7·50 85
34 – ½ a. on 2 r. (No. 31) 11·00 1·75
35 **7** 1 a. on 1¼ a. green (No. 19) 11·00 40

1941.
36 **9** ¼ a. orange 2·00 10
37 ½ a. red 1·60 10
38 1 a. green 8·00 10
39 1¼ a. green 14·00 45
40 2 a. blue 11·00 1·00
41 4 a. yellow 12·00 9·50
42 – 2 r. black and red 9·00 £100
43 – 5 r. black and orange 9·00 £140
The rupee values are larger 23 × 28 mm.

OFFICIAL STAMPS

1904. Optd **SERVICE**.
S1 **5** ¼ a. orange 10 50
S2 ½ a. red 10 10
S3 1 a. green 10 20
S4 2 a. brown 30 30
S5 3 a. violet 2·00 1·60
S6 4 a. blue 3·00 1·50

INHAMBANE Pt. 9

A district of Mozambique which used its own stamps from 1895 to 1920.

1895. 1000 reis = 1 milreis.
1913. 100 centavos = 1 escudo.

1895. 700th Birth Anniv of St. Anthony. Optd **CENTENARIO DE S. ANTONIO Inhambane MDCCCXCV**.

(a) "Embossed" key-type inscr "PROVINCIA DE MOCAMBIQUE".
1 Q 5 r. black 11·00 9·50
2 10 r. green 10·00 7·50
3 20 r. red 19·00 15·00
5 40 r. brown 22·00 14·00
6 50 r. blue 22·00 14·00
8 200 r. violet 27·00 25·00
9 300 r. orange 27·00 25·00

(b) "Figures" key type inscr "MOCAMBIQUE".
12 R 50 r. blue 17·00 15·00
16 75 r. red 19·00 16·00
13 80 r. green 19·00 16·00
14 100 r. brown on yellow 27·00 21·00
17 150 r. red on rose 24·00 19·00

1903. "King Carlos" key type inscr "INHAMBANE".
18 S 2½ r. grey 20 20
19 5 r. orange 20 20
20 10 r. green 20 20
21 15 r. green 50 40
22 20 r. lilac 50 40
23 25 r. red 50 40
24 50 r. brown 80 55
25 65 r. blue 5·00 2·50
26 75 r. purple 75 70
27 100 r. blue on blue 75 70
28 115 r. brown on pink 2·10 2·10
29 130 r. brown on yellow 2·10 2·10
30 200 r. purple on pink 2·10 2·10
31 400 r. blue on yellow 3·75 3·00
32 500 r. black on blue 5·50 4·00
33 700 r. grey on yellow 6·25 5·50

1905. No. 25 surch **50 REIS** and bar.
34 S 50 r. on 65 r. blue 1·00 90

1911. 1903 issue optd **REPUBLICA**
35 S 2½ r. grey 15 15
36 5 r. orange 15 15
37 10 r. green 15 15
38 15 r. green 15 15
39 20 r. lilac 15 15
40 25 r. red 30 20
41 50 r. brown 20 15
42 75 r. purple 20 15
43 100 r. blue on blue 15 15
44 115 r. brown on pink 35 30
45 130 r. brown on yellow 35 30
46 200 r. purple on pink 45 30
47 400 r. blue on yellow 70 50
48 500 r. black on blue 70 50
49 700 r. black on yellow 90 75

1913. Surch **REPUBLICA INHAMBANE** and value on "Vasco da Gama" stamps of (a) Portuguese Colonies.
50 ¼ c. on 2½ r. green 35 25
51 ½ c. on 5 r. red 35 25
52 1 c. on 10 r. purple 35 25
53 2½ c. on 25 r. green 35 25
54 5 c. on 50 r. blue 45 35
55 7½ c. on 75 r. brown 75 65
56 10 c. on 100 r. brown 75 65
57 15 c. on 150 r. bistre 75 65

(b) Macao.
58 ¼ c. on ½ a. green 55 45
59 ½ c. on 1 a. red 55 45
60 1 c. on 2 a. purple 55 45
61 2½ c. on 4 a. green 55 45
62 5 c. on 8 a. blue 55 45
63 7½ c. on 12 a. brown 95 80
64 10 c. on 16 a. brown 70 45
65 15 c. on 24 a. bistre 70 45

(c) Timor.
66 ¼ c. on ½ a. green 55 45
67 ½ c. on 1 a. red 55 45
68 1 c. on 2 a. purple 55 45
69 2½ c. on 4 a. green 55 45
70 5 c. on 8 a. blue 55 45
71 7½ c. on 12 a. brown 1·00 75
72 10 c. on 16 a. brown 70 45
73 15 c. on 24 a. bistre 70 45

1914. No. 34 optd **REPUBLICA**.
74 S 50 r. on 65 r. blue 95 70

1914. "Ceres" key type inscr "INHAMBANE".
75 U ¼ c. olive 30 20
76a ½ c. black 35 30
77 1 c. green 30 20
78 1½ c. brown 30 20
79 2 c. red 30 20
80 2½ c. violet 10 10
81 5 c. blue 20 20
82 7½ c. brown 55 30
83 8 c. grey 55 30
84 10 c. red 55 40
85 15 c. red 65 50
86 20 c. green 65 50
87 30 c. brown on green 85 60
88 40 c. brown on red 85 60
89 50 c. orange on pink 1·50 1·00
90 1 e. green on blue 1·50 1·00

ININI Pt. 6

A territory in French Guiana, in the N.E. of S. America, separately administered from 1930 but reunited with Fr. Guiana in 1946.

100 centimes = 1 franc.

1931. Stamps of French Guiana optd **TERRITOIRE DE L'ININI** (Type **20**) or **Territoire de l'ININI** (others).
1 **20** 1 c. green and lilac 40 60
2 2 c. green and red 50 75
3 3 c. green and violet 50 75
4 4 c. mauve and brown 50 75
5 5 c. orange and blue 50 75
6 10 c. brown and mauve 40 65
7 15 c. orange and brown 40 65
8 20 c. green and blue 50 75
9 25 c. brown and red 70 90
10 **21** 30 c. green & deep green 1·00 1·40
11 30 c. brown and green 70 90
12 35 c. green and blue 80 1·00
13 40 c. grey and brown 70 90
14 45 c. green and olive 70 90
15 50 c. grey and blue 70 90
16 55 c. red and blue 2·25 3·00
17 60 c. green and red 70 90
18 65 c. green and red 1·10 1·50
19 70 c. green and blue 70 90
20 75 c. blue and deep blue 1·40 1·60
21 80 c. blue and black 75 1·00
22 90 c. red and carmine 1·00 1·40
23 90 c. brown and mauve 70 90
24 1 f. brown and mauve 7·50 8·00
25 1 f. red 75 1·00
26 1 f. blue and black 70 90
27 **22** 1 f. 25 green and brown 80 1·10
28 1 f. 25 red 70 90
29 1 f. 40 mauve and brown 75 1·00
30 1 f. 50 light blue and blue 70 90
31 1 f. 60 green and brown 75 1·00
32 1 f. 75 brown and red 11·00 12·00
33 1 f. 75 blue and deep blue 85 1·25
34 2 f. red and green 80 1·10
35 2 f. 25 blue 80 1·10
36 2 f. 50 brown and red 80 1·10
37 3 f. mauve and red 80 1·10
38 5 f. green and violet 80 1·10
39 10 f. blue and green 80 1·10
40 20 f. green and blue 1·00 1·40

1939. New York World's Fair. As T **58c** of Guadeloupe.
51 1 f. 25 red 2·50 3·00
52 2 f. 25 blue 2·50 3·00

1939. 150th Anniv of French Revolution. As T **58d** of Guadeloupe.
53 45 c. + 25 c. green & black 7·25 7·50
54 70 c. + 30 c. brown & black 7·50 7·50
55 90 c. + 35 c. orange & black 7·50 7·50
56 1 f. 25 + 1 f. red & black 7·50 7·50
57 2 f. 25 + 2 f. blue & black 7·50 7·50

POSTAGE DUE STAMPS

1932. Postage Due Stamps of French Guiana optd **TERRITOIRE DE L'ININI**.

D41	D 23	5 c. blue & deep blue	25	45
D42		10 c. blue and brown	50	75
D43		20 c. red and green	35	50
D44		30 c. red and brown	35	50
D45		50 c. brown & mauve	80	1·00
D46		60 c. brown and red	80	1·00
D47	D 24	1 f. brown and blue	1·25	1·75
D48		2 f. green and red	1·50	2·00
D49		3 f. grey and mauve	2·00	3·00

IONIAN ISLANDS Pt. 1

A group of islands off the W. coast of Greece, placed under the protection of Gt. Britain in 1815 and ceded to Greece in 1864.

12 pence = 1 shilling
20 shillings = 1 pound

1

1859. Imperf.

1	1	(½d.) orange	75·00	£500
2		(1d.) blue	20·00	£180
3		(2d.) red	15·00	£180

IRAN Pt. 16

A State of W. Asia.

1868. 20 shahis (or chahis) = 1 kran;
10 krans = 1 toman.
1932. 100 dinars = 1 rial.

NOTE.—The word "English" in the descriptive headings to various Persian issues is to be taken as referring to the lettering or figures and not to the language which is often French.

1

3 Nasred-Din

4 Nasred-Din

1868. Imperf or roul.

1	1	1 (sh.) violet	70·00	
1c		1 (sh.) grey	80·00	
15		1 (sh.) black	10·00	15·00
2		2 (sh.) green	50·00	
16		2 (sh.) blue	80·00	40·00
35		2 (sh.) black	£250	£3000
3		4 (sh.) blue	70·00	
17		4 (sh.) red	70·00	35·00
4		8 (sh.) red	70·00	
8a		8 (sh.) green	70·00	70·00
13		1 (kr.) yellow	£1000	
18		1 kr. red	£100	45·00
38		1 kr. red on yellow	£1100	50·00
19		4 kr. yellow	£300	45·00
36		4 kr. blue	£120	70·00
40		5 kr. violet	£225	£180
41		5 kr. gold	£750	£200
39		1 to. bronze on blue	£15000	£2500

1876. Perf.

20	3	1 (sh.) black and mauve	4·00	2·00
24		2 (sh.) black and green	5·00	1·50
25		5 (sh.) black and pink	4·50	75
30		10 (sh.) black and blue	6·00	3·00

1879. Perf.

45a	4	1 (sh.) black and red	11·00	1·00
46a		2 (sh.) black and yellow	14·00	1·10
47		5 (sh.) black and green	13·00	60
48		10 (sh.) black and mauve	£130	10·00
49		1 (kr.) black and brown	40·00	90
50c		5 (kr.) black and blue	18·00	50

5

6

1881.

56	5	5 c. mauve	5·00	2·00
57a		10 c. red	4·50	1·50
61		25 c. green	£100	1·00
62	6	50 c. black, yellow & orge	75·00	6·00
69		50 c. black	20·00	3·00
63		1 f. black and blue	14·00	1·25
64		5 f. black and red	14·00	1·00
65		10 f. black, yellow & red	15·00	2·75

The 10 f. is larger (30½ × 36 mm.).

1882. As T **5** and **6**.

66	–	5 s. green	5·00	20
68	–	10 s. black, yellow & orange	15·00	90

10

11

13

14

15
16

1885.

70	10	1 c. green	5·00	60
71		2 c. red	5·00	50
72		5 c. blue	5·00	10
73	11	10 c. brown	6·50	20
74		1 k. grey	7·00	40
75		5 k. purple	70·00	5·50

1885. Surch **OFFICIEL** and value in English and Persian.

81a	–	3 on 5 s. green (No. 66)	18·00	5·50
76	–	6 on 5 s. green (No. 66)	40·00	6·00
83	–	6 on 10 s. (No. 68)	32·00	5·50
84	6	8 on 50 c. black	60·00	9·00
78		12 on 50 c. black	70·00	9·00
79	–	18 on 10 s. (No. 68)	60·00	7·00
80	6	1 t. on 5 f. black and red	60·00	4·00

1889.

85	13	1 c. pink	25	10
86		2 c. blue	20	10
87		5 c. mauve	20	10
88		7 c. brown	1·00	30
89	14	10 c. black	35	10
90		1 k. orange	45	10
91		2 k. red	3·00	90
92		5 k. green	2·25	1·00

1891.

93	15	1 c. black	20	10
94		2 c. brown	30	10
95		5 c. blue	15	10
96		7 c. grey	65·00	2·00
97		10 c. red	55	10
98		14 c. orange	40	20
99	16	1 k. green	7·00	15
100		2 k. orange	£100	5·50
101		5 k. orange	80	40

17 18

21 Muzaffer-ed-Din

1894.

102	17	1 c. mauve	30	10
103		2 c. green	30	10
104		5 c. blue	30	10
105		8 c. brown	30	10
106	18	10 c. yellow	50	15
107		16 c. pink	2·50	60
108		1 k. pink and yellow	2·00	15
109		2 k. brown and blue	2·00	15
110		5 k. violet and silver	2·25	30
111		10 k. pink and gold	10·00	2·50
112		50 k. green and gold	7·00	4·50

See also Nos. 116/24.

1897. Surch in English and Persian in frame.

113	17	5 c. on 8 c. brown	1·75	20
114	18	1 k. on 5 k. violet & silver	5·50	1·50
115		2 k. on 5 k. violet & silver	5·50	2·00

1898. Chahi values on white or green paper.

116	17	1 c. grey	20	10
117		2 c. brown	30	10
118		3 c. purple	30	10
119		4 c. red	30	10
120		5 c. yellow	30	10
121		8 c. orange	1·00	35
154		10 c. blue	60	10
123		12 c. red	90	10
124		16 c. green	1·50	35
125	21	1 k. blue	2·00	10
157		1 k. red	1·75	20
126		2 k. pink	2·00	10
158		2 k. green	3·50	60
127		3 k. yellow	2·00	20
159		3 k. brown	5·00	1·00
128		4 k. grey	2·00	50
160		4 k. red	5·00	1·00
129		5 k. green	2·00	50
161		5 k. brown	7·50	1·00
130		10 k. orange	3·50	75
162		10 k. blue	17·00	3·50
131		50 k. mauve	9·50	4·00
163		50 k. brown	12·00	2·25

(21a)

(22)

(24)

1899. Optd with control mark of various scroll devices as T **21a**.

132	17	1 c. grey	60	10
133		2 c. brown	60	10
134		3 c. purple	60	10
135		4 c. red	60	10
136		5 c. yellow	60	10
137		8 c. orange	1·50	15
138		10 c. blue	60	10
139		12 c. red	1·25	10
140		16 c. green	1·25	35
141	21	1 k. blue	1·50	10
142		2 k. pink	2·75	45
143		3 k. yellow	8·50	1·50
144		4 k. grey	8·50	1·50
145		5 k. green	4·50	1·50
146		10 k. orange	12·00	1·50
147		50 k. mauve	10·00	4·00

1900. Optd with T **22** across two stamps.

164	17	1 c. grey	20·00	2·00
165		2 c. brown	20·00	2·00
166		3 c. purple	28·00	3·00
167		4 c. red	65·00	8·50
168		5 c. yellow	7·50	1·00
169		10 c. blue	£275	£110
170		12 c. red	28·00	2·00

Prices quoted in this issue are for pairs.

1901. Surch in various ways in English and Persian.

176	17	5 on 8 c. brown	2·00	25
179	21	12 c. on 1 k. red	10·00	4·00
180		5 k. on 50 k. brown	45·00	12·00

1902. Surch with T **24**.

177	17	5 c. on 10 c. blue	1·50	60
178	21	5 c. on 1 k. red	1·50	80

1902. Optd **PROVISOIRE 1319** in ornamental frame.

181	17	1 c. grey	2·00	1·00
182		2 c. brown	3·50	2·50
183		3 c. purple	2·00	1·00
184		4 c. red	2·00	1·00
185		5 c. yellow	1·75	65
197		5 on 8 c. brown (No. 176)	5·00	40
186		8 c. orange	2·00	1·50
187		10 c. blue	2·00	1·00
188		12 c. red	3·50	1·00
198	21	12 c. on 1 k. (No. 179)	7·50	2·50
189	17	16 c. green	7·00	3·00
190	21	1 k. red	6·50	2·25
191		2 k. green	—	10·00
192		3 k. brown	—	25·00
193		4 k. red	—	28·00
194		5 k. brown	—	30·00
199		5 k. on 50 k. (No. 180)	25·00	9·00
195		10 k. blue	—	30·00
196		50 k. brown	—	32·00

28

(29)

1902. Inscr "CHAHIS" or "KRANS" in capital letters. Optd with T **29**.

200	28	1 c. grey	1·25	10
201		2 c. brown	4·00	20
202		3 c. green	7·00	10
203		5 c. red	2·00	10
204		10 c. yellow	6·00	10
205		12 c. blue	9·00	40
206		1 k. mauve	22·00	50
207		2 k. green	25·00	2·00
208		10 k. blue	55·00	13·00
209		50 k. red	£375	£250

1902. Surch **5 KRANS** in English and Persian.

210	28	5 k. on 5 k. yellow	60·00	7·00

1902. Optd **PROVISOIRE 1319** in ornamental frame.

211	28	1 c. grey	20·00	10·00
212		2 c. brown	20·00	10·00
213		3 c. green	20·00	10·00
214		5 c. red	20·00	10·00
215		12 c. blue	20·00	10·00

34

1902. Inscr "Chahis" or "Krans" in lower case letters.

227	34	1 c. grey	11·00	
228		2 c. brown	20·00	
229		3 c. green	11·00	
230		5 c. red	11·00	10
231		10 c. yellow	13·00	90
232		12 c. blue	16·00	1·10
233		1 k. mauve		
234		2 k. green		
235		10 k. blue		
236		50 k. red	£425	

1902. Surch **5 KRANS** without T **29** opt.

237	34	5 k. on 5 k. yellow	30·00	

1903. Optd **PROVISOIRE 1903** and lion in frame, but without Arms opt (T **29**).

239	28	1 c. grey	—	4·00
240		2 c. brown	—	4·00
241		5 c. red	—	4·00
242		10 c. yellow	—	6·00
243		12 c. blue	—	10·00
244		1 k. mauve	—	11·00

38

39 Muzaffer ed-Din

1903.

246	38	1 c. lilac	20	10
247		2 c. grey	25	10
248		3 c. green	30	10
249		5 c. red	40	10
250		10 c. brown	40	10
251		12 c. blue	40	10
252	39	1 k. purple	1·25	15
253		2 k. blue	2·00	10
254		5 k. brown	3·00	15
255		10 k. red	7·50	30
256		20 k. orange	12·00	60
257		30 k. green	14·00	1·50
258		50 k. green	55·00	14·00

See also Nos. 298/303.

1903. Surch in both English and Persian except those marked* which are surch in English only.

272	38	"1 CHAHI" on 3 c. green	5·00	1·25
287		"1 CHAI" on 3 c. green	3·50	40
288	39	1 c. on 1 k. purple	12·00	3·50
273	38	2 c. on 3 c. green	10·00	4·25
289	39	2 c. on 5 k. brown	17·00	6·00
277	38	3 c. on 5 c. red	2·50	10
278		6 c. on 10 c. brown	4·00	10
279	39	9 c. on 1 k. purple	5·00	15
274		12 c. on 10 k. red	16·00	3·75
275		2 t. on 50 k. green*	55·00	25·00
280		2 t. on 50 k. green	55·00	25·00
276		3 t. on 50 k. green*	55·00	25·00
281		3 t. on 50 k. green	55·00	25·00

50

52 Shah Muhammad Ali Mirza

1906. Optd **PROVISOIRE** and lion. Imperf. or perf.

292	50	1 c. violet	50	10
293		2 c. grey	60	10
294		3 c. green	60	10
295		6 c. red	1·00	10
296		10 c. brown	11·00	50
297		13 c. blue	6·00	35

1907.

298	38	1 ch. violet on blue	15	10
299		2 ch. grey on blue	15	10
300		3 ch. green on blue	15	10
301		6 ch. red on blue	15	10
302		9 ch. yellow on blue	20	10
303		10 ch. sepia on blue	20	10
305	52	13 c. blue	50	10
306		26 c. brown	50	10
307		1 k. red	50	10
308		2 k. green	50	10
309		3 k. blue	60	10
311		4 k. brown	1·75	30
312		5 k. brown	1·25	15
313		10 k. pink	2·00	15
314		20 k. brown	4·75	25
315		30 k. purple	5·00	40
316	–	50 k. red and gold	20·00	17·00

The 50 k. is larger with the head facing the other way.

(54)

56

1909. Nos. 298/315 optd as T **54**. Imperf.
320 **38** 1 ch. on 1 ch. violet on bl 30·00 20·00
321 1 ch. on 2 ch. grey on bl 30·00 20·00
322 1 ch. on 3 ch. grn on bl 30·00 20·00
323 1 ch. on 6 ch. red on blue 30·00 20·00
324 1 ch. on 9 ch. yell on bl 30·00 20·00
325 1 ch. on 10 ch. brn on bl 30·00 20·00
326 **52** 2 ch. on 13 ch. blue 32·00 22·00
327 2 ch. on 26 ch. brown 32·00 22·00
328 2 ch. on 1 kr. red 32·00 22·00
329 2 ch. on 2 kr. green 32·00 22·00
330 2 ch. on 3 kr. blue 32·00 22·00
331 2 ch. on 4 kr. yellow 32·00 22·00
333 2 ch. on 5 kr. brown 32·00 22·00
334 2 ch. on 10 kr. pink 32·00 22·00
335 2 ch. on 20 kr. black 35·00 24·00
336 2 ch. on 30 kr. purple 35·00 24·00

1909.
337 **56** 1 c. purple and orange 35 10
338 2 c. purple and violet 35 10
339 3 c. purple and green 35 10
340 6 c. purple and red 35 10
341 9 c. purple and grey 40 10
342 10 c. maroon and purple 70 10
343 13 c. purple and blue 70 10
344 26 c. purple and green 3·00 10
345 1 k. brown, violet & silver 6·00 10
346 2 k. brown, green & silver 6·00 10
347 3 k. brown, grey & silver 7·00 15
348 4 k. brown, blue & silver 12·00 40
349 5 k. sepia, brown & gold 16·00 40
350 10 k. brown, orge & gold 30·00 70
351 20 k. brown, grn & gold 30·00 1·40
352 30 k. brown, red & gold 40·00 1·90

Stamps of this issue offered at very low prices are reprints.

For stamps as Type **56** but with curved inscriptions, see Nos. O836 etc.

57 Ahmed Mirza (65)

1911.
361 **57** 1 c. orange and green 15 10
362 2 c. brown and red 15 10
363 3 c. green and grey 15 10
364 3 c. green and brown 15 10
365 5 c. red and brown 15 10
366 6 c. red and grey 15 10
367 6 c. red and green 15 10
368 9 c. lilac and brown 15 10
369 10 c. brown and red 15 10
370 12 c. blue and green 15 10
371 13 c. blue and violet 15 10
372 24 c. green and purple 15 10
373 26 c. green and blue 4·00 2·00
374 1 k. red and blue 10 10
375 2 k. purple and green 20 10
376 3 k. black and lilac 25 10
377 4 k. black and blue 4·00 2·00
378 5 k. blue and red 20 10
379 10 k. pink and brown 35 10
380 20 k. buff and brown 55 10
381 30 k. green and red 80 10

1911. Various stamps optd **Relais** in English and Persian.
382 **56** 2 ch. purple and violet 13·00 3·00
383 3 ch. purple and green 13·00 3·00
384 6 ch. purple and red 13·00 3·00
385 13 ch. purple and blue 13·00 3·00
386 **57** 2 ch. brown and red 13·00 3·00
387 3 ch. green and grey 13·00 3·00
388 6 ch. red and grey 13·00 3·00
388a 13 ch. blue and violet 13·00 3·00

1912. Optd **Officiel** in English and Persian.
389 **57** 1 c. orange and green 40 10
390 2 c. brown and red 40 10
391 3 c. green and grey 40 10
392 6 c. red and grey 1·75 10
393 9 c. lilac and brown 85 15
394 10 c. brown and red 85 15
395 13 c. blue and violet 5·00 35
396 26 c. green and blue 13·00 70
397 1 k. red and blue 10·00 20
398 2 k. purple and green 11·00 20
399 3 k. black and lilac 15·00 20
400 5 k. blue and red 17·00 20
401 10 k. pink and brown 30·00 1·25
402 20 k. buff and brown 30·00 2·00
403 30 k. green and red 30·00 2·75

1914. Surch with new value and **1914** in English and Persian.
412 **57** 1 c. on 13 c. blue & violet 2·00 15
413 3 c. on 26 c. green & blue 2·00 15

1915. Surch with new value in frame and **1915** in English and Persian.
414 **57** 1 c. on 5 c. red & brown 1·75 10
415b 2 c. on 5 c. red & brown 1·75 10
416 6 c. on 12 c. blue & green 2·50 10

1915. Surch with new value in English and Persian.
417 **56** 5 c. on 1 k. (No. 345) 2·50 10
418 12 c. on 13 c. (No. 343) 3·25 10

1915. Optd with T **65** ("1333").
419 **56** 1 c. purple and orange 40 10
420 2 c. purple and violet 70 10
421 3 c. purple and green 1·50 10
422 6 c. purple and red 1·75 10
423 9 c. purple and grey 3·50 10
424 10 c. purple and mauve 7·00 20
425 1 k. brown, violet & silver 7·50 15

66 The Imperial Crown

67 King Darius on his Throne

1915. Coronation of Shah Ahmed.
426 **66** 1 c. blue and red 10 10
427 2 c. red and blue 10 10
428 3 c. green 10 10
429 5 c. red 10 10
430 6 c. red and green 10 10
431 9 c. violet and brown 10 10
432 10 c. brown and green 15 10
433 12 c. blue 15 10
434 24 c. sepia and brown 45 10
435 **67** 1 k. black, brown & silver 45 10
436 2 k. red, blue and silver 45 15
437 3 k. brown, lilac & silver 45 15
438 5 k. grey, brown & silver 45 15
439 – 1 t. black, violet & gold 70 30
440 – 2 t. brown, green & gold 70 30
441 – 3 t. red, crimson & gold 1·00 30
442 – 5 t. grey, blue and gold 1·00 30

DESIGNS: 1 t. to 5 t. Gateway of the Palace of Persepolis.

(69) (73)

1915. Optd with T **69** ("1334").
477 **56** 1 k. brown, violet & silver 5·50 40
478 10 k. brown, orge & gold 20·00 75
479 20 k. brown, grn & gold 90·00 8·50
480 30 k. brown, red & gold 35·00 2·75

1917. Surch with value in English only.
481 **57** 12 c. on 1 k. red & blue £225 80·00
482 24 c. on 1 k. red & blue £100 40·00

1917. Optd with T **73** ("1335") or surch also with new value in English and Persian.
483 **56** 1 c. purple and orange 35·00 9·00
484 1 c. on 2 c. (No. 338) 4·00 10
485 1 c. on 9 c. (No. 341) 4·00 10
486 1 c. on 10 c. (No. 342) 4·00 10
490 **57** 1 c. on 10 c. brown & red 4·00 10
487 **56** 3 c. on 9 c. purple & grey 4·00 10
491 **57** 3 c. on 10 c. brown & red 4·00 35
488 **56** 3 c. on 26 c. (No. 344) 4·50 10
489 5 c. on 13 c. (No. 343) 4·25 10
492 **57** 5 c. on 1 k. red and blue 6·50 70
493 6 c. on 10 c. brown & red 4·25 80
494 6 c. on 12 c. blue & green 4·75 10

(78) (82)

1918. Optd with T **78** ("1336").
507 **56** 2 k. brown, green & silver 12·00 55

1918. Surch as T **78** and new value in English and Persian.
508 **56** 24 c. on 4 k. (No. 348) 13·00 50
509 10 k. on 5 k. (No. 349) 14·00 1·25

1918. Coronation issue of 1915 optd **Novembre 1918** (date also in Persian).
510 **67** 2 k. red, blue and silver 2·00 1·50
511 3 k. brown, lilac & silver 2·00 1·50
512 5 k. grey, brown & silver 3·00 1·50
513 – 1 t. black, violet & gold 3·00 1·50
514 – 2 t. brown, green & gold 3·25 1·50
515 – 3 t. red, crimson & gold 4·00 1·50
516 – 5 t. grey, blue and gold 4·50 2·50

1918. Surch as T **82** and new value in English and Persian.
517 **57** 3 c. on 12 c. blue & green 5·00 10
518 6 c. on 10 c. brown & red 5·00 10
519 6 c. on 1 k. red and blue 5·00 10

1918. Optd with T **82** ("1337").
520 **56** 2 k. brown, green & silver 28·00 1·50
521 3 k. brown, grey & silver 12·00 70
522 4 k. brown, blue & silver 65·00 2·75
523 5 k. sepia, brown & gold 35·00 1·50
524 10 k. brown, orge & gold 28·00 1·50
525 20 k. brown, grn & gold £150 18·00
526 30 k. brown, red & gold 48·00 3·25

84 Ahmed Mirza

92 Ahmed Mirza

1919. Type **84** surch **Provisoire 1919** and value in English and Persian.
527 **84** 1 c. yellow 70 10
528 3 c. green 1·00 10
529 5 c. purple 2·00 10
530 6 c. violet 4·00 10
531 12 c. blue 6·00 15

1919. Surch **1919** and value in English and Persian.
532 **13** 2 k. on 5 c. mauve 1·60 70
533 3 k. on 5 c. mauve 1·60 70
534 4 k. on 5 c. mauve 1·60 70
535 5 k. on 5 c. mauve 1·60 70
536 **15** 10 k. on 10 c. red 1·60 70
537 20 k. on 10 c. red 2·25 1·10
538 30 k. on 10 c. red 2·25 1·10
539 50 k. on 14 c. orange 2·25 1·75

1921. Surch **6-CHAHIS** in English and Persian.
539a **57** 6 c. on 12 c. blue & green 17·00 15

1921. Coup d'Etat of Reza Khan. Coronation issue of 1915 optd **21. FEV. 1921** in English and Persian.
540 **66** 3 c. green 4·00
541 5 c. red 4·00
542 6 c. red and green 4·00
543 10 c. brown and green 4·00
544 12 c. blue 4·00
545 **67** 1 k. black, brown & silver 4·00
546 2 k. red, blue and silver 5·00
547 5 k. grey, brown & silver 6·00
548 – 2 t. brown, green & gold 6·00
549 – 3 t. red, crimson & gold 6·00
550 – 5 t. grey, blue and gold 6·00

1922. Surch with value in English only.
551 **57** 10 c. on 6 c. brown & green 22·00 2·25
552 1 k. on 12 c. blue & green 22·00 3·50

1922. Surcharged with value in English only over **BENADERS.**
553 **57** 10 c. on 6 c. brown & green 15·00 2·25
554 1 k. on 12 c. blue & grn 15·00 2·75

1922. Optd **CONTROLE 1922** in English and Persian.
555 **57** 1 c. orange and green 35 10
556 2 c. brown and red 35 10
557 3 c. green and grey 35 10
558 3 c. green and brown 40 10
559 3 c. red and brown 20·00 3·50
560 6 c. brown and green 35 10
561 9 c. lilac and brown 70 10
562 10 c. brown and red 70 10
563 12 c. blue and green 1·10 10
564 24 c. green and purple 3·50 10
565 1 k. red and blue 9·00 10
566 2 k. purple and green 13·00 10
567 3 k. black and lilac 25·00 10
568 4 k. blue and black 60·00 80
569 5 k. blue and red 30·00 10
570 10 k. red and brown 75·00 15
571 20 k. yellow and brown 75·00 15
572 30 k. green and red 85·00 15

1922. Surch in English and Persian.
573 **57** 3 c. on 12 c. (No. 563) 2·50 10
574 6 c. on 24 c. (No. 564) 3·25 10
575 10 c. on 20 k. (No. 571) 5·50 1·50
576 1 k. on 30 k. (No. 572) 14·00 3·00

1924.
577 **92** 1 c. orange 20 10
578 2 c. red 20 10
579 3 c. brown 30 10
580 6 c. sepia 30 10
581 9 c. green 50 10
582 10 c. violet 50 10
583 12 c. red 50 10
584 1 k. blue 1·00 10
585 2 k. red and blue 2·00 10
586 3 k. purple and violet 8·00 15
587 5 k. sepia and red 12·00 30
588 10 k. violet and sepia 25·00 1·25
589 20 k. sepia and green 30·00 1·25
590 30 k. black and orange 35·00 1·75

1924. Surch **p. re. 1924** and value in English and Persian.
591 **84** 1 c. brown 15 10
592 2 c. grey 15 10
593 3 c. red 20 10
594 6 c. orange 70 15

1925. Surch **p. re. 1925** and value in English and Persian.
595 **84** 2 c. green 15 10
596 3 c. red 20 10
597 6 c. blue 35 10
598 9 c. brown 1·50 10
599 10 c. grey 3·25 15
600 1 k. green 3·25 10
601 2 k. mauve 15·00 20

94

(95 "Provisional Pahlavi Government, 31 Oct 1925")

1925. Deposition of Shah Ahmed and Provisional Government of Riza Khan Pahlavi. Fiscal stamps as T **94** (various frames) optd with T **95**.
602 **94** 1 c. red 1·50 70
603 2 c. yellow 1·50 70
604 3 c. green 1·50 70
605 5 c. grey 7·00 1·10
606 10 c. red 1·50 1·60
607 1 k. blue 3·00 70

(96)

1926. Optd with T **96**.
608 **92** 1 c. orange 30 10
609 2 c. red 35 10
610 3 c. brown 70 15
611 6 c. sepia 20·00 18·00

1926. Optd **Regne de Pahlavi 1926** in English and Persian.
612 **56** 1 c. purple and orange 20 10
613 2 c. purple and violet 20 10
614 3 c. purple and green 20 10
615 6 c. purple and red 30 10
616 9 c. purple and grey 65 10
617 10 c. maroon and purple 65 10
618 13 c. purple and blue 1·75 10
619 26 c. purple and green 5·50 10
620 1 k. brown, violet & silver 4·00 10
621 2 k. brown, green & silver 4·50 10
622 3 k. brown, grey & silver 4·50 15
623 4 k. brown, blue & silver 55·00 30
624 5 k. sepia, brown & gold 35·00 15
625 10 k. brown, orge & gold £200 15
626 20 k. brown, grn & gold £225 30
627 30 k. brown, red & gold £225 1·10

98 Riza Shah Pahlavi 99

1926.
628 **98** 1 c. green 15 10
629 2 c. blue 30 10
630 3 c. green 55 10
631 6 c. red 65 10
632 9 c. red 7·50 10
633 10 c. brown 13·00 10
634 12 c. orange 17·00 10
635 15 c. blue 20·00 10
636 **99** 1 k. blue 32·00 65
637 2 k. mauve 70·00 10·00

1927. Air. Optd with airplane and **POSTE AERIENNE** in English and Persian.
642 **56** 1 c. purple and orange 30 20
643 2 c. purple and violet 70 35
644 3 c. purple and green 40 30
645 6 c. purple and red 55 30
646 9 c. purple and grey 55 30
647 10 c. maroon and purple 70 35
648 13 c. purple and blue 1·25 70
649 26 c. purple and green 1·40 70
650 1 k. brown, violet & silver 1·40 70
651 2 k. brown, green & silver 3·00 1·50
652 3 k. brown, grey & silver 4·50 1·75
653 4 k. brown, blue & silver 10·00 4·75
654 5 k. sepia, brown & gold 10·00 6·00
655 10 k. brown, orge & gold £400 £130
656 20 k. brown, grn & gold £275 £130
657 30 k. brown, red & gold £275 £130

1928. Air. Fiscal stamps surch with Junkers F-13 airplane, **Poste aerien** and new value in French and Persian.
657a **94** 3 k. brown 55·00 16·00
657b 5 k. brown 10·00 2·75
657c 1 t. violet 10·00 4·00
657d 2 t. green 16·00 7·00
657e 3 t. green 23·00 8·00

102

104 Riza Shah Pahlavi

1929. Air. Fiscal stamps as T **102** (various frames) surch with Junkers F-13 airplane, **Poste aerienne** and value in French and Persian.
658 **102** 1 c. green 10 10
659 2 c. blue 20 10
660 3 c. red 10 10
661 5 c. brown 10 10
662 10 c. green 15 10
663 1 k. violet 35 10
664 2 k. orange 70 20
665 3 k. brown (22 × 30 mm) 50·00 8·00
666 5 k. brown (22 × 33 mm) 6·00 3·00
667 10 k. vio (21 × 31 mm) 15·00 5·50
668 20 k. grn (21 × 31 mm) 22·00 4·00
669 30 k. grn (21 × 31 mm) 27·00 8·00

1929.

No.	Type	Description	Mint	Used
670	104	1 c. red and green	25	10
671		2 c. blue and red	25	10
672		3 c. green and red	25	10
673		6 c. green and brown	25	10
674		9 c. red and blue	50	10
675		10 c. brown and green	85	10
676		12 c. violet and black	1·10	10
677		15 c. blue and yellow	2·00	10
678		24 c. lake and olive	3·50	10
679		1 k. black and blue	4·00	10
680		2 k. violet and orange	8·00	10
681		3 k. red and green	10·00	15
682		5 k. green and brown	9·00	20
683		1 t. red and blue	12·00	45
684		2 t. black and red	25·00	2·00
685	–	3 t. violet and gold	30·00	3·25

DESIGN: 3 t. Shah enthroned (28½ × 39 mm.).

106 Riza Shah Pahlavi and Elburz Mts

1930. Air.

No.	Type	Description	Mint	Used
686	106	1 c. blue and yellow	10	10
687		2 c. black and blue	15	10
688		3 c. violet and olive	15	10
689		4 c. blue and violet	15	10
690		5 c. red and green	15	10
691		6 c. green and red	15	10
692		8 c. violet and grey	15	10
693		10 c. red and blue	20	10
694		12 c. orange and grey	25	10
695		15 c. olive and brown	25	10
696		1 k. red and blue	55	25
697		2 k. blue and black	55	35
698		3 k. green and brown	70	45
699		5 k. black and red	1·75	55
700		1 t. purple and orange	2·50	70
701		2 t. brown and green	5·50	2·50
702		3 t. green and purple	22·00	16·00

107 · 108 Riza Shah Pahlavi · 109

1931.

No.	Type	Description	Mint	Used
703	107	1 c. blue and brown	20	10
704		2 c. black and red	30	10
705		3 c. brown and mauve	25	10
706		6 c. violet and red	35	10
707		9 c. red and blue	2·00	10
708		10 c. grey and red	5·00	10
709		11 c. red and blue	7·00	10
710		12 c. mauve and blue	6·00	10
711		16 c. red and black	5·50	10
712		27 c. blue and black	12·00	10
713		1 k. blue and red	12·00	10

1933. New Currency.

No.	Type	Description	Mint	Used
714	108	5 d. brown	15	10
715		10 d. blue	15	10
716		15 d. grey	30	10
717		30 d. green	30	10
718		45 d. blue	60	10
719		50 d. mauve	60	10
720		60 d. green	1·75	10
721		75 d. brown	1·75	10
722		90 d. red	1·75	10
723	109	1 r. black and red	2·50	10
724		1 r. 20 red and black	7·00	15
725		1 r. 50 blue and yellow	12·00	15
726		2 r. brown and blue	10·00	15
727		3 r. green and mauve	25·00	35
728		5 r. red and brown	32·00	7·00

110 "Justice" · 112 Cement Works, Chah-Abdul-Azim

1935. 10th Anniv of Riza Khan's Advent to Power.

No.	Type	Description	Mint	Used
729	110	5 d. green and brown	20	10
730	–	10 d. grey and orange	20	10
731	–	15 d. blue and red	20	10
732	–	30 d. green and black	55	10
733	–	45 d. lake and olive	65	10
734	112	75 d. brown and green	2·50	40
735	–	90 d. red and blue	6·00	70
736	–	1 r. violet and brown	14·00	3·75
737	–	1 r. 50 blue and purple	6·00	2·00

DESIGNS: 10 d. Ruins of Persepolis (40 × 26 mm); 15 d. "Education" (23 × 33 mm); 30 d. De Havilland Tiger Moth biplanes over Teheran Aerodrome (38 × 25 mm); 45 d. Sakhtessar Sanatorium, Mazanderan (40 × 27 mm); 90 d. Gunboat "Palang" (38 × 24 mm); 1 r. Railway bridge over R. Karun (42 × 29 mm); 1 r. 50, Post and Customs House, Teheran (42 × 27 mm).

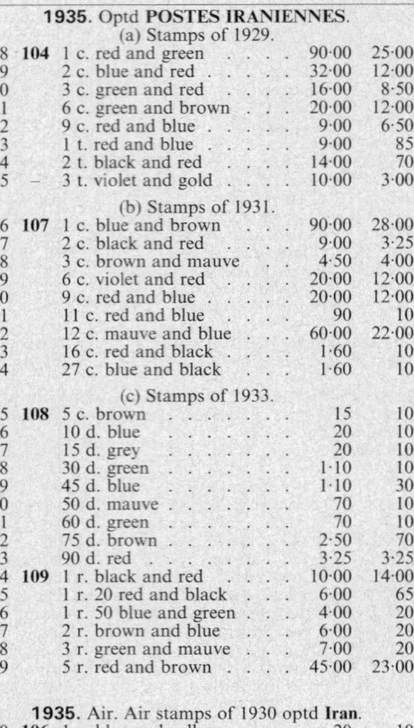

1935. Optd **POSTES IRANIENNES**.

(a) Stamps of 1929.

No.	Type	Description	Mint	Used
738	104	1 c. red and green	90·00	25·00
739		2 c. blue and red	32·00	12·00
740		3 c. green and red	16·00	8·50
741		6 c. green and brown	20·00	12·00
742		9 c. red and blue	9·00	6·50
743		1 t. red and blue	9·00	85
744		2 t. black and red	14·00	70
745	–	3 t. violet and gold	10·00	3·00

(b) Stamps of 1931.

No.	Type	Description	Mint	Used
746	107	1 c. blue and brown	90·00	28·00
747		2 c. black and red	9·00	3·25
748		3 c. brown and mauve	4·50	4·00
749		6 c. violet and red	20·00	12·00
750		9 c. red and blue	20·00	12·00
751		11 c. red and blue	90	10
752		12 c. mauve and blue	60·00	22·00
753		16 c. red and black	1·60	10
754		27 c. blue and black	1·60	10

(c) Stamps of 1933.

No.	Type	Description	Mint	Used
755	108	5 c. brown	15	10
756		10 d. blue	20	10
757		15 d. grey	20	10
758		30 d. green	1·10	10
759		45 d. blue	1·10	30
760		50 d. mauve	70	10
761		60 d. green	70	10
762		75 d. brown	2·50	70
763		90 d. red	3·25	3·25
764	109	1 r. black and red	10·00	14·00
765		1 r. 20 red and black	6·00	65
766		1 r. 50 blue and green	4·00	20
767		2 r. brown and blue	6·00	20
768		3 r. green and mauve	7·00	20
769		5 r. red and brown	45·00	23·00

1935. Air. Air stamps of 1930 optd **Iran**.

No.	Type	Description	Mint	Used
770	106	1 c. blue and yellow	20	10
771		2 c. black and blue	20	10
772		3 c. violet and olive	20	10
773		4 c. blue and violet	20	10
774		5 c. red and green	20	10
775		6 c. green and red	20	10
776		8 c. violet and grey	20	10
777		10 c. red and blue	20	10
778		12 c. orange and blue	20	10
779		15 c. olive and brown	55	20
780		1 k. red and blue	1·75	70
781		2 k. blue and black	2·25	70
782		3 k. green and brown	2·75	2·25
783		5 k. black and red	1·50	70
784		1 t. purple and orange	35·00	17·00
785		2 t. brown and green	4·50	1·75
786		3 t. green and purple	6·50	2·00

116 · 117 Riza Shah Pahlavi · 117a

1935. Rial values are larger, 22 × 31 mm.

No.	Type	Description	Mint	Used
787	116	5 d. violet	20	10
788		10 d. purple	20	10
789		15 d. blue	20	10
790		30 d. green	35	10
791		45 d. orange	75	10
792		50 d. brown	1·50	10
793		60 d. blue	6·50	10
794		75 d. red	4·50	10
795		90 d. red	4·50	10
796		1 r. purple	7·50	10
797		1 r. 50 blue	13·00	35
798		2 r. green	12·00	15
799		3 r. brown	13·00	30
800		5 r. grey	22·00	6·00

1936. Rial values are larger, 23 × 31 mm.

No.	Type	Description	Mint	Used
801	117	5 d. violet	15	10
802		10 d. mauve	15	10
803		15 d. blue	30	10
804		30 d. green	40	10
805		45 d. red	55	10
806		50 d. brown	80	10
807		60 d. brown	55	10
808		75 d. red	1·00	10
809		90 d. red	1·60	10
810		1 r. green	6·00	10
811		1 r. 50 blue	3·00	10
812		2 r. blue	11·00	10
813		3 r. purple	15·00	10
814		5 r. green	20·00	45
815		10 r. blue and brown	35·00	5·50

1938. 60th Birthday of Shah. Perf or imperf.

No.	Type	Description	Mint	Used
815a	117a	5 d. blue	15	10
815b		10 d. red	15	10
815c		30 d. blue	15	10
815d		60 d. brown	20	10
815e		90 d. red	30	15
815f		1 r. violet	1·00	
815g		1 r. 50 blue	35	15
815h		2 r. red	1·00	
815i		5 r. mauve	1·40	1·00
815j		10 r. red	3·25	1·75

118 Riza Shah Pahlavi · 119 Princess Fawzieh and Crown Prince

1938. Rial values are larger, 23 × 31 mm.

No.	Type	Description	Mint	Used
816	118	5 d. violet	15	10
817		10 d. mauve	15	10
818		15 d. blue	15	10
819		30 d. green	20	10
820		45 d. red	30	10
821		50 d. brown	30	10
822		60 d. orange	30	10
823		75 d. red	35	10
824		90 d. red	70	10
825		1 r. green	1·25	10
826		1 r. 50 blue	7·50	10
827		2 r. blue	10·00	10
828		3 r. purple	13·00	10
829		5 r. green	20·00	25
830		10 r. blue and brown	42·00	1·75

1939. Royal Wedding.

No.	Type	Description	Mint	Used
831	119	5 d. brown	15	10
832		10 d. violet	20	10
833		30 d. green	70	20
834		90 d. red	2·00	30
835		1 r. 50 blue	3·00	1·10

120 Railway Bridge over Karun River · 123 Mohammed Riza Pahlavi

1942.

No.	Type	Description	Mint	Used
850	120	5 d. violet	1·50	10
851		5 d. orange	35	10
852	–	10 d. mauve	2·75	20
853	–	10 d. green	1·50	10
854	–	20 d. violet	30	10
855	–	20 d. mauve	30	10
856	–	25 d. red	12·50	90
857	–	25 d. violet	1·50	10
858	–	35 d. green	25	10
859	–	50 d. blue	50	10
860	–	50 d. green	1·60	10
861	–	70 d. brown	50	10
862	–	75 d. purple	50	10
863	–	75 d. red	7·75	10
864	–	1 r. red	2·75	10
865	–	1 r. purple	10·00	10
866	–	1 r. 50 red	1·60	10
867	120	2 r. blue	4·00	10
868	–	2 r. green	5·25	10
869	–	2 r. 50 blue	5·25	10
870	–	3 r. green	80·00	10
871	–	3 r. purple	10·50	10
872	–	5 r. green	80·00	20
873	–	5 r. blue	5·25	10
874	123	10 r. black and orange	20·00	2·00
875		10 r. black and brown	12·00	10
876		20 r. violet and brown	£600	16·00
877		20 r. black and orange	18·00	15
878		30 r. green and black	£1400	9·75
879		30 r. black and green	18·00	20
880		50 r. red and blue	£200	12·00
881		50 r. black and purple	32·00	25
882		100 r. black and red	£250	28·00
883		200 r. black and blue	£275	32·00

DESIGNS—HORIZ: 10 d. Vereshk Railway Bridge, N. Iran; 20 d. Granary, Ahwaz; 25 d. Steam train on Karj Bridge; 50 d. Ministry of Justice; 70 d. School building. VERT: 35 d. Museum; 75 d. Side view of museum; 1 to 5 r. Full-face portrait of Mohammed Riza Pahlavi.

124 Lion and Bull, Persepolis

1948. Fund to rebuild Avicenna's Tomb at Hamadan (1st issue).

No.	Type	Description	Mint	Used
899	124	50 d. + 25 d. green	20	35
900	–	1 r. + 50 d. red	40	50
901	–	2½ r. + 1¼ r. blue	80	70
902	–	5 r. + 2½ r. violet	1·75	1·50
903	–	10 r. + 5 r. purple	3·00	2·00

DESIGNS—VERT: 1 r. Persian Warrior, Persepolis. HORIZ: 2½ r. Palace of Darius, Persepolis; 5 r. Tomb of Cyrus, Pasargades; 10 r. King Darius enthroned.

See also Nos. 909/13, 930/4, 939/43, and 1024/28.

126 National Flag

1949. Iran's War Effort.

No.	Type	Description	Mint	Used
904	126	25 d. multicoloured	50	15
905	–	50 d. violet	3·50	70
906	–	1 r. 50 red	3·50	70
907	–	2 r. 50 blue	9·00	45
908	–	5 r. green	9·00	1·00

DESIGNS: 50 d. Bandar Shahpur (port); 1 r. 50, Lorries on winding road; 2 r. 50, Vereshk Railway Bridge; 5 r. Mohammed Riza Pahlavi and map of Iran.

127 King Ardashir II · 128 King Ardashir I and Ahura Mazda

1949. Fund to rebuild Avicenna's Tomb (2nd issue).

No.	Type	Description	Mint	Used
909	127	50 d. + 25 d. green	20	20
910	–	1 r. + 50 d. red	30	20
911	–	2½ r. + 1¼ r. blue	60	35
912	–	5 r. + 2½ r. plum	1·10	1·00
913	128	10 r. + 5 r. green	1·90	1·75

DESIGNS—VERT: 1 r. King Narses. HORIZ: 2½ r. King Shapur I and Emperor Valerian; 5 r. Arch of Ctesiphon.

129 Mohammed Riza Pahlavi and Post and Customs House, Teheran

130 Old G.P.O., Teheran · 131 Mohammed Riza Pahlavi

1949.

No.	Type	Description	Mint	Used
914	–	5 d. green and red	10	10
915	–	10 d. brown and blue	10	10
916	–	20 d. blue and violet	20	10
917	–	25 d. blue and brown	25	10
918	–	50 d. blue and green	30	10
919	–	75 d. red and brown	50	10
920	–	1 r. green and violet	60	10
921	–	1 r. 50 red and green	1·50	10
922	129	2 r. brown and red	2·25	10
923	–	2 r. 50 blue	2·25	10
924	–	3 r. orange and blue	4·50	10
925	–	5 r. violet and red	6·75	10
926	130	10 r. green and red	14·50	15
927		20 r. red and black	£225	12·00
928	131	30 r. blue and brown	26·00	2·00
929		50 r. blue and red	42·00	1·90

DESIGNS—HORIZ: All show buildings. In the dinar values, portrait is to right of stamp, and in rial values, to left; 5 d. Ramsar Hotel, Darband, Caspian Sea; 10 d. Zayende River Bridge; 20 d. Bank Melli Iran building; 25 d. Old Royal Palace, Isfahan; 50 d. Chaharbagh School, Isfahan; 75 d. Railway Square; 1 r. Justice Ministry; 1 r. 50, Shah Mosque, Teheran; 2 r. 50, Parliament Building; 3 r. The Great Gate, Isfahan; 5 r. Isfahan.

132 Tomb of Ali Abarquh · 134 Allegory

1949. Fund to rebuild Avicenna's Tomb (3rd issue).

No.	Type	Description	Mint	Used
930	132	50 d. + 25 d. green	20	20
931	–	1 r. + 50 d. brown	25	20
932	–	2½ r. + 1¼ r. blue	45	35
933	–	5 r. + 2½ r. red	85	85
934	–	10 r. + 5 r. olive	1·75	1·75

DESIGNS—VERT: 1 r. Jami Mosque, Isfahan. HORIZ: 2½ r. Tomb tower, Hamadan; 5 r. Jami Mosque, Ardistan; 10 r. Seljuk coin.

1950. 75th Anniv of U.P.U.

No.	Type	Description	Mint	Used
935	–	50 d. lake	20·00	14·00
936	134	2 r. 50 blue	28·00	18·00

DESIGN—HORIZ: 50 d. Hemispheres and doves.

135 Riza Shah Pahlavi and Mausoleum

1950. Interment of Riza Shah Pahlavi at Shah Abdul Azim.

937	135	50 d. brown	6·50	2·50
938		2 r. black	13·50	3·50

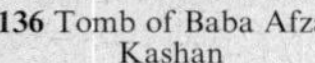

136 Tomb of Baba Afzal, Kashan

139 Flag and Book

1950. Fund to Rebuild Avicenna's Tomb (4th issue).

939	136	50 d. + 25 d. green	15	15
940	–	1 r. + 50 d. blue	20	20
941	–	$2\frac{1}{2}$ r. + $1\frac{1}{4}$ r. purple	35	30
942	–	5 r. + $2\frac{1}{2}$ r. red	85	75
943	–	10 r. + 5 r. grey	1·90	1·50

DESIGNS—VERT: 1 r. Gorgan vase; $2\frac{1}{2}$ r. Ghazan Tower, Bistam. HORIZ: 5 r. Masjid-i Gawhar Shad Mosque, Meshed; 10 r. Niche in wall of Mosque at Rezaieh.

1950. 2nd Economic Conference of Islamic Countries.

944	139	1 r. 50 + 1 r. multicoloured	12·00	3·25

140 Mohammed Riza Pahlavi in Military School Uniform

142 Memorial

1950. Shah's 31st Birthday. Portraits of Shah at different ages, framed as T **140**.

945	140	25 d. black and red	2·00	20
946	–	50 d. black and orange	2·00	30
947	–	75 d. black and brown	12·00	1·40
948	–	1 r. black and green	8·00	1·60
949	–	2 r. 50 black and blue	14·00	2·00
950	–	5 r. black and red	20·00	2·50

PORTRAITS—Shah in uniform: 50 d. Naval cadet; 75 d. Boy scout; 1 r. Naval officer; 2 r. 50, Army officer-cadet; 5 r. Army general.

1950. 4th Anniv of Re-establishment of Control in Azerbaijan.

951	–	10 d. + 5 d. brown	7·00	1·25
952	142	50 d. + 25 d. purple	7·50	1·40
953	–	1 r. + 50 d. purple	15·00	1·75
954	–	1 r. 50 + 75 d. red & grn	15·00	3·25
955	–	2 r. 50 + 1 r. 25 blue	16·00	5·00
956	–	3 r. + 1 r. 50 blue	22·00	5·00

DESIGNS—VERT: 10 d. Shah and map; 1 r. 50, Map and battle scene; 2 r. 50, Shah and flags. HORIZ: 1 r. Troops marching; 3 r. Cavalry parade.

143 Shah and Queen Soraya

144 Farabi

1951. Royal Wedding. T **143** and similar portraits.

959	143	5 d. purple	1·10	35
960		25 d. orange	1·50	45
961		50 d. green	3·25	55
962	–	1 r. brown	3·75	90
963	–	1. 50 r. red	5·25	2·10
964	–	2. 50 r. blue	7·00	2·75

DESIGNS: 1 r. to 2 r. 50, As T **143** but portraits centrally placed.

1951. Millenary of Death of Farabi (philosopher).

965	144	50 d. red	3·00	60
966		2 r. 50 blue	11·00	1·75

145 Mohammed Riza Pahlavi 146

1951.

967	145	5 d. red	10	10
968		10 d. violet	10	10
969		20 d. sepia	10	10
970		25 d. blue	10	10
971		50 d. green	40	10
972		50 d. deep green	5·25	10
973		75 d. red	30	10
974	146	1 r. green	50	10
975		1 r. turquoise	50	10
976		1 r. 50 red	80	10
977		2 r. brown	2·75	10
978		2 r. 50 blue	2·50	10
979		3 r. orange	10·00	10
980		5 r. green	10·00	10
981		10 r. olive	26·00	80
982		20 r. brown	13·50	30
983		30 r. blue	7·75	40
984		50 r. black	26·00	1·25

147 Coran Gate, Shiraz

1951. 600th Death Anniv of Saadi (Muslih-ad-Din) (poet).

985	147	25 d. + 25 d. green	1·50	45
986	–	50 d. + 50 d. green	1·50	55
987	–	1 r. 50 + 50 d. blue	7·00	1·25

DESIGNS—HORIZ: 50 d. Tomb of Saadi. VERT: (as T **144**): 1 r. 50, Saadi.

150 Shah and Lockheed Super Constellation over Mosque

151 Oil Well and Mosque

1952. Air.

988	–	50 d. green	10	10
989	150	1 r. red	15	10
990		2 r. blue	20	10
991		3 r. sepia	30	10
992		5 r. lilac	45	10
993		10 r. red	65	10
994		20 r. violet	1·75	20
995		30 r. olive	2·25	30
996		50 r. brown	6·00	40
997		100 r. sepia	65·00	3·50
998		200 r. green	25·00	5·50

DESIGN: 50 d. Shah and Lockheed Super Constellation airplane over Mt. Demavend.

1953. Discovery of Oil at Qum. (a) Postage.

999	151	50 d. bistre and green	1·00	10
1000	–	1 r. bistre and mauve	1·00	10
1001	151	2 r. 50 bistre and blue	1·50	35
1002	–	5 r. bistre and brown	2·10	80

(b) Air. With Lockheed Super Constellation airplane.

1003	151	3 r. bistre and violet	26·00	6·00
1004	–	5 r. bistre and brown	35·00	8·00
1005	151	10 r. bistre and green	45·00	12·00
1006	–	20 r. bistre and purple	55·00	14·00

DESIGN: 1 r., 5 r. (2), 20 r. As Type **151** but horiz.

153 Power Station Boiler Plant

1953. 2nd Anniv of Nationalization of Oil Industry.

1007	153	50 d. green	1·25	15
1008	–	1 r. red	1·75	15
1009	–	2 r. 50 blue	7·00	40
1010	–	5 r. orange	7·50	60
1011	–	10 r. lilac	8·50	85

DESIGNS—HORIZ: 1 r. Crude oil stabilizer; 5 r. Pipe-lines; 10 r. View of Abadan. VERT: 2 r. 50, Super fractionaters.

154 Family and U.N. Emblem

155 Gymnast

1953. United Nations Day.

1012	154	1 r. green & turquoise	50	20
1013		2 r. 50 blue & light blue	1·00	45

1953. Ancient Persian Sports.

1014	155	1 r. green	1·40	85
1015	–	2 r. 50 blue	6·00	1·10
1016	–	3 r. grey	18·00	1·40
1017	–	5 r. ochre	12·00	3·25
1018	–	10 r. violet	24·00	4·50

DESIGNS—HORIZ: 2 r. 50, Archer; 3 r. Mountaineers. VERT: 5 r. Polo-player (Persian Sports Club Badge); 10 r. Lion-hunter.

156 Iranian Roach

157 Machinery

1954. Nationalization of Fishing Industry.

1019	156	1 r. multicoloured	2·00	55
1020	–	2 r. 50 multicoloured	30·00	1·75
1021	–	3 r. red	12·00	1·25
1022	157	5 r. green	11·00	2·25
1023	–	10 r. multicoloured	20·00	5·50

DESIGNS—HORIZ: As Type **156**: 2 r. 50, Clupeid; 10 r. Sturgeon. As Type **157**: 3 r. Refrigeration machinery.

158 Hamadan

159 Avicenna

1954. Fund to Rebuild Avicenna's Tomb (5th issue).

1024	158	50 d. + 25 d. green	15	15
1025	159	1 r. + $\frac{1}{2}$ r. brown	20	20
1026	–	$2\frac{1}{2}$ r. + $1\frac{1}{4}$ r. blue	45	30
1027	–	5 r. + $2\frac{1}{2}$ r. red	70	50
1028	–	10 r. + 5 r. olive	1·40	1·25

DESIGNS—VERT: As Type **159**: $2\frac{1}{2}$ r. Qabus tower, Gargan, HORIZ: As Type **158**: 5 r. Old tomb of Avicenna; 10 r. New tomb of Avicenna.

160 Shah in Military Uniform

161 Hands breaking Chain

1954.

1029	160	5 d. brown	10	10
1062		5 d. violet	10	10
1030		10 d. violet	10	10
1063		10 d. red	10	10
1031		25 d. red	10	10
1064		25 d. brown	10	10
1032		50 d. brown	10	10
1065		50 d. red	10	10
1066	–	1 r. green	1·25	10
1034	–	1 r. 50 red	75	10
1067	–	1 r. 50 brown	20·00	10
1035	–	2 r. brown	75	10
1068	–	2 r. green	1·90	10
1069	–	2 r. 50 blue	75	10
1037	–	3 r. green	1·25	10
1070	–	3 r. brown	5·25	10
1038	–	5 r. green	2·50	10
1071	–	5 r. purple	2·50	10
1039	–	10 r. lilac	6·25	2·00
1072	–	10 r. blue	4·25	10
1040	–	20 r. blue	50·00	6·00
1073	–	20 r. green	26·00	10
1041	–	30 r. brown	£110	20·00
1074	–	30 r. orange	£130	12·00
1042	–	50 r. orange	38·00	2·00
1075	–	50 r. brown	£110	16·00
1043	–	100 r. violet	£475	38·00
1044	–	200 r. yellow	£110	12·00

DESIGN: 1 r. to 200 r. Shah in naval uniform.

1954. 1st Anniv of Return of Shah. Mult.

1045	2 r. Type **161**	3·25	45
1046	3 r. Hand holding torch and Iranian flag	5·00	70
1047	5 r. Man clasping Iranian flag	9·00	1·25

SIZES: 3 r. ($19\frac{1}{2} \times 27\frac{1}{2}$ mm.); 5 r. ($20\frac{1}{2} \times 28\frac{1}{2}$ mm.).

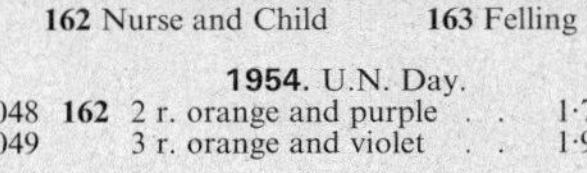

162 Nurse and Child

163 Felling Trees

1954. U.N. Day.

1048	162	2 r. orange and purple	1·75	50
1049		3 r. orange and violet	1·90	1·00

1954. 4th World Forestry Congress. Inscr "4eme congres mondial forestier".

1050	163	1 r. green and brown	16·00	3·50
1051	–	2 r. 50 blue and green	25·00	7·00
1052	–	5 r. brown and lavender	50·00	15·00
1053	–	10 r. lake and blue	60·00	28·00

DESIGNS: 2 r. 50, Man carrying logs; 5 r. Man operating circular saw; 10 r. Ancient Persian galley.

164

165 Parliament Building

1955. National Costumes.

1054	164	1 r. multicoloured	1·25	45
1055	–	2 r. multicoloured	2·25	65
1056	–	2 r. 50 multicoloured	14·00	1·25
1057	–	3 r. multicoloured	6·00	1·25
1058	–	5 r. multicoloured	10·00	2·50

DESIGNS—2 r. Male costume; 2 r. 50, 3 f., 5 r. Female costumes.

1955. 50th Anniv of Constitution.

1059	–	2 r. green and purple	1·75	40
1060	–	3 r. blue	3·50	60
1061	165	5 r. orange and green	4·25	95

DESIGNS—HORIZ: 2 r. Gateway of Parliament Building. VERT: 3 r. Winged Statue.

167 U.N. Emblem and Hemispheres

168 Wrestlers

1955. United Nations Day.

1077	167	1 r. orange and red	65	30
1078		2 r. 50 lt blue & blue	1·10	35

1955. International Success of Iranian Wrestlers.

1079	168	2 r. 50 multicoloured	3·25	70

169 Hospital Buildings

170

1956. Opening of Nemazi Hospital, Shiraz. Multicoloured.

1080	–	50 d. ($24 \times 33\frac{1}{2}$ mm)	70	40
1081	169	1 r. ($36 \times 24\frac{1}{2}$ mm)	2·75	60
1082	–	2 r. 50 ($24 \times 33\frac{1}{2}$ mm)	3·50	1·25
1083	–	5 r. (36×23 mm)	8·25	2·00
1084	–	10 r. ($24 \times 33\frac{1}{2}$ mm)	13·50	5·00

DESIGNS: 50 d. Hospital garden; 2 r. 50, Spear thrower; 5 r. Koran gate, Shiraz; 10 r. Poet Hafiz and his tomb.

1956. 10th Anniv of National Olympic Committee.

1085	170	5 r. lilac	15·00	5·50

171 Tusi's Tomb, Maragheh

172 Reveille

1956. 700th Death Anniv of Nasir ed-Din Tusi, 1201–74 (astronomer and scientist).

1086	171	1 r. orange	2·00	40
1087	–	2 r. 50 blue (Astrolabe)	4·00	60
1088	–	5 r. lilac and sepia (Portrait)	6·50	1·00

1956. National Scout Jamboree.

1089	172	2 r. 50 blue & ultram	7·00	3·50
1090	–	5 r. mauve and lilac	13·00	4·00

DESIGN: 5 r. Shah in scout's uniform and badge.

173

174 U.N. Emblem and Young People

1956. World Health Organization.
1091 **173** 6 r. mauve . . . . 1·60 70

1956. United Nations Day.
1092 **174** 1 r. green 50 30
1093 – 2 r. 50 blue and green . . 1·25 50
DESIGN: 2 r. 50, U.N. emblem and scales of justice.

175 Telecommunications Centre, Teheran

1956. Centenary of Persian Telegraphs.
1094 **175** 2 r. 50 green and blue . . 2·00 90
1095 – 6 r. mauve and pink . . . 6·00 1·40
DESIGN: 6 r. Telegraph poles and mosque.

176 Shah and Pres. Mirza

1956. Visit of President of Pakistan.
1096 **176** 1 r. multicoloured . . . . 1·00 20

177 Mohammed Riza Pahlavi **178**

1956.
1097 **177** 5 d. red and rose 10 10
1098 10 d. violet and blue . . . 10 10
1099 25 d. brown and sepia . . 10 10
1100 50 d. olive and sepia . . . 10 10
1101 1 r. green and brown . . 10 10
1102 1 r. 50 brown & mauve . . 50 10
1103 2 r. red and mauve . . . 50 10
1104 2 r. 50 blue & ultram . . 55 10
1105 3 r. bistre and brown . . 1·25 10
1106 5 r. red . . . . 1·50 10
1132 6 r. blue and light blue . . 2·00 10
1133 10 r. turquoise & green . . 2·50 10
1134 20 r. olive and green . . . 2·50 10
1135 30 r. sepia and blue . . . 15·00 80
1136 50 r. brown and sepia . . 26·00 80
1137 100 r. red & brt purple . . £160 4·00
1138 200 r. bistre and violet . . £100 32·00

1956.
1122 **178** 5 d. plum and violet . . . 10 10
1123 10 d. mauve & purple . . . 10 10
1124 25 d. orange and red . . . 10 10
1125 50 d. green and grey . . . 10 10
1126 1 r. turquoise & green . . 10 10
1127 1 r. 50 pur & mauve . . . 50 10
1128 2 r. turquoise and blue . . 55 10
1129 2 r. 50 turquoise & blue . . 55 10
1130 3 r. red and rose . . . . 1·00 10
1131 5 r. violet and blue . . . 95 10
1107 6 r. mauve and lilac . . . 1·40 10
1108 10 r. green and blue . . . 2·50 10
1109 20 r. blue and green . . . 3·50 15
1110 30 r. orange and red . . . 26·00 8·00
1111 50 r. sage and green . . . 13·00 2·00
1112 100 r. red and purple . . £425 30·00
1113 200 r. violet & purple . . £225 40·00

179 Lord Baden-Powell

180 Steam Express Train and Mosque

1957. Birth Centenary of Lord Baden-Powell (founder of Boy Scout movement).
1114 **179** 10 r. brown and green . . 4·00 2·00

1957. Inauguration of Teheran–Meshed Railway. Multicoloured.
1115 2 r. 50 Track and signal . . . 5·00 85
1116 5 r. Diesel train and map (horiz) . . . . 8·00 1·50
1117 10 r. Type **180** . . . . . . 18·00 8·75

181 President Gronchi and Shah

1957. Visit of President of Italy.
1118 **181** 2 r. grey, green & red . . 75 50
1119 – 6 r. blue, green & red . . 2·00 75
DESIGN: 6 r., Plaque and flags between ruins of Persepolis and Colosseum.

183 Queen Soraya and Ramsar Hotel

1957. 6th Medical Congress, Ramsar.
1120 **183** 2 r. green and blue . . . 1·00 20

184 Shah and King Faisal II of Iraq

1957. Visit of King of Iraq.
1121 **184** 2 r. blue, red & green . . 75 15

185 Globes within Laurel Sprays

1957. Int Cartographical Conf, Teheran.
1140 **185** 10 r. multicoloured . . . 4·00 65

186 "Flight"

187 "The Weightlifter"

1957. Air. United Nations Day.
1141 **186** 10 r. red and mauve . . . 1·10 60
1142 20 r. purple and violet . . 1·60 1·00

1957. Int Weightlifting Championships.
1143 **187** 10 r. blue, green & red . . 1·50 35

188 Radio Mast and Buildings

189 Oil Derrick and "Bowl of Flames"

1958. 30th Anniv of Iranian Broadcasting Service.
1144 **188** 10 r. sepia, buff & blue . . 1·75 65

1958. 50th Anniv of Iranian Oil Industry.
1145 **189** 2 r. brown, yell & grey . . 2·25 30
1146 10 r. brown, yell & blue . 5·75 80

190 Exhibition Emblem

191 Steam Train on Viaduct

1958. Brussels International Exn.
1147 **190** 2 r. 50 red 45 10
1148 6 r. red 80 20

1958. Inaug of Teheran–Tabriz Railway.
1149 **191** 6 r. lilac . . . . 12·00 3·00
1150 – 8 r. green . . . . 16·00 6·50
DESIGN: 8 r. Steam express train and route map.

192 Mohammed Riza Pahlavi

193 U.N. Emblem and Map of Persia

1958.
1162 **192** 5 d. violet 10 10
1163 5 d. brown 10 10
1164 10 d. red 10 10
1165 10 d. green 10 10
1166 10 d. turquoise 10 10
1167 25 d. red 10 10
1168 25 d. orange 20 10
1169 50 d. blue 20 10
1170 50 d. red 10 10
1171 1 r. green 35 10
1172 1 r. violet 35 10
1232 2 r. brown . . . . 2·50 10
1176 3 r. brown 50 10
1177 6 r. blue 40 10
1179 8 r. purple . . . . . . 1·40 10
1180 8 r. brown 50 10
1181 10 r. black 50 10
1182 14 r. blue . . . . 3·00 10
1183 14 r. green 50 10
1185 20 r. green . . . . . . 2·00 10
1186 30 r. red . . . . 2·50 20
1187 30 r. brown 50 10
1188 50 r. purple . . . . . . 26·00 25
1189 50 r. blue . . . . 1·40 10
1190 100 r. orange . . . . . . 2·50 75
1191 100 r. green . . . . . . £100 2·00
1192 200 r. green . . . . . . 26·00 1·40
1193 200 r. mauve . . . . . . £225 2·40

1958. United Nations Day.
1194 **193** 6 r. blue & light blue . . 75 60
1195 10 r. violet and green . . 95 80

194 Clasped Hands

195 Rudagi playing Lyre

1958. 10th Anniv of Declaration of Human Rights.
1196 **194** 6 r. brown & chocolate . . 35 20
1197 8 r. olive and green . . . 90 35

1958. 1100th Birth Anniv of Rudagi (poet and musician).
1198 **195** 2 r. 50 blue . . . . . . 2·75 25
1199 – 5 r. violet . . . . . . 5·75 45
1200 **195** 10 r. sepia . . . . . . 10·00 90
DESIGN: 5 r. Rudagi meditating.

196

1959. Red Cross Commemoration.
1201 **196** 1 r. multicoloured 85 20
1202 6 r. multicoloured . . . . 1·40 55

197 Wrestlers

198 Torch of Freedom

1959. World Wrestling Championships.
1203 **197** 6 r. multicoloured . . . . 4·25 75

1959. United Nations Day.
1204 **198** 6 r. red, brown & bistre . 65 25

199 Shah and President Khan

1959. Visit of President of Pakistan.
1205 **199** 6 r. multicoloured . . . . 2·50 45

200 I.L.O. Emblem

201 Pahlavi Foundation Bridge, Khorramshahr

1959. 40th Anniv of I.L.O.
1206 **200** 1 r. blue & light blue . . 50 20
1207 5 r. brown & lt brown . . 75 35

1960. Opening of Pahlavi Foundation Bridge, Khorramshahr.
1208 **201** 1 r. blue and brown . . . 75 10
1209 – 5 r. green and blue . . . 1·00 30
DESIGN: 5 r. Close-up view of bridge.

202 "Uprooted Tree"

203 Insecticide Sprayer

1960. World Refugee Year.
1210 – 1 r. blue 10 10
1211 **202** 6 r. black and green . . . 35 20
DESIGN: 1 r. "Uprooted tree" and columns.

1960. Anti-Malaria Campaign.
1212 – 1 r. blk & red on yell . . 30 15
1213 **203** 2 r. blue, blk & light-bl . . 80 20
1214 – 3 r. blk & red on green . . 1·40 50
DESIGNS (30 × 37 mm.): 1 r., 3 r. Different views of mosquito crossed out in red.

204 Polo Player

206 Scout Emblem within Flower

205 Shah and King Hussein

1960. "Olympic Games Week".
1215 **204** 1 r. purple 50 20
1216 – 6 r. violet and blue . . . 1·10 50
DESIGN: 6 r. Archer.

1960. Visit of King of Jordan.
1217 **205** 6 r. multicoloured . . . . 2·50 60

1960. 3rd National Scout Jamboree.
1218 **206** 1 r. green 30 10
1219 – 6 r. ochre, sep & blue . . 60 20
DESIGN: 6 r. Scout camp, Persepolis.

207 Shah and Queen Farah

1960. Royal Wedding.

1220 207 1 r. green . . . . 1·00 40
1221 5 r. blue . . . . 2·75 70

208 UN Emblem

209 Shah and Queen Elizabeth II

1960. 15th Anniv of U.N.O.

1222 208 6 r. sepia, blue & bistre . 55 15

1961. Visit of Queen Elizabeth II.

1223 209 1 r. brown 65 10
1224 6 r. blue . . . . 1·10 20

210 Girl playing Pan-pipes

1961. International Music Congress, Teheran.

1225 210 1 r. stone and brown . . 50 10
1226 – 6 r. slate 90 15

DESIGN—(24 × 39½ mm): 6 r. Safiaddin Anmavi (musician).

211 Royal Family

1961. Birth of Crown Prince.

1227 211 1 r. purple . . . . 1·00 50
1228 6 r. blue . . . . 4·50 1·25

212 U.N. Emblem and Birds

213 Tree-planting

1961. United Nations Day.

1236 212 2 r. red and blue 15 10
1237 6 r. violet and blue . . . 45 20

1962. Afforestation Week.

1238 213 2 r. blue, cream & green . 25 10
1239 6 r. green, blue & ultram . 55 20

214 Worker

215 Family on Map

1962. Workers' Day.

1240 214 2 r. multicoloured 15 10
1241 6 r. multicoloured 45 30

1962. Social Insurance.

1242 215 2 r. vio, black & yellow . 15 10
1243 6 r. blue, blk & lt blue . . 45 30

216 Sugar Plantation

217 Karaj Dam

1962. Sugar Cane Production.

1244 216 2 r. green, bl & ultram . . 25 15
1245 6 r. bl, cream & ultram . . 65 30

1962. Inauguration of Karaj Dam.

1246 217 2 r. green & brown . . . 1·00 10
1247 6 r. bl & ultramarine . . 1·40 20

218 Sefid Rud Dam

1962. Inauguration of Sefid Rud Dam.

1248 218 2 r. buff, blue & myrtle . . 1·00 15
1249 – 6 r. black, blue & brown . 1·40 30

DESIGN: 6 r. Distant view of dam.

219 U.N. Emblem

1962. 15th Anniv of U.N.E.S.C.O.

1250 219 2 r. black, green & red . . 40 15
1251 6 r. blue, green & red . . 85 30

220 Arrow piercing Mosquito

221 Mohammed Riza Pahlavi

222 Shah and Palace of Darius, Persepolis

223 Oil Pipelines

1962. Malaria Eradication.

1252 220 2 r. black and green . . . 15 10
1253 – 6 r. blue and red 50 20
1254 – 10 r. ultram and blue . . 90 25

DESIGNS—VERT: (29½ × 34½ mm): 6 r. Mosquito and insecticide-sprayer. HORIZ: (As Type **220**)—10 r. Globe and campaign emblem.

1962.

1255 221 5 d. green 10 10
1256 10 d. brown 10 10
1257 25 d. blue 10 10
1336 50 d. turquoise 10 10
1337 1 r. orange 15 10
1338 2 r. violet 20 10
1339 5 r. brown 65 10
1340 222 6 r. blue . . . . 1·00 10
1341 8 r. green 70 10
1342 10 r. blue . . . . 1·00 10
1265a 11 r. green 60 10
1266a 14 r. violet . . . . 1·00 10
1345 20 r. brown . . . . 1·10 20
1346 50 r. red . . . . 1·25 45

1962. 2nd Petroleum Symposium of Economic Commission for Asia and the Far East.

1269 223 6 r. brown and blue . . . 40 15
1270 14 r. brown and grey . . . 85 35

224 Hippocrates and Avicenna

225 New Houses

1962. W.H.O. Medical Congress, Teheran.

1271 224 2 r. blue, brn & cream . . 1·00 15
1272 6 r. blue, sage & green . . 1·50 30

1962. United Nations Day.

1273 225 6 r. blue and indigo . . . 45 15
1274 – 14 r. green and blue . . . 95 20

DESIGN—HORIZ: 14 r. Laying foundation stone.

226 "Bouquet for the Crown Prince"

1962. Crown Prince's Birthday.

1275 226 6 r. blue . . . . 1·50 30
1276 14 r. green . . . . 3·00 70

227 Persian Gulf Map

228 Hilton Hotel, Teheran

1962. Persian Gulf Seminar.

1277 227 6 r. blue, pink & pale bl . 40 15
1278 14 r. blue, flesh & pink . . 85 30

1963. Opening of Royal Teheran Hilton Hotel.

1279 228 6 r. blue . . . . 1·40 20
1280 14 r. brown . . . . . . 2·25 45

229 Refugees

1963. Earthquake Relief Fund.

1281 229 14 r. + 6 r. bl, brn & grn . 90 60

230 Mohammed Riza Shah Dam

1963. Inaug of Mohammed Riza Shah Dam.

1282 230 6 r. multicoloured . . . . 1·75 30
1283 14 r. multicoloured . . . 3·75 65

231 Worker with Pickaxe

232 Bird and Globe

1963. Workers' Day.

1283a 231 2 r. black and yellow . . 45 10
1283b 6 r. black and blue . . . 60 20

1963. Freedom from Hunger.

1284 232 2 r. ultram, bl & bis . . . 50 10
1285 – 6 r. black, bistre & blue . 90 20
1286 – 14 r. bistre and green . . 2·00 45

DESIGNS: 6 r. Globe and ears of wheat (stylized); 14 r. Globe encircled by scroll, and campaign emblem.

233 Shah and Scroll

1963. Agrarian Reform Act.

1287 233 6 r. green and blue . . . 90 20
1288 14 r. green and yellow . . 2·00 55

234 Shah and King Frederick

1963. Visit of King of Denmark.

1289 234 6 r. blue and indigo . . . 1·25 25
1290 14 r. brown and sepia . . 3·00 50

235 Flags of Iran and India; Ibn Sina Mosque, Teheran, and Taj Mahal, India

1963. Visit of President Radhakrishnan of India.

1291 235 6r. multicoloured . . . . 1·60 25
1292 14 r. multicoloured . . . 3·50 50

236 Shahnaz Dam

1963. Inauguration of Shahnaz Dam.

1293 236 6 r. ultram, bl & grn . . . 1·50 25
1294 14 r. green, blue & buff . . 2·25 50

237 Centenary Emblem

238 Shah and Queen Juliana

1963. Red Cross Centenary.

1295 237 6 r. multicoloured . . . . 1·75 30
1296 14 r. grey, red & buff . . 3·75 60

1963. Visit of Queen of the Netherlands.

1304 238 6 r. blue & ultramarine . . 2·50 30
1305 14 r. green & black . . . 3·25 60

240 Students in Class

1963. Formation of Literacy Teaching Corps.

1306 240 6 r. multicoloured . . . . 1·50 15
1307 14 r. multicoloured . . . 2·50 30

241 Pres. De Gaulle and View of Teheran

1963. Visit of President of France.

1308 241 6 r. ultramarine & blue . . 1·75 30
1309 14 r. brown and ochre . . 3·50 60

242 Plant, Route Map and Emblem

1963. Opening of Chemical Fertiliser Plant, Shiraz.

1310 **242** 6 r. black, yellow & red . 1·75 30
1311 – 14 r. black, blue & yell . . 3·50 60

DESIGN—HORIZ: 14 r. Fertiliser plant and emblem.

243 Pres. Lubke and Shah Mosque, Isfahan

1963. Visit of President of German Federal Republic.

1312 **243** 6 r. blue and violet . . . 1·75 30
1313 14 r. brown and grey . . 3·50 55

244 U.N. Emblem

1963. United Nations Day.

1314 **244** 8 r. multicoloured . . . . 1·25 20

245 Aircraft crossing U.N. Emblem
246 Crown Prince Riza

1963. Iranian Air Force in Congo.

1315 **245** 6 r. multicoloured . . . . 1·25 20

1963. Children's Day.

1316 **246** 2 r. brown 75 15
1317 6 r. blue . . . . 1·00 25

247 Chairman Brezhnev

1963. Visit of Chairman of Soviet Presidium.

1318 **247** 5 r. multicoloured . . . . 1·75 30
1319 11 r. multicoloured . . . 2·75 50

248 Ataturk's Mausoleum

1963. 25th Death Anniv of Kemal Ataturk.

1320 **248** 4 r. brown, grey & grn . . 1·50 15
1321 – 5 r. black, red & yellow . 1·75 20

DESIGN: 5 r. Kemal Ataturk.

249 Scales of Justice and Globe
250 Mother and Child

1963. 15th Anniv of Declaration of Human Rights.

1322 **249** 6 r. black, blue & green . 1·10 20
1323 14 r. blk, cream & brn . . 1·75 30

1963. Mothers Day.

1324 **250** 2 r. multicoloured . . . . 1·00 15
1325 4 r. multicoloured . . . . 2·00 20

251 Cogwheel and Map
252 Hand with Document (Profit-sharing)

1963. Industrial Development.

1326 **251** 8 r. bl, cream & turquoise 1·75 30

1964. Six-Point Reform Law.

1327 **252** 2 r. brn, violet & blue . . 40 10
1328 – 4 r. brown and grey . . . 1·10 15
1329 – 6 r. multicoloured . . . . 2·00 20
1330 – 8 r. multicoloured . . . . 2·25 25
1331 – 10 r. red, green & dp grn . 2·50 30
1332 – 12 r. brown and red . . . 3·25 35

DESIGNS: 4 r. Factory and documents on scales (Sale of Shares to Workers); 6 r. Worker on Globe (Education Corps); 8 r. Tractor (Land reform); 10 r. Trees (Nationalization of forests); 12 r. Silhouettes within gateway (Votes for Women).

253 U.N. Emblem
254 Blossom

1964. 20th Economic Commission for Asia and the Far East Session, Teheran.

1347 **253** 14 r. black and green . . 1·25 30

1964. New Year Greetings.

1348 **254** 50 d. orge, sepia & grn . . 15 10
1349 1 r. orange, black & bl . . 15 10

255 Weather Vane
256 "Tourism"

1964. World Meteorological Day.

1350 **255** 6 r. violet and blue . . . 75 20

1964. 1st Anniv of Iranian Tourist Organization (INTO).

1351 **256** 6 r. green, vio & black . . 90 20
1352 – 11 r. orange, brn & blk . . 1·60 45

DESIGN: 11 r. Winged beasts, column and INTO emblem.

257 Rudagi (blind poet)
258 Sculptured Head

1964. Opening of Blind Institute.

1353 **257** 6 r. blue 90 20
1354 8 r. brown . . . . 1·60 30

1964. "7000 Years of Persian Art" Exhibition.

1355 **258** 2 r. blue and grey . . . . 1·50 10
1356 – 4 r. ultramarine & blue . . 5·00 20
1357 – 6 r. yellow and brown . . 3·00 30
1358 – 10 r. green and yellow . . 5·00 50

DESIGNS—HORIZ: 4 r. Sumerian war chariot on map. VERT: 6 r. Golden cup with lion decorations; 10 r. Sculptured head of man.

259 Shah and Emperor Haile Selassie

1964. Visit of Emperor of Ethiopia.

1359 **259** 6 r. ultramarine & blue . . 1·25 20

260 Congress Emblem
261 Bark Beetle under Lens

1964. 2nd Iranian Dental Assn Congress.

1360 **260** 2 r. red, dp bl & bl . . 40 15
1361 – 4 r. multicoloured . . . 1·00 30

DESIGN: 4 r. "2 IDA" in symbolic form.

1964. Inauguration of Plant Parasites and Diseases Research Institute.

1362 – 2 r. brown, red & buff . . 1·00 15
1363 **261** 6 r. indigo, brown & bl . 1·75 30

DESIGN: 2 r. Microscope, plants and research centre.

262 Plaque
263 Eleanor Roosevelt

1964. Mehregan Festival.

1364 **262** 8 r. red and yellow . . . 1·25 15

1964. Eleanor Roosevelt Commemoration

1365 **263** 10 r. blue and violet . . . 1·50 25

264 Clasped Hands and U.N. Emblem
265 Gymnast

1964. United Nations Day.

1366 **264** 6 r. multicoloured 85 15
1367 – 14 r. red, blue & orge . . 1·40 30

DESIGN: 14 r. U.N. and "Bird" emblems.

1964. Olympic Games, Tokyo.

1368 **265** 4 r. sepia, turq & brn . . 70 15
1369 – 6 r. red and blue . . . . 1·00 25

DESIGN—Diamond (39 × 39 mm): 6 r. Polo.

266 Crown Prince Riza
267 Conference and U.N. Emblems

1964. Children's Day.

1370 **266** 1 r. green and brown . . 50 10
1371 2 r. red and blue . . . 1·25 15
1372 6 r. blue and red . . . . 2·25 30

1964. Petro-Chemical Conf and Gas Seminar.

1373 **267** 6 r. multicoloured 50 15
1374 8 r. multicoloured . . . . 1·00 25

268 Shah and King Baudouin

1964. Visit of King of Belgium.

1375 **268** 6 r. black, orge & yell . . 40 15
1376 8 r. black, orge & grn . . 85 15

269 Rhazes

1964. 1100th Birth Anniv of Rhazes (Zakariya Ar-Razi, alchemist).

1377 **269** 2 r. multicoloured 60 15
1378 6 r. multicoloured 90 20

270 Shah and King Olav

1965. Visit of King of Norway.

1379 **270** 2 r. mauve and purple . . 50 15
1380 4 r. green and olive . . . 90 20

271 Crown, Map and Star
272 Woman and U.N. Emblem

1965. Six-Point Reform Law.

1381 **271** 2 r. orange, blk & blue . . 30 15

1965. 18th Session of United Nations Commission on Status of Women, Teheran.

1382 **272** 6 r. black, blue & lt blue . 45 10
1383 8 r. blue, red & lt red . . 80 15

273 Festival Plant
274 Pres. Bourguiba and Minarets

1965. New Year Festival.

1384 **273** 50 d. multicoloured . . . 10 10
1385 1 r. multicoloured 20 10

1965. Visit of President of Tunisia.

1386 **274** 4 r. multicoloured 75 15

275 Map of Oil Pipelines

1965. 14th Anniv of Nationalisation of Oil Industry.

1387 **275** 6 r. multicoloured 90 20
1388 14 r. multicoloured . . . 1·75 40

276 I.T.U. Emblem and Symbols

1965. Centenary of I.T.U.
1389 **276** 14 r. red and grey 90 30

277 I.C.Y. Emblem

1965. International Co-operation Year.
1390 **277** 10 r. green and blue 1·40 20

278 Boeing 727-100 and Airline Emblem

1965. Inaug of Jet Services by Iranian National Airlines.
1391 **278** 14 r. multicoloured 1·00 35

279 "Co-operation" (Hands holding Book)

1965. 1st Anniv of Regional Development Co-operation Plan. Multicoloured.
1392 2 r. Type **279** 20 10
1393 4 r. Globe and flags of Turkey, Iran and Pakistan (40½ × 24½ mm) 30 15

280 Moot Emblem and Arabesque Pattern

1965. Middle East Rover (Scout) Moot.
1394 **280** 2 r. multicoloured 40 15

281 Gateway of Parliament Building

1965. 60th Anniv of Iranian Constitution.
1397 **281** 2 r. brown and mauve 30 10

282 Congress Emblem

283 Teacher and Class

1965. Iranian Dental Congress.
1398 **282** 6 r. blue, mve & silver 35 15

1965. World Eradication of Illiteracy Congress, Teheran. Multicoloured.
1399 2 r. Type **283** 10 10
1400 5 r. Globe showing alphabets (25 × 30 mm.) 20 10
1401 6 r. U.N.E.S.C.O. emblem and symbols (diamond, 36 × 36 mm.) 30 15
1402 8 r. Various scripts (35 × 23 mm.) 30 15
1403 14 r. Shah and multi-lingual inscriptions (41 × 52 mm.) 1·10 30

284 Shah Riza Pahlavi

1965. 25th Anniv (actually 24th) of Shah's Accession.
1404 **284** 1 r. red and grey 35 10
1405 2 r. red and yellow 70 10

285 Congress Emblem

1965. 14th Medical Congress.
1406 **285** 5 r. ultram, bl & gold 40 10

286 President Jonas

1965. Visit of President of Austria.
1407 **286** 6 r. blue and brown 85 20

287 Plaque

1965. Mehregan Festival.
1408 **287** 4 r. multicoloured 30 15
See also No. 1464.

289 U.N. Emblem and "Flowers"

290 Emblem and "Arches"

1965. United Nations Day.
1409 **289** 5 r. multicoloured 30 15

1965. Iranian Industrial Exn, Teheran.
1410 **290** 3 r. multicoloured 20 10

291 Crown Prince Riza

292 "Weightlifting"

1965. Children's Day.
1411 **291** 2 r. choc, brn & gold 40 10

1965. World Weightlifting Championships, Teheran.
1412 **292** 10 r. mve, vio & blue 45 15

293 Open Book

295 Scales of Justice

294 Shah and King Faisal

1965. Book Week.
1416 **293** 8 r. multicoloured 40 20

1965. Visit of King of Saudi Arabia.
1417 **294** 4 r. brown and bistre 70 15

1965. Human Rights Day.
1418 **295** 14 r. multicoloured 45 20

296 Tractor (Land Reform)

1966. 3rd Anniv of Shah's White Revolution (Parliamentary Assent to Shah's Reform Plan).
1419 **296** 1 r. brown and yellow 10 10
1420 – 2 r. green & light green 15 10
1421 – 3 r. brown and silver 15 10
1422 – 4 r. violet & light violet 15 10
1423 – 5 r. lake and red 15 10
1424 – 6 r. brown and bistre 20 10
1425 – 7 r. ultramarine & blue 30 15
1426 – 8 r. ultramarine & blue 30 15
1427 – 9 r. brown & light brown 35 20
DESIGNS: 2 r. Trees (Nationalization of Forests); 3 r. Cogwheel emblem (Sale of shares to workers); 4 r. Cylinders (Profit-sharing); 5 r. Parliament gateway (Votes for Women); 6 r. Blackboard and pupils (Education Corps); 7 r. Staff of Aesculapius (Medical Corps); 8 r. Scales (Justice); 9 r. Girders (Construction Corps).

297 Mohammed Riza Pahlavi

298 Shah and Ruins of Persepolis

1966.
1428 **297** 5 d. green 10 10
1429 10 d. brown 10 10
1430 25 d. blue 10 10
1431 50 d. turquoise 10 10
1432 1 r. orange 10 10
1433 2 r. violet 10 10
1434 4 r. brown 3·00 10
1435 5 r. sepia 15 10
1436 **298** 6 r. blue 15 10
1437 8 r. green 30 10
1438 10 r. blue 20 10
1439 11 r. green 70 10
1440 14 r. violet 1·40 10
1441 20 r. brown 10·00 10
1442 50 r. red 3·50 10
1443 100 r. blue 9·00 40
1444 200 r. brown 7·00 75

299 Nurse taking Oath

300 Narcissus

1966. Nurses' Day.
1445 **299** 5 r. blue and deep blue 25 15
1446 5 r. mauve and red 25 15

1966. New Year Festival.
1447 **300** 50 d. multicoloured 15 10
1448 1 r. multicoloured 15 10
See also Nos. 1530/3.

301 Oil Rigs

1966. Inauguration of Six New Oil Companies in Persian Gulf.
1449 **301** 14 r. black, purple & bl 70 20

302 Radar Aerial

1966. C.E.N.T.O. (Iran, Pakistan and Turkey) Telecommunications Organization.
1450 **302** 2 r. green 15 10
1451 – 4 r. orange and blue 15 10
1452 – 6 r. grey and purple 25 10
1453 – 8 r. indigo and blue 35 10
1454 – 10 r. brown and ochre 45 30
DESIGNS—VERT: 4 r. Aerial and radio "waves"; 6 r. "CENTO" and emblem; 8 r. Emblem and "waves"; 10 r. Bowl aerial and "waves".

303 W.H.O. Building

1966. Inaug of W.H.O. Headquarters, Geneva.
1455 **303** 10 r. black, blue & yellow 35 25

304 Globe Emblem and Motto

1966. Conference of International Women's Council, Teheran.
1456 **304** 6 r. multicoloured 20 10
1457 8 r. multicoloured 30 15

305 U.N.E.S.C.O. Emblem

1966. Air. 20th Anniv of U.N.E.S.C.O.
1458 **305** 14 r. multicoloured 75 30

306 Ruins of Persepolis, Map and Globe

1966. Int Iranology Congress, Teheran.
1459 **306** 14 r. multicoloured 50 15

307 Medical Emblem

1966. 15th Medical Congress, Teheran.
1460 **307** 4 r. gold, blue & ultram 30 10

308 Parliament Gateway

1966. 55th Interparliamentary Union Conference, Teheran.
1461 **308** 6 r. grn, blue and red 25 10
1462 – 8 r. grn, blue & mauve 25 15
DESIGN: 8 r. Senate Building.

309 President Sunay

1966. Visit of President of Turkey.
1463 **309** 6 r. brown and violet . . 30 10

1966. Mehregan Festival. Plaque design similar to T **287** but vert (30 × 40 mm).
1464 6 r. brown and bistre 25 10

310 Farmers

1966. Rural Courts of Justice.
1465 **310** 5 r. brown and bistre . . 35 25

311 U.N. Emblem

1966. U.N. Day and 21st Anniv of U.N.O.
1466 **311** 6 r. brown and black . . 20 10

312 Crown Prince
313 I.W.O. Emblem

1966. Children's Day.
1467 **312** 1 r. blue 30 10
1468 2 r. violet 30 10

1966. Iranian Women's Organization.
1469 **313** 5 r. blue, black & gold . . 15 10

314 Strip of Film

1966. 1st Children's Film Festival, Teheran.
1470 **314** 4 r. black, purple & vio . 30 10

315 Counting on the Fingers
316 Cover of Book

1966. National Census.
1471 **315** 6 r. brown and grey . . . 30 10

1966. Book Week.
1472 **316** 8 r. brown, ochre & blue . 20 15

317 Riza Shah Pahlavi

1966. Riza Shah Pahlavi Commemoration.
1473 **317** 1 r. brown 60 10
1474 1 r. blue 60 10
1475 – 2 r. blue 60 10
1476 – 2 r. green 60 10
Nos. 1475/6 show Riza Shah Pahlavi bare-headed.

318 E.R.O.P.A. Emblem and Map

1966. 4th General Assembly of Public Administrators Organization (E.R.O.P.A.).
1477 **318** 8 r. brown and green . . 30 15

319 Shah with Farmers

1967. 5th Anniv of Land Reform Laws.
1485 **319** 6 r. brown, yellow & bis . 30 10

320 Torch and Stars

1967. 4th Anniv of Shah's White Revolution.
1486 **320** 2 r. multicoloured 45 10
1487 – 6 r. multicoloured 60 15
DESIGN: 6 r. Shah acknowledging greetings.

321 Golden "Bull"

1967. Museum Week. Multicoloured.
1488 3 r. Type **321** 20 10
1489 5 r. Golden "leopard" 25 15
1490 8 r. Capital with rams' heads . 60 25

322 Planting a Tree
323 Goldfish

1967. Tree-planting Week.
1491 **322** 8 r. green and brown . . 35 10

1967. New Year Festival.
1492 **323** 1 r. blue, red & brown . . 10 10
1493 – 8 r. ultram, bl & red . . . 60 15
DESIGN—35 × 27 mm: 8 r. Barn swallows.

324 Microscope, Horses and Emblem

1967. 2nd Veterinary Congress.
1494 **324** 5 r. red, black & grey . . 20 10

325 Pres. Arif and Mosques

1967. Visit of President of Iraq.
1495 **325** 6 r. green and blue . . . 30 10

326 U.N. Emblem and Fireworks

1967. U.N. Stamp Day.
1496 **326** 5 r. multicoloured 30 10

327 Map showing Pipeline Routes

1967. Nationalization of Oil Industry.
1497 **327** 6 r. multicoloured 60 15

328 Fencing

1967. Int Youth Fencing Championships, Teheran.
1498 **328** 5 r. yellow and violet . . 30 10

329 Shah and King Bhumibol

1967. Visit of King of Thailand.
1499 **329** 6 r. brown & lt brown . . 40 20

330 Emblem, Old and Young Couples

1967. 15th Anniv of Social Insurance Scheme.
1500 **330** 5 r. blue and bistre . . . 20 10

331 Skiing

1967. Olympic Committee Meeting, Teheran.
1501 **331** 3 r. brown and black . . 15 10
1502 – 6 r. multicoloured 15 10
1503 – 8 r. brown and blue . . . 25 15
DESIGNS: 6 r. Olympic "shield"; 8 r. Wrestling.

332 "LIONS" and Lions Head

1967. 50th Anniv of Lions International. Mult.
1504 3 r. Type **332** 15 10
1505 7 r. Lions emblem (36 × 42 mm) 40 15

333 President Stoica

1967. Visit of President of Rumania.
1506 **333** 6 r. blue and orange . . . 25 10

334 I.T.Y. Emblem
335 Iranian Pavilion

1967. International Tourist Year
1507 **334** 3 r. blue and red 10 10

1967. World Fair, Montreal.
1508 **335** 4 r. red, gold & brown . . 10 10
1509 10 r. brown, gold & red . 20 10

336 First Persian Stamp
337 Globe and Schoolchildren

1967. Stamp Centenary.
1510 **336** 6 r. purple, blue & lt blue . 20 10
1511 8 r. purple, myrtle & grn . 25 10

1967. Campaign Against Illiteracy.
1512 **337** 3 r. violet and blue . . . 15 10
1513 5 r. brown and yellow . . 15 10

338 "Musician"
339 "Helping Hand"

1967. International Musical Education in Oriental Countries Conference, Teheran.
1514 **338** 14 r. purple and brown . . 45 20

1967. 1st "S.O.S." Children's Village in Iran.
1515 **339** 8 r. brown and yellow . . 1·60 60

340 Winged Ram
341 U.N. Emblem

1967. 1st Shiraz Arts Festival, Persepolis.
1516 **340** 8 r. brown and bistre . . 35 10

1967. United Nations Day.
1517 **341** 6 r. blue and bistre . . . 20 10

342 Shah Mohammed Riza Pahlavi and Empress Farah

343 Crown Prince Riza

1967. Coronation of Shah and Empress Farah.
1518 **342** 2 r. brown, blue & silver . 35 10
1519 10 r. violet, blue & silver . 70 25
1520 14 r. multicoloured . . . 1·10 25

1967. Children's Day.
1521 **343** 2 r. violet and silver . . . 15 10
1522 8 r. brown and silver . . 40 15

344 Pres. G. Traikov

345 Scout Emblem and Neckerchiefs

1967. Visit of President of Bulgaria.
1523 **344** 10 r. brown and violet . . 20 10

1967. Boy Scouts Co-operation Week.
1524 **345** 8 r. brown and green . . 40 15

346 "Co-operation" (linked hands)

347 Shaikh Sabah

1967. Co-operation Year.
1525 **346** 6 r. multicoloured 20 10

1968. Visit of Shaikh of Kuwait.
1526 **347** 10 r. green and blue . . . 25 10

348 Shah and Text of Reform Plan

1968. 5th Anniv of Shah's White Revolution.
1527 **348** 2 r. green, sepia & flesh . 40 10
1528 8 r. violet, green & blue . 55 10
1529 14 r. brown, blue & mve . 80 20

1968. New Year Festival. As T **300**. Mult.
1530 1 r. Almond blossom 10 10
1531 2 r. Red tulips 10 10
1532 2 r. Yellow tulips 15 10
1533 6 r. Festival dancer 65 10

349 Oil Technician and Rig

350 W.H.O. Emblem

1968. National Oil Industry.
1534 **349** 14 r. black, yellow & grn . 45 10

1968. 20th Anniv of W.H.O.
1535 **350** 14 r. orange, blue & pur . 40 10

351 Ancient Chariot (sculpture)

353 Human Rights Emblem

352 Shah and King Hassan

1968. 5th World Congress of Persian Archaeology and Art, Teheran.
1536 **351** 8 r. multicoloured 25 10

1968. Visit of King of Morocco.
1537 **352** 6 r. violet and flesh . . . 55 15

1968. Human Rights Conference, Teheran.
1538 **353** 8 r. red and green 15 10
1539 – 14 r. ultramarine & blue . 20 15
DESIGN: 14 r. As Type **353**, but rearranged, and inscr "INTERNATIONAL CONFERENCE ON HUMAN RIGHTS—TEHERAN 1968".

354 Footballer

355 Oil Refinery

1968. Asian Football Cup Finals, Teheran.
1540 **354** 8 r. multicoloured 20 10
1541 10 r. multicoloured . . . 40 15

1968. Inauguration of Teheran Oil Refinery.
1542 **355** 14 r. multicoloured . . . 55 25

356 Empress Farah in Guides' Uniform

357 Mosquito Emblem

1968. Iranian Girl Guides "Great Camp".
1543 **356** 4 r. blue and purple . . . 75 15
1544 6 r. brown and red . . 1·00 25

1968. 8th International Tropical Medicine and Malaria Congresses, Teheran.
1545 **357** 6 r. purple and black . . 20 10
1546 14 r. green and purple . . 45 15

358 Allegory of Literacy

359 "Horseman" and "Flower"

1968. World Illiteracy Eradication Campaign Day.
1547 **358** 6 r. blue, brown & lilac . 15 10
1548 14 r. green, brown & yell . 30 10

1968. 2nd Shiraz Arts Festival, Persepolis.
1549 **359** 14 r. multicoloured . . . 45 15

MINIMUM PRICE

The minimum price quoted is 10p which represents a handling charge rather than a basis for valuing common stamps. For further notes about prices see introductory pages.

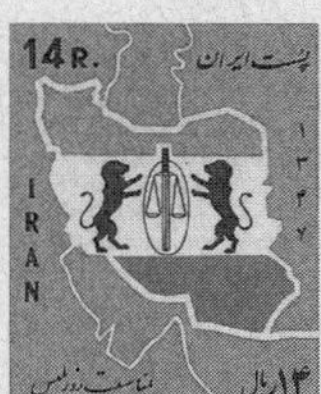

360 Police Emblem on Map

361 Interpol Emblem

1968. Police Day.
1550 **360** 14 r. multicoloured . . . 90 15

1968. 37th Interpol General Assembly.
1551 **361** 10 r. purple, blk & blue . 50 15

362 U.N. Emblem and Dove

1968. United Nations Day.
1552 **362** 14 r. ultram and blue . . 35 15

363 Empress Farah

1968. 1st Anniv of Coronation. Mult.
1553 6 r. Type **363** . . . . 2·50 1·00
1554 8 r. Shah Mohammed Riza Pahlavi . . . . 2·50 1·00
1555 10 r. Family group . . . . . 2·50 1·00

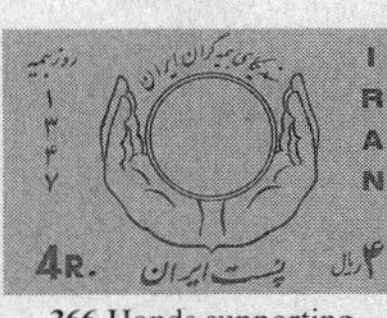

364 Imperial Crown and Bulls' Heads Capital (festival emblem)

365 "Landscape"

1968. National Festival of Art and Culture, Teheran.
1556 **364** 14 r. multicoloured . . . 45 15

1968. Children's Day. Children's Paintings. Multicoloured.
1557 2 r. Type **365** 10 10
1558 3 r. "Boat and House" (35 × 29 mm) 15 10
1559 5 r. "Flowers" (35 × 29 mm) . 20 10

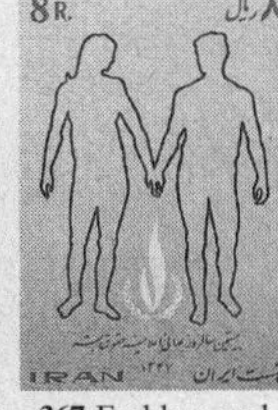

366 Hands supporting Globe

367 Emblem and Human Figures

1968. Insurance Day.
1560 **366** 4 r. blue and grey 10 10
1561 – 5 r. multicoloured 20 10
1562 – 8 r. multicoloured 15 10
1563 – 10 r. multicoloured . . . 75 20
DESIGNS: 5 r. Factory aflame ("Fire risk"); 8 r. Urban workers ("Life"); 10 r. Insurance Institute emblem and transport ("Travel insurance").

1968. 20th Anniv of Declaration of Human Rights.
1564 **367** 8 r. pur, ultram & bl . . . 20 10

368 Justice, Construction Corps and Medical Corps

1969. 6th Anniv of Shah's White Revolution. Each green, brown and lilac.
1565 2 r. Type **368** 30 10
1566 4 r. Working conditions, civil engineering and irrigation . 40 15
1567 6 r. Land reform, nationalization of forests and sale of shares to workers 50 20
1568 8 r. Profit-sharing, votes for women and education corps . 80 20
Nos. 1565/8, each showing symbols of three of the reforms, were issued, se-tenant, forming a composite design of a rosette.

369 Shah Mohammed Riza Pahlavi

1969. 10,000th Day of Shah's Reign.
1569 **369** 6 r. brown, red & blue . . 55 15

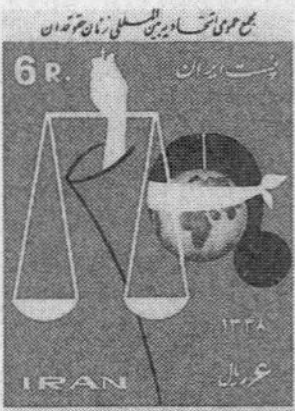

370 Goldfinch

1969. New Year Festival. Multicoloured.
1570 1 r. Type **370** 30 10
1571 2 r. Ring-necked Pheasant . . 30 10
1572 8 r. Roses 70 15

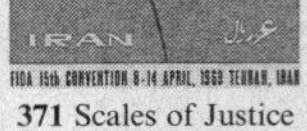

371 Scales of Justice and "Blindfold Globe"

372 Symbols of I.L.O.

1969. 15th FIDA (Female Jurists) Convention, Teheran.
1573 **371** 6 r. black and blue . . . 30 10

1969. 50th Anniv of I.L.O.
1574 **372** 10 r. violet and blue . . . 30 10

373 Wrestling "Throw"

1969. 3rd Aryamehr Cup International Wrestling Championships.
1575 **373** 10 r. multicoloured . . . 40 10

374 "Flower and Birds" 375 Mask and Cord

1969. World Handicrafts Day.
1576 **374** 10 r. multicoloured . . . 40 10

1969. "Philia 1969". Outdoor Course for Scout Patrol Leaders.
1577 **375** 6 r. multicoloured 40 15

376 Mughal Miniature (Pakistan)

1969. 5th Anniv of Regional co-operation for Development. Miniatures. Multicoloured.
1578 25 r. Type **376** . . . . 1·10 50
1579 25 r. "Kneeling Figure" (Safavi, Iran) . . . . 1·10 50
1580 25 r. "Suleiman the Magnificent and Court" (Ottoman, Turkey) . . . . 1·10 50

377 Astronauts on Moon

1969. 1st Man on the Moon.
1581 **377** 24 r. brown, blue & buff . 2·50 85

378 "Education" (quotation from Shah's Declaration)

1969. Education Reform Conference.
1582 **378** 10 r. red, green & buff . . 40 20

379 Oil Rig

1969. 10th Anniv of Iranian–Italian Marine Drilling Project.
1583 **379** 8 r. multicoloured 70 15

380 Festival Emblem 381 Thumb-print and Cross

1969. Third Shiraz Arts Festival.
1584 **380** 6 r. multicoloured 15 10
1585 8 r. multicoloured 25 10

1969. International Anti-Illiteracy Campaign.
1586 **381** 4 r. multicoloured 20 10

382 Shah, Persepolis and U.P.U. Emblem

1969. 16th U.P.U. Congress, Tokyo.
1587 **382** 10 r. multicoloured . . . 65 20
1588 14 r. multicoloured . . . 1·60 30

383 Fair Emblem 384 "Justice"

1969. 2nd International Asian Trade Fair, Teheran. Multicoloured.
1589 8 r. Type **383** 15 10
1590 14 r. As T **383**, but inscr "ASIA 69" 20 10
1591 20 r. Emblem and sections of globe (horiz) 50 20

1969. Rural Courts of Justice Day.
1592 **384** 8 r. brown and green . . 30 10

385 U.N. Emblem 386 Festival Emblem

1969. 25th Anniv of United Nations Day.
1593 **385** 2 r. blue and pale blue . . 15 10

1969. National Festival of Art and Culture, Teheran.
1594 **386** 2 r. multicoloured 35 10

387 "In the Garden" 388 Global Emblem

1969. Children's Week. Children's drawings. Multicoloured.
1595 1 r. Type **387** 15 10
1596 2 r. "Three Children" (horiz) . . 20 10
1597 5 r. "Mealtime" (horiz) . . . 50 15

1969. National Association of Parents and Teachers Congress, Teheran.
1598 **388** 8 r. brown and blue . . . 20 10

389 Earth Station 391 Mahatma Gandhi

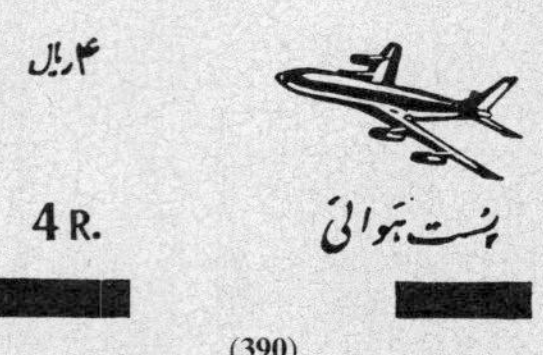

(390)

1969. Opening of 1st Iranian Satellite Communications Earth Station.
1599 **389** 6 r. brown and ochre . . 20 10

1969. Air. 50th Anniv of 1st England–Australia Flight. No. 1281 surch as T **390**.
1600 **229** 4 r. on 14 r. + 6 r. . . . . 1·10 45
1601 10 r. on 14 r. + 6 r. . . . 1·10 45
1602 14 r. on 14 r. + 6 r. . . . 1·10 45

1969. Birth Centenary of Mahatma Gandhi.
1603 **391** 14 r. brown and grey . . 2·75 70

392 Globe and Flags

1969. 50th Anniv of League of Red Cross Societies. Multicoloured.
1604 2 r. Type **392** 30 10
1605 6 r. Red Cross emblems on Globe 40 15

393 Shah and Reform Symbols

1970. 7th Anniv of Shah's White Revolution.
1606 **393** 1 r. multicoloured 55 15
1607 2 r. multicoloured 65 15

394 Pansies 396 "EXPO" Emblem

395 Nationalization Decree

1970. New Year Festival. Multicoloured.
1608 1 r. Type **394** 15 10
1609 8 r. New Year table (40 × 26 mm) . . . . 1·00 20

1970. 20th Anniv of Oil Industry Nationalization. Multicoloured.
1610 2 r. Type **395** 50 15
1611 4 r. Laying pipeline 70 15
1612 6 r. Part of Kharg Island plant 75 15
1613 8 r. Ocean terminal, Kharg Island (vert) . . . . 1·10 30
1614 10 r. Refinery, Teheran . . . . 1·10 35

1970. "EXPO 70" World Fair, Osaka Japan.
1615 **396** 4 r. blue and mauve . . . 15 10
1616 10 r. violet and blue . . . 35 15

397 Dish Aerial and Satellite 398 New U.P.U. H.Q.

1970. Asian Plan Communications Committee Meeting, Teheran.
1617 **397** 14 r. multicoloured . . . 65 20

1970. New U.P.U. Headquarters Building, Berne.
1618 **398** 2 r. sepia, mve & grn . . 20 10
1619 4 r. sepia, mve & lilac . . 30 10

399 A.P.Y. Emblem 400 Stork carrying Baby

1970. Asian Productivity Year.
1620 **399** 8 r. multicoloured 20 10

1970. 50th Anniv of Midwifery School.
1621 **400** 8 r. blue and brown . . . 30 15

401 Tomb of Cyrus the Great

1970. 2,500th Anniv of Persian Empire (1st issue). Achaemenian Era.
1622 **401** 6 r. violet, red & grey . . 50 15
1623 – 8 r. green, black & pink . . 55 15
1624 – 10 r. brown, red & yell . . 80 30
1625 – 14 r. brown, blk & blue . 1·40 70
DESIGNS—HORIZ: 10 r. Religious ceremony (Median bas-relief); 14 r. Achaemenian officers (bas-relief). VERT: 8 r. Columns, Palace of Apadana.
See also Nos. 1629/32, 1633/6, 1640/2, 1658/61, 1664/7, 1674/7 and 1679/82.

402 Saiful Malook Lake (Pakistan)

1970. 6th Anniv of Regional Co-operation for Development. Multicoloured.
1626 2 r. Type **402** 40 15
1627 2 r. Seeyo-Se-Pol Bridge, Isfahan (Iran) (62 × 46 mm) 40 15
1628 2 r. View from Fethiye (Turkey) 40 15

1970. 2500th Anniv of Persian Empire (2nd issue). Achaemenian Era. Designs as T **401**.
1629 2 r. gold, dp green & green . . 50 15
1630 6 r. gold, violet and green . . 50 20
1631 8 r. gold, blue and orange . . 1·00 30
1632 14 r. red, black and blue . . 1·40 75
DESIGNS—VERT: 2 r. Eagle amulet; 6 r. "Lion" goblet; 8 r. Winged ibex statue. HORIZ: 14 r. Tapestry.

1970. 2500th Anniv of Persian Empire (3rd issue). Coins of Sassanid and Parthian Eras. Designs as T **401**. Multicoloured, frames in gold.
1633 1 r. Queen Buran dirham . . . 50 15
1634 2 r. Mithridates I dirham . . . 55 15
1635 6 r. Shapur I dirham . . . . . 1·00 20
1636 8 r. Ardeshir I dirham . . . . 1·40 55

405 Candle and Globe Emblem

1970. World Literacy Day.
1637 **405** 1 r. multicoloured 10 10
1638 2 r. multicoloured 15 10

406 Isfahan Tile

408 Councils Emblem

1970. International Architects' Congress, Isfahan.
1639 **406** 6 r. multicoloured 20 15

1970. 2500th Anniv of Persian Empire (4th issue). Achaemenian and Sassanid Eras. Designs as T **401**.
1640 2 r. multicoloured 50 15
1641 6 r. brown, blue and lilac . . . 1·00 20
1642 8 r. green, red and lilac . . . . 1·25 30
DESIGNS—VERT: 2 r. Sassanid arch and art. HORIZ: 6 r. Archaemenian mounted courier; 8 r. Seal of Darius I.

1970. 1st Congress of Provincial Councils.
1643 **408** 2 r. violet and blue . . . 10 10

409 Dove and U.N. Emblem

411 Festival Emblem

410 "1970" and I.A.T.A. Emblem

1970. United Nations Day.
1644 **409** 2 r. ultram, purple & bl . 10 10

1970. Air. 26th International Air Transport Association General Meeting, Teheran.
1645 **410** 14 r. multicoloured . . . 2·50 40

1970. National Festival of Art and Culture, Teheran.
1646 **411** 2 r. multicoloured 15 10

412 "Goatherd and Goats"

1970. Children's Week. Children's Drawings. Multicoloured,.
1647 50 d. Type **412** 15 10
1648 1 r. "Family picnic" 20 10
1649 2 r. "Mosque" 40 10

413 Shah Mohammed Riza Pahlavi

1971. 8th Anniv of Shah's White Revolution.
1650 **413** 2 r. multicoloured 20 20

414 Common Shelduck

1971. International Wetland and Waterfowl Conference, Ramsar. Multicoloured.
1651 1 r. Type **414** 50 10
1652 2 r. Ruddy Shelduck 50 10
1653 8 r. Greater Flamingo (vert) . . 1·25 25

415 Riza Shah Pahlavi

416 Red Junglefowl

1971. 50th Anniv of Rise of Pahlavi Dynasty.
1654 **415** 6 r. multicoloured . . . . 1·40 30

1971. New Year Festival. Birds. Multicoloured.
1655 1 r. Type **416** 40 10
1656 2 r. Barn swallow at nest . . . 1·00 10
1657 6 r. Hoopoe . . . . 3·25 35

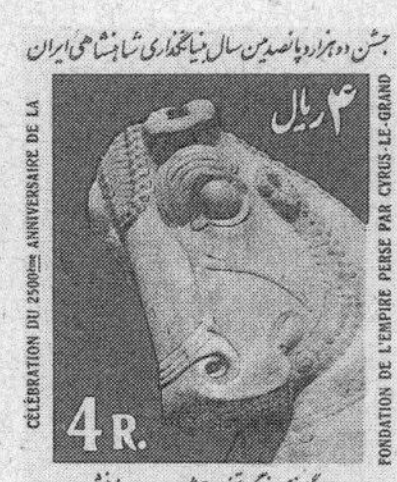
417 Stone Bull's Head, Persepolis

1971. 2,500th Anniv of Persian Empire (5th issue). Age of Cyrus the Great. Multicoloured.
1658 4 r. Type **417** 90 15
1659 5 r. Winged lion ornament . . 1·25 15
1660 6 r. Persian Archer (bas-relief) . 1·25 20
1661 8 r. Imperial audience (bas-relief) . . . . 1·50 30

418 Prisoners' Rehabilitation

421 "Shiraz Arts"

420 Badshahi Mosque, Lahore (Pakistan)

1971. Rehabilitation Week.
1662 **418** 6 r. multicoloured . . . . 1·00 15
1663 8 r. multicoloured . . . . 1·50 15

1971. 2500th Anniv of Persian Empire (6th issue). Art of Ancient Persia. As T **417**.
1664 1 r. multicoloured 70 15
1665 2 r. black and brown 70 15
1666 2 r. brown, black and purple . 70 15
1667 10 r. black, blue & brown . . . 90 30
DESIGNS—VERT: No. 1664, "Harpist" (mosaic); No. 1667, Bronze head of Parthian prince. HORIZ: No. 1665. "Shapur I hunting" (ornamental plate); No. 1666. "Investiture of Ardashir I" (bas-relief).

1971. 7th Anniv of Regional Co-operation for Development. Multicoloured.
1668 2 r. Type **420** 30 15
1669 2 r. Selimiye Mosque, Edirne, Turkey (vert) 30 15
1670 2 r. Chaharbagh School, Isfahan (Iran) (vert) 30 15

1971. 5th Shiraz Arts Festival, Persepolis.
1671 **421** 2 r. multicoloured 30 15

422 "Book-reading"

1971. World Literacy Day.
1672 **422** 2 r. multicoloured 20 10

423 Kings Abdullah and Hussein II

1971. 50th Anniv of Hashemite Kingdom of Jordan.
1673 **423** 2 r. multicoloured 20 10

424 National Steel Foundry

1971. 2,500th Anniv of Persian Empire (7th issue). Modern Iran. Multicoloured.
1674 1 r. Type **424** 30 15
1675 2 r. Shahyad Aryamehr Memorial 65 15
1676 3 r. Senate Building, Teheran . 65 20
1677 11 r. Shah Abbas the Great Dam . . . . 1·25 40

425 Ghatur Railway Bridge

1971. Inaug. of Iran–Turkey Railway Link.
1678 **425** 2 r. multicoloured . . . . 1·00 10

426 Shah Mohammed Riza Pahlavi

1971. 2,500th Anniv of Persian Empire (8th issue). Pahlavi Era. Multicoloured.
1679 1 r. Type **426** . . . . 1·40 50
1680 2 r. Riza Shah Pahlavi . . . . 1·50 50
1681 5 r. Proclamation tablet of Cyrus the Great (horiz) . . 1·60 50
1682 10 r. Pahlavi Crown . . . . . 3·25 75

427 Racial Equality Year Emblem

428 Shah Mohammed Riza Pahlavi

1971. Racial Equality Year.
1683 **427** 2 r. multicoloured . . . 10 10

1971.
1684 **428** 5 d. purple 10 10
1685 10 d. red 10 10
1686 50 d. green 10 10
1687 1 r. green 10 10
1688 2 r. brown 10 10
1689 6 r. green 50 10
1690 8 r. violet 90 30
1691 **428** 10 r. purple 70 10
1692 11 r. green . . . . 2·00 10
1693 14 r. blue . . . . 7·50 10
1694 20 r. mauve . . . . 5·50 15
1695 50 r. ochre . . . . 3·25 50
Nos. 1689/95 are larger, 27 × 37 mm.
See also Nos. 1715/26b and 1846/50.

429 "Waiters at a Banquet"

1971. Children's Week. Children's Drawings. Multicoloured.
1696 2 r. Type **429** 20 15
1697 2 r. "Persepolis Ruins" (vert) . 20 15
1698 2 r. "Persian Archer" (vert) . . 20 15

430 U.N.E.S.C.O. Emblem

1971. 25th Anniv of U.N.E.S.C.O.
1699 **430** 6 r. blue and purple . . . 30 15

431 Congress Emblem and Livestock

1971. 4th Iranian Veterinary Congress.
1700 **431** 2 r. red, black and grey . 30 10

432 I.L.O. Emblem and Globe

1971. 7th Asian International Labour Organization Regional Conference, Teheran.
1701 **432** 2 r. orange, blue & blk . . 20 10

433 Bird feeding Young

434 Shah Mohammed Riza Pahlavi

1971. 25th Anniv of U.N.I.C.E.F.
1702 **433** 2 r. multicoloured 20 10

1972. 9th Anniv of Shah's White Revolution.
1703 **434** 2 r. multicoloured . . . . 1·00 15

435 Chukar Partridge

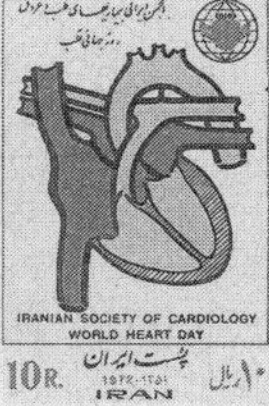
436 Human Heart

1972. New Year Festival. Birds. Mult.
1705 1 r. Type **435** 30 15
1706 1 r. Pin-tailed sandgrouse . . . 30 15
1707 2 r. Yellow-bellied waxbill and red-cheeked cordon-bleu . 1·60 20

1972 World Heart Day.
1708 **436** 10 r. multicoloured . . . 80 20

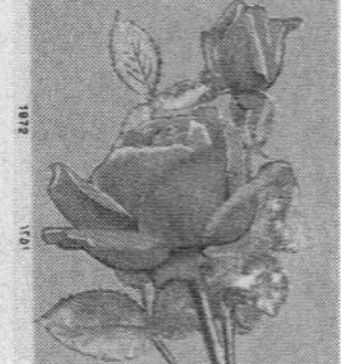

437 Winged Ibex Symbol **438** Scarlet Roses

1972. International Film Festival, Teheran.
1709 **437** 6 r. gold and blue 70 15
1710 – 8 r. multicoloured . . . . 1·25 20
DESIGN: 8 r. Symbolic spectrum.

1972. Roses. Multicoloured.
1711 1 r. Type **438** 20 10
1712 2 r. Yellow roses 50 10
1713 5 r. Red rose 75 15

1972. As Nos. 1684/95, but with bistre frames and inscriptions.
1715 **428** 5 d. purple 10 10
1716 10 d. brown 10 10
1717 50 d. green 10 10
1718 1 r. green 10 10
1719 2 r. brown 40 10
1720 6 r. green 30 10
1721 8 r. violet 35 15
1722 10 r. purple 55 10
1723 11 r. blue 70 15
1724 14 r. blue . . . . . . 3·50 20
1725 20 r. mauve . . . . . . 7·00 30
1726 50 r. blue . . . . . . 2·50 65
1726a 110 r. violet . . . . . . 3·50 75
1726b 200 r. black . . . . . . 7·50 3·50
Nos. 1720/26b are larger, 27 × 37 mm.

439 "U.I.T." Emblem

1972. World Telecommunications Day.
1726c **439** 14 r. multicoloured . . . 1·50 30

440 "Fisherman" (Cevat Dereli, Turkey) **442** Pens

441 Floral Patterns

1972. 8th Anniv of Regional Co-operation for Development. Paintings. Multicoloured.
1727 5 r. Type **440** . . . . 1·00 25
1728 5 r. "Iranian Woman" (Behzad, Iran) 90 25
1729 5 r. "Will and Power" (A.R. Chughtai, Pakistan) 90 25

1972. 6th Shiraz Arts Festival.
1730 **441** 6 r. black, red & green . . 75 15
1731 8 r. black and purple . . 1·00 20

1972. World Literacy Day.
1732 **442** 1 r. multicoloured 15 10
1733 2 r. multicoloured 20 10

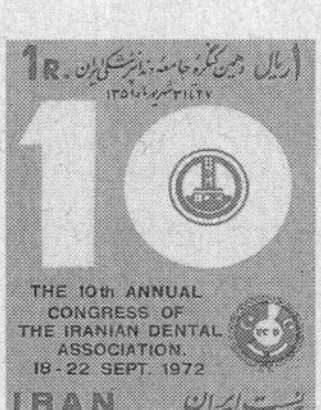

443 "10" and Dental Emblem **444** A.B.U. Emblem within "9"

1972. 10th Annual Congress of Iranian Dental Association.
1734 **443** 1 r. multicoloured 20 10
1735 2 r multicoloured 30 10

1972. 9th General Assembly of Asian Broadcasting Union, Teheran.
1736 **444** 6 r. multicoloured 50 10
1737 8 r. multicoloured 75 20

445 3ch. stamp of 1910 on Cover **447** Communications Emblem

446 Chess

1972. World Stamp Day.
1738 **445** 10 r. multicoloured . . . 1·25 30

1972. Olympic Games, Munich. Iranian Sports. Multicoloured.
1739 1 r. Type **446** . . . . 1·25 20
1740 2 r. Hunting . . . . 1·25 20
1741 3 r. Archery . . . . 1·50 20
1742 5 r. Horse-racing . . . . . . 1·50 20
1743 6 r. Polo . . . . 1·50 20
1744 8 r. Wrestling . . . . 1·60 25

1972. United Nations Day.
1746 **447** 10 r. multicoloured . . . 1·10 25

448 "Children in Garden" **449** Festival Emblem

1972. Children's Week. Children's Drawings. Multicoloured.
1747 2 r. Type **448** 35 10
1748 2 r. "At the Theatre" 55 10
1749 6 r. "Children at play" (horiz) . 1·25 20

1972. National Festival of Art and Culture, Teheran.
1750 **449** 10 r. multicoloured . . . 2·75 30

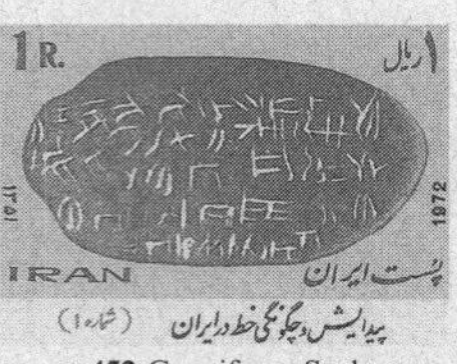

450 Family Planning Emblem **451** Scouting Emblem

1972. Family Planning Campaign.
1751 **450** 1 r. multicoloured 15 10
1752 2 r. multicoloured 20 10

1972. 20th Anniv of Scouting in Iran.
1753 **451** 2 r. multicoloured 40 10

452 Cuneiform Seal

1973. "Origins of Writing" (1st issue). Impressions from ancient seals. Multicoloured. Background colours given.
1754 **452** 1 r. blue 40 15
1755 – 1 r. yellow 40 15
1756 – 1 r. mauve 40 15
1757 – 2 r. orange 45 15
1758 – 2 r. green 45 15
1759 – 2 r. buff 45 15
See also Nos. 1774/9 and 1822/7.

453 Open Books in Space **454** "Twelve Reforms"

1973. International Book Year. Multicoloured.
1760 2 r. Type **453** 55 10
1761 6 r. Illuminated manuscript . . 85 15

1973. 10th Anniv of Shah's White Revolution. Multicoloured.
1762 1 r. Type **454** 15 10
1763 2 r. Pyramid of 12 balls . . . 20 10
1764 6 r. As Type **454** but size 71 × 92 mm. . . . . 1·00 45

455 Long-spined Seabream ("Sparus spinifer") **457** "Footballers"

456 W.H.O. Emblem

1973. New Year Festival. Fishes. Mult.
1766 1 r. Type **455** 55 10
1767 1 r. Purple tang ("Acanthurus sp.") 55 10
1768 2 r. Two-banded seabream ("Anisotremus sp.") 75 15
1769 2 r. Sergeant major ("Abdufef") 75 15
1770 2 r. Black-spotted snapper ("Lutyanus fulniflamma") . 75 15

1973. 25th Anniv of W.H.O.
1771 **456** 10 r. multicoloured . . . 80 20

1973. 15th Asian Youth Football Tournament, Teheran.
1772 **457** 14 r. multicoloured . . . 1·00 25

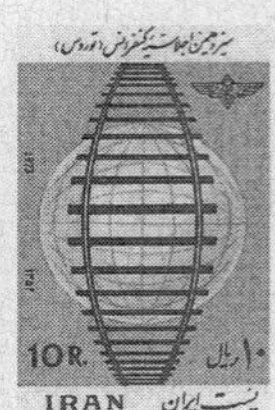

458 Railway Track encircling Globe **459** Ancient Aryan Script

1973. International Railway Conference, Teheran
1773 **458** 10 r. blue, blk & mve . . 1·25 20

1973. "Origins of Writing". Multicoloured.
1774 1 r. Type **459** 25 15
1775 1 r. Achaemenian priest and text 25 15
1776 1 r. Kharochtani tablet 25 15
1777 2 r. Parthian medallion (Arsacid) 45 15
1778 2 r. Parthian coin (Mianeh) . . 45 15
1779 2 r. Gachtak inscribed medallion (Dabireh) 45 15

INDEX

Countries can be quickly located by referring to the index at the end of this volume.

460 Orchid **461** Carved Head, Tomb of Antiochus I (Turkey)

1973. Flowers. Multicoloured.
1780 1 r. Type **460** 20 10
1781 2 r. Hyacinth 30 10
1782 6 r. Wild rose 90 30

1973. 9th Anniv of Regional Co-operation for Development. Multicoloured.
1783 2 r. Type **461** 30 15
1784 2 r. Statue, Lut excavations (Iran) 30 15
1785 2 r. Street in Moenjodaro (Pakistan) 30 15

462 Shah and Oil Installations **463** Soldiers and "Sun"

1973. Full Independence for Iranian Oil Industry.
1786 **462** 5 r. black and blue . . . 90 20

1973. 20th Anniv of Gen. Zahedi's Uprising.
1787 **463** 2 r. multicoloured 20 10

464 Sportswomen and Globe

1973. 7th International Women's Congress on Physical Education and Sport, Teheran.
1788 **464** 2 r. multicoloured (blue background) 20 10
1789 2 r. multicoloured (green background) 20 10

465 Festival Poster **467** Wrestling

466 Shahyad Monument and Rainbow

1973. 7th Shiraz Arts Festival.
1790 **465** 1 r. multicoloured 15 10
1791 5 r. multicoloured 20 15

1973. Centenary of World Meteorological Organization.
1792 **466** 5 r. multicoloured 60 15

1973. World Wrestling Championships, Teheran.
1793 **467** 6 r. multicoloured 55 10

468 Alphabetic "Sun"

469 Globe wearing Earphones

1973. World Literacy Day.
1794 **468** 2 r. multicoloured 15 10

1973. Int Audio-visual Exhibition, Teheran.
1795 **469** 10 r. multicoloured . . . 45 15

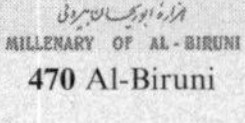
470 Al-Biruni

472 Crown Prince Cup

471 C.I.S.M. Badge and Emblem

1973. Birth Millenary of Abu al-Rayhan al-Biruni (mathematician and philosopher).
1796 **470** 10 r. black and brown . . 80 20

1973. 25th Anniv of International Military Sports Council (C.I.S.M.)
1797 **471** 8 r. multicoloured 30 15

1973. Crown Prince Cup Football Championship.
1798 **472** 2 r. brown, black & lilac . 15 10

473 Interpol Emblem

475 U.P.U. Emblem, Post-horn and Letter

474 Curves on Globe

1973. 50th Anniv of International Criminal Police Organization (Interpol).
1799 **473** 2 r. multicoloured 30 10

1973. 25th Anniv of World Mental Health Federation.
1800 **474** 10 r. multicoloured . . . 50 15

1973. World Post Day.
1801 **475** 6 r. orange and blue . . . 30 10

476 Emblems within Honeycomb

477 Festival Emblem and "People"

1973. 5th Anniv of United Nations Volunteers.
1802 **476** 2 r. multicoloured (brown background) 10 10
1803 2 r. multicoloured (green background) 10 10

1973. National Festival of Art and Culture. Teheran.
1804 **477** 2 r. multicoloured 20 10

478 Bosphorus Bridge

1973. 50th Anniv of Turkish Republic. Mult.
1805 2 r. Type **478** 50 10
1806 8 r. Meeting of Kemal Ataturk and Reza Shah Pahlavi . . . 60 20

479 "House and Garden"

481 Cylinder of Cyrus and Red Cross Emblems

480 Ear of Grain and Cow

1973. Children's Week. Children's Drawings. Multicoloured.
1807 2 r. Type **479** 25 15
1808 2 r. "Collecting Fruit" 25 15
1809 2 r. "Caravan" (horiz) 25 15

1973. 10th Anniv of World Food Programme.
1810 **480** 10 r. multicoloured . . . 75 15

1973. 22nd Int Red Cross Conference, Teheran
1811 **481** 6 r. multicoloured 35 10

482 IATA Emblem

483 Emblem, Film and Flags

1973. Tourist Managers Congress, Teheran.
1812 **482** 10 r. multicoloured . . . 35 15

1973. International Film Festival, Teheran.
1813 **483** 2 r. multicoloured 20 10

484 Flame Emblem

485 Harp Emblem

1973. 25th Anniv of Declaration of Human Rights.
1814 **484** 8 r. multicoloured 30 10

1973. "Art of Music" Festival.
1815 **485** 10 r. red, green & blk . . 40 15
1816 – 10 r. ultram, bl & pur . . 40 15
DESIGN: No. 1816, Musical symbols.

486 Reform Symbols

1974. 11th Anniv of Shah's White Revolution. Multicoloured.
1817 1 r. Type **486** 20 15
1818 1 r. Tractor, factory in cog-wheel, women and parliament gate 20 15
1819 2 r. Girders, hose and worker . 20 15
1820 2 r. Rod of Aesculapius, scales and road passing house . . 20 15

487 Pir Amooz Ketabaty Script

1974. "Origins of Writing" (3rd issue). Multicoloured.
1822 1 r. Din Dabireh Avesta . . . 40 15
1823 1 r. Mo Eghely Ketabaty . . . 40 15
1824 1 r. Type **487** 40 15
1825 2 r. Pir Amooz, Naskh style . . 40 15
1826 2 r. Pir Amooz, decorative . . 40 15
1827 2 r. Pir Amooz, decorative and architectural 40 15

488 Chicken, Cow and Syringe

1974. Fifth Iranian Veterinary Congress.
1828 **488** 6 r. multicoloured 40 15

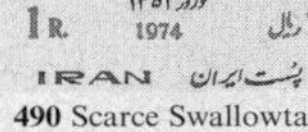
490 Scarce Swallowtail

491 Mevlana

1974. Nawrooz and Spring Festivals. Butterflies. Multicoloured, background colours given.
1841 **490** 1 r. mauve 30 10
1842 – 1 r. purple 30 10
1843 – 2 r. green 65 10
1844 – 2 r. brown 65 10
1845 – 2 r. blue 65 10
DESIGNS: No. 1842, Swallowtail; 1843, Peacock; 1844, Painted lady; 1845, Cardinal.

1974. As Nos. 1684/95, but colours changed.
1846 **428** 50 d. blue and orange . . 20 10
1847 1 r. blue and green . . . 25 10
1848 2 r. blue and red 40 10
1849 10 r. blue and green . . . 4·50 10
1850 20 r. blue and mauve . . 2·75 20
Nos. 1849/50 are larger, 27 × 37 mm.

1974. 700th Death Anniv of Jalal-udin Mevlana (poet).
1851 **491** 2 r. multicoloured 20 10

492 Palace of Forty Columns, Isfahan

1974. 9th Near- and Middle-East Medical Congress, Isfahan.
1852 **492** 10 r. multicoloured . . . 40 15

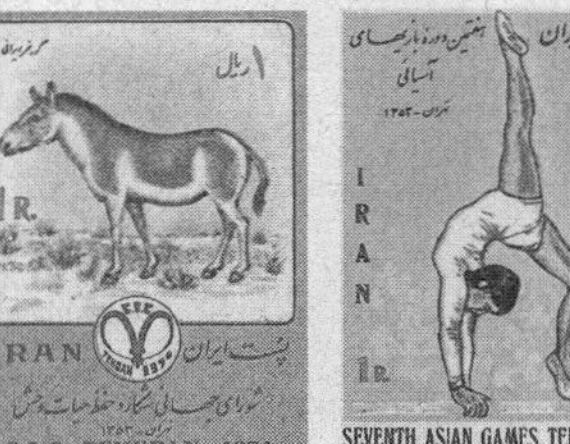
493 Asiatic Wild Ass
494 Gymnastics

1974. International Game and Wild Life Protection Congress, Teheran. Multicoloured.
1853 1 r. Type **493** 20 15
1854 2 r. Great Bustard 40 15
1855 6 r. Fawn and Fallow deer . . 45 20
1856 8 r. Georgian Black grouse . . 1·00 20

1974. 7th Asian Games, Teheran (1st series). Multicoloured.
1857 1 r. Type **494** 15 10
1858 1 r. Table tennis 20 10
1859 2 r. Boxing 50 10
1860 2 r. Hurdling 50 10
1861 6 r. Weightlifting 70 15
1862 8 r. Handball . . . . 1·25 15
See also Nos. 1874/9, 1890/3 and 1909.

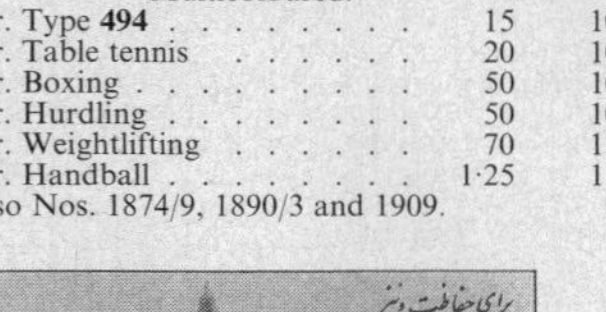

495 Lion of St Mark's

1974. U.N.E.S.C.O. "Save Venice" Campaign. Multicoloured.
1863 6 r. Type **495** 30 10
1864 8 r. Merchants at the Doge's court 65 15

496 Chain Link

497 Shah and Douglas DC-9-80 Super Eighty

1974. Farm Co-operatives' Day.
1865 **496** 2 r. multicoloured 15 10

1974. Air.
1866 **497** 4 r. black and orange . . 10 10
1867 10 r. black and blue . . . 60 15
1868 12 r. black and brown . . 70 20
1869 14 r. black and green . . 1·00 20
1870 20 r. black and mauve . . 1·25 30
1871 50 r. black and blue . . . 5·50 80

498 De Havilland D.H.9A, 1924

1974. 50th Anniv of Imperial Iranian Air Force. Multicoloured.
1872 10 r. Type **498** . . . . . . 1·10 15
1873 10 r. McDonnell Douglas F-4D Phantom II fighter of 1974 . 1·10 15

499 Tennis (men's doubles)

500 Mazanderan Costume

1974. 7th Asian Games, Teheran (2nd series). Multicoloured.
1874 1 r. Type **499** 15 10
1875 1 r. Swimming 15 10
1876 2 r. Wrestling 20 10
1877 2 r. Hockey 20 10
1878 4 r. Volleyball 60 15
1879 10 r. Tennis (women's singles) . 1·25 15

1974. Regional Costumes. Multicoloured.
1880 2 r. Type **500** 70 20
1881 2 r. Bakhtiari 70 20
1882 2 r. Turkoman 70 20
1883 2 r. Ghasgai 70 20
1884 2 r. Kirmanshah (Kurdistan) . . 70 20
1885 2 r. Sanandadj (Kurdistan) . . . 70 20

501 Gold Cup

502 Iranian Carpet

1974. Iranian Football Championships.
1886 **501** 2 r. yellow, brn and grn . . 20 10

1974. 10th Anniv of Regional Co-operation for Development. Multicoloured.
1887 2 r. Pakistani carpet (diamond) centre 35 15
1888 2 r. Turkish carpet (striped) . . 35 15
1889 2 r. Type **502** 35 15

503 Rifle-shooting **504** Persian King

1974. Seventh Asian Games, Teheran (3rd series). Multicoloured.
1890 2 r. Type **503** 30 15
1891 2 r. Fencing 30 15
1892 2 r. Football 30 15
1893 2 r. Cycling 35 15

1974. 8th Shiraz Arts Festival, Persepolis.
1894 **504** 2 r. multicoloured 15 10

506 Petrochemical Works, Khark

1974.
1896 **506** 5 d. green and brown . . 10 10
1897 – 10 d. orange & brown . . 25 10
1898 – 50 d. green and brown . . 10 10
1899 – 1 r. blue and brown . . 15 10
1900 – 2 r. purple and brown . . 20 10
1901 – 6 r. brown and blue . . 15 10
1902 – 8 r. turquoise and blue . . 20 10
1903 – 10 r. purple and blue . . 45 10
1904 – 14 r. green and blue . . 11·00 10
1905 – 20 r. red and blue . . . 1·00 10
1906 – 50 r. violet and blue . . 1·75 20

DESIGNS—As T **506**: 10 d. Railway bridge, Ghatur; 50 d. Dam, Farahnaz; 1 r. Oil Refinery; 2 r. Radio telescope; 37 × 27 mm: 6 r. Steelworks, Aryamehr; 8 r. Tabriz University; 10 r. Shah Abbas Kabir Dam; 14 r. Teheran Opera House; 20 r. Shahyad Square; 50 r. Aryamehr Stadium.
See also Nos. 1939/49.

507 Family within Hands **509** Plan of Hasanlu

508 Aryamehr Stadium, Teheran

1974. State Education and Health Services. Multicoloured.
1907 2 r. Type **507** 15 10
1908 2 r. Children, pen and book within hands 15 10

1974. Seventh Asian Games, Teheran (4th series).
1909 **508** 6 r. multicoloured 40 10

1974. 2nd International Architectural Congress, Shiraz.
1910 **509** 8 r. multicoloured 30 10

510 Charioteer

1974. Centenary of U.P.U. Multicoloured.
1911 6 r. Type **510** 30 10
1912 14 r. U.P.U. emblem and letters 50 20

511 Road through Park

1974. Opening of Farahabad Park, Teheran. Multicoloured.
1913 1 r. Type **511** 10 10
1914 2 r. Recreation pavilion . . . 15 10

512 Festival Emblem

1974. National Festival of Art and Culture, Teheran.
1915 **512** 2 r. multicoloured 15 10

513 Crown Prince in Aircraft

1974. Air. Crown Prince's Birthday.
1916 **513** 14 r. multicoloured . . . 45 15

514 Destroyer "Palang"

1974. Navy Day.
1917 **514** 10 r. multicoloured . . . 80 20

515 Scarecrow **516** Winged Bull Emblem

1974. Children's Week. Children's Drawings. Multicoloured.
1918 2 r. Type **515** 15 10
1919 2 r. Girl at spinning wheel . . 15 10
1920 2 r. New Year picnic 15 10
Nos. 1919/20 are horiz.

1974. 3rd International Film Festival, Teheran.
1921 **516** 2 r. multicoloured 15 10

517 W.P.Y. Emblem

1974. World Population Year.
1922 **517** 8 r. multicoloured 30 10

518 Gold Butterfly Brooch

1974. 14th Wedding Anniv of Shah and Empress Farah. Multicoloured.
1923 6 r. Type **518** 15 10
1924 8 r. Gold diadem 20 10

519 Angel with Banner

1975. International Women's Year.
1925 **519** 2 r. orange, blue & red . . 15 10

520 Emblems of Agriculture, Industry and the Arts **521** Tourism Year Emblem

1975. 12th Anniv of Shah's White Revolution.
1926 **520** 2 r. multicoloured 15 10

1975. South Asia Tourism Year.
1927 **521** 6 r. multicoloured 15 10

522 Farabi's Initial **523** Ornament

1975. 1100th Birth Anniv of Abu-Nasr al-Farabi (philosopher).
1928 **522** 2 r. multicoloured 15 10

1975. New Year Festival. Multicoloured.
1929 1 r. Type **523** 15 10
1930 1 r. Blossoms and tree 15 10
1931 1 r. Arabesque and patterns . . 15 10

524 Nasser Khosrov **525** Persian Warriors

1975. Birth Millenary of Nasser Khosrov (poet).
1932 **524** 2 r. black, red & bistre . . 15 10

1975. 70th Anniv of Rotary International. Multicoloured.
1933 2 r. Type **525** 55 10
1934 10 r. Charioteer (horiz) . . . . 1·50 15

526 Biochemical Emblem **527** "Co-operative Peoples"

1975. Fifth Biochemical Symposium.
1935 **526** 2 r. multicoloured 15 10

1975. Co-operatives Day.
1936 **527** 2 r. multicoloured 10 10

528 Ancient Signal-beacons

1975. World Telecommunications Day. Mult.
1937 6 r. Type **528** 20 10
1938 8 r. Telecommunications satellite 30 15

1975. As Nos. 1896/1906 but colours changed.
1939 **506** 5 d. orange & turquoise . 10 10
1940 – 10 d. purple & turquoise . 25 10
1941 – 50 d. mauve & turquoise . 10 10
1942 – 1 r. blue and turquoise . . 20 10
1943 – 2 r. brown & turquoise . . 20 10
1944 – 6 r. violet and brown . . 50 10
1945 – 8 r. red and brown . . . 70 10
1946 – 10 r. green and brown . . 90 15
1947 – 14 r. mauve and brown . 6·00 25
1948 – 20 r. turquoise & brown . 1·75 30
1949 – 50 r. blue and brown . . 1·75 70

529 "Iran Air" Boeing 747SP

1975. "Iran Air's" First Teheran–New York Flight.
1950 **529** 10 r. multicoloured . . . 35 15

530 Environmental Emblem **532** Party Emblem

531 Dam and Reservoir

1975. World Environment Day.
1951 **530** 6 r. multicoloured 20 10

1975. 25th Anniv of International Commission on Irrigation and Drainage.
1952 **531** 10 r. multicoloured . . . 25 15

1975. Formation of Resurgence Party.
1953 **532** 2 r. multicoloured 10 10

533 Saluting Hand **534** Festival Motif

1975. 2nd National Girl Scout Camp, Teheran.
1954 **533** 2 r. multicoloured 20 10

1975. Festival of Tus (honouring poet Firdausi).
1955 **534** 2 r. multicoloured 10 10

535 Iranian Tile

1975. 11th Anniv of Regional Co-operation for Development. Multicoloured.
1956 2 r. Type **535** 15 10
1957 2 r. Pakistani camel-skin vase (vert) 15 10
1958 2 r. Turkish porcelain vase (vert) 15 10

536 Parliament Gateway

1975. 70th Anniv of Iranian Constitution.
1959 **536** 10 r. multicoloured . . . 25 15

537 Stylised Column **538** Flags over Globe

1975. 9th Shiraz Arts Festival.
1960 **537** 8 r. multicoloured 25 15

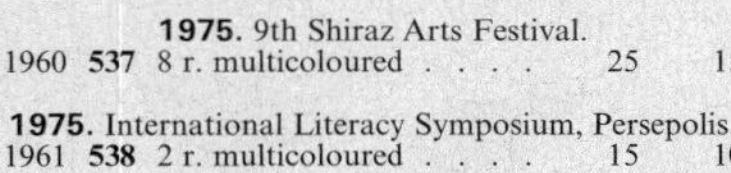

1975. International Literacy Symposium, Persepolis.
1961 **538** 2 r. multicoloured 15 10

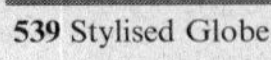
539 Stylised Globe **541** Festival Emblem

540 Envelope on World Map

1975. 3rd International Trade Fair, Teheran.
1962 **539** 2 r. multicoloured 15 10

1975. World Post Day.
1963 **540** 14 r. multicoloured . . . 45 15

1975. National Festival of Art and Culture, Teheran.
1964 **541** 2 r. multicoloured 15 10

542 Face within Film **543** "Mother's Face"

1975. International Festival of Children's Films, Teheran.
1965 **542** 6 r. multicoloured 15 10

1975. Children's Week. Multicoloured.
1966 2 r. Type **543** 15 10
1967 2 r. "Young Girl" 15 10
1968 2 r. "Our House" (horiz) . . . 15 10

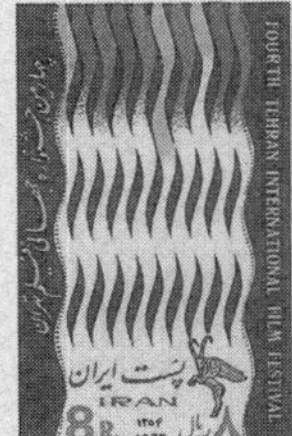

544 "Sound Film" **545** Reform Symbols

1975. 4th International Film Festival, Teheran.
1969 **544** 8 r. multicoloured . . . 20 15

1976. 13th Anniv of Shah's White Revolution. Multicoloured.
1970 2 r. Type **545** 10 10
1971 2 r. Symbols representing "People" 10 10
1972 2 r. Five reform symbols . . . 10 10

546 Motor Cycle Patrol **547** Football Cup

1976. Highway Police Day. Multicoloured.
1973 2 r. Type **546** 40 15
1974 6 r. Bell Model 205 Iroquois police helicopter (horiz) . . 85 20

1976. Third International Football Cup.
1975 **547** 2 r. multicoloured 15 10

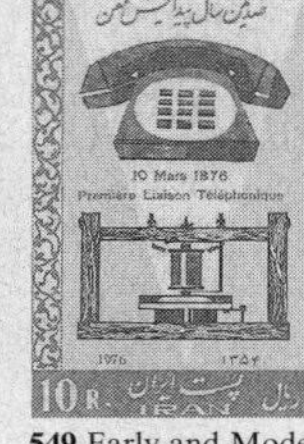

548 Candlestick **549** Early and Modern Telephones

1976. New Year. Multicoloured.
1976 1 r. Type **548** 15 10
1977 1 r. Incense burner 15 10
1978 1 r. Rosewater jug 15 10

1976. Telephone Centenary.
1979 **549** 10 r. multicoloured . . . 25 15

550 Human Eye

1976. World Health Day.
1980 **550** 6 r. multicoloured 30 10

551 Nurse holding Child

1976. 30th Anniv of Social Services Organization. Multicoloured.
1981 2 r. Type **551** 15 10
1982 2 r. Workshop apprentices . . 15 10
1983 2 r. Handclasp (help the aged) (vert) 15 10

552 Linked Men on Map **553** Sound Waves and Headphones

1976. 10th Anniv of Iranian Co-operative Movement.
1984 **552** 2 r. multicoloured 15 10

1976. World Telecommunications Day.
1985 **553** 14 r. multicoloured . . . 30 15

554 "Patriotism" **555** Nasser-Khosrow and Landmarks on Map

1976. National Resistance Organization.
1986 **554** 2 r. multicoloured 15 10

1976. Tourism Day and Birth Anniv of Nasser-Khosrow "The Great Iranian Tourist".
1987 **555** 6 r. multicoloured 15 10

556 Riza Shah Pahlavi **557** Olympic Flame and Emblem

1976. 12th Anniv of Regional Co-operation for Development. Multicoloured.
1988 2 r. Type **556** 15 10
1989 6 r. Mohammed Ali Jinnah (Pakistan) 25 15
1990 8 r. Kemal Ataturk (Turkey) . 35 15

1976. Olympic Games, Montreal.
1991 **557** 14 r. multicoloured . . . 45 20

558 Riza Shah Pahlavi in Coronation Dress

1976. 50th Anniv of Pahlavi Dynasty. Mult.
1992 2 r. Riza Shah Pahlavi and Mohammed Riza Pahlavi (horiz) 20 10
1993 6 r. Type **558** 75 15
1994 14 r. Mohammed Riza Pahlavi in Coronation dress . . . . 1·00 25

559 Festival Emblem **560** Conference Emblem

1976. 10th Shiraz Arts Festival.
1995 **559** 10 r. multicoloured . . . 30 15

1976. 10th Asia–Pacific Scout Conference, Teheran.
1996 **560** 2 r. multicoloured 15 10

561 Radiation Treatment **562** Target and Presentation to Policewoman

1976. Campaign against Cancer.
1997 **561** 2 r. multicoloured 20 10

1976. Police Day.
1998 **562** 2 r. multicoloured 30 10

564 U.P.U. Emblem and Iranian Stamp on Envelope

1976. International Post Day.
2000 **564** 10 r. multicoloured . . . 30 15

565 Crown Prince presenting Cup **566** Mohammed Riza Pahlavi, Riza Shah Pahlavi and Steam Train

1976. Society of Village Culture Houses.
2001 **565** 6 r. multicoloured 20 10

1976. Railway Day.
2002 **566** 8 r. multicoloured . . . . 1·25 50

567 Festival Emblem **568** Census Symbols

1976. National Festival of Art and Culture, Teheran.
2003 **567** 14 r. multicoloured . . . 35 15

1976. National Census.
2004 **568** 2 r. multicoloured 15 10

569 Flowers and Birds **570** Mohammed Ali Jinnah (Quaid-i-Azam)

1976. Children's Week. Multicoloured.
2005 2 r. Type **569** 15 10
2006 2 r. Flowers and bird 15 10
2007 2 r. Flowers and butterfly . . . 15 10

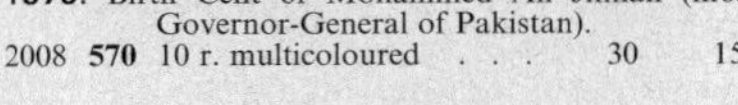

1976. Birth Cent of Mohammed Ali Jinnah (first Governor-General of Pakistan).
2008 **570** 10 r. multicoloured . . . 30 15

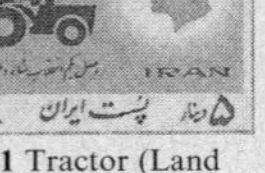

571 Tractor (Land reform) **572** Man in Guilan Costume

1977. 14th Anniv of Shah's White Revolution. Shah's head and frame in gold.
2009 **571** 5 d. green and pink . . . 10 10
2010 – 10 d. green and brown . . 10 10
2011 – 50 d. blue and orange . . 10 10
2012 – 1 r. blue and mauve . . . 10 10
2013 – 2 r. green and orange . . 10 10
2014 – 3 r. red and blue 10 10
2015 – 5 r. lilac and green . . . 20 10
2016 – 6 r. purple, brn & blk . . 30 10
2017 – 8 r. purple, blue & blk . . 30 10
2018 – 10 r. blue, green & blk . 1·40 10
2019 – 12 r. brn, lilac & blk . . 70 10
2020 – 14 r. red, orange & blk . . 1·00 10

2021 – 20 r. orge, grey & blk . . 2·00 10
2022 – 30 r. green, blue & blk . . 1·75 10
2023 – 50 r. red, yellow & blk . . 3·50 10
2024 – 100 r. blue, mve & blk . . 3·25 55
2025 – 200 r. violet, grn & blk . . 6·50 1·50

DESIGNS:—21 × 28 mm: 10 d. Trees (Nationalization of forests); 50 d. Bank notes (Profit-sharing); 1 r. Factory workers (Sale of shares to workers); 2 r. Parliament gate (Votes for women); 3 r. Teacher and pupils (Education corps); 5 r. Doctor examining patient (Medical corps). 36 × 27 mm: 6 r. Bulldozer (Civil engineering); 8 r. Scales (Justice); 10 r. Dam (Irrigation); 12 r. Building site (Construction corps); 14 r. Clock and receptionist (Working conditions); 20 r. Screen and students (Adult literacy); 30 r. Sound waves (Telecommunications); 50 r. Students and pupils (Education); 100 r. Baby in hands (Child care); 200 r. Elderly couple (Care of the aged).

1977. New Year Festival. Multicoloured.
2026 1 r. Type **572** 10 10
2027 2 r. Women in Guilan costume 15 10

573 Circuit Diagram
574 Riza Shah Dam

1977. World Telecommunications Day.
2028 **573** 20 r. multicoloured . . . 55 15

1977. Inauguration of Riza Shah Dam.
2029 **574** 5 r. multicoloured 20 10

575 Olympic Rings

1977. Olympic Day.
2030 **575** 14 r. multicoloured . . . 35 15

576 Turkish "Human Face" Vase

1977. 13th Anniv of Regional Co-operation for Development. Multicoloured.
2031 5 r. Type **576** 20 10
2032 5 r. Pakistani toy bullock cart . 20 10
2033 5 r. Iranian buff earthenware 20 10

577 Flowers on Map of Asia
578 Map and Emblem

1977. 2nd Asia-Pacific Jamboree, Nishapur
2034 **577** 10 r. multicoloured . . . 25 10

1977. 9th Asian Electronics Conference, Teheran.
2035 **578** 3 r. multicoloured 15 10

579 "Tree" in Farsi Script
580 Globe and Envelope

1977. Teachers' Day.
2036 **579** 10 r. multicoloured . . . 30 10

1977. Centenary of Iran's Admission to U.P.U.
2037 **580** 14 r. multicoloured . . . 30 10

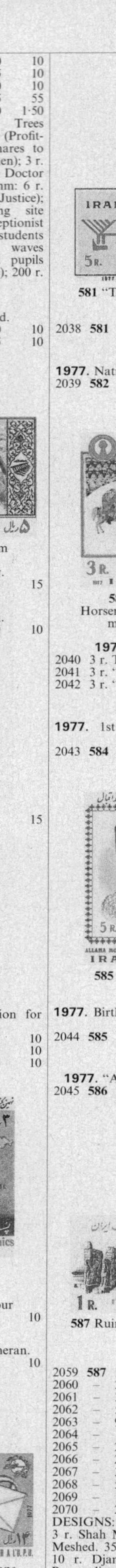
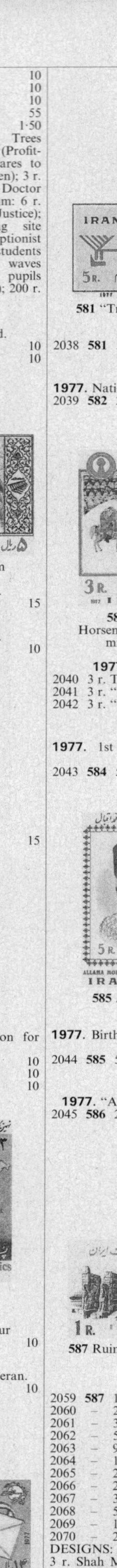
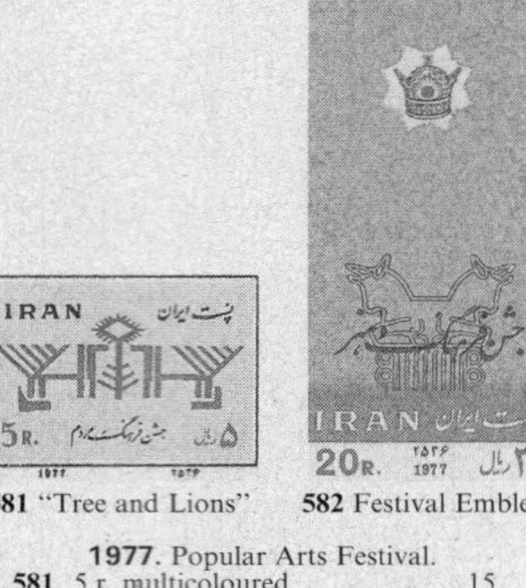
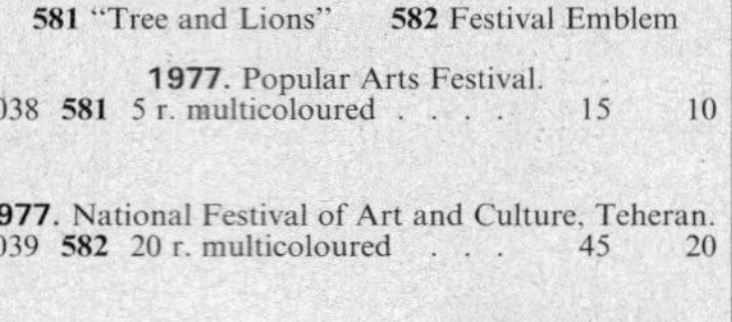

581 "Tree and Lions"
582 Festival Emblem

1977. Popular Arts Festival.
2038 **581** 5 r. multicoloured 15 10

1977. National Festival of Art and Culture, Teheran.
2039 **582** 20 r. multicoloured . . . 45 20

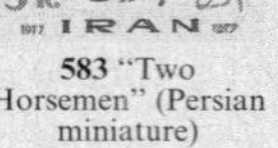

583 "Two Horsemen" (Persian miniature)
584 Seminar Emblem

1977. Children's Week. Multicoloured.
2040 3 r. Type **583** 15 10
2041 3 r. "Lover and his mistress" . 15 10
2042 3 r. "Five people round a bed" 15 10

1977. 1st Regional Seminar on Education and Welfare of the Deaf.
2043 **584** 5 r. multicoloured 15 10

585 A. M. Iqbal
586 Bronze Head from Nigeria

1977. Birth Centenary of Allama Mohammad Iqbal (Pakistani poet).
2044 **585** 5 r. multicoloured 15 10

1977. "Art of Black Africa" Exhibition, Teheran.
2045 **586** 20 r. multicoloured . . . 1·60 30

587 Ruins at Persepolis
588 Mohammed Riza Pahlavi

1978.
2059 **587** 1 r. brown and gold . . . 10 10
2060 – 2 r. green and gold . . . 20 10
2061 – 3 r. purple and gold . . . 30 10
2062 – 5 r. green and gold . . . 40 10
2063 – 9 r. brown and gold . . . 85 30
2064 – 10 r. blue and gold . . . 3·50 35
2065 – 20 r. red and gold . . . 1·00 30
2066 – 25 r. blue and gold . . . 17·00 2·75
2067 – 30 r. red and gold . . . 1·75 35
2068 – 50 r. green and gold . . . 2·75 1·75
2069 – 100 r. blue and gold . . . 9·00 4·25
2070 – 200 r. violet and gold . . . 12·00 9·00

DESIGNS: 30 × 23 mm: 2 r. Khajou Bridge, Isfahan; 3 r. Shah Mosque, Isfahan; 5 r. Imam Riza Shrine, Meshed. 35 × 26 mm: 9 r. Warrior frieze, Persepolis; 10 r. Djameh Mosque, Isfahan; 20 r. Bas-relief, Persepolis; 25 r. Shaikh Lotfollah Mosque; 30 r. Ruins, Persepolis (different); 50 r. Ali Ghapou Palace, Isfahan; 100 r. Stone relief, Tagh Bastan; 200 r. Relief, Naqsh Rostam.

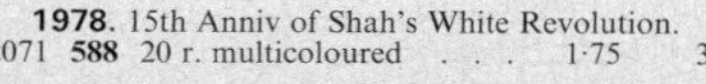

1978. 15th Anniv of Shah's White Revolution.
2071 **588** 20 r. multicoloured . . . 1·75 30

589 Animals (carpet)
590 Costume of Mazandera Province

1978. Inauguration of Persian Carpets Museum, Teheran. Multicoloured.
2072 3 r. Type **589** 15 10
2073 5 r. Court scene 20 10
2074 10 r. Floral pattern 30 15

1978. New Year Festival. Multicoloured.
2075 3 r. Type **590** 15 10
2076 5 r. Woman in costume of Mazandera Province 25 10

591 Riza Shah Pahlavi and Crown Prince inspecting Girls' School

1978. Birth Centenary of Riza Shah Pahlavi. Multicoloured.
2077 3 r. Type **591** 15 10
2078 5 r. Riza Shah Pahlavi and Crown Prince at inauguration of Trans-Iranian Railway . . 1·25 30
2079 10 r. Riza Shah Pahlavi and Crown Prince at Palace of Persepolis 55 15
2080 14 r. Shah handing Crown Prince officer's diploma . . 60 20

592 Satellite and Receiving Station

1978. 10th Anniv of Admission to International Telecommunications Union.
2081 **592** 20 r. multicoloured . . . 65 20

593 Microwave Antenna

1978. World Telecommunications Day.
2082 **593** 15 r. multicoloured . . . 55 20

594 Welfare Legion Emblem
595 Pink Roses

1978. 10th Anniv of Universal Welfare Legion.
2083 **594** 10 r. multicoloured . . . 20 10

1978. 14th Anniv of Regional Co-operation for Development. Roses. Multicoloured.
2084 5 r. Type **595** 15 10
2085 10 r. Salmon rose 35 10
2086 15 r. Red roses 60 15

596 Rhazes and Pharmaceutical Equipment

1978. Pharmacists' Day.
2087 **596** 5 r. multicoloured 20 10

597 Girl Guides and Aryamehr Arch

1978. 23rd World Girl Guides Conference, Teheran.
2088 **597** 5 r. multicoloured 20 10

598 Riza Shah Pahlavi

1978. 50th Anniv of Bank Melli Iran. Mult.
2089 3 r. Type **598** 40 15
2090 5 r. Mohammed Riza Pahlavi . 60 15

599 Young Girl and Bird

1978. Children's Week.
2091 **599** 3 r. multicoloured 20 10

600 U.P.U. Emblem over Map of Iran

1978. World Post Day.
2092 **600** 14 r. multicoloured . . . 50 10

601 Classroom and Communications Equipment

1978. 50th Anniv of Communications Faculty.
2093 **601** 10 r. multicoloured . . . 60 10

602 Human Rights Emblem
603 Rose

1978. 30th Anniv of Human Rights Declaration.
2094 **602** 20 r. multicoloured . . . 1·60 15

1979. New Year Festival. Multicoloured.
2095 2 r. Type **603** 15 10
2096 3 r. Man in Khurdistan costume 60 10
2097 5 r. Woman in Khurdistan costume 90 15

604 Revolutionary Crowd

1979. Islamic Revolution. Multicoloured.
2098 3 r. Type **604** 80 15
2099 5 r. Hands holding flower, gun and torch 60 15
2100 10 r. Protest march 70 30
2101 20 r. Bloodied hands releasing dove (vert) . . . . . . 1·60 30

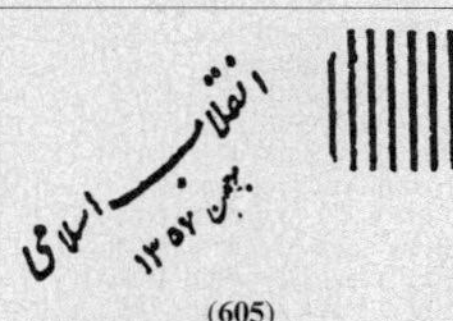

(605)

1979. Designs as T **587** optd with T **605**.
(a) Nos. 1945/6.
2102 8 r. red and brown . . . . . 1·00 15
2103 10 r. green and brown . . . . 24·00 85
(b) Nos. 2063/4, 2068/70 and unissued 15 r. and 19 r. stamps.
2104 9 r. brown and gold . . . . . 1·00 15
2105 10 r. turquoise and gold . . . 30 15
2106 15 r. mauve and gold 30 15
2107 19 r. green and gold 65 15
2108 50 r. green and gold . . . . . 2·50 35
2109 100 r. blue and gold . . . . . 5·00 70
2110 200 r. violet and gold . . . . 6·25 1·75
DESIGNS—HORIZ: (36 × 26 mm): 15 r. Rock carvings, Naqsh Rostam; 19 r. Chehel Sotoon Palace, Isfahan.

606 Tulip formed from "Allah" and "Islamic Republic"

607 "Iranian Goldsmith" (Kamal el Molk)

1979. Islamic Republic.
2111 **606** 5 r. multicoloured 85 15

1979. 15th Anniv of Regional Co-operation for Development. Paintings. Multicoloured.
2112 5 r. Type **607** . . . . 1·50 15
2113 5 r. "Turkish Harvest" (Namik Ismail) . . . . 1·50 15
2114 5 r. "Pakistan Village Scene" (Allah Baksh) . . . . . . 1·50 15

608 "Telecom 79"

1979. Third World Telecommunications Exhibition, Geneva.
2115 **608** 20 r. gold, black & red . . 3·50 20

609 Tulip rising from Blood of Revolutionary

610 Persian Rug

1979. International Year of the Child. Children's Paintings. Multicoloured.
2116 2 r. Type **609** 40 15
2117 3 r. Children greeting the rising sun (vert) 50 15
2118 5 r. Children with banners . . 1·00 15

1979.
2119 **610** 50 d. brown & orange . . 10 10
2120 1 r. blue & light blue . . 10 10
2121 2 r. red and yellow . . . 10 10
2122 3 r. blue and mauve . . . 10 10
2123 5 r. olive and green . . . 15 10
2124 10 r. black and pink . . . 25 10
2125 20 r. brown and grey . . 35 10
2126 50 r. violet and grey . . . 85 10
2127 100 r. black and green . . 4·00 70
2128 200 r. blue and stone . . 3·00 1·50
Nos. 2126/8 are larger, 27 × 37 mm.

611 Globe in Envelope

612 Kashani and Astrolabe

1979. World Post Day.
2134 **611** 10 r. multicoloured . . . . 1·50 15

1979. 550th Death Anniv of Ghyath-al-din Jamshid Kashani (mathematician and astronomer).
2135 **612** 5 r. black and brown . . . 85 15

613 Kaaba, Mecca

1980. 1400th Anniv of Hegira (1st issue). Multicoloured.
2136 3 r. Type **613** 10 10
2137 5 r. Koran and globe (vert) . . 15 10
2138 10 r. Pilgrim and Kaaba . . . 30 10
See also Nos. 2148/51.

614 Flag and Revolutionaries

615 Dehkhoda

1980. 1st Anniv of Islamic Revolution. Mult.
2139 1 r. Type **614** (28 × 40 mm) . 10 10
2432 1 r. As No. 2139 but 24 × 35 mm 10 10
2140 3 r. Dagger and dripping blood (28 × 40 mm) 10 10
2433 3 r. As No. 2140 but 24 × 36 mm 15 15
2141 5 r. Open window and rising sun (28 × 40 mm) 15 10
2435 5 r. As No. 2141 but 24 × 36 mm 20 20

1980. Birth Centenary of Dehkhoda (compiler, Iranian encyclopedia).
2142 **615** 10 r. multicoloured 20 10

616 Female Costume of East Azerbaijan

617 M. Mossadegh

1980. New Year Festival. Multicoloured.
2143 3 r. Type **616** 15 10
2144 5 r. Male costume of East Azerbaijan 20 10

1980. Birth Centenary of Dr. Mohammed Mossadegh (statesman).
2145 **617** 20 r. multicoloured 45 20

618 Morteza Mottahari

619 Telephone

1980. 1st Death Anniv of Prof. Morteza Mottahari.
2146 **618** 10 r. black and red 20 10

1980. World Telecommunications Day.
2147 **619** 20 r. black, green & red . . 40 15

620 Mosque Interior

1980. 1400th Anniv of Hegira (2nd issue). Multicoloured.
2148 50 d. Type **620** 10 10
2149 1 r. Crowd with banner . . . 10 10
2150 3 r. Al-Biruni, Farabi and Avicenna 10 10
2151 5 r. Mosque and Kaaba . . . 15 10

621 Dr. Ali Shariati

622 Kaaba and Banner

1980. Dr. Ali Shariati (educator) Commemoration.
2152 **621** 5 r. multicoloured 20 10

1980. Birth Anniv of Hazrat Mehdi (Shiite Imam).
2153 **622** 5 r. green, red & black . . 20 10

623 Ayatollah Teleghani

624 O.P.E.C. Emblem and Globe

1980. Ayatollah Teleghani Commemoration.
2154 **623** 5 r. multicoloured 35 10

1980. 20th Anniv of Organization of Petroleum Exporting Countries. Multicoloured.
2155 5 r. Type **624** 20 10
2156 10 r. Figures supporting O.P.E.C. emblem 35 10

625 Hands breaking Star of David around Dome of the Rock

626 Tulip and Feizieh Theological College

1980. "Let us Liberate Jerusalem".
2157 **625** 5 r. multicoloured 20 10
2158 20 r. multicoloured 45 20

1981. 2nd Anniv of Islamic Revolution. Mult.
2159 3 r. Type **626** (dated "1981" at right) 20 10
2434 3 r. As No. 2159 but dated at left 15 15
2160 5 r. Tulip (in red), drops of blood and "Martyr" in Persian script 25 10
2436 5 r. As No. 2160 but orange tulip 20 20
2161 20 r. Open tulip (in red) and crest of Republic 50 20
2441 20 r. As No. 2161 but orange tulip 50 50

627 Male Costume of Lorestan

628 I.T.U. and W.H.O. Emblems with Ribbons forming Caduceus

1981. New Year Festival. Multicoloured.
2162 5 r. Type **627** 20 10
2163 10 r. Female costume, Lorestan 40 10

1981. World Telecommunications Day.
2164 **628** 5 r. orange, blk & grn . . 20 10

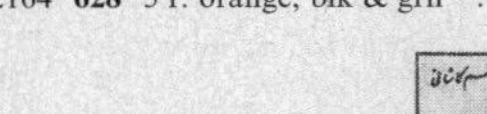

630 Militia Training

631 Ayatollah Kashani

1981.
2165 **630** 50 d. black and brown . . 10 10
2166 – 1 r. purple and green . . 10 10
2167 – 2 r. brown and blue . . . 10 10
2168 – 3 r. black and green . . . 10 10
2169 – 5 r. blue and brown . . . 15 10
2170 – 10 r. ultramarine & blue . 20 10
2171 – 20 r. black and red . . . 50 20
2172 – 50 r. black and mauve . . 80 30
2173 – 100 r. black and brown . 1·50 55
2174 – 200 r. blue and black . . 3·50 75
DESIGNS—As Type **630**: 1 r. Man and boy at school desk (Literacy campaign); 2 r. Digging irrigation ditch. 37 × 27 mm: 3 r. Massed prayers; 20 r. Woman with rifle; 50 r. Worker at lathe; 100 r. Pilgrims around Kaaba. 27 × 37 mm: 5 r. Revolutionary Guards emblem and crowd; 10 r. Arabic tapestry; 200 r. Niche in Mosque illuminated by sun.

1981. Birth Centenary of Ayatollah Kashani.
2175 **631** 15 r. purple and green . . 35 15

632 Armed Forces

1981. Islamic Iranian Army.
2176 **632** 5 r. multicoloured 20 10

633 Carrier Pigeon flying over Gun Barrels

1981. U.P.U. Day.
2177 **633** 20 r. black and blue . . . 55 15

634 Inscription

1981. Millenary of "Nabj al-Blagah" (sacred book).
2178 **634** 25 r. green, blue & black . . 50 15

635 Victims of Bomb at Islamic Party's Headquarters

1981. Iranian Bomb and War Victims, Commemoration.
2179 **635** 3 r. black and red 15 10
2180 – 5 r. brown & dp brown . . 20 10
2181 – 10 r. multicoloured . . . 30 15
DESIGNS: 5 r. President Rajai and Prime Minister Bahomar (bomb victims); 10 r. Dr. Chamran (killed in Iran–Iraq War).

636 Ayatollah Tabatabaee

637 Hand writing on Board

1981. Death Centenary of Ayatollah Ghazi Tabatabaee.
2182 **636** 5 r. brown, grn & gold . . 15 10

1982. Literacy Campaign.
2183 **637** 5 r. blue and gold 15 10

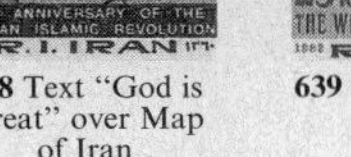

638 Text "God is Great" over Map of Iran

639 Banner around Globe

1982. 3rd Anniv of Islamic Revolution. Mult.
2184 5 r. Type **638** 15 10
2185 10 r. Dove forming tulip . . . 25 15
2186 20 r. "God is Great" over Globe 45 25

1982. Islamic Unity Week.

2187 **639** 25 r. multicoloured . . . 50 15

640 Manacled Hands reaching towards Christ

1982. Glorification of Christ's Birth.

2188 **640** 20 r. multicoloured . . . 55 20

641 Male Costume of Khuzestan

642 National Flag

1982. New Year Festival. Multicoloured.

2189 3 r. Type **641** 10 10

2190 5 r. Female costume of Khuzestan 15 10

1982. 3rd Anniv of Islamic Republic.

2191 **642** 30 r. black, red & green . 50 20

643 Ayatollah Sadr

1982. 2nd Death Anniv of Ayatollah Sadr.

2192 **643** 50 r. multicoloured . . . 60 30

644 Ayatollahs Madani and Dastghib

1982. Ayatollahs Sayed Assadollah Madani and Sayed Abdolhossein Dastghib Commemoration.

2193 **644** 50 r. red, black & gold . . 60 30

645 Hand holding Cogwheels

646 Geometric Pattern

1982. Labour Day.

2194 **645** 100 r. multicoloured . . . 1·40 50

1982. World Telecommunications Day.

2195 **646** 100 r. multicoloured . . . 1·40 50

647 Symbolic Design

648 Rifles and Clenched Fist

1982. Ma'bas Festival.

2196 **647** 32 r. multicoloured . . . 60 20

1982. 19th Anniv of 1963 Islamic Rising.

2197 **648** 20 r. blk, red & silver . . 60 20

649 Lieutenant Islambuli

650 Ayatollah Beheshti

1982. Lieutenant Khaled Islambuli (assassin of Pres. Sadat of Egypt). Commemoration.

2198 **649** 2 r. multicoloured 20 10

1982. 1st Death Anniv of Ayatollah Mohammed Hossein Beheshti.

2199 **650** 10 r. multicoloured . . . 30 15

651 Soldiers, Tanks and Hand holding Banner

1982. Victims of War against Iraq Commemoration.

2200 **651** 5 r. multicoloured 20 10

652 Dome of the Rock

1982. World Jerusalem Day.

2201 **652** 1 r. multicoloured 20 10

653 Pilgrims around Kaaba

654 Globe and Letters

1982. Pilgrimage to Mecca.

2202 **653** 10 r. multicoloured . . . 25 10

1982. World U.P.U. Day.

2203 **654** 30 r. multicoloured . . . 65 20

655 Bloodied Hand releasing Dove

656 Casting Vote

1983. 4th Anniv of Islamic Revolution.

2204 **655** 30 r. multicoloured (crowd in brown) 60 15

2445 30 r. multicoloured (crowd in orange) 75 75

1983. 4th Anniv of Islamic Republic.

2205 **656** 10 r. red, black & green . 30 10

657 "Enlightenment"

658 Microwave Antenna and "83"

1983. Teachers' Day.

2206 **657** 5 r. multicoloured 15 10

1983. World Communications Year.

2207 **658** 20 r. blue, mauve & brn . 55 10

659 Assembly

660 Doves and Crowd

1983. First Session of Islamic Consultative Assembly.

2208 **659** 5 r. multicoloured 15 10

1983. 20th Anniv of 1963 Islamic Rising.

2209 **660** 10 r. multicoloured . . . 25 10

661 Map of Persian Gulf and burning Oil Wells at Nowruz

1983. Ecology Week.

2210 **661** 5 r. black, red and blue . 30 10

662 Sadooghi

663 Hands holding Rifle over Dome of the Rock

1983. Ayatollah Mohammad Sadooghi Commemoration.

2211 **662** 20 r. black and red . . . 55 10

1983. World Jerusalem Day.

2212 **663** 5 r. yellow, brown & blue . 20 10

664 Rajai and Bahomar

1983. Government Week (death anniv of Pres. Rajai and Prime Minister Dr. Bahomar).

2213 **664** 3 r. orange and blue . . . 20 10

665 Cartridges and Text

666 Stamps and Map of Iran around Globe

1983. War Week.

2214 **665** 5 r. green and red 20 10

1983. World U.P.U. Day.

2215 **666** 10 r. multicoloured . . . 30 10

667 Esfahani

668 Mirza Kuchik Khan

1983. 4th Death Anniv of Ayatollah Ashrafi Esfahani.

2216 **667** 5 r. multicoloured 15 10

1983. Religious and Political Personalities.

2217 – 1 r. black and pink . . . 10 10

2218 **668** 2 r. black and orange . . 10 10

2219 – 3 r. black and blue . . . 10 10

2220 – 5 r. black and red . . . 15 10

2221 – 10 r. black and green . . 30 10

2222 – 20 r. black and purple . . 55 20

2223 – 30 r. black and brown . . 75 30

2224 – 50 r. black and blue . . . 95 50

2225 – 100 r. black and red . . . 2·00 65

2226 – 200 r. black and green . . 4·00 1·25

DESIGNS: 1 r. Sheikh Mohammed Khiabani; 3 r. Seyd Modjtaba Navab Safavi; 5 r. Seyd Jamal-ed-Din Assadabadi; 10 r. Seyd Hassah Modaress; 20 r. Sheikh Fazel Assad Nouri; 30 r. Mirza Mohammed Hossein Naieni; 50 r. Sheikh Mohammed Hossein Kashef; 100 r. Seyd Hassan Shirazi; 200 r. Mirza Reza Kermani.

669 Sword severing "Right of Veto" Hand

670 Storming the U.S. Embassy, Hostage and burning American Flag

1983. United Nations Day.

2228 **669** 32 r. multicoloured . . . 60 30

1983. 4th Anniv of Storming of United States Embassy.

2229 **670** 28 r. multicoloured . . . 40 10

671 Avicenna and Globe

1983. International Medical Seminar, Teheran.

2230 **671** 3 r. purple and blue . . . 20 10

672 Young and Old Soldiers

1983. Preparation Day.

2231 **672** 20 r. green, black & red . 55 20

673 Fist with Gun and Dove

1983. Saddam's Crimes Conference.

2232 **673** 5 r. black and mauve . . 20 10

674 Dr. Mohammad Mofatteh

675 Light shining on Globe

1983. 4th Death Anniv of Dr. Mohammed Mofatteh.

2233 **674** 10 r. mve, blk & gold . . 30 10

1983. Mohammed's Birth Anniv.

2234 **675** 5 r. blue, brown & green . 20 10

676 Tulips and Flag

677 Nurse tending Wounded Soldier

1984. 5th Anniv of Islamic Revolution.
2235 **676** 10 r. multicoloured . . . 30 10

1984. Nurses' Day.
2240 **677** 20 r. multicoloured . . . 55 20

678 Soldier in Wheelchair

679 "Lotus gebelia"

1984. Invalids' Day.
2241 **678** 5 r. multicoloured 20 10

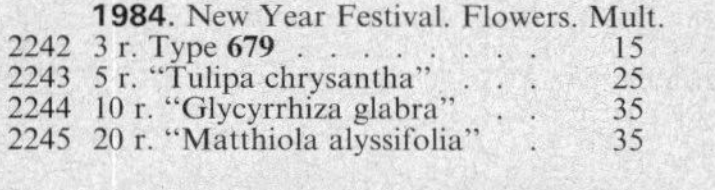
1984. New Year Festival. Flowers. Mult.
2242 3 r. Type **679** 15 10
2243 5 r. "Tulipa chrysantha" . . . 25 10
2244 10 r. "Glycyrrhiza glabra" . . 35 15
2245 20 r. "Matthiola alyssifolia" . . 35 25

680 Malcolm Little (founder of Union of Moslem Mosques and Organization for African-American Unity)

1984. Struggle Against Racial Discrimination.
2246 **680** 5 r. multicoloured 20 10

681 Flag around Globe

683 Harb

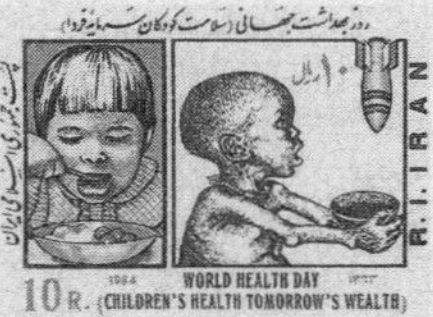

682 Well-fed and Starving Children

1984. 5th Anniv of Islamic Republic.
2247 **681** 5 r. multicoloured 20 10

1984. World Health Day.
2248 **682** 10 r. multicoloured . . . 30 15

1984. 22nd Death Anniv of Sheikh Ragheb Harb.
2249 **683** 5 r. black, red and green . . 20 10

684 Family holding Red Crescent Banner

685 Transmitter

1984. World Red Cross and Red Crescent Day.
2250 **684** 5 r. multicoloured 20 10

1984. World Telecommunications Day.
2251 **685** 20 r. black, blue and red . 30 10

686 Ghotb

688 Jerusalem, Map of Israel and Koran

687 Kaaba and Destruction of Images

1984. 19th Death Anniv of Seyyed Ghotb.
2252 **686** 10 r. black, gold & orge . 25 15

1984. Conquest of Mecca.
2253 **687** 5 r. multicoloured 20 10

1984. World Jerusalem Day (5 r.) and Fetr Feast (10 r.). Multicoloured.
2254 5 r. Type **688** 20 10
2255 10 r. Crowd around Mosque . 30 20

689 Choga Zanbil, Susa

1984. Preservation of Cultural Heritage. Mult.
2256 5 r. Type **689** 20 10
2257 5 r. Emamzadeh Hossein shrine, Qazvin (Arabic date at left) . 20 10
2258 5 r. Imam Mosque, Isfahan . . 20 10
2259 5 r. Ark Fortress, Tabriz . . . 20 10
2260 5 r. Prophet Daniel's Mausoleum, Susa (with conical tower) 20 10

691 Crowd around Kaaba

692 Spirit Nebula

1984. Feast of Sacrifices.
2261 **691** 10 r. multicoloured . . . 25 15

1984. 10th International Trade Fair, Teheran.
2262 **692** 10 r. blue and red 25 15

693 Rifle and Cartridges on Flower

694 Stylized Pigeon and U.P.U. Emblem

1984. War Week.
2263 **693** 5 r. multicoloured 20 10

1984. World Universal Postal Union Day.
2264 **694** 20 r. multicoloured . . . 45 30

MINIMUM PRICE

The minimum price quoted is 10p which represents a handling charge rather than a basis for valuing common stamps. For further notes about prices see introductory pages.

695 Khomeini

696 Tabatabaie

1984. 7th Death Anniv of Haj Seyyed Mostafa Khomeini.
2265 **695** 5 r. multicoloured 20 10

1984. Ghazi Tabatabaie Commemoration.
2266 **696** 5 r. black, gold and red . 20 10

697 Saadi

698 Clasped Hands, Mosque and Koran

1984. 800th Birth Anniv of Saadi (poet) Congress.
2267 **697** 10 r. multicoloured . . . 25 15

1984. Mohammed's Birth Anniv and Unity Week.
2268 **698** 5 r. multicoloured 20 10

699 Doves as Petals

700 Sapling and Forest

1985. 6th Anniv of Islamic Revolution (1st issue).
2269 **699** 40 r. multicoloured (tulip emblem in red) 60 35
2446 40 r. multicoloured (tulip emblem in mauve) . . 75 45
See also No. 2277.

1985. Tree Planting Day. Multicoloured.
2270 3 r. Type **700** 15 10
2271 5 r. Sapling growing near forest 20 10

701 Crown Imperial ("Fritillaria imperialis")

702 Procession of Women with Flags

1985. New Year Festival. Multicoloured.
2272 5 r. Type **701** 20 10
2273 5 r. Pilewort ("Ranunculus ficarioides") 20 10
2274 5 r. Saffron crocus ("Crocus sativus") 20 10
2275 5 r. "Primula heterochroma" . 20 10

1985. Women's Day and Birth Anniv of Fatima.
2276 **702** 10 r. multicoloured . . . 25 15

703 Tulip and Ballot Box

704 Koran

1985. 6th Anniv of Islamic Republic (2nd issue).
2277 **703** 20 r. multicoloured . . . 50 30

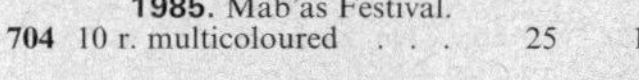
1985. Mab'as Festival.
2278 **704** 10 r. multicoloured . . . 25 15

705 Globe, Chain, Banner, Kaaba and Scales

706 I.T.U. Emblem and Telephone Handsets

1985. World Day of the Oppressed.
2279 **705** 5 r. multicoloured 20 10

1985. World Telecommunications Day.
2280 **706** 20 r. multicoloured . . . 50 30

707 Soldier saluting and Bridge

708 Fist, Rifles and Qum Theological College

1985. Liberation of Khorramshahr.
2281 **707** 5 r. multicoloured 25 10

1985. 22nd Anniv of 1963 Islamic Rising.
2282 **708** 10 r. multicoloured . . . 25 15

709 Decorated Plates and Vases

1985. World Handicrafts Day.
2283 **709** 20 r. multicoloured . . . 50 30

710 Map of Israel and Dome of the Rock

711 Arabic Script

1985. World Jerusalem Day.
2284 **710** 5 r. multicoloured 20 10

1985. Fetr Feast.
2285 **711** 5 r. blue, red and black . 20 10

712 Organization Emblem

1985. 4th Anniv of Islamic Propagation Organization.
2286 **712** 5 r. brown, green & blk . 20 10

713 Abdolhossein Amini and the Koran

714 Pilgrims around Holy Kaaba

1985. Ayatollah Sheikh Abdolhossein Amini (theologian) Commemoration.
2287 **713** 5 r. multicoloured 20 10

1985. Pilgrimage to Mecca.
2288 **714** 10 r. multicoloured . . . 30 15

715 Two Swords Pattern

716 Revolutionaries and Mosque

1985. Preservation of Cultural History. Ancient Ceramic Plates from Nishabur. Multicoloured.
2289 5 r. Type **715** 20 10
2290 5 r. Plate with border of Farsi script 20 10
2291 5 r. Stylised bird pattern . . . 20 10
2292 5 r. Four leaves and knot pattern 20 10

1985. 50th Anniv of Rising in Goharshad Mosque, Meshed.
2293 **716** 10 r. multicoloured . . . 30 15

717 Health Services

718 Red Tulips dripping Blood

1985. Government and People Week. Multicoloured.
2294 5 r. Envelope, crane and mechanical digger 20 10
2295 5 r. Factory, cogwheel and ear of wheat 20 10
2296 5 r. Type **717** 20 10
2297 5 r. Literacy campaign emblem on book 20 10

1985. 7th Anniv of "Bloody Friday" Riots.
2298 **718** 10 r. multicoloured . . . 30 15

719 O.P.E.C. Emblem and "25"

720 Dead Iranian

1985. 25th Anniv of Organization of Petroleum Exporting Countries.
2299 **719** 5 r. yellow and brown . . 20 10
2300 – 5 r. blue and green . . . 20 10
DESIGN: No. 2300, O.P.E.C. emblem and world map.

1985. 5th Anniv of Iran–Iraq War. Mult.
2301 5 r. Type **720** 20 10
2302 5 r. Dome of mosque and text "Ashura" 20 10
2303 5 r. White doves with map of Iran under a hail of bombs . 20 10
2304 5 r. Oasis and exploding rifle . 20 10

721 Symbolic Design

722 Envelopes and Posthorn

1985. Death Millenary of Ash-Sharif Ar-Radi (writer).
2305 **721** 20 r. blue, gold & ultram . 50 30

1985. World U.P.U. Day.
2306 **722** 20 r. multicoloured . . . 50 30

723 Emblem

724 Seedling and Ear of Wheat in Hand

1985. World Standards Day.
2307 **723** 20 r. multicoloured . . . 50 30

1985. Agricultural Training and Extension Year.
2308 **724** 5 r. multicoloured 20 10

725 Seal of U.S. Embassy

726 Kaaba, Mosque and Clasped Hands

1985. 6th Anniv of Storming of United States Embassy.
2309 **725** 40 r. multicoloured . . . 60 30

1985. Mohammed's Birth Anniv and Unity Week.
2310 **726** 10 r. multicoloured . . . 30 15

727 Rose growing from Pen Nib and Tulip

728 Profiles and Symbols of Learning

1985. High Council of Cultural Revolution Anniv.
2311 **727** 5 r. multicoloured 20 10

1985. International Youth Year. Mult.
2312 5 r. Type **728** 20 10
2313 5 r. Profiles and symbols of war 20 10
2314 5 r. Profiles and symbols of industry and agriculture . . 20 10
2315 5 r. Profiles and sports pictograms 20 10

729 Ezzeddin Al-Qassam

730 Bayonets, Map and Clenched Fists

1985. 50th Death Anniv of Ezzeddin Al-Qassam.
2316 **729** 20 r. brown, red & silver . 50 30

1985. Afghan Resistance to Occupation.
2317 **730** 40 r. multicoloured . . . 75 40

731 Mirza Taqi Khan Amir Kabir

732 Tulips and Crowd destroying Statue

1986. 135th Death Anniv of Mirza Taqi Khan Amir Kabir.
2318 **731** 5 r. multicoloured 20 15

1986. 7th Anniv of Islamic Revolution.
2319 **732** 20 r. multicoloured . . . 60 35

733 Sulayman Khater and Dome of the Rock

1986. 40th Death Anniv of Sulayman Khater.
2320 **733** 10 r. black, blue & red . . 30 15

734 Woman, Child and Crowd

735 "Papaver orientale"

1986. Women's Day and Birth Anniv of Fatima.
2321 **734** 10 r. multicoloured . . . 30 15

1986. New Year Festival. Flowers. Mult.
2322 5 r. Type **735** 20 10
2323 5 r. "Anemone coronaria" . . 20 10
2324 5 r. "Papaver bracteatum" . . 20 10
2325 5 r. "Anemone biflora" . . . 20 10

736 Fist and Text

737 Rose, Globe and Coloured Bands

1986. "2000th Day of Sacred Defence" (Iran–Iraq war).
2326 **736** 5 r. green and red . . . 20 15

1986. Struggle against Racial Discrimination.
2327 **737** 5 r. multicoloured 20 15

738 Iranian Flag and Map

1986. 7th Anniv of Islamic Republic.
2328 **738** 10 r. multicoloured . . . 30 15

739 Dome

740 Insignia

1986. Mab'as Festival.
2329 **739** 40 r. multicoloured . . . 50 25

1986. Army Day.
2330 **740** 5 r. multicoloured 25 15

741 Dead Soldier and Wrecked Helicopter

742 Text

1986. 6th Anniv of United States Landing at Tabas.
2331 **741** 40 r. orange, grn & blk . . 90 40

1986. World Day of the Oppressed. Birth Anniv of Imam Mahdi.
2332 **742** 10 r. black, red & gold . . 30 20

743 Symbolic Design

744 Antennae and Radio Waves

1986. Teachers' Day.
2333 **743** 5 r. multicoloured 20 15

1986. World Communications Day.
2334 **744** 20 r. black, silver & bl . . 60 35

745 Soldier and Tanks

1986. International Children's Day.
2335 **745** 15 r. multicoloured . . . 40 30
2336 – 15 r. black, bl & mve . . 40 30
DESIGN: No. 2336, Boy and text.

746 Qum Theological College and Sun Rays

747 Dome of the Rock, Map of Israel and Barbed Wire

1986. 23rd Anniv of 1963 Islamic Rising.
2337 **746** 10 r. multicoloured . . . 30 15

1986. World Jerusalem Day.
2338 **747** 10 r. multicoloured . . . 40 15

748 Crowd at Prayer

1986. Fetr Festival.
2339 **748** 10 r. multicoloured . . . 30 15

749 Baluchi Needle Work

1986. World Handicrafts Day. Multicoloured.
2340 10 r. Type **749** 30 20
2341 10 r. Master craftswomen at work 30 20
2342 10 r. Carpet 30 20
2343 10 r. Engraved copper vase . . 30 20

750 Linked Hands around Map on Globe

751 Dr. Beheshti, Doves and Explosion

1986. Solidarity with South African People.
2344 **750** 10 r. multicoloured . . . 30 15

1986. 5th Anniv of Bomb Explosion at Islamic Party Headquarters, Teheran.
2345 **751** 10 r. multicoloured . . . 30 15

752 Ayatollah Mohammad Taqi Shirazi and Map

753 Shrine, Meshed

1986. Iraqi Muslim Rising.
2346 **752** 20 r. multicoloured . . . 50 30

1986. Birth Anniv of Imam Riza.
2347 **753** 10 r. multicoloured . . . 30 15

754 Crowd around Kaaba, Flag and Clenched Fists

755 Soltanieh Mosque

1986. Feast of Sacrifices.
2348 **754** 10 r. multicoloured . . . 30 15

1986. Preservation of Cultural Heritage. Mult.
2349 5 r. Type **755** 20 10
2350 5 r. Mausoleum of Sohel Ben Ali, Astaneh 20 10
2351 5 r. Bam fortress 20 10
2352 5 r. Gateway of Blue Mosque, Tabriz 20 10

756 "Eid-ul-Ghadir" in Arabic

757 Graph, Roof and People

1986. Ghadir Festival.
2353 **756** 20 r. light green, green and black 50 30

1986. Population and Housing Census.
2354 **757** 20 r. multicoloured . . . 50 30

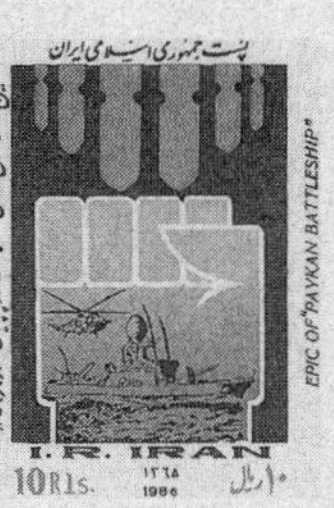

758 Missle Boat "Paykan" in Fist below Bombs

1986. 6th Anniv of Iran–Iraq War. Mult.
2355 **758** 10 r. blue, black & red . . 55 15
2356 – 10 r. red and black . . . 30 15
2357 – 10 r. yellow, black & red . 30 15
2358 – 10 r. blue, black & red . 30 15
2359 – 10 r. green, black & red . 30 15
DESIGNS: No. 2356, Khorramshar; 2357, Howeizah; 2358, Siege of Abadan; 2359, Susangard.

759 Wrestling

1986. 10th Asian Games, Seoul. Multicoloured.
2360 15 r. Type **759** 35 20
2361 15 r. Rifle shooting 35 20

760 Bird with Envelopes as Wings on Globe

1986. World Universal Postal Union Day.
2362 **760** 20 r. multicoloured . . . 50 30

761 Emblem

762 Allameh Tabatabaie

1986. 40th Anniv of U.N.E.S.C.O.
2363 **761** 45 r. blue, black and red . 75 35

1986. 5th Death Anniv of Allameh Tabatabaie.
2364 **762** 10 r. green, gold & blk . . 20 15

763 Sun behind Dome and Minaret

764 Militiamen with Flags

1986. Mohammed's Birth Anniv and Unity Week.
2365 **763** 10 r. multicoloured . . . 20 15

1986. "Mobilization of the Oppressed" Week.
2366 **764** 5 r. multicoloured 20 15

765 Guerrilla Fighters

1986. Afghan Resistance to Occupation.
2367 **765** 40 r. multicoloured . . . 65 30

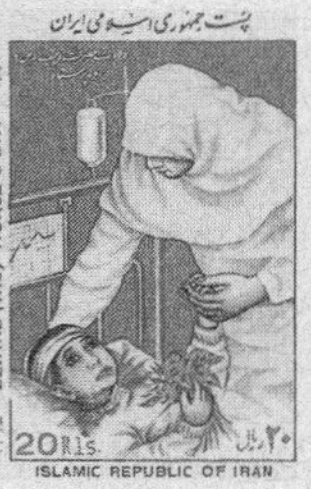

766 Nurse tending Boy

767 Emblem and Tulip on Globe

1987. Nurses' Day.
2368 **766** 20 r. multicoloured . . . 50 30

1987. 5th Islamic Theology Conference, Teheran.
2369 **767** 20 r. multicoloured . . . 50 30

768 Emblems of Revolution

1987. 8th Anniv of Islamic Revolution.
2370 **768** 20 r. multicoloured (38 × 58 mm) 50 30
2444 20 r. multicoloured (24 × 37 mm) 50 50

769 Emblem and Crowd

770 Woman and Soldiers

1987. 8th Anniv of Revolutionary Committees.
2371 **769** 10 r. yellow, blue & red . 30 15

1987. Women's Day and Birth Anniv of Fatima.
2372 **770** 10 r. multicoloured . . . 30 15

771 Airbus Industrie A300 Aircraft and Banner around Globe

1987. 25th Anniv of Iranair.
2373 **771** 30 r. multicoloured . . . 90 45

772 Ayatollah Naeini

773 Flag Irises

1987. 50th Death Anniv of Ayatollah Mirza Mohammad Hossein Naeini.
2374 **772** 10 r. multicoloured . . . 30 15

1987. New Year Festival. Flowers. Mult.
2375 5 r. Type **773** 20 10
2376 5 r. Tulips 20 10
2377 5 r. Dutch irises 20 10
2378 5 r. Roses 20 10

774 Arabic Text and Arched Window

775 Flag as Star on Map

1987. Mab'as Festival.
2379 **774** 45 r. lt green, grn & gold . 70 35

1987. 8th Anniv of Islamic Republic.
2380 **775** 20 r. multicoloured . . . 45 30

776 Soldiers with Flag

777 Emblems on Map and Dome of the Rock

1987. Revolutionary Guards' Day. Birth Anniv of Imam Hossein.
2381 **776** 5 r. multicoloured 20 15

1987. Commemoration of Lebanese Hizbollah Dead.
2382 **777** 10 r. red, green and grey . 30 15

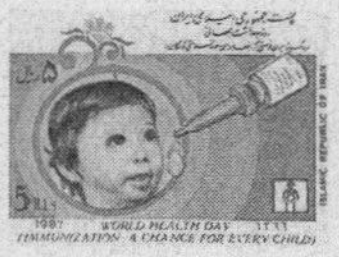

778 Child and Vaccination Dropper

779 Stars around Holy Kaaba

1987. World Health Day. Multicoloured.
2383 3 r. Syringe and children . . . 15 10
2384 5 r. Type **778** 20 10

1987. World Day of the Oppressed. Birth Anniv of Imam Mahdi.
2385 **779** 20 r. multicoloured . . . 50 30

780 Worker with Rifle and Koran, Factory and Cogwheel

781 Ayatollah Mottahari, Candle and Book

1987. International Labour Day.
2386 **780** 5 r. multicoloured 20 15

1987. Teachers' Day.
2387 **781** 5 r. red, yellow & blue . . 20 15

782 Map in Telephone Dial

783 12th-century Ceramic Lidded Pot, Rey

1987. World Telecommunications Day.
2388 **782** 20 r. violet and blue . . . 50 30

1987. International Museums Day.
2389 **783** 20 r. chestnut, brn & grey 50 30
2390 – 20 r. brown, blk & grn . . 50 30
DESIGN: No. 2390, Sassanian silver-gilt flower vase.

784 Dove, Globe and Dome of the Rock dripping Blood onto Star

785 Qum Theological College, Crown and Bayonets

1987. World Jerusalem Day.
2391 **784** 20 r. multicoloured . . . 50 30

1987. 24th Anniv of 1963 Islamic Rising.
2392 **785** 20 r. multicoloured . . . 50 30

786 Blown Glass

1987. World Crafts Day. Multicoloured.
2393 5 r. Type **786** 20 10
2394 5 r. Khatam marquetry 20 10
2395 5 r. Ceramic ware 20 10
2396 5 r. Ceramic master-craftsman . 20 10

787 Factory, Freighter and Dam

788 Figures in Cupped Hand

1987. Campaign against Tax Evasion.

2397 **787** 10 r. gold, blk & silver . . 30 15

1987. Welfare Week.

2398 **788** 15 r. multicoloured . . . 35 25

789 Crowd around Mosque

1987. Feast of Sacrifices.

2399 **789** 12 r. turq, silver & blk . . 35 20

790 Design from Mosque Tile

791 Hands clasped over National Emblem

1987. Ghadir Festival.

2400 **790** 18 r. gold, green & blk . . 45 30

1987. Islamic Banking Week.

2401 **791** 15 r. brn, bl & gold . . . 35 25

792 Typical Persian Calligraphy

1987. 1st Iranian Calligraphers' Cultural and Artistic Congress.

2402 **792** 20 r. multicoloured . . . 50 30

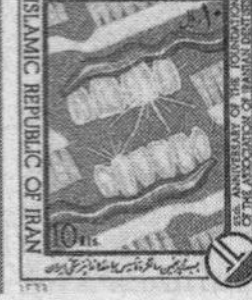

793 Blood running from Heart as Globe, Mosque and Kaaba

794 Toothbrushes as Mouths

1987. Commemoration of Pilgrims killed at Mecca.

2403 **793** 8 r. multicoloured 30 15

1987. 25th Anniv of Iranian Dentists Association.

2404 **794** 10 r. multicoloured . . . 35 15

795 Dove with Globe as Eye

796 Rifleman and Armed Launch

1987. International Peace Day.

2405 **795** 20 r. bronze and blue . . 50 30

1987. 7th Anniv of Iran–Iraq War.

2406 **796** 25 r. green, blue & blk . . 60 40

2407 – 25 r. red, black & blue . . 60 40

DESIGN: No. 2407, Rifleman and soldiers.

797 Open Book on Crossed Pistols

798 People in Cupped Hands

1987. Police Day.

2408 **797** 10 r. multicoloured . . . 50 20

1987. International Social Security Co-operation Week.

2409 **798** 15 r. black, blue & gold . . 35 25

799 Dove with Envelopes as Tail on Globe

800 American Flag, Great Seal and Capitol

1987. World Post Day. Multicoloured.

2410 15 r. Type **799** 35 25

2411 15 r. Dr. M. Ghandi (Postal Minister) commemoration . 35 25

1987. 6th Anniv of Storming of United States Embassy.

2412 **800** 40 r. multicoloured . . . 75 55

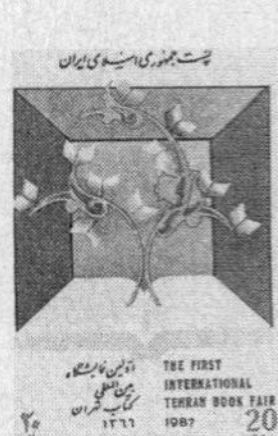

801 Tree growing from Open Book

802 Clasped Hands

1987. 1st Teheran Book Fair.

2413 **801** 20 r. multicoloured . . . 50 30

1987. Mohammed's Birth Anniv and Unity Week.

2414 **802** 25 r. brn, flesh & grn . . 55 35

803 Ayatollah Modarres

804 Djameh Mosque, Urmia

1987. 50th Death Anniv of Ayatollah Seyyed Hassan Modarres.

2415 **803** 10 r. brown and ochre . . 25 15

1987. Mosques.

2415a – 1 r. orange and silver . . 10 10

2416 **804** 2 r. mauve and silver . . 10 10

2416a – 3 r. green and silver . . 10 10

2417 – 5 r. red and silver . . 15 10

2594 – 10 r. blue and silver . . 15 10

2419 – 20 r. violet and silver . . 35 20

2420 – 30 r. red and silver . . 45 25

2421 – 40 r. blue and silver . . 55 30

2422 – 50 r. brown and silver . . 90 40

2423 – 100 r. green and silver . 1·60 95

2602 – 200 r. black and silver . 3·00 1·75

2604 – 500 r. green and silver . 7·25 4·25

DESIGNS—HORIZ: 1 r. Djameh Mosque, Schuschter; 3 r. Djameh Mosque, Kerman; 5 r. Qazvin; 10 r. Veramin; 20 r. Saveh; 40 r. Shiraz; 100 r. Hamadan. VERT: 30 r. Natanz; 50 r. Isfahan; 200 r. Dizful; 500 r. Yezd.

805 Open Book, Profiles and Ear of Wheat

1987. Agricultural Training and Extension Week.

2426 **805** 10 r. multicoloured . . . 25 15

806 Guerrilla Fighters on Map

1987. Afghan Resistance to Occupation.

2427 **806** 40 r. multicoloured . . . 75 55

807 Crowd with Banners

1988. 10th Anniv of Qum Uprising.

2428 **807** 20 r. multicoloured . . . 50 30

808 Bombs and Pencils

809 Takhti and Mountain

1988. Iranian Schools Victims' Commemoration.

2429 **808** 10 r. multicoloured . . . 25 15

1988. Victory of Gholamreza Takhti in World Freestyle Wrestling Championships.

2430 **809** 15 r. multicoloured . . . 35 25

810 Woman carrying armed Man

811 Text

1988. Women's Day and Birth Anniv of Fatima.

2431 **810** 20 r. multicoloured . . . 50 30

1988. 9th Anniv of Islamic Revolution.

2447 **811** 40 r. multicoloured . . . 75 45

812 Crowd burning Statue

1988. 10th Anniv of Tabriz Uprising.

2448 **812** 25 r. multicoloured . . . 60 35

813 Tree in Hand

814 "Anthemis hyalina"

1988. Tree Day.

2449 **813** 15 r. multicoloured . . . 35 25

1988. New Year Festival. Flowers. Mult.

2450 10 r. Type **814** 25 15

2451 10 r. Common mallows . . . 25 15

2452 10 r. Violets 25 15

2453 10 r. "Echium amaenum" . . 25 15

815 Hand putting Ballot Paper into Box

816 Calligraphy

1988. 9th Anniv of Islamic Republic.

2454 **815** 20 r. multicoloured . . . 50 30

1988. World Day of the Oppressed. Birth Anniv of Imam Mahdi.

2455 **816** 20 r. brown and blue . . 50 30

817 Shahid Mottahari Mosque and Theology School, Teheran

818 Bomb, Gas Cloud and Victims

1988. Preservation of Cultural Heritage. Multicoloured.

2456 10 r. Type **817** 25 15

2457 10 r. Colonnade of Tarikhaneh Mosque, Damghan . . 25 15

2458 10 r. Gateway of Sepahdari Mosque and Theology School, Arak (horiz) . . . 25 15

2459 10 r. Agha Bozorg Mosque and Theology School, Kashan (courtyard with pool) (horiz) 25 15

1988. Halabja Chemical Attack Victims' Commemoration.

2460 **818** 20 r. multicoloured . . . 50 30

819 Map, Dome of the Rock and Palestinian

820 Satellite and Telephone Handset

1988. Palestinian "Intifida" Movement. Each brown, red and black.

2461 10 r. Type **819** 30 15

2462 10 r. Man with rounded beard . 30 15

2463 10 r. Man wearing crew-necked jumper 30 15

2464 10 r. Man with long pointed beared 30 15

2465 10 r. Crowd and hand holding stone 30 15

1988. World Telecommunications Day.

2466 **820** 20 r. blue and green . . . 50 30

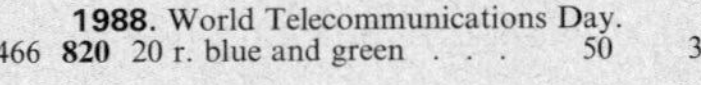

821 Ceramic Vase

822 Miners pushing Coal Truck

1988. International Museum Day. Mult.

2467 10 t. Type **821** 25 15
2468 10 r. Iran Bastan Museum porch 25 15
2469 10 r. 14th-century Tabriz silk rug 25 15
2470 10 r. 7th-century B.C. gold ring, Arjan, Behbahan 25 15

1988. Mining Day.

2471 **822** 20 r. multicoloured . . . 3·25 90

823 Children playing by River

824 Bleeding Dove and Broken Bayonets

1988. International Children's Day.

2472 **823** 10 r. multicoloured . . . 30 15

1988. 25th Anniv of 1963 Islamic Rising.

2473 **824** 10 r. multicoloured . . . 30 15

825 Glim Weaving

826 Child in Flower

1988. World Handicrafts Day. Multicoloured.

2474 10 r. Type **825** 25 15
2475 10 r. Miniature of horsemen . . 25 15
2476 10 r. Glim weaver (horiz) . . . 25 15
2477 10 r. Straw basket (horiz) . . . 25 15

1988. Child Health Campaign.

2478 **826** 20 r. blue, green & black . 35 20

827 Symbols of Industry and Agriculture

828 Balkhi

1988. Campaign Against Tax Evasion.

2479 **827** 20 r. gold, blue & silver . 35 20

1988. Allameh Balkhi (Afghan revolutionary writer) Commemoration.

2480 **828** 20 r. black, red & silver . 35 20

829 Blood raining on Holy Kaaba

830 Missile hitting Boeing 737 Airplane

1988. 1st Anniv of Death of Mecca Pilgrims. Multicoloured.

2481 10 r. Type **829** 20 15
2482 10 r. Holy Kaaba and blood-stained robe 20 15

1988. Destruction of Iranair Passenger Airplane.

2483 **830** 45 r. multicoloured . . . 1·00 45

HAVE YOU READ THE NOTES AT THE BEGINNING OF THIS CATALOGUE?
These often provide answers to the enquiries we receive.

831 Seyyed Ali Andarzgou

832 Central Bank, Teheran

1988. 10th Death Anniv of Seyyed Ali Andarzgou (revolutionary).

2484 **831** 20 r. blue, black & brn . . 35 20

1988. Islamic Banking Week.

2485 **832** 20 r. grey, brn & gold . . 35 20

833 Carrying away Victim

834 Weightlifting

1988. 10th Anniv of "Bloody Friday" Riots.

2486 **833** 25 r. green, purple & red . 45 25

1988. Olympic Games, Seoul. Multicoloured.

2487 10 r. Type **834** 20 15
2488 10 r. Men's gymnastics 20 15
2489 10 r. Judo 20 15
2490 10 r. Football 20 15
2491 10 r. Wrestling 20 15

835 Plant

836 Iranians and Rifle

1988. Agricultural Census.

2492 **835** 30 r. yellow, blk & grn . . 50 35

1988. 8th Anniv of Iran–Iraq War.

2493 **836** 20 r. multicoloured . . . 35 20

837 Envelopes around Globe

1988. World Post Day.

2494 **837** 20 r. green, black & blue . 35 20

838 Child's Face and Profiles

839 Clasped Hands and Emblem

1988. Parents' and Teachers' Co-operation Week.

2495 **838** 20 r. multicoloured . . . 35 20

1988. Mohammed's Birth Anniv and Unity Week.

2496 **839** 10 r. multicoloured . . . 20 15

840 Fist and Shattered Eagle

841 Tree as Umbrella

1988. 7th Anniv of Storming of United States Embassy.

2497 **840** 45 r. multicoloured . . . 75 45

1988. Insurance Day.

2498 **841** 10 r. multicoloured . . . 20 15

842 Tomb of Hafiz

1988. International Hafiz (writer) Congress, Shiraz.

2499 **842** 20 r. blue, gold & mve . . 35 20

843 Agricultural Symbols on Open Book

845 Map and Armed Afghan

844 Parvin Etessami (writer)

1988. Agricultural Training and Extension Week.

2500 **843** 15 r. multicoloured . . . 30 15

1988. Iranian Celebrities of Science, Art and Literature. Multicoloured.

2501 10 r. Type **844** 20 15
2502 10 r. Qaem Maqam Farahani (writer) 20 15
2503 10 r. Kamal al-Molk (artist) . . 20 15
2504 10 r. Jalal al-Ahmad (writer) . . 20 15
2505 10 r. Dr. Mohammad Mo'in (writer) 20 15

1988. Afghan Resistance to Occupation.

2506 **845** 40 r. multicoloured . . . 75 45

846 Satellite, Envelopes and Dish Aerial

847 Tulips and Script

1989. Asian and Pacific Transport and Communications Decade. Multicoloured.

2507 20 r. Type **846** 45 30
2508 20 r. Air transport 45 30
2509 20 r. Road and rail transport . 1·75 60
2510 20 r. Shipping 65 30

1989. Air. 10th Anniv of Islamic Revolution.

2511 **847** 40 r. mauve, gold & blk . . 80 55
2512 50 r. violet, gold & blk . . 80 55

848 Sun illuminating Koran

849 Hands protecting Tree

1989. Mab'as Festival.

2513 **848** 20 r. multicoloured . . . 35 25

1989. Tree Day.

2514 **849** 20 r. multicoloured . . . 35 25

850 "Cephalanthera kurdica"

851 Wind Gauge and Wheat

1989. New Year Festival. Flowers. Mult.

2515 10 r. Type **850** 20 15
2516 10 r. "Dactylorhiza romana" . . 20 15
2517 10 r. "Comperia comperiana" . 20 15
2518 10 r. "Orchis mascula" 20 15

1989. World Meteorological Day. Mult.

2519 20 r. Type **851** 40 25
2520 30 r. Wind gauge, airplane and weather ship 80 35

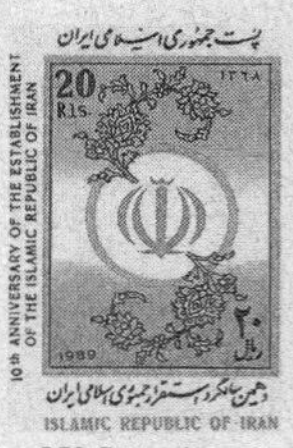

852 State Arms

853 Refinery

1989. 10th Anniv of Islamic Republic.

2521 **852** 20 r. multicoloured . . . 35 25

1989. Commissioning of First Phase of Abadan Oil Refinery.

2522 **853** 20 r. multicoloured . . . 40 25

854 Mottahari

855 Dome of the Rock and Barbed Wire

1989. Teachers' Day. 10th Death Anniv of Ayatollah Mottahari.

2523 **854** 20 r. multicoloured . . . 35 25

1989. World Jerusalem Day.

2524 **855** 30 r. multicoloured . . . 60 35

856 Satellite, Globe and Dish Aerial

857 Jar

1989. World Telecommunications Day.

2525 **856** 20 r. multicoloured . . . 40 25

1989. International Museums Day. 6th-century Gurgan Artefacts.

2526 **857** 20 r. yellow, blue & blk . 40 25
2527 – 20 r. blue, black & mve . 40 25

DESIGN: No. 2527, Flagon.

858 Armed Men, Tent and Family with Sheep

1989. Nomad's Day.

2528 **858** 20 r. multicoloured . . . 35 20

859 Man engraving Vase

1989. World Crafts Day. Multicoloured.

2529 20 r. Type **859** 35 25
2530 20 r. Engraved copper vase . . 35 25
2531 20 r. Engraved copper plate (vert) 35 25
2532 20 r. Engraved copper wall-hanging (vert) 35 25

860 Khomeini and Crowd

861 Pasteur, Avicenna and Hand holding Quill

1989. Ayatollah Khomeini Commemoration.

2533 **860** 20 r. orange, black and blue (postage) 40 20
2534 – 70 r. blk, vio & gold (air) . 1·10 70

DESIGN—HORIZ: 70 r. Ayatollah Khomeini.

1989. "Philexfrance 89" International Stamp Exhibition, Paris. Each black, blue and brown, background colour given.

2535 **861** 30 r. blue 50 35
2536 50 r. brown 75 55

862 Map and Satellite

1989. 10th Anniv of Asia–Pacific Telecommunity.

2537 **862** 30 r. orange, black & bl . 50 30

863 Araghi

1989. 10th Death Anniv of Mehdi Araghi.

2538 **863** 20 r. orange and purple . 35 20

864 Shahryar and Monument

1989. Mohammed Hossein Shahryar (poet) Commemoration.

2539 **864** 20 r. multicoloured . . . 35 20

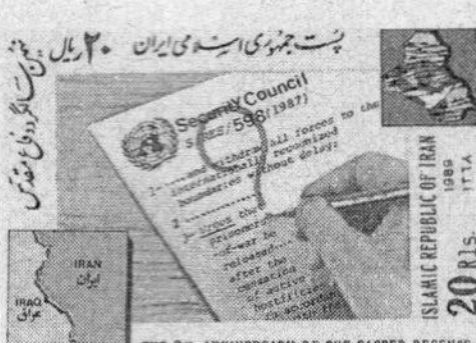

865 U.N. Security Council Document

1989. 9th Anniv of Iran–Iraq War.

2540 **865** 20 r. multicoloured . . . 35 20

866 Khomeini addressing Crowd

1989. Ayatollah Khomeini.

2541 – 1 r. multicoloured 10 10
2542 – 2 r. multicoloured 10 10
2543 **866** 3 r. multicoloured 10 10
2544 – 5 r. multicoloured 25 10
2545 – 10 r. multicoloured . . . 60 10
2546 – 20 r. multicoloured . . . 35 10
2547 – 30 r. multicoloured . . . 50 30
2548 – 40 r. multicoloured . . . 65 50
2549 – 50 r. multicoloured . . . 80 50
2550 – 70 r. multicoloured . . . 1·10 65
2551 – 100 r. ultram, bl & grn . . 1·60 95
2552 – 200 r. brown, yell & grn . . 3·00 1·50
2553 – 500 r. multicoloured . . . 7·50 4·00
2554 – 1000 r. multicoloured . . 15·00 8·25

DESIGNS: 1 r. Rose and courtyard; 2 r. Khomeini as young man; 5 r. Khomeini going into exile; 10 r. Khomeini's return from exile; 20 r. Khomeini making speech; 30 r. Boy kissing Khomeini; 40 r. Ayatollahs; 50 r. Khomeini; 70 r. Meeting in house; 100 r. Arabic inscription; 200 r. Microphones and chair; 500 r. Qum Mosque and roses; 1000 r. Sun's rays.

867 Pigeon carrying Letter

1989. World Post Day.

2561 **867** 20 r. multicoloured . . . 35 20

868 Multi-pointed Star in Window Arch

869 U.S. Emblem and Crowd in Dove

1989. Mohammed's Birth Anniv and Unity Week.

2562 **868** 10 r. multicoloured . . . 15 10

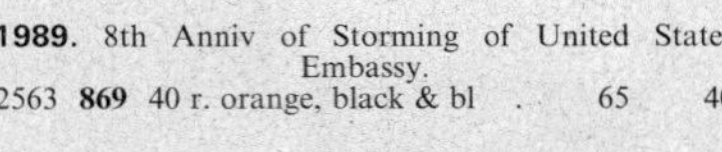

1989. 8th Anniv of Storming of United States Embassy.

2563 **869** 40 r. orange, black & bl . 65 40

870 Iranian and Launch with Machine Gun

1989. 10th Anniv of People's Militia.

2564 **870** 10 r. multicoloured . . . 30 15

871 Mehdi Elahi Ghomshei

1989. Iranian Celebrities of Science, Art and Literature.

2565 **871** 10 r. red, black and gold . 15 10
2566 – 10 r. green, blk and gold . 15 10
2567 – 10 r. yellow, blk & gold . 15 10
2568 – 10 r. green, black & gold . 15 10
2569 – 10 r. mauve, blk & gold . 15 10

DESIGNS: No. 2566, Grand Ayatollah Seyyed Hossein Boroujerdi; 2567, Grand Ayatollah Sheikh Abdulkarim Haeri; 2568, Dr. Abdulazim Gharib; 2569, Seyyed Hossein Mirkhani.

872 Guiding Child's Hand

873 Book as Profiles forming Flower

1990. International Literacy Year.

2570 **872** 20 r. multicoloured . . . 35 20

1990. Identity Cards.

2571 **873** 10 r. multicoloured . . . 15 10

874 Drinking Vessel

875 Crowd

1990. Cultural Heritage.

2572 **874** 20 r. black and orange . . 35 20
2573 – 20 r. black and green . . 35 20

DESIGN: No. 2563, Vase with stem.

1990. 11th Anniv of Islamic Revolution.

2574 **875** 50 r. multicoloured . . . 80 50

876 Emblem

877 Soldier in Wheelchair

1990. Int Koran Recitation Competition.

2575 **876** 10 r. black, blue & green . 15 10

1990. Invalids' Day.

2576 **877** 10 r. multicoloured . . . 15 10

878 Figures encircling Tree

879 "Coronilla varia"

1990. Tree Day.

2577 **878** 20 r. multicoloured . . . 35 20

1990. New Year Festival. Flowers. Mult.

2578 10 r. Type **879** 15 10
2579 10 r. "Astragalus cornucaprae" 15 10
2580 10 r. "Astragalus obtusifolius" . 15 10
2581 10 r. "Astragalus straussii" . . 15 10

880 Crowd and Ballot Box

881 Flower growing from Globe

1990. 11th Anniv of Islamic Republic.

2582 **880** 30 r. multicoloured . . . 50 30

1990. World Health Day.

2583 **881** 40 r. multicoloured . . . 65 40

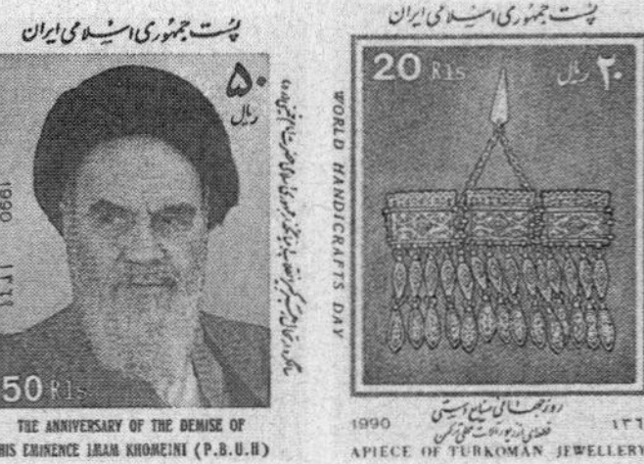

882 Khomeini

883 Turkoman Jewellery

1990. 1st Death Anniv of Ayatollah Khomeini.

2584 **882** 50 r. multicoloured . . . 80 50

1990. World Handicrafts Day.

2585 20 r. Type **883** 35 20
2586 50 r. Gilded-steel bird 80 50

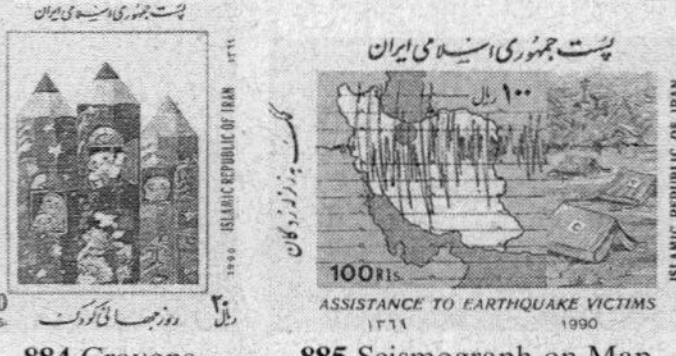

884 Crayons

885 Seismograph on Map and Red Crescent Camp

1990. International Children's Day.

2587 **884** 20 r. multicoloured . . . 35 20

1990. Aid for Earthquake Victims.

2588 **885** 100 r. multicoloured . . . 1·60 95

886 P.O.W. and Roses

887 Ayatollah Khomeini and Dome of the Rock

1990. Returned Prisoners of War.

2589 **886** 250 r. multicoloured . . . 3·75 2·00

1990. World Jerusalem Day.

2590 **887** 100 r. multicoloured . . . 1·60 95

889 Flowers, Crowd and Khomeini

1991. 12th Anniv of Islamic Revolution.
2605 **889** 100 r. multicoloured . . . 1·60 95

890 11th-century Gold Jug

1991. International Museum Day. Mult.
2606 50 r. Type **890** 80 50
2607 50 r. 14th-century silver-inlaid brass basin 80 50

891 Flowers and Fists — 892 Museum

1991. 11th Anniv of Iran–Iraq War.
2608 **891** 100 r. multicoloured . . . 1·60 95

1991. Inauguration of Post Museum, Teheran.
2609 **892** 200 r. brown and black . 3·25 2·00

893 Headset on Globe — 894 "Iris spuria"

1991. World Telecommunications Day (1990).
2610 **893** 50 r. multicoloured . . . 80 50

1991. New Year Festival. Irises. Multicoloured.
2611 20 r. Type **894** 35 20
2612 20 r. "Iris lycotis" 35 20
2613 20 r. "Iris demawendica" . . . 35 20
2614 20 r. "Iris meda" 35 20

895 Map, Dome of the Rock and Hosseini — 897 Revolutionaries

896 Light Beam on Mountains

1991. 10th Death Anniv of Saleh Hosseini.
2615 **895** 30 r. red and black . . . 50 30

1991. Mab'as Festival.
2616 **896** 100 r. multicoloured . . . 1·60 95

1991. 25th Death Anniv (1990) of Revolutionaries.
2617 **897** 50 r. brown and orange . 80 50

898 Arabic Script — 899 Crowd, Flag, and Ballot Box

1991. World Day of the Oppressed. Birth Anniv of Mahdi.
2618 **898** 50 r. multicoloured . . . 80 50

1991. 12th Anniv of Islamic Republic.
2619 **899** 20 r. multicoloured . . . 35 20

900 Map and Bayonets — 901 Mother and Child

1991. World Jerusalem Day.
2620 **900** 100 r. multicoloured . . 1·60 95

1991. Women's Day and Birth Anniv of Fatima.
2621 **901** 50 r. multicoloured . . . 80 50

902 Boroujerdi — 903 Disasters

1991. 30th Death Anniv of Ayatollah Boroujerdi.
2622 **902** 200 r. black and green . . 3·25 2·00

1991. International Decade for Natural Disaster Reduction.
2623 **903** 100 r. multicoloured . . . 2·00 1·10

904 Book, Candle and Dr. Mottahari

1991. Teachers' Day.
2624 **904** 50 r. yellow, orge & blk . 80 50

905 Rays striking Globe — 906 Mausoleum, Meshed

1991. World Telecommunications Day. "Telecommunications and Safety of Human Life".
2625 **905** 100 r. multicoloured . . . 1·60 95

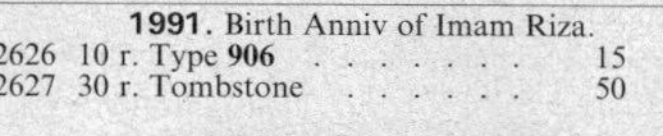
1991. Birth Anniv of Imam Riza.
2626 10 r. Type **906** 15 10
2627 30 r. Tombstone 50 30

907 Khomeini

1991. 2nd Death Anniv of Ayatollah Khomeini.
2628 **907** 100 r. multicoloured . . . 1·60 95

908 Karbala Shrine

1991. Iraqi Attack on Shi'ite Shrine, Karbala.
2629 **908** 70 r. multicoloured . . . 1·10 65

909 Nisami

1991. 900th Birth Anniv of Nisami (writer) International Congress, Tabris.
2630 **909** 50 r. multicoloured . . . 80 50

910 Archway

1991. 1330th Death Anniv of Ali ibn Ali Talib (Caliph).
2631 **910** 50 r. multicoloured . . . 80 50

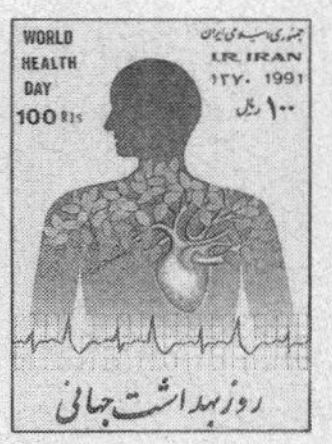
911 Hands reaching through Parched Earth to Blood Drop — 912 Heart as Tree and Cardiograph

1991. Blood Donation.
2632 **911** 50 r. multicoloured . . . 80 50

1991. World Health Day,
2633 **912** 100 r. multicoloured . . . 1·60 95

913 Nedjefi

1991. Marashi Nedjefi Commemoration.
2634 **913** 30 r. multicoloured . . . 50 30

914 Doves flying from Cage

1991. 1st Anniv of Return of Prisoners of War.
2635 **914** 100 r. multicoloured . . . 1·60 95

915 Engraved Brassware

1991. World Crafts Day. Multicoloured.
2636 40 r. Type **915** 65 40
2637 40 r. Gilded samovar 65 40

916 Ayatollah Lari

1991.
2638 **916** 30 r. multicoloured . . . 50 30

917 Fist and Roses in Cartouche — 918 Islamic Symbols

1991. 11th Anniv of Iran–Iraq War.
2639 **917** 20 r. multicoloured . . . 35 20

1991. Islamic Unity Week.
2640 **918** 30 r. multicoloured . . . 50 30

919 13th-century Kashan Ewer — 920 Gharib

1991. International Museum Day. Mult.
2641 20 r. Type **919** 35 20
2642 40 r. 13th-century Kashan ewer with bird's head lip 65 40

1991. Dr. Mohammed Gharib.
2643 **920** 100 r. black and blue . . 1·60 95

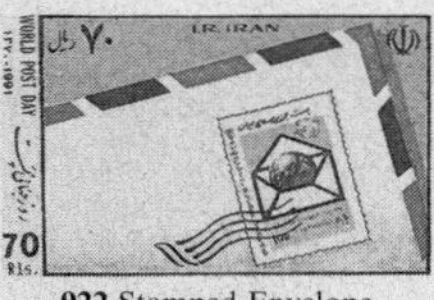
921 Banners — 922 Stamped Envelope

1991. Liberation of Khorramshahr.
2644 **921** 30 r. multicoloured . . . 50 30

1991. World Post Day.
2645 **922** 70 r. multicoloured . . . 1·10 65

923 Khaju-Ye Kermani

1991. International Congress on Khaju-Ye Kermani (writer).
2646 **923** 30 r. multicoloured . . . 50 30

924 Globe and Seismograph

925 Cogwheel, Grain, Tree, Figures and Globe

1991. 1st International Seismology and Earthquake Engineering Conference.
2647 **924** 100 r. multicoloured . . . 1·60 95

1991. World Food Day.
2648 **925** 80 r. multicoloured . . . 1·25 75

926 Conference Emblem

927 Green Woodpecker and Flower Decoration

1991. Palestinian Peoples Conference.
2649 **926** 40 r. gold and violet . . . 65 40

1991. 1st Asian Biennial Exhibition of Children's Book Illustrations.
2650 **927** 100 r. multicoloured . . . 2·00 95

928 Script and Emblem

929 Festival Award

1991. Children's Book Fair, Teheran.
2651 **928** 20 r. multicoloured . . . 35 20

1991. Roshd International Educational Film Festival.
2652 **929** 50 r. multicoloured . . . 80 50

930 Meeting Emblem

932 Child throwing Stone at Star of David

931 Militia Members

1991. 7th Ministerial Meeting of Group of 77.
2653 **930** 30 r. green and violet . . 50 30

1991. People's Militia Week.
2654 **931** 30 r. multicoloured . . . 50 30

1991. World Children's Day.
2655 **932** 50 r. multicoloured . . . 80 50

933 Globe and Doves

1991. World Tourism Day.
2656 **933** 200 r. black, mauve & bl . 3·00 1·60

934 Emblems

935 Trees, Hand, Water and Wheat

1991. World Standards Day.
2657 **934** 100 r. multicoloured . . . 1·60 95

1991. Agricultural Training Week.
2658 **935** 70 r. multicoloured . . . 1·10 65

936 Araf Hosseini

938 Revolutionary Scenes

937 Sadegh Ghanji

1992.
2659 **936** 50 r. multicoloured . . . 55 35

1992.
2660 **937** 50 r. multicoloured . . . 55 35

1992. 13th Anniv of Islamic Revolution. Mult.
2661 30 r. Type **938** 35 20
2662 50 r. Revolutionary scenes (different) 55 35

939 Members' Flags

1992. Economic Co-operation Organization Summit, Teheran.
2663 **939** 200 r. multicoloured . . . 2·25 1·40

940 Seyd Abbas Musawi (Hezbollah Secretary-General) and Dome of the Rock

941 Planets, Satellite, Globe and Mobile Dish Aerial

1992. World Jerusalem Day.
2664 **940** 200 r. multicoloured . . . 2·25 1·40

1992. World Meteorological Day.
2665 **941** 100 r. multicoloured . . . 1·10 75

942 Badshahi Mosque, Lahore, Pakistan

943 Ayatollah Khomeini Voting

1992. South and West Asia Postal Union. Multicoloured.
2666 50 r. Type **942** 60 35
2667 50 r. Imam's Mosque, Isfahan . 60 35
2668 50 r. St. Sophia's, Istanbul, Turkey 60 35

1992. 13th Anniv of Islamic Republic.
2669 **943** 50 r. multicoloured . . . 60 35

944 Embraer Bandeirante and Crates

1992. Establishment of Postal Air Service.
2670 **944** 60 r. multicoloured . . . 80 45

945 Hands holding Trees

946 Tulips

1992. National Resources Week.
2671 **945** 100 r. multicoloured . . . 1·10 75

1992. New Year Festival. Flowers. Multicoloured.
2672 20 r. Type **946** 40 25
2673 20 r. Rose 40 25
2674 40 r. Orange blossom 50 30
2675 40 r. Yellow jasmine 50 30

947 Members' Flags

1992. Economic Co-operation Organization.
2676 **947** 20 r. multicoloured . . . 40 25

948 Morse Apparatus

1992. World Telecommunications Day. Mult.
2677 20 r. Type **948** 40 25
2678 20 r. Telegraph poles and wires 40 25
2679 20 r. Old wall and candlestick telephones 40 25
2680 40 r. Dish aerials 50 30
2681 40 r. Satellite and Earth . . . 50 30
Nos. 2677/81 were issued together, se-tenant, forming a composite design.

949 Sabzevari

950 Emblem

1992. Science, Art and Literature. Multicoloured.
2682 50 r. Type **949** 60 35
2683 50 r. Madjlessi (in turban) . . 60 35
2684 50 r. Arabic script by Mir Emad 60 35
2685 50 r. Samani (in fez) 60 35

1992. 21st Near East Regional Conference Session of F.A.O., Teheran.
2686 **950** 40 r. green, blue & black . 50 25

951 Globe, Equipment and Charts

952 Palm Trees

1992. International Surveying and Mapping Conf.
2687 **951** 40 r. multicoloured . . . 50 25

1992. 2nd Anniv of Unification of Yemen.
2688 **952** 50 r. multicoloured . . . 60 35

953 Dome of the Rock, Oasis and Child

1992. World Children's Day.
2689 **953** 50 r. multicoloured . . . 50 30

954 Khomeini

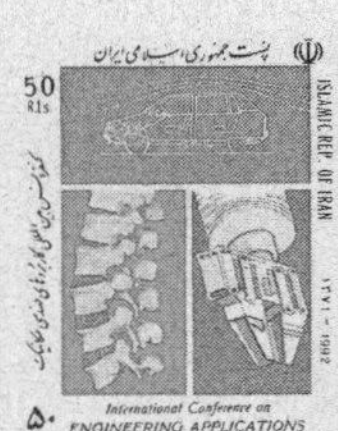
955 Diagram of Wind Tunnel Test, Section of Spine and Robot Hand

1992. 3rd Death Anniv of Ayatollah Khomeini.
2690 **954** 100 r. multicoloured . . . 1·10 70

1992. International Engineering Applications of Mechanics Conference, Teheran.
2691 **955** 50 r. multicoloured . . . 50 30

956 Building and Books

1992. Hajia Nosrat Baygom Amin Mo'in (lawyer) Commemoration.
2692 **956** 20 r. multicoloured . . . 35 20

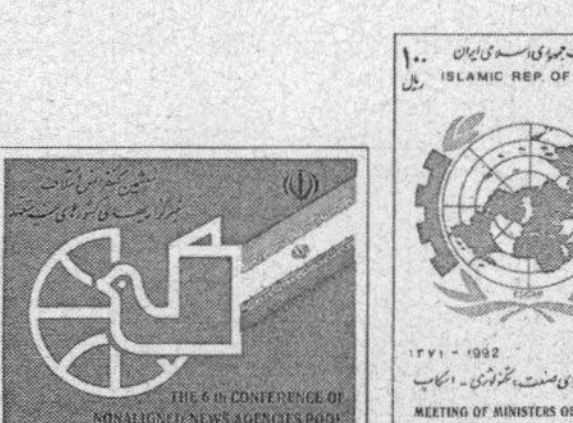
957 Emblem and Iranian Flag

958 ESCAP Emblem

1992. 6th Non-aligned News Agencies Pool Conference, Teheran.
2693 **957** 100 r. multicoloured . . . 1·10 70

1992. Meeting of Economic and Social Commission for Asia and the Pacific Industry and Technology Ministers.
2694 **958** 100 r. green, gold & blk . 1·10 70

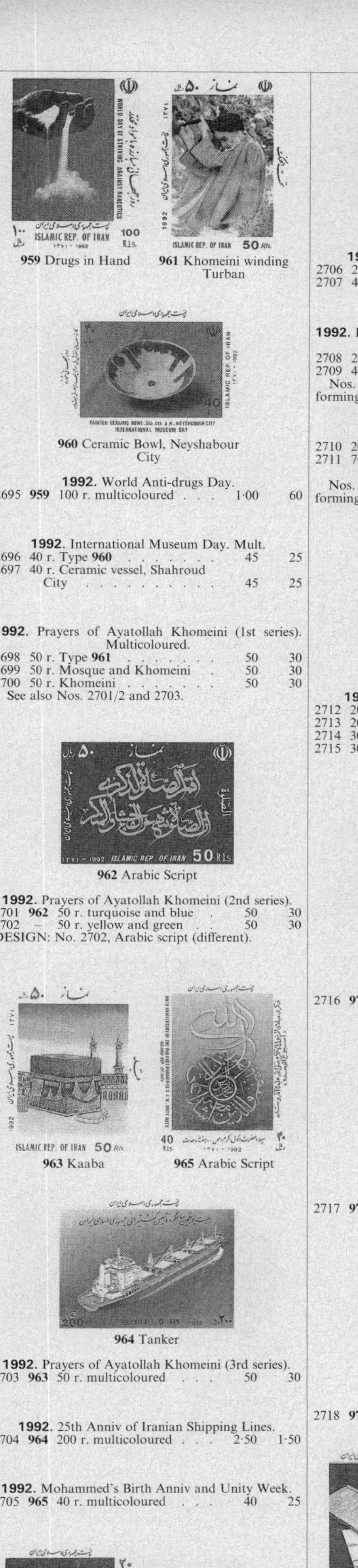

959 Drugs in Hand

961 Khomeini winding Turban

960 Ceramic Bowl, Neyshabour City

1992. World Anti-drugs Day.
2695 **959** 100 r. multicoloured . . . 1·00 60

1992. International Museum Day. Mult.
2696 40 r. Type **960** 45 25
2697 40 r. Ceramic vessel, Shahroud City 45 25

1992. Prayers of Ayatollah Khomeini (1st series). Multicoloured.
2698 50 r. Type **961** 50 30
2699 50 r. Mosque and Khomeini . . 50 30
2700 50 r. Khomeini 50 30
See also Nos. 2701/2 and 2703.

962 Arabic Script

1992. Prayers of Ayatollah Khomeini (2nd series).
2701 **962** 50 r. turquoise and blue . 50 30
2702 – 50 r. yellow and green . . 50 30
DESIGN: No. 2702, Arabic script (different).

963 Kaaba

965 Arabic Script

964 Tanker

1992. Prayers of Ayatollah Khomeini (3rd series).
2703 **963** 50 r. multicoloured . . . 50 30

1992. 25th Anniv of Iranian Shipping Lines.
2704 **964** 200 r. multicoloured . . . 2·50 1·50

1992. Mohammed's Birth Anniv and Unity Week.
2705 **965** 40 r. multicoloured . . . 40 25

966 Soldiers and Sun

968 Foundry and Steel Products

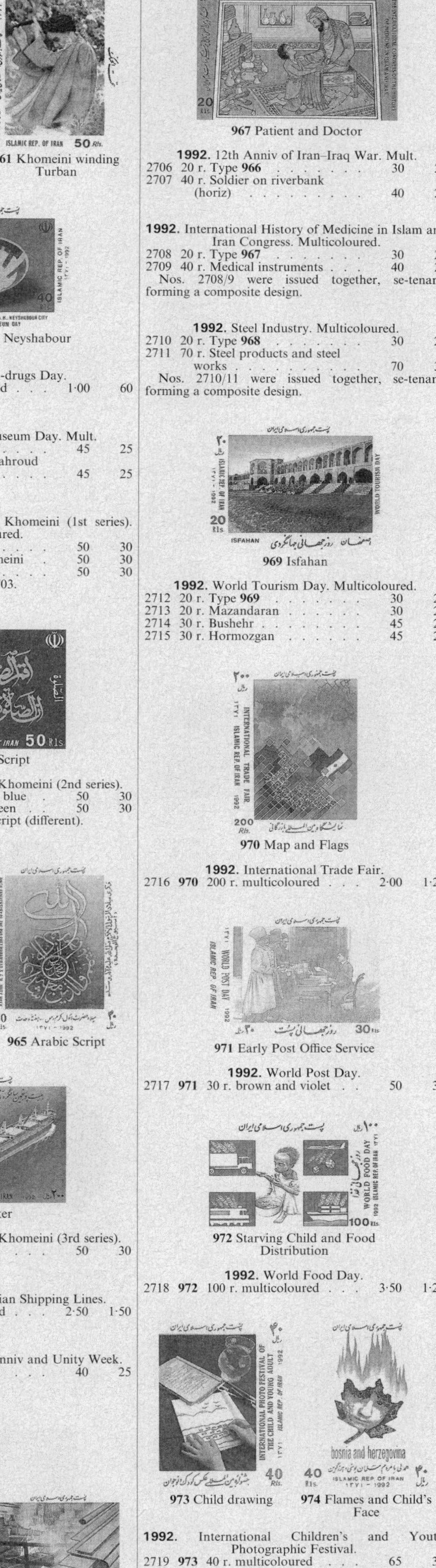

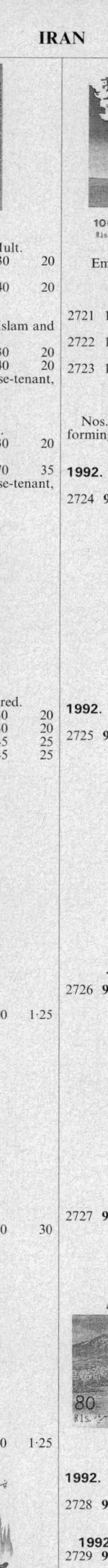

967 Patient and Doctor

1992. 12th Anniv of Iran–Iraq War. Mult.
2706 20 r. Type **966** 30 20
2707 40 r. Soldier on riverbank (horiz) 40 20

1992. International History of Medicine in Islam and Iran Congress. Multicoloured.
2708 20 r. Type **967** 30 20
2709 40 r. Medical instruments . . . 40 20
Nos. 2708/9 were issued together, se-tenant, forming a composite design.

1992. Steel Industry. Multicoloured.
2710 20 r. Type **968** 30 20
2711 70 r. Steel products and steel works 70 35
Nos. 2710/11 were issued together, se-tenant, forming a composite design.

969 Isfahan

1992. World Tourism Day. Multicoloured.
2712 20 r. Type **969** 30 20
2713 20 r. Mazandaran 30 20
2714 30 r. Bushehr 45 25
2715 30 r. Hormozgan 45 25

970 Map and Flags

1992. International Trade Fair.
2716 **970** 200 r. multicoloured . . . 2·00 1·25

971 Early Post Office Service

1992. World Post Day.
2717 **971** 30 r. brown and violet . . 50 30

972 Starving Child and Food Distribution

1992. World Food Day.
2718 **972** 100 r. multicoloured . . . 3·50 1·25

973 Child drawing

974 Flames and Child's Face

1992. International Children's and Youth Photographic Festival.
2719 **973** 40 r. multicoloured . . . 65 35

1992. Bosnia and Herzegovina.
2720 **974** 40 r. multicoloured . . . 55 35

975 Storming Embassy, Doves and Crow

976 Emblem

1992. Multicoloured.
2721 100 r. Type **975** (11th anniv of storming of U.S. Embassy) . 1·00 50
2722 100 r. Soldiers, crows and doves (Students' Day) . . . . . 1·00 50
2723 100 r. Ayatollah Khomeini, crows and doves (13th anniv of Khomeini's return from exile) . . . . 1·00 50
Nos. 2721/3 were issued together, se-tenant, forming a composite design.

1992. 17th Annual Meeting of Islamic Development Bank Board of Governors.
2724 **976** 20 r. multicoloured . . . 25 15

977 Flags and Dish Aerials on Maps

1992. Azerbaijan–Iran Telecommunications Co-operation.
2725 **977** 40 r. multicoloured . . . 55 35

978 Star

1992. 10th Anniv of Islamic University.
2726 **978** 200 r. green & dp green . 2·00 1·25

979 Soldiers in Armed Motor Boat

1992. People's Militia Week.
2727 **979** 40 r. multicoloured . . . 55 35

980 Shahryar

981 "Heaven and Hell"

1992. International Congress on Mohammed Hossein Shahryar (poet).
2728 **980** 80 r. multicoloured . . . 75 40

1992. Women's Day and Birth Anniv of Fatima.
2729 **981** 70 r. multicoloured . . . 65 35

982 Oil Derrick

1992. Oil Industry. Multicoloured.
2730 100 r. Type **982** . . . . . . 1·00 50
2731 100 r. Drilling . . . . 1·00 50

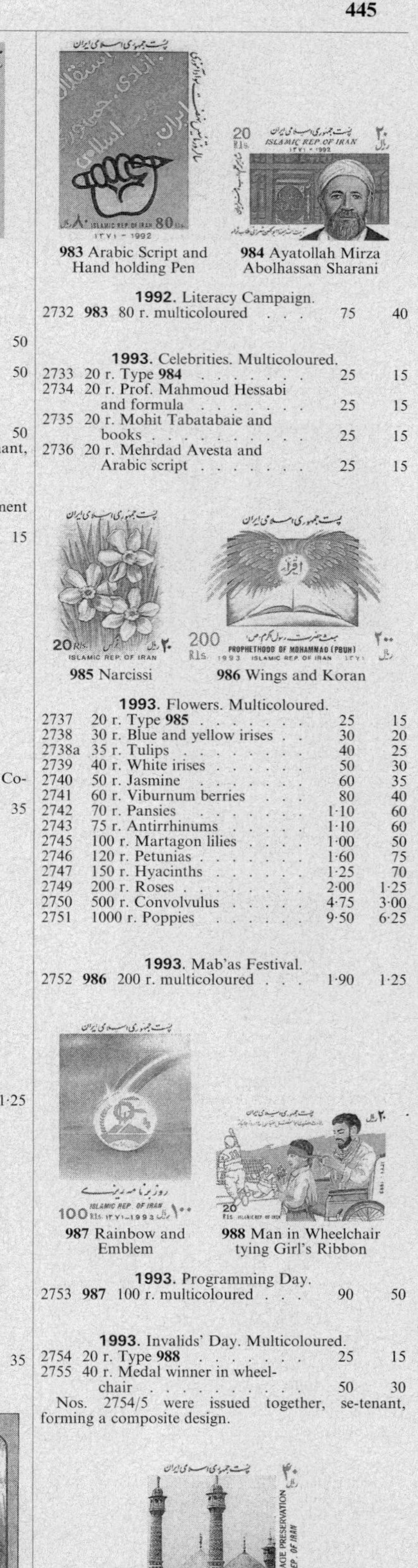

983 Arabic Script and Hand holding Pen

984 Ayatollah Mirza Abolhassan Sharani

1992. Literacy Campaign.
2732 **983** 80 r. multicoloured . . . 75 40

1993. Celebrities. Multicoloured.
2733 20 r. Type **984** 25 15
2734 20 r. Prof. Mahmoud Hessabi and formula 25 15
2735 20 r. Mohit Tabatabaie and books 25 15
2736 20 r. Mehrdad Avesta and Arabic script 25 15

985 Narcissi

986 Wings and Koran

1993. Flowers. Multicoloured.
2737 20 r. Type **985** 25 15
2738 30 r. Blue and yellow irises . . 30 20
2738a 35 r. Tulips 40 25
2739 40 r. White irises 50 30
2740 50 r. Jasmine 60 35
2741 60 r. Viburnum berries . . . 80 40
2742 70 r. Pansies . . . . 1·10 60
2743 75 r. Antirrhinums . . . . . 1·10 60
2745 100 r. Martagon lilies . . . . 1·00 50
2746 120 r. Petunias . . . . . . 1·60 75
2747 150 r. Hyacinths . . . . . . 1·25 70
2749 200 r. Roses . . . . 2·00 1·25
2750 500 r. Convolvulus . . . . . 4·75 3·00
2751 1000 r. Poppies . . . . . . 9·50 6·25

1993. Mab'as Festival.
2752 **986** 200 r. multicoloured . . . 1·90 1·25

987 Rainbow and Emblem

988 Man in Wheelchair tying Girl's Ribbon

1993. Programming Day.
2753 **987** 100 r. multicoloured . . . 90 50

1993. Invalids' Day. Multicoloured.
2754 20 r. Type **988** 25 15
2755 40 r. Medal winner in wheelchair 50 30
Nos. 2754/5 were issued together, se-tenant, forming a composite design.

989 Fatima Mosque, Qom

1993. Preservation of Cultural Heritage. Mult.
2756 40 r. Type **989** 50 30
2757 40 r. Interior of mosque . . . 50 30

990 Hands reaching towards Sun

1993. World Day of the Oppressed. Birth Anniv of Mahdi.
2758 **990** 60 r. multicoloured . . . 50 30

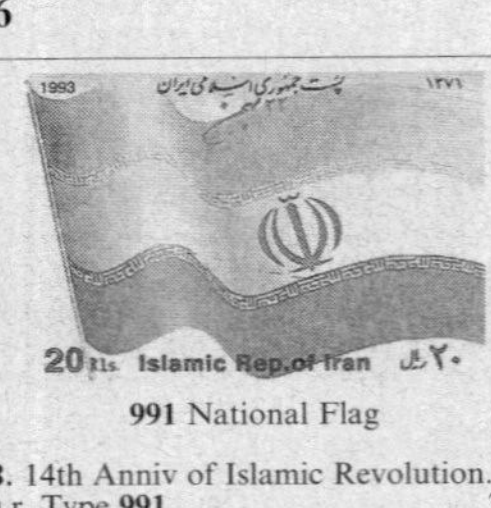

991 National Flag

1993. 14th Anniv of Islamic Revolution. Mult.

2759 20 r. Type **991** 25 15
2760 20 r. Flag and soldiers 25 15
2761 20 r. Guerrillas 25 15
2762 20 r. Oil derricks, harvesters and crowd 25 15
2763 20 r. Ayatollah Khomeini in motorcade and on arrival in Iran 25 15

Nos. 2759/63 were issued together, se-tenant, forming a composite design.

992 Volleyball

993 Ansari

1993. 1st Islamic Countries Women's Games. Multicoloured.

2764 40 r. Type **992** 50 30
2765 40 r. Basketball 50 30
2766 40 r. Gold medal 50 30
2767 40 r. Swimming 50 30
2768 40 r. Running 50 30

Nos. 2764/8 were issued together, se-tenant, forming a compostite design.

1993. Congress on Sheikh Morteza Ansari.

2769 **993** 40 r. multicoloured . . . 50 30

994 World Map as Tree Foliage and Rainbow

1993. Tree Day.

2770 **994** 70 r. multicoloured . . . 90 55

995 Burning Tank and Man with Sling

996 Butterfly and Tulip

1993. World Jerusalem Day.

2771 **995** 20 r. multicoloured . . . 25 15

1993. New Year Festival. Flowers and Butterflies. Multicoloured.

2772 20 r. Type **996** 25 15
2773 20 r. Butterfly and narcissus . . 25 15
2774 40 r. Butterfly, tulips and rose . 50 30
2775 40 r. Butterfly and roses . . . 50 30

997 Grass and Goldfish in Bowl

1993. Fetr Feast.

2776 **997** 100 r. multicoloured . . . 2·25 1·25

998 Open Music Book

1993. 14th Anniv of Islamic Republic.

2777 **998** 40 r. multicoloured . . . 40 25

999 Door and Landscape

1993. International Birth Millenary of Sheikh Mofeed Congress.

2778 **999** 80 r. multicoloured . . . 80 50

1000 Emblem

1001 Globe

1993. 13th Asian and Pacific Labour Ministers' Conference, Teheran.

2779 **1000** 100 r. multicoloured . . 1·00 60

1993. Int Congress for Advancement of Science and Technology in Islamic World.

2780 **1001** 50 r. multicoloured . . . 50 30

1002 Mirror Box

1993. International Museum Day.

2781 **1002** 40 r. multicoloured . . . 40 25

1003 Khomeini

1004 Girl on Swing

1993. 4th Death Anniv of Ayatollah Khomeini.

2782 **1003** 20 r. multicoloured . . . 25 10

1993. World Children's Day.

2783 **1004** 50 r. multicoloured . . . 50 30

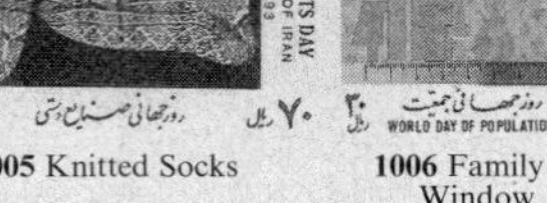

1005 Knitted Socks

1006 Family at Window

1993. World Crafts Day.

2784 **1005** 70 r. multicoloured . . . 70 45

1993. World Population Day.

2785 **1006** 30 r. multicoloured . . . 30 20

1007 Football

1993. Student Games. Multicoloured.

2786 20 r. Type **1007** 20 10
2787 40 r. Judo and wrestling . . . 40 25
2788 40 r. Long jumping, weight-lifting, badminton and basketball 40 25

1008 Butterfly and Film Frame

1993. International Children's and Youths' Film Festival, Isfahan.

2789 **1008** 60 r. multicoloured . . . 60 30

1009 Postal Messenger

1010 Stars and Birds

1993. World Post Day.

2790 **1009** 60 r. multicoloured . . . 60 30

1993. 3rd International Biennial Children's Book Illustrations Exhibition, Teheran. Multicoloured.

2791 30 r. Type **1010** 40 25
2792 30 r. Moon and girl in boat . . 85 50
2793 30 r. Cherub blowing trumpet . 40 25
2794 30 r. Trees and clouds 40 25

Nos. 2791/4 were issued together, se-tenant, forming a composite design.

1011 Khaje Nassireddin Tussy

1013 Ayatollah Golpayegani

1012 Militia Member

1993. 719th Death Anniv of Khaje Nassireddin Tussy (scientist).

2795 **1011** 30 r. multicoloured . . . 35 20

1993. People's Militia Week. Multicoloured.

2796 50 r. Type **1012** 50 25
2797 50 r. Woman tying headband for Militia member 50 25

1993. Ayatollah Golpayegani Commem.

2798 **1013** 300 r. multicoloured . . 3·00 1·50

1014 Hopscotch Grid drawn in Blood

1015 Flags

1993. Support for Moslems of Bosnia and Herzegovina. Multicoloured.

2799 40 r. Type **1014** 45 15
2800 40 r. Youth giving "V" sign . . 45 15
2801 40 r. Woman and mosque . . . 45 15

1994. Invalids' Day and Birthday of Abalfazil el Abbas.

2802 **1015** 80 r. multicoloured . . . 80 50

1016 Trees and Ploughed Field in Book

1994. Agricultural Week.

2803 **1016** 60 r. multicoloured . . . 65 40

1017 Electrification of Villages

1018 Dome of the Rock

1994. 15th Anniv of Islamic Revolution. Mult.

2804 40 r. Type **1017** 65 40
2805 40 r. Ayatollah Khomeini and workers with flag 65 40
2806 40 r. Fishing and new roads . . 65 40
2807 40 r. Harvesting wheat and weaving 65 40

Nos. 2804/7 were issued together, se-tenant, forming a composite design.

1994. Congress on Islamic Law.

2808 **1018** 60 r. multicoloured . . . 70 40

1019 Doctor, Gymnast, Camera, Paintbrush, Book and Student

1994. Youth Welfare.

2809 **1019** 30 r. multicoloured . . . 50 30

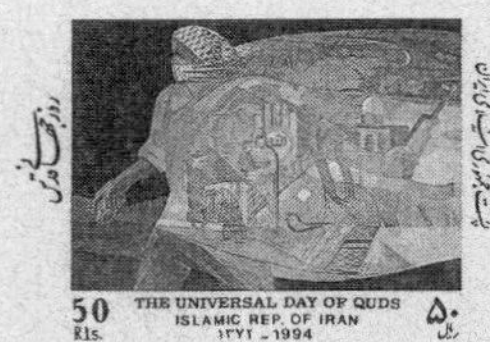

1020 Palestinian and Peaceful Scene

1994. World Jerusalem Day.

2810 **1020** 50 r. multicoloured . . . 55 30

1021 Black-crowned Night Heron

1022 Ball and Rectangles

1994. New Year Festival. Birds. Multicoloured.

2811 40 r. Type **1021** 65 40
2812 40 r. Eurasian bittern 65 40
2813 40 r. Chukar partridges (horiz) 65 40
2814 40 r. Ring-necked pheasants (horiz) 65 40

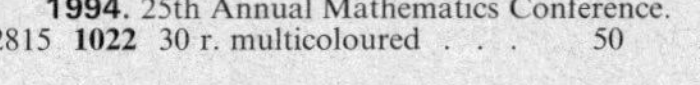

1994. 25th Annual Mathematics Conference.

2815 **1022** 30 r. multicoloured . . . 50 30

1023 Book and Roses

1994. 15th Anniv of Islamic Republic.

2816 **1023** 40 r. multicoloured . . . 40 20

1024 Child and Roses

1994. World Heath Day.
2817 **1024** 100 r. multicoloured . . 1·00 40

1025 Delvari, Cavalrymen and Ship

1994. 80th Death Anniv of Raiss Ali Delvari (revolutionary).
2818 **1025** 50 r. multicoloured . . . 50 20

1026 I.Y.F. Emblem

1994. International Year of the Family.
2819 **1026** 50 r. multicoloured . . . 50 20

1027 Old Telephone System and Computer Operator

1994. World Telecommunications Day.
2820 **1027** 50 r. multicoloured . . . 50 20

1028 Marlik Gold Cup
1029 Kufic Enamelled Pot

1994. International Museum Day.
2821 **1028** 40 r. multicoloured . . . 50 20

1994. Cultural Preservation.
2822 **1029** 40 r. multicoloured . . . 50 20

1030 Khomeini
1031 Motahhari

1994. 5th Death Anniv of Ayatollah Khomeini.
2823 **1030** 30 r. multicoloured . . . 30 15

1994. 15th Death Anniv of Ayatollah Motahhari.
2824 **1031** 30 r. multicoloured . . . 30 15

INDEX

Countries can be quickly located by referring to the index at the end of this volume.

1032 Rose-water Sprinkler
1034 Mosaic and Rose

1033 Games Emblem

1994. World Crafts Day.
2825 60 r. Type **1032** 60 30
2826 60 r. Silk weaving, Khorassan . 60 30

1994. Islamic Countries' University Student Games.
2827 **1033** 60 r. multicoloured . . . 55 30

1994. Mohammed's Birth Anniv and Unity Week.
2828 **1034** 30 r. multicoloured . . . 30 15

1035 Cameraman

1994. 14th Anniv of Iran–Iraq War.
2829 **1035** 70 r. multicoloured . . . 70 30

1036 Envelope

1994. World Post Day.
2830 **1036** 50 r. multicoloured . . . 50 25

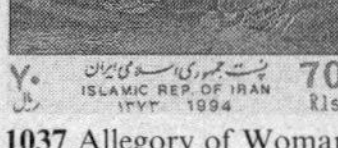

1037 Allegory of Woman
1038 Soldier

1994. Women's Day and Birth Anniv of Fatima.
2831 **1037** 70 r. multicoloured . . . 70 30

1994. People's Militia Week.
2832 **1038** 30 r. multicoloured . . . 35 15

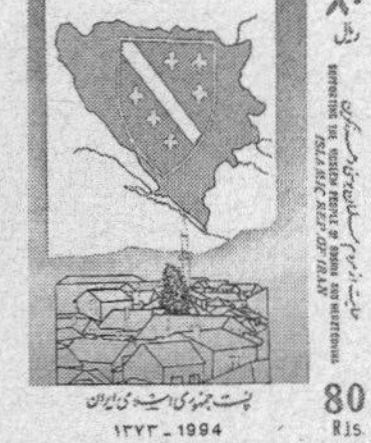
1039 Book
1040 Arms, Map and Town

1994. Book Week.
2833 **1039** 40 r. multicoloured . . . 40 20

1994. Support for Moslems of Bosnia and Herzegovina. Multicoloured.
2834 80 r. Type **1040** 85 40
2835 80 r. Commander Adnan (deceased) and family . . . 85 40

1041 Araki
1042 Arabic Script

1995. 2nd Death Anniv of Grand Ayatollah Mohammad Ali Araki (Shia leader).
2836 **1041** 100 r. multicoloured . . 1·00 50

1995. World Day of the Oppressed. Birth Anniv of Mahdi.
2837 **1042** 50 r. multicoloured . . . 50 25

1043 Flag, Dome and Man
1044 Crowd, National Flag and Ayatollah Khomeini

1995. Revolutionaries (1st series). Multicoloured.
2838 50 r. Type **1043** 50 25
2839 50 r. Man in patterned shirt . . 50 25
2840 50 r. Man with full beard wearing grey shirt 50 25
2841 50 r. Man in jacket and sweater looking to right 50 25
See also Nos. 2874/7, 2909/16 and 2953/6.

1995. 16th Anniv of Islamic Revolution.
2842 **1044** 100 r. multicoloured . . 1·00 50

1045 Dome of the Rock
1046 Hand holding Tree

1995. World Jerusalem Day.
2843 **1045** 100 r. multicoloured . . 1·00 50

1995. Tree Day.
2844 **1046** 50 r. multicoloured . . . 50 25

1047 Hyacinths

1995. New Year Festival. Multicoloured.
2845 50 r. Type **1047** 60 30
2846 50 r. Pansies 60 30
2847 50 r. Grass and bow 60 30
2848 50 r. Tulips, bow and goldfish bowl 80 50

1048 Diesel Goods Train on Bridge

1995. Inauguration of Bafq–Bandar Abbas Railway.
2849 **1048** 100 r. multicoloured . . 1·50 80

1049 Phoenix rising from Tulips
1050 Shapes

1995. 16th Anniv of Islamic Republic.
2850 **1049** 100 r. multicoloured . . 1·00 50

1995. Press Festival.
2851 **1050** 100 r. multicoloured . . 1·00 50

1051 Khomeini
1052 Arabic Script

1995. Ayatollah Ahmad Khomeini Commem.
2852 **1051** 50 r. multicoloured . . . 50 25

1995. Invalids' Day.
2853 **1052** 80 r. multicoloured . . . 80 40

1053 Yezd Mosque and Vaziri

1995. Ayatollah Ali Vaziri Commemoration.
2854 **1053** 100 r. multicoloured . . 1·00 50

1054 Telecommunications

1995. World Telecommunications Day.
2855 **1054** 100 r. multicoloured . . 1·00 50

1055 Khomeini
1056 Immunizing Baby

1995. 6th Death Anniv of Ayatollah Khomeini.
2856 **1055** 100 r. multicoloured . . 1·00 50

1995. 50th Anniv of U.N.O. Multicoloured.
2857 100 r. Type **1056** . . . . . 1·00 50
2858 100 r. Child laughing . . . . 1·00 50
2859 100 r. Cereals and world map . 1·00 50
2860 100 r. Woman reading . . . . 1·00 50

1057 Ashtiany
1059 Man with Gun and Book

1058 Dam Workers

1995. Iqbal Ashtiany (historian) Commem.
2861 **1057** 100 r. multicoloured . . 1·00 50

1995. Government Week.
2862 **1058** 100 r. multicoloured . . 1·00 50

1995. People's Militia Week.
2863 **1059** 100 r. multicoloured . . 1·00 50

1060 Envelopes and Globe forming Flower — 1061 Cypher

1995. World Post Day.
2864 **1060** 100 r. multicoloured . . 1·00 50

1995. Prophet Mohammed Commemoration.
2865 **1061** 100 r. multicoloured . . 1·00 50

1062 Tondgoyan — 1063 Shaghaghi

1995. M. J. Tondgoyan (oil minister) Commem.
2866 **1062** 100 r. multicoloured . . 1·00 50

1996. Fathi Shaghaghi (Islamic Jihad Secretary-General) Commemoration.
2867 **1063** 100 r. multicoloured . . 1·00 50

1064 Crowd, Flowers and Ayatollah Khomeini — 1065 Dome of the Rock

1996. 17th Anniv of Islamic Revolution.
2868 **1064** 100 r. multicoloured . . 1·00 50

1996. World Jerusalem Day.
2869 **1065** 100 r. multicoloured . . 1·00 50

1066 Crested Bird

1996. New Year Festival. Birds. Multicoloured.
2870 100 r. Type **1066** . . . . . . 1·50 80
2871 100 r. Budgerigar . . . . . . 1·50 80
2872 100 r. Yellow-headed bird . . 1·50 80
2873 100 r. Blue-headed bird . . 1·50 80

1996. Revolutionaries (2nd series). As T **1043**. Multicoloured.
2874 100 r. Colonel-pilot Abbas Babaiy . . . . 1·00 50
2875 100 r. Officer-pilot Ali Akbar Sharoudi . . . . 1·00 50
2876 100 r. Commandant Mohammad Ebrahim Hemmat . . . . 1·00 50
2877 100 r. Commandant Mohammad Boroudjerdi . . 1·00 50

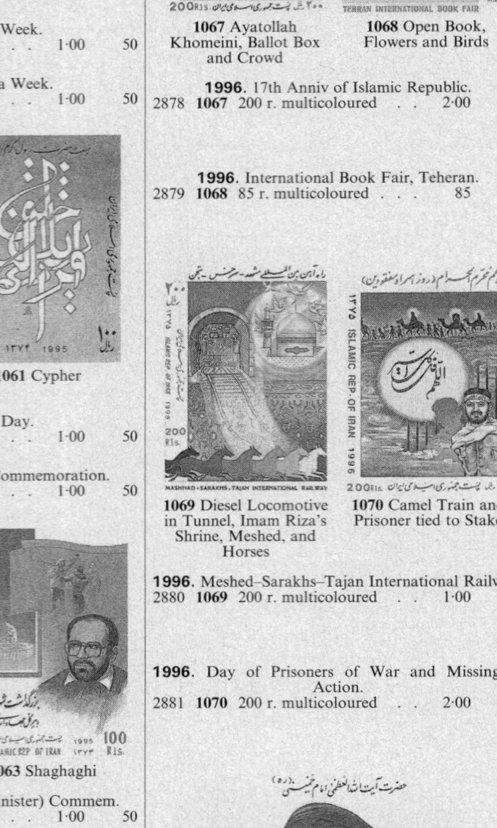

1067 Ayatollah Khomeini, Ballot Box and Crowd — 1068 Open Book, Flowers and Birds

1996. 17th Anniv of Islamic Republic.
2878 **1067** 200 r. multicoloured . . 2·00 1·00

1996. International Book Fair, Teheran.
2879 **1068** 85 r. multicoloured . . . 85 40

1069 Diesel Locomotive in Tunnel, Imam Riza's Shrine, Meshed, and Horses — 1070 Camel Train and Prisoner tied to Stake

1996. Meshed–Sarakhs–Tajan International Railway.
2880 **1069** 200 r. multicoloured . . 1·00 40

1996. Day of Prisoners of War and Missing in Action.
2881 **1070** 200 r. multicoloured . . 2·00 1·00

1071 Khomeini

1996. 7th Death Anniv of Ayatollah Khomeini.
2882 **1071** 200 r. multicoloured . . 2·00 1·00

1072 Carpet

1996. World Crafts Day.
2883 **1072** 200 r. multicoloured . . 2·00 1·00

1073 Emblem

1996. 3rd Posts and Telecommunications Ministerial Conference, Teheran.
2884 **1073** 200 r. multicoloured . . 2·00 1·00

1074 Zouqeblateyne Mosque

1996. Mohammed's Birth Anniv and Unity Week. Multicoloured.
2885 200 r. Type **1074** . . . . . . 2·00 1·00
2886 200 r. Tomb of Imam Hossein (dome with flag flying to right) . . . . 2·00 1·00
2887 200 r. Prophet's Mosque (dome without flag) . . . . . . 2·00 1·00
2888 200 r. Tomb of Imam Riza (dome with flag flying to left) . . . . 2·00 1·00
2889 200 r. Qaba Mosque (with four corner minarets) . . . . . 2·00 1·00

1075 Teheran Underground

1996. Government Week. Multicoloured.
2890 200 r. Type **1075** . . . . . . 1·00 40
2891 200 r. Ispahan iron works . . 1·00 40
2892 200 r. Merchant fleet . . . . . 1·00 40
2893 200 r. Bandar-e-Imam oil refinery . . . . 1·00 40
2894 200 r. Boumehen Earth Station 1·00 40

1076 Ardabily and Mosque Interior

1996. Allameh Moghaddas Ardabily Commem.
2895 **1076** 200 r. multicoloured . . 2·00 1·00

1077 Artillery Position and Soldier praying

1996. 16th Anniv of Iran—Iraq War.
2896 **1077** 200 r. multicoloured . . 2·00 1·00

1078 Cogs and Equipment

1996. World Standards Day.
2897 **1078** 200 r. multicoloured . . 2·00 1·00

MORE DETAILED LISTS
are given in the Stanley Gibbons Catalogues referred to in the country headings.
For lists of current volumes see Introduction.

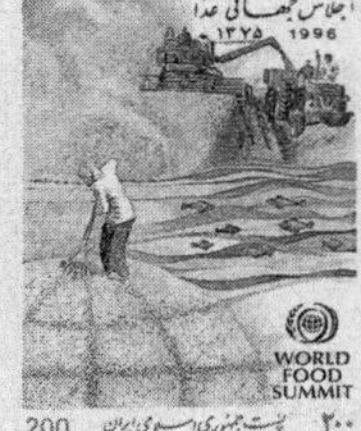

1079 Harvesting and Man working on "Globe" Rick

1996. World Food Summit, Rome.
2898 **1079** 200 r. multicoloured . . 2·00 1·00

1080 Men, Houses and Women

1996. National Population and Housing Census.
2899 **1080** 200 r. multicoloured . . 2·00 1·00

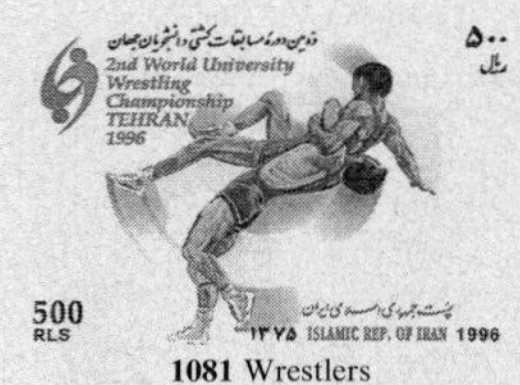

1081 Wrestlers

1996. 2nd World University Wrestling Championship, Teheran.
2900 **1081** 500 r. multicoloured . . 4·75 2·40

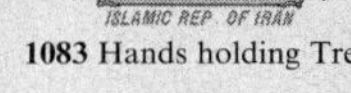

1082 Ayatollah Khomeini embracing Youth — 1083 Hands holding Tree

1997. 18th Anniv of Islamic Revolution. Mult.
2901 200 r. Type **1082** . . . . . . 2·25 1·00
2902 200 r. Banner of Khomeini above crowd . . . . 2·25 1·00
2903 200 r. Khomeini waving . . 2·25 1·00
2904 200 r. Khomeini returning from exile in France . . . . . . 2·25 1·00
2905 200 r. Soldiers . . . . 2·25 1·00

1997. Tree Day.
2906 **1083** 200 r. multicoloured . . 2·25 1·00

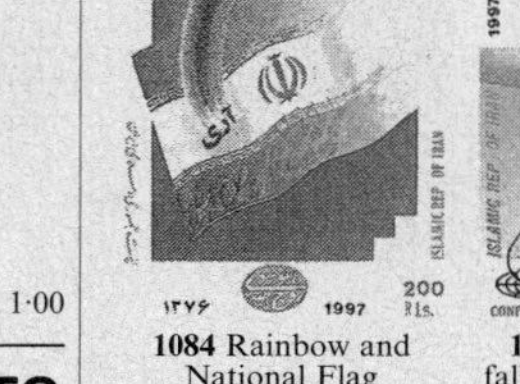

1084 Rainbow and National Flag — 1085 Water Droplet falling to "Globe" Pool in Cupped Hands

1997. 18th Anniv of Islamic Republic.
2907 **1084** 200 r. multicoloured . . 2·25 1·00

1997. 8th International Rainwater Catchment Systems Conference.
2908 **1085** 200 r. multicoloured . . 2·25 1·00

1997. Revolutionaries (3rd series). As T **1043**. Multicoloured.

2909 100 r. Alireza Mowahhed Danesh (blue flag, white turban) . . . . 1·25 50
2910 100 r. Mohammad Reza Dastwareh (orange flag, white turban) . . . . 1·25 50
2911 100 r. Abbas Karimi (blue flag, full-face without glasses) . . 1·25 50
2912 100 r. Nasser Kazemi (orange flag, white vest with red trim) . . . . 1·25 50
2913 100 r. Youssef Kolahdouz (blue flag, three-quarter face) . . 1·25 50
2914 100 r. Yadollah Kolhar (orange flag, full-face) . . . . . . 1·25 50
2915 100 r. Fazlollah Mahallati (blue flag, full-face with glasses) . . 1·25 50
2916 100 r. Abdollah Meyssami (orange flag, green vest and coat) . . . . 1·25 50

1086 Satellite, Letter, Globe and Computer

1087 Khomeini

1997. Post, Telecommunications and Productivity.

2917 **1086** 200 r. multicoloured . . 2·25 1·00

1997. 10th Death Anniv of Ayatollah Khomeini.

2918 **1087** 200 r. multicoloured . . 2·00 1·00

1088 Teheran Underground Railway Map and Tunnel

1089 Flora and Fauna

1997. National Achievements. Multicoloured.

2919 40 r. Type **1088** 15 10
2920 50 r. Cornfield and silo 20 10
2921 65 r. Medals from Student Scientific Olympiads 25 10
2922 70 r. Steelworks, Mobarakeh . . 30 15
2923 100 r. Modern communications systems 40 20
2924 130 r. Harbour and tanker . . 50 25
2925 150 r. Oil refinery, Bandar Abbas 60 30
2926 200 r. Martyr Radja-ee dam . . 75 35
2927 350 r. Martyr Radja-ee power station . . . . 1·40 70
2928 400 r. Foreign Ministry building . . . . 1·75 80
2929 500 r. Child receiving oral vaccination . . . . 2·10 1·00
2930 650 r. Koran Printing House and Koran . . . . 2·75 1·40
2931 1000 r. Imam Khomeini International Airport, Teheran . . . . 4·25 2·10
2932 2000 r. Tomb of Imam Khomeini, Teheran . . . . 8·25 4·00

1997. 10th Anniv of Montreal Protocol (on reduction of use of chlorofluorocarbons).

2933 **1089** 200 r. multicoloured . . 2·25 1·00

1090 Crowd with Flags and Banners

1091 Allama Mohammad Iqbal (Pakistani poet)

1997. 17th Anniv of Iran–Iraq War.

2934 **1090** 200 r. multicoloured . . 2·25 1·00

1997. Iranian–Pakistani Culture. Mult.

2935 200 r. Type **1091** . . . . . . 2·25 1·00
2936 200 r. Jalal-ad-din Moulana Rumi (Persian mystic) . . . 2·25 1·00

1092 Airplane, Letters and Computer

1997. World Post Day.

2937 **1092** 200 r. multicoloured . . 2·25 1·00

1093 Frasheri and Etehemberg Mosque, Tirana

1997. 150th Birth Anniv (1996) of Naim Frasheri (Albanian writer).

2938 **1093** 200 r. multicoloured . . 2·25 1·00

1094 Calligraphy

1095 Games Emblem

1997. 8th Islamic Summit, Teheran. Illustrated pages from the Koran. Each green, gold and red.

2939 300 r. Type **1094** . . . . . 3·00 1·50
2940 300 r. Page with rose at bottom left . . . . 3·00 1·50
2941 300 r. Page with rose on right-hand side . . . . . . 3·00 1·50
2942 300 r. Page with rose at top left-hand corner . . . . . . 3·00 1·50
2943 300 r. Summit emblem . . . . 3·00 1·50

1997. 2nd Islamic Countries Women's Games, Teheran.

2944 **1095** 200 r. multicoloured . . 2·25 1·00

1096 Dome of the Rock

1998. World Jerusalem Day.

2945 **1096** 250 r. multicoloured . . 10 10

1097 State Flags and Poppies

1998. 19th Anniv of Islamic Revolution. Mult.

2946 200 r. Type **1097** 10 10
2947 200 r. Harvesting grain 10 10
2948 200 r. Soldiers with flags . . . 10 10
2949 200 r. Crowd with banner of Khomeini 10 10
2950 200 r. Ayatollah Khomeini . . 10 10

Nos. 2946/50 were issued together, se-tenant, forming a composite design.

1098 Tree and Town

1998. Tree Day.

2951 **1098** 200 r. multicoloured . . 10 10

1099 Flower Arrangement and Gifts

1998. New Year Festival.

2952 **1099** 200 r. multicoloured . . 10 10

1998. Revolutionaries (4th series). As T **1043**. Multicoloured.

2953 100 r. Man in open-necked shirt 10 10
2954 100 r. Man in vest and jacket (three-quarter face) . . . 10 10
2955 100 r. Man in vest and jacket (profile) 10 10
2956 100 r. Man in crew-neck jumper and jacket 10 10

1100 M. Shahryar (poet)

1101 Khomeini

1998.

2957 **1100** 200 r. multicoloured . . 10 10

1998. 9th Death Anniv of Ayatollah Khomeini.

2958 **1101** 200 r. multicoloured . . 10 10

1102 Map and Emblem

1998. 2nd South and West Asia Postal Union Congress.

2959 **1102** 250 r. multicoloured . . 10 10

1103 Player, Ball and Stadium

1998. World Cup Football Championship, France.

2960 **1103** 500 r. multicoloured . . 20 10

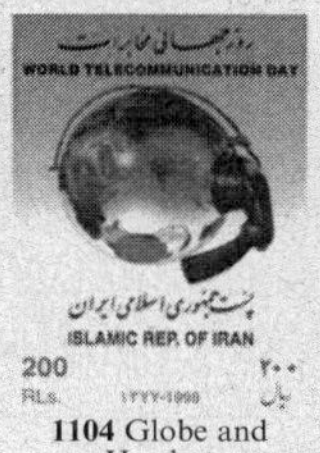

1104 Globe and Headset

1105 Silver Vessel

1998. World Telecommunications Day.

2961 **1104** 200 r. multicoloured . . 10 10

1998. World Handicrafts Day.

2962 **1105** 200 r. multicoloured . . 10 10

1106 State Flag as Dove, Birds and Flowers

1998. 1st Anniv of Presidential Election.

2963 **1106** 200 r. multicoloured . . 10 10

1107 Khomeini voting

1998. 19th Anniv of Islamic Republic.

2964 **1107** 250 r. multicoloured . . 10 10

1108 Handshake, Rainbow and Doves

1109 Arabic Script

1998. Co-operation Day.

2965 **1108** 250 r. multicoloured . . 10 10

1998. "1000th Friday of Public Prayer".

2966 **1109** 250 r. blue, gold and black 10 10

200 R ٢٠٠ ریال

(1110)

1998. Mosques. Nos. 2415a and 2416a surch as T **1110**.

2967 **1110** 200 r. on 1 r. orange and silver 10 10
2968 200 r. on 3 r. green and silver 10 10

1111 Globe and Shark's Fin

1998. International Year of the Ocean.

2969 **1111** 250 r. multicoloured . . 10 10

1112 Arabic Script

1998. Sacred Defence Week.

2970 **1112** 250 r. multicoloured . . 10 10

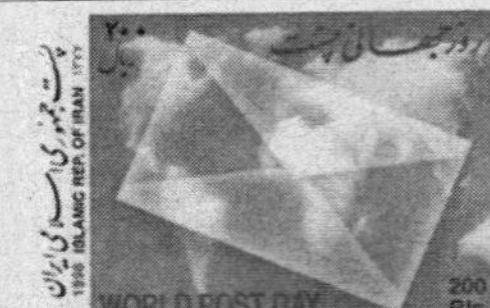

1113 Envelope and Clouds as World Map

1998. World Post Day.
2971 **1113** 200 r. multicoloured . . . 10 10

1114 Wrestlers

1998. World Wrestling Championship, Iran.
2972 **1114** 250 r. multicoloured . . 10 10

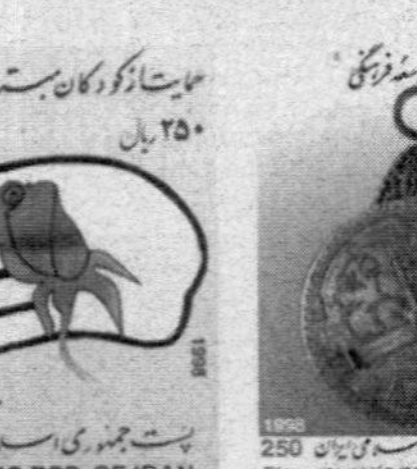

1115 Rosebud in Hand **1116** Navigation Instrument

1998. Children's Cancer Relief.
2973 **1115** 250 r. multicoloured . . . 10 10

1999. Museum Exhibit.
2974 **1116** 250 r. multicoloured . . . 10 10

NEWSPAPER POSTAGE DUE STAMPS

1909. Optd **Imprimes** in English and Persian.
N319 **38** 2 ch. grey on blue . . . . 13·00 2·00

OFFICIAL STAMPS

1902. Stamp of 1898 surch **Service** and value in English and Persian.
O224 **21** 5 c. on 1 k. red . . . . . 4·00 50
O225 10 c. on 1 k. red . . . . . 3·00 60
O226 12 c. on 1 k. red . . . . . 4·25 1·40

1903. Stamps of 1903 optd **Service**.
O259 **38** 1 c. lilac 15 10
O260 2 c. grey 15 10
O261 3 c. green 15 10
O262 5 c. red 15 10
O263 10 c. brown 15 10
O264 12 c. blue 20 10
O265 **39** 1 k. purple 40 10
O266 2 k. blue 80 10
O267 5 k. brown . . . . 6·00 20
O268 10 k. red . . . . 6·00 50
O269 20 k. orange . . . . . . 9·00 50
O270 30 k. green . . . . 12·00 1·00
O271 50 k. green . . . . 55·00 14·00

1905. Nos. 275/6 and 280/1 optd **Service**.
O283 **39** 2 t. on 50 k. green (275) . 45·00 22·00
O285 2 t. on 50 k. green (280) . 45·00 22·00
O284 3 t. on 50 k. green (276) . 45·00 25·00
O286 3 t. on 50 k. green (281) . 45·00 22·00

(O 57)

O 120

1911. Stamps of 1909 optd **Service** and with Type O **57**.
O353 **56** 1 c. purple and orange . . 3·00 15
O354 2 c. purple and violet . . . 3·00 15
O355 3 c. purple and green . . . 3·00 20
O356 6 c. purple and red . . . 3·00 20
O357 9 c. purple and grey . . . 3·00 50
O358 10 c. purple and mauve . . 6·00 60
O359 1 k. brown, violet & silver . 7·00 2·00
O360 2 k. brown, green & silver . 12·00 5·00

1915. Coronation stamps of 1915 optd **SERVICE** in English and Persian.
O460 **66** 1 c. blue and red 10 10
O461 2 c. red and blue 10 10
O462 3 c. green 10 10
O463 5 c. red 10 10
O464 6 c. red and green 20 10
O465 9 c. violet and brown . . . 20 10
O466 10 c. brown and green . . 20 10
O467 12 c. blue 20 10
O468 24 c. chocolate & brown . 20 10
O469 **67** 1 k. black, brn & silver . . 80 15
O470 2 k. red, blue and silver . . 80 15
O471 – 3 k. sepia, lilac & silver . . 80 20
O472 **67** 5 k. grey, sepia & silver . . 85 20
O473 – 1 t. black, violet & gold . . 85 35
O474 – 2 t. brown, grn & gold . . 90 35
O475 – 3 t. red, crimson & gold . 90 55
O476 – 5 t. grey, blue and gold . . 1·25 60

1941.
O836 O **120** 5 d. violet 55 10
O837 10 d. mauve 55 10
O838 25 d. red 55 10
O839 50 d. black 55 10
O840 75 d. red 80 10
O841 1 r. green . . . . . . 2·00 10
O842 1 r. 50 blue . . . . . 2·25 10
O843 2 r. blue . . . . . . 4·25 10
O844 3 r. purple . . . . . 8·50 10
O845 5 r. green . . . . . . 12·00 20
O846 10 r. blue & brown . . 35·00 40
O847 20 r. mauve & blue . . £130 1·50
O848 30 r. green & violet . . £250 2·75
O849 50 r. brown & blue . . £300 45·00
The rial values are larger (23 × 30 mm)

O **489** Red Lion and Sun Emblem

1974.
O1829 O **489** 5 d. violet & mauve . 10 10
O1830 10 d. mauve & blue . 10 10
O1831 50 d. orange & grn . 10 10
O1832 1 r. blue and gold . . 10 10
O2046 1 r. black and green . 10 10
O1833 2 r. green & orange . 10 10
O2047 2 r. brown and grey . 10 10
O2048 3 r. blue & orange . . 10 10
O2049 5 r. green and pink . 15 15
O1834 6 r. green & yellow . 35 10
O2050 6 r. black and blue . . 15 15
O1835 8 r. blue & yellow . . 35 15
O2051 8 r. red and green . . 20 15
O1836 10 r. blue & mauve . 2·00 20
O2052 10 r. turq & green . . 35 20
O1837 11 r. purple & blue . 70 20
O2053 11 r. blue & yellow . 70 25
O1838 14 r. red and blue . . 70 50
O2054 14 r. green & grey . . 75 30
O2055 15 r. blue & mauve . 1·50 70
O1839 20 r. blue & orange . 70 55
O2056 20 r. purple & yellow . 1·75 30
O2057 30 r. brown & orange 1·75 90
O1840 50 r. brown & green . 3·50 1·40
O2058 50 r. black & gold . . 3·50 1·00
The 6 r. to 50 r. are larger, 23 × 37 mm.

PARCEL POST STAMPS

1915. Coronation stamps of 1915 optd **COLIS POSTAUX** in English and Persian.
P443 **66** 1 c. blue and red 10 10
P444 2 c. red and blue 10 10
P445 3 c. green 10 10
P446 5 c. red 10 10
P447 6 c. red and green 20 10
P448 9 c. violet and brown . . . 20 10
P449 10 c. brown and green . . 20 10
P450 12 c. blue 20 10
P451 24 c. choc & brown . . . 20 10
P452 **67** 1 k. black, brn & silver . . 70 15
P453 2 k. red, blue and silver . . 70 15
P454 3 k. sepia, lilac & silver . . 70 20
P455 5 k. grey, sepia & silver . . 70 20
P456 – 1 t. black, violet & gold . . 75 35
P457 – 2 t. brown, grn & gold . . 75 35
P458 – 3 t. red, crimson & gold . . 80 55
P459 – 5 t. grey, blue and gold . . 1·25 55

P **192**

1958.
P1151 P **192** 50 d. drab 10 10
P1152 1 r. red 10 10
P1153 2 r. blue 20 10
P1154 3 r. myrtle 15 10
P1478 5 r. violet 15 10
P1479 10 r. brown 30 15
P1480 20 r. orange 50 35
P1481 30 r. mauve . . . . . 1·00 15
P1482 50 r. lake . . . . . . 1·25 85
P1483 100 r. yellow . . . . 2·75 1·00
P1484 200 r. green . . . . . 6·00 3·75
The word "IRAN" with a black frame is printed in reverse on the back of the above stamps and is intended to show through the stamps when attached to parcels.

INDEX

Countries can be quickly located by referring to the index at the end of this volume.

POSTAL TAX STAMPS

T **142a** Red Lion and Sun Emblem (8 lines to each ray)

1950. Hospitals Fund.
T1139 T **142a** 50 d. red & green . . 50 15
T1396 2 r. red and lilac . . 80 15

1976. As T **142a** but with five lines to each ray.
T2007 T **142a** 50 d. red & green . . 1·25 20
T2008 2 r. red and blue . . 1·75 20

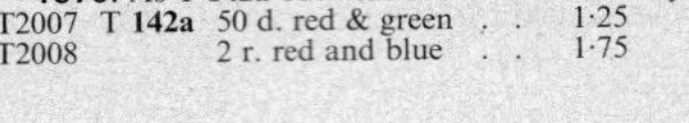

IRAQ Pt. 1, Pt. 19

A country W. of Persia, formerly under Turkish dominion, then under British mandate after the 1914–18 War. An independent kingdom since 1932 until 14 July, 1958, when the king was assassinated and a republic proclaimed.

1917. 16 annas = 1 rupee.
1931. 1000 fils = 1 dinar.

1918. Stamps of Turkey (Pictorial issue, Nos. 501/514) surch **IRAQ IN BRITISH OCCUPATION** and value in Indian currency.

No.	Type	Description	Unused	Used
1		½ a. on 5 pa. purple	30	80
2		½ a. on 10 pa. green	30	15
3		1 a. on 20 pa. red	30	10
17		1½ a. on 5 pa. purple	1·00	95
5		2½ a. on 1 pi. blue	90	1·25
6	3	a. on 1½ pi. grey and red	80	25
7		4 a. on 1¾ pi. brown & grey	80	25
8		6 a. on 2 pi. black and green	1·60	1·25
9		8 a. on 2½ pi. green & orange	90	60
10		12 a. on 5 pi. lilac	1·75	3·00
11		1 r. on 10 pi. brown	2·25	1·40
12		2 r. on 25 pi. green	7·50	2·50
13		5 r. on 50 pi. red	20·00	20·00
14		10 r. on 100 pi. blue	48·00	17·00

2 Sunni Mosque, Muadhdham

3 Winged Cherub

4 Allegory of Date Palm — 10 King Faisal I

1923.

No.	Type	Description	Unused	Used
41	2	½ a. green	60	10
42	–	1 a. brown	1·00	10
43	3	1½ a. red	50	10
44	–	2 a. buff	50	15
45	–	3 a. blue	85	15
46	–	4 a. violet	1·75	30
47	–	6 a. blue	1·00	30
48	–	8 a. bistre	2·00	30
49	4	1 r. brown and green	3·00	1·00
50	2	2 r. black	12·00	7·00
51		2 r. bistre	30·00	3·25
52	–	5 r. orange	26·00	13·00
53	–	10 r. red	32·00	20·00

DESIGNS—30 × 24 mm: 1 a. Gufas on the Tigris; 2 a. Bull from Babylonian wall-sculpture; 6 a., 10 r. Shiah Mosque, Kadhimain. 34 × 24 mm: 3 a. Arch of Ctesiphon. 24 × 30 mm: 4, 8 a., 5 r. Tribal Standard, Dulaim Camel Corps.

1927.

No.	Type	Description	Unused	Used
78	10	1 r. brown	6·00	50

11 King Faisal I 12

1931.

No.	Type	Description	Unused	Used
80	11	½ a. green	80	10
81		1 a. brown	90	10
82		1½ a. red	80	30
83		2 a. orange	80	10
84		3 a. blue	80	10
85		4 a. purple	1·25	1·10
86		6 a. blue	1·25	60
87		8 a. green	1·25	1·75
88	12	1 r. brown	3·00	1·25
89		2 r. brown	5·50	4·00
90		5 r. orange	18·00	30·00
91		10 r. red	50·00	70·00
92	10	25 r. violet	£500	£650

1932. Nos. 80/92 and 46 surch in "Fils" or "Dinar".

No.	Type	Description	Unused	Used
106	11	2 f. on ½ a. green	20	10
107		3 f. on ½ a. green	20	10
108		4 f. on 1 a. brown	1·75	25
109		5 f. on 1 a. brown	45	10
110		8 f. on 1½ a. red	35	30
111		10 f. on 2 a. orange	35	10
112		15 f. on 3 a. blue	85	1·00
113		20 f. on 4 a. purple	1·25	1·25
114	–	25 f. on 4 a. vio (No. 46)	1·75	3·00
115	11	30 f. on 6 a. blue	1·50	60
116		40 f. on 8 a. green	2·25	2·50
117	12	75 f. on 1 r. brown	1·75	2·50
118		100 f. on 2 r. brown	5·50	3·75
119		200 f. on 5 r. orange	11·00	17·00
120		½ d. on 10 r. red	45·00	60·00
121	10	1 d. on 25 r. violet	80·00	£130

1932. As Types 10/12 but value in FILS or DINAR.

No.	Type	Description	Unused	Used
138	11	2 f. blue	40	10
139		3 f. green	40	10
140		4 f. purple	40	10
141		5 f. green	50	10
142		8 f. red	1·00	10
143		10 f. yellow	1·00	10
144		15 f. blue	1·00	10
145		20 f. orange	1·00	40
146		25 f. mauve	1·00	30
147		30 f. olive	1·75	15
148		40 f. violet	1·00	70
149	12	50 f. brown	1·00	20
150		75 f. blue	2·00	2·00
151		100 f. green	3·50	70
152		200 f. red	12·00	3·25
153	10	½ d. blue	35·00	32·00
154		1 d. purple	65·00	65·00

16 King Ghazi 17

1934.

No.	Type	Description	Unused	Used
172	16	1 f. violet	45	30
173		2 f. blue	20	15
174		3 f. green	20	15
175		4 f. purple	25	15
176		5 f. green	25	15
177		8 f. red	35	15
178		10 f. yellow	45	15
179		15 f. blue	45	15
180		20 f. orange	45	15
181		25 f. mauve	85	20
182		30 f. green	65	20
183		40 f. violet	75	25
184	17	50 f. brown	1·75	25
185		75 f. blue	1·50	30
186		100 f. green	1·90	45
187		200 f. red	3·50	75
188	–	½ d. blue	5·50	2·40
189	–	1 d. red	38·00	12·00

DESIGN—23 × 27½ mm: ½, 1 d. Portrait as in Types **16/17** but different frame.

19 Mausoleum of Sitt Zubaidah

21 Lion of Babylon

22 Spiral Tower of Samarra

1941.

No.	Type	Description	Unused	Used
208	19	1 f. purple	10	10
209		2 f. brown	10	10
210	–	3 f. green	10	10
211	–	4 f. violet	10	10
212	–	5 f. red	20	10
213	21	8 f. red	50	10
214		8 f. yellow	10	10
215		10 f. yellow	9·25	2·10
216		10 f. red	50	10
217		15 f. blue	85	20
218a		15 f. black	85	30
219		20 f. black	1·25	40
220		20 f. blue	45	20
221	22	25 f. purple	20	10
222		30 f. orange	25	15
223b		40 f. brown	85	40
224b	–	50 f. blue	1·25	45
225a	–	75 f. mauve	85	45
226	–	100 f. olive	1·25	75
227	–	200 f. orange	2·10	75
228	–	½ d. blue	10·00	3·50
229a	–	1 d. green	20·00	8·00

DESIGNS—HORIZ: 3 f., 4 f., 5 f. King Faisal's Mausoleum (24 × 20 mm). ½ d., 1 d. Mosque of the Golden Dome, Samarra (24 × 21 mm). VERT: 50 f., 75 f. as Type **22**, but larger (21 × 24 mm); 100 f., 200 f. Oil Wells (20 × 22 mm).

26 King Faisal II 27

1942.

No.	Type	Description	Unused	Used
255	26	1 f. brown and violet	35	35
256		2 f. brown and blue	35	35
257		3 f. brown and green	35	35
258		4 f. sepia and brown	35	35
259		5 f. brown and green	35	35
260		6 f. brown and red	35	35
261		10 f. brown and pink	35	35
262		12 f. brown and green	35	35

1948.

No.	Type	Description	Unused	Used
271	27	1 f. blue	30	10
272		2 f. brown	15	10
273		3 f. green	15	10
274		3 f. red	3·50	90
275		4 f. lilac	15	10
276		5 f. red	15	10
277		5 f. green	4·25	1·75
278		6 f. mauve	1·00	10
279		8 f. brown	2·50	45
280		10 f. red	25	10
281		12 f. green	20	10
282		14 f. green	1·40	10
283		15 f. black	4·25	85
284		16 f. red	65	25
285		20 f. blue	45	10
286		25 f. purple	50	10
287	27	28 f. blue	85	25
288		30 f. orange	50	10
289		40 f. brown	1·25	45
290		50 f. blue	4·25	85
291		60 f. blue	85	45
292		75 f. mauve	85	45
293		100 f. green	3·50	85
294		200 f. orange	2·75	85
295		½ d. blue	7·25	2·75
296		1 d. green	24·00	10·00

The 50 f. to 1 d. are larger (22½ × 27½ mm).

29 Vickers Viking "Al Mahfoutha" over Basrah Aerodrome

31 King Faisal I and Equestrian Statue

1949. Air.

No.	Type	Description	Unused	Used
330	29	3 f. green	20	20
331	–	4 f. purple	20	20
332	–	5 f. brown	20	20
333	29	10 f. red	2·50	85
334	–	20 f. blue	85	45
335	–	35 f. orange	75	45
336	–	50 f. green	1·60	70
337	–	100 f. violet	3·75	1·40

DESIGNS—As Type **29**: 4, 20 f. "Al Mahfoutha" over Kut Barrage; 5, 35 f. "Al Mahfoutha" over Faisal II Bridge. 31 × 22½ mm: 50, 100 f. "Al Mahfoutha" over Dhiyala Railway Bridge.

1949. 75th Anniversary of U.P.U.

No.	Type	Description	Unused	Used
339	–	20 f. blue	1·75	1·25
340	31	40 f. orange	2·50	1·25
341	–	50 f. violet	5·50	4·50

DESIGNS: 20 f. King Ghazi and mounted postman; 50 f. King Faisal II, globe and wreath.

32 King Faisal II 33 (35)

1953. Coronation of King Faisal II.

No.	Type	Description	Unused	Used
342	32	3 f. red	85	85
343		14 f. brown	1·75	85
344		28 f. blue	4·75	1·25

1954.

No.	Type	Description	Unused	Used
346	33	1 f. blue	35	15
347		2 f. brown	15	10
348		3 f. lake	15	10
349		4 f. violet	15	10
350		5 f. green	20	10
351		6 f. mauve	20	10
352		8 f. brown	20	10
353		10 f. blue	20	10
354		15 f. black	1·10	75
355		16 f. red	1·75	1·50
356		20 f. olive	85	20
357		25 f. purple	85	10
358		30 f. red	85	10
359		40 f. brown	90	35
360		50 f. blue	1·25	50
361		75 f. mauve	2·10	60
362		100 f. olive	3·75	60
363		200 f. salmon	6·25	1·25

The 50 f. to 200 f. are larger (22 × 28 mm).

1955. Abrogation of Anglo-Iraqi Treaty. Optd with T **35**.

No.	Type	Description	Unused	Used
380	33	3 f. lake	80	35
381		10 f. blue	80	35
382	27	28 f. blue	1·25	60

36 King Faisal II

1955. 6th Arab Engineers' Conference, Baghdad.

No.	Type	Description	Unused	Used
383	36	3 f. red	65	30
384		10 f. blue	1·40	55
385		28 f. blue	2·10	1·25

37 King Faisal II and Globe

1956. 3rd Arab Postal Union Conference, Baghdad.

No.	Type	Description	Unused	Used
386	37	3 f. red	85	45
387		10 f. blue	90	45
388		28 f. blue	1·25	85

38 King Faisal II and Power Loom

39 King Faisal II and Exhibition Emblem

1957. Development Week.

No.	Type	Description	Unused	Used
389	38	1 f. blue and buff	30	20
390	–	3 f. multicoloured	35	20
391	–	5 f. multicoloured	30	25
392	–	10 f. multicoloured	55	25
393	–	40 f. multicoloured	1·25	85

DESIGNS: 3 f. Irrigation dam; 5 f. Residential road, Baghdad; 10 f. Cement kiln; 40 f. Tigris Bridge.

1957. Agricultural and Industrial Exn, Baghdad.

No.	Type	Description	Unused	Used
394	39	10 f. brown and cream	60	50

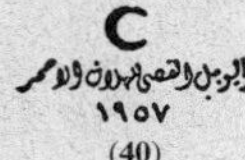

(40)

1957. Silver Jubilee of Iraqi Red Crescent Society. No. 388 optd with T **40**.

No.	Type	Description	Unused	Used
395	37	28 f. blue	3·00	1·25

41 King Faisal II

42 King Faisal II and Tanks

1957.

No.	Type	Description	Unused	Used
396	41	1 f. blue	25	35
397		2 f. brown	25	35
398		3 f. red	25	35
399		4 f. violet	25	35
400		5 f. green	50	35
401		6 f. red	50	50
402		8 f. brown	1·00	75
403		10 f. blue	75	70

1958. Army Day.

No.	Type	Description	Unused	Used
411	42	8 f. grey and green	60	60
412	–	10 f. black and brown	75	75
413	–	20 f. brown and blue	75	75
414	–	30 f. violet and red	1·25	85

DESIGNS—As T **42**: King Faisal II and: 10 f. Platoon marching; 20 f. Mobile artillery unit and De Havilland D.H.112 Venom jet fighters. 22½ × 27½ mm: 30 f. King Faisal II (full-length portrait).

1958. Development Week. As T **38**, inscr "1958".

No.	Type	Description	Unused	Used
415		3 f. green, drab and violet	25	25
416		5 f. multicoloured	35	35
417		10 f. multicoloured	1·10	65

DESIGNS—VERT: 3 f. Sugar beet and refining plant. HORIZ: 5 f. Building and pastoral scene; 10 f. Irrigation dam.

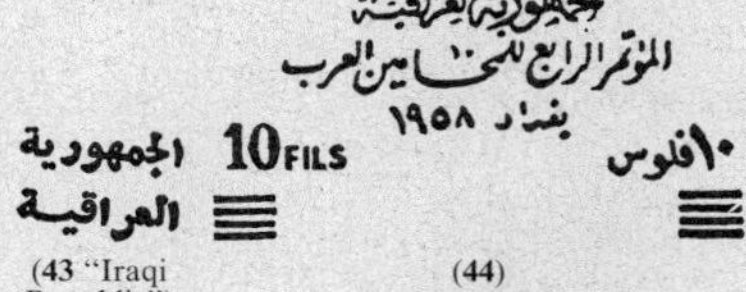

(43 "Iraqi Republic") (44)

1958. Optd with T **43**. (a) On No. 189.

No.	Type	Description	Unused	Used
418		1 d. purple	17·00	17·00
		(b) On T **27**.		
418a		1 f. blue	21·00	7·00
419		12 f. olive	35	20
420		14 f. olive	35	20
421		16 f. red	6·50	2·10
422		28 f. blue	35	35
423		60 f. blue	85	1·25
424		½ d. blue	8·25	4·25
425		1 d. green	21·00	8·25
		(c) On T **33**.		
426		1 f. blue	15	10
427		2 f. brown	15	10
428		4 f. violet	20	20
429		5 f. green	20	20
430		6 f. mauve	20	20
431		8 f. brown	25	20
432		10 f. blue	25	20
433		15 f. black	45	20
434		16 f. red	1·40	25
435		20 f. olive	1·90	1·25
436		25 f. purple	25	20
437		30 f. red	35	20
438		40 f. brown	45	35
439		50 f. blue	5·50	3·00
440		75 f. mauve	1·75	85
441		100 f. olive	4·25	85
442		200 f. salmon	6·75	4·25

Nos. 439/42 are larger (22 × 28 mm).

(d) On T **41**.

443 1 f. blue . . . . 1·75 60
444 2 f. brown 20 20
445 3 f. red 20 20
446 4 f. violet 35 20
447 5 f. green 45 20
448 6 f. red 45 20
449 8 f. brown 45 20
450 10 f. blue 45 20
451 20 f. green 45 20
452 25 f. purple 75 45
453 30 f. red 65 45
454 40 f. brown . . . . 2·50 1·25
455 50 f. purple . . . . 1·25 85
456 75 f. green . . . . 1·25 85
457 100 f. orange . . . . 1·50 85
458 200 f. blue . . . . 7·00 1·25
Nos. 455/8 are larger (22½ × 27½ mm).

1958. Arab Lawyers Conf., Baghdad. Surch with T **44**.
506 **36** 10 f. on 28 f. blue . . . . . 2·25 2·00

45 Republican Soldier and Flag  **45a** Orange Tree

1959. Army Day.
507 **45** 3 f. blue 35 25
508 10 f. olive 50 40
509 40 f. violet . . . . 1·25 1·00

1959. Afforestation Day.
510 **45a** 10 f. orange and green . . 45 20

الجمهورية العراقية
يوم الطفل العالمي
١ حزيران ١٩٥٩
10 FILS ١٠ فلوس

(46)

1959. International Children's Day. Surch with T **46**.
511 **37** 10 f. on 28 f. blue 95 50

47 Worker and Buildings  **48** Harvesters

1959. 1st Anniv of Revolution. Inscr "14TH JULY 1958".
512 **47** 10 f. blue and ochre 45 45
513 – 30 f. green and ochre . . . 85 45
DESIGN—HORIZ: 30 f. Revolutionaries brandishing weapons.

1959. Agricultural Reform.
514 **48** 10 f. black and green . . . 45 25

اسبوع
الصحة والثقافة

49 Republican Emblem (50)

1959.
515 **49** 1 f. multicoloured 15 10
516 2 f. multicoloured 15 10
517 3 f. multicoloured 15 10
518 4 f. multicoloured 15 10
519 5 f. multicoloured 15 10
520 10 f. multicoloured 15 10
521 15 f. multicoloured 45 20
522 20 f. multicoloured 45 20
523 30 f. multicoloured 45 25
524 40 f. multicoloured 70 25
525 50 f. multicoloured . . . . 3·00 75
526 75 f. multicoloured 85 20
527 100 f. multicoloured . . . 1·50 45
528 200 f. multicoloured . . . 2·50 45
529 500 f. multicoloured . . . 4·25 1·90
530 1 d. multicoloured . . . . 10·50 5·50

1959. "Health and Hygiene". Optd with T **50**.
531 **49** 10 f. multicoloured 65 45

51 Gen. Kassem and Military Parade  **52** Gen. Kassem

1960. Army Day.
532 **51** 10 f. lake and green 45 45
533 – 16 f. red and blue 70 45
534 – 30 f. olive, brown & buff . . 70 45
535 – 40 f. violet and buff . . . 1·10 65
536 – 60 f. buff, choc & brown . . 1·40 85
DESIGNS—Gen. Kassem and: HORIZ: 16 f. Infantry on manoeuvres; 60 f. Partisans. VERT: 30 f. Anti-aircraft gun-crew; 40 f. Oilfield guards on parade.

1960. Gen. Kassem's Escape from Assassination.
537 **52** 10 f. violet 45 25
538 30 f. green 85 45

53 Al Rasafi (poet)  **54** Gen. Kassem at Tomb of Unknown Soldier

1960. Al Rasafi Commemoration. Optd **1960** in English and Arabic.
539 **53** 10 l. red . . . . 2·10 1·25
See also No 732.

1960. 2nd Anniv of Revolution.
540 – 6 f. gold, olive & orange . . 45 45
541 **54** 10 f. orange, green & blue . 45 45
542 16 f. orange, vio & blue . . 65 65
543 – 18 f. gold, blue & orange . . 65 65
544 – 30 f. gold, brown & orange . 85 85
545 **54** 60 f. orge, sep & blue . . . 1·75 1·25
DESIGN—VERT: 6 f., 18 f., 30 f. Symbol of Republic.

55 Gen. Kassem, Flag and Troops  **56** Gen. Kassem with Children

1961. Army Day.
546 **55** 3 f. multicoloured 20 15
547 6 f. multicoloured 20 15
548 10 f. multicoloured 45 15
549 – 20 f. black, yellow & green . 45 40
550 – 30 f. black, yellow & brn . 45 40
551 – 40 f. black, yellow & blue . 85 55
DESIGN: 20 f., 30 f., 40 f. Kassem and triumphal arch.

1961. World Children's Day. Main design brown; background colours given.
558 **56** 3 f. yellow 55 40
559 6 f. blue 75 40
560 10 f. pink . . . . 1·00 40
561 30 f. lemon . . . . 1·00 40
562 50 f. green . . . . 1·75 40

57 Gen. Kassem saluting  **58** Gen. Kassem and Army Emblem

1961. 3rd Anniv of Revolution.
563 – 1 f. multicoloured 15 10
564 – 3 f. multicoloured 15 10
565 **57** 5 f. multicoloured 15 10
566 – 6 f. multicoloured 15 10
567 – 10 f. multicoloured 25 20
568 **57** 30 f. multicoloured 45 35
569 40 f. multicoloured 65 45
570 – 50 f. multicoloured . . . . 1·25 90
571 – 100 f. multicoloured . . . 4·00 2·10
DESIGN: 1, 3, 6, 10, 50, 100 f. Gen. Kassem and Iraqi flag.

1962. Army Day.
572 – 1 f. multicoloured 15 10
573 – 3 f. multicoloured 15 10
574 – 6 f. multicoloured 20 10
575 **58** 10 f. black, gold & lilac . . 40 20
576 30 f. black, gold & orange . 75 45
577 50 f. black, gold & green . . 1·25 85
DESIGN—VERT: 1, 3, 6 f. Gen. Kassem saluting and part of speech.

مؤتمر
العالم الاسلامي
بغداد
١٣٨١هـ-١٩٦٢م

(59) **60** Gen. Kassem, Flag and Handclasp

1962. 5th Islamic Congress. Optd with T **59**.
578 **49** 3 f. multicoloured 25 25
579 10 f. multicoloured 25 25
580 30 f. multicoloured 65 60

1962. 4th Anniv of Revolution. Flag in green and gold.
581 **60** 1 f. orange and sepia . . . 10 10
582 3 f. green and sepia 10 10
583 6 f. brown and black . . . 10 10
584 10 f. lilac and sepia 35 35
585 30 f. red and sepia 50 40
586 50 f. grey and sepia . . . . 1·00 70

61 Fanfare  **62** Republican Emblem

1962. Millenary of Baghdad. Multicoloured.
603 3 f. Type **61** 15 15
604 6 f. Al Kindi (philosopher) . . 25 15
605 10 f. Map of old "Round City" of Baghdad 45 20
606 40 f. Gen. Kassem and flag . . 1·25 85

1962. Aerogramme Stamps.
607 **62** 14 f. black and green . . . 85 50
608 35 f. black and red . . . . 1·25 75
Nos. 607/8 were originally issued only attached to aerogramme forms covering the old imprinted King Faisal II stamps, but later appeared in sheets.

63 Campaign Emblem  **64** Gen. Kassem and Tanks

1962. Malaria Eradication.
609 **63** 3 f. multicoloured 20 20
610 10 f. multicoloured 50 20
611 40 f. multicoloured 85 50

1963. Army Day.
612 **64** 3 f. black and yellow . . . 10 10
613 5 f. sepia and purple . . . 10 10
614 6 f. black and green 10 10
615 10 f. black and blue 25 20
616 10 f. black and pink 25 20
617 20 f. black and blue 50 35
618 40 f. black and mauve . . . 85 45
619 50 f. sepia and blue . . . . 1·25 70

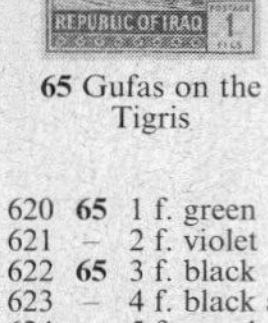

65 Gufas on the Tigris  **66** Shepherd with Sheep

1963.
620 **65** 1 f. green 20 10
621 – 2 f. violet 25 15
622 **65** 3 f. black 25 10
623 – 4 f. black and yellow . . . 30 15
624 – 5 f. purple and green . . . 40 15
625 – 10 f. red 65 20
626 – 15 f. brown and yellow . . 1·00 20
627 – 20 f. violet . . . . 1·25 20
628 – 30 f. orange 70 25
629 – 40 f. green . . . . 1·40 15
630 – 50 f. brown . . . . 5·25 45
631 – 75 f. black and green . . . 1·50 25
632 – 100 f. purple . . . . 2·00 25
633 – 200 f. brown . . . . 3·00 35
634 – 500 f. blue . . . . 6·75 1·75
635 – 1 d. purple . . . . 10·00 3·25
DESIGNS: 2 f., 500 f. Spiral tower of Samarra; 4 f., 15 f. Sumerian Harp; 5 f., 75 f. Republican emblem; 10 f., 50 f. Lion of Babylon; 20 f., 40 f. Koranic school of Abbasid period; 30 f., 200 f. Mosque and minarets; 100 f., 1 d. Winged bull of Kharsabad.

1963. Freedom from Hunger.
636 **66** 3 f. black and green 35 15
637 – 10 f. mauve and brown . . 45 25
638 – 20 f. brown and blue . . . 95 45
DESIGNS: 10 f. Harvester; 20 f. Trees.

67 Centenary Emblem  **68** Helmet, Rifle and Flag

1963. Red Cross Centenary.
640 **67** 3 f. violet and red 25 20
641 10 f. blue and red 40 35
642 – 30 f. blue and red 45 35
DESIGN—HORIZ:: 30 f. Hospital.

1964. Army Day.
643 **68** 3 f. sepia, green & blue . . 20 15
644 10 f. sepia, green & pink . . 45 25
645 30 f. sepia, green & yellow . 85 50

69 Revolutionaries and Flag

1964. 1st Anniv of 14th Ramadan Revolution. Flag in red, green and black.
646 **69** 10 f. violet 45 25
647 30 f. brown 85 45

70 Shamash (Sun-God) and Hammurabi  **71** Soldier raising Flag on Map of Iraq

1964. 15th Anniv of Declaration of Human Rights.
649 **70** 6 f. olive and purple 45 35
650 – 10 f. violet and orange . . . 85 40
651 **70** 30 f. green and blue . . . . 1·25 50
DESIGN: 10 f. U.N. Emblem and Scales of Justice.

1964. 6th Anniv of Revolution.
652 – 3 f. orange, grey & black . . 15 20
653 **71** 10 f. red, black and green . . 25 20
654 20 f. red, black and green . . 45 20
655 – 30 f. orange, grey & black . . 85 50
DESIGNS—HORIZ: 3 f., 30 f. Soldier "protecting" people and factories with outstretched arm.

72 Soldier, Civilians and Star Emblem  **73** Musician

1964. 1st Anniv of Nov 18th Revolution.
656 **72** 5 f. orange and brown . . . 35 20
657 10 f. orange and blue . . . 45 20
658 50 f. orange and violet . . . 95 65

1964. International Arab Music Conf, Baghdad.
659 **73** 3 f. multicoloured 40 25
660 10 f. multicoloured 40 25
661 30 f. multicoloured . . . . 1·10 55

74 Conference Emblem and Map

75 A.P.U. Emblem

1964. 9th Arab Engineer's Conf, Baghdad.

662 **74** 10 f. green and mauve . . . 50 35

1964. 10th Anniv of Arab Postal Union's Permanent Office.

663 **75** 3 f. blue and red 20 20

664 10 f. slate and purple . . . 30 20

665 30 f. blue and orange . . . 85 45

76 Soldier, Civilians and Flag

77 Cogwheel and Factory

1965. Army Day.

666 **76** 5 f. multicoloured 25 20

667 15 f. multicoloured 30 20

668 30 f. multicoloured 85 45

1965. 1st Arab Ministers of Labour Conf, Baghdad.

670 **77** 10 f. multicoloured 45 25

78 Oil Tanker

79 Armed Soldier with Flag

1965. Inauguration of Deep Sea Terminal for Tankers.

671 **78** 10 f. multicoloured 70 15

1965. 2nd Anniv of 14th Ramadan Revolution.

672 **79** 10 f. multicoloured 45 25

80 Tree

81 Federation Emblem

1965. Tree Week.

673 **80** 6 f. multicoloured 20 10

674 20 f. multicoloured 65 35

1965. Arab Insurance Federation. Sun in gold.

675 **81** 3 f. ultramarine & blue . . . 25 20

676 10 f. black and grey 25 20

677 30 f. red and pink 80 45

82 Dagger of Deir Yassin, Palestine

83 "Threat of Disease"

1965. Deir Yassin Massacre.

678 **82** 10 f. drab and black 35 25

679 20 f. brown and blue 65 45

1965. World Health Day.

680 **83** 3 f. multicoloured 35 20

681 10 f. multicoloured 50 25

682 20 f. multicoloured . . . . 1·10 65

84 I.T.U. Emblem and Symbols

1965. Centenary of I.T.U.

683 **84** 10 f. multicoloured 45 20

684 20 f. multicoloured . . . . 1·10 45

85 Flag and Map

86 Revolutionary and Flames

85a Lamp and Burning Library

1965. 1st Anniv of Iraq–U.A.R. Pact.

686 **85** 10 f. multicoloured 35 20

1965. Reconstitution of Algiers University Library.

687 **85a** 5 f. red, green and black . . 20 20

688 10 f. green, red and black . . 30 20

1965. 45th Anniv of 1920 Rebellion.

689 **86** 5 f. multicoloured 30 20

690 10 f. multicoloured 30 20

87 Mosque

1965. Mohammed's Birthday.

691 **87** 10 f. multicoloured 50 50

88 Factory and Ear of Wheat

90 Fair Emblem

89 I.C.Y. Emblem

1965. 7th Anniv of 14 July Revolution.

693 **88** 10 f. multicoloured 35 35

1965. Air. International Co-operation Year.

694 **89** 5 f. black and brown . . . 50 50

695 10 f. brown and green . . . 75 60

696 30 f. black and blue . . . . 2·10 75

1965. Baghdad Fair.

697 **90** 10 f. multicoloured 25 20

91 Pres. Arif (photo by Studio Jean)

1965. 2nd Anniv of 18 November Revolution.

698 **91** 5 f. blue and orange 20 20

699 10 f. sepia and blue 45 25

700 50 f. blue and mauve . . . 1·50 1·00

92 Census Graph

1965. National Census.

701 **92** 3 f. black and purple . . . 25 20

702 5 f. red and brown 25 20

703 15 f. bistre and blue 85 45

93 Hawker Siddeley Trident 1E Airliner

1965. Air. Inauguration of Hawker Siddeley Trident 1E Aircraft by Iraqi Airways.

704 **93** 5 f. multicoloured 40 30

705 10 f. multicoloured 50 35

706 40 f. multicoloured . . . . 1·50 85

94 Date Palms

95 Army Memorial

1965. 2nd F.A.O. Dates Conference, Baghdad.

707 **94** 3 f. multicoloured 25 20

708 10 f. multicoloured 55 20

709 15 f. multicoloured . . . . 1·10 70

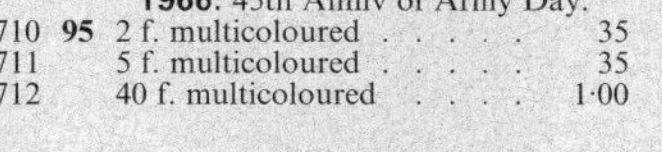

1966. 45th Anniv of Army Day.

710 **95** 2 f. multicoloured 35 25

711 5 f. multicoloured 35 25

712 40 f. multicoloured . . . . 1·00 65

96 "Eagle" and Flag

96a Arab League Emblem

1966. 3rd Anniv of 14th Ramadan Revolution.

713 **96** 5 f. multicoloured 20 20

714 10 f. multicoloured 25 20

1966. Arab Publicity Week.

715 **96a** 5 f. green, brown & orange 25 25

716 15 f. blue, purple and olive 40 25

97 Footballers

1966. Arab Football Cup, Baghdad. Mult.

717 2 f. Type **97** 25 25

718 5 f. Goalkeeper with ball . . . 25 25

719 15 f. Type **97** 85 45

99 Excavator

100 Queen Nefertari

1966. Labour Day.

721 **99** 15 f. multicoloured 25 15

722 25 f. black, silver & red . . 35 20

1966. Nubian Monuments Preservation.

723 **100** 5 f. yellow, black & olive . 60 35

724 15 f. yellow, brown & blue . 85 35

725 – 40 f. brown, chest & red . . 1·50 1·00

DESIGN—HORIZ: (41 × 32 mm): 40 f. Rock temples, Abu Simbel.

101 President Arif

1966. 8th Anniv of 14 July Revolution.

726 **101** 5 f. multicoloured 25 20

727 15 f. multicoloured . . . 45 20

728 50 f. multicoloured . . . . 1·25 70

102

1966. Mohammed's Birthday.

729 **102** 5 f. multicoloured 20 20

730 15 f. multicoloured . . . 25 20

731 30 f. multicoloured . . . . 1·00 90

1966. As No. 539 but without opt.

732 **53** 10 f. red . . . . 4·00 5·00

103 Iraqi Museum, Statue and Window

104 Revolutionaries

1966. Inauguration of Iraqi Museum, Baghdad. Multicoloured.

733 15 f. Type **103** 40 40

734 50 f. Gold head-dress . . . . . 1·10 65

735 80 f. Sumerian head (vert) . . . 1·90 1·10

1966. 3rd Anniv of 18 November Revolution.

736 **104** 15 f. multicoloured 45 25

737 25 f. multicoloured 85 45

105 "Magic Carpet"

1966. Air. Meeting of Arab International Tourist Union, Baghdad. Multicoloured.

738		2 f. White stork emblem ($27\frac{1}{2}$ × 39 mm)	20	20
739		5 f. Type **105**	20	20
740		15 f. As 2 f.	95	25
741		50 f. Type **105**	1·75	70

106 U.N.E.S.C.O. Emblem

1966. 20th Anniv of U.N.E.S.C.O.

742	**106**	5 f. brown, black & blue	20	10
743		15 f. green, black & red	45	25

107 Soldier and Rocket-launchers

1967. Army Day.

744	**107**	15 f. ochre, brown & yell	35	20
745		20 f. ochre, brown & lilac	50	25

108 Oil Refinery

1967. 6th Arab Petroleum Congress, Baghdad. Multicoloured.

747		5 f. Congress emblem (vert)	20	20
748		15 f. Type **108**	30	20
749		40 f. Congress emblem (vert)	55	45
750		50 f. Type **108**	1·25	75

109 "Spider's Web" Emblem

110 Worker holding Cogwheel

1967. Hajeer Year (1967).

751	**109**	5 f. multicoloured	25	15
752		15 f. multicoloured	30	20

1967. Labour Day.

753	**110**	10 f. multicoloured	25	15
754		15 f. multicoloured	30	15

111

1967. Mohammed's Birthday.

755	**111**	5 f. multicoloured	25	20
756		15 f. multicoloured	50	25

112 Flag and Hands with Clubs

1967. 47th Anniv of 1920 Rebellion.

757	**112**	5 f. multicoloured	20	10
758		15 f. multicoloured	30	15

113 Um Qasr Port

114 Costume

1967. 9th Anniv of 14 July Revolution and Inaug of Um Qasr Port. Multicoloured.

759		5 f. Type **113**	40	20
760		10 f. Freighter at quayside	45	20
761		15 f. As 10 f.	75	20
762		40 f. Type **113**	2·25	1·10

1967. Iraqi Costumes. Designs showing different costumes.

765	**114**	2 f. mult (postage)	25	20
766	–	5 f. multicoloured	25	15
767	–	10 f. multicoloured	35	20
768	–	15 f. multicoloured	75	45
769	–	20 f. multicoloured	95	45
770	–	25 f. multicoloured	1·00	50
771	–	30 f. multicoloured	1·25	50
772	–	40 f. multicoloured (air)	85	65
773	–	50 f. multicoloured	1·50	85
774	–	80 f. multicoloured	1·90	1·00

115 Pres. Arif and Map

1967. 4th Anniv of November 18 Revolution. Multicoloured.

775		5 f. President Arif	30	15
776		15 f. Type **115**	45	20

116 Ziggurat of Ur

1967. International Tourist Year. Multicoloured.

777		2 f. Type **116** (postage)	25	15
778		5 f. Statues of Nimroud	25	15
779		10 f. Babylon (arch)	30	15
780		15 f. Minaret of Mosul	35	15
781		25 f. Arch of Ctesiphon	45	15
782		50 f. Statue, Temple of Hatra (air)	1·75	25
783		80 f. Spiral Minaret of Samarra	2·10	45
784		100 f. Adam's Tree	1·75	60
785		200 f. Aladdin ("Aladdin's Cave")	4·25	2·10
786		500 f. Golden Mosque of Kadhimain	13·50	7·50

Nos. 780 and 782/785 are vert.

117 Guide Emblem and Saluting Hand

1967. Iraqi Scouts and Guides. Multicoloured.

787		2 f. Type **117**	40	35
788		5 f. Guides by camp-fire	50	35
789		10 f. Scout emblem and saluting hand	60	40
790		15 f. Scouts setting up camp	1·00	45

118 Soldiers Drilling

1968. Army Day.

792	**118**	5 f. brown, green & blue	30	20
793		15 f. indigo, olive & blue	55	25

119 White-cheeked Bulbul

1968. Iraqi Birds. Multicoloured.

794		5 f. Type **119**	50	20
795		10 f. Hoopoe	65	20
796		15 f. Jay	95	25
797		25 f. Peregrine Falcon	1·50	35
798		30 f. White Stork	1·90	35
799		40 f. Black Partridge	2·25	55
800		50 f. Marbled Teal	2·75	75

120 Battle Scene

1968. 5th Anniv of 14th Ramadan Revolution.

801	**120**	15 f. orange, black & blue	50	30

121 Symbols of "Labour"

1968. Labour Day.

802	**121**	15 f. multicoloured	30	20
803		25 f. multicoloured	50	25

122 Football

1968. 23rd International Military Sports Council Football Championship. Multicoloured.

804		2 f. Type **122**	30	20
805		5 f. Goalkeeper in mid air	30	20
806		15 f. Type **122**	55	20
807		25 f. As 5 f.	75	45

123 Soldier with Iraqi Flag

1968. 10th Anniv of 14 July Revolution.

809	**123**	15 f. multicoloured	30	15

124 Anniversary and W.H.O. Emblems

1968. 20th Anniv of W.H.O.

810	–	5 f. multicoloured	25	20
811	–	10 f. multicoloured	25	20
812	**124**	15 f. red, blue & black	30	25
813	–	25 f. red, green & black	55	30

DESIGN—VERT: 5, 10 f. Combined anniversary and W.H.O. emblems.

125 Human Rights Emblem

126 Mother and children

1968. Human Rights Year.

814	**125**	10 f. red, yellow and blue	25	20
815		25 f. red, yellow & green	30	20

1968. U.N.I.C.E.F. Commemoration.

817	**126**	15 f. multicoloured	25	20
818		25 f. multicoloured	40	30

127 Army Tanks

1969. Army Day.

820	**127**	25 f. multicoloured	1·50	75

128 Agricultural Scene

1969. 6th Anniv of 14th Ramadan Revolution.

821	**128**	15 f. multicoloured	45	25

129 Mosque and Worshippers

1969. Hajeer Year.

822	**129**	15 f. multicoloured	45	25

130 Emblem of Iraqi Veterinary Medical Association

1969. 1st Arab Veterinary Union Conf, Baghdad.

823	**130**	10 f. multicoloured	45	25
824		15 f. multicoloured	60	35

131 Mahseer

1969. Multicoloured. (a) Postage. Fishes.

825		2 f. Type **131**	50	35
826		3 f. Sharpey's barbel	50	35
827		10 f. Silver pomfret	60	35
828		100 f. Pike barbel	2·50	1·25

(b) Air. Fauna.

829		2 f. Striped hyena	20	15
830		3 f. Leopard	20	15
831		5 f. Mountain gazelle	20	15
832		10 f. Head of Arab horse	75	50
833		200 f. Arab horse	3·75	2·25

132 Kaaba, Mecca

1969. Mohammed's Birthday.
834 132 15 f. multicoloured 45 20

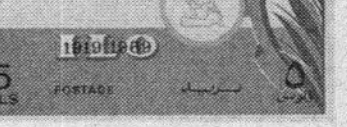

133 I.L.O. Emblem — 134 Weightlifting

1969. 50th Anniv of I.L.O.
835 133 5 f. yellow, blue & black . 15 10
836 15 f. yellow, green & black . 20 10
837 50 f. yellow, red & black 1·10 85

1969. Olympic Games, Mexico (1968). Mult.
839 3 f. Type **134** 50 35
840 5 f. High jumping 50 35
841 10 f. As Type **134** 50 35
842 35 f. As 5 f. 1·00 70

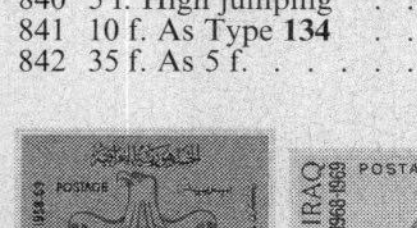

135 Arms of Iraq and "Industry" — 136 Rebuilding Roads

1969. 11th Anniv of 14 July Revolution.
844 135 10 f. multicoloured 20 20
845 15 f. multicoloured 25 20

1969. Anniv of 17 July Revolution and Inaug of Baghdad International Airport. Mult.
846 10 f. Type **136** 20 20
847 15 f. Type **136** 35 25
848 20 f. Airport building 70 45
849 200 f. President Bakr (vert) 4·25 2·10

137 Ear of Wheat and Fair Emblem — 139 Radio Beacon and Outline of Palestine

138 Floating Crane "Antara"

6th International Baghdad Fair.
850 137 10 f. brown, gold & grn 35 25
851 15 f. red, gold and blue 50 30

1969. 50th Anniv of Port of Basra. Mult.
852 15 f. Type **138** 30 15
853 20 f. Harbour tender "Al-Walid" 40 15
854 30 f. Pilot boat "Al-Rashid" 70 15
855 35 f. Dredger "Hillah" 1·00 35
856 50 f. Survey ship "Al-Fao" 1·75 65

1969. 10th Anniv of Iraqi News Agency.
857 139 15 f. multicoloured 35 25
858 50 f. multicoloured 75 45

140 Emblem, Book and Hands — 141 Ross and Keith Smith's Vickers Vimy Biplane

1969. Campaign Against Illiteracy.
859 140 15 f. multicoloured 25 15
860 20 f. multicoloured 40 30

1969. Air. 50th Anniv of 1st England–Australia Flight.
861 141 15 f. multicoloured 1·75 85
862 35 f. multicoloured 2·50 1·75

142 Newspaper Headline — 144 Iraqis supporting Wall

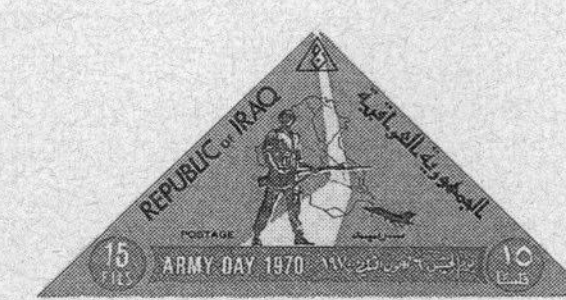

143 Soldier and Map

1969. Centenary of Iraqi Press.
864 142 15 f. black, orange & yell 45 45

1970. Army Day.
865 143 15 f. multicoloured 45 30
866 20 f. multicoloured 65 55

1970. 7th Anniv of 14th Ramadan Revolution.
867 144 10 f. multicoloured 20 20
868 15 f. multicoloured 25 20

(145) — (147)

146 Map of Arab Countries, and Slogans

1970. New Year ("Nawrooz"). Nos. 891/6 optd with T **145**.
869 2 f. multicoloured 25 25
870 3 f. multicoloured 25 25
871 5 f. multicoloured 25 25
872 10 f. multicoloured 50 25
873 15 f. multicoloured 65 25
874 50 f. multicoloured 1·75 1·10

1970. 23rd Anniv of Al-Baath Party. Mult.
875 15 f. Type **146** 25 25
876 35 f. Type **146** 45 45
877 50 f. Iraqis acclaiming Party 1·25 55

1970. Mosul Spring Festival. Nos. 891/6 optd with T **147**.
879 2 f. multicoloured 60 60
880 3 f. multicoloured 60 60
881 5 f. multicoloured 60 60
882 10 f. multicoloured 60 60
883 15 f. multicoloured 80 70
884 50 f. multicoloured 1·25 85

148 Iraqis celebrating Labour Day

1970. Labour Day.
885 148 10 f. multicoloured 15 15
886 15 f. multicoloured 15 15
887 35 f. multicoloured 1·00 85

149 Kaaba, Mecca, Broken Statues and Koran

1970. Mohammed's Birthday.
888 149 15 f. multicoloured 25 15
889 20 f. multicoloured 30 25

1970 ١٩٧٠
عيد الصحافة

150 Poppies — (151)

1970. Spring Festival. Flowers. Multicoloured.
891 2 f. Type **150** 40 25
892 3 f. Narcissi 40 25
893 5 f. Tulip 40 25
894 10 f. Carnations 45 30
895 15 f. Roses 85 45
896 50 f. As 10 f. 1·75 1·10

1970. Press Day. No. 864 optd with T **151**.
896a 142 15 f. black, orange & yell 45 45

152 Revolutionaries

1970. 50th Anniv of Revolution of 1920.
897 152 10 f. black and green 20 20
898 15 f. black and gold 30 20
899 – 35 f. black and orange 70 35
DESIGN: 35 f. Revolutionary and rising sun.

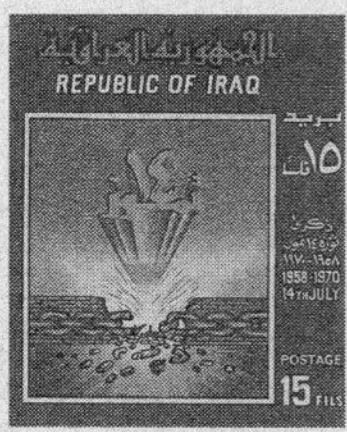

153 Bomb-burst and Broken Chain

1970. 12th Anniv of 14 July Revolution.
901 153 15 f. multicoloured 25 15
902 20 f. multicoloured 30 20

154 Hands and Map of Iraq

1970. 2nd Anniv of 17 July Revolution.
903 154 15 f. multicoloured 25 15
904 25 f. multicoloured 45 25

155 Pomegranates

1970. Fruits. Multicoloured.
905 3 f. Type **155** 35 15
906 5 f. Grapefruit 35 15
907 10 f. Grapes 35 15
908 15 f. Oranges 70 20
909 35 f. Dates 1·75 1·50
The Latin inscriptions on Nos. 906/7 are transposed.

156 Kaaba, Mecca

1970. Hajeer Year.
910 156 15 f. multicoloured 25 15
911 25 f. multicoloured 45 25

الدورة السابعة

970 – ٩٧٠

(157)

1970. 7th Int Baghdad Fair. Optd with T **157**.
912 137 10 f. brown, gold & green 2·10 1·25
913 15 f. red, gold and blue 2·10 1·25

158 Arab League Flag and Map

1970. 25th Anniv of Arab League.
914 158 15 f. purple, green & olive 20 15
915 35 f. red, green & grey 45 40

159 Euphrates Bridge

1970. Air. National Development. Multicoloured.
916 10 f. Type **159** 1·25 35
917 15 f. Type **159** 2·00 50
918 1 d. Pres. Bakr and banknotes (37 × 27 mm) 32·00 14·00

160 I.E.Y. Emblem

1970. International Education Year.
919 160 5 f. multicoloured 20 15
920 15 f. multicoloured 40 25

161 Baghdad Hospital and Society Emblem

1970. 50th Anniv of Iraq Medical Society.
922 161 15 f. multicoloured 25 20
923 40 f. multicoloured 85 50

162 Union Emblem — 163 Sugar Beet

1970. Air. 10th Arab Telecommunications Union Conference, Baghdad.
924 162 15 f. multicoloured 25 15
925 25 f. multicoloured 45 35

1970. 12th Anniv of Mosul Sugar Refinery. Multicoloured.
926 5 f. Type **163** 20 10
927 15 f. Sugar refinery (horiz) 35 15
928 30 f. Type **163** 1·25 60

164 O.P.E.C. Emblem

1970. 10th Anniv of Organization of Petroleum Exporting Countries (O.P.E.C.).
929 164 10 f. blue, bistre & purple 45 25
930 40 f. blue, bistre & green 1·50 1·00

165 Soldiers, Tank and Aircraft

1971. 50th Anniv of Army Day.
931 **165** 15 f. black, mve & gold . . 50 20
932 – 40 f. multicoloured . . . . 1·50 85
DESIGN—42 × 35 mm: 40 f. Soldiers and map of Middle East.

166 "Revolutionary Army"

1971. 8th Anniv of 14th Ramadan Revolution.
934 **166** 15 f. multicoloured 30 20
935 40 f. multicoloured 85 55

167 Pilgrims and Web

1971. Hajeer Year.
936 **167** 10 f. multicoloured 15 10
937 15 f. multicoloured 35 25

168 Pres. Bakr with Torch

1971. 1st Anniv of 11th March Manifesto.
938 **168** 15 f. multicoloured 60 45
939 100 f. multicoloured . . . 1·90 1·60

169 Boatman in Marshland

1971. Tourism Week. Multicoloured.
940 5 f. Type **169** 20 10
941 10 f. Stork over Baghdad . . . 55 25
942 15 f. Landscape ("Summer Resorts") 60 35
943 100 f. "Return of Sinbad" . . . 2·75 1·75

170 Blacksmith taming Serpent

1971. New Year ("Nawrooz").
944 **170** 15 f. multicoloured 45 25
945 25 f. multicoloured 55 35

1971. World Meteorological Day. Nos. 780 and 783 optd **W.M. DAY 1971** in English and Arabic.
946 15 f. multicoloured (postage) . . 2·00 85
947 80 f. multicoloured (air) . . . . 4·25 3·25

172 Emblem and Workers

1971. 24th Anniv of Al-Baath Party. Mult.
948 15 f. Type **172** 30 30
949 35 f. Type **172** 50 50
950 250 f. As Type **172** but central portion of design only (42 × 42 mm) . . . . 6·75 6·75
On No. 950 the circular centre is also perforated.

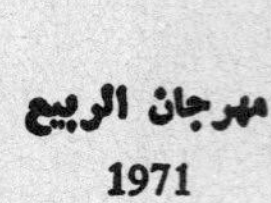
(173)

174 Worker and Farm-girl

1971. Mosul Spring Festival. Nos. 765/6 and 770 optd with T **173**.
951 **114** 2 f. multicoloured 40 25
952 – 5 f. multicoloured 40 25
953 – 25 f. multicoloured . . . . 1·25 75

1971. Labour Day.
954 **174** 15 f. multicoloured 35 25
955 40 f. multicoloured 60 50

175 Muslim at Prayer

1971. Mohammed's Birthday.
956 **175** 15 f. multicoloured 35 25
957 100 f. multicoloured . . . 1·40 1·10

176 Revolutionaries, and Hands with Broken Chains

1971. 13th Anniv of 14 July Revolution.
958 **176** 25 f. multicoloured 45 20
959 50 f. multicoloured . . . . 1·10 55

177 Rising Sun and "Prosperity"

1971. 3rd Anniv of 17 July Revolution.
960 **177** 25 f. multicoloured 45 20
961 70 f. multicoloured . . . . 1·60 85

182 Bank Emblem

1971. 30th Anniv of Rafidain Bank.
989 **182** 10 f. multicoloured 45 30
990 15 f. multicoloured 45 30
991 25 f. multicoloured 45 30
992 65 f. multicoloured . . . 2·10 1·10
993 250 f. multicoloured . . . 10·00 10·00
Nos. 992/3 are larger, 42 × 42 mm.

التعداد الزراعي العام

١٩٧١/١٠/١٥

(183)

1971. Agricultural Census. Nos. 905, 908/9 optd with T **183**.
994 3 f. multicoloured . . . . . . 1·40 1·50
995 15 f. multicoloured . . . . . . 1·40 1·50
996 35 f. multicoloured . . . . . . 1·40 1·50

184 Football

1971. 4th Pan-Arab Schoolboy Games, Baghdad. Multicoloured.
997 15 f. Type **184** 35 25
998 25 f. Throwing the discus and running 50 25
999 35 f. Table tennis 85 50
1000 70 f. Gymnastics . . . . . . 1·50 1·00
1001 95 f. Volleyball and basketball . 1·90 1·00

يوم الطالب
٢٣ تشرين الثاني
٩٦١ – ٩٧١

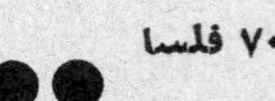

(185)

186 Society Emblem

1971. Students' Day. Nos. 892/3 surch and 895 optd as T **185**.
1003 15 f. multicoloured . . . . . 1·00 1·00
1004 25 f. on 5 f. multicoloured . . 1·50 1·50
1005 70 f. on 3 f. multicoloured . . 3·00 3·00

1971. Air. 20th Anniv of Iraqi Philatelic Society.
1006 **186** 25 f. multicoloured . . . 1·10 75
1007 70 f. multicoloured . . . 1·50 1·40

1971. 25th Anniv of U.N.I.C.E.F. Nos. 817/18 optd **25th Anniversary 971**.
1008 **126** 15 f. multicoloured . . . 2·25 2·10
1009 25 f. multicoloured . . . 2·25 2·10

188 Schoolchildren on Zebra Crossing

1971. 2nd Traffic Week.
1010 **188** 15 f. multicoloured . . . 2·50 1·60
1011 25 f. multicoloured . . . 2·50 1·60

189 A.P.U. Emblem

190 Racial Equality Year Symbol

1971. 25th Anniv of Founding of Arab Postal Union at Sofar Conference.
1012 **189** 25 f. brown, yell & grn . . 25 15
1013 70 f. red, yellow & blue . . 1·10 70

1971. Racial Equality Year.
1014 **190** 25 f. multicoloured . . . 20 20
1015 70 f. multicoloured . . . 85 75

191 Soldiers with Flag and Torch

192 Workers

1972. Army Day.
1016 **191** 25 f. multicoloured . . . 1·10 35
1017 70 f. multicoloured . . . 2·00 1·40

1972. 9th Anniv of 14th Ramadan Revolution.
1018 **192** 25 f. multicoloured . . . 1·40 45
1019 95 f. multicoloured . . . 2·50 1·75

193 Mosque and Crescent

1972. Hajeer Year.
1020 **193** 25 f. multicoloured . . . 25 20
1021 35 f. multicoloured . . . 65 45

المؤتمر التاسع للاتحاد الوطني
لطلبة العراق
٢٥ شباط – ٢ آذار / ١٩٧٢

(194)

1972. Air. 9th Iraqi Students' Union Congress. Nos. 916/17 optd with T **194**.
1022 **159** 10 f. multicoloured . . . 1·75 1·75
1023 15 f. multicoloured . . . 1·75 1·75

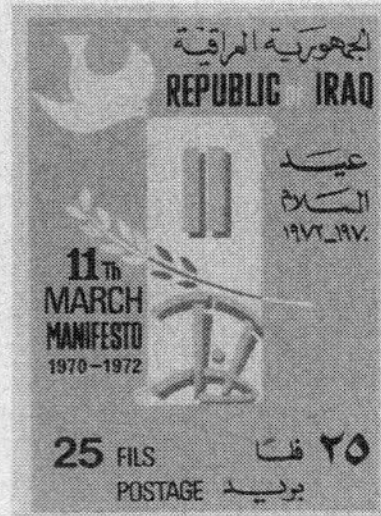

195 Dove, Olive Branch and Manifesto

1972. 2nd Anniv of 11 March Manifesto.
1024 **195** 25 f. blue, lt blue & blk . 55 20
1025 70 f. pur, mve & blk . . . 2·00 1·10

196 Observatory and Weather Balloon on Isobar Map

197 Cogwheel Emblem

1972. World Meteorological Day.
1026 **196** 25 f. multicoloured . . . 1·25 45
1027 35 f. multicoloured . . . 2·25 1·25

1972. Iraqi Chamber of Commerce.
1028 **197** 25 f. multicoloured . . . 35 20
1029 35 f. multicoloured . . . 60 35

198 Oil Rig and Flame

1972. Inauguration of North Rumaila Oilfield.

1030	198	25 f. multicoloured	1·00	25
1031		35 f. multicoloured	1·10	85

199 Party Emblem

1972. 25th Anniv of Al Baath Party. Mult.

1032	10 f. Type **199**	30	25
1033	25 f. Emblem and inscription	50	35
1034	35 f. Type **199**	65	45
1035	70 f. As 25 f.	1·90	1·60

SIZES—HORIZ: 25 f. 70 f. 51 × 27 mm.

200 Mountain Scene

1972. New Year ("Nawrooz").

1036	200	25 f. mauve, yellow & bl	90	35
1037		70 f. brown, yellow & bl	2·10	1·60

201 Congress "Quills" Emblem — 204 Hand holding Spanner

202 Federation Emblem

1972. 3rd Arab Journalists Congress.

1038	201	25 f. orange, black & grn	45	35
1039		35 f. blue, black & grn	1·25	1·10

1972. 4th Anniv of Iraqi Women's Federation.

1040	202	25 f. multicoloured	45	25
1041		35 f. multicoloured	1·25	1·10

1972. Labour Day.

1046	204	25 f. multicoloured	35	15
1047		35 f. multicoloured	65	20

205 Kaaba, Mecca

1972. Mohammed's Birthday.

1048	205	25 f. black, gold & green	45	25
1049		35 f. black, gold & violet	1·40	1·10

206 Shooting for Goal

1972. Air. 25th International Military Sports Council Football Championship, Baghdad. Multicoloured.

1050	10 f. Type **206**	55	25
1051	20 f. Players in goalmouth	80	35
1052	25 f. Type **206**	1·10	45
1053	35 f. As 20 f.	1·60	65

207 Soldiers and Artillery

1972. 14th Anniv of 14 July Revolution.

1055	207	35 f. multicoloured	1·10	65
1056		70 f. multicoloured	2·40	1·60

208 "Spirit of Revolution"

1972. 4th Anniv of 17 July Revolution.

1057	208	25 f. multicoloured	90	50
1058		95 f. multicoloured	2·50	2·00

209 Scout Badge and Camp Scene

1972. 10th Jamboree and Conference of Arab Scouts, Mosul.

1059	209	20 f. multicoloured	1·50	1·00
1060		25 f. multicoloured	1·90	1·00

210 Guide Badge and Camp

1972. 4th Conference and Camp of Arab Guides, Mosul.

1061	210	10 f. multicoloured	90	60
1062		45 f. multicoloured	3·00	1·50

(211)

1972. 3rd Traffic Week. Nos. 1010/11 surch or optd as T **211**.

1063	188	25 f. multicoloured	3·00	2·10
1064		70 f. on 15 f. mult	4·75	4·25

(212)

213 "Strong Man" Statuette

1972. Festival of Palm Trees and Feast of Dates. Nos. 707 and 709 surch as T **212**.

1065	94	25 f. on 3 f. mult	2·10	1·25
1066		70 f. on 15 f. mult	4·25	3·25

1972. Air. World Body-building Championships and Asian Congress, Baghdad. Multicoloured.

1067	25 f. Type **213**	1·00	55
1068	70 f. Ancient warriors and modern Strong Man	2·10	1·50

214 Bank Building

1972. 25th Anniv of Central Bank of Iraq.

1069	214	25 f. multicoloured	95	35
1070		70 f. multicoloured	1·90	1·90

216 International Railway Union Emblem

1972. 50th Anniv of Int Railway Union.

1073	216	25 f. multicoloured	1·25	35
1074		45 f. multicoloured	3·00	1·90

1973. Various "Faisal" definitives with portrait obliterated with 3 bars. (a) 1954 issue.

1075	33	10 f. blue	2·25	85
1076		15 f. black	2·25	85
1077		25 f. purple	2·25	85

(b) 1957 issue.

1078	41	10 f. blue	2·25	85
1079		15 f. black	2·25	85
1080		25 f. purple	2·25	85

المؤتمر الدولي
للتاريخ/١٩٧٣
(219)

1973. International History Congress. Nos. 780, 783 and 786 optd with T **219**.

1094	15 f. multicoloured (postage)	2·50	2·50
1095	80 f. multicoloured (air)	4·25	4·25
1096	500 f. multicoloured	38·00	38·00

220 Iraqi Oil Workers

1973. 1st Anniv of Nationalisation of Iraqi Oil Industry.

1097	220	25 f. multicoloured	1·75	1·25
1098		70 f. multicoloured	3·75	2·10

221 Harp — 225a Iraqis and Flags

1973.

1099	221	5 f. black and orange	15	10
1100		10 f. black and brown	15	10
1101		20 f. black and mauve	20	10
1102	–	25 f. black and blue	35	15
1103	–	35 f. black and green	40	20
1104	–	45 f. black and blue	40	25
1105	–	50 f. yellow and green	65	25
1106	–	70 f. yellow and violet	70	40
1107	–	95 f. yellow and brown	1·25	65

DESIGNS: 25, 35, 45 f. Minaret of Mosul; 50, 70, 95 f. Statue of a Goddess.

1973. July Festivals.

1122	225a	25 f. multicoloured	70	25
1123		35 f. multicoloured	1·40	85

1973. Int. Journalists' Conference. Nos. 857/8 optd **I.O.J. SEPTEMBER 26-29, 1973.**

1124	139	15 f. multicoloured	2·10	2·10
1125		50 f. multicoloured	3·00	3·00

227 Interpol H.Q., Paris — 228 Flags and Fair Emblems

1973. 50th Anniv of International Criminal Police Organization (Interpol).

1126	227	25 f. multicoloured	70	25
1127		70 f. multicoloured	3·50	2·25

1973. 10th Baghdad International Fair.

1128	228	10 f. multicoloured	30	15
1129		20 f. multicoloured	70	30
1130		55 f. multicoloured	1·40	75

229 W.M.O. Emblem — 230 Arab Flags and Map

1973. Centenary of World Meteorological Organization.

1148	229	25 f. black, grn & orge	45	15
1149		35 f. black, grn & mve	1·40	95

1973. 11th Session of Arab States' Civil Aviation Council, Baghdad.

1150	230	20 f. multicoloured	35	25
1151		35 f. multicoloured	1·10	75

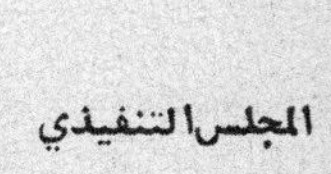

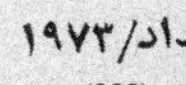

(232)

233 Human Rights Emblem

1973. Sixth Executive Council Meeting of Arab Postal Union, Baghdad. No. 665 optd with T **232**.

1153	75	30 f. blue and orange	3·25	2·10

1973. 25th Anniv of Declaration of Human Rights.

1154	233	25 f. multicoloured	35	15
1155		70 f. multicoloured	1·40	85

234 Shield and Military Activities

1974. 50th Anniv of Military College.

1156	234	25 f. multicoloured	35	25
1157		35 f. multicoloured	1·25	85

236 U.P.U. Emblem

1974. Centenary of Universal Postal Union.

1159	236	25 f. multicoloured	60	20
1160		35 f. multicoloured	65	35
1161		70 f. multicoloured	1·75	1·10

237 Allegory of Nationalization

1974. 2nd Anniv of Nationalization of Iraqi Oil Industry.
1162 **237** 10 f. multicoloured . . . 25 15
1163 25 f. multicoloured . . . 65 25
1164 70 f. multicoloured . . . 1·75 1·75

238 Festival Theme

240 Cement Plant

239 National Front Emblem and Heads

1975. July Festivals.
1165 **238** 20 f. multicoloured . . . 30 15
1166 35 f. multicoloured . . . 85 45

1975. 1st Anniv of Progressive National Front.
1167 **239** 20 f. multicoloured . . . 35 15
1168 50 f. multicoloured . . . 1·40 85

1975. 25th Anniv of Iraqi Cement Industry.
1169 **240** 20 f. multicoloured . . . 40 25
1170 25 f. multicoloured . . . 40 30
1171 70 f. multicoloured . . . 1·25 95

1975. Surch.
1172 **155** 10 f. on 3 f. multicoloured . 2·50 1·10
1173 – 25 f. on 3 f. mult (No. 892) 3·75 1·25

242 W.P.Y. Emblem

1975. World Population Year (1974).
1174 **242** 25 f. green and blue . . . 40 20
1175 35 f. blue and mauve . . . 70 30
1176 70 f. violet and olive . . . 1·75 1·10

243 Festival Emblems

1975. July Festivals.
1177 **243** 5 f. multicoloured 20 15
1178 10 f. multicoloured . . . 25 20
1179 35 f. multicoloured . . . 1·10 65

244 Map and Emblems

245 "Equality, Development, Peace"

1975. 10th Anniv of Arab Labour Organization.
1180 **244** 25 f. multicoloured . . . 40 15
1181 35 f. multicoloured . . . 65 55
1182 45 f. multicoloured . . . 70 55

1975. International Women's Year.
1183 **245** 10 f. multicoloured . . . 35 15
1184 35 f. multicoloured . . . 65 35
1185 70 f. multicoloured . . . 2·00 1·75

246 Diyala Barrage

1975. 25th Anniv of International Commission on Irrigation and Drainage.
1187 **246** 3 f. multicoloured 20 15
1188 25 f. multicoloured . . . 45 25
1189 70 f. multicoloured . . . 1·75 1·10

247 Company Seal

1975. 25th Anniv of National Insurance Company, Baghdad.
1190 **247** 20 f. multicoloured . . . 35 15
1191 25 f. multicoloured . . . 70 50

248 Court Musicians

1975. International Music Conference, Baghdad.
1193 **248** 25 f. multicoloured . . . 55 25
1194 45 f. multicoloured . . . 1·25 75

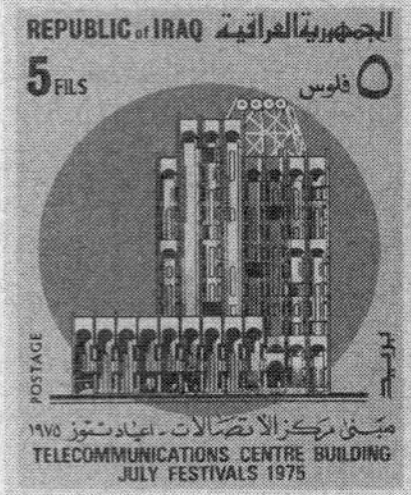

250 Telecommunications Centre

1975. Opening of Telecommunications Centre.
1203 **250** 5 f. multicoloured 15 15
1204 10 f. multicoloured . . . 20 15
1205 60 f. multicoloured . . . 1·40 95

251 Diesel Train

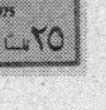

252 Goddess (statue)

1975. 15th Taurus Railway Conference, Baghdad. Multicoloured.
1206 25 f. Type **251** . . . . . . 2·75 2·25
1207 30 f. Diesel locomotive . . . . 3·75 3·00
1208 35 f. Tank locomotive and train . . . . 5·50 4·25
1209 50 f. Steam locomotive . . . . 8·00 6·75

1976.
1210 **252** 5 f. multicoloured 10 10
1211 10 f. multicoloured . . . 10 10
1212 15 f. multicoloured . . . 15 10
1213 – 20 f. multicoloured . . . 20 10
1214 – 25 f. multicoloured . . . 30 10
1215 – 30 f. multicoloured . . . 40 10
1216 – 35 f. multicoloured . . . 50 20
1217 – 50 f. multicoloured . . . 70 20
1218 – 75 f. multicoloured . . . 1·00 50

DESIGNS: 20, 25, 30 f. Two females forming column; 35, 50, 75 f. Head of bearded man.

253 Soldier and Symbols of Industry and Agriculture

254 Crossed-out Thumbprint

1976. Arab Day.
1219 **253** 5 f. multicoloured 20 15
1220 25 f. mult on silver . . . 45 15
1221 50 f. mult on gold . . . . 1·25 50

1976. Arab Literacy Day.
1222 **254** 5 f. multicoloured 15 10
1223 15 f. multicoloured . . . 20 15
1224 35 f. multicoloured . . . 1·25 45

255 Iraq Earth Station

256 Early and Modern Telephones

1976. 13th Anniv of Revolution of 14th Ramadan.
1225 **255** 10 f. multicoloured . . . 25 10
1226 25 f. mult on silver . . . 60 30
1227 75 f. mult on gold . . . 2·10 1·40

1976. Telephone Centenary.
1228 **256** 35 f. multicoloured . . . 55 25
1229 50 f. multicoloured . . . 1·10 60
1230 75 f. multicoloured . . . 1·60 1·10

257 Map and Emblem

258 Iraqi Family on Map

1976. 20th Int. Arab Trade Unions Conf.
1231 **257** 5 f. mult (postage) . . . 25 20
1232 10 f. multicoloured . . . 25 20
1233 75 f. multicoloured (air) . 2·10 1·10

1976. Police Day.
1234 **258** 5 f. multicoloured 25 15
1235 15 f. multicoloured . . . 35 15
1236 35 f. multicoloured . . . 1·50 85

259 "Strategy" Pipeline

260 Human Eye

1976. 4th Anniv of Oil Nationalization.
1237 **259** 25 f. multicoloured . . . 65 35
1238 75 f. multicoloured . . . 2·10 1·25

1976. Air. World Health Day. "Foresight Prevents Blindness".
1240 **260** 25 f. blue and black . . . 25 15
1241 35 f. green and black . . 35 25
1242 50 f. orange & brown . . 70 45

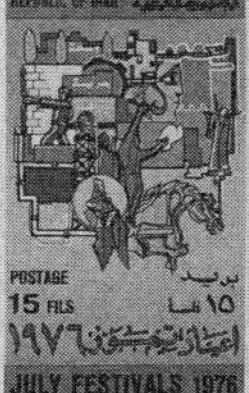

261 "Agriculture, Industry and Construction"

262 Basketball

1976. July Festivals.
1243 **261** 15 f. multicoloured . . . 25 15
1244 35 f. multicoloured . . . 70 30

1976. Olympic Games, Montreal. Mult.
1245 25 f. Type **262** 35 35
1246 35 f. Volleyball 50 40
1247 50 f. Wrestling 75 50
1248 75 f. Boxing . . . . 1·40 85

263 Bishop Capucci, Wounded Dove and Map of Palestine

264 Common Kingfisher

1976. 2nd Anniv of Bishop Capucci's Arrest.
1250 **263** 25 f. multicoloured . . . 40 20
1251 35 f. multicoloured . . . 50 30
1252 75 f. multicoloured . . . 1·60 1·10

1976. Birds. Multicoloured.
1253 5 f. Type **264** 85 20
1254 10 f. Turtle dove 95 30
1255 15 f. Pin-tailed sandgrouse . . 1·10 35
1256 25 f. Blue rock thrush . . . . 1·90 40
1257 50 f. Purple heron and grey heron . . . . 3·00 80

See also Nos. O1258/62.

265 Emblem within "15"

266 Children with Banner

1976. 15th Anniv of Iraqi Students' Union.
1263 **265** 30 f. multicoloured . . . 35 10
1264 70 f. multicoloured . . . 1·60 75

1976. 30th Anniv of U.N.E.S.C.O. "Children's Books". Multicoloured.
1265 10 f. Type **266** 30 10
1266 25 f. Children in garden . . . 35 15
1267 75 f. Children with Iraqi flag . 1·90 1·40

267 Tanker "Rumaila" and Emblem

1976. 4th Anniv of First Iraqi Oil Tanker and 1st Anniv of Basrah Petroleum Co Nationalization. Multicoloured.
1268 10 f. Type **267** 35 10
1269 15 f. Type **267** 45 15
1270 25 f. Oil jetty and installations . 65 25
1271 50 f. As 25 f. . . . . 1·75 1·00

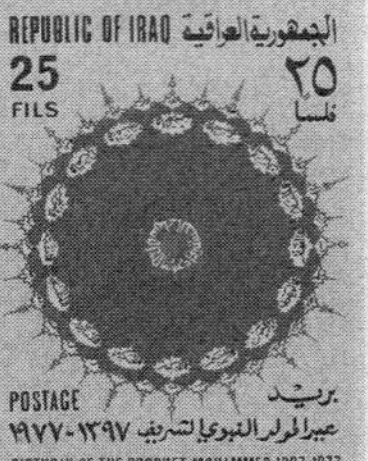

268 Islamic Design with Inscriptions

269 Dove Emblem

1977. Birthday of Prophet Mohammed.
1272 **268** 25 f. multicoloured . . . 35 15
1273 35 f. multicoloured . . . 70 65

1977. Peace Day.
1274 269 25 f. multicoloured 30 20
1275 30 f. multicoloured 45 30

270 Dahlia

1977. Flowers. Multicoloured.
1276 5 f. Type 270 20 10
1277 10 f. "Lathyrus odoratus" 20 10
1278 35 f. "Chrysanthemum coronarium" 65 25
1279 50 f. "Verbena hybrida" 1·00 90

271 "V" Emblem with Doves

1977. 30th Anniv of Al-Baath Party. Mult.
1280 25 f. Type 271 35 15
1281 75 f. Human figures as a flame 1·40 70

272 A.P.U. Emblem and Flags

273 1st May Emblem

1977. 25th Anniv of Arab Postal Union.
1283 272 25 f. multicoloured 35 15
1284 35 f. multicoloured 55 40

1977. Labour Day.
1285 273 10 f. multicoloured 20 10
1286 30 f. multicoloured 45 15
1287 35 f. multicoloured 65 50

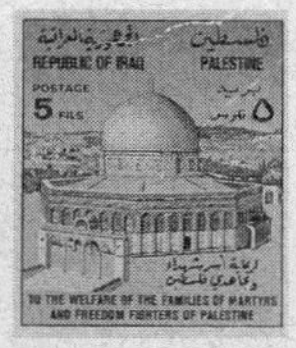

274 First Stage of Lift

275 Dome of the Rock

1977. 8th Asian Weightlifting Championships, Baghdad. Multicoloured.
1288 25 f. Type 274 60 45
1289 75 f. Press-up stage of lift 1·60 1·00

1977. Palestinian Welfare.
1291 275 5 f. multicoloured 70 15

276 Arabian Garden

277 Dove and Ear of Wheat

1977. Arab Tourism Year. Multicoloured.
1292 5 f. Type 276 15 10
1293 10 f. Town view with Minarets (horiz) 20 15
1294 30 f. Country stream 50 25
1295 50 f. Oasis (horiz) 1·50 90

1977. July Festivals.
1296 277 25 f. multicoloured 45 20
1297 30 f. multicoloured 70 30

278 Map of Middle East and North Africa

279 Emblem

1977. U.N. Conference on Desertification.
1298 278 30 f. multicoloured 50 35
1299 70 f. multicoloured 1·40 70

1977. Census Day.
1300 279 20 f. multicoloured 20 15
1301 30 f. multicoloured 50 15
1302 70 f. multicoloured 90 60

280 Abstract Calligraphic Emblem

281 Kamal Jumblatt and Political Caricatures

1977. Al-Mutanabby Festival.
1303 280 25 f. multicoloured 20 15
1304 50 f. multicoloured 55 35

1977. Kamal Jumblatt (Lebanese socialist). Commemoration.
1305 281 20 f. multicoloured 20 15
1306 30 f. multicoloured 30 15
1307 70 f. multicoloured 75 50

282 Hajeer Year Emblem

283 Girl, Boy and National Flag Ribbon

1977. Hajeer Year.
1308 282 30 f. multicoloured 35 15
1309 35 f. multicoloured 40 15

1978. Youth Day.
1310 283 10 f. multicoloured 15 15
1311 15 f. multicoloured 15 15
1312 35 f. multicoloured 40 30

284 Hand placing Coin in Box

285 Transmitting and Receiving Equipment

1978. 6th Anniv of Postal Savings Bank.
1313 284 15 f. multicoloured 25 15
1314 25 f. multicoloured 35 15
1315 35 f. multicoloured 70 35

1978. 10th World Telecommunications Day and 1st Anniv of Iraqi Microwave Network.
1316 285 25 f. multicoloured 30 15
1317 35 f. multicoloured 35 15
1318 75 f. multicoloured 65 35

286 Map and Flags

287 Silver Coins

1978. 1st Conference of Arabian Gulf Postal Ministers.
1319 286 25 f. multicoloured 45 15
1320 35 f. multicoloured 65 40

1978. Ancient Iraqi Coins.
1321 287 1 f. black, silver & yell 15 10
1322 – 2 f. black, gold & blue 15 10
1323 – 3 f. black, silver & orge 15 10
1324 – 4 f. black, gold & grn 15 10
1325 – 75 f. black, gold & grn 1·50 1·50
DESIGNS—HORIZ: 2 f. Two gold coins; 3 f. Two silver coins; 4 f. Two gold coins. VERT: 75 f. Gold coin.

288 Flower Emblem

1978. July Festivals.
1326 288 25 f. multicoloured 25 15
1327 35 f. multicoloured 40 25

289 Nurse, Hospital and Sick Child

1978. Global Eradication of Smallpox.
1329 289 25 f. multicoloured 25 15
1330 35 f. multicoloured 50 25
1331 75 f. multicoloured 1·40 75

290 Altharthar–Euphrates Canal

1978.
1332 290 5 f. multicoloured 15 10
1333 10 f. multicoloured 15 10
1334 15 f. multicoloured 15 15
1335 25 f. multicoloured 15 15
1336 35 f. multicoloured 35 15
1337 50 f. multicoloured 45 35
See also Nos. O1338/41.

291 I.M.C.O. Emblem

1978. World Maritime Day.
1342 291 25 f. multicoloured 45 15
1343 75 f. multicoloured 75 65

292 Workers in the Countryside

1978. 10th Anniv of People's Work Groups.
1344 292 10 f. multicoloured 15 10
1345 25 f. multicoloured 35 15
1346 35 f. multicoloured 55 50

293 Fair Emblem

294 Map, Rule and Emblem

1978. Baghdad International Fair.
1347 293 25 f. multicoloured 15 15
1348 35 f. multicoloured 25 15
1349 75 f. multicoloured 1·40 60

1978. World Standards Day.
1350 294 25 f. multicoloured 15 15
1351 35 f. multicoloured 25 15
1352 75 f. multicoloured 1·10 65

295 Conference Chamber

296 Congress Emblem

1978. Ninth Arab Summit Conference, Baghdad.
1353 295 25 f. multicoloured 20 15
1354 35 f. multicoloured 30 20
1355 75 f. multicoloured 85 70

1978. 4th Congress of Association of Thoracic and Cardiovascular Surgeons of Asia.
1356 296 25 f. multicoloured 30 15
1357 75 f. multicoloured 85 60

297 Pilgrims and Kaaba

1978. Pilgrimage to Mecca.
1358 297 25 f. multicoloured 30 15
1359 35 f. multicoloured 45 25

298 Map and Symbol

1978. U.N. Conference for Technical Co-operation among Developing Countries.
1360 298 25 f. multicoloured 25 15
1361 50 f. multicoloured 45 20
1362 75 f. multicoloured 75 50

299 Hands holding Emblem

300 Globe and Human Rights Emblem

1978. International Year to Combat Racism.
1363 299 25 f. multicoloured 25 15
1364 50 f. multicoloured 45 25
1365 75 f. multicoloured 1·25 50

1978. 30th Anniv of Declaration of Human Rights.
1366 300 25 f. multicoloured 25 15
1367 75 f. multicoloured 1·00 85

301 Candle and Emblem

302 Open Book, Pencil and Flame

1979. Police Day.
1368 301 10 f. multicoloured 15 15
1369 25 f. multicoloured 30 15
1370 35 f. multicoloured 65 35

1979. Anniv of Application of Compulsory Education Law.
1371 302 15 f. multicoloured 15 15
1372 25 f. multicoloured 25 15
1373 35 f. multicoloured 70 25

303 School, Teacher and Assyrian Relief

304 Clenched Fist, Pencil and Book

1979. Teachers' Day.
1374 303 10 f. multicoloured 15 15
1375 15 f. multicoloured 20 15
1376 50 f. multicoloured 60 35

1979. National Literacy Campaign.
1377 304 15 f. multicoloured . . . 15 15
1378 25 f. multicoloured . . . 30 15
1379 35 f. multicoloured . . . 55 25

305 World map, Koran and Symbols of Arab Achievements
306 Girl playing Flute

1979. The Arabs.
1380 305 35 f. multicoloured . . . 45 20
1381 75 f. multicoloured . . . 1·25 65

1979. Mosul Spring Festival.
1382 306 15 f. multicoloured . . . 25 15
1383 25 f. multicoloured . . . 40 20
1384 35 f. multicoloured . . . 85 35

307 Iraqi Map and Flag with U.P.U. Emblem
308 Championship Emblem with Sea and Sky

1979. 50th Anniv of Admission to Universal Postal Union.
1385 307 25 f. multicoloured . . . 40 15
1386 35 f. multicoloured . . . 55 25
1387 75 f. multicoloured . . . 1·00 45

1979. Fifth Arabian Gulf Football Championship.
1388 308 10 f. multicoloured . . . 15 15
1389 15 f. multicoloured . . . 25 15
1390 50 f. multicoloured . . . 70 45

309 Child with Globe and Candle
310 Flower and Branch

1979. International Year of the Child.
1391 309 25 f. multicoloured . . . 45 25
1392 75 f. multicoloured . . . 1·10 75

1979. July Festivals.
1394 310 15 f. multicoloured . . . 15 10
1395 25 f. multicoloured . . . 25 25
1396 35 f. multicoloured . . . 45 25

311 Children supporting Globe
312 Jawad Selim (sculptor)

1979. 50th Anniv of International Bureau of Education.
1397 311 25 f. multicoloured . . . 45 25
1398 50 f. multicoloured . . . 75 40
1399 100 f. multicoloured . . . 1·10 85

1979. Writers and Artists. Multicoloured.
1400 25 f. Type 312 . . . . 35 15
1401 25 f. S. al-Hosari (philosopher) 35 15
1402 25 f. Mustapha Jawad (historian) 35 15

313 The Kaaba, Mecca
314 Figure "20" and Globe

1979. Pilgrimage to Mecca.
1403 313 25 f. multicoloured . . . 30 15
1404 50 f. multicoloured . . . 55 25

1979. 20th Anniv of Iraqi News Agency.
1405 314 25 f. multicoloured . . . 30 15
1406 50 f. multicoloured . . . 65 20
1407 75 f. multicoloured . . . 1·00 35

315 Wave Pattern and Television Screen

1979. World Telecommunications Exhibition and Radio Conference, Geneva.
1408 315 25 f. multicoloured . . . 35 15
1409 50 f. multicoloured . . . 50 30
1410 75 f. multicoloured . . . 85 50

316 Clenched Fists and Refugee

1979. Palestinian Solidarity Day.
1411 316 25 f. multicoloured . . . 45 15
1412 50 f. multicoloured . . . 65 35
1413 75 f. multicoloured . . . 1·10 65

317 Ahmed Hassan Al-Bakir
318 Boy with Violin

1979. Inauguration of President Saddam Hussain. Multicoloured.
1414 25 f. Type 317 . . . . . . 25 15
1415 35 f. Pres. Hussain taking the oath 45 20
1416 75 f. Type 317 . . . . . . 75 45
1417 100 f. As No. 1415 . . . . 1·10 85

1979. Activities of Vanguards (youth organization). Multicoloured.
1418 10 f. Type 318 . . . . . . 10 10
1419 15 f. Boys on building site . . 15 15
1420 25 f. Boys on assault course and in personal combat 20 15
1421 35 f. Vanguards emblem . . . 45 20

319 Wind-speed Indicator and Thermometer
320 Lighting Cigarette and Cancerous Lungs

1980. World Meteorological Day.
1422 319 15 f. multicoloured . . . 15 15
1423 25 f. multicoloured . . . 25 15
1424 35 f. multicoloured . . . 45 25

1980. World Health Day. Anti-Smoking Campaign.
1425 320 25 f. multicoloured . . . 30 15
1426 35 f. multicoloured . . . 45 15
1427 75 f. multicoloured . . . 75 45

321 Festivals Emblem
322 Hurdling

1980. July Festivals.
1428 321 25 f. multicoloured . . . 20 15
1429 35 f. multicoloured . . . 25 15

1980. Olympic Games, Moscow. Multicoloured.
1431 15 f. Type 322 . . . . . . 20 15
1432 20 f. Weightlifting (vert) . . . 30 15
1433 30 f. Boxing 45 25
1434 35 f. Football (vert) 50 35

323 "Rubus sanctus"

1980. Fruit. Multicoloured.
1436 5 f. Type 323 . . . . 20 10
1437 15 f. Peaches 35 15
1438 20 f. Pears 50 15
1439 25 f. Apples 60 15
1440 35 f. Plums 80 30

324 Conference Emblem and Arabic Text
325 A.P.U. Emblem Posthorn and Map

1980. World Tourism Conference, Manila.
1441 324 25 f. multicoloured . . . 25 15
1442 50 f. multicoloured . . . 50 25
1443 100 f. multicoloured . . . 95 65

1980. 11th Congress of Arab Postal Union, Baghdad.
1444 325 10 f. multicoloured . . . 15 10
1445 30 f. multicoloured . . . 25 15
1446 35 f. multicoloured . . . 40 25

326 O.P.E.C. Emblem and Globe

1980. 20th Anniv of Organization of Petroleum Exporting Countries.
1447 326 30 f. multicoloured . . . 50 20
1448 75 f. multicoloured . . . 1·00 65

327 African Monarch

1980. Butterflies. Multicoloured.
1449 10 f. Swallowtail 25 20
1450 15 f. Type 327 . . . . . . 50 25
1451 20 f. Red admiral 70 40
1452 30 f. Clouded yellow . . . . 1·00 45

328 Mosque and Kaaba

1980. 1400th Anniv of Hegira.
1453 328 15 f. multicoloured . . . 20 15
1454 25 f. multicoloured . . . 35 15
1455 35 f. multicoloured . . . 45 20

329 Riflemen and Dome of the Rock on Map of Israel

1980. Palestinian Solidarity Day.
1456 329 25 f. multicoloured . . . 30 15
1457 35 f. multicoloured . . . 45 20
1458 75 f. multicoloured . . . 1·00 50

330 Soldier and Rocket
331 "8" and Flags forming Torch

1981. 60th Anniv of Army Day.
1459 330 5 f. multicoloured 15 10
1460 30 f. multicoloured . . . 40 15
1461 75 f. multicoloured . . . 90 50

1981. 18th Anniv of 14th Ramadan Revolution.
1462 331 15 f. multicoloured . . . 15 10
1463 30 f. multicoloured . . . 30 15
1464 35 f. multicoloured . . . 40 20

332 Map of Arab States tied with Ribbon

1981. The Arabs.
1465 332 5 f. multicoloured 10 10
1466 25 f. multicoloured . . . 30 15
1467 35 f. multicoloured . . . 45 20

333 Pres. Hussain, Saddam and Modern Military Equipment
334 I.T.U. and W.H.O. Emblems and Ribbons forming Caduceus

1981. Saddam's Battle of Qadisiya.
1468 333 30 f. multicoloured . . . 30 15
1469 35 f. multicoloured . . . 40 15
1470 75 f. multicoloured . . . 70 35

1981. World Telecommunications Day.
1472 334 25 f. multicoloured . . . 35 20
1473 50 f. multicoloured . . . 70 30
1474 75 f. multicoloured . . . 1·10 60

335 Mil Mi-24 Helicopters attacking Ground Forces
336 Map and Flower enclosing Ballot Box

1981. 50th Anniv of Air Force. Mult.
1475 5 f. Type 335 (postage) 15 15
1476 10 f. Antonov An-2 biplane trainer 25 15
1477 15 f. "SAM-15" missile . . . 25 15
1478 120 f. De Havilland Dragon Rapide biplane and Mikoyan Gurevich MiG-21 jet fighters (vert) (air) . . . . 2·50 1·50

1981. 1st Anniv of National Assembly Election.
1479 336 30 f. multicoloured . . . 30 10
1480 35 f. multicoloured . . . 45 15
1481 45 f. multicoloured . . . 55 25

337 Festivals Emblem
338 Basket Weaver

1981. July Festivals.
1482 337 15 f. multicoloured . . . 20 10
1483 25 f. multicoloured . . . 30 15
1484 35 f. multicoloured . . . 45 20

1981. Popular Industries. Multicoloured.

1485	5 f. Type **338**	10	10
1486	30 f. Copper worker	35	20
1487	35 f. Potter	55	20
1488	50 f. Weaver (horiz)	70	30

339 Saddam Hussain Gymnasium

1981. Modern Buildings. Multicoloured.

1489	45 f. Type **339**	45	20
1490	50 f. Palace of Conferences	45	20
1491	120 f. As 50 f.	1·25	95
1492	150 f. Type **339**	1·75	1·10

340 Pilgrims

1981. Pilgrimage to Mecca.

1493	**340**	25 f. multicoloured	40	15
1494		45 f. multicoloured	65	25
1495		50 f. multicoloured	65	25

341 Harvesting

1981. World Food Day.

1496	**341**	30 f. multicoloured	30	15
1497		45 f. multicoloured	60	30
1498		75 f. multicoloured	90	55

343 Teacher with Deaf Child

344 Medal and Map

1981. International Year of Disabled Persons.

1501	**343**	30 f. multicoloured	30	15
1502		45 f. multicoloured	70	25
1503		75 f. multicoloured	95	60

1981. Martyr's Day.

1504	**344**	45 f. multicoloured	50	20
1505		50 f. multicoloured	50	20
1506		120 f. multicoloured	1·50	1·00

See also Nos. O1507/9.

345 "Ibn Khaldoon" (freighter)

1981. 5th Anniv of United Arab Shipping Company.

1507	**345**	50 f. multicoloured	75	35
1508		120 f. multicoloured	2·00	1·10

346 Woman and Symbols of Technology

347 President Hussain, "7" and "Flowers"

1982. Iraqi Women's Day.

1509	**346**	25 f. multicoloured	35	15
1510		45 f. multicoloured	60	30
1511		50 f. multicoloured	60	35

1982. 35th Anniv of Al-Baath Party. Mult.

1512	25 f. Type **347**	35	15
1513	30 f. Rainbow and "7 7 7"	35	15
1514	45 f. Type **347**	55	35
1515	50 f. As 30 f.	55	35

348 A.P.U. Emblem and Globe

349 White Storks

1982. 30th Anniv of Arab Postal Union.

1517	**348**	25 f. multicoloured	30	15
1518		45 f. multicoloured	50	25
1519		50 f. multicoloured	55	25

1982. Mosul Spring Festival. Multicoloured.

1520	25 f. Type **349**	75	15
1521	30 f. Doll	45	15
1522	45 f. Type **349**	75	35
1523	50 f. As 30 f.	65	30

350 World Map, Factories and "1"

1982. Labour Day.

1524	**350**	25 f. multicoloured	30	10
1525		45 f. multicoloured	45	25
1526		50 f. multicoloured	50	30

351 Geometric Figure and I.T.U. Problem

352 Oil Gusher

1982. World Telecommunications Day.

1527	**351**	5 f. multicoloured	10	10
1528		45 f. multicoloured	50	25
1529		100 f. multicoloured	1·10	70

1982. 10th Anniv of Oil Nationalization. Mult.

1530	5 f. Type **352**	10	10
1531	25 f. Type **352**	45	15
1532	45 f. Bronze sculpture of bull and horse flanking couple holding model of oil rig	75	35
1533	50 f. As 45 f.	85	45

353 Nuclear Power Emblem and Lion

354 Footballers

1982. 1st Anniv of Attack on Iraqi Nuclear Reactor. Multicoloured.

1534	30 f. Type **353**	45	15
1535	45 f. Bomb aimed at egg	70	25
1536	50 f. Type **353**	75	35
1537	120 f. As No. 1535	1·50	95

1982. World Cup Football Championship, Spain. Multicoloured.

1538	5 f. Type **354**	15	10
1539	45 f. Three footballers	50	30
1540	50 f. Type **354**	50	30
1541	100 f. As 45 f.	1·10	75

355 President Hussain and Fireworks

356 Green Lizard

1982. July Festivals.

1543	**355**	25 f. multicoloured	25	15
1544		45 f. multicoloured	45	25
1545		50 f. multicoloured	45	30

1982. Reptiles. Multicoloured.

1546	25 f. Type **356**	1·40	60
1547	30 f. Asp	1·50	60
1548	45 f. Two green lizards	1·75	80
1549	50 f. "Natrix tessellata"	2·00	1·10

357 Pandit Nehru (India)

1982. Seventh Non-Aligned Countries Conference, Baghdad. Multicoloured.

1550	50 f. Type **357**	55	25
1551	50 f. Josef Tito (Yugoslavia)	55	25
1552	50 f. Abdul Nasser (Egypt)	55	25
1553	50 f. Kwame Nkrumah (Ghana)	55	25
1554	100 f. President Hussain (Iraq)	1·25	70

358 Microscope and Bacilli

1982. Cent of Discovery of Tubercule Bacillus.

1555	**358**	20 f. multicoloured	45	15
1556		50 f. multicoloured	80	25
1557		100 f. multicoloured	1·40	80

359 U.P.U. Building, Berne

360 Drums

1982. U.P.U. Day.

1561	**359**	5 f. multicoloured	15	10
1562		45 f. multicoloured	45	25
1563		100 f. multicoloured	1·10	70

1982. Musical Instruments. Multicoloured.

1564	5 f. Type **360**	15	10
1565	10 f. Stringed board instrument	20	10
1566	35 f. Bowed instruments	55	20
1567	100 f. Mandolin	1·75	75

361 Mosque and Minaret, Mecca

1982. Prophet Mohammed's Birthday. Mult.

1568	25 f. Type **361**	25	15
1569	30 f. Courtyard of mosque	25	15
1570	45 f. Type **361**	40	25
1571	50 f. As No. 1569	45	40

362 Flowers

1982. Flowers. Multicoloured.

1572	10 f. Type **362**	20	15
1573	20 f. Flowers (different)	30	15
1574	30 f. Type **362**	35	20
1575	40 f. As No. 1573	50	35
1576	50 f. Type **362**	65	35
1577	100 f. As No. 1573	1·10	60

1983. Nos. 1489/51 surch.

1578	60 f. on 50 f. Palace of Conferences	75	30
1579	70 f. on 45 f. Type **339**	1·10	45
1580	160 f. on 120 f. Palace of Conferences	2·50	1·50

364 President Hussain

1983. July Festivals.

1583	**364**	30 f. multicoloured	30	15
1584		60 f. multicoloured	70	35
1585		70 f. multicoloured	75	35

365 Emblem and Interlocked Bands

366 Horseman and Map

1983. World Communications Year. Mult.

1586	5 f. Type **365**	15	15
1587	25 f. Hexagons of primary colours	25	15
1588	60 f. Type **365**	75	45
1589	70 f. As No. 1587	85	50

1983. Battle of Thiqar. Multicoloured.

1591	20 f. Type **366**	25	15
1592	50 f. Eagle swooping on pyre	65	30
1593	60 f. Type **366**	70	35
1594	70 f. As No. 1592	80	45

367 Fair Emblem and Silhouette of Baghdad

368 Pres. Hussain within Figure "9"

1983. Baghdad International Fair.

1595	**367**	60 f. multicoloured	65	30
1596		70 f. multicoloured	70	45
1597		160 f. multicoloured	1·50	1·10

1983. Ninth Al-Baath Party Congress. Mult.

1598	30 f. Type **368**	25	15
1599	60 f. Eagle, torch, map and book	60	35
1600	70 f. Type **368**	70	40
1601	100 f. As No. 1599	1·00	55

369 Fishermen hauling Boat

1983. Paintings. Multicoloured.

1602	60 f. Type **369**	65	45
1603	60 f. Festive crowd	65	45
1604	60 f. Hanging decorations	65	45
1605	70 f. Crowd	75	55
1606	70 f. Bazaar	75	55

370 Dove and Victim

371 Apartment Building

1983. Massacre of Palestinians in Sabra and Shatila Refugee Camps, Lebanon. Multicoloured.

1607	10 f. Type **370**	20	10
1608	60 f. Type **370**	70	35
1609	70 f. Dove and clasped fist shedding blood and victims	75	45
1610	160 f. As No. 1609	1·60	1·10

1983. Buildings.
1611 371 60 f. lt grn, blk & grn . . 60 35
1612 – 70 f. purple, blk & grey . . 65 45
1613 – 160 f. pur, blk & grey . . 1·50 85
1614 371 200 f. green, blk & ol . . 2·00 1·10
DESIGNS: 70, 160 f. Apartment building (different).
See also Nos. O1615/16.

372 President Hussain

1983. 4th Anniv of President Hussain as Party and State Leader.
1617 372 60 f. multicoloured . . . 65 35
1618 70 f. multicoloured . . . 75 45
1619 250 f. multicoloured . . . 2·50 1·50

373 Congress Emblem

1984. 25th International Military Medicine and Pharmacy Congress.
1620 373 60 f. multicoloured . . . 65 35
1621 70 f. multicoloured . . . 75 45
1622 200 f. multicoloured . . . 2·25 1·10

374 President Hussain and Flowers
375 Boxing

1984. Pres. Saddam Hussain's 47th Birthday. Multicoloured.
1623 60 f. Type 374 . . . . . . 45 25
1624 70 f. Pres. Hussain in army uniform 55 35
1625 160 f. As No. 1623 . . . . . 1·60 1·25
1626 200 f. Type 374 . . . . . . 1·90 1·25

1984. Olympic Games, Los Angeles. Multicoloured.
1628 50 f. Type 375 . . . . . . 50 40
1629 60 f. Hurdling, weightlifting and wrestling 70 40
1630 70 f. Type 375 . . . . . . 85 50
1631 100 f. As No. 1629 . . . . . 1·10 65

376 Pres. Hussain and Horses' Heads
377 Flag as Ribbon and Two Domes

1984. Battle of Qadisiya. Multicoloured.
1633 50 f. Type 376 . . . . . . 45 30
1634 60 f. President Hussain and symbolic representation of battle 65 35
1635 70 f. Type 376 . . . . . . 75 55
1636 100 f. As No. 1634 . . . . . 1·10 60

1984. Martyr's Day. Multicoloured.
1638 50 f. Type 377 . . . . . . 50 25
1639 60 f. Woman holding rifle and medal 60 35
1640 70 f. Type 377 . . . . . . 70 50
1641 100 f. As No. 1639 . . . . . 1·00 65

378 Text

1985. 5th Anniv of President Hussain's Visit to Al-Mustansiriyah University.
1646 378 60 f. red and blue 60 40
1647 70 f. red and green . . . 70 45
1648 250 f. red and black . . . 2·40 85

379 Pres. Hussain and Jet Fighters
380 Pres. Hussain within Flower

1985. 54th Anniv of Iraqi Air Force. Mult.
1649 10 f. Type 379 . . . . 25 10
1650 60 f. Fighter airplanes trailing flag and "54" (horiz) . . . . 1·00 55
1651 70 f. As No. 1650 . . . . . . 1·10 60
1652 160 f. Type 379 . . . . 2·75 1·40

1985. 48th Birthday of President Saddam Hussain. Multicoloured.
1654 30 f. Type 380 . . . . 30 20
1655 60 f. Pres. Hussain, candle and flowers 60 40
1656 70 f. Type 380 . . . . 75 55
1657 100 f. As No. 1655 . . . . . 1·10 75

381 Graph and Modern Office

1985. Posts and Telecommunications Development. Multicoloured.
1659 20 f. Type 381 . . . . 20 15
1660 50 f. Dish aerial and graph . . 60 30
1661 60 f. Type 381 . . . . 65 30
1662 70 f. As No. 1660 . . . . . . 75 45

382 Arms at Crossroads, and Building

1985. Saddam's Battle of Qadisiya. Multicoloured.
1663 10 f. Type 382 . . . . 15 10
1664 20 f. Pres. Hussain and emblem of Al-Baath Party 20 15
1665 60 f. Type 382 . . . . 65 35
1666 70 f. As No. 1664 . . . . . . 70 55

383 Solar Energy Research Centre

1985.
1668 383 10 f. multicoloured . . . 15 10
1669 50 f. multicoloured . . . 60 30
1670 100 f. multicoloured . . . 1·10 70

384 Disabled Children
385 Hand holding Quill

1985. U.N.I.C.E.F. Child Survival Campaign. Multicoloured.
1671 10 f. Type 384 . . . . 15 10
1672 15 f. Toddler and baby 25 15
1673 50 f. Type 384 . . . . 60 30
1674 100 f. As No. 1672 . . . . . 1·10 80

1985. Death Millenary of Al-Sharif Al-Radhi (poet).
1675 385 10 f. multicoloured . . . 15 10
1676 50 f. multicoloured . . . 45 30
1677 100 f. multicoloured . . . 95 65

386 U.N. Emblem

1985. 40th Anniv of U.N.O.
1678 386 10 f. multicoloured . . . 15 10
1679 40 f. blue, black & yellow . 45 25
1680 100 f. multicoloured . . . 1·10 65

387 World Map

1985. Palestinian Solidarity Day.
1681 387 10 f. multicoloured . . . 15 10
1682 50 f. multicoloured . . . 55 30
1683 100 f. multicoloured . . . 1·40 70

388 Flag, Man and Blood Vessels as Roots
389 I.Y.Y. Emblem and Soldier with Flag

1985. Martyr's Day.
1684 388 10 f. multicoloured . . . 15 10
1685 40 f. multicoloured . . . 45 30
1686 100 f. multicoloured . . . 95 60

1985. International Youth Year. Multicoloured.
1687 40 f. Type 389 . . . . 35 20
1688 50 f. Young couple, flag and I.Y.Y. emblem 50 25
1689 100 f. Type 389 . . . . 90 60
1690 200 f. As No. 1688 . . . . . 1·75 1·40

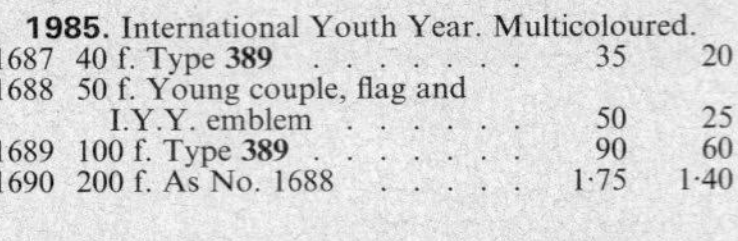

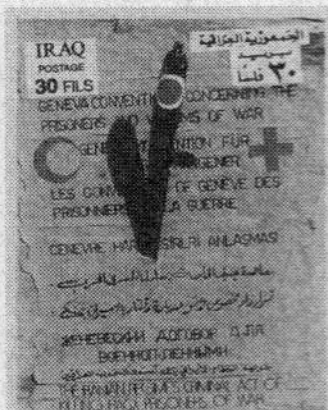

390 Pres. Hussain and Soldier in "6"
391 Pen as Knife in Sheet of Text

1986. Army Day. Multicoloured.
1692 10 f. Type 390 . . . . 15 15
1693 40 f. Pres. Hussain, cogwheel, "6" and missiles (horiz) . . 45 20
1694 50 f. Type 390 . . . . 55 30
1695 100 f. As No. 1693 . . . . . 1·25 70

1986. Iraqi Prisoners of War Commemoration. Multicoloured.
1697 30 f. Type 391 . . . . 30 20
1698 70 f. Dove, cherub holding flag and three prisoners 75 45
1699 100 f. Type 391 . . . . 95 60
1700 200 f. As No. 1698 . . . . . 2·00 1·40

392 Pres. Hussain with Children
393 Worker, Globe and Cogwheel

1986. 49th Birthday of President Saddam Hussain. Multicoloured.
1702 30 f. Type 392 . . . . 30 15
1703 50 f. Pres. Hussain and doves holding flag 60 20
1704 100 f. Type 392 . . . . 90 65
1705 150 f. As No. 1703 . . . . . 1·60 1·00

1986. Labour Day. Multicoloured.
1707 10 f. Type 393 . . . . 10 10
1708 40 f. Candle in cogwheel . . . 35 15
1709 100 f. Type 393 . . . . 90 65
1710 150 f. As No. 1708 . . . . . 1·25 90

394 Pres. Hussain and "30 July 17"

1986. July Festivals and 7th Anniv of Pres. Hussain's State Leadership. Multicoloured.
1711 20 f. Type 394 . . . . 15 10
1712 30 f. Pres. Hussain and "17 1986" 25 15
1713 100 f. Type 394 . . . . 90 60
1714 150 f. As No. 1712 . . . . . 1·40 95

395 Pres. Hussain and Jet Fighter

1986. 55th Anniv of Iraqi Air Force. Multicoloured.
1716 30 f. Type 395 . . . . 55 20
1717 50 f. Pres. Hussain and jet fighters . . . . 1·10 30
1718 100 f. Type 395 . . . . 2·10 1·25
1719 150 f. As No. 1717 . . . . . 3·00 1·60

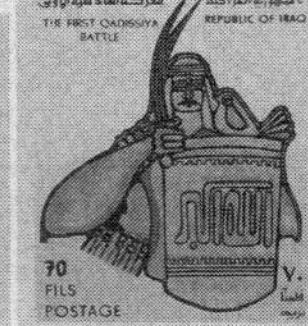

396 Refinery
397 Arab Warrior

1986. Oil Nationalization Day. Multicoloured.
1721 10 f. Type 396 . . . . 15 10
1722 40 f. Derrick and pipeline within flag (vert) 45 20
1723 100 f. Type 396 . . . . 1·10 60
1724 150 f. As No. 1722 . . . . . 1·60 1·10

1986. 1st Battle of Qadisiya. Multicoloured.
1725 20 f. Type 397 . . . . 30 15
1726 60 f. Pres. Hussain and battle scene 60 35
1727 70 f. Type 397 . . . . 65 45
1728 100 f. As No. 1726 . . . . . 95 60

398 Pres. Hussain, Battlefield and Cheering Soldiers
399 Pres. Hussain

1986. Saadam's Battle of Qadisiya. Mult.
1729 30 f. Type 398 . . . . 65 25
1730 40 f. Pres. Hussain within flag "swords" and symbols of ancient and modern warfare (horiz) 90 35
1731 100 f. Type 398 . . . . 1·50 1·00
1732 150 f. As No. 1730 . . . . . 3·00 1·50

1986.
1734 399 30 f. multicoloured . . . 50 15
1735 50 f. multicoloured . . . 75 20
1736 100 f. multicoloured . . . 1·40 40
1737 150 f. multicoloured . . . 2·00 60
1738 250 f. multicoloured . . . 3·50 1·10
1739 350 f. multicoloured . . . 5·00 1·50

401 Women
402 Flag and Treble Clef forming Dove

1986. Iraqi Women's Day. Multicoloured.
1744 30 f. Type **401** 30 15
1745 50 f. Woman and battle scenes (horiz) 70 25
1746 100 f. Type **401** 95 60
1747 150 f. As No. 1745 . . . . . 1·90 95

1986. International Peace Year. Multicoloured.
1748 50 f. Type **402** 45 15
1749 100 f. Globe, dove with flag and hand holding rifle and olive branch 95 55
1750 150 f. Type **402** . . . . . . 1·40 90
1751 250 f. As No. 1749 . . . . . 2·10 1·10

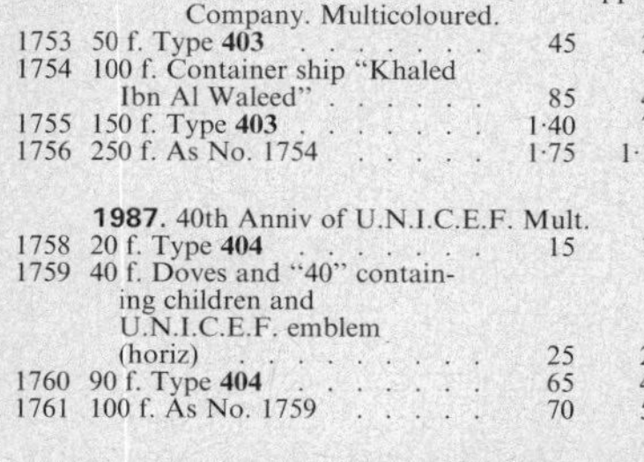

403 Freighter "Al Alwah" and Map
404 Activities on Tree

1987. 10th Anniv of United Arab Shipping Company. Multicoloured.
1753 50 f. Type **403** 45 20
1754 100 f. Container ship "Khaled Ibn Al Waleed" 85 45
1755 150 f. Type **403** . . . . . . 1·40 70
1756 250 f. As No. 1754 . . . . . 1·75 1·10

1987. 40th Anniv of U.N.I.C.E.F. Mult.
1758 20 f. Type **404** 15 15
1759 40 f. Doves and "40" containing children and U.N.I.C.E.F. emblem (horiz) 25 20
1760 90 f. Type **404** 65 40
1761 100 f. As No. 1759 . . . . . 70 50

405 Pres. Hussain in "6"
406 Torch, Cogwheel, Wheat and Map

1987. Army Day. Multicoloured.
1762 20 f. Type **405** 15 10
1763 40 f. Pres. Hussain and military scenes 25 15
1764 90 f. Type **405** 50 25
1765 100 f. As No. 1763 . . . . . 65 35

1987. 40th Anniv of Al-Baath Party. Mult.
1766 20 f. Type **406** 15 10
1767 40 f. Pres. Hussain, map and flag as "7" 20 15
1768 90 f. Type **406** 50 25
1769 100 f. As No. 1767 . . . . . 60 30

407 Pres. Hussain
408 Pres. Hussain, Civilians, Soldiers and buried Soldier

1987. 50th Birthday of President Saddam Hussain. Multicoloured.
1770 20 f. Type **407** 15 10
1771 40 f. Anniversary dates, flowers and Pres. Hussain 20 15
1772 90 f. Type **407** 50 30
1773 100 f. As No. 1771 . . . . . 60 35

1987. July Festivals and 8th Anniv of Pres. Hussain's State Leadership. Multicoloured.
1774 20 f. Pres. Hussain and flag (horiz) 15 10
1775 40 f. Type **408** 30 15
1776 90 f. As No. 1174 . . . . . 55 35
1777 100 f. Type **408** 70 45

409 Symbolic Family on Graph

1987. Census. Multicoloured.
1778 20 f. Type **409** 20 10
1779 30 f. People on graph 30 15
1780 50 f. As No. 1779 . . . . . 40 20
1781 500 f. Type **409** . . . . . . 3·50 2·50

410 Pres. Hussain in "6" and Troops
412 Flag as "V" and Lyre

411 "8" and Pres. Hussain

1988. Army Day. Multicoloured.
1782 20 f. Type **410** 20 10
1783 30 f. Soldier and medal (horiz) . 20 15
1784 50 f. Type **410** 35 20
1785 150 f. As No. 1783 . . . . . 85 50

1988. 18th Anniv of People's Army (1786, 1788) and 25th Anniv of 8th February Revolution (others). Multicoloured.
1786 20 f. Type **411** 20 10
1787 30 f. Pres. Hussain and eagle on "8" (vert) 25 15
1788 50 f. Type **411** 35 20
1789 150 f. As No. 1787 . . . . . 1·00 60

1988. Art Day. Multicoloured.
1790 20 f. Type **412** 20 10
1791 30 f. Pres. Hussain, rifle as torch, clef and dove on film strip 25 15
1792 50 f. Type **412** 35 25
1793 100 f. As No. 1791 . . . . . 70 45

413 Rally and Ears of Wheat

1988. 41st Anniv of Al-Baath Party. Mult.
1795 20 f. Type **413** 15 10
1796 30 f. Flowers and "7 April 1947–1988" 15 15
1797 50 f. Type **413** 35 25
1798 150 f. As No. 1796 . . . . . 85 60

414 Emblem
415 Pres. Hussain

1988. Regional Marine Environment Day. Multicoloured.
1799 20 f. Type **414** 15 10
1800 40 f. Fishes (horiz) 25 15
1801 90 f. Type **414** 60 45
1802 100 f. As No. 1800 . . . . . 80 50

1988. 51st Birthday of President Saddam Hussain. Multicoloured.
1803 20 f. Type **415** 15 10
1804 30 f. Pres. Hussain and hands holding flowers 20 15
1805 50 f. Type **415** 35 20
1806 100 f. As No. 1804 . . . . . 65 45

416 Emblem

1988. 40th Anniv of W.H.O. Multicoloured.
1808 20 f. Type **416** 15 10
1809 40 f. Red crescent protecting line of people (vert) 20 15
1810 90 f. Type **416** 65 45
1811 100 f. As No. 1809 . . . . . 75 55

417 Bomb and Open Book showing School, Child and Wreath
418 Hand holding Flash of Lightning

1988. Bilat Al-Shuhada School Bomb Victims. Multicoloured.
1812 20 f. Type **417** 15 10
1813 40 f. Explosion and girl (horiz) 25 15
1814 90 f. Type **417** 60 45
1815 100 f. As No. 1813 . . . . . 70 50

1988. July Festivals and 9th Anniv of President Hussain's State Leadership. Multicoloured.
1817 50 f. Type **418** 35 25
1818 90 f. Sun, map and Pres. Hussain 50 35
1819 100 f. Type **418** 65 45
1820 150 f. As No. 1818 . . . . . 1·00 70

419 Pres. Hussain and al-Sail al-Kabir Miqat

1988. President Hussain's Pilgrimage to Mecca.
1822 **419** 90 f. multicoloured . . . 60 40
1823 100 f. multicoloured . . . 70 50
1824 150 f. multicoloured . . . 1·00 70

420 Mosul

1988. Tourism. Multicoloured.
1825 50 f. Type **420** 60 40
1826 100 f. Basrah 80 55
1827 150 f. Baghdad (vert) . . . . 1·50 1·00

421 Pres. Hussain and Soldiers

1988. "Victorious Iraq".
1828 **421** 50 f. multicoloured . . . 2·00 2·00
1829 100 f. multicoloured . . . 4·25 4·25
1830 150 f. multicoloured . . . 6·25 6·25

422 Emblem

1988. Navy Day. Multicoloured.
1831 50 f. Type **422** 40 30
1832 90 f. Missile boats 40 20
1833 100 f. Type **422** 85 60
1834 150 f. As No. 1832 . . . . . 70 30

423 Map and Hands holding Flag

1988. Liberation of Fao City.
1836 **423** 100 f. multicoloured . . . 60 40
1837 150 f. multicoloured . . . 1·25 90

424 Missile Launch from Winged Map
425 Boxer and Hodori (mascot)

1988. Iraq Missile Research.
1839 **424** 100 f. multicoloured . . . 60 40
1840 150 f. multicoloured . . . 85 60

1988. Olympic Games, Seoul. Multicoloured.
1842 100 f. Type **425** 85 60
1843 150 f. Games emblem . . . . 1·25 90

426 Dancers and Golden Cow
427 Crescent and Camel Train

1988. 2nd Babylon International Festival.
1845 **426** 100 f. multicoloured . . . 50 35
1846 150 f. multicoloured . . . 80 55

1988. Mohammed's Birth Anniv.
1848 **427** 100 f. multicoloured . . . 50 35
1849 150 f. multicoloured . . . 75 55
1850 1 d. multicoloured . . . 5·50 4·00

انتصر العراق
١٩٨٨/٨/٨

428 Hand holding Candle
(**429** "Victory")

1988. Martyr's Day.
1851 **428** 100 f. multicoloured . . . 55 40
1852 150 f. multicoloured . . . 80 55
1853 500 f. multicoloured . . . 2·50 1·75

1988. Nos. 1738/9 optd with T **429**.
1854 **399** 250 f. multicoloured . . . 1·40 1·00
1855 350 f. multicoloured . . . 2·00 1·40

430 Family on Pedestrian Crossing

1989. Police Day.
1856 **430** 50 f. multicoloured . . . 30 20
1857 100 f. multicoloured . . . 55 40
1858 150 f. multicoloured . . . 85 60

431 Children and Money

1989. Postal Savings Bank. (a) Size 32 × 32 mm.
1859 **431** 50 f. multicoloured . . . 25 20

(b) Size 24 × 25 mm. With or without Arabic opt.
1860 – 100 f. multicoloured 55 40
1861 – 150 f. multicoloured 80 55

DESIGN: 100, 150 f. Motif as Type **431** but with inscriptions differently arranged and inscr "REPUBLIC OF IRAQ".

Nos. 1860/1 were not issued without overprint.

432 Members' Flags and Leaders

1989. Formation of Arab Co-operation Council (Egypt, Iraq, Jordan and Yemen Arab Republic). Multicoloured.

1862		100 f. Type **432**	55	40
1863		150 f. Leaders in formal pose	80	55

433 Dates

1989. 1st Anniv of Liberation of Fao City.

1864	**433**	100 f. multicoloured	55	40
1865		150 f. multicoloured	80	55

434 Pres. Hussain

1989. 52nd Birthday of President Saddam Hussain.

1867	**434**	100 f. multicoloured	70	50
1868		150 f. multicoloured	1·10	75

435 Khairalla **436** Hussain laying Mortar

1989. General Adnan Khairalla Commem.

1870	**435**	50 f. multicoloured	35	25
1871		100 f. multicoloured	70	50
1872		150 f. multicoloured	1·00	70

1989. Completion of Basrah Reconstruction Project.

1873	**436**	100 f. multicoloured	70	50
1874		150 f. multicoloured	1·00	70

437 Crane and Buildings **438** "Women"

1989. Start of Reconstruction of Fao City.

1875	**437**	100 f. multicoloured	70	50
1876		150 f. multicoloured	1·00	70

1989.

1877	**438**	100 f. multicoloured	70	50
1878		150 f. multicoloured	1·10	75
1879		1 d. multicoloured	5·75	4·00
1880		5 d. multicoloured	25·00	17·00

439 Pres. Hussain **440** Flag and Victory Signs

1989. July Festivals and 10th Anniv of President Hussain's State Leadership.

1881	**439**	50 f. multicoloured	30	20
1882		100 f. multicoloured	55	40
1883		150 f. multicoloured	90	65

1989. Victory Day.

1884	**440**	100 f. multicoloured	55	40
1885		150 f. multicoloured	90	65

441 Children, Heart and Bride

1989. Iraqi Family.

1887	**441**	50 f. multicoloured	30	20
1888		100 f. multicoloured	60	40
1889		150 f. multicoloured	95	65

442 Najaf

1989. Tourism. Multicoloured.

1890		100 f. Type **442**	60	40
1891		100 f. Arbil	60	40
1892		100 f. Marsh Arab punt and Ziggurat of Ur	45	20

443 Map and Means of Transport

1989. 5th Session of Arab Ministers of Transport Council, Baghdad. Multicoloured.

1893		50 f. Type **443**	60	20
1894		100 f. Sun, means of transport and map	90	30
1895		150 f. Means of transport, and members' flags (vert)	1·25	40

444 City and Pres. Hussain placing Final Stone **445** Anniversary Emblem

1989. Completion of Fao City Reconstruction.

1896	**444**	100 f. multicoloured	70	50
1897		150 f. multicoloured	1·00	70

1989. 30th Anniv of Iraqi News Agency.

1898	**445**	50 f. multicoloured	30	20
1899		100 f. multicoloured	60	40
1900		150 f. multicoloured	85	60

446 Emblem **447** Pansies

1989. 1st Anniv of Declaration of Palestinian State. Multicoloured.

1901		25 f. Type **446**	15	10
1902		50 f. Crowd of children	30	20
1903		100 f. Type **446**	60	40
1904		150 f. As No. 1902	95	65

1989. Flowers. Multicoloured.

1905		25 f. Type **447**	15	10
1906		50 f. Antirrhinums	30	20
1907		100 f. "Hibiscus trionum"	60	40
1908		150 f. Mesembryanthemums	1·00	70

448 Map and Emblem

1989. Centenary of Interparliamentary Union.

1910	**448**	25 f. multicoloured	20	10
1911		100 f. multicoloured	60	40
1912		150 f. multicoloured	90	60

449 Sun, Flag, Doves and Mosque Domes **450** Dove, Red Crescent and Pres. Hussain

1989. Martyr's Day.

1913	**449**	50 f. multicoloured	25	20
1914		100 f. multicoloured	55	40
1915		150 f. multicoloured	80	55

1989. Iraqi Red Crescent Society.

1916	**450**	100 f. multicoloured	50	35
1917		150 f. multicoloured	75	55
1918		500 f. multicoloured	2·50	1·75

451 Members' Flags on Map

1990. 1st Anniv of Arab Co-operation Council.

1919	**451**	50 f. multicoloured	60	40
1920		100 f. multicoloured	1·00	70

مؤتمر القمة العربي

الاستثنائي

بغداد ٢٨/أيار/١٩٩٠

(452)

1990. Arab League Summit Conference, Baghdad. Nos. 1906 and 1908 optd with T **452**.

1922		50 f. multicoloured	30	20
1923		150 f. multicoloured	85	60

453 Doves and Flag as Flame

1990. 2nd Anniv of Liberation of Fao City.

1924	**453**	50 f. multicoloured	30	20
1925		100 f. multicoloured	60	40

OBLIGATORY TAX

28a King Faisal II 28b

مالية
فلسان
انقاذ فلسطين

(28c "Tax 2 Fils Save Palestine")

مالية
انقاذ فلسطين

(28d "Tax Save Palestine")

انقاذ
فلسطين

(28e "Save Palestine") (size varies)

١٠ فلوس
انقاذ فلسطين

(28g "Tax 10 Fils Save Palestine") (size varies)

مالية
٥ فلوس
انقاذ فلسطين

(28h "Tax 5 Fils Save Palestine")

1949. Aid for Palestine.

(a) Nos. O300 and 278 surch as T **28**.

T324	**27**	2 f. on 3 f. green	9·00	7·50
T325		2 f. on 6 f. mauve	8·50	6·75

(b) Nos. O299 and O303 optd as T **28d** but smaller.

T326	**27**	2 f. brown	5·00	4·25
T327		5 f. red	12·50	10·00

(c) No. O234 optd with T **28d**.

T328	**20**	5 f. red	3·00	4·25

(d) Revenue stamp surch in Arabic (="2 Fils Save Palestine") as bottom two lines of T **28c**.

T329	**28a**	2 f. on 5 f. blue	4·00	2·50

(e) Revenue stamps optd with T **28e**.

T330	**28a**	5 f. blue	1·90	35
T335		10 f. orange	6·75	3·00
T332	**28b**	10 f. orange	—	13·50

(f) Revenue stamp surch as T **28g**.

T336	**28b**	10 f. on 20 f. green	15·00	9·25

(h) No. 278 surch with T **28h**.

T337	**27**	5 f. on 6 f. mauve	17·00	6·50

دفاع
وطني

113a (113b)

1968. Flood Relief.

T763	**113a**	5 f. brown	20	15

1968. Defence Fund. Optd with Type **113b**.

T764	**113a**	5 f. brown	20	15

دفاع وطني
٥ فلوس

(164a) (215)

1970. Obligatory Tax. Defence Fund. Nos. 620 and 625/9 surch with Type T **164a**.

T931	**65**	5 f. on 1 f. green	1·75	2·00
T932	–	5 f. on 10 f. red	2·50	2·75
T933	–	5 f. on 15 f. brn & yell	2·50	2·75
T934	–	5 f. on 20 f. violet	2·50	2·75
T935	–	5 f. on 30 f. orange	2·50	2·75
T936	–	5 f. on 40 f. green	2·50	2·75

1973. Obligatory Tax. Defence Fund. Nos. 607/8 surch with Type **215**.

T1071	**62**	5 f. on 14 f. blk & grn	3·50	3·50
T1072		5 f. on 35 f. blk & red	3·50	3·50

دفاع وطني
٥ فلوس

(223) (231)

1973. Nos. 738, 765, 777, 787 and 891 optd similar to Type **215** (No. T1119) or as Type **223** (others).

T1117	–	5 f. on 2 f. mult	2·75	3·00
T1118	**114**	5 f. on 2 f. mult	2·75	3·00
T1119	**116**	5 f. on 2 f. mult	2·75	3·00
T1120	**117**	5 f. on 2 f. mult	2·75	3·00
T1121	**150**	5 f. on 2 f. mult	2·75	3·00

1973. No. 1099 optd with Type **231**.

T1152	**221**	5 f. black and orange	2·40	1·00

235 Soldier

1974. Defence Fund.

T1158	**235**	5 f. black, yell & brn	60	80

OFFICIAL STAMPS

1920. Issue of 1918 (surch Turkish stamps) optd **ON STATE SERVICE**.

O33	½ a. on 10 pa. green	80	80
O20	1 a. on 20 pa. red	1·50	60
O35	1½ a. on 5 pa. brown	2·00	55
O22	2½ a. on 1 pi. blue	1·75	2·25
O23	3 a. on 1½ pi. black & pink	9·00	80
O36	4 a. on 1¾ pi. brown & blue	2·00	1·00
O25	6 a. on 2 pi. black & green	12·00	4·75
O38	8 a. on 2½ pi. green & brown	3·00	2·00
O27	12 a. on 5 pi. purple	8·50	4·75
O28	1 r. on 10 pi. brown	9·00	4·25
O29	2 r. on 25 pi. green	18·00	10·00
O30	5 r. on 50 pi. red	32·00	23·00
O31	10 r. on 100 pi. blue	50·00	£110

1923. Nos. 41/50 and 52/3 optd **ON STATE SERVICE** in English only.

O54	**2**	½ a. green	90	40
O55	–	1 a. brown	90	10
O56	**3**	1½ a. red	1·75	60
O57	–	2 a. buff	1·75	20
O58	–	3 a. blue	2·50	85
O59	–	4 a. violet	3·50	50
O60	–	6 a. blue	3·75	1·25
O61	–	8 a. bistre	4·00	1·75
O62	**4**	1 r. brown and green	6·00	1·25
O63	**2**	2 r. black	20·00	8·00
O64	–	5 r. orange	48·00	26·00
O65	–	10 r. red	70·00	48·00

1924. Nos. 41/9 and 51/3 optd **ON STATE SERVICE** in English and Arabic.

O66	**2**	½ a. green	85	10
O67	–	1 a. brown	60	10
O68	**3**	1½ a. red	70	20
O69	–	2 a. buff	1·00	10
O70	–	3 a. blue	1·25	10
O71	–	4 a. violet	3·25	30
O72	–	6 a. blue	1·75	20
O73	–	8 a. bistre	2·50	35
O74	**4**	1 r. brown and green	9·50	1·00
O75	**2**	2 r. bistre	27·00	3·75
O76	–	5 r. orange	45·00	42·00
O77	–	10 r. red	65·00	42·00

1927. Optd **ON STATE SERVICE** in English and Arabic.

O79	**10**	1 r. brown	5·50	1·75

1931. Optd **ON STATE SERVICE** in English and Arabic.

O 93	**11**	½ a. green	50	2·75
O 94		1 a. brown	70	10
O 95		1½ a. red	4·50	17·00
O 96		2 a. orange	70	10
O 97		3 a. blue	85	85
O 98		4 a. purple	95	1·00
O 99		6 a. blue	4·00	15·00
O100		8 a. green	4·00	15·00
O101	**12**	1 r. brown	13·00	14·00
O102		2 r. brown	20·00	50·00
O103		5 r. orange	40·00	90·00
O104		10 r. red	70·00	£150
O105	**10**	25 r. violet	£550	£700

1932. Official stamps of 1924 and 1931 surch in "Fils" or "Dinar".

O122	**11**	3 f. on ½ a. green	3·25	3·25
O123		4 f. on 1 a. brown	2·25	10
O124		5 f. on 1 a. brown	2·25	10
O125	**4**	8 f. on 1½ a. red	3·75	50
O126c	**11**	10 f. on 2 a. orange	2·50	10
O127		15 f. on 3 a. blue	3·50	1·00
O128		20 f. on 4 a. purple	3·50	1·40
O129		25 f. on 4 a. purple	3·75	1·50
O130	–	30 f. on 6 a. bl (No. O72)	3·75	1·75
O131	**11**	40 f. on 8 a. green	3·75	3·50
O132	**12**	50 f. 1 r. brown	3·75	3·50
O133		75 f. on 1 r. brown	6·00	6·00
O134	**2**	100 f. on 2 r. bistre	11·00	3·50
O135	–	200 f. on 5 r. orange (No. O76)	20·00	20·00
O136	–	½ d. on 10 r. red (No. 77)	50·00	70·00
O137	**10**	1 d. on 25 r. violet	85·00	£140

1932. Issue of 1932 optd **ON STATE SERVICE** in English and Arabic.

O155	**11**	2 f. blue	1·00	10
O156		3 f. green	1·00	10
O157		4 f. purple	1·00	10
O158		5 f. green	1·00	10
O159		8 f. red	1·00	10
O160		10 f. yellow	1·75	10
O161		15 f. blue	2·25	10
O162		20 f. orange	2·25	15
O163		25 f. mauve	2·00	15
O164		30 f. olive	3·25	20
O165		40 f. violet	4·25	20
O166	**12**	50 f. brown	3·00	20
O167		75 f. blue	2·25	90
O168		100 f. green	9·00	1·00
O169		200 f. red	17·00	6·50
O170	**10**	½ d. blue	12·00	21·00
O171		1 d. purple	50·00	70·00

1934. Issue of 1934 optd **ON STATE SERVICE** in English and Arabic.

O190	**16**	1 f. violet	1·10	40
O191		2 f. blue	90	15
O192		3 f. green	50	15
O193		4 f. purple	1·00	15
O194		5 f. green	90	15
O195		8 f. red	3·50	25
O196		10 f. yellow	35	15
O197		15 f. blue	8·00	1·25
O198		20 f. orange	75	15
O199		25 f. mauve	16·00	4·75
O200		30 f. green	3·50	25
O201		40 f. violet	4·50	25
O202	**17**	50 f. brown	70	55
O203		75 f. blue	5·00	65
O204		100 f. green	1·40	85
O205		200 f. red	3·50	2·00
O206	–	½ d. blue (No. 188)	10·00	15·00
O207	–	1 d. red (No. 189)	38·00	45·00

1941. Issue of 1941 optd **ON STATE SERVICE** in English and Arabic.

O230	**19**	1 f. purple	20	15
O231		2 f. brown	20	15
O232	–	3 f. green (No. 210)	20	15
O233	–	4 f. violet (No. 211)	20	15
O234	–	5 f. red (No. 212)	20	15
O235	**21**	8 f. red	65	15
O236b		8 f. yellow	15	15
O237		10 f. yellow	4·25	35
O238		10 f. red	50	15
O239		15 f. blue	4·25	65
O240		15 f. black	85	25
O241		20 f. black	1·25	25
O242		20 f. blue	40	15
O244	**22**	25 f. purple	65	25
O246a		30 f. orange	35	25
O248a		40 f. brown	45	25
O249c	–	50 f. blue (No. 224)	75	50
O250	–	75 f. mauve (No. 225)	85	25
O251	–	100 f. olive (No. 226)	1·75	25
O252	–	200 f. orange (No. 227)	2·00	70
O253	–	½ d. blue (No. 228)	9·00	4·25
O254	–	1 d. green (No. 229)	14·00	7·50

1942. Issue of 1942 optd **ON STATE SERVICE** in English and Arabic.

O263	**26**	1 f. brown and violet	25	25
O264		2 f. brown and blue	25	25
O265		3 f. brown and green	25	25
O266		4 f. sepia and brown	35	25
O267		5 f. brown and green	35	35
O268		6 f. brown and red	35	35
O269		10 f. brown and pink	45	45
O270		12 f. brown and green	45	45

1948. Issue of 1948 optd **ON STATE SERVICE** in English and Arabic.

O298	**27**	1 f. blue	15	25
O299		2 f. brown	15	30
O300		3 f. green	15	30
O301		3 f. red	2·10	20
O302		4 f. lilac	15	25
O303		5 f. red	15	20
O304		5 f. green	2·50	20
O305		6 f. mauve	20	30
O306		8 f. brown	20	30
O307		10 f. red	20	25
O308		12 f. green	20	25
O309		14 f. green	90	25
O310		15 f. black	4·00	5·00
O311		16 f. red	2·00	30
O312		20 f. blue	20	15
O313		25 f. purple	20	15
O314		28 f. blue	65	30
O315		30 f. orange	20	20
O316		40 f. brown	45	35
O317		50 f. blue	50	30
O318		60 f. blue	45	20
O319		75 f. mauve	85	20
O320		100 f. green	85	85
O321		200 f. orange	1·40	85
O322		½ d. blue	11·50	12·00
O323		1 d. green	17·00	25·00

1955. Issue of 1954 optd **ON STATE SERVICE** in English and Arabic.

O364	**33**	1 f. blue	20	20
O365		2 f. brown	20	20
O366		3 f. lake	20	20
O367		4 f. violet	20	20
O368		5 f. green	20	20
O369		6 f. mauve	20	20
O370		8 f. brown	20	20
O371		10 f. blue	20	20
O372		16 f. red	17·00	20·00
O373		20 f. olive	35	25
O374		25 f. purple	1·75	85
O375		30 f. red	75	25
O376		40 f. brown	35	25
O377	–	50 f. blue	1·90	65
O378	–	60 f. purple	10·00	4·50
O379	–	100 f. olive	24·00	11·00

No. O378 does not exist without opt.

1958. Issue of 1957 optd **ON STATE SERVICE** in English and Arabic.

O404	**41**	1 f. blue	1·50	1·50
O405		2 f. brown	2·10	2·10
O406		3 f. red	2·10	2·10
O407		4 f. violet	1·50	1·50
O408		5 f. green	1·50	1·50
O409		6 f. red	1·50	1·50
O410		10 f. blue	1·50	1·50

1958. Official stamps optd with T **43**.

(a) Nos. O251/2.

O459		100 f. green		
O459a		200 f. orange	2·75	1·50

(b) Nos. O298 etc.

O460	**27**	1 f. blue	17·00	17·00
O461		2 f. brown	17·00	17·00
O462		3 f. green	17·00	17·00
O463		3 f. red	17·00	17·00
O464		4 f. lilac	17·00	17·00
O465		5 f. red	17·00	17·00
O466		5 f. green	17·00	17·00
O467		6 f. mauve	17·00	17·00
O468		8 f. brown	17·00	17·00
O470		12 f. green	50	45
O471		14 f. green	85	40
O472		15 f. black	85	45
O473		16 f. red	2·10	1·25
O474		25 f. purple	1·75	1·25
O475		28 f. blue	1·25	65
O476		40 f. brown	85	70
O477		60 f. blue	3·00	2·10
O478		75 f. mauve	1·25	1·50
O479		200 f. orange	2·10	1·50
O480		½ d. blue	6·75	5·00
O481		1 d. green	12·50	10·00

(c) Nos. O364 etc.

O482	**33**	1 f. blue	45	20
O483		2 f. brown	45	20
O484		3 f. red	45	20
O485		4 f. violet	45	20
O486		5 f. green	50	20
O487		6 f. mauve	45	20
O488		8 f. brown	45	20
O489		10 f. blue	45	20
O490		16 f. red	4·25	4·75
O491		20 f. green	45	20
O492		25 f. purple	45	25
O493		30 f. red	45	35
O494		40 f. brown	65	35
O495	–	50 f. blue	65	45
O496	–	60 f. purple	65	50
O497	–	100 f. green	1·25	50

(d) Nos. O404 etc.

O498	**41**	1 f. blue	20	20
O499		2 f. brown	20	20
O500		3 f. red	25	20
O501		4 f. violet	25	20
O502		5 f. green	25	20
O503		6 f. red	20	20
O504		8 f. brown	45	10
O505		10 f. blue	40	20

No. O504 does not exist without opt T **43**.

1961. Nos. 515, etc. optd **On State Service** in English and Arabic.

O552	**49**	1 f. multicoloured	15	10
O553		2 f. multicoloured	15	10
O554		4 f. multicoloured	15	10
O555		5 f. multicoloured	35	10
O556		10 f. multicoloured	40	10
O557		50 f. multicoloured	5·00	3·00

1962. Nos. 515, etc. optd **ON STATE SERVICE** in English and Arabic.

O587	**49**	1 f. multicoloured	10	10
O588		2 f. multicoloured	10	10
O589		3 f. multicoloured	10	10
O590		4 f. multicoloured	10	10
O591		5 f. multicoloured	10	10
O592		10 f. multicoloured	10	10
O593		15 f. multicoloured	15	10
O594		20 f. multicoloured	20	20
O595		30 f. multicoloured	25	20
O596		40 f. multicoloured	30	20
O597		50 f. multicoloured	30	20
O598		75 f. multicoloured	55	30
O599		100 f. multicoloured	85	60
O600		200 f. multicoloured	2·10	1·25
O601		500 f. multicoloured	5·50	4·25
O602		1 d. multicoloured	11·00	8·50

1971. Various stamps optd or surch **Official** in English and Arabic.

(a) Costumes. Nos. 768 and 770/4.

O962		15 f. multicoloured (postage)	1·25	40
O963		25 f. multicoloured	3·25	2·75
O964		30 f. multicoloured	3·25	2·75
O965		40 f. multicoloured (air)	2·10	85
O966		50 f. multicoloured	2·10	85
O967		80 f. multicoloured	3·50	1·75

(b) International Tourist Year. Nos. 778 and 780/2.

O969		5 f. multicoloured (postage)	1·90	30
O970		15 f. multicoloured	1·90	45
O971		25 f. multicoloured	1·90	90
O972		50 f. multicoloured (air)	2·10	1·10

(c) Birds. No. 798.

O1178		30 f. multicoloured	3·50	2·75

(d) 20th Anniv of W.H.O. Nos. 811/13.

O973	–	10 f. multicoloured	2·25	50
O974	**124**	15 f. red, blue & black	2·25	50
O975		25 f. red, green & black	2·25	50

(e) Human Rights Year. Nos. 814/15.

O976	**125**	10 f. red, yellow & blue	3·25	40
O977		25 f. red, yellow & green	3·25	70

(f) U.N.I.C.E.F. Nos. 817/18.

O978	**126**	15 f. multicoloured	3·25	35
O979		25 f. multicoloured	3·25	35

(g) Army Day. No. 820.

O980	**127**	25 f. multicoloured	7·50	2·75

(h) Fish and Fauna. Nos. 825/7, 829/30 and 832.

O981		10 f. mult (postage)	3·25	2·50
O982		15 f. on 3 f. multicoloured	3·25	2·50
O983		25 f. on 2 f. multicoloured	3·25	2·50
O984		10 f. multicoloured (air)	3·25	2·75
O985		15 f.+3 f. multicoloured	3·25	2·75
O986		25 f.+2 f. multicoloured	3·25	2·75

(i) Fruits. Nos. 906/9.

O987		5 f. multicoloured	3·25	2·75
O988		10 f. multicoloured	3·25	2·75
O989		15 f. multicoloured	3·25	2·75
O990		35 f. multicoloured	3·25	2·75

(j) Arab Football Cup, Baghdad. No. 717.

O991	**97**	2 f. multicoloured	3·25	2·75

(k) 50th Anniv of I.L.O. No. 836.

O992	**133**	15 f. yellow, grn & blk	3·25	2·75

1972. Nos. 625/8 optd **Official** in English and Arabic.

O1042		10 f. red	4·50	4·50
O1043		15 f. brown and yellow	4·50	4·50
O1044		20 f. violet	4·50	4·50
O1045		30 f. orange	4·50	4·50

1973. Various stamps with portrait obliterated by 3 bars. (i) 1948 issue.

O1081	**27**	25 f. pur (No. O313)	2·50	60
O1082		50 f. blue (No. O317)	2·50	2·25

(ii) 1955 issue.

O1083	**33**	25 f. pur (No. O374)	2·50	60
O1084	–	50 f. blue (No. O377)	2·50	2·75

(iii) Similar to 1958 issue (T **41**) but size $22\frac{1}{2} \times 27\frac{1}{2}$ mm.

O1085		50 f. purple	2·50	2·25

(O **218**) (size varies) (O **237a**)

1973. "Faisal" stamps with portrait obliterated. (a) Optd with 3 bars and Type O **218**.

O1086	**33**	10 f. blue	2·75	2·75
O1087	**41**	15 f. black	2·75	3·00

(b) Optd with Type O **218** only.

O1090	**33**	15 f. black	2·75	75
O1091	**41**	15 f. black	2·75	75
O1096	**27**	25 f. purple	11·00	11·50
O1092	**33**	25 f. purple	2·75	75
O1093	**41**	25 f. purple	2·75	75

1973. No. 1097 optd **Official** in English and Arabic.

O1099	**220**	25 f. multicoloured	35	15

1973. Nos. 1099/1107 optd **OFFICIAL** in English and Arabic.

O1108	**221**	5 f. black and orange	15	15
O1109		10 f. black and brown	15	10
O1110		20 f. black and mauve	25	15
O1111	–	25 f. black and blue	40	15
O1112	–	35 f. black and green	50	20
O1113	–	45 f. black and blue	50	30
O1114	–	50 f. yellow and green	80	30
O1115	–	70 f. yellow and violet	1·10	45
O1116	–	95 f. yellow and brown	1·75	90

1973. Various "Faisal" Official stamps optd **ON STATE SERVICE** in English and Arabic, with portrait obliterated by "leaf" motif similar to that used in Type O **218**. (a) 1948 issue.

O1130a	**27**	12 f. olive	3·50	80
O1131		14 f. olive	3·50	1·00
O1132		15 f. black	3·50	1·00
O1133		16 f. red	7·00	6·50
O1134		28 f. blue	3·50	1·00
O1134a		30 f. orange	3·50	1·60
O1134b		40 f. brown	3·50	1·60
O1135		60 f. blue	4·25	1·60
O1136		100 f. green	16·00	6·50
O1137		½ d. blue	35·00	14·00
O1138		1 d. green	55·00	23·00

(b) 1955 issue.

O1139	**33**	3 f. lake	3·50	80
O1140		6 f. mauve	4·25	1·40
O1141		8 f. brown	3·50	80
O1142		16 f. red	7·00	6·50
O1142a		20 f. green	3·50	80
O1142b		30 f. red	3·50	80
O1142c		40 f. brown	3·50	80
O1143	–	60 f. purple	6·25	2·00
O1144	–	100 f. green	14·00	3·25

(c) 1958 issue.

O1145	**41**	3 f. lake	3·50	80
O1146		6 f. mauve	3·50	80
O1147		8 f. brown	3·50	80
O1147a		30 f. red	3·50	80

1974. No. T1168 optd with Type O **237a**.

O1165	**235**	5 f. black, yell & brn	1·60	1·40

O **249** Eagle Emblem

O **342** Entrance to Baghdad University

1975.

O1195	O **249**	5 f. multicoloured	10	10
O1196		10 f. multicoloured	15	10
O1197		15 f. multicoloured	25	10
O1198		20 f. multicoloured	35	10
O1199		25 f. multicoloured	45	10
O1200		30 f. multicoloured	55	20
O1201		50 f. multicoloured	90	35
O1202		100 f. multicoloured	2·00	85

1976. Nos. 1253/7 additionally inscr "OFFICIAL" in English and Arabic.

O1258	**264**	5 f. multicoloured	80	65
O1259	–	10 f. multicoloured	85	70
O1260	–	15 f. multicoloured	90	75
O1261	–	25 f. multicoloured	2·50	1·10
O1262	–	50 f. multicoloured	3·50	2·00

1978. As T **290**, but additionally inscr "OFFICIAL" in English and Arabic.

O1338		5 f. multicoloured	15	10
O1339		10 f. multicoloured	15	15
O1340		15 f. multicoloured	25	15
O1341		25 f. multicoloured	45	15

1981.

O1499	O **342**	45 f. multicoloured	45	20
O1500		50 f. multicoloured	45	20

1982. As Nos. 1504/6, additionally inscr "OFFICIAL" in English and Arabic.

O1507		45 f. multicoloured	65	20
O1508		50 f. multicoloured	65	25
O1509		120 f. multicoloured	1·50	1·10

1983. Nos. O1499/1500 surch.

O1591	O **342**	60 f. on 45 f. mult	90	35
O1582		70 f. on 50 f. mult	1·25	50

1983. Design as T **371**.

O1615		60 f. yellow, black & pink	65	35
O1616		70 f. yellow, black & pink	75	45

DESIGN: Nos. O1615/16, Aerial view of building.

1984. Multicoloured.

O1642		20 f. Type **377**	15	15
O1643		30 f. Type **377**	30	15
O1644		50 f. As No. 1639	45	25
O1645		60 f. As No. 1639	55	40

O **400** Pres. Hussain

1986.

O1740	O **400**	30 f. multicoloured	50	10
O1741		50 f. multicoloured	75	20
O1742		100 f. multicoloured	1·40	45
O1743		150 f. multicoloured	2·00	75

Nos. O1740/3 are inscribed "POSTAGE".

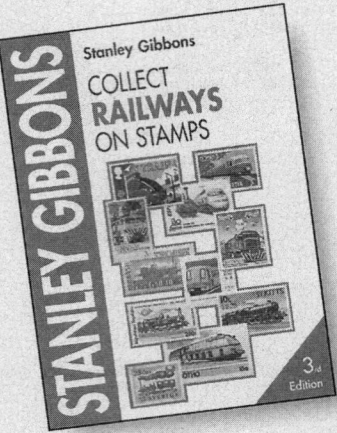

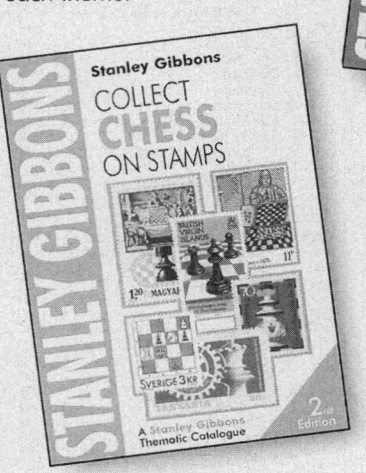

IRELAND (REPUBLIC) Pt. 1

Ireland (Eire) consisting of Ireland less the six counties of Ulster, became the Irish Free State in 1922 and left the British Empire in 1949 when it became an independent republic.

1949. 12 pence = 1 shilling. 20 shillings = 1 pound.
1971. 100 (new) pence = 1 pound (Punt).

Rialtas Sealadach na hÉireann 1922 — Rialtas Sealadach na hÉireann 1922.

(1) "Provisional Government (2) of Ireland, 1922"

1922. Optd with T **1** (date in thin figures and no full point).

1	**105**	½d. green	1·00	40
2	**104**	1d. red	1·50	35
4a		2½d. blue	1·00	3·50
5	**106**	3d. violet	4·25	3·75
6		4d. green	3·50	10·00
7	**107**	5d. brown	4·00	8·50
8	**108**	9d. brown	11·00	21·00
9		10d. blue	8·50	40·00
17	**109**	2s. 6d. brown	35·00	65·00
19		5s. red	60·00	£120
21		10s. blue	£120	£250

On Nos. 17, 19 and 21 the overprint is in four lines instead of five.

1922. Optd with T **2** (date in thick figures followed by full point).

30	**105**	½d. green	2·00	80
31	**104**	1d. red	1·50	50
10	**105**	1½d. brown	1·40	85
12	**106**	2d. orange	2·50	50
35	**104**	2½d. blue	6·00	18·00
36	**106**	3d. violet	2·50	2·00
37		4d. green	3·25	5·00
38	**107**	5d. brown	4·25	9·00
39		6d. purple	8·00	3·25
40	**108**	9d. black	12·00	15·00
41		9d. green	4·75	32·00
42		10d. blue	26·00	50·00
43		1s. brown	8·50	12·00

Saorstát Éireann 1922

(**5** "Irish Free State, 1922")

1922. Optd with T **5**.

52	**105**	½d. green	1·25	30
53	**104**	1d. red	75	40
54	**105**	1½d. brown	3·50	8·50
55	**106**	2d. orange	1·25	1·00
56	**104**	2½d. blue	6·50	8·00
57	**106**	3d. violet	3·50	11·00
58		4d. green	3·25	6·50
59	**107**	5d. brown	3·50	4·75
60		6d. purple	2·00	2·00
61	**108**	9d. green	3·00	5·50
62		10d. blue	16·00	50·00
63		1s. brown	7·00	11·00
86	**109**	2s. 6d. brown	40·00	42·00
87		5s. red	60·00	80·00
88		10s. blue	£150	£170

6 "Sword of Light"

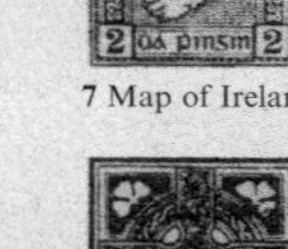
7 Map of Ireland

8 Arms of Ireland

9 Celtic Cross

1922.

71	**6**	½d. green	90	90
112	**7**	1d. red	30	10
73		1½d. purple	1·60	2·00
114		2d. green	30	10
75	**8**	2½d. brown	4·00	3·75
116	**9**	3d. blue (18½ × 22½ mm)	60	10
227		3d. blue (17 × 21 mm)	40	15
117	**8**	4d. blue	55	10
118	**6**	5d. violet (18½ × 22½ mm)	65	10
228		5d. violet (17 × 21 mm)	30	15
119b		6d. purple	1·25	20
119c		8d. red	80	80
120	**8**	9d. violet	1·50	80
121	**9**	10d. brown	60	80
121b		11d. red	1·50	2·25
82	**6**	1s. blue	17·00	5·50

12 Daniel O'Connell

13 Shannon Barrage

1929. Centenary of Catholic Emancipation.

89	**12**	2d. green	50	45
90		3d. blue	4·00	8·50
91		9d. violet	4·00	4·00

1930. Completion of Shannon Hydro-Electric Scheme.

92	**13**	2d. deep brown	80	55

14 Reaper

15 The Cross of Cong

1931. Bicentenary of Royal Dublin Society.

93	**14**	2d. blue	65	30

1932. International Eucharistic Congress.

94	**15**	2d. green	1·00	30
95		3d. blue	2·25	5·00

16 Adoration of the Cross

17 Hurler

1933. "Holy Year".

96	**16**	2d. green	1·25	15
97		3d. blue	2·50	2·00

1934. 50th Anniv of Gaelic Athletic Assn.

98	**17**	2d. green	75	55

18 St. Patrick

19 Ireland and New Constitution

1937.

123a	**18**	2s. 6d. green	1·50	2·25
124ca		5s. purple	6·00	7·50
125ba		10s. blue	7·00	16·00

1937. Constitution Day.

105	**19**	2d. red	1·00	20
106		3d. blue	4·00	3·75

For similar stamps see Nos. 176/7.

20 Father Mathew

1938. Centenary of Temperance Crusade.

107	**20**	2d. brown	1·50	30
108		3d. blue	8·50	6·00

21 George Washington, American Eagle and Irish Harp

1939. 150th Anniv of U.S. Constitution and Installation of First U.S. President.

109	**21**	2d. red	1·75	65
110		3d. blue	3·25	4·25

24 Volunteer and G.P.O., Dublin

1941. 25th Anniv of Easter Rising (1916). (a) Provisional issue. Optd with two lines of Irish characters between the dates "1941" and "1916".

126	**7**	2d. orange	1·00	50
127	**9**	3d. blue	24·00	9·50

(b) Definitive Issue.

128	**24**	2½d. blue	70	60

25 Dr. Douglas Hyde

26 Sir William Rowan Hamilton

1943. 50th Anniv of Gaelic League.

129	**25**	½d. green	40	30
130		2½d. purple	1·25	10

1943. Centenary of Announcement of Discovery of Quaternions.

131	**26**	½d. green	40	40
132		2½d. brown	1·75	10

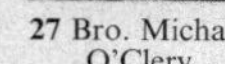
27 Bro. Michael O'Clery

28 Edmund Ignatius Rice

1944. Death Tercentenary of Michael O'Clery (Franciscan historian) (commemorating the "Annals of the Four Masters").

133	**27**	½d. green	10	10
134		1s. brown	70	10

1944. Death Centenary of Edmund Rice (founder of Irish Christian Brothers).

135	**28**	2½d. slate	60	45

29 "Youth sowing Seeds of Freedom"

30 "Country and Homestead"

1945. Death Centenary of Thomas Davis (founder of Young Ireland Movement).

136	**29**	2½d. blue	1·00	25
137		6d. purple	6·00	3·75

1946. Birth Centenaries of Michael Davitt and Charles Parnell (land reformers).

138	**30**	2½d. red	1·50	20
139		3d. blue	2·75	3·50

31 Angel Victor over Rock of Cashel

1948. Air. Inscr "VOX HIBERNIAE".

140	**31**	1d. brown	1·50	3·50
141	–	3d. blue	3·00	2·25
142	–	6d. purple	80	1·50
142b	–	8d. lake	6·00	7·00
143	–	1s. green	80	1·50
143a	**31**	1s. 3d. orange	7·00	1·25
143b		1s. 5d. blue	2·75	1·00

DESIGNS: 3d., 8d. Angel Victor over Lough Derg; 6d. Over Croagh Patrick; 1s. Over Glendalough.

35 Theobald Wolfe Tone

1948. 150th Anniv of Insurrection.

144	**35**	2½d. purple	1·00	10
145		3d. violet	3·25	3·25

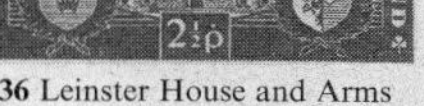
36 Leinster House and Arms of Provinces

37 J. C. Mangan

1949. International Recognition of Republic.

146	**36**	2½d. brown	1·50	10
147		3d. blue	5·50	4·25

1949. Death Centenary of James Clarence Mangan (poet).

148	**37**	1d. green	1·50	20

38 Statue of St. Peter, Rome

39 Thomas Moore

1950. Holy Year.

149	**38**	2½d. violet	1·00	40
150		3d. blue	8·00	8·50
151		9d. brown	8·00	10·00

1952. Death Centenary of Thomas Moore (poet).

152	**39**	2½d. purple	50	10
153		3½d. olive	1·75	2·75

40 Irish Harp

1953. "An Tostal" (Ireland at Home) Festival.

154	**40**	2½d. green	1·75	35
155		1s. 4d. blue	15·00	24·00

41 Robert Emmet

42 Madonna and Child (Della Robbia)

1953. 150th Death Anniv of Emmet (patriot).

156	**41**	3d. green	3·75	15
157		1s. 3d. red	42·00	9·50

1954. Marian Year.

158	**42**	3d. blue	1·50	10
159		5d. green	2·75	5·50

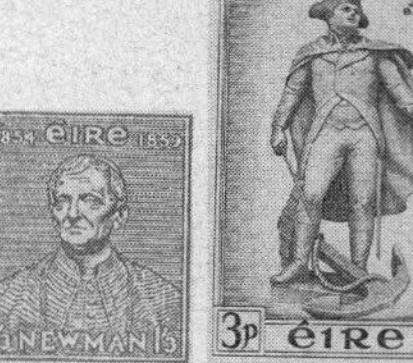
43 Cardinal Newman (first Rector)

44 Statue of Commodore Barry

45 John Redmond

1954. Centenary of Founding of Catholic University of Ireland.

160	**43**	2d. purple	1·50	10
161		1s. 3d. blue	16·00	6·00

1956. Barry Commemoration.

162	**44**	3d. lilac	1·50	10
163		1s. 3d. blue	5·50	9·00

1957. Birth Centenary of John Redmond (politician).

164	**45**	3d. blue	1·00	10
165		1s. 3d. purple	8·00	15·00

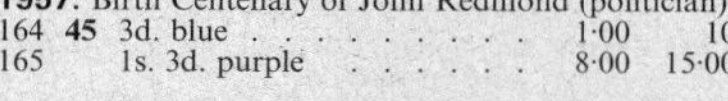

46 Thomas O'Crohan

47 Admiral Brown

48 "Father Wadding" (Ribera)

1957. Birth Cent of Thomas O'Crohan (author).

166	**46**	2d. purple	1·50	15
167		5d. violet	1·50	5·50

1957. Death Cent of Admiral William Brown.

168	**47**	3d. blue	2·25	20
169		1s. 3d. red	30·00	16·00

1957. Death Tercentenary of Father Luke Wadding (theologian).

170	**48**	3d. blue	2·00	10
171		1s. 3d. lake	15·00	8·50

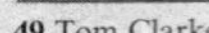

49 Tom Clarke

50 Mother Mary Aikenhead

1958. Birth Centenary of Thomas J. ("Tom") Clarke (patriot).

172 **49** 3d. green . . . . 2·50 10
173 1s. 3d. brown . . . . . . 5·00 13·00

1958. Death Centenary of Mother Mary Aikenhead (foundress of Irish Sisters of Charity).

174 **50** 3d. blue . . . . 1·75 10
175 1s. 3d. red . . . . 15·00 10·00

1958. 21st Anniv of Irish Constitution.

176 **19** 3d. brown . . . . 1·25 10
177 5d. green . . . . 2·25 4·50

51 Arthur Guinness

52 "The Flight of the Holy Family"

1959. Bicentenary of Guinness Brewery.

178 **51** 3d. purple . . . . 3·00 10
179 1s. 3d. blue . . . . . . 11·00 12·00

1960. World Refugee Year.

180 **52** 3d. purple 50 10
181 1s. 3d. sepia . . . . . . 75 3·25

53 Conference Emblem

1960. 1st Anniv of Europa.

182 **53** 6d. brown . . . . 4·00 3·00
183 1s. 3d. violet . . . . . . 10·00 20·00

54 Dublin Airport, De Havilland Dragon Mk 2 "Iolar" and Boeing 720

55 St Patrick

1961. Silver Jubilee of Aer Lingus Airlines.

184 **54** 6d. blue . . . . 1·00 3·25
185 1s. 3d. green . . . . . . 1·50 4·75

1961. 15th Death Centenary of St. Patrick.

186 **55** 3d. blue . . . . 1·00 10
187 8d. purple . . . . 2·00 5·50
188 1s. 3d. green . . . . . . 2·00 1·60

56 John O'Donovan and Edugen O'Curry

1962. Death Centenaries of O'Donovan and O'Curry (scholars).

189 **56** 3d. red 30 10
190 1s. 3d. purple . . . . . . 1·25 2·25

57 Europa "Tree"

1962. Europa.

191 **57** 6d. red . . . . 50 1·00
192 1s. 3d. turquoise . . . . . 90 1·50

58 Campaign Emblem

1963. Freedom from Hunger.

193 **58** 4d. violet 50 10
194 1s. 3d. red . . . . 1·75 2·75

59 "Co-operation"

1963. Europa.

195 **59** 6d. red 75 75
196 1s. 3d. blue . . . . 2·00 3·75

60 Centenary Emblem

1963. Centenary of Red Cross.

197 **60** 4d. red and grey 50 10
198 1s. 3d. red, grey & green . . 1·25 2·25

61 Wolfe Tone

1964. Birth Bicentenary of Wolfe Tone (revolutionary).

199 **61** 4d. black 90 10
200 1s. 3d. blue . . . . 1·90 2·25

62 Irish Pavilion at Fair

63 Europa "Flower"

1964. New York World's Fair.

201 **62** 5d. multicoloured 50 10
202 1s. 5d. multicoloured . . . 2·25 3·75

1964. Europa.

203 **63** 8d. green and blue . . . . 1·00 1·25
204 1s. 5d. brown and orange . . 3·00 2·75

64 "Waves of Communications"

65 W. B. Yeats (poet)

1965. Centenary of I.T.U.

205 **64** 3d. blue and green 40 10
206 8d. black and green . . . . 1·40 2·00

1965. Birth Centenary of Yeats.

207 **65** 5d. black, brown and green . 30 10
208 1s. 5d. black, grn & brn . . 2·25 1·75

66 I.C.Y. Emblem

1965. International Co-operation Year.

209 **66** 3d. blue 60 10
210 10d. brown . . . . 1·00 3·00

67 Europa "Sprig"

1965. Europa.

211 **67** 8d. black and red . . . . . 1·00 1·00
212 1s. 5d. purple & turquoise . 3·25 3·50

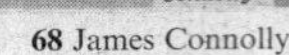

68 James Connolly

76 Roger Casement

1966. 50th Anniv of Easter Rising.

213 **68** 3d. black and blue 35 10
214 – 3d. black and bronze . . . 35 10
215 – 5d. black and olive 35 10
216 – 5d. black, orange & green . 35 10
217 – 7d. black and brown . . . . 40 2·25
218 – 7d. black and green . . . . 40 2·25
219 – 1s. 5d. black & turquoise . . 40 1·50
220 – 1s. 5d. black and green . . . 40 1·50

DESIGNS: No. 214, Thomas J. Clarke; No. 215, P. H. Pearse; No. 216, "Marching to Freedom"; No. 217, Eamonn Ceannt; No. 218, Sean MacDiarmada; No. 219, Thomas MacDonagh; No. 220, Joseph Plunkett.

1966. 50th Death Anniv of Roger Casement (patriot).

221 **76** 5d. black 15 10
222 1s. brown 30 50

77 Europa "Ship"

78 Interior of Abbey (from lithograph)

1966. Europa.

223 **77** 7d. green and orange . . . 35 40
224 1s. 5d. green and grey . . . 90 1·00

1966. 750th Anniv of Ballintubber Abbey.

225 **78** 5d. brown 10 10
226 1s. black 20 25

79 Cogwheels

80 Maple Leaves

1967. Europa.

229 **79** 7d. green, gold & cream . . 30 40
230 1s. 5d. red, gold & cream . . 70 1·00

1967. Canadian Centennial.

231 **80** 5d. multicoloured 10 10
232 1s. 5d. multicoloured . . . 20 75

81 Rock of Cashel (from photo by Edwin Smith)

1967. International Tourist Year.

233 **81** 7d. sepia 15 20
234 10d. blue 15 40

82 1 c. Fenian Stamp Essay

84 Jonathan Swift

1967. Centenary of Fenian Rising.

235 **82** 5d. black and green 10 10
236 – 1s. black and pink 20 30

DESIGN: 1s. 24 c. Fenian Stamp Essay.

1967. 300th Birth Anniv of Jonathan Swift.

237 **84** 3d. black and grey 10 10
238 – 1s. 5d. brown and blue . . . 20 30

DESIGN: 1s. 5d. Gulliver and Lilliputians.

86 Europa Key

1968. Europa.

239 **86** 7d. red, gold and brown . . 25 50
240 1s. 5d. blue, gold & brown . 40 1·00

87 St Mary's Cathedral, Limerick

1968. 800th Anniv of St. Mary's Cathedral, Limerick.

241 **87** 5d. blue 10 10
242 10d. green 20 60

88 Countess Markievicz

89 James Connolly

1968. Birth Centenary of Countess Markievicz (patriot).

243 **88** 3d. black 10 10
244 1s. 5d. indigo and blue . . . 20 20

1968. Birth Centenary of James Connolly (patriot).

245 **89** 6d. brown & chocolate . . . 15 50
246 1s. grn, lt grn & myrtle . . . 15 10

90 Stylised Dog (brooch)

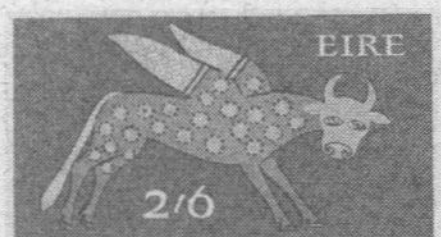

92 Winged Ox (Symbol of St Luke)

1968.

247 **90** ½d. orange 10 30
248 1d. green 15 10
249 2d. ochre 50 10
250 3d. blue 35 10
251 4d. red 30 10
252 5d. green 40 35
253 6d. brown 30 10
254 – 7d. brown and yellow . . . 45 3·50
255 – 8d. brown and chestnut . . 45 1·25
256 – 9d. blue and green 50 10
257 – 10d. brown and violet . . . 1·50 1·50
258 – 1s. chocolate and brown . . 40 10
259 – 1s. 9d. black & turquoise . . 4·00 1·50
260 **92** 2s. 6d. multicoloured . . . 1·75 30
261 5s. multicoloured . . . . 3·00 1·50
262 – 10s. multicoloured . . . . 4·50 3·75

DESIGNS—As Type **90**: 7d., 8d., 9d., 10d., 1s., 1s. 9d., Stag. As Type **92**: 10s Eagle (Symbol of St. John The Evangelist).

See also Nos. 287, etc.

94 Human Rights Emblem

95 Dail Eireann Assembly

1968. Human Rights Year.

263 **94** 5d. yellow, gold & black . . 15 10
264 7d. yellow, gold and red . . 15 40

1969. 50th Anniv of Dail Eireann (1st National Parliament).

265 **95** 6d. green 15 10
266 9d. blue 15 30

96 Colonnade

97 Quadruple I.L.O. Emblems

1969. Europa.

267 **96** 9d. grey, ochre and blue . . 40 1·10

268 1s. 9d. grey, gold and red . . 70 1·40

1969. 50th Anniv of I.L.O.

269 **97** 6d. black and grey 20 10

270 9d. black and yellow 20 25

98 "The Last Supper and Crucifixion" (Evie Hone Window, Eton Chapel)

1969. Contemporary Irish Art (1st issue).

271 **98** 1s. multicoloured . . . . 30 1·50

See also Nos. 280, 306, 317, 329, 362, 375, 398, 408, 452, 470 and 498.

99 Mahatma Gandhi

1969. Birth Centenary of Mahatma Gandhi.

272 **99** 6d. black and green 20 10

273 1s. 9d. black and yellow . . 30 90

100 Symbolic Bird in Tree

1970. European Conservation Year.

274 **100** 6d. bistre and black . . . 20 10

275 9d. violet and black . . . 25 80

101 "Flaming Sun"

1970. Europa.

276 **101** 6d. violet and silver . . . 30 10

277 9d. brown and silver . . . 45 1·25

278 1s. 9d. grey and silver . . . 65 2·00

102 "Sailing Boats" (Peter Monamy)

103 "Madonna of Eire" (Mainie Jellett)

1970. 250th Anniv of Royal Cork Yacht Club.

279 **102** 4d. multicoloured 15 10

1970. Contemporary Irish Art (2nd issue).

280 **103** 1s. multicoloured 15 20

104 Thomas MacCurtain

106 Kevin Barry

1970. 50th Death Annivs. of Irish Patriots.

281 **104** 9d. black, violet & grey . . 50 25

282 – 9d. black, violet & grey . . 50 25

283 **104** 2s. 9d. black, blue & grey . 1·40 1·50

284 – 2s. 9d. black, blue & grey . 1·40 1·50

DESIGN: Nos. 282 and 284, Terence MacSwiney.

1970. 50th Death Anniv of Kevin Barry (patriot).

285 **106** 6d. green 30 10

286 1s. 2d. blue . . . . 40 1·10

1971. Decimal Currency. As Nos. 247/62 but with face values in new currency, without "p", and some colours changed.

287 **90** ½p. green 10 10

340 1p. blue 10 10

289 1½p. brown 15 15

341 2p. green 10 10

291 2½p. brown 15 10

342 3p. brown 10 10

293 3½p. brown 15 10

294 4p. violet 15 10

295 – 5p. brown and olive . . . 70 20

344 **90** 5p. green 60 10

296 – 6p. grey and brown . . . 3·50 30

346 **90** 6p. grey 20 10

347 – 7p. blue and green 90 35

348 **90** 7p. green 35 10

297 – 7½p. mauve and brown . . . 50 85

349 – 8p. brown & dp brown . . 75 50

350 **90** 8p. brown 30 10

351 – 9p. black and green . . . 90 30

352 **90** 9p. green 30 10

352a 9½p. red 35 20

353 **92** 10p. multicoloured . . . . 1·50 30

354 – 10p. black and lilac . . . 85 10

354a **90** 10p. mauve 70 10

355 – 11p. black and red . . . 45 30

299b **92** 12p. multicoloured 60 80

355a – 12p. black and green . . . 55 10

355b **90** 12p. green 30 10

355c – 13p. brown . . . . 40 1·25

356 **92** 15p. multicoloured 55 40

356a **90** 15p. blue 40 10

356b – 16p. black and green . . . 40 80

356c **92** 17p. multicoloured 50 50

478 **90** 18p. red 45 50

479 19p. blue . . . . 55 1·75

357 **92** 20p. multicoloured 50 15

480 **90** 22p. blue 65 10

481 24p. brown 75 95

482 26p. green . . . . 1·50 40

483 29p. mauve . . . . 1·75 2·00

358 – 50p. multicoloured 70 30

359 – £1 multicoloured . . . . 1·25 30

DESIGNS—As Type **90**: 5p. (295); 6p. (296); 7p. (347); 7½p., 8p., 9p. (351) 10p. (354), 11p., 12p. (No. 355a), 13p., 16p. Stag. As Type **92**: 50p., £1, Eagle (symbol of St. John the Evangelist).

107 "Europa Chain"

108 J. M. Synge

1971. Europa.

302 **107** 4p. brown and green . . . 50 10

303 6p. black and blue . . . . 1·75 2·25

1971. Birth Cent. of J. M. Synge (playwright).

304 **108** 4p. multicoloured 15 10

305 10p. multicoloured 60 80

109 "An Island Man" (Jack B. Yeats)

110 Racial Harmony Symbol

1971. Contemporary Irish Art (3rd issue). Birth Centenary of J. B. Yeats (artist).

306 **109** 6p. multicoloured 55 55

1971. Racial Equality Year.

307 **110** 4p. red 20 10

308 10p. black 50 75

111 "Madonna and Child" (statue by J. Hughes)

112 Heart

1971. Christmas.

309 **111** 2½p. black, gold & green . . 10 10

310 6p. black, gold and blue . . 55 65

1972. World Health Day.

311 **112** 2½ p. gold and brown . . . 30 15

312 12 p. silver and grey . . . 1·10 1·75

113 "Communications"

114 Dove and Moon

1972. Europa.

313 **113** 4p. orange, blk & silver . . 1·25 25

314 6p. blue, black & silver . . 3·25 4·75

1972. Patriot Dead 1922–23.

315 **114** 4p. multicoloured 10 10

316 6p. yellow, green & dp grn . 45 40

115 "Black Lake" (Gerard Dillon)

116 "Horseman" (Carved Slab)

1972. Contemporary Irish Art (4th issue).

317 **115** 3p. multicoloured 50 35

1972. 50th Anniv of Olympic Council of Ireland.

318 **116** 3p. yellow, black and gold . 15 10

319 6p. pink, black & gold . . 55 60

117 Madonna and Child (from Book of Kells)

118 2d. Stamp of 1922

1972. Christmas.

320 **117** 2½p. multicoloured 10 10

321 4p. multicoloured 20 10

322 12p. multicoloured 55 65

1972. 50th Anniv of 1st Irish Postage Stamp.

323 **118** 6p. grey and green 30 60

119 Celtic Head Motif

1973. Entry into European Communities.

325 **119** 6p. multicoloured 40 90

326 12p. multicoloured . . . . 60 1·10

120 Europa "Posthorn"

1973. Europa.

327 **120** 4p. blue 50 10

328 6p. black . . . . 1·25 2·00

121 "Berlin Blues II" (W. Scott)

1973. Contemporary Irish Art (5th issue).

329 **121** 5p. blue and black 40 30

122 Weather Map

123 Tractor ploughing

1973. Centenary of I.M.O./W.M.O.

330 **122** 3½p. multicoloured 30 10

331 12p. multicoloured . . . . 80 2·00

1973. World Ploughing Championships, Wellington Bridge.

332 **123** 5p. multicoloured 15 10

333 7p. multicoloured 75 50

124 "Flight into Egypt" (Jan de Cock)

125 Daunt Island Lightship and "Mary Stanford" (Ballycotton Lifeboat), 1936

1973. Christmas.

334 **124** 3½p. multicoloured 15 10

335 12p. multicoloured . . . . 1·10 1·50

1974. 150th Anniv of R.N.L.I.

336 **125** 5p. multicoloured 30 30

126 "Edmund Burke" (statue by J. H. Foley)

127 "Oliver Goldsmith" (Statue by J. H. Foley)

1974. Europa.

337 **126** 5p. black and blue 50 10

338 7p. black and green . . . 2·25 2·50

1974. Death Bicentenary of Oliver Goldsmith (writer).

360 **127** 3½p. black and yellow . . . 15 10

361 12p. black and green . . . 60 1·00

128 "Kitchen Table" (Norah McGuiness)

129 Rugby Players

1974. Contemporary Irish Art (6th issue).

362 **128** 5p. multicoloured 35 30

1974. Centenary of Irish Rugby Football.

363 **129** 3½p. green 30 10

364 12p. multicoloured . . . . 1·75 2·75

130 U.P.U. "Postmark"

131 "Madonna and Child" (Bellini)

1974. Centenary of Universal Postal Union.

365 **130** 5p. green and black . . . 25 10

366 7p. blue and black 35 80

1974. Christmas.

367 **131** 5p. multicoloured 15 10

368 15p. multicoloured 60 90

132 "Peace"

1975. International Women's Year.
369 132 8p. purple and blue 25 75
370 15p. blue and green . . . 50 1·25

133 "Castletown Hunt" (R. Healy)

1975. Europa.
371 133 7p. grey 75 15
372 9p. green . . . . 1·25 2·50

134 Putting

1975. Ninth European Amateur Golf Team Championship, Killarney.
373 134 6p. multicoloured 75 45
374 – 9p. multicoloured . . . . 1·50 1·50
No. 374 is similar to Type 134 but shows a different view of the putting green.

135 "Bird of Prey" (sculpture by Oisin Kelly)

1975. Contemporary Irish Art (7th issue).
375 135 15p. brown 65 75

136 Nano Nagle (founder) and Waifs

137 Tower of St. Anne's Church, Shandon

1975. Bicentenary of Presentation Order of Nuns.
376 136 5p. black and blue 20 10
377 7p. black and brown . . . 30 30

1975. European Architectural Heritage Year.
378 137 5p. brown 20 10
379 6p. multicoloured 40 85
380 – 7p. blue 40 10
381 – 9p. multicoloured 45 80
DESIGN: Nos. 380/1, Interior of Holycross Abbey, Co. Tipperary.

138 St. Oliver Plunkett (commemorative medal by Imogen Stuart)
139 "Madonna and Child" (Fra Filippo Lippi)

1975. Canonisation of Oliver Plunkett.
382 138 7p. black 15 10
383 15p. brown 55 45

1975. Christmas.
384 139 5p. multicoloured 15 10
385 7p. multicoloured 15 10
386 10p. multicoloured 45 30

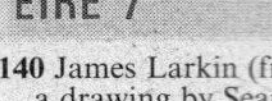

140 James Larkin (from a drawing by Sean O'Sullivan)
141 Alexander Graham Bell

1975. Birth Centenary of James Larkin (Trade Union Leader).
387 140 7p. green and grey 20 10
388 11p. brown and yellow . . 40 55

1976. Centenary of Telephone.
389 141 9p. multicoloured 20 10
390 15p. multicoloured 45 50

142 1847 Benjamin Franklin Essay

1976. Bicentenary of American Revolution.
391 – 7p. blue, red and silver . . 15 10
392 – 8p. blue, red and silver . . 20 1·10
393 142 9p. blue, orange & silver . 20 10
394 15p. red, grey and silver . . 30 75
DESIGNS: 7p. Thirteen Stars; 8p. Fifty Stars.

143 Spirit Barrel

1976. Europa. Irish Delft. Multicoloured.
396 9p. Type 143 . . . . 40 20
397 11p. Dish . . . . 70 1·60

144 "The Lobster Pots, West of Ireland" (Paul Henry)

1976. Contemporary Irish Art (8th issue).
398 144 15p. multicoloured 60 60

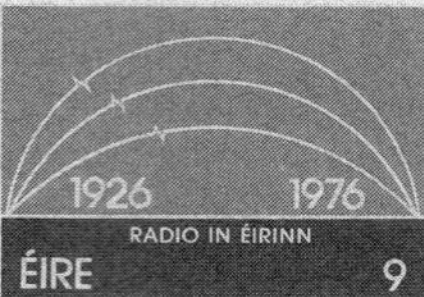

145 Radio Waves

1976. 50th Anniv of Irish Broadcasting Service.
399 145 9 p. blue and green 20 10
400 – 11p. brown, red & blue . . 60 1·00
DESIGN—VERT: 11p. Transmitter, radio waves and globe.

146 "The Nativity" (Lorenzo Monaco)

1976. Christmas.
401 146 7p. multicoloured 15 10
402 9p. multicoloured 15 10
403 15p. multicoloured 55 55

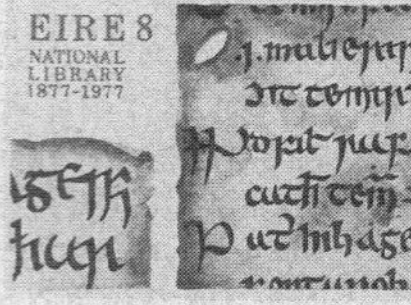

147 16th Century Manuscript

1977. Centenaries of National Library (8p.) and National Museum (10p.) Multicoloured.
404 8p. Type 147 . . . . 30 30
405 10p. Prehistoric stone 40 35

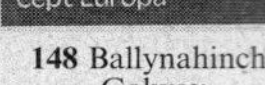

148 Ballynahinch, Galway
149 "Head" (Louis le Brocquy)

1977. Europa. Multicoloured.
406 10p. Type 148 . . . . 30 25
407 12p. Lough Tay, Wicklow . . . 90 1·50

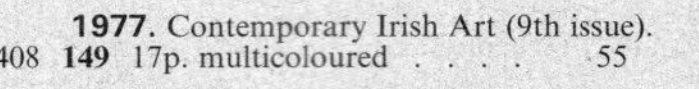
1977. Contemporary Irish Art (9th issue).
408 149 17p. multicoloured 55 75

150 Guide and Tents

1977. Scouting and Guiding. Multicoloured.
409 8p. Type 150 . . . . 35 10
410 17p. Tent and Scout saluting . . 75 1·75

151 "The Shanachie" (drawing by Jack B. Yeats)

1977. Anniversaries.
411 151 10p. black 25 15
412 – 12p. black . . . . 35 1·00
DESIGNS AND EVENTS: 10p. Type 151 (Golden Jubilee of Irish Folklore Society); 12p. The philosopher Eriugena (1100th death anniv).

152 "Electricity" (Golden Jubilee of Electricity Supply Board)

1977. Golden Jubilees.
413 152 10p. multicoloured 15 10
414 – 12p. multicoloured . . . . 30 1·40
415 – 17p. black and brown . . . 40 35
DESIGNS: 12p. Bulls (from Irish coins) (Agricultural Credit Act); 17p. Greyhound (Greyhound Track Racing).

153 "The Holy Family" (Giorgione)
154 Junkers W.33 "Bremen" in Flight

1977. Christmas.
416 153 8p. multicoloured 15 10
417 10p. multicoloured 15 10
418 17p. multicoloured . . . . 55 1·25

1978. 50th Anniv of 1st East–West Transatlantic Flight.
419 154 10p. black and blue . . . 20 15
420 17p. black and brown . . . 35 1·10

155 Spring Gentian
156 Catherine McAuley

1978. Wild Flowers. Multicoloured.
421 8p. Type 155 . . . . 20 40
422 10p. Strawberry tree 25 15
423 11p. Large-flowered Butterwort . 30 50
424 17p. St. Dabeoc's Heath . . . . 40 2·00

1978. Anniversaries and Events. Multicoloured.
425 10p. Type 156 (founder of Sisters of Mercy) (birth bicent) . . . 20 10
426 11p. Doctor performing vaccination (Global Eradication of Smallpox) (horiz) 30 80
427 17p. "Self-portrait" (Sir William Orpen (painter) (birth cent) . 40 1·10

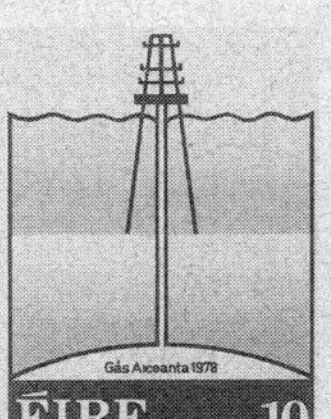

157 Diagram of Drilling Rig
159 "Virgin and Child" (Guercino)

158 Farthing

1978. Arrival Onshore of Natural Gas.
428 157 10p. multicoloured 30 30

1978. 50th Anniv of Irish Currency.
429 158 8p. black, copper & green . 20 20
430 – 10p. black, silver & green . . 25 10
431 – 11p. black, copper & brn . 25 50
432 – 17p. black, silver & blue . . 40 1·00
DESIGNS: 10p. Florin; 11p. Penny; 17p. Half-crown.

1978. Christmas.
433 159 8p. brown, blue and gold . 15 10
434 10p. brown, blue & purple . 15 10
435 17p. brown, blue & grn . . 45 1·40

160 Conolly Folly, Castletown

1978. Europa.
436 160 10p. brown 30 15
437 – 11p. green . . . . 30 1·00
DESIGN: 11p. Dromoland Belvedere.

161 Athletes in Cross-country Race

1979. 7th World Cross-country Championships, Limerick. Multicoloured
438 161 8p. multicoloured 20 30

MINIMUM PRICE

The minimum price quoted is 10p which represents a handling charge rather than a basis for valuing common stamps. For further notes about prices see introductory pages.

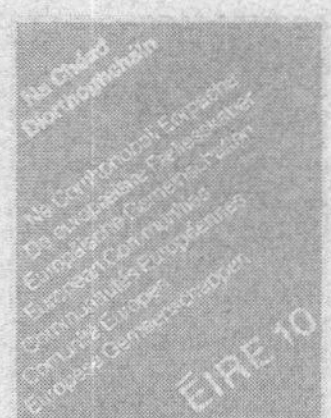

162 "European Communities" (in languages of member nations)
163 Sir Rowland Hill

1979. 1st Direct Elections to European Assembly.
439 **162** 10p. green 15 15
440 11p. violet 15 35

1979. Death Centenary of Sir Rowland Hill.
441 **163** 17p. black, grey and red . . 30 60

164 Winter Wren

1979. Birds. Multicoloured.
442 8p. Type **164** 40 70
443 10p. Great Crested Grebe . . . 40 15
444 11p. White-fronted Goose . . . 45 70
445 17p. Peregrine Falcon . . . . . 70 2·00

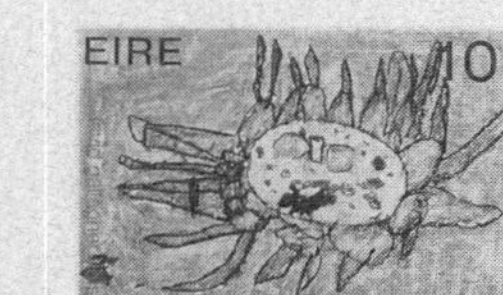

165 "A Happy Flower" (David Gallagher)

1979. International Year of the Child. Paintings by Children. Multicoloured.
446 10p. Type **165** 20 10
447 11p. "Myself and My Skipping Rope" (Lucy Norman) (vert) . 25 60
448 17p. "Swans on a Lake" (Nicola O'Dwyer) 35 85

166 Pope John Paul II

1979. Visit of Pope John Paul II.
449 **166** 12p. multicoloured 30 20

167 Brother with Child

1979. Anniversaries and Events.
450 **167** 9½p. brown and mauve . . 20 10
451 – 11p. orange, black & blue . 20 70
452 – 20p. multicoloured . . . . 40 1·40
DESIGNS—VERT: 11p. Windmill and sun (Int Energy Conservation Month). HORIZ: 9½p. Type **167** (Cent of Hospitaller Order of St. John of God in Ireland); 20p. "Seated Figure" (sculpture F. E. McWilliam) (Contemporary Irish Art (10th issue)).

168 Patrick Pearse, "Liberty" and G.P.O., Dublin
169 "Madonna and Child" (panel painting from the Domnach Airgid Shrine)

1979. Birth Centenary of Patrick Pearse (patriot).
453 **168** 12p. multicoloured 30 15

1979. Christmas.
454 **169** 9½p. multicoloured 15 10
455 20p. multicoloured 30 55

170 Bianconi Long Car, 1836

1979. Europa. Multicoloured.
456 12p. Type **170** 20 30
457 13p. Transatlantic cable, Valentia, 1866 . . . . 30 1·40

171 John Baptist de la Salle (founder)
172 George Bernard Shaw

1980. Cent of Arrival of De La Salle Order.
458 **171** 12p. multicoloured 30 30

1980. Europa. Personalities. Multicoloured.
459 12p. Type **172** 40 50
460 13p. Oscar Wilde (28 × 38 mm) . 40 1·00

173 Stoat
174 Playing Bodhran and Whistle

1980. Wildlife. Multicoloured.
461 12p. Type **173** 20 40
462 15p. Arctic hare 20 15
463 16p. Red fox 20 50
464 25p. Red deer . . . . 30 1·40

1980. Traditional Music and Dance. Mult.
466 12p. Type **174** 15 10
467 15p. Playing Uilleann pipes . . 20 15
468 25p. Dancing . . . . 35 1·10

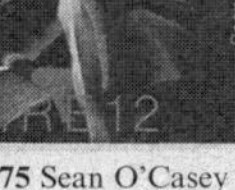
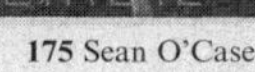

175 Sean O'Casey
176 Nativity Scene (painting by Geraldine McNulty)

1980. Commemorations.
469 12p. multicoloured 15 10
470 25p. black, buff and brown . . 30 55
DESIGNS AND COMMEMORATIONS: 12p. Type **175** (playwright) (birth centenary); 25p. "Gold Painting No. 57" (P. Scott) (Contemporary Irish Art (11th issue)).

1980. Christmas.
471 **176** 12p. multicoloured 15 10
472 15p. multicoloured 20 10
473 25p. multicoloured . . . . 40 1·25

177 Boyle Air-pump, 1659
178 "The Legend of the Cock and the Pot"

1981. Irish Science and Technology. Mult.
474 12p. Type **177** 20 10
475 15p. Ferguson tractor, 1936 . . 25 10
476 16p. Parsons turbine, 1884 . . . 25 90
477 25p. Holland submarine, 1878 . 30 1·25

1981. Europa. Folklore. Paintings by Maria Simonds-Gooding.
491 **178** 18p. black, yellow & red . 25 10
492 – 19p. black, orge & yell . . 35 70
DESIGN: 19p. "The Angel with the Scales of Judgement".

179 Cycling
180 Jeremiah O'Donovan Rossa

1981. 50th Anniv of "An Oige" (Irish Youth Hostel Association). Multicoloured.
493 15p. Type **179** 25 40
494 18p. Hill-walking (horiz) . . . 25 10
495 19p. Mountaineering (horiz) . . 25 95
496 30p. Rock-climbing 40 95

1981. 150th Birth Anniv of Jeremiah O'Donovan Rossa (politician).
497 **180** 15p. multicoloured 30 30

181 "Railway Embankment" (W. J. Leech)

1981. Contemporary Irish Art (12th issue).
498 **181** 30p. multicoloured 60 60

182 James Hoban and White House

1981. 150th Death Anniv of James Hoban (White House architect).
499 **182** 18p. multicoloured 30 30

183 "Arkle" (steeplechaser)

1981. Famous Irish Horses. Multicoloured.
500 18p. Type **183** . . . . 40 1·00
501 18p. "Boomerang" (show-jumper) . . . . 40 1·00
502 22p. "King of Diamonds" (Draught horse) 40 30
503 24p. "Ballymoss" (flat-racer) . . 40 70
504 36p. "Coosheen Finn" (Connemara pony) . . . . . 60 1·00

184 "Nativity" (F. Barocci)
185 Eviction Scene

1981. Christmas.
505 **184** 18p. multicoloured 20 10
506 22p. multicoloured 25 10
507 36p. multicoloured . . . . 45 2·00

1981. Anniversaries. Multicoloured.
508 18p. Type **185** 35 25
509 22p. Royal Dublin Society emblem 40 30
ANNIVERSARIES: 18p. Centenary of Land Law (Ireland) Act. 22p. Royal Dublin Society (organization for the advancement of agriculture, industry, art and science). 250th Anniv

186 Upper Lake, Killarney National Park

1982. 50th Anniv of Killarney National Park. Multicoloured.
510 18p. Type **186** 35 20
511 36p. Eagle's Nest . . . . . . 65 1·60

187 "The Stigmatization of St. Francis" (Sassetta)
188 The Great Famine, 1845–50

1982. Religious Anniversaries.
512 **187** 22p. multicoloured 85 15
513 – 24p. brown 40 80
DESIGNS AND ANNIVERSARIES: 22p. Type **187** (St. Francis of Assisi (founder of Franciscan order) (500th birth anniv); 24p. Francis Makemie (founder of American Presbyterianism) and old Presbyterian Church, Ramelton, Co. Donegal (300th anniv of ordination).

1982. Europa. Historic Events.
514 **188** 26p. black and stone . . . 80 50
515 – 29p. multicoloured . . . . 80 2·00
DESIGN—HORIZ: 29p. The coming of Christianity to Ireland.

189 Padraic O. Conaire (writer) (birth centenary)
191 "St. Patrick" (Galway hooker)

190 Porbeagle Shark

1982. Anniversaries of Cultural Figures.
516 **189** 22p. black and blue . . . 25 30
517 – 26p. black and brown . . . 30 30
518 – 29p. black and blue . . . 40 1·75
519 – 44p. black and grey . . . 50 1·60
DESIGNS AND ANNIVERSARIES: 26p. James Joyce (writer) (birth centenary); 29p. John Field (musician) (birth centenary); 44p. Charles Kickham (writer) (death centenary).

1982. Marine Life. Multicoloured.
520 22p. Type **190** . . . . 55 1·25
521 22p. Common European oyster . 55 1·25
522 26p. Atlantic salmon 70 30
523 29p. Dublin Bay prawn . . . . 70 2·25

1982. Irish Boats. Multicoloured.
524 22p. Type **191** . . . . 60 1·25
525 22p. Currach (horiz) . . . . . 60 1·25
526 26p. "Asgard II" (cadet brigantine) (horiz) 60 30
527 29p. "Howth" 17-foot yacht . . 60 2·25

192 "Irish House of Commons" (painting by Francis Wheatley)

1982. Bicentenary of Grattan's Parliament and Birth Centenary of Éamon de Valera. Multicoloured.
528 22p. Type **192** . . . . 35 1·25
529 26p. Eamon de Valera (vert) . . 40 40

193 "Madonna and Child" (sculpture)
194 Aughnanure Castle

1982. Christmas.
530 **193** 22p. multicoloured 30 90
531 26p. multicoloured 30 35

1983. Irish Architecture.
532 – 1p. blue 10 10
533 – 2p. green 20 10
534 – 3p. black 20 10
535 – 4p. red 20 10
536 – 5p. brown 30 10
537 – 6p. blue 30 15
538 – 7p. green 30 15
539 – 10p. black 30 10
540 – 12p. brown 30 30
541 **194** 15p. green 45 35
542 20p. purple 50 45
543 22p. blue 50 10
544 – 23p. green 85 80
544a – 24p. brown . . . . . . 1·25 35
545 – 26p. brown 75 10
545c – 28p. red 75 45
546 – 29p. green 90 65
547 – 30p. black 70 30
547c – 32p. brown . . . . . . 1·75 2·50
547d – 37p. blue . . . . 90 1·60
547e – 39p. red . . . . 2·25 2·75
548 – 44p. black and grey . . . 90 90
548b – 46p. green and grey . . . 5·00 2·00
549 – 50p. blue and grey . . . 1·00 65
550 – £1 brown and grey . . . 3·75 3·00
550b – £1 blue and grey . . . . 3·25 1·25
550c – £2 green and black . . . 4·25 4·50
551 – £5 red and grey . . . . . 10·00 5·00
DESIGNS—HORIZ: (As T **194**): 1 to 5p. Central Pavilion, Dublin Botanic Gardens; 6 to 12p. Dr. Steevens' Hospital, Dublin; 28 to 37p. St. MacDara's Church. (37 × 21 mm); 46p., £1 (No. 550) Cahir Castle; 50p., £2 Casino Marino. £5 Central Bus Station, Dublin. VERT: (As T **194**): 23 to 26p., 39p. Cormac's Chapel. (21 × 37 mm); 44p., £1 (No. 550b) Killarney Cathedral.

195 Ouzel Gallery Goblet
196 Padraig O. Siochfhradha (writer and teacher)

1983. Bicentenaries of Dublin Chamber of Commerce (22p.) and Bank of Ireland (26p.). Multicoloured.
552 22p. Type **195** 30 55
553 26p. Bank of Ireland building (horiz) 35 35

1983. Anniversaries. Multicoloured.
554 26p. Type **196** (Birth cent.) . . . 50 75
555 29p. Young Boys' Brigade member (Centenary) . . . . 60 1·50

197 Neolithic Carved Pattern, Newgrange Tomb

1983. Europa.
556 **197** 26p. black and yellow . . . 1·75 50
557 – 29p. black, brn & yell . . . 4·00 5·00
DESIGN: 29p. Sir William Rowan Hamilton's formulae for the multiplication of quaternions.

198 Kerry Blue Terrier

1983. Irish Dogs. Multicoloured.
558 22p. Type **198** 65 35
559 26p. Irish Wolfhound 75 45
560 26p. Irish Water Spaniel . . . 75 45
561 29p. Irish Terrier . . . . 95 2·25
562 44p. Irish Setters . . . . 1·40 2·50

199 Animals (Irish Society for the Prevention of Cruelty to Animals)

1983. Anniversaries and Commemorations.
564 **199** 22p. multicoloured . . . . 50 1·00
565 – 22p. multicoloured . . . . 50 1·00
566 – 26p. multicoloured 50 60
567 – 26p. multicoloured 50 60
568 – 44p. blue and black . . . 75 2·00
DESIGNS—VERT: No. 565, Sean MacDiarmada (patriot) (birth cent.); No. 567, "St. Vincent de Paul in the Streets of Paris" (150th anniv of Society of St. Vincent de Paul); No. 568, "Andrew Jackson" (Frank McKelvey) (President of the United States). HORIZ: No. 566, "100" (Centenary of Industrial Credit Company).

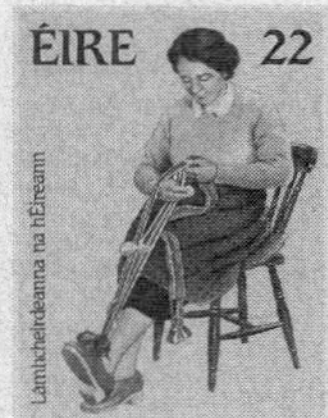

200 Postman with Bicycle
201 Weaving

1983. World Communications Year. Multicoloured.
569 22p. Type **200** 55 75
570 29p. Dish antenna . . . . . . 70 2·00

1983. Irish Handicrafts. Multicoloured.
571 22p. Type **201** 40 50
572 26p. Basket making 40 35
573 29p. Irish crochet . . . . . . 45 1·25
574 44p. Harp making . . . . . . 70 2·00

202 "La Natividad" (R. van der Weyden)

1983. Christmas.
575 **202** 22p. multicoloured 30 30
576 26p. multicoloured 40 30

203 Dublin and Kingstown Railway Steam Locomotive "Princess"

1984. 150th Anniv of Irish Railways. Mult.
577 23p. Type **203** . . . . 75 1·25
578 26p. Great Southern Railways steam locomotive "Macha" . 75 35
579 29p. Great Northern Railway steam locomotive No. 87 "Kestrel" . . . . 85 1·75
580 44p. Two-car electric train Coras Iompair Eireann . . . . . . 1·10 2·25

204 "Sorbus hibernica"

1984. Irish Trees. Multicoloured.
582 22p. Type **204** 65 70
583 26p. "Taxus baccata fastigiata" . 70 40
584 29p. "Salix hibernica" . . . . 85 2·00
585 44p. "Betula pubescens" . . . . 1·10 2·75

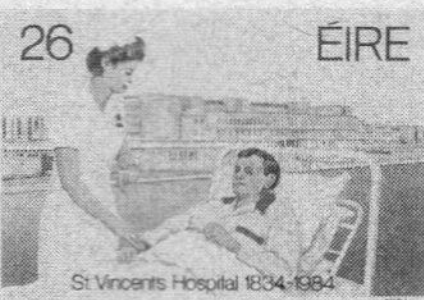

205 St. Vincent's Hospital, Dublin

1984. 150th Anniv of St. Vincent's Hospital and Bicentenary of Royal College of Surgeons. Multicoloured.
586 26p. Type **205** 50 30
587 44p. Royal College and logo . . 90 1·50

206 C.E.P.T. 25th Anniversary Logo

1984. Europa.
588 **206** 26 p. bl, dp bl & blk . . . 1·75 50
589 29p. lt grn, grn & blk . . . 2·25 2·50

207 Flags on Ballot Box
208 John McCormack

1984. Second Direct Elections to European Assembly.
590 **207** 26p. multicoloured 50 70

1984. Birth Centenary of John McCormack (tenor).
591 **208** 22p. multicoloured 50 70

209 Hammer-throwing

1984. Olympic Games, Los Angeles.
592 **209** 22p. mauve, blk & gold . . 35 80
593 – 26p. violet, blk & gold . . 40 65
594 – 29p. blue, black & gold . . 60 1·25
DESIGNS: 26p. Hurdling; 29p. Running.

210 Hurling

1984. Centenary of Gaelic Athletic Association. Multicoloured.
595 22p. Type **210** 50 90
596 26p. Irish football (vert) 60 90

211 Galway Mayoral Chain

1984. Anniversaries. Multicoloured.
597 26p. Type **211** (500th anniv of mayoral charter) 35 50
598 44p. St. Brendan (from 15th-cent Bodleian manuscript) (1500th birth anniv) (horiz) . . . . . 75 1·50

212 Hands passing Letter

1984. Bicentenary of Irish Post Office.
599 **212** 26p. multicoloured 60 70

213 "Virgin and Child" (Sassoferrato)

1984. Christmas. Multicoloured.
600 17p. Christmas star (horiz) . . . 45 80
601 22p. Type **213** . . . . 45 1·25
602 26p. Type **213** 65 40

214 "Love" and Heart-shaped Balloon

1985. Greetings Stamps. Multicoloured.
603 22p. Type **214** 50 75
604 26p. Bouquet of hearts and flowers (vert) 60 75

215 Dunsink Observatory (bicentenary)
216 "Polyommatus icarus"

1985. Anniversaries. Multicoloured.
605 22p. Type **215** 50 50
606 26p. "A Landscape at Tivoli, Cork, with Boats" (Nathaniel Grogan) (800th anniv of City of Cork) (horiz) 50 30
607 37p. Royal Irish Academy (bicentenary) . . . . 70 1·75
608 44p. Richard Crosbie's balloon flight (bicentenary of first aeronautic flight by an Irishman) . 80 1·75

1985. Butterflies. Multicoloured.
609 22p. Type **216** . . . . 1·25 1·00
610 26p. "Vanessa atalanta" . . . . 1·25 70
611 28p. "Gonepteryx rhamni" . . 1·50 2·75
612 44p. "Eurabyas aurinia" . . . 2·00 3·00

217 Charles Villiers Stanford (composer)

1985. Europa. Irish Composers. Multicoloured.
613 26p. Type **217** . . . . 2·00 50
614 37p. Turlough Carolan (composer and lyricist) . . . . . . 4·00 5·50

218 George Frederick Handel

1985. European Music Year. Composers. Mult.
615 22p. Type **218** . . . . 1·25 2·50
616 22p. Guiseppe Domenico Scarlatti . . . . 1·25 2·50
617 26p. Johann Sebastian Bach . . 1·50 50

219 U.N. Patrol of Irish Soldiers, Congo, 1960

1985. Anniversaries. Multicoloured.
618 22 p. Type **219** (25th anniv of Irish Participation in U.N. Peace-keeping Force) 65 80
619 26p. Thomas Ashe (patriot) (birth cent) (vert) 65 60
620 44p. "Bishop George Berkeley" (James Lathan) (philosopher, 300th birth anniv) (vert) . . . 1·00 3·00

220 Group of Young People

1985. International Youth Year. Mult.
621 22p. Type **220** 55 50
622 26p. Students and young workers (vert) 55 50

221 Visual Display Unit

1985. Industrial Innovation. Multicoloured.
623 22p. Type **221** 65 75
624 26p. Turf cutting with hand tool and with modern machinery . 70 55
625 44p. "The Key Man" (Sean Keating) (150th anniv of Institution of Engineers of Ireland) . . . . 1·25 2·50

222 Lighted Candle and Holly

224 Stylised Love Bird with Letter

1985. Christmas. Multicoloured.
626 22p. Type **222** 75 65
627 22p. "Virgin and Child in a Landscape" (Adrian van Ijsenbrandt) . . . . 90 2·25
628 22p. "The Holy Family" (Murillo) . . . . 90 2·25
629 26p. "The Adoration of the Shepherds" (Louis le Nain) (horiz) 90 25

No. 626 was only issued in sheetlets of 16 sold at £3, providing a discount of 52p. off the face value of the stamps.

1986. Greetings Stamps. Multicoloured.
630 22p. Type **224** 55 90
631 26p. Heart-shaped pillar-box . . 55 90

225 Hart's Tongue Fern

226 "Harmony between Industry and Nature"

1986. Ferns. Multicoloured.
632 24p. Type **225** 70 70
633 28p. Rusty-back Fern 80 70
634 46p. Killarney Fern . . . . . . 1·25 2·10

1986. Europa. Protection of the Environment. Multicoloured.
635 28p. Type **226** . . . . 1·75 50
636 39p. "Vanessa atalanta" (butterfly) and tractor in field ("Preserve hedgerows") (horiz) . . . . 3·25 5·00

227 Boeing 747-200 over Globe showing Aer Lingus Routes

1986. 50th Anniv of Aer Lingus (airline). Multicoloured.
637 28p. Type **227** . . . . 1·40 75
638 46p. De Havilland Dragon Mk 2 "Iolar" (first airplane) . . . 1·90 3·00

228 Grand Canal at Robertstown

1986. Irish Waterways. Multicoloured.
639 24p. Type **228** . . . . 1·00 1·00
640 28p. Fishing in County Mayo (vert) . . . . 1·25 1·00
641 30p. Motor cruiser on Lough Derg . . . . 1·50 2·50

229 "Severn" (19th-century paddlesteamer)

1986. 150th Anniv of British and Irish Steam Packet Company. Multicoloured.
642 24p. Type **229** . . . . 75 1·00
643 28p. "Leinster" (modern ferry) . 85 60

230 Kish Lighthouse and Bell JetRanger III Helicopter

231 J. P. Nannetti (first president) and Linotype Operator (Dublin Council of Trade Unions centenary)

1986. Irish Lighthouses. Multicoloured.
644 24p. Type **230** 75 75
645 30p. Fastnet Lighthouse . . . . 1·75 2·75

1986. Anniversaries and Commemorations.
646 **231** 24p. multicoloured 50 90
647 – 28p. black and grey . . . 60 80
648 – 28p. multicoloured 60 80
649 – 30p. multicoloured . . . . 65 1·00
650 – 46p. multicoloured . . . . 70 1·75

DESIGNS:—VERT: No. 647, Arthur Griffith (statesman); 649, Clasped hands (International Peace Year). HORIZ: No. 648, Woman surveyor (Women in Society); 650, Peace dove (International Peace Year).

232 William Mulready and his Design for 1840 Envelope

1986. Birth Bicentenaries of William Mulready (artist) (24p.) and Charles Bianconi (originator of Irish mail coach service) (others). Multicoloured.
651 24p. Type **232** 65 70
652 28p. Bianconi car outside Hearns Hotel, Clonmel (vert) 75 55
653 39p. Bianconi car on the road . 1·25 1·75

233 "Adoration of the Shepherds" (Francesco Pascucci)

1986. Christmas. Multicoloured.
654 21p. Type **233** . . . . 1·10 1·40
655 28p. "Adoration of the Magi" (Frans Francken III) (vert) . . 65 60

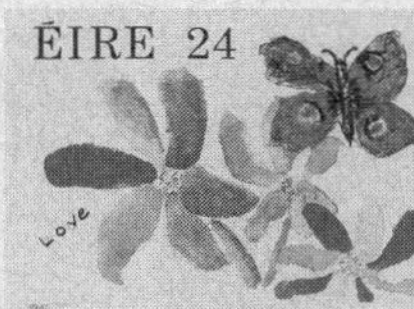

234 "Butterfly and Flowers" (Tara Collins)

1987. Greetings Stamps. Children's Paintings. Multicoloured.
656 24p. Type **234** . . . . 70 1·25
657 28p. "Postman on Bicycle delivering Hearts" (Brigid Teehan) (vert) . . . . 80 1·25

235 Cork Electric Tram

1987. Irish Trams. Multicoloured.
658 24p. Type **235** 65 65
659 28p. Dublin standard tram No. 29 . . . . 70 85
660 30p. Howth (Great Northern Railway) tram . . . . 80 2·00
661 46p. Galway horse tram . . . . 1·25 2·25

236 Ships from Crest (Bicentenary of Waterford Chamber of Commerce)

1987. Anniversaries.
663 **236** 24p. black, blue & grn . . 70 60
664 – 28p. multicoloured 70 60
665 – 30p. multicoloured . . . . 70 2·00
666 – 39p. multicoloured . . . . 75 1·75

DESIGNS—HORIZ: 28p. Canon John Hayes and symbols of agriculture and development (birth centenary and 50th anniv of Muintir na Tire programme); 39p. Mother Mary Martin and International Missionary Training Hospital, Drogheda (50th anniv of Medical Missionaries of Mary). VERT: 30p. "Calceolaria burbidgei" and College crest (300th anniv of Trinity College Botanic Gardens, Dublin).

237 Bord na Mona Headquarters and "The Turf Cutter" (sculpture, John Behan), Dublin

1987. Europa. Modern Architecture. Mult.
667 28p. Type **237** . . . . 1·50 60
668 39p. St. Mary's Church, Cong . 3·50 5·00

238 Kerry Cow

1987. Irish Cattle. Multicoloured.
669 24p. Type **238** 70 75
670 28p. Friesian cow and calf . . . 85 60
671 30p. Hereford bullock . . . . . 90 2·25
672 39p. Shorthorn bull . . . . . 1·00 2·25

239 Fleadh Nua, Ennis

1987. Festivals. Multicoloured.
673 24p. Type **239** 65 70
674 28p. Rose of Tralee International Festival 70 60
675 30p. Wexford Opera Festival (horiz) . . . . 80 2·00
676 46p. Ballinasloe Horse Fair (horiz) . . . . 1·10 2·00

240 Flagon (1637), Arms and Anniversary Ornament (1987) (350th anniv of Dublin Goldsmiths' Company)

1987. Anniversaries and Commemorations.
677 **240** 24p. multicoloured 55 80
678 – 24p. grey and black . . . 55 80
679 – 28p. multicoloured 65 60
680 – 46p. multicoloured . . . . 1·00 1·10

DESIGNS—VERT: 24p. (No. 678) Cathal Brugha (patriot); 46p. Woman chairing board meeting (Women in Society). HORIZ: 28p. Arms of Ireland and inscription (50th anniv of Constitution).

241 Scenes from "The Twelve Days of Christmas" (carol)

1987. Christmas. Multicoloured.
681 21p. Type **241** . . . . 60 1·00
682 24p. The Nativity (detail, late 15th-century Waterford Vestments) (vert) . . . . . . 75 1·00
683 28p. Figures from Neapolitan crib, c. 1850 (vert) 75 80

242 Acrobatic Clowns spelling "LOVE"

1988. Greetings Stamps. Multicoloured.
684 24p. Type **242** 60 60
685 28p. Pillar box and hearts (vert) 65 65

243 "Robert Burke" (Sidney Nolan) and Map of Burke and Wills Expedition Route

1988. Bicentenary of Australian Settlement. Multicoloured.
686 24p. Type **243** 40 60
687 46p. "Eureka Stockade" (mural detail, Sidney Nolan) . . . . 85 1·75

244 Past and Present Buildings of Dublin

1988. Dublin Millennium.
688 **244** 28p. multicoloured 45 55

245 Showjumping

1988. Olympic Games, Seoul. Multicoloured.

689 28p. Type **245** . . . . 1·00 1·40
690 28p. Cycling . . . . 1·00 1·40

246 William T. Cosgrave (statesman)

1988. Anniversaries and Events.

691 **246** 24p. grey and black . . . 45 45
692 – 30p. multicoloured . . . . 80 1·00
693 – 50p. multicoloured . . . . 1·00 1·90

DESIGNS—HORIZ: 30p. Members with casualty and ambulance (50th anniv of Order of Malta Ambulance Corps). VERT: 50p. Barry Fitzgerald (actor) (birth centenary).

247 Air Traffic Controllers and Airbus Industrie A320

1988. Europa. Transport and Communications. Multicoloured.

694 28p. Type **247** . . . . 1·25 55
695 39p. Globe with stream of letters from Ireland to Europe . . . 1·75 2·50

248 "Sirius" (paddle-steamer)

1988. Transatlantic Transport Anniversaries. Multicoloured.

696 24p. Type **248** (150th anniv of regular transatlantic steamship services) 75 50
697 46p. Short S.20 seaplane "Mercury" and Short S.21 flying boat "Maia" (Short Mayo composite aircraft) in Foynes Harbour (50th anniv of first commercial transatlantic flight) . . . . 1·50 2·75

249 Cottonweed **251** Computer and Abacus

250 Garda on Duty

1988. Endangered Flora of Ireland. Mult.

698 24p. Type **249** 65 55
699 28p. Hart's saxifrage 75 55
700 46p. Purple milk-vetch . . . . 1·10 2·00

1988. Irish Security Forces. Multicoloured.

701 28p. Type **250** . . . . 60 1·00
702 28p. Army unit with personnel carrier . . . . 60 1·00
703 28p. Navy and Air Corps members with "Eithne" (helicopter patrol vessel) . . . . 60 1·00
704 28p. Army and Navy reservists . 60 1·00

1988. Anniversaries. Multicoloured.

705 24p. Type **251** (Institute of Chartered Accountants in Ireland centenary) 40 40
706 46p. "Duquesa Santa Ana" off Donegal (400th anniv of Spanish Armada) (horiz) . . 1·25 1·25

252 "President Kennedy" (James Wyeth) **253** St. Kevin's Church, Glendalough

1988. 25th Death Anniv of John F. Kennedy (American statesman).

707 **252** 28p. multicoloured 70 80

1988. Christmas. Multicoloured.

708 21p. Type **253** 80 80
709 24p. The Adoration of the Magi 50 60
710 28p. The Flight into Egypt . . . 60 55
711 46p. The Holy Family . . . . 90 2·25

The designs of Nos. 709/11 are from a 15th-century French Book of Hours.

254 Spring Flowers spelling "Love" in Gaelic

1989. Greetings Stamps. Multicoloured.

712 24p. Type **254** 60 55
713 28p. "The Sonnet" (William Mulready) (vert) 65 55

255 Italian Garden, Garinish Island

1989. National Parks and Gardens. Multicoloured.

714 24p. Type **255** 80 55
715 28p. Lough Veagh, Glenveagh National Park 95 55
716 32p. Barnaderg Bay, Connemara National Park . . . . 1·00 1·25
717 50p. St. Stephen's Green, Dublin . . . . 1·50 1·75

256 "Silver Stream", 1908

1989. Classic Irish Cars. Multicoloured.

718 24p. Type **256** 50 55
719 28p. Benz "Comfortable", 1898 . 50 55
720 39p. "Thomond", 1929 . . . . 1·25 1·50
721 46p. Chambers' 8 h.p. model, 1905 . . . . 1·50 1·50

257 Ring-a-ring-a-roses

1989. Europa. Children's Games. Multicoloured.

722 28p. Type **257** 75 75
723 39p. Hopscotch . . . . 1·00 2·25

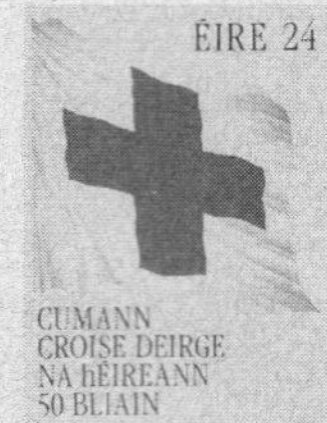

258 Irish Red Cross Flag (50th anniv)

1989. Anniversaries and Events.

724 **258** 24p. red and black 55 60
725 – 28p. blue, black & yellow . 1·10 1·10

DESIGN: 28p. Circle of twelve stars (third direct elections to European Parliament).

259 Saints Kilian, Totnan and Colman (from 12th-century German manuscript)

1989. 1300th Death Anniv of Saints Kilian, Totnan and Colman.

726 **259** 28p. multicoloured . . . . 65 1·10

260 19th-century Mail Coach passing Cashel

1989. Bicentenary of Irish Mail Coach Service.

727 **260** 28p. multicoloured . . . . 1·00 75

261 Crest and 19th-century Dividers (150th anniv of Royal Institute of Architects of Ireland)

1989. Anniversaries and Commemorations.

728 – 24p. grey and black . . . 65 55
729 **261** 28p. multicoloured 65 55
730 – 30p. multicoloured . . . . 1·40 1·75
731 – 46p. brown . . . . 1·60 1·75

DESIGNS—VERT: 24p. Sean T. O'Kelly (statesman) (drawing by Sean O'Sullivan); 46p. Jawaharlal Nehru (birth centenary). HORIZ: 30p. Margaret Burke-Sheridan (soprano) (portrait by De Gennaro) and scene from "La Boheme" (birth centenary).

262 "NCB Ireland' rounding Cape Horn" (Des Fallon)

1989. First Irish Entry in Whitbread Round the World Yacht Race.

732 **262** 28p. multicoloured . . . . 1·25 1·25

263 Willow/Red Grouse **264** "The Annunciation"

1989. Game Birds. Multicoloured.

733 24p. Type **263** . . . . 1·00 55
734 28p. Lapwing . . . . 1·10 55
735 39p. Woodcock . . . . 1·40 2·25
736 46p. Ring-necked Pheasant . . 1·50 2·25

1989. Christmas. Multicoloured.

738 21p. Children decorating crib . . 75 75
739 24p. Type **264** 85 60
740 28p. "The Nativity" 90 55
741 46p. "The Adoration of the Magi" . . . . 1·75 2·50

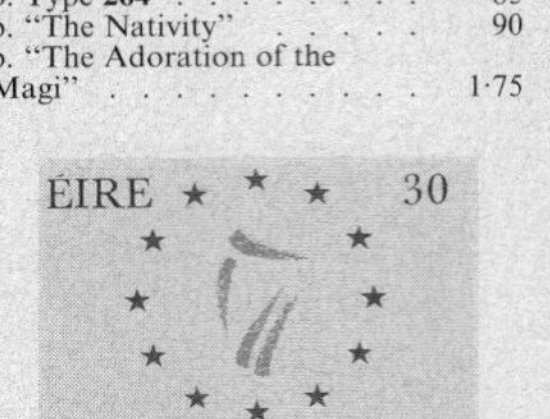

265 Logo (Ireland's Presidency of the European Communities)

1990. European Events. Multicoloured.

742 30p. Type **265** 75 60
743 50p. Logo and outline map of Ireland (European Tourism Year) . . . . 2·00 3·00

266 Dropping Messages from Balloon

1990. Greetings Stamps.

744 **266** 26p. multicoloured . . . . 1·25 1·25
745 – 30p. red, buff & brown . . 1·25 1·25

DESIGN: 30p. Heart and "Love" drawn in lipstick.

267 Silver Kite Brooch **268** Posy of Flowers

1990. Irish Heritage.

746 **267** 1p. black and blue . . . 10 10
747 2p. black and orange . . 10 10
748 – 4p. black and violet . . . 10 10
749 – 5p. black and green . . . 15 10
750 – 10p. black and orange . . 20 25
751 – 20p. black and yellow . . 35 40
752 – 26p. black and violet . . 45 50
809 – 28p. black and orange . . 45 50
754 – 30p. black and blue . . . 55 60
810 – 32p. black and green . . 50 55
756 – 34p. black and yellow . . 1·00 1·00
757 – 37p. black and green . . 1·25 1·25
758 – 38p. black and violet . . 1·25 1·25
758b – 40p. black and blue . . . 1·25 1·25
759 – 41p. black and orange . . 80 75
760 – 44p. brown and yellow . . 85 80
760a – 45p. black and violet . . 1·25 1·50
761 – 50p. black and yellow . . 1·25 1·25
762 – 52p. black and blue . . . 1·50 1·50
763 – £1 black and yellow . . . 1·75 1·90
764 – £2 black and green . . . 3·25 3·00
765 – £5 black and blue . . . . 9·00 9·25

DESIGNS: 4, 5p. Dunamase food vessel; 26, 28p. Lismore crozier; 34, 37, 38, 40p. Gleninsheen collar; 41, 44p. Silver thistle brooch; 45, 50, 52p. Broighter boat. 22×38 mm: £5 St. Patrick's Bell Shrine. HORIZ: As T **267**: 10p. Derrinboy armlets; 20p. Gold dress fastener; 30p. Enamelled latchet brooch: 32p. Broighter collar. 38×22 mm: £1 Ardagh Chalice; £2 Tara brooch.

For 32p. value as No. 755 but larger, 27×20 mm, see No. 823.

1990. Greetings Stamps. Multicoloured.

766 26p. Type **268** . . . . 2·00 2·50
767 26p. Birthday presents . . . . 2·00 2·50
768 30p. Flowers, ribbon and horseshoe . . . . 2·00 2·50
769 30p. Balloons . . . . 2·00 2·50

269 Player heading Ball

1990. World Cup Football Championship, Italy. Multicoloured.

770 30p. Type **269** . . . . 1·50 2·00
771 30p. Tackling . . . . 1·50 2·00

270 Battle of the Boyne, 1690

1990. 300th Anniv of the Williamite Wars (1st issue). Multicoloured.
772 30p. Type **270** . . . . 1·25 1·75
773 30p. Siege of Limerick, 1690 . . 1·25 1·75
See also Nos. 806/7.

271 1990 Irish Heritage 30p. Stamp and 1840 Postmark

1990. 150th Anniv of the Penny Black. Mult.
774 30p. Type **271** 90 90
775 50 p. Definitive stamps of 1922, 1969, 1982 and 1990 . . . . 1·25 2·00

272 General Post Office, Dublin

274 Narcissus "Foundling" and Japanese Gardens, Tully

273 Medical Missionary giving Injection

1990. Europa Post Office Buildings. Mult.
776 30p. Type **272** . . . . 1·00 60
777 41p. Westport Post Office, County Mayo . . . . 1·40 2·75

1990. Anniversaries and Events.
778 **273** 26p. multicoloured 80 30
779 – 30p. black . . . . 1·00 2·25
780 – 50p. multicoloured . . . . 1·00 1·25
DESIGNS—VERT: 30p. Michael Collins (statesman) (birth centenary). HORIZ: 50p. Missionaries working at water pump (Irish missionary service).

1990. Garden Flowers. Multicoloured.
781 26p. Type **274** 60 55
782 30p. "Rosa x hibernica" and Mulahide Castle gardens . . 70 80
783 41p. Primula "Rowallane Rose" and Rowallane garden . . . 1·40 2·00
784 50p. "Erica erigena" "Irish Dusk" and Palm House, National Botanical Gardens . 1·75 2·25

275 "Playboy of the Western World" (John Synge)

1990. Irish Theatre. Multicoloured.
785 30p. Type **275** . . . . 1·25 1·75
786 30p. "Juno and the Pay-cock" (Sean O'Casey) . . . . . . 1·25 1·75
787 30p. "The Field" (John Keane) . 1·25 1·75
788 30p. "Waiting for Godot" (Samuel Beckett) . . . . . . 1·25 1·75

276 Nativity

277 Hearts in Mail Sack and Postman's Cap

1990. Christmas. Multicoloured.
789 26p. Child praying by bed . . . 70 80
790 26p. Type **276** 70 60
791 30p. Madonna and Child . . . 90 90
792 50p. Adoration of the Magi . . 1·60 2·25

1991. Greetings Stamps. Multicoloured.
793 26p. Type **277** . . . . 85 1·00
794 30p. Boy and girl kissing . . . 90 1·00

278 Starley "Rover" Bicycle, 1886

1991. Early Bicycles. Multicoloured.
795 26p. Type **278** 80 60
796 30p. Child's horse tricycle, 1875 . 90 1·00
797 50p. "Penny Farthing", 1871 . . 1·60 2·00

279 "Cuchulainn" (statue by Oliver Sheppard) and Proclamation

1991. 75th Anniv of Easter Rising.
799 **279** 32p. multicoloured . . . . 85 1·40

280 Scene from "La Traviata" (50th anniv of Dublin Grand Opera Society)

1991. "Dublin 1991 European City of Culture". Multicoloured.
800 28p. Type **280** 65 80
801 32p. City Hall and European Community emblem . . . . 85 1·50
802 44p. St. Patrick's Cathedral (800th anniv) . . . . 90 1·60
803 52p. Custom House (bicent) (41×24 mm) . . . . 1·00 1·60

281 "Giotto" Spacecraft approaching Halley's Comet

1991. Europa. Europe in Space. Multicoloured.
804 32p. Type **281** . . . . 1·00 1·00
805 44p. Hubble Telescope orbiting Earth . . . . 1·50 3·00

282 Siege of Athlone

1991. 300th Anniv of the Williamite Wars (2nd issue). Multicoloured.
806 28p. Type **282** . . . . 90 1·40
807 28p. Generals Ginkel and Sarsfield (signatories of Treaty of Limerick) . . . . 90 1·40

283 John A. Costello (statesman)

1991. Anniversaries.
811 **283** 28p. black 70 70
812 – 32p. multicoloured . . . . 85 1·00
813 – 52p. multicoloured . . . . 1·40 2·50
DESIGNS—VERT: 28p. Type **283** (birth cent) (drawing by Sean O'Sullivan); 32p. "Charles Stewart Parnell" (Sydney Hall) (death cent); HORIZ: 52p. Meeting of United Irishmen.

284 Player on 15th Green, Portmarnock (Walker Cup)

1991. Golf Commemorations. Multicoloured.
814 28p. Type **284** . . . . 1·00 75
815 32p. Logo and golfer of 1900 (cent of Golfing Union of Ireland) (vert) . . . . 1·25 1·00

285 Wicklow Cheviot

1991. Irish Sheep. Multicoloured.
816 32p. Type **285** . . . . 1·00 80
817 38p. Donegal Blackface . . . . 1·40 1·75
818 52p. Galway (horiz) . . . . . 2·00 3·50

286 Boatyard

1991. Fishing Fleet. Multicoloured.
819 28p. Type **286** 60 65
820 32p. Traditional inshore trawlers 70 80
821 44p. Inshore lobster pot boat . 1·40 2·25
822 52p. "Veronica" (fish factory ship) . . . . 1·75 2·50

1991. As No. 755, but larger, 27×20 mm. Self-adhesive.
823 32p. black and green 65 80

287 The Annunciation

289 Healthy Family on Apple

288 Multicoloured Heart

1991. Christmas.
827 – 28p. multicoloured 80 80
828 **287** 28p. blue, green & black . . 75 65
829 – 32p. red and black . . . 85 75
830 – 52p. multicoloured . . . . 1·60 2·50
DESIGNS: No. 827, Three Kings; No. 829, The Nativity; No. 830, Adoration of the Kings:

1992. Greetings Stamps. Multicoloured.
831 28p. Type **288** 85 95
832 32p. "LOVE" at end of rainbow (vert) . . . . 95 1·10

1992. "Healthy Living" Campaign.
833 **289** 28p. multicoloured 85 85

290 Boxing

1992. Olympic Games, Barcelona. Mult.
834 32p. Type **290** 75 90
835 44p. Sailing . . . . 1·00 2·25

291 "Mari" (cog) and 14th-century Map

1992. Irish Maritime Heritage. Multicoloured.
837 32p. Type **291** . . . . 1·00 90
838 52p. "Ovoca" (trawler) and chart (vert) . . . . 1·50 2·75

292 Chamber Logo and Commercial Symbols

1992. Bicentenary of Galway Chamber of Commerce and Industry.
839 **292** 28p. multicoloured 70 85

293 Cliffs and Cove

1992. Greetings Stamps. Multicoloured.
840 28p. Type **293** . . . . 75 1·10
841 28p. Meadow . . . . 75 1·10
842 32p. Fuchsia and honeysuckle . 75 1·10
843 32p. Lily pond and dragonfly . . 75 1·10

294 Fleet of Columbus

1992. Europa. 500th Anniv of Discovery of America by Columbus. Multicoloured.
844 32p. Type **294** 75 90
845 44p. Columbus landing in the New World . . . . 1·25 2·50

295 Irish Immigrants

1992. Irish Immigrants in the Americas. Multicoloured.
846 52p. Type **295** . . . . 1·60 1·75
847 52p. Irish soldiers, entertainers and politicians . . . . 1·60 1·75

296 Pair of Pine Martens

1992. Endangered Species. Pine Marten. Mult.
848 28p. Type **296** . . . . 1·00 70
849 32p. Marten on branch . . . . 1·00 80
850 44p. Female with kittens . . . 1·60 1·50
851 52p. Marten catching great tit . 2·00 1·75

297 "The Rotunda and New Rooms" (James Malton)

1992. Dublin Anniversaries. Multicoloured.

852 28p. Type **297** 70 65
853 32p. Trinity College Library (28 × 45 mm) . . . . 1·00 1·00
854 44p. "Charlemont House" . . . 1·10 2·00
855 52p. Trinity College main gate (28 × 45 mm) . . . . . . 1·40 2·25

ANNIVERSARIES: 28, 44p. Bicentenary of Publication of Malton's "Views of Dublin"; 32, 52p. 400th anniv of Founding of Trinity College.

298 European Star and Megalithic Dolmen

1992. Single European Market.

856 **298** 32p. multicoloured 70 80

299 Farm Produce **300** "The Annunciation" (from illuminated manuscript)

1992. Irish Agriculture. Multicoloured.

857 32p. Type **299** . . . . 1·00 1·25
858 32p. Dairy and beef herds . . . 1·00 1·25
859 32p. Harvesting cereals . . . . 1·00 1·25
860 32p. Market gardening . . . . 1·00 1·25

Nos. 857/60 were printed together, se-tenant, forming a composite design.

1992. Christmas. Multicoloured.

861 28p. Congregation entering church 80 65
862 28p. Type **300** 80 65
863 32p. "Adoration of the Shepherds" (Da Empoli) . . 1·10 1·00
864 52p. "Adoration of the Magi" (Rottenhammer) . . . . . . 1·40 1·50

301 Queen of Hearts **303** Bee Orchid

302 "Evening at Tangier" (Sir John Lavery)

1993. Greetings Stamps. Multicoloured.

865 28p. Type **301** 75 75
866 32p. Hot air balloon trailing hearts (horiz) 85 85

1993. Irish Impressionist Painters. Multicoloured.

867 28p. Type **302** 75 60
868 32p. "The Goose Girl" (William Leech) 80 65
869 44p. "La Jeune Bretonne" (Roderic O'Conor) (vert) . . 1·25 1·60
870 52p. "Lustre Jug" (Walter Osborne) (vert) . . . . . . 1·75 2·25

1993. Irish Orchids. Multicoloured.

871 28p. Type **303** 90 60
872 32p. O'Kelly's orchid . . . . 1·10 80
873 38p. Dark red helleborine . . . 1·60 2·25
874 52p. Irish lady's tresses . . . . 1·90 2·75

304 "Pears in a Copper Pan" (Hilda van Stockum)

1993. Europa. Contemporary Art. Mult.

876 32p. Type **304** 75 75
877 44p. "Arrieta Orzola" (Tony O'Malley) . . . . 1·10 1·10

305 Cultural Activities

1993. Centenary of Conradh Na Gaelige (cultural organization). Multicoloured.

878 32p. Type **305** 85 75
879 52p. Illuminated manuscript cover (vert) . . . . 1·50 1·50

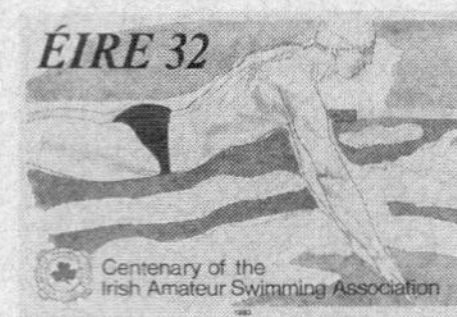

306 Diving

1993. Centenary of Irish Amateur Swimming Association. Multicoloured.

880 32p. Type **306** . . . . 1·00 1·25
881 32p. Swimming . . . . 1·00 1·25

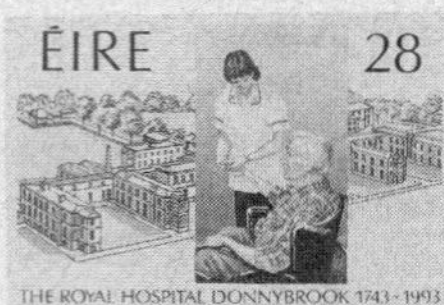

307 Nurse with Patient and Hospital Buildings

1993. Anniversaries and Events. Multicoloured.

882 28p. Type **307** (250th anniv of Royal Hospital, Donnybrook) 80 60
883 32p. College building and crest (bicentenary of St. Patrick's College, Carlow) (vert) . . . 80 60
884 44p. Map of Neolithic field system, Ceide (opening of interpretative centre) . . . . 1·25 1·40
885 52p. Edward Bunting (musicologist) (150th death anniv) (25 × 42 mm) . . . . 1·40 1·60

308 Great Northern Railways Gardner at Drogheda

1993. Irish Buses. Multicoloured.

886 28p. Type **308** 60 65
887 32p. C.I.E. Leyland Titan at College Green, Dublin . . . 65 70
888 52p. Horse-drawn omnibus at Old Baal's Bridge, Limerick . 1·50 2·00
889 52p. Char-a-banc at Lady's View, Killarney . . . . . . 1·50 2·00

309 The Annunciation

1993. Christmas. Multicoloured.

890 28p. The flight into Egypt (vert) 60 65
891 28p. Type **309** 60 55
892 32p. Holy Family 70 70
893 52p. Adoration of the shepherds 1·60 2·25

310 Biplane skywriting "Love"

1994. Greetings Stamps. Multicoloured.

894 28p. Type **310** 75 75
895 32p. Couple within heart (vert) . 85 85

311 Smiling Sun

1994. Greetings Stamps. Multicoloured.

896 32p. Type **311** 85 90
897 32p. Smiling daisy 85 90
898 32p. Smiling heart 85 90
899 32p. Smiling rose 85 90

312 Stylised Logo of Macra na Feirme (50th anniv)

1994. Anniversaries and Events.

901 **312** 28p. gold and blue 75 65
902 – 32p. multicoloured . . . . 1·25 75
903 – 38p. multicoloured . . . . 1·25 1·75
904 – 52p. black, cobalt & blue . 1·40 2·00

DESIGNS—38 × 35 mm: 32p. "The Taking of Christ" (Caravaggio) (loan of painting to National Gallery). $37\frac{1}{2} \times 27$ mm: 38p. Sir Horace Plunkett with 19th-century milk carts and modern tankers (centenary of Irish Co-operative Organization Society); 52p. Congress emblem (centenary of Irish Congress of Trade Unions).

313 St. Brendan visiting Iceland

1994. Europa. St. Brendan's Voyages. Mult.

905 32p. Type **313** 75 70
906 44p. Discovering Faroe Islands . 1·50 2·00

314 First Meeting of Dail, 1919

1994. Parliamentary Anniversaries. Multicoloured.

908 32p. Type **314** (75th anniv) . . . 90 1·00
909 32p. European Parliament (4th direct elections) . . . . . . 90 1·00

315 Irish and Argentine Footballers **317** Statue of Edmund Rice and Class

316 "Arctia caja"

1994. Sporting Anniversaries and Events. Multicoloured.

910 32p. Type **315** . . . . 80 1·00
911 32p. Irish and German footballers . . . . 80 1·00
912 32p. Irish and Dutch women's hockey match (horiz) . . . . 1·25 1·00
913 52p. Irish and English women's hockey match (horiz) . . . . 1·50 2·00

ANNIVERSARIES AND EVENTS: Nos. 910/11, World Cup Football Championship, U.S.A.; 912, Women's Hockey World Cup, Dublin; 913, Centenary of Irish Ladies' Hockey Union.

1994. Moths. Mult (a) Size 37 × 26 mm.

914 28p. Type **316** 65 60
915 32p. "Calamia tridens" 75 70
916 38p. "Saturnia pavonia" . . . 90 1·10
917 52p. "Deilephila elpenor" . . . 1·50 2·00

(b) Size 34 × 22 mm. Self-adhesive.

919 32p. "Calamia tridens" . . . . 90 1·25
920 32p. Type **316** . . . . 90 1·25
921 32p. "Deilephila elpenor" . . . 90 1·25
922 32p. "Saturnia pavonia" . . . 90 1·25

1994. Anniversaries and Events. Multicoloured.

923 28p. St. Laurence Gate, Drogheda ($41\frac{1}{2} \times 25$ mm) . . 70 80
924 32p. Type **317** . . . . 75 1·10
925 32p. Edmund Burke (politician) . 75 1·10
926 52p. Vickers FB-27 Vimy and map (horiz) . . . . 1·25 1·40
927 52p. Eamonn Andrews (broadcaster) . . . . 1·50 1·50

ANNIVERSARIES AND EVENTS: No. 923, 800th anniv of Drogheda; 924, 150th death anniv of Edmund Rice (founder of Irish Christian Brothers); 925, 927, The Irish abroad; 926, 75th anniv of Alcock and Brown's first transatlantic flight.

318 George Bernard Shaw (author) and "Pygmalion" Poster

1994. Irish Nobel Prize Winners. Multicoloured.

928 28p. Type **318** 60 75
929 28p. Samuel Beckett (author) and pair of boots 60 75
930 32p. Sean MacBride (human rights campaigner) and peace doves 70 75
931 52p. William Butler Yeats (poet) and poem . . . . 1·10 1·75

319 "The Annunciation" (ivory plaque) **320** Tree of Hearts

1994. Christmas. Multicoloured.

932 28p. Nativity 70 60
933 28p. Type **319** 70 60
934 32p. "Flight into Egypt" (wood carving) 80 70
935 52p. "Nativity" (ivory plaque) . 1·10 2·00

1995. Greetings Stamps. Multicoloured.

936 32p. Type **320** 80 95
937 32p. Teddy bear holding balloon 80 95
938 32p. Clown juggling hearts . . . 80 95
939 32p. Bouquet of flowers 80 95

321 West Clare Railway Steam Locomotive No. 1 "Kilkee" at Kilrush Station

1995. Transport. Narrow Gauge Railways. Multicoloured.

941 28p. Type **321** 75 60
942 32p. County Donegal Railway tank locomotive No. 2 "Blanche" at Donegal Station 90 90
943 38p. Cork and Muskerry Railway tank locomotive No. 1 "City of Cork" on Western Road, Cork . . . . 1·25 1·75
944 52p. Cavan and Leitrim Railway tank locomotive No. 3 "Lady Edith" on Arigna Tramway . 1·75 2·50

322 English and Irish Rugby Players

1995. World Cup Rugby Championship, South Africa. Multicoloured.
946 32p. Type **322** 75 75
947 52p. Australian and Irish players . . . . 1·25 1·75

323 Peace Dove and Skyscrapers

1995. Europa. Peace and Freedom. Mult.
(a) Size 38 × 26 mm. Ordinary gum.
949 32p. Type **323** 85 75
950 44p. Peace dove and map of Europe and North Africa . . 1·40 2·00
(b) Size 34½ × 23 mm. Self-adhesive.
951 32p. Type **323** 90 90
952 32p. As No. 950 . . . . 90 90

324 Soldiers of the Irish Brigade and Memorial Cross

325 Irish Brigade, French Army, 1745

1995. 250th Anniv of Battle of Fontenoy.
953 **324** 32p. multicoloured 80 80

1995. Military Uniforms. Multicoloured.
954 28p. Type **325** 70 60
955 32p. Tercio Irlanda, Spanish army in Flanders, 1605 . . . 80 75
956 32p. Royal Dublin Fusiliers, 1914 . . . . 80 75
957 38p. St. Patrick's Battalion, Papal Army, 1860 . . . . . 1·10 1·25
958 52p. 69th Regiment, New York State Militia, 1861 . . . . . 1·60 1·75

326 Guglielmo Marconi and Original Radio Transmitter

1995. Centenary of Radio. Multicoloured.
959 32p. Type **326** . . . . 90 1·25
960 32p. Traditional radio dial . . . 90 1·25

327 Bartholomew Mosse (founder) and Hospital Building

1995. Anniversaries. Multicoloured.
961 28p. Type **327** (250th anniv of Rotunda Hospital) 70 70
962 32p. St. Patrick's House, Maynooth College (bicent) (25 × 41 mm) 80 80
963 32p. Laurel wreath and map of Europe (50th anniv of end of Second World War) 80 80
964 52p. Geological map of Ireland (150th anniv of Geological Survey of Ireland) (32½ × 32½ mm) . . . . 1·25 1·50

INDEX
Countries can be quickly located by referring to the index at the end of this volume.

328 Natterjack Toad

1995. Reptiles and Amphibians. Multicoloured.
(a) Size 40 × 27 mm. Ordinary gum.
965 32p. Type **328** . . . . 1·00 1·25
966 32p. Common lizards . . . . . 1·00 1·25
967 32p. Smooth newts . . . . . . 1·00 1·25
968 32p. Common frog . . . . . . 1·00 1·25
(b) Size 34 × 23 mm. Self-adhesive.
969 32p. Type **328** . . . . 1·00 1·25
970 32p. Common lizard . . . . . 1·00 1·25
971 32p. Smooth newts . . . . . . 1·00 1·25
972 32p. Common frog . . . . . . 1·00 1·25
Nos. 965/8 were printed together, se-tenant, with the backgrounds forming a composite design.

329 "Crinum moorei"

1995. Bicentenary of National Botanic Gardens, Glasnevin. Flowers. Multicoloured.
973 32p. Type **329** 85 70
974 38p. "Sarracenia x moorei" . . 1·10 1·10
975 44p. "Solanum crispum" "Glasnevin" . . . . 1·50 2·50

330 Anniversary Logo and Irish United Nations Soldier

1995. 50th Anniv of United Nations. Mult.
976 32p. Type **330** 80 70
977 52p. Emblem and "UN" . . . 1·25 1·40

331 "Adoration of the Shepherds" (illuminated manuscript) (Benedotto Bardone)

1995. Christmas. Multicoloured.
978 28p. Adoration of the Magi . . 70 65
979 28p. Type **331** 70 65
980 32p. "Adoration of the Magi" (illuminated manuscript) (Bardone) 80 70
981 52p. "The Holy Family" (illuminated manuscript) (Bardone) . 1·40 1·90

332 Zig and Zag on Heart

333 Wheelchair Athlete

1996. Greetings Stamps. Multicoloured.
982 32p. Type **332** 95 50
983 32p. Zig and Zag waving . . . 1·25 1·25
984 32p. Zig and Zag in space suits . 1·25 1·25
985 32p. Zig and Zag wearing hats . 1·25 1·25

1996. Olympic and Paralympic Games, Atlanta. Multicoloured.
987 28p. Type **333** 70 65
988 32p. Running 80 80
989 32p. Throwing the discus . . . 80 80
990 32p. Single kayak 80 80

334 Before the Start, Fairyhouse Race Course

1996. Irish Horse Racing. Multicoloured.
991 28p. Type **334** 70 65
992 32p. Steeplechase, Punchestown . 80 80
993 32p. On the Flat, The Curragh . 80 80
994 38p. Steeplechase, Galway . . . 1·25 1·25
995 52p. After the race, Leopardstown . . . . 1·50 1·50

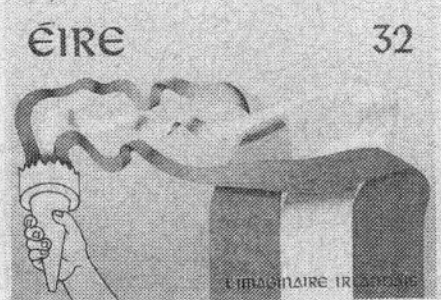

335 Irish and French Coloured Ribbons merging

1996. "L'Imaginaire Irlandais" Festival of Contemporary Irish Arts, France.
996 **335** 32p. multicoloured 80 80

336 Louie Bennett (suffragette)

1996. Europa. Famous Women.
(a) Size 40 × 29 mm. Ordinary gum.
997 **336** 32p. violet 80 70
998 – 44p. green . . . . 1·10 1·25
(b) Size 34 × 23 mm. Self-adhesive.
999 **336** 32p. violet . . . . 90 1·25
1000 – 32p. green . . . . 90 1·25
DESIGN: Nos. 998, 1000. Lady Augusta Gregory (playwright).

337 Newgrange Passage Tomb (Boyne Valley World Heritage Site)

1996. Anniversaries and Events.
1001 **337** 28p. brown and black . . 85 60
1002 – 32p. multicoloured . . . 90 90
DESIGN: 32p. Children playing (50th anniv of U.N.I.C.E.F.).

338 Stanley Woods

1996. Isle of Man Tourist Trophy Motor Cycle Races. Irish Winners. Multicoloured.
1004 32p. Type **338** 80 70
1005 44p. Artie Bell . . . . 1·25 1·50
1006 50p. Alec Bennett . . . . . . 1·50 1·75
1007 52p. Joey and Robert Dunlop . 1·50 1·75

339 Michael Davitt (founder of The Land League)

1996. Anniversaries and Events. Multicoloured.
1009 28p. Type **339** (150th birth anniv) 70 60
1010 32p. Presidency logo (Ireland's Presidency of European Union) (horiz) 80 70

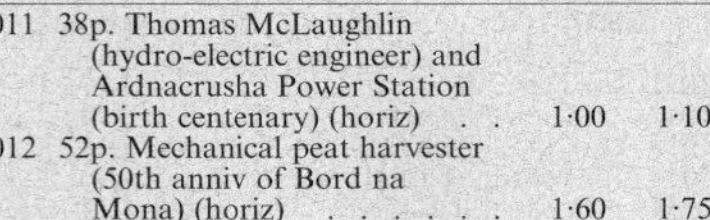
1011 38p. Thomas McLaughlin (hydro-electric engineer) and Ardnacrusha Power Station (birth centenary) (horiz) . . 1·00 1·10
1012 52p. Mechanical peat harvester (50th anniv of Bord na Mona) (horiz) . . . . . . 1·60 1·75

340 "Ciara" (coastal patrol vessel)

1996. 50th Anniv of Irish Naval Service. Multicoloured.
1013 32p. Type **340** 80 70
1014 44p. "Cliona" (corvette) . . . 1·40 1·50
1015 52p. "M-1" (motor torpedo boat) (vert) . . . . 1·50 1·60

341 Blind Woman with Child

1996. People with Disabilities. Multicoloured.
1016 28p. Type **341** 55 60
1017 28p. Man in wheelchair playing bowls 55 60

342 Green-winged Teal

1996. Freshwater Ducks. Multicoloured.
1018 32p. Type **342** 85 70
1019 38p. Common shoveler . . . . 1·00 1·00
1020 44p. European wigeon . . . . 1·25 1·50
1021 52p. Mallard . . . . 1·50 1·75

343 "Man of Aran"

1996. Centenary of Irish Cinema. Multicoloured.
1023 32p. Type **343** 85 90
1024 32p. "My Left Foot" 85 90
1025 32p. "The Commitments" . . 85 90
1026 32p. "The Field" 85 90

344 Visit of the Magi

1996. Christmas. Designs from 16th-century "Book of Hours" (Nos.1028/30). Multicoloured.
1027 28p. The Holy Family 75 60
1028 28p. Type **344** 60 60
1029 32p. The Annunciation 80 75
1030 52p. The Shepherds receiving new of Christ's birth . . . . 1·40 1·60

345 Magpie

346 Pair of Doves

1997. Birds. Ordinary gum. Multicoloured.
(a) Size 21 × 24 mm or 24 × 21 mm.

1031 1p. Type **345** 10 10
1032 2p. Gannet (vert) 10 10
1033 4p. Corncrake (vert) 10 10
1034 5p. Wood pigeon (horiz) . . . 10 10
1035 10p. Kingfisher (vert) 15 20
1036 20p. Lapwing (vert) 30 35
1037 28p. Blue tit (horiz) 45 50
1038 30p. Blackbird (vert) 45 50
1039 30p. Goldcrest (vert) 45 50
1040 30p. Stonechat (vert) 45 50
1041 30p. As No. 1036 . . . . . . 45 50
1042 30p. As No. 1032 . . . . . . 45 50
1043 30p. As No. 1033 . . . . . . 45 50
1044 30p. Type **345** 45 50
1045 30p. As No. 1035 . . . . . . 45 50
1046 30p. Peregrine falcon (vert) . . 45 50
1047 30p. Barn owl (vert) 45 50
1048 30p. Robin (vert) 45 50
1049 30p. Song thrush (vert) 45 50
1050 30p. Wren (vert) 45 50
1051 30p. Pied wagtail (vert) 45 50
1052 30p. Puffin (vert) 45 50
1053 32p. As No. 1048 . . . . . . 50 55
1054 35p. As No. 1040 . . . . . . 50 55
1055 40p. Ringed plover (horiz) . . 60 65
1056 44p. As No. 1052 . . . . . . 70 75
1057 45p. As No. 1049 . . . . . . 70 75
1058 50p. European sparrow hawk (horiz) 80 85
1059 52p. As No. 1047 . . . . . . 80 85

(b) Size 24 × 45 mm or 45 × 24 mm.

1060 £1 Greenland white-fronted goose (vert) . . . . . . 1·60 1·75
1061 £2 Pintail (horiz) . . . . . 3·25 3·50
1062 £5 Shelduck (vert) . . . . . 8·00 8·25

(c) Size 17 × 21 mm or 21 × 17 mm.

1080 4p. Corncake 10 10
1081 5p. Wood pigeon 10 10
1082 30p. Blackbird 45 50
1083 30p. Goldcrest 45 50
1084 32p. Robin 50 55
1085 32p. Peregrine falcon 50 55

(d) Size 25 × 30 mm. Self-adhesive.

1086a 30p. Goldcrest 45 50
1087a 30p. Blackbird 45 50
1088 32p. Peregrine falcon . . . . 1·00 1·00
1089 32p. Robin . . . . 1·00 1·00

1197. Greetings Stamps. Multicoloured.

1100 32p. Type **346** 85 50
1101 32p. Cow jumping over moon . . 1·10 1·10
1102 32p. Pig going to market . . . 1·10 1·10
1103 32p. Cockerel . . . . 1·10 1·10

347 Troops on Parade

1997. 75th Anniv of Irish Free State. Mult.

1105 28p. Page from the "Annals of the Four Masters" and quill, 1944 ½d. O'Clery stamp . . . 55 55
1106 32p. Type **347** 60 65
1107 32p. The Dail, national flag and Constitution 60 65
1108 32p. Athlete, footballer and hurling player 60 65
1109 32p. Singer, violinist and bodhran player 60 65
1110 32p. Stained glass window and 1929 9d. O'Connell stamp . . 60 60
1111 32p. 1923 2d. map stamp and G.P.O., Dublin 60 60
1112 52p. Police personnel and Garda badge . . . . 1·00 1·25
1113 52p. The Four Courts and Scales of Justice . . . . . 1·00 1·25
1114 52p. Currency, blueprint and food-processing plant . . . 1·00 1·25
1115 52p. Books, palette and Seamus Heaney manuscript . . . . 1·00 1·25
1116 52p. Air Lingus airliner and 1965 1s. 5d. air stamp . . . 1·00 1·25

348 Grey Seals

1997. Marine Mammals. Multicoloured.

1118 28p. Type **348** 75 60
1119 32p. Bottle-nosed dolphins . . 85 80
1120 44p. Harbour porpoises (horiz) 1·25 1·40
1121 52p. Killer whale (horiz) . . . 1·40 1·50

349 Dublin Silver Penny of 997

1997. Millenary of Irish Coinage.

1123 **349** 32p. multicoloured . . . 65 65

350 "The Children of Lir"

1997. Europa. Tales and Legends. Multicoloured.
(a) Size 38 × 28 mm. Ordinary gum.

1124 32p. Type **350** 70 60
1125 44p. Oisin and Niamh . . . . 1·00 1·10

(b) Size 36 × 25 mm. Self-adhesive.

1126 32p. Type **350** 70 70
1127 32p. Oisin and Niamh 70 70

351 Emigrants waiting to board Ship

1997. 150th Anniv of The Great Famine.

1128 **351** 28p. blue, red and stone . 75 60
1129 – 32p. orange, bl & stone . 90 70
1130 – 52p. brown, blue & stone . 1·40 1·10

DESIGNS: 32p. Family and dying child; 52p. Irish Society of Friends soup kitchen.

352 Kate O'Brien (novelist) (birth centenary)

1997. Anniversaries. Multicoloured.

1132 28p. Type **352** 60 70
1133 28p. St. Columba crossing to Iona (stained glass window) (1400th death anniv) . . . 60 70
1134 32p. "Daniel O'Connell" (J. Haverty) (politician) (150th death anniv) (27 × 49 mm) 70 70
1135 52p. "John Wesley" (N. Hone) (founder of Methodism) (250th anniv of first visit to Ireland) . . . . 1·25 1·60

353 The Baily Lighthouse

1997. Lighthouses. Multicoloured.

1136 32p. Type **353** 80 80
1137 32p. Tarbert 80 80
1138 38p. Hookhead (vert) 85 85
1139 50p. The Fastnet (vert) . . . . 1·10 1·25

354 Commemorative Cross

355 Dracula and Bat

1997. Ireland–Mexico Joint Issue. 150th Anniv of Mexican St. Patrick's Battalion.

1140 **354** 32p. multicoloured . . . 55 60

1997. Centenary of Publication of Bram Stoker's "Dracula". Multicoloured.

1141 28p. Type **355** 60 55
1142 32p. Dracula and female victim 65 60
1143 38p. Dracula emerging from coffin (horiz) 80 80
1144 52p. Dracula and wolf (horiz) . 1·10 1·10

356 "The Nativity" (Kevin Kelly)

357 Christmas Tree

1997. Christmas. Multicoloured.
(a) Stained-glass Windows. Ordinary gum.

1146 28p. Type **356** 60 55
1147 32p. The Nativity (Sarah Purser and A. E. Child) 70 65
1148 52p. The Nativity (A. E. Child) . . . . 1·25 1·40

(b) Self-adhesive.

1149 28p. Type **357** 55 65

358 Holding Heart

1998. Greetings Stamps (1st series). Designs based on the "love is" cartoon characters of Kim Casali. Multicoloured.

1150 32p. Type **358** 70 50
1151 32p. Receiving letter . . . . . 70 1·00
1152 32p. Sitting on log . . . . . . 70 1·00
1153 32p. With birthday presents . . 70 1·00

See also Nos. 1173/6.

359 Lady Mary Heath and Avro Avian over Pyramids

1998. Pioneers of Irish Aviation. Multicoloured.

1155 28p. Type **359** 60 55
1156 32p. Col. James Fitzmaurice and Junkers W.33 "Bremen" over Labrador 65 60
1157 44p. Captain J. P. Saul and Fokker F.VIIa/3m "Southern Cross" . . . . 1·25 1·25
1158 52p. Captain Charles Blair and Sikorsky V-s 44 (flying boat) 1·50 1·50

360 Show-jumping

1998. Equestrian Sports. Multicoloured.

1159 30p. Type **360** 70 60
1160 32p. Three-day eventing . . . 75 65
1161 40p. Gymkhana . . . . 90 1·25
1162 45p. Dressage (vert) . . . . . 90 1·25

361 Figure of "Liberty"

1998. Bicentenary of United Irish Rebellion. Mult.

1164 30p. Type **361** 90 90
1165 30p. United Irishman 90 90
1166 30p. French soldiers 90 90
1167 45p. Wolfe Tone . . . . . . 1·00 1·25
1168 45p. Henry Joy McCracken . . 1·00 1·25

362 Gathering of the Boats, Kinvara

1998. Europa. Festivals. Multicoloured.
(a) Size 39 × 27 mm.

1169 30p. Type **362** 70 80
1170 40p. Puck Fair, Killorglin . . 80 95

(b) Size 34 × 23 mm. Self-adhesive.

1171 30p. Type **362** 65 70
1172 30p. Puck Fair, Killorglin . . 65 70

1998. Greetings Stamps (2nd series). As Nos. 1105/8, but with changed face value. Multicoloured.

1173 30p. As No. 1153 . . . . . . 70 80
1174 30p. As No. 1152 . . . . . . 70 80
1175 30p. As No. 1151 . . . . . . 70 80
1176 30p. Type **358** 70 80

363 Cyclists rounding Bend

1998. Visit of "Tour de France" Cycle Race to Ireland. Multicoloured.

1177 30p. Type **363** 70 70
1178 30p. Two cyclists ascending hill 70 70
1179 30p. "Green jersey" cyclist and other competitor 70 70
1180 30p. "Yellow jersey" (race leader) 70 70

364 Voter and Local Councillors of 1898

1998. Democracy Anniversaries. Multicoloured.

1181 30p. Type **364** (cent of Local Government (Ireland) Act) . 60 60
1182 32p. European Union flag and harp symbol (25th anniv of Ireland's entry into European Community) 65 65
1183 35p. Woman voter and suffragettes, 1898 (cent of women's right to vote in local elections) 75 75
1184 45p. Irish Republic flag (50th anniv of Republic of Ireland Act) . . . . 1·00 1·00

365 "Asgard II" (cadet brigantine)

366 Ashworth Pillbox (1856)

1998. "Cutty Sark" International Tall Ships Race, Dublin. Multicoloured. (a) Ordinary gum.

1185 30p. Type **365** (26 × 38 mm) . . 55 60
1186 30p. U.S.C.G. "Eagle" (cadet barque) (26 × 38 mm) . . . 55 60
1187 45p. "Boa Esperanza" (replica caravel) (38 × 26 mm) . . . 80 85
1188 £1 "Royalist" (training brigantine) (38 × 26 mm) . . . . 1·75 1·90

(b) Self-adhesive.

1189 30p. "Boa Esperanza" (34 × 23 mm) 55 60
1190 30p. Type **365** (23 × 34 mm) . . 55 60
1191 30p. U.S.C.G. "Eagle" (23 × 34 mm) 55 60
1192 30p. "Royalist" (34 × 23 mm) . 55 60

1998. Irish Postboxes. Multicoloured.

1193 30p. Type **366** 55 65
1194 30p. Irish Free State wallbox (1922) 55 65
1195 30p. Double pillarbox (1899) . . 55 65
1196 30p. Penfold pillarbox (1866) . 55 65

367 Mary Immaculate College, Limerick (centenary)

1998. Anniversaries. Multicoloured.

1197 30p. Type **367** 65 60
1198 40p. Newtown School, Waterford (bicent) (vert) . . 80 90
1199 45p. Trumpeters (50th anniv of Universal Declaration of Human Rights) . . . . . . 95 1·10

368 Cheetah

1998. Endangered Animals. Multicoloured.

1201 30p. Type **368** 75 75
1202 30p. Scimitar-horned oryx . . 75 75
1203 40p. Golden lion tamarin (vert) . . . . 1·00 1·00
1204 45p. Tiger (vert) . . . . . . 1·25 1·25

369 The Holy Family **370** Choir Boys

1998. Christmas. Mult. (a) Ordinary gum.

1206 30p. Type **369** 60 60
1207 32p. Shepherds 65 65
1208 45p. Three Kings . . . . . . 85 1·10

(b) Self-adhesive.

1209 30p. Type **370** 55 60

371 Puppy and Heart **372** Micheal Mac Liammoir

1999. Greetings Stamps. Pets. Multicoloured.

1210 30p. Type **371** 45 50
1211 30p. Kitten and ball of wool . 45 50
1212 30p. Goldfish 45 50
1213 30p. Rabbit with lettuce leaf . 45 50

1999. Irish Actors and Actresses.

1215 **372** 30p. black and brown . . 55 60
1216 – 45p. black and green . . 80 85
1217 – 50p. black and blue . . . 90 95

DESIGNS: 45p. Siobhan McKenna, 50p. Noel Purcell.

373 Irish Emigrant Ship

1999. Ireland-U.S.A. Joint Issue. Irish Emigration.

1218 **373** 45p. multicoloured . . . 80 85

374 "Polly Woodside" (barque) **375** Sean Lemass

1999. Maritime Heritage. Multicoloured.

1219 30p. Type **374** 55 60
1220 35p. "Ilen" (schooner) 65 70
1221 45p. R.N.L.I. Cromer class lifeboat (horiz) 80 85
1222 £1 "Titanic" (liner) (horiz) . . 1·75 1·90

1999. Birth Centenary of Sean Lemass (politician).

1225 **375** 30p. black and green . . 60 65

376 European Currency Emblem

1999. Introduction of Single European Currency.

1226 **376** 30p. multicoloured . . . 60 65

The face value of No. 1226 is shown in both Irish and Euro currency.

377 European Flags **379** Father James Cullen and St. Francis Xavier Church, Dublin

378 Swans, Kilcolman Nature Reserve

1999. 50th Anniv of Council of Europe.

1227 **377** 45p. multicoloured . . . 80 85

1999. Europa. Parks and Gardens. Multicoloured. (a) Size 36 × 26 mm. Ordinary gum.

1228 30p. Type **378** 70 50
1229 40p. Fallow deer, Phoenix Park . . . . 90 1·00

(b) Size 34 × 23 mm. Self-adhesive.

1230 30p. Type **378** 65 65
1231 30p. Fallow deer, Phoenix Park 65 65

1999. Centenary of Pioneer Total Abstinence Association.

1232 **379** 32p. brown, bistre and black 60 65

380 Elderly Man and Child using Computer

1999. International Year of Older Persons.

1233 **380** 30p. multicoloured . . . 60 65

381 Postal Van, 1922

1999. 125th Anniv of Universal Postal Union.

1234 **381** 30p. green and deep green 65 65
1235 – 30p. multicoloured . . . 65 65

DESIGN: No. 1235, Modern postal lorries.

382 Danno Keeffe

1999. Gaelic Athletic Association "Millennium Football Team". Multicoloured. (a) Size 37 × 25 mm. Ordinary gum.

1236 30p. Type **382** 45 50
1237 30p. Enda Colleran 45 50
1238 30p. Joe Keohane 45 50
1239 30p. Sean Flanagan 45 50
1240 30p. Sean Murphy 45 50
1241 30p. John Joe Reilly 45 50
1242 30p. Martin O'Connell 45 50
1243 30p. Mick O'Connell 45 50
1244 30p. Tommy Murphy 45 50
1245 30p. Sean O'Neill 45 50
1246 30p. Sean Purcell 45 50
1247 30p. Pat Spillane 45 50
1248 30p. Mikey Sheehy 45 50
1249 30p. Tom Langan 45 50
1250 30p. Kevin Heffernan 45 50

(b) Size 33 × 23 mm. Self-adhesive.

1251 30p. Type **382** 45 50
1252 30p. Enda Colleran 45 50
1253 30p. Joe Keohane 45 50
1254 30p. Sean Flanagan 45 50
1255 30p. Sean Murphy 45 50
1256 30p. John Joe Reilly 45 50
1257 30p. Martin O'Connell 45 50
1258 30p. Mick O'Connell 45 50
1259 30p. Tommy Murphy 45 50
1260 30p. Sean O'Neill 45 50
1261 30p. Sean Purcell 45 50
1262 30p. Pat Spillane 45 50
1263 30p. Mikey Sheehy 45 50
1264 30p. Tom Langan 45 50
1265 30p. Kevin Heffernan 45 50

383 Douglas DC3

1999. Commercial Aviation. Multicoloured.

1266 30p. Type **383** 45 50
1267 32p. Britten Norman Islander . 50 55
1268 40p. Boeing 707 . . . . 60 65
1269 45p. Lockheed Constellation . 70 75

384 Mammoth **386** Grace Kelly (American actress)

385 Holy Family

1999. Extinct Irish Animals. Multicoloured. (a) Size 26 × 38 mm (vert) or 38 × 26 mm (horiz). Ordinary gum.

1270 30p. Type **384** 45 50
1271 30p. Giant deer 45 50
1272 45p. Wolves (horiz) 70 75
1273 45p. Brown bear (horiz) . . . 70 75

(b) Size 33 × 23 mm (horiz) or 22 × 34 mm (vert). Self-adhesive.

1275 30p. Brown bear (horiz) . . . 45 50
1276 30p. Type **384** 45 50
1277 30p. Wolves (horiz) 45 50
1278 30p. Giant deer 45 50

1999. Christmas. Children's Nativity Plays. Mult. (a) Size 35 × 25 mm. Ordinary gum.

1279 30p. Type **385** 45 50
1280 32p. Visit of the Shepherds . . 50 55
1281 45p. Adoration of the Magi . . 70 75

(b) Size 16 × 26 mm. Self-adhesive.

1282 30p. Angel 55 60

1999. New Millennium (1st issue). Famous People of the 20th Century. Multicoloured.

1283 30p. Type **386** 45 50
1284 30p. Jesse Owens (American athlete) 45 50
1285 30p. John F. Kennedy (former American President) 45 50
1286 30p. Mother Teresa (missionary) 45 50
1287 30p. John McCormack (tenor) . 45 50
1288 30p. Nelson Mandela (South African statesman) 45 50

387 Ruined Castle (Norman Invasion, 1169)

2000. New Millennium (2nd issue). Irish Historic Events. Multicoloured.

1289 30p. Type **387** 45 50
1290 30p. Flight of the Earls, 1607 . 45 50
1291 30p. Opening of Irish Parliament, 1782 . . . . . 45 50
1292 30p. Eviction (formation of the Land League) 45 50
1293 30p. First four Irish Prime Ministers (Irish Independence) 45 50
1294 30p. Irish soldier and personnel carrier (U.N. Peace-keeping) 45 50

388 Frog Prince **389** Revd. Nicholas Callan (electrical scientist)

2000. Greetings Stamps. Mythical Creatures. Multicoloured.

1295 30p. Type **388** 45 50
1296 30p. Pegasus 45 50
1297 30p. Unicorn 45 50
1298 30p. Dragon 45 50

2000. New Millennium (3rd issue). Discoveries. Multicoloured.

1300 30p. Type **389** 45 50
1301 30p. Birr Telescope 45 50
1302 30p. Thomas Edison (inventor of light bulb) 45 50
1303 30p. Albert Einstein (mathematical physicist) 45 50
1304 30p. Marie Curie (physicist) . . 45 50
1305 30p. Galileo (astronomer and mathematician) 45 50

390 "Jeanie Johnston" (emigrant ship)

2000. Completion of "Jeanie Johnston" Replica.

1306 **390** 30p. multicoloured . . . 45 50

POSTAGE DUE STAMPS

D 1

1925.

D 1 D 1 ½d. green . . . . 12·00 16·00
D 6 1d. red . . . . 1·50 70
D 7 1½d. red . . . . 1·75 6·50
D 8 2d. green . . . . 2·75 70
D 9 3d. blue . . . . 2·25 2·75
D10 5d. violet . . . . 4·50 3·00
D11a 6d. plum 80 90
D12 8d. orange . . . . . . 8·50 8·00
D13 10d. purple . . . . . . 8·50 7·50
D14 1s. green . . . . 6·00 9·00

1971. Decimal Currency. Colours changed.

D15 D 1 1p. brown 30 60
D16 1½p. green . . . . 60 1·50
D17 3p. stone . . . . 90 2·00
D18 4p. orange . . . . . . 90 1·25
D19 5p. blue . . . . 95 3·00
D20 7p. yellow . . . . . . 40 3·50
D21 8p. red . . . . 40 2·75

D 2 D 3

1980.

D25 D 2 1p. green 30 55
D26 2p. blue 30 55
D27 4p. green 40 55
D28 6p. flesh 40 70
D29 8p. blue 40 75
D30 18p. green . . . . . . 75 1·25
D31 20p. red . . . . 2·25 4·50
D32 24p. green . . . . . . 75 2·00
D33 30p. violet . . . . . . 3·00 5·50
D34 50p. pink . . . . 3·75 6·50

1988.

D35 D 3 1p. black, red & yellow . . 10 10
D36 2p. black, red & brown . . 10 10
D37 3p. black, red & purple . . 10 10
D38 4p. black, red & violet . . 10 10
D39 5p. black, red & blue . . 10 10
D40 17p. black, red & green . . 30 35
D41 20p. black, red & blue . . 35 40
D42 24p. black, red & green . . 40 45
D43 30p. black, red & grey . . 50 55
D44 50p. black, red & grey . . 90 95
D45 £1 black, red & brown . . 1·75 1·90

ISLE OF MAN Pt. 1

An island in the Irish Sea to the north-west of England. Man became a possession of the English Crown during the Middle Ages, but retains its own Assembly.

Regional issues from 1958–71 are listed at end of "GREAT BRITAIN".

Isle of Man had an independent postal administration from 1973.

100 pence = 1 pound

4 Castletown

5 Manx Cat

1973. Multicoloured.

12	½p. Type **4**	10	10
13	1p. Port Erin	10	10
14	1½p. Snaefell	10	10
15	2p. Laxey	10	10
16	2½p. Tynwald Hill	10	10
17	3p. Douglas Promenade	10	10
18	3½p. Port St. Mary	15	15
19	4p. Fairy Bridge	15	15
20	4½p. As 2½p.	20	20
21	5p. Peel	20	20
22	5½p. As 3p.	25	25
23	6p. Cregneish	25	25
24	7p. As 2p.	30	30
25	7½p. Ramsey Bay	25	25
26	8p. As 7½p.	35	35
27	9p. Douglas Bay	30	35
28	10p. Type **5**	40	35
29	11p. Monk's Bridge, Ballasalla	30	30
30	13p. Derbyhaven	40	40
31	20p. Manx loaghtyn ram	50	50
32	50p. Manx shearwater	1·50	1·25
33	£1 Viking longship	3·00	2·50

SIZES: Nos. 13/27 and 29/30 as Type **4**; Nos. 31/3 as Type **5**.

6 Viking Landing on Man, A.D. 938

1973. Inauguration of Postal Independence.

34 **6**	15p. multicoloured	60	60

7 No. 1 "Sutherland", 1873

1973. Cent of Steam Railway. Multicoloured.

35	2½p. Type **7**	20	20
36	3p. No. 4 "Caledonia", 1885	20	20
37	7½p. No. 13 "Kissack", 1910	80	90
38	9p. No. 3 "Pender", 1873	1·00	90

8 Leonard Randles, First Winner, 1923

1973. Golden Jubilee of Manx Grand Prix. Multicoloured.

39	3p. Type **8**	30	20
40	3½p. Alan Holmes, Double Winner, 1957	30	20

9 Princess Anne and Capt. Mark Phillips

1973. Royal Wedding.

41 **9**	25p. multicoloured	1·00	1·00

10 Badge, Citation and Sir William Hillary (founder)

1974. 150th Anniv of Royal National Lifeboat Institution. Multicoloured.

42	3p. Type **10**	10	10
43	3½p. Wreck of "St. George", 1830	15	15
44	8p. R.N.L.B. "Manchester and Salford", 1868–87	40	40
45	10p. R.N.L.B. "Osman Gabriel"	45	45

11 Stanley Woods, 1935

1974. Tourist Trophy Motor-cycle Races (1st issue). Multicoloured.

46	3p. Type **11**	10	10
47	3½p. Freddy Frith, 1937	10	10
48	8p. Max Deubel and Emil Horner, 1961	45	45
49	10p. Mike Hailwood, 1961	60	45

See also Nos. 63/6.

12 Rushen Abbey and Arms

1974. Historical Anniversaries. Multicoloured.

50	3½p. Type **12**	10	10
51	4½p. Magnus Haraldson rows King Edgar on the Dee	10	10
52	8p. King Magnus and Norse fleet	40	40
53	10p. Bridge at Avignon and bishop's mitre	50	50

COMMEMORATIONS: Nos. 50 and 53, William Russell, Bishop of Sodor and Man, 600th death anniv; Nos. 51/2, 1000th anniv of rule of King Magnus Haraldson.

13 Churchill and Bugler Dunne at Colenso, 1899

1974. Birth Centenary of Sir Winston Churchill. Multicoloured.

54	3½p. Type **13**	10	10
55	4½p. Churchill and Government Buildings, Douglas	10	10
56	8p. Churchill and Manx ack-ack crew	25	35
57	20p. Churchill as Freeman of Douglas	75	55

14 Cabin School and Names of Pioneers

1975. Manx Pioneers in Cleveland, Ohio. Multicoloured.

59	4½p. Type **14**	10	10
60	5½p. Terminal Tower Building, J. Gill and R. Carran	15	10
61	8p. Clague House Museum, and Robert and Margaret Clague	35	40
62	10p. S.S. "William T. Graves" and Thomas Quayle	50	50

15 Tom Sheard, 1923

1975. Tourist Trophy Motor-cycle Races (2nd issue). Multicoloured.

63	5½p. Type **15**	20	15
64	7p. Walter Handley, 1925	30	20
65	10p. Geoff Duke, 1955	50	30
66	12p. Peter Williams, 1973	50	45

16 Sir George Goldie and Birthplace

1975. 50th Death Anniv of Sir George Goldie. Multicoloured.

67	5½p. Type **16**	10	15
68	7p. Goldie and map of Africa (vert)	20	20
69	10p. Goldie as President of Geographical Society (vert)	40	30
70	12p. River scene on the Niger	40	45

17 Title Page of Manx Bible

18 William Christian listening to Patrick Henry

1975. Christmas and Bicentenary of Manx Bible. Multicoloured.

71	5½p. Type **17**	15	15
72	7p. Rev. Philip Moore and Ballaugh Old Church	20	20
73	11p. Bishop Hildesley and Bishops Court	35	35
74	13p. John Kelly saving Bible manuscript	40	40

1976. Bicent of American Independence. Mult.

75	5½p. Type **18**	15	15
76	7p. Conveying the Fincastle Resolutions	20	20
77	13p. Patrick Henry and William Christian	35	35
78	20p. Christian as an Indian fighter	50	50

19 First Horse Tram, 1876

1976. Cent of Douglas Horse-Trams. Mult.

80	5½p. Type **19**	10	15
81	7p. "Toast-rack" tram, 1890	15	15
82	11p. Horse-bus, 1895	45	35
83	13p. Royal tram, 1972	50	45

20 Barrose Beaker

21 Diocesan Banner

1976. Europa. Ceramic Art. Multicoloured.

84	5p. Type **20**	25	20
85	5p. Souvenir teapot	25	20
86	5p. Laxey jug	25	20
87	10p. Cronk Aust food vessel (horiz)	40	35
88	10p. Sansbury bowl (horiz)	40	35
89	10p. Knox urn (horiz)	40	35

1976. Christmas and Centenary of Mothers' Union. Multicoloured.

90	6p. Type **21**	15	15
91	7p. Onchan banner	15	15
92	11p. Castletown banner	40	35
93	13p. Ramsey banner	40	45

22 Queen Elizabeth II

1977. Silver Jubilee. Multicoloured.

94	6p. Type **22**	20	20
95	7p. Queen Elizabeth and Prince Philip (vert)	20	20
96	25p. Queen Elizabeth (different)	80	70

23 Carrick Bay from "Tom-the-Dipper"

1977. Europa. Landscapes. Multicoloured.

97	6p. Type **23**	20	20
98	10p. View from Ramsey	30	30

24 F. A. Applebee, 1912

1977. Linked Anniversaries. Multicoloured.

99	6p. Type **24**	20	15
100	7p. St. John's Ambulance Brigade at Governor's Bridge, 1938	20	20
101	11p. Scouts operating the scoreboard	50	40
102	13p. John Williams, 1976	50	40

The events commemorated are: 70th anniv of Manx TT races; 70th anniv of Boy Scouts; Centenary of St. John's Ambulance Brigade.

25 Old Summer House, Mount Morrison, Peel

27 Watch Tower, Langness

1977. Bicent of First Visit of John Wesley. Multicoloured.

103	6p. Type **25**	20	15
104	7p. Wesley preaching in Castletown Square	30	20
105	11p. Wesley preaching outside Braddan Church	45	35
106	13p. New Methodist Church, Douglas	50	40

Nos. 104/5 are larger, 38 × 26 mm.

26 Short Type 184 Seaplane and H.M.S. "Ben-My-Chree", 1915

1978. 60th Anniv of Royal Air Force. Mult.

107	6p. Type **26**	20	15
108	7p. Bristol Scout C and H.M.S. "Vindex", 1915	30	20
109	11p. Boulton Paul Defiant over Douglas Bay, 1941	45	35
110	13p. Sepecat Jaguar over Ramsey, 1977	50	40

1978. Multicoloured.

111	½p. Type **27**	10	10
112	1p. Jurby Church (horiz)	10	10
113	6p. Government Buildings	30	30
114	7p. Tynwald Hill (horiz)	35	35
115	8p. Milner's Tower	25	25
116	9p. Laxey Wheel	35	35
117a	10p. Castle Rushen (horiz)	35	35
118	11p. St. Ninian's Church	40	40
119a	12p. Tower of Refuge (horiz)	50	40
120a	13p. St. German's Cathedral (horiz)	40	40
121a	14p. Point of Ayre Lighthouse (horiz)	50	50
122a	15p. Corrin's Tower (horiz)	40	40
123	16p. Douglas Head Lighthouse (horiz)	90	90
124	20p. Fuchsia	40	40
125	25p. Manx cat	50	50
126	50p. Chough	1·00	1·00
127	£1 Viking warrior	2·00	2·00
128	£2 Queen Elizabeth II	4·50	4·50

Nos. 124/7 are larger, 25 × 31 mm and No. 128, 38 × 48 mm.

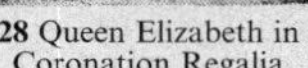

28 Queen Elizabeth in Coronation Regalia — **29** Wheel-headed Cross-slab

1978. 25th Anniv of Coronation.

132 **28** 25p. multicoloured 75 75

1978. Europa. Celtic and Norse Crosses. Multicoloured.

133 6p. Type **29** 20 15
134 6p. Celtic wheel-cross 20 15
135 6p. Keeil Chiggyrt Stone . . . 20 15
136 11p. Olaf Liotulfson Cross . . 35 30
137 11p. Odd's and Thorleif's Crosses 35 30
138 11p. Thor Cross 35 30

30 J. K. Ward and Ward Library, Peel

1978. Anniversaries and Events. Multicoloured.

139 6p. Type **30** 15 15
140 7p. Swimmer, cyclist and walker (42 × 26 mm) 20 20
141 11p. American bald eagle, Manx arms and maple leaf (42 × 26 mm) 35 35
142 13p. Lumber camp, Three Rivers, Quebec 40 40

ANNIVERSARIES AND EVENTS: 6, 13p. James Kewley Ward (Manx pioneer in Canada) commemoration; 7p. Commonwealth Games, Edmonton; 11p. 50th anniv of North American Manx Association.

31 Hunt the Wren — **33** Postman, 1859

32 P. M. C. Kermode and "Nassa kermodei"

1978. Christmas.

143 **31** 5p. multicoloured 50 50

1979. Centenary of Natural History and Antiquarian Society. Multicoloured.

144 6p. Type **32** 15 15
145 7p. Peregrine falcon 20 20
146 11p. Fulmar 35 35
147 13p. "Epitriptus cowini" (fly) . 40 40

1979. Europa. Communications. Multicoloured.

148 6p. Type **33** 25 25
149 11p. Postman, 1979 . . . . . 50 50

34 Viking Longship Emblem — **35** Viking Raid at Garwick

1979. Millennium of Tynwald. Multicoloured.

150b 3p. Type **34** 10 10
151 4p. "Three Legs of Man" emblem 15 15
152 6p. Type **35** 15 15
153 7p. 10th-century meeting of Tynwald 20 20
154 11p. Tynwald Hill and St. John's Church 30 30
155 13p. Procession to Tynwald Hill 45 35

The 4p. value is as Type **34** and the remainder as Type **35**.

36 Queen and Court on Tynwald Hill

1979. Royal Visit. Multicoloured.

156 7p. Type **36** 35 35
157 13p. Queen and procession from St. John's Church to Tynwald Hill 50 50

37 "Odin's Raven"

1979. Voyage of "Odin's Raven".

158 **37** 15p. multicoloured 70 70

38 John Quilliam seized by the Press Gang

1979. 150th Death Anniv of Captain John Quilliam. Multicoloured.

159 6p. Type **38** 15 15
160 8p. Steering H.M.S. "Victory", Battle of Trafalgar 20 20
161 13p. Captain John Quilliam and H.M.S. "Spencer" 35 35
162 15p. Captain John Quilliam (member of the House of Keys) 40 40

39 Young Girl with Teddybear and Cat

1979. Christmas. Int Year of the Child. Mult.

163 5p. Type **39** 25 25
164 7p. Father Christmas with young children 35 35

40 Conglomerate Arch, Langness

1980. 150th Anniv of Royal Geographical Society. Multicoloured.

165 7p. Type **40** 20 20
166 8p. Braaid Circle 20 20
167 12p. Cashtal-yn-Ard 25 25
168 13p. Volcanic rocks at Scarlett 35 35
169 15p. Sugar-loaf Rock 40 40

41 "Mona's Isle I"

1980. 150th Anniv of Isle of Man Steam Packet Company. Multicoloured.

170 7p. Type **41** 20 20
171 8p. "Douglas I" 20 20
172 11½p. H.M.S. "Mona's Queen II" sinking U-boat 30 30
173 12p. H.M.S. "King Orry III" at surrender of German fleet, 1918 . . . . 30 30
174 13p. "Ben-My-Chree IV" . . . 40 35
175 15p. "Lady of Mann II" . . . 50 40

42 Stained Glass Window, T. E. Brown Room, Manx Museum

1980. Europa. Personalities. Thomas Edward Brown (poet and scholar) Commemoration. Multicoloured.

177 7p. Type **42** 20 20
178 13½p. Clifton College, Bristol . 40 40

43 King Olav V and "Norge" (Norwegian royal yacht)

1980. Visit of King Olav of Norway, August 1979.

179 **43** 12p. multicoloured 50 50

44 Winter Wren and View of Calf of Man

1980. Christmas and Wildlife Conservation Year. Multicoloured.

181 6p. Type **44** 20 20
182 8p. European robin and view of Port Erin Marine Biological Station 30 30

45 William Kermode and Brig "Robert Quayle", 1819 — **46** Peregrine Falcon

1980. Kermode Family in Tasmania Commemoration. Multicoloured.

183 7p. Type **45** 20 20
184 9p. "Mona Vale", Van Diemen's Land, 1834 . . . . 25 25
185 13½p. Ross Bridge, Tasmania . 40 35
186 15p. "Mona Vale", Tasmania (completed 1868) 45 40
187 17½p. Robert Quayle Kermode and Parliament Buildings, Tasmania 50 45

1980. Multicoloured.

188 1p. Type **46** 40 40
189 5p. Loaghtyn ram 40 40

47 Luggers passing Red Pier, Douglas

1981. Centenary of Royal National Mission to Deep Sea Fishermen. Multicoloured.

190 8p. Type **47** 25 25
191 9p. Peel Lugger "Wanderer" rescuing survivors from "Lusitania" 30 30
192 18p. Nickeys leaving Port St. Mary 45 45
193 20p. Nobby entering Ramsey Harbour 50 50
194 22p. Nickeys "Sunbeam" and "Zebra" at Port Erin . . . 50 50

48 "Crosh Cuirn" Superstition

1981. Europa. Folklore. Multicoloured.

195 8p. Type **48** 25 25
196 18p. "Bollan Cross" superstition 75 75

49 Lt. Mark Wilks (Royal Manx Fencibles) and Peel Castle

1981. 150th Death Anniv of Colonel Mark Wilks. Multicoloured.

197 8p. Type **49** 25 25
198 20p. Ensign Mark Wilks and Fort St. George, Madras 50 50
199 22p. Governor Mark Wilks and Napoleon, St. Helena 70 55
200 25p. Col. Mark Wilks (Speaker of the House of Keys) and estate, Kirby 80 80

50 Miss Emmeline Goulden (Mrs. Pankhurst) and Mrs. Sophia Jane Goulden

1981. Centenary of Manx Women's Suffrage.

201 **50** 9p. black, grey and stone . . 50 50

51 Prince Charles and Lady Diana Spencer

1981. Royal Wedding.

202 **51** 9p. black, blue and lt blue . . 50 50
203 25p. black, blue and pink . . 1·50 1·50

52 Douglas War Memorial, Poppies and Commemorative Inscription

1981. 60th Anniv of The Royal British Legion. Multicoloured.

205 8p. Type **52** 25 25
206 10p. Major Robert Cain (war hero) 30 35
207 18p. Festival of Remembrance, Royal Albert Hall 65 65
208 20p. T.S.S. "Tynwald" at Dunkirk, May 1940 . . . . 75 75

53 Nativity Scene (stained glass window, St. George's Church)

1981. Christmas. Multicoloured.

209 7p. Type **53** 25 25
210 9p. Children from Special School performing nativity play (48 × 30 mm) 35 35

54 Joseph and William Cunningham (founders of Isle of Man Boy Scout Movement) and Cunningham House Headquarters

1982. 75th Anniv of Boy Scout Movement and 125th Birth Anniv of Lord Baden-Powell. Multicoloured.

211 9p. Type **54** 30 30
212 10p. Baden-Powell visiting Isle of Man, 1911 . . . . 30 30
213 19½p. Baden-Powell and Scout emblem (40 × 31 mm) 60 60
214 24p. Scouts and Baden-Powell's last message 70 70
215 29p. Scout salute, handshake, emblem and globe 90 90

55 "The Principals and Duties of Christianity" (Bishop T. Wilson) (first book printed in Manx, 1707)

1982. Europa. Historic Events. Multicoloured.

No.	Description	Unused	Used
216	9p. Type **55**	25	25
217	19½p. Landing at Derbyhaven (visit of Thomas, 2nd Earl of Derby, 1507)	50	50

56 Charlie Collier (first TT race (single cylinder) winner) and Tourist Trophy Race, 1907

1982. 75th Anniv of Tourist Trophy Motorcycle Racing. Multicoloured.

No.	Description	Unused	Used
218	9p. Type **56**	20	20
219	10p. Freddie Dixon (Sidecar and Junior TT winner) and Junior TT Race, 1927	25	25
220	24p. Jimmie Simpson (TT winner and first to lap at 60, 70 and 80 mph) and Senior TT, 1932	80	70
221	26p. Mike Hailwood (winner of fourteen TT's) and Senior TT, 1961	85	75
222	29p. Jock Taylor (Sidecar TT winner, 1978, 1980 and 1981) and Sidecar TT (with Benga Johansson), 1980	1·00	90

57 "Mona I"

1982. 150th Anniv of Isle of Man Steam Packet Company Mail Contract. Multicoloured.

No.	Description	Unused	Used
223	12p. Type **57**	50	50
224	19½p. "Manx Maid II"	75	75

58 Three Wise Men bearing Gifts

1982. Christmas. Multicoloured.

No.	Description	Unused	Used
225	8p. Type **58**	50	50
226	11p. Christmas snow scene (vert)	50	50

60 Opening of Salvation Army Citadel, and T. H. Cannell, J.P.

1983. Centenary of Salvation Army in Isle of Man. Multicoloured.

No.	Description	Unused	Used
228	10p. Type **60**	30	30
229	12p. Early meeting place and Gen. William Booth	40	40
230	19½p. Salvation Army band	60	60
231	26p. Treating lepers and Lt.-Col. Thomas Bridson	90	90

61 Atlantic Puffins

61a "Queen Elizabeth II" (Ricardo Macarron)

1983. Sea Birds. Multicoloured.

No.	Description	Unused	Used
232	1p. Type **61**	30	30
233	2p. Northern gannets	30	30
234	5p. Lesser black-backed gulls	60	40
235	8p. Common cormorants	60	40
236	10p. Kittiwakes	60	35
237	11p. Shags	60	35
238	12p. Grey herons	70	40
239	13p. Herring gulls	70	40
240	14p. Razorbills	70	40
241	15p. Great black-backed gulls	80	50
242	16p. Common shelducks	80	50
243	18p. Oystercatchers	80	60
244	20p. Arctic terns	90	1·00
245	25p. Common guillemots	1·00	1·00
246	50p. Redshanks	1·75	1·75
247	£1 Mute swans	3·25	3·00
248	£5 Type **61a**	12·00	12·00

Nos. 244/7 are larger, 39 × 26 mm.

62 Design Drawings by Roger Casement for the Great Laxey Wheel (½-size illustration)

1983. Europa. The Great Laxey Wheel.

No.	Type	Description	Unused	Used
249	62	10p. black, blue and buff	40	35
250	–	20½p. multicoloured	60	70

DESIGN: 20½p. Roger Casement and the Great Laxey Wheel.

63 Nick Keig (international yachtsman) and Trimaran "Three Legs of Man III"

1983. 150th Anniv of King William's College. Multicoloured.

No.	Description	Unused	Used
251	10p. Type **63**	20	20
252	12p. King William's College, Castletown	30	30
253	28p. Sir William Bragg (winner of Nobel Prize for Physics) and spectrometer	80	80
254	31p. General Sir George White, V.C. and action at Charasiah	1·00	1·00

64 New Post Office Headquarters, Douglas

1983. World Communications Year and 10th Anniv of Isle of Man Post Office Authority. Multicoloured.

No.	Description	Unused	Used
255	10p. Type **64**	40	40
256	15p. As Type **64** but inscr "POST OFFICE DECENNIUM 1983"	60	60

65 Shepherds

1983. Christmas. Multicoloured.

No.	Description	Unused	Used
257	9p. Type **65**	50	50
258	12p. Three Kings	50	50

66 "Manx King" (full-rigged ship)

1984. The Karran Fleet. Multicoloured.

No.	Description	Unused	Used
259	10p. Type **66**	40	40
260	13p. "Hope" (barque)	55	55
261	20½p. "Rio Grande" (brig)	85	85
262	28p. "Lady Elizabeth" (barque)	1·00	1·00
263	31p. "Sumatra" (barque)	1·10	1·10

67 C.E.P.T. 25th Anniversary Logo

69 Window from Glencrutchery House, Douglas

68 Railway Air Services De Havilland D.H.84 Dragon Mk 2

1984. Europa.

No.	Type	Description	Unused	Used
265	67	10p. orange, brown and light orange	35	35
266		20½p. blue, deep blue and light blue	70	70

1984. 50th Anniv of First Official Airmail to the Isle of Man and 40th Anniv of International Civil Aviation Organization. Multicoloured.

No.	Description	Unused	Used
267	11p. Type **68**	45	45
268	13p. West Coast Air Services De Havilland D.H. 86A Dragon Express "Ronaldsway"	55	55
269	26p. B.E.A. Douglas DC-3	1·00	1·00
270	28p. B.E.A. Vickers Viscount 800	1·10	1·10
271	31p. Telair Britten Norman Islander	1·40	1·40

1984. Christmas. Stained-glass Windows. Multicoloured.

No.	Description	Unused	Used
272	10p. Type **69**	50	50
273	13p. Window from Lonan Old Church	50	50

70 William Cain's Birthplace, Ballasalla

1984. William Cain (civic leader, Victoria) Commemoration. Multicoloured.

No.	Description	Unused	Used
274	11p. Type **70**	35	35
275	22p. The "Anna" leaving Liverpool, 1852	75	75
276	28p. Early Australian railway	1·00	1·00
277	30p. William Cain as Mayor of Melbourne, and Town Hall	1·10	1·10
278	33p. Royal Exhibition Building, Melbourne	1·25	1·25

71 Queen Elizabeth II and Commonwealth Parliamentary Association Badge

1984. Links with the Commonwealth. 30th Commonwealth Parliamentary Association Conference. Multicoloured.

No.	Description	Unused	Used
279	14p. Type **71**	50	50
280	33p. Queen Elizabeth II and Manx emblem	1·10	1·10

72 Cunningham House Headquarters and Mrs. Willie Cunningham and Mrs. Joseph Cunningham (former Commissioners)

1985. 75th Anniv of Girl Guide Movement. Multicoloured.

No.	Description	Unused	Used
281	11p. Type **72**	45	45
282	14p. Princess Margaret, Isle of Man standard and guides	75	75
283	29p. Lady Olave Baden-Powell opening Guide Headquarters, 1955	1·10	1·10
284	31p. Guide uniforms from 1910 to 1985	1·40	1·40
285	34p. Guide handclasp, salute and early badge	1·60	1·60

73 Score of Manx National Anthem

1985. Europa. European Music Year.

No.	Type	Description	Unused	Used
286	73	12p. black, light brown and brown	50	45
287	–	12p. black, light brown and brown	50	45
288	–	22p. black, lt blue and blue	1·00	95
289	–	22p. black, lt blue and blue	1·00	95

DESIGNS: No. 287, William H. Gill (lyricist); 288, Score of hymn "Crofton"; 289, Dr. John Clague (composer).

74 Charles Rolls in 20 h.p. Rolls-Royce (1906 Tourist Trophy Race)

1985. Century of Motoring. Multicoloured.

No.	Description	Unused	Used
290	12p. Type **74**	40	40
291	12p. W. Bentley in 3 litre Bentley (1922 Tourist Trophy Race)	40	40
292	14p. F. Gerrard in E.R.A. (1950 British Empire Trophy Race)	55	55
293	14p. Brian Lewis in Alfa Romeo (1934 Mannin Moar Race)	55	55
294	31p. Jaguar "XJ-SC" ("Roads Open" car, 1984 Motor Cycle TT Races)	1·40	1·25
295	31p. Tony Pond and Mike Nicholson in Vauxhall "Chevette" (1981 Rothmans International Rally)	1·40	1·25

75 Queen Alexandra and Victorian Sergeant with Wife

1985. Centenary of Soldiers', Sailors' and Airmen's Families Association. Association Presidents. Multicoloured.

No.	Description	Unused	Used
296	12p. Type **75**	40	40
297	15p. Queen Mary and Royal Air Force family	55	55
298	29p. Earl Mountbatten and Royal Navy family	1·10	1·10
299	34p. Prince Michael of Kent and Royal Marine with parents, 1982	1·25	1·25

76 Kirk Maughold (birthplace)

1985. Birth Bicentenary of Lieutenant-General Sir Mark Cubbon (Indian administrator). Mult.

No.	Description	Unused	Used
300	12p. Type **76**	45	45
301	22p. Lieutenant-General Sir Mark Cubbon (vert)	1·10	1·10
302	45p. Memorial statue, Bangalore, India (vert)	1·90	1·90

77 St. Peter's Church, Onchan

1985. Christmas. Manx Churches. Multicoloured.

303 11p. Type **77** 45 45
304 14p. Royal Chapel of St. John, Tynwald 55 55
305 31p. Bride Parish Church . . . 1·25 1·25

78 Swimming

1986. Commonwealth Games, Edinburgh. Multicoloured.

306 12p. Type **78** 40 40
307 15p. Race walking 50 50
308 31p. Rifle-shooting . . . . . 1·50 1·50
309 34p. Cycling . . . . 1·50 1·50

No. 309 also commemorates the 50th anniversary of Manx International Cycling Week.

79 Viking Necklace and Peel Castle

1986. Centenary of Manx Museum. Multicoloured.

310 12p. Type **79** 35 35
311 15p. Meayll Circle, Rushen . . 45 45
312 22p. Skeleton of Great Deer and Manx Museum (vert) . . . . 1·00 1·00
313 26p. Viking longship model (vert) 1·25 1·25
314 29p. Open Air Museum, Cregneash . . . . 1·40 1·40

80 Viking Longship

81 "Usnea articulata" (lichen) and "Neotinea intacta" (orchid), The Ayres

1986. Manx Heritage Year.

315 **80** 2p. multicoloured 25 25
316 – 10p. black, green and grey 75 75

DESIGN: 10p. Celtic cross logo.

1986. Europa. Protection of Nature and the Environment. Multicoloured.

317 12p. Type **81** 60 60
318 12p. Hen harrier, Calf of Man 60 60
319 22p. Manx stoat, Eary Cushlin 95 95
320 22p. "Stenobothus stigmaticus" (grasshopper), St. Michael's Isle 95 95

82 Ellanbane (home of Myles Standish)

1986. "Ameripex '86" International Stamp Exhibition, Chicago. Captain Myles Standish of the "Mayflower". Multicoloured.

321 12p. Type **82** 35 35
322 15p. "Mayflower" crossing the Atlantic, 1620 . . . . 55 55
323 31p. Pilgrim Fathers landing at Plymouth, 1620 . . . . . . 1·40 1·40
324 34p. Captain Myles Standish 1·60 1·60

83 Prince Andrew in Naval Uniform and Miss Sarah Ferguson

1986. Royal Wedding. Multicoloured.

326 15p. Type **83** 75 75
327 40p. Engagement photograph . 1·75 1·50

84 Prince Philip (from photo by Karsh)

85 European Robins on Globe and "Peace and Goodwill" in Braille

1986. Royal Birthdays. Multicoloured.

328 15p. Type **84** 80 80
329 15p. Queen Elizabeth II (from photo by Karsh) 80 80
330 34p. Queen Elizabeth and Prince Philip (from photo by Karsh) (48 × 35 mm) . . . . 1·75 1·75

Nos. 328/30 also commemorate "Stockholmia '86" International Stamp Exhibition, Sweden and the 350th anniversary of the Swedish Post Office.

1986. Christmas and International Peace Year. Multicoloured.

331 11p. Type **85** 50 50
332 14p. Hands releasing peace dove 55 55
333 31p. Clasped hands and "Peace" in sign language . . . . . . 1·25 1·25

86 North Quay

1987. Victorian Douglas. Multicoloured.

334 2p. Type **86** 10 10
335 3p. Old Fishmarket 10 10
336 10p. The Breakwater 35 35
337 15p. Jubilee Clock 50 50
338 31p. Loch Promenade . . . . 1·60 1·60
339 34p. Beach . . . . 1·90 1·90

87 "The Old Fishmarket and Harbour, Douglas"

1987. Paintings by John Miller Nicholson. Multicoloured.

340 12p. Type **87** 35 35
341 26p. "Red Sails at Douglas" . . 90 90
342 29p. "The Double Corner, Peel" . . . . 1·50 1·50
343 34p. "Peel Harbour" . . . . . 1·75 1·75

88 Sea Terminal, Douglas

1987. Europa. Architecture. Multicoloured.

344 12p. Type **88** 60 60
345 12p. Tower of Refuge, Douglas 60 60
346 22p. Gaiety Theatre, Douglas 1·10 1·10
347 22p. Villa Marina, Douglas . . 1·10 1·10

89 Supercharged "BMW" 500cc Motor Cycle, 1939

1987. 80th Anniv of Tourist Trophy Motor Cycle Races. Multicoloured.

348 12p. Type **89** 40 40
349 15p. Manx "Kneeler" Norton 350cc, 1953 . . . . 60 60
350 29p. MV Agusta 500cc 4, 1956 1·00 1·00
351 31p. Guzzi 500cc V8, 1957 . . 1·10 1·10
352 34p. Honda 250cc 6, 1967 . . . 1·40 1·40

Nos. 348/52 also commemorate the Centenary of the St. John Ambulance Brigade.

90 Fuchsia and Wild Roses

91 Stirring the Christmas Pudding

1987. Wild Flowers. Multicoloured.

354 16p. Type **90** 60 60
355 29p. Field scabious and ragwort 1·10 1·10
356 31p. Wood anemone and celandine . . . . 1·25 1·25
357 34p. Violets and primroses . . 1·50 1·50

1987. Christmas. Victorian Scenes. Multicoloured.

358 12p. Type **91** 50 50
359 15p. Bringing home the Christmas tree 75 75
360 31p. Decorating the Christmas tree . . . . 1·25 1·25

92 Russell Brookes in Vauxhall "Opel" (Manx Rally winner, 1985)

1988. Motor Sport. Multicoloured.

361 13p. Type **92** 75 70
362 26p. Ari Vatanen in Ford "Escort" (Manx Rally winner, 1976) . . . . 1·25 1·10
363 31p. Terry Smith in Repco "March 761" (Hill Climb winner, 1980) . . . . 1·40 1·25
364 34p. Nigel Mansell in Williams/Honda (British Grand Prix winner, 1986 and 1987) . . . 1·60 1·40

93 Horse Tram Terminus, Douglas Bay Tramway

93a Queen Elizabeth II taking Salute at Trooping the Colour

1988. Manx Railways and Tramways. Mult.

365 1p. Type **93** 10 10
366 2p. Snaefell Mountain Railway 10 10
367 3p. Marine Drive Tramway . . 10 10
367c 4p. Douglas Cable Tramway . 10 10
368 5p. Douglas Head Incline Railway 20 20
369 10p. Douglas & Laxey Coast Electric Tramway car at Maughold Head 30 30
370 13p. As 4p. 50 50
371 14p. Manx Northern Railway No. 4, "Caledonia", at Gob-y-Deigan 50 50
372 15p. Laxey Mine Railway Lewin locomotive "Ant" 50 50
373 16p. Port Erin Breakwater Tramway locomotive "Henry B. Loch" 50 50
374 17p. Ramsey Harbour Tramway 50 50
375 18p. Locomotive No. 7, "Tynwald", on Foxdale line 55 55
375a 18p. T.P.O. Special leaving Douglas, 3 July 1991 . . . 55 55
376 19p. Baldwin Reservoir Tramway steam locomotive No. 1, "Injebreck" 60 60
377 20p. I.M.R. No. 13, "Kissack", near St. Johns 60 60
377a 21p. As 14p. 60 60
377b 23p. Double-deck horse tram, Douglas 60 60
378 25p. I.M.R. No. 12, "Hutchinson", leaving Douglas 70 70
379 50p. Groudle Glen Railway locomotive "Polar Bear" . . 1·50 1·50
380 £1 I.M.R. No. 11, "Maitland", pulling Royal Train, 1963 . 3·00 3·00
380a £2 Type **93a** . . . . 6·00 6·00

94 Laying Isle of Man–U.K. Submarine Cable

1988. Europa. Transport and Communications. Multicoloured.

381 13p. Type **94** 60 60
382 13p. "Flex Services" (cable ship) 60 60
383 22p. Earth station, Braddan . . 1·00 1·00
384 22p. "INTELSAT 5" satellite 1·00 1·00

Nos. 381/2 and 383/4 were each printed together, se-tenant Nos. 381/2 forming a composite design.

95 "Euterpe" (full-rigged ship) off Ramsey, 1863

1988. Manx Sailing Ships. Multicoloured.

385 16p. Type **95** 50 50
386 29p. "Vixen" (topsail schooner) leaving Peel for Australia, 1853 1·10 1·10
387 31p. "Ramsey" (full-rigged ship) off Brisbane, 1870 . . . . 1·40 1·40
388 34p. "Star of India" (formerly "Euterpe") (barque) off San Diego, 1976 . . . . 1·50 1·50

Nos. 386/7 also commemorate the Bicent of Australian Settlement.

96 "Magellanica"

1988. 50th Anniv of British Fuchsia Society. Multicoloured.

390 13p. Type **96** 50 50
391 16p. "Pink Cloud" 60 60
392 22p. "Leonora" 80 80
393 29p. "Satellite" . . . . 1·10 1·00
394 31p. "Preston Guild" . . . . . 1·25 1·25
395 34p. "Thalia" . . . . 1·40 1·40

97 Long-eared Owl

1988. Christmas. Manx Birds. Multicoloured.

396 12p. Type **97** 70 70
397 15p. European robin . . . . . 1·00 1·00
398 31p. Grey partridge . . . . . 1·60 1·60

98 Ginger Cat

1989. Manx Cats. Multicoloured.

399 16p. Type **98** 50 50
400 27p. Black and white cat . . . 1·00 1·00
401 30p. Tortoiseshell and white cat 1·50 1·50
402 40p. Tortoiseshell cat . . . . . 1·75 1·75

99 Tudric Pewter Clock, c. 1903

1989. 125th Birth Anniv of Archibald Knox (artist and designer). Multicoloured.

403 13p. Type **99** 35 35
404 16p. "Celtic Cross" watercolour 45 45
405 23p. Silver cup and cover 1902–03 . . . . 75 75
406 32p. Gold and silver brooches from Liberty's Cymric range (horiz) . . . . 1·40 1·40
407 35p. Silver jewel box, 1900 (horiz) . . . . 1·50 1·50

100 William Bligh and Old Church, Onchan

1989. Bicentenary of the Mutiny on the "Bounty". Multicoloured.

408 13p. Type **100** 40 40
409 16p. Bligh and loyal crew cast adrift 40 40
410 23p. Pitcairn Islands 1989 Settlement Bicentenary 90 c., No. 345 1·25 1·25
411 27p. Norfolk Island 1989 Bicentenary 39 c., No. 461 1·25 1·25
412 30p. Midshipman Peter Heywood and Tahiti 70 70
413 32p. H.M.S. "Bounty" anchored off Pitcairn Island 75 75
414 35p. Fletcher Christian and Pitcairn Island 80 80

101 Skipping and Hopscotch

1989. Europa. Children's Games. Multicoloured.

416 13p. Type **101** 65 65
417 13p. Wheelbarrow, leapfrog and piggyback 65 65
418 23p. Completing model house and blowing bubbles 1·00 1·00
419 23p. Girl with doll and doll's house 1·00 1·00

Nos. 416/17 and 418/19 were printed together, se-tenant, forming composite designs.

102 Atlantic Puffin

104 Mother with Baby, Jane Crookall Maternity Home

103 Red Cross Cadets learning Resuscitation

1989. Sea Birds. Multicoloured.

420 13p. Type **102** 80 80
421 13p. Black guillemot 80 80
422 13p. Common cormorant 80 80
423 13p. Kittiwake 80 80

1989. 125th Anniv of International Red Cross and Centenary of Noble's Hospital, Isle of Man.

424 **103** 14p. multicoloured 40 40
425 – 17p. grey and red 65 65
426 – 23p. multicoloured 90 90
427 – 30p. multicoloured 1·25 1·25
428 – 35p. multicoloured 1·50 1·50

DESIGNS: 17p. Anniversary logo; 23p. Signing Geneva Convention, 1864; 30p. Red Cross ambulance; 35p. Henri Dunant (founder).

1989. Christmas. 50th Anniv of Jane Crookall Maternity Home and 75th Anniv of St. Ninian's Church, Douglas. Multicoloured.

429 13p. Type **104** 55 55
430 16p. Mother with child 70 70
431 34p. Madonna and Child 1·25 1·25
432 37p. Baptism, St. Ninian's Church 1·40 1·40

105 "The Isle of Man Express going up a Gradient"

1990. Isle of Man Edwardian Postcards. Mult.

433 15p. Type **105** 30 30
434 19p. "A way we have in the Isle of Man" 55 55
435 32p. "Douglas—waiting for the male boat" 1·00 1·00
436 34p. "The last toast rack home, Douglas Parade" 1·40 1·40
437 37p. "The last Isle of Man boat" 1·50 1·50

106 Modern Postman

107 Penny Black

1990. Europa. Post Office Buildings. Mult.

438 15p. Type **106** 65 65
439 15p. Ramsey Post Office, 1990 (40 × 26 mm) 65 65
440 24p. Postman, 1890 1·00 1·00
441 24p. Douglas Post Office, 1890 (40 × 26 mm) 1·00 1·00

1990. 150th Anniv of the Penny Black.

442 **107** 1p. black, buff and gold 10 10
443 – 19p. gold, black & buff 65 65
444 – 32p. multicoloured 1·40 1·40
445 – 34p. multicoloured 1·40 1·40
446 – 37p. multicoloured 1·60 1·60

DESIGNS: 19p. Wyon Medal, 1837; 32p. Wyon's stamp essay; 34p. Perkins Bacon engine-turned essay, 1839; 37p. Twopence Blue, 1840.

108 Queen Elizabeth the Queen Mother

110 Churchill with Freedom of Douglas Casket

109 Hawker Hurricane Mk 1, Bristol Type 142 Blenheim Mk 1 and Home Defence

1990. 90th Birthday of Queen Elizabeth the Queen Mother.

448 **108** 90p. multicoloured 4·00 4·00

1990. 50th Anniv of Battle of Britain. Mult.

449 15p. Type **109** 50 50
450 15p. Supermarine Spitfire with Westland Lysander Mk I rescue aircraft and launch 50 50
451 24p. Rearming Hawker Hurricanes Mk I fighters 1·00 1·00
452 24p. Ops room and scramble 1·00 1·00
453 29p. Civil Defence personnel 1·25 1·25
454 29p. Anti-aircraft battery 1·25 1·25

1990. 25th Death Anniv of Sir Winston Churchill. Multicoloured.

455 19p. Type **110** 60 60
456 32p. Churchill and London blitz 1·10 1·10
457 34p. Churchill and searchlights over Westminster 1·40 1·40
458 37p. Churchill with R.A.F. Hawker Hurricane Mk I fighters 1·40 1·40

111 Boy on Toboggan and Girl posting Letter

112 Henry Bloom Noble and Orphans (Marshall Wane)

1990. Christmas. Multicoloured.

459 14p. Type **111** 40 40
460 18p. Girl on toboggan and skaters 60 60
461 34p. Boy with snowman 1·25 1·25
462 37p. Children throwing snowballs 1·40 1·40

1991. Manx Photography.

464 **112** 17p. brown, grey & black 45 45
465 – 21p. brown and ochre 60 60
466 – 26p. brown, stone & blk 90 90
467 – 31p. brown, lt brn & blk 1·25 1·25
468 – 40p. multicoloured 1·50 1·50

DESIGNS: 21p. Douglas (Frederick Frith); 26p. Studio portrait of three children (Hilda Newby); 31p. Cashtal yn Ard (Christopher Killip); 40p. Peel Castle (Colleen Corlett).

113 Lifeboat "Sir William Hillary", Douglas

1991. Manx Lifeboats. Multicoloured.

469 17p. Type **113** 45 45
470 21p. "Osman Gabriel", Port Erin 60 60
471 26p. "Ann and James Ritchie", Ramsey 90 90
472 31p. "The Gough Ritchie", Port St. Mary 1·25 1·25
473 37p. "John Batstone", Peel 1·50 1·50

No. 469 is inscribed "HILARY" and No. 471 "JAMES & ANN RITCHIE", both in error.

114 "Intelsat" Communications Satellite

116 Laxey Hand-cart, 1920

115 Oliver Godfrey with Indian 500cc at Start, 1911

1991. Europa. Europe in Space. Multicoloured.

474 17p. Type **114** 80 80
475 17p. "Ariane" rocket launch and fishing boats in Douglas harbour 80 80
476 26p. Weather satellite and space station 1·10 1·10
477 26p. Ronaldsway Airport, Manx Radio transmitter and Space shuttle launch 1·10 1·10

Nos. 474/5 and 476/7 were each printed together, se-tenant, each pair forming a composite design.

1991. 80th Anniv of Tourist Trophy Mountain Course. Multicoloured.

478 17p. Type **115** 40 40
479 21p. Freddie Dixon on Douglas "banking" sidecar, 1923 60 60
480 26p. Bill Ivy on Yamaha 125cc, 1968 85 85
481 31p. Giacomo Agostini on MV Agusta 500cc, 1972 1·25 1·25
482 37p. Joey Dunlop on RVF Honda 750cc, 1985 1·40 1·40

1991. Fire Engines. Multicoloured.

485 17p. Type **116** 40 40
486 21p. Horse-drawn steamer, Douglas, 1909 60 60
487 30p. Merryweather "Hatfield" pump, 1936 85 85
488 33p. Dennis "F8" pumping appliance, Peel, 1953 1·25 1·25
489 37p. Volvo turntable ladder, Douglas, 1989 1·40 1·40

117 Mute Swans, Douglas Harbour

1991. Swans. Multicoloured.

490 17p. Type **117** 55 55
491 17p. Black swans, Curraghs Wildlife Park 55 55
492 26p. Whooper swans, Bishop's Dub, Ballaugh 1·10 1·10
493 26p. Whistling ("Bewick's") swans, Eairy Dam, Foxdale 1·10 1·10
494 37p. Coscoroba swans, Curraghs Wildlife Park 1·40 1·40
495 37p. Whooper ("Trumpeter") swans, Curraghs Wildlife Park 1·40 1·40

The two designs of each value were printed together, se-tenant, forming a composite design.

118 The Three Kings

120 Queen Elizabeth II at Coronation, 1953

119 North African and Italian Campaigns, 1942–43

1991. Christmas. Paper Sculptures. Multicoloured.

496 16p. Type **118** 50 40
497 20p. Mary with manger 75 80
498 26p. Shepherds with sheep 95 95
499 37p. Choir of angels 1·25 1·25

1992. 50th Anniv of Parachute Regiment. Mult.

502 23p. Type **119** 80 80
503 23p. D-Day, 1944 80 80
504 28p. Arnhem, 1944 90 90
505 28p. Rhine crossing, 1945 90 90
506 39p. Operations in Near, Middle and Far East, 1945–68 1·40 1·40
507 39p. Liberation of Falkland Islands, 1982 1·40 1·40

1992. 40th Anniv of Accession. Multicoloured.

508 18p. Type **120** 50 50
509 23p. Queen visiting Isle of Man, 1979 70 70
510 28p. Queen in evening dress 80 80
511 33p. Queen visiting Isle of Man, 1989 1·40 1·40
512 39p. Queen arriving for film premiere, 1990 1·50 1·50

121 Brittle-stars

1992. Centenary of Port Erin Marine Laboratory. Multicoloured.

513 18p. Type **121** 50 50
514 23p. Phytoplankton 60 60
515 28p. Atlantic herring 80 80
516 33p. Great scallop 1·40 1·40
517 39p. Dahlia anemone and delesseria 1·50 1·50

122 The Pilgrim Fathers embarking at Delfshaven

1992. Europa. 500th Anniv of Discovery of America by Columbus. Multicoloured.

518 18p. Type **122** 75 75
519 18p. "Speedwell" leaving Delfshaven 75 75
520 28p. "Mayflower" setting sail for America 1·50 1·50
521 28p. "Speedwell" anchored at Dartmouth 1·50 1·50

The two designs for each value were printed together, se-tenant, in horizontal pairs forming composite designs.

123 Central Pacific Locomotive "Jupiter", 1869

1992. Construction of the Union Pacific Railroad, 1866–69. Multicoloured.

522 33p. Type **123** 1·10 1·10
523 33p. Union Pacific locomotive No. 119, 1869 1·10 1·10
524 39p. Union Pacific locomotive No. 844, 1992 1·60 1·60
525 39p. Union Pacific locomotive No. 3985, 1992 1·60 1·60

124 "King Orry V" in Douglas Harbour

1992. Manx Harbours. Multicoloured.

527 18p. Type **124** 50 50
528 23p. Castletown 60 60
529 37p. Port St. Mary 1·40 1·40
530 40p. Ramsey 1·40 1·40

126 Stained Glass Window, St. German's Cathedral, Peel

127 Mansell on Lap of Honour, British Grand Prix, 1992

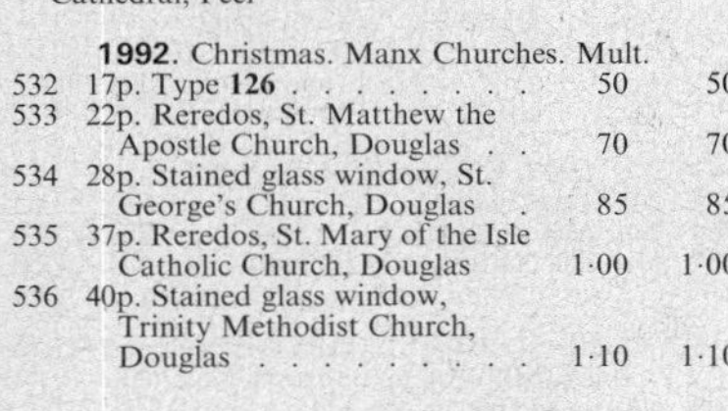

1992. Christmas. Manx Churches. Mult.

532 17p. Type **126** 50 50
533 22p. Reredos, St. Matthew the Apostle Church, Douglas 70 70
534 28p. Stained glass window, St. George's Church, Douglas 85 85
535 37p. Reredos, St. Mary of the Isle Catholic Church, Douglas 1·00 1·00
536 40p. Stained glass window, Trinity Methodist Church, Douglas 1·10 1·10

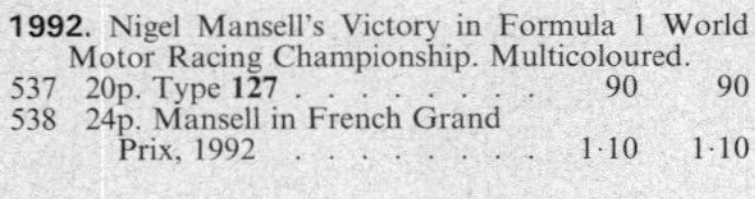

1992. Nigel Mansell's Victory in Formula 1 World Motor Racing Championship. Multicoloured.

537 20p. Type **127** 90 90
538 24p. Mansell in French Grand Prix, 1992 1·10 1·10

128 H.M.S. "Amazon" (frigate)

128a Manx Red Ensign

128b Queen Elizabeth II (hologram)

1993. Ships. Multicoloured.

539 1p. Type **128** 10 10
540 2p. "Fingal" (lighthouse tender) 10 10
541 4p. "Sir Winston Churchill" (cadet schooner) 10 10
542 5p. "Dar Mlodziezy" (full-rigged cadet ship) 10 10
543 20p. "Tynwald I" (paddle-steamer) 45 45
544 21p. "Ben Veg" (freighter) 50 50
545 22p. "Waverley" (paddle-steamer) 50 50
546 23p. Royal Yacht "Britannia" 55 55
547 24p. "Francis Drake" (ketch) 55 55
548 25p. "Royal Viking Sky" (liner) 60 60
549 26p. "Lord Nelson" (cadet barque) 65 65
550 27p. "Europa" (liner) 65 65
551 30p. "Snaefell V" (ferry) leaving Ardrossan 75 75
552 35p. "Seacat" (catamaran ferry) 85 85
553 40p. "Lady of Man I" (ferry) off Ramsey 1·00 1·00
554 50p. "Mona's Queen II" (paddle ferry) leaving Fleetwood 1·25 1·25
555 £1 "Queen Elizabeth 2" (liner) and "Mona's Queen V" (ferry) off Liverpool 2·50 2·50
556 £2 Type **128a** 5·00 5·00
557 £5 Type **128b** 15·00 15·00

For 4, 20 and 24p. in smaller size, 21 × 18 mm, see Nos. 687/93.

129 No. 1 Motor Car and No. 13 Trailer at Groudle Glen Hotel

1993. Cent of Manx Electric Railway. Mult.

559 20p. Type **129** 60 60
560 24p. No. 9 Tunnel Car and No. 19 Trailer at Douglas Bay Hotel 90 90
561 28p. No. 19 Motor Car and No. 59 Royal Trailer Special at Douglas Bay 1·00 1·00
562 39p. No. 33 Motor Car, No. 45 Trailer and No. 13 Van at Derby Castle 1·40 1·40

130 "Sir Hall Caine" (statue) (Bryan Kneale)

1993. Europa. Contemporary Art. Works by Bryan Kneale. Multicoloured.

563 20p. Type **130** 70 70
564 20p. "The Brass Bedstead" (painting) 70 70
565 28p. Abstract bronze sculpture 1·00 1·00
566 28p. "Polar Bear Skeleton" (drawing) 1·00 1·00

131 Graham Oates and Bill Marshall (1933 International Six Day Trial) on Ariel Square Four

1993. Manx Motor Cycling Events. Mult.

567 20p. Type **131** 50 50
568 24p. Sergeant Geoff Duke (1947 Royal Signals Display Team) on Triumph 3T Twin 70 70
569 28p. Denis Parkinson (1953 Senior Manx Grand Prix) on Manx Norton 90 90
570 33p. Richard Swallow (1991 Junior Classic MGP) on Aermacchi 1·25 1·25
571 39p. Steve Colley (1992 Scottish Six Day Trial) on Beta Zero 1·40 1·40

132 "Inachis io" (Peacock)

133 Children decorating Christmas Tree

1993. Butterflies. Multicoloured.

573 24p. Type **132** 80 80
574 24p. "Argynnis aglaja" (Dark green fritillary) 80 80
575 24p. "Cynthia cardui" (Painted lady) 80 80
576 24p. "Celastrina argiolus" (Holly blue) 80 80
577 24p. "Vanessa atalanta" (Red admiral) 80 80

1993. Christmas. Multicoloured.

578 19p. Type **133** 55 55
579 23p. Girl with snowman 65 65
580 28p. Boy opening presents 80 80
581 39p. Girl with teddy bear 1·25 1·25
582 40p. Children with toboggan 1·25 1·25

134 White-throated Robin

1994. Calf of Man Bird Observatory. Mult.

583 20p. Type **134** 60 60
584 20p. Black-eared wheatear 60 60
585 24p. Goldcrest 90 90
586 24p. Northern oriole 90 90
587 30p. Common kingfisher 1·10 1·10
588 30p. Hoopoe 1·10 1·10

135 Gaiety Theatre, Douglas

1994. Manx Tourism Centenary. Multicoloured.

590 24p. Type **135** 60 60
591 24p. Sports 60 60
592 24p. Artist at work and yachts racing 60 60
593 24p. TT Races and British Aerospace Hawk T.1s of Red Arrows display team 60 60
594 24p. Musical instruments 60 60
595 24p. Laxey Wheel and Manx cat 60 60
596 24p. Tower of Refuge, Douglas, with bucket and spade 60 60
597 24p. Cyclist 60 60
598 24p. Tynwald Day and classic car 60 60
599 24p. Santa Mince Pie train, Groudle Glen 60 60

136 "Eubranchus tricolor" (sea slug)

1994. Europa. Discoveries of Edward Forbes (marine biologist). Multicoloured.

600 20p. Type **136** 60 60
601 20p. "Loligo forbesii" (common squid) 60 60
602 20p. Edward Forbes and signature 60 60
603 30p. "Solaster moretonis" (fossil starfish) 1·00 1·00
604 30p. "Adamsia carciniopados" (anenome) on hermit crab 1·00 1·00
605 30p. "Solaster endeca" (starfish) 1·00 1·00

137 Maj-Gen. Bedell Smith and Naval Landing Force including "Ben-my-Chree IV" (ferry)

1994. 50th Anniv of D-Day. Multicoloured.

606 4p. Type **137** 15 15
607 4p. Admiral Ramsay and naval ships including "Victoria" and "Lady of Man" (ferries) 15 15
608 20p. Gen. Montgomery and British landings 70 70
609 20p. Lt-Gen. Dempsey and 2nd Army landings 70 70
610 30p. Air Chief Marshal Leigh-Mallory and U.S. paratroops and aircraft 1·00 1·00
611 30p. Air Chief Marshal Tedder and British paratroops and aircraft 1·00 1·00
612 41p. Lt-Gen. Bradley and U.S. 1st Army landings 1·25 1·25
613 41p. Gen. Eisenhower and American landings 1·25 1·25

138 Postman Pat, Jess and Ffinlo at Sea Terminal, Douglas

1994. Postman Pat visits the Isle of Man. Multicoloured.

614 1p. Type **138** 15 15
615 20p. Laxey Wheel 70 70
616 24p. Cregneash 90 90
617 30p. Manx Electric Railway trains 1·00 1·00
618 36p. Peel Harbour 1·25 1·25
619 41p. Douglas Promenade 1·40 1·40

139 Cycling

1994. Centenary of International Olympic Committee. Multicoloured.

621 10p. Type **139** 30 30
622 20p. Downhill skiing 55 55
623 24p. Swimming 70 70
624 35p. Hurdling 95 95
625 48p. Centenary logo 1·40 1·40

140 Santa Train to Santon

1994. Christmas. Father Christmas in the Isle of Man. Multicoloured.

626 19p. Type **140** 60 60
627 23p. Father Christmas and Postman Pat on mini tractor, Douglas (vert) 80 80
628 60p. Father Christmas and majorettes in sleigh, Port St. Mary 2·00 2·00

141 Foden Steam Wagon, Highway Board Depot, Douglas

1995. Steam Traction Engines. Multicoloured.

629 20p. Type **141** 60 60
630 24p. Clayton & Shuttleworth and Fowler engines pulling dead whale 70 70
631 30p. Wallis and Steevens engine at Ramsey Harbour 85 85
632 35p. Marshall engine with threshing machine, Ballarhenny 1·10 1·10
633 41p. Marshall convertible steam roller 1·25 1·25

142 Car No. 2 and First Train, 1895

1995. Centenary of Snaefell Mountain Railway. Multicoloured.

634 20p. Type **142** 70 70
635 24p. Car No. 4 in green livery and Car No. 3 in Laxey Valley 80 80
636 35p. Car No. 6 and Car No. 5 in 1971 1·10 1·10
637 42p. Goods Car No. 7 and "Caledonia" steam locomotive pulling construction train 1·25 1·25

143 Peace Doves forming Wave and Tower of Refuge, Douglas Bay

1995. Europa. Peace and Freedom. Multicoloured.

639 20p. Type **143** 75 75
640 30p. Peace dove breaking barbed wire 1·00 1·00

144 Spitfire, Tank and Medals

1995. 50th Anniv of End of Second World War. Multicoloured.

641 10p. Type **144** 30 30
642 10p. Typhoon, anti-aircraft gun and medals 30 30
643 20p. Lancaster, H.M.S. "Biter" (escort carrier) and medals 55 55
644 20p. U.S. Navy aircraft, jungle patrol and medals 55 55
645 24p. Celebrations in Parliament Square 70 70
646 24p. V.E. Day bonfire 70 70
647 40p. Street party 1·10 1·10
648 40p. King George VI and Queen Elizabeth on Isle of Man in July 1945 1·10 1·10

145 Reg Parnell in Maserati "4 CLT", 1951

1995. 90th Anniv of Motor Racing on Isle of Man. Multicoloured.

649 20p. Type **145** 60 60
650 24p. Stirling Moss in Frazer Nash, 1951 75 75
651 30p. Richard Seaman in Delage, 1936 85 85
652 36p. Prince Bira in ERA R2B "Romulus", 1937 1·00 1·00
653 41p. Kenelm Guinness in Sunbeam 1, 1914 1·10 1·10
654 42p. Freddie Dixon in Riley, 1934 1·10 1·10

146 Thomas the Tank Engine and Bertie Bus being Unloaded

1995. 50th Anniv of Thomas the Tank Engine Stories by Revd. Awdry. "Thomas the Tank Engine's Dream". Multicoloured.

656 20p. Type **146** 60 60
657 24p. Mail train 75 75
658 30p. Bertie and engines at Ballasalla 85 85
659 36p. "Viking" the diesel engine, Port Erin 1·00 1·00
660 41p. Thomas and railcar at Snaefell summit 1·10 1·10
661 45p. Engines racing past Laxey Wheel 1·25 1·25

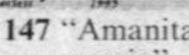

147 "Amanita muscaria"

148 St. Catherine's Church, Port Erin

1995. Fungi. Multicoloured.

662 20p. Type **147** 50 50
663 24p. "Boletus edulis" 65 65
664 30p. "Coprinus disseminatus" 85 85
665 35p. "Pleurotus ostreatus" 95 95
666 45p. "Geastrum triplex" 1·50 1·50

1995. Christmas. Multicoloured.

668 19p. Type **148** 50 50
669 23p. European robin on holly branch 65 65
670 42p. St. Peter's Church and wild flowers 1·25 1·25
671 50p. Hedgehog hibernating under farm machinery 1·50 1·50

149 Langness Lighthouse

151 Douglas Borough Arms

150 White Manx Cat and Celtic Interlaced Ribbons

1996. Lighthouses. Multicoloured.

672 20p. Type **149** 55 55
673 24p. Point of Ayre lighthouse (horiz) 65 65
674 30p. Chicken Rock lighthouse 85 85
675 36p. Calf of Man lighthouse (horiz) 1·00 1·00
676 41p. Douglas Head lighthouse 1·10 1·10
677 42p. Maughold Head lighthouse (horiz) 1·10 1·10

1996. Manx Cats. Multicoloured.

678 20p. Type **150** 60 60
679 24p. Cat and Union Jack ribbons 75 75
680 36p. Cat on rug in German colours, mouse and Brandenburg Gate 1·00 1·00
681 42p. Cat, U.S.A. flag and Statue of Liberty 1·25 1·25
682 48p. Cat, map of Australia and kangaroo 1·40 1·40

1996. Centenary of Douglas Borough. Self-adhesive.

684 **151** (20p.) multicoloured 60 60

1996. Ships. As Nos. 541, 543 and 547, but smaller, 21 × 18 mm. Multicoloured.

687 4p. "Sir Winston Churchill" (cadet schooner) 15 15
689 20p. "Tynwald I" (paddle-steamer), 1846 65 65
693 24p. "Francis Drake" (ketch) 85 85

The 20p. and 24p. show the positions of the face value and Queen's head reversed.

152 Princess Anne (President, Save the Children Fund) and Children

1996. Europa. Famous Women. Multicoloured.

701 24p. Type **152** 75 75
702 30p. Queen Elizabeth II and people of the Commonwealth 1·00 1·00

153 Alec Bennett

1996. Tourist Trophy Motorcycle Races. Irish Winners. Multicoloured.

703 20p. Type **153** 65 65
704 24p. Stanley Woods 80 80
705 45p. Artie Bell 1·25 1·25
706 60p. Joey and Robert Dunlop 1·75 1·75

154 National Poppy Appeal Trophy

1996. 75th Anniv of Royal British Legion. Mult.

708 20p. Type **154** 60 60
709 24p. Manx War Memoial, Braddan 65 65
710 42p. Poppy appeal collection box 1·10 1·10
711 75p. Royal British Legion badge 2·10 2·10

155 U.N.I.C.E.F. Projects in Mexico

1996. 50th Anniv of U.N.I.C.E.F. Multicoloured.

713 24p. Type **155** 60 60
714 24p. Projects in Sri Lanka 60 60
715 30p. Projects in Colombia 75 75
716 30p. Projects in Zambia 75 75
717 42p. Projects in Afghanistan 1·10 1·10
718 42p. Projects in Vietnam 1·10 1·10

156 Labrador

1996. Dogs. Multicoloured.

719 20p. Type **156** 55 55
720 24p. Border collie 65 65
721 31p. Dalmatian 90 90
722 38p. Mongrel 1·00 1·00
723 43p. English setter 1·25 1·25
724 63p. Alsatian 1·75 1·75

157 "Snowman and Pine Trees" (David Bennett)

158 Primroses and Cashtyl ny Ard

1996. Christmas. Children's Paintings. Multicoloured.

726 19p. Type **157** 50 50
727 23p. "Three-legged Father Christmas" (Louis White) 65 65
728 50p. "Family around Christmas Tree" (Robyn Whelan) 1·40 1·40
729 75p. "Father Christmas in Sleigh" (Claire Bradley) 1·90 1·90

1997. Spring in Man. Multicoloured.

730 20p. Type **158** 50 50
731 24p. Lochtan sheep and lambs 70 70
732 43p. Daffodils, duck and ducklings 1·10 1·10
733 63p. Dabchick with young and frog on lily pad 1·60 1·60

159 Barn Owl

160 Moddey Dhoo, Peel Castle

1997. Owls. Multicoloured.

734 20p. Type **159** 60 60
735 24p. Short-eared owl 75 75
736 31p. Long-eared owl 90 90
737 36p. Little owl 1·10 1·10
738 43p. Snowy owl 1·25 1·25
739 56p. Tawny owl 1·50 1·50

1997. Europa. Tales and Legends. Multicoloured.

741 21p. Type **160** 50 50
742 25p. Fairies in tree and cottage 60 60
743 31p. Fairies at Fairy Bridge 80 80
744 36p. Giant Finn Macooil and Calf of Man 1·00 1·00
745 37p. The Buggane of St. Trinian's 1·00 1·00
746 43p. Fynoderee and farm 1·25 1·25

Nos. 742/3 include the "EUROPA" emblem.

161 Sopwith Tabloid

1997. Manx Aircraft. Multicoloured.

747 21p. Type **161** 50 50
748 21p. Grumman Tiger (1996 Schneider Trophy) 50 50
749 25p. BAe ATP (15th anniv of Manx Airlines) 60 60
750 25p. BAe 146-200 (15th anniv of Manx Airlines) 60 60
751 31p. Boeing 757-200 (largest aircraft to land on Isle of Man) 75 75
752 31p. Farman biplane (1st Manx flight, 1911) 75 75
753 36p. Spitfire 90 90
754 36p. Hawker Hurricane 90 90

Nos. 747/8, 749/50, 751/2 and 753/4 respectively were each printed together, se-tenant, the backgrounds forming composite of Isle of Man.

No. 752 is inscribed "EARMAN BIPLANE" in error.

162 14th Hole, Ramsey Golf Club

1997. Golf. Multicoloured.

755 21p. Type **162** 50 50
756 25p. 15th Hole, King Edward Bay Golf and Country Club 60 60
757 43p. 17th Hole, Rowany Golf Club 1·10 1·10
758 50p. 8th Hole, Castletown Golf Links 1·50 1·50

163 Steve Colley

1997. F.I.M. "Trial de Nations" Motorcycle Team Trials. Multicoloured.

761 21p. Type **163** 50 50
762 25p. Steve Saunders (vert) 60 60
763 37p. Sammy Miller (vert) 1·00 1·00
764 44p. Don Smith 1·25 1·25

164 Angel and Shepherd

165 Engagement of Princess Elizabeth and Lieut. Philip Mountbatten, 1947

1997. Christmas. Multicoloured.

765 20p. Type **164** 55 55
766 24p. Angel and King 70 70
767 63p. The Nativity (54 × 39 mm) 1·50 1·50

1997. Golden Wedding of Queen Elizabeth and Prince Philip. Multicoloured (except No. 768).

768 50p. Type **165** (brown and gold) 1·25 1·25
769 50p. Wedding photograph, 1947 1·25 1·25
770 50p. At Ascot, 1952 1·25 1·25
771 50p. Golden Wedding photograph, 1997 1·25 1·25

166 Shamrock

168 Viking Figurehead

167 Queen Elizabeth II and Queen Elizabeth the Queen Mother

1998. Flowers. Multicoloured

773 1p. Bearded iris 10 10
774 2p. Daisy 10 10
775 4p. Type **166** 10 10
776 5p. Silver Jubilee rose 10 15
777 10p. Oriental poppy 20 25
778 20p. Heath spotted orchid 40 45
779 21p. Cushag 40 45
780 22p. Gorse 45 50
781 25p. Princess of Wales rose 50 55
782 26p. Dog rose 50 55
783 30p. Fuchsia "Lady Thumb" 60 65
784 50p. Daffodil 1·00 1·10
785 £1 Spear thistle 2·00 2·10
790 £2.50 Type **167** 5·00 5·25

1998. Viking Longships. Multicoloured.

793 21p. Type **168** 50 50
794 25p. Viking longship at sea 70 70
795 31p. Viking longship on beach 80 80
796 75p. Stern of ship 2·00 2·00

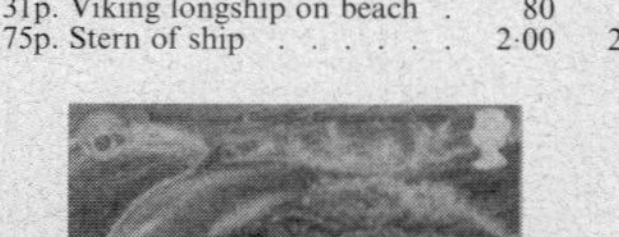

169 Bottle-nosed Dolphins

1998. U.N.E.S.C.O. International Year of the Ocean. Multicoloured.

798 10p. Type **169** 30 30
799 21p. Basking shark 50 50
800 25p. Front view of basking shark 70 70
801 31p. Minke whale 80 80
802 63p. Killer whale and calf 1·60 1·60

170 Locomotive No. 12 "Hutchinson"

1998. 125th Anniv of Isle of Man Steam Railway. Multicoloured.

803 21p. Type **170** 50 50
804 25p. Locomotive No. 10 "G. H. Wood" 60 60
805 31p. Locomotive No. 11 "Maitland" 80 80
806 63p. Locomotive No. 4 "Loch" . 1·60 1·60

171 Purple Helmets Display Team

1998. Isle of Man T.T. Races and 50th Anniv of Honda (manufacturer). Multicoloured.

808 21p. Type **171** 45 45
809 25p. Joey Dunlop 55 55
810 31p. Dave Molyneux 75 75
811 43p. Naomi Taniguchi . . . . 1·10 1·10
812 63p. Mike Hailwood . . . . . 1·60 1·60

172 Princess Diana wearing Protective Clothing, Angola

1998. Diana, Princess of Wales Commemoration. Multicoloured.

813 25p. Type **172** 65 65
814 25p. Receiving award from United Cerebral Palsy Charity, New York, 1995 . . . . . . 65 65
815 25p. With children, South Korea, 1992 . . . . 65 65
816 25p. Wearing blue jacket, July 1993 . . . . 65 65

173 Tynwald Day Ceremony

1998. Europa. Festivals. Multicoloured.

817 25p. Type **173** 65 65
818 30p. Traditional dancers, Tynwald Fair 75 75

174 Father Christmas at North Pole

1998. Christmas. "A Very Special Delivery". Multicoloured.

819 20p. Type **174** 50 50
820 24p. Father Christmas checking list 60 60
821 30p. Flying over Spring Valley sorting office 90 90
822 43p. Passing through Baldrine village . . . . 1·10 1·10
823 63p. Father Christmas delivering presents . . . . 1·60 1·60

175 Large Oval Pillar Box, Kirk Onchan

176 Cottage, Ballaglass Glen

1999. Local Post Boxes. Multicoloured.

824 10p. Type **175** 20 25
825 20p. Wall box, Ballaterson . . 40 45
826 21p. King Edward VII pillar box, Laxey Station 45 50
827 25p. Wall box, Spaldrick . . . 50 55
828 44p. Small oval pillar box, Derby Road, Douglas 90 95
829 63p. Wall box, Baldrine Station . 1·25 1·40

1999. Europa. Parks and Gardens. Multicoloured.

830 25p. Type **176** 50 55
831 30p. Glen Maye Waterfall . . . 60 65

177 "Ann and James Ritchie", Ramsey

1999. 175th Anniv of Royal National Lifeboat Institution. Multicoloured.

832 21p. Type **177** 45 50
833 25p. "Sir William Hillary", Douglas 50 55
834 37p. "Ruby Clery, Peel" . . . 75 80
835 43p. "Herbert and Edith" (inshore lifeboat), Port Erin . 85 90
836 43p. 1974 150th Anniv 8p. stamp 85 90
837 56p. "Gough Ritchie II", Port St. Mary . . . . 1·10 1·25
838 56p. 1991 Manx Lifeboats 21p. stamp . . . . 1·10 1·25

178 Winter

1999. Centenary of Yn Cheshaght Ghailckagh (Manx Gaelic Society). The Seasons. Multicoloured.

840 22p. Type **178** 45 50
841 26p. Spring 50 55
842 50p. Summer . . . . 1·00 1·10
843 63p. Autumn . . . . 1·25 1·40

Nos. 840/3 are inscribed "Ellan Vannin", the Manx name for the Isle of Man.

180 Tilling-Stevens Double-deck Bus, 1922

1999. Manx Buses. Multicoloured.

845 22p. Type **180** 45 50
846 26p. Thornycroft BC single-deck, 1928 . . . . 50 55
847 28p. Cumberland ADC 416 single-deck, 1927 . . . . . 55 60
848 37p. Straker-Squire single-deck, 1914 . . . . 75 80
849 38p. Thornycroft A2 single-deck, 1927 . . . . 75 80
850 40p. Leyland Lion LT9 single-deck, 1938 . . . . 80 85

181 Miss Sophie Rhys-Jones

1999. Royal Wedding. Multicoloured.

851 22p. Type **181** 45 50
852 26p. Leaving St. George's Chapel, Windsor 50 55
853 39p. Prince Edward 80 85
854 44p. Miss Sophie Rhys-Jones and Prince Edward (horiz) . . 90 95
855 53p. In landau (horiz) . . . . . 1·10 1·25

182 St. Luke's Church, Baldwin

1999. Christmas. Churches. Multicoloured.

857 21p. Type **182** 40 45
858 25p. St. Mark's Chapel, Malew . 50 55
859 30p. St. German's Parish Church and Cathedral, Peel 60 65
860 64p. Kirk Christ Church, Rushen . . . . 1·25 1·40

183 "Massachusetts", 1967

1999. Legends of Music. The Bee Gees (pop group). Designs showing compact discs. Multicoloured.

861 22p. Type **183** 45 50
862 26p. "Words", 1968 . . . . . . 50 55
863 29p. "I've Gotta Get a Message to You", 1968 . . . . 60 65
864 37p. "Ellan Vannin", 1998 . . . 75 80
865 38p. "You Win Again", 1987 . . 75 80
866 66p. "Night Fever", 1978 . . . 1·25 1·40

185 Harrison's Chronometer, 1735, and Map

2000. "The Story of Time". Multicoloured.

869 22p. Type **185** 45 50
870 26p. Daniels' chronometer, 2000, and clock face 50 55
871 29p. Harrison's chronometer, 1767, map and clock 60 65
872 34p. Mudge's chronometer, 1769, and steam locomotives . . . 70 75
873 38p. Arnold's chronometer, 1779, and map of Africa 75 80
874 44p. Earnshaw's chronometer, 1780, and map of Caribbean . 90 95

186 Duke and Duchess of York on Wedding Day, 1923

2000. "Queen Elizabeth the Queen Mother's Century". Multicoloured (except 26p. and 30p).

875 22p. Type **186** 45 50
876 26p. Queen Elizabeth with Princess Elizabeth, 1940 (brown and black) 50 55
877 30p. King George VI and Queen Elizabeth visiting troops, 1944 (brown and black) 60 65
878 44p. Queen Mother and Queen Elizabeth, 1954 . . . . . . 85 90
879 52p. Queen Mother with Prince Charles, 1985 . . . . . . 1·00 1·10
880 64p. Queen Mother, 1988 . . . 1·25 1·25

POSTAGE DUE STAMPS

D 1

D 2

1973.

D1 **D 1** ½p. red, black and yellow . 1·75 1·50
D2 1p. red, black and brown . 65 65
D3 2p. red, black and green . 15 20
D4 3p. red, black and grey . . 25 25
D5 4p. red, black and pink . . 35 35
D6 5p. red, black and blue . . 40 40
D7 10p. red, black and violet . 50 50
D8 20p. red, black and green . 90 90

1975.

D 9 **D 2** ½p. yellow, black & red . . 10 10
D10 1p. brown, black & red . . 10 10
D11 4p. lilac, black and red . . 10 10
D12 7p. blue, black and red . . 20 20
D13 9p. grey, black and red . . 25 25
D14 10p. mauve, black and red 30 30
D15 50p. orange, black and red . . . . 1·25 1·25
D16 £1 green, black & red . . 1·50 1·50

D 3

D 4

1982.

D17 **D 3** 1p. multicoloured 10 10
D18 2p. multicoloured 10 10
D19 5p. multicoloured 10 10
D20 10p. multicoloured . . . 20 25
D21 20p. multicoloured . . . 40 45
D22 50p. multicoloured . . . 1·00 1·10
D23 £1 multicoloured . . . . 2·00 2·10
D24 £2 multicoloured . . . . 4·00 4·25

1992.

D25 **D 4** £5 multicoloured . . . . 10·00 10·50

ISRAEL Pt. 19

The former British Mandate over Palestine was ended by the partition plan approved by the United Nations General Assembly on 29 November, 1947, and on 14 May, 1948, the new state of Israel was proclaimed.

1948. 1000 prutot (mils) = 1 Israeli pound.
1960. 100 agorot = 1 Israeli pound.
1980. 100 agorot = 1 shekel.

> **"TABS"** All Israeli stamps (except the Postage Dues) exist with descriptive sheet margin attached. These so-called "Tabs" are popular and in some cases scarce.
> Prices are for stamps without "tab". Separate prices for stamps with "tabs" are given in Stanley Gibbons Catalogue, Part 19 (Middle East).

1 Palm Tree and Baskets with Dates

2 Silver Shekel and Pomegranates

1948. Ancient Jewish Coins. Perf or roul.

1	**1**	3 m. orange	50	10
2	–	5 m. green	50	10
3a	–	10 m. mauve	40	15
4	–	15 m. red	1·00	10
5	–	20 m. blue	2·50	10
6	–	50 m. brown	12·50	65
7	**2**	250 m. green	32·00	12·50
8		500 m. red on buff	£120	45·00
9		1000 m. blue on blue (36 × 24 mm)	£250	£100

DESIGNS ON COINS: 5 m. Vine leaf; 10 m. Ritual jar; 15 m. Bunch of grapes; 20 m. Ritual cup; 50 m. Tied palm branches and lemon.

See also Nos. 21/6, 40/51 and 90/93.

3 "Flying Scroll" Emblem

1948. Jewish New Year.

10	**3**	3 m. brown and blue	40	25
11		5 m. green and blue	40	25
12		10 m. red and blue	50	40
13		20 m. blue and light blue	2·75	90
14		65 m. brown and red	11·00	4·25

4 Road to Jerusalem

5 National Flag

1949. Inauguration of Constituent Assembly.

15	**4**	250 pr. brown and grey	1·50	1·25

1949. Adoption of New National Flag.

16	**5**	20 pr. blue	60	35

6 Petah Tiqwa Well

7 Air Force Badge

1949. 70th Anniv of Founding of Petah Tiqwa.

17	**6**	40 pr. brown and green	9·50	75

1949. Jewish New Year.

18	**7**	5 pr. blue	90	40
19	–	10 pr. green	90	40
20	–	35 pr. brown	7·25	4·25

BADGES: 10 pr. Navy; 35 pr. Army.

MINIMUM PRICE

The minimum price quoted is 10p which represents a handling charge rather than a basis for valuing common stamps. For further notes about prices see introductory pages.

8 Ancient Jewish Coin

10 Stag and Globe

1949. 2nd Jewish Coins issue. Inscr at left of 6 or 8 characters.

21	**8**	3 pr. grey	10	10
22	–	5 pr. violet (as No. 2)	10	10
23	–	10 pr. green (as No. 3)	10	10
24	–	15 pr. red (as No. 4)	15	10
25	–	30 pr. blue	35	10
26	–	50 pr. brown (as No. 6)	1·25	15

DESIGN: 30 p.r. Ritual vessel.

For designs with larger inscription at left, see Nos. 40/51 and 90/93.

1950. Israel's Membership and 75th Anniv of U.P.U.

27	**10**	40 pr. violet	90	65
28		80 pr. red	1·00	75

11 Landing of Immigrants

1950. 2nd Anniv of Independence.

29	**11**	20 pr. brown	2·25	1·75
30	–	40 pr. green	9·75	5·50

DESIGN: 40 pr. Line of immigrant ships.

12 Library and Book

1950. 25th Anniv of Founding of Hebrew University, Jerusalem.

31	**12**	100 pr. green	40	25

13 Eagle

1950. Air.

32	–	5 pr. blue	50	25
33	–	30 pr. grey	40	25
34	–	40 pr. green	40	25
35	–	50 pr. brown	40	25
36	**13**	100 pr. red	15·00	11·00
37	–	250 pr. blue	2·25	90

DESIGNS—VERT: 5 pr. Doves pecking grapes; 30 pr. Eagle; 40 pr. Ostrich; 50 pr. Dove. HORIZ: 250 pr. Dove with olive branch.

14 Star of David and Fruit

16 Runner and Track

1950. Jewish New Year.

38	**14**	5 pr. violet and orange	15	10
39		15 pr. brown and green	60	40

1950. 3rd Jewish Coins issue. Inscr at left of 13 characters.

40	3 pr. grey	10	10
41	5 pr. violet	10	10
42	10 pr. green	10	10
43	15 pr. red	10	10
44	20 pr. orange	10	10
45	30 pr. blue	10	10
46	35 pr. green	30	10
47	40 pr. brown	10	10
48	45 pr. mauve	10	10
49	50 pr. brown	10	10
50	60 pr. red	10	10
51	85 pr. blue	10	10

DESIGNS ON COINS: 3, 20 pr. Palm tree and baskets with dates; 5, 35 pr. Vine leaf; 10, 40 pr. Ritual jar; 15, 45 pr. Bunch of grapes; 30, 60 pr. Ritual vessel; 50, 85 pr. Tied palm branches and lemon.

For further designs with value at right, see Nos. 90/93.

1950. 3rd Maccabiah (sports meeting).

52	**16**	80 pr. green and olive	1·90	1·25

17 "The Negev" (after R. Rubin)

1950. Opening of Post Office at Elat.

53	**17**	500 pr. brown & light brown	9·50	4·50

19 Memorial Tablet

1951. 40th Anniv of Founding of Tel Aviv.

54	**19**	40 pr. brown	40	25

20 "Supporting Israel"

21 Metsudat Yesha

1951. Independence Bonds Campaign.

55	**20**	80 pr. red	25	15

1951. 3rd Anniv of State of Israel.

56	**21**	15 pr. red	20	15
57	–	40 pr. blue (Hakastel)	50	40

22 Tractor

23 Ploughing and Savings Stamp

1951. 50th Anniv of Jewish National Fund.

58	**22**	15 pr. brown	10	10
59	–	25 pr. green	10	10
60	**23**	80 pr. blue	1·00	70

DESIGN—As Type **22**: 25 pr. Stylised tree.

24 Dr. T. Herzl

25 Carrier Pigeons

1951. 23rd Zionist Congress.

61	**24**	80 pr. green	25	20

1951. Jewish New Year. As T **25**.

62	**25**	5 pr. blue	10	10
63	–	15 pr. red	10	10
64	–	40 pr. violet	25	20

DESIGNS: 15 pr. Woman and dove; 40 pr. Scroll of the Law.

26 Menora and Emblems

1952.

64a	**26**	1000 pr. black and blue	16·00	7·50

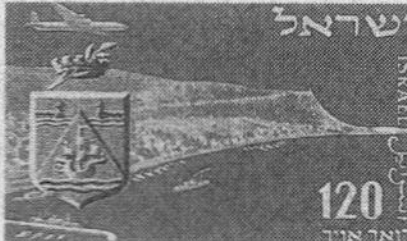

26a Haifa Bay, Mt. Carmel and City Seal

1952. Air. National Stamp Exn ("TABA").

64b	–	100 pr. blue & black	40	30
64c	**26a**	120 pr. purple & black	40	30

DESIGN: 100 pr. Haifa Bay and City Seal.

27 Thistle and Yad Mordechai

1952. 4th Anniv of Independence.

65	**27**	30 pr. brown and mauve	15	10
66	–	60 pr. slate and blue	20	10
67	–	110 pr. brown and red	45	30

DESIGNS: 60 pr. Cornflower and Deganya; 110 pr. Anemone and Safed.

28 New York Skyline and Z.O.A. Building

29 Figs

1952. Opening of American Zionist Building, Tel Aviv.

68	**28**	220 pr. grey and blue	45	30

1952. Jewish New Year.

69	**29**	15 pr. yellow and green	20	10
70	–	40 pr. yellow, blue & violet	25	15
71	–	110 pr. grey and red	40	30
72	–	220 pr. green, brn & orge	50	35

FLOWERS: 40 pr. Lily ("Rose of Sharon"); 110 pr. Dove; 220 pr. Nuts.

30 Dr. C. Weizmann (from sketch by R. Errell)

1952. Death of First President.

73	**30**	30 pr. blue	10	10
74		110 pr. black	35	30

31

32 Douglas DC-4 Airliner over Tel Aviv Yafo

1952. 70th Anniv of Bet Yaakov Lechu Venelcha Immigration Organization.

75	**31**	110 pr. buff, green & brown	25	15

1953. Air.

76	–	10 pr. deep green & green	10	10
77	–	70 pr. violet and lilac	10	10
78	–	100 pr. deep green & green	10	10
79	–	150 pr. brown & orange	10	10
80	–	350 pr. red and pink	15	10
81	–	500 pr. deep blue and blue	20	10
81a	–	750 pr. dp brown & brown	20	10
82	**32**	1000 pr. dp green & green	3·75	95
82a	–	3000 pr. purple	50	45

DESIGNS—HORIZ: 10 pr. Olive tree; 70 pr. Sea of Galilee; 100 pr. Shaar Hogay on road to Jerusalem; 150 pr. Lion Rock, Negev; 350 pr. Bay of Elat. VERT: 500 pr. Tanour Falls, near Metoulla; 750 pr. Lake Hula; 3000 pr. Tomb of Meir Baal Haness.

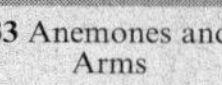

33 Anemones and Arms

35 Maimonides (philosopher)

1953. 5th Anniv of Independence.

83	**33**	110 pr. red, green & blue	25	20

1953. 7th Int. Congress of History of Science.

84	**35**	110 pr. brown	95	60

36 Holy Ark, Petah-Tikvah **37** Hand holding Globe/Football

1953. Jewish New Year.
85 – 20 pr. blue 10 10
86 **36** 45 pr. red 10 10
87 – 200 pr. violet 35 25
DESIGNS: 20 pr. Holy Ark, Jerusalem; 200 pr. Holy Ark, Zefat.

1953. 4th Maccabiah.
88 **37** 110 pr. brown and blue 20 20

38 Exhibition Emblem **39** Ancient Jewish Coin

1953. "Conquest of the Desert" Exhibition.
89 **38** 200 pr. multicoloured 20 15

1954. 4th Jewish Coins issue.
90 **39** 80 pr. bistre 10 10
91 – 95 pr. green 10 10
92 – 100 pr. brown 10 10
93 – 125 pr. blue 15 10
DESIGNS ON COINS: 95 pr. Wheat; 100 pr. Gate; 125 pr. Lyre.

40 Gesher and Narcissus **41** Dr. T. Z. Herzl

1954. 6th Anniv of Independence.
94 – 60 pr. blue, red & grey 10 10
95 **40** 350 pr. brown, yellow & grn 20 15
DESIGN: 60 pr. Yehiam and helichrysum.

1954. 50th Death Anniv of Herzl (founder of World Zionist Movement).
96 **41** 160 pr. sepia, buff & blue 20 15

43

1954. Jewish New Year.
97 **43** 25 pr. sepia 15 10

44 19th century Mail Coach and P.O.

1954. National Stamp Exhibition.
98 **44** 60 pr. black, yellow & blue 10 10
99 – 200 pr. black, red & green 25 15
DESIGN: 200 pr. Mail van and G.P.O., 1954.

45 Baron Edmond de Rothschild

1954. 20th Death Anniv of De Rothschild (financier).
100 **45** 300 pr. turquoise 20 10

46 Lamp of Knowledge

1955. 50th Anniv of Teachers' Association.
101 **46** 250 pr. blue 15 10

47 Parachutist and Barbed Wire **48** Menora and Olive Branches

1955. Jewish Mobilisation during 2nd World War.
102 **47** 120 pr. black & turquoise 15 10

1955. 7th Anniv of Independence.
103 **48** 150 pr. orange, blk & grn 25 15

49 Immigrants and Ship **50** Musicians playing Timbrel and Cymbals

1955. 20th Anniv of Youth Immigration Scheme.
104 **49** 5 pr. black and blue 10 10
105 – 10 pr. black and red 10 10
106 – 25 pr. black and green 10 10
107 – 30 pr. black and orange 10 10
108 – 60 pr. black and violet 10 10
109 – 750 pr. black and brown 45 35
DESIGNS: 10 pr. Immigrants and Douglas DC-3 airplane; 25 pr. Boy and calf; 30 pr. Girl watering flowers; 60 pr. Boy making pottery; 750 pr. Boy using theodolite.

1955. Jewish New Year.
110 **50** 25 pr. green and orange 10 10
111 – 60 pr. grey and orange 10 10
112 – 120 pr. blue and yellow 10 10
113 – 250 pr. brown and orange 25 15
DESIGNS—Musicians playing: 60 pr. Ram's horn; 120 pr. Tuba; 250 pr. Harp.

51 Ambulance **52** "Reuben"

1955. 25th Anniv of Magen David Adom (Jewish Red Cross).
114 **51** 160 pr. green, black & red 20 15

1955. Twelve Tribes of Israel.
115 **52** 10 pr. green 10 10
116 – 20 pr. mauve 10 10
117 – 30 pr. blue 10 10
118 – 40 pr. brown 10 10
119 – 50 pr. blue 10 10
120 – 60 pr. bistre 10 10
121 – 80 pr. violet 10 10
122 – 100 pr. red 10 10
123 – 120 pr. olive 10 10
124 – 180 pr. mauve 15 10
125 – 200 pr. green 15 10
126 – 250 pr. grey 15 10
EMBLEMS: 20 pr. "Simeon" (castle); 30 pr. "Levi" (High Priest's breastplate); 40 pr. "Judah" (lion); 50 pr. "Dan" (scales); 60 pr. "Naphtali" (gazelle); 80 pr. "Gad" (tents); 100 pr. "Asher" (tree); 120 pr. "Issachar" (sun and stars); 180 pr. "Zebulun" (ship); 200 pr. "Joseph" (sheaf of wheat); 250 pr. "Benjamin" (wolf).

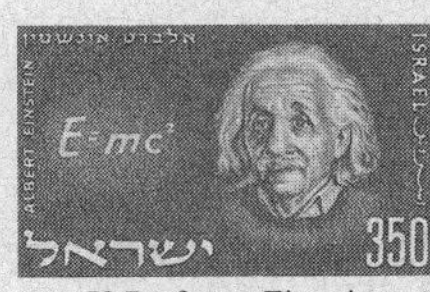

53 Professor Einstein

1956. Einstein Commemoration.
127 **53** 350 pr. brown 15 15

54 Technion **55** "Eight Years of Independence"

1956. 30th Anniv of Israel Institute of Technology, Haifa.
128 **54** 350 pr. green and black 15 10

1956. 8th Anniv of Independence.
129 **55** 150 pr. multicoloured 15 10

56 Oranges **57** Musican playing Lyre **58** Insignia of "Haganah"

1956. 4th International Congress of Mediterranean Citrus Fruit Growers.
130 **56** 300 pr. multicoloured 20 15

1956. Jewish New Year. Musicians playing instruments.
131 **57** 30 pr. brown and blue 10 10
132 – 50 pr. violet and orange 10 10
133 – 150 pr. turquoise & orge 20 15
INSTRUMENTS—VERT: 50 pr. Sistrum. HORIZ: 150 pr. Double oboe.

1957. Defence Fund.
134 **58** 80 pr. + 20 pr. green 10 10
135 150 pr. + 50 pr. red 10 10
136 350 pr. + 50 pr. blue 15 10

59 Airplane sky-writing Figure "9" **60** Bezalel Museum and Candelabrum

1957. 9th Anniv of Independence.
137 **59** 250 pr. black, blue & lt blue 15 10

1957. 50th Anniv of Bezalel Museum, Jerusalem.
138 **60** 400 pr. multicoloured 15 10

61 Seal of Tamach and Horse **62** Throwing the Hammer

1957. Jewish New Year. Ancient Hebrew Seals.
139 **61** 50 pr. blk & brn on blue 10 10
140 – 160 pr. blk & grn on buff 10 10
141 – 300 pr. blk & red on pink 15 10
DESIGNS: 160 pr. Seal of Shema and lion; 300 pr. Seal of Netanyahuv Ne'avadyahu and gazelle.

1958. 25th Anniv of Maccabiah Games.
142 **62** 500 pr. red and bistre 15 10

63 Ancient Hebrew Ship

1958. Israel Merchant Marine Commemoration.
143 **63** 10 pr. red, blue & brown 10 10
144 – 20 pr. brown and green 10 10
145 – 30 pr. grey and red 10 10
146 – 1000 pr. green and blue 45 35
DESIGNS—As T **63**: 10 pr. Immigration ship "Nirit"; 20 pr. Freighter "Shomron". 57 × 22½ mm: 1000 pr. Liner "Zion".

64 Menora and Olive Branch **65** Dancing Children forming "10"

1958. 10th Anniv of Independence.
147 **64** 400 pr. green, black & gold 20 15

1958. 1st World Conference of Jewish Youth, Jerusalem.
148 **65** 200 pr. green and orange 20 15

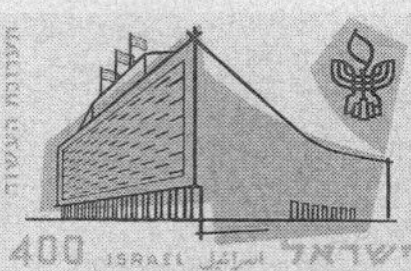

66 Convention Centre, Jerusalem, and Exhibition Emblem

1958. 10th Anniv (of Israel) Exn, Jerusalem.
149 **66** 400 pr. orange and lilac on cream 20 15

67 Wheat **68** Ancient Stone

1958. Jewish New Year.
150 **67** 50 pr. brown and ochre 10 10
151 – 60 pr. black and yellow 10 10
152 – 160 pr. purple and violet 15 10
153 – 300 pr. green and apple 20 15
DESIGNS: 60 pr. Barley; 160 pr. Grapes; 300 pr. Figs.
See also Nos. 166/8.

1958. 10th Anniv of Declaration of Human Rights.
154 **68** 750 pr. black, yellow & bl 20 15

69 Post Office Emblem **70** Sholem Aleichem

1959. 10th Anniv of Israel Postal Services.
155 **69** 60 pr. black, red & olive 10 10
156 – 120 pr. black, red & olive 10 10
157 – 250 pr. black, red & olive 10 10
158 – 500 pr. black, red & olive 20 15
DESIGNS—HORIZ: 120 pr. Mail van. VERT: 250 pr. Radio-telephone equipment; 500 pr. "Telex" dial and keyboard.

1959. Birth Cent of Sholem Aleichem (writer).
159 **70** 250 pr. brown and green 20 15

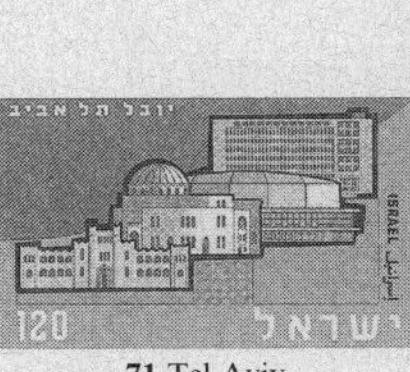

71 Tel Aviv **72** Anemone

1959. 50th Anniv of Tel Aviv.
160 **71** 120 pr. multicoloured 20 15

1959. 11th Anniv of Independence. Mult.
161 60 pr. Type **72** 10 10
162 120 pr. Cyclamen 10 10
163 300 pr. Narcissus 20 15
See also Nos. 188/9, 211/3 and 257/9.

73 C. N. Bialik

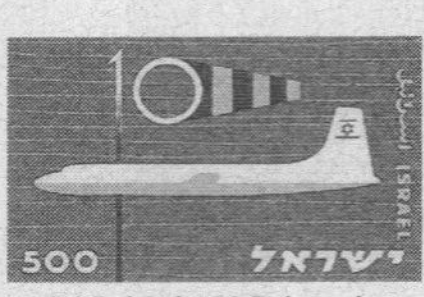

74 Bristol 175 Britannia Airliner and Wind-sock

1959. 25th Anniv of Chaim Bialik (poet).
164 **73** 250 pr. olive and orange . . 20 15

1959. 10th Anniv of Civil Aviation in Israel.
165 **74** 500 pr. multicoloured . . . 20 15

1959. Jewish New Year. As T **67**.
166 60 pr. red and brown 10 10
167 200 pr. green & deep green . . . 15 10
168 350 pr. orange and brown . . . 25 15
DESIGNS: 60 pr. Pomegranates; 200 pr. Olives; 350 pr. Dates.

76 E. Ben-Yehuda

77 Merhavya Settlement

1959. Birth Centenary of Ben-Yehuda (pioneer of Hebrew language).
169 **76** 250 pr. deep blue & blue . . 25 50

1959. 50th Anniv of Merhavya and Deganya Settlements. 75th Anniv of Yesud Ha-Maala Settlement.
170 **77** 60 pr. green and yellow . . 10 10
171 – 120 pr. brown & lt brown . . 15 10
172 – 180 pr. green and blue . . . 30 20
DESIGNS: 120 pr. Yesud Ha-Maala; 180 pr. Deganya.

78 Ancient Jewish Coin

79 Tiberias

1960. New currency. Values in black.
173 **78** 1 a. bistre on pink 10 10
174 3 a. red on pink 10 10
175 5 a. slate on pink 10 10
176 6 a. green on blue 10 10
176a 7 a. grey on blue 10 10
177 8 a. mauve on blue 10 10
178 12 a. blue on blue 10 10
179 18 a. orange 10 10
180 25 a. blue 15 10
181 30 a. red 15 10
182 50 a. lilac 15 10

1960. Air.
183 – 15 a. black and lilac . . . 15 10
184 – 20 a. black and green . . . 15 10
184a – 25 a. black and orange . . . 15 10
184b – 30 a. black & turquoise . . 15 10
184c – 35 a. black and green . . . 15 10
184d – 40 a. black and lilac . . . 50 25
184e – 50 a. black and olive . . . 50 25
185 **79** 65 a. black and blue . . . 35 15
185a – I£1 black and pink 75 35
DESIGNS—VERT: 15 a. Old town, Zefat; 20 a. Tower, Ashqelon; 25 a. Akko Tower and boats; 30 a. View of Haifa from Mt. Carmel. HORIZ: 35 a. Ancient synagogue, Capernaum; 40 a. Kefar Hittim—Tomb of Jethro; 50 a. City walls, Jerusalem. I£1, Old city, Yafo (Jaffa).

80 Operation "Magic Carpet"

1960. World Refugee Year.
186 **80** 25 a. brown 15 10
187 – 50 a. green 20 15
DESIGN: 50 a. Resettled family.

1960. 12th Anniv of Independence. Flowers as T **72**.
188 12 a. multicoloured 15 10
189 32 a. yellow, green & brown . . 20 15
DESIGNS: 12 a. "Pancratium maritimum"; 32 a. "Oenothera drummondi".

81 Atomic Symbol and Reactor Building

83 King Saul

1960. Inauguration of Atomic Reactor.
190 **81** 50 a. red, black and blue . . 25 20

1960. Jewish New Year. Centres multicoloured.
191 **83** 7 a. green 10 10
192 – 25 a. brown 20 20
193 – 40 a. blue 30 20
DESIGNS: 25 a. King David; 40 a. King Solomon.

84 Dr. Theodor Herzl

85 Postal Courier, Prague, 1741

1960. Birth Cent. of Dr. Theodor Herzl (founder of World Zionist Movement).
194 **84** 25 a. sepia and cream . . . 25 20

1960. "TAVIV" National Stamp Exhibition, Tel Aviv.
195 **85** 25 a. black and grey 30 25

86 Henrietta Szold

1960. Birth Cent. of Henrietta Szold (founder of Youth Immigration Scheme).
196 **86** 25 a. violet and blue 20 15

87 Badges of First Zionist Congress and Jerusalem

1960. 25th Zionist Congress, Jerusalem.
197 **87** 50 a. light and deep blue . . 25 20

88 Ram (Aries)

89 The Twelve Signs

1961. Signs of the Zodiac.
198 **88** 1 a. green 10 10
199 – 2 a. red 10 10
200 – 6 a. blue 10 10
201 – 7 a. brown 10 10
202 – 8 a. myrtle 10 10
203 – 10 a. orange 10 10
204 – 12 a. violet 10 10
205 – 18 a. mauve 10 10
206 – 20 a. olive 10 10
207 – 25 a. purple 10 10
208 – 32 a. black 15 10
209 – 50 a. turquoise 15 10
210 **89** I£1 blue, gold & indigo . . 40 35
DESIGNS—As Type **88**: 2 a. Bull (Taurus); 6 a. Twins (Gemini); 7 a. Crab (Cancer); 8 a. Lion (Leo); 10 a. Virgin (Virgo); 12 a. Scales (Libra); 18 a. Scorpion (Scorpio); 20 a. Archer (Sagittarius); 25 a. Goat (Capricorn); 32 a. Waterman (Aquarius); 50 a. Fishes (Pisces).

1961. 13th Anniv of Independence. Flowers as T **72**.
211 7 a. yellow, brown & green . . 10 10
212 12 a. green, purple & mve . . 15 10
213 32 a. red, green and blue . . 25 15
FLOWERS: 7 a. Myrtle; 12 a. Squill; 32 a. Oleander.

91 Throwing the Javelin

92 "A Decade of Israel Bonds"

1961. 7th "Hapoel" Sports Association Int Congress, Ramat Gan.
214 **91** 25 a. multicoloured 25 20

1961. 10th Anniv of Israel Bond Issue.
215 **92** 50 a. blue 25 20

93 Samson

94 Bet Hamidrash (synagogue), Medzibozh (Russia)

1961. Jewish New Year. Heroes of Israel. Centres multicoloured.
216 **93** 7 a. red 15 10
217 – 25 a. grey 20 15
218 – 40 a. lilac 30 20
HEROES: 25 a. Yehuda Maccabi; 40 a. Bar Kochba.

1961. Death Bicent of Rabbi Baal Shem Tov (founder of Hassidism movement).
219 **94** 25 a. sepia and yellow . . . 25 20

95 Fir Cone

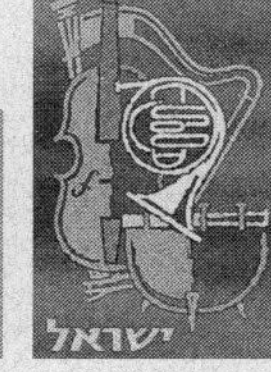

96 Musical Instruments

1961. Afforestation Achievements.
220 **95** 25 a. yellow, black & green . 25 20
221 – 30 a. multicoloured 25 20
DESIGN: 30 a. Symbol of afforestation.

1961. 25th Anniv of Israel Philharmonic Orchestra.
222 **96** 50 a. multicoloured 55 45

97 Bay of Elat

1962. Air.
223 **97** I£3 multicoloured . . . . . 2·00 1·25

1962. As Nos. 198, 201 and 208 but colours changed and surch.
224 **88** 3 a. on 1 a. mauve 10 10
225 – 5 a. on 7 a. grey 10 10
226 – 30 a. on 32 a. green 15 10

99 Symbolic Flame

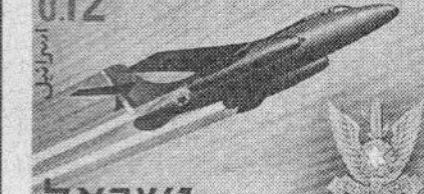

100 Sud Aviation Vatour IIA Bomber

1962. Heroes and Martyrs Day.
227 **99** 12 a. yellow, red & black . . 15 10
228 – 55 a. multicoloured 45 35
DESIGN: 55 a. Nazi "Yellow Star" and candles.

1962. 14th Anniv of Independence.
229 **100** 12 a. blue 20 15
230 – 30 a. green 40 25
DESIGN: 30 a. Flight of Vatour IIA bombers.

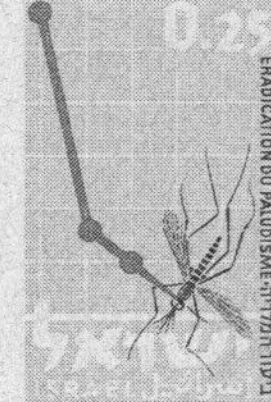

101 Mosquito and Malaria Graph

102 Rosh Pinna

1962. Malaria Eradication.
231 **101** 25 a. bistre, red & black . . 25 20

1962. 80th Anniv of Rosh Pinna.
232 **102** 20 a. green and yellow . . 25 20

103 Fair Flags

104 "The wolf also shall dwell with the lamb..."

1962. Near East International Fair, Tel Aviv.
233 **103** 55 a multicoloured 25 30

1962. Jewish New Year. Illustrating quotations from the Book of Isaiah.
234 **104** 8 a. black, red and olive . . 10 10
235 – 28 a. black, purple & olive . 25 20
236 – 43 a. black, orange & olive 35 25
DESIGNS: 28 a. "And the leopard shall lie down with the kid..."; 43 a. "And the suckling child shall play on the hole of the asp...".

105 Boeing 707 Jetliner

1962. El Al Airline Commemoration.
237 **105** 55 a. indigo, lilac & blue . 45 30

106 Pennant Coralfish

1962. Red Sea Fish (1st series). Multicoloured.
238 3 a. Type **106** 20 10
239 6 a. Racoon butterflyfish . . . 20 10
240 8 a. Indian Ocean lionfish . . . 25 10
241 12 a. Royal angelfish 25 15
See also Nos. 265/8.

107 Symbolic Cogwheels

1962. 25th Anniv of United Jewish Appeal.
242 **107** 20 a. blue, silver and red . 30 25

108 J. Korczak (child educator)

109 Houbara Bustard

1962. Janusz Korczak Commemoration.
243 **108** 30 a. sepia and grey . . . 40 30

1963. Air. Birds.
244 – 5 a. pink, brown & violet . 10 10
245 – 20 a. turq, brn & red . . . 20 15
246 – 28 a. black, brown & grn . 25 15
247 – 30 a. multicoloured 25 15
248 – 40 a. multicoloured 30 20
249 – 45 a. multicoloured 50 40

250 **109** 55 a. orange, blk & turq . . 50 40
251 – 70 a. bistre, brn & blk . . 55 50
252 – I£1 orange, black & red . . 55 50
253 – I£3 multicoloured . . . . 1·90 1·90
DESIGNS—HORIZ: 5 a. Sinai rosefinch; 20 a. White-breasted kingfisher; 28 a. Mourning wheatear. VERT: 30 a. European bee eater; 40 a. Graceful prinia; 45 a. Palestine sunbird; 70 a. Scops owl; I£1 Purple heron; I£3, White-tailed sea eagle.

110 Bird in the Hand

1963. Freedom from Hunger.
254 **110** 55 a. grey and black . . . 30 35

111 Construction at Daybreak **112** Compositor

1963. 25th Anniv of Stockade and Tower Settlements.
255 **111** 12 a. brown, blk & yell . . 15 10
256 – 30 a. purple, blk & blue . . 25 25
DESIGN: 30 a. Settlement at night.

1963. 15th Anniv of Independence. Flowers. As T **72**.
257 8 a. multicoloured 25 15
258 30 a. yellow, rose and pink . . . 40 25
259 37 a. multicoloured 50 25
FLOWERS: 8 a. White lily; 30 a. Bristly hollyhock; 37 a. Sharon tulip.

1963. Centenary of Hebrew Press.
260 **112** 12 a. purple and buff . . . 40 30
No. 260 comes in sheets of 16 (4 × 4) with overall background of replica of front page of first issue of Hebrew newspaper "Halbanon".

113 "And the sun beat upon the head of Jonah..." **114** Hoe clearing Thistles

1963. Jewish New Year. Illustrating quotations from the Book of Jonah. Multicoloured.
261 8 a. Type **113** 15 10
262 30 a. "And there was a mighty tempest in the sea" 40 25
263 55 a. "And Jonah was in the belly of the fish" 35 30
Nos. 262/3 are horiz.

1963. 80th Anniv of Israeli Agricultural Settlements.
264 **114** 37 a. multicoloured 25 20

1963. Red Sea Fish (2nd series). As T **106**. Multicoloured.
265 2 a. Undulate triggerfish 15 10
266 6 a. Radial lionfish 25 10
267 8 a. Catalufa 30 20
268 12 a. Emperor angelfish 30 20

115 "Shalom"

1963. Maiden Voyage of Liner "Shalom".
269 **115** I£1 blue, turquoise & pur . 1·25 1·00

116 "Old Age and Survivors" **117** Pres. Ben-Zvi

1964. 10th Anniv of National Insurance. Multicoloured.
270 12 a. Type **116** 15 15
271 25 a. Nurse and child within hands ("Maternity") 20 20
272 37 a. Family within hand ("Large families") 30 25
273 50 a. Hand with arm and crutch ("Employment injuries") . . 35 25

1964. 1st Death Anniv of President Izhak Ben-Zvi.
274 **117** 12 a. brown 15 10

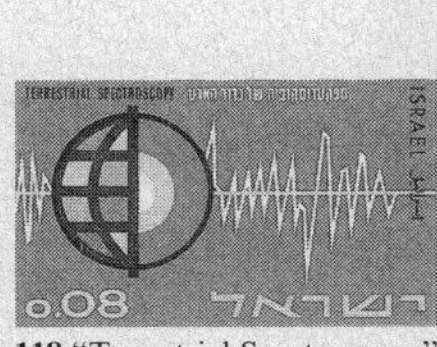

118 "Terrestrial Spectroscopy" **119** Running

1964. 16th Anniv of Independence. Israel's Contribution to Science. Multicoloured.
275 8 a. Type **118** 15 10
276 35 a. Macromolecules of living cell 35 25
277 70 a. Electronic computer . . . 40 30

1964. Olympic Games, Tokyo.
278 **119** 8 a. black and red 10 10
279 – 12 a. black and mauve . . 15 10
280 – 30 a. red, black & blue . . 20 15
281 – 50 a. red, purple & green . 20 20
DESIGNS: 12 a. Throwing the discus; 30 a. Basketball; 50 a. Football.

120 3rd Century Glass Vessel **121** Congress Emblem

1964. Jewish New Year. Showing glass vessels in Haaretz Museum, Tel Aviv. Multicoloured.
282 8 a. Type **120** 15 10
283 35 a. 1st-2nd century vessel . . 20 20
284 70 a. 1st century vessel 30 20

1964. 6th Israel Medical Assn's World Congress.
285 **121** I£1 multicoloured 40 30

122 "Exodus" (immigrant ship) **123** Eleanor Roosevelt

1964. "Year of the Blockade-Runners".
286 **122** 25 a. black, blue & turq . . 25 20

1964. 80th Birth Anniv of Eleanor Roosevelt.
287 **123** 70 a. purple 35 30

124 Olympics Symbols and Knight

1964. 16th Chess Olympics.
288 **124** 12 a. brown 30 25
289 – 70 a. green 90 85
DESIGN: 70 a. Olympics symbol and rook.

125 "African-Israeli Friendship" **126** Masada

1964. "TABAI" National Stamp Exn, Haifa.
290 **125** 57 a. multicoloured 45 30

1965. Masada.
291 **126** 25 a. green 25 20
292 – 36 a. blue 35 20
293 – I£1 brown 40 40
DESIGNS—HORIZ: 36 a. "Northern Palace", lower section. VERT: I£1, "Northern Palace" aerial view.

127 Ashdod **128** Fair Emblem

1965. Civic Arms (1st series).
294 – 1 a. brown (Lod) 10 10
295 – 2 a. mauve (Qiryat Shmona) 10 10
296 – 5 a. black (Petah Tiqwa) . . 10 10
297 – 6 a. violet (Nazareth) . . 10 10
298 – 8 a. orge (Beer Sheva) . . 10 10
299 – 10 a. green (Bet Shean) . . 10 10
300 – 12 a. purple (Tiberias) . . 10 10
301 **127** 15 a. green 10 10
302 – 20 a. red (Elat) 10 10
303 – 25 a. blue (Akko) 10 10
304 – 35 a. purple (Dimona) . . 10 10
305 – 37 a. green (Zefat) . . . 40 10
305a – 40 a. brown (Mizpe Ramon) 15 10
306 – 50 a. blue (Rishon Le Zion) 15 10
306a – 55 a. red (Ashqelon) . . . 15 10
307 – 70 a. brown (Jerusalem) . . 20 15
307a – 80 a. red (Rosh Pinna) . . 40 25
308 – I£1 green (Tel Aviv-Yafo) . 25 25
309 – I£3 mauve (Haifa) 40 30
Nos. 307, 308/9 are $22\frac{1}{2} \times 27$ mm, in size.
See also Nos. 413/24.

1965. 2nd International Book Fair, Jerusalem.
310 **128** 70 a. black, blue & grn . . 30 25

129 Hands reaching for barbed wire **130** "National Water Supply"

1965. 20th Anniv of Concentration Camps Liberation.
311 **129** 25 a. black, yell & grey . . 25 20

1965. 17th Anniv of Independence.
312 **130** 37 a. brown, dp blue & bl . 25 20

131 Potash Works, Sedom **132** "Syncom" Satellite and Telegraph Pole

1965. Dead Sea Industrial Development. Mult.
313 12 a. Potash Works, Sedom . . 15 10
314 50 a. Type **131** 30 25
The two stamps form one composite design when placed side by side.

1965. I.T.U. Centenary.
315 **132** 70 a. violet, black & blue . 25 20

133 "Co-operation" **134** "Light"

1965. International Co-operation Year.
316 **133** 36 a. multicoloured 25 20

1965. Jewish New Year. "The Creation". Multicoloured.
317 6 a. Type **134** 10 10
318 8 a. "Heaven" 10 10
319 12 a. "Earth" 10 10
320 25 a. "Stars" 25 20
321 35 a. "Birds and Beasts" . . . 35 25
322 70 a. "Man" 45 30

135 Foxy Charaxes **136** War of Independence Memorial

1965. Butterflies and Moths. Multicoloured.
323 2 a. Type **135** 10 10
324 6 a. Southern swallowtail . . . 15 10
325 8 a. Oleander hawk moth . . . 20 15
326 12 a. Sooty orange-tip 20 15

1966. Memorial Day.
327 **136** 40 a. brown and black . . 20 15

137 Flags

1966. 18th Anniv of Independence. Mult.
328 12 a. Type **137** 10 10
329 30 a. Fireworks 15 15
330 80 a. Dassault Mirage IIICJ jet fighters and warships 25 20

138 Knesset Building

1966. Inaug of Knesset Building, Jerusalem.
331 **138** I£1 blue 30 25

139 Scooter Rider **140** Spice Box

1966. Road Safety. Multicoloured.
332 2 a. Type **139** 10 10
333 5 a. Cyclist 10 10
334 10 a. Pedestrian on crossing . . 10 10
335 12 a. Child with ball 10 10
336 15 a. Motorist in car 10 10

1966. Jewish New Year. Religious Ceremonial Objects. Multicoloured.
337 12 a. Type **140** 10 10
338 15 a. Candlesticks 10 10
339 35 a. Kiddush cup 20 15
340 40 a. Torah pointer 20 15
341 80 a. Hanging lamp 20 20

141 Panther (bronze)

1966. Israel Museum Exhibits. Multicoloured.
342 15 a. Type **141** 35 15
343 30 a. Synagogue menora (stone) . 35 15
344 40 a. Phoenician sphinx (ivory) . 35 20
345 55 a. Earring (gold) 45 25
346 80 a. Miniature capital (gold) . . 70 35
347 I£1.15 Drinking horn (gold) . . 1·25 90
No. 347 is vert.

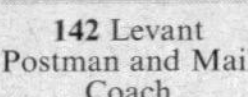

142 Levant Postman and Mail Coach

143 "Fight Cancer and Save Life"

1966. Stamp Day.

348	**142**	12 a. green and brown . .	10	10
349	–	15 a. mauve, brown & grn .	10	10
350	–	40 a. blue and mauve . . .	25	10
351	–	I£1 brown and blue . . .	35	30

DESIGNS: 15 a. Turkish postman and camels; 40 a. Palestine postman and steam locomotive. I£1, Israeli postman and Boeing 707 jetliner.

1966. Cancer Research.

352	**143**	15 a. green and red	20	15

144 Akko (Acre)

145 Book and Crowns

1967. Ancient Israeli Ports.

353	**144**	15 a. purple	15	10
354	–	40 a. green	25	20
355	–	80 a. blue	35	30

PORTS: 40 a. Caesarea; 80 a. Yafo (Jaffa).

1967. Shulhan Arukh ("Book of Wisdom").

356	**145**	40 a. multicoloured	25	20

146 War of Independence Memorial

1967. Memorial Day.

357	**146**	55 a. silver, blue & turq . .	25	20

147 Taylorcraft Auster AOP.5 Reconnaissance Plane

1967. Independence Day. Military Aircraft.

358	**147**	15 a. blue and green . . .	15	15
359	–	30 a. brown and orange . .	20	15
360	–	80 a. violet & turquoise . .	30	20

AIRCRAFT: 30 a. Dassault Mystere IVA jet fighter; 80 a. Dassault Mirage IIICJ jet fighters.

148 Freighter "Dolphin" in Straits of Tiran

149 Law Scroll

1967. Victory in Arab-Israeli War.

361	–	15 a. black, yellow & red .	10	10
362	**148**	40 a. green	15	15
363	–	80 a. violet	20	20

DESIGNS—VERT: 15 a. Sword emblem of "Zahal" (Israeli Defence Forces). HORIZ: 80 a. "Wailing Wall", Jerusalem.

1967. Jewish New Year. Scrolls of the Torah (Mosaic Law), and similar designs.

364	**149**	12 a. multicoloured	10	10
365	–	15 a. multicoloured	10	10
366	–	35 a. multicoloured	20	20
367	–	40 a. multicoloured	20	20
368	–	80 a. multicoloured	20	20

150 "Welcome to Israel"

151 Lord Balfour

1967. International Tourist Year. Each with "Sun" emblem. Multicoloured.

369	30 a. Type **150**	15	15
370	40 a. "Air hostess"	15	15
371	80 a. "Orange" child	20	20

1967. 50th Anniv of Balfour Declaration.

372	–	15 a. green	10	10
373	**151**	40 a. brown	25	15

DESIGN: 15 a. Dr. C. Weizmann.

152 Ibex

153 Diamond

1967. Israeli Nature Reserves. Multicoloured.

374	12 a. Type **152**	15	15
375	18 a. Caracal	20	15
376	60 a. Dorcas gazelle	25	20

1968. Air. Israeli Exports.

377	–	10 a. multicoloured	10	10
378	–	30 a. multicoloured	10	10
379	–	40 a. multicoloured	15	10
380	–	50 a. multicoloured	15	10
381	–	55 a. multicoloured	15	10
382	–	60 a. multicoloured	20	20
383	–	80 a. multicoloured	20	20
384	–	I£1 multicoloured	25	15
385	–	I£1.50 multicoloured . . .	35	20
386	**153**	I£3 violet and green . . .	55	30

DESIGNS: 10 a. Draped curtains ("Textiles"); 30 a. "Stamps"; 40 a. Jar and necklace ("Arts and Crafts"); 50 a. Chick and egg ("Chicks"); 55 a. Melon, avocado and strawberries ("Fruits"); 60 a. Gladioli ("Flowers"); 80 a. Telecommunications equipment ("Electronics"). I£1, Atomic equipment ("Isotopes"). I£1.50, Models ("Fashion").

154 Beflagged Football

155 "Immigration"

1968. Pre-Olympic Football Tournament.

387	**154**	80 a. multicoloured	25	20

1968. Independence Day. Multicoloured.

388	15 a. Type **155**	10	10
389	80 a. "Settlement"	25	20

156 Rifles and Helmet

157 Zahal Emblem

1968. Memorial Day.

390	**156**	55 a. multicoloured	20	15

1968. Independence Day (Zahal–Israel Defence Forces).

391	**157**	40 a. multicoloured	20	15

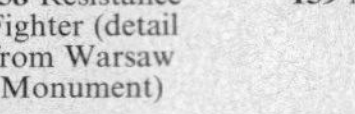

158 Resistance Fighter (detail from Warsaw Monument)

159 Moshe Sharett

1968. 25th Anniv of Warsaw Ghetto Rising.

392	**158**	60 a. bistre	25	20

1968. 27th Zionist Congress, Jerusalem.

393	**159**	I£1 sepia	35	25

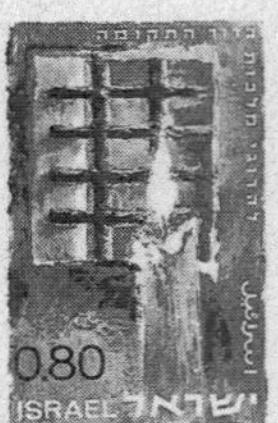
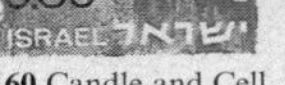
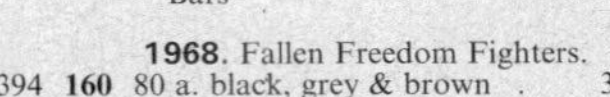

160 Candle and Cell Bars

161 Jerusalem

1968. Fallen Freedom Fighters.

394	**160**	80 a. black, grey & brown .	30	25

1968. Jewish New Year.

395	**161**	12 a. multicoloured	10	10
396	–	15 a. multicoloured	10	10
397	–	35 a. multicoloured	20	20
398	–	40 a. multicoloured	20	15
399	–	60 a. multicoloured	20	20

DESIGNS: Jerusalem—views of the Old City (12, 15, 35 a.) and of the New City (40, 60 a.).

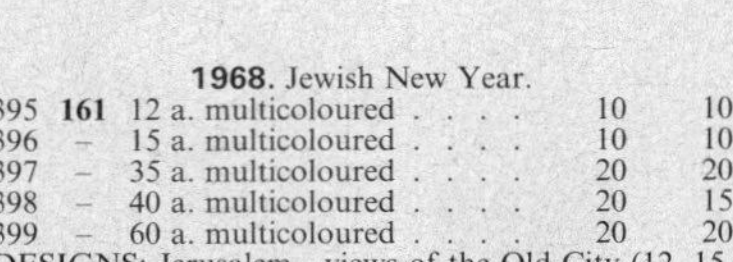

162 Scout Badge and Knot

163 "Lions' Gate", Jerusalem (detail)

1968. 50th Anniv of Jewish Scout Movement.

400	**162**	30 a. multicoloured	20	15

1968. "Tabira" Stamp Exhibition, Jerusalem.

401	**163**	I£1 brown	20	15

164 A. Mapu

165 Paralytics playing Basketball

1968. Death Cent of Abraham Mapu (writer).

403	**164**	30 a. olive	20	15

1968. International Games for the Paralysed.

404	**165**	40 a. green and lt green . .	20	15

166 Elat

1969. Israeli Ports.

405	**166**	30 a. mauve	30	20
406	–	60 a. brown (Ashdod) . . .	35	25
407	–	I£1 green (Haifa)	45	30

167 "Worker" and I.L.O. Emblem

168 Israeli Flag at Half-mast

1969. 50th Anniv of I.L.O.

408	**167**	80 a. green and lilac . . .	20	15

1969. Memorial Day.

409	**168**	55 a. gold, blue and violet .	25	15

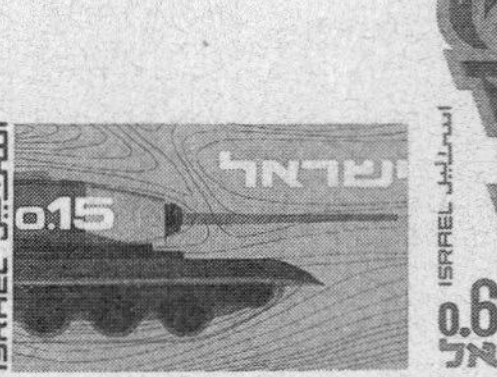

169 Army Tank

170 Flaming Torch

1969. Independence Day. Multicoloured.

410	15 a. Type **169**	15	10
411	80 a. "Elat" (destroyer)	30	25

1969. 8th Maccabiah.

412	**170**	60 a. multicoloured	25	20

171 Arms of Hadera

172 Building the Ark

1969. Civic Arms (2nd series).

413	2 a. green (Type **171**)	10	10
414	3 a. purple (Herzliyya)	10	10
415	5 a. orange (Holon)	10	10
416	15 a. red (Bat Yam)	10	10
417	18 a. blue (Ramla)	15	10
418	20 a. brown (Kefar Sava) . . .	15	10
419	25 a. blue (Giv'atayim)	15	10
420	30 a. mauve (Rehovot)	15	10
421	40 a. violet (Netanya)	25	10
422	50 a. blue (Bene Beraq)	25	10
423	60 a. green (Nahariyya)	25	10
424	80 a. green (Ramat Gan) . . .	25	10

1969. Jewish New Year, showing scenes from "The Flood". Multicoloured.

425	12 a. Type **172**	10	10
426	15 a. Animals going aboard . .	10	10
427	35 a. Ark afloat	20	20
428	40 a. Dove with olive branch . .	20	15
429	60 a. Ark on Mt. Ararat . . .	20	15

173 "King David" (Chagall)

174 Atomic "Plant"

1969. "King David".

430	**173**	I£3 multicoloured	1·10	75

1969. 25th Anniv of Weizmann Institute of Science.

431	**174**	I£1.15 multicoloured . . .	85	60

175 Dum Palms, Emeq He-Arava

176 Immigrant "Aircraft"

1970. Nature Reserves.

No.	Type	Description	Unused	Used
432	**175**	2 a. olive	10	10
433	–	3 a. blue	10	10
434	–	5 a. red	10	10
435	–	6 a. green	10	10
436	–	30 a. violet	25	20

DESIGNS: 3 a. Tahana Waterfall, Nahal Iyon; 5 a. Nahal Baraq Canyon, Negev; 6 a. Ha-Masreq, Judean Hills; 30 a. Soreq Cave, Judean Hills.

1970. 20th Anniv of Operation "Magic Carpet" (Immigration of Yemenite Jews).

No.	Type	Description	Unused	Used
437	**176**	30 a. multicoloured	20	15

177 Joseph Trumpeldor

178 Prime Minister Levi Eshkol

1970. 50th Anniv of Defence of Tel Hay.

No.	Type	Description	Unused	Used
438	**177**	I£1 violet	40	35

1970. Levi Eshkol Commemoration.

No.	Type	Description	Unused	Used
439	**178**	15 a. multicoloured	20	15

179 Ze'ev Jabotinsky (commander)

180 Camel and Diesel Train

1970. 50th Anniv of Defence of Jerusalem.

No.	Type	Description	Unused	Used
440	**179**	80 a. green and cream	45	30

1970. Opening of Dimona-Oron Railway.

No.	Type	Description	Unused	Used
441	**180**	80 a. multicoloured	70	30

181 Mania Schochat (author)

183 Memorial Flame

184 "Orchis laxifloris"

182 Scene from "The Dybbuk"

1970. 60th Anniv of "Ha-Shomer".

No.	Type	Description	Unused	Used
442	**181**	40 a. purple and cream	25	20

1970. 50th Anniv of Habimah National Theatre.

No.	Type	Description	Unused	Used
443	**182**	I£1 multicoloured	45	30

1970. Memorial Day.

No.	Type	Description	Unused	Used
444	**183**	55 a. black, red & violet	30	25

1970. Independence Day. Israeli Wild Flowers. Multicoloured.

No.	Description	Unused	Used
445	12 a. Type **184**	20	15
446	15 a. "Iris mariae"	20	20
447	80 a. "Lupinus pilosus"	75	65

185 C. Netter (founder)

186 I.A.I. Arava Transport Airplane

1970. Centenary of Miqwe Yisrael Agricultural College. Multicoloured.

No.	Description	Unused	Used
448	40 a. Type **185**	30	25
449	80 a. College building and gate	45	40

1970. Israeli Aircraft Industry.

No.	Type	Description	Unused	Used
450	**186**	I£1 silver, violet & blue	30	25

187 Yachts

188 Keren Hayesod

1970. World "420" Class Sailing Championships. Multicoloured.

No.	Description	Unused	Used
451	15 a. Type **187**	25	20
452	30 a. Yacht with spinnaker	25	25
453	80 a. Yachts turning around buoy	45	35

1970. 50th Anniv of Keren Hayesod.

No.	Type	Description	Unused	Used
454	**188**	40 a. multicoloured	30	25

189 Old Synagogue, Cracow

191 Mother and Child

190 Jewish "Bird" heading for Sun

1970. Jewish New Year. Multicoloured.

No.	Description	Unused	Used
455	12 a. Type **189**	10	10
456	15 a. Great Synagogue, Tunis	10	10
457	35 a. Portuguese Synagogue, Amsterdam	15	15
458	40 a. Great Synagogue, Moscow	20	15
459	60 a. Shearith Israel Synagogue, New York	20	15

1970. "Operation Ezra and Nehemiah" (Exodus of Iraqi Jews to Israel).

No.	Type	Description	Unused	Used
460	**190**	80 a. multicoloured	30	20

1970. 50th Anniv of Women's International Zionist Organization (W.I.Z.O.).

No.	Type	Description	Unused	Used
461	**191**	80 a. yellow, grn & silver	30	25

192 Tel Aviv Post Office, 1920

193 Histadrut Emblem

1970. "Tabit" Stamp Exhibition, Tel Aviv, and 50th Anniv of Tel Aviv Post Office.

No.	Type	Description	Unused	Used
462	**192**	I£1 multicoloured	30	25

1970. 50th Anniv of "Histadrut" (General Federation of Labour).

No.	Type	Description	Unused	Used
464	**193**	35 a. multicoloured	20	15

194 "Landscape with Bridge" (C. Pissaro)

1970. Paintings in Tel Aviv Museum. Mult.

No.	Description	Unused	Used
465	85 a. "Jewish Wedding" (J. Israels)	35	25
466	I£1 Type **194**	35	30
467	I£2 "Flowers in a Vase" (F. Leger)	45	40

195 "Inn of the Ghosts" (Cameri Theatre)

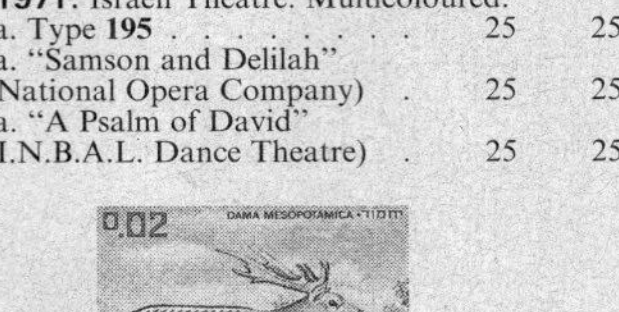

1971. Israeli Theatre. Multicoloured.

No.	Description	Unused	Used
468	50 a. Type **195**	25	25
469	50 a. "Samson and Delilah" (National Opera Company)	25	25
470	50 a. "A Psalm of David" (I.N.B.A.L. Dance Theatre)	25	25

196 Fallow Deer

1971. Nature Reserves. Animals of Biblical Times. Multicoloured.

No.	Description	Unused	Used
471	2 a. Type **196**	10	10
472	3 a. Asiatic wild ass	10	10
473	5 a. Arabian oryx	10	10
474	78 a. Cheetah	40	30

197 "Haganah" Emblem

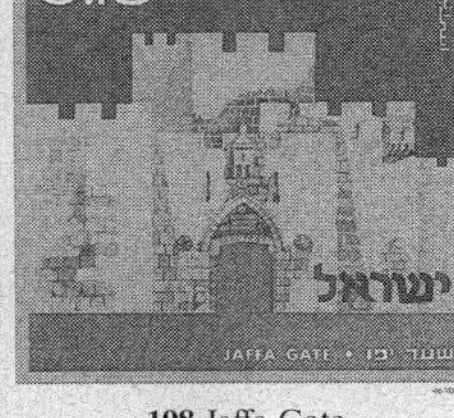

198 Jaffa Gate

1971. Memorial Day.

No.	Type	Description	Unused	Used
475	**197**	78 a. multicoloured	30	20

1971. Independence Day. Gates of Jerusalem (1st series). Multicoloured.

No.	Description	Unused	Used
476	15 a. Type **198**	45	25
477	18 a. New Gate	50	25
478	35 a. Damascus Gate	50	35
479	85 a. Herod's Gate	50	35

See also Nos. 527/30.

199 Gymnastics

200 "...and he wrote upon the tables..."

1971. 9th "Hapoel" Games. Multicoloured.

No.	Description	Unused	Used
481	50 a. Type **199**	25	20
482	50 a. Basketball	25	20
483	50 a. Running	25	20

1971. Feast of Weeks ("Shavuot"). Illuminated verses from the Bible. Multicoloured.

No.	Description	Unused	Used
484	50 a. Type **200**	35	30
485	85 a. "The first of the first-fruits..."	45	40
486	I£1. 50 "...and ye shall observe the feast..."	60	45

See also Nos. 488/92.

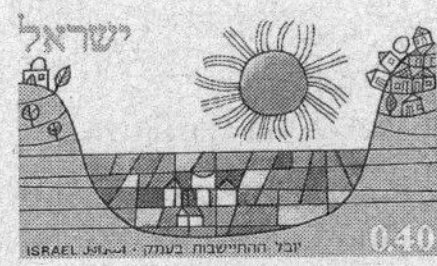

201 "Sun over the Emeq"

1971. 50th Anniv of Settlements in the "Emeq" (Yezreel Valley).

No.	Type	Description	Unused	Used
487	**201**	40 a. multicoloured	25	20

1971. Jewish New Year. Feast of the Tabernacles ("Sukkot"). Illuminated Verses from the Bible. As Type **200** Multicoloured.

No.	Description	Unused	Used
488	15 a. "You shall rejoice in your feast"	15	10
489	18 a. "You shall dwell in booths..."	15	10
490	20 a. "That I made the people..."	15	15
491	40 a. "...gathered in the produce"	20	15
492	65 a. "...I will give you your rains..."	25	20

202 Kinneret

203 "Agricultural Research"

1971. Landscapes (1st series).

No.	Type	Description	Unused	Used
493	–	3 a. blue	20	10
494	–	5 a. green	10	10
495	–	15 a. orange	10	10
496	**202**	18 a. purple	65	10
497	–	20 a. green	10	10
498	–	22 a. blue	80	10
498a	–	25 a. red	10	10
499	–	30 a. mauve	15	10
500	–	35 a. purple	10	10
501	–	45 a. blue	15	10
502	–	50 a. green	20	10
503	–	55 a. green	20	10
504	–	65 a. brown	15	10
505	–	70 a. red	20	10
505apa	–	80 a. blue	20	10
506	–	88 a. blue	80	30
507	–	95 a. red	80	35
508	–	I£1.10 brown	20	10
508a	–	I£1.30 blue	25	15
508b	–	I£1.70 brown	20	10
509pa	–	I£2 brown	15	15
510pa	–	I£3 violet	25	20
510a	–	I£10 blue	90	50

DESIGNS—As T **202**: 3 a. Judean desert; 5 a. Gan Ha-Shelosha; 15 a. Negev desert; 20 a. Tel Dan; 22 a. Yafo; 25 a. Arava; 30 a. En Avedat; 35 a. Brekhat Ram; 45 a. Mt. Hermon; 50 a. Rosh Pinna; 55 a. Natanya; 65 a. Plain of Zebulun; 70 a. Engedi; 80 a. Beach at Elat; 88 a. Akko (Acre); 95 a. Hamifratz Hane'Elam; I£1.10, Aqueduct near Acre; I£1.30, Zefat; I£1.70, Nazerat Illit; I£2, Coral Island; I£3, Haifa. 28 × 27 mm: I£10, Elat.

See also Nos. 682/4a.

1971. 50th Anniv of Volcani Institute of Agricultural Research.

No.	Type	Description	Unused	Used
511	**203**	I£1 multicoloured	30	20

204 Hebrew Text

205 "The Scribe" (sculpture, B. Schatz)

1971. Educational Development. Multicoloured.

No.	Description	Unused	Used
512	15 a. Type **204**	10	10
513	18 a. Mathematical formulae	10	10
514	20 a. Engineering symbols	10	10
515	40 a. University degree abbreviations	15	15

1972. Jewish Art.

No.	Type	Description	Unused	Used
516	**205**	40 a. brown, copper & blk	20	15
517	–	55 a. multicoloured	20	15
518	–	70 a. multicoloured	20	15
519	–	85 a. black and yellow	25	20
520	–	I£1 multicoloured	25	20

DESIGNS—VERT: 55 a. "Sarah" (A. Pann); 85 a. "Old Jerusalem" (woodcut, J. Steinhardt); I£1; "Resurrection" (A. Kahana). HORIZ: 70 a. "Zefat" (M. Shemi).

206 The Flight from Egypt

207 "Let My People Go"

1972. Passover Feast ("Pesah"). Multicoloured.

No.	Description	Unused	Used
521	18 a. Type **206**	25	20
522	45 a. Baking unleavened bread	25	25
523	95 a. "Seder" table	35	30

1972. Campaign for Jewish Immigration.

No.	Type	Description	Unused	Used
524	**207**	55 a. multicoloured	85	60

INDEX

Countries can be quickly located by referring to the index at the end of this volume.

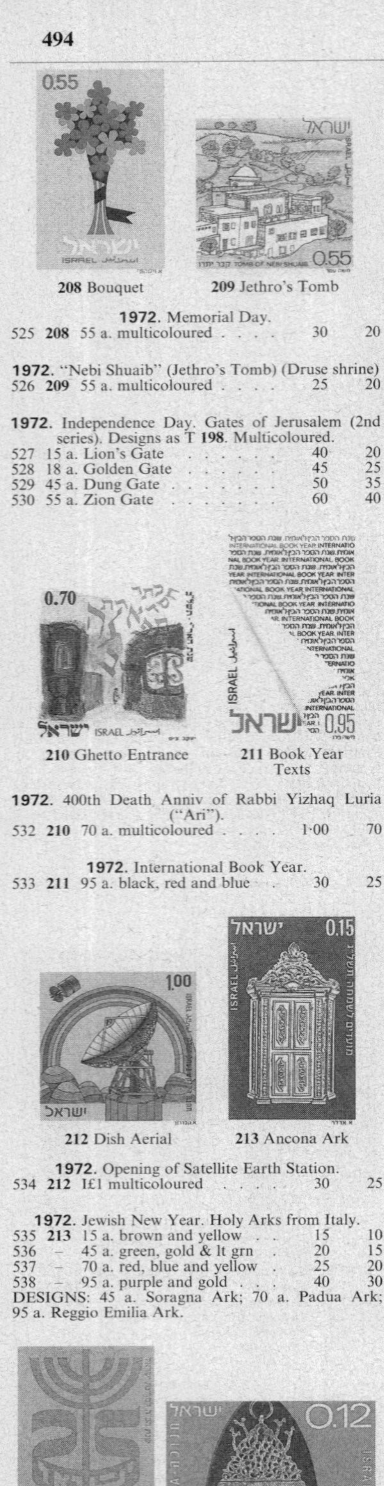

208 Bouquet 209 Jethro's Tomb

1972. Memorial Day.
525 **208** 55 a. multicoloured 30 20

1972. "Nebi Shuaib" (Jethro's Tomb) (Druse shrine)
526 **209** 55 a. multicoloured 25 20

1972. Independence Day. Gates of Jerusalem (2nd series). Designs as T **198**. Multicoloured.
527 15 a. Lion's Gate 40 20
528 18 a. Golden Gate 45 25
529 45 a. Dung Gate 50 35
530 55 a. Zion Gate 60 40

210 Ghetto Entrance 211 Book Year Texts

1972. 400th Death Anniv of Rabbi Yizhaq Luria ("Ari").
532 **210** 70 a. multicoloured . . . . 1·00 70

1972. International Book Year.
533 **211** 95 a. black, red and blue . . 30 25

212 Dish Aerial 213 Ancona Ark

1972. Opening of Satellite Earth Station.
534 **212** I£1 multicoloured 30 25

1972. Jewish New Year. Holy Arks from Italy.
535 **213** 15 a. brown and yellow . . 15 10
536 – 45 a. green, gold & lt grn . . 20 15
537 – 70 a. red, blue and yellow . . 25 20
538 – 95 a. purple and gold . . . 40 30
DESIGNS: 45 a. Soragna Ark; 70 a. Padua Ark; 95 a. Reggio Emilia Ark.

214 Menora Emblem 215 Hanukka Lamp (Morocco, 18th-19th century)

1972. 25th Anniv of State of Israel.
539 **214** I£1 blue, purple & silver . . . 30 25

1972. Festival of Lights ("Hanukka"). Ceremonial Lamps. Multicoloured.
540 12 a. Type **215** 15 15
541 25 a. 18th-century Polish lamp . . 20 15
542 70 a. 17th-century German silver lamp 20 20

216 Pendant 217 "Horse and Rider"

1973. Immigration of North African Jews.
543 **216** 18 a. multicoloured 20 15

1973. Children's Drawings. Multicoloured.
544 2 a. Type **217** 10 10
545 3 a. "Balloon ride" (17 × 48 mm) 10 10
546 55 a. "Party-time" 15 15

218 "Reuben" Window 219 Flame of Remembrance

1973. "Tribes of Israel" Stained-glass Windows by Chagall, Hadassah Synagogue, Jerusalem. Multicoloured.
547 I£1 "Levi" 65 50
548 I£1 "Simeon" 65 50
549 I£1 Type **218** 65 50
550 I£1 "Issachar" 65 50
551 I£1 "Zebulun" 65 50
552 I£1 "Judah" 65 50
553 I£1 "Asher" 65 45
554 I£1 "Gad" 65 45
555 I£1 "Dan" 65 45
556 I£1 "Benjamin" 65 45
557 I£1 "Joseph" 65 45
558 I£1 "Naphtali" 65 45

1973. Memorial Day.
559 **219** 65 a. multicoloured 25 15

220 Skeletal Hand

1973. Holocaust (Persecution of European Jews 1933–45) Memorial.
560 **220** 55 a. blue 20 15

221 Signatures of Declaration of Independence

1973. Independence Day.
561 **221** I£1 multicoloured 25 20

222 Star of David and Runners 223 Isaiah

1973. 9th Maccabiah.
563 **222** I£1.10 multicoloured . . . 25 15

1973. Jewish New Year. Prophets of Israel.
564 18 a. Type **223** 10 10
565 65 a. Jeremiah 10 10
566 I£1.10 Ezekiel 20 15

224 Jews in Boat, and Danish Flag 225 Institute Emblem and Cogwheel

1973. 30th Anniv of Rescue of Danish Jews.
567 **224** I£5 black, red & brown . . 60 45

1973. 50th Anniv of "Technion" Israel Institute of Technology.
568 **225** I£1.25 multicoloured . . . 25 20

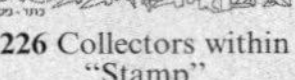

226 Collectors within "Stamp" 227 Soldier with Prayer Shawl

1973. "Jerusalem 73" International Stamp Exhibition. Multicoloured.
569 20 a. Type **226** 10 10
570 I£1 Collectors within "Stamp" (different) 20 20

1974. Memorial Day.
572 **227** I£1 black and blue 20 15

228 Quill and Bottle of Ink 229 "Woman in Blue" (M. Kisling)

1974. 50th Anniv of Hebrew Writers' Association.
573 **228** I£2 black and gold 20 15

1974. Jewish Art. Multicoloured.
574 I£1.25 Type **229** 15 15
575 I£2 "Mother and Child" (bronze, C. Orloff) 20 15
576 I£3 "Girl in Blue" (C. Soutine) . 25 20
See also Nos. 604/6.

230 Spanner

1974. 50th Anniv of Young Workers' Movement.
577 **230** 25 a. multicoloured 30 25

231 Lady Davis Technical Centre, Tel Aviv

1974. "Architecture in Israel" (1st series).
578 **231** 25 a. grey 10 10
579 – 60 a. blue 15 10
580 – I£1.45 brown 20 15
DESIGNS: 60 a. Elias Sourasky Library, Tel Aviv University. I£1.45, Mivtahim Rest-home, Zikhron Yaaqov.
See also Nos. 596/8.

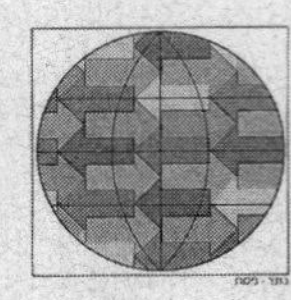

232 Istanbuli Synagogue 233 Arrows on Globe

1974. Jewish New Year. Rebuilt Synagogues in Jerusalem's Old City. Multicoloured.
581 25 a. Type **232** 10 10
582 70 a. Emtzai Synagogue 15 10
583 I£1 Raban Yohanan Ben Zakai Synagogue 15 15

1974. Centenary of U.P.U. Multicoloured.
584 25 a. Type **233** 10 10
585 I£1.30 Dove "postman" (27 × 27 mm) 25 20

234 David Ben Gurion (statesman)

1974. Ben Gurion Memorial.
586 **234** 25 a. brown 10 10
587 I£1.30 green 20 20

236 Child with Plant, and Rainbow 238 Welding

237 Hebrew University, Jerusalem

1975. Arbour Day. Multicoloured.
588 1 a. Type **236** 10 10
589 35 a. Bird in tree 10 10
590 I£2 Child with plant and sun . . 20 15

1975. 50th Anniv of Hebrew University, Jerusalem.
591 **237** I£2.50 multicoloured . . . 25 20

1975. "Occupational Safety". Multicoloured.
592 30 a. Type **238** 10 10
593 80 a. Tractor-driving 10 10
594 I£1.20 Telegraph line maintenance 15 15

239 Harry S. Truman 240 Memorial

1975. Truman Commemoration.
595 **239** I£5 brown 25 20

1975. "Architecture in Israel" (2nd series). As T **231**.
596 80 a. brown 15 10
597 I£1.30 green 15 10
598 I£1.70 brown 20 15
DESIGNS: 80 a. Hebrew University Synagogue, Jerusalem. I£1.30, Museum, Yad Mordechai. I£1.70, City Hotel, Bat Yam.

1975. Memorial Day.
599 **240** I£1 red, black & mauve . . 20 15

241 Text and Poppy **242** Hurdling

1975. Fallen Soldiers' Memorial.
600 **241** I£1.45 black, red & grey . . 20 15

1975. 10th Hapoel Games. Multicoloured.
601 25 a. Type **242** 10 10
602 I£1.70 Cycling 10 10
603 I£3 Volleyball 20 15

1975. Jewish Art. As T **229**. Multicoloured.
604 I£1 "Hanukka" (M. D. Oppenheim) 20 15
605 I£1.40 "The Purim Players" (J. Adler) (horiz) 20 15
606 I£4 "Yom Kippur" (M. Gottlieb) 25 20

243 Old People **244** Gideon

1975. Gerontology.
607 **243** I£1.85 multicoloured . . . 20 15

1975. Jewish New Year. Judges of Israel. Mult.
608 35 a. Type **244** 10 10
609 I£1 Deborah 15 10
610 I£1.40 Jephthah 20 15

245 Zalman Shazar **246** Emblem of Pioneer Women

1975. 1st Death Anniv of Zalman Shazar (President 1963–73).
611 **245** 35 a. black and silver . . . 20 15

1975. 50th Anniv of Pioneer Women's Organization.
612 **246** I£5 multicoloured 35 30

247 New Hospital Buildings

1975. Return of Hadassah Hospital to Mt. Scopus.
613 **247** I£4 multicoloured 25 20

248 Pratincole **249** "Air Pollution"

1975. Protected Wild Birds. Multicoloured.
614 I£1.10 Type **248** 30 30
615 I£1.70 Spur-winged plover . . . 40 40
616 I£2 Black-winged stilt 50 50

1975. "Environmental Quality". Multicoloured.
617 50 a. Type **249** 15 10
618 80 a. "Water pollution" 15 10
619 I£1.70 "Noise pollution" 15 15

250 Star of David **251** Symbolic "Key"

1975.
620 **250** 75 a. blue and red 20 10
621 I£1.80 blue and grey . . . 15 10
622 I£1.85 blue and brown . . 25 10
623 I£2.45 blue and green . . 25 10
623a I£2.70 blue and mauve . . 20 10
623b I£4.30 blue and red . . . 20 10
624 I£5.40 blue and bistre . . 25 15
625 I£8 blue and turquoise . . 30 15

1976. 70th Anniv of Bezalel Academy of Arts and Design, Jerusalem.
626 **251** I£1.85 multicoloured 20 15

252 "Border Settlements" **253** "In the days of Ahasuerus..."

1976. Jewish Border Settlements.
627 **252** I£1.50 multicoloured . . . 20 15

1976. "Purim" Festival. Multicoloured.
628 40 a. Type **253** 10 10
629 80 a. "He set the royal crown..." 15 10
630 I£1.60 "Thus shall it be done..." 15 15

254 Monument to the Fallen **255** "Dancers of Meron" (R. Rubin)

1976. Memorial Day.
632 **254** I£1.85 multicoloured . . . 30 25

1976. Lag Ba-Omer Festival.
633 **255** I£1.30 multicoloured . . . 30 25

256 "200" Flag

1976. Bicentenary of American Revolution.
634 **256** I£4 multicoloured 40 30

258 High Jump

1976. Olympic Games, Montreal.
636 **258** I£1.60 black and red . . . 20 15
637 – I£2.40 black and blue . . . 20 15
638 – I£4.40 black and mauve . . 25 20
DESIGNS: I£2.40, Swimming. I£4.40, Gymnastics.

259 Multiple Tent Emblems **260** "Truth"

1976. Camping.
639 **259** I£1.60 multicoloured . . . 25 20

1976. Jewish New Year. Multicoloured.
640 45 a. Type **260** 10 10
641 I£1.50 "Judgement" 15 15
642 I£1.90 "Peace" 20 20

261 Excavated Byzantine House

1976. Archaeology in Jerusalem (1st series). Multicoloured.
643 I£1.30 Type **261** 30 20
644 I£2.40 Arch of 2nd Temple . . 35 30
645 I£2.80 Staircase to 2nd Temple . 35 30

262 Pawn **263** Clearing Ground

1976. 22nd Chess Olympiad, Haifa. Mult.
646 I£1.30 Type **262** 15 15
647 I£1.60 Rook 20 15

1976. Archaeology in Jerusalem (2nd series). Designs as T **261**. Multicoloured.
648 70 a. City Wall, First Temple period 25 10
649 I£5 Omayyad palace 45 40

1976. Pioneers.
650 **263** 5 a. brown and gold . . . 10 10
651 – 10 a. lilac and gold . . . 10 10
652 – 60 a. red and gold 10 10
653 – I£1.40 blue and gold . . . 15 15
654 – I£1.80 green and gold . . . 20 15
DESIGNS—HORIZ: 10 a. Building breakwater. I£1.40, Ploughing. I£1.80, Ditch-clearing. VERT: 60 a. Road construction.

264 "Grandfather's Carrot"

1977 Voluntary Service.
655 **264** I£2.60 multicoloured . . . 25 20

265 "By the Rivers of Babylon"

1977. Drawings of E. M. Lilien.
656 **265** I£1.70 brown, grey & blk . 40 35
657 – I£1.80 black, stone & brn . 40 35
658 – I£2.10 green, lt grn & blk . 40 35
PAINTINGS—VERT: I£1.80, "Abraham". HORIZ: I£2.10, "May Our Eyes Behold".

266 Jew and Arab shaking Hands

1977. Children's Drawings on Peace. Mult.
659 50 a. Type **266** 15 10
660 I£1.40 Arab and Jew holding hands 25 20
661 I£2.70 Peace dove, Jew and Arab 35 25

267 Parachute Troops Memorial

1977. Memorial Day.
662 **267** I£3.30 multicoloured . . . 35 30

268 Embroidery showing Sabbath Loaves **269** Trumpet

1977. Sabbath.
663 **268** I£3 multicoloured 30 25

1977. Ancient Musical Instruments. Mult.
664 I£1.50 Type **269** 25 20
665 I£2 Lyre 25 20
666 I£5 "Jingle" (cymbals) 35 25

270 Fencing **272** American Zionist Emblem

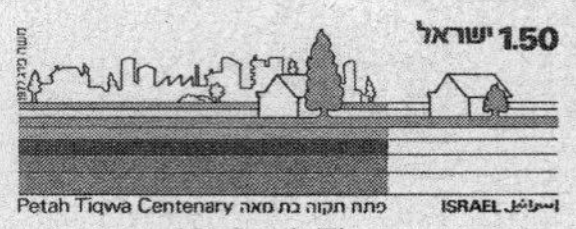

271 Petah Tiqwa

1977. 10th Maccabiah Games.
667 **270** I£1 grey, blue and black . . 25 20
668 – I£2.50 grey, red & black . . 25 25
669 – I£3.50 grey, green & blk . . 30 30
DESIGNS: I£2.50, Putting the shot. I£3.50, Judo.

1977. Centenary of Petah Tiqwa.
670 **271** I£1.50 multicoloured . . . 35 20

1977. Zionist Organization of America Convention.
671 **272** I£4 multicoloured 30 30

273 Page of 16th-cent Book "Kohelet Yaakov" **274** Sarah

1977. 400th Anniv of Hebrew Printing at Zefat.
672 **273** I£4 black, gold and red . . 30 25

1977. Jewish New Year. Matriarchs of Israel. Multicoloured.
673 70 a. Type **274** 15 10
674 I£1.50 Rebekah 25 20
675 I£2 Rachel 35 30
676 I£3 Leah 35 35
See also Nos. 728/30.

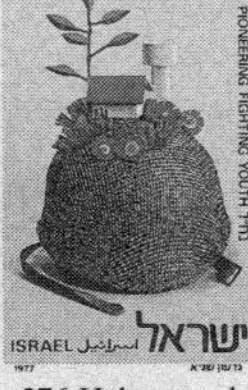

275 Police **276** Helmet and Model Settlement

1977. National Police Force. Multicoloured.
677 I£1 Type **275** 25 20
678 I£1 Civil Guard 25 20
679 I£1 Frontier Guard 25 20

1977. "Nahal" Pioneering Fighting Youth.
680 **276** I£3.50 multicoloured . . . 30 25

277 Accelerator Building, Weizmann Institute

278 Caesarea

1977. Inauguration of Koffler Accelerator.
681 **277** I£8 blue and black 60 50

1977. Landscapes (2nd series).
682 **278** 10 a. blue 10 10
683b – I£1 bistre 15 15
684 – I£20 green and orange . . 75 30
684a – I£50 multicoloured . . . 95 60
DESIGNS—As T **278**: I£1, Arava. 29 × 27 mm: I£20, Rosh Pinna. 27½ × 36½ mm: I£50, Soreq Cave.

279 "Mogul" Steam Locomotive, 1892

280 Blood-stained Scallop ("Gloripallium pallium")

1977. Railways in the Holy Land. Mult.
685 65 a. Type **279** 10 10
686 I£1.50 Steam locomotive . . . 25 20
687 I£2 4-6-0 Class P steam locomotive 35 30
688 I£2.50 Diesel locomotive . . . 40 35

1977. Red Sea Shells. Multicoloured.
690 I£2 Type **280** 20 20
691 I£2 Pacific grinning tun ("Malea pomum") 20 20
692 I£2 Isabelle cowrie ("Cypraea isabella") 20 20
693 I£2 Camp Pitar venus ("Lioconcha castrensis") . . . 20 20

281 "The Marriage Parties" (Dutch Ketubah)

1978. Illuminated Jewish Marriage Contracts (Ketubah). Multicoloured.
694 75 a. Type **281** 15 15
695 I£3.90 Moroccan Ketubah . . . 25 20
696 I£6 Jerusalem Ketubah 40 30

282 "A Street in Jerusalem" (H. Gliksberg)

283 Eliyahu Golomb (leader of Hagana)

1978. Jewish Art.
697 **282** I£3 multicoloured 25 25
698 – I£3.80 black, yell & grey . 30 25
699 – I£4.40 multicoloured . . . 35 25
DESIGNS: I£3.80, "Thistles" (L. Krakauer). I£4.40, "An Alley in Zefat" (M. Levanon).

1978. Historical Personalities (1st series).
700 **283** I£2 green and yellow . . . 20 15
701 – I£2 blue and grey 20 15
702 – I£2 purple and stone . . . 20 15
703 – I£2 brown and stone . . . 20 15
704 – I£2 black and grey 20 15
DESIGNS: No. 701, David Raziel (Irgun commander); 702, Yitzhak Sadeh (nationalist and military commander); 703, Dr. Moshe Sneh (Zionist politician); 704, Abraham Stern (underground fighter).
See also Nos. 721/2, 725/6, 732/3, 738/40, 763/5, 809/11 and 831/3.

284 Children's Flower Paintings (from mural, Petah Tikvah Museum)

286 Y.M.C.A. Building Jerusalem

1978. Memorial Day.
705 **284** I£1.50 multicoloured . . . 20 10
706 – I£1.50 multicoloured . . . 20 10
707 – I£1.50 multicoloured . . . 20 10
708 – I£1.50 multicoloured . . . 20 10
709 – I£1.50 multicoloured . . . 20 10
710 – I£1.50 multicoloured . . . 20 10
711 – I£1.50 multicoloured . . . 20 10
712 – I£1.50 multicoloured . . . 20 10
713 – I£1.50 multicoloured . . . 20 10
714 – I£1.50 multicoloured . . . 20 10
715 – I£1.50 multicoloured . . . 20 10
716 – I£1.50 multicoloured . . . 20 10
717 – I£1.50 multicoloured . . . 20 10
718 – I£1.50 multicoloured . . . 20 10
719 – I£1.50 multicoloured . . . 20 10
Nos. 705/19 issued together form a composite design, each showing a different portion of the Memorial Wall.

1978. Historical Personalities (2nd series). As T **283**.
721 I£2 blue and stone 20 15
722 I£2 brown and grey 20 15
DESIGNS: No. 721, Dr. Chaim Weizmann (first president of Israel); No. 722, Dr. Theodor Herzl (founder of Zionism).

1978. Centenary of Jerusalem Y.M.C.A.
723 **286** I£5.40 multicoloured . . . 35 30

287 Verse of National Anthem

288 Family Groups

1978. Cent of Publication of "Hatiqwa" (Jewish National Anthem).
724 **287** I£8.40 silver, dp blue & bl . 55 40

1978. Historical Personalities (3rd series). As T **283**.
725 I£2 purple and cream 20 15
726 I£2 green and cream 20 15
DESIGNS: No. 725, Rabbi Ouziel; No. 726, Rabbi Kook.

1978. Social Welfare.
727 **288** I£5.10 multicoloured . . . 35 30

1978. Jewish New Year, Patriarchs of Israel. As T **274**. Multicoloured.
728 I£1.10 Abraham 20 15
729 I£5.20 Isaac 35 30
730 I£6.60 Jacob 40 35

289 Star of David, Young Tree and Globe showing U.S.A.

291 Indian Silver and Enamelled Vase

290 Shaare Zedek Medical Centre, New and Old Buildings

1978. United Jewish Appeal.
731 **289** I£8.40 multicoloured . . . 65 60

1978. Historical Personalities (4th series). As T **283**.
732 I£2 purple and stone 20 15
733 I£2 blue and grey 20 15
DESIGNS: No. 732, David Ben-Gurion (first Prime Minister); No. 733, Ze'ev Jabotinsky (Zionist leader).

1978. Opening of New Shaare Zedek Medical Centre, Jerusalem.
734 **290** I£5.40 multicoloured . . . 40 30

1978. Institute for Islamic Art, Jerusalem. Multicoloured.
735 I£2.40 Type **291** 25 20
736 I£3 13th-century Persian pottery chess rook (elephant with howdah) 30 25
737 I£4 Syrian Mosque lamp . . . 35 25

1978. Historical Personalities (5th series). As T **283**.
738 I£2 black and stone 20 15
739 I£2 blue and grey 20 15
740 I£2 black and stone 20 15
DESIGNS: No. 738, Menahem Ussishkin (president of Jewish National Fund); No. 739, Berl Katzenelson (pioneer of Zionist socialism); No. 740, Dr. Max Nordau (journalist).

292 "Iris lortetii"

293 Agricultural Mechanization

1978. Wild Irises. Multicoloured.
741 I£1.10 Type **292** 20 15
742 I£5.40 "Iris haynei" 40 30
743 I£8.40 "Iris nazarena" 50 45

1979. Technological Achievements. Mult.
744 I£1.10 Type **293** 15 10
745 I£2.40 Sea water desalination . . 20 15
746 I£4.30 Electronics 20 15
747 I£5 Chemical fertilizers 25 20

294 Jewish Brigade Flag

295 "Good from Evil"

1979. Yishuv Volunteers serving in Second World War.
748 **294** I£5.10 yell, bl & dp bl . . . 45 40

1979. "Salute to the Righteous among Nations".
749 **295** I£5.40 multicoloured . . . 45 40

296 Prayer for Peace in Western Wall

297 Naval Memorial, Ashdod

1979. Signing of Egyptian–Israeli Peace Treaty.
750 **296** I£10 multicoloured 35 30

1979. Memorial Day.
752 **297** I£5.10 multicoloured . . . 30 20

298 Weightlifting

299 "50" and Rotary Emblem

1979. 11th Hapoel Games. Multicoloured.
753 I£1.50 Type **298** 25 15
754 I£6 Tennis 35 35
755 I£11 Gymnastics 50 45

1979. 50th Anniv of Rotary in Israel.
756 **299** I£7 multicoloured 45 40

300 Rabbi Joshua Ben Hananiah (blacksmith)

301 Tiberias Hot Springs

1979. Jewish New Year. The "Hazal" (sages and craftsmen). Multicoloured.
757 I£1.80 Type **300** 25 20
758 I£8.50 Rabbi Meir Ba'al Ha-Nes (scribe) 45 40
759 I£13 Rabbi Johanan the Sandal-maker 60 55

1979. Health Resorts. Multicoloured.
760 I£8 Type **301** 30 25
761 I£12 Dead Sea Hot Spring . . . 50 35

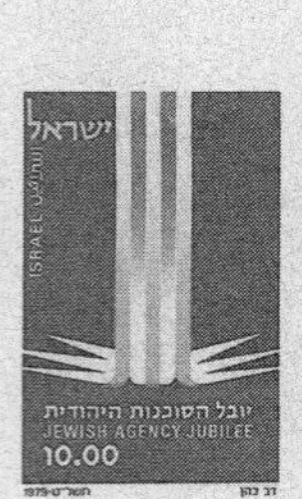

302 "Searchlight Beam"

303 Arab and Jew before Jerusalem

1979. 50th Anniv of Jewish Agency.
762 **302** I£10 blue, grey & turq . . 45 30

1979. Historical Personalities (6th series). As T **283**.
763 I£7 purple and grey 30 25
764 I£9 blue 35 35
765 I£13 black and stone 45 40
DESIGNS: I£7, Dr. Arthur Ruppin ("father of Zionist settlement"). I£9, Joseph Trumpeldor (founder of Zion Mule Corps and Jewish Legion). I£13, Aaron Aaronsohn (botanist).

1979. Children Paint Jerusalem. Multicoloured.
766 I£1.80 Type **303** 20 15
767 I£4 Jewish, Christian and Muslim citizens of Jerusalem (horiz) 20 20
768 I£5 Worshippers at the Western Wall (horiz) 25 25

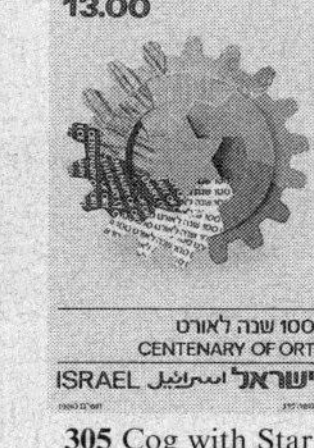

304 Boy sliding down Rainbow

305 Cog with Star of David

1979. International Year of the Child.
769 **304** I£8.50 multicoloured . . . 40 30

1980. Centenary of Organization for Rehabilitation through Training.
770 **305** I£13 multicoloured 55 45

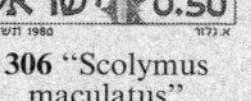

306 "Scolymus maculatus"

307 "The Road of Courage" Monument

1980. Thistles. Multicoloured.
771 50 a. Type **306** 20 15
772 I£5.50 "Echinops viscosus" . . 35 25
773 I£8.50 "Cynara syriaca" 65 60

1980. Memorial Day.
774 **307** I£12 multicoloured 40 30

308 Symbolical Human Figure with Blood-drop

309 Sabbath Lamp, Netherlands, 18th Century

1980. 50th Anniv of Magden David Adom (voluntary medical corps).
775 **308** I£2.70 red, grey & black . . 15 15
776 – I£13 multicoloured 40 35
DESIGN: I£13, Mobile intensive care unit and graph.

1980. Jewish New Year. Sabbath Lamps. Multicoloured.
778 I£4.30 Type **309** 35 20
779 I£20 Germany, 18th century . . 50 45
780 I£30 Morocco, 19th century . . 65 50

310 Yizhak Gruenbrum

311 Tree and Flowers

1980. 10th Death Anniv of Yizhak Gruenbaum (Zionist and politician).
781 **310** I£32 brown . . . . 1·25 1·10

1980. Renewal of Jewish Settlement in Gush Etzion.
782 **311** I£19 multicoloured 70 60

New currency. 1 (new) Shekel = 10 (old) Israeli Pounds.

313 "Shekel"

314 Golda Meir

1980.
784 **313** 5 a. green & emerald . . 10 10
785 10 a. red and mauve . . 10 10
786 20 a. turquoise & blue . . 10 10
787 30 a. violet & dp violet . 10 10
788 50 a. orange and red . . 10 10
789a 60 a. green & purple . . 15 10
790 70 a. blue and black . . 15 10
791 90 a. violet & brown . . 15 10
792 1 s. mauve and green . . 15 10
793 1 s. 10 green and red . . 15 10
794 1 s. 20 blue and red . . 15 10
795 2 s. green and purple . . 20 10
796 2 s. 80 brown & green . . 25 10
797a 3 s. red and blue 20 15
798 3 s. 20 grey and red . . 40 30
799b 4 s. purple & mauve . . 25 15
800 4 s. 20 blue & violet . . 25 10
801a 5 s. green and black . . 25 10
802pa 10 s. brown & dp brown 30 15

1981. Golda Meir (former Prime Minister). Commemoration.
803 **314** 2 s. 60 purple 60 55

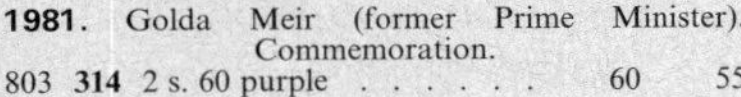

315 Landscape (Anna Ticho)

1981. Paintings of Jerusalem. Multicoloured.
804 50 a. Type **315** 20 15
805 1 s. 50 "View of City" (Joseph Zaritsky) (vert) 40 30
806 2 s. 50 Landscape (Mordechai Ardon) 50 45

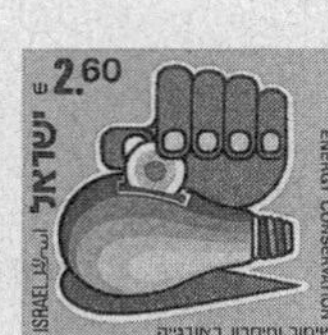
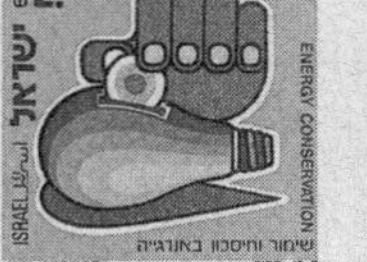

316 Hand putting Coin into Light Bulb

317 A. H. Silver (Zionist)

1981. Energy. Multicoloured.
807 2 s. 60 Type **316** 50 40
808 4 s. 20 Hand squeezing energy from the sun 60 50

1981. Historical Personalities (7th series).
809 – 2 s. blue 55 45
810 – 2 s. 80 green 55 45
811 **317** 3 s. 20 ochre and black . . 55 45
DESIGNS—As T **283**: 2 s. Shmuel Yosef Agnon (writer); 2 s. 80, Moses Montefiore (Zionist).

318 Biq'at Ha-yarden Memorial

319 Board Sailing

1981. Memorial Day.
812 **318** 1 s. multicoloured 30 25

1981. 11th Maccabiah Games. Multicoloured.
813 80 a. Type **319** 45 30
814 4 s. Basketball 65 50
815 6 s. High jump 85 75

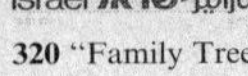

320 "Family Tree"

321 Moses and the Burning Bush

1981. The Jewish Family Heritage.
816 **320** 3 s. multicoloured 55 45

1981. Jewish New Year. Moses. Multicoloured.
817 70 a. Type **321** 25 10
818 1 s. Moses and Aaron petitioning Pharoah for Israelites' freedom 30 20
819 3 s. Israelites crossing the Red Sea 50 30
820 4 s. Moses with the Tablets . . 55 50

322 "Rosa damascena"

1981. Roses. Multicoloured.
821 90 a. Type **322** 40 25
822 3 s. 50 "Rosa phoenicia" . . . 50 40
823 4 s. 50 "Rosa hybrida" 65 50

323 Ha-Shiv'a Interchange

1981. Ha-Shiv'a Motorway Interchange.
824 **323** 8 s. multicoloured . . . . 1·25 1·10

324 Balonea Oak

325 Elat Stone

1981. Trees. Multicoloured.
825 3 s. Type **324** 40 35
826 3 s. Wild strawberry 40 35
827 3 s. Judas tree 40 35

1981. Precious Stones. Multicoloured.
828 2 s. 50 Type **325** 25 20
829 5 s. 50 Star sapphire 60 40
830 7 s. Emerald 70 50

1982. Historical Personalities (8th series). Vert designs as T **283**.
831 7 s. multicoloured 75 60
832 8 s. brown, stone and black . . 75 60
833 9 s. blue and grey 75 60
DESIGNS: 7 s. Perez Bernstein (politician); 8 s. Rabbi Arye Levin; 9 s. Joseph Gedaliah Klausner (writer, editor and President of Hebrew Language Academy).

327 Child crossing Road

1982. Road Safety.
834 **327** 7 s. multicoloured 75 60

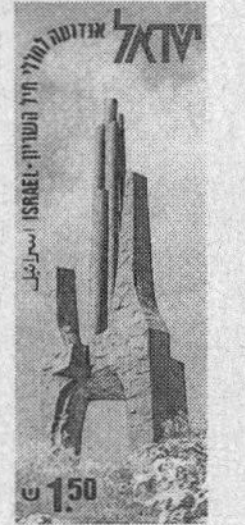
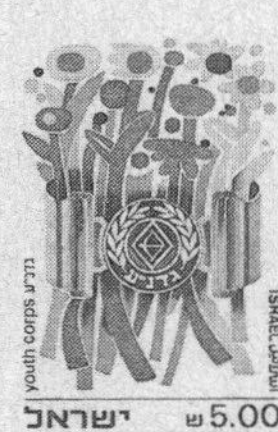

328 Armoured Brigade Memorial, En Zetim

330 Emblem and Flowers

329 Landscape (Aryeh Lubin)

1982. Memorial Day.
836 **328** 1 s. 50 multicoloured . . . 30 20

1982. Israeli Art. Multicoloured.
837 7 s. Type **329** 85 70
838 8 s. "Landscape" (Sionah Tagger) (vert) 90 85
839 15 s. "Pastorale" (Israel Paldi) . 1·25 1·25

1982. 40th Anniv of Gadna (Youth Corps).
840 **330** 5 s. multicoloured 80 70

331 Agricultural Products

332 Joshua and Israelites setting out for Canaan

1982.
841 **331** 40 a. blue and green . . . 10 10
842 80 a. blue and mauve . . 10 10
843 1 s. 40 green and red . . 20 15
844a 6 s. mauve and red . . . 30 20
845 7 s. red and green 15 10
846 8 s. green and red 20 15
847 9 s. green and brown . . 10 10
848a 15 s. red and green . . . 25 15
849 30 s. purple and red . . . 20 15
850b 50 s. bistre and red . . . 50 20
851a 100 s. black and green . . 70 50
852a 500 s. red and black . . . 70 60

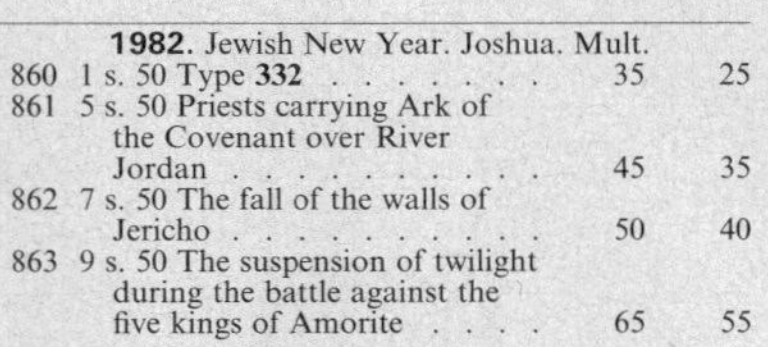

1982. Jewish New Year. Joshua. Mult.
860 1 s. 50 Type **332** 35 25
861 5 s. 50 Priests carrying Ark of the Covenant over River Jordan 45 35
862 7 s. 50 The fall of the walls of Jericho 50 40
863 9 s. 50 The suspension of twilight during the battle against the five kings of Amorite 65 55

333 Rosh Pinna

334 Symbolic Figures on Star of David

1982. Centenaries of Rosh Pinna and Rishon Le Zion Settlements. Multicoloured.
864 2 s. 50 Type **333** 45 40
865 3 s. 50 Rishon Le Zion 45 40
See also Nos. 868/9, 905/6 and 967.

1982. 70th Anniv of Hadassah (Women's Zionist Organization of America).
866 **334** 12 s. multicoloured . . . . 1·10 90

335 Branch

336 Flower

1982. No value expressed.
867 **335** (–) brown and orange . . . 55 20
No. 867 was initially sold at 1 s. 70 but this value was subsequently increased several times.

1982. Centenaries of Zikhron Yaaqov and Mazkeret Batya. As T **333**. Multicoloured.
868 6 s. Zikhron Yaaqov 45 40
869 9 s. Mazkeret Batya 45 40

1982. Council for a Beautiful Israel.
870 **336** 17 s. multicoloured . . . . 1·25 1·10

337 Eliahu Bet Tzuri

338 Honey Bee, Honeycomb and Flowers

1982. "Martyrs of the Struggle for Israel's Independence".
872 **337** 3 s. grey, black & brown . 35 25
873 – 3 s. grey, black & olive . . 35 25
874 – 3 s. grey, black & blue . . 35 25
875 – 3 s. grey, black & olive . . 35 25
876 – 3 s. grey, black & brown . 35 25
877 – 3 s. grey, black & blue . . 35 25
878 – 3 s. grey, black & brown . 35 25
879 – 3 s. grey, black & olive . . 35 25
880 – 3 s. grey, black & blue . . 35 25
881 – 3 s. grey, black & olive . . 35 25
882 – 3 s. grey, black & brown . 35 25
883 – 3 s. grey, black & olive . . 35 25
884 – 3 s. grey, black & blue . . 35 25
885 – 3 s. grey, black & brown . 35 25
886 – 3 s. grey, black & blue . . 35 25
887 – 3 s. grey, black & olive . . 35 25
888 – 3 s. grey, black & blue . . 35 25
889 – 3 s. grey, black & brown . 35 25
890 – 3 s. grey, black & olive . . 35 25
891 – 3 s. grey, black & brown . 35 25
DESIGNS: No. 873, Hannah Szenes; 874, Shlomo Ben Yosef; 875, Yosef Lishanski; 876, Naaman Belkind; 877, Eliezer Kashani; 878, Yechiel Dresner; 879, Dov Gruner; 880, Mordechai Alkachi; 881, Eliahu Hakim; 882, Meir Nakar; 883, Avshalom Haviv; 884, Ya'akov Weiss; 885, Meir Feinstein; 886, Moshe Barazani; 887, Eli Cohen; 888, Samuel Azaar; 889, Dr. Moshe Marzouk; 890, Shalom Salih; 891, Yosef Basri.

1983. Bee-keeping.
892 **338** 30 s. multicoloured . . . . 1·90 1·75

339 Sweets in Ashtray

340 Golan Settlement

1983. Anti-Smoking Campaign.
893 **339** 7 s. multicoloured 55 45

1983. Settlements. Multicoloured.
894 8 s. Type **340** 65 50
895 15 s. Galil settlement 90 75
896 20 s. Yehuda and Shomeron settlements . . . . 1·25 1·00

341 84th Division "of Steel" Memorial, Besor (Israel Godowitz)

1983. Memorial Day.
897 **341** 3 s. multicoloured 30 25

342 Star of David

1983. 35th Anniv of Independence.
898 **342** 25 s. multicoloured . . . . 1·90 1·75

343 Running

1983. 12th Hapoel Games.
900 **343** 6 s. multicoloured 50 40

344 Missile and Blueprint

1983. 50th Anniv of Israel Military Industries.
901 **344** 12 s. multicoloured 80 60

345 "The Last Way" (Iosef Kuzhovsky)

1983. Babi Yar Massacre.
902 **345** 35 s. multicoloured . . . . 1·90 1·50

347 Raoul Wallenberg

348 Ohel Moed Synagogue, Tel Aviv

1983. Raoul Wallenberg (Swedish diplomat) Commemoration.
904 **347** 14 s. stone and brown . . 1·10 90

1983. Centenary of Yesud Ha-Maala and Nes Ziyyona. As T **333**. Multicoloured.
905 11 s. Yesud Ha-Maala 60 55
906 13 s. Nes Ziyyona 65 60

1983. Jewish New Year. Synagogues. Mult.
907 3 s. Type **348** 35 25
908 12 s. Yeshurun Synagogue, Jerusalem 60 50
909 16 s. Ohel Aharon Synagogue, Haifa 85 70
910 20 s. Khalaschi Synagogue, Beer Sheva 95 85

349 Afula Landscape

1983. Afula Urban Centre, Jezreel Valley.
911 **349** 15 s. multicoloured 75 60

351 Israeli Aircraft Industry Kfir-C2 Jet Fighter

1983. Military Equipment. Multicoloured.
913 8 s. Type **351** 25 20
914 18 s. "Reshef" (missile vessel) . . 45 40
915 30 s. "Merkava" battle tank . . 60 55

352 Rabbi Meir Bar-Ilan

353 "Aliya" ("immigration")

1983. 34th Death Anniv of Rabbi Meir Bar-Ilan (Zionist leader).
916 **352** 9 s. blue and green 35 30

1983. 50th Anniv of Jewish Immigration from Germany.
917 **353** 14 s. red, gold and blue . . 45 35

354 Michael Halperin

355 Yigal Allon

1984. 65th Death Anniv of Michael Halperin (nationalist).
918 **354** 7 s. brown, stone & dp brn 40 30

1984. 4th Death Anniv of Yigal Allon (politician).
919 **355** 15 s. blue, green & blk . . 40 30

356 Uri Zvi Grinberg

357 Hevel Ha-Besor

1984. 3rd Death Anniv of Uri Zvi Grinberg (poet).
920 **356** 16 s. brown and red . . . 40 30

1984. Settlements. Multicoloured.
921 12 s. Type **357** 45 40
922 17 s. Arava 60 50
923 40 s. Hevel Azza 70 65

358 Alexander Zaid Monument (David Polus)

1984. Sculptures.
924 **358** 15 s. stone, black & blue . . 50 45
925 – 15 s. stone, black & brn . . 50 45
926 – 15 s. green, black & grey . . 50 45
DESIGNS: No. 925, Tel Hay Memorial (Abraham Melnikov); 926, Dov Gruner monument (Chana Orloff).

359 Oliphant House, Dalyat Al Karmil (memorial to Druse Community)

360 Worker with Flag

1984. Memorial Day.
927 **359** 10 s. multicoloured 30 25

1984. 50th Anniv of National Labour Federation.
928 **360** 35 s. multicoloured 75 70

361 Leon Pinsker

362 Stars and Hearts

1984. 93rd Death Anniv of Leon Pinsker (Zionist leader).
929 **361** 20 s. lilac and purple . . . 70 60

1984. 70th Anniv of American Jewish Joint Distribution Committee.
930 **362** 30 s. red, blue & black . . 70 60

363 Dove on Olympic Podium

364 General Charles Orde Wingate

1984. Olympic Games, Los Angeles.
931 **363** 80 s. multicoloured . . . . 1·40 1·25

1984. 40th Death Anniv of Gen. Charles Orde Wingate (military strategist).
933 **364** 20 s. grey, black & green . 70 60

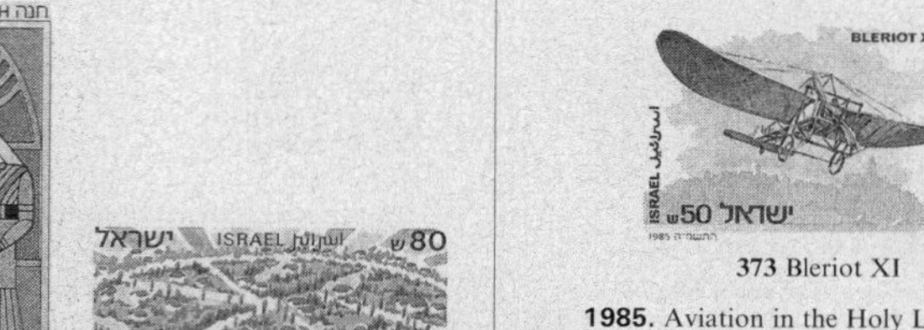

365 Hannah

366 Nahalal (first Moshav)

1984. Jewish New Year. Women in the Bible. Multicoloured.
934 15 s. Type **365** 40 30
935 70 s. Ruth 65 55
936 100 s. Huldah the prophetess . . 90 80

1984. Moshavim (Co-operative Workers' Settlements).
937 **366** 80 s. multicoloured . . . . 1·10 90

367 David Wolffsohn

368 "Apartment to Let" (Leah Goldberg, illus Shemuel Katz)

1984. 70th Death Anniv of David Wolffsohn (president of Zionist Organization).
938 **367** 150 s. brown, blue & blk . . 1·90 1·75

1984. Children's Books. Multicoloured.
939 20 s. Type **368** 30 25
940 30 s. "Why is the Zebra wearing pyjamas?" (O. Hille, illus Alona Frankel) (28 × 28 mm) 30 30
941 50 s. "Across the Sea" (Haim Nahman Bialik, illus Nahum Gutman) 35 30

369 Bread and Wheat

1984. World Food Day.
942 **369** 200 s. multicoloured . . . 1·50 1·25

370 Isaac Herzog

1984. 25th Death Anniv of Isaac Herzog (Israel's first Chief Rabbi).
943 **370** 400 s. multicoloured . . . 2·50 2·00

371 Lappet-faced Vulture

1985. Biblical Birds of Prey (1st series). Multicoloured.
944 100 s. Type **371** 90 90
945 200 s. Bonelli's eagle . . . . . 1·25 1·25
946 300 s. Sooty falcon . . . . . . 1·50 1·25
947 500 s. Griffon vulture . . . . . 2·40 2·00
See also Nos. 1015/18.

372 Golani Brigade Monument and Museum

1985. Memorial Day.
949 **372** 50 s. multicoloured 30 25

373 Bleriot XI

1985. Aviation in the Holy Land. Mult.
950 50 s. Type **373** (landing by Jules Vedrines, 1913) 45 35
951 150 s. Short S.17 Kent flying boat "Scipio" (Imperial Airways regular flights via Palestine, 1931–42) 60 45

952 250 s. De Havilland D.H.82A Tiger Moth (foundation of Palestine Flying Club, 1934) . 75 70
953 300 s. Short S.16 Scion II (international flights by Palestine Airways, 1937–40) 90 85

374 Zivia and Yitzhak Zuckerman

1985. Zivia and Yitzhak Zuckerman (Polish Jewish freedom fighters) Commemoration.
954 **374** 200 s. brown, grey & black 95 85

375 Nurses tending Patients

1985. 18th International Congress of Nurses.
955 **375** 400 s. multicoloured . . . 1·40 1·25

377 Ark of the Covenant

378 "Medals"

1985. Jewish New Year. Tabernacle Furnishings. Multicoloured.
957 100 s. Type **377** 35 25
958 150 s. The table 35 25
959 200 s. Candlestick 40 40
960 300 s. Incense altar 50 45

1985. International Youth Year.
961 **378** 150 s. multicoloured . . . 35 30

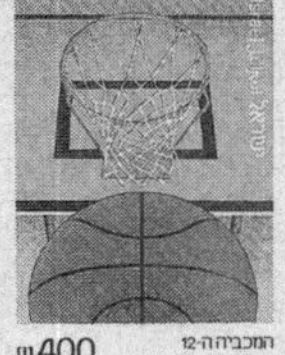

379 Basketball

380 Recanati

1985. 12th Maccabiah Games. Multicoloured.
962 400 s. Type **379** 90 75
963 500 s. Tennis . . . . 1·00 90
964 600 s. Windsurfing . . . . . . 1·25 1·00

1985. 40th Death Anniv of Leon Yehuda Racanati (founder of Palestine Discount Bank).
965 **380** 200 s. brn, grey & bl . . . 45 40

381 Dizengoff (after J. Steinhardt and M. Sima)

1985. 49th Death Anniv of Meir Dizengoff (founder and Mayor of Tel Aviv).
966 **381** 500 s. black, brown & sil . 1·00 75

1985. Centenary of Gedera. As T **333**. Mult.
967 600 s. Gedera . . . . 1·10 95

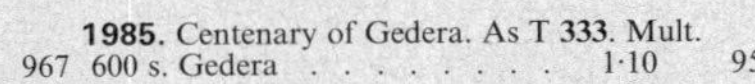

382 Kibbutz Members

1985. The Kibbutz.
968 **382** 900 s. multicoloured . . . 1·75 1·25

Currency Reform.
1000 (old) Shekalim = 1 (new) Shekel

383 Dr. Theodor Herzl

384 Corinthian Capital, 1st Century B.C.

1986.
969 **383** 1 a. blue and red 10 10
970 2 a. blue and green . . . 10 10
971 3 a. blue and bistre . . . 10 10
972 5 a. blue & turquoise . . 10 10
973 10 a. blue and orange . . 20 15
974a 20 a. blue and purple . . 25 20
975a 30 a. blue and yellow . . 40 25
976a 50 a. blue and violet . . . 60 35

1986. Jerusalem Archaeology.
977 – 40 a. green, orange & blk . 30 15
978 – 60 a. brown, violet & blk . 45 15
979 – 70 a. green, brn & blk . . 50 15
980 – 80 a. purple, bis & blk . . 55 20
981 – 90 a. yellow, lilac & blk . 60 20
982 **384** 1 s. brown, green & blk . 60 20
983a – 2 s. blue, green & black . 1·25 35
984 – 3 s. mauve, blue & black . 1·75 55
987 – 10 s. green, blue & black . 2·00 55

DESIGNS—As T **384**: 40 a. Relief, 1st century B.C. (Second Temple); 60 a. Byzantine capital, 6th century A.D.; 3 s. Archaic Ionic capital, 1st century B.C. (Second Temple). 32 × 23 mm: 70 a. Relief from palace of Umayyid Caliphs, 8th century A.D.; 80 a. Crusader capital from Church of Ascension, Mount of Olives, 12–13th centuries; 90 a. Relief from Suleiman's Wall, 16th century A.D.; 2 s. Insignia of Sayif addin Attaz from Mameluke Academy, 14th century A.D.; 10 s. Frieze from burial cave entrance, end of Second Temple period.

385 "Balanophyllia coccinea"

387 Microphone and Map

386 Sketches of Rubinstein (Pablo Picasso)

1986. Red Sea Corals. Multicoloured.
991 30 a. Type **385** 60 50
992 40 a. "Goniopora" 60 50
993 50 a. "Dendronephthya" . . . 60 50

1986. Birth Cent (1987) of Arthur Rubinstein and 5th International Rubinstein Piano Competition.
994 **386** 60 a. multicoloured . . . . 1·25 1·10

1986. 50th Anniv of Broadcasting from Jerusalem.
995 **387** 70 a. multicoloured . . . . 1·25 1·10

388 Negev Bridge Monument, Beer Sheva

389 El-Jazzar Mosque, Akko

1986. Memorial Day.
996 **388** 20 a. multicoloured 45 35

1986. Id Al-Fitr (end of Ramadan).
997 **389** 30 a. emerald, green & ol . 55 45

390 Hebrew Union College, Cincinnati

1986. "Ameripex '86" International Stamp Exhibition, Chicago. Jewish Institutes of Higher Learning. Multicoloured.
998 50 a. Type **390** 85 75
999 50 a. Yeshiva University, New York 85 75
1000 50 a. Jewish Theology Seminary, New York . . . 85 75

391 Nabi Sabalan's Tomb, Hurfeish

1986. Feast of Nabi Sabalan (Druse feast).
1002 **391** 40 a. multicoloured . . . 70 55

392 Graffiti on Wall

1986. Anti-Racism Campaign.
1003 **392** 60 a. multicoloured . . . 1·25 95

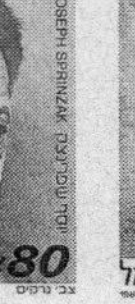
393 Sprinzak

395 Gates of Heaven, with Jerusalem above, opening to Power of Prayer

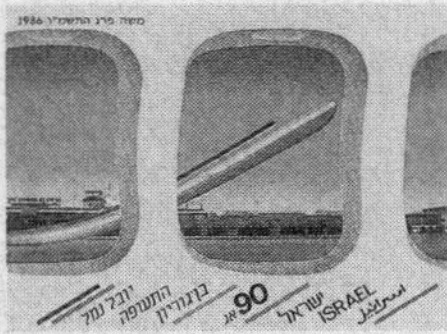
394 Airport through Cabin Windows

1986. Birth Centenary (1985) of Joseph Sprinzak (first Speaker of Knesset).
1004 **393** 80 a. blue, green & black . 1·25 1·10

1986. 50th Anniv of Ben Gurion Airport.
1005 **394** 90 a. multicoloured . . . 1·90 1·50

1986. Jewish New Year. Pages from Worms Mahzor (prayer book). Multicoloured.
1006 20 a. Type **395** (prayers for Yom Kippur) 60 50
1007 40 a. Man weighing shekel for Temple (prayer for Sheqalim, first special Sabbath) 65 65
1008 90 a. Roses (illustration of liturgical poem) 85 75

396 David Ben Gurion

1986. Birth Centenary of David Ben Gurion (Prime Minister, 1948–53 and 1955–63).
1009 **396** 1 s. bistre, brown & black 1·75 1·50

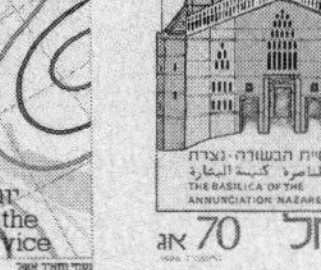
398 Satellite and Isobars over Map

399 Basilica of the Annunciation, Nazareth

1986. 50th Anniv of Meteorological Service.
1011 **398** 50 a. multicoloured . . . 1·10 90

1986. Christmas.
1012 **399** 70 a. multicoloured . . . 1·40 1·25

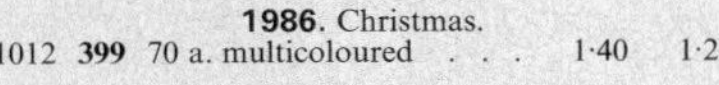

400 Bronislaw Huberman (violinist and founder)

1986. 50th Anniv of Israel Philharmonic Orchestra.
1013 **400** 1 s. 50 brn, blk & yell . . 2·25 1·90
1014 – 1 s. 50 grey, blk & yell . . 2·25 1·90

DESIGN: No. 1014, Arturo Toscanini (conductor of Orchestra's first concert, 1936).

401 Hume's Tawny Owl

1987. Biblical Birds of Prey (2nd series). Owls. Multicoloured.
1015 30 a. Eagle owl 50 45
1016 40 a. Striated scops owl . . . 65 60
1017 50 a. Barn owl 85 70
1018 80 a. Type **401** . . . . 1·50 95

402 Six-Day War Memorial, Ammunition Hill, Jerusalem

1987. Memorial Day.
1020 **402** 30 a. multicoloured . . . 55 45

403 Emblem

1987. 13th Hapoel Games.
1021 **403** 90 a. multicoloured . . . 1·25 1·10

405 Street Cleaner

406 Saluki

1987. "A Clean Environment".
1023 **405** 40 a. multicoloured . . . 55 40

1987. World Dog Show. Dogs of Israeli Origin. Multicoloured.
1024 40 a. Type **406** . . . . 1·25 1·00
1025 50 a. Sloughi . . . . 1·25 1·00
1026 2 s. Canaan dog . . . . . . 2·75 2·50

407 Radio Operators and Globe

1987. Israel Radio Amateurs.
1027 **407** 2 s. 50 multicoloured . . 3·75 3·00

408 Altneuschul Synagogue, Prague

409 Rabbi Amiel

1987. Jewish New Year. Synagogue Models in Museum of the Diaspora, Tel Aviv (1st issue). Multicoloured.
1028 30 a. Type **408** 45 45
1029 50 a. Main Synagogue, Aleppo, Syria 60 50
1030 60 a. Israelite Temple, Florence 70 60

See also Nos. 1054/6.

1987. 104th Birth Anniv of Rabbi Moshe Avigdor Amiel (Chief Rabbi of Tel Aviv).
1031 **409** 1 s. 40 multicoloured . . 1·75 1·25

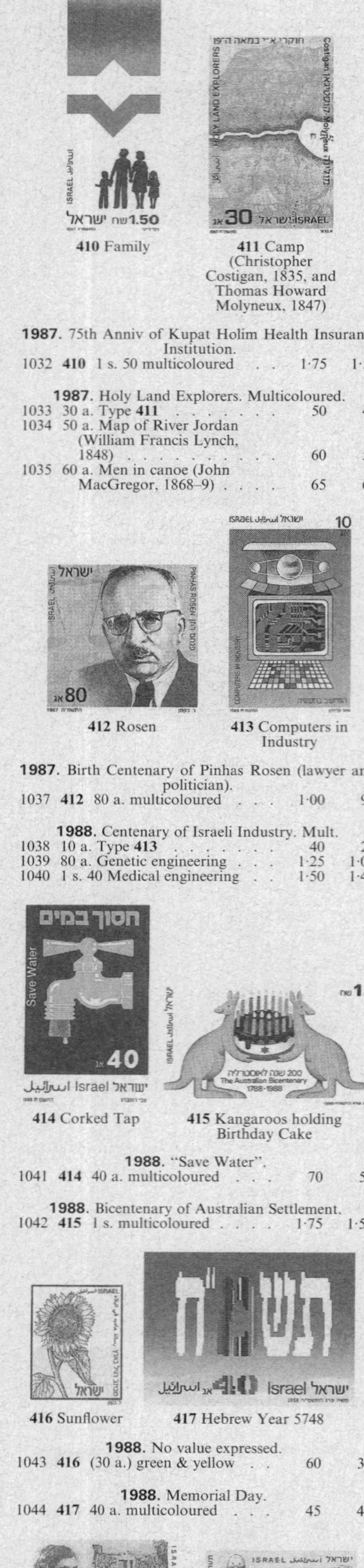

410 Family

411 Camp (Christopher Costigan, 1835, and Thomas Howard Molyneux, 1847)

1987. 75th Anniv of Kupat Holim Health Insurance Institution.
1032 **410** 1 s. 50 multicoloured . . 1·75 1·50

1987. Holy Land Explorers. Multicoloured.
1033 30 a. Type **411** 50 45
1034 50 a. Map of River Jordan (William Francis Lynch, 1848) 60 50
1035 60 a. Men in canoe (John MacGregor, 1868–9) 65 60

412 Rosen

413 Computers in Industry

1987. Birth Centenary of Pinhas Rosen (lawyer and politician).
1037 **412** 80 a. multicoloured . . . 1·00 95

1988. Centenary of Israeli Industry. Mult.
1038 10 a. Type **413** 40 25
1039 80 a. Genetic engineering . . . 1·25 1·00
1040 1 s. 40 Medical engineering . . 1·50 1·40

414 Corked Tap

415 Kangaroos holding Birthday Cake

1988. "Save Water".
1041 **414** 40 a. multicoloured . . . 70 55

1988. Bicentenary of Australian Settlement.
1042 **415** 1 s. multicoloured . . . . 1·75 1·50

416 Sunflower

417 Hebrew Year 5748

1988. No value expressed.
1043 **416** (30 a.) green & yellow . . . 60 30

1988. Memorial Day.
1044 **417** 40 a. multicoloured . . . 45 40

418 Anne Frank and House, Amsterdam

419 Jerusalem

1988. 43rd Death Anniv of Anne Frank (concentration camp victim).
1046 **418** 60 a. multicoloured . . . 85 70

1988. "Independence 40" National Stamp Exhibition, Jerusalem.
1047 **419** 1 s. lt brown & brown . . 1·40 1·25

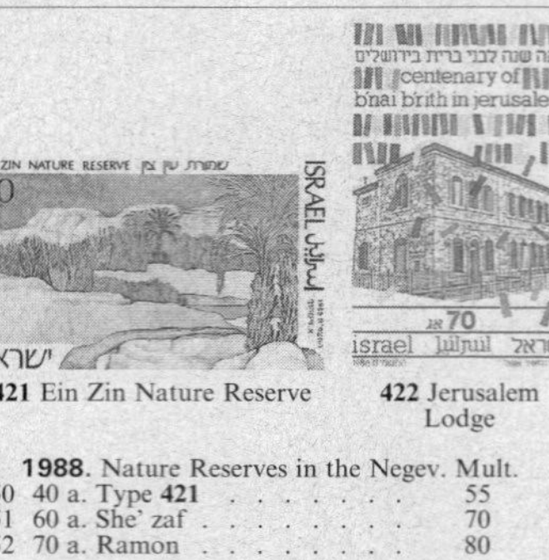

421 Ein Zin Nature Reserve

422 Jerusalem Lodge

1988. Nature Reserves in the Negev. Mult.
1050 40 a. Type **421** 55 50
1051 60 a. She' zaf 70 60
1052 70 a. Ramon 80 65

1988. Centenary of B'nai B'rith in Jerusalem.
1053 **422** 70 a. multicoloured . . . 95 85

1988. Jewish New Year. Synagogue Models in Museum of the Diaspora, Tel Aviv (2nd issue). As T **408**. Multicoloured.
1054 35 a. 12th-century Kai-Feng Fu Synagogue, China 60 50
1055 60 a. 17th-century Zabludow Synagogue, Poland 65 60
1056 70 a. 18th-century Touro Synagogue, Newport, Rhode Island 70 65

423 Havivah Reik

1988. Jewish World War II Underground Fighters. Multicoloured.
1057 **423** 40 a. multicoloured . . . 55 50
1058 – 1s. 65 dp blue, blue & blk 2·25 1·90
DESIGN: 1 s. 65, Enzo Hayyim Sereni.

424 Dayan

425 Burning Illustration of German Synagogue

1988. 7th Death Anniv of Moshe Dayan (soldier and politician).
1059 **424** 40 a. multicoloured . . . 60 50

1988. 50th Anniv of "Kristallnacht" (Nazi pogrom).
1060 **425** 80 a. multicoloured . . . 1·25 95

426 Menorah and Soldiers

1988. 74th Anniv of Formation of Jewish Legion.
1061 **426** 2 s. dp brn, brn & bis . . 2·50 1·90

427 Avocado (fruit-growing)

1988. Agricultural Achievements in Israel. Multicoloured.
1062 50 a. Type **427** 75 65
1063 60 a. Easter lily (plant breeding) 90 75
1064 90 a. Plants and drip-pipe (irrigation systems) . . . . 1·00 90

428 Red Sea

429 Rabbi Maimon

1989. Tourism. Multicoloured.
1065 40 a. Type **428** 65 60
1066 60 a. Dead Sea 75 70
1067 70 a. Mediterranean . . . . . 1·00 85
1068 1 s.70 Sea of Galilee . . . . . 1·40 1·40

1989. 114th Birth Anniv of Rabbi Judah Leib Maimon (writer).
1069 **429** 1 s. 70 multicoloured . . 2·25 2·00

430 "Rashi" in Rashi Script

431 Airforce Memorial, Har Tayassim

1989. 950th Birth Anniv of Rashi (Rabbi Solomon Ben Isaac of Troyes) (scholar).
1070 **430** 4 s. cream and brown . . 4·50 3·75

1989. Memorial Day.
1071 **431** 50 a. multicoloured . . . 60 50

432 Child

433 Games Emblem

1989. 20th Anniv of Israel United Nations Children's Fund National Committee.
1072 **432** 90 a. multicoloured . . . 1·25 1·00

1989. 13th Maccabia Games.
1073 **433** 80 a. multicoloured . . . 90 75

434 Smoira

436 Garganey

1989. Birth Centenary (1988) of Moshe Smoira (first President of Israel's Supreme Court).
1074 **434** 90 a. blue . . . . 1·25 1·00

1989. Ducks. Multicoloured.
1076 80 a. Type **436** 95 85
1077 80 a. Mallard 95 85
1078 80 a. Green-winged teal . . . 95 85
1079 80 a. Common shelduck . . . 95 85

437 Printed Circuit and Pencil

438 Lion Design (Ukraine, 1921)

1989. 13th International Council of Graphic Design Associations Congress.
1080 **437** 1 s. multicoloured . . . . 1·10 1·10

1989. Jewish New Year. Paper-cuts. Mult.
1081 50 a. Type **438** 50 45
1082 70 a. Hand design (Morocco, 1800s) 65 50
1083 80 a. Stag design (Germany, 1818) 75 60

439 Founders of Safa Brurah

440 Rabbi Alkalai

1989. Centenaries of Safa Brurah ("Clear Language") and Hebrew Language Committee (precursors of Hebrew Language Council).
1084 **439** 1 s. multicoloured . . . . 1·10 1·10

1989. 11th Death Anniv of Rabbi Hai Alkalai (Zionist).
1085 **440** 2 s. 50 multicoloured . . 2·50 1·90

441 "Stag"

442 Postal Authority Emblem

1989. "Tevel 89" Youth Stamp Exhibition.
1086 **441** 50 a. multicoloured . . . 55 50

1989. First Stamp Day.
1087 **442** 1 s. multicoloured . . . . 1·00 90

443 "See You Again"

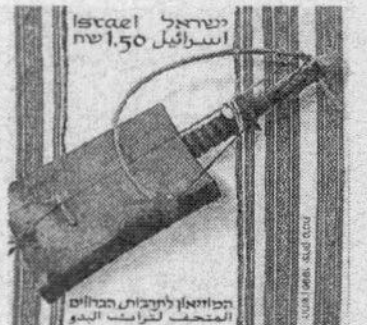

444 Rebab and Carpet

1989. Greetings Stamps. No value expressed. Multicoloured.
1088 (–) Type **443** 40 35
1089 (–) Patched heart ("With Love") 40 35
1090 (–) Flower ("Good Luck") . . 40 35
See also Nos. 1111/13 and 1128/30.

1990. The Bedouin in Israel.
1092 **444** 1 s. 50 multicoloured . . 1·40 1·10

445 Traditional Dancing

446 Photograph Album and Orange

1990. Circassians in Israel.
1093 **445** 1 s. 50 multicoloured . . 1·25 1·10

1990. Centenary of Rehovot Settlement.
1094 **446** 2 s. multicoloured . . . . 1·90 1·50

447 Artillery Corps Monument, Zikhron Yaaqov

1990. Memorial Day.
1095 **447** 60 a. multicoloured . . . 55 45

448 Ruins of Gamla, Yehudiyya

449 School, Deganya Kibbutz (Richard Kauffmann)

1990. Nature Reserves (1st series). Mult.
1096 60 a. Type **448** 55 45
1097 80 a. Huleh 70 55
1098 90 a. Mt. Meron 80 70
See also Nos. 1200/2.

1990. Architecture.
1099b 75 a. Type **449** 30 25
1100 1 s. 10 Dining hall, Tel Yosef Kibbutz (Leopold Krakauer) 60 35
1101 1 s. 20 Engel House, Tel Aviv (Ze'ev Rechter) 70 45
1102 1 s. 40 Weizmann House, Rehovot (Erich Mendelsohn) 75 45
1103 1 s. 60 National Institutions Building, Jerusalem (Yohanan Ratner) 75 45

1990. Greetings Stamps. As Nos. 1088/90 but with value.

1111 55 a. As No. 1090 . . . . . 50 35
1112a 80 a. Type **443** 35 25
1113a 1 s. As No. 1089 . . . . . . 55 35

451 Badges

452 Dancers

1990. 70th Anniv of Formation of Hagana (underground military organization).

1114 **451** 1 s. 50 multicoloured . . 1·40 1·10

1990. 8th International Folklore Festival, Haifa. Multicoloured.

1115 1 s. 90 Type **452** . . . . . 1·90 1·75
1116 1 s. 90 Dancers and accordion player . . . . 1·90 1·75

Nos. 1115/16 were printed together, se-tenant, forming a composite design.

453 19th-century Austro-Hungarian Spice Box

454 People forming Star of David

1990. Jewish New Year. Silver Spice Boxes. Multicoloured.

1117 55 a. Type **453** 65 50
1118 80 a. 19th century Italian box . 75 65
1119 1 s. German painted and gilt box by Matheus Wolf, 1700 . 90 75

1990. Absorption of Immigrants.

1120 **454** 1 s. 10 multicoloured . . 1·10 95

455 Ancient and Modern Means of Communication

457 Basketball

1990. Electronic Mail.

1121 **455** 1 s. 20 green, blk & yell . 1·10 95

1990. Computer Games. Multicoloured.

1123 60 a. Type **457** 65 55
1124 60 a. Chess 65 55
1125 60 a. Racing cars 65 55

458 Tel Aviv-Yafo Post Office and 1948 20 m. Stamp

459 Jabotinsky

1990. Stamp Day.

1126 **458** 1 s. 20 multicoloured . . 1·10 1·00

1990. 50th Death Anniv of Ze'ev Jabotinsky (Zionist leader).

1127 **459** 1 s. 90 multicoloured . . 1·90 1·50

1991. Greetings Stamps. No value expressed. As T **443**. Multicoloured.

1128 (–) Birthday cake ("Happy Birthday") 40 30
1129 (–) Champagne bottle ("Greetings") 40 30
1130 (–) Envelopes ("Keep in Touch") 40 30

Nos. 1128/30 were sold at the current inland letter rate.

460 Sarah Aaronsohn (intelligence agent)

1991. Anniversaries. Multicoloured.

1131 1 s. 30 Type **460** (birth centenary (1990)) . . . . 1·00 75
1132 1 s. 30 Rahel Bluwstein (poet, 60th death anniv) . . . . . 1·00 75
1133 1 s. 30 Lea Goldberg (writer and translator, 80th birth anniv) . . . . 1·00 75

461 Eucalyptus Tree and Hadera

1991. Centenary of Hadera.

1134 **461** 2 s. 50 multicoloured . . 2·00 1·75

462 Karate

1991. 14th Hapoel Games. Multicoloured.

1135 60 a. Type **462** 65 50
1136 90 a. Table tennis 75 65
1137 1 s. 10 Football 90 75

463 Intelligence Services Memorial, Centre for Special Studies, Tel Aviv

1991. Memorial Day.

1138 **463** 65 a. multicoloured . . . 55 45

464 First (Diesel) Power Station, Tel Aviv

465 Rabbi Shimon Hakham (co-founder) and Armon Building

1991. Inauguration of Rutenberg Power Station. Multicoloured.

1139 70 a. Type **464** 65 45
1140 90 a. Yarden Hydro-electric Station, Naharayim 90 55
1141 1 s. 20 Rutenberg coal fired power station, Ashqelon . . 1·00 70

1991. Centenary (1990) of Bukharim Quarter of Jerusalem.

1142 **465** 2 s. 10 multicoloured . . 1·50 1·25

467 Ram's Head and Man blowing Shofar

468 Front Page of First Edition

1991. Festivals. Multicoloured.

1144 65 a. Type **467** (Jewish New Year) 65 50
1145 1 s. "Penitence Cock", father blessing children and men blowing shofars (Day of Atonement) 75 65
1146 1 s. 20 Family in booth (Festival of Tabernacles) . . 90 75

1991. 150th Anniv of "Jewish Chronicle" (weekly newspaper).

1147 **468** 1 s. 50 black, blue & red . 1·40 1·10

469 Colonists and Baron Maurice de Hirsch (founder)

1991. Centenary of Jewish Colonization Association.

1148 **469** 1 s. 60 multicoloured . . 1·40 1·10

471 Cancelled 1948 5 m. Stamp

1991. Stamp Day.

1150 **471** 70 a. multicoloured . . . 55 45

472 Rahel Yanait Ben-Zvi (Zionist)

473 Runner

1991. Multicoloured.

1151 1 s. Type **472** 75 70
1152 1 s. 10 Dona Gracia Nasi (supporter of 16th-century Jewish settlement in Tiberias) . . . 80 75

1991. Olympic Games, Barcelona.

1153 **473** 1 s. 10 multicoloured . . 95 60

474 Flame and Hebrew Script

475 Southern Wing of Acre Prison

1991. 51st Anniv of Lehi (resistance organization).

1154 **474** 1 s. 50 multicoloured . . 1·25 1·10

1991. 60th Anniv of Etzel (resistance organization).

1155 **475** 1 s. 50 black, red & grey . 1·25 1·10

476 Mozart and Score of "Don Giovanni"

477 Anemone

1991. Death Bicentenary of Wolfgang Amadeus Mozart (composer).

1156 **476** 2 s. multicoloured . . . . 1·75 1·50

1992. No value expressed.

1157 **477** (–) red and green 30 15

No. 1157 was sold at the current inland letter rate, initially 75 a.

478 Hanna Rovina (actress)

479 Trees

1992. Multicoloured.

1158 80 a. Type **478** 50 45
1159 1 s. 30 Rivka Guber (teacher and writer) 65 55

1992. Sea of Galilee. Multicoloured.

1160 85 a. Type **479** 65 50
1161 85 a. Sailboard 65 50
1162 85 a. Fishes 65 50

480 Palmah Emblem

481 Samaritans praying on Mount Gerizim

1992. 51st Anniv of Palmah (resistance organization).

1163 **480** 1 s. 50 gold, blue & mve . 1·10 95

1992. The Samaritans.

1164 **481** 2 s. 60 multicoloured . . 2·00 1·90

482 Border Guard Memorial, Eiron Junction (Yechiel Arad)

1992. Memorial Day.

1165 **482** 85 a. multicoloured . . . 45 40

483 Azulai

484 Hayyim

1992. 186th Death Anniv of Rabbi Hayyim Joseph David Azulai (scholar).

1166 **483** 85 a. multicoloured . . . 45 40

1992. 83rd Death Anniv of Rabbi Joseph Hayyim Ben Elijah.

1167 **484** 1 s. 20 multicoloured . . 60 45

485 "Almanach Perpetuum" and Models of Columbus's Ships

1992. 500th Anniv of Discovery of America by Columbus.

1168 **485** 1 s. 60 multicoloured . . 1·00 80

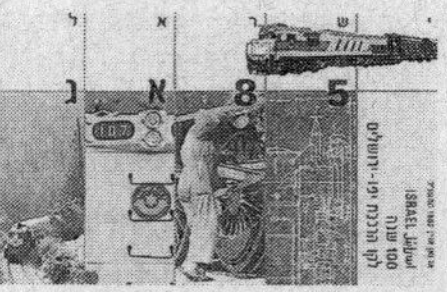

487 Diesel Trains, Greasing of Wheels and Blueprint of Baldwin Engine

1992. Cent of Jaffa–Jerusalem Railway. Mult.

1170 85 a. Type **487** 50 45
1171 1 s. Scottish steam locomotive, track plan at Lod, electric signalling board at Tel Aviv, semaphore arms and points at Lod 55 50
1172 1 s. 30 Diesel locomotive, interior and exterior of passenger carriages, Palestine Railways ticket and 1926 timetable . . 70 65
1173 1 s. 60 Diesel train, drawing of facade of Jerusalem station, platform at Lod, Jaffa station in 1900 and points at Bar-Giora station 90 70

488 Cover of "Or-HaHayyim" ("Light of Life") (Rabbi Hayyim Benatar, 250th (1993) anniv)

489 Leopard

1992. Death Anniversaries.
1175 **488** 1 s. 30 lilac, grn & gold . 75 65
1176 – 3 s. lilac, green & gold . . 1·75 1·60
DESIGN: 3 s. 19th-century drawing of Bet-El Yeshiva, Jerusalem (Rabbi Shalom Sharabi, 215th anniv).

1992. Zoo Animals. Multicoloured.
1177 50 a. Type **489** 35 30
1178 50 a. Indian elephant 35 30
1179 50 a. Chimpanzee 35 30
1180 50 a. Lion 35 30

490 "Parables" (Yitzhak ben Shlomo ibn Sahula) (1st edition, Brescia, 1491)

1992. Jewish New Year. Centenary of Jewish National and University Library, Jerusalem. Multicoloured.
1181 85 a. Type **490** 50 45
1182 1 s. Mahzor (prayer book) (15th-century manuscript by Leon ben Yehoshua de Rossi) 65 55
1183 1 s. 20 Draft of translation by Martin Buber of Leviticus 25: 10–13 . . . . 75 70

491 Court Building
492 Wallcreeper

1992. Inauguration of New Supreme Court Building.
1184 **491** 3 s. 60 multicoloured . . 2·25 1·90

1992. Songbirds. Multicoloured.
1185 10 a. Type **492** 10 10
1186 20 a. Tristram's grackle . . . 10 10
1187 30 a. Pied ("White") wagtail . 15 10
1188 50 a. Palestine sunbird 20 10
1189 85 a. Sinai rosefinch 35 20
1190 90 a. Barn swallows 40 25
1191 1 s. Trumpeter finches 40 25
1192 1 s. 30 Graceful prinia ("warbler") 55 35
1193 1 s. 50 Black-eared wheatear . 65 40
1194 1 s. 70 Black-capped ("Common") bulbuls . . . 70 45

493 "Judah Released"
494 European Community Emblem on Graph

1992. 75th Anniv of First All-Hebrew Film. Scenes from films. Multicoloured.
1195 80 a. Type **493** (first Hebrew film) 75 70
1196 2 s. 70 "Oded the Wanderer" (first Hebrew feature film) . . 1·50 1·40
1197 3 s. 50 "This is the Land" (first Hebrew talking film) . . . . 1·90 1·75

1992. Stamp Day. European Single Market.
1198 **494** 1 s. 50 multicoloured . . 85 75

495 Begin
496 Shrine of the Bab

1993. 1st Death Anniv of Menahem Begin (Prime Minister, 1977–83).
1199 **495** 80 a. multicoloured . . . 45 40

1993. Nature Reserves (2nd series). As T **448**. Multicoloured.
1200 1 s. 20 Hof Dor 75 65
1201 1 s. 50 Nahal Ammud 90 75
1202 1 s. 70 Nahal Ayun . . . . 1·00 90

1993. Baha'i World Centre, Haifa.
1203 **496** 3 s. 50 multicoloured . . 1·90 1·75

497 Medical Corps Memorial, Carmel, Haifa (Akiva Lomnitz)
498 "The Eye's Memory"

1993. Memorial Day.
1204 **497** 80 a. multicoloured . . . 45 40

1993. Illustration of Scientific Concepts. Exhibits from the Israel National Museum of Science, Haifa (Nos. 1205/6) or the Bernard M. Bloomfield Science Museum, Jerusalem (others).
1205 80 a. Type **498** 45 40
1206 80 a. Colour mixing 45 40
1207 80 a. Waves 45 40
1208 80 a. Floating balls (principle of lift) 45 40

499 Prisoner
500 Hurbat Rabbi Yehuda Hassid Synagogue, Jerusalem

1993. 50th Anniv of Uprisings in the Ghettos and Concentration Camps.
1209 **499** 1 s. 20 black, yell & bl . . 70 55

1993. 45th Anniv of Independence.
1210 **500** 3 s. 60 multicoloured . . 2·10 1·90

501 Giulio Racah
502 Family using Crossing (Lior Abohovsky)

1993. Physicists. Multicoloured.
1211 80 a. Type **501** 45 40
1212 1 s. 20 Aharon Katchalsky-Katzir 65 55

1993. Road Safety. Children's Paintings. Mult.
1213 80 a. Type **502** 55 50
1214 1 s. 20 Vehicles and road signs (Elinor Paz) 70 60
1215 1 s. 50 Road signals on "man" (Moran Dadush) 80 75

503 Poppy
504 Passing Baton

1993. Anti-drugs Campaign.
1216 **503** 2 s. 80 multicoloured . . 1·50 1·40

1993. 14th Maccabiah Games.
1217 **504** 3 s. 60 multicoloured . . 2·25 1·90

505 Tree
506 Ear of Wheat

1993. International Day of the Elderly.
1218 **505** 80 a. multicoloured . . . 40 30

1993. Jewish New Year. Multicoloured.
1219 80 a. Type **506** 40 30
1220 1 s. 20 Grapes 65 45
1221 1 s. 50 Olives 90 75

507 Environmental Concerns

1993. Environment Year.
1222 **507** 1 s. 20 multicoloured . . 60 45

508 Emblems

1993. 150th Anniv of B'nai B'rith (cultural and social organization).
1223 **508** 1 s. 50 multicoloured . . 60 45

510 Talmudic Oil Lamp

1993. Festival of Hanukka. Multicoloured.
1225 90 a. Type **510** 45 30
1226 1 s. 30 Hanukka lamp in shape of building 65 45
1227 2 s. "Lighting the Hanukka Lamp" (illustration from the "Rothschild Miscellany") . . 1·00 75

511 Cover of First Issue

1993. Stamp Day. Centenary (1992) of "Miniature World" (children's magazine).
1228 **511** 1 s. 50 multicoloured . . 75 55

512 Yellow-banded Borer ("Chlorophorus varius")

1994. Beetles. Multicoloured.
1229 85 a. Type **512** 40 30
1230 85 a. Copper beetle ("Potosia cuprea") 40 30
1231 85 a. Pied ground beetle ("Graphopterus serrator") . 40 30
1232 85 a. Seven-spotted ladybird ("Coccinella septempunctata") 40 30

513 Man carrying Car ("Exercise Regularly")

1994. Health and Well-being. Multicoloured.
1233 85 a. Type **513** 40 30
1234 1 s. 30 Blowing soap bubbles ("Don't Smoke") 65 45
1235 1 s. 60 Inspecting food through magnifying glass ("Eat Sensibly") 90 75

MINIMUM PRICE

The minimum price quoted is 10p which represents a handling charge rather than a basis for valuing common stamps. For further notes about prices see introductory pages.

514 Haffkine
515 Communications, Electronics and Computer Corps Memorial, Yehud (Claude Grundman)

1994. 64th Death Anniv of Dr. Mordecai Haffkine (bacteriologist).
1236 **514** 3 s. 85 multicoloured . . 1·90 1·50

1994. Memorial Day.
1237 **515** 85 a. multicoloured . . . 40 30

516 Assuta Private Hospital (Yosef Neufeld)

1994. International Style Architecture in Tel Aviv. Each grey, blue and green.
1238 85 a. Type **516** 40 30
1239 85 a. Co-operative workers' housing (flats with separate balconies) (Arieh Sharon) . . 40 30
1240 85 a. Citrus House (Karl Rubin) 40 30

517 Battered Child

1994. "No to Violence" Campaign.
1241 **517** 3 s. 85 black and red . . . 1·90 1·50

518 Saul Adler

1994. Birth Centenary (1995) of Saul Adler (scientist).
1242 **518** 4 s. 50 multicoloured . . 2·25 1·75

519 Inflating Balloon
521 Israeli Team at Munich Games, 1972, and National Committee Emblem

520 Chemistry Class at Bialystok and Physical Education at Wolyn

1994. Ayalon Valley International Hot-Air Balloon Race. Multicoloured.
1243 85 a. Type **519** 40 30
1244 85 a. Balloons in air 40 30
1245 85 a. Balloon hovering over target (cross on ground) . . 40 30

1994. 75th Anniv of Tarbut Schools (Hebrew schools in Eastern Europe).
1246 **520** 1 s. 30 multicoloured . . 60 45

1994. Centenary of Int Olympic Committee.
1247 **521** 2 s. 25 multicoloured . . 1·10 85

522 The Little Prince (book character) and Saint-Exupery

1994. 50th Death Anniv of Antoine de Saint-Exupery (writer and pilot).
1248 **522** 5 s. multicoloured . . . . 2·25 1·90

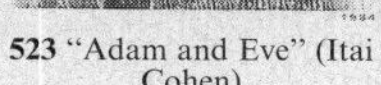

523 "Adam and Eve" (Itai Cohen)

524 Jewish and Arab Houses merging

1994. Jewish New Year. Entries in the "Children and Young People draw the Bible" exhibition. Multicoloured.
1249 85 a. Type **523** 40 30
1250 1 s. 30 "Jacob's Dream" (Moran Sheinberg) 65 45
1251 1 s. 60 "Moses in the Bulrushes" (Carmit Crspi) . 85 75

1994. Israeli–Palestinian Peace Process.
1253 **524** 90 a. multicoloured . . . 45 35

525 Silicat Brick Factory, Tel Aviv (Fourth Aliya, 1924–28)

526 Road to Peace

1994. Aliyot (immigration of Jews to Israel). Multicoloured.
1254 1 s. 40 Settlers and booklet distributed in Poland to encourage Jews to settle the Valley of Jezreel (Third Aliya, 1919–23) 60 50
1255 1 s. 70 Type **525** 85 60

1994. Signing of Israel–Jordan Peace Treaty.
1256 **526** 3 s. 50 multicoloured . . 1·50 1·10

527 Ford Model "T" Converted Car, 1920s

1994. Public Transport. Multicoloured.
1257 90 a. Type **527** 40 30
1258 1 s. 40 "White Super" bus, 1940s 60 45
1259 1 s. 70 Leyland "Royal Tiger" bus, 1960s 70 55

528 Hanukka Lamp from Mazagan, Morocco

1994. Festival of Hanukka.
1260 **528** 1 s. 50 multicoloured . . 65 50

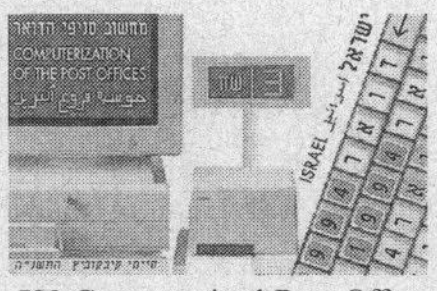

529 Computerized Post Office Counter

1994. Stamp Day. Computerization of the Post Office.
1261 **529** 3 s. multicoloured . . . . 1·25 95

530 Breaking Dreyfus's Sword

1994. Centenary of "The Dreyfus Affair" (conviction for treason of French Army Captain Alfred Dreyfus).
1262 **530** 4 s. 10 multicoloured . . 1·75 1·25

531 "Serpentine" (Itzhak Danziger), Yarkon Park, Tel Aviv

1995. Outdoor Sculptures. Multicoloured.
1263 90 a. Type **531** 40 30
1264 1 s. 40 "Stabile" (Alexander Calder), Mount Herzl, Jerusalem 60 45
1265 1 s. 70 Hall of Remembrance Gate (David Palombo), Yad Vashem, Jerusalem 70 55

532 Score from "Schelomo", Solomon (after Dore) and Ernest Bloch

1995. Composers (1st series). Multicoloured.
1266 4 s. 10 Type **532** . . . . . . 1·75 1·25
1267 4 s. 10 Score from "Jeremiah", Jeremiah (after Gustave Dore) and Leonard Bernstein . . . . 1·75 1·25
See also Nos. 1272/3, 1330 and 1338.

533 Ordnance Corps Memorial, Netanya

1995. Memorial Day.
1268 **533** 1 s. multicoloured 40 30

534 Liberation of Dachau Concentration Camp

1995. 50th Anniv of End of Second World War.
1269 **534** 1 s. multicoloured 40 30

535 U.N. Projects

1995. 50th Anniv of U.N.O.
1271 **535** 1 s. 50 multicoloured . . 65 50

1995. Composers (2nd series). As T **532**. Multicoloured.
1272 2 s. 40 Arnold Schoenberg and scene from "Moses and Aaron" . . . . 1·00 75
1273 2 s. 40 Darius Milhaud and score and scene from opera "David" . . . . 1·00 75

537 Canoeist

1995. 15th Hapoel Games.
1275 **537** 1 s. multicoloured 40 30

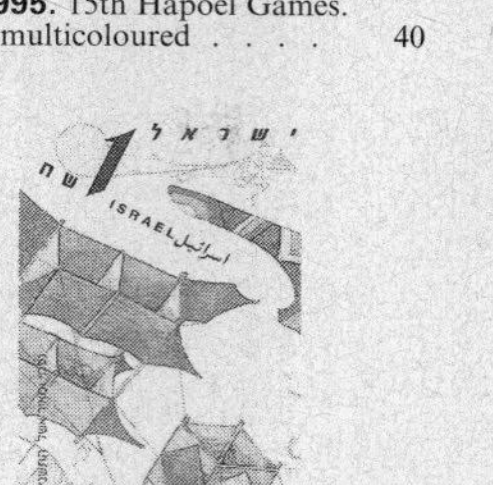

538 Box Kite and Cody "War" Kite

1995. Kites. Multicoloured.
1276 1 s. Type **538** 40 30
1277 1 s. Bird-shaped, hexagonal "Tiara" and rhombic "Eddy" kites 40 30
1278 1 s. Multiple rhombic and triangular "Deltic" aerobatic kites 40 30
Nos. 1276/8 were printed together, se-tenant, forming a composite design.

539 "Stars in a Bucket" (Anda Amir-Pinkerfeld, illus. Hava Nathan)

1995. Children's Books. Designs illustrating poems. Multicoloured.
1279 1 s. Type **539** 40 30
1280 1 s. 50 "Hurry, Run, Dwarfs" (Miriam Yallan-Stekelis, illus. Tirzah Tanny) 65 50
1281 1 s. 80 "Daddy's Big Umbrella" (Levin Kipnis, illus. Pazit Meller-Dushi) 75 55

540 "Zim Israel" (container ship)

1995. 50th Anniv of Zim Navigation Company.
1282 **540** 4 s. 40 multicoloured . . 1·90 1·40

541 Elijah's Chair (German, 1768)

1995. Jewish New Year. Multicoloured.
1283 1 s. Type **541** (circumcision) . . 40 30
1284 1 s. 50 Velvet bag for prayer shawl (Moroccan, 1906) (Bar-Mitzvah) 65 50
1285 1 s. 80 Marriage stone (from Bingen Synagogue, Germany, 1700) 75 55

542 King David playing Harp (mosaic pavement, Gaza Synagogue)

1995. 3000th Anniv of City of David (Jerusalem). Multicoloured.
1286 1 s. Type **542** 40 30
1287 1 s. 50 Illustration of Jerusalem from 19th-century map by Rabbi Pinie 65 50
1288 1 s. 80 Aerial view of Knesset (parliament) 75 55

543 "Sheep" (Menashe Kadishman)

1995. 75th Anniv of Veterinary Services.
1289 **543** 4 s. 40 multicoloured . . 1·90 1·40

544 Rabin

1995. Yitzhak Rabin (Prime Minister) Commemoration.
1290 **544** 5 s. multicoloured . . . . 2·10 1·60

545 Putting out Fire

1995. 70th Anniv of Fire and Rescue Service. Multicoloured.
1291 1 s. Type **545** 40 30
1292 1 s. Cutting crash victim out of car 40 30

546 Miniature Silver Menorah (Zusia Ejbuszyc)

1995. Festival of Hanukka.
1293 **546** 1 s. 50 multicoloured . . 60 45

547 Flying Model Plane

1995. Stamp Day.
1294 **547** 1 s. 80 multicoloured . . 75 55

548 Film Stars

550 Cycling

1995. Centenary of Motion Pictures.
1295 **548** 4 s. 40 multicoloured . . 1·90 1·40
The stars depicted are the Marx Brothers, Simone Signoret, Peter Sellers, Danny Kaye and Al Jolson.

1996. Sport. Multicoloured.
1301 1 s. 05 Type **550** 40 30
1302 1 s. 10 Show jumping 40 30
1303 1 s. 80 Water skiing 50 40
1304 1 s. 90 Paragliding 70 55
1305 2 s. Volleyball 75 55
1306 2 s. 30 Whitewater rafting . . . 65 50
1307 3 s. Bat and ball 85 65
1308 5 s. Archery . . . . 1·75 1·25
1309 10 s. Abseiling . . . . 3·50 2·50

552 Cow and Computer

553 Abraham Shlonsky (poet)

1996. 70th Anniv of Israel Dairy Cattle Breeders' Association.
1311 **552** 4 s. 65 multicoloured . . 1·75 1·25

1996. Modern Hebrew Writers. Multicoloured.
1313 40 a. Type **553** 15 10
1314 40 a. Joseph Brenner (novelist and essayist) 15 10
1315 40 a. Judah Gordon (poet) . . 15 10
1316 40 a. Haim Hazaz (novelist) . . 15 10
1317 40 a. Devorah Baron (novelist) 15 10
1318 40 a. Yehuda Burla (novelist) . 15 10
1319 40 a. Micha Berdyczewski (novelist and historian) . . . 15 10
1320 40 a. Yaakov Shabtai (novelist) 15 10
1321 40 a. Isaac Peretz (novelist) . . 15 10
1322 40 a. Nathan Alterman (poet) . 15 10
1323 40 a. Saul Tchernichowsky (poet) 15 10
1324 40 a. Amir Gilboa (poet) . . . 15 10
1325 40 a. Yokheved Bat-Miriam (poet) 15 10
1326 40 a. Mendele Sefarim (novelist) 15 10

554 Fallen Policemen Monument, National Police Academy, Kiryat Ata (Yosef Assa)

1996. Memorial Day.
1327 **554** 1 s. 05 multicoloured . . 40 30

555 Circuit Boards **556** Emblem and Old Photographs

1996. 75th Anniv of Manufacturers' Association.
1328 **555** 1 s. 05 multicoloured . . 40 30

1996. Centenary of Metulla.
1329 **556** 1 s. 90 multicoloured . . 70 55

1996. Composers (3rd series). As T **532**. Multicoloured.
1330 4 s. 65 Gustav Mahler, score from "Resurrection Symphony" and creation of light . . . . 1·75 1·25

557 Plant growing in Cracked Earth **558** Fencing

1996. 50th Anniv of the 11 Negev Settlements.
1331 **557** 1 s. 05 multicoloured . . 40 30

1996. Olympic Games. Atlanta. Multicoloured.
1332 1 s. 05 Type **558** 40 30
1333 1 s. 60 Pole vaulting 60 45
1334 1 s. 90 Wrestling 70 55

559 Jaffa Orange Tree and Citrus Fruit

1996. Israeli Fruit Production. Multicoloured.
1335 1 s. 05 Type **559** 40 30
1336 1 s. 60 Grape vine, avocado, date, sharon fruit and mango 60 45
1337 1 s. 90 Star fruit plant and exotic fruit 70 55

1996. Composers (4th series). As T **532**. Multicoloured.
1338 4 s. 65 Felix Mendelssohn, Prophet Elijah (after Albrecht Durer) and score from oratorio "Elijah" . . . . . 1·75 1·25

560 Road Systems

1996. 75th Anniv of Public Works Department.
1339 **560** 1 s. 05 multicoloured . . 40 30

561 New Year

1996. Jewish Festivals. Paintings by Sahar Pick. Multicoloured.
1340 1 s. 05 Type **561** 40 30
1341 1 s. 60 Booth decoration (Festival of Tabernacles) . . 60 45
1342 1 s. 90 Pulpit (Simchat Torah Festival) 70 55

562 Herzl looking out at David's Tower (wall hanging)

1996. Centenary of 1st Zionist Congress, Basel, Switzerland.
1343 **562** 4 s. 65 multicoloured . . 1·75 1·25

563 Lighted Candles

1996. Festival of Hanukkah. Self-adhesive.
1345 **563** 2 s. 50 multicoloured . . 95 70

564 Bird and Fighter Aircraft

1996. Coexistence between Man and Animals. Multicoloured.
1346 1 s. 10 Type **564** 40 30
1347 1 s. 75 Dog, people and cat . . 60 45
1348 2 s. Dolphins and diver 70 55

565 Ahad Ha'am

1996. Cent of First Edition of "Ha-Shilo'ah" (periodical) and 140th Birth Anniv of Ahad Ha'am (editor and Zionist).
1349 **565** 1 s. 15 multicoloured . . 40 30

566 Shavit Rocket, Earth and "Ofeq-3" (satellite)

1996. Stamp Day. Space Research.
1350 **566** 2 s. 05 multicoloured . . 70 55

567 Equal Opportunities Emblem **570** Windmills, Don Quixote and Sancho Panza (Ya'acov Farkas (Ze'ev))

568 Woman, Ethiopia

1996. Equal Opportunities for Disabled People.
1351 **567** 5 s. multicoloured . . . . 1·75 1·25

1997. Traditional Costumes of Jewish Communities Abroad. Multicoloured.
1352 1 s. 10 Type **568** 40 30
1353 1 s. 70 Man, Kurdistan 60 45
1354 2 s. Woman, Salonica 70 55

1997. 450th Birth Anniv of Miguel de Cervantes (writer).
1356 **570** 3 s. multicoloured . . . . 1·00 75

571 Logistics Corps Memorial, Hadir

1997. Memorial Day.
1357 **571** 1 s. 10 multicoloured . . 40 30

572 Ark of the Torah, Old-New Synagogue (east side) **573** Rabbi Elijah (Mario Sermoneta)

1997. Jewish Monuments in Prague. Mult.
1358 1 s. 70 Type **572** 60 45
1359 1 s. 70 Grave of Rabbi Loew (chief Rabbi of Prague), Old Jewish Cemetery 60 45

1997. Death Bicentenary of Vilna Gaon (Rabbi Elijah ben Solomon).
1360 **573** 2 s. multicoloured 70 55

574 "Exodus" in Haifa Port **577** Drunk Driver

576 Classroom (Navit Mangashsa)

1997. Clandestine Immigration, 1934–48.
1361 **574** 5 s. multicoloured . . . . 1·75 1·25

1997. Winning Entry in "Hello First Grade!" Stamp Drawing Competition.
1363 **576** 1 s. 10 multicoloured . . 40 30

1997. Road Safety. Multicoloured.
1364 1 s. 10 Type **577** ("Don't Drink and Drive") 40 30
1365 1 s. 10 Car sinking in water ("Keep in Lane") 40 30
1366 1 s. 10 Car hitting bird ("Keep your Distance") 40 30

578 Ice Skating

1997. 15th Maccabiah Games.
1367 **578** 5 s. multicoloured . . . . 1·75 1·25

579 Abraham and Tamarisk Tree **580** Mt. Scopus (Jerusalem) and Choirs

1997. Festival of Sukkot. The Visiting Patriarchs (1st series). Paintings from the Sukkah of Rabbi Loew Immanuel of Szeged, Hungary. Multicoloured.
1368 1 s. 10 Type **579** 40 30
1369 1 s. 70 Abraham preparing to sacrifice Isaac 60 45
1370 2 s. Jacob dreaming of angels on ladder to heaven 70 55
See also Nos. 1453/6.

1997. Music and Dance Festivals. Mult.
1371 1 s. 10 Type **580** (Zimriya World Assembly of Choirs, Hebrew University) 40 30
1372 2 s. Fireworks over Karmiel and dancers (Dance Festival) 70 55
1373 3 s. Zefat and klezmers (Hassidic musicians) (Klezmer Festival) . . . . . 1·00 75

581 "The Night of 29th November" (Ya'acov Eisenscher) **583** National Flag and Srulik with Flower

1997. 50th Anniv of U.N. Resolution on Establishment of State of Israel.
1374 **581** 5 s. multicoloured . . . . 1·75 1·25

1997. 50th Anniv (1998) of State of Israel. (1st issue). No value expressed. (a) Size $18 \times 23\frac{1}{2}$ mm.
1376 **583** (–) multicoloured 30 25

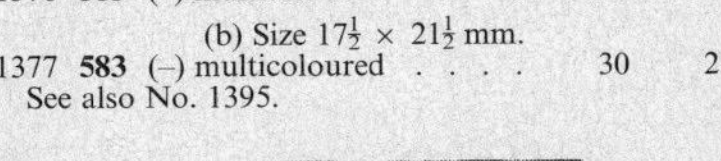

(b) Size $17\frac{1}{2} \times 21\frac{1}{2}$ mm.
1377 **583** (–) multicoloured 30 25
See also No. 1395.

584 Norseman Aircraft, Soldier, Missile Corvette and Cannon "Napoleon-Chick"

1997. 50th Anniv of Arrival in Israel of Machal (overseas volunteers) (1377) and Gachal (overseas recruits) (1378). Multicoloured.
1378 1 s. 15 Type **584** 40 30
1379 1 s. 80 Infantry soldier and Holocaust survivors 60 45

585 Bezalel (spinning-top)

1997. Festival of Hanukka. Museum Exhibits. Multicoloured.
1380 1 s. 80 Type **585** (Eretz Israel Museum, Tel Aviv) 60 45
1381 2 s. 10 Coin of Bar-Kokhba during war against the Romans (Israel Museum, Jerusalem) 70 55

586 Children leaving Airliner

1997. Chabad Children of Chernobyl Organization (for evacuation of Jewish children from radiated areas of Europe to Israel).
1382 **586** 2 s. 10 multicoloured . . 70 55

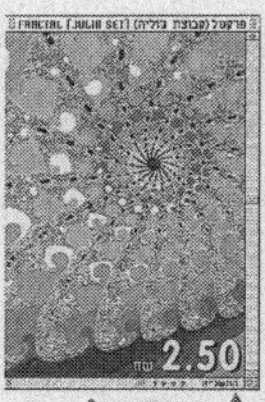

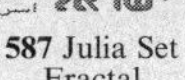

587 Julia Set Fractal **588** Photograph of Soldiers of Palmach Battalion and Civilians (Zefat)

1997. Stamp Day.
1383 **587** 2 s. 50 multicoloured . . 85 65

1998. 50th Anniv of War of Independence. Battle Fronts. Multicoloured.
1384 1 s. 15 Type **588** 40 30
1385 1 s. 15 "Castel Conquered" (Arieh Navon) superimposed on armoured vehicles (Jerusalem) 40 30
1386 1 s. 15 Soldiers raising flag (Elat) 40 30

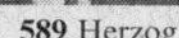

589 Herzog **590** Franz Kafka (writer)

1998. 80th Birth Anniv of Chaim Herzog (President 1983–93).
1388 **589** 5 s. 35 multicoloured . . 1·75 1·25

1998. Jewish Contribution to World Culture (1st series). Multicoloured.
1389 90 a. Type **590** 30 25
1390 90 a. George Gershwin (composer) 30 25
1391 90 a. Lev Davidovich Landau (physicist) 30 25
1392 90 a. Albert Einstein (physicist and mathematician) 30 25
1393 90 a. Leon Blum (writer) . . . 30 25
1394 90 a. Elizabeth Rachel Felix (actress) 30 25
See also Nos. 1436/41.

591 Declaration Ceremony, 1948 **592** Olive Branch

1998. 50th Anniv of State of Israel (2nd issue).
1395 **591** 1 s. 15 multicoloured . . 40 30

1998. Memorial Day.
1396 **592** 1 s. 15 multicoloured . . 40 30

593 Swearing In Ceremony in 1948 and Badge entwined with Medal Ribbons **595** Kitten

594 Giorgio Perlasca, Aristides de Sousa Mendes, Charles Lutz, Sempo Sugihara and Selahattin Ulkumen (diplomats) (½-size illustration)

1998. 50th Anniv of Defence Forces.
1397 **593** 5 s. 35 multicoloured . . 1·75 1·25

1998. Holocaust Memorial Day. Righteous Among the Nations (non-Jews who risked their lives to save Jews during the Holocaust).
1398 **594** 6 s. multicoloured . . . . 2·00 1·50

1998. Children's Pets. Multicoloured.
1399 60 a. Type **595** 20 15
1400 60 a. Puppy 20 15
1401 60 a. Parrot 20 15
1402 60 a. Goldfish 20 15
1403 60 a. Hamster 20 15
1404 60 a. Rabbit 20 15
Nos. 1399/1404 were issued together in se-tenant sheetlets of six stamps and six triangular labels bearing the emblem of "Israel 98" International Stamp Exhibition, each label with an adjacent stamp completing a square. The complete sheetlet forms a composite design.

598 De Havilland D.H.89 Dragon Rapide

1998. Aircraft of War of Independence. Mult.
1407 2 s. 20 Type **598** 75 55
1408 2 s. 20 Supermarine Spitfire . . 75 55
1409 2 s. 20 Boeing B-17 Flying Fortress 75 55

600 "Amos" Satellite, Immigration, Grapes, Dove and Lion's Gate, Jerusalem

1998. "Israel Jubilee" Exhibition, Tel Aviv.
1411 **600** 5 s. 35 multicoloured . . 1·60 1·25

601 Holding Hands (Nitzan Shupak)

1998. "Living in a World of Mutual Respect" Elementary Education Programme.
1412 **601** 1 s. 15 multicoloured . . 35 25

602 Birds (Hechal Yitshak Synagogue, Moshav Yonatan)

1998. Jewish New Year. Synagogue Curtains. Multicoloured.
1413 1 s. 15 Type **602** 35 25
1414 1 s. 80 Lions (Ohal Chanah Synagogue, Neve Tsuf) . . . 50 40
1415 2 s. 20 Leaves (Hatzvi Israel Synagogue, Jerusalem) . . . 65 50

603 Hebron

1998. Jewish Life in Eretz Israel (1st series). Design showing sections from Holy Cities Wall Plaque. Multicoloured.
1416 1 s. 80 Type **603** 50 40
1417 2 s. 20 Jerusalem 65 50
See also Nos. 1430/1.

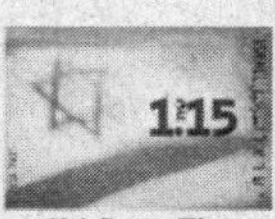

604 State Flag

1998. Self-adhesive.
1418 **604** 1 s. 15 blue and deep blue 35 25
1419 2 s. 15 blue and green . . 65 50
1420 3 s. 25 blue and mauve . . 1·00 75
1421 5 s. 35 blue and yellow . . 1·60 1·25

605 Hanukka Lamp showing Mattathias (Boris Schatz) **606** "Hyacinthus orientalis"

1999. Festival of Hanukka.
1426 **605** 2 s. 15 multicoloured . . 65 50

1999. Wild Hyacinths. No value expressed.
1427 **606** (1 s. 15) green and lilac . . 35 25

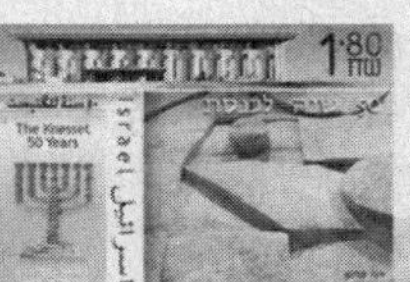

607 The Knesset, Menorah and Knesset Stone Wall (des. Danny Karavan)

1999. 50th Anniv of the Knesset (Parliament).
1428 **607** 1 s. 80 multicoloured . . 50 40

608 Manuscript

1999. 380th Birth Anniv of Rabbi Shalem Shabazi (Yemeni poet).
1429 **608** 2 s. 20 multicoloured . . 65 50

1999. Jewish Life in Eretz Israel (2nd series). As T **603**, showing sections from Holy Cities Wall Plaque. Multicoloured.
1430 1 s. 15 Zefat 35 25
1431 5 s. 35 Tiberias . . . . 1·60 1·25

609 Part of £1 Share Certificate

1999. Centenary of Jewish Colonial Trust.
1432 **609** 1 s. 80 multicoloured . . 50 40

610 Yemeni Woman

1999. Traditional Costumes of Jewish Communities (1st series). Multicoloured.
1433 2 s. 15 Type **610** 65 50
1434 3 s. 25 Woman wearing sari, India 95 70
See also Nos. 1457/8.

1999. Jewish Contribution to World Culture (2nd series). As T **590**. Multicoloured.
1436 90 a. Emile Durkheim (sociologist) 25 20
1437 90 a. Paul Ehrlich (medical researcher) 25 20
1438 90 a. Rosa Luxemburg (revolutionary) 25 20
1439 90 a. Norbert Wiener (mathematician) 25 20
1440 90 a. Sigmund Freud (psychologist) 25 20
1441 90 a. Martin Buber (philosopher) 25 20

612 Memorial to Bedouin Soldiers, Rish Lakish

1999. Memorial Day.
1442 **612** 1 s. 20 multicoloured . . 35 25

613 Flags of U.N., Israel and Other States

1999. 50th Anniv of Israel's Admission to United Nations.
1443 **613** 2 s. 30 multicoloured . . 65 50

614 Holtzberg

1999. 75th Birth Anniv of Simcha Holtzberg.
1444 **614** 2 s. 50 multicoloured . . 70 55

615 "My Favourite Room" (detail)

1999. 50th Death Anniv of James Ensor (artist).
1445 **615** 2 s. 30 multicoloured . . 65 50

616 Ouza the Goose

1999. Lovely Butterfly (children's television programme). Multicoloured.
1446 1 s. 20 Type **616** 35 25
1447 1 s. 20 Nooly the chick and Shabi the snail 35 25
1448 1 s. 20 Batz the tortoise and Pingi the penguin 35 25

617 "Church of the Holy Sepulchre, Jerusalem" (F. Geyer)

1999. Paintings of Christian Pilgrimage Sites. Multicoloured.
1449 3 s. Type **617** 90 70
1450 3 s. "Mary's Well, Nazareth" (W. H. Bartlett) 90 70
1451 3 s. "The River Jordan" (E. Finden after A. W. Callcott) 90 70

618 Illustration from Nehemia Emshel's Manuscript of Musa-Nameh by Shahin (poet)

1999. 205th Death Anniv of Rabbi Or Sharga from Persia.
1452 **618** 5 s. 60 multicoloured . . 1·60 1·25

1999. Festival of Sukkot. The Visiting Patriarchs (2nd series). As T **579**, showing paintings from the Sukkah of Rabbi Loew Immanuel of Szeged, Hungary. Multicoloured.
1453 1 s. 20 Joseph interpreting Pharaoh's dreams 35 20
1454 1 s. 90 Moses and the burning bush 55 40
1455 2 s. 30 Aaron and Holy Ark . 65 50
1456 5 s. 60 David playing harp . . 1·60 1·25

1999. Traditional Costumes of Jewish Communities (2nd series). As T **610**. Multicoloured.
1457 2 s. 30 Woman from Seus region, Morocco 65 50
1458 3 s. 40 Man from Bukhara . . 1·00 75

619 Family and Part of 1948 250 m. Stamp

1999. Stamp Day.
1459 **619** 5 s. 35 multicoloured . . 1·60 1·25

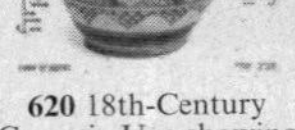

620 18th-Century Ceramic Urn showing Funeral Procession

622 "The Street of the Jews in Old Jersusalem" (Ludwig Blum)

621 View over Town from Arch of Columns

1999. Jewish Culture in Slovakia. Multicoloured.

1460	1 s. 90 Type **620**	55	40
1461	1 s. 90 18th-century urn showing visit to a sick man	55	40

1999. 50th Anniv of Kiryat Shemona.

1462	**621**	1 s. 20 multicoloured	35	25

1999. 50th Anniv of Proclamation of Jerusalem as Capital.

1463	**622**	3 s. 40 multicoloured	1·00	75

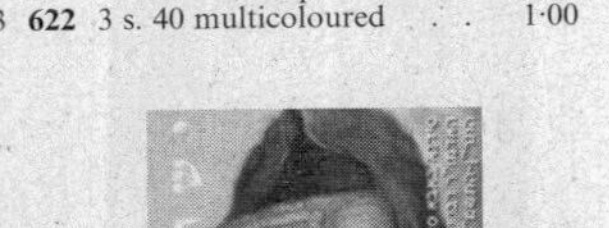

623 Sali

1999. 15th Death Anniv of Admor (Rabbi) Israel Abihssira Sidna "Baba Sali".

1464	**623**	4 s. 40 multicoloured	1·25	95

624 Children and Aliens holding Hands (Renana Barak)

2000. "Stampin' the Future" Children's Painting Competition. Multicoloured.

1465	1 s. 20 Type **624**	35	25
1466	1 s. 90 Man and robot (Tal Engelsten)	55	40
1467	2 s. 30 Futuristic street scene (Asia Aizenshteyn)	70	50
1468	3 s. 40 Alien's and child's heads (Ortal Hasid)	1·00	75

625 Globe, Joggers and Skiers

2000. Year 2000. Multicoloured.

1469	1 s. 40 Type **625** (quality of life)	40	30
1470	1 s. 90 Da Vinci's "Proportion of Man", ear of corn and scientist (biotechnology)	55	40
1471	2 s. 30 Computer, satellite dish and website address (information technology)	70	50
1472	2 s. 80 Moon's surface, astronaut and globe (space research)	80	60

OFFICIAL STAMPS

בול שרות

(O 18)

1951. As Nos. 41 etc but colours changed. Optd with Type O **18**.

O54	5 pr. mauve	10	10
O55	15 pr. red	10	10
O56	30 pr. blue	10	10
O57	40 pr. brown	20	15

POSTAGE DUE STAMPS

דמי דאר

(D 3)

1948. As T **1** optd with Type D **3**.

D10	**1**	3 m. orange on yellow	1·90	1·00
D11		5 m. green on yellow	1·90	1·25
D12		10 m. mauve on yellow	6·25	3·25
D13		20 m. blue on yellow	19·00	10·50
D14		50 m. brown on yellow	75·00	60·00

D 9

D 30

1949.

D27	D **9**	2 pr. orange	15	10
D28		5 pr. violet	35	15
D29		10 pr. green	20	10
D30		20 pr. red	25	10
D31		30 pr. blue	40	25
D32		50 pr. brown	65	55

1952.

D73	D **30**	5 pr. brown	10	10
D74		10 pr. blue	10	10
D75		20 pr. purple	10	10
D76		30 pr. black	10	10
D77		40 pr. green	10	10
D78		50 pr. sepia	10	10
D79		60 pr. violet	10	10
D80		100 pr. red	15	10
D81		250 pr. blue	25	15

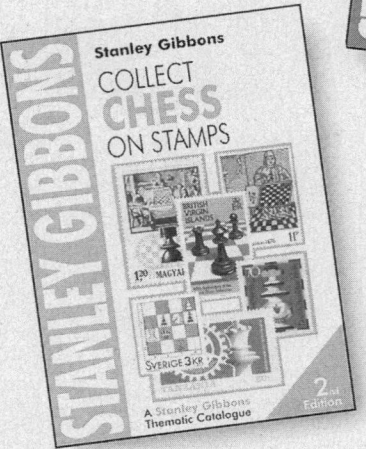

PALESTINIAN AUTHORITY

Following negotiations in Oslo, during which the Israeli government recognised the Palestine Liberation Organization as representing the Arab inhabitants of those areas occupied by Israel since 1967 and the P.L.O. accepted Israel's right to exist within secure borders, an agreement was signed in Washington on 13 September 1993 under which there was to be limited Palestinian self-rule in the Gaza Strip and in an enclave around Jericho on the West Bank. Further talks followed, leading to the Cairo Agreement of 4 May 1994 which inaugurated Palestinian Authority rule in Gaza and Jericho.

Under the Taba Accord of 28 September 1995 the Israeli army progressively withdrew from much of the remainder of the West Bank which was then placed under Palestinian Authority administration.

CURRENCY Israeli currency continued to be used in the Palestinian Authority areas. The first stamp issues had face values in mils, the currency of the Palestine Mandate period, but the Israeli authorities objected to this notional currency with the result that the face values were subsequently shown in the Jordanian currency of 1000 fils = 1 dinar.

PA **1** Monument from Hisham Palace, Jericho

1994. Multicoloured.
PA 1 5 m. Type PA **1** 10 10
PA 2 10 m. Type PA **1** 10 10
PA 3 20 m. Type PA **1** 10 10
PA 4 30 m. Church of the Holy Sepulchre, Jerusalem . . . 10 10
PA 5 40 m. As No. PA4 . . . . . 15 15
PA 6 50 m. As No. PA4 . . . . . 20 20
PA 7 75 m. As No. PA4 . . . . . 25 25
PA 8 125 m. Flags of Palestinian Authority 30 30
PA 9 150 m. As No. PA8 . . . . . 40 40
PA10 250 m. As No. PA8 . . . . . 65 65
PA11 300 m. As No. PA8 . . . . . 75 75
PA12 500 m. Flags of Palestinian Authority (51 × 29 mm) . . 1·25 1·25
PA13 1000 m. Dome of the Rock, Jerusalem (51 × 29 mm) . 2·50 2·50

PA **2** Arms of Palestinian Authority

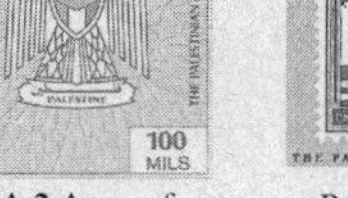
PA **6** Palestine Mandate 1927 2 m. Stamp

1994.
PA14 PA **2** 50 m. yellow 15 15
PA15 100 m. green 25 25
PA16 125 m. blue 30 30
PA17 200 m. orange 50 50
PA18 250 m. yellow 65 65
PA19 400 m. purple . . . . 1·00 1·00

CURRENCY From No. PA23 the face values are expressed as 1000 fils = 1 Jordanian dinar.

1995. Palestine Postal History.
PA23 PA **6** 150 f. green & black . . 45 45
PA24 – 350 f. orange & black . . 95 95
PA25 – 500 f. red and black . . 1·40 1·40
DESIGNS: 350 f. Palestine Mandate 1927; 5 m. stamp; 500 f. Palestine Mandate 1932; 8 m. stamp.

PA **7** Woman in Embroidered Costume

1995. Traditional Palestinian Women's Costumes. Multicoloured.
PA26 250 f. Type PA **7** 70 70
PA27 300 f. Woman carrying basket 85 85
PA28 550 f. Woman in cloak . . . 1·60 1·60
PA29 900 f. Woman in veiled head-dress . . . . 2·50 2·50

1995. Nos. PA1/13 surch **FILS** in English and Arabic.
PA30 PA **1** 5 f. on 5 m. mult . . . 10 10
PA31 10 f. on 10 m. mult . . 10 10
PA32 20 f. on 20 m. mult . . 10 10
PA33 – 30 f. on 30 m. mult . . 10 10
PA34 – 40 f. on 40 m. mult . . 10 10
PA35 – 50 f. on 50 m. mult . . 15 15
PA36 – 75 f. on 75 m. mult . . 20 20
PA37 – 125 f. on 125 m. mult . . 35 35
PA38 – 150 f. on 150 m. mult . 40 40
PA39 – 250 f. on 250 m. mult . 70 70
PA40 – 300 f. on 300 m. mult . 80 80
PA41 – 500 f. on 500 m. mult . 1·40 1·40
PA42 – 1000 f. on 1000 m. mult 3·00 3·00

1995. Handstamped **Fils** within circle in English and Arabic, twice on each stamp. (a) On Nos. PA1/13.
PA43 PA **1** 5 f. on 5 m. mult . .
PA44 10 f. on 10 m. mult . .
PA45 20 f. on 20 m. mult . .
PA46 – 30 f. on 30 m. mult . .
PA47 – 40 f. on 40 m. mult . .
PA48 – 50 f. on 50 m. mult . .
PA49 – 75 f. on 75 m. mult . .
PA50 – 125 f. on 125 m. mult
PA51 – 150 f. on 150 m. mult
PA52 – 250 f. on 250 m. mult
PA53 – 300 f. on 300 m. mult
PA54 – 500 f. on 500 m. mult
PA55 – 1000 f. on 1000 m. mult

(b) On Nos. PA14/19.
PA56 PA **2** 50 f. on 50 m. yellow .
PA57 100 f. on 100 m. grn . .
PA58 125 f. on 125 m. blue .
PA59 200 f. on 200 m. orange
PA60 250 f. on 250 m. yell . .
PA61 400 f. on 400 m. pur . .

PA **10** Bethlehem (old print)

1995. Christmas. Multicoloured.
PA63 10 f. Type PA **10** 10 10
PA64 20 f. Manger Square, Bethlehem 10 10
PA65 50 f. Entrance to Church of the Nativity (vert) 15 15
PA66 100 f. Pope John Paul II with Yasser Arafat 30 30
PA67 1000 f. Site of the Nativity . . 3·25 3·25

PA **11** Yasser Arafat

PA **14** Boxing

PA **12** Summer Palace, Peking

1996.
PA68 PA **11** 10 f. black & lilac . . 10 10
PA69 20 f. black & yellow . 10 10
PA70 50 f. black & blue . . 15 15
PA71 100 f. black & green . 20 20
PA72 1000 f. black & brown 2·00 2·00

1996. Int Stamp Exhibitions and Fairs. Mult.
PA73 20 f. Type PA **12** ("China '96") 10 10
PA74 50 f. Hagia Sofia Mosque, Istanbul ("Istanbul '96") . . 20 20
PA75 100 f. Villa Hugel, Essen (Essen stamp fair) 40 40
PA76 1000 f. Modern skyline, Toronto ("Capex '96") . . 3·75 3·75

1996. Olympic Games, Atlanta. Multicoloured.
PA78 30 f. Type PA **14** 10 10
PA79 40 f. Olympic medal of 1896 . 15 15
PA80 50 f. Running 20 20
PA81 150 f. Olympic flame and flag . 60 60
PA82 1000 f. Palestinian Olympic Committee emblem . . . . 3·50 3·50

PA **15** Poppy

PA **17** Great Tits

1996. Flowers and Fruits. Multicoloured.
PA84 10 f. Type PA **15** 10 10
PA85 25 f. Hibiscus 10 10
PA86 100 f. Thyme 40 40
PA87 150 f. Lemon 55 55
PA88 750 f. Orange . . . . 2·75 2·75

1997. Birds. Multicoloured.
PA91 25 f. Type PA **17** 10 10
PA92 75 f. Blue rock thrushes . . . 20 20
PA93 150 f. Golden orioles 45 45
PA94 350 f. Hoopoes . . . . . . 1·10 1·10
PA95 600 f. Peregrine falcons . . . 1·90 1·90

PA **18** Gaza

1997. Palestinian Towns in 1839. Each brown and black.
PA96 350 f. Type PA **18** . . . . . 1·10 1·10
PA97 600 f. Hebron . . . . 1·90 1·90

PA **20** Yasser Arafat and Wischnewski

1997. Friends of Palestine (1st series). Hans-Jurgen Wischnewski (German politician). Multicoloured.
PA 99 600 f. Type PA **20** . . . . . 1·25 1·25
PA100 600f. Wischnewski congratulating Yasser Arafat . . . 1·25 1·25
See also Nos. PA103/4.

PA **21** "The Young Jesus in the Temple" (Anton Wollenek)

1997. Christmas.
PA101 PA **21** 350 f. multicoloured . 75 75
PA102 700 f. multicoloured . . 1·50 1·50

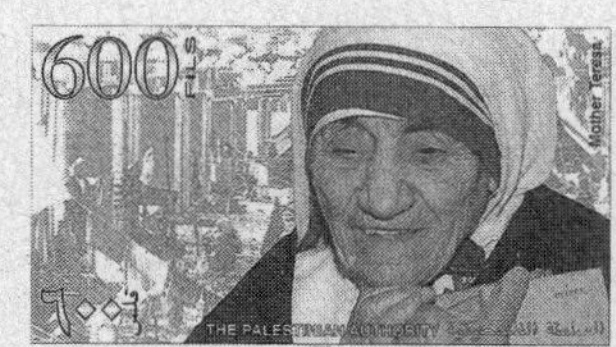
PA **22** Mother Teresa and Street Scene

1997. Friends of Palestine (2nd series). Mother Teresa (founder of Missionaries of Charity). Multicoloured.
PA103 600 f. Type PA **22** . . . . . 1·25 1·25
PA104 600 f. Mother Teresa with Yasser Arafat . . . . . 1·25 1·25

PA **24** Hare and Palm Tree

PA **25** Sea Onion

1998. Mosaics from Jabalia. Multicoloured.
PA106 50 f. Type PA **24** 10 10
PA107 125 f. Goat, hare and hound . 20 20
PA108 200 f. Lemon tree and baskets 50 50
PA109 400 f. Lion 90 90

1998. Medicinal Plants. Multicoloured.
PA110 40 f. Type PA **25** 10 10
PA111 80 f. "Silybum marianum" . 10 10
PA112 500 f. "Foeniculum vulgare" 1·10 1·10
PA113 800 f. "Inula viscosa" . . . 1·90 1·90

PA **27** Bonelli's Eagle

1998. Birds of Prey. Multicoloured.
PA115 20 f. Type PA **27** 10 10
PA116 60 f. Hobby 10 10
PA117 340 f. Verreaux's eagle . . . 80 80
PA118 600 f. Bateleur . . . . . . 1·40 1·40
PA119 900 f. Buzzard . . . . . . 2·10 2·10

PA **31** Control Tower

1999. Inauguration of Gaza International Airport. Multicoloured.
PA123 80 f. Type PA **31** 10 10
PA124 300 f. Fokkar F.27 Friendship airliner (horiz) 70 70
PA125 700 f. Terminal building (horiz) . . . . 1·60 1·60

PA **32** Peking ("China'99")

1999. International Stamp Exhibitions and Anniversary. Multicoloured.
PA126 20 f. Type PA **32** 10 10
PA127 80 f. Melbourne ("Australia 99") 10 10
PA128 260 f. Nuremberg ("iBRA'99") 60 60
PA129 340 f. Paris ("Philexfrance 99") 80 80
PA130 400 f. Emblem and landscape (face value at right) (125th anniv of U.P.U.) 90 90
PA131 400 f. As No. PA130 but face value at left 90 90

PA **33** Relief by Anton Wollenek

PA **34** Horse and Foal

1999. Hebron.
PA132 PA **33** 400 f. multicoloured . 90 90
PA133 500 f. multicoloured . 1·25 1·25

1999. Arabian Horses. Multicoloured.
PA134 25 f. Type PA **34** 10 10
PA135 75 f. Black horse 10 10
PA136 150 f. Horse rearing 30 30
PA137 350 f. Horse trotting 80 80
PA138 800 f. Brown horse . . . . 1·90 1·90

ITALIAN COLONIES Pt. 8

GENERAL ISSUES

100 centesimi = 1 lira.

1932. As Garibaldi stamps of Italy, but inscr "POSTE COLONIALI ITALIANE".

1 – 10 c. green (postage) . . . . 1·40 3·75
2 **128** 20 c. red . . . . 1·40 3·75
3 – 25 c. green . . . . 1·40 3·75
4 **128** 30 c. green . . . . 1·40 3·75
5 – 50 c. red . . . . 1·40 3·75
6 – 75 c. red . . . . 1·40 3·75
7 – 1 l. 25 c. blue . . . . 1·40 3·75
8 – 1 l. 75 c. + 25 c. blue . . . 2·75 8·00
9 – 2 l. 55 c. + 50 c. sepia . . . 2·75 8·00
10 – 5 l. + 1 l. blue . . . . 2·75 8·00

11 **130** 50 c. red (air) . . . . 1·40 4·25
12 – 80 c. green . . . . 1·40 4·25
13 **130** 1 l. + 25 c. sepia . . . . 3·50 8·00
14 – 2 l. + 50 c. sepia . . . . 3·50 8·00
15 – 5 l. + 1 l. sepia . . . . 3·50 8·00

1932. Dante stamps of Italy (colours changed) optd **COLONIE ITALIANE**.

18 – 10 c. slate (postage) 20 45
19 – 15 c. sepia 20 45
20 – 20 c. green 20 35
21 – 25 c. green 20 35
22 – 30 c. brown 20 60
23 – 50 c. blue 20 15
24 – 75 c. red 50 80
25 – 1 l. 25 c. blue 50 75
26 – 1 l. 75 c. violet . . . . 60 1·40
27 – 2 l. 75 c. orange . . . . 60 1·40
28 – 5 l. + 2 l. olive . . . . 60 1·40
29 **124** 10 l. + 2 l. 50 c. blue . . . 60 1·40

30 **125** 50 c. slate (air) . . . . 50 1·10
31 – 1 l. blue . . . . 50 1·10
32 – 3 l. green . . . . 90 1·90
33 – 5 l. sepia . . . . 90 1·90
34 **125** 7 l. 70 c. + 2 l. red . . . . 90 1·90
35 – 10 l. + 2 l. 50 c. orange . . . 90 1·90
36 **127** 100 l. sepia and green . . . 10·00 20·00

No. 36 is inscribed instead of overprinted.

9 Ploughing

10 Savoia Marchetti S-55X Flying Boat

1933. 50th Anniv of Foundation of Colony of Eritrea.

37 **9** 10 c. brown (postage) . . . . 2·25 3·50
38 – 20 c. purple . . . . 2·25 3·50
39 – 25 c. green . . . . 2·25 2·50
40 **9** 50 c. violet . . . . 2·25 2·50
41 – 75 c. red . . . . 2·25 5·50
42 – 1 l. 25 blue . . . . 2·25 5·50
43 **9** 2 l. 75 red . . . . 4·50 9·00
44 – 5 l. + 2 l. green . . . . 6·50 18·00
45 – 10 l. + 2 l. brown . . . . 6·50 18·00

46 – 50 c. brown (air) . . . . 2·25 4·50
47 – 1 l. black . . . . 2·25 4·50
48 **10** 3 l. red . . . . 2·75 8·00
49 5 l. brown . . . . 2·75 8·00
50 – 7 l. 70 + 2 l. green . . . . 6·50 16·00
51 **10** 10 l. + 2 l. 50 blue . . . . 6·50 16·00
52 – 50 l. violet . . . . 6·50 16·00

DESIGNS—VERT: (Postage): 20, 75 c., 5 l. Camel transport; 25 c., 1 l. 25; 10 l. Lioness with star on left shoulder (Arms). HORIZ: (Air): 50 c., 1 l., 7 l. 70, Eagle; 50 l. Savoia Marchetti S-55X flying boat over map of Eritrea.

11 Agricultural Implements

13 Macchi Castoldi MC-72 Seaplane

1933. 10th Anniv of Fascist March on Rome.

(a) Postage.

53 **11** 5 c. orange . . . . 2·50 3·75
54 – 25 c. green . . . . 2·50 3·75
55 – 50 c. violet . . . . 2·50 3·75
56 **11** 75 c. red . . . . 2·50 5·00
57 – 1 l. 25 blue . . . . 2·50 5·00
58 – 1 l. 75 red . . . . 2·50 6·00
59 **11** 2 l. 75 blue . . . . 2·50 7·50
60 – 5 l. black . . . . 4·00 9·50
61 – 10 l. blue . . . . 4·00 9·50
62 – 25 l. olive . . . . 5·00 12·00

DESIGNS—HORIZ: 50 c., 1 l. 75, 10 l. Tractor. VERT: 25 c., 1 l. 25, 5 l. Arab and camel; 25 l. Soldier.

(b) Air.

63 **13** 50 c. brown . . . . 3·00 6·00
64 – 75 c. purple . . . . 3·00 6·00
65 **13** 1 l. sepia . . . . 3·00 6·00
66 – 3 l. green . . . . 3·00 11·00
67 **13** 10 l. violet . . . . 3·00 11·00
68 – 12 l. blue . . . . 3·00 11·00
69 – 20 l. green . . . . 5·00 15·00
70 – 50 l. blue . . . . 7·00 17·00

DESIGNS—HORIZ: 75 c., 3, 12 l. Savoia Marchetti S-71 airplane. VERT: 20 l. Pilot swinging propeller; 50 l. Propeller.

15

16 Hailing Marina Fiat MF5 Flying Boat

1934. 15th Milan Exhibition.

71 **15** 20 c. red . . . . 40 1·50
72 30 c. green . . . . 40 1·50
73 50 c. black . . . . 40 1·50
74 1 l. 25 blue . . . . 40 1·50

1934. Air. Honouring the Duke of the Abruzzi (explorer).

75 **16** 25 l. black . . . . 12·00 45·00

17 Scoring a Goal

18 Marina Fiat MF.5 Flying Boat over Stadium

1934. World Football Championship.

76 **17** 10 c. green (postage) . . . . 6·00 14·00
77 50 c. violet . . . . 15·00 10·00
78 1 l. 25 blue . . . . 15·00 35·00
79 – 5 l. brown . . . . 19·00 60·00
80 – 10 l. blue . . . . 19·00 60·00

DESIGN—VERT: 5, 10 l. Fascist salute before kick-off.

81 **13** 50 c. brown (air) . . . . 5·00 10·00
82 75 c. purple . . . . 5·00 10·00
83 – 5 l. black . . . . 12·00 32·00
84 – 10 l. red . . . . 12·00 32·00
85 **18** 15 l. red . . . . 12·00 32·00
86 – 25 l. green . . . . 12·00 32·00
87 – 50 l. green . . . . 12·00 32·00

DESIGNS—VERT: 5, 10, 25 l. "Saving a goal". HORIZ: 50 l. Giant football and Marina Fiat MF.5 flying boat.

EXPRESS STAMPS

1932. Air. As Garibaldi stamps of Italy.

E16 **E 131** 2 l. 25 + 1 l. blk & vio . . 3·50 8·00
E17 4 l. 50 + 1 l. 50 grn & brn . . 3·50 8·00

ITALIAN EAST AFRICA Pt. 8

Italian Empire in East Africa comprising Eritrea, Ethiopia and Italian Somaliland, constituted by Royal Decree of 1 June 1936. Occupied by British Forces 1942–43 (see BRITISH OCCUPATION OF ITALIAN COLONIES (MIDDLE EAST FORCES) in Volume 3).

100 centesimi = 1 lira

1 Grant's Gazelle

2 R. Nile Statue and Lake Tsana

1938.

1 **1** 2 c. red 20 70
2 A 5 c. brown 25 20
3 B 7½ c. violet . . . . 40 1·10
4 **2** 10 c. brown 25 20
5 C 15 c. green 25 35
6 B 20 c. red 25 15
7 D 25 c. green 25 15
8 **1** 30 c. brown 35 60
9 A 35 c. blue . . . . 70 1·60
10 B 50 c. violet 25 10
11 C 75 c. red 45 15
12 D 1 l. green 30 10
13 B 1 l. 25 blue 45 35
14 **2** 1 l. 75 orange . . . . 9·00 10
15 A 2 l. red 65 40
16 D 2 l. 55 brown . . . . 3·50 6·50
17 **1** 3 l. 70 violet . . . . 16·00 9·50
18 C 5 l. blue . . . . 1·40 65
19 A 10 l. red . . . . 5·50 3·25
20 **2** 20 l. green . . . . 3·50 2·50

DESIGN—VERT: A, Italian eagle and Lion of Judah; B, Profile of King Emmanuel III; C, Soldier implanting Fascist emblem. HORIZ: D, Shadows on road.

5 Mussolini Monument and Mt. Amba Aradam

1938. Air.

21 E 25 c. green . . . . 70 1·75
22 **5** 50 c. brown . . . . 22·00 10
23 F 60 c. red . . . . 70 2·25
24 E 75 c. brown . . . . 1·25 1·50
25 G 1 l. blue 30 10
26 **5** 1 l. 50 violet 35 20
27 F 2 l. blue 35 40
28 E 3 l. red . . . . 55 1·25
29 G 5 l. brown . . . . 1·50 1·60
30 **5** 10 l. purple . . . . 2·50 2·25
31 E 25 l. blue . . . . 4·50 3·25

DESIGNS—HORIZ: E, Savoia Marchetti S-73 airplane, rock sculpture of eagle and Mt. Amba Aradam; F, Savoia Marchetti S-73 airplane over Lake Tsana. VERT: G, Bateleur.

9 Statue of Augustus

10 Eagle and Serpent

1938. Birth Bimillenary of Augustus the Great.

36 **9** 5 c. brown (postage) 10 60
37 – 10 c. red 10 60
38 **9** 25 c. green 40 40
39 – 50 c. violet 40 20
40 **9** 75 c. red . . . . 40 1·40
41 – 1 l. 25 blue . . . . 40 1·40

DESIGN: 10 c., 50 c., 1 l. 25, Statue of Goddess of Abundance.

42 **10** 50 c. brown (air) 30 60
43 1 l. violet . . . . 40 1·60

11 Ethiopian Canoe

1940. Naples Exhibition.

44 **11** 5 c. brown (postage) 10 35
45 – 10 c. orange 10 35
46 – 25 c. green 45 85
47 **11** 50 c. violet 45 85
48 – 75 c. red . . . . 45 1·40
49 – 1 l. 25 blue . . . . 45 1·50
50 – 2 l. + 75 c. red . . . . 45 2·25

DESIGNS—VERT: 10 c., 75 c., 2 l. Soldier; 25 c., 1 l. 25, Allegory of Italian Conquest of Ethiopia.

51 50 c. grey (air) . . . . 30 1·50
52 1 l. violet . . . . 30 1·50
53 2 l. + 75 c. blue . . . . 55 2·25
54 5 l. + 2 l. brown . . . . 55 2·25

DESIGNS—VERT: 50 c., 2 l. Savoia Marchetti S-66 flying boat over tractor. HORIZ: Savoia Marchetti S.M.83 airplane over city.

15 Hitler and Mussolini

1941. Axis Commemoration.

55 **15** 5 c. yellow (postage) 20
56 10 c. brown 20
57 20 c. black 45
58 25 c. green 45
59 50 c. purple 45
60 75 c. red 45
61 1 l. 25 blue 45

62 1 l. blue (air) . . . . 12·00
63 1 l. blue . . . . 1·10

In No. 62 the "l lira" tablet is in the centre; in No. 63 it is in the lower left corner.

EXPRESS LETTER STAMPS

E 7 Plough and Native Huts

1938. Air.

E32 **E 7** 2 l. blue 35 90
E33 2 l. 50 brown . . . . 45 1·75

E 8 King Victor Emmanuel III

1938.

E34 **E 8** 1 l. 25 green 35 45
E35 2 l. 50 red (inscr "EXPRESS") . . . . 55 3·75

POSTAGE DUE STAMPS

1941. Nos. D395/407 of Italy optd **A.O.I.**

D64 **D 141** 5 c. brown 35
D65 10 c. blue 35
D66 20 c. red 85
D67 25 c. green 85
D68 30 c. orange . . . . 1·90
D69 40 c. brown . . . . 2·25
D70 50 c. violet . . . . 2·25
D71 60 c. blue . . . . 4·00
D72 **D 142** 1 l. orange . . . . 16·00
D73 2 l. green . . . . 16·00
D74 5 l. violet . . . . 16·00
D75 10 l. blue . . . . 16·00
D76 20 l. red . . . . 16·00

ITALIAN OCCUPATION OF CEPHALONIA AND ITHACA Pt. 3

Two of the Greek Ionian Islands off the W. coast of Greece, under Italian occupation in 1941.

100 lepta = 1 drachma.

PRICES Prices are for unsevered pairs. Single stamps from severed pairs are worth ⅓ unused and ½ used prices.

1941. Stamps of Greece optd **ITALIA Occupazione Militare Italiana isole Cefalonia e Itaca** across a pair of stamps. (a) On postage stamps of 1937.

1 **86** 5 l. blue and brown . . . . 2·75 3·50
2 – 10 l. brown and blue . . . . 2·75 3·50
3 – 20 l. green and black . . . . 2·75 3·50
4 – 40 l. black and green . . . . 2·75 3·50
5 – 50 l. black and brown . . . . 2·75 3·50
6 – 80 l. brown and violet . . . . 9·00 9·00
7 **89** 1 d. green . . . . 60·00 45·00
8 **89a** 1 d. 50 green . . . . 45·00 35·00
9 – 2 d. blue . . . . 4·00 4·75
10 – 5 d. red . . . . 18·00 15·00
11 – 6 d. brown . . . . 18·00 15·00
12 – 7 d. brown . . . . 18·00 15·00
13 **89** 8 d. blue . . . . 25·00 22·00
14 – 10 d. brown . . . . 22·00 12·00
15 – 15 d. green . . . . 35·00 18·00
16 – 25 d. blue . . . . 50·00 40·00
17 **89a** 30 d. red £140 £100

(b) On air stamps of 1938 and 1935.

18 **D 20** 50 l. brown (No. 521) . . . . 65·00 50·00
19 **79** 1 d. red . . . . 20·00 20·00
20 – 2 d. blue . . . . 12·00 12·00
21 – 5 d. mauve . . . . 20·00 25·00
22 – 7 d. blue . . . . 30·00 25·00
23 – 25 d. red . . . . 90·00 85·00
24 – 30 d. green . . . . £110 80·00
25 – 50 d. mauve £750 £550
26 – 100 d. brown £300 £250

(c) On Charity Tax stamps.

27 **D 20** 10 l. red (No. C498) . . . . 6·50 6·50
28 **C 96** 10 l. red . . . . 8·50 5·00
29 50 l. green (No. C525) . . . . 2·75 2·75
30 50 l. green (No. C554) £150
31 1 d. blue (No. C526) . . . . 15·00 10·00

ITALIAN OCCUPATION OF CORFU — Pt. 3

One of the Greek Ionian Islands situated off the coast of Albania temporarily occupied by Italy during a dispute with Greece in 1923. For later Occupation Issues see ITALIAN OCCUPATION OF CORFU AND PAXOS below.

100 centesimi = 1 lira.
100 lepta = 1 drachma.

1923. Stamps of Italy optd **CORFU**.

No.	Type	Description	Unused	Used
1	37	5 c. green	1·75	1·50
2		10 c. red	1·75	1·50
3		15 c. grey	1·75	1·50
4	41	20 c. orange	1·75	1·50
5	39	30 c. brown	1·75	1·50
6		50 c. mauve	1·75	1·50
7		60 c. blue	1·75	1·50
8	34	1 l. brown and green	1·75	1·50

1923. Stamps of Italy surch **CORFU** and value.

No.	Type	Description	Unused	Used
9	37	25 l. on 10 c. red	6·00	2·00
10	39	60 l. on 25 c. blue	2·75	
11		70 l. on 30 c. brown	2·75	
12		1 d. 20 on 50 c. mauve	4·00	2·50
13	34	2 d. 40 on 1 l. brn & grn	4·00	2·75
14		4 d. 75 on 2 l. grn & orge	2·75	

ITALIAN OCCUPATION OF CORFU AND PAXOS — Pt. 3

Greek Ionian Islands occupied by Italy in 1941.

100 lepta = 1 drachma.

1941. Stamps of Greece optd **CORFU**.

(a) On postage stamps of 1937.

No.	Type	Description	Unused	Used
1	86	5 l. blue and brown	1·00	75
2	–	10 l. brown and blue	50	45
4	–	20 l. green and black	50	45
5	–	40 l. black and green	50	45
6	–	50 l. black and brown	50	45
7	–	80 l. brown and violet	50	45
8	89	1 d. green	1·25	1·00
9	89a	1 d. 50 green	2·75	2·75
10	–	2 d. blue	75	65
11	89	3 d. brown	1·25	1·00
12	–	5 d. red	75	65
13	–	6 d. olive	75	65
14	–	7 d. brown	1·50	1·00
15	89	8 d. blue	9·00	4·25
16	–	10 d. brown	60·00	35·00
17	–	15 d. green	3·50	2·50
18	–	25 d. blue	3·50	2·50
19	89a	30 d. red	25·00	18·00
20	89	100 d. red	70·00	30·00

(b) On air stamps of 1938 and 1935.

No.	Type	Description	Unused	Used
22	D 20	50 l. brown (No. 521)	1·25	50
23	79	1 d. red	70·00	25·00
24		2 d. blue	1·25	1·00
25		5 d. mauve	1·25	1·00
26		7 d. blue	1·25	1·00
27		10 d. brown	70·00	22·00
28		10 d. orange	14·00	8·00
29		25 d. red	14·00	8·00
30		30 d. green	22·00	14·00
31		50 d. mauve	22·00	14·00
32		100 d. brown	£200	£140

(c) On Charity Tax stamps of 1939.

No.	Type	Description	Unused	Used
33	C 96	10 l. red	1·25	75
34		50 l. green	1·25	1·00
35		1 d. blue	6·00	5·00

(d) On Postage Due stamps of 1902 and 1913.

No.	Type	Description	Unused	Used
D36	D 20	10 l. red	1·00	1·00
D37		25 l. blue	1·50	1·50
D38		80 l. purple	£160	90·00
D39		1 d. blue	£200	75·00
D40		2 d. red	2·50	1·25
D41		5 d. blue	7·50	5·00
D42		10 d. green	5·00	3·75
D43		15 d. brown	7·50	5·00
D44		25 d. red	7·50	5·00
D45		50 d. orange	7·50	5·00
D46		100 d. green	75·00	75·00

ITALIAN OCCUPATION OF IONIAN ISLANDS — Pt. 3

A group of islands off the W. coast of Greece, placed under the protection of Gt. Britain in 1815 and ceded to Greece in 1864. Under Italian occupation in 1941.

For use in all islands except Kithyra.

100 lepta = 1 drachma.

1941. Stamps of Italy optd **ISOLE JONIE**.

(a) On postage stamps of 1929.

No.	Type	Description	Unused	Used
1	98	5 c. brown	25	75
2	–	10 c. brown	25	75
3	99	20 c. red	25	75
4	–	25 c. green	25	75
5	103	30 c. brown	25	75
6		50 c. violet	25	75
7	–	75 c. red	25	75
8	–	1 l. 25 blue	25	75

(b) On air stamp of 1930.

No.	Type	Description	Unused	Used
9	110	50 c. brown	25	1·00

(c) On Postage Due stamps of 1934.

No.	Type	Description	Unused	Used
D10	D 141	10 c. blue	30	75
D11		20 c. red	30	75
D12		30 c. orange	30	75
D13	D 142	1 l. orange	30	75

ITALIAN POST OFFICES IN CHINA — Pt. 8

Italian Military Posts in China, including Peking and Tientsin, now closed.

100 centesimi = 1 lira. 100 cents = 1 dollar.

Stamps of Italy overprinted or surcharged.

A. PEKING

1917. Surch **PECHINO** and value.

No.	Type	Description	Unused	Used
1	37	2 c. on 5 c. green	50·00	24·00
2	33	4 c. on 10 c. red	£3000	£2500
3	37	4 c. on 10 c. pink	90·00	50·00
4	41	6 c. on 15 c. grey	£225	£125
5		8 c. on 20 c. on 15 c. grey	£1500	£650
6		8 c. on 20 c. orange	£2500	£550
7	39	20 c. on 50 c. violet	£14000	£7500
8	34	40 c. on 1 l. brown & grn	£70000	£10000

1917. Optd **Pechino**.

No.	Type	Description	Unused	Used
9	30	1 c. brown	3·00	5·00
10	31	2 c. brown	3·00	5·00
11	37	5 c. green	1·00	2·50
12		10 c. pink	1·00	2·50
13	41	20 c. orange	24·00	26·00
14	39	25 c. blue	1·00	4·00
15		50 c. violet	1·75	5·00
16	34	1 l. brown and green	2·00	6·00
17		5 l. blue and pink	4·00	11·00
18		10 l. green and pink	38·00	75·00

1918. Surch **Pechino** and value.

No.	Type	Description	Unused	Used
19	30	½ c. on 1 c. brown	20·00	32·00
20	31	1 c. on 2 c. brown	1·25	2·75
21	37	2 c. on 5 c. green	1·00	2·50
22		4 c. on 10 c. pink	1·00	2·50
23	41	8 c. on 20 c. orange	3·00	5·00
28	39	10 c. on 25 c. blue	2·00	3·25
25		20 c. on 50 c. violet	2·75	5·00
26	34	40 c. on 1 l. brown & green	30·00	40·00
27		2 dollari on 5 l. blue & pink	£120	£140
30		2 DOLLARI on 5 l. blue and pink	£20000	£22000

EXPRESS LETTER STAMPS

1917. Express Letter stamp optd **Pechino** or surch **12 CENTS** also.

No.	Type	Description	Unused	Used
E28	E 41	12 c. on 30 c. bl & pink	20·00	38·00
E19		30 c. blue and pink	5·00	10·00

POSTAGE DUE STAMPS

1917. Postage Due stamps optd **Pechino**.

No.	Type	Description	Unused	Used
D19	D 12	10 c. mauve & orange	2·00	3·00
D20		20 c. mauve & orange	2·00	3·00
D21		30 c. mauve & orange	2·00	4·00
D22		40 c. mauve & orange	2·00	4·00

1918. Surch **Pechino** and value.

No.	Type	Description	Unused	Used
D28	D 12	4 c. on 10 c. mauve and orange	£20000	£18000
D29		8 c. on 20 c. mauve and orange	3·00	7·00
D30		12 c. on 30 c. mauve and orange	15·00	32·00
D31		16 c. on 40 c. mauve and orange	60·00	£100

B. TIENTSIN

1917. Surch **TIENTSIN** and value.

No.	Type	Description	Unused	Used
31	37	2 c. on 5 c. green	90·00	65·00
32		4 c. on 10 c. pink	£180	£110
33b	41	6 c. on 15 c. grey	£350	£225

Prices for the above are for stamps with surcharge inverted.

1917. Optd **Tientsin**.

No.	Type	Description	Unused	Used
34	30	1 c. brown	2·00	4·00
35	31	2 c. brown	2·00	4·50
36	37	5 c. green	75	1·50
37		10 c. pink	75	1·50
38	41	20 c. orange	25·00	32·00
39	39	25 c. blue	1·00	2·25
40		50 c. violet	1·00	3·25
41	34	1 l. brown and green	2·25	6·50
42		5 l. blue and pink	2·75	12·00
43		10 l. green and pink	40·00	75·00

1918. Surch **Tientsin** and value.

No.	Type	Description	Unused	Used
44	30	½ c. on 1 c. brown	18·00	32·00
45	31	1 c. on 2 c. brown	1·00	3·25
46	37	2 c. on 5 c. green	1·00	1·75
47		4 c. on 10 c. pink	1·00	1·75
48	41	8 c. on 20 c. orange	2·50	4·00
49	39	10 c. on 25 c. blue	2·00	4·00
50		20 c. on 50 c. violet	2·50	4·50
51	34	40 c. on 1 l. brown & green	25·00	35·00
52		2 Dollari on 5 l. blue & pink	£140	£150
54		2 dollari on 5 l. blue & pink	£4000	£3000

EXPRESS LETTER STAMPS

1917. Express Letter stamp optd **Tientsin** or surch **12 CENTS** also.

No.	Type	Description	Unused	Used
E53	E 41	12 c. on 30 c. blue and pink	20·00	50·00
E44		30 c. blue and pink	4·00	14·00

POSTAGE DUE STAMPS

1917. Postage Due stamps optd **Tientsin**.

No.	Type	Description	Unused	Used
D44	D 12	10 c. mauve & orange	2·00	3·25
D45		20 c. mauve & orange	2·00	3·25
D46		30 c. mauve & orange	2·00	3·25
D47		40 c. mauve & orange	2·00	3·25

1918. Surch **Tientsin** and value.

No.	Type	Description	Unused	Used
D53	D 12	4 c. on 10 c. mauve and orange	£650	£900
D54		8 c. on 20 c. mauve and orange	3·00	7·00
D55		12 c. on 30 c. mauve and orange	15·00	28·00
D56		16 c. on 40 c. mauve and orange	65·00	£110

ITALIAN POST OFFICES IN CRETE — Pt. 8

Italian P.O.s in Crete, now closed.
1900. 40 paras = 1 piastre.
1906. 100 centesimi = 1 lira.

Stamps or Italy surcharged or overprinted.

1900. Surch **1 PIASTRA 1**.

No.	Type	Description	Unused	Used
1	27	1 pi. on 25 c. blue	2·40	16·00

1901. Surch **LA CANEA 1 PIASTRA 1**.

No.	Type	Description	Unused	Used
2	33	1 pi. on 25 c. blue	1·75	2·75

1906. 1901 stamps optd **LA CANEA**.

No.	Type	Description	Unused	Used
3	30	1 c. brown	40	70
4	31	2 c. brown	40	70
5		5 c. green	60	85
6	33	10 c. red	70·00	45·00
7		15 c. on 20 c. orange	1·00	1·25
8		25 c. blue	2·75	3·00
9		40 c. brown	2·75	3·00
10		45 c. green	2·75	3·00
11		50 c. mauve	2·75	3·25
12	34	1 l. brown and green	14·00	18·00
13		5 l. blue and pink	42·00	65·00

1907. 1906 stamps optd **LA CANEA**.

No.	Type	Description	Unused	Used
14	37	5 c. green	35	75
15		10 c. red	35	75
16	41	15 c. black	90	1·90
17	39	25 c. blue	1·10	2·25
18		40 c. brown	5·50	8·50
19		50 c. violet	90	2·25

EXPRESS LETTER STAMP

1906. Express Letter stamp optd **LA CANEA**.

No.	Type	Description	Unused	Used
E1	E 35	25 c. red	2·00	4·00

ITALIAN POST OFFICES IN THE TURKISH EMPIRE — Pt. 8

Currency: Italian and Turkish.

Stamps of Italy overprinted and surcharged.

A. GENERAL ISSUES.

The following were in use in P.O.s in Alexandria, Assab, La Goletta, Massawa, Susa, Tripoli and Tunis and also at Consular post offices at Buenos Aires and Montevideo.

1874. 1863 type, slightly altered, optd **ESTERO**.

No.	Type	Description	Unused	Used
1	4	1 c. green	60	4·50
2	5	2 c. brown	70	6·00
3	6	5 c. grey	£100	5·00
4		10 c. orange	£400	12·00
10		10 c. blue	65·00	3·50
5	10	20 c. blue	£300	6·00
11		20 c. orange	£900	3·00
6	6	30 c. brown	70	3·25
7		40 c. red	70	4·00
8		60 c. mauve	70	20·00
9	7	2 l. red	40·00	£200

1881. 1879 type, slightly altered, optd **ESTERO**.

No.	Type	Description	Unused	Used
12	12	5 c. green	3·00	3·00
13		10 c. red	1·00	2·00
14		20 c. orange	1·00	2·00
15		25 c. blue	1·00	2·00
16		50 c. mauve	1·25	20·00

B. OFFICES IN TURKISH EMPIRE.

(a) **Albania.**

1902. Surch **ALBANIA** and value.

No.	Type	Description	Unused	Used
18	31	10 pa. on 5 c. green	1·25	1·00
24	37	10 pa. on 5 c. green	18·00	20·00
25		20 pa. on 10 c. red	10·00	8·00
19	33	35 pa. on 20 c. orange	2·00	1·75
20		40 pa. on 25 c. blue	3·25	1·75
26		80 pa. on 50 c. mauve	10·00	8·00

1902. Surch with figures of value repeated twice and currency in words thus, **20 Para 20**.

No.	Type	Description	Unused	Used
21	31	10 pa. on 5 c. green	4·00	1·00
27	37	10 pa. on 5 c. green	1·00	1·00
28		20 pa. on 10 c. red	1·00	1·25
22	33	35 pa. on 20 c. orange	1·50	1·50
23		40 pa. on 25 c. blue	8·00	2·50
29		80 pa. on 50 c. mauve	20·00	14·00

(b) **General Offices in Europe and Asia.**

1908. Surch with figures of value repeated twice and currency in words thus, **30 Para 30**.

No.	Type	Description	Unused	Used
32	41	30 pa. on 15 c. grey	75	1·00
30	39	40 pa. on 25 c. blue	1·00	85
31		80 pa. on 50 c. mauve	1·25	1·00

EXPRESS LETTER STAMPS

1908. Express Letter stamps surch **LEVANTE** and new value.

No.	Type	Description	Unused	Used
E33	E 35	1 pi. on 25 c. red	75	1·00
E34	E 41	60 pa. on 30 c. bl & red	1·25	1·60

C. INDIVIDUAL OFFICES IN EUROPE AND ASIA.

(a) **Constantinople.**

1908. Surch in one line with figure of value and currency in words.

No.	Type	Description	Unused	Used
40	37	10 pa. on 5 c. green	1·00	2·00
41		20 pa. on 10 c. pink	1·00	2·00
47	41	30 pa. on 15 c. grey	1·00	1·00
43	39	1 pi. on 25 c. blue	1·00	2·00
44		2 pi. on 50 c. mauve	16·00	16·00
45	34	4 pi. on 1 l. brown & green	£400	£300
46		20 pi. on 5 l. blue & pink	£1400	£1000

1908. Surch in two lines with figures of value repeated twice and currency in words.

No.	Type	Description	Unused	Used
48	34	4 pi. on 1 l. brown & grn	20·00	24·00
51		20 pi. on 5 l. blue & pink	24·00	26·00

1909. Surch **Costantinopoli** (10 pa. to 2 pi.) or **COSTANTINOPOLI** (4 to 40 pi.) and value in figures twice repeated and currency in words.

No.	Type	Description	Unused	Used
52	37	10 pa. on 5 c. green	40	50
53		20 pa. on 10 c. pink	40	50
54	41	30 pa. on 15 c. grey	40	50
55	39	1 pi. on 25 c. blue	40	50
56		2 pi. on 50 c. mauve	1·00	1·50
57	34	4 pi. on 1 l. brown & green	1·00	1·50
58		20 pi. on 5 l. blue & pink	18·00	20·00
59		40 pi. on 10 l. green & pink	2·00	8·00

1921. Surch with value in figures and currency in words thus, **4 PIASTRE**.

No.	Type	Description	Unused	Used
60	37	1 pi. on 5 c. green	80·00	£160
61		2 pi. on 15 c. grey	2·00	3·00
62	41	4 pi. on 20 c. orange	12·00	20·00
63	39	5 pi. on 25 c. blue	12·00	20·00
64		10 pi. on 60 c. red	1·00	2·00

1921. Surch with value in figures and currency in words thus, **PARA 20**.

No.	Type	Description	Unused	Used
65	30	10 pa. on 1 c. brown	60	2·00
66	31	20 pa. on 2 c. brown	60	2·00
67	37	30 pa. on 5 c. green	1·50	2·00
68		1 pi. 20 on 15 c. grey	1·60	1·50
69	41	3 pi. on 20 c. orange	2·50	5·00
70	39	3 pi. 30 on 25 c. blue	1·10	2·00
71		7 pi. 20 on 60 c. red	1·75	2·00
72	34	15 pi. on 1 l. brown & green	10·00	15·00

1922. Surch **COSTANTINOPOLI** and value in figures once only after currency in words.

No.	Type	Description	Unused	Used
73	37	20 pa. on 5 c. green	6·00	14·00
74		1 pi. 20 on 15 c. grey	75	1·00
75	39	3 pi. on 30 c. brown	75	1·50
76		3 pi. 30 on 40 c. brown	75	1·00
77	34	7 pi. 20 on 1 l. brn & grn	75	1·00

1922. Surch **Piastre 3,75** in two lines.

No.	Type	Description	Unused	Used
78	39	3,75 pi. on 25 c. blue	1·25	1·00

1922. Para values surch in one line thus **30 PARA** and piastre values with **PIASTRE** over new value except Nos. 81, 86, 98 and 99 where the figures of value are above.

No.	Type	Description	Unused	Used
79	31	30 pa. on 2 c. brown	60	2·00
80	37	30 pa. on 5 c. green	2·00	4·00
81	41	1,50 pi. on 20 c. orange	60	2·00
82	39	1,50 pi. on 25 c. blue	75	2·50
83		3,75 pi. on 40 c. brown	1·00	2·50
84		4,50 pi. on 50 c. mauve	3·00	5·00
85		7,50 pi. on 60 c. red	3·00	4·75
86		15 pi. on 85 c. brown	4·00	10·00
87	34	18,75 pi. on 1 l. brn & grn	2·00	6·50
98		45 pi. on 5 l. blue and red	30·00	40·00
99		90 pi. on 10 l. olive & red	30·00	45·00

1922. Para values surch in two lines and piastre values with **PIASTRE** under new value.

No.	Type	Description	Unused	Used
90	37	30 pa. on 5 c. green	60	1·25
91		1½ pi. on 10 c. red	65	1·25
92	39	3 pi. on 25 c. blue	4·50	3·00
93		3¾ pi. on 40 c. brown	75	1·00
94		4½ pi. on 50 c. mauve	18·00	15·00
95		7½ pi. on 85 c. brown	2·00	4·00
96	34	7½ pi. on 1 l. brown & grn	2·50	5·00
97		15 pi. on 1 l. brown & grn	24·00	42·00

1923. Surch **COSTANTINOPOLI** and value in figures once only after currency in words.

No.	Type	Description	Unused	Used
100	37	30 pa. on 5 c. green	1·50	1·50
101	39	1 pi. 20 on 25 c. blue	1·50	1·50
103		4 pi. 20 on 50 c. mauve	1·50	1·50
104		7 pi. 20 on 60 c. red	1·50	1·50
105		15 pi. on 85 c. brown	1·50	2·25
106	34	18 pi. 30 on 1 l. brown and green	1·75	2·25
107		45 pi. on 5 l. blue & pink	2·00	4·00
108		90 pi. on 10 l. green & pink	2·00	5·00

EXPRESS LETTER STAMPS

1922. Express Letter stamps surch **15 PIASTRE**.

No.	Type	Description	Unused	Used
E 90	E 41	15 pi. on 1 l. 20 on 30 c. blue and red	6·00	16·00
E100		15 pi. on 30 c. blue and red	£100	£200

1923. Express Letter stamp surch **COSTANTINOPOLI 15 PIASTRE**.

No.	Type	Description	Unused	Used
E109	E 41	15 pi. on 1 l. 20 blue and red	3·00	10·00

POSTAGE DUE STAMPS

1922. Postage Due stamps optd **Costantinopoli**.
D100 D **12** 10 c. mauve & orange . 2·00 5·00
D101 30 c. mauve & orange . 2·00 5·00
D102 60 c. mauve & orange . 2·00 5·00
D103 1 l. mauve and blue . . 2·00 5·00
D104 2 l. mauve and blue . . £425 £600
D105 5 l. mauve and blue . . £150 £250
Nos. D100/5 bear a control cachet applied over blocks of four so that a quarter of the circle falls in a corner of each stamp.

(b) **Durazzo.**

1909. Surch **Durazzo** (10 pa. to 2 pi.) or **DURAZZO** (4 to 40 pi.) and value.
109 **37** 10 pa. on 5 c. green . . . . 50 1·00
110 20 pa. on 10 c. pink . . . . 50 1·00
111 **41** 30 pa. on 15 c. grey . . . . 2·00 2·00
112 **39** 1 pi. on 25 c. blue . . . . 60 1·00
113 2 pi. on 50 c. mauve . . . . 60 1·25
114 **34** 4 pi. on 1 l. brown & green . 80 2·00
115 20 pi. on 5 l. blue & pink . . 75·00 80·00
116 40 pi. on 10 l. grn & pink . . 6·00 25·00

1915. No. 111 of Durazzo surch **CENT. 20.**
116a **41** 20 c. on 30 pa. on 15 c. grey . . . . 1·60 8·50

(c) **Janina.**

1909. Surch **Janina** (10 pa. to 2 pi.) or **JANINA** (4 to 40 pi.) and value.
117 **37** 10 pa. on 5 c. green . . . . 50 1·00
118 20 pa. on 10 c. pink . . . . 50 1·00
119 **41** 30 pa. on 15 c. grey . . . . 50 1·25
120 **39** 1 pi. on 25 c. blue . . . . 50 2·00
121 2 pi. on 50 c. mauve . . . . 50 2·00
122 **34** 4 pi. on 1 l. brown & green . 60 2·00
123 20 pi. on 5 l. blue & pink . . £100 £100
124 40 pi. on 10 l. grn & pink . . 8·00 30·00

(d) **Jerusalem.**

1909. Surch **Gerusalemme** (10 pa. to 2 pi.) or **GERUSALEMME** (4 to 40 pi.) and value.
125 **37** 10 pa. on 5 c. green . . . . 60 2·00
126 20 pa. on 10 c. pink . . . . 60 2·00
127 **41** 30 pa. on 15 c. grey . . . . 60 2·00
128 **39** 1 pi. on 25 c. blue . . . . 60 2·00
129 2 pi. on 50 c. mauve . . . . 2·50 5·00
130 **34** 4 pi. on 1 l. brown & green . 5·00 7·50
131 20 pi. on 5 l. blue & pink . . £180 £180
132 40 pi. on 10 l. grn & pink . . 20·00 60·00

(e) **Salonica.**

1909. Surch **Salonicco** (10 pa. to 2 pi.) or **SALONICCO** (4 to 40 pi.) and value.
133 **37** 10 pa. on 5 c. green . . . . 60 1·00
134 20 pa. on 10 c. pink . . . . 60 1·00
135 **41** 30 pa. on 15 c. grey . . . . 60 1·00
136 **39** 1 pi. on 25 c. blue . . . . 60 1·00
137 2 pi. on 50 c. mauve . . . . 60 1·25
138 **34** 4 pi. on 1 l. brown & green . 75 2·00
139 20 pi. on 5 l. blue & pink . . £140 £160
140 40 pi. on 10 l. grn & pink . . 10·00 28·00

(f) **Scutari.**

1909. Surch **Scutari di Albania** (4 pa. to 2 pi.) or **SCUTARI DI ALBANIA** (4 to 40 pi.) and value.
141 **31** 4 pa. on 2 c. brown . . . . 60 1·75
142 **37** 10 pa. on 35 c. green . . . . 60 1·00
143 20 pa. on 10 c. pink . . . . 60 1·00
144 **41** 30 pa. on 15 c. grey . . . . 5·00 5·00
145 **39** 1 pi. on 25 c. blue . . . . 60 1·00
146 2 pi. on 50 c. mauve . . . . 60 1·25
147 **34** 4 pi. on 1 l. brown & green . 75 1·50
148 20 pi. on 5 l. blue & pink . . 12·00 16·00
149 40 pi. on 10 l. grn & pink . . 40·00 50·00

1916. No. 144 of Scutari surch **CENT. 20.**
150 **41** 20 c. on 30 pa. on 15 c. grey 3·00 10·00

(g) **Smyrna.**

1909. Surch **Smirne** (10 pa. to 2 pi.) or **SMIRNE** (4 to 40 pi.) and value.
151 **37** 10 pa. on 5 c. green . . . . 50 1·00
152 20 pa. on 10 c. pink . . . . 50 1·00
153 **41** 30 pa. on 15 c. grey . . . . 50 1·00
154 **39** 1 pi. on 25 c. blue . . . . 50 1·25
155 2 pi. on 50 c. mauve . . . . 60 1·25
156 **34** 4 pi. on 1 l. brown & green . 1·00 2·00
157 20 pi. on 5 l. blue & pink . . 60·00 50·00
158 40 pi. on 10 l. grn & pink . . 14·00 28·00

(h) **Valona.**

1909. Surch **Valona** (10 pa. to 2 pi.) or **VALONA** (4 to 40 pi.) and value.
159 **37** 10 pa. on 5 c. green . . . . 50 1·00
160 20 pa. on 10 c. pink . . . . 50 1·00
161 **41** 30 pa. on 15 c. grey † . . . 5·00 4·00
167 30 pa. on 15 c. grey † . . . 2·25 5·00
162 **39** 1 pi. on 25 c. blue . . . . 50 1·25
163 2 pi. on 50 c. mauve . . . . 50 1·25
164 **34** 4 pi. on 1 l. brown & green . 60 1·75
165 20 pi. on 5 l. blue & pink . . 24·00 28·00
166 40 pi. on 10 l. grn & pink . . 32·00 55·00
† On No. 161 the surcharge is **Para**, on No. 167 **PARA**.

1916. No. 167 of Valona surch **CENT. 20.**
168 **41** 20 c. on 30 pa. on 15 c. grey 1·00 6·00

D. OFFICES IN AFRICA.

(a) **Benghazi.**

1901. Surch **BENGASI 1 PIASTRA 1**.
169 **33** 1 pi. on 25 c. blue . . . . . 25·00 50·00
170 **39** 1 pi. on 25 c. blue . . . . . 22·00 60·00

(b) **Tripoli.**

1909. Optd **Tripoli di Barberia** (1 to 50 c.) or **TRIPOLI DI BARBERIA** (1, 2 l.).
171 **30** 1 c. brown . . . . 1·40 2·00
173 **31** 2 c. brown . . . . 1·00 1·00
174 **37** 5 c. green . . . . 30·00 6·00
175 10 c. red . . . . 1·25 1·40
176 **41** 15 c. grey . . . . 2·00 2·25
177 **39** 25 c. blue . . . . 90 1·25
178 40 c. brown . . . . 3·00 3·25
179 50 c. violet . . . . 3·00 3·25
180 **34** 1 l. brown and green . . . 55·00 35·00
181 5 l. blue and pink . . . . 20·00 75·00

EXPRESS LETTER STAMPS

1909. Express Letter stamps optd **TRIPOLI DI BARBERIA**.
E182 E **35** 25 c. pink . . . . . . 3·00 4·00
E183 E **41** 30 c. blue and pink . . . 4·00 8·00

ITALY Pt. 8

A Republic in S. Europe on the Mediterranean and Adriatic Seas. Originally a kingdom formed by the union of various smaller kingdoms and duchies that issued their own stamps.

100 centesimi = 1 lira.

1 King Victor Emmanuel II 3

1862. Head embossed. Imperf (15 c.) or perf (others).
1 **1** 10 c. bistre £4500 £130
5 15 c. blue . . . . 35·00 28·00
2a 20 c. blue . . . . 4·25 14·00
3 40 c. red . . . . £170 75·00
4 80 c. yellow . . . . 20·00 £1000
For stamps of this type imperf, see Sardinia Nos. 27 etc.

1863. Imperf.
7 **3** 15 c. blue . . . . 1·10 2·75

4 5 6

7 10

1863. Perf.
8 **4** 1 c. green . . . . 1·40 20
9 **5** 2 c. brown . . . . 5·00 20
10 **6** 5 c. grey £800 40
11 10 c. brown £1200 60
21 10 c. blue . . . . £2750 1·25
12 15 c. blue £1000 60
20a **10** 20 c. blue £500 55
22 20 c. orange £2000 60
13 **6** 30 c. brown . . . . 6·50 1·40
14 40 c. red . . . . £2500 1·50
15 60 c. mauve . . . . 5·00 7·00
16 **7** 2 l. red . . . . 10·00 35·00

1865. Surch **C 20 20 C** and curved bar.
17 **6** 20 c. on 15 c. blue £300 55

1878. Official stamps surch **2 C** and wavy bars.
23 **O 11** 2 c. on 2 c. red . . . . . 85·00 4·00
24 2 c. on 5 c. red . . . . . 85·00 5·00
25 2 c. on 20 c. red . . . . . £400 1·75
26 2 c. on 30 c. red . . . . . £250 2·00
27 2 c. on 1 l. red . . . . . £300 1·90
28 2 c. on 2 l. red . . . . . £300 2·75
29 2 c. on 5 l. red . . . . . £400 4·00
30 2 c. on 10 l. red . . . . . £275 4·75

12 King Umberto I 13 Arms of Savoy 14

1879. Corners vary for each value.
31 **12** 5 c. green . . . . 5·00 20
32 10 c. red £275 20
33 20 c. orange £225 20
34 25 c. blue £300 50
35 30 c. brown . . . . 90·00 £1000
36 50 c. mauve . . . . 7·50 3·25
37 2 l. orange . . . . 30·00 £140

1889. Figures in four corners. Various frames.
38 **13** 5 c. green £300 90
39 **14** 40 c. brown . . . . 7·00 1·75
40 45 c. green . . . . £1000 1·75
41 60 c. mauve . . . . 7·00 7·00
42 1 l. brown and orange . . . 8·00 1·75
43 5 l. red and green . . . . . 9·00 £325

1890. Surch **Cmi. 2** or **Cmi 20.**
44 **12** 2 c. on 5 c. green . . . . . 10·00 30·00
45 20 c. on 30 c. brown . . . . £200 3·00
46 20 c. on 50 c. mauve . . . . £200 14·00

1890. Parcel Post stamps surch **Valevole per le stampe Cmi. 2** and bars.
47 **P 13** 2 c. on 10 c. grey . . . . . 2·50 2·75
48 2 c. on 20 c. blue . . . . . 3·50 2·75
49 2 c. on 50 c. pink . . . . . 22·00 12·00
50 2 c. on 75 c. green . . . . . 2·25 2·25
51 2 c. on 1 l. 25 orange . . . 24·00 10·00
52 2 c. on 1 l. 75 brown . . . 11·00 20·00

21 22 23

24 25 26

27 29

1891.
53 **21** 1 c. brown . . . . 3·00 1·75
54 **22** 2 c. brown . . . . 3·00 30
55 **23** 5 c. green £275 75
56 **24** 5 c. green . . . . 8·00 25
57 **25** 10 c. red . . . . 4·00 30
58 **26** 20 c. orange . . . . 4·00 30
59 **27** 25 c. blue . . . . 4·00 55
60 45 c. olive . . . . 4·00 1·00
61 **29** 5 l. red and blue . . . . . . 30·00 60·00

30 31

33 King Victor Emmanuel III 34

1901. Designs vary.
62 **30** 1 c. brown 10 10
63 **31** 2 c. brown 10 10
64 5 c. green . . . . 24·00 10
65 **33** 10 c. red . . . . 26·00 10
66 20 c. orange . . . . 4·25 10
67 25 c. blue . . . . 30·00 10
68 40 c. brown . . . . £275 2·50
69 45 c. green . . . . 3·00 10
70 50 c. violet . . . . £300 4·00
71 **34** 1 l. brown and green . . . . 1·60 10
72 5 l. blue and pink . . . . 12·00 1·00
85 10 l. green and pink . . . . 30·00 5·50
See also Nos. 171s, 181, 185 and 186/7.

1905. Surch **C. 15.**
73 **33** 15 c. on 20 c. orange . . . . 40·00 30

37 39 41

1906.
75 **37** 5 c. green 15 10
76 10 c. red 15 10
90 **41** 15 c. grey . . . . 12·00 30
77 **39** 25 c. blue 55 10
78 40 c. brown 85 10
79 50 c. violet 70 10
See also Nos. 104 etc. 171d/h and 171j/r.

42 Garibaldi 43

1910. 50th Anniv of Plebiscite in Naples and Sicily.
81 **42** 5 c. (+ 5 c.) green . . . . . 8·00 14·00
82 15 c. (+ 5 c.) red . . . . . 16·00 30·00

1910. National Plebiscite of Southern States, 1860.
83 **43** 5 c. (+ 5 c.) pink . . . . . 50·00 60·00
84 15 c. (+ 5 c.) green . . . . 85·00 85·00

45 46 50

1911. Jubilee of Italian Kingdom.
86 **45** 2 c. (+ 3 c.) brown . . . . . 1·00 2·25
87 **46** 5 c. (+ 5 c.) green . . . . . 3·00 10·00
88 – 10 c. (+ 5 c.) red . . . . . 3·00 10·00
89 – 15 c. (+ 5 c.) grey . . . . . 3·00 10·00
DESIGNS: Symbolic of the Genius of Italy (10 c.) and the Glory of Rome (15 c.).

1912. Re-erection of Campanile of St. Mark, Venice.
91 **50** 5 c. black . . . . 3·00 3·50
92 15 c. brown . . . . 8·00 14·00

1913. Surch **2 2.**
93 **46** 2 on 5 c. green . . . . . . 40 1·10
94 – 2 on 10 c. red (No. 88) . . . 40 1·10
95 – 2 on 15 c. grey No. 89) . . . 40 1·10

53 Banner of United Italy

54 Italian Eagle and Arms of Savoy

1915. Red Cross Society. No. 98 is surch **20.**
96 **53** 10 c. + 5 c. red . . . . . . 1·40 3·50
97 **54** 15 c. + 5 c. grey . . . . . . 1·40 4·75
98 20 on 15 c. + 5 c. grey . . . 2·75 15·00
99 20 c. + 5 c. orange . . . . . 2·00 12·00

1916. Surch **CENT. 20.**
100 **41** 20 c. on 15 c. grey . . . . . 5·50 30

1917. Air. Express Letter stamp optd **ESPERIMENTO POSTA AEREA MAGGIO 1917 TORINO = ROMA = ROMA = TORINO.**
102 E **35** 25 c. red . . . . 4·00 6·00

1917. Air. Express Letter stamp surch **IDROVOLANTE NAPOLI-PALERMO NAPOLI 25 CENT 25.**
103 E **59** 25 c. on 40 c. violet . . . 5·00 11·00

1917.
104 **37** 15 c. grey 85 10
105 **41** 20 c. orange 85 10
178 **39** 20 c. orange 55 10
179 20 c. green 35 10
180 20 c. purple . . . . 1·10 10
181 **34** 25 c. green & light green . . 25 10
182 **39** 25 c. green . . . . 3·50 3·25
106 30 c. brown . . . . 1·10 25
183 30 c. grey 90 10
107 55 c. purple . . . . 3·75 3·25
108 60 c. red 90 10
109 60 c. blue . . . . 3·25 12·00
184 60 c. orange . . . . 2·25 10
185 **34** 75 c. red and carmine . . . 1·60 15
110 **39** 85 c. brown . . . . 2·50 1·00
186 **34** 1 l. 25 blue & ultramarine . 1·90 10
111 2 l. green and orange . . . 9·00 1·00
187 2 l. 50 green and orange . . 20·00 1·10
See also Nos. 171a/c and 171i.

59 Ancient Seal of Republic of Trieste

60

1921. Union of Venezia Giulia with Italy.

112	59	15 c. red and black	1·00	10·00
113		25 c. red and blue	1·00	10·00
114		40 c. red and brown	1·00	10·00

1921. 600th Death Anniv of Dante.

115	60	15 c. red	1·00	8·00
116	–	25 c. green	1·00	8·00
117	–	40 c. brown	1·00	8·00

DESIGNS: 25 c. Woman with book; 40 c. Dante.

62 "Victory"

64

1921. Victory of 1918.

118	62	5 c. green	20	1·00
119		10 c. red	35	1·40
120		15 c. grey	60	4·25
121		25 c. blue	35	3·00

1922. 9th Italian Philatelic Congress. Trieste. Optd **IX CONGRESSO FILATELICO ITALIANO TRIESTE 1922**.

122	37	10 c. red	£160	£100
123		15 c. grey	£120	£100
124	39	25 c. blue	£120	£100
125		40 c. brown	£160	£100

1922. 50th Death Anniv of Mazzini.

126	64	25 c. purple	2·00	11·00
127	–	40 c. purple	3·00	11·00
128	–	80 c. blue	2·00	11·00

DESIGNS VERT: 40 c. Mazzini. HORIZ: 80 c. Tomb of Mazzini.

66

1923. Tercentenary of Propagation of the Faith.

129	66	20 c. orange and green	1·00	26·00
130		30 c. orange and red	1·00	26·00
131		50 c. orange and violet	1·00	26·00
132		1 l. orange and blue	1·00	26·00

The portraits and arms in the corners at right vary for each value.

1923. Surch in words and figures. (15 c. surch **DIECI** only).

133	39	7½ c. on 85 c. brown	15	40
135	30	10 c. on 1 c. brown	15	15
136	31	10 c. on 2 c. brown	15	15
137	37	10 c. on 15 c. grey	10	10
138	39	20 c. on 25 c. blue	10	10
139	33	25 c. on 45 c. olive	15	2·50
140	39	25 c. on 60 c. blue	70	35
141		30 c. on 50 c. mauve	10	10
142		30 c. on 55 c. purple	25	20
143		50 c. on 40 c. brown	35	15
144		50 c. on 55 c. purple	15·00	4·50
145	34	1 l. 75 on 10 l. olive & red	5·50	9·50

73

74

75

1923. 1st Anniv of Fascist March on Rome.

146	73	10 c. green	1·00	2·50
147		30 c. violet	1·10	2·50
148		50 c. red	1·25	3·75
149	74	1 l. blue	1·00	2·50
150		2 l. brown	1·10	4·50
151	75	5 l. black and blue	3·25	17·00

76

1923. Fascist "Black Shirt" Fund.

152	76	30 c. + 30 c. brown	15·00	40·00
153		50 c. + 50 c. mauve	17·00	40·00
154		1 l. + 1 l. grey	15·00	40·00

77

1923. 50th Death Anniv of A. Manzoni (writer).

155	77	10 c. black and red	90	20·00
156	–	15 c. black and green	90	20·00
157	–	30 c. black	90	20·00
158	–	50 c. black and brown	90	20·00
159	–	1 l. black and blue	13·00	£100
160	–	5 l. black and purple	£240	£1000

DESIGNS: 10 c. to 50 c. Scenes from Manzoni's "I Promessi Sposi"; 1 l. Manzoni's home, Milan; 5 l. Portrait of Manzoni.

1924. Victory stamps surch **LIRE UNA** between stars.

161	62	1 l. on 5 c. green	7·00	42·00
162		1 l. on 10 c. red	4·50	42·00
163		1 l. on 15 c. grey	7·00	42·00
164		1 l. on 25 c. blue	4·50	42·00

1924. Trade Propaganda. Optd **CROCIERA ITALIANA 1924**.

165	37	10 c. red	60	7·00
166	39	30 c. brown	60	7·00
167		50 c. violet	60	7·00
168		60 c. blue	4·75	28·00
169		85 c. brown	2·50	28·00
170	34	1 l. brown and green	21·00	£120
171		2 l. green and orange	17·00	£120

Used on an Italian cruiser which visited South America for trade propaganda.

1924. Previous issues with attached advertising labels (imperf between stamp and label). Colour of label given.

171a	15 c. (104) + Columbia (blue)	12·00	14·00
171b	15 c. (104) + Bitter Campari (blue)	1·00	5·00
171c	15 c. (104) + Cordial Campari (black)	1·00	5·00
171d	25 c. (77) + Coen (green)	75·00	12·00
171e	25 c. (77) + Piperno (brown)	£650	£140
171f	25 c. (77) + Tagliacozzo (brown)	£300	£140
171g	25 c. (77) + Abrador (blue)	40·00	30·00
171h	25 c. (77) + Reinach (green)	40·00	20·00
171i	30 c. (106) + Columbia (green)	12·00	12·00
171j	50 c. (79) + Coen (blue)	£600	24·00
171k	50 c. (79) + Columbia (red)	6·00	2·00
171l	50 c. (79) + De Montel (blue)	1·00	4·00
171m	50 c. (79) + Piperno (green)	£700	50·00
171n	50 c. (79) + Reinach (blue)	75·00	15·00
171o	50 c. (79) + Singer (red)	1·00	70
171p	50 c. (79) + Tagliacozzo (green)	£900	£100
171q	50 c. (79) + Siero Casali (blue)	6·00	12·00
171r	50 c. (79) + Tantal (red)	£100	35·00
171s	1 l. (71) + Columbia (blue)	£300	£200

81 Church of St. John Lateran

1924. Holy Year (1925).

172	–	20 c. + 10 c. brown & grn	1·00	5·00
173	81	30 c. + 15 c. brown & choc	1·00	5·00
174	–	50 c. + 25 c. brown & vio	1·00	5·00
175	–	60 c. + 30 c. brown & red	1·00	10·00
176	–	1 l. + 50 c. purple & blue	1·00	10·00
177	–	5 l. + 2 l. 50 purple & red	1·00	30·00

DESIGNS: 20 c. Church of St. Maria Maggiore; 50 c. Church of St. Paul; 60 c. St. Peter's; 1 l. Pope opening Holy Door; 5 l. Pope shutting Holy Door.

82

83 Vision of St. Francis

1925. Royal Jubilee.

188	82	60 c. red	20	20
189		1 l. blue	20	20
190		1 l. 25 blue	1·75	70

1926. 700th Death Anniv of St. Francis of Assisi.

191	83	20 c. green	10	30
194	–	30 c. black	10	15
192	–	40 c. violet	10	20
193	–	60 c. red	15	20
195	–	1 l. 25 blue	10	20
196	–	5 l. + 2 l. 50 brown	4·50	40·00

DESIGNS—HORIZ: 40 c. St. Damian's Church and Monastery, Assisi; 60 c. St. Francis's Monastery, Assisi; 1 l. 25, Death of St. Francis, from fresco in Church of the Holy Cross, Florence. VERT: 30 c., 5 l. St. Francis (after Luca della Robbia).

88

1926. Air.

197	88	50 c. red	1·25	2·75
198		60 c. grey	1·10	2·25
199		80 c. brown and purple	7·00	21·00
200		1 l. blue	60	2·75
201		1 l. 20 brown	7·00	35·00
202		1 l. 50 orange	4·50	7·50
203		5 l. green	12·00	26·00

89 Castle of St. Angelo

1926. 1st National Defence issue.

204	89	40 c. + 20 c. black & brn	60	4·75
205	–	60 c. + 30 c. brown & red	60	4·75
206	–	1 l. 25 + 60 c. black & grn	60	14·00
207	–	5 l. + 2 l. 50 black & blue	90	45·00

DESIGNS: 60 c. Aqueduct of Claudius; 1 l. 25, Capitol; 5 l. Porta del Popolo.

See also Nos. 219/22 and 278/81.

90 Volta

91

92

1927. Death Centenary of Volta.

208	90	20 c. red	20	25
209		50 c. green	65	10
210		60 c. purple	80	1·10
211		1 l. 25 blue	80	1·10

1927.

216	91	50 c. grey and brown	75	10
212		1 l. 75 brown	1·50	10
213		1 l. 85 black	40	30
214		2 l. 55 red	1·90	3·25
215		2 l. 65 purple	1·90	21·00

No. 216 is smaller (17½ × 21½ mm).

1927. Air. Surch.

217	88	50 c. on 60 c. grey	2·00	15·00
218		80 c. on 1 l. blue	10·00	60·00

1928. 2nd National Defence issue. As Nos. 204/7.

219	89	30 c. + 10 c. black & vio	2·00	9·50
220	–	50 c. + 20 c. black & olive	2·00	6·50
221	–	1 l. 25 + 50 c. black & blue	5·00	21·00
222	–	5 l. + 2 l. black & red	8·00	55·00

1928.

223	92	7½ c. brown	70	2·00
224		15 c. orange	70	15
225		35 c. grey	1·10	3·50
226		50 c. mauve	1·60	15

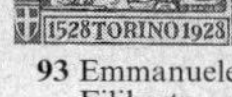

93 Emmanuele Filiberto

94 Soldier of First World War and Statue

95 Statue, Turin (Maroghetti)

96 King Victor Emmanuel II

1928. 400th Birth Anniv of Emmanuele Filiberto, Duke of Savoy, and 10th Anniv of Victory in World War.

227a	93	20 c. blue and brown	35	50
228a		25 c. green and red	35	50
229a		30 c. brown and green	45	70
230	94	50 c. red and blue	25	15
231		75 c. red and pink	35	25
232	95	1 l. 25 black and blue	55	30
233	94	1 l. 75 green and blue	1·10	1·25
234	93	5 l. green and mauve	3·50	35·00
235	94	10 l. black and pink	7·00	80·00
236	95	20 l. green and mauve	12·00	£250

1929. 50th Death Anniv of King Victor Emmanuel II. Veterans' Fund.

237	96	50 c. + 10 c. green	1·10	3·00

97 Fascist Arms of Italy

98 Romulus, Remus and Wolf

99 Julius Caesar

103 King Victor Emmanuel III

1929. Imperial Series.

238	97	2 c. orange	10	10
239	98	5 c. brown	10	10
240	99	7½ c. violet	10	10
241	–	10 c. brown	10	10
242	–	15 c. green	10	10
243	99	20 c. red	10	10
244	–	25 c. green	10	10
245	103	30 c. brown	10	10
246	–	35 c. blue	10	10
247	103	50 c. violet	10	10
248	–	75 c. red	10	10
249	99	1 l. violet	10	10
250	–	1 l. 25 blue	10	10
251	–	1 l. 75 orange	10	10
252	–	2 l. red	10	10
253	98	2 l. 55 green	10	10
254		3 l. 70 violet	10	10
255		5 l. red	10	10
256	–	10 l. violet	25	25
257	99	20 l. green	85	3·75
258	–	25 l. black	1·90	12·00
259	–	50 l. violet	2·75	18·00

DESIGNS—As Type **99**: 10 c., 1 l. 75, 25 l. Augustus the Great; 15 c., 35 c., 2 l., 10 l. Italia (Woman with castle on her head); 25 c., 75 c., 1 l. 25, 50 l. Profile of King Victor Emmanuel III.

For stamps as above but without Fascist emblems, see Nos. 633 etc, and for stamps with integral label for armed forces see Nos. 563/74.

104 Bramante Courtyard

1929. 1400th Anniv of Abbey of Montecassino.

260	104	20 c. orange	30	25
261	–	25 c. green	30	25
262	–	50 c. + 10 c. brown	1·25	6·00
263	–	75 c. + 15 c. red	1·40	8·50
264	104	1 l. 25 + 25 c. blue	1·75	10·00
265	–	5 l. + 1 l. purple	1·75	32·00
266	–	10 l. + 2 l. green	2·75	55·00

DESIGNS—HORIZ: 25 c. "Death of St. Benedict" (fresco); 50 c. Monks building Abbey; 75 c., 5 l. Abbey of Montecassino. VERT: 10 l. St. Benedict.

109

1930. Marriage of Prince Umberto and Princess Marie Jose.

267	109	20 c. orange	25	25
268		50 c. + 10 c. brown	65	1·60
269		1 l. 25 + 25 c. blue	1·10	5·00

110 Pegasus   113

1930. Air.

270	–	25 c. green	10	10
271	110	50 c. brown	10	10
272	–	75 c. brown	10	10
273	–	80 c. orange	10	25
274	–	1 l. violet	10	10
275	113	2 l. blue	10	10
276	110	5 l. green	10	25
277		10 l. red	15	55

DESIGNS—As Type **110**: 25 c., 80 c. Wings; 75 c., 1 l. Angel.

1930. 3rd National Defence issue. Designs as Nos. 204/7.

278	89	30 c. + 10 c. violet & grn	40	6·00
279	–	50 c. + 10 c. blue & green	40	3·50
280	–	1 l. 25 + 30 c. green & bl	55	11·00
281	–	5 l. + 1 l. 50 choc & brn	2·75	42·00

114 Ferrucci on Horseback   117 Francesco Ferrucci

1930. 400th Death Anniv of Francesco Ferrucci.

282	114	20 c. red (postage)	20	35
283	–	25 c. green	25	35
284	–	50 c. violet	15	15
285	–	1 l. 25 blue	1·00	70
286	–	5 l. + 2 l. orange	3·25	35·00
287	117	50 c. violet (air)	80	4·00
288		1 l. brown	80	7·00
289		5 l. + 2 l. purple	2·50	45·00

DESIGNS—HORIZ: 25 c., 50 c., 1 l. 25, Ferrucci assassinated by Maramaldo. VERT: 5 l. Ferrucci in helmet.

119 Jupiter sending forth Eagle

1930. Birth Bimillenary of Virgil.

290	–	15 c. brown (postage)	40	30
291	–	20 c. orange	40	30
292	–	25 c. green	50	20
293	–	30 c. purple	55	30
294	–	50 c. violet	40	15
295	–	75 c. red	85	1·00
296	–	1 l. 25 blue	85	70
297	–	5 l. + 1 l. 50 brown	23·00	70·00
298	–	10 l. + 2 l. 50 olive	23·00	80·00
299	119	50 c. brown (air)	2·50	3·50
300		1 l. orange	3·50	5·50
301		7 l. 70 + 1 l. 30 purple	18·00	75·00
302		9 l. + 2 l. blue	19·00	80·00

DESIGNS (scenes from "Aeneid" or "Georgics"): 15 c. Helenus and Anchises; 20 c. The passing legions; 25 c. Landing of Aeneas; 30 c. Earth's bounties; 50 c. Harvesting; 75 c. Rural life; 1 l. 25, Aeneas sights Italy; 5 l. A shepherd's hut; 10 l. Turnus, King of the Rutuli.

120 Savoia Marchetti S-55A Flying Boats

1930. Air. Transatlantic Mass Formation Flight.

303	120	7 l. 70 blue and brown	£120	£375

121 St. Antony's Installation as a Franciscan   123 Tower of the Marzocco

1931. 700th Death Anniv of St. Antony of Padua.

304	121	20 c. purple	40	25
305	–	25 c. green	45	25
306	–	30 c. brown	75	40
307	–	50 c. violet	40	15
308	–	75 c. lake	3·50	1·40
309	–	1 l. 25 c. blue	2·50	65
310	–	5 l. + 2 l. 50 c. olive	15·00	65·00

DESIGNS—HORIZ: 25 c. Sermon to the Fishes; 30 c. Hermitage of Olivares; 50 c. Basilica of the Saint at Padua; 75 c. Death of St. Antony; 1 l. 25, St. Antony liberating prisoners. VERT: 5 l. Vision of St. Antony.

1931. 50th Anniv of Naval Academy, Leghorn.

311	123	20 c. red	75	30
312	–	50 c. violet	75	15
313	–	1 l. 25 blue	3·25	85

DESIGNS—HORIZ: 50 c. Cadet ship "Amerigo Vespucci"; 1 l. 25, Cruiser "Trento".

124 Dante (1265–1321)

125 Leonardo da Vinci's Drawing "Flying Man"   127 Leonardo da Vinci

1932. Dante Alighieri Society. (a) Postage.

314	–	10 c. brown	40	30
315	–	15 c. green	45	30
316	–	20 c. red	40	20
317	–	25 c. green	45	25
318	–	30 c. brown	75	35
319	–	50 c. violet	35	15
320	–	75 c. red	1·25	1·00
321	–	1 l. 25 blue	1·00	70
322	–	1 l. 75 orange	1·25	1·00
323	–	2 l. 75 green	8·00	12·00
324	–	5 l. + 2 l. red	13·00	60·00
325	124	10 l. + 2 l. 50 olive	14·00	75·00

DESIGNS: 10 c. Giovanni Boccaccio (writer); 15 c. Niccolo Machiavelli (statesman); 20 c. Fra Paolo Sarpi (philosopher); 25 c. Vittorio Alfieri (poet); 30 c. Ugo Foscolo (writer); 50 c. Giacomo Leopardi (poet); 75 c. Giosue Carducci (poet); 1 l. 25, Carlo Botta (historian); 1 l. 75, Torquato Tasso (poet); 2 l. 75, Francesco Petrarch (poet); 5 l. Ludovico Ariosto (poet).

(b) Air.

326	125	50 c. brown	75	3·25
327	–	1 l. violet	75	2·00
328	–	3 l. red	2·00	8·00
329	–	5 l. green	2·25	10·00
330	125	7 l. 70 + 2 l. blue	3·50	42·00
331	–	10 l. + 2 l. 50 grey	4·00	42·00
332	127	100 l. green and blue	20·00	£140

DESIGN—HORIZ: 1, 3, 5, 10 l. Leonardo da Vinci.

128 Garibaldi and Victor Emmanuel   130 Caprera

1932. 50th Death Anniv of Garibaldi.

333	–	10 c. blue (postage)	40	30
334	128	20 c. brown	45	20
335	–	25 c. green	70	35
336	128	30 c. orange	75	50
337	–	50 c. violet	40	15
338	–	75 c. red	2·50	1·50
339	–	1 l. 25 blue	1·75	70
340	–	1 l. 75 + 25 c. blue	9·00	38·00
341	–	2 l. 55 + 50 c. brown	15·00	50·00
342	–	5 l. + 1 l. lake	15·00	55·00

DESIGNS—HORIZ: 10 c. Garibaldi's birthplace, Nice; 25 c., 50 c. "Here we make Italy or die"; 75 c. Death of Anita (Garibaldi's wife); 1 l. 25, Garibaldi's tomb; 1 l. 75, Quarto Rock. VERT: 2 l. 55, Garibaldi's statue in Rome; 5 l. Garibaldi.

343	130	50 c. lake (air)	65	2·25
344	–	80 c. green	1·25	4·00
345	130	1 l. + 25 c. brown	1·75	12·00
346	–	2 l. + 50 c. blue	3·25	24·00
347	–	5 l. + 1 l. green	4·25	28·00

DESIGNS—VERT: 80 c. The Ravenna hut; 2 l. Anita; 5 l. Garibaldi.

132 Agriculture

1932. 10th Anniv of Fascist March on Rome. (a) Postage.

350	132	5 c. sepia	30	25
351	–	10 c. sepia	40	25
352	–	15 c. green	45	30
353	–	20 c. red	40	20
354	–	25 c. green	45	20
355	–	30 c. sepia	60	90
356	–	35 c. blue	2·00	3·00
357	–	50 c. violet	30	15
358	–	60 c. brown	2·00	2·00
359	–	75 c. red	90	40
360	–	1 l. violet	1·75	90
361	–	1 l. 25 blue	90	30
362	–	1 l. 75 orange	1·10	40
363	–	2 l. 55 green	13·00	18·00
364	–	2 l. 75 green	13·00	19·00
365	–	5 l. + 2 l. 50 red	25·00	£110

DESIGNS: 10 c. Fascist soldier; 15 c. Fascist coastguard; 20 c. Italian youth; 25 c. Tools forming a shadow of the Fasces; 30 c. Religion; 35 c. Imperial highways; 50 c. Equestrian statue of Mussolini; 60 c. Land reclamation; 75 c. Colonial expansion; 1 l. Marine development; 1 l. 25, Italians abroad; 1 l. 75, Sport, 2 l. 55, Child Welfare; 2 l. 75. "O.N.D." Recreation; 5 l. Caesar's statue.

(b) Air.

366		50 c. brown	1·50	3·75
367		75 c. brown	4·50	11·00

DESIGNS: 50 c. Eagle (front of Air Ministry Building, Rome); 75 c. Aerial view of Italian cathedrals.

134 Airship "Graf Zeppelin"

1933. Air. "Graf Zeppelin" issue.

372	134	3 l. green and black	6·00	22·00
373	–	5 l. brown and green	6·00	22·00
374	–	10 l. blue and red	6·00	50·00
375	–	12 l. orange and blue	6·00	75·00
376	–	15 l. black and brown	6·00	90·00
377	–	20 l. blue and brown	6·00	£100

DESIGNS (all with airship): 3 l. S. Paola Gate and tomb of Consul Caius Cestius; 5 l. Appian Way and tomb of Cecilia Metella; 10 l. Portion of Mussolini Stadium; 12 l. S. Angelo Castle; 15 l. Forum Romanum; 20 l. Empire Way, Colosseum and Baths of Domitian.

Italian Flag

Italian Flag   King Victor Emmanuel III   "Flight"
135

Italian Flag   King Victor Emmanuel III   Rome—Chicago
136
(½-size illustrations)

1933. Air. Balbo Transatlantic Mass Formation Flight by Savoia Marchetti S-55X Flying Boats.

378	135	5 l. 25 + 19 l. 75 red, green and blue	42·00	£850
379	136	5 l. 25 + 44 l. 75 red, green and blue	42·00	£850

The first part of the illustration in each group is of the Registered Air Express label and has an abbreviation of one of the pilots' names overprinted on it; the second part is the stamp for Ordinary Postage and the third is the actual Air Mail stamp.

137 Athlete

1933. International University Games, Turin.

380	137	10 c. brown	20	30
381		20 c. red	20	35
382		50 c. violet	35	15
383		1 l. 25 blue	85	1·60

138 Dome of St. Peter's   139 St. Peter's and Church of the Holy Sepulchre

1933. "Holy Year". (a) Postage.

384	138	20 c. red	40	30
385	–	25 c. green	55	40
386	–	50 c. violet	40	15
387	138	1 l. 25 blue	75	65
388	–	2 l. 55 + 2 l. 50 black	2·25	45·00

DESIGNS: 25, 50 c. Angel with Cross; 2 l. 55, Cross with Doves of Peace.

(b) Air.

389	139	50 c. + 25 c. brown	60	6·00
390		75 c. + 50 c. purple	1·10	8·00

1934. Air. Rome–Buenos Aires Flight. Surch with airplane, **1934 XII PRIMO VOLO DIRETTO ROMA = BUENOS-AYRES TRIMOTORE "LOMBARDI MAZZOTTI"**, value and fasces.

391	113	2 l. on 2 l. yellow	1·50	28·00
392		3 l. on 2 l. green	1·50	35·00
393		5 l. on 2 l. red	1·50	42·00
394		10 l. on 2 l. violet	1·50	48·00

141 Anchor of the "Emmanuele Filiberto"   142 Antonio Pacinotti

1934. 10th Anniv of Annexation of Fiume.

395	141	10 c. brown (postage)	1·60	40
396		20 c. red	20	25
397	–	50 c. violet	20	15
398	–	1 l. 25 blue	20	75
399	–	1 l. 75 + 1 l. blue	35	21·00
400	–	2 l. 55 + 2 l. purple	45	24·00
401	–	2 l. 75 + 2 l. 50 olive	45	24·00

DESIGNS: 50 c. Gabriele d'Annunzio; 1 l. 25, St. Vito's Tower barricaded; 1 l. 75, Hands supporting crown of historical monuments; 2 l. 55, Victor Emmanuel III's arrival in the "Brindisi" (cruiser); 2 l. 75, Galley, gondola and battleship.

402		25 c. green (air)	20	1·00
403		50 c. brown	20	55
404		75 c. brown	20	1·25
405		1 l. + 50 c. purple	20	9·50
406		2 l. + 1 l. 50 blue	20	12·00
407		3 l. + 2 l. black	20	13·50

DESIGNS—Marina Fiat MF.5 flying boat over: 25, 75 c. Fiume Harbour; 50 c., 1 l. War Memorial; 2 l. Three Venetian lions; 3 l. Roman Wall.

1934. 75th Anniv of Invention of Pacinotti's Dynamo.

411	142	50 c. violet	40	15
412		1 l. 25 blue	60	1·25

143   145 Luigi Galvani

1934. World Cup Football Championship, Italy.

413	143	20 c. red (postage)	2·25	2·75
414	–	25 c. green	2·25	80
415	–	50 c. violet	2·25	30
416	–	1 l. 25 blue	8·50	4·00
417	–	5 l. + 2 l. 50 brown	40·00	£140

DESIGNS—VERT: 5 l. Players heading the ball. HORIZ: 25 c., 50 c., 1 l. 25, Two footballers.

418		50 c. red (air)	4·00	6·00
419		75 c. blue	7·00	7·50
420		5 l. + 2 l. 50 olive	21·00	70·00
421		10 l. + 5 l. brown	24·00	80·00

DESIGNS—HORIZ: 50 c. Marina Fiat MF.5 flying boat over Mussolini Stadium, Turin; 5 l. Marina Fiat MF.5 flying boat over Stadium, Rome. VERT: 75 c. Savoia Marchetti S-55X flying boat over footballer; 10 l. Marina Fiat MF.5 flying boat over Littoral Stadium, Bologna.

1934. 1st Int Congress of Electro-Radio-Biology.

422	145	30 c. brown on buff	50	40
423		75 c. red on pink	75	1·75

146 Military Symbol

148 King Victor Emmanuel III

1934. Military Medal Centenary.

424 **146** 10 c. brown (postage) . . . 55 55
425 – 15 c. green . . . . 65 1·00
426 – 20 c. red 55 35
427 – 25 c. green 85 35
428 – 30 c. brown . . . . 1·40 1·40
429 – 50 c. violet 85 20
430 – 75 c. red . . . . 3·50 1·50
431 – 1 l. 25 blue . . . . 2·75 85
432 – 1 l. 75 + 1 l. red . . . . 9·50 32·00
433 – 2 l. 55 + 2 l. purple . . . 10·00 35·00
434 – 2 l. 75 + 2 l. violet . . . . 11·00 35·00

DESIGNS—VERT: 25 c. Mountaineers; 1 l. 75, Cavalry. HORIZ: 15 c., 50 c. Barbed-wire cutter; 20 c. Throwing hand-grenade; 30 c. Cripple wielding crutch; 75 c. Artillery; 1 l. 25, Soldiers cheering; 2 l. 55, Sapper; 2 l. 75, First Aid.

435 25 c. green (air) . . . . 60 2·00
436 50 c. grey . . . . 60 2·25
437 75 c. brown . . . . 80 2·50
438 80 c. blue . . . . 1·10 3·00
439 1 l. + 50 c. brown . . . . . . 2·25 15·00
440 2 l. + 1 l. blue . . . . . . 3·50 17·00
441 3 l. + 2 l. black . . . . . . 4·75 19·00

DESIGNS—HORIZ: 25, 80 c. Italian "P" Type airship under fire; 50, 75 c. Naval launch; 1 l. Caproni Ca 101 airplane and troops in desert; 2 l. Pomilio PC type biplane and troops. VERT: 3 l. Unknown soldier's tomb.

1934. Air. Rome–Mogadiscio Flight and King's visit to Italian Somaliland.

444 **148** 1 l. violet . . . . 50 7·50
445 2 l. blue . . . . 50 9·50
446 4 l. brown . . . . 1·10 45·00
447 5 l. green . . . . 1·10 55·00
448 8 l. red . . . . 5·00 75·00
449 10 l. brown . . . . 5·00 85·00

149 Man with Fasces

150

1935. University Contests. Inscr "LITTORIALI".

450 **149** 20 c. red 15 30
451 – 30 c. brown . . . . . . 90 2·25
452 – 50 c. violet 15 15

DESIGNS: 30 c. Eagle and soldier. Standard-bearer and bayonet attack.

1935. National Militia. Inscr "PRO OPERA PREVID. MILIZIA".

453 **150** 20 c. + 10 c. red (post.) . . 2·75 4·75
454 – 25 c. + 15 c. green . . . . 2·75 5·50
455 – 50 c. + 30 c. violet . . . . 2·75 6·50
456 – 1 l. 25 + 75 c. blue . . . . 2·75 8·00
457 – 50 c. + 50 c. brown (air) . . 3·75 11·00

DESIGNS: 25 c. Roman standards; 50 c. Soldier and cross; 50 c. + 50 c. Wing over Globe; 1 l. 25, Soldiers and arch.

152 Symbol of Flight

153 Leonardo da Vinci

1935. International Aeronautical Exn, Milan.

458 **152** 20 c. red . . . . 2·25 55
459 30 c. brown . . . . 5·50 1·90
460 **153** 50 c. violet . . . . . . 11·00 20
461 1 l. 25 blue . . . . 8·00 1·00

MINIMUM PRICE

The minimum price quoted is 10p which represents a handling charge rather than a basis for valuing common stamps. For further notes about prices see introductory pages.

154 Vincenzo Bellini

155 "Music"

1935. Death Centenary of Bellini (composer).

462 **154** 20 c. red (postage) 75 45
463 30 c. brown . . . . 1·00 95
464 50 c. violet 75 20
465 1 l. 25 blue . . . . 3·00 1·25
466 – 1 l. 75 + 1 l. orange . . . 20·00 55·00
467 – 2 l. 75 + 2 l. olive . . . . 21·00 60·00

DESIGNS—VERT: 2 l. 75, Bellini's villa. HORIZ: 1 l. 75, Hands at piano.

468 **155** 25 c. brown (air) . . . . . 1·10 2·00
469 50 c. brown . . . . 1·10 2·00
470 60 c. red . . . . 1·90 2·50
471 – 1 l. + 1 l. violet . . . . . 7·50 48·00
472 – 5 l. + 2 l. green . . . . . 11·00 60·00

DESIGNS: 1 l. Angelic musicians; 5 l. Mountain landscape (Bellini's birthplace).

156 "Commerce" and Industrial Map of Italy

1936. 17th Milan Fair. Inscr as in T **156**.

473 **156** 20 c. red 20 30
474 – 30 c. brown 25 45
475 – 50 c. violet 20 20
476 **156** 1 l. 25 blue 50 70

DESIGN—HORIZ: 30 c., 50 c. Cog-Wheel and plough.

157 "Fertility"

1936. 2000th Birth Anniv of Horace.

477 **157** 10 c. green (postage) . . . 1·40 40
478 – 20 c. red . . . . 1·40 40
479 – 30 c. brown . . . . 1·40 70
480 – 50 c. violet . . . . 1·10 15
481 – 75 c. red . . . . 2·00 90
482 – 1 l. 25 + 1 l. blue . . . . 11·00 40·00
483 – 1 l. 75 + 1 l. red . . . . 13·00 50·00
484 – 2 l. 55 + 1 l. blue . . . . 15·00 55·00

DESIGNS—HORIZ: 20 c., 1 l. 25, Landscape; 75 c. Capitol; 2 l. 55, Dying gladiator. VERT: 30 c. Ajax defying lightning; 50 c. Horace; 1 l. 75, Pan.

485 – 25 c. green (air) . . . . . . 1·10 1·90
486 – 50 c. brown . . . . 1·60 1·90
487 – 60 c. red . . . . 1·90 3·50
488 – 1 l. + 1 l. violet . . . . . 7·00 50·00
489 – 5 l. + 2 l. green . . . . . 11·00 70·00

DESIGNS—HORIZ: 25 c. Savoia Marchetti S-55A flying boat; 50 c., 1 l. Caproni Ca 101 airplane over lake; 60 c. Eagle and oak tree; 5 l. Rome.

159

160

1937. Child Welfare. Inscr as in T **159/60**.

490 **159** 10 c. brown (postage) . . . 65 40
491 **160** 20 c. red 65 40
492 **159** 25 c. green 80 45
493 – 30 c. sepia . . . . 1·10 85
494 **160** 50 c. violet 65 20
495 – 75 c. red . . . . 3·50 1·25
496 **160** 1 l. 25 blue . . . . 4·25 1·25
497 – 1 l. 75 + 75 c. orange . . 19·00 50·00
498 – 2 l. 75 + 1 l. 25 green . . 14·00 55·00
499 **160** 5 l. + 3 l. blue . . . . . 16·00 60·00

DESIGNS—As Type **159**: 30 c., 1 l. 75, Boy between Fasces; 75 c., 2 l. 75, "Bambino" (after della Robbia).

500 – 25 c. green (air) . . . . . . 2·00 3·50
501 – 50 c. brown . . . . 2·75 3·50
502 – 1 l. violet . . . . 2·00 4·50
503 – 2 l. + 1 l. blue . . . . . . 8·50 50·00
504 – 3 l. + 2 l. orange . . . . . 10·00 55·00
505 – 5 l. + 3 l. red . . . . . . 11·00 60·00

DESIGNS—As Type **160**: 25 c., 1 l., 3 l. Little child with rifle. As Type **159**: 50 c., 2 l., 5 l. Children's heads.

163 Naval Memorial

164 Augustus the Great

1937. 2000th Birth Anniv of Augustus the Great.

506 **163** 10 c. green (postage) . . . 40 40
507 – 15 c. brown 40 45
508 – 20 c. red 40 40
509 – 25 c. green 40 40
510 – 30 c. brown 70 50
511 – 50 c. violet 40 15
512 – 75 c. red 75 80
513 – 1 l. 25 blue . . . . 1·10 80
514 – 1 l. 75 + 1 l. purple . . . 20·00 42·00
515 – 2 l. 55 + 2 l. black . . . . 21·00 45·00

DESIGNS—VERT: 15 c. Military trophies; 20 c. Reconstructing temples of Rome; 25 c. Census (with reference to birth of Jesus Christ); 30 c. Statue of Julius Caesar; 50 c. Election of Augustus as Emperor; 75 c. Head of Augustus (conquest of Ethiopia); 1 l. 25, Constructing new fleet; 1 l. 75, Building Altar of Peace; 2 l. 55, The Capitol.

516 – 25 c. purple (air) . . . . . 1·75 2·75
517 – 50 c. brown . . . . 1·75 2·00
518 – 80 c. brown . . . . 3·75 4·25
519 – 1 l. + 1 l. blue . . . . . 10·00 32·00
520 **164** 5 l. + 1 l. violet . . . . . 15·00 50·00

DESIGNS—HORIZ: 25 c. "Agriculture"; 50 c. Prosperity of the Romans; 80 c. Horses of the Sun Chariot; 1 l. Staff and map of ancient Roman Empire.

165 Gasparo Spontini (composer)

166 Marconi

1937. Famous Italians.

521 **165** 10 c. sepia 15 40
522 – 20 c. red 15 40
523 – 25 c. green 15 20
524 – 30 c. brown 15 60
525 – 50 c. violet 15 15
526 – 75 c. red 40 90
527 – 1 l. 25 blue 50 90
528 **165** 1 l. 75 orange 50 90
529 – 2 l. 55 + 2 l. green . . . . 4·00 38·00
530 – 2 l. 75 + 2 l. brown . . . . 4·00 38·00

DESIGNS: 20 c., 2 l. 55, Antonio Stradivarius (violin maker); 25, 50 c. Giacomo Leopardi (poet); 30, 75 c., Giovanni Battista Pergolesi (composer); 1 l. 25, 2 l. 75, Giotto di Bondone (painter and architect).

1938. Guglielmo Marconi (telegraphy pioneer) Commemoration.

531 **166** 20 c. red 40 35
532 50 c. violet 20 25
533 1 l. 25 blue . . . . 25 1·10

167 Founding of Rome

168 Victor Emmanuel III

1938. 2nd Anniv of Proclamation of Italian Empire.

534 **167** 10 c. brown (postage) . . . 35 20
535 – 20 c. red 35 20
536 – 25 c. green 35 20
537 – 30 c. brown 35 35
538 – 50 c. violet 35 15
539 – 75 c. red 45 35
540 – 1 l. 25 blue 70 35
541 – 1 l. 75 violet 80 45
542 – 2 l. 75 green . . . . . . 4·25 13·00
543 – 5 l. red . . . . 5·00 17·00

DESIGNS—VERT: 20 c. Emperor Augustus; 25 c. Dante; 30 c. Columbus; 50 c. Leonardo da Vinci; 75 c. Garibaldi and Victor Emmanuel II; 1 l. 25, Italian Unknown Warrior's Tomb; 1 l. 75, "March on Rome"; 2 l. 75, Wedding ring on map of Ethiopia; 5 l. Victor Emmanuel III.

544 **168** 25 c. green (air) . . . . . 70 1·10
545 – 50 c. brown . . . . 70 1·10
546 – 1 l. violet . . . . 85 1·25
547 – 2 l. blue . . . . 1·25 8·50
548 **168** 3 l. red . . . . 1·50 13·00
549 – 5 l. green . . . . 2·50 16·00

DESIGNS—HORIZ: 50 c., 1 l. Dante: 2, 5 l. Leonardo da Vinci.

169 Steam Locomotive and ETR 200 Express Train

170 Hitler and Mussolini

171 Hitler and Mussolini

172 Roman Cavalry

1939. Centenary of Italian Railways.

550 **169** 20 c. red 35 25
551 50 c. violet 45 15
552 1 l. 25 blue . . . . 75 1·25

1941. Italo-German Friendship.

553 **170** 10 c. brown 40 30
554 20 c. orange 40 30
555 25 c. green 40 30
556 **171** 50 c. violet 50 15
557 75 c. red 60 60
558 1 l. 25 blue 60 70

1941. 2000th Birth Anniv of Livy (Latin historian).

559 **172** 20 c. + 10 c. red 20 80
560 30 c. + 15 c. brown . . . 20 85
561 – 50 c. + 25 c. violet . . . . 25 1·00
562 – 1 l. 25 + 1 l. blue . . . . 25 1·25

DESIGN: 50 c., 1 l. 25, Roman legionary.

1942. War Propaganda. Nos. 244/5 and 247 with attached labels (imperf between stamp and label) to encourage war effort.

563 25 c. green (Navy) 10 60
564 25 c. green (Army) 10 60
565 25 c. green (Air Force) 10 60
566 25 c. green (Militia) 10 60
567 30 c. brown (Navy) . . . . . . 10 1·00
568 30 c. brown (Army) . . . . . . 10 1·00
569 30 c. brown (Air Force) . . . . 10 1·00
570 30 c. brown (Militia) . . . . . 10 1·00
571 50 c. violet (Navy) 10 30
572 50 c. violet (Army) 10 30
573 50 c. violet (Air Force) 10 30
574 50 c. violet (Militia) 10 30

173 Galileo teaching at Padua

174 Rossini

1942. Death Tercentenary of Galileo.

575 **173** 10 c. red and orange . . . 15 30
576 – 25 c. green and olive . . . 15 35
577 – 50 c. violet and purple . . 15 15
578 – 1 l. 25 blue and grey . . . 20 70

DESIGNS: Galileo at Venice (25 c.) and at Arcetri, near Florence (1 l. 25), 50 c. Portrait of Galileo.

1942. 150th Birth Anniv of Rossini (composer).

579 – 25 c. green 15 25
580 – 30 c. brown 15 30
581 **174** 50 c. violet 15 20
582 1 l. blue 15 55

DESIGN: 25 c., 30 c. Rossini Monument, Pescaro.

175

187 Romulus, Remus and Wolf (after Pollaiuolo)

1943. Allied Military Government issue.

583 **175** 15 c. orange 25 60
584 25 c. bistre 25 60
585 30 c. grey 25 60
586 50 c. violet 25 60
587 60 c. yellow 25 80
588 1 l. green . . . . 25 1·00
589 2 l. red . . . . 25 1·00
590 5 l. blue . . . . 25 2·00
591 10 l. brown . . . . 25 3·00

1943. Allied Military Government issue Stamps of 1929 optd **GOVERNO MILITARE ALLEATO**.

592 **99** 20 c. red . . . . 55 1·75
593 35 c. blue . . . . 4·50 15·00
594 **103** 50 c. violet . . . . 10 1·00

1944.

619 **187** 50 c. purple 10 15

1944. As issue of 1929, but with Fascist emblems removed.

633 – 10 c. brown (Augustus the Great) 10 10
640 **99** 20 c. red 10 10
620 **103** 30 c. brown 30 20
635 – 50 c. violet (Italia) 10 10
621 **103** 50 c. violet . . . . 30 1·00
636 – 60 c. orange (Italia) 10 10
641 **103** 60 c. green 10 10
637 **99** 1 l. violet 10 10
643 – 1 l. 20 brown (Italia) . . . 10 10
638 – 2 l. red (Italia) 10 10
645 **98** 5 l. red 10 10
646 – 10 l. violet (Italia) . . . . 1·00 2·50

1945. Stamps of Italy surch **L. 2,50** (No. 629) and stamps of Italian Social Republic surch **POSTE ITALIANE** and new value (Nos. 627/8).

627 1 l. 20 on 20 c. red (No. 102) . . 10 10
628 2 l. on 25 c. green (No. 103) . . 10 10
629 2 l. 50 on 1 l. 75 orange (No. 251) 10 10

193 "Work, Justice and Family"

195 Planting a Sapling

196 "Peace"

197 "Work Justice and Family"

1945.

647 – 10 c. brown 10 10
648 **193** 20 c. brown 10 10
649 – 25 c. blue 10 10
650 **195** 40 c. grey 10 10
651 – 50 c. violet 10 10
652 – 60 c. green 10 15
653 – 80 c. red 10 10
654 **195** 1 l. green 10 10
655 – 1 l. 20 brown 10 10
656 – 2 l. brown 10 10
657 – 3 l. red 10 10
658 – 4 l. red 25 10
659 **193** 5 l. blue 70 10
660 **195** 6 l. violet . . . . 3·75 10
661 – 8 l. green . . . . 1·75 10
662 – 10 l. grey 70 10
663 **193** 10 l. red . . . . 11·00 10
664 **195** 15 l. blue . . . . 5·00 10
665 – 20 l. purple 85 10
666 **196** 25 l. green . . . . . . 10·00 10
667 – 30 l. blue £225 10
668 **196** 50 l. purple . . . . . . 4·00 10
669 **197** 100 l. red . . . . £200 1·10

DESIGNS: 10, 50, 80 c., 8, 10 (662) l. Hammer breaking chain ("Freedom"); 25 c., 1 l. 20, 3, 4, 20, 30 l. Flaming torch ("Enlightenment"); 60 c., 2 l. Gardener tying sapling to stake.

198 Clasped Hands and Caproni Campini N-1 Jet

200 Amalfi

1945. Air.

670 **198** 1 l. grey 10 15
671 – 2 l. blue 25 10
672 **198** 3 l. 20 red 15 20
673 – 5 l. green 15 10
674 **198** 10 l. red 15 10
675 – 25 l. blue . . . . 14·00 10·00
676 – 25 l. brown 10 10
677 **198** 50 l. green . . . . . . 19·00 11·00
678 50 l. violet 15 10

DESIGN: 2, 5, 25 l. Barn swallows in flight.

1946. Mediaeval Italian Republics.

679 **200** 1 l. sepia 10 10
680 – 2 l. blue 10 10
681 – 3 l. green 10 10
682 – 4 l. orange 10 10
683 – 5 l. violet 10 10
684 – 10 l. red 10 10
685 – 15 l. blue 35 25
686 – 20 l. brown 20 15

DESIGNS—VERT: 2 l. Lucca; 3 l. Siena; 4 l. Florence. HORIZ: 5 l. Pisa; 10 l. Genoa; 15 l. Venice; 20 l. "The Oath of Pontida".

1947. Air. Surch **LIRE 6–**.

687 **198** 6 l. on 3 l. 20 orange . . . 15 10

202 Wireless Mast

204 Douglas DC-2 over Rome

1947. Air. 50th Anniv of Radio.

688 **202** 6 l. violet 15 10
689 – 10 l. red 15 10
690 – 20 l. orange 85 85
691 **202** 25 l. blue . . . . 1·00 1·00
692 – 35 l. blue . . . . 1·25 1·25
693 – 50 l. purple . . . . . . 2·25 2·25

DESIGNS: 10, 35 l. Ship's aerial; 20, 50 l. Heinkel He 70 Blitz wireless-equipped airplane.

1948. Air.

911 **204** 100 l. green 60 10
912 300 l. mauve 50 30
913 500 l. blue 70 55
914 1000 l. brown . . . . . . 1·50 1·25

For No. 911 in smaller size see No. 1297.

205 St. Catherine giving her Cloak to a Beggar

206 St. Catherine carrying the Cross

1948. 600th Birth Anniv of St. Catherine of Siena.

698 **205** 3 l. blue & green (postage) . 20 15
699 – 5 l. blue and violet 20 20
700 – 10 l. violet and brown . . 2·50 1·00
701 – 30 l. grey and bistre . . . 6·00 4·00
702 **206** 100 l. violet & brown (air) . 40·00 25·00
703 – 200 l. blue and bistre . . . 15·00 12·00

DESIGNS—All show St. Catherine. VERT: 5 l. Carrying the Cross; 10 l. Extending her arms to Italy; 30 l. Dictating "The Dialogue" to a Disciple. HORIZ: 200 l. Extending her arms to Italy.

207 "Proclamation of New Constitution"

1948. Proclamation of New Constitution.

704 **207** 10 l. violet 40 55
705 30 l. blue . . . . 2·00 1·25

208 Rising at Palermo

1948. Centenary of Revolution of 1848.

706 **208** 3 l. brown 50 20
707 – 4 l. purple 50 20
708 – 5 l. blue . . . . 1·60 25
709 – 6 l. green 85 75
710 – 8 l. brown 95 50
711 – 10 l. red . . . . 2·00 25
712 – 12 l. green . . . . 4·75 1·75
713 – 15 l. black . . . . 13·00 70
714 – 20 l. red . . . . 30·00 6·00
715 – 30 l. blue . . . . 6·00 55
716 – 50 l. violet . . . . . . 80·00 2·00
717 – 100 l. blue . . . . £110 17·00

DESIGNS: 4 l. Rising at Padua; 5 l. Concession of Statute, Turin; 6 l. Storming Porta Tosa, Milan; 8 l. Proclamation of Venetian Republic; 10 l. Defence of Vicenza; 12 l. Hero of Curtatone; 15 l. Hero of Goito; 20 l. Austrian retreat from Bologna; 30 l. Fighting at Brescia; 50 l. Garibaldi; 100 l. Goffredo Mameli (party patriot) on death bed, July 1849.

209 Alpinist and Bassano Bridge

210 Gaetano Donizetti

1948. Rebuilding of Bassano Bridge.

718 **209** 15 l. green . . . . 1·40 1·25

1948. Death Centenary of Donizetti (composer).

719 **210** 15 l. brown . . . . 1·40 1·10

211 Exhibition Grounds

212

1949. 27th Milan Fair.

720 **211** 20 l. sepia . . . . 6·25 1·60

1949. 25th Biennial Art Exhibition. Venice.

721 **212** 5 l. red and flesh 25 20
722 – 15 l. green and cream . . . 2·00 1·10
723 – 20 l. brown and buff . . . 8·00 20
724 – 50 l. blue and yellow . . . 30·00 1·10

DESIGNS: 15 l. Clock bell-ringers, St. Mark's Column and Campanile; 20 l. Emblem of Venice and "Bucentaur" (state gallery); 50 l. Winged lion on St. Mark's Column.

213 Globes and Forms of Transport

1949. 75th Anniv of U.P.U.

725 **213** 50 l. blue . . . . 55·00 4·25

214 Vascello Castle

1949. Centenary of Roman Republic.

726 **214** 100 l. brown . . . . . . £200 60·00

215 Worker and Ship

216 Statue of Mazzini

1949. European Recovery Plan.

727 **215** 5 l. green . . . . 4·00 3·75
728 15 l. violet . . . . 18·00 14·00
729 20 l. brown . . . . 85·00 15·00

1949. Honouring Giuseppe Mazzini (founder of "Young Italy").

730 **216** 20 l. black . . . . 7·50 1·25

217 V. Alfieri

218 San Giusto Cathedral

1949. Birth Bicentenary of Vittorio Alfieri (poet).

731 **217** 20 l. brown . . . . 7·00 1·25

1949. First Trieste Free Election.

732 **218** 20 l. lake . . . . 10·00 8·00

219 Staff of Aesculapius and Globe

220 A. Palladio and Vicenza Basilica

1949. 2nd World Health Congress, Rome.

733 **219** 20 l. violet . . . . 26·00 7·50

1949. 400th Anniv of Completion of Palladio's Basilica at Vicenza.

734 **220** 20 l. violet . . . . 14·00 5·00

221 Lorenzo de Medici

222 Galleon and Exhibition Buildings

1949. 500th Birth Anniv of Lorenzo de Medici "The Magnificent".

735 **221** 20 l. blue . . . . 10·00 1·25

1949. 13th Levant Fair, Bari.

736 **222** 20 l. red . . . . 6·00 1·25

223 Voltaic Pile

224 Count Alessandro Volta

1949. 150th Anniv of Volta's Discovery of the Electric Cell.

737 **223** 20 l. red . . . . 4·00 1·25
738 **224** 50 l. blue . . . . £100 26·00

225 Holy Trinity Bridge, Florence

226 Caius Valerius Catullus

1949. Rebuilding of Holy Trinity Bridge Florence.

739 **225** 20 l. green . . . . 12·00 1·25

1949. Death Bimillenary of Catullus (poet).

740 **226** 20 l. blue . . . . 12·00 1·25

227 Domenico Cimarosa

228 Entrance to Exhibition

1949. Birth Bicentenary of Cimarosa (composer).

741 **227** 20 l. violet . . . . 10·00 90

1950. 28th Milan Fair.

742 **228** 20 l. brown . . . . 2·25 90

229 Car and Flags

1950. 32nd Int Automobile Exhibition, Turin.

743 **229** 20 l. violet . . . . 10·00 90

230 Statue of Perseus

231 St. Peter's Basilica

1950. 5th General U.N.E.S.C.O. Conference, Florence.

744 – 20 l. green . . . . 4·00 1·10
745 **230** 55 l. blue . . . . 35·00 4·00

DESIGN—HORIZ: 20 l. Pitti Palace, Florence.

1950. Holy Year.

746 **231** 20 l. violet . . . . 3·00 50
747 55 l. blue . . . . 40·00 1·25

232 Gaudenzio Ferrari

233 Town Hall, Florence, Statue of Columbus and Wireless Mast

1950. Honouring Gaudenzio Ferrari (painter).

748	**232**	20 l. green	14·00	1·50

1950. International Radio Conf, Florence.

749	**233**	20 l. violet	10·00	4·00
750		55 l. blue	£140	60·00

234 L. Muratori

1950. Death Bicentenary of Ludovico Muratori (historian).

751	**234**	20 l. brown	7·00	1·25

235 Guido D'Arezze

236 Galleon

1950. 9th Death Cent of D'Arezzo (musician).

752	**235**	20 l. green	15·00	1·25

1950. 14th Levant Fair, Bari.

753	**236**	20 l. brown	10·00	1·25

237 Marzotto and Rossi

238 Tobacco Plant and Factory

1950. Pioneers of Wool Industry.

754	**237**	20 l. blue	80	65

1950. European Tobacco Conference, Rome.

755	**238**	5 l. green and mauve	80	1·60
756	–	20 l. green and brown	2·25	65
757	–	55 l. brown and blue	45·00	10·00

DESIGNS: 20 l. Plant; 55 l. Girl and plant.

239 Seal of Academy

240 A. Righi

1950. Bicentenary of Academy of Fine Arts, Venice.

758	**239**	20 l. lt brown & brown	4·00	1·00

1950. Birth Centenary of Augusto Righi (physicist).

759	**240**	20 l. black and buff	2·75	1·25

INDEX

Countries can be quickly located by referring to the index at the end of this volume.

241 Blacksmith

1950. Provincial Occupations. As T **241**.

760	**241**	50 c. blue	10	10
881	–	1 l. violet	10	10
762	–	2 l. brown	10	10
763	–	5 l. black	50	10
764	–	6 l. brown	25	10
765	–	10 l. green	4·75	10
766	–	12 l. green	2·00	10
883	–	15 l. blue	60	10
768	–	20 l. violet	10·00	10
769	–	25 l. brown	3·25	10
770	–	30 l. purple	1·90	10
771	–	35 l. red	8·50	35
772	–	40 l. brown	55	10
773	–	50 l. violet	14·00	10
774	–	55 l. blue	80	10
775	–	60 l. red	4·50	25
776	–	65 l. green	90	10
777	–	100 l. brown	30·00	10
778	–	200 l. brown	16·00	15

DESIGNS: 1 l. Motor mechanic; 2 l. Stonemason; 5 l. Potter; 6 l. Girls embroidering and water-carrying; 10 l. Weaver; 12 l. Fisherman at tiller; 15 l. Boat builder; 20 l. Fisherman trawling; 25 l. Girl packing oranges; 30 l. Girl carrying grapes; 35 l. Gathering olives; 40 l. Carter and wagon; 50 l. Shepherd; 55 l. Ploughman; 60 l. Ox-cart; 65 l. Girl harvester; 100 l. Women handling maize; 200 l. Woodcutter.

242 First Tuscan Stamp

243 Car and Flags

1951. Centenary of First Tuscan Stamp.

779	**242**	20 l. red and purple	1·25	80
780		55 l. blue & ultramarine	20·00	14·00

1951. 33rd International Motor Show, Turin.

781	**243**	20 l. green	14·00	1·60

244 Peace Hall, Rome

1951. Consecration of Hall of Peace, Rome.

782	**244**	20 l. violet	8·75	1·60

245 Westland W.81 Helicopter over Fair

246 Fair Building

1951. 29th Milan Fair.

783	**245**	20 l. brown	10·00	1·10
784	**246**	55 l. blue	30·00	20·00

247 Allegory

248 Columbus disembarking

1951. 10th International Textile Art and Fashion Exhibition, Turin.

785	**247**	20 l. violet	16·00	1·75

1951. 500th Birth Anniv of Columbus.

786	**248**	20 l. green	20·00	2·25

249 Gymnastics Symbols

250 Montecassino Abbey restored

1951. Int. Gymnastic Festival, Florence.

787	**249**	5 l. red and brown	18·00	£150
788		10 l. red and green	18·00	£150
789		15 l. red and blue	18·00	£150

1951. Restoration of Montecassino Abbey.

790	**250**	20 l. violet	3·50	90
791	–	55 l. blue	40·00	16·00

DESIGN: 55 l. Abbey in ruins, 1944.

251 Perugino

252 Modern Art

1951. 500th Birth Anniv of Perugino (painter).

792	**251**	20 l. brown and sepia	3·25	2·00

1951. Triennial Art Exhibition, Milan.

793	**252**	20 l. black and green	4·75	1·75
794	–	55 l. pink and blue	20·00	16·00

DESIGN—HORIZ: 55 l. Jug and symbols.

253 Cyclist and Globe

254 Galleon and Hemispheres

1951. World Cycling Championship.

795	**253**	25 l. black	3·00	1·60

1951. 15th Levant Fair, Bari.

796	**254**	25 l. blue	5·50	1·25

255 "Jorio's Daughter"

1951. Birth Centenary of Francesco Paolo Michetti (painter).

797	**255**	25 l. brown	6·00	1·25

256 T 1 of Sardinia and Arms of Cagliari

1951. Sardinian Postage Stamp Centenary.

798	**256**	10 l. black and sepia	1·00	1·75
799	–	25 l. green and red	1·50	1·00
800	–	60 l. red and blue	9·00	7·00

DESIGNS: 25 l. 20 c. stamp and arms of Genoa; 60 l. 40 c. stamp and arms of Turin.

257 "Industry and Commerce"

258 Census in Ancient Rome

1951. 3rd Industrial and Commercial Census.

801	**257**	10 l. green	1·25	1·25

1951. 9th National Census.

802	**258**	25 l. black	1·75	1·00

259 G. Verdi and Roncole Church

260 Mountain Forest

1951. 50th Death Anniv of Giuseppe Verdi (composer).

803	–	10 l. green and purple	1·50	1·00
804	**259**	25 l. brown & chocolate	6·00	1·00
805	–	60 l. blue and green	20·00	9·00

DESIGNS: 10 l. Verdi, Theatre Royal and Cathedral, Parma; 60 l. Verdi, La Scala Opera House and Cathedral, Milan.

1951. Forestry Festival. Inscr "FESTA DEGLI ALBERI".

806	**260**	10 l. green and olive	1·75	1·75
807	–	25 l. green	3·50	75

DESIGN—HORIZ: 25 l. Tree and wooded hills.

261 V. Bellini

262 Royal Palace, Caserta

1952. 150th Birth Anniv of Bellini (composer).

808	**261**	25 l. black	2·50	50

1952. Bicentenary of Construction of Caserta Palace by Vanvitelli.

809	**262**	25 l. bistre and green	2·75	50

263

264 Motor-boat Pavilion

1952. 1st Int Sports Stamps Exhibition, Rome.

810	**263**	25 l. brown and black	90	65

1952. 30th Milan Fair.

811	**264**	60 l. blue	8·00	6·00

265 Leonardo da Vinci

267 Campaniles and First Stamps

1952. 500th Birth Anniv of Leonardo da Vinci.

812	**265**	25 l. orange	35	10
813	–	60 l. blue	3·00	3·75
814	**265**	80 l. red	18·00	30

DESIGN — (inscr "LEONARDO DA VINCI 1452–1952"): 60 l. "The Virgin of the Rocks".

1952. Modena and Parma Stamp Centenary.

815	**267**	25 l. black and brown	80	65
816		60 l. indigo and blue	5·00	5·00

268 Hand, Torch and Globe

269 Lion of St. Mark

1952. Overseas Fair, Naples.

817	**268**	25 l. blue	1·40	50

1952. 26th Biennial Art Exhibition, Venice.

818	**269**	25 l. black and cream	1·40	50

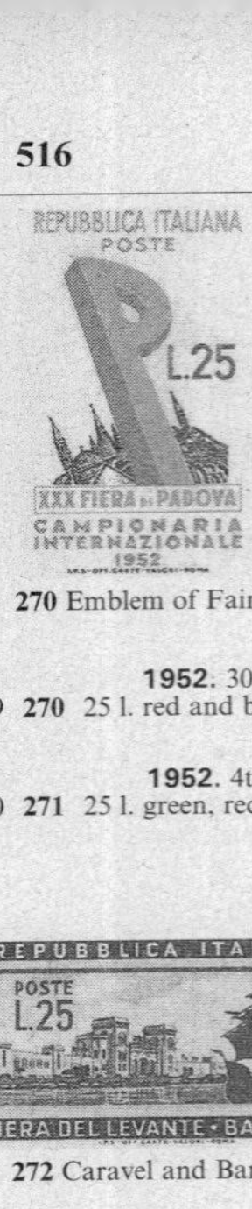

270 Emblem of Fair

271 San Giusto Cathedral and Flag

1952. 30th Padua Fair.
819 **270** 25 l. red and blue . . . . . 2·25 60

1952. 4th Trieste Fair.
820 **271** 25 l. green, red & brown . 1·75 60

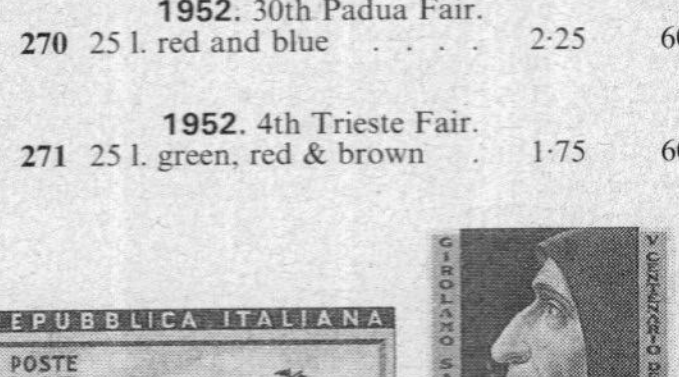

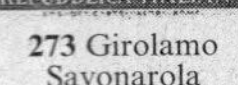

272 Caravel and Bari Fair

273 Girolamo Savonarola

1952. 16th Levant Fair, Bari.
821 **272** 25 l. green . . . . 1·60 60

1952. 5th Birth Cent of Savonarola (reformer).
822 **273** 25 l. violet . . . . 2·50 60

274 Savoia Marchetti S.M.95C over Colosseum

275 Alpine Climbing Equipment

1952. 1st Civil Aeronautics Law Conf, Rome.
823 **274** 60 l. blue & ultramarine . . 16·00 14·00

1952. Alpine Troops National Exhibition.
824 **275** 25 l. black . . . . 1·00 40

276 Army, Navy and Air Force Symbols

277 Sailor, Soldier and Airman

1952. Armed Forces Day.
825 **276** 10 l. green 15 10
826 **277** 25 l. sepia and brown . . . 35 10
827 – 60 l. black and blue . . . 3·00 2·50
DESIGN—As Type **277**: 60 l. Airplane, motor torpedo boat and tank.

278 Cardinal Massaia and Map

279 V. Gemito

1952. Centenary of Mission to Ethiopia.
828 **278** 25 l. dp brown & brown . . 1·60 1·00

1952. Birth Centenary of Gemito (sculptor).
829 **279** 25 l. brown . . . . 1·25 45

280 A. Mancini

281

1952. Birth Centenary of Mancini (painter).
830 **280** 25 l. myrtle . . . . 1·25 45

1952. Centenary of Martyrdom of Belfiore.
831 **281** 25 l. blue and black . . . 1·60 45

282 Antonello da Messina

283 Cars Racing

1953. Antonello Exhibition, Messina.
832 **282** 25 l. red . . . . 1·50 45

1953. 20th "Mille Miglia" Car Race.
833 **283** 25 l. violet . . . . 1·25 50

284 Bee and Medals

285 Arcangelo Corelli

286 Coin of Syracuse

1953. Creation of Orders of Meritorious Labour.
834 **284** 25 l. violet . . . . 1·00 45

1953. Birth Tercentenary of Corelli (composer).
835 **285** 25 l. brown . . . . 1·50 45

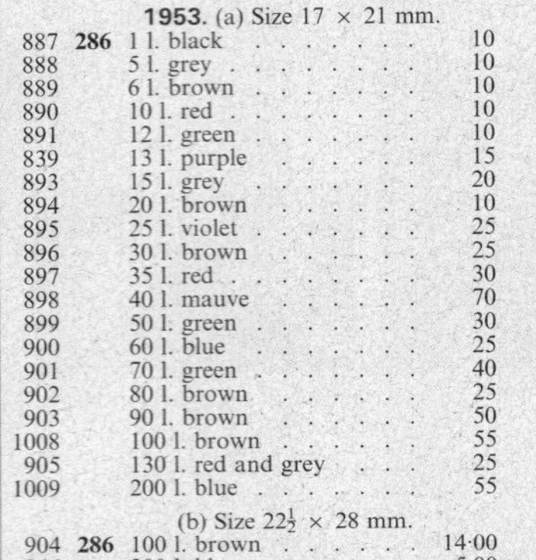

1953. (a) Size 17 × 21 mm.
887 **286** 1 l. black 10 10
888 5 l. grey 10 10
889 6 l. brown 10 10
890 10 l. red 10 10
891 12 l. green 10 10
839 13 l. purple 15 10
893 15 l. grey 20 10
894 20 l. brown 10 10
895 25 l. violet 25 10
896 30 l. brown 25 10
897 35 l. red 30 10
898 40 l. mauve 70 10
899 50 l. green 30 10
900 60 l. blue 25 10
901 70 l. green 40 10
902 80 l. brown 25 10
903 90 l. brown 50 10
1008 100 l. brown 55 10
905 130 l. red and grey 25 10
1009 200 l. blue 55 10

(b) Size $22\frac{1}{2}$ × 28 mm.
904 **286** 100 l. brown . . . . . . 14·00 10
846 200 l. blue . . . . 5·00 30
See also Nos. 1202/19b.

287 St. Clare of Assisi

288 Mountains and Reservoirs

289 "Agriculture"

1953. 700th Death Anniv of St. Clare.
847 **287** 25 l. red and brown . . . 85 30

1953. Mountains Festival.
848 **288** 25 l. green . . . . 2·50 30

1953. International Agricultural Exn, Rome.
849 **289** 25 l. brown . . . . 1·25 10
850 60 l. blue . . . . 4·00 1·50

290 Rainbow over Atlantic

291 L. Signorelli

1953. 4th Anniv of Atlantic Pact.
851 **290** 25 l. turquoise & orange . . 4·00 20
852 60 l. blue and mauve . . . 11·00 2·50

1953. 500th Birth Anniv of Signorelli (painter).
853 **291** 25 l. green and brown . . . 55 20

292 A. Bassi

293 Capri

1953. 6th Int Microbiological Congress, Rome.
854 **292** 25 l. brown and black . . . 85 20

1953. Tourist Series.
855 – 10 l. brown and sepia . . . 10 10
856 – 12 l. black and blue . . . 15 15
857 – 20 l. brown and orange . . 40 10
858 – 25 l. green and blue . . . 1·25 10
859 – 35 l. brown and buff . . . 2·00 20
860 **293** 60 l. blue and green . . . 3·00 50
DESIGNS—VERT: 10 l. Siena; 25 l. Cortina d'Ampezzo. HORIZ: 12 l. Rapallo; 20 l. Gardone; 35 l. Taormina.

294 Lateran Palace

295 Television Aerial and Screen

1954. 25th Anniv of Lateran Treaty.
861 **294** 25 l. brown and sepia . . . 65 15
862 60 l. blue and bright blue . 2·25 1·50

1954. Introduction of Television in Italy.
863 **295** 25 l. violet . . . . 1·00 15
864 60 l. turquoise . . . . . . 4·50 2·00

296 "Everyone Must Contribute to the Public Expense"

297 Vertical Flight Trophy

1954. "Encouragement to Taxpayers".
865 **296** 25 l. violet . . . . 2·50 15

1954. 1st Experimental Helicopter Mail Flight, Milan–Turin.
866 **297** 25 l. green 85 55

298 Golden Eagle and Campanile

299 A. Catalani

1954. 10th Anniv of Resistance Movement.
867 **298** 25 l. black and brown . . . 40 20

1954. Birth Centenary of Catalani (composer).
868 **299** 25 l. green 50 20

300 Marco Polo, Lion of St. Mark, Venice, and Dragon Pillar, Peking

1954. 7th Birth Centenary of Marco Polo.
869 **300** 25 l. brown 50 20
870 60 l. green . . . . 3·25 2·25

301 Cyclist, Car and Landscape

1954. 60th Anniv of Italian Touring Club.
871 **301** 25 l. green and red 70 20

302 "St. Michael the Archangel" (after Guido Reni)

303 "Pinocchio"

304 Amerigo Vespucci

1954. International Police Congress, Rome.
872 **302** 25 l. red . . . . 1·00 10
873 60 l. blue . . . . 1·75 1·50

1954. 64th Death Anniv of Carlo Lorenzini (Collodi) (writer).
874 **303** 25 l. red 50 20

1954. 5th Birth Cent of Vespucci (explorer).
875 **304** 25 l. purple 45 10
876 60 l. blue . . . . 2·50 1·25

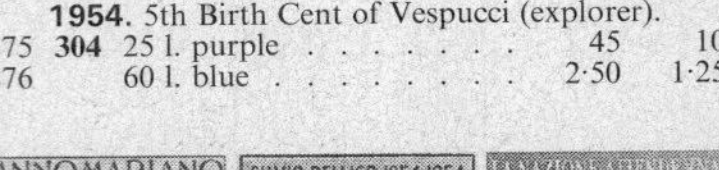

305 "Madonna" (Perugino)

306 Silvio Pellico

308 "The Nation Expects a Faithful Declaration of Your Income"

1954. Termination of Marian Year.
877 **305** 25 l. brown and buff . . . 30 15
878 – 60 l. black and cream . . . 1·60 1·25
DESIGN: 60 l. Madonna's head (Michelangelo).

1955. Death Centenary of Pellico (dramatist).
879 **306** 25 l. blue and violet . . . 55 20

1955. "Encouragement to Taxpayers".
907 **308** 25 l. lilac . . . . 2·25 10

309

310 A. Rosmini

1955. 4th World Petroleum Congress.
908 **309** 25 l. green . . . . 1·00 10
909 – 60 l. red . . . . 1·75 1·25
DESIGN: 60 l. Oil derricks and globe.

1955. Death Cent of Rosmini (theologian).
910 **310** 25 l. brown 65 15

311 Girolamo Fracastoro (physician) and Roman Arena, Verona

1955. International Medical Conf, Verona.
915 **311** 25 l. brown and black . . . 65 15

312 Basilica of St. Francis

313 Scholar and Drawing-board

1955. Bicentenary of Elevation of Basilica of St. Francis of Assisi to Papal Chapel.
916 **312** 25 l. black and cream . . . 35 15

1955. Centenary of "Montani" Institute, Fermo.
917 **313** 25 l. green 30 15

314 "The Harvester" **315** F.A.O. Building, Rome

1955. 50th Anniv of Int Agricultural Institute.
918 **314** 25 l. brown and red 30 15

1955. 10th Anniv of F.A.O.
919 **315** 60 l. violet and black 85 60

316 G. Matteotti **317** B. Grassi

1955. 70th Birth Anniv of Giacomo Matteotti (politician).
920 **316** 25 l. red 70 15

1955. 30th Death Anniv of Grassi (biologist).
921 **317** 25 l. green 50 15

318 "St. Stephen giving Alms to the Poor" **319** G. Pascoli

1955. 5th Death Cent of Fra Angelico (painter).
922 **318** 10 l. black and cream 20 10
923 – 25 l. blue and cream 35 10
DESIGN—HORIZ: 25 l. "St. Lawrence giving goods of the Church to the poor".

1955. Birth Centenary of Pascoli (poet).
924 **319** 25 l. black 40 15

320 G. Mazzini **321** "Italia" Ski-jump

1955. Air. 150th Birth Anniv of Mazzini (founder of "Young Italy").
925 **320** 100 l. green 2·25 1·00

1956. 7th Winter Olympic Games, Cortina d'Ampezzo.
926 **321** 10 l. green and orange 10 10
927 – 12 l. black and yellow 15 20
928 – 25 l. purple and orange 15 10
929 – 60 l. blue and orange 2·25 1·10
DESIGNS: 12 l. Snow Stadium; 25 l. Ice Stadium; 60 l. Skating Arena, Misurina.

1956. Air. Italian President's Visit to U.S.A. and Canada. Surch **1956 Visita del Presidente della Repubblica negli U.S.A. e nel Canada L. 120**.
930 **198** 120 l. on 50 l. mauve 1·25 1·90

323 Coach and Steam Train

1956. 50th Anniv of Simplon Tunnel.
931 **323** 25 l. green 5·00 20

324

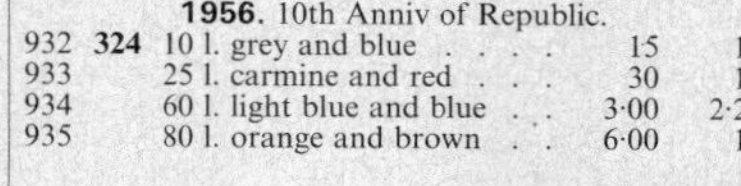

1956. 10th Anniv of Republic.
932 **324** 10 l. grey and blue 15 10
933 25 l. carmine and red 30 10
934 60 l. light blue and blue 3·00 2·25
935 80 l. orange and brown 6·00 15

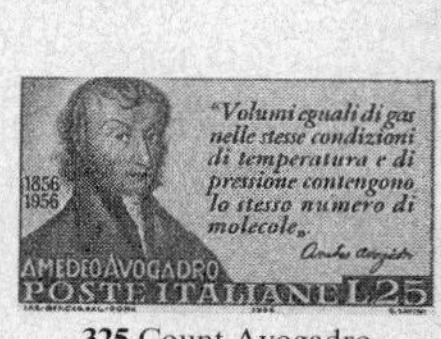

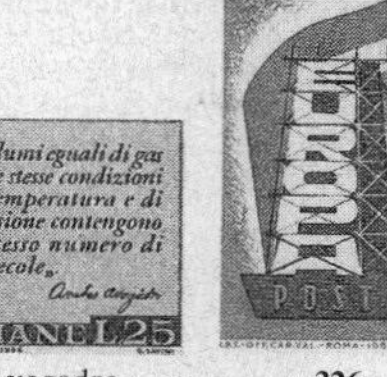

325 Count Avogadro **326**

1956. Death Centenary of Avogadro (physicist).
936 **325** 25 l. black 30 10

1956. Europa.
937 **326** 25 l. deep green & green 80 10
938 60 l. deep blue and blue 8·00 35

327 **328** The Globe

1956. Int Astronautical Congress, Rome.
939 **327** 25 l. blue 30 10

1956. 1st Anniv of Admission to U.N.
940 **328** 25 l. red & green on pink 15 10
941 60 l. green & red on green 30 10

329 Savings Bank, Books and Certificates **330** Ovid

1956. 80th Anniv of Post Office Savings Bank.
942 **329** 25 l. blue and slate 20 10

1957. Birth Bimillenary of Ovid (poet).
943 **330** 25 l. black and olive 30 10

331 St. George (after Donatello) **332** Antonio Canova

1957.
944 **331** 500 l. green 1·60 10
945a 1000 l. red 2·25 20

1957. Birth Bicentenary of Canova (sculptor).
946 **332** 25 l. brown 15 10
947 – 60 l. slate 25 30
948 – 80 l. blue 25 15
DESIGNS—VERT: 60 l. Hercules and Lica. HORIZ: 80 l. Pauline Borghese (bust).

333 Traffic Lights at Crossroads **334** "Europa" Flags

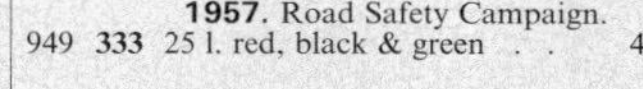

1957. Road Safety Campaign.
949 **333** 25 l. red, black & green 40 10

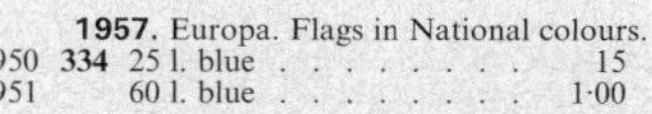

1957. Europa. Flags in National colours.
950 **334** 25 l. blue 15 10
951 60 l. blue 1·00 20

335 Giosue Carducci **336** Filippino Lippi (after self-portrait)

1957. 50th Death Anniv of Carducci (poet).
954 **335** 25 l. sepia 30 10

1957. 500th Birth Anniv of Filippino Lippi (painter).
955 **336** 25 l. brown 20 10

337 Cicero (bust) **338** Garibaldi (after M. Lorusso)

1957. 2,000th Death Anniv of Cicero (statesman).
956 **337** 25 l. red 25 10

1957. 150th Birth Anniv of Garibaldi.
957 **338** 15 l. grey 10 10
958 – 110 l. lilac 45 25
DESIGN—HORIZ: 110 l. Statue of Garibaldi on horseback (after Romanelli).

339 St. Domenico Savio and Youths **340** St. Francis of Paola

1957. Death Centenary of St. Domenico Savio.
959 **339** 15 l. black and violet 10 10

1957. 450th Death Anniv of St. Francis of Paola.
960 **340** 25 l. black 30 10

341 Dams, Peasant and Map of Sardinia **342** Statue of the Holy Virgin and Lourdes Basilica

1958. Inaug of Flumendosa—Mulargia Irrigation Scheme, Sardinia.
961 **341** 25 l. turquoise 10 10

1958. Centenary of Apparition of Virgin Mary at Lourdes.
962 **342** 15 l. purple 10 10
963 60 l. blue 15 10

343 "The Constitution" **344** Exhibition Emblem and Ancient Roman Road

1958. 10th Anniv of Constitution.
964 **343** 25 l. green and brown 10 10
965 – 60 l. sepia and blue 15 10
966 – 110 l. sepia and brown 40 15
DESIGNS—VERT: 60 l. Oak tree with new growth. HORIZ: 110 l. Montecitorio Palace, Rome.

1958. Brussels International Exhibition.
967 **344** 60 l. yellow and blue 10 10

345 Rodolfo's Attic ("La Boheme") **346** The Prologue ("I Pagliacci")

1958. Birth Centenary of Puccini (operatic composer).
968 **345** 25 l. blue 30 10

1958. Birth Centenary of Leoncavallo (operatic composer).
969 **346** 25 l. red and indigo 40 10

347 "Ave Maria" (after Segantini) **348** "Fattori in his Studio" (self-portrait)

1958. Birth Centenary of Giovanni Segantini (painter).
970 **347** 110 l. green on cream 35 15

1958. 50th Death Anniv of Giovanni Fattori (painter).
971 **348** 110 l. brown 50 20

349 Federal Palace, Brasilia and Arch of Titus, Rome **349a** "Europa"

1958. Visit of Pres. Gronchi to Brazil.
972 **349** 175 l. green 90 1·25

1958. Europa.
973 **349a** 25 l. blue and red 10 10
974 60 l. red and blue 30 10

350 Naples ½ grano stamp of 1858 **351** "Winged Horse" (sculpture in Sorrento Cathedral)

1958. 1st Naples Postage Stamps Centenary.
975 **350** 25 l. brown 10 10
976 – 60 l. brown and sepia 20 10
DESIGN: 60 l. Naples 1 grano stamp of 1858.

1958. Visit of Shah of Iran.
977 **351** 25 l. sepia & lavender 10 10
978 60 l. blue & pale blue 35 50

352 E. Torricelli **353** "Triumphs of Julius Caesar" (after fresco by Mantegna)

1958. 350th Birth Anniv of Evangelista Torricelli (physicist).
979 **352** 25 l. red 60 30

1958. 40th Anniv of Victory in World War I.
980 **353** 15 l. green 10 10
981 – 25 l. slate 10 10
982 – 60 l. red 15 15
DESIGNS—HORIZ: 25 l. Arms of Trieste, Rome and Trento. VERT: 60 l. Memorial bell of Rovereto.

354 Eleonora Duse

355 "Drama"

1958. Birth Centenary of Eleonora Duse (actress).
983 **354** 25 l. blue 15 10

1958. 10th Anniv of "Premio Italia" (international contest for radio and television plays).
984 **355** 25 l. black, blue & red . . 10 10
985 – 60 l. black and blue . . . 15 10
DESIGN: 60 l. "Music" (radio mast and grand piano).

356 Sicily 5 gr. stamp of 1859

357 Capitol, Quirinal Square Obelisk and Dome of St. Peter's

1959. 1st Sicilian Postage Stamps Centenary.
986 – 25 l. turquoise 10 10
987 **356** 60 l. orange 20 10
DESIGN: 25 l. Sicily 2 gr. stamp of 1859.

1959. 30th Anniv of Lateran Treaty.
988 **357** 25 l. blue 10 10

358 N.A.T.O. Emblem and Map

1959. 10th Anniv of N.A.T.O.
989 **358** 25 l. blue and yellow . . . 10 10
990 60 l. blue and green . . . 20 15

359 Arms of Paris and Rome

360 Olive Branch growing from shattered Tree

1959. Rome–Paris Friendship.
991 **359** 15 l. red, brown & blue . . 15 10
992 25 l. red, brown & blue . . 15 10

1959. Int War Veterans' Assn Convention, Rome.
993 **360** 25 l. green 10 10

361 Lord Byron Monument

362 C. Prampolini

1959. Unveiling of Lord Byron Monument, Rome.
994 **361** 15 l. green 10 10

1959. Birth Centenary of Camillo Prampolini (politician).
995 **362** 15 l. red . . . . 1·25 10

363 Quirinal Square Obelisk, Rome

364 Victor Emmanuel II, Garibaldi, Cavour and Mazzini

1959. Olympic Games Propaganda. Roman Monuments and Ruins. Inscr "ROMA MCMLX".
996 **363** 15 l. sepia and orange . . 15 10
997 – 25 l. sepia and blue . . . 15 10
998 – 35 l. sepia and buff . . . 20 10
999 – 60 l. sepia and mauve . . 30 15
1000 – 110 l. sepia and yellow . . 40 15
DESIGNS—VERT: 25 l. Tower of City Hall, Quirinal Hill. HORIZ: 35 l. Baths of Caracalla; 60 l. Arch of Constantine (Colosseum); 110 l. Basilica of Massentius.

1959. Centenary of 2nd War of Independence.
1001 **364** 15 l. black 10 10
1002 – 25 l. red and brown . . . 15 10
1003 – 35 l. violet 15 15
1004 – 60 l. blue 15 15
1005 – 110 l. lake 20 15
DESIGNS—VERT: 25 l. Italian camp after the Battle of Magenta (after painting by Fattori); 110 l. Battle of Magenta (after painting by Induno). HORIZ: 35 l. Battle of San Fermo (after painting by Trezzini); 60 l. Battle of Palestro.
The 25 l. is also a Red Cross commemorative.

365 Workers' Monument and I.L.O. Building, Geneva

366 Romagna 8 b. Stamp of 1859

1959. 40th Anniv of I.L.O.
1006 **365** 25 l. violet 10 10
1007 60 l. brown 10 10

1959. Romagna Postage Stamps Centenary.
1010 **366** 25 l. brown and black . . . 10 10
1011 – 60 l. green and black . . . 10 10
DESIGN: 60 l. Romagna 20 b. stamp of 1859.

366a "Europa"

367

1959. Europa.
1012 **366a** 25 l. green 10 10
1013 60 l. blue 10 10

1959. Stamp Day.
1014 **367** 15 l. red, black & grey . . 10 10

368 "The Fire of Borgo" (after Raphael)

369 Garibaldi's Message to Sicilians

1960. World Refugee Year.
1015 **368** 25 l. red 10 10
1016 60 l. purple 10 10

1960. Cent of Garibaldi's Expedition to Sicily.
1017 **369** 15 l. brown 10 10
1018 – 25 l. red 10 10
1019 60 l. blue 20 20
DESIGNS—VERT: 25 l. Garibaldi meeting King Victor Emmanuel II near Naples (after Matania). HORIZ: 60 l. Embarkation of volunteers at Quarto, near Genoa (after T. van Elven).

370 "The Discus Thrower" (after Miron)

371 Vittorio Bottego (after Ettore Ximenes)

1960. Olympic Games. Inscr as in T **370**.
1020 – 5 l. brown 10 10
1021 – 10 l. blue and orange . . 10 10
1022 – 15 l. blue 10 10
1023 – 25 l. sepia and lilac . . . 10 10
1024 **370** 35 l. red 10 10
1025 – 60 l. sepia and green . . . 15 10
1026 – 110 l. purple 20 10
1027 – 150 l. brown and blue . . 1·40 1·10
1028 – 200 l. green 70 20
DESIGNS—VERT: 5 l. Games emblem; 15 l. "Starting the Race" (statue); 110 l. "Pugilist at rest" (after Apollonius); 200 l. "The Apoxiomenos" (after Lisippos). HORIZ: 10 l. Olympic Stadium, Rome; 25 l. Cycling Stadium, Rome; 60 l. Sports Palace, Rome; 150 l. Little Sports Palace.

1960. Birth Centenary of Vittorio Bottego (explorer).
1029 **371** 30 l. brown 10 10

371a Conference Emblem

1960. Europa.
1030 **371a** 30 l. brown & green . . . 10 10
1031 70 l. orange and blue . . 20 10

372 Caravaggio

373 Coach and Posthorn

1960. 350th Death Anniv of Caravaggio (painter).
1032 **372** 25 l. brown 10 10

1960. Stamp Day.
1033 **373** 15 l. sepia and red 10 10

374 Michelangelo

375 Douglas DC-8 Jetliner crossing Atlantic Ocean

1961. Works of Michelangelo. Frescoes on ceiling of Sistine Chapel. (a) Size 17 × 20½ mm.
1034 – 1 l. black 10 10
1035 – 5 l. orange 10 10
1036 – 10 l. red 10 10
1037 – 15 l. purple 10 10
1038 – 20 l. green 15 10
1039 – 25 l. brown 15 10
1040 – 30 l. purple 15 10
1041 – 40 l. red 15 10
1042 – 50 l. green 20 10
1043 – 55 l. brown 15 10
1044 – 70 l. blue 20 10
1045 – 85 l. green 20 10
1046 – 90 l. mauve 35 20
1047 – 100 l. violet 40 10
1048 – 115 l. blue 20 10
1049 – 150 l. brown 70 10
1050 **374** 200 l. blue . . . . . . 1·40 10

(b) Size 22 × 26½ mm.
1051 – 500 l. green . . . . . . 2·75 10
1052 – 1000 l. red . . . . . . 4·00 2·00
DESIGNS: 1, 5, 10, 115, 150 l. Ignudo (different versions); 15 l. Joel; 20 l. Libyan Sibyl; 25 l. Isaiah; 30 l. Erythraean Sibyl; 40 l. Daniel; 50 l. Delphic Sibyl; 55 l. Cumaean Sibyl; 70 l. Zachariah; 85 l. Jonah; 90 l. Jeremiah; 100 l. Ezekiel; 500 l. Adam; 1000 l. Eve.

1961. Visit of President Gronchi to S. America.
1053 **375** 170 l. blue (Argentina) . . 3·50 4·25
1054 185 l. green (Uruguay) . . 3·50 4·25
1055 205 l. violet (Peru) . . . 9·50 10·00
The countries indicated are shown in deep colours on the map.

376 Pliny the Younger

377 Ippolito Nievo

1961. 19th Birth Cent of Pliny the Younger.
1056 **376** 30 l. brown and buff . . . 10 10

1961. Birth Centenary of Ippolito Nievo (poet).
1057 **377** 30 l. blue and red 10 10

378 St. Paul in Ship (from 15th-century Bible of Borso d'Este)

1961. 19th Cent of St. Paul's Arrival in Rome.
1058 **378** 30 l. multicoloured . . . 20 10
1059 70 l. multicoloured . . . 40 30

379 Cannon and Gaeta Fortress

1961. Cent of Italian Unification and Independence.
1060 **379** 15 l. brown and blue . . . 20 10
1061 – 30 l. brown and blue . . . 20 10
1062 – 40 l. brown and blue . . . 25 25
1063 – 70 l. mauve and brown . . 35 10
1064 – 115 l. blue and brown . . 1·25 10
1065 – 300 l. red, brown & green . 4·25 4·50
DESIGNS: 30 l. Carignano Palace, Turin; 40 l. Montecitorio Palace, Rome; 70 l. Vecchio Palace, Florence; 115 l. Madama Palace, Rome; 300 l. Capitals, "Palace of Work", Int. Exn. of Work, Turin.

380 Doves

381 G. Romagnosi

1961. Europa.
1066 **380** 30 l. red 10 10
1067 70 l. green 10 10

1961. Birth Bicent of Romagnosi (philosopher).
1068 **381** 30 l. green 10 10

382 Imprint of 50 c. Provisional Postal Franked Paper of Sardinia, 1819

1961. Stamp Day.
1069 **382** 15 l. mauve and black . . 10 10

383 "The Sweet-burning Lamp" from Pascoli's "La Poesia" (after wood-eng by P. Morbiducci)

1962. 50th Death Anniv of G. Pascoli (poet).
1070 **383** 30 l. red 15 10
1071 70 l. blue 30 40

384 Pacinotti's Dynamo (diagram)

385 St. Catherine (after 15th-century woodcut)

1962. 50th Death Anniv of Antonio Pacinotti (physicist).
1072 **384** 30 l. black and red . . . 15 10
1073 70 l. black and blue . . . 30 40

1962. 5th Cent of Canonization of St. Catherine of Siena.
1074 – 30 l. violet 15 10
1075 **385** 70 l. black and red . . . 40 50
DESIGN: 30 l. St. Catherine (after A. Vanni).

386 Camera Lens **387** Cyclist being paced

1962. 30th Anniv of Int Cinematograph Art Fair. Venice.
1076 **386** 30 l. black and blue . . . 25 10
1077 – 70 l. black and red . . . 30 35
DESIGN: 70 l. Lion of St. Mark.

1962. World Cycling Championships.
1078 **387** 30 l. black and green . . 20 10
1079 – 70 l. blue and black . . . 20 10
1080 – 300 l. black and red . . . 3·00 3·00
DESIGNS: 70 l. Cyclists road-racing; 300 l. Cyclists on track.

388 Europa "Tree"

1962. Europa.
1081 **388** 30 l. red and carmine . . 40 10
1082 70 l. ultramarine & blue . 40 30

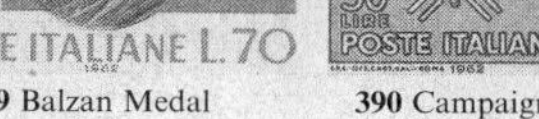

389 Balzan Medal **390** Campaign Emblem

1962. International Balzan Foundation.
1083 **389** 70 l. red and green . . . 10 10

1962. Malaria Eradication.
1084 **390** 30 l. violet 10 10
1085 70 l. blue 25 25

391 10 c. Stamp of 1862 and 30 l. Stamp of 1961 **392** "The Pentecost" (from "Codex Syriacus")

1962. Stamp Day.
1086 **391** 15 l. multicoloured . . . 10 10

1962. Ecumenical Council, Vatican City.
1087 **392** 30 l. orge & bl on cream . 10 10
1088 70 l. bl & orge on cream . 15 15

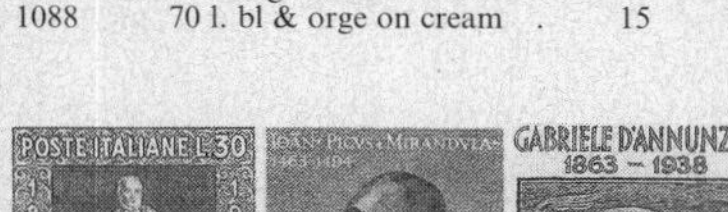

393 Statue of Cavour (statesman) **394** Pico della Mirandola (scholar) **395** D'Annunzio

1962. Centenary of Court of Accounts.
1089 **393** 30 l. green 10 10

1983. 5th Birth Cent of G. Pico della Mirandola.
1090 **394** 30 l. violet 10 10

1963. Birth Centenary of Gabriele D'Annunzio (author and soldier).
1091 **395** 30 l. green 10 10

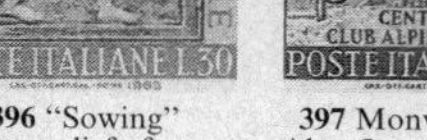

396 "Sowing" (bas-relief after G. and N. Pisano) **397** Monviso, Italian Alps, Ice-axe and Rope

1963. Freedom from Hunger.
1092 **396** 30 l. sepia and red 10 10
1093 – 70 l. sepia and blue . . . 20 30
DESIGN: 70 l. "Harvesting" (bas-relief after G. and N. Pisano).

1963. Italian Alpine Club Centenary.
1094 **397** 115 l. sepia and blue . . . 10 10

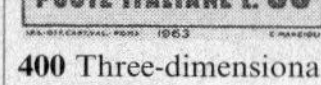

398 "I.N.A." Lighthouse **399** Posthorn and Globe

1963. 50th Anniv of Italian National Insurance Corporation.
1095 **398** 30 l. black and green . . 10 10

1963. Paris Postal Conference Centenary.
1096 **399** 70 l. blue and green . . . 10 10

400 Three-dimensional Emblem **401** "World Tourism"

1963. Red Cross Centenary.
1097 **400** 30 l. red and purple . . . 10 10
1098 70 l. red and blue 25 30

1963. U.N. Tourism Conference, Rome.
1099 **401** 15 l. blue and olive . . . 10 10
1100 70 l. brown and blue . . . 15 20

402 "Co-operation" **403** "Naples"

1963. Europa.
1101 **402** 30 l. brown and red . . . 10 10
1102 70 l. green and brown . . 20 10

1963. 4th Mediterranean Games, Naples. Inscr "NAPOLI 1963".
1103 **403** 15 l. ochre and blue . . . 10 10
1104 – 70 l. orange and green . . 20 30
DESIGN: 70 l. Greek "Olympic" vase.

404 Mascagni and Costanzi Theatre **405** G. Belli

1963. 150th Birth Anniv of Verdi (1105) and Birth Centenary of Mascagni (1106) (composers).
1105 – 30 l. brown and green . . 15 10
1106 **404** 30 l. green and brown . . 15 10
DESIGN: No. 1105, Verdi and La Scala Opera House.

1963. Death Centenary of Giuseppei Belli (poet).
1107 **405** 30 l. brown 10 10

406 Stamp "Flower" **407** Galileo Galilei

1963. Stamp Day.
1108 **406** 15 l. red and blue 10 10

1964. 400th Birth Anniv of Galileo Galilei.
1109 **407** 30 l. brown 15 10
1110 70 l. black 15 15

408 Nicodemus (from Michelangelo's "Pieta") **410** Carabinieri on Parade

1964. 400th Death Anniv of Michelangelo.
1111 **408** 30 l. sepia (postage) . . . 10 10
1112 – 185 l. black (air) 35 50
DESIGN: 185 l. Michelangelo's "Madonna of Bruges".

1964. 150th Anniv of Carabinieri (military police).
1113 **410** 30 l. red and blue 10 10
1114 – 70 l. brown 15 15
DESIGN: 70 l. "The Charge at Pastrengo (1848)" (De Albertis).

411 G. Bodoni **412** Europa "Flower"

1964. 150th Death Anniv (1963) of Giambattista Bodoni (type-designer and printer).
1115 **411** 30 l. red 10 10

1964. Europa.
1116 **412** 30 l. purple 10 10
1117 70 l. blue 10 10

413 European Buildings **414** Victor Emannuel Monument, Rome

1964. 7th European Municipalities' Assembly.
1118 **413** 30 l. brown and green . . 10 10
1119 70 l. brown and blue . . . 10 10
1120 500 l. red . . . . 1·25 1·40

1964. War Veterans' Pilgrimage to Rome.
1121 **414** 30 l. brown 10 10
1122 70 l. blue 10 10

415 G. da Verrazzano and Verrazano Bridge

1964. Opening of Verrazano Narrows Bridge, New York.
1123 **415** 30 l. black and brown (postage) 10 10
1124 130 l. black & grn (air) . . 20 35
This American bridge is designated "Verrazano" with one "z".

416 Italian Stamps **417** Prisoners of War

1964. Stamp Day.
1125 **416** 15 l. brown and bistre . . 10 10

1965. 20th Anniv of Resistance.
1126 **417** 10 l. black 10 15
1127 – 15 l. black, red & green . 10 10
1128 – 30 l. purple 10 10
1129 – 70 l. blue 15 15
1130 – 115 l. red 15 15
1131 – 130 l. brown, grn & red . 15 15
DESIGNS—VERT: 15 l. Servicemen and casualty ("Liberation Army"); 70 l. Alpine soldiers ("Resistance in the mountains"). HORIZ: 30 l. Gaunt hands and arms on swastika ("Political and Racial Persecution"); 115 l. Patriots with banners ("Resistance in the Towns"); 130 l. Ruined building and torn flags ("Martyred Cities").

418 I.T.U. Emblem, Meucci and Marconi

1965. I.T.U. Centenary.
1132 **418** 70 l. red and green . . . 10 10

419 "Flying Dutchman" Dinghies

1965. World Sailing Championships, Alassio and Naples.
1133 **419** 30 l. black and red . . . 15 10
1134 – 70 l. black and blue . . . 15 10
1135 – 500 l. black & grey-blue . 50 60
DESIGNS—VERT: 70 l. "5.5 S.1" class yachts. HORIZ: 500 l. "Lightning" dinghies.

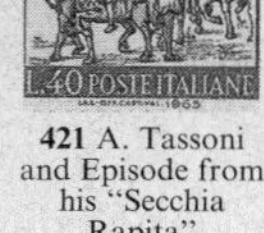

420 Mont Blanc and Tunnel **421** A. Tassoni and Episode from his "Secchia Rapita"

1965. Opening of Mont Blanc Road Tunnel.
1136 **420** 30 l. black 10 10

1965. 400th Birth Anniv of Alessandro Tassoni (poet).
1137 **421** 40 l. multicoloured . . . 10 10

422 Europa "Sprig" **423** "Hell" (Codex, Vatican Library)

1965. Europa.
1138 **422** 40 l. green and orange . . 10 10
1139 90 l. green and blue . . . 10 10

1965. 700th Birth Anniv of Dante.
1140 **423** 40 l. multicoloured . . . 10 10
1141 – 90 l. multicoloured . . . 15 15
1142 – 130 l. multicoloured . . . 15 15
1143 – 500 l. green 40 45
DESIGNS—VERT: 90 l. "Purgatory" (codex, Marciana Library, Venice); 500 l. Head of Dante (bronze, Naples Museum). HORIZ: 130 l. "Paradise" (codex, British Museum).

424 House and Savings-bank **425** Douglas DC-6B Airliner passing Control-tower

1965. Savings Day.
1144 **424** 40 l. multicoloured . . . 10 10

1965. Night Airmail Service.
1145 **425** 40 l. red and blue 15 10
1146 – 90 l. multicoloured . . . 15 10
DESIGN: 90 l. Sud Aviation Caravelle jetliner within airmail envelope "border".

426 Map of "Highway to the Sun" **427** Two-man Bobsleigh

1965. Stamp Day.
1147 **426** 20 l. multicoloured . . . 10 10

1966. World Bobsleigh Championships, Cortina d'Ampezzo.
1148 **427** 40 l. red, blue & grey . . 15 10
1149 – 90 l. violet and blue . . . 15 10
DESIGN: 90 l. Four-man bobsleigh.

428 Skier carrying Torch **429** B. Croce

1966. University Winter Games, Turin.
1150 **428** 40 l. black and red . . . 15 10
1151 – 90 l. violet and red . . . 15 10
1152 – 500 l. brown and red . . 35 45
DESIGNS—VERT: 90 l. Ice skating; 500 l. Ice hockey.

1966. Birth Centenary of Benedetto Croce (philosopher).
1153 **429** 40 l. sepia 10 10

430 Arms of Cities of Venezia

1966. Centenary of Union of Venezia and Italy.
1154 **430** 40 l. multicoloured . . . 10 10

431 Pine, Palatine Hill, Rome **432** "Visit Italy"

1966. "Trees and Flowers". Multicoloured.
1155 20 l. Type **431** 10 10
1156 25 l. Apples 15 10
1157 40 l. Carnations 15 10
1158 50 l. Irises 15 10
1241 55 l. Cypresses 20 10
1159 90 l. Anthemis (Golden Marguerite) 15 15
1160 170 l. Olive tree, Villa Adriana, Tivoli 20 15
1242 180 l. Broom 40 20
Nos. 1241 and 1242 are 26 × 35½ mm.

1966. Tourist Propaganda.
1161 **432** 20 l. multicoloured . . . 10 10

433 Capital "I" **434** Battle Scene

1966. 20th Anniv of Republic.
1162 **433** 40 l. multicoloured . . . 10 10
1163 90 l. multicoloured . . . 10 10

1966. Centenary of Battle of Bezzecca.
1164 **434** 90 l. olive 10 10

435 "Singing Angels" (from copper panel on altar of St. Antony's Basilica, Padua) **436** Europa "Ship"

1966. 5th Death Centenary of Donatello.
1165 **435** 40 l. multicoloured . . . 10 10

1966. Europa.
1166 **436** 40 l. violet 10 10
1167 90 l. blue 10 10

437 "Madonna in Maesta" (after Giotto) **438** Filzi, Battisti, Chiesa and Sauro

1966. Giotto's 700th Birth Anniv.
1168 **437** 40 l. multicoloured . . . 10 10

1966. 50th Death Annivs of World War I Heroes.
1169 **438** 40 l. green and slate . . . 10 10

439 Postal Emblem **440** Compass and Globe

1966. Stamp Day.
1170 **439** 20 l. multicoloured . . . 10 10

1967. Centenary of Italian Geographical Society.
1171 **440** 40 l. blue and black . . . 10 10

441 Toscanini

1967. Birth Centenary of Arturo Toscanini (orchestral conductor).
1172 **441** 40 l. buff and blue 30 10

442 Campidoglio, Rome

1967. 10th Anniv of Rome Treaties.
1173 **442** 40 l. brown and black . . 10 10
1174 90 l. purple and black . . 10 10

443 Cogwheels **444** Brown Bear (Abruzzo Park)

1967. Europa.
1175 **443** 40 l. purple and pink . . 10 10
1176 90 l. blue and cream . . . 10 10

1967. Italian National Parks. Multicoloured.
1177 20 l. Ibex (Gran Paradiso Park) (vert) 10 10
1178 40 l. Type **444** 10 10
1179 90 l. Red deer stag (Stelvio Park) 20 15
1180 170 l. Tree (Circeo Park) (vert) 30 20

445 Monteverdi

1967. 400th Death Anniv of Claudio Monteverdi (composer).
1181 **445** 40 l. brown & chestnut . . 15 10

446 Racing Cyclists

1967. 50th Tour of Italy Cycle Race. Designs showing cyclists.
1182 **446** 40 l. multicoloured . . . 10 10
1183 – 90 l. multicoloured . . . 10 10
1184 – 500 l. multicoloured . . . 65 80

447 Pirandello and Stage

1967. Birth Centenary of Luigi Pirandello (dramatist).
1185 **447** 40 l. multicoloured . . . 10 10

448 Stylised Mask

1967. Two Worlds Festival, Spoleto.
1186 **448** 20 l. black and green . . 10 10
1187 40 l. black and red . . . 10 10

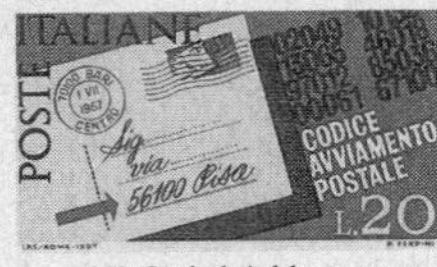

449 Coded Addresses

1967. Introduction of Postal Codes.
1188 **449** 20 l. black, blue & yellow . 10 10
1189 25 l. black, red & yellow . 10 10
1190 40 l. black, purple & yell . 10 10
1191 50 l. black, green & yell . 10 10

450 Pomilio PE Type Biplane and Postmark **451** St. Ivo's Church, Rome

1967. 50th Anniv of 1st Airmail Stamp.
1192 **450** 40 l. black and blue . . . 10 10

1967. 300th Death Anniv of Francesco Borromini (architect).
1193 **451** 90 l. multicoloured . . . 10 10

452 U. Giordano and Music from "Andrea Chenier" **453** "The Oath of Pontida" (from painting by Adolfo Cao)

1967. Birth Centenary of Umberto Giordano (composer).
1194 **452** 20 l. brown and black . . 10 10

1967. 800th Anniv of Oath of Pontida.
1195 **453** 20 l. brown 10 10

454 I.T.Y. Emblem **455** Lions Emblem

1967. International Tourist Year.
1196 **454** 20 l. black, blue & yell . . 10 10
1197 50 l. black, blue & orge . 10 10

1967. 50th Anniv of Lions International.
1198 **455** 50 l. multicoloured . . . 10 10

456 Sentry **457** E. Fermi (scientist) and Reactor

1967. 50th Anniv of Stand on the Piave.
1199 **456** 50 l. multicoloured . . . 10 10

1967. 25th Anniv of 1st Nuclear Chain Reaction.
1200 **457** 50 l. black and brown . . 10 10

458 Stamp and Dove

1967. Stamp Day.
1201 **458** 25 l. multicoloured . . . 10 10

1968. As Nos. 887, etc. (1952) size 16 × 20 mm.
1202 **286** 1 l. black 10 10
1203 5 l. slate 10 10
1204 6 l. brown 10 10
1205 10 l. red 10 10
1206 15 l. violet 10 10
1207 20 l. sepia 10 10
1208 25 l. violet 10 10
1209 30 l. brown 10 10
1210 40 l. purple 10 10
1211 50 l. olive 10 10
1212 55 l. violet 20 10
1213 60 l. blue 10 10
1214 70 l. green 10 10
1215 80 l. brown 10 10
1215a 90 l. brown 10 10
1216 100 l. brown 10 10
1216a 120 l. blue and green . . 10 10
1216b 125 l. purple & brown . . 35 10
1217 130 l. red and grey . . . 10 10
1217a 150 l. violet 30 10
1217b 170 l. green & brown . . 30 10
1218 180 l. purple and grey . . 40 10
1218a 200 l. blue 20 10
1219 300 l. green 55 10
1219a 350 l. orge, red & yell . . 50 10
1219b 400 l. red 55 20

459 Scouts around Campfire

460 Europa "Key"

1968. Italian Boy Scouts.
1220 **459** 50 l. multicoloured . . . 10 10

1968. Europa.
1221 **460** 50 l. green and pink . . . 10 10
1222 90 l. brown and blue . . . 10 10

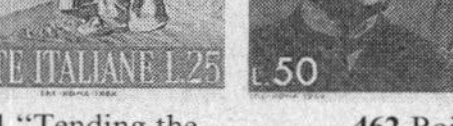

461 "Tending the Sick"

462 Boito and "Mephistopheles"

1968. 400th Birth Anniv of Luigi Gonzaga (St. Aloysius).
1223 **461** 25 l. violet and brown . . 10 10

1968. 50th Death Anniv of Arrigo Boito (composer and librettist).
1224 **462** 50 l. multicoloured . . . 15 10

GIAMBATTISTA VICO 1668 1744 POSTE ITALIANE L.50

463 F. Baracca and "Aerial Combat" (abstract by G. Balla)

464 Giambattista Vico (300th Birth Anniv)

1968. 500th Death Anniv of Francesco Baracca (airman of World War I).
1225 **463** 25 l. multicoloured . . . 10 10

1968. Italian Philosophers' Birth Annivs.
1226 **464** 50 l. blue 10 10
1227 – 50 l. black 10 10
DESIGN: No. 1227, Tommaso Campanella (400th birth anniv).

465 Cycle Wheel and Stadium

467 Rossini

466 "St. Mark's Square, Venice" (Canaletto)

1968. World Road Cycling Championships.
1228 **465** 25 l. bl, pink & brn . . 15 10
1229 – 90 l. indigo, red & blue . . 15 10
DESIGN: 90 l. Cyclists and Imola Castle.

1968. Death Bicentenary of Canaletto (painter).
1230 **466** 50 l. multicoloured . . . 20 10

1968. Death Centenary of Gioacchino Rossini (composer).
1231 **467** 50 l. red 15 10

468 Mobilization

469 "Conti Correnti Postali"

1968. 50th Anniv of Victory in World War I. Multicoloured.
1232 20 l. Type **468** 10 10
1233 25 l. Trench warfare 10 10
1234 40 l. Naval forces 10 10
1235 50 l. Air Force 10 10
1236 90 l. Battle of Vittorio Veneto . 15 15
1237 180 l. Tomb of Unknown Soldier 20 20

1968. 50th Anniv of Postal Cheque Service.
1238 **469** 50 l. multicoloured . . . 10 10

X giornata del francobollo poste italiane L 25

470 Tracking Equipment and Buildings

471 "Postal Development"

1968. Space Telecommunications Centre, Fucino.
1239 **470** 50 l. multicoloured . . . 10 10

1968. Stamp Day.
1240 **471** 25 l. red and yellow . . . 10 10

472 Commemorative Medal

473 Colonnade

1969. Centenary of State Audit Department.
1243 **472** 50 l. black and pink . . . 10 10

1969. Europa.
1244 **473** 50 l. multicoloured . . . 15 10
1245 90 l. multicoloured . . . 15 15

Organizzazione Internazionale del Lavoro 1919-1969 POSTE ITALIANE L.50

474 Machiavelli

475 I.L.O. Emblem

1969. 500th Birth Anniv of Niccolo Machiavelli (statesman).
1246 **474** 50 l. multicoloured . . . 10 10

1969. 50th Anniv of I.L.O.
1247 **475** 50 l. black and green . . 10 10
1248 90 l. black and red . . . 10 10

476 Postal Emblem

1969. 50th Anniv of Italian Philatelic Federation.
1249 **476** 50 l. multicoloured . . . 10 10

477 Sondrio-Tirano Mailcoach of 1903

1969. Stamp Day.
1250 **477** 25 l. blue 15 10

ITALIA L.20 1483 RAFFAELLO 1520

478 Skiing

479 "Galatea" (detail of fresco by Raphael)

1970. World Skiing Championships, Val Gardena. Multicoloured.
1251 50 l. Type **478** 15 10
1252 90 l. Dolomites 15 10

1970. 450th Death Anniv of Raphael. Mult.
1253 20 l. Type **479** 15 10
1254 50 l. "Madonna of the Goldfinch" 15 10

480 Symbols of Flight

1970. 50th Anniv of Rome–Tokyo Flight by A. Ferrarin.
1255 **480** 50 l. multicoloured . . . 15 10
1256 90 l. multicoloured . . . 15 10

481 "Flaming Sun"

482 Erasmo da Narni (from statue by Donatello)

1970. Europa.
1257 **481** 50 l. yellow and red . . . 15 10
1258 90 l. yellow and green . . 30 10

1970. 600th Birth Anniv of Erasmo da Narni "Il Gattamelata" (Condottiere).
1259 **482** 50 l. green 10 10

483 Running

1970. World University Games, Turin. Mult.
1260 20 l. Type **483** 10 10
1261 180 l. Swimming 20 20

484 Dr. Montessori and children

1970. Birth Cent of Dr. Maria Montessori (educationist).
1262 **484** 50 l. multicoloured . . . 15 10

485 Map and Cavour's Declaration

1970. Centenary of Union of Rome and Papal States with Italy.
1263 **485** 50 l. multicoloured . . . 15 10

486 Loggia of Campanile, St. Mark's Square, Venice

1970. 400th Death Anniv of Jacopo Tatti, "Il Sansovino" (architect).
1264 **486** 50 l. brown 10 10

487 "Garibaldi at Dijon" (engraving)

1970. Centenary of Garibaldi's Participation in Franco-Prussian War.
1265 **487** 20 l. grey and blue . . . 20 15
1266 50 l. purple and blue . . . 20 15

488 U.N. Emblem within Tree

489 Rotary Emblem

1970. 25th Anniv of United Nations.
1267 **488** 25 l. green, blk & brn . . 10 10
1268 90 l. yell, black & blue . . 20 15

1970. 65th Anniv of Rotary International.
1269 **489** 25 l. ultram, yell & bl . . 15 10
1270 90 l. ultram, yell & bl . . 25 10

490 Telephone Dial and "Network"

491 Urban Complex and Tree

1970. Completion of Telephone Trunk-dialling System.
1271 **490** 25 l. green and red . . . 20 10
1272 90 l. blue and red 25 10

1970. Nature Conservation Year.
1273 **491** 20 l. red and green . . . 15 10
1274 25 l. grey and green . . . 15 10

492 Electric Locomotive "Tartaruga"

493 "The Adoration" (F. Lippi)

1970. Stamp Day.
1275 **492** 25 l. black 40 10

1970. Christmas. Multicoloured.
1276 25 l. Type **493** (postage) . . . 10 10
1277 150 l. "The Adoration of the Magi" (Gentile da Fabriano). (air) 20 15
No. 1277 is horiz., size 44 × 35 mm.

494 Saverio Mercadante

1970. Death Centenary of Saverio Mercadante (composer).
1278 **494** 25 l. violet and grey . . . 15 10

495 "Mercury" (part of Cellini's "Perseus with the Head of Medusa")

496 Bramante's "Little Temple", St. Peter's Montorio, Rome

1971. 400th Death Anniv of Benvenuto Cellini (goldsmith and sculptor).

1279 **495** 50 l. blue 10 10

1971.

1280 **496** 50 l. black and brown . . 10 10

497 Adenauer, Schuman and De Gasperi

1971. 20th Anniv of European Coal and Steel Community.

1281 **497** 50 l. brown, blk & grn . . 15 10
1282 90 l. brown, black & red . 15 10

498 Europa Chain

499 Mazzini

1971. Europa.

1283 **498** 50 l. red 10 10
1284 90 l. purple 20 10

1971. 25th Anniv of Republic.

1285 **499** 50 l. multicoloured . . . 15 10
1286 90 l. multicoloured . . . 15 10

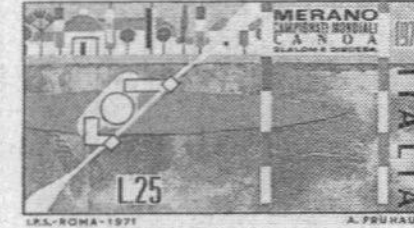

500 Canoeist in Slalom

1971. World Canoeing Slalom and Free Descent Championships, Merano. Multicoloured.

1287 25 l. Type **500** 10 10
1288 90 l. Canoeist making free descent 20 15

501 Three Sports

1971. Youth Games.

1289 **501** 20 l. black, grn & brn . . 10 10
1290 – 50 l. blk, violet & orge . . 10 10

DESIGN: 50 l. Four other sports.

502 Alitalia Emblem

1971. 25th Anniv of Alitalia State Airline. Multicoloured.

1291 50 l. Type **502** 10 10
1292 90 l. Emblem and Globe . . . 15 15
1293 150 l. Tailplane of Boeing 747 . 25 20

503 Grazia Deledda

504 Boy in "Savings" Barrel

1971. Birth Cent of Grazia Deledda (writer).

1294 **503** 50 l. black and brown . . 10 10

1971. Postal Savings Bank.

1295 **504** 25 l. multicoloured . . . 10 10
1296 50 l. multicoloured . . . 10 10

1971. Air. As No. 911 but smaller, 20 × 36 mm.

1297 **204** 100 l. green 30 10

505 U.N.I.C.E.F. Emblem and Paper Dolls

1971. 25th Anniv of U.N.I.C.E.F. Multicoloured.

1301 25 l. Type **505** 10 10
1302 90 l. Children acclaiming U.N.I.C.E.F. emblem . . . 20 15

506 Liner "Tirrenia"

1971. Stamp Day.

1303 **506** 25 l. green 30 10

507 "The Nativity"

1971. Christmas. Miniatures from "Matilda's Evangelarium", Nonantola Abbey, Modena. Multicoloured.

1304 25 l. Type **507** 10 10
1305 90 l. "The Adoration of the Magi" 20 15

508 G. Verga and Sicilian Cart

1972. 50th Death Anniv of Giovanni Verga (writer).

1306 **508** 25 l. multicoloured . . . 15 10
1307 50 l. multicoloured . . . 15 10

509 G. Mazzini

510 Stylized Flags

1972. Death Cent of Giuseppe Mazzini (statesman).

1308 **509** 25 l. green and black . . 10 10
1309 90 l. grey and black . . . 15 15
1310 150 l. red and black . . . 20 20

1972. 50th International Fair, Milan.

1311 **510** 25 l. green and black . . 10 10
1312 – 50 l. red and black . . . 10 10
1313 – 90 l. blue and black . . . 15 15

DESIGNS: 50 l. "Windows, stand and pavilions" (abstract); 90 l. Abstract general view of Fair.

INDEX

Countries can be quickly located by referring to the index at the end of this volume.

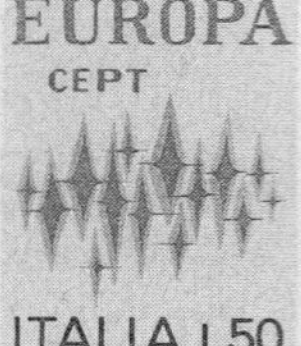

511 "Communications"

512 Alpine Soldier

1972. Europa.

1314 **511** 50 l. multicoloured . . . 15 10
1315 90 l. multicoloured . . . 25 15

1972. Centenary of Alpine Corps. Multicoloured.

1316 25 l. Type **512** 10 10
1317 50 l. Soldier's hat 15 15
1318 90 l. Soldier and mountains . . 20 20

513 Brenta Mountains

1972. Centenary of Tridentine Alpinists Society. Multicoloured.

1319 25 l. Type **513** 10 10
1320 50 l. Alpinist 10 10
1321 180 l. Mt. Crozzon 35 30

514 Diagram of Conference Hall

1972. 60th Interparliamentary Union Conference, Rome.

1322 **514** 50 l. multicoloured . . . 15 10
1323 90 l. multicoloured . . . 15 15

515 "St. Peter Damiani" (miniature, after G. di Paolo)

516 "The Three Graces" (Canova)

1972. 900th Death Anniv of St. Peter Damiani.

1324 **515** 50 l. multicoloured . . . 10 10

1972. 150th Death Anniv of Antonio Canova (sculptor).

1325 **516** 50 l. green 15 10

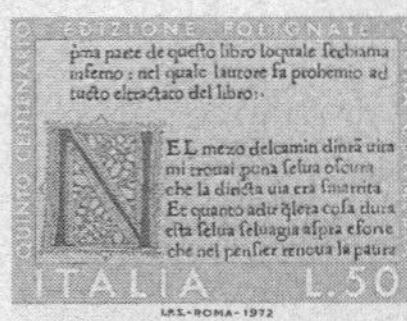

517 Initial and First Verse (Foligno edition)

1972. 500th Anniv of "The Divine Comedy". Multicoloured.

1326 50 l. Type **517** 10 10
1327 90 l. Initial and first verse (Mantua edition) (vert) . . . 15 10
1328 180 l. Initial and first verse ("Jesino" edition) 35 20

518 "Angel"

1972. Christmas. Multicoloured.

1329 20 l. Type **518** 10 10
1330 25 l. "Holy Child in Crib" (horiz) 10 10
1331 150 l. "Angel" (looking to left) 20 20

519 Postal Coach

1972. Stamp Day.

1332 **519** 25 l. red 15 10

520 L. B. Alberti (from bronze by M. de Pasti, Louvre)

521 L. Perosi

1972. 500th Death Anniv of Leon B. Alberti (writer and savant).

1333 **520** 50 l. blue and yellow . . . 15 10

1972. Birth Cent of Lorenzo Perosi (composer and priest).

1334 **521** 50 l. brown and yellow . . 10 10
1335 90 l. black and green . . 20 15

522 Don Orione

523 Oceanic Survey

1972. Birth Centenary of Don Orione (child-welfare pioneer).

1336 **522** 50 l. blue and turquoise . 10 10
1337 90 l. green and yellow . . 20 15

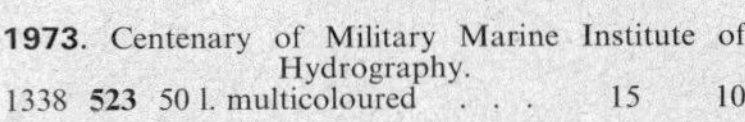

1973. Centenary of Military Marine Institute of Hydrography.

1338 **523** 50 l. multicoloured . . . 15 10

524 Grand Staircase, Royal Palace, Caserta

1973. Death Bicentenary of Luigi Vanvitelli (architect).

1339 **524** 25 l. green 15 10

525 Schiavoni Shore

1973. "Save Venice" Campaign. Multicoloured.

1340 20 l. Type **525** 15 10
1341 25 l. "The Tetrarchs" (sculpture) (vert) 15 10
1342 50 l. "The Triumph of Venice" (V. Carpaccio) 20 10
1343 90 l. Bronze horses, St. Mark's Basilica (vert) 20 15
1344 300 l. Piazetta S. Marco . . . 65 45

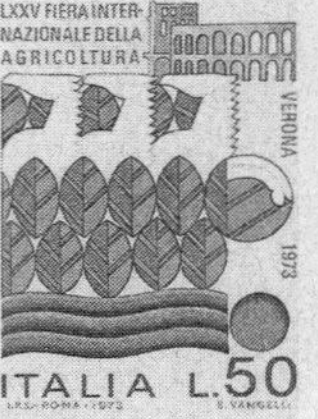

526 Fair Theme

527 Title-page of "Diverse Figure"

1973. 75th Int Agricultural Fair, Verona.

1345 **526** 50 l. multicoloured . . . 15 10

1973. 300th Death Anniv of Salvator Rosa (painter and poet).

1346 **527** 25 l. black and orange . . 10 10

528 Formation of Fiat PAN Acrobatic Jet Aircraft

1973. 50th Anniv of Military Aviation. Mult.

1349 20 l. Type **528** (postage) . . . 10 10
1350 25 l. Formation of Savoia Marchetti S-55X flying boats . . . 10 10
1351 50 l. Fiat G-91Y jet fighters on patrol . . . 10 10
1352 90 l. Fiat CR-32 biplanes performing aerobatics . . . 15 10
1353 180 l. Caproni Campini N-1 jet airplane . . . 30 20
1354 150 l. Lockheed F-104S Starfighter over Aeronautical Academy, Pozzuoli (air) . . 30 20

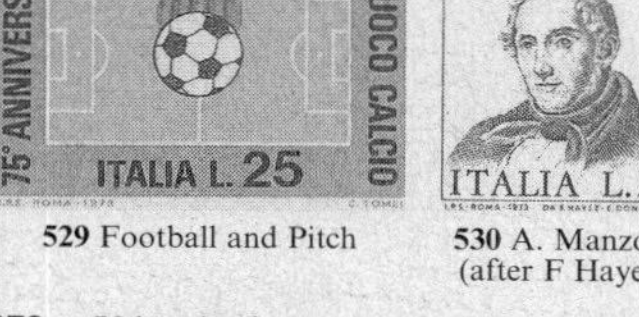

529 Football and Pitch **530** A. Manzoni (after F Hayez)

1973. 75th Anniversary of Italian Football Association. Multicoloured.

1355 25 l. Type **529** . . . 20 10
1356 90 l. Players in goal mouth . . 45 20

1973. Death Centenary of Alessandro Manzoni (writer and politician).

1357 **530** 25 l. brown and black . . 10 10

531 Palladio's "Rotunda", Vicenza **532** Spring and Cogwheels

1973. Andrea Palladio Commemoration.

1358 **531** 90 l. multicoloured . . . 30 15

1973. 50th Anniv of Italian State Supplies Office.

1359 **532** 50 l. multicoloured . . . 10 10

533 Europa "Posthorn"

1973. Europa.

1360 **533** 50 l. gold, lilac & yellow . . 10 10
1361 90 l. gold, green & yell . . 30 20

534 "Catcher" and Baseball Field

1973. 1st Intercontinental Baseball Cup. Multicoloured.

1362 25 l. Type **534** . . . 10 10
1363 90 l. "Striker" and baseball field . . . 20 15

535 Carnival Setting **536** "Argenta Episode"

1973. Viareggio Carnival.

1364 **535** 25 l. multicoloured . . . 10 10

1973. 50th Death Anniv of Don Giovanni Minzoni (military chaplain).

1365 **536** 50 l. multicoloured . . . 15 10

537 G. Salvemini **538** Farnese Palace, Caprorola

1973. Birth Centenary of Gaetano Salvemini (political historian).

1366 **537** 50 l. multicoloured . . . 10 10

1973. 400th Birth Anniv of "Vignola" (Jacopa Barozzi—architect).

1367 **538** 90 l. purple and yellow . . 20 15

539 "St. John the Baptist" **540** Leaning Tower of Pisa

1973. 400th Birth Anniv of Caravaggio (painter).

1368 **539** 25 l. black and yellow . . 10 10

1973. Tourism.

1369 **540** 50 l. multicoloured . . . 20 10

541 Botticelli **542** Immacolatella Fountain, Naples

1973. Italian Painters (1st series).

1370 **541** 50 l. brown and red . . . 10 10
1371 – 50 l. blue and brown . . . 10 10
1372 – 50 l. green and emerald . . 10 10
1373 – 50 l. black and red . . . 10 10
1374 – 50 l. brown and blue . . . 10 10

PAINTERS: No. 1371, Piranesi; No. 1372, Veronese; No. 1373, Verrocchio; No. 1374, Tiepolo.

See also Nos. 1392/6, 1456/61, 1495/9 and 1518/22.

1973. Italian Fountains (1st series). Mult.

1375 25 l. Type **542** . . . 10 10
1376 25 l. Trevi Fountain, Rome . . 10 10
1377 25 l. Pretoria Fountain, Palermo . . . 10 10

See also Nos. 1418/20, 1453/5, 1503/5, 1529/31, 1570/2 and 1618/20.

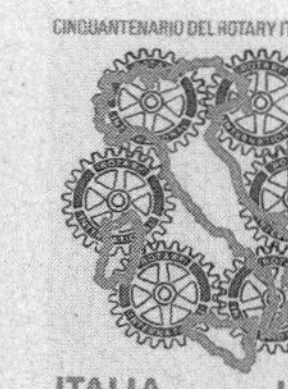

543 "Angels" **544** Map and Emblems

1973. Christmas. Sculptures by A. di Duccio.

1378 **543** 20 l. black and green . . 10 10
1379 – 25 l. black and blue . . . 10 10
1380 – 150 l. black & yellow . . 15 20

DESIGNS: 25 l. "Virgin and Child"; 150 l. "Angels" (different).

1973. 50th Anniv of Italian Rotary.

1381 **544** 50 l. blue, green & red . . 10 10

545 Sud Aviation Super Caravelle 12 **546** Military Medal for Valour

1973. Stamp Day.

1382 **545** 25 l. blue . . . 25 10

1973. 150th Anniv of Holders of the Gold Medal for Military Valour Organisation.

1383 **546** 50 l. multicoloured . . . 10 10

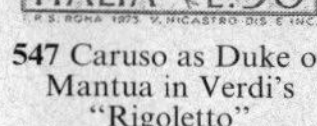

547 Caruso as Duke of Mantua in Verdi's "Rigoletto" **548** "Christ crowning King Roger" (Martorana Church, Palermo)

1973. Birth Centenary of Enrico Caruso (operatic tenor).

1384 **547** 50 l. red . . . 30 10

1974. Norman Art in Sicily. Mosaics.

1385 **548** 20 l. blue and yellow . . . 15 10
1386 – 50 l. red and green . . . 15 10

DESIGN: 50 l. "King William offering Church to the Virgin Mary" (Monreale Cathedral).

549 Pres. L. Einaudi **550** G. Marconi in Headphones

1974. Birth Centenary of Luigi Einaudi (President 1948–55).

1387 **549** 50 l. green . . . 10 10

1974. Birth Centenary of Guglielmo Marconi (radio pioneer).

1388 **550** 50 l. brown and green . . 15 10
1389 – 90 l. multicoloured . . . 15 15

DESIGN: 90 l. Marconi and world map.

551 "David" (Bernini) **552** Guards from Lombardy-Venetia (1848), Sardinian Marines (1815) and Tebro Battalion (1849)

1974. Europa. Sculptures. Multicoloured.

1390 50 l. Type **551** . . . 10 10
1391 90 l. "Spirit of Victory" (Michelangelo) . . . 20 15

1974. Italian Painters (2nd series). As T **541**.

1392 50 l. blue and green . . . 10 10
1393 50 l. brown and blue . . . 10 10
1394 50 l. black and red . . . 10 10
1395 50 l. brown and yellow . . . 10 10
1396 50 l. blue and brown . . . 10 10

PORTRAITS: No. 1392, Borromini; No. 1393, Carriera; No. 1394, Giambellino (Giovanni Bellini); No. 1395, Mantegna; No. 1396, Raphael.

1974. Bicentenary of Italian Excise Guards. Uniforms. Multicoloured.

1397 40 l. Sardinian chasseurs, 1774 and 1795, and Royal Fusilier of 1817 . . . 15 10
1398 50 l. Type **552** . . . 15 10
1399 90 l. Lieutenant (1866), Sergeant-major of Marines (1892) and guard (1880) . . 20 15
1400 180 l. Helicopter pilot, naval and alpine guards of 1974 . 35 20

553 Feather Headdress

1974. 50th Anniv of National Bersaglieri Association. Multicoloured.

1401 40 l. Type **553** . . . 10 10
1402 50 l. Bersaglieri emblem on rosette . . . 10 10

554 Running **555** Francesco Petrarch

1974. European Athletics Championships, Rome. Multicoloured.

1403 40 l. Type **554** . . . 15 10
1404 50 l. Pole vaulting . . . 15 10

1974. 600th Death Anniv of Francesco Petrarch (poet and scholar).

1405 **555** 40 l. multicoloured . . . 15 10
1406 – 50 l. blue, yellow & brn . . 15 10

DESIGN: 50 l. Petrarch at work in his study.

556 Portofino

1974. Tourist Publicity (1st series). Mult.

1407 40 l. Type **556** . . . 20 10
1408 40 l. Gradara . . . 20 10

See also Nos. 1442/4, 1473/5, 1513/14, 1515/17, 1543/5, 1596/9, 1642/5, 1722/5, 1762/5, 1806/9, 1845/8, 1877/80, 1917/20, 1963/6, 1992/5, 2031/4, 2088/91, 2115/18, 2165/8, 2212/15, 2248/51, 2315/16, 2365/8, 2425/8, 2486/9 and 2550/3.

557 Tommaseo's Statue, Sebenico **558** Giacomo Puccini

1974. Death Centenary of Niccolo Tommaseo (writer).

1409 **557** 50 l. green and pink . . . 15 10

1974. 50th Death Anniv of Giacomo Puccini (composer).

1410 **558** 40 l. multicoloured . . . 30 15

559 Cover Engraving of Ariosto's "Orlando Furioso" **560** Commemoration Tablet (Quotation from Varrone's "Menippean Satire")

1974. 500th Birth Anniv of Ludovico Ariosto (poet).

1411 **559** 50 l. blue and red . . . 15 10

1974. 2000th Death Anniv of Marco Varrone (Varrone Reatino) (author).

1412 **560** 50 l. lake, red and yellow . 15 10

561 "The Month of October" (detail from 15th-century mural)

1974. 14th International Wine Congress.

1413 **561** 50 l. multicoloured . . . 15 15

562 "U.P.U." and Emblem

1974. Centenary of Universal Postal Union. Mult.
1414 50 l. Type **562** 15 10
1415 90 l. "U.P.U." emblem and letters 15 15

563 "The Triumph of St. Thomas Aquinas" (detail—F. Traini)
564 Detail of Bas-relief, Ara Pacis

1974. 700th Death Anniv of St. Thomas Aquinas.
1416 **563** 50 l. multicoloured . . . 15 10

1974. Centenary of Italian Order of Advocates.
1417 **564** 50 l. black, green & brn . 15 10

1974. Italian Fountains (2nd series). As Type **542** Multicoloured.
1418 40 l. Oceanus Fountain, Florence 15 15
1419 40 l. Neptune Fountain, Bologna 15 15
1420 40 l. Maggiore Fountain, Perugia 15 15

565 "The Adoration" (Presepe di Greccio)

1974. Christmas.
1421 **565** 40 l. multicoloured . . . 15 10

566 Pulcinella
567 "God admonishing Adam" (Jacopo della Quercia (sculptor) (1374–1438))

1974. Children's Comic Characters. Mult.
1422 40 l. Type **566** 15 10
1423 50 l. Clowns 15 10
1424 90 l. Pantaloon from Bisognosi 15 15

1974. Italian Artists' Anniversaries (1st series).
1425 **567** 90 l. violet 20 15
1426 – 90 l. multicoloured 20 15

DESIGN: No. 1426, Uffizi Gallery, Florence (Giorgio Vasari (architect and painter) (1511–1574)).

See also Nos. 1445/6, 1480/2, 1523/4, 1564/5, 1593/4, 1699/1700, 1731/2, 1774/5, 1824/5, 1885/6, 1949/50 and 1987.

568 "Angel with Tablet"
569 "Pitti Madonna"

1975. Holy Year. Multicoloured.
1427 40 l. Type **568** 10 10
1428 50 l. Angel with column . . . 10 10
1429 90 l. Bridge of the Holy Angels, Rome (49 × 40 mm) . . . 15 10
1430 150 l. Angel with crown of thorns 25 25
1431 180 l. Angel with cross 25 25

1975. 500th Birth Anniv of Michelangelo.
1432 **569** 40 l. green 10 10
1433 – 50 l. brown 10 10
1434 – 90 l. red 15 15

DESIGNS: 50 l. Sculptured niche, Vatican Palace; 90 l. Detail from fresco "Flood of the Universe" (Sistine Chapel).

570 "The Four Days of Naples" (M. Mazzacurati)
571 "The Flagellation of Christ" (Caravaggio)

1975. 30th Anniv of Italian Resistance Movement. Resistance Monuments. Multicoloured.
1435 70 l. Type **570** 15 15
1436 100 l. "Martyrs of the Ardeatine Caves" (F. Coccia) 15 15
1437 150 l. "The Resistance Fighters of Cuneo" (U. Mastroianni) 20 15

1975. Europa. Paintings. Multicoloured.
1438 100 l. Type **571** 20 10
1439 150 l. "The Appearance of the Angel to Agar and Ishmael in the Desert" (Tiepolo) . . . 20 20

572 Globe and Emblems

1975. International Women's Year.
1440 **572** 70 l. multicoloured 15 10

573 "San Marco III" (satellite) and "Santa Rita" (marine launching pad)
574 Cover Engraving from Palestrina's "Primo Libro delle Messe"

1975. Italian Space Project.
1441 **573** 70 l. multicoloured . . . 30 10

1975. Tourist Publicity (2nd series). As T **556**. Multicoloured.
1442 150 l. Cefalu 25 15
1443 150 l. Isola Bella 25 15
1444 150 l. Montecatini Terme . . . 25 15

1975. Italian Artists' Annivs. (2nd series). As T **567**. Multicoloured.
1445 90 l. "Flora" (Guido Reni (1575–1642)) 15 15
1446 90 l. "Artist and Model" (Armando Spadini (1883–1925)) 15 15

1975. 450th Birth Anniv of Giovanni Pierluigi da Palestrina (composer).
1447 **574** 100 l. purple & brown . . 20 10

575 Boat in Harbour

1975. Italian Emigration.
1448 **575** 70 l. multicoloured 15 10

576 Notoriat Emblem

1975. Centenary of Unification of Italian Laws.
1449 **576** 100 l. mauve, stone & bl . . 15 10

577 Railway Steam Locomotive Driving-wheels

1975. 21st International Railway Congress, Bologna.
1450 **577** 70 l. multicoloured . . . 35 10

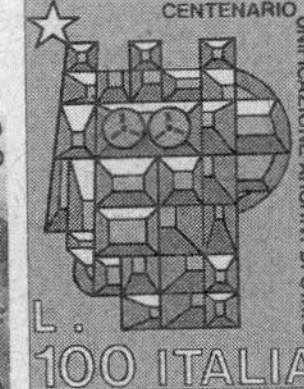

578 "D'Acquisto's Sacrifice" (Vittorio Pisani)
579 Symbolised Head representing Files

1975. 32nd Death Anniv of Salvo d'Acquisto (carabiniere who sacrificed himself to save 22 hostages).
1451 **578** 100 l. multicoloured . . . 20 10

1975. Centenary of State Archives Unification.
1452 **579** 100 l. multicoloured . . . 15 10

1975. Italian Fountains (3rd series). As T **542**. Multicoloured.
1453 70 l. Rosello Fountain, Sassari . 20 15
1454 70 l. 99 Channel Fountain, L'Aquila 20 15
1455 70 l. Piazza Fountain, Milan . 20 15

1975. Italian Composers. As T **541**.
1456 100 l. blue, pink and red . . . 20 15
1457 100 l. blue, green & dp green . 20 15
1458 100 l. green, brown & dp brn . 20 15
1459 100 l. brown, red and lake . . 20 15
1460 100 l. purple, grey & green . . 20 15
1461 100 l. black, lt yellow & yellow 20 15

DESIGNS: No. 1456, Ferruccio Busoni; 1457, Alessandro Scarlatti; 1458, Francesco Cilea; 1459, Antonio Vivaldi; 1460, Franco Alfa; No. 1461, Gaspare Spontini.

581 "Annunciation to the Shepherds"

1975. Christmas. Alatri Cathedral Carvings. Multicoloured.
1462 70 l. Type **581** 15 10
1463 100 l. "The Nativity" 15 10
1464 150 l. "Annunciation to the Kings" 20 20

582 "Children on Horseback"
583 "Boccaccio" (from fresco by A. del Castagno)

1975. Stamp Day. Children's Stories. Mult.
1465 70 l. Type **582** 15 10
1466 100 l. "The Magic Orchard" (vert) 20 10
1467 150 l. "Church Procession" . . 25 20

1975. 600th Death Anniv of Giovanni Boccaccio. Multicoloured.
1468 100 l. Type **583** 15 10
1469 150 l. Cover engraving from Boccaccio's "Fiammetta" . . 20 20

584 Entrance to State Advocate's Office
585 "Italia 1976" Emblem

1976. Centenary of State Advocate's Office.
1470 **584** 150 l. multicoloured . . . 20 15

1976. "Italia 76" International Stamp Exhibition, Milan (1st issue).
1471 **585** 150 l. red, green & black . 20 15
1472 – 180 l. multicoloured . . . 20 15

DESIGN: 180 l. Exhibition Hall, Milan.

See also Nos. 1487/91.

1976. Tourist Publicity (3rd series). As T **556**. Multicoloured.
1473 150 l. Fenis Castle, Aosta . . . 25 15
1474 150 l. Forio Ischia 25 15
1475 150 l. Itria Valley 25 15

586 Majolica Plate
587 Republican Flags

1976. Europa. Italian Crafts. Multicoloured.
1476 150 l. Type **586** 20 15
1477 180 l. Vase in form of woman's head 25 15

1976. 30th Anniv of Republic. Multicoloured.
1478 100 l. Type **587** 15 10
1479 150 l. Statesmen 20 15

588 "Fortitude" (Giacomo Serpotta) (1656–1732)

1976. Italian Artists' Annivs. (3rd series).
1480 **588** 150 l. blue 25 15
1481 – 150 l. multicoloured . . . 25 15
1482 – 150 l. black and red . . . 25 15

DESIGNS: No. 1481, "Woman at Table" (Umberto Boccioni (1882–1916)); 1482, "Gunner's Letter from the Front" (Filippo Tommaso Marinetti (1876–1944)).

589 "The Dragon"

1976. 450th Death Anniv of Vittore Carpaccio (painter).
1483 **589** 150 l. red 20 15
1484 – 150 l. red 20 15

DESIGN: No. 1484, "St. George".

Nos. 1483/4 form Carpaccio's "St. George and the Dragon".

590 "Flora" (Titian)

1976. 400th Death Anniv of Titian.
1485 **590** 150 l. red 30 15

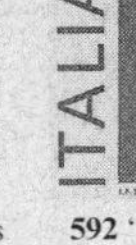

591 St. Francis (13th-century fresco)
592 "Cursus Publicus" Post Cart

1976. 750th Death Anniv of St. Francis of Assisi.
1486 **591** 150 l. brown & lt brn . . 30 15

1976. "Italia 76" International Stamp Exhibition, Milan (2nd issue).
1487 **592** 70 l. black, grey & blue . 10 10
1488 – 100 l. black, grey & yell . 15 10
1489 – 150 l. black, grey & brn . 20 10
1490 – 200 l. multicoloured . . . 25 15
1491 – 400 l. multicoloured . . . 55 20
DESIGNS: 100 l. Emblem of Royal Sardinian Posts; 150 l. 19th-century "Lion's head" letterbox; 200 l. Early cancelling machine; 400 l. Modern letter-coding machine.

593 Girl with "Protective Umbrella" and Animals

594 "The Visit" (S. Lega)

1976. Stamp Day. Nature Protection. Multicoloured.
1492 40 l. Type **593** 10 10
1493 100 l. "Protective scarf" . . . 15 10
1494 150 l. Doctor with bandaged tree 15 15

1976. Italian Painters (3rd series). As T **541**.
1495 170 l. green, yellow & red . . . 25 15
1496 170 l. black, turquoise & grn . 25 15
1497 170 l. black, purple & mve . . 25 15
1498 170 l. brown, lavender & vio . 25 15
1499 170 l. black and brown 25 15
DESIGNS: No. 1495, Carlo Dolci; 1496, Lorenzo Ghiberti (sculptor); 1497, Domenico Ghirlandaio; 1498, Giovanni Piazzetta; 1499, "Sassoferrato" (Giovanni Salvi).

1976. 150th Birth Anniv of Silvestro Lega (painter).
1500 **594** 170 l. multicoloured . . . 30 15

595 "Adoration of the Magi" (Bartolo di Fredi)

596 Net of Serpents obscuring the Sun

1976. Christmas. Multicoloured.
1501 70 l. Type **595** 15 20
1502 120 l. "The Nativity" (Taddao Gaddi) 25 20

1976. Italian Fountains (4th series). As Type **542** Multicoloured.
1503 170 l. Antique Fountain, Gallipoli 30 15
1504 170 l. Erbe Madonna Fountain, Verona 30 15
1505 170 l. Fountain of Palazzo Doria, Gerona 30 15

1977. Campaign against Drug Abuse. Mult.
1506 120 l. Type **596** 20 15
1507 170 l. "Addict" and poppy . . 30 15

597 Igniting Explosives

598 "Globe" and Cross

1977. 300th Birth Anniv of Pietro Micca (national hero).
1508 **597** 170 l. multicoloured . . . 20 15

1977. Salesian Missionaries. Multicoloured.
1509 70 l. Type **598** 15 10
1510 120 l. St. John Bosco and "United people" 15 20

599 Article 53 of the Italian Constitution

1977. "Encouragement to Taxpayers".
1511 **599** 120 l. black, brn & stone . 25 10
1512 170 l. black, olive & grn . 30 10

1977. Europa. As T **556** but with C.E.P.T. emblem. Multicoloured.
1513 170 l. Mount Etna 40 15
1514 200 l. Castel del Monte 50 15

1977. Tourist Publicity (4th series). As T **556**. Multicoloured.
1515 170 l. Canossa Castle 30 15
1516 170 l. Castellana Grotto . . . 30 15
1517 170 l. Fermo 30 15

1977. Famous Italians. As T **541**.
1518 70 l. brown, green & dp grn . . 20 15
1519 70 l. black, blue and green . . 20 15
1520 70 l. brown, yellow & lt brn . . 20 15
1521 70 l. blue, pink and red 20 15
1522 70 l. black, brown & dp brn . . 20 15
DESIGNS: No. 1518, Filippo Brunelleschi (architect); 1519, Pietro Aretino (satirist); 1520, Carlo Goldoni (dramatist); 1521, Luigi Cherubini (composer); 1522, Edoardo Bassini (surgeon).

1977. Italian Artists' Anniversaries (4th series). As Type **567** Multicoloured.
1523 170 l. "Winter" (G. Arcimboldi (c. 1527–1593)) 30 15
1524 170 l. "Justice" (Andrea Delitio (15th century)) 25 15

601 Paddle-steamer "Ferdinando Primo"

1977. Italian Ship-building (1st series). Multicoloured.
1525 170 l. Type **601** 35 20
1526 170 l. Sail corvette "Carracciolo" 35 20
1527 170 l. Liner "Saturnia" 35 20
1528 170 l. Hydrofoil missile boat "Sparviero" 35 20
See also Nos. 1552/5, 1621/4 and 1691/4.

1977. Italian Fountains (5th series). As T **542**. Multicoloured.
1529 120 l. Pacassi Fountain, Gorizia 30 15
1530 120 l. Fraterna Fountain, Isernia 30 15
1531 120 l. Palma Fountain, Palmi . 30 15

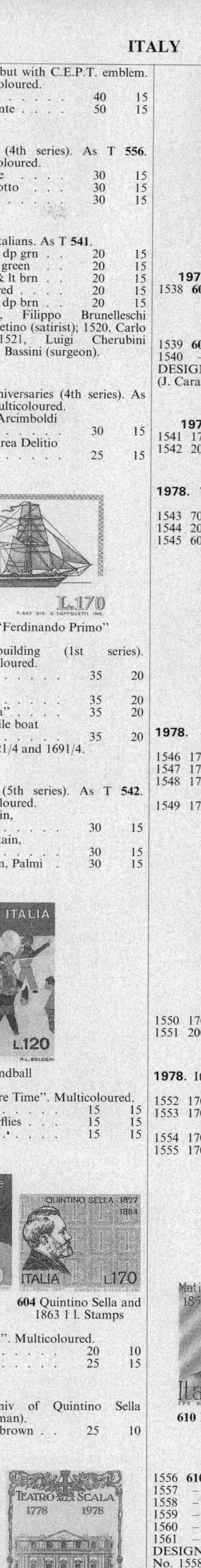

602 Handball

1977. Stamp Day. "Leisure Time". Multicoloured.
1532 120 l. Type **602** 15 15
1533 120 l. Catching butterflies . . . 15 15
1534 120 l. Kites 15 15

603 "Pulse"

604 Quintino Sella and 1863 1 l. Stamps

1977. "Give Blood". Multicoloured.
1535 70 l. Type **603** 20 10
1536 120 l. "Transfusion" 25 15

1977. 150th Birth Anniv of Quintino Sella (statesman).
1537 **604** 170 l. green and brown . . 25 10

605 Dina Galli

607 La Scala Opera House

606 "Adoration of the Shepherds" (P. Testa)

1977. Birth Centenary of Dina Galli (actress).
1538 **605** 170 l. multicoloured . . . 20 10

1977. Christmas.
1539 **606** 70 l. black and green . . 10 10
1540 – 120 l. black and green . . 20 15
DESIGN: 120 l. "The Adoration of the Shepherds" (J. Caraglio).

1978. Bicentenary of La Scala Opera House.
1541 170 l. Type **607** 30 15
1542 200 l. Theatre interior 40 15

1978. Tourist Publicity (5th series). As T **556**. Multicoloured.
1543 70 l. Gubbio 15 10
1544 200 l. Udine 30 15
1545 600 l. Paestum 75 45

608 Dusky Grouper

1978. Environmental Protection. Mediterranean Fauna. Multicoloured.
1546 170 l. Type **608** 70 30
1547 170 l. Leathery turtle 70 30
1548 170 l. Mediterranean monk seal 70 30
1549 170 l. Audouin's gull . . . . . 1·50 30

609 Maschio Angioino Castle, Naples

1978. Europa. Multicoloured.
1550 170 l. Type **609** 35 10
1551 200 l. Pantheon, Rome 35 15

1978. Italian Ship-building (2nd series). As T **601**. Multicoloured.
1552 170 l. Brigantine "Fortuna" . . 55 25
1553 170 l. Cruiser "Benedetto Brin" 55 25
1554 170 l. Frigate "Lupo" 55 25
1555 170 l. Container ship "Africa" . 55 25

610 Matilde Serao (writer)

611 First and Last Paragraphs of Constitution

1978. Famous Italians.
1556 **610** 170 l. black and red . . . 20 15
1557 – 170 l. brown and blue . . . 20 15
1558 – 170 l. blue & pale blue . . 20 15
1559 – 170 l. black and green . . 20 15
1560 – 170 l. brown and green . . 20 15
1561 – 170 l. blue and red . . . 20 15
DESIGNS: No. 1557, Vittorino da Feltre (scientist); No. 1558, Victor Emmanuel II; No. 1559, Pope Pius IX; No. 1560, Marcello Malpighi (biologist); No. 1561, Antonio Meucci (telephone pioneer).
See also Nos. 1600/4.

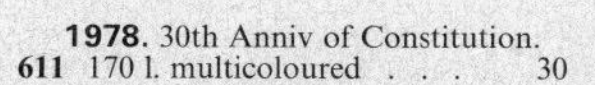

1978. 30th Anniv of Constitution.
1562 **611** 170 l. multicoloured . . . 30 10

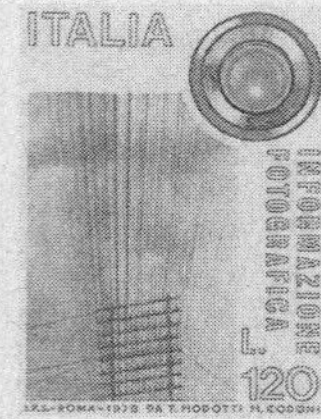

612 Telephone Wires and Lens

1978. Photographic Information.
1563 **612** 120 l. grey, blue & green . 20 10

1978. Italian Artists' Annivs. (5th series). As T **567**. Multicoloured.
1564 170 l. "The Ivy" (Tranquillo Cremona 1837–1878) . . . 1·25 15
1565 520 l. "The Cook" (Bernardo Strozzi 1581–1644) . . . . 2·00 1·25

613 The Holy Shroud of Turin

1978. 400th Anniv of Translation of the Holy Shroud from Savoy to Turin.
1566 **613** 220 l. yellow, black & red . 40 15

614 Volleyball Players

615 Detail from "St. Peter distributing Ananias's Silver"

1978. World Volleyball Championships.
1567 **614** 80 l. black, red & blue . . 25 10
1568 – 120 l. black, blue & orge . 40 15
DESIGN: 120 l. Players with ball.

1978. 550th Death Anniv of Tommaso Guidi (Masaccio).
1569 **615** 170 l. blue 30 10

1978. Italian Fountains (6th series). As T **542**. Multicoloured.
1570 120 l. Neptune Fountain, Trento 25 15
1571 120 l. Fountain of Fortune, Fano 25 15
1572 120 l. Cavallina Fountain, Genzano di Lucania 25 15

616 "Madonna and Child" (Giorgione)

617 "Flowers"

1978. Christmas.
1573 **616** 80 l. red and brown . . . 15 10
1574 – 120 l. multicoloured . . . 15 15
DESIGN—HORIZ: (48 × 27 mm); 120 l. "Adoration of the Magi" (Giorgione).

1978. Stamp Day. United Europe. Mult.
1575 120 l. Type **617** 15 10
1576 120 l. Flags and ribbon 15 10
1577 120 l. Figures raising globe inscribed "E" 15 10

618

619 State Polygraphic Institute

1978.
1578 **618** 1500 l. multicoloured . . 1·00 10
1579 2000 l. multicoloured . . 1·40 10
1580 3000 l. multicoloured . . 2·00 10
1581 4000 l. multicoloured . . 2·50 10
1582 5000 l. multicoloured . . 3·25 10
1583 10000 l. multicoloured . . 7·00 60
1584 20000 l. multicoloured . . 14·00 4·00

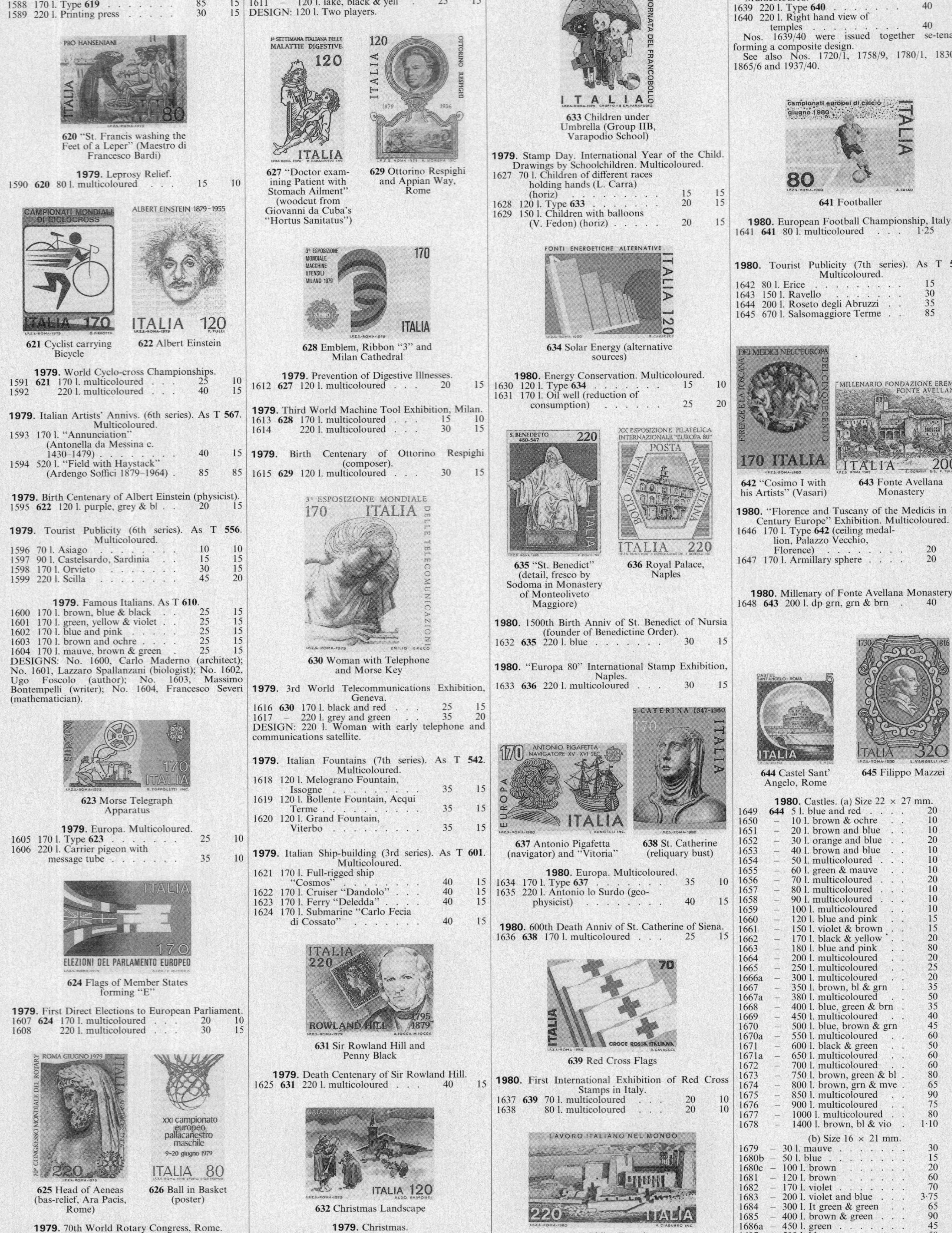

1979. 50th Anniv of State Polygraphic Institute. Multicoloured.
1588 170 l. Type **619** 85 15
1589 220 l. Printing press 30 15

620 "St. Francis washing the Feet of a Leper" (Maestro di Francesco Bardi)

1979. Leprosy Relief.
1590 **620** 80 l. multicoloured . . . 15 10

621 Cyclist carrying Bicycle

622 Albert Einstein

1979. World Cyclo-cross Championships.
1591 **621** 170 l. multicoloured . . . 25 10
1592 220 l. multicoloured . . . 40 15

1979. Italian Artists' Annivs. (6th series). As T **567**. Multicoloured.
1593 170 l. "Annunciation" (Antonella da Messina c. 1430–1479) 40 15
1594 520 l. "Field with Haystack" (Ardengo Soffici 1879–1964) . 85 85

1979. Birth Centenary of Albert Einstein (physicist).
1595 **622** 120 l. purple, grey & bl . . 20 15

1979. Tourist Publicity (6th series). As T **556**. Multicoloured.
1596 70 l. Asiago 10 10
1597 90 l. Castelsardo, Sardinia . . 15 15
1598 170 l. Orvieto 30 15
1599 220 l. Scilla 45 20

1979. Famous Italians. As T **610**.
1600 170 l. brown, blue & black . . 25 15
1601 170 l. green, yellow & violet . . 25 15
1602 170 l. blue and pink 25 15
1603 170 l. brown and ochre 25 15
1604 170 l. mauve, brown & green . . 25 15
DESIGNS: No. 1600, Carlo Maderno (architect); No. 1601, Lazzaro Spallanzani (biologist); No. 1602, Ugo Foscolo (author); No. 1603, Massimo Bontempelli (writer); No. 1604, Francesco Severi (mathematician).

623 Morse Telegraph Apparatus

1979. Europa. Multicoloured.
1605 170 l. Type **623** 25 10
1606 220 l. Carrier pigeon with message tube 35 10

624 Flags of Member States forming "E"

1979. First Direct Elections to European Parliament.
1607 **624** 170 l. multicoloured . . . 20 10
1608 220 l. multicoloured . . . 30 15

625 Head of Aeneas (bas-relief, Ara Pacis, Rome)

626 Ball in Basket (poster)

1979. 70th World Rotary Congress, Rome.
1609 **625** 220 l. multicoloured . . . 30 15

1979. 21st European Basketball Championships.
1610 **626** 80 l. multicoloured . . . 15 10
1611 – 120 l. lake, black & yell . 25 15
DESIGN: 120 l. Two players.

627 "Doctor examining Patient with Stomach Ailment" (woodcut from Giovanni da Cuba's "Hortus Sanitatus")

629 Ottorino Respighi and Appian Way, Rome

628 Emblem, Ribbon "3" and Milan Cathedral

1979. Prevention of Digestive Illnesses.
1612 **627** 120 l. multicoloured . . . 20 15

1979. Third World Machine Tool Exhibition, Milan.
1613 **628** 170 l. multicoloured . . . 15 10
1614 220 l. multicoloured . . . 30 15

1979. Birth Centenary of Ottorino Respighi (composer).
1615 **629** 120 l. multicoloured . . . 30 15

630 Woman with Telephone and Morse Key

1979. 3rd World Telecommunications Exhibition, Geneva.
1616 **630** 170 l. black and red . . . 25 15
1617 – 220 l. grey and green . . 35 20
DESIGN: 220 l. Woman with early telephone and communications satellite.

1979. Italian Fountains (7th series). As T **542**. Multicoloured.
1618 120 l. Melograno Fountain, Issogne 35 15
1619 120 l. Bollente Fountain, Acqui Terme 35 15
1620 120 l. Grand Fountain, Viterbo 35 15

1979. Italian Ship-building (3rd series). As T **601**. Multicoloured.
1621 170 l. Full-rigged ship "Cosmos" 40 15
1622 170 l. Cruiser "Dandolo" . . . 40 15
1623 170 l. Ferry "Deledda" 40 15
1624 170 l. Submarine "Carlo Fecia di Cossato" 40 15

631 Sir Rowland Hill and Penny Black

1979. Death Centenary of Sir Rowland Hill.
1625 **631** 220 l. multicoloured . . . 40 15

632 Christmas Landscape

1979. Christmas.
1626 **632** 120 l. multicoloured . . . 20 10

633 Children under Umbrella (Group IIB, Varapodio School)

1979. Stamp Day. International Year of the Child. Drawings by Schoolchildren. Multicoloured.
1627 70 l. Children of different races holding hands (L. Carra) (horiz) 15 15
1628 120 l. Type **633** 20 15
1629 150 l. Children with balloons (V. Fedon) (horiz) 20 15

634 Solar Energy (alternative sources)

1980. Energy Conservation. Multicoloured.
1630 120 l. Type **634** 15 10
1631 170 l. Oil well (reduction of consumption) 25 20

635 "St. Benedict" (detail, fresco by Sodoma in Monastery of Monteoliveto Maggiore)

636 Royal Palace, Naples

1980. 1500th Birth Anniv of St. Benedict of Nursia (founder of Benedictine Order).
1632 **635** 220 l. blue 30 15

1980. "Europa 80" International Stamp Exhibition, Naples.
1633 **636** 220 l. multicoloured . . . 30 15

637 Antonio Pigafetta (navigator) and "Vitoria"

638 St. Catherine (reliquary bust)

1980. Europa. Multicoloured.
1634 170 l. Type **637** 35 10
1635 220 l. Antonio lo Surdo (geo-physicist) 40 15

1980. 600th Death Anniv of St. Catherine of Siena.
1636 **638** 170 l. multicoloured . . . 25 15

639 Red Cross Flags

1980. First International Exhibition of Red Cross Stamps in Italy.
1637 **639** 70 l. multicoloured . . . 20 10
1638 80 l. multicoloured . . . 20 10

640 Philae Temples

1980. Italian Work for the World (1st series). Preservation of Philae Temples, Egypt. Multicoloured.
1639 220 l. Type **640** 40 20
1640 220 l. Right hand view of temples 40 20
Nos. 1639/40 were issued together se-tenant, forming a composite design.
See also Nos. 1720/1, 1758/9, 1780/1, 1830/1, 1865/6 and 1937/40.

641 Footballer

1980. European Football Championship, Italy.
1641 **641** 80 l. multicoloured . . . 1·25 40

1980. Tourist Publicity (7th series). As T **556**. Multicoloured.
1642 80 l. Erice 15 10
1643 150 l. Ravello 30 15
1644 200 l. Roseto degli Abruzzi . . 35 15
1645 670 l. Salsomaggiore Terme . . 85 85

642 "Cosimo I with his Artists" (Vasari)

643 Fonte Avellana Monastery

1980. "Florence and Tuscany of the Medicis in 16th Century Europe" Exhibition. Multicoloured.
1646 170 l. Type **642** (ceiling medallion, Palazzo Vecchio, Florence) 20 15
1647 170 l. Armillary sphere 20 15

1980. Millenary of Fonte Avellana Monastery.
1648 **643** 200 l. dp grn, grn & brn . 40 15

644 Castel Sant' Angelo, Rome

645 Filippo Mazzei

1980. Castles. (a) Size 22 × 27 mm.
1649 **644** 5 l. blue and red 20 10
1650 – 10 l. brown & ochre . . 10 10
1651 – 20 l. brown and blue . . 10 10
1652 – 30 l. orange and blue . . 20 10
1653 – 40 l. brown and blue . . 10 10
1654 – 50 l. multicoloured . . . 10 10
1655 – 60 l. green & mauve . . 10 10
1656 – 70 l. multicoloured . . . 20 10
1657 – 80 l. multicoloured . . . 10 10
1658 – 90 l. multicoloured . . . 10 10
1659 – 100 l. multicoloured . . 10 10
1660 – 120 l. blue and pink . . 15 10
1661 – 150 l. violet & brown . . 15 10
1662 – 170 l. black & yellow . . 20 10
1663 – 180 l. blue and pink . . 80 35
1664 – 200 l. multicoloured . . 20 10
1665 – 250 l. multicoloured . . 25 10
1666a – 300 l. multicoloured . . 20 10
1667 – 350 l. brown, bl & grn . 35 10
1667a – 380 l. multicoloured . . 50 10
1668 – 400 l. blue, green & brn . 35 10
1669 – 450 l. multicoloured . . 40 10
1670 – 500 l. blue, brown & grn 45 10
1670a – 550 l. multicoloured . . 60 10
1671 – 600 l. black & green . . 50 10
1671a – 650 l. multicoloured . . 60 10
1672 – 700 l. multicoloured . . 60 10
1673 – 750 l. brown, green & bl . 80 10
1674 – 800 l. brown, grn & mve . 65 10
1675 – 850 l. multicoloured . . 90 10
1676 – 900 l. multicoloured . . 75 10
1677 – 1000 l. multicoloured . . 80 10
1678 – 1400 l. brown, bl & vio 1·10 10

(b) Size 16 × 21 mm.
1679 – 30 l. mauve 30 10
1680b – 50 l. blue 15 10
1680c – 100 l. brown 20 10
1681 – 120 l. brown 60 20
1682 – 170 l. violet 70 20
1683 – 200 l. violet and blue . . 3·75 4·00
1684 – 300 l. lt green & green . . 65 40
1685 – 400 l. brown & green . . 90 55
1686a – 450 l. green 45 25
1687 – 500 l. blue 50 30

1687a – 600 l. green 50 30
1688 – 650 l. mauve 60 40
1689 – 750 l. violet 70 25
1690 – 800 l. red 65 35

DESIGNS: 10 l. Sforzesco Castle, Milan; 20 l. Castel del Monte, Andria; 30 l. (1652), L'Aquila Castle; 30 l. (1679), 100 l. (1680c), Santa Severa Castle; 40 l. Ursino Castle, Catania; 50 l. (1654), Rocca di Calascio, L'Aquila; 50 l. (1680b), Scilla; 60 l. Norman Tower, San Mauro; 70 l. Aragonese Castle, Reggio Calabria; 80 l. Sabbionara, Avio; 90 l. Isola Capo Rizzuto; 100 l. (1659), Aragonese Castle, Ischia; 120 l. (1660), Estense Castle, Ferrara; 120 l. (1681), Lombardia Enna; 150 l. Miramare, Trieste; 170 l. (1662), Ostia; 170 l. (1682), 650 l. (1688), Serralunga d'Alba; 180 l. Castel Gavone, Finale Ligure; 200 l. (1664), Cerro al Volturno; 200 l. (1683), Svevo Angioina Fortress, Lucera; 250 l. Rocca di Mondavio, Pesaro; 300 l. (1666a), Norman Castle, Svevo, Bari; 300 l. (1684), 500 l. (1687), Norman Castle, Melfi; 350 l. Mussomeli; 380 l. Rocca di Vignola, Modena; 400 l. (1668), Emperor's Castle, Prato; 400 l. (1685), 750 l. (1689), Venafro; 450 l. (1669), Bosa; 450 l. (1686a) Piobbico Castle, Pesaro; 500 l. (1670), Rovereto; 550 l. Rocca Sinibalda; 600 l. Scaligero Castle, Sirmione; 650 l. (1671a), Montecchio; 700 l. Ivrea; 750 l. (1673), Rocca di Urbisaglia; 800 l. Rocca Maggiore, Assisi; 850 l. Castello di Arechi, Salerno; 900 l. Castello di Saint-Pierre, Aosta; 1000 l. Montagnana, Padua; 1400 l. Caldoresco Castle, Vasto.

1980. Italian Ship-building (4th series). As T **601**. Multicoloured.
1691 200 l. Corvette "Gabbiano" . . 60 15
1692 200 l. Destroyer "Audace" . . 60 15
1693 200 l. Barque "Italia" 60 15
1694 200 l. Pipe-layer "Castoro Sei" 60 15

1980. 250th Birth Anniv of Filippo Mazzei (writer and American revolutionary).
1695 **645** 320 l. multicoloured . . . 50 30

646 Villa Foscari Malcontenta, Venice

1980. Italian Villas (1st series). Multicoloured.
1696 80 l. Type **646** 25 25
1697 150 l. Barbaro Maser, Treviso . 45 15
1698 170 l. Godi Valmarana, Vicenza 70 15
See also Nos. 1737/9, 1770/2, 1811/14, 1853/6, 1893/6 and 1943/7.

1980. Italian Artists Anniversaries (7th series). As T **567**. Multicoloured.
1699 520 l. "Saint Barbara" (Jacopo Palma, the Elder (1480–1528)) 75 55
1700 520 l. "Apollo and Daphne" (Gian Lorenzo Bernini (1598–1680)) 75 55

647 "Nativity" (Federico Brandani)

1980. Christmas.
1701 **647** 120 l. green and brown . . 20 10

648 "My Town" (Treviso)

1980. Stamp Day. Paintings by School-children entitled "My Town". Multicoloured.
1702 70 l. Type **648** 10 10
1703 120 l. Sansepolcro 15 15
1704 170 l. Sansepolcro (different) . 20 15

649 Daniele Comboni and African Village

1981. 150th Birth Anniv and Death Centenary of Daniele Comboni (missionary).
1705 **649** 80 l. brown, indigo and blue 15 10

650 Alcide de Gasperi

651 Landscape outlined by Person in Wheelchair

1981. Birth Centenary of Alcide de Gasperi (politician).
1706 **650** 200 l. green 30 10

1981. International Year of Disabled Persons.
1707 **651** 300 l. multicoloured . . . 45 15

652 Anemone

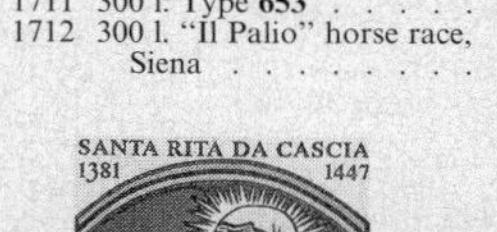

653 Human Chess Game, Marostica

1981. Flowers (1st series). Multicoloured.
1708 200 l. Type **652** 35 15
1709 200 l. Oleander 35 15
1710 200 l. Rose 35 15
See also Nos. 1753/5 and 1797/9.

1981. Europa. Multicoloured.
1711 300 l. Type **653** 60 15
1712 300 l. "Il Palio" horse race, Siena 60 15

654 St. Rita of Cascia

655 Ciro Menotti

1981. 600th Birth Anniv of St. Rita of Cascia.
1713 **654** 600 l. multicoloured . . . 90 35

1981. 150th Death Anniv of Ciro Menotti (patriot).
1714 **655** 80 l. black and brown . . 15 10

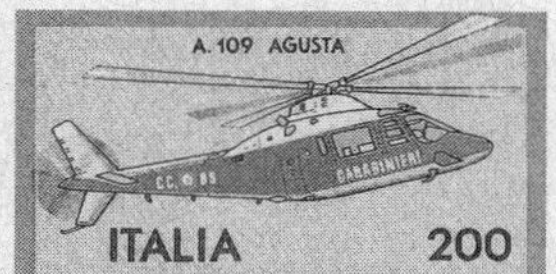

656 Agusta A.109 Helicopter

1981. Italian Aircraft (1st series). Multicoloured.
1715 200 l. Type **656** 40 20
1716 200 l. Partenavia P.68B Victor airplane 40 20
1717 200 l. Aeritalia G.222 transport 40 20
1718 200 l. Aermacchi MB 339 jet trainer 40 20
See also Nos. 1748/51 and 1792/5.

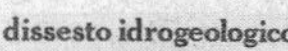

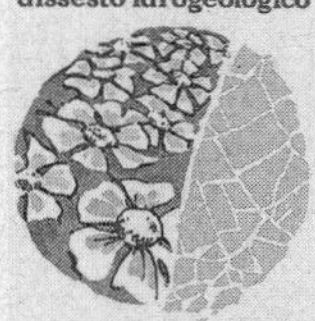

657 Fertile and Barren Soil

1981. Water Conservation.
1719 **657** 80 l. multicoloured . . . 15 10

1981. Italian Work for the World (2nd series). As T **640**.
1720 300 l. blue 35 20
1721 300 l. red 35 20
DESIGNS: No. 1720, Sao Simao, Brazil; No. 1721, High Island, Hong Kong.

1981. Tourist Publicity (8th series). As T **556**. Multicoloured.
1722 80 l. Matera 15 10
1723 150 l. Riva del Garda 20 20
1724 300 l. Santa Teresa di Gallura . 55 15
1725 900 l. Tarquinia . . . . 2·10 60

658 Naval Academy and Badge

1981. Centenary of Naval Academy, Livorno. Multicoloured.
1726 80 l. Type **658** 15 10
1727 150 l. Aerial view of Academy . 20 20
1728 200 l. "Amerigo Vespucci" (cadet ship) and sailor using sextant 45 10

659 Spada Palace, Rome, and Decorative Motif from Grand Hall

1981. 150th Anniv of Council of State.
1729 **659** 200 l. brown, green & bl . 30 15

660 Running

661 Riace Bronze

1981. World Cup Light Athletics Championships, Rome.
1730 **660** 300 l. multicoloured . . . 40 15

1981. Italian Artists' Annivs. (8th series). Designs as T **567**. Multicoloured.
1731 200 l. "Harbour" (Carlo Carra (1881–1966)) 35 30
1732 200 l. "Nightfall" (Giuseppe Ugonia (1881–1944)) 35 30

1981. Riace Bronzes (ancient Greek statues). Multicoloured.
1733 200 l. Type **661** 35 15
1734 200 l. Riace bronze (different) . 35 15

662 Virgil (Treviri mosaic)

1981. Death Bimillenary of Virgil (poet).
1735 **662** 600 l. multicoloured . . . 75 40

663 "Still-life" (Gregorio Sciltian)

1981. World Food Day.
1736 **663** 150 l. multicoloured . . . 30 25

1981. Italian Villas (2nd series). As T **646**. Multicoloured.
1737 100 l. Villa Campolieto, Ercolano 15 10
1738 200 l. Villa Cimbrone, Ravello . 35 15
1739 300 l. Villa Pignatelli, Naples . 50 15

664 "Adoration of the Magi" (Giovanni da Campione d'Italia)

1981. Christmas.
1740 **664** 200 l. dp bl, brn & bl . . 30 10

665 Pope John XXIII

666 Envelopes forming Railway Track

1981. Birth Centenary of Pope John XXIII.
1741 **665** 200 l. multicoloured . . . 40 10

1981. Stamp Day.
1742 **666** 120 l. green, red & black . 75 20
1743 – 200 l. multicoloured . . . 50 20
1744 – 300 l. multicoloured . . . 60 15
DESIGNS—VERT: 200 l. Caduceus, chest, envelopes and cherub blowing posthorn. HORIZ: 300 l. Letter seal.

667 "St. Francis receiving the Stigmata" (Pietro Cavaro)

668 Paganini (after Ingres)

1982. 800th Birth Anniv of St. Francis of Assisi.
1745 **667** 300 l. brown and blue . . 40 15

1982. Birth Bicentenary of Niccolo Paganini (composer and violinist).
1746 **668** 900 l. multicoloured . . . 1·60 1·40

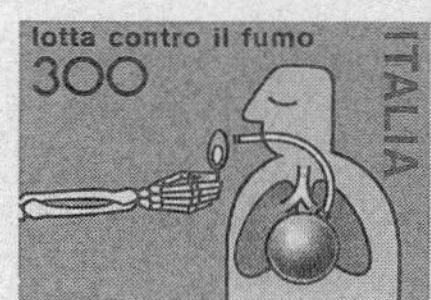

669 Skeletal Hand lighting Cigarette "Bomb"

1982. Anti-Smoking Campaign.
1747 **669** 300 l. multicoloured . . . 40 10

1982. Italian Aircraft (2nd series). As T **656**. Multicoloured.
1748 300 l. Panavia (inscr "Aeritalia") MRCA Tornado jet fighter 50 20
1749 300 l. Savoia SIAI 260 Turbo trainer 50 20
1750 300 l. Piaggio P-166 DL-3 Turbo 50 20
1751 300 l. Nardi NH 500 helicopter 50 20

670 Church of Santo Spirito o del Vespro, Palermo

671 Coronation of Charlemagne, 799

1982. 700th Anniv of Sicilian Vespers (uprising).
1752 **670** 120 l. red, blue & purple . 20 10

1982. Flowers (2nd series). As T **652**. Mult.
1753 300 l. Camellias 70 30
1754 300 l. Carnations 70 30
1755 300 l. Cyclamen 70 30

1982. Europa.
1756 **671** 200 l. brown, black & bl . 40 30
1757 – 450 l. multicoloured . . . 70 30
DESIGN: 450 l. Stars and signatures to Treaty of Rome, 1957.

1982. Italian Work for the World (3rd series). As T **640**. Multicoloured.
1758 450 l. Radio communication across Red Sea 50 25
1759 450 l. Automatic letter sorting . 50 25

672 Garibaldi **673** Bridge Game, Pisa

1982. Death Centenary of Giuseppe Garibaldi.
1760 **672** 200 l. multicoloured . . . 65 20

1982. Folk Customs (1st series).
1761 **673** 200 l. multicoloured . . . 45 35
See also Nos. 1804, 1850, 1875/6, 1914, 1972, 2004, 2028 and 2092.

1982. Tourist Publicity (9th series). As T **556**. Multicoloured.
1762 200 l. Frasassi Grotto 40 35
1763 200 l. Fai della Paganella . . . 40 25
1764 450 l. Rodi Garganico 70 30
1765 450 l. Temples of Agrigento . . 70 30

674 Coxless Four

1982. World Junior Rowing Championships.
1766 **674** 200 l. multicoloured . . . 45 40

675 Ducal Palace, Urbino, Montefeltro and Palazzo dei Consoli, Gubbio

1982. 500th Death Anniv of Federico da Montefeltro, Duke of Urbino.
1767 **675** 200 l. multicoloured . . . 30 20

676 Footballer holding aloft World Cup

1982. Italy's World Cup Football Victory.
1768 **676** 1000 l. multicoloured . . 2·40 1·75

677 Seating Plan

1982. 69th Interparliamentary Union Conference.
1769 **677** 450 l. multicoloured . . . 50 25

1982. Italian Villas (3rd series). As T **646**. Multicoloured.
1770 150 l. Temple of Aesculapius, Villa Borghese, Rome . . . 50 20
1771 250 l. Villa D'Este, Tivoli . . . 95 15
1772 350 l. Villa Lante, Bagnaia, Viterbo . . . . 1·60 35

678 Francis of Taxis

1982. Commemoration of Establishment of First Public Postal System in Europe.
1773 **678** 300 l. red, blue & verm . . 35 20

1982. Italian Artists' Annivs. (9th series). As T **567**. Multicoloured.
1774 300 l. "Portrait of Antonietta Negroni Prati Morosini as a Child" (Francesco Hayez (1791–1882)) 60 20
1775 300 l. "The Fortuneteller" (Giovanni Piazzetta (1682–1754)) 60 20

679 Tree, Chair and Bed (Maria di Pastena)

1983. Stamp Day. Timber in Human Life. Drawings by Schoolchildren. Multicoloured.
1776 150 l. Type **679** 35 20
1777 250 l. Tree with timber products in branches (Lucia Andreoli) 55 20
1778 350 l. Forest (Marco Gallea) . 80 25

680 Microscope

1983. Cancer Control.
1779 **680** 400 l. multicoloured . . . 70 15

1983. Italian Work for the World (4th series). Automobile Industry. As T **640**. Multicoloured.
1780 400 l. Factories on globe . . . 35 25
1781 400 l. Assembly line 35 25

681 Academy Emblem **682** Shooting

1983. 400th Anniv of Accademia della Crusca (Florentine Academy of Letters).
1782 **681** 400 l. red, brown & blue . . 70 15

1983. World Biathlon Championships, Antholz.
1783 **682** 200 l. multicoloured . . . 50 30

683 Gabriele Rossetti **684** Guicciardini (after G. Bugiardini)

1983. Birth Centenary of Gabriele Rossetti (poet).
1784 **683** 300 l. blue and brown . . 30 10

1983. 500th Birth Anniv of Francesco Guicciardini (lawyer and diplomat).
1785 **684** 450 l. brown 70 30

685 Saba and Trieste **686** Pope Pius XII

1983. Birth Centenary of Umberto Saba (poet).
1786 **685** 600 l. multicoloured . . . 1·00 35

1983. 25th Death Anniv of Pope Pius XII.
1787 **686** 1400 l. blue . . . . . . 2·40 60

687 Pope and St. Paul's Basilica **688** Launch of Ship

1983. Holy Year. Multicoloured.
1788 250 l. Type **687** 40 30
1789 300 l Pope John Paul II and Basilica of Santa Maria Maggiore 50 15
1790 400 l. Pope and St. John's Basilica 65 15
1791 500 l. Pope and St. Peter's Cathedral. 85 25

1983. Italian Aircraft (3rd series). As T **656**. Multicoloured.
1792 400 l. Savoia SIAI 211 . . . . 75 25
1793 400 l. Agusta A.129 Mangusta helicopter 75 25
1794 400 l. Caproni C22J glider . . 75 25
1795 400 l. Aeritalia/Aermacchi AM-X jet fighter 75 25

1983. Labour Day.
1796 **688** 1200 l. blue . . . . . . 2·00 60

1983. Flowers (3rd series). As T **652**. Mult.
1797 200 l. Gladiolus 90 50
1798 200 l. Mimosa 90 50
1799 200 l. Rhododendron 90 50

689 Galileo (after O. Leoni) and Telescope

1983. Europa. Multicoloured.
1800 400 l. Type **689** . . . . 4·00 40
1801 500 l. Archimedes (marble bust) and screw . . . . 4·00 25

690 Moneta and Doves

1983. 150th Birth Anniv of Ernesto Teodoro Moneta (Nobel Peace Prize winner).
1802 **690** 500 l. multicoloured . . . 90 25

691 Quadriga, Globe and V.D.U.

1983. Third International Juridical Information Congress, Rome.
1803 **691** 500 l. multicoloured . . . 90 25

1983. Folk Customs (2nd issue). As T **673**. Multicoloured.
1804 300 l. Ceri procession, Gubbio . 65 20

692 Elevation of Host **693** Frescobaldi

1983. 20th National Eucharistic Congress, Milan.
1805 **692** 300 l. multicoloured . . . 50 20

1983. Tourist Publicity (10th series). As T **556**. Multicoloured.
1806 250 l. Alghero . . . . 1·00 90
1807 300 l. Bardonecchia 95 25
1808 400 l. Riccione . . . . 1·50 25
1809 500 l. Taranto . . . . 2·25 25

1983. 400th Birth Anniv of Girolamo Frescobaldi (composer).
1810 **693** 400 l. green, bl, & brn . . 60 25

1983. Italian Villas (4th series). As T **646**. Multicoloured.
1811 250 l. Villa Fidelia, Spello . . 95 65
1812 300 l. Villa Imperiale, Pesaro . 85 15
1813 400 l. Michetti Convent, Francavilla al Mare . . . . 1·25 15
1814 500 l. Villa di Riccia . . . . . 1·50 25

694 Francesco de Sanctis **695** "Madonna of the Chair"

1983. Death Centenary of Francesco de Sanctis (writer).
1815 **694** 300 l. multicoloured . . . 50 15

1983. Christmas. 500th Birth Anniv of Raphael (artist). Multicoloured.
1816 250 l. Type **695** 60 20
1817 400 l. "Sistine Madonna" . . . 85 15
1818 500 l. "Madonna of the Candles" 95 15

696 Chain of Letters (Roberta Rizzi) **697** Battered Road Sign

1983. Stamp Day. Drawings by school-children. Multicoloured.
1819 200 l. Type **696** 60 15
1820 300 l. Space postman delivering letter (Maria Grazia Federico) (vert) 85 15
1821 400 l. Steam train leaving envelope and globe (Paolo Bucciarelli) . . . . 1·90 50

1984. Road Safety. Multicoloured.
1822 300 l. Type **697** 70 15
1823 400 l. Crashed car and police-man 80 15

1984. Italian Artists Anniversaries (10th series). As T **567**. Multicoloured.
1824 300 l. "Races at Bois de Boulogne" (Giuseppe de Nittis (1846–1884)) 60 20
1825 400 l. "Paul Guillaume" (Amedeo Modigliani (1884–1920)) 80 20

698 Maserati "Biturbo"

1984. Italian Motor Industry (1st series). Multicoloured.
1826 450 l. Type **698** . . . . 1·40 25
1827 450 l. Iveco "190.38 Special" lorry . . . . 1·40 25
1828 450 l. Same Trattori "Galaxy" tractor . . . . 1·40 25
1829 450 l. Alfa "33" . . . . 1·40 25
See also Nos. 1867/70 and 1933/6.

699 Glassblower, Glasses and Jug

1984. Italian Work for the World (5th series). Ceramic and Glass Industries. Multicoloured.
1830 300 l. Ceramic plaque and furnace 45 20
1831 300 l. Type **699** 45 20

700 European Parliament Building Strasbourg

1984. Second European Parliament Direct Elections.
1832 **700** 400 l. multicoloured . . . 70 30

701 State Forest Corps Helicopter

1984. Nature Protection. Forests. Multicoloured.
1833 450 l. Type **701** . . . . 1·50 80
1834 450 l. Forest animals and burning cigarette . . . . . 1·10 80
1835 450 l. River and litter . . . . 1·75 80
1836 450 l. Wildlife and building construction . . . . 1·75 80

702 Ministry of Posts and Telecommunications, Rome

1984. "Italia '85" International Stamp Exhibition, Rome (1st issue). Multicoloured.
1837 450 l. Type **702** 90 25
1838 550 l. Appian Way . . . . . . 1·10 30
See also Nos. 1857/9, 1862/4, 1871/3 and 1898/1911.

703 G. di Vittorio, B. Buozzi and A. Grandi

1984. 40th Anniv of Rome Pact (foundation of Italian Trade Unions).
1839 **703** 450 l. multicoloured . . . 1·00 25

704 Bridge

1984. Europa. 25th Anniv of European Post and Telecommunications Conference.
1840 **704** 450 l. multicoloured . . . 3·00 50
1841 550 l. multicoloured . . . 5·00 2·00

705 Symposium Emblem

706 Horse-race

1984. Int Telecommunications Symposium, Florence.
1842 **705** 550 l. multicoloured . . . 1·25 35

1984. Centenary of Italian Derby. Multicoloured.
1843 250 l. Type **706** . . . . 1·50 1·25
1844 400 l. Horse-race (different) . . 2·00 40

1984. Tourist Publicity (11th series). As T **556**. Multicoloured.
1845 350 l. Campione d'Italia . . . 1·10 85
1846 400 l. Chiancianco Terme . . . 1·10 15
1847 450 l. Padula . . . . 1·25 20
1848 550 l. Syracuse . . . . 1·25 40

1984. Folk Customs (3rd issue). As T **673**. Multicoloured.
1850 400 l. Procession of Shrine of Santa Rosa, Viterbo . . . . 1·00 20

708 Harvester, Thresher and Medieval Fields Map

1984. Peasant Farming. Multicoloured.
1851 250 l. Type **708** 45 45
1852 350 l. Hand oil press, cart and medieval fields map 75 20

1984. Italian Villas (5th series). As T **646**. Multicoloured.
1853 250 l. Villa Caristo, Stignano . 1·00 85
1854 350 l. Villa Doria Pamphili, Genoa . . . . 1·10 70
1855 400 l. Villa Reale, Stupinigi . . 1·25 20
1856 450 l. Villa Mellone, Lecce . . 1·40 25

709 Etruscan Bronze of Warrior

710 Dish Aerial, Globe and Punched Tape

1984. "Italia '85" International Stamp Exhibition, Rome (2nd issue). Multicoloured.
1857 550 l. Type **709** 70 30
1858 550 l. Exhibition emblem . . . 70 30
1859 550 l. Etruscan silver-backed mirror 70 30

1985. Information Technology.
1860 **710** 350 l. multicoloured . . . 70 15

711 Man helping Old Woman

712 "Venus in her Chariot" (fresco, Raphael)

1985. Problems of Elderly People.
1861 **711** 250 l. multicoloured . . . 55 35

1985. "Italia '85" International Stamp Exhibition, Rome (3rd issue). Multicoloured.
1862 600 l. Type **712** 70 30
1863 600 l. Exhibition emblem . . . 70 30
1864 600 l. Warriors (detail of fresco, Baldassare Peruzzi) 70 30

713 Plate, Vase and Pot

1985. Italian World Aid (6th series). Ceramics. Multicoloured.
1865 600 l. Type **713** 60 30
1866 600 l. Decorated plate 60 30

1985. Italian Motor Industry (2nd series). As T **698**. Multicoloured.
1867 450 l. Fiat "Uno" 80 25
1868 450 l. Lamborghini "Countach LP500" 80 25
1869 450 l. Lancia "Thema" 80 25
1870 450 l. Fiat Abarth "100 Bialbero" 80 25

714 St. Mary of Peace Church, Rome

715 Pope Sixtus V

1985. "Italia '85" International Stamp Exhibition, Rome (4th issue). Baroque Art. Multicoloured.
1871 250 l. Type **714** 35 25
1872 250 l. Exhibition emblem . . . 35 25
1873 250 l. Fountain obelisk and Saint Agnes's Church, Rome 35 25

1985. 400th Anniv of Election of Pope Sixtus V.
1874 **715** 1500 l. multicoloured . . 3·00 1·00

1985. Folk Customs (4th series). As T **673**. Multicoloured.
1875 250 l. March of the Turks, Potenza 90 30
1876 350 l. Republican regatta, Amalfi . . . . 1·10 15

1985. Tourist Publicity (12th series). As T **556**. Multicoloured.
1877 350 l. Bormio 85 70
1878 400 l. Castellammare di Stabia . 90 20
1879 450 l. Stromboli . . . . . . 1·00 25
1880 600 l. Termoli . . . . 1·90 35

716 European Otter

717 Aureliano Pertile and Giovanni Martinelli (singers)

1985. Nature Protection. Multicoloured.
1881 500 l. Type **716** 65 30
1882 500 l. Primulas 65 30
1883 500 l. Fir tree 65 30
1884 500 l. Black winged stilts . . . 2·00 50

1985. Anniversaries of Italian Artists (11th series). As T **567**. Multicoloured.
1885 350 l. "Madonna" (Giambattista Salvi (1609–85)) 90 60
1886 400 l. "The Pride of Work" (Mario Sironi (1885–1961) . 1·10 15

1985. Europa. Music Year. Multicoloured.
1887 500 l. Type **717** . . . . 3·00 25
1888 600 l. Vicenzo Bellini and Johann Sebastian Bach (composers) . . . . 4·50 50

718 San Salvatore Abbey

1985. 950th Anniv of San Salvatore Abbey, Mt. Amiata.
1889 **718** 450 l. multicoloured . . . 1·25 20

719 Cyclists

1985. World Cycling Championships, Bassano del Grappa.
1890 **719** 400 l. multicoloured . . . 1·25 15

720 U.N. and Congress Emblems and Globe

1985. Seventh United Nations Crime Prevention Congress, Milan.
1891 **720** 600 l. multicoloured . . . 1·90 30

721 Profile and Emblem

1985. International Youth Year.
1892 **721** 600 l. multicoloured . . . 1·90 30

1985. Villas (6th series). As T **646**. Multicoloured.
1893 300 l. Villa Nitti, Maratea . . 1·10 30
1894 400 l. Villa Aldrovandi Mazzacorati, Bologna . . . 1·50 20
1895 500 l. Villa Santa Maria, Pula . 2·00 30
1896 600 l. Villa de Mersi, Villazzano . . . . 2·25 40

722 State Emblems of Italy and Vatican City and Medallion (Mario Soccorsi)

1985. Ratification of the Modification of 1929 Lateran Concordat.
1897 **722** 400 l. multicoloured . . . 1·10 15

723 Parma Town Hall and 1857 25 c. Stamp

724 Basel 1845 $2\frac{1}{2}$ r. Stamp

1985. "Italia '85" International Stamp Exhibition. Rome (5th issue). Multicoloured. (a) As T **723**.
1898 300 l. Type **723** 55 40
1899 300 l. Naples New Castle and 1858 2 g. stamp 55 40
1900 300 l. Palermo Cathedral and Sicily 1859 $\frac{1}{2}$ g. stamp . . . 55 40
1901 300 l. Modena Cathedral and 1852 15 c. stamp 55 40
1902 300 l. Piazzo Navona, Rome, and Papal States 1852 7 b. stamp 55 40
1903 300 l. Palazzo Vecchio, Florence, and Tuscany 1851 2 c. stamp 55 40
1904 300 l. Turin and Sardinia 1861 3 l. stamp 55 40
1905 300 l. Bologna and Romagna 1859 6 b. stamp 55 40
1906 300 l. Palazzo Litta, Milan, and Lombardy and Venetia 1850 15 c. stamp 55 40

(b) As T **724**.
1907 500 l. Type **724** . . . . 1·00 35
1908 500 l. Japan 1871 48 m. stamp . 1·00 35
1909 500 l. United States 1847 10 c. stamp . . . . 1·00 35
1910 500 l. Western Australia 1854 1d. stamp . . . . 1·00 35
1911 500 l. Mauritius 1848 2d. stamp . . . . 1·00 35

725 Skiers

1986. Cross-country Skiing.
1913 **725** 450 l. multicoloured . . . 1·00 20

1986. Folk Customs (5th series). As T **673**. Multicoloured.
1914 450 l. Le Candelore, Catania . 90 20

726 Amilcare Ponchielli and Scene from "La Gioconda"

1986. Composers. Multicoloured.
1915 2000 l. Type **726** (death centenary) . . . . 3·25 80
1916 2000 l. Giovan Battista Pergolesi (250th death anniv) . . . . 3·25 80

727 Acitrezza

1986. Tourist Publicity (13th series). Mult.
1917 350 l. Type **727** 65 30
1918 450 l. Capri 85 20
1919 550 l. Merano . . . . . . 1·10 30
1920 650 l. San Benedetto del Tronto . . . . 1·25 40

728 Heart-shaped Tree (life) 729 "Eyes"

1986. Europa. Multicoloured.
1921 650 l. Type **728** . . . . 1·10 45
1922 650 l. Star-shaped tree (poetry) 1·10 45
1923 650 l. Butterfly-shaped tree (colour) . . . . 1·10 45
1924 650 l. Sun-shaped tree (energy) 1·10 45

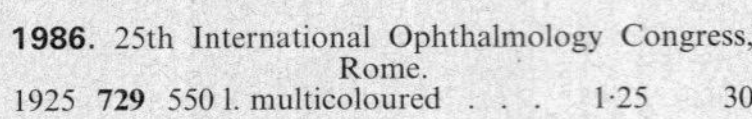

1986. 25th International Ophthalmology Congress, Rome.
1925 **729** 550 l. multicoloured . . . 1·25 30

730 Italian Police

1986. European Police Meeting, Chianciano Terme.
1926 **730** 550 l. multicoloured . . . 75 25
1927 650 l. multicoloured . . . 1·00 35

731 Battle Scene

1986. 120th Anniv of Battle of Bezzecca.
1928 **731** 550 l. multicoloured . . . 1·10 25

732 Figure with Flag 733 Bersagliere and Helmets

1986. National Independence Martyrs' Day.
1929 **732** 2000 l. multicoloured . . 3·50 60

1986. 150th Anniv of Turin Bersaglieri Corps (alpine troops).
1930 **733** 450 l. multicoloured . . . 1·40 15

734 Dish Aerial, Transmitter and "Messages"

1986. Telecommunications.
1931 **734** 350 l. multicoloured . . . 60 15

735 Varallo

1986. Holy Mountain of Varallo.
1932 **735** 2000 l. green and blue . . 3·25 55

1986. Italian Motor Industry (3rd series). As T **698**. Multicoloured.
1933 450 l. Alfa Romeo "AR 8 Turbo" 65 25
1934 450 l. Innocenti "650 SE" . . . 65 25
1935 450 l. Ferrari "Testarossa" . . 65 25
1936 450 l. Fiatallis "FR 10B" . . . 65 25

736 Clothes and Woman (fashion)

1986. Italian World Aid (7th series). Mult.
1937 450 l. Type **736** 80 20
1938 450 l. Man and clothes (fashion) 80 20
1939 650 l. Olivetti personal computer, keyboard and screen . . 1·10 30
1940 650 l. Breda steam turbine . . 1·10 30

737 Airplane flying through "40" 738 "Madonna and Child" (bronze sculpture by Donatello)

1986. 40th Anniv of Alitalia (national airline). Multicoloured.
1941 550 l. Type **737** . . . . 1·25 20
1942 650 l. Airplane and landing lights . . . . 1·40 25

1986. Villas (7th series). As T **646**. Mult.
1943 350 l. Villa Necker, Trieste . . 65 15
1944 350 l. Villa Borromeo, Cassana d'Adda 65 15
1945 450 l. Villa Palagonia, Bagheria 85 15
1946 550 l. Villa Medicea, Poggio a Caiano . . . . 1·10 20
1947 650 l. Issogne Castle . . . . 1·25 25

1986. Christmas.
1948 **738** 450 l. bistre . . . . . . 1·00 10

1986. Anniversaries of Italian Artists (12th series). As T **567**.
1949 450 l. black and orange . . . 1·25 20
1950 550 l. multicoloured . . . . . 1·50 20
DESIGNS: 450 l. Drawing of woman (Andrea del Sarto (1486–1531)); 550 l. "Daphne at Pavarola" (Felice Casorati (1883–1963)).

739 Lockheed Hercules Transport dropping Squares in National Colours onto Globe 740 Engraving 1862 Stamp

1986. International Peace Year. Multicoloured.
1951 550 l. Type **739** . . . . 1·00 20
1952 650 l. Airplane, Cross and people (commemoration of Italian airmen killed on mission to Kindu, Congo) . 1·25 20

1986. Stamp Day. Francesco Maria Matraire (engraver).
1953 **740** 550 l. multicoloured . . . 1·25 15

741 Woven Threads (Marzotto Textile Industry)

1987. Italian Industry.
1954 **741** 700 l. multicoloured . . . 1·10 30
1955 – 700 l. blue & turquoise . . 1·10 30
DESIGN: No. 1955, Clouds and flame (Italgas Gas Corporation).

742 River Volturno 743 Gramsci

1987. Nature Protection. Rivers and Lakes. Multicoloured.
1956 500 l. Type **742** 85 30
1957 500 l. Lake Garda 85 30
1958 500 l. Lake Trasimeno 85 30
1959 500 l. River Tirso 85 30

1987. 50th Death Anniv of Antonio Gramsci (politician).
1960 **743** 600 l. grey, black & red . 90 15

744 Church of the Motorway of the Sun, Florence (Giovanni Michelucci) 745 View of Naples on Football

1987. Europa. Architecture. Multicoloured.
1961 600 l. Type **744** . . . . . . 1·25 20
1962 700 l. Termini station, Rome (Nervi) . . . . 1·75 35

1987. Tourist Publicity (14th series). As T **556**. Multicoloured.
1963 380 l. Verbania Pallanza . . . 85 30
1964 400 l. Palmi 95 20
1965 500 l. Vasto . . . . 1·10 20
1966 600 l. Villacidro . . . . . . 1·40 30

1987. S.S.C. Naples, National Football Champion, 1986–87.
1967 **745** 500 l. multicoloured . . . 2·75 40

746 "The Absinthe Drinker" (Edgar Degas)

747 Liguori and Gulf of Naples

1987. Anti-alcoholism Campaign.
1968 **746** 380 l. multicoloured . . . 1·00 15

1987. Death Bicentenary of St. Alfonso Maria de Liguori (co-founder of Redemptorists).
1969 **747** 400 l. multicoloured . . . 80 15

748 Emblem and Olympic Stadium, Rome

1987. World Light Athletics Championships, Rome (1970) and "Olymphilex '87" Stamp Exhibition, Rome (1971).
1970 700 l. Type **748** . . . . . . 1·00 20
1971 700 l. International Olympic Committee building, Foro Italico, Rome . . . . . . 1·00 20

1987. Folk Customs (6th series). As T **673**. Multicoloured.
1972 380 l. Joust, Foligno 85 15

749 Piazza del Popolo, Ascoli Piceno

750 "The Adoration in the Manger" (St. Francis's Basilica, Assisi)

1987. Piazzas (1st series). Multicoloured.
1973 380 l. Type **749** 70 20
1974 500 l. Piazza Giuseppe Verdi, Palermo 85 15
1975 600 l. Piazza San Carlo, Turin . 95 15
1976 700 l. Piazza dei Signori, Verona . . . . 1·10 15
See also Nos. 2002/3 and 2023/4.

1987. Christmas. Frescoes by Giotto. Mult.
1977 500 l. Type **750** . . . . . . 1·00 15
1978 600 l. "Epiphany" (Scrovegni Chapel, Padua) . . . . . . 1·10 15

751 Battle Scene

1987. 120th Anniv of Battle of Mentana.
1979 **751** 380 l. multicoloured . . . 85 15

752 "Christ Pantocrator" (mosaic, Monreale Cathedral)

1987. Artistic Heritage. Multicoloured.
1980 500 l. Type **752** . . . . . . 1·40 20
1981 500 l. San Carlo Theatre, Naples (18th-century engraving) . . . . 1·40 20

753 College and 1787 and 1987 Uniforms   **754** Marco de Marchi (philatelist) and Milan Cathedral

1987. Bicentenary of Nunziatella Military Academy, Naples.
1982 **753** 600 l. multicoloured . . . 1·25 20

1987. Stamp Day.
1983 **754** 500 l. multicoloured . . . 1·25 15

755 Man chipping Flints   **756** Lyceum

1988. "Homo aeserniensis".
1984 **755** 500 l. multicoloured . . . 85 15

1988. E.Q. Visconti Lyceum, Rome.
1985 **756** 500 l. multicoloured . . . 85 15
See also Nos. 2019, 2109 and 2127.

757 Statue, Bosco and Boy   **758** 15th-Century Soncino Bible

1988. Death Centenary of St. John Bosco (founder of Salesian Brothers).
1986 **757** 500 l. multicoloured . . . 70 15

1988. Anniversaries of Italian Artists (13th series). As T **567**. Multicoloured.
1987 650 l. "Archaeologists" (Giorgio de Chirico (1888–1978)) . . . 1·25 20

1988. 500th Anniv of First Printing of Bible in Hebrew.
1988 **758** 550 l. multicoloured . . . 1·25 20

759 St Valentine, Epileptics and Wave Patterns

1988. Anti-epilepsy Campaign.
1989 **759** 500 l. multicoloured . . . 90 15

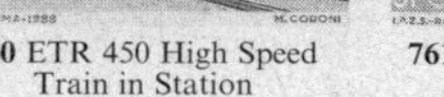

760 ETR 450 High Speed Train in Station   **761** Golfer on Ball

1988. Europa. Transport and Communications. Multicoloured.
1990 650 l. Type **760** . . . 55 30
1991 750 l. Map and keyboard operator (electronic postal systems) . . . 1·50 40

1988. Tourist Publicity (15th series). As T **556**. Multicoloured.
1992 400 l. Castiglione della Pescaia . 65 30
1993 500 l. Lignano Sabbiadoro . . 80 30
1994 650 l. St. Domenico's Church, Noto . . . 90 15
1995 750 l. Vieste . . . 95 40

1988. Golf.
1996 **761** 500 l. multicoloured . . . 90 15

762 Stadium and Mascot   **763** Milan Cathedral on Football

1988. World Cup Football Championship, Italy (1990) (1st series).
1997 **762** 3150 l. multicoloured . . 4·00 2·75
See also Nos. 2049 and 2052/87.

1988. A. C. Milan. National Football Champion, 1987–88.
1998 **763** 650 l. multicoloured . . . 90 40

764 Horse's Head

1988. Artistic Heritage. Pergola Bronzes. Multicoloured.
1999 500 l. Type **764** . . . 80 30
2000 650 l. Bust of woman . . . 1·00 40

765 Student (bas-relief)   **766** Emblem and Appian Way

1988. 900th Anniv of Bologna University.
2001 **765** 500 l. violet . . . 70 15

1988. Piazzas (2nd series). As T **749**. Mult.
2002 400 l. Piazza del Duomo, Pistoia . . . 70 20
2003 550 l. Piazza del Unita d'Italia, Trieste . . . 80 20

1988. Folk Customs (7th series). As T **673**. Multicoloured.
2004 500 l. Candle procession, Sassari . . . 90 15

1988. "Roma 88" Int Gastroenterology and Digestive Endoscopy Congress.
2005 **766** 750 l. multicoloured . . . 1·25 30

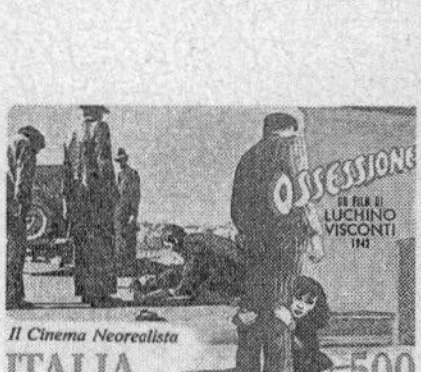

767 "Ossessione" (Luchino Visconti, 1942)   **769** "Holy Family" (Pasquale Celommi)

768 Bird (aluminium)

1988. Italian Films. Scenes from and Advertising Posters of named Films. Multicoloured.
2006 500 l. Type **767** . . . 90 30
2007 650 l. "Ladri di Biciclette" (Vittorio de Sica, 1948) . . . 1·00 30
2008 2400 l. "Roma Citta Aperta" (Roberto Rossellini, 1945) . 3·25 70
2009 3050 l. "Riso Amaro" (Giuseppe de Santis, 1949) . 5·00 1·00

1988. Italian Industry. Multicoloured.
2010 750 l. Type **768** . . . 80 25
2011 750 l. Oscilloscope display (electronics) . . . 80 25
2012 750 l. Banknote engraving, 1986 tourism stamp and medals (60th anniv of State Polygraphic Institute) . . . 80 25

1988. Christmas (1st issue).
2013 **769** 650 l. multicoloured . . . 1·25 10
See also No. 2015.

770 Borromeo and Plague Victims

1988. 450th Birth Anniv of St. Carlo Borromeo, Archbishop of Milan.
2014 **770** 2400 l. multicoloured . . 2·75 75

771 "Nativity" (bas-relief)   **772** Edoardo Chiossone (stamp designer) and Japanese 1879 2 s. "Koban" Stamp

1988. Christmas (2nd issue).
2015 **771** 500 l. green and brown . . 1·10 10

1988. Stamp Day.
2016 **772** 500 l. multicoloured . . . 60 10

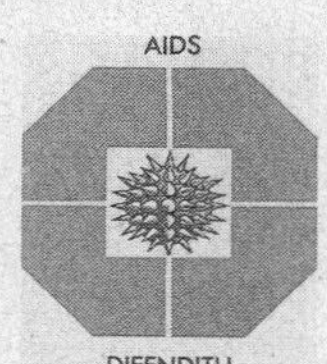

773 AIDS Virus

1989. Anti-AIDS Campaign.
2017 **773** 650 l. multicoloured . . . 1·00 15

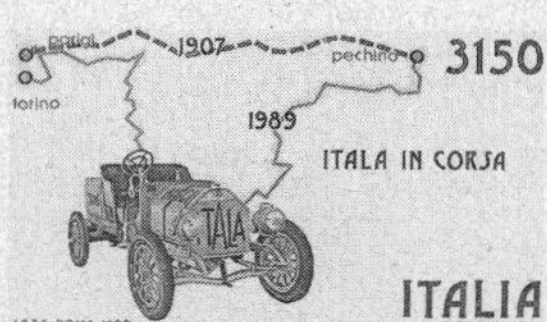

774 1907 Itala Car and Route Map

1989. Re-enactment of 1907 Peking–Paris Car Rally.
2018 **774** 3150 l. multicoloured . . 4·00 3·00

1989. Giuseppe Parini Lyceum, Milan. As T **756**.
2019 650 l. multicoloured . . . 1·10 20

776 Fresco, Ragione Palace, Padua   **777** Stylized Yachts

1989. Artistic Heritage.
2020 **776** 500 l. multicoloured . . . 90 30
2021 – 650 l. blue . . . 1·00 20
DESIGN: 650 l. Crypt, Basilica of St. Nicolas, Bari.

1989. World Sailing Championships, Alassio, Naples and Porto Cervo.
2022 **777** 3050 l. multicoloured . . 3·75 60

1989. Piazzas (3rd series). As T **749**. Mult.
2023 400 l. Piazza di Spagna, Rome . 50 30
2024 400 l. Piazza del Duomo, Catanzaro . . . 50 30

778 Leap-frog (Luca Rizzello)

1989. Europa. Children's Games. Mult.
2025 500 l. Type **778** . . . 65 15
2026 650 l. Girl dressing up (Serena Forcuti) (vert) . . . 80 15
2027 750 l. Sack race (Adelise Lahner) . . . 1·25 30

1989. Folk Customs (8th series). As T **673**. Multicoloured.
2028 400 l. Spello flower paintings . 55 35

779 Cloisters

1989. Pisa University.
2029 **779** 500 l. violet . . . 70 35

780 Parliamentary Emblem as Tree on Map   **781** 1889 5 c. Savoy Arms Stamp

1989. 3rd Direct Elections to European Parliament.
2030 **780** 500 l. multicoloured . . . 90 35
No. 2030 is also inscribed with the European Currency Unit rate of 0.31 ECU.

1989. Tourist Publicity (16th series). As T **556**. Multicoloured.
2031 500 l. Grottammare . . . 85 35
2032 500 l. Spotorno . . . 85 35
2033 500 l. Pompeii . . . 85 35
2034 500 l. Giardini Naxos . . . 85 35

1989. Centenary of Ministry of Posts and Telecommunications. Multicoloured.
2035 500 l. Type **781** . . . 1·00 60
2036 2400 l. Globe within posthorn . 3·25 75

782 Ball and Club Emblem

1989. Inter Milan, National Football Champion, 1988–89.
2037 **782** 650 l. multicoloured . . . 1·00 45

783 Stylized Chamber

1989. Centenary of Interparliamentary Union.
2038 **783** 750 l. multicoloured . . . 1·10 40

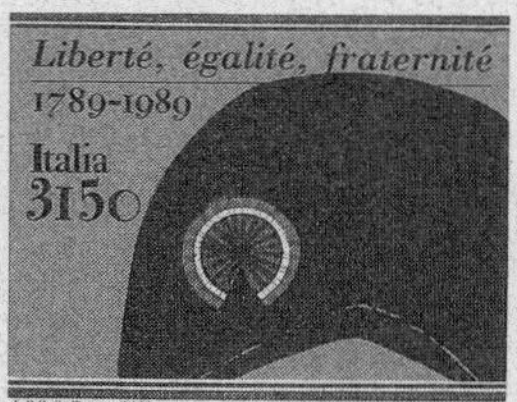

784 Phrygian Cap

1989. Bicentenary of French Revolution.
2039 **784** 3150 l. multicoloured . . 3·50 3·00

785 Corinaldo Wall

1989. Artistic Heritage. 550th Birth Anniv of Francesco di Giorgio Martini (architect).

2040	**785**	500 l. multicoloured . . .	75	25

786 Chaplin in Film Scenes

1989. Birth Centenary of Charlie Chaplin (film actor and director).

2041	**786**	750 l. black and brown . .	1·50	40

787 "Inauguration of Naples—Portici Line" (left-hand detail, S Fergola)

1989. 150th Anniv of Naples–Portici Railway. Multicoloured.

2042	550 l. Type **787**	1·00	30
2043	550 l. Right-hand detail . . .	1·00	30

Nos. 2042/3 were printed together, se-tenant, forming a composite design.

788 Castelfidardo, Accordion and Stradella

1989. Italian Industry. Multicoloured.

2044	450 l. Type **788**	50	25
2045	450 l. Books (Arnoldo Mondadori Publishing House)	50	25

789 Madonna and Child
790 Emilio Diena (stamp dealer)

1989. Christmas. Details of "Adoration of the Magi" (Correggio). Multicoloured.

2046	500 l. Type **789**	80	25
2047	500 l. Magi	80	25

Nos. 2046/7 were printed together, se-tenant, forming a composite design.

1989. Stamp Day.

2048	**790**	500 l. black, brown & bl .	70	15

791 Monument (Mario Ceroli) and Football Pitch
792 Old Map (left half) with Route superimposed

1989. World Cup Football Championship, Italy (1990) (2nd issue).

2049	**791**	450 l. multicoloured . . .	1·00	35

1990. Columbus's First Voyages, 1474–84, Multicoloured.

2050	700 l. Type **792**	85	35
2051	700 l. Right half of map . . .	85	35

Nos. 2050/1 were printed together, se-tenant, forming a composite design.

793 Italy

1990. World Cup Football Championship, Italy (3rd issue). Designs showing finalists' emblems or playing venues. Multicoloured.

2052	450 l. Type **793**	50	30
2053	450 l. U.S.A.	50	30
2054	450 l. Olympic Stadium, Rome	50	30
2055	450 l. Comunale Stadium, Florence	50	30
2056	450 l. Austria	50	30
2057	450 l. Czechoslovakia	50	30
2058	600 l. Argentina	70	35
2059	600 l. U.S.S.R.	70	35
2060	600 l. San Paolo-Stadium, Naples	70	35
2061	600 l. New Stadium, Bari . . .	70	35
2062	600 l. Cameroun	70	35
2063	600 l. Rumania	70	35
2064	650 l. Brazil	75	40
2065	650 l. Costa Rica	75	40
2066	650 l. Delle Alpi Stadium, Turin	75	40
2067	650 l. Ferraris Stadium, Genoa	75	40
2068	650 l. Sweden	75	40
2069	650 l. Scotland	75	40
2070	700 l. United Arab Emirates .	85	45
2071	700 l. West Germany	85	45
2072	700 l. Dall'Ara Stadium, Bologna	85	45
2073	700 l. Meazza Stadium, Milan .	85	45
2074	700 l. Colombia	85	45
2075	700 l. Yugoslavia	85	45
2076	800 l. Belgium	90	50
2077	800 l. Uruguay	90	50
2078	800 l. Bentegodi Stadium, Verona	90	50
2079	800 l. Friuli Stadium, Udine . .	90	50
2080	800 l. South Korea	90	50
2081	800 l. Spain	90	50
2082	1200 l. England	1·50	75
2083	1200 l. Netherlands	1·50	75
2084	1200 l. Sant'Elia Stadium, Cagliari	1·50	75
2085	1200 l. La Favorita Stadium, Palermo	1·50	75
2086	1200 l. Ireland	1·50	75
2087	1200 l. Egypt	1·50	75

See also No. 2104.

1990. Tourist Publicity (17th series). As T **556**. Multicoloured.

2088	600 l. San Felice Circeo . . .	75	30
2089	600 l. Castellammare del Golfo	75	30
2090	600 l. Montepulciano	75	30
2091	600 l. Sabbioneta	75	30

1990. Folk Customs (9th series). As T **673**. Multicoloured.

2092	600 l. Avelignesi horse race, Merano	75	30

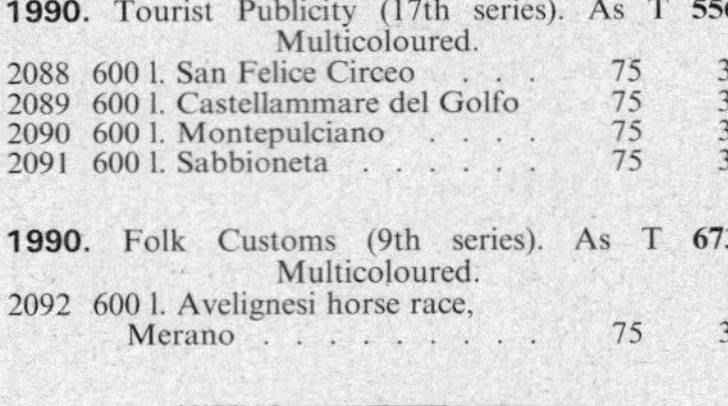

794 National Colours

1990. Death Centenary of Aurelio Saffi.

2093	**794**	700 l. multicoloured . . .	85	35

795 Giovanni Giorgi (inventor)
796 Flags, Globe and Workers (after "The Four States" (Pellizza da Volpedo))

1990. 55th Anniv of Invention of Giorgi/MKSA System of Electrotechnical Units.

2094	**795**	600 l. multicoloured . . .	75	30

1990. Centenary of Labour Day.

2095	**796**	600 l. multicoloured . . .	75	30

797 Ball on Map
798 Piazza San Silvestro Post Office, Rome

1990. S. S. C. Naples, National Football Champion, 1989–90.

2096	**797**	700 l. multicoloured . . .	1·00	35

1990. Europa. Post Office Buildings. Mult.

2097	700 l. Type **798**	85	35
2098	800 l. Fondaco Tedeschi post office, Venice	1·00	40

799 Paisiello
800 Globe, Open Book and Bust of Dante

1990. 250th Birth Anniv of Giovanni Paisiello (composer).

2099	**799**	450 l. multicoloured . . .	60	20

1990. Centenary of Dante Alighieri Society.

2100	**800**	700 l. multicoloured . . .	85	35

801 Byzantine Mosaic, Ravenna
802 Malatestiana Temple, Rimini

1990. Artistic Heritage. Multicoloured.

2101	450 l. Type **801**	55	20
2102	700 l. "Christ and Angels" (detail of Rachis altar, Friuli) (Lombard art)	85	35

1990. 40th Anniv of Malatestiana Religious Music Festival.

2103	**802**	600 l. multicoloured . . .	75	30

1990. West Germany, Winner of World Cup Football Championship. As No. 2071 but value changed and additionally inscr "CAMPIONE DEL MONDO".

2104	600 l. multicoloured	1·50	1·00

803 "Still Life"

1990. Birth Cent of Giorgio Morandi (painter).

2105	**803**	750 l. black	90	35

804 Ancient and Modern Wrestlers

1990. World Greco-Roman Wrestling Championships, Rome.

2106	**804**	3200 l. multicoloured . .	3·50	1·50

805 "New Life" (Emidio Vangelli)

1990. Christmas. Multicoloured.

2107	600 l. Type **805**	75	30
2108	750 l. "Adoration of the Shepherds" (fresco by Pellegrino in St. Daniel's Church, Friuli)	90	35

806 Catania University

1990.

2109	–	600 l. multicoloured . . .	80	30
2110	**806**	750 l. blue & ultramarine .	1·00	35

DESIGN—As T **756**: 600 l. Bernardino Telesio High School, Cosenza.

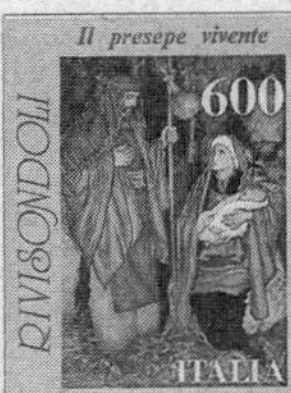

807 Corrado Mezzana (stamp designer, self-portrait)
808 Holy Family

1990. Stamp Day.

2111	**807**	600 l. multicoloured . . .	80	30

1991. "The Living Tableau", Rivisondoli.

2112	**808**	600 l. multicoloured . . .	70	30

809 Fair Emblem
810 Emblem

1991. "EuroFlora '91" Fair, Genoa.

2113	**809**	750 l. multicoloured . . .	90	30

1991. 750th Anniv of Siena University.

2114	**810**	750 l. gold, black & blue .	80	30

1991. Tourist Publicity (18th series). As T **556**. Multicoloured.

2115	600 l. Cagli	70	30
2116	600 l. La Maddalena	70	30
2117	600 l. Roccaraso	70	30
2118	600 l. Sanremo	1·10	30

811 European Community Flag
812 City and Columbus's Fleet

1991. Europa Youth Meeting, Venice.

2119	**811**	750 l. multicoloured . . .	80	30

No. 2119 is also valued in ECUs (European Currency Unit).

1991. 500th Anniv (1992) of Discovery of America by Christopher Columbus (1st issue). Multicoloured.

2120	750 l. Type **812**	1·25	40
2121	750 l. Map, Columbus, seal and King and Queen of Spain . .	80	30

Nos. 2120/1 were printed together, se-tenant, forming a composite design.

See also Nos. 2151/4.

813 Belli and View of Rome

1991. Birth Bicentenary of Giuseppe Gioachino Belli (poet).
2122 **813** 600 l. brown and blue . . 60 25

814 St Gregory's Church, Rome

1991. Artistic Heritage.
2123 **814** 3200 l. multicoloured . . 3·25 1·25

815 "DRS" Satellite

1991. Europa. Europe in Space. Multicoloured.
2124 750 l. Type **815** 90 30
2125 800 l. "Hermes" spaceship and "Columbus" space station . 90 30

816 Sta Maria Maggiore Church, Lanciano

817 Football and Genoa Lantern

1991. Artistic Heritage.
2126 **816** 600 l. brown 60 25

1991. D. A. Azuni Lyceum, Sassari. As T **756**.
2127 600 l. multicoloured 60 25

1991. Sampdoria, National Football Champion, 1990–91.
2128 **817** 3000 l. multicoloured . . 3·00 1·25

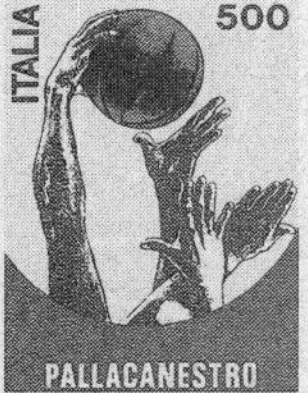

818 Hands and Ball

819 Children and Butterflies

1991. Centenary of Basketball.
2129 **818** 500 l. multicoloured . . . 50 20

1991. United Nations Conference on Rights of the Child. Multicoloured.
2130 600 l. Type **819** 60 25
2131 750 l. Child with balloon on man's shoulders 75 30

820 "Youth and Gulls" (sculpture, Pericle Fazzini)

821 Winged Sphinx

1991. Artistic Heritage. Multicoloured.
2132 **820** 600 l. yellow, blue & blk . 60 25
2133 – 3200 l. multicoloured . . 3·25 1·25
DESIGN: 3200 l. Palazzo Esposizioni, Turin (Pier Luigi Nervi (birth centenary)).

1991. Egyptian Museum, Turin.
2134 **821** 750 l. gold, green & yell . 75 30

822 Luigi Galvani (physiologist) and Experimental Equipment

823 Mozart at Spinet

1991. 100 Years of Radio (1st issue).
2135 **822** 750 l. multicoloured . . . 75 30
Galvani carried out experiments in electricity.
See also Nos. 2148, 2203, 2241 and 2321/2.

1991. Death Bicentenary of Wolfgang Amadeus Mozart (composer).
2136 **823** 800 l. multicoloured . . . 80 30

824 Bear

825 "The Angel of Life" (Giovanni Segantini)

1991. Nature Protection. Multicoloured.
2137 500 l. Type **824** 60 25
2138 500 l. Peregrine falcon 70 25
2139 500 l. Deer 70 25
2140 500 l. Marine life . . . . . . 1·25 25

1991. Christmas.
2141 **825** 600 l. multicoloured . . . 65 25

826 Giulio and Alberto Bolaffi (stamp catalogue publishers)

1991. Stamp Day.
2142 **826** 750 l. multicoloured . . . 80 30

827 Signature and National Flag

1991. Birth Cent of Pietro Nenni (politician).
2143 **827** 750 l. multicoloured . . . 80 30

828 Runners

1992. 22nd European Indoor Light Athletics Championships, Genoa.
2144 **828** 600 l. multicoloured . . . 75 25

829 Neptune Fountain, Florence

830 Statue of Marchese Alberto V of Este (founder) and University

1992. 400th Death Anniv of Bartolomeo Ammannati (architect and sculptor).
2145 **829** 750 l. multicoloured . . . 80 30

1992. 600th Anniv (1991) of Ferrara University.
2146 **830** 750 l. multicoloured . . . 80 30

831 Pediment

1992. Naples University.
2147 **831** 750 l. multicoloured . . . 80 30

1992. 100 Years of Radio (2nd issue). As T **822**. Multicoloured.
2148 750 l. Alessandro Volta (physicist) and Voltaic pile 80 30
Volta formulated the theory of current electricity and invented an electric battery.

832 Emblem and Venue

833 Medal of Lorenzo (Renato Beradi)

1992. "Genova '92" International Thematic Stamp Exhibition (1st issue).
2149 **832** 750 l. multicoloured . . . 75 30
See also Nos. 2170/5.

1992. 500th Death Anniv of Lorenzo de Medici, "The Magnificent".
2150 **833** 750 l. multicoloured . . . 75 30

834 Columbus before Queen Isabella

835 Scenes from Life of St. Maria Filippini (altar, Montefiascone Cathedral)

1992. 500th Anniv of Discovery of America by Columbus (2nd issue). Multicoloured.
2151 500 l. Type **834** 65 20
2152 500 l. Columbus's fleet 75 25
2153 500 l. Sighting land 65 20
2154 500 l. Landing in the New World 75 25

1992. 300th Anniv of Maestre Pie Filippini Institute.
2155 **835** 750 l. multicoloured . . . 75 30

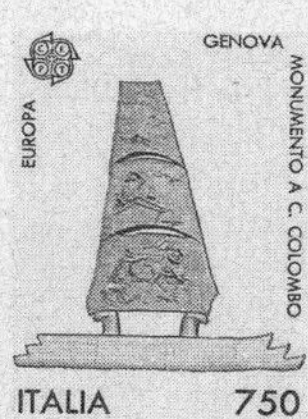

836 Columbus Monument, Genoa (G. Giannetti)

1992. Europa. 500th Anniv of Discovery of America by Columbus. Multicoloured.
2156 750 l. Type **836** . . . . 1·00 30
2157 850 l. Emblem of "Colombo '92" exhibition, Genoa . . . 1·25 35

MORE DETAILED LISTS
are given in the Stanley Gibbons Catalogues referred to in the country headings.
For lists of current volumes see Introduction.

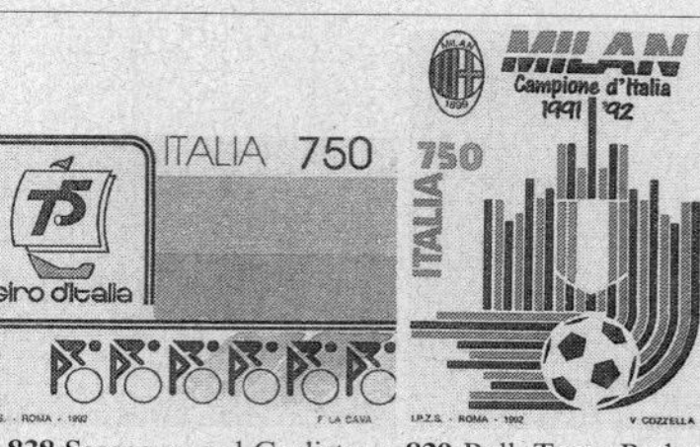

838 Seascape and Cyclists

839 Ball, Team Badge and Stylization of Milan Cathedral

1992. 75th "Tour of Italy" Cycle Race. Mult.
2159 750 l. Type **838** 75 30
2160 750 l. Mountains and cyclists . 75 30
Nos. 2159/60 were issued together, se-tenant, forming a composite design.

1992. A.C. Milan, National Football Champion, 1991–92.
2161 **839** 750 l. green, red & black . 75 30

840 Viareggio

1992. Seaside Resorts. Multicoloured.
2162 750 l. Type **840** 75 30
2163 750 l. Rimini 75 30

841 Nuvolari

1992. Birth Centenary of Tazio Nuvolari (racing driver).
2164 **841** 3200 l. multicoloured . . 3·25 1·25

1992. Tourist Publicity (19th series). As T **556**. Multicoloured.
2165 600 l. Arcevia 60 25
2166 600 l. Braies 60 25
2167 600 l. Maratea 60 25
2168 600 l. Pantelleria 60 25

842 "Adoration of the Shepherds" (detail)

1992. 400th Death Anniv of Jacopo da Ponte (painter).
2169 **842** 750 l. multicoloured . . . 75 30

843 Columbus's House, Genoa

844 Woman's Eyes and Mouth

1992. "Genova '92" International Thematic Stamp Exhibition (2nd issue). Multicoloured.
2170 500 l. Type **843** 50 20
2171 600 l. Departure of Columbus's fleet from Palos, 1492 . . . 80 25
2172 750 l. Route map of Columbus's first voyage . . 75 30
2173 850 l. Columbus sighting land . 85 35
2174 1200 l. Columbus landing on San Salvador . . . . . . 1·60 70
2175 3200 l. Columbus, "Man" (Leonardo da Vinci), "Fury" (Michelangelo) and Raphael's portrait of Michelangelo . . 3·25 1·25

1992. Stamp Day. Ordinary or self-adhesive gum.
2176 **844** 750 l. multicoloured . . . 75 30

845 Map of Europe and Lions Emblem

1992. 75th Anniv of Lions International and 38th Europa Forum, Genoa.
2178 **845** 3000 l. multicoloured . . . 3·00 1·25

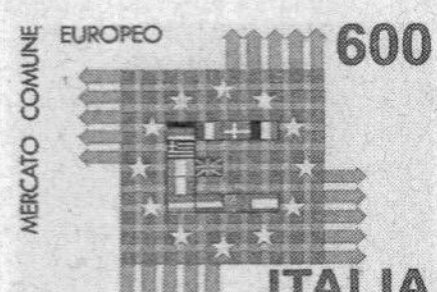

846 European Community Emblem and Members' Flags

1992. European Single Market (1st issue).
2179 **846** 600 l. multicoloured . . . 60 25
See also Nos. 2182/93.

847 Woman with Food Bowl

1992. International Nutrition Conference, Rome.
2180 **847** 500 l. multicoloured . . . 50 20

848 Caltagirone Crib **849** Buildings on Flag of Italy

1992. Christmas.
2181 **848** 600 l. multicoloured . . . 60 25

1993. European Single Market (2nd issue). Designs differing in flag of country and language of inscription. Multicoloured.
2182 750 l. Type **849** 75 30
2183 750 l. Belgium 75 30
2184 750 l. Denmark 75 30
2185 750 l. France 75 30
2186 750 l. Germany 75 30
2187 750 l. Greece 75 30
2188 750 l. Ireland 75 30
2189 750 l. Luxembourg 75 30
2190 750 l. Netherlands 75 30
2191 750 l. Portugal 75 30
2192 750 l. United Kingdom 75 30
2193 750 l. Spain 75 30

850 Russian and Italian Alpine Veterans **851** Mezzettino, Colombina and Arlecchino

1993. 50th Anniv Meeting of Veterans of Battle of Nikolayevka.
2194 **850** 600 l. multicoloured . . . 60 25

1993. Death Bicentenary of Carlo Goldoni (dramatist). Multicoloured.
2195 500 l. Type **851** 40 20
2196 500 l. Arlecchino and portrait of Goldoni 40 20

INDEX

Countries can be quickly located by referring to the index at the end of this volume.

852 "Africa" (mosaic, Roman villa, Piazza Armerina)

1993. Artistic Heritage.
2197 **852** 750 l. multicoloured . . . 80 25

853 Wedge stopping Heart-shaped Cog

1993. National Health Day. Campaign against Heart Disease.
2198 **853** 750 l. multicoloured . . . 70 20

854 Tabby

1993. Domestic Cats. Multicoloured.
2199 600 l. Type **854** 50 30
2200 600 l. White Persian 50 30
2201 600 l. Devon rex (vert) 50 30
2202 600 l. Maine coon (vert) 50 30

1993. 100 Years of Radio (3rd issue). As T **822**. Multicoloured.
2203 750 l. Temistocle Calzecchi Onesti (physicist) and apparatus for detecting electromagnetic waves 80 20

855 "The Piazza" **856** Horace

1993. Death Bicentenary of Francesco Guardi (artist).
2204 **855** 3200 l. multicoloured . . . 3·25 1·60

1993. 2000th Death Anniv of Horace (Quintus Horatius Flaccus) (poet).
2205 **856** 600 l. multicoloured . . . 55 30

857 Cottolengo and Small House of the Divine Providence, Turin **858** "Carousel Horses" (Lino Bianchi Barriviera)

1993. St. Giuseppe Benedetto Cottolengo Commemoration.
2206 **857** 750 l. multicoloured . . . 70 20

1993. Europa. Contemporary Art. Mult.
2207 750 l. Type **858** 80 20
2208 850 l. "Dynamism of Coloured Shapes" (Gino Severini) . . 90 30

859 Medal (Giuseppe Romagnoli) **860** Emblem

1993. 400th Anniv of San Luca National Academy.
2209 **859** 750 l. multicoloured . . . 70 20

1993. "Family Fest '93" International Conference, Rome.
2210 **860** 750 l. multicoloured . . . 70 30

861 Player and Club Badge **863** Canoeing

862 Carloforte

1993. Milan, National Football Champion, 1992–93.
2211 **861** 750 l. multicoloured . . . 80 30

1993. Tourist Publicity (20th series). Mult.
2212 600 l. Type **862** 50 30
2213 600 l. Palmanova 50 30
2214 600 l. Senigallia 50 30
2215 600 l. Sorrento 50 30
See also Nos. 2248/51 and 2315/18.

1993. World Canoeing Championships, Trentino.
2216 **863** 750 l. multicoloured . . . 70 20

864 Observatory **865** Staircase, St. Salome's Cathedral, Veroli

1993. Centenary of Regina Margherita Observatory.
2217 **864** 500 l. multicoloured . . . 55 30

1993. Artistic Heritage.
2218 **865** 750 l. multicoloured . . . 70 20

866 Soldier, Boy with Rifle and German Helmet **867** Carriage

1993. Second World War 50th Anniversaries (1st series). Multicoloured.
2219 750 l. Type **866** (the Four Days of Naples) 70 20
2220 750 l. Menorah, people in railway truck and Star of David (deportation of Roman Jews) 70 20
2221 750 l. Seven Cervi brothers (execution) 70 20
See also Nos. 2259/61.

1993. The Taxis Family in Postal History. Multicoloured.
2222 750 l. Type **867** 60 20
2223 750 l. Taxis arms 60 20
2224 750 l. Gig 60 20
2225 750 l. 17th-century postal messenger 60 20
2226 750 l. 18th-century postal messenger 60 20

868 Head Office, Rome

1993. Centenary of Bank of Italy. Mult.
2227 750 l. Type **868** 80 20
2228 1000 l. 1000 lire banknote (first note issued by Bank) . . . . 1·25 40

869 Colonies Express Letter Stamp Design

1993. Stamp Day. Centenary of First Italian Colonies Stamps.
2229 **869** 600 l. red and blue . . . 55 25

870 Tableau Vivant, Corchiano

1993. Christmas. Multicoloured.
2230 600 l. Type **870** 50 25
2231 750 l. "The Annunciation" (Piero della Francesca) . . . 70 20

871 17th-century Map of Foggia

1993. Treasures from State Archives and Museums (1st series). Multicoloured.
2232 600 l. Type **871** (Foggia Archives) 55 25
2233 600 l. "Concert" (Bartolomeo Manfredi) (Uffizi Gallery, Florence) 55 25
2234 750 l. View of Siena from 15th-century illuminated manuscript (Siena Archives) (vert) 65 20
2235 850 l. "The Death of Adonis" (Sebastiano del Piombo) (Uffizi Gallery) 65 30
See also Nos. 2266/9, 2306/9 and 2346/9.

872 Ringmaster and Bareback Riders **873** Mother and Child inside House

1994. The Circus. Multicoloured.
2236 600 l. Type **872** 45 25
2237 750 l. Clowns 60 20

1994. "The Housewife, a Presence that Counts".
2238 **873** 750 l. multicoloured . . . 60 20

874 "Bread" (Dario Piazza) **876** "The Risen Christ" (statue)

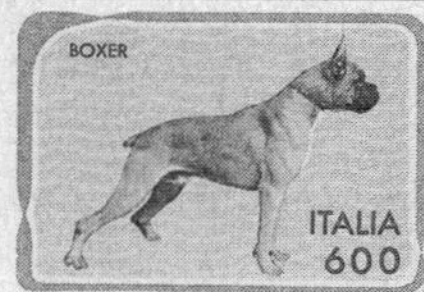

875 Boxer

1994. Paintings of Italian Food. Multicoloured.
2239 500 l. Type **874** 40 25
2240 600 l. "Italian Pasta in the World" (Erminia Scaglione) . 45 25

1994. 100 Years of Radio (4th issue). As T **822**. Multicoloured.
2241 750 l. Augusto Righi (physicist) and his Hertzian oscillator . 60 20

1994. Dogs. Multicoloured.
2242 600 l. Type **875** 45 30
2243 600 l. Dalmatian 45 30
2244 600 l. Maremma sheepdog . . 45 30
2245 600 l. German shepherd . . . 45 30

1994. Procession of "The Risen Christ", Tarquinia.
2246 **876** 750 l. multicoloured . . . 60 20

877 Pacioli in Study

1994. 500th Anniv of Publication of "Summary of Arithmetic, Geometry, Proportion and Proportionality" by Fra' Luca Pacioli.
2247 **877** 750 l. multicoloured . . . 60 20

1994. Tourist Publicity (21st series). As T **862**. Multicoloured.
2248 600 l. Odescalchi Castle, Santa Marinella 45 30
2249 600 l. St. Michael's Abbey, Monticchio 45 30
2250 600 l. Orta San Giulio 45 30
2251 600 l. Cathedral, Messina . . . 45 30

878 Kossuth

879 Women's High-diving

1994. Death Centenary of Lajos Kossuth (Hungarian statesman).
2252 **878** 3750 l. multicoloured . . 3·00 1·50

1994. World Water Sports Championships. Multicoloured.
2253 600 l. Type **879** 45 25
2254 750 l. Water polo 60 20

880 Club Badge, Football and Colours

1994. Milan, National Football Champion, 1993–94.
2255 **880** 750 l. multicoloured . . . 80 30

881 Camillo Golgi (cytologist) and Golgi Cells

882 "Goddess of Caldevigo" (bronze statuette, 5th century B.C.)

1994. Europa. Discoveries. Italian Nobel Prize winners. Multicoloured.
2256 750 l. Type **881** (medicine, 1906) 70 20
2257 850 l. Giulio Natta (chemist) and diagram of polymer structure (chemistry, 1963) . 70 30

1994. "Ancient Peoples of Italy" Archaeological Exhibition, Rimini.
2258 **882** 750 l. multicoloured . . . 60 20

883 Destruction of Montecassino

884 Washing of Feet

1994. Second World War 50th Anniversaries (2nd series). Multicoloured.
2259 750 l. Type **883** 60 20
2260 750 l. Bound prisoners (Ardeatine Caves Massacre) . 60 20
2261 750 l. Family (Marzabotto Massacre) 60 20

1994. 22nd National Eucharistic Congress, Siena.
2262 **884** 600 l. multicoloured . . . 45 25

885 "Ariadne, Venus and Bacchus"

1994. Artistic Heritage. 400th Death Anniv of Tintoretto (artist).
2263 **885** 750 l. multicoloured . . . 60 20

886 "Piazza del Duomo during the Plague, 1630" (attr Cigoli)

1994. 750th Anniv of Arciconfraternita della Misericordia, Florence.
2264 **886** 750 l. multicoloured . . . 60 20

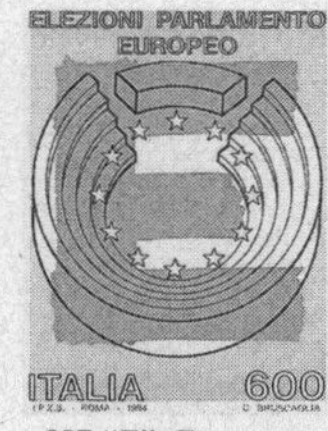

887 "E", European Union Emblem and Parliament

888 Olympic Rings and Pierre de Coubertin (founder)

1994. European Parliament Elections.
2265 **887** 600 l. multicoloured . . . 45 25

1994. Treasures from State Archives and Museums (2nd series). As T **871**. Multicoloured.
2266 600 l. Frontispiece of notary's register, 1623–24 (Catania Archives) (vert) 45 25
2267 600 l. "Death of Patroclus" (Attic vase, 5th century B.C.) (Agrigento Archaeological Museum) (vert) 45 25
2268 750 l. "Galata and his Wife" (statue) (National Roman Museum) (vert) 60 20
2269 850 l. Civic seal, 1745 (Campobasso Archives) (vert) 65 30

1994. Centenary of Int Olympic Committee.
2270 **888** 850 l. multicoloured . . . 65 30

889 Vesuvius and "G 7"

890 Church of the Holy House and "Madonna and Child"

1994. Group of Seven (industrialized countries) Summit, Naples.
2271 **889** 600 l. bl, ultram & grn . . 45 25

1994. 700th Anniv of Shrine of the Nativity of the Virgin, Loreto.
2272 **890** 500 l. multicoloured . . . 40 25

891 Pietro Miliani (papermaker) (after Francesco Rosaspina)

892 Frederick II (sculpture, Bitonto Cathedral)

1994. Stamp Day. Multicoloured.
2273 600 l. Type **891** 45 25
2274 750 l. Paper and Watermark Museum (former St. Dominic's Monastery), Fabriano 60 20

1994. 800th Birth Anniv of Frederick II, Holy Roman Emperor.
2275 **892** 750 l. multicoloured . . . 60 20

893 St. Mark's Basilica

1994. 900th Anniv of Dedication of St. Mark's Basilica, Venice.
2276 **893** 750 l. multicoloured . . . 70 60

894 "The Annunciation" (Melozzo da Forli)

895 Club Emblem on Globe

1994. Christmas. Multicoloured.
2278 600 l. Type **894** 45 25
2279 750 l. "Sacred Conversation" (detail, Lattanzio da Rimini) 60 20

1994. Centenary of Italian Touring Club.
2280 **895** 600 l. multicoloured . . . 45 25

896 Headquarters, Rome

897 New Emblem

1994. 75th Anniv of Credit for Businesses and Public Works.
2281 **896** 750 l. multicoloured . . . 60 20

1994. Incorporation of Italian Post. Size 34 × 26 mm.
2282 – 600 l. red and silver . . . 45 25
2283 **897** 750 l. black, grn & red . . 60 20
2284 – 750 l. red 60 20
DESIGN—VERT: 600 l. Palazzo Querini Dubois, Venice (restored with Post Office help).
For 750 and 850 l. values, size 26 × 17 mm, see Nos. 2343/4.

898 Gentile

899 Rainbow, Dove, Olive Tree and Flood

1994. 50th Death Anniv of Giovanni Gentile (philosopher).
2285 **898** 750 l. multicoloured . . . 60 20

1995. For Flood Victims.
2286 **899** 750 l. + 2250 l. mult . . 4·00 3·00

900 Skater

1995. World Speed Skating Championships, Baselga di Pine.
2287 **900** 750 l. multicoloured . . . 60 20

901 First Issue of "La Domenica del Corriere"

902 Rice

1995. 50th Death Anniv of Achille Beltrame (painter).
2288 **901** 500 l. multicoloured . . . 40 25

1995. Italian Food. Multicoloured.
2289 500 l. Type **902** 40 25
2290 750 l. Olives and olive oil . . . 60 20

903 Grey Herons

1995. Birds. Multicoloured.
2291 600 l. Type **903** 50 25
2292 600 l. Griffon vultures ("Grifone") 50 25
2293 600 l. Golden eagles ("Aquila Reale") 50 25
2294 600 l. Snow finches ("Fringuello Alpino") 50 25

904 Anniversary Emblem

1995. 50th Anniv of U.N.O.
2295 **904** 850 l. black, blue & gold . . 65 30

905 Detail of Monument (Giuseppe Grande)

1995. Centenary of Monument to the Fallen of the Five Days of Milan (1848 uprising).
2296 **905** 750 l. multicoloured . . . 60 20

906 Princess Mafalda of Savoy and Concentration Camp

1995. 50th Anniv of End of Second World War. Multicoloured.
2297 750 l. Type **906** 60 20
2298 750 l. DUKW at Anzio . . . 60 20
2299 750 l. Teresa Gullace and scene of her death 60 20
2300 750 l. Florence Town Hall and Military Medal 60 20
2301 750 l. Vittorio Veneto Town Hall and Military Medal . . 60 20
2302 750 l. Cagliari Town Hall and Military Medal 60 20
2303 750 l. Battle of Mount Lungo . 60 20
2304 750 l. Parachuting supplies in the Balkans 60 20
2305 750 l. Light cruisers of the Eighth Division in Atlantic . 60 20

1995. Treasures from State Archives and Museums (3rd series). As T **871**. Multicoloured.

2306 500 l. Illuminated letter "P" from statute of Pope Innocent III (Rome Archives) (vert) 40 25
2307 500 l. "Port of Naples" (detail, Bernardo Strozzi) (St. Martin National Museum, Naples) . 40 25
2308 750 l. Illuminated letter "I" showing the Risen Christ from 1481 document (Mantua Archives) (vert) . . 60 20
2309 850 l. "Sacred Love and Profane Love" (Titian) (Borghese Museum and Gallery, Rome) 65 30

907 Emblem

908 Santa Croce Basilica, Florence

1995. Centenary of Venice Biennale.

2310 **907** 750 l. blue, gold & yellow . 60 20

1995. Artistic Heritage.

2311 **908** 750 l. brown 60 20

911 Experiment demonstrating X-rays

1995. Europa. Peace and Freedom. Mult.

2312 750 l. Type **909** (50th anniv of end of Second World War in Europe) 60 20
2313 850 l. Mostar Bridge, (Bosnia) and Council of Europe emblem 65 30

909 Soldiers and Civilians celebrating

910 Players

1995. Centenary of Volleyball.

2314 **910** 750 l. blue, orge & grn . . 60 20

1995. Tourist Publicity (22nd series). As T **862**. Multicoloured.

2315 750 l. Alatri 60 20
2316 750 l. Nuoro 60 20
2317 750 l. Susa 60 20
2318 750 l. Venosa 60 20

1995. Centenary of Discovery of X-rays by Wilhelm Rontgen.

2319 **911** 750 l. multicoloured . . . 60 20

912 Player and Club Badge

1995. Juventus, National Football Champion, 1994–95.

2320 **912** 750 l. multicoloured . . . 60 25

913 Villa Griffone (site of Marconi's early experiments)

1995. 100 Years of Radio (5th issue). Centenary of First Radio Transmission. Multicoloured.

2321 750 l. Type **913** 60 20
2322 850 l. Guglielmo Marconi and transmitter (36 × 21 mm) . 65 30

914 St. Antony, Holy Basilica (Padua) and Page of Gospel

916 Milan Cathedral and Eye (congress emblem)

915 Durazzo Pallavicini, Pegli

1995. 800th Birth Anniv of St. Antony of Padua. Multicoloured.

2323 750 l. Type **914** 60 20
2324 850 l. St. Antony holding Child Jesus (painting, Vieira Lusitano) (horiz) 65 30

1995. Public Gardens (1st series). Multicoloured.

2325 750 l. Type **915** 60 20
2326 750 l. Boboli, Florence 60 20
2327 750 l. Ninfa, Cisterna di Latina 60 20
2328 750 l. Parco della Reggia, Caserta 60 20

See also Nos. 2439/42.

1995. 10th European Ophthalmological Society Congress, Milan.

2329 **916** 750 l. multicoloured . . . 60 20

917 "Sailors' Wives"

1995. Birth Centenary of Massimo Campigli (painter).

2330 **917** 750 l. multicoloured . . . 60 20

918 Dome of Santa Maria del Fiore (Florence), Galileo and Albert Einstein

1995. 14th World Relative Physics Conference, Florence.

2331 **918** 750 l. blue, brown & blk . 60 20

919 Rudolph Valentino in "The Son of the Sheik"

1995. Centenary of Motion Pictures.

2332 **919** 750 l. black, blue & red . 60 20
2333 – 750 l. multicoloured . . . 60 20
2334 – 750 l. multicoloured . . . 60 20
2335 – 750 l. multicoloured . . . 60 20

DESIGNS: No. 2333, Toto in "The Gold of Naples"; 2334, Frederico Fellini's "Cabiria Nights"; 2335, Poster (by Massimo Geleng) for "Cinecitta 95" film festival.

920 Wheatfield and Anniversary Emblem

1995. 50th Anniv of F.A.O.

2336 **920** 850 l. multicoloured . . . 65 30

921 St. Albert's Stone Coffin (detail) and Basilica

1995. 900th Anniversaries of Pontida Basilica and Death of St. Albert of Prezzate.

2337 **921** 1000 l. brown and blue . . 80 40

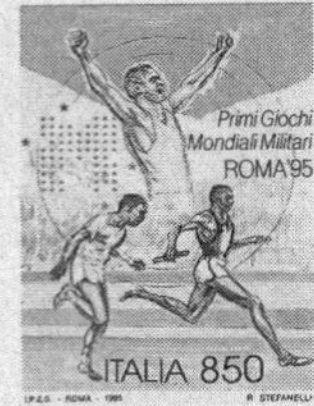

922 Athletes

1995. 1st World Military Games, Rome.

2338 **922** 850 l. multicoloured . . . 65 30

923 Globe and Means of Communication

1995. 50th Anniv of Ansa News Agency.

2339 **923** 750 l. multicoloured . . . 60 20

924 Crib (Stefano da Putignano), Polignano Cathedral

1995. Christmas. Multicoloured.

2340 750 l. Type **924** 60 20
2341 850 l. "Adoration of the Wise Men" (detail, Fra Angelico) . 65 30

925 Renato Mondolfo (philatelist) and Trieste 1949 20 l. Stamp

1995. Stamp Day.

2342 **925** 750 l. multicoloured . . . 60 20

1995. 1st Anniv of Incorporation of Italian Post. Size 26 × 17 mm.

2343 **897** 750 l. red 60 20
2344 850 l. black, grn & red . . 65 30

926 Collage representing Marinetti's Works

1996. 120th Birth Anniv of Filippo Marinetti (writer and founder of Futurist movement).

2345 **926** 750 l. multicoloured . . . 60 20

1996. Treasures from State Archives and Museums (4th series). As T **871**. Multicoloured.

2346 750 l. Arms (Georgofili Academy, Florence) 60 20
2347 750 l. Illuminated letter showing St. Luke and his ox from Constitution of 1372 (Lucca Archives) (vert) 60 20
2348 850 l. Inkwells, pen and manuscript of Gabriele d'Annunzio (writer) (Il Vittoriale, Gardone Riviera) 65 30
2349 850 l. "Life of King Modus and Queen Racio" from 1486 miniature (Turin Archives) . 65 30

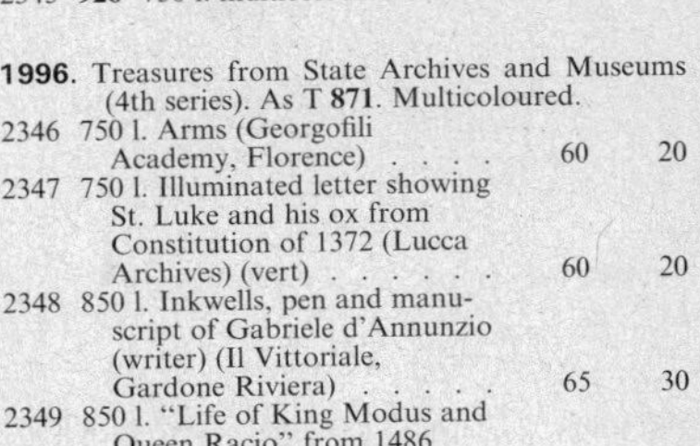

927 "Sarah and the Angel" (fresco, Archbishop's Palace, Udine)

1996. 300th Birth Anniv of Giambattista Tiepolo (painter).

2350 **927** 1000 l. multicoloured . . 80 40

928 White Wine

1996. Italian Wine Production. Multicoloured.

2351 500 l. Type **928** 40 25
2352 750 l. Red wine 60 20

929 Marco Polo and Palace in the Forbidden City

1996. 700th Anniv (1995) of Marco Polo's Return from Asia and "China '96" International Stamp Exhibition, Peking.

2353 **929** 1250 l. multicoloured . . 1·00 50

930 Milan Cathedral (left detail)

931 Quill pen and Satellite (50th Anniv of National Federation of Italian Press)

1996. "Italia 98" International Stamp Exhibition, Milan (1st issue). Multicoloured.

2354 750 l. Type **930** 60 20
2355 750 l. Cathedral (right detail) . 60 20

Nos. 2354/5 were issued together, se-tenant, forming a composite design of the Cathedral.

See also Nos. 2518, 2523, 2528/30 and 2531.

1996. Anniversaries.

2356 **931** 750 l. multicoloured . . . 60 20
2357 – 750 l. blue, pink & black . . 60 20

DESIGN—HORIZ: No. 2357, Globe (centenary of "La Gazetta dello Sport" (newspaper)).

HAVE YOU READ THE NOTES AT THE BEGINNING OF THIS CATALOGUE?

These often provide answers to the enquiries we receive.

932 Postman and Emblem

933 Uniforms of Different Periods

1996. International Museum of Postal Images, Belvedere Ostrense.
2358 **932** 500 l. multicoloured . . . 40 25

1996. Centenary of Academy of Excise Guards.
2359 **933** 750 l. multicoloured . . . 60 20

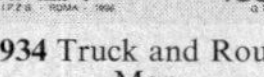

934 Truck and Route Map

935 Carina Negrone (pilot)

1996. Trans-continental Drive, Rome–New York.
2360 **934** 4650 l. multicoloured . . 3·75 1·75

1996. Europa. Famous Women. Multicoloured.
2361 750 l. Type **935** 60 20
2362 850 l. Adelaide Ristori (actress) 65 30

936 Fishes, Sea and Coastline from St. Raphael to Genoa

1996. 20th Anniv of Ramoge Agreement on Environmental Protection of the Mediterranean.
2363 **936** 750 l. multicoloured . . . 80 20

937 Celestino V and Town of Fumone

1996. 700th Death Anniv of Pope Celestino V.
2364 **937** 750 l. multicoloured . . . 60 20

938 St Anthony's Church, Diano Marina

1996. Tourist Publicity (23rd series). Mult.
2365 750 l. Type **938** 60 20
2366 750 l. Pienza Cathedral 60 20
2367 750 l. Belltower of St. Michael the Archangel's Church, Monte Sant'Angelo 60 20
2368 750 l. Prehistoric stone dwelling, Lampedusa 60 20

939 Abbey and Relief from 12th-century Ivory Reliquary

1996. 500th Anniv of Reconsecration of Farfa Abbey.
2369 **939** 1000 l. black, yell & orge . 80 40

940 Fair Entrance and Mt. Pellegrino

1996. Mediterranean Fair, Palermo.
2370 **940** 750 l. multicoloured . . . 60 20

941 State Arms

942 Rider and Emblem

1996. 50th Anniv of Italian Republic.
2371 **941** 750 l. multicoloured . . . 60 20

1996. 50th Anniv of Production of Vespa Motor Scooters.
2372 **942** 750 l. multicoloured . . . 60 20

943 Views of Messina and Venice

1996. 40th Anniv of Founding Meetings of European Economic Community, Messina and Venice.
2373 **943** 750 l. multicoloured . . . 60 20

944 Athlete on Starting Block and 1896 Athletes

1996. Centenary of Modern Olympic Games and Olympic Games, Atlanta. Multicoloured.
2374 500 l. Type **944** 40 25
2375 750 l. Putting the shot and view of Atlanta (vert) 60 20
2376 850 l. Gymnast, stadium and basketball player 65 30
2377 1250 l. 1896 stadium, Athens, and 1996 stadium, Atlanta (vert) . . . . 1·00 50

945 "Acanthobrahmaea europaea"

1996. Butterflies. Multicoloured.
2378 750 l. Type **945** 60 20
2379 750 l. "Melanargia arge" . . . 60 20
2380 750 l. "Papilio hospiton" . . . 60 20
2381 750 l. "Zygaena rubicundus" . 60 20

946 "Prima Comunione"

1996. Italian Films (1st series).
2382 **946** 750 l. black, red & blue . . 60 20
2383 – 750 l. multicoloured . . . 60 20
2384 – 750 l. multicoloured . . . 60 20
DESIGNS: No. 2383, Poster for "Cabiria"; 2384, "Scusate il Ritardo".
See also Nos. 2453/5 and 2528/30.

947 Santa Maria del Fiore

1996. 700th Anniv of Cathedral of Santa Maria del Fiore, Florence.
2385 **947** 750 l. blue 60 20

948 Player, Shield and Club Badge

949 Choppy (congress mascot)

1996. Milan, National Football Champion, 1995–96.
2386 **948** 750 l. multicoloured . . . 60 20

1996. 13th International Prehistoric and Protohistoric Sciences Congress.
2387 **949** 850 l. multicoloured . . . 65 30

950 Games Emblem and Pictograms

952 Rejoicing Crowd and Club Badge

951 Fair Entrance

1996. Mediterranean Games, Bari (1997).
2388 **950** 750 l. multicoloured . . . 60 20

1996. Levant Fair, Bari.
2389 **951** 750 l. multicoloured . . . 60 20

1996. Juventus, European Football Champion, 1995–96.
2390 **952** 750 l. multicoloured . . . 60 20

953 Pertini

954 Montale and Hoopoe

1996. Birth Centenary of Alessandro Pertini (President 1978–85).
2391 **953** 750 l. multicoloured . . . 60 20

1996. Birth Centenary of Eugenio Montale (poet).
2392 **954** 750 l. brown and blue . . 60 20

955 "The Annunciation"

1996. 400th Birth Anniv of Pietro Berrettini da Cortona (artist).
2393 **955** 500 l. multicoloured . . . 40 25

956 Tex Willer (Galep)

1996. Stamp Collecting. Strip Cartoons. Mult.
2394 750 l. Type **956** 60 20
2395 850 l. Corto Maltese (Hugo Pratt) 65 30

957 Vortex and "Stamps"

958 Bell Tower and Former Benedictine Abbey (seat of faculty)

1996. Stamp Day.
2396 **957** 750 l. multicoloured . . . 60 20

1996. Universities.
2397 **958** 750 l. brown 60 20
2398 – 750 l. blue 60 20
2399 – 750 l. green 60 20
DESIGNS—VERT: No. 2397, Type **958** (centenary of Faculty of Agriculture, Perugia University); 2398, Former St. Matthew's Cathedral (seat of Medical School), Salerno University. HORIZ: No. 2399, Athenaeum, Sassari University.

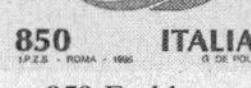

959 Emblem

960 "Madonna of the Quail" (Antonio Pisanello)

1996. World Food Summit, Rome.
2400 **959** 850 l. green and black . . 65 30

1996. Christmas. Multicoloured.
2401 750 l. Type **960** 60 20
2402 850 l. Father Christmas and toys (horiz) 65 30

961 "UNESCO" and Globe

962 Headquarters, Rome

1996. 50th Anniversaries of U.N.E.S.C.O. and U.N.I.C.E.F.
2403 750 l. Type **961** 60 20
2404 850 l. U.N.I.C.E.F. emblem on kite, baby and globe 65 30

1996. 70th Anniv of National Statistics Institute.
2405 **962** 750 l. multicoloured . . . 60 20

963 Bookcase

964 Hall of the Tricolour, Reggio Emilia

1996. 50th Anniv of Strega Prize.
2406 **963** 3400 l. multicoloured . . 2·75 1·25

1997. Bicentenary of First Tricolour (now national flag), Cispalpine Republic.
2407 **964** 750 l. multicoloured . . . 55 30

965 Tower Blocks and Skier

1997. World Alpine Skiiing Championships, Sestriere. Multicoloured.
2408 750 l. Type **965** 55 30
2409 850 l. Olympic colours forming ski run and ski 60 30

966 Ferraris, Early Motor and Ferraris National Electrotechnology Institute, Turin

1997. Death Centenary of Galileo Ferraris (physicist).
2410 **966** 750 l. multicoloured . . . 55 30

967 Loi

1997. 5th Death Anniv of Emanuela Loi (bodyguard killed in Mafia car bombing).
2411 **967** 750 l. multicoloured . . . 55 30

969 Statue of Marcus Aurelius

970 St. Germiniano (after Bartolomeo Schedoni) holding Modena Cathedral

1997. 40th Anniv of Treaty of Rome (foundation of European Economic Community).
2413 **969** 750 l. multicoloured . . . 55 30

1997. 1600th Death Anniv of St. Germiniano (patron saint of Modena).
2414 **970** 750 l. multicoloured . . . 50 25

971 "Baptism of St. Ambrose" and "Hand of God recalling him to City"

972 Statue of Minerva, Central Square

1997. 1600th Death Anniv of St. Ambrose, Bishop of Milan.
2415 **971** 1000 l. multicoloured . . 70 35
The illustrations are taken from reliefs by Volvinio on the Golden Altar in St. Ambrose's Cathedral, Milan.

1997. Universities.
2416 **972** 750 l. red 50 25
2417 – 750 l. blue 50 25
DESIGN: (Rome University); No. 2417, Palace of Bo, Padua University.

973 St. Peter's Cathedral and Colosseum within "Wolf suckling Romulus and Remus"

1997. 2750th Anniv of Foundation of Rome.
2418 **973** 850 l. multicoloured . . . 60 30

974 Pre-Roman Walls, Gela

975 First Page of Prison Notebook and Signature

1997.
2419 **974** 750 l. multicoloured . . . 50 25

1997. 60th Death Anniv of Antonio Gramsci (politician).
2420 **975** 850 l. multicoloured . . . 60 30

976 Teracotta Relief and Cloisters

978 Detail of 1901 Poster for "Tosca" and Theatre

977 Shoemaker's Workshop

1997. 500th Anniv of Consecration of Pavia Church.
2421 **976** 1000 l. multicoloured . . 70 35

1997. Europa. Tales and Legends. Mult.
2422 800 l. Type **977** ("He who becomes the Property of Others works for his Soup") 55 30
2423 900 l. Street singer (19th-century copper etching) 65 35

1997. Centenary of Teatro Massimo, Palermo.
2424 **978** 800 l. multicoloured . . . 55 30

979 St. Sebastian's Church, Acireale

1997. Tourist Publicity (24th series). Mult.
2425 800 l. Type **979** 55 30
2426 800 l. Cicero and his tomb, Formia 55 30
2427 800 l. St. Mary of the Assumption, Positano . . . 55 30
2428 800 l. St. Vitale's Basilica, Ravenna 55 30

980 Books and Marble Floor

1997. 10th Book Salon, Turin.
2429 **980** 800 l. multicoloured . . . 55 30

981 Queen Paola and Castel Sant'Angelo, Rome

1997. 60th Birthday of Queen Paola of Belgium.
2430 **981** 750 l. multicoloured . . . 50 25

982 Palazzo della Civilta del Lavoro and Fair Pavilions

1997. Rome Fair.
2431 **982** 800 l. multicoloured . . . 55 30

983 Orvieto Cathedral

984 Morosini in Via Tasso Prison, 1944

1997.
2432 **983** 450 l. violet 30 15

1997. 53rd Death Anniv of Father Giuseppe Morosini.
2433 **984** 800 l. multicoloured . . . 55 30

985 Player, Club Emblem and Football

986 Chamois and "Iris marsica"

1997. Juventus, National Football Champion, 1996–97.
2434 **985** 800 l. multicoloured . . . 55 30

1997. 75th Anniv of Abruzzo National Park.
2435 **986** 800 l. multicoloured . . . 55 30

987 Towers and Fair Complex

1997. Bologna Fair.
2436 **987** 800 l. multicoloured . . . 55 30

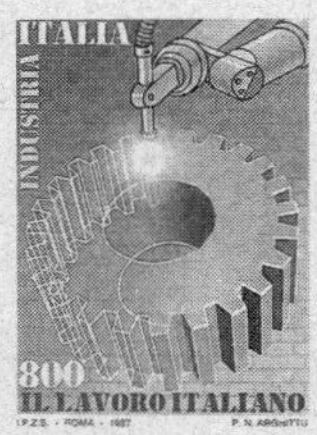

988 Pennant and Ships' Bows

990 Cogwheel and Robot Arm (industry)

989 Runner, High Jumper and Gymnast

1997. Centenary of Italian Naval League.
2437 **988** 800 l. multicoloured . . . 55 30

1997. 13th Mediterranean Games, Bari.
2438 **989** 900 l. multicoloured . . . 65 35

1997. Public Gardens (2nd series). As T **915**. Multicoloured.
2439 800 l. Orto Botanico, Palermo . 55 30
2440 800 l. Villa Sciarra, Rome . . 55 30
2441 800 l. Cavour, Santena 55 30
2442 800 l. Miramare, Trieste . . . 55 30

1997. Italian Work. Multicoloured.
2443 800 l. Type **990** 55 30
2444 900 l. Cereals, fruit trees, grapes and sun (agriculture) (horiz) . 65 35

991 Globe and the "Matthew"

1997. 500th Anniv of John Cabot's Discovery of North America.
2445 **991** 1300 l. multicoloured . . 90 45

992 Verri

993 "Madonna of the Rosary" (Pomarancio il Vecchio)

1997. Death Bicentenary of Pietro Verri (illuminist).
2446 **992** 3600 l. multicoloured . . 2·50 1·25

1997. Painters' Anniversaries. Multicoloured.
2447 450 l. Type **993** (400th death anniv) 30 15
2448 650 l. "The Miracle of Ostia" ((detail, Paolo Uccello) (600th birth anniv)) (26 × 37 mm) 45 25

994 Procession

1997. Varia Festival, Palmi.
2449 **994** 800 l. multicoloured . . . 55 30

995 Basketball

1997. University Games, Sicily. Multicoloured.
2450 450 l. Type **995** 30 15
2451 800 l. High jumping 55 30

996 Rosmini

1997. Birth Bicentenary of Antonio Rosmini (philosopher).
2452 **996** 800 l. multicoloured . . . 55 30

1997. Italian Films (2nd series). As T **946**.
2453 800 l. multicoloured 55 30
2454 800 l. black, blue and red . . . 55 30
2455 800 l. multicoloured 55 30
DESIGNS: No. 2453, Pietro Germi in "Il Ferroviere"; 2454, Anna Magnani in "Mamma Roma"; 2455, Ugo Tognazzi in "Amici Miei".

997 Open Book and Beach, Viareggio

1997. Viareggio-Repaci Prize.
2456 **997** 4000 l. multicoloured . . 2·75 1·40

998 Venue and Bell Tower

1997. International Trade Fair, Bolzano.
2457 **998** 800 l. multicoloured . . . 55 30

999 Bronze Head (500 BC)

1000 Pope Paul VI and Door of Death, St. Peter's Cathedral, Rome

1997. Museum Exhibits. Multicoloured.
2458 450 l. Type **999** (National Museum, Reggio Calabria) . 30 15
2459 650 l. "Madonna and Child with Two Vases of Roses" (Ercole de Roberti) (National Picture Gallery, Ferrara) . . 45 25
2460 800 l. Miniature of poet Sordello da Goito (Arco Palace Museum, Mantua) . 55 30
2461 900 l. "St. George and the Dragon" (Vitale di Bologna) (National Picture Gallery, Bologna) 60 30

1997. Birth Centenary of Pope Paul VI.
2462 **1000** 4000 l. blue . . . . . . 3·00 1·50

1001 Portello Pavilion (venue) and Milan Cathedral

1002 War-ravaged and Reconstructed Cities

1997. Milan Fair.
2463 **1001** 800 l. multicoloured . . 60 30

1997. 50th Anniv of European Recovery Programme ("Marshall Plan").
2464 **1002** 800 l. multicoloured . . 60 30

1003 Nativity (crib, St Francis's Church, Leonessa)

1997. Christmas. Multicoloured.
2465 800 l. Type **1003** 60 30
2466 900 l. "Nativity" (painting, Sta. Maria Maggiore, Spelo) . . 65 35

1004 Production Plant and Merloni

1005 Cavalcaselle and Drawings

1997. Birth Centenary of Aristide Merloni (entrepreneur).
2467 **1004** 800 l. multicoloured . . 60 30

1997. Death Centenary of Giovanni Battista Cavalcaselle (art historian).
2468 **1005** 800 l. multicoloured . . 60 30

1006 Magnifying Glass and Fleur-de-lis

1997. Stamp Day.
2469 **1006** 800 l. multicoloured . . 60 30

1007 Refugees aboard "Toscana" (steamer)

1997. 50th Anniv of Exodus of Italian Inhabitants from Istria, Fiume and Dalmatia.
2470 **1007** 800 l. multicoloured . . 60 30

1008 Arms of State Police and Badge of Traffic Police

1997. 50th Anniv of Traffic Police.
2471 **1008** 800 l. multicoloured . . 60 30

1009 Map of Italy in Column and Flag

1998. 50th Anniv of Constitution.
2472 **1009** 800 l. black, red & green 60 30

1010 "Hercules and the Hydra"

1998. 500th Death Anniv of Antonio del Pollaiuolo (painter).
2473 **1010** 800 l. multicoloured . . 60 30

1011 Bertolt Brecht

1998. Writers' Birth Centenaries.
2474 **1011** 450 l. multicoloured . . 30 15
2475 – 650 l. multicoloured . . 45 25
2476 – 800 l. multicoloured . . 60 30
2477 – 900 l. blue, green & blk . 65 35
DESIGNS—HORIZ: 650 l. Federico Garcia Lorca (poet); 800 l. Curzio Malaparte. VERT: 900 l. Leonida Repaci.

1012 Fair Complex

1998. Verona Fair.
2478 **1012** 800 l. multicoloured . . 60 30

1013 Memorial Tablet in Casale Montferrato Synagogue

1998. 150th Anniv of Granting of Full Citizen Rights to Italian Jews.
2479 **1013** 800 l. multicoloured . . 60 30

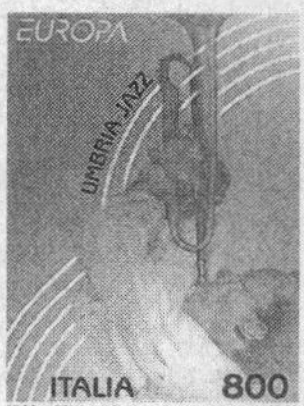

1014 Trombonist

1998. Europa. National Festivals. Mult.
2480 800 l. Type **1014** (Umbria Jazz Festival) 60 30
2481 900 l. Boy holding animal (Giffoni Film Festival) . . . 65 35

1015 "The Last Supper"

1998. 500th Anniv of Completion of "The Last Supper" (mural) by Leonardo da Vinci.
2482 **1015** 800 l. brown 60 30

1016 Costumes designed by Bernardo Buontalenti for First Opera in Florence

1017 Turin Cathedral and Holy Shroud

1998. Italian Theatre. Multicoloured.
2483 800 l. Type **1016** (400th anniv of opera) 60 30
2484 800 l. Gaetano Donizetti (composer, 150th death anniv) (horiz) 60 30

1998. 500th Anniv of Turin Cathedral. Display of the Holy Shroud.
2485 **1017** 800 l. multicoloured . . 60 30

1018 Otranto Castle

1998. Tourist Publicity (25th series). Mult.
2486 800 l. Type **1018** 60 30
2487 800 l. Mori Fountain and Orsini Tower, Marino . . . 60 30
2488 800 l. Valfederia Chapel, Livigno 60 30
2489 800 l. Marciana Marina, Elba . 60 30

1019 Cagliari Cathedral, Drummer and Fair Building

1998. International Sardinia Fair, Cagliari.
2490 **1019** 800 l. multicoloured . . 60 30

1020 "Charge of the Carabinieri at Pastrengo" (Sebastiano de Albertis)

1021 Flags

1998. 150th Anniv of Battle of Pastrengo.
2491 **1020** 800 l. multicoloured . . 60 30

1998. Padua Fair.
2492 **1021** 800 l. multicoloured . . 60 30

1022 Player and Club Badge

1998. Juventus, National Football Champion, 1997–98.
2493 **1022** 800 l. multicoloured . . 60 30

1023 Turin Polytechnic

1024 Emblem

1998. Universities.
2494 **1023** 800 l. blue 60 30

1998. World Food Programme.
2495 **1024** 900 l. multicoloured . . 65 35

1025 Santa Maria de Pesio Carthusian Monastery

1998. Artistic Heritage.
2496 **1025** 800 l. multicoloured . . 60 30

1026 Ammonites and Pergola

1998. 4th International "Fossils, Evolution, Ambience" Congress, Pergola.
2497 **1026** 800 l. multicoloured . . 60 30

1027 Flag at Half-mast

1028 Endoscope and Globe

1998. "The Forces of Order, the Fallen".
2498 **1027** 800 l. multicoloured . . 60 30

1998. 6th World General Endoscopic Surgery Congress, Rome.
2499 **1028** 900 l. multicoloured . . 65 35

1029 First Parliamentary Chamber

1998. National Museums. Multicoloured.
2500 800 l. Type **1029** (Italian Risorgimento Museum, Turin) 60 30
2501 800 l. Statue of an ephebus (Athenian youth), Temple of Concord and column of Temple of Vulcan (Regional Archaeology Museum, Agrigento) (vert) 60 30
2502 800 l. Sculpture by Umberto Boccioni and Palazzo Venier dei Leoni (venue) (Peggy Guggenheim Collection, Venice) 60 30

1030 Fair Complex and Basilica

1998. Vicenza Trade Fair.
2503 **1030** 800 l. multicoloured . . 60 30

1031 Leopardi (after Luigi Lolli) and Palazzo Leopardi, Recanati

1998. Birth Bicentenary of Giacomo Leopardi (poet).
2504 **1031** 800 l. brown and black . . 60 30

1032 Young Etruscan Girl (detail of tomb painting)

1033 Pitch, Pitcher and Batter

1998. Women in Art.
2505 **1032** 100 l. black, green & sil . 10 10
2506 – 450 l. multicoloured . . 30 15
2507 – 650 l. multicoloured . . 45 25
2508 – 800 l. brown & black . . 60 30
2509 – 1000 l. blue, brn & blk . 70 35

DESIGNS: 450 l. Detail of "Herod's Banquet and the Dance of Salome" (fresco by Filippo Lippi in Prato Cathedral); 650 l. "Profile of a Woman" (Antonio del Pollaiuolo); 800 l. "Lady with a Unicorn" (detail, Raphael); 1000 l. "Constanza Buonarelli" (bust by Gian Lorenzo Bernini).

For these designs but with face values in euros added, see Nos. 2537/41.

1998. 33rd World Cup Baseball Championship, Florence.
2510 **1033** 900 l. multicoloured . . 65 35

1034 Columbus and Vespucci

1998. 500th Anniversaries of Landing of Christopher Columbus in Venezuela and of Amerigo Vespucci's Explorations.
2511 **1034** 1300 l. multicoloured . . 95 50

1035 Emblem

1998. 50th International Stamp Fair, Riccione.
2512 **1035** 800 l. multicoloured . . 60 30

1036 Mother Teresa and Child

1998. 1st Death Anniv of Mother Teresa (founder of Missionaries of Charity). Multicoloured.
2513 800 l. Type **1036** 60 30
2514 900 l. Mother Teresa (vert) . . 65 35

1037 Father Pio and Monastery Church, San Giovanni Rotondo

1998. 30th Death Anniv of Father Pio da Pietrelcina (Capuchin friar who bore the stigmata).
2515 **1037** 800 l. blue 60 30

1038 Titus Arch, Rome, and Sicilian Mosaic of Rider

1998. World Equestrian Championships, Rome.
2516 **1038** 4000 l. multicoloured . . 2·75 1·40

1039 Telecommunications College, Rome

1998. Universities.
2517 **1039** 800 l. blue 60 30

1040 Pope John Paul II and his Message

1998. "Italia 98" International Stamp Exhibition, Milan (3rd issue). Stamp Day.
2518 **1040** 800 l. multicoloured . . 60 30

1041 "Giuseppe Garibaldi" (aircraft carrier)

1998. Armed Forces Day. Multicoloured.
2519 800 l. Type **1041** (Navy) . . . 60 30
2520 800 l. Eurofighter 2000 (75th anniv of Air Force) . . . 60 30
2521 800 l. Carabiniere (vert) . . . 60 30
2522 800 l. Battle of El-Alamein at night (Army) (vert) 60 30

1042 "Dionysus" (bronze statue)

1045 Cogwheels and "Proportions of Man" (Leonardo da Vinci)

1044 Hand releasing Birds

1998. "Italia 98" International Stamp Exhibition, Milan (4th issue). Art Day.
2523 **1042** 800 l. multicoloured . . 60 30

1998. 50th Anniv of Universal Declaration of Human Rights.
2525 **1044** 1400 l. multicoloured . . 1·00 50

1998. Europa Day. Ordinary or self-adhesive gum.
2526 **1045** 800 l. multicoloured . . 60 30

1998. "Italia 98" International Stamp Exhibition, Milan (6th issue). Cinema Day. As T **946**. Multicoloured.
2528 450 l. "Ti Conosco Mascherino" (dir. Eduardo de Filippo) 30 15
2529 800 l. "Fantasmia a Roma" (Antonio Pietrangeli) . . . 50 25
2530 900 l. "Il Signor Max" (Mario Camerini) 60 30

1046 Satellite Dish, Type, Book and "Internet"

1048 "Epiphany" (sculpture, St. Mark's Church, Seminara)

1998. "Italia 98" International Stamp Exhibition, Milan (7th issue). Communications Day.
2531 **1046** 800 l. multicoloured . . 50 25

1998. Christmas.
2533 **1048** 800 l. blue 50 25
2534 – 900 l. brown 60 30

DESIGN—HORIZ: 900 l. "Adoration of the Shepherds" (drawing, Giulio Romano).

1049 "Ecstasy of St. Teresa"

1998. 400th Birth Anniv of Gian Lorenzo Bernini (sculptor).
2535 **1049** 900 l. multicoloured . . 60 30

1050 Royal Decree and Waldensian Emblem

1998. 150th Anniv of Toleration of the Waldenses (religious sect).
2536 **1050** 800 l. multicoloured . . 50 25

DENOMINATION. From No. 2537 Italian stamps are denominated both in lira and in euros. As no cash for the latter is in circulation, the catalogue continues to use the lira value.

1999. As Nos. 2505/9 but with face value in euros added.
2537 100 l. black, green and silver . 10 10
2538 450 l. multicoloured 30 15
2539 650 l. multicoloured 40 20
2540 800 l. brown and black . . . 50 25
2541 1000 l. blue, brown and black . 70 35

1051 "Space Concept–Wait"

1999. Birth Centenary of Lucio Fontana (artist).
2542 **1051** 450 l. blue and black . . 30 15

1052 La Sila National Park, Calabria

1053 Holy Door, St. Peter's Cathedral

1999. Europa. Parks and Gardens. Multicoloured.
2543 800 l. Type **1052** 50 25
2544 900 l. Tuscan Archipelago National Park (horiz) . . . 60 30

1999. Holy Year 2000.
2545 **1053** 1400 l. multicoloured . . 90 45

1054 St. Egidius's Church, Cellere

1999. Artistic Heritage.
2546 **1054** 800 l. brown 50 25

1055 Holy Year 2000 and 11th-century Bells

1999. Museums. Multicoloured.
2547 800 l. Type **1055** (History of Campanology Museum, Agnone) 50 25
2548 800 l. "Lake with Swan" (stained glass) (Casina delle Civette Museum, Rome) . . 50 25
2549 800 l. Renaissance majolica dish (International Ceramics Museum, Faenza) (vert) . . 50 25

1056 Earth Pyramids, Segonzano

1999. Tourist Publicity (26th series). Multicoloured.
2550 800 l. Type **1056** 50 25
2551 800 l. Marmore Waterfall, Terni 50 25
2552 800 l. Cathedral, Lecce 50 25
2553 800 l. Lipari 50 25

1057 Audience Chamber

1999. Constitutional Court.
2554 **1057** 800 l. multicoloured . . 50 25

1058 Fire Engine at Fire

1999. Fire Brigade.
2555 **1058** 800 l. multicoloured . . 50 25

1059 Cadet and Academy

1999. Modena Military Academy.
2556 **1059** 800 l. multicoloured . . 50 25

1060 Players and Airplane

1999. 50th Anniv of Death in Aircrash of Grand Turin Football Team. Multicoloured.
2557 800 l. Type **1060** 50 25
2558 900 l. Superga Basilica, club arms and names of victims . 60 30

1061 Council Seat, Strasbourg

1999. 50th Anniv of Council of Europe.
2559 **1061** 800 l. multicoloured . . 50 25

1062 Players and Club Emblem

1999. Milan, National Football Champion, 1998–99.
2560 **1062** 800 l. multicoloured . . 50 25

1063 Ballot Box and Parliament Chamber, Strasbourg

1999. 20th Anniv of First Direct Elections to European Parliament.
2561 **1063** 800 l. multicoloured . . 50 25

1064 Coppi

1999. 80th Birth Anniv of Fausto Coppi (racing cyclist).
2562 **1064** 800 l. multicoloured . . 50 25

INDEX

Countries can be quickly located by referring to the index at the end of this volume.

1065 "P"

1999. Priority Mail stamp. Self-adhesive.
2563 **1065** 1200 l. black and gold . . 80 40

1066 First Fiat Car (advertising poster)

1067 "Our Lady of the Snow"

1999. Centenary of Fiat (motor manufacturer).
2564 **1066** 4800 l. multicoloured . . 3·00 1·50

1999. Centenary of Erection of Statue of "Our Lady of the Snow" on Mt. Rocciamelone.
2565 **1067** 800 l. multicoloured . . 50 25

1068 Pimentel and St. Elmo Castle, Naples

1999. Death Bicentenary of Eleonora de Fonseca Pimentel (writer and revolutionary).
2566 **1068** 800 l. multicoloured . . 50 25

1069 Canoes

1999. 30th World Speed Canoeing Championships.
2567 **1069** 900 l. multicoloured . . 60 30

1070 "Goethe in the Rome Countryside" (Johann Tischbein)

1999. 250th Birth Anniv of Johann Wolfgang Goethe (poet and playwright).
2568 **1070** 4000 l. multicoloured . . 2·75 1·40

1071 Cyclist and Stopwatch

1072 Child with Rucksack

1999. World Cycling Championships, Treviso and Verona.
2569 **1071** 1400 l. multicoloured . . 90 45

1999. Stamp Day.
2570 **1072** 800 l. multicoloured . . 50 25

1073 Architectural Drawing of Basilica

1999. Re-opening of Upper Basilica of St. Francis of Assisi.
2571 **1073** 800 l. multicoloured . . 50 25

1074 Parini (after Francesco Rosaspina)

1075 Volta (bust by Giovan Commolli) and Voltaic Pile

1999. Death Bicentenary of Giuseppe Parini (poet).
2572 **1074** 800 l. steel blue 50 25

1999. Bicentenary of Invention of Electrochemical Battery by Alessandro Volta.
2573 **1075** 3000 l. multicoloured . . 2·00 1·00

1076 Forms and U.P.U. Emblem

1999. 125th Anniv of Universal Postal Union.
2574 **1076** 900 l. multicoloured . . 60 30

1077 Mameli with 1948 and 1949 100 l. Stamps

1999. 150th Death Anniv of Goffredo Mameli (poet and patriot) and 150th Anniv of Roman Republic.
2575 **1077** 1500 l. multicoloured . . 1·00 50

1078 Man and Town

1079 First World War Soldiers (after postcard)

1999. "The Stamp Our Friend". Multicoloured.
2576 450 l. Type **1078** 30 15
2577 650 l. Campaign emblem 40 20
2578 800 l. Schoolchildren 50 25
2579 1000 l. Windmill (toy) 65 35

1999. Centenary of Generation of '99.
2580 **1079** 900 l. multicoloured . . 60 30

1080 Santa Claus

1999. Christmas. Multicoloured.
2581 800 l. Type **1080** 50 25
2582 1000 l. "Nativity" (Dosso Dossi) 65 35

1081 Peutinger Tablet (medieval map showing pilgrim route by C. Celtes and Conrad Peutinger)

1999. Holy Year 2000. Multicoloured.
2583 1000 l. Type **1081** 65 35
2584 1000 l. 18th-century pilgrim's stamp 65 35
2585 1000 l. 13th-century bas-relief of pilgrims (facade of Fidenza Cathedral) 65 35

1082 Urbino State Art Institute

1999. Schools and Universities.
2586 **1082** 450 l. black 30 15
2587 – 650 l. brown 40 20
DESIGN: 650 l. Pisa High School.

1083 "Leopard bitten by Tarantula"

1999. Birth Centenary of Antonio Ligabue (artist).
2588 **1083** 1000 l. multicoloured . . 65 35

1084 Robot's Hand meeting Man's Hand (after Michelangelo)

1999. Year 2000.
2589 **1084** 4800 l. multicoloured . . 3·25 1·75

CONCESSIONAL LETTER POST

CL **93** Arms of Savoy and Fasces

CL **109** Arms and Fasces

1928.

CL227	CL **93**	10 c. blue	50	10

1930.

CL267	CL **109**	10 c. brown	10	10

1945. No. CL267, surch with Royal Arms (obliterating fasces) and new value.

CL647	CL **109**	40 c. on 10 c. brn	10	10

1945. As Type CL **109**, but Arms redrawn without fasces.

CL648		10 c. brown	10	10
CL649		1 l. brown	2·00	2·00

CL **201** Italia

CL **220** Italia

1947.

CL687	CL **201**	1 l. green	15	10
CL688		8 l. red	12·00	20

1948.

CL734	CL **220**	15 l. violet	85·00	10
CL916		20 l. violet	20	10
CL917		30 l. green	15	10
CL918		35 l. brown	15	10
CL919		110 l. blue	15	10
CL920		270 l. mauve	75	20
CL921		300 l. green & pink	40	15
CL922		370 l. brown & orge	45	20

CONCESSIONAL PARCEL POST

CP **288**

1953.

CP918	CP **288**	40 l. orange	75	15
CP919		50 l. blue	1·75	15
CP920		60 l. violet	5·00	75
CP921		70 l. green	35·00	2·75
CP850		75 l. sepia	£100	2·00
CP923		80 l. brown	25	10
CP924		90 l. lilac	25	10
CP851		110 l. red	£100	2·50
CP926		110 l. yellow	25	10
CP927		120 l. green	25	10
CP928		140 l. black	25	10
CP929		150 l. red	25	10
CP930		180 l. red	35	10
CP931		240 l. slate	35	10
CP932		500 l. brown	80	30
CP933		600 l. turquoise	1·40	30
CP934		900 l. blue	1·60	30

Unused prices are for the complete pair. Used prices are for the left half; right halves are worth more.

CP **707**

1984.

CP1849	CP **707**	3000 l. blue & red	3·50	2·50

EXPRESS LETTER STAMPS

E **35**

1903. For inland letters.

E 73	E **35**	25 c. red	8·00	30
E113		50 c. red	65	35
E129		60 c. red	60	30
E178		70 c. red	15	20
E179		1 l. 25 blue	15	10

E **41** King Victor Emmanuel III

1908. For foreign letters.

E 80	E **41**	30 c. blue and pink	40	1·00
E180		2 l. blue and pink	40	20·00
E181		2 l. 50 blue and pink	40	1·10

E **59**

1917. Surch **25** and bars.

E112	E **59**	25 c. on 40 c. violet	8·00	20·00

1921. Surch with new value.

E118	E **41**	L. 1.20 on 30 c. blue and pink	35	5·50
E173		L. 1.60 on 1 l. 20 blue and pink	40	23·00

1922. Surch in words and figures.

E122	E **35**	60 c. on 50 c. red	7·00	30
E172		70 c. on 60 c. red	20	40

E **131** "Garibaldi" (statue), Savoia Marchetti S-55A Flying Boat and "Anita Garibaldi" (statue)

1932. Air. 50th Death Anniv of Garibaldi.

E348	E **131**	2 l. 25 + 1 l. violet and red	4·75	24·00
E349		4 l. 50 + 1 l. 50 brown and green	5·50	26·00

E **132** King Victor Emmanuel III

1932.

E350	E **132**	1 l. 25 green	10	10
E351		2 l. 50 orange	10	1·00

1932. 10th Anniv of March on Rome. As Type **132**.

(a) For inland letters. Inscribed "ESPRESSO".

E368	1 l. 25 green	40	80

(b) For foreign letters. Inscribed "EXPRES".

E369	2 l. 50 orange	2·25	70·00

DESIGNS: 1 l. 25, Roman road; 2 l. 50, Flags and head of Mussolini.

E **133** Savoia Marchetti S-55A Flying Boat

1933. Air.

E370	E **133**	2 l. black	10	75
E371		2 l. 25 black	1·75	60·00

1934. Air. 10th Anniv of Annexation of Fiume. Inscr as in T **141**.

E408	2 l. + 1 l. 25 blue	50	17·00
E409	2 l. 25 + 1 l. 25 green	20	13·00
E410	4 l. 50 + 2 l. red	20	14·00

DESIGN: Foundation of Fiume.

1934. Air. Military Medal Centenary. Inscr as in T **146**.

E442	2 l. + 1 l. 25 brown	3·50	15·00
E443	4 l. 50 + 2 l. red	5·50	17·00

DESIGN—HORIZ: 2 l., 4 l. 50, Caproni Ca 101 airplane over triumphal arch.

E **192** Italia

1945.

E647	E **192**	5 l. red	10	50

E **200** Winged Foot of Mercury

1945.

E679	E **200**	5 l. red	10	10
E680	–	10 l. blue	10	10
E681	–	15 l. red	3·00	10
E682	E **200**	25 l. orange	30·00	10
E683		30 l. violet	4·00	75
E915		50 l. purple	5·00	10
E685	–	60 l. red	35·00	20

DESIGN: 10, 15, 60 l. Horse and torch bearer.

E **209** Rising at Naples

1948. Centenary of 1848 Revolution.

E718	E **209**	35 l. violet	60·00	10·00

E **341** Etruscan Horses

1958.

E 961	E **341**	75 l. purple	25	10
E1220		150 l. green	20	10
E1221		250 l. blue & lt blue	30	10
E1222		300 l. brown & lt brn	35	10

MILITARY POST STAMPS

1943. Stamps of Italy optd **P.M.**

(a) Postage stamps of 1929 (Nos. 239/56).

M583	5 c. brown	20	35
M584	10 c. brown	20	35
M585	15 c. green	20	35
M586	20 c. red	20	35
M587	25 c. green	20	35
M588	30 c. brown	20	35
M589	50 c. violet	20	20
M590	1 l. violet	20	5·00
M591	1 l. 25 blue	20	55
M592	1 l. 75 orange	20	35
M593	2 l. red	20	50
M594	5 l. red	20	2·25
M595	10 l. violet	20	7·00

(b) Air stamps of 1930 (Nos. 271/7).

M596	50 c. brown	20	35
M597	1 l. violet	20	55
M598	2 l. blue	20	4·00
M599	5 l. green	20	5·50
M600	10 l. red	20	11·00

(c) Air Express stamp of 1933 (No. E370).

M601	2 l. black	20	8·50

(d) Express Letter stamp of 1932 (No. E350).

M602	1 l. 25 green	20	80

NEWSPAPER STAMPS

N **2**

1862. Imperf.

N5	N **2**	2 c. yellow	20·00	50·00

For similar stamps in black, see Sardinia.

OFFICIAL STAMPS

O **11**

1875.

O21	O **11**	2 c. red	70	75
O22		5 c. red	70	75
O23		20 c. red	15	15
O24		30 c. red	25	25
O25		1 l. red	1·60	3·00
O26		2 l. red	8·00	10·00
O27		5 l. red	50·00	55·00
O28		10 l. red	85·00	30·00

1934. Air. Optd **SERVIZIO DI STATO**.

O450	**148**	10 l. grey	£275	£5000

PARCEL POST STAMPS

P **13** King Umberto I

1884. Various frames.

P38	P **13**	10 c. grey	65·00	16·00
P39		20 c. blue	£110	28·00
P40		50 c. pink	5·00	3·50
P41		75 c. green	5·00	3·50
P42		1 l. 25 orange	12·00	10·00
P43		1 l. 75 brown	14·00	26·00

The left-hand portion of the following parcel post stamps is affixed to the packet-card, the right-hand portion to the receipt. Unused prices are for the complete pair and used prices for the half-stamp. Unsevered stamps in used condition are usually from cancelled-to-order material and are worth more than the half-stamp.

P **53**

1914.

P 96	P **53**	5 c. brown	10	10
P 97		10 c. blue	10	10
P 98		20 c. black	20	10
P 99		25 c. red	35	10
P100		50 c. orange	45	10
P101		1 l. violet	55	10
P102		2 l. green	75	10
P103		3 l. yellow	90	10
P104		4 l. grey	1·25	10
P105		10 l. purple	11·00	1·00
P106		12 l. brown	80·00	10·00
P107		15 l. olive	80·00	10·00
P108		20 l. purple	80·00	10·00

1923. Surch with figures on left half and words and figures on right half.

P146	P **53**	30 c. on 5 c. brown	30	10
P147		60 c. on 5 c. brown	55	10
P148		1 l. 50 on 5 c. brown	1·75	50
P149		3 l. on 10 l. purple	1·75	50

P **92**

1927.

P217	P **92**	5 c. brown	10	10
P218		10 c. blue	10	10
P219		25 c. red	10	10
P220		30 c. blue	10	10
P221		50 c. orange	10	10
P222	–	60 c. red	10	10
P223	P **92**	1 l. violet	10	10
P224		2 l. green	10	10
P225		3 l. bistre	10	10
P226		4 l. black	10	10
P227		10 l. purple	45	10
P228		20 l. purple	70	10

The value in the right-hand portion of the 60 c. is in figures.

1945. Optd with ornamental device obliterating Fascist emblems in centre.

P647	P **92**	5 c. brown	50	10
P648		10 c. blue	50	10
P649		25 c. red	50	10
P650		30 c. blue	6·00	40
P651		50 c. orange	50	10
P652	–	60 c. red	50	10
P653	P **92**	1 l. violet	50	10
P654		2 l. green	50	10
P655		3 l. bistre	50	10
P656		4 l. black	50	10
P657		10 l. purple	5·00	45
P658		20 l. purple	12·00	1·00

1946. As Type P **92**, but without fasces between stamps.

P679	P **92**	1 l. mauve	75	10
P680		2 l. green	60	10
P681		3 l. orange	1·25	10
P682		4 l. black	2·00	10
P683		10 l. purple	30·00	40
P684		20 l. purple	35·00	90

P **201**

1946.

P 687	P **201**	25 c. blue	10	10
P 688		50 c. brown	40	10
P 689		1 l. brown	40	10
P 690		2 l. blue	80	10
P 691		3 l. orange	30	10
P 692		4 l. grey	4·75	40
P 910		5 l. purple	10	10
P 911		10 l. violet	10	10
P 912		20 l. purple	15	10
P1348		30 l. purple	15	10
P 914		40 l. violet	10	10
P 915		50 l. red	10	10
P 916		60 l. violet	10	10
P 917		100 l. blue	15	10
P 918		140 l. red	15	10

P 919	P 201	150 l. brown	25	10
P 920		200 l. green	25	10
P 921		280 l. yellow	35	10
P 922		300 l. purple	30	10
P 923		400 l. black	40	10
P 924		500 l. brown	75	10
P 925		600 l. brown	70	20
P 926		700 l. blue	85	15
P 927		800 l. orange	90	15

P 298

1954.

P928a	P 298	1000 l. blue	1·10	10
P929		2000 l. red and brown	3·00	15

PNEUMATIC POST LETTERS

PE 53

1913.

PE 96	PE 53	10 c. brown	1·10	7·50
PE 97		15 c. lilac	1·40	10·00
PE191		15 c. pink	80	5·00
PE192		15 c. purple	2·00	10·00
PE193		20 c. purple	3·75	13·00
PE 98		30 c. blue	2·50	25·00
PE194		35 c. red	5·00	60·00
PE195		40 c. red	7·00	65·00

1924. Surch.

PE165	PE 53	15 c. on 10 c. brown	1·75	10·00
PE166		15 c. on 20 c. purple	2·75	14·00
PE167		20 c. on 10 c. brown	2·75	18·00
PE168		20 c. on 15 c. lilac	1·75	10·00
PE169		35 c. on 40 c. red	5·50	60·00
PE170		40 c. on 30 c. blue	2·75	45·00

PE 134 Galileo Galilei PE 204 Minerva

1933.

PE372	–	15 c. purple	10	45
PE373	PE 134	35 c. red	10	45

DESIGN: 15 c. Dante Alighieri.

1945. As Type PE 134, but inscr "ITALIA" instead of "REGNO D'ITALIA".

PE679	–	60 c. brn (Dante)	20	40
PE680	PE 134	1 l. 40 blue	20	40

1947.

PE694	PE 204	3 l. purple	8·00	12·00
PE695		5 l. blue	15	10
PE961		10 l. red	15	10
PE962		20 l. blue	15	10

POSTAGE DUE STAMPS

D 3 D 11

1863. Imperf.

D6	D 3	10 c. yellow	50·00	90·00

1869. Perf.

D21	D 11	10 c. brown	£2500	10·00

D 12 D 13

(D 20)

1870.

D22	D 12	1 c. mauve & orange	1·25	2·50
D23		2 c. mauve & orange	9·50	11·00
D24		5 c. mauve & orange	20	10
D25		10 c. mauve & orange	30	10
D26		20 c. mauve & orange	50	10
D27		30 c. mauve & orange	1·25	25
D28		40 c. mauve & orange	1·40	35
D29		50 c. mauve & orange	1·25	15
D30	D 12	60 c. mauve & orange	50·00	60
D31		60 c. brown & orange	9·50	2·25
D32		1 l. brown and blue	£2250	5·00
D33		1 l. mauve and blue	50	15
D34		2 l. brown and blue	£2750	6·50
D35		2 l. mauve and blue	15·00	60
D36		5 l. brown and blue	£150	4·75
D37		5 l. mauve and blue	48·00	1·40
D38		10 l. brown and blue	£4000	7·50
D39		10 l. mauve and blue	50·00	60

1884.

D40	D 13	50 l. green	20·00	10·00
D73		50 l. yellow	26·00	13·00
D41		100 l. red	25·00	5·00
D74		100 l. blue	20·00	5·00

1890. Surch over numeral as Type D 20.

D47	D 12	10 (c.) on 2 c. (D23)	50·00	10·00
D48		20 (c.) on 1 c. (D22)	£250	7·50
D49		30 (c.) on 2 c. (D23)	£900	3·75

D 141 D 142

1934. With Fascist emblems.

D395	D 141	5 c. brown	10	10
D396		10 c. blue	10	10
D397		20 c. red	10	10
D398		25 c. green	10	10
D399		30 c. orange	10	10
D400		40 c. brown	10	20
D401		50 c. violet	10	10
D402		60 c. blue	15	45
D403	D 142	1 l. orange	10	10
D404		2 l. green	10	10
D405		5 l. violet	25	15
D406		10 l. blue	60	20
D407		20 l. red	70	25

D 191 D 192 D 201

1945. Fascist emblems removed.

D630	D 191	5 c. brown	15	10
D631		10 c. blue	10	10
D632		20 c. red	15	10
D633		25 c. green	10	10
D634		30 c. orange	10	10
D635		40 c. black	10	15
D636		50 c. violet	10	10
D637		60 c. blue	10	15
D685	D 192	1 l. orange	15	10
D639		2 l. green	15	10
D640		5 l. violet	10	10
D641		10 l. blue	10	10
D642		20 l. red	20	20

1947.

D690	D 201	1 l. orange	10	10
D691		2 l. green	25	10
D692		3 l. red	1·25	85
D693		4 l. brown	85	70
D924		5 l. violet	15	10
D695		6 l. blue	3·75	80
D696		8 l. mauve	14·00	1·40
D926		10 l. blue	15	10
D698		12 l. brown	4·75	1·10
D927		20 l. purple	15	10
D928		25 l. red	15	10
D929		30 l. purple	15	10
D930		40 l. brown	15	10
D931		50 l. green	15	10
D932		100 l. orange	15	10
D935		500 l. red and blue	70	15
D936		500 l. purple & blue	60	20
D937		900 l. mve, blk & grn	1·25	55
D938		1500 l. orange & brn	1·60	55

PUBLICITY ENVELOPE STAMPS

1921. Optd **B.L.P.**

B129	37	10 c. red	35·00	6·50
B137		15 c. grey	£130	38·00
B138	41	20 c. orange	£130	38·00
B132	39	25 c. blue	42·00	10·00
B140		30 c. brown	85·00	20·00
B115		40 c. brown	27·00	1·75
B134		50 c. violet	£325	65·00
B135		60 c. red	£1300	£425
B141		85 c. brown	£130	38·00
B136	34	1 l. brown and green	£2500	£700

ITALIAN SOCIAL REPUBLIC

Following the surrender of Italy on 3 September 1943, and his rescue from imprisonment on 12 September, Mussolini proclaimed the Italian Social Republic at Salo on 23 September 1943. From this town on Lake Garda the Republican government administered those parts of Italy, north of the Gustav Line, which were under German occupation.

1944. Stamps of Italy optd **G. N. R.**
(a) Postage. (i) Nos. 239 and 241/59.

1	98	5 c. brown	1·00	2·00
2	–	10 c. brown	1·00	2·00
3	–	15 c. green	1·00	2·00
4	99	20 c. red	1·00	2·00
5	–	25 c. green	1·00	2·00
6	103	30 c. brown	1·00	2·00
7	–	35 c. blue	40·00	60·00
8	103	50 c. violet	1·00	2·00
9	–	75 c. red	1·00	2·00
10	99	1 l. violet	1·00	2·00
11	–	1 l. 25 blue	1·00	2·00
12	–	1 l. 75 red	2·75	12·00
13	–	2 l. red	3·00	14·00
14	98	2 l. 55 green	20·00	80·00
15		3 l. 70 violet	18·00	65·00
16		5 l. red	3·00	12·00
17	–	10 l. violet	30·00	40·00
18	99	20 l. green	£150	£300
19	–	25 l. black	£350	£800
20	–	50 l. violet	£300	£800

(ii) War Propaganda issue. Nos. 563/74.

21	25 c. green (Navy)	1·25	5·00
22	25 c. green (Army)	1·25	5·00
23	25 c. green (Air Force)	1·25	5·00
24	25 c. green (Militia)	1·25	5·00
25	30 c. brown (Navy)	1·25	7·50
26	30 c. brown (Army)	1·25	7·50
27	30 c. brown (Air Force)	1·25	7·50
28	30 c. brown (Militia)	1·25	7·50
29	50 c. violet (Navy)	1·25	5·00
30	50 c. violet (Army)	1·25	5·00
31	50 c. violet (Air Force)	1·25	5·00
32	50 c. violet (Militia)	1·25	5·00

(b) Air. Nos. 270/7.

33	–	25 c. green	4·00	14·00
34	110	50 c. brown	2·00	2·50
35	–	75 c. brown	5·00	18·00
36	–	80 c. red	18·00	70·00
37	–	1 l. violet	2·00	8·50
38	113	2 l. blue	18·00	70·00
39	110	5 l. green	30·00	£100
40		10 l. red	£400	£1000

(4) (5)

1944. Stamps of Italy. (a) Optd with T **4**.

57	–	25 c. green (No. 244)	10	10
60	–	75 c. red (No. 248)	10	10

(b) Optd with T **5**.

58	103	30 c. brown	10	10
61	–	1 l. 25 blue (No. 250)	10	10
77	–	50 l. violet (No. 259)	£130	£700

(c) Optd **REPUBBLICA SOCIALE ITALIANA**.

59	103	50 c. violet	10	10

1944. War Propaganda stamps. Nos. 563/74 optd with T **4** (25 c.), T **5** (30 c.) or **REPUBBLICA SOCIALE ITALIANA** (50 c.).

64	25 c. green (Navy)	10	45
65	25 c. green (Army)	10	45
66	25 c. green (Air Force)	10	45
67	25 c. green (Militia)	10	45
68	30 c. brown (Navy)	15	60
69	30 c. brown (Army)	15	60
70	30 c. brown (Air Force)	15	60
71	30 c. brown (Militia)	15	60
72	50 c. violet (Navy)	10	45
73	50 c. violet (Army)	10	45
74	50 c. violet (Air Force)	10	45
75	50 c. violet (Militia)	10	45

Prices are for examples overprinted on the stamp part only; items overprinted twice (on stamp and label) are worth more.

10 Loggia dei Mercanti, Bologna 11

12 Basilica de St. Lorenzo, Rome 13

1944. Inscr "REPUBBLICA SOCIALE ITALIANA".

106	–	5 c. brown	10	15
107	–	10 c. brown	10	15
102	10	20 c. red	10	15
108	11	20 c. red	10	15
103	12	25 c. green	10	15
109	13	25 c. green	10	15
110	–	30 c. brown	10	15
111	–	50 c. violet	10	15
112	–	75 c. red	10	15
113	–	1 l. violet	10	15
114	–	1 l. 25 blue	10	1·75
115	–	3 l. green	10	9·50

DESIGN: 5 c. St. Ciriaco's Church, Ancona; 10 c., 1 l. Montecassino, Abbey; 30 c., 75 c. Drummer; 50 c. Fascist allegory; 1 l. 25, 3 l. St. Mary of Grace, Milan.

17 Bandiera Brothers

1944. Death Centenary of Attilio and Emilio Bandiera (revolutionaries).

117	17	25 c. green	10	15
118		1 l. violet	10	15
119		2 l. 50 red	10	2·00

CONCESSIONAL LETTER POST

1944. Concessional Letter Post stamp of Italy optd as T **5** but smaller.

CL76	CL 109	10 c. brown	10	10

EXPRESS LETTER STAMPS

1944. Express stamps of Italy optd **G. N. R.**

E41	E 132	1 l. 25 green (postage)	2·00	10·00
E42		2 l. 50 red	70·00	£180
E43	E 133	2 l. black (air)	£325	£750

(E 7)

1944. Express stamps of Italy optd with Type E **7**.

E62	E 132	1 l. 25 green	10	10
E63		2 l. 50 orange	10	1·00

E 16 Palermo Cathedral

1944.

E116	E 16	1 l. 25 green	10	40

PARCEL POST STAMPS

1944. Parcel Post stamps of Italy optd **REP. SOC. ITALIANA** on left-hand side and Fascist Emblem on right.

P77	P 92	5 c. brown	1·00	2·00
P78		10 c. blue	1·00	2·00
P79		25 c. red	1·00	2·00
P80		30 c. blue	1·00	2·00
P81		50 c. orange	1·00	2·00
P82		60 c. red	1·00	2·00
P83		1 l. violet	1·00	2·00
P84		2 l. green	£120	£160
P85		3 l. bistre	2·00	4·00
P86		4 l. black	2·00	4·00
P87		10 l. purple	70·00	£100
P88		20 l. purple	£200	£300

The unused and used prices are for unsevered stamps.

POSTAGE DUE STAMPS

1944. Postage Due stamps of Italy optd **G. N. R.**

D44	D 141	5 c. brown	4·50	18·00
D45		10 c. blue	4·50	18·00
D46		20 c. red	2·00	10·00
D47		25 c. green	1·75	10·00
D48		30 c. orange	3·00	16·00
D49		40 c. brown	1·75	10·00
D50		50 c. violet	25·00	80·00
D51		60 c. blue	£140	£300
D52	D 142	1 l. orange	3·00	15·00
D53		2 l. green	5·00	18·00
D54		5 l. violet	70·00	£140
D55		10 l. blue	35·00	£100
D56		20 l. red	35·00	£100

1944. Postage Due stamps of Italy optd with small Fascist emblems.

D 89	D 141	5 c. brown	20	80
D 90		10 c. blue	20	60
D 91		20 c. red	20	60
D 92		25 c. green	20	60
D 93		30 c. orange	20	1·40
D 94		40 c. brown	20	1·60
D 95		50 c. violet	20	35
D 96		60 c. blue	55	5·00
D 97	D 142	1 l. orange	20	35
D 98		2 l. green	1·00	3·50
D 99		5 l. violet	10·00	30·00
D100		10 l. blue	26·00	65·00
D101		20 l. red	26·00	65·00

IVORY COAST Pt. 6; Pt. 13

A French colony in W. Africa on the Gulf of Guinea, incorporated in French West Africa in 1944. In 1958 it became an autonomous republic within the French Community, and in 1960 it became fully independent.

100 centimes = 1 franc.

1892. "Tablet" key-type inscr "COTE D'IVOIRE" in blue (Nos. 2, 3, 5, 14, 7, 9/11) or red (others).

1	D	1 c. black on blue	65	85
2		2 c. brown on buff	1·00	1·10
3		4 c. brown on grey	1·50	1·50
4a		5 c. green on green	5·75	3·75
5		10 c. black on lilac	5·00	5·25
14		10 c. red	70·00	45·00
6		15 c. blue	9·50	7·00
15		15 c. grey	5·00	1·75
7		20 c. red on green	9·50	8·75
8		25 c. black on pink	9·50	1·60
16		25 c. blue	17·00	12·50
9		30 c. brown on drab	16·00	12·50
10		40 c. red on yellow	11·00	4·50
11		50 c. red on pink	45·00	35·00
17		50 c. brown on blue	11·00	6·75
12		75 c. brown on yellow	8·00	12·50
13		1 f. green	28·00	20·00

1904. Surch in figures and bars.
18 D 0.05 on 30 c. brown . . . . . 42·00 45·00
19 0.10 on 75 c. brown on yellow 2·50 8·25
20 0.15 on 1 f. olive . . . . . . 9·00 9·50

1906. "Faidherbe", "Palms" and "Balay" key-types inscr "COTE D'IVOIRE" in blue (10 c., 5 f.) or red (others).
22 I 1 c. grey 30 40
23 2 c. brown 30 40
24 4 c. brown on blue 90 75
25 5 c. green . . . . 2·40 40
26 10 c. pink . . . . 4·25 1·75
27 J 20 c. black on blue . . . . . 4·00 3·00
28 25 c. blue . . . . 3·50 1·75
29 30 c. brown on pink . . . . . 5·75 5·00
30 35 c. black on yellow . . . . 4·00 2·25
32 45 c. brown on green . . . . 7·75 6·00
33 50 c. violet . . . . 7·25 6·00
34 75 c. green on orange . . . . 8·50 6·00
35 K 1 f. black on blue . . . . . 20·00 19·00
36 2 f. blue on pink . . . . . . 32·00 27·00
37 5 f. red on yellow . . . . . . 50·00 50·00

1912. Surch in figures.
38 D 05 on 15 c. grey 25 40
39 05 on 30 c. brown on drab . . 70 80
40 10 on 40 c. red on yellow . . 50 75
41 10 on 50 c. brown on blue . . 60 1·10
42 10 on 75 c. brown on orange . 2·00 3·50

7 River Scene

1913.
43 7 1 c. violet and purple 10 10
44 2 c. black and brown 10 25
45 4 c. purple and violet 10 25
46 5 c. green and light green . . . 50 50
61 5 c. brown and chocolate . . . 25 40
47 10 c. pink and red 50 65
62 10 c. green and light green . . . 25 40
63 10 c. pink on blue 15 20
48 15 c. red and orange 30 50
49 20 c. grey and black 40 60
50 25 c. blue and ultramarine . . 4·25 2·75
64 25 c. violet and black 30 30
51 30 c. brown and chocolate . . . 65 80
65 30 c. pink and red 80 85
66 30 c. red and blue 20 30
67 30 c. green and olive 25 40
52 35 c. orange and violet 65 80
53 40 c. green and grey 60 80
54 45 c. brown and red 40 50
68 45 c. purple and red . . . . 3·00 4·00
55 50 c. violet and black . . . . 1·90 2·00
69 50 c. blue and ultramarine . . . 50 65
70 50 c. blue and green 50 50
71 60 c. violet on pink 40 55
72 65 c. green and red 85 95
56 75 c. pink and brown 30 45
73 75 c. ultramarine and blue . . 1·90 2·00
74 85 c. black and purple . . . . 85 1·00
75 90 c. carmine and red . . . . 6·00 7·25
57 1 f. black and yellow 65 55
76 1 f. 10 brown and green . . . 3·75 4·00
77 1 f. 50 blue and light blue . . 4·25 4·00
78 1 f. 75 mauve and blue . . . . 6·75 6·00
58 2 f. blue and brown . . . . . 1·50 85
79 3 f. mauve on pink . . . . . 4·25 2·50
59 5 f. brown and blue . . . . . 3·00 3·00

1915. Surch **5c** and red cross.
60 7 10 c. + 5 c. pink and red . . . 40 65

1934. Surch with new value twice.
80 7 50 on 45 c. purple and red . . 1·60 1·60
81 50 on 75 c. ultram & blue . . 1·00 95
82 50 on 90 c. pink and red . . 1·00 95
83 60 on 75 c. violet on pink . . 50 50
84 65 on 15 c. red and orange . . 50 60
85 85 on 75 c. pink and brown . . 50 60

1922. Surch in figures and bars.
86 7 25 c. on 2 f. blue and brown . 40 50
87 25 c. on 5 f. brown and blue . 40 50
88 90 c. on 75 c. pink and red . . 50 65
89 1 f. 25 on 1 f. ultram & blue . 35 50
90 1 f. 50 on 1 f. blue & lt blue . 50 55
91 3 f. on 5 f. green and red . . 1·25 2·00
92 10 f. on 5 f. mauve and red . . 5·00 8·00
93 20 f. on 5 f. red and green . . 9·00 9·00

1931. "Colonial Exhibition" key-types inscr "COTE D'IVOIRE".
94 E 40 c. black and green . . . . 1·25 40
95 F 50 c. black and mauve . . . 3·00 3·25
96 G 90 c. black and red . . . . . 1·10 1·40
97 H 1 f. 50 black and blue . . . . 3·00 3·50

1933. Stamps of Upper Volta optd **Cote d'Ivoire** or surch also.
98 3 2 c. brown and violet 10 25
99 4 c. black and yellow 20 30
100 5 c. indigo and blue 30 40
101 10 c. blue and pink 35 40
102 15 c. brown and blue 40 50
103 20 c. brown and green 40 50
104 – 25 c. brown and yellow . . . 50 1·00
105 – 30 c. deep green and green . . 50 1·00
106 – 45 c. brown and blue . . . . 5·00 4·00
107 – 65 c. indigo and blue . . . . 1·50 1·75
108 – 75 c. black and violet . . . . 60 1·40
109 – 90 c. red and mauve . . . . 85 1·50
110 6 1 f. brown and green . . . . 1·60 1·40
111 – 1 f. 25 on 40 c. blk & pink . . 65 75
112 6 1 f. 50 ultramarine & blue . . 1·60 1·00
113 – 1 f. 75 on 50 c. black & grn . 1·60 90

12 Baoule Woman

16 General Binger

1936.
114 12 1 c. red 10 25
115 2 c. blue 10 25
116 3 c. green 10 25
117 4 c. brown 10 30
118 5 c. violet 10 25
119 10 c. blue 10 20
120 15 c. red 10 20
121 – 20 c. blue 10 25
122 – 25 c. red 10 20
123 – 30 c. green 10 25
124 – 30 c. brown 10 25
125 12 35 c. green 15 30
126 – 40 c. red 10 25
127 – 45 c. brown 25 45
128 – 45 c. green 40 60
129 – 50 c. purple 10 10
130 – 55 c. violet 45 60
131 – 60 c. red 45 60
132 – 65 c. brown 30 45
133 – 70 c. brown 35 45
134 – 75 c. violet 25 30
135 – 80 c. brown 30 35
136 – 90 c. red . . . . 2·00 3·25
137 – 90 c. green 75 90
138 – 1 f. green 70 75
139 – 1 f. red 30 50
140 – 1 f. violet 30 30
141 – 1 f. 25 red 25 25
142 – 1 f. 40 blue 60 75
143 – 1 f. 50 blue 30 30
144 – 1 f. 50 grey 60 60
145 – 1 f. 60 brown 45 60
146 – 1 f. 75 red 30 50
147 – 1 f. 75 blue 40 55
148 – 2 f. blue 30 30
149 – 2 f. 50 blue 50 65
150 – 2 f. 50 red 40 60
151 – 3 f. green 30 35
152 – 5 f. brown 30 40
153 – 10 f. violet 35 50
154 – 20 f. red . . . . 1·40 95
DESIGNS—HORIZ: 20 c. to 30 c. and 40 c. to 55 c. Mosque at Bobo-Dioulasso; 60 c. to 1 f. 60, Coastal scene. VERT: 1 f. 75, to 20 f. Comoe Rapids.

1937. International Exhibition, Paris. As Nos. 157/62 of Guadeloupe.
155 20 c. violet 35 60
156 30 c. green 35 60
157 40 c. red 35 75
158 50 c. brown and blue 35 75
159 90 c. red 35 60
160 1 f. 50 blue 45 80

1937. 50th Anniv of Gen. Binger's Exploration.
161 16 65 c. brown 20 15

1938. International Anti-Cancer Fund. As T **58b** of Guadeloupe.
162 1 f. 75 + 50 c. blue . . . . . . 2·50 5·25

1939. Caillie Cent. As T **27** of Muaritania.
163 90 c. orange 25 40
164 2 f. violet 30 55
165 2 f. 25 blue 55 65

1939. New York World's Fair. As T **58c** of Guadeloupe.
166 1 f. 25 red 60 65
167 2 f. 25 blue 60 65

1939. 150th Anniv of French Revolution. As T **58d** of Guadeloupe.
168 45 c. + 25 c. green & black . . 3·50 4·25
169 70 c. + 30 c. brown & black . . 3·50 4·25
170 90 c. + 35 c. orange & black . . 3·50 4·25
171 1 f. 25 + 1 f. red and black . . 3·50 4·25
172 2 f. 25 + 2 f. blue and black . . 3·50 4·25

1940. Air. As T **30** of Mauritania.
173 1 f. 90 blue 30 45
174 2 f. 90 red 35 55
175 4 f. 50 green 35 55
176 4 f. 90 olive 35 55
177 6 f. 90 orange . . . . 85 1·00

1941. National Defence Fund. Surch **SECOURS NATIONAL** and value.
178 + 1 f. on 50 c. (No. 129) . . . 2·00 2·00
178a + 2 f. on 80 c. (No. 135) . . . 6·50 6·75
178b + 2 f. on 1 f. 50 (No. 143) . . 6·50 6·75
178c + 3 f. on 2 f. (No. 148) . . . 6·50 6·50

16a Pirogue

1942. Marshal Petain issue.
178d 16a 1 f. green . . . . 20 1·25
178e 2 f. 50 blue . . . . 20 1·25

1942. Air. Colonial Child Welfare Fund. As Nos. 98g/i of Niger.
178f 1 f. 50 + 3 f. 50 green 35
178g 2 f. + 6 f. brown 30
178h 3 f. + 9 f. red 30

1942. Air Imperial Fortnight. As No. 98j of Niger.
178i 1 f. 20 + 1 f. 80 blue & red . . 30

1942. Air. As T **32** of Mauritania but inscr "COTE D'IVOIRE".
179 50 f. olive and green . . . . . 95 1·40

REPUBLIC

17 African Elephant

19 Pres. Houphouet-Boigny

18 Place Lapalud, Abidjan

1959.
180 17 10 f. black and green . . . 40 20
181 25 f. brown and bistre . . . 75 30
182 30 f. olive and turquoise . . 1·00 40

1959. Air.
183 18 100 f. brn, grn & choc . . . 2·25 60
184 – 200 f. brn, myrtle & turq . . 3·75 1·25
185 – 500 f. turquoise, brn & grn . 8·50 3·25
DESIGNS: 200 f. Houphouet-Boigny railway bridge, Abidjan; 500 f. Ayame Barrage.

1959. 1st Anniv of Republic.
186 19 25 f. brown 50 30

20 Bete Mask

22 "Thoningia sanguinea"

21a "World Peace"

1960. Native Masks.
187 20 50 c. chocolate & brown . . 10 10
188 – 1 f. violet and red 10 10
189 – 2 f. green and blue 10 10
190 – 4 f. red and green 15 15
191 – 5 f. brown and red 20 20
192 – 6 f. blue and purple 25 20
193 – 45 f. purple and green . . . 1·25 50
194 – 50 f. blue and brown . . . . 1·75 75
195 – 85 f. green and red . . . . 3·00 1·25
DESIGNS—VERT: MASKS OF: 1 f. Guere; 2 f. Guere (different type); 45 f. Bete (different type); 50 f. Gouro; 85 f. Gouro (different type). HORIZ: 4 f. Baole; 5 f. Senoufo; 6 f. Senoufo (different type).

1960. 10th Anniv of African Technical Co-operation Commission. As T **4** of Malagasy.
196 25 f. violet and turquoise . . . 50 40

1960. 1st Anniv of Conseil de l'Entente. As T **9** of Niger.
197 25 f. multicoloured 50 50

1961. 1st Anniv of Independence.
198 21a 25 f. black, green & brown . 55 35

1961.
199 – 5 f. red, yellow and green . . 55 15
200 – 10 f. yellow red and blue . . 30 20
201 – 15 f. purple, grn & orange . 1·10 30
202 22 20 f. yellow, red & brown . . 60 30
203 – 25 f. yellow, red & green . . 70 30
204 – 30 f. red, green & black . . 90 50
205 – 70 f. yellow red & green . . 2·50 1·00
206 – 85 f. multicoloured . . . . 3·25 1·40
FLOWERS: 5 f. "Plumeria rubra"; 10 f. "Haemanthus cinnabarinus"; 15 f. "Bougainvillea spectabilis"; 25 f. "Eulophia cucullata"; 30 f. "Newbouldia laevis"; 70 f. "Mussaenda erythrophylla"; 85 f. "Strophantus sarmentosus".

23 Mail-carriers

1961. Stamp Day.
207 23 25 f. brown, blue & green . . 55 40

24 Ayame Dam

26 Palms

25 Swimming

1961.
208 24 25 f. sepia, blue and green . . 55 30

1961. Abidjan Games. Inscr as in T **25**.
209 25 5 f. sepia, green and blue (postage) 20 10
210 – 20 f. brn, green & grey . . 35 20
211 – 25 f. brn, green & blue . . 55 25
211a – 100 f. blk, red & bl (air) . . 2·75 1·60
DESIGNS: 20 f. Basketball; 25 f. Football; 100 f. High-jumping.

1962. 17th Session of African Technical Co-operation Commission, Abidjan.
212 26 25 f. multicoloured 55 35

1962. Air. "Air Afrique" Airline. As T **42** of Mauritania.
213 50 f. blue, brown & chestnut . . 1·25 65

1962. Malaria Eradication. As T **43** of Mauritania.
214 25 f. + 5 f. green 65 65

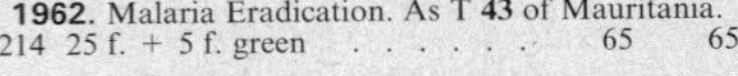

27 Fort Assinie

1962. Postal Centenary.
215 27 85 f. multicoloured . . . . 1·90 1·10

28 Village, Man Region

1962. Air.
216 – 200 f. sepia, purple & green . 5·00 1·90
217 28 500 f. green, purple & blk . 8·50 4·00
DESIGN—VERT: 200 f. Street Scene, Odienne.

1962. 1st Anniv of Union of African and Malagasy States. As No. 155 of Mauritania.
218 72 30 f. red . . . . 1·00 55

29 U.N. Headquarters and Emblem

1962. Air. 2nd Anniv of Admission to U.N.
219 29 100 f. multicoloured . . . . 1·90 85

30 Bouake Arms and Cotton Exhibit

1963. Bouake Fair.
220 **30** 50 f. sepia, brown & green . 65 35

1963. Freedom from Hunger. As T **51** of Mauritania.
221 25 f. + 5 f. violet, brown & pur 85 85

31 Map of Africa

1963. Conference of African Heads of State, Addis Ababa.
222 **31** 30 f. green and blue 60 60

32 Sassandra Bay

1963. Air.
223 – 50 f. green, brown & blue . 1·25 45
224 **32** 100 f. brown, blue & myrtle . 1·90 95
225 – 200 f. turquoise, grn & brn . 3·50 1·60
DESIGNS: 50 f. Moosou Bridge; 200 f. River Comoe.

1963. Air. African and Malagasian Posts and Telecommunications Union. As T **56** of Mauritania.
226 85 f. multicoloured . . . . . . 1·40 85

33 Hartebeest

34 Scales of Justice, Globe and UNESCO Emblem

1963. "Tourism and Hunting".
227 – 1 f. multicoloured 30 10
228 – 2 f. multicoloured 30 15
229 – 4 f. multicoloured 25 15
230 – 5 f. multicoloured 25 10
247 – 5 f. green, yellow & brn . . 45 20
231 **33** 10 f. brown, green & grey . 45 20
248 – 10 f. brown, green & purple . 1·00 20
232 – 15 f. black, green & brn . . 60 30
249 – 15 f. brown, green & purple . 1·60 30
233 – 20 f. brown, green & red . . 85 30
234 – 25 f. brown, green & yellow . 1·40 50
235 – 45 f. purple, green & turq . 2·75 1·00
236 – 50 f. black, green & brn . . 3·75 1·40
DESIGNS—HORIZ: 1 f. Yellow-backed duiker; 4 f. Beecroft's hyrax; 5 f. (No. 247) African manatee; 10 f. (No. 248) Pygmy hippopotamus; 15 f. (No. 232) Giant forest hog; 20 f. Warthog; 45 f. Hunting dogs. VERT: 2 f. Potto; 5 f. (No. 230) Water chevrotain; 15 f. (No. 249) Royal antelope; 25 f. Bongo; 50 f. Western black and white colobus.

1963. Air. 1st Anniv of "Air Afrique" and "DC–8" Service Inaug. As T **59** of Mauritania.
237 25 f. multicoloured 55 25

1963. 15th Anniv of Declaration of Human Rights.
238 **34** 85 f. black, blue & orange . 1·25 70

35 Rameses II and Nefertari, Abu Simbel

36 Map of Africa

1964. Air. Nubian Monuments Preservation.
239 **35** 60 f. black, brown & red . . 1·60 85

1964. Inter-African National Education Ministers' Conference, Abidjan.
240 **36** 30 f. red, green and blue . . 60 35

37 Weather Balloon

38 Doctor tending Child

1964. World Meteorological Day.
241 **37** 25 f. multicoloured 60 40

1964. National Red Cross Society.
242 **38** 50 f. multicoloured 95 50

39 Arms of the Ivory Coast

1964. Air.
243 **39** 200 f. gold, blue & green . . 3·00 1·40

40 Globe and Athletes

41 Symbolic Tree

1964. Olympic Games. Tokyo.
244 **40** 35 f. brown, green & violet . 95 45
245 – 65 f. ochre, brown & blue . 1·90 95
DESIGN—HORIZ: 65 f. Wrestling and Globe.

1964. 1st Anniv of European-African Convention.
246 **41** 30 f. multicoloured 65 35

1964. French, African and Malagasy Co-operation. As T **68** of Mauritania.
250 25 f. brown, red and green . . . 55 35

42 Pres. Kennedy

43 Korhogo Mail-carriers, 1914

1964. Air. Pres. Kennedy Commemoration.
251 **42** 100 f. brown and grey . . . 1·90 1·40

1964. Stamp Day.
252 **43** 85 f. sepia, brown & blue . . 1·60 95

44 Pottery

1965. Native Handicrafts.
253 **44** 5 f. black, red and green . . 20 15
254 – 10 f. black, purple & green . 25 15
255 – 20 f. blue, chocolate & brn . 50 20
256 – 25 f. brown, red and olive . 55 30
DESIGNS: 10 f. Wood-carving; 20 f. Ivory-carving; 25 f. Weaving.

45 Mail coming ashore

1965. Stamp Day.
257 **45** 30 f. multicoloured 60 45

46 I.T.U. Emblem and Symbols

1965. I.T.U. Centenary.
258 **46** 85 f. blue, red and green . . 1·40 85

47 Abidjan Railway Station

1965.
259 **47** 30 f. multicoloured . . . . 1·25 45

48 Pres. Houphouet-Boigny and Map

49 Hammerkop

1965. 5th Anniv of Independence.
260 **48** 30 f. multicoloured 55 35

1965. Birds.
261 – 1 f. green, yellow & violet . 1·50 50
262 – 2 f. multicoloured . . . . . 1·50 55
263 – 5 f. purple, red and olive . . 1·60 65
264 **49** 10 f. brown, black & pur . . 2·25 60
265 – 15 f. red, grey and green . . 1·90 65
266 – 30 f. brown, green & lake . . 2·75 65
267 – 50 f. blue, black & brown . 5·25 1·25
268 – 75 f. red, green & orange . . 5·25 1·50
269 – 90 f. multicoloured . . . . 7·50 3·25
BIRDS—HORIZ: 1 f. Yellow-bellied Green Pigeon; 2 f. Spur-winged Goose; 30 f. Namaqua Dove; 50 f. Lizard Buzzard. VERT: 5 f. Stone Partridge; 15 f. White-breasted Guineafowl; 75 f. Yellow-billed Stork; 90 f. Latham's Francolin.

50 Lieupleu Rope-bridge

1965. Air.
270 **50** 100 f. brown, green & lt grn 1·90 1·10
271 – 300 f. purple, flesh & blue . 5·50 2·75
DESIGN: 300 f. Street in Kong.

51 Steam Mail Train, 1906

52 "Maternity"

1966. Stamp Day.
272 **51** 30 f. green, black & pur . . 3·25 1·60

1966. World Festival of Negro Arts. Dakar.
273 **52** 5 f. black and green 20 15
274 – 10 f. black and violet . . . 30 20
275 – 20 f. black and orange . . . 90 45
276 – 30 f. black and red . . . . 1·10 65
DESIGNS—CARVED WORK: 10 f. Pomade box; 20 f. Drums; 30 f. "Ancestor".

53 Ivory Hotel

1966. Inauguration of Ivory Hotel.
277 **53** 15 f. multicoloured 45 25

54 Tractor Cultivation

1966. 6th Anniv of Independence.
278 **54** 30 f. multicoloured 50 35

1966. Air. Inaug of Douglas DC-8F Air Services. As T **87** of Mauritania.
279 30 f. grey, black and green . . . 55 30

55 Open-air Class

1966. National School of Administration.
280 **55** 30 f. black, blue and lake . . 55 35

56 Inoculating Cattle

57 U.N.E.S.C.O. "Waves" enveloping "Man"

1966. Campaign for Prevention of Cattle Plague.
281 **56** 30 f. brown, green & blue . 65 40

1966. 20th Anniv of U.N.E.S.C.O.
282 **57** 30 f. violet and blue 60 40
283 – 30 f. black, brown & blue . 55 35
DESIGN: No. 283, Distributing food parcels to children.

58 Bouake Hospital

59 "Air Afrique" Headquarters

1966.
284 **58** 30 f. multicoloured 55 35

1966. Air.
285 **59** 500 f. blue, ochre & green . 8·25 3·25

60 Sikorsky S-43 Amphibian (30th anniv)

1967. Stamp Day.
286 **60** 30 f. blue, brown & turq . . 1·25 80

61 Cutting Pineapples

62 "African Mythology"

1967. Fruits.
287 **61** 20 f. purple, brown & grn . 35 15
288 – 30 f. red, brown & green . . 45 30
289 – 100 f. brown, olive & blue . 1·90 85
DESIGNS: 30 f. Cutting palm-nuts; 100 f. Cutting bananas.

1967. 35th Pen Club Int Congress, Abidjan.
290 **62** 30 f. black, green and lake . 60 40

63 "Improvement of Rural Housing"

1967. 7th Anniv of Independence.
291 **63** 30 f. multicoloured 50 30

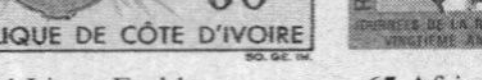

64 Lions Emblems 65 African Man and Woman

1967. 50th Anniv of Lions International.
292 **64** 30 f. multicoloured 80 45

1967. Air. 5th Anniv of U.A.M.P.T. As T **101** of Mauritania.
293 100 f. red, blue and violet . . . 1·60 85

1967. 5th Anniv of West African Monetary Union. As T **103** of Mauritania.
294 30 f. black, green and mauve . . 50 30

1967. 20th Anniv of Recognition Days.
295 **65** 90 f. multicoloured . . . . 1·10 65
See also No. 342.

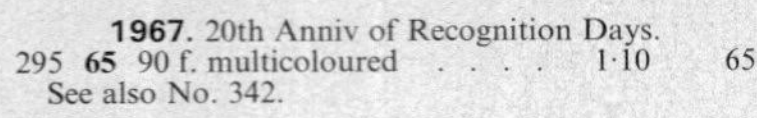

66 Senoufo Village

1968. Air.
296 **66** 100 f. brown, yellow & grn . 1·90 90
297 – 500 f. brown, blue & grn . . 8·25 3·25
DESIGN: 500 f. Tiegba lake village.

67 Tabou Radio Station, 1912

1968. Stamp Day.
298 **67** 30 f. green, brn & turq . . . 60 35

68 Cotton Loom

1968. Industries.
299 – 5 f. black, red and green . . 20 10
300 **68** 10 f. brown, green, & slate . 30 15
301 – 15 f. black, blue and red . . 70 45
302 – 20 f. blue and purple . . . 50 30
303 – 30 f. brown, green & blue . 65 35
304 – 50 f. black, grn & mauve . . 95 45
305 – 70 f. chocolate, blue & brn . 1·40 70
306 – 90 f. black, purple & blue . 1·60 1·10
DESIGNS—HORIZ: 5 f. Palm-oil works; 30 f. Flour mills; 50 f. Cocoa-butter extraction machine; 90 f. Timber sawmill and logs. VERT: 15 f. Oil refinery, Abidjan; 20 f. Raw cotton and reeling machine; 70 f. Soluble-coffee plant.
See also Nos. 335/7.

69 Canoeing

1968. Olympic Games, Mexico.
307 **69** 30 f. brown, blue & green . 60 30
308 – 100 f. purple, ultram & blue 1·60 65
DESIGN: 100 f. 100-metres sprint.

70 Sacrificial Offering

1968. 8th Anniv of Independence.
309 **70** 30 f. multicoloured 55 30

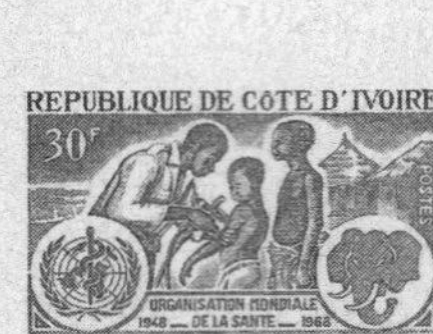

71 Doctor inoculating Patient 72 Impala in Forest

1968. 20th Anniv of W.H.O.
310 **71** 30 f. chocolate, brn & bl . . 55 30

1968. Fauna and Flora Protection.
311 **72** 30 f. brown, green & blue . 1·10 55

73 Museum and Carved Screen

1968. Opening of Abidjan Museum.
312 **73** 30 f. brown, red & blue . . 55 30

74 Human Rights Emblem and "Justice" Totems

1968. Human Rights Year.
313 **74** 30 f. orge, purple & blue . . 55 30

1969. Air. "Philexafrique" Stamp Exn, Abidjan, Ivory Coast (1st issue). As T **113a** of Mauritania. Multicoloured.
314 100 f. "Grand Bassam" (Achalme) . . . . 3·25 3·25

1969. Air. "Philexafrique" Stamp Exn, Abidjan, Ivory Coast (2nd issue). As T **114a** of Mauritania.
315 50 f. red, blue and green . . . . 1·90 1·90
316 100 f. blue, brown & orange . . 3·00 3·00
317 200 f. slate, blue & brown . . . 4·50 4·50
DESIGNS—HORIZ: 50 f. Aerial view of San Pedro village and stamp of 1936; 200 f. Chambers of Agriculture and Industry building, Abidjan, and 5 f. stamp of 1913. VERT: 100 f. Chief's costume and 5 f. stamp of 1936.

75 "Ville de Maranhao" (mail steamer) at Grand-Bassam

1969. Stamp Day.
319 **75** 30 f. purple, blue & green . 65 30

76 Ivory Hotel

1969. Opening of Ivory Hotel.
320 **76** 30 f. blue, red and green . . 65 30

77 "Man on Horse-back" (statuette) 78 Hertzian-wave Radio Station, Man

1969. Ivory Coast Art Exn, Vevey, Switzerland.
321 **77** 30 f. black, purple & red . . 65 45

1969. 9th Anniv of Independence.
322 **78** 30 f. green, brown & blue . 60 35

1969. 5th Anniv of African Development Bank. As T **122a** of Mauritania.
323 30 f. brown, green and lake . . 50 30

80 Arms of Bouake 81 Game Fishing

1969. Coats of Arms.
324 **80** 10 f. multicoloured 20 10
325 – 15 f. multicoloured 30 15
326 – 30 f. black, gold & green . . 45 15
ARMS: 15 f. Abidjan; 30 f. Ivory Coast Republic.
See also Nos. 402/3 and 432/36.

1969. Int SKAL Tourist Assn Congress, Abidjan.
327 **81** 30 f. blue, purple & violet . 2·00 50
328 – 100 f. multicoloured . . . . 3·00 1·50
DESIGN: 100 f. Assinie Holiday Village.

1969. 10th Anniv of Aerial Navigation Security Agency for Africa and Madagascar (A.S.E.C.N.A.). As T **147** of Gabon.
329 30 f. red 55 35

82 Man Waterfall

1970. Air.
330 **82** 100 f. blue, green & brown . 1·90 1·00
331 – 200 f. red, green & emerald . 2·75 1·10
DESIGN: 200 f. Mt. Niangbo.

83 University Hospital Centre, Abidjan

1970. "10 Years of Higher Education".
332 **83** 30 f. indigo, green & blue . . 55 35

84 Telegraphist and Gabriel Dadie (Postal administrator)

1970. Stamp Day.
333 **84** 30 f. black, green and red . . 50 30

85 Abidjan University

1970. 3rd A.U.P.E.L.F. (Association of French Speaking Universities). General Assembly, Abidjan.
334 **85** 30 f. purple, green & blue . 55 35

86 Safety-match Manufacture 88 Wild Life

87 Dish Aerial and Television Class

1970. Industrial Expansion.
335 **86** 5 f. brown, blue & choc . . 20 15
336 – 20 f. red, green & grey . . 40 15
337 – 50 f. brown, blue & green . 90 35
DESIGNS: 20 f. Textile-printing; 50 f. Ship-building.

1970. World Telecommunications Day.
338 **87** 40 f. green, drab and red . . 65 40

1970. New U.P.U. Headquarters Building, Berne. As T **81** of New Caledonia.
339 30 f. brown, green & purple . . 65 35

1970. 25th Anniv of United Nations.
340 **88** 30 f. brown, green & blue . 90 55

89 Coffee Plant 90 African Man and Woman

1970. 10th Anniv of Independence (1st issue).
341 **89** 30 f. green, brown & orge . 55 35
See also Nos. 344/9.

1970. 5th P.D.C.I. (Ivory Coast Democratic Party) Congress.
342 **90** 40 f. multicoloured 65 35

91 Power Station

1970. Thermal Power Plant, Vridi.
343 **91** 40 f. brown, blue & green . 60 20

92 Pres. Houphouet-Boigny and De Gaulle

1970. 10th Anniv of Independence (2nd issue). Embossed on silver (300 f. values) or gold foil.
344 300 f. Type **92** (postage) . . . . . . 9·00
345 300 f. Ivory Coast Arms . . . . . . 7·75
346 1000 f. Type **92** . . . . 32·00
347 1000 f. As No. 345 . . . . 29·00
348 300 f. Pres. Houphouet-Boigny and African elephants (air) . . . . . . 7·25
349 1200 f. As No. 348 . . . . 29·00

93 Mail Bus, 1925

1971. Stamp Day.
350 **93** 40 f. purple, green & brn . . 70 30

94 Port of San Pedro

1971. Air.
351 **94** 100 f. red, blue and green . . 1·50 55
352 – 500 f. green, blue & brown . 7·75 3·50
DESIGN: 500 f. African Riviera coastline.

95 Desjardin's Marginella

1971. Marine Life.
353 – 1 f. brn, blue and green . . 15 10
354 – 5 f. red, lilac and blue . . . 20 15
355 – 10 f. red, blue and green . . 45 20
356 **95** 15 f. brown, purple & blue . 50 25
357 – 15 f. brown, violet & red . . 75 25
358 – 20 f. red and yellow . . . . 1·10 40
359 – 20 f. lake, purple & red . . 1·25 45
360 – 25 f. brown, black & lake . . 75 25
361 – 35 f. red, yellow & green . . 1·40 55
362 – 40 f. brown, blue & green . 3·00 1·25
363 – 40 f. red, turquoise & brn . 2·25 90
364 – 45 f. brown, green & emer . 2·75 1·25
365 – 50 f. green, red and violet . 2·75 1·10
366 – 65 f. blue, green & brown . 3·25 2·25
DESIGNS—HORIZ: 1 f. African's pelican's-foot; 5 f. "Neptunus validus"; 20 f. (No. 359) Digitate carrier shell; 25 f. Butterfly cone; 40 f. (No. 362) Garter cone; 45 f. Bubonion conch; 65 f. Rat cowrie. VERT: 10 f. "Hermodice carunculata"; 15 f. (No. 357) Fanel moon; 20 f. (No. 358) "Goniaster cuspidatus"; 35 f. "Polycheles typhiops"; 40 f. (No. 363) African fan scallop; 50 f. "Enoplometopus callistas".

96 Telegraph Station, Grand Bassam, 1891

1971. World Telecommunications Day.
367 **96** 100 f. brown, green & blue . 1·10 65

97 Treichville Swimming Pool

1971. Air.
368 **97** 100 f. multicoloured . . . . 1·90 70

98 Tool-making **99** African Telecommunications Map

1971. Technical Training and Instruction.
369 **98** 35 f. blue, red and green . . 60 30

1971. Pan-African Telecommunications Network.
370 **99** 45 f. yellow, red & purple . 60 30

100 Bondoukou Market

1971. 11th Anniv of Independence.
371 **100** 35 f. brown, blue and grey (postage) 60 35
372 – 200 f. black and blue on gold (air) . . . . 2·50 1·60
No. 372 has a similar design to Type **100** but in smaller format, size 38 × 27 mm.

101 Children of Three Races

1971. Racial Equality Year. Multicoloured.
373 40 f. Type **101** 55 20
374 45 f. Children around Globe . . 55 20

1971. 10th Anniv of U.A.M.P.T. As T **139a** of Mauritania. Multicoloured.
375 100 f. H.Q. and Ivory Coast Arms . . . . 1·40 65
U.A.M.P.T. = African and Malagasy Posts and Telecommunications Union.

102 Gaming Table

1971. National Lottery.
376 **102** 35 f. multicoloured 50 20

103 Technicians working on Power Cables **105** Cogwheel and Students

104 Lion of St. Mark's

1971. Electricity Works Centre, Akovai-Santai.
377 **103** 35 f. multicoloured 70 35

1972. Air. U.N.E.S.C.O. "Save Venice" Campaign. Multicoloured.
378 100 f. Type **104** . . . . 1·60 85
379 200 f. St. Mark's Square . . . . 3·25 1·60

1972. Technical Instruction Week.
380 **105** 35 f. blue, brown & red . . 50 35

106 Heart Emblem **107** Child learning to write

1972. World Heart Month.
381 **106** 40 f. blue, red & green . . 60 35

1972. International Book Year.
382 – 35 f. brown, orange & grn . 40 20
383 **107** 40 f. black, orange & grn . 55 30
DESIGN—HORIZ: 35 f. Students and open book.

108 Gouessesso Tourist Village

1972. Air.
384 **108** 100 f. brown, green & blue . 1·90 85
385 – 200 f. green, brown & bl . 2·75 1·10
386 – 500 f. brown, bistre & blue 7·75 3·50
DESIGNS: 200 f. Jacqueville Lake; 500 f. Mosque of Kawara.

109 Regional Postal Training Centre, Abidjan **110** Aerial Mast, Abobo Hertzian Centre

1972. Stamp Day.
387 **109** 40 f. bistre, green & pur . . 60 35

1972. World Telecommunications Day.
388 **110** 40 f. red, blue and green . . 70 35

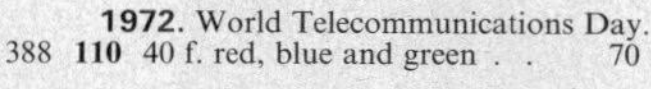

112 Computer Operator

1972. Development of Information Services.
393 **112** 40 f. blue, brown & green . 70 35

113 Odienne

1972. 12th Anniv of Independence.
394 **113** 35 f. brown, green & blue . . 55 35

1972. 10th Anniv of West African Monetary Union. As Type **149** of Mauritania.
395 40 f. grey, purple & brown . . . 60 35

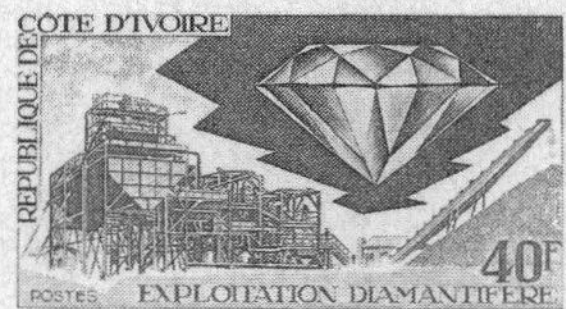

115 Diamond and Mine

1972. Development of the Diamond Industry.
396 **115** 40 f. blue, grey & brown . 1·60 85

116 Lake-dwellings, Bletankoro

1972. Air.
397 **116** 200 f. purple, grn & blue . 2·50 1·10
398 – 500 f. brown, grn & blue . 7·75 3·50
DESIGN: 500 f. Kossou Dam.

117 Louis Pasteur and Institute

1972. Inauguration of Pasteur Institute, Abidjan.
399 **117** 35 f. blue, green & brown . 60 35

118 Satellite Earth Station

1972. Air. Opening of Satellite Earth Station Akakro.
400 **118** 200 f. brown, green & blue . 2·75 1·10

119 Child pumping Water **120** Dr. G. A. Hansen

1972. "Conserve Water" Campaign.
401 **119** 35 f. black, green & red . . 60 30
See also No. 414.

1973. Coats of Arms. As Type **80**. Multicoloured.
402 5 f. Arms of Daloa 15 10
403 10 f. Arms of Gagnoa 20 10
See also Nos. 432/36.

1973. Centenary of Hansen's Identification of Leprosy Bacillus.
404 **120** 35 f. brown, blue & pur . . 60 30

121 Pearly Razorfish

1973. Fishes
405 – 15 f. blue and green . . . 60 40
406 – 20 f. red and brown . . . 1·00 55
406a – 25 f. red and green . . . 1·50 40
406b – 35 f. red and green . . . 1·90 85
407 **121** 50 f. red, blue and black . 2·75 1·40
FISHES: 15 f. Grey triggerfish; 20 f. West African goatfish; 25 f. African hind; 35 f. Bigeye.

122 Child and Emblem

1973. Establishment of first S.O.S. Children's Village in Africa.
408 **122** 40 f. black, red & green . . 55 30

123 National Assembly Building

1973. 112th Interparliamentary Council Session, Abidjan.
409 **123** 100 f. multicoloured . . . 85 35

124 Classroom and Shop **125** "Women's Work"

1973. "Commercial Action" Programme.
410 **124** 40 f. multicoloured 45 15

1973. Technical Instruction for Women.
411 **125** 35 f. multicoloured 50 30

126 Scouts helping with Food Cultivation

1973. 24th World Scouting Congress, Nairobi, Kenya.
412 **126** 40 f. multicoloured 65 35

127 Party Headquarters

1973. New Party Headquarters Building, Yamoussokro.

413 **127** 35 f. multicoloured 45 25

128 Children at Dry Pump

1973. Pan-African Drought Relief.

414 **128** 40 f. sepia, brown & red . . 60 30

129 "The Judgment of Solomon" (Nandjui Legue)

1973. Air. 6th World Peace and Justice Conf.

415 **129** 500 f. multicoloured . . . 9·00 4·00

1973. U.A.M.P.T. As T **155a** of Mauritania.

416 100 f. black, red and violet . . . 1·10 60

130 "Arrow-heads" **132** Motorway Junction

131 Ivory Coast 1 c. Stamp of 1892

1973. Abidjan Museum.

417 **130** 5 f. black, red & brown . . 15 10

1973. Stamp and Post Day.

418 **131** 40 f. black, orange & grn . 65 35

1973. Motorway Projects. Indenie Interchange, Abidjan.

419 **132** 35 f. black, green & blue . 55 30

133 Map of Africa and Emblem **134** "Elephants" Ticket

1973. 18th General Assembly of International Social Security Association.

420 **133** 40 f. brn, ultram & bl . . . 50 20

1973. Travel-Agents' Assns, 7th World Congress.

421 **134** 40 f. multicoloured 50 20

136 Kong Mosque

1974.

426 **136** 35 f. brown, blue & grn . . 55 35

137 Grand-Lahou Post Office

1974. Stamp Day.

427 **137** 35 f. brown, green & bl . . 55 20

138 Converging Columns

1974. "Formation Permanente".

428 **138** 35 f. multicoloured 40 20

139 Sassandra Bridge

1974. Air.

429 **139** 100 f. brown & green . . . 1·10 50

430 500 f. black & green . . . 7·25 2·50

1974. 15th Anniv of Conseil de l'Entente. As T **184** of Niger.

431 40 f. multicoloured 45 20

141 Arms of Ivory Coast

1974.

432 **141** 35 f. gold, green & brn . . 35 10

433 40 f. gold, green & blue . . 40 10

434 60 f. gold, green & red . . 50 20

435 65 f. gold, lt green & grn . . 55 20

436 70 f. gold, green & blue . . 60 30

142 View of Factory

1974. Air. Vridi Soap Factory Abidjan.

437 **142** 200 f. multicoloured . . . 2·25 1·10

143 Pres. Houphouet-Boigny **144** WPY Emblem

1974.

438 **143** 25 f. brown, orge & grn . . 35 15

1974. World Population Year.

439 **144** 40 f. blue and green . . . 55 20

145 Cotton-Picking **146** Pres. Houphouet-Boigny

1974. Cotton Production (1st series).

440 **145** 50 f. multicoloured 60 30

See also Nos. 456/7.

1974.

889 **146** 5 f. brown, mve & red . . 10 10

890 10 f. brown, blue & grn . . 10 10

891 20 f. lt brown, brn & red . . 15 10

892 25 f. brown, mve & bl . . 15 10

893 30 f. lt brown, brn & red . . 20 10

441 35 f. brown, grn & orge . . 30 10

894 40 f. brown, orge & grn . . 25 10

895 50 f. brown, pur & red . . 30 15

443 60 f. brown, red & blue . . 55 15

444 65 f. brown, blue & red . . 55 10

896 90 f. brown, red & pur . . 55 15

897 125 f. brown, red & pur . . 65 20

898 155 f. brown, blue & lilac . 85 35

147 UPU Emblem **148** Flag and UPU Emblems

1974. Centenary. of U.P.U.

445 **147** 40 f. green, blue and brown (postage) 60 30

446 **148** 200 f. multicoloured (air) . 3·00 1·60

447 300 f. multicoloured . . . 4·00 2·25

149 Raoul Follereau **150** Civic Service Emblem

1974. Follereau (leprosy pioneer). Commem.

448 **149** 35 f. red, yellow & green . 50 30

1974. 14th Anniv of Independence.

449 **150** 35 f. multicoloured 50 20

151 Library Building and Students

1975. 1st Anniv of Inauguration of National Library.

450 **151** 40 f. multicoloured 50 20

152 Congress Emblem **153** Coffee Flower

1975. 52nd International Seedcrushers Association Congress, Abidjan.

451 **152** 40 f. black and green . . . 45 20

1975. Coffee Production. Multicoloured.

452 5 f. Type **153** 20 10

453 10 f. Coffee-berries 30 15

154 Sassandra Wharf

1975.

454 **154** 100 f. brown, green & bl . 1·10 65

155 Postal Sorters

1975. Stamp Day.

455 **155** 40 f. multicoloured 60 30

156 Cotton Flower

1975. Cotton Production (2nd series). Multicoloured.

456 5 f. Type **156** 20 15

457 10 f. Cotton bolls 35 15

157 Marie Kore and I.W.Y. Emblem

1975. International Women's Year.

458 **157** 45 f. brown, blue & grn . . 55 30

158 Dabou Fort

1975.

459 **158** 50 f. violet, blue & grn . . 55 30

159 Abidjan Harbour

1975. 25th Anniv of Abidjan Port.

460 **159** 35 f. multicoloured . . . . 1·25 40

160 Cocoa Tree

1975.

462 **160** 35 f. multicoloured 80 35

161 Rural Activities

1975. Promotion of Rural Development.

463 **161** 50 f. mauve, violet & black 55 35

162 Railway Bridge over the N'Zi, Dimbokro

1975. 15th Anniv of Independence.
464 **162** 60 f. multicoloured . . . . 1·25 45

163 "Mother" (statue) **164** Baoule Mask

1976. Mothers' Day.
465 **163** 65 f. multicoloured 85 45

1976. Ivory Coast Art. Multicoloured.
466 20 f. Type **164** (postage) . . . 30 15
467 25 f. Senoufo statuette 35 20
468 150 f. Chief Abron's chair . . . 1·75 85
469 200 f. Akans royal symbols: fly swatter and panga (air) . . . 3·25 1·40

165 Early and Modern Telephones **166** Effigy, Map and Carrier Pigeon

1976. Telephone Centenary.
470 **165** 70 f. blue, brown & black . 65 40

1976. 20th Anniv of Stamp Day and Ivory Coast Philatelic Club.
471 **166** 65 f. multicoloured 55 35

167 "Smiling Trees" and Cat **168** Children Reading

1976. Nature Protection.
472 **167** 65 f. multicoloured 65 35

1976. Literature for Children.
473 **168** 65 f. multicoloured 60 35

169 Throwing the Javelin

1976. Olympic Games, Montreal. Multicoloured.
474 60 f. Type **169** 55 30
475 65 f. Running (horiz) 55 30

170 Mohammed Ali Jinnah

1976. Birth Centenary of Mohammed Ali Jinnah (first Governor-General of Pakistan).
476 **170** 50 f. multicoloured . . . . 28·00 5·50

171 Cashew-nut

1976.
477 **171** 65 f. multicoloured . . . . 1·10 45

172 Houphouet-Boigny Bridge, Abidjan

1976. 3rd African Roads Conference, Abidjan.
478 **172** 60 f. multicoloured . . . . 2·50 60

173 John Paul Jones (after Peale) and detail of "First Salute to the Stars and Stripes" (E. Moran)

1976. Bicentenary of American Revolution. Multicoloured.
479 100 f. Type **173** 90 35
480 125 f. Comte de Rochambeau, grenadier and flag . . . . . 1·10 30
481 150 f. Admiral D'Estaing, French marine and French warships . . . . 1·40 55
482 175 f. Marquis de Lafayette (after Peale), grenadier and flag . . . . 1·40 40
483 200 f. Thomas Jefferson (after Peale), militiaman and Declaration of Independence . 1·60 45

174 Independence Motif **175** Ife Bronze Mask

1976. 16th Anniv of Independence.
485 **174** 60 f. multicoloured 60 35

1977. 2nd World Festival of Negro Arts. Lagos.
486 **175** 65 f. multicoloured 65 45

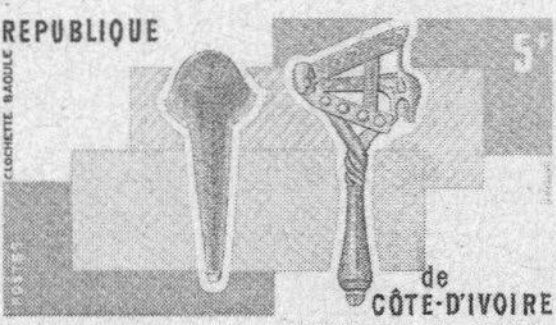

176 Baoule Handbells

1977. Musical Instruments (1st series).
487 **176** 5 f. brown and green . . . 15 15
488 – 10 f. black and red 20 15
489 – 20 f. black and violet . . . 35 15
DESIGNS: 10 f. Senoufo xylophone; 20 f. Dida tom-tom.
See also Nos. 603/4.

177 Unloading Mail from Douglas DC-8

1977. Stamp Day.
490 **177** 60 f. multicoloured 60 30

178 "Charaxes jasius epijasius"

1977. Butterflies (1st series). Multicoloured.
491 30 f. "Epiphora rectifascia boolana" . . . . 1·60 55
492 60 f. Type **178** . . . . 10·00 5·00
493 65 f. "Imbrasia arata" . . . . 2·75 1·10
494 100 f. "Palla decius" . . . . . 3·25 1·60
See also Nos. 546/9 and 585/7.

179 Tingrela Mosque

1977. Air.
495 **179** 500 f. brown, green & bl . 5·00 2·75

180 Chateau Sassenage, Grenoble

1977. 10th Anniv of International French Language Council.
496 **180** 100 f. multicoloured . . . 80 40

181 Wright Brothers and Wright Type A Biplane

1977. History of Flying. Multicoloured.
497 60 f. Type **181** 45 15
498 75 f. Louis Bleriot crossing English Channel 65 20
499 100 f. Ross Smith and Vickers Vimy aircraft 90 20
500 200 f. Charles Lindbergh and "Spirit of St. Louis" . . . . 1·75 45
501 300 f. Concorde . . . . 2·75 85

182 Santos Dumont's "Ville de Paris"

1977. History of the Airship. Multicoloured.
503 60 f. Type **182** 55 15
504 65 f. Launch of LZ-1 . . . . . 55 15
505 150 f. "Schwaben" . . . . . . 1·25 35
506 200 f. "Bodensee" . . . . . . 1·90 55
507 300 f. "Graf Zeppelin" over Egypt . . . . 2·50 85

183 Congress Emblem

1977. 17th International Congress of Administrative Sciences in Africa.
509 **183** 60 f. green and emerald . . 50 30

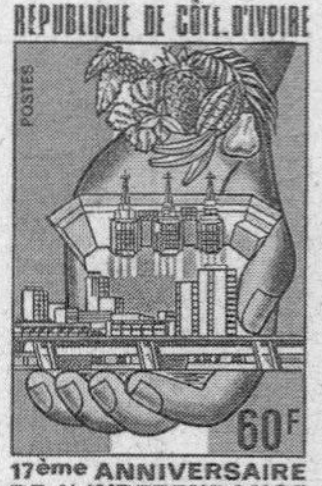

184 Pres. Houphouet-Boigny **185** Container Ship "Yamoussoukro"

1977.
510 **184** 35 f. black, mauve & brn . 20 10
511 40 f. black, orange & grn . 90 30
512 45 f. black, green & orge . 1·10 30
513 60 f. black, purple & brn . 1·25 35
514 65 f. black, orange & grn . 1·40 45

1977. Yamoussoukro Container Port.
515 **185** 65 f. multicoloured 85 45

186 Hand holding Symbols of Development **187** "Strophantus hispidus"

1977. 17th Anniv of Independence.
516 **186** 60 f. black, orange & grn . 55 30

1977. Flowers (1st series). Multicoloured.
517 5 f. Type **187** 15 10
518 20 f. "Anthurium cultorum" . . 30 20
519 60 f. "Arachnis flos-aeris" . . . 50 30
520 65 f. "Renanthera storiei" . . . 55 35
See also Nos. 571/3, 622/5, 678/80, 791c/e, 827a/b and 873e/f.

188 Presidents Giscard d'Estaing and Houphouet-Boigny

1978. Visit of President Giscard d'Estaing of France
521 **188** 60 f. multicoloured 70 30
522 65 f. multicoloured 70 30
523 100 f. multicoloured . . . 1·10 55

189 "St. George and the Dragon"

1978. 400th Birth Anniv of Peter Paul Rubens (artist).
525 65 f. Type **189** 50 15
526 150 f. "Head of a Child" . . . 1·25 45
527 250 f. "The Annunciation" . . 1·90 65
528 300 f. "The Birth of Louis XIII" . . . . 2·75 95

190 Members of the Royal Guard

1978. Images of History.
530 **190** 60 f. red, black & blue . . 80 35
531 – 65 f. black, blue & red . . 80 35
DESIGN: 65 f. Figures of traditional cosmology.

191 Rural Post Office

1978. Stamp Day.
532 **191** 60 f. multicoloured 55 30

192 Microwave Antenna

1978. Telecommunications Day.
533 **192** 60 f. multicoloured 60 35

193 S. A. Arrhenius and Equipment (Chemistry, 1903)

1978. Nobel Prize Winners. Multicoloured.
534 60 f. Type **193** 45 10
535 75 f. Jules Bordet (Medicine, 1920) 55 15
536 100 f. André Gide (Literature, 1947) 80 20
537 200 f. John Steinbeck (Literature, 1962) . . . . 1·40 45
538 300 f. U.N.I.C.E.F. (Peace, 1965) . . . . 2·40 70

194 Player kicking Ball

1978. World Cup Football Championship, Argentina. Multicoloured.
540 60 f. Football and player (horiz) 45 15
541 65 f. Type **194** 50 20
542 100 f. Football and player (different) (horiz) 70 35
543 150 f. Goalkeeper (horiz) . . . 1·10 35
544 300 f. Football "sun" and player . . . . 2·25 65

1978. Butterflies (2nd series). As T **178**. Multicoloured.
546 60 f. "Miniodes discolor" . . . 90 45
547 65 f. "Charaxes lactetinctus" . . 90 45
548 100 f. "Papilio zalmoxis" . . . 1·40 80
549 200 f. "Papilio antimachus" . . 3·00 1·60

195 Banded Cricket

1978. Insects (1st series). Multicoloured.
550 10 f. Type **195** 20 15
551 20 f. "Nepa cinerea" (water scorpion) 30 15
552 60 f. Horned tree-hopper . . . 70 35
553 65 f. "Goliathus cassicus" (beetle) . . . . 1·00 45
See also Nos. 600/2.

196 Passengers in Train

1978. Educational Television. Multicoloured.
554 60 f. Figures emerging from television screen 45 20
555 65 f. Type **196** . . . . 1·50 60

197 "Astragale" (oil exploration ship)

1978. 1st Anniv of Discovery of Oil in Ivory Coast. Multicoloured.
556 60 f. Type **197** . . . . 1·10 35
557 65 f. Ram, map of Ivory Coast and gold goblets 85 35

1978. Air. "Philexafrique" Stamp Exhibition, Gabon (1st issue) and Int Stamp Fair, Essen, West Germany. As T **262** of Niger. Multicoloured.
559 100 f. Ring-necked pheasant and Bavaria 1849 1 k. stamp . . . 2·10 1·60
560 100 f. African elephant and Ivory Coast 1965 90 f. stamp . . . 2·10 1·60
See also Nos. 588/9.

198 National Assembly Building, Paris
199 African with Ballot Box

1978. Centenary of Paris U.P.U. Congress.
561 **198** 200 f. multicoloured . . . 1·40 55

1978. 18th Anniv of Independence.
562 **199** 60 f. multicoloured 55 30

200 Ribbon of Flags

1978. Technical Co-operation among Developing Countries. Multicoloured.
563 60 f. Type **200** 50 20
564 65 f. Ribbon of flags forming arrows 50 20

201 Ploughing

1979. Agriculture.
565 **201** 100 f. multicoloured . . . 90 35

202 King Hassan and Pres Houphouet-Boigny

1979. Visit of King Hassan of Morocco.
566 **202** 60 f. multicoloured . . . . 1·60 35
567 65 f. multicoloured . . . . 2·25 35
568 500 f. multicoloured . . . 10·00 2·50

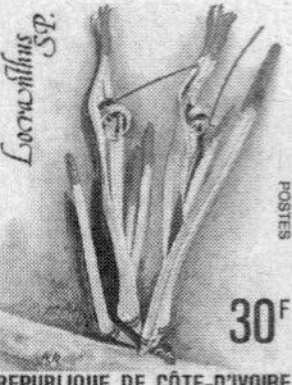

203 Isis

1979. U.N.E.S.C.O. Campaign for Preservation of Nubian Monuments.
569 **203** 200 f. silver, grn & turq . . 1·60 85
570 – 500 f. gold, brn & orge . . 4·00 2·25
DESIGN: 500 f. Gold medal.

204 "Loranthus sp."
205 Sable Antelopes

1979. Flowers (2nd series). Mult.
571 30 f. Type **204** 45 35
572 60 f. "Vanda josephine" . . . 90 45
573 65 f. "Renanthera storiei" . . . 90 55

1979. Endangered Animals (1st series). Mult.
574 5 f. Type **205** 20 15
575 20 f. Yellow-backed duiker . . 35 20
576 50 f. Pygmy hippopotamus . . . 55 20
577 60 f. Aardvark . . . . 1·10 55
See also Nos. 613/18.

206 Children and Globe

1979. International Year of the Child. Mult.
578 60 f. Type **206** 45 30
579 65 f. Child on dove 50 30
580 100 f. Type **206** 95 55
581 500 f. As 65 f. . . . . 3·75 2·25

207 Travelling Post Office

1979. Stamp Day.
582 **207** 60 f. multicoloured 55 20

208 Korhogo Cathedral

1979. 75th Anniv of Arrival of Holy Fathers.
583 **208** 60 f. multicoloured 55 30

209 Crying Child
210 "Euphaedra xypete"

1979. 10th Anniv of S.O.S. Children's Village.
584 **209** 65 f. multicoloured 55 30

1979. Butterflies (3rd series). Multicoloured.
585 60 f. Type **210** 80 35
586 65 f. "Pseudacraea bois duvali" . 90 35
587 70 f. "Auchenisa schausi" . . . 1·40 55

211 Carved Figure and Antelope
212 Astronaut Greeting Boy

1979. "Philexafrique", Stamp Exhibition, Gabon (2nd issue).
588 **211** 70 f. multicoloured . . . . 1·40 1·10
589 – 70 f. green, turq & red . . . 1·40 1·10
DESIGN: No. 589, U.P.U. emblem antenna, ship and truck.

1979. 10th Anniv of Moon Landing. Mult.
590 60 f. Type **212** 65 45
591 65 f. Trajectory between Earth and Moon (horiz) 65 45
592 70 f. Type **212** . . . . 1·10 55
593 150 f. As 65 f. . . . . 2·00 1·40

213 "Flying Scotsman" and Great Britain £1 stamp, 1878

1979. Death Centenary of Sir Rowland Hill. Multicoloured.
594 60 f. Type **213** 30 10
595 75 f. Steam locomotive and Ivory Coast 45 c. stamp, 1936 . . . 45 15
596 100 f. Diesel locomotive No. 105, U.S.A. and Hawaiian 13 c. "missionary" stamp, 1852 . . 70 20
597 150 f. Steam locomotive No. 1, Japan and Japanese 20 s. stamp, 1872 . . . . 1·00 30
598 300 f. Class BB 15000 electric locomotive, France and French 15 c. stamp, 1850 . . 2·00 60

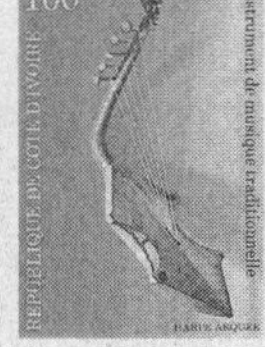

214 "Delta sp."
215 Harp

1979. Insects (2nd series). Mult.
600 30 f. Type **214** . . . . 2·25 1·10
601 60 f. "Mantis religiosa" (vert) . 4·00 1·60
602 65 f. "Locusta migratorius" . . 4·50 1·60

1979. Musical Instruments (2nd series). Mult.
603 100 f. Type **215** . . . . . . 11·00 4·50
604 150 f. Senoufo funeral horns . . 17·00 6·75

216 "Telecom 79"
217 Carved Head

1979. Third World Telecommunications Exhibition, Geneva.
605 **216** 60 f. grey, orange & blue . 55 30

1979. Culture Days.
606 **217** 65 f. multicoloured 55 20

218 Boxing

1979. Pre-Olympic Year. Multicoloured.
607 60 f. Type **218** 45 15
608 65 f. Running 45 15
609 100 f. Football 70 30
610 150 f. Cycling . . . . 1·10 45
611 300 f. Wrestling . . . . 2·25 80
See also Nos. 642/5.

219 Jentink's Duiker

1979. Endangered Animals (2nd series). Multicoloured.
613 40 f. Type **219** 45 20
614 60 f. Olive colobus 50 20
615 75 f. African manatees 70 25
616 100 f. Temminck's giant squirrel . . . . 1·00 35
617 150 f. Pygmy hippopotamus . . 1·40 45
618 300 f. Chimpanzee . . . . . . 2·75 90

220 Raoul Follereau and Institute

1979. Raoul Follereau d'Adzope Institute.
619 **220** 60 f. multicoloured 60 35

221 Post, Adze and Plant **222** Concorde and Map of Africa

1979. 19th Anniv of Independence.
620 **221** 60 f. multicoloured 55 15

1979. 20th Anniv of ASECNA (African Air Safety Organization).
621 **222** 60 f. multicoloured 75 30

222a Coelancanth

1979. Fishes (1st series). Multicoloured.
621a 60 f. Lionfish . . . .
621b 65 f. Type **222a** . . . .
See also Nos. 629/31 and 666/8.

MINIMUM PRICE

The minimum price quoted is 10p which represents a handling charge rather than a basis for valuing common stamps. For further notes about prices see introductory pages.

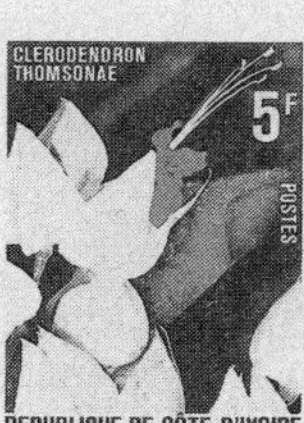

223 "Clerodendron thomsonae" **224** Elephant, Map and Rotary Emblem

1980. Flowers (3rd series). Multicoloured.
622 5 f. Type **223** 10 10
623 10 f. "La Boule de Feu" (horiz) . 15 10
624 50 f. "Costus incanusiamus" . . 55 15
625 60 f. "Ficus elastica" 55 20

1980. 75th Anniv of Rotary International.
626 **224** 65 f. multicoloured 55 30

225 Seal

1980. International Archives Day.
627 **225** 65 f. multicoloured 55 35

226 Boys with Stamp Album

1980. Stamp Day.
628 **226** 65 f. brown & turquoise . . 60 20

1980. Fishes (2nd series). As T **222a**.
629 60 f. Emperor snapper 90 40
630 65 f. Guinean fingerfish (vert) . 90 40
631 100 f. Banded gourami . . . . 1·50 75

228 Missionary and Church, Aboisso

1980. 75th Anniv of Settlement of Holy Fathers at Aboisso.
632 **228** 60 f. multicoloured 60 35

229 Hands protecting Child from Cigarettes

1980. Anti-Smoking Campaign.
633 **229** 60 f. multicoloured 60 20

230 Pope John-Paul II and President Houphouet-Boigny

1980. Papal Visit.
634 **230** 65 f. yell, brn & dp brn . . 1·00 45

231 "Le Belier" Express Train, Abidjan–Bouake **232** Headquarters Building, Dakar

1980. Railways. Multicoloured.
635 60 f. Type **231** 60 35
636 65 f. Abidjan Station, 1904 . . 60 35
637 100 f. Steam train, 1908 . . . . 1·10 45
638 150 f. Steam goods train, 1940 . 1·75 80

1980. West African Central Bank. First Anniv.
639 **232** 60 f. multicoloured 60 35

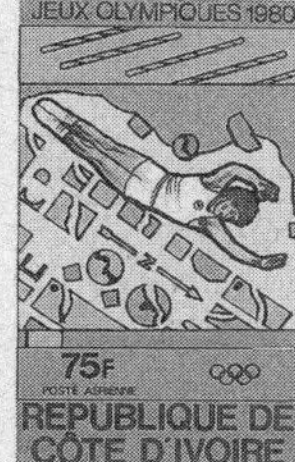

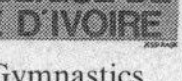

233 Cobra

1980. Animals. Multicoloured.
640 60 f. Type **233** 55 20
641 150 f. Toad . . . . 1·50 65

234 Gymnastics **235** World Tourism Conference Emblem

1980. Air. Olympic Games, Moscow. Multicoloured.
642 75 f. Type **234** 65 15
643 150 f. Ring exercise . . . . . 1·10 30
644 250 f. Vaulting horse (horiz) . . 2·00 55
645 350 f. Bar exercise . . . . . . 3·00 85

1980. Tourism. Multicoloured.
647 60 f. Village scene 45 15
648 65 f. Type **235** 45 15

1980. Insects (3rd series). As Type **214**. Multicoloured.
649 60 f. "Ugada limbata" (25 × 35 mm) 85 55
650 60 f. "Forticula auricularia" (36 × 26 mm) . . . . 1·60 95
651 65 f. "Mantis religiosa" (26 × 32 mm) . . . . 1·60 85
652 200 f. Grasshopper (35 × 25 mm) . . . . 2·25 1·40

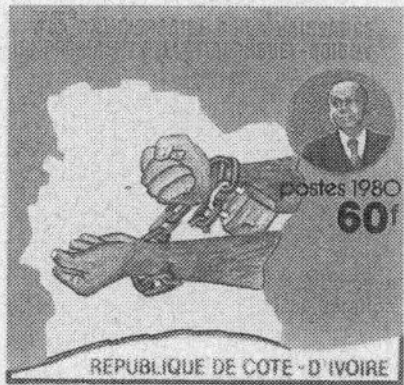

236 Hands breaking Chains, Map and President

1980. President Houphouet-Boigny's 75th Birthday.
653 **236** 60 f. mult (postage) . . . 55 30
654 – 65 f. multicoloured . . . 55 30
655 – 70 f. multicoloured . . . 70 45
656 **236** 150 f. multicoloured . . . 1·75 1·10
657 – 300 f. multicoloured . . . 3·25 1·75
658 – 2000 f. silver (air) . . . . 15·00 15·00
659 – 3000 f. gold . . . . . . 22·00 22·00
DESIGNS: SQUARE; 70 f. Presidential speech on map in national colours. HORIZ: (44 × 29 mm) 65 f.; 300 f. President and symbols of progress. VERT: (35 × 45 mm) 2000 f.; 3000 f. President Houphouet-Boigny.

237 Map of Ivory Coast

1980. Seventh P.D.C.I.–R.D.A. Congress.
660 **237** 60 f. green, orange & blk . 45 15
661 65 f. green, orange & blk . 45 15

238 "Sotra" (ferry)

1980. New Lagoon Transport.
662 **238** 60 f. multicoloured 55 30

239 Abidjan

1980. 20th Anniv of Independence.
663 **239** 60 f. multicoloured . . . . 1·50 45

240 Conference Emblem **241** Map of Africa and Posthorn

1980. 5th General Conference of African Universities Association, Yamoussoukro.
664 **240** 60 f. multicoloured 55 30

1980. 5th Anniv of African Posts and Telecommunications Union.
665 **241** 150 f. multicoloured . . . 1·10 35

241a Red-billed Dwarf Hornbill **242** Rio Grande Cichlid

1980. Birds. Multicoloured.
665a 60 f. Superb starling . . . . . 13·50 8·50
665b 65 f. Type **241a** . . . . . . 13·50 8·50
665c 65 f. South African crowned crane . . . . 14·00 9·00
665d 100 f. Saddle-bill stork . . . . 38·00 24·00

1981. Fishes (3rd series). Multicoloured.
666 60 f. Type **242** 80 50
667 65 f. Red-tailed black shark . . 80 50
668 200 f. Green pufferfish . . . . 2·25 1·25

243 Post Office, Grand Lahou

1981. Stamp Day.
669 **243** 60 f. multicoloured 55 20

244 Mask

1981. 25th Anniv of Ivory Coast Philatelic Club.
670 **244** 65 f. black, lt brown & brn . . . 45 20

245 Red Cross Aircraft, Satellite and Globe (Telecommunications and Health)

1981. World Telecommunications Day.
671 **245** 30 f. multicoloured 20 10
672 60 f. multicoloured 45 20

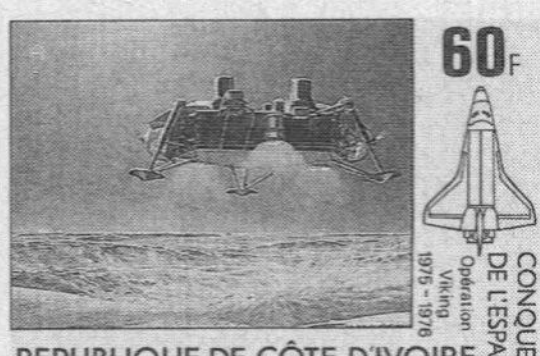

246 "Viking" landing on Mars

1981. Conquest of Space. Multicoloured.
673 60 f. Type **246** 45 15
674 75 f. Space Shuttle on launch pad 55 20
675 125 f. Space Shuttle erecting experiment 85 40
676 300 f. Space Shuttle performing experiment . . . . 2·10 90

247 "Amorphophallus sp." 249 Map formed of Flag

248 Prince Charles, Lady Diana Spencer and Coach

1981. Flowers (4th series). Multicoloured.
678 50 f. Type **247** 55 20
679 60 f. Sugar cane flowers 65 35
680 100 f. "Heliconia ivoirea" . . . 1·25 55
See also Nos. 791c/e, 827a/b and 873e/f.

1981. Royal Wedding.
681 **248** 80 f. multicoloured 55 20
682 – 100 f. multicoloured 65 35
683 – 125 f. multicoloured . . . 85 40
DESIGNS: 100 f., 125 f. Similar designs showing portraits and coaches.

1981.
684a **249** 5 f. multicoloured . . . 10 10
684aa 10 f. multicoloured . . . 15 10
684ab 20 f. multicoloured . . . 15 10
684b 25 f. multicoloured . . . 15 10
684c 30 f. multicoloured . . . 20 10
684ca 35 f. multicoloured . . . 20 10
684d 40 f. multicoloured . . . 30 10
684e 50 f. multicoloured . . . 35 10
685 80 f. multicoloured . . . 50 20
686 100 f. multicoloured . . 60 35
687 125 f. multicoloured . . 85 40

250 Goalkeeper

1981. World Cup Football Championships, Spain (1982). Multicoloured.
688 70 f. Type **250** 45 30
689 80 f. Saving a goal 55 35
690 100 f. Diving for ball (vert) . . 65 40
691 150 f. Goalmouth scene . . . . 1·00 60
692 350 f. Fighting for ball (vert) . . 2·40 1·10

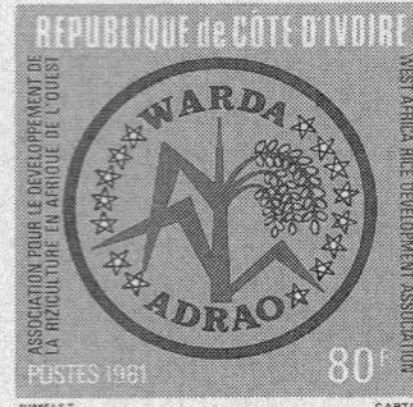

251 Association Emblem

1981. West Africa Rice Development Association.
694 **251** 80 f. multicoloured 60 30

252 Post Office

1981. Stamp Day.
695 **252** 70 f. multicoloured 45 20
696 80 f. multicoloured 55 35
697 100 f. multicoloured . . . 65 35

253 Hands with and without Fruit, and F.A.O. Emblem

1981. World Food Day.
698 **253** 100 f. multicoloured . . . 65 35

254 Felice Nazarro

1981. 75th Anniv of French Grand Prix Motor Race. Multicoloured.
699 15 f. Type **254** 15 10
700 40 f. Jim Clark 35 15
701 80 f. Fiat, 1907 . . . . 65 40
702 100 f. Auto Union, 1936 . . . . 80 45
703 125 f. Ferrari, 1961 . . . . . . 1·10 55

255 Symbols of Economic Growth

1981. 21st Anniv of Independence.
705 **255** 50 f. multicoloured 35 15
706 80 f. multicoloured 55 30

256 "Queue de Cheval" 258 Rotary Emblem on Map of Africa

257 Bingerville Post Office, 1902

1982. Hairstyles. Multicoloured.
707 80 f. Type **256** 55 30
708 100 f. "Belier" . . . . 1·10 45
709 125 f. "Cheri regarde mon visage" . . . . 1·40 55

1982. Stamp Day.
710 **257** 100 f. multicoloured . . . 65 35

1982. Rotary International Conference, Abidjan.
711 **258** 100 f. blue and gold . . . 70 40

259 George Washington

1982. Celebrities' Anniversaries. Multicoloured.
712 80 f. Type **259** (250th birth anniv) 55 20
713 100 f. Auguste Picard (20th death anniv) 65 30
714 350 f. Goethe (150th death anniv) . . . . 2·25 85
715 450 f. Princess of Wales (21st birthday) . . . . 3·00 1·25

260 Hexagonal Pattern and Telephone

1982. World Telecommunications Day.
717 **260** 80 f. multicoloured 55 20

261 Presidents Mitterand and Houphouet-Boigny

1982. Visit of President Mitterand of France.
718 **261** 100 f. multicoloured . . . 90 45

262 Dr. Koch, Bacillus and Microscope 263 Scouts in Dinghy

1982. Cent of Discovery of Tubercle Bacillus.
719 **262** 30 f. multicoloured 30 20
720 80 f. multicoloured 85 45

1982. 75th Anniv of Boy Scout Movement. Multicoloured.
721 80 f. Type **263** 60 40
722 100 f. Dinghy (horiz) 70 50
723 150 f. Leaning into wind . . . 1·00 65
724 350 f. Hauling sail . . . . . . 2·50 80

264 Aerial View of Coastline 265 Congress Emblem

1982. 10th Anniv of U.N. Environmental Programme.
726 **264** 40 f. multicoloured 35 15
727 80 f. multicoloured 55 30

1982. First League of Ivory Coast Secretaries Congress, Abidjan.
728 **265** 80 f. multicoloured 55 20
729 100 f. multicoloured . . . 65 35

1982. Birth of Prince William of Wales. Nos. 681/3 optd **NAISSANCE ROYALE 1982.**
730 **247** 80 f. multicoloured 55 30
731 – 100 f. multicoloured . . . 65 35
732 – 125 f. multicoloured . . . 85 40

267 "Child with Dove"

1982. Picasso Paintings. Multicoloured.
734 80 f. Type **267** 55 20
735 100 f. "Self-portrait" 65 20
736 185 f. "Les Demoiselles d'Avignon" . . . . 1·60 40
737 350 f. "The Dream" . . . . . 2·75 85
738 500 f. "La Colombe de l'Avenir" (horiz) . . . . 4·00 1·10

268 Post Office Counter, Abidjan 17

1982. World U.P.U. Day. Multicoloured.
739 80 f. Type **268** 55 30
740 100 f. Postel 2001 Building, Abidjan (vert) 85 35
741 350 f. Counter clerks at Abidjan 17 Post Office . . . . 2·50 95
742 500 f. Exterior and interior views of Postel 2001 (48 × 36 mm) . 3·50 1·50

1982. World Cup Football Championship Results. Nos. 688/92 optd.
743 70 f. Type **249** 45 25
744 80 f. Saving a goal 55 25
745 100 f. Diving for ball (vert) . . 60 35
746 150 f. Goalmouth scene 90 55
747 350 f. Fighting for ball (vert) . . 2·25 1·10
OVERPRINTS: 70 f. **1966 VAINQUEUR GRANDE-BRETAGNE**; 80 f. **1970 VAINQUEUR BRESIL**; 100 f. **1974 VAINQUEUR ALLEMAGNE (RFA)**; 150 f. **1978 VAINQUEUR ARGENTINE**; 350 f. **1982 VAINQUEUR ITALIE.**

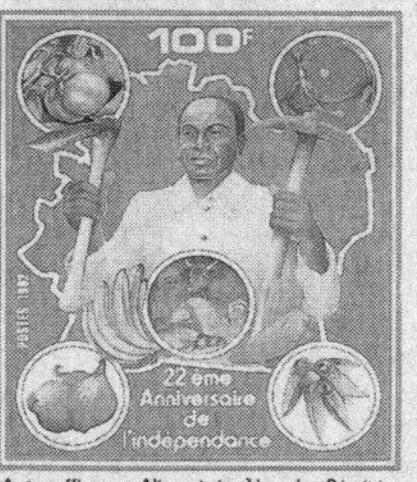

270 President Houphouet-Boigny with Farming Implements and Agricultural Produce

1982. 22nd Anniv of Independence.
749 **270** 100 f. multicoloured . . . 70 35

271 Emblem and Map of Member Countries

1982. 20th Anniv of West African Monetary Union.
750 **271** 100 f. brown, blue & dp bl . 65 35

272 Man Waterfall

1982. Landscapes. Multicoloured.
751 80 f. Type **272** . . . . 2·25 55
752 80 f. Wooded savanna 70 35
753 500 f. Type **272** . . . . 9·00 2·75

273 Child and S.O.S. Village **274** Long-tailed Pangolin

1983. S.O.S. Children's Village.
754 **273** 125 f. multicoloured . . . 90 40

1983. Animals. Multicoloured.
755 35 f. Type **274** 30 15
756 90 f. Bush pig (horiz) 65 35
757 100 f. Eastern black-and-white colobus 70 40
758 125 f. African buffalo (horiz) . . 95 50

275 Post Office, Grand Bassam, 1903

1983. Stamp Day.
759 **275** 100 f. multicoloured . . . 2·00 60

276 Montgolfier Balloon, 1783

1983. Bicentenary of Manned Flight. Mult.
760 100 f. Type **276** 70 25
761 125 f. Charles's hydrogen balloon, 1783 . . . . 95 30
762 150 f. Balloon "Armand Barbes" (Paris siege post, 1870) (horiz) . . . . 1·10 35
763 350 f. Balloon "Double Eagle II" over Atlantic . . . . 2·50 80
764 500 f. Advertising airship (horiz) . . . . 4·00 1·10

277 "Descent from the Cross"

1983. Easter. Multicoloured.
765 100 f. Type **277** 65 20
766 125 f. "The Resurrection of Christ" (horiz) 85 30
767 350 f. "The Raising of the Cross" (horiz) . . . . 2·25 85
768 400 f. "The Piercing of the Lance" . . . . 2·75 90
769 500 f. "Descent from the Cross" 3·25 1·10

278 Safe containing U.N. Emblem

1983. 25th Anniv of U.N. Economic Commission for Africa.
770 **278** 100 f. multicoloured . . . 65 30

279 African Fish Eagle

1983. Birds. Multicoloured.
771 100 f. Type **279** . . . . 2·00 85
772 125 f. Grey parrot (horiz) . . . 2·50 65
773 150 f. Violet turaco (horiz) . . . 3·75 1·00

280 Swimming

1983. Air. Pre-Olympic Year. Multicoloured.
774 100 f. Type **280** 65 20
775 125 f. Diving 90 30
776 350 f. Backstroke . . . . . . 2·40 80
777 400 f. Butterfly stroke . . . . . 2·75 95

281 Forest destroyed by Fire

1983. Ecology in Action. Multicoloured.
779 25 f. Type **281** 35 20
780 100 f. Animals running from fire . . . . 1·10 45
781 125 f. Protected animals . . . . 1·40 65

282 Flali Dance

1983. Traditional Dances. Multicoloured.
782 50 f. Type **282** 35 15
783 100 f. Mask dance 65 30
784 125 f. Stilt dance 95 40

283 Hotel Ivoire

1983. 20th Anniv of Hotel Ivoire, Abidjan.
785 **283** 100 f. multicoloured . . . 65 35

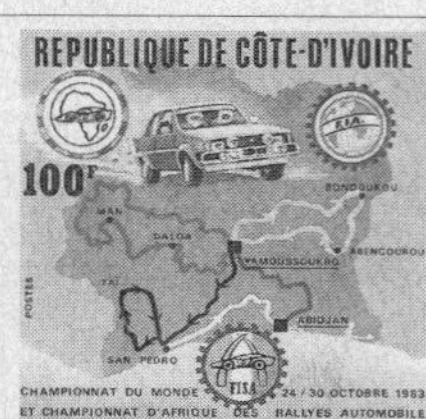

284 Rally Car and Route

1983. World and African Car Rally Championships.
786 **284** 100 f. multicoloured . . . 90 45

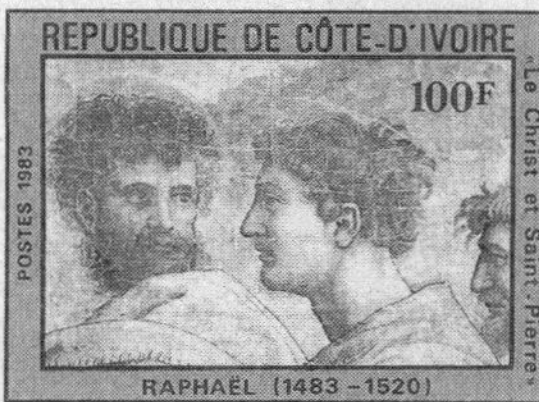

285 "Christ and St. Peter"

1983. Christmas. Paintings by Raphael. Multicoloured.
787 100 f. Type **285** 65 30
788 125 f. Study for St. Joseph . . . 90 35
789 350 f. "Virgin of the House of Orleans" . . . . 2·40 80
790 500 f. "Virgin of the Blue Diadem" . . . . 3·25 1·10

286 President Houphouet-Boigny

1983. 23rd Anniv of Independence.
791 **286** 100 f. multicoloured . . . 65 30

286a Telegraphist, Dish Aerial and National Postal Sorting Centre

1983. World Communications Year. Mult.
791a 100 f. Cable-laying, Postel 2001 building, Abidjan, and telephonists . . . . . .
791b 125 f. Type **286a** . . . . . .

1983. Flowers (5th series). As T **247**. Multicoloured.
791c 100 f. Pineapple flowers . . . 40 35
791d 125 f. "Heliconia rostrata" . . 2·25 85
791e 150 f. "Rose de Porcelaine" . . 2·75 1·40

287 Arrow piercing Television Screen

1984. First Audio-Visual Forum.
792 **287** 100 f. black and green . . 65 30

288 Competition Emblem **289** Spider

1984. Africa Cup Football Competition.
793 **288** 100 f. multicoloured . . . 65 30
794 – 200 f. orge, grn & blk . . . 1·40 55
DESIGN: 200 f. Maps of Africa and Ivory Coast shaking hands.

1984. Multicoloured.
795 100 f. Type **289** . . . . 1·00 55
796 125 f. "Polistes gallicus" (wasp) . 1·25 65

290 Abidjan Post Office, 1934

1984. Stamp Day.
797 **290** 100 f. multicoloured . . . 65 30

291 Swimming

1984. Air. Olympic Games, Los Angeles. Multicoloured.
798 100 f. Type **291** 65 30
799 125 f. Cross-country 80 30
800 185 f. Pistol shooting . . . . . 1·25 45
801 350 f. Fencing . . . . 2·40 65

292 Lions Club Badge

1984. Third Lions Multi District 403 Convention. Multicoloured.
803 100 f. Type **292** 85 35
804 125 f. As T **292** but with badge at right . . . . 1·00 55

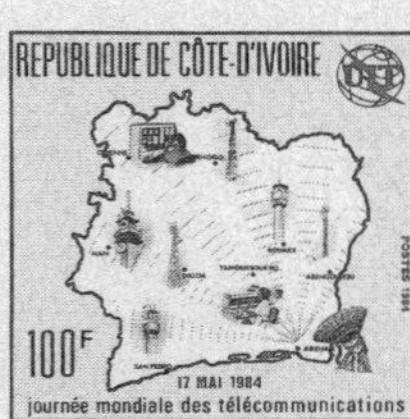

293 Telecommunications Stations on Map of Ivory Coast

1984. World Telecommunications Day.
805 **293** 100 f. multicoloured . . . 65 30

294 Flags, Agriculture and Symbols of Unity and Growth

1984. 25th Anniv of Council of Unity.
806 **294** 100 f. multicoloured . . . 65 30
807 125 f. multicoloured . . . 85 35

295 First Government House, Grand-Bassam

1984. Old Buildings (1st series). Multicoloured.
808 100 f. Type **295** 65 30
809 125 f. Palace of Justice Grand-Bassam 85 35
See also Nos. 873a/c.

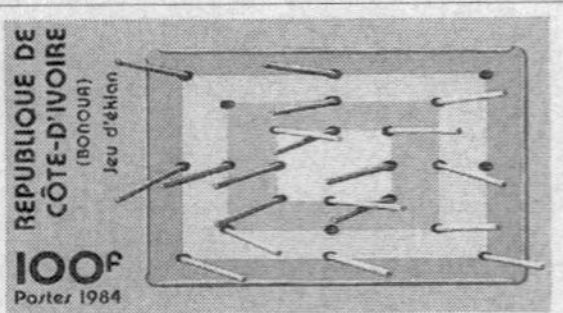

296 Eklan Board

1984. Eklan. Multicoloured.

810 100 f. Type **296** 65 35
811 125 f. Two Eklan players 85 45

297 "La Gazelle" Express Train, Abidjan-Ouagadougou

1984. Transport. Mult. (a) Locomotives.

812 100 f. Type **297** 75 30
813 125 f. Steam locomotive, 1931, France 1·00 40
814 350 f. Type 10 steam locomotive, Belgium 3·00 70
815 500 f. Class GT2 Mallet steam locomotive 5·25 1·10

(b) Ships.

816 100 f. Container Ship 65 40
817 125 f. Cargo liner 90 50
818 350 f. "Queen Mary" (liner) 2·40 1·60
819 500 f. "France" (liner) 4·25 2·50

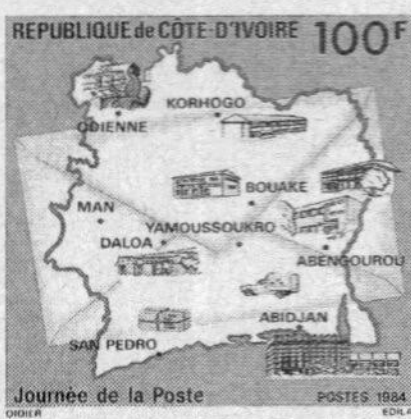

298 Envelope, Map and Symbols of Postal Service

1984. Stamp Day.

820 **298** 100 f. multicoloured 85 45

299 Emblem

1984. 10th Anniv of West African Economic Community.

821 **299** 100 f. multicoloured 65 30

300 Book Cover

1984. 90th Anniv (1982) of Ivory Coast Postage Stamps.

822 **300** 125 f. multicoloured 95 65

301 Map Outline, People and Flag

1984. 24th Anniv of Independence.

823 **301** 100 f. multicoloured 65 30

INDEX

Countries can be quickly located by referring to the index at the end of this volume.

302 G. Tiacoh (400 metres silver) **302a** Serval

1984. Air. Olympic Games Medallists. Mult.

824 100 f. Type **302** 65 20
825 150 f. C. Lewis (100 and 200 metres gold) 1·00 35
826 200 f. A. Babers (400 metres gold) 1·40 45
827 500 f. J. Cruz (800 metres gold) 3·25 1·00

1984. Flowers (6th series). As T **247**. Mult.

827a 100 f. "Allamanda cathartica" 22·00 8·25
827b 125 f. Baobab flowers 22·00 8·25

1984. Animals. Multicoloured.

827c 100 f. Bushbuck 22·00 8·25
827d 150 f. Type **302a** 22·00 8·25

302b Valtur Club, Assouinde

1984.

827e 50 f. Type **302b** 19·00 3·25
827f 100 f. Azagni Canal 19·00 5·00

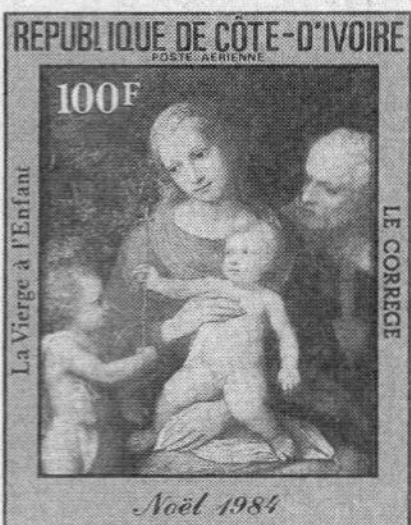

303 "Virgin and Child" (Correggio)

1985. Air. Christmas. Multicoloured.

828 100 f. Type **303** 80 30
829 200 f. "Virgin and Child" (Andrea del Sarto) 1·40 55
830 400 f. "Virgin and Child" (Jacopo Bellini) 2·75 1·10

Nos. 829/30 are wrongly inscribed "Le Correge" (Correggio).

304 Map, Hands, Emblem and Dove **305** "Le Babou" (Dan costume)

1985. African Conference of Rotary International, Abidjan.

831 **304** 100 f. multicoloured 65 30
832 125 f. multicoloured 85 35

1985. Traditional Costumes. Multicoloured.

833 90 f. Type **305** 70 35
834 100 f. Avikam post-natal dress 95 45

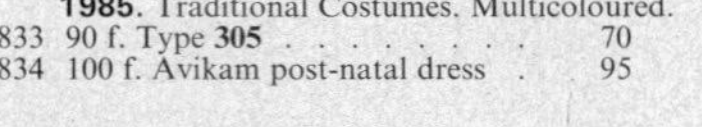

305a Hadada Ibis **308** Emblem

306 River Steamer "Adjame"

1985. Birds. Multicoloured.

834a 25 f. Marabou stork
834b 100 f. African jacana
834c 350 f. Type **305a**

1985. Stamp Day.

835 **306** 100 f. multicoloured 1·00 55

1985. 7th Conference of District 18 of Zonta International, Abidjan.

836 **308** 125 f. multicoloured 85 30

309 Airplane, Van and Industrial Landscape

1985. "Philexafrique" Stamp Exhibition, Lome, Togo (1st issue). Multicoloured.

837 200 f. Type **309** 1·60 1·25
838 200 f. Sports and agriculture 1·60 1·25

See also Nos. 864/5.

310 Red-breasted Mergansers

1985. Air. Birth Bicentenary of John J. Audubon (ornithologist). Multicoloured.

839 100 f. Type **310** 95 75
840 150 f. American white pelican (vert) 1·50 80
841 200 f. American wood stork (vert) 3·00 90
842 350 f. Velvet scoters 4·50 1·10

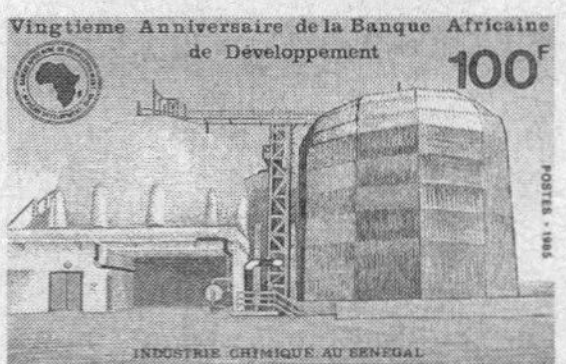

311 Chemical Plant, Senegal

1985. 20th Anniv of African Development Bank.

843 100 f. Type **311** 65 20
844 125 f. Tree seedlings, Gambia 85 35

312 Profiles within Map and IYY Emblem

1985. International Youth Year.

845 **312** 125 f. multicoloured 85 35

313 Presidential Guard Shoulder Flash **314** Ivory Coast Arms

1985. 25th Anniv of National Armed Forces.

846 **313** 100 f. gold and purple 65 20
847 – 100 f. gold and blue 65 20
848 – 125 f. gold and black 95 30
849 – 200 f. gold and brown 1·50 45
850 – 350 f. silver and blue 2·40 80

DESIGNS: Shoulder flashes of—No. 847, F.A.N.C.I. (army); 848, Air Force; 849, Navy; 850, Gendarmerie.

1985. Postal Convention with Sovereign Military Order of Malta. Multicoloured.

851 125 f. Type **314** 85 35
852 350 f. Sovereign Military Order of Malta arms 2·50 1·40

315 Footballers

1985. World Cup Football Championship, Mexico. Multicoloured.

853 100 f. Type **315** 65 20
854 150 f. Footballers (different) 1·00 35
855 200 f. Footballers (different) 1·40 40
856 350 f. Footballers (different) 2·50 70

316 Pope and Abidjan Cathedral

1985. Visit of Pope John Paul II.

858 **316** 100 f. multicoloured 1·00 55

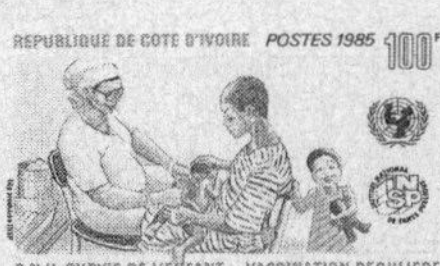

317 Vaccinating Baby

1985. U.N.I.C.E.F. Child Survival Campaign. Multicoloured.

859 100 f. Type **317** 65 30
860 100 f. Mother breast-feeding baby while child plays 65 30
861 100 f. Mother spoon-feeding child 65 30
862 100 f. Mother giving child a drink (oral rehydration) 65 30

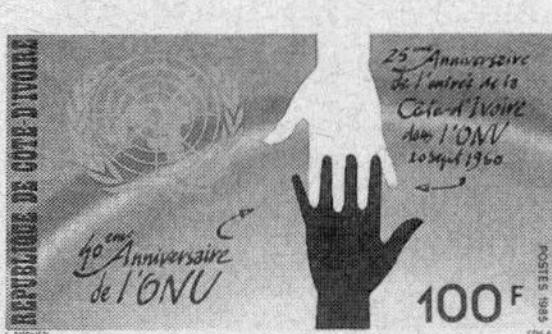

318 Rainbow, UN Emblem and Joined Hands

1985. 40th Anniv of U.N.O. and 25th Anniv of Ivory Coast Membership.

863 **318** 100 f. multicoloured 65 20

319 Footballers and Children with Injured Animal

1985. Air. "Philexafrique" International Stamp Exhibition, Lome, Togo (2nd issue). Multicoloured.

864 250 f. Type **319** 2·00 1·40
865 250 f. Dish aerial, rocket and container ship 2·00 1·40

320 City Skyline

1985. "Expo 85" World's Fair, Tsukuba, Japan.
866 **320** 125 f. multicoloured . . . 85 30

321 Young Duiker

1985. World Wildlife Fund. Banded Duiker. Multicoloured.
867 50 f. Type **321** 45 20
868 60 f. Duiker in front of bushes . 55 20
869 75 f. Two duikers . . . . . . 1·10 35
870 100 f. Duiker (different) . . . . 1·60 45

322 Children on Open Ground

323 Woman spinning Cotton

1985. "Return to the Earth".
871 **322** 125 f. multicoloured . . . 85 35

1985. Rural Handicrafts. Multicoloured.
872 125 f. Type **323** 85 35
873 155 f. Man painting on cotton cloth . . . . 1·10 45

323a Samatiguila Mosque

1985. Old Buildings (2nd series). Multicoloured.
873a 100 f. Bondoukou Market . . 17·00 5·50
873b 125 f. Type **323a** . . . . . 17·00 5·50
873c 200 f. Samory House, Bondoukou . . . . 17·00 5·50

1985. Flowers (7th series). As T **247**. Mult.
873d 100 f. "Amorphophallus staudtii" . . . . 22·00 5·50
873e 125 f. Crinum . . . . 22·00 5·50
873f 200 f. "Triphyophyllum peltotum" . . . . 22·00 5·50

324 Edmond Halley and Computer Picture of Comet

1986. Air. Appearance of Halley's Comet. Multicoloured.
874 125 f. Type **324** 85 25
875 155 f. Sir William Herschel and Uranus . . . . 1·00 30
876 190 f. Space telescope and comet . . . . 1·25 40
877 350 f. "MS T-5" space probe and comet . . . . 2·50 85
878 440 f. "Skylab" and Kohoutek's comet . . . . 2·75 1·00

325 "Millettia takou"

326 Vase from We

1986. Plants. Multicoloured.
879 40 f. "Omphalocarpum elatum" 30 15
880 50 f. "Momordica charantia" . 35 15
881 125 f. Type **325** 85 40
882 200 f. "Costus afer" . . . . . 1·40 65

1986. Traditional Kitchenware and Tools. Multicoloured.
883 20 f. Type **326** 15 10
884 30 f. Baoule vase 20 10
885 90 f. Baoule dish 60 20
886 125 f. Dan knife (vert) 90 30
887 440 f. Baoule pottery jug (vert) . 3·25 1·25

327 Institute Building

1986. 10th Anniv of Institute for Higher Technical and Professional Education.
888 **327** 125 f. multicoloured . . . 85 30

329 Cable Ship "Stephan", 1910

1986. Stamp Day.
899 **329** 125 f. multicoloured . . . 1·50 65

330 Footballers

1986. Air. World Cup Football Championship, Mexico.
900 **330** 90 f. multicoloured 60 20
901 – 125 f. multicoloured . . . 85 25
902 – 155 f. multicoloured . . . 1·10 35
903 – 440 f. multicoloured . . . 3·00 90
904 – 500 f. multicoloured . . . 3·25 1·10
DESIGNS: 125 f. to 500 f. Different football scenes.

331 Emblem

333 Sacred Tom-tom

332 Endlicher's Bichir

1986. 25th Anniv of National Youth and Sports Institute.
906 **331** 125 f. green and orange . . 85 30

1986. Fishes. Multicoloured.
907 5 f. Type **332** 10 10
908 125 f. Daget's squeaker . . . . 1·10 70
909 150 f. West African lung-fish . . 1·40 90
910 155 f. Ivory Coast squeaker . . 1·75 90
911 440 f. Electric catfish . . . . . 4·50 2·50

1986. Enthronement of King of the Agni. Multicoloured.
912 50 f. Type **333** 35 20
913 350 f. King being carried . . . 2·50 1·40
914 440 f. King and his Court . . . 3·25 1·90

334 Baoule Village, Aoulo

1986. Rural Dwellings (1st series). Multicoloured.
915 125 f. Type **334** 85 45
916 155 f. Avikam village, Eva . . . 1·10 65
917 350 f. Lobi village, Soukala . . 2·50 1·40
See also Nos. 938/9, 990 and 1012.

335 Ivory Coast Arms

336 Rocky Coastline

1986.
921 **335** 50 f. red 30 10
924 125 f. green 70 15
926 155 f. red 95 20
927 195 f. blue . . . . 1·10 30

1986. Coastal Landscapes. Multicoloured.
930 125 f. Type **336** . . . . 1·00 55
931 155 f. Sandy beach . . . . . . 1·40 85

337 Fishery Lake

338 Pres. Houphouet-Boigny, Rainbow and Dove

1986. Oceanographic Research Centre. Mult.
932 125 f. Type **337** 85 45
933 155 f. Fishermen hauling in net . 1·75 80

1986. International Peace Year.
934 **338** 155 f. multicoloured . . . 1·00 55

339 Bull

1986. Research and Development. Mult.
935 125 f. Type **339** . . . . 1·10 65
936 155 f. Rice (IDSA 6) . . . . . 1·10 65

340 Pres. Houphouet-Boigny and Symbols of Development

1986. 26th Anniv of Independence.
937 **340** 155 f. multicoloured . . . 1·10 55

341 Guesseple Dan Village

1987. Rural Dwellings (2nd series). Mult.
938 190 f. Type **341** . . . . 1·40 90
939 550 f. M'Bagui Senoufo village . 4·00 2·25

342 Postman, 1918

343 Elephant and Cockerel

1987. Stamp Day.
940 **342** 155 f. multicoloured . . . 1·10 65

1987. 25th Anniv of French–Ivory Coast Cultural Friendship. Jean Mermoz College. Multicoloured.
941 40 f. Type **343** 30 15
942 155 f. Children's faces in dove . 1·10 55

344 Child running to Adult

1987. World Red Cross Day.
943 **344** 195 f. + 5 f. multicoloured 1·50 1·40

345 "Soling" Class Yachts

1987. Air. Olympic Games, Seoul (1988) (1st issue). Sailing. Multicoloured.
944 155 f. Type **345** . . . . 1·10 85
945 195 f. Windsurfers . . . . . . 1·40 80
946 250 f. "470" class dinghies . . . 1·90 90
947 550 f. Windsurfer . . . . . . 4·00 1·60
See also Nos. 959/62.

346 "Excavations" (Krah N'Guessan)

347 Airplane and Van

1987. Paintings. Multicoloured.
949 195 f. Type **346** . . . . 1·40 90
950 500 f. "Ceremonial Cortege" (Santoni Gerard) . . . . . . 3·25 2·25

1987. World Post Day. International Express Post.
951 **347** 155 f. multicoloured . . . 1·10 80
952 195 f. multicoloured . . . 1·40 90

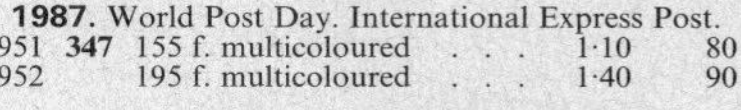

348 Map and Forms of Communication

1987. 100 Years of International Mail and Communications Exchanges.
953 **348** 155 f. multicoloured . . . 1·10 65

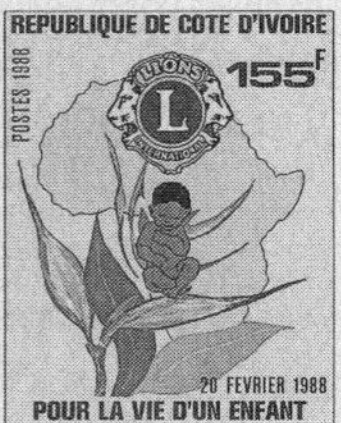

349 Tower Block reflecting Symbols of Progress

350 Baby in Aloe Plant on Map

1987. 27th Anniv of Independence.
954 **349** 155 f. multicoloured . . . 1·10 65

1988. Lions International. "For the Life of a Child".
955 **350** 155 f. multicoloured . . . 1·10 65

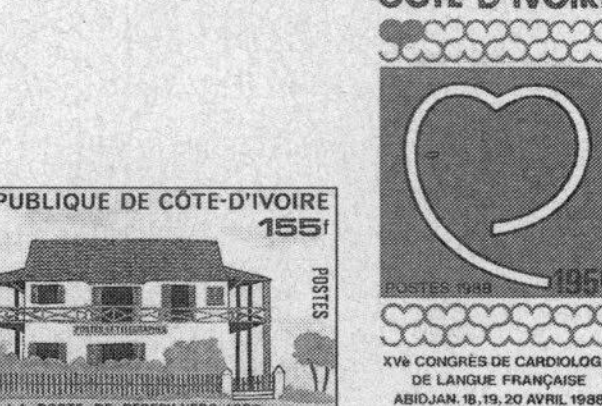

351 Bereby Post Office, 1900

352 Heart

1988. Stamp Day.
956 **351** 155 f. multicoloured . . . 1·00 55

1988. 15th Francophone Cardiological Congress, Abidjan.
957 **352** 195 f. red and black . . . 1·60 1·10

353 Man working Soil

1988. 10th Anniv of International Agricultural Development Fund.
958 **353** 195 f. multicoloured . . . 1·40 80

354 Gymnastics (rings)

1988. Air. Olympic Games, Seoul (2nd issue). Multicoloured.
959 100 f. Type **354** 65 35
960 155 f. Women's handball . . . 1·00 45
961 195 f. Boxing . . . . 1·40 45
962 500 f. Gymnastics (parallel bar) . 3·25 1·25

355 Stone Sculpture with Deep Nostrils **356** Healthy Youth and Drug Addict

1988. Archaeological Research. Stone Sculptures from Niangoran-Bouah Collection.
964 **355** 5 f. brown and flesh . . . 10 10
965 – 10 f. brown and green . . 10 10
966 – 30 f. brown and green . . 20 10
967 – 155 f. brown & yellow . . 1·00 55
968 – 195 f. brown and green . . 1·40 80
DESIGNS: 10 f. Sculpture with full lips; 30 f. Sculpture with large nose; 155 f. Sculpture with triangular mouth; 195 f. Sculpture with sunken eyes.

1988. 1st International Drug Abuse and Illegal Trafficking Day.
969 **356** 155 f. multicoloured . . . 1·10 80

357 "The Couple" (K. J. Houra)

1988. Paintings by Local Artists. Multicoloured.
970 20 f. Type **357** 15 10
971 30 f. "The Canary of Gentleness" (Monne Bou) (horiz) 20 10
972 150 f. "The Eternal Dancer" (Monne Bou) . . . . 1·00 55
973 155 f. "The Termite Hill" (Mathilde Moro) . . . . . . 1·00 55
974 195 f. "The Sun of Independence" (Michel Kodjo) . . . . 1·25 70

358 Emblem

1988. 25th Anniv of Organization of African Unity.
975 **358** 195 f. + 5 f. multicoloured 1·40 1·25

359 Collector with Album

1988. World Post Day.
976 **359** 155 f. multicoloured . . . 1·00 65

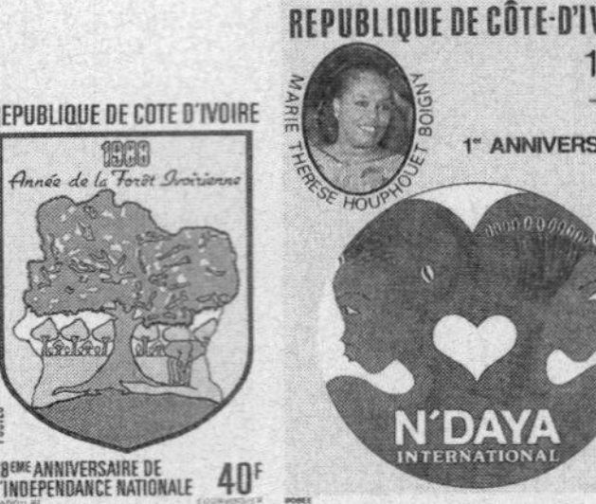

360 Emblem **361** Marie Therese Houphouet-Boigny and Emblem

1988. 28th Anniv of Independence. Forestry Year. Multicoloured.
977 40 f. Type **360** 30 20
978 155 f. "To each his tree" . . . 1·10 65
979 155 f. "Stop fires" . . . . . . 1·10 65

1988. 1st Anniv of N'Daya International.
980 **361** 195 f. + 5 f. multicoloured 1·40 1·25

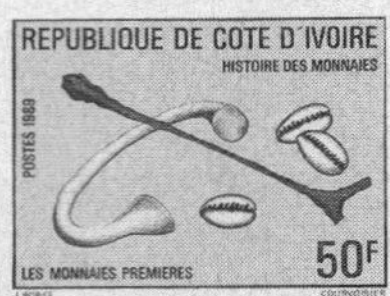

362 Money Cowries and Bones

1989. History of Money (1st series).
981 **362** 50 f. multicoloured 70 30
982 – 195 f. black, grey & blue . 1·50 90
DESIGN: 195 f. Bank of Senegal notes.
See also Nos. 1004/5, 1019/21 and 1053.

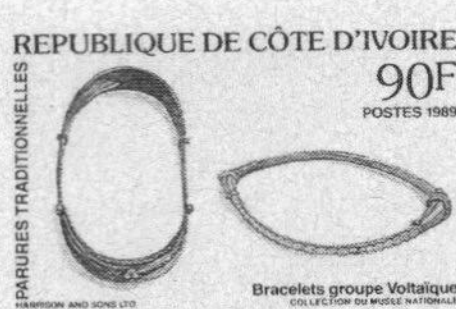

363 Voltaic Bracelets

1989. Traditional Jewellery. Multicoloured.
983 90 f. Type **363** 70 45
984 155 f. Dan ankle bracelets . . . 1·25 90

364 Stamp used as Money **365** "Old Man and Child"

1989. Stamp Day.
985 **364** 155 f. multicoloured . . . 1·25 85

1989. Carvings by Christian Lattier. Mult.
986 40 f. Type **365** 30 20
987 155 f. "Saxophone Player" . . . 1·10 55
988 550 f. "Panther" (horiz) . . . . 3·50 2·00

366 Map and Tractor

1989. 30th Anniv of Council of Unity.
989 **366** 75 f. multicoloured 50 30

367 Sirikukube Dan

1989. Rural Dwellings (3rd series).
990 **367** 155 f. multicoloured . . . 1·10 65

368 Congress Venue and Pres. Houphouet-Boigny

1989. International Peace Congress, Yamoussoukro.
991 **368** 195 f. multicoloured . . . 1·40 80

369 Map and King holding Court

1989. Anniversaries. Multicoloured.
992 200 f. Type **369** (279th anniv of accession of King Sekou Watara of Kong) . . . . . 1·50 1·00
993 200 f. Bastille and detail of Declaration of Rights of Man (bicentenary of French Revolution) . . . . 1·50 1·00

370 Nile Monitor

1989. Reptiles. Multicoloured.
994 25 f. Type **370** 15 10
995 100 f. Nile crocodile 70 50

371 Globe and Emblem

1989. World Post Day.
996 **371** 195 f. multicoloured . . . 1·40 65

372 Telephone Kiosks and Mail Boxes

1989. 30th Anniv of West African Posts and Telecommunications Association.
997 **372** 155 f. multicoloured . . . 1·10 65

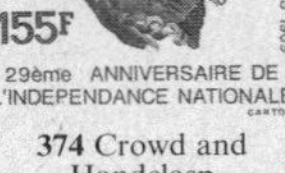
373 Milan **374** Crowd and Handclasp

1989. Air. World Cup Football Championship (1990) Preliminary Rounds. Multicoloured.
998 195 f. Type **373** . . . . 1·40 45
999 300 f. Genoa . . . . 2·00 65
1000 450 f. Turin . . . . 2·75 1·00
1001 550 f. Bologna . . . . 4·00 1·25

1989. 29th Anniv of Independence.
1002 **374** 155 f. multicoloured . . . 1·00 55

375 Emblem **376** West African Bank 25 f. Banknote

1990. 10th Anniv of Pan-African Postal Union.
1003 **375** 155 f. multicoloured . . . 1·00 55

1990. History of Money (2nd series).
1004 **376** 155 f. black and green . . 1·00 55
1005 – 195 f. black and orange . . 1·50 85
DESIGN: 195 f. Banknotes, 1917–44.
See also Nos. 1019/21 and 1053.

377 "Afrique" (steam packet)

1990. Stamp Day.
1006 **377** 155 f. multicoloured . . . 2·00 85

378 Envelopes on Map

1990. 20th Anniv of Multinational Postal Training School, Abidjan.
1007 **378** 155 f. multicoloured . . . 1·10 55

379 Footballers

1990. Air. World Cup Football Championship, Italy. Designs showing match scenes. Multicoloured.
1008 155 f. Type **379** . . . . . . 1·00 35
1009 195 f. Brazil v. West Germany . 1·25 45
1010 500 f. England v. Russia . . . 3·25 1·10
1011 600 f. England v. Netherlands . 4·25 1·40

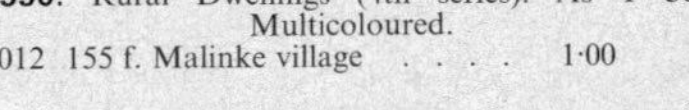
1990. Rural Dwellings (4th series). As T **367**. Multicoloured.
1012 155 f. Malinke village . . . . 1·00 45

380 Teacher writing Letters on Blackboard

1990. International Literacy Year.
1013 **380** 195 f. multicoloured . . . 1·40 65

381 Cathedral

1990. Consecration of Our Lady of Peace Cathedral, Yamoussoukro. Multicoloured.
1014 155 f. Type **381** . . . . 1·00 55
1015 195 f. Aerial view . . . . . . 1·40 80

382 Pres. Houphouet-Boigny and Pope

1990. 3rd Visit of Pope John Paul II.
1016 **382** 500 f. multicoloured . . . 3·50 1·90

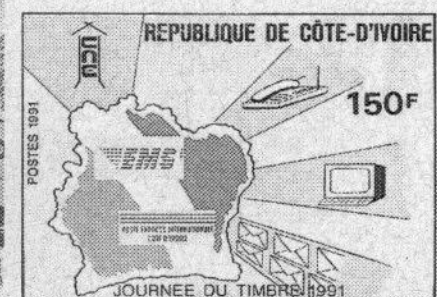

383 Postman delivering to Village **385** Communications

384 Modern Building and Road Network

1990. World Stamp Day.
1017 **383** 195 f. multicoloured . . . 1·40 80

1990. 30th Anniv of Independence.
1018 **384** 155 f. multicoloured . . . 1·00 55

1991. History of Money (3rd series). As T **376**.
1019 40 f. black and yellow 30 15
1020 155 f. black and green . . . . 1·00 65
1021 195 f. black and mauve . . . . 1·25 85
DESIGNS: 40, 155 f. West African Bank; 100 f. and 5 f. notes, 1942; 195 f. Issuing Institute for French West Africa and Togo; 50 f. and 500 f. notes.

1991. Stamp Day.
1022 **385** 150 f. multicoloured . . . 1·00 35

386 Suzanne Lenglen

1991. Centenary of French Open Tennis Championships. Tennis players. Multicoloured.
1023 200 f. Type **386** . . . . 1·40 1·10
1024 200 f. Helen Wills Moody . . . 1·40 1·10
1025 200 f. Simone Mathieu . . . . 1·40 1·10
1026 200 f. Maureen Connolly . . . 1·40 1·10
1027 200 f. Francoise Durr . . . . 1·40 1·10
1028 200 f. Margaret Court . . . . 1·40 1·10
1029 200 f. Chris Evert . . . . . 1·40 1·10
1030 200 f. Martina Navratilova . . 1·40 1·10
1031 200 f. Steffi Graf . . . . . 1·40 1·10
1032 200 f. Henri Cochet . . . . . 1·40 1·10
1033 200 f. Rene Lacoste . . . . . 1·40 1·10
1034 200 f. Jean Borotra . . . . . 1·40 1·10
1035 200 f. Donald Budge . . . . . 1·40 1·10
1036 200 f. Marcel Bernard . . . . 1·40 1·10
1037 200 f. Ken Rosewall . . . . . 1·40 1·10
1038 200 f. Rod Laver . . . . . . 1·40 1·10
1039 200 f. Bjorn Borg . . . . . . 1·40 1·10
1040 200 f. Yannick Noah . . . . 1·40 1·10

387 "Europe"

1991. Steam Packets. Multicoloured.
1041 50 f. Type **387** 35 20
1042 550 f. "Asie" . . . . 3·50 2·25

1991. Various stamps surch.
1043 – 150 f. on 155 f. mult (987) 1·00 35
1044 **367** 150 f. on 155 f. mult . . . 1·00 35
1045 – 150 f. on 155 f. black and green (1020) . . . . . 1·10 45
1046 – 200 f. on 195 f. black and mauve (1021) . . . . . 1·40 55

389 Post and Savings Society's Emblem and Letter-box **390** We Drum

1991. World Post Day. Multicoloured.
1047 50 f. Type **389** 35 20
1048 100 f. S.I.P.E. emblem and globe 65 35

1991. Drums.
1049 **390** 5 f. purple and lilac . . . 10 10
1050 – 25 f. red and pink 15 10
1051 – 150 f. green & turquoise . 1·10 80
1052 – 200 f. green and brown . . 1·40 1·00
DESIGNS: 25 f. Krou drum, Soubre; 150 f. Nafana drum, Sinematiau; 200 f. Akye drum, Alepe.

1991. History of Money (4th series). As T **376**.
1053 100 f. black and mauve 65 45
DESIGN: 100 f. French West Africa and Togo banknotes.

391 Government Buildings

1991. 31st Anniv of Independence.
1054 **391** 150 f. multicoloured . . . 1·00 45

392 Orchid **394** African Civet

393 Footballer and Cup

1991. Orchids.
1055 **392** 150 f. mauve, grn & blk . 1·00 35
1056 – 200 f. red, emer & grn . . 1·25 45
DESIGNS—HORIZ: 200 f. Different orchid.

1992. Ivory Coast Victory in African Nations Football Cup Championship, Senegal. Mult.
1057 20 f. Type **393** 20 15
1058 150 f. Elephants supporting cup with their trunks (vert) . . . 1·10 95

1992. Animals in Abidjan Zoo.
1059 **394** 5 f. brown, red & green . 10 10
1060 – 40 f. brown, green & orge 30 15
1061 – 150 f. brown, green & red 1·00 55
1062 – 500 f. brown, grn & ochre 3·25 2·25
DESIGNS: 40 f. African palm civet; 150 f. Bongo; 500 f. Leopard.

395 World Map

1992. World Post Day.
1063 **395** 150 f. blue and black . . 1·00 55

396 1892 "Tablet" and 1962 Postal Centenary Stamps

1992. Stamp Day. Centenary of First Ivory Coast Stamps. Multicoloured.
1064 150 f. Type **396** . . . . . . 1·00 65
1065 150 f. 1961 Independence and 1991 World Post Day stamps . . . . 1·00 65

397 Tomb Entrance

1992. Tourism, Funerary Monuments.
1067 **397** 5 f. red, green and blue . . 10 10
1068 – 50 f. brown, green & bl . 50 15
1069 – 150 f. brown, blue & grn . 1·10 35
1070 – 400 f. green, blue & red . 2·75 1·40
DESIGNS (tombs): 50 f. Angels, lions and figures; 150 f. Drummer, angel, sentry and animals; 400 f. Angels, figures and tree.

398 Dove, Flag and Head of Statue of Liberty **400** Emblem and Map

399 Runners and Flags

1992. 32nd Anniv of Independence. Mult.
1071 30 f. Type **398** 20 10
1072 150 f. Crowd waving flags, Statue of Liberty and map . 70 35

1992. International Marathon. Multicoloured.
1073 150 f. Type **399** 70 35
1074 200 f. Runners and landmarks . 1·40 50

1992. 1st Anniv of Ity Gold Mine.
1075 **400** 200 f. multicoloured . . . 1·40 50

400a Dent de Man

1992. Tourist Sites. Multicoloured.
1075a 10 f. Hotel complex . . . .
1075b 25 f. Type **400a** . . . . .
1075c 100 f. Holiday village (horiz) .
1075d 200 f. Tourist map . . . . .

401 Girl with Stockbook and Collectors swapping Stamp **402** "Argemone mexicana"

1993. Stamp Day. Youth Philately. Multicoloured.
1076 50 f. Type **401** 25 15
1077 50 f. Girl pointing at stamps . 25 15
1078 150 f. Boy perusing album and girls viewing exhibition display . . . . 1·00 35

1993. Medicinal Plants. Multicoloured.
1079 5 f. Type **402** 10 10
1080 20 f. "Hibiscus esculentus" . . 35 10
1081 200 f. "Cassia alata" . . . . . 1·40 90

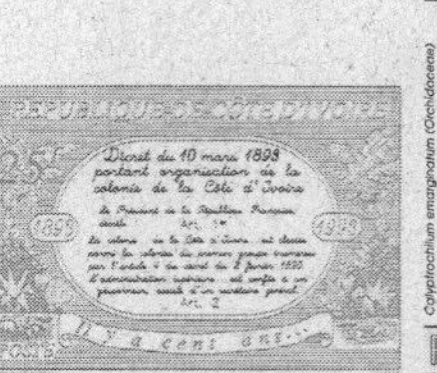
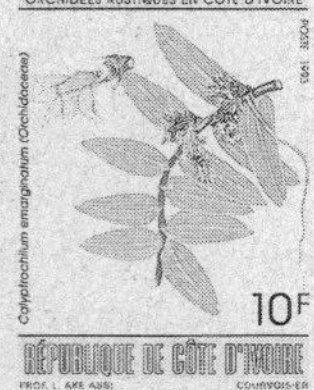

403 Presidential Decree establishing Colony **404** "Calyptrochilum emarginatum"

1993. Centenary of Ivory Coast.
1082 **403** 25 f. black and green . . 10 10
1083 – 100 f. blue and black . . 70 50
1084 – 500 f. black and brown . . 3·25 2·25
DESIGNS: 100 f. Louis Binger (first Governor) and Felix Houphouet-Boigny (President); 500 f. Factory.

1993. Orchids. Multicoloured.
1085 10 f. Type **404** 10 10
1086 50 f. "Plectrelminthus caudathus" 25 15
1087 150 f. "Eulophia guineensis" . 1·00 65

405 Heading Ball **407** Abstract Design

406 19th-century Map of Ivory Coast

1993. World Cup Football Championship, U.S.A. (1994). Multicoloured.
1088 150 f. Type **405** 70 35
1089 200 f. Players jumping . . . . 1·40 50
1090 300 f. Player dribbling ball past opponent . . . . 2·00 1·40
1091 400 f. Ball ricocheting off players . . . . 2·75 1·60

1993. World Post Day.
1092 **406** 30 f. red, black and blue . 15 10
1093 – 200 f. multicoloured . . . 1·40 90
DESIGN: 200 f. Bouake post office.

1993. African Plastic Arts Biennale, Abidjan.
1094 **407** 200 f. multicoloured . . . 90 45

408 Map of Mining Centre

1993. 33rd Anniv of Independence.
1095 **408** 200 f. multicoloured . . . 1·40 70

409 Boigny and Modern Developments

1994. Felix Houphouet-Boigny (President, 1960–93) Commemoration. Multicoloured.

1096 150 f. Type **409** 35 20
1097 150 f. Boigny, tractor, ploughing with oxen and container ship 35 20
1098 150 f. Boigny and Our Lady of the Peace Cathedral, Yamoussoukro 35 20
1099 200 f. Type **409** 50 25
1100 200 f. As No. 1097 . . . . . 50 25
1101 200 f. As No. 1098 . . . . . 50 25

410 Raoul Follereau and Globe

1994. 50th Anniv (1992) of World Anti-leprosy Campaign.

1103 **410** 150 f. multicoloured . . . 35 20

411 Globe, Satellites and Flags

412 Country-woman with Basket on Back

1994. 1st Meeting of Regional African Satellite Communications Organization Board of Directors, Abidjan.

1104 **411** 150 f. multicoloured . . . 35 20

1994. Multicoloured, colour of frame given.

1105 **412** 5 f. orange 10 10
1106 25 f. blue 10 10
1107 30 f. bistre 10 10
1108 40 f. green 10 10
1109 50 f. brown 15 10
1110 75 f. purple 20 10
1111 150 f. green 40 20
1112 180 f. purple 45 25
1115 280 f. grey 75 40
1116 300 f. violet 80 40

413 "Christ"

414 Modern Developments

1994. Stained Glass Windows by Pierre Fakhoury from Our Lady of Peace Cathedral, Yamoussoukro. Multicoloured.

1120 25 f. Type **413** 10 10
1121 150 f. "The Fisher of Men" . . . 40 20
1122 200 f. "Madonna and Child" . . 50 25

1994. 34th Anniv of Independence. The Family.

1124 **414** 150 f. multicoloured . . . 40 20

415 Green Mamba

1995. Snakes. Multicoloured.

1125 10 f. Royal python 10 10
1126 20 f. Green bush snake 10 10
1127 100 f. Type **415** 25 15
1128 180 f. Common puff adder . . . 70 50
1129 500 f. Rhinoceros viper . . . . 1·50 1·10

416 Women collecting Water

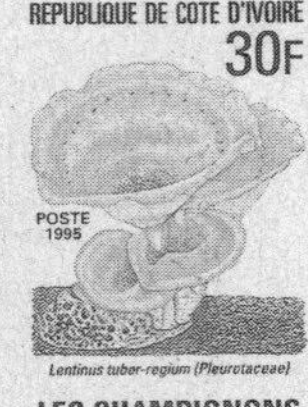

417 "Lentinus tuber-regium"

1995. 50th Anniversaries. Multicoloured.

1130 100 f. Type **416** (F.A.O.) . . . 25 15
1131 280 f. Dove on globe (U.N.O.) 75 40

1995. Fungi. Multicoloured.

1132 30 f. Type **417** 20 10
1133 50 f. Chinese mushroom . . . 30 15
1134 180 f. "Dictyophora indusiata" 90 45
1135 250 f. Termite mushroom . . . 1·25 60

418 Laboratory Worker and Pasteur

1995. Death Centenary of Louis Pasteur (chemist).

1136 **418** 280 f. multicoloured . . . 1·00 60

419 GSR Emblem on Butterfly Wing

1995. School Philatelic Clubs. Multicoloured.

1137 50 f. Type **419** 10 10
1138 180 f. LBP emblem on butterfly wing 70 50

420 Palla

1995. Butterflies. Multicoloured.

1139 180 f. Type **420** 70 50
1140 280 f. Mocker swallowtail . . 1·00 65
1141 550 f. Emperor swallowtail . . 1·75 1·10

421 Motor Vehicles and Handcart

1996. Abidjan Transport. Multicoloured.

1142 180 f. Type **421** 45 25
1143 280 f. Catching bus 70 35

422 African Bonytongue

1996. Fishes. Multicoloured.

1144 50 f. Type **422** 10 10
1145 180 f. Western grunter 55 30
1146 700 f. Guinean butter catfish . 2·10 1·25

423 "Cyrtorchis arcuata"

424 Boxing

1996. Flowers. Multicoloured.

1147 40 f. Type **423** 10 10
1148 100 f. "Eulophia horsfalii" . . 25 15
1149 180 f. "Eulophidium maculatum" 45 25
1150 200 f. "Ansellia africana" . . . 50 25

1996. Centenary of Modern Olympic Games and Olympic Games, Atlanta. Multicoloured.

1151 200 f. Type **424** 50 25
1152 280 f. Running 70 35
1153 400 f. Long jumping 95 50
1154 500 f. National Olympic Committee arms and pictograms . . . . 1·25 65

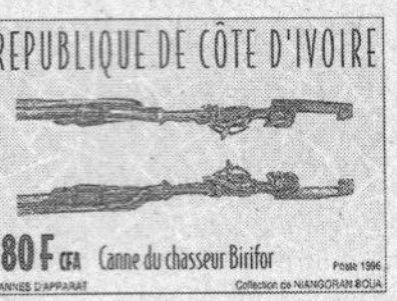

425 Huntsmens' Sticks, Birifor

1996. Ceremonial Sticks.

1155 **425** 180 f. black and green . . 45 25
1156 – 200 f. black and orange . . 50 25
1157 – 280 f. black and lilac . . 70 35

DESIGNS: 200 f. Lobi chief's stick from Bindam; 280 f. Lobi chief's stick from Gboberi.

426 Sacred Lotus

1997. Water Plants. Multicoloured.

1158 50 f. Type **426** 10 10
1159 180 f. White lotus 40 20
1160 280 f. Cape Blue water-lily . . 60 30
1161 700 f. White water-lily . . . . 1·50 75

427 Pres. Houphouet-Boigny and Cathedral

1997. Our Lady of Peace Cathedral, Yamoussoukro. Multicoloured.

1162 180 f. Type **427** 40 20
1163 200 f. Interior of church . . . 45 25
1164 280 f. Pope John Paul II and elevated view of cathedral . 60 30

428 Pearl Necklace

429 Stone Head

1997. Traditional Necklaces. Each lilac and black.

1165 50 f. Type **428** 10 10
1166 100 f. Necklace of small pearls . 20 10
1167 180 f. Broken necklace of pearls 40 20

1997. Stone Heads from Gohitafla. Multicoloured.

1168 100 f. Type **429** 20 10
1169 180 f. Stone head (full-face) . . 40 20
1170 500 f. Stone head (side-view) . 1·10 55

430 Pulley

431 Manatees

1997. Wooden Weaving Tools.

1171 **430** 180 f. multicoloured . . . 40 20
1172 – 280 f. blk, grn & dp grn . 60 30
1173 – 300 f. black, bl & ultram . 65 35

DESIGNS—VERT: 280 f. Combing frame. HORIZ: 300 f. Shuttle.

1997. Endangered Species. Multicoloured.

1174 180 f. Type **431** 40 20
1175 280 f. Jentink's duiker 60 30
1176 400 f. Waterbuck 85 45

432 Goalkeeper

1998. World Cup Football Championship, France. Multicoloured.

1177 180 f. Type **432** 40 20
1178 280 f. Player composed of flags of competing nations (vert) . 60 30
1179 400 f. Match scene showing trajectory of ball 85 45
1180 500 f. Players and ball as mascot (vert) . . . . 1·10 55

433 "Agaricus bingensis"

434 "Hutchinsonia barbata"

1998. Fungi. Multicoloured.

1181 50 f. Type **433** 10 10
1182 180 f. "Lactarius gymnocarpus" 40 20
1183 280 f. "Termitomyces letestui" . 60 30

1998. Plants. Multicoloured.

1184 40 f. Type **434** 10 10
1185 100 f. "Synsepalum aubrevillei" 20 10
1186 180 f. "Cola lorougnonis" . . 40 20

435 Tapa Woman

1998. Traditional Costumes. Multicoloured.

1187 180 f. Type **435** 35 20
1188 280 f. Raphia woman 55 30

436 Steam Locomotive, South Africa, 1918

1999. Railways of Africa. Multicoloured.

1189 180 f. Type **436** 35 20
1190 280 f. Beyer Peacock 15th Class Garratt type steam locomotive, 1925 (wrongly inscr "Garret") 55 30

MILITARY FRANK STAMP

MF 59

1967. No value indicated.

MF1 MF **59** (–) multicoloured . . 1·90 1·90

OFFICIAL STAMPS

O **135** Arms of Ivory Coast

1973. No value indicated. Multicoloured. Background colours given.

O422 O **135** (–) green & turquoise . 45 20
O423 (–) yellow & orange . . 75 35
O424 (–) pink & mauve . . . 1·00 55
O425 (–) violet & blue . . . 2·75 1·10

Nos. O422/25 represent the following face values. No. O422, 35 f. No. O423, 75 f. No. O424, 100 f. No. O425, 250 f.

PARCEL POST STAMPS

1903. Postage Due stamps of French Colonies optd.

(a) **Cote d'Ivoire COLIS Postaux**.

P18	U	50 c. purple	22·00	22·00
P20		1 f. pink on buff	22·00	22·00

(b) **Colis Postaux**.

P19	U	50 c. purple	£2000	£2000
P21		1 f. pink on buff	£2000	£2000

(c) **Cote d'Ivoire Colis Postaux**.

P22	U	50 c. purple	75·00	75·00
P23		1 f. pink on buff	42·00	42·00

1903. Postage Due stamps of French Colonies surch.

(a) **Cote d'Ivoire Colis Postaux** and new value.

P24	U	50 c. on 15 c. green	6·50	6·50
P25		50 c. on 60 c. brown on buff	27·00	23·00
P26		1 f. on 5 c. blue	8·25	6·25
P27		1 f. on 10 c. brown	11·00	11·00
P30		4 f. on 60 c. brown on buff	85·00	55·00

(b) **Colis Postaux Cote d'Ivoire** and new value.

P35	U	4 f. on 5 c. blue	£140	£160
P28		4 f. on 15 c. green	85·00	55·00
P29		4 f. on 30 c. pink	85·00	55·00
P36		8 f. on 15 c. green	£160	£160

1904. Postage Due stamps of French Colonies optd.

(a) **C. P. Cote d'Ivoire**.

P31	U	50 c. purple	22·00	22·00
P32		1 f. pink on buff	20·00	22·00

(b) **Cote d'Ivoire C.P**.

P33	U	50 c. purple	22·00	19·00
P34		1 f. pink on buff	28·00	27·00

1905. Postage Due stamps of French Colonies surch **Cote d'Ivoire C. P.** and new value.

P39	U	2 f. on 1 f. pink on buff	£160	£160
P40		4 f. on 1 f. pink on buff	£180	£180
P41		8 f. on 1 f. pink on buff	£400	£400

POSTAGE DUE STAMPS

1906. "Natives" key-type inscr "COTE D'IVOIRE".

D38	L	5 c. green	75	75
D39		10 c. purple	75	60
D40		15 c. blue on blue	75	75
D41		20 c. black on yellow	75	75
D42		30 c. red on cream	2·50	4·00
D43		50 c. violet	2·00	3·00
D44		60 c. black on buff	5·50	12·00
D45		1 f. black on pink	19·00	22·00

1915. "Figure" key-type inscr "COTE D'IVOIRE".

D60	M	5 c. green	10	25
D61		10 c. red	10	25
D62		15 c. grey	10	25
D63		20 c. brown	15	25
D64		30 c. blue	20	35
D65		50 c. black	20	40
D66		60 c. orange	50	55
D67		1 f. violet	50	75

1927. Surch in figures.

D94	M	"2 F." on 1 f. purple	40	85
D95		"3 F." on 1 f. brown	40	85

D **21** Guere Mask

D **30** Mask

D **70** Baoule Weight

1960. Values in black.

D196	D **21**	1 f. violet	15	15
D197		2 f. green	15	15
D198		5 f. yellow	30	30
D199		10 f. blue	55	55
D200		20 f. mauve	95	95

1962.

D220	D **30**	1 f. blue and orange	15	15
D221	–	2 f. red and black	20	20
D222	–	5 f. green and red	30	30
D223	–	10 f. purple and green	55	55
D224	–	20 f. black and violet	90	90

DESIGNS: 2 f. to 20 f. Various native masks from Bingerville Art School.

1968. Designs showing different types of weights.

D309	D **70**	5 f. multicoloured	15	15
D310	–	10 f. multicoloured	20	20
D311	–	15 f. multicoloured	50	50
D312	–	20 f. multicoloured	80	80
D313	–	30 f. multicoloured	1·10	1·10

D **111** "Animal" Weight

1972. Gold Weights and Measures.

D389	D **111**	20 f. brown & violet	65	65
D390	–	40 f. brown & red	1·00	1·00
D391	–	50 f. purple & orange	1·50	1·50
D392	–	100 f. brown & green	3·00	3·00

DESIGNS: 40 f. "Dagger"; 50 f. "Bird"; 100 f. "Triangle".

JAIPUR Pt. 1

A state of Rajasthan, India. Now uses Indian stamps.

12 pies = 1 anna; 16 annas = 1 rupee

2 Chariot of the Sun God, Surya 3

1904.

3	2	½ a. blue	2·75	4·50
4		1 a. red	4·25	12·00
5		2 a. green	3·50	10·00

1904.

9	3	¼ a. olive	55	45
10a		½ a. blue	55	40
28		1 a. red	1·75	1·60
12		2 a. green	1·00	75
13		4 a. brown	5·00	2·00
14		8 a. violet	3·00	2·75
15a		1 r. yellow	15·00	16·00

This set was issued engraved in 1904 and surface-printed in 1913.

4 Chariot of the Sun God, Surya (5)

1911. No gum.

17	4	¼ a. olive	30	60
18		½ a. blue	30	60
20		1 a. red	45	65
21a		2 a. green	2·00	5·50

1926. Surch with T **5**.

32	3	3 a. on 8 a. violet	1·25	1·90
33		3 a. on 1 r. yellow	2·00	3·75

6 Chariot of the Sun God, Surya 7 Maharaja Sawai Man Singh II

1931. Investiture of Maharaja. Centres in black.

40	6	¼ a. purple	90	1·25
58	7	¼ a. red	30	15
41		½ a. violet	30	10
59		¾ a. red	4·50	2·75
42	–	1 a. blue	5·00	5·50
60	7	1 a. blue	5·50	2·00
43	–	2 a. orange	3·50	5·50
61	7	2 a. orange	5·50	2·75
44	–	2½ a. red	28·00	45·00
62	7	2½ a. red	2·25	1·50
45	–	3 a. green	10·00	38·00
63	7	3 a. green	1·40	40
46	–	4 a. green	12·00	40·00
64	7	4 a. green	17·00	80·00
47	–	6 a. blue	6·00	38·00
65	7	6 a. blue	2·25	18·00
48	–	8 a. brown	10·00	55·00
66	7	8 a. brown	14·00	75·00
49	–	1 r. olive	25·00	£160
67	7	1 r. bistre	20·00	£100
50	–	2 r. green	22·00	£170
51	–	5 r. purple	32·00	£180

DESIGNS—VERT: 1 a. (No. 42), Elephant and banner; 2 a. (No. 43), Sowar in armour; 2½ a. (No. 44), Common peafowl; 8 a. (No. 48), Sireh-Deorhi Gate. HORIZ: 3 a. (No. 45), Bullock carriage; 4 a. (No. 46), Elephant carriage; 6 a. (No. 47), Albert Museum; 1 r. (No. 49), Chandra Mahal; 2 r. Amber Palace; 5 r. Maharajas Sawai Jai Singh and Man Singh.

1932. As T **7**, but inscr "POSTAGE & REVENUE". Portrait in black.

52		1 a. blue	50	55
53		2 a. brown	1·75	1·10
54		4 a. green	3·25	5·50
55		8 a. brown	4·50	8·50
56		1 r. bistre	16·00	70·00
57		2 r. green	70·00	£275

1936. Nos. 57 and 51 surch **One Rupee**.

68		1 r. on 2 r. green	6·00	65·00
69		1 r. on 5 r. purple	6·00	50·00

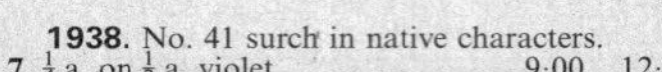

1938. No. 41 surch in native characters.

70	7	¼ a. on ½ a. violet	9·00	12·00

13 Maharaja and Amber Palace

1947. Silver Jubilee of Maharaja's Accession to the Throne. Inscr as in T **13**.

71	–	¼ a. brown and green	70	2·75
72	13	½ a. green and violet	20	2·50
73	–	¾ a. black and red	70	3·25
74	–	1 a. brown and blue	40	2·50
75	–	2 a. violet and red	40	2·75
76	–	3 a. green and black	90	3·75
77	–	4 a. blue and brown	50	2·50
78	–	8 a. red and brown	60	3·50
79	–	1 r. purple and green	1·40	19·00

DESIGNS: ¼ a. Palace Gate; ¾ a. Map of Jaipur; 1 a. Observatory; 2 a. Wind Palace; 3 a. Coat of Arms; 4 a. Amber Fort Gate; 8 a. Chariot of the Sun; 1 r. Maharaja's portrait between State flags.

1947. No. 41 surch **3 PIES** and bars.

80	7	3 p. on ½ a. violet	14·00	22·00

OFFICIAL STAMPS

1929. Optd **SERVICE**. No gum (except for No. O6a).

O1	3	¼ a. bistre	1·25	1·50
O2		½ a. blue	65	20
O3c		1 a. red	70	25
O5		2 a. green	65	40
O6a		4 a. brown (with gum)	2·00	1·75
O7		8 a. violet	16·00	48·00
O8		1 r. orange	32·00	£190

1931. Stamps of 1931–32 optd **SERVICE**.

O23	7	¼ a. red	40	10
O13		½ a. violet	30	10
O24		¾ a. red	1·50	40
O25		1 a. blue	7·50	30
O14	–	1 a. blue (No. 42)	£225	1·75
O18	–	1 a. blue (No. 52)	1·50	10
O15	–	2 a. orange (No. 43)	2·25	4·25
O19	–	2 a. brown (No. 53)	2·00	10
O26	7	2 a. orange	6·50	1·75
O27		2½ a. red	9·00	70·00
O16	–	4 a. green (No. 46)	25·00	23·00
O20	–	4 a. green (No. 54)	£225	5·50
O28	7	4 a. green	5·00	3·25
O21	–	8 a. brown (No. 55)	5·50	1·10
O29	7	8 a. brown	5·00	4·50
O22	–	1 r. bistre (No. 56)	14·00	15·00
O30	7	1 r. bistre	£100	

1932. No. O5 surch in native characters.

O17	3	½ a. on 2 a. green	£130	1·00

1947. Official stamps surch.

O33	7	3 p. on ½ a. violet	4·00	10·00
O32		9 p. on 1 a. blue	2·50	2·50

1949. No. O13 surch in native characters.

O34	7	¾ a. on ½ a. violet	13·00	13·00

For later issues see **RAJASTHAN**.

JAMAICA Pt. 1

An island in the W. Indies. Part of the Br. Caribbean Federation from 3 Jan. 1958, until 6 Aug. 1962 when Jamaica became an independent state within the Commonwealth.

1860. 12 pence = 1 shilling;
20 shillings = 1 pound.
1969. 100 cents = 1 dollar.

8 11

1860. Portrait as T **8**. Various frames.

7	8	½d. red	13·00	3·50
16a		½d. green	80	10
8		1d. blue	55·00	75
18a		1d. red	27·00	60
9		2d. red	55·00	70
20a		2d. grey	55·00	50
21a		3d. green	2·50	1·00
22a		4d. orange	2·00	35
52a		6d. lilac	9·50	17·00
23a		6d. yellow	4·00	3·50
24		1s. brown	5·00	6·00
25		2s. red	27·00	20·00
26		5s. lilac	48·00	65·00

See also Nos. 47a etc.

1889.

27	11	1d. purple and mauve	2·25	20
28a		2d. green	4·50	6·00
29		2½d. purple and blue	4·75	50

1890. No. 22a surch **TWO PENCE HALF-PENNY**.

30	8	2½d. on 4d. orange	27·00	8·50

13 Llandovery Falls, Jamaica

1900.

31	13	1d. red	1·25	20
32		1d. black and red	2·25	20

14 Arms of Jamaica 16

1903.

33	14	½d. grey and green	1·50	30
34		1d. grey and red	1·50	10
35		2½d. grey and blue	2·25	30
42		2½d. blue	2·50	1·25
36		5d. grey and yellow	15·00	23·00
44		6d. purple	12·00	12·00
45		5s. grey and violet	40·00	30·00

1906.

38a	16	½d. green	3·75	20
40		1d. red	1·25	10

1908. Queen Victoria portraits as 1860.

47a		3d. purple on yellow	2·00	1·50
48		4d. brown	70·00	60·00
49		4d. black on yellow	7·00	38·00
50		4d. red on yellow	1·50	8·00
54		1s. black on green	3·75	8·50
56		2s. purple on blue	6·00	3·50

17

1911.

57	17	2d. grey	2·25	13·00

1912. As T **17**, but King George V.

89a		½d. green	1·50	10
58		1d. red	1·25	10
59		1½d. orange	1·00	60
60		2d. grey	1·75	1·75
61		2½d. blue	1·00	15
62		3d. purple on yellow	40	45
63		4d. black and red on yellow	50	3·50
64a		6d. purple and mauve	70	1·00
65		1s. black on green	1·25	2·00
66		2s. purple and blue on blue	12·00	25·00
67		5s. green and red on yellow	48·00	80·00

1916. Optd **WAR STAMP.** in one line (with full point).

68	16	½d. green	10	35
69a	–	3d. purple on yellow (62)	1·00	17·00

See also Nos. 76/77a.

1916. Optd **WAR STAMP.** in two lines.

73	16	½d. green	10	20
74	–	1½d. orange (No. 59)	10	10
75	–	3d. purple on yellow (No. 62)	15	1·25

1919. Optd **WAR STAMP** in one line (no full point).

76	15	½d. green	10	15
77a	–	3d. purple on yell (No. 62)	2·00	1·25

23 Jamaica Exhibition, 1891 24 Arawak Woman preparing Cassava

27 Return of War Contingent, 1919 34

1919.

91a	23	½d. green and olive	25	50
79	24	1d. red and orange (A)*	1·75	1·75
92		1d. red and orange (B)*	1·50	10
93	–	1½d. green	40	45
81	–	2d. blue and green	1·00	4·00
82a	27	2½d. blue	1·50	1·75
96a	27	3d. green and blue	80	15
97a	–	4d. brown and green	75	30
98a	–	6d. black and blue	12·00	1·50
99a	–	1s. orange	1·75	65
100	–	2s. blue and brown	3·25	65
101	–	3s. violet and orange	11·00	9·00
102c	–	5s. blue and bistre	25·00	22·00
103	34	10s. green	50·00	70·00

*Two types of the 1d. (A) Without and (B) with "POSTAGE & REVENUE" at foot.

DESIGNS—HORIZ (41½ × 26 mm): 1½d. War Contingent embarking, 1915; 6d. Port Royal, 1853. (27 × 22 mm): 3d. Landing of Columbus, 1494. VERT (22 × 29 mm): 2d. King's House, Spanish Town; 4d. Cathedral, Spanish Town. (25 × 30 mm): 1s. Statue of Queen Victoria, Kingston; 2s. Admiral Rodney Memorial, Spanish Town; 3s. Sir Charles Metcalfe Monument; 5s. Jamaican scenery.

37 41

1923. Child Welfare. Designs as T **37**.

104	37	½d. + ½d. black and green	60	5·50
105	–	1d. + ½d. black and red	1·75	10·00
106	–	2½d. + ½d. black and blue	8·50	18·00

1929. Various frames.

108	41	1d. red	1·75	10
109		1½d. brown	1·75	15
110		9d. red	3·25	1·00

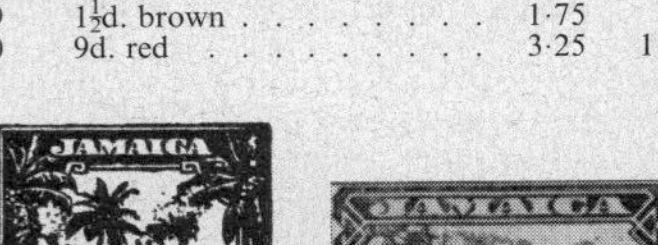

43 Coco Palms at Don Christopher's Cove 45 Priestman's River, Portland

1932.

111	43	2d. black and green	8·00	2·25
112	–	2½d. turquoise and blue	1·75	1·50
113	45	6d. black and purple	8·00	1·25

DESIGN—As T **43**: 2½d. Wag Water River, St. Andrew.

1935. Silver Jubilee. As T **10a** of Gambia.

114		1d. blue and red	20	15
115		1½d. blue and black	50	1·00
116		6d. green and blue	5·00	11·00
117		1s. grey and purple	4·00	7·00

1937. Coronation. As T **10b** of Gambia.

118		1d. red	30	15
119		1½d. grey	50	30
120		2½d. blue	85	70

48 King George VI 49 Coco Palms at Don Christopher's Cove

50 Bananas

54 Bamboo Walk

1938.

121	48	½d. green	1·50	10
121b		½d. orange	30	30
122		1d. red	80	10
122a		1d. green	50	10
123		1½d. brown	80	10
124b	49	2d. black and green	75	10
125	–	2½d. green and blue	3·00	1·50
126	50	3d. blue and green	70	1·25

126b 50 3d. green and blue . . . . 1·25 1·25
126c 3d. green and red . . . . 1·50 30
127 – 4d. brown and green . . . 40 10
128a – 6d. black and purple . . . 1·75 10
129 – 9d. red 40 50
130 – 1s. green and brown . . . 6·00 20
131 54 2s. blue and brown . . . 20·00 90
132ba – 5s. blue and brown . . . 6·50 3·00
133aa – 10s. green . . . . . . 9·00 5·00
133a – £1 brown and violet . . . 27·00 26·00
DESIGNS—As Type **49**: 2½d. Wag Water River, St. Andrew. As Type **50**: 4d. Citrus grove; 9d. Kingston Harbour; 1s. Sugar industry; £1 Tobacco growing and cigar making. As previous issues, but with portrait of King George VI: 6d. As Type **45**; 5 s. As No. 102c; 10s. As Type **34**.

57 Courthouse, Falmouth

59 Institute of Jamaica

1945. New Constitution..
134 57 1½d. brown 20 30
135a – 2d. green 30 50
136 59 3d. blue 20 50
137 – 4½d. black 30 30
138 – 2s. brown 30 50
139 – 5s. blue . . . . 1·00 1·00
140 59 10s. green . . . . . . 85 2·25
DESIGNS—VERT (as Type **57**): 2s. "Labour and Learning". HORIZ (as Type **57**): 2d. Kings Charles II and George VI. (As Type **59**): 4½d. House of Assembly; 5s. Scroll, flag and King George VI.

1946. Victory. As T **11a** of Gambia.
141a 1½d. brown 30 65
142 3d. blue . . . . 2·50 2·25

1948. Silver Wedding. As T **11b/c** of Gambia.
143 1½d. brown 30 10
144 £1 red . . . . 24·00 45·00

1949. U.P.U. As T **11d/f** of Gambia.
145 1½d. brown 30 15
146 2d. green . . . . 1·00 1·75
147 3d. blue . . . . 55 1·25
148 6d. purple . . . . 65 2·50

1951. Inauguration of B.W.I. University College. As T **43a/b** of Grenada.
149 2d. black and brown 30 30
150 6d. black and purple 35 30

69 Scout Badge and Map of Caribbean

70 Scout Badge and Map of Jamaica

1952. 1st Caribbean Scout Jamboree.
151 69 2d. blue, green and black . . 15 10
152 70 6d. green, red and black . . 15 50

1953. Coronation. As T **11h** of Gambia.
153 2d. black and green 50 10

1953 Royal Visit. As T **49** but with portrait of Queen Elizabeth II and inscr "ROYAL VISIT 1953".
154 2d. black and green 40 10

73 H.M.S. "Britannia" (ship of the line) at Port Royal

1955. Tercentenary Issue.
155 73 2d. black and green 35 10
156 – 2½d. black and blue 15 35
157 – 3d. black and claret 15 30
158 – 6d. black and red 20 20
DESIGNS: 2½d. Old Montego Bay; 3d. Old Kingston; 6d. Proclamation of Abolition of Slavery, 1838.

74 Coconut Palms

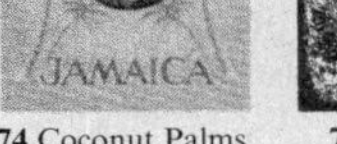

76 Blue Mountain Peak

75 Mahoe

77 Arms of Jamaica

1956.
159 74 ½d. black and red 10 10
160 – 1d. black and green 10 10
161 – 2d. black and red 10 10
162 – 2½d. black and blue 30 40
163 75 3d. green and brown 20 10
164 – 4d. green and blue 20 10
165 – 5d. red and green . . . . . 20 1·00
166 – 6d. black and red . . . . . 1·25 10
167 76 8d. blue and orange 15 10
168 – 1s. green and blue 60 10
169 – 1s. 6d. blue and purple . . . 80 10
170 – 2s. blue and green . . . . . 7·00 1·50
171 77 3s. black and blue . . . . . 1·50 1·75
172 – 5s. black and red . . . . . 3·75 3·00
173 – 10s. black and green . . . . 25·00 13·00
174 – £1 black and purple . . . . 25·00 13·00
DESIGNS—As Type **74**: 1d. Sugar cane; 2d. Pineapples; 2½d. Bananas. As Type **75**: 4d. Breadfruit; 5d. Ackee; 6d. Streamertail. As Type **76**: 1s. Royal Botanic Gardens, Hope; 1s. 6d. Rafting on the Rio Grande; 2s. Fort Charles. As Type **77** but vert: 10s., £1 Arms without portrait.

1958. British Caribbean Federation. As T **47a** of Grenada.
175 2d. green 50 10
176 5d. blue . . . . 95 3·50
177 6d. red 95 40

81 Bristol Britannia 312 flying over "City of Berlin", 1860

83 1s. Stamps of 1860 and 1956

1960. Centenary of Jamaica Postage Stamps.
178 81 2d. blue and purple 45 10
179 – 6d. red and olive 45 25
180 83 1s. brown, green and blue . 45 30
DESIGN—As Type **81**: 6d. Postal mule-cart and motor-van.

1962. Independence. (a) Nos. 159/74 optd **INDEPENDENCE** and **1962** (3d. to 2s.) or **1962 1962** (others).
205 74 ½d. black and red 10 15
182 – 1d. black and green 10 10
183 – 2½d. black and blue 10 85
184 75 3d. green and brown 10 10
185 – 5d. red and olive 15 60
186 – 6d. black and red . . . . . 2·50 10
187 76 8d. blue and orange 15 10
188 – 1s. green and blue 15 10
189 – 2s. blue and olive . . . . . 80 1·50
190 77 3s. black and blue . . . . . 90 1·50
191 – 10s. black and green . . . . 2·75 4·25
192 – £1 black and purple . . . . 2·75 5·50

86 Military Bugler and Map

(b) As T **86** inscr "INDEPENDENCE".
193 86 2d. multicoloured 75 10
194 4d. multicoloured 75 10
195 – 1s. 6d. black and red . . . 2·50 85
196 – 5s. multicoloured . . . . . 3·25 4·00
DESIGNS: 1s. 6d. Gordon House and banner; 5s. Map, factories and fruit.

89 Kingston Seal, Weightlifting, Boxing, Football and Cycling

1962. 9th Central American and Caribbean Games, Kingston.
197 89 1d. sepia and red 20 10
198 – 6d. sepia and blue 20 10
199 – 8d. sepia and bistre 20 10
200 – 2s. multicoloured 30 80
DESIGNS: 6d. Diver, sailing, swimming and water polo; 8d. Javelin, discus, pole-vault, hurdles and relay-racing; 2s. Kingston coat of arms and athlete.

93 Farmer and Crops

1963. Freedom from Hunger.
201 93 1d. multicoloured 20 10
202 8d. multicoloured 60 60

1963. Cent of Red Cross. As T **20b** of Gambia.
203 2d. red and black 20 10
204 1s. 6d. red and blue . . . . . 70 1·50

95 Carole Joan Crawford ("Miss World 1963")

1964. "Miss World 1963" Commem.
214 95 3d. multicoloured 10 10
215 1s. multicoloured 15 10
216 1s. 6d. multicoloured . . . 20 50

96 Lignum Vitae

103 Gypsum Industry

1964.
217 96 1d. blue, green & brown . 10 10
218 – 1½d. multicoloured 15 10
219 – 2d. red, yellow and green . 15 10
220 – 2½d. multicoloured 90 60
221 – 3d. yellow, black & grn . . 15 10
222 – 4d. ochre and violet . . . 45 10
223 – 6d. multicoloured . . . . 2·25 10
224 – 8d. multicoloured . . . . 2·25 1·50
225 103 9d. blue and bistre . . . 1·50 10
226 – 1s. black and brown . . . 20 10
227 – 1s. 6d. black, blue & buff 3·00 15
228 – 2s. brown, black & blue . 2·75 15
229b – 3s. blue and green 35 65
230 – 5s. black, ochre & blue . . 1·25 1·00
231 – 10s. multicoloured . . . . 1·25 1·25
232 – £1 multicoloured . . . . 1·50 1·00
DESIGNS—HORIZ (As T **96**): 1½d. Ackee (fruit); 2½d. Land shells; 3d. National flag over Jamaica; 4d. Antillean murex (sea shell); 6d. "Papilio homerus" (butterfly); 8d. Streamertail. VERT (As T **96**): 2d. Blue Mahoe (tree). HORIZ (As T **103**): 1s. National Stadium; 1s. 6d. Palisadoes International Airport; 2s. Bauxite mining; 3s. Blue marlin (sport fishing); 5s. Exploration of sunken city, Port Royal; £1 Queen Elizabeth II and national flag. VERT (As T **96**): 10s. Arms of Jamaica.

114 Scout Badge and Alligator

1964. 6th Inter-American Scout Conf, Kingston.
233 – 3d. red, black and pink . . 10 10
234 – 8d. blue, olive and black . . 15 25
235 114 1s. gold, blue & light blue 20 45
DESIGNS—VERT (25½ × 30 mm): 3d. Scout belt; 8d. Globe, scout hat and scarf.

115 Gordon House, Kingston

118 Eleanor Roosevelt

1964. 10th Commonwealth Parliamentary Conf, Kingston.
236 115 3d. black and green 10 10
237 – 6d. black and red 30 10
238 – 1s. 6d. black and blue . . . 50 30
DESIGNS: 6d. Headquarters House, Kingston; 1s. 6d. House of Assembly, Spanish Town.

1964. 16th Anniv of Declaration of Human Rights.
239 118 1s. black, red & green . . . 10 10

119 Guides' Emblem on Map

121 Uniform Cap

1965. Golden Jubilee of Jamaica Girl Guides' Assn. Inscr "1915–1965".
240 119 3d. yellow, green & black 10 10
241 – 1s. yellow, black & green 20 40
DESIGN—TRIANGULAR (61½ × 30½ mm): 1s. Guide emblems.

1965. Centenary of Salvation Army. Mult.
242 3d. Type **121** 25 10
243 1s. 6d. Flag-bearer and drummer (vert) 50 50

123 Paul Bogle, William Gordon and Morant Bay Court House

1965. Centenary of Morant Bay Rebellion.
244 123 3d. brown, blue & black . 10 10
245 1s. 6d. brown, green & blk 20 10
246 3s. brown, red & black . . 30 75

124 Abeng-blower, "Telstar", Morse Key and I.T.U. Emblem

1965. Centenary of I.T.U.
247 124 1s. black, slate & red . . . 40 15

1966. Royal Visit. Nos. 221, 223, 226/7 optd **ROYAL VISIT MARCH 1966**.
248 3d. yellow, black and green . . 15 10
249 6d. multicoloured . . . . . . 1·75 30
250 1s. black and brown 55 10
251 1s. 6d. black, blue and buff . . 2·00 2·00

126 Sir Winston Churchill

1966. Churchill Commemoration.
252 126 6d. black and green 50 30
253 1s. brown and blue 75 80

127 Statue of Athlete and Flags

1966. 8th British Empire and Commonwealth Games.
254 127 3d. multicoloured 10 10
255 – 6d. multicoloured 40 10
256 – 1s. multicoloured 10 10
257 – 3s. gold and blue 35 45
DESIGNS: 6d. Racing cyclists; 1s. National Stadium, Kingston; 3s. Games emblem.

131 Bolivar's Statue and Flags of Jamaica and Venezuela

133 Sir Donald Sangster (Prime Minister)

132 Jamaican Pavilion

1966. 150th Anniv of "Jamaica Letter".
259 **131** 8d. multicoloured 20 10

1967. World Fair, Montreal.
260 **132** 6d. multicoloured 10 15
261 1s. multicoloured 10 15

1967. Sangster Memorial Issue.
262 **133** 3d. multicoloured 10 10
263 1s. 6d. multicoloured . . . 20 20

134 Traffic Duty

1967. Centenary of Constabulary Force. Mult
264 3d. Type **134** 40 10
265 1s. Personnel of the Force ($56\frac{1}{2} \times 20\frac{1}{2}$ mm) 40 10
266 1s. 6d. Badge and Constables of 1867 and 1967 . . . . . . 50 75

1968. M.C.C.'s West Indies Tour. As Nos. 445/7 of Guyana.
267 6d. multicoloured 50 50
268 6d. multicoloured 50 50
269 6d. multicoloured 50 50

137 Sir Alexander and Lady Bustamante

1968. Labour Day.
270 **137** 3d. red and black 10 15
271 1s. olive and black 10 15

138 Human Rights Emblem over Map of Jamaica

1968. Human Rights Year. Multicoloured.
272 3d. Type **138** 10 10
273 1s. Hands cupping Human Rights emblem 10 10
274 3s. Jamaican holding "Human Rights" 30 90

141 I.L.O. Emblem

1969. 50th Anniv of I.L.O.
275 **141** 6d. yellow and brown . . . 10 10
276 3s. green and brown . . . 30 30

142 Nurse and Children being Weighed and Measured

146 "The Adoration of the Kings" (detail, Foppa)

1969. 20th Anniv of W.H.O. Multicoloured.
277 6d. Type **142** 10 10
278 1s. Malaria eradication (horiz) 10 10
279 3s. Trainee nurse 20 55

1969. Decimal Currency. Nos. 217, 219, 221/3 and 225/32 surch **C-DAY 8th September 1969** and value.
280 **95** 1 c. on 1d. bl, grn & brn . . 10 10
281 – 2 c. on 2d. red, yellow & grn 10 10
282 – 3 c. on 3d. yellow, blk & grn 10 10
283 – 4 c. on 4d. ochre & violet 1·25 10
284 – 5 c. on 6d. multicoloured 1·25 10
285 **103** 8 c. on 9d. blue & bistre . . 10 10
286 – 10 c. on 1s. black & brn . . 10 10
287 – 15 c. on 1s. 6d. black, blue and buff 30 90
288 – 20 c. on 2s. brn, blk & bl 1·50 1·50
289 – 30 c. on 3s. blue & green 1·50 2·75
290 – 50 c. on 5s. black, ochre and blue . . . . 1·25 3·00
291 – $1 on 10s. multicoloured 1·25 6·50
292 – $2 on £1 multicoloured . . 1·50 6·50

1969. Christmas. Paintings. Multicoloured.
293 2 c. Type **146** 20 40
294 5 c. "Madonna, Child and St. John" (Raphael) 25 40
295 8 c. "The Adoration of the Kings" (detail, Dosso Dossi) 25 40

149 Half Penny, 1869

1969. Centenary of 1st Jamaican Coins.
296 **149** 3 c. silver, black and mauve 15 25
297 – 15 c. silver, black & grn . . 10 10
DESIGN: 15 c. One penny, 1869.

151 George William Gordon

156 "Christ appearing to St. Peter" (Carracci)

1970. National Heroes. Multicoloured; background colours given.
298 **151** 1 c. mauve 10 10
299 – 3 c. blue 10 10
300 – 5 c. grey 10 10
301 – 10 c. red 15 10
302 – 15 c. green 30 25
PORTRAITS: 3 c. Sir Alexander Bustamante; 5 c. Norman Manley; 10 c. Marcus Garvey; 15 c. Paul Bogle.

1970. Easter. Centres multicoloured; frame colours given.
303 **156** 3 c. red 10 10
304 – 10 c. green 10 10
305 – 20 c. grey 20 60
DESIGNS: 10 c. "Christ Crucified" (Antonello); 20 c. Easter lily.

1970. No. 219 surch **2c**.
306 2 c. on 2d. red, yellow & grn . . 20 20

160 Lignum Vitae

164 Bananas, Citrus, Sugar-Cane and Tobacco

161 Cable Ship "Dacia"

1970. Decimal Currency. Designs as Nos. 217, 219, 221/23, 225/32, but with values inscr as T **160** in new currency.
307 **160** 1 c. blue, green & brown . 60 1·50
308 – 2 c. red, yellow and green (as 2d.) 30 10
309 – 3 c. yellow, black and green (as 3d.) 45 60
310 – 4 c. ochre and violet (as 4d.) 2·25 10
311 – 5 c. multicoloured (as 6d.) 3·00 30
312 **103** 8 c. blue and yellow . . . 1·75 10
313 – 10 c. black & brn (as 1s.) 40 10
314 – 15 c. black, blue and buff (as 1s. 6d.) . . . . 2·00 2·50
315 – 20 c. brown, black and blue (as 2s.) . . . . 1·25 2·25
316 – 30 c. blue & green (as 3s.) 3·00 3·75
317 – 50 c. black, ochre and blue (as 5s.) . . . . 1·25 3·75
318 – $1 multicoloured (as 10s.) 1·00 3·75
319 – $2 multicoloured (as £1) . . 1·25 4·00

1970. Centenary of Telegraph Service.
320 **161** 3 c. yellow, black and red . 15 10
321 – 10 c. black and green . . . 20 10
322 – 50 c. multicoloured . . . . 50 1·00
DESIGNS: 10 c. Bright's cable gear aboard "Dacia"; 50 c. Morse key and chart.

1970. 75th Anniv of Jamaican Agricultural Society.
323 **164** 2 c. multicoloured 25 60
324 10 c. multicoloured 45 10

165 Locomotive "Projector" (1845)

168 Church of St. Jago de la Vega

1970. 125th Anniv of Jamaican Railways.
325 3 c. Type **165** 30 10
326 15 c. Steam locomotive No. 54 (1944) 80 30
327 50 c. Steam locomotive No. 102 (1967) . . . . 2·00 2·00

1971. Centenary of Disestablishment of Church of England in Jamaica.
328 **168** 3 c. multicoloured 10 10
329 10 c. multicoloured 10 10
330 20 c. multicoloured 30 30
331 – 30 c. multicoloured 30 80
DESIGN: 30 c. Emblem of Church of England in Jamaica.

169 Henry Morgan and Ships

1971. Pirates and Buccaneers. Multicoloured.
332 3 c. Type **169** 75 10
333 15 c. Mary Read, Anne Bonny and trial pamphlet . . . . . . 1·00 15
334 30 c. Pirate schooner attacking merchantman . . . . 1·75 1·25

170 1s. Stamp of 1919 with Frame Inverted

1971. Tercentenary of Post Office.
335 – 3 c. black and brown . . . 20 20
336 – 5 c. black and green . . . 20 20
337 – 8 c. black and violet . . . 20 10
338 – 10 c. brown, black and blue 20 10
339 – 20 c. multicoloured 50 45
340 **170** 50 c. brown, blk & grey . . 75 1·50
DESIGNS—HORIZ: 3 c. Dummer packet letter, 1705; 5 c. Pre-stamp inland letter, 1793; 8 c. Harbour St. P.O., Kingston, 1820; 10 c. Modern stamp and cancellation; 20 c. British stamps used in Jamaica, 1859.

171 Satellite and Dish Aerial

172 Causeway, Kingston Harbour

1972. Opening of Jamaican Earth Satellite Station.
341 **171** 3 c. multicoloured 15 10
342 15 c. multicoloured 20 15
343 50 c. multicoloured . . . . 65 1·25

1972. Multicoloured.
344 1 c. Pimento (vert) 10 10
345 2 c. Red ginger (vert) 10 10
346 3 c. Bauxite Industry 10 10
347 4 c. Type **172** 10 10
348 5 c. Oil refinery 10 10
349 6 c. Senate Building, University of the West Indies 10 10
350 8 c. National Stadium 30 10
351 9 c. Devon House 10 10
352 10 c. Air Jamaica Hostess and Vickers VC-10 . . . . . . 20 10
353 15 c. Old Iron Bridge, Spanish Town (vert) . . . . 2·00 10
354 20 c. College of Arts, Science and Technology 30 15
355 30 c. Dunn's River Falls (vert) . 35 15
356 50 c. River rafting . . . . . . 1·50 40
357 $1 Jamaica House . . . . . . 75 1·50
358 $2 Kings House . . . . 1·00 1·50
Designs for 8 c. to $2 are larger, 35×27 or 27×35 mm..

1972. 10th Anniv of Independence Nos. 346, 352 and 356 optd **TENTH ANNIVERSARY INDEPENDENCE 1962-1972**.
359 3 c. multicoloured 30 30
360 10 c. multicoloured 30 10
361 50 c. multicoloured . . . . . . 75 2·00

175 Arms of Kingston

1972. Centenary of Kingston as Capital.
362 **175** 5 c. multicoloured 10 10
363 30 c. multicoloured 20 35
364 – 50 c. multicoloured . . . . 40 1·75
DESIGN—HORIZ: 50 c. design similar to Type **175**.

176 Mongoose on Map

1973. Centenary of Introduction of the Small Indian Mongoose.
365 **176** 8 c. green, yellow & black . 15 10
366 – 40 c. dp blue, blue & blk . 35 50
367 – 60 c. pink, salmon & blk . 60 1·00
DESIGNS: 40 c. Mongoose and rat; 60 c. Mongoose and chicken.

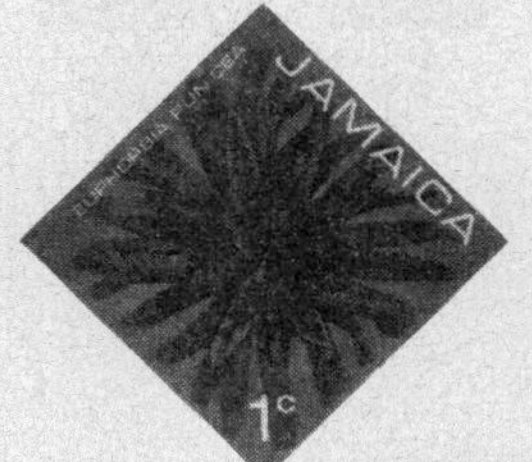

177 "Euphorbia punicea"

1973. Flora. Multicoloured.
369 1 c. Type **177** 10 10
370 6 c. "Hylocereus triangularis" . 15 10
371 9 c. "Columnea argentea" . . 15 10
372 15 c. "Portlandia grandiflora" . 25 15
373 30 c. "Samyda pubescens" . . 50 60
374 50 c. "Cordia sebestena" . . . 80 1·25

178 "Broughtonia sanguinea"

1973. Orchids. Multicoloured.

No.		Description	Unused	Used
375		5 c. Type **178**	40	10
376		10 c. "Arpophyllum jamaicense" (vert)	50	10
377		20 c. "Oncidium pulchellum" (vert)	1·25	25
378		$1 "Brassia maculata"	2·75	2·75

179 "Mary", 1808–15

1974. Mail Packet Boats. Multicoloured.

No.		Description	Unused	Used
380		5 c. Type **179**	55	10
381		10 c. "Queensbury", 1814–27	55	10
382		15 c. "Sheldrake", 1829–34	90	40
383		50 c. "Thames I", 1842	2·00	2·50

180 "Journeys"

1974. National Dance Theatre Company. Mult.

No.		Description	Unused	Used
385		5 c. Type **180**	10	10
386		10 c. "Jamaican Promenade"	10	10
387		30 c. "Jamaican Promenade" (different)	30	30
388		50 c. "Misa Criolla"	50	80

181 U.P.U. Emblem and Globe

1974. Centenary of U.P.U.

No.		Description	Unused	Used
390	**181**	5 c. multicoloured	10	10
391		9 c. multicoloured	10	10
392		50 c. multicoloured	35	80

182 Senate Building and Sir Hugh Wooding

1975. 25th Anniv of University of West Indies. Mult.

No.		Description	Unused	Used
393		5 c. Type **182**	10	10
394		10 c. University Chapel and Princess Alice	10	10
395		30 c. Type **182**	20	25
396		50 c. As 10 c.	35	60

183 Commonwealth Symbol

1975. Heads of Commonwealth Conf. Mult.

No.		Description	Unused	Used
397		5 c. Type **183**	10	10
398		10 c. Jamaican coat of arms	10	10
399		30 c. Dove of Peace	15	30
400		50 c. Jamaican flag	30	1·40

184 Jamaican Kite Swallowtail

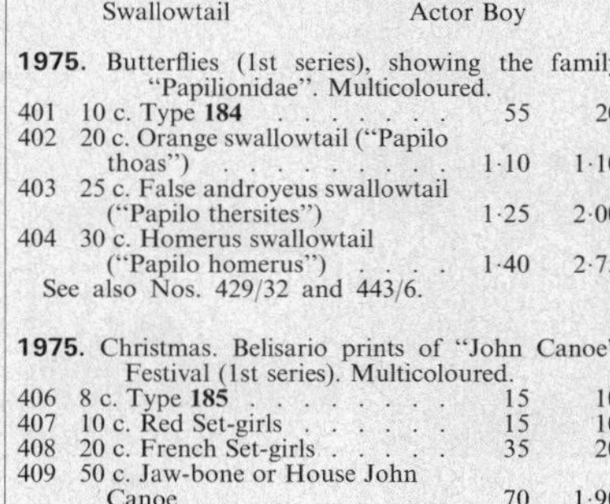

185 Koo Koo or Actor Boy

1975. Butterflies (1st series), showing the family "Papilionidae". Multicoloured.

No.		Description	Unused	Used
401		10 c. Type **184**	55	20
402		20 c. Orange swallowtail ("Papilo thoas")	1·10	1·10
403		25 c. False androyeus swallowtail ("Papilo thersites")	1·25	2·00
404		30 c. Homerus swallowtail ("Papilo homerus")	1·40	2·75

See also Nos. 429/32 and 443/6.

1975. Christmas. Belisario prints of "John Canoe" Festival (1st series). Multicoloured.

No.		Description	Unused	Used
406		8 c. Type **185**	15	10
407		10 c. Red Set-girls	15	10
408		20 c. French Set-girls	35	20
409		50 c. Jaw-bone or House John Canoe	70	1·90

See also Nos. 421/3.

186 Bordone Map, 1528

1976. 16th Century Maps of Jamaica.

No.		Description	Unused	Used
411	**186**	10 c. brown, lt brn & red	20	10
412	–	20 c. multicoloured	35	25
413	–	30 c. multicoloured	60	85
414	–	50 c. multicoloured	85	2·25

DESIGNS: 20 c. Porcacchi map, 1576; 30 c. De Bry map, 1594; 50 c. Langenes map, 1598.

See also Nos. 425/8.

187 Olympic Rings

1976. Olympic Games, Montreal.

No.		Description	Unused	Used
415	**187**	10 c. multicoloured	15	10
416		20 c. multicoloured	30	20
417		25 c. multicoloured	30	25
418		50 c. multicoloured	45	2·00

1976. West Indian Victory in World Cricket Cup. As T **223a** of Grenada.

No.		Description	Unused	Used
419		10 c. Map of the Caribbean	40	50
420		25 c. Prudential Cup	85	1·75

1976. Christmas. Belisario Prints (2nd series). As T **185**. Multicoloured.

No.		Description	Unused	Used
421		10 c. Queen of the set-girls	10	10
422		20 c. Band of the Jaw-bone John Canoe	25	10
423		50 c. Koo Koo (actor-boy)	45	1·75

1977. 17th Cent Maps of Jamaica. As T **186**.

No.		Description	Unused	Used
425		9 c. multicoloured	30	30
426		10 c. red, brown and buff	30	10
427		25 c. black, blue and lt blue	70	60
428		40 c. black, blue and green	80	2·00

DESIGNS: 9 c. Hickeringill map, 1661; 10 c. Ogilby map, 1671; 25 c. Visscher map, 1680; 40 c. Thornton map, 1689.

1977. Butterflies (2nd series). As T **184**. Mult.

No.		Description	Unused	Used
429		10 c. False barred sulphur ("Eurema elathea")	35	10
430		20 c. Bronze wing ("Dynamine egaea")	75	55
431		25 c. Jamaican harlequin ("Chlosyne pantoni")	1·00	1·50
432		40 c. Mimic ("Hypolimnas misippus")	1·50	3·25

188 Map, Scout Emblem and Streamertail

190 Half-figure with Canopy

189 Trumpeter

1977. Sixth Caribbean Scout Jamboree, Jamaica.

No.		Description	Unused	Used
434	**188**	10 c. multicoloured	35	10
435		20 c. multicoloured	70	25
436		25 c. multicoloured	75	35
437		50 c. multicoloured	1·00	1·75

1977. 50th Anniv of Jamaica Military Band. Mult.

No.		Description	Unused	Used
438		9 c. Type **189**	15	10
439		10 c. Clarinet players	15	10
440		20 c. Two kettle drummers (vert)	40	35
441		25 c. Double-bass player and trumpeter (vert)	55	65

1978. Butterflies (3rd series). As T **184**. Multicoloured.

No.		Description	Unused	Used
443		10 c. Jamaican hairstreak ("Callophrys crethona")	50	10
444		20 c. Malachite ("Siproeta stelenes")	85	20
445		25 c. Common long-tailed skipper ("Urbanus proteus")	95	65
446		50 c. Troglodyte ("Anaea troglodyta")	2·00	3·00

1978. Arawak Artefacts (1st series).

No.		Description	Unused	Used
448	**190**	10 c. brown, yellow & black	10	10
449	–	20 c. brown, mauve. & black	15	10
450	–	50 c. brown, green & blk	35	35

DESIGNS: 20 c. Standing figure; 50 c. Birdman.

See also Nos. 479/83.

191 Norman Manley (statue)

193 "Negro Aroused" (sculpture by Edna Manley)

192 Band and Banner

1978. 24th Commonwealth Parliamentary Conference. Multicoloured.

No.		Description	Unused	Used
452		10 c. Type **191**	10	10
453		20 c. Sir Alexander Bustamante (statue)	20	15
454		25 c. City of Kingston Crest	20	20
455		40 c. Gordon House Chamber, House of Representatives	30	55

1978. Christmas. Centenary of Salvation Army. Multicoloured.

No.		Description	Unused	Used
456		10 c. Type **192**	40	10
457		20 c. Trumpeter	45	20
458		25 c. Banner	45	30
459		50 c. William Booth (founder)	80	2·50

1978. International Anti-Apartheid Year.

No.		Description	Unused	Used
460	**193**	10 c. multicoloured	30	20

194 Tennis, Montego Bay

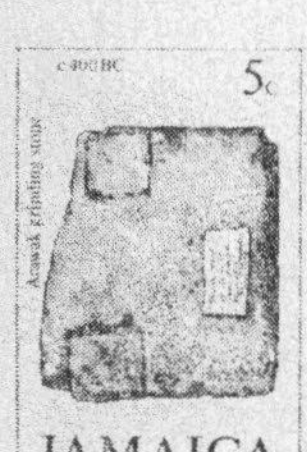

197 Grinding Stone, circa 400 B.C.

1979. Multicoloured.

No.		Description	Unused	Used
461		1 c. Type **194**	70	55
462		2 c. Golf, Tryall, Hanover	1·75	2·25
463		4 c. Horse riding, Negril Beach	40	80
464		5 c. Old waterwheel, Tryall, Hanover	55	20
465		6 c. Fern Gully, Ocho Rios	70	1·50
466		7 c. Dunn's River Falls, Ocho Rios	40	30
467		8 c. Jamaican tody	1·00	65
468		10 c. Jamaican mango	1·00	20
469		12 c. Yellow-billed amazon	80	1·00
470		15 c. Streamertail	1·00	30
471		35 c. White-chinned thrush	1·25	30
472		50 c. Jamaican woodpecker	1·50	30
473		65 c. Rafting, Martha Brae Trelawny	70	1·50
474		75 c. Blue Marlin fleet, Port Antonio	1·25	30
475		$1 Scuba diving, Ocho Rios	1·50	1·50
476		$2 Sailing boats, Montego Bay	75	50
477		$5 Arms and map of Jamaica (37 × 27 mm)	1·00	1·60

1979. 10th Anniv of Air Jamaica. No. 352 optd **TENTH ANNIVERSARY AIR JAMAICA 1st APRIL 1979**.

No.		Description	Unused	Used
478		10 c. multicoloured	50	50

1979. Arawak Artefacts (2nd series). Multicoloured.

No.		Description	Unused	Used
479		5 c. Type **197**	10	10
480		10 c. Stone implements, c. 500 B.C. (horiz)	10	10
481		20 c. Cooking pot, c. 300 A.D. (horiz)	10	15
482		25 c. Serving boat, c. 300 A.D. (horiz)	10	20
483		50 c. Storage jar fragment, c. 300 A.D.	25	35

198 1962 1s. 6d. Independence Commemorative Stamp

1979. Death Centenary of Sir Rowland Hill.

No.		Description	Unused	Used
484	**198**	10 c. black, brown and red	15	10
485	–	20 c. yellow and brown	20	15
486	–	25 c. mauve and blue	25	20
487	–	50 c. multicoloured	35	70

DESIGNS: 20 c. 1920 1s. with frame inverted; 25 c. 1860 6d. stamp; 50 c. 1968 3d. Human Rights Year commemorative.

199 Group of Children

1979. Christmas. International Year of the Child. Multicoloured.

No.		Description	Unused	Used
489		10 c. Type **199**	10	10
490		20 c. Doll (vert)	10	10
491		25 c. "The Family" (painting by child)	15	15
492		50 c. "House on the Hill" (painting by child)	25	40

200 Date Tree Hall, 1886 (original home of Institute)

1980. Centenary of Institute of Jamaica. Mult.

No.		Description	Unused	Used
493		5 c. Type **200**	10	10
494		15 c. Institute building, 1980	15	10
495		35 c. Microfilm reader (vert)	25	20
496		50 c. Hawksbill turtle and green turtle	45	85
497		75 c. Jamaican owl (vert)	1·50	2·75

201 Don Quarrie (200 Metres, 1976)

1980. Olympic Games, Moscow. Jamaican Olympic Gold Medal Winners. Multicoloured.

No.		Description	Unused	Used
498		15 c. Type **201**	40	15
499		35 c. Arthur Wint (4 × 400 Metres Relay, 1952)	45	70
500		35 c. Leslie Laing (4 × 400 Metres Relay, 1952)	45	70
501		35 c. Herbert McKenley (4 × 400 Metres Relay, 1952)	45	70
502		35 c. George Rhoden (4 × 400 Metres Relay, 1952)	45	70

202 Parish Church

1980. Christmas. Churches (1st series). Multicoloured.

503 15 c. Type **202** 10 10
504 20 c. Coke Memorial Church 10 10
505 25 c. Church of the Redeemer 15 10
506 $5 Holy Trinity Cathedral 1·00 2·00

See also No. 537/9 and 570/2.

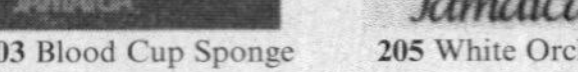

203 Blood Cup Sponge **205** White Orchid

204 Brown's Hutia (or Indian Coney)

1981. Marine Life (1st series). Multicoloured.

508 20 c. Type **203** 15 10
509 45 c. Tube sponge (horiz) 25 35
510 60 c. Black coral 35 45
511 75 c. Tyre reef (horiz) 40 75

See also Nos. 541/5.

1981. Brown's Hutia (or Indian Coney).

512 20 c. Hutia facing right 15 20
513 20 c. Type **204** 15 20
514 20 c. Hutia facing left and eating 15 20
515 20 c. Hutia family 15 20

1981. Royal Wedding. Multicoloured.

516 20 c. Type **205** 10 10
517 45 c. Royal Coach 15 10
518 60 c. Prince Charles and Lady Diana Spencer 20 20
519 $5 St. James' Palace 60 85

206 Blind Man at Work

1981. International Year for Disabled Persons. Multicoloured.

521 20 c. Type **206** 15 15
522 45 c. Painting with the mouth 40 40
523 60 c. Deaf student communicating with sign language 50 75
524 $1.50 Basketball players 1·25 2·00

207 W.F.D. Emblem on 1964 1½d. Definitive **208** "Survival" (song title)

1981. World Food Day. Stamps on Stamps.

525 **207** 20 c. multicoloured 35 15
526 – 45 c. black, red and orge 70 40
527 – $2 black, blue and green 2·00 1·40
528 – $4 black, green and brown 3·25 2·50

DESIGNS—VERT (As T **207**): 45 c. 1922 1d. value. HORIZ (40 × 26 mm): $2 As 1938 3d. but with W.F.D. emblem replacing King's head; $4 As 1938 1s. but with W.F.D. emblem replacing King's head.

1981. Bob Marley (musician) Commemoration. Song Titles. Multicoloured.

529 1 c. Type **208** 50 40
530 2 c. "Exodus" 50 40
531 3 c. "Is this Love" 50 40
532 15 c. "Coming in from the Cold" 2·25 30
533 20 c. "Positive Vibration" 2·25 30
534 60 c. "War" 3·00 2·75
535 $3 "Could you be Loved" 5·50 10·00

No. 533 is incorrectly inscribed "OSITIVE VIBRATION".

209 Webb Memorial Baptist Church

1981. Christmas. Churches (2nd series). Multicoloured.

537 10 c. Type **209** 10 10
538 45 c. Church of God in Jamaica 30 15
539 $5 Bryce United Church 1·75 2·50

210 Gorgonian Coral **211** Cub Scout

1982. Marine Life (2nd series). Multicoloured.

541 20 c. Type **210** 45 10
542 45 c. Hard sponge and diver (horiz) 65 25
543 60 c. American manatee (horiz) 90 55
544 75 c. Plume worm (horiz) 1·00 65
545 $3 Coral banded shrimp (horiz) 2·50 1·75

1982. 75th Anniv of Boy Scout Movement. Mult.

546 20 c. Type **211** 50 15
547 45 c. Scout camp 85 40
548 60 c. "Out of Many, One People" 1·10 90
549 $2 Lord Baden-Powell 1·75 2·50

212 "Lignum vitae" (national flower) **213** Prey Captured

1982. 21st Birthday of Princess of Wales.

551 20 c. Type **212** 20 20
552 45 c. Carriage ride 35 35
553 60 c. Wedding 50 60
554 75 c. "Saxifraga longifolia" 1·00 1·75
555 $2 Princess of Wales 1·40 2·00
556 $3 "Viola gracilis major" 1·40 2·75

1982. Birth of Prince William of Wales. Nos. 551/6 optd **ROYAL BABY 21.6.82.**

558 20 c. Type **212** 20 20
559 45 c. Carriage ride 30 35
560 60 c. Wedding 40 60
561 75 c. "Saxifraga longifolia" 70 1·00
562 $2 Princess of Wales 75 1·50
563 $3 "Viola gracilis major" 1·00 2·50

1982. Jamaican Birds (1st series). Jamaican Lizard Cuckoo. Multicoloured.

565 $1 Type **213** 1·40 1·40
566 $1 Searching for prey 1·40 1·40
567 $1 Calling prior to prey search 1·40 1·40
568 $1 Adult landing 1·40 1·40
569 $1 Adult flying in 1·40 1·40

See also Nos. 642/5 and 707/10.

1982. Christmas. Churches (3rd series). As T **209**. Multicoloured.

570 20 c. United Pentecostal Church 40 10
571 45 c. Disciples of Christ Church 75 25
572 75 c. Open Bible Church 1·40 2·75

214 Queen Elizabeth II

1983. Royal Visit. Multicoloured.

573 $2 Type **214** 3·00 3·50
574 $3 Coat of arms 4·00 5·00

215 Folk Dancing

1983. Commonwealth Day. Multicoloured.

575 20 c. Type **215** 15 15
576 45 c. Bauxite mining 35 35
577 75 c. World map showing position of Jamaica 45 45
578 $2 Coat of arms and family 60 1·40

216 General Cargo Ship at Wharf

1983. 25th Anniv of International Maritime Organization. Multicoloured.

579 15 c. Type **216** 75 30
580 20 c. "Veendam" (cruise liner) at Kingston 1·00 40
581 45 c. "Astronomer" (container ship) entering port 1·75 85
582 $1 Tanker passing International Seabed Headquarters Building 2·75 3·75

217 Norman Manley and Sir Alexander Bustamante **218** Ship-to-Shore Radio

1983. 21st Anniv of Independence.

583 **217** 15 c. multicoloured 15 20
584 20 c. multicoloured 15 25
585 45 c. multicoloured 30 50

1983. World Communications Year. Multicoloured.

586 20 c. Type **218** 40 15
587 45 c. Postal services 75 40
588 75 c. Telephone communications 1·00 2·00
589 $1 T.V. via satellite 1·25 2·50

219 "Racing at Caymanas" (Sidney McLaren)

1983. Christmas. Paintings. Multicoloured.

590 15 c. Type **219** 15 10
591 20 c. "Seated Figures" (Karl Parboosingh) 15 10
592 75 c. "The Petitioner" (Henry Daley) (vert) 50 50
593 $2 "Banana Plantation" (John Dunkley) (vert) 1·25 2·25

220 Sir Alexander Bustamante

1984. Birth Centenary of Sir Alexander Bustamante. Multicoloured.

594 20 c. Type **220** 65 1·00
595 20 c. Birthplace, Blenheim 65 1·00

221 De Havilland Gipsy Moth Seaplane

1984. Seaplanes and Flying Boats. Multicoloured.

596 25 c. Type **221** 1·50 20
597 55 c. Consolidated Commodore flying boat 2·00 85
598 $1.50 Sikorsky S-38A flying boat 3·25 4·00
599 $3 Sikorsky S-40 flying boat "American Clipper" 4·00 6·00

222 Cycling

1984. Olympic Games, Los Angeles. Multicoloured.

600 25 c. Type **222** 75 30
601 55 c. Relay running 60 30
602 $1.50 Start of race 1·00 2·25
603 $3 Finish of race 1·40 3·25

1984. Nos. 465 and 469 surch.

605 5 c. on 6 c. Fern Gully, Ocho Rios 15 40
606 10 c. on 12 c. Yellow-billed amazon 85 60

224 Head of Jamaican Boa Snake

1984. Jamaican Boa Snake. Multicoloured.

607 25 c. Type **224** 3·50 40
608 55 c. Boa snake on branch over tree 4·50 80
609 70 c. Snake with young 5·50 3·00
610 $1 Snake on log 6·50 3·50

225 Locomotive "Enterprise" (1845)

1984. Railway Locomotives (1st series). Mult.

612 25 c. Type **225** 1·50 30
613 55 c. Tank locomotive (1880) 1·75 70
614 $1.50 Kitson-Meyer tank locomotive (1904) 2·50 3·00
615 $3 Super-heated locomotive No. 40 (1916) 3·75 5·50

See also Nos. 634/7.

226 "Accompong Madonna" (Namba Roy) **227** Brown Pelicans flying

1984. Christmas. Sculptures. Multicoloured.

616 20 c. Type **226** 30 10
617 25 c. "Head" (Alvin Marriott) 35 10
618 55 c. "Moon" (Edna Manley) 80 65
619 $1.50 "All Women are Five Women" (Mallica Reynolds (Kapo)) 1·90 3·75

1985. Birth Bicentenary of John J. Audubon (ornithologist). Brown Pelican. Multicoloured.

620 20 c. Type **227** 1·00 20
621 55 c. Diving for fish 1·50 40
622 $2 Young pelican taking food from adult 2·50 3·25
623 $5 "Brown Pelican" (John J. Audubon) 3·75 6·50

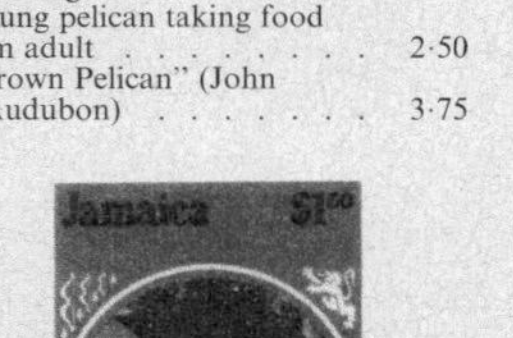

228 The Queen Mother at Belfast University

1985. Life and Times of Queen Elizabeth the Queen Mother. Multicoloured.

625 25 c. With photograph album, 1963 20 10
626 55 c. With Prince Charles at Garter Ceremony, Windsor Castle, 1983 25 15
627 $1.50 Type **228** 50 75
628 $3 With Prince Henry at his christening (from photo by Lord Snowdon) 85 1·75

229 Maps and Emblems

1985. International Youth Year and 5th Pan-American Scout Jamboree.

No.	Type	Description	Unused	Used
630	229	25 c. multicoloured	40	10
631		55 c. multicoloured	55	25
632		70 c. multicoloured	70	80
633		$4 multicoloured	2·50	4·50

1985. Railway Locomotives (2nd series). As T **225**. Multicoloured.

No.	Description	Unused	Used
634	25 c. Baldwin steam locomotive No. 16	1·25	30
635	55 c. Rogers locomotive	1·50	35
636	$1.50 Locomotive "Projector", 1845	2·25	2·50
637	$4 Diesel locomotive No. 102	3·50	5·00

230 "The Old Settlement" (Ralph Campbell)

1985. Christmas. Jamaican Paintings. Mult.

No.	Description	Unused	Used
638	20 c. Type **230**	10	10
639	55 c. "The Vendor" (Albert Huie) (vert)	15	15
640	75 c. "Road Menders" (Gaston Tabois)	20	35
641	$4 "Woman, must I not be about my Father's business?" (Carl Abrahams) (vert)	1·10	2·25

1986. Jamaican Birds (2nd series). As T **213**. Multicoloured.

No.	Description	Unused	Used
642	25 c. Chestnut-bellied cuckoo	50	10
643	55 c. Jamaican becard	65	30
644	$1.50 White-eyed thrush	85	1·75
645	$5 Rufous-tailed flycatcher	1·75	4·00

1986. 60th Birthday of Queen Elizabeth II. As T **120a** of Hong Kong. Multicoloured.

No.	Description	Unused	Used
646	20 c. Princess Elizabeth and Princess Margaret, 1939	15	10
647	25 c. With Prince Charles and Prince Andrew, 1962	15	10
648	70 c. Queen visiting War Memorial, Montego Bay, 1983	25	25
649	$3 On state visit to Luxembourg, 1976	50	90
650	$5 At Crown Agents Head Office, London, 1983	75	1·75

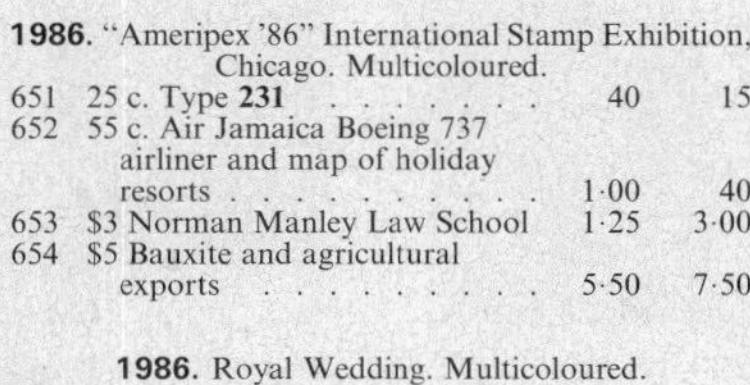

231 Bustamante Children's Hospital

231a Prince Andrew and Miss Sarah Ferguson, Ascot, 1985

1986. "Ameripex '86" International Stamp Exhibition, Chicago. Multicoloured.

No.	Description	Unused	Used
651	25 c. Type **231**	40	15
652	55 c. Air Jamaica Boeing 737 airliner and map of holiday resorts	1·00	40
653	$3 Norman Manley Law School	1·25	3·00
654	$5 Bauxite and agricultural exports	5·50	7·50

1986. Royal Wedding. Multicoloured.

No.	Description	Unused	Used
656	20 c. Type **231a**	15	10
657	$5 Prince Andrew making speech, Fredericton, Canada, 1985	1·00	1·90

232 Richard "Shrimpy" Clarke

1986. Jamaican Boxing Champions. Multicoloured.

No.	Description	Unused	Used
658	45 c. Type **232**	20	15
659	70 c. Michael McCallum	30	30
660	$2 Trevor Berbick	70	1·25
661	$4 Richard "Shrimpy" Clarke, Michael McCallum and Trevor Berbick	1·25	2·25

1986. Nos. 472/3 surch.

No.	Description	Unused	Used
662	5 c. on 50 c. Jamaican woodpecker	1·50	2·00
663	10 c. on 65 c. Rafting, Martha Brae Trelawny	1·00	1·40

234 "Heliconia wagneriana"

235 Crown Cone

1986. Christmas. Flowers (1st series). Mult.

No.	Description	Unused	Used
664	20 c. Type **234**	10	10
665	25 c. "Heliconia psittacorum" (horiz)	10	10
666	55 c. "Heliconia rostrata"	20	30
667	$5 "Strelitzia reginae" (horiz)	1·60	3·50

See also Nos. 703/6 and 739/42.

1987. Sea Shells. Multicoloured.

No.	Description	Unused	Used
668	35 c. Type **235**	45	15
669	75 c. Measled cowrie	65	60
670	$1 Atlantic trumpet triton	75	90
671	$5 Rooster-tail conch	1·50	3·50

236 Norman Manley

237 Arms of Jamaica

1987. Portraits.

No.	Type	Description	Unused	Used
672A	236	1 c. red and pink	10	30
673A		2 c. red and pink	10	30
674A		3 c. green and stone	10	30
675A		4 c. green & light green	10	30
676B		5 c. blue and grey	10	30
677A		6 c. blue and grey	20	30
678A		7 c. violet and mauve	20	30
679A		8 c. mauve and pink	20	10
680A		9 c. sepia and brown	20	10
681B	–	10 c. red and pink	10	10
682B	–	20 c. orange and flesh	20	10
683A	–	30 c. green & light green	40	10
684B	–	40 c. dp green & green	30	20
685B	–	50 c. green and grey	30	20
685cB	–	55 c. bistre and cream	30	10
686A	–	60 c. blue & light blue	30	20
687A	–	70 c. violet & light violet	30	20
688A	–	80 c. violet and lilac	30	30
689B	–	90 c. brown & lt brown	60	30
690A	237	$1 brown and cream	50	30
690cB		$1.10 brown and cream	40	30
691aB		$2 orange and cream	40	50
692A		$5 green and stone	60	85
693A		$10 blue and azure	70	1·25
693cB		$25 violet and lilac	90	1·40
693dB		$50 mauve and lilac	1·75	2·50

DESIGN: 10 c. to 90 c. Sir Alexander Bustamante.

The 5, 20, 40, 50, 90 c. and $1 exist with or without imprint date at foot.

238 Jamaican Flag and Coast at Sunset

239 Marcus Garvey

1987. 25th Anniv of Independence. Multicoloured.

No.	Description	Unused	Used
694	55 c. Type **238**	75	60
695	70 c. Jamaican flag and inscription (horiz)	1·00	2·00

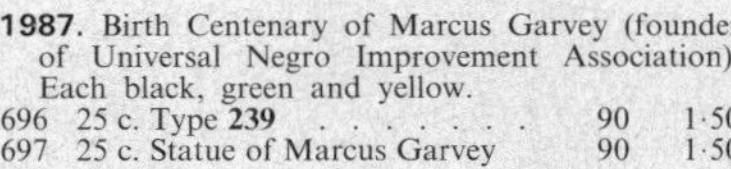

1987. Birth Centenary of Marcus Garvey (founder of Universal Negro Improvement Association). Each black, green and yellow.

No.	Description	Unused	Used
696	25 c. Type **239**	90	1·50
697	25 c. Statue of Marcus Garvey	90	1·50

240 Salvation Army School for the Blind

1987. Cent of Salvation Army in Jamaica. Mult.

No.	Description	Unused	Used
698	25 c. Type **240**	1·25	30
699	55 c. Col. Mary Booth and Bramwell Booth Memorial Hall	1·25	30
700	$3 Welfare Service lorry, 1929	3·25	4·25
701	$5 Col. Abram Davey and S.S. "Alene", 1887	4·25	6·00

1987. Christmas. Flowers (2nd series). As T **234**. Multicoloured.

No.	Description	Unused	Used
703	20 c. Hibiscus hybrid	15	10
704	25 c. "Hibiscus elatus"	15	10
705	$4 "Hibiscus cannabinus"	2·00	3·00
706	$5 "Hibiscus rosasinensis"	2·25	3·00

1988. Jamaican Birds (3rd series). As T **213**. Multicoloured.

No.	Description	Unused	Used
707	45 c. Chestnut-bellied cuckoo, black-billed amazon and Jamaican euphonia	1·75	2·25
708	45 c. Black-billed amazon, jamaican white-eyed vireo, rufous-throated solitaire and yellow elaenia	1·75	2·25
709	$5 Snowy plover, little blue heron and great blue heron (white phase)	4·25	4·75
710	$5 Black-necked stilt, snowy egret, snowy plover and black-crowned night heron	4·25	4·75

The two designs of each value were printed together, se-tenant, each pair forming a composite design.

243 Blue Whales

1988. Marine Mammals. Multicoloured.

No.	Description	Unused	Used
711	20 c. Type **243**	2·00	70
712	25 c. Gervais's whales	2·00	70
713	55 c. Killer whales	3·00	80
714	$5 Common dolphins	5·00	7·50

243a Jackie Hendriks

1988. West Indian Cricket. Each showing portrait, cricket equipment and early belt buckle. Multicoloured.

No.	Description	Unused	Used
715	25 c. Type **243a**	1·50	40
716	55 c. George Headley	1·60	40
717	$2 Michael Holding	3·25	2·75
718	$3 R. K. Nunes	3·50	4·25
719	$4 Allan Rae	3·75	4·50

244 Jamaican Red Cross Workers with Ambulance

1988. 125th Anniv of Int Red Cross. Mult.

No.	Description	Unused	Used
720	55 c. Type **244**	50	30
721	$5 Henri Dunant (founder) in field hospital	2·00	3·25

245 Boxing

1988. Olympic Games, Seoul. Multicoloured.

No.	Description	Unused	Used
722	25 c. Type **245**	15	10
723	45 c. Cycling	55	30
724	$4 Athletics	1·25	2·00
725	$5 Hurdling	1·25	2·00

246 Bobsled Team Members and Logo

1988. Jamaican Olympic Bobsled Team. Mult.

No.	Description	Unused	Used
727	25 c. Type **246**	50	75
728	25 c. Two-man bobsled	50	75
729	$5 Bobsled team members (different) and logo	1·40	2·25
730	$5 Four-man bobsled	1·40	2·25

1988. Hurricane Gilbert Relief Fund. Nos. 722/5 surch + **25c HURRICANE GILBERT RELIEF FUND**.

No.	Description	Unused	Used
731	25 c. + 25 c. Type **245**	10	15
732	45 c. + 45 c. Cycling	20	25
733	$4 + $4 Athletics	1·10	1·90
734	$5 + $5 Hurdling	1·10	2·25

248 Nurses and Firemen

1988. Year of the Worker. Multicoloured.

No.	Description	Unused	Used
735	25 c. Type **248**	45	20
736	55 c. Woodcarver	45	30
737	$3 Textile workers	1·00	2·50
738	$5 Workers on fish farm	1·25	3·00

1988. Christmas. Flowers (3rd series). As T **234**. Multicoloured.

No.	Description	Unused	Used
739	25 c. "Euphorbia pulcherrima"	50	10
740	55 c. "Spathodea campanulata" (horiz)	60	15
741	$3 "Hylocereus triangularis"	1·10	1·60
742	$4 "Broughtonia sanguinea" (horiz)	1·10	1·75

249 Old York Castle School

1989. Bicent of Methodist Church in Jamaica.

No.	Type	Description	Unused	Used
743	249	25 c. black and blue	20	10
744	–	45 c. black and red	25	10
745	–	$5 black and green	2·50	3·50

DESIGNS: 45 c. Revd. Thomas Coke and Parade Chapel, Kingston; $5 Father Hugh Sherlock and St. John's Church.

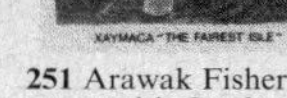

250 "Syntomidopsis variegata"

251 Arawak Fisherman with Catch

1989. Jamaican Moths (1st series). Multicoloured.

No.	Description	Unused	Used
746	25 c. Type **250**	50	10
747	55 c. "Himantoides perkinsae"	80	30
748	$3 "Arctia nigriplaga"	1·50	2·75
749	$5 "Sthenognatha toddi"	1·90	3·50

See also Nos. 758/61 and 790/3.

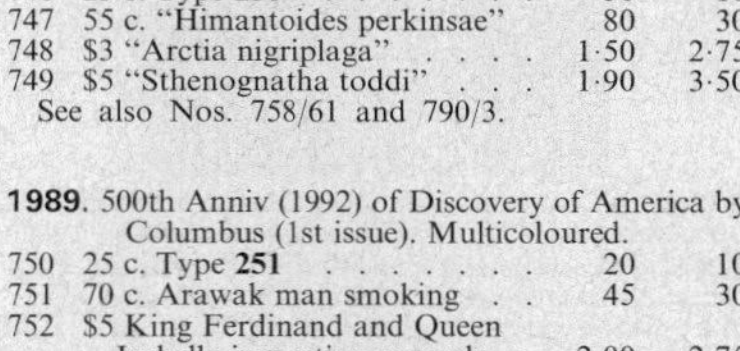

1989. 500th Anniv (1992) of Discovery of America by Columbus (1st issue). Multicoloured.

No.	Description	Unused	Used
750	25 c. Type **251**	20	10
751	70 c. Arawak man smoking	45	30
752	$5 King Ferdinand and Queen Isabella inspecting caravels	2·00	2·75
753	$10 Columbus with chart	3·75	5·50

See also Nos. 774/7 and 802/7.

252 Girl Guide

1990. 75th Anniv of Girl Guide Movement in Jamaica. Multicoloured.

No.	Description	Unused	Used
755	45 c. Type **252**	75	30
756	55 c. Guide leader	85	30
757	$5 Brownie, guide and ranger	4·00	6·00

1990. Jamaican Moths (2nd series). As T **250**. Multicoloured.

No.	Description	Unused	Used
758	25 c. "Eunomia rubripunctata"	85	35
759	55 c. "Perigonia jamaicensis"	1·25	35
760	$4 "Uraga haemorrhoa"	2·50	3·75
761	$5 "Empyreuma pugione"	2·50	3·75

1990. "EXPO '90" International Garden and Greenery Exhibition, Osaka. Nos. 758/61 optd **EXPO '90** and logo.

No.	Description	Unused	Used
762	25 c. "Eunomia rubripunctata"	85	35
763	55 c. "Perigonia jamaicensis"	1·25	35
764	$4 "Uraga haemorrhoa"	2·50	3·75
765	$5 "Empyreuma pugione"	2·50	3·75

254 Teaching English

1990. International Literacy Year. Mult.

766	55 c. Type **254**	40	25
767	$5 Teaching maths	3·00	4·00

255 "To the Market"

1990. Christmas. Children's Paintings. Mult.

768	20 c. Type **255**	35	10
769	25 c. "House and Garden"	35	10
770	55 c. "Jack and Jill"	50	15
771	70 c. "Market"	65	40
772	$1.50 "Lonely"	1·50	2·25
773	$5 "Market Woman" (vert)	3·00	4·50

256 Map of First Voyage, 1492

1990. 500th Anniv (1992) of Discovery of America by Columbus (2nd issue). Multicoloured.

774	25 c. Type **256**	60	20
775	45 c. Map of second voyage, 1493	75	20
776	$5 Map of third voyage, 1498	3·00	3·75
777	$10 Map of fourth voyage, 1502	4·25	5·50

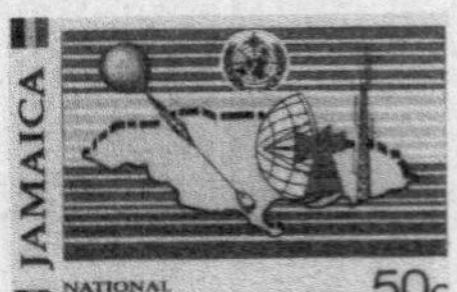

257 Weather Balloon, Dish Aerial and Map of Jamaica

1991. 11th World Meteorological Congress, Kingston.

780	**257**	50 c. multicoloured	50	20
781		$10 multicoloured	5·50	7·00

258 Bust of Mary Seacole

1991. International Council of Nurses Meeting of National Representatives. Multicoloured.

782	50 c. Type **258**	50	30
783	$1.10 Mary Seacole House	1·25	1·75

259 Jamaican Iguana

1991. 50th Anniv of Natural History Society of Jamaica. Jamaican Iguana. Multicoloured.

785	$1.10 Type **259**	55	70
786	$1.10 Head of iguana looking right	55	70
787	$1.10 Iguana climbing	55	70
788	$1.10 Iguana on rock looking left	55	70
789	$1.10 Close-up of iguana's head	55	70

1991. Jamaican Moths (3rd series). As T **250**. Multicoloured.

790	50 c. "Urania sloanus"	65	20
791	$1.10 "Phoenicoprocta jamaicensis"	90	60
792	$1.40 "Horama grotei"	1·10	90
793	$8 "Amplypterus gannascus"	3·25	6·00

1991. "Phila Nippon '91" International Stamp Exhibition, Tokyo. Nos. 790/3 optd **PHILA NIPPON 91** and emblem.

794	50 c. "Urania sloanus"	65	20
795	$1.10 "Phoenicoprocta jamaicensis"	90	60
796	$1.40 "Horama grotei"	1·10	90
797	$8 "Amplypterus gannascus"	3·25	6·00

261 "Doctor Bird"

1991. Christmas. Children's Paintings. Mult.

798	50 c. Type **261**	40	10
799	$1.10 "Road scene"	80	25
800	$5 "Children and house"	2·00	2·50
801	$10 "Cows grazing"	3·25	5·00

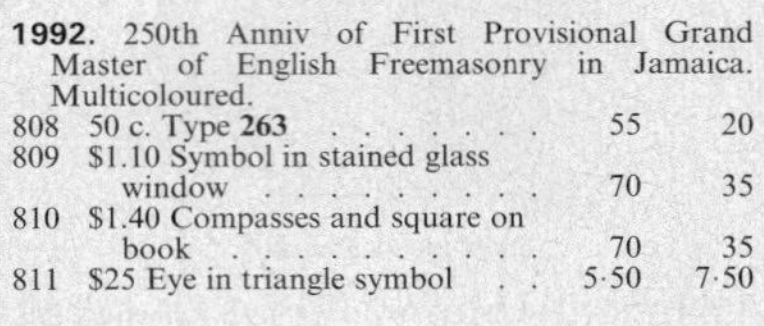

262 Indians threatening Ships

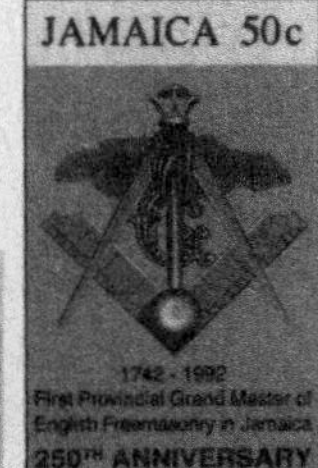

263 Compasses and Square Symbol

1991. 500th Anniv (1992) of Discovery of America by Columbus (3rd issue). Multicoloured.

802	50 c. Type **262**	45	15
803	$1.10 Spaniards setting dog on Indians	55	30
804	$1.40 Indian with gift of pineapple	55	30
805	$25 Columbus describes Jamaica with crumpled paper	5·50	7·50

1992. 250th Anniv of First Provisional Grand Master of English Freemasonry in Jamaica. Multicoloured.

808	50 c. Type **263**	55	20
809	$1.10 Symbol in stained glass window	70	35
810	$1.40 Compasses and square on book	70	35
811	$25 Eye in triangle symbol	5·50	7·50

264 Ship in Flooded Street

1992. 300th Anniv of Destruction of Port Royal. Multicoloured.

813	50 c. Type **264**	45	30
814	$1.10 Church tower falling	60	40
815	$1.40 Houses collapsing	60	40
816	$25 Inhabitants falling into fissure	3·75	5·50

265 Credit Union Symbol

1992. 50th Anniv of Credit Union Movement.

818	**265**	50 c. blue, emerald. & grn	75	40
819	–	$1.40 multicoloured	1·40	1·75

DESIGN: $1.40, O'Hare Hall.

266 Jamaican Flag and Beach Scene

1992. 30th Anniv of Independence.

820	**266**	50 c. multicoloured	10	10
821		$1.10 multicoloured	20	20
822		$25 multicoloured	2·75	4·50

MINIMUM PRICE

The minimum price quoted is 10p which represents a handling charge rather than a basis for valuing common stamps. For further notes about prices see introductory pages.

267 "Rainbow" (Cecil Baugh)

269 Cadet, Armoured Car and Emblem

268 Girls' Brigade Parade

1993. Art Ceramics and Pottery. Multicoloured.

823	50 c. Type **267**	10	10
824	$1.10 "Yabba Pot" (Louisa Jones)	20	20
825	$1.40 "Sculptured Vase" (Gene Pearson)	20	20
826	$25 "Lidded Form" (Norma Harrack)	3·50	4·50

1993. Centenary of Girls' Brigade. Mult.

827	50 c. Type **268**	60	40
828	$1.10 Brigade members	65	70

1993. 50th Anniv of Jamaica Combined Cadet Force. Multicoloured.

829	50 c. Type **269**	25	20
830	$1.10 Cadet and Britten Norman Islander aircraft (horiz)	40	30
831	$1.40 Cadet and patrol boats	40	30
832	$3 Cadet and emblem (horiz)	60	1·40

270 Constant Spring Golf Course

1993. Golf Courses. Multicoloured.

833	50 c. Type **270**	20	10
834	$1.10 Type **270**	20	10
835	$1.40 Half Moon	25	15
836	$2 As $1.40	30	35
837	$3 Jamaica Jamaica	35	45
838	$10 As $3	90	1·75

271 Norman Manley

273 Flags of Great Britain and Jamaica

1994. Birth Centenary of Norman Manley.

840	**271**	$25 multicoloured	2·00	2·75
841		$50 multicoloured	2·50	3·25

1994. Royal Visit. Multicoloured.

843	$1.10 Type **273**	20	10
844	$1.40 Royal Yacht "Britannia"	50	20
845	$25 Queen Elizabeth II	1·50	2·50
846	$50 Queen Elizabeth and Prince Philip	2·50	3·50

274 Douglas DC-9

1994. 25th Anniv of Air Jamaica. Mult.

847	50 c. Type **274**	25	20
848	$1.10 Douglas DC-8	25	20
849	$5 Boeing 727	50	65
850	$50 Airbus A300	3·25	5·00

275 Giant Swallowtail

1994. Giant Swallowtail Butterfly Conservation. Multicoloured.

851	50 c. Type **275**	25	20
852	$1.10 With wings closed	35	20
853	$10 On flower	1·25	2·00
854	$25 With wings spread	2·50	3·75

276 "Royal Botanical Gardens" (Sidney McLaren)

1994. Tourism. Multicoloured.

856	50 c. Type **276**	30	20
857	$1.10 Blue Mountains	45	30
858	$5 Tourist in hammock and water sports	1·50	2·00

277 Jamaican Red Poll Calf

1994. Jamaican Red Poll Cattle. Multicoloured.

860	50 c. Type **277**	10	10
861	$1.10 Red Poll heifer	10	10
862	$25 Red Poll cow	1·25	2·25
863	$50 Red Poll bull	2·50	3·75

278 Refuse Collectors

1994. Christmas. Children's Paintings. Multicoloured.

864	50 c. Type **278**	10	10
865	90 c. Hospital ward	10	10
866	$1.10 House	10	10
867	$50 Landscape	2·75	4·00

279 Jamaican Band-tailed Pigeon ("Ring-tailed Pigeon")

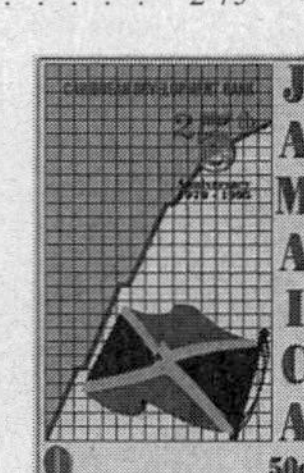

280 Graph, National Flag and Logo

1995. Jamaican Wild Birds. Multicoloured.

868	50 c. Type **279**	40	20
869	90 c. Yellow-billed amazon ("Yellow-billed parrot")	50	30
870	$1.10 Black-billed amazon ("Black-billed parrot")	50	30
871	$50 Jamaican owl ("Brown owl")	4·00	5·00

1995. 25th Anniv of Caribbean Development Bank.

873	**280**	50 c. green, black and yellow	10	10
874		$1 green, black and yellow	10	10
875	–	$1.10 multicoloured	10	10
876	–	$50 multicoloured	2·75	4·00

DESIGNS—HORIZ: $1.10, Industry, agriculture and commerce; $50 Jamaican currency.

281 "Song of Freedom"

1995. 50th Birth Anniv of Bob Marley (reggae singer). Record covers. Multicoloured.

877	50 c. Type **281**	15	10
878	$1.10 "Fire"	20	15
879	$1.40 "Time will Tell"	20	15
880	$3 "Natural Mystic"	35	40
881	$10 "Live at Lyceum"	1·10	1·75

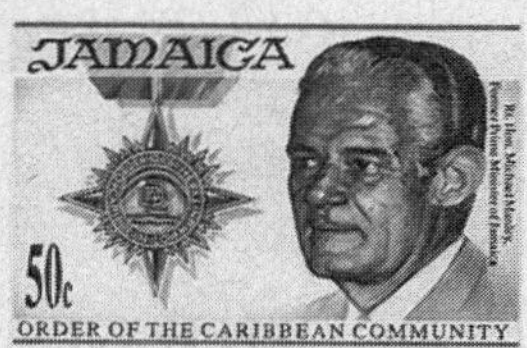

283 Michael Manley

1995. Recipients of the Order of the Caribbean Community. Multicoloured.

884	50 c. Type **283**	10	10
885	$1.10 Sir Alister McIntyre	10	10
886	$1.40 Justice P. Telford Georges	10	10
887	$50 Dame Nita Barrow	2·75	4·00

284 Dish Aerial and Landrover, Balkans

1995. 50th Anniv of United Nations. Multicoloured.

889	50 c. Type **284**	15	10
890	$1.10 Antonov An-32 aircraft, Balkans	25	15
891	$3 Bedford articulated road tanker, Balkans	40	50
892	$5 Fairchild C-119 Flying Boxcar, Korea	55	75

285 Landing of Indian Immigrants

1996. 150th Anniv of Indian Immigration to Jamaica. Multicoloured.

894	$2.50 Type **285**	20	10
895	$10 Indian musicians and traditional dancers	60	80

286 Jamaican Flag and U.N.I.C.E.F. Emblem

1996. 50th Anniv of U.N.I.C.E.F.

896	**286**	$2.50 multicoloured	15	10
897		$8 multicoloured	45	70
898		$10 multicoloured	50	75

287 Brown's Hutia

1996. Endangered Species. Brown's Hutia ("Jamaican Hutia"). Multicoloured.

899	$2.50 Type **287**	15	10
900	$10 Hutia on rock	50	65
901	$12.50 Female with young	60	80
902	$25 Head of hutia	1·25	1·75

288 High Altar, Church of St. Thomas the Apostle

1997. 300th Anniv of Kingston Parish Church. Multicoloured.

903	$2 Type **288**	15	10
904	$8 Church of St. Thomas the Apostle	60	60
905	$12.50 "The Angel" (wood carving by Edna Manley) (vert)	90	1·25

No. 903 is inscribed "ALTER" in error.

289 Child's Face and U.N.E.S.C.O. Emblem

1998. 10th Anniv of Chernobyl Nuclear Disaster.

907	**289**	$55 multicoloured	1·75	2·25

290 "Coelia triptera"

291 Diana, Princess of Wales

1997. Orchids. Multicoloured.

908A	$1 Type **290**	10	10
909A	$2 "Oncidium pulchellum" (horiz)	10	10
910A	$2.50 "Oncidium triquetium"	10	10
911A	$3 "Broughtonia negrilensis"	10	10
912A	$4.50 "Oncidium gauntlettii" (horiz)	10	15
913A	$5 "Encyclia fragans" (horiz)	15	20
914A	$8 "Broughtonia sanguinea" (horiz)	25	30
915A	$12 "Phaius tankervilleae"	35	40
916B	$25 "Cochleanthes flabelliformis" (horiz)	75	80
917A	$50 "Broughtonia sanguinea" (three varieties) (horiz)	1·50	1·60

1998. Diana, Princess of Wales Commemoration.

918	**291**	$20 multicoloured	85	90

292 University Chapel, Mona

1998. 50th Anniv of University of West Indies. Multicoloured.

920	$8 Type **292**	40	40
921	$10 Philip Sherlock Centre for Creative Arts, Mona	40	40
922	$50 University arms (vert)	2·25	2·75

293 Flags of Jamaica and CARICOM

1998. 25th Anniv of Caribbean Community.

923	**293**	$30 multicoloured	1·40	1·40

294 Jamaican Footballer

295 Coral Reef

1998. World Cup Football Championship, France. Multicoloured.

924	$10 Type **294**	45	40
925	$25 Jamaican team (horiz)	1·10	1·25
926	$100 As $25	4·00	5·00

1998. Christmas. International Year of the Ocean. Multicoloured.

927	$10 Type **295**	45	40
928	$30 Fishing boats, Negril	1·25	1·25
929	$50 Black spiny sea urchin	2·00	2·25
930	$100 Composite design as Nos. 927/9 (22 × 41 mm)	4·00	4·50

296 Michael Collins (astronaut)

1999. 30th Anniv of First Manned Landing on Moon. Multicoloured.

931	$7 Type **296**	30	25
932	$10 Service module docking with lunar module	40	40
933	$25 Buzz Aldrin on Moon's surface	90	95
934	$30 Command module in Earth orbit	1·00	1·10

297 Lesley Ann Masterton and Fong-Yee (polo)

1999. Jamaican Sporting Personalities. Mult.

936	$5 Type **297**	25	20
937	$10 Lawrence Rowe, Collie Smith and Alfred Valentine (cricket)	40	40
938	$20 Vivalyn Latty-Scott (women's cricket) (vert)	75	80
939	$25 Lindy Delapenha (football) (vert)	80	95
940	$30 Joy Grant-Charles (netball) (vert)	90	95
941	$50 Percy Hayles, Gerald Gray and Bunny Grant (boxing)	1·50	1·75

298 "Spey" (mail ship), 1891

1999. 125th Anniv of Universal Postal Union. Multicoloured.

943	$7 Type **298**	30	25
944	$10 "Jamaica Planter" (mail ship), 1936	40	40
945	$25 Lockheed Constellation (aircraft), 1950	90	95
946	$30 Airbus A-310 (aircraft), 1999	1·00	1·10

299 Airbus A-310

1999. 30th Anniv of Air Jamaica. Multicoloured.

947	$10 Type **299**	40	40
948	$25 A-320	90	95
949	$30 A-340	1·00	1·10

300 Shih Tzu

1999. Dogs. Multicoloured.

950	$7 Type **300**	35	25
951	$10 German shepherd	45	40
952	$30 Doberman pinscher	1·10	1·40

301 Nelson Mandela Park

1999. Parks and Gardens. Multicoloured.

953	$7 Type **301**	20	25
954	$10 St. William Grant Park	30	35
955	$25 Seaview Park	75	80
956	$30 Holruth Park	90	95

302 "The Prophet" (sculpture)

2000. Birth Centenary of Edna Manley (artist). Multicoloured.

957	$10 Type **302**	30	35
958	$25 "Horse of the Morning"	75	80
959	$30 "The Angel"	90	95
960	$100 Edna Manley	3·00	3·25

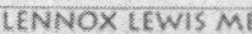

303 Lennox Lewis

2000. Lennox Lewis, World Heavyweight Boxing Champion. Multicoloured.

962	$10 Holding W.B.C. Championship belt	30	35
963	$10 In ring with right arm raised	30	35
964	$10 Holding W.B.C. belt above head	30	35
965	$25 Taking punch on chin	75	80
966	$25 Type **303**	75	80
967	$25 In corner	75	80
968	$30 With W.B.C. belt after fight	90	95
969	$30 Holding all four belts	90	95
970	$30 With belts in front of sky-scraper	90	95

OFFICIAL STAMPS

1890. Optd **OFFICIAL**.

O3	**8**	½d. green	6·50	40
O4	**11**	1d. red	4·00	80
O5		2d. grey	7·50	1·00

JAMMU AND KASHMIR — Pt. 1

A state in the extreme N. of India.

12 pies = 1 anna; 16 annas = 1 rupee

1

Gum. The stamps of Jammu and Kashmir were issued without gum.

1866. Imperf.

41	1	$\frac{1}{2}$ a. black	19·00	42·00
26		$\frac{1}{2}$ a. red	24·00	42·00
44		$\frac{1}{2}$ a. blue	32·00	£200
20		$\frac{1}{2}$ a. green	70·00	£180
48		$\frac{1}{2}$ a. yellow	£100	
15		1 a. black	£200	
27		1 a. red	28·00	£150
34		1 a. blue	20·00	£200
21		1 a. green	75·00	£180
24		1 a. yellow	£600	
16		4 a. black	£200	
10		4 a. red	50·00	90·00
19		4 a. blue	£140	
37		4 a. green	£110	
25		4 a. yellow	£350	

Prices for the circular stamps (Nos. 5/48) are for cut-square examples. Cut-to-shape examples are worth from 10% to 20% of these prices, according to condition.

$\frac{1}{2}$ a. $\frac{1}{2}$ a

1 a. **4** $\frac{1}{2}$ a

1867.

69a	4	$\frac{1}{2}$ a. black	£100	£130
58		$\frac{1}{2}$ a. blue	£140	75·00
60		$\frac{1}{2}$ a. red	4·75	2·50
64		$\frac{1}{2}$ a. orange	85·00	90·00
68		$\frac{1}{2}$ a. green	£1300	£800
69b		1 a. black	£1200	£1000
55		1 a. blue	£500	£275
61		1 a. red	11·00	8·00
65		1 a. orange	£1500	£950
69		1 a. green	£2250	£1400

The characters denoting the value are in the upper part of the inner circle.

8 ($\frac{1}{4}$ a.) **12** ($\frac{1}{4}$ a.)

1867. Imperf.

90	8	$\frac{1}{4}$ a. black	2·00	2·25
91		$\frac{1}{2}$ a. blue	2·00	1·00
93		1 a. blue	£2750	£1200
94		1 a. orange	7·50	8·00
97		2 a. yellow	10·00	12·00
99		4 a. green	26·00	26·00
101		8 a. red	28·00	26·00

1878. Imperf or perf.

139	12	$\frac{1}{8}$ a. yellow	70	1·00
125		$\frac{1}{4}$ a. red	2·50	2·75
131		$\frac{1}{4}$ a. orange	8·00	9·50
130a		$\frac{1}{4}$ a. blue	£750	£450
142		$\frac{1}{4}$ a. brown	55	45
105		$\frac{1}{2}$ a. violet	13·00	12·00
126		$\frac{1}{2}$ a. red	50	55
132		$\frac{1}{2}$ a. orange	18·00	12·00
143		$\frac{1}{2}$ a. blue	4·25	
127		1 a. red	2·00	2·50
106		1 a. mauve	19·00	20·00
133		1 a. orange	17·00	9·00
148		1 a. grey	65	50
150		1 a. green	65	50
108		2 a. violet	20·00	20·00
110		2 a. blue	38·00	38·00
128		2 a. red	2·75	3·50
134		2 a. orange	14·00	9·00
152		2 a. red on yellow	1·25	90
153		2 a. red on green	2·00	2·50
129		4 a. red	6·50	6·50
135		4 a. orange	26·00	40·00
155		4 a. green	2·50	3·25
130		8 a. red	6·50	7·50
136		8 a. orange	50·00	60·00
159		8 a. blue	5·00	7·00
161a		8 a. lilac	10·00	15·00

OFFICIAL STAMPS

1878. Imperf or perf.

O 6	12	$\frac{1}{4}$ a. black	65	70
O 7		$\frac{1}{2}$ a. black	15	30
O 8		1 a. black	20	45
O 9		2 a. black	30	40
O10		4 a. black	35	70
O11		8 a. black	1·00	1·00

JAPAN — Pt. 18

An empire of E. Asia, consisting of numerous islands.

1871. 100 mon = 1 sen.
1872. 10 rin = 1 sen; 100 sen = 1 yen.

1 (48 mon)

1871. Imperf.

1	1	48 m. brown	£180	£225
3		100 m. blue	£200	£180
5		200 m. red	£350	£225
15b		500 m. green	£400	£400

1872. Perf.

17	1	$\frac{1}{2}$ s. brown	80·00	£125
19		1 s. blue	£170	£160
21		2 s. red	£350	£275
22		5 s. green	£375	£425

5 **12** **13** Bean Goose

1872. Various sizes. Design details differ.

34	5	$\frac{1}{2}$ s. brown	18·00	24·00
66		$\frac{1}{2}$ s. grey	16·00	15·00
35		1 s. blue	70·00	28·00
67		1 s. brown	30·00	13·00
36		2 s. red	£110	30·00
74		2 s. yellow	70·00	12·00
46		4 s. red	£100	30·00
68		4 s. green	£110	18·00
75	12	5 s. green	£200	85·00
57		6 s. brown	£110	40·00
69		6 s. orange	75·00	15·00
58	5	10 s. green	£110	45·00
70		10 s. blue	£125	17·00
59		20 s. violet	£200	70·00
71		20 s. red	£100	12·00
60		30 s. black	£250	70·00
72		30 s. violet	£125	35·00

1875.

61	13	12 s. red	£400	£190
62	–	15 s. lilac (Pied Wagtail)	£325	£160
63	–	45 s. red (Northern Goshawk)	£500	£250

20 **21** **22**

23 **24**

1876.

116	20	5 r. grey	3·50	30
77		1 s. black	25·00	3·00
78		1 s. brown	12·00	1·00
113		1 s. green	5·50	25
79		2 s. grey	50·00	2·00
102		2 s. violet	24·00	1·50
114		2 s. red	7·50	10
95		3 s. orange	50·00	24·00
117		3 s. red	12·00	25
82a		4 s. blue	32·00	2·75
103		4 s. green	40·00	1·75
118		4 s. bistre	8·50	30
83	21	5 s. brown	50·00	18·00
115		5 s. blue	14·00	15
104		6 s. orange	£150	70·00
105		8 s. brown	45·00	2·75
119		8 s. violet	15·00	90
86		10 s. blue	40·00	1·50
120		10 s. brown	16·00	30
87		12 s. red	£200	£160
88	22	15 s. green	£125	6·50
121		15 s. violet	45·00	40
89		20 s. blue	£150	12·00
122		20 s. orange	55·00	1·40
123	23	25 s. green	90·00	1·25
90	22	30 s. mauve	£200	75·00
111		45 s. red	£500	£500
112		50 s. red	£160	10·00
124		50 s. brown	85·00	3·00
125	24	1 y. red	£120	2·50

25 Imperial Crest and Cranes

1894. Emperor's Silver Wedding.

126	25	2 s. red	20·00	30
127		5 s. blue	25·00	4·00

26 Prince Kitashirakawa **27** Prince Arisugawa

1896. China War.

128	26	2 s. red	14·00	75
129	27	2 s. red	14·00	75
130	26	5 s. blue	35·00	2·00
131	27	5 s. blue	35·00	2·00

Both 2 s. have an oval medallion, and both 5 s. a circular one.

28 **29** **30**

31 **32** Empress Jingu

1899.

132	28	5 r. grey	5·50	1·00
133		$\frac{1}{2}$ s. grey	3·50	10
134		1 s. brown	4·50	10
135		$1\frac{1}{2}$ s. blue	15·00	85
136		$1\frac{1}{2}$ s. violet	8·00	15
137		2 s. green	6·00	10
138		3 s. purple	6·50	10
139		3 s. red	6·00	10
140		4 s. red	6·00	1·00
141		5 s. yellow	14·00	10
142	29	6 s. red	30·00	3·00
143		8 s. olive	35·00	4·00
144		10 s. blue	10·00	15
145		15 s. violet	40·00	1·00
146		20 s. orange	32·00	10
147	30	25 s. green	70·00	75
148		50 s. brown	65·00	80
149	31	1 y. red	80·00	1·00
183	32	5 y. green	£475	4·50
184		10 y. violet	£650	6·50

33 Rice Cakes used at Japanese Weddings

1900. Prince Imperial Wedding.

152	33	3 s. red	25·00	30

34 Symbols of Korea and Japan **35** Gun and Japanese Flag

1905. Amalgamation of Japanese and Korean Postal Services.

153	34	3 s. red	90·00	20·00

1906. Triumphal Military Review of Russo-Japanese War.

154	35	$1\frac{1}{2}$ s. blue	40·00	3·50
155		3 s. red	70·00	14·00

36 **37** **38**

1914.

167	36	$\frac{1}{2}$ s. brown	2·25	10
168		1 s. orange	3·25	10
232		$1\frac{1}{2}$ s. blue	3·00	10
170		2 s. green	5·50	10
298		3 s. red	1·50	20
172	37	4 s. red	16·00	1·50
300		5 s. violet	7·50	10
174		6 s. brown	24·00	4·00
302		7 s. orange	12·00	15
175		8 s. grey	18·00	15·00
176		10 s. blue	12·00	10
236		13 s. brown	10·00	10
178		20 s. red	60·00	15
179		25 s. olive	18·00	50
180	38	30 s. brown	22·00	45
238		30 s. orange and green	25·00	25
181		50 s. brown	30·00	25
239		50 s. brown and blue	15·00	30
309		1 y. green and brown	80·00	75

40 Ceremonial Cap **42** Hall of Ceremony

1915. Emperor's Coronation.

185	40	$1\frac{1}{2}$ s. grey and red	3·00	50
186	–	3 s. violet and brown	3·50	65
187	42	4 s. red	16·00	7·50
188		10 s. blue	38·00	15·00

DESIGN—As T **40**: 3 s. Imperial throne.

43 Mandarin Duck **44** "Kammuri" (ceremonial headband)

1916. Investiture of Prince Hirohito as Heir Apparent.

189	43	$1\frac{1}{2}$ s. green, red and yellow	4·00	85
190		3 s. red and yellow	5·00	1·00
191	44	10 s. blue	£800	£300

45 Dove of Peace **46** Dove of Peace

1919. Restoration of Peace.

192	45	$1\frac{1}{2}$ s. brown	2·50	1·00
193	46	3 s. green	3·50	1·25
194	45	4 s. red	7·00	3·50
195	46	10 s. blue	22·00	8·00

1919. Air. 1st Tokyo–Osaka Airmail Service. Optd with airplane.

196	36	$1\frac{1}{2}$ s. blue	£275	£100
197		3 s. red	£425	£250

48 7th Century Censor **49** Meiji Shrine

1920. First Census.

198	48	$1\frac{1}{2}$ s. purple	8·00	4·25
199		3 s. red	9·00	4·25

1920. Dedication of Meiji (Emperor Mutsuhito) Shrine.

200	49	$1\frac{1}{2}$ s. violet	3·00	1·50
201		3s. red	3·00	1·50

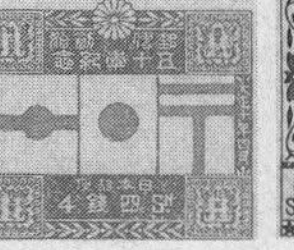

50 Postal and National Flags **51** Dept. of Communications, Tokyo

1921. 50th Anniv of Japanese Post.

202	50	1½ s. red and green	3·00	1·50
203	51	3 s. brown	3·50	1·75
204	50	4 s. red and pink	50·00	25·00
205	51	10 s. blue	£250	90·00

52 Warships "Katori" and "Kashima"

53 Mt. Fuji and Sika Deer

1921. Return of Crown Prince from European Tour.

206	52	1½ s. violet	3·00	2·10
207		3 s. olive	3·50	2·25
208		4 s. red	42·00	35·00
209		10 s. blue	60·00	35·00

1922.

293	53	4 s. green	3·25	20
266		4 s. orange	12·00	30
211		8 s. red	20·00	8·00
267		8 s. green	20·00	15
303		8 s. bistre	14·00	75
305		20 s. blue	16·00	60
268		20 s. purple	65·00	30

54 Mt. Niitaka

55

56

58 Empress Jingu

1923. Crown Prince's visit to Taiwan.

213	54	1½ s. yellow	20·00	18·00
214		3 s. violet	25·00	8·00

1923. Imperf.

215	55	½ s. grey	3·00	2·75
216		1½ s. blue	5·00	60
217		2 s. brown	5·00	60
218		3 s. red	2·50	50
219		4 s. green	30·00	15·00
220		5 s. violet	14·00	60
221		8 s. red	45·00	35·00
222	56	10 s. brown	24·00	50
223		20 s. blue	30·00	1·00

1924.

224	58	5 y. green	£225	3·50
225		10 y. violet	£425	2·75

59 Cranes

60 Phoenix

1925. Imperial Silver Wedding.

226	59	1½ s. purple	2·25	1·40
227a	60	3 s. brown and silver	3·00	3·00
228	59	8 s. red	25·00	15·00
229b	60	20 s. green and silver	65·00	50·00

61a Yomei Gate, Tosho Shrine, Nikko

1926.

241	–	2 s. green	2·40	10
242	61a	6 s. red	12·00	25
243	–	10 s. blue	10·00	10
304	–	10 s. red	10·00	15

DESIGNS: 2 s. Mt. Fuji; 10 s. Nagoya Castle.

62 Baron Maeshima

63 Globe

1927. 50th Anniv of Membership of U.P.U.

244	62	1½ s. purple	2·75	1·75
245		3 s. olive	2·75	1·75
246	63	6 s. red	85·00	60·00
247		10 s. blue	95·00	50·00

64 Phoenix

65 Ceremonial Shrines

1928. Emperor's Enthronement.

248	64	1½ s. green on yellow	1·00	50
249	65	3 s. purple on yellow	1·00	50
250	64	6 s. red on yellow	3·75	3·00
251	65	10 s. blue on yellow	5·00	3·75

66 Shrine of Ise

67 Nakajima-built Fokker F.VIIb/3m over Lake Ashi, Hakone

1929. 58th Vicennial Removal of Shrine of Ise.

255	66	1½ s. violet	2·00	1·50
256		3 s. red	2·75	1·50

1929. Air.

257	67	8½ s. brown	50·00	40·00
258		9½ s. red	15·00	12·00
259		16½ s. green	15·00	14·00
260		18 s. blue	16·00	8·00
261		33 s. black	35·00	5·00

68 Map of Japan

69 Meiji Shrine

1930. 3rd Census.

262	68	1½ s. purple	2·75	1·25
263		3 s. red	3·00	1·25

Although Type **68** is inscr "Second Census", this was actually the third census.

1930. 10th Anniv of Meiji Shrine Dedication.

264	69	1½ s. green	2·00	1·50
265		3 s. orange	2·75	1·50

70 Insignia of Red Cross Society

1934. 15th International Red Cross Conference, Tokyo.

272	70	1½ s. green	2·50	1·40
273	–	3 s. violet	2·75	1·90
274	70	6 s. red	10·00	7·00
275	–	10 s. blue	14·00	10·00

DESIGN—HORIZ: 3 s.; 10 s. Red Cross Society Buildings, Tokyo.

72 Cruiser "Hiyei" and Pagoda, Liaoyang

73 Akasaka Palace, Tokyo

1935. Visit of Emperor of Manchukuo.

276	72	1½ s. green	2·50	1·60
277	73	3 s. brown	2·00	1·00
278	72	6 s. red	14·00	7·50
279	73	10 s. blue	10·00	7·00

74 Mt. Fuji (after Kazan Watanabe)

75c Mt. Fuji from Mishima

1935. New Year's Greetings.

280	74	1½ s. red	15·00	10

1936. Fuji-Hakone National Park.

281	–	1½ s. brown	5·00	4·00
282	–	3 s. green	7·00	6·00
283	–	6 s. red	16·00	14·00
284	75c	10 s. blue	22·00	15·00

DESIGNS: Mt. Fuji (1½ s.), from Lake Ashi; (3 s.), from Lake Kawaguchi; (6 s.).

76 Dove of Peace

77 Shinto Shrine Port Arthur

1936. 30 Years of Occupation of Kwantung.

285	76	1½ s. violet	12·00	12·00
286	77	3 s. brown	15·00	16·00
287	–	10 s. green	£180	£225

DESIGN—HORIZ: 10 s. Govt. House, Kwantung.

78 Imperial Diet

80 Wedded Rocks, Futami Bay

1936. Inauguration of New Houses of the Imperial Diet, Tokyo.

288	78	1½ s. green	1·50	1·25
289	–	3 s. purple	1·50	1·50
290	–	6 s. red	5·50	5·00
291	78	10 s. blue	12·00	4·50

DESIGN: 3, 6 s. Grand Staircase.

1936. New Year's Greetings.

292	80	1½ s. red	6·00	10

82 Goshuinsen (16th-cent trading ship)

83 General Nogi

84 Lake Taisho, Kamikochi

85 Mitsubishi B5N1 and Map

86 Kamatari Fujiwara

87 Plum Tree

1937. Imperf or perf (424), perf (others). Without gum (424), or without gum (392, 394, 396), with gum (others).

313	82	½ s. violet	1·50	80
314	–	1 s. brown	2·00	50
392b	83	2 s. red	15	10
316	–	3 s. green	75	10
394	83	3 s. brown	75	20
317	–	4 s. green	1·00	10
318	84	5 s. blue	2·00	10
396	–	5 s. purple	30	10
319	–	6 s. orange	4·00	2·00
320	–	7 s. green	75	20
398	–	7 s. red	25	15
321	–	8 s. violet	1·00	50
322	–	10 s. red	6·00	10
323	85	12 s. blue	60	60
324	–	14 s. red and brown	1·00	30
325	–	20 s. blue	1·00	10
326	–	25 s. lt brown & brown	80	10
327	–	30 s. blue	3·00	10
328	–	50 s. green and bistre	2·00	10
329	–	1 y. lt brown & brown	6·00	75
424	86	5 y. green	5·50	60
331	87	10 y. purple	20·00	1·50

DESIGNS: 1 s. Rice harvesting; 3 s. Hydroelectric Power Station; 4, 5 s. (No. 396), 7 s. (No. 398), Admiral Togo; 6 s. Garambi Lighthouse, Taiwan; 7 s. (No. 320), Diamond Mountains, Korea; 8 s. Meiji Shrine; 10 s. Yomei Gate, Tosho Shrine, Nikko; 14 s. Inner Gate, Kasuga Shrine; 20 s. Mt. Fuji and cherry blossom; 25 s. Horyu Temple; 30 s. Torii, Itsukushima Shrine at Miyajima; 50 s. Temple of Golden Pavilion, Kyoto; 1 y. Great Buddha, Kamakura.

88 Nakajima-built Douglas DC-2 Airliner

89 New Year's Emblem

1937. Aerodrome Fund.

336	88	2 s. + 2 s. red	2·25	1·25
337		3 s. + 2 s. violet	2·25	1·50
338		4 s. + 2 s. green	3·25	1·25

1937. New Year's Greetings.

339	89	2 s. red	12·00	10

90 Nantai Volcano

92 Shinkyo Bridge

91 Kegon Falls

93 Hiuchi Volcano

1938. Nikko National Park.

340	90	2 s. orange	75	55
341	91	4 s. green	75	55
342	92	10 s. red	7·00	4·00
343	93	20 s. blue	8·00	5·00

94 Daisen Volcano and Meadow

95 Yashima Plateau and Estuary

96 Abuto Kwannon Shrine

97 Tomo Bay

1939. Daisen and Setonaikai National Parks.

345	94	2 s. brown	50	60
346	95	4 s. green	2·25	2·00
347	96	10 s. red	8·00	7·00
348	97	20 s. blue	8·00	6·00

98 Mt Kuju and Village

99 Naka Volcano

100 Naka Crater

101 Volcanic Cones of Mt. Aso

1939. Aso National Park.

350	**98**	2 s. brown	60	70
351	**99**	4 s. green	3·25	3·25
352	**100**	10 s. red	26·00	18·00
353	**101**	20 s. blue	30·00	20·00

102 Globe

1939. 75th Anniv of Membership of International Red Cross Union.

355	**102**	2 s. brown	2·00	1·25
356	–	4 s. green	2·25	1·40
357	**102**	10 s. red	12·00	8·50
358	–	20 s. blue	14·00	8·50

DESIGN: 4 s., 20 s. Count Tsunetami Sano.

104 Golden Bird

105 Mt. Takachiho

106 Sake Jar and Ayu

107 Kashiwara Shrine

1940. 2600th Anniv of Japanese Empire.

359	**104**	2 s. orange	90	85
360	**105**	4 s. green	45	40
361	**106**	10 s. red	4·00	4·25
362	**107**	20 s. blue	1·00	75

108 Mt. Hokuchin

109 Mt. Asahi

110 Sounkyo Gorge, Kobako

111 Tokachi Range

1940. Daisetsu-zan National Park.

363	**108**	2 s. brown	60	60
364	**109**	4 s. green	2·50	2·50
365	**110**	10 s. red	8·50	6·50
366	**111**	20 s. blue	11·00	5·00

112 Mt. Shimmoe

113 Takachiho Peak

114 Kirishima Shrine

115 Lake Roku-Kwannon

1940. Kirishima National Park, Kyushu.

368	**112**	2 s. brown	60	60
369	**113**	4 s. green	1·00	1·00
370	**114**	10 s. red	7·50	5·00
371	**115**	20 s. blue	10·00	5·00

116 Ceremonial Shrine (after Y Araka)

117 "Loyalty and Filial Piety"

1940. 50th Anniv of Promulgation of Imperial Re-script on Education.

373	**116**	2 s. violet	85	1·00
374	**117**	4 s. green	1·25	1·40

118 Mt. Daiton

119 Central Peak, Mt. Niitaka

120 Buddhist Temple, Mt. Kwannon

121 View of Mt. Niitaka

1941. Daiton and Niitaka-Arisan National Parks.

375	**118**	2 s. brown	80	60
376	**119**	4 s. green	1·25	1·00
377	**120**	10 s. red	5·00	3·00
378	**121**	20 s. blue	6·00	2·75

122 Seisui Precipice, East Taiwan Coast

124 Taroko Gorge, Taiwan

123 Mt. Tsugitaka

125 Mt. Taroko, Source of R. Takkiri

1941. Tsugitaka and Taroko National Parks.

380	**122**	2 s. brown	75	60
381	**123**	4 s. green	1·25	1·00
382	**124**	10 s. red	4·00	4·25
383	**125**	20 s. blue	5·50	4·00

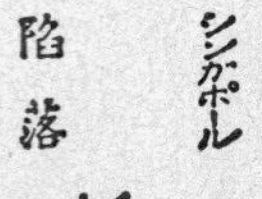

(126)

1942. Surrender of Singapore. Surch as T **126**.

385	**83**	2 s. + 1 s. red	1·00	1·25
386	–	4 s. + 2 s. green (No. 317)	1·00	1·25

127 Kenkoku Shrine

129 Orchids and Crest of Manchukuo

1942. 10th Anniv of Establishment of Manchukuo.

387	**127**	2 s. brown	40	50
388	–	5 s. olive	60	90
389	**127**	10 s. red	85	1·25
390	**129**	20 s. blue	3·00	2·75

DESIGN—VERT: 5 s. Boys of Japan and Manchukuo.

130 Girl War-worker

135 "The Enemy will Surrender"

140 Garambi Lighthouse, Taiwan

141 Garambi Lighthouse, Taiwan

1942. Imperf (418/19, 421), imperf or perf (400, 420), perf (others). With or without gum (398, 420), without gum (400, 418/19, 421), with gum (others).

391	**130**	1 s. brown	10	10
393	–	2 s. green	80	45
395	–	4 s. green	20	10
397	–	6 s. blue	60	60
399	–	10 s. red and pink	85	10
400	**135**	10 s. grey	7·50	8·00
418		10 s. blue	25·00	
419	–	10 s. orange	30	10
401	–	15 s. blue	2·00	50
402	–	17 s. violet	60	25
420	–	20 s. blue	30	10
404	–	27 s. red	65	80
405	–	30 s. green	3·00	1·00
421	–	30 s. blue	2·00	40

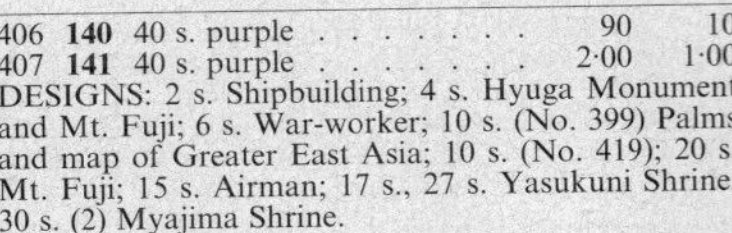

406	**140**	40 s. purple	90	10
407	**141**	40 s. purple	2·00	1·00

DESIGNS: 2 s. Shipbuilding; 4 s. Hyuga Monument and Mt. Fuji; 6 s. War-worker; 10 s. (No. 399) Palms and map of Greater East Asia; 10 s. (No. 419); 20 s. Mt. Fuji; 15 s. Airman; 17 s., 27 s. Yasukuni Shrine; 30 s. (2) Myajima Shrine.

142 Class C59 Steam Locomotive No. 28

143 Tanks in action at Bataan

1942. 70th Anniv of First National Railway.

408	**142**	5 s. green	4·00	6·00

1942. 1st Anniv of Declaration of War.

409	**143**	2 s. + 1 s. brown	2·00	2·75
410	–	5 s. + 2 s. blue	2·50	3·25

DESIGN: 5 s. Attack on Pearl Harbour.

144 Yasukuni Shrine

145 Kwantung Shrine and Map of Kwantung Peninsula

1944. 75th Anniv of Yasukuni Shrine.

411	**144**	7 s. green	85	1·00

1944. Dedication of Kwantung Shrine.

412	**145**	3 s. brown	3·00	10·00
413		7 s. grey	3·00	10·00

146 Sun and Cherry Blossom

149 Torii of Yasukuni Shrine

1945. Imperf or perf and with or without gum (422), imperf without gum (others).

415	**146**	3 s. red	35	40
416	–	5 s. green	40	20
422	–	50 s. brown	60	10
423	**149**	1 y. olive	1·50	85

DESIGNS: 5 s. Sunrise and Kawasaki Ki-61 Hien fighter; 50 s. Coal miners.

150 Pagoda of Horyu Temple, Nara

153 Kiyomizu Temple, Kyoto

154 Noh Mask

1946. Imperf or perf (30 s., 50, 100 y.), imperf (others). With or without gum (30 s., 5, 50, 100 y.), without gum (others).

426	–	15 s. green	45	45
427	**150**	30 s. violet	75	10
428a	–	1 y. blue	1·00	10
429	–	1 y. 30 bistre	5·00	1·60
430	–	1 y. 50 grey	3·00	50
431	**153**	2 y. red	2·50	10
432	–	5 y. mauve	7·50	25
433b	**154**	50 y. brown	80·00	30
434a	–	100 y. purple	80·00	40

DESIGNS: 15 s. Baron H. Maeshima; 1 y. Mt. Fuji, after Hokusai; 1 y. 30, Snow and white-fronted geese (after Hokusai); 1 y. 50, Kintai Bridge, Iwakuni; 5 y. Veil-tailed goldfish; 100 y. Plum tree.

For 30 s., 1 y. 20, 4 y. and 10 y. as Nos. 427, 429 and 434a but with Japanese characters reading in reverse order, see Nos. 441, 445/6 and 449.

156 Mediaeval Postman's Bell

157 Baron Maeshima

1946. 75th Anniv of Government Postal Service.

436	**156**	15 s. orange	4·00	3·00
437	**157**	30 s. green	6·00	5·00
438	–	50 s. red	3·25	2·50
439	–	1 y. blue	4·50	4·50

DESIGNS—As Type **156**: 50 s. First Japanese Postage Stamp; 1 y. Symbols of communication.

160 **161** Baron Maeshima **163** National Art

1947. As issues of 1946 but with Japanese characters in reverse order and new designs. Imperf without gum (449), perf with gum (others).

441	**150**	30 s. violet	3·00	2·00
442	**160**	35 s. green	75	30
443	–	45 s. mauve	85	50
444	**161**	1 y. brown	3·25	40
445	**150**	1 y. 20 green	2·00	30
446	–	4 y. blue (as No. 429)	6·00	30
447	–	5 y. blue	8·00	10
448	**163**	10 y. violet	14·00	10
449	–	10 y. purple (as No. 434a)	28·00	70

DESIGNS—VERT: 45 s. Numeral; 5 y. Whaling.

For similar designs, but without the chrysanthemum emblem, see Nos. 467/70.

164 Mother and Child **165** Roses and Wisteria

1947. Inauguration of New Constitution.

451	**164**	50 s. red	60	40
452	**165**	1 y. blue	70	40

166 National Products **167** Lily of the Valley

1947. Re-opening of Private Foreign Trade.

455	**166**	1 y. 20 brown	3·00	1·25
456		4 y. blue	5·00	1·50

1947. Relief of Ex-convicts Day.

458	**167**	2 y. green	4·00	1·75

169 Hurdling **170**

1947. 2nd National Athletic Meeting. Kanazawa. Each mauve.

460	1 y. 20 Type **169**	10·00	6·00
461	1 y. 20 Diving	10·00	6·00
462	1 y. 20 Throwing the discus	10·00	6·00
463	1 y. 20 Volleyball	10·00	6·00

1947. Community Chest.

465	**170**	1 y. 20 + 80 s. red	75	85

172 Kiyomizu Temple, Kyoto **173** National Art

1948. Designs without chrysanthemum.

467	–	1 y. 50 blue	2·50	50
468	**172**	2 y. red	8·00	10
469	–	3 y. 80 brown	8·00	6·50
470	**173**	10 y. violet	12·00	10

DESIGNS: 1 y. 50, 3 y. 80, Numeral types.

174 Stylised Tree **176** Boy and Girl reading

1948. Encouragement of Afforestation.

474	**174**	1 y. 20 green	80	60

1948. Re-organization of Educational System.

480	**176**	1 y. 20 red	65	65

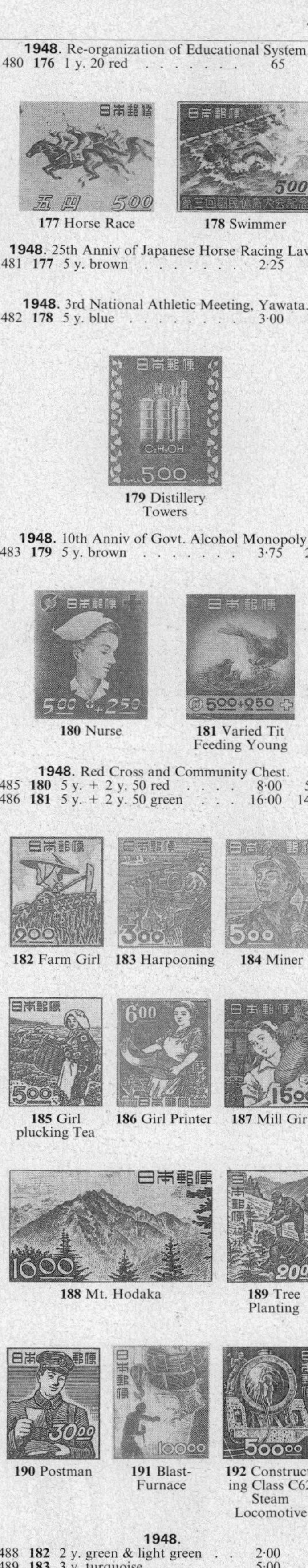

177 Horse Race **178** Swimmer

1948. 25th Anniv of Japanese Horse Racing Laws.

481	**177**	5 y. brown	2·25	85

1948. 3rd National Athletic Meeting, Yawata.

482	**178**	5 y. blue	3·00	1·25

179 Distillery Towers

1948. 10th Anniv of Govt. Alcohol Monopoly.

483	**179**	5 y. brown	3·75	2·25

180 Nurse **181** Varied Tit Feeding Young

1948. Red Cross and Community Chest.

485	**180**	5 y. + 2 y. 50 red	8·00	5·00
486	**181**	5 y. + 2 y. 50 green	16·00	14·50

182 Farm Girl **183** Harpooning **184** Miner

185 Girl plucking Tea **186** Girl Printer **187** Mill Girl

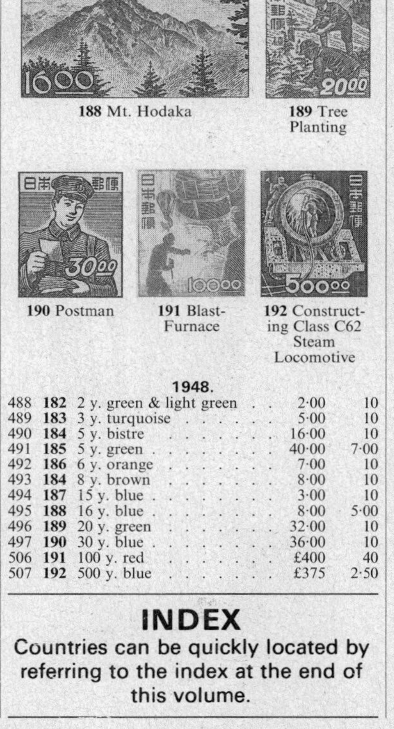

188 Mt. Hodaka **189** Tree Planting

190 Postman **191** Blast-Furnace **192** Constructing Class C62 Steam Locomotive

1948.

488	**182**	2 y. green & light green	2·00	10
489	**183**	3 y. turquoise	5·00	10
490	**184**	5 y. bistre	16·00	10
491	**185**	5 y. green	40·00	7·00
492	**186**	6 y. orange	7·00	10
493	**184**	8 y. brown	8·00	10
494	**187**	15 y. blue	3·00	10
495	**188**	16 y. blue	8·00	5·00
496	**189**	20 y. green	32·00	10
497	**190**	30 y. blue	36·00	10
506	**191**	100 y. red	£400	40
507	**192**	500 y. blue	£375	2·50

INDEX

Countries can be quickly located by referring to the index at the end of this volume.

193 Baseball

1948. 3rd National Athletic Meeting, Fukuoke.

509	**193**	5 y. green	12·00	5·00
510	–	5 y. green (bicycle race)	12·00	5·00
511	–	5 y. green (sprinter)	12·00	5·00
512	–	5 y. green (high jumper)	12·00	5·00

194 "Beauty Looking Back" (Moronobu Hishikawa) **195** Girl playing with Shuttlecock

1948. Philatelic Week.

514	**194**	5 y. brown	60·00	40·00

1948. New Year's Greetings.

516	**195**	2 y. red	3·75	2·25

196 Skater **197** Ski Jumper

1949. 4th National Athletic Meeting.

(a) Suwa City.

517	**196**	5 y. violet	3·50	2·00

(b) Sapporo, Hokkaido.

518	**197**	5 y. blue	4·00	2·00

198 "Koan Maru" (ferry) in Beppu Harbour **199** Exhibition Grounds

1949.

519	**198**	2 y. blue and red	2·00	1·25
520		5 y. blue and green	5·50	1·50

1949. Foreign Trade Fair, Yokohama. Perf or imperf.

521	**199**	5 y. red	2·50	1·00

200 Seto Inland Sea **201** Stylised Trees

1949. Matsuyama, Okayama and Takamatsu Exhibitions.

522	**200**	10 y. red (Matsuyama)	30·00	15·00
523		10 y. pink (Okayama)	35·00	20·00
524		10 y. claret (Takamatsu)	50·00	25·00

1949. Encouragement of Afforestation.

525	**201**	5 y. green	5·00	2·00

202 Shishi-Iwa (Lion Rock)

203 Mt. Omine

204 Doro-Hatcho River Pool

205 Hashikui-Iwa

1949. Yoshino-Kumano National Park.

526	**202**	2 y. brown	1·00	60
527	**203**	5 y. green	3·25	1·00
528	**204**	10 y. red	14·00	8·00
529	**205**	16 y. blue	7·50	2·25

206 Boy

1949. Children's Day.

531	**206**	5 y. purple and buff	5·00	1·50

208 Observatory Tower **209** Radio Mast, Pigeon and Globe

1949. 75th Anniv of Central Meteorological Observatory, Tokyo.

534	**208**	8 y. green	3·50	1·40

1949. Establishment of Joint Ministries of Postal and Electrical Communications.

535	**209**	8 y. blue	3·50	1·25

210 Park in Autumn

211 Park in Spring

212 Park in Summer

213 Park in Winter

1949. Fuji-Hakone National Park.

536	**210**	2 y. brown	2·50	60
537	**211**	8 y. green	3·00	1·00
538	**212**	14 y. red	1·75	30
539	**213**	24 y. blue	3·25	40

214 Woman holding Rose **215** Doves

1949. Establishment of Memorial City at Hiroshima.
541 **214** 8 y. brown . . . . 6·00 2·00

1949. Establishment of International Cultural City at Nagasaki.
542 **215** 8 y. green . . . . 5·00 2·00

216 Swimmer

1949. 4th National Athletic Meeting, Yokohama.
543 **216** 8 y. blue . . . . 4·00 1·25

217 Boy Scout **218** Symbolical of Writing and Printing

1949. 1st National Scout Jamboree, Tokyo.
544 **217** 8 y. brown . . . . 7·50 2·00

1949. Press Week.
545 **218** 8 y. blue . . . . 4·50 2·00

219 Map of Japan and Letters **220** Globe and Forms of Transport

1949. 75th Anniv of U.P.U.
546 **219** 2 y. green . . . . 2·75 1·50
547 **220** 8 y. red . . . . 4·75 1·60
548 **219** 14 y. red . . . . 9·50 4·00
549 **220** 24 y. blue . . . . 17·00 9·25

221 Throwing the Javelin **222** Telescope

1949. 4th National Athletic Meeting, Tokyo. Each brown.
551 8 y. Type **221** . . . . 4·00 1·50
552 8 y. Dinghy sailing . . . . . . 4·00 1·50
553 8 y. Relay racing . . . . 4·00 1·50
554 8 y. Tennis . . . . 4·00 1·50

1949. 50th Anniv of Establishment of Latitude Observatory, Mizusawa.
555 **222** 8 y. green . . . . 3·50 2·00

223 "Moon and Brent Geese" (after Hiroshige) **224** Dr. H. Noguchi

A B C D

E F G H I

J K L M N

O P Q R

1949. Postal Week.
556 **223** 8 y. violet . . . . £130 60·00

1949. Various portraits as illustrated, in frame as T **224**.
557 A 8 y. green . . . . 10·00 1·00
558 B 8 y. green . . . . 4·00 1·00
559 C 8 y. green . . . . 4·00 1·00
560 D 8 y. green . . . . 3·50 1·00
561 E 8 y. violet . . . . 10·00 4·00
562 F 8 y. purple . . . . 3·50 1·00
563 G 8 y. green . . . . 8·00 2·00
564 H 8 y. violet . . . . 8·00 2·00
565 I 8 y. red . . . . 16·00 2·00
566 J 8 y. red . . . . 30·00 2·50
567 K 8 y. brown . . . . 15·00 2·25
568 L 8 y. blue . . . . 9·00 2·25
569 M 10 y. green . . . . 60·00 4·50
570 N 10 y. purple . . . . 9·00 1·50
571 O 10 y. red . . . . 4·00 1·40
572 P 10 y. grey . . . . 7·00 1·40
573 Q 10 y. brown . . . . 6·00 1·40
574 R 10 y. blue . . . . 6·00 1·40
PORTRAITS: A, Hideyo Noguchi (bacteriologist); B, Y. Fukuzawa (educationist); C, Soseki Natsume (novelist); D, Shoyo Tsubouchi (dramatist); E, Danjuro Ichikawa (actor); F, Jo Niijima (religious leader); G, Hogai Kano (painter); H, Kanzo Uchimura (religious leader); I, Mme. Higuchi (author); J, Ogai Mori (doctor); K, S. Masaoka (poet); L, S. Hishida (painter); M, A. Nishi (scholar); N, K. Ume (lawyer); O, H. Kimura (astrophysicist); P, I. Nitobe (statesman); Q, T. Torada (physicist); R, Tenshin Okakura (writer).

225 Japanese Pheasant and Pampas Grass **226** Tiger (after Maruyama Okyo)

1950. Air.
575 **225** 16 y. grey . . . . 38·00 18·00
576 34 y. purple . . . . 70·00 23·00
577 59 y. red . . . . £100 18·00
578 103 y. orange . . . . . . 75·00 30·00
579 144 y. olive . . . . 75·00 30·00

1950. New Year's Greetings.
580 **226** 2 y. red . . . . 8·00 1·00

227 Microphones of 1925 and 1950 **228** Dove

1950. 25th Anniv of Japanese Broadcasting System.
582 **227** 8 y. blue . . . . 4·00 1·50

1950. 1st Anniv of Joint Ministries of Postal and Electrical Communications.
583 **228** 8 y. green . . . . 3·75 1·25

229 Lake Akan and Mt. O-Akani

230 Lake Kutcharo

231 Mt. Akan-Fuji

232 Lake Mashu

1950. Akan National Park.
584 **229** 2 y. brown . . . . 1·10 50
585 **230** 8 y. green . . . . 1·75 75
586 **231** 14 y. red . . . . 8·50 2·25
587 **232** 24 y. blue . . . . 10·00 2·25

233 Gymnast on Rings

1950. 5th National Athletic Meeting.
589 **233** 8 y. red . . . . 30·00 12·00
590 – 8 y. red (Pole vaulting) . . . 30·00 12·00
591 – 8 y. red (Football) . . . . 30·00 12·00
592 – 8 y. red (Horse jumping) . . 30·00 12·00

234 Tahoto Pagoda, Ishiyama Temple **235** Baron Maeshima **236** Long-tailed Cock

237 Kannon Bosatsu (detail of wall painting, Horyu Temple) **238** Himeji Castle

239 Phoenix Temple, Uji **240** Buddhisattva Statue, Chugu Temple

1950. With noughts for sen after value.
593 **234** 80 s. red . . . . 2·00 1·75
594 **235** 1 y. brown . . . . 4·75 30
595 **236** 5 y. green and brown . . . 8·00 30
596 **237** 10 y. lake and mauve . . . 18·00 10
597 **238** 14 y. brown . . . . 50·00 35·00
598 **239** 24 y. blue . . . . 40·00 16·00
599 **240** 50 y. brown . . . . £140 1·00
For designs without noughts see Nos. 653 etc and for designs additionally inscr "NIPPON" see Nos. 1041/59.

241 Girl and Rabbit **242** Skiing, Mt. Zao

1951. New Year's Greetings.
604 **241** 2 y. red . . . . 7·00 1·00
For 50 y. in this design dated "1999" see No. 2565.

1951. Tourist Issue. Mt. Zao.
606 **242** 8 y. olive . . . . 14·00 3·00
607 – 24 y. blue . . . . 15·00 5·00
DESIGN—HORIZ: 24 y. Two skiers on Mt. Zao.

243 Nihon-Daira **244** Mt. Fuji from Nihon Daira

1951. Tourist Issue. Nihon-Daira.
608 **243** 8 y. green . . . . 14·00 3·00
609 **244** 24 y. blue . . . . 70·00 18·00

245 Child's Head

1951. Children's Charter.
611 **245** 8 y. brown . . . . 25·00 3·00

246 Hot Springs, Owaki Valley **247** Lake Ashi

1951. Tourist Issue. Hakone Spa.
612 **246** 8 y. brown . . . . 10·00 2·00
613 **247** 24 y. blue . . . . 8·00 3·00

248 Senju Waterfall **249** Ninai Waterfall

1951. Tourist Issue. Akame Waterfalls.
614 **248** 8 y. green . . . . 10·00 2·00
615 **249** 24 y. blue . . . . 10·00 3·00

250 Waka-no-Ura **251** Tomo-ga-Shima

1951. Tourist Issue. Coastal Resorts.

616	**250**	8 y. brown	8·00	2·00
617	**251**	24 y. blue	8·00	3·00

252 Oirase River

253 Lake Towada

254 View from Kankodai

255 Hakkoda Mountains

1951. Towada National Park.

618	**252**	2 y. brown	1·25	30
619	**253**	8 y. green	6·50	70
620	**254**	14 y. red	5·50	4·00
621	**255**	24 y. blue	7·50	4·00

256 Uji River **257** Uji Bridge

1951. Tourist Issue. Uji River.

623	**256**	8 y. brown	9·00	2·00
624	**257**	24 y. blue	8·00	3·00

258 Douglas DC-4 Airliner over Horyuji Pagoda **259** Airplane and Mt. Tate

1951. Air. With noughts for sen after numerals of value.

625	**258**	15 y. violet	4·00	3·25
626		20 y. blue	32·00	1·00
627		25 y. green	35·00	15
628		30 y. red	26·00	15
629		40 y. black	7·00	30
630	**259**	55 y. blue	£225	45·00
631		75 y. red	£175	28·00
632		80 y. mauve	30·00	3·50
633		85 y. black	22·00	12·00
634		125 y. brown	18·00	3·25
635		160 y. green	40·00	5·50

For similar designs, but without noughts after numerals of value, see Nos. 671/81.

260 Chrysanthemum **261** Japanese Flag

1951. Peace Treaty.

636	**260**	2 y. brown	2·50	1·00
637	**261**	8 y. red and blue	7·00	2·00
638	**260**	24 y. green	18·00	6·00

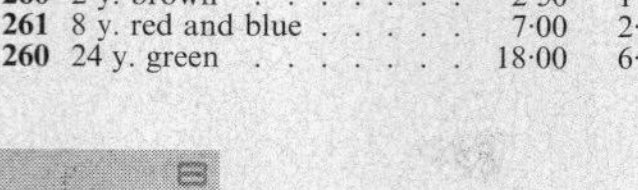

262 Oura Catholic Church, Nagasaki **263** Gateway, Sofuku Temple

1951. Tourist Issue. Nagasaki.

639	**262**	8 y. red	10·00	2·00
640	**263**	24 y. blue	8·00	3·00

264 Lake Marunuma **265** Lake Sugenuma

1951. Tourist Issue.

641	**264**	8 y. purple	10·00	2·00
642	**265**	24 y. green	8·00	3·00

266 Shosenkyo Valley **267** Nagatoro Bridge

1951. Tourist Issue. Shosenkyo.

643	**266**	8 y. red	9·50	2·00
644	**267**	24 y. blue	9·00	3·00

268 Putting the Shot **269** Noh Mask

1951. 6th National Athletic Meeting.

645	**268**	2 y. brown	3·50	1·00
646	–	2 y. blue (hockey)	3·50	1·00

1952. New Year's Greetings.

647	**269**	5 y. red	10·00	90

270 Ship's Davit and Southern Cross **271** Red Cross and Lily

1952. 75th Anniv of U.P.U. Membership.

649	**270**	5 y. violet	5·00	1·25
650	–	10 y. green	16·00	3·00

DESIGN: 10 y. Earth and Ursa Major. Inscr "1952".

1952. 75th Anniv of Japanese Red Cross.

651	**271**	5 y. red	5·00	1·00
652	–	10 y. green & red (Nurse)	11·00	2·00

272 Akita Dog **273** Little Cuckoo **274** Tahoto Pagoda, Ishiyama Temple

275 Mandarins **276** Japanese Serow **277** Chuson Temple

278 Veil-tailed Goldfish **279** Yomei Gate, Tosho Shrine, Nikko **280** "Marimo" (water plant) and Sockeye Salmon

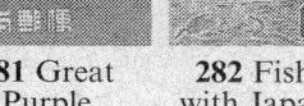

281 Great Purple **282** Fishing with Japanese Cormorants **283** "Bridge and Irises" (from lacquered box)

1952. Without noughts after numerals of value.

653	**235**	1 y. brown	30	10
654	**272**	2 y. black	40	10
655	**273**	3 y. turquoise	25	10
656	**274**	4 y. purple and red	2·50	10
657	**275**	5 y. brown and blue	25	10
658	**276**	8 y. brown & lt brown	30	10
659	**237**	10 y. red and mauve	6·00	10
660	**238**	14 y. green	7·50	1·25
661	**277**	20 y. green	1·00	10
662	**239**	24 y. violet	16·00	2·00
663		30 y. purple	35·00	40
664	**278**	35 y. orange	10·00	10
665	**279**	45 y. blue	4·50	10
666	**240**	50 y. brown	4·50	10
667	**280**	55 y. green, black & blue	16·00	30
668	**281**	75 y. multicoloured	14·00	90
669	**282**	100 y. red	38·00	10
670	**283**	500 y. purple	85·00	10

For 1, 2, 3, 50, 55 and 75 y. in same designs, but inscr "NIPPON", see Nos. 1041, 1582a, 1226, 1058/60, 1232 and 1064.

1952. Air. As. Nos. 625/35 but without noughts after numerals of value.

671	**258**	15 y. violet	2·00	1·10
672		20 y. blue	50·00	70
673		25 y. green	1·00	10
674		30 y. red	3·50	10
675		40 y. black	4·00	10
676	**259**	55 y. blue	75·00	4·50
677		75 y. red	£140	10·00
678		80 y. mauve	95·00	3·00
679		85 y. black	5·00	1·25
680		125 y. brown	10·00	1·40
681		160 y. green	40·00	1·75

284 Mt. Yari **285** Kurobe Valley

286 Mt. Shirouma

287 Mt. Norikura

1952. Chubu-Sangaku National Park.

682	**284**	5 y. brown	2·75	40
683	**285**	10 y. green	18·00	2·00
684	**286**	14 y. red	5·50	2·00
685	**287**	24 y. blue	8·00	2·75

288 Central Hall **289** Wrestlers

1952. 75th Anniv of Tokyo University.

687	**288**	10 y. green	11·00	2·00

1952. 7th National Athletic Meeting.

688	–	5 y. blue (Mountaineer)	6·00	1·00
689	**289**	5 y. brown	6·00	1·00

290 Mt. Azuma-Kofuji

291 Mt. Asahi

292 Mt. Bandai

293 Mt. Gessan

1952. Bandai-Asahi National Park.

690	**290**	5 y. brown	2·00	40
691	**291**	10 y. olive	11·00	1·75
692	**292**	14 y. red	4·25	2·75
693	**293**	24 y. blue	8·00	4·00

294 "Kirin" and Chrysanthemums **295** Flag of Crown Prince

1952. Investiture of Crown Prince Akihito.

695	**294**	5 y. orange and brown	2·75	50
696		10 y. orange and green	3·00	75
697	**295**	24 y. blue	15·00	4·25

296 Dancing Doll **297** First Japanese Electric Lamp

1953. New Year's Greetings.

699	**296**	5 y. red	7·00	1·00

1953. 75th Anniv of Electric Lamp in Japan.

701	**297**	10 y. brown	7·50	2·00

299 Kintai Bridge **302** Great Buddha, Kamakura

300 Lake Shikotsu **301** Mt. Yotei

(Illustrations reduced: each 40 × 23 mm)

1953. Tourist Issue. Kintai Bridge.

702 – 10 y. brown 7·50 2·00

703 **299** 24 y. blue 7·50 3·00

DESIGN—VERT: 10 y. Kintai Bridge (after Hiroshige).

1953. Shikotsu-Toya National Park.

704 **300** 5 y. blue 1·75 35

705 **301** 10 y. green 5·50 75

1953. Air.

707 **302** 70 y. brown 3·50 10

708 80 y. blue 5·00 10

709 115 y. olive 2·75 30

710 145 y. turquoise 18·00 2·00

303 Wedded Rocks, Futami Bay

304 Nakiri Coast

(Illustrations reduced: each 40 × 23 mm)

1953. Ise Shima National Park.

711 **303** 5 y. red 1·75 30

712 **304** 10 y. blue 4·00 70

305 "Ho-o" (Happy Phoenix)

1953. Return of Crown Prince from Overseas Tour.

714 **305** 5 y. lake 3·00 1·50

715 – 10 y. blue 8·75 3·25

DESIGN: 10 y. Manchurian crane in flight.

306 Judo

307 Tokyo Observatory

1953. 8th National Athletic Meeting, Matsuyama.

716 **306** 5 y. green 8·00 2·00

717 – 5 y. black 8·00 2·00

DESIGN: 5 y. Rugby footballers.

1953. 75th Anniv of Tokyo Observatory.

718 **307** 10 y. blue 10·00 2·00

308 Mt. Unzen **309**

(Illustrations reduced: each 40 × 23 mm)

1953. Unzen National Park.

719 **308** 5 y. red 1·50 25

720 **309** 10 y. blue 4·00 65

310 Wooden Horse

311 Ice Skaters

1953. New Year's Greetings.

722 **310** 5 y. red 5·50 25

1954. World Speed Skating Championships, Sapporo.

724 **311** 10 y. blue 4·00 1·10

312

313 Wrestlers

1954. International Trade Fair, Osaka

725 **312** 10 y. red 4·25 1·10

1954. Int Free-style Wrestling Championship.

726 **313** 10 y. green 4·00 1·00

314 Mt. Asama

315 Mt. Tanigawa

(Illustrations reduced: each 40 × 23 mm)

1954. Jo-Shin-Etsu Kogen National Park.

727 **314** 5 y. sepia 1·50 25

728 **315** 10 y. turquoise 3·75 65

316 Archery

317 Telegraph Table

1954. 9th National Athletic Meeting, Sapporo.

730 **316** 5 y. green 5·00 1·50

731 – 5 y. brown (Table tennis) 5·00 1·50

1954. 75th Anniv of Japan's Membership of I.T.U.

732 **317** 5 y. purple 2·25 75

733 – 10 y. blue 6·00 1·00

DESIGN—HORIZ: 10 y. I.T.U. Monument.

318 Tumbler

319 Tama Gorge

320 Chichibu Mountains

1954. New Year's Greetings.

735 **318** 5 y. red and black 7·00 80

1955. Chichibu-Tama National Park.

737 **319** 5 y. blue 1·25 25

738 **320** 10 y. lake 1·50 40

321 Paper Carp

1955. 15th International Chamber of Commerce Congress, Tokyo.

740 **321** 10 y. multicoloured 6·00 1·50

322 Bentenzaki Peninsula

323 Jodoga Beach

1955. Rikuchu-Kaigan National Park.

741 **322** 5 y. green 1·50 25

742 **323** 10 y. red 2·00 40

324 Gymnastics

325 "Girl Playing Glass Flute" (Utamaro)

1955. 10th National Athletic Meeting, Kanagawa.

744 **324** 5 y. red 3·00 1·00

745 – 5 y. blue (Running) 3·00 1·00

1955. Philatelic Week.

746 **325** 10 y. multicoloured 12·00 8·00

326 "Kokeshi" Dolls

327 Table Tennis

1955. New Year's Greetings.

747 **326** 5 y. green and red 3·00 20

1956. World Table Tennis Championships.

749 **327** 10 y. brown 1·10 35

328 Judo

1956. World Judo Championships.

750 **328** 10 y. purple and green 1·40 40

329 Children and Paper Carps

1956. International Children's Day.

751 **329** 5 y. black and blue 1·00 30

330 Osezaki Lighthouse

331 Kujuku Island

(Illustrations reduced: each 40 × 22 mm)

1956. 25th Anniv of National Park Law. Saikai National Park.

752 **330** 5 y. brown 1·25 50

753 **331** 10 y. indigo and blue 1·75 85

332 Imperial Palace, and Modern Buildings

333 Sakuma Dam

1956. 5th Centenary of Tokyo.

755 **332** 10 y. purple 3·25 50

1956. Completion of Sakuma Dam.

756 **333** 10 y. blue 2·50 50

334 Basketball

335 Ebizo Ichikawa (actor), (after Sharaku)

1956. 11th National Athletic Meeting, Kobe.

757 **334** 5 y. green 1·50 30

758 – 5 y. purple (Long jumping) 1·50 30

1956. Philatelic Week.

759 **335** 10 y. black, orge & grey 13·00 4·75

336 Mt. Manaslu and Mountaineer

1956. Conquest of Mt. Manaslu.

760 **336** 10 y. multicoloured 4·50 1·25

337 View of Yui (after Hiroshige) and Type EF 58 Electric Locomotive No. 4

1956. Electrification of Tokaido Railway Line.

761 **337** 10 y. black, green & brn 10·00 3·00

338 Cogwheel, Valve and Freighter "Nissyo Maru"

339 Whale (float)

1956. Floating Machinery Fair.

762 **338** 10 y. blue 1·60 70

1956. New Year's Greetings.

763 **339** 5 y. multicoloured 2·00 15

340 U.N.O. Emblem

341 I.G.Y. Emblem, Emperor Penguin and Antarctic Research Vessel "Soya"

1957. 1st Anniv of Japan's Admission into U.N.

765 **340** 10 y. red and blue 1·00 95

1957. International Geophysical Year.

766 **341** 10 y. blue, yellow & black 2·25 75

342 Atomic Reactor

343 Gymnast

1957. Completion of Atomic Reactor at Tokai-Mura.

767 **342** 10 y. violet 50 15

1957. 12th National Athletic Meeting, Shizuoka.

768 **343** 5 y. blue 60 15

769 – 5 y. red (Boxing) 60 15

344 "Girl Bouncing Ball" (after Harunobu)

345 Ogochi Dam

1957. Philatelic Week.

770 **344** 10 y. multicoloured 4·00 1·50

1957. Completion of Ogochi Dam.

771 **345** 10 y blue 45 15

346 Japan's First Blast Furnace and Modern Plant

347 "Inu-hariko" (toy dog)

1957. Centenary of Japanese Iron Industry.

772 **346** 10 y. purple and orange 35 15

1957. New Year's Greetings.

773 **347** 5 y. multicoloured 30 15

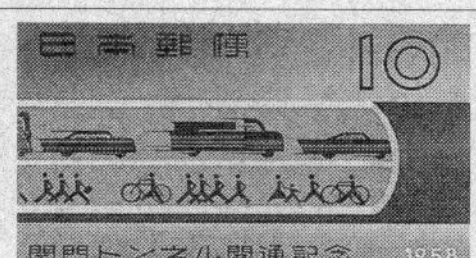

348 Kan-Mon Tunnel

1958. Opening of Kan-Mon Undersea Tunnel.
775 **348** 10 y. multicoloured 50 10

349 "Lady returning from Bath-house" (after Kiyonaga)

1958. Philatelic Week.
776 **349** 10 y. multicoloured . . . . 1·00 15

350 Statue of Ii Naosuke, "Powhattan" (1858 paddle-steamer) and Modern Liner

351 National Stadium, Tokyo

1958. Centenary of Opening of Ports to Traders.
777 **350** 10 y. red and blue 30 10

1958. 3rd Asian Games, Tokyo. Inscr as in T **351**. Multicoloured.
778 5 y. Type **351** 30 10
779 10 y. Flame and Games emblem 45 50
780 14 y. Runner breasting tape . . 35 15
781 24 y. High-diver 40 50

352 Emigration Ship "Kasato Maru" and South American Map

1958. 50th Anniv of Japanese Emigration to Brazil.
782 **352** 10 y. multicoloured 50 10

353 Dado-Okesa Dancer on Sado Island

354 Mt. Yahiko and Echigo Plain

1958. Sado-Yahiko Quasi-National Park.
783 **353** 10 y. multicoloured 70 10
784 **354** 10 y. multicoloured 40 10

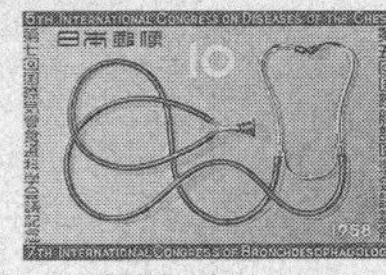

355 Stethoscope

1958. Int Congresses of Chest Diseases and Bronchoesophagology, Tokyo.
785 **355** 10 y. turquoise 60 10

356 "Old Kyoto Bridge" (after Hiroshige)

357 Badminton Player

1958. International Correspondence Week.
786 **356** 24 y. multicoloured . . . . 4·50 50

The design is taken from the series of 53 woodcuts, showing stages of the Tokaido Road. Others from this series are shown on Nos. 810, 836, 878 and 908.

1958. 13th National Athletic Meeting, Toyama.
787 **357** 5 y. purple 75 10
788 – 5 y. blue (Weightlifting) . . 75 10

358 Yukichi Fukuzawa (founder) and Keio University

359 Children Skipping across Globe

1958. Centenary of Keio University.
789 **358** 10 y. red 30 10

1958. International Child and Social Welfare Conferences, Tokyo.
790 **359** 10 y. green 30 10

360 "Flame of Freedom"

361 Ebisu with Madai Seabream (toy)

1958. 10th Anniv of Declaration of Human Rights.
791 **360** 10 y. multicoloured 30 10

1958. New Year's Greetings.
792 **361** 5 y. multicoloured 50 10

362 Map of Kojima Bay and Tractor

1959. Completion of Kojima Bay Reclamation Project.
794 **362** 10 y. purple and ochre . . 50 15

363 Karst Plateau

364 Akiyoshi Cavern

1959. Akiyoshidai Quasi-National Parks.
795 **363** 10 y. multicoloured . . . . 1·75 10
796 **364** 10 y. multicoloured . . . . 2·25 10

365 Map of Asia

366 Crown Prince Akihito and Princess Michiko

1959. Asian Congress Commemorating of 2500th Anniv of Buddha's Death.
797 **365** 10 y. red 40 10

1959. Imperial Wedding.
798 – 5 y. violet and purple . . . 35 10
799 **366** 10 y. purple and brown . . 85 10
800 – 20 y. sepia and brown . . 1·00 15
801 **366** 30 y. deep green & green . 2·00 15
DESIGN: 5, 20 y. Ceremonial fan.

367 "Ladies reading poems" (from "Ukiyo Genji" after Eishi)

368 Graduated Glass and Scales

1959. Philatelic Week.
803 **367** 10 y. multicoloured . . . . 2·50 1·25

1959. Ratification of Adoption of Metric System in Japan.
804 **368** 10 y. sepia and blue . . . 30 10

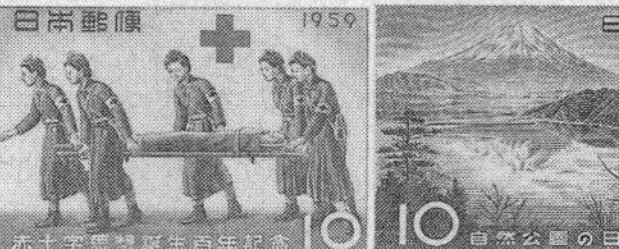

369 Stretcher-party with Casualty

370 Mt. Fuji from Lake Motosu

1959. Red Cross.
805 **369** 10 y. red and green 40 10

1959. National Parks Day.
806 **370** 10 y. green, purple & blue . 60 10

371 Ao Caves, Yabakei

372 Japanese Cormorant with Hita and Mt. Hiko background

1959. Yaba-Hita-Hikosan Quasi-National Parks.
807 **371** 10 y. multicoloured . . . . 2·00 30
808 **372** 10 y. multicoloured . . . . 3·75 30

373 Nagoya and Golden Dolphin

374 "Kuwana" (after Hiroshige)

1959. 350th Anniv of Nagoya.
809 **373** 10 y. gold, black & blue . . 60 10

1959. International Correspondence Week.
810 **374** 30 y. multicoloured . . . . 10·00 2·00

375 Flying Manchurian Crane and I.A.T.A. Emblem

376 Throwing the Hammer

1959. 15th Int Air Transport Association Meeting, Tokyo
811 **375** 10 y. blue . . . . 1·40 30

1959. 14th National Athletic Meeting, Tokyo.
812 **376** 5 y. blue . . . . 1·00 10
813 – 5 y. brown (Fencer) . . . 1·00 10

377 Open Book showing portrait of Shoin Yoshida

378 Halves of Globe

1959. Death Centenary of Shoin Yoshida (educator) and Nat. Parents/Teachers Assoc. Convention.
814 **377** 10 y. brown 40 10

1959. 15th Session of Contracting Parties to G.A.T.T.
815 **378** 10 y. brown 60 10

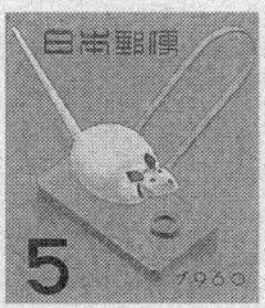

379 Rice-eating Rat of Kanazawa (toy)

380 Yukio Ozaki and Clock Tower Memorial Hall

1959. New Year's Greetings.
816 **379** 5 y. multicoloured . . . . 1·00 10

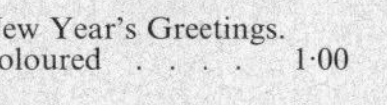

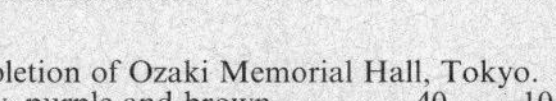

1960. Completion of Ozaki Memorial Hall, Tokyo.
818 **380** 10 y. purple and brown . . 40 10

381 Deer

1960. 1250th Anniv of Transfer of Capital to Nara.
819 **381** 10 y. olive 70 10

382 Godaido Temple, Matsushima

383 Bridge of Heaven (sandbank), Miyazu Bay

384 Miyajima from the Sea

1960. "Scenic Trio".
820 **382** 10 y. turquoise & brown . 2·50 25
821 **383** 10 y. green and blue . . . 3·00 25
822 **384** 10 y. green and violet . . . 3·00 25

385 Takeshima-Gamagori Causeway

1960. Mikawa Bay Quasi-National Park.
823 **385** 10 y. multicoloured . . . . 1·25 20

386 "Ise" (from Satake picture scroll "Thirty-six Immortal Poets")

1960. Philatelic Week.
824 **386** 10 y. black, red & brown . 3·75 2·00

387 "Kanrin Maru" (barque) crossing the Pacific

388 Japanese Crested Ibis

1960. Centenary of Japanese-American Treaty.
825 **387** 10 y. sepia and green . . . 2·25 30
826 – 30 y. black and red . . . . 1·60 20
DESIGN: 30 y. Pres. Buchanan receiving Japanese mission.

1960. 12th Int Bird Preservation Congress, Tokyo.
827 **388** 10 y. red, pink and grey . . 1·75 50

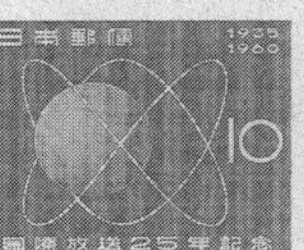

389 Radio Waves around Globe

390 Abashiri Flower Gardens

1960. 25th Anniv of Japanese Overseas Broadcasting Service, "Radio Japan".
828 **389** 10 y. red 40 10

1960. Abashiri Quasi-National Park.
829 **390** 10 y. multicoloured . . . . 1·50 25

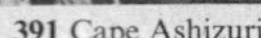
391 Cape Ashizuri

392 Rainbow linking Hawaii and Japan

1960. Ashizuri Quasi-National Park.
830 **391** 10 y. multicoloured . . . . 1·00 25

1960. 75th Anniv of Japanese Emigration to Hawaii.
831 **392** 10 y. multicoloured . . . . 1·00 20

393 Douglas DC-8 Jetliner and Farman H.F.III Biplane

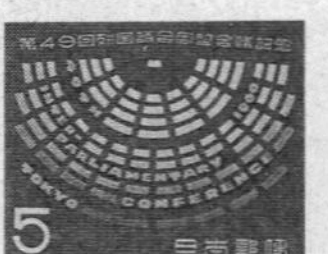
394 Seat Plan of the Diet

1960. 50th Anniv of Japanese Aviation.
832 **393** 10 y. brown and grey . . . 1·25 25

1960. 49th Inter-Parliamentary Union Conf. Inscr "49TH INTER-PARLIAMENTARY CONFERENCE TOKYO 1960".
833 **394** 5 y. orange and blue . . . 70 10
834 – 10 y. brown and blue . . . 1·60 20
DESIGN: 10 y. "Clear Day with Southern Breeze" (from "36 Views of Mt. Fuji" by Hokusai Katsushika).

395 "Kambara" (after Hiroshige)

1960. International Correspondence Week.
836 **395** 30 y. multicoloured . . . . 18·00 4·00

396 Okayama Observatory

1960. Opening of Okayama Astrophysical Observatory.
837 **396** 10 y. violet 90 25

397 "Kendo" (Japanese fencing)

398 Lieut. Shirase and Map of Antarctica

1960. 15th National Athletic Meeting, Kumamoto.
838 **397** 5 y. blue . . . . 1·00 15
839 – 5 y. purple (Vaulting) . . . 1·00 15

1960. 50th Anniv of 1st Japanese Antarctic Expedition.
840 **398** 10 y. black and brown . . 1·00 15

399 Red Beko and Golden Bekokko (Japanese toys)

400 Diet Building and Stars

1960. New Year's Greetings.
841 **399** 5 y. multicoloured 50 10

1960. 70th Anniv of Diet.
843 **400** 5 y. violet and black . . . 60 10
844 – 10 y. red 75 15
DESIGN: 10 y. Opening ceremony of first session of Diet.

401 Narcissus

402 Pearl-divers at Shirahama

1961. Japanese Flowers. Flowers in natural colours. Background colours given.
845 10 y. purple (T **401**) . . . . . 5·00 80
846 10 y. brown (Plum blossom) . . 3·00 80
847 10 y. bistre (Camellia) . . . . . 2·00 70
848 10 y. grey (Cherry blossom) . . 2·00 70
849 10 y. sepia (Peony) . . . . . 1·90 55
850 10 y. grey (Iris) . . . . . . 1·50 55
851 10 y. turquoise (Lily) . . . . . 1·00 30
852 10 y. blue (Morning Glory) . . . 1·00 30
853 10 y. sage (Bellflower) . . . . 1·00 30
854 10 y. orange (Gentian) . . . . 1·00 30
855 10 y. blue (Chrysanthemum) . . 1·25 30
856 10 y. slate (Camellia) . . . . . 1·00 30

1961. Minami-Boso Quasi-National Park.
857 **402** 10 y. multicoloured . . . . 1·00 10

403 Hirase's Slit Shell

404 Nanten

405 Cherry Blossoms

406 Engaku Temple

407 Yomei Gate, Tosho Shrine, Nikko

408 Noh Mask

409 Copper Pheasant

410 "The Wind God"

411 Manchurian Cranes

412 "Kalavinka" (legendary bird)

1961.
858 **403** 4 y. red and brown 35 10
859 **404** 6 y. red and green 20 10
860 **405** 10 y. mauve and purple . . 45 10
861 **406** 30 y. violet . . . . 5·00 10
862 **407** 40 y. red . . . . 6·00 10
863 **408** 70 y. black and ochre . . . 3·00 10
864 **409** 80 y. brown and red . . . 1·75 10
865 **410** 90 y. green . . . . . . 35·00 15
866 **411** 100 y. grey, black & pink . 18·00 10
867 **412** 120 y. violet . . . . . . 12·00 30
For 70, 80, 90, 100, and 120 y. in different colours and additionally inscr "NIPPON" see Nos. 1065/6, 1068, 1234/6 and 1238.

413 Baron Maeshima

414 "Dancing Girl" (from 17th-century screen)

1961. 90th Anniv of Japanese Postal Service.
868 **413** 10 y. green and black . . . 1·00 15

1961. Philatelic Week.
869 **414** 10 y. multicoloured . . . . 1·75 90

415 Lake Biwa

416 Rotary Emblem and "Peoples of the World"

1961. Lake Biwa Quasi-National Park.
870 **415** 10 y. multicoloured . . . . 1·10 20

1961. 52nd Rotary International Convention
871 **416** 10 y. orange and black . . 45 10

417 "Benefits Irrigation"

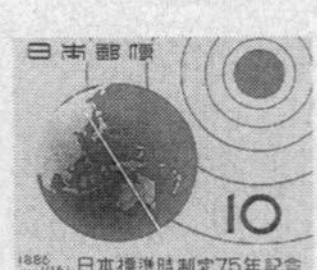
418 Globe showing Longitude 135° E. and Sun

1961. Inauguration of Aichi Irrigation Scheme.
872 **417** 10 y. blue and purple . . . 50 15

1961. 75th Anniv of Japanese Standard Time.
873 **418** 10 y. red, black & ochre . . 50 15

419 Parasol Dancer, Tottori Beach

420 Komagatake Volcano

1961. San'in Kaigan Quasi-National Park.
874 **419** 10 y. multicoloured 80 20

1961. Onuma Quasi-National Park.
875 **420** 10 y. multicoloured 80 20

421 Gymnast

422 "Hakone" (after Hiroshige)

1961. 16th National Athletic Meeting, Akita.
876 **421** 5 y. green . . . . 1·00 10
877 – 5 y. blue (Rowing) . . . . 1·00 10

1961. International Correspondence Week.
878 **422** 30 y. multicoloured . . . . 9·00 4·00

423 Throwing the Javelin

424 Library and Book

1961. Olympic Games, Tokyo, 1964 (1st issue).
879 **423** 5 y.+5 y. brown . . . . . 1·50 70
880 – 5 y.+5 y. green . . . . . 1·50 70
881 – 5 y.+5 y. red . . . . . . 1·50 70
DESIGNS: No. 880, Wrestling; No. 881, Diver (Woman).
See also Nos. 899/901, 909/11, 935/7, 949/52, 969/72 and 981/5.

1961. Opening of National Diet Library.
882 **424** 10 y. blue and gold 60 15

425 Tiger (Izumo toy)

1961. New Year's Greetings.
883 **425** 5 y. multicoloured 75 10

426 Mt. Fuji from Lake Aishi

427 Minokake-Iwa, Irozaki

428 Mt. Fuji from Mitsutoge

429 Mt. Fuji from Osezaki

1962. Fuji-Hakone-Izu National Park.
885 **426** 5 y. green . . . . 1·00 10
886 **427** 5 y. blue . . . . 1·00 10
887 **428** 10 y. brown . . . . 1·75 25
888 **429** 10 y. black . . . . 1·25 25

430 Omishima Island

431 Doll Festival

1962. Kitanagato-Kaigan Quasi-National Park.
889 **430** 10 y. multicoloured 60 20

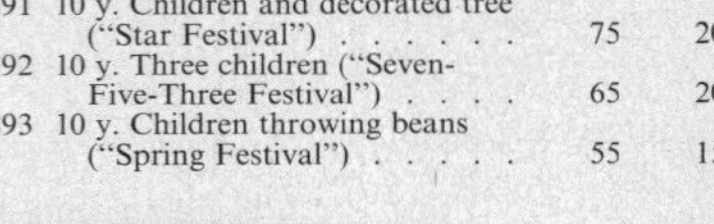

1962. National Festivals. Multicoloured.
890 10 y. Type **431** . . . . 1·75 25
891 10 y. Children and decorated tree ("Star Festival") 75 20
892 10 y. Three children ("Seven-Five-Three Festival") 65 20
893 10 y. Children throwing beans ("Spring Festival") 55 15

432 "Dancer" (after N. Kano)

433 Sakurajima Volcano

1962. Philatelic Week.
894 **432** 10 y. multicoloured . . . . 1·50 1·00

1962. Kinkowan Quasi-National Park.
895 **433** 10 y. multicoloured 60 20

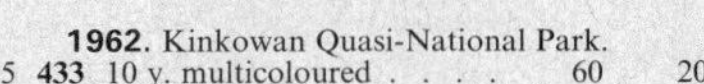

434 Mount Kongo

1962. Kongo-Ikoma Quasi-National Park.
896 **434** 10 y. multicoloured 60 20

435 Suigo View

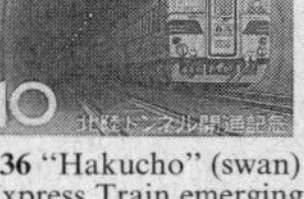
436 "Hakucho" (swan) Express Train emerging from Tunnel

1962. Suigo Quasi-National Park.
897 **435** 10 y. multicoloured 80 20

1962. Opening of Hokuriku Railway Tunnel.
898 **436** 10 y. brown . . . . 2·50 45

1962. Olympic Games, Tokyo, 1964 (2nd issue). Sports designs as T **423**.
899 5 y. + 5 y. red 75 35
900 5 y. + 5 y. green 75 35
901 5 y. + 5 y. purple 75 35
SPORTS: No. 899 Judo; 900, Water-polo; 901, Gymnastics (female).

437 Scout's Hat on Map

1962. Asian Scout Jamboree, Mt. Fuji.
902 **437** 10 y. black, bistre & red . . 40 10

438 Mt. Shibutsu and Ozegahara Swamp

439 Smoking Summit of Mt. Chausu, Nasu

440 Lake Chuzenji and Mt. Nantai

441 Senryu-kyo Narrows, Shiobara

1962. Nikko National Park.
903 **438** 5 y. turquoise 60 10
904 **439** 5 y. lake 60 10
905 **440** 10 y. purple 80 10
906 **441** 10 y. olive 80 10

442 Wakato Suspension Bridge
443 "Nihonbashi" (after Hiroshige)

1962. Opening of Wakato Suspension Bridge.
907 **442** 10 y. red . . . . 1·50 35

1962. International Correspondence Week.
908 **443** 40 y. multicoloured . . . . 7·50 3·00

1962. Olympic Games, Tokyo, 1964 (3rd issue). Sports designs as T **423**.
909 5 y. + 5 y. green 65 25
910 5 y. + 5 y. lilac 65 25
911 5 y. + 5 y. red 65 25
SPORTS: No. 909, Basketball; No. 910, Rowing; No. 911, Fencing.

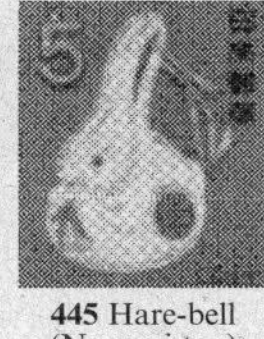

444 Rifle-shooting
445 Hare-bell (Nogomi toy)

1962. 17th National Athletic Meeting, Okayama.
912 **444** 5 y. purple 40 10
913 – 5 y. blue 40 10
DESIGN: No. 913, Softball.

1962. New Year's Greetings.
914 **445** 5 y. multicoloured 40 10
For 50 y. in this design dated "1999" see No. 2566.

446 Mt. Ishizuchi and Kamega Forest
447 "Five Towns"

1963. Ishizuchi Quasi-National Park.
916 **446** 10 y. multicoloured 30 10

1963. Amalgamation of Five Towns as Kita-Kyushu.
917 **447** 10 y. brown 25 10

448 Frosted Foliage, Fugen Peak
449 Amakusa Islands and Mt. Unzen

1963. Unzen-Amakusa National Park.
918 **448** 5 y. blue 35 10
919 **449** 10 y. red 65 10

450 Midorigaike (Green Pond)
451 Hakusan Mountains

1963. Hakusan National Park.
920 **450** 5 y. brown 45 10
921 **451** 10 y. green 75 10

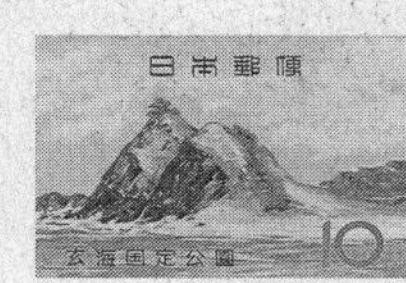

452 Great Rocks, Keya

1963. Genkai Quasi-National Park.
922 **452** 10 y. multicoloured 25 10

453 Globe and Emblem

1963. Freedom from Hunger.
923 **453** 10 y. green 40 10

454 "Portrait of Heihachiro Honda" (anon-Yedo period)
455 Centenary Emblem and World Map

1963. Philatelic Week.
924 **454** 10 y. multicoloured 85 45

1963. Centenary of Red Cross.
925 **455** 10 y. multicoloured 35 10

456 Globe and Leaf

1963. 5th International Irrigation and Drainage Commission Congress, Toyko.
926 **456** 10 y. blue 15 10

457 Mt. Ito, Asahi Range
458 Mt. Bandai across Lake Hibara

(Illustrations reduced: each 33 × 23 mm)

1963. Bandai-Asahi National Park.
927 **457** 5 y. green 45 10
928 **458** 10 y. brown 75 10

459 Purple Jay

1963. Japanese Birds. Multicoloured.
929 10 y. Type **459** . . . . . . 2·00 65
930 10 y. Rock ptarmigan 60 15
931 10 y. Eastern turtle dove . . . 60 15
932 10 y. White stork 60 15
933 10 y. Japanese bush warbler . . 60 15
934 10 y. Siberian meadow bunting . 60 15

1963. Olympic Games, Tokyo, 1964 (4th issue). Sports designs as T **423**.
935 5 y. + 5 y. blue 75 25
936 5 y. + 5 y. brown 75 25
937 5 y. + 5 y. brown 75 25
SPORTS: No. 935, Dinghy sailing; No. 936, Boxing; No. 937, Volleyball.

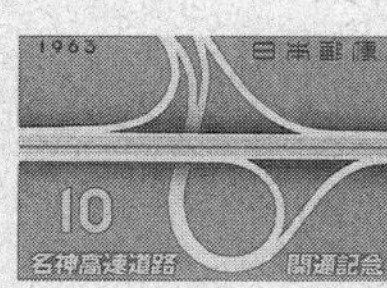

460 Road Junction, Ritto, Shiga
461 Girl Scout and Flag

1963. Opening of Nagoya-Kobe Expressway.
938 **460** 10 y. green, black & orge . . 35 10

1963. Asian Girl Scout Camp, Nagano.
939 **461** 10 y. multicoloured 35 10

462 Mt. Washiu
463 Whirlpool at Naruto

1963. Seto Inland Sea National Park.
940 **462** 5 y. brown 25 10
941 **463** 10 y. green 35 10

464 Lake Shikaribetsu
465 Mt. Kurodake

1963. Daisetsuzan National Park.
942 **464** 5 y. blue 25 10
943 **465** 10 y. purple 35 10

466 Antennae
467 "Great Wave off Kanagawa" (from "36 Views of Mt. Fuji" by Hokusai Katsushika)

1963. 14th International Scientific Radio Union Conference, Tokyo.
944 **466** 10 y multicoloured 25 10

1963. International Correspondence Week.
945 **467** 40 y. multicoloured . . . . 4·25 50
The design is taken from the series of 36 woodcuts showing Mt. Fuji. Others from this series are shown as Nos. 989, 1010, 1075, 1100, 1140 and 1185.

468 Athletes
469 Wrestling

1963. "Pre-Olympic" Athletic Meeting, Tokyo.
946 **468** 10 y. multicoloured 15 10

1963. 18th National Athletic Meeting, Yamaguchi.
947 **469** 5 y. brown 20 10
948 – 5 y. green 20 10
DESIGN: No. 948, Free-style gymnastics.

1963. Olympic Games, Tokyo, 1964 (5th issue). Sports designs as T **423**.
949 5 y. + 5 y. blue 35 10
950 5 y. + 5 y. olive 35 10
951 5 y. + 5 y. black 35 10
952 5 y. + 5 y. purple 35 10
SPORTS: No. 949, Cycling; 950, Show jumping; 951, Hockey; 952, Pistol-shooting.

470 Hachijo Island
471 Kai and Iwai Dragon Toys

1963. Izu Islands Quasi-National Park.
953 **470** 10 y. multicoloured 25 10

1963. New Year's Greetings.
954 **471** 5 y. multicoloured 35 10

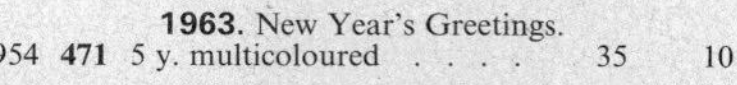

472 Wakasa Bay
473 View from Horikiri Pass and Agave Plant

1964. Wakasa Bay Quasi-National Park.
956 **472** 10 y. multicoloured 35 10

1964. Nichinan-Kaigan Quasi-National Park.
957 **473** 10 y. multicoloured 15 10

474 Uji Bridge
475 View of Toba

1964. Ise-Shima National Park.
958 **474** 5 y. brown 15 10
959 **475** 10 y. purple 20 10

476 Festival Float and Mt. Norikura (Tokayama Festival)
477 "Yamaboko" Shrine (Gion Festival)

478 Warriors on Horseback (Soma Horse Festival)

479 Festival Scene (Chichibu Festival)

1964. Regional Festivals.

960 **476** 10 y. multicoloured 35 10
961 **477** 10 y. multicoloured 35 10
962 **478** 10 y. multicoloured 35 10
963 **479** 10 y. multicoloured 35 10

480 Prince Niou playing for Lady Nakanokimi (detail of Takayoshi "Yadorigi" scroll illustrating "Tale of Genji" by Lady Murasaki)

1964. Philatelic Week.

964 **480** 10 y. multicoloured 40 15

481 Himeji Castle

482 Handball

1964. Rebuilding of Himeji Castle.

965 **481** 10 y. brown 15 10

1964. 19th National Athletic Meeting, Niigata.

966 **482** 5 y. green 10 10
967 – 5 y. red (Gymnastics) . . . 10 10

483 Cross-section of Cable

1964. Opening of Japan–U.S. Submarine Telephone Cable.

968 **483** 10 y. multicoloured 15 10

1964. Olympic Games, Tokyo (6th issue). Sports designs as T **423**.

969 5 y. + 5 y. violet 45 10
970 5 y. + 5 y. blue 45 10
971 5 y. + 5 y. lake 45 10
972 5 y. + 5 y. olive 45 10

SPORTS: No. 969, Modern pentathlon; 970, Canoeing; 971, Football; 972, Weightlifting.

484 Nihonbashi Bridge

485 "Coins"

1964. Opening of Tokyo Expressway.

973 **484** 10 y. green, silver & blk . . 25 10

1964. Int. Monetary Fund Convention, Tokyo.

980 **485** 10 y. gold and red 25 10

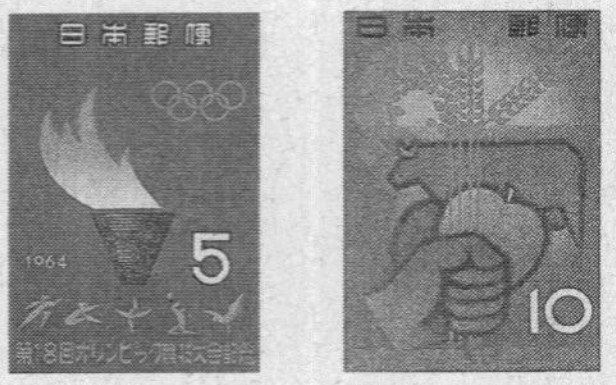

486 Olympic Flame

487 "Agriculture"

1964. Olympic Games, Tokyo (7th issue). Inscr "1964". Multicoloured.

981 5 y. Type **486** 20 15
982 10 y. Main stadium (horiz) . . . 30 20
983 30 y. Fencing hall (horiz) . . . 50 30
984 40 y. Indoor stadium (horiz) . . 70 30
985 50 y. Komazawa hall (horiz) . . 90 30

1964. Reclamation of Hachirogata Lagoon.

987 **487** 10 y. gold and purple . . . 15 10

488 "Hikari" (light) Express Train

1964. Inauguration of Tokyo–Osaka Shinkansen Railway Line.

988 **488** 10 y. blue and black . . . 1·00 20

489 "Tokaido Highway" (from "36 Views of Mt. Fuji" by Hokusai Katsushika)

490 Straw Snake

1964. International Correspondence Week.

989 **489** 40 y. multicoloured . . . . 1·75 10

1964. New Year's Greetings.

990 **490** 5 y. multicoloured 15 10

491 Mt. Daisen and Akamatsu Pond

492 Jodo-ga-Ura (Paradise Islands) of Oki

(Illustrations reduced: each 33 × 23 mm)

1965. Daisen-Oki National Park.

992 **491** 5 y. blue 25 10
993 **492** 10 y. brown 35 10

493 Niseko-Annupuri Mountains

494 Radar Station

1965. Niseko Shakotan Otaru Quasi-National Park.

994 **493** 10 y. multicoloured 30 10

1965. Completion of Meteorological Radar Station, Mt. Fuji.

995 **494** 10 y. multicoloured 25 10

495 Kiyotsu Gorge

496 Mt. Myoko across Lake Nojiri

1965. Jo-Shin-Etsu Kogen National Park.

996 **495** 5 y. brown 20 10
997 **496** 10 y. purple 35 10

497 Postal Museum

1965. Inauguration of Postal Museum, Ote-machi, Tokyo, and Stamp Exhibition.

998 **497** 10 y. green 15 10

498 "The Prelude" (after Shoen Uyemura)

499 Children at Play

1965. Philatelic Week.

999 **498** 10 y. multicoloured 50 10

1965. Inaug of National Children's Gardens.

1000 **499** 10 y. multicoloured . . . 20 10

500 Tree within "Leaf"

501 Globe and Symbols

1965. Reafforestation.

1001 **500** 10 y. multicoloured . . . 20 10

1965. Centenary of I.T.U.

1002 **501** 10 y. multicoloured . . . 35 10

502 Mt. Naka Crater

503 Aso Peaks

(Illustrations reduced: each 33 × 23 mm)

1965. Aso National Park.

1003 **502** 5 y. red 25 10
1004 **503** 10 y. green 35 10

504 I.C.Y. Emblem and Doves

1965. International Co-operation Year.

1005 **504** 40 y. multicoloured . . . 75 10

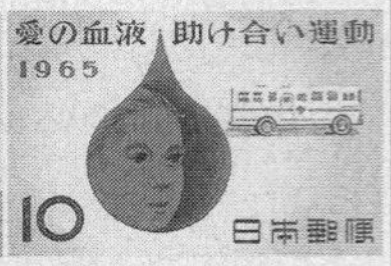

505 "Meiji Maru" (cadet ship) and Japanese Gulls

506 "Blood Donation"

1965. 25th Maritime Day.

1006 **505** 10 y. multicoloured . . . 1·25 10

1965. Campaign for Blood Donors.

1007 **506** 10 y. multicoloured . . . 25 10

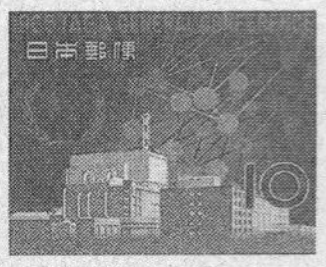

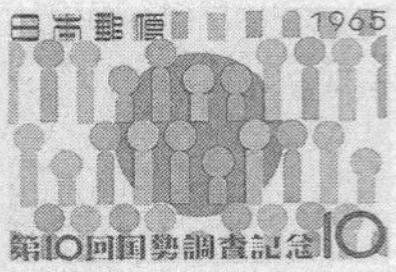

507 Atomic Power Station, Tokyo

508 "Population"

1965. 9th International Atomic Energy Authority Conference, Tokyo.

1008 **507** 10 y. multicoloured . . . 35 10

1965. 10th National Census.

1009 **508** 10 y. multicoloured . . . 20 10

509 "Water at Misaka" (from "36 Views of Mt. Fuji" by Hokusai Katsushika)

510 Emblems and Plan of Diet

1965. International Correspondence Week.

1010 **509** 40 y. multicoloured . . . 80 60

1965. 75th Anniv of National Suffrage.

1011 **510** 10 y. multicoloured . . . 20 10

511 Walking

512 Outline of Face, and Baby

1965. 20th National Athletic Meeting, Gifu.

1012 **511** 5 y. green 15 10
1013 – 5 y. brown (Gymnastics) . . . 15 10

1965. Int Conferences of Otology, Rhinology and Laryngology (ICORL) and Pediatrics (ICP), Tokyo.

1014 **512** 30 y. multicoloured . . . 40 10

513 Mt. Iwo

514 Mt. Rausu

1965. Shiretoko National Park.

1015 **513** 5 y. turquoise 25 10
1016 **514** 10 y. blue 35 10

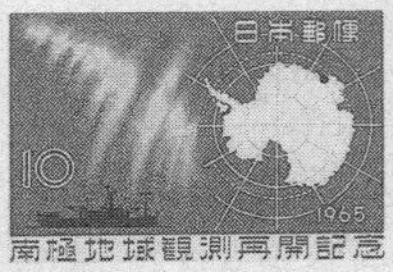

515 Antarctic Map, Research Vessel "Fuji" and Aurora Australis

516 "Straw Horse"

1965. Antarctic Expedition of 1965.

1017 **515** 10 y. multicoloured . . . 1·40 15

1965. New Year's Greetings.

1018 **516** 5 y. multicoloured 15 10

517 Telephone Switchboard (1890) and Modern Dial

518 Spiny Lobster

1965. 75th Anniv of Japanese Telephone Service.

1020 **517** 10 y. multicoloured . . . 15 10

NIPPON. From this point onwards all stamps are additionally inscribed "NIPPON".

1966. Fishery Products. Multicoloured.

1021 10 y. Type **518** 30 15
1022 10 y. Golden carp 30 15
1023 10 y. Madai seabream 30 15
1024 10 y. Skipjack tuna 30 15
1025 10 y. Ayu 30 15
1026 15 y. Japanese eel 40 15
1027 15 y. Chub mackerel 40 15
1028 15 y. Chum salmon 40 15
1029 15 y. Buri 60 15
1030 15 y. Tiger pufferfish 60 20
1031 15 y. Japanese common squid . 75 30
1032 15 y. Horned turban (shellfish) 85 30

519 Pleasure Garden, Mito

519a Pleasure Garden and Manchurian Cranes, Okayama

519b Kerokuen Garden, Kanazawa

1966. Famous Japanese Gardens.

1033 **519** 10 y. green, blk & gold . 25 10
1034 **519a** 15 y. black, red & blue . 1·25 10
1035 **519b** 15 y. black, green & sil . 35 10

520 Crater of Mt. Zao

1966. Zao Quasi-National Park.

1036 **520** 10 y. multicoloured . . . 35 10

521 Muroto Cape

522 Senba Cliffs, Anan

1966. Muroto-Anan Kaigan Quasi-National Park.

1037 **521** 10 y. multicoloured . . . 25 10
1038 **522** 10 y. multicoloured . . . 30 10

523 A.I.P.P.I. Emblem

1966. General Assembly of Int Association for Protection of Industrial Property (A.I.P.P.I.).
1039 **523** 40 y. multicoloured . . . 35 10

524 "Butterflies" (after T. Fujishima)

1966. Philatelic Week.
1040 **524** 10 y. multicoloured . . . 35 10

525 Goldfish **526** Chrysanthemums **527** Fuji (wisteria)

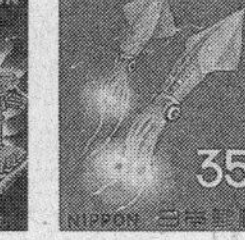
528 Hydrangea **529** Golden Hall, Chuson Temple **530** "Watasenia scintillans" (squid)

531 Yomei Gate, Tosho Shrine, Nikko **532** Mizubasho **533** Konponchudo Hall, Enryaku Temple

534 Ancient Clay Horse **535** Garden of Katsura Palace

536 Onjo Bosatsu (relief from bronze lantern, Todai Temple) **537** Kongo-Rikishi Statue, Todai Temple Nara

1966. Inscr "NIPPON".
1041 **235** 1 y. bistre 10 10
1047 **525** 7 y. orange and green . . 40 10
1049 **526** 15 y. yellow and blue . . 1·25 10
1050 15 y. yellow and blue . . 25 10
1052 **527** 20 y. green and violet . . 1·25 10
1053 **528** 25 y. blue and green . . 60 10
1054 **529** 30 y. gold and blue . . . 40 10
1055 **530** 35 y. black, brown & blue 3·25 10
1056 **531** 40 y. green and brown . . 60 10
1057 **532** 45 y. multicoloured . . . 50 10
1058 **240** 50 y. red . . . . . . 11·00 10
1059 50 y. mauve 80 10
1060 **280** 55 y. green, black & blue . 75 10
1061 **533** 60 y. green . . . . . . 1·00 10
1062 **534** 65 y. brown . . . . . 16·00 10
1063 65 y. orange . . . . . . 1·00 10
1064 **281** 75 y. multicoloured . . . 1·40 10
1065 **410** 90 y. brown and gold . . 2·00 10
1066 **411** 100 y. grey, black & red . 1·75 10
1067 **535** 110 y. brown . . . . . 1·50 10
1068 **412** 120 y. red . . . . . . 3·50 10
1069 **536** 200 y. green . . . . . 7·50 10
1070 **537** 500 y. purple . . . . . 8·50 10
No. 1050 is as T **526** but with white figures of value.
See also Nos. 1226/49.

538 U.N. and U.N.E.S.C.O. Emblems **539** Pacific Ocean

1966. 20th Anniv of U.N.E.S.C.O.
1071 **538** 15 y. multicoloured . . . 15 10

1966. 11th Pacific Science Congress, Tokyo.
1072 **539** 15 y. multicoloured . . . 20 10

540 Amakusa Bridges

1966. Completion of Amakusa Bridges.
1073 **540** 15 y. multicoloured . . . 20 10

541 Family and Emblem **542** "Sekiya on the Sumida" (from "36 Views of Mt. Fuji" by Hokusai Katsushika)

1966. 50th Anniv of Post Office Life Insurance Office.
1074 **541** 15 y. multicoloured . . . 15 10

1966. International Correspondence Week.
1075 **542** 50 y. multicoloured . . . 1·75 15

543 Rotary Cobalt Radiator **544** Triple Jump

1966. 9th. International Cancer Congress, Tokyo.
1076 **543** 7 y. + 3 y. black & orge . 25 15
1077 – 15 y. + 5 y. mult . . . 35 15
DESIGN—VERT: 15 y. Detection by X-rays.

1966. 21st National Athletic Meeting, Oita.
1078 **544** 7 y. red 30 10
1079 – 7 y. blue (clay-pigeon shooting) 30 10

545 National Theatre Building **546** Rice Year Emblem

1966. Inauguration of Japanese National Theatre. Multicoloured.
1080 15 y. Type **545** 25 10
1081 25 y. "Kabuki" performance ($48 \times 33\frac{1}{2}$ mm) 90 10
1082 50 y. "Bunraku" puppet act ($33\frac{1}{2} \times 48$ mm) . . . . . 1·00 10

1966. International Rice Year.
1083 **546** 15 y. black, ochre & red . 15 10

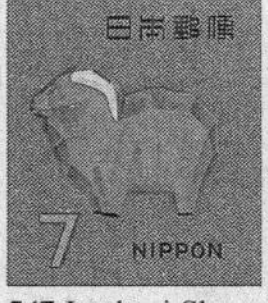

547 Ittobori Sheep (sculpture) **548** Satellite "Intelsat 2", Earth and Moon

1966. New Year's Greetings.
1084 **547** 7 y. multicoloured 15 10

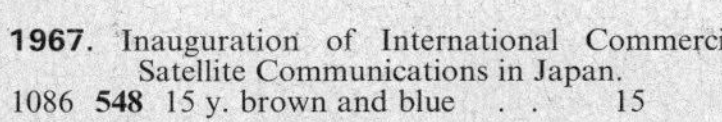
1967. Inauguration of International Commercial Satellite Communications in Japan.
1086 **548** 15 y. brown and blue . . 15 10

549 Douglas DC-8 and Flight Route **550** Literature Museum

1967. Inauguration of Round-the-World Air Service.
1087 **549** 15 y. multicoloured . . . 50 10

1967. Opening of Japanese Modern Literature Museum, Meguro-ku, Tokyo.
1088 **550** 15 y. multicoloured . . . 15 10

551 "Lakeside" (after S. Kuroda)

1967. Philatelic Week.
1089 **551** 15 y. multicoloured . . . 60 10

552 Port of Kobe **553** Emblem of Welfare Service

1967. 5th International Association of Ports and Harbours Congress, Tokyo.
1090 **552** 50 y. multicoloured . . . 80 10

1967. 50th Anniv of Welfare Commissioner Service.
1091 **553** 15 y. gold and agate . . 25 10

554 Pedestrian Road Crossing

1967. 20th Anniv of Road Safety Campaign.
1092 **554** 15 y. multicoloured . . . 15 10

555 Mts. Kita and Koma **556** Mts. Akashi, Hijiri and Higashi

1967. Southern Alps National Park.
1093 **555** 7 y. blue 25 10
1094 **556** 15 y. purple 35 10

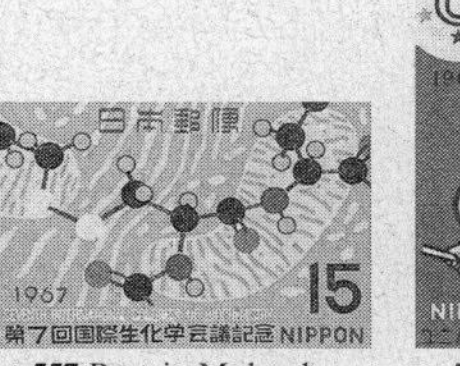

557 Protein Molecules **558** Gymnast

1967. 7th Int Biochemistry Congress, Tokyo.
1095 **557** 15 y. multicoloured . . . 15 10

1967. "Universiade 1967" (Sports Meeting), Tokyo. Multicoloured.
1096 15 y. Type **558** 20 10
1097 50 y. Universiade "U" emblem ($25 \times 35\frac{1}{2}$ mm) 90 10

559 Paper Lantern

560 Mt. Fuji (after T. Yokoyama)

1967. International Tourist Year.
1098 **559** 15 y. multicoloured . . . 25 10
1099 **560** 50 y. multicoloured . . . 3·25 3·25

561 "Kajikazawa in Kai Province" (from "36 Views of Mt. Fuji" by Hokusai Katsushika) **562** Athlete

1967. International Correspondence Week.
1100 **561** 50 y. multicoloured . . . 2·75 15

1967. 22nd National Athletic Meeting, Saitama.
1101 **562** 15 y. multicoloured . . . 50 10

563 Buddha, Koryu Temple, Kyoto **564** Kudara Kannon (Budda), Horyu Temple, Nara

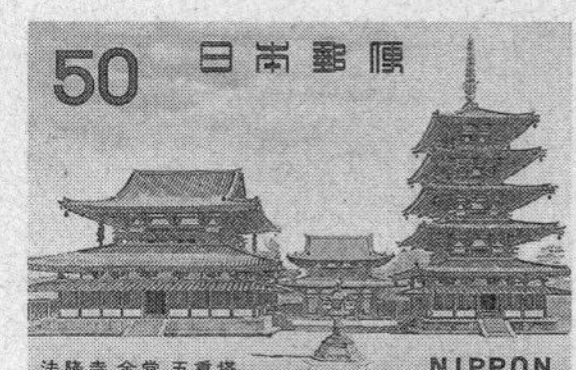
565 Horyu Temple, Nara

1967. National Treasures. Asuka Period.
1102 **563** 15 y. multicoloured . . . 40 10
1103 **564** 15 y. multicoloured . . . 60 10
1104 **565** 50 y. multicoloured . . . 2·50 20
See also Nos. 1113/15, 1120/2, 1134/6, 1152/4, 1170/2 and 1177/80.

566 Motor Expressway **569** "Noborizaru" (Miyazaki toy)

567 Mt. Kumotori

568 Lake Chichibu

1967. 13th World Road Congress, Tokyo.
1105 **566** 50 y. multicoloured . . . 75 10

1967. Chichibu-Tama National Park.
1106 **567** 7 y. olive 35 10
1107 **568** 15 y. violet 45 10

1967. New Year's Greetings.
1108 **569** 7 y. multicoloured 35 10

570 Mt. Sobo **571** Takachiho Gorge

1967. Sobo-Katamuki Quasi-National Park.
1110 **570** 15 y. multicoloured . . . 35 10
1111 **571** 15 y. multicoloured . . . 35 10

572 Boy and Girl and Cruise Liner "Sakura Maru" **573** Asura Statue, Kofuku Temple, Nara

574 Gakko Bosatsu, Todai Temple, Nara **575** Srimaha devi (painting), Yakushi Temple, Nara

1968. Youth Goodwill Cruise to mark Meiji Centenary.
1112 **572** 15 y. violet, yellow & blue 15 10

1968. National Treasures. Nara Period (710–784).
1113 **573** 15 y. multicoloured . . . 45 10
1114 **574** 15 y. multicoloured . . . 70 10
1115 **575** 50 y. multicoloured . . . 2·50 20

576 Mt. Yatsugatake and Cattle **577** Mt. Tateshina and Lake

1968. Yatsugatake-Chushin Kogen Quasi-National Park.
1116 **576** 15 y. multicoloured . . . 30 10
1117 **577** 15 y. multicoloured . . . 30 10

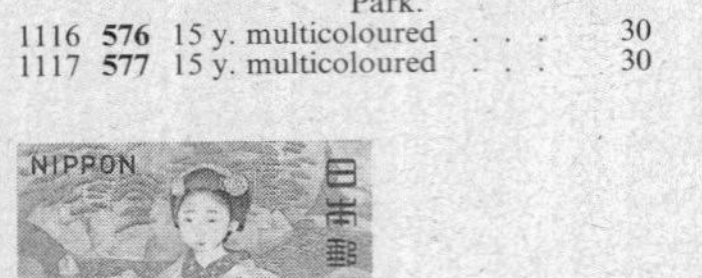

578 "Dancer in a Garden" (after Bakusen Tsuchida) **579** View of Rishiri Island from Rebun Island

1968. Philatelic Week.
1118 **578** 15 y. multicoloured . . . 40 10

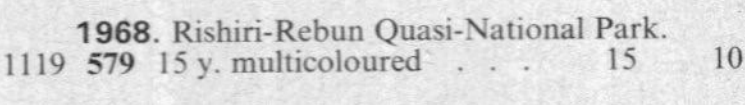

1968. Rishiri-Rebun Quasi-National Park.
1119 **579** 15 y. multicoloured . . . 15 10

580 Lacquer Casket **582** "Fugen Bosatsu" (painting of Bodishattva Samantabhadva)

581 "The Origin of Shigisan" (painting in Chogo-sonshi Temple)

1968. National Treasures. Heinan Period (794–1185).
1120 **580** 15 y. multicoloured . . . 30 10
1121 **581** 15 y. multicoloured . . . 60 10
1122 **582** 50 y. multicoloured . . . 4·25 35

583 Centenary Tower and Star **584** Biro Trees and Pacific Sunrise

1968. Hokkaido Centenary.
1123 **583** 15 y. multicoloured . . . 15 10

1968. Return of Ogasawara Islands to Japan.
1124 **584** 15 y. multicoloured . . . 15 10

585 "Map of Japan" in Figures

1968. Postal Codes Campaign.
1125 **585** 7 y. red, brown & grn (I) . 2·75 10
1126 – 7 y. red, brown & grn (II) 2·75 10
1127 **585** 15 y. mve, vio & bl (I) . . 1·00 10
1128 – 15 y. mve, vio & bl (II) . . 1·00 10
(I) Inscr as in Type **585** reading "Don't omit postal code on the address" measures 11 mm.
(II) Inscr reading "Postal code also on your address" measures 12 mm.

586 River Kiso **587** Inuyama Castle and View

1968. Hida-Kisogawa Quasi-National Park.
1129 **586** 15 y. multicoloured . . . 25 10
1130 **587** 15 y. multicoloured . . . 25 10

588 Federation Emblem and "Sun"

1968. Int Youth Hostel Conference, Tokyo.
1131 **588** 15 y. multicoloured . . . 20 10

589 Humans forming Emblem **590** Baseball "Pitcher"

1968. 50th All-Japan High School Baseball Championships, Koshi-en, Tokyo.
1132 **589** 15 y. multicoloured . . . 60 10
1133 **590** 15 y. multicoloured . . . 60 10

591 "Minamoto Yoritomo" (Jingo Temple Collection) **593** Red-braided Armour (Kasuga Grand Shrine Collection)

592 Emperor Nijo escaping from Black Palace (from "Tale of Heiji" picture scroll)

1968. National Treasures. Kamakura Period (1185–1334).
1134 **591** 15 y. multicoloured . . . 40 10
1135 **592** 15 y. multicoloured . . . 40 10
1136 **593** 50 y. multicoloured . . . 3·00 30

594 Mount Iwate **595** Lake Towada

1968. Towada-Hachimantai National Park.
1137 **594** 7 y. brown 25 10
1138 **595** 15 y. green 45 10

596 Gymnastics **597** "Fujimihara in Owari Province" (from "36 Views of Mt. Fuji" by Hokusai Katsushika)

1968. 23rd National Athletic Meeting.
1139 **596** 15 y. multicoloured . . . 40 10

1968. International Correspondence Week.
1140 **597** 50 y. multicoloured . . . 2·00 25

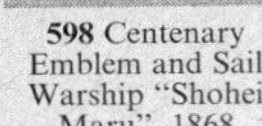

598 Centenary Emblem and Sail Warship "Shohei Maru", 1868 **599** "Arrival of the Imperial Carriage in Tokyo" (after Tomone Kobori)

1968. Centenary of Meiji Era.
1141 **598** 15 y. multicoloured . . . 15 10
1142 **599** 15 y. multicoloured . . . 15 10

600 Old and New Kannonzaki Lighthouses

1968. Centenary of Japanese Lighthouses.
1143 **600** 15 y. multicoloured . . . 30 10

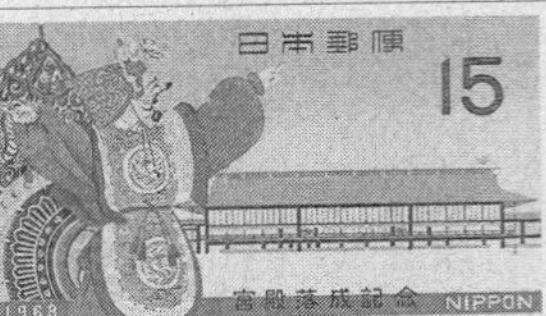

601 Ryo's Dancer and State Hall

1968. Completion of Imperial Palace.
1144 **601** 15 y. multicoloured . . . 20 10

602 Mount Takachiho **603** Mount Motobu, Yaku Island

1968. Kirishima-Yaku National Park.
1145 **602** 7 y. violet 20 10
1146 **603** 15 y. orange 25 10

604 "Niwatori" (Yamagata toy) **605** Human Rights Emblem and Dancers

1968. New Year's Greetings.
1147 **604** 7 y. multicoloured 25 10

1968. Human Rights Year.
1149 **605** 50 y. multicoloured . . . 25 15

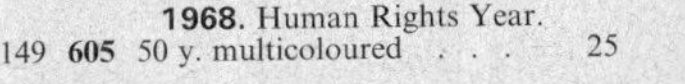

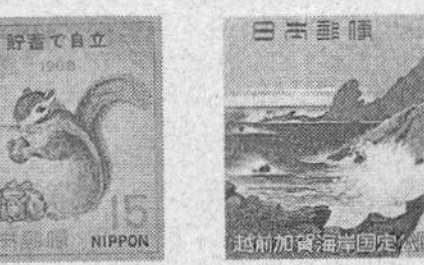

606 Siberian Chipmunk with Nuts **607** Coastal Scenery

1968. Savings Promotion.
1150 **606** 15 y. sepia and green . . 70 10

1969. Echizen-Kaga-Kaigan Quasi-National Park.
1151 **607** 15 y. multicoloured . . . 15 10

608 Silver Pavilion, Jisho Temple, Kyoto **609** Pagoda, Anraku Temple, Nagano

610 "Winter Landscape" (Sesshu)

1969. National Treasures. Muromachi Period.
1152 **608** 15 y. multicoloured . . . 40 10
1153 **609** 15 y. multicoloured . . . 40 10
1154 **610** 50 y. multicoloured . . . 2·00 30

611 Mt. Chokai, from Tobishima

1969. Chokai Quasi-National Park.
1155 **611** 15 y. multicoloured . . . 35 10

612 "Expo" Emblem and Globe

613 "Cherry Blossom" (from mural Chichakuin Temple, Kyoto)

1969. "EXPO 70" World Fair, Osaka (1st issue).
1156 **612** 15 y. + 5 y. mult 35 15
1157 **613** 50 y. + 10 y. mult 85 50
See also Nos. 1193/5 and 1200/2.

614 Mt. Koya from Jinnogamine — **615** Mt. Gomadan and Rhododendrons

1969. Koya-Ryujin Quasi-National Park.
1158 **614** 15 y. multicoloured . . . 15 10
1159 **615** 15 y. multicoloured . . . 15 10

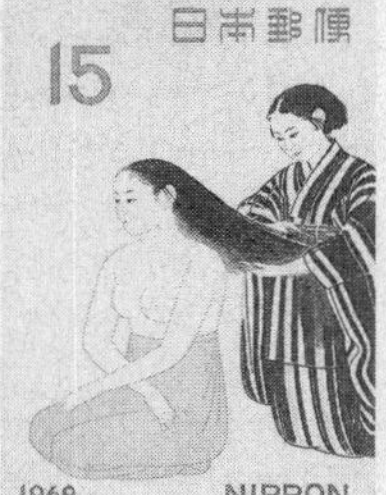
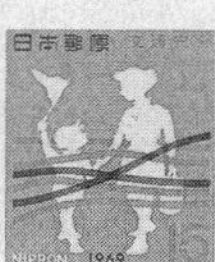

616 "Hair" (Kokei Kobayashi) — **617** Woman and Child crossing "Roads"

1969. Philatelic Week.
1160 **616** 15 y. multicoloured . . . 40 10

1969. Road Safety Campaign.
1161 **617** 15 y. green, blue & red . . 15 10

618 Sakawagawa Bridge

1969. Completion of Tokyo-Nagoya Expressway.
1162 **618** 15 y. multicoloured . . . 30 10

619 Museum Building

1969. Opening of National Museum of Modern Art, Tokyo.
1163 **619** 15 y. multicoloured . . . 15 10

620 Nuclear-powered Freighter "Mutsu" and Atomic Symbol

1969. Launching of Japan's 1st Nuclear Ship "Mutsu".
1164 **620** 15 y. multicoloured . . . 30 10

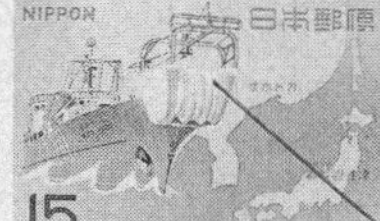

621 Cable Ship "KDD Maru" and Map — **622** Symbol and Cards

1969. Opening of Japanese Ocean Cable.
1165 **621** 15 y. multicoloured . . . 15 10

1969. Postal Codes Campaign.
1166 **622** 7 y. red and green 15 10
1167 – 15 y. red and blue 20 10
DESIGN: 15 y. Symbol, postbox and code numbers.

624 Lions Emblem and Rose — **625** Hotoke-ga-ura (coast)

1969. 52nd Lions Int Convention, Tokyo.
1168 **624** 15 y. multicoloured . . . 20 10

1969. Shimokita-Hanto Quasi-National Park.
1169 **625** 15 y. multicoloured . . . 15 10

626 Himeji Castle, Hyogo Prefecture — **627** "Pinewoods" (T. Hasegawa)

628 "The Japanese Cypress" (artist unknown)

1969. National Treasures. Momoyama Period.
1170 **626** 15 y. multicoloured . . . 50 10
1171 **627** 15 y. black and drab . . . 50 10
1172 **628** 50 y. multicoloured . . . 1·00 10

629 Harano-fudo Waterfalls — **630** Mount Nagisan

1969. Hyonosen-Ushiroyama-Nagisan Quasi-National Park.
1173 **629** 15 y. multicoloured . . . 25 10
1174 **630** 15 y. multicoloured . . . 25 10

631 Mount O-akan — **632** Mount Iwo

1969. Akan National Park.
1175 **631** 7 y. blue 25 10
1176 **632** 15 y. sepia 25 10

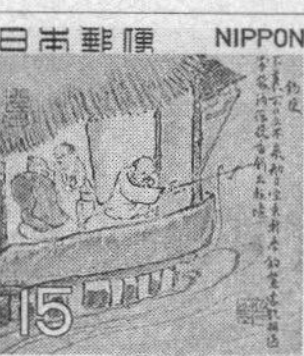

633 "Choben" (T. Ikeno)

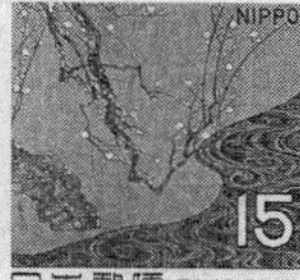

634 "The Red-plum Tree" (K. Ogata) — **635** "The White-plum Tree" (K. Ogata)

636 "Japanese Pheasant" Incense-burner (after Ninsei)

1969. National Treasures. Edo Period.
1177 **633** 15 y. multicoloured . . . 40 10
1178 **634** 15 y. multicoloured . . . 50 10
1179 **635** 15 y. multicoloured . . . 50 10
1180 **636** 50 y. multicoloured . . . 1·25 95

637 Globe and Doves

638 "Woman Reading a Letter" (Utamaro Kitagawa)

639 "Reading a Letter" (Harunobu Suzuki)

640 "Miyako Dennai" (Sharaku Toshusai)

1969. 16th U.P.U. Congress, Tokyo.
1181 **637** 15 y. multicoloured . . . 30 10
1182 **638** 30 y. multicoloured . . . 65 10
1183 **639** 50 y. multicoloured . . . 1·25 10
1184 **640** 60 y. multicoloured . . . 1·40 10

641 "Mishima Pass" (from "36 Views of Mt. Fuji" by Hokusai Katsushika) — **642** Rugby Football

1969. International Correspondence Week.
1185 **641** 50 y. multicoloured . . . 1·00 10

1969. 24th National Athletic Meeting.
1186 **642** 15 y. multicoloured . . . 50 10

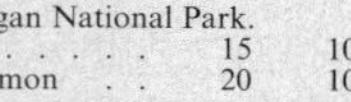

643 Cape Kitayama — **644** Goishi Coast

1969. Rikuchu-Kaigan National Park.
1187 **643** 7 y. blue 15 10
1188 **644** 15 y. red and salmon . . 20 10

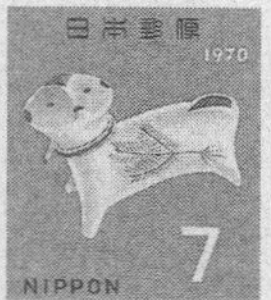

645 Worker in Safety Helmet — **646** Guardian Dog, Hokkeji Temple

1969. 50th Anniv of I.L.O.
1189 **645** 15 y. multicoloured . . . 15 10

1969. New Year's Greetings.
1190 **646** 7 y. multicoloured 35 10

647 Peasants, Tsushima Island

1970. Iki-Tsushima Quasi-National Park.
1192 **647** 15 y. multicoloured . . . 20 10

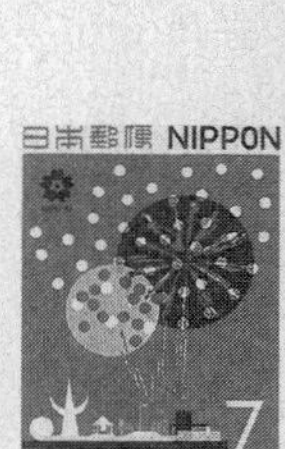

648 View of Fair and Firework Display — **651** "Woman with Drum" (Saburosuke Okada)

1970. "EXPO 70" World Fair, Osaka (2nd issue). Multicoloured.
1193 7 y. Type **648** 15 10
1194 15 y. Earth and Cherry Blossom Garland 25 10
1195 50 y. "Irises" (Korin Ogata) . . 45 10
No. 1195 is horiz size 48 × 33 mm.

1970. Philatelic Week.
1197 **651** 15 y. multicoloured . . . 40 10

652 Cherry Blossom, Mt. Yoshino — **653** Waterfall, Nachi

1970. Yoshino-Kumano National Park.
1198 **652** 7 y. black and pink . . . 30 10
1199 **653** 15 y. dp green, green & bl 45 10

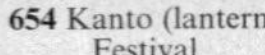
654 Kanto (lantern) Festival

655 Japanese Pavilions

656 "Flowers of Autumn" (detail, Hoitsu Sakai)

1970. "EXPO 70" World Fair, Osaka (3rd issue).

1200 **654** 7 y. multicoloured 20 10
1201 **655** 15 y. multicoloured . . . 30 10
1202 **656** 50 y. multicoloured . . . 45 10

657 Houses and Code Symbol

658 Utaemon Nakamura VI as Hanako in "Musume Dojoji"

659 Danjuro Ichikawa XI as Sukeroku in "Sukeroku"

661 Girl Scout saluting

660 "Kanjincho"

1970. Postal Codes Campaign.

1204 **657** 7 y. violet and green . . . 25 10
1205 15 y. purple and blue . . . 35 10

1970. Japanese Theatre "Kabuki".

1206 **658** 15 y. multicoloured . . . 25 10
1207 **659** 15 y. multicoloured . . . 25 10
1208 **660** 50 y. multicoloured . . . 75 10

See also Nos. 1250/2, 1284/6 and 1300/2.

1970. 50th Anniv of Japanese Girl Scouts.

1209 **661** 15 y. multicoloured . . . 35 10

662 Festival Drummer and Kinoura Coastline

663 Mt. Tate from Himi Shore

1970. Noto-Hanto Quasi-National Park.

1210 **662** 15 y. multicoloured . . . 25 10
1211 **663** 15 y. multicoloured . . . 25 10

664 "Sunflower" and U.N. Emblem

667 "Tokyo Post Office" (woodcut, Hiroshige III)

665 Mt. Myogi

666 Mt. Arafune

1970. 4th U.N. Congress on Prevention of Crime and Treatment of Offenders, Kyoto.

1212 **664** 15 y. multicoloured . . . 25 10

1970. Myogi-Arafune-Sakukuogen Quasi-National Park.

1213 **665** 15 y. multicoloured . . . 20 10
1214 **666** 15 y. multicoloured . . . 20 10

1970. International Correspondence Week.

1215 **667** 50 y. multicoloured . . . 85 10

668 Show Jumping, Mt. Iwate and Paulownia Flowers

669 "Hodogaya Stage" (print, Hiroshige III)

1970. 25th National Athletic Meeting, Iwate.

1216 **668** 15 y. multicoloured . . . 50 10

1970. Centenary of Telegraph Service.

1217 **669** 15 y. multicoloured . . . 45 10

670 U.N. Emblem within "Tree"

672 Competition Emblem

1970. 25th Anniv of U.N.O. Multicoloured.

1218 15 y. Type **670** 15 10
1219 50 y. U.N. emblem, New York H.Q. and flags 40 10

1970. 19th International Vocational Training Competition, Chiba City.

1220 **672** 15 y. multicoloured . . . 15 10

673 Diet Building and Doves

674 "Wild Boar" (folk-handicraft)

1970. 80th Anniv of Japanese Diet.

1221 **673** 15 y. multicoloured . . . 15 10

1970. New Year's Greetings.

1222 **674** 7 y. multicoloured 20 10

675 Ski Jumping

1971. Winter Olympic Games, Sapporo (1972) (1st issue). Multicoloured.

1224 15 y. + 5 y. Type **675** 30 10
1225 15 y. + 5 y. Ice-hockey (horiz) 30 10

See also Nos. 1280/82

677 Mute Swan

678 Sika Deer

679 "Allomyrina dichotomus"

680 "Pine Tree" (T. Kano)

682 Golden Eagle

684 "Ho-o" (Phoenix), Byodoin Temple, Uji

692 Statue of Kissho, Joruri Temple

1971. Inscr "NIPPON".

1226 **273** 3 y. green 10 10
1227 **677** 5 y. blue 10 10
1228 **678** 10 y. brown & green . . 25 10
1229 **679** 12 y. brown 20 10
1230 **680** 20 y. brown & green . . 20 10
1231 **528** 25 y. blue and green . . 35 10
1232 **240** 50 y. green 35 10
1233 – 60 y. green & yellow . . 40 10
1234 **408** 70 y. black & orange . . 95 10
1235 **409** 80 y. brown and red . . 1·50 10
1236 **410** 90 y. brown & orange . . 1·40 10
1237 **682** 90 y. black and red . . 2·00 10
1238 **412** 120 y. brown & green . . 55 10
1239 – 140 y. purple & mauve . . 75 10
1240 **684** 150 y. turq & green . . 1·75 10
1240a 150 y. brown and red . . 60 10
1241 – 200 y. red . . . . 3·00 10
1242 – 200 y. brown . . . . . . 3·50 10
1243 – 200 y. red . . . . 1·25 10
1244 – 250 y. blue . . . . . . 1·25 10
1245 – 300 y. blue . . . . . . 3·50 10
1246 – 350 y. brown . . . . . . 2·00 10
1247 – 400 y. red . . . . 2·40 10
1248 – 500 y. green . . . . . . 3·00 10
1249 **692** 1000 y. multicoloured . . 5·50 60

DESIGNS: 60 y. Narcissi; 140 y. Noh mask of aged man; 200 y. (No. 1241), Onjo Bosatsu (relief), Todai Temple; 200 y. (Nos. 1242/3), Warrior (statuette); 250 y. Komainu (guardian dog), Katori Shrine; 300 y. Buddha, Kofuku Temple; 350 y. Goddess of Mercy, Yaluski Temple, Nara; 400 y. Tentoki (demon); 500 y. Buddhist deity.

No. 1231 is Type **528**, redrawn. The inscription and face value are smaller, but the main difference is in the position of the leaves. On No. 1053 they touch the left edge of the design, but on No. 1231 they are completely clear of it.

No. 1241 is as Type **536** but smaller, 18 × 22 mm.

For 210 y. as Nos. 1242/3 and 360 y. as No. 1246, see Nos. 1600 and 1604.

693 "Gen-jo-raku"

694 "Ko-cho"

695 "Tai-hei-raku"

1971. Japanese Theatre "Gagaku".

1250 **693** 15 y. multicoloured . . . 30 10
1251 **694** 15 y. multicoloured . . . 30 10
1252 **695** 50 y. multicoloured . . . 85 10

696 Voter and Diet Building

697 Pine Trees and Maple Leaves

1971. 25th Anniv of Women's Suffrage.

1253 **696** 15 y. multicoloured . . . 15 10

1971. National Afforestation Campaign.

1254 **697** 7 y. black, violet & green . 40 10

698 "Tsukiji-akashicho" (K. Kaburagi)

699 "Posting a Letter" (K. Dogishi)

700 "Postman" (K. Kasai)

701 "Railway Post Office" (S. Onozaki)

1971. Philatelic Week.

1255 **698** 15 y. multicoloured . . . 40 10

1971. Centenary of Japanese Postal Services.

1256 **699** 15 y. multicoloured . . . 20 10
1257 **700** 15 y. black & brown . . . 20 10
1258 **701** 15 y. multicoloured . . . 40 10

702 Great Tit

703 Adelie Penguins

1971. 25th Bird Week.

1259 **702** 15 y. multicoloured . . . 1·25 10

1971. 10th Anniv of Antarctic Treaty.

1260 **703** 15 y. multicoloured . . . 1·50 20

704 Goto-Wakamatsu-Seto

705 Kuzyuku-shima

1971. Saikai National Park.

1261 **704** 7 y. green 25 10
1262 **705** 15 y. brown 35 10

706 Postal Code Numerals **707** Scout Bugler

1971. Postal Code Campaign.
1263 **706** 7 y. red and green 20 10
1264 15 y. red and blue 30 10

1971. 13th World Scout Jamboree, Asagiri.
1265 **707** 15 y. multicoloured . . . 40 10

708 Rose Emblem **709** "Tokyo Horse Tram" (Yoshimura)

1971. 50th Anniv of Family Conciliation System.
1266 **708** 15 y. multicoloured . . . 25 10

1971. International Correspondence Week.
1267 **709** 50 y. multicoloured . . . 60 25

710 Emperor's Standard **712** Tennis

1971 European Tour by Emperor Hirohito and Empress Nagako. Multicoloured.
1268 15 y. Type **710** 15 10
1269 15 y. "Beyond the Sea" (drawing by Empress Nagako) . . 15 10

1971. 26th National Athletic Meeting.
1271 **712** 15 y. multicoloured . . . 30 10

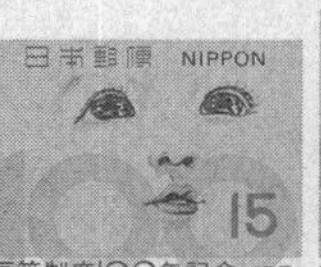

713 Child's Face and "100" **714** "Dragon" (G. Hashimoto)

1971. Centenary of National Family Registration System.
1272 **713** 15 y. multicoloured . . . 15 10

1971. Centenary of Government Printing Works, Tokyo. Multicoloured.
1273 15 y. Type **714** 20 10
1274 15 y. "Tiger" (from same drawing as above) 20 10

716 Mt. Yotei from Lake Toya **718** Takarabune ("Treasure Ship")

717 Mt. Showa-Shinzan

1971. Shikotsu-Toya National Park.
1275 **716** 7 y. green and olive . . . 25 10
1276 **717** 15 y. blue and brown . . . 40 10

1971. New Year's Greetings.
1277 **718** 7 y. multicoloured 25 10
1278 10 y. multicoloured . . . 35 10

719 Skiing

1972. Winter Olympic Games, Sapporo (2nd issue). Multicoloured.
1280 20 y. Type **719** 15 10
1281 20 y. Bobsleighing 15 10
1282 50 y. Figure skating (pair) (52 × 36 mm) 45 10

722 "Kumagai-jinya" **723** "Nozaki-mura"

724 "Awa-no-Naruto"

1972. Japanese Theatre. "Banraku" Puppet Theatre.
1284 **722** 20 y. multicoloured . . . 30 10
1285 **723** 20 y. multicoloured . . . 30 10
1286 **724** 50 y. multicoloured . . . 70 10

725 "Hikari" Express Train **727** Fishing, Taishakukyo Valley

726 Hiba Mountains

1972. Centenary of Japanese Railways (1st issue) and Opening of Sanyo Shinkansen Line.
1287 **725** 20 y. multicoloured . . . 25 10
See also Nos. 1305/6.

1972. Hiba-Dogo-Taishaku Quasi-National Park.
1288 **726** 20 y. multicoloured . . . 15 10
1289 **727** 20 y. multicoloured . . . 20 10

728 Adult with Human Heart **729** "Rising Balloon" (Gakuryo Nakamura)

1972. World Heart Month.
1290 **728** 20 y. multicoloured . . . 15 10

1972. Philatelic Week.
1291 **729** 20 y. multicoloured . . . 15 10

730 Courtesy Gate, Shuri **731** Japanese Camellia

1972. Return of Ryukyu Islands to Japan.
1292 **730** 20 y. multicoloured . . . 15 10

1972. National Afforrestation Campaign.
1293 **731** 20 y. yellow blue & green . 35 10

732 Mt. Kurikoma and Kokeshi Doll

733 Naruko-kyo Gorge and Kokeshi Doll

1972. Kurikoma Quasi-National Park.
1294 **732** 20 y. multicoloured . . . 15 10
1295 **733** 20 y. multicoloured . . . 15 10

734 Envelope and Code Symbol **736** Mt. Hodaka

737 Mt. Tate

1972. Postal Codes Campaign (5th issue).
1296 **734** 10 y. black, purple & bl . 10 10
1297 – 20 y. red and green . . . 15 10
DESIGN: 20 y. Mail-box and code symbol.

1972. Chubu Sangaku National Park.
1298 **736** 10 y. violet and mauve . . 20 10
1299 **737** 20 y. blue and brown . . 30 10

738 "Tamura" **739** "Aoi-no-ue"

740 "Hagoromo"

1972. Japanese Theatre. "Noh".
1300 **738** 20 y. multicoloured . . . 20 10
1301 **739** 20 y. multicoloured . . . 20 10
1302 **740** 50 y. multicoloured . . . 45 15

741 "Profiles of Schoolchildren" **742** "Eitai Bridge" (Hiroshige III)

1972. Centenary of Japanese Educational System.
1303 **741** 20 y. multicoloured . . . 15 10

1972. International Correspondence Week.
1304 **742** 50 y. multicoloured. . . . 60 10

743 "Inauguration of Railway Service" (Hiroshige III) **745** Kendo (Japanese Fencing)

1972. Centenary of Japanese Railways (2nd issue). Multicoloured.
1305 20 y. Type **743** 50 10
1306 20 y. Class C-62 steam locomotive No. 2 . . . . . 50 10

1972. 27th National Athletic Meeting, Kagoshima.
1307 **745** 10 y. multicoloured . . . 35 10

746 Scout and Cub **747** "Harbour and Bund, Yokohama" (Hiroshige III)

1972. 50th Anniv of Japanese Boy Scouts.
1308 **746** 20 y. multicoloured . . . 35 10

1972. Centenary of Japanese Customs Service.
1309 **747** 20 y. multicoloured . . . 55 10

748 "Plum Blossoms" Plate (K. Ogata) **749** Mt. Tsurugi

750 River Yoshino, Oboke Valley

1972. New Year's Greetings.
1310 **748** 10 y. multicoloured . . . 15 10

1973. Tsurugi-San Quasi-National Park.
1312 **749** 20 y. multicoloured . . . 30 10
1313 **750** 20 y. multicoloured . . . 30 10

751 Mt. Takao **752** Minoo Falls and Japanese Macaques

1973. Meiji-no-mori Quasi-National Park.
1314 **751** 20 y. multicoloured . . . 20 10
1315 **752** 20 y. multicoloured . . . 20 10

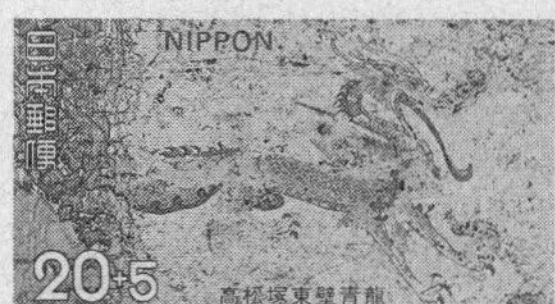
753 "Dragon" (East Wall)

754 "Male Figures" (East Wall) **755** "Female Figures" (West Wall)

1973. Asuka Archaeological Conservation Fund. Takamatsuzuka Kofun Tomb Murals.
1316 **753** 20 y. + 5 y. mult 30 10
1317 **754** 20 y. + 5 y. mult 30 10
1318 **755** 50 y. + 10 y. mult 80 35

756 Phoenix Tree **757** "Sumiyoshimode" (R. Kishida)

1973. National Afforestation Campaign.
1319 **756** 20 y. multicoloured . . . 35 10

1973. Philatelic Week.
1320 **757** 20 y. multicoloured . . . 15 10

758 Mt. Kama **759** Rock Outcrops, Mt. Haguro

1973. Suzuka Quasi-National Park.
1321 **758** 20 y. multicoloured . . . 25 10
1322 **759** 20 y. multicoloured . . . 25 10

760 Chichi-jima Island Beach **761** Coral Reef, Minami-jimi Island

1973. Ogasawara Islands National Park.
1323 **760** 10 y. blue 25 10
1324 **761** 20 y. purple 35 10

762 Postal Code Symbol and Tree **765** Waterfall, Sanden-kyo Gorge

764 Mt. Shinnyu

1973. Postal Codes Campaign.
1325 **762** 10 y. gold and green . . . 10 10
1326 – 20 y. lilac, red & blue . . 15 10
DESIGN: 20 y. Postman and symbol.

1973. Nishi-Chugoku-Sanchi Quasi-National Park.
1327 **764** 20 y. multicoloured . . . 30 10
1328 **765** 20 y. multicoloured . . . 30 10

766 Valley of River Tenryu **767** Scops Owl and Woodland Path, Mt. Horaiji

1973. Tenryu-Okumikowa Quasi-National Park.
1329 **766** 20 y. multicoloured . . . 25 10
1330 **767** 20 y. blue, green & silver . 1·25 20

768 "Cock" (J. Ito) **769** Sprinting

1973. International Correspondence Week.
1331 **768** 50 y. multicoloured . . . 65 10

1973. 28th National Athletic Meeting. Chiba.
1332 **769** 10 y. multicoloured . . . 20 10

770 Kan-Mon Bridge

1973. Opening of Kan-Mon Suspension Bridge.
1333 **770** 20 y. multicoloured . . . 40 10

771 Hanasaka-jijii and his Dog

772 Hanasaka-jijii finds the Gold

773 Hanasaka-jijii and Tree in Blossom

1973. Japanese Folk Tales (1st series). "Hanasaki-jijii".
1334 **771** 20 y. multicoloured . . . 15 10
1335 **772** 20 y. multicoloured . . . 15 10
1336 **773** 20 y. multicoloured . . . 15 10
See also Nos. 1342/4, 1352/4, 1358/60, 1362/4, 1378/80 and 1387/9.

774 Lantern **775** Niju-bashi Bridge

1973. New Year's Greetings.
1337 **774** 10 y. multicoloured . . . 10 10

1974. Imperial Golden Wedding. Mult.
1339 20 y. Type **775** 15 10
1340 20 y. Imperial Palace 15 10

777 "The Crane Damsel"

1974. Japanese Folk Tales (2nd series). "Tsuru-Nyobo". Multicoloured.
1342 20 y. Type **777** 15 10
1343 20 y. Manchurian Crane "weaving" 50 10
1344 20 y. Manchurian Cranes in flight 50 10

780 "A Reefy Coast" (Hyakusui Hirafuku)

1974. International Ocean Exposition, Okinawa (1975) (1st issue).
1345 **780** 20 y. + 5 y. mult 15 10
See also Nos. 1401/3.

781 Marudu Falls **782** Seascape

1974. Iriomote National Park.
1346 **781** 20 y. multicoloured . . . 25 10
1347 **782** 20 y. multicoloured . . . 25 10

783 Iriomote Cat

1974. Nature Conservation (1st series).
1348 **783** 20 y. multicoloured . . . 25 10
See also Nos. 1356, 1361, 1372, 1377, 1381, 1405, 1419, 1422, 1430, 1433/4, 1449, 1457, 1469, 1470, 1475, 1490, 1497 and 1502.

784 "Finger" (Shinsui Ito)

1974. Philatelic Week.
1349 **784** 20 y. multicoloured . . . 40 10

785 Nambu Red Pine **786** Supreme Court Building

1974. National Afforestation Campaign.
1350 **785** 20 y. multicoloured . . . 20 10

1974. Completion of Supreme Court Building, Tokyo.
1351 **786** 20 y. brown 15 10

787 "Sailing in a Wooden Bowl"

788 "Conquering the Goblins"

789 "Wielding the Little Magic Mallet"

1974. Japanese Folk Tales (3rd series). "The Dwarf".
1352 **787** 20 y. multicoloured . . . 15 10
1353 **788** 20 y. multicoloured . . . 15 10
1354 **789** 20 y. multicoloured . . . 15 10

790 "Uniform Rivalry" (detail after Kunimasa Baido) **792** World Blood Donation

1974. Centenary of Japanese Police System.
1355 **790** 20 y. multicoloured . . . 15 10

1974. Nature Conservation (2nd series). As T **783**. Multicoloured.
1356 20 y. European otter ("Lutra lutra") 25 10

1974. International Red Cross Day.
1357 **792** 20 y. multicoloured . . . 15 10

793 "Discovery of Kaguya Hime"

794 "Kaguya Hime as Young Woman"

795 "The Ascent to Heaven"

1974. Japanese Folk Tales (4th series). "Kaguya Hime".
1358 **793** 20 y. multicoloured . . . 25 10
1359 **794** 20 y. multicoloured . . . 25 10
1360 **795** 20 y. multicoloured . . . 25 10

1974. Nature Conservation (3rd series). As T **783**. Multicoloured.
1361 20 y. Ryukyu rabbit ("Pentalagus furnessi") . . . 25 10

797 Old Men in front of Yahata Shrine

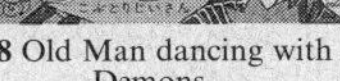

798 Old Man dancing with Demons

799 Old Man with Two Warts

1974. Japanese Folk Tales (5th series). "Kobutori-Jiisan".
1362 **797** 20 y. multicoloured . . . 15 10
1363 **798** 20 y. multicoloured . . . 15 10
1364 **799** 20 y. multicoloured . . . 15 10

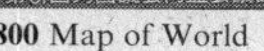

800 Map of World

802 "Pine and Northern Goshawk" (detail, Sesson)

1974. 61st Inter-Parliamentary Union Congress, Tokyo. Multicoloured.
1365 20 y. Type **800** 25 10
1366 50 y. "Aizen"–Mandarins in pond (Kawabata) (48 × 33 mm) . . . . 1·00 10

1974. International Correspondence Week.
1367 **802** 50 y. brown & purple . . 90 15

803 U.P.U. Emblem

805 Footballers

1974. Centenary of U.P.U. Multicoloured.
1368 20 y. Type **803** 10 10
1369 50 y. "Tending a Cow" (fan-painting—Sotatsu Tawaraya) (50 × 29 mm) 30 10

1974. 29th National Athletic Meeting.
1370 **805** 10 y. multicoloured . . . 15 10

806 Shii-take Mushrooms

808 Class D51 Locomotive

809 Class C57 Locomotive

1974. 9th International Scientific Congress on Cultivation of Edible Fungi.
1371 **806** 20 y. multicoloured . . . 40 10

1974. Nature Conservation (4th series). As T **783**. Multicoloured.
1372 20 y. Bonin Islands flying fox ("Pteropus pselaphon") . . 15 10

1974. Railway Steam Locomotives (1st series).
1373 **808** 20 y. multicoloured . . . 65 15
1374 **809** 20 y. multicoloured . . . 65 15
See also Nos. 1382/3, 1385/6, 1395/6 and 1398/9.

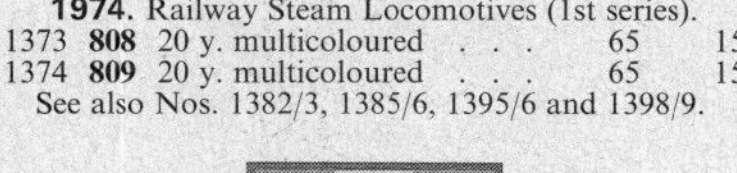

810 "Kugikakushi" (ornamental nail-covering) in the form of a daffodil

1974. New Year's Greetings.
1375 **810** 10 y. multicoloured. . . . 15 10

1975. Nature Conservation (5th series). As T **783**. Multicoloured.
1377 20 y. Short-tailed albatrosses ("Diomedea albatrus") (vert) 65 10

812 Taro releasing Tortoise

813 Sea-God's Palace

814 Taro and Pandora's Box

1975. Japanese Folk Tales (6th series). "Urashima Taro".
1378 **812** 20 y. multicoloured . . . 25 10
1379 **813** 20 y. multicoloured . . . 25 10
1380 **814** 20 y. multicoloured . . . 25 10

1975. Nature Conservation (6th series). As T **783**. Multicoloured.
1381 20 y. Manchurian cranes ("Grus japonensis") (vert) . 75 10

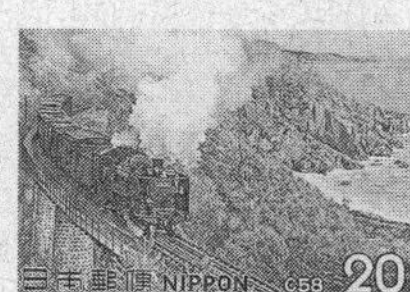

816 Class C58 Locomotive

817 Class D52 Locomotive

1975. Railway Steam Locomotives (2nd series).
1382 **816** 20 y. multicoloured . . . 65 10
1383 **817** 20 y. multicoloured . . . 65 10

818 "Sight and Hearing" (Shiko Munakata)

1975. 50th Anniv of Japanese Broadcasting Corporation.
1384 **818** 20 y. multicoloured . . . 15 10

819 Class 8620 Locomotive No. 68622

820 Class C11 Locomotive

1975. Railway Steam Locomotives (3rd series).
1385 **819** 20 y. multicoloured . . . 65 10
1386 **820** 20 y. multicoloured . . . 65 10

821 Old Man feeding Mouse

822 Old Man holding Mouse's Tail

823 Mice giving Feast to Old Man

1975. Japanese Folk Tales (7th series). "Nezumi No Jodo".
1387 **821** 20 y. multicoloured . . . 25 10
1388 **822** 20 y. multicoloured . . . 25 10
1389 **823** 20 y. multicoloured . . . 25 10

824 Matsuura Screen **825**

1975. Philatelic Week.
1390 **824** 20 y. multicoloured . . . 30 10
1391 **825** 20 y. multicoloured . . . 30 10

827 Oil Rigs

1975. Ninth World Petroleum Congress, Tokyo.
1394 **827** 20 y. multicoloured . . . 15 10

828 Class 9600 Locomotive No. 69820

829 Class C51 Locomotive No. 225

830 Plantation

1975. Railway Steam Locomotives (4th series).
1395 **828** 20 y. multicoloured . . . 65 10
1396 **829** 20 y. multicoloured . . . 65 10

1975. National Land Afforestation Campaign.
1397 **830** 20 y. multicoloured . . . 15 10

831 Class 7100 Locomotive "Benkei", 1880

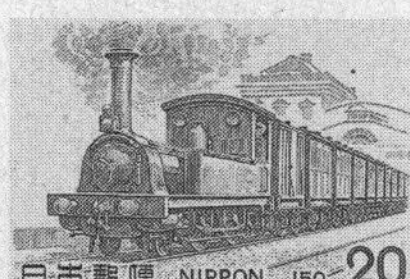

832 Class 150 Locomotive, 1872

1975. Railway Steam Locomotives (5th series).
1398 **831** 20 y. black and buff . . . 65 10
1399 **832** 20 y. black and yellow . . 65 10

833 Woman's Head and I.W.Y. Emblem

834 Okinawa Dance

1975. International Women's Year.
1400 **833** 20 y. multicoloured . . . 15 10

1975. International Ocean Exposition, Okinawa (2nd issue). Multicoloured.
1401 20 y. Type **834** 25 10
1402 30 y. Bingata textile pattern . . 40 10
1403 50 y. "Aquapolis and Globe" emblem (48 × 34 mm) . . . 55 10

1975. Nature Conservation (7th series). As T **783**. Multicoloured.
1405 20 y. Bonin Island honey-eater ("Apalopteron familiare") . 70 10

838 Kentoshisen (7th–9th centuries)

839 Kenminsen (7th–9th centuries)

1975. Japanese Ships (1st series).
1406 **838** 20 y. red 45 15
1407 **839** 20 y. brown 45 15
See also Nos. 1409/10, 1420/1, 1423/4, 1428/9 and 1431/2.

840 Apple

843 "Green Peafowl" (after K. Ogata)

841 Goshuin-sen (16th-century trading ship)

842 "Tenchi-maru" (state barge), 1630

1975. Centenary of Apple Cultivation in Japan.
1408 **840** 20 y. multicoloured . . . 15 10

1975. Japanese Ships (2nd series).
1409 **841** 20 y. green 45 15
1410 **842** 20 y. blue 45 15

1975. International Correspondence Week.
1411 **843** 50 y. multicoloured . . . 1·00 15

844 United States Flag

1975. American Tour by Emperor Hirohito and Empress Nagako. Multicoloured.
1412 20 y. Type **844** 25 10
1413 20 y. Japanese flag 25 10

846 Savings Box **847** Weightlifting

1975. Centenary of Japanese Post Office Savings Bank.
1415 **846** 20 y. multicoloured . . . 15 10

1975. 30th National Athletic Meeting.
1416 **847** 10 y. multicoloured . . . 20 10

848 "Tatsu-guruma" (toy) **850** Sengoku-bune (fishing boat)

851 "Shohei Maru" (sail warship)

1975. New Year's Greetings.
1417 **848** 10 y. multicoloured . . . 35 10

1976. Nature Conservation (8th series). As T **783**. Multicoloured.
1419 50 y. Ryukyu robin ("Erithacus komadori") 60 25

1976. Japanese Ships (3rd series).
1420 **850** 50 y. blue 65 15
1421 **851** 50 y. violet 65 15

1976. Nature Conservation (9th series). As T **783**. Multicoloured.
1422 50 y. Tortoise ("Goemyda spengleri") 60 15

853 "Taisei Maru" (cadet ship)

854 "Tenyo Maru" (liner)

1976. Japanese Ships (4th series).
1423 **853** 50 y. black 65 15
1424 **854** 50 y. brown 65 15

855 Section of Hikone Folding Screen **857** Cedar Forest, Plum Blossom, and Mt. Tsukuba

1976. Philatelic Week. Multicoloured.
1425 50 y. Type **855** 45 10
1426 50 y. Similar to Type **855** . . . 45 10
NOTE: The two stamps form a composite design of the "Hikone Folding Screen".

1976. National Land Afforestation Campaign.
1427 **857** 50 y. multicoloured . . . 30 10

858 "Asama Maru" (liner)

859 "Kinai Maru" (cargo liner)

1976. Japanese Ships (5th series).
1428 **858** 50 y. green 65 15
1429 **859** 50 y. brown 65 15

1976. Nature Conservation (10th series). As T **783**. Multicoloured.
1430 50 y. Green tree frog ("Racophorus arboreus") (vert) 50 10

861 "Kamakura Maru" (container ship)

862 "Nissei Maru" (oil tanker)

1976. Japanese Ships (6th series).
1431 **861** 50 y. blue 65 15
1432 **862** 50 y. blue 65 15

1976. Nature Conservation (11th and 12th series). As T **783**. Multicoloured.
1433 50 y. Tokyo bitterling ("Tanakia tanago") 95 10
1434 50 y. Three-spined sticklebacks ("Gasterosteus aculeatus") . 95 10

865 "Kite and Rooks" (detail, Yosa Buson) **866** Gymnastics

1976. International Correspondence Week.
1435 **865** 100 y. multicoloured . . . 1·25 25

1976. 31st National Athletic Meeting.
1436 **866** 20 y. multicoloured . . . 35 10

867 "KDD Maru" (cable ship) laying cable

1976. Opening of Sino-Japanese Cable.
1437 **867** 50 y. multicoloured . . . 60 10

868 Man-zai-raku (classical dance) **870** Children at First Kindergarten

1976. Golden Jubilee of Emperor's Accession.
1438 **868** 50 y. multicoloured . . . 40 10
1439 – 50 y. red, gold & black . . . 40 10
DESIGN: No. 1439, Coronation coach.

1976. Centenary of First Kindergarten. Tokyo.
1441 **870** 50 y. multicoloured . . . 50 10

871 Family Group **872** Bamboo Snake

1976. 50th Anniv (1977) of Health Insurance System.
1442 **871** 50 y. multicoloured . . . 40 10

1976. New Year's Greetings.
1443 **872** 20 y. multicoloured . . . 20 10

873 East Pagoda, Yakushi Temple

1976. National Treasures (1st series). Mult.
1445 50 y. Type **873** 50 10
1446 100 y. Deva King, Todai Temple (33 × 48 mm) . . . 1·25 10
See also Nos. 1447/8, 1452/3, 1463/4, 1471/2, 1480/1 and 1486/9.

875 Golden Pavilion, Toshodai Temple

1977. National Treasures (2nd series). Mult.
1447 50 y. Type **875** 50 10
1448 100 y. Illustration from "Heike Nokyo Sutra" (33 × 48 mm) . . . . 1·25 10

1977. Nature Conservation (13th series). As T **783**. Multicoloured.
1449 50 y. Horseshoe crabs ("Tachypleus tridentatus") . 45 10

878 Figure Skating **879**

1977. World Figure Skating Championships, Tokyo.
1450 **878** 50 y. multicoloured . . . 55 10
1451 **879** 50 y. multicoloured . . . 55 10

880 Detail of Picture Scroll (attr Toba Sojo Kakuyu)

881 Wood Carving of Buddhist Saint (attr Jocho) Byodoin Temple, Uji

1977. National Treasures (3rd series).
1452 **880** 50 y. multicoloured . . . 50 10
1453 **881** 100 y. dp brn, brn & grn . 1·25 10

882 Forest in Sunshine

1977. National Land Afforestation Campaign.
1454 **882** 50 y. multicoloured . . . 40 10

883 "Women" Weavers (part) **884** "Women" Weavers (part)

1977. Philatelic Week.
1455 **883** 50 y. multicoloured . . . 50 10
1456 **884** 50 y. multicoloured . . . 50 10
Nos. 1455/6 were issued in se-tenant pairs, forming a composite design.

1977. Nature Conservation (14th series). As T **783**. Multicoloured.
1457 50 y. Mikado swallowtail ("Graphium doson") (vert) . 60 10

886 Nurses **887** Central Part of Nuclear Reactor

1977. 16th Congress of the International Council of Nurses.
1458 **886** 50 y. multicoloured . . . 40 10

1977. Reaching of Critical Mass by Joyo Fast-Breeder Reactor, Oarai Town.
1459 **887** 50 y. multicoloured . . . 40 10

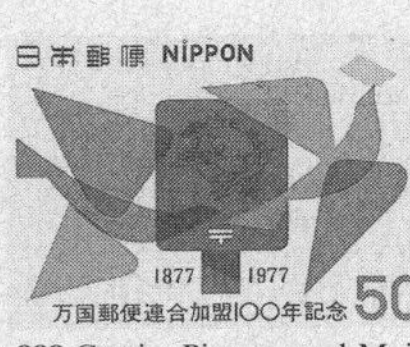

888 Carrier Pigeons and Mail Box with U.P.U. Emblem

889 U.P.U. Emblem and World Map

1977. Centenary of Japan's Admission to U.P.U.
1460 **888** 50 y. multicoloured . . . 40 10
1461 **889** 100 y. multicoloured . . . 1·40 10

890 Illustration from "Picture Scroll of Lady Murasaki's Diary"

891 Statue of Seitaka Doji

892 Green Cross (safety emblem) and Workmen

1977. National Treasures (4th series).
1463 **890** 50 y. multicoloured . . . 55 10
1464 **891** 100 y. brown, deep brown and light brown . . . 1·40 10

1977. National Safety Week. Multicoloured.
1465 50 y. Type **892** 80 10
1466 50 y. Worker and high-rise building 80 10
1467 50 y. Unloading freight 80 10
1468 50 y. Machine-worker 80 10

1977. Nature Conservation (15th series). As T **783**. Multicoloured.
1469 50 y. Firefly ("Luciola cruciata") 50 10

1977. Nature Conservation (16th series). As T **783**. Multicoloured.
1470 50 y. Cicada ("Euterpnosia chibensis" 60 10

898 Drawing of Han Shan by Kao

899 Matsumoto Castle

1977. National Treasures (5th series).
1471 **898** 50 y. multicoloured . . . 60 10
1472 **899** 100 y. multicoloured . . . 1·40 10

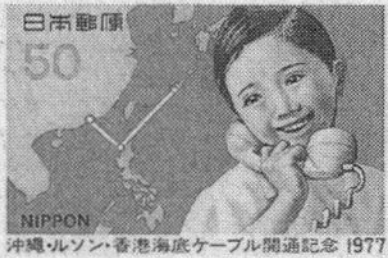

900 Map and Child on Telephone

1977. Opening of Okinawa-Luzon-Hong Kong Submarine Cable.
1473 **900** 50 y. multicoloured . . . 40 10

901 Surgeon

1977. 27th Congress of International Society of Surgeons.
1474 **901** 50 y. multicoloured . . . 50 10

1977. Nature Conservation (17th series). As T. **783**. Multicoloured.
1475 50 y. Dragonfly ("Boninthemis insularis") (vert) 60 10

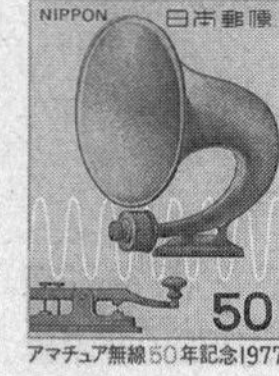

903 Horn-shaped Speaker and Telegraph Key

904 Racing Cyclist and Mt. Iwaki

1977. 50th Anniv of Amateur Radio League.
1476 **903** 50 y. multicoloured . . . 40 10

1977. 32nd National Athletic Meeting.
1477 **904** 20 y. multicoloured . . . 40 10

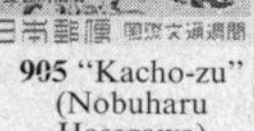

905 "Kacho-zu" (Nobuharu Hasegawa)

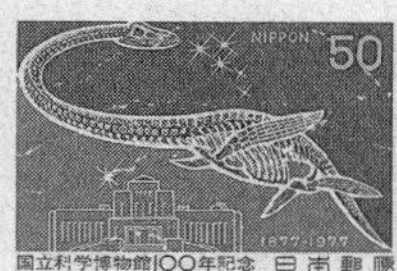

906 Long-necked Dinosaur and Museum

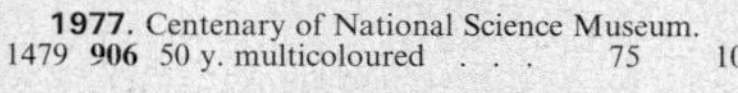

1977. International Correspondence Week.
1478 **905** 100 y. multicoloured . . . 1·40 25

1977. Centenary of National Science Museum.
1479 **906** 50 y. multicoloured . . . 75 10

907 Detail, Folding Screen, Chishakuin Temple, Kyoto

908 Kiyomizu-dera Temple

1977. National Treasures (6th series).
1480 **907** 50 y. multicoloured . . . 50 10
1481 **908** 100 y. brn, grn & bl . . . 1·25 10

909 Toy Horse

1977. New Year's Greetings.
1482 **909** 20 y. multicoloured . . . 25 10

910 Underground Train, 1927

911 Underground Train No. 1101, 1977

1977. 50th Anniv of Japanese Underground Railway.
1484 **910** 50 y. multicoloured . . . 90 10
1485 **911** 50 y. multicoloured . . . 90 10

912 Genji's Carriage at Sumiyoshi Shrine (scene on folding screen (Sotatsu Tawaraya) from "Tale of Genji" by Lady Murasaki)

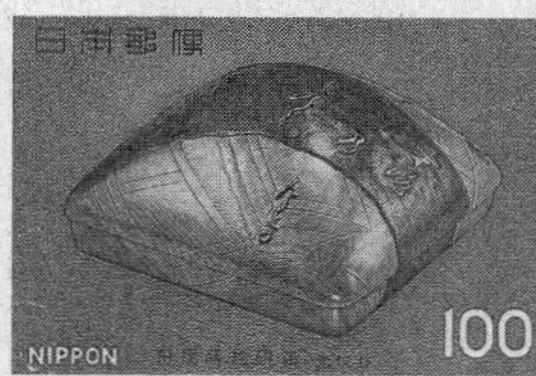

913 Inkstone Case (Koetsu Honami)

1978. National Treasures (7th series).
1486 **912** 50 y. multicoloured . . . 50 10
1487 **913** 100 y. multicoloured . . . 1·40 10

914 "Noryozu" (Morikage Kusumi)

915 Yomei Gate, Tosho Shrine, Nikko

1978. National Treasures (8th series).
1488 **914** 50 y. multicoloured . . . 50 10
1489 **915** 100 y. multicoloured . . . 1·40 10

916 "Primula Sieboldi"

1978. Nature Conservation (18th series).
1490 **916** 50 y. multicoloured . . . 50 10

917 Seated Woman With Flower (hanging scroll)

918 Dancing Woman (hanging scroll)

1978. Philatelic Week. "Kanbun Bijinzu" Genre Paintings.
1491 **917** 50 y. multicoloured . . . 40 10
1492 **918** 50 y. multicoloured . . . 40 10

919 Rotary Emblem and Mt Fuji (from "36 Views of Mt. Fuji" by Hokusai Katsushita)

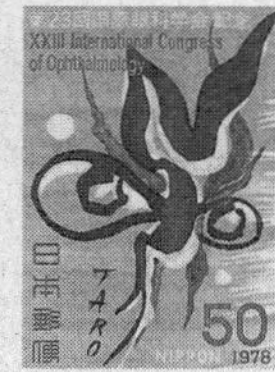

920 Congress Emblem

1978. Rotary International Convention, Tokyo.
1493 **919** 50 y. multicoloured . . . 70 20

1978. 23rd Int Ophthalmological Congress.
1494 **920** 50 y. multicoloured . . . 45 10

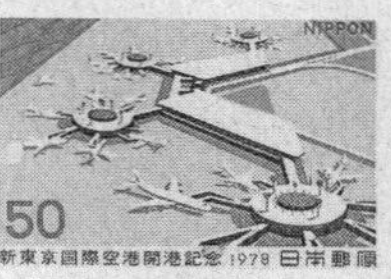

921 Passenger Terminal Buildings

922 Cape Ashizuri, Rainbow and Cedar Trees

1978. Opening of Narita Airport, Tokyo.
1495 **921** 50 y. multicoloured . . . 60 10

1978. National Afforestation Campaign.
1496 **922** 50 y. multicoloured . . . 50 10

923 "Pinguicula ramosa"

924 "Karashishi" (attr Sotatsu Tawaraya) and Lions Emblem

1978. Nature Conservation (19th series).
1497 **923** 50 y. multicoloured . . . 50 10

1978. 61st Lions International Convention, Tokyo.
1498 **924** 50 y. multicoloured . . . 55 10

925 "Grand Champion Raigoyo **926** Hidenoyama in the Ring" (Toyokuni III)

927 "Drum Tower of Ekoin Temple, Ryogoku" (Hiroshige)

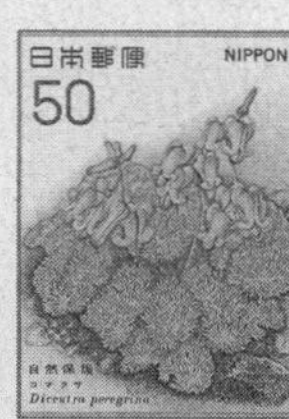

928 "Dicentra peregrina"

1978. Sumo (Japanese Wrestling) Pictures (1st series).
1499 **925** 50 y. multicoloured . . . 50 10
1500 **926** 50 y. multicoloured . . . 50 10
1501 **927** 50 y. multicoloured . . . 60 10
Nos. 1499/500, were issued together se-tenant forming a composite design.
See also Nos. 1505/7, 1513/15, 1519/21 and 1523/5.

1978. Nature Conservation (20th series).
1502 **928** 50 y. multicoloured . . . 35 10

929 Keep Fit Exercise **930** Chamber of Commerce and Industry Building and Centenary Emblem

1978. 50th Anniv of Radio Gymnastic Exercises.
1503 **929** 50 y. multicoloured . . . 1·25 10

1978. Centenary of 1st Chambers of Commerce, Tokyo and Osaka.
1504 **930** 50 y. multicoloured . . . 40 10

MINIMUM PRICE

The minimum price quoted is 10p which represents a handling charge rather than a basis for valuing common stamps. For further notes about prices see introductory pages.

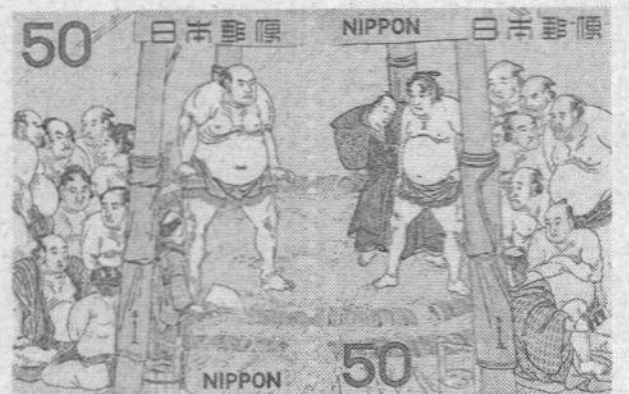

931 "Dohyoiri" wrestlers Tanikaze 932 and Onogawa (Shunsho Katsukawa)

933 "Jinmaku versus Raiden" (Shunnei Katsukawa)

934 Statues on Tokyo Securities Exchange Building

1978. Sumo Pictures (2nd series).

1505 **931** 50 y. multicoloured . . . 50 10
1506 **932** 50 y. multicoloured . . . 50 10
1507 **933** 50 y. multicoloured . . . 60 10

Nos. 1505/6 were issued together se-tenant, forming a composite design.

1978. Centenary of Tokyo and Osaka Stock Exchanges.

1508 **934** 50 y. brown, purple & grn 50 10

935 Copper Pheasant (detail of door painting attr Sanraku Kano)

936 Mt. Yari and Softball Players

1978. International Correspondence Week.

1509 **935** 100 y. multicoloured . . . 1·25 25

1978. 33rd National Athletic Meeting.

1510 **936** 20 y. multicoloured . . . 40 10

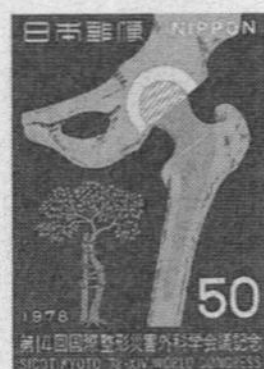

937 Artificial Joint

938 Refracting Telescope and Stars

1978. 14th Congress of Int Society of Orthopaedic and Traumatic Surgeons, Kyoto.

1511 **937** 50 y. blue, ultram & silver 55 10

1978. Centenary of Tokyo Astronomical Observatory.

1512 **938** 50 y. multicoloured . . . 55 10

939 "The then Heroic Champion's 940 Sumo Wrestling" (detail, Toyokuni III)

941 "Children's Charming Sumo Play" (Utamaro Kitagawa)

942 Sheep Bell (folk toy)

1978. Sumo Pictures (3rd series).

1513 **939** 50 y. multicoloured . . . 50 10
1514 **940** 50 y. multicoloured . . . 50 10
1515 **941** 50 y. multicoloured . . . 60 10

Nos. 1513/14 were issued together se-tenant, forming a composite design.

1978. New Year's Greetings.

1516 **942** 20 y. multicoloured . . . 35 10

943 Family and Human Rights Emblem

1978. 30th Anniv of Declaration of Human Rights.

1518 **943** 50 y. multicoloured . . . 45 10

944/5 "Great Sumo Wrestlers crossing Ryogoku Bridge" (Toyokuni III)

946 "Yumitori Ceremony at Grand Fund-raising Tournament" (Kunisada II)

947 Hands protecting Children

1979. Sumo Pictures. (4th series).

1519 **944** 50 y. multicoloured . . . 50 10
1520 **945** 50 y. multicoloured . . . 50 10
1521 **946** 50 y. multicoloured . . . 60 10

Nos. 1519/20 were issued together se-tenant, forming a composite design.

1979. Education for the Handicapped.

1522 **947** 50 y. multicoloured . . . 45 10

948/9 "Takekuma versus Iwamigata" (Kuniyoshi Utagawa)

950 "Daidozan's Dohyoiri" (Sharaku Toshusai)

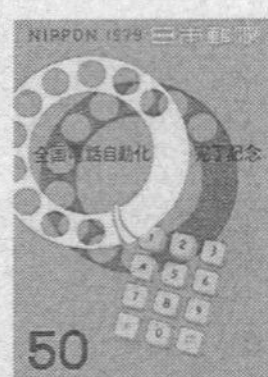

951 Telephone Dial and Pushbuttons

1979. Sumo Pictures (5th series).

1523 **948** 50 y. multicoloured . . . 50 10
1524 **949** 50 y. multicoloured . . . 50 10
1525 **950** 50 y. multicoloured . . . 60 10

Nos. 1523/4 were issued together se-tenant, forming a composite design.

1979. Telephone Automation Completion.

1526 **951** 50 y. multicoloured . . . 50 10

952 Drawing by Leonardo da Vinci

1979. Centenary of Western Medicine in Japan.

1527 **952** 50 y. multicoloured . . . 55 10

953 "Standing Beauties" 954 (Kaigetsudo School)

1979. Philatelic Week.

1528 **953** 50 y. multicoloured . . . 50 10
1529 **954** 50 y. multicoloured . . . 50 10

955 Mt. Horaiji and Maple Leaves

1979. National Afforestation Campaign.

1530 **955** 50 y. multicoloured . . . 50 10

956 "Goddess of Maternal Mercy" (Kano Hogai)

957 "The Princess of the Sea God" (Aoki Shigeru)

1979. Modern Japanese Art (1st series).

1531 **956** 50 y. multicoloured . . . 60 10
1532 **957** 50 y. multicoloured . . . 60 10

See also Nos. 1533/4, 1544/5, 1550/1, 1558/9, 1567/8, 1574/5, 1610/11, 1618/19, 1628/9, 1650/1, 1656/7, 1675/6, 1689/90, 1693/4 and 1697/8.

958 "Fire Dance" (Gyosha Hayami)

959 "Leaning Figure" (Tetsugoro Yorozu)

1979. Modern Japanese Art (2nd series).

1533 **958** 50 y. multicoloured . . . 60 10
1534 **959** 50 y. multicoloured . . . 60 10

960 Quarantine Officers

1979. Centenary of Quarantine System.

1535 **960** 50 y. multicoloured . . . 75 10

961 Girl with Letter

962 Hakata Doll

1979. Letter writing Day.

1536 **961** 20 y. multicoloured . . . 30 10
1537 **962** 50 y. multicoloured . . . 45 10

963 Baseball Pitcher and Ball

1979. 50th National Inter-City Amateur Baseball Tournament.

1538 **963** 50 y. multicoloured . . . 70 10

964 Girl collecting Stars

965 Boy catching Toy Insects

1979. International Year of the Child.

1539 **964** 50 y. multicoloured . . . 50 10
1540 **965** 50 y. multicoloured . . . 50 10

966 "The Moon over the Castle Ruins" (Bansui Doi and Rentaro Taki)

967 "Evening Glow" (Uko Nakamura and Shin Kusakawa)

1979. Japanese Songs (1st series).

1542 **966** 50 y. multicoloured . . . 70 10
1543 **967** 50 y. multicoloured . . . 70 10

See also Nos. 1552/3, 1556/7, 1561/2, 1565/6, 1572/3, 1580/1, 1616/17 and 1620/1.

968 "Black Cat" (Shunso Hishida)

969 "Kinyo" (Sotaro Yasui)

1979. Modern Japanese Art (3rd series).

1544 **968** 50 y. multicoloured . . . 70 10
1545 **969** 50 y. multicoloured . . . 70 10

970 "Steep Mountains and the Dark Dale" (Okyo Maruyama)

971 Long Distance Runner

1979. International Correspondence Week.
1546 **970** 100 y. multicoloured . . . 1·75 30

1979. 34th National Athletic Meeting, Miyazaki.
1547 **971** 20 y. multicoloured . . . 60 10

972 "ITU" and Globe

973 Woman and Embryo

1979. Centenary of Admission to International Telecommunications Union.
1548 **972** 50 y. multicoloured . . . 60 10

1979. 9th International Obstetrics and Gynaecology Convention, Tokyo.
1549 **973** 50 y. multicoloured . . . 60 10

974 "Nude" (Kagaku Murakami)

975 "Harvest" (Asai Chu)

1979. Modern Japanese Art (4th series).
1550 **974** 50 y. multicoloured . . . 50 10
1551 **975** 50 y. multicoloured . . . 50 10

976 "Maple Leaves" (Tatsuyuki Takano and Teiichi Okano)

977 "Birthplace" (Tatsuyuki Takano and Teiichi Okano)

1979. Japanese Songs (2nd series).
1552 **976** 50 y. multicoloured . . . 50 10
1553 **977** 50 y. multicoloured . . . 50 10

978 "Happy Monkeys" (folk toy)

979 "Winter Scene" (anon)

980 "Mount Fuji" (anon)

1979. New Year's Greeting.
1554 **978** 20 y. multicoloured . . . 30 10

1980. Japanese Songs (3rd series).
1556 **979** 50 y. multicoloured . . . 50 20
1557 **980** 50 y. multicoloured . . . 50 10

981 "Salmon" (Yuichi Takahashi)

982 "Hall of the Supreme Buddha" (Kokei Kobayashi)

1980. Modern Japanese Art (5th series).
1558 **981** 50 y. multicoloured . . . 55 10
1559 **982** 50 y. multicoloured . . . 55 10

983 Scales

1980. Centenary of Government Auditing Bureau.
1560 **983** 50 y. multicoloured . . . 50 10

984 "Spring Brook" (Tatsuyuki Takano and Teiichi Okano)

985 "Cherry Blossoms" (anon)

1980. Japanese Songs (4th series).
1561 **984** 50 y. multicoloured . . . 55 10
1562 **985** 50 y. multicoloured . . . 55 10

986/7 "Scenes of Outdoor Play in Spring" (Sukenobu Nishikawa)

1980. Philatelic Week.
1563 **986** 50 y. multicoloured . . . 30 10
1564 **987** 50 y. multicoloured . . . 50 10

988 "Sea" (Ryuha Hayashi and Takeshi Inoue)

989 "Misty Moonlight Night" (Tatsuyuki Takano and Teiichi Okano)

1980. Japanese Songs (5th series).
1565 **988** 50 y. multicoloured . . . 55 10
1566 **989** 50 y. multicoloured . . . 55 10

990 "Maiko Girls" (Seiki Kuroda)

991 "Mother and Child" (Shoen Uemura)

1980. Modern Japanese Art (6th series).
1567 **990** 50 y. multicoloured . . . 55 10
1568 **991** 50 y. multicoloured . . . 55 10

992 "Nippon Maru I"

993 Mount Gozaisho and Cedars

1980. 50th Anniv of Training Cadet Ships "Nippon Maru I" and "Kaio Maru".
1569 **992** 50 y. multicoloured . . . 75 20

1980. National Afforestation Campaign.
1570 **993** 50 y. multicoloured. . . . 60 10

994 "Acrobatic Performances on a Ladder at New Year's Parade of Yayosu Fire Brigades" (Hiroshige III)

1980. Centenary of Fire Fighting System.
1571 **994** 50 y. multicoloured . . . 60 10

995 "The Sun" (Taksuyuki Takano and Teiichi Okano)

996 "Memories of Summer" (Shoko Ema and Yoshinao Nakata)

1980. Japanese Songs (6th series).
1572 **995** 50 y. multicoloured . . . 60 10
1573 **996** 50 y. multicoloured . . . 60 10

997 "Black Fan" (Takeji Fujishima)

998 "The Dance 'Are Yudachi ni' " (Seiho Takeuchi)

1980. Modern Japanese Art (7th series).
1574 **997** 50 y. multicoloured . . . 65 10
1575 **998** 50 y. multicoloured . . . 65 10

999 Teddy Bear holding Letter

1000 Knotted Letter

1980. Letter Writing Day.
1576 **999** 20 y. multicoloured . . . 30 10
1577 **1000** 50 y. multicoloured . . . 50 10

1001 "Luehdorfia japonica"

1980. 16th International Congress of Entomology, Kyoto.
1578 **1001** 50 y. multicoloured . . . 90 10

1002 Map on Three-dimensional Graph

1980. 24th International Geographical Congress and 10th International Cartographic Conference, Tokyo.
1579 **1002** 50 y. multicoloured . . . 40 10

1003 "Red Dragonfly" (Rofu Miki and Kosaku Yamada)

1004 "Song by the Sea" (Kokui Hayashi and Tamezo Narita)

1980. Japanese Songs (7th series).
1580 **1003** 50 y. multicoloured . . . 70 10
1581 **1004** 50 y. multicoloured . . . 70 10

1005 Integrated Circuit

1980. 8th World Computer Congress and Third World Conference on Medical Informatics, Tokyo.
1582 **1005** 50 y. multicoloured . . . 60 10

1006 Akita Dog

1007 Adonis

1008 Lily

1009 Camellia

1010 Small Cabbage Whites on Rape Blossom

1011 Japanese Babylonia

1012 Noble Scallops

1013 Flowering Cherry

1014 Hanging Bell, Byodoin Temple, Uji

1015 Yoka Star Shell

1016 Precious Wentletrap

1017 Flautist, Horyu Temple

1018 Deer (from lacquer writing box)

1019 Mirror with Figures

1020 Heart-shaped Earthen Figurine

1021 Silver Crane, Kasuga Taisha Shrine, Nara

1022 Miroku Bosatsu, Horyu Temple

1023 Dainichi Buddha, Chuson Temple

1024 Keiki Doji, Kongobu Temple

1025 Komoku Ten, Todai Temple, Nara

1026 Lady Maya, Horyu Temple

1027 Tea Jar with Wisteria Decoration (Ninsei Nonomura)

1028 Miroku Bosatsu

1980. 41 y. and 62 y. perf or imperf (self-adhesive), others perf.

1582a	**1006**	2 y. blue	10	10
1583	**1007**	10 y. yell, grn & brn	10	10
1584	**1008**	20 y. yellow, bl & grn	15	10
1585	**1009**	30 y. multicoloured	20	25
1586	**1010**	40 y. multicoloured	40	10
1587	**1011**	40 y. multicoloured	35	10
1588	**1012**	41 y. multicoloured	35	10
1589	**1013**	50 y. multicoloured	60	10
1590	**1014**	60 y. green and black	70	10
1591	**1015**	60 y. multicoloured	50	10
1592	**1016**	62 y. multicoloured	50	10
1593	**1017**	70 y. blue and yellow	90	10
1594	**1018**	70 y. yellow, blk & bl	60	10
1594a		72 y. yellow, blk & bl	60	10
1595	**1019**	80 y. green & black	1·25	10
1596	**1020**	90 y. yell, blk & grn	1·25	10
1597	**1021**	100 y. black, blue and ultramarine	85	10
1598	**1022**	170 y. purple & bistre	65	10
1599		175 y. brn, grn & bis	1·25	10
1600	–	210 y. orange and lilac (as No. 1242)	1·25	10
1601	**1023**	260 y. brown & red	2·00	10
1602	**1024**	300 y. brown	2·00	10
1603	**1025**	310 y. brown & vio	2·00	10
1604	–	360 y. purple and pink (as No. 1246)	2·25	10
1605	**1026**	410 y. orange & blue	5·50	10
1606	**1027**	410 y. multicoloured	1·50	10
1607	**1028**	600 y. yellow, purple and lilac	4·00	10

1031 "Manchurian Cranes" (door painting, Motooki Watanabe)

1032 Archery and Mt. Nantai

1980. International Correspondence Week.
1608 **1031** 100 y. multicoloured . . 1·00 35

1980. 35th National Athletic Meeting, Tochigi.
1609 **1032** 20 y. multicoloured . . . 40 10

HAVE YOU READ THE NOTES AT THE BEGINNING OF THIS CATALOGUE?
These often provide answers to the enquiries we receive.

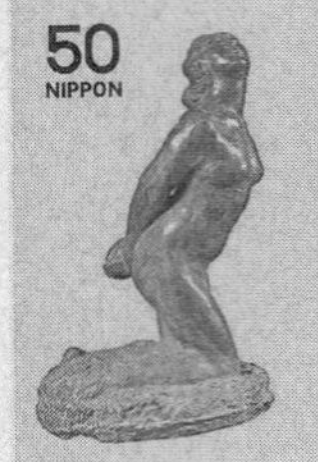
1033 "Woman" (sculpture, Morie Ogiwara)

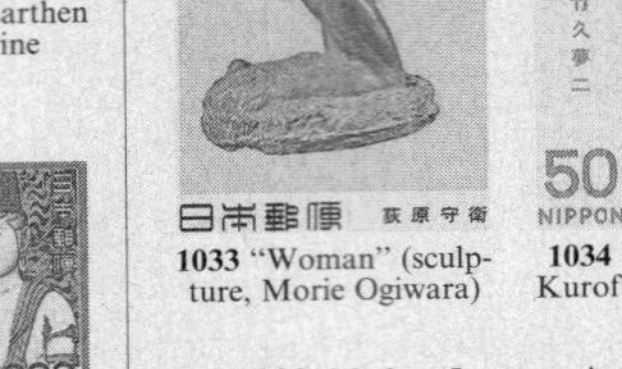
1034 "Woman of the Kurofune-ya" (Yumeji Takehisa)

1980. Modern Japanese Art (8th series).
1610 **1033** 50 y. multicoloured . . . 65 10
1611 **1034** 50 y. multicoloured . . . 65 10

1035 "Energy"

1036 Diet Building and Doves

1980. 35th World Congress of Junior Chambers of Commerce, Osaka.
1612 **1035** 50 y. multicoloured . . . 45 10

1980. 90th Anniv of Japanese Diet.
1613 **1036** 50 y. multicoloured . . . 35 10

1037 Toy Rooster

1980. New Year's Greetings.
1614 **1037** 20 y. multicoloured . . . 40 10

1038 "Komori-Uta" (nursery song)

1039 "Coconut" (Toson Shimazaki and Toraji Ohaka)

1981. Japanese Songs (8th series).
1616 **1038** 60 y. multicoloured . . . 55 10
1617 **1039** 60 y. multicoloured . . . 55 10

1040 "Power Station in the Snow" (Shiskanosuke Oka)

1041 "Nukada-no-Okimi of Asuka in Spring" (Yukihiko Yasuda)

1981. Modern Japanese Art (9th series).
1618 **1040** 60 y. multicoloured . . . 60 10
1619 **1041** 60 y. multicoloured . . . 60 10

1042 "Spring has Come" (Tatsuyuki Takano and Teiichi Okano)

1043 "Cherry Blossoms" (Hagoromo Takeshima and Rentaro Taki)

1981. Japanese Songs (9th series).
1620 **1042** 60 y. multicoloured . . . 60 10
1621 **1043** 60 y. multicoloured . . . 60 10

1044 Port Island and Exposition Emblem

1981. Kobe Port Island Exposition, Kobe City.
1622 **1044** 60 y. multicoloured . . . 35 10

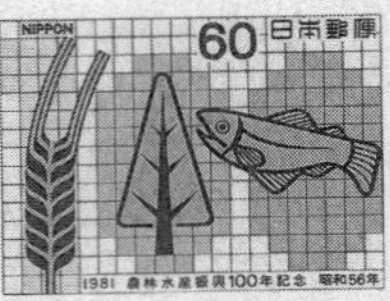
1045 Cereal, Tree and Fish on "100"

1981. Centenary of Agricultural, Forestry and Fishery Promotion.
1623 **1045** 60 y. multicoloured . . . 50 10

1046 "Yugao" (Lady of the Evening Roses)

1047 Genji

1981. Philatelic Week. Details of Harunobu Suzuki's Illustrations of "Tale of Genji" by Lady Murasaki.
1624 **1046** 60 y. multicoloured . . . 50 10
1625 **1047** 60 y. multicoloured . . . 50 10
Nos. 1624/5 were issued together, se-tenant, forming a composite design.

1048 Pagodas at Nara and Double Cherry Blossom

1049 Container Ship and Crane

1981. National Afforestation Campaign.
1626 **1048** 60 y. multicoloured . . . 55 10

1981. 12th International Port and Harbour Association Conference.
1627 **1049** 60 y. multicoloured . . . 75 10

1050 "N's Family" (Narashinge Koide)

1051 "Bamboo Shoots" (Heihachiro Fukuda)

1981. Modern Japanese Art (10th series).
1628 **1050** 60 y. multicoloured . . . 65 10
1629 **1051** 60 y. multicoloured . . . 65 10

1052 Stylized Debris Barriers

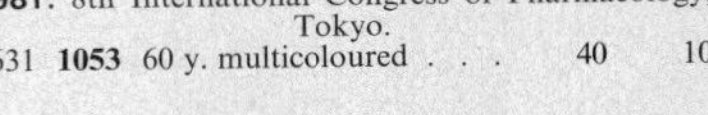
1053 Human Figure and Dose Response Chart

1981. Centenary of Land Erosion Control.
1630 **1052** 60 y. multicoloured . . . 40 10

1981. 8th International Congress of Pharmacology, Tokyo.
1631 **1053** 60 y. multicoloured . . . 40 10

1054 Girl writing Letter

1055 Boy with Pencil and Stamp

1981. Letter Writing Day.
1632 **1054** 40 y. multicoloured . . . 40 10
1633 **1055** 60 y. multicoloured . . . 55 10

1056 Japanese Crested Ibis

1981. 50th Anniv of National Parks.
1634 **1056** 60 y. multicoloured . . . 1·25 30

1057 Electric Plug and dripping Tap

1058 Energy Recycling

1981. Energy Conservation.
1635 **1057** 40 y. dp bl, lilac & bl . . 40 10
1636 **1058** 60 y. multicoloured . . . 50 10

1059 Oura Cathedral, Nagasaki

1060 Hyokei Hall, Tokyo

1981. Modern Western-style Architecture (1st series).
1637 **1059** 60 y. multicoloured . . . 55 10
1638 **1060** 60 y. multicoloured . . . 55 10
See also Nos. 1648/9, 1654/5, 1658/9, 1669/70, 1680/1, 1695/6, 1705/6, 1710/11 and 1732/3.

1061 Bluebird and I.Y.D.P. Emblem

1062 Globe in Brain

1981. International Year of Disabled Persons.
1639 **1061** 60 y. + 10 y. mult . . . 45 10

1981. International Neurological Conferences, Kyoto.
1640 **1062** 60 y. multicoloured . . . 35 10

1063 Convention Emblem

1064 "Eastern Turtle Doves" (Sanraku Kano)

1981. International Federation of Postal, Telegram and Telephone Workers' Unions World Convention, Tokyo.
1641 **1063** 60 y. multicoloured . . . 45 10

1981. International Correspondence Week.
1642 **1064** 130 y. multicoloured . . 2·25 75

1065 48 m. Stamp 1871

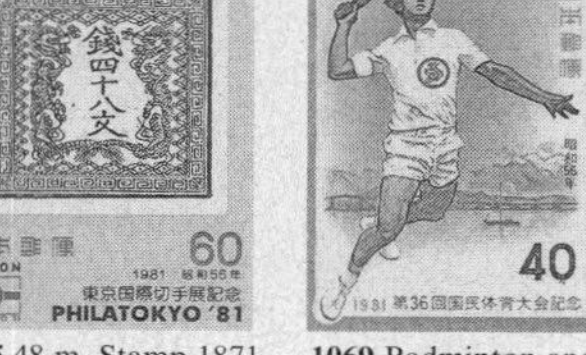

1069 Badminton and Lake Biwa

1981. "Philatokyo '81" International Stamp Exhibition, Tokyo. Multicoloured, frame colour of stamp within design given.
1643 **1065** 60 y. brown 60 10
1644 – 60 y. blue 60 10
1645 – 60 y. red 60 10
1646 – 60 y. green 60 10
DESIGNS: No. 1644, 100 m. stamp, 1871; 1645, 200 m. stamp, 1871; 1646, 500 m. stamp, 1871.

1981. 36th National Athletic Meeting, Shiga.
1647 **1069** 40 y. multicoloured . . . 50 10

1070 Former Kaichi School Matsumoto

1071 Doshisha Chapel, Kyoto

1981. Modern Western-style Architecture (2nd series).
1648 **1070** 60 y. multicoloured . . . 50 10
1649 **1071** 60 y. multicoloured . . . 50 10

1072 "Portrait of Reiko" (Ryusei Kishida)

1073 "Ichiyo" (Kiyokata Kaburagi)

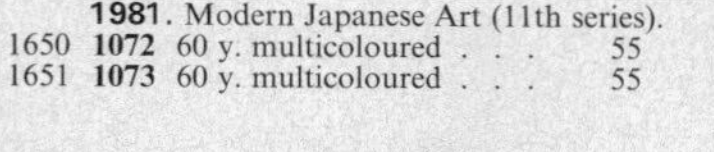

1981. Modern Japanese Art (11th series).
1650 **1072** 60 y. multicoloured . . . 55 10
1651 **1073** 60 y. multicoloured . . . 55 10

1074 Clay Dog (folk toy)

1981. New Year's Greetings.
1652 **1074** 40 y. multicoloured . . . 45 10

1075 St John's Church, Inuyama

1076 Military Exercise Hall, Sapporo Agricultural School

1982. Modern Western-style Architecture (3rd series).
1654 **1075** 60 y. multicoloured . . . 55 10
1655 **1076** 60 y. multicoloured . . . 55 10

1077 "Yoritomo in a Cave" (Seison Maeda)

1078 "Posters on a Terrace" (Yuzo Saeki)

1982. Modern Japanese Art (12th series).
1656 **1077** 60 y. multicoloured . . . 55 10
1657 **1078** 60 y. multicoloured . . . 55 10

1079 Bank of Japan, Kyoto Branch (now museum)

1080 Saiseikan Hospital, Yamagata

1982. Modern Western-style Architecture (4th series).
1658 **1079** 60 y. multicoloured . . . 50 10
1659 **1080** 60 y. multicoloured . . . 50 10

1081 Gorilla and Greater Flamingo

1982. Ueno Zoo. Centenary. Multicoloured.
1660 60 y. Type **1081** . . . . 1·25 65
1661 60 y. Lion and king penguins . 1·25 65
1662 60 y. Giant panda and Indian elephants . . . . 1·00 55
1663 60 y. Giraffe and common zebras . . . . 1·00 55

INDEX

Countries can be quickly located by referring to the index at the end of this volume.

1085/6 "Enjoying Snow Landscape of Matsuchi-yama" (Torii Kiyonaga)

1982. Philatelic Week.
1664 **1085** 60 y. multicoloured . . . 50 10
1665 **1086** 60 y. multicoloured . . . 50 10
Nos. 1664/5 were issued together se-tenant forming a composite design.

1087 Lion

1088 Arbor Festival Emblem and Blue and White Fly-catcher

1982. 10th Anniv of Return of Okinawa (Ryukyu Islands).
1666 **1087** 60 y. multicoloured . . . 60 10

1982. National Afforestation Campaign.
1667 **1088** 60 y. multicoloured . . . 60 25

1089 Noh Mask

1982. 16th World Dermatology Congress, Tokyo.
1668 **1089** 60 y. multicoloured . . . 65 10

1090 Divine Gate of Oyama Shrine, Kanazawa

1091 Former Iwasaki Mansion, Taito-ku, Tokyo (now Training Institute)

1982. Modern Western-style Architecture (5th series).
1669 **1090** 60 y. multicoloured . . . 50 10
1670 **1091** 60 y. multicoloured . . . 50 10

1092 Class 1290 Locomotive "Zenko", 1881

1093 "Yamabiko" (echo) Express Train

1982. Opening of Tohoku Shinkansen Railway Line.
1671 **1092** 60 y. multicoloured . . . 1·00 30
1672 **1093** 60 y. multicoloured . . . 1·00 30

1094 Gull and Balloon with Letter

1095 Bird carrying Letter to Fairy

1982. Letter Writing Day.
1673 **1094** 40 y. multicoloured . . . 40 10
1674 **1095** 60 y. multicoloured . . . 55 10

1096 "Garment Patterned with Irises" (Saburosuke Okada)

1097 "Buddhisattva Kannon on Potalaka Island" (Tessai Tomioka)

1982. Modern Japanese Art (13th series).
1675 **1096** 40 y. multicoloured . . . 65 10
1676 **1097** 60 y. multicoloured . . . 65 10

1098 Wreath (condolences)

1099 Folded Paper Crane (congratulations)

1100 Pine, Plum and Bamboo Blossom (congratulations)

1982. Special Correspondence Stamps.
1677 **1098** 60 y. multicoloured . . . 75 10
1678 **1099** 60 y. multicoloured . . . 75 10
1679 **1100** 70 y. multicoloured . . . 95 10
For other values see Nos. 1722/3, 2013/16 and 2289/92.

1101 Hokkaido Prefectural Building, Sapporo

1102 Saigo Tsugumichi Mansion, Meguro (now in Inuyama)

1982. Modern Western-style Architecture (6th series).
1680 **1101** 60 y. multicoloured . . . 75 10
1681 **1102** 60 y. multicoloured . . . 75 10

1103 16th-century Portuguese Galleon and World Map

1982. 400th Anniv of Christian Boys' Delegation to Europe.
1682 **1103** 60 y. multicoloured . . . 70 10

1104 "T'ien T'an in the Clouds" (Ryuzaburo Umehara)

1982. 10th Anniv of Restoration of Diplomatic Relations with China.
1683 **1104** 60 y. multicoloured . . . 55 10

1105 Table Tennis and Monument of the Meet

1106 "Amusement" (wooden doll by Goyo Hirata)

1982. 37th National Athletic Meeting. Matsue.
1684 **1105** 40 y. multicoloured . . . 60 10

1982. International Correspondence Week.
1685 **1106** 130 y. multicoloured . . 2·00 10

1107 "Bank of Japan near Eitaibashi in Snow" (Yasuji Inoue)

1982. Centenary of Central Bank System.
1686 **1107** 60 y. multicoloured . . . 45 10

1108 "Asahi" (rising sun) Express Train

1109 ED 16 Electric Locomotive No. 8

1982. Opening of Joetsu Shinkansen Railway Line.
1687 **1108** 60 y. multicoloured . . . 1·00 30
1688 **1109** 60 y. multicoloured . . . 1·00 30

1110 "Srimhadevi" (Shiko Munakata)

1111 "Saltimbanque" (Seiji Togo)

1982. Modern Japanese Art (14th series).
1689 **1110** 60 y. multicoloured . . . 65 10
1690 **1111** 60 y. multicoloured . . . 65 10

1112 "Kintaro on a Wild Boar" (clay Tsutsumi doll)

1982. New Year Greetings.
1691 **1112** 40 y. multicoloured . . . 45 10

1113 "Snowstorm" (Shinsui Ito)

1114 "Spiraea and Calla in a Perrian Vase" (Zenzaburo Kojima)

1983. Modern Japanese Art (15th series).
1692 **1113** 60 y. multicoloured . . . 75 10
1693 **1114** 60 y. multicoloured . . . 75 10

1115 Fujimura Memorial Hall, Kofu (formerly Mutsuzawa School)

1116 Porch of Sakuranomiya Public Hall, Osaka

1983. Modern Western-style Architecture (7th series).
1695 **1115** 60 y. multicoloured . . . 75 10
1696 **1116** 60 y. multicoloured . . . 75 10

1117 "Selflessness" (Taikan Yokoyama)

1118 "Aged Monkey" (wood carving, Koun Takamura)

1983. Modern Japanese Art (16th series).
1697 **1117** 60 y. multicoloured . . . 75 10
1698 **1118** 60 y. multicoloured . . . 75 10

1119 Museum and Japanese Characters representing History, Folklore and Antiquity

1983. Opening of National Museum of History and Folklore.
1699 **1119** 60 y. multicoloured . . . 40 10

1120/1 "Women working in the Kitchen" (Utamaro Kitagawa)

1983. Philatelic Week.
1700 **1120** 60 y. multicoloured . . . 75 10
1701 **1121** 60 y. multicoloured . . . 75 10
Nos. 1695/6 were issued together, se-tenant, forming a composite design.

1122 "Hiba arbor-vitae", Japanese Black Fritillary and Hakusan Mountains

1123 Colt and Racehorse

1983. National Afforestation Campaign.
1702 **1122** 60 y. multicoloured . . . 75 10

1983. 50th Nippon Derby.
1703 **1123** 60 y. multicoloured . . . 85 10

1124 Rabbit and Empty Can

1983. Islands Clean-up Campaign.
1704 **1124** 60 y. multicoloured . . . 70 10

1125 Hohei-kan House (Wedding Hall), Sapporo

1126 Glover House, Nagasaki

1983. Modern Western-style Architecture (8th series).
1705 **1125** 60 y. multicoloured . . . 75 10
1706 **1126** 60 y. multicoloured . . . 75 10

1127 First Issue and Nihonbashi Bulletin Board

1983. Centenary of "Government Journal".
1707 **1127** 60 y. multicoloured . . . 75 10

1128 Boy with Letter

1129 Fairy with Letter

1983. Letter Writing Day.
1708 **1128** 40 y. multicoloured . . . 35 10
1709 **1129** 60 y. multicoloured . . . 65 10

1130 59th Bank, Hirosaki

1131 Auditorium of Gakushuin Elementary School (now in Narita)

1983. Modern Western-style Architecture (9th series).
1710 **1130** 60 y. multicoloured . . . 75 10
1711 **1131** 60 y. multicoloured . . . 75 10

1132 Theatre and Noh Player

1983. Opening of National Noh Theatre, Tokyo.
1712 **1132** 60 y. multicoloured . . . 75 10

1133 Okinawa Rail

1983. Endangered Birds (1st series). Multicoloured.
1713 60 y. Type **1133** . . . . 1·10 80
1714 60 y. Blakiston's fish owl ("Ketupa blakistoni") (horiz) . . . . 1·10 80
See also Nos. 1724/5, 1729/30, 1735/6 and 1742/3.

1135 "Chi-kyu" (paper doll by Juzo Kagoshima)

1136 Naginata Player and Myogi Mountains

1983. International Correspondence Week.
1715 **1135** 130 y. multicoloured . . 1·75 25

1983. 38th National Athletic Meeting, Gumman.
1716 **1136** 40 y. multicoloured . . . 40 10

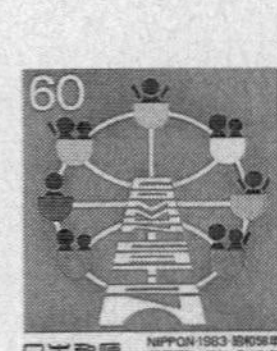

1137 Ferris Wheel

1138 Children supporting Globe

1983. World Communications Year.
1717 **1137** 60 y. multicoloured . . . 50 10
1718 **1138** 60 y. multicoloured . . . 50 10

1139 Park and Monument

1140 Congress Emblem and Mouth Mirror

1983. Opening of Showa Memorial National Park.
1719 **1139** 60 y. multicoloured . . . 60 10

1983. 71st World Dental Congress, Tokyo.
1720 **1140** 60 y. multicoloured . . . 60 10

1141 "Shirase"

1983. Maiden Voyage of Antarctic Research Ship "Shirase".
1721 **1141** 60 y. multicoloured . . . 2·50 45

1983. Special Correspondence Stamps.
1722 **1098** 40 y. multicoloured . . . 45 10
1723 **1099** 40 y. multicoloured . . . 45 10

1983. Endangered Birds (2nd series). As T **1133**. Multicoloured.
1724 60 y. Pryer's woodpecker ("Sapheopipo noguchii") . . 1·25 40
1725 60 y. Canada goose ("Branta canadensis leucopareia") (horiz) . . . . 1·25 40

1144 "Mouse riding a Small Hammer" (folk toy)

1145 Human Rights Emblem

1983. New Year's Greetings.
1726 **1144** 40 y. multicoloured . . . 60 10

1983. 35th Anniv of Declaration of Human Rights.
1728 **1145** 60 y. multicoloured . . . 45 10

1984. Endangered Birds (3rd series). As T **1133**. Multicoloured.
1729 60 y. Japanese marsh warbler ("Megalurus pryeri pryeri") (horiz) . . . . 1·25 30
1730 60 y. Crested Serpent Eagle ("Spilornis cheela perplexus") . . . . 1·25 30

1148 Exhibition Emblem and Mascot

1984. "Expo '85" International Science and Technology Exhibition, Tsukuba (1985).
1731 **1148** 60 y. + 10 y. mult . . . 80 15

1149 Bank of Japan Head Office

1150 Hunter House, Kobe

1984. Modern Western-style Architecture (10th series).
1732 **1149** 60 y. multicoloured . . . 75 10
1733 **1150** 60 y. multicoloured . . . 75 10

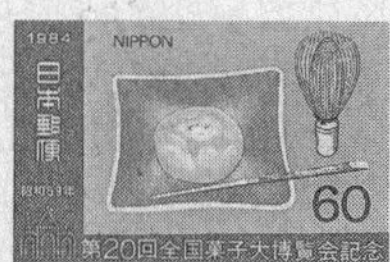
1151 Japanese-style Cake and Bamboo Tea Whisk

1984. 20th Confectionery Fair, Tokyo.
1734 **1151** 60 y. multicoloured . . . 55 10

1984. Endangered Birds (4th series). As T **1133**. Multicoloured.
1735 60 y. Black wood pigeon ("Columba janthina nitens") 1·25 30
1736 60 y. Spotted greenshank ("Tringa guttifer") (horiz) . 1·25 30

1154 Bunraku Puppet and Theatre

1984. Opening of National Bunraku Theatre, Osaka.
1737 **1154** 60 y. multicoloured . . . 75 10

1155 "Otani Oniji as Edobeh" (Toshusai Sharaku)

1156 "Iwai Hanshiro IV as Shigenoi" (Toshusai Sharaku)

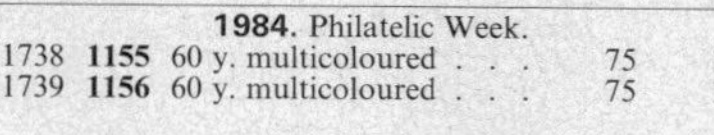
1984. Philatelic Week.
1738 **1155** 60 y. multicoloured . . . 75 10
1739 **1156** 60 y. multicoloured . . . 75 10

1157 Kaikozu Tree and Sakura Volcano

1158 "Himawari" Weather Satellite and Chart

1984. National Afforestation Campaign.
1740 **1157** 60 y. multicoloured . . . 75 10

1984. Centenary of National Weather Forecasts.
1741 **1158** 60 y. multicoloured . . . 75 10

1984. Endangered Birds (5th series). As T **1133**. Multicoloured.
1742 60 y. White-backed woodpecker ("Dendrocopos leucotos owstoni") (horiz) . 1·25 30
1743 60 y. Peregrine falcon ("Falco peregrinus fruitii") . . . . 1·25 30

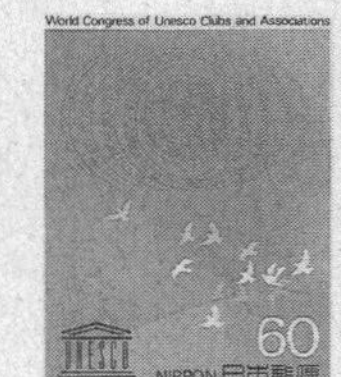
1161 Doves

1984. Federation of U.N.E.S.C.O. Clubs and Associations World Congress, Sendai.
1744 **1161** 60 y. multicoloured . . . 45 10

1162 Birds in Tree

1163 Bird and Flowers

1984. Letter Writing Day.
1745 **1162** 40 y. multicoloured . . . 35 10
1746 **1163** 60 y. multicoloured . . . 60 10

1164 "Fire and Wind" (Motomi Hagimoto)

1165 "Bonds" (Noboru Kanda)

1984. Disaster Prevention Week.
1747 **1164** 40 y. multicoloured . . . 35 10
1748 **1165** 60 y. black and yellow . . 60 10

1166 "Leontopodium fauriei"

1168 Basho's Crossroads, Sendai

1984. Alpine Plants (1st series). Multicoloured.
1749 60 y. Type **1166** 70 10
1750 60 y. "Lagotis glauca" (horiz) . 70 10
See also Nos. 1752/3, 1769/70, 1775/6, 1802/3, 1813/14 and 1827/8.

1984. 6th International Virology Congress, Sendai.
1751 **1168** 60 y. multicoloured . . . 55 10

1984. Alpine Plants (2nd series). As T **1166**. Multicoloured.
1752 60 y. Globe Flower ("Trollius riederianus") 75 10
1753 60 y. "Primula cuneifolia" . . . 75 10

1171 Logo

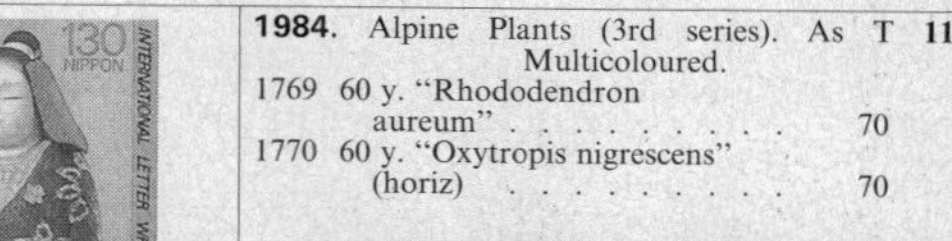
1172 "Serenity" (doll by Ryujo Hori)

1984. Electronic Mail.
1754 **1171** 500 y. multicoloured . . 8·00 3·00

1984. International Correspondence Week.
1755 **1172** 130 y. multicoloured . . 2·00 15

1173 Silver Pavilion, Jisho Temple

1174 Hockey and East Pagoda of Yakushi Temple

1984. 17th International Internal Medicine Congress, Kyoto City.
1756 **1173** 60 y. multicoloured . . . 55 10

1984. 39th National Athletic Meeting, Nara.
1757 **1174** 40 y. multicoloured . . . 70 10

1175 Birds in Tree

1176 Flowers

1177 Chrysanthemums Design

1178 Leaf and Bird Design

1984. Traditional Crafts (1st series). Kutani Porcelain Plates and Nishijin Silk Weavings.
1758 **1175** 60 y. multicoloured . . . 80 10
1759 **1176** 60 y. multicoloured . . . 80 10
1760 **1177** 60 y. multicoloured . . . 80 10
1761 **1178** 60 y. multicoloured . . . 80 10
See also Nos. 1771/4, 1787/90, 1795/8, 1805/8, 1820/3 and 1829/32.

1179 Eiji Sawamura (pitcher)

1984. 50th Anniv of Japan Tokyo Baseball Club. Multicoloured.
1762 60 y. Type **1179** 60 10
1763 60 y. Masaru Kageura (striker) 60 10
1764 60 y. Ball, birds and Matsutaro Shoriki (founder) 60 10

1182 Workers' Profiles and Symbols

1183 Bamboo Ox (Sakushu folk toy)

1984. Centenary of Technical Education.
1765 **1182** 60 y. multicoloured . . . 45 10

1984. New Year's Greetings.
1766 **1183** 40 y. multicoloured . . . 40 10

1984. Alpine Plants (3rd series). As T **1166**. Multicoloured.
1769 60 y. "Rhododendron aureum" 70 10
1770 60 y. "Oxytropis nigrescens" (horiz) 70 10

1186 Dolls

1187 Doll with Cat

1188 Bird and Flower Design

1189 Birds and Chrysanthemums Design

1985. Traditional Crafts (2nd series). Edo Kimekomi Dolls and Okinawa Bingata Cloth.
1771 **1186** 60 y. multicoloured . . . 75 10
1772 **1187** 60 y. multicoloured . . . 75 10
1773 **1188** 60 y. multicoloured . . . 75 10
1774 **1189** 60 y. multicoloured . . . 75 10

1985. Alpine Plants (4th Series). As T **1166**. Multicoloured.
1775 60 y. "Dryas octopetala" (horiz) 75 10
1776 60 y. "Draba japonica" . . . 75 10

1192 Theme Pavilion and Symbol Tower

1194 University Buildings, Chiba City, and Transmitter

1985. "EXPO '85" World Fair, Tsukuba. Multicoloured.
1777 40 y. Type **1192** 40 10
1778 60 y. Geometric city 60 10

1985. Inauguration of University of the Air.
1780 **1194** 60 y. multicoloured . . . 45 10

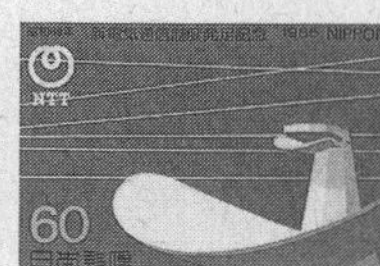
1195 Aerial and Communication Lines

1985. Privatisation of Nippon Telegraph and Telephone Corporation.
1781 **1195** 60 y. multicoloured . . . 45 10

1196 Map of Japan (after Teixeira's Map in Ortelius's "Atlas", 1595)

1197 Korekiyo Takahashi (proposer of Patent Laws)

1985. World Import Fair, Nagoya.
1782 **1196** 60 y. multicoloured . . . 60 10

1985. Centenary of Industrial Patents System.
1783 **1197** 60 y. multicoloured . . . 45 10

1198 "Winter in the North" (Yumeji Takehisa)

1199 "Toward the Morning Light" (Yumeji Takehisa)

1985. Philatelic Week.
1784 **1198** 60 y. multicoloured . . . 75 10
1785 **1199** 60 y. multicoloured . . . 75 10

1200 Mt. Aso and Gentian

1985. National Afforestation Campaign.
1786 **1200** 60 y. multicoloured . . . 50 10

1201 Hawk **1202** Ducks

1203 Bowl 1204 Plate

1985. Traditional Crafts (3rd series). Yew Wood Carvings and Arita Porcelain.
1787 **1201** 60 y. multicoloured . . . 60 10
1788 **1202** 60 y. multicoloured . . . 60 10
1789 **1203** 60 y. multicoloured . . . 50 10
1790 **1204** 60 y. multicoloured . . . 50 10

1205 "Cherry Trees at Night" **1206** (Taikan Yokoyama)

1985. 50th Anniv of Radio Japan (overseas broadcasting station).
1791 **1205** 60 y. multicoloured . . . 60 10
1792 **1206** 60 y. multicoloured . . . 60 10
Nos. 1791/2 were issued together, se-tenant, forming a composite design.

1207 Maeshima and "Tokyo Post Office" (Hiroshige III) **1208** Bridge

1985. 150th Birth Anniv of Baron Hisoka Maeshima (first Postmaster-General).
1793 **1207** 60 y. multicoloured . . . 55 10

1985. Opening of Great Naruto Bridge.
1794 **1208** 60 y. multicoloured . . . 70 10

1209 Weaving **1210** Weaving

1211 Dish **1212** Panel

1985. Traditional Crafts (4th series). Ojiya Linen Weavings and Kamakura Lacquered Wood Carvings.
1795 **1209** 60 y. multicoloured . . . 50 10
1796 **1210** 60 y. multicoloured . . . 50 10
1797 **1211** 60 y. multicoloured . . . 50 10
1798 **1212** 60 y. multicoloured . . . 50 10

1213 Silhouette of Laurel and Couple

1985. International Youth Year.
1799 **1213** 60 y. multicoloured . . . 50 10

1214 Owl with Letter **1215** Girl holding Bird, Letter and Cat

1985. Letter Writing Day.
1800 **1214** 40 y. multicoloured . . . 60 10
1801 **1215** 60 y. multicoloured . . . 60 10

1985. Alpine Plants (5th series). As T **1166**. Multicoloured.
1802 60 y. Gentian ("Gentiana nipponica") 70 10
1803 60 y. "Callianthemum insigne" 70 10

1218 Logo

1985. Electronic Mail.
1804 **1218** 500 y. multicoloured . . 5·00 30

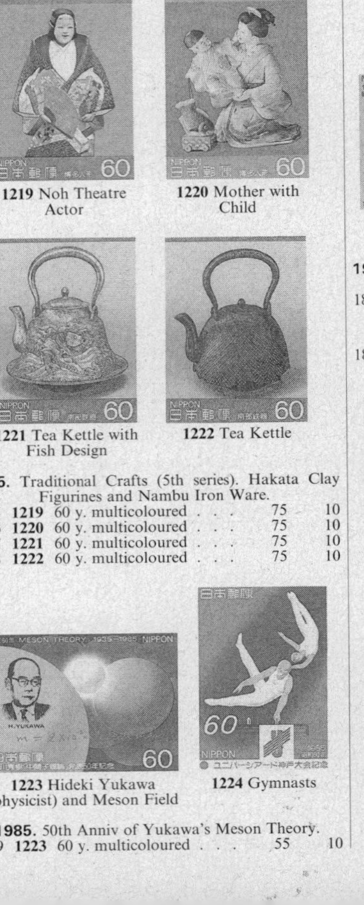

1219 Noh Theatre Actor **1220** Mother with Child

1221 Tea Kettle with Fish Design **1222** Tea Kettle

1985. Traditional Crafts (5th series). Hakata Clay Figurines and Nambu Iron Ware.
1805 **1219** 60 y. multicoloured . . . 75 10
1806 **1220** 60 y. multicoloured . . . 75 10
1807 **1221** 60 y. multicoloured . . . 75 10
1808 **1222** 60 y. multicoloured . . . 75 10

1223 Hideki Yukawa (physicist) and Meson Field **1224** Gymnasts

1985. 50th Anniv of Yukawa's Meson Theory.
1809 **1223** 60 y. multicoloured . . . 55 10

1985. University Games, Kobe.
1810 **1224** 60 y. multicoloured . . . 70 10

1225 Competitor filing Test Piece **1226** "Hibiscus syriacus" (national flower of S. Korea)

1985. 28th International Vocational Training Competition, Osaka.
1811 **1225** 40 y. multicoloured . . . 40 10

1985. 20th Anniv of Japan–South Korea Diplomatic Relations.
1812 **1226** 60 y. multicoloured . . . 75 10

1985. Alpine Plants (6th series). As T **1166**. Multicoloured.
1813 60 y. "Viola crassa" (horiz) . . 1·00 10
1814 60 y. "Campanula chamissonis" . . . . 1·00 10

1229 Tunnels and Section through Mt. Tanigawa **1230** "Seisen" (doll by Goyo Hirata)

1985. Opening of North-bound Kan-Etsu Tunnel.
1815 **1229** 60 y. multicoloured . . . 70 10

1985. International Correspondence Week.
1816 **1230** 130 y. multicoloured . . 1·50 10

1231 Youth helping African Farmer

1985. 20th Anniv of Japanese Overseas Co-operation Volunteers.
1817 **1231** 60 y. multicoloured . . . 50 10

1232 Honey Bee on Strawberry Blossom **1233** Handball Player and Mt. Daisen

1985. 30th International Bee-keeping Congress, Nagoya.
1818 **1232** 60 y. multicoloured . . . 80 10

1985. 40th Int Athletic Meeting, Tottori.
1819 **1233** 40 y. multicoloured . . . 70 10

1234 Table **1235** Bowl

1236 Lantern on Column **1237** Lantern

1985. Traditional Crafts (6th series). Wajima Lacquerware and Izumo Sandstone Lanterns.
1820 **1234** 60 y. multicoloured . . . 60 10
1821 **1235** 60 y. multicoloured . . . 60 10
1822 **1236** 60 y. multicoloured . . . 60 10
1823 **1237** 60 y. multicoloured . . . 60 10

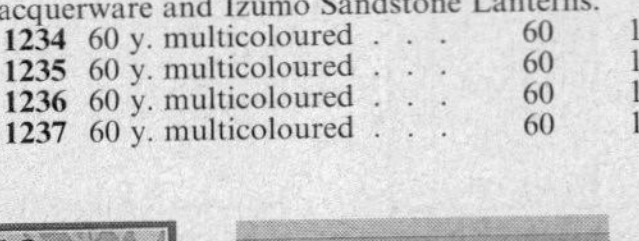

1238 Osaka Papier-mache Tiger **1239** Cabinet Emblem and Official Seal

1985. New Year's Greetings.
1824 **1238** 40 y. multicoloured . . . 50 10

1985. Cent of Cabinet System of Government.
1826 **1239** 60 y. multicoloured . . . 55 10

1986. Alpine Plants (7th series). As T **1166**. Multicoloured.
1827 60 y. "Diapensia lapponica" . 55 10
1828 60 y. "Pedicularis apodochila" . 55 10

1242 Fan with Tree Design **1243** Fan with Flower Design

1244 Flask with Fish Pattern **1245** Tea Caddy

1986. Traditional Craft (7th series). Kyoto Fans and Tobe Porcelain.
1829 **1242** 60 y. multicoloured . . . 75 10
1830 **1243** 60 y. multicoloured . . . 75 10
1831 **1244** 60 y. multicoloured . . . 75 10
1832 **1245** 60 y. multicoloured . . . 75 10

1246 Gothic Style Finial and "Golden Norm"

1986. Centenary of Architecture Institute, Shiba, Tokyo.
1833 **1246** 60 y. multicoloured . . . 60 10

1247 Standing Lady **1248** Seated Lady

1986. Philatelic Week. Details of "South of Hateruma" by Kaigetsu Kikuchi.
1834 **1247** 60 y. multicoloured . . . 80 10
1835 **1248** 60 y. multicoloured . . . 80 10

1249 Phoenix and Enthronement Hall, Kyoto Palace

1250 Imperial Palace Ridge Decoration

1986. 60th Anniv of Emperor Hirohito's Accession.
1836 **1249** 60 y. multicoloured . . . 70 10
1837 **1250** 60 y. multicoloured . . . 70 10

1251 "Mt. Fuji in Early Morning" (Yukihiko Yasuda)

1252 Bull-headed Shrike in Reeds

1986. 12th Economic Summit of Industrialised Countries, Tokyo.
1839 **1251** 60 y. multicoloured . . . 75 10

1986. National Afforestation Campaign.
1840 **1252** 60 y. multicoloured . . . 1·25 30

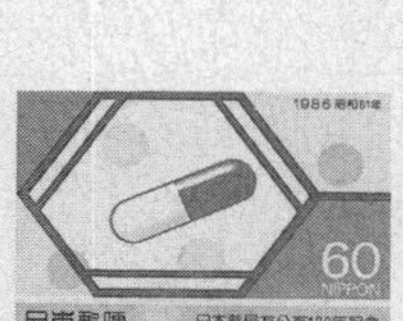

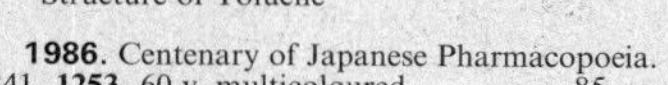

1253 Capsule, Tablets and Structure of Toluene

1254 Map and Clock

1986. Centenary of Japanese Pharmacopoeia.
1841 **1253** 60 y. multicoloured . . . 85 10

1986. Centenary of Japanese Standard Time.
1842 **1254** 60 y. multicoloured . . . 65 10

1255 Bird on Chair and Letter on Table

1257 Yataro Iwasaki, Makoto Kondo and Cadet Ship "Nippon Maru II"

1986. Letter Writing Day. Multicoloured.
1843 40 y. Type **1255** 40 10
1844 60 y. Girl holding rabbit and letter 70 10

1986. 110th Anniv of Merchant Navy Education.
1846 **1257** 60 y. multicoloured . . . 1·75 35

1258 Asian Apollo ("Parnassius eversmanni")

1262 "Folkways in Twelve Months" (detail, Shunsho Katsukawa)

1986. Insects (1st series). Multicolored.
1847 60 y. Type **1258** . . . . 1·00 10
1848 60 y. Shieldbug ("Poecilocoris lewisi") . . . . 1·00 10
1849 60 y. Longhorn beetle ("Rosalia batesi") . . . . 1·00 10
1850 60 y. "Epiophlebia superstes" . 1·00 10
See also Nos. 1854/7, 1861/4, 1869/72, 1878/81 and 1911/12.

1986. 52nd International Federation of Library Associations General Conference, Tokyo.
1851 **1262** 60 y. multicoloured . . . 75 10

1263 Electron Microscope

1264 Couple and Conference Emblem

1986. 11th International Electron Microscopy Congress, Kyoto.
1852 **1263** 60 y. multicoloured . . . 85 10

1986. 23rd International Social Welfare Conference, Tokyo.
1853 **1264** 60 y. multicoloured . . . 60 10

1986. Insects (2nd series). As T **1258**. Mult.
1854 60 y. Dragonflies ("Sympetrum pedemonatanum") . . . . 1·00 10
1855 60 y. Weevil ("Damaster blaptoides") . . . . 1·00 10
1856 60 y. Stag beetle ("Dorcus hopei") . . . . 1·00 10
1857 60 y. Wonderful hair-streak ("Thermozephyrus ataxus") . 1·00 10

1269 "Ohmori Miyage" (shiso doll, Juzoh Kagoshima)

1270 Gymnast and Mt. Fuji

1986. International Correspondence Week.
1858 **1269** 130 y. multicoloured . . 1·50 15

1986. 41st National Athletic Meeting, Yamanashi.
1859 **1270** 40 y. multicoloured . . . 70 10

1271 "Flowers in Autumn and Girl in Rakuhoku"

1276 Stylized Dove

1986. 5th World Ikebana Convention, Kyoto.
1860 **1271** 60 y. multicoloured . . . 85 10

1986. Insects (3rd series). As T **1258**. Mult.
1861 60 y. "Elcysma westwoodii" (moth) . . . . 1·00 10
1862 60 y. "Rhyothemis variegata" . 1·00 10
1863 60 y. Cicada ("Tibicen japonicus") . . . . 1·00 10
1864 60 y. "Chrysochroa holstii" . . 1·00 10

1986. International Peace Year. Mult.
1865 40 y. Type **1276** 40 10
1866 60 y. Circle of children (horiz) . 60 10

1278 "Rabbits making Rice Cake" (Nagoya clay model)

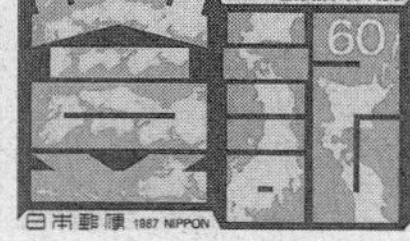

1283 Characters for "Toki" (Registry) and Map

1986. New Year's Greetings.
1867 **1278** 40 y. multicoloured . . . 75 10
For 50 y. in this design dated "1999" see No. 2567.

1987. Insects (4th series). As T **1258**. Mult.
1869 60 y. "Cheirotonus jambar" . . 1·00 10
1870 60 y. Chestnut tiger ("Parantica sita") . . . . 1·00 10
1871 60 y. "Anotogaster sieboldii" . 1·00 10
1872 60 y. Stag beetle ("Lucanus maculifemoratus") . . . . 1·00 10

1987. Centenary of Land Registration.
1873 **1283** 60 y. multicoloured . . . 65 10

1284 Basho Matsuo (after Haritsu Ogawa)

1285 "Departing Spring" (Senju)

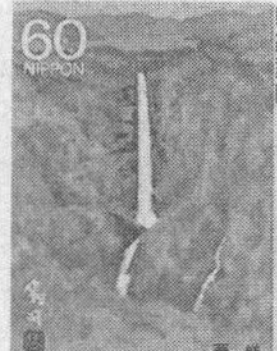

1286 Kegon Falls

1287 "Sunlight" (Toshu Shrine)

1987. "Narrow Road to a Far Province" (travel diary) by Basho Matsuo (1st series).
1874 **1284** 60 y. multicoloured . . . 75 10
1875 **1285** 60 y. multicoloured . . . 75 10
1876 **1286** 60 y. multicoloured . . . 75 10
1877 **1287** 60 y. multicoloured . . . 75 10
In this series each pair of stamps (except Nos. 1874/5) illustrates one "haiku" (17-syllable poem) from the diary. The full text of the "haiku" is printed on one stamp and given in calligraphy on the other with appropriate illustrations. Each "haiku" was written at a particular point in the journey (given in brackets in the caption to the second stamp of each pair).
See also Nos. 1896/9, 1906/9, 1925/8, 1932/5, 1945/8, 1962/5, 1973/6, 1982/5 and 2000/3.

1987. Insects (5th series). As T **1258**. Mult.
1878 60 y. Owl-fly ("Ascaraphus ramburi") . . . . 1·00 10
1879 60 y. Cockchafer ("Polyphylla laticollis") . . . . 1·00 10
1880 60 y. Leaf butterfly ("Kallima inachus") . . . . 1·00 10
1881 60 y. "Calopteryx cornelia" . . 1·00 10

1294 Wind Orchid

1295 Lobster-root

1987. 12th International Orchid Conference, Tokyo.
1883 **1294** 60 y. multicoloured . . . 70 10
1884 **1295** 60 y. multicoloured . . . 70 10

1296 Early Mail Sorting Carriage

1987. Ending of Railway Mail Carriage Contracts.
1885 60 y. Type **1296** . . . . 1·00 30
1886 60 y. Loading mail sacks (detail of scroll painting by Beisen Kubota) . . . . 1·00 30

1298 Class 860 Tank Locomotive No. 137, 1893

1987. Privatisation of Japan Railways. Mult.
1887 60 y. Type **1298** . . . . 1·00 30
1888 60 y. Maglev MLU 002 . . . 1·00 30

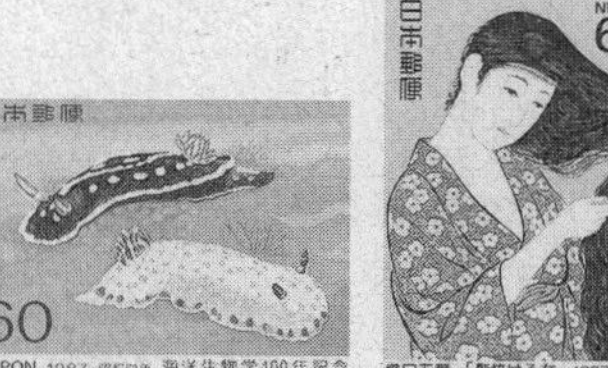

1300 Nudibranchs

1301 "Woman with a Comb"

1987. Centenary of Marine Biology Studies in Japan.
1889 **1300** 60 y. multicoloured . . . 85 15

1987. Philatelic Week. Paintings by Goyo Hashiguchi. Multicoloured.
1890 60 y. Type **1301** 85 10
1891 60 y. "Woman putting on make-up" 85 10

1303 Map and Emblem

1304 Magpie and Forested Coastline

1987. 20th Annual General Meeting of Asian Development Bank.
1892 **1303** 60 y. multicoloured . . . 60 10

1987. National Afforestation Campaign.
1893 **1304** 60 y. multicoloured . . . 1·25 10

1305 Yatsuhashi Gold Lacquer and Nacre Inkstone Case (Kohrin Ogata)

1306 Hikone Castle

1987. National Treasures (1st series).
1894 **1305** 60 y. multicoloured . . . 75 10
1895 **1306** 110 y. multicoloured . . 1·50 15
See also Nos. 1900/1, 1929/30, 1949/50, 1968/9, 1980/1, 2006/7 and 2017/18.

1307 European Cuckoo

1308 Horse and River (Nasu)

1309 "In the Shade of the Willow"

1310 Paddy Field (Ashino)

1987. "Narrow Road to a Far Province" by Basho Matsuo (2nd series).
1896 **1307** 60 y. multicoloured . . . 80 10
1897 **1308** 60 y. multicoloured . . . 60 10
1898 **1309** 60 y. multicoloured . . . 60 10
1899 **1310** 60 y. multicoloured . . . 60 10

1311 Golden Turtle Reliquary for Buddha's Ashes (Tashodai Temple)

1312 Inuyama Castle

1987. National Treasures (2nd series). Multicoloured.
1900 **1311** 60 y. multicoloured . . . 85 10
1901 **1312** 110 y. multicoloured . . 1·40 15

1313 Flowers in Envelope

1315 Flood Barrier across Rivers

1987. Letter Writing Day. Multicoloured.
1902 40 y. Type **1313** 35 10
1903 60 y. Elephant holding letter in trunk 45 10

1987. Centenary of Modern Flood Control of Rivers Kiso, Nagara and Ibi.
1905 **1315** 60 y. multicoloured . . . 60 10

1316 Chestnut Blossoms

1317 Chestnut Leaves (Sukagawa)

1318 Transplanting Rice

1319 Fern Leaves ("Dyeing Stone", Shinobu)

1987. "Narrow Road to a Far Province" by Basho Matsuo (3rd series).
1906 **1316** 60 y. multicoloured . . . 60 10
1907 **1317** 60 y. multicoloured . . . 60 10
1908 **1318** 60 y. multicoloured . . . 60 10
1909 **1319** 60 y. multicoloured . . . 60 10

1320 Temple of Emerald Buddha and Cherry Blossom

1321 "Gensho Kanto" (Ryujo Hori)

1987. Centenary of Japan–Thailand Friendship Treaty.
1910 **1320** 60 y. multicoloured . . . 65 10

1987. Insects (6th series). As T **1258**. Mult.
1911 40 y. Orange-tip ("Anthocaris cardamines") 75 10
1912 40 y. Great purple ("Sasakia charonda") 75 10

1987. International Correspondence Week. Multicoloured.
1913 130 y. Type **1321** . . . . . . 1·40 10
1914 150 y. "Utage-no-Hana" (Goyo Hirata) . . . . 1·60 10

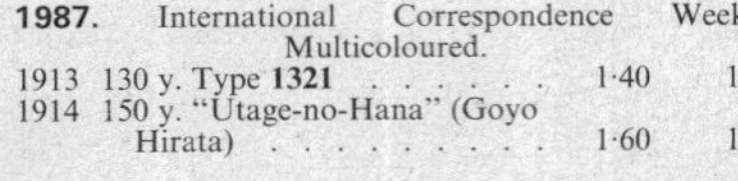

1323 "Three Beauties" (detail, Toyokuni Utagawa)

1324 Lion's Head Public Water Tap

1987. 13th International Certified Public Accountants Congress, Tokyo.
1915 **1323** 60 y. multicoloured . . . 55 10

1987. Centenary of Yokohama Waterworks.
1916 **1324** 60 y. multicoloured . . . 55 10

1325 Basketball Players and Shuri Gate, Naha

1326 Playing Card with Queen holding Bird and King smoking

1987. 42nd National Athletic Meeting, Okinawa.
1917 **1325** 40 y. multicoloured . . . 45 10

1987. 6th International Smoking and Health Conference, Tokyo.
1918 **1326** 60 y. multicoloured . . . 70 10

1327 Dish Aerial, Kashima Station

1328 Nijo Castle

1987. International Telecommunications Conference, Tokyo.
1919 **1327** 60 y. multicoloured . . . 65 10

1987. World Historic Cities Conference, Kyoto.
1920 **1328** 60 y. multicoloured . . . 65 10

1329 "Family in Tree" (Takahiro Nagahama)

1331 Kurashiki Papier-mache Dragon

1987. International Year of Shelter for the Homeless. Multicoloured.
1921 40 y. Type **1329** 40 10
1922 60 y. "Houses" (Yoko Sasaki) . . . 60 10

1987. New Year's Greetings.
1923 **1331** 40 y. multicoloured . . . 50 10

1332 Sweet Flags

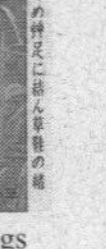

1333 Sweet Flags and Birds (Sendai)

1334 "Recollecting the Past"

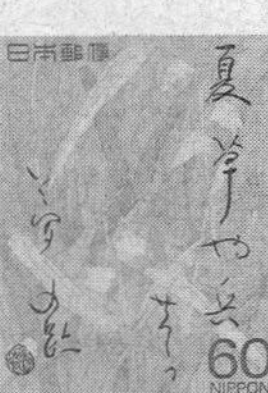

1335 "Summer Grasses" (Hiraizumi)

1988. "Narrow Road to a Far Province" by Basho Matsuo (4th series).
1925 **1332** 60 y. multicoloured . . . 60 10
1926 **1333** 60 y. multicoloured . . . 60 10
1927 **1334** 60 y. multicoloured . . . 60 10
1928 **1335** 60 y. multicoloured . . . 60 10

1336 Kongo Samma-in Pagoda, Mt. Koya

1337 Ekoh-Doji, Kongobu Temple

1988. National Treasures (3rd series).
1929 **1336** 60 y. multicoloured . . . 60 10
1930 **1337** 110 y. multicoloured . . 1·25 10

1338 Class ED 79 Locomotive "Sea of Japan" leaving Tunnel and Map

1988. Opening of Seikan (Aomori–Hakodate) Railway Tunnel.
1931 **1338** 60 y. multicoloured . . . 70 30

1339 Safflower

1340 Willow Trees (Obanazawa)

1341 Risshaku (or Mountain) Temple

1342 Pine Trees (Risshaku Temple)

1988. "Narrow Road to a Far Province" by Basho Matsuo (5th series).
1932 **1339** 60 y. multicoloured . . . 60 10
1933 **1340** 60 y. multicoloured . . . 60 10
1934 **1341** 60 y. multicoloured . . . 60 10
1935 **1342** 60 y. multicoloured . . . 60 10

1343 South Bisan Section from Kagawa Side **1344**

1345 Shimotsui Section from Okayama Side **1346**

1988. Opening of Seto Great Road and Rail Bridge.
1936 **1343** 60 y. multicoloured . . . 85 30
1937 **1344** 60 y. multicoloured . . . 85 30
1938 **1345** 60 y. multicoloured . . . 85 30
1939 **1346** 60 y. multicoloured . . . 85 30
Nos. 1936/7 and 1938/9 were printed together, se-tenant, each pair forming composite design.

1347 "Long Undergarment" (Kotondo Torii)

1349 Detail of Biwa Plectrum Guard

1988. Philatelic Week. Multicoloured.
1940 60 y. Type **1347** 60 10
1941 60 y. "Kimono Sash" (Kotondo Torii) 60 10

1988. "Silk Road" Exhibition. Nara.
1943 **1349** 60 y. multicoloured . . . 60 10

1350 Yashima, Little Cuckoo and Olive Tree

1988. National Afforestation Campaign.
1944 **1350** 60 y. multicoloured . . . 70 10

1351 River Mogami

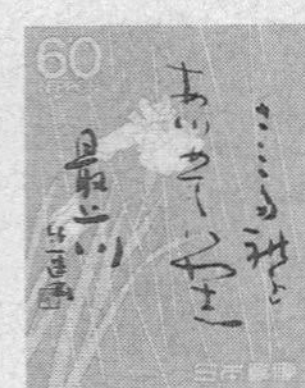

1352 Irises in the Rain (Oishida)

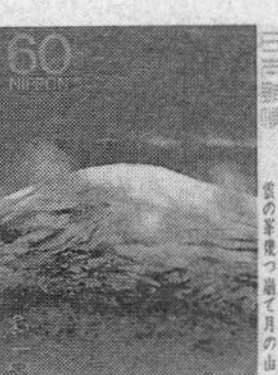

1353 Moon Mountain

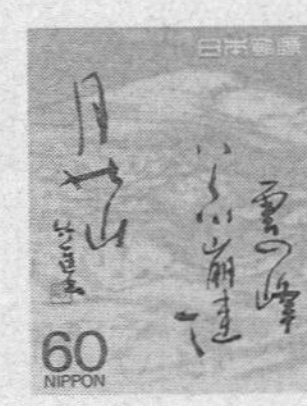

1354 Moon Mountain (Gassan)

1988. "Narrow Road to a Far Province" by Basho Matsuo (6th series).
1945 **1351** 60 y. multicoloured . . . 80 15
1946 **1352** 60 y. multicoloured . . . 60 10
1947 **1353** 60 y. multicoloured . . . 60 10
1948 **1354** 60 y. multicoloured . . . 60 10

1355 Morodo Shrine, Itsukushima

1356 Kozakura-gawa Braided Armour

1988. National Treasures (4th series).
1949 **1355** 60 y. multicoloured . . . 60 10
1950 **1356** 100 y. multicoloured . . 95 20

1357 Mt. Sakura

1358 Cat with Letter

1988. International Conference on Volcanoes, Kagoshima.
1951 **1357** 60 y. multicoloured . . . 60 10

1988. Letter Writing Day. Multicoloured.
1952 40 y. Type **1358** 45 10
1953 40 y. Crab with letter (34 × 25 mm) 45 10
1954 60 y. Fairy with letter 60 10
1955 60 y. Girl and letter (25 × 32 mm) 60 10
Nos. 1952 and 1954 exist both perforated with ordinary gum and imperforate with self-adhesive gum.

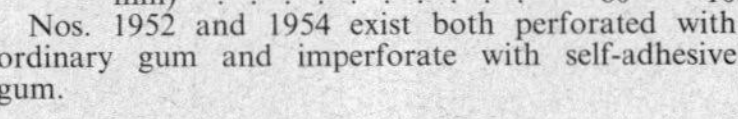

1362 Ohana (Kinosuke puppet, Japan)

1366 Peonies

1988. International Puppetry Festival, Nagoya, Iida and Tokyo. Multicoloured.
1956 60 y. Type **1362** 60 10
1957 60 y. Stick puppet of girl (Czechoslovakia) 60 10
1958 60 y. Shadow puppet (China) . 60 10
1959 60 y. Knight (Italy) 60 10

1988. 10th Anniv of Japanese–Chinese Treaty of Peace and Friendship. Multicoloured.
1960 60 y. Type **1366** 60 10
1961 60 y. Ton-ton (giant panda) . . 75 10

1368 Mimosa Flowers

1369 Lagoon and Grass (Kisagata)

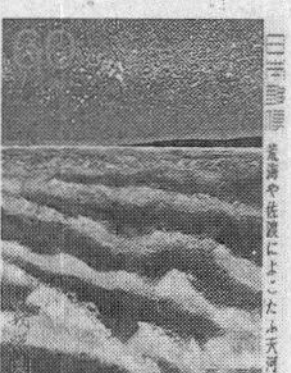
1370 Rough Sea

1371 Waves (Ichiburi)

1988. "Narrow Road to a Far Province" by Basho Matsuo (7th series).

1962	**1368**	60 y. multicoloured . . .	60	10
1963	**1369**	60 y. multicoloured . . .	60	10
1964	**1370**	60 y. multicoloured . . .	60	10
1965	**1371**	60 y. multicoloured . . .	60	10

1372 Nagoya and Egg

1373 Globe and "Rehabilitation" in Braille

1988. 18th International Poultry Congress, Nagoya.

1966	**1372**	60 y. multicoloured . . .	70	10

1988. 16th Rehabilitation International World Congress, Tokyo.

1967	**1373**	60 y. multicoloured . . .	60	10

1374 Nakatsuhime-no-mikoto, Yakushi Temple

1375 Murou Temple

1988. National Treasures (5th series).

1968	**1374**	60 y. multicoloured . . .	60	10
1969	**1375**	100 y. multicoloured . .	95	20

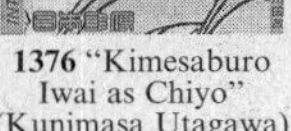
1376 "Kimesaburo Iwai as Chiyo" (Kunimasa Utagawa)

1378 Gymnast and Temple of the Golden Pavilion

1988. International Correspondence Week. Multicoloured.

1970	80 y. Type **1376**	85	10
1971	120 y. "Komazo Ichikawa III as Ganryu Sasaki" (Toyokuni Utagawa) . . .	1·25	20

1988. 43rd National Athletic Meeting, Kyoto.

1972	**1378**	40 y. multicoloured . . .	45	10

1379 Rice

1380 Ariso Sea (Kurikara Pass)

1381 Sun

1382 "Autumn Wind and Sun" (Kanazawa)

1988. "Narrow Road to a Far Province" by Basho Matsuo (8th series).

1973	**1379**	60 y. multicoloured . . .	60	10
1974	**1380**	60 y. multicoloured . . .	60	10
1975	**1381**	60 y. multicoloured . . .	60	10
1976	**1382**	60 y. multicoloured . . .	60	10

1383 Mexican State Arms

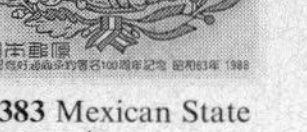
1384 Snake (Shimotsuke clay bell)

1988. Centenary of Japan–Mexico Friendship and Trade Treaty.

1977	**1383**	60 y. multicoloured . . .	60	10

1988. New Year's Greetings.

1978	**1384**	40 y. multicoloured . . .	45	10

1385 Figures on Globe

1988. 40th Anniv of Declaration of Human Rights.

1979	**1385**	60 y. multicoloured . . .	60	10

1386 Gold-plated Silver Pot with Hunting Design, Todai Temple

1387 Bronze Figure of Yakushi (Buddha of Medicine), Horyu Temple

1989. National Treasures (6th series).

1980	**1386**	60 y. multicoloured . . .	60	10
1981	**1387**	100 y. multicoloured . .	95	20

1388 Nata Temple

1389 Pampas Grass (Natadera)

1390 Moonlight, Kehi Shrine

1391 Moon and Pine Trees (Tsuruga)

1989 "Narrow Road to a Far Province" by Basho Matsuo (9th series).

1982	**1388**	60 y. multicoloured . . .	60	10
1983	**1389**	60 y. multicoloured . . .	60	10
1984	**1390**	60 y. multicoloured . . .	60	10
1985	**1391**	60 y. multicoloured . . .	60	10

1392 Globe and Exhibition Site

1989. "Fukuoka '89" Asian–Pacific Exhibition, Fukuoka.

1989	**1392**	60 y. multicoloured . . .	60	10
1996		62 y. multicoloured . . .	60	10

1393 "Russian Ladies sight-seeing at Port" (detail, Yoshitora) and Art Gallery

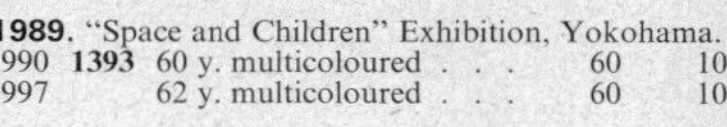
1394 Bonsai Japanese White Pine

1989. "Space and Children" Exhibition, Yokohama.

1990	**1393**	60 y. multicoloured . . .	60	10
1997		62 y. multicoloured . . .	60	10

1989. World Bonsai Convention, Omiya.

1993	**1394**	62 y. multicoloured . . .	60	10

1395 Lute-player

1397 "Dutch East Indiaman entering Harbour" (Nagasaki wood-block print)

1989. Philatelic Week. Details of "Awa Dance" (painting) by Tsunetomi Kitano. Multicoloured.

1994	62 y. Type **1395**	60	10
1995	62 y. Dancer	60	10

1989. "Holland Festival '89".

1998	**1397**	62 y. multicoloured . . .	1·00	15

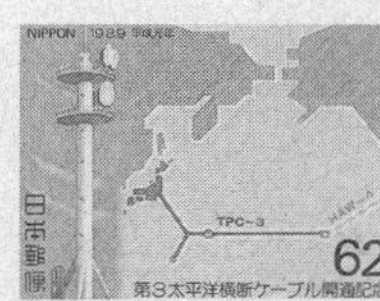
1398 Chikura Communication Tower and Cable Route

1989. Opening of 3rd Trans-Pacific Submarine Telephone Cable (Japan–Hawaii).

1999	**1398**	62 y. multicoloured . . .	60	10

1399 Beach in Autumn

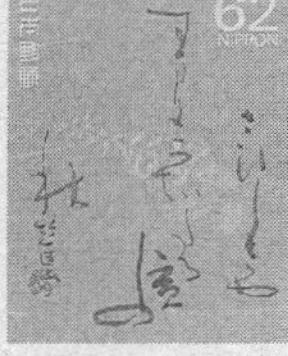
1400 Bush Clover (Ironohama)

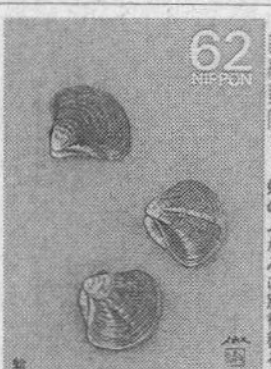
1401 Poker-drop Venuses

1402 Wedded Rocks, Futami Bay (Ohgaki)

1989. "Narrow Road to a Far Province" by Basho Matsuo (11th series).

2000	**1399**	62 y. multicoloured . . .	60	10
2001	**1400**	62 y. multicoloured . . .	60	10
2002	**1401**	62 y. multicoloured . . .	70	15
2003	**1402**	62 y. multicoloured . . .	60	10

1403 Mt. Tsurugi, Lime and Bay Trees

1404 Children in Bird and Flower "Balloon"

1989. National Afforestation Campaign.

2004	**1403**	62 y. multicoloured . . .	60	10

1989. International Garden and Greenery Exposition, Osaka (1990) (1st issue).

2005	**1404**	62 y. + 10 y. mult . . .	70	10

See also Nos. 2035/6.

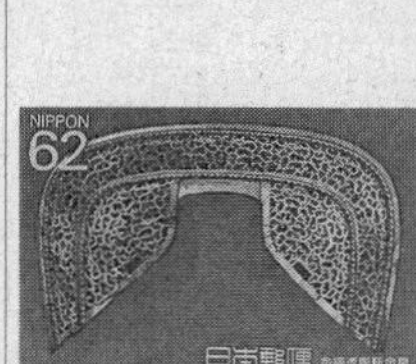
1405 Saddle Fitting from Burial Mound, Konda

1406 "Beetle Wings" Zushi, Horyu Temple

1989. National Treasures (7th series).

2006	**1405**	62 y. multicoloured . . .	60	10
2007	**1406**	100 y. multicoloured . .	95	20

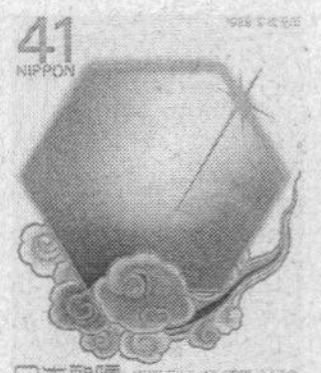
1407 "Crystal of Light and Auspicious Clouds"

1409 Bird as Vase holding Envelope

1989. World Design Exposition, Nagoya. Multicoloured.

2008	41 y. Type **1407**	45	10
2009	62 y. "design"	60	10

1989. Letter Writing Day. Multicoloured.

2010	41 y. Type **1409**	45	10
2011	62 y. Mother Rabbit reading letter	60	10

1989. Special Correspondence Stamps.

2013	**1098**	41 y. multicoloured . . .	40	10
2014	**1099**	41 y. multicoloured . . .	40	10
2015		62 y. multicoloured . . .	55	10
2016	**1100**	72 y. multicoloured . . .	65	10

1411 Gold Stamp

1412 Bronze Mirror

1989. National Treasures (8th series).

2017	**1411**	62 y. multicoloured . . .	60	10
2018	**1412**	100 y. multicoloured . .	95	20

1413 Bouquet of Orchids and Stephanotis

1414 Wheelchair Race

1989. 6th Interflora World Congress, Tokyo.
2019 **1413** 62 y. multicoloured . . . 60 10

1989. Far East and South Pacific Games for the Disabled, Kobe.
2020 **1414** 62 y. multicoloured . . . 60 10

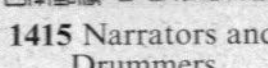

1415 Narrators and Drummers

1419 Ear of Rice and Paddy Field

1417 New Emperor and Kaoru playing Go ("Yadorigi" scroll)

1989. "Europalia 89 Japan" Festival, Belgium. Details of "Okuni Theatre" (painting on folding screen). Multicoloured.
2021 62 y. Type **1415** 60 10
2022 70 y. Okuni (actress) 60 10

1989. International Correspondence Week. Details of Takayoshi Picture Scrolls illustrating "Tale of Genji" by Lady Murasaki. Multicoloured.
2023 80 y. Type **1417** 75 10
2024 120 y. Yugao's granddaughters playing Go ("Takekawa scroll") . . . . 1·25 20

1989. 7th Asian/African Conference of Int. Irrigation and Drainage Commission.
2025 **1419** 62 y. multicoloured . . . 60 10

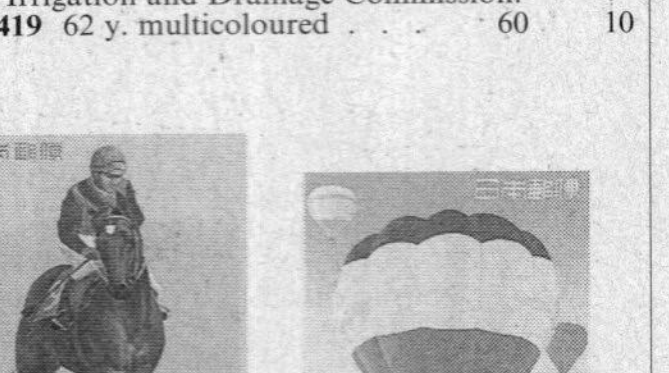

1420 Shinzan (first winner of all five major races)

1421 Hot-air Balloons

1989. 100th Tenno Sho Horse Race.
2026 **1420** 62 y. multicoloured . . . 70 10

1989. 9th Hot Air Balloon World Championship, Saga City.
2027 **1421** 62 y. multicoloured . . . 60 10

1422 Conductor

1423 Yawata Wooden Horse

1989. 50th Anniv of Japanese Copyright Control Act.
2028 **1422** 62 y. multicoloured . . . 60 10

1989. New Year's Greetings.
2029 **1423** 41 y. multicoloured . . . 45 10

1424 Hamamatsu Papier-mache Horse

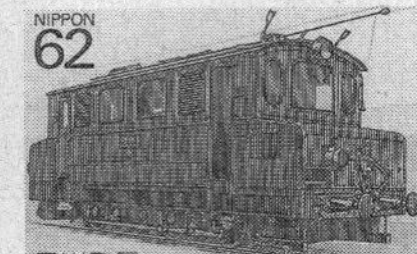

1425 Type 10000

1989. New Year Lottery Stamp.
2030 **1424** 62 y. multicoloured . . . 60 10
Each stamp carries a lottery number.

1990. Electric Railway Locomotives (1st series).
2031 **1425** 62 y. purple, lilac & grn . 1·25 25
2032 – 62 y. multicoloured . . . 1·25 25
DESIGN: No. 2032, Type EF 58 No. 38, 1946.
See also Nos. 2033/4, 2039/40, 2089/90 and 2101/2.

1990. Electric Railway Locomotives (2nd series). As T **1425**. Multicoloured.
2033 62 y. Type ED 40 No. 12, 1919 1·25 25
2034 62 y. Type EH 10 No. 8, 1954 . 1·25 25

1429 Fairies on Flower

1431 "Women gazing at the Stars" (Chou Ohta)

1990. "Expo 90" International Garden and Greenery Exposition, Osaka. Multicoloured.
2035 41 y. + 4 y. Type **1429** 45 10
2036 62 y. Bicycle under tree 55 10

1990. Philatelic Week.
2037 **1431** 62 y. multicoloured . . . 55 10

1990. Electric Railway Locomotives (3rd series). As T **1425**. Multicoloured.
2039 62 y. Type EF 53, 1932 . . . . 1·25 25
2040 62 y. Type ED 70, 1957 . . . . 1·25 25

1434 Sweet Briar (Hokkaido)

1435 Apple Blossom (Aomori)

1436 "Paulownia tomentosa" (Iwate)

1437 Japanese Bush Clover (Miyagi)

1438 Butterbur Flower (Akita)

1439 Safflower (Yamagata)

1440 Rhododendron (Fukushima)

1441 Rose (Ibaraki)

1442 Yashio Azalea (Tochigi)

1443 Japanese Azalea (Gunma)

1444 Primrose (Saitama)

1445 Rape (Chiba)

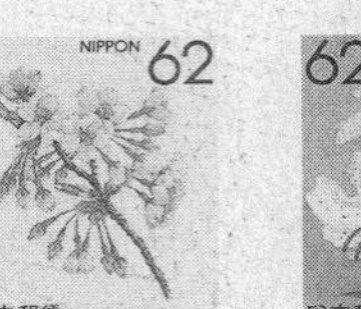

1446 Cherry Blossom (Yamanashi)

1447 Gold-banded Lily (Kanagawa)

1448 Cherry Blossom (Tokyo)

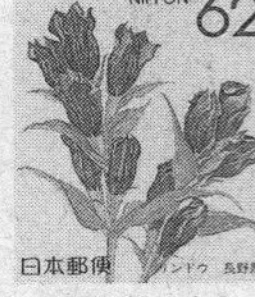

1449 Gentian (Nagano)

1450 Tulip (Niigata)

1451 Tulip (Toyama)

1452 Fritillaria (Ishikawa)

1453 Narcissi (Fukui)

1454 Chinese Milk Vetch (Gifu)

1455 Azalea (Shizuoka)

1456 Rabbit-ear Iris (Aichi)

1457 Iris (Mie)

1458 Rhododendron (Shiga)

1459 Weeping Cherry Blossom (Kyoto)

1460 Japanese Apricot and Primrose (Osaka)

1461 Marguerites (Hyogo)

1462 Double Cherry Blossom (Nara)

1463 Japanese Apricot (Wakayama)

1464 Pear Blossom (Tottori)

1465 Peony (Shimane)

1466 Peach Blossom (Okayama)

1467 Japanese Maple (Hiroshima)

1468 Summer Orange Blossom (Yamaguchi)

1469 Sudachi Orange Blossom (Tokushima)

1470 Olive Blossom (Kagawa)

1471 Mandarin Orange Blossom (Ehime)

1472 "Myrica rubra" (Kochi)

1473 Japanese Apricot (Fukuoka)

1474 Laurel (Saga)

1475 Unzen Azalea (Nagasaki)

1476 Gentian (Kumamoto)

1477 Japanese Apricot (Oita)

1478 Crinum (Miyazaki)

1479 Rhododendron (Kagoshima)

1480 Coral Tree (Okinawa)

1990. Prefecture Flowers.

2041 **1434** 62 y. multicoloured . . . 60 10
2042 **1435** 62 y. multicoloured . . . 60 10
2043 **1436** 62 y. multicoloured . . . 60 10
2044 **1437** 62 y. multicoloured . . . 60 10
2045 **1438** 62 y. multicoloured . . . 60 10
2046 **1439** 62 y. multicoloured . . . 60 10
2047 **1440** 62 y. multicoloured . . . 60 10
2048 **1441** 62 y. multicoloured . . . 60 10
2049 **1442** 62 y. multicoloured . . . 60 10
2050 **1443** 62 y. multicoloured . . . 60 10
2051 **1444** 62 y. multicoloured . . . 60 10
2052 **1445** 62 y. multicoloured . . . 60 10
2053 **1446** 62 y. multicoloured . . . 60 10
2054 **1447** 62 y. multicoloured . . . 60 10
2055 **1448** 62 y. multicoloured . . . 60 10
2056 **1449** 62 y. multicoloured . . . 60 10
2057 **1450** 62 y. multicoloured . . . 60 10
2058 **1451** 62 y. multicoloured . . . 60 10
2059 **1452** 62 y. multicoloured . . . 60 10
2060 **1453** 62 y. multicoloured . . . 60 10
2061 **1454** 62 y. multicoloured . . . 60 10
2062 **1455** 62 y. multicoloured . . . 60 10
2063 **1456** 62 y. multicoloured . . . 60 10
2064 **1457** 62 y. multicoloured . . . 60 10
2065 **1458** 62 y. multicoloured . . . 60 10
2066 **1459** 62 y. multicoloured . . . 60 10
2067 **1460** 62 y. multicoloured . . . 60 10
2068 **1461** 62 y. multicoloured . . . 60 10
2069 **1462** 62 y. multicoloured . . . 60 10
2070 **1463** 62 y. multicoloured . . . 60 10
2071 **1464** 62 y. multicoloured . . . 60 10
2072 **1465** 62 y. multicoloured . . . 60 10
2073 **1466** 62 y. multicoloured . . . 60 10
2074 **1467** 62 y. multicoloured . . . 60 10
2075 **1468** 62 y. multicoloured . . . 60 10
2076 **1469** 62 y. multicoloured . . . 60 10
2077 **1470** 62 y. multicoloured . . . 60 10
2078 **1471** 62 y. multicoloured . . . 60 10
2079 **1472** 62 y. multicoloured . . . 60 10
2080 **1473** 62 y. multicoloured . . . 60 10
2081 **1474** 62 y. multicoloured . . . 60 10
2082 **1475** 62 y. multicoloured . . . 60 10
2083 **1476** 62 y. multicoloured . . . 60 10
2084 **1477** 62 y. multicoloured . . . 60 10
2085 **1478** 62 y. multicoloured . . . 60 10
2086 **1479** 62 y. multicoloured . . . 60 10
2087 **1480** 62 y. multicoloured . . . 60 10

1481 Mt. Unzen and Unzen Azalea

1484 Fritillary on Thistle

1990. National Afforestation Campaign.

2088 **1481** 62 y. multicoloured . . . 55 10

1990. Electric Railway Locomotives (4th series). As T **1425**. Multicoloured.

2089 62 y. Type EF 55, 1936 . . . . 1·25 25
2090 62 y. Type ED 61 No. 13, 1958 . 1·25 25

1990. Winning Entries in Postage Stamp Design Contest. Multicoloured.

2091 62 y. Type **1484** 55 25
2092 70 y. "Communication" . . . 65 20

1486 17th-century Ottoman Tile

1990. Century of Japan–Turkey Friendship.

2093 **1486** 62 y. multicoloured . . . 55 10

1487/91 Folding Screen ($\frac{1}{2}$ size illustration)

1492 "Ponies" (Kayo Yamaguchi)

1493 Emblem and Landscape

1990. The Horse in Culture (1st series).

2094 **1487** 62 y. multicoloured . . . 65 10
2095 **1488** 62 y. multicoloured . . . 65 10
2096 **1489** 62 y. multicoloured . . . 65 10
2097 **1490** 62 y. multicoloured . . . 65 10
2098 **1491** 62 y. multicoloured . . . 65 10
2099 **1492** 62 y. multicoloured . . . 65 10

Nos. 2094/8 were printed together, se-tenant, forming a composite design showing a 17th-century folding screen painting.

See also Nos. 2106/8, 2113/14, 2132/4 and 2135/6.

1990. 38th International Youth Hostel Federation Congress. Muikamachi and Kashiwazaki.

2100 **1493** 62 y. multicoloured . . . 55 10

1990. Electric Railway Locomotives (5th series). As T **1425**. Multicoloured.

2101 62 y. Type ED 57, 1941 . . . 1·25 25
2102 62 y. Type EF 30 Nos. 3 and 6, 1961 . . . . 1·25 25

1496 Bluebird and Heart

1497 Fairy on Horse

1990. Letter Writing Day.

2103 **1496** 41 y. multicoloured . . . 40 10
2104 **1497** 62 y. multicoloured . . . 55 10

For similar design to No. 2104, see No. 2157.

1500 "A Horse" (Suisho Nishiyama)

1990. The Horse in Culture (2nd series). Multicoloured.

2106 62 y. 16th-century lacquered saddle 65 10
2107 62 y. 16th-century lacquered stirrups 65 10
2108 62 y. Type **1500** 65 10

1501 Origami Polyhedron

1502 Track Race

1990. Int. Mathematicians Congress, Kyoto.

2109 **1501** 62 y. multicoloured . . . 60 10

1990. World Cycling Championships. Maebashi and Tochigi Prefecture.

2110 **1502** 62 y. multicoloured . . . 60 10

1503 Ogai Mori (translator) and Passage from Goethe's "Faust"

1504 "Ji" (character) and Rosetta Stone

1990. 8th International Association for Germanic Studies Congress, Tokyo.

2111 **1503** 62 y. blue, yellow & brn . 55 10

1990. International Literacy Year.

2112 **1504** 62 y. multicoloured . . . 55 10

1505 "Kurabeuma Race" (detail of Kimono)

1506 "Kettei" (Shodo Sasaki)

1990. The Horse in Culture (3rd series).

2113 **1505** 62 y. multicoloured . . . 65 10
2114 **1506** 62 y. multicoloured . . . 65 10

1507 Peaceful Landscape

1990. International Decade for Natural Disaster Reduction Conference, Yokohama.

2115 **1507** 62 y. multicoloured . . . 55 10

1508 Animals at Dance

1990. International Correspondence Week. Details from "Choju-jinbutsu-giga" Picture Scroll. Multicoloured.

2116 80 y. Type **1508** 75 10
2117 120 y. Dancing frogs . . . . . 1·10 20

1510 Midwife, Mother and Baby

1990. 22nd International Confederation of Midwives Congress, Kobe City.

2118 **1510** 62 y. multicoloured . . . 55 10

1511 "Letter Bearer" (detail, Harunobu Suiendo)

1990. "Phila Nippon '91" International Stamp Exhibition, Tokyo (1st issue).

2119 **1511** 100 y. multicoloured . . 1·00 20

See also No. 2170.

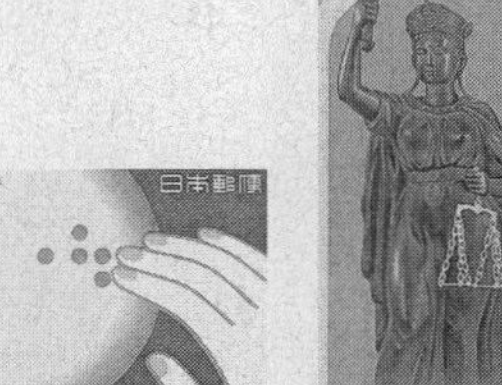

1512 Hand reading Braille

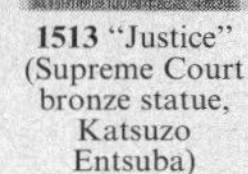

1513 "Justice" (Supreme Court bronze statue, Katsuzo Entsuba)

1990. Centenary of Japanese Braille.

2121 **1512** 62 y. multicoloured . . . 55 10

1990. Centenary of Modern Judiciary System.

2122 **1513** 62 y. multicoloured . . . 55 10

1514 Chinese Phoenix (detail from dais of Emperor's enthronement seat)

1516 Stained Glass Window (Diet building)

1990. Enthronement of Emperor. Multicoloured.

2123 62 y. Type **1514** 55 10
2124 62 y. Pattern from robe of Manzai Raku dancers . . . 55 10

1990. Centenary of Diet.

2126 **1516** 62 y. multicoloured . . . 55 10

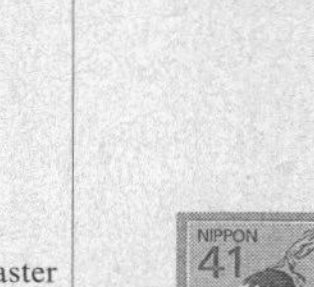

1517 Sheep (Nogomi ceramic bell)

1519 Tsuneishi-Hariko Papiermache Ram

1990. New Year's Greetings.

2127 **1517** 41 y. multicoloured . . . 40 10

1990. New Year Lottery Stamps. Multicoloured.

2128 41 y. Sheep (Tosa ceramic bell) 40 10
2129 62 y. Type **1519** 55 10

Each stamp carries a lottery number.

1520 Dr. Nishina and Radio Isotope

1521 "Lady using Telephone" (Senseki Nakamura)

1990. Birth Centenary of Dr. Yoshio Nishina (physicist) and 50th Anniv of First Japanese Cyclotron (radio isotope generator).

2130 **1520** 62 y. multicoloured . . . 55 10

1990. Centenary of Telephone Service in Japan.

2131 **1521** 62 y. multicoloured . . . 55 10

1522 Horse-drawn Post Carriages **1523** (details of scroll painting by Beisen Kubota)

1524 Inkstone Case (Korin Ogata)

1991. The Horse in Culture (4th series).

2132 **1522** 62 y. multicoloured . . . 60 10
2133 **1523** 62 y. multicoloured . . . 60 10
2134 **1524** 62 y. multicoloured . . . 60 10

Nos. 2132/3 were issued together, se-tenant, forming a composite design.

1525 "Spring Warmth" (Kogetsu Saigo)

1526 "Senju in Musashi Province" (from "36 Views of Mt. Fuji" by Hokusai Katsushika)

1991. The Horse in Culture (5th series).

2135 **1525** 62 y. multicoloured . . . 65 10
2136 **1526** 62 y. multicoloured . . . 65 10

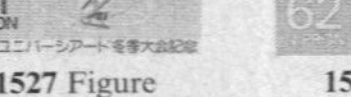

1527 Figure Skating

1529 Bouquet

1991. Winter Universiade, Sapporo and Furano. Multicoloured.

2137 41 y. Type **1527** 45 10
2138 62 y. Short-track speed skating (horiz) 60 10

1991. New Postal Life Insurance System.

2139 **1529** 62 y. multicoloured . . . 55 10

1530 "Glory of the Earth" (Komei Bekki)

1531 "Beauty looking Back" (Moronobu Hishikawa)

1991. "Ceramic World Shigaraki '91" Exn.

2140 **1530** 62 y. multicoloured . . . 55 10

1991. Philatelic Week. 120th Anniv of First Japanese Stamps.

2141 62 y. Type **1531** 60 10
2142 62 y. "The Prelude" (Shuho Yamakawa) 60 10

1533 Weeping Cherry Blossom and Phoenix Hall, Byodoin Temple

1534 Early Leveller and Standard Datum Repository, Tokyo

1991. National Afforestation Campaign.

2144 **1533** 41 y. multicoloured . . . 40 10

1991. Centenary of Standard Datum of Levelling.

2145 **1534** 62 y. multicoloured . . . 55 10

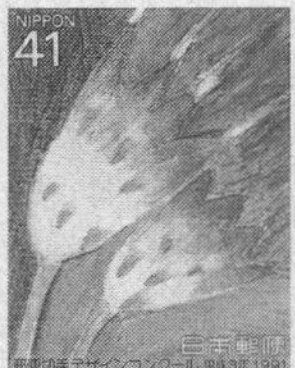

1535 Flowers

1539 Japanese Snipe ("Gallinago hardwickii")

1991. Winning Entries in Postage Stamp Design Contest.

2146 **1535** 41 y. multicoloured . . . 40 10
2147 – 62 y. multicoloured . . . 55 10
2148 – 70 y. brown, blue & blk . . 65 10
2149 – 100 y. multicoloured . . . 90 20

DESIGNS—HORIZ: 62 y. Couple in traditional dress; 100 y. Butterfly. VERT: 70 y. "World Peace".

1991. Water Birds (1st series). Multicoloured.

2150 62 y. Type **1539** 95 10
2151 62 y. Brown booby ("Sula leucogaster") 95 10

See also Nos. 2162/3, 2179/80, 2184/5, 2198/9, 2241/2, 2247/8 and 2251/2.

1541 Kikugoro Onoe VI in Title Role of "Spirit of the Lion"

1542 Utaemon Nakamura VI as Princess Yaegaki in "24 Examples of Filial Piety"

1991. Kabuki Theatre (1st series).

2152 **1541** 62 y. green, gold & blk . . 55 10
2153 **1542** 100 y. multicoloured . . . 90 20

See also Nos. 2164/5, 2172/3, 2181/2, 2186/7 and 2190/1.

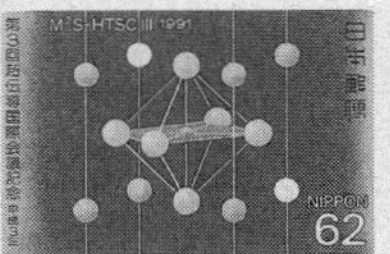

1543 "Solidarity" in Sign Language and Congress Emblem

1544 Crystal Structure

1991. 11th World Federation of the Deaf International Congress, Tokyo.

2154 **1543** 62 y. + 10 y. mult . . . 65 10

The premium was assigned to programmes for helping the deaf.

1991. International Conf on Materials and Mechanism of Superconductivity, Kanazawa.

2155 **1544** 62 y. multicoloured . . . 55 10

1545 Girl sitting on Morning Glory

1546 Fairy on Horse

1991. Letter Writing Day.

2156 **1545** 41 y. multicoloured . . . 40 10
2157 **1546** 62 y. multicoloured . . . 55 10

For design similar to No. 2157 but with central motif drawn larger, see No. 2104.

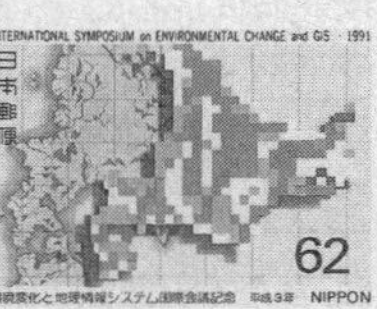

1547 High Jumping

1549 Map and Computer Image of Hokkaido

1991. 3rd World Athletics Championships, Tokyo. Multicoloured.

2159 41 y. Type **1547** 50 10
2160 62 y. Putting the shot 70 15

1991. International Symposium on Environmental Change and Geographic Information Systems, Asahikawa, Hokkaido.

2161 **1549** 62 y. multicoloured . . . 70 15

1991. Water Birds (2nd series). As T **1539**. Multicoloured.

2162 62 y. Japanese gull ("Larus crassirostris") 95 20
2163 62 y. Little grebe ("Podiceps ruficollis") 95 20

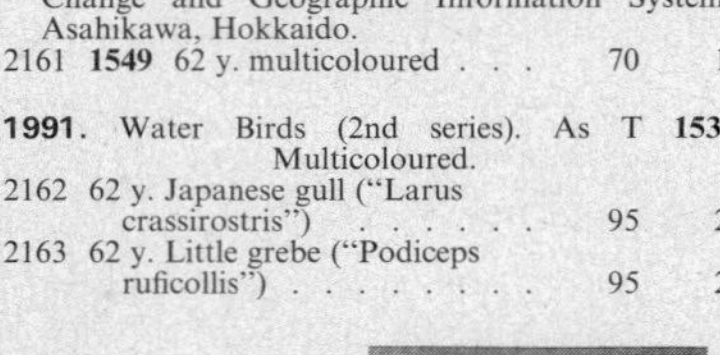

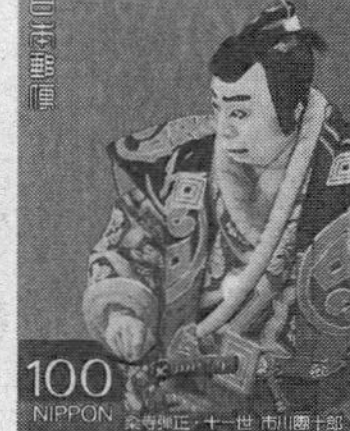

1552 Koshiro Matsumoto VII as Benkei in "The Subscription List"

1553 Danjuro Ichikawa XI as Danjo in "Tweezers"

1991. Kabuki Theatre (2nd series).

2164 **1552** 62 y. black, grey & gold . . 70 15
2165 **1553** 100 y. multicoloured . . 1·25 30

1554 Nobles watching burning Oten Gate

1991. International Correspondence Week. Details from Ban Dainagon Picture Scrolls by Mitsunaga Tokiwa. Multicoloured.

2166 80 y. Type **1554** 95 20
2167 120 y. Arrest of Yoshio Tomo (arsonist) . . . . 1·40 30

1556 "Clear Day with Southern Breeze" (from "36 Views of Mt. Fuji" by Hokusai Katsushika) and Seismographic Wave

1557 Tea Utensils and Flower

1991. Earthquake and Natural Disaster Countermeasures Conference. Tokyo.

2168 **1556** 62 y. multicoloured . . . 70 15

1991. 800th Anniv of Introduction of Green Tea into Japan.

2169 **1557** 62 y. multicoloured . . . 70 15

1558 "Saucy Girl" (from "A Selection of Beautiful Women" by Kunisada Utagawa)

1991. "Phila Nippon '91" International Stamp Exhibition, Tokyo (2nd issue).

2170 **1558** 62 y. multicoloured . . . 70 15

1559 Baigyoku Nakamura III as the Ogiya Courtesan Yugiri in "Yoshida-ya"

1560 Ganjiro Nakamura III as Jihei Kamiya in "Shinju-Ten no Amijima"

1991. Kabuki Theatre (3rd series). Works by Chikamatsu Monzaemon.

2172 **1559** 62 y. black, pur & gold . . 70 15
2173 **1560** 100 y. multicoloured . . 1·25 30

1561 Boy building Toy Town

1562 Ishikawa Papier-Mache Monkey

1991. 30th Anniv of Administrative Councillors System.

2174 **1561** 62 y. multicoloured . . . 70 15

1991. New Year's Greetings. Multicoloured.

2175 41 y. Type **1562** 50 10
2176 62 y. Obata monkey 70 15

1565 Obata Monkey

1991. New Year Lottery Stamps. Multicoloured.

2177 41 y. + 3 y. Ishikawa papier-mache monkey 50 10
2178 62 y. + 3 y. Type **1565** 75 15

Each stamp carries a lottery number.

1992. Water Birds (3rd series). As T **1539**. Multicoloured.

2179 62 y. Tufted puffin ("Lunda cirrhata") 95 20
2180 62 y. Hooded cranes ("Grus monacha") 95 20

1568 Kichiemon Nakamura I as Jiro Naozane Kumagai in "Chronicle of Two Boys in Battle of Ichinotani" by Munesuke Namiki

1569 Nizaemon Kataoka XIII as Old Man in "Kotobuki Shiki Sambaso"

1992. Kabuki Theatre (4th series).

2181 **1568** 62 y. multicoloured . . . 70 15
2182 **1569** 100 y. multicoloured . . 1·25 30

1570 Orchid and Chimpanzees

1992. 8th Conference of Parties to Convention on International Trade in Endangered Species, Kyoto City.

2183 **1570** 62 y. multicoloured . . . 70 15

1992. Water Birds (4th series). As T **1539**. Multicoloured.

2184 62 y. Whooper swan ("Cygnus cygnus") 95 20
2185 62 y. Painted snipe ("Rostratula benghalensis") 95 20

1573 Enjaku Jitsukawa II as Ishikawa-Geomon in "Two-Storey Gate—Pawlonia" by Gohei Namiki

1574 Hakuo Matsumoto I as Oishi-Kuranosuke in "Loyal Retainers in Genroku" by Seika Mayama

1992. Kabuki Theatre (5th series).

2186 **1573** 62 y. multicoloured . . . 70 15
2187 **1574** 100 y. multicoloured . . 1·25 30

1575 "Flowers on Chair" (Hoshun Yamaguchi)

1576 Shuri Castle

1992. Philatelic Week.
2188 **1575** 62 y. multicoloured . . . 70 15

1992. 20th Anniv of Return of Okinawa (Ryukyu Islands).
2189 **1576** 62 y. multicoloured . . . 70 15

1577 Baiko Onoe VII as the Wisteria Maiden

1578 Shoroku Onoe II as Goro Soga and Kanzaburo Nakamura XVII as Juro Soga in "Kotobuki-Soga-taimen"

1992. Kabuki Theatre (6th series).
2190 **1577** 62 y. multicoloured . . . 70 15
2191 **1578** 100 y. multicoloured . . 1·25 30

1579 "ADEOS" Observation Satellite

1581 Bird delivering Letter to Flower

1992. International Space Year. Multicoloured.
2192 62 y. Type **1579** 70 15
2193 62 y. "BS-3" broadcasting satellite and space station 70 15
Nos. 2192/3 were printed together, se-tenant, forming a composite design.

1992. Letter Writing Day. Multicoloured.
2194 41 y. Type **1581** 50 10
2195 62 y. Bird delivering letter to dog 70 15

1583 Ammonite, Map and Stratigraphic Plan

1586 Canoeing

1992. 29th Int Geological Congress, Kyoto.
2197 **1583** 62 y. multicoloured . . . 75 15

1992. Water Birds (5th series). As T **1539**. Multicoloured.
2198 62 y. White-faced shearwater ("Calonectris leucomelas") . 70 15
2199 62 y. Ruddy kingfisher ("Halcyon coromanda") . . 70 15

1992. 47th National Athletic Meeting, Yamagata.
2200 **1586** 41 y. multicoloured . . . 50 10

1587 Japanese Jar (Ninsei Nonomura)

1588 Chinese Vase (Tang dynasty)

1992. 20th Anniv of Restoration of Diplomatic Relations with China.
2201 **1587** 62 y. multicoloured . . . 70 15
2202 **1588** 62 y. multicoloured . . . 70 15

1589 Nobles arriving at Taiken Gate

1590 Fujiwarano Nobuyori giving Audience

1992. International Correspondence Week. Details from "Tale of Heiji" Shinzei Picture Scroll.
2203 **1589** 80 y. multicoloured . . . 95 20
2204 **1590** 120 y. multicoloured . . 1·40 30

1591 "Friends" (Tomoko Komoto)

1593 "Kyo" Ideograph, Mt. Fuji, Sun and Waves

1992. 3rd Stamp Design Competition Winners. Multicoloured.
2205 62 y. Type **1591** 70 15
2206 70 y. "Gaiety on Christmas Night" (Brat Anca) 80 20

1992. 30th International Co-operative Alliance Congress, Tokyo.
2207 **1593** 62 y. multicoloured . . . 70 15

1594 Takakazu Seki (mathematician, 350th birth)

1595 Akiko Yosano (poet, 50th death)

1992. Anniversaries.
2208 **1594** 62 y. multicoloured . . . 70 15
2209 **1595** 62 y. multicoloured . . . 70 15

1596 Certified Public Tax Accountants' Assn Emblem

1992. 50th Anniv of Tax Accountants Law.
2210 **1596** 62 y. multicoloured . . . 70 15

1597 Papier-mache and Clay Cock

1600 Tsuyazaki Clay Cock on Drum

1992. New Year's Greetings. Multicoloured.
2211 41 y. Type **1597** 50 10
2212 62 y. Tsuyazaki clay cock on drum 70 15

1992. New Year Lottery Stamps. Multicoloured.
2213 41 y. + 3 y. Papier-mache and clay cock 50 10
2214 62 y. + 3 y. Type **1600** 75 15
Each stamp carries a lottery number.

1601 "Orthetrum albistylum" (dragonfly)

1601a "Oxycetonia jucunda" (beetle)

1602 Mikado Swallowtail

1603 Ladybirds

1603a Honey Bee

1603b "Lycaena phleas" (copper butterfly)

1604 Mandarin

1605 Japanese White Eye

1606 Eastern Turtle Dove

1606a Great Tit

1607 Varied Tit

1608 Greater Pied Kingfisher

1609 Spotbill Duck

1609a Little Ringed Plover

1609b Bull-headed Shrike

1610 Bullfinch

1610a Japanese Grosbeak

1610b Jay

1611 Orchids

1612 Wild Pink

1613 Adder's Tongue Lily

1614 Day-flowers

1615 Iris

1616 Violets

1617 Praying Mantis, Chrysanthemums and Hibiscus (after Hatsu Sakai)

1618 "Pine and Hawk" (Sesson Shukei)

1992.
2215 **1601** 9 y. yellow, blk & bl . 10 10
2215a **1601a** 10 y. multicoloured . . 10 10
2216 **1602** 15 y. brown, light green and green . . 20 10
2217 **1603** 18 y. green, grey and red 20 10
2217a **1603a** 20 y. multicoloured . . 20 10
2217b **1603b** 30 y. multicoloured . . 30 10
2218 **1604** 41 y. orge, dp bl & bl . 50 10
2219 **1605** 50 y. yell, bl & blk . . 60 15
2220 **1606** 62 y. orge, dp bl & bl . 75 15
2220a **1606a** 70 y. multicoloured . . 70 15
2221 **1607** 72 y. orge, bl & grn . 85 20
2222 **1608** 80 y. blue, stone and green . . . . . . 1·00 20
2223 **1609** 90 y. brn, yell & bl . 1·10 25
2223a **1609a** 110 y. multicoloured . 1·10 25
2223b **1609b** 120 y. multicoloured . 1·10 25
2224 **1610** 130 y. multicoloured . 1·75 40
2224a **1610a** 140 y. multicoloured . 1·40 25
2224b **1610b** 160 y. multicoloured . 1·60 35
2225 **1611** 190 y. multicoloured . 2·25 45
2226 **1612** 270 y. multicoloured . 3·25 65
2227 **1613** 350 y. mauve, lilac and green . . . . . . 4·00 80
2228 **1614** 390 y. multicoloured . 4·50 90
2229 **1615** 420 y. violet, lt green & green . . . . . . 5·00 1·00
2230 **1616** 430 y. multicoloured . 5·00 1·00
2231 **1617** 700 y. multicoloured . 8·25 1·60
2232 **1618** 1000 y. multicoloured . 12·00 2·40
The 41, 50, 62 and 80 y. also exist imperforate with self-adhesive gum.

1993. Water Birds (6th series). As T **1539**. Multicoloured.
2241 62 y. Common kingfisher ("Alcedo atthis") 75 15
2242 62 y. Cattle egret ("Bubulcus ibis") 75 15

1623 Super Giant Slalom

1625 Poppies (after Hochu Nakamura)

1993. World Alpine Skiing Championships, Shizukuishi (nr. Morioka). Multicoloured.
2243 41 y. Type **1623** 50 10
2244 62 y. Downhill 75 15

1993. Seasonal Flowers (1st series). Multicoloured.
2245 41 y. Type **1625** 50 10
2246 62 y. Cherry Blossoms (after Haitsu Sakai) (25 × 35 mm) 75 15
See also Nos. 2258/9, 2269/70 and 2287/8.

1993. Water Birds (7th series). As T **1539**. Multicoloured.
2247 62 y. White-fronted geese ("Anser albifrons") 75 15
2248 62 y. Japanese white-necked cranes ("Grus vipio") . . . 75 15
No. 2247 is wrongly inscribed "Ansner".

1629 "In the Studio" (Nanpu Katayama)

1630 Coral Trees and Reef, Minnajima Island

1993. Philatelic Week.
2249 **1629** 62 y. multicoloured . . . 75 15

1993. National Afforestation Campaign.
2250 **1630** 41 y. multicoloured . . . 50 10

1993. Water Birds (8th series). As T **1539**. Multicoloured.
2251 62 y. Baikal teal ("Anas formosa") 75 15
2252 62 y. White-tailed sea eagle ("Haliaeetus albicilla") . . . 75 15

1635 "Mandarin Duck in Nest" and "Gardenia in Nest"

1993. Wedding of Crown Prince Naruhito and Masako Owada. Multicoloured.
2253 62 y. "Mandarin Duck in Nest" (pattern of groom's jacket) (vert) 75 15
2254 62 y. "Gardenia in Nest" (pattern of bride's robe) (vert) . 75 15
2255 70 y. Type **1635** 80 20

1636 Manchurian Crane with Chicks

1640 Stylized Ideographs for "Commercial Registration"

1993. 5th Meeting of Ramsar Convention for the Preservation of Wetlands, Kushiro (Hokkaido).

2256 62 y. Type **1636** 75 15
2257 62 y. Head of Manchurian crane 75 15

1993. Seasonal Flowers (2nd series) As T **1615**. Multicoloured.

2258 41 y. Lily (after Kiitsu Suzuki) . 50 10
2259 62 y. Thistle (after Shiko Watanabe) (25 × 35 mm) . . . 75 15

1993. Centenary of Commercial Registration System.

2260 **1640** 62 y. multicoloured . . . 75 15

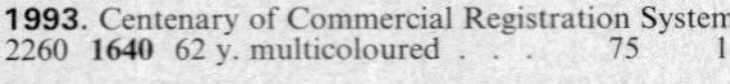
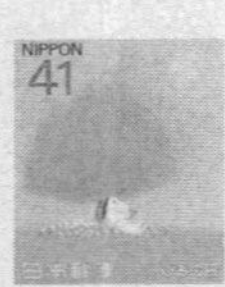

1641 Puppy reading Letter under Tree

1643 Heart, Clouds and Flowers

1993. Letter Writing Day. Multicoloured.

2261 41 y. Type **1641** 50 10
2262 62 y. Man pointing at flying letter (23 × 27 mm) 75 15

1993. World Federation for Mental Health Congress, Chiba City.

2264 **1643** 62 y. multicoloured . . . 75 15

1644 "Glaucidium palmatum"

1993. 15th International Botanical Congress, Yokohama. Multicoloured.

2265 62 y. Type **1644** 75 15
2266 62 y. "Sciadopitys verticillata" . 75 15

1646 Swimming

1650 "Arrival of Portuguese" (folding screen)

1993. 48th National Athletic Meeting, Kagawa Prefecture. Multicoloured.

2267 41 y. Type **1646** 50 10
2268 41 y. Karate 50 10

1993. Seasonal Flowers (3rd series). As T **1615**. Multicoloured.

2269 41 y. "Chinese Bell-flowers" (Korin Ogata) 50 10
2270 62 y. Chrysanthemums (detail of "Cranes and Plants in Spring and Autumn", Kiitsu Suzuki) (25 × 35 mm) . . . 75 15

1993. 450th Anniv of First Portuguese Visit to Japan. Multicoloured.

2271 62 y. Type **1650** 75 15
2272 62 y. Jesuit mother-of-pearl inlaid host box 75 15

1652 Ki no Tsurayuki (Agetatami Scrolls)

1993. International Correspondence Week. Picture Scrolls of the Thirty-six Immortal Poets

2273 80 y. Type **1652** 95 20
2274 120 y. Kodai no Kimi (Satake Scrolls) . . . . 1·40 30

1654 Sprinter

1656 Toson Shimazaki (writer, 50th death)

1993. 10th International Veterans' Athletic Championships, Miyazaki.

2275 **1654** 62 y. multicoloured . . . 75 15

1993. Anniversaries. Multicoloured.

2277 62 y. Type **1656** 75 15
2278 62 y. Umetaro Suzuki (scientist, 50th death) 75 15
2279 62 y. Kazan Watanabe (after Chinzan Tsubaki) (artist, birth bicentenary) 75 15

1659 Shibahara Clay Dog

1662 Kosen Clay Tosa Dog

1993. New Year's Greetings. Multicoloured.

2280 41 y. Type **1659** 50 10
2281 62 y. Kosen clay tosa dog . . . 75 15

1993. New Year Lottery Stamps. Multicoloured.

2282 41 y. Shibahara clay dog . . . 50 10
2283 62 y. Type **1662** 75 15

1663 Rice Flowers

1664 Man and Bird (Soichiro Asaba)

1993. Centenary of Agricultural Research Centre, Nishigahara.

2284 **1663** 62 y. multicoloured . . . 75 15

1993. 45th Anniv of Declaration of Human Rights. Stamp design contest winning entries.

2285 62 y. Type **1664** 75 15
2286 70 y. Symbols (Armand Clotagatilde) 80 20

1994. Seasonal Flowers (4th series). As T **1625**. Multicoloured.

2287 50 y. Plum Blossom (after Korin Ogata) 60 15
2288 80 y. Winter Camellia (after Hoitsu Sakai) (26 × 35 mm) 95 20

1994. Special Correspondence Stamps. As Nos. 1677/9 but values changed.

2289 **1098** 50 y. multicoloured . . . 60 15
2290 **1099** 50 y. multicoloured . . . 60 15
2291 80 y. multicoloured . . . 95 20
2292 **1100** 90 y. multicoloured . . . 1·10 25

1668 Ladies' Figure Skating

1672 "Irises" (Heihachiro Fukuda)

1994. World Figure Skating Championships, Chiba City. Multicoloured.

2293 50 y. Type **1668** 60 15
2294 50 y. Ice dancing 60 15
2295 80 y. Men's figure skating . . . 95 20
2296 80 y. Pairs figure skating . . . 95 20

1994. Philatelic Week.

2297 **1672** 80 y. multicoloured . . . 95 20

1673 "Love" (Chieko Kitajima)

1677 White Stork, Marguerites and Camphor Tree

1994. International Year of the Family. Winning Entries in Stamp Design Contest. Multicoloured.

2298 50 y. Type **1673** 60 15
2299 50 y. "Happiness Flower" (Shigenobu Nagaishi) . . . 60 15
2300 80 y. "Family flowering at Home" (Junichi Mineta) . . 95 20
2301 80 y. "Family in Flight" (Soichiro Asaba) 95 20

1994. National Afforestation Campaign.

2302 **1677** 50 y. multicoloured . . . 65 15

1678 Houses by the Waterside

1679 Pylon and Monju Building

1994. International Conference on Reduction of Natural Disasters, Yokohama.

2303 **1678** 80 y. multicoloured . . . 95 20

1994. Achievement of Initial Criticality (self-sustaining reaction) in Monju Nuclear Fast Breeder Reactor, Tsuruga.

2304 **1679** 80 y. multicoloured . . . 95 20

1680 Wildlife

1681 Envelope "Ship" and Man

1994. Environment Day.

2305 **1680** 80 y. multicoloured . . . 95 20

1994. Letter Writing Day. Multicoloured.

2306 50 y. Type **1681** 60 15
2307 80 y. Giraffe carrying envelope 95 20

1683 Emblem in Eye

1684 Baron Maeshima (Postal Minister) and 1871 48 mon "Dragon" Stamp

1994. 10th Int AIDS Conference, Yokohama.

2309 **1683** 80 y. multicoloured . . . 95 20

1994. History of Stamps (1st series). First Japanese Issue. Multicoloured, frame colour of "Dragon" stamp given.

2310 **1684** 80 y. brown 95 20
2311 – 80 y. blue 95 20
2312 – 80 y. red 95 20
2313 – 80 y. green 95 20

DESIGNS: No. 2311, 100 mon "Dragon" stamp; 2312, 200 mon "Dragon" stamp; 2313, 500 mon "Dragon" stamp.

The central portion of the stamp portrayed varies according to value.

See also Nos. 2339/42, 2345/6, 2363/4, 2382/5 and 2416/19.

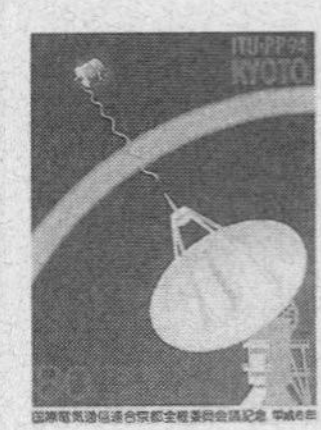

1685/1686 Airport and Airplane bearing Airport Code

1688 Dish Aerial and Satellite

1994. Opening of Kansai International Airport, Osaka. Multicoloured.

2314 80 y. Type **1685** 95 20
2315 80 y. Type **1686** 95 20
2316 80 y. Airplane approaching Airport 95 20

Nos. 2314/15 form the composite design shown.

1994. I.T.U. Plenipotentiary Conference, Kyoto.

2317 **1688** 80 y. multicoloured . . . 95 20

1689 Kickball

1695 Handball

1692 Sugoroku

1994. 12th Asian Games, Hiroshima. Mult.

2318 50 y. Type **1689** 60 15
2319 80 y. Steeplechase 95 20
2320 80 y. Synchronized swimming . 95 20

1994. International Correspondence Week. Details of "House of Entertainment" (folding screen). Multicoloured.

2321 90 y. Type **1692** . . . . 1·10 25
2322 110 y. Shogi . . . . 1·25 25
2323 130 y. Go . . . . 1·50 30

1994. 49th National Athletic Meeting, Aichi.

2324 **1695** 50 y. multicoloured . . . 60 15

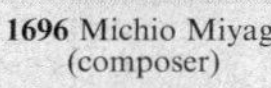

1696 Michio Miyagi (composer)

1698 Fujiwara no Michinaga and Insulin Crystals

1994. Birth Anniversaries. Multicoloured.

2325 80 y. Type **1696** 95 20
2326 80 y. Gyoshu Hayami (painter) and "Moths" 95 20

1994. 15th International Diabetes Federation Congress, Kobe.

2327 **1698** 80 y. multicoloured . . . 95 20

Fujiwara no Michinaga (966–1028) was the earliest known Japanese diabetic.

1699/1703 "Viewing Maple Leaves at Takao" (folding screen, Hideyori Kano) (⅗-size illustration)

1704 "Yokuryuchi Pool, Shugakuin Imperial Villa" (Kenji Kawai)

1705 "Rock Garden, Ryoan Temple" (Eizo Kato)

1994. 1200th Anniv of Kyoto. Paintings.

2328 **1699** 80 y. multicoloured . . . 95 20
2329 **1700** 80 y. multicoloured . . . 95 20
2330 **1701** 80 y. multicoloured . . . 95 20
2331 **1702** 80 y. multicoloured . . . 95 20
2332 **1703** 80 y. multicoloured . . . 95 20
2333 **1704** 80 y. multicoloured . . . 95 20
2334 **1705** 80 y. multicoloured . . . 95 20

Nos. 2328/32 were issued together, se-tenant, forming the composite design illustrated.

1706 Izumo Papier-mache Boar

1709 Boar (Takayama soft toy)

1994. New Year's Greetings. Multicoloured.

2335 50 y. Type **1706** 60 15
2336 80 y. Boar (Takayama soft toy) 95 20

1994. New Year's Greetings. Lottery Stamps. Multicoloured.

2337 50 y. + 3 y. Izumo Papier-mache boar 60 15
2338 80 y. + 3 y. Type **1709** . . . . 1·00 20

Each stamp carries a lottery number.

1710 5 r. Stamp and Eduardo Chiossone (designer)

1994. History of Stamps (2nd series). "Koban" issue of 1876–88. Multicoloured, colour of featured stamp given.

2339 **1710** 80 y. grey 95 20
2340 – 80 y. brown 95 20
2341 – 80 y. red 95 20
2342 – 80 y. blue 95 20

FEATURED STAMPS: No. 2340, 1 s. stamp (Type **20**); 2341, 12 s. stamp (Type **21**); 2342, 20 s. stamp (Type **22**).

1711 Himeji Castle Tower

1712 "Himeji Castle" (Masami Takahashi)

1994. World Heritage Sites (1st series).

2343 **1711** 80 y. multicoloured . . . 95 20
2344 **1712** 80 y. multicoloured . . . 95 20

See also Nos. 2347/8, 2373/4 and 2400/1.

1713 2 s. Stamp and Postal Delivery by Hand-drawn Cart

1715 "Kannon Bosatsu" (wall painting, Kondo Hall)

1716 Kondo Hall, Horyu Temple

1995. History of Stamps (3rd series). 1894 Emperor's Silver Wedding issue and paintings by Shinsai Shibata. Multicoloured.

2345 80 y. Type **1713** 95 20
2346 80 y. 5 s. Stamp and postal delivery by horse-drawn carriage 95 20

1995. World Heritage Sites (2nd series). Multicoloured.

2347 **1715** 80 y. multicoloured . . . 95 20
2348 **1716** 110 y. multicoloured . . 1·25 25

1717 Emblem and National Flowers

1995. Centenary of Japan–Brazil Treaty of Friendship. Multicoloured.

2349 80 y. Type **1717** 95 20
2350 80 y. Emblem and sports . . . 95 20

1719 Unebi and Nijo Mountains and Tile from Palace

1720 "Remembering Times Past" (Saburosuke Okada)

1995. 1300th Anniv of Fujiwara Palace, Kashihara.

2351 **1719** 50 y. multicoloured . . . 60 15
2352 **1720** 80 y. multicoloured . . . 95 20

1721 "Dissection" (Seison Maeda)

1722 "National Census" and "16"

1995. Modern Anatomy Education.

2353 **1721** 80 y. multicoloured . . . 95 20

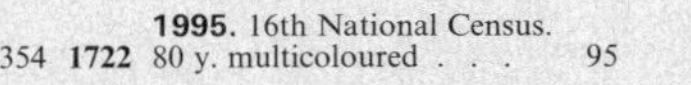

1995. 16th National Census.

2354 **1722** 80 y. multicoloured . . . 95 20

1723 Volunteer teaching Bangladeshi Woman to Read

1724 "Visitor to Art Studio" (Keika Kanashima)

1995. 30th Anniv of Japanese Overseas Co-operation Volunteers Service.

2355 **1723** 80 y. multicoloured . . . 95 20

1995. Philatelic Week.

2356 **1724** 80 y. + 20 y. mult . . . 1·25 25

The premium was for the Osaka/Kobe and Awaji earthquake victims' fund.

1725 Auspicious Clouds

1726 Reeds (mourning)

1727 Water Lily (mourning)

1728 Cloud, "Wind" and Pine Bark Pattern

1729 "Daphniphyllum macropodum"

1730 Maple and Shrine Island, Akiteline

1995. Special Correspondence Stamps.

2357 **1725** 50 y. multicoloured . . . 60 15
2358 **1726** 50 y. multicoloured . . . 60 15
2359 **1727** 80 y. multicoloured . . . 95 20
2360 **1728** 80 y. multicoloured . . . 95 20
2361 **1729** 90 y. multicoloured . . . 1·10 25

1995. National Afforestation Campaign.

2362 **1730** 50 y. multicoloured . . . 60 15

1731 8½ s. Stamp and First Airmail Flight from Osaka to Tokyo

1733 Hearts forming Flower

1995. History of Stamps (4th series). 1929 First Airmail issue. Multicoloured.

2363 110 y. Type **1731** . . . . . . 1·25 25
2364 110 y. 18 s. Stamp and loading freight onto airplane . . . . 1·25 25

1995. Greetings Stamps. Multicoloured. Self-adhesive.

2365 80 y. Type **1733** 95 20
2366 80 y. Child with balloon . . . 95 20
2367 80 y. Flower and pencil . . . 95 20
2368 80 y. Star, sun and moon . . . 95 20
2369 80 y. Child with dog 95 20

1738 Postman

1740 Cedar

1995. Letter Writing Day. Multicoloured.

2370 50 y. Type **1738** 60 15
2371 80 y. Ostrich 95 20

1995. World Heritage Sites (3rd series). Yaku Island. Multicoloured.

2373 80 y. Type **1740** 95 20
2374 80 y. Sika deer 95 20

1742 "Friends, One and All" (Yuki Ogawa)

1743 Atomic Bomb Dome, Hiroshima (Nobuya Nagata)

1744 "Light of Peace" (Nobuo Suenaga)

1745 Marathon Runners

1995. 50th Anniv of End of Second World War. Stamp Design Contest Winners.

2375 **1742** 50 y. multicoloured . . . 60 15
2376 **1743** 80 y. multicoloured . . . 95 20
2377 **1744** 80 y. multicoloured . . . 95 20

1995. 18th International University Games, Fukuoka.

2378 **1745** 80 y. multicoloured . . . 95 20

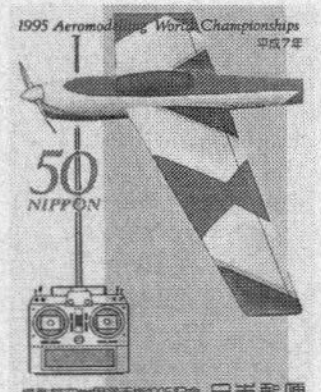
1746 Radio-controlled Plane

1748 Horse, Cow and Labrador

1995. World Aeromodel Championships, Kasaoka. Multicoloured.

2379 50 y. Type **1746** 60 15
2380 80 y. Radio-controlled helicopter 95 20

1995. World Veterinary Congress, Yokohama.

2381 **1748** 80 y. multicoloured . . . 95 20

1749 5 y. Stamp and Cherub and Tokyo Mailbox

1753 Judo (Makuhari, Chiba)

1995. History of Stamps (5th series). Industries issue of 1948–49. Multicoloured.

2382 80 y. Type **1749** 95 20
2383 80 y. 500 y. Stamp and mail van . . . . 1·60 25
2384 80 y. 90 y. Stamp and mail van 95 20
2385 80 y. 100 y. Stamp and cherub on Tokyo mailbox 95 20

1995. World Sports Championships. Mult.

2386 80 y. Type **1753** 95 20
2387 80 y. Gymnastics (Sabae, Fukui) 95 20

1755 Shell Matching Game (from "New Year's Amusements")

1995. International Correspondence Week. Details of paintings on folding screens. Multicoloured.

2388 90 y. Type **1755** . . . . 1·10 25
2389 110 y. Battledore and Shuttlecock (from "Twelve Months") . . . . 1·25 25
2390 130 y. Playing Cards (from "Matsuura Folding Screen") 1·50 30

1758 Cyclists

1759 Patchwortk Hearts (Tomoko Suzuki)

1995. 50th Anniv of National Athletic Meeting, Fukushima.

2391 **1758** 50 y. multicoloured . . . 60 15

1995. 50th Anniversaries of U.N.O. (2392) and U.N.E.S.C.O. (2393). Multicoloured.

2392 80 y. Type **1759** 95 20
2393 80 y. Children with Heart Balloon (Yukino Ikeda) . . 95 20

1761 Tadataka Ino (cartographer, 250th birth)

1995. Anniversaries. Multicoloured.

2394 80 y. Type **1761** 95 20
2395 80 y. Kitaro Nishida (philosopher, 50th death) 95 20

1763 Tsutsumi Clay Rat on Cayenne Pepper

1766 Satsuma Papier-Mache Rat in Rice Store

1995. New Year's Greetings. Multicoloured.

2396 50 y. Type **1763** 60 15
2397 80 y. Satsuma papier-mache rat in rice store 95 20

1995. New Year's Lottery Stamps. Multicoloured.

2398 50 y. +3 y. Tsutsumi clay rat on turnip 60 15
2399 80 y. +3 y. Type **1766** . . . . . 1·00 20

Each stamp carries a lottery number.

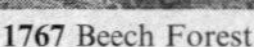

1767 Beech Forest

1769 Obi Material showing Choson Dynasty Boxes (Keisuke Serizawa)

1995. World Heritage Sites (4th series). Shirakami Mountains. Multicoloured.

2400 80 y. Type **1767** 95 20
2401 80 y. Black woodpecker 95 20

1995. 30th Anniv of Resumption of Japan–Korea Diplomatic Relations.

2402 **1769** 80 y. multicoloured . . . 95 20

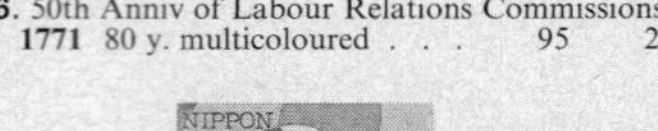

1770 Siebold

1771 Twined Ropes

1996. Birth Bicentenary of Philipp Franz von Siebold (physician and Japanologist).

2403 **1770** 80 y. multicoloured . . . 95 20

1996. 50th Anniv of Labour Relations Commissions.

2404 **1771** 80 y. multicoloured . . . 95 20

1772 Turtle and Crane

1996. Senior Citizens.

2405 **1772** 80 y. multicoloured . . . 95 20

1773 Driving to Diet for Promulgation of Constitution, 1946

1774 Signing San Francisco Peace Treaty, 1951

1775 Return of Okinawa, 1972

1776 Woman and Diet Building

1996. 50 Post-war Years (1st series).

2406 **1773** 80 y. mve, lil & gold . . 95 20
2407 **1774** 80 y. dp grn, grn & gold . 95 20
2408 **1775** 80 y. indigo, blue and gold 95 20

See also Nos. 2420/1, 2429/30, 2443/4 and 2449/54.

1996. 50th Anniv of Women's Suffrage.

2409 **1776** 80 y. multicoloured . . . 95 20

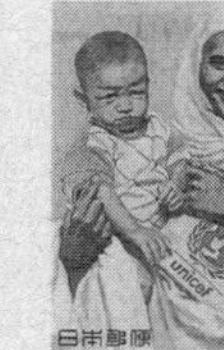

1777 "Window" (Yukihiko Yasuda)

1778 Mother and Child

1996. Philatelic Week.

2410 **1777** 80 y. multicoloured . . . 95 20

1996. 50th Anniv of U.N.I.C.E.F.

2411 **1778** 80 y. multicoloured . . . 95 20

1779 Children and Sun

1780 Narcissus Flycatcher

1996. Child Welfare Week.

2412 **1779** 80 y. multicoloured . . . 95 20

1996. Bird Week. Multicoloured.

2413 80 y. Type **1780** 95 20
2414 80 y. Binoculars and bird feeding nestlings 95 20

1782 Cherry Blossom and Tokyo Buildings

1996. National Afforestation Campaign.

2415 **1782** 50 y. multicoloured . . . 60 15

1783 1991 Design

1784 1949 Design

1996. History of Stamps (6th series). Philatelic Week Issues.

2416 **1783** 80 y. brown, ochre and lilac 95 20
2417 80 y. multicoloured . . . 95 20
2418 **1784** 80 y. deep lilac & lilac . 95 20
2419 80 y. multicoloured . . . 95 20

1785 Olympic Flame (Olympic Games, Tokyo, 1964)

1786 Sun Tower ("EXPO 70" World Fair, Osaka)

1996. 50 Post-war Years (2nd series).

2420 **1785** 80 y. multicoloured . . . 95 20
2421 **1786** 80 y. multicoloured . . . 95 20

1787/1788 "Oirase no Keiryu" (Chikkyo Ono)

1996. Centenary of Modern River Control Systems.

2422 **1787** 80 y. multicoloured . . . 95 20
2423 **1788** 80 y. multicoloured . . . 95 20

Nos. 2422/3 were issued together, se-tenant, forming the composite design illustrated.

1789 Emblem

1790 "Nippon Maru II" (cadet ship)

1996. Marine Day.

2424 **1789** 50 y. multicoloured . . . 60 15
2425 **1790** 80 y. multicoloured . . . 95 20

1791 Cat

1996. Letter Writing Day. Multicoloured.

2426 50 y. Type **1791** 60 15
2427 80 y. Toy horse 95 20

1793 "Hikari" Express Train and Motorway

1794 Woman and Modern Appliances

1996. 50 Post-war Years (3rd series). Modern Life.

2429 **1793** 80 y. multicoloured . . . 95 20
2430 **1794** 80 y. multicoloured . . . 95 20

1795 Kenji Miyazawa (writer, centenary)

1797 Archer

1996. Birth Anniversaries. Multicoloured.

2431 80 y. Type **1795** 95 20
2432 80 y. Hokiichi Hanawa (scholar and editor, 250th) 95 20

1996. 51st National Athletic Meeting, Hiroshima.

2433 **1797** 50 y. multicoloured . . . 95 20

1798 Paper-chain People around Red Feather (donor pin)

1799 Piano Keys and Double Clef

1996. 50th Anniv of Community Chest.

2434 **1798** 80 y. multicoloured . . . 95 20

1996. International Music Day.

2435 **1799** 80 y. multicoloured . . . 95 20

1800 "Water Mill in Onden"

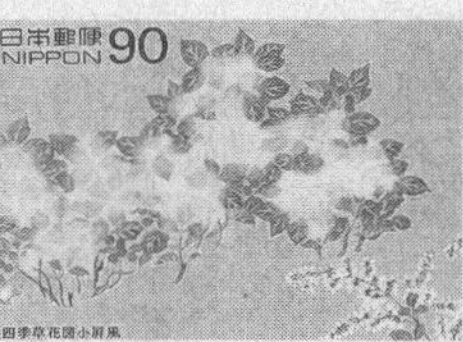

1801 Flowers

1803 Flowers

1805 Flowers

1996. International Correspondence Week. Paintings from "36 Views of Mt. Fuji" by Hokusai Katsushika (2436, 2438, 2440) and details of paintings on folding screen by Kohrin Ogata (others).

2436 **1800** 90 y. multicoloured . . . 95 20
2437 **1801** 90 y. multicoloured . . . 95 20
2438 – 110 y. multicoloured . . 1·10 25
2439 **1803** 110 y. multicoloured . . 1·10 25
2440 – 130 y. multicoloured . . 1·40 30
2441 **1805** 130 y. multicoloured . . 1·40 30

DESIGNS—As T **1800**: No. 2438; "Fine Day with a South Wind"; 2440, "Lake in Sosyu Hakone".

1806 Congress Emblem and Squirrel

1996. 18th International Savings Banks Congress, Tokyo.

2442 **1806** 80 y. multicoloured . . . 85 20

1807 Mobile Telephone, Fibre-optic Cable and Communications Satellite

1808 Satellite Photograph of Earth

1996. 50 Post-war Years (4th series). Telecommunications and Environmental Protection.

2443 **1807** 80 y. multicoloured . . . 85 20
2444 **1808** 80 y. multicoloured . . . 85 20

1809 Okinawa Papier-mache Fighting Bull

1812 Child on Bull (Takamatus Wedding Doll)

1996. New Year's Greetings. Multicoloured.

2445 50 y. Type **1809** 55 15
2446 80 y. Child on bull (Takamatsu wedding doll) 85 20

1996. New Year Lottery Stamps. Multicoloured.

2447 50 y. +3 y. Okinawa papier-mache fighting bull 55 15
2448 80 y. +3 y. Type **1812** 85 20

Each stamp carries a lottery number.

1813 Yujiro Ishihara (actor) as Youth

1814 Ishihara smoking Pipe

1815 Hibari Misora (actress' and singer) in "Kanashiki Kuchibue"

1816 Misora singing

1817 Osamu Tezuka (cartoonist) and Cartoon Characters

1818 Self-portrait and Astroboy

1997. 50 Post-war Years (5th series). Entertainers.

2449 **1813** 80 y. blk, brn & gold . . 80 20
2450 **1814** 80 y. multicoloured . . . 80 20
2451 **1815** 80 y. black, bl & gold . . 80 20
2452 **1816** 80 y. multicoloured . . . 80 20
2453 **1817** 80 y. multicoloured . . . 80 20
2454 **1818** 80 y. multicoloured . . . 80 20

1819 Emblem

1821 "Daigo" (Togyu Okumura)

1997. Winter Olympic Games, Nagano (1998). Multicoloured.

2455 80 y. +10 y. Type **1819** . . . 90 20
2456 80 y. +10 y. Snowlets (mascots) 90 20

1997. Philatelic Week.

2457 **1821** 80 y. multicoloured . . . 75 15

1822 Main Court Room

1997. 50th Anniv of Supreme Court.

2458 **1822** 80 y. multicoloured . . . 80 20

1823 Parachutist

1824 Waving to Mechanical Doll

1825 Stamp Lover

1826 Helicopter Postman

1827 With Love Letter

1828 Mexican Mythological Figures (Luis Nishizawa)

1997. Greetings Stamps. Doraemon (cartoon character). Self-adhesive gum.

2459 **1823** 80 y. multicoloured . . . 80 20
2460 **1824** 80 y. multicoloured . . . 80 20
2461 **1825** 80 y. multicoloured . . . 80 20
2462 **1826** 80 y. multicoloured . . . 80 20
2463 **1827** 80 y. multicoloured . . . 80 20

1997. Centenary of Japanese Emigration to Mexico.

2464 **1828** 80 y. multicoloured . . . 80 20

1829 Zao Crater Lake and Bush Clover

1830 House's Seal and Diet Building

1997. National Afforestation Campaign.

2465 **1829** 50 y. multicoloured . . . 50 10

1997. 50th Anniv of House of Councillors.

2466 **1830** 80 y. multicoloured . . . 80 20

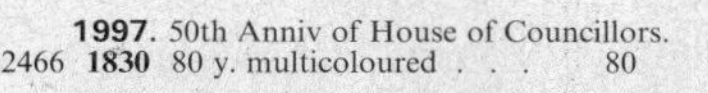

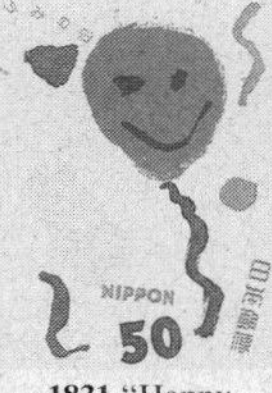

1831 "Happy Balloon" (Orville Isaac)

1832 "Bird Friends" (Haruka Kumiya)

1833 "Message from Rainbow Forest" (Anna Romanovskaya)

1834 "Greetings" (Yumi Kiryu)

1997. Letter Writing Day.

2467 **1831** 50 y. multicoloured . . . 50 10
2468 **1832** 70 y. multicoloured . . . 70 15
2469 **1833** 80 y. multicoloured . . . 80 20
2470 **1834** 90 y. multicoloured . . . 90 20

1835 Bird with Letter and Owl on Blackboard

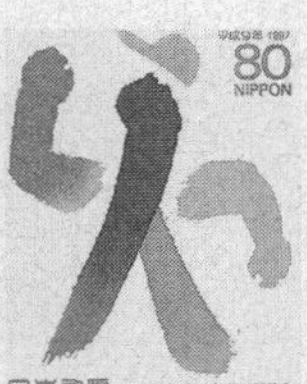

1836 Stylized Worker

1997. 50th Anniv of High School Part-time and Correspondence Courses.

2472 **1835** 50 y. multicoloured . . . 50 10

1997. 50th Anniv of Labour Standards Law.

2473 **1836** 80 y. multicoloured . . . 80 20

1837 Pacific Ocean and Mt. Osorno (after Hokusai Katsushika)

1838 Mopi (mascot) and Synchronized Swimmers

1997. Centenary of Japan–Chile Relations.

2474 **1837** 80 y. multicoloured . . . 80 20

1997. 52nd National Athletic Meeting, Osaka.

2475 **1838** 80 y. multicoloured . . . 80 20

1839 "Hodogaya" (from "53 Stations of Tokaido")

1840 Woodpecker and Flower

1842 Foliage

1844 Snow-covered Tree

1997. International Correspondence Week. Paintings by Hiroshige Ando (2476, 2478, 2480) and details from "The Four Seasons" by Hoitsu Sakai (others). Multicoloured.

2476 90 y. Type **1839** 90 20
2477 90 y. Type **1840** 90 20
2478 110 y. "Kameyama" (from "53 Stations of Tokaido") . . . 1·10 25
2479 110 y. Type **1842** . . . . 1·10 25
2480 130 y. "Snow View from Sumida River Revetment" (from "Edo Scenic Sites: Snow, Moon and Flower") . 1·25 25
2481 130 y. Type **1844** . . . . 1·25 25

1845 Auditorium, Takeru (opera character) and Ballerina

1997. Inaug of New National Theatre, Tokyo.

2482 **1845** 80 y. multicoloured . . . 80 20

1846 "Iihi Tabidachi" (Shinji Tanimura)

1847 "Tsuki no Sabaku" (Masao Kato and Suguru Sasaki)

1997. Favourite Songs (1st series).

2483 **1846** 50 y. multicoloured . . . 50 10
2484 **1847** 80 y. multicoloured . . . 80 20

See also Nos. 2497/8, 2499/2500, 2522/3, 2527/8, 2531/2, 2558/9, 2568/9 and 2578/9.

1848 Rohan Kouda (writer, 130th anniv)

1997. Birth Anniversaries. Multicoloured.

2485 80 y. Type **1848** 80 20
2486 80 y. Hiroshige Ando (after Toyo Kuni III) (painter, bicentenary) 80 20

1850 Miharu Hariko Paper Tiger

1853 Hakata Hariko Paper Tiger

1997. New Year's Greetings. Multicoloured.

2487 50 y. Type **1850** 50 10
2488 80 y. Hakata Hariko paper tiger 80 20

1997. New Year Lottery Stamps. Multicoloured.

2489 50 y. + 3 y. Miharu Hariko paper tiger 55 15
2490 80 y. + 3 y. Type **1853** 85 20

Each stamp carries a lottery number.

1854 "Yotsutake, Ryukyu Dance" (Taiji Hamada)

1997. 25th Anniv of Return of Okinawa (Ryukyu Islands).

2491 **1854** 80 y. multicoloured . . . 80 20

1855 Former Shibuya House, Yamagata

1856 Tomizawa House

1997. Traditional Houses (1st series).

2492 **1855** 80 y. multicoloured . . . 80 20
2493 **1856** 80 y. multicoloured . . . 80 20

See also Nos. 2513/14, 2529/30, 2539/40 and 2570/2.

1857 "Mother Sea" (Bokunen Naka)

1858 "Mother Earth" (Bokunen Naka)

1997. United Nations Framework Convention on Climate Change, Kyoto.

2494 **1857** 80 y. multicoloured . . . 80 20
2495 **1858** 80 y. multicoloured . . . 80 20

1859 Drying Harvested Rice

1997. 50th Anniv of Agricultural Insurance System.

2496 **1859** 80 y. multicoloured . . . 80 20

1860 "Sunayama" (Hakushu Kitahara and Shinpei Nakayama)

1861 "Jingle Bells" (Shoji Miyazawa and J. Pierpont)

1997. Favourite Songs (2nd series).

2497 **1860** 50 y. multicoloured . . . 50 10
2498 **1861** 80 y. multicoloured . . . 80 20

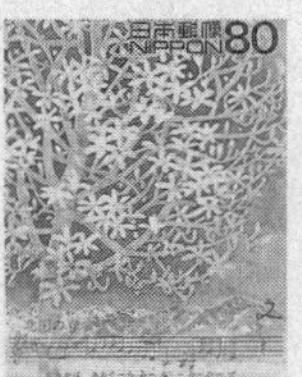

1862 "Shabondama" (Ujo Noguchi and Shinpei Nakayama)

1863 "Kitaguni no Haru" (Haku Ide and Minoru Endo)

1998. Favourite Songs (3rd series).

2499 **1862** 50 y. multicoloured . . . 50 10
2500 **1863** 80 y. multicoloured . . . 80 20

1864 Hollyhock

1998. Winter Paralympics, Nagano. Mult.

2501 50 y. Type **1864** 50 10
2502 80 y. Ice sledge hockey 80 20

1866 Miyama Gentian ("Gentiana nipponica")

1871 Snow-boarding

1998. Winter Olympic Games, Nagano. Mult.

2503 50 y. Type **1866** 50 10
2504 50 y. Marsh marigold ("Caltha palustris") 50 10
2505 50 y. Black lily ("Fritillaria camtschaensis") 50 10
2506 50 y. Peony ("Paeonia japonica") 50 10
2507 50 y. Adder's tongue lily ("Erythronium japonicum") . 50 10
2508 80 y. Type **1871** 80 20
2509 80 y. Curling 80 20
2510 80 y. Speed skating 80 20
2511 80 y. Cross-country skiing . . 80 20
2512 80 y. Alpine skiing 80 20

1876 Former Baba House, Nagano

1877 Naka House

1998. Traditional Houses (2nd series).

2513 **1876** 80 y. multicoloured . . . 80 20
2514 **1877** 80 y. multicoloured . . . 80 20

1878 Fireman and Ambulance

1879 Fireman and Fire Engine

1998. 50th Anniv of Japanese Fire Service.

2515 **1878** 80 y. multicoloured . . . 80 20
2516 **1879** 80 y. multicoloured . . . 80 20

The firemen in the designs are taken from paintings of actors by Kunichika Toyohara.

1880 Puppy

1998. Greetings Stamps. Self-adhesive. Mult.

2517 80 y. Type **1880** 80 20
2518 80 y. Kitten 80 20
2519 80 y. Budgerigars 80 20
2520 80 y. Pansies 80 20
2521 80 y. Rabbit 80 20

1885 "Medaka-no-Gakko" (Shigeru Chaki and Yoshinao Nakada)

1886 "Aoi Sanmyaku" (Yaso Saijo and Ryoichi Hattori)

1998. Favourite Songs (4th series).

2522 **1885** 50 y. multicoloured . . . 50 10
2523 **1886** 80 y. multicoloured . . . 80 20

1887 "Poppies" (Kokei Kobayashi)

1889 Trout and Japanese Azalea

1888 "Liberty Leading the People" (Eugene Delacroix)

1998. Philatelic Week.

2524 **1887** 80 y. multicoloured . . . 80 20

1998. Year of France in Japan.

2525 **1888** 110 y. multicoloured . . 1·10 25

1998. National Afforestation Campaign.

2526 **1889** 50 y. multicoloured . . . 50 10

1890 "Wild Roses" (Sakufu Kondo and Franz Schubert)

1891 "Hill abloom with Tangerine Flowers" (Minoru Uminuma and Shogo Kato)

1998. Favourite Songs (5th series).

2527 **1890** 50 y. multicoloured . . . 50 10
2528 **1891** 80 y. multicoloured . . . 80 20

1892 Kowata Residence, Shinji

1893 Kamihaga Residence, Uchiko

1998. Traditional Houses (3rd series).

2529 **1892** 80 y. multicoloured . . . 80 20
2530 **1893** 80 y. multicoloured . . . 80 20

1894 "This Road" (Hakusyu Kitahara and Kousaku Yamada)

1895 "I'm a Boy of the Sea" (anon)

1998. Favourite Songs (6th series).

2531 **1894** 50 y. multicoloured . . . 50 10
2532 **1895** 80 y. multicoloured . . . 80 20

1896 Boy writing

1998. Letter Writing Day. Multicoloured.

2533 50 y. Type **1896** 80 20
2534 50 y. Girl with letter 80 20
2535 80 y. Girl holding pen 80 20
2536 80 y. Boy holding pen 80 20
2537 80 y. Boy and girl reading letters (horiz) 80 20

1901 Kamio Residence, Oita

1902 Nakamura Residence, Okinawa

1998. Traditional Houses (4th series).

2539 **1901** 80 y. multicoloured . . . 80 20
2540 **1902** 80 y. multicoloured . . . 80 20

1903 FJ Class Dinghy Racing

1998. 53rd National Athletic Meeting, Kanagawa.

2541 **1903** 50 y. multicoloured . . . 50 10

1904 "Sketch of Maple Leaf" (detail)

1905 "Parakeet in Oak Tree"

1907 "Coloured Chicken in Snow-laden Bamboo"

1909 "Parakeet in Rose Bush"

1998. International Correspondence Week. Paintings by Shakuchu Ito. Multicoloured.

2542 90 y. Type **1904** 90 20
2543 90 y. Type **1905** 90 20
2544 110 y. "Drake and Duck in Snow" (detail) . . . . . 1·25 25
2545 110 y. Type **1907** . . . . . . 1·10 25
2546 130 y. "Butterfly in the Peonies" (detail) . . . . . 1·25 25
2547 130 y. Type **1909** . . . . . . 1·25 25

1910 Serving **1911** Receiving

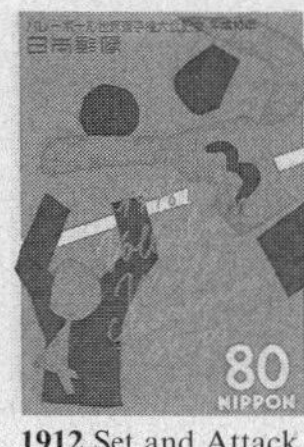 

1912 Set and Attack **1913** Blocking

1998. World Volleyball Championships, Japan.

2548 **1910** 80 y. multicoloured . . . 80 20
2549 **1911** 80 y. multicoloured . . . 80 20
2550 **1912** 80 y. multicoloured . . . 80 20
2551 **1913** 80 y. multicoloured . . . 80 20

1914 Bakin Takizawa (writer, 150th death anniv) **1915** Yoshie Fujiwara (opera singer, birth centenary)

1998. Anniversaries.

2552 **1914** 80 y. multicoloured . . . 80 20
2553 **1915** 80 y. multicoloured . . . 80 20

1916 Sahara Papier-mache Rabbit making Rice Cake **1919** Yamagata Papier-mache Rabbit on Ball

1998. New Year's Greetings. Multicoloured.

2554 50 y. Type **1916** 50 10
2555 80 y. Yamagata papier-mache rabbit on ball 80 20

1998. New Year's Lottery Stamps. Multicoloured.

2556 50 y. + 3 y. Sahara papier-mache rabbit making rice cake 55 15
2557 50 y. + 3 y. Type **1919** 55 15

Each stamp carries a lottery number.

1920 "The Apple Song" (Hachiro Sato and Tadashi Manjome) **1921** "The Toy Cha-Cha-Cha" (Akiyuki Nasaka and Osamu Yoshioka)

1998. Favourite Songs (7th series).

2558 **1920** 50 y. multicoloured . . . 50 10
2559 **1921** 80 y. multicoloured . . . 80 20

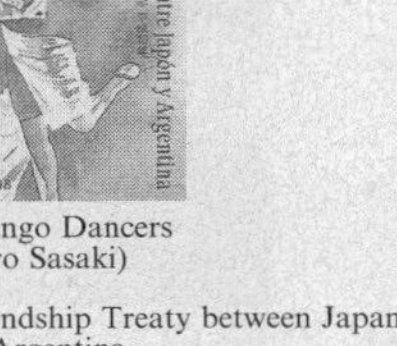

1922 Tango Dancers (Goro Sasaki)

1998. Centenary of Friendship Treaty between Japan and Argentina.

2560 **1922** 80 y. multicoloured . . . 80 20

1923 "Family" (Chakou Wiam) **1924** "Heart Tree" (Atsuko Niizato)

1925 "Hito" (Shozo Somekawa) **1926** "Happiness" (Mary Carmel Mulloor)

1998. 50th Anniv of Universal Declaration of Human Rights.

2561 **1923** 50 y. multicoloured . . . 50 10
2562 **1924** 70 y. multicoloured . . . 50 10
2563 **1925** 80 y. multicoloured . . . 80 20
2564 **1926** 90 y. multicoloured . . . 90 20

1998. 50th Anniv of New Year's Greetings Stamps. Previous issues now dated "1999".

2565 **241** 50 y. mauve 50 10
2566 **445** 50 y. multicoloured . . . 50 10
2567 **1278** 50 y. multicoloured . . . 50 10

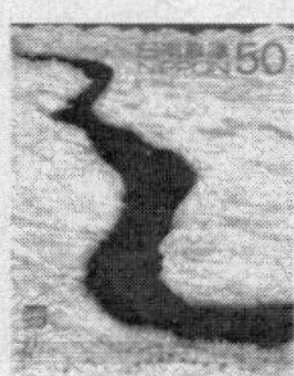 

1927 "Flowing like a River" (Yasushi1 Akimoto and Akira Mitake) **1928** "Song of the Four Seasons" (Toyohisa Araki)

1999. Favourite Songs (8th series).

2568 **1927** 50 y. multicoloured . . . 60 15
2569 **1928** 80 y. multicoloured . . . 95 20

1929 Iwase Residence, Nishi-Akao

1930/1 Ogimachi Houses, Shirakawa (Illustration reduced. Actual size 69 × 33 mm)

1999. Traditional Houses (5th series).

2570 **1929** 80 y. multicoloured . . . 95 20
2571 **1930** 80 y. multicoloured . . . 95 20
2572 **1931** 80 y. multicoloured . . . 95 20

Nos. 2571/2 were issued together, se-tenant, forming the composite design illustrated.

1932 "The Kaen-daiko Drum" (Shinsho Kokontei V) **1933** "Toku the Boatman" (Bunraku Katsura VIII)

1934 "Mr. Kobee, the Faultfinder" (Ensho Sanyutei VI) **1935** "Time Noodles" (Kosan Yanagiya V)

1936 "Once in a Hundred Years" (Beicho Katsura III)

1999. Comic Stories.

2573 **1932** 80 y. multicoloured . . . 95 20
2574 **1933** 80 y. multicoloured . . . 95 20
2575 **1934** 80 y. multicoloured . . . 95 20
2576 **1935** 80 y. multicoloured . . . 95 20
2577 **1936** 80 y. multicoloured . . . 95 20

1937 "Sukiyaki" (Rokusuke Ei and Hachidai Nakamura) **1938** "Early Spring" (Kazumasa Yoshimaru and Akira Nakada)

1999. Favourite Songs (9th series).

2578 **1937** 50 y. multicoloured . . . 60 15
2579 **1938** 80 y. multicoloured . . . 95 20

1939 Kitten

1999. Greetings Stamps. Mult. Self-adhesive.

2580 80 y. Type **1939** 95 20
2581 80 y. Roses 95 20
2582 80 y. Puppy (47 × 37 mm) . . . 95 20
2583 80 y. Brown rabbit 95 20
2584 80 y. Grey and white rabbit (41 × 38 mm) 95 20

1944 Body Parts and Staff of Asclepius

1999. 25th General Assembly of Japan Medical Congress.

2585 **1944** 80 y. multicoloured . . . 95 20

1945/6 "Hare playing on the field in Spring" (Insho Domoto)

1999. Philatelic Week.

2586 **1945** 80 y. multicoloured . . . 95 20
2587 **1946** 80 y. multicoloured . . . 95 20

Nos. 2586/7 were issued together, se-tenant, forming the composite design illustrated.

1947 Nazca Lines, Llama and Machu Picchu Ruins

1948 Amagi Alpine Rose and Mount Fuji

1999. 100 Years of Japanese Emigration to Peru.

2588 **1947** 80 y. multicoloured . . . 95 20

1999. National Afforestation Campaign.

2589 **1948** 50 y. multicoloured . . . 60 15

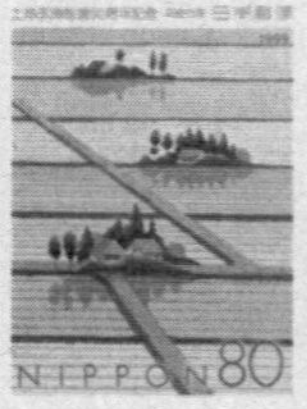

1949 Tholos, Delphi

1950 Demon Dancer (Ouro Carnival), Lake Titicaca and Andean Condor

1999. Centenary of Japan–Greece Treaty of Commerce and Navigation.

2590 **1949** 80 y. multicoloured . . . 95 20

1999. 100 Years of Japanese Emigration to Bolivia.

2591 **1950** 80 y. multicoloured . . . 95 20

1951 Houses and Paddy Fields

1952 "Hill where Camellias Bloom" (detail of statue, Naoki Tominaga) and "Hope" (detail of stained glass window, Louis Fransen)

1999. 50th Anniv of Land Improvement Law.

2592 **1951** 80 y. multicoloured . . . 95 20

1999. 50th Anniv of Family Court.

2593 **1952** 80 y. multicoloured . . . 95 20

1953 Primroses

1954 Rickshaw, 1899

1999. 50th Anniv of Rehabilitation Support Programme.

2594 **1953** 80 y. multicoloured . . . 95 20

1999. Centenary of Patent Attorney System.

2595 **1954** 80 y. multicoloured . . . 95 20

1955 Masaakira Tomii, Kenjiro Ume and Nobushige Hozumi (drafters)

1956 Sayo-chan, Saku-chan and Ken-chan (originator, developer and inspector) (Takashi Yanase)

1999. Centenaries of Civil (1998) and Commercial (1999) Laws.

2596 **1955** 80 y. multicoloured . . . 95 20

1999. Centenary of Japanese Copyright System.

2597 **1956** 80 y. multicoloured . . . 95 20

1957 Children and Envelope

1971 Doves and Hearts

1999. Letter Writing Day. 50th Anniv of Japanese Association of Pen Friend Clubs.

2598 **1957** 50 y. multicoloured . . . 60 15
2599 – 50 y. multicoloured . . . 60 15
2600 – 50 y. multicoloured . . . 60 15
2601 – 50 y. multicoloured . . . 60 15
2602 – 80 y. blue, black & yell . 95 20
2603 – 80 y. multicoloured . . . 95 20
2604 – 80 y. black, blue & yell . 95 20
2605 – 80 y. black, red & yellow 95 20
2606 – 80 y. multicoloured . . . 95 20
2607 – 80 y. black, yellow & bl . 95 20
2608 – 80 y. multicoloured . . . 95 20
2609 – 80 y. black and red . . . 95 20
2610 – 80 y. black, yellow & grn 95 20
2611 – 80 y. green, black & yell . 95 20

DESIGNS: As T **1957**—No. 2599, Bear and crayon; 2600, Girl with pen; 2601, Clown jumping from envelope; 2604, Boy and star; 2606, Miffie and Barbara; 2610, Girl with letter. 52 × 27 mm—2602, Giraffes. 35 × 27 mm— 2603, Kite. 29 × 29 mm—2605, Girl with pencil; 2609, Girl; 2611, Ducklings. 38 × 38 mm—2607, Boy playing trumpet. 27 × 36 mm—2608, Girl playing cello.

1999. Greetings Stamps.

2613 50 y. Type **1971** 60 15
2614 80 y. Japanese character . . . 95 20
2615 90 y. Crane and leaves . . . . 1·10 20

1974 "Wagahai wa Neko de Aru" (novel by Natsume Soseki)

1976 Yosano Akiko (poet)

1978 Tram, Tokyo, 1903

1980 "Haikara" (western-style fashion)

1982 Moving Casualties, Russo–Japanese War, 1904-05

1984 Golfer and Gentian

1999. The Twentieth Century (1st series). The 1900s. Multicoloured.

2616 50 y. Type **1974** 60 15
2617 50 y. "Bochan" (novel by Natsume Soseki) 60 15
2618 80 y. Type **1976** 95 20
2619 80 y. Denkikan Cinema, Asakusa 95 20
2620 80 y. Type **1978** 95 20
2621 80 y. Kawakami Otojirou and Sadayakko (actor couple) . . 95 20
2622 80 y. Type **1980** 95 20
2623 80 y. Sumo wrestlers (opening of Sumo Ring, Ryogoku, Tokyo, 1909) 95 20
2624 80 y. Type **1982** 95 20
2625 80 y. Military hospital, Russo–Japanese War 95 20

See also Nos. 2627/36.

1999. 54th National Sports Festival, Kumamoto.

2626 **1984** 50 y. multicoloured . . . 60 15

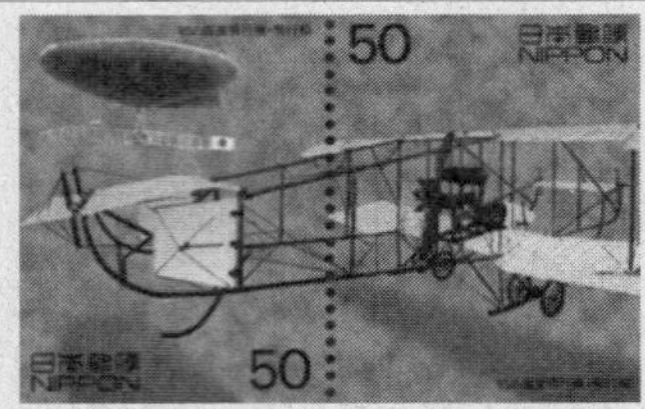

1985/86 Biplane "Kaishiki No. 1" and Airship "Yamadashiki No. 1" (first Japanese-built aircraft)

1987 Children singing (School Song Book, 1910)

1989 Dr. Noguchi Hideyo (discovery of Oroya Fever germ, 1926)

1991 Kanaguri Shizo and Mishima Yahiko at Opening Parade, Olympic Games, Stockholm, 1912

1993 Matsui Sumako as Kachucha in "Resurrection" (play by Shimamura Hogetsu), 1914

1999. The Twentieth Century (2nd series). Multicoloured.

2627 50 y. Type **1985** 60 15
2628 50 y. Type **1986** 60 15
2629 80 y. Type **1987** 95 20
2630 80 y. Explorer and dog (Shirase Antarctic Expedition, 1910) . 95 20
2631 80 y. Type **1989** 95 20
2632 80 y. Wolf (extinction of indigenous wolves, 1905) . . 95 20
2633 80 y. Type **1991** 95 20
2634 80 y. Dancers (formation of Takarazuka Musical Company, 1913) 95 20
2635 80 y. Type **1993** 95 20
2636 80 y. Mother and children (first sale of milk caramel in Japan, 1913) 95 20

Nos. 2627/8 were issued together, se-tenant forming the composite design illustrated.

1995 Stork on Elephant

1999. International Year of the Elderly.

2637 **1995** 80 y. multicoloured . . . 95 20

1996 "Sea Route in Kazusa Area" (from "36 Views of Mt. Fuji" by Hokusai Katsushika)

1998 "Rain beneath the Mountain Top" (from "36 Views of Mt. Fuji")

1999 "Chrysanthemums and a Horsefly"

2000 "Under the Fukagawa Mannen Bridge" (from "36 Views of Mt. Fuji")

1999. International Correspondence Week. 125th Anniv of Universal Postal Union. Multicoloured

2638 90 y. Type **1996** . . . . 1·10 20
2639 90 y. "Confederate Roses and a Sparrow" . . . . 1·10 20
2640 110 y. Type **1998** . . . . . . 1·30 25
2641 110 y. Type **1999** . . . . . . 1·30 25
2642 130 y. Type **2000** . . . . . . 1·50 30
2643 130 y. "Peonies and a Butterfly" . . . . 1·50 30

MILITARY FRANK STAMPS

(M 36)

1910. No. 139 optd with Type M **36**.

M156 **28** 3 s. red . . . . £225 35·00

1913. No. 298 optd with Type M **36**.

M185 **36** 3 s. red . . . . 30·00 11·00

1921. No. 37 of Japanese Post Offices in China optd with Type M **36**.

M202 **36** 3 s. red £7000 £3250

PREFECTURE STAMPS

Since 1 April 1989 the Japanese Ministry of Posts and Telecommunications has issued stamps, some apparently commemorative, inscribed for various prefectures.

The Japanese local government system contains 47 prefectures which vary from Tokyo, Osaka, Kyoto, Hokkaido and Okinawa to rural areas; the powers of the prefectures are similar to those of English or Welsh counties. Each prefecture issue is sold within the area for which it is inscribed and also in other prefectures grouped with it in one of 11 postal regions; the stamps are also available from the Tokyo Central Post Office. All issues are valid for postal purposes throughout Japan.

These issues do not fulfil the published criteria for full listing in the Stanley Gibbons catalogue and, in consequence, are recorded in abbreviated form below.

The sheet of 47 prefecture flowers was sold throughout Japan and is given full listing as Nos. 2041/87.

1989

Nagano. Monkeys in hot spring. 62 y.

Yamagata. Cherries. 62 y.

Okinawa. Courtesy Gate, Shuri. 62 y.

Ehime. Dogo Hot Spa buildings. 62 y.

Kanagawa. Doll and gas lamps. 62 y.

Hiroshima. Seto Inland Sea. 62 y. × 2.

Niigata. Memorial Hall and Bandai Bridge. 62 y.

Aichi. Nagoya Castle and golden dolphin. 62 y.

Oita. Monkey and Mt. Takasaki. 62 y.

Hokkaido. Old Prefectural Building, Sapporo. 62 y.

Hokkaido. Runner and wild rose (athletic meeting). 62 y.

Kumamoto. Kumamoto Castle. 62 y.

Ishikawa. Stone lantern, Kenroku Park. 62 y.

Aomori. Apples. 62 y.

Osaka. Bunraku puppets and Nakanoshima Theatre. 62 y.

Shiga. Lake Biwa and racoon-dog. 62 y.

Chiba. Racoon-dogs dancing. 62 y.

Tokyo. Railway station. 62 y.

Yamaguchi. Blowfish lanterns. 62 y.

1990

Hokkaido. Ice hockey (Asian Winter Olympics). 62 y.

Toyama. Mt. Tate and Shomyo Falls. 62 y.

Ibaraki. "Seven Baby Crows" (nursery rhyme). 62 y.

Nagano. Old inns of Tsumago and Magome. 62 y. × 2.

Shizuoka. Mt. Fuji and tea picker. 62 y.

Fukushima. Peaches. 62 y.

Akita. Omagari Fireworks Festival. 62 y.

Kagoshima. Mt. Sakura. 62 y.

Nagasaki. Sailing ship. 62 y.

Okinawa. Ryukyu dancer. 62 y.

Tokyo. New post office and logger. 62 y.

Shimane. Male dancer with basket. 62 y.

Fukuoka. High jumping and Fukuoka Tower (athletic meeting). 62 y.

Kyoto. Dancing girl crossing bridge. 62 y.

Wakayama. Three pilgrims on old path to Kumano. 62 y.

Miyagi. Izunuma Swamp and five whistling swans. 62 y.

Gifu. Four seasons in Hida. 62 y. × 4.

Saitama. Tenjin Shrine and children playing song game. 62 y.

Hokkaido. Two Manchurian cranes. 62 y.

1991

Kagawa. Mounted archer at Battle of Yashima. 62 y.

Okayama. Water jars (Bizen ware). 62 y. × 2.

Saga. Watchtower, Yoshinogari. 62 y.

Yamanashi. "Bride under Cherry Blossoms" (nursery rhyme). 62 y.

Niigata. Two fancy carps. 62 y.

Hokkaido. Lily of the valley, lilac, lily, rowanberries. 62 y. × 4.

Tochigi. Mt. Nikkou and ramblers. 62 y.

Iwate. Mt. Iwate. 62 y.

Kochi. Sakamoto Ryoma and child standing on whale. 62 y.

Tokushima. Wooden puppet. 62 y.

Tokyo, Fringed orchid. 41 y.

Miyazaki. Cape Toi and wild horses. 62 y.

Kumamoto. Tsu-jun Aqueduct releasing water into river. 62 y.

Okinawa. Black pearls in oyster and Kabira Bay. 41 y.

Tottori. Pears. 62 y.

Ishikawa. Genki (mascot) and sunrise (46th National Athletic Meeting). 41 y.

Mie. Ninja holding shuriken (throwing weapon), rainbow, Iga Ueno Castle and Ninja house. 62 y.

Fukui. Woman wearing spectacles. 62 y.

Gunma. "Hare and Tortoise" (fable). 62 y.

Hyogo. Weathercock and Kobe City lights. 62 y.

Nara. Mt. Yoshino in spring and autumn. 62 y. × 2.

1992

Niigata. Ryokan's Hermitage, Bunsui, 41 y.

Fukuoka. Mt. Togami, Japanese bush warbler and azaleas (National Afforestation Campaign). 41 y.

Hokkaido. Arctic foxes. 62 y.

Toyama. Mt. Tate and tulips. 62 y.

Ehime. Islets in Kurushima Strait. 62 y.

Iwate. Cape Kitayama, Rikuchu, in winter. 62 y.

Ohita. Three Tsurusaki dancers. 62 y.

Yamaguchi. Tanabata lantern festival. 62 y.

Kanagawa. Shasui waterfall. 62 y.

Fukuoka. Mari Tahei with spear and sake dish (Kuroda samurai folk song). 62 y.

Okinawa. Naha regatta. 62 y.

Osaka. Osaka Business Park and Castle. 41 y.

Aichi. Scops owl. 62 y.

1993

Akita. Rocks at Oga Peninsula. 41 y.

Ibaraki. Fukuroda waterfall. 62 y.

Ishikawa. Nanao Bay and Notojima Bridge. 62 y.

Tokyo. Cherry blossom and Tama District mountain ranges. 62 y.

Hokkaido. Harbour seals. 62 y.

Kagawa. Peace statue. 62 y.

Hiroshima. Drummer (rice transplanting ritual). 62 y.

Shizuoka. Black paradise flycatcher and Mt. Fuji. 41 y.

Shiga. Yachts on Lake Biwa. 62 y.

Nagano. Matsumoto Castle and mountains. 62 y.

Kagoshima. Drummer and dancer (Ohara Festival) and Mt. Sakura. 41 y.

Aomori. Oirase mountain stream. 62 y.

Chiba. Waterfall in Yoro Gorge. 41 y.

1994

Tokyo. Rainbow Bridge. 50 y.

Toyama. Kurobe Dam and Gorge. 80 y.

Shimane. Izumo no Okuni (Kabuki dancer) and Izumo Shrine. 80 y.

Nagano. Home at Kashiwabara of Issa Kobayushi (poet). 80 y.

Gunma. Fukiwari Waterfalls. 80 y.

Hokkaido. Sika deer. 50 y.

Hyogo. White stork and Drum Tower, Izushi. 50 y.

Wakayama. Yachts off Wakaura Coast and Marina City. 80 y.

Mie. Kentish plovers and Wedded Rocks, Futami Bay. 80 y.

Tokushima. Awa dance 50 y.

Okinawa. Tug-of-war. 50 y.

Fukui. Pine grove in Kehi. 50 y.

Miyagi. Junks and Godaido Temple, Matsushima. 80 y.

Nagasaki. Dragon Festival. 80 y.

1995

Hokkaido. Chipmunks. 80 y.

Kyoto, Ushiwaka and Benkei on bridge. 80 y.

Gifu. Flowers (Rose, cyclamen, African violets etc). 80 y.

Niigata. Jade and Gyofu Soma (poet). 80 y.

Kochi. Cape Ashizuri-Misaki Lighthouse. 80 y.

Ishikawa. Kanizawa Castle. 80 y.

Hokkaido. Lady's slipper orchid. 80 y.

Saitama. Kuroyama Waterfall. 80 y.

Tokyo. Red Gate, Tokyo University. 50 y.

Okinawa. Procession of drummers (folk festival dance). 80 y.

Miyagi. Avenue of zelkova trees. 50 y.

Osaka. Float in Kishiwada Danjiri Festival. 80 y.

Yamagata. Yamadera (or Risshaku) Temple, Mt. Houju, in autumn. 80 y.

Hida. Four seasons in Hida. 80 y. × 4 se-tenant.

Saga Boy and fish (Karatsu Kunchi Festival). 80 y.

Okayama. Woman writing (Niimi Estate festival). 80 y.

Tochigi. Kirihuri Waterfall. 50 y.

Nara. Yoshino in autumn and spring. 80 y. × 2.

Chiba. Cows in field ("Farmpia '95" dairy farming exhibition). 80 y.

1996

Hokkaido. Sea butterflies. 80 y.

Kumamoto. Boy dancing, bridge and ships (Ushibuka Haiya festival). 80 y.

Fukushima. Pink peony. 80 y.

Mie. Wild crinums (flowers). 80 y. and Women collecting shells. 80 y. se-tenant.

Saga. Jar, flames and pavilion (ceramics exhibition). 80 y.

Yamanashi. Waterfall in Shosenkyo Gorge. 50 y.

Fukui. Murasaki Shikibu (author of "Tale of Genji") and Mt. Hino. 80 y.

Shiga. Enryaku Temple and ancient trees, Mt. Hiei. 80 y.

Ehime. Nishiumi Marine Park. 80 y.

Hokkaido. Wild rose. 80 y.

Aomori. Kabuki characters (Nebuta festival). 80 y.

1997

Miyazaki. Dancers with drums (Shimozuru Usudaiko Odori folk dance). 80 y.

Okinawa. Main Palace of Shuri Castle and stone dragon's head. 80 y.

Tokyo. Kaminari Gate, Asakusa. 80 y.

Tottori. Umbrella Dance, Shanshan Festival. 80 y.

Nagano. Orchestra (Saito Memorial Festival, Matsumoto). 80 y.

Nagano. Gentians. 80 y.

Kanagawa. Mountains and flowers, Sengokubara Marsh. 80 y.

Aichi. Floats, Nagoya Festival. 80 y. × 2 se-tenant.

Nara. Pagodas on Mt. Wakakusa (grassburning rite). 50 y.

Kumamoto. Ball in air above temple (Men's World Handball Championship). 80 y.

Hokkaido. Dahurian rhododendron. 80 y.

Shizuoka. Tea picking. 50 y.

Shizuoka. Mt. Fuji in summer (cows and daisies) and autumn (dry grass). 80 y. × 2 se-tenant.

Kagawa. Visitors at foot of Marugame Castle. 80 y.

Hokkaido. Ermine. 50 y.

Okayama. Castle. 80 y.

Okinawa. Pineapples and mangoes. 50 y. × 2 se-tenant.

Nagasaki, Saga and Fukuoka. Nagasaki Kaido Highway route map. 80 y. × 4 se-tenant.

Kyoto. University clock tower. 80 y.

Niigata. "Bride" by Fukiya Koji. 50 y.

Akita. Lanterns on bamboo poles (Kanto Festival). 80 y.

Tottori. Ship, flower, dolphin and buildings (Expo Tottori 97). 80 y.

Saitama. Waterwheel plant at Hozoji-numa Pond, Hanyu. 50 y.

Toyama. Street dancers (Good Wind Festival). 80 y. × 2 se-tenant.

Ibaraki. Sailing dinghies on Lake Kasumigaura. 80 y.

Tokyo. Tokyo Big Site (exhibition buildings overlooking lake), Telecom Centre (monorail), Rainbow Bridge, Tokyo International Forum (glass building), Edo Tokyo Museum (steps leading to building). 80 y. × 5 se-tenant.

Saitama. Two birds on tree and three walkers (First World Walking Festival). 80 y.

Chiba and Kanagawa. Kanagawa–Chiba Bridge and Tunnel. 80 y. × 2 se-tenant.

1998

Hokkaido. Rowanberries in snow and pink moss in spring. 80 y. × 2 se-tenant.

Kyoto. Hiyoshi Dam. 80 y.

Okinawa. Sanshin (musical instrument), towel and banana plant cloth. 80 y.

Gifu. Crowd surrounding float (Okoshi Daiko drum festival). 80 y.

Hyogo and Tokushima. Ko–Awaj–Naruto Motorway. Ohnaruto Bridge (with whirlpool), Akashi Kaikyo Bridge (with spring blossom). 80 y. × 2 se-tenant.

Nagano. "Jomon's Venus" (figurine from Chino). 80 y.

Iwate. Procession of caparisoned horses. 80 y.

Tokyo. Towers as hand (Business Show). 80 y.

Nagasaki. Mt. Heisei Shinzan. 80 y.

Gunma. 80 y. Oze Moor in spring and autumn. 80 y. × 2 se-tenant.

Yamagata. Two dancers carrying hats (Flower Hat Dance). 50 y.

Shizuoka. Women's World Softball Championship. 80 y.

Ishikawo. Mt. Hakusan (with woods in foreground). 50 y.

Oita. Decorated cart (Gion Festival). 50 y.

Nagano. World Puppet Festival. 50 y. × 2 se-tenant.

Hiroshima. Views of Seto Inland Sea. Itsukushima Shrine with torii gate; bridge over Ondo Strait. 80 y. × 2 se-tenant.

Okinawa. First and last Ryukyu Islands stamps. 80 y. × 2 se-tenant.

Kagoshima. Ceramic teabowl and vase (400th anniv of Satsuma-yoki Pottery). 80 y. × 2 se-tenant.

Kagawa. Seto Great Road and Rail Bridge. 80 y.

Hyogo. Kobe Lights. 80 y.

Aomori. Apples. 80 y. (as 1989 issue but face value changed).

Wakayama. Three pilgrims on old path to Kumano. 80 y. (as 1990 issue).

Tokyo. Tama intercity monorail. 80 y.

JAPANESE TAIWAN (FORMOSA)

From 1895 to 1945 Taiwan was part of the Japanese Empire, using the stamps of Japan. During 1945 American naval and air forces disrupted communications between Taiwan and Japan. The following were issued when supplies of Japanese stamps ran short.

1 Numeral and Chrysanthemum

1945. Imperf.

J1 **1** 3 s. red . . . . 25·00 28·00
J2 5 s. green . . . . 25·00 23·00
J3 10 s. blue . . . . 35·00 35·00

JAPANESE OCCUPATION OF CHINA — Pt. 17

100 cents = 1 dollar.

I. KWANGTUNG

Japanese troops occupied Canton in 1938 and by 1945 had overrun much of Kwangtung province. Unoverprinted stamps of China were used until the following stamps were issued.

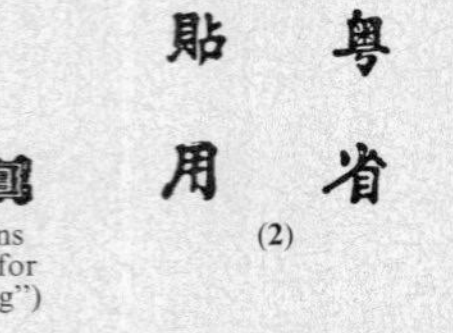

貼 粵

用 省

(**1**) (Trans "Special for Kwantung") (**2**)

1942. Stamps of China optd with T **1**.

1 – 1 c. orange (411) . . . . . . 70 1·25
2 **77** 1 c. orange . . . . 90 1·50
3 **58** 2 c. green . . . . 7·50 4·25
4 **72** 3 c. red . . . . 50 1·25
5 **77** 5 c. green . . . . 95 1·00
7 **72** 8 c. olive . . . . 1·25 60
8 **77** 8 c. green . . . . 1·40 1·25
9 **72** 10 c. green . . . . 1·25 1·10
11 **77** 10 c. emerald . . . . . . 2·00 2·00
12 **72** 16 c. brown . . . . 2·50 2·75
13 17 c. green . . . . 2·75 3·25
14 – 20 c. blue (519) . . . . . . 2·75 2·50
15 **72** 30 c. red . . . . 2·50 2·50
16 **77** 30 c. red . . . . 3·00 3·50
17 **72** 50 c. blue . . . . 3·75 3·00
18 **77** 50 c. blue . . . . 3·00 2·25
19 **72** $1 sepia and brown . . . . 6·00 5·00
20 $2 brown and blue . . . . . 6·00 5·00
21 $5 green and red . . . . . 7·00 4·50
22 $10 violet and green . . . . 12·00 7·50
23 $20 blue and purple . . . . 8·00 5·50

1942. Stamps of China optd with T **2**.
(a) On 1938 issue.

24 **72** 2 c. green . . . . 30 1·00
25 3 c. red . . . . 30 1·00
26 5 c. green 35 25
28 8 c. green 30 30
29 10 c. green 55 75
30 16 c. brown . . . . 60 1·50
31 25 c. blue . . . . 1·25 2·25
32 30 c. red . . . . 1·50 2·25
33 50 c. blue . . . . 1·25 1·25
35 $1 brown and red . . . . . 5·00 5·50
37 $2 brown and blue . . . . . 5·00 6·00
39 $5 green and red . . . . . 6·50 6·50
40 $10 violet and green . . . . 12·00 9·00
42 $20 blue and purple . . . . 7·00 10·00

(b) On 1941 issue.

44 **77** 2 c. blue . . . . 25 1·50
45 5 c. green . . . . 25 1·25
46 8 c. orange . . . . 90 2·25
47 8 c. green . . . . 70 2·25
48 10 c. green . . . . 75 2·25
49 17 c. green . . . . 75 3·00
50 25 c. purple . . . . 1·00 2·75
51 30 c. red . . . . 1·00 2·25
52 50 c. blue . . . . 1·25 2·25
53 $1 black and brown . . . . 6·00 4·50
54 $2 black and blue . . . . . 6·00 4·25
55 $5 black and red . . . . . 9·00 7·00
56 $10 black and green . . . . 10·00 8·00
57 $20 black and purple . . . . 7·00 6·00

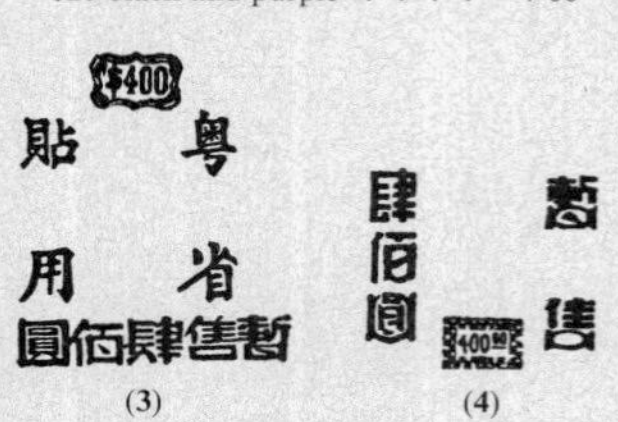

(**3**) (**4**)

1945. Canton provisionals. Surch as T **3**.

58 **72** $200 on 10 c. green (No. 29) . 55·00 45·00
59 $400 on 8 c. olive (No. 28) . . 55·00 45·00

1945. Swatow provisional. No. 508 of China surch with T **4**.

60 $400 on 1 c. orange £375 £300

POSTAGE DUE STAMP

(**D 3**)

1945. Postage Due stamp of China surch with T D **3**.

D58 D **62** $100 on $2 orange . . . £400 £400

II. MENGKIANG (INNER MONGOLIA)

The autonomous area of Mengkiang ("the Mongolian Borderlands"), consisting of Suiyuan, South Chahar and North Shansi, was established by the Japanese in November, 1937.

For the first issue in 1941 see the note at the beginning of III North China.

疆 蒙

分 半

(**3**)

1942. Stamps of China optd "Mengkiang" and surch half original value at T **3**.

86 – ½ c. on 1 c. orange (411) . . 1·00 1·00
93 **58** 1 c. on 2 c. green . . . . . 1·00 1·00
69 **72** 1 c. on 2 c. green 75 75
94 **58** 2 c. on 4 c. green 10 50
87 **60** 2 c. on 4 c. lilac . . . . . . 3·25 2·25
72 **72** 4 c. on 8 c. green . . . . . 1·50 75
73 **72** 5 c. on 10 c. green . . . . . 1·50 1·50
99 – 5 c. on 10 c. purple (515) . . 75 1·75
95 **72** 8 c. on 16 c. brown . . . . 1·25 40
68 **58** 10 c. on 20 c. blue . . . . . 28·00 23·00
100 – 10 c. on 20 c. red (418) . . . 75 1·75
88 – 10 c. on 20 c. blue (519) . . 2·50 2·25
101 – 15 c. on 30 c. pur (542) . . 2·25 2·00
75 **72** 15 c. on 30 c. red . . . . . 3·00 3·25
102 – 20 c. on 40 c. orge (524) . . 3·25 2·25
103 – 25 c. on 50 c. green (525) . . 2·75 2·25
77 **72** 25 c. on 50 c. blue . . . . . 5·00 5·50
96 50 c. on $1 sepia & brown . 6·00 5·00
82 $1 on $2 brown and blue . . 9·00 9·00
98 $5 on $10 violet & green . . 30·00 30·00
84 $10 on $20 blue & purple . . 75·00 65·00

4 Dragon Pillar, Peking

5 Miners

1943. 5th Anniv of Establishment of Mengkiang Post and Telegraph Service.

104 **4** 4 c. orange . . . . 2·00 2·50
105 8 c. blue . . . . 2·00 2·50

1943. 2nd Anniv of War in East Asia.

106 **5** 4 c. green . . . . 2·00 2·75
107 8 c. red . . . . 2·00 2·75

6 Stylised Horse

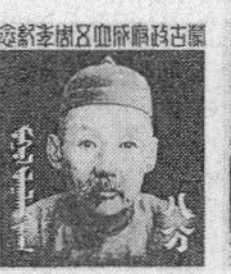

7 Prince Yun

8 Blast Furnace

1943. 1st Anniv of Federation of Autonomous Governments of Mongolian Provinces.

108 **6** 3 c. red . . . . 1·50 2·75
109 **7** 8 c. blue . . . . 1·50 2·75

1944. Productivity Campaign.

110 **8** 8 c. brown . . . . 2·00 3·50

1945. Stamps of China optd "Mengkiang" as top characters in T **3**.

117 – 1 c. orange (411) 50 50
111 **58** 2 c. green . . . . 1·25 1·00
112 4 c. green . . . . 4·50 3·00
113 5 c. green . . . . 1·75 1·00
118 – 8 c. orange (514) 10 35
119 – 10 c. purple (515) 10 40
120 – 20 c. red (418) 15 40
121 – 30 c. red (542) 15 50
122 – 40 c. orange (524) 10 50
123 – 50 c. green (525) 70 80
114 **72** $1 sepia and brown . . . . 2·75 2·25
115 $2 brown and blue . . . . . 7·00 5·50
116 $5 green and red . . . . . 24·00 17·00

角 伍

(**10**)

1945. Stamps of China optd "Mengkiang" (as T **3** of North China) and surch as T **10**.

124B **60** 10 c. on ½ c. sepia . . . . 50 2·00
126B – 10 c. on 1 c. orange (411) . 25 2·00
135 **58** 50 c. on 2 c. olive . . . . 55 2·25
130 **72** 50 c. on 2 c. olive . . . . 35 2·50
136 **58** 50 c. on 4 c. green . . . . 2·00 3·75
131 **60** 50 c. on 4 c. lilac . . . . 85 3·25
137 **58** 50 c. on 5 c. green . . . . 50 2·50
132B **72** 50 c. on 5 c. olive . . . . 50 2·00
138 – $1 on 8 c. orange (514) . . 15 3·25

III. NORTH CHINA

The Japanese conquered North China in 1937 and formed a puppet Government in Peking.

疆 蒙

(**2.** of Meng Kiang "Mengkiang")

(**B.** "Honan")

北 河

(**D.** "Hopeh")

西 山

(**E.** "Shansi")

東 山

(**H.** "Shantung")

北 蘇

(**J.** "Supeh")

Types **2** of Meng Kiang and **B** to **J** are the six "district" overprints comprising North China (including Mengkiang) and a detailed list of the overprints on the stamps of China is given in the Stanley Gibbons' Catalogue, Part 17 (China).

坡 嘉 新
念 紀 落 陷

(**1**)

國建洲滿
念紀年週十

(**2**)

In 1942 stamps of China overprinted with Types **B** to **J** were further overprinted with Type **1** (to commemorate the Fall of Singapore) or with Type **2** (to commemorate the tenth Anniversary of Manchukuo). These stamps are also listed in the Stanley Gibbons' Catalogue Part 17 (China).

分 半

(**3**)

1942. Stamps of China optd "Hwa Pei" (= North China) and surch half original value at T **3**.

111 – ½ c. on 1 c. orange (No. 411) 45 45
128 **58** 1 c. on 2 c. olive 75 20
114 – 1 c. on 2 c. blue (No. 509) . 1·50 1·00
88 **72** 1 c. on 2 c. olive 50 40
129 **58** 2 c. on 4 c. green 10 10
116 **60** 2 c. on 4 c. lilac . . . . . 1·10 1·10
134 – 4 c. on 8 c. orge (No. 514) . 10 10
91 **72** 4 c. on 8 c. olive 60 25
120 – 5 c. on 10 c. pur (No. 515) . 2·25 2·25
92 **72** 5 c. on 10 c. green 80 25
130 8 c. on 16 c. olive 75 20
135 – 10 c. on 20 c. lake (No. 418) 40 10
122 – 10 c. on 20 c. blue (No. 519) 75 1·10
96 **72** 15 c. on 30 c. red . . . . . 1·50 1·10
136 – 15 c. on 30 c. purple (No. 542) 45 10
137 – 20 c. on 40 c. orge (No. 542) 1·00 15
138 – 25 c. on 50 c. grn (No. 525) . 1·25 25
98 **72** 25 c. on 50 c. blue . . . . . 1·10 85
131 50 c. on $1 brown & red . . 3·00 1·25
132 $1 on $2 brown and blue . . 6·00 5·50
133 $5 on $10 violet & green . . 20·00 15·00
109 $10 on $20 blue & purple . . 60·00 40·00

邦友
界租 還交

念紀

(**4**)

局總 政郵
立成
念紀年週五

(**5**)

1943. Return to China of Foreign Concessions. Optd with T **4**.

139 **58** 2 c. on 4 c. green (No. 129) . 2·00 2·00
140 **72** 4 c. on 8 c. olive (No. 91) . . 2·00 2·00
141 8 c. on 16 c. olive (No. 130) . 2·00 2·00

1943. 5th Anniv of Directorate-General of Posts for North China. Optd with T **5**.

142 **58** 2 c. on 4 c. green (No. 129) . 2·00 2·00
143 **72** 4 c. on 8 c. olive (No. 91) . . 2·00 2·00
144 8 c. on 16 c. olive (No. 130) . 2·00 2·00

1943. Stamps of China optd "Hwa Pei" as top characters in T **3**.

164 – 1 c. orange (No. 411) . . . 20 25
153 **58** 2 c. olive 10 15
154 4 c. green 10 10
155 5 c. green 10 10
156 **72** 9 c. olive 15 25
165 – 10 c. purple (No. 515) . . . 10 15
145 **72** 10 c. green . . . . 3·00 1·50
157 16 c. olive 15 15
158 18 c. olive 20 25
166 – 20 c. lake (No. 418) 15 15
167 – 30 c. red (as No. 542) . . . 10 15
168 – 40 c. orange (No. 524) . . . 15 15
169 – 50 c. green (No. 525) . . . 20 15
159 **72** $1 brown and red . . . . . 5·00 1·00
160 $2 brown and blue . . . . . 2·75 75
161 $5 green and red . . . . . 4·00 2·25
162 $10 violet and green . . . . 7·00 5·50
163 $20 blue and purple . . . . 8·00 6·50

戰 參
念紀年週一

(**6**)

會員委務政
念紀年週四

(**7**)

1944. 1st Anniv of Declaration of War on Allies by Japanese-controlled Nanking Govt. Optd with T **6**.

170 **58** 4 c. green (No. 154) . . . . 3·00 3·00
171 **72** 10 c. green (No. 149) . . . 3·00 3·00

1944. 4th Anniv of North China Political Council. Optd with T **7**.

172 **72** 9 c. olive (No. 156) . . . . 2·00 2·00
173 18 c. olive (No. 158) . . . . 2·00 2·25
174 – 50 c. green (No. 169) . . . 2·00 2·25
175 **72** $1 brown & red (No.159) . . 4·00 3·00

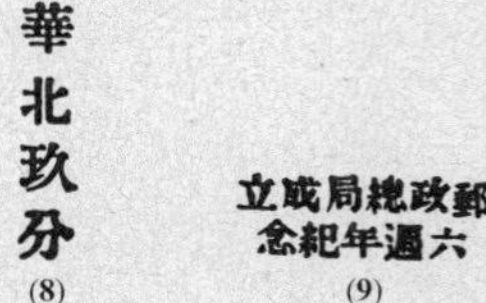

(**8**) (**9**)

1944. Stamps of Japanese Occupation of Shanghai and Nanking optd "Hwa Pei" and surch as T **8**.

176 **5** 9 c. on 50 c. orange . . . . 2·00 2·25
177 18 c. on $1 green . . . . . 2·25 2·25
178 **6** 36 c. on $2 blue . . . . . . 3·00 2·75
179 90 c. on $5 red . . . . . . 3·25 3·00

1944. 6th Anniv of Directorate-General of Posts for North China. Optd with T **9**.

180 **72** 9 c. olive (No. 156) . . . . 2·00 2·25
181 18 c. olive (No. 158) . . . . 2·00 2·25
182 – 50 c. green (No. 169) . . . 2·50 2·25
183 **72** $1 brown & red (No. 159) . 5·00 3·25

席 主 汪
念紀典葬

(**10**)

年週二戰參
念 紀

(**11**)

華北壹圓

(**12**)

1944. Death of Wang Ching-wei. Optd with T **10**.

184 – 20 c. lake (No. 166) . . . . 2·25 2·25
185 – 50 c. green (No. 169) . . . 2·25 2·25
186 **72** $1 brown & red (No. 159) . 3·00 2·50
187 $2 brown & blue (No. 160) . 3·00 2·75

1945. 2nd Anniv of Declaration of War on Allies by Nanking Govt. Optd with T **11**.

188 – 20 c. lake (No. 166) . . . . 2·25 2·25
189 – 50 c. green (No. 169) . . . 2·25 2·25
190 **72** $1 brown & red (No. 159) . 3·00 2·50
191 $2 brown & blue (No. 160) . 3·00 2·75

1945. Stamps of Japanese Occupation of Shanghai and Nanking surch as T **12**.

192 **7** 50 c. on $3 orange . . . . . 4·50 6·25
193 $1 on $6 blue . . . . 4·50 6·25

13 Dragon Pillar

14 Long Bridge

15 Imperial City Tower

16 Marble Boat, Summer Palace

17

1945. 5th Anniv of Establishment of North China Political Council. Views of Peking.

194 **13** $1 yellow . . . . 1·25 1·50
195 **14** $2 blue . . . . 1·50 1·50
196 **15** $5 red . . . . 1·50 1·25
197 **16** $10 green . . . . 2·00 1·75

1945. Optd "Hwa Pei" as top characters in T **3**.

198 **17** $1 brown . . . . 1·25 25
199 $2 blue . . . . 1·40 15
200 $5 red . . . . 1·50 45
201 $10 green . . . . 1·75 1·00
202 $20 purple . . . . 3·25 1·10
203 $50 brown . . . . 15·00 8·50

18 Wutai Mountain, Shansi

19 Kaifeng Iron Pagoda, Honan

20 International Bridge, Tientsin

21 Taishan Mountain, Shantung

22 GPO, Peking

1945. 7th Anniv of Directorate General of Posts for North China.

204 **18** $5 green . . . . 60 1·25
205 **19** $10 brown . . . . 65 1·10
206 **20** $20 purple . . . . 75 1·10
207 **21** $30 grey . . . . 1·00 1·00
208 **22** $50 red . . . . 1·10 1·00

IV. NANKING AND SHANGHAI

The Japanese captured Shanghai and Nanking in 1937 and Hankow in 1938. During the same year Nanking was made the seat of Japanese-controlled administration for the Yangtse Basin. The stamps listed below were used in parts of Anhwei, Southern Kiangsu, Chekiang, Hupeh, Kiangsi, Hunan and Fukien.

N.B. With the exception of Nos. 114 to 119 the following are all surcharged on stamps of China.

20
國內信函航空費已付
(1)

1941. Air. Surch as T **1**.

1 **61** 10 s. on 50 c. brown . . . . . 25 2·50
2 18 s. on 90 c. olive . . . . . 60 3·50
4 20 s. on $1 green . . . . . 1·00 4·00
5 25 s. on 90 c. olive . . . . . 25 2·75
6 35 s. on $2 brown . . . . . 25 2·50
7 60 s. on 35 s. on $2 brown (No. 6) . . . . . 25 3·50

收回租界紀念
八月一日 三十二年
伍角
(2)

1943. Return to China of Shanghai Concessions. Surch as T **2**.

8 **72** 25 c. on 5 c. green . . . . . 2·00 1·75
9 **77** 50 c. on 8 c. orange . . . . . 2·00 1·75
10 **72** $1 on 16 c. olive . . . . . 2·00 1·75
11 **77** $2 on 50 c. blue . . . . . 2·00 1·75

1943. As No. 422 but colour changed. Issued at Shanghai.

12 **72** 15 c. brown . . . . 15·00 16·00

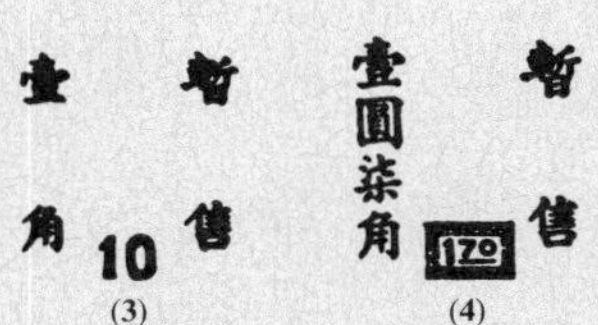
(3) (4)

1943. Stamps of China and No. 12 above surch as T **3** (cent values) or T **4** (dollar values). (a) On T **58**.

13 **58** $6 on 5 c. green . . . . . 1·50 2·50
14 $20 on 15 c. red . . . . . 1·50 1·75
15 $500 on 15 c. green . . . . . 1·50 1·75
17 $1000 on 20 c. blue . . . . . 2·75 3·25
18 $1000 on 25 c. blue . . . . . 3·00 3·25

(b) On Martyrs issue (as T **60**).

88 **60** $7.50 c. on ½ c. sepia . . . . 35 4·50
89 – $15 on 1 c. orange . . . . 25 1·50
91 – $30 on 2 c. blue . . . . 45 1·50
93 – $200 on 1 c. orange . . . . 40 1·00
94 – $200 on 8 c. orange . . . . 45 1·25

(c) On T **72**.

19 **72** 25 c. on 5 c. green . . . . 50 2·25
20 30 c. on 2 c. green . . . . 1·00 2·50
21 50 c. on 3 c. red 10 45
22 50 c. on 5 c. green 20 40
23 50 c. on 8 c. green . . . . 1·00 1·75
24 $1 on 8 c. green 10 15
26 $1 on 15 c. brown . . . . 70 1·00
27 $1.30 on 16 c. brown . . . . 10 1·00
28 $1.50 on 3 c. red 10 50
54 $1.70 on 30 c. red . . . . 1·40 2·75
55 $2 on 5 c. green 15 45
30 $2 on 10 c. green 10 40
56 $2 on $1 sepia & brown . . . . 4·00 3·50
59 $3 on 8 c. green 10 15
31 $3 on 15 c. brown 25 50
32 $4 on 16 c. brown 30 50
33 $5 on 15 c. brown 75 60
61 $6 on 5 c. green 50 75
62 $6 on 8 c. green 15 35
38 $6 on 10 c. green 50 70
39 $10 on 10 c. green 10 30
40 $10 on 16 c. brown 10 20
41 $20 on 3 c. red 10 40
42 $20 on 15 c. red . . . . 2·00 4·00
43 $20 on 15 c. brown . . . . 35 1·00
64 **72** $20 on $2 brown & blue . . 1·75 2·25
65 $50 on 30 c. red . . . . 75 1·90
66 $50 on 50 c. blue . . . . 75 2·00
67 $50 on $5 green and red . . 1·25 2·00
68 $50 on $20 blue & purple . . 2·25 3·00
45 $100 on 3 c. red . . . . 1·00 1·00
83 $100 on $10 violet & grn . . 45 75
84 $200 on $20 blue & purple . . 45 75
46 $500 on 8 c. green . . . . 1·75 2·25
47 $500 on 10 c. green . . . . 1·50 2·25
48 $500 on 15 c. red . . . . 4·00 3·50
49 $500 on 15 c. brown . . . . 3·50 3·25
50 $500 on 16 c. brown . . . . 2·50 3·25
51 $1000 on 25 c. blue . . . . 3·00 4·25
86 $1000 on 30 c. red . . . . 2·00 3·50
75 $1000 on 50 c. blue . . . . 2·50 3·50
76 $1000 on $2 brown & blue . . 2·25 4·75
77 $2000 on $5 green & red . . 2·50 3·75
87a $5000 on $10 violet & grn . . 15·00 18·00

(d) On T **77**.

95 **77** 5 c. on ½ c. sepia . . . . 10 1·50
96 10 c. on 1 c. orange . . . . 10 1·25
97 20 c. on 1 c. orange . . . . 15 1·00
98 40 c. on 5 c. green . . . . 10 1·10
99 $5 on 5 c. green 15 35
100 $10 on 10 c. green 35 70
101 $50 on ½ c. sepia 25 50
102 $50 on 1 c. orange 35 50
103 $50 on 17 c. olive . . . . 75 1·00
104 $200 on 5 c. green . . . . 50 1·00
105 $200 on 8 c. green . . . . 60 1·10
106 $200 on 8 c. orange . . . . 1·25 2·00
107 $500 on $5 black and red . . 1·75 3·00
108 $1000 on 1 c. orange . . . . 1·50 2·75
109 $1000 on 25 c. purple . . . . 1·75 2·50
110 $1000 on 30 c. red . . . . 2·00 2·75
111 $1000 on $2 black & blue . . 2·25 3·00
112 $1000 on $10 black & grn . . 2·75 2·75
113 $2000 on $5 black & red . . 3·25 3·00

5 Wheat and Cotton Flower

6 Purple Mountain, Nanking

1944. 4th Anniv of Establishment of Chinese Puppet Government at Nanking.

114 **5** 50 c. orange 10 50
115 $1 green 10 50
116 **6** $2 blue 10 50
117 $5 red 10 50

7 Map of Shanghai and Foreign Concessions

1944. 1st Anniv of Return to China of Shanghai Foreign Concessions.

118 **7** $3 orange . . . . 35 1·50
119 $6 blue . . . . 35 1·50

1945. 5th Anniv of Establishment of Chinese Puppet Government at Nanking. Surch as T **4**.

124 **5** $15 on 50 c. orange . . . . 10 1·50
125 $30 on $1 green . . . . 10 1·50
126 **6** $60 on $2 blue . . . . 10 1·50
127 $200 on $5 red . . . . 10 1·25

(9)

1945. Air Raid Precautions Propaganda. Air stamps surch as T **9**.

128 **61** $150 on 15 c. green . . . . 75 1·25
129 $250 on 25 c. orange . . . . 75 1·25
130 $600 on 60 c. blue . . . . 75 1·25
131 $1000 on $1 green . . . . 75 1·25

POSTAGE DUE STAMPS

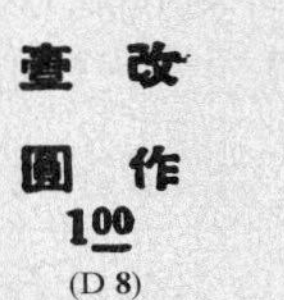
(D 8)

1945. Postage Due stamps surch as Type D **8**.

D120 D **62** $1 on 2 c. orange . . . 35 2·75
D121 $2 on 5 c. orange . . . 35 2·50
D122 $5 on 10 c. orange . . . 35 2·50
D123 $10 on 20 c. orange . . . 35 2·25

JAPANESE OCCUPATION OF NETHERLANDS INDIES Pt. 4

The Japanese occupied the Netherlands Indies from March 1942 to 1945.

100 sen (cents) = 1 rupee (gulden).

I. JAVA

1 Eastern Asia

1943. 1st Anniv of Japanese Occupation of Java.

1 **1** 2 s. brown . . . . 1·75 1·75
2 – 3½ s. red . . . . 1·75 1·75
3 – 5 s. green . . . . 3·00 1·75
4 – 10 s. blue . . . . 5·50 1·75

DESIGNS: 3½ s. Farmer ploughing ricefield; 5 s. Mt. Soemer; 10 s. Bantam Bay.

2 Wayang puppet

4 Bird of Vishnu and Mt Soemer

5 Native soldier

1943. Designs with rectangular panel of characters as at foot of T **2**/**4**.

5 – 3½ c red 50 50
6 **2** 5 c. green 50 50
7 – 10 c. blue 50 45
8 – 20 c. olive 85 50
9 – 40 c. purple . . . . 1·50 50
10 **4** 60 c. orange . . . . 1·75 80
11 – 80 c. brown . . . . 3·50 80
12 – 1 r. violet . . . . 8·50 1·40

DESIGNS—As Type **2**: 3½ c. Native head; 10 c. Boroboudur Temple; 20 c. Map of Java; 40 c. Seated dancer and Temple. As Type **4**: 80 c. Ploughing with oxen; 1 r. Terraced ricefields.

1943. Savings Campaign.

13 **5** 3½ c. red . . . . 13·00 6·00
14 10 c. blue . . . . 15·00 2·25

II. SUMATRA

6 Lake Toba

1943. Designs with rectangular panel characters as at foot of T **6**.

15 – 1 c. olive 60 90
16 – 2 c. green 60 90
17 – 3 c. blue 60 90
18 – 3½ c. red . . . . 60 1·00
19 – 4 c. blue 60 90
20 – 5 c. orange 60 90
21 – 10 c. blue 75 95
22 – 20 c. brown . . . . 1·25 1·50
23 **6** 30 c. purple . . . . 1·50 2·00
24 40 c. brown . . . . 1·75 2·50
25 – 50 c. bistre . . . . 6·00 7·00
26 – 1 r. violet . . . . 11·00 13·00

DESIGNS: 1 c. to 3 c. Batak house; 3½ c. to 5 c. Minangkabau house; 10 c., 20 c. Ploughing with oxen; 50 c., 1 r. Carabao Canyon (20 × 28 mm).

(7)

1944. Various stamps optd with T **7**.
(a) On Netherlands Indies stamps of 1933.

38 **46** 1 c. violet 30 80
39 2 c. purple 30 80
40 2½ c. bistre 30 80
41 3 c. green . . . . 5·50 7·50
27 3½ c. grey 30 75
42 **47** 10 c. red . . . . 5·50 7·50
51 15 c. blue . . . . 1·60 4·75
52 20 c. purple 30 55
37 25 c. green . . . . 1·75 2·00
46 30 c. blue . . . . 13·00 17·00
54 35 c. violet . . . . 1·50 2·25
55 40 c. green . . . . 70 1·25
34 42½ c. yellow . . . . 38·00 48·00
35 50 c. blue . . . . 15·00 18·00
49 2 g. green . . . . 32·00 42·00
36 2 g. 50 purple . . . . 48·00 60·00
56 5 g. bistre . . . . 9·50 14·00

(b) On Nos. 429/44 of Netherlands Indies.

57 – 10 c. red 35 55
59 – 15 c. blue 60 90
60 – 17½ c. orange . . . . 80 1·25
61 – 20 c. mauve . . . . 16·00 20·00
62 – 25 c. green . . . . 2·25 4·75
63 – 30 c. brown . . . . 70 1·50
64 – 35 c. purple . . . . 15·00 18·00
65 – 40 c. green . . . . 70 1·50
66 – 50 c. red . . . . 1·50 1·75
67 – 60 c. blue . . . . 1·10 1·40
68 – 80 c. red . . . . 1·50 2·00
69 – 1 g. violet . . . . 1·50 2·00
70 – 2 g. green . . . . 2·00 3·00
71 – 5 g. brown . . . . 55·00 75·00
72 – 10 g. green . . . . 18·00 24·00
73 **68** 25 g. orange £120 £160

(c) On Nos. 463/6 of Netherlands Indies.

74 – 3 c. green 30 75
75 **71** 4 c. green 30 75
76 – 5 c. blue 30 75
77 – 7½ c. violet 30 75

(d) On Nos. 506 and 509 of Netherlands.

78 **94** 5 c. green . . . . 8·50 11·00
79 12½ c. blue . . . . 4·50 10·00

III. JAPANESE NAVAL CONTROL AREA

(9)

1942. Various stamps optd with T **9**.
(a) On Netherlands Indies stamps of 1933.

89 **46** 1 c. violet . . . . 40 1·60
90 2 c. purple . . . . 40 1·60
91 2½ c. bistre . . . . 30 1·40
92 3 c. green . . . . 40 2·00
83 4 c. green . . . . 7·00 11·00
84 5 c. blue . . . . 8·50 13·00
95 **47** 10 c. red . . . . 24·00 32·00
96 15 c. blue . . . . 3·75 5·50
97 20 c. purple . . . . 80 3·00
98 25 c. green . . . . 2·50 5·50
86 30 c. blue . . . . 10·00 16·00
100 35 c. violet . . . . 80 3·00
101 40 c. green . . . . 80 3·00
88 50 c. blue . . . . 25·00 38·00
102 80 c. red . . . . 28·00 42·00
103 1 g. violet . . . .
104 2 g. green . . . .
105 5 g. bistre . . . .

(b) On Nos. 270 and 360 of Netherlands Indies.

107 – 5 c. blue . . . . 40 1·40
106 **48** 30 c. blue £110 £150

(c) On Nos. 429/44 of Netherlands Indies.

108 – 10 c. red . . . . 1·25 1·60
110 – 15 c. blue . . . . 55 2·25
111 – 17½ c. orange . . . . 65 2·25
112 – 20 c. mauve . . . . 18·00 27·00
113 – 25 c. green . . . . 16·00 25·00
114 – 30 c. brown . . . . 80 2·00
115 – 35 c. purple . . . . 42·00 50·00
116 – 40 c. green . . . . 16·00 25·00
117 – 50 c. red . . . . 2·50 3·50
118 – 60 c. blue . . . . 3·00 5·50
119 – 80 c. red . . . . 3·00 5·50
120 – 1 g. violet . . . . 2·50 4·75
121 – 2 g. green . . . . 20·00 32·00
122 – 5 g. brown . . . .
123 **68** 2 g. orange . . . .

(d) On Nos. 462/6 of Netherlands Indies.

124 – 2½ c. purple . . . . 3·75 6·00
125 – 3 c. green . . . . 1·60 3·25
126 **71** 4 c. green . . . . 60 2·25
127 – 5 c. blue . . . . 2·50 6·00
128 – 7½ c. violet . . . . 45 2·25

(e) On Nos. 506 and 509 of Netherlands.

129 **94** 5 c. green . . . .
130 12½ c. blue . . . .

1943. Air. Nos. 89 and 91 surch.

148 **46** "f. 2" on 1 c. violet . . . . 9·00 14·00
149 "f. 8.50" on 2½ c. bistre . . . 12·00 18·00

10 Japanese Flag and Palms

11 Mt Fuji, Flag and Bird

1943.

152 **10** 2 c. brown 30 85
153 3 c. green 30 85
154 3½ c. orange 30 85
155 5 c. blue 30 85
156 10 c. red 30 85
157 15 c. blue . . . . 50 1·00
158 20 c. violet . . . . 50 1·00
159 **11** 25 c. orange . . . . 1·40 2·00
160 30 c. blue . . . . 1·75 2·50
161 50 c. green . . . . 4·50 7·00
162 1 g. purple . . . . 13·00 18·00

POSTAGE DUE STAMPS

1942. Netherlands Indies Postage Due stamps of 1913 and 1937 optd with T **9**.

D142 1 c. orange . . . . 2·75 5·50
D132 2½ c. orange . . . . 50 1·10
D133 3½ c. orange . . . . 2·50 5·50
D134 5 c. orange . . . . 1·00 2·00
D135 7½ c. orange . . . . 1·00 2·00
D136 10 c. orange . . . . 60 1·75
D144 15 c. orange . . . . 1·00 2·00
D137 20 c. orange . . . . 1·00 2·00
D138 20 c. on 37½ c. orange . . . . 9·00 14·00
D139 25 c. orange . . . . 1·00 2·25
D140 30 c. orange . . . . 1·00 2·25
D146 40 c. orange . . . . 1·00 2·00
D147 1 g. blue . . . . 3·75 6·50

JAPANESE OCCUPATION OF PHILIPPINES Pt. 22

100 centavos or sentimos = 1 peso.

1942. Stamps of Philippines optd with bars or surch also.

No.	Type	Description	Unused	Used
J1	**104**	2 c. green	10	10
J4a	–	5 c. on 6 c. brn (No. 526)	10	10
J2	–	12 c. black (No. 529)	10	15
J3	–	16 c. blue (No. 530)	3·50	2·50
J5	–	16 c. on 30 c. red (No. 505)	20	20
J6	–	50 c. on 1 p. black and orange (No. 534)	50	55
J7	–	1 p. on 4 p. black and blue (No. 508)	75·00	85·00

1942. No. 460 of Philippines surch **CONGRATULATIONS FALL OF BATAAN AND CORREGIDOR 1942 2**.

No.	Type	Description	Unused	Used
J8		2 c. on 4 c. green	4·00	4·00

J 4 Agricultural Produce

1942. Red Cross Fund.

No.	Type	Description	Unused	Used
J9	**J 4**	2 c. + 1 c. violet	15	15
J10		5 c. + 1 c. green	15	15
J11		16 c. + 2 c. orange	17·00	16·00

1942. 1st Anniv of "Greater East Asia War". No. 460 of Philippines surch with native characters, **12-8-1942** and **5**.

No.	Type	Description	Unused	Used
J12		5 c. on 4 c. green	40	35

1943. 1st Anniv of Philippine Executive Commission. Nos. 566 and 569 of Philippines surch with native characters, **1-23-43** and value.

No.	Type	Description	Unused	Used
J13	**105**	2 c. on 8 c. red	30	30
J14		5 c. on 1 p. sepia	45	45

J 7 Nipa Hut

J 9 Mts Mayon and Fuji

1943.

No.	Type	Description	Unused	Used
J15	**J 7**	1 c. orange	10	10
J16	–	2 c. green	10	10
J17	**J 7**	4 c. green	10	10
J18	**J 9**	5 c. brown	10	10
J19	–	6 c. red	10	10
J20	**J 9**	10 c. blue	10	10
J21	–	12 c. blue	80	80
J22	–	16 c. brown	10	10
J23	**J 7**	20 c. purple	95	95
J24	**J 9**	21 c. violet	30	30
J25	–	25 c. brown	10	10
J26	**J 9**	1 p. red	55	55
J27	–	2 p. purple	3·75	3·75
J28	–	5 p. olive	6·50	6·00

DESIGNS—VERT: 2, 6, 25 c. Rice planter; 12, 16 c., 2 p., 5 p. Morro vinta (sailing canoe).

J 11 Map of Manila Bay

J 13 Filipino Girl

1943. 1st Anniv of Fall of Bataan and Corregidor.

No.	Type	Description	Unused	Used
J29	**J 11**	2 c. red	20	20
J30		5 c. green	20	20

1943. 350th Anniv of Printing in the Philippines. No. 531 of Philippines surch **Limbagan 1593–1943** and value.

No.	Type	Description	Unused	Used
J31		12 c. on 20 c. bistre	25	25

1943. Japanese Declaration of the "Independence of the Philippines". Imperf or perf.

No.	Type	Description	Unused	Used
J32	**J 13**	5 c. blue	15	15
J33		12 c. orange	15	15
J34		17 c. red	15	15

1943. Luzon Flood Relief. Surch **BAHA 1943** + and premium.

No.	Type	Description	Unused	Used
J36	–	12 c. + 21 c. bl (No. J21)	15	15
J37	**J 7**	20 c. + 36 c. purple	10	10
J38	**J 9**	21 c. + 40 c. violet	10	10

J 17 Rev. Jose Burgos

J 24 Jose P Laurel

1944. National Heroes. Imperf or perf.

No.	Type	Description	Unused	Used
J39	–	5 c. blue (Rizal)	20	20
J40	**J 17**	12 c. red	10	10
J41	–	17 c. orange (Mabini)	15	15

1944. 2nd Anniv of Fall of Bataan and Corregidor. Nos. 567/8 of Philippines surch **REPUBLIKA NG PILIPINAS 5-7-44** and value.

No.	Type	Description	Unused	Used
J43	**105**	5 c. on 20 c. blue	45	45
J44		12 c. on 60 c. green	95	95

1945. 1st Anniv of Republican Government. Imperf.

No.	Type	Description	Unused	Used
J45	**J 24**	5 s. brown	10	10
J46		7 s. green	10	10
J47		20 s. blue	10	10

POSTAGE DUE STAMP

1942. Postage Due stamp of Philippines surch **3 CVOS. 3** and bar.

No.	Type	Description	Unused	Used
JD 9	**D 51**	3 c. on 4 c. red	23·00	13·00

OFFICIAL STAMPS

1943. Stamps of Philippines optd variously with bars, **(K.P.)** and Japanese characters or surch also.

No.	Type	Description	Unused	Used
JO29	**104**	2 c. green (No. 563)	10	10
JO30	–	5 c. on 6 c. brown (No. 526)	15	15
JO32	–	16 c. on 30 c. red (No. 505)	40	40

1944. No. 526 of Philippines surch **5 REPUBLIKA NG PILIPINAS (K.P.)** and four bars.

No.	Type	Description	Unused	Used
JO45	–	5 c. on 6 c. brown	10	10

1944. Official stamp of Philippines (No. 531 optd **O.B.**), optd **Pilipinas REPUBLIKA K.P.** and bars.

No.	Type	Description	Unused	Used
JO46	–	20 c. bistre	30	30

1944. Air stamp of Philippines optd **REPUBLIKA NG PILIPINAS (K.P.)** and two bars.

No.	Type	Description	Unused	Used
JO47	**105**	1 p. sepia	55	60

JAPANESE POST OFFICES IN CHINA Pt. 17

Post Offices at Shanghai and other Treaty Ports operated between 1876 and 1922.

10 rin = 1 sen; 100 sen = 1 yen.

那 支
(1)

1900. Stamps of Japan, 1899, optd with T **1**.

No.	Type	Description	Unused	Used
1	**28**	5 r. grey	4·50	5·00
2		½ s. grey	3·25	1·75
3		1 s. brown	3·50	1·25
4		1½ s. blue	10·00	4·00
5		1½ s. violet	5·50	1·50
6		2 s. green	6·00	1·50
7		3 s. purple	7·00	1·00
8		3 s. red	4·50	1·00
9		4 s. red	7·00	2·25
10		5 s. yellow	16·00	2·25
11	**29**	6 s. red	20·00	16·00
12		8 s. green	13·00	15·00
13		10 s. blue	11·00	1·00
14		15 s. purple	20·00	2·00
15		20 s. orange	20·00	1·25
16	**30**	25 s. green	40·00	10·00
17		50 s. brown	45·00	2·00
18	**31**	1 y. red	75·00	3·00
19	**32**	5 y. green	£475	75·00
20		10 y. violet	£750	£130

1900. Imperial Wedding issue of Japan optd with T **1**.

No.	Type	Description	Unused	Used
21	**33**	3 s. red	50·00	35·00

1913. Stamps of Japan, 1913, optd with T **1**.

No.	Type	Description	Unused	Used
33	**36**	½ s. brown	3·00	2·00
34		1 s. orange	3·00	2·00
35		1½ s. blue	3·25	2·00
36		2 s. green	4·25	2·00
37		3 s. red	3·00	1·00
38	**37**	4 s. red	12·00	10·00
39		5 s. violet	16·00	3·00
40		6 s. brown	30·00	30·00
41		8 s. grey	40·00	40·00
42		10 s. blue	15·00	2·00
43		20 s. red	35·00	6·00
44		25 s. olive	45·00	8·00
45	**38**	30 s. brown	75·00	50·00
46		50 s. brown	£100	50·00
47		1 y. green and brown	£140	10·00
48		5 y. green	£1500	£600
49		10 y. violet	£2500	£1500

JAPANESE POST OFFICES IN KOREA Pt. 18

10 rin = 1 sen; 100 sen = 1 yen.

鮮 朝
(1)

1900. Stamps of Japan, 1899, optd with T **1**.

No.	Type	Description	Unused	Used
1	**28**	5 r. grey	12·00	10·00
2		1 s. brown	18·00	6·50
3a		1½ s. blue	£225	£140
4		2 s. green	24·00	16·00
5		3 s. purple	16·00	6·00
6		4 s. red	70·00	30·00
7		5 s. yellow	60·00	30·00
8	**29**	8 s. green	£225	£160
9		10 s. blue	30·00	3·00
10		15 s. purple	75·00	6·00
11		20 s. orange	75·00	5·00
12	**30**	25 s. green	£200	50·00
13		50 s. brown	£150	18·00
14	**31**	1 y. red	£400	14·00

1900. Wedding of Prince Imperial. No. 152 of Japan optd with T **1**.

No.	Type	Description	Unused	Used
15	**33**	3 s. red	90·00	22·00

JASDAN Pt. 1

A state of India. Now uses Indian Stamps.

12 pie = 1 anna; 16 annas = 1 rupee

1 Sun

1942.

No.	Type	Description	Unused	Used
4	**1**	1 a. green	12·00	95·00

JERSEY Pt. 1

Island in the English Channel off N.W. coast of France. Occupied by German forces from June 1940 to May 1945 with separate stamp issues.

The general issue of 1948 for Channel Islands and the regional issues of 1958 are listed at end of GREAT BRITAIN.

Jersey had its own postal administration from 1969.

1941. 12 pence = 1 shilling;
20 shillings = 1 pound.
1971. 100 (new) pence = 1 pound sterling.

(a) War Occupation Issues.

1

2 Old Jersey Farm

1941.

No.	Type	Description	Unused	Used
1	**1**	½d. green	4·00	3·25
2		1d. red	4·25	3·25

1943.

No.	Type	Description	Unused	Used
3	**2**	½d. green	8·00	7·25
4	–	1d. red	2·25	1·00
5	–	1½d. brown	4·00	4·00
6	–	2d. yellow	5·25	4·00
7a	–	2½d. blue	1·50	2·25
8	–	3d. violet	1·50	3·75

DESIGNS: 1d. Portelet Bay; 1½d. Corbiere Lighthouse; 2d. Elizabeth Castle; 2½d. Mont Orgueil Castle; 3d. Gathering vraic (seaweed).

(b) Independent Postal Administration.

10 Elizabeth Castle

1969. Multicoloured.

No.	Type	Description	Unused	Used
15		½d. Type **10**	10	70
16		1d. La Hougue Bie (prehistoric tomb)	15	20
17		2d. Portelet Bay	10	15
18		3d. La Corbiere Lighthouse	20	15
19		4d. Mont Orgueil Castle by night	15	10
20		5d. Arms and Royal Mace	15	10
21		6d. Jersey cow	25	30
22		9d. Chart of the English Channel	40	75
23		1s. Mont Orgueil Castle by day	75	75
24		1s. 6d. Chart of the English Channel	1·25	1·25
25		1s. 9d. Queen Elizabeth II (after Cecil Beaton) (vert)	1·25	1·25
26		2s. 6d. Jersey Airport	2·00	1·75
27		5s. Legislative Chamber	8·00	5·00
28		10s. The Royal Court	24·00	16·00
29		£1 Queen Elizabeth II (after Cecil Beaton) (vert)	2·00	2·00

24 First Day Cover

1969. Inauguration of Post Office.

No.	Type	Description	Unused	Used
30	**24**	4d. multicoloured	25	20
31		5d. multicoloured	30	30
32		1s. 6d. multicoloured	1·00	1·10
33		1s. 9d. multicoloured	1·25	1·40

INDEX
Countries can be quickly located by referring to the index at the end of this volume.

25 Lord Coutanche, former Bailiff of Jersey

1970. 25th Anniv of Liberation. Multicoloured.

No.	Type	Description	Unused	Used
34		4d. Type **25**	25	25
35		5d. Sir Winston Churchill	25	25
36		1s. 6d. "Liberation" (Edmund Blampied)	1·40	1·40
37		1s. 9d. S.S. "Vega"	1·50	1·50

Nos. 36/7 are horiz.

29 "A Tribute to Enid Blyton"

1970. "Battle of Flowers" Parade. Multicoloured.

No.	Type	Description	Unused	Used
38		4d. Type **29**	25	25
39		5d. "Rags to Riches" (Cinderella and pumpkin)	40	40
40		1s. 6d. "Gourmet's Delight" (lobster and cornucopia)	5·50	2·50
41		1s. 9d. "We're the Greatest" (ostriches)	6·00	2·50

33 Jersey Airport

1970. Decimal Currency. Nos. 15, etc, but with new colours, new design (6p.) and decimal values, as T **33**.

No.	Type	Description	Unused	Used
42		½p. mult (as No. 15)	10	10
43		1p. mult (as No. 18)	10	10
44		1½p. mult (as No. 21)	10	10
45		2p. mult (as No. 19)	10	10
46		2½p. mult (as No. 20)	10	10
47		3p. mult (as No. 16)	10	10
48		3½p. mult (as No. 17)	15	15
49		4p. mult (as No. 22)	15	15
49a		4½p. mult (as No. 20)	20	20
50		5p. mult (as No. 23)	10	15
50a		5½p. mult (as No. 21)	40	25
51		6p. multicoloured (Martello Tower, Archirondel, 23 × 22 mm)	25	30
52		7½p. mult (as No. 24)	30	40
52a		8p. mult (as No. 19)	25	25
53		9p. mult (as No. 25)	50	30
54		10p. mult (as No. 26)	50	55
55		20p. mult (as No. 27)	75	75
56		50p. mult (as No. 28)	1·75	1·75

34 White Eared-Pheasant

1971. Wildlife Preservation Trust (1st series). Multicoloured.

No.	Type	Description	Unused	Used
57		2p. Type **34**	50	25
58		2½p. Thick-billed parrot (vert)	50	25
59		7½p. Western black-and-white colobus monkey (vert)	6·00	3·75
60		9p. Ring-tailed lemur	6·50	3·75

See also Nos. 73/6, 217/21, 324/9, 447/51 and 824/9.

35 Poppy Emblem and Field

1971. 50th Anniv of Royal British Legion. Mult.

No.	Type	Description	Unused	Used
61		2p. Royal British Legion Badge	25	25
62		2½p. Type **35**	25	25
63		7½p. Jack Counter and Victoria Cross	2·00	2·00
64		9p. Crossed Tricolour and Union Jack	2·00	2·00

36 "Tante Elizabeth" (E. Blampied) **37** Jersey Fern

1971. Paintings (1st series). Multicoloured.
65 2p. Type **36** 15 15
66 2½p. "English Fleet in the Channel" (P. Monamy) (horiz) 25 20
67 7½p. "The Boyhood of Raleigh" (Millais) (horiz) 2·75 2·25
68 9p. "The Blind Beggar" (W. W. Ouless) 3·00 2·50
See also Nos. 115/118.

1972. Wild Flowers of Jersey. Multicoloured.
69 3p. Type **37** 25 15
70 5p. Jersey thrift 60 45
71 7½p. Jersey orchid 2·25 2·25
72 9p. Jersey viper's bugloss 2·50 2·25

1972. Wildlife Preservation Trust (2nd series). As T **34**. Multicoloured.
73 2½p. Cheetah 65 20
74 3p. Rothschild's mynah (vert) 40 35
75 7½p. Spectacled bear 1·40 1·50
76 9p. Tuatara 2·00 1·75

38 Artillery Shako **39** Princess Anne

1972. Royal Jersey Militia. Multicoloured.
77 2½p. Type **38** 15 15
78 3p. Shako (2nd North Regt.) 20 20
79 7½p. Shako (5th South-West Regt.) 85 50
80 9p. Helmet (3rd Jersey Light Infantry) 1·00 60

1972. Royal Silver Wedding. Multicoloured.
81 2½p. Type **39** 10 10
82 3p. Queen Elizabeth and Prince Philip (horiz) 10 10
83 7½p. Prince Charles 40 50
84 20p. The Royal Family (horiz) 60 70

40 Armorican Bronze Coins

1973. Centenary of La Societe Jersiaise. Mult.
85 2½p. Silver cups 10 10
86 3p. Gold torque (vert) 10 10
87 7½p. Royal Seal of Charles II (vert) 40 40
88 9p. Type **40** 50 50

41 Balloon "L'Armee de la Loire" and Letter, Paris, 1870

1973. Jersey Aviation History. Multicoloured.
89 3p. Type **41** 10 10
90 5p. Astra seaplane, 1912 15 15
91 7½p. Supermarine Sea Eagle 60 60
92 9p. De Havilland Dragon Express "Giffard Bay" 80 80

42 "North Western", 1870

1973. Centenary of Jersey Eastern Railway. Early Locomotives. Multicoloured.
93 2½p. Type **42** 10 10
94 3p. "Calvados", 1873 10 10
95 7½p. "Carteret" at Grouville station, 1893 60 40
96 9p. "Caesarea", 1873, and route map 80 50

43 Princess Anne and Capt. Mark Phillips

1973. Royal Wedding.
97 **43** 3p. multicoloured 10 10
98 20p. multicoloured 90 90

44 Spider Crab

1973. Marine Life. Multicoloured.
99 2½p. Type **44** 10 10
100 3p. Conger eel 10 10
101 7½p. Lobster 50 50
102 20p. Tuberculate ormer 70 70

45 Freesias **47** John Wesley

46 First Letter Box and Contemporary Cover

1974. Spring Flowers. Multicoloured.
103 3p. Type **45** 10 10
104 5½p. Anemones 20 10
105 8p. Carnations and Gladioli 60 40
106 10p. Daffodils and Iris 80 50

1974. Centenary of U.P.U. Multicoloured.
107 2½p. Type **46** 10 10
108 3p. Postmen, 1862 and 1969 10 10
109 5½p. Letter-box and letter, 1974 35 30
110 20p. R.M.S. "Aquila" (1874) and B.A.C. One Eleven 200 (1974) 85 60

1974. Anniversaries.
111 **47** 3p. black and brown 10 10
112 – 3½p. violet and blue 10 10
113 – 8p. black and lilac 30 35
114 – 20p. black and stone 70 65
PORTRAITS AND EVENTS: 3p. (Bicentenary of Methodism in Jersey). 3½p. Sir William Hillary, founder (150th anniv of R.N.L.I.). 8p. Canon Wace (poet and historian) (800th death anniv. 20p. Sir Winston Churchill (Birth cent)

48 "Catherine" and "Mary" (Royal yachts)

1974. Marine Paintings by Peter Monamy. Mult.
115 3½p. Type **48** 10 10
116 5½p. French two-decker 20 15
117 8p. Dutch vessel (horiz) 30 35
118 25p. Battle of Cap La Hague, 1692 (55 × 27 mm) 80 80

49 Potato Digger

1975. 19th-Century Farming. Multicoloured.
119 3p. Type **49** 10 10
120 3½p. Cider crusher 10 15
121 8p. Six-horse plough 35 35
122 10p. Hay cart 55 50

50 H.M. Queen Elizabeth, the Queen Mother (photograph by Cecil Beaton) **51** Nautilus Shell

1975. Royal Visit.
123 **50** 20p. multicoloured 1·00 1·00

1975. Jersey Tourism. Multicoloured.
124 5p. Type **51** 10 10
125 8p. Parasol 15 15
126 10p. Deckchair 35 55
127 12p. Sandcastle with flags of Jersey and the U.K. 60 60

52 Common Tern **53** Armstrong Whitworth Siskin IIIA

1975. Sea Birds. Multicoloured.
129 4p. Type **52** 15 15
130 5p. British storm petrel 15 15
131 8p. Brent geese 50 40
132 25p. Shag 85 40

1975. 50th Anniv of Royal Air Force Association, Jersey Branch. Multicoloured.
133 4p. Type **53** 10 10
134 5p. Supermarine Southampton I flying boat 15 15
135 10p. Supermarine Spitfire Mk I 50 35
136 25p. Folland Gnat T.1 95 80

54 Map of Jersey Parishes

55 Parish Arms and Island Scene

1976. Multicoloured. (a) Parish Arms and Views.
137 ½p. Type **54** 10 10
138 1p. Zoological Park 10 10
139 5p. St. Mary's Church 15 15
140 6p. Seymour Tower 15 15
141 7p. La Corbiere Lighthouse 20 20
142 8p. St. Saviour's Church 20 20
143 9p. Elizabeth Castle 25 25
144 10p. Gorey Harbour 25 25
145 11p. Jersey Airport 30 25
146 12p. Grosnez Castle 30 30
147 13p. Bonne Nuit Harbour 35 35
148 14p. Le Hocq Tower 35 40
149 15p. Morel Farm 40 45

(b) Emblems.
150 20p. Type **55** 50 50
151 30p. Flag and map 75 75
152 40p. Postal H.Q. and badge 1·00 1·00
153 50p. Parliament, Royal Court and arms 1·25 1·00
154 £1 Lieutenant-Governor's flag and Government House 2·50 2·50
155 £2 Queen Elizabeth II (vert) 4·50 4·50

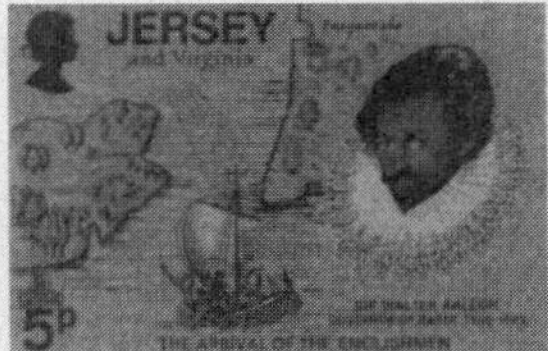

56 Sir Walter Raleigh and Map of Virginia

1976. Bicentenary of American Independence. Multicoloured.
160 5p. Type **56** 10 10
161 7p. Sir George Carteret and map of New Jersey 15 15
162 11p. Philippe Dauvergne and Long Island landing 40 50
163 13p. John Copley and sketch 45 65

57 Dr. Grandin and Map of China

1976. Birth Centenary of Dr. Lilian Grandin (medical missionary).
164 **57** 5p. multicoloured 10 10
165 – 7p. yellow, brown & black 15 15
166 – 11p. multicoloured 50 35
167 – 13p. multicoloured 50 50
DESIGNS: 7p. Sampan on the Yangtze; 11p. Overland trek; 13p. Dr. Grandin at work.

58 Coronation, 1953 (photographed by Cecil Beaton)

1977. Silver Jubilee. Multicoloured.
168 5p. Type **58** 25 15
169 7p. Visit to Jersey, 1957 30 20
170 25p. Queen Elizabeth II (photo by Peter Grugeon) 90 80

59 Coins of 1871 and 1877

1977. Centenary of Currency Reform. Mult.
171 5p. Type **59** 10 10
172 7p. One-twelfth shilling, 1949 15 15
173 11p. Silver crown, 1966 40 35
174 13p. £2 piece, 1972 45 50

60 Sir William Weston and "Santa Anna", 1530

1977. Centenary of St. John Ambulance. Mult.
175 5p. Type **60** 10 10
176 7p. Sir William Drogo and ambulance, 1877 15 15
177 11p. Duke of Connaught and ambulance, 1917 40 35
178 13p. Duke of Gloucester and stretcher-team, 1977 45 50

61 Arrival of Queen Victoria, 1846

1977. 125th Anniv of Victoria College. Mult.
179 7p. Type **61** 20 20
180 10½p. Victoria College, 1852 25 20
181 11p. Sir Galahad Statue, 1924 (vert) 30 35
182 13p. College Hall (vert) 35 35

62 Harry Vardon Statuette and Map of Royal Jersey Course

1978. Cent of Royal Jersey Golf Club. Mult.
183 6p. Type **62** 15 15
184 8p. Harry Vardon's grip and swing 20 20
185 11p. Harry Vardon's putt 65 50
186 13p. Golf trophies and book by Harry Vardon 65 55

63 Mont Orgueil Castle

1978. Europa. Castles from Paintings by Thomas Phillips. Multicoloured.

187 6p. Type **63** 20 20
188 8p. St. Aubin's Fort 40 40
189 10½p. Elizabeth Castle 50 50

64 "Gaspe Basin" (P. J. Ouless)

1978. Links with Canada. Multicoloured.

190 6p. Type **64** 15 15
191 8p. Map of Gaspe Peninsula . . 20 20
192 10½p. "Century" (brigantine) . . 25 30
193 11p. Early map of Jersey . . . 40 35
194 13p. St. Aubin's Bay, town and harbour 45 40

65 Queen Elizabeth and Prince Philip **66** Mail Cutter, 1778–1827

1978. 25th Anniv of Coronation.

195 **65** 8p. silver, black and red . . 30 30
196 – 25p. silver, black and blue . . 70 70

DESIGN: 25p. Hallmarks of 1953 and 1977.

1978. Bicentenary of England–Jersey Government Mail Packet Service.

197 **66** 6p. black, brown & yellow . 15 15
198 – 8p. black, green & yellow . . 20 20
199 – 10½p. black, ultram & bl . . 40 40
200 – 11p. black, purple and lilac . 45 45
201 – 13p. black, red and pink . . 50 50

DESIGNS—SHIPS: 8p. "Flamer", 1831–7; 10½p. "Diana", 1877–90; 11p. "Ibex", 1891–1925; 13p. "Caesarea", 1960–75.

67 Jersey Calf **68** Jersey Pillar Box, c. 1860

1979. 9th Conference of World Jersey Cattle Bureau. Multicoloured.

202 6p. Type **67** 20 20
203 25p. "Ansom Designette" (calf presented to the Queen, 1978) (46 × 29 mm) 80 80

1979. Europa. Multicoloured.

204 8p. Type **68** 25 25
205 8p. Clearing modern post box . 25 25
206 10½p. Telephone switchboard, c. 1900 . . . . 30 30
207 10½p. Modern SPC telephone system 30 30

69 Percival Mew Gull "Golden City" **70** "My First Sermon"

1979. 25th International Air Rally. Mult.

208 6p. Type **69** 15 15
209 8p. De Havilland Chipmunk . . 20 25
210 10½p. Druine Turbulent 40 25
211 11p. De Havilland Tiger Moth . 45 35
212 13p. North American Harvard . 50 40

1979. International Year of the Child and 150th Birth Anniversary of Sir John Millais (painter). Paintings. Multicoloured.

213 8p. Type **70** 25 20
214 10½p. "Orphans" 35 35
215 11p. "The Princes in the Tower" 35 40
216 25p. "Christ in the House of his Parents" (50 × 32 mm) . . . 75 75

1979. Wildlife Preservation Trust (3rd series). As T **34**. Multicoloured.

217 6p. Pink pigeon (vert) 15 15
218 8p. Orang-utan (vert) 20 30
219 11½p. Waldrapp 50 35
220 13p. Lowland gorilla (vert) . . 65 40
221 15p. Rodriguez flying fox (vert) 75 530

71 Plan of Mont Orgueil **72** Sir Walter Raleigh

1980. Jersey Fortresses. Drawings by Thomas Phillips. Multicoloured.

222 8p. Type **71** 30 25
223 11½p. Plan of La Tour de St. Aubin 35 30
224 13p. Plan of Elizabeth Castle . 55 45
225 25p. Map of Jersey (38 × 27 mm) 80 70

1980. Europa. Links with Britain. Multicoloured.

226 9p. Type **72** 20 20
227 9p. Paul Ivy (engineer) discussing Elizabeth Castle 20 20
228 13½p. Sir George Carteret receiving deeds to Smith's Island, Virginia from Charles II 45 45
229 13½p. Lady Carteret, maid and Jean Chevalier 45 45

Nos. 226/7 and 228/9 were issued together, se-tenant, forming composite designs.

73 Planting

1980. Cent of Jersey Royal Potato. Mult.

230 7p. Type **73** 15 15
231 15p. Digging 35 35
232 17½p. Weighbridge 60 60

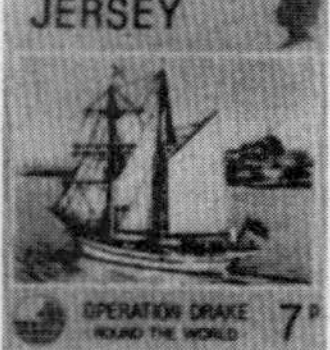

74 Three Lap Event **75** "Eye of the Wind"

1980. 60th Anniv of Jersey Motor Cycle and Light Car Club. Multicoloured.

233 7p. Type **74** 25 25
234 9p. Jersey International Road Race 25 25
235 13½p. Scrambling 45 45
236 15p. Sand racing (saloon cars) . 50 50
237 17½p. National Hill Climb . . 55 55

1980. "Operation Drake" and 150th Anniv of Royal Geographical Society (14p). Multicoloured.

238 7p. Type **75** 20 20
239 9p. Inflatable raft 25 25
240 13½p. Shooting rapids 35 35
241 14p. "Discovery" 45 35
242 15p. Aerial walkway 45 35
243 17½p. Goodyear Aerospace airship "Europa" 55 45

76 Detail of "The Death of Major Peirson"

1981. Bicentenary of Battle of Jersey. Details of J. S. Copley's painting.

244 **76** 7p. multicoloured 25 25
245 – 10p. multicoloured 30 30
246 – 15p. multicoloured 60 60
247 – 17½p. multicoloured 80 80

77 De Bagot **78a** "Queen Elizabeth II" (Norman Hepple)

1981. Crests of Jersey Families.

249 **77** ½p. black, silver & grn . . 20 20
250 – 1p. multicoloured 10 10
251 – 2p. multicoloured 10 10
252 – 3p. multicoloured 10 10
253 – 4p. silver, black & mve . . 25 15
254 – 5p. multicoloured 15 15
255 – 6p. multicoloured 20 20
256 – 7p. multicoloured 20 20
257 – 8p. multicoloured 25 25
258 – 9p. multicoloured 30 30
259b – 10p. multicoloured . . . 35 35
260 – 11p. multicoloured . . . 35 35
261a – 12p. multicoloured . . . 40 25
262 – 13p. multicoloured . . . 40 40
263 – 14p. multicoloured . . . 45 45
264 – 15p. multicoloured . . . 45 45
265 – 16p. multicoloured . . . 45 45
266 – 17p. multicoloured . . . 50 50
266a – 18p. multicoloured . . . 75 75
266b – 19p. multicoloured . . . 80 80
267 – 20p. black, silver & yellow 60 60
268 – 25p. black and blue . . . 60 60
268a **77** 26p. black, silver & red . . 60 60
269 – 30p. multicoloured . . . 90 90
270a – 40p. multicoloured . . . 1·25 1·25
271 – 50p. multicoloured . . . 1·50 1·60
272 – 75p. multicoloured . . . 2·25 1·75
273 – £1 multicoloured . . . . 3·25 3·00
274 **78a** £5 multicoloured . . . 15·00 12·00

DESIGNS—As T **77**: 1p. De Carteret; 2p. La Cloche; 3p. Dumaresq; 4p. Payn; 5p. Janvrin; 6p. Poingdestre; 7p. Pipon; 8p. Marett; 9p. Le Breton; 10p. Le Maistre; 11p. Bisson; 12p. Robin; 13p. Herault; 14p. Messervy; 15p. Fiott; 16p. Malet; 17p. Mabon; 18p. De St. Martin; 19p. Hamptonne; 20p. Badier; 25p. L'Arbalestier; 30p. Journeaux; 40p. Lempriere; 50p. Auvergne; 75p. Remon. 38 × 22 mm: £1 Jersey crest and map of Channel.

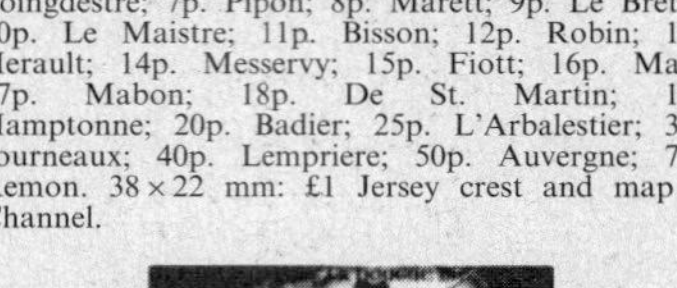
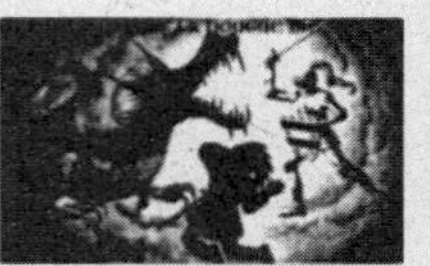

79 Knight of Hambye slaying Dragon

1981. Europa. Folklore. Multicoloured.

275 10p. Type **79** 25 25
276 10p. Servant slaying Knight of Hambye and awaiting execution 25 25
277 18p. St. Brelade celebrating Easter on island 50 50
278 18p. Island revealing itself as a huge fish 50 50

LEGENDS: 10p. (both) Slaying of the Dragon of Lawrence by the Knight of Hambye; 18p. (both) Voyages of St. Brelade.

80 The Harbour by Gaslight

1981. 150th Anniv of Gas in Jersey. Multicoloured.

279 7p. Type **80** 25 25
280 10p. The Quay 30 30
281 18p. Royal Square 45 45
282 22p. Halkett Place 55 55
283 25p. Central Market 65 65

81 Prince Charles and Lady Diana Spencer

1981. Royal Wedding.

284 **81** 10p. multicoloured 75 75
285 25p. multicoloured . . . . 1·75 1·75

82 Christmas Tree in Royal Square **83** Jersey, 16,000 B.C.

1981. Christmas. Multicoloured.

286 7p. Type **82** 25 25
287 10p. East window, Parish Church, St. Helier 40 40
288 18p. Boxing Day meet of Jersey Drag Hunt 50 50

1982. Europa. Formation of Jersey. Mult.

289 11p. Type **83** 30 30
290 11p. In 10,000 B.C. (vert) . . . 30 30
291 19½p. In 7,000 B.C. (vert) . . . 70 60
292 19½p. In 4,000 B.C. 70 60

84 Duke Rollo of Normandy, William the Conqueror and "Clameur de Haro" (traditional procedure for obtaining justice)

1982. Links with France. Multicoloured.

293 8p. Type **84** 25 25
294 8p. John of England, Philippe Auguste of France, and Siege of Rouen 25 25
295 11p. Jean Martell (brandy merchant), early still and view of Cognac 35 35
296 11p. Victor Hugo, "Le Rocher des Proscrits" (rock where he used to meditate) and Marine Terrace 35 35
297 19½p. Pierre Teilhard de Chardin (philosopher) and "Maison Saint Louis" (science institute) 60 60
298 19½p. Pere Charles Rey (scientist), anemotachymeter and The Observatory, St. Louis . . . 60 60

85 Sir William Smith, Founder of Boys' Brigade

1982. Youth Organizations. Multicoloured.

299 8p. Type **85** 25 25
300 11p. Boys' Brigade "Old Boys" band, Liberation Parade, 1945 (vert) 30 30
301 24p. William Smith and Lord Baden-Powell at Royal Albert Hall, 1903 . . . . 70 70
302 26p. Lord and Lady Baden-Powell, St. Helier, 1924 (vert) 90 90
303 29p. Scouts at "Westward Ho" campsite, St. Ouen's Bay . . 1·00 1·00

Nos. 299/301 commemorate the centenary of the Boys' Brigade and Nos. 302/3 the 75th anniversary of the Boy Scout Movement.

86 H.M.S. "Tamar" and H.M.S. "Dolphin" at Port Egmont

1983. Jersey Adventurers (1st series). Mult.

304 8p. Type **86** 25 25
305 11p. H.M.S. "Dolphin" and H.M.S. "Swallow" off Magellan Strait 30 30
306 19½p. Discovering Pitcairn Island 50 50
307 24p. Carteret taking possession of English Cove, New Ireland 70 70
308 26p. H.M.S. "Swallow" sinking a pirate, Macassar Strait . . . 85 75
309 29p. H.M.S. "Endymion" leading convoy from West Indies . . 1·00 85

See also Nos. 417/21 and 573/8.

HAVE YOU READ THE NOTES AT THE BEGINNING OF THIS CATALOGUE?

These often provide answers to the enquiries we receive.

87 1969 5s. Legislative Chamber Definitive

1983. Europa. Multicoloured.
310 11p. Type **87** 50 50
311 11p. Royal Mace (23 × 32 mm) 50 50
312 19½p. 1969 10s. Royal Court definitive showing green border error. 75 75
313 19½p. Bailiff's Seal (23 × 32 mm) 75 75

88 Charles Le Geyt and Battle of Minden (1759)

1983. World Communications Year and 250th Birth Anniv of Charles Le Geyt (1st Jersey postmaster). Multicoloured.
314 8p. Type **88** 25 25
315 11p. London to Weymouth mail coach 35 35
316 24p. P.O. Mail Packet "Chesterfield" attacked by French privateer 75 75
317 26p. Mary Godfray and the Hue Street Post Office 90 90
318 29p. Mail steamer leaving St. Helier harbour . . . . . . 1·10 1·10

89 Assembly Emblem

1983. 13th General Assembly of the A.I.P.L.F. (Association Internationale des Parlementaires de Langue Francaise) Jersey.
319 **89** 19½p. multicoloured 75 75

90 "Cardinal Newman" **91** Golden Lion Tamarin

1983. 50th Death Anniv of Walter Ouless (artist). Multicoloured.
320 8p. Type **90** 25 25
321 11p. "Incident in the French Revolution" 45 45
322 20½p. "Thomas Hardy" 85 85
323 31p. "David with the head of Goliath" (38 × 32 mm) . . . 1·25 1·25

1984. Wildlife Preservation Trust (4th series). Multicoloured.
324 9p. Type **91** 30 30
325 12p. Snow leopard 40 40
326 20½p. Jamaican boa 70 70
327 26p. Round island gecko . . . 1·10 1·10
328 28p. Coscoroba swan . . . . 1·25 1·25
329 31p. St. Lucia amazon . . . . 1·25 1·25

92 C.E.P.T. 25th Anniversary Logo

1984. Europa.
330 **92** 9p. lt blue, blue & black . . 30 30
331 12p. lt green, grn & blk . . 40 40
332 20½p. lilac, purple & blk . . 70 70

94 "Sarah Bloomshoft" at Demie de Pas Light, 1906

1984. Centenary of Jersey R.N.L.I. Lifeboat Station. Multicoloured.
334 9p. Type **94** 40 40
335 9p. "Hearts of Oak" and "Maurice Georges", 1949 . . 40 40
336 12p. "Elizabeth Rippon" and "Hanna", 1949 . . . . . 50 50
337 12p. "Elizabeth Rippon" and "Santa Maria", 1951 . . . . 50 50
338 20½p. "Elizabeth Rippon" and "Bacchus", 1973 . . . . . 90 75
339 20½p. "Thomas James King" and "Cythara", 1983 . . . . . 90 75

95 Bristol Type 170 Freighter Mk 32

1984. 40th Anniv of I.C.A.O. Multicoloured.
340 9p. Type **95** 30 30
341 12p. Airspeed A.S.57 Ambassador 2 . . . . . . 40 40
342 26p. De Havilland D.H.114 Heron 1B . . . . 1·10 1·10
343 31p. De Havilland D.H.89A Dragon Rapide . . . . . . 1·40 1·40

96 "Robinson Crusoe leaves the Wreck"

1984. Links with Australia. Paintings by John Alexander Gilfillan. Multicoloured.
344 9p. Type **96** 30 30
345 12p. "Edinburgh Castle" . . . 40 40
346 20½p. "Maori Village" 75 75
347 26p. "Australian Landscape" . 95 95
348 28p. "Waterhouse's Corner, Adelaide" . . . . 1·00 1·00
349 31p. "Captain Cook at Botany Bay" . . . . 1·10 1·10

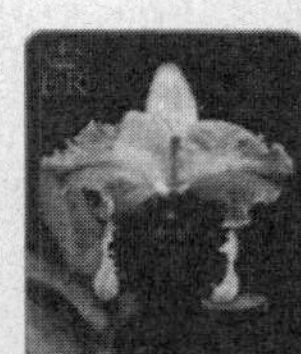

97 "B.L.C. St. Helier" Orchid

1984. Christmas. Jersey Orchids (1st series). Multicoloured.
350 9p. Type **97** 50 45
351 12p. "Oda Mt. Bingham" . . . 75 65
See also Nos. 433/7, 613/17 and 892/7.

98 "'Hebe' off Corbiere, 1874"

1984. Death Centenary of Philip John Ouless (artist). Multicoloured.
352 9p. Type **98** 30 30
353 12p. "The 'Gaspe' engaging the 'Diomede'" 40 40
354 22p. "The Paddle-steamer 'London' entering Naples, 1856" 80 80
355 31p. "'The Rambler' entering Cape Town, 1840" . . . . . 1·40 1·40
356 34p. "St. Aubin's Bay from Mount Bingham, 1871" . . . 1·50 1·50

99 John Ireland (composer) and Faldouet Dolmen

1985. Europa. European Music Year. Mult.
357 10p. Type **99** 40 40
358 13p. Ivy St. Helier (actress) and His Majesty's Theatre, London 55 55
359 22p. Claude Debussy (composer) and Elizabeth Castle . . . . 1·00 90

100 Girls' Brigade **101** "Duke of Normandy" at Cheapside

1985. International Youth Year. Mult.
360 10p. Type **100** 30 30
361 13p. Girl Guides (75th anniversary) 50 50
362 29p. Prince Charles and Jersey Youth Service Activities Base 1·00 1·00
363 31p. Sea Cadet Corps . . . . 1·10 1·00
364 34p. Air Training Corps . . . 1·25 1·10

1985. The Jersey Western Railway. Mult.
365 10p. Type **101** 55 55
366 13p. Saddletank at First Tower 70 70
367 22p. "La Moye" at Millbrook 1·10 1·10
368 29p. "St. Heliers" at St. Aubin 1·25 1·25
369 34p. "St. Aubyns" at Corbiere 1·40 1·40

102 Memorial Window to Revd. James Hemery (former Dean) and St. Helier Parish Church

1985. 300th Anniv of Huguenot Immigration. Multicoloured.
370 10p. Type **102** 30 30
371 10p. Judge Francis Jeune, Baron St. Helier, and Houses of Parliament 30 30
372 13p. Silverware by Pierre Amiraux 45 45
373 13p. Francis Voisin (merchant) and Russian port 45 45
374 22p. Robert Brohier, Schweppes carbonation plant and bottles 75 75
375 22p. George Ingouville, V.C. R.N. and attack on Viborg . 75 75

103 Howard Davis Hall, Victoria College

1985. Thomas Benjamin Davis (philanthropist) Commemoration. Multicoloured.
376 10p. Type **103** 40 40
377 13p. Racing schooner "Westward" 60 60
378 31p. Howard Davis Park, St. Helier . . . . 1·10 1·10
379 34p. Howard Davis Experimental Farm, Trinity . . . . 1·25 1·25

104 "Amaryllis belladonna" (Pandora Sellars)

1986. Jersey Lilies. Multicoloured.
380 13p. Type **104** 75 75
381 34p. "A Jersey Lily" (Lily Langtry) (Sir John Millais) (30 × 48 mm) . . . . 1·75 1·75

105 King Harold, William of Normandy and Halley's Comet, 1066 (from Bayeux Tapestry)

1986. Appearance of Halley's Comet. Multicoloured.
383 10p. Type **105** 40 40
384 22p. Lady Carteret, Edmond Halley, map and Comet . . 1·00 1·00
385 31p. Aspects of communications in 1910 and 1986 on TV screen 1·40 1·40

106 Dwarf Pansy **107** Queen Elizabeth II (from photo by Karsh)

1986. Europa. Environmental Conservation. Multicoloured.
386 10p. Type **106** 40 40
387 14p. Sea stock 75 75
388 22p. Sand crocus . . . . . . 1·10 1·10

1986. 60th Birthday of Queen Elizabeth II.
389 **107** £1 multicoloured . . . . . 3·25 3·25
See also No. 491b.

108 Le Rat Cottage

1986. 50th Anniv of National Trust for Jersey. Multicoloured.
390 10p. Type **108** 30 30
391 14p. The Elms (Trust headquarters) 45 45
392 22p. Morel Farm 80 80
393 29p. Quetivel Mill 90 90
394 31p. La Vallette 95 95

109 Prince Andrew and Miss Sarah Ferguson **110** "Gathering Vraic"

1986. Royal Wedding.
395 **109** 14p. multicoloured 50 50
396 40p. multicoloured . . . . 1·50 1·50

1986. Birth Centenary of Edmund Blampied (artist).
397 **110** 10p. multicoloured 40 40
398 – 14p. black, blue & grey . . 70 70
399 – 29p. multicoloured . . . . 1·00 1·00
400 – 31p. black, orge & grey . . 1·25 1·25
401 – 34p. multicoloured . . . . 1·40 1·40
DESIGNS: 14p. "Driving Home in the Rain"; 29p. "The Miller"; 31p. "The Joy Ride"; 34p. "Tante Elizabeth".

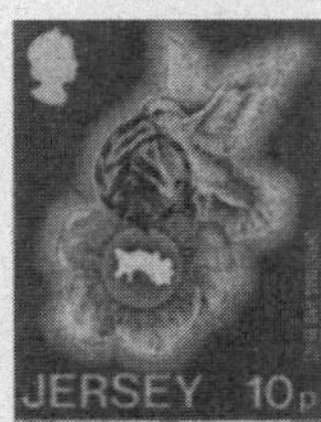

111 Island Map on Jersey Lily, and Dove holding Olive Branch

1986. Christmas. Int Peace Year. Mult.
402 10p. Type **111** 40 40
403 14p. Mistletoe wreath encircling European robin and dove . . 60 60
404 34p. Christmas cracker releasing dove . . . . 1·25 1·25

112 "Westward" under Full Sail

1987. Racing Schooner "Westward". Mult.
405 10p. Type **112** 40 40
406 14p. T. B. Davis at the helm . . 60 60
407 31p. "Westward" overhauling "Britannia" . . . . 1·25 1·10
408 34p. "Westward" fitting-out at St. Helier . . . . 1·40 1·25

113 De Havilland Dragon Express "Belcroute Bay"

1987. 50th Anniv of Jersey Airport. Multicoloured.

409 10p. Type **113** 30 30
410 14p. Boeing 757 and Douglas DC-9-15 . . . . 50 50
411 22p. Britten Norman "long nose" Trislander and Islander aircraft 70 70
412 29p. Short 330 and Vickers Viscount 800 . . . . 1·00 1·10
413 31p. B.A.C. One Eleven 500 and Handley Page Dart Herald . 1·25 1·25

114 St. Mary and St. Peter's Roman Catholic Church

1987. Europa. Modern Architecture. Mult.

414 11p. Type **114** 45 45
415 15p. Villa Devereux, St. Brelade 65 65
416 22p. Fort Regent Leisure Centre, St. Helier (57 × 29 mm) . . . 90 90

115 H.M.S. "Racehorse" and H.M.S. "Carcass" (bomb ketches) trapped in Arctic

1987. Jersey Adventurers (2nd series). Philippe D'Auvergne. Multicoloured.

417 11p. Type **115** 40 40
418 15p. H.M.S. "Alarm" on fire, Rhode Island 50 50
419 29p. H.M.S. "Arethusa" wrecked off Ushant 90 90
420 31p. H.M.S. "Rattlesnake" stranded on Isle de Trinidad 1·00 1·00
421 34p. Mont Orgueil Castle and fishing boats . . . . 1·10 1·10

See also Nos. 501/6 and 539/44.

116 Grant of Lands to Normandy, 911 and 933

1987. 900th Death Anniv of William the Conqueror. Multicoloured.

422 11p. Type **116** 40 40
423 15p. Edward the Confessor and Duke Robert I of Normandy landing on Jersey, 1030 . . . 45 45
424 22p. King William's coronation, 1066 and fatal fall, 1087 . . 80 80
425 29p. Death of William Rufus, 1100 and Battle of Tinchebrai, 1106 . . . . 95 95
426 31p. Civil war between Matilda and Stephen, 1135–41 . . . 1·10 1·10
427 34p. Henry inherits Normandy, 1151; John asserts ducal rights in Jersey, 1213 . . . . . 1·25 1·25

117 "Grosnez Castle"

1987. Christmas. Paintings by John Le Capelain. Multicoloured.

428 11p. Type **117** 40 40
429 15p. "St. Aubin's Bay" 60 60
430 22p. "Mont Orgueil Castle" . . 80 80
431 31p. "Town Fort and Harbour, St. Helier" . . . . 1·10 1·10
432 34p. "The Hermitage" . . . . 1·25 1·25

HAVE YOU READ THE NOTES AT THE BEGINNING OF THIS CATALOGUE?
These often provide answers to the enquiries we receive.

118 "Cymbidium pontac"

1988. Jersey Orchids (2nd series). Multicoloured.

433 11p. Type **118** 50 50
434 15p. "Odontioda" "Eric Young" (vert) 60 60
435 29p. "Lycaste auburn" "Seaford" and "Ditchling" . 1·00 1·00
436 31p. "Odontoglossum" "St. Brelade" (vert) . . . . . . 1·10 1·10
437 34p. "Cymbidium mavourneen" "Jester" . . . . 1·25 1·25

119 Labrador Retriever

1988. Centenary of Jersey Dog Club. Mult.

438 11p. Type **119** 50 50
439 15p. Wire-haired dachshund . . 75 75
440 22p. Pekingese . . . . 1·10 1·10
441 31p. Cavalier King Charles spaniel . . . . 1·10 1·10
442 34p. Dalmatian . . . . 1·25 1·25

120 De Havilland D.H.C.7 Dash Seven, London Landmarks and Jersey Control Tower

1988. Europa. Transport and Communications. Multicoloured.

443 16p. Type **120** 50 50
444 16p. Weather radar and Jersey airport landing system (vert) 50 50
445 22p. Hydrofoil, St. Malo and Elizabeth Castle, St. Helier . 90 90
446 22p. Port control tower and Jersey Radio maritime communication centre, La Moye (vert) 90 90

121 Rodriguez Fody **122** Rain Forest Leaf Frog, Costa Rica

1988. Wildlife Preservation Trust (5th series). Multicoloured.

447 12p. Type **121** 55 55
448 16p. Volcano rabbit (horiz) . . . 70 70
449 29p. White-faced marmoset . . 1·10 1·10
450 31p. Ploughshare tortoise (horiz) 1·25 1·25
451 34p. Mauritius kestrel . . . . . 1·40 1·40

1988. Operation Raleigh. Multicoloured.

452 12p. Type **122** 45 45
453 16p. Archaeological survey, Peru 55 55
454 22p. Climbing glacier, Chile . . 80 80
455 29p. Red Cross Centre, Solomon Islands . . . . 1·00 1·00
456 31p. Underwater exploration, Australia . . . . 1·10 1·10
457 34p. "Zebu" (brigantine) returning to St. Helier . . . 1·25 1·25

123 St. Clement Parish Church

1988. Christmas. Jersey Parish Churches (1st series). Multicoloured.

458 12p. Type **123** 35 35
459 16p. St. Ouen 60 60
460 31p. St. Brelade . . . . 1·00 1·00
461 34p. St. Lawrence . . . . 1·10 1·10

See also Nos. 535/8 and 597/600.

124 Talbot "Type 4 CT Tourer", 1912

1989. Vintage Cars (1st series). Multicoloured.

462 12p. Type **124** 40 40
463 16p. De Dion "Bouton Type 1-D", 1920 . . . . 60 60
464 23p. Austin 7 "Chummy", 1926 75 75
465 30p. Ford "Model T", 1926 . . 90 90
466 32p. Bentley 8 litre, 1930 . . . 1·10 1·10
467 35p. Cadillac "452A–V16 Fleetwood Sports Phaeton", 1931 . . . . 1·25 1·25

See also Nos. 591/6 and 905/10.

125 Belcroute Bay **125a** Arms of King George VI

1989. Jersey Scenes. Multicoloured.

468 1p. Type **125** 10 10
469 2p. High Street, St. Aubin . . 10 10
470 4p. Royal Jersey Golf Course 10 10
471 5p. Portelet Bay 15 15
472 10p. Les Charrieres D'Anneport 30 30
473 13p. St. Helier Marina 40 40
474 14p. Sand yacht racing, St. Ouen's Bay 40 40
475 15p. Rozel Harbour 45 45
476 16p. St. Aubin's Harbour . . 50 50
477 17p. Jersey Airport 50 50
478 18p. Corbiere Lighthouse . . 55 55
479 19p. Val de la Mare 55 55
480 20p. Elizabeth Castle 60 60
481 21p. Greve de Lecq 50 50
482 22p. Samares Manor 65 65
483 23p. Bonne Nuit Harbour . . 65 50
484 24p. Grosnez Castle 65 65
485 25p. Augres Manor 70 70
486 26p. Central Market 75 75
487 27p. St. Brelade's Bay 80 80
488 30p. St. Ouen's Manor 85 85
489 40p. La Hougue Bie 90 90
490 50p. Mont Orgueil Castle . . 1·25 1·25
491 75p. Royal Square, St. Helier 2·25 2·25
491b £2 Type **107** . . . . 6·00 6·00
491c £4 Type **125a** . . . . . . 8·00 8·25

Nos. 469/91 are as Type **125**.

126 Agile Frog

1989. Endangered Jersey Fauna. Multicoloured.

492 13p. Type **126** . . . . 1·00 1·00
493 13p. "Heteropterus morpheus" (butterfly) (vert) . . . . . 1·00 1·00
494 17p. Barn owl (vert) . . . . . 1·10 1·10
495 17p. Green lizard . . . . . . 1·10 1·10

127 Toddlers' Toys

1989. Europa. Children's Toys and Games. Designs showing clay plaques. Multicoloured.

496 17p. Type **127** 50 50
497 17p. Playground games 50 50
498 23p. Party games 90 90
499 23p. Teenage sports 90 90

128 Queen Elizabeth II and Royal Yacht "Britannia" in Elizabeth Harbour

1989. Royal Visit.

500 **128** £1 multicoloured . . . . . 3·00 3·25

129 Philippe D'Auvergne presented to Louis XVI, 1786

1989. Bicentenary of the French Revolution. Philippe D'Auvergne. Multicoloured.

501 13p. Type **129** 45 45
502 17p. Storming the Bastille, 1789 . . . . 60 60
503 23p. Marie de Bouillon and revolutionaries, 1790 . . . . 80 80
504 30p. Auvergne's headquarters at Mont Orgueil, 1795 . . . . 1·10 1·10
505 32p. Landing arms for Chouan rebels, 1796 . . . . 1·25 1·25
506 35p. The last Chouan revolt, 1799 . . . . 1·40 1·40

See also Nos. 539/44.

130 "St. Helier" off Elizabeth Castle

1989. Centenary of Great Western Railway Steamer Service to Channel Islands. Multicoloured.

507 13p. Type **130** 40 40
508 17p. "Caesarea II" off Corbiere Lighthouse 50 50
509 27p. "Reindeer" in St. Helier harbour . . . . 1·00 1·00
510 32p. "Ibex" racing "Frederica" off Portelet . . . . 1·25 1·25
511 35p. "Lynx" off Noirmont . . 1·40 1·40

131 "Gorey Harbour"

1989. 150th Birth Anniv of Sarah Louisa Kilpack (artist). Multicoloured.

512 13p. Type **131** 40 40
513 17p. "La Corbiere" 50 50
514 23p. "Greve de Lecq" . . . . 1·00 1·00
515 32p. "Bouley Bay" . . . . . . 1·25 1·25
516 35p. "Mont Orgueil" . . . . . 1·40 1·40

132 Head Post Office, Broad Street, 1969 **133** "Battle of Flowers" Parade

1990. Europa. Post Office Buildings. Mult.

517 18p. Type **132** 50 50
518 18p. Postal Headquarters, Mont Millais, 1990 . . . . 50 50
519 24p. Hue Street Post Office, 1815 (horiz) 90 90
520 24p. Head Post Office, Halkett Place, 1890 (horiz) 90 90

1990. Festival of Tourism. Multicoloured.

521 18p. Type **133** 60 60
522 24p. Sports 75 75
523 29p. Mont Orgueil Castle and German Underground Hospital Museum 95 95
524 32p. Salon Culinaire . . . . . 1·00 1·00

134 Early Printing Press and Jersey Newspaper Mastheads

1990. International Literacy Year. Jersey News Media. Multicoloured.
526 14p. Type **134** 55 55
527 18p. Modern press, and offices of "Jersey Evening Post" in 1890 and 1990 60 60
528 34p. Radio Jersey broadcaster 1·10 1·10
529 37p. Channel Television studio cameraman 1·10 1·10

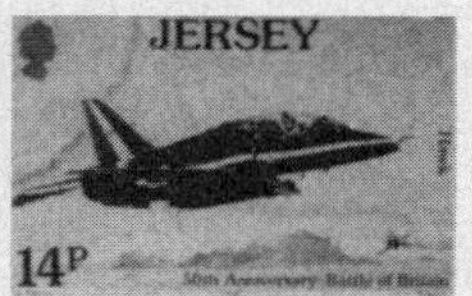

135 British Aerospace Hawk T.1

1990. 50th Anniv of Battle of Britain. Multicoloured.
530 14p. Type **135** 45 45
531 18p. Supermarine Spitfire 60 60
532 24p. Hawker Hurricane Mk I 90 90
533 34p. Vickers-Armstrong Wellington 1·60 1·60
534 37p. Avro Lancaster 1·75 1·75

1990. Christmas. Jersey Parish Churches (2nd series). As T **123**. Multicoloured.
535 14p. St. Helier 40 40
536 18p. Grouville 60 60
537 34p. St. Saviour 1·25 1·25
538 37p. St. John 1·40 1·40

1991. 175th Death Anniv of Philippe d'Auvergne. As T **129**. Multicoloured.
539 15p. Prince's Tower, La Hougue Bie 50 50
540 20p. Auvergne's arrest in Paris 60 60
541 26p. Auvergne plotting against Napoleon 80 80
542 31p. Execution of George Cadoudal 1·00 1·00
543 37p. H.M.S. "Surly" (cutter) attacking French convoy 1·25 1·25
544 44p. Auvergne's last days in London 1·40 1·40

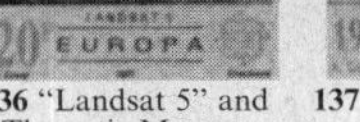

136 "Landsat 5" and Thematic Mapper Image over Jersey
137 1941 1d. Stamp (50th anniv of first Jersey postage stamp)

1991. Europa. Europe in Space. Multicoloured.
545 20p. Type **136** 55 55
546 20p. "ERS-1" earth resources remote sensing satellite 55 55
547 26p. "Meteosat" weather satellite 85 85
548 26p. "Olympus" direct broadcasting satellite 85 85

1991. Anniversaries. Multicoloured.
549 15p. Type **137** 40 40
550 20p. Steam train (centenary of Jersey Eastern Railway extension to Gorey Pier) 60 60
551 26p. Jersey cow and Herd Book (125th anniv of Jersey Herd Book) 80 80
552 31p. Stone-laying ceremony (from painting by P. J. Ouless) (150th anniv of Victoria Harbour) 90 90
553 53p. Marie Bartlett and hospital (250th anniv of Marie Bartlett's hospital bequest) 1·75 1·75

138 "Melitaea cinxia"

1991. Butterflies and Moths. Multicoloured.
554 15p. Type **138** 40 40
555 20p. "Euplagia quadripunctaria" 50 50
556 37p. "Deilephilia porcellus" 1·60 1·60
557 57p. "Inachis io" 2·00 2·00

139 Drilling for Water, Ethiopia

1991. Overseas Aid. Multicoloured.
558 15p. Type **139** 50 40
559 20p. Building construction, Rwanda 60 65
560 26p. Village polytechnic, Kenya 80 80
561 31p. Treating leprosy, Tanzania 1·00 1·00
562 37p. Ploughing, Zambia 1·25 1·25
563 44p. Immunisation clinic, Lesotho 1·40 1·40

140 "This is the Place for Me"
141 Pied Wagtail

1991. Christmas. Illustrations by Edmund Blampied for J. M. Barrie's "Peter Pan". Multicoloured.
564 15p. Type **140** 40 40
565 20p. "The Island Come True" 65 65
566 37p. "The Never Bird" 1·25 1·25
567 53p. "The Great White Father" 1·60 1·60

1992. Winter Birds. Multicoloured.
568 16p. Type **141** 55 55
569 22p. Firecrest 80 80
570 28p. Common snipe 90 90
571 39p. Lapwing 1·40 1·40
572 57p. Fieldfare 1·90 1·90
See also Nos. 635/9.

142 Shipping at Shanghai, 1860

1992. Jersey Adventurers (3rd series). 150th Birth Anniv of William Mesny. Multicoloured.
573 16p. Type **142** 50 50
574 16p. Mesny's junk running Taiping blockade, 1862 50 50
575 22p. General Mesny outside river gate, 1874 75 75
576 22p. Mesny in Burma, 1877 75 75
577 33p. Mesny and Governor Chang, 1882 1·00 1·00
578 33p. Mesny in mandarin's sedan chair, 1886 1·00 1·00

143 "Tickler" (brigantine)

1992. Jersey Shipbuilding. Multicoloured.
579 16p. Type **143** 50 50
580 22p. "Hebe" (brig) 80 80
581 50p. "Gemini" (barque) 1·60 1·60
582 57p. "Percy Douglas" (full-rigged ship) 1·90 1·90

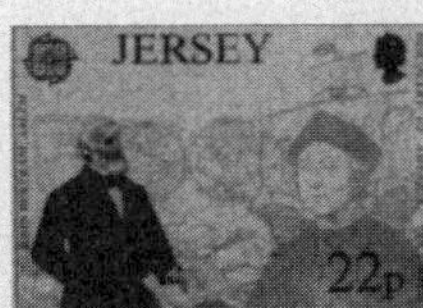

144 John Bertram (ship owner) and Columbus

1992. Europa. 500th Anniv of Discovery of America by Columbus. Multicoloured.
584 22p. Type **144** 70 70
585 28p. Sir George Carteret (founder of New Jersey) 85 85
586 39p. Sir Walter Raleigh (founder of Virginia) 1·25 1·25

145 "Snow Leopards" (Allison Griffiths)
146 Farmhouse

1992. Batik Designs. Multicoloured.
587 16p. Type **145** 50 50
588 22p. "Three Elements" (Nataly Miorin) 70 70
589 39p. "Three Men in a Tub" (Amanda Crocker) 1·25 1·25
590 57p. "Cockatoos" (Michelle Millard) 1·75 1·75

1992. Vintage Cars (2nd series). As T **124**. Multicoloured.
591 16p. Morris Cowley "Bullnose", 1925 35 35
592 22p. Rolls Royce "20/25", 1932 50 50
593 28p. Chenard and Walcker "T5", 1924 80 80
594 33p. Packard 900 series "Light Eight", 1932 1·00 1·00
595 39p. Lanchester "21", 1927 1·25 1·25
596 50p. Buick "30 Roadster", 1913 1·75 1·75

1992. Christmas. Jersey Parish Churches (3rd series). As T **123**. Multicoloured.
597 16p. Trinity 40 35
598 22p. St. Mary 65 70
599 39p. St. Martin 1·25 1·25
600 57p. St. Peter 1·60 1·60

1993. Multicoloured.
601 (–) Type **146** 50 50
602 (–) Trinity Church 50 50
603 (–) Daffodils and cows 50 50
604 (–) Jersey cows 50 50
605 (–) Sunbathing 60 60
606 (–) Windsurfing 60 60
607 (–) Crab (Queen's head at left) 60 60
608 (–) Crab (Queen's head at right) 60 60
609 (–) "Singin' in the Rain" float 75 75
610 (–) "Dragon Dance" float 75 75
611 (–) "Bali, Morning of the World" float 75 75
612 (–) "Zulu Fantasy" float 75 75

The above do not show face values, but are inscribed "BAILIWICK POSTAGE PAID" (Nos. 601/4), "U.K. MINIMUM POSTAGE PAID" (Nos. 605/8) or "EUROPE POSTAGE PAID" (Nos. 609/12). They were initially sold at 17p., 23p. or 28p., but it is intended that these face values will be increased to reflect postage rate changes in the future.

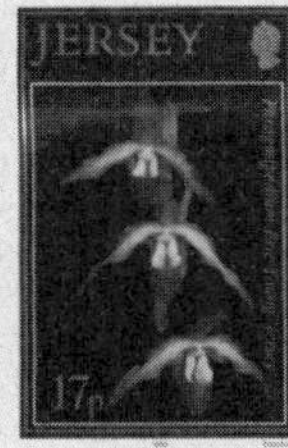

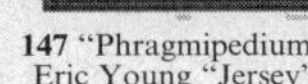
147 "Phragmipedium" Eric Young "Jersey"
149 "Jersey's Opera House" (Ian Rolls)

148 Douglas DC-3 Dakota

1993. Jersey Orchids (3rd series). Multicoloured.
613 17p. Type **147** 50 50
614 23p. "Odontoglossum" Augres "Trinity" 75 75
615 28p. "Miltonia" St. Helier "Colomberie" 90 90
616 39p. "Phragmipedium pearcei" 1·50 1·50
617 57p. "Calanthe" Grouville "Grey" 2·00 2·00

1993. 75th Anniv of Royal Air Force. Mult.
618 17p. Type **148** 50 50
619 23p. Wight seaplane 70 70
620 28p. Avro Shackleton A.E.W.2 80 80
621 33p. Gloster Meteor Mk III and De Havilland Vampire FB.5 90 90
622 39p. Hawker Siddeley Harrier GR.IA 1·10 1·10
623 57p. Panavia Tornado F Mk 3 1·60 1·60

Nos. 618/23 also commemorate the 50th anniv of the Royal Air Force Association and the 40th anniv of the first air display on Jersey.

1993. Europa. Contemporary Art. Multicoloured.
625 23p. Type **149** 70 70
626 28p. "The Ham and Tomato Bap" (Jonathan Hubbard) 85 85
627 39p. "Vase of Flowers" (Neil MacKenzie) 1·25 1·25

150 1943 $\frac{1}{2}$d. Occupation Stamp

1993. 50th Anniv of Edmund Blampied's Occupation Stamps. Designs showing stamps from the 1943 issue.
628 **150** 17p. green, lt grn & blk 40 45
629 – 23p. red, pink & black 55 55
630 – 28p. brown, cinnamon and black 75 75
631 – 33p. orange, salmon & blk 1·00 1·00
632 – 39p. blue, cobalt & black 1·40 1·40
633 – 50p. mauve, lt mve & blk 1·50 1·50

DESIGNS: 23p. 1d. value; 28p. $1\frac{1}{2}$d. value; 33p. 2d. value; 39p. $2\frac{1}{2}$d. value; 50p. 3d. value.

151 Queen Elizabeth II (from painting by Marca McGregor)

1993. 40th Anniv of Coronation.
634 **151** £1 multicoloured 3·50 3·50

152 Short-toed Treecreeper
153 Two Angels holding "Hark the Herald Angels Sing" Banner

1993. Summer Birds. Multicoloured.
635 17p. Type **152** 50 50
636 23p. Dartford warbler 75 75
637 28p. Common wheatear 85 85
638 39p. Cirl bunting 1·25 1·25
639 57p. Jay 1·75 1·75

1993. Christmas. Stained Glass Windows by Henry Bosdet from St. Aubin on the Hill Church. Multicoloured.
640 17p. Type **153** 45 45
641 23p. Two angels playing harps 65 65
642 39p. Two angels playing violins 1·25 1·25
643 57p. Two angels holding "Once in Royal David's City" banner 1·90 1·90

154 "Coprinus comatus"
156 Maine Coon

1994. Fungi. Multicoloured.
644 18p. Type **154** 45 45
645 23p. "Amanita muscaria" 70 70
646 30p. "Cantharellus cibarius" 90 90
647 41p. "Macrolepiota procera" 1·25 1·25
648 60p. "Clathrus ruber" 1·75 1·75

1994. 21st Anniv of Jersey Cat Club. Mult.
650 18p. Type **156** 45 45
651 23p. British shorthair (horiz) 70 70
652 35p. Persian 90 90
653 41p. Siamese (horiz) 1·25 1·25
654 60p. Non-pedigree 1·75 1·75

157 Mammoth Hunt, La Cotte de St. Brelade

1994. Europa. Archaeological Discoveries. Multicoloured.
655 23p. Type **157** 55 55
656 23p. Stone Age hunters pulling mammoth into cave 55 55
657 30p. Chambered passage, La Hougue Bie 85 85
658 30p. Transporting stones 85 85

158 Gliders and Towing Aircraft approaching France

1994. 50th Anniv of D-Day. Multicoloured.

659 18p. Type **158** 60 60
660 18p. Landing craft approaching beaches . . . 60 60
661 23p. Disembarking from landing craft on Gold Beach 80 80
662 23p. British troops on Sword Beach . . . 80 80
663 30p. Spitfires over beaches . . 90 90
664 30p. Invasion map 90 90

159 Sailing

1994. Centenary of International Olympic Committee. Multicoloured.

665 18p. Type **159** 45 45
666 23p. Rifle shooting 60 60
667 30p. Hurdling 85 85
668 41p. Swimming . . . . 1·25 1·25
669 60p. Hockey . . . . 1·60 1·60

160 Strawberry Anemone

1994. Marine Life. Multicoloured.

670 18p. Type **160** 50 50
671 23p. Hermit crab and parasitic anemone 75 75
672 41p. Velvet swimming crab . . . 1·40 1·40
673 60p. Common jellyfish . . . . 1·75 1·75

161 "Condor 10" (catamaran)

1994. 25th Anniv of Jersey Postal Administration. Multicoloured.

674 18p. Type **161** 45 45
675 23p. Map of Jersey and pillar box 60 60
676 35p. Vickers Type 953 Vanguard of B.E.A. 85 85
677 41p. Shorts 360 of Aurigny Air Services . . . . 1·10 1·10
678 60p. "Caesarea" (Sealink ferry) . 1·50 1·50

162 "Away in a Manger"

1994. Christmas. Carols. Multicoloured.

680 18p. Type **162** 45 45
681 23p. "Hark! the Herald Angels Sing" 60 60
682 41p. "While Shepherds watched" 1·25 1·25
683 60p. "We Three Kings of Orient Are" . . . . 1·60 1·60

163 Dog and "GOOD LUCK"

164 Camellia "Captain Rawes"

1995. Greetings Stamps. Multicoloured.

684 18p. Type **163** 45 45
685 18p. Rose and "WITH LOVE" . 45 45
686 18p. Chick and "CONGRATULATIONS" . 45 45
687 18p. Bouquet of flowers and "THANK YOU" 45 45
688 23p. Dove with letter and "WITH LOVE" 55 55
689 23p. Cat and "GOOD LUCK" . 55 55
690 23p. Carnations and "THANK YOU" 55 55
691 23p. Parrot and "CONGRATULATIONS" . 55 55
692 60p. Pig and "HAPPY NEW YEAR" (25 × 63 mm) . . . 1·40 1·40

No. 692 commemorates the Chinese New Year of the Pig.

1994. Camellias. Multicoloured.

693 18p. Type **164** 60 60
694 23p. "Brigadoon" 80 80
695 30p. "Elsie Jury" 95 95
696 35p. "Augusto L'Gouveia Pinto" 1·00 1·00
697 41p. "Bella Romana" . . . . 1·10 1·10

165 "Liberation" (sculpture, Philip Jackson)

1995. Europa. Peace and Freedom

698 **165** 23p. black and blue . . . 55 55
699 30p. black and pink . . . 70 75

166 Bailiff and Crown Officers in Launch

1995. 50th Anniv of Liberation. Multicoloured.

700 18p. Type **166** 40 40
701 18p. "Vega" (Red Cross supply ship) 40 40
702 23p. H.M.S. "Beagle" (destroyer) 60 60
703 23p. British troops in Ordnance Yard, St. Helier 60 60
704 60p. King George VI and Queen Elizabeth in Jersey . . . . 1·50 1·50
705 60p. Unloading supplies from landing craft, St. Aubin's . . 1·50 1·50

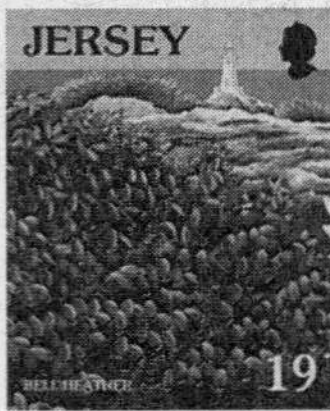

167 Bell Heather

1995. European Nature Conservation Year. Wild Flowers. Multicoloured.

707 19p. Type **167** 55 55
708 19p. Sea campion 55 55
709 19p. Spotted rock-rose 55 55
710 19p. Thrift 55 55
711 19p. Sheep's-bit scabious . . . 55 55
712 23p. Field bind-weed 65 65
713 23p. Common bird's-foot-trefoil 65 65
714 23p. Sea-holly 65 65
715 23p. Common centaury 65 65
716 23p. Dwarf pansy 65 65

Nos. 707/11 and 712/16 respectively were printed together, se-tenant, forming composite designs.

168 "Precis almana"

1995. Butterflies. Multicoloured.

717 19p. Type **168** 55 55
718 23p. "Papilio palinurus" . . . 70 70
719 30p. "Catopsilia scylla" . . . 90 90
720 41p. "Papilio rumanzovia" . . 1·10 1·10
721 60p. "Troides helena" . . . . 1·75 1·75

169 Peace Doves and United Nations Anniversary Emblem

1995. 50th Anniv of United Nations.

723 **169** 19p. cobalt and blue . . . 55 55
724 – 23p. turquoise and green . . 65 65
725 – 41p. green and turquoise . 1·10 1·10
726 **169** 60p. blue and cobalt . . . 1·60 1·60

DESIGN: 23p., 41p. Symbolic wheat and anniversary emblem.

170 "Puss in Boots"

1995. Christmas. Pantomimes. Multicoloured.

727 19p. Type **170** 55 55
728 23p. "Cinderella" 70 70
729 41p. "Sleeping Beauty" . . . . 1·00 1·00
730 60p. "Aladdin" . . . . 1·60 1·60

172 African Child and Map

1996. 50th Anniv of U.N.I.C.E.F. Multicoloured.

732 19p. Type **172** 50 50
733 23p. Children and globe . . . 60 60
734 30p. European child and map . 80 80
735 35p. South American child and map 95 95
736 41p. Asian child and map . . . 1·10 1·10
737 60p. South Pacific child and map 1·60 1·60

173 Queen Elizabeth II (from photo by T. O'Neill)

1996. 70th Birthday of Queen Elizabeth II.

738 **173** £5 multicoloured . . . . . 10·00 10·50

174 Elizabeth Garrett (first British woman doctor)

1996. Europa. Famous Women. Multicoloured.

739 23p. Type **174** 60 60
740 30p. Emmeline Pankhurst (suffragette) 80 80

175 Player shooting at Goal

1996. European Football Championship, England. Multicoloured.

741 19p. Type **175** 50 50
742 23p. Two players chasing ball . 70 70
743 35p. Player avoiding tackle . . 95 95
744 41p. Two players competing for ball . . . . 1·10 1·10
745 60p. Players heading ball . . . 1·75 1·75

176 Rowing

1996. Sporting Anniversaries. Multicoloured.

746 19p. Type **176** 50 50
747 23p. Judo 70 70
748 35p. Fencing 95 95
749 41p. Boxing . . . . 1·10 1·10
750 60p. Basketball . . . . 1·75 1·75

ANNIVERSARIES: Nos. 746/8, 750/1, Centenary of modern Olympic Games; 749, 50th anniv of International Amateur Boxing Association.

177 Bay on North Coast

1996. Tourism. Beaches. Multicoloured.

752 19p. Type **177** 50 50
753 23p. Portelet Bay 60 60
754 30p. Greve de Lecq Bay . . . 80 80
755 35p. Beauport Beach 95 95
756 41p. Plemont Bay . . . . . . 1·10 1·10
757 60p. St. Brelade's Bay . . . . 1·60 1·60

178 Drag Hunt

1996. Horses. Multicoloured.

758 19p. Type **178** 50 50
759 23p. Pony and trap 60 60
760 30p. Training racehorses on beach 80 80
761 35p. Show jumping 95 95
762 41p. Pony Club event . . . . 1·10 1·10
763 60p. Shire mare and foal . . . 1·60 1·60

179 The Journey to Bethlehem

1996. Christmas. Multicoloured.

764 19p. Type **179** 60 60
765 23p. The Shepherds 70 70
766 30p. The Nativity . . . . . . 1·00 1·00
767 60p. The Three Kings . . . . 1·60 1·60

181 Lillie the Cow on the Beach

182 Red-breasted Merganser

1997. Tourism. "Lillie the Cow". Multicoloured. Self-adhesive.

770 (23p.) Type **181** 70 70
771 (23p.) Lillie taking photograph . 70 70
772 (23p.) Carrying bucket and spade 70 70
773 (23p.) Eating meal at Mont Orgueil 70 70

1997. Seabirds and Waders. Multicoloured.

774 1p. Type **182** 10 10
775 2p. Sanderling 10 10
776 4p. Northern gannet 10 10
777 5p. Great crested grebe . . . 10 15
778 10p. Common tern 20 25
779 15p. Black-headed gull 30 35
780 20p. Dunlin 40 45
781 21p. Sandwich tern 40 45
782 22p. Ringed plover 40 50
783 23p. Bar-tailed godwit 45 50
784 24p. Puffin 45 50
785 25p. Brent goose 50 55
786 26p. Grey plover 50 55
787 27p. Common scoter 55 60
788 28p. Lesser black-backed gull . 60 65
789 29p. Little egret 60 65
790 30p. Fulmar 60 65
791 31p. Golden plover 60 65
792 32p. Greenshank 65 70
793 33p. Little grebe 65 70
794 34p. Common comorant 70 75
795 35p. Curlew 70 75
796 37p. Oystercatcher 75 80
797 40p. Turnstone 80 85
798 44p. Herring gull 90 95
799 45p. Rock pipit 90 95
800 50p. Great black-backed gull . 1·00 1·10
801 60p. Avocet . . . . 1·25 1·40

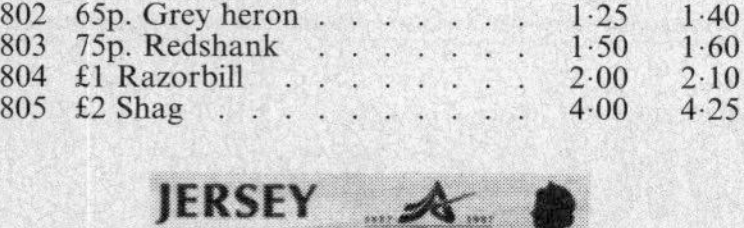

802 65p. Grey heron . . . . 1·25 1·40
803 75p. Redshank . . . . 1·50 1·60
804 £1 Razorbill . . . . 2·00 2·10
805 £2 Shag . . . . 4·00 4·25

183 De Havilland D.H.95 Flamingo

1997. 60th Anniv of Jersey Airport. Multicoloured.
807 20p. Type **183** 55 55
808 24p. Handley Page H.P.R. Marathon 65 65
809 31p. De Havilland D.H.114 Heron 80 80
810 37p. Boeing 737-236 . . . . . 1·00 1·00
811 43p. Britten Norman Trislander . . . . 1·10 1·10
812 63p. BAe 146-200 . . . . . . 1·75 1·75

184 The Bull of St. Clement

1997. Europa. Tales and Legends. Multicoloured.
813 20p. Type **184** 50 50
814 24p. The Black Horse of St. Ouen 60 60
815 31p. The Black Dog of Bouley Bay 70 70
816 63p. Les Fontaines des Mittes . 1·40 1·40
Nos. 814/15 include the "EUROPA" emblem.

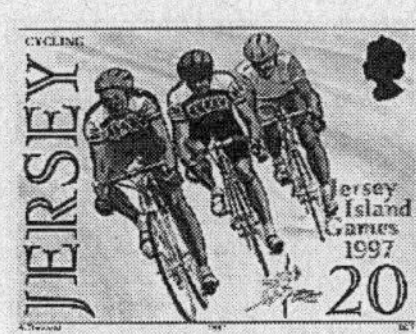

185 Cycling

1997. 7th Island Games, Jersey. Multicoloured.
818 20p. Type **185** 55 55
819 24p. Archery 65 65
820 31p. Windsurfing 80 80
821 37p. Gymnastics . . . . . . 1·00 1·00
822 43p. Volleyball . . . . 1·10 1·10
823 63p. Running . . . . 1·75 1·75

186 Mallorcan Midwife Toad

1997. Wildlife Preservation Trust (6th series). Multicoloured.
824 20p. Type **186** 55 50
825 24p. Aye-aye 65 65
826 31p. Echo parakeet 80 80
827 37p. Pigmy hog . . . . 1·00 1·00
828 43p. St. Lucia whip-tail . . . 1·10 1·10
829 63p. Madagascar teal . . . . 1·75 1·75

187 Ash

1997. Trees. Multicoloured.
830 20p. Type **187** 55 55
831 24p. Elder 65 65
832 31p. Beech 80 80
833 37p. Sweet chestnut . . . . . 1·00 1·00
834 43p. Hawthorn . . . . 1·10 1·10
835 63p. Common oak . . . . . 1·75 1·75

188 Father Christmas and Reindeer outside Jersey Airport

1997. Christmas. Multicoloured.
836 20p. Type **188** 55 55
837 24p. Father Christmas with presents, St. Aubin's Harbour 65 65
838 31p. Father Christmas in sleigh, Mont Orgueil Castle 90 90
839 63p. Father Christmas with children, Royal Square, St. Helier . . . . 1·75 1·75

189 Wedding Photograph, 1947

1997. Golden Wedding of Queen Elizabeth and Prince Philip. Multicoloured.
840 50p. Type **189** . . . . 1·50 1·50
841 50p. Queen Elizabeth and Prince Philip, 1997 . . . . 1·50 1·50

191 J.M.T. Bristol 4 Tonner, 1923

1998. 75th Anniv of Jersey Motor Transport Company. Buses. Multicoloured.
844 20p. Type **191** 55 55
845 24p. Safety Coach Service Regent double decker, 1934 . . . . 65 65
846 31p. Slade's Dennis Lancet, circa 1936 . . . . 75 75
847 37p. Tantivy Leyland PLSC Lion, 1947 . . . . 1·00 1·00
848 43p. J.B.S. Morris, circa 1958 . 1·10 1·10
849 63p. J.M.T. Titan TD4 double decker, circa 1961 . . . . . 1·50 1·50

192 Creative Arts Festival

193 Hobie Cat and "Duke of Normandy" (launch)

1998. Europa. National Festivals. Multicoloured.
850 20p. Type **192** 60 60
851 24p. Jazz Festival 65 65
852 31p. Good Food Festival . . . 85 85
853 63p. Floral Festival . . . . . 1·50 1·50
Nos. 851/2 include the "EUROPA" emblem.

1998. Opening of Elizabeth Marina, St. Helier. Multicoloured.
854 20p. Type **193** 50 50
855 20p. Hobie Cat with white, yellow, red and green sails . 50 50
856 20p. Hobie Cats with pink, purple and orange sails 50 50
857 20p. Bow of Hobie Cat with yellow, blue and purple sail . 50 50
858 20p. Hobie Cat heeling 50 50
859 24p. Yacht with red, white and blue spinnaker 60 60
860 24p. Yacht with pink spinnaker 60 60
861 24p. Yacht with two white sails 60 60
862 24p. Trimaran 60 60
863 24p. Yacht with blue, white and yellow spinnaker in foreground 60 60
Nos. 854/8 and 859/63 respectively were printed together, se-tenant, forming composite designs of yacht races.

194 Bass

1998. International Year of the Ocean. Fishes. Multicoloured.
864 20p. Type **194** 50 50
865 24p. Red gurnard 65 65
866 31p. Skate 80 80
867 37p. Mackerel . . . . 1·00 1·00
868 43p. Tope . . . . 1·10 1·10
869 63p. Cuckoo wrasse . . . . . 1·50 1·50

195 Cider-making

196 Irises

1998. Days Gone By. Multicoloured. Self-adhesive.
870 (20p.) Type **195** 40 45
871 (20p.) Potato barrels on cart . . 40 45
872 (20p.) Collecting seaweed for fertiliser 40 45
873 (20p.) Milking Jersey cows . . 40 45

1998. Flowers. Multicoloured.
874 20p. Type **196** 50 50
875 24p. Carnations 65 65
876 31p. Chrysanthemums 80 80
877 37p. Pinks . . . . 1·00 1·00
878 43p. Roses . . . . 1·10 1·10
879 63p. Lilies . . . . 1·50 1·50

197 Central Market Crib

1998. Christmas. Cribs. Multicoloured.
881 20p. Type **197** 45 45
882 24p. St. Thomas's Church crib . 55 55
883 31p. Trinity Parish Church crib . 65 65
884 63p. Royal Square crib . . . . 1·40 1·40

199 Jersey Eastern Railway Mail Train

1999. 125th Anniv of U.P.U. Multicoloured.
886 20p. Type **199** 40 45
887 24p. "Brighton" (paddle-steamer) 50 55
888 43p. De Havilland D.H.86 Dragon Express at Jersey Airport 85 90
889 63p. Jersey Postal Service Morris Minor van . . . . 1·25 1·40

200 "Jessie Eliza", St. Catherine

1999. 175th Anniv of Royal National Lifeboat Institution. Multicoloured.
890 75p. Type **200** . . . . 1·50 1·60
891 £1 "Alexander Coutanche", St. Helier . . . . 2·00 2·10

201 "Cymbidium" Maufant "Jersey"

1999. Jersey Orchids (4th series). Multicoloured.
892 21p. Type **201** 45 50
893 25p. "Miltonia" Millbrook "Jersey" 50 55
894 31p. "Paphiopedilum" "Transvaal" 65 70
895 37p. "Paphiopedilum" "Elizabeth Castle" 75 80
896 43p. "Calanthe" "Five Oaks" . 85 90
897 63p. "Cymbidium" Icho Tower "Trinity" . . . . 1·25 1·40

202 Howard Davis Park

1999. Europa. Parks and Gardens. Multicoloured.
899 21p. Type **202** 45 50
900 25p. Sir Winston Churchill Memorial Park 50 55
901 31p. Coronation Park 65 70
902 63p. La Collette Gardens . . . 1·25 1·40
Nos. 900/1 include the "EUROPA" logo at top left and all four values show the "iBRA '99" International Stamp Exhibition, Nuremberg, emblem at top right.

203 Prince Edward and Miss Sophie Rhys-Jones

1999. Royal Wedding.
903 **203** 35p. multicoloured (yellow background) . . . . . 1·00 1·00
904 35p. multicoloured (blue background) . . . . . 1·00 1·00

204 Jersey-built Benz, 1899

1999. Vintage Cars (3rd series). Centenary of Motoring in Jersey. Multicoloured.
905 21p. Type **204** 40 45
906 25p. Star Tourer, 1910 . . . . 50 55
907 31p. Citroen "Traction Avant", 1938 . . . . 60 65
908 37p. Talbot BG110 Tourer, 1937 . . . . 75 80
909 43p. Morris Cowley Six Special Coupe, 1934 . . . . . . 85 90
910 63p. Ford Anglia Saloon, 1946 . 1·25 1·40

205 West European Hedgehog

1999. Small Mammals. Multicoloured.
911 21p. Type **205** 40 45
912 25p. Eurasian red squirrel . . . 50 55
913 31p. Nathusius pipistrelle . . . 60 65
914 37p. Jersey bank vole 75 80
915 43p. Lesser white-toothed shrew 85 90
916 63p. Common mole . . . . . 1·25 1·40

206 Gorey Pierhead Light

207 Mistletoe

1999. 150th Anniv of First Lighthouse on Jersey. Multicoloured.
917 21p. Type **206** 40 45
918 25p. La Corbiere 50 55
919 34p. Noirmont Point 70 75
920 38p. Demie de Pas 75 80
921 44p. Greve d'Azette 90 95
922 64p. Sorel Point . . . . 1·25 1·40

1999. Christmas. Festive Foliage. Multicoloured.
923 21p. Type **207** 40 45
924 25p. Holly 50 55
925 34p. Ivy 70 75
926 64p. Christmas Rose . . . . . 1·25 1·40

208 Jersey Crest

2000. New Millennium.

927 **208** £10 gold, red and carmine . 20·00 21·00

POSTAGE DUE STAMPS

D 1

D **3** Arms of St. Clement and Dovecote at Samares

1969.

D1 D **1** 1d. violet . . . . 1·50 1·50
D2 2d. sepia . . . . 2·25 2·00
D3 3d. mauve . . . . 3·00 2·75
D4 – 1s. green . . . . 9·00 7·50
D5 – 2s. 6d. grey . . . . 21·00 16·00
D6 – 5s. red . . . . 30·00 27·00
DESIGNS: 1s., 2s. 6d. and 5s. Map.

1971. Decimal Currency. Design as Nos. D4/6, but values in new currency.

D 7 ½p. black 10 10
D 8 1p. blue 10 10
D 9 2p. brown 10 10
D10 3p. purple 10 10
D11 4p. red 10 10
D12 5p. green 15 15
D13 6p. orange 20 15
D14 7p. yellow 20 15
D15 8p. blue 30 25
D16 10p. green 40 35
D17 11p. brown 40 40
D18 14p. violet 45 45
D19 25p. green 90 90
D20 50p. purple . . . . 1·50 1·50

1978. Parish Arms and Views.

D21 D **3** 1p. black and green . . . 10 10
D22 – 2p. black and yellow . . 10 10
D23 – 3p. black and brown . . 10 10
D24 – 4p. black and red 10 10
D25 – 5p. black and blue . . . 10 10
D26 – 10p. black and olive . . . 30 20
D27 – 12p. black and blue . . . 35 25
D28 – 14p. black and orange . . 35 30
D29 – 15p. black and mauve . . 35 30
D30 – 20p. black and green . . 50 40
D31 – 50p. black and brown . . 1·10 1·10
D32 – £1 black and blue . . . . 2·25 2·25
DESIGNS: 2p. Arms of St. Lawrence and Handois Reservoir; 3p. Arms of St. John and Sorel Point; 4p. Arms of St. Ouen and Pinnacle Rock; 5p. Arms of St. Peter and Quetivel Mill; 10p. Arms of St. Martin and St. Catherine's Breakwater; 12p. Arms of St. Helier and Harbour; 14p. Arms of St. Saviour and Highlands College; 15p. Arms of St. Brelade and Beauport Bay; 20p. Arms of Grouville and La Hougue Bie; 50p. Arms of St. Mary and Perry Farm; £1 Arms of Trinity and Bouley Bay.

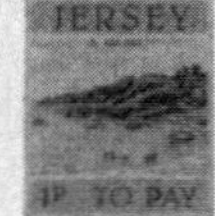

D **4** St. Brelade

1982. Jersey Harbours.

D33 D **4** 1p. green 10 10
D34 – 2p. yellow 10 10
D35 – 3p. brown 10 10
D36 – 4p. red 10 10
D37 – 5p. blue 10 10
D38 – 6p. green 10 15
D39 – 7p. mauve 15 20
D40 – 8p. red 15 20
D41 – 9p. green 20 45
D42 – 10p. blue 20 25
D43 – 20p. green 40 45
D44 – 30p. purple 60 65
D45 – 40p. orange 80 85
D46 – £1 violet . . . . 2·00 2·10
DESIGNS: 2p. St. Aubin; 3p. Rozel; 4p. Greve de Lecq; 5p. Bouley Bay; 6p. St. Catherine; 7p. Gorey; 8p. Bonne Nuit; 9p. La Roque; 10p. St. Helier; 20p. Ronez; 30p. La Collette; 40p. Elizabeth Castle; £1 Upper Harbour Marina.

JHALAWAR Pt. 1

A state of Rajasthan, India. Now uses Indian stamps.

4 paisa = 1 anna

1 Apsara (dancing nymph of Hindu Paradise)

1886. Imperf.
1 **1** 1 p. green . . . 3·25 8·50
2 – ¼ a. green . . . 70 1·60
The ¼ a. is larger and has a different frame.

JIND Pt. 1

A "convention" state of the Punjab, India, which now uses Indian stamps.

12 pies = 1 anna; 16 annas = 1 rupee

J 1 (½ a.) J 6 (¼ a.)

1874. Imperf.
J 8 **J 1** ½ a. blue . . . 60 3·25
J 9 1 a. purple . . . 1·40 7·50
J 3 2 a. bistre . . . 1·00 3·25
J11 4 a. green . . . 1·50 10·00
J12 8 a. purple . . . 7·00 10·00

1882. Various designs and sizes. Imperf or perf.
J16A **J 6** ¼ a. brown . . . 30 1·25
J19A ½ a. bistre . . . 70 60
J20A 1 a. brown . . . 1·60 3·25
J22A 2 a. blue . . . 2·25 1·00
J23A 4 a. green . . . 1·25 90
J25A 8 a. red . . . 5·00 4·25

Stamps of India (Queen Victoria) overprinted.

1885. Optd **JHIND STATE** vert (curved).
1 **23** ½ a. turquoise . . . 1·75 2·75
2 – 1 a. purple . . . 22·00 30·00
3 – 2 a. blue . . . 7·50 12·00
4 – 4 a. green (No. 71) . . . 45·00 60·00
5 – 8 a. mauve . . . £400
6 – 1 r. grey (No. 101) . . . £400

1885. Optd **JEEND STATE.**
7 **23** ½ a. turquoise . . . 80·00
8 – 1 a. purple . . . 85·00
9 – 2 a. blue . . . 85·00
10 – 4 a. green (No. 71) . . . £110
11 – 8 a. mauve . . . £120
12 – 1 r. grey (No. 101) . . . £130

1886. Optd **JHIND STATE** horiz.
17 **23** ½ a. turquoise . . . 25 10
18 – 1 a. purple . . . 75 20
20 – 1 a. 6 p. brown . . . 1·10 2·50
21 – 2 a. blue . . . 1·25 40
23 – 3 a. orange . . . 1·25 50
15 – 4 a. green (No. 71) . . . 38·00
24 – 4 a. green (No. 96) . . . 2·50 1·75
27 – 6 a. brown . . . 90 7·00
28 – 8 a. mauve . . . 3·75 11·00
30 – 12 a. purple on red . . . 3·75 16·00
31 – 1 r. grey (No. 101) . . . 7·00 32·00
32 **37** 1 r. green and red . . . 7·50 38·00
33 **38** 2 r. red and orange . . . £225 £650
34 3 r. brown and green . . . £375 £650
35 5 r. blue and violet . . . £425 £650

1900. Optd **JHIND STATE** horiz.
36 **40** 3 p. red . . . 80 1·00
37 3 p. grey . . . 15 2·50
38 **23** ½ a. green . . . 2·50 4·00
40 – 1 a. red . . . 20 4·00

Stamps of India optd **JHIND STATE.**

1903. King Edward VII.
41 **41** 3 p. grey . . . 10 10
43 – ½ a. green (No. 122) . . . 50 1·40
44 – 1 a. red (No. 123) . . . 2·00 1·25
46 – 2 a. lilac . . . 1·50 60
47 – 2½ a. blue . . . 30 4·75
48 – 3 a. orange . . . 35 40
50 – 4 a. olive . . . 5·00 7·00
51 – 6 a. bistre . . . 5·00 14·00
52 – 8 a. mauve . . . 2·25 17·00
54 – 12 a. purple on red . . . 1·90 11·00
55 – 1 r. green and red . . . 2·50 12·00

1907. King Edward VII (inscr "INDIA POSTAGE and REVENUE").
56 ½ a. green (No. 149) . . . 10 20
57 1 a. red (No. 150) . . . 15 60

1913. King George V.
58 **55** 3 p. grey . . . 10 1·60
59 **56** ½ a. green . . . 10 60
60 **57** 1 a. red . . . 10 35
61 **59** 2 a. lilac . . . 15 3·75
62 **62** 3 a. orange . . . 1·50 8·50
63 **64** 6 a. bistre . . . 4·50 21·00

1914. Stamps of India (King George V) optd **JIND STATE** in two lines.
64 **55** 3 p. grey . . . 40 20
65 **56** ½ a. green . . . 1·50 15
66 **57** 1 a. red . . . 70 15
80 1 a. brown . . . 3·00 1·25
67 **58** 1½ a. brown (A. No. 163) . . . 70 3·25
68 1½ a. brown (B. No. 165) . . . 35 1·50
81 1½ a. red (B.) . . . 20 1·50
69 **59** 2 a. lilac . . . 1·25 45
70 **61** 2 a. 6 p. blue . . . 35 3·75
82 2 a. 6 p. orange . . . 40 5·00
71 **62** 3 a. orange . . . 50 2·25
83 3 a. blue . . . 1·40 3·25
72 **63** 4 a. olive . . . 1·25 5·00
73 **64** 6 a. brown . . . 1·25 9·50
74 **65** 8 a. mauve . . . 3·50 5·50
75 **66** 12 a. red . . . 1·50 9·50
76 **67** 1 r. brown and green . . . 6·50 12·00
77 2 r. red and orange . . . 5·00 85·00
78 5 r. blue and violet . . . 30·00 £170

1922. No. 192 of India optd **JIND.**
79 **57** 9 p. on 1 a. red . . . 1·25 13·00

Stamps of India optd **JIND STATE** in one line.

1927. King George V.
84 **55** 3 p. grey . . . 10 10
85 **56** ½ a. green . . . 10 35
86 **80** 9 p. green . . . 50 40
87 **57** 1 a. brown . . . 15 10
88 **82** 1 a. 3 p. mauve . . . 20 30
89 **58** 1½ a. red . . . 40 1·60
90 **70** 2 a. lilac . . . 1·10 35
91w **61** 2 a. 6 p. orange . . . 80 7·00
92 **62** 3 a. blue . . . 2·00 8·00
93w **83** 3 a. 6 p. blue . . . 50 12·00
94w **71** 4 a. green . . . 1·00 1·75
95 **64** 6 a. bistre . . . 55 13·00
96 **65** 8 a. mauve . . . 2·00 2·00
97w **66** 12 a. red . . . 3·25 14·00
98 **67** 1 r. brown and green . . . 3·25 3·50
99 2 r. red and orange . . . 25·00 95·00
100 5 r. blue and violet . . . 10·00 30·00
101 10 r. green and red . . . 12·00 18·00
102 15 r. blue and olive . . . 60·00 £400
103 25 r. orange and blue . . . 90·00 £475

1934. King George V.
104 **79** ½ a. green . . . 30 15
105 **81** 1 a. brown . . . 1·00 25
106 **59** 2 a. orange . . . 90 60
107 **62** 3 a. red . . . 1·40 40
108 **63** 4 a. olive . . . 2·00 90

1937. King George VI.
109 **91** 3 p. slate . . . 6·00 1·50
110 ½ a. brown . . . 60 2·50
111 9 p. green . . . 60 2·25
112 1 a. red . . . 60 45
113 **92** 2 a. red . . . 1·50 11·00
114 – 2 a. 6 p. violet . . . 1·00 12·00
115 – 3 a. green . . . 5·00 11·00
116 – 3 a. 6 p. blue . . . 2·00 12·00
117 – 4 a. brown . . . 6·00 12·00
118 – 6 a. green . . . 3·50 15·00
119 – 8 a. violet . . . 2·50 15·00
120 – 12 a. red . . . 1·75 17·00
121 **93** 1 r. slate and brown . . . 15·00 28·00
122 2 r. purple and brown . . . 17·00 80·00
123 5 r. green and blue . . . 30·00 60·00
124 10 r. purple and red . . . 55·00 60·00
125 15 r. brown and green . . . £150 £600
126 25 r. slate and purple . . . £325 £600

1941. Stamps of India (King George VI) optd **JIND.**
(a) On issue of 1937.
127 **91** 3 p. slate . . . 10·00 14·00
128 ½ a. brown . . . 1·00 50
129 9 p. green . . . 9·00 11·00
130 1 a. red . . . 1·00 3·25
131 **93** 1 r. slate and brown . . . 8·00 20·00
132 2 r. purple and brown . . . 16·00 26·00
133 5 r. green and blue . . . 38·00 70·00
134 10 r. purple and red . . . 55·00 70·00
135 15 r. brown and green . . . £120 £130
136 25 r. slate and purple . . . £100 £325

(b) On issue of 1940.
137 **100a** 3 p. slate . . . 50 60
138 ½ a. mauve . . . 50 85
139 9 p. green . . . 60 2·25
140 1 a. red . . . 65 85
141 **101** 1 a. 3 p. yellow-brown . . . 1·00 2·75
142 1½ a. violet . . . 5·00 3·50
143 2 a. red . . . 1·75 2·50
144 3 a. violet . . . 12·00 2·75
145 3½ a. blue . . . 6·00 6·00
146 **102** 4 a. brown . . . 3·50 2·75
147 6 a. green . . . 3·75 9·50
148 8 a. violet . . . 2·50 9·00
149 12 a. purple . . . 11·00 9·00

OFFICIAL STAMPS

Postage stamps of Jind optd **SERVICE.**

1885. Nos. 1/3 (Queen Victoria).
O1 **23** ½ a. green . . . 40 30
O2 – 1 a. purple . . . 30 10
O3 – 2 a. blue . . . 28·00 38·00

1886. Nos. 17/32 and No. 38 (Q.V.).
O12 **23** ½ a. turquoise . . . 50 10
O22 – ½ a. green (No. 38) . . . 1·25 20
O14 – 1 a. purple . . . 7·50 30
O16 – 2 a. blue . . . 50 30
O17 – 4 a. green (No. 24) . . . 1·00 50
O19 – 8 a. mauve . . . 3·00 2·00
O21 **37** 1 r. green and red . . . 6·00 28·00

1903. Nos. 42/55 (King Edward VII).
O23 **41** 3 p. grey . . . 10 10
O25 – ½ a. green (No. 43) . . . 2·00 10
O26 – 1 a. red (No. 44) . . . 90 10
O28 – 2 a. lilac . . . 40 10
O29 – 4 a. olive . . . 40 45
O31 – 8 a. mauve . . . 3·00 1·50
O32 – 1 r. green and red . . . 2·50 2·25

1907. Nos. 56/7 (King Edward VII).
O33 ½ a. green . . . 15 10
O34 1 a. red . . . 30 10

1914. Official stamps of India. Nos. O75/96 (King George V) optd **JIND STATE.**
O35 **55** 3 p. grey . . . 10 10
O36 **56** ½ a. green . . . 10 10
O37 **57** 1 a. red . . . 25 10
O46 1 a. brown . . . 50 10
O39 **59** 2 a. lilac . . . 15 15
O40 **63** 4 a. olive . . . 45 15
O41 **64** 6 a. bistre . . . 50 2·25
O42 **65** 8 a. mauve . . . 30 1·00
O43 **67** 1 r. brown and green . . . 1·00 1·60
O44 2 r. red and orange . . . 12·00 55·00
O45 5 r. blue and violet . . . 18·00 £150

Stamps of India optd **JIND STATE SERVICE.**

1927. King George V.
O47 **55** 3 p. grey . . . 10 20
O48 **56** ½ a. green . . . 10 90
O49 **80** 9 p. green . . . 40 15
O50 **57** 1 a. brown . . . 10 10
O51 **82** 1 a. 3 p. mauve . . . 40 15
O52 **70** 2 a. lilac . . . 25 15
O64 **59** 2 a. orange . . . 30 15
O53 **61** 2 a. 6 p. orange . . . 50 15·00
O54 **71** 4 a. green . . . 35 25
O55w **64** 6 a. bistre . . . 2·00 13·00
O56w **65** 8 a. mauve . . . 45 1·50
O57 **66** 12 a. red . . . 1·00 10·00
O58 **67** 1 r. brown and green . . . 2·25 2·50
O59 2 r. red and orange . . . 30·00 24·00
O60 5 r. blue and purple . . . 13·00 £160
O61 10 r. green and red . . . 26·00 90·00

1934. King George V.
O62 **79** ½ a. green . . . 20 15
O63 **81** 1 a. brown . . . 20 15
O65 **63** 4 a. olive . . . 3·75 30

1937. King George VI.
O66 **91** ½ a. brown . . . 48·00 30
O67 9 p. green . . . 85 7·50
O68 1 a. red . . . 55 30
O69 **93** 1 r. slate and brown . . . 26·00 42·00
O70 2 r. purple and brown . . . 45·00 £180
O71 5 r. green and blue . . . 85·00 £325
O72 10 r. purple and red . . . £180 £750

1939. Official stamps of India optd **JIND.**
O73 **O 20** 3 p. slate . . . 50 70
O74 ½ a. brown . . . 1·50 50
O75 ½ a. purple . . . 60 30
O76 9 p. green . . . 1·50 7·50
O77 1 a. red . . . 1·60 15
O78 1½ a. violet . . . 6·00 1·00
O79 2 a. orange . . . 3·00 30
O80 2½ a. violet . . . 2·00 6·00
O81 4 a. brown . . . 3·75 1·40
O82 8 a. violet . . . 3·50 3·00

1943. Stamps of India (King George VI) optd **JIND SERVICE.**
O83 **93** 1 r. slate and brown . . . 18·00 42·00
O84 2 r. purple and brown . . . 42·00 £120
O85 5 r. green and blue . . . 90·00 £300
O86 10 r. purple and red . . . £160 £375

JOHORE Pt. 1

A state of the Federation of Malaya incorporated in Malaysia in 1963.

100 cents = 1 dollar (Straits or Malayan)

Queen Victoria stamps of Straits Settlements overprinted.

1876. Optd with Crescent and Star.
1 **1** 2 c. brown . . . £8500 £3500

1882. Optd **JOHORE.**
8 **1** 2 c. pink (no full point) . . . 65·00 80·00
6 2 c. pink (with full point) . . . £130 £140

1884. Optd **JOHOR.**
10 **1** 2 c. pink (no full point) . . . 6·50 4·50
14 2 c. pink (with full point) . . . 90·00 45·00

1891. Surch **JOHOR Two CENTS.**
17 **1** 2 c. on 24 c. green . . . 23·00 35·00

21 Sultan Aboubakar 24 Sultan Ibrahim

1891.
21 **21** 1 c. purple . . . 30 50
22 2 c. purple and yellow . . . 50 1·50
23 3 c. purple and red . . . 55 50
24 4 c. purple and black . . . 2·75 12·00
25 5 c. purple and green . . . 7·00 20·00
26 6 c. purple and blue . . . 8·00 20·00
27 $1 green and red . . . 60·00 £130

1892. Surch **3 cents.**
28 **21** 3 c. on 4 c. purple and black . . . 2·00 50
29 3 c. on 5 c. purple and green . . . 80 2·00
30 3 c. on 6 c. purple and blue . . . 2·00 2·25
31 3 c. on $1 green and red . . . 10·00 48·00

1896. Sultan's Coronation. Optd **KEMAHKOTAAN.**
32 **21** 1 c. purple . . . 45 85
33 2 c. purple and yellow . . . 45 1·00
34 3 c. purple and red . . . 55 1·00
35 4 c. purple and black . . . 80 2·25
36 5 c. purple and green . . . 5·50 7·50
37 6 c. purple and blue . . . 3·50 6·00
38 $1 green and red . . . 40·00 90·00

1896.
39 **24** 1 c. green . . . 70 45
40 2 c. green and blue . . . 40 30
41 3 c. green and purple . . . 2·75 1·75
42 4 c. green and red . . . 50 60
43 4 c. yellow and red . . . 75 75
44 5 c. green and brown . . . 75 1·40
45 6 c. green and yellow . . . 80 2·50
46 10 c. green and black . . . 7·00 45·00
47 25 c. green and mauve . . . 9·00 38·00
48 50 c. green and red . . . 13·00 40·00
49 $1 purple and green . . . 26·00 65·00
50 $2 purple and red . . . 27·00 65·00
51 $3 purple and blue . . . 28·00 90·00
52 $4 purple and brown . . . 28·00 75·00
53 $5 purple and yellow . . . 60·00 £110

1903. Surch in figures and words.
54 **24** 3 c. on 4 c. yellow and red . . . 50 1·10
55 10 c. on 4 c. grn & red (A) . . . 2·50 7·00
59 10 c. on 4 c. grn & red (B) . . . 9·00 35·00
58 10 c. on 4 c. yell & red (B) . . . 20·00 35·00
56 50 c. on $3 purple & blue . . . 27·00 80·00
60 50 c. on $5 purple & yellow . . . 65·00 £130
57 $1 on $2 purple and red . . . 60·00 £110
10 c. on 4 c. Type A, "cents" in small letters. Type B, "CENTS" in capitals.

33 Sultan Sir Ibrahim

1904.
78 **33** 1 c. purple and green . . . 40 15
90 2 c. purple and orange . . . 50 2·75
63 3 c. purple and black . . . 3·00 50
91 4 c. purple and red . . . 90 60
109 5 c. purple and green . . . 30 30
83 8 c. purple and blue . . . 4·00 5·00
84 10 c. purple and black . . . 38·00 3·00
116 25 c. purple and green . . . 2·25 1·00
119 50 c. purple and red . . . 3·00 1·60
120 $1 green and mauve . . . 3·00 85
121 $2 green and red . . . 5·50 3·50
72 $3 green and blue . . . 23·00 70·00
73 $4 green and brown . . . 24·00 90·00
124 $5 green and orange . . . 50·00 50·00
75 $10 green and black . . . 48·00 £130
76 $50 green and blue . . . £140 £200
77 $100 green and red . . . £275 £425
128 $500 blue and red . . . £16000

1912. Surch **3 CENTS.** and bars.
88 **33** 3 c. on 8 c. purple and blue . . . 2·75 5·00

1918.
103 **33** 1 c. purple and black . . . 30 20
89 2 c. purple and green . . . 40 80
104 2 c. purple and sepia . . . 85 3·00
105 2 c. green . . . 40 40
106 3 c. green . . . 1·50 4·00
107 3 c. purple and sepia . . . 1·10 1·50
110 6 c. purple and red . . . 40 45
93 10 c. purple and blue . . . 1·75 1·40
112 10 c. purple and yellow . . . 30 25
113 12 c. purple and blue . . . 1·00 1·25
114 12 c. blue . . . 35·00 4·00
115 21 c. purple and orange . . . 2·00 3·00
117 30 c. purple and orange . . . 5·00 4·00
118 40 c. purple and brown . . . 5·00 4·50

37 Sultan Sir Ibrahim and Sultana 38 Sultan Sir Ibrahim

1935.
129 **37** 8 c. violet and grey . . . 3·00 50

1940.
130 **38** 8 c. black and blue . . . 14·00 30

1948. Silver Wedding. As T **11b/11c** of Gambia.
131 10 c. violet . . . 20 30
132 $5 green . . . 24·00 35·00

39 Sultan Sir Ibrahim 40 Sultan Sir Ibrahim

1949.
133 **39** 1 c. black . . . 10 10
134 2 c. orange . . . 10 10
135 3 c. green . . . 35 60
136 4 c. brown . . . 10 10
136a 5 c. purple . . . 30 10
137 6 c. grey . . . 20 10
138 8 c. red . . . 2·50 90
138a 8 c. green . . . 3·00 1·50
139 10 c. mauve . . . 40 10
139a 12 c. red . . . 2·25 3·00
140 15 c. blue . . . 2·00 10
141 20 c. black and green . . . 45 1·00
141a 20 c. blue . . . 80 10
142 25 c. purple and orange . . . 60 10
142a 30 c. red and purple . . . 1·75 2·25

142b 39 35 c. red and purple . . . 3·25 1·00
143 40 c. red and purple . . . 3·50 7·50
144 50 c. black and blue . . . 1·00 10
145 $1 blue and purple . . . . 3·50 1·50
146 $2 green and red . . . . . 14·00 3·50
147 $5 green and brown . . . . 40·00 9·00

1949. U.P.U. As T **11d/11g** of Gambia.
148 10 c. purple 30 15
149 15 c. blue . . . . 1·25 1·00
150 25 c. orange . . . . 65 2·25
151 50 c. black . . . . 1·25 2·25

1953. Coronation. As T **11h** of Gambia.
152 10 c. black and purple 50 10

1955. Diamond Jubilee of Sultan.
153 **40** 10 c. red 10 10

41 Sultan Sir Ismail and Johore Coat of Arms

1960. Coronation of Sultan.
154 **41** 10 c. multicoloured 20 20

1960. As Nos. 92/102 of Kedah but with inset portrait of Sultan Sir Ismail.
155 1 c. black 10 30
156 2 c. red 10 50
157 4 c. sepia 10 10
158 5 c. lake 10 10
159 8 c. green . . . . 1·50 2·25
160 10 c. purple 30 10
161 20 c. blue . . . . 1·00 30
162 50 c. black and blue 30 10
163 $1 blue and purple . . . . . 1·25 2·00
164 $2 green and red . . . . . . 7·50 11·00
165 $5 brown and green . . . . . 24·00 25·00

42 "Vanda hookeriana"

1965. Inset portrait of Sultan Ismail. Multicoloured.
166 1 c. Type **42** 10 30
167 2 c. "Arundina graminifolia" . . 10 50
168 5 c. "Paphiopedilum niveum" . . 10 10
169 6 c. "Spathoglottis plicata" . . 40 30
170 10 c. "Arachnis flos-aeris" . . 40 10
171 15 c. "Rhyncostylis retusa" . . 1·50 10
172 20 c. "Phalaenopsis violacea" . . 1·50 60

The higher values used in Johore were Nos. 20/7 of Malaysia (National Issues).

44 "Delias ninus"

1971. Butterflies. Inset portrait of Sultan Ismail. Multicoloured.
175 1 c. Type **44** . . . . 30 1·00
176 2 c. "Danaus melanippus" . . 75 1·25
177 5 c. "Parthenos sylvia" 95 20
178 6 c. "Papilio demoleus" . . . . 95 1·60
179 10 c. "Hebomoia glaucippe" . . 95 20
180 15 c. "Precis orithya" 95 10
181 20 c. "Valeria valeria" 95 30

The higher values in use with this issue were Nos. 64/71 of Malaysia (National Issues).

45 "Rafflesia hasseltii" (inset portrait of Sultan Ismail)

46 Coconuts. (Inset portrait of Sultan Mahmood)

1979. Flowers. Multicoloured.
188 1 c. Type **45** 10 50
189 2 c. "Pterocarpus indicus" . . 10 50
190 5 c. "Lagerstroemia speciosa" . 10 30
191 10 c. "Durio zibethinus" . . . 15 10
192 15 c. "Hibiscus rosa-sinensis" . 15 10
193 20 c. "Rhododendron scortechinii" 20 10
194 25 c. "Etlingera elatior" (inscr "Phaeomeria speciosa") . . 40 20

1986. Agricultural Products of Malaysia. Mult.
202 1 c. Coffee 10 10
203 2 c. Type **46** 10 10
204 5 c. Cocoa 10 10
205 10 c. Black pepper 10 10
206 15 c. Rubber 10 10
207 20 c. Oil palm 10 10
208 30 c. Rice 15 20

POSTAGE DUE STAMPS

D 1

1938.
D1 D 1 1 c. red . . . . 12·00 35·00
D2 4 c. green . . . . 40·00 40·00
D3 8 c. orange . . . . 48·00 £140
D4 10 c. brown . . . . 48·00 48·00
D5 12 c. purple . . . . 55·00 £110

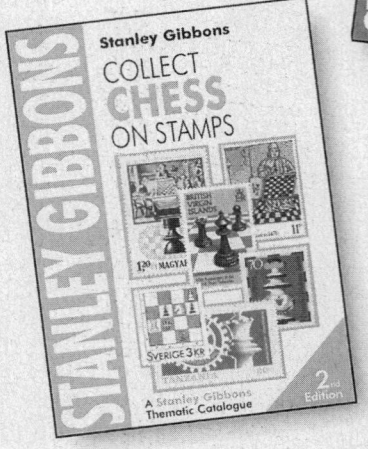

JORDAN Pt. 1, Pt. 19

A territory to the E. of Israel, formerly called Transjordan; under British mandate from 1918 to 1946. Independent kingdom since 1946.

1920. 1000 milliemes = 100 piastres = £1 Egyptian.
1927. 1000 milliemes = £1 Palestinian.
1950. 1000 fils = 1 Jordan dinar.

شرق الاردن

(**1** "East of Jordan")

1920. Stamps of Palestine optd with T **1**.

1 **3** 1 m. brown 50 1·25
10 2 m. green 50 70
3 3 m. brown 90 1·25
4 4 m. red 95 1·25
5 5 m. orange 1·50 1·25
14 1 p. blue 1·50 1·75
15 2 p. olive 3·50 3·00
16 5 p. purple 2·25 6·00
17 9 p. ochre 3·50 20·00
18 10 p. blue 4·25 20·00
19 20 p. grey 8·00 35·00

(**2**) (Tenth of a piastre) (**3**) (Piastre)

1922. Handstamped with T **2** or **3** (piastre values).

(a) 1920 issue of Jordan (No. 1 etc).

28 **2** $\frac{1}{10}$ p. on 1 m. brown 20·00 25·00
29 $\frac{2}{10}$ p. on 2 m. green 25·00 25·00
22 $\frac{3}{10}$ p. on 3 m. brown 10·00 10·00
23 $\frac{4}{10}$ p. on 4 m. red 50·00 50·00
24 $\frac{5}{10}$ p. on 5 m. orange £180 £100
31 **3** 1 p. on 1 p. blue £200 60·00
25 2 p. on 2 p. olive £250 75·00
26 5 p. on 5 p. purple 50·00 70·00
27a 9 p. on 9 p. ochre £130 £140
33 10 p. on 10 p. blue £850 £1000
34 20 p. on 20 p. grey £650 £850

(b) Type **3** of Palestine.

35 **3** 10 p. on 10 p. blue £1800 £2500
36 20 p. on 20 p. grey £2500 £3000

(**4** "Arab Government of the East, April, 1921")

1922. Stamps of Jordan handstamped with T **4**.

45 **3** 1 m. brown 12·00 15·00
46a 2 m. green 8·00 8·00
39b 3 m. brown 7·00 7·00
40 4 m. red 45·00 50·00
41a 5 m. orange 15·00 10·00
48a 1 p. blue 15·00 9·00
42c 2 p. olive 12·00 10·00
43a 5 p. purple 60·00 80·00
44b 9 p. ochre 65·00 80·00
52a 10 p. blue £1100 £1600
53a 20 p. grey £1100 £1800

حكومة الشرق
العربية
نيسان سنة ٩٢١

(**5** "Arab Government of the East, April, 1921")

1923. Stamps of Jordan optd with T **5**.

62 **3** 1 m. brown 16·00 24·00
63 2 m. green 14·00 18·00
56 3 m. brown 12·00 15·00
57 4 m. red 10·00 12·00
64 5 m. orange 10·00 12·00
65 1 p. blue 10·00 14·00
59 2 p. olive 15·00 15·00
60 5 p. purple 60·00 80·00
66 9 p. ochre 75·00 £100
67 10 p. blue 70·00 £100
68 20 p. grey 70·00 £100

(**6**) (**7**)

(**8**) (**9**)

1923. Various stamps surch as T **6/9**.

(a) 1920 issue of Jordan (No. 1 etc).

70 – $2\frac{1}{2}$/10ths p. on 5 m. £160 £160
70c **6** $\frac{5}{10}$ p. on 3 m. † £5000
70d $\frac{5}{10}$ p. on 5 m.
70e **9** 2 p. on 20 p.

(b) No. 7 of Palestine.

71 **6** $\frac{5}{10}$ p. on 3 m. £3000

(c) 1922 issue of Jordan (Nos. 22 etc).

72 **6** $\frac{5}{10}$ p. on 3 m. £7000
73 $\frac{5}{10}$ p. on 5 p. 70·00 8·00
73b $\frac{5}{10}$ p. on 9 p. £1200
74 **7** $\frac{1}{2}$ p. on 5 p. 70·00 80·00
75a $\frac{1}{2}$ p. on 9 p. £350 £400
77 **8** 1 p. on 5 p. 80·00 £100

(d) 1922 issue of Jordan (Nos. 396 etc).

78b **6** $\frac{5}{10}$ p. on 3 m. 40·00 50·00
79 $\frac{5}{10}$ p. on 5 p. 8·00 14·00
79d $\frac{5}{10}$ p. on 9 p. — £1200
80c **7** $\frac{1}{8}$ p. on 2 p. 60·00 £110
82 $\frac{1}{8}$ p. on 5 p. £1800
83b **8** 1 p. on 5 p. £2000 £2250

(e) 1923 issue of Jordan (Nos. 56 etc).

84 **6** $\frac{5}{10}$ p. on 3 m. 25·00 30·00
85 **7** $\frac{1}{8}$ p. on 9 p. 90·00 £150
87 **9** 1 p. on 10 p. £2250 £2500
88 2 p. on 20 p. 60·00 80·00

حكومة
الشرق العربية
٩ شعبان ١٣٤١

(**10** "Arab Government of the East, 9 Sha'ban, 1341")

1923. Stamps of Saudi Arabia optd with T **10**.

89 **11** $\frac{1}{8}$ p. brown 2·00 1·75
96 $\frac{1}{4}$ on $\frac{1}{8}$ p. brown (47) 4·00 5·50
90 $\frac{1}{8}$ p. red 2·00 1·75
91 1 p. blue 1·25 80
92 $1\frac{1}{8}$ p. lilac 1·50 1·75
93 2 p. orange 2·00 5·50
94 3 p. brown 3·00 8·00
95 5 p. green 5·00 9·00
97 10 on 5 p. green (49) 15·00 22·00

(**11** "Arab Government of the East, Commemoration of Independence, 25 May, 1923")

1923. Stamps of Palestine optd with T **11**.

98A **3** 1 m. brown 17·00 17·00
99A 2 m. green 28·00 35·00
100A 3 m. brown 10·00 12·00
101A 4 m. red 10·00 12·00
102A 5 m. orange 50·00 60·00
103B 1 p. blue 50·00 60·00
104A 2 p. olive 50·00 70·00
105A 5 p. purple 60·00 70·00
106B 9 p. ochre 50·00 60·00
107A 10 p. blue 60·00 80·00
108B 20 p. grey 70·00 90·00

1923. No. 107 surch with T **9**.

109 1 p. on 10 p. blue £6000

نصف قرش

(**12**)

1923. No. 92 surch with T **12**.

110 $\frac{1}{2}$ p. on $1\frac{1}{2}$ p. lilac 6·00 6·00

حكومة
الشرق العربية
٩ شعبان ١٣٤١

(**13** "Arab Government of the East, 9 Sha'ban, 1341")

1923. Stamp of Saudi Arabia handstamped as T **13**.

112 **11** $\frac{1}{2}$ p. red 6·00 7·00

(**15** "Arab Government of the East")

1924. Stamps of Saudi Arabia optd with T **15**.

114 **11** $\frac{1}{2}$ p. red 6·00 8·00
115 1 p. blue £300 £200
116 $1\frac{1}{2}$ p. violet £350

ملك العرب

(**16** "Commemorating the coming of His Majesty the King of the Arabs" and date)

1924. Stamps of Saudi Arabia optd with T **15** and **16**.

117 **11** $\frac{1}{2}$ p. red 1·00 1·00
118 1 p. blue 1·25 1·25
119 $1\frac{1}{2}$ p. violet 2·00 2·00
120 2 p. orange 4·00 4·00

حكومة الشرق
العربي
١٣٤٢

(**17** "Government of the Arab East, 1342")

1924. Stamps of Saudi Arabia optd with T **17**.

125 **11** $\frac{1}{8}$ p. brown 35 25
126 $\frac{1}{4}$ p. green 30 30
127 $\frac{1}{2}$ p. red 30 30
129 1 p. blue 2·50 1·50
130 $1\frac{1}{2}$ p. lilac 2·50 2·50
131 2 p. orange 2·00 2·00
132 3 p. red 1·50 1·50
133 5 p. green 2·00 2·50
134 10 p. purple and mauve 4·00 5·00

(**18** "Government of the Arab East, 1343")

1925. Stamps as T **20** of Saudi Arabia optd with T **18**.

135 $\frac{1}{8}$ p. brown 30 70
136 $\frac{1}{4}$ p. blue 30 70
137 $\frac{1}{2}$ p. red 50 40
138 1 p. green 40 40
139 $1\frac{1}{2}$ p. orange 90 1·75
140 2 p. blue 1·25 2·00
141 3 p. green 1·75 3·00
142 5 p. brown 2·00 7·00

شرق
الاردن

(**19** "East of the Jordan")

1925. Stamps of Palestine (without Palestine opt) optd with T **19**.

143 **3** 1 m. brown 10 65
144 2 m. yellow 10 30
145 3 m. blue 20 30
146 4 m. red 20 65
147 5 m. orange 20 30
148 6 m. green 20 50
149 7 m. brown 20 50
150 8 m. red 30 30
151 13 m. blue 50 60
152 1 p. grey 50 50
153 2 p. olive 1·00 1·25
154 5 p. purple 3·00 4·00
155 9 p. ochre 6·00 8·00
156 10 p. blue 12·00 14·00
157 20 p. violet 20·00 25·00

22 Emir Abdullah **23**

1927. Figures at left and right.

159 **22** 2 m. blue 15 30
160 3 m. red 60 70
161 4 m. green 70 1·25
162 5 m. orange 30 30
163 10 m. red 50 1·00
164 15 m. blue 60 30
165 20 m. olive 80 90
166 **23** 50 m. purple 2·50 4·00
167 90 m. brown 6·00 12·00
168 100 m. blue 8·00 9·00
169 200 m. violet 17·00 24·00
170 500 m. brown 60·00 85·00
171 1000 m. grey £100 £140

(**24** "Constitution")

1928. Optd with T **24**.

172 **22** 2 m. blue 80 2·00
173 3 m. red 90 3·00
174 4 m. green 1·00 3·50
175 5 m. orange 1·00 2·00
176 10 m. red 1·50 4·00
177 15 m. blue 1·50 2·00
178 20 m. olive 3·00 8·00
179 **23** 50 m. purple 5·00 9·00
180 90 m. brown 14·00 40·00
181 100 m. blue 22·00 45·00
182 200 m. violet 65·00 £100

1930. "Locust campaign". Optd **LOCUST CAMPAIGN** in English and Arabic.

183 **22** 2 m. blue 1·10 4·00
184 3 m. red 1·50 5·00
185 4 m. green 1·50 5·00
186 5 m. orange 15·00 14·00
187 10 m. red 1·50 4·00
188 15 m. blue 1·50 2·25
189 20 m. olive 1·50 4·00
190 **23** 50 m. purple 5·00 9·50
191 90 m. brown 10·00 40·00
192 100 m. blue 12·00 40·00
193 200 m. violet 30·00 85·00
194 500 m. brown 75·00 £170

28 Emir **29** Emir

1930.

230 **28** 1 m. brown 20 75
195 2 m. green 30 50
258 3 m. pink 15 15
196a 3 m. green 1·75 85
259 4 m. green 15 15
233 4 m. pink 1·75 1·25
198 5 m. orange 40 40
199 10 m. red 90 15
260 10 m. violet 15 15
261 12 m. red 35 30
200 15 m. blue 65 20
262 15 m. green 40 40
201 20 m. green 1·25 35
263 20 m. blue 45 45
202 **29** 50 m. purple 1·75 1·25
203 90 m. bistre 2·50 4·25
240 100 m. blue 5·00 1·75
241 200 m. violet 9·00 6·50
242 500 m. brown 13·00 12·00
243 £P1 grey 24·00 22·00

30 Mushetta **32** The Khasneh at Petra

1933.

208 **30** 1 m. black and purple 50 1·40
209 – 2 m. black and red 60 1·00
210 – 3 m. green 75 1·40
211 – 4 m. black and brown 1·25 2·25
212 – 5 m. black and orange 1·25 1·25
213 – 10 m. red 1·50 3·00
214 **32** 15 m. blue 2·50 1·25
215 – 20 m. black and olive 3·50 5·00
216 – 50 m. black and purple 9·00 10·00
217 **30** 90 m. black and yellow 13·00 25·00
218 – 100 m. black and blue 13·00 25·00
219 – 200 m. black and violet 45·00 60·00
220 **32** 500 m. red and brown £130 £170
221 – \$P1 black and green £350 £550

DESIGNS—HORIZ: 2 m. Nymphaeum, Jerash; 3., 90 m. Kasr Kharana; 4 m. Kerak Castle; 5., 100 m. Temple of Artemis, Jerash; 10., 200 m. Ajlun Castle; 20 m. Allenby Bridge over Jordan; 50 m. Threshing. VERT: £P1, Emir Abdullah; Nos. 216 to 221 are larger ($33\frac{1}{2}$ × 24 mm. or 24 × $33\frac{1}{2}$ mm).

35 Map of Jordan **39** Parliament Building

1946. Installation of King Abdullah and National Independence.

249 **35** 1 m. purple 10 10
250 2 m. orange 10 10
251 3 m. green 10 10
252 4 m. violet 10 10
253 10 m. brown 15 15
254 12 m. red 15 15
255 20 m. blue 20 20
256 50 m. blue 40 40
257 200 m. green 1·60 2·00

1947. Inauguration of 1st National Parliament.
276 39 1 m. violet 10 20
277 3 m. red 10 20
278 4 m. green 10 20
279 10 m. purple 10 20
280 12 m. red 10 20
281 20 m. blue 10 20
282 50 m. red 40 40
283 100 m. pink 75 90
284 200 m. green 1·50 1·50

40 Globe and Forms of Transport

44 Lockheed Constellation Airliner and Globe

1949. 75th Anniv of U.P.U.
285 40 1 m. brown 15 25
286 4 m. green 25 30
287 10 m. red 30 55
288 20 m. blue 50 65
289 – 50 m. green 1·10 1·40
DESIGN: 50 m. King Abdullah.

1950. Air.
295 44 5 f. purple and yellow 40 25
296 10 f. brown and violet 40 25
297 15 f. red and olive 40 40
298 20 f. black and blue 50 40
299 50 f. green and mauve 90 75
300 100 f. brown and blue 1·25 90
301 150 f. orange and black 2·25 1·50

1952. Optd **FILS** and bars or **J.D.** (on 1 d.).
313 28 1 f. on 1 m. brown 25 25
314 2 f. on 2 m. green 25 25
315 3 f. on 3 m. green 20·00
316 3 f. on 3 m. pink 25 25
310 4 f. on 4 m. pink 6·00 2·75
318 4 f. on 4 m. green 25 25
319 5 f. on 5 m. orange 30 30
320 10 f. on 10 m. red 22·00
321 10 f. on 10 m. violet 30 30
322 12 f. on 12 m. red 30 30
312 15 f. on 15 m. blue 20·00 10·00
325 15 f. on 15 m. green 45 30
326 20 f. on 20 m. green 23·00
327 20 f. on 20 m. blue 1·00 50
328 29 50 f. on 50 m. purple 80 70
329 90 f. on 90 m. bistre 7·00 4·50
330 100 f. on 100 m. blue 4·00 1·75
331 200 f. on 200 m. violet 6·50 2·50
332 500 f. on 500 m. brown 15·00 4·50
333 1 d. on £P1 grey 30·00 8·00

48 Dome of the Rock and Khazneh at Petra

49 King Abdullah

1952. Unification of Jordan and Palestine.
355 48 1 f. green and brown 20 20
356 2 f. red and green 20 20
357 3 f. black and red 20 20
358 4 f. orange and green 20 20
359 5 f. purple and brown 25 25
360 10 f. brown and violet 25 25
361 20 f. black and blue 65 35
362 100 f. sepia and brown 2·50 1·75
363 200 f. orange and violet 5·75 3·25

1952. (a) Size 18 × 21½ mm.
364 49 5 f. orange 20 20
365 10 f. lilac 20 20
366 12 f. red 75 50
367 15 f. olive 45 20
368 20 f. blue 50 25
(b) Size 20 × 24½ mm.
369 49 50 f. purple 1·10 45
370 90 f. brown 3·25 1·75
371 100 f. blue 3·50 95

1953. Optd with two horiz bars across Arabic commemorative inscription.
378 48 1 f. green and brown 20 20
379 2 f. red and green 20 20
380 3 f. black and red 20 20
381 4 f. orange and green 20 20
382 5 f. purple and brown 20 20
383 10 f. brown and violet 65 35
384 20 f. black and blue 65 50
385 100 f. brown and blue 3·50 1·00
386 200 f. orange and violet 5·00 3·50

51 Omar Mosque, Jerusalem

51a King Hussein

1953. Obligatory Tax stamps optd for postal use as in T **51**. (a) Inscr "MILS".
387 T 36 1 m. blue 20 20
388 3 m. green 20 20
389 5 m. purple 60·00 55·00
390 – 10 m. red 18·00 18·00
391 – 15 m. black 45 45
392 – 20 m. brown 60·00 40·00
393 – 50 m. violet 45 40
394 – 100 m. red 4·75 3·75
(b) Inscr "MILS" and optd **PALESTINE**.
395 T 36 1 m. blue 25·00 23·00
396 3 m. green 25·00 23·00
397 5 m. purple 25·00 23·00
398 – 10 m. red 25·00 23·00
399 – 15 m. black 28·00 23·00
400 – 20 m. brown 28·00 23·00
400a – 50 m. violet
401 – 100 m. red 40·00 35·00
(c) Inscr "MILS", optd **FILS** (T334, etc).
402 T 36 1 f. on 1 m. blue 27·00 24·00
403 3 f. on 3 m. green 27·00 24·00
404 – 10 f. on 10 m. red 27·00 24·00
405 – 15 f. on 15 m. black 27·00 24·00
406 – 20 f. on 20 m. brown 27·00 24·00
407 – 100 f. on 100 m. red 30·00 30·00
(d) Inscr "FILS".
408 T 36 5 f. purple 20 15
409 – 10 f. red 25 15
410 – 15 f. black 55 45
411 – 20 f. brown 1·00 70
412 – 100 f. orange 2·40 1·40

1953. Enthronement of King Hussein.
413 51a 1 f. black and green 15 15
414 4 f. black and red 15 10
415 15 f. black and blue 1·00 20
416 20 f. black and lilac 1·60 20
417 50 f. black and green 3·50 1·75
418 100 f. black and blue 7·00 4·75

52 El-Deir Temple, Petra

54a Temple of Artemis Jerash

1954.
445 52 1 f. brn & grn (postage) 10 10
446 – 2 f. black and red 10 10
447 52 3 f. violet and purple 10 10
448 – 4 f. green and brown 10 10
449 52 5 f. green and violet 15 10
450 – 10 f. green and purple 20 10
451 – 12 f. sepia and red 70 10
452 – 15 f. red and brown 45 15
453 – 20 f. green & blue 30 15
454 – 50 f. red and blue 70 15
428 – 100 f. blue and green 1·50 55
456 – 200 f. blue and lake 4·00 1·25
457 – 500 f. purple and brown 15·00 7·00
458 – 1 d. lake and olive 23·00 10·00
470 54a 5 f. orange and blue (air) 15 10
433 10 f. red and brown 25 10
434 25 f. blue and green 40 15
435 35 f. blue and mauve 50 20
436 40 f. slate and red 60 20
437 50 f. orange and blue 75 35
438 100 f. brown and blue 1·00 75
439 150 f. lake and turquoise 1·60 1·00
DESIGNS—VERT: 2 f., 4 f., 500 f., 1 d. King Hussein. HORIZ: 10 f., 15 f., 20 f. Dome of the Rock, Jerusalem; 12 f., 50 f., 100 f., 200 f. Facade of Mosque of El Aqsa.

1955. Arab Postal Union. As T **80** of Egypt but inscr "H. K. JORDAN" at top and "ARAB POSTAL UNION" at foot.
440 15 f. green 30 15
441 20 f. violet 30 15
442 25 f. brown 40 30

56 King Hussein and Queen Dina

1955. Royal Wedding.
443 56 15 f. blue 1·00 50
444 100 f. lake 3·50 2·00

58 Envelope with Postmarks in English and Arabic

59 "Flame of Freedom"

1956. 1st Arab Postal Congress, Amman.
459 58 1 f. brown and black 10 10
460 4 f. red and black 10 10
461 15 f. blue and black 10 10
462 20 f. bistre and black 15 10
463 50 f. blue and black 45 30
464 100 f. orange and black 70 50

1958. 10th Anniv of Declaration of Human Rights.
476 59 5 f. red and blue 10 10
477 15 f. black and brown 15 10
478 35 f. purple and green 35 25
479 45 f. black and red 50 30

60 King Hussein

1959. Centres in black.
480 60 1 f. green 10 10
481 2 f. violet 10 10
482 3 f. red 20 10
483 4 f. purple 20 10
484 7 f. green 25 10
485 12 f. red 40 10
486 15 f. red 40 10
487 21 f. green 40 10
488 25 f. brown 55 10
489 35 f. blue 80 10
490 40 f. green 1·10 15
491 50 f. red 1·50 15
492 100 f. green 2·00 40
493 200 f. purple 5·00 1·50
494 500 f. blue 13·50 5·50
495 1 d. purple 24·00 14·00

61 Arab League Centre, Cairo

1960. Inaug. of Arab League Centre, Cairo.
496 61 15 f. black and green 20 15

62 "Care of Refugees"

1960. World Refugee Year.
497 62 15 f. red and blue 15 10
498 35 f. blue and bistre 15 15

63 Shah of Iran and King Hussein

1960. Visit of Shah of Iran.
499 63 15 f. multicoloured 25 15
500 35 f. multicoloured 40 35
501 50 f. multicoloured 60 50

64 Petroleum Refinery, Zarka

1961. Inaug of Jordanian Petroleum Refinery.
502 64 15 f. blue and violet 20 10
503 35 f. brown and violet 30 20

65 Jordanian Families and Graph

67 Campaign Emblem

1961. 1st Jordanian Census Commemoration.
504 65 15 f. brown 25 10

1961. Dag Hammarskjold Memorial Issue. Optd **IN MEMORIAL OF DAG HAMMARSKJOELD 1904–1961** in English and Arabic and laurel leaves at top and bottom.
505 62 15 f. red and blue 1·75 1·75
506 35 f. blue and bistre 2·00 2·00

1962. Malaria Eradication.
507 67 15 f. mauve 20 10
508 35 f. blue 40 20

68 Telephone Exchange, Amman

1962. Inauguration of Amman's Automatic Telephone Exchange.
510 68 15 f. blue and purple 15 15
511 35 f. purple and green 35 15

69 Aqaba Port and King Hussein

1962. Opening of Aqaba Port.
512 69 15 f. black and purple 25 10
513 35 f. black and blue 60 25

70 Dag Hammarskjold and UN Headquarters

1963. 17th Anniv of U.N.O.
515 70 15 f. red, olive and blue 15 15
516 35 f. blue, red and olive 55 30
517 50 f. olive, blue and red 80 55

71 Church of Holy Virgin's Tomb, Jerusalem

72 League Centre, Cairo and Emblem

1963. "Holy Places". Multicoloured.
519 50 f. Type **71** 85 85
520 50 f. Basilica of the Agony, Gethsemane 85 85
521 50 f. Holy Sepulchre, Jerusalem 85 85
522 50 f. Nativity Church, Bethlehem 85 85
523 50 f. Haram of Ibrahim, Hebron 85 85
524 50 f. Dome of the Rock, Jerusalem 85 85
525 50 f. Omer-el-Khetab Mosque, Jerusalem 85 85
526 50 f. El-Aqsa Mosque, Jerusalem 85 85

1963. Arab League.
527 72 15 f. blue 20 15
528 35 f. red 65 30

73 Wheat and F.A.O. Emblem

74 Canal and Symbols

1963. Freedom from Hunger.
529 73 15 f. green, black & blue 15 10
530 35 f. green, black & apple 35 20

1963. East Ghor Canal Project.
532 74 1 f. black and bistre 15 10
533 4 f. black and blue 15 10
534 5 f. black and purple 15 10
535 10 f. black and green 25 10
536 35 f. black and orange 1·50 1·00

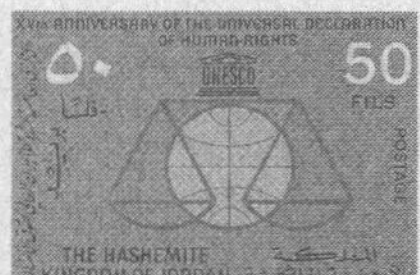

75 Scales of Justice and Globe

1963. 15th Anniv of Declaration of Human Rights.
537 **75** 50 f. red and blue 40 20
538 50 f. blue and red 40 20

1963. Surch in English and Arabic.
539 **60** 1 f. on 21 f. black & green . 20 15
540 2 f. on 21 f. black & green . 20 15
541 4 f. on 12 f. black & red . . 7·75 7·50
542 – 4 f. on 12 f. sepia and red (No. 451) 30 25
543 **60** 5 f. on 21 f. black & green . 50 35
544 25 f. on 35 f. blue . . . . . 2·00 70

77 King Hussein and Red Crescent

1963. Red Crescent Commemoration.
545 **77** 1 f. purple and red 10 10
546 2 f. turquoise and red . . . 10 10
547 3 f. blue and red 10 10
548 4 f. turquoise and red . . . 10 10
549 5 f. sepia and red 10 10
550 85 f. green and red . . . . 1·75 1·40

78 Red Cross Emblem

1963. Centenary of Red Cross.
552 **78** 1 f. purple and red 10 10
553 2 f. turquoise and red . . . 10 10
554 3 f. blue and red 10 10
555 4 f. turquoise and red . . . 10 10
556 5 f. sepia and red 10 10
557 85 f. green and red . . . . 2·75 1·75

79 Kings Hussein of Hejaz and Hussein of Jordan

1963. Arab Renaissance Day.
559 **79** 15 f. multicoloured 35 25
560 25 f. multicoloured 50 35
561 35 f. multicoloured 90 70
562 50 f. multicoloured . . . . 2·00 1·75

80 Al Aqsa Mosque, Pope Paul and King Hussein

1964. Pope Paul's Visit to the Holy Land.
564 **80** 15 f. green and black . . . 20 15
565 – 35 f. mauve and black . . . 50 35
566 – 50 f. brown and black . . . 80 50
567 – 80 f. blue and black . . . 1·50 90
DESIGNS: 35 f. Dome of the Rock (Mosque of Omar), Jerusalem; 50 f. Church of the Holy Sepulchre, Jerusalem; 80 f. Church of the Nativity, Bethlehem.

81 Prince Abdullah

1964. 2nd Birthday of Prince Abdullah. Mult.
568 5 f. Prince standing by wall . . 30 10
569 10 f. Head of Prince and roses . 35 25
570 35 f. Type **81** 75 50
SIZES: 5 f. as Type **81** but vert; 10 f. diamond (63 × 63 mm).

NOTE.—A set of ten triangular 20 f. stamps showing astronauts and rockets was issued, but very few were put on sale at the Post Office and we are not listing them unless we receive satisfactory evidence as to their status.

82 Basketball 83 Woman and Child

1964. Olympic Games, Tokyo (1st issue).
571 **82** 1 f. red 10 10
572 – 2 f. blue 10 10
573 – 3 f. green 10 10
574 – 4 f. buff 10 10
575 – 5 f. violet 10 10
576 – 35 f. red . . . . 1·40 60
577 – 50 f. green . . . . 2·50 1·25
578 – 100 f. brown . . . . 4·00 2·25
DESIGNS—VERT: 2 f. Volleyball; 3 f. Football; 5 f. Running. HORIZ: 4 f. Table tennis; 35 f. Cycling; 50 f. Fencing; 100 f. Pole vaulting.
See also Nos. 610/17 and 641/6.

1964. 4th Session of Social Studies Seminar, Amman.
580 **83** 5 f. multicoloured 10 10
581 10 f. multicoloured 20 10
582 25 f. multicoloured 30 20

84 King Hussein Sports Stadium, Amman

1964. Air. Inaug of "Hussein Sports City".
583 **84** 1 f. multicoloured 10 10
584 4 f. multicoloured 10 10
585 10 f. multicoloured 20 15
586 35 f. multicoloured 35 25

85 President Kennedy

1964. Pres. Kennedy Memorial Issue.
588 **85** 1 f. violet 20 20
589 2 f. red 20 20
590 3 f. blue 20 20
591 4 f. brown 20 20
592 5 f. green 20 20
593 85 f. red . . . . 12·50 5·75

86 Statues at Abu Simbel

1964. Nubian Monuments Preservation.
595 **86** 4 f. black and blue 10 10
596 15 f. violet and yellow . . . 25 20
597 25 f. red and green 30 30

87 King Hussein and Map of Palestine in 1920

1964. Arab Summit Conference.
598 **87** 10 f. multicoloured 10 10
599 15 f. multicoloured 20 10
600 25 f. multicoloured 25 10
601 50 f. multicoloured 60 20
602 80 f. multicoloured . . . . 1·10 90

88 Pope Paul VI, King Hussein and Ecumenical Patriarch

1964. Meeting of Pope, King and Patriarch, Jerusalem. Multicoloured, background colour given.
604 **88** 10 f. green 15 10
605 15 f. purple 15 10
606 25 f. brown 25 15
607 50 f. blue 75 50
608 80 f. green . . . . 1·25 1·00

89 Olympic Flame

1964. Olympic Games, Tokyo (2nd issue).
610 **89** 1 f. red 10 10
611 2 f. violet 10 10
612 3 f. green 10 10
613 4 f. brown 10 10
614 5 f. red 10 10
615 35 f. blue 65 55
616 50 f. olive . . . . 1·00 90
617 100 f. blue . . . . 2·25 2·00

90 Scouts crossing River

1964. Jordanian Scouts.
619 **90** 1 f. brown 10 10
620 – 2 f. violet 10 10
621 – 3 f. ochre 10 10
622 – 4 f. lake 10 10
623 – 5 f. green 10 10
624 – 35 f. blue . . . . 3·00 1·10
625 – 50 f. green . . . . 3·25 1·75
DESIGNS: 2 f. First aid; 3 f. Exercising; 4 f. Practising knots; 5 f. Cooking meal; 35 f. Sailing; 50 f. Around camp-fire.

91 Four-coloured Bush Shrike

1964. Air. Birds. Multicoloured.
627 150 f. Type **91** . . . . 11·00 5·00
628 500 f. Ornate Hawk Eagle . . . 35·00 20·00
629 1000 f. Grey-headed Kingfisher . 65·00 35·00
Nos. 628/9 are vert.

92 Bykovsky

1965. Russian Astronauts.
630 40 f. brown and green (Type **92**) 75 75
631 40 f. violet and brown (Gagarin) 75 75
632 40 f. maroon and blue (Nikolaev) 75 75
633 40 f. lilac and bistre (Popovich) . 75 75
634 40 f. sepia and blue (Tereshkova) 75 75
635 40 f. green and pink (Titov) . . 75 75

93 U.N. Headquarters and Emblem

1965. 19th Anniv (1964) of U.N.
638 **93** 30 f. vio, turq & brn 40 20
639 70 f. brown, blue & vio . . 60 45

94 Olympic Flame

1965. Air. Olympic Games, Tokyo (3rd issue).
641 **94** 10 f. red 10 10
642 15 f. violet 10 10
643 20 f. blue 25 10
644 30 f. green 60 35
645 40 f. brown 80 35
646 60 f. mauve . . . . 1·25 70

95 Dagger on Deir Yassin, Palestine

1965. Deir Yassin Massacre.
648 **95** 25 f. red and olive . . . . . 1·00 80

96 Horse-jumping 97 Volleyball Player and Cup

1965. Army Day.
649 **96** 5 f. green 15 10
650 – 10 f. blue 30 10
651 – 35 f. brown 95 45
DESIGNS: 10 f. Tank; 35 f. King Hussein making inspection in army car.

1965. Arab Volleyball Championships.
652 **97** 15 f. olive 60 20
653 35 f. lake . . . . 1·10 50
654 50 f. blue . . . . 1·90 1·10

98 President J. F. Kennedy

1965. 1st Death Anniv of Pres. Kennedy.
656 **98** 10 f. black and green . . . 20 15
657 15 f. violet and orange . . . 40 20
658 25 f. brown and blue . . . 55 30
659 50 f. purple and green . . . 95 60

99 Pope Paul, King Hussein and Dome of the Rock

1965. 1st Anniv of Pope Paul's Visit to the Holy Land.
661 **99** 5 f. brown and mauve . . . 35 10
662 10 f. lake and green . . . 65 25
663 15 f. blue and flesh . . . 90 35
664 50 f. grey and pink . . . 2·50 1·10

100 Cathedral Steps

1965. Air. Jerash Antiquities. Multicoloured.
666 55 f. Type **100** 90 90
667 55 f. Artemis Temple Gate . . . 90 90
668 55 f. Street of Columns . . . 90 90
669 55 f. Columns of South Theatre . 90 90
670 55 f. Forum (horiz) 90 90
671 55 f. South Theatre (horiz) . . . 90 90
672 55 f. Triumphal Arch (horiz) . . 90 90
673 55 f. Temple of Artemis (horiz) . 90 90

101 Jordan Pavilion at Fair

1965. New York World's Fair.
674 **101** 15 f. multicoloured 15 10
675 25 f. multicoloured 35 20
676 50 f. multicoloured 75 45

102 Lamp and Burning Library

1965. Burning of Algiers Library.
678 **102** 25 f. green, red and black . 25 15

103 I.T.U. Emblem and Symbols

1965. Centenary of I.T.U.
679 **103** 25 f. blue and light blue . . 30 15
680 45 f. black and green . . . 50 45

104 "Syncom" Satellite and Pagoda

1965. Space Achievements. Multicoloured.
682 5 f. Type **104** 15 10
683 10 f. North American X-15 rocket airplane 25 10
684 15 f. Astronauts 55 25
685 20 f. As 10 f. 55 25
686 50 f. Type **104** . . . . 1·00 60

105 Dead Sea

1985. Dead Sea. Multicoloured.
688 35 f. Type **105** 60 40
689 35 f. Boats and palms 60 40
690 35 f. Qumran Caves 60 40
691 35 f. Dead Sea Scrolls 60 40

1965. Air. Space Flight of McDivitt and White. Nos. 641/6 optd **James McDivitt Edward White 2-6-1965** in English and Arabic and rocket.
692 **94** 10 f. red . . . . 1·90 70
693 15 f. violet . . . . 1·90 70
694 20 f. blue . . . . 2·75 1·50
695 30 f. green . . . . 3·75 2·50
696 40 f. brown . . . . 4·50 3·25
697 60 f. mauve . . . . 7·50 5·00

107 King Hussein, U.N. Emblem and Headquarters

1965. King Hussein's Visit to France and the U.S.A.
699 **107** 5 f. sepia, blue and pink . . 10 10
700 – 10 f. sepia, green & grey . . 15 10
701 – 20 f. agate, brown & blue . . 30 25
702 **107** 50 f. lilac, brown & blue . . 90 65
DESIGNS: 10 f. King Hussein, Pres. de Gaulle and Eiffel Tower; 20 f. King Hussein, Pres. Johnson and Statue of Liberty.

108 I.C.Y. Emblem

109 A.P.U. Emblem

1965. International Co-operation Year.
704 **108** 5 f. red and orange . . . 20 15
705 10 f. violet and blue . . . 45 20
706 45 f. purple and green . . . 1·75 1·40

1965. 10th Anniv (1964) of Arab Postal Union's Permanent Office at Cairo.
707 **109** 15 f. black and blue . . . 15 15
708 25 f. black and green . . . 45 20

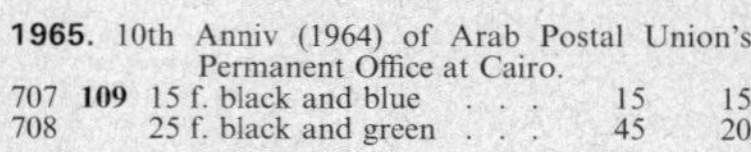

110 Dome of the Rock

1965. Inaug (1964) of "Dome of the Rock".
709 **110** 15 f. multicoloured 75 30
710 25 f. multicoloured . . . . 1·25 80

111 King Hussein

115 First Station of the Cross

114 Agricultural Symbols

1966. (a) Postage. Portraits in blue (1 f. to 15 f.) or purple (21 f. to 150 f.); background colours given.
711 **111** 1 f. orange 10 10
712 2 f. blue 10 10
713 3 f. violet 10 10
714 4 f. purple 10 10
715 7 f. brown 20 10
716 12 f. mauve 20 10
717 15 f. brown 25 10
718 21 f. green 40 10
719 25 f. blue 45 10
720 35 f. stone 60 15
721 40 f. yellow 65 20
722 50 f. green 70 35
723 100 f. green . . . . 1·25 70
724 150 f. violet . . . . 2·75 1·10
(b) Air. Portraits in brown; background colours given.
725 **111** 200 f. turquoise . . . . . 4·25 1·25
726 500 f. green . . . . 7·00 5·00
727 1 d. blue . . . . 12·50 8·25

1966. Space Flights of Belyaev and Leonov. Nos. 630/5 optd **Alexei Leonov Pavel Belyaev 18 3-1965** in English and Arabic and spacecraft motif.
728 **92** 40 f. brown and green . . . 4·50 3·00
729 – 40 f. violet and brown . . . 4·50 3·00
730 – 40 f. purple and blue . . . 4·50 3·00
731 – 40 f. lilac and bistre . . . 4·50 3·00
732 – 40 f. sepia and blue . . . 4·50 3·00
733 – 40 f. green and pink . . . 4·50 3·00

1966. Pope Paul's Visit to U.N. (1965). Nos. 604/8 optd **PAPA PAULUS VI WORLD PEACE VISIT TO UNITED NATIONS 1965** in English and Arabic.
736 **88** 10 f. green 20 10
737 15 f. purple 45 20
738 25 f. brown 45 25
739 50 f. blue 85 45
740 80 f. green . . . . 1·50 75

1966. Anti-T.B. Campaign. (a) Unissued "Freedom from Hunger" stamps optd as in T **114**.
741 **114** 15 f. multicoloured 35 25
742 35 f. multicoloured 80 60
743 50 f. multicoloured . . . . 1·40 1·25
(b) As Nos. 741/3 but with additional premium obliterated by bars.
745 – 15 f. multicoloured 35 25
746 – 35 f. multicoloured 80 60
747 – 50 f. multicoloured . . . . 1·40 1·25

1966. Christ's Passion. The Stations of the Cross.
749 **115** 1 f. multicoloured 10 10
750 – 2 f. multicoloured 10 10
751 – 3 f. multicoloured 20 10
752 – 4 f. multicoloured 20 15
753 – 5 f. multicoloured 35 20
754 – 6 f. multicoloured 50 30
755 – 7 f. multicoloured 65 40
756 – 8 f. multicoloured 65 40
757 – 9 f. multicoloured 85 50
758 – 10 f. multicoloured 95 60
759 – 11 f. multicoloured . . . . 1·10 70
760 – 12 f. multicoloured . . . . 1·10 70
761 – 13 f. multicoloured . . . . 1·10 70
762 – 14 f. multicoloured . . . . 1·25 85
DESIGNS: The 14 Stations. The denominations, expressed in Roman numerals, correspond to the numbers of the stations.

116 Schirra and "Gemini 6"

118 Dag Hammarskjold

117 The Three Kings

1966. Space Achievements.
764 **116** 1 f. blue, violet & green . . 10 10
765 – 2 f. green, violet & blue . . 10 10
766 – 3 f. violet, blue & green . . 10 10
767 – 4 f. violet, green & ochre . 15 10
768 – 30 f. turquoise, brn & vio . 1·40 90
769 – 60 f. brown, turq & vio . . 1·75 1·40
DESIGNS: 2 f. Stafford and "Gemini 6"; 3 f. Borman and "Gemini 7"; 4 f. Lovell and "Gemini 7"; 30 f. Armstrong and "Gemini 8"; 60 f. Scott and "Gemini 8".

1966. Christmas. Multicoloured.
771 5 f. Type **117** 20 10
772 10 f. The Magi presenting gifts to the infant Christ 30 15
773 35 f. The flight to Egypt (vert) . 2·50 85

1967. "Builders of World Peace". Multicoloured.
775 5 f. Type **118** 10 10
781 5 f. U Thant 10 10
776 10 f. Pandit Nehru 20 10
782 10 f. Pres. De Gaulle 20 10
777 35 f. Pres. Kennedy 60 30
783 35 f. Pres. Johnson 60 25
778 50 f. Pope John XXIII . . . . 1·50 50
784 50 f. Pope Paul VI . . . . . 1·50 50
779 100 f. King Abdullah I (of Jordan) . . . . 1·60 1·40
785 100 f. King Hussein . . . . . 1·60 90

119 King Hussein

1967. "Gold Coins". Circular designs, centre and rim embossed on gold foil. Imperf.
(a) As T **119**. (i) Diameter 41 mm.
787 **119** 5 f. orange and blue . . . 30 30
788 10 f. orange and violet . . 30 30
(ii) Diameter 47 mm.
789 **119** 50 f. lilac and brown . . . 1·50 1·50
790 100 f. pink and green . . . 2·00 2·00
(iii) Diameter 54 mm.
791 **119** 200 f. blue & deep blue . . 5·00 5·00
(b) Crown Prince Hassan of Jordan. (i) Diam 41 mm.
792 – 5 f. black and green 55 55
793 – 10 f. black and lilac 55 55
(ii) Diameter 47 mm.
794 – 50 f. black and blue . . . . 3·00 3·00
795 – 100 f. black and brown . . . 4·00 4·00
(iii) Diameter 54 mm.
796 – 200 f. black and mauve . . . 7·50 7·50
A similar set was also issued in the same values and sizes but different colours with portrait of John F. Kennedy.

120 University City, Statue and Olympic Torch

1967. Preparation for Olympic Games in Mexico (1968).
797 **120** 1 f. red, black and violet . 10 10
798 – 2 f. black, violet and red . 10 10
799 – 3 f. violet, red and black . 10 10
800 – 4 f. blue, brown & green . 10 10
801 – 30 f. green, blue & brown . 40 40
802 – 60 f. brown, green & blue . 1·00 50
DESIGNS (each with Olympic torch): 2 f. Fishermen on Lake Patzcuaro; 3 f. University City and skyscraper, Mexico City; 4 f. Avenida de la Reforma, Mexico City; 30 f. Guadalajara Cathedral; 60 f. Fine Arts Theatre, Mexico City.

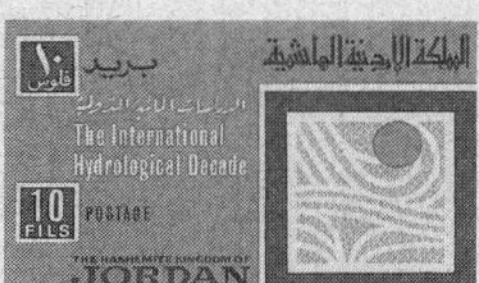

121 Decade Emblem

1967. International Hydrological Decade.
804 **121** 10 f. black and red 25 10
805 15 f. black & turquoise . . . 45 25
806 25 f. black and purple . . . 75 50

122 U.N.E.S.C.O. Emblem

1967. 20th Anniv of U.N.E.S.C.O.
807 **122** 100 f. multicoloured 1·00 60

123 Dromedary

1967. Animals. Multicoloured.
808 1 f. Type **123** (postage) 10 10
809 2 f. Karakul sheep 15 10
810 3 f. Angora goat 15 10
811 4 f. Striped hyena (air) 25 15
812 30 f. Arab horses 1·25 35
813 60 f. Goitred gazelle 2·10 80

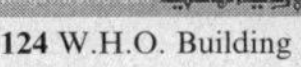

124 W.H.O. Building **125** Arab League Emblem, Open Book and Reaching Hands

1967. Inaug of W.H.O. Headquarters, Geneva.
815 **124** 5 f. black and green 15 10
816 45 f. black and orange 55 30

1968. Literacy Campaign.
817 **125** 20 f. green and orange 40 25
818 20 f. blue and mauve 40 25

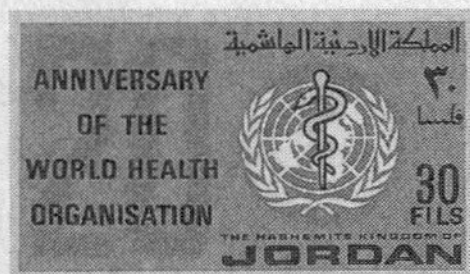

126 W.H.O. Emblem and "20"

1968. 20th Anniv of W.H.O.
819 **126** 30 f. multicoloured 50 25
820 100 f. multicoloured 1·40 75

127 Goldfinch **128** Human Rights Emblem

1968. Game Protection. Multicoloured.
821 5 f. Type **127** (postage) 1·50 65
822 10 f. Chukar partridge (vert) 2·50 65
823 15 f. Ostriches (vert) 3·50 80
824 20 f. Sand partridge 3·50 95
825 30 f. Mountain gazelle 2·25 70
826 40 f. Arabian oryx 3·25 75
827 50 f. Houbara bustard 5·00 1·75
828 60 f. Ibex (vert) (air) 4·00 2·00
829 100 f. Flock of mallard 6·00 4·00

1968. Human Rights Year.
830 **128** 20 f. black, buff & brown 30 20
831 60 f. black, blue & green 70 50

129 I.L.O. Emblem

1969. 50th Anniv of I.L.O.
832 **129** 10 f. black and blue 20 10
833 20 f. black and brown 20 10
834 25 f. black and green 30 25
835 45 f. black and mauve 50 35
836 60 f. black and orange 70 40

130 Horses in Pasture

1969. Arab Horses. Multicoloured.
837 10 f. Type **130** 50 15
838 20 f. White horse 1·25 35
839 45 f. Black mare and foal 2·50 1·10

131 Kaaba, Mecca, and Dome of the Rock, Jerusalem

1969. Multicoloured.
840 5 f. As Type **131** 30 10
841 10 f. Dome of the Rock (30 × 36 mm) 50 35
842 20 f. As 10 f. 90 50
843 45 f. As 5 f. 2·25 55

132 Oranges **133** Prince Hassan and Bride

1969. Fruits. Multicoloured.
844 10 f. Type **132** 25 10
845 20 f. Gooseberry 40 20
846 30 f. Lemons 80 20
847 40 f. Grapes 1·10 30
848 50 f. Olives 1·60 75
849 100 f. Apples 2·50 1·50

1969. Wedding of Prince Hassan (1968).
850 – 20 f. multicoloured 70 50
851 – 60 f. multicoloured 1·10 80
852 **133** 100 f. multicoloured 1·25 90
Nos. 850/1 show a similar design to Type **133**.

134 Wrecked Houses

1970. "Tragedy of the Refugees". Various vert. designs as T **134**. Multicoloured.
853/82 1 f. to 30 f. inclusive
Set of 30 10·00 10·00

135 Bombed Mosque **136** Pomegranate

1970. "Tragedy in the Holy Lands". Various vert. designs as T **135** Multicoloured.
883/912 1 f. to 30 f. inclusive
Set of 30 10·00 10·00

1970. Flowers. Multicoloured.
913 5 f. Type **136** 30 10
914 15 f. Wattle 50 10
915 25 f. Caper 75 10
916 35 f. Convolvulus 1·10 25
917 45 f. Desert scabious 1·50 55
918 75 f. Black iris 2·40 2·00
Nos. 913/5 and 917 are wrongly inscribed on the stamps.

137 Football

1970. Sports. Multicoloured.
919 5 f. Type **137** 15 10
920 10 f. Diving 20 10
921 15 f. Boxing 35 10
922 50 f. Running 1·00 45
923 100 f. Cycling (vert) 2·50 90
924 150 f. Basketball (vert) 3·50 2·00

138 Arab Children **139** White-crowned Black Wheatear

1970. Children's Day. Multicoloured.
925 5 f. Type **138** 20 10
926 10 f. Refugee boy with kettle 25 10
927 15 f. Refugee girl in camp 45 15
928 20 f. Refugee child in tent 70 20
Nos. 926/8 are vert.

1970. Birds.
929 **139** 120 f. black and orange 5·50 1·75
930 – 180 f. brn, blk & lilac 6·75 3·50
931 – 200 f. multicoloured 7·75 4·50
DESIGNS: 180 f. Masked shrike; 200 f. Palestine sunbird.

140 Grotto of the Nativity, Bethlehem

1970. Christmas. Church of the Nativity, Bethlehem. Multicoloured.
932 5 f. Type **140** 20 10
933 10 f. Christmas crib 30 15
934 20 f. Crypt Altar 50 20
935 25 f. Nave, Church of the Nativity 60 45

141 Arab League Flag, Emblem and Map

1971. 25th Anniv (1970) of Arab League.
936 **141** 10 f. green, violet & orge 15 15
937 20 f. green, brown & blue 35 15
938 30 f. green, blue & olive 50 25

142 Heads of Four Races and Emblem

1971. Racial Equality Year. Multicoloured.
939 5 f. Type **142** 10 10
940 10 f. "Plant" and emblem 15 10
941 15 f. Doves and emblem (horiz) 30 20
No. 939 is inscribed "KINIGDOM" in error.

143 Shore of the Dead Sea **144** Ibn Sinai (Avicenna)

1971. Tourism. Multicoloured.
942 5 f. Type **143** 20 10
943 30 f. Ed Deir, Petra 60 30
944 45 f. Via Dolorosa, Jerusalem (vert) 90 35
945 60 f. River Jordan 1·50 80
946 100 f. Christmas Bell, Bethlehem (vert) 2·10 1·50

1971. Famous Arab Scholars, Multicoloured.
947 5 f. Type **144** 15 10
948 10 f. Ibn Rushd 25 10
949 20 f. Ibn Khaldun 35 10
950 25 f. Ibn Tufail 60 10
951 30 f. Ibn El Haytham 80 45

145 New U.P.U. H.Q. Building

1971. Inauguration of New U.P.U. Headquarters Building, Berne.
952 **145** 10 f. brown, green & yell 25 10
953 20 f. purple, green & yell 75 35

146 Young Pupil **147** Mothers and Children

1972. International Education Year.
954 **146** 5 f. multicoloured 10 10
955 15 f. multicoloured 20 10
956 20 f. multicoloured 35 10
957 30 f. multicoloured 75 40

1972. Mothers Day. Multicoloured.
958 10 f. Type **147** 30 10
959 20 f. Mother and child (vert) 50 10
960 30 f. Bedouin mother and child (vert) 1·00 50

148 Pope Paul VI leaving Holy Sepulchre, Jerusalem

1972. Easter. Multicoloured.
961 30 f. Type **148** (postage) 70 15
962 60 f. The Calvary, Church of the Holy Sepulchre (air) 1·40 50
963 100 f. "Washing of the Feet", Jerusalem 2·75 1·25

149 Children and U.N.I.C.E.F. Emblem

1972. 25th Anniv of U.N.I.C.E.F.
964 **149** 10 f. turquoise, bl & brn 15 10
965 – 20 f. brown, grn & pur 50 25
966 – 30 f. brown, mve & bl 75 35
DESIGNS—VERT: 20 f. Child with toy bricks. HORIZ: 30 f. Nurse holding baby.

150 Dove of Peace **152** Arab with Kestrel

151 Al Aqsa Mosque and Pilgrims

1972. 25th Anniv (1970) of United Nations.
967 **150** 5 f. green, violet & yellow . 10 10
968 10 f. green, red & yellow . 20 10
969 15 f. blue, black & yellow . 40 10
970 20 f. blue, green & yellow . 55 20
971 30 f. green, brn & yellow . 1·00 50

1972. Burning of Al Aqsa Mosque (1970). Mult.
972 30 f. Type **151** . 1·00 20
973 60 f. Mosque in flames . 1·50 80
974 100 f. Mosque Interior . 3·50 1·60

1972. Jordanian Desert Life. Multicoloured.
975 5 f. Type **152** . 20 10
976 10 f. Desert bungalow (horiz) . 20 10
977 15 f. Camel trooper, Arab Legion (horiz) . 40 15
978 20 f. Boring operations (horiz) . 45 15
979 25 f. Shepherd (horiz) . 55 20
980 30 f. Dromedaries at water-trough (horiz) . 80 35
981 35 f. Chicken farm (horiz) . 90 55
982 45 f. Irrigation scheme (horiz) . 1·75 1·10

153 Wasfi el Tell and Dome of the Rock, Jerusalem

1972. Wasfi el Tell (assassinated statesman) Memorial Issue. Multicoloured.
983 5 f. Type **153** . 20 10
984 10 f. Wasfi el Tell, map and flag . 30 10
985 20 f. Type **153** . 60 10
986 30 f. As 10 f. . 70 55

154 Clay-pigeon shooting

155 Aero Club Emblem

1972. World Clay-pigeon Shooting Championships. Multicoloured.
987 25 f. Type **154** . 60 10
988 75 f. Marksman on range (horiz) . 1·90 80
989 120 f. Marksman taking aim (horiz) . 1·50 1·75

1973. Royal Jordanian Aero Club.
990 **155** 5 f. blk, bl & yell (postage) 15 10
991 10 f. black, blue & yellow . 15 10
992 – 15 f. multicoloured (air) . 35 10
993 – 20 f. multicoloured . 55 15
994 – 40 f. multicoloured . 1·10 50
DESIGNS: 15 f. Piper Cherokee 140 aircraft; 20 f. Beech B55 Baron airplane; 40 f. Winged horse emblem.

156 Dove and Flag

1973. 50th Anniv of Hashemite Kingdom of Jordan. Multicoloured.
995 5 f. Type **156** . 10 10
996 10 f. Anniversary emblem . 20 10
997 15 f. King Hussein . 50 10
998 30 f. Map and emblems . 1·00 90

157 Map and Jordanian Advance

1973. 5th Anniv of Battle of Karama. Multicoloured.
999 5 f. Type **157** . 20 10
1000 10 f. Jordanian attack, and map . 40 20
1001 15 f. Map, and King Hussein on tank . 1·00 70

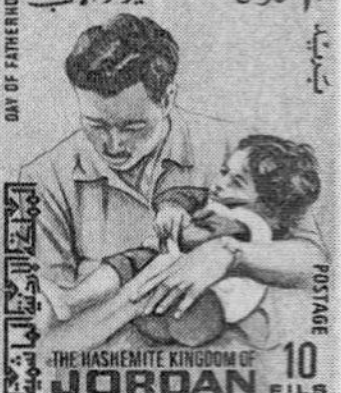

158 Father and Son **159** Phosphate Mines

1973. Fathers' Day. Multicoloured.
1002 10 f. Type **158** . 15 10
1003 20 f. Father and daughter . 50 15
1004 30 f. Family group . 75 35

1973. Development Projects. Multicoloured.
1005 5 f. Type **159** . 25 10
1006 10 f. Cement factories . 35 10
1007 15 f. Sharhabil Dam . 55 15
1008 20 f. Kafrein Dam . 75 35

160 Racing Camel

1973. Camel Racing. Multicoloured.
1009 5 f. Type **160** . 25 10
1010 10 f. Camels in "paddock" . 50 15
1011 15 f. Start of race . 75 25
1012 20 f. Camel racing . 1·75 50

161 Book Year Emblem

1973. International Book Year (1972).
1013 **161** 30 f. multicoloured . 75 10
1014 60 f. multicoloured . 1·25 50

162 Family Group

1973. Family Day.
1015 **162** 20 f. multicoloured . 40 10
1016 – 30 f. multicoloured . 60 15
1017 – 60 f. multicoloured . 1·00 50
DESIGNS: 30, 60 f. Different family groups.

163 Shah of Iran, King Hussein, Cyrus's Tomb and Mosque of Omar

1973. 2500th Anniv of Iranian Monarchy.
1018 **163** 5 f. multicoloured . 25 10
1019 10 f. multicoloured . 30 10
1020 15 f. multicoloured . 50 15
1021 30 f. multicoloured . 1·00 50

164 Emblem of Palestine Week

1973. Palestine Week. Multicoloured.
1022 5 f. Type **164** . 30 10
1023 10 f. Torch and emblem . 50 10
1024 15 f. Refugees (26 × 47mm) . 1·00 30
1025 30 f. Children and map on Globe . 1·50 40

165 Traditional Harvesting

1973. Ancient and Modern Agriculture. Multicoloured.
1026 5 f. Type **165** (postage) . 15 10
1027 10 f. Modern harvesting . 20 10
1028 15 f. Traditional seeding . 40 10
1029 20 f. Modern seeding . 60 15
1030 30 f. Traditional ploughing . 70 20
1031 35 f. Modern ploughing . 80 25
1032 45 f. Pest Control . 1·00 25
1033 60 f. Horticulture . 1·75 90
1034 100 f. Agricultural landscape (air) . 2·00 1·00

166 Long-nosed Butterflyfish **168** "The Club-footed Boy" (Murillo)

167 Battle of Muta

1974. Red Sea Fishes. Multicoloured.
1035 5 f. Type **166** . 25 10
1036 10 f. Monocle bream . 35 10
1037 15 f. As No. 1036 . 65 15
1038 20 f. Slender-spined mojarra . 75 15
1039 25 f. As No. 1038 . 1·10 30
1040 30 f. Russell's snapper . 1·10 30
1041 35 f. As No. 1040 . 1·75 45
1042 40 f. Blue-barred orange parrotfish . 2·00 50
1043 45 f. As No. 1042 . 2·10 55
1044 50 f. Type **166** . 2·50 60
1045 60 f. Yellow-edged lyretail . 3·00 60

1974. Islamic Battles against the Crusaders. Multicoloured.
1046 10 f. Type **167** . 35 10
1047 20 f. Battle of Yarmouk . 90 25
1048 30 f. Battle of Hattin . 1·60 65

1974. Famous Paintings. Multicoloured.
1049 5 f. Type **168** . 25 10
1050 10 f. "Praying Hands" (Durer) . 40 10
1051 15 f. "St. George and the Dragon" (Uccello) . 50 10
1052 20 f. "The Mona Lisa" (L. da Vinci) . 60 10
1053 30 f. "Hope" (F. Watts) . 75 15
1054 40 f. "The Angelus" (Jean Millet) (horiz) . 1·00 20
1055 50 f. "The Artist and her Daughter" (Angelica Kauffmann) . 2·00 25
1056 60 f. "Whistler's Mother" (J. Whistler) (horiz) . 2·00 70
1057 100 f. "Master Hare" (Sir J. Reynolds) . 2·50 1·25

المؤتمر الدولي لتاريخ بلاد الشام
٢٠ – ١٩٧٤/٤/٢٥
الجامعة الاردنية

(169)

1974. International Conference for Damascus History. Nos. 1013/4 optd with T **169**.
1058 **161** 30 f. multicoloured . 40 25
1059 60 f. multicoloured . 85 50

170 U.P.U. Emblem **171** Camel Caravan

1974. Centenary of Universal Postal Union.
1060 **170** 10 f. multicoloured . 15 10
1061 30 f. multicoloured . 40 20
1062 60 f. multicoloured . 70 70

1974. The Dead Sea. Multicoloured.
1063 2 f. Type **171** . 10 10
1064 3 f. Palm and shore . 15 10
1065 4 f. Hotel on coast . 15 10
1066 5 f. Jars from Qumram Caves . 15 10
1067 6 f. Copper scrolls (vert) . 30 10
1068 10 f. Cistern steps, Qumram (vert) . 45 10
1069 20 f. Type **171** . 55 15
1070 30 f. As 3 f. . 80 15
1071 40 f. As 4 f. . 85 40
1072 50 f. As 5 f. . 1·40 50
1073 60 f. As 6 f. . 1·75 70
1074 100 f. As 10 f. . 2·75 1·10

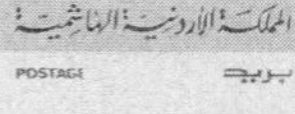

172 W.P.Y. Emblem **173** Water-skier

1974. World Population Year.
1075 **172** 5 f. purple, green & blk . 15 10
1076 10 f. red, green & blk . 25 10
1077 20 f. orange, grn & blk . 50 20

1974. Water-skiing. Multicoloured.
1078 5 f. Type **173** . 10 10
1079 10 f. Water-skier (side view) (horiz) . 20 10
1080 20 f. Skier turning (horiz) . 50 10
1081 50 f. Type **173** . 1·10 30
1082 100 f. As 10 f. . 2·10 75
1083 200 f. As 20 f. . 2·75 2·00

174 Ka'aba, Mecca, and Pilgrims

1974. "Pilgrimage Season".
1084 **174** 10 f. multicoloured . 25 15
1085 20 f. multicoloured . 65 45

175 Amrah Palace **176** King Hussein at Wheel of Car

1974. Desert Ruins. Multicoloured.
1086 10 f. Type **175** . 25 15
1087 20 f. Hisham Palace . 50 45
1088 30 f. Kharana Castle . 1·25 60

1975. Air. Royal Jordanian Automobile Club.
1089 **176** 30 f. multicoloured . 40 15
1090 60 f. multicoloured . 1·25 70

177 Woman in Costume **178** Treasury, Petra

1975. Jordanian Women's Costumes.
1091 **177** 5 f. multicoloured . 15 10
1092 – 10 f. multicoloured . 25 10
1093 – 15 f. multicoloured . 40 15
1094 – 20 f. multicoloured . 65 20
1095 – 25 f. multicoloured . 85 50
DESIGNS: 10 f. to 25 f. Various costumes as Type **177**.

1975. Tourism. Multicoloured.
1096 15 f. Type **178** (postage) . 25 10
1097 20 f. Ommayyad Palace, Amman (horiz) . 40 15
1098 30 f. Dome of the Rock, Jerusalem (horiz) . 70 30
1099 40 f. Forum columns, Jerash (horiz) . 1·00 60
1100 50 f. Palms, Aqaba (air) . 65 30
1101 60 f. Obelisj Tomb, Petra (horiz) . 1·50 70
1102 80 f. Fort of Wadi Rum (horiz) . 2·10 1·40

179 King Hussein

180 Globe and "Desert"

1975.

1103 179 5 f. blue and green . . . 20 10
1104 10 f. blue and violet . . . 20 10
1105 15 f. blue and pink . . . 10 10
1106 20 f. blue and brown . . 40 15
1107 25 f. blue & ultramarine . 40 15
1108 30 f. blue and brown . . 15 10
1109 35 f. blue and violet . . . 20 15
1110 40 f. blue and red 50 25
1111 45 f. blue and mauve . . 30 20
1112 50 f. blue and green . . . 30 20
1113 60 f. brown and green . . 90 35
1114 100 f. brown & lt brown . 1·50 40
1115 120 f. brown and blue . . 75 60
1116 180 f. brown and mauve . 1·25 90
1117 200 f. brown and blue . . 1·50 1·25
1118 400 f. brown and purple . 2·50 2·00
1119 500 f. brown and red . . 3·25 3·00
Nos. 1113/19 are larger, 27 × 27 mm.

1975. 10th Anniv of ALIA (Royal Jordanian Airlines). Multicoloured.
1120 10 f. Type **180** 20 10
1121 30 f. Boeing 707 linking globe and map of Jordan (horiz) . 70 25
1122 60 f. Globe and "ALIA" logo . 1·40 60

181 Satellite and Earth Station

1975. Satellite Earth Station Opening.
1123 181 20 f. multicoloured . . . 60 15
1124 30 f. multicoloured . . . 1·00 50

182 Emblem of Chamber of Commerce

1975. 50th Anniv of Amman Chamber of Commerce.
1125 182 10 f. multicoloured . . . 15 10
1126 15 f. multicoloured . . . 30 15
1127 20 f. multicoloured . . . 45 30

183 Emblem and Hand with Spanner

1975. Completion of Three Year Development Plan.
1128 183 5 f. black, red & green . . 10 10
1129 10 f. black, red & green . 20 20
1130 20 f. black, red & green . 50 30

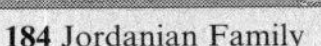

184 Jordanian Family

185 A.L.O. Emblem and Salt Mine

1976. International Women's Year (1975). Mult.
1131 5 f. Type **184** 10 10
1132 25 f. Woman scientist 45 25
1133 60 f. Woman graduate . . . . 1·10 65

1976. Arab Labour Organization. Multicoloured.
1134 10 f. Type **185** 15 10
1135 30 f. Welding 50 25
1136 60 f. Quayside, Aqaba . . . . 1·10 75

1976. Nos. 853/82, surch in English and Arabic.
1137/46 25 f. on 1 f. to 10 f. . . . .
1147/51 40 f. on 11 f. to 15 f. . . .
1152/56 50 f. on 16 f. to 20 f. . . .
1157/61 75 f. on 21 f. to 25 f. . . .
1162/66 125 f. on 26 f. to 30 f. . . .
Set of 30 . . . . 40·00 28·00

1976. Nos. 883/912, surch in English and Arabic.
1167/76 25 f. on 1 f. to 10 f. . . . .
1178/82 40 f. on 11 f. to 15 f. . . .
1183/87 50 f. on 16 f. to 20 f. . . .
1188/92 75 f. on 21 f. to 25 f. . . .
1192/96 125 f. on 26 f. to 30 f. . . .
Set of 30 . . . . 40·00 28·00

187 Tennis

188 Schu'aib Dam

1976. Sports and Youth. Multicoloured.
1197 5 f. Type **187** 10 10
1198 10 f. Body-building 20 10
1199 15 f. Football 30 10
1200 20 f. Show jumping 45 10
1201 30 f. Weightlifting 70 25
1202 100 f. Stadium, Amman . . . 2·75 1·50

1976. Dams. Multicoloured.
1203 30 f. Type **188** 60 15
1204 60 f. Al-Kafrein Dam . . . . 1·40 50
1205 100 f. Ziqlab Dam . . . . . . 2·50 1·00

189 Early and Modern Telephones

190 Road Crossing and Traffic Lights

1977. Telephone Centenary. Multicoloured.
1206 75 f. Type **189** . . . . 1·00 60
1207 125 f. Early telephone and modern receiver . . . . 1·75 1·00

1977. International Traffic Day. Multicoloured.
1208 5 f. Type **190** 20 10
1209 75 f. Roundabout and traffic lights . . . . 2·10 60
1210 125 f. Motorcycle policemen, road signs and traffic lights . 3·75 1·90

191 Airliner over Ship

192 Child, Toys and Money-box

1977. Silver Jubilee of King Hussein. Mult.
1211 10 f. Type **191** 20 10
1212 25 f. Pylons and factories . . . 30 10
1213 40 f. Fertilizer plant 45 15
1214 50 f. Ground-to-air missile . . 60 25
1215 75 f. Mosque . . . . 1·25 75
1216 125 f. Ground satellite receiving aerial . . . . 1·75 1·50

1977. Postal Savings Bank. Multicoloured.
1218 10 f. Type **192** . . . . . . 1·00 50
1219 25 f. Child with piggy bank . . 30 10
1220 50 f. Savings Bank emblem . . 60 30
1221 75 f. Boy and bank teller . . . 1·25 65

193 King Hussein and Queen Alia

194 Queen Alia

1977.
1222 193 10 f. multicoloured . . . 15 10
1223 25 f. multicoloured . . . 30 15
1224 40 f. multicoloured . . . 50 25
1225 50 f. multicoloured . . . 60 45

1977. Queen Alia Commemoration.
1226 194 10 f. multicoloured . . . 15 10
1227 25 f. multicoloured . . . 30 15
1228 40 f. multicoloured . . . 50 25
1229 50 f. multicoloured . . . 60 45

195 Mohammed Ali Jinnah

196 A.P.U. Emblem and Flags

1977. Birth Cent. of Mohammed Ali Jinnah (1st Governor-General of Pakistan).
1230 195 25 f. multicoloured . . . 40 20
1231 75 f. multicoloured . . . 2·00 80

1978. 25th Anniv (1977) of Arab Postal Union.
1232 196 25 f. multicoloured . . . 35 10
1233 40 f. multicoloured . . . 85 35

197 Coffee Pots and Cups

198 Roman Amphitheatre, Jerash

1978. Handicrafts. Multicoloured.
1234 25 f. Type **197** 30 10
1235 40 f. Porcelain plate and ashtray 40 15
1236 75 f. Vase, necklace and chains 95 45
1237 125 f. Containers holding pipes 1·60 1·00

1978. Tourism. Multicoloured.
1238 5 f. Type **198** 15 10
1239 20 f. Roman columns, Jerash . 35 10
1240 40 f. Roman mosaic, Madaba . 50 30
1241 75 f. Rock formations, Rum . 1·25 55

199 King Hussein and Pres. Sadat of Egypt

200 Cement Works

1978. Visits of Arab Leaders to Jordan. Mult.
1242 40 f. Type **199** 40 15
1243 40 f. King Hussein and Pres. Assad (horiz) 40 15
1244 40 f. King Hussein and King Khalid (horiz) 40 15

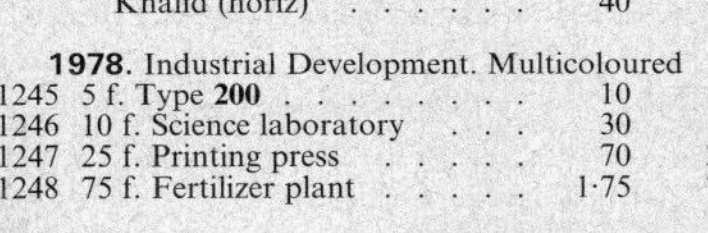

1978. Industrial Development. Multicoloured
1245 5 f. Type **200** 10 10
1246 10 f. Science laboratory . . . 30 10
1247 25 f. Printing press 70 20
1248 75 f. Fertilizer plant . . . . 1·75 70

201 U.N.E.S.C.O. Emblem

202 King Hussein

1978. 30th Anniv of U.N.E.S.C.O.
1249 201 40 f. multicoloured . . . 40 25
1250 75 f. multicoloured . . . 1·00 75

1979. Dated "1979".
1251 202 25 f. brown, flesh & blue . . 40 10
1252 40 f. brown, flesh & pur . 70 15
See also 1265/72 for values dated "1980" and Nos. 1309/13 for those dated "1981".

203 Emblems within Cogwheels

204 I.Y.C. Emblem and Flag of Jordan

1979. Five Year Development Plan.
1253 203 25 f. multicoloured . . . 1·40 20
1254 40 f. multicoloured . . . 1·75 30
1255 50 f. multicoloured . . . 2·10 90

1979. International Year of the Child.
1256 204 25 f. multicoloured . . . 60 25
1257 40 f. multicoloured . . . 90 35
1258 50 f. multicoloured . . . 1·00 75

205 Census Emblem

206 Nurse holding Baby

1979. Population and Housing Census.
1259 205 25 f. multicoloured . . . 30 15
1260 40 f. multicoloured . . . 50 15
1261 50 f. multicoloured . . . 70 35

1980. International Nursing Day.
1262 206 25 f. multicoloured . . . 40 15
1263 40 f. multicoloured . . . 70 30
1264 50 f. multicoloured . . . 90 55

1980.
1265 202 5 f. brown, pink & grn . . 10 10
1266 10 f. brown, pink & vio . 10 10
1267 20 f. brown and pink . . 15 10
1268 25 f. brown, pink & blue . 20 10
1269 40 f. brown and mauve . . 30 15
1270 50 f. brown, pink & grn . 40 25
1271 75 f. brown, pink & grey . 30 20
1272 125 f. brown, pink & red . 1·25 30
Nos. 1265/72 are similar to Nos. 1251/2 but are inscr "1980".

207 El Deir Temple, Petra

208 Mosque and Kaaba, Mecca

1980. World Tourism Conference, Manila.
1273 207 25 f. black, grey & green . 75 25
1274 40 f. black, grey & blue . 1·00 50
1275 50 f. black, grey & purple . 1·25 1·00

1980. 1400th Anniv of Hegira.
1276 208 25 f. multicoloured . . . 30 10
1277 40 f. multicoloured . . . 40 15
1278 50 f. multicoloured . . . 50 20
1279 75 f. multicoloured . . . 80 60
1280 100 f. multicoloured . . . 1·00 80

209 Conference Emblem

210 Picking Crops, examining Patients and Flag-raising Ceremony

1980. 11th Arab Summit Conference, Amman.
1282 209 25 f. multicoloured . . . 30 10
1283 40 f. multicoloured . . . 50 15
1284 50 f. multicoloured . . . 55 25
1285 75 f. multicoloured . . . 80 50
1286 100 f. multicoloured . . . 95 75

1981. Red Crescent.
1288 210 25 f. multicoloured . . . 50 20
1289 40 f. multicoloured . . . 90 40
1290 50 f. multicoloured . . . 1·10 65

211 I.T.U. and W.H.O. Emblems and Ribbons forming Caduceus

212 Jordan Stamps of 1930 and 1975

1981. World Telecommunications Day.
1291 211 25 f. multicoloured . . . 50 20
1292 40 f. multicoloured . . . 90 40
1293 50 f. multicoloured . . . 1·10 65

1981. Opening of Postal Museum. Multicoloured.
1294 25 f. Type **212** 50 15
1295 40 f. Jordan stamps of 1933 and 1954 (vert) 75 30
1296 50 f. Jordan stamps of 1946 and 1952 . . . . 1·00 55

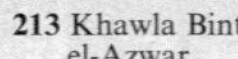
213 Khawla Bint el-Azwar

214 F.A.O. Emblem and Olive Branches

1981. Arab Women in History. Multicoloured.
1297 25 f. Type **213** 75 20
1298 40 f. El-Khansa (writer) 1·25 40
1299 50 f. Rabia el-Adawiyeh (Sufi religious leader) 2·00 1·00

1981. World Food Day.
1300 **214** 25 f. multicoloured 60 15
1301 40 f. multicoloured 80 35
1302 50 f. multicoloured 1·10 70

215 I.Y.D.P. Emblem

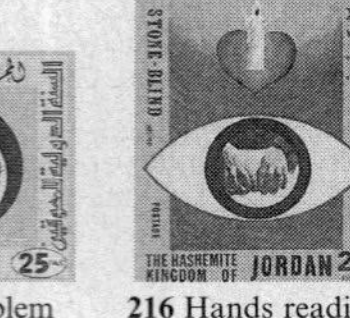
216 Hands reading Braille

1981. International Year of Disabled Persons.
1303 **215** 25 f. multicoloured 60 20
1304 40 f. multicoloured 90 30
1305 50 f. multicoloured 1·10 70

1981. The Blind.
1306 **216** 25 f. multicoloured 60 20
1307 40 f. multicoloured 90 30
1308 50 f. multicoloured 1·10 70

1982.
1309 **202** 5 f. brown, pink & grn 10 10
1310 10 f. brown, pink & vio 10 10
1311 20 f. brown and pink 20 10
1312 25 f. brown, pink & blue 25 20
1313 40 f. brown, pink & pur 65 45
Nos. 1309/13 are similar to Nos. 1251/2, but are inscr "1981".

217 Hand holding Jug and Stone Tablets

218 A.P.U. Emblem

1982. Jordan Monuments.
1314 **217** 25 f. multicoloured 55 15
1315 40 f. multicoloured 85 25
1316 50 f. multicoloured 1·10 60

1982. 30th Anniv of Arab Postal Union.
1317 **218** 10 f. multicoloured 15 10
1318 25 f. multicoloured 40 15
1319 40 f. multicoloured 65 30
1320 50 f. multicoloured 75 50
1321 100 f. multicoloured 1·40 1·25

219 King Hussein and Jet Fighter

1982. Independence, Army Day and 30th Anniv of King's Accession to Throne. Multicoloured.
1322 10 f. King Hussein and rockets 20 10
1323 25 f. King Hussein and tanks 45 20
1324 40 f. Type **219** 1·00 30
1325 50 f. King Hussein and tanks (different) 1·10 60
1326 100 f. King Hussein and flag being hoisted by armed forces 2·40 1·50

220 Salt Secondary School

1982. Salt Secondary School.
1327 **220** 10 f. multicoloured 15 10
1328 25 f. multicoloured 50 15
1329 40 f. multicoloured 80 25
1330 50 f. multicoloured 1·25 50
1331 100 f. multicoloured 2·75 1·50

221 City Gate, Jerusalem

222 Soldiers, Flags and Badge

1982. Jerusalem. Multicoloured.
1332 10 f. Type **221** 20 10
1333 25 f. Minaret 55 15
1334 40 f. Mosque 80 40
1335 50 f. Mosque (different) 95 60
1336 100 f. Dome of the Rock 1·90 1·25

1982. Yarmouk Forces.
1337 **222** 10 f. multicoloured 20 10
1338 25 f. multicoloured 55 15
1339 40 f. multicoloured 80 40
1340 50 f. multicoloured 95 60
1341 100 f. multicoloured 1·90 1·25

223 Dish Aerial, Earth and U.N. Emblem

224 King Abdullah and Dome of the Rock

1982. 2nd U.N. Conference on the Exploration and Peaceful Uses of Outer Space, Vienna.
1343 **223** 10 f. multicoloured 20 10
1344 25 f. multicoloured 40 15
1345 40 f. multicoloured 70 40
1346 50 f. multicoloured 95 70
1347 100 f. multicoloured 1·90 1·50

1982. Birth Centenary of King Abdullah.
1348 **224** 10 f. multicoloured 20 10
1349 25 f. multicoloured 40 15
1350 40 f. multicoloured 70 40
1351 50 f. multicoloured 95 70
1352 100 f. multicoloured 1·90 1·50

225 King Hussein and Temple Colonnade

226 King Hussein

1982. Roman Ruins at Jerash. Multicoloured.
1353 10 f. Type **225** 25 10
1354 25 f. Archway 45 15
1355 40 f. Temple of Artemis 95 40
1356 50 f. Amphitheatre 1·25 70
1357 100 f. Hippodrome 2·00 1·50

1983.
1358 **226** 10 f. multicoloured 10 10
1359 25 f. multicoloured 25 10
1360 40 f. multicoloured 35 15
1361 60 f. multicoloured 70 35
1362 100 f. multicoloured 80 50
1363 125 f. multicoloured 1·10 80

227 Massacre Victims

1983. Massacre of Palestinian Refugees in Sabra and Shatila Camps. Multicoloured.
1364 10 f. Type **227** 25 10
1365 25 f. Covered bodies 60 15
1366 40 f. Orphans 95 35
1367 50 f. Massacre victims in street 1·50 70
1368 100 f. Massacre victims (different) 2·25 1·75

228 Control Tower and Airport Buildings

1983. Opening of Queen Alia International Airport. Multicoloured.
1370 10 f. Type **228** 20 10
1371 25 f. Tower and terminal building 40 15
1372 40 f. Tower and hangar 90 35
1373 50 f. Tower and aerial view of airport 1·40 55
1374 100 f. Tower and embarkation bridge 2·10 1·60

229 King Hussein with Radio Equipment

1983. Royal Jordanian Radio Amateurs Society.
1375 **229** 10 f. multicoloured 20 10
1376 25 f. multicoloured 40 15
1377 40 f. multicoloured 80 30
1378 50 f. multicoloured 1·00 50
1379 100 f. multicoloured 2·00 1·40

230 Academy Building, Amman

1983. Establishment of Royal Academy for Islamic Civilization Research. Multicoloured.
1380 10 f. Type **230** 20 10
1381 25 f. Silk rug 45 15
1382 40 f. View of Amman 80 30
1383 50 f. Panorama of Jerusalem 1·00 50
1384 100 f. Holy sites of Islam 2·00 1·40

231 Irrigation Canal

1983. Food Security. Multicoloured.
1386 10 f. Type **231** 20 10
1387 25 f. Growing crops under glass 45 15
1388 40 f. Battery hens 85 30
1389 50 f. Harvesting 1·00 50
1390 100 f. Flock of sheep 2·00 1·40

232 Switchboard and Emblem

1983. World Communications Year. Mult.
1391 10 f. Type **232** 25 10
1392 25 f. Aerial view of satellite receiving station 60 15
1393 40 f. Microwave antenna and emblems of communication 90 30
1394 50 f. W.C.Y. emblems 1·25 55
1395 100 f. Airmail letter 2·25 1·50

233 Dome of the Rock, Jerusalem

1983. Palestinian Solidarity.
1396 **233** 5 f. multicoloured 40 15
1397 10 f. multicoloured 80 30

234 Human Rights Emblems

1983. 35th Anniv of Declaration of Human Rights.
1398 **234** 10 f. multicoloured 20 10
1399 25 f. multicoloured 50 15
1400 40 f. multicoloured 80 30
1401 50 f. multicoloured 1·00 50
1402 100 f. multicoloured 1·90 1·40

235 "Stop Polio Campaign" Emblem

1984. Anti-poliomyelitis Campaign.
1403 **235** 40 f. orange, black & bl 50 20
1404 60 f. silver, black & red 1·50 35
1405 100 f. green, black & yell 1·75 95

236 Bomb and Cogwheel

1984. Israel's Attack on Iraqi Nuclear Reactor. Multicoloured.
1406 40 f. Type **236** 1·00 20
1407 60 f. Hand with dagger attacking nuclear symbol 1·90 75
1408 100 f. Aircraft bombing nuclear symbol 3·25 1·50

237 King Hussein and Tanks

1984. Independence and Army Day. Mult.
1409 10 f. Type **237** 20 10
1410 25 f. King Hussein and naval patrol boat 50 15
1411 40 f. King Hussein and Camel Corps 85 30
1412 60 f. King Hussein and soldiers at Independence Monument 1·50 50
1413 100 f. Parading soldiers 2·00 1·50

238 Sports Pictogram

1984. Olympic Games. Los Angeles. Mult.
1414 25 f. Type **238** 30 15
1415 40 f. Swimming 50 20
1416 60 f. Shooting and archery pictograms 90 50
1417 100 f. Gymnastics (floor exercises) 1·40 1·25

239 Amman Power Station

1984. Water and Electricity Year. Multicoloured.
1419 25 f. Power lines and factories 40 15
1420 40 f. Type **239** 75 20
1421 60 f. Reservoirs and water pipe 1·00 55
1422 100 f. Telephone lines, street light, water tap and pipeline 1·75 1·00

240 Omayyid Coins

1984. Coins. Multicoloured.
1423 40 f. Type **240** 60 20
1424 60 f. Abbasid coins 1·00 45
1425 125 f. Hashemite coins 1·90 1·25

241 Shield and Antelope

1984. Release of Antelope in Jordan. Multicoloured.
1426 25 f. Type **241** 50 15
1427 40 f. Four antelope 90 30
1428 60 f. Three antelope . . . . . . 1·40 65
1429 100 f. Duke of Edinburgh, King Hussein and Queen Alia . . 2·40 1·00

242 Mu'ta Military University, Karak City

1984. Jordanian Universities. Multicoloured.
1430 40 f. Type **242** 50 20
1431 60 f. Yarmouk University, Irbid City 75 45
1432 125 f. Jordan University, Amman . . . . 1·75 1·00

243 Tombs of El-Hareth bin Omier el-Azdi and Derar bin el-Azwar

1984. Al Sahaba Tombs. Multicoloured.
1433 10 f. Type **243** 20 10
1434 25 f. Tombs of Sharhabil bin Hasna and Abu Obaidah Amer bin el-Jarrah 50 15
1435 40 f. Muath bin Jabal's tomb . 75 20
1436 50 f. Tombs of Zaid bin Haretha and Abdullah bin Rawaha 90 35
1437 60 f. Tomb of Amer bin Abi Waqqas . . . . 1·25 65
1438 100 f. Jafar bin Abi Taleb's tomb . . . . 1·90 1·25

244 Soldier descending Mountain and King Hussein

1985. Independence and Army Day. Mult.
1439 25 f. Type **244** 45 15
1440 40 f. Flags on map, King Abdullah and King Hussein . 70 30
1441 60 f. Flag, monument and arms . . . . 1·25 60
1442 100 f. King Hussein, flag, King Abdullah and arms . . . . 2·00 1·40

245 Sir Rowland Hill (instigator of first stamps)

1985. Postal Celebrities. Multicoloured.
1443 40 f. Type **245** 70 25
1444 60 f. Heinrich von Stephan (founder of Universal Postal Union) . . . . 1·00 50
1445 125 f. Yacoub Sukker (first Jordanian stamp designer) . 2·10 1·25

246 Emblem and Delegates round Table

1985. 1st Jordanians Abroad Conference. Mult.
1446 40 f. Type **246** 70 25
1447 60 f. Conference emblem and globe and hand over torch . 1·00 50
1448 125 f. Globe encircled by Jordanian flags . . . . . . 2·10 1·25

247 I.Y.Y. Emblem

1985. International Youth Year. Multicoloured.
1449 10 f. Type **247** 20 10
1450 25 f. Arab couple on map, flag and emblem 50 20
1451 40 f. Stylised figures flanking globe, flag and emblem . . . 75 30
1452 60 f. Part of cogwheel, laurel branch and ribbons in jug decorated with emblem . . . 1·25 75
1453 125 f. Stylised figures and emblem . . . . 2·25 1·50

248 El-Deir Temple, Petra

1985. 10th Anniv of World Tourist Organization. Multicoloured.
1454 10 f. Type **248** 20 10
1455 25 f. Temple of Artemis (ruins), Jerash 45 20
1456 40 f. Amrah Palace 65 25
1457 50 f. Hill town, Jordan valley . 90 35
1458 60 f. Sailing in Aqaba bay . . 1·25 65
1459 125 f. Roman amphitheatre, Amman and city arms . . . 2·10 1·40

249 Mother and Baby and Hospital

1985. U.N.I.C.E.F. Child Survival Campaign. Multicoloured.
1461 25 f. Type **249** 45 20
1462 40 f. Child being weighed . . . 65 30
1463 60 f. Childrens' heads as balloons . . . . 1·25 75
1464 125 f. Mother feeding baby . . 2·10 1·60

250 Dancers

1985. 5th Anniv of Jerash Festival. Mult.
1466 10 f. Opening ceremony, 1980 . 20 10
1467 25 f. Type **250** 45 20
1468 40 f. Dancers (different) . . . 65 40
1469 60 f. Male choir at Roman theatre . . . . 1·25 75
1470 100 f. King Hussein and his wife . . . . 2·00 1·60

251 Flag and Emblem forming "40"

1985. 40th Anniv of U.N.O.
1471 **251** 60 f. multicoloured . . . 1·25 80
1472 125 f. multicoloured . . . 1·90 1·50

252 Hussein comforting Boy

1985. 50th Birthday of King Hussein. Mult.
1473 10 f. Type **252** 20 10
1474 25 f. Hussein in Arab robes . . 50 25
1475 40 f. Hussein piloting aircraft . 70 35
1476 60 f. Hussein in army uniform . 1·10 70
1477 100 f. Hussein in Arab head-dress . . . . 1·90 1·60

253 El Aqsa Mosque

1985. Compulsory Tax. Restoration of El Aqsa Mosque, Jerusalem.
1479 **253** 5 f. multicoloured 25 15
1480 10 f. multicoloured . . . 75 45

254 Policeman beside Car

1985. The Police. Multicoloured.
1481 40 f. Type **254** . . . . 1·25 60
1482 60 f. Policeman and crowd of children . . . . 1·75 80
1483 125 f. Policeman taking oath . 3·00 1·60

255 Satellite over Map of Arab Countries

1986. 1st Anniv of Launch of "Arabsat 1" Communications Satellite. Multicoloured.
1484 60 f. Satellite . . . . 1·00 40
1485 100 f. Type **255** . . . . 1·60 80

256 King presenting Colours

1986. 30th Anniv of Arabisation of Jordanian Army. Multicoloured.
1486 40 f. Type **256** 55 20
1487 60 f. King Hussein shaking hands with soldier 70 30
1488 100 f. King Hussein addressing Army . . . . 1·50 90

257 King Abdullah decorating Soldier

1986. 40th Anniv of Independence.
1490 **257** 160 f. multicoloured . . . 2·00 1·25

258 King Hussein of Hejaz and Sons

1986. 70th Anniv of Arab Revolt. Multicoloured.
1491 40 f. Type **258** 60 15
1492 60 f. King Abdullah with armed men . . . . 1·00 30
1493 160 f. King leading soldiers on horseback . . . . 2·00 1·40

259 Emblem

1986. International Peace Year.
1495 **259** 160 f. multicoloured . . . 2·00 1·25
1496 240 f. blk, orge & grn . . 2·50 1·75

260 Cardiac Centre Building

1986. King Hussein Medical City. Multicoloured.
1497 40 f. Type **260** 50 20
1498 60 f. Patient undergoing operation . . . . 1·00 50
1499 100 f. View of operating theatre during operation . . . . 1·50 90

261 Extract of King Hussein's Speech in Arabic

1986. 40th Anniv of U.N.O. Multicoloured.
1500 40 f. Type **261** 50 20
1501 80 f. Extract of speech in Arabic (different) . . . . . 1·10 50
1502 100 f. Extract of speech in English . . . . 1·40 90

262 Head Post Office, Amman

1987. 35th Anniv of Arab Postal Union. Mult.
1504 80 f. Type **262** 80 50
1505 160 f. Ministry of Communications, Amman . 1·60 1·25

263 Jaber ibn Hayyan al-Azdi

1987. Arab and Muslim Pharmacists. Mult.
1506 60 f. Type **263** 60 30
1507 80 f. Abu-al-Qasem al-Majreeti 75 40
1508 240 f. Abu-Bakr al-Razi . . . 2·25 1·90

264 Village

1987. S.O.S. Childrens' Village, Amman. Mult.
1509 80 f. Type **264** . . . . 1·25 70
1510 240 f. Child and mural . . . . 2·40 1·90

265 Soldiers on Wall

1987. 40th Anniv of 4th Army Brigade. Multicoloured.
1511 60 f. Type **265** . . . . 1·00 50
1512 80 f. Mortar crew . . . . . . 1·50 70

266 Black-headed Bunting

1987. Birds. Multicoloured.
1514 10 f. Hoopoe 30 20
1515 40 f. Palestine sunbird . . . . 1·00 50
1516 50 f. Type **266** . . . . 1·40 70
1517 60 f. Spur-winged plover . . . 1·50 75
1518 80 f. Greenfinch . . . . . . 2·10 1·25
1519 100 f. Black-winged stilt . . . 2·50 1·50

267 King Hussein

268 Horsemen Charging

1987.
1520 **267** 60 f. multicoloured . . . 50 10
1521 80 f. multicoloured . . . 70 25
1522 160 f. multicoloured . . . 1·25 55
1523 240 f. multicoloured . . . 2·00 80

1987. 800th Anniv of Battle of Hattin. Mult.
1524 60 f. Type **268** 90 45
1525 80 f. Horseman and Dome of the Rock . . . . 1·25 75
1526 100 f. Saladin, horsemen and Dome of the Rock . . . . 1·50 1·00

269 Arms

1987.
1528 **269** 80 f. multicoloured . . . 90 40
1529 160 f. multicoloured . . . 1·50 70

270 Amman Industrial Estate, Sahab

1987.
1530 **270** 80 f. multicoloured . . . 75 25

271 University Crest

1987. 25th Anniv of Jordan University. Multicoloured.
1531 60 f. Type **271** 70 30
1532 80 f. Entrance to campus (47 × 32 mm) 90 45

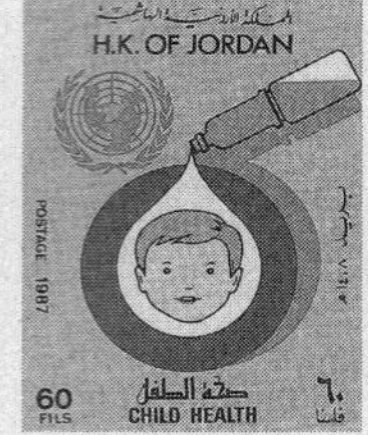

272 Child's Head in Droplet

1987. U.N.I.C.E.F. Child Survival Campaign. Multicoloured.
1533 60 f. Type **272** 60 35
1534 80 f. Hands reaching towards child and flag as "J" . . . . 1·25 80
1535 160 f. Baby on scales and children reading . . . . . 1·75 1·25

273 Parliament in Session, 1987

1987. 40th Anniv of Jordanian Parliament.
1536 – 60 f. mauve and gold . . 75 50
1537 **273** 80 f. multicoloured . . . 1·25 1·10
DESIGN: 60 f. 1947 opening ceremony.

274 Emblem

1987. Extraordinary Arab Summit Conference, Amman.
1538 **274** 60 f. multicoloured . . . 65 30
1539 80 f. multicoloured . . . 85 40
1540 160 f. multicoloured . . . 1·50 1·00
1541 240 f. multicoloured . . . 2·25 1·50

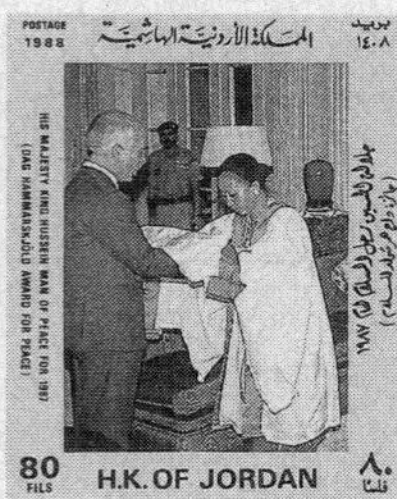

275 King Hussein receiving Cape

1988. Award of 1987 Dag Hammarskjold Peace Prize to King Hussein. Multicoloured.
1543 80 f. Type **275** 85 40
1544 160 f. King Hussein receiving Prize . . . . 1·60 1·40

276 Golden Sword

1988. Jordanian Victory in 1987 Arab Military Basketball Championship. Multicoloured.
1545 60 f. Type **276** 65 25
1546 80 f. King Hussein congratulating winners 90 45
1547 160 f. Match scene . . . . . 1·75 1·50

277 Anniversary Emblem and National Flag

278 Emblems and Globe

1988. 40th Anniv of W.H.O.
1548 **277** 60 f. multicoloured . . . 80 30
1549 80 f. multicoloured . . . 1·00 50

1988. 75th Anniv of Arab Scout Movement.
1550 **278** 60 f. multicoloured . . . 80 30
1551 80 f. multicoloured . . . 1·00 50

279 Crested Lark

1988. Birds. Multicoloured.
1552 10 f. Type **279** 20 10
1553 20 f. Stone-curlew 35 15
1554 30 f. Redstart 40 15
1555 40 f. Blackbird 60 25
1556 50 f. Rock dove 70 30
1557 160 f. White-breasted kingfisher . . . . 2·40 1·25

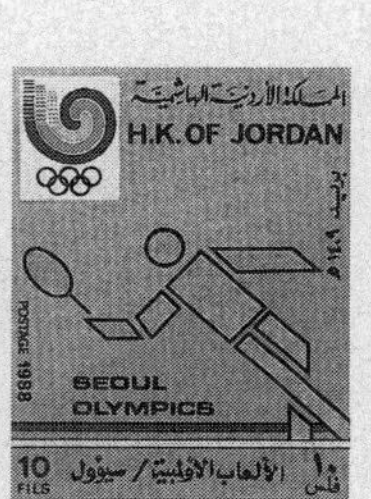

280 City cupped in Hands

282 Tennis

281 Um al-Rasas

1988. Restoration of Sana'a, Yemen Arab Republic.
1559 **280** 80 f. multicoloured . . . 75 40
1560 160 f. multicoloured . . . 1·00 75

1988. Historic Sites. Multicoloured.
1561 60 f. Type **281** 60 35
1562 80 f. Umm Qais 80 45
1563 160 f. Iraq al-Amir . . . . . 1·25 70

1988. Olympic Games, Seoul. Multicoloured.
1565 10 f. Type **282** 15 10
1566 60 f. Mascot 60 35
1567 80 f. Running and swimming . 80 45
1568 120 f. Basketball . . . . . . 1·00 70
1569 160 f. Football . . . . 1·25 1·00

283 Flame and Figures

1988. 40th Anniv of Declaration of Human Rights.
1571 **283** 80 f. multicoloured . . . 80 45
1572 160 f. multicoloured . . . 1·25 75

284 El-Deir Temple, Petra

1988. 25th Anniv of Royal Jordanian Airline. Multicoloured.
1573 60 f. Type **284** 75 50
1574 80 f. Boeing 737 airliner and map of world . . . . 1·00 60

285 Dome of the Rock, Jerusalem

1989. Palestinian Welfare.
1575 **285** 5 f. multicoloured . . . 10 10
1576 10 f. multicoloured . . . 20 15

286 Treasury, Petra, Flags and King Hussein

1989. Formation of Arab Co-operation Council (economic grouping of four states). Multicoloured.
1577 10 f. Type **286** 10 10
1578 30 f. Sana'a, Yemen 30 15
1579 40 f. Spiral Tower of Samarra, Iraq 40 20
1580 60 f. Pyramids, Egypt 55 25

287 Jordanian Parliament Building

1989. Centenary of Interparliamentary Union.
1581 **287** 40 f. multicoloured . . . 35 15
1582 60 f. multicoloured . . . 50 25

288 Modern Flats and Emblems

1989. Arab Housing Day and World Refugee Day. Multicoloured.
1583 5 f. Type **288** 10 10
1584 40 f. Hand supporting refugee family (horiz) 45 20
1585 60 f. Modern blocks of flats (horiz) 65 30

289 King Abdullah, Mosque and King Hussein

1989. Inauguration of King Abdullah Ibn al-Hussein Mosque, Amman.
1586 **289** 40 f. multicoloured . . . 35 15
1587 60 f. multicoloured . . . 55 25

290 Horse's Head

1989. Arabian Horse Festival. Multicoloured.
1589 5 f. Horse in paddock and emblem of Royal Stables (horiz) 10 10
1590 40 f. Horse rearing and Treasury, Petra (horiz) . . . 60 25
1591 60 f. Type **290** 90 40

291 Trees

1989. 50th Anniv of Ministry of Agriculture. Multicoloured.
1593 5 f. Type **291** 10 10
1594 40 f. Tree and "50" 45 20
1595 60 f. Orange trees and hives . . 65 30

292 Open Book, Globe and Flags

1989. Jordan Library Association.
1596 **292** 40 f. multicoloured . . . 40 15
1597 60 f. multicoloured . . . 60 25

293 Man carrying Basket

1989. Mosaics. Multicoloured.
1598 5 f. Type **293** 10 10
1599 10 f. Philadelphia (modern Amman) 15 10
1600 40 f. Deer 55 25
1601 60 f. Man with stick 85 40
1602 80 f. Jerusalem (horiz) . . . . 1·10 55

294 Flags and Map

1990. 1st Anniv of Arab Co-operation Council.
1604 **294** 5 f. multicoloured 10 10
1605 20 f. multicoloured 10 10
1606 60 f. multicoloured 15 10
1607 80 f. multicoloured 20 15

295 Wild Asses at Oasis

1990. Nature Conservation. Multicoloured.
1608 40 f. Type **295** 15 10
1609 60 f. Rock formation, Rum . . 20 10
1610 80 f. Desert palm trees 25 15

296 Horsemen and Building

1990. 70th Anniv of Arrival of Prince Abdullah in Ma'an.
1611 **296** 40 f. multicoloured . . . 15 10
1612 60 f. multicoloured . . . 20 15

297 Emblem

1990. 40th Anniv of United Nations Development Programme.
1614 **297** 60 f. multicoloured . . . 15 10
1615 80 f. multicoloured . . . 20 15

298 King Hussein

299 Nubian Ibex

1990. Multicoloured, frame colour given.
1616 **298** 5 f. yellow 10 10
1620 20 f. green 10 10
1621 40 f. red 10 10
1617 60 f. blue 15 10
1618 80 f. mauve 15 10
1622 240 f. brown 45 20
1623 320 f. purple 60 30
1624 1 d. green . . . . 1·75 90

1991. Endangered Animals. Multicoloured.
1631 5 f. Type **299** 10 10
1632 40 f. Onager 30 15
1633 80 f. Arabian gazelles 55 25
1634 160 f. Arabian oryx . . . . . 1·10 50

300 Electric Light Bulbs

1991. Energy Rationalization. Multicoloured.
1635 5 f. Type **300** 10 10
1636 40 f. Solar energy (vert) . . . 20 10
1637 80 f. Angle-poise lamp by window (vert) 40 20

301 Grain

1991. Grain Production. Multicoloured.
1638 5 f. Type **301** 10 10
1639 40 f. Ear of wheat and leaves . 20 10
1640 80 f. Ear of wheat and field . . 40 20

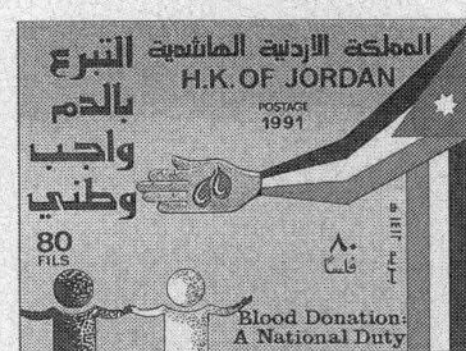

302 Drops of Blood on Hand

1991. National Blood Donation Campaign.
1641 **302** 80 f. multicoloured . . . 65 35
1642 160 f. multicoloured . . . 1·10 50

303 Jerusalem and Map

1991. Palestinian "Intifida" Movement.
1643 **303** 20 f. multicoloured . . . 15 10

304 Emblem

1992. "Expo '92" World's Fair, Seville.
1644 **304** 80 f. multicoloured . . . 15 10
1645 320 f. multicoloured . . . 70 35

305 Man and Woman balancing Scales

1992. World Health Day. "Heartbeat—the Rhythm of Health".
1646 80 f. Type **305** 20 10
1647 125 f. Man and heart in balance and cardiograph (horiz) . . 35 20

306 Children

1992. S.O.S. Children's Village, Aqaba. Mult.
1648 80 f. Type **306** 20 10
1649 125 f. Village 35 20

307 Judo and Olympic Flame

1992. Olympic Games, Barcelona. Multicoloured.
1650 5 f. Type **307** 10 10
1651 40 f. Runners and track (vert) . . 15 10
1652 80 f. Gymnast 35 20
1653 125 f. Mascot (vert) 50 25
1654 160 f. Table tennis 65 35

308 King Hussein

1992. 40th Anniv of King Hussein's Accession. Multicoloured.
1656 40 f. Type **308** 10 10
1657 80 f. National colours, crown and King (horiz) 25 15
1658 125 f. King and flags (horiz) . . . 35 20
1659 160 f. King, crown and anniversary emblem (horiz) 45 25

309 African Monarch

310 Hadrian's Triumphal Arch, Jerash

1992. Butterflies. Multicoloured.
1661 5 f. Type **309** 10 10
1662 40 f. Black-veined white . . . 30 15
1663 80 f. Swallowtail 55 20
1664 160 f. "Pseudochazara telephassa" . . . . 1·10 45

1993. Variously dated "1992" to "1996".
1666 **310** 5 f. brown, blue & blk . . 10 10
1788 25 f. brown, pur & blk . . 10 10
1718 40 f. brown, grn & blk . . 10 10
1798 50 f. brown, yell & blk . . 10 10
1799 75 f. brn, cinn & blk . . . 15 10
1667 80 f. brown, grn & blk . . 10 10
1668 100 f. brn, red & blk . . . 20 10
1800 100 f. brn, grn & blk . . . 20 15
1801 120 f. brn, grn & blk . . . 20 15
1669 125 f. brn, pink & blk . . 25 15
1721 125 f. brown, bl & blk . . 20 15
1802 150 f. brn, pink & blk . . 25 15
1670 160 f. brn, yell & blk . . 30 20
1803 200 f. brn, grey & blk . . 35 20
1671 240 f. brn, pur & blk . . 45 25
1804 300 f. brn, pink & blk . . 55 30
1672 320 f. brn, chest & blk . . 55 30
1805 400 f. brown, bl & blk . . 70 40
1793 500 f. brn, ochre & blk . . 90 50
1674 1 d. brown, yell & blk . . 1·75 95

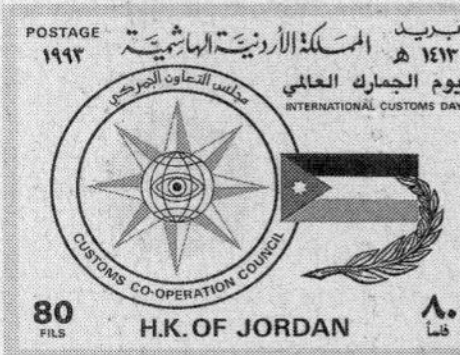

311 Customs Co-operation Council Emblem, Flag and Laurel

1993. International Customs Day.
1680 **311** 80 f. multicoloured . . . 20 10
1681 125 f. multicoloured . . . 35 15

312 King Hussein and Military Equipment

1993. Army Day and 77th Anniv of Arab Revolt. Multicoloured.
1682 5 f. Type **312** 10 10
1683 40 f. King Hussein, soldier, surgeons and tank 25 10
1684 80 f. King Abdullah and Dome of the Rock 45 20
1685 125 f. King Hussein of Hejaz, Dome of the Rock and horsemen 70 25

313 Society Emblem and Natural Energy Resources

1993. 23rd Anniv of Royal Scientific Society.
1687 **313** 80 f. multicoloured . . . 15 10

314 Courtyard

1993. Centenary of Salt Municipality.
1688 **314** 80 f. multicoloured . . . 20 10
1689 125 f. multicoloured . . . 35 15

315 Long-tailed Blue

1993. Butterflies. Multicoloured.

1691 5 f. Type **315** 10 10
1692 40 f. "Melanargria titea" . . . 20 10
1693 80 f. "Allancastria deyrollei" . . 30 15
1694 160 f. "Gonepteryx cleopatra" . 75 35

316 Eyes, Candle and White Cane

1993. White Cane Day. Multicoloured.

1696 80 f. Type **316** 20 10
1697 125 f. Globe, white cane and eye (vert) 35 15

317 King Hussein in Army Uniform

1993. 40th Anniv of King Hussein's Enthronement. Multicoloured.

1698 40 f. Type **317** 15 10
1699 80 f. King wearing Bedouin costume 25 10
1700 125 f. King wearing suit . . . 40 20
1701 160 f. King with Queen Noor (horiz) 50 25

318 Saladin and Dome of the Rock, Jerusalem

1993. 800th Death Anniv of Saladin.

1703 **318** 40 f. multicoloured . . . 20 10
1704 80 f. multicoloured . . . 40 15
1705 125 f. multicoloured . . . 60 25

319 King Hussein and Crowd

1993. King Hussein's Return from Surgery in U.S.A. (1992). Multicoloured.

1706 80 f. Type **319** 30 10
1707 125 f. King waving at crowd . 50 15
1708 160 f. King embracing his mother 60 20

320 Virus, Emblem and Silhouettes

1993. World AIDS Day.

1710 **320** 80 f. multicoloured . . . 20 15
1711 125 f. multicoloured . . . 35 20

321 Emblems and Flag

1993. 45th Anniv of United Nations Declaration of Human Rights.

1713 **321** 40 f. multicoloured . . . 10 10
1714 160 f. multicoloured . . . 35 25

322 Loading Airplane

1994. Jordan Hashemite Charity Organization. Multicoloured.

1715 80 f. Type **322** 20 10
1716 125 f. Transport plane 35 15

323 Mosque and King Hussein

1994. Refurbishment of El Aqsa Mosque and Dome of the Rock.

1726 80 f. Type **323** 30 15
1727 125 f. Dome of the Rock and King Hussein 50 20
1728 240 f. Dome of the Rock and King Hussein (different) . . 95 45

324 Emblems on Doves

1994. 75th Anniv of International Red Cross and Red Crescent Societies. Multicoloured.

1730 80 f. Child and emblems (horiz) 25 10
1731 160 f. Type **324** 50 25

325 Globe, Emblem and "75"

1994. 75th Anniv of I.L.O.

1733 **325** 80 f. multicoloured . . . 20 10
1734 125 f. multicoloured . . . 35 20

326 Sports Pictograms and Olympic Rings

1994. Centenary of International Olympic Committee. Multicoloured.

1735 80 f. Type **326** 20 10
1736 125 f. Sports pictograms, flame and "100" 30 10
1737 160 f. Olympic rings, track and athlete (horiz) 40 15
1738 240 f. Olympic rings and hand holding torch (horiz) 60 25

327 King Hussein greeting Soldiers

1994. Jordanian Participation in United Nations Peace-keeping Forces. Multicoloured.

1740 80 f. Type **327** 20 10
1741 125 f. King Hussein inspecting troops 30 15
1742 160 f. U. N. checkpoint . . . 35 15

328 Flag, Emblem, Globe, Wheat and Family

1994. International Year of the Family.

1743 **328** 80 f. multicoloured . . . 20 10
1744 125 f. multicoloured . . . 30 15
1745 160 f. multicoloured . . . 35 15

329 Aircraft and Emblem

1994. 50th Anniv of I.C.A.O.

1746 **329** 80 f. multicoloured . . . 25 15
1747 125 f. multicoloured . . . 40 20
1748 160 f. multicoloured . . . 50 25

330 Hands around Water Droplet

1994. Water Conservation Campaign. Mult.

1749 80 f. Type **330** 20 10
1750 125 f. Glass beneath running tap, foodstuffs and industry . 35 20
1751 160 f. Water droplets and boy on lush hillside 45 30

331 Crown Prince Hassan

1994. 10th Anniv of Crown Prince's Award.

1752 **331** 80 f. multicoloured . . . 20 10
1753 125 f. multicoloured . . . 35 20
1754 160 f. multicoloured . . . 45 30

332 University Emblem

1995. Inauguration of Al al-Bayt University.

1755 **332** 80 f. gold, blue & black 20 10
1756 125 f. gold, green & blk 35 20

333 U. N. Emblem and "50"

1995. 50th Anniv of U.N.O.

1758 **333** 80 f. multicoloured . . . 20 10
1759 125 f. multicoloured . . . 35 20

334 Labour Emblem and Crowd with Flag

1995. Labour Day. Multicoloured.

1760 80 f. Type **334** 20 10
1761 125 f. Emblem, world map and miner's head 35 20
1762 160 f. Hands holding spanner and torch 40 25

335 Flags and Globe

1995. Jordan Week in Japan. Multicoloured.

1763 80 f. Type **335** 20 10
1764 125 f. Hemispheres and flags . 35 20
1765 160 f. Flags, brick wall and globe 40 25

336 Artefacts

1995. Petra, "The Rose City". Multicoloured.

1766 50 f. Amphitheatre 10 10
1767 75 f. Type **336** 20 10
1768 80 f. Treasury seen through cleft in rocks (vert) 20 10
1769 160 f. Treasury (vert) 40 25

337 Emblem

1995. 50th Anniv of Arab League.

1771 **337** 80 f. multicoloured . . . 20 10
1772 125 f. multicoloured . . . 35 20
1773 160 f. multicoloured . . . 40 25

338 Leaves and Emblem

1995. 50th Anniv of F.A.O. Multicoloured.

1774 80 f. Type **338** 20 10
1775 125 f. Ears of wheat and "50" incorporating F.A.O. emblem 35 20
1776 160 f. United Nations emblem and "50" incorporating F.A.O. emblem 40 25

339 Knotted Ropes, Summit Emblem and National Flags

1995. Middle Eastern and North African Economic Summit, Amman.

1777 339 80 f. multicoloured . . . 15 10
1778 125 f. multicoloured . . . 20 15

340 King Hussein

1995. 60th Birthday of King Hussein. Mult.

1779 25 f. Type **340** 10 10
1780 40 f. Hussein within shield . . . 10 10
1781 80 f. Dove incorporating "60", El-Deir Temple (Petra) and Hussein 15 10
1782 100 f. Hussein in military uniform and anniversary emblem 20 15
1783 125 f. King Hussein 20 15
1784 160 f. Hussein, national flag and "60 60 60" 30 20

341 Hands and Hard of Hearing Emblem

1995. The Deaf. Multicoloured.

1786 80 f. Type **341** 15 10
1787 125 f. Emblems, sign language and hard of hearing emblem 20 15

342 Anniversary Emblem and Map of Jordan

1996. 50th Anniv of Independence. Mult.

1794 100 f. Type **342** 15 10
1795 200 f. King Hussein, map of Jordan and King Abdullah . 35 20
1796 300 f. King Hussein 55 35

343 Games Emblem, Olympic Rings and Pictograms

1996. Olympic Games. Atlanta. Multicoloured.

1806 50 f. Type **343** 10 10
1807 100 f. Games emblem and pictograms 20 15
1808 200 f. Games emblem forming torch and figure 35 20
1809 300 f. Games emblem, torch and national flag 55 35

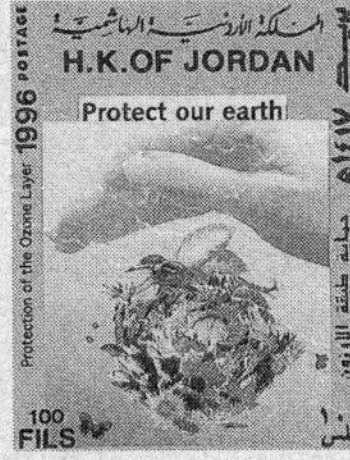

344 Hand protecting Animals and Plants

1996. Protection of the Ozone Layer.

1810 344 100 f. multicoloured . . . 15 10

345 Anniversary Emblem

1996. 50th Anniv of U.N.I.C.E.F. Fund.

1811 345 100 f. multicoloured . . . 15 10
1812 200 f. multicoloured . . . 35 20

346 Playing Polo

1997. 50th Birthday of Crown Prince Hassan. Multicoloured.

1813 50 f. Type **346** 10 10
1814 100 f. Wearing western dress (vert) 15 10
1815 200 f. In military uniform . . . 35 20

347 Karak

1997. Centenary of Discovery of Madaba Mosaic Map. Multicoloured.

1817 100 f. Type **347** 15 10
1818 200 f. River Jordan (horiz) . . 35 20
1819 300 f. Jerusalem 50 30

348 Von Stephan

1997. Death Centenary of Heinrich von Stephan (founder of U.P.U.).

1821 348 100 f. multicoloured . . . 15 10
1822 200 f. multicoloured . . . 35 20

349 Rosefinch

1997. The Jordanian Rosefinch.

1823 349 50 f. multicoloured . . . 10 10
1824 100 f. multicoloured . . . 15 10
1825 150 f. multicoloured . . . 25 15
1826 200 f. multicoloured . . . 35 20

350 Performers and Hadrian's Triumphal Arch

1997. 15th Anniv of Jerash Festival. Mult.

1827 50 f. Type **350** 10 10
1828 100 f. Orchestra, Festival emblem and Jerash ruins . . 15 10
1829 150 f. Temple of Artemis and marching band 25 15
1830 200 f. Women dancers and audience at performance . . 35 20

351 Current and Previous Parliament Buildings

1997. 50th Anniv of First National Parliament. Multicoloured.

1832 100 f. Type **351** 15 10
1833 200 f. King Hussein addressing, and view of, Chamber of Deputies 35 20

352 Meeting Emblem

1997. 53rd International Air Transport Assn Annual General Meeting, Amman.

1834 352 100 f. multicoloured . . . 15 10
1835 200 f. multicoloured . . . 35 20
1836 300 f. multicoloured . . . 50 30

353 King Hussein and Queen Noor

1997. 62nd Birthday of King Hussein.

1837 353 100 f. multicoloured . . . 15 10
1838 200 f. multicoloured . . . 35 20
1839 300 f. multicoloured . . . 50 30

354 Jerusalem and Dome of the Rock

1997. Jerusalem.

1841 354 100 f. + 10 f. mult . . . 20 15
1842 200 f. + 20 f. mult . . . 35 20
1843 300 f. + 30 f. mult . . . 55 30

355 Opening Ceremony

1997. Jordan, Arab Football Champion, 1997. Multicoloured.

1844 50 f. Type **355** 10 10
1845 75 f. Team saluting national anthem 15 10
1846 100 f. Posing for team photograph and police officers patrolling crowd 15 10

356 Women

1997. National Women's Forum. Mult.

1848 50 f. Type **356** 10 10
1849 100 f. National flag, women's profiles and emblems (horiz) 15 10
1850 150 f. Forum meeting and emblem (horiz) 25 15

357 Air Pollution by Factories and Cars

1998. Earth Day. Children's Paintings. Mult.

1851 50 f. Polluted air, land and water 10 10
1852 100 f. Type **357** 15 10
1853 150 f. "Earth" being strangled by pollution (vert) 25 15

358 King Abdullah and Camel in Desert

1998. 75th Anniv of Recognition of Transjordan as Autonomous State. Multicoloured.

1864 100 f. Type **358** 15 10
1865 200 f. King Hussein and camel in desert 35 20
1866 300 f. King Abdullah, King Hussein and May 1923 9 p. stamp 50 30

359 Thistle

1998. Flowers. Multicoloured.

1868 50 f. Type **359** 10 10
1869 100 f. Poppy 15 10
1870 150 f. Carnation 25 15

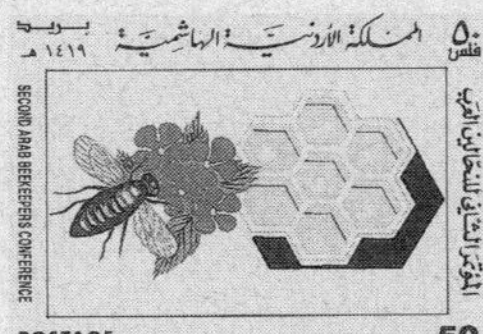

360 Animals and Trees

1998. Mosaics from Um ar-Rasas. Mult.

1872 100 f. Type **360** 15 10
1873 200 f. City buildings 35 20
1874 300 f. Mosiac panel 50 30

361 Honey Bee and Honeycomb

1998. 2nd Arab Bee-keeping Conference. Mult.

1875 50 f. Type **361** 10 10
1876 100 f. Bee on flower (vert) . . 15 10
1877 150 f. Bee, flower and honeycomb 25 15

المملكة الأردنية الهاشمية

50 FILS

INTERNATIONAL STAMP DAY

H. K. OF JORDAN POSTAGE 1998

362 Dove with Stamp

1998. International Stamp Day. Multicoloured.

1879	50 f. Type **362**	10	10
1880	100 f. World map and U.P.U. emblem	15	10
1881	150 f. Stamps encircling globe	25	15

363 King Hussein and Map of Jordan

1998. 63rd Birthday of King Hussein.

1882	**363**	100 f. multicoloured	15	10
1883		200 f. multicoloured	35	20
1884		300 f. multicoloured	50	30

364 King Hussein and Emblem

1998. 25th Anniv of Arab Police and Security Chiefs' Meeting. Multicoloured.

1886	100 f. Type **364**	15	10
1887	200 f. Flags of member countries of Arab League (vert)	35	20
1888	300 f. Police beret and map of Jordan	50	30

365 Family and Anniversary Emblem

1998. 50th Anniv of Universal Declaration of Human Rights. Multicoloured.

1889	100 f. Type **365**	15	10
1890	200 f. Silhouettes of people and United Nations emblem	35	20

366 Wahbi al Tal

1999. Birth Centenary and 50th Death Anniv of Mustafa Wahbi al Tal (poet).

1891	**366**	100f. multicoloured	15	10

OBLIGATORY TAX

T 36 Mosque in Hebron

T 43 Ruins at Palmyra, Syria

1947.

T264	T 36	1 m. blue	30	20
T265		2 m. red	35	25
T266		3 m. green	45	35
T267		5 m. red	55	40
T268	–	10 m. red	60	55
T269	–	15 m. grey	90	60
T270	–	20 m. brown	1·25	70
T271	–	50 m. violet	2·10	1·50
T272	–	100 m. red	6·00	4·25
T273	–	200 m. blue	18·00	11·00
T274	–	500 m. green	42·00	30·00
T275	–	£P1 brown	90·00	75·00

DESIGNS: Nos. T268/71, Dome of the Rock; Nos. T272/75, Acre.

1950. Optd **Aid** in English and Arabic.

T290	28	5 m. orange		6·75
T291		10 m. violet		10·00
T292		15 m. green		12·00

1950. Revenue stamps optd **Aid** in English and Arabic.

T296	T 43	5 m. orange	10·00	7·50
T297		10 m. violet	12·00	7·50

1951. Values in "FILS".

T302	T 36	5 f. red	30	30
T303	–	10 f. red	40	40
T304	–	15 f. black	45	45
T305	–	20 f. brown	60	60
T306	–	100 f. orange	2·40	2·40

DESIGNS: Nos. T303/305, Dome of the Rock; No. T306, Acre.

1952. Nos. T264/75 optd **J.D.** (T344) or **FILS** (others).

T334	T 36	1 f. on 1 m. blue	25	25
T335		2 f. on 2 m. red	60·00	
T336		3 f. on 3 m. green	30	25
T337	–	10 f. on 10 m. red	30	25
T338	–	15 f. on 15 m. grey	65	50
T339	–	20 f. on 20 m. brown	85	85
T340	–	50 f. on 50 m. violet	1·50	1·50
T341	–	100 f. on 100 m. orge	8·00	5·00
T342	–	200 f. on 200 m. blue	20·00	13·00
T343	–	500 f. on 500 m. green	48·00	35·00
T344	–	1 d. on £P1 brown	£110	70·00

OFFICIAL STAMPS

(حكومة)
الشرق العربي
١٣٤٢

(O 16 "Arab Government of the East, 1342")

1924. Type **11** of Saudi Arabia optd with Type O **16**.

O117		½ p. red	20·00	£100

POSTAGE DUE STAMPS

حكومة
مستحق
الشرق العربية
٩ شعبان ١٣٤١ مستحق

(D 12 "Due") (D 13)

1923. Issue of 1923 (with opt T **10**) further optd

(a) With Type D **12** (the 3 p. also surch as T **12**).

D112	11	½ p. on 3 p. brown	13·00	16·00
D113		1 p. blue	8·50	9·50
D114		1½ p. lilac	8·50	9·50
D115		2 p. orange	10·00	11·00

(b) With Type D **13** and surch as T **12**.

D116	11	½ p. on 3 p. brown	42·00	50·00

حكومة
الشرق العربية
مستحق
٩ شعبان ١٣٤١

(D 14)

1923. Stamps of Saudi Arabia handstamped with Type D **14**.

D117	11	½ p. red	1·00	2·25
D118		1 p. blue	2·00	2·50
D119		1½ p. violet	2·00	3·25
D120		2 p. orange	2·75	3·75
D121		3 p. brown	4·00	7·50
D122		5 p. olive	7·00	11·00

مستحق

مستحق
شرق الاردن

١ مليم

(D 20 "Due East of the Jordan") (D 21)

1925. Stamps of Palestine (without Palestine opt) optd with Type D **20**.

D159	3	1 m. brown	1·40	4·50
D160		2 m. yellow	1·75	3·25
D161		4 m. red	2·75	5·50
D162		8 m. red	3·75	8·50
D163		13 m. blue	4·50	8·50
D164		5 p. purple	5·00	11·00

1926. Stamps of Palestine as last surch as Type D **21** ("DUE" and new value in Arabic).

D165	3	1 m. on 1 m. brown	3·00	5·00
D166		2 m. on 1 m. brown	3·00	5·00
D167		4 m. on 3 m. blue	3·25	6·00
D168		8 m. on 3 m. blue	3·25	6·00
D169		13 m. on 13 m. blue	3·75	7·00
D170		5 p. on 13 m. blue	4·50	10·00

The lower line of the surcharge differs for each value.

(D 25) D 26 D 50

1928. Surch as Type D **25** or optd only.

D183	22	1 m. on 3 m. red	70	3·50
D184		2 m. blue	80	3·50
D185		4 m. on 15 m. blue	1·25	4·00
D186		10 m. red	1·25	4·00
D187	23	20 m. on 100 m. blue	3·75	10·00
D188		50 m. purple	4·75	13·00

1929.

D244	D 26	1 m. brown	15	2·75
D245		2 m. yellow	30	3·25
D246		4 m. green	55	4·25
D247		10 m. red	1·10	4·75
D193		20 m. olive	6·50	11·00
D194		50 m. blue	7·50	17·00

1952. Optd **FILS FILS.** in English and Arabic

D350	D 26	1 f. on 1 m. brown	30	30
D351		2 f. on 2 m. yellow	30	30
D352		4 f. on 4 m. green	55	70
D353		10 f. on 10 m. red	1·50	1·25
D354		20 f. on 20 m. olive	3·75	3·50
D346		50 f. on 50 m. blue	3·50	3·25

1952. Inscr "THE HASHEMITE KINGDOM OF THE JORDAN".

D372	D 50	1 f. brown	15	45
D373		2 f. yellow	20	45
D374		4 f. green	20	45
D375		10 f. red	45	65
D376		20 f. brown	45	90
D377		50 f. blue	1·25	2·25

1957. As Type D **50**, but inscr "THE HASHEMITE KINGDOM OF JORDAN".

D465		1 f. brown	15	35
D466		2 f. yellow	15	35
D467		4 f. green	25	50
D468		10 f. red	35	50
D469		20 f. brown	75	1·40

JORDANIAN OCCUPATION OF PALESTINE Pt. 19

1948. Stamps of Jordan optd **PALESTINE** in English and Arabic.

P 1	28	1 m. brown	35	35
P 2		2 m. green	35	35
P 3		3 m. green	35	35
P 4		3 m. pink	25	25
P 5		4 m. green	25	25
P 6		5 m. orange	25	25
P 7		10 m. violet	65	65
P 8		12 m. red	65	40
P 9		15 m. green	90	90
P10		20 m. blue	1·25	65
P11	29	50 m. purple	1·40	1·60
P12		90 m. bistre	7·75	1·60
P13		100 m. blue	8·50	4·50
P14		200 m. violet	3·25	6·95
P15		500 m. brown	27·00	12·50
P16		£P1 grey	60·00	32·00

1949. 75th Anniv of U.P.U. Stamps of Jordan optd **PALESTINE** in English and Arabic.

P30	40	1 m. brown	25	60
P31		4 m. green	40	80
P32		10 m. red	50	90
P33		20 m. blue	80	95
P34	–	50 m. green (No. 289)	1·40	1·50

OBLIGATORY TAX

1950. Nos. T264/75 of Jordan optd **PALESTINE** in English and Arabic.

PT35	T 36	1 m. blue	10	25
PT36		2 m. red	15	25
PT37		3 m. green	30	40
PT38		5 m. purple	40	30
PT39	–	10 m. red	40	30
PT40	–	15 m. black	1·25	40
PT41	–	20 m. brown	2·00	75
PT42	–	50 m. violet	2·75	1·40
PT43	–	100 m. red	4·75	2·25
PT44	–	200 m. blue	12·00	5·75
PT45	–	500 m. green	38·00	19·00
PT46	–	£P1 brown	70·00	42·00

POSTAGE DUE STAMPS

1948. Postage Due stamps of Jordan optd **PALESTINE** in English and Arabic.

PD25	D 26	1 m. brown	1·40	1·75
PD26		2 m. yellow	1·60	2·10
PD18		4 m. green	1·60	2·10
PD28		10 m. red	1·60	1·75
PD20		20 m. olive	1·00	1·00
PD21		50 m. blue	1·60	2·10

After a time the stamps of Jordan were used in the occupied areas.

JUBALAND Pt. 8

A district in E. Africa, formerly part of Kenya, ceded by Gt. Britain to Italy in 1925, and incorporated in Italian Somaliland.

100 centesimi = 1 lira.

1925. Stamps of Italy optd **OLTRE GIUBA**.

1	30	1 c. brown	2·00	2·00
2	31	2 c. brown	2·00	2·00
3	37	5 c. green	2·00	2·00
4		10 c. pink	2·00	2·00
5		15 c. grey	2·00	2·00
6	41	20 c. orange	2·00	2·00
39	39	20 c. green	2·50	5·00
7		25 c. blue	2·00	2·00
8		30 c. brown	2·00	2·00
40		30 c. grey	3·00	5·00
9		40 c. brown	2·00	2·00
10		50 c. mauve	2·00	2·00
11		60 c. red	2·00	2·00
41	44	75 c. red and carmine	16·00	35·00
12		1 l. brown and green	4·00	3·75
42		1 l. 25 blue & ultramarine	19·00	38·00
13		2 l. green and orange	30·00	17·00
43		2 l. 50 green and orange	24·00	48·00
14		5 l. blue and pink	35·00	22·00
15		10 l. green and pink	7·00	22·00

1925. Royal Jubilee stamps of Italy optd **OLTRE GIUBA**.

44	82	60 c. red	20	3·00
45		1 l. blue	25	3·00
46		1 l. 25 blue	50	8·50

1926. St. Francis of Assisi stamps of Italy. as Nos. 191/6, optd **OLTRE GIUBA**.

47		20 c. green	1·00	4·25
48		40 c. violet	1·00	4·25
49		60 c. red	1·00	4·25
50		1 l. 25 blue	1·00	4·25
51		5 l. + 2 l. 50 olive	2·00	5·50

8 Map of Jubaland

1926. 1st Anniv of Acquisition of Jubaland.

54	3	5 c. orange	60	2·50
55		20 c. green	60	2·50
56		25 c. brown	60	2·50
57		40 c. red	60	2·50
58		60 c. purple	60	2·50
59		1 l. blue	60	2·50
60		2 l. grey	60	2·50

1926. As Colonial Propaganda T **6** of Cyrenaica, but inscr "OLTRE GIUBA".

61		5 c. + 5c. brown	20	2·25
62		10 c. + 5 c. olive	20	2·25
63		20 c. + 5 c. green	20	2·25
64		40 c. + 5 c. red	20	2·25
65		60 c. + 5 c. orange	20	2·25
66		1 l. + 5 c. blue	20	2·25

EXPRESS LETTER STAMPS

1926. Express Letter stamps of Italy optd **OLTRE GIUBA**.

E52	E 35	70 c. red	8·00	20·00
E53	E 41	2 l. 50 blue and pink	13·00	25·00

PARCEL POST STAMPS.

1925. Parcel Post stamps of Italy optd **OLTRE GIUBA**.

P16	P 53	5 c. brown	4·00	1·25
P17		10 c. blue	1·90	75
P18		20 c. black	1·90	75
P19		25 c. red	1·90	75
P20		50 c. orange	3·50	75
P21		1 l. violet	2·25	75
P22		2 l. green	2·25	75
P23	P 53	3 l. yellow	3·50	1·00
P24		4 l. grey	4·25	1·25
P25		10 l. purple	19·00	3·00
P26		12 l. brown	48·00	8·00
P27		15 l. olive	38·00	8·00
P28		20 l. purple	38·00	8·00

Unused prices are for complete stamps, used prices for half-stamps.

POSTAGE DUE STAMPS

1925. Postage Due stamps of Italy optd **OLTRE GIUBA**.

D29	D 12	5 c. purple and orange	4·75	7·50
D30		10 c. purple & orange	3·75	7·50
D31		20 c. purple & orange	3·75	7·50
D32		30 c. purple & orange	3·75	7·50
D33		40 c. purple & orange	4·75	7·50
D34		50 c. purple & orange	5·50	7·50
D35		60 c. brown & orange	5·50	7·50
D36		1 l. purple and blue	7·00	7·50
D37		2 l. purple and blue	26·00	45·00
D38		5 l. purple and blue	32·00	45·00

KAMPUCHEA Pt. 21

Following the fall of the Khmer Rouge government, which had terminated the Khmer Republic, the People's Republic of Kampuchea was proclaimed on 10 January 1979.

Kampuchea was renamed Cambodia in 1989.

100 cents = 1 riel.

105 Soldiers with Flag and Independence Monument, Phnom Penh

106 Moscow Kremlin and Globe

1980. Multicoloured. Without gum.

402	0.1 r. Type **105**	1·90	1·90
403	0.2 r. Khmer people and flag	3·75	3·75
404	0.5 r. Fisherman pulling in nets	5·00	5·00
405	1 r. Armed forces and Kampuchean flag	8·25	8·25

1982. 60th Anniv of U.S.S.R. Multicoloured.

406	50 c. Type **106**	15	10
407	1 r. Industrial complex and map of U.S.S.R.	30	10

107 Arms of Kampuchea

1983. 4th Anniv of People's Republic of Kampuchea. Multicoloured.

408	50 c. Type **107**	25	10
409	1 r. Open book illustrating national flag and arms (horiz)	50	15
410	3 r. Stylized figures and map	1·40	40

108 Runner with Olympic Torch

109 Orange Tiger

1983. Olympic Games, Los Angeles (1984) (1st issue). Multicoloured.

412	20 c. Type **108**	10	10
413	50 c. Javelin throwing	15	10
414	80 c. Pole vaulting	20	10
415	1 r. Discus throwing	35	15
416	1 r. 50 Relay (horiz)	50	20
417	2 r. Swimming (horiz)	85	30
418	3 r. Basketball	1·25	45

See also Nos. 526/32.

1983. Butterflies. Multicoloured.
420 20 c. Type **109** 15 10
421 50 c. "Euploea althaea" . . . 20 15
422 80 c. "Byasa polyeuctes" (horiz) 40 20
423 1 r. "Stichophthalma howqua" (horiz) 70 25
424 1 r. 50 Leaf butterfly . . . . . 1·25 45
425 2 r. Blue argus . . . . . . 1·75 60
426 3 r. Lemon migrant . . . . . 2·75 80

110 Srah Srang

1983. Khmer Culture. Multicoloured.
427 20 c. Type **110** 10 10
428 50 c. Bakong 15 10
429 80 c. Ta Som (vert) 25 10
430 1 r. North gate, Angkor Thom (vert) 40 15
431 1 r. 50 Kennora (winged figures) (vert) 70 25
432 2 r. Apsara (carved figures), Angkor (vert) 75 25
433 3 r. Banteai Srei (goddess), Tevoda (vert) . . . . 1·25 40

111 Dancers with Castanets

1983. Folklore. Multicoloured.
434 50 c. Type **111** 25 10
435 1 r. Dancers with grass headdresses 55 20
436 3 r. Dancers with scarves . . . 1·25 40

112 Detail of Fresco

1983. 500th Birth Anniv of Raphael (artist).
438 **112** 20 c. multicoloured 10 10
439 – 50 c. multicoloured 15 10
440 – 80 c. multicoloured 25 10
441 – 1 r. multicoloured 50 15
442 – 1 r. 50 multicoloured . . . 85 25
443 – 2 r. multicoloured . . . . 1·10 25
444 – 3 r. multicoloured . . . . 1·40 40
DESIGNS: Nos. 439/44, different details of frescoes by Raphael.

113 Montgolfier Balloon **114** Cobra

1983. Bicentenary of Manned Flight. Mult.
446 20 c. Type **113** 10 15
447 30 c. "La Ville d'Orleans", 1870 20 10
448 50 c. Charles's hydrogen balloon 30 15
449 1 r. Blanchard and Jeffries crossing Channel, 1785 . . . 50 20
450 1 r. 50 Salomon Andree's balloon flight over Arctic 85 35
451 2 r. Auguste Piccard's stratosphere balloon "F.N.R.S." 90 40
452 3 r. Hot-air balloon race . . . 1·50 50

1983. Reptiles. Multicoloured.
454 20 c. Crested lizard (horiz) . . 15 10
455 30 c. Type **114** 20 10
456 80 c. Trionyx turtle (horiz) . . . 25 10
457 1 r. Chameleon 45 15
458 1 r. 50 Boa constrictor 75 25
459 2 r. Crocodile (horiz) 90 25
460 3 r. Turtle (horiz) . . . . . . 1·40 40

115 Rainbow Lory **116** Sunflower

1983. Birds. Multicoloured.
461 20 c. Type **115** 20 10
462 50 c. Barn swallow 30 15
463 80 c. Golden eagle (horiz) . . . 50 25
464 1 r. Griffon vulture (horiz) . . . 85 40
465 1 r. 50 Javanese collared dove (horiz) . . . . 1·25 55
466 2 r. Magpie . . . . 1·60 70
467 3 r. Great Indian hornbill . . . 2·50 1·10

1983. Flowers. Multicoloured.
468 20 c. Type **116** 10 10
469 50 c. "Caprifoliaceae" 15 10
470 80 c. "Bougainvillea" 25 10
471 1 r. "Ranunculaceae" 40 15
472 1 r. 50 "Nyctagynaeceae" . . . 75 25
473 2 r. Cockscomb 90 25
474 3 r. Roses . . . . 1·40 40

117 Luge

1983. Winter Olympic Games, Sarajevo (1984) (1st issue). Multicoloured.
475 1 r. Type **117** 40 15
476 2 r. Biathlon 90 25
477 4 r. Ski-jumping . . . . . . 1·75 50
478 5 r. Two-man bobsleigh . . . . 1·90 60
479 7 r. Ice hockey . . . . 2·75 85
See also Nos. 496/502.

118 Cyprinid

1983. Fishes. Multicoloured.
481 20 c. Type **118** 20 10
482 50 c. Loach 30 10
483 80 c. Bubblebee catfish 35 10
484 1 r. Spiny eel 80 15
485 1 r. 50 Cyprinid (different) . . 1·25 30
486 2 r. Cyprinid (different) . . . . 1·50 30
487 3 r. Aberrant fish . . . . . . 2·25 60

119 Factory and Gearwheel

1983. Festival of Rebirth. Multicoloured.
488 50 c. Type **119** 20 10
489 1 r. Tractor and cow (horiz) . . 35 15
490 3 r. Bulk carrier, diesel locomotive, car and bridge . . . 2·75 60

120 Red Cross and Sailing Ship

1984. 5th Anniv of Liberation. Multicoloured.
492 50 c. Type **120** 20 10
493 1 r. Three soldiers, flags and temple 35 15
494 3 r. Crowd surrounding temple 1·00 35

121 Speed Skating **122** Ilyushin Il-62M Jet over Angkor Vat

1984. Winter Olympic Games, Sarajevo (2nd issue). Multicoloured.
496 20 c. Type **121** 10 10
497 50 c. Ice hockey 15 10
498 80 c. Skiing 20 10
499 1 r. Ski jumping 50 15
500 1 r. 50 Skiing (different) . . . 75 25
501 2 r. Cross-country skiing . . . 90 25
502 3 r. Ice skating (pairs) . . . . 1·25 40

1984. Air.
504 **122** 5 r. multicoloured . . . . 2·50 75
505 10 r. multicoloured . . . . 4·75 1·50
506 15 r. multicoloured . . . . 7·25 2·25
507 25 r. multicoloured . . . . 12·25 3·75
For design as Type **122** but inscribed "R.P. DU KAMPUCHEA", see Nos. 695/8.

123 Cattle Egret **124** Doves and Globe

1984. Birds. Multicoloured.
508 10 c. Type **123** 15 10
509 40 c. Black-headed shrike . . . 40 25
510 80 c. Slaty-headed parakeet . . . 75 35
511 1 r. Golden-fronted leafbird . . 1·10 35
512 1 r. 20 Red-winged crested cuckoo . . . . 1·25 40
513 2 r. Grey wagtail . . . . . . 2·10 85
514 2 r. 50 Forest wagtail . . . . . 2·50 95

1984. International Peace in South-East Asia Forum, Phnom Penh. Mult, background colour given.
515 **124** 50 c. green 20 10
516 1 r. blue 40 15
517 3 r. violet . . . . 1·25 35

125 "Luna 2"

1984. Space Research. Multicoloured.
518 10 c. "Luna 1" 10 10
519 40 c. Type **125** 15 10
520 80 c. "Luna 3" 25 10
521 1 r. "Soyuz 6" and cosmonauts (vert) 40 15
522 1 r. 20 "Soyuz 7" and cosmonauts (vert) 65 20
523 2 r. "Soyuz 8" and cosmonauts (vert) 75 25
524 2 r. 50 Book, rocket and S. P. Korolev (Russian spaceship designer) (vert) . . . . . . 1·25 40

126 Throwing the Discus

1984. Olympic Games, Los Angeles (2nd issue). Multicoloured.
526 20 c. Type **126** 10 10
527 50 c. Long jumping 15 10
528 80 c. Hurdling 25 10
529 1 r. Relay 50 15
530 1 r. 50 Pole vaulting 75 25
531 2 r. Throwing the javelin . . . 90 25
532 3 r. High jumping . . . . . . 1·25 40

INDEX
Countries can be quickly located by referring to the index at the end of this volume.

128 Coyote

1984. Dog Family. Multicoloured.
535 10 c. Type **128** 10 10
536 40 c. Dingo 15 10
537 80 c. Hunting dog 25 10
538 1 r. Golden jackal 45 15
539 1 r. 20 Red fox 75 20
540 2 r. Maned wolf (vert) . . . . 1·25 25
541 2 r. 50 Wolf . . . . 1·75 40

129 Class BB 1002 Diesel Locomotive, 1966, France

1984. Railway Locomotives. Multicoloured.
542 10 c. Type **129** 10 10
543 40 c. Class BB 1052 diesel locomotive, 1966, France . . 15 10
544 80 c. Franco-Belgian-built steam locomotive, 1945, France . . 25 15
545 1 r. Steam locomotive No. 231-505, 1929, France 50 20
546 1 r. 20 Class 803 diesel railcar, 1968, Germany 90 25
547 2 r. Class BDE-405 diesel locomotive, 1957, France . . 1·40 40
548 2 r. 50 Class DS-01 diesel railcar, 1925, France . . . . 2·00 50

130 Magnolia

1984. Flowers. Multicoloured.
549 10 c. Type **130** 10 10
550 40 c. "Plumeria" sp. 15 10
551 80 c. "Himenoballis" sp. . . . 25 15
552 1 r. "Peltophorum roxburghii" 45 20
553 1 r. 20 "Couroupita guianensis" 70 25
554 2 r. "Lagerstroemia" sp. . . . 1·10 30
555 2 r. 50 "Thevetia perubiana" . . 1·75 50

131 Mercedes Benz

1984. Cars. Multicoloured.
556 20 c. Type **131** 10 10
557 50 c. Bugatti 15 10
558 80 c. Alfa Romeo 35 15
559 1 r. Franklin 50 20
560 1 r. 50 Hispano-Suiza 85 25
561 2 r. Rolls Royce . . . . . . 1·25 30
562 3 r. Tatra . . . . 1·50 50

132 Sra Lai (Rattle) **133** Gazelle

1984. Musical Instruments. Multicoloured.
564 10 c. Type **132** 10 10
565 40 c. Skor drum (horiz) 15 10
566 80 c. Skor drums (different) . . 35 15
567 1 r. Thro khmer (stringed instrument) (horiz) 40 20
568 1 r. 20 Raneat ek (xylophone) (horiz) 70 25
569 2 r. Raneat kong (bells) (horiz) 75 30
570 2 r. 50 Thro khe (stringed instrument) (horiz) . . . . . 1·25 50

1984. Mammals. Multicoloured.
571 10 c. Type **133** 10 10
572 40 c. Roe deer 15 10
573 80 c. Hare (horiz) 25 15
574 1 r. Red deer 50 20
575 1 r. 20 Indian elephant 75 30
576 2 r. Genet (horiz) 90 40
577 2 r. 50 Kouprey (horiz) . . . . 1·25 60

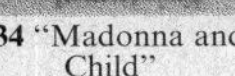

134 "Madonna and Child" **136** Footballers

135 Bullock Cart

1984. 450th Death Anniv of Correggio (artist). Multicoloured.
578 20 c. Type **134** 10 10
579 50 c. Detail showing man striking monk 15 10
580 80 c. "Madonna and Child" (different) 25 15
581 1 r. "Madonna and Child" (different) 40 20
582 1 r. 50 "Mystical Marriage of St. Catherine" 70 30
583 2 r. "Pieta" 75 40
584 3 r. Detail showing man descending ladder . . . . . 1·25 60

1985. National Festival (6th Anniv of People's Republic). Multicoloured.
586 50 c. Type **135** 40 10
587 1 r. Horse-drawn passenger cart 65 25
588 3 r. Elephants . . . . 1·60 50

1985. World Cup Football Championship, Mexico (1986) (1st issue). Designs showing footballers.
590 **136** 20 c. multicoloured 10 10
591 – 50 c. multicoloured 25 10
592 – 80 c. multicoloured 45 15
593 – 1 r. multicoloured (horiz) . 55 25
594 – 1 r. 50 multicoloured (horiz) 80 35
595 – 2 r. multicoloured . . . . 1·00 45
596 – 3 r. multicoloured . . . . 1·60 70
See also Nos. 680/6.

137 Eska-Mofa Motor Cycle, 1939

1985. Centenary of Motor Cycle. Multicoloured.
598 20 c. Type **137** 10 10
599 50 c. Wanderer, 1939 . . . . . 25 10
600 80 c. Premier, 1929 . . . . . 45 15
601 1 r. Ardie, 1939 . . . . . . 55 25
602 1 r. 50 Jawa, 1932 . . . . . 80 35
603 2 r. Simson, 1983 . . . . . . 1·00 45
604 3 r. "CZ 125", 1984 . . . . 1·60 70

138 Glistening Ink Cap

1985. Fungi. Multicoloured.
606 20 c. "Gymnophilus spectabilis" (horiz) 15 10
607 50 c. Type **138** 40 15
608 80 c. Panther cap 70 20
609 1 r. Fairy cake mushroom . . . 90 35
610 1 r. 50 Fly agaric . . . . . . 1·40 45
611 2 r. Shaggy ink cap . . . . . 1·60 60
612 3 r. Caesar's mushroom . . . . 2·75 95

139 "Sputnik 1"

1985. Space Exploration. Multicoloured.
613 20 c. Type **139** 10 10
614 50 c. "Soyuz" rocket on transporter and Yury Gagarin (first man in space) 40 10
615 80 c. "Vostok 6" and Valentina Tereshkova (first woman in space) 45 15
616 1 r. Space walker 55 25
617 1 r. 50 "Salyut"–"Soyuz" link . 80 35
618 2 r. "Lunokhod 1" (lunar vehicle) . . . . 1·00 45
619 3 r. "Venera" (Venus probe) . . 1·60 70

140 Absara Dancer **140a** Captured Nazi Standards, Red Square, Moscow

1985. Traditional Dances. Multicoloured.
621 50 c. Absara group (horiz) . . 35 10
622 1 r. Tepmonorom dance (horiz) . 70 25
623 3 r. Type **140** . . . . 1·75 75

1985. 40th Anniv of End of Second World War. Multicoloured.
623a 50 c. Rejoicing soldiers in Berlin 30 10
623b 1 r. Type **140a** 55 25
623c 3 r. Tank battle . . . . . . 1·75 75

141 Tortoiseshell Cat **142** "Black Dragon" Lily

1985. Domestic Cats. Multicoloured.
624 20 c. Type **141** 10 10
625 50 c. Tortoiseshell (different) 25 10
626 80 c. Tabby 45 15
627 1 r. Long-haired Siamese . . . 60 25
628 1 t. 50 Sealpoint Siamese . . . 1·00 35
629 2 r. Grey cat . . . . 1·25 45
630 3 r. Black cat . . . . 2·00 70

1985. Flowers. Multicoloured.
631 20 c. Type **142** 10 10
632 50 c. "Iris delavayi" 25 10
633 80 c. "Crocus aureus" 45 15
634 1 r. "Cyclamen persicum" . . . 60 25
635 1 r. 50 Fairy primrose 90 35
636 2 r. Pansy "Ullswater" . . . . 1·10 45
637 3 r. "Crocus purpureus grandiflorus" . . . . 1·75 70

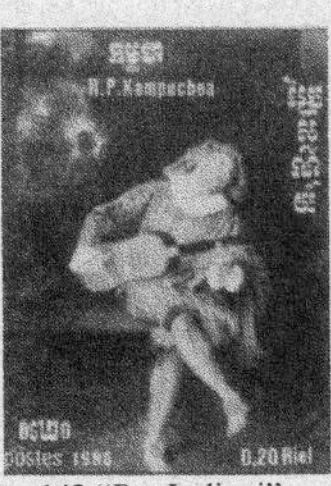

143 "Per Italiani" (Antoine Watteau) **144** Lenin and Arms

1987. International Music Year. Multicoloured.
638 20 c. Type **143** 10 10
639 50 c. "St. Cecilia" (Carlos Saraceni) 25 10
640 80 c. "Still Life with Violin" (Jean Baptiste Oudry) (horiz) 45 15
641 1 r. "Three Musicians" (Fernand Leger) 55 25
642 1 r. 50 Orchestra 80 35
643 2 r. "St. Cecilia" (Bartholomeo Schedoni) . . . . 1·00 45
644 3 r. "Harlequin with Violin" (Christian Caillard) . . . . 1·60 70

1985. 115th Birth Anniv of Lenin. Multicoloured.
646 1 r. Type **144** 60 25
647 3 r. Lenin on balcony and map 1·60 70

145 Saffron-cowled Blackbird

1985. "Argentina '85" International Stamp Exhibition, Buenos Aires. Birds. Multicoloured.
648 20 c. Type **145** 15 10
649 50 c. Saffron finch (vert) . . . 30 15
650 80 c. Blue and yellow tanager (vert) 50 20
651 1 r. Scarlet-headed blackbird . 70 25
652 1 r. 50 Amazon kingfisher (vert) 1·40 35
653 2 r. Toco toucan (vert) . . . . 1·90 45
654 3 r. Rufous-bellied thrush . . . 2·50 70

146 River Launch, Cambodia, 1942

1985. Water Craft. Multicoloured.
655 10 c. Type **146** 15 10
656 40 c. River launch, Cambodia, 1948 . . . . 25 15
657 80 c. Tug, Japan, 1913 . . . . 45 20
658 1 r. Dredger, Holland 65 25
659 1 r. 20 Tug, U.S.A. . . . . . 1·10 35
660 2 r. River freighter . . . . . 1·50 45
661 2 r. 50 River tanker, Panama . 2·00 70

147 "The Flood" (Michelangelo) **148** Son Ngoc Minh

1985. "Italia '85" International Stamp Exhibition, Rome. Paintings. Multicoloured.
662 20 r. Type **147** 10 10
663 50 r. "The Virgin of St. Marguerite" (Mazzola) . . . 25 10
664 80 r. "The Martyrdom of St. Peter" (Zampieri Domenichino) 45 15
665 1 r. "Allegory of Spring" (detail) (Sandro Botticelli) 55 25
666 1 r. 50 "The Sacrifice of Abraham" (Caliari) 80 35
667 2 r. "The Meeting of Joachim and Anne" (Giotto) . . . . . . 1·00 45
668 3 r. "Bacchus" (Michel Angelo Carravaggio) . . . . 1·60 70

1985. Festival of Rebirth.
670 **148** 50 c. multicoloured 15 10
671 1 r. multicoloured 40 15
672 3 r. multicoloured . . . . 1·10 45

149 Tiger Barbs

1985. Fishes. Multicoloured.
673 20 c. Type **149** 15 10
674 50 c. Giant snakehead 40 15
675 80 c. Veil-tailed goldfish . . . 75 20
676 1 r. Pearl gourami 90 35
677 1 r. 50 Six-banded tiger barbs . 1·25 45
678 2 r. Siamese fighting fish . . . 1·60 60
679 3 r. Siamese tigerfish . . . . 2·75 90

150 Footballers **152** "Mir" Space Station and Spacecraft

151 Cob

1986. World Cup Football Championship, Mexico (2nd issue).
680 **150** 20 c. multicoloured 10 10
681 – 50 c. multicoloured 25 10
682 – 80 c. multicoloured 45 15
683 – 1 r. multicoloured 55 25
684 – 1 r. 50 multicoloured . . . 80 35
685 – 2 r. multicoloured . . . . 1·00 45
686 – 3 r. multicoloured . . . . 1·60 70
DESIGNS: 50 c. to 3 r. Various footballing scenes.

1986. Horses. Multicoloured.
688 20 c. Type **151** 10 10
689 50 c. Arab 25 10
690 80 c. Australian pony 45 15
691 1 r. Appaloosa 55 25
692 1 r. 50 Quarter horse 80 35
693 2 r. Vladimir heavy draught horse . . . . 1·00 45
694 3 r. Andalusian . . . . 1·60 70

1986. 27th Russian Communist Party Congress. Multicoloured.
694a 50 c. Type **152** 25 10
694b 1 r. Lenin 55 25
694c 5 r. Statue and launch of space rocket . . . . 2·50 1·00

1986. Air. As Nos. 504/7 but inscr "R.P. DU KAMPUCHEA".
695 **122** 5 r. multicoloured . . . . 2·75 95
696 10 r. multicoloured . . . . 5·75 1·60
697 15 r. multicoloured . . . . 8·50 2·50
698 25 r. multicoloured . . . . 15·00 4·25

153 Edaphosaurus (⅔-size illustration)

1986. Prehistoric Animals. Multicoloured.
699 20 c. Type **153** 10 10
700 50 c. Sauroctonus 25 10
701 80 c. Mastodonsaurus 45 15
702 1 r. Rhamphorhynchus (vert) . 60 25
703 1 r. 50 "Brachiosaurus brancai" (vert) 90 35
704 2 r. "Tarbosaurus bataar" (vert) 1·10 45
705 3 r. Indricotherium (vert) . . . 1·75 70

154 "Luna 16"

1986. 25th Anniv of First Man in Space. Multicoloured.
706 10 c. Type **154** 10 10
707 40 c. "Luna 3" 25 10
708 80 c. "Vostok" 45 15
709 1 r. Cosmonaut Leonov on space walk 55 25
710 1 r. 20 "Apollo" and "Soyuz" preparing to dock 80 35
711 2 r. "Soyuz" docking with "Salyut" space station . . . 1·00 45
712 2 r. 50 Yury Gagarin (first man in space) and spacecraft . . . . 1·60 75

155 Baksei Chmkrong Temple, 920

1986. Khmer Culture. Multicoloured.
713 20 c. Type **155** 10 10
714 50 c. Buddha's head 25 10
715 80 c. Prea Vihear monastery, Dangrek 45 15
716 1 r. Fan with design of man and woman 55 25
717 1 r. 50 Fan with design of men fighting 80 35
718 2 r. Fan with design of dancer 1·00 45
719 3 r. Fan with design of dragon-drawn chariot 1·60 70

156 Tricar, 1885

1986. Centenary (1985) of Motor Car. Mercedes Benz Models. Multicoloured.
720 20 c. Type **156** 10 10
721 50 c. Limousine, 1935 25 10
722 80 c. Open tourer, 1907 45 15
723 1 r. Light touring car, 1920 55 25
724 1 r. 50 Cabriolet, 1932 80 35
725 2 r. "SKK" tourer, 1938 1·00 45
726 3 r. "190", 1985 1·60 70

157 Orange Tiger

159 Solar System, Copernicus, Galileo and Tycho Brahe (astronomers)

158 English Kogge of Richard II's Reign

1986. Butterflies. Multicoloured.
727 20 c. Type **157** 15 10
728 50 c. Five-bar swallowtail 35 15
729 80 c. Chequered swallowtail 65 20
730 1 r. Chestnut tiger 75 35
731 1 r. 50 "Idea blanchardi" 1·10 45
732 2 r. Common mormon 1·40 60
733 3 r. "Dabasa payeni" 2·25 95

1986. Medieval Ships.
734 20 c. Type **158** 10 10
735 50 c. Kogge 25 10
736 80 c. Knarr 45 15
737 1 r. Galley 55 25
738 1 r. 50 Norman ship 80 35
739 2 r. Mediterranean usciere 1·10 45
740 3 r. French kogge 1·75 70

1986. Appearance of Halley's Comet. Multicoloured.
741 10 c. Type **159** 10 10
742 20 c. "Nativity" (Giotto) and comet from Bayeux Tapestry 10 10
743 50 c. Comet, 1910, and Mt. Palomar observatory, U.S.A. 25 10
744 80 c. Edmond Halley and "Planet A" space probe 45 15
745 1 r. 20 Diagram of comet's trajectory and "Giotto" space probe 60 25
746 1 r. 50 "Vega" space probe and camera 80 35
747 2 r. Thermal pictures of comet 1·00 45

160 Ruy Lopez

1986. "Stockholmia 86" International Stamp Exhibition. Chess. Multicoloured.
749 20 c. Type **160** 10 10
750 50 c. Francois-Andre Philidor 25 10
751 80 c. Karl Anderssen and Houses of Parliament, London 45 15
752 1 r. Wilhelm Steinitz and Charles Bridge, Prague 60 25
753 1 r. 50 Emanuel Lasker and medieval knight 90 35
754 2 r. Jose Raul Capablanca and Morro Castle, Cuba 1·10 45
755 3 r. Aleksandr Alekhine 1·75 70

161 "Parodia maassii"

162 Bananas

1986. Cacti. Multicoloured.
757 20 c. Type **161** 10 10
758 50 c. "Rebutia marsoneri" 25 10
759 80 c. "Melocactus evae" 45 15
760 1 r. "Gymnocalycium valnicekianum" 55 25
761 1 r. 50 "Discocactus silichromus" 80 35
762 2 r. "Neochilenia simulans" 1·00 45
763 3 r. "Weingartia chiquichuquensis" 1·60 70

1986. Fruit. Multicoloured.
764 10 c. Type **162** 10 10
765 40 c. Papaya 20 10
766 80 c. Mangoes 45 15
767 1 r. Breadfruit 55 35
768 1 r. 20 Lychees 60 25
769 2 r. Pineapple 1·00 45
770 2 r. 50 Grapefruit (horiz) 1·40 55

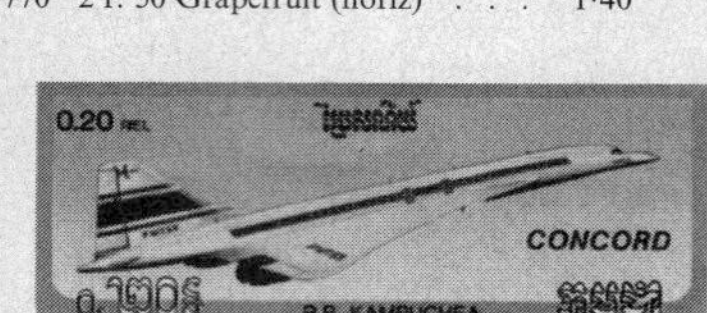
163 Concorde ($\frac{2}{3}$-size illustration)

1986. Aircraft. Multicoloured.
771 20 c. Type **163** (wrongly inscr "Concord") 10 10
772 50 c. Douglas DC-10 25 10
773 80 c. Boeing 747SP 45 15
774 1 r. Ilyushin Il-62M 55 25
775 1 r. 50 Ilyushin Il-86 80 35
776 2 r. Antonov An-24 (wrongly inscr "AN-124") 1·10 45
777 3 r. Airbus Industrie A300 1·75 70

164 Elephant and Silver Containers on Tray

1986. Festival of Rebirth. Silverware. Mult.
778 50 c. Type **164** 25 10
779 1 r. Tureen 55 20
780 3 r. Dish on stand 1·60 45

165 Kouprey

1986. Endangered Animals. Cattle. Mult.
781 20 c. Type **165** 10 10
782 20 c. Gaur 10 10
783 80 c. Bateng cow and calf 45 15
784 1 r. 50 Asiatic water buffalo 90 30

166 Tou Samuth (revolutionary)

1987. National Festival. 8th Anniv of People's Republic.
785 **166** 50 c. multicoloured 20 10
786 1 r. multicoloured 40 15
787 3 r. multicoloured 1·10 35

167 Biathlon

1987. Winter Olympic Games, Calgary (1988) (1st issue). Multicoloured.
788 20 c. Type **167** 10 10
789 50 c. Figure skating 25 10
790 80 c. Speed skating 45 15
791 1 r. Ice hockey 55 25
792 1 r. 50 Two-man luge 80 35
793 2 r. Two-man bobsleigh 1·00 45
794 3 r. Cross-country skiing 1·60 70
See also Nos. 864/70.

168 Weightlifting

1987. Olympic Games, Seoul (1988) (1st issue). Designs showing ancient Greek and modern athletes. Multicoloured.
796 20 c. Type **168** 10 10
797 50 c. Archery (horiz) 25 10
798 80 c. Fencing (horiz) 45 15
799 1 r. Gymnastics 55 25
800 1 r. 50 Throwing the discus (horiz) 80 35
801 2 r. Throwing the javelin 1·00 45
802 3 r. Hurdling 1·60 70
See also Nos. 875/81.

169 Papillon

1987. Dogs. Multicoloured.
804 20 c. Type **169** 10 10
805 50 c. Greyhound 25 10
806 80 c. Great dane 45 15
807 1 r. Dobermann 55 25
808 1 r. 50 Samoyed 80 35
809 2 r. Borzoi 1·00 45
810 3 r. Rough collie 1·60 70

170 "Sputnik 1" **171** Flask

1987. Space Exploration. Multicoloured.
811 20 c. Type **170** 10 10
812 50 c. "Soyuz 10" 25 10
813 80 c. "Proton" 45 15
814 1 r. "Vostok 1" 55 25
815 1 r. 50 "Elektron 2" 80 35
816 2 r. "Kosmos" 1·00 45
817 3 r. "Luna 2" 1·60 70

1987. Metalwork. Multicoloured.
819 50 c. Type **171** 20 10
820 1 r. Repousse box (horiz) 50 25
821 1 r. 50 Teapot and cups on tray (horiz) 75 35
822 3 r. Ornamental sword 1·50 70

172 Carmine Bee Eater

1987. "Capex'87" International Stamp Exhibition, Toronto. Birds. Multicoloured.
823 20 c. Type **172** 10 10
824 50 c. Hoopoe (vert) 25 10
825 80 c. South African crowned crane (vert) 45 15
826 1 r. Barn owl (vert) 55 25
827 1 r. 50 Grey-headed kingfisher (vert) 80 35
828 2 r. Red-whiskered bulbul 1·00 45
829 3 r. Purple heron (vert) 1·60 70

173 Horatio Phillip's "Multiplane" Model, 1893

1987. Experimental Aircraft Designs. Mult.
831 20 c. Type **173** 10 10
832 50 c. John Stringfellow's steam-powered model, 1848 25 10
833 80 c. Thomas Moy's model "Aerial Steamer", 1875 45 15
834 1 r. Leonardo da Vinci's "ornithopter", 1490 55 25
835 1 r. 50 Sir George Cayley's "convertiplane", 1843 80 35
836 2 r. Sir Hiram Maxim's "Flying Test Rig", 1894 1·00 45
837 3 r. William Henson's "Aerial Steam Carriage", 1842 1·60 70

174 Giant Tortoise

1987. Reptiles. Multicoloured.
839 20 c. Type **174** 10 10
840 50 c. African spiny-tailed lizard 25 10
841 80 c. Iguana 45 15
842 1 r. Coast horned lizard 55 25
843 1 r. 50 Northern chuckwalla 80 35
844 2 r. Glass lizard 1·00 45
845 3 r. Common garter snake 1·60 70

175 Kamov Ka-15

1987. "Hafnia 87" International Stamp Exhibition, Copenhagen. Helicopters. Multicoloured.
846 20 c. Type **175** 10 10
847 50 c. Kamov Ka-18 25 10
848 80 c. Westland Lynx 45 15
849 1 r. Sud Aviation Gazelle 55 25
850 1 r. 50 Sud Aviation SA 330E Puma 80 35
851 2 r. Boeing-Vertol CH-47 Chinook 1·00 45
852 3 r. Boeing UTTAS 1·60 70

176 Revolutionaries

178 Earth Station Dish Aerial

177 Magirus-Deutz No. 21

1987. 70th Anniv of Russian October Revolution. Multicoloured.

853a	2 r. Revolutionaries on street corner (horiz)	95	40
853b	3 r. Type **176**	1·25	50
853c	5 r. Lenin receiving ticker-tape message (horiz)	2·50	1·00

1987. Fire Engines. Multicoloured.

854	20 c. Type **177**	10	10
855	50 c. "SIL-131" rescue vehicle	25	10
856	80 c. "Cas-25" fire pump	45	15
857	1 r. Sirmac Saab "424"	60	25
858	1 r. 50 Rosenbaum-Falcon	85	35
859	2 r. Tatra "815-PRZ"	1·10	45
860	3 r. Chubbfire "C-44-20"	1·60	70

1987. Telecommunications. Multicoloured.

861	50 c. Type **178**	10	10
862	1 r. Technological building with radio microwave aerial (27 × 44 mm)	55	25
863	3 r. Intersputnik programme earth station (44 × 27 mm)	1·60	70

179 Speed Skating

1988. Winter Olympic Games, Calgary (2nd issue). Multicoloured.

864	20 c. Type **179**	10	10
865	50 c. Ice hockey	25	10
866	80 c. Slalom	45	15
867	1 r. Ski jumping	55	25
868	1 r. 50 Biathlon	80	35
869	2 r. Ice dancing	1·00	45
870	3 r. Cross-country skiing	1·60	70

180 Irrigation Canal Bed

1988. Irrigation Projects. Multicoloured.

872	50 c. Type **180**	10	10
873	1 r. Dam construction	50	20
874	3 r. Dam and bridge	1·50	65

181 Beam Exercise

1988. Olympic Games, Seoul (2nd issue). Women's Gymnastics. Multicoloured.

875	20 c. Type **181**	10	10
876	50 c. Bar exercise (horiz)	25	10
877	80 c. Ribbon exercise	45	15
878	1 r. Hoop exercise	55	25
879	1 r. 50 Baton exercise	80	35
880	2 r. Ball exercise (horiz)	1·00	45
881	3 r. Floor exercise (horiz)	1·60	70

182 Abyssinian

1988. "Juvalux 88" 9th Youth Philately Exhibition, Luxembourg. Cats. Multicoloured.

883	20 c. White long-haired (horiz)	10	10
884	50 c. Type **182**	25	10
885	80 c. Ginger and white long-haired	45	15
886	1 r. Tortoiseshell queen and kitten (horiz)	55	25
887	1 r. 50 Brown cat	80	35
888	2 r. Black long-haired cat	1·00	45
889	3 r. Grey cat	1·60	70

183 "Emerald Seas" (liner)

1988. "Essen 88" International Stamp Fair. Ships. Multicoloured.

891	20 c. Type **183**	10	10
892	50 c. Car ferry	20	10
893	80 c. "Mutsu" (nuclear-powered freighter)	35	10
894	1 r. "Kosmonavt Yury Gagarin" (research ship)	50	15
895	1 r. 50 Tanker	55	20
896	2 r. Hydrofoil	75	30
897	3 r. Hovercraft	1·25	35

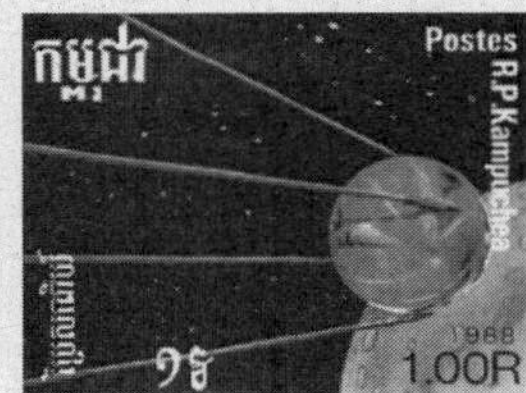

184 Satellite

1988. Space Exploration. Designs showing different satellites.

899	–	20 c. multicoloured (vert)	10	10
900	–	50 c. multicoloured (vert)	20	10
901	–	80 c. multicoloured (vert)	35	10
902	**184**	1 r. multicoloured	50	15
903	–	1 r. 50 multicoloured	55	20
904	–	2 r. multicoloured	75	30
905	–	3 r. multicoloured	1·25	35

185 Swordtail

1988. "Finlandia 88" International Stamp Exhibition, Helsinki. Tropical Fish. Multicoloured.

907	20 c. Type **185**	15	10
908	50 c. Head-and-taillight tetra	30	10
909	80 c. Paradise fish	55	15
910	1 r. Black moor goldfish	85	20
911	1 r. 50 Cardinal tetra	90	30
912	2 r. Sword-tailed characin	1·25	45
913	3 r. Sail-finned molly	2·10	60

186 Flowery Helicostyla

188 "Cattleya aclandiae"

187 Seven-spotted Ladybird

1988. Sea Shells. Multicoloured.

915	20 c. Type **186**	10	10
916	50 c. Changing helicostyla	20	10
917	80 c. Shining helicostyla	35	10
918	1 r. Marinduque helicostyla	50	15
919	1 r. 50 Siren chlorena	55	20
920	2 r. Miraculous helicostyla	75	30
921	3 r. "Helicostyla limansauensis"	1·25	35

1988. Insects. Multicoloured.

922	20 c. Type **187**	10	10
923	50 c. "Zonabride geminata" (blister beetle)	20	10
924	80 c. "Carabus auronitens" (ground beetle)	35	10
925	1 r. Honey bee	50	15
926	1 r. 50 Praying mantis	55	20
927	2 r. Dragonfly	75	30
928	3 r. Soft-winged flower beetle	1·25	35

1988. Orchids. Multicoloured.

929	20 c. Type **188**	10	10
930	50 c. "Odontoglossum" "Royal Sovereign"	20	10
931	80 c. "Cattleya labiata"	35	10
932	1 r. Bee orchid	50	15
933	1 r. 50 "Laelia anceps"	55	20
934	2 r. "Laelia pumila"	75	30
935	3 r. "Stanhopea tigrina" (horiz)	1·25	35

189 Egyptian Banded Cobra

190 Walking Dance

1988. Reptiles. Multicoloured.

936	20 c. Type **189**	10	10
937	50 c. Common iguana	20	10
938	80 c. Long-nosed vine snake (horiz)	35	10
939	1 r. Common box turtle (horiz)	50	15
940	1 r. 50 Iguana (horiz)	55	20
941	2 r. Viper (horiz)	75	30
942	3 r. Common cobra	1·25	35

1988. Festival of Rebirth. Khmer Culture. Multicoloured.

943	50 c. Type **190**	20	10
944	1 r. Peacock dance (horiz)	50	15
945	3 r. Kantere dance (horiz)	1·25	35

191 Bridge

1989. Multicoloured.

946	50 c. Type **191**	25	10
947	1 r. More distant view of bridge	50	20
948	3 r. Closer view of bridge	1·60	65

192 Cement Works

1989. National Festival. 10th Anniv of People's Republic of Kampuchea. Multicoloured.

949	3 r. Bayon Earth Station (horiz)	20	10
950	12 r. Electricity generating station 4 (horiz)	75	30
951	30 r. Type **192**	2·10	85

193 Footballers

1989. World Cup Football Championship, Italy (1990).

952	**193**	2 r. multicoloured	10	10
953	–	3 r. multicoloured	20	10
954	–	5 r. multicoloured	30	10
955	–	10 r. multicoloured	65	25
956	–	15 r. multicoloured	1·00	40
957	–	20 r. multicoloured	1·25	50
958	–	35 r. multicoloured	2·40	95

DESIGNS: 3 r. to 35 r. Various footballing scenes.

194 Tram

1989. Trams and Trains. Multicoloured.

960	2 r. Type **194**	10	10
961	3 r. ETR 401 Pendolino express train, 1976, Italy	20	10
962	5 r. High speed train, Germany	35	15
963	10 r. Theme park monorail train	80	25
964	15 r. German Trans Europe Express (TEE) train	1·25	35
965	20 r. "Hikari" express train, Sanyo Shinkansenline, Japan	1·50	50
966	35 r. TGV express train, France	3·00	85

195 Fidel Castro

196 Scarlet Macaw

1989. 30th Anniv of Cuban Revolution.

968	**195**	12 r. multicoloured	90	40

1989. Parrots. Multicoloured.

969	20 c. Type **196**	10	10
970	80 c. Sulphur-crested cockatoo	10	10
971	3 r. Rose-ringed parakeet	25	10
972	6 r. Blue and yellow macaw	50	15
973	10 r. Cape parrot	90	30
974	15 r. Blue-fronted amazon	1·40	45
975	25 r. White-capped parrot (horiz)	2·10	70

197 Skiing

1989. Winter Olympic Games, Albertville (1992). Multicoloured.

977	2 r. Type **197**	10	10
978	3 r. Biathlon	20	10
979	5 r. Cross-country skiing	30	10
980	10 r. Ski jumping	65	25
981	15 r. Speed skating	1·00	40
982	20 r. Ice hockey	1·25	50
983	35 r. Two-man bobsleighing	2·40	95

198 "Nymphaea capensis" (pink)

1989. Water Lilies. Multicoloured.

985	20 c. Type **198**	10	10
986	80 c. "Nymphaea capensis" (mauve)	10	10
987	3 r. "Nymphaea lotus dentata"	25	10
988	6 r. "Dir. Geo. T. Moore"	50	15
989	10 r. "Sunrise"	90	30
990	15 r. "Escarboncle"	1·40	45
991	25 r. "Cladstoniana"	2·10	70

199 Wrestling

1989. Olympic Games, Barcelona (1992). Multicoloured.

993		2 r. Type **199**	10	10
994		3 r. Gymnastics (vert)	20	10
995		5 r. Putting the shot	30	10
996		10 r. Running (vert)	65	25
997		15 r. Fencing	1·00	40
998		20 r. Canoeing (vert)	1·40	50
999		35 r. Hurdling (vert)	2·40	95

200 Downy Boletus

1989. Fungi. Multicoloured.

1001		20 c. Type **200**	10	10
1002		80 c. Red-staining inocybe	10	10
1003		3 r. Honey fungus	35	15
1004		6 r. Field mushroom	70	25
1005		10 r. Brown roll-rim	1·25	45
1006		15 r. Shaggy ink cap	1·90	65
1007		25 r. Parasol mushroom	3·00	1·00

201 Shire Horse

1989. Horses. Multicoloured.

1008		2 r. Type **201**	10	10
1009		3 r. Brabant	20	10
1010		5 r. Bolounais	30	10
1011		10 r. Breton	65	25
1012		15 r. Vladimir heavy draught horse	1·00	40
1013		20 r. Italian heavy draught horse	1·25	50
1014		35 r. Freiberger	2·40	95

KATANGA Pt. 14

The following stamps were issued by Mr. Tshombe's Government for independent Katanga. In 1963 Katanga was reunited with the Central Government of Congo.

1960. Various stamps of Belgian Congo optd **KATANGA** and bar or surch also. (a) Masks issue of 1948.

1		1 f. 50 on 1 f. 25 mauve and blue	50	20
2		3 f. 50 on 2 f. 50 green & brown	50	25
3		20 f. purple and red	1·75	90
4		50 f. black and brown	4·00	3·25
5		100 f. black and red	30·00	22·00

(b) Flowers issue of 1952. Flowers in natural colours; colours given are of backgrounds and inscriptions.

6		10 c. yellow and purple	10	10
7		15 c. green and red	10	10
8		20 c. grey and green	15	15
9		25 c. orange and green	15	15
10		40 c. salmon and green	15	15
11		50 c. turquoise and red	20	20
12		60 c. purple and green	15	15
13		75 c. grey and lake	20	20
14		1 f. lemon and red	25	25
15		2 f. buff and olive	30	30
16		3 f. pink and green	40	35
17		4 f. lavender and sepia	60	50
18		5 f. green and purple	60	50
19		6 f. 50 lilac and red	60	45
20		7 f. brown and green	80	70
21		8 f. yellow and green	80	70
22		10 f. olive and purple	11·50	9·00

(c) Wild animals issue of 1959.

23		10 c. brown, sepia and blue	15	10
24		20 c. blue and red	15	10
25		40 c. brown and blue	15	10
26		50 c. multicoloured	15	10
27		1 f. black, green and brown	5·25	3·25
28		1 f. 50 black and yellow	8·75	6·00
29		2 f. black, brown and red	40	10
30		3 f. black, purple and slate	3·25	2·50
31		5 f. brown, green and sepia	60	25
32		6 f. 50 brown, yellow and blue	75	25
33		8 f. bistre, violet and brown	1·10	35
34		10 f. multicoloured	1·60	50

(d) Madonna.

35	**102**	50 c. brown, ochre & chest	15	15
36		1 f. brown, violet and blue	15	15
37		2 f. brown, blue and slate	20	20

(e) African Technical Co-operation Commission. Inscr in French or Flemish.

38	**103**	3 f. salmon and slate	7·00	7·00
39		3 f. 50 on 3 f. sal & slate	2·10	2·10

1960. Independence. Independence issue of Congo optd **11 JUILLET DE L'ETAT DU KATANGA**.

40	**106**	20 c. bistre	10	10
41		50 c. red	10	10
42		1 f. green	10	10
43		1 f. 50 brown	10	10
44		2 f. mauve	10	10
45		3 f. 50 violet	15	10
46		5 f. blue	15	10
47		6 f. 50 black	15	10
48		10 f. orange	25	20
49		20 f. blue	45	30

5

1961. Katanga Art.

50	**5**	10 c. green	10	10
51		20 c. violet	10	10
52		50 c. blue	10	10
53		1 f. 50 green	10	10
54		2 f. brown	10	10
55	–	3 f. 50 blue	10	10
56	–	5 f. turquoise	10	10
57	–	6 f. brown	10	10
58	–	6 f. 50 blue	10	10
59	–	8 f. purple	15	10
60	–	10 f. brown	15	10
61	–	20 f. myrtle	25	20
62	–	50 f. brown	50	40
63	–	100 f. turquoise	85	70

DESIGNS: 3 f. 50 to 8 f. "Preparing food"; 10 f. to 100 f. "Family circle".

6 Pres. Tshombe

1961. 1st Anniv of Independence. Portrait in brown.

64	**6**	6 f. 50 + 5 f. red, green & gold	1·25	1·00
65		8 f. + 5 f. red, green and gold	1·25	1·00
66		10 f. + 5 f. red, green and gold	1·25	1·00

7 "Tree"

8 Early Aircraft, Steam Train and Safari

1961. Katanga International Fair. Vert symbolic designs as T **7**.

67	**7**	50 c. red, green and black	10	10
68	–	1 f. black and blue	10	10
69	–	2 f. 50 black and yellow	15	15
70	**7**	3 f. 50 red, brown and black	15	15
71	–	5 f. black and violet	25	25
72	–	6 f. 50 black and yellow	30	30

1961. Air.

73	**8**	3 f. 50 multicoloured	4·75	5·50
74	–	6 f. 50 multicoloured	1·10	1·10
75	**8**	8 f. multicoloured	4·75	5·50
76	–	10 f. multicoloured	2·10	1·10

DESIGNS: 6 f. 50, 10 f. Tail of Boeing 707.

9 Gendarme in armoured Vehicle

1962. Katanga Gendarmerie.

77	**9**	6 f. multicoloured	2·25	2·25
78		8 f. multicoloured	35	35
79		10 f. multicoloured	45	45

POSTAGE DUE STAMPS

1960. Postage Due stamps of Belgian Congo handstamped **KATANGA**. (a) On Nos. D 270/4.

D50	**D 86**	10 c. olive	80	80
D51		20 c. blue	80	80
D52		50 c. green	1·00	1·00
D53		1 f. brown		
D54		2 f. orange		

(b) On Nos. D 330/6.

D55	**D 99**	10 c. brown	3·25	3·25
D56		20 c. purple	3·25	3·25
D57		50 c. green	3·25	3·25
D58		1 f. blue	1·00	1·00
D59		2 f. red	2·00	2·00
D60		4 f. violet	2·75	2·75
D61		6 f. blue	3·25	3·25

KAZAKHSTAN Pt. 10

Formerly a constituent republic of the Soviet Union, Kazakhstan declared its independence on 16 December 1991.

1992. 100 kopeks = 1 rouble.
1994. 100 tyin (ty.) = 1 tenge (t.).

1 "Golden Warrior"

(2)

1992. "Golden Warrior" (from 5th-century B.C. tomb).

1	**1**	50 k. multicoloured	15	15

1992. Nos. 6079/80 of Russia optd as T **2**, in Cyrillic (2, 4) English (3, 5) Capitals.

2		12 k. purple	2·75	2·25
3		12 k. purple	2·75	2·25
4		13 k. violet	2·75	2·25
5		13 k. violet	2·75	2·25

(3)

4 Saiga

1992. Russian–French Space Flight. Nos. 6072/4 of Russia surch as T **3**.

6		30 k. on 2 k. brown	50	20
7		75 k. on 3 k. green	35	35
8		1 r. on 1 k. brown	45	45

1992.

9	**4**	75 k. multicoloured	15	15

5 "Turksib" (E. K. Kasteev)

1992. Kazakh Art.

10	**5**	1 r. multicoloured	25	25

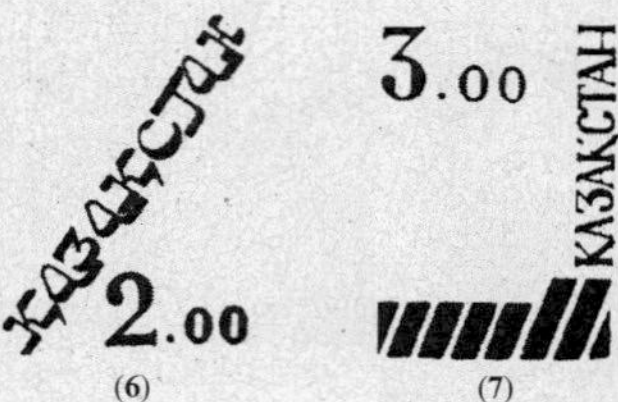

(6) (7)

(8)

9 National Flag and Arms

1992. Various stamps of Russia surch as T **6** (11/12), **7** (13/14) or **8** (15/16).

11		1 r. 50 on 1 k. brown (No. 5940)	15	10
12		2 r. on 2 k. brown (No. 6073)	40	20
13		3 r. on 6 k. blue (No. 4673)	25	20
14		5 r. on 6 k. blue (No. 4673)	25	20
15		10 r. on 1 k. brown (No. 5940)	40	30
16		24 r. 50 on 1 k. brown (No. 5940)	40	30

1992. Republic Day.

17	**9**	5 r. multicoloured	25	15

10 Rocket Launch

11 National Flag

1993.

18	**10**	1 r. green	10	10
19		3 r. red	10	10
20		10 r. bistre	15	10
21		25 r. violet	30	15
22	**11**	50 r. yellow, blue and deep blue	60	30

See also Nos. 45 etc.

12 Rocket and Earth

1993. Space Mail.

23	**12**	100 r. multicoloured	35	30

13 Cock

1993. New Year. Year of the Cock.

24	**13**	60 r. black, red and yellow	35	30

14 Space Station

1993. Cosmonauts Day.

25	**14**	90 r. multicoloured	35	30

15 Nazarbaev and Flag on Map

1993. President Nursultan Nazarbaev (1st series).

26	**15**	50 r. multicoloured	35	25

See also No. 28.

16 Kalkaman-Uly

1993. 325th Birth Anniv of Bukar Zhyrau Kalkaman-Uly (poet).

27	**16**	15 r. multicoloured	35	25

17 Arms, Flag on Map and Nazarbaev

1993. President Nursultan Nazarbaev (2nd series).

28	**17**	100 r. multicoloured	35	25

INDEX

Countries can be quickly located by referring to the index at the end of this volume.

18 Desert Dormouse

1993. Mammals. Multicoloured.

29 5 r. Type **18** . . . 10 10
30 10 r. Porcupine . . . 10 10
31 15 r. Marbled polecat . . . 20 10
32 20 r. Asiatic wild ass . . . 25 15
33 25 r. Mouflon . . . 30 15
34 30 r. Cheetah . . . 35 20

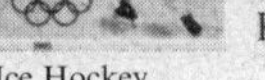

19 Ice Hockey **20** Skiers

1994. Winter Olympic Games, Lillehammer, Norway (1st issue). Multicoloured.

35 15 t. Type **19** . . . 10 10
36 25 t. Skiing . . . 10 10
37 90 t. Ski jumping . . . 35 15
38 150 t. Speed skating . . . 60 30

1994. Winter Olympic Games, Lillehammer, Norway (2nd issue). Multicoloured.

39 2 t. Type **20** . . . 20 10
40 6 t. 80 Vladimir Smirnov (Kazakh skier) . . . 55 20

See also No. 42.

21 Dog **22** Smirnov

1994. New Year. Year of the Dog.

41 **21** 30 t. black, blue and green . . 25 10

1994. Vladimir Smirnov, Winter Olympic Games Medals Winner. As No. 40 but face value changed and with additional inscription in Kazakh.

42 **22** 12 t. multicoloured . . . 75 35

23 Launch of "Soyuz TM16" at Baikonur

1994. Cosmonautics Day.

43 **23** 2 t. multicoloured . . . 25 10

1994.

45 **10** 15 ty. blue . . . 10 10
76 20 ty. orange . . . 10 10
77 25 ty. yellow . . . 10 10
78 50 ty. grey . . . 10 10
46 80 ty. purple . . . 15 10
79 1 t. green . . . 20 10
80 2 t. blue . . . 35 15
81 4 t. mauve . . . 60 25
82 6 t. green . . . 90 40
83 12 t. mauve . . . 1·90 90

25 Mt. Abay

1994. 5th "Asia Dauysy" International Music Festival, Almaty. Multicoloured.

47 10 t. Type **25** . . . 50 25
48 15 t. Medeo Ice Stadium, Almaty . 85 45

26 Horsfield's Tortoises

1994. Reptiles. Multicoloured.

49 1 t. Type **26** . . . 10 10
50 1 t. 20 Toad-headed agamas . . 10 10
51 2 t. Halys vipers . . . 10 10
52 3 t. Turkestan plate-tailed geckos . 15 10
53 5 t. Steppe agamas . . . 25 15
54 7 t. Glass lizards . . . 35 20

27 National Arms

1994. Republic Day.

56 **27** 2 t. multicoloured . . . 15 10

28 "Why does the Swallow have a Forked Tail?" (dir. Amen Khaidorov)

1994. Children's Fund. Kazakh Children's Films. Multicoloured.

57 1 t. + 30 ty. Type **28** . . . 10 10
58 1 t. + 30 ty. "The Calf and Hare seek a Better Life" (E. Abdrakhmanov) . . . 10 10
59 1 t. + 30 ty. Asses ("Lame Kulan" dir. Amen Khaidarov) . . . 10 10

29 Entelodon

1994. Prehistoric Animals. Multicoloured.

60 1 t. Type **29** . . . 10 10
61 1 t. 20 Saurolophus . . . 10 10
62 2 t. Plesiosaurus . . . 10 10
63 3 t. "Sordes pilosus" . . . 15 10
64 5 t. Mosasaurus . . . 25 15
65 7 t. "Megaloceros giganteum" . . 35 20

1995. Nos. 45/6 surch.

67 **24** 1 t. on 15 ty. blue . . . 10 10
68 2 t. on 15 ty. blue . . . 15 10
69 3 t. on 80 ty. purple . . . 25 10
70 4 t. on 80 ty. purple . . . 35 15
71 6 t. on 80 ty. purple . . . 45 20
72 8 t. on 80 ty. purple . . . 50 25
73 12 t. on 80 ty. purple . . . 1·10 50
74 20 t. on 80 ty. purple . . . 2·10 85

31 Pig **32** Kunanbaev

1994. New Year. Year of the Pig.

75 **31** 10 t. blue, black and light blue . 25 15

1995. 150th Birth Anniv of Abai Kunanbaev (writer). Multicoloured.

86 4 t. Type **32** . . . 10 10
87 9 t. Kunanbaev holding pen and book . . . 25 15

33 Flight Path of "Soyuz" Spacecraft

1995. Cosmonautics Day. Multicoloured.

88 2 t. Type **33** . . . 80 40
89 10 t. Yuri Malenchenko, Talgat Musabaev and Ulf Merbold (cosmonauts) . . . 3·75 1·50

34 Manshuk Mametova and Battle Scene

1995. 50th Anniv of End of Second World War. Multicoloured.

90 1 t. Type **34** . . . 35 15
91 3 t. Aliya Moldafulova and tank . 65 30
92 5 t. Wheat field, dove and eternal flame . . . 1·25 60

35 "Spring" (S. Membeev)

1995. Paintings. Multicoloured.

93 4 t. Type **35** . . . 35 15
94 9 t. "Mountains" (Zh. Shardenov) . . . 65 30
95 15 t. "Kulash Baiseitova in role of Kyz Zhibek" (G. Ismailova) (vert) . . . 1·25 60
96 28 t. "Kokpar" (K. Telzhanov) . 2·00 1·10

1995. "Asia Dauysy" International Music Festival, Almaty. Nos. 47/8 optd **KAZAKSTAN '95 1995.**

97 10 t. multicoloured . . . 85 40
98 15 t. multicoloured . . . 1·25 60

37 Dauletkerei

1995. 175th Birth Anniv of Dauletkerei (composer and poet).

99 **37** 2 t. multicoloured . . . 25 15
100 28 t. multicoloured . . . 3·75 1·75

38 Gandhi, Temple and Spinning Wheel

1995. 125th Birth Anniv (1994) of Mahatma Gandhi.

101 **38** 9 t. red and black . . . 1·50 75
102 22 t. red and black . . . 3·00 1·60

39 Anniversary Emblem **40** Cathedral of the Ascension

1995. 50th Anniv of U.N.O.

103 **39** 10 t. gold and blue . . . 90 45
104 36 t. gold and blue . . . 3·00 1·60

1995. Buildings in Almaty.

105 **40** 1 t. green . . . 15 15
106 – 2 t. blue . . . 20 10
107 – 3 t. red . . . 30 15
108 – 48 t. brown . . . 4·25 2·40

DESIGNS: 2 t. Culture Palace; 3 t. Opera and Ballet House; 48 t. Theatre.

See also Nos. 124/5.

41 White-tailed Sea Eagle

1995. Birds of Prey. Multicoloured.

109 1 t. Type **41** . . . 10 10
110 3 t. Osprey . . . 20 10
111 5 t. Lammergeier . . . 35 15
112 6 t. Himalayan griffon . . . 40 20
113 30 t. Saker falcon . . . 2·10 1·00
114 50 t. Golden eagle . . . 3·50 1·75

42 Rat and Lunar Cycle **43** Baikonur Launch Pad highlighted on Globe

1996. Chinese New Year. Year of the Rat.

115 **42** 25 t. red, black and lilac . . 90 45

1996. Cosmonauts Day. Multicoloured.

116 6 t. Type **43** . . . 65 35
117 15 t. Yury Gagarin . . . 1·60 85
118 20 t. Proposed "Alpha" space station . . . 2·25 1·10

45 Cycling **46** Zhabaev (after embroidery by G. Atknin)

1996. Olympic Games, Atlanta. Multicoloured.

120 4 t. Type **45** . . . 35 20
121 6 t. Wrestling . . . 55 25
122 30 t. Boxing . . . 2·75 1·40

1996. As T **40** but smaller, size 24 x 19 mm.

124 1 t. green . . . 10 10
125 6 t. green . . . 20 10

DESIGNS: 1 t. Circus; 6 t. Academy of Sciences (50th anniv).

1996. 150th Birth Anniv of Zhambil Zhabaev (writer).

126 **46** 12 t. multicoloured . . . 30 15

47 Tomb, Dombauyl

1996. Ancient Buildings. Multicoloured.

127 1 t. Type **47** . . . 20 10
128 3 t. Mausoleum, Aisha Biy . . 75 40
129 6 t. Mausoleum, Syrly Tam . . 1·60 1·90

48 "Soyuz TM-13" docked with "Mir" Space Station **49** Map of Kazakhstan and Dove with Letter

1996. 5th Anniv of Toktar Aubakirov's (cosmonaut) Service on "Mir". Multicoloured.

131 46 t. Type **48** . . . 1·00 65
132 46 t. Aubakirov . . . 1·00 65

Nos. 131/2 were issued together, se-tenant, forming a composite design.

1996. World Post Day.

133 **49** 9 t. blue . . . 35 20
134 – 40 t. orange . . . 1·75 90

DESIGN: 40 t. Dove with letter and Universal Postal Union emblem.

1996. Republic Day. No. 56 surch **KAZAKSTAN 1. 1996.**

135 **27** 21 t. on 2 t. multicoloured . 60 40

51 "Saturnia schenki"

1996. Butterflies. Multicoloured.

136 4 t. Type **51** . . . 15 10
137 6 t. "Parnassius patricius" . . 20 10
138 12 t. "Parnasssius ariadne" . . 40 20
139 46 t. "Colias draconis" . . . 1·50 85

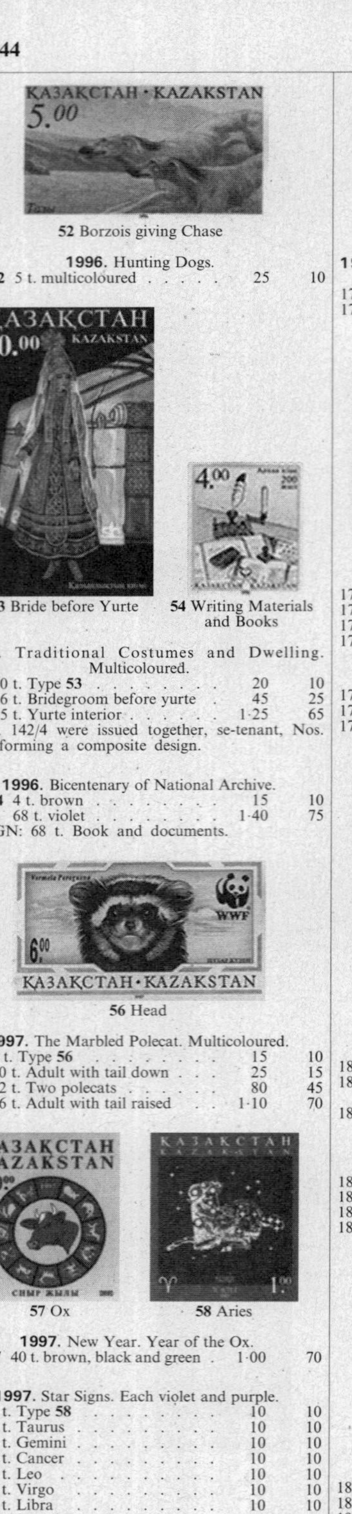

52 Borzois giving Chase

1996. Hunting Dogs.
140 52 5 t. multicoloured 25 10

53 Bride before Yurte
54 Writing Materials and Books

1996. Traditional Costumes and Dwelling. Multicoloured.
142 10 t. Type 53 . . . . 20 10
143 16 t. Bridegroom before yurte . 45 25
144 45 t. Yurte interior . . . . . . 1·25 65
Nos. 142/4 were issued together, se-tenant, Nos. 142/3 forming a composite design.

1996. Bicentenary of National Archive.
145 54 4 t. brown 15 10
146 – 68 t. violet . . . . 1·40 75
DESIGN: 68 t. Book and documents.

56 Head

1997. The Marbled Polecat. Multicoloured.
148 6 t. Type 56 . . . . 15 10
149 10 t. Adult with tail down . . . 25 15
150 32 t. Two polecats 80 45
151 46 t. Adult with tail raised . . 1·10 70

57 Ox
58 Aries

1997. New Year. Year of the Ox.
152 57 40 t. brown, black and green . 1·00 70

1997. Star Signs. Each violet and purple.
153 1 t. Type 58 . . . . 10 10
154 2 t. Taurus 10 10
155 3 t. Gemini 10 10
156 4 t. Cancer 10 10
157 5 t. Leo 10 10
158 6 t. Virgo 10 10
159 7 t. Libra 10 10
160 8 t. Scorpio 10 10
161 9 t. Sagittarius 10 10
162 10 t. Capricorn 10 10
163 12 t. Aquarius 15 10
164 20 t. Pisces 20 15

59 Saturn and Automatic Transfer Vehicle
60 Emblem

1997. Cosmonauts Day. Multicoloured.
166 10 t. Type 59 . . . . 50 30
167 10 t. Space shuttle and "Mir" space station 50 30
168 10 t. "Sputnik 1" and Earth . . 50 30
Nos. 166/8 were issued together, se-tenant, forming a composite design.

1997. World Book and Copyright Day.
169 60 15 t. yellow and green . . . 30 15
170 60 t. yellow and green . . . 1·25 20

61 Auezov Museum, Almaty

1997. Birth Centenary of Mukhtar Auezov (philologist). Multicoloured.
171 25 t. Type 61 . . . . 50 35
172 40 t. Auezov at table (after Shcherkassky) 70 50

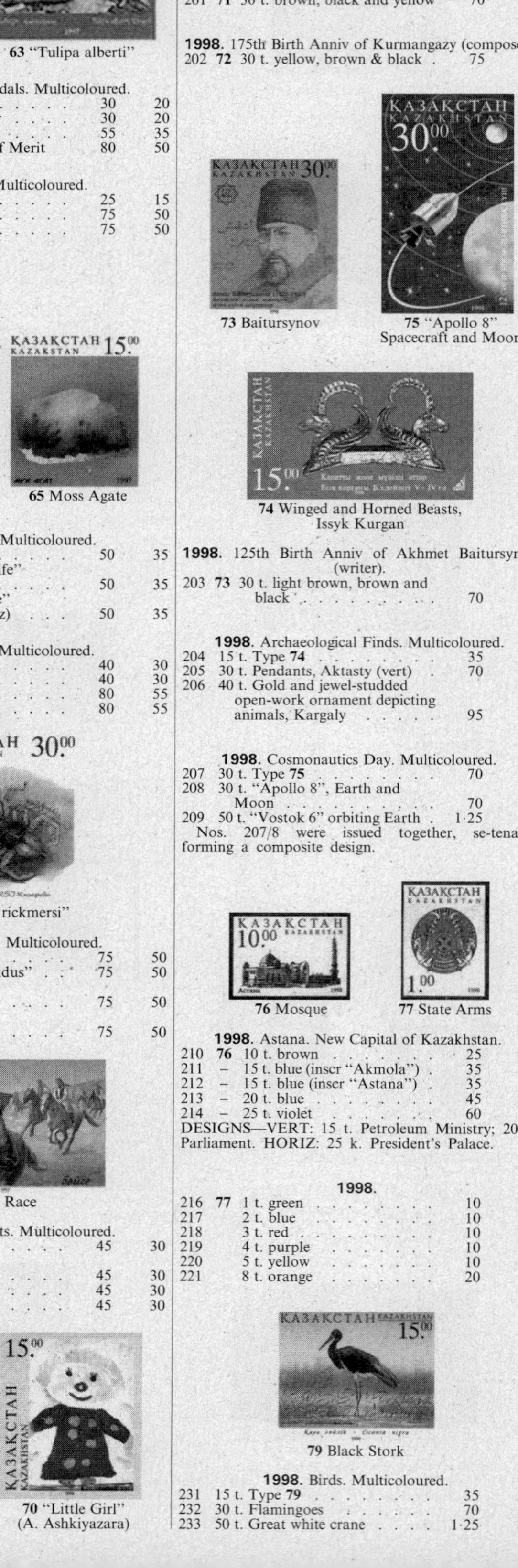

62 Order of Bravery
63 "Tulipa alberti"

1997. Orders and Medals. Multicoloured.
173 15 t. Type 62 . . . . 30 20
174 15 t. Medal of Honour 30 20
175 20 t. Order of Victory 55 35
176 30 t. National Order of Merit . . 80 50

1997. Tulips. Multicoloured.
177 15 t. "Tulipa regelii" 25 15
178 35 t. Type 63 . . . . 75 50
179 35 t. "Tulipa greigii" 75 50

64 "Shepherd" (Sh. Sariev)
65 Moss Agate

1997. Paintings. Multicoloured.
180 25 t. Type 64 . . . . 50 35
181 25 t. "Fantastic Still Life" (S. Kalmykov) 50 35
182 25 t. "Capturing Horse" (M. Kenbaev) (horiz) . . . 50 35

1997. Minerals. Multicoloured.
183 15 t. Type 65 . . . . 40 30
184 15 t. Chalcedony 40 30
185 20 t. Azurite 80 55
186 20 t. Malachite 80 55

66 "Gylippus rickmersi"

1997. Arachnidae. Multicoloured.
188 30 t. Type 66 . . . . 75 50
189 30 t. "Latrodectus pallidus" . . 75 50
190 30 t. "Oculicosa supermirabilis" 75 50
191 30 t. "Anomalobuthus rickmersi" 75 50

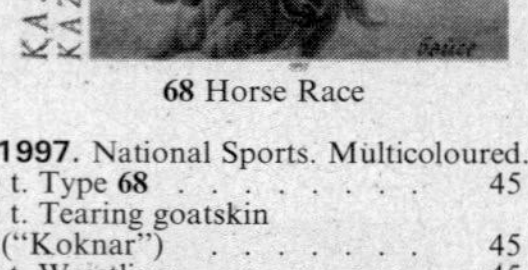

68 Horse Race

1997. National Sports. Multicoloured.
193 20 t. Type 68 . . . . 45 30
194 20 t. Tearing goatskin ("Koknar") 45 30
195 20 t. Wrestling 45 30
196 20 t. Two-horse race 45 30

69 Ice Dancing
70 "Little Girl" (A. Ashkiyazara)

1998. Winter Sports. Multicoloured.
197 15 t. Type 69 . . . . 35 25
198 30 t. Biathlon 70 50

1997. Children's Paintings. Multicoloured.
199 15 t. Type 70 . . . . 35 25
200 15 t. "My House" (M. Tarakara) (horiz) 35 25

71 Tiger and Lunar Cycle
72 Kurmangazy

1997. New Year. Year of the Tiger.
201 71 30 t. brown, black and yellow 70 50

1998. 175th Birth Anniv of Kurmangazy (composer).
202 72 30 t. yellow, brown & black . 75 50

73 Baitursynov
75 "Apollo 8" Spacecraft and Moon

74 Winged and Horned Beasts, Issyk Kurgan

1998. 125th Birth Anniv of Akhmet Baitursynov (writer).
203 73 30 t. light brown, brown and black 70 50

1998. Archaeological Finds. Multicoloured.
204 15 t. Type 74 . . . . 35 25
205 30 t. Pendants, Aktasty (vert) . 70 50
206 40 t. Gold and jewel-studded open-work ornament depicting animals, Kargaly 95 65

1998. Cosmonautics Day. Multicoloured.
207 30 t. Type 75 . . . . 70 50
208 30 t. "Apollo 8", Earth and Moon 70 50
209 50 t. "Vostok 6" orbiting Earth . 1·25 55
Nos. 207/8 were issued together, se-tenant, forming a composite design.

76 Mosque
77 State Arms

1998. Astana. New Capital of Kazakhstan.
210 76 10 t. brown 25 20
211 – 15 t. blue (inscr "Akmola") . 35 25
212 – 15 t. blue (inscr "Astana") . 35 25
213 – 20 t. blue 45 30
214 – 25 t. violet 60 40
DESIGNS—VERT: 15 t. Petroleum Ministry; 20 t. Parliament. HORIZ: 25 k. President's Palace.

1998.
216 77 1 t. green 10 10
217 2 t. blue 10 10
218 3 t. red 10 10
219 4 t. purple 10 10
220 5 t. yellow 10 10
221 8 t. orange 20 15

79 Black Stork

1998. Birds. Multicoloured.
231 15 t. Type 79 . . . . 35 25
232 30 t. Flamingoes 70 50
233 50 t. Great white crane . . . . 1·25 85

80 Lynx
82 Stamp and U.P.U. Emblem

1998. Wild Cats. Multicoloured.
234 15 t. Type 80 . . . . 30 25
235 30 t. Sand dune cat 70 50
236 50 t. Snow leopard . . . . . 1·25 85

1998. World Post Day.
238 82 30 t. bistre 70 50

83 Anniversary Emblem
84 Warrior with Sword

1998. 5th Anniv of the Tenge (currency unit).
239 83 40 t. orange 95 65

1998. Kazakh Horsemen. Multicoloured.
240 20 t. Type 84 . . . . 45 30
241 30 t. Using bow and arrow . . 70 50
242 40 t. With spear and shield . . 95 65

86 Rabbit and Lunar Cycle
87 Steam Locomotive and Railway Route Map

1999. New Year. Year of the Rabbit.
244 86 40 t. green, black and yellow 95 65

1999. Railway Locomotives. Multicoloured.
245 40 t. Type 87 . . . . 95 65
246 50 t. Electric locomotive . . . . 1·25 85
247 60 t. Diesel railcar . . . . . 1·40 95
248 80 t. Electric locomotive (different) . . . . 1·90 1·25

88 Family (census)
89 Satellite

1999.
249 88 1 t. green 10 10
250 – 15 t. red 35 25
251 – 20 t. brown 45 30
252 – 30 t. brown 70 50
DESIGNS—HORIZ: 15 t. Kanysh Satbaev and book; 20 t. Satbaev and building. VERT: 30 t. Dish aerial and "Intelsat" satellite.

1999. Cosmonautics Day. Multicoloured.
253 50 t. Type 89 . . . . 1·25 85
254 90 t. Astronaut on Moon (30th anniv of first manned Moon landing) (horiz) . . . . . . 2·10 1·40

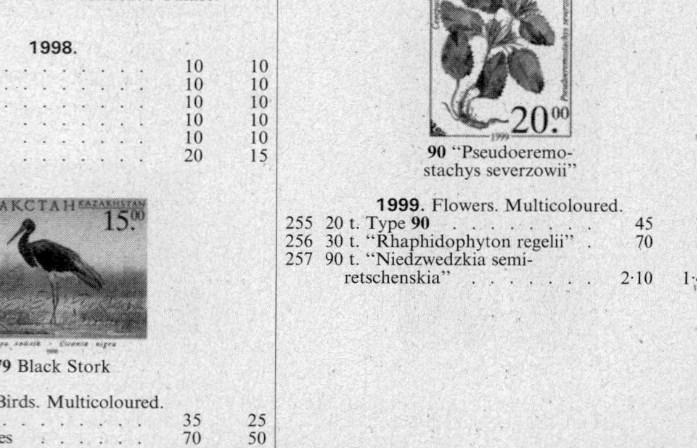

90 "Pseudoeremostachys severzowii"

1999. Flowers. Multicoloured.
255 20 t. Type 90 . . . . 45 30
256 30 t. "Rhaphidophyton regelii" . 70 50
257 90 t. "Niedzwedzkia semiretschenskia" . . . . . . 2·10 1·40

KEDAH Pt. 1

A state of the Federation of Malaya, incorporated in Malaysia in 1963.

100 cents = 1 dollar (Straits or Malayan)

1 Sheaf of Rice 2 Malay ploughing

1912.

No.	Type	Description	Unused	Used
1	1	1 c. black and green	50	25
26		1 c. brown	50	20
52		1 c. black	50	10
27		2 c. green	1·25	20
2		3 c. black and red	2·75	30
19		3 c. purple	65	70
53		3 c. green	1·75	90
3		4 c. red and grey	9·50	25
20		4 c. red	2·25	20
54		4 c. violet	90	10
4		5 c. green and brown	2·25	3·00
55		5 c. yellow	1·50	10
56		6 c. red	70	65
5		8 c. black and blue	2·75	3·50
57		8 c. black	9·50	10
6	2	10 c. blue and brown	1·75	90
58		12 c. black and blue	2·25	4·00
31		20 c. black and green	4·00	2·00
32		21 c. mauve and purple	2·00	13·00
33		25 c. blue and purple	2·25	6·00
34		30 c. black and pink	3·00	7·00
59		35 c. purple	5·00	25·00
9		40 c. black and purple	3·50	14·00
36		50 c. brown and blue	2·25	11·00
37w	–	$1 black and red on yellow	6·50	7·50
38	–	$2 green and brown	13·00	80·00
39w	–	$3 black and blue on blue	50·00	60·00
40w	–	$5 black and red	55·00	£110

DESIGN:—As Type **2**: $1 to $5, Council Chamber.

1919. Surch in words.

No.	Type	Description	Unused	Used
24		50 c. on $2 green and brown	55·00	65·00
25		$1 on $3 black and blue on blue	20·00	85·00

1922. Optd **MALAYA- BORNEO EXHIBITION.**

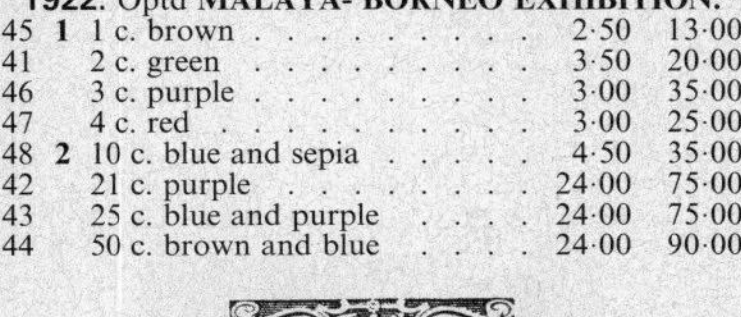

No.	Type	Description	Unused	Used
45	1	1 c. brown	2·50	13·00
41		2 c. green	3·50	20·00
46		3 c. purple	3·00	35·00
47		4 c. red	3·00	25·00
48	2	10 c. blue and sepia	4·50	35·00
42		21 c. purple	24·00	75·00
43		25 c. blue and purple	24·00	75·00
44		50 c. brown and blue	24·00	90·00

6 Sultan Abdul Hamid Halimshah

1937.

No.	Type	Description	Unused	Used
60	6	10 c. blue and brown	4·00	80
61		12 c. black and violet	27·00	12·00
62		25 c. blue and purple	7·50	4·50
63		30 c. green and red	8·50	10·00
64		40 c. black and purple	4·00	16·00
65		50 c. brown and blue	6·00	4·50
66		$1 black and green	4·00	10·00
67		$2 green and brown	£120	90·00
68		$5 black and red	32·00	£140

1948. Silver Wedding. As T **11b/11c** of Gambia.

No.	Type	Description	Unused	Used
70		10 c. violet	20	20
71		$5 red	25·00	32·00

1949. U.P.U. As T **11d/11g** of Gambia.

No.	Type	Description	Unused	Used
72		10 c. purple	25	20
73		15 c. blue	1·50	1·25
74		25 c. orange	65	1·25
75		50 c. black	1·00	2·25

7 Sheaf of Rice 8 Sultan Badlishah

1950.

No.	Type	Description	Unused	Used
76	7	1 c. black	30	30
77		2 c. orange	30	15
78		3 c. green	1·40	1·00
79		4 c. brown	60	10
79ab		5 c. purple	60	70
80		6 c. grey	50	15
81		8 c. red	1·25	2·25
81a		8 c. green	75	1·75
82		10 c. mauve	50	10
82a		12 c. red	85	2·50
83		15 c. blue	80	35
84		20 c. black and green	85	2·50
84a		20 c. blue	85	10
85	8	25 c. purple and orange	90	30
85a		30 c. red and purple	1·25	1·25
85b		35 c. red and purple	85	1·50
86		40 c. red and purple	2·25	6·00
87	8	50 c. black and blue	1·75	20
88		$1 blue and purple	2·75	2·50
89		$2 green and red	20·00	22·00
90		$5 green and brown	42·00	32·00

1953. Coronation. As T **11h** of Gambia.

No.	Type	Description	Unused	Used
91		10 c. black and purple	65	30

15 Fishing Craft 20 Sultan Abdul Halim Mu' Adzam Shah

1957. Inset portrait of Sultan Badlishah.

No.	Type	Description	Unused	Used
92	–	1 c. black	10	35
93	–	2 c. red	10	60
94	–	4 c. sepia	10	30
95	–	5 c. lake	10	30
96	–	8 c. green	2·00	6·00
97	–	10 c. sepia	40	20
98	15	20 c. blue	1·75	1·50
99	–	50 c. black and blue	1·50	2·25
100	–	$1 blue and purple	3·50	8·00
101	–	$2 green and red	19·00	21·00
102	–	$5 brown and green	38·00	32·00

DESIGNS—HORIZ: 1 c. Copra; 2 c. Pineapples; 4 c. Ricefield; 5 c. Masjid Alwi Mosque, Kangar; 8 c. East Coast Railway "Golden Blowpipe" Express; $1 Govt Offices; $2 Bersilat (form of wrestling); $5 Weaving. VERT: 10 c. Tiger; 50 c. Aborigines with blowpipe.

1959. Installation of Sultan.

No.	Type	Description	Unused	Used
103	20	10 c. yellow, brown and blue	10	10

21 Sultan Abdul Halim Shah

1959. As Nos. 92/102 but with inset portrait of Sultan Abdul Halim Shah as in T **21**.

No.	Type	Description	Unused	Used
104		1 c. black	10	40
105		2 c. red	10	70
106		4 c. sepia	10	30
107		5 c. lake	10	10
108		8 c. green	3·50	2·75
109		10 c. sepia	75	10
109a		10 c. purple	3·50	30
110		20 c. blue	60	30
111a		50 c. black and blue	30	20
112		$1 blue and purple	1·75	2·25
113		$2 green and red	13·00	15·00
114a		$5 brown and green	22·00	11·00

22 "Vanda hookeriana"

1965. Flowers. Multicoloured.

No.	Type	Description	Unused	Used
115		1 c. Type **22**	10	50
116		2 c. "Arundina graminifolia"	10	80
117		5 c. "Paphiopedilum niveum"	10	10
118		6 c. "Spathoglottis plicata"	15	30
119		10 c. "Arachnis flos-aeris"	30	10
120		15 c. "Rhyncostylis retusa"	1·50	10
121		20 c. "Phalaenopsis violacea"	1·75	60

The higher values used in Kedah were Nos. 20/7 of Malaysia.

23 "Danaus melanippus"

1971. Butterflies. Multicoloured.

No.	Type	Description	Unused	Used
124		1 c. "Delias ninus"	30	85
125		2 c. Type **23**	40	85
126		5 c. "Parthenos sylvia"	1·00	10
127		6 c. "Papilio demoleus"	1·00	1·00
128		10 c. "Hebomoia glaucippe"	75	10
129		15 c. "Precis orithya"	1·00	10
130		20 c. "Valeria valeria"	1·25	45

The higher values in use with this issue were Nos. 64/71 of Malaysia.

24 "Pterocarpus indicus"

1979. Flowers. Multicoloured.

No.	Type	Description	Unused	Used
135		1 c. "Rafflesia hasseltii"	10	50
136		2 c. Type **24**	10	50
137		5 c. "Lagerstroemia speciosa"	10	30
138		10 c. "Durio zibethinus"	15	10
139		15 c. "Hibiscus rosa-sinensis"	15	10
140		20 c. "Rhododendron scortechinii"	20	10
141		25 c. "Etlingera elatior" (inscr "Phaeomeria speciosa")	40	10

25 Sultan Abdul Halim Shah 26 Cocoa

1983. Silver Jubilee of Sultan's Installation. Multicoloured.

No.	Type	Description	Unused	Used
142		20 c. Type **25**	70	30
143		40 c. Paddy fields (horiz)	1·75	1·00
144		60 c. Paddy fields and Mount Jerai (horiz)	2·50	4·25

1986. Agricultural Products of Malaysia. Mult.

No.	Type	Description	Unused	Used
152		1 c. Coffee	10	10
153		2 c. Coconuts	10	10
154		5 c. Type **26**	10	10
155		10 c. Black pepper	10	10
156		15 c. Rubber	10	10
157		20 c. Oil palm	10	10
158		30 c. Rice	15	20

KELANTAN Pt.1

A state in the Federation of Malaya, incorporated in Malaysia in 1963.

100 cents = 1 dollar (Straits or Malayan)

1

3 Sultan Ismail

1911.

1a	1	1 c. green	2·75	30
15		1 c. black	50	50
16		2 c. brown	4·50	3·75
16a		2 c. green	1·50	40
2		3 c. red	4·00	15
16b		3 c. brown	3·00	1·00
17		4 c. black and red	1·25	10
18		5 c. green & red on yellow	80	10
19		6 c. purple	2·50	1·50
19a		6 c. red	4·00	5·50
5		8 c. blue	5·50	1·00
20		10 c. black and mauve	2·00	10
21		30 c. purple and red	4·00	5·50
8		50 c. black and orange	7·50	2·50
9		$1 green	45·00	48·00
9a		$1 green and brown	35·00	2·00
10		$2 green and red	1·50	4·00
11		$5 green and blue	4·00	7·50
12		$25 green and orange	38·00	75·00

1922. Optd **MALAYA BORNEO EXHIBITION.**

37	1	1 c. green	2·50	38·00
30		4 c. black and red	3·25	38·00
31		5 c. green and red on yellow	4·50	38·00
38		10 c. black and mauve	5·00	48·00
32		30 c. purple and red	4·50	55·00
33		50 c. black and orange	7·50	60·00
34		$1 green and brown	22·00	80·00
35		$2 green and red	48·00	£150
36		$5 green and blue	£140	£300

1928.

40	3	1 c. olive and yellow	30	55
41		2 c. green	2·50	10
42		4 c. red	4·75	70
43		5 c. brown	4·75	10
44		6 c. red	11·00	5·50
45		8 c. olive	4·75	10
46		10 c. purple	22·00	2·75
47		12 c. blue	3·25	4·00
48		25 c. red and purple	4·75	3·50
49		30 c. violet and red	40·00	16·00
50		40 c. orange and green	8·00	23·00
51		50 c. olive and orange	55·00	6·50
39		$1 blue	11·00	75·00
52		$1 violet and green	48·00	12·00
53		$2 red	£180	£180
54		$5 red	£325	£450

All except No. 39 are larger than T **3**.

1948. Silver Wedding. As T **11b/11c** of Gambia.

55	10 c. violet	60	1·75
56	$5 red	24·00	48·00

1949. U.P.U. As T **11d/11g** of Gambia.

57	10 c. purple	25	30
58	15 c. blue	1·50	90
59	25 c. orange	60	2·25
60	50 c. black	1·00	2·25

5 Sultan Ibrahim

6 Sultan Yahya Petra and Crest of Kelantan

1951.

61	5	1 c. black	30	30
62		2 c. orange	80	35
63		3 c. green	3·50	1·25
64		4 c. brown	40	15
65		5 c. purple	45	50
66		6 c. grey	40	20
67		8 c. red	1·75	3·25
68		8 c. green	75	1·75
69		10 c. mauve	40	10
70		12 c. red	75	2·25
71		15 c. blue	3·25	60
72		20 c. black and green	45	5·50
73		20 c. blue	80	25
74		25 c. purple and orange	1·00	55
75		30 c. red and purple	1·25	1·75
76		35 c. red and purple	90	1·50
77		40 c. red and purple	5·50	12·00
78		50 c. black and blue	2·00	40
79		$1 blue and purple	7·00	4·25
80		$2 green and red	23·00	20·00
81		$5 green and brown	48·00	40·00

1953. Coronation. As T **11h** of Gambia.

82	10 c. black and purple	60	90

1957. As Nos. 92/102 of Kedah but inset portrait of Sultan Ibrahim.

83	1 c. black	10	30
84	2 c. red	50	60
85	4 c. sepia	10	10
86	5 c. lake	10	10
87	8 c. green	90	2·50
88	10 c. sepia	1·25	10
89	10 c. purple	5·50	5·50
90	20 c. blue	1·25	30
91	50 c. black and blue	50	50
92	$1 blue and purple	4·50	1·50
93	$2 green and red	11·00	6·00
94	$5 brown and green	15·00	12·00

1961. Coronation of the Sultan.

95	6	10 c. multicoloured	40	30

7 Sultan Yahya Petra

8 "Vanda hookeriana"

1961. As Nos. 83, etc, but with inset portrait of Sultan Yahya Petra as in T **7**.

96	1 c. black	10	85
97	2 c. red	10	85
98	4 c. sepia	20	30
99	5 c. lake	20	10
100	8 c. green	6·00	7·00
101	10 c. purple	80	10
102	20 c. blue	3·25	55

1965. As Nos. 115/21 of Kedah but with inset portrait of Sultan Yahya Petra as in T **8**.

103	8	1 c. multicoloured	10	50
104	–	2 c. multicoloured	10	75
105	–	5 c. multicoloured	15	10
106	–	6 c. multicoloured	70	1·25
107	–	10 c. multicoloured	30	10
108	–	15 c. multicoloured	1·50	20
109	–	20 c. multicoloured	1·50	1·25

The higher values used in Kelantan were Nos. 20/7 of Malaysia (National Issues).

9 "Parthenos sylvia"

1971. Butterflies. As Nos. 124/30 of Kedah but with portrait of Sultan Yahya Petra as in T **9**.

112	–	1 c. multicoloured	30	1·50
113	–	2 c. multicoloured	40	1·50
114	9	5 c. multicoloured	1·25	30
115	–	6 c. multicoloured	1·25	1·75
116	–	10 c. multicoloured	1·25	20
117	–	15 c. multicoloured	1·25	10
118	–	20 c. multicoloured	1·75	1·00

The higher values in use with this series were Nos. 64/71 of Malaysia (National Issues).

10 "Lagerstroemia speciosa"

1979. Flowers. As Nos. 135/41 of Kedah but with portrait of Sultan Yahya Petra as in T **10**.

123	1 c. "Rafflesia hasseltii"	10	60
124	2 c. "Pterocarpus indicus"	10	60
125	5 c. Type **10**	10	50
126	10 c. "Durio zibethinus"	15	10
127	15 c. "Hibiscus rosa-sinensis"	15	10
128	20 c. "Rhododendron scortechinii"	20	10
129	25 c. "Etlingera elatior" (inscr "Phaeomeria speciosa")	40	50

11 Sultan Tengku Ismail Petra

12 Black Pepper

1980. Coronation of Sultan Tengku Ismail Petra.

130	11	10 c. multicoloured	40	75
131		15 c. multicoloured	40	15
132		50 c. multicoloured	90	2·75

1986. Agricultural Products of Malaysia. Mult.

140	1 c. Coffee	10	10
141	2 c. Coconuts	10	10
142	5 c. Cocoa	10	10
143	10 c. Type **12**	10	10
144	15 c. Rubber	10	10
145	20 c. Oil palm	10	10
146	30 c. Rice	15	20

KENYA Pt.1

Formerly part of Kenya, Uganda and Tanganyika (q.v.). Became Independent in 1963 and a Republic in 1964.

100 cents = 1 shilling

1 Cattle Ranching

4 Cockerel

3 National Assembly

1963. Independence.

1	1	5 c. multicoloured	10	55
2	–	10 c. brown	10	10
3	–	15 c. mauve	85	10
4	–	20 c. black and green	15	10
5	–	30 c. black and yellow	15	10
6	–	40 c. brown and blue	15	30
7	–	50 c. red, black and green	15	10
8	–	65 c. turquoise and yellow	55	65
9	3	1 s. multicoloured	20	10
10	–	1 s. 30 brown, black & grn	4·25	20
11	–	2 s. multicoloured	1·25	40
12	–	5 s. brown, blue and green	1·25	40
13	–	10 s. brown and blue	8·50	2·50
14	–	20 s. black and red	5·50	7·50

DESIGNS—As Type **1**: 10 c. Wood-carving; 15 c. Heavy industry; 20 c. Timber industry; 30 c. Jomo Kenyatta facing Mt. Kenya; 40 c. Fishing industry; 50 c. Kenya flag; 65 c. Pyrethrum industry. As Type **3**: 1 s. 30, Tourism (Treetops hotel); 2 s. Coffee industry; 5 s. Tea industry; 10 s. Mombasa Port; 20 s. Royal College, Nairobi.

1964. Inauguration of Republic. Multicoloured.

15	15 c. Type **4**	20	15
16	30 c. Pres. Kenyatta	20	10
17	50 c. African lion	20	10
18	1 s. 30 Hartlaub's turaco	3·75	50
19	2 s. 50 Nandi flame	50	3·75

5 Thomson's Gazelle

7 Greater Kudu

1966.

20	5	5 c. orange, black and sepia	20	20
21	–	10 c. black and green	10	10
22	–	15 c. black and orange	10	10
23	–	20 c. ochre, black and blue	10	15
24	–	30 c. indigo, blue and black	20	10
25	–	40 c. black and brown	60	30
26	–	50 c. black and orange	60	10
27	–	65 c. black and green	1·25	2·00
28	–	70 c. black and red	6·00	1·25
29	7	1 s. brown, black and blue	30	10
30	–	1 s. 30 blue, green and black	4·00	20
31	–	1 s. 50 black, brown and green	4·25	2·00
32	–	2 s. 50 yellow, black & brown	3·25	1·25
33	–	5 s. yellow, black and green	75	70
34	–	10 s. ochre, black and brown	1·75	3·00
35	–	20 s. multicoloured	7·00	13·00

DESIGNS—As Type **5**: 10 c. Sable antelope; 15 c. Aardvark ("Ant Bear"); 20 c. Lesser bushbaby; 30 c. Warthog; 40 c. Common zebra; 50 c. African buffalo; 65 c. Black rhinoceros; 70 c. Ostrich. As Type **7**: 1 s. 30, African elephant; 1 s. 50, Bat-eared fox; 2 s. 50, Cheetah; 5 s. Savanna monkey ("Vervet Monkey"); 10 s. Giant ground pangolin; 20 s. Lion.

8 Perna Tellin

9 Ramose Murex

1971. Sea Shells. Multicoloured.

36	5 c. Type **8**	10	30
37	10 c. Episcopal mitre	15	10
38	15 c. Purplish clanculus	15	20
39	20 c. Humpback cowrie	15	20
40	30 c. Variable abalone	20	10
41	40 c. Flame top shell	20	10
42	50 c. Common purple janthina	30	20
43	50 c. Common purple janthina	9·50	2·25
44	60 c. Bullmouth helmet	30	1·25
45	70 c. Chambered or pearly nautilus	45	1·50
46	70 c. Chambered or pearly nautilus	9·00	4·50
47a	1 s. Type **9**	20	10
48	1 s. 50 Trumpet triton	1·00	10
49	2 s. 50 Trapezium horse conch	1·00	10
50a	5 s. Great green turban	1·00	10
51	10 s. Textile or cloth of gold cone	3·25	15
52a	20 s. Scorpion conch	3·25	25

INSCRIPTIONS: No. 42, "Janthina globosa"; 43, "Janthina janthina"; 45, "Nautilus pompileus"; 46, "Nautilus pompilius".

Nos. 47/52 are larger, as Type **9**.

1975. Nos. 48/9 and 52a surch.

53	2 s. on 1 s. 50 Trumpet triton	6·00	4·50
54	3 s. on 2 s. 50 Trapezium horse conch	9·50	18·00
55	40 s. on 20 s. Scorpion conch	6·00	13·00

11 Microwave Tower

1976. Telecommunications Development. Mult.

56	50 c. Type **11**	10	10
57	1 s. Cordless switchboard (horiz)	10	10
58	2 s. Telephones	20	30
59	3 s. Message switching centre (horiz)	25	45

12 Akii Bua, Ugandan Hurdler

1976. Olympic Games, Montreal. Multicoloured.

61	50 c. Type **12**	10	10
62	1 s. Filbert Bayi, Tanzanian runner	15	10
63	2 s. Steve Muchoki, Kenyan boxer	45	35
64	3 s. Olympic flame and East African flags	60	50

13 Diesel-hydraulic Train, Tanzania–Zambia Railway

1976. Railway Transport. Multicoloured.

66	50 c. Type **13**	35	10
67	1 s. Nile Bridge, Uganda	60	15
68	2 s. Nakuru Station, Kenya	1·75	1·25
69	3 s. Uganda Railway Class A steam locomotive, 1896	1·75	1·75

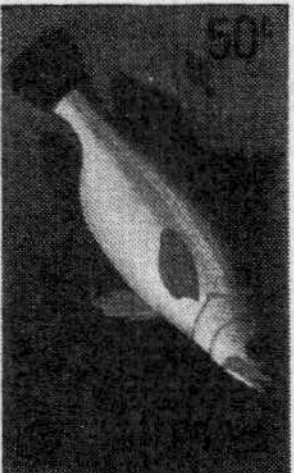

14 Nile Perch

1977. Game Fish of East Africa. Multicoloured.

71	50 c. Type **14**	25	10
72	1 s. Nile mouthbrooder ("Tilapia")	35	10
73	3 s. Sailfish	75	60
74	5 s. Black marlin	90	80

15 Maasai Manyatta (village), Kenya

1977. Second World Black and African Festival of Arts and Culture, Nigeria. Multicoloured.

76	50 c. Type **15**	15	10
77	1 s. "Heartbeat of Africa" (Ugandan dancers)	20	10
78	2 s. Makonde sculpture, Tanzania	75	1·25
79	3 s. "Early man and technology" (skinning hippopotamus)	1·00	1·75

16 Rally Car and Villagers

1977. 25th Anniv of Safari Rally. Multicoloured.

81	50 c. Type **16**	15	10
82	1 s. Pres. Kenyatta starting rally	15	10
83	2 s. Car fording river	50	60
84	5 s. Car and elephants	1·40	1·50

17 Canon Kivebulaya

1977. Centenary of Ugandan Church. Multicoloured.

86	50 c. Type **17**	10	10
87	1 s. Modern Namirembe Cathedral	10	10
88	2 s. The first Cathedral	30	55
89	5 s. Early congregation, Kigezi	50	1·00

18 Sagana Royal Lodge, Nyeri, 1952

1977. Silver Jubilee. Multicoloured.

91	2 s. Type **18**	15	15
92	5 s. Treetops Hotel (vert)	20	35
93	10 s. Queen Elizabeth and Pres. Kenyatta	30	60
94	15 s. Royal visit, 1972	45	1·00

19 Pancake Tortoise

1977. Endangered Species. Multicoloured.

96	50 c. Type **19**	30	10
97	1 s. Nile crocodile	40	10
98	2 s. Hunter's hartebeest	1·60	55
99	3 s. Red colobus monkey	1·75	70
100	5 s. Dugong	2·00	1·10

20 Kenya-Ethiopia Border Point

1977. Nairobi–Addis Ababa Highway. Mult.

102	50 c. Type **20**	15	10
103	1 s. Archer's Post	15	10
104	2 s. Thika Flyover	40	40
105	5 s. Marsabit Game Lodge	1·00	1·10

21 Gypsum

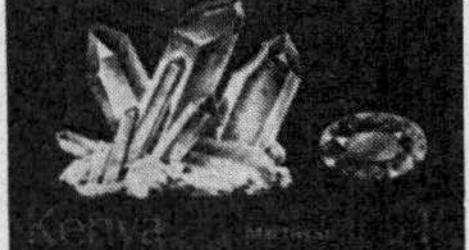

22 Amethyst

1977. Minerals. Multicoloured.

107	10 c. Type **21**	1·25	20
108	20 c. Trona	1·25	20
109	30 c. Kyanite	1·40	20
110	40 c. Amazonite	1·40	10
111	50 c. Galena	1·40	10
112	70 c. Silicified wood	5·50	40
113	80 c. Fluorite	5·50	60
114	1 s. Type **22**	1·40	10
115	1 s. 50 Agate	1·50	30
116	2 s. Tourmaline	1·50	20
117	3 s. Aquamarine	1·75	55
118	5 s. Rhodolite garnet	1·75	1·40
119	10 s. Sapphire	1·75	2·50
120	20 s. Ruby	6·00	3·50
121	40 s. Green grossular garnet	16·00	16·00

23 Joe Kadenge (Kenya) and Forwards

1978. World Cup Football Championship, Argentina. Multicoloured.

122	50 c. Type **23**	10	10
123	1 s. Mohamed Chuma (Tanzania) and cup presentation	10	10
124	2 s. Omari Kidevu (Zanzibar) and goalmouth scene	30	70
125	3 s. Polly Ouma (Uganda) and three forwards	40	95

24 Boxing

1978. Commonwealth Games, Edmonton. Mult.

127	50 c. Type **24**	15	10
128	1 s. Welcoming the Olympic Games Team, 1968	20	10
129	3 c. Javelin throwing	60	1·00
130	5 s. Pres. Kenyatta admiring boxer's trophy	75	1·60

25 "Overloading is Dangerous"

1978. Road Safety. Multicoloured.

131	50 c. Type **25**	50	10
132	1 s. "Speed does not pay"	70	20
133	1 s. 50 "Ignoring Traffic Signs may cause death"	85	55
134	2 s. "Slow down at School Crossing"	1·25	1·00
135	3 s. "Never cross a continuous line"	1·40	2·50
136	5 s. "Approach Railway Level Crossing with extreme caution"	2·00	3·50

26 Pres. Kenyatta at Mass Rally, 1963

1978. Kenyatta Day. Multicoloured.

137	50 c. "Harambee Water Project"	15	10
138	1 s. Handing over of Independence Instruments, 1963	15	10
139	2 s. Type **26**	40	50
140	3 s. "Harambee, 15 Great Years"	75	1·25
141	5 s. "Struggle for Independence, 1952"	1·00	2·00

27 Freedom Fighters, Namibia

1978. International Anti-Apartheid Year.

142	**27**	50 c. multicoloured	15	10
143	–	1 s. black and blue	15	10
144	–	2 s. multicoloured	40	30
145	–	3 s. multicoloured	60	65
146	–	5 s. multicoloured	75	1·00

DESIGNS: 1 s. International seminar on apartheid; 2 s. Steve Biko's tombstone; 3 s. Nelson Mandela; 5 s. Bishop Lamont.

28 Children Playing

1979. International Year of the Child. Multicoloured.

147	50 c. Type **28**	20	10
148	2 s. Boy fishing	60	60
149	3 s. Children singing and dancing	80	1·00
150	5 s. Children with camels	1·00	1·60

29 "The Lion and the Jewel"

1979. Kenya National Theatre. Multicoloured.

151	50 c. Type **29**	15	10
152	1 s. "Utisi"	15	10
153	2 s. Theatre programmes	30	30
154	3 s. Kenya National Theatre	45	45
155	5 s. "Genesis"	75	75

30 Blind Telephone Operator

31 "Father of the Nation" (Kenyatta's funeral procession)

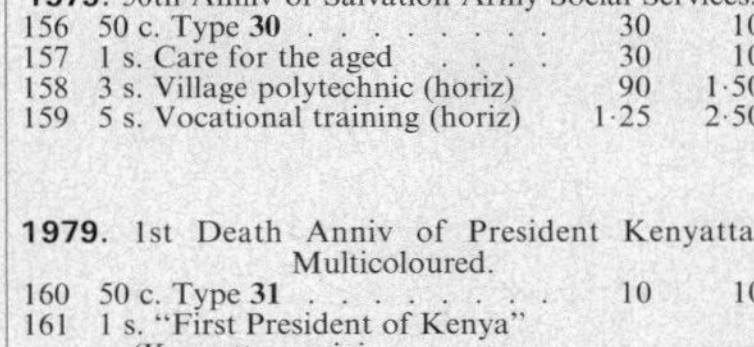

1979. 50th Anniv of Salvation Army Social Services.

156	50 c. Type **30**	30	10
157	1 s. Care for the aged	30	10
158	3 s. Village polytechnic (horiz)	90	1·50
159	5 s. Vocational training (horiz)	1·25	2·50

1979. 1st Death Anniv of President Kenyatta. Multicoloured.

160	50 c. Type **31**	10	10
161	1 s. "First President of Kenya" (Kenyatta receiving independence)	10	10
162	3 s. "Kenyatta the politician" (speaking at rally)	30	50
163	5 s. "A true son of Kenya" (Kenyatta as a boy carpenter)	40	95

32 British East Africa Company 1890 1 a. Stamp

1979. Death Centenary of Sir Rowland Hill.

164	**32**	50 c. multicoloured	15	10
165	–	1 s. multicoloured	15	10
166	–	2 s. black, red and brown	20	40
167	–	5 s. multicoloured	35	1·00

DESIGNS: 1 s. Kenya, Uganda and Tanganyika 1935 1 s. stamp; 2 s. Penny Black; 5 s. 1964 2 s. 50, Inauguration of Republic commemorative.

33 Roads, Globe and Conference Emblem

1980. International Road Federation. African Highway Conference, Nairobi. Multicoloured.

168	50 c. Type **33**	15	10
169	1 s. New weighbridge, Athi River	15	10
170	3 s. New Nyali Bridge, Mombasa	40	85
171	5 s. Highway to Jomo Kenyatta International Airport	50	2·00

34 Mobile Unit in action in Masailand

1980. Flying Doctor Service. Multicoloured.

172	50 c. Type **34**	10	10
173	1 s. Donkey transport to Turkana airstrip (vert)	20	10
174	3 s. Surgical team in action at outstation (vert)	65	1·00
175	5 s. Emergency airlift from North Eastern Province	90	1·60

35 Statue of Sir Rowland Hill

37 Blue-spotted Stingray

36 Pope John Paul II

1980. "London 1980" International Stamp Exhibition.

177	**35**	25 s. multicoloured	1·00	2·50

1980. Papal Visit. Multicoloured.

179	50 c. Type **36**	40	10
180	1 s. Pope, arms and cathedral (vert)	50	10
181	5 s. Pope, flags and dove (vert)	1·10	70
182	10 s. Pope, President Moi and map of Africa	1·60	1·40

1980. Marine Life. Multicoloured.

183	50 c. Type **37**	30	10
184	2 s. Allard's anemonefish	1·00	80
185	3 s. Four-coloured nudibranch	1·25	1·75
186	5 s. "Eretmochelys imbricata"	1·75	2·75

38 National Archives

1980. Historic Buildings. Multicoloured.

187	50 c. Type **38**	10	10
188	1 s. Provincial Commissioner's Office, Nairobi	15	10
189	1 s. 50 Nairobi House	20	20
190	2 s. Norfolk Hotel	25	50
191	3 s. McMillan Library	35	75
192	5 s. Kipande House	55	1·25

39 "Disabled enjoys Affection"

1981. Int Year for Disabled Persons. Mult.

193	50 c. Type **39**	15	10
194	1 s. President Moi presenting flag to Disabled Olympic Games team captain	15	10
195	3 s. Blind people climbing Mount Kenya, 1975	55	55
196	5 s. Disabled artist at work	70	1·00

40 Longonot Complex

1981. Satellite Communications. Multicoloured.
197 50 c. Type **40** 15 10
198 2 s. "Intelsat V" 40 35
199 3 s. "Longonot I" 45 55
200 5 s. "Longonot II" 60 85

41 Kenyatta Conference Centre

1981. O.A.U. (Organization of African Unity) Summit Conference, Nairobi.
201 **41** 50 c. multicoloured 15 10
202 – 1 s. black, yellow & blue . . 15 10
203 – 3 s. multicoloured 40 40
204 – 5 s. multicoloured 70 65
205 – 10 s. multicoloured . . . . 80 1·00
DESIGNS: 1 s. "Panaftel" earth stations; 3 s. Parliament Building; 5 s. Jomo Kenyatta International Airport; 10 s. O.A.U. flag.

42 St. Paul's Cathedral **43** Giraffe

1981. Royal Wedding. Multicoloured.
207 50 c. Prince Charles and President Daniel Arap Moi 10 10
208 3 s. Type **42** 15 20
209 5 s. Royal Yacht "Britannia" . 25 30
210 10 s. Prince Charles on safari in Kenya 40 55

1981. Rare Animals. Multicoloured.
212 50 c. Type **43** 15 10
213 2 s. Bongo 35 25
214 5 s. Roan antelope . . . . . . 70 1·25
215 10 s. Agile mangabey . . . . . 1·00 2·75

44 "Technical Development" **45** Kamba

1981. World Food Day. Multicoloured.
216 50 c. Type **44** 10 10
217 1 s. "Mwea rice projects" . . . 15 10
218 2 s. "Irrigation schemes" . . . 30 55
219 5 s. "Breeding livestock" . . . 60 1·75

1981. Ceremonial Costumes (1st series). Mult.
220 50 c. Type **45** 40 10
221 1 s. Turkana 45 10
222 2 s. Giriama . . . . 1·25 85
223 3 s. Masai . . . . 1·60 2·00
224 5 s. Luo . . . . 1·75 3·00
See also Nos. 329/33, 413/17 and 515/19.

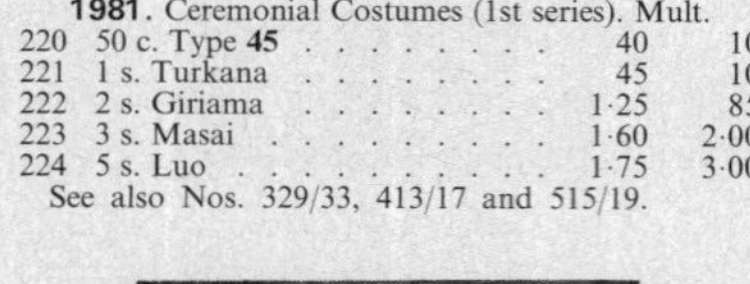

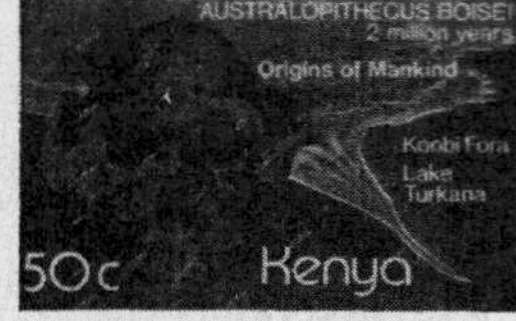

46 "Australopithecus boisei"

1982. "Origins of Mankind". Skulls. Multicoloured.
225 50 c. Type **46** . . . . 1·10 20
226 2 s. "Homo erectus" . . . . . 2·50 1·50
227 3 s. "Homo habilis" . . . . . 3·00 3·75
228 5 s. "Proconsul africanus" . . 3·50 5·00

47 Tree-planting

1982. 75th Anniv of Boy Scout Movement (Nos. 229, 231, 233 and 235) and 60th Anniv of Girl Guide Movement (Nos. 230, 232, 234 and 236). Multicoloured.
229 70 c. Type **47** 50 65
230 70 c. Paying homage 50 65
231 3 s. 50 "Be Prepared" . . . . 1·25 1·75
232 3 s. 50 "International Friendship" . . . . 1·25 1·75
233 5 s. Helping disabled . . . . . 1·75 2·50
234 5 s. Community service . . . . 1·75 2·50
235 6 s. 50 Paxtu Cottage (Lord Baden-Powell's home) . . . 2·00 2·75
236 6 s. 50 Lady Baden-Powell . . 2·00 2·75

48 Footballer displaying Shooting Skill

1982. World Cup Football Championship, Spain. Footballers silhouetted against Map of World. Multicoloured.
238 70 c. Type **48** . . . . 1·50 65
239 3 s. 50 Heading . . . . 2·75 2·75
240 5 s. Goalkeeping . . . . . . 3·25 4·25
241 10 s. Dribbling . . . . 5·50 8·00

49 Cattle Judging **50** Micro-wave Radio System

1982. 80th Anniv of Agricultural Society of Kenya. Multicoloured.
243 70 c. Type **49** 50 10
244 2 s. 50 Farm machinery . . . . 1·25 1·25
245 3 s. 50 Musical ride . . . . . 1·50 2·50
246 6 s. 50 Agricultural Society emblem . . . . 2·00 4·25

1982. I.T.U. Plenipotentiary Conference, Nairobi. Multicoloured.
247 70 c. Type **50** 50 10
248 3 s. 50 Sea-to-shore service link 1·75 1·75
249 5 s. Rural telecommunications system . . . . 2·25 3·75
250 6 s. 50 I.T.U. emblem . . . . 2·50 4·50

1982. No. 113 surch **70c.**
251 70 c. on 80 c. Fluorite . . . . 1·00 1·00

52 Container Cranes

1983. 5th Anniv of Kenya Ports Authority. Mult.
252 70 c. Type **52** 85 10
253 2 s. Port by night . . . . . . 1·75 1·90
254 3 s. 50 Container cranes (different) . . . . 2·50 3·50
255 5 s. Map of Mombasa Port . . 3·25 4·50

53 Shada Zambarau **54** Waridi Kikuba

1983. Flowers. Multicoloured.
257 10 c. Type **53** 40 40
258 20 c. Kilua Kingulima 55 40
259 30 c. Mwalika Mwiya 55 40
260 40 c. Ziyungi Buluu 55 40
261 50 c. Kilua Habashia 55 30
262 70 c. Chanuo Kato 60 20
262a 80 c. As 40 c. . . . . 4·00 2·75
262b 1 s. Waridi Kikuba . . . . . 4·00 80
263 1 s. Type **54** 65 20
264 1 s. 50 Mshomoro Mtambazi 1·75 60
265 2 s. Papatuo Boti . . . . . . 1·75 60
266 2 s. 50 Tumba Mboni . . . . 2·25 60
266a 3 s. Mkuku Mrembo . . . . 7·50 7·50
267 3 s. 50 Mtongo Mbeja . . . . 2·00 1·50
267b 4 s. Mnukia Muuma . . . . 4·75 6·50
268 5 s. Nyungu Chepuo . . . . 2·00 1·50
268a 7 s. Mlua Miba . . . . . . 6·50 8·50
269 10 s. Muafunili . . . . 2·00 2·00
270 20 s. Mbake Nyanza . . . . 2·00 3·00
271 40 s. Njuga Pagwa . . . . . 3·75 8·00
The 1 s. 50 to 40 s. are in the same format as T **54**.

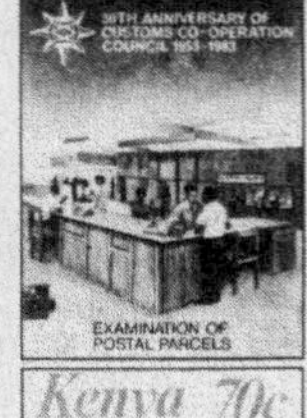

55 Coffee Plucking **56** Examining Parcels

1983. Commonwealth Day. Multicoloured.
272 70 c. Type **55** 10 10
273 2 s. President Daniel Arap Moi 15 20
274 5 s. Satellite view of Earth (horiz) 35 45
275 10 s. Masai dance (horiz) . . . 65 1·00

1983. 30th Anniv of Customs Co-operation Council. Multicoloured.
276 70 c. Type **56** 25 10
277 2 s. 50 Customs Headquarters, Mombasa 65 30
278 3 s. 50 Customs Council Headquarters, Brussels . . . 75 40
279 10 s. Customs patrol boat . . . 2·40 2·50

57 Communications via Satellite

1983. World Communications Year. Multicoloured.
280 70 c. Type **57** 60 10
281 2 s. 50 "Telephone and Postal Services" . . . . 1·50 1·75
282 3 s. 50 Communications by sea and air (horiz) . . . . . 2·00 3·00
283 5 s. Road and rail communications (horiz) . . . 2·50 4·00

58 "Craftsman" (freighter) in Kilindini Harbour

1983. 25th Anniv of Intergovernmental Maritime Organization. Multicoloured.
284 70 c. Type **58** 95 10
285 2 s. 50 Life-saving devices . . . 2·00 1·75
286 3 s. 50 Mombasa container terminal . . . . 2·50 3·00
287 10 s. Marine park . . . . . . 3·50 6·50

59 President Moi signing Visitors' Book

1983. 29th Commonwealth Parliamentary Conference. Multicoloured.
288 70 c. Type **59** 25 10
289 2 s. 50 Parliament building, Nairobi (vert) . . . . . . 90 1·10
290 5 s. State opening of Parliament (vert) . . . . 1·60 2·75

60 Kenyan and British Flags

1983. Royal Visit. Multicoloured.
292 70 c. Type **60** 50 10
293 3 s. 50 Sagana State Lodge . . 2·00 1·50
294 5 s. Treetops Hotel . . . . . 2·25 2·50
295 10 s. Queen Elizabeth II and President Moi . . . . 3·50 6·50

61 President Moi

1983. 20th Anniv of Independence. Mult.
297 70 c. Type **61** 10 10
298 2 s. President Moi planting tree 15 20
299 3 s. 50 Kenyan flag and emblem 25 35
300 5 s. School milk scheme 40 50
301 10 s. People of Kenya . . . . 75 1·10

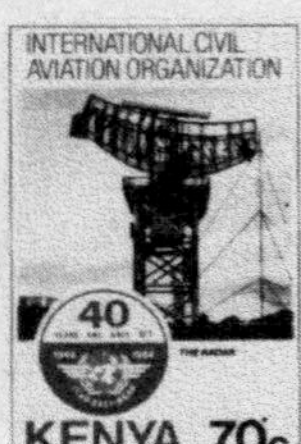

62 White-backed Night Heron **63** Radar Tower

1984. Rare Birds of Kenya. Multicoloured.
303 70 c. Type **62** . . . . 1·75 30
304 2 s. 50 Quail plover . . . . . 3·00 2·50
305 3 s. 50 Taita olive thrush . . . 3·75 3·75
306 5 s. Mufumbiri shrike . . . . 4·25 4·25
307 10 s. White-winged apalis . . . 5·50 7·00

1984. 40th Anniv of International Civil Aviation Organization. Multicoloured.
308 70 c. Type **63** 15 10
309 2 s. 50 Kenya School of Aviation (horiz) 45 45
310 3 s. 50 Boeing 707 taking off from Moi airport (horiz) 65 80
311 5 s. Air traffic control centre . . 95 1·25

64 Running

1984. Olympic Games, Los Angeles.
312 **64** 70 c. black, green & dp green 30 10
313 – 2 s. 50 black, purple & vio . 60 70
314 – 5 s. black, blue & dp blue . 1·50 2·50
315 – 10 s. black, yellow & brn . . 3·50 5·50
DESIGNS: 2 s. 50, Hurdling; 5 s. Boxing; 10 s. Hockey.

65 Conference and Kenya Library Association Logos

1984. 50th Conference of the International Federation of Library Associations. Multicoloured.
317 70 c. Type **65** 10 10
318 3 s. 50 Mobile library 50 60
319 5 s. Adult library . . . . . . 65 1·25
320 10 s. Children's library . . . . 1·00 2·50

66 Doves and Cross **67** Export Year Logo

1984. 4th World Conference on Religion and Peace. As T **66**, each design showing a different central symbol. Multicoloured.
321 70 c. Type **66** 30 10
322 2 s. 50 Arabic inscription . . . 1·25 1·50
323 3 s. 50 Peace emblem . . . . . 1·60 2·25
324 6 s. 50 Star and Crescent . . . 2·00 3·50

1984. Kenya Export Year. Multicoloured.
325 70 c. Type **67** 30 10
326 3 s. 50 Forklift truck with air cargo (horiz) . . . . 1·75 2·00
327 5 s. Loading ship's cargo . . . 2·50 2·75
328 10 s. Kenyan products (horiz) . 3·75 5·25

1984. Ceremonial Costumes (2nd series). As T **45**. Multicoloured.
329 70 c. Luhya 70 15
330 2 s. Kikuyu . . . . 1·75 1·75
331 3 s. 50 Pokomo . . . . . . 2·25 2·25
332 5 s. Nandi . . . . 2·50 2·50
333 10 s. Rendile . . . . 3·50 5·00

68 Staunton Knight and Nyayo National Stadium

1984. 60th Anniv of International Chess Federation. Multicoloured.
334 70 c. Type **68** . . . . 1·50 30
335 2 s. 50 Staunton rook and Fort Jesus . . . . 2·50 1·75
336 3 s. 50 Staunton bishop and National Monument . . . . 3·00 2·50
337 5 s. Staunton queen and Parliament Building . . . . 3·25 3·50
338 10 s. Staunton king and Nyayo Fountain . . . . 5·00 7·00

69 Cooking with Wood-burning Stove and Charcoal Fire

1985. Energy Conservation. Multicoloured.
339 70 c. Type **69** 20 10
340 2 s. Solar energy panel on roof 65 75
341 3 s. 50 Production of gas from cow dung . . . . 75 1·25
342 10 s. Ploughing with oxen . . . 2·25 4·50

70 Crippled Girl Guide making Table-mat

1985. 75th Anniv of Girl Guide Movement. Multicoloured.
344 1 s. Type **70** 75 15
345 3 s. Girl Guides doing community service . . . . 1·75 1·50
346 5 s. Lady Olave Baden-Powell (founder) . . . . 2·50 3·00
347 7 s. Girl Guides gardening . . 4·00 6·00

71 Stylised Figures and Globe

1985. World Red Cross Day.
348 **71** 1 s. black and red 80 15
349 – 4 s. multicoloured . . . . . 3·00 3·00
350 – 5 s. multicoloured . . . . . 3·25 3·50
351 – 7 s. multicoloured . . . . . 4·50 6·00
DESIGNS: 4 s. First Aid team; 5 s. Hearts containing crosses ("Blood Donation"); 7 s. Cornucopia ("Famine Relief").

72 Man with Malaria **73** Repairing Water Pipes

1985. 7th International Congress of Protozoology, Nairobi. Multicoloured.
352 1 s. Type **72** 90 15
353 3 s. Child with Leishmaniasis . 2·75 2·75
354 5 s. Cow with Trypanosomiasis 3·25 3·50
355 7 s. Dog with Babesiosis . . . 4·75 6·50

1985. United Nations Women's Decade Conference. Multicoloured.
356 1 s. Type **73** 20 10
357 3 s. Traditional food preparation 60 70
358 5 s. Basket-weaving . . . . . 75 1·25
359 7 s. Dressmaking . . . . . . 1·00 2·50

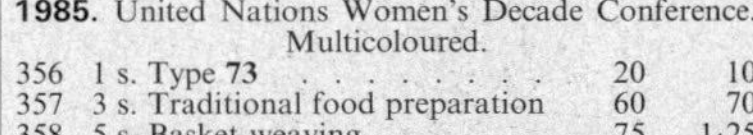

74 The Last Supper

1985. 43rd International Eucharistic Congress, Nairobi. Multicoloured.
360 1 s. Type **74** 50 10
361 3 s. Village family ("The Eucharist and the Christian Family") . . . . 2·25 2·00
362 5 s. Congress altar, Uhuru Park 2·50 2·75
363 7 s. St. Peter Claver's Church, Nairobi . . . . 3·00 4·50

75 Black Rhinoceros

1985. Endangered Animals. Multicoloured.
365 1 s. Type **75** . . . . 1·75 40
366 3 s. Cheetah . . . . 3·00 2·75
367 5 s. De Brazza's monkey . . . 3·25 3·75
368 10 s. Grevy's zebra . . . . . 5·50 7·50

76 "Borassus aethiopum"

1986. Indigenous Trees. Multicoloured.
370 1 s. Type **76** 65 15
371 3 s. "Acacia xanthophloea" . . 2·50 2·50
372 5 s. "Ficus natalensis" . . . . 3·50 3·75
373 7 s. "Spathodea nilotica" . . . 4·50 6·00

77 Dove and U.N. Logo (from poster) **78** Dribbling the Ball

1986. International Peace Year. Multicoloured.
375 1 s. Type **77** 30 10
376 3 s. U.N. General Assembly (horiz) . . . . 1·00 65
377 7 s. Nuclear explosion . . . . 2·25 2·75
378 10 s. Quotation from Wall of Isaiah, U.N. Building, New York (horiz) . . . . 3·00 3·25

1986. World Cup Football Championship, Mexico. Multicoloured.
379 1 s. Type **78** 80 15
380 3 s. Scoring from a penalty . . 2·25 1·25
381 5 s. Tackling . . . . 3·00 2·00
382 7 s. Cup winners . . . . . . 3·75 3·50
383 10 s. Heading the ball . . . . 4·75 4·25

79 Rural Post Office and Telephone

1986. "Expo '86" World Fair, Vancouver. Mult.
385 1 s. Type **79** 50 15
386 3 s. Container depot, Embakasi 2·50 1·75
387 5 s. Piper Twin Commanche airplane landing at game park airstrip . . . . 3·50 2·75
388 7 s. Container ship . . . . . . 4·00 4·50
389 10 s. Transporting produce to market . . . . 4·25 13·00

80 Telephone, Computer and Dish Aerial

1986. African Telecommunications. Multicoloured.
390 1 s. Type **80** 35 10
391 3 s. Telephones of 1876, 1936 and 1986 . . . . 1·00 85
392 5 s. Dish aerial, satellite, telephones and map of Africa 1·25 1·25
393 7 s. Kenyan manufacture of telecommunications equipment . . . . 1·75 2·25

81 Mashua

1986. Dhows of Kenya. Multicoloured.
394 1 s. Type **81** 65 20
395 3 s. Mtepe . . . . 1·75 1·50
396 5 s. Dau La Mwao . . . . . . 2·25 2·75
397 10 s. Jahazi . . . . 3·75 5·00

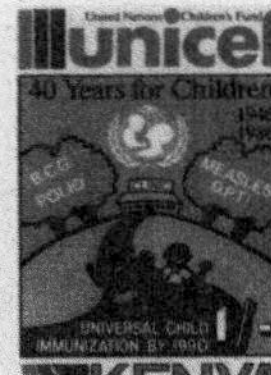

82 Nativity **83** Immunization

1986. Christmas. Multicoloured.
399 1 s. Type **82** 30 10
400 3 s. Shepherd and sheep . . . 1·00 55
401 5 s. Angel and slogan "LOVE PEACE UNITY" (horiz) . . 1·60 1·40
402 7 s. The Magi riding camels (horiz) . . . . 1·90 2·75

1987. 40th Anniv of U.N.I.C.E.F. Multicoloured.
403 1 s. Type **83** 45 10
404 3 s. Food and nutrition . . . . 1·00 70
405 4 s. Oral rehydration therapy . 1·75 1·50
406 5 s. Family planning . . . . . 1·75 1·50
407 10 s. Female literacy . . . . . 2·50 3·50

84 Akamba Woodcarvers

1987. Tourism. Multicoloured.
408 1 s. Type **84** 30 10
409 3 s. Tourism on beach . . . . 2·00 1·75
410 5 s. Tourist and guide at view point . . . . 2·75 3·50
411 7 s. Pride of lions . . . . . . 4·00 5·50

1987. Ceremonial Costumes (3rd series). As T **45**. Multicoloured.
413 1 s. Embu 50 10
414 3 s. Kisii . . . . 1·50 70
415 5 s. Samburu . . . . 1·75 1·40
416 7 s. Taita . . . . 2·50 2·50
417 10 s. Boran . . . . 2·75 3·00

85 Telecommunications by Satellite

1987. 10th Anniv of Kenya Posts and Telecommunications Corporation. Multicoloured.
418 1 s. Type **85** 35 30
419 3 s. Rural post office, Kajiado 80 90
420 4 s. Awarding trophy, Welfare Sports . . . . 1·10 1·40
421 5 s. Village and telephone box . 1·25 1·50
422 7 s. Speedpost labels and outline map of Kenya . . . . . . 1·75 2·50

86 Volleyball **87** "Aloe volkensii"

1987. 4th All-Africa Games, Nairobi. Mult.
424 1 s. Type **86** 20 10
425 3 s. Cycling 25 30
426 4 s. Boxing 35 55
427 5 s. Swimming 40 60
428 7 s. Steeplechasing . . . . . . 50 1·10

1987. Medicinal Herbs. Multicoloured.
430 1 s. Type **87** 40 10
431 3 s. "Cassia didymobotrya" . . 1·10 1·00
432 5 s. "Erythrina abyssinica" . . 1·75 1·75
433 7 s. "Adenium obesum" . . . 2·25 2·50
434 10 s. Herbalist's clinic . . . . 2·50 2·75

88 "Epamera sidus" **89** "Papilio rex"

1988. Butterflies. Multicoloured.
434a 10 c. "Cyrestis camillus" . . . 90 1·50
435 20 c. Type **88** 30 70
436 40 c. "Cynthia cardui" 40 70
437 50 c. "Colotis evippe" 40 70
438 70 c. "Precis westermanni" . . 40 70
439 80 c. "Colias electo" 40 70
440 1 s. "Eronia leda" 40 30
440a 1 s. 50 "Papilio dardanus" . . 2·25 30
441 2 s. Type **89** 70 40
442 2 s. 50 "Colotis phisadia" . . . 75 90
443 3 s. "Papilio desmondi" . . . 80 90
444 3 s. 50 "Papilio demodocus" . . 80 60
445 4 s. "Papilio phorcas" 85 60
446 5 s. "Charaxes druceanus" . . . 90 70
447 7 s. "Cymothoe teita" . . . . . 1·00 1·75
448 10 s. "Charaxes zoolina" . . . 1·25 1·75
449 20 s. "Papilio dardanus" . . . 1·60 3·00
450 40 s. "Charaxes cithaeron" . . 3·00 5·50
The 10 c. to 1 s. 50 are in the same format as T **88**.

90 Samburu Lodge and Crocodiles

1988. Kenyan Game Lodges. Multicoloured.
451 1 s. Type **90** 30 10
452 3 s. Naro Moru River Lodge and rock climbing 75 60
453 4 s. Mara Serena Lodge and zebra with foal . . . . 85 1·00
454 5 s. Voi Safari Lodge and buffalo 95 1·10
455 7 s. Kilimanjaro Buffalo Lodge and giraffes . . . . 1·25 1·75
456 10 s. Meru Mulika Lodge and rhinoceroses . . . . 1·75 2·00

91 Athletes and Stadium, Commonwealth Games, Brisbane, 1982

1988. "Expo '88" World Fair, Brisbane, and Bicent of Australian Settlement. Multicoloured.

457 1 s. Type **91** 30 10
458 3 s. Flying Doctor Service De Havilland Drover 3 and Piper Twin Commanche aircraft . 1·50 1·00
459 4 s. H.M.S. "Sirius" (frigate), 1788 . . . . 1·75 1·60
460 5 s. Ostrich and emu . . . . 2·00 1·90
461 7 s. Queen Elizabeth II, Pres. Arap Moi of Kenya and Prime Minister Hawke of Australia 2·00 2·75

92 W.H.O. Logo and Slogan

1988. 40th Anniv of W.H.O.

463 **92** 1 s. blue, gold & dp blue . . 25 10
464 – 3 s. multicoloured 85 70
465 – 5 s. multicoloured . . . . . 1·25 1·25
466 – 7 s. multicoloured . . . . . 1·75 2·25

DESIGNS: 3 s. Mother with young son and nutritious food; 5 s. Giving oral vaccine to baby; 7 s. Village women drawing clean water from pump.

93 Handball

94 Calabashes

1988. Olympic Games, Seoul. Multicoloured.

467 1 s. Type **93** 20 10
468 3 s. Judo 45 40
469 5 s. Weightlifting 60 60
470 7 s. Javelin 75 85
471 10 s. Relay racing . . . . . . 90 1·25

1988. Kenyan Material Culture (1st issue). Mult.

473 1 s. Type **94** 20 10
474 3 s. Milk gourds 60 55
475 5 s. Cooking pots (horiz) . . . 70 65
476 7 s. Winnowing trays (horiz) . . 95 1·10
477 10 s. Reed baskets (horiz) . . . 1·40 1·60

See also Nos. 646/50.

95 Pres. Arap Moi taking Oath, 1978

1988. 10th Anniv of "Nyayo" Era. Mult.

479 1 s. Type **95** 25 10
480 3 s. Building soil conservation barrier 85 70
481 3 s. 50 Passengers boarding bus 1·50 1·00
482 4 s. Metalwork shop . . . . . 1·25 1·25
483 5 s. Moi University, Eldoret . . 1·25 1·25
484 7 s. Aerial view of hospital . . 2·75 3·00
485 10 s. Pres. Arap Moi and Mrs. Thatcher at Kapsabet Telephone Exchange . . . . 4·25 3·75

96 Kenya Flag

1988. 25th Anniv of Independence. Mult.

486 1 s. Type **96** 30 10
487 3 s. Coffee picking 50 50
488 5 s. Proposed Kenya Posts and Telecommunications Headquarters building . . . 95 95
489 7 s. Kenya Airways Airbus Industrie A310-300 "Harambee Star" . . . . . . 3·00 2·00
490 10 s. New diesel locomotive No. 9401 . . . . 4·25 3·50

97 Gedi Ruins, Malindi

1989. Historic Monuments. Multicoloured.

491 1 s. 20 Type **97** 30 10
492 3 s. 40 Vasco Da Gama Pillar, Malindi (vert) 85 80
493 4 s. 40 Ishiakani Monument, Kiunga 90 95
494 5 s. 50 Fort Jesus, Mombasa . . 1·25 1·40
495 7 s. 50 She Burnan Omwe, Lamu (vert) . . . . 1·75 2·25

98 125th Anniversary and Kenya Red Cross Logos

1989 125th Anniv of International Red Cross. Multicoloured.

496 1 s. 20 Type **98** 30 10
497 3 s. 40 Red Cross workers with car crash victim . . . . . . 1·00 85
498 4 s. 40 Disaster relief team distributing blankets . . . . 1·10 1·25
499 5 s. 50 Henri Dunant (founder) 1·25 1·50
500 7 s. 70 Blood donor . . . . . 1·50 2·50

99 Female Giraffe and Calf

100 "Lentinus sajor-caju"

1989. Reticulated Giraffe. Multicoloured.

501 1 s. 20 Type **99** . . . . 1·75 30
502 3 s. 40 Giraffe drinking . . . . 3·25 3·00
503 4 s. 40 Two giraffes . . . . . 3·75 3·75
504 5 s. 50 Giraffe feeding . . . . 4·50 5·00

1989. Mushrooms. Multicoloured.

506 1 s. 20 Type **100** . . . . . . 1·50 30
507 3 s. 40 "Agaricus bisporus" . . 2·25 2·00
508 4 s. 40 "Agaricus bisporus" (different) . . . . 2·50 2·50
509 5 s. 50 "Termitomyces schimperi" . . . . 3·25 3·50
510 7 s. 70 "Lentinus edodes" . . . 4·00 5·00

101 Independence Monuments

1989. Birth Centenary of Jawaharlal Nehru (Indian statesman). Multicoloured.

511 1 s. 20 Type **101** 80 30
512 3 s. 40 Nehru with graduates and open book . . . . 2·25 1·75
513 5 s. 50 Jawaharlal Nehru . . . 3·25 3·75
514 7 s. 70 Industrial complex and cogwheels . . . . 3·75 5·00

1989. Ceremonial Costumes (4th series). As T **45**. Multicoloured.

515 1 s. 20 Kipsigis 75 20
516 3 s. 40 Rabai . . . . 1·75 1·50
517 5 s. 50 Duruma . . . . 2·25 2·50
518 7 s. 70 Kuria . . . . 3·00 3·50
519 10 s. Bajuni . . . . 3·25 4·00

102 EMS Speedpost Letters and Parcel

1990. 10th Anniv of Pan African Postal Union. Multicoloured.

520 1 s. 20 Type **102** 15 10
521 3 s. 40 Mail runner 35 35
522 5 s. 50 Mandera Post Office . . 55 70
523 7 s. 70 EMS Speedpost letters and globe (vert) . . . . 80 1·60
524 10 s. P.A.P.U. logo (vert) . . . 90 1·60

103 "Stamp King" with Tweezers and Magnifying Glass

104 Moi Golden Cup

1990. "Stamp World London '90" International Stamp Exhibition.

525 **103** 1 s. 50 multicoloured . . . 35 10
526 – 4 s. 50 multicoloured . . . 1·25 1·25
527 – 6 s. 50 black, red and blue . 1·40 1·60
528 – 9 s. multicoloured . . . . 1·75 2·75

DESIGNS: 4 s. 50, Penny Black and Kenya Stamp Bureau postmark; 6 s. 50, Early British cancellations; 9 s. Ronald Ngala Street Post Office, Nairobi.

1990. World Cup Football Championship, Italy. Trophies. Multicoloured.

530 1 s. 50 Type **104** 60 10
531 4 s. 50 East and Central Africa Challenge Cup . . . . . . 1·75 1·60
532 6 s. 50 East and Central Africa Club Championship Cup . . 2·75 3·00
533 9 s. World Cup . . . . 3·00 4·00

105 K.A.N.U. Flag

1990. 30th Anniv of Kenya African National Union. Multicoloured.

534 1 s. 50 Type **105** 15 10
535 2 s. 50 Nyayo Monument . . . 15 15
536 4 s. 50 Party Headquarters . . 35 35
537 5 s. Jomo Kenyatta (Party founder) 40 40
538 6 s. 50 President Arap Moi . . 50 75
539 9 s. President Moi addressing rally . . . . 70 1·40
540 10 s. Queue of voters . . . . . 80 1·40

106 Desktop Computer

1990. 125th Anniv of I.T.U. Multicoloured.

541 1 s. 50 Type **106** 15 10
542 4 s. 50 Telephone switchboard assembly, Gilgil 35 50
543 6 s. 50 "125 YEARS" 45 80
544 9 s. Urban and rural telecommunications . . . . 70 2·00

107 Queen Mother at British Museum, 1988

108 Queen Elizabeth at Hospital Garden Party, 1947

1990. 90th Birthday of Queen Elizabeth the Queen Mother.

545 **107** 10 s. multicoloured . . . . 1·50 1·75
546 **108** 40 s. black and green . . . 3·25 4·75

109 Kenya 1988 2 s. Definitive

110 Adult Literacy Class

1990. Cent of Postage Stamps in Kenya. Mult.

547 1 s. 50 Type **109** 75 10
548 4 s. 50 East Africa and Uganda 1903 1 a . . . . 1·50 90
549 6 s. 50 British East Africa Co 1890 ½ a. optd on G.B. 1d. . 2·00 1·75
550 9 s. Kenya and Uganda 1922 20 c. . . . . 2·50 2·75
551 20 s. Kenya, Uganda, Tanzania 1971 2 s. 50 railway commemorative . . . . . . 4·25 6·50

1990. International Literacy Year. Multicoloured.

552 1 s. 50 Type **110** 30 10
553 4 s. 50 Teaching by radio . . . 1·00 90
554 6 s. 50 Technical training . . . 1·25 1·40
555 9 s. International Literacy Year logo . . . . 2·00 3·00

111 National Flag

1991. Olympic Games, Barcelona (1992) (1st issue). Multicoloured.

556 2 s. Type **111** 30 10
557 6 s. Basketball . . . . 1·75 1·25
558 7 s. Hockey . . . . 2·00 1·75
559 8 s. 50 Table tennis . . . . . 2·00 2·75
560 11 s. Boxing . . . . 2·00 3·00

See also Nos. 580/4.

112 Symbolic Man and Pointing Finger

114 Leopard

1992. AIDS Day. Multicoloured.

561 2 s. Type **112** 60 15
562 6 s. Victim and drugs . . . . . 1·50 90
563 8 s. 50 Male and female symbols 2·00 2·25
564 11 s. Symbolic figure and hypodermic syringe . . . . 2·75 3·75

1992. 40th Anniv of Queen Elizabeth II's Accession. As T **179a** of Gibraltar. Multicoloured.

565 3 s. Queen and Prince Philip with Pres. Moi 40 10
566 8 s. Marabou storks in tree . . 1·00 70
567 11 s. Treetops Hotel . . . . . 1·00 90
568 14 s. Three portraits of Queen Elizabeth . . . . 1·10 1·25
569 40 s. Queen Elizabeth II . . . 2·50 4·25

1992. Kenya Wildlife. Multicoloured.

570 3 s. Type **114** 80 30
571 8 s. Lion . . . . 1·75 1·50
572 10 s. Elephant . . . . 2·75 2·50
573 11 s. Buffalo . . . . 1·75 2·50
574 14 s. Black rhinoceros . . . . 3·50 3·50

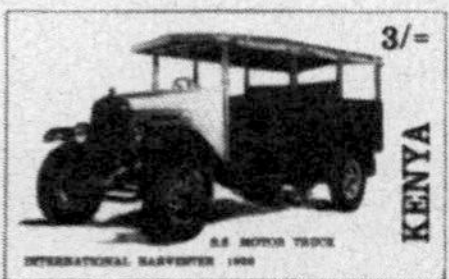

115 International Harvester Safari Truck. 1926

1992. Vintage Cars. Multicoloured.

575 3 s. Type **115** 90 20
576 8 s. Fiat "509", 1924 . . . . . 1·75 1·25
577 10 s. Hupmobile, 1923 . . . . 2·00 2·00
578 11 s. Chevrolet "Box Body", 1928 . . . . 2·00 2·00
579 14 s. Bentley/Parkward, 1934 . 2·25 2·75

116 Kenyan Athlete winning Race

1992. Olympic Games, Barcelona (2nd issue). Mult.

580 3 s. Type **116** 65 10
581 8 s. Men's judo . . . . 1·25 1·25
582 10 s. Kenyan women's volleyball players . . . . 2·00 2·00
583 11 s. Kenyan men's 4 × 100 metres relay runners . . . . 2·00 2·00
584 14 s. Men's 10,000 metres . . . 2·25 2·75

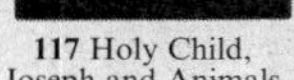
117 Holy Child, Joseph and Animals

118 Asembo Bay Lighthouse, Lake Victoria

1992. Christmas. Multicoloured.
585 3 s. Type **117** 20 10
586 8 s. Mary with Holy Child 55 50
587 11 s. Christmas tree 70 80
588 14 s. Adoration of the Magi 1·00 1·75

1993. Lighthouses. Multicoloured.
589 3 s. Type **118** 90 30
590 8 s. Old Ras Serani lighthouse, Mombasa 1·75 1·40
591 11 s. New Ras Serani lighthouse, Mombasa 2·00 2·00
592 14 s. Gingira, Lake Victoria 2·50 3·00

119 Superb Starling

120 Yellow-billed Hornbill

1993. Birds. Multicoloured. (a) As T **119**.
593 50 c. Type **119** 10 10
594 1 s. Red and yellow barbet 10 10
594a 1 s. 50 Lady Ross's turaco 10 10
595 3 s. Black-throated honeyguide ("Greater honeyguide") 10 10
595a 5 s. African fish eagle 10 10
595b 6 s. Vulturine guineafowl 10 10
596 7 s. Malachite kingfisher 15 20
597 8 s. Speckled pigeon 15 20
598 10 s. Cinnamon-chested bee eater 20 25
599 11 s. Scarlet-chested sunbird 20 25
600 14 s. Bagalafecht weaver ("Reichenow's weaver") 25 30

(b) As T **120**.
601 50 s. Type **120** 1·00 1·10
602 80 s. Lesser flamingo 1·60 1·75
603 100 s. Hadada ibis 2·00 2·10

121 Nurse bandaging Boy's Legs

123 "Ansellia africana"

122 Maendeleo House, Nairobi

1993. 17th World Congress of Rehabilitation International.
611 **121** 3 s. multicoloured 50 10
612 – 8 s. multicoloured 75 65
613 – 10 s. multicoloured 85 90
614 – 11 s. multicoloured 85 90
615 – 14 s. black, blue & orge 1·10 1·60
DESIGNS—HORIZ: 8 s. Singing group on crutches; 10 s. Vocational training; 11 s. Wheelchair race. VERT: 14 s. Congress emblem.

1994. 40th Anniv of Maendeleo Ya Wanawake Organization. Multicoloured.
616 3 s. 50 Type **122** 35 10
617 9 s. Planting saplings 60 50
618 11 s. Rural family planning clinic (vert) 70 70
619 12 s. 50 Women carrying water 85 1·25
620 15 s. 50 Improved wood-burning cooking stove (vert) 1·10 1·60

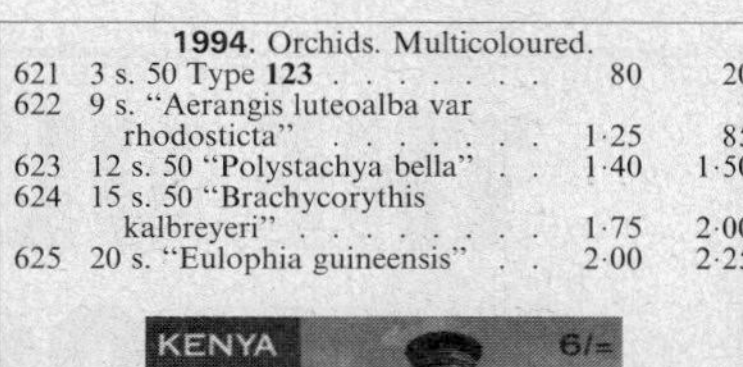
1994. Orchids. Multicoloured.
621 3 s. 50 Type **123** 80 20
622 9 s. "Aerangis luteoalba var rhodosticta" 1·25 85
623 12 s. 50 "Polystachya bella" 1·40 1·50
624 15 s. 50 "Brachycorythis kalbreyeri" 1·75 2·00
625 20 s. "Eulophia guineensis" 2·00 2·25

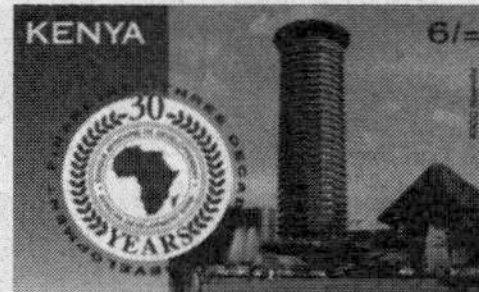

124 Emblem and K.I.C.C. Building, Nairobi

1994. 30th Anniv of African Development Bank. Multicoloured.
626 6 s. Type **124** 50 25
627 25 s. Isinya-Kajiado project 2·00 2·75

125 Kenyan Family

126 Paul Harris (founder of Rotary)

1994. International Year of the Family. Mult.
628 6 s. Type **125** 50 10
629 14 s. 50 Nurse with mother and baby 1·75 1·40
630 20 s. Schoolchildren and teacher (horiz) 2·00 2·25
631 25 s. Emblem (horiz) 2·25 2·75

1994. 50th Anniv of Rotary Club of Mombasa. Multicoloured.
632 6 s. Type **126** 25 10
633 14 s. 50 Anniversary logo 70 70
634 17 s. 50 Administering polio vaccine 1·00 1·25
635 20 s. Women at stand pipe 1·00 1·40
636 25 s. Rotary emblem 1·10 1·60

127 Donkey

128 Male Golfer in Bunker

1995. Kenya Society for Prevention of Cruelty to Animals. Multicoloured.
637 6 s. Type **127** 30 10
638 14 s. 50 Cow 45 45
639 17 s. 50 Sheep 55 75
640 20 s. Dog 1·10 1·50
641 25 s. Cat 1·25 1·75

1995. Golf. Multicoloured.
642 6 s. Type **128** 50 15
643 17 s. 50 Female golfer on fairway 1·25 1·25
644 20 s. Male golfer teeing-off 1·40 1·75
645 25 s. Head of golf club 1·60 2·00

129 Perfume Containers

1995. Kenyan Material Culture (2nd issue). Mult.
646 6 s. Type **129** 30 10
647 14 s. 50 Basketry 75 75
648 17 s. 50 Preserving pots 85 1·00
649 20 s. Gourds 1·10 1·50
650 25 s. Wooden containers 1·25 1·75

130 Tsetse Fly

131 Maize

1995. 25th Anniv of I.C.I.P.E. Insect Pests. Multicoloured.
651 14 s. Type **130** 50 30
652 26 s. Tick 80 80
653 32 s. Wild silkmoth 95 95
654 33 s. Maize borer 1·00 1·50
655 40 s. Locust 1·60 2·00

1995. 50th Anniv of F.A.O. Multicoloured.
656 14 s. Type **131** 55 30
657 28 s. Cattle 90 80
658 32 s. Chickens 1·10 1·10
659 33 s. Fisherman with catch 1·25 1·75
660 40 s. Fruit 1·75 2·50

132 Kenyan and United Nations Flags over Headquarters, Nairobi

1995. 50th Anniv of United Nations.
661 **132** 23 s. multicoloured 70 70
662 – 26 s. multicoloured 80 90
663 – 32 s. multicoloured 95 1·10
664 – 40 s. blue, red and black 1·40 2·00
DESIGNS: 26 s. Multi-racial group with emblem; 32 s. United Nations helmet; 40 s. 50th anniversary emblem.

133 Swimming

1996. Olympic Games, Atlanta (1st issue). Events and Gold Medal Winners. Multicoloured.
665 14 s. Type **133** 70 80
666 20 s. Archery 70 80
667 20 s. Weightlifting 70 80
668 20 s. Pole vault (vert) 70 80
669 20 s. Equestrian (vert) 70 80
670 20 s. Diving (vert) 70 80
671 20 s. Sprinting (vert) 70 80
672 20 s. Athlete carrying Olympic Torch (vert) 70 80
673 20 s. Hurdling (vert) 70 80
674 20 s. Kayak (vert) 70 80
675 20 s. Boxing (vert) 70 80
676 20 s. Gymnastics (vert) 70 80
677 25 s. Greg Louganis (U.S.A.) (diving, 1984 and 1988) (vert) 70 80
678 25 s. Cassius Clay (U.S.A.) (boxing, 1960) (vert) 70 80
679 25 s. Nadia Comaneci (Rumania) (gymnastics, 1980) (vert) 70 80
680 25 s. Daley Thompson (Great Britain) (decathlon, 1980 and 1984) (vert) 70 80
681 25 s. Kipchoge Keino (Kenya) (running, 1968) (vert) 70 80
682 25 s. Kornelia Enders (Germany) (swimming, 1976) (vert) 70 80
683 25 s. Jackie Joyner-Kersee (U.S.A.) (long jump, 1988) (vert) 70 80
684 25 s. Michael Jordan (U.S.A.) (basketball, 1984) (vert) 70 80
685 25 s. Shun Fujimoto (Japan) (gymnastics, 1972) (vert) 70 80
686 32 s. Javelin 70 80
687 40 s. Fencing 80 85
688 50 s. Discus 1·00 1·10
Nos. 665/7 with 686/8, 668/76 and 677/85 respectively were printed together, se-tenant, forming composite designs.
See also Nos. 702/6.

134 Lions

135 Water Buck

1996. Tourism. Multicoloured. (a) Designs as T **134**.
690 6 s. Type **134** 30 10
691 14 s. Mt. Kenya 35 30
692 20 s. Sail boards 55 70
693 25 s. Hippopotami 1·00 1·40
694 40 s. Couple in traditional dress 1·25 2·00

(b) Horiz designs as T **135**.
696 20 s. Type **135** 70 90
697 20 s. Pair of rhinoceroses 70 90
698 20 s. Cheetah 70 90
699 20 s. Group of oryx 70 90
700 20 s. Pair of giraffes 70 90
701 20 s. Monkey and bongo 70 90

136 Women's 10,000 Metres

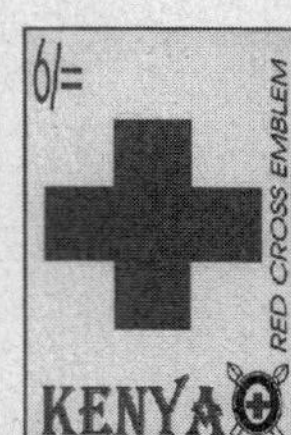

137 Red Cross Emblem

1996. Olympic Games, Atlanta (2nd issue). Multicoloured.
702 6 s. Type **136** 25 10
703 14 s. Steeple-chasing 45 30
704 20 s. Victorious athletes with flag 70 80
705 25 s. Boxing 70 1·00
706 40 s. Men's 1500 metres 1·25 2·00

1996. Kenya Red Cross Society.
707 **137** 6 s. red and black 25 10
708 – 14 s. multicoloured 45 35
709 – 20 s. multicoloured 70 80
710 – 25 s. multicoloured 80 95
711 – 40 s. multicoloured 1·40 2·00
DESIGNS: 14 s. Giving blood; 20 s. Immunization; 25 s. Refugee child with food; 40 s. Cleaning the environment.

138 Impala

139 Kenya Lions Club Logo

1996. East African Wildlife Society. Multicoloured.
712 6 s. Type **138** 20 10
713 20 s. Colobus monkey 60 60
714 25 s. African elephant 1·10 1·25
715 40 s. Black rhinoceros 1·75 2·25

1996. Work of Lions Club International in Kenya. Multicoloured.
716 6 s. Type **139** 15 10
717 14 s. Eye operation 45 45
718 20 s. Two disabled children in wheelchair 70 80
719 25 s. Modern ambulance 80 1·00

140 C.O.M.E.S.A. Logo

1997. Inauguration of Common Market for Eastern and Southern Africa. Multicoloured.
720 6 s. Type **140** 15 15
721 20 s. Kenyan flag and logo 70 95

141 "Haplochromis cinctus"

1997. Endangered Species. Lake Victoria Cichlid Fishes. Multicoloured.
722 25 s. Type **141** 75 90
723 25 s. "Haplochromis" "Orange Rock Hunter" 75 90
724 25 s. "Haplochromis chilotes" 75 90
725 25 s. "Haplochromis nigricans" 75 90

142 Class 94 Diesel-electric Locomotive No. 9401, 1981

1997. Kenya Railway Locomotives. Multicoloured.

726	6 s. Type **142**	25	15
727	14 s. Class 87 diesel-electric No. 8721, 1964	45	40
728	20 s. Class 59 Garratt steam No. 5905, 1955	65	60
729	25 s. Class 57 Garratt steam No. 5701, 1939	70	70
730	30 s. Class 23 steam No. 2305, 1923	75	90
731	40 s. Class 10 steam No. 1001, 1914	90	1·40

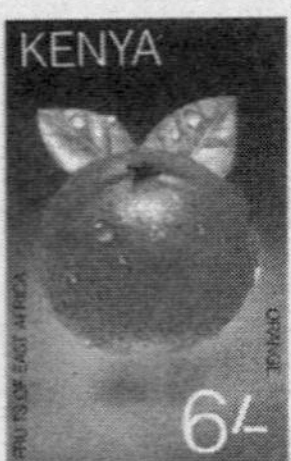

143 Orange

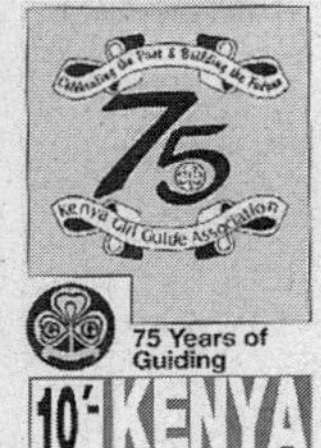

145 Girl Guides Anniversary Logo

144 Crocodile

1997. Fruits of East Africa. Multicoloured.

732	6 s. Type **143**	35	15
733	14 s. Pineapple	55	45
734	20 s. Mango	80	90
735	25 s. Pawpaw	85	1·00

1997. Local Tourist Attractions. Multicoloured.

736	10 s. Type **144**	55	25
737	27 s. Lake Bogoria hot springs	95	90
738	30 s. Warthogs	1·00	1·00
739	33 s. Windsurfing	1·25	1·40
740	42 s. Traditional huts	1·50	2·00

1997. 75th Anniv of Kenyan Girl Guides Anniversary. Multicoloured.

741	10 s. Type **145**	30	35
742	10 s. Lord Baden Powell	30	35
743	27 s. Girl guides hiking	70	75
744	27 s. Rangers in camp	70	75
745	33 s. Girl guides planting seedlings	80	90
746	33 s. Boy scouts giving first aid	80	90
747	42 s. Boy scouts in camp	90	1·00
748	42 s. Brownies entertaining the elderly	90	1·00

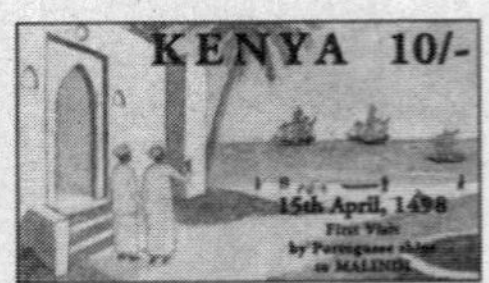

146 Portuguese Ships arriving at Malinda

1998. 500th Anniv of Vasco da Gama's Arrival at Malinda. Multicoloured.

749	10 s. Type **146**	30	25
750	24 s. Portuguese ships	70	70
751	33 s. Map of Africa	90	1·10
752	42 s. Vasco da Gama Pillar and harbour	1·00	1·40

147 Lion

1998. 18th Anniv of Pan African Postal Union. Wildlife. Multicoloured.

753	10 s. Type **147**	40	25
754	24 s. Buffalo	80	70
755	35 s. Grant's gazelle	1·00	1·10
756	42 s. Cheetah	1·75	2·00

148 Pres. Arap Moi taking Oath, 1998

1998. Daniel Arap Moi's 5th Presidential Term.

758	**148**	14 s. multicoloured	40	40

OFFICIAL STAMPS

Intended for use on official correspondence of the Kenya Government only, but there is no evidence that they were so used.

1964. Stamps of 1963 optd **OFFICIAL**.

O21	**46**	5 c. multicoloured	10
O22	–	10 c. brown	10
O23	–	15 c. mauve	1·25
O24	–	20 c. black and green	20
O25	–	30 c. black and yellow	30
O26	–	50 c. red, black and green	2·75

POSTAGE DUE STAMPS

D 3

1967.

D13	D 3	5 c. red	15	2·50
D41		10 c. green	30	75
D42		20 c. blue	30	75
D44		30 c. brown	15	50
D45		40 c. purple	15	50
D49		50 c. green	10	10
D46		80 c. red	20	55
D50		1 s. orange	10	10
D51		2 s. violet	10	10
D52		3 s. blue	10	10
D53		5 s. red	10	10

KENYA, UGANDA AND TANGANYIKA (TANZANIA) Pt. 1

From 1903 joint issues were made for British East Africa (later Kenya) and Uganda. In 1933 the postal administrations of Kenya, Uganda and Tanganyika were combined.

On independence of the constituent territories in the 1960s the postal administration became the East African Posts and Telecommunications Corporation. As well as separate issues for each state (q.v.), joint commemorative issues (which however were not valid in Zanzibar) were made until the dissolution of the Corporation in 1977.

1903. 16 annas = 100 cents = 1 rupee.
1922. 100 cents = 1 shilling.

1

2

1903.
17a 1 ½ a. green . . . . 4·50 3·00
2 1 a. grey and red . . . . . . 1·75 50
19a 2 a. purple . . . . 2·50 2·25
21 2½ a. blue . . . . 7·50 17·00
22a 3 a. purple and green . . . 3·75 26·00
23 4 a. green and black . . . 7·50 18·00
24 5 a. grey and brown . . . 8·00 15·00
25 8 a. grey and blue . . . 7·00 8·50
9 2 1 r. green . . . . 16·00 50·00
27 2 r. purple . . . . 38·00 55·00
28 3 r. green and black . . . 55·00 95·00
29 4 r. grey and green . . . 60·00 £130
30 5 r. grey and red . . . 70·00 £100
31 10 r. grey and blue . . . £140 £160
15 20 r. grey and stone . . . £450 £900
16 50 r. grey and brown . . . £1100 £2000

1907.
34 1 1 c. brown . . . . 2·00 15
35 3 c. green . . . . 8·00 50
36 6 c. red . . . . 2·75 10
37 10 c. lilac and olive . . . 9·00 8·50
38 12 c. purple . . . . 9·00 2·75
39 15 c. blue . . . . 12·00 8·50
40 25 c. green and black . . . 6·00 7·00
41 50 c. green and brown . . . 12·00 12·00
42 75 c. grey and blue . . . 4·50 32·00

1912. As T **1/2** but portraits of King George V.
44 1 c. black . . . . 30 1·75
45 3 c. green . . . . 2·00 60
46 6 c. red 70 60
47 10 c. orange . . . . 2·00 40
48 12 c. grey . . . . 2·75 50
49 15 c. blue . . . . 2·75 80
50 25 c. black & red on yellow . . 45 1·25
51 50 c. black and lilac . . . 1·50 1·25
52b 75 c. black and green . . . 6·00 7·00
53 1 r. black and green . . . 1·75 4·00
54 2 r. red and black on blue . . 20·00 35·00
55 3 r. violet and green . . . 20·00 70·00
56 4 r. red and green on yellow . . 45·00 £100
57 5 r. blue and purple . . . 48·00 £120
58 10 r. red and green on green . . 85·00 £150
59 20 r. black & purple on red . . £275 £300
60 20 r. purple & blue on blue . . £300 £325
61 50 r. red and green . . . £500 £600
62 100 r. purple & black on red . . £3500 £2250
63 500 r. green & red on green . . £15000

1919. No. 46 surch **4 cents**.
64 4 c. on 6 c. red 85 15

6

7

1922.
76 6 1 c. brown . . . . 80 2·50
77 5 c. violet . . . . 3·25 75
78 5 c. green . . . . 2·00 30
79 10 c. green . . . . 1·50 30
80 10 c. black . . . . 4·00 20
81a 12 c. black . . . . 3·25 26·00
82 15 c. red . . . . 1·25 10
83 20 c. orange . . . . 3·25 10
84 30 c. blue . . . . 2·00 50
85 50 c. grey . . . . 2·50 10
86 75 c. olive . . . . 3·00 9·00
87 7 1 s. green . . . . 3·75 2·50
88 2 s. purple . . . . 8·00 9·00
89 2 s. 50 brown . . . . . . 18·00 65·00
90 3 s. grey . . . . 17·00 6·50
91 4 s. grey . . . . 20·00 75·00
92 5 s. red . . . . 22·00 20·00
93 7 s. 50 orange . . . . . . 60·00 £140
94 10 s. blue . . . . 48·00 48·00
95 £1 black and orange . . . £140 £200
96 £2 green and purple . . . £600
97 £3 purple and yellow . . . £750
98 £4 black and mauve . . . £1400
99 £5 black and blue . . . £1700
100 £10 black and green . . . £7500
101 £20 red and green . . . £15000
102 £25 black and red . . . £18000
103 £50 black and brown . . . £25000
104 £75 purple and grey . . . £55000
105 £100 red and black . . . £55000

8 South African Crowned Cranes

9 Dhow on Lake Victoria

1935. King George V.
110 8 1 c. black and brown . . . 50 1·50
111 9 5 c. black and green . . . 1·75 60
112 – 10 c. black and yellow . . . 3·00 60
113 – 15 c. black and red . . . 1·25 10
114 8 20 c. black and orange . . . 2·00 20
115 – 30 c. black and blue . . . 2·00 1·50
116 9 50 c. purple and black . . . 1·75 10
117 – 65 c. black and brown . . . 2·75 2·00
118 – 1 s. black and green . . . 1·00 65
119 – 2 s. red and purple . . . 4·50 4·00
120 – 3 s. blue and black . . . 6·50 15·00
121 – 5 s. black and red . . . 17·00 27·00
122 8 10 s. purple and blue . . . 50·00 75·00
123 – £1 black and red . . . £120 £140
DESIGNS—VERT: 10 c., £1 Lion; 30 c., 5 s. Nile Railway Bridge, Ripon Falls. HORIZ: 15 c., 2 s. Kilimanjaro; 65 c. Mt. Kenya; 1 s., 3 s. Lake Naivasha.

1935. Silver Jubilee. As T **10a** of Gambia.
124 20 c. blue and olive . . . 50 10
125 30 c. brown and blue . . . 2·50 3·50
126 65 c. green and blue . . . 1·75 2·75
127 1 s. grey and purple . . . 2·00 2·50

1937. Coronation. As T **10b** of Gambia.
128 5 c. green 20 10
129 20 c. orange 40 30
130 30 c. blue . . . . 60 1·25

15 Dhow on Lake Victoria

1938. As 1935 (except 10 c.) but with portrait of King George VI as in T **15**.
131a 8 1 c. black and brown . . . 30 40
132 15 5 c. black and green . . . 2·75 50
133 5 c. brown and orange . . . 40 3·00
134 – 10 c. brown and orange . . . 1·75 10
135 – 10 c. black and green . . . 30 85
136 – 10 c. brown and grey . . . 75 55
137a – 15 c. black and red . . . 3·75 3·75
138 – 15 c. black and green . . . 1·60 3·00
139b 8 20 c. black and orange . . . 6·00 10
140 15 25 c. black and red . . . 1·25 2·25
141b – 30 c. black and blue . . . 2·75 10
142 – 30 c. purple and brown . . . 1·50 40
143 8 40 c. black and blue . . . 1·75 3·00
144e 15 50 c. purple and black . . . 7·00 55
145a – 1 s. black and brown . . . 9·50 30
146b – 2 s. red and purple . . . 15·00 30
147ab – 3 s. blue and black . . . 23·00 2·00
148b – 5 s. black and red . . . 23·00 1·00
149b 8 10 s. purple and blue . . . 30·00 3·00
150a – £1 black and red . . . 17·00 15·00
DESIGN—HORIZ: 10 c. Lake Naivasha.

1941. Stamps of South Africa surch **KENYA TANGANYIKA UGANDA** and value. Alternate stamps inscr in English or Afrikaans.
151 7 5 c. on 1d. black and red . . 60 15
152 22a 10 c. on 3d. blue . . . . 1·00 30
153 8 20 c. on 6d. green & red . . 1·00 20
154 – 70 c. on 1s. brown and blue (No. 120) . . . . . . 9·50 40
Prices for Nos. 151/4 are for unused pairs and used singles.

1946. Victory. As T **11a** of Gambia.
155 20 c. orange 30 10
156 30 c. blue 30 50

1948. Silver Wedding. As T **11b/11c** of Gambia.
157 20 c. orange 15 10
158 £1 red . . . . 35·00 50·00

1949. U.P.U. As T **11d/11g** of Gambia.
159 20 c. orange 20 10
160 30 c. blue . . . . 1·50 1·25
161 50 c. grey 75 20
162 1 s. brown 75 40

1952. Visit of Queen Elizabeth II (as Princess) and Duke of Edinburgh. As Nos. 135 and 145ba but inscr "ROYAL VISIT 1952".
163 10 c. black and green . . . 10 1·50
164 1 s. black and brown . . . 20 1·75

1953. Coronation. As T **11h** of Gambia.
165 20 c. black and orange . . . 15 10

1954. Royal Visit. As No. 171 but inscr "ROYAL VISIT 1954".
166 18 30 c. black and blue . . . 20 15

18 Owen Falls Dam

21 Queen Elizabeth II

20 Royal Lodge, Sagana

1954.
167 18 5 c. black and brown . . . 40 50
168 – 10 c. red 75 10
169a – 15 c. black and blue . . . 55 1·00
170 – 20 c. black and orange . . . 80 10
171 18 30 c. black and blue . . . 80 10
172 – 40 c. brown . . . . . . 2·50 75
173 – 50 c. purple . . . . . . 1·50 10
174 – 65 c. green and purple . . . 2·75 1·50
175 – 1 s. black and purple . . . 1·25 10
176 – 1 s. 30 lilac and orange . . . 8·00 10
177 – 2 s. black and green . . . 5·00 80
178 – 5 s. black and orange . . . 14·00 1·50
179 20 10 s. black and blue . . . 20·00 2·25
180 21 £1 red and black . . . 16·00 11·00
DESIGNS—VERT (Size as Type **18**): 10 c., 50 c. Giraffe; 20 c., 40 c., 1 s. Lion. HORIZ: 1 c., 1 s. 30, 5 s. Elephants; 65 c., 2 s. Mount Kilimanjaro.

25 Map of E. Africa showing Lakes

1958. Cent of Discovery of Lakes Tanganyika and Victoria by Burton and Speke.
181 25 40 c. blue and green . . . 30 40
182 1 s. 30 green and purple . . 30 1·40

26 Sisal

29 Queen Elizabeth II

28 Mt. Kenya and Giant Plants

1960.
183 26 5 c. blue 10 15
184 – 10 c. green 10 10
185 – 15 c. purple 30 10
186 – 20 c. mauve 20 10
187 – 25 c. green . . . . 3·25 1·00
188 – 30 c. red 15 10
189 – 40 c. blue 15 10
190 – 50 c. violet 15 10
191 – 65 c. olive 30 75
192 28 1 s. violet and purple . . . 80 10
193 – 1 s. 30 brown and red . . . 2·50 15
194 – 2 s. indigo and blue . . . 2·50 30
195 – 2 s. 50 olive & turquoise . . 4·00 2·75
196 – 5 s. red and purple . . . 3·75 60
197 – 10 s. myrtle and green . . . 8·00 6·50
198 29 20 s. blue and lake . . . 16·00 17·00
DESIGNS—As Type **26**: 10 c. Cotton; 15 c. Coffee; 20 c. Blue wildebeest; 25 c. Ostrich; 30 c. Thomson's gazelle; 40 c. Manta; 50 c. Common zebra; 65 c. Cheetah. As Type **28**: 1 s. 30, Murchison Falls and hippopotamus; 2 s. Mt. Kilimanjaro and giraffe; 2 s. 50, Candelabra tree and black rhinoceros; 5 s. Crater Lake and Mountains of the Moon; 10 s. Ngorongoro Crater and African buffalo.

30 Land Tillage

1963. Freedom from Hunger.
199 30 15 c. blue and olive . . . 10 10
200 – 30 c. brown and yellow . . 20 10
201 30 50 c. blue and orange . . . 30 10
202 – 1 s. 30 brown and blue . . . 55 1·75
DESIGN: 30 c., 1 s. 30, African with corncob.

31 Scholars and Open Book

1963. Founding of East African University.
203 31 30 c. multicoloured . . . 10 10
204 1 s. 30 multicoloured . . . 20 20

32 Red Cross Emblem

1963. Centenary of Red Cross.
205 32 30 c. red and blue . . . 1·00 10
206 50 c. red and brown . . . 1·25 55

35 East African "Flags"

1964. Olympic Games, Tokyo.
207 – 30 c. yellow and purple . . 10 10
208 – 50 c. purple and yellow . . 15 10
209 35 1 s. 30 yellow, green & blue . 30 10
210 2 s. 50 mauve, violet & bl . . 40 1·40
DESIGN—VERT: 30 c., 50 c. Chrysanthemum emblem.

36 Rally Badge

1965. 13th East African Safari Rally.
211 36 30 c. black, yellow & turq . . 10 10
212 50 c. black, yellow & brn . . 10 10
213 – 1 s. 30 green, ochre & blue . . 25 10
214 – 2 s. 50 green, red and blue . . 40 1·50
DESIGN: 1 s. 30, 2 s. 50, Cars en route.

38 I.T.U. Emblem and Symbols

1965. Centenary of I.T.U. "I.T.U." and symbols in gold.
215 38 30 c. brown and mauve . . 20 10
216 50 c. brown and grey . . . 20 10
217 1 s. 30 brown and blue . . . 55 10
218 2 s. 50 brown and turquoise . 1·00 2·25

39 I.C.Y. Emblem

1965. International Co-operation Year.
219 39 30 c. green and gold . . . 10 10
220 50 c. black and gold . . . 15 10
221 1 s. 30 blue and gold . . . 30 10
222 2 s. 50 red and gold . . . 75 2·50

40 Game Park Lodge, Tanzania

1966. Tourism. Multicoloured.
223 30 c. Type **40** 15 10
224 50 c. Murchison Falls, Uganda 50 10
225 1 s. 30 Lesser flamingoes, Lake Nakuru, Kenya . . . . . . 2·25 30
226 2 s. 50 Deep sea fishing, Tanzania . . . . 2·00 3·00

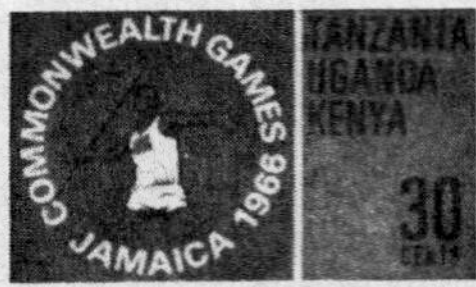

41 Games Emblem

1966. 8th British Empire and Commonwealth Games, Jamaica.
227 **41** 30 c. multicoloured 10 10
228 50 c. multicoloured 15 10
229 1 s. 30 multicoloured . . . 20 10
230 2 s. 50 multicoloured . . . 35 1·50

42 U.N.E.S.C.O. Emblem

1966. 20th Anniv of U.N.E.S.C.O.
231 **42** 30 c. black, green & red . . 25 10
232 50 c. black, green & brn . . 35 10
233 1 s. 30 black, green & grey . 85 15
234 2 s. 50 black, green & yell . 1·50 3·00

43 De Havilland Dragon Rapide

1967. 21st Anniv of East African Airways.
235 **43** 30 c. violet, blue and green . 30 10
236 – 50 c. multicoloured 40 10
237 – 1 s. 30 multicoloured 85 30
238 – 2 s. 50 multicoloured . . . 1·25 3·00
DESIGNS: 50 c. Vickers Super VC-10; 1 s. 30, Hawker Siddeley Comet 4B; 2 s. 50, Fokker Friendship.

44 Pillar Tomb

1967. Archaeological Relics.
239 **44** 30 c. ochre, black & purple . 15 10
240 – 50 c. red, black & brown . . 65 10
241 – 1 s. 30 black, yellow & grn . 85 15
242 – 2 s. 50 black, ochre & red . 1·40 3·00
DESIGNS: 50 c. Rock painting; 1 s. 30, Clay head; 2 s. 50, Proconsul skull.

48 Unified Symbols of Kenya, Tanzania, and Uganda.

1967. Foundation of East African Community.
243 **48** 5 s. gold, black and grey . . 40 1·25

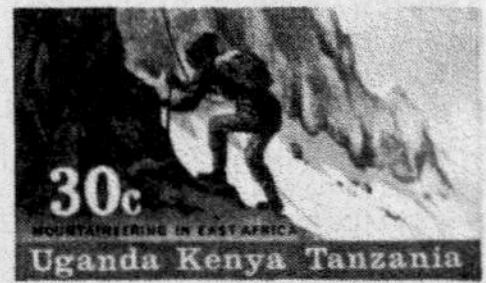

49 Mountaineering

1968. Mountains of East Africa. Multicoloured.
244 30 c. Type **49** 15 10
245 50 c. Mount Kenya 30 10
246 1 s. 30 Mount Kilimanjaro . . 60 10
247 2 s. 50 Ruwenzori Mountains . 90 2·25

50 Family and Rural Hospital

1968. World Health Organization.
248 **50** 30 c. green, lilac & brown . . 10 10
249 – 50 c. slate, lilac and black . . 15 10
250 – 1 s. 30 brown, lilac & lt brown 20 15
251 – 2 s. 50 grey, black & lilac . . 30 1·90
DESIGNS: 50 c. Family and nurse; 1 s. 30, Family and microscope; 2 s. 50, Family and hypodermic syringe.

51 Olympic Stadium, Mexico City

1968. Olympic Games, Mexico.
252 **51** 30 c. green and black . . . 10 10
253 – 50 c. green and black . . . 15 10
254 – 1 s. 30 red, black & grey . . 25 15
255 – 2 s. 50 sepia and brown . . 35 1·50
DESIGNS—HORIZ: 50 c. High-diving boards; 1 s. 30, Running tracks. VERT: 2 s. 50, Boxing ring.

52 "Umoja" (railway ferry)

1969. Water Transport.
256 **52** 30 c. blue and grey 40 10
257 – 50 c. multicoloured 45 10
258 – 1 s. 30 green and blue . . . 85 20
259 – 2 s. 50 orange and blue . . 1·40 3·25
DESIGNS: 50 c. S.S. "Harambee"; 1 s. 30, M.V. "Victoria"; 2 s. 50, "St. Michael".

53 I.L.O. Emblem and Agriculture

1969. 50th Anniv of Int Labour Organization.
260 **53** 30 c. black, green & yellow . 10 10
261 – 50 c. multicoloured 10 10
262 – 1 s. 30 black, brown and orange 10 10
263 – 2 s. 50 black, blue & turq . . 20 90
DESIGNS—I.L.O. emblem and: 50 c. Building-work; 1 s. 30, Factory-workers; 2 s. 50, Shipping.

54 Pope Paul VI and Ruwenzori Mountains

55 Euphorbia Tree shaped as Africa, and Emblem

1969. Visit of Pope Paul VI to Uganda.
264 **54** 30 c. black, gold and blue . 15 10
265 70 c. black, gold and red . . 20 10
266 1 s. 50 black, gold & blue . . 25 20
267 2 s. 50 black, gold & violet . 30 1·40

1969. 5th Anniv of African Development Bank.
268 **55** 30 c. green and gold 10 10
269 70 c. green, gold & violet . . 15 10
270 1 s. 50 green, gold & blue . . 30 10
271 2 s. 50 green, gold & brown 35 1·00

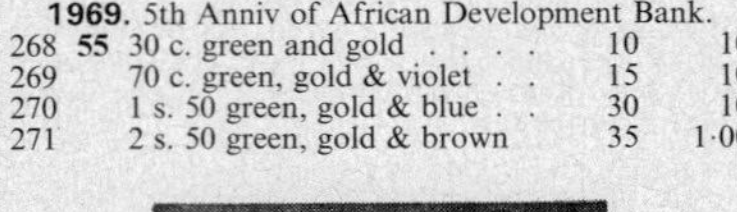

56 Marimba

1970. Musical Instruments.
272 **56** 30 c. buff and brown . . . 15 10
273 – 70 c. green, brown & yell . . 25 10
274 – 1 s. 50 brown & yellow . . . 50 10
275 – 2 s. 50 orange, yellow & brn 75 2·25
DESIGNS: 70 c. Amadinda; 1 s. 50, Nzomari; 2 s. 50, Adeudeu.

57 Satellite Earth Station

1970. Inauguration of Satellite Earth Station.
276 **57** 30 c. multicoloured 10 10
277 – 70 c. multicoloured 15 10
278 – 1 s. 50 black, violet & orge 25 10
279 – 2 s. 50 multicoloured . . . 55 2·25
DESIGNS: 70 c. Transmitter—daytime; 1 s. 50, Transmitter—night; 2 s 50, Earth and satellite.

58 Athlete

1970. 9th Commonwealth Games.
280 **58** 30 c. brown and black . . . 10 10
281 70 c. green, brown and black 10 10
282 1 s. 50 lilac, brown and black 15 10
283 2 s. 50 blue, brown and black 20 1·25

59 "25" and U.N. Emblem

1970. 25th Anniversary of United Nations.
284 **59** 30 c. multicoloured 10 10
285 70 c. multicoloured 10 10
286 1 s. 50 multicoloured . . . 20 10
287 2 s. 50 multicoloured . . . 45 2·00

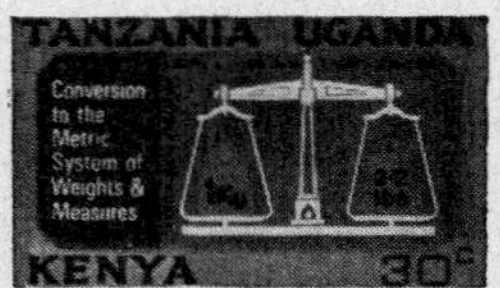

60 Balance and Weight Equivalents

1970. Conversion to Metric System. Multicoloured.
288 30 c. Type **60** 10 10
289 70 c. Fahrenheit and Centigrade thermometers 10 10
290 1 s. 50 Petrol pump and liquid capacities 15 10
291 2 s. 50 Surveyors and land measures . . . . 35 2·00

61 Class 11 Tank Locomotive

1971. Railway Transport. Multicoloured.
292 30 c. Type **61** 35 10
293 70 c. Class 90 diesel-electric locomotive 55 10
294 1 s. 50 Class 59 steam locomotive 1·00 30
295 2 s. 50 Class 30 steam locomotive 1·75 2·75

62 Syringe and Cow

1971. O.A.U. Rinderpest Campaign.
297 **62** 30 c. black, brown & grn . . 10 10
298 – 70 c. black, blue & brown . 10 10
299 **62** 1 s. 50 black, purple & brn . 15 10
300 – 2 s. 50 black, red & brown . 25 70
DESIGN: 70 c., 2 s 50, As Type **62** but with bull facing right.

63 Livingstone meets Stanley

1971. Centenary of Livingstone and Stanley meeting at Ujiji.
301 **63** 5 s. multicoloured 30 75

64 Pres. Nyerere and Supporters

1971. 10th Anniv of Tanzanian Independence. Multicoloured.
302 30 c. Type **64** 10 10
303 70 c. Ujamaa village 15 10
304 1 s. 50 Dar-es-Salaam University 30 25
305 2 s. 50 Kilimanjaro International Airport . . . . 1·00 3·25

65 Flags and Trade Fair Emblem

1972. All-Africa Trade Fair.
306 **65** 30 c. multicoloured 10 10
307 70 c. multicoloured 10 10
308 1 s. 50 multicoloured . . . 10 10
309 2 s. 50 multicoloured . . . 25 80

66 Child with Cup

1972. 25th Anniv of U.N.I.C.E.F. Multicoloured.
310 30 c. Type **66** 10 10
311 70 c. Children with ball 10 10
312 1 s. 50 Child at blackboard . . 10 10
313 2 s. 50 Child and tractor . . . 25 80

67 Hurdling

1972. Olympic Games, Munich. Multicoloured.
314 40 c. Type **67** 10 10
315 70 c. Running 10 10
316 1 s. 50 Boxing 20 15
317 2 s. 50 Hockey . . . . 30 1·75

68 Ugandan Kobs

1972. 10th Anniv of Ugandan Independence. Multicoloured.
319 40 c. Type **68** 30 10
320 70 c. Conference Centre . . . 30 10
321 1 s. 50 Makerere University . . 65 30
322 2 s. 50 Coat of arms . . . . . 1·00 3·25

69 Community Flag

1972. 5th Anniv of East African Community.
324 **69** 5 s. multicoloured . . . . . 55 1·60

70 Run-of-the-wind Anemometer

1972. Centenary of IMO/WMO. Multicoloured.
325 40 c. Type **70** 10 10
326 70 c. Weather balloon (vert) 15 10
327 1 s. 50 Meteorological rocket 25 15
328 2 s. 50 Satellite receiving aerial 55 2·25

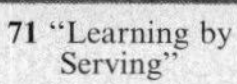
71 "Learning by Serving" **73** Police Dog-handler

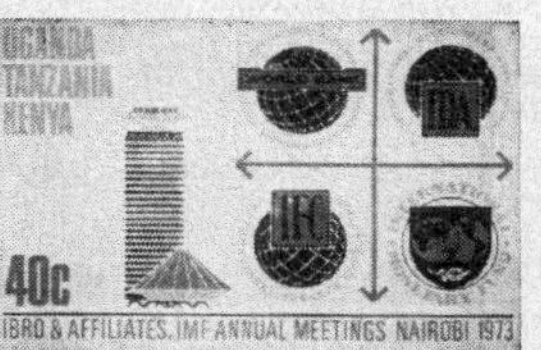

72 Kenyatta Conference Centre

1973. 24th World Scouting Conference, Nairobi.
329 **71** 40 c. multicoloured 15 10
330 – 70 c. red, violet & black 20 10
331 – 1 s. 50 blue, violet & black 45 30
332 – 2 s. 50 multicoloured 1·00 2·25
DESIGN: 70 c. Baden-Powell's grave, Nyeri; 1 s. 50, World Scout emblem; 2 s. 50, Lord Baden-Powell.

1973. I.M.F./World Bank Conference.
333 **72** 40 c. green, grey & black 10 10
334 – 70 c. brown, grey & black 10 10
335 – 1 s. 50 multicoloured 25 35
336 – 2 s. 50 orange, grey & black 35 1·75
DESIGNS: Nos. 334/6 show different arrangements of Bank emblems and the Conference Centre, the 1 s. 50 being vertical.

1973. 50th Anniv of Interpol.
338 **73** 40 c. yellow, blue & black 55 15
339 – 70 c. green, yellow & blk 90 15
340 – 1 s. 50 violet, yellow & blk 1·50 90
341 – 2 s. 50 green, orange & blk 3·75 6·00
342 – 2 s. 50 green, orange & blk 3·75 6·00
DESIGNS: 70 c. East African policemen; 1 s. 50, Interpol emblem; 2 s. 50 (2), Interpol H.Q. No. 341 is inscribed "St. Clans" and No. 342 "St. Cloud".

74 Tea Factory

1973. 10th Anniv of Kenya's Independence. Mult.
343 40 c. Type **74** 10 10
344 70 c. Kenyatta Hospital 15 10
345 1 s. 50 Nairobi Airport 50 20
346 2 s. 50 Kindaruma hydro-electric scheme 65 1·75

75 Party H.Q.

1973. 10th Anniv of Zanzibar's Revolution. Mult.
347 40 c. Type **75** 10 10
348 70 c. Housing scheme 15 10
349 1 s. 50 Colour T.V. 35 30
350 2 s. 50 Amaan Stadium 70 2·50

76 "Symbol of Union"

1974. 10th Anniv of Tanganyika–Zanzibar Union. Multicoloured.
351 40 c. Type **76** 10 10
352 70 c. Handclasp and map 15 10
353 1 s. 50 "Communications" 35 30
354 2 s. 50 Flags of Tanu, Tanzania and Afro-Shirazi Party 70 2·50

77 East African Family ("Stability of the Home")

1974. 17th Social Welfare Conference, Nairobi.
355 **77** 40 c. yellow, brown & blk 10 10
356 – 70 c. multicoloured 10 10
357 – 1 s. 50 yellow, green & blk 20 30
358 – 2 s. 50 red, violet & black 1·00 2·00
DESIGNS: 70 c. Dawn and drummer (U.N. Second Development Plan); 1 s. 50, Agricultural scene (Rural Development Plan); 2 s. 50, Transport and telephone ("Communications").

78 New Postal H.Q., Kampala

1974. Centenary of U.P.U. Multicoloured.
359 40 c. Type **78** 10 10
360 70 c. Mail-train and post-van 20 10
361 1 s. 50 U.P.U. Building, Berne 15 20
362 2 s. 50 Loading mail into Vickers Super VC-10 55 1·50

79 Family-planning Clinic

1974. World Population Year.
363 **79** 40 c. multicoloured 10 10
364 – 70 c. mauve and red 10 10
365 – 1 s. 50 multicoloured 15 20
366 – 2 s. 50 blue, emerald and green 30 1·90
DESIGNS: 70 c. "Tug of War"; 1 s. 50, "Population scales"; 2 s. 50, W.P.Y. emblem.

80 Seronera Wildlife Lodge, Tanzania

1975. East African Game Lodges. Multicoloured.
367 40 c. Type **80** 15 10
368 70 c. Mweya Safari Lodge, Uganda 20 10
369 1 s. 50 "Ark"—Aberdare Forest Lodge, Kenya 35 30
370 2 s. 50 Paraa Safari Lodge, Uganda 80 2·25

81 Kitana (wooden comb), Bajun of Kenya **83** Ahmed ("Presidential" Elephant)

82 International Airport, Entebbe

1975. African Arts. Multicoloured.
371 50 c. Type **81** 10 10
372 1 s. Earring, Chaga of Tanzania 15 10
373 2 s. Okoco (armlet), Acholi of Uganda 35 70
374 3 s. Kitete, Kamba gourd, Kenya 65 1·40

1975. O.A.U. Summit Conf, Kampala. Mult.
375 50 c. Type **82** 30 10
376 1 s. Map of Africa and flag (vert) 30 10
377 2 s. Nile Hotel, Kampala 30 85
378 3 s. Martyrs' Shrine, Namugongo (vert) 40 1·60

1975. Rare Animals. Multicoloured.
379 50 c. Type **83** 50 10
380 1 s. Albino buffalo 50 10
381 2 s. Ahmed in grounds of National Museum 1·60 1·50
382 3 s. Abbott's duiker 1·60 3·00

84 Maasai Manyatta (village), Kenya

1975. 2nd World Black and African Festival of Arts and Culture, Nigeria (1977). Multicoloured.
383 50 c. Type **84** 15 10
384 1 s. "Heartbeat of Africa" (Ugandan Dancers) 15 10
385 2 s. Makonde sculpture, Tanzania 50 85
386 3 s. "Early Man and Technology" (Skinning animal) 75 1·40

85 Fokker Friendship at Nairobi Airport

1975. 30th Anniv of East African Airways. Multicoloured.
387 50 c. Type **85** 1·00 30
388 1 s. Douglas DC-9 at Kilimanjaro Airport 1·10 30
389 2 s. Vickers Super VC-10 at Entebbe Airport 3·50 3·00
390 3 s. East African Airways crest 3·75 3·75

Further commemorative sets were released during 1976–78 using common designs, but each inscribed for one republic only. See Kenya, Tanzania and Uganda.

Co-operation between the postal services of the three member countries virtually ceased after 30 June 1977. The postal services of Kenya, Tanzania and Uganda then operated independently.

OFFICIAL STAMPS

For use on official correspondence of the Tanganyika Government only.

1959. Stamps of 1954 optd **OFFICIAL**.
O 1 **18** 5 c. black and brown 10 60
O 2 – 10 c. red 15 60
O 3 – 15 c. black and blue 30 70
O 4 – 20 c. black and orange 20 20
O 5 **18** 30 c. black and blue 15 40
O 6 – 50 c. purple 20 20
O 7 – 1 s. black and red 20 40
O 8 – 1 s. 30 orange and lilac 1·90 1·25
O 9 – 2 s. black and green 1·25 1·00
O10 – 5 s. black and orange 3·00 2·25
O11 **20** 10 s. black and blue 2·00 2·75
O12 **21** £1 red and black 6·50 13·00

1960. Stamps of 1960 optd **OFFICIAL**.
O13 **26** 5 c. blue 10 75
O14 – 10 c. green 10 75
O15 – 15 c. purple 10 75
O16 – 20 c. mauve 10 10
O17 – 30 c. red 10 10
O18 – 50 c. violet 30 30
O19 **28** 1 s. violet and purple 30 10
O20 – 5 s. red and purple 9·00 65

POSTAGE DUE STAMPS

D 1 D 2

1923.
D1 **D 1** 5 c. violet 2·50 50
D2 10 c. red 2·50 15
D3 20 c. green 2·50 3·00
D4 30 c. brown 17·00 14·00
D5 40 c. blue 6·50 14·00
D6 1 s. green 48·00 95·00

1935.
D 7 **D 2** 5 c. violet 2·75 1·75
D 8 10 c. red 30 50
D 9 **D 2** 20 c. green 30 50
D10 30 c. brown 80 50
D11 40 c. blue 1·50 3·00
D12 1 s. grey 19·00 19·00

KHMER REPUBLIC Pt. 21

Cambodia was renamed Khmer Republic on 9th October 1970.

Following the fall of the Khmer Republic, the People's Republic of Kampuchea was proclaimed on 10 January 1979.

100 cents = 1 riel.

78 "Attack"

1971. Defence of Khmer Territory.
285 **78** 1 r. multicoloured 10 10
286 3 r. multicoloured 20 10
287 10 r. multicoloured 50 20

79 "World Races" and U.N. Emblem

1971. Racial Equality Year.
288 **79** 3 r. multicoloured 10 10
289 7 r. multicoloured 35 15
290 8 r. multicoloured 55 25

80 General Post Office, Phnom Penh

1971.
291 **80** 3 r. multicoloured 20 15
292 9 r. multicoloured 40 20
293 10 r. multicoloured 50 30

81 Global Emblem

1971. World Telecommunications Day.
294 **81** 3 r. multicoloured 10 10
295 4 r. multicoloured 20 10
296 – 7 r. multicoloured 30 15
297 – 8 r. red, black and orange 40 20
DESIGN: 7, 8 r. I.T.U. emblem.

82 Indian Coral Bean

1971. Wild Flowers. Multicoloured.
298 2 r. Type **82** 25 20
299 3 r. Orchid tree 35 25
300 6 r. Flame-of-the-forest 70 30
301 10 r. Malayan crape myrtle (vert) 90 50

83 Arms of the Republic **84** Monument and Flag

1971. 1st Anniv of Republic.
302 **83** 3 r. bistre and green 15 10
303 **84** 3 r. multicoloured 10 10
304 4 r. multicoloured 20 10
305 **83** 8 r. bistre and orange 25 15
306 10 r. bistre and brown 50 20
307 **84** 10 r. multicoloured 50 25

85 U.N.I.C.E.F. Emblem — 86 Book Year Emblem

1971. 25th Anniv of U.N.I.C.E.F.

309	85	3 r. purple	20	10
310		5 r. blue	25	15
311		9 r. red and violet	45	30

1972. International Book Year.

312	86	3 r. green, purple & blue	15	10
313		8 r. blue, green and purple	25	15
314		9 r. bistre, blue and green	45	20

87 Lion of St. Mark's

1972. U.N.E.S.C.O. "Save Venice" Campaign.

316	87	3 r. brown, buff and purple	20	10
317	–	5 r. brown, buff and green	35	20
318	–	10 r. brown, blue & green	65	20

DESIGNS—HORIZ: 5 r. St. Mark's Basilica. VERT: 10 r. Bridge of Sighs.

88 U.N. Emblem — 89 Dancing Apsaras (relief), Angkor

1972. 25th Anniv of Economic Commission for Asia and the Far East (C.E.A.E.O.)

320	88	3 r. red	15	10
321		6 r. blue	20	15
322		9 r. red	35	20

1972.

324	89	1 r. brown	10	10
325		3 r. violet	15	10
326		7 r. purple	25	15
327		8 r. brown	30	15
328		9 r. green	40	20
329		10 r. blue	55	20
330		12 r. purple	70	25
331		14 r. blue	85	40

90 "UIT" on TV Screen — 91 Conference Emblem

1972. World Telecommunications Day.

332	90	3 r. black, blue and yellow	15	10
333		9 r. black, blue and mauve	35	15
334		14 r. black, blue and brown	55	25

1972. United Nations Environmental Conservation Conference, Stockholm.

335	91	3 r. green, brown and violet	15	10
336		12 r. violet and green	40	20
337		15 r. green and violet	55	35

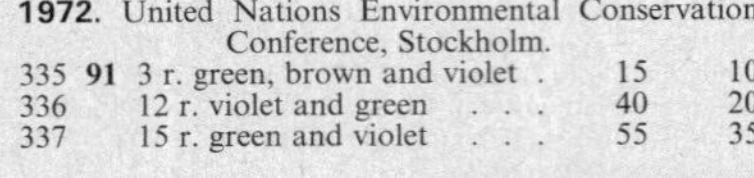

92 Javan Rhinoceros — 94 Hoisting Flag

1972. Wild Animals.

339	92	3 r. black, red and violet	25	10
340	–	4 r. violet, bistre and purple	35	10
341	–	6 r. brown, green and blue	60	20
342	–	7 r. ochre, green and brown	60	20
343	–	8 r. black, green and blue	85	30
344	–	10 r. black, blue and green	1·25	30

DESIGNS: 4 r. Mainland serow; 6 r. Thamin; 7 r. Banteng; 8 r. Water buffalo; 10 r. Gaur.

1972. Olympic Games, Munich. Nos. 164 of Cambodia and 302, 306 and 336/7 of Khmer Republic optd **XXe JEUX OLYMPIQUES MUNICH 1972**, Olympic rings and emblem.

345	83	3 r. bistre and green	25	20
346		10 r. bistre and brown	60	50
347	–	12 r. green and brown	1·50	50
348	91	12 r. violet and green	70	50
349		15 r. green and violet	75	50

1972. 2nd Anniv of Republic.

350	94	3 r. multicoloured	10	10
351		5 r. multicoloured	15	10
352		9 r. multicoloured	35	20

1972. Red Cross Aid for War Victims. No. 164 of Cambodia and 302, 306 and 336/7 of Khmer Republic surch **SECOURS AUX VICTIMES DE GUERRE**, red cross and value.

353	83	3 r. + 2 r. bistre & green	20	20
354		10 r. + 6 r. bistre & brown	45	45
355	–	12 r. + 7 r. green & brown	1·75	55
356	91	12 r. + 7 r. violet & green	55	55
357		15 r. + 8 r. green & violet	1·00	1·00

96 Garuda — 97 Crest and Temple

1973. Air.

358	96	3 r. red	10	15
359		30 r. blue	1·40	70
360		50 r. lilac	2·50	1·40
361		100 r. green	4·00	2·25

1973. New Constitution.

362	97	3 r. multicoloured	10	10
363		12 r. multicoloured	15	15
364		14 r. multicoloured	35	20

98 Apsara — 99 Interpol Emblem

1972. Angkor Sculptures.

366	98	3 r. black	10	10
367	–	8 r. blue	15	10
368	–	10 r. brown	35	20

DESIGNS: 8 r. Devata (12th century); 10 f. Devata (10th century).

1973. 50th Anniv of International Criminal Police Organization (Interpol).

370	99	3 r. green and turquoise	10	10
371		7 r. green and red	20	15
372		10 r. green and brown	30	20

100 Marshal Lon Nol

1973. Honouring Marshal Lon Nol, 1st President of Republic.

374	100	3 r. black, brown & green	10	10
375		8 r. black, brown and green	20	15
376		14 r. black, brown and agate	20	15

102 Copernicus and Space Rocket

1974. 500th Birth Anniv of Nicolas Copernicus (astronomer). Multicoloured.

382		1 r. Type **102** (postage)	10	10
383		5 r. Copernicus and "Mariner II"	10	10
384		10 r. Copernicus and "Apollo"	25	15
385		25 r. Copernicus and "Telstar"	70	35
386		50 r. Copernicus and space-walker	1·25	70
387		100 r. Copernicus and spaceship landing on Moon	3·00	1·50
388		150 r. Copernicus, and Moon-landing craft leaving "Apollo"	4·25	2·75
389		200 r. Copernicus and "Skylab III" (air)	5·25	2·75
390		250 r. Copernicus and Concorde	7·50	3·75

1974. 4th Anniv of Republic. Various stamps optd **4E ANNIVERSAIRE DE LA REPUBLIQUE**.

391	78	10 r. multicoloured	70	50
392	77	50 r. on 3 r. multicoloured	1·75	1·40
393	94	100 r. on 5 r. multicoloured	3·75	3·25

No. 392 is additionally optd **REPUBLIQUE KHMERE** in French and Cambodian.

104 Xylophone

1975. Unissued stamps of Cambodia showing musical instruments, surch **REPUBLIQUE KHMERE** in French and Cambodian and new value. Multicoloured.

394	5 r. on 8 r. Type **104**		
395	20 r. on 1 r. So (two-stringed violin)		
396	160 r. on 7 r. Khoung vong (bronze gongs)		
397	180 r. on 14 r. Two drums		
398	235 r. on 12 r. Barrel-shaped drum		
399	500 r. on 9 r. Xylophone (different)		
400	1000 r. on 10 r. Boat-shaped xylophone		
401	2000 r. on 3 r. Twenty-stringed guitar on legs		
	Set of 8	£130	

POSTAGE DUE STAMPS

D 101 Frieze, Angkor Vat

1974.

D378	D 101	2 r. brown	15	15
D379		6 r. green	25	25
D380		8 r. red	30	30
D381		10 r. blue	35	35

APPENDIX

The following stamps have either been issued in excess of postal needs or have not been available to the public in reasonable quantities at face value. Such stamps may later be given full listing if there is evidence of regular postal use.

1972.

Moon Landing of "Apollo 16". Embossed on gold foil. Air 900 r. x 2.

Visit of Pres. Nixon to China. Embossed on gold foil. Air 900 r. x 2.

Olympic Games, Munich. Embossed on gold foil. Air 900 r. x 2.

1973.

Gold Medal Winners, Munich Olympics. Embossed on gold foil. Air 900 r. x 2.

World Cup Football Championships, West Germany (1974). Embossed on gold foil. Air 900 r. x 4.

1974.

Pres. Kennedy and "Apollo 11". Embossed on gold foil. Air 1100 r. x 2.

500th Birth Anniv of Nicolas Copernicus (astronomer). Embossed on gold foil. Air 1200 r.

Centenary of U.P.U. (1st issue). Postage 10, 60 r.; Air 700 r.; 1200 r. embossed on gold foil.

1975.

Olympic Games, Montreal (1976). Postage 5, 10, 15, 25 r.; Air 50, 100, 150, 200, 250 r.; 1200 r. embossed on gold foil.

World Cup Football Championships, West Germany (1974). Postage 1, 5, 10, 25 r.; Air 50, 100, 150, 200, 250 r.; 1200 r. embossed on gold foil.

Centenary of U.P.U. (2nd issue). Postage 15, 20, 70, 160, 180, 235 r.; Air 500, 1000, 2000 r.; 2000 r. embossed on gold foil.

KHOR FAKKAN Pt. 19

From 1965 various issues were produced for this dependency, some being overprinted on, or in the same designs as, issues for Sharjah.

APPENDIX

The following stamps have either been issued in excess of postal needs or have not been available to the public in reasonable quantities at face value. Such stamps may later be given full listing if there is evidence of regular postal use.

1965.

Views. Nos. 75/80 of Sharjah optd. Air 10, 20, 30, 40, 75, 100 n.p.

Boy and Girl Scouts. Nos. 74 and 89 of Sharjah optd. 2, 2 r.

Birds. Nos. 101/6 of Sharjah optd. Air 30, 40, 75, 150 n.p., 2, 3 r.

Olympic Games, Tokyo 1964. Nos. 95/7 of Sharjah optd. 40, 50 n.p. 2 r.

New York World's Fair. Nos. 81/3 of Sharjah optd. Air 20, 40 n.p. 1 r.

Pres. Kennedy Commem. Nos. 98/100 of Sharjah optd. Air 40, 60, 100 n.p.

Centenary of I.T.U. Postage 1, 2, 3, 4, 5, 50 n.p., 1 r., 120 n.p.

Pan-Arab Games, Cairo. 50 p.65.

1966.

International Co-operation Year. 50 n.p.68.

Churchill Commemoration. 2, 3, 4, 5 r.

Roses. 20, 35, 60, 80 n.p., 1 r., 125 n.p.

Fish. 1, 2, 3, 4, 5, 15, 20, 30, 40, 50, 75 n.p., 1, 2, 3, 4, 5, 10 r.

Int. Stamp Exhibition, Washington D.C. (SIPEX). 80, 120 n.p., 2 r.

New Currency Surcharges in Rials and Piastres.

(a) 1965 I.T.U. Centenary issue. 10 p. on 50 n.p., 16 p. on 120 n.p., 1 r. on 1 r.

(b) Churchill issue. 1 r. on 2 r., 2 r. on 3 r., 3 r. on 4 r., 4 r. on 5 r.

(c) Roses issue. 1 p. on 20 n.p., 2 p. on 35 n.p., 4 p. on 60 n.p., 6 p. on 80 n.p., 10 p. on 125 n.p., 12 p. on 1 r.

New Currency Surcharges in Dirhams and Riyals.

(a) 1965 Pan-Arab Games issue. 20 d. on 50 p.65.

(b) Fish issue. 1 d. on 1 n.p., 2 d. on 2 n.p., 3 d. on 3 n.p., 4 d. on 4 n.p., 5 d. on 5 n.p., 15 d. on 15 n.p., 20 d. on 20 n.p., 30 d. on 30 n.p., 40 d. on 40 n.p., 50 d. on 50 n.p., 75 d. on 75 n.p., 1 r. on 1 r., 2 r. on 2 r., 3 r. on 3 r., 4 r. on 4 r., 5 r. on 5 r., 10 r. on 10 r.

3rd Death Anniv of Pres. J. Kennedy. Optd on Int. Stamp Exhibition, Washington issue. 80 d. on 80 n.p., 120 d. on 120 n.p., 2 r. on 2 r.

World Football Cup Championship, England. ½ r. × 7.

1967.

4th Death Anniv of Pres. J. Kennedy. Optd on 1966 Int. Stamp Exhibition issue. 80 d. on 80 n.p., 120 d. on 120 n.p., 2 r. on 2 r.

1968.

Famous Paintings. Optd on Sharjah. Postage 1, 2, 3, 4, 5, 30, 40, 60, 75 d.; Air 1, 2, 3, 4, 5 r.

Winter Olympic Games, Grenoble. Optd on Sharjah. Postage 1, 2, 3, 4, 5 d.; Air 1, 2, 3 r.

Previous Olympic Games. Optd on Sharjah. Air 25, 50, 75 d., 1 r. 50, 3, 4 r.

Olympic Games, Mexico. Optd on Sharjah. 10, 20, 30 d., 2, 2 r. 40, 5 r.

1969.

12th World Jamboree. Optd on 1968 issue of Sharjah. Postage 1, 2, 3, 4, 5, 10 d.; Air 30, 50, 60 d., 1 r. 50.

Martyrs of Liberty. Optd on 1968 issue of Sharjah. Air 35 d.64, 60 d.64, 1 r.64.

Sportsmen and Women. Optd on 1968 issue of Sharjah. Postage 20, 30, 40, 60 d., 1 r. 50, 2 r. 50; Air 35, 50 d., 1, 2, 3 r. 25, 4, 4 r.

A number of issues on gold or silver foil also exist, but it is understood that these were mainly for presentation purposes, although valid for postage.

In common with the other states of the United Arab Emirates the Khor Fakkan stamp contract was terminated on 1 August 1972, and any further new issues released after that date were unauthorised.

KIAUTSCHOU (KIAOCHOW) Pt. 7

A port in Shantung, China, leased by Germany from China in 1898. It was occupied by Japan in 1914, but reverted to China in 1922.

1900. 100 pfennige = 1 mark.
1905. 100 cents = 1 dollar (Chinese).

1900. No. 9 of German Post Offices in China surch **5 Pfg.**

3 5 pf. on 10 pf. red . . . . 48·00 50·00

1901. "Yacht" key-types inscr "KIAUTSCHOU".

11 N 3 pf. brown . . . . 2·00 2·00
12 5 pf. green . . . . 2·40 1·00
13 10 pf. red . . . . 4·25 1·75
14 20 pf. blue . . . . 10·00 8·75
15 25 pf. black & red on yell . . 22·00 32·00
16 30 pf. black & orge on buff . 22·00 27·00
17 40 pf. black and red . . . . 24·00 29·00
18 50 pf. black & pur on buff . 25·00 29·00
19 80 pf. black & red on pink . 48·00 70·00
20 O 1 m. red . . . . 85·00 £140
21 2 m. blue £130 £150
22 3 m. black £110 £275
23 5 m. red and black £400 £800

1905. Chinese currency. "Yacht" key-types inscr "KIAUTSCHOU".

34 N 1 c. brown . . . . 85 1·25
35 2 c. green . . . . 1·00 1·00
36 4 c. red . . . . 1·25 75
37 10 c. blue . . . . 1·00 1·10
38 20 c. black and red . . . . 1·50 18·00
39 40 c. black and red on pink . 2·50 55·00
40 O ½ d. red . . . . 6·00 75·00
41 1 d. blue . . . . 7·50 65·00
42 1½ d. black . . . . 8·50 £150
43 2½ d. red and black . . . . 40·00 £450

KING EDWARD VII LAND Pt. 1

Stamp issued in connection with the Shackleton Antarctic Expedition in 1908. The expedition landed at Cape Royds in Victoria Land, instead of King Edward VII Land the intended destination.

1908. Stamp of New Zealand optd **KING EDWARD VII LAND.**

A1 **42** 1d. red . . . . £400 35·00

KIONGA Pt. 9

Part of German E. Africa, occupied by the Portuguese during the 1914/18 war, and now incorporated in Mozambique.

1916. "King Carlos" key-type of Lourenco Marques optd **REPUBLICA** and surch **KIONGA** and new value.

1 S ½ c. on 100 r. blue on blue . . 5·50 5·00
2 1 c. on 100 r. blue on blue . . 5·50 5·00
3 2½c. on 100 r. blue on blue . . 5·50 5·00
4 5 c. on 100 r. blue on blue . . 5·50 5·00

KIRIBATI Pt. 1

This group of islands in the Pacific, formerly known as the Gilbert Islands, achieved independence on 12 July 1979 and was renamed Kiribati.

100 cents = 1 dollar

15 National Flag

1979. Independence. Multicoloured.

84 10 c. Type **15** 10 25
85 45 c. Houses of Parliament and Maneaba ni Maungatabu (House of Assembly) 20 65

16 "Teraaka" (training ship)

1979. Multicoloured.

86 1 c. Type **16** 10 75
122 3 c. "Tautunu" (inter-island freighter) 15 30
123 5 c. Hibiscus 10 15
124 7 c. Catholic Cathedral, Tarawa . 10 15
125 10 c. Maneaba, Bikenibeu . . . 10 15
91 12 c. Betio Harbour 15 20
92 15 c. Eastern reef heron . . . 35 25
93 20 c. Flamboyant tree 20 25
129 25 c. Moorish idol (fish) . . . 30 30
95 30 c. Frangipani 25 30
96 35 c. G.I.P.C. Chapel, Tangintebu 25 30
97 50 c. "Hypolimnas bolina" (butterfly) 75 55
98 $1 "Tabakea" (Tarawa Lagoon ferry) 70 75
99 $2 Evening scene 50 80
135 $5 National flag . . . . 1·00 2·50

17 Gilbert and Ellice Islands 1911 ½d. Stamp
18 Boy with Giant Clam Shell

1979. Death Cent of Sir Rowland Hill. Mult.

100 10 c. Type **17** 10 10
101 20 c. Gilbert & Ellice Islands 1956 2s. 6d. definitive 15 20
102 25 c. G.B. Edward VII 2s. 6d. . . 15 20
103 45 c. Gilbert and Ellice Islands 1924 10s. 25 35

1979. International Year of the Child. Mult.

105 10 c. Type **18** 10 10
106 20 c. Child climbing coconut palm (horiz) 10 10
107 45 c. Girl reading 15 20
108 $1 Child in traditional costume . 30 50

19 Downrange Station, Christmas Island

1980. Satellite Tracking. Multicoloured.

109 25 c. Type **19** 10 10
110 45 c. Map showing satellite trajectory 15 15
111 $1 Rocket launch, Tanegashima, Japan (vert) 30 35

20 T.S. "Teraaka"

1980. "London 1980" Int Stamp Exhibition. Mult.

112 12 c. Type **20** 15 10
113 25 c. Loading Air Tungaru Britten Norman Islander, Bonriki Airport 15 10
114 30 c. Radio operator 15 10
115 $1 Bairiki Post Office 20 35

21 "Achaea janata"

1980. Moths. Multicoloured.

117 12 c. Type **21** 10 10
118 25 c. "Ethmia nigroapicella" . . 15 15
119 30 c. "Utetheisa pulchelloides" . 15 15
120 50 c. "Anua coronata" 25 25

22 Captain Cook Hotel

1980. Development. Multicoloured.

136 10 c. Type **22** 10 10
137 20 c. Sports stadium 10 10
138 25 c. International Airport, Bonriki 15 10
139 35 c. National Library and Archives, Bairiki 15 10
140 $1 Otintai Hotel, Bikenibeu . . 20 40

23 "Acalypha godseffiana"

1981. Flowers. Multicoloured.

141 12 c. Type **23** 10 10
142 30 c. "Hibiscus schizopetalus" . 15 15
143 35 c. "Calotropis gigantea" . . 15 15
144 50 c. "Euphorbia pulcherrima" . 20 20

25 Maps of Abaiang and Marakei, and String Figures

1981. Islands (1st series). Multicoloured.

145 12 c. Type **25** 15 10
146 30 c. Maps of Little Makin and Butaritari, and village house . 20 10
147 35 c. Map of Maiana and coral road 25 15
148 $1 Map of Christmas Island, and Captain Cook's H.M.S. "Resolution" 70 75

See also Nos. 201/4, 215/18, 237/40, 256/60 and 270/3.

26 "Katherine"

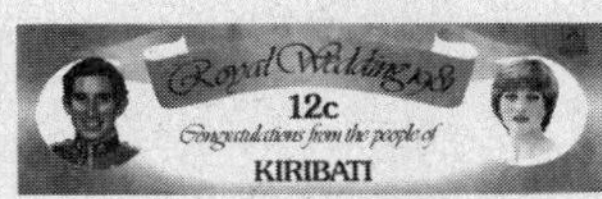

27 Prince Charles and Lady Diana Spencer (½-size illustration)

1981. Royal Wedding. Royal Yachts. Multicoloured.

149 12 c. Type **26** 10 15
150 12 c. Type **27** 20 30
151 50 c. "Osborne" 25 40
152 50 c. Type **27** 50 75
153 $2 "Britannia" 35 80
154 $2 Type **27** . . . . 1·50 2·50

28 Tuna Bait Breeding Centre, Bonriki Fish Farm

1981. Tuna Fishing Industry. Multicoloured.

158 12 c. Type **28** 15 10
159 30 c. Tuna fishing 20 20
160 35 c. Cold storage, Betio . . . 20 25
161 50 c. Government Tuna Fishing Vessel "Nei Manganibuka" . 30 50

29 Pomarine Skua

1982. Birds. Multicoloured.

163 1 c. Type **29** 15 15
164 2 c. Mallard 15 15
165 4 c. Collared petrel 20 20
166 5 c. Blue-faced booby 20 20
167 7 c. Friendly quail dove . . . 20 20
168 8 c. Common shoveler 20 20
169 12 c. Polynesian reed warbler . 20 20
170 15 c. American golden plover . 25 25
171 20 c. Eastern reef heron . . . 30 30
171a 25 c. Common noddy . . . . 3·00 1·50
172 30 c. Brown booby 30 30
173 35 c. Audubon's shearwater . . 30 35
174 40 c. White-throated storm petrel (vert) 35 40
175 50 c. Bristle-thighed curlew (vert) 40 45
175a 55 c. White tern (vert) . . . . 11·00 16·00
176 $1 Kuhl's lory (vert) 70 40
177 $2 Long-tailed koel (vert) . . 90 55
178 $5 Great frigate bird (vert) . . 1·75 1·25

30 Riley Turbo Skyliner

1982. Air. Inaug of Tungaru Airline. Mult.

179 12 c. Type **30** 15 10
180 30 c. Britten Norman "short nose" Trislander 20 20
181 35 c. Casa-212 Aviocar 20 25
182 50 c. Boeing 727-200 . . . . . 30 35

No. 179 is inscr "De Havilland DH114 Heron" in error.

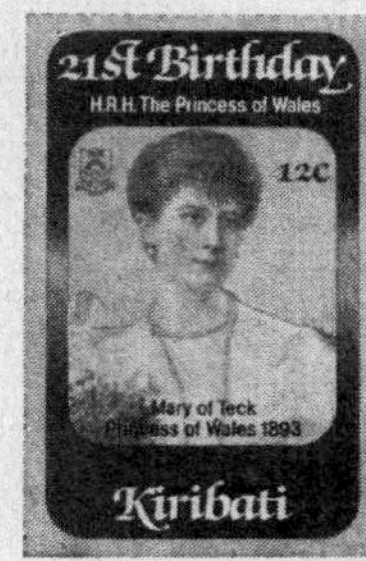

31 Mary of Teck, Princess of Wales, 1893

1982. 21st Birthday of Princess of Wales. Mult.

183 12 c. Type **31** 10 10
184 50 c. Coat of arms of Mary of Teck 20 20
185 $1 Diana, Princess of Wales . . 30 35

1982. Birth of Prince William of Wales. Nos. 183/5 optd **ROYAL BABY.**

186 12 c. Type **31** 10 10
187 50 c. Coat of arms of Mary of Teck 25 25
188 $1 Diana, Princess of Wales . . 40 45

32 First Aid Practice

1982. 75th Anniv of Boy Scout Movement. Mult.

189 12 c. Type **32** 20 15
190 25 c. Boat repairs 20 30
191 30 c. On parade 25 35
192 40 c. Gilbert Islands 1977 8 c. Scouting stamp and "75" . . 25 60

33 Queen and Duke of Edinburgh with Local Dancer

1982. Royal Visit. Multicoloured.

193 12 c. Type **33** 15 15
194 25 c. Queen, Duke of Edinburgh and outrigger canoe 20 20
195 35 c. New Philatelic Bureau building 30 30

34 "Obaia, The Feathered" (Kiribati legend)

1983. Commonwealth Day. Multicoloured.

197 12 c. Type **34** 10 10
198 30 c. Robert Louis Stevenson Hotel, Abemama 15 20
199 50 c. Container ship off Betio . 15 25
200 $1 Map of Kiribati 20 50

1983. Island Maps (2nd series). As T **25**. Mult.

201 12 c. Beru, Nikunau and canoe . 20 15
202 25 c. Abemama, Aranuka, Kuria and fish 20 20
203 35 c. Nonouti and reef fishing (vert) 25 35
204 50 c. Tarawa and House of Assembly (vert) 30 50

35 Collecting Coconuts

1983. Copra Industry. Multicoloured.
205 12 c. Type **35** . . . 25 20
206 25 c. Selecting coconuts for copra 45 35
207 30 c. Removing husks . . . 45 40
208 35 c. Drying copra . . . 45 45
209 50 c. Loading copra at Betio . . 50 55

36 War Memorials

1983. 40th Anniv of Battle of Tarawa. Multicoloured.
210 12 c. Type **36** . . . 15 15
211 30 c. Maps of Tarawa and Pacific Ocean . . . 25 30
212 35 c. Gun emplacement . . . 25 35
213 50 c. Modern and war-time landscapes . . . 35 55
214 $1 Aircraft carrier U.S.S. "Tarawa" . . . 55 75

1983. Island Maps (3rd series). As T **25**. Mult.
215 12 c. Teraina and Captain Fanning's ship "Betsey", 1798 25 15
216 30 c. Nikumaroro and hawksbill turtle . . . 30 35
217 35 c. Kanton and local postmark 35 40
218 50 c. Banaba and flying fish . . 40 55

37 Tug "Riki"

1984. Kiribati Shipping Corporation. Mult.
219 12 c. Type **37** . . . 50 15
220 35 c. Ferry "Nei Nimanoa" . . 90 35
221 50 c. Ferry "Nei Tebaa" . . 1·25 60
222 $1 Cargo ship "Nei Momi" . . 1·50 1·10

38 Water and Sewage Schemes

1984. "Ausipex" International Stamp Exhibition, Melbourne. Multicoloured.
224 12 c. Type **38** . . . 20 15
225 30 c. "Nouamake" (game fishing boat) . . . 25 30
226 35 c. Overseas training schemes 25 40
227 50 c. International communications link . . . 35 55

39 "Tabakea supporting Banaba"

1984. Kiribati Legends (1st series). Multicoloured.
228 12 c. Type **39** . . . 15 20
229 30 c. "Nakaa, Judge of the Dead" . . . 20 35
230 35 c. "Naareau and Dragonfly" 20 45
231 50 c. "Whistling Ghosts" . . . 30 55
See also Nos. 245/8.

40 Sail-finned Tang

1985. Reef Fishes. Multicoloured.
232 12 c. Type **40** . . . 60 25
233 25 c. Picasso triggerfish . . . 1·00 65
234 35 c. Clown surgeonfish . . . 1·25 85
235 80 c. Red squirrelfish . . . 2·00 2·50

1985. Island Maps (4th series). As T **25**. Mult.
237 12 c. Tabuaeran and great frigate bird . . . 75 15
238 35 c. Rawaki and germinating coconuts . . . 1·40 40
239 50 c. Arorae and xanthid crab 1·60 65
240 $1 Tamana and fish hook . . . 2·25 1·25

41 Youths playing Football on Beach

1985. International Youth Year. Multicoloured.
241 15 c. Type **41** . . . 75 70
242 35 c. Logos of I.Y.Y. and Kiribati Youth Year . . . 1·10 1·40
243 40 c. Girl preparing food (vert) 1·25 1·60
244 55 c. Map illustrating Kiribati's youth exchange links . . . 1·40 2·25

1985. Kiribati Legends (2nd series). As T **39**. Mult.
245 15 c. "Nang Kineia and the Tickling Ghosts" . . . 50 30
246 35 c. "Auriaria and Tituabine" 85 85
247 40 c. "The first coming of Babai at Arorae" . . . 1·00 1·25
248 55 c. "Riiki and the Milky Way" 1·25 1·75

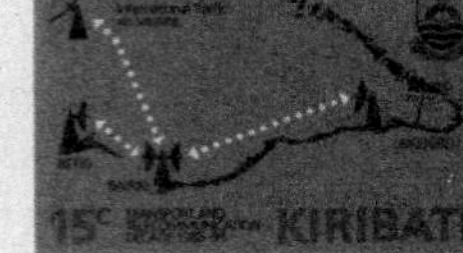

42 Map showing Telecommunications Satellite Link

1985. Transport and Telecommunications Decade (1st issue). Multicoloured.
249 15 c. Type **42** . . . 1·50 1·00
250 40 c. M. V. "Moanaraoi" (Tarawa–Suva service) . . . 2·75 3·00
See also Nos. 268/9, 293/4 and 314/15.

1986. 60th Birthday of Queen Elizabeth II. As T **120a** of Hong Kong. Multicoloured.
251 15 c. Princess Elizabeth in Girl Guide uniform, Windsor Castle, 1938 . . . 15 15
252 35 c. At Trooping the Colour, 1980 . . . 20 30
253 40 c. With Duke of Edinburgh in Kiribati, 1982 . . . 20 35
254 55 c. At banquet, Austrian Embassy, London, 1966 . . 25 50
255 $1 At Crown Agents Head Office, London, 1983 . . . 45 1·25

1986. Island Maps (5th series). As T **25**. Mult.
256 15 c. Manra and coconut crab 1·75 85
257 30 c. Birnie and McKean Islands and cowrie shells . . . 2·75 2·00
258 35 c. Orona and red-footed booby . . . 3·25 2·25
259 40 c. Malden Island and whaling ship, 1844 . . . 3·25 3·00
260 55 c. Vostok, Flint and Caroline Islands and Bellingshausen's "Vostok", 1820 . . . 3·25 3·50

43 "Lepidodactylus lugubris"

1986. Geckos. Multicoloured.
261 15 c. Type **43** . . . 1·50 70
262 35 c. "Gehyra mutilata" . . . 1·75 1·50
263 40 c. "Hemidactylus frenatus" 1·90 1·75
264 55 c. "Gehyra oceanica" . . . 2·25 2·50
See also Nos. 274/7.

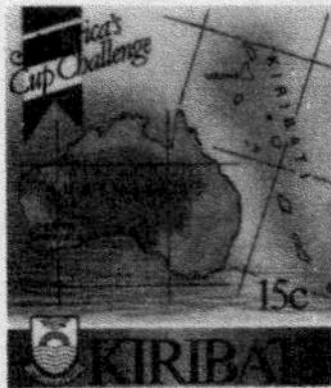

44 Maps of Australia and Kiribati

46 Henri Dunant (founder)

45 Freighter "Moamoa"

1986. America's Cup Yachting Championship. Multicoloured.
265 15 c. Type **44** . . . 20 65
266 55 c. America's Cup and map of course . . . 50 1·25
267 $1.50 "Australia II" (1983 winner) . . . 1·25 1·50

1987. Transport and Telecommunications Decade (2nd issue). Multicoloured.
268 30 c. Type **45** . . . 2·25 2·25
269 55 c. Telephone switchboard and automatic exchange . . . 3·25 3·50

1987. Island Maps (6th series). As T **25**. Multicoloured.
270 15 c. Starbuck and red-tailed tropic bird . . . 55 60
271 30 c. Enderbury and white tern 65 65
272 55 c. Tabiteuea and pandanus tree . . . 65 80
273 $1 Onotoa and okai (house) . . 70 2·00

1987. Skinks. As T **43**. Multicoloured.
274 15 c. "Emoia nigra" . . . 15 20
275 35 c. "Cryptoblepharus sp." . . 20 35
276 40 c. "Emoia cyanura" . . . 25 45
277 $1 "Lipinia noctua" . . . 40 1·00

1987. Royal Ruby Wedding. Nos. 251/5 optd **40TH WEDDING ANNIVERSARY.**
279 15 c. Princess Elizabeth in Girl Guide uniform, Windsor Castle, 1938 . . . 15 25
280 35 c. At Trooping the Colour, 1980 . . . 20 30
281 40 c. With Duke of Edinburgh in Kiribati, 1982 . . . 25 35
282 55 c. At banquet, Austrian Embassy, London, 1966 . . 30 45
283 $1 At Crown Agents Head Office, London, 1983 . . . 50 1·25

1988. 125th Anniv of Int Red Cross. Mult.
284 15 c. Type **46** . . . 80 65
285 35 c. Red Cross workers in Independence parade, 1979 . 1·25 1·50
286 40 c. Red Cross workers with patient . . . 1·25 1·60
287 55 c. Gilbert & Ellice Islands 1970 British Red Cross Centenary 10 c. stamp . . . 1·60 1·75

47 Causeway built by Australia

1988. Bicent of Australian Settlement and "Sydpex '88" National Stamp Exn, Sydney. Mult.
288 15 c. Type **47** . . . 25 20
289 35 c. Capt. Cook and Pacific map 60 60
290 $1 Obverse of Australian $10 Bicentenary banknote . . . 1·25 1·75
291 $1 Reverse of $10 Bicentenary banknote . . . 1·25 1·75

48 Manual Telephone Exchange and Map of Kiritimati

1988. Transport and Telecommunications Decade (3rd issue). Multicoloured.
293 35 c. Type **48** . . . 75 75
294 45 c. Betio–Bairiki Causeway . 1·00 1·00

49 "Hound" (brigantine), 1835

1989. Nautical History (1st series). Multicoloured.
295 15 c. Type **49** . . . 90 55
296 30 c. "Phantom" (brig), 1854 . 1·50 1·10
297 40 c. H.M.S. "Alacrity" (schooner), 1873 . . . 1·60 1·60
298 $1 "Charles W. Morgan" (whaling ship), 1851 . . . 3·00 3·75
See also Nos. 343/7 and 523/6.

50 Eastern Reef Heron

51 House of Assembly

1989. Birds with Young. Multicoloured.
299 15 c. Type **50** . . . 1·25 1·50
300 15 c. Eastern reef heron chicks in nest . . . 1·25 1·50
301 $1 White-tailed tropic bird . . 2·50 3·25
302 $1 Young white-tailed tropic bird 2·50 3·25
Nos. 299/300 and 301/2 were each printed together, se-tenant, each pair forming a composite design.

1989. 10th Anniv of Independence. Mult.
303 15 c. Type **51** . . . 25 25
304 $1 Constitution . . . 1·25 1·75

51a "Apollo 10" on Launch Gantry

1989. 20th Anniv of First Manned Landing on Moon. Multicoloured.
305 20 c. Type **51a** . . . 30 30
306 50 c. Crew of "Apollo 10" (30 × 30 mm) . . . 70 90
307 60 c. "Apollo 10" emblem (30 × 30 mm) . . . 80 1·00
308 75 c. "Apollo 10" splashdown, Hawaii . . . 95 1·25

51c Examining Fragment of Statue

1989. "Philexfrance 89" International Stamp Exhibition, Paris and "World Stamp Expo '89", Washington. Designs showing Statue of Liberty. Multicoloured.
311 35 c. Type **51c** . . . 1·10 1·40
312 35 c. Workman drilling Statue . 1·10 1·40
313 35 c. Surveyor with drawing . . 1·10 1·40

52 Telecommunications Centre

1989. Transport and Telecommunications Decade (4th issue). Multicoloured.
314 30 c. Type **52** . . . 1·50 1·25
315 75 c. "Mataburo" (inter-island freighter) . . . 3·00 3·75

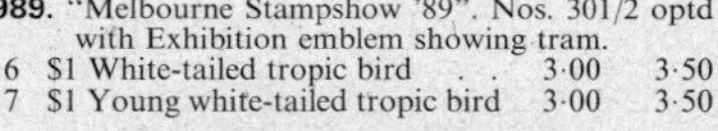
1989. "Melbourne Stampshow '89". Nos. 301/2 optd with Exhibition emblem showing tram.
316 $1 White-tailed tropic bird . . 3·00 3·50
317 $1 Young white-tailed tropic bird 3·00 3·50

54 Virgin and Child (detail, "The Adoration of the Holy Child" (Denys Calvert)

1989. Christmas. Paintings. Multicoloured.
318 10 c. Type **54** . . . 65 30
319 15 c. "The Adoration of the Holy Child" (Denys Calvert) . . 85 40
320 55 c. "The Holy Family and St. Elizabeth" (Rubens) . . . 2·50 1·25
321 $1 "Madonna with Child and Maria Magdalena" (School of Correggio) . . . 3·75 6·00

55 Gilbert and Ellice Islands 1912 1d. and G.B. Twopence Blue Stampss

1990. 150th Anniv of the Penny Black and "Stamp World London 90" International Stamp Exhibition. Multicoloured.

322 15 c. Type **55** 90 55
323 50 c. Gilbert and Ellice Islands 1911 ½d. and G.B. Penny Black 2·25 2·25
324 60 c. Kiribati 1982 1 c. bird and G.B. 1870 ½d. . . . . 2·25 2·25
325 $1 Gilbert Islands 1976 1 c. ship and G.B. 1841 1d. brown . . 2·75 3·25

56 Blue-barred Orange Parrotfish

1990. Fishes. Multicoloured.

326 1 c. Type **56** 30 60
327 5 c. Honeycomb grouper 45 60
328 10 c. Blue-finned trevally . . . 55 70
329 15 c. Hump-backed snapper . . 70 40
330 20 c. Variegated emperor . . . 75 60
356 23 c. Bennett's pufferfish . . . 80 80
331 25 c. Rainbow runner 80 65
332 30 c. Black-saddled coral grouper 90 65
333 35 c. Great barracuda . . . . . 1·00 75
334 40 c. Convict tang . . . . . . 1·00 80
335 50 c. Violet squirrelfish . . . . 1·25 90
336 60 c. Stocky hawkfish . . . . . 1·75 1·40
337 75 c. Pennant coralfish . . . . 1·90 1·60
338 $1 Common blue-striped snapper ("Yellow and blue sea perch") . . . . 2·25 1·90
339 $2 Sailfish . . . . 3·25 4·50
340 $5 White-tipped reef shark . . 6·50 9·50

1990. 90th Birthday of Queen Elizabeth the Queen Mother. As T **107** (75 c.) or **108** ($2) of Kenya.

341 75 c. multicoloured . . . . . 1·25 1·50
342 $2 black and green . . . . . 2·75 3·50

DESIGNS—21 × 36 mm: 75 c. Queen Elizabeth the Queen Mother. 29 × 37 mm: $2 King George VI and Queen Elizabeth with air raid victim, London, 1940.

1990. Nautical History (2nd series). As T **49**. Multicoloured.

343 15 c. "Herald" (whaling ship), 1851 . . . . 75 55
344 50 c. "Belle" (barque), 1849 . . 1·50 1·50
345 60 c. "Supply" (schooner), 1851 1·75 2·25
346 75 c. "Triton" (whaling ship), 1848 . . . . 1·75 2·25

57 Manta

1991. Endangered Species. Fishes. Multicoloured.

348 15 c. Type **57** . . . . 1·10 55
349 20 c. Manta (different) . . . . 1·25 90
350 30 c. Whale shark . . . . . . 1·75 2·00
351 35 c. Whale shark (different) . . 2·00 2·25

58 Queen Elizabeth II

1991. 65th Birthday of Queen Elizabeth II and 70th Birthday of Prince Philip. Multicoloured.

366 65 c. Type **58** . . . . 1·25 1·50
367 70 c. Prince Philip in R.A.F. uniform . . . . 1·25 1·50

59 Aerial View of Hospital

1991. "Phila Nippon '91" International Stamp Exhibition, Tokyo, and Opening of Tungaru Central Hospital. Multicoloured.

368 23 c. Type **59** 40 30
369 50 c. Traditional dancers . . . 75 85
370 60 c. Hospital entrance . . . . 85 1·10
371 75 c. Foundation stone and plaques . . . . 1·25 1·60

60 Mother and Child

1991. Christmas. Multicoloured.

373 23 c. Type **60** 60 40
374 50 c. The Holy Family in Pacific setting . . . . 1·10 90
375 60 c. The Holy Family in traditional setting . . . . . 1·25 1·50
376 75 c. Adoration of the Shepherds 1·50 2·00

1992. 40th Anniv of Queen Elizabeth II's Accession. As T **179a** of Gibraltar. Multicoloured.

377 23 c. Kiribati village 30 30
378 30 c. Lagoon at sunset 40 45
379 50 c. Tarawa waterfront . . . 60 70
380 60 c. Three portraits of Queen Elizabeth 70 90
381 75 c. Queen Elizabeth II . . . 90 1·10

1992. "EXPO '92" Worlds Fair, Seville. Nos. 356, 336/7 and 339 optd **EXPO'92 SEVILLA**.

382 23 c. Bennett's pufferfish . . . 55 40
383 60 c. Stocky hawkfish . . . . 1·25 1·50
384 75 c. Pennant coralfish . . . . 1·40 1·60
385 $2 Sailfish . . . . 3·00 4·00

62 Marine Training Centre Sign

1992. 25th Anniv of Marine Training Centre. Multicoloured.

386 23 c. Type **62** 45 40
387 50 c. Cadets on parade 80 90
388 60 c. Fire school 80 90
389 75 c. Lifeboat training . . . . 1·10 1·40

63 Healthy Children

1992. United Nations World Health and Food and Agriculture Organizations. Multicoloured.

390 23 c. Type **63** 55 50
391 50 c. Fishing at night . . . . 1·00 1·00
392 60 c. Fruit . . . . 1·25 1·50
393 75 c. "Papuan Chief" (container ship) . . . . 1·75 2·25

64 Phoenix Petrel 65 "Chilocorus nigritus"

1993. Birds. Multicoloured.

394 23 c. Type **64** 40 50
395 23 c. Cook's petrel 40 50
396 60 c. European pintail . . . . 90 1·10
397 60 c. Eurasian wigeon . . . . 90 1·10
398 75 c. Spectacled tern . . . . . 1·00 1·25
399 75 c. Black-naped tern . . . . 1·00 1·25
400 $1 Australian stilt . . . . . . 1·25 1·40
401 $1 Wandering tattler . . . . . 1·25 1·40

1993. Insects. Multicoloured.

402 23 c. Type **65** 85 55
403 60 c. "Rodolia pumila" (ladybird) . . . . 1·75 2·00
404 75 c. "Rodolia cardinalis" (ladybird) . . . . 2·00 2·25
405 $1 "Cryptolaemus montrouzieri" 2·25 2·75

66 U.S. Air Reconnaissance Consolidated B-24 Liberator

1993. 50th Anniv of Battle of Tarawa. Multicoloured.

406 23 c. Type **66** 60 65
407 23 c. U.S.S. "Nautilus" (submarine) 60 65
408 23 c. U.S.S. "Indianapolis" (cruiser) 60 65
409 23 c. U.S.S. "Pursuit" (destroyer) 60 65
410 23 c. Vought Sikorsky Kingfisher spotter seaplane 60 65
411 23 c. U.S.S. "Ringgold" and "Dashiell" (destroyers) . . . 60 65
412 23 c. Sherman tank on seabed . 60 65
413 23 c. Grumman Hellcat fighter aircraft in lagoon 60 65
414 23 c. Naval wreck on seabed . . 60 65
415 23 c. First U.S. aircraft to land on Betio 60 65
416 75 c. Landing craft leaving transports . . . . 1·00 1·10
417 75 c. Marines landing on Betio . 1·00 1·10
418 75 c. Landing craft approaching beach . . . . 1·00 1·10
419 75 c. Marines pinned down in surf . . . . 1·00 1·10
420 75 c. U.S.S. "Maryland" (battleship) . . . . 1·00 1·10
421 75 c. Aerial view of Betio Island . 1·00 1·10
422 75 c. U.S. Navy memorial . . . 1·00 1·10
423 75 c. Memorial to expatriates . . 1·00 1·10
424 75 c. Japanese memorial . . . . 1·00 1·10
425 75 c. Plan of Betio Island . . . 1·00 1·10

67 Shepherds and Angels

1993. Christmas. Pacific Nativity Scenes. Mult.

426 23 c. Type **67** 30 25
427 40 c. Three Kings 55 60
428 60 c. Holy Family . . . . . . 85 1·00
429 75 c. Virgin and Child . . . . 1·10 1·40

69 Bryde's Whale and Calf

1994. Whales. Multicoloured.

432 23 c. Type **69** . . . . 90 1·00
433 23 c. Bryde's whale with two calves . . . . 90 1·00
434 40 c. Blue whale and calf (face value at left) . . . . 1·10 1·25
435 40 c. Blue whales and calf (face value at right) . . . . . . 1·10 1·25
436 60 c. Humpback whale and calf (face value at left) . . . . . 1·75 2·25
437 60 c. Humpback whale and calf (face value at right) . . . . 1·75 2·25
438 75 c. Killer whale and calf . . . 1·75 2·25
439 75 c. Killer whale and two calves 1·75 2·25

70 Family silhouetted on Beach

1994. 15th Anniv of Independence. Protecting the Environment. Multicoloured.

440 40 c. Type **70** 60 60
441 60 c. Fish and coral . . . . . 1·00 1·25
442 75 c. Great frigate birds in flight . . . . 1·25 1·50

71 "Diaphania indica" 72 "Nerium oleander"

1994. Butterflies and Moths. Multicoloured.

443 1 c. Type **71** 10 10
444 5 c. "Herpetogramma licarsisalis" 10 10
445 10 c. "Parotis suralis" 10 10
446 12 c. "Sufetula sunidesalis" . . 10 10
447 20 c. "Aedia sericea" 15 20
448 23 c. "Anomis vitiensis" . . . 20 25
449 30 c. "Anticarsia irrorata" . . . 25 30
450 35 c. "Spodoptera litura" . . . 25 30
451 40 c. "Mocis frugalis" 30 35
452 45 c. "Agrius convolvuli" . . . 35 40
453 50 c. "Cephonodes picus" . . . 40 45
454 55 c. "Gnathothlibus erotus" . . 40 45
455 60 c. "Macroglossum hirundo" . 45 50
456 75 c. "Badamia exclamationis" . 60 65
457 $1 "Precis villida" 80 85
458 $2 "Danaus plexippus" . . . . 1·60 1·75
459 $3 "Hypolimnas bolina" (male) . 2·40 2·50
460 $5 "Hypolimnas bolina" (female) 4·00 4·25

1994. Seasonal Flowers. Multicoloured.

461 23 c. Type **72** 30 30
462 60 c. "Catharanthus roseus" . . 80 1·00
463 75 c. "Ipomea pes-caprae" . . 1·00 1·25
464 $1 "Calophyllum inophyllum" . 1·40 2·00

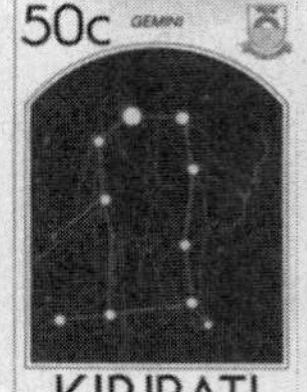

73 Gemini (The Twins) 74 Church and Traditional Meeting Hut

1995. Night Sky over Kiribati. Multicoloured.

465 50 c. Type **73** 75 70
466 60 c. Cancer (The Crab) . . . 85 90
467 75 c. Cassiopeia (The Queen of Ethiopia) . . . . 1·00 1·25
468 $1 Southern Cross . . . . . . 1·25 1·75

1995. Tourism. Multicoloured.

469 30 c. Type **74** 60 70
470 30 c. Fishermen and outrigger canoes 60 70
471 30 c. Gun emplacement and map 60 70
472 30 c. Children with marine creatures 60 70
473 30 c. Sports 60 70
474 40 c. Local girls in traditional costume 60 70
475 40 c. Windsurfing 60 70
476 40 c. Fishermen and wood carver 60 70
477 40 c. Under water sport 60 70
478 40 c. Women weaving 60 70

75 Grumman TBF Avenger

1995. 50th Anniv of End of Second World War. American Aircraft. Multicoloured.

489 23 c. Type **75** 60 45
490 40 c. Curtiss SOC.3-1 Seagull seaplane 80 70
491 50 c. Consolidated B-24 Liberator bomber 90 90
492 60 c. Grumman G-21 Goose amphibian . . . . 1·10 1·10
493 75 c. Martin B-26 Marauder bomber . . . . 1·40 1·50
494 $1 Northrop P-61 Black Widow bomber . . . . 1·60 1·75

76 Eclectus Parrots, Great Frigate Bird and Coconut Crabs

1995. Protecting the Environment. Multicoloured.

496 60 c. Type **76** 85 95
497 60 c. Red-tailed tropic birds, common dolphin and pantropical spotted dolphin . 85 95
498 60 c. Blue-striped snapper ("Yellow and blue sea perch"), blue-barred orange parrotfish and green turtle 85 95
499 60 c. Red-breasted wrasse, pennant coralfish and violet squirrelfish 85 95

1995. "Jakarta '95" Stamp Exhibition, Indonesia. Nos. 496/9 optd **JAKARTA 95** within emblem.

500 60 c. Type **76** . . . . 1·25 1·40
501 60 c. Red-tailed tropic birds, common dolphin and pantropical spotted dolphin . 1·25 1·40
502 60 c. Blue-striped snapper, blue-barred orange parrotfish and green turtle . . . . 1·25 1·40
503 60 c. Red-breasted wrasse, pennant coralfish and violet squirrelfish . . . . 1·25 1·40

79 "Teanoai" (police patrol boat)

1995. Police Maritime Unit. Multicoloured.
506 75 c. Type **79** . . . . 1·40 1·50
507 75 c. "Teanoai" at sea . . . . 1·40 1·50

80 Pantropical Spotted Dolphins

1996. Dolphins. Multicoloured.
508 23 c. Type **80** 80 55
509 60 c. Spinner dolphins . . . . 1·50 1·25
510 75 c. Fraser's dolphins . . . . 1·75 1·75
511 $1 Rough-toothed dolphins . . 1·90 2·25

81 Tap and Top Left Segment of U.N.I.C.E.F. Emblem

1996. 50th Anniv of U.N.I.C.E.F. Multicoloured.
512 30 c. Type **81** 50 60
513 30 c. Documents and top right segment 50 60
514 30 c. Syringe and bottom left segment 50 60
515 30 c. Open book and bottom right segment 50 60
Nos. 512/15 were printed together, se-tenant, with each block of 4 showing the complete emblem.

84 Rathbun Red Crab

1996. Sea Crabs. Multicoloured.
518 23 c. Type **84** 40 40
519 60 c. Red and white painted crab 80 80
520 75 c. Red-spotted crab . . . . 95 1·10
521 $1 Red-spotted white crab . . . . . 1·40 4·00

1996. Nautical History (3rd series). As T **49**. Multicoloured.
523 23 c. "Potomac" (whaling ship), 1843 . . . . 50 40
524 50 c. "Southern Cross IV" (missionary ship), 1891 . . . 80 80
525 60 c. "John Williams III" (missionary sailing ship), 1890 . . . . 90 1·00
526 $1 H.M.S. "Dolphin" (frigate), 1765 . . . . 1·40 1·75

1997. "Pacific '97" International Stamp Exhibition, San Francisco. Nos. 489/94 optd **PACIFIC 97 World Philatelic Exhibition San Francisco, California 29 May - 8 June**.
528 23 c. Type **75** 40 35
529 40 c. Curtiss SOC.3-1 Seagull seaplane 60 55
530 50 c. Consolidated B-24 Liberator bomber 70 70
531 60 c. Grumman G-21 Goose amphibian 80 90
532 75 c. Martin B-26 Marauder bomber . . . . 90 1·10
533 $1 Northrop P-61 Black Widow bomber . . . . 1·10 1·40

87 Queen Elizabeth II in 1996

88 Young Rock Dove

1997. Golden Wedding of Queen Elizabeth and Prince Philip. Multicoloured.
535 50 c. Type **87** . . . . 90 1·00
536 50 c. Prince Philip carriage-driving at Windsor Horse Show . . . . 90 1·00
537 60 c. Queen in phaeton at Trooping the Colour . . . 1·00 1·25
538 60 c. Prince Philip on Montserrat, 1993 . . . . 1·00 1·25
539 75 c. Queen Elizabeth and Prince Philip, 1989 . . . . . . 1·25 1·40
540 75 c. Prince Edward on horseback . . . . 1·25 1·40
Nos. 535/6, 537/8 and 539/40 respectively were printed together, se-tenant, with the backgrounds forming composite designs.

1997. Birds. Multicoloured.
542 50 c. Type **88** 75 80
543 50 c. Adult rock dove 75 80
544 60 c. Adult Pacific pigeon . . 80 90
545 60 c. Young Pacific pigeon . . 80 90
546 75 c. Adult Micronesian pigeon 90 1·00
547 75 c. Young Micronesian pigeon . . . . 90 1·00

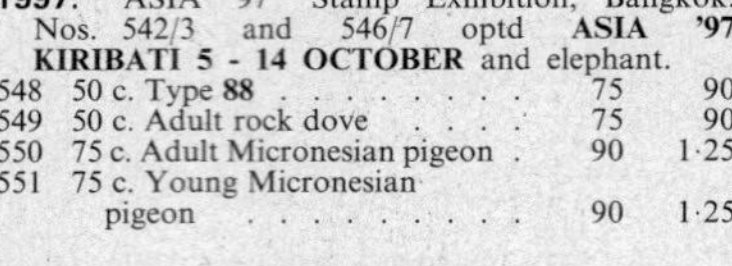

1997. "ASIA '97" Stamp Exhibition, Bangkok. Nos. 542/3 and 546/7 optd **ASIA '97 KIRIBATI 5 - 14 OCTOBER** and elephant.
548 50 c. Type **88** 75 90
549 50 c. Adult rock dove 75 90
550 75 c. Adult Micronesian pigeon . 90 1·25
551 75 c. Young Micronesian pigeon . . . . 90 1·25

90 Spiny Lobster

1998. Endangered Species. Spiny Lobster. Multicoloured.
552 25 c. Type **90** 30 40
553 25 c. Facing right 30 40
554 25 c. With coral in foreground 30 40
555 25 c. On sponge 30 40

91 Diana, Princess of Wales, 1992

1998. Diana, Princess of Wales Commemoration.
557 **91** 25 c. multicoloured 30 40

93 Indo-Pacific Humpbacked Dolphin

1998. Whales and Dolphins. Multicoloured.
560 25 c. Type **93** 45 55
561 25 c. Bottlenose dolphin . . . 45 55
562 60 c. Short-snouted spinner dolphin 80 90
563 60 c. Risso's dolphin 80 90
564 75 c. Striped dolphin . . . . 90 1·00
565 75 c. Sei whale . . . . 90 1·00
566 $1 Fin whale . . . . 1·00 1·25
567 $1 Minke whale . . . . 1·00 1·25

95 Pollutants and Harmful Emissions

1998. The Greenhouse Effect. Multicoloured.
569 25 c. Type **95** 20 25
570 50 c. Diagram of greenhouse effect 40 45
571 60 c. Diagram of rising sea levels on Tarawa 45 50
572 75 c. Diagram of rising sea levels on Kiritimati 55 60

97 Common Shoveler ("Northern Shoveler") (male)

1999. "iBRA '99" International Stamp Exhibition, Nuremberg. Ducks. Multicoloured.
575 25 c. Type **97** 20 25
576 50 c. Common Shoveler ("Northern Shoveler") (female) and ducklings . . 40 45
577 60 c. Green-winged teal (male) . 45 50
578 75 c. Green-winged teal (female) and ducklings 55 60

98 Map of Millennium Island

1999. "Towards the Millennium". 20th Anniv of Independence. Multicoloured.
580 25 c. Type **98** 35 35
581 60 c. Map of Kiribati 65 65
582 75 c. Map of Nikumaroro . . . 75 75
583 $1 Amelia Earhart (aviator) . . 95 95
No. 581 shows Tarawa as "TAROWA" in error.
See also Nos. 594/8.

1999. 30th Anniv of First Manned Landing on Moon. As T **296** of Jamaica. Multicoloured.
585 25 c. Buzz Aldrin (astronaut) . . 35 35
586 60 c. Service module docking with lunar module 65 65
587 75 c. "Apollo 11" on Moon's surface 75 75
588 $1 Command module separating from service section 95 95

99 Santa Claus in Sailing Canoe

1999. Christmas and 125th Anniv of Universal Postal Union. Multicoloured.
590 25 c. Type **99** 30 25
591 60 c. Santa and unloading freighter 55 55
592 75 c. Santa in sleigh passing aircraft 70 70
593 $1 Santa using computer 90 95

100 Open Hands around Globe ("FAITH")

2000. "Towards the Millennium". "A Region of Peace". Multicoloured.
594 25 c. Type **100** 30 30
595 40 c. Solar eclipse ("HARMONY") 45 45
596 60 c. Stars and Sun over Earth ("HOPE") 60 60
597 75 c. Sun over Earth ("ENLIGHTENMENT") . . 75 75
598 $1 Dove over Earth ("PEACE") 90 90

101 Bert feeding Pigeons

2000. "Sesame Street" (children's T.V. programme). Multicoloured.
599 20 c. T **101** 15 20
600 20 c. Little Bear flying kite . . . 15 20
601 20 c. Grover calling 15 20
602 20 c. Elmo and Cookie Monster 15 20
603 20 c. Telly leaning out of window 15 20
604 20 c. Zoe painting house . . . 15 20
605 20 c. Ernie with bird 15 20
606 20 c. Big Bird and Rosita reading 15 20
607 20 c. Oscar the Grouch and Slimey in dustbin 15 20
Nos. 599/607 were printed together, se-tenant, with the backgrounds forming a composite design.

OFFICIAL STAMPS

1981. Nos. 86/135 optd **O.K.G.S.**
O11 1 c. Type **16** 10 30
O12 3 c. M.V. "Tautunu" (inter-island freighter) 10 20
O13 5 c. Hibiscus 10 15
O14 7 c. Catholic Cathedral, Tarawa 10 15
O15 10 c. Maneaba, Bikenibeu . . 10 15
O16 12 c. Betio Harbour 30 30
O17 15 c. Eastern reef heron . . . 1·50 30
O18 20 c. Flamboyant tree 20 30
O19 25 c. Moorish idol (fish) . . . 30 30
O20 30 c. Frangipani 30 35
O21 35 c. G.I.P.C. Chapel, Tangintebu 35 40
O22 50 c. "Hypolimnas bolina" (butterfly) 50 55
O23 $1 "Tabakea" (Tarawa Lagoon ferry) . . . . 1·00 75
O24 $2 Evening scene . . . . . . 1·50 1·25
O25 $5 National flag . . . . . . 3·00 3·25

1983. Nos. 169, 172/3, 175 and 177 optd **O.K.G.S.**
O36 12 c. Polynesian reed warbler . 40 30
O37 30 c. Brown booby 70 50
O38 35 c. Audubon's shearwater . . 80 60
O39 50 c. Bristle-thighed curlew . . 1·00 80
O40 $2 Long-tailed koel . . . . . 3·00 2·75

POSTAGE DUE STAMPS

D **1** Kiribati Coat of Arms

1981.
D1 D **1** 1 c. black and mauve . . . 10 10
D2 2 c. black and blue 10 10
D3 5 c. black and green . . . 10 10
D4 10 c. black and brown . . 10 15
D5 20 c. black and blue . . . 15 25
D6 30 c. black and brown . . 20 35
D7 40 c. black and purple . . 25 45
D8 50 c. black and green . . . 25 50
D9 $1 black and red 40 75

KISHANGARH — Pt. 1

A state of Rajasthan, India. Now uses Indian stamps.

12 pies = 1 anna; 16 annas = 1 rupee

1

1899. Imperf or perf.

1 1 1 a. green . . . 21·00 55·00
3 1 a. blue . . . £400

2 (¼ a.) 5 (2 a.) Maharaja Sardul Singh

1899. Various arms designs. Perf or imperf.

21 2 ¼ a. green . . . £200 £350
22a ¼ a. red . . . 25 40
25 ½ a. green . . . 13·00 16·00
8 ½ a. red . . . £1800 £1100
26a ½ a. blue . . . 75 50
7 ½ a. lilac . . . £100 £180
27 2 1 a. grey . . . 4·50 3·00
29 1 a. mauve . . . 75 1·00
12b 1 a. pink . . . 50·00 £150
15 5 2 a. orange . . . 4·25 4·50
31 2 4 a. brown . . . 2·00 5·00
32 1 r. green . . . 10·00 15·00
17 1 r. lilac . . . 20·00 25·00
33 1 r. yellow . . . £650
34 2 r. red . . . 38·00 48·00
35 5 r. mauve . . . 32·00 48·00

11 (½ a.) 12 Maharaja Sardul Singh

1903. Imperf or perf.

39 11 ½ a. pink . . . 8·50 3·00
40 12 2 a. orange . . . 3·00 5·50
41 2 8 a. grey . . . 5·00 7·50

13 Maharaja Madan Singh 14 Maharaja Madan Singh

1904.

42 13 ¼ a. red . . . 45 45
43a ½ a. brown . . . 50 30
44a 1 a. blue . . . 1·50 1·40
45 2 a. orange . . . 13·00 7·00
46a 4 a. brown . . . 11·00 14·00
47 8 a. violet . . . 6·00 17·00
48 1 r. green . . . 22·00 28·00
49 2 r. yellow . . . 22·00 £100
50 5 r. brown . . . 21·00 £130

1912.

63 14 ¼ a. blue . . . 20 45
64 ½ a. green . . . 20 80
65 1 a. red . . . 1·00 2·50
54 2 a. purple . . . 2·50 5·00
67 4 a. blue . . . 6·00 8·00
68 8 a. brown . . . 7·00 38·00
69 1 r. mauve . . . 15·00 £100
70 2 r. green . . . 75·00 £200
71 5 r. brown . . . 75·00 £350

15 16 Maharaja Yagyanarayan Singh

1913.

59 15 ¼ a. blue . . . 20 90
60 2 a. purple . . . 7·00 18·00

1928.

72 16 ¼ a. blue . . . 70 2·00
73 ½ a. green . . . 2·25 1·25
74 – 1 a. red . . . 65 1·50
75 – 2 a. purple . . . 3·00 7·50
76 16 4 a. brown . . . 1·40 1·75
77 8 a. violet . . . 3·50 23·00
78 1 r. green . . . 12·00 45·00
79 2 r. yellow . . . 26·00 £140
80 5 r. red . . . 30·00 £160

Nos. 74/5 are larger.

OFFICIAL STAMPS

1918. Optd **ON K S D**.

O 5 2 ¼ a. green . . . — £120
O 6 ¼ a. pink . . . 2·25 60
O 7 ½ a. blue . . . £130 35·00
O 9 1 a. mauve . . . 30·00 1·50
O10 5 2 a. orange . . . — £120
O11 2 4 a. brown . . . 42·00 16·00
O16 8 a. grey . . . 60·00 22·00
O12 1 r. green . . . £130 95·00
O13 2 r. brown . . . — £750
O14 5 r. mauve . . . — £1500

1918. Optd **ON K S D**.

O15 12 2 a. orange . . . 60·00 5·00

1918. Optd **ON K S D**.

O17 13 ¼ a. red . . . — £225
O18 ½ a. brown . . . 75 35
O19 1 a. blue . . . 7·00 4·00
O20 2 a. orange . . . — £800
O21 4 a. brown . . . 45·00 18·00
O22 8 a. violet . . . £250 £160
O23 1 r. green . . . £500 £450
O24 5 r. brown

1918. Optd **ON K S D**.

O28 14 ¼ a. blue . . . 50 50
O29 ½ a. green . . . 75 75
O30a 1 a. red . . . 1·00 1·00
O31 2 a. purple . . . 6·00 4·00
O32 4 a. blue . . . 20·00 15·00
O33 8 a. brown . . . 95·00 40·00
O34 1 r. mauve . . . £300 £300
O35 2 r. green
O36 5 r. brown . . . £1300

1918. Optd **ON K S D**.

O25 15 ¼ a. blue . . . 6·00
O27 2 a. purple . . . £375 £400

For later issues see **RAJASTHAN**.

KOREA — Pt. 18

A peninsula to the S. of Manchuria in E. Asia. Formerly an empire under Chinese suzerainty, it was annexed by Japan in 1910 and used Japanese stamps. After the defeat of Japan in 1945, Russian and United States Military administrations were set up in Korea to the north and south of the 38th Parallel respectively; in 1948 South Korea and North Korea became independent republics.

KOREAN EMPIRE

1884. 100 mon = 1 tempo.
1895. 5 poon = 1 cheun.
1900. 10 re (or rin) = 1 cheun; 100 cheun = 1 weun.

1 3 Korean Flag (4)

1894.

1 1 5 m. pink . . . 34·00 £4000
2 – 10 m. blue . . . 7·50 £2500

DESIGN: 10 m. Central motif as in Type 1 but different frame and inscribed "CORGAN POST POST".

1895.

7 3 5 p. green . . . 14·00 12·00
8 10 p. blue . . . 18·00 10·00
9 25 p. red . . . 14·00 16·00
10a 50 p. lilac . . . 12·00 6·50

1897. Optd with T 4.

12 3 5 p. green . . . 20·00 15·00
13 10 p. blue . . . 24·00 20·00
14 25 p. red . . . 30·00 24·00
16 50 p. lilac . . . 30·00 20·00

1899. Surch in Korean characters.

17 3 1 (p.) on 5 p. green (No. 7) . . £1200 £750
20 1 (p.) on 5 p. green (No. 12) . . £250 £200
18 1 (p.) on 25 p. red (No. 9) . . £150 75·00
21 1 (p.) on 25 p. red (No. 14) . . 50·00 32·00

6 7 National Emblems 8

1900. T 6, 7 (2 ch.), 8 (2 ch.) and similar designs.

22a 2 r. grey . . . 75 1·50
23 1 ch. green . . . 5·50 4·00
24 2 ch. blue (T 7) . . . 35·00 38·00
25 2 ch. blue (T 8) . . . 8·00 7·00
26 3 ch. orange . . . 7·50 7·50
27 4 ch. red . . . 10·00 9·00
28 5 ch. pink . . . 10·00 10·00
29 6 ch. blue . . . 12·00 11·00
30 10 ch. purple . . . 18·00 16·00
31a 15 ch. purple . . . 30·00 25·00
32 20 ch. red . . . 50·00 38·00
33 50 ch. green and pink . . . £200 £140
34 1 wn. multicoloured . . . £300 £200
35 2 wn. green and purple . . . £500 £250

9 Imperial Crown 17 Falcon, Sceptre and Orb

1902. 40th Anniv of Emperor's Accession as King.

36 9 3 ch. orange . . . 32·00 25·00

(10) (11) (12) (16)

Types **10** to **12** are in two parts, the horizontal strokes (one, two or three) representing the value figures and the bottom part being the character for "cheun".

Some variation can be found in these woodblock overprints.

1902.

(a) Surch as Types **10** to **12**.

37 3 1 ch. on 25 p. red (No. 9) . . 8·50 6·50
38 1 ch. on 25 p. red (No. 14) . . 45·00 45·00
39 2 ch. on 25 p. red (No. 9) . . 8·50 7·00
40 1 ch. on 25 p. red (No. 14) . . 42·00 40·00
42 2 ch. on 50 p. lilac (No 10a) . . — £350
43 3 ch. on 25 p. red (No. 9) . . 42·00 90·00
44 3 ch. on 25 p. red (No. 14)
46 3 ch. on 50 p. lilac (No. 10a) . . 8·00 10·00
47 3 ch. on 50 p. lilac (No. 16) . . 12·00 12·00

(b) Surch as T **16** (Japanese "sen" character) and strokes.

49 3 3 ch. on 50 p. lilac . . . £650 £500

1903.

50 17 2 r. grey . . . 50 75
51 1 ch. purple . . . 4·50 4·50
52 2 ch. green . . . 4·50 4·50
53 3 ch. orange . . . 5·50 5·50
54 4 ch. pink . . . 6·50 6·00
55 5 ch. brown . . . 9·00 8·00
56 6 ch. lilac . . . 9·00 8·50
57 10 ch. blue . . . 12·00 10·00
58 15 ch. red on yellow . . . 22·00 22·00
59 20 ch. purple on yellow . . . 30·00 32·00
60 50 ch. red on green . . . 90·00 95·00
61 1 wn. lilac on lilac . . . £150 £160
62 2 wn. purple on orange . . . £250 £250

SOUTH KOREA

1946. 100 cheun = 1 weun.
1953. 100 weun = 1 hwan.
1962. 100 chon = 1 won.

A. UNITED STATES MILITARY GOVERNMENT

조 선
우표
5 전

(31) 33 National Emblem

1946. Stamps of Japan surch as T **31**.

69 5 ch. on 5 s. purple (No. 396) . 7·00 7·00
70 5 ch. on 14 s. red & brn (No. 324) 1·50 1·75
71 10 ch. on 40 s. purple (No. 407) . 1·50 1·50
72 20 ch. on 6 s. blue (No. 397) . . 1·50 1·25
73 30 ch. on 27 s. red (No. 404) . . 1·50 1·25
74 5 w. on 17 s. violet (No. 402) . 6·50 5·50

1946. Liberation from Japanese Rule.

75 – 3 ch. orange . . . 75 65
76 – 5 ch. green . . . 75 55
77 – 10 ch. red . . . 75 45
78 – 20 ch. blue . . . 75 45
79 33 50 ch. purple . . . 1·10 80
80 1 w. brown . . . 1·40 70

DESIGN: 3 ch. to 20 ch. Family and flag.

34 Dove of Peace and Map of Korea

1946. 1st Anniv of Liberation.

81 34 50 ch. violet . . . 5·00 2·75

35 U.S. and Korean Flags 36 Kyongju Observatory

39 Golden Crown of Silla 40 Admiral Li Sun Sin

1946. Resumption of Postal Service between Korea and U.S.A.

82 35 10 w. red . . . 6·00 4·00

1946.

83 36 50 ch. blue . . . 75 45
84 – 1 w. brown . . . 1·25 60
85 – 2 w. blue . . . 1·25 40
86 39 5 w. mauve . . . 14·00 6·00
87 40 10 w. green . . . 14·00 7·00

DESIGNS—As Type **36**: 1 w. Hibiscus; 2 w. Map of Korea.

41 Korean Alphabet 42 Li Jun, patriot

44 16th-century "Turtle" Ship 45 Letters Surrounding Globe

1946. 500th Anniv of Creation of Korean Alphabet.

88 41 50 ch. blue . . . 3·50 2·00

1947.

89 42 5 w. green . . . 8·50 3·00
90 – 10 w. blue . . . 8·50 3·00
91 – 20 w. red . . . 3·00 65
92 44 50 w. brown . . . 40·00 10·00

DESIGNS: 10 w. Admiral Li Sun Sin; 20 w. Independence Arch, Seoul.

1947. Resumption of Int Postal Service.

93 45 10 w. blue . . . 12·00 5·00

46 Douglas DC-4 Airliner

1947. Air. Inauguration of Air Mail Service.

94 46 50 w. red . . . 6·00 2·50
126 150 w. blue . . . 1·00 90
127 150 w. green . . . 8·50 4·00

47 Hand and Ballot Slip 48 Casting Votes

1948. South Korea Election.

95	47	2 w. orange	10·00	7·00
96		5 w. mauve	10·00	6·00
97		10 w. violet	20·00	8·00
98	48	20 w. red	30·00	16·00
99		50 w. blue	28·00	17·00

49 Korean Flag and Laurel Wreath

1948. Olympic Games.

100	49	5 w. green	65·00	35·00
101	–	10 w. violet	25·00	14·00

DESIGN—VERT: 10 w. Runner with torch

50 Capitol and Ears of Rice
51 Korean Family

1948. Meeting of First National Assembly.

102	50	4 w. brown	16·00	8·00

1948. Promulgation of Constitution.

103	51	4 w. green	45·00	16·00
104	–	10 w. brown	32·00	10·00

DESIGN—HORIZ: 10 w. Flag of Korea.

52 Dr. Syngman Rhee (First President)

53 Hibiscus

1948. Election of First President.

105	52	5 w. blue	60·00	25·00

B. REPUBLIC OF KOREA

1948. Proclamation of Republic.

106	–	4 w. blue	30·00	18·00
107	53	5 w. mauve	26·00	16·00

DESIGN: 4 w. Dove and olive branch.

54 Li Jun
55 Kyongju Observatory

1948.

108	54	4 w. red	40	20
109	55	14 w. blue	40	25

56 Doves and U.N. Emblem

57 Citizen and Date

1949. Arrival of U.N. Commission.

110	56	10 w. blue	30·00	14·00

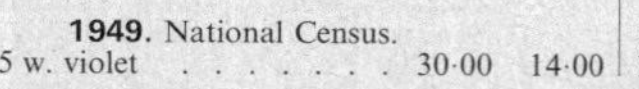
1949. National Census.

111	57	15 w. violet	30·00	14·00

58 Children and Plant

1949. 20th Anniv of Children's Day.

112	58	15 w. violet	15·00	7·00

59 Hibiscus

60 Map of Korea and Magpies

61 Dove and Globe

62 Admiral Li Sun Sin

1949.

113	–	1 w. red	3·00	1·50
114	–	2 w. grey	1·50	60
115	–	5 w. green	7·50	2·25
116	–	10 w. green	3·00	60
117	59	15 w. red	45	20
118	–	20 w. brown	45	20
119	–	30 w. green	50	20
120	–	50 w. blue	45	20
121	60	65 w. blue	2·00	60
122	–	100 w. green	50	20
123	61	200 w. green	60	35
124	–	400 w. brown	60	40
125	62	500 w. blue	60	45

DESIGNS—AS TYPE **59**: 1 w. Postman; 2 w. Worker and factory; 5 w. Harvesting rice; 10 w. Manchurian cranes; 20 w. Diamond Mountains; 30 w. Ginseng plant; 50 w. South Gate, Seoul; 100 w. Tabo Pogoda, Kyongju. AS TYPE **61**: 400 w. Diamond Mountains.

63 Symbol and Phoenix

64 Steam Train

1949. 1st Anniv of Independence.

128	63	15 w. blue	18·00	7·50

1949. 50th Anniv of Korean Railways.

129	64	15 w. blue	65·00	35·00

65 Korean Flag

66 Post-horse Warrant

1949. 75th Anniv of U.P.U.

130	65	15 w. multicoloured	12·00	8·00

1950. 50th Anniv of Membership of U.P.U.

131	66	15 w. green	15·00	6·00
132		65 w. brown	10·00	3·50

67 Douglas DC-2 Airplane and Globe

68 Demonstrators

69 Capitol, Seoul

1950. Air. Opening of Internal Air Mail Service.

133	67	60 w. blue	10·00	3·50

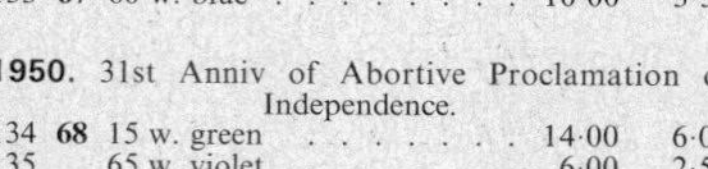
1950. 31st Anniv of Abortive Proclamation of Independence.

134	68	15 w. green	14·00	6·00
135		65 w. violet	6·00	2·50

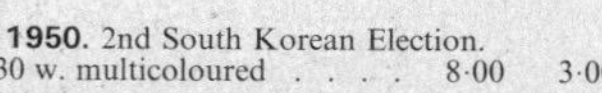
1950. 2nd South Korean Election.

136	69	30 w. multicoloured	8·00	3·00

70 Dr. Syngman Rhee

71 Flag and Mountains

1950. Unification of Korea.

137	70	100 w. blue	2·50	1·00
138	71	100 w. green	3·50	1·00
139	–	200 w. green	2·00	75

DESIGN—35 × 24 mm: 200 w. Map of Korea and flags of U.N. and Korea.

73 Manchurian Crane

76 Post-horse Warrant

77 Fairy (8th cent painting)

1951. Perf or roul.

140	73	5 w. brown	2·75	60
181	–	20 w. violet	1·00	30
187	–	50 w. green	2·00	30
183	76	100 w. blue	1·25	25
193	77	1000 w. green	2·25	40

DESIGNS—HORIZ: 20 w. Astrological Tiger (ancient painting); 50 w. Dove and Korean flag.

1951. Surch with new value.

145	54	100 w. on 4 w. red	2·75	75
146	59	200 w. on 15 w. red	4·50	2·00
147	54	300 w. on 4 w. red	1·50	1·00
156	–	300 w. on 10 w. green (116)	10·00	2·00
149	55	300 w. on 14 w. blue	2·25	75
150	59	300 w. on 15 w. red	1·75	75
151	–	300 w. on 20 w. brown (118)	2·50	85
152	–	300 w. on 30 w. green (119)	2·00	75
153	–	300 w. on 50 w. blue (120)	2·00	80
154	60	300 w. on 65 w. blue	4·50	1·60
155	–	300 w. on 100 w. green (122)	2·25	75

80 Statue of Liberty and Flags

1951. Participation in Korean War. Flags in national colours. A. As Type **80** in green. B. As Type **80** but showing U.N. Emblem and doves in blue.

			A	B
158		500 w. Australia	6·00	6·00
159		500 w. Belgium	6·00	6·00
160		500 w. Britain	6·00	6·00
161		500 w. Canada	6·00	6·00
162		500 w. Colombia	6·00	6·00
163		500 w. Denmark	12·00	15·00
164		500 w. Ethiopia	6·00	6·00
165		500 w. France	6·00	6·00
166		500 w. Greece	6·00	6·00
167		500 w. India	10·00	10·00
168		500 w. Italy (with crown)	15·00	15·00
169		500 w. Italy (without crown)	7·00	7·00
170		500 w. Luxembourg	10·00	10·00
171		500 w. Netherlands	6·00	6·00
172		500 w. New Zealand	6·00	6·00
173		500 w. Norway	10·00	10·00
174		500 w. Philippines	6·00	6·00
175		500 w. Sweden	6·00	6·00
176		500 w. Thailand	6·00	6·00
177		500 w. Turkey	6·00	6·00
178		500 w. Union of S. Africa	6·00	6·00
179		500 w. U.S.A.	5·00	5·00

The prices are the same for unused or used.

1951. Air. No. 126 surch **500 WON**.

180	46	500 w. on 150 w. blue	2·50	75

82 Buddha of Sokkuram

83 Pulguksa Temple, Kyongju

84 Monument to King Muryol, Kyongju

85 Shrine of Admiral Li Sun Sin, Tongyong

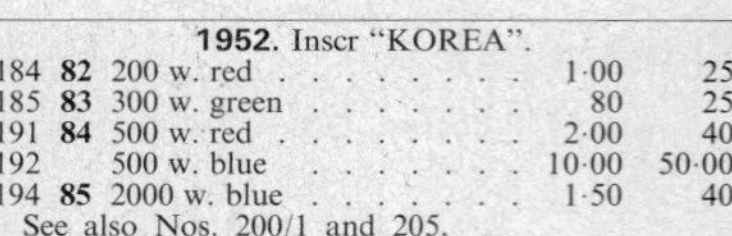
1952. Inscr "KOREA".

184	82	200 w. red	1·00	25
185	83	300 w. green	80	25
191	84	500 w. red	2·00	40
192		500 w. blue	10·00	50·00
194	85	2000 w. blue	1·50	40

See also Nos. 200/1 and 205.

86 President Syngman Rhee

1952. President's Election to 2nd Term of Office.

195	86	1000 w. green	2·00	70

87 Douglas DC-3 over Freighter

1952. Air.

196	87	1200 w. brown	1·10	40
197		1800 w. blue	1·25	40
198		4200 w. violet	1·50	50

For stamps in new currency, see Nos. 210/12.

88 Tree-planting

89 Monument to King Muryol, Kyongju

91 Pagoda Park, Seoul

92 Sika Deer

93 Sika Deer

1953. New currency. With character "hwan" after figure of value.

244	88	1 h. blue	25	10
200	84	2 h. blue	50	10
201		5 h. green	60	10
202	89	5 h. green	50	10
203	88	10 h. green	1·00	10
204	–	10 h. brown	2·50	10
205	85	20 h. brown	3·25	10
206	91	30 h. blue	1·00	10
242	92	100 h. brown	7·50	30
243	91	200 h. violet	3·50	25
208	93	500 h. orange	28·00	1·60
209		1000 h. brown	60·00	3·00

DESIGN: No. 204, "Metopta rectifasciata" (moth) and Korean flag.

For designs without character after figure of value, see 1955 issue (No. 273 etc).

1953. Air. Colours changed and new Currency.

210	87	12 h. blue	1·25	35
211		18 h. violet	1·50	40
212		42 h. green	2·00	70

94 Field Hospital

1953. Red Cross Fund. Crosses in red.

213	94	10 h. + 5 h. green	5·00	1·50
214	–	10 h. + 5 h. blue	5·00	1·50

DESIGN—VERT: No. 214, Nurses supporting wounded soldier.

95 Y.M.C.A. Badge and Map

96 Douglas DC-6 over East Gate, Seoul

1953. 50th Anniv of Korean Young Men's Christian Association.

215	95	10 h. red and black	2·00	70

1954. Air.
216 **96** 25 h. brown . . . . 2·00 80
217 35 h. purple . . . . 2·75 1·00
218 38 h. green . . . . 2·75 1·10
219 58 h. blue . . . . 2·50 1·25
258 70 h. green . . . . 4·75 2·00
220 71 h. blue . . . . 6·50 1·50
259 110 h. brown . . . . 4·75 2·00
260 205 h. mauve . . . . 7·00 2·00

98 Tokto Island **99** Erosion Control

1954.
221 – 2 h. purple . . . . 1·00 15
222 – 5 h. blue 80 15
223 **98** 10 h. green . . . . 1·25 15
DESIGN: 2 h., 5 h. Rocks off Tokto Is.

1954. 4th World Forestry Congress, Dehru Dun.
224 **99** 10 h. light green and green . 1·00 15
225 19 h. light green and green . 1·00 15

100 Presidents Syngman Rhee and Eisenhower **101** "Rebirth of Industry"

1954. Korea–United States Mutual Defence Treaty.
226 **100** 10 h. blue . . . . 1·75 40
227 19 h. brown . . . . 1·25 40
228 71 h. green . . . . 2·50 85

1955. Reconstruction.
229 **101** 10 h. brown . . . . 2·50 15
230 15 h. violet . . . . 2·25 15
231 20 h. blue . . . . 2·25 15
232 50 h. mauve . . . . 3·00 25
269 50 h. red . . . . 5·00 15

102 Rotary Emblem **103** Pres. Syngman Rhee

1955. 50th Anniv of Rotary International.
236 **102** 20 h. violet . . . . 2·50 85
237 25 h. green . . . . 1·25 45
238 71 h. purple . . . . 1·50 50

1955. 80th Birthday of President.
239 **103** 20 h. blue . . . . 3·25 1·00

104 Independence Arch, Seoul

1955. 10th Anniv of Liberation.
240 **104** 40 h. green . . . . 2·00 70
241 100 h. brown . . . . 2·00 1·00

105 Hibiscus **106** King Sejong **107** Kyongju Observatory

1955. Without character after figure of value.
273 **88** 2 h. blue 25 10
309 **89** 4 h. blue 60 10
310 5 h. green 60 10
247 **105** 10 h. mauve . . . . 1·00 10
277 – 10 h. green 75 10
248 **106** 20 h. purple . . . . 2·50 10
279 **105** 20 h. mauve 60 15
280 – 30 h. violet 75 15
281 **106** 40 h. purple 85 15
249 **107** 50 h. violet . . . . 2·75 10
315 – 55 h. purple . . . . 2·00 10
250 **92** 100 h. purple . . . . 12·00 10
284 **107** 100 h. violet . . . . 2·75 15
285 **92** 200 h. purple . . . . 3·25 15
286 **91** 400 h. violet . . . . 32·00 35
251 **93** 500 h. brown . . . . 28·00 40
288 1000 h. brown . . . . . . 50·00 2·25

DESIGNS—HORIZ: No. 277, South Gate, Seoul; 280, Tiger. VERT: No. 315, Haegumgang (cliff face).

108 Runners and Torch **109** U.N. Emblem

1955. 36th National Athletic Meeting.
252 **108** 20 h. purple . . . . 3·00 1·00
253 55 h. green . . . . 3·00 1·00

1955. 10th Anniv of U.N.
254 **109** 20 h. green . . . . 2·25 60
255 55 h. blue . . . . 2·25 60

110 Admiral Li Sun Sin and 16th-century "Turtle" Ship

1955. 10th Anniv of Korean Navy.
256 **110** 20 h. blue . . . . 3·00 1·50

111 Admiration Pagoda **112** Pres. Syngman Rhee

1956. 81st Birthday of President.
257 **111** 20 h. green . . . . 3·00 1·00

1956. President's Election to Third Term of Office.
261 **112** 20 h. brown . . . . 16·00 5·00
262 55 h. blue . . . . 7·50 3·00

113 Torch and Olympic Rings **114** Central P.O., Seoul

1956. Olympic Games.
263 **113** 20 h. brown . . . . 3·00 80
264 55 h. green . . . . 3·00 80

1956. Stamp Day. Inscr "4289.12.4".
265 **114** 20 h. turquoise . . . . . 3·00 55
266 – 50 h. red . . . . 3·75 1·00
267 – 55 h. green . . . . 1·50 55
DESIGNS—VERT: 50 h. Stamp of 1884. HORIZ: 55 h. Man leading post-pony.

119 I.T.U. Emblem and Radio Mast **120** Korean Scout and Badge

1957. 5th Anniv of Korea's Admission to I.T.U.
290 **119** 40 h. blue . . . . 1·50 60
291 55 h. green . . . . 1·50 60

1957. 50th Anniv of Boy Scout Movement.
293 **120** 40 h. purple . . . . 1·75 60
294 55 h. purple . . . . 1·75 60

1957. Flood Relief Fund. As No. 281 but Korean inscr and premium added and colour changed.
299 40 h. + 10 h. green . . . . . 2·50 50

123 Mercury, Flags and Freighters **124** Star of Bethlehem and Pine Cone

1957. Korean-American Friendship Treaty.
301 **123** 40 h. orange . . . . 1·25 60
302 205 h. green . . . . 1·60 80

1957. Christmas and New Year Issue.
304 **124** 15 h. brown, green & orange 2·50 50
305 – 25 h. green, red & yellow 2·50 30
306 – 30 h. blue, green & yellow 4·25 1·25
DESIGNS: 25 h. Christmas tree and tassels; 30 h. Christmas tree and dog by window.

125 Winged Letter **126** Korean Children regarding future

1958. Postal Week.
321 **125** 40 h. blue and red 80 25

1958. 10th Anniv of Republic of Korea.
323 **126** 20 h. grey 80 25
324 – 40 h. red . . . . 1·25 25
DESIGN—HORIZ: 40 h. Hibiscus flowers forming figure "10".

127 U.N.E.S.C.O. Headquarters, Paris **128** Children flying Kites

1958. Inaug of U.N.E.S.C.O. Building, Paris.
326 **127** 40 h. orange and green . . 1·00 25

1958. Christmas and New Year.
330 **128** 15 h. green . . . . 1·00 30
331 – 25 h. red, yellow and blue 1·00 30
332 – 30 h. red, blue and yellow 2·00 50
DESIGNS—VERT: 25 h. Christmas tree, tassels and wicker basket (cooking sieve); 30 h. Children in traditional festive costume.

129 Rejoicing Crowds in Pagoda Park, Flag and Torch

1959. 40th Anniv of Abortive Proclamation of Independence.
334 **129** 40 h. purple and brown . . 1·00 25

130 Marines going Ashore from Landing-craft

1959. 10th Anniv of Korean Marine Corps.
336 **130** 40 h. green . . . . 1·00 25

131

1959. 10th Anniv of Korea's Admission to W.H.O.
339 **131** 40 h. purple and pink . . . 1·00 25

132 Diesel Train

1959. 60th Anniv of Korean Railways.
341 **132** 40 h. sepia and brown . . 1·90 1·00

133 Runners in Relay Race

1959. 40th Korean National Games.
343 **133** 40 h. brown and blue . . . 1·00 25

134 Red Cross and Korea

1959. Red Cross. Inscr "1959 4292".
345 **134** 40 h. red and green . . . . 1·00 25
346 – 55 h. red and mauve . . . 1·00 25
DESIGN: 55 h. Red Cross on Globe.

135 Korean Postal Flags Old and New **136** Mice in Korean Costume and New Year Emblem

1959. 75th Anniv of Korean Postal Service.
348 **135** 40 h. red and blue . . . . 1·00 25

1959. Christmas and New Year.
350 **136** 15 h. pink, blue and grey . 1·00 15
351 – 25 h. red, green and blue . 80 15
352 – 30 h. red, black & mauve . 1·40 15
DESIGNS: 25 h. Carol singers; 30 h. Crane.

137 U.P.U. Monument **138** Honey Bee and Clover

1960. 60th Anniv of Admission of Korea to U.P.U.
354 **137** 40 h. brown and blue . . 1·60 75

1960. Children's Savings Campaign.
356 **138** 10 h. yellow, brown & green 75 10
357 – 20 h. brown, blue & pink . 1·25 10
DESIGN: 20 h. Snail and Korean money-bag.
For these stamps in new currency, see Nos. 452 etc.

139 "Uprooted Tree" **140** Pres. Eisenhower

1960. World Refugee Year.
358 **139** 40 h. red, blue and green . 80 10

1960. Visit of President Eisenhower of United States.
360 **140** 40 h. blue, red and green . 3·00 80

141 Schoolchildren

1960. 75th Anniv of Educational System.
362 **141** 40 h. purple, brown & green 1·00 25

142 Assembly **143** "Liberation"

1960. Inauguration of House of Councillors.
364 **142** 40 h. blue . . . . 1·00 25

1960. 15th Anniv of Liberation.
366 **143** 40 h. red, blue and brown 1·00 25

144 Weightlifting **145** Barn Swallow and Insulators

1960. Olympic Games.
368 **144** 20 h. brown, flesh & turq . 1·00 35
369 – 40 h. brown, blue & turq . 1·00 35
DESIGN: 40 h. South Gate, Seoul.

1960. 75th Anniv of Korean Telegraph Service.
371 **145** 40 h. violet, grey and blue 1·10 60

146 "Rebirth of Republic" **147** "Torch of Culture"

1960. Establishment of New Government.
373 **146** 40 h. green, blue & orange . 1·00 25

1960. Cultural Month.
376 **147** 40 h. yellow, lt blue & bl . 1·00 25

148 U.N. Flag **149** U.N. Emblem and Gravestones

1960. 15th Anniv of U.N.
378 **148** 40 h. blue, green & mauve . 1·00 25

1960. Establishment of U.N. Memorial Cemetery.
380 **149** 40 h. brown and orange . . 1·00 25

150 "National Stocktaking" **151** Festival Stocking

1960 Census of Population and Resources.
382 **150** 40 h. red, drab and blue . . 1·00 25

1960. Christmas and New Year Issue.
384 – 15 h. brown, yellow & grey . 50 15
385 **151** 25 h. red, green and blue . 40 10
386 – 30 h. red, yellow and blue . 75 15
DESIGNS: 15 h. Ox's head; 30 h. Girl bowing in New Year's greeting.

152 Wind-sock and Ancient Rain-gauge

1961. World Meteorological Day.
388 **152** 40 h. ultramarine and blue . 1·00 25

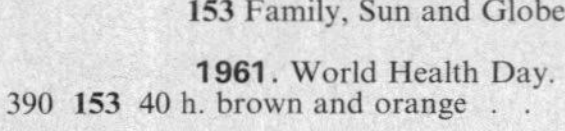

153 Family, Sun and Globe

1961. World Health Day.
390 **153** 40 h. brown and orange . . 1·00 25

154 Students' Demonstration **155** Workers and Conference Emblem

1961. 1st Anniv of April Revolution (Overthrow of Pres. Syngman Rhee).
392 **154** 40 h. green, red and blue . 1·00 30

1961. Int Community Development Conf, Seoul.
394 **155** 40 h. green 80 25

156 Girl Guide, Camp and Badge **157** Soldier's Grave

1961. 15th Anniv of Korean Girl Guide Movement.
396 **156** 40 h. green . . . . 1·00 25

1961. Memorial Day.
398 **157** 40 h. black and drab . . . 1·00 30

158 Soldier with Torch **159** "Three Liberations"

1961. Revolution of 16 May (Seizure of Power by Gen. Pak Chung Hi).
400 **158** 40 h. brown and yellow . . 1·00 30

1961. Liberation Day.
402 **159** 40 h. multicoloured . . . . 1·00 30

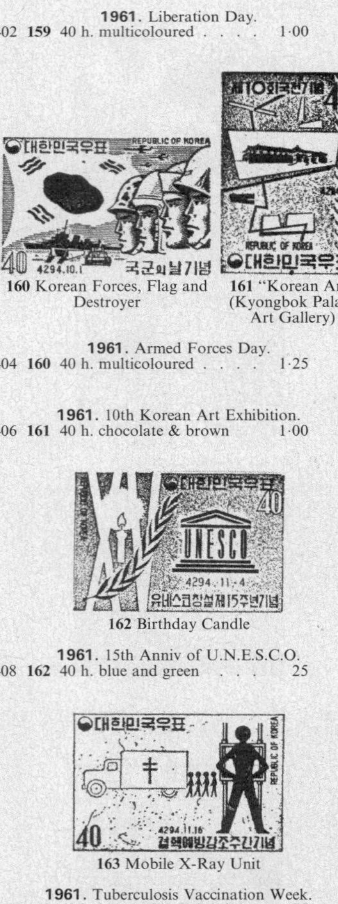

160 Korean Forces, Flag and Destroyer **161** "Korean Art" (Kyongbok Palace Art Gallery)

1961. Armed Forces Day.
404 **160** 40 h. multicoloured . . . . 1·25 30

1961. 10th Korean Art Exhibition.
406 **161** 40 h. chocolate & brown 1·00 25

162 Birthday Candle

1961. 15th Anniv of U.N.E.S.C.O.
408 **162** 40 h. blue and green . . . 25 25

163 Mobile X-Ray Unit

1961. Tuberculosis Vaccination Week.
410 **163** 40 h. brown, black & lt brn 75 25

164 Ginseng **165** King Sejong

166 White-bellied Black Woodpecker **167** Rice Harvester

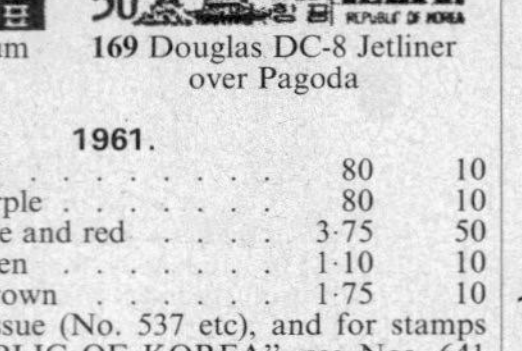

168 Korean Drum **169** Douglas DC-8 Jetliner over Pagoda

1961.
412 **164** 20 h. red 80 10
413 **165** 30 h. purple 80 10
414 **166** 40 h. blue and red . . . . 3·75 50
415 **167** 40 h. green . . . . 1·10 10
416 **168** 100 h. brown . . . . . . 1·75 10
See also 1962 issue (No. 537 etc), and for stamps inscribed "REPUBLIC OF KOREA", see Nos. 641 etc and 785/95.

1961. Air.
417 **169** 50 h. violet and blue . . . 10·00 3·50
418 – 100 h. brown and blue . . 15·00 12·00
419 – 200 h. brown and blue . . 20·00 6·00
420 – 400 h. green and blue . . 20·00 6·50
DESIGNS—Plane over: 100 h. West Gate, Suwon; 200 h. Gateway and wall of Toksu Palace, Seoul; 400 h. Pavilion, Kyongbok Palace, Seoul.
See also Nos. 454 etc.

170 I.T.U. Emblem as Satellite

1962. 10th Anniv of Admission to I.T.U.
421 **170** 40 h. red and blue . . . . 1·25 40

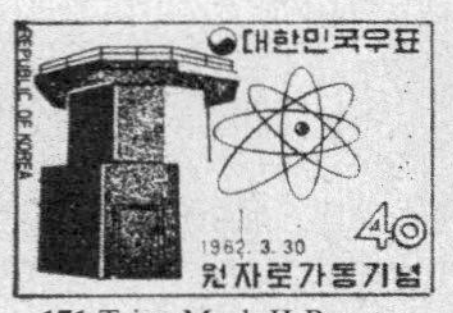

171 Triga Mark II Reactor

1962. 1st Korean Atomic Reactor.
423 **171** 40 h. green, drab and blue 1·00 25

172 Mosquito and Emblem

1962. Malaria Eradication.
424 **172** 40 h. red and green 50 25

173 Girl and Y.W.C.A. Emblem

1962. 40th Anniv of Korean Young Women's Christian Association.
426 **173** 40 h. blue and orange . . . 1·00 30

MINIMUM PRICE

The minimum price quoted is 10p which represents a handling charge rather than a basis for valuing common stamps. For further notes about prices see introductory pages.

174 Emblem of Asian Film Producers' Federation **175** Soldiers crossing Han River Bridge

1962. 9th Asian Film Festival, Seoul.
427 **174** 40 h. violet, red & turquoise 1·25 25

1962. 1st Anniv of 16th May Revolution.
428 – 30 h. green and brown . . 1·50 50
429 **175** 40 h. brown, green & turq 1·50 50
430 – 200 h. yellow, red & blue 11·00 3·00
DESIGNS—HORIZ: 30 h. "Industrial Progress" (men moving cogwheel up slope); 200 h. "Egg" containing Korean badge and industrial skyline.

176 20-oared "Turtle" Ship

1962. 370th Anniv of Hansan Naval Victory over Japanese.
433 **176** 2 w. blue and light blue . . 1·50 70
434 – 4 w. black, violet & turq . . 2·75 1·00
DESIGN: 4 w. 16-oared "turtle" ship.

177 Chindo Dog **178** "Hanabusaya asiatica"

179 Statue of Goddess Mikuk Besal **213** Longhorn Beetle

180 Farmers' Dance **181** 12th-century Wine-jug

214 Factory, Fishes and Corn **182** Mison

183 13th-century Printing-block and Impression used for "Tripitaka Koreana" **191** Sika Deer

192 Bell of King Kyongdok **215** Boddhisatva, Sokkuram Shrine

216 Tile, Silla Dynasty

217 "Azure Dragon", Koguryo period

1962. New Currency.
537 **177** 20 ch. brown 25 10
436 **178** 40 ch. blue 30 10
785 – 40 ch. green 40 10
539 **179** 50 ch. brown 30 10
540 **213** 60 ch. brown 40 10
541 **180** 1 w. blue . . . . 1·00 10
542 **179** 1 w. 50 grey 30 10
543 **164** 2 w. red . . . . 1·25 10
472 **165** 3 w. purple . . . . 2·25 10
545 **167** 4 w. green 30 10
442 **181** 5 w. blue . . . . 4·25 10
547 **214** 7 w. mauve . . . . 1·10 10
548 **168** 10 w. brown . . . . 2·00 10
549 **182** 20 w. mauve . . . . 3·00 10
550 **183** 40 w. purple . . . . 4·50 10
551 **191** 50 w. brown . . . . 6·00 15
552 **192** 100 w. green . . . . 15·00 20
553 **215** 200 w. dp green and green . . 5·00 10
554 **216** 300 w. green and brown . . 10·00 10
555 **217** 500 w. blue and lt blue . . 7·00 10
DESIGN—18 × 72 mm: No. 785, motif as Type **178** but inscriptions differently arranged.
See also Nos. 607, 609 and 641/9.

184 Scout Badge and Korean Flag

185 Chub Mackerel, Trawler and Nets

1962. 40th Anniv of Korean Scout Movement.
446 **184** 4 w. brown, red and blue 80 25
447 4 w. green, red and blue 80 25

1962. 10th Indo-Pacific Fishery Council Meeting, Seoul.
449 **185** 4 w. ultramarine and blue . 1·40 30

186 I.C.A.O. Emblem

1962. 10th Anniv of Korea's Entry into I.C.A.O.
450 **186** 4 w. blue and brown . . . 1·25 25

1962. Children's Savings Campaign. As Nos. 356/7 but new currency.
452 1 w. yellow, brown and green 3·25 10
453 2 w. brown, blue and pink . 8·25 65

1962. Air. New Currency.
454 **169** 5 w. blue and violet . . . 12·50 2·40
512 – 10 w. brown and green (As No. 418) . . . . . 2·75 30
513 – 20 w. brown and green (As No. 419) . . . . . 3·50 35
563 **169** 39 w. drab and blue . . 4·75 35
514 – 40 w. green and blue (As No. 420) . . . . . 4·00 50
564 – 64 w. green and blue (As No. 418) . . . . . 2·10 25
565 – 78 w. blue and green (As No. 419) . . . . . 3·00 30
566 – 112 w. green and blue (As No. 420) . . . . . 3·00 30

187 Electric Power Plant

1962. Inauguration of 1st Korean Economic Five Year Plan.
458 **187** 4 w. violet and orange . . 1·25 40
459 – 4 w. ultramarine and blue 1·25 40
DESIGN: No. 459, Irrigation Dam.
See also Nos. 482/3, 528/9, 593/4 and 634/5.

188 Campaign Emblem

1963. Freedom from Hunger.
460 **188** 4 w. green, buff and blue 75 25

189 Globe and Letters

1963. 1st Anniv of Asian-Oceanic Postal Union.
462 **189** 4 w. purple, green & blue 90 25

190 Centenary Emblem and Map

1963. Centenary of Red Cross.
464 **190** 4 w. red, grey and blue . . 90 25
465 4 w. red, grey and orange 90 25

1963. Flood Relief. As No. 545, but new colour and inscr with premium.
479 4 w. + 1 w. blue . . . . . . 1·50 45

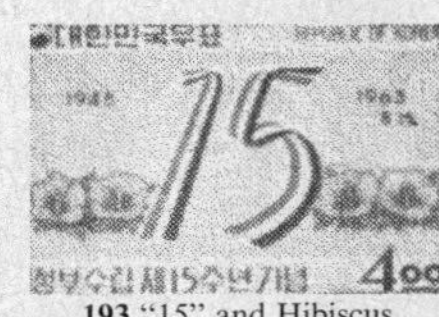
193 "15" and Hibiscus

1963. 15th Anniv of Republic.
480 **193** 4 w. red, violet and blue . . 1·40 30

194 Nurse and Emblem

1963. 15th Anniv of Korean Army Nursing Corps.
481 **194** 4 w. black, turquoise & grn 1·00 25

1963. Five Year Plan. Dated "1963". As T **187**.
482 4 w. violet and blue 90 25
483 4 w. chocolate and brown . . . 4·25 85
DESIGNS: No. 482, Cement Factory, Mun'gyong, and bag of cement; 483, Miner and coal train, Samch'ok region.

195 Rock Temples of Abu Simbel **196**

1963. Nubian Monuments Preservation.
484 **195** 3 w. green and drab . . . 2·25 40
485 **196** 4 w. green and drab . . . 2·25 40
Nos. 484/5 were issued together, se-tenant, forming a composite design.

197 Rugby Football and Athlete

198 Nurse and Motor Clinic

1963. 44th National Games.
487 **197** 4 w. green, brown & blue 1·00 25

1963. 10th Anniv of Korean Tuberculosis Prevention Society.
488 **198** 4 w. blue and red . . . . 1·00 25

199 Eleanor Roosevelt

200 U.N. Headquarters

1963. 15th Anniv of Declaration of Human Rights.
489 **199** 3 w. brown and blue . . . 80 25
490 – 4 w. blue, green and buff 80 25
DESIGN: 4 w. Freedom torch and globe.

1963. 15th Anniv of U.N. Recognition of Korea.
492 **200** 4 w. green, blue and black 1·00 25

201 Pres. Pak Chong Hi and Capitol

202 "Tai-Keum" (Bamboo Flute)

1963. Inaug of President Pak Chong Hi.
494 **201** 4 w. blue, turquoise & blk 11·00 3·50

1963. Musical Instruments and Players. As T **202**.
495 4 w. green, brown and drab . . 2·25 60
496 4 w. black, blue and light blue 2·25 60
497 4 w. green, mauve and pink . . 2·25 60
498 4 w. brown, violet and grey . . 2·25 60
499 4 w. blue, brown and pink . . 2·25 60
500 4 w. turquoise, black and blue 2·25 60
501 4 w. violet, bistre and yellow 2·25 60
502 4 w. blue, brown and mauve 2·25 60
503 4 w. black, blue and purple . . 2·25 60
504 4 w. black, brown and pink . . 2·25 60
MUSICAL INSTRUMENTS (and players)—VERT: No. 495, Type **202**; 496, "Wul-keum" (banjo); 497, "Tang-piri" (flageolet); 498, "Na-bal" (trumpet); 499, "Hyang-pipa" (lute); 500, "Pyenkyeng" jade chimes; 501, "Taipyeng-so" (clarinet); 502, "Chang-ko" (double-ended drum). HORIZ: No. 503, "Wa-kong-hu" (harp); 504, "Kaya-ko" (zither).

203 Symbols of Metric System

204 "U.N.E.S.C.O."

1964. Introduction of Metric System in Korea.
505 **203** 4 w. multicoloured 90 25

1964. 10th Anniv of Korean U.N.E.S.C.O. Committee.
506 **204** 4 w. ultramarine, red & bl 90 25

205 Symbols of Industry and Census

1964. National Industrial Census (1963).
507 **205** 4 w. brown, black & grey 1·25 60

206 Y.M.C.A. Emblem and Profile of Young Man

1964. 50th Anniv of Korean Young Men's Christian Association.
508 **206** 4 w. red, blue and green 75 25

207 Fair Emblem, Ginseng Root and Freighter

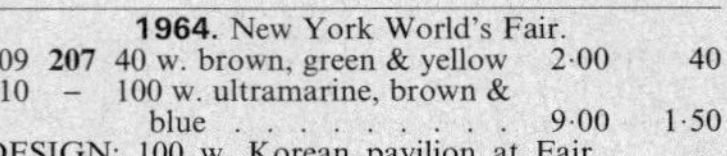
1964. New York World's Fair.
509 **207** 40 w. brown, green & yellow 2·00 40
510 – 100 w. ultramarine, brown & blue . . . . 9·00 1·50
DESIGN: 100 w. Korean pavilion at Fair.

208 Secret Garden

1964. Background in light blue.
517 **208** 1 w. green 60 20
518 – 2 w. green . . . . 1·00 25
519 – 3 w. green . . . . 1·00 25
520 – 4 w. green . . . . 1·50 30
521 – 5 w. violet . . . . 2·00 30
522 – 6 w. blue . . . . 2·00 40
523 – 7 w. brown . . . . 2·40 40
524 – 8 w. brown . . . . 2·50 40
525 – 9 w. violet . . . . 2·50 40
526 – 10 w. green . . . . 2·75 45
DESIGNS: 2 w. Whahong Gate; 3 w. Uisang Pavilion; 4 w. Mt. Songni; 5 w. Paekma River; 6 w. Anab Pond; 7 w. Choksok Pavilion; 8 w. Kwanghan Pavilion; 9 w. Whaom Temple; 10 w. Chonjeyon Falls.

1964. Five Year Plan. Dated "1964". As T **187**.
528 4 w. black and blue . . . . . 1·50 30
529 4 w. blue and yellow . . . . . 1·00 30
DESIGNS: No. 528, Trawlers and fish; 529, Oil refinery and barrels.

209 Wheel and Globe

1964. Colombo Plan Day.
530 **209** 4 w. lt brown, brn & grn 70 25

210 "Helping Hand"

1964. 15th Anniv of Korea's Admission to W.H.O.
532 **210** 4 w. black, green and light green 50 25

211 Running

1964. 45th National Games, Inchon.
534 **211** 4 w. pink, green & purple 1·00 25

212 U.P.U. Monument, Berne, and Ribbons

1964. 90th Anniv of U.P.U.
535 **212** 4 w. brown, blue and pink 75 25

218 Federation Emblem

219 Olympic "V" Emblem

1964. 5th Meeting of Int Federation of Asian and Western Pacific Contractors' Assns.
556 **218** 4 w. green, light green and brown 75 25

1964. Olympic Games, Tokyo.
557 **219** 4 w. blue, turquoise & brn 1·50 60
558 – 4 w. mauve, blue & green 1·50 60
559 – 4 w. brown, ultram & blue 1·50 60
560 – 4 w. red, brown and blue 1·50 60
561 – 4 w. brown, purple and blue 1·50 60
DESIGNS—HORIZ: No. 558, Running; 559, Rowing; 560, Horse-jumping; 561, Gymnastics.

220 Unissued 1884 100 m. Stamp

221 Pine Cone

1964. 80th Anniv of Korean Postal Services.
567 **220** 3 w. blue, violet & mauve 1·00 40
568 – 4 w. black, violet & green 1·60 60
DESIGNS: 4 w. Hong Yong Sik, 1st Korean Postmaster-general.

1965. Korean Plants. Plants multicoloured, background colours given.
571 **221** 4 w. green 1·25 40
572 – 4 w. brown (Plum blossom) 1·25 40
573 – 4 w. blue (Forsythia) 1·25 40
574 – 4 w. green (Azalea) 1·25 40
575 – 4 w. pink (Lilac) 1·25 40
576 – 4 w. grey (Wild rose) 1·25 40
577 – 4 w. green (Balsam) 1·25 40
578 – 4 w. grey (Hibiscus) 1·25 40
579 – 4 w. flesh (Crepe myrtle) 1·25 40
580 – 4 w. blue (Ullung chrysanthemum) 1·25 40
581 – 4 w. buff (Paulownia, tree) 1·25 40
582 – 4 w. blue (Bamboo) 1·25 40

222 Folk Dancing

1965. Pacific Area Travel Assn Conf, Seoul.
584 **222** 4 w. violet, brown & green 1·00 25

223 Flag and Doves

1965. Military Aid for Vietnam.
586 **223** 4 w. brown, blue & yellow 60 50

224 "Food Production"

225 "Family Scales"

1965. Agricultural Seven Year Plan.
588 **224** 4 w. brown, green & black 50 25

1965. Family Planning Month.
589 **225** 4 w. green, drab & lt green 65 25

226 I.T.U. Emblem and Symbols

1965. Centenary of I.T.U.
591 **226** 4 w. black, red and blue 65 20

1965. Five Year Plan. Dated "1965". As T **187**.
593 4 w. blue and pink 1·00 25
594 4 w. sepia and brown 80 25
DESIGNS: No. 593, "Korea" (freighter) at quayside and crates; 594, Fertiliser plant and wheat.

227 Flags of Australia, Belgium, Great Britain, Canada and Colombia

1965. 15th Anniv of Outbreak of Korean War.
595 **227** 4 w. multicoloured 1·00 40
596 – 4 w. multicoloured 1·00 40
597 – 4 w. multicoloured 1·00 40
598 – 4 w. multicoloured 1·00 40
599 – 10 w. multicoloured 2·50 60
DESIGNS—U.N. Emblem and flags of: No. 596, Denmark, Ethiopia, France, Greece and India; 597, Italy, Luxembourg, Netherlands, New Zealand and Norway; 598, Philippines, Sweden, Thailand, Turkey and South Africa; 599, General MacArthur and flags of Korea, U.N. and U.S.A.

228 Flag and Sky-writing ("20")

229 Ants and Leaf

1965. 20th Anniv of Liberation.
601 **228** 4 w. red, violet and blue 65 25
602 – 10 w. red, blue and violet 1·10 40
DESIGN: 10 w. South Gate and fireworks.

1965. Savings Campaign.
603 **229** 4 w. brown, ochre & green 50 25

230 Hoisting Flag

231 Radio Aerial

1965. 15th Anniv of Recapture of Seoul.
604 **230** 3 w. green, blue & orange 1·10 35

1965. 80th Anniv of Korean Telecommunications.
605 **231** 3 w. green, black and blue 60 25
606 – 10 w. black, blue & yellow 1·00 35
DESIGN: 10 w. Telegraphist of 1885.

1965. Flood Relief. As No. 545 (1962 issue), but colour changed and inscr with premium.
607 4 w. + 2 w. blue 1·00 30

232 Pole Vaulting

1965. National Athletic Meeting, Kwangju.
608 **232** 3 w. multicoloured 1·00 40

1965. Aid for Children. As No. 545 (1962 issue), but colour changed and inscr with premium.
609 4 w. + 2 w. purple 1·10 30

233 I.C.Y. Emblem

1965. International Co-operation Year and 20th Anniv of United Nations.
610 **233** 3 w. red, green & dp green 50 25
611 – 10 w. ultramarine, grn & bl 1·10 25
DESIGN—VERT: 10 w. U.N. flag and headquarters, New York.

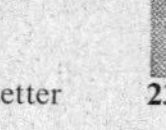
234 Child posting Letter

235 Children with Toboggan

1965. 10th Communications Day.
613 **234** 3 w. multicoloured 1·00 25
614 – 10 w. red, blue and green 1·60 30
DESIGN: 10 w. Airmail envelope and telephone receiver.

1965. Christmas and New Year.
615 **235** 3 w. blue, red and green 60 25
616 – 4 w. blue, red & green 75 25
DESIGN: 4 w. Boy and girl in traditional costume.

236 Freedom House

1966. Opening of Freedom House, Panmunjom.
618 **236** 7 w. black, emer & grn 1·00 40
619 39 w. black, lilac & green 4·25 60

237 Mandarins

1966. Korean Birds. Multicoloured.
621 3 w. Type **237** 1·75 1·00
622 5 w. Manchurian crane 1·90 1·00
623 7 w. Ring-necked pheasant 2·40 1·00

238 Pine Forest

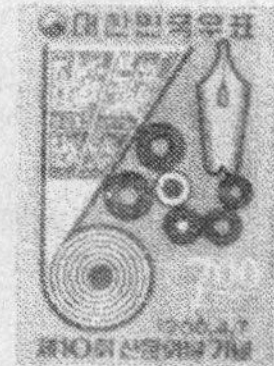
239 Printing Press and Pen

1966. Reafforestation Campaign.
625 **238** 7 w. brown, green and light green 70 15

1966. 10th Newspaper Day.
626 **239** 7 w. purple, yellow & green 60 15

240 Curfew Bell and Young Koreans

241 W.H.O. Building

1966. Youth Guidance Month.
627 **240** 7 w. orange, green & blue 60 15

1966. Inauguration of W.H.O. Headquarters, Geneva.
628 **241** 7 w. black, blue & yellow 1·00 40
629 39 w. red, grey and yellow 4·00 1·00

242 Pres. Pak, Handclasp and Flags

1966. Pres. Pak Chung Hi's State Tour of South-East Asia.
631 **242** 7 w. multicoloured 3·00 1·00

243 Girl Scout and Flag

1966. 20th Anniv of Korean Girl Scouts.
632 **243** 7 w. black, green & yellow 1·00 20

244 Student and Ehwa Women's University

1966. 80th Anniv of Korean Women's Education.
633 **244** 7 w. multicoloured 65 20

1966. 5-Year Plan. Dated "1966". As T **187**.
634 7 w. ultramarine and blue 1·75 60
635 7 w. black and yellow 1·00 30
DESIGNS: No. 634, Map and transport; 635, Radar aerials and telephone.

246 Wall-eyed Pollack

1966. Korean Fishes. Multicoloured.
637 3 w. Type **246** 1·00 45
638 5 w. Lenok 1·60 45
639 7 w. Manchurian croaker 1·75 45

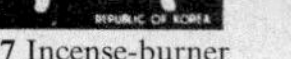
247 Incense-burner

249 Buddha, Kwanchok Temple

1966. As previous issues (some redrawn) and new designs, all inscr "REPUBLIC OF KOREA".
641 **213** 60 ch. green 20 10
642 **180** 1 w. green 1·10 10
643 **164** 2 w. green 15 10
644 **165** 3 w. brown 15 10
645 **181** 5 w. blue 2·00 10
646 **214** 7 w. blue 1·75 10
789 **168** 10 w. blue (22 × 18 mm) 3·50 10
647 **247** 13 w. blue 1·90 10
709 **182** 20 w. green and light green 6·00 10
710 **183** 40 w. green and olive 7·00 10
793 40 w. blue and pink (18 × 22 mm) 6·50 10
711 **191** 50 w. brown and bistre 5·75 10
648 – 60 w. green 2·25 10
649 **249** 80 w. green 2·25 10
DESIGN—As Type **247**: 60 w. 12th-century porcelain vessel.

250 Children and Hemispheres

1966. 15th Assembly of World Conf of Teaching Profession (WCOTP), Seoul.
650 **250** 7 w. violet, brown & blue 45 15

251 Factory within Pouch

1966. Savings Campaign.
652 **251** 7 w. multicoloured 45 15

252 People on Map of Korea

1966. National Census.
653 **252** 7 w. multicoloured 45 15

253 "Lucida lateralis"

1966. Insects. Multicoloured.
654 3 w. Type **253** 90 50
655 5 w. "Hexacentrus japonicus" (grasshopper) 90 50
656 7 w. "Sericinus montela" (butterfly) 1·00 50

254 C.I.S.M. Emblem and "Round Table" Meeting

1966. 21st General Assembly of International Military Sports Council (C.I.S.M.), Seoul.
658 **254** 7 w. multicoloured 50 15

255 Soldiers and Flags

1966. 1st Anniv of Korean Troops in Vietnam.
660 **255** 7 w. multicoloured . . . . 3·00 90

256 Wrestling

1966. 47th Athletic Meeting, Seoul.
661 **256** 7 w. multicoloured . . . . 2·00 45

257 Lions Emblem and Map

1966. 5th Orient and South-East Asian Lions Convention, Seoul.
662 **257** 7 w. multicoloured 50 15

258 University Emblem, "20" and Shields

1966. 20th Anniv of Seoul University.
664 **258** 7 w. multicoloured 40 15

259 A.P.A.C.L. Emblem

1966. 12th Conference of Asian People's Anti-Communist League (A.P.A.C.L.), Seoul.
665 **259** 7 w. multicoloured 50 25

260 Presidents Pak and Johnson

261 U.N.E.S.C.O. Symbols and Emblem

1966. President Johnson's Visit to Korea.
667 **260** 7 w. multicoloured . . . . 1·00 25
668 83 w. multicoloured . . . . 5·00 70

1966. 20th Anniv of U.N.E.S.C.O.
670 **261** 7 w. multicoloured 55 20

1966. Hurricane Relief. As No. 646 but colour changed and premium added.
672 **214** 7 w. + 2 w. red . . . . . 1·10 15

262 "Lucky Bag"

263 Eurasian Badger

1966. Christmas and New Year. Multicoloured.
673 5 w. Type **262** 45 15
674 7 w. Sheep (vert) 45 15

1966. Korean Fauna. Multicoloured.
676 3 w. Type **263** . . . . 1·25 25
677 5 w. Asiatic black bear . . . . 1·25 25
678 7 w. Tiger . . . . 1·50 25

264 "Syncom" Satellite

265 Presidents Pak and Lubke

1967. 15th Anniv of Korea's Admission to I.T.U.
680 **264** 7 w. multicoloured 70 30

1967. Visit of Pres. Lubke of West Germany to Korea.
682 **265** 7 w. multicoloured . . . . 2·00 80

266 Coin, Factories and Houses

267 Okwangdae Mask

1967. 1st Anniv of Korean Revenue Office.
684 **266** 7 w. sepia and green . . . 50 25

1967. Folklore. Multicoloured.
685 4 w. Type **267** . . . . 1·00 25
686 5 w. Sandi mask (horiz) . . . . 1·00 25
687 7 w. Mafoe mask . . . . . . 1·00 25

268 J.C.I. Emblem and Pavilion

269 Map Emblem

1967. International Junior Chamber of Commerce Conference, Seoul.
689 **268** 7 w. multicoloured 50 25

1967. 5th Asian Pacific Dental Congress, Seoul.
691 **269** 7 w. multicoloured 55 25

270 Korean Pavilion

271 Worker and Soldier

1967. World Fair, Montreal.
693 **270** 7 w. black, red and yellow 1·00 35
694 83 w. black, red and blue 6·50 70

1967. Veterans' Day.
696 **271** 7 w. multicoloured 50 25

272 Railway Wheel and Rail

1967. 2nd Five Year Plan. Dated "1967".
697 **272** 7 w. black, yellow & brn 2·40 1·10
698 – 7 w. orange, brown & blk 1·00 30
DESIGN: No. 698, Nut and bolt.
See also 773/4, 833/4, 895/6 and 981/2.

273 Sword Dance

1967. Folklore. Multicoloured.
699 4 w. Type **273** 85 25
700 5 w. Peace dance (vert) . . . 85 25
701 7 w. Buddhist dance (vert) . . 1·10 25

274 Soldier and Family

275 President Pak and Phoenix

1967. Fund for Korean Troops Serving in Vietnam.
703 **274** 7 w. + 3 w. black & purple 1·00 15

1967. Inaug of President Pak for 2nd Term.
704 **275** 7 w. multicoloured . . . . 4·00 1·00

276 Scout, Badge and Camp

1967. 3rd Korean Scout Jamboree. Multicoloured.
706 7 w. Type **276** . . . . 1·00 30
707 20 w. Scout badge, bridge and tent . . . . 2·50 50

280 Girls on Swing

1967. Folklore. Multicoloured.
712 4 w. Type **280** . . . . 1·00 25
713 5 w. Girls on seesaw (vert) . . 1·00 25
714 7 w. Girls dancing (vert) . . . 1·40 25

281 Freedom Centre

282 Boxing

1967. 1st World Anti-Communist League Conference, Taipei. Multicoloured.
716 5 w. Type **281** 50 25
717 7 w. Hand grasping chain (vert) . 50 25

1967. National Athletic Meeting, Seoul. Mult.
719 5 w. Type **282** . . . . 1·10 25
720 7 w. Basketball . . . . 1·10 25

283 Students' Memorial, Kwangjoo

284 Decade Emblem

1967. Students' Day.
721 **283** 7 w. multicoloured 50 25

1967. International Hydrological Decade.
722 **284** 7 w. multicoloured 50 25

285 Children spinning Top

286 Playing Shuttlecock

1967. Christmas and New Year.
723 **285** 5 w. blue, red and pink . . 50 15
724 – 7 w. brown, blue & bistre 50 15
DESIGN: 7 w. Monkey and Signs of the Zodiac.

1967. Folklore. Multicoloured.
726 4 w. Type **286** 90 25
727 5 w. "Dalmaji" (horiz) 90 25
728 7 w. Archery . . . . 1·25 25

287 Microwave Transmitter

1967. Inauguration of Microwave Telecommunications Service.
730 **287** 7 w. black, green and blue 50 25

288 Carving, King Songdok's Bell

289 5th–6th century Earrings

290 Korean Flag

1968.
732 **288** 1 w. brown and yellow . . 25 10
733 **289** 5 w. yellow and green . . 1·25 10
734 **290** 7 w. red and blue 70 10
787 7 w. blue 45 10
788 7 w. blue* 30 10
790 10 w. blue* 60 10
*Nos. 788 and 790 have their face values shown as "7" or "10" only, omitting the noughts shown on Nos. 734 and 787.
For designs similar to Type **290** see Nos. 771, 780 and 827.

291 W.H.O. Emblem

292 E.A.T.A. Emblem and Korean Motif

1968. 20th Anniv of W.H.O.
735 **291** 7 w. multicoloured 55 25

1968. 2nd East Asia Travel Association Conference, Seoul.
737 **292** 7 w. multicoloured 50 25

293 C.A.C.C.I. Emblem, Korean Doorknocker and Factories

1968. 2nd Conference of Confederation of Asian Chambers of Commerce and Industry (C.A.C.C.I.), Seoul.
739 **293** 7 w. multicoloured 50 25

294 Pres. Pak and Emperor Haile Selassie

1968. Visit of Emperor of Ethiopia.
741 **294** 7 w. multicoloured . . . . 2·00 75

295 Post-bag

1968. Postman's Day. Multicoloured.
743 5 w. Type **295** . . . . 1·25 50
744 7 w. Postman 50 25

296 Atomic and Development Symbols

1968. Promotion of Science and Technology.
745 **296** 7 w. blue, green and red 50 25

297 Kyung Hi University and Conference Emblem

1968. 2nd Conf of Int Assn of University Presidents.
746 **297** 7 w. multicoloured 50 25

298 "Liberation" **299** Reservist

1968. Liberation of Suppressed Peoples' Campaign.
748 **298** 7 w. multicoloured 50 25

1968. Army Reservists' Fund.
749 **299** 7 w. + 3 w. black & green 1·50 30

300 Stylised Peacock **301** Fair Entrance

1968. 20th Anniv of Republic.
750 **300** 7 w. multicoloured 60 25

1968. 1st Korean Trade Fair, Seoul.
751 **301** 7 w. multicoloured 50 25

302 Assembly Emblem **303** Scout Badge

1968. 3rd General Assembly of Asian Pharmaceutical Association Federation.
752 **302** 7 w. multicoloured 50 25

1968. 6th Far East Scout Conference, Seoul.
753 **303** 7 w. multicoloured . . . . 1·25 25

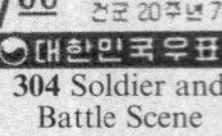

304 Soldier and Battle Scene **305** Colombo Plan Emblem and Globe

1968. 20th Anniv of Korean Armed Forces.
754 **304** 7 w. orange and green . . 2·00 40
755 – 7 w. blue and light blue . . 2·00 40
756 – 7 w. blue and orange . . 2·00 40
757 – 7 w. light blue and blue . . 2·00 40
758 – 7 w. green and orange . . 2·00 40
DESIGNS: No. 755, Sailor and naval guns; 756, Servicemen and flags; 757, Airman and jet fighters; 758, Marine and landings.

1968. 19th Meeting of Colombo Plan Consultative Committee, Seoul.
759 **305** 7 w. multicoloured 50 15

306 (I) Olympic Emblems **307** (II)

1968. Olympic Games, Mexico. Multicoloured.
760 7 w. Type **306** . . . . 2·00 60
761 7 w. Type **307** . . . . 2·00 60
762 7 w. Cycling (I) . . . . 2·00 60
763 7 w. Cycling (II) . . . . 2·00 60
764 7 w. Boxing (I) . . . . 2·00 60
765 7 w. Boxing (II) . . . . 2·00 60
766 7 w. Wrestling (I) . . . . . . 2·00 60
767 7 w. Wrestling (II) . . . . . . 2·00 60

The two types of each design may be identified by the position of the country name at the foot of the design–ranged right in types I, and left in types II. On three of the designs (excluding "Cycling") the figures of value are on left and right respectively. Types I and II of each design were issued together horizontally se-tenant within the sheets of 50 stamps.

308 Statue of Woman **309** Coin and Symbols

1968. 60th Anniv of Women's Secondary Education.
769 **308** 7 w. multicoloured 50 20

1968. National Wealth Survey.
770 **309** 7 w. multicoloured 50 20

1968. Disaster Relief Fund. As No. 734, but with additional inscr and premium added.
771 **290** 7 w. + 3 w. red and blue 5·00 50
The face value on No. 771 is expressed as "7 00 + 3 00", see also Nos. 780 and 827.

310 Shin Eui Ju Memorial **311** Demonstrators

1968. Anniv of Student Uprising, Shin Eui Ju (1945).
772 **310** 7 w. multicoloured 50 20

1968. 2nd Five Year Plan. As T **272**. Dated "1968". Multicoloured.
773 7 w. Express motorway 60 25
774 7 w. "Clover-leaf" road junction 60 25

1968. Human Rights Year.
775 **311** 7 w. multicoloured 50 20

312 Christmas Lanterns **314** Korean House and UN Emblems

1968. Christmas and New Year. Multicoloured.
776 5 w. Type **312** 75 10
777 7 w. Cockerel 75 10

1968. 20th Anniv of South Korea's Admission to U.N.
779 **314** 7 w. multicoloured 50 20

1969. Military Helicopter Fund. As No. 734 but colours changed and inscr with premium added.
780 **290** 7 w. + 3 w. red, bl & grn 1·25 40

315 Torch and Monument, Pagoda Park, Seoul **316** Hyun Choong Sa and "Turtle" Ships

1969. 50th Anniv of Samil (Independence) Movement.
781 **315** 7 w. multicoloured 60 25

1969. Dedication of Rebuilt Hyun Choong Sa (Shrine of Admiral Li Sun Sin).
782 **316** 7 w. multicoloured 80 25

317 President Pak and Yang di-Pertuan Agong **318** Stone Temple Lamp

1969. Visit of Yang di-Pertuan Agong (Malaysian Head-of-State).
783 **317** 7 w. multicoloured . . . . 2·00 75

1969.
786 **318** 5 w. purple 50 10
791 – 20 w. green . . . . 1·50 10
792 – 30 w. green . . . . 2·25 10
794 – 40 w. mauve and blue . . . 1·75 10
795 – 100 w. brown and purple 28·00 10
DESIGNS—As Type **318**. VERT: 20 w. Wine jug. 40 w. Porcelain Jar, Yi Dynasty; 100 w. Seated Buddha (bronze). HORIZ: 30 w. "Duck" vase.

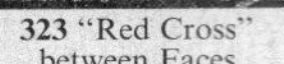

323 "Red Cross" between Faces **324** "Building the Nation's Economy"

1969. 50th Anniv of League of Red Cross Societies.
796 **323** 7 w. multicoloured 85 20

1969. "Second Economy Drive".
798 **324** 7 w. multicoloured 40 15

325 Presidents Pak and Nguyen van Thieu

1969. Visit of President Nguyen van Thieu of South Vietnam.
799 **325** 7 w. multicoloured . . . . 2·00 65

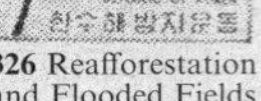

326 Reafforestation and Flooded Fields **327** Ignition of Second-stage Rocket

1969. Flood and Drought Damage Prevention Campaign. Multicoloured.
801 7 w. Type **326** 60 25
802 7 w. Withered and flourishing plants 60 25

1969. First Man on the Moon.
803 **327** 10 w. blue, black and red 1·50 50
804 – 10 w. blue, black and red 1·50 50
805 – 20 w. multicoloured . . . 1·50 50
806 – 20 w. multicoloured . . . 1·50 50
807 – 40 w. blue, red and black 1·50 50
DESIGNS: No. 804, Separation of modules from rocket; No. 805, Diagram of lunar orbit; No. 806, Astronauts on Moon; No. 807, Splashdown of "Apollo 11".

328 Stepmother admonishing Kongji **332** Steam Locomotive of 1899

1969. Korean Fairy Tales (1st series). "Kongji and Patji". Multicoloured.
809 5 w. Type **328** 65 25
810 7 w. Kongji and sparrows . . . 75 25
811 10 w. Kongji and ox . . . . . 1·10 40
812 20 w. Kongji in sedan-chair . . 1·25 40
See also Nos. 828/31, 839/42, 844/7 and 853/6.

1969. 70th Anniv of Korean Railways. Multicoloured.
814 7 w. Type **332** . . . . 1·50 50
815 7 w. Early steam and modern diesel locomotives . . . . . 1·50 50

333 Northrop F-5A Freedom Jet Fighters **334** Game of Cha-jun

1969. 20th Anniv of Korean Air Force. Multicoloured.
816 10 w. Type **333** . . . . 1·25 25
817 10 w. McDonnell-Douglas F-4D Phantom II jet fighter . . . 1·25 25

1969. 10th Korean Traditional Arts Contest, Taegu.
818 **334** 7 w. multicoloured 60 15

335 Molecule and Institute Building **336** Presidents Pak and Hamani

1969. Completion of Korean Institute of Science and Technology.
819 **335** 7 w. multicoloured 60 15

1969. Visit of President Hamani of Niger Republic.
820 **336** 7 w. multicoloured . . . . 1·25 40

337 Football **342** Students ringing "Education"

1969. 50th Anniv of National Athletic Meeting. Multicoloured.
822 10 w. Type **337** . . . . 1·10 40
823 10 w. Volleyball . . . . 1·10 40
824 10 w. Korean wrestling . . . . 1·10 40
825 10 w. Fencing . . . . 1·10 40
826 10 w. Taekwondo (karate) . . 1·10 40
Nos. 824/6 are horiz.

1969. Searchlight Fund. As T **290** but with additional inscr and premium. Face value expressed as "7+3".
827 7 w. + 3 w. red and blue . . . 80 25

1969. Korean Fairy Tales (2nd series). "The Hare's Liver". As T **328**. Multicoloured.
828 5 w. Princess and Doctors . . . 65 30
829 7 w. Hare arriving at Palace . . 70 30
830 10 w. Preparing to remove the Hare's liver . . . . 1·10 40
831 20 w. Escape of the Hare . . . 1·25 40

1969. 2nd Five-year Plan. As T **272**. Dated "1969". Multicoloured.
833 7 w. "Agriculture and Fisheries" 75 40
834 7 w. Industrial emblems . . . 50 15

1969. 1st Anniv of National Education Charter.
835 **342** 7 w. multicoloured 50 15

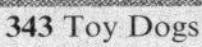
343 Toy Dogs **344** Woman with Letter and U.P.U. Monument, Berne

1969. Lunar New Year ("Year of the Dog"). Multicoloured.
836 5 w. Type **343** 60 25
837 7 w. Candle and lattice doorway 60 25

1970. 70th Anniv of Korea's Admission to U.P.U.
838 **344** 10 w. multicoloured . . . 3·00 70

1970. Korean Fairy Tales (3rd series). "The Sun and the Moon". As T **328**. Multicoloured.
839 5 w. Mother meets the tiger . . 65 25
840 7 w. Tiger in disguise 70 25
841 10 w. Children chased up a tree 1·10 40
842 20 w. Children escape to Heaven 1·25 40

1970. Korean Fairy Tales (4th series). "The Woodcutter and the Fairy". As T **328**. Mult.
844 10 w. Woodcutter hiding Fairy's dress . . . . 1·10 40
845 10 w. Fairy as Woodcutter's Wife 1·10 40
846 10 w. Fairy and children fly to Heaven . . . . 1·10 40
847 10 w. Happy reunion . . . . . 1·10 40

353 I.E.Y. Emblem on Open Book **354** Seated Buddha and Korean Pavilion

1970. International Education Year.
849 **353** 10 w. multicoloured . . . 3·00 70

1970. "EXPO 70" World Fair, Osaka, Japan.
850 **354** 10 w. multicoloured . . . 2·25 60

355 "4-11" Club Emblem

356 Bank Emblem and Cash

1970. 15th "4-11" Club (young farmers' organization) Central Contest, Suwon.
851 **355** 10 w. multicoloured . . . 80 30

1970. 3rd General Meeting of Asian Development Bank, Seoul.
852 **356** 10 w. multicoloured . . . 80 30

1970. Korean Fairy Tales (5th series). "Heungbu and Nolbu". As T **328**. Multicoloured.
853 10 w. Heungbu tending swallow 1·00 25
854 10 w. Heungbu finds treasure in pumpkin . . . . 1·00 25
855 10 w. Nolbu with pumpkin . . 1·00 25
856 10 w. Nolbu chased by devil 1·00 25

361 Royal Palanquin (Yi dynasty)

362 New Headquarters Building

1970. Early Korean Transport.
858 **361** 10 w. multicoloured . . . 1·00 25
859 – 10 w. multicoloured . . . 2·25 85
860 – 10 w. multicoloured . . . 1·00 25
861 – 10 w. black, stone and blue 1·25 25
DESIGNS—HORIZ: No. 859, Tramcar, 1899; 860, Emperor Sunjong's cadillac, 1903; 861, An Chang Nam's Nieuport 28 biplane, 1922.

1970. Opening of New U.P.U. Headquarters Building, Berne.
862 **362** 10 w. multicoloured . . . 70 30

363 Dish Aerial and Hemispheres

1970. Inauguration of Satellite Communications Station, Kum San.
863 **363** 10 w. multicoloured . . . 1·10 30

364 "PEN" and Quill Pen

366 Postal Code Symbol

365 Section of Motorway

1970. 37th International P.E.N. (literary organization) Congress, Seoul.
864 **364** 10 w. multicoloured . . . 70 25

1970. Opening of Seoul–Pusan Motorway.
865 **365** 10 w. multicoloured . . . 1·25 30

1970. Introduction of Postal Codes.
866 **366** 10 w. multicoloured . . . 60 25

367 Parcel Sorting Area

368 Children's Hall and Boy

1970. Inauguration of Postal Mechanization.
867 **367** 10 w. multicoloured . . . 60 25

1970. Opening of Children's Hall, Seoul.
869 **368** 10 w. multicoloured . . . 60 30

369 "Mountain and River" (Yi In Moon)

1970. Korean Paintings of Yi Dynasty (1st series). Multicoloured.
870 10 w. Type **369** . . . . 1·25 30
871 10 w. "Jongyangsa Temple" (Chong Son) . . . . 1·25 30
872 10 w. "Mountain and River by Moonlight" (Kim Doo Ryang) (vert) . . . . 1·25 30
See also Nos. 887/89, 897/899, 947/52, 956/8 and 961/5.

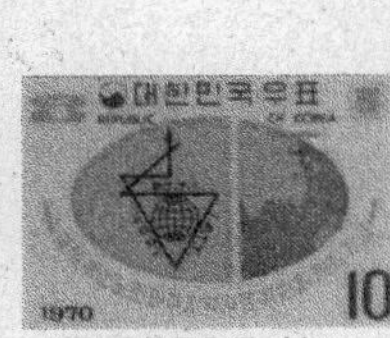
370 P.T.T.I. Emblem

371 WAC and Corps Badge

1970. Councillors' Meeting, Asian Chapter of Postal, Telegraph and Telephone International (Post Office Trade Union Federation).
874 **370** 10 w. multicoloured . . . 55 25

1970. 20th Anniv of Korean Women's Army Corps.
875 **371** 10 w. multicoloured . . . 60 25

372 Pres. Pak and Flag

1970.
876 **372** 10 w. multicoloured . . . 3·75 55
877 – 10 w. black, green & blue 2·75 50
DESIGN—VERT: No. 877, Pres. Pak and industrial complex.

373 Presidents Pak and Sanchez Hernandez

1970. Visit of Pres. Sanchez Hernandez of El Salvador.
878 **373** 10 w. multicoloured . . . 2·00 60

374 "People and Houses"

1970. National Census.
880 **374** 10 w. multicoloured . . . 90 25

375 Diving

1970. 51st National Athletic Games, Seoul.
881 10 w. Type **375** . . . . 1·40 50
882 10 w. Hockey . . . . 1·40 50
883 10 w. Baseball . . . . 1·40 50

376 Police Badge and Activities

377 Bell and Globe

1970. National Police Day.
885 **376** 10 w. multicoloured . . . 1·00 30

1970. 25th Anniv of United Nations.
886 **377** 10 w. multicoloured . . . 75 30

1970. Korean Paintings of the Yi Dynasty (2nd series). Vert designs at T **369**, showing animals. Multicoloured.
887 30 w. "Fierce Tiger" (Shim Sa Yung) . . . . 2·50 75
888 30 w. "Cats and Sparrows" (Pyun Sang Byuk) . . . . 2·50 75
889 30 w. "Dog with Puppies" (Yi Am) . . . . 2·50 75

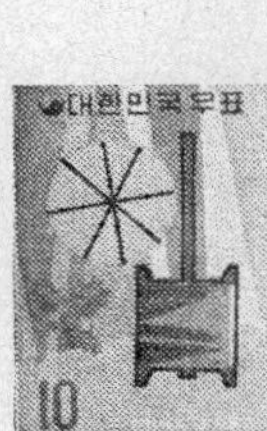
378 Kite and Reel

380 Fields ("Food Production")

379 Quotation and Emblems on Globe

1970. Lunar New Year ("Year of the Pig"). Multicoloured.
891 10 w. Type **378** 65 20
892 10 w. Toy pig 65 20

1970. 15th Communications Day.
894 **379** 10 w. multicoloured . . . 65 30

1970. 2nd Five Year Plan. At T **272**. Dated "1970". Multicoloured.
895 10 w. "Port Development" . . 50 20
896 10 w. "House Construction" . . 50 20

1970. Korean Paintings of the Yi Dynasty (3rd series). Vert designs as T **369**. Multicoloured.
897 10 w. "Chokpyokdo" (river cliff) (Kim Hong Do) . . . . . . 1·75 30
898 10 w. "Hen and Chicks" (Pyn Sang Byuk) . . . . 1·75 30
899 10 w. "The Flute-player" (Shin Yun Bok) . . . . 1·75 30

1971. Economic Development (1st series). Mult.
901 10 w. Type **380** 65 30
902 10 w. Dam ("Electric Power") (horiz) 65 30
903 10 w. Map on crate ("Exports") (horiz) 65 30
See also Nos. 905/7 and 910/12.

381 Coal-mining

382 Globe, Torch and Spider

1971. Economic Development (2nd series). Mult.
905 10 w. Type **381** . . . . 1·10 40
906 10 w. Cement works (vert) . . 60 20
907 10 w. Fertilizer plant 60 20

1971. Anti-Espionage Month.
909 **382** 10 w. multicoloured . . . 70 20

383 Motorway Junction

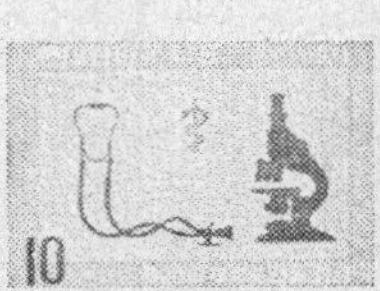
384 Reservist and Badge

1971. Economic Develepment (3rd series). Mult.
910 10 w. Type **383** 60 20
911 10 w. Scales ("Gross National Income") (horiz) 60 20
912 10 w. Bee and coins ("Increased Savings") (horiz) 60 20

1971. 3rd Home Reserve Forces Day.
914 **384** 10 w. multicoloured . . . 1·00 30

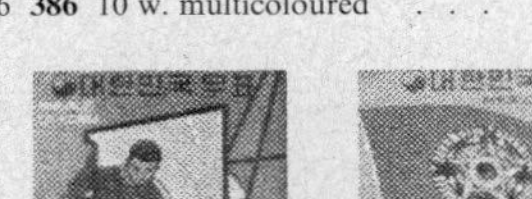
385 W.H.O. Emblem, Stethoscope and Microscope

386 Underground Train

1971. 20th World Health Day.
915 **385** 10 w. multicoloured . . . 50 30

1971. Construction of Seoul Underground Railway System.
916 **386** 10 w. multicoloured . . . 1·10 20

387 Footballer

388 Veteran and Association Flag

1971. 1st Asian Soccer Games, Seoul.
917 **387** 10 w. multicoloured . . . 1·40 40

1971. 20th Korean Veterans' Day.
918 **388** 10 w. multicoloured . . . 50 20

389 Girl Scouts

390 Torch and Economic Symbols

1971. 25th Anniv of Korean Girl Scouts Federation.
919 **389** 10 w. multicoloured . . . 55 20

1971. 10th Anniv of May 16th Revolution.
920 **390** 10 w. multicoloured . . . 50 20

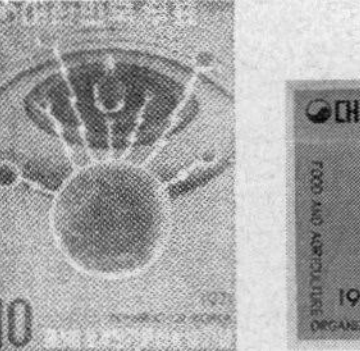
391 "Telecommunications"

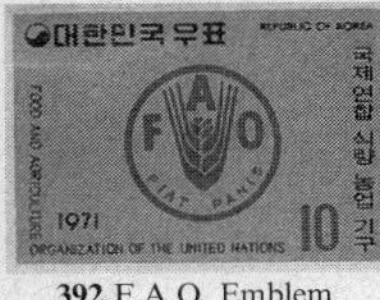
392 F.A.O. Emblem

1971. 3rd World Telecommunications Day.
921 **391** 10 w. multicoloured . . . 50 20

1971. "The Work of the United Nations Organization".
922 – 10 w. mauve, black & grn 1·50 50
923 **392** 10 w. blue, black & mauve 1·50 50
924 – 10 w. multicoloured . . . 1·50 50
925 – 10 w. blue, black & mauve 1·50 50
926 – 10 w. mauve, black & grn 1·50 50
927 – 10 w. blue, black & mauve 1·50 50
928 – 10 w. mauve, black & blue 1·50 50
929 – 10 w. black, green & mauve 1·50 50
930 – 10 w. mauve, black & blue 1·50 50
931 – 10 w. blue, black & mauve 1·50 50
932 – 10 w. mauve, black & blue 1·50 50
933 – 10 w. black, mauve & grn 1·50 50
934 – 10 w. mauve, blue & black 1·50 50
935 – 10 w. black, mauve & grn 1·50 50
936 – 10 w. mauve, black & blue 1·50 50
937 – 10 w. blue, black & mauve 1·50 50

938 – 10 w. mauve, black & blue 1·50 50
939 – 10 w. black, mauve & grn 1·50 50
940 – 10 w. mauve, black & blue 1·50 50
941 – 10 w. blue, black & mauve 1·50 50
942 – 10 w. mauve, black & grn 1·50 50
943 – 10 w. black, blue & mauve 1·50 50
944 – 10 w. multicoloured . . . 1·50 50
945 – 10 w. black, blue & mauve 1·50 50
946 – 10 w. black, mauve & grn 1·50 50

EMBLEMS: No. 992, I.L.O.; No. 924, General Assembly and New York Headquarters; No. 925, U.N.E.S.C.O.; No. 926, W.H.O.; No. 927, World Bank; No. 928, International Development Association; No 929, Security Council; No. 930, International Finance Corporation; No. 931, International Monetary Fund; No. 932, International Civil Aviation Organization; No. 933, Economic and Social Council; No. 934, South Korean flag; No. 935, Trusteeship Council; No. 936, U.P.U.; No. 937, I.T.U.; No. 938, World Meteorological Organization; No. 939, Int Court of Justice; No. 940, I.M.C.O.; No. 941, U.N.I.C.E.F.; No. 942, International Atomic Energy Agency; No. 943, United Nations Industrial Development Organization; No. 944, United Nations Commission for the Unification and Rehabilitation of Korea; No. 945, United Nations Development Programme; No. 946, United Nations Conference on Trade and Development.

393 "Boating" (Shin Yun Bok)

1971. Korean Paintings of the Yi Dynasty (4th series). Multicoloured.
947 10 w. Type **393** . . . . 2·75 75
948 10 w. "Greeting Travellers" . . 2·75 75
949 10 w. "Tea Ceremony" . . . . 2·75 75
950 10 w. "Lady and Servants on Country Road" . . . . . . 2·75 75
951 10 w. "Couple Walking" . . . 2·75 75
952 10 w. "Fairy and Boy beneath Pine Tree" (Li Chae Kwan) (vert) . . . . 2·75 75

Nos. 947/51 show "Folk Customs" paintings by Shin Yun Bok.

394 Pres. Pak, Emblem and Motorway

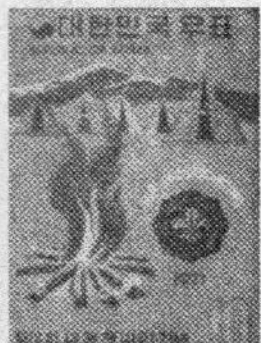

395 Campfire and Badge

1971. Re-election of Pres. Pak for 3rd Term.
954 **394** 10 w. multicoloured . . . 2·00 1·00

1971. Korean Paintings of the Yi Dynasty (5th series). As T **393**. Multicoloured.
956 10 w. "Chasing the Cat" (Kim Deuk Shin) . . . . 2·00 50
957 10 w. "Valley Family" (Li Chae Kwan) (vert) . . . . 2·00 50
958 10 w. "Man Reading" (Li Chae Kwan) (vert) . . . . 2·00 50

1971. 13th World Scout Jamboree, Asagiri, Japan.
960 **395** 10 w. multicoloured . . . 55 20

1971. Korean Paintings of the Yi Dynasty (6th series). As T **393** but vert. Multicoloured.
961 10 w. "Classroom" . . . . . 2·50 85
962 10 w. "Wrestling Match" . . . 2·50 85
963 10 w. "Dancer with Musicians" 2·50 85
964 10 w. "Weavers" . . . . . . 2·50 85
965 10 w. "Drawing Water at the Well" . . . . 2·50 85

Nos. 961/5 depict genre paintings by Kim Hong Do.

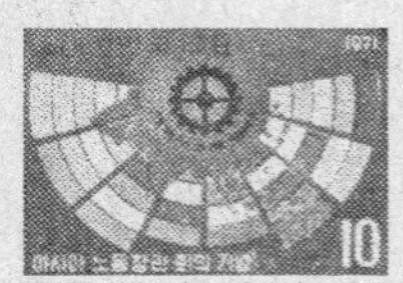

396 Cogwheel and Asian Map

1971. 3rd Asian Labour Minister's Conference, Seoul.
967 **396** 10 w. multicoloured . . . 50 20

397 Judo

1971. 52nd National Athletic Meeting, Seoul. Multicoloured.
969 10 w. Type **397** . . . . 1·25 40
970 10 w. Archery . . . . 1·25 40

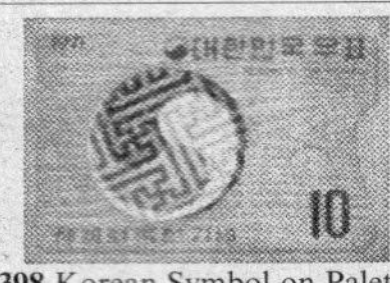

398 Korean Symbol on Palette

1971. 20th National Fine Art Exhibition.
972 **398** 10 w. multicoloured . . . 50 20

399 Doctor and Globe

400 Emblems and "Vocational Skills"

1971. 7th Congress of Medical Associations from Asia and Oceania.
973 **399** 10 w. multicoloured . . . 55 20

1971. 2nd National Vocational Skill Contest for High School Students.
974 **400** 10 w. multicoloured . . . 50 20

401 Callipers and "K" Emblem

1971. 10th Anniv of Industrial Standardisation.
976 **401** 10 w. multicoloured . . . 50 20

402 Fairy Tale Rats

403 Emblem and Hangul Alphabet

1971. Lunar New Year ("Year of the Rat"). Multicoloured.
977 10 w. Type **402** . . . . . . 1·00 50
978 10 w. Flying crane . . . . . . 1·00 50

1971. 50th Anniv of Hangul Hakhoe (Korean Language Research Society).
980 **403** 10 w. multicoloured . . . 50 20

1971. 2nd Five Year Plan. As T **272**. Dated "1971". Multicoloured.
981 10 w. Atomic power plant . . . 60 20
982 10 w. Hydro-electric power project 65 20

404 Korean Red Cross Building on Map

405 Globe and Open Book

1971. South–North Korean Red Cross Conference, Panmunjom.
983 **404** 10 w. multicoloured . . . 1·00 30

1971. International Book Year.
985 **405** 10 w. multicoloured . . . 60 20

406 "Intelsat 4" and Korean Earth Station

407 Speed Skating

1971. 20th Anniv of Korea's Membership of I.T.U.
987 **406** 10 w. multicoloured . . . 50 20

1972. Winter Olympic Games, Sapporo, Japan. Multicoloured.
988 10 w. Type **407** . . . . 1·00 30
989 10 w. Figure-skating . . . . . 1·00 30

408 Forestry Map

410 E.C.A.F.E. Emblem and Industrial Symbols

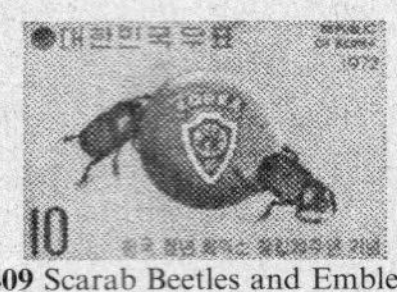

409 Scarab Beetles and Emblem

1972. "Trees for Unity" Campaign.
991 **408** 10 w. multicoloured . . . 50 20

1972. 20th Anniv of Korean Junior Chamber of Commerce.
992 **409** 10 w. multicoloured . . . 70 20

1972. 25th Anniv of U.N. Economic Commission for Asia and the Far East.
993 **410** 10 w. multicoloured . . . 55 20

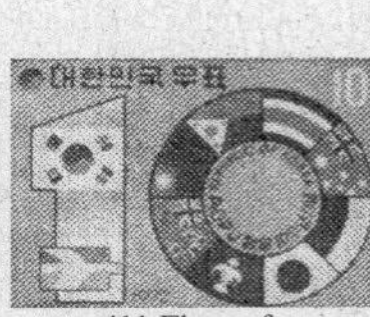

411 Flags of Member Countries

412 Reserve Forces' Flag

1972. 10th Anniv of Asian and Oceanic Postal Union.
994 **411** 10 w. multicoloured . . . 50 20

1972. Home Reserve Forces Day.
995 **412** 10 w. multicoloured . . . 1·00 30

413 Emblem and "Terias harina"

414 Rural Activities

1972. 50th Anniv of Korean Young Women's Christian Association.
996 **413** 10 w. multicoloured . . . 1·75 50

1972. "New Community" (rural development) Movement.
997 **414** 10 w. multicoloured . . . 50 20

415 "Anti-Espionage" and Korean Flag

416 Children with Balloons

1972. Anti-Espionage Month.
998 **415** 10 w. multicoloured . . . 50 20

1972. 50th Children's Day.
999 **416** 10 w. multicoloured . . . 50 20

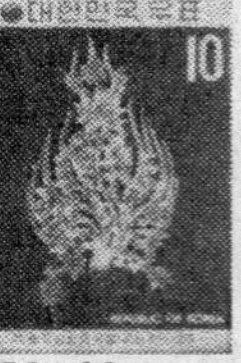

417 Leaf Ornament from Gold Crown

418 Lake Paengnokdam, Mt. Halla Park

419 Kalkot, Koje Island, Hanryo Straits Park

1972. Treasures from King Munyong's Tomb. Multicoloured.
1000 10 w. Type **417** 60 20
1001 10 w. Gold earrings (horiz) 65 20

1972. National Parks (1st series).
1002 **418** 10 w. multicoloured . . . 75 40
1003 **419** 10 w. multicoloured . . . 75 40

See also Nos. 1018/19 and 1026/7.

420 Marguerite and Conference Emblem

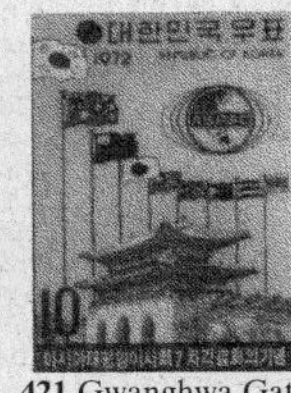

421 Gwanghwa Gate and National Flags

1972. U.N. Environmental Conservation Conference, Stockholm.
1004 **420** 10 w. multicoloured . . . 45 20

1972. 7th Asian and Pacific Council (ASPAC) Ministerial Meeting, Seoul.
1006 **421** 10 w. multicoloured . . . 60 25

422 Pasture ("Development of Rural Economy")

423 "Love Pin"

1972. 3rd Five Year Plan. Dated "1972". Multicoloured.
1007 10 w. Type **422** 60 25
1008 10 w. Foundry ladle ("Heavy Industries") 60 25
1009 10 w. Crate and Globe ("Increased Exports") . . . 60 25

1972. Disaster Relief Fund.
1010 **423** 10 w. + 5 w. red & blue . 75 20

424 Judo

425 Family Reunion through Red Cross

1972. Olympic Games, Munich. Multicoloured.
1011 20 w. Type **424** 75 20
1012 20 w. Weightlifting 75 20
1013 20 w. Wrestling 75 20
1014 20 w. Boxing 75 20

1972. 1st Plenary Meeting of South-North Korean Red Cross Conference, Pyongyang.
1016 **425** 10 w. multicoloured . . . 1·25 35

426 Bulkuk Temple, Kyongju Park

428 Conference Emblem within "5"

427 Statue and Bopju Temple, Mt. Sokri Park

1972. National Parks (2nd series).
1018 **426** 10 w. multicoloured . . . 75 40
1019 **427** 10 w. multicoloured . . . 75 40

1972. 5th Asian Judicial Conference, Seoul.
1020 **428** 10 w. multicoloured . . . 55 20

429 Lions Badge between Korean Emblems

1972. 11th Orient and South-East Asian Lions Convention, Seoul.
1021 **429** 10 w. multicoloured . . . 50 20

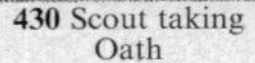

430 Scout taking Oath **431** Dolls and Ox's Head

1972. 50th Anniv of Korean Boy Scouts Movement.
1022 **430** 10 w. multicoloured . . . 1·00 25

1972. Lunar New Year ("Year of the Ox"). Multicoloured.
1023 10 w. Type **431** 60 20
1024 10 w. Revellers in balloon . . 60 20

432 Temple, Mt. Naejang Park **433** Madeungryong Pass, Mt. Sorak Park

1972. National Parks. (3rd series).
1026 **432** 10 w. multicoloured . . . 75 40
1027 **433** 10 w. multicoloured . . . 75 40

434 President Pak, Flag and "Development"

1972. Re-election of President Pak.
1028 **434** 10 w. multicoloured . . . 2·00 65

435 National Central Museum, Kyongbok Palace **437** Korean Family

436 Temple, Mt. Sorak

1973. Korean Tourist Attractions (1st series).
1030 **435** 10 w. multicoloured . . . 75 15
1031 **436** 10 w. multicoloured . . . 75 15
See also Nos. 1042/3, 1048/9, 1057/8 and 1075/6.

1973. Korean Unification Campaign.
1032 **437** 10 w. multicoloured . . . 50 15

438 "V" Sign and Flags **439** Construction Workers and Cogwheel

1973. Return of Korean Forces from South Vietnam.
1033 **438** 10 w. multicoloured . . . 60 20

1973. 10th Workers' Day.
1034 **439** 10 w. multicoloured . . . 50 15

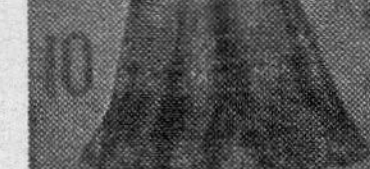

440 W.M.O. Emblem and Satellite **442** Wonsam Costume (woman's ceremonial)

1973. Centenary of World Meteorological Organization.
1035 **440** 10 w. multicoloured . . . 50 15

1973. Korean Court Costumes of the Yi Dynasty (1st series). Multicoloured. Background colours given.
1037 – 10 w. orange . . . . . . 1·10 30
1038 **442** 10 w. orange . . . . . . 1·10 30
DESIGN: No. 1037, Kujangbok (king's ceremonial costume);
See also Nos. 1045/6, 1053/4, 1060/1 and 1078/9.

443 Nurse with Lamp **444** Reservists and Flag

1973. 50th Anniv of Korean Nurses' Association.
1040 **443** 10 w. multicoloured . . . 65 15

1973. Home Reserve Forces Day.
1041 **444** 10 w. multicoloured . . . 75 30

445 Palmi Island **446** Sain-am Rock, Mt. Dokjol

1973. Korean Tourist Attractions (2nd series).
1042 **445** 10 w. multicoloured . . . 75 25
1043 **446** 10 w. multicoloured . . . 75 25

447 Table Tennis Player

1973. Victory of South Korean Women's Team in World Table Tennis Championships, Sarajevo.
1044 **447** 10 w. multicoloured . . . 1·25 30

1973. Korean Court Costumes of the Yi Dynasty (2nd series). As T **442**. Mult. Background colours given.
1045 10 w. purple 80 15
1046 10 w. green 80 15
DESIGNS: No. 1045, Konryongpo (king's costume); No. 1046, Jokui (queen's ceremonial costume).

450 Admiral Li Sun Sin's Shrine, Asan **451** Limestone Cavern, Kusan-ni

1973. Korean Tourist Attractions (3rd series).
1048 **450** 10 w. multicoloured . . . 80 25
1049 **451** 10 w. multicoloured . . . 80 25

452 Children's Choir

1973. 20th Anniv of World Vision Int.
1050 **452** 10 w. multicoloured . . . 75 25

453 Love Pin and "Disasters"

1973. Disaster Relief Fund.
1051 **453** 10 w. + 5 w. mult 45 15

454 Steel Converter **457** Table Tennis Bat and Ball

1973. Inauguration of Pohang Steel Works.
1052 **454** 10 w. multicoloured . . . 50 15

1973. Korean Court Costumes of the Yi Dynasty (3rd series). As T **442**. Mult. Background colours given.
1053 10 w. blue . . . . 1·25 15
1054 10 w. pink . . . . 1·25 15
DESIGNS: No. 1053, Kangsapo (crown prince's) costume; No. 1054, Tangui (princess's) costume.

1973. Table Tennis Gymnasium Construction Fund.
1056 **457** 10 w. + 5 w. mve & grn 75 20

458 Namhae Suspension Bridge **459** Hongdo Island

1973. Korean Tourist Attractions (4th series).
1057 **458** 10 w. multicoloured . . . 55 10
1058 **459** 10 w. multicoloured . . . 55 10

460 Interpol and Korean Police Emblems

1973. 50th Anniv of International Criminal Police Organization (Interpol).
1059 **460** 10 w. multicoloured . . . 65 10

1973. Korean Court Costumes of the Yi Dynasty (4th series). As T **442**. Mult. Background colours given.
1060 10 w. yellow 75 10
1061 10 w. blue 75 10
DESIGNS: No. 1060, Kumkwanchobok (court official's) costume; 1061, Hwalot (queen's wedding) costume.

465 Manchurian Cranes **466** Sommal Lily **467** Motorway and Farm

1973.
1063 – 1 w. brown 40 10
1063a – 3 w. black and blue . . . 50 15
1064 – 5 w. brown 10 10
1064a – 6 w. turquoise and green 30 10
1065 **465** 10 w. ultramarine & blue 75 15
1066 **466** 10 w. red, black & green 75 10
1067 **467** 10 w. green and red . . 50 10
1068 – 30 w. brown and yellow 65 10
1068a – 50 w. green and brown 50 10
1068b – 60 w. brown and yellow 50 10
1068c – 80 w. black and brown 75 10
1069 – 100 w. yellow & brown 15·00 40
1069a – 100 w. red . . . . . . 1·00 15
1069b – 200 w. brown and pink 1·40 20
1069c – 300 w. red and lilac . . 2·00 25
1069d – 500 w. multicoloured . . 10·00 30
1069e – 500 w. purple & brown 4·00 25
1069f – 1000 w. green . . . . . 5·00 60

DESIGNS—VERT: 1 w. Mask of old man; 5 w. Siberian chipmunk; 6 w. Lily; 30 w. Honey bee; 50 w. Pot with lid; 60 w. Jar; 100 w. (No. 1069) Gold Crown, Silla dynasty; 100 w. (No. 1069a) Admiral Yi Soon Shin; 300 w. Pobjusa Temple; 500 w. (No. 1069d) Gold Crown; 500 w. (No. 1069e) Carved dragon (tile Backje Dynasty). LARGER 24633 mm: 100 w. Flying deities (relief from bronze bell, Sangweon Temple). HORIZ: 3 w. Magpie; 80 w. Ceramic horseman; 200 w. Muryangsujeon Hall, Busok Temple.
For designs similar to Type **465** but with frame, see Type **703**.

470 Tennis

1973. 54th National Athletic Meeting, Pusan. Multicoloured.
1070 10 w. Type **470** 65 15
1071 10 w. Hurdling 65 15

471 Children with Stamp Albums

1973. Philatelic Week.
1072 **471** 10 w. multicoloured . . . 40 10

472 Soyang River Dam

1973. Inauguration of Soyang River Dam.
1074 **472** 10 w. multicoloured . . . 40 10

473 Mt. Mai, Chinan **474** Tangerine Grove, Cheju Island

1973. Korean Tourist Attractions (5th series).
1075 **473** 10 w. multicoloured . . . 50 10
1076 **474** 10 w. multicoloured . . . 50 10

475 Match, Cigarette and Flames **478** Tiger and Candles

1973. 10th Fire Prevention Day.
1077 **475** 10 w. multicoloured . . . 40 10

1973. Korean Court Costumes of the Yi Dynasty (5th series). As T **442**. Mult. Back-ground colours given.
1078 10 w. orange 75 10
1079 10 w. pink 75 10
DESIGNS: No. 1078, Pyongsangbok (official's wife) costume; 1079, Kokunbok (military officer's) costume.

1973. Lunar New Year ("Year of the Tiger"). Multicoloured.
1081 10 w. Type **478** 75 10
1082 10 w. Decorated top 75 10

479 Korean Girl and Flame Emblem

1973. 25th Anniv of Declaration of Human Rights.
1084 **479** 10 w. multicoloured . . . 40 10

480 Boeing 747-200 Jetliner and Polar Zone

1973. Air.
1085 **480** 110 w. blue and pink . . . 3·00 30
1086 – 135 w. red and green . . . 3·00 30
1087 – 145 w. red and blue . . . 3·00 30
1088 – 180 w. yellow and lilac . . . 3·00 30
DESIGNS—Boeing 747-200 jetliner and postal zones on map; 135 w. South-east Asia; 145 w. India, Australasia and North America; 180 w. Europe, Africa and South America.

481 "Komunko" (zither)

1974. Traditional Musical Instruments (1st series). Multicoloured. Background colours given.
1089 **481** 10 w. blue . . . . 1·00 10
1090 – 30 w. orange . . . . . . 1·00 40
DESIGN: 30 w. "Nagak" (trumpet triton).
See also Nos. 1098/9, 1108/9, 1117/18 and 1132/3.

483 Apricots

485 Reservist and Factory

1974. Fruits (1st series). Multicoloured.
1092 10 w. Type **483** 30 10
1093 30 w. Strawberries 60 15
See also Nos. 1104/5, 111/2, 1120/1 and 1143/4.

1974. Home Reserve Forces Day.
1095 **485** 10 w. multicoloured . . . 30 10

486 W.P.Y. Emblem

489 Diesel Mail Train and Communications Emblem

1974. World Population Year.
1096 **486** 10 w. multicoloured . . . 25 10

1974. Traditional Musical Instruments (2nd series). As T **481**. Multicoloured. Background colours given.
1098 10 w. blue 75 10
1099 30 w. green . . . . 1·50 15
DESIGNS: 10 w. "Tchouk"; 30 w. "Eu".

1974. Communications Day.
1101 **489** 10 w. multicoloured . . . 75 15

490 C.A.F.E.A.-I.C.C. Emblem on Globe

491 Port Installations

1974. 22nd Session of International Chamber of Commerce's Commission on Asian and Far Eastern Affairs, Seoul.
1102 **490** 10 w. multicoloured . . . 30 10

1974. Inaug of New Port Facilities, Inchon.
1103 **491** 10 w. multicoloured . . . 40 10

1974. Fruits (2nd series). As T **483**. Mult.
1104 10 w. Peaches 40 10
1105 30 w. Grapes 60 15

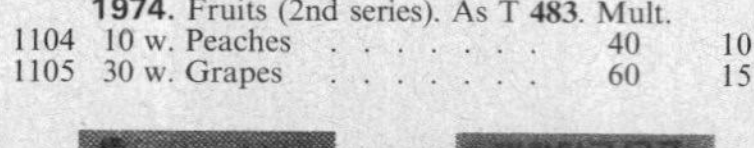

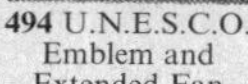
494 U.N.E.S.C.O. Emblem and Extended Fan

499 Cross and Emblems

1974. 20th Anniv of South Korean U.N.E.S.C.O. Commission.
1107 **494** 10 w. multicoloured . . . 30 10

1974. Traditional Musical Instruments (3rd series). As T **481**. Multicoloured. Background colours given.
1108 10 w. orange 65 10
1109 30 w. pink . . . . 1·25 15
DESIGNS: 10 w. "A-chaing" (stringed instrument); 30 w. "Kyobang-ko" (drum).

1974. Fruits (3rd series). As T **483**. Multicoloured.
1111 10 w. Pears 40 10
1112 30 w. Apples 60 15

1974. "Explo 74" 2nd International Training Congress on Evangelism. Multicoloured.
1114 10 w. Type **499** 30 10
1115 10 w. Emblem and Korean map on Globe 30 10

501 Underground Train

1974. Opening of Seoul Underground Railway.
1116 **501** 10 w. multicoloured . . . 85 10

1974. Traditional Musical Instruments (4th series). As T **481**. Multicoloured. Background colours given.
1117 10 w. blue 65 10
1118 30 w. pink . . . . 1·10 15
DESIGNS: No. 1117, So ("Pan pipes"); No. 1118, Haikem (Two-stringed fiddle).

1974. Fruits (4th series). As T **483**. Multicoloured.
1120 10 w. Cherries 40 10
1121 30 w. Persimmons 60 10

506 Rifle Shooting

1974. 55th National Athletic Meeting, Seoul. Multicoloured.
1123 10 w. Type **506** 30 10
1124 30 w. Rowing 80 10

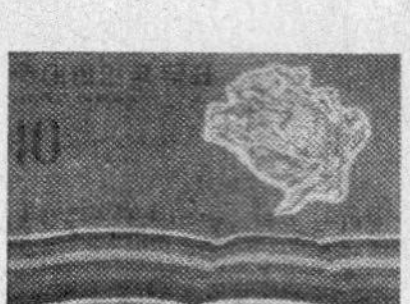
508 U.P.U. Emblem

509 Symbols of Member Countries

1974. Centenary of U.P.U.
1125 **508** 10 w. multicoloured (postage) 30 10
1126 110 w. multicoloured (air) . 1·25 50

1974. 1st World Conference of People-to-People International.
1128 **509** 10 w. multicoloured . . . 30 10

510 Korean Stamps of 1884

1974. Philatelic Week and 90th Anniv of First Korean Stamps.
1129 **510** 10 w. multicoloured . . . 50 10

511 Taekwondo Contestants

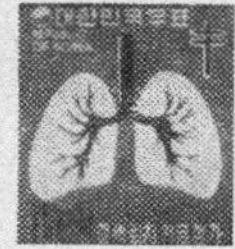
514 Lungs

1974. 1st Asian Taekwondo Championships, Seoul.
1131 **511** 10 w. multicoloured . . . 50 10

1974. Traditional Musical Instruments (5th series). As T **481**. Multicoloured. Background colours given.
1132 10 w. pink 50 10
1133 30 w. ochre 75 15
DESIGNS: 10 w. Pak (clappers); 30 w. Pyenchong (chimes).

1974. Tuberculosis Control Fund.
1135 **514** 10 w. + 5 w. red & green 40 10

515 Presidents Pak and Ford

516 Yook Young Soo (wife of Pres. Pak)

1974. State Visit of President Ford of United States.
1136 **515** 10 w. multicoloured . . . 55 20

1974. Yook Young Soo Memorial Issue.
1138 **516** 10 w. green 50 15
1139 10 w. orange 50 15
1140 10 w. violet 50 15
1141 10 w. blue 50 15

1974. Fruits (5th series). As T **483**. Multicoloured.
1143 10 w. Tangerines 40 10
1144 30 w. Chestnuts 50 15

519 "Good Luck" Purse

521 U.P.U. Emblem and "75"

1974. Lunar New Year ("Year of the Rabbit"). Multicoloured.
1146 10 w. Type **519** 40 10
1147 10 w. Toy rabbits 40 10

1975. 75th Anniv of Korea's Membership of U.P.U. Multicoloured.
1149 10 w. Type **521** 30 10
1150 10 w. U.P.U. emblem and paper dart 30 10

523 Dove with "Good Luck" Card

1975. Inauguration of National Welfare Insurance System.
1151 **523** 10 w. multicoloured . . . 20 10

524 Dr. Schweitzer, Map and Syringe

525 Salpuli Dancer

1975. Birth Centenary of Dr. Albert Schweitzer.
1152 **524** 10 w. bistre 50 15
1153 10 w. mauve 50 15
1154 10 w. orange 50 15
1155 10 w. green 50 15

1975. Korean Folk Dances (1st series). Multicoloured, background colour given.
1156 **525** 10 w. green 40 10
1157 – 10 w. blue 40 10
DESIGN: No. 1157, Exorcism in dance.
See also Nos. 1168/9, 1175/6, 1193/4 and 1208/9.

527 Globe and Rotary Emblem

1975. 70th Anniv of Rotary International.
1159 **527** 10 w. multicoloured . . . 25 10

528 Women and I.W.Y. Emblem

1975. International Women's Year.
1160 **528** 10 w. multicoloured . . . 25 10

529 Violets

531 Saemaeul Township

1975. Flowers (1st series). Multicoloured.
1161 10 w. Type **529** 40 10
1162 10 w. Anemones 40 10
See also Nos. 1171/2, 1184/5, 1199/1200 and 1213/4.

1975. National Afforestation Campaign. Multicoloured.
1163 10 w. Type **531** 50 10
1164 10 w. Lake and trees 50 10
1165 10 w. "Green" forest 50 10
1166 10 w. Felling timber 50 10
Nos. 1163/6 were issued together, se-tenant, forming a composite design.

535 H.R.F. Emblem on Map of Korea

536 Butterfly Dance

1975. Homeland Reserve Forces Day.
1167 **535** 10 w. multicoloured . . . 40 10

1975. Folk Dances (2nd series). Multicoloured, background colour given.
1168 **536** 10 w. green 45 10
1169 – 10 w. yellow 45 10
DESIGN: No. 1169, Victory dance.

538 Rhododendron

540 Metric Symbols

1975. Flowers (2nd series). Multicoloured.
1171 10 w. Type **538** 40 10
1172 10 w. Clematis 40 10

1975. Centenary of Metric Convention.
1173 **540** 10 w. multicoloured . . . 25 10

541 Soldier and Incense Pot

542 Mokjoong Dance

1975. 20th Memorial Day.
1174 **541** 10 w. multicoloured . . . 25 10

1975. Folk Dances (3rd series). Multicoloured.
1175 **542** 10 w. blue 45 10
1176 – 10 w. pink 45 10
DESIGN: No. 1176, Malttungi dancer.

544 Flags of South Korea, U.N. and U.S

1975. 25th Anniv of Korean War. Multicoloured.
1178 10 w. Type **544** 45 10
1179 10 w. Flags of Ethiopia, France, Greece, Canada and South Africa 45 10

1180 10 w. Flags of Luxembourg, Australia, U.K., Colombia and Turkey . . . 45 10
1181 10 w. Flags of Netherlands, Belgium, Philippines, New Zealand and Thailand . . . 45 10

548 Presidents Pak and Bongo
549 Iris

1975. State Visit of President Bongo of Gabon.
1182 **548** 10 w. multicoloured . . . 40 10

1975. Flowers (3rd series). Multicoloured.
1184 10 w. Type **549** 40 10
1185 10 w. Thistle 40 10

551 Scout Scarf
552 Freedom Flame

1975. "Nordjamb 75" World Scout Jamboree, Norway. Multicoloured.
1186 10 w. Type **551** 40 10
1187 10 w. Scout oath 40 10
1188 10 w. Scout camp 40 10
1189 10 w. Axe and rope 40 10
1190 10 w. Camp fire 40 10

1975. 30th Anniv of Liberation. Multicoloured.
1191 20 w. Type **552** 45 10
1192 20 w. Balloon emblems 45 10

554 Drum Dance
556 Taekwondo Contestant

1975. Folk Dances (4th series). Multicoloured, background colour given.
1193 **554** 20 w. yellow 60 10
1194 – 20 w. orange 60 10
DESIGN: No. 1194, Bara dance.

1975. 2nd World Taekwondo Championships, Seoul.
1196 **556** 20 w. multicoloured . . . 30 10

557 Assembly Hall

1975. Completion of National Assembly Hall.
1197 **557** 20 w. multicoloured . . . 30 10

558 Dumper Truck and Emblem
559 Broad-bell Flower

1975. Contractors' Association Convention, Seoul.
1198 **558** 20 w. multicoloured . . . 40 10

1975. Flowers (4th series). Multicoloured.
1199 20 w. Type **559** 45 10
1200 20 w. Bush clover 45 10

561 Morse Key and Dish Aerial

1975. 90th Anniv of Korean Telecommunications.
1201 **561** 20 w. black, orge & pur 35 10

562 Yeongweol Caves
564 Flag and Missiles

1975. International Tourism Day. Multicoloured.
1202 20 w. Type **562** 30 10
1203 20 w. Mount Sorak 30 10

1975. Korean Armed Forces Day.
1204 **564** 20 w. multicoloured . . . 30 10

565 "Gymnastics"
567 "Kangaroo" Collector

1975. 56th National Athletic Meeting. Multicoloured.
1205 20 w. Type **565** 25 10
1206 20 w. "Handball" 25 10

1975. Philatelic Week.
1207 **567** 20 w. multicoloured . . . 30 10

568 Sogo Dance
570 U.N. Emblem and Handclasps

1975. Folk Dances (5th series). Multicoloured, background colour given.
1208 **568** 20 w. blue 45 10
1209 – 20 w. yellow 55 10
DESIGN: No. 1209, Bupo Nori dance.

1975. 30th Anniv of United Nations.
1211 **570** 20 w. multicoloured . . . 25 10

571 Red Cross and Emblems
572 Camellia

1975. 70th Anniv of Korean Red Cross.
1212 **571** 20 w. multicoloured . . . 35 10

1975. Flowers (5th series). Multicoloured.
1213 20 w. Type **572** 50 10
1214 20 w. Gentian 50 10

574 Union Emblem
575 Children Playing

1975. 10th Anniv of Asian Parliamentary Union.
1215 **574** 20 w. multicoloured . . . 30 10

1975. Lunar New Year. Multicoloured.
1216 20 w. Type **575** 30 10
1217 20 w. Dragon ("Year of the Dragon") 30 10

577 Electric Train

1975. Opening of Cross-country Electric Railway.
1219 **577** 20 w. multicoloured . . . 50 10

578 "Dilipa fenestra"

1976. Butterflies (1st series). Multicoloured, background colour given.
1220 **578** 20 w. red . . . . 1·00 10
1221 – 20 w. blue . . . . 1·00 10
DESIGN: No. 1221, "Luehdorfia puziloi".
See also Nos. 1226/7, 1246/7, 1254/5 and 1264/5.

580 Institute Emblem and Science Emblems
581 Japanese White-necked Crane

1976. 10th Anniv of Korean Institute of Science and Technology.
1222 **580** 20 w. multicoloured . . . 25 10

1976. Birds (1st series). Multicoloured.
1223 20 w. Type **581** 75 25
1224 20 w. Great bustard 75 25
See also Nos. 1243/4, 1251/2, 1257/8 and 1266/7.

583 Globe and Telephones

1976. Telephone Centenary.
1225 **583** 20 w. multicoloured . . . 20 10

584 "Papilio xuthus"

1976. Butterflies (2nd series). Multicoloured, background colour given.
1226 **584** 20 w. yellow . . . . . . 1·00 10
1227 – 20 w. green . . . . . . 1·00 10
DESIGN: No. 1227, "Parnassius bremeri".

586 "National Development"
587 Eye and People

1976. Homeland Reserve Forces Day.
1228 **586** 20 w. multicoloured . . . 30 10

1976. World Health Day. Prevention of Blindness.
1229 **587** 20 w. multicoloured . . . 30 10

588 Pres. Pak and Flag
589 Ruins of Moenjodaro

1976. 6th Anniv of Saemaul Movement (community self-help programme). Multicoloured.
1230 20 w. Type **588** 45 15
1231 20 w. People ("Intellectual edification") 45 15
1232 20 w. Village ("Welfare") . . 45 15
1233 20 w. Produce and fields ("Production") 45 15
1234 20 w. Produce and factory ("Increase of Income") . . 45 15

1976. Moenjodaro (Pakistan) Preservation Campaign.
1235 **589** 20 w. multicoloured . . . 40 10

590 U.S. Flags of 1776 and 1976
591 Camp Scene on Emblem

1976. Bicentenary of American Revolution. Each black, blue and red.
1236 100 w. Type **590** . . . . . . 1·60 45
1237 100 w. Statue of Liberty . . . 1·60 45
1238 100 w. Map of United States . 1·60 45
1239 100 w. Liberty Bell . . . . . 1·60 45
1240 100 w. American astronaut . . 1·60 45

1976. 30th Anniv of Korean Girl Scouts Federation.
1242 **591** 20 w. multicoloured . . . 60 10

592 Blue-winged Pitta
594 Buddha and Temple

1976. Birds (2nd series). Multicoloured.
1243 20 w. Type **592** 80 25
1244 20 w. White-bellied black woodpecker 80 25

1976. U.N.E.S.C.O. Campaign for Preservation of Borobudur Temple (in Indonesia).
1245 **594** 20 w. multicoloured . . . 25 10

595 Eastern Pale Clouded Yellow

1976. Butterflies (3rd series). Multicoloured, background colour given.
1246 **595** 20 w. olive 75 10
1247 – 20 w. violet 75 10
DESIGN: No. 1247, Chinese windmill.

597 Protected Family
598 Volleyball

1976. National Life Insurance.
1248 **597** 20 w. multicoloured . . . 30 10

1976. Olympic Games, Montreal. Multicoloured.
1249 20 w. Type **598** 35 10
1250 20 w. Boxing 35 10

600 Black Wood Pigeon
602 Children and Books

1976. Birds (3rd series). Multicoloured.
1251 20 w. Type **600** 80 25
1252 20 w. Oystercatcher 80 25

1976. Books for Children.
1253 **602** 20 w. multicoloured . . . 25 10

603 "Hestina assimilis"

1976. Butterflies (4th series). Multicoloured, background colour given.
1254 **603** 20 w. brown 75 10
1255 – 20 w. drab 75 10
DESIGN: No. 1255, Blue triangle.

604a Corps Members and Flag — **605** Black-faced Spoonbill

1976. 1st Anniv of Korean Civil Defence Corps.
1256 **604a** 20 w. multicoloured . . 30 10

1976. Birds (4th series). Multicoloured.
1257 20 w. Type **605** 75 25
1258 20 w. Black stork 75 25

607 Chamsungdan, Mani Mountain

1976. International Tourism Day. Multicoloured.
1259 20 w. Type **607** 40 10
1260 20 w. Ilchumun Gate, Tongdosa 40 10

609 Cadet and Parade — **610** "Musa basjoo" (flower arrangement, Cheong Jo the Great)

1976. 30th Anniv of Korean Military Academy.
1261 **609** 20 w. multicoloured . . . 25 10

1976. Philatelic Week.
1262 **610** 20 w. black, red and drab 25 10

611 Yellow-legged Tortoiseshell — **613** European Black Vulture

1976. Butterflies (5th series). Multicoloured, background colour given.
1264 **611** 20 w. light green 75 10
1265 – 20 w. purple 75 10
DESIGN: No. 1265, "Fabriciana nerippe".

1976. Birds (5th series). Multicoloured.
1266 20 w. Type **613** . . . . 2·75 1·25
1267 20 w. Whistling Swan . . . . 2·75 1·25

615 Snake (bas-relief, Kim Yu Shin's tomb) — **619** Dish Aerial

617 "Training Technicians"

1976. Lunar New Year (Year of the Snake). Multicoloured.
1268 20 w. Type **615** 50 10
1269 20 w. Door knocker with Manchurian cranes 50 10

1977. 4th Five Year Economic Development Plan. Multicoloured.
1271 20 w. Type **617** 40 10
1272 20 w. Tanker ("Heavy Industries") 50 10

1977. 25th Anniv of Korea's I.T.U. Membership.
1273 **619** 20 w. multicoloured . . . 30 10

620 Korean Broadcasting Centre — **621** Jar with Grape Design

1977. 50th Anniv of Broadcasting in Korea.
1274 **620** 20 w. multicoloured . . . 35 10

1977. Korean Ceramics (1st series). Multicoloured, background colours given.
1275 20 w. Type **621** (brown) . . . 75 10
1276 20 w. Celadon vase (grey) . . 75 10
See also Nos. 1285/6, 1287/8, 1290/1 and 1300/1.

623 "Two-children" Family — **624** Reserve Soldier

1977. Family Planning.
1277 **623** 20 w. green, turq & orge 30 10

1977. 9th Homeland Reserve Forces Day.
1278 **624** 20 w. multicoloured . . . 35 10

625 Diagram of Brain — **626** Medical Book and Equipment

1977. 10th Anniv of Science Day.
1279 **625** 20 w. multicoloured . . . 25 10

1977. 35th International Military Medicine Meeting.
1280 **626** 20 w. multicoloured . . . 45 10

627 Child with Flowers — **628** Veterans' Flag and Emblem

1977. 20th Anniv of Children's Charter.
1281 **627** 20 w. multicoloured . . . 25 10

1977. 25th Anniv of Korean Veterans' Day.
1282 **628** 20 w. multicoloured . . . 40 10

629 Statue of Buddha, Sokkulam Grotto — **630** Celadon Jar

1977. 2600th Birth Anniv of Buddha.
1283 **629** 20 w. green and brown . . 40 10

1977. Korean Ceramics (2nd series). Multicoloured, background colours given.
1285 20 w. Type **630** (pink) 45 10
1286 20 w. Porcelain vase (blue) (vert) 45 10

632 "Buddha" Celadon Wine Jar

1977. Korean Ceramics (3rd series). Multicoloured, background colours given.
1287 20 w. Type **632** (mauve) . . . 45 10
1288 20 w. Celadon vase (pale blue) 45 10

수해구제
+10
(**634**)

635 Celadon Vase, Black Koryo Ware

1977. Flood Relief. No. 791 surch with T **634**.
1289 20 w. + 10 w. green . . . . 1·25 40

1977. Korean Ceramics (4th series). Multicoloured, background colours given.
1290 20 w. Type **635** (stone) 45 10
1291 20 w. White porcelain bowl (green) (horiz) 45 10

637 Ulleung-do Island — **639** Servicemen

1977. World Tourism Day. Multicoloured.
1292 20 w. Type **637** 30 10
1293 20 w. Haeundae Beach . . . 30 10

1977. Armed Forces Day.
1294 **639** 20 w. multicoloured . . . 20 10

640 — **641**
"Mount Inwang Clearing-up after the Rain" (detail from drawing by Chung Seon)

1977. Philatelic Week.
1295 **640** 20 w. multicoloured . . . 40 10
1296 **641** 20 w. multicoloured . . . 40 10
Nos. 1294/5 were issued together, se-tenant, forming a composite design.

642 Rotary Emblem and Koryo Dynasty Bronze Bell — **643** South Korean Flag over Everest

1977. 50th Anniv of Korean Rotary Club.
1298 **642** 20 w. multicoloured . . . 50 10

1977. South Korean Conquest of Mount Everest.
1299 **643** 20 w. multicoloured . . . 50 10

644 Punch'ong Bottle — **646** Hands preserving Nature

1977. Korean Ceramics (5th series). Multicoloured, background colours given.
1300 20 w. Type **644** (brown) . . . 50 10
1301 20 w. Celadon cylindrical bottle (pale brown) 50 10

1977. Nature Conservation.
1302 **646** 20 w. blue, green & brn 30 10

647 Children with Kites — **649** Clay Pigeon Shooting

1977. Lunar New Year ("Year of the Horse"). Multicoloured.
1303 20 w. Type **647** 30 10
1304 20 w. Horse (bas-relief, Kim Yu Shin's tomb) 30 10

1977. 42nd World Shooting Championships, Seoul. Multicoloured.
1306 20 w. Type **649** 35 10
1307 20 w. Air pistol shooting . . . 35 10
1308 20 w. Air rifle shooting . . . 35 10

652 Korean Airlines Boeing 747-200

1977. 25th Anniv of Korean Membership of I.C.A.O.
1310 **652** 20 w. multicoloured . . . 45 10

653 "Exports"

1977. Korean Exports.
1311 **653** 20 w. multicoloured . . . 35 10

654 Ships and World Map

1978. National Maritime Day.
1312 **654** 20 w. multicoloured . . . 30 10

655 Three-storey Pagoda, Hwaom Temple — **656** Seven-storey Pagoda, T'app'yong-ri

1978. Stone Pagodas (1st series).
1313 **655** 20 w. multicoloured . . . 35 10
1314 **656** 20 w. multicoloured . . . 35 10
See also Nos. 1319/20, 1322/5 and 1340/1.

657 Ants with Coins — **658** Seoul Sejong Cultural Centre, Hahoe Mask and Violin

1978. Savings Encouragement.
1315 **657** 20 w. multicoloured . . . 30 10

1978. Opening of Seoul Sejong Cultural Centre.
1316 **658** 20 w. multicoloured . . . 60 10

659 Standard Bearer

660 Pigeon and Young

1978. 10th Homeland Reserve Forces Day.
1317 **659** 20 w. multicoloured . . . 25 10

1978. Family Planning.
1318 **660** 20 w. black and green . . 35 10

661 Pagoda, Punhwang Temple

662 Pagoda, Miruk Temple

1978. Stone Pagodas (2nd series).
1319 **661** 20 w. multicoloured . . . 35 10
1320 **662** 20 w. multicoloured . . . 35 10

663 National Assembly

1978. 30th Anniv of National Assembly.
1321 **663** 20 w. multicoloured . . . 25 10

664 Tabo Pagoda, Pulguk Temple

665 Three-storey Pagoda, Pulguk Temple

1978. Stone Pagodas (3rd series).
1322 **664** 20 w. multicoloured . . . 35 10
1323 **665** 20 w. multicoloured . . . 35 10

666 Ten-storey Pagoda, Kyongch'on Temple

667 Nine-storey Octagonal Pagoda, Wolchong Temple

1978. Stone Pagodas (4th series).
1324 **666** 20 w. multicoloured . . . 45 10
1325 **667** 20 w. multicoloured . . . 45 10

668 Emblem and Hands with Tools

669 Crater Lake, Mt. Baeguda and Bell of Joy

1978. 24th International Youth Skill Olympics, Pusan.
1326 **668** 20 w. multicoloured . . . 25 10

1978. 30th Anniv of Republic of Korea.
1328 **669** 20 w. multicoloured . . . 25 10

670 Army Nursing Officer

671 Sobaeksan Observatory and Telescope

1978. 30th Anniv of Army Nursing Corps.
1329 **670** 20 w. multicoloured . . . 25 10

1978. Opening of Sobaeksan Observatory.
1330 **671** 20 w. multicoloured . . . 40 10

672 Kyonghoeru Pavilion, Kyonbok Palace

673 Baeg-do Island

1978. World Tourism Day.
1331 **672** 20 w. multicoloured . . . 30 10
1332 **673** 20 w. multicoloured . . . 30 10

674 Customs Officers and Flag

1978. Centenary of Custom House.
1333 **674** 20 w. multicoloured . . . 25 10

675 Armed Forces

676 Earthenware Figures, Silla Dynasty

1978. 30th Anniv of Korean Armed Forces.
1334 **675** 20 w. multicoloured . . . 40 10

1978. Culture Month.
1335 **676** 20 w. black and green . . 25 10

677 Painting of a Lady (Shin Yoon-bok)

678 Young Men and Y.M.C.A. Emblem

1978. Philatelic Week.
1336 **677** 20 w. multicoloured . . . 35 10

1978. 75th Anniv of Korean Y.M.C.A.
1338 **678** 20 w. multicoloured . . . 25 10

679 Hand smothering Fire

1978. Fire Prevention Campaign.
1339 **679** 20 w. multicoloured . . . 25 10

680 Thirteen-storey Pagoda, Jeonghye Temple

681 Three-storey Pagoda, Jinjeon Temple

1978. Stone Pagodas (5th series).
1340 **680** 20 w. multicoloured . . . 30 10
1341 **681** 20 w. multicoloured . . . 30 10

682 Snow Scene

684 People within Hibiscus

1978. Lunar New Year ("Year of the Sheep"). Multicoloured.
1342 20 w. Type **682** 30 10
1343 20 w. Sheep (bas-relief, Kim Yu Shin's tomb) 30 10

1978. 10th Anniv of National Education Charter.
1345 **684** 20 w. multicoloured . . . 25 10

685 President Pak

1978. Re-election of President Pak.
1346 **685** 20 w. multicoloured . . . 40 10

686 Golden Mandarinfish

687 Lace Bark Pine

1979. Nature Conservation.
1348 **686** 20 w. multicoloured . . . 35 10
1349 **687** 20 w. multicoloured . . . 35 10

688 Samil Monument

689 Worker and Bulldozer

1979. 60th Anniv of Samil Independence Movement.
1350 **688** 20 w. multicoloured . . . 25 10

1979. Labour Day.
1351 **689** 20 w. multicoloured . . . 25 10

690 Tabo Pagoda, Pulgak Temple

695 Hand holding Symbols of Security

1979. Korean Art. Multicoloured.
1352 20 w. Type **690** 25 10
1353 20 w. Gilt-bronze Maitreya 25 10
1354 20 w. Gold crown of Silla . . 25 10
1355 20 w. Celadon vase 25 10
1356 60 w. "Tano Day Activities" (silk screen) (50633 mm) 45 10

1979. Strengthening National Security.
1358 **695** 20 w. multicoloured . . . 25 10

696 Pulguk Temple and P.A.T.A. Emblem

1979. 28th Pacific Area Travel Association Conference, Seoul.
1359 **696** 20 w. multicoloured . . . 25 10

697 Presidents Pak and Senghor

1979. Visit of President Senghor of Senegal.
1360 **697** 20 w. multicoloured . . . 25 10

698 Basketball

699 Children playing

1979. 8th World Women's Basketball Championships, Seoul.
1362 **698** 20 w. multicoloured . . . 40 10

1979. International Year of the Child.
1363 **699** 20 w. multicoloured . . . 30 10

700 Children on Swing

1979. Family Planning.
1364 **700** 20 w. multicoloured . . . 30 10

701 Mandarins

702 "Neofinettia falcata" (orchid)

1979. Nature Conservation.
1365 **701** 20 w. multicoloured . . . 60 15
1366 **702** 20 w. multicoloured . . . 40 10

703 Manchurian Cranes

1979.
1367 **703** 10 w. black and green 50 15
1368 – 15 w. dp green & green 15 10
1369 – 20 w. bistre, black & blue 20 10
1370 – 30 w. multicoloured . . 25 10
1371 – 40 w. multicoloured . . 30 10
1372 – 50 w. brown, red & orge 20 10
1373 – 60 w. grey, purple & mve 30 10
1374 – 70 w. multicoloured . . 50 10
1375 – 80 w. yellow, blk & red 60 10
1376 – 90 w. buff, green and orange 75 10
1377 – 100 w. purple & mauve 45 10
1377a – 100 w. black 45 10
1378 – 150 w. black, bistre and blue 50 10
1379 – 200 w. brown and green 1·10 10
1380 – 300 w. blue . . . . . . 2·00 20
1381 – 400 w. green, brown and deep green . . . . . 2·25 20
1381a – 400 w. blue, ochre, brown and grey . . . . . . 3·00 30
1382 – 450 w. brown . . . . . 1·60 40
1383 – 500 w. dp green & green 2·00 40
1383a – 550 w. black . . . . . . 2·00 50
1384 – 600 w. multicoloured . . 2·25 1·00
1385 – 700 w. multicoloured . . 3·25 40
1386 – 800 w. multicoloured . . 2·40 50
1387 – 1000 w. lt brown & brn 3·25 40
1388 – 1000 w. lt brown & brn 3·25 40
1389 – 5000 w. multicoloured . . 18·00 4·00

DESIGNS:—As T **703**: HORIZ: 15 w. Mt. Sorak; 50 w. Earthenware model of wagon; 90 w. Paikryung Island; 1000 w. Duck earthenware vessels (1387 facing right; 1388 facing left). VERT: 20 w. Tolharubang (stone grandfather); 30 w. National flag; 40 w. "Hibiscus syriacus"; 60 w. Porcelain jar, Yi Dynasty; 70 w. Kyongju Observatory; 80 w. Mounted warrior (pottery vessel); 100 w. (1377) Ryu Kwan Soon; 100 w. (1377a) Chung Yak Yong (writer); 150 w. Porcelain jar, Chosun Dynasty; 200 w. Ahn Joong Geun; 300 w. Ahn Chang Ho; 400 w. Koryo celadon incense burner; 450, 550 w. Kim Ku (organizer of Korean Independence Party); 500 w. Brick with mountain landscape; 600 w. Hong Yung Sik (postal reformer); 700 w. Duck (lid of incense burner). 29641 mm: 800 w. Dragon's head flagpole finial; 5000 w. Tiger.

See also No. 1065.

725 People suffering from Traffic Pollution

1979. Environmental Protection.

1390 **725** 20 w. brown and green 30 10

726 Common Goral

727 "Convallaria leiskei" Miquel

1979. Nature Conservation.

1391 **726** 20 w. multicoloured . . . 40 10
1392 **727** 20 w. multicoloured . . . 40 10

728 Presidents Pak and Carter

1979. Visit of President Carter of United States.

1393 **728** 20 w. multicoloured . . . 20 10

729 Exhibition Building and Emblem

1979. Opening of Korea Exhibition Centre.

1395 **729** 20 w. multicoloured . . . 20 10

730 Boeing 747-200 Jetliner and Globe

1979. 10th Anniv of Korean Air Lines.

1396 **730** 20 w. multicoloured . . . 30 10

731 "The Courtesans' Sword Dance" (Shin Yun-bok)

1979. United States "5000 Years of Korean Art" Exhibition (1st issue).

1397 **731** 60 w. multicoloured . . . 75 15

See also Nos. 1402/3, 1406/7, 1420/1, 1426/7, 1433/4, 1441/2 and 1457/8.

732 Mount Mai, North Cholla Province

733 Dragon's Head Rock, Cheju Island

1979. World Tourism Day.

1399 **732** 20 w. multicoloured . . . 25 10
1400 **733** 20 w. multicoloured . . . 25 10

734 Heart, Donors and Blood Drop

1979. Blood Donors.

1401 **734** 20 w. red and green . . . 50 10

735 White Porcelain Jar with Grape Design

736 Mounted Warrior (pottery vessel)

1979. "5000 Years of Korean Art" Exhibition (2nd issue).

1402 **735** 20 w. multicoloured . . . 40 10
1403 **736** 20 w. multicoloured . . . 40 10

737 "Moon Travel" (Park Chung Jae)

1979. Philatelic Week.

1404 **737** 20 w. multicoloured . . . 20 10

738 Hahoe Mask

739 Golden Amitabha with Halo

1979. "5000 Years of Korean Art" Exhibition (3rd issue).

1406 **738** 20 w. multicoloured . . . 40 10
1407 **739** 20 w. multicoloured . . . 40 10

740 Rain Frog

741 Asian Polypody

1979. Nature Conservation.

1408 **740** 20 w. multicoloured . . . 45 10
1409 **741** 20 w. multicoloured . . . 45 10

742 Monkey (bas-relief, Kim Yun Shin's tomb)

743 Children playing Yut

1979. Lunar New Year ("Year of the Monkey").

1410 **742** 20 w. multicoloured . . . 20 10
1411 **743** 20 w. multicoloured . . . 20 10

744 President Choi Kyu Hah

1979. Presidential Inauguration.

1413 **744** 20 w. multicoloured . . . 30 10

745 Firefly

746 Meesun Tree

1980. Nature Conservation (5th series).

1415 **745** 30 w. multicoloured . . . 45 10
1416 **746** 30 w. multicoloured . . . 45 10

747 President Pak

748 Earthenware Kettle

749 "Landscape" (Kim Hong Do)

1980. President Pak Commemoration.

1417 **747** 30 w. red 25 10
1418 30 w. purple 25 10

1980. Exhibition "5000 Years of Korean Art" (4th issue).

1420 **748** 30 w. multicoloured . . . 40 10
1421 **749** 60 w. multicoloured . . . 55 10

750 "Lotus"

751 "Magpie and Tiger"

1980. Folk Paintings (1st series).

1423 **750** 30 w. multicoloured . . . 45 20
1424 **751** 60 w. multicoloured . . . 1·25 40

See also Nos. 1429/31, 1437/40 and 1453/6.

752 Merchant Ships

1980. Korean Merchant Navy.

1425 **752** 30 w. multicoloured . . . 30 10

753 "Heavenly Horse" (tomb painting)

754 Banner Staff with Dragonhead Finial

1980. Exhibition "5000 Years of Korean Art" (5th series).

1426 **753** 30 w. multicoloured . . . 40 10
1427 **754** 30 w. multicoloured . . . 40 10

755 "Fruition"

1980. 10th Anniv of Saemaul Movement (community self-help programme).

1428 **755** 30 w. multicoloured . . . 25 10

756 "Red Phoenix"

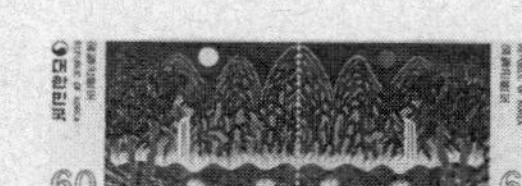

757/8 "Sun and Moon over Mt. Konryun" (½-size illustration)

1980. Folk Paintings (2nd series).

1429 **756** 30 w. multicoloured . . . 30 10
1430 **757** 60 w. multicoloured . . . 50 40
1431 **758** 60 w. multicoloured . . . 50 40

Nos. 1430/1 were issued together, se-tenant, forming a composite design.

759 "Man on a Horse" (mural, Koguryo period)

760 "Tiger" (granite sculpture)

1980. Exhibition "5000 Years of Korean Art" (6th issue).

1433 **759** 30 w. multicoloured . . . 40 10
1434 **760** 30 w. multicoloured . . . 40 10

761 U.N. Flag and Rifle

762 "Venus de Milo" and Contestants

1980. 30th Anniv of Intervention of U.N. Forces in Korean War.

1435 **761** 30 w. multicoloured . . . 30 10

1980. "Miss Universe" Beauty Contest, Seoul.

1436 **762** 30 w. multicoloured . . . 30 10

763 "Rabbits pounding Grain in a Mortar"

764 "Dragon in Cloud"

1980. Folk Paintings (3rd series).

1437 **763** 30 w. multicoloured . . . 40 10
1438 **764** 30 w. multicoloured . . . 40 10

765 "Pine Tree"

766 "Flowers and Manchurian Cranes" (detail, folding screen)

1980. Folk Paintings (4th series).

1439 **765** 30 w. multicoloured . . . 40 10
1440 **766** 30 w. multicoloured . . . 75 20

767 Human faced Roof Tile

768 "White Tiger" (mural)

1980. Exhibition "5000 Years of Korean Art" (7th issue).

1441 **767** 30 w. multicoloured . . . 30 10
1442 **768** 30 w. multicoloured . . . 30 10

769 Football

770 President Chun Doo Hwan

1980. 10th President's Cup Football Tournament.

1443 **769** 30 w. multicoloured . . . 30 10

1980. Presidential Inauguration.

1444 **770** 30 w. multicoloured . . . 25 10

771 Woman Soldier and Emblem

1980. 30th Anniv of Women's Army Corps.

1446 **771** 30 w. multicoloured . . . 25 10

772 River Baegma

773 Three Peaks of Dodam

1980. World Tourism Day.

1447 **772** 30 w. pink and purple . . 30 10
1448 **773** 30 w. yellow, green & bl 30 10

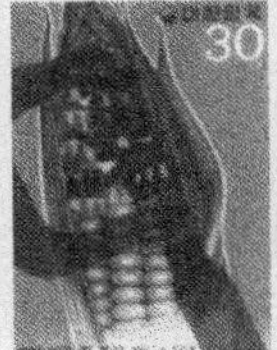
774 Corn-cob and Micrometer

775 Tree

1980. Population and Housing Census.

1449 **774** 30 w. multicoloured . . . 30 10

1980. 75th Anniv of Korean Red Cross.

1450 **775** 30 w. multicoloured . . . 35 10

776 "Angels delivering Mail" (Kim Ki Chul)

1980. Philatelic Week.

1451 **776** 30 w. multicoloured . . . 25 10

777 "Ten Long-life Symbols"

781 Deva King (sculpture)

1980. Folk Paintings (5th series). Multicoloured.

1453 30 w. Type **777** 30 10
1454 30 w. "Herb of eternal youth" and deer 30 10
1455 30 w. Pine and deer eating herb 30 10
1456 30 w. Pine, water and rock . . 30 10

Nos. 1453/6 were issued together, se-tenant, forming a composite design.

1980. Exhibition "5000 Years of Korean Art" (8th series).

1457 **781** 30 w. black 40 10
1458 30 w. red 40 10

782 "Cable Enterprise" (cable ship) and Cross-section of Cable

1980. Inauguration of Korea-Japan Submarine Cable.

1459 **782** 30 w. multicoloured . . . 35 10

783 Cock (bas-relief Kim Yu Shin's tomb)

784 Cranes

1980. Lunar New Year ("Year of the Cock").

1460 **783** 30 w. multicoloured . . . 30 10
1461 **784** 30 w. multicoloured . . . 30 10

785 President Chun Doo Hwan and Factory within "Hibiscus syriacus"

1981. Presidential Inauguration.

1463 **785** 30 w. multicoloured . . . 25 10

786 "Korea Sun" (tanker)

787 "Asia Yukho" (freighter)

1981. Ships (1st series).

1465 **786** 30 w. multicoloured . . . 55 15
1466 **787** 90 w. multicoloured . . . 85 25

See also Nos. 1470/1, 1482/5 and 1501/2.

788 National Assembly Building

1981. Inaugural Session of 11th National Assembly.

1467 **788** 30 w. brown and gold . . 30 10

789 Symbols of Disability and I.Y.D.P. Emblem

790 Disabled Person in Wheelchair at Foot of Steps

1981. International Year of Disabled Persons.

1468 **789** 30 w. multicoloured . . . 30 10
1469 **790** 90 w. multicoloured . . . 60 35

791 "Saturn" (bulk-carrier)

792 "Hanjin Seoul" (container ship)

1981. Ships (2nd series).

1470 **791** 30 w. deep purple, purple and blue 55 15
1471 **792** 90 w. grey, blue and red 85 25

793 Council Emblem on Ribbon

1981. Advisory Council on Peaceful Unification Policy.

1472 **793** 40 w. multicoloured . . . 30 10

794 "Clean Rivers and Air"

795 White Storks visiting Breeding Grounds

1981. World Environment Day.

1473 **794** 30 w. multicoloured . . . 30 10
1474 **795** 90 w. multicoloured . . . 70 20

796 Presidents Chun and Suharto of Indonesia

1981. Presidential Visit to A.S.E.A.N. Countries. Multicoloured.

1475 40 w. Type **796** 50 10
1476 40 w. Pres. Chun and Sultan of Malaysia 50 10
1477 40 w. Handshake and flags of South Korea and Singapore 50 10
1478 40 w. Pres. Chun and King of Thailand 50 10
1479 40 w. Presidents Chun and Marcos of Philippines . . . 50 10
1480 40 w. Pres. Chun and flags of Korea, Singapore, Malaysia and Philippines (39643 mm) 50 10

802 "Chung Ryong No. 3" (tug)

803 "Soo Gong No. 71" (trawler)

1981. Ships (3rd series).

1482 **802** 40 w. multicoloured . . . 65 15
1483 **803** 100 w. multicoloured . . 95 25

804 "Aldebaran" (log carrier)

805 "Hyundai No. 1" (car carrier)

1981. Ships (4th series).

1484 **804** 40 w. multicoloured . . . 65 15
1485 **805** 100 w. multicoloured . . 95 25

806 Korean with Flag and Dates on Graph

812 W.H.O. Emblem and Citizens

807 Glider

1981. 36th Anniv of Liberation.

1486 **806** 40 w. multicoloured . . . 30 10

1981. 3rd Model Aeronautic Competition. Multicoloured.

1487 10 w. Type **807** 40 10
1488 20 w. Elastic-powered airplane 40 10
1489 40 w. Line-controlled airplane 40 15
1490 50 w. Radio-controlled airplane 60 20
1491 80 w. Radio-controlled helicopter 75 30

1981. 32nd Session of W.H.O. Regional Committee for the Western Pacific, Seoul.

1492 **812** 40 w. multicoloured . . . 30 10

813 Seoul Communications Tower

814 Ulreung Island

1981. World Tourism Day.

1493 **813** 40 w. multicoloured . . . 30 10
1494 **814** 40 w. multicoloured . . . 30 10

815 Cycling

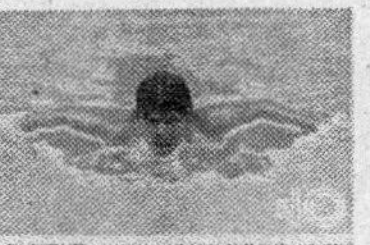
816 Swimming

1981. 62nd National Sports Meeting, Seoul.

1495 **815** 40 w. multicoloured . . . 35 10
1496 **816** 40 w. multicoloured . . . 35 10

817 Presidents Chun and Carazo Odio

818 Hand holding Plate with F.A.O. Emblem

1981. Visit of President Carazo Odio of Costa Rica.
1497 **817** 40 w. multicoloured . . . 30 10

1981. World Food Day.
1498 **818** 40 w. multicoloured . . . 30 10

819 Airliner and Clouds

820 South Gate of Seoul and Olympic Rings

1981. National Aviation Day.
1499 **819** 40 w. orange, brown and silver 40 10

1981. Choice of Seoul as 1988 Olympic Host City.
1500 **820** 40 w. multicoloured . . . 30 10

821 "Stolt Hawk" (chemical carrier)

822 Passenger Ferry

1981. Ships (5th series).
1501 **821** 40 w. black 65 15
1502 **822** 100 w. blue 95 25

823 "Hang-gliding" (Kim Kyung Jun)

1981. Philatelic Week.
1503 **823** 40 w. multicoloured . . . 30 10

824 Camellia and Dog

825 Children flying Kite

1981. Lunar New Year ("Year of the Dog").
1505 **824** 40 w. multicoloured . . . 30 10
1506 **825** 40 w. multicoloured . . . 30 10

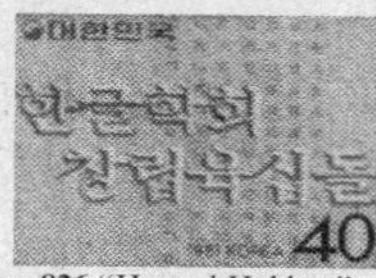

826 "Hangul Hakhoe"

1981. 60th Anniv of Hangul Hakhoe (Korean Language Society).
1508 **826** 40 w. multicoloured . . . 35 10

INDEX

Countries can be quickly located by referring to the index at the end of this volume.

827 Telephone and Dish Aerial

828 Scout Emblem and Logs forming "75"

1982. Inauguration of Korea Telecommunication Authority.
1509 **827** 60 w. multicoloured . . . 40 10

1982. 75th Anniv of Boy Scout Movement.
1510 **828** 60 w. multicoloured . . . 60 10

829 Young Woman

830 Dividers and World Map

1982. 60th Anniv of Korean Young Women's Christian Association.
1511 **829** 60 w. multicoloured . . . 35 10

1982. Centenary of International Polar Year.
1512 **830** 60 w. multicoloured . . . 50 10

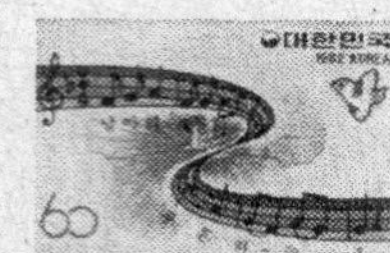

831 Music and "Hibiscus syriacus"

1982. Children's Day.
1513 **831** 60 w. multicoloured . . . 40 10

832 President Chun and Samuel Doe

1982. Visit of Samuel Doe (Liberian Head of State).
1514 **832** 60 w. multicoloured . . . 35 10

833 Centenary Emblem

1982. Centenary of Korea–United States Friendship Treaty.
1516 **833** 60 w. multicoloured . . . 30 10
1517 – 60 w. multicoloured . . . 30 10
DESIGN: No. 1517, Statue of Liberty and Seoul South Gate.

835 Presidents Chun and Mobutu

1982. Visit of President Mobutu of Zaire.
1519 **835** 60 w. multicoloured . . . 30 10

836 "Territorial Expansion by Kwanggaeto the Great" (Lee Chong Sang)

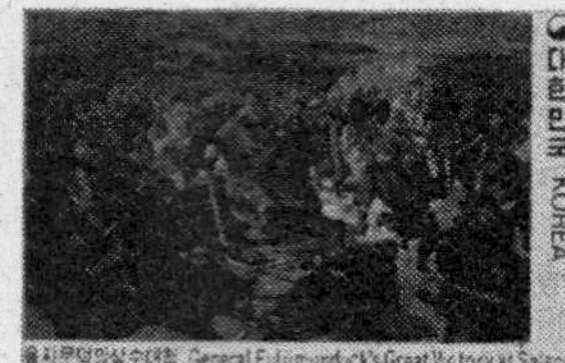

837 "General Euljimunduck's Great Victory at Salsoo" (Park Kak Soon)

1982. Documentary Paintings (1st series).
1521 **836** 60 w. multicoloured . . . 40 10
1522 **837** 60 w. multicoloured . . . 40 10
See also Nos. 1523/4, 1537/8 and 1548/9.

838 "Shilla's Repulse of Invading Tang Army" (Oh Seung Woo)

839 "General Kang Kam Chan's Great Victory at Kyiju" (Lee Yong Hwan)

1982. Documentary Paintings (2nd series).
1523 **838** 60 w. multicoloured . . . 40 10
1524 **839** 60 w. multicoloured . . . 40 10

840 Convention Emblem and Globe

841 Presidents Chun and Moi of Kenya

1982. 55th International Y's Men's Club Convention, Seoul.
1525 **840** 60 w. multicoloured . . . 20 10

1982. Presidential Visits to Africa and Canada. Multicoloured.
1526 60 w. Type **841** 35 10
1527 60 w. Presidents Chun and Shagari of Nigeria 35 10
1528 60 w. Presidents Chun and Bongo of Gabon 35 10
1529 60 w. Presidents Chun and Diouf of Senegal 35 10
1530 60 w. Flags of South Korea and Canada 35 10

846 National Flag

1982. Centenary of National Flag.
1532 **846** 60 w. multicoloured . . . 40 10

847 Emblem and Player

1982. 2nd Seoul Table Tennis Championships.
1534 **847** 60 w. multicoloured . . . 40 10

848 Baseball Player

1982. 27th World Baseball Championship Series, Seoul.
1535 **848** 60 w. brown 40 10

849 Exhibition Centre

1982. Seoul International Trade Fair.
1536 **849** 60 w. multicoloured . . . 30 10

850 "Admiral Yi Sun Sin's Great Victory at Hansan" (Kim Hyung Ku)

851 "General Kim Chwa Jin's Chungsanri Battle" (Sohn Soo Kwang)

1982. Documentary Paintings (3rd series).
1537 **850** 60 w. multicoloured . . . 60 15
1538 **851** 60 w. multicoloured . . . 35 10

852 "Miners reading Consolatory Letters" (Um Soon Keun)

1982. Philatelic Week.
1539 **852** 60 w. multicoloured . . . 45 10

853 Presidents Chung and Suharto

1982. Visit of President Suharto of Indonesia.
1541 **853** 60 w. multicoloured . . . 30 10

854 J.C.I. Emblem over World Map

855 "Intelsat 5" and "4-A" orbiting Globe

1982. 37th Junior Chamber International World Congress, Seoul.
1543 **854** 60 w. multicoloured . . . 30 10

1982. Second U.N. Conference on the Exploration and Peaceful Uses of Outer Space, Vienna.
1544 **855** 60 w. multicoloured . . . 30 10

856 Pig (bas-relief, Kim Yu Shin's tomb)

1982. Lunar New Year ("Year of the Pig").
1545 60 w. Type **856** 35 10
1546 60 w. Magpies and Korean moneybag 40 10

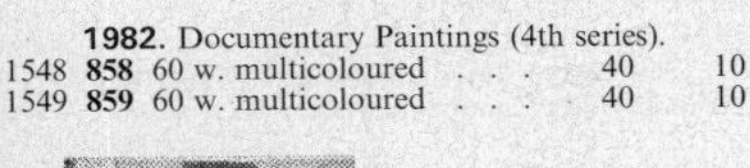

858 "General Kwon Yul's Great Victory at Haengju" (Oh Seung Woo)

859 "Kim Chong Suh's Exploitation of Yukin" (Kim Tae)

1982. Documentary Paintings (4th series).
1548 **858** 60 w. multicoloured . . . 40 10
1549 **859** 60 w. multicoloured . . . 40 10

860 Flags of South Korea and Turkey

861 Hand writing Letter

1982. Visit of President Evran of Turkey.
1550 **860** 60 w. multicoloured . . . 35 10

1982. Letter Writing Campaign.
1552 **861** 60 w. multicoloured . . . 30 10

862 Emblem, Airliner, Container Ship and Cranes

863 Hyundai "Pony 2"

1983. International Customs Day.
1553 **862** 60 w. multicoloured . . . 50 15

1983. Korean-made Vehicles (1st series). Multicoloured.
1554 60 w. Type **863** 50 10
1555 60 w. Keohwa Jeep 50 10
See also Nos. 1558/9, 1564/5, 1572/3 and 1576/7.

865 President Chun and Sultan of Malaysia

1983. Visit of King of Malaysia.
1556 **865** 60 w. multicoloured . . . 30 10

866 Daewoo "Maepsy"

867 Kia "Bongo" Minibus

1983. Korean-made Vehicles (2nd series).
1558 **866** 60 w. multicoloured . . . 50 10
1559 **867** 60 w. multicoloured . . . 50 10

868 Former General Bureau of Postal Administration

869 Central Post Office, Seoul

1983. "Philakorea 84" International Stamp Exhibition, Seoul. Centenary of Korean Postal Service (1st series).
1560 **868** 60 w. multicoloured . . . 30 10
1561 **869** 60 w. multicoloured . . . 30 10
See also Nos. 1566/7, 1574/5 and 1603/6.

870 Old Village Schoolroom

1983. Teachers' Day.
1562 **870** 60 w. multicoloured . . . 35 10

871 Asia Motor Co. Bus

872 Kia "Super Titan" Truck

1983. Korean-made Vehicles (3rd series).
1564 **871** 60 w. multicoloured . . . 45 10
1565 **872** 60 w. multicoloured . . . 45 10

873 Early Postman

1983. "Philakorea 84" International Stamp Exhibition, Seoul. Centenary of Korean Postal Service (2nd series).
1566 **873** 70 w. multicoloured . . . 40 10
1567 – 70 w. multicoloured . . . 40 10
DESIGN: No. 1567, Modern postman on motor-cycle.

875 "Communications in Outer Space" (Chun Ja Eun)

1983. World Communications Year.
1568 **875** 70 w. multicoloured . . . 35 10

876 Whooper Swans at Sunrise

1983. Inaug of Communications Insurance.
1570 **876** 70 w. multicoloured . . . 60 15

877 Emblems of Science and Engineering

1983. Korean Symposium on Science and Technology, Seoul.
1571 **877** 70 w. multicoloured . . . 35 10

878 Daewoo Dump Truck

879 Hyundai Cargo Lorry

1983. Korean-made Vehicles (4th series).
1572 **878** 70 w. multicoloured . . . 45 10
1573 **879** 70 w. multicoloured . . . 45 10

880 Mail carried by Horse

1983. "Philakorea 84" International Stamp Exhibition, Seoul. Centenary of Korean Postal Service (3rd series). Multicoloured.
1574 70 w. Type **880** 35 10
1575 70 w. Mail truck and Douglas DC-8-60 Super Sixty jetliner 40 10

882 Dong-A Concrete Mixer Truck

883 Dong-A Tanker

1983. Korean-made Vehicles (5th series).
1576 **882** 70 w. multicoloured . . . 50 10
1577 **883** 70 w. multicoloured . . . 50 10

884 President Chun and King Hussein

885 Woman with Fan

1983. Visit of King Hussein of Jordan.
1578 **884** 70 w. multicoloured . . . 35 10

1983. 53rd American Society of Travel Agents World Congress, Seoul.
1580 **885** 70 w. multicoloured . . . 35 10

886 I.P.U. Emblem and Flags

1983. 70th Inter-Parliamentary Union Conference, Seoul.
1581 **886** 70 w. multicoloured . . . 35 10

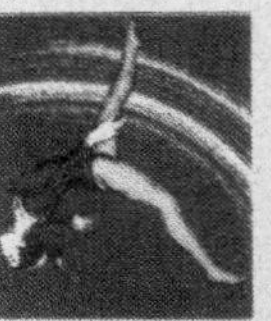

887 Gymnastics

888 Football

1983. 64th National Sports Meeting, Inchon.
1583 **887** 70 w. multicoloured . . . 40 10
1584 **888** 70 w. multicoloured . . . 40 10

889 Presidents Chun and U San Yu of Burma

894 Rain Drops containing Symbols of Industry, Light and Food

1983. Presidential Visits. Multicoloured.
1585 70 w. Type **889** 60 50
1586 70 w. Presidents Chun and Giani Zail Singh of India 60 50
1587 70 w. Presidents Chun and Jayewardene of Sri Lanka 60 50
1588 70 w. Flags of South Korea and Australia 60 50
1589 70 w. Flags of South Korea and New Zealand 60 50

1983. Development of Water Resources and 10th Anniv of Soyang-gang Dam.
1591 **894** 70 w. multicoloured . . . 35 10

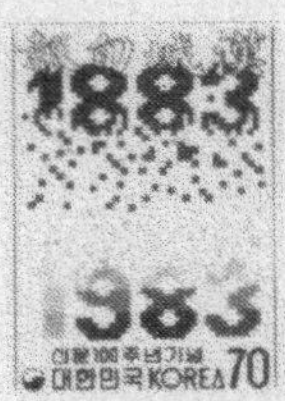

895 Centenary Dates

896 Tree with Lungs and Cross of Lorraine

1983. Centenary of 1st Korean Newspaper "Hansong Sunbo".
1592 **895** 70 w. multicoloured . . . 35 10

1983. 30th Anniv of Korean National Tuberculosis Association.
1593 **896** 70 w. multicoloured . . . 35 10

897 Presidents Chun and Reagan

898 Child collecting Stamps

1983. Visit of President Reagan of United States of America.
1594 **897** 70 w. multicoloured . . . 35 10

1983. Philatelic Week.
1596 **898** 70 w. multicoloured . . . 35 10

899 Rat (bas-relief, Kim Yu Shin's tomb)

1983. Lunar New Year ("Year of the Rat"). Multicoloured.
1598 70 w. Type **899** 35 10
1599 70 w. Manchurian cranes and pine 45 10

901 Bicentenary Emblem

902 5 m. and 10 m. Stamps, 1884

1984. Bicentenary of Catholic Church in Korea.
1601 **901** 70 w. red, violet & silver 35 10

1984. "Philakorea 84" International Stamp Exhibition, Seoul. Centenary of Korean Postal Service (4th series). Multicoloured.
1603 70 w. Type **902** 40 10
1604 70 w. 5000 w. stamp, 1983 . . 40 10

904 Old Postal Emblem and Post Box

1984. "Philakorea 84" International Stamp Exhibition, Seoul. Centenary of Korean Postal Service (5th series). Multicoloured.
1605 70 w. Type **904** 40 10
1606 70 w. Modern postal emblem and post box 40 10

906 President Chun and Sultan

1984. Visit of Sultan of Brunei.
1607 **906** 70 w. multicoloured . . . 40 10

907 President Chun and Sheikh Khalifa

1984. Visit of Sheikh Khalifa of Qatar.
1609 **907** 70 w. multicoloured . . . 35 10

908 Child posting Letter

1984. Centenary of Korean Postal Administration. Multicoloured.
1611 70 w. Type **908** 35 10
1612 70 w. Postman in city 35 10

910 Pope John Paul II

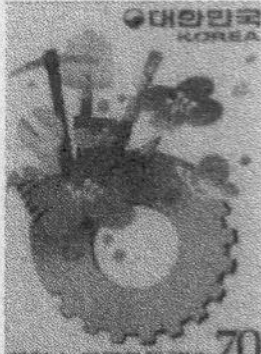

911 Cogwheel, Worker's Tools and Flowers

1984. Visit of Pope John Paul II.
1614 **910** 70 w. black 35 10
1615 70 w. multicoloured . . . 35 10

1984. Labour Festival.
1617 **911** 70 w. multicoloured . . 30 10

912 Globe, Jetliner, Container Ship and Emblem

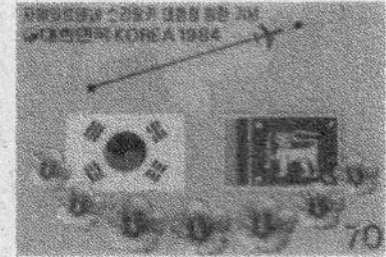

913 Map and Flags of S. Korea and Sri Lanka

1984. 63rd/64th Sessions of Customs Co-operation Council, Seoul.
1618 **912** 70 w. multicoloured . . . 65 15

1984. Visit of President Jayewardene of Sri Lanka.
1619 **913** 70 w. multicoloured . . . 35 10

914 Symbols and Punctuation Marks

915 Expressway

1984. 14th Asian Advertising Congress, Seoul.
1621 **914** 70 w. multicoloured . . . 35 10

1984. Opening of 88 Olympic Expressway.
1622 **915** 70 w. multicoloured . . . 35 10

916 Laurel, "Victory" and Olympic Rings

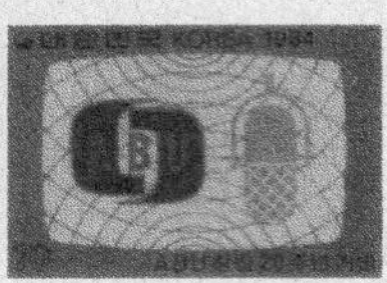

917 A.B.U. Emblem and Microphone

1984. 90th Anniv of International Olympic Committee.
1623 **916** 70 w. multicoloured . . . 35 10

1984. 20th Anniv of Asia-Pacific Broadcasting Union.
1624 **917** 70 w. multicoloured . . . 35 10

918 Flags of S. Korea and Senegal

1984. Visit of President Abdou Diouf of Senegal.
1625 **918** 70 w. multicoloured . . . 35 10

919 Archery

921 Crucifixion

1984. Olympic Games, Los Angeles. Multicoloured.
1627 70 w. Type **919** 40 10
1628 440 w. Fencing . . . . 1·60 35

1984. Centenary of Korean Protestant Church. Multicoloured.
1629 70 w. Type **921** 40 10
1630 70 w. Cross, vine and dove . . 40 10

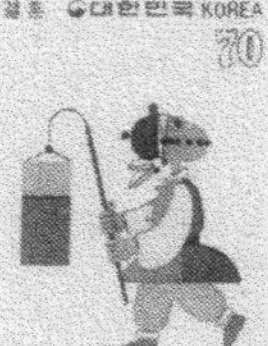

923 Man carrying Silk-covered Lantern

1984. Folk Customs (1st series). "Wedding" (Kim Kyo Man). Multicoloured.
1632 70 w. Type **923** 40 10
1633 70 w. Bridegroom on horse . . 40 10
1634 70 w. Man playing clarinet . . 40 10
1635 70 w. Bride in sedan chair (51635 mm) 40 10

See also Nos. 1657/8, 1683/4, 1734/8, 1808/11, 1840/3, 1858/61 and 1915/18.

927 Pres. Chun and Mt. Fuji

1984. Pres. Chun's Visit to Japan.
1637 **927** 70 w. multicoloured . . . 40 10

928 Flags of S. Korea and Gambia

1984. Visit of President Sir Dawada Kairaba Jawara of Gambia.
1639 **928** 70 w. multicoloured . . . 40 10

929 Symbols of International Trade

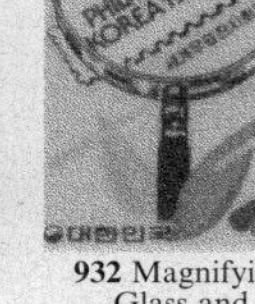

930 Namsan Tower and National Flags

1984. "Sitra '84" International Trade Fair, Seoul.
1641 **929** 70 w. multicoloured . . . 40 10

1984. Visit of President El Hadj Omar Bongo of Gabon.
1642 **930** 70 w. multicoloured . . . 40 10

931 Badminton

932 Magnifying Glass and Exhibition Emblem

1984. 65th National Sports Meeting, Taegu. Multicoloured.
1644 70 w. Type **931** 40 10
1645 70 w. Wrestling 40 10

1984. "Philakorea 1984" International Stamp Exhibition, Seoul. Multicoloured.
1646 70 w. Type **932** 40 10
1647 70 w. South Gate, Seoul, and stamps (horiz) 40 10

934 Presidents Chun and Gayoom

1984. Visit of President Maumoon Abdul Gayoom of the Maldives.
1650 **934** 70 w. multicoloured . . . 40 10

935 "100" and Industrial Symbols

1984. Centenary of Korean Chamber of Commerce and Industry.
1652 **935** 70 w. multicoloured . . . 40 10

936 Children playing Jaegi-chagi

937 Ox (bas-relief, Kim Yu Shin's tomb)

1985. Lunar New Year ("Year of the Ox").
1653 **936** 70 w. multicoloured . . . 40 10
1654 **937** 70 w. multicoloured . . . 40 10

938 I.Y.Y. Emblem

1985. International Youth Year.
1656 **938** 70 w. multicoloured . . . 40 10

939 Pounding Rice for New Year Rice Cake

940 Welcoming Year's First Full Moon

1985. Folk Customs (2nd series).
1657 **939** 70 w. multicoloured . . . 40 10
1658 **940** 70 w. multicoloured . . . 40 10

941 Seoul Olympic Emblem

1985. Olympic Games, Seoul (1988) (1st issue). Multicoloured.
1659 70 w. + 30 w. Type **941** . . . 45 20
1660 70 w. + 30 w. Hodori (mascot) 45 20

See also Nos. 1673/4, 1678/8, 1694/5, 1703/10, 1747/50, 1752/5, 1784/7, 1814/17, 1826/7, 1835/6 and 1844/7.

943 "Still Life with Doll" (Lee Chong Woo)

944 "Rocky Mountain in Early Spring Morning" (Ahn Jung Shik)

1985. Modern Art (1st series).
1662 **943** 70 w. multicoloured . . . 40 10
1663 **944** 70 w. multicoloured . . . 40 10

See also Nos. 1680/1, 1757/60, 1791/4 and 1875/8.

945 Flags, Statue of Liberty and President Chun

946 Flags, Seoul South Gate and National Flower

1985. Presidential Visit to United States.
1664 **945** 70 w. multicoloured . . . 40 10

1985. Visit of President Mohammed Zia-ul-Haq of Pakistan.
1666 **946** 70 w. multicoloured . . . 40 10

947 Underwood Hall

1985. Centenary of Yonsei University.
1668 **947** 70 w. black, buff & green . 40 10

948 Flags and Map

1985. Visit of President Luis Alberto Monge of Costa Rica.
1669 **948** 70 w. multicoloured . . . 40 10

949 Rasbora

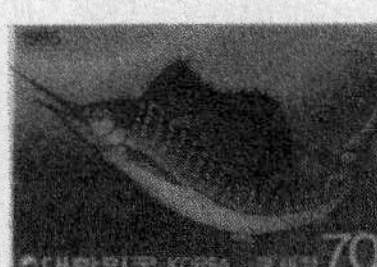
950 Sailfish

1985. Fishes (1st series).
1671 **949** 70 w. multicoloured . . . 75 15
1672 **950** 70 w. multicoloured . . . 75 15
See also Nos. 1730/3, 1797/1800, 1881/4, 1903/6 and 1951/4.

951 Rowing

952 National Flags

1985. Olympic Games, Seoul (1988) (2nd issue). Multicoloured.
1673 70 w. + 30 w. Type **951** . . . 45 30
1674 70 w. + 30 w. Hurdling . . . 45 30

1985. Visit of President Hussain Muhammed Ershad of Bangladesh.
1676 **952** 70 w. multicoloured . . . 40 10

953 National Flags

1985. Visit of President Joao Bernardo Vieira of Guinea-Bissau.
1678 **953** 70 w. multicoloured . . . 40 10

954 "Spring Day on the Farm" (Huh Paik Ryun)

955 "The Exorcist" (Kim Chung Hyun)

1985. Modern Art (2nd issue).
1680 **954** 70 w. multicoloured . . . 40 10
1681 **955** 70 w. multicoloured . . . 40 10

956 Heavenly Lake, Paekdu and National Flower

1985. 40th Anniv of Liberation.
1682 **956** 70 w. multicoloured . . . 40 10

957 Wrestling

958 Janggi

1985. Folk Customs (3rd series).
1683 **957** 70 w. multicoloured . . . 40 10
1684 **958** 70 w. multicoloured . . . 40 10

959 "The Spring of My Home" (Lee Won Su and Hong Nan Pa)

960 "A Leaf Boat" (Park Hong Keun and Yun Yong Ha)

1985. Korean Music (1st series).
1685 **959** 70 w. multicoloured . . . 45 10
1686 **960** 70 w. multicoloured . . . 45 10
See also Nos. 1728/9, 1776/7, 1854/5, 1862/3, 1893/4, 1935/6, 1996/7 and 2064/5.

1985. Olympic Games, Seoul (1988) (3rd issue). As T **951**. Multicoloured.
1687 70 w. + 30 w. Basketball . . 45 20
1688 70 w. + 30 w. Boxing 45 20

961 Satellite, "100" and Dish Aerial

962 Meetings Emblem

1985. Centenary of First Korean Telegraph Service.
1690 **961** 70 w. multicoloured . . . 40 10

1985. World Bank and International Monetary Fund Meetings, Seoul.
1691 **962** 70 w. multicoloured . . . 40 10

963 U.N. Emblem and Doves

964 Red Cross and Hands (detail "Creation of Adam", Michelangelo)

1985. 40th Anniv of U.N.O.
1692 **963** 70 w. multicoloured . . . 40 10

1985. 80th Anniv of Korea Red Cross.
1693 **964** 70 w. black, red and blue 45 10

1985. Olympic Games, Seoul (1988) (4th issue). As T **951**. Multicoloured.
1694 70 w. + 30 w. Cycling 40 20
1695 70 w. + 30 w. Canoeing . . . 40 20

965 Cancelled Stamp on Envelope

966 Tiger (bas-relief, Kim Yu Shin's tomb)

1985. Philatelic Week.
1697 **965** 70 w. multicoloured . . . 40 10

1985. Lunar New Year ("Year of the Tiger").
1698 **966** 70 w. multicoloured . . . 40 10

967 Mount Fuji and Boeing 747 Jetliner

1985. 20th Anniv of Korea-Japan Treaty on Basic Relations.
1699 **967** 70 w. mult (postage) . . . 45 10
1700 370 w. multicoloured (air) . 1·50 50

968 Doves and Globe

970 Pres. Chun, Big Ben and Korean and British Flags

1986. International Peace Year.
1701 **968** 70 w. multicoloured . . . 35 10
1702 400 w. multicoloured . . 1·75 40

1986. Olympic Games, Seoul (1988) (5th series). As T **951**. Multicoloured.
1703 70 w. + 30 w. Show jumping (postage) 40 20
1704 70 w. + 30 w. Fencing . . . 40 20
1705 70 w. + 30 w. Football . . . 40 20
1706 70 w. + 30 w. Gymnastics . . 40 20
1707 370 w. + 100 w. As No. 1703 (air) . . . . 1·60 70
1708 400 w. + 100 w. As No. 1704 1·75 70
1709 440 w. + 100 w. As No. 1705 1·90 70
1710 470 w. + 100 w. As No. 1706 2·00 70

1986. Presidential Visit to Europe. Multicoloured.
1711 70 w. Type **970** 40 10
1712 70 w. Pres. Chun, Eiffel Tower and Korean and French flags 40 10
1713 70 w. Pres. Chun, Belgian Parliament and Korean and Belgian flags 40 10
1714 70 w. Pres. Chun, Cologne Cathedral and Korean and West German flags 40 10

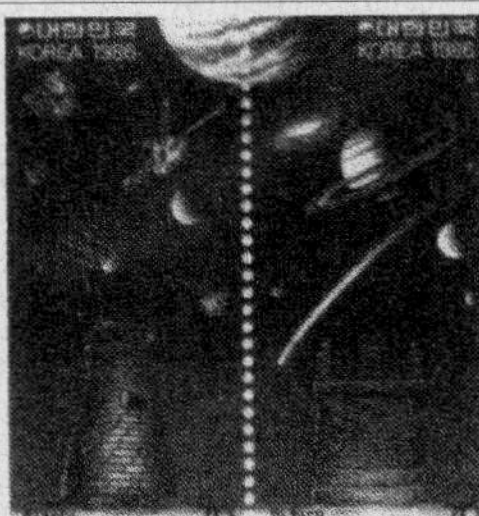
974 Kyongju Observatory

975 Kwanchon Observatory

1986. Science (1st series). Appearance of Halley's Comet.
1716 **974** 70 w. multicoloured . . . 30 10
1717 **975** 70 w. multicoloured . . . 30 10
See also Nos. 1781/2, 1833/4, 1864/5 and 1898/9.

976 General Assembly Emblem

977 Swallowtail and Flowers

1986. 5th Association of National Olympic Committees General Assembly, Seoul.
1718 **976** 70 w. multicoloured . . . 45 10

1986. "Ameripex '86" International Stamp Exhibition, Chicago. Multicoloured.
1719 70 w. Type **977** . . . . 2·00 75
1720 370 w. "Papilio bianor" . . . 2·00 75
1721 400 w. Swallowtails . . . . . 2·00 75
1722 440 w. Swallowtail and frog 2·00 75
1723 450 w. Swallowtail . . . . . 2·00 75
1724 470 w. "Papilio bianor" . . . 2·00 75
Nos. 1719/24 were printed together, se-tenant, forming a composite design.

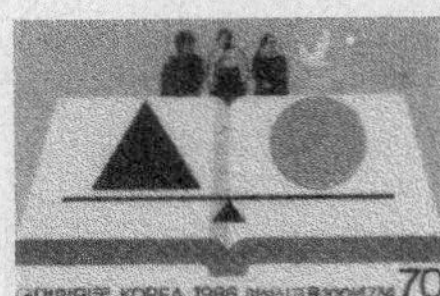
983 Male and Female Symbols in Balance

1986. Centenary of Korean Women's Education.
1725 **983** 70 w. multicoloured . . . 35 10

984 National Flags

1986. Visit of President Andre Kolingba of Central African Republic.
1726 **984** 70 w. multicoloured . . . 35 10

985 "Half Moon" (Yun Keuk Young)

986 "Let's Go and Pick the Moon" (Yun Seok Jung and Park Tae Hyun)

1986. Korean Music (2nd series).
1728 **985** 70 w. multicoloured . . . 35 10
1729 **986** 70 w. multicoloured . . . 35 10

987 Cyprinid Fish

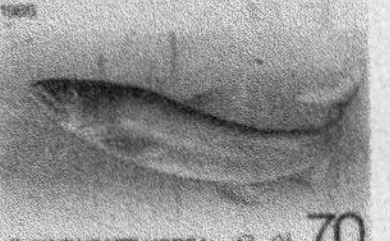
988 Ayu

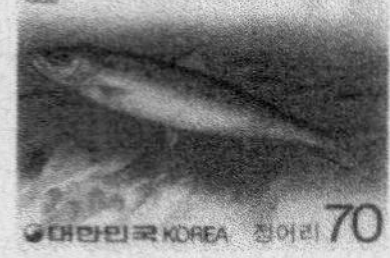

989 Black-spotted Sardine

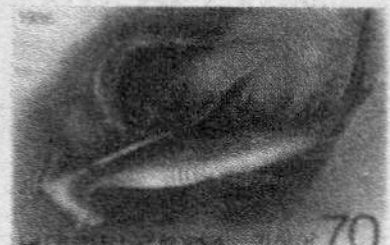
990 Hammerheads

1986. Fishes (2nd series).

1730 **987** 70 w. multicoloured . . . 85 20
1731 **988** 70 w. multicoloured . . . 85 20
1732 **989** 70 w. multicoloured . . . 85 20
1733 **990** 70 w. multicoloured . . . 85 20

991 Flag Carrier and Gong Player

996 Child

1986. Folk Customs (4th series). Farm Music. Multicoloured.

1734 70 w. Type **991** 30 10
1735 70 w. Drummer and piper . . 30 10
1736 70 w. Drummer and gong player 30 10
1737 70 w. Men with ribbons . . . 30 10
1738 70 w. Man and woman with child 30 10

Nos. 1734/8 were printed together, se-tenant, forming a composite design.

1986. Family Planning.

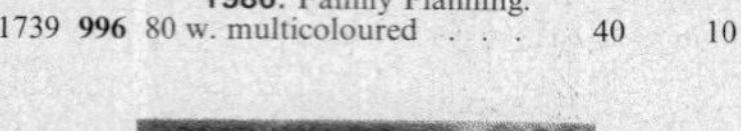
1739 **996** 80 w. multicoloured . . . 40 10

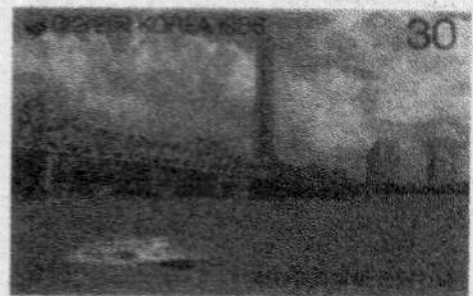
997 Bridge and "63" Building, Seoul

1986. Completion of Han River Development. Multicoloured.

1740 30 w. Type **997** 85 25
1741 60 w. Buildings and excursion boat 60 25
1742 80 w. Rowing boat and Seoul Tower 40 10

Nos. 1740/2 were printed together, se-tenant, forming a composite design.

1000 Emblem

1004 Boy fishing for Stamp

1002 "5", Delegates and Juan Antonio Samaranch (President of International Olympic Committee)

1986. 10th Asian Games, Seoul. Multicoloured.

1743 80 w. Type **1000** 40 10
1744 80 w. Firework display 40 10

1986. 5th Anniv of Choice of Seoul as 1988 Olympic Games Host City.

1746 **1002** 80 w. multicoloured . . 45 10

1986. Olympic Games, Seoul (1988) (6th issue). As T **951**. Multicoloured.

1747 80 w. + 50 w. Weightlifting (postage) . . . . 1·25 60
1748 80 w. + 50 w. Handball . . . 1·25 60
1749 370 w. + 100 w. As No. 1747 (air) . . . . 1·75 75
1750 400 w. + 100 w. As No. 1748 1·90 75

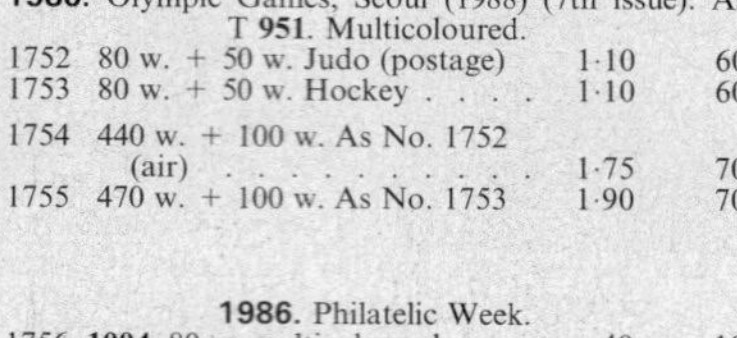
1986. Olympic Games, Seoul (1988) (7th issue). As T **951**. Multicoloured.

1752 80 w. + 50 w. Judo (postage) 1·10 60
1753 80 w. + 50 w. Hockey . . . . 1·10 60
1754 440 w. + 100 w. As No. 1752 (air) . . . . 1·75 70
1755 470 w. + 100 w. As No. 1753 1·90 70

1986. Philatelic Week.

1756 **1004** 80 w. multicoloured . . 40 10

1005 "Chunhyang-do" (Kim Un Ho)

1006 "Flowers" (Lee Sang Bum)

1007 "Portrait of a Friend" (Ku Bon Wung)

1008 "Woman in a Ski Suit" (Son Ung Seng)

1986. Modern Art (3rd series).

1757 **1005** 80 w. multicoloured . . 40 10
1758 **1006** 80 w. multicoloured . . 40 10
1759 **1007** 80 w. multicoloured . . 40 10
1760 **1008** 80 w. multicoloured . . 40 10

1009 Rabbit

1010 Eastern Broad-billed Roller

1986. Lunar New Year ("Year of the Rabbit").

1761 **1009** 80 w. multicoloured . . 35 10

1986. Birds. Multicoloured.

1762 80 w. Type **1010** 90 30
1763 80 w. Japanese waxwing . . . 90 30
1764 80 w. Black-naped oriole . . . 90 30
1765 80 w. Black-capped kingfisher 90 30
1766 80 w. Hoopoe 90 30

1011 Siberian Tiger

1012 Bleeding Heart ("Dicentra spectabilis")

1987. Endangered Animals. Multicoloured.

1767 80 w. Type **1011** . . . . . . 1·00 30
1768 80 w. Leopard cat . . . . . 1·00 30
1769 80 w. Red fox . . . . 1·00 30
1770 80 w. Wild boar . . . . . . 1·00 30

1987. Flowers. Multicoloured.

1771 550 w. Type **1012** . . . . . . 1·50 25
1772 550 w. Diamond bluebell ("Hanabusaya asiatica") . . 1·50 25
1773 550 w. "Erythronium japonicum" . . . . 1·50 25
1774 550 w. Pinks ("Dianthus chinensis") . . . . 1·50 25
1775 550 w. "Chrysanthemum zawadskii" . . . . 1·50 25

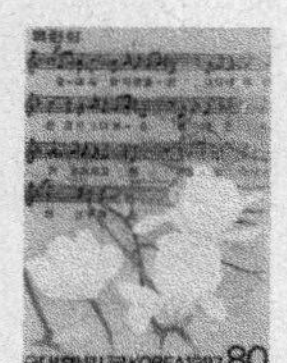

1013 "Barley Field" (Park Wha Mok and Yun Yong Ha)

1014 "Magnolia" (Cho Young Shik and Kim Dong Jin)

1987. Korean Music (3rd series).

1776 **1013** 80 w. multicoloured . . 40 10
1777 **1014** 80 w. multicoloured . . 40 10

1015 National Flags and Korean National Flower

1987. Visit of President Ahmed Abdallah Abderemane of Comoros.

1778 **1015** 80 w. multicoloured . . 35 10

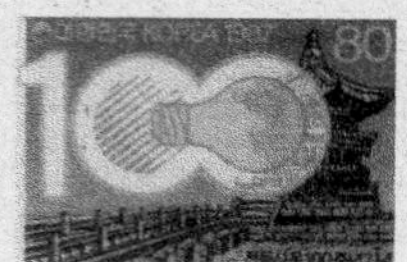
1016 "100", Light Bulb and Hyang Woen Jeong

1987. Centenary of Electric Light in Korea.

1780 **1016** 80 w. multicoloured . . 35 10

1017 Punggi Wind Observatory

1019 Globes, Crane and Ship

1987. Science (2nd series).

1781 **1017** 80 w. dp brown & brown 40 10
1782 – 80 w. brown & dp brown 40 10

DESIGN: No. 1782, Rain gauge.

1987. 15th International Association of Ports and Harbours General Session, Seoul.

1783 **1019** 80 w. multicoloured . . 40 10

1987. Olympic Games, Seoul (1988) (8th issue). As T **951**. Multicoloured.

1784 80 w. + 50 w. Wrestling . . . 80 25
1785 80 w. + 50 w. Tennis 80 25
1786 80 w. + 50 w. Diving 80 25
1787 80 w. + 50 w. Show jumping 80 25

1020 Flags and Doves

1987. Visit of President U San Yu of Burma.

1789 **1020** 80 w. multicoloured . . 40 10

1021 "Valley of Peach Blossoms" (Pyen Kwan Sik)

1022 "Rural Landscape" (Lee Yong Wu)

1023 "Man" (Lee Ma Dong)

1024 "Woman with Water Jar on Head", (sculpture Yun Hyo Chung)

1987. Modern Art (4th series).

1791 **1021** 80 w. multicoloured . . 35 10
1792 **1022** 80 w. multicoloured . . 35 10
1793 **1023** 80 w. multicoloured . . 35 10
1794 **1024** 80 w. multicoloured . . 35 10

1025 Map and Digital Key Pad

1987. Completion of Automatic Telephone Network (1795) and Communications for Information Year (1796).

1795 80 w. Type **1025** 35 10
1796 80 w. Emblem 35 10

1027 Cyprinid Fishes

1028 Russell's Oarfish

1029 Cyprinid Fish

1030 Spine-tailed Mobula

1987. Fishes (3rd series).
1797 **1027** 80 w. multicoloured . . 85 20
1798 **1028** 80 w. multicoloured . . 85 20
1799 **1029** 80 w. multicoloured . . 85 20
1800 **1030** 80 w. multicoloured . . 85 20

1031 Statue of Indomitable Koreans (detail) and Flags
1033 Map and Pen within Profile

1987. Opening of Independence Hall. Mult.
1801 80 w. Type **1031** 35 10
1802 80 w. Monument of the Nation and aerial view of Hall . . 35 10

1987. 16th Pacific Science Congress, Seoul.
1804 **1033** 80 w. multicoloured . . 35 10

1034 Flags and Seoul South Gate

1987. Visit of President Virgilio Barco of Colombia.
1806 **1034** 80 w. multicoloured . . 40 10

1035/1038 Festivities (½-size illustration)

1987. Folk Customs (5th series). Harvest Moon Day.
1808 **1035** 80 w. multicoloured . . 35 10
1809 **1036** 80 w. multicoloured . . 35 10
1810 **1037** 80 w. multicoloured . . 35 10
1811 **1038** 80 w. multicoloured . . 35 10
Nos. 1808/11 were issued together, se-tenant, forming a composite design.

1039 Telephone Dials forming Number
1040 Service Flags and Servicemen

1987. Installation of over 10,000,000 Telephone Lines.
1812 **1039** 80 w. multicoloured . . 40 10

1987. Armed Forces Day.
1813 **1040** 80 w. multicoloured . . 40 10

1987. Olympic Games, Seoul (1988) (9th issue). As T **951**. Multicoloured.
1814 80 w. + 50 w. Table tennis 70 20
1815 80 w. + 50 w. Shooting . . . 70 20
1816 80 w. + 50 w. Archery . . . 70 20
1817 80 w. + 50 w. Volleyball . . . 70 20

1041 Stamps around Child playing Trumpet
1042 Korean Scientist and Map

1987. Philatelic Week.
1819 **1041** 80 w. multicoloured . . 35 10

1987. 1st Anniv of South Korea's Signing of Antarctic Treaty.
1820 **1042** 80 w. multicoloured . . 1·25 30

1043 Dragon
1044 Scattered Sections of Apple

1987. Lunar New Year ("Year of the Dragon").
1821 **1043** 80 w. multicoloured . . 35 10

1988. Compulsory Pension Programme.
1822 **1044** 80 w. multicoloured . . 30 10

1045 Base and Gentoo Penguins
1046 Flag, Olympic Stadium and President Roh Tae Woo

1988. Completion of Antarctic Base.
1823 **1045** 80 w. multicoloured . . 90 30

1988. Presidential Inauguration.
1824 **1046** 80 w. multicoloured . . 30 10

1047 Dinghy Racing
1049 Crane

1988. Olympic Games, Seoul (1988) (10th issue). Multicoloured.
1826 80 w. + 20 w. Type **1047** . . 35 20
1827 80 w. + 20 w. Taekwondo . . 35 20

1988. Japanese White-necked Crane. Mult.
1829 80 w. Type **1049** 75 45
1830 80 w. Crane taking off 75 45
1831 80 w. Crane with wings spread 75 45
1832 80 w. Two cranes in flight . . 75 45

1053 Water Clock
1055 Torch Carrier

1988. Science (3rd series). Multicoloured.
1833 80 w. Type **1053** 30 10
1834 80 w. Sundial 30 10
Nos. 1833/4 were issued together, se-tenant, forming a composite design.

1988. Olympic Games, Seoul (1988) (11th issue). Multicoloured.
1835 80 w. + 20 w. Type **1055** . . 35 20
1836 80 w. + 20 w. Stadium . . . 35 20

1057 Globe and Red Cross as Candle
1058 Computer Terminal

1988. 125th Anniv of International Red Cross.
1838 **1057** 80 w. multicoloured . . 30 10

1988. 1st Anniv of National Use of Telepress.
1839 **1058** 80 w. multicoloured . . 30 10

1059 Woman sitting by Pool and Woman on Swing
1063 Olympic Flag and Pierre de Coubertin (founder of modern Games)

1988. Folk Customs (6th series). Tano Day. Multicoloured.
1840 80 w. Type **1059** 65 35
1841 80 w. Women dressing their hair 65 35
1842 80 w. Woman on swing and boy smelling flowers 65 35
1843 80 w. Boys wrestling 65 35
Nos. 1840/3 were issued together, se-tenant, forming a composite design.

1988. Olympic Games, Seoul (1988) (12th issue). Multicoloured.
1844 80 w. Type **1063** 30 10
1845 80 w. Olympic monument . . 30 10
1846 80 w. View of Seoul (vert) 30 10
1847 80 w. Women in Korean costume (vert) 30 10

1067 Stamps forming Torch Flame
1068 Pouring Molten Metal from Crucible

1988. "Olymphilex '88" Olympic Stamps Exhibition, Seoul.
1849 **1067** 80 w. multicoloured . . 30 10

1988. 22nd International Iron and Steel Institute Conference, Seoul.
1851 **1068** 80 w. multicoloured . . 30 10

1069 Gomdoori (mascot)

1988. Paralympic Games, Seoul.
1852 80 w. Type **1069** . . . . . . 1·00 50
1853 80 w. Archery 50 10

1071 "Homesick" (Lee Eun Sang and Kim Dong Jin)
1072 "The Pioneer" (Yoon Hae Young and Cho Doo Nam)

1988. Korean Music (4th series).
1854 **1071** 80 w. multicoloured . . 35 10
1855 **1072** 80 w. multicoloured . . 35 10

1073 Girls on See-saw
1074 Dancers

1988. Lunar New Year ("Year of the Snake").
1856 **1073** 80 w. multicoloured . . 25 10

1989. Folk Customs (7th series). Mask Dance. Multicoloured.
1858 80 w. Type **1074** 25 10
1859 80 w. Dancer with fans . . . 25 10
1860 80 w. Dancer holding branch 25 10
1861 80 w. Dancer with "Lion" . . 25 10
Nos. 1858/61 were issued together, se-tenant, forming a composite design.

1079 "Arirang"
1080 "Doraji-taryong"

1989. Korean Music (5th series).
1862 **1079** 80 w. multicoloured . . 25 10
1863 **1080** 80 w. multicoloured . . 25 10

1081 Wooden Type Printing
1082 Metal Type Printing

1989. Science (4th series).
1864 **1081** 80 w. brn, bis & stone 25 10
1865 **1082** 80 w. brn, bis & stone 25 10
Nos. 1864/5 were issued together, se-tenant, forming a composite design.

1083 Teeth, Globe, Pencil and Book
1084 Hand with Stick in Heart

1989. 14th Asian–Pacific Dental Congress.
1866 **1083** 80 w. multicoloured . . 25 10

1989. Respect for the Elderly.
1867 **1084** 80 w. multicoloured . . 25 10

1085 Emblem
1086 Profiles within Heart

1989. Rotary Int Convention, Seoul.
1868 **1085** 80 w. multicoloured . . 25 10

1989. 19th International Council of Nurses Congress, Seoul.
1869 **1086** 80 w. multicoloured . . 25 10

1087 "Communication"
1088 "Longevity"

1989. National Information Technology Month.
1870 **1087** 80 w. multicoloured . . 25 10

1989. World Environment Day.
1871 **1088** 80 w. multicoloured . . 30 10

1089 Satellite, Globe and Dish Aerial
1090 "Liberty guiding the People" (detail, Eugene Delacroix)

1989. 10th Anniv of Asia–Pacific Telecommunity.
1872 **1089** 80 w. multicoloured . . 25 10

1989. Bicentenary of French Revolution.
1873 **1090** 80 w. multicoloured . . 25 10

1091 Apple and Flask

1989. 5th Asian and Oceanic Biochemists Federation Congress, Seoul.
1874 **1091** 80 w. multicoloured . . 25 10

1092 "White Ox" (Lee Joong Sub)

1093 "Street Stall" (Park Lae Hyun)

1094 "Little Girl" (Lee Bong Sang)

1095 "Autumn Scene" (Oh Ji Ho)

1989. Modern Art (5th series).
1875 **1092** 80 w. multicoloured . . 30 10
1876 **1093** 80 w. multicoloured . . 30 10
1877 **1094** 80 w. multicoloured . . 30 10
1878 **1095** 80 w. multicoloured . . 30 10

1096 Hunting Scene **1097** Goddess of Law and Ancient Law Code

1989. Seoul Olympics Commemorative Festival and World Sports Festival for Ethnic Koreans.
1879 **1096** 80 w. multicoloured . . 25 10

1989. 1st Anniv of Constitutional Court.
1880 **1097** 80 w. multicoloured . . 25 10

1098 Banded Knifejaw

1099 Banded Loach

1100 Torrent Catfish

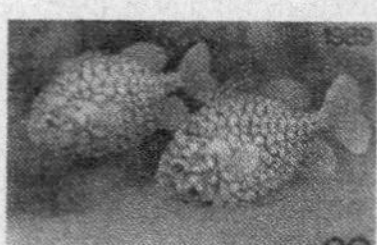
1101 Japanese Pinecone Fish

1989. Fishes (4th series).
1881 **1098** 80 w. multicoloured . . 85 20
1881 **1099** 80 w. multicoloured . . 85 20
1882 **1100** 80 w. multicoloured . . 85 20
1883 **1101** 80 w. multicoloured . . 85 20

1102 Emblem

1989. 44th International Eucharistic Congress, Seoul.
1885 **1102** 80 w. multicoloured . . 25 10

1103 Control Tower and Boeing 747 Jetliner

1989. 29th International Civil Airports Association World Congress, Seoul.
1886 **1103** 80 w. multicoloured . . 35 10

1104 Scissors cutting Burning Banner **1105** Lantern

1989. Fire Precautions Month.
1887 **1104** 80 w. multicoloured . . 25 10

1989. Philatelic Week.
1888 **1105** 80 w. multicoloured . . 25 10

1106 Cranes **1107** New Year Custom

1989. Lunar New Year ("Year of the Horse").
1890 **1106** 80 w. multicoloured . . 25 10
1891 **1107** 80 w. multicoloured . . 25 10

1108 "Pakyon Fall" **1109** "Chonan Samgori"

1990. Korean Music (6th series).
1893 **1108** 80 w. multicoloured . . 25 10
1894 **1109** 80 w. multicoloured . . 25 10

1110 Clouds, Umbrella and Satellite **1111** Child with Rose

1990. World Meteorological Day.
1895 **1110** 80 w. multicoloured . . 40 10

1990. 40th Anniv of U.N.I.C.E.F. Work in Korea.
1896 **1111** 80 w. multicoloured . . 25 10

1112 Cable, Fish and Route Map

1990. Completion of Cheju Island–Kohung Optical Submarine Cable.
1897 **1112** 80 w. multicoloured . . 40 10

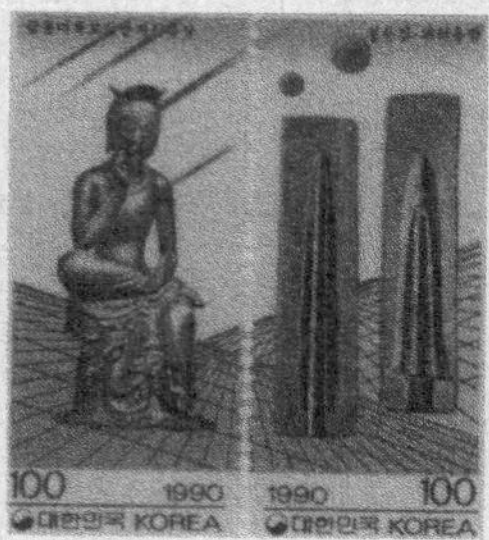
1113 Gilt-bronze Maitreya **1114** Spear and Dagger Moulds

1990. Science (5th series). Metallurgy.
1898 **1113** 100 w. multicoloured . . 30 15
1899 **1114** 100 w. multicoloured . . 30 15
Nos. 1898/9 were issued together, se-tenant, forming the composite design illustrated.

1115 Housing and "20"

1990. 20th Anniv of Saemaul Movement (community self-help programme).
1900 **1115** 100 w. multicoloured . . 30 15

1116 Youths **1117** Butterfly Net catching Pollution

1990. Youth Month.
1901 **1116** 100 w. multicoloured . . 30 15

1990. World Environmental Day.
1902 **1117** 100 w. multicoloured . . 30 15

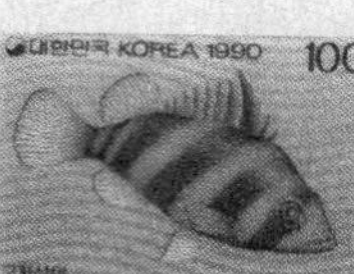
1118 Belted Bearded Grunt

1119 Kusa Pufferfish

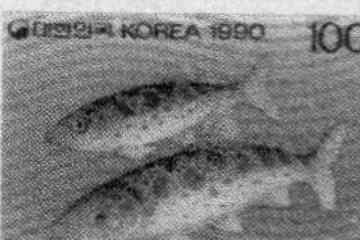
1120 Cherry Salmon

1121 Rosy Bitterling

1990. Fishes (5th series).
1903 **1118** 100 w. multicoloured . . 75 20
1904 **1119** 100 w. multicoloured . . 75 20
1905 **1120** 100 w. multicoloured . . 75 20
1906 **1121** 100 w. multicoloured . . 75 20

1122 Automatic Sorting Machines **1123** Bandaged Teddy Bear in Hospital Bed

1990. Opening of Seoul Mail Centre.
1907 **1122** 100 w. multicoloured . . 30 15

1990. Road Safety Campaign.
1909 **1123** 100 w. multicoloured . . 75 30

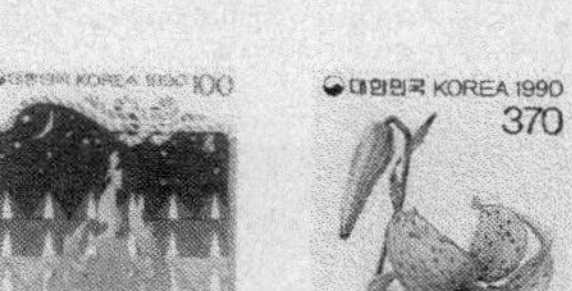

1124 Campfire **1125** Lily

1990. 8th Korean Boy Scouts Jamboree, Kosong.
1910 **1124** 100 w. multicoloured . . 30 15

1990. Wild Flowers (1st series). Multicoloured.
1911 370 w. Type **1125** . . . . . . 1·25 60
1912 400 w. Asters . . . . 1·40 60
1913 440 w. Pheasant's eye . . . . 1·25 60
1914 470 w. Scabious . . . . . . 1·90 60
See also Nos. 1956/9, 1992/5, 2082/5, 2133/6, 2162/5, 2191/4 and 2244/7.

1129 Washing Wool **1133** Church

1990. Folk Customs (8th series). Hand Weaving.
1915 **1129** 100 w. red, yellow & blk 30 15
1916 – 100 w. multicoloured . . 30 15
1917 – 100 w. multicoloured . . 30 15
1918 – 100 w. multicoloured . . 30 15
DESIGNS: No. 1916, Spinning; 1917, Dyeing spun yarn; 1918, Weaving.

1990. Centenary of Anglican Church in Korea.
1919 **1133** 100 w. multicoloured . . 30 15

1134 Top of Tower **1135** Peas in Pod

1990. 10th Anniv of Seoul Communications Tower.
1920 **1134** 100 w. black, blue & red 30 15

1990. Census.
1921 **1135** 100 w. multicoloured . . 30 15

1136 "40" and U.N. Emblem
1137 Inlaid Case with Mirror

1990. 40th Anniv of U.N. Development Programme.
1922 **1136** 100 w. multicoloured . . 30 15

1990. Philatelic Week.
1923 **1137** 100 w. multicoloured . . 30 15

1138 Children feeding Ram
1140 Mascot

1990. Lunar New Year ("Year of the Sheep"). Multicoloured.
1925 100 w. Type **1138** 30 15
1926 100 w. Crane flying above mountains 30 15

1990. "Expo '93" World's Fair, Taejon (1st issue). Multicoloured.
1928 100 w. Type **1140** 30 20
1929 440 w. Yin and Yang (exhibition emblem) . . . . 1·25 60
See also Nos. 1932/3, 2000/1 and 2058/61.

1142 Books and Emblem
1143 Earth

1991. 30th Anniv of Saemaul Minlibrary.
1931 **1142** 100 w. multicoloured . . 30 15

1991. "Expo '93" World's Fair, Taejon (2nd issue). Multicoloured.
1932 100 w. Type **1143** 30 15
1933 100 w. Expo Tower 30 15

1145 "In a Flower Garden" (Uh Hyo Sun and Kwon Kil Sang)
1146 "Way to the Orchard" (Park Hwa Mok and Kim Kong Sun)

1991. Korean Music (7th series).
1935 **1145** 100 w. multicoloured . . 30 15
1936 **1146** 100 w. multicoloured . . 30 15

1147 Moth
1148 Beetle

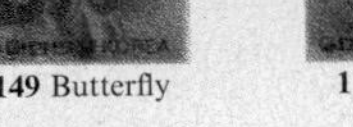

1149 Butterfly
1150 Beetle

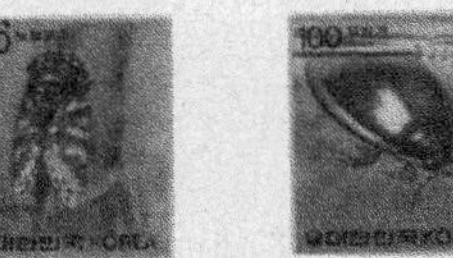

1151 Cicada
1152 Water Beetle

1153 Hornet
1154 Ladybirds

1155 Dragonfly
1156 Grasshopper

1991. Insects.
1937 **1147** 100 w. multicoloured . . 40 15
1938 **1148** 100 w. multicoloured . . 40 15
1939 **1149** 100 w. multicoloured . . 40 15
1940 **1150** 100 w. multicoloured . . 40 15
1941 **1151** 100 w. multicoloured . . 40 15
1942 **1152** 100 w. multicoloured . . 40 15
1943 **1153** 100 w. multicoloured . . 40 15
1944 **1154** 100 w. multicoloured . . 40 15
1945 **1155** 100 w. multicoloured . . 40 15
1946 **1156** 100 w. multicoloured . . 40 15

1157 Flautist and Centre
1158 Flag and Provisional Government Building

1991. 40th Anniv of Korean Traditional Performing Arts Centre.
1947 **1157** 100 w. multicoloured . . 30 15

1991. 72nd Anniv of Establishment of Korean Provisional Government in Shanghai.
1948 **1158** 100 w. multicoloured . . 30 15

1159 Urban Landscape and Emblem

1991. Employment for Disabled People.
1949 **1159** 100 w. multicoloured . . 30 15

1160 Bouquet

1991. Teachers' Day.
1950 **1160** 100 w. multicoloured . . 30 15

1161 Asian Minnow

1162 Majime Minnows

1163 Blotched Grunter

1164 Ijima's Left-eyed Flounder

1991. Fishes (6th series).
1951 **1161** 100 w. multicoloured . . 65 25
1952 **1162** 100 w. multicoloured . . 65 25
1953 **1163** 100 w. multicoloured . . 65 25
1954 **1164** 100 w. multicoloured . . 65 25

1165 Animals waiting to Board Bus
1166 "Aerides japonicum"

1991. "Waiting One's Turn" Campaign.
1955 **1165** 100 w. multicoloured . . 30 15

1991. Wild Flowers (2nd series). Mult.
1956 100 w. Type **1166** 35 15
1957 100 w. "Heloniopsis orientalis" 35 15
1958 370 w. "Aquilegia buergeriana" 90 40
1959 440 w. "Gentiana zollingeri" 1·25 40

1167 Scout with Semaphore Flags
1168 "Y.M.C.A."

1991. 17th World Scout Jamboree.
1960 **1167** 100 w. multicoloured . . 30 10

1991. Young Men's Christian Association World Assembly, Seoul.
1962 **1168** 100 w. multicoloured . . 25 10

1169 Derelict Steam Locomotive and Family Members Reunited
1170 Globe, Rainbow, Dove and U.N. Emblem

1991. "North–South Reunification".
1963 **1169** 100 w. multicoloured . . 90 20

1991. Admission of South Korea to United Nations Organization.
1964 **1170** 100 w. multicoloured . . 25 10

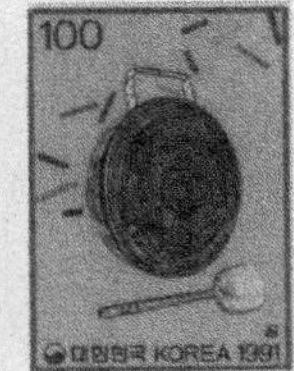

1171 Unra
1172 Jing

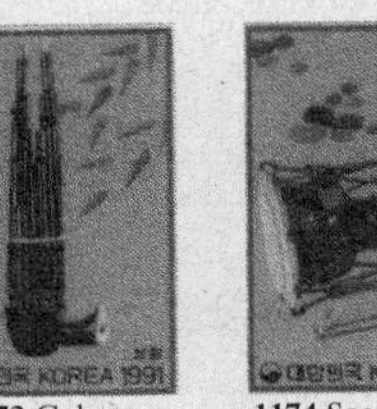

1173 Galgo
1174 Saeng-hwang

1991. Traditional Musical Instruments (1st series).
1965 **1171** 100 w. multicoloured . . 40 20
1966 **1172** 100 w. multicoloured . . 40 20
1967 **1173** 100 w. multicoloured . . 40 20
1968 **1174** 100 w. multicoloured . . 40 20
See also Nos. 1981/4.

1175 Film and Theatrical Masks
1176 Globe and Satellite

1991. Culture Month.
1969 **1175** 100 w. multicoloured . . 25 10

1991. "Telecom 91" International Telecommunications Exhibition, Geneva.
1970 **1176** 100 w. multicoloured . . 25 10

1177 Hexagonals
1178 Bamboo

1179 Geometric
1180 Tree

1991. Korean Beauty (1st series). Kottams (patterns on walls) from Jakyung Hall, Kyungbok Palace.
1971 **1177** 100 w. multicoloured . . 55 25
1972 **1178** 100 w. multicoloured . . 55 25
1973 **1179** 100 w. multicoloured . . 55 25
1974 **1180** 100 w. multicoloured . . 55 25
See also Nos. 2006/9, 2068/71, 2103/6, 2157/60, 2219/22, 2257/60 and 2308/15.

1181 Light Bulb turning off Switch
1182 "Longevity"

1991. Energy Saving Campaign.
1975 **1181** 100 w. multicoloured . . 25 10

1991. Lunar New Year ("Year of the Monkey"). Multicoloured.
1976 100 w. Type **1182** 25 10
1977 100 w. Flying kites 55 10

1184 Stamps

1991. Philatelic Week.
1979 **1184** 100 w. multicoloured . . 25 10

1185 Yonggo
1186 Chwago

1187 Kkwaenggwari
1188 T'ukchong

1992. Traditional Musical Instruments (2nd series).
1981 **1185** 100 w. multicoloured . . 40 15
1982 **1186** 100 w. multicoloured . . 40 15
1983 **1187** 100 w. multicoloured . . 40 15
1984 **1188** 100 w. multicoloured . . 40 15

1189 White Hibiscus

1191 Satellite

1992. "Hibiscus syriacus" (national flower). Multicoloured.
1985 100 w. Type **1189** 45 25
1986 100 w. Pink hibiscus 45 25

1992. Science Day.
1987 **1191** 100 w. multicoloured . . 25 10

1192 Yoon Pong Gil

1193 Children and Heart

1992. 60th Death Anniv of Yoon Pong Gil (independence fighter).
1988 **1192** 100 w. multicoloured . . 25 10

1992. Child Protection.
1989 **1193** 100 w. multicoloured . . 30 10

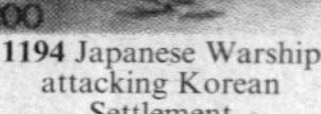
1194 Japanese Warship attacking Korean Settlement

1195 Farmer

1992. 400th Anniv of Start of Im-Jin War.
1990 **1194** 100 w. multicoloured . . 35 10

1992. 60th International Fertilizer Industry Association Conference, Seoul.
1991 **1195** 100 w. multicoloured . . 25 10

1992. Wild Flowers (3rd series). As T **1166**. Multicoloured.
1992 100 w. "Lychnis wilfordii" . . 30 10
1993 100 w. "Lycoris radiata" . . 30 10
1994 370 w. "Commelina communis" 1·00 45
1995 440 w. "Calanthe striata" . . 1·00 45

1196 "Longing for Mt. Keumkang" (Han Sang Ok and Choi Young Shurp)

1197 "The Swing" (Kim Mal Bong and Geum Su Hyeon)

1992. Korean Music (8th series).
1996 **1196** 100 w. multicoloured . . 30 10
1997 **1197** 100 w. multicoloured . . 30 10

1198 Gymnastics

1199 Stylized View of Exhibition

1992. Olympic Games, Barcelona. Multicoloured.
1998 100 w. Type **1198** 30 10
1999 100 w. Pole vaulting 30 10

1992. "Expo '93" World's Fair, Taejon (3rd issue). Multicoloured.
2000 100 w. Type **1199** 25 10
2001 100 w. "Expo 93" 25 10

1201 Korea Exhibition Centre and South Gate, Seoul

1992. 21st Universal Postal Union Congress, Seoul (1st issue). Multicoloured.
2003 100 w. Type **1201** 25 10
2004 100 w. Tolharubang (stone grandfather), Cheju 25 10
See also Nos. 2075/6, 2088 and 2112/15.

1203 Woven Pattern

1204 Fruit and Flower Decorations

1205 Carved Decorations

1206 Coral, Butterfly and Pine Resin Decorations

1992. Korean Beauty (2nd series). Maedeups (tassels).
2006 **1203** 100 w. multicoloured . . 40 15
2007 **1204** 100 w. multicoloured . . 40 15
2008 **1205** 100 w. multicoloured . . 40 15
2009 **1206** 100 w. multicoloured . . 40 15

1207 Lee Pong Chang

1208 Hwang Young Jo (Barcelona, 1992)

1992. 60th Death Anniv of Lee Pong Chang (independence fighter).
2010 **1207** 100 w. brown & orange 30 10

1992. Korean Winners of Olympic Marathon. Multicoloured.
2011 100 w. Type **1208** 60 15
2012 100 w. Shon Kee Chung (Berlin, 1936) 60 15

1209 Sails on Map of Americas

1210 Heads and Speech Balloon

1992. 500th Anniv of Discovery of America by Columbus.
2014 **1209** 100 w. multicoloured . . . 70 10

1992. Campaign for Purification of Language.
2015 **1210** 100 w. multicoloured . . 70 10

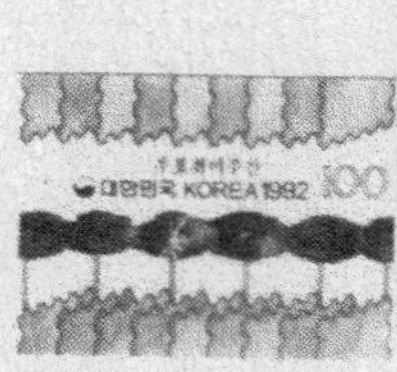
1211 Flowers and Stamps

1212 Cockerels in Snow-covered Yard

1992. Philatelic Week.
2016 **1211** 100 w. multicoloured . . 70 10

1992. Lunar New Year ("Year of the Cock"). Mult.
2018 100 w. Type **1212** 60 10
2019 100 w. Flying kites 60 10

1214 Emblem, Globe and Woman holding Bowl

1992. International Nutrition Conference, Rome.
2021 **1214** 100 w. multicoloured . . 85 10

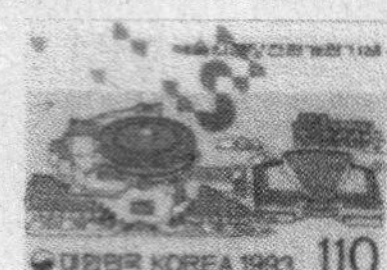
1215 View of Centre and Logo

1993. Inauguration of Seoul Arts Centre's Opera House.
2022 **1215** 110 w. multicoloured . . 85 15

1216 Pres. Kim Young Sam, Flag and Mt. Paekdu Lake

1217 National Flag

1993. Inauguration of 14th President.
2023 **1216** 110 w. multicoloured . . 85 15

1993. No. 2036a orange, black and pink, others multicoloured.
2025 10 w. Type **1217** 10 10
2026 20 w. White stork 10 10
2027 30 w. White magnolia . . . 10 10
2028 40 w. Korean white pine . . 10 10
2028a 50 w. Water cock 10 10
2029 60 w. Squirrel 10 10
2030 70 w. Chinese lanterns (plant) 10 10
2030a 80 w. Japanese white eye on japonica branch 10 10
2031 90 w. Scops owl 15 10
2031a 100 w. Dishcloth gourd . . . 15 10
2032 110 w. "Hibiscus syriacus" (plant) 25 10
2033 120 w. As 110 w. 15 10
2034 130 w. Narcissi 20 10
2034c 140 w. As 130 w. 15 10
2035 150 w. Painted porcelain jar . 25 10
2036 160 w. Pine tree (horiz) . . . 30 10
2036a 170 w. Crayfish 20 10
2036c 170 w. Far eastern curlew . . 20 10
2037 180 w. Little tern (horiz) . . 30 10
2037a 190 w. As 110 w. 20 10
2038 200 w. Turtle (horiz) 30 10
2038a 210 w. As 180 w. 35 10
2038b 260 w. As 180 w. 25 10
2039 300 w. Sky lark (horiz) . . . 45 15
2040 370 w. Drum and drum dance (horiz) 65 15
2041 400 w. Celadon cockerel water dropper (horiz) 65 15
2042 420 w. As 370 w. 65 15
2043 440 w. Haho'i mask and Ssirum wrestlers (horiz) . 80 15
2044 480 w. As 440 w. 75 15
2045 500 w. Celadon pomegranate water dropper 80 15
2046 700 w. Gilt-bronze Bongnae-san incense burner (23 × 34 mm) . . . . 1·10 25
2046a 710 w. King Sejong and alphabet . . . . 1·25 25
2046b 800 w. Cheju ponies . . . . 1·25 20
2047 900 w. Gilt-bronze buddha triad (23 × 34 mm) . . . . 1·60 30
2048 910 w. As 710 w. . . . . . 1·60 30
2049 930 w. Celadon pitcher (blue background) (23 × 31 mm) . . . . 1·50 25
2049a 930 w. As No. 2049 (brown background) . . . . . . 1·60 25
2049b 1000 w. Stone guardian animal (from tomb of King Muryong) (32 × 21 mm) . . 1·60 35
2050 1050 w. As 930 w. . . . . . 1·60 40
2050a 1170 w. Bronze incense burner . . . . 2·25 25
2050b 1190 w. As 930 w. . . . . . 2·75 30

1243 Student and Computer

1244 Emblem and Map

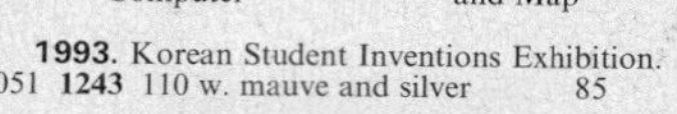

1993. Korean Student Inventions Exhibition.
2051 **1243** 110 w. mauve and silver 85 10

1993. International Human Rights Conference, Vienna, Austria.
2052 **1244** 110 w. multicoloured . . 85 10

1245 Hand scooping Globe from Water

1246 Matsu-take Mushroom ("Tricholoma matsutake")

1993. "Water is Life".
2053 **1245** 110 w. multicoloured . . 85 10

1993. Fungi (1st series). Multicoloured.
2054 110 w. Type **1246** 60 10
2055 110 w. "Ganoderma lucidum" 60 10
2056 110 w. "Lentinula edodes" . . 60 10
2057 110 w. Oyster fungus ("Pleurotus ostreatus") . . 60 10
See also Nos. 2095/8, 2146/9, 2207/10, 2249/52 and 2293/6.

1247 Government Pavilion

1248 International Pavilion and Mascot

1249 Recycling Art Pavilion

1250 Telecom Pavilion

1993. "Expo '93" World's Fair, Taejon (4th issue).
2058 **1247** 110 w. multicoloured . . 50 10
2059 **1248** 110 w. multicoloured . . 50 10
2060 **1249** 110 w. multicoloured . . 50 10
2061 **1250** 110 w. multicoloured . . 50 10

1251 Emblems

1993. 19th Congress of International Society of Orthopaedic and Trauma Surgery.
2063 **1251** 110 w. multicoloured . . 85 10

1252 "O Dol Ddo Gi" (Cheju Island folk song)

1253 "Ong He Ya" (barley threshing song)

1993. Korean Music (9th series).
2064 **1252** 110 w. multicoloured . . 60 10
2065 **1253** 110 w. multicoloured . . 60 10

1254 Janggu Drum Dance

1255 Emblem

1993. "Visit Korea" Year (1994) (1st issue).
2066 **1254** 110 w. multicoloured . . 50 10
2067 **1255** 110 w. multicoloured . . 50 10
See also Nos. 2086/7.

1256 "Twin Tigers" (military officials, 1st to 3rd rank)

1260 Campaign Emblem

1993. Korean Beauty (3rd series). Hyoongbae (embroidered insignia of the Chosun dynasty). Multicoloured.
2068 110 w. Type **1256** 50 10
2069 110 w. "Single Crane" (civil officials, 4th to 9th rank) . . 50 10
2070 110 w. "Twin Cranes" (civil officials, 1st to 3rd rank) . . 50 10
2071 110 w. "Dragon" (King) . . . 50 10

1993. Anti-litter Campaign.
2072 **1260** 110 w. multicoloured . . 50 10

1261 "Eggplant and Oriental Long-nosed Locust" (Shin Saim Dang)

1262 "Weaving"

1993. Philatelic Week.
2073 **1261** 110 w. multicoloured . . 50 10

1993. 21st U.P.U. Congress, Seoul (2nd issue). Paintings by Kim Hong Do. Multicoloured.
2075 110 w. Type **1262** 50 10
2076 110 w. "Musicians and a Dancer" (vert) 50 10

1263 Ribbon and Globe as "30", Freighter and Ilyushin Il-86 Airliner

1993. 30th Trade Day.
2078 **1263** 110 w. multicoloured . . 60 10

1264 Sapsaree and Kite

1993. Lunar New Year ("Year of the Dog"). Multicoloured.
2079 110 w. Type **1264** 50 10
2080 110 w. Puppy with New Year's Greetings bow 50 10

1993. Wild Flowers (4th series). As T **1166**.
2082 110 w. "Weigela hortensis" . . 75 10
2083 110 w. "Iris ruthenica" . . . 75 10
2084 110 w. "Aceriphyllum rossii" . . 75 10
2085 110 w. Marsh marigold ("Caltha palustris") 75 10

1266 Flautist on Cloud

1267 T'alch'um Mask Dance

1994. "Visit Korea" Year (2nd issue).
2086 **1266** 110 w. multicoloured . . 50 10
2087 **1267** 110 w. multicoloured . . 50 10

1268 Map'ae, Horse, Envelope and Emblem

1269 Monument

1994. 21st U.P.U. Congress, Seoul (3rd issue).
2088 **1268** 300 w. multicoloured . . 1·25 15
The map'ae was a token which gave authority to impress post horses.

1994. 75th Anniv of Samil (Independence) Movement.
2090 **1269** 110 w. multicoloured . . 65 10

1270 Great Purple ("Sasakia charonda")

1994. Protection of Wildlife and Plants (1st series). Multicoloured.
2091 110 w. Type **1270** (butterfly) . 60 10
2092 110 w. "Allomyrina dichotoma" (beetle) 60 10
See also Nos. 2143/4, 2186/7, 2241/2, 2275/8 and 2326/9.

1271 Family of Mandarins

1994. International Year of the Family.
2094 **1271** 110 w. multicoloured . . 65 10

1994. Fungi (2nd series). As T **1246**. Multicoloured.
2095 110 w. Common morel ("Morchella esculenta") . . 50 10
2096 110 w. "Gomphus floccosus" . 50 10
2097 110 w. "Cortinarius purpurascens" 50 10
2098 110 w. "Oudemansiella platyphylla" 50 10

1272 Museum

1994. Inauguration of War Memorial Museum, Yongsan (Seoul).
2100 **1272** 110 w. multicoloured . . 65 10

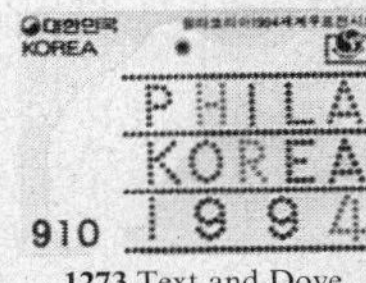

1273 Text and Dove

1994. "Philakorea 1994" International Stamp Exhibition, Seoul (1st issue).
2101 **1273** 910 w. multicoloured . . 2·00 40
See also Nos. 2107/9.

1274 Taeguk (Yin-Yang) Fan

1275 Crane Fan

1276 Pearl Fan

1277 Wheel Fan

1994. Korean Beauty (4th series). Fans.
2103 **1274** 110 w. multicoloured . . 50 10
2104 **1275** 110 w. multicoloured . . 50 10
2105 **1276** 110 w. multicoloured . . 50 10
2106 **1277** 110 w. multicoloured . . 50 10

1278 "Wintry Days" (Kim Chong Hui)

1282 "Sword Dance" (Sin Yun Bok)

1994. "Philakorea 1994" International Stamp Exhibition, Seoul (2nd issue). Multicoloured.
2107 130 w. Type **1278** 50 10
2108 130 w. "Grape" (Choe Sok Hwan) 50 10
2109 130 w. "Riverside Scene" (Kim Duk Sin) 50 10

1994. 21st U.P.U. Congress, Seoul (4th issue). Mult.
2112 130 w. Type **1282** 50 10
2113 130 w. "Book Shelves" (detail of folk painting showing stamps) 50 10
2114 130 w. Congress emblem . . . 50 10
2115 130 w. Hong Yung Sik (postal reformer) and Heinrich von Stephan (founder of U.P.U.) (horiz) 75 10

1283 Old Map

1284 Mail Van

1994. 600th Anniv of Adoption of Seoul as Capital of Korea (1st issue).
2118 **1283** 130 w. multicoloured . . 60 10
See also No. 2139.

1994. Transport. Multicoloured.
2121 300 w. Type **1284** 60 15
2122 330 w. Airplane 80 15
2122a 340 w. Airplane facing left . . 70 10
2122b 380 w. As 340 w. 60 10
2123 390 w. Airplane (different) . . 1·10 15
2124 400 w. As 330 w. . . . . . 1·25 15
2126 540 w. Streamlined diesel train 2·10 15
2127 560 w. As 330 w. . . . . . 2·25 15
2130 1190 w. River cruiser . . . . 3·75 25
2131 1300 w. As 330 w. . . . . 4·00 40
2132 1340 w. As 340 w. . . . . 4·25 35
2132a 1380 w. As 340 w. . . . . 4·50 35

1994. Wild Flowers (5th series). As T **1166**. Multicoloured.
2133 130 w. "Gentiana jamesii" . . 45 10
2134 130 w. "Geranium eriostemon var. megalanthum" 45 10
2135 130 w. "Leontopodium japonicum" 45 10
2136 130 w. "Lycoris aurea" . . . 45 10

1285 "Water Melon and Field Mice" (detail of folding screen, Shin Saimdang)

1286 "600"

1994. Philatelic Week.
2137 **1285** 130 w. multicoloured . . 65 10

1994. 600th Anniv of Seoul as Capital (2nd issue).
2139 **1286** 130 w. multicoloured . . 65 10

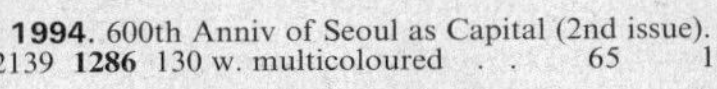

1287 Pigs travelling in Snow

1994. Lunar New Year ("Year of the Pig"). Multicoloured.
2140 130 w. Type **1287** 60 10
2141 130 w. Family in forest 60 10

1995. Protection of Wildlife and Plants (2nd series). Multicoloured.
2143 130 w. Plancy's green pond frog ("Rana plancyi") 60 10
2144 130 w. Common toad ("Bufo bufo") 60 10

1995. Fungi (3rd series). As T **1246**. Multicoloured.
2146 130 w. Shaggy ink caps ("Coprinus comatus") . . 45 10
2147 130 w. Chicken mushroom ("Laetiporus sulphureus") 45 10
2148 130 w. "Lentinus lepideus" . . 45 10
2149 130 w. Cracked green russula ("Russula virescens") . . . 45 10

1290 Spheres around Reactor

1291 Scales of Justice

1995. Completion of Hanaro Research Reactor.
2151 **1290** 130 w. multicoloured . 65 10

1995. Centenary of Judicial System.
2152 **1291** 130 w. multicoloured . . 65 10

MINIMUM PRICE

The minimum price quoted is 10p which represents a handling charge rather than a basis for valuing common stamps. For further notes about prices see introductory pages.

1292 Tiger

1995. Centenary of Law Education.
2153 **1292** 130 w. multicoloured . 65 10

1293 Dooly the Little Dinosaur (Kim Soo Jeung)

1294 Kochuboo (Kim Yong Hwan)

1995. Cartoons (1st series). Multicoloured.
2154 **1293** 130 w. multicoloured . . 70 10
2155 **1294** 440 w. multicoloured . . 1·25 15
See also Nos. 2196/7, 2234/5, 2280/1 and 2322/4.

1295 Gate of Eternal Youth, Changdokkung Palace

1296 Fish Water Gate, Chuhamru Pavilion, Changdokkung Palace

1297 Pomosa Temple Gate, Pusan City

1298 Yangban Residence Gate, Hahoe Village

1995. Korean Beauty (5th series). Gates.
2157 **1295** 130 w. multicoloured . . 50 10
2158 **1296** 130 w. multicoloured . . 50 10
2159 **1297** 130 w. multicoloured . . 50 10
2160 **1298** 130 w. multicoloured . . 50 10

1299 Lion and Emblem

1995. 78th Convention of Lions Clubs International.
2161 **1299** 130 w. multicoloured . . 65 10

1995. Wild Flowers (6th series). As T **1166**. Multicoloured.
2162 130 w. "Halenia corniculata" . 50 10
2163 130 w. "Erythronium japonicum" 50 10
2164 130 w. "Iris odaesanensis" . . 50 10
2165 130 w. "Leontice microrrhyncha" 50 10

1300 National Flag

1301 Telescope

1995. 50th Anniv of Liberation. Multicoloured.
2166 130 w. Type **1300** 60 10
2167 440 w. Anniversary emblem (96 × 19 mm) . . . . . . 1·40 15

1995. Inauguration of Mt. Bohyun Optical Astronomy Observatory.
2169 **1301** 130 w. multicoloured . . 65 10

1302 Turtle's Back Song

1303 Song from "Standards of Musical Science"

1995. Literature (1st series).
2170 **1302** 130 w. multicoloured . . 60 10
2171 **1303** 130 w. multicoloured . . 60 10
See also Nos. 2212/13, 2269/70 and 2301/2.

1304 "50 Th" incorporating Man with Wheat

1995. 50th Anniv of F.A.O.
2172 **1304** 150 w. black and violet . 70 10

1305 Open Bible

1306 Families in Houses

1995. Centenary of Korean Bible Society.
2174 **1305** 150 w. multicoloured . . 70 10

1995. Population and Housing Census.
2175 **1306** 150 w. multicoloured . . 70 10

1307 Dove of Flags

1995. 50th Anniv of United Nations Organization.
2176 **1307** 150 w. multicoloured . . 70 10

1308 Rontgen

1309 "Water Pepper and Mantis" (detail of folding screen, Shin Saim Dang)

1995. Centenary of Discovery of X-Rays by Wilhelm Rontgen.
2177 **1308** 150 w. multicoloured . . 70 10

1995. Philatelic Week.
2178 **1309** 150 w. multicoloured . . 70 10

1310 Rat and Snowman

1312 Miroku Bosatsu, Koryu Temple, Kyoto

1995. Lunar New Year ("Year of the Rat"). Multicoloured.
2180 150 w. Type **1310** 60 10
2181 150 w. Cranes and pine trees (horiz) 60 10

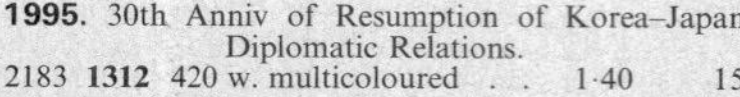

1995. 30th Anniv of Resumption of Korea–Japan Diplomatic Relations.
2183 **1312** 420 w. multicoloured . . 1·40 15

1313 Caoble Route

1314 "30" and Molecule

1996. Inauguration of Korea–China Submarine Cable.
2184 **1313** 420 w. multicoloured . . 70 15

1996. 30th Anniv of Korea Institute of Science and Technology.
2185 **1314** 150 w. multicoloured . . 70 10

1996. Protection of Wildlife and Plants (3rd series). As T **1270.** Multicoloured.
2186 150 w. Black pond turtle ("Geoclemys reevesii") . . 60 10
2187 150 w. Ground skink ("Scincella laterale") 60 10

1315 Satellite and Launching Pad

1996. Launch of "Mugunghwa 2" Telecommunications Satellite.
2189 **1315** 150 w. multicoloured . . 70 10

1316 So Chae P'il (founder) and Leader from First Issue

1996. Centenary of "Tongnip Shinmun" (first independent newspaper).
2190 **1316** 150 w. multicoloured . . 70 10

1996. Wild Flowers (7th series). As T **1166.** Multicoloured.
2191 150 w. "Cypripedium macranthum" 55 10
2192 150 w. "Trilium tschonoskii" . . 55 10
2193 150 w. "Viola variegata" . . . 55 10
2194 150 w. "Hypericum ascyron" 55 10

1317 Anniversary Emblem and Cadets

1996. 50th Anniv of Korean Military Academy.
2195 **1317** 150 w. multicoloured . . 70 10

1318 Gobau (Kim Song Hwan)

1319 Battle between Kkach'i and Caesarius (Lee Hyun Se) (from film "Armageddon")

1996. Cartoons (2nd series).
2196 **1318** 150 w. multicoloured . . 60 10
2197 **1319** 150 w. multicoloured . . 60 10

1320 Anniversary Emblem

1321 Globe and Congress Emblem

1996. 50th Anniv of Korean Girl Scouts.
2199 **1320** 150 w. multicoloured . . 70 10

1996. 35th World Congress of International Advertising Association, Seoul.
2200 **1321** 150 w. multicoloured . . 70 10

1322 Syringes and Drugs

1996. International Anti-drug Day.
2201 **1322** 150 w. multicoloured . . 70 10

1323 Skater

1324 Torch Bearer

1996. World University Students' Games, Muju and Chonju (1st issue). Multicoloured.
2202 150 w. Type **1323** 90 10
2203 150 w. Games emblem (vert) . 90 10
See also Nos. 2228/9.

1996. Olympic Games, Atlanta. Multicoloured.
2204 150 w. Type **1324** 65 10
2205 150 w. Games emblem 65 10

1996. Fungi (4th series). As T **1246.** Multicoloured.
2207 150 w. "Amanita inaurata" . . 70 10
2208 150 w. "Paxillus atrotomentosus" 70 10
2209 150 w. "Rhodophyllus crassipes" 70 10
2210 150 w. "Sarcodon imbricatum" 70 10

1327 Requiem for a Deceased Sister

1328 Ode to Knight Kip'a

1996. Literature (2nd series).
2212 **1327** 150 w. multicoloured . . 75 10
2213 **1328** 150 w. multicoloured . . 75 10

1329 Alphabet

1330 Castle

1996. 550th Anniv of Han-Gul (Korean alphabet created by King Sejong).
2215 **1329** 150 w. black and grey . . 70 10

1996. Bicentenary of Suwon Castle.
2217 **1330** 400 w. multicoloured . . 1·90 15

1331 Front Gate, University Flag and Emblem

1996. 50th Anniv of Seoul National University.
2218 **1331** 150 w. multicoloured . . 70 10

1332 Five-direction Pouch

1333 Chinese Phoenix Pouch (Queen's Court pouch)

1334 Princess Pokon's Wedding Pouch

1335 Queen Yunbi's Pearl Pouch

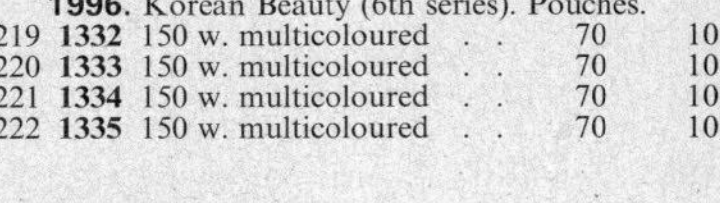

1996. Korean Beauty (6th series). Pouches.
2219 **1332** 150 w. multicoloured . . 70 10
2220 **1333** 150 w. multicoloured . . 70 10
2221 **1334** 150 w. multicoloured . . 70 10
2222 **1335** 150 w. multicoloured . . 70 10

1336 "Poppy and Lizard" (detail of folding screen, Shin Saimdang)

1337 Children riding Ox

1996. Philatelic Week.
2223 **1336** 150 w. multicoloured . . 70 10

1996. Lunar New Year ("Year of the Ox"). Multicoloured.
2225 150 w. Type **1337** 95 10
2226 150 w. Boy piper and resting ox 95 10

1339 Figure Skating

1340 Coins forming "100"

1997. World University Students' Games, Muju and Chonju (2nd issue). Multicoloured.
2228 150 w. Type **1339** 95 10
2229 150 w. Skiing 95 10

1997. Centenary of Foundation of Hansong Bank (first commercial bank in Korea).
2231 **1340** 150 w. multicoloured . . 70 10

1341 "Auspicious Turtles" (painting)

1342 Globe, Pen and open Book (Jeon Chong Kwan)

1997. Interparliamentary Union Conference, Seoul.
2232 **1341** 150 w. multicoloured . . 70 10

1997. World Book and Copyright Day.
2233 **1342** 150 w. multicoloured . . 70 10

1343 A Long, Long Journey in Search of Mummy (Kim Chong Nae)

1344 Run, Run, Hannie (Lee Chin Ju)

1997. Cartoons (3rd series).
2234 **1343** 150 w. multicoloured . . 70 10
2235 **1344** 150 w. multicoloured . . 70 10

1345 Torch Bearer

1997. 2nd East Asian Games, Pusan.
2237 **1345** 150 w. multicoloured . . 70 10

1346 Jules Rimet (founder)

1347 "Chukkuk" (Lee Chul Joo)

1997. World Cup Football Championship (2002), South Korea and Japan (1st issue).
2238 **1346** 150 w. multicoloured . . 60 10
2239 **1347** 150 w. multicoloured . . 60 10
See also Nos. 2284/7.

1997. Protection of Wildlife and Plants (4th series). As **T 1270.** Multicoloured.
2241 150 w. Chinese nine-spined sticklebacks ("Pungitius sinensis") 70 10
2242 150 w. Spot-eared brook perch ("Coreoperca kawamebari") 70 10

1997. Wild Flowers (8th series). As **T 1166.** Multicoloured.
2244 150 w. "Belamcanda chinensis" 75 10
2245 150 w. "Belamcanda chinensis" 75 10
2246 150 w. "Campanula takesimana" 75 10
2247 150 w. "Magnolia sieboldii" . 75 10

1348 Emblem and "97" forming Face

1349 Seoul South Gate and Emblem

1997. 2nd Art Biennale, Kwangju.
2248 **1348** 150 w. multicoloured . . 70 10

1997. Fungi (5th series). As **T 1246.** Multicoloured.
2249 150 w. "Inocybe fastigiata" . . 75 10
2250 150 w. "Panaeolus papilionaceus" 75 10
2251 150 w. "Ramaria flava" . . . 75 10
2252 150 w. Fly agaric ("Amanita muscaria") 75 10

1997. 85th World Dental Congress, Seoul.
2254 **1349** 170 w. multicoloured . . 20 10

1350 Harbour and Score

1997. Centenary of Mokpo Port.
2255 **1350** 170 w. multicoloured . . 70 10

1351 Main Building, Pyongyang

1997. Centenary of Founding of Soongsil Academy in Pyongyang (now situated in Seoul).
2256 **1351** 170 w. multicoloured . . 70 10

1352 Concentric Squares

1353 Green Silk

1354 Pattern of Squares

1355 Pattern of Squares and Triangles

1997. Korean Beauty (7th series). Patchwork Pojagi (wrapping cloths).
2257 **1352** 170 w. multicoloured . . 65 10
2258 **1353** 170 w. multicoloured . . 65 10
2259 **1354** 170 w. multicoloured . . 65 10
2260 **1355** 170 w. multicoloured . . 65 10

1356 "Hollyhock and Frog" (detail of folding screen, Shin Saimdang)

1357 Tiger's Head

1997. Philatelic Week.
2261 **1356** 170 w. multicoloured . . 70 10

1997. Lunar New Year ("Year of the Tiger"). Multicoloured.
2263 170 w. Type **1357** 70 10
2264 170 w. "Magpie and Tiger" (folk painting) 70 10

1359 Buddha, Sokkuram Shrine

1360 Pulguk Temple

1997. World Heritage Sites (1st series).
2266 **1359** 170 w. multicoloured . . 20 10
2267 **1360** 380 w. multicoloured . . 40 10
See also Nos. 2317/18.

1361 "Poem to Sui General Yu Zhong Wen" (Ulchi Mundok)

1362 "Record of Travel to Five Indian Kingdoms" (Hye Ch'o)

1997. Literature (3rd series).
2269 **1361** 170 w. multicoloured . . 70 10
2270 **1362** 170 w. multicoloured . . 70 10

1363 Neon Lights on Globe and Nuclear Power Plant

1998. Centenary of Introduction of Electricity to Korea.
2272 **1363** 170 w. multicoloured . . 70 10

1364 Pres. Kim Dae Jung and Flag

1998. Inauguration of 15th President of South Korea.
2273 **1364** 170 w. multicoloured . . 60 10

1998. Protection of Wildlife and Plants (5th series). Vert designs as **T 1270.** Multicoloured.
2275 340 w. Korean leopard ("Panthera pardus orientalis") . . . . 1·25 75
2276 340 w. Asiatic black bears ("Selenarctos thibetanus") 1·25 75
2277 340 w. European otters ("Lutra lutra") . . . . 1·25 75
2278 340 w. Siberian musk deers ("Moschus moschiferus") . 1·25 75

1365 Aktong-i (Lee Hi Jae)

1366 Challenger (Park Ki Jong)

1998. Cartoons (4th series).
2280 **1365** 170 w. multicoloured . . 40 10
2281 **1366** 340 w. multicoloured . . 70 10

1367 Assembly Building and Firework Display

1368 Player with Ball

1998. 50th Anniv of National Assembly.
2283 **1367** 170 w. multicoloured . . 60 10

1998. World Cup Football Championship (2002), Korea and Japan (2nd issue). Multicoloured.
2284 170 w. Type **1368** 50 10
2285 170 w. Two players chasing ball 50 10
2286 170 w. Players heading ball . . 50 10
2287 170 w. Player kicking ball over head 50 10

1369 Writing on Stone Tablets

1998. Information Technology. Multicoloured.
2289 170 w. Type **1369** 50 10
2290 170 w. Pony Express 50 10
2291 170 w. Man using telephone and post box 50 10
2292 170 w. Old and modern forms of communication (68 × 22 mm) 50 10

1998. Fungi (6th series). As **T 1246.** Multicoloured.
2293 170 w. "Pseudocolus schellenbergiae" 50 10
2294 170 w. "Cyptotrama asprata" . 50 10
2295 170 w. "Laccaria vinaceoavellanea" . . . 50 10
2296 170 w. "Phallus rugulosus" . . 50 10

1373 Flag and Runners

1374 "Grapes" (Lady Shin Saimdang)

1998. 50th Anniv of Proclamation of Republic.
2298 **1373** 170 w. multicoloured . . 60 10

1998. Philatelic Week.
2299 **1374** 170 w. multicoloured . . 60 10

1375 Thinking of Mother

1376 Would You Leave Me Now?

1998. Literature (4th series). Sogyo Songs.
2301 **1375** 170 w. multicoloured . . 60 10
2302 **1376** 170 w. multicoloured . . 60 10

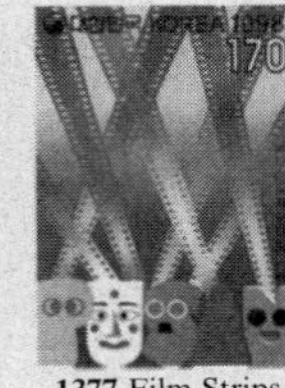
1377 Film Strips and Masks

1998. 3rd Pusan International Film Festival.
2304 **1377** 170 w. multicoloured . . 20 10

1378 Myungnyundang Hall

1998. 600th Anniv of Sungkyunkwan University.
2305 **1378** 170 w. multicoloured . . 20 10

1379 National Constabulary, Badge and Lake Ch'onji

1380 Hot-air Balloon

1998. 50th Anniv of Korean Armed Forces.
2306 **1379** 170 w. multicoloured . . 20 10

1998. World Stamp Day.
2307 **1380** 170 w. multicoloured . . 20 10

1381 Peach

1382 Double Crane

1383 Carp

1384 Peach

1385 Toad

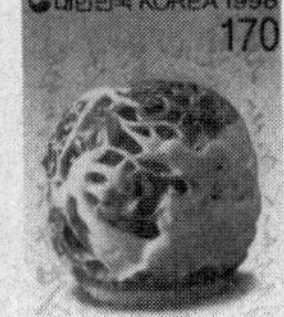
1386 Dragon and Cloud

1387 Monkey

1388 House

1998. Korean Beauty (8th series). Porcelain Water Droppers.

2308 **1381** 170 w. multicoloured . . 20 10
2309 **1382** 170 w. multicoloured . . 20 10
2310 **1383** 170 w. multicoloured . . 20 10
2311 **1384** 170 w. multicoloured . . 20 10
2312 **1385** 170 w. multicoloured . . 20 10
2313 **1386** 170 w. multicoloured . . 20 10
2314 **1387** 170 w. multicoloured . . 20 10
2315 **1388** 170 w. multicoloured . . 20 10

1389 Rabbits

1390 Tripitaka Koreana (scriptures engraved on wooden blocks)

1391 Changgyong P'anjon (woodblock repository)

1998. Lunar New Year ("Year of the Rabbit").

2316 **1389** 170 w. multicoloured . . 20 10

1998. World Heritage Sites (2nd series). Haein Temple.

2317 **1390** 170 w. multicoloured . . 20 10
2318 **1391** 380 w. multicoloured . . 40 10

1392 Maize, Compass and Ship's Wheel

1999. Centenary of Kunsan Port.

2320 **1392** 170 w. multicoloured . . 20 10

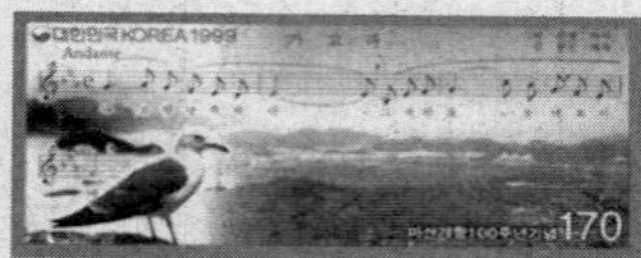
1393 Masan and Score of "I Want to Go" by Lee Eun Sang

1999. Centenary of Masan Port.

2321 **1393** 170 w. multicoloured . . 20 10

1394 Rai-Fi (Kim San Ho)

1395 Tokgo T'ak (Lee Sang Mu)

1396 Im Kkuk Jung (Lee Du Ho)

1999. Cartoons (5th series).

2322 **1394** 170 w. multicoloured . . 20 10
2323 **1395** 170 w. multicoloured . . 20 10
2324 **1396** 170 w. multicoloured . . 20 10

1999. Protection of Wildlife and Plants (6th series). Vert designs as T **1270**.

2326 170 w. Peregrine falcon ("Falco peregrinus") 20 10
2327 170 w. Grey frog hawk ("Accipiter soloensis") . . . 20 10
2328 340 w. Steller's sea eagle ("Haliaeetus pelagicus") . . 35 10
2329 340 w. Eagle owl ("Bubo bubo") 35 10

1397 Five clasped Hands

1398 Goethe (after Joseph Stieler)

1999. 109th International Olympic Committee Congress, Seoul.

2331 **1397** 170 w. multicoloured . . 20 10

1999. 250th Birth Anniv of Johann Wolfgang von Goethe (poet and playwright).

2332 **1398** 170 w. multicoloured . . 20 10

1399 "Kumgang Mountain" (Kyomjae Chong Son)

1999. Philatelic Week.

2334 **1399** 170 w. multicoloured . . 20 10

1400 Mogul Tank Locomotive No. 101 (first locomotive in Korea)

1999. Centenary of Railway in Korea.

2336 **1400** 170 w. multicoloured . . 20 10

C. NORTH KOREAN OCCUPATION.

(**1** "Democratic People's Republic of Korea")

1950. Nos. 116 and 118/19, optd with Type **1**.

1 10 w. green . . . . 45·00
2 20 w. brown . . . . 12·50
3 30 w. green . . . . 15·00

NORTH KOREA

100 cheun = 1 won.

GUM. All stamps of North Korea up to No. N1506 are without gum, except where otherwise stated.

A. RUSSIAN OCCUPATION

1 Hibiscus

2 Diamond Mountains

1946. Perf, roul or imperf.
N1 **1** 20 ch. red . . . . 55·00 38·00
N2 **2** 50 ch. green . . . . 17·00 15·00
N4b 50 ch. red . . . . 10·00 10·00
N5b 50 ch. violet . . . . 10·00 12·00

4 Gen. Kim Il Sung and Flag

5 Peasants

1946. 1st Anniv of Liberation from Japan.
N6 **4** 50 ch. brown £190 £190

1947. Perf, roul or imperf.
N 7 **5** 1 wn. green . . . . 5·00 4·00
N 8 1 wn. violet . . . . 15·00 10·00
N 9 1 wn. blue on buff . . . . . 5·50 4·50
N10 1 wn. blue . . . . 3·25 2·50

6

7

8

1948. 2nd Anniv of Labour Law.
N11 **6** 50 ch. blue £225 £180

1948. 3rd Anniv of Liberation from Japan.
N12 **7** 50 ch. red . . . . — £325

1948. Promulgation of Constitution.
N13 **8** 50 ch. blue and red . . . . £160 40·00

B. KOREAN PEOPLE'S DEMOCRATIC REPUBLIC

9 North Korean Flag **10**

1948. Establishment of People's Republic. Roul.
N16 **9** 25 ch. violet . . . . 3·50 3·50
N17 50 ch. blue . . . . 6·00 6·00

1949. Roul or perf.
N18 **10** 6 wn. red and blue . . . . 2·00 2·00

11 Kim Il Sung University, Pyongyang

12 North Korean Flags

11a Kim Il Sung University, Pyongyang

1949. Roul.
N19 **11** 1 wn. violet . . . . 45·00 20·00
N20 **11a** 1 wn. blue . . . . 45·00 20·00

1949. 4th Anniv of Liberation from Japan. Roul or perf.
N22 **12** 1 wn. red, green and blue 35·00 14·00

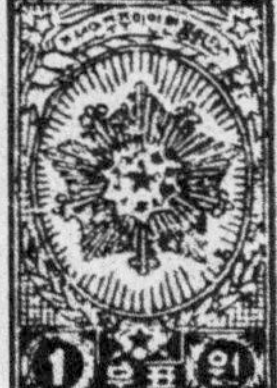
13 Order of the National Flag

14 Liberation Monument, Pyongyang

15 Soldier and Flags

16 Peasant and Worker

17 Tractor

18 Capitol, Seoul

1950. Perf, roul or imperf. Various sizes.
N24 **13** 1 wn. green (A) . . . . . 4·00 1·00
N25 1 wn. orange (A) . . . . . — 25·00
N26 1 wn. orange (B) . . . . . 17·00 12·00
N27 1 wn. green (C) . . . . . 4·00 1·25
N28 1 wn. olive (D) . . . . . 7·00 4·50
SIZES: (A) $23\frac{1}{4}\times37\frac{1}{2}$ mm. (B) $20\times32\frac{1}{2}$ mm. (C) $22\times35\frac{1}{2}$ mm. (D) $22\frac{1}{2}\times36\frac{1}{2}$ mm.

1950. 5th Anniv of Liberation from Japan. Roul, perf or imperf. Various sizes.
N29 **14** 1 wn. red, indigo and blue 1·25 90
N30 1 wn. orange . . . . . . 7·00 5·00
N31 **15** 2 wn. black, blue red . . . 1·25 90
N32 **16** 6 wn. green (A) . . . . . 1·75 1·25
N36 6 wn. red (B) . . . . . 12·50 11·00
N33 **17** 10 wn. brown (C) . . . . . 2·50 2·00
N37 10 wn. brown (D) . . . . 18·00 13·50
SIZES: (A) 20×30 mm. (B) 22×33 mm. (C) 20×28 mm. (D) 22×30 mm.

1950. Capture of Seoul by North Korean Forces.
N38 **18** 1 wn. red, blue and green 40·00 32·00

19

20 Kim Gi Ok and Aeroplane

1951. Order of Admiral Li Sun Sin. Imperf or perf.
N39 **19** 6 wn. orange . . . . . . 6·50 5·00

1951. Air Force Hero Kim Gi Ok. Imperf.
N40 **20** 1 wn. blue . . . . 8·00 3·00

21 Russian and North Korean Flags

22 Kim Ki U (hero)

23 N. Korean and Chinese Soldiers

1951. 6th Anniv of Liberation from Japan. Roul or perf.
N41 **21** 1 wn. blue . . . . 3·50 2·50
N42 1 wn. red . . . . 3·50 2·50
N43 **22** 1 wn. blue . . . . 3·50 2·50
N44 1 wn. red . . . . 3·75 2·50
N45 **23** 2 wn. blue . . . . 6·50 5·00
N46 2 wn. red . . . . 10·00 7·50
All values exist on buff and on white paper.

24 Order of Soldier's Honour

25

26 Woman Partisan, Li Su Dok

1951. Imperf or perf.
N47 **24** 40 wn. red . . . . 9·00 4·50

1951. Co-operation of Chinese People's Volunteers. Imperf or perf.
N49 **25** 10 wn. blue . . . . 5·00 3·25

1952. Partisan Heroes. Imperf or perf.
N50 **26** 70 wn. brown . . . . . . 4·00 1·00

27

28 Gen. P'eng Teh-huai

29 Munition Worker

1952. Peace Propaganda. Imperf or perf.
N51 **27** 20 wn. blue, green & red 6·00 2·00

1952. Honouring Commander of Chinese People's Volunteers. Imperf.
N52 **28** 10 wn. purple . . . . . . 8·00 4·00

1952. Labour Day. Imperf or perf.
N53 **29** 10 wn. red . . . . 17·00 17·00

30

31

32

1952. 6th Anniv of Labour Law. Imperf or perf.
N54a **30** 10 wn. blue . . . . . . 11·00 11·00

1952. Anti-U.S. Imperialism Day. Imperf or perf.
N55 **31** 10 wn. red . . . . 13·00 13·00

1952. North Korean and Chinese Friendship. Imperf or perf.
N56b **32** 20 wn. deep blue . . . . 9·00 9·00

33

34

1952. 7th Anniv of Liberation from Japan. Imperf or perf.
N57 **33** 10 wn. red . . . . 10·00 10·00
N58 **34** 10 wn. red . . . . 12·00 12·00

35

1952. Int Youth Day. With gum. Imperf or perf.
N59 **35** 10 wn. green . . . . . . 8·00 8·00

36

37

1953. 5th Anniv of People's Army. Imperf or perf.
N60 **36** 10 wn. red . . . . 12·50 12·50
N61 **37** 40 wn. purple . . . . . . 12·50 12·50

38

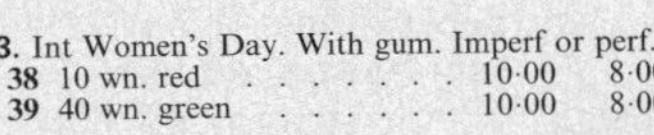
39

1953. Int Women's Day. With gum. Imperf or perf.
N62 **38** 10 wn. red . . . . 10·00 8·00
N63 **39** 40 wn. green . . . . . . 10·00 8·00

40

41

1953. Labour Day. Imperf or perf.
N64 **40** 10 wn. green . . . . . . 7·50 7·50
N65 **41** 40 wn. orange . . . . . . 7·50 7·50

42

43

1953. Anti-U.S. Imperialism Day. With gum. Imperf or perf.
N66 **42** 10 wn. turquoise . . . . . 15·00 13·00
N67 **43** 40 wn. red . . . . 15·00 13·00

44

45

1953. 4th World Youth Festival, Bucharest. With gum. Imperf or perf.
N68 **44** 10 wn. blue and green . . . 4·00 3·25
N69 **45** 20 wn. green and pink . . . 4·00 3·25

46

47

1953. Armistice and Victory Issue. With gum. Imperf or perf.
N70a **46** 10 wn. brown & yellow 38·00 32·00

1953. 8th Anniv of Liberation from Japan. Imperf.
N71 **47** 10 wn. red . . . . £120 90·00

48

49 Liberation Monument, Pyongyang

1953. 5th Anniv of People's Republic. Imperf or perf.
N72 **48** 10 wn. blue and red . . . . 11·00 11·00

1953. With gum. Imperf or perf.
N73 **49** 10 wn. slate . . . . 3·75 3·50

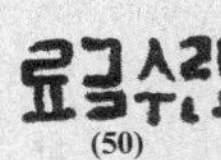
(50)

(51)

1954. No. N18 optd "Fee Collected" in Korean characters, T **50**.
N74 **10** 6 wn. red and blue £150 £150

1954. Nos. N18 and N39 surch with T **51**.
N75 **10** 5 wn. on 6 wn. red & blue 12·00 12·00
N76 **19** 5 wn. on 6 wn. orange . . 55·00 45·00

52

53

1954. Post-war Economic Reconstruction. With gum. Imperf or perf.
N77 **52** 10 wn. blue . . . . 15·00 9·00

1954. 6th Anniv of People's Army. With gum. Imperf or perf.
N78 **53** 10 wn. red . . . . 13·00 10·00

54 55

1954. Int Women's Day. With gum. Imperf or perf.
N79 **54** 10 wn. red . . . . 5·50 5·50

1954. Labour Day. With gum. Imperf or perf.
N80 **55** 10 wn. red . . . . 6·00 6·00

56 57 Taedong Gate, Pyongyang

1954. Anti-U.S. Imperialism Day. With gum. Imperf or perf.
N81 **56** 10 wn. red . . . . 17·00 15·00

1954. Imperf or perf.
N82 **57** 5 wn. lake . . . . 2·00 75
N83 5 wn. brown . . . . 2·00 75

58 59 Soldier

1954. National Young Activists' Conf. With gum. Imperf or perf.
N84 **58** 10 wn. red, blue and slate 3·00 3·00

1954. 9th Anniv of Liberation from Japan. With gum. Imperf or perf.
N85 **59** 10 wn. red . . . . 6·00 6·00

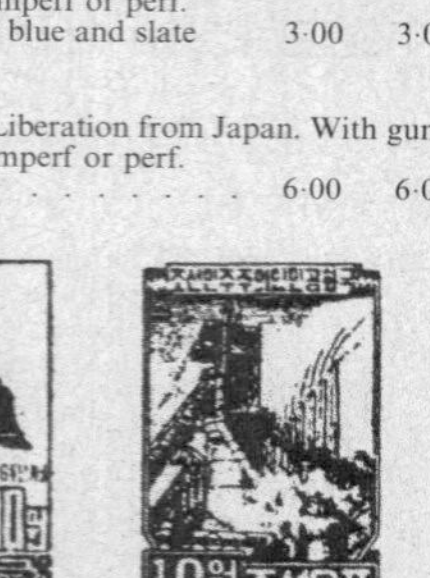

60 North Korean Flag 61 Hwanghae Iron Works

62 Hwanghae Iron Works and Workers

194. 6th Anniv of People's Republic. With gum. Imperf or perf.
N86 **60** 10 wn. blue and red . . . . 5·00 5·00

1954. Economic Reconstruction. Imperf or perf.
N87 **61** 10 wn. blue . . . . 4·50 50
N88 **62** 10 wn. brown . . . . 4·50 50

63

64

1955. 7th Anniv of People's Army. With gum. Imperf or perf.
N89 **63** 10 wn. red . . . . 4·50 3·50

1955. Int. Women's Day. With gum. Imperf or perf.
N90 **64** 10 wn. deep blue . . . . . 5·00 3·50

65

66

1955. Labour Day. With gum. Imperf or perf.
N91 **65** 10 wn. green . . . . 3·25 3·25
N92 **66** 10 wn. red . . . . 3·25 3·25

67 Admiral Li Sun Sin

68

1955. Imperf or perf.
N93 **67** 1 wn. blue on green . . . . 1·25 20
N94 2 wn. red on buff . . . . . 1·75 25
N95 2 wn. red . . . . 3·00 50

1955. 9th Anniv of Labour Law. With gum. Imperf or perf.
N96 **68** 10 wn. red . . . . 3·50 2·50

69 Liberation Monument and Flags

1955. 10th Anniv of Liberation from Japan. Imperf or perf.
N97 **69** 10 wn. green . . . . . . 2·00 1·50
N98 10 wn. red, blue and brown (29½ × 42½ mm) . . . . . 1·25 1·00

70

71

1955. Soviet Union Friendship Month. Imperf or perf.
N 99 **70** 10 wn. red . . . . 1·50 1·00
N100 10 wn. red and blue . . . 2·25 1·50
N101 **71** 20 wn. red and slate . . . 3·25 2·50
N102 20 wn. red and blue . . . 1·50 1·25
SIZES: No. N99, 22 × 32½ mm; N100, 29½ × 43 mm; N101, 18½ × 32 mm; N102, 25 × 43 mm.

72 Son Rock

73

1956. Haegumgang Maritime Park. Imperf or perf.
N103 **72** 10 wn. blue on blue . . . 3·00 1·75

1956. 8th Anniv of People's Army. Imperf or perf.
N104 **73** 10 wn. red on green . . . 5·50 5·50

74

1956. Labour Day. Imperf or perf.
N105 **74** 10 wn. blue . . . . . . 4·50 2·75

75 Machinist

76 Taedong Gate, Pyongyang

77 Woman Harvester

78 Moranbong Theatre, Pyongyang

1956. Imperf or perf.
N106 **75** 1 wn. brown . . . . . . 1·25 60
N107 **76** 2 wn. blue 90 60
N108 **77** 10 wn. red 90 60
N109 **78** 40 wn. green . . . . . . 8·00 3·50

79 Miner

80 Boy Bugler and Girl Drummer

1956. 10th Anniv of Labour Law. Imperf or perf.
N110 **79** 10 wn. brown . . . . . . 2·50 1·00

1956. 10th Anniv of Children's Union. Imperf or perf.
N111 **80** 10 wn. brown . . . . . . 4·00 2·75

81 Workers

82 Industrial Plant

1956. 10th Anniv of Sex Equality Law. Imperf or perf.
N112 **81** 10 wn. brown . . . . . . 2·00 1·40

1956. 10th Anniv of Nationalization of Industry. Imperf or perf.
N113 **82** 10 wn. brown . . . . . . 45·00 16·00

83 Liberation Tower

84 Kim Il Sung University

1956. 11th Anniv of Liberation from Japan. Imperf or perf.
N114 **83** 10 wn. red . . . . 3·00 1·25

1956. 10th Anniv of Kim Il Sung University. Imperf or perf.
N115 **84** 10 wn. brown . . . . . . 2·50 1·75

85 Boy and Girl

86 Pak Ji Won

1956. 4th Democratic Youth League Congress. Imperf or perf.
N116 **85** 10 wn. brown . . . . . . 2·50 1·50

1957. 220th Birth Anniv of Pak Ji Won "Yonam", (statesman). Imperf or perf.
N117 **86** 10 wn. blue . . . . . . 1·50 90

87 Tabo Pagoda, Pulguksa

88 Ulmil Pavilion, Pyongyang

89 Furnaceman

1957. Imperf, perf or roul.
N118 **87** 5 wn. blue . . . . 1·00 75
N119 **88** 40 wn. green . . . . . . 2·00 1·25

1957. Production and Economy Campaign. With or without gum. Imperf or perf.
N121 **89** 10 wn. blue . . . . . . 2·50 1·25

90 Furnaceman

91 Voters and Polling Booth

1957. 2nd General Election. Imperf or perf.
N122 **90** 1 wn. orange 75 30
N123 2 wn. brown 75 30
N124 **91** 10 wn. red . . . . 3·75 1·25

92 Ryongwangjong, Pyongyang

93 Lenin and Flags

94 Kim Il Sung at Pochonbo

95 Lenin

96 Pouring Steel

1957. 1530th Anniv of Pyongyang. Imperf or perf.
N125 **92** 10 wn. green . . . . . . 1·00 25

1957. 40th Anniv of Russian Revolution. Imperf or perf.
N126 **93** 10 wn. green 75 40
N127 **94** 10 wn. red 75 40
N128 **95** 10 wn. blue 75 40
N129 **96** 10 wn. orange . . . . . 2·00 40
No. N126 exists with gum.

97 Congress Emblem

98 Liberation Monument, Spassky Tower and Flags

1957. 4th World Trade Unions Federation Congress. Leipzig. Imperf (with or without gum) or perf.
N130 **97** 10 wn. blue and green . . 1·25 50

1957. Russian Friendship Month. Imperf or perf.
N131 **98** 10 wn. green . . . . . . 1·75 50

99 Weighing a Baby

100 Bandaging a Hand

1957. Red Cross. Imperf, perf or roul.
N132 **99** 1 wn. red . . . . 6·00 1·00
N133 2 wn. red . . . . 6·00 1·00
N134 **100** 10 wn. red . . . . . . 15·00 2·75
No. N133 exists with or without gum.

101 Koryo Celadon Jug (12th century)

102 Koryo Incense-burner (12th century)

1958. Korean Antiquities. Imperf (with or without gum) or perf.
N135 **101** 10 wn. blue . . . . . . 4·50 75
N136 **102** 10 wn. green . . . . . . 4·50 75

103 Woljong Temple Pagoda

104 Soldier

1958. With gum (5 wn.), without gum (10 wn.). Imperf or perf.
N137 **103** 5 wn. green . . . . . . 1·00 50
N138 10 wn. blue . . . . . . 1·50 75

1958. 10th Anniv of People's Army. No gum (No. N139) with or without gum (No. N140). Imperf or perf.
N139 **104** 10 wn. blue . . . . . . 1·75 50
N140 – 10 wn. red . . . . . . 4·50 65
DESIGN—HORIZ: (37½×26 mm.): No. N140, Soldier, flag and Hwanghae Iron Works.

106 Lisunov Li-2 Airliner over Pyongyang

1958. Air. Imperf or perf.
N141 **106** 20 wn. blue . . . . . . 5·50 1·00

107 Sputniks

108 Sputnik encircling Globe

1958. I.G.Y. Inscr "1957-1958". Imperf or perf.
N142 **107** 10 wn. slate 45 10
N143 **108** 20 wn. slate 45 10
N144 – 40 wn. slate . . . . . . 1·75 30
N145 **107** 70 wn. slate 50 20
DESIGN—HORIZ: 40 wn. Sputnik over Pyongyang Observatory.
Nos. N142/4 exist with or without gum.

109 Furnaceman

110 Hwanghae Iron Works

1958. Young Socialist Constructors' Congress, Pyongyang. Imperf or perf.
N146 **109** 10 wn. blue . . . . . . 2·75 50

1958. Opening of Hwanghae Iron Works. Imperf or perf.
N147 **110** 10 wn. blue . . . . . . 4·25 65

111 Commemorative Badge

112 Federation Emblem

1958. Farewell to Chinese People's Volunteers (1st issue). Imperf or perf.
N148 **111** 10 wn. purple and blue 1·50 40
See also No. N158.

1958. 4th International Women's Federation Democratic Congress. Imperf or perf.
N149 **112** 10 wn. blue . . . . . . 1·00 35

113 Conference Emblem

1958. 1st World Young Workers' Trade Union Federation Conference, Prague. Imperf or perf.
N150 **113** 10 wn. brown & green 1·75 35

114 Flats, East Ward, Pyongyang

115 Workers' Flats, Pyongyang

1958. Rehousing Progress. Imperf or perf.
N151 **114** 10 wn. blue . . . . . . 2·00 50
N152 **115** 10 wn. green . . . . . . 2·00 50

117 Pyongyang Railway Station

119 Textile Worker

1958. 10th Anniv of Korean People's Republic. Imperf or perf.
N153 – 10 wn. green . . . . . . 3·00 50
N154 **117** 10 wn. green . . . . . . 11·00 1·50
N155 – 10 wn. brown and buff 1·50 50
N156 **119** 10 wn. brown . . . . . 7·50 1·75
N157 – 10 wn. brown . . . . . 6·50 1·00
DESIGNS—HORIZ: No. N153, Hungnam Fertiliser Plant; N157, Yongp'ung Dam, Pyongyang. VERT: No. N155, Arms of People's Republic.

121 Volunteer and Steam Troop Train

122 Transplanting Rice

1958. Farewell to Chinese People's Volunteers (2nd issue). Imperf or perf.
N158 **121** 10 wn. sepia . . . . . . 24·00 8·00

1958. Imperf or perf.
N159 **122** 10 wn. sepia 75 15

123 Winged Horse of Chollima

124 N. Korean and Chinese Flags

1958. National Production Executives' Meeting, Pyongyang. With or without gum. Imperf or perf.
N160 **123** 10 wn. red . . . . . . 1·60 30

1958. North Korean–Chinese Friendship Month. With or without gum. Imperf or perf.
N161 **124** 10 wn. red, blue & green 1·25 30

125 Farm Workers

126 Gen. Ulji Mun Dok

1959. National Co-operative Farming Congress, Pyongyang. With or without gum. Imperf or perf.
N162 **125** 10 wn. blue 90 25

1959. With gum. Imperf or perf.
N163 **126** 10 wn. red and yellow . . 2·00 50
See also Nos. N165/7 and N216/19.

127 Women with Banner

128 Rocket and Moon

1959. National Conference of Women Socialist Constructors, Pyongyang. With or without gum.
N164 **127** 10 ch. brown and red . . 75 30

1959. Revalued currency. Portraits as T **126**. Imperf (with or without gum) or perf (with gum).
N165 – 2 ch. blue on green . . . 60 10
N166 – 5 ch. purple on buff . . . 70 10
N167 **126** 10 ch. red on cream . . . 85 10
PORTRAITS: 2 ch. General Kang Gam Chan; 5 ch. General Chon Bong Jun.

1959. Launch of Soviet Moon Rocket. With or without gum. Imperf or perf.
N168 **128** 2 ch. purple on buff . . . 1·25 25
N169 10 ch. blue on green . . 1·50 35

129 "Irrigation"

130 Inscribed Tree at Partisan H.Q., Chongbong

131 Kim Il Sung Statue

132 Mt. Paekdu

1959. Land Irrigation Project. Imperf or perf.
N170 **129** 10 ch. multicoloured . . 3·75 65

1959. Partisan Successes against Japanese 1937–39. With gum (No. N172) or no gum (others). Perf (N172) or imperf or perf (others).
N171 **130** 5 ch. multicoloured . . . 2·75 45
N172 **131** 10 ch. blue & turquoise 1·00 10
N173 **132** 10 ch. violet . . . . . . 2·25 40

133 "Flying Horse" Tractor

1959. "Great Perspectives" (1st issue: Development of Industrial Mechanisation). With or without gum. Perf, roul or imperf.
N174 **133** 1 ch. red, olive and green 65 10
N175 – 2 ch. multicoloured . . 3·25 75
N176 – 2 ch. red, pink and violet 60 10
N177 – 5 ch. orange, brown and ochre 60 15
N178 – 10 ch. blue, green & brn . 70 15
N179 – 10 ch. grn, lt grn & brn . 1·50 25
DESIGNS: No. N175, Electric mine locomotive; N176, "Red Star 58" bulldozer; N177, "Flying Horse" excavator; N178, "SU-50" universal lathe; N179, "Victory 58" lorry.
See also Nos. N189a/200 and N275/79.

134 Armistice Building, Panmunjom

135 Protest Meeting

136 "Hoisting link between N. and S. Korea"

137 Emigration "Pickets"

1959. Campaign for Withdrawal of U.S. Forces from S. Korea. With gum. Perf (20 ch.) or imperf or perf (others).
N180 **134** 10 ch. blue & ultramarine 55 20
N181 **135** 20 ch. deep blue & blue 75 30
N182 **136** 70 ch. brown, cream and purple . . . . . . 13·00 6·00

1959. Campaign Against Emigration of South Koreans. With gum.
N183 **137** 20 ch. brown and sepia . 3·50 1·00

138 Korean Type of "1234"

139 Books breaking Chains

140 Emblems of Peace, Labour and Letters

141 Korean Alphabet of 1443

1959. International Book Exibition, Leipzig. With gum (No. N184, N186) or no gum (others).
N184 **138** 5 ch. sepia . . . . . . 15·00 5·00
N185 **139** 5 ch. red and green . . . 4·50 1·50
N186 **140** 10 ch. blue . . . . . . 4·50 1·50
N187 **141** 10 ch. violet and blue . . 7·00 2·50

142 Pig Farm

143 Rotary Cement Kiln

1959. Animal Husbandry. With gum (5 ch.) or no gum (2 ch.).
N188 – 2 ch. brown, grn & buff 75 15
N189 **142** 5 ch. cream, blue & brn 1·00 20
DESIGN—HORIZ: 2 ch. Cow-girl with Cattle.

1959. "Great Perspectives" (2nd issue: Production Targets). With gum (Nos. N190 and N192) or no gum (others). Perf (N197/8 and N200), perf or imperf (others).
N189a **143** 1 ch. cinnamon, brn & bl 40 10
N190 – 2 ch. multicoloured . . 60 10
N191 – 5 ch. multicoloured . . 1·00 25
N192 – 10 ch. multicoloured . . 1·25 35
N193 – 10 ch. purple, yell & bl 60 10
N194 – 10 ch. yellow, grn & red . 90 10
N195 – 10 ch. multicoloured . . 60 10
N196 – 10 ch. blue, light blue and green 75 10
N197 – 10 ch. multicoloured . . 60 10
N198 – 10 ch. green, buff and brown 90 10
N199 – 10 ch. brown & orange 60 10
N200 – 10 ch. multicoloured . . 1·10 15
DESIGNS—VERT: No. N190, Electric power lines and dam; N191, Loading fertilizers into goods wagon; HORIZ: No. N192, Factory, electric power lines and dam; N193, Harvesting; N194, Sugar-beet, factory and pieces of sugar; N195, Steel furnace; N196, Trawlers; N197, Pig-iron workers; N198, Coal miners; N199, Girl picking apples; N200, Textile worker.

144 Sika Deer

145 Congress Emblem

1959. Game Preservation. No gum (5 ch.), with gum (10 ch.).
N201 – 5 ch. multicoloured . . 1·75 20
N202 – 5 ch. yellow, brown & bl 1·75 10
N203 – 5 ch. sepia, green & brn 1·75 10
N204 – 5 ch. brown, black & blue 1·75 10
N205 **144** 10 ch. multicoloured . . 1·75 25
N206 – 10 ch. red, brown and green on cream . . . 4·50 65
DESIGNS—HORIZ: No. N201, Chinese water deer; N202, Siberian weasel; N203, Steppe polecat; N204, European otter; N206, Ring-necked pheasant.

1960. 3rd Korean Trade Unions Federation Congress. With gum.
N207 **145** 5 ch. multicoloured . . . 45 20

146 "Chungnyon-ho" (freighter)

1959. Transport. With gum.

N208 – 5 ch. purple . . . . . . 6·75 75
N209 **146** 10 ch. green . . . . . . 2·50 60
DESIGN: 5 ch. Electric train.

147 Soldier, Tractor and Plough **148** Knife Dance

1960. 12th Anniv of Korean People's Army. With gum.

N210 **147** 5 ch. violet and blue . . 35·00 28·00

1960. Korean National Dances. Multicoloured.

N211 5 ch. Type **148** . . . . . . 3·50 20
N212 5 ch. Drum dance . . . . . 3·50 20
N213 10 ch. Farmers' dance . . . 3·50 25

149 Women of Three Races **150** Kim Jong Ho (geographer)

1960. 50th Anniv of Int Women's Day. With gum.

N214 **149** 5 ch. mauve and blue . . 90 15
N215 – 10 ch. green and orange 90 25
DESIGN—VERT: 10 ch. Woman operating lathe.

1960. Korean Celebrities. With gum.

N216 **150** 1 ch. grey and green . . 75 10
N217 – 2 ch. blue and yellow . . 90 10
N218 – 5 ch. blue and yellow . . 3·00 20
N219 – 10 ch. brown and ochre 85 10
PORTRAITS: 2 ch. Kim Hong Do (painter); 5 ch. Pak Yon (musician); 10 ch. Chong Da San (scholar).

151 Grapes **152** Lenin

1960. Wild Fruits. Fruits in natural colours. With or without gum (N221/2), with gum (others).

N220 5 ch. olive and turquoise . . 80 15
N221 5 ch. drab and blue . . . 80 15
N222 5 ch. olive and blue . . . 80 15
N223 10 ch. olive and orange . . 1·25 20
N224 10 ch. green and pink . . . 1·25 20
FRUITS: No. N220, T **151**; N221, Fruit of "Actinidia arguta planch"; N222, Pine-cone; N223, Hawthorn berries; N224, Horse-chestnut.

1960. 90th Birth Anniv of Lenin. With gum.

N225 **152** 10 ch. purple 55 15

153 Koreans and American Soldier (caricature) **154** Arch of Triumph Square, Pyongyang

1960. Campaign Day for Withdrawal of U.S. Forces from South Korea. With gum.

N226 **153** 10 ch. blue . . . . . . 3·25 40

1960. Views of Pyongyang.

N227 **154** 10 ch. green 75 20
N228 – 20 ch. slate . . . . . . 1·00 30
N229 – 40 ch. green . . . . . . 2·25 50
N230 – 70 ch. green . . . . . . 3·00 60
N231 – 1 wn. blue . . . . . . 4·50 90
VIEWS OF PYONGYANG: 20 ch. River Taedong promenade; 40 ch. Youth Street; 70 ch. People's Army Street; 1 wn. Sungri Street.

155 Russian Flag on Moon (14.9.59) **156** "Mirror Rock"

1960. Russian Cosmic Rocket Flights. With gum (5 ch.) or no gum (10 ch.).

N232 – 5 ch. turquoise . . . . . 2·00 1·10
N233 **155** 10 ch. multicoloured . . 2·00 75
DESIGN: 5 ch. "Lunik 3" approaching Moon (4.10.59).

1960. Diamond Mountains Scenery (1st issue). Multicoloured.

N234 5 ch. Type **156** . . . . . . 1·00 10
N235 5 ch. Devil-faced Rock . . . 1·00 10
N236 10 ch. Dancing Dragon Bridge (horiz) . . . . 3·00 25
N237 10 ch. Nine Dragon Falls . . 3·50 25
N238 10 ch. Mt. Diamond on the Sea (horiz) 90 10
See also Nos. N569/72, N599/601 and N1180/4.

157 Lily **158** Guerrillas in the Snow

1960. Flowers. Multicoloured. With gum (N242), with or without gum (others).

N239 5 ch. Type **157** 90 15
N240 5 ch. Rhododendron 90 15
N241 10 ch. Hibiscus . . . . . . 1·75 20
N242 10 ch. Blue campanula . . . 1·75 20
N243 10 ch. Mauve campanula . . 1·75 20

1960. Revolutionary Leadership of Kim Il Sung.

N244 **158** 5 ch. red 45 10
N245 – 10 ch. blue 70 10
N246 – 10 ch. red 70 10
N247 – 10 ch. blue 70 10
N248 – 10 ch. red 70 10
DESIGNS: No. N245, Kim Il Sung talks to guerrillas; N246, Kim Il Sung at Pochonbo; N247, Kim Il Sung on bank of Amnok River; N248, Kim Il Sung returns to Pyongyang.

159 Korean and Soviet Flags **160** "North Korean–Soviet Friendship"

1960. 15th Anniv of Liberation from Japan.

N249 **159** 10 ch. red, blue & brown 60 15

1960. North Korean–Soviet Friendship Month.

N250 **160** 10 ch. lake on cream . . 35 15

161 Okryu Bridge, Pyongyang

1960. Pyongyang Buildings.

N251 **161** 10 ch. blue . . . . . . 2·25 20
N252 – 10 ch. violet . . . . . 1·50 15
N253 – 10 ch. green 75 10
DESIGNS: No. N252, Grand Theatre, Pyongyang; N253, Okryu Restaurant.

162 Tokro River Dam

1960. Inauguration of Tokro River Hydro-electric Power Station. With gum.

N254 **162** 5 ch. blue 70 10

163 **164** Quayside Welcome

1960. 15th Anniv of World Federation of Trade Unions.

N255 **163** 10 ch. light blue, ultram and blue 25 10

1960. Repatriation of Korean Nationals from Japan.

N256 **164** 10 ch. purple . . . . . 2·50 35

165 Lenin and Workers **166** Football

1960. Korea–Soviet Friendship. With gum.

N257 **165** 10 ch. brown and flesh 35 15

1960. Liberation Day Sports Meeting, Pyongyang. Multicoloured.

N258 5 ch. Running (vert) 60 10
N259 5 ch. Weightlifting (vert) . . 60 10
N260 5 ch. Cycling (vert) . . . . . 2·25 15
N261 5 ch. Gymnastics (vert) . . . 60 10
N262 5 ch. Type **166** . . . . . . 1·10 15
N263 10 ch. Swimming 60 10
N264 10 ch. Moranbong Stadium, Pyongyang 60 10

167 Friendship Monument, Pyongyang **168** Federation Emblem

1960. 10th Anniv of Entry of Chinese Volunteers into Korean War. With gum.

N265 – 5 ch. mauve 30 10
N266 **167** 10 ch. blue 30 10
DESIGN—HORIZ: 5 ch. Chinese and Korean soldiers celebrating.

1960. 15th Anniv of World Democratic Youth Federation.

N267 **168** 10 ch. multicoloured . . 30 10

169 White-backed Woodpecker **170** Korean Wrestling

1960. Birds.

N268 **169** 2 ch. multicoloured . . 3·25 10
N268a – 5 ch. multicoloured . . 4·50 25
N269 – 5 ch. brown, yell & bl 6·00 60
N270 – 10 ch. yellow, brn & grn 3·75 45
DESIGNS—HORIZ: 5 ch. (N268a), Mandarins; 10 ch. Black-naped oriole. VERT: 5 ch. (N269), Scops owl.

1960. Sports and Games. Multicoloured.

N271 5 ch. Type **170** 60 10
N272 5 ch. Riding on swing (vert) 60 10
N273 5 ch. Archery . . . . . . 2·25 30
N274 10 ch. Jumping on see-saw (vert) 60 10

171 Cogwheel and Corn ("Mechanization of Rural Economy") **172** Cultivated Ginseng

1961. "Great Perspectives" (3rd issue: Targets of Seven-Year Plan, 1961–67. Inscr "1961"). Mult.

N275 5 ch. Type **171** 60 10
N276 5 ch. Cogwheel and textiles 1·10 10

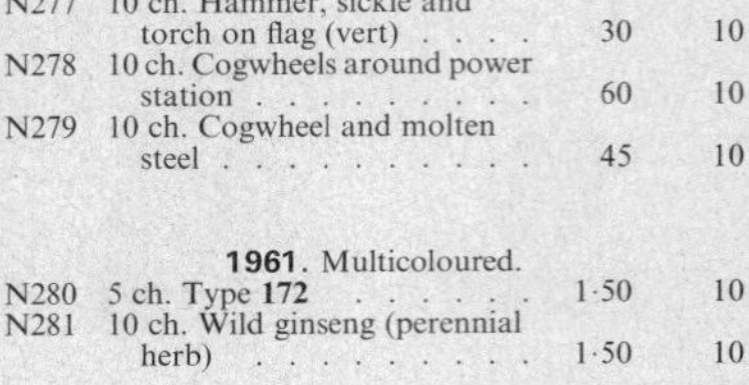

N277 10 ch. Hammer, sickle and torch on flag (vert) 30 10
N278 10 ch. Cogwheels around power station 60 10
N279 10 ch. Cogwheel and molten steel 45 10

1961. Multicoloured.

N280 5 ch. Type **172** . . . . . . 1·50 10
N281 10 ch. Wild ginseng (perennial herb) . . . . 1·50 10

173 Aldehyde Shop

1961. Construction of Vinalon Factory. With gum.

N282 **173** 5 ch. red and yellow . . 60 10
N283 – 10 ch. green and yellow 1·10 10
N284 – 10 ch. blue and yellow 1·10 10
N285 – 20 ch. purple and yellow 1·25 15
DESIGNS: No. N283, Glacial acetic acid shop; N284, Polymerization and saponification shop; N285, Spinning shop.
See also Nos. N338/41.

174 Construction Work **175** Museum Building

1961. Construction of Children's Palace, Pyongyang. With gum.

N286 **174** 2 ch. red on yellow . . . 35 15

1961. Completion of Museum of Revolution, Pyongyang. With gum.

N287 **175** 10 ch. red 25 10

176 Cosmic Rocket **177** Wheat Harvester

1961. Launching of Soviet Venus Rocket.

N288 **176** 10 ch. red, yellow & blue 60 15

1961. Agricultural Mechanisation. With gum.

N289 – 5 ch. violet 50 10
N290 – 5 ch. green 50 10
N291 **177** 5 ch. green 50 10
N292 – 10 ch. blue 60 10
N293 – 10 ch. purple 60 10
DESIGNS: No. N289, Tractor-plough; N290, Disc-harrow; N292, Maize-harvester; N293, Tractors.

178 **179** Agriculture

1961. Opening of Training Institute.

N294 **178** 10 ch. brown on buff . . 25 10

1961. 15th Anniv of Land Reform Law. With gum.

N295 **179** 10 ch. green on yellow 45 15

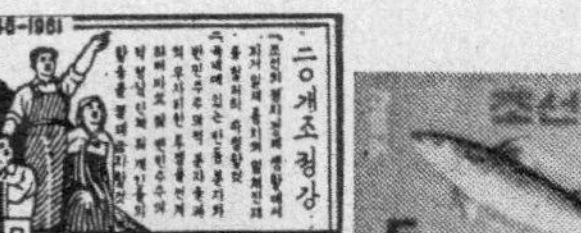

180 **181** Chub Mackerel

1961. 15th Anniv of National Programme. With gum.

N296 **180** 10 ch. purple & yellow 20 10

1961. Marine Life.

N297 **181** 5 ch. multicoloured . . . 1·25 10
N298 – 5 ch. black and blue . . 2·00 25
N299 – 10 ch. blue, black & lt bl 2·50 25
N300 – 10 ch. multicoloured . . 1·25 10
N301 – 10 ch. brown, yell & grn 1·25 10
DESIGNS: No. N298, Common dolphin; N299, Whale sp; N300, Yellow-finned tuna; N301, Pacific cod.

182 Tractor-crane

183 Tree-planting

1961. With gum.

N302 **182** 1 ch. brown 65 10
N303 – 2 ch. brown 65 10
N304 – 5 ch. green 90 10
N305 – 10 ch. violet 90 20

DESIGNS—HORIZ: 2 ch. Heavy-duty lorry; 5 ch. Eight-metres turning lathe. VERT: 10 ch. 3000-ton press.

See also Nos. N378/9c.

1961. Re-afforestation Campaign. With gum.

N306 **183** 10 ch. green . . . . . . 1·00 25

184 "Peaceful Unification" Banner

1961. Propaganda for Peaceful Reunification of Korea.

N307 **184** 10 ch. multicoloured . . 6·50 1·50

185 Pioneers visiting Battlefield

1961. 15th Anniv of Children's Union. Mult.

N308 5 ch. Pioneers bathing . . . 40 10
N309 10 ch. Pioneer bugler . . . . 1·25 20
N310 10 ch. Type **185** 40 10

186 "Labour Law"

187 Apples

1961. 15th Anniv of Labour Law. With gum.

N311 **186** 10 ch. blue on yellow . . 45 20

1961. Fruit. Multicoloured.

N312 5 ch. Peaches 75 10
N313 5 ch. Plums 75 10
N314 5 ch. Type **187** 75 10
N315 10 ch. Persimmons 75 10
N316 10 ch. Pears 75 10

188 Yury Gagarin and "Vostok 1"

1961. World's First Manned Space Flight.

N317 **188** 10 ch. ultramarine & bl 35 10
N318 10 ch. violet and blue . . 35 10

189 Power Station

1961. 15th Anniv of Nationalization of Industries Law. With gum.

N319 **189** 10 ch. brown . . . . . 4·50 60

190 Women at Work

191 Children planting Tree

1961. 15th Anniv of Sex Equality Law. With gum.

N320 **190** 10 ch. red 35 10

1961. Children. Multicoloured.

N321 5 ch. Type **191** 60 10
N322 5 ch. Reading book 30 10
N323 10 ch. Playing with ball . . . 30 10
N324 10 ch. Building a house . . . 30 10
N325 10 ch. Waving flag 30 10

192 Poultry and Stock-breeding

193 Soldiers on March (statue)

1961. Improvement in Living Standards. Mult.

N326 5 ch. Type **192** 60 10
N327 10 ch. Fabrics and textile factory . . . . . . 1·10 10
N328 10 ch. Trawler and fish (horiz) 1·50 20
N329 10 ch. Grain-harvesting (horiz) 50 10

1961. 25th Anniv of Fatherland Restoration Association. With gum.

N330 – 10 ch. violet 40 10
N331 – 10 ch. violet 25 10
N332 **193** 10 ch. blue and buff . . . 25 10

DESIGNS—Marshal Kim Il Sung: No. N330, Seated under tree; N331, Working at desk.

194 Party Emblem and Members

195 Miner

1961. 4th Korean Workers' Party Congress, Pyongyang. With gum.

N333 **194** 10 ch. green 20 10
N334 – 10 ch. purple 20 10
N335 – 10 ch. red 20 10

DESIGNS—VERT: No. N334, "Chollima" statue, Pyongyang. HORIZ: No. N335, Marshal Kim Il Sung.

1961. Miners' Day. With gum.

N336 **195** 10 ch. brown . . . . . 1·75 60

196 Pak in Ro

197 Aldehyde Shop

1961. 400th Birth Anniv of Pak in Ro (poet).

N337 **196** 10 ch. indigo on blue . . 45 15

1961. Completion of Vinalon Factory. With gum.

N338 **197** 5 ch. red and yellow . . 60 10
N339 – 10 ch. brown & yellow 90 10
N340 – 10 ch. blue and yellow 90 10
N341 – 20 ch. purple & yellow 1·40 20

DESIGNS: No. N339, Glacial-acetic shop; N340, Polymerization and saponification shop; N341, Spinning shop.

198 Korean and Chinese Flags

199 Basketball

1961. North Korean Friendship Treaties with China and the U.S.S.R.

N342 – 10 ch. multicoloured . . 40 10
N343 **198** 10 ch. red, blue & yellow 40 10

DESIGN: No. N342, Korean and Soviet flags.

1961. Physical Culture Day. With gum.

N344 – 2 ch. grey 75 10
N345 – 5 ch. blue 90 10
N346 **199** 10 ch. blue 90 10
N347 – 10 ch. blue 90 10
N348 – 10 ch. purple 90 10
N349 – 20 ch. purple 75 10

DESIGNS: 2 ch. Table tennis; 5 ch. Flying model glider; 10 ch. (N347) Rowing; 10 ch. (N348) High jumping; 20 ch. Sports emblem.

5전 대동여지도 100
(200)

201 General Rock

1961. Centenary of Publication of Map "Taidong Yu Jido" by Kim Jung Ho. No. N216 surch with T **200**.

N350 **150** 5 ch. on 1 ch. grey and green . . . . 38·00 24·00

1961. Mt. Chilbo Scenery. With gum.

N351 **201** 5 ch. blue 75 10
N352 – 5 ch. brown 75 10
N353 – 10 ch. violet . . . . . 1·40 20
N354 – 10 ch. blue . . . . . . 1·40 20
N355 – 10 ch. blue . . . . . . 1·40 20

DESIGNS—HORIZ: No. N352, Chonbul Peak; N354, Tiled House Rock; N355, Rainbow Rock. VERT: No. N353, Mansa Peak.

202 "Agriculture and Industry"

203 Winged Horse and Congress Emblem

1961. With gum.

N356 **202** 10 ch. green 35 10

1961. 5th World Federation of Trade Unions Congress, Moscow. With gum.

N357 **203** 10 ch. blue, purple & vio 25 10

204 Class "Red Banner" Electric Locomotive

205 Ice Hockey

1961. Railway Electrification. With gum.

N358 **204** 10 ch. violet and yellow . 4·00 1·60

1961. Winter Sports. With gum.

N359 – 10 ch. brown and green . 75 10
N360 – 10 ch. brown and green . 75 10
N361 **205** 10 ch. brown and blue . . 75 10
N362 – 10 ch. brown and blue . . 75 10

DESIGNS: No. N359, Figure skating; N360, Speed skating; N362, Skiing.

206 Grain Harvest

207 Tiger

1962. "Six Heights" of Production Targets (1st series). Inscr "1962". With gum.

N363 – 5 ch. red, violet and grey 30 10
N364 – 5 ch. brown and grey . . 1·75 30
N365 **206** 10 ch. yellow, black & bl 30 10
N366 – 10 ch. red, yellow & blue 90 10
N367 – 10 ch. black and blue . . 1·10 15
N368 – 10 ch. yellow, brn & blue 30 10

DESIGNS: No. N363, Ladle and molten steel; N364, Electric mine train; N366, Fabrics and mill; N367, Trawler and catch; N368, Construction of flats.

See also Nos. N440/5.

1962. Animals.

N369 **207** 2 ch. multicoloured . . . 2·00 15
N370 – 2 ch. brown and green 1·50 10
N371 – 5 ch. yellow and green 1·50 10
N372 – 10 ch. brown and green 1·75 15

ANIMALS—HORIZ: 2 ch. (N370), Racoon-dog; 5 ch. Chinese ferret-badger; 10 ch. Asiatic black bear.

208 Kayagum Player

209 "Leuhdorfia puziloi"

1962. Musical Instruments and Players (1st series). Multicoloured.

N373 10 ch. Type **208** . . . . . . 1·75 20
N374 10 ch. Man playing haegum (two-stringed bowed instrument) . . . . . . 1·75 20
N375 10 ch. Woman playing wolgum (banjo) . . . . 1·75 20
N376 10 ch. Man playing chotdae (flute) . . . . 1·75 20
N377 10 ch. Woman playing wagonghu (harp) . . . . 1·75 20

See also Nos. N473/7.

1962. As T **182**. Inscr "1962". With gum (Nos. N379 and 379b), no gum (others).

N378 5 ch. green 50 10
N379 10 ch. blue 75 15
N379a 10 ch. brown . . . . - 3·75
N379b 5 wn. brown . . . . 9·50 3·00
N379c 10 wn. purple . . . . . . 11·50 6·00

DESIGNS—VERT: 5 ch. Hydraulic press; 10 ch. (2), Three-ton hammer; 10 wn. Tunnel drill. HORIZ: 5 wn. Hobbing machine.

See also Nos. N415/22, N513/15 and 573.

1962. Butterflies. Multicoloured.

N380 5 ch. Type **209** . . . . . . 2·50 15
N381 10 ch. "Sericinus telamon" (purple background) . . . 2·50 15
N382 10 ch. Keeled apollo (lilac background) . . . . . . 2·50 15
N383 10 ch. Peacock (green background) . . . . . . 2·50 15

210 G. S. Titov and "Vostok 2"

1962. 2nd Soviet Manned Space Flight.

N384 **210** 10 ch. multicoloured . . 45 15

211 Marshal Kim Il Sung and (inset) addressing Workers

1962. Marshal Kim Il Sung's 50th Birthday. With gum.

N385 **211** 10 ch. red 45 15
N386 – 10 ch. green 45 15
N387 – 10 ch. blue 45 10

DESIGN: No. 387, Kim Il Sung in fur hat and (inset) inspecting battle-front.

212 Kim Chaek

214 Black-faced Spoonbill

213 Mother with Children

1962. Korean Revolutionaries (1st series). With gum.

N388 **212** 10 ch. sepia 35 10
N389 – 10 ch. blue 35 10
N390 – 10 ch. red 35 10
N391 – 10 ch. purple 35 10
N392 – 10 ch. green 35 10
N393 – 10 ch. blue 35 10
N394 – 10 ch. brown 35 10

PORTRAITS: No. N389, Kang Gon; N390, An Gil; N391, Ryu Gyong Su; N392/3, Kim Jong Suk; N394, Choe Chun Guk.

See also Nos. N478/82 and N733/5.

1962. National Mothers' Meeting, Pyongyang.

N395 **213** 10 ch. multicoloured . . 30 10

1962. Birds. Inscr "1962". Multicoloured.
N396 5 ch. Type **214** . . . . . . 1·25 15
N397 5 ch. Brown hawk owl . . . 4·25 15
N398 10 ch. Eastern broad-billed roller . . . . 2·40 35
N399 10 ch. Black paradise flycatcher . . . . 2·40 35
N400 20 ch. Whistling swan . . . 3·00 65

215 Victory Flame

216 Japanese Croaker

1962. 25th Anniv of Battle of Pochonbo.
N401 **215** 10 ch. multicoloured . . 55 10

1962. Fishes. Multicoloured.
N402 5 ch. Type **216** . . . . . . 1·50 10
N403 5 ch. Hairtail . . . . 1·50 10
N404 10 ch. Dotted gizzard shad (head pointing to right) . . 1·75 20
N405 10 ch. Japanese spotted seabass (blue background) . . . . 1·75 20
N406 10 ch. Japanese croaker (green background) . . . . . . 1·75 20

217 Waterdropper

218 Radial Drill

1962. Antiques. With gum.
N407 – 4 ch. black and blue . . 1·00 10
N408 **217** 5 ch. black and ochre . . 1·00 10
N409 A 10 ch. black and green . . 1·25 10
N410 B 10 ch. black and orange . 1·25 10
N411 C 10 ch. black and purple . 1·25 10
N412 D 10 ch. black and brown . 1·25 10
N413 E 10 ch. black and yellow . 1·25 10
N414 – 40 ch. black and grey . . 3·50 35
DESIGNS—VERT: 4 ch. Brush pot; 40 ch. Porcelain decanter. HORIZ: A, Inkstand; B, Brushstand; C, Turtle paperweight; D, Inkstone; E, Document case.

1962. Double frame-line. With gum.
N415 – 2 ch. green 40 10
N415a – 2 ch. brown . . . . . . — 4·00
N416 – 4 ch. blue . . . . . . 1·75 10
N417 **218** 5 ch. blue 40 10
N418 – 5 ch. purple 40 10
N419 – 10 ch. purple 50 10
N420 – 40 ch. blue . . . . . 3·75 20
N421 – 90 ch. blue . . . . . 1·60 30
N422 – 1 wn. brown . . . . . 4·75 50
DESIGNS—VERT: 2 ch. Vertical milling machine; 5 ch. (N418), Hydraulic hammer; 1 wn. Spindle drill. HORIZ: 4 ch. "Victory April 15" motor-car; 10 ch. All-purpose excavator; 40 ch. Trolley-bus; 90 ch. Planning machine.
See also Nos. N513/15 and N573.

219 Chong Da San

220 Voter

1962. Birth Bicentenary of Chong Da San (philosopher).
N423 **219** 10 ch. purple 35 10

1962. Election of Deputies to National Assembly. Multicoloured.
N424 10 ch. Type **220** 80 10
N425 10 ch. Family going to poll 80 10

221 Pyongyang

1962. 1535th Anniv of Pyongyang. With gum.
N426 **221** 10 ch. black and blue . . 65 10

222 Globe and "Vostok 3" and "4"

223 Spiraea

1962. 1st "Team" Manned Space Flight.
N427 **222** 10 ch. indigo, blue & red 60 20

1962. Korean Plants. Plants in natural colours; frame and inscr colours given.
N428 **223** 5 ch. lt green and green 1·25 10
N429 – 10 ch. green and red . . 1·25 10
N430 – 10 ch. blue and purple 1·25 10
N431 – 10 ch. green and olive . . 1·25 10
PLANTS: No. N429, Ginseng; N430, Campanula; N431, "Rheumcoreanum makai (Polyonaceae)".

224 "Uibang Ryuchui"

225 Science Academy

1962. 485th Anniv of Publication of "Uibang Ryuchui" (medical encyclopaedia).
N432 **224** 10 ch. multicoloured . . 3·50 30

1962. 10th Anniv of Korean Science Academy.
N433 **225** 10 ch. blue & turquoise 1·00 10

226 Fisherwomen

227 European Mink

1962.
N434 **226** 10 ch. blue . . . . . . 1·00 10

1962. Animals.
N435 **227** 4 ch. brown and green 70 10
N436 – 5 ch. blue, drab & green 70 10
N437 – 10 ch. blue and yellow 90 10
N438 – 10 ch. sepia & turquoise 90 10
N439 – 20 ch. brown and blue 1·50 15
ANIMALS—HORIZ: No. N436, Chinese hare. VERT: No. N437, Eurasian red squirrel; N438, Common goral; N439, Siberian chipmunk.

228 Harvesting

1963. "Six Heights" of Production Targets (2nd issue). Inscr "1963". Multicoloured.
N440 5 ch. Miner . . . . 1·00 20
N441 10 ch. Type **228** 40 10
N442 10 ch. Furnaceman 30 10
N443 10 ch. Construction worker 30 10
N444 10 ch. Textiles loom operator 65 10
N445 40 ch. Fisherman and trawler 2·25 40

229 Soldier

230 Peony

1963. 15th Anniv of Korean People's Army. With gum.
N446 – 5 ch. brown 50 10
N447 **229** 10 ch. red 60 10
N448 – 10 ch. blue 85 10
DESIGNS: 5 ch. Airman; 10 ch. Sailor.

1963. Korean Flowers. Multicoloured.
N449 5 ch. Type **230** 60 10
N450 10 ch. Rugosa rose 90 10
N451 10 ch. Azalea 90 10
N452 20 ch. Campion 90 10
N453 40 ch. Orchid . . . . 2·50 35

231 "Sadang-ch'um" (Korean folk dance)

232 Revolutionaries

1963. International Music and Dancing Contest, Pyongyang. Multicoloured.
N454 10 ch. Type **231** . . . . . . 1·75 15
N455 10 ch. Dancer with fan . . . 1·75 15

1963. 3rd Anniv of South Korean Rising of April, 1960.
N456 **232** 10 ch. multicoloured . . 40 15

233 Karl Marx

234 Children in Chemistry Class

1963. 145th Birth Anniv of Karl Marx. With gum.
N457 **233** 10 ch. blue 30 10

1963. Child Care and Amenities. Multicoloured.
N458 2 ch. Type **234** 80 20
N459 5 ch. Children running . . . 70 15
N460 10 ch. Boy conducting choir 1·75 20
N461 10 ch. Girl chasing butterfly 3·50 25

235 Armed Koreans and American Soldier (caricature)

1963. Campaign Month for Withdrawal of U.S. Forces from South Korea.
N462 **235** 10 ch. multicoloured . . 45 10

236 "Cyrtoclytus capra"

237 Soldier with Flag

1963. Korean Beetles. Multicoloured designs. Colours of beetles given.
N463 5 ch. Type **236** 75 10
N464 10 ch. multicoloured . . . . 1·10 10
N465 10 ch. red and blue . . . . . 1·10 10
N466 10 ch. indigo, blue & purple 1·10 10
BEETLES: No. N464, "Cicindela chinensis" (tiger beetle); N465, "Purpuricenus lituratus"; N466, "Agapanthia pilicornis".

1963. 10th Anniv of Victory in Korean War.
N467 **237** 10 ch. multicoloured . . 50 10

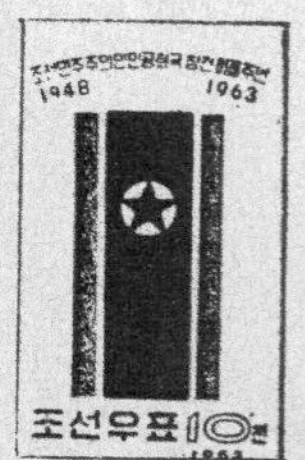
238 North Korean Flag

239 Namdae Gate, Kaesong

1963. 15th Anniv of People's Republic. Mult.
N468 10 ch. Type **238** 30 10
N469 10 ch. North Korean Badge . 30 10

1963. Ancient Korean Buildings (1st series). With gum.
N470 **239** 5 ch. black 20 10
N471 – 10 ch. blue 40 10
N472 – 10 ch. brown 40 10
BUILDINGS: No. N471, Taedong Gate, Pyongyang; N472, Potong Gate, Pyongyang.
See also Nos. N537/8.

240 Ajaeng (bowed zither)

241 Nurse with Children

1963. Musical Instruments and Players (2nd series). Multicoloured. Nos. N473 and N476 with gum.
N473 3 ch. Type **240** . . . . . . 1·25 15
N474 5 ch. Pyongyon (jade chimes) 1·25 15
N475 10 ch. Saenap (brass bowl) 1·50 15
N476 10 ch. Rogo (drums in frame) 1·50 15
N477 10 ch. Piri ("wooden pipe") 1·50 15

1963. Korean Revolutionaries (2nd issue). As T **212**. With gum.
N478 5 ch. brown 40 10
N479 5 ch. purple 40 10
N480 10 ch. rose 50 10
N481 10 ch. slate 50 10
N482 10 ch. dull purple 50 10
PORTRAITS: No. N478, Kwon Yong Byok; N479, Ma Dong Hui; N480, Li Je Sun; N481, Pak Dal; N482, Kim Yong Bom.

1963. Child Welfare. Multicoloured.
N483 10 ch. Type **241** 50 10
N484 10 ch. Children in playground 50 10

242 Hwajang Hall

243 Furnaceman

1963. Mount Myohyang Resort. Multicoloured.
N485 5 ch. Type **242** 35 10
N486 10 c. Mountain stream and chalet 75 10
N487 10 ch. Kwanum Pavilion and stone pagoda 65 10
N488 10 ch. Rope bridge across river 1·75 15
Nos. N487/8 are horiz.

1963. Seven Year Plan. With gum.
N489 **243** 5 ch. red 20 10
N490 – 10 ch. grey . . . . . . 1·50 20
N491 – 10 ch. red . . . . . . 1·50 20
N492 – 10 ch. lilac 85 10
DESIGNS—VERT: No. N490, Construction workers. HORIZ: No. N491, Power technicians; N492, Miners.

244 Children hoeing

1963. "Hung Bo" (fairytale). Multicoloured.
N493 5 ch. Type **244** 30 10
N494 10 ch. Tying up broken leg of swallow 90 10
N495 10 ch. Barn swallow dropping gourd seed 90 10
N496 10 ch. Sawing through giant gourd 50 10
N497 10 ch. Treasure inside gourd 50 10

245 Marksman

1963. Marksmanship. Multicoloured.
N498 5 ch. Type **245** 30 10
N499 10 ch. Marksman with small-bore rifle 55 10
N500 10 ch. Marksman with standard rifle 55 10

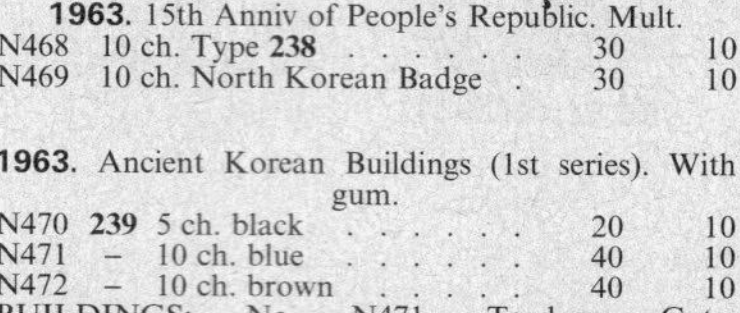
246 Sinuiju Chemical Fibre Factory

248 Korean Alphabet

247 Strikers

1964. Chemical Fibres Factories. With gum.
N501 **246** 10 ch. slate 75 10
N052 – 10 ch. purple 75 10
DESIGN: No. N502, Chongjin Chemical Fibre Factory.

1964. 35th Anniv of Wonsan General Strike. With gum.
N503 **247** 10 ch. brown 60 10

1964. 520th Anniv of Korean Alphabet.
N504 **248** 10 ch. green, buff & brn 60 20

249 Lenin **250** Whale-catcher

1964. 40th Death Anniv of Lenin. With gum.
N505 **249** 10 ch. red 30 10

1964. Fishing Industry. Multicoloured.
N506 5 ch. Type **250** 50 10
N507 5 ch. Trawler No. 051 . . . . 50 10
N508 10 ch. Trawler No. 397 . . . 1·00 20
N509 10 ch. Trawler No. 738 . . . 1·00 20

251 Insurgents

1964. 45th Anniv of Rising of 1st March. With gum.
N510 **251** 10 ch. purple 30 10

252 Warring Peasants

1964. 70th Anniv of Kabo Peasants' War. With gum.
N511 **252** 10 ch. purple 30 10

253 Students' Palace, Pyongyang **254** "Changbaek" Excavator

1964. With gum.
N512 **253** 10 ch. green 30 10

1964. Single frame-line. Dated "1964" or "1965" (No. N573). With gum.
N513 – 5 ch. violet 60 10
N514 **254** 10 ch. green 90 10
N515 – 10 ch. blue 90 10
N573 – 10 ch. violet 75 20
DESIGNS—VERT: 5 ch. 200 Metre drill; 10 ch. (N573) "Horning 500" machine. HORIZ: 10 ch. (N515) 400 h.p. Diesel engine.

255 "On the March"

1964. 5th Korean Democratic Youth League Congress, Pyongyang.
N516 **255** 10 ch. multicoloured . . 30 10

256 Electric Train

1964. Inauguration of Pyongyang–Sinuiju Electric Railway.
N517 **256** 10 ch. multicoloured . . 2·50 20

257 Rejoicing in Chongsan-ri Village

1964. Popular Movement at Chongsan-ri. With gum.
N517a **257** 5 ch. brown . . . . .

258 Drum Dance **259** "For the Sake of the Fatherland"

1964. Korean Dances.
N518 **258** 2 ch. mauve, buff & blk 1·50 15
N519 – 5 ch. red, black & yellow 1·75 15
N520 – 10 ch. multicoloured . . 2·00 15
DESIGNS: 5 ch. "Ecstasy" (solo); 10 ch. Tabor.

1964. Li Su Bok Commemorative. With gum.
N521 **259** 5 ch. red 20 10

260 Nampo Smelting Works

1964. With gum.
N522 **260** 5 ch. green . . . . . . 2·50 10
N523 – 10 ch. slate . . . . . . 2·75 20
DESIGN: 10 ch. Hwanghae iron works.

261 Torch, Chollima Statue and Cogwheel

1964. Asian Economic Seminar, Pyongyang. Multicoloured.
N524 5 ch. Type **261** 25 10
N525 10 ch. Flags, statue and cogwheel 30 10

262 Korean People and Statue of Kang Ho Yong (war hero)

1964. Struggle for Reunification of Korea.
N526 **262** 10 ch. multicoloured . . 45 10

263 Hawk Fowl

1964. Domestic Poultry. Multicoloured.
N527 2 ch. Type **263** 35 10
N528 4 ch. White fowl 35 10
N529 5 ch. Ryongyon fowl 55 10
N530 5 ch. Black fowl 55 10
N531 40 ch. Helmet guineafowl . . 2·00 60

264 Skiing

1964. Winter Olympic Games, Innsbruck.
N532 **264** 5 ch. red, blue and buff 50 10
N533 – 10 ch. blue, green & buff 75 10
N534 – 10 ch. blue, red & buff 75 10
DESIGNS: No. N533, Ice skating; N534, Skiing (slalom).

265 "Tobolsk" (passenger ship) and Flags **266** Tonggun Pavilion Uiju

1964. 5th Anniv of Agreement for Repatriation of Koreans in Japan.
N535 **265** 10 ch. red, blue & lt blue 1·40 30
N536 – 30 ch. multicoloured . . 1·10 15
DESIGN: 30 ch. Return of repatriates.

1964. Ancient Korean Buildings (2nd series). With gum.
N537 **266** 5 ch. purple 20 10
N538 – 10 ch. green 30 10
DESIGN: 10 ch. Inpang Pavilion, Kanggye City.

267 Cycling **268** Burning of the "General Sherman"

1964. Olympic Games, Tokyo.
N539 – 2 ch. brown and blue . . 25 10
N540 **267** 5 ch. brown and green . . 75 10
N541 – 10 ch. orange and blue . . 35 10
N542 – 10 ch. orange and green . . 35 10
N543 – 40 ch. brown and blue . . 60 35
DESIGNS—HORIZ: 2 ch. Rifle-shooting; 10 ch. blue, Running. VERT: 10 ch. green, Wrestling; 40 ch. Volleyball.

1964. The "General Sherman" Incident, 1866. With gum.
N544 **268** 30 ch. brown . . . . . 2·00 30

269 Organizing Guerrillas

1964. Guerrilla Operations in the 1930's against the Japanese. With gum.
N545 **269** 2 ch. violet 25 10
N546 – 5 ch. blue 35 10
N547 – 10 ch. black 45 10
DESIGNS: 5 ch. Kim Il Sung addressing guerrillas; 10 ch. Battle scene at Xiaowangqing.

270 Students attacking **271** Weightlifting

1964. Kwangju Students Rising, 1929. With gum.
N548 **270** 10 ch. violet . . . . . . 1·60 15

1964. "GANEFO" Athletic Games, Djakarta, Indonesia (1963). Multicoloured.
N549 2 ch. Type **271** 40 10
N550 5 ch. Athlete breasting tape 40 10
N551 5 ch. Boxing 40 10
N552 10 ch. Football . . . . . . 1·00 15
N553 10 ch. Globe Emblem 40 15
Nos. N551/3 are horiz.

272 Lynx **273** Vietnamese Attack

1964. Animals. With gum.
N554 2 ch. sepia (Type **272**) . . . 75 10
N555 5 ch. sepia (Leopard cat) . . 1·75 10
N556 10 ch. brown (Leopard) . . . 2·25 10
N557 10 ch. sepia (Yellow-throated marten) . . . . 2·25 10

1964. Support for People of Vietnam.
N558 **273** 10 ch. multicoloured . . 30 10

274 Prof. Kim Bong Han and Emblems

1964. Kyongrak Biological Systems.
N559 **274** 2 ch. purple and olive . . 65 10
N560 – 5 ch. green, orange & bl . 90 10
N561 – 10 ch. red, yellow & blue . 1·25 10
DESIGNS—33 × 23½ mm: 5 ch. "Bonghan" duct; 10 ch. "Bonghan" corpuscle. Each include emblems as in Type **274**.

275 Farmers, Tractor and Lorry

1964. Agrarian Programme. Multicoloured.
N562 5 ch. Type **275** 20 10
N563 10 ch. Peasants with scroll and book 30 10
N564 10 ch. Peasants, one writing in book 30 10

276 Chung Jin gets a Pistol **277** Girl with Korean Products

1964. The Struggle to capture Japanese Arms. With gum.
N565 **276** 4 ch. brown 25 10

1964. Economic 7 Year Plan. Multicoloured. With gum (5 ch.) or no gum (others).
N566 5 ch. Type **277** 40 10
N567 10 ch. Farm girl 40 10
N568 10 ch. Couple on winged horse (23½ × 23½ mm) 25 10

278 Three Fairies Rock **280** Soldiers Advancing, Fusong

1964. Diamond Mountains Scenery (2nd issue). Inscr "1964". Multicoloured. Without gum (2, 4 ch.) or with gum (others).
N569 2 ch. Type **278** 75 10
N570 4 ch. Ryonju Falls . . . . . 2·75 10
N571 10 ch. The Ten Thousand Rocks, Manmulsang . . . 75 10
N572 10 ch. Chinju Falls . . . . . 2·75 10

1965. Guerrilla Operations against the Japanese, 1934–40. With gum.
N574 **280** 10 ch. violet 50 10
N575 – 10 ch. violet 50 10
N576 – 10 ch. green 50 10
DESIGNS: No. N575, Soldiers descending hill, Hongqihe; N576, Soldiers attacking hill post, Luozigou.

281 Tuman River **282** Union Badge

1965. Korean Rivers. Multicoloured.
N577 2 ch. Type **281** 60 10
N578 5 ch. Taedong (vert) . . . . 1·75 15
N579 10 ch. Amnok 75 10

1965. 1st Congress of Landworkers' Union, Pyongyang. With gum.
N580 **282** 10 ch. multicoloured . . 30 10

283 Furnacemen and Workers

1965. 10 Major Tasks of 7 Year Plan. With gum.
N581 **283** 10 ch. multicoloured . . 30 10

284 Miners' Strike, Sinhung Colliery

1965. 35th Anniv of Strikes and Peasants' Revolt. With gum.
N582 **284** 10 ch. olive . . . . . . 1·25 15
N583 – 10 ch. brown . . . . . 1·50 15
N584 – 40 ch. purple . . . . . 1·00 15
DESIGNS: 10 ch. Strikers at Pyongyang Rubber Factory; 40 ch. Revolt of Tanchon peasants.

285 Embankment Construction

286 Hand holding Torch

1965. Sunhwa River Works. With gum.
N585 **285** 10 ch. multicoloured . . 30 10

1965. 5th Anniv of South Korean Rising of April 19th. Multicoloured. With gum.
N586 10 ch. Type **286** 20 10
N587 40 ch. Student-hero, Kim Chio 45 20

287 Power Station under Construction

1965. Construction of Thermal Power Station, Pyongyang. With gum.
N588 **287** 5 ch. brown and blue . . 25 10

288 African and Asian

1965. 10th Anniv of 1st Afro-Asian Conference, Bandung. With gum.
N589 **288** 10 ch. multicoloured . . 30 10

289 Rejoicing of Koreans

1965. 10th Anniv of General Assn of Koreans in Japan. With gum.
N590 **289** 10 ch. blue and red . . 25 10
N591 – 40 ch. indigo, blue & red 45 15
DESIGN: 40 ch. Patriot and flag.

290 Workers in Battle

291 "Victory 64" 10-ton Lorry

1965. 2nd Afro-Asian Conf, Algiers. With gum.
N592 **290** 10 ch. black, yellow & red 75 10
N593 – 40 ch. black, yellow & red 1·25 25
DESIGN: 40 ch. Korean and African soldiers.
The Algiers Conference did not take place.

1965. With gum.
N594 **291** 10 ch. green . . . . . . 1·25 20

292 Kim Chang Gol

1965. War Heroes (1st series). With gum.
N595 **292** 10 ch. green 30 10
N596 – 10 ch. brown 30 10
N597 – 40 ch. purple 75 20
PORTRAITS: No. N596, Cho Gun Sil and machine-gun; N597, An Hak Ryong and machine-gun.
See also Nos. N781/3 and N842/3.

293 Marx and Lenin

1965. Postal Ministers' Congress, Peking. With gum.
N598 **293** 10 ch. black, yell & red 1·50 15

294 Lake Samil

1965. Diamond Mountains Scenery (3rd issue). Multicoloured. With gum.
N599 2 ch. Type **294** 60 10
N600 5 ch. Chipson Peak . . . . 1·00 10
N601 10 ch. Kwanum Falls . . . . 2·75 25

295 Amnok River, Kusimuldong

1965. Scenes of Japanese War. With gum.
N602 **295** 5 ch. green and blue . . 35 10
N603 – 10 ch. turquoise & blue 60 10
DESIGN: 10 ch. Lake Samji.

296 Footballer and Games' Emblem

297 Workers and Map

1965. "GANEFO" Football Games, Pyongyang. Multicoloured. With gum.
N604 10 ch. Type **296** . . . . . . 1·25 10
N605 10 ch. Games emblem and Moranbong Stadium . . . 1·25 10

1965. 20th Anniv of Liberation from Japan. With gum.
N606 **297** 10 ch. multicoloured . . 30 10

298 Engels

299 Pole Vaulting

1965. 145th Birth Anniv of Engels. With gum.
N607 **298** 10 ch. brown 30 10

1965. Sports. Multicoloured. With gum.
N608 2 ch. Type **299** 50 10
N609 4 ch. Throwing the javelin 1·75 20
N610 10 ch. Throwing the discus 50 10
N611 10 ch. High jumping (horiz) 50 10
N612 10 ch. Putting the shot (horiz) 50 10

301 Korean Fighters

1965. 20th Anniv of Korean Workers' Party. Each black, yellow and red. With gum.
N613 10 ch. Type **301** 45 10
N614 10 ch. Party emblem 45 10
N615 10 ch. Lenin and Marx . . . 45 10
N616 10 ch. Workers marching . . 45 10
N617 10 ch. Fighters 45 10
N618 40 ch. Workers 45 10
Nos. N613/8 each have a red banner in the background and were issued together in blocks of 6 (3 × 2), forming a composite design, within the sheet.

302 Kim Chaek Iron Works

303 Grass Carp

1965. With gum.
N620 **302** 10 ch. purple . . . . . 3·50 10
N621 – 10 ch. brown . . . . . 3·50 10
DESIGN: No. 621, Chongjin Steel Works.

1965. Freshwater Fish. Multicoloured. With gum.
N622 2 ch. Rainbow trout 70 10
N623 4 ch. Dolly Varden charr . . 90 10
N624 10 ch. Brown trout (surfacing water) . . . . 2·25 15
N625 10 ch. Common carp diving (date at left) 2·25 15
N626 10 ch. Type **303** . . . . . . 2·25 15
N627 40 ch. Crucian carp . . . . 3·25 55

304 Building House

305 Children in Workshop

1965. Kim Hong Do's Drawings. With gum.
N628 2 ch. green (Type **304**) . . . 45 10
N629 4 ch. purple (Weaving) . . . 90 10
N630 10 ch. brown (Wrestling) . . 80 10
N631 10 ch. blue (School class) . . 80 10
N632 10 ch. red (Dancing) . . . . 1·25 10
N633 10 ch. violet (Blacksmiths) 1·10 10

1965. Life at Pyongyang Children's and Students' Palace. Multicoloured. With gum.
N634 2 ch. Type **305** 20 10
N635 4 ch. Boxing 20 10
N636 10 ch. Chemistry 75 10
N637 10 ch. Playing violin and accordion 75 10

306 Whale-catcher

1965. Korean Fishing Boats. With gum.
N638 **306** 10 ch. blue . . . . . . 1·40 25
N639 – 10 ch. green . . . . . . 1·40 25
DESIGN: No. N639, Fishing fleet service vessel.

307 Great Tit

308 Silkworm Moth ("Bombyx mori") and Cocoon

1965. Korean Birds. Inscr "1965". Multicoloured. With gum.
N640 4 ch. Black-capped kingfisher (vert) . . . . 1·75 10
N641 10 ch. Type **307** . . . . . . 2·40 25
N642 10 ch. Pied wagtail (facing left) 2·40 25
N643 10 ch. Azure-winged magpie (facing right) . . . . . . 2·40 25
N644 40 ch. Black-tailed hawfinch 5·50 85

1965. Korean Sericulture. With gum.
N645 **308** 2 ch. green . . . . . . 5·00 20
N646 – 10 ch. brown . . . . . 5·00 30
N647 – 10 ch. purple . . . . . 5·00 30
MOTHS AND COCOONS: No. N646, Ailathus silk moth ("Samia cynthia"); N647, Chinese oak silk moth ("Antheraea pernyi").

309 Hooded Crane

310 Japanese Common Squid

1965. Wading Birds. With gum.
N648 **309** 2 ch. brown . . . . . . 3·00 10
N649 – 10 ch. blue . . . . . . 3·25 30
N650 – 10 ch. purple . . . . . 3·25 30
N651 – 40 ch. green . . . . . . 6·00 70
BIRDS: No. N649, Japanese white-necked crane; N650, Manchurian crane; N651, Grey heron.

1965. Korean Molluscs. Multicoloured. With gum.
N652 5 ch. Type **310** . . . . . . 1·25 10
N653 10 ch. Giant Pacific octopus . 1·75 10

311 Spotbill Duck

1965. Korean Ducks. Multicoloured. With gum.
N654 2 ch. Type **311** . . . . . . 2·40 10
N655 4 ch. Ruddy shelduck . . . . 2·40 15
N656 10 ch. Mallard . . . . . . 3·50 35
N657 40 ch. Baikal teal . . . . . 5·00 85

312 Circus Theatre, Pyongyang

313 "Marvel of Peru" ("Mirabilis jalapa")

1965. Korean Circus. With gum except No. N661.
N658 **312** 2 ch. blue, black & brn 75 10
N659 – 10 ch. blue, red & black 1·50 10
N660 – 10 ch. red, black & green 1·50 10
N661 – 10 ch. orange, sepia & grn 1·50 10
N662 – 10 ch. red, yellow & turq 1·50 10
DESIGNS—VERT: No. N659, Trapeze artistes; N660, Performer with hoops on seesaw; N661, Tightrope dancers; N662, Performer with revolving cap on stick.

1965. Korean Flowers. Multicoloured. With gum except No. N663.
N663 4 ch. Type **313** . . . . . . 1·10 10
N664 10 ch. Peony . . . . 1·50 10
N665 10 ch. Moss rose . . . . . . 1·50 10
N666 10 ch. Magnolia . . . . . . 1·50 10

314 "Finn" Class Dinghy

315 Cuban, Korean and African

1965. Yachts. Multicoloured. With gum.
N667 2 ch. Type **314** 70 20
N668 10 ch. "5.5m" class yacht . . 1·00 30
N669 10 ch. "Dragon" class yacht . 1·00 30
N670 40 ch. "Star" class yacht . . 2·00 60

1966. African-Asian and Latin American Friendship Conference, Havana. With gum.
N671 **315** 10 ch. multicoloured . . 30 10

316 Hosta **317** Farmer and Wife

1966. Wild Flowers. Mult. With gum. (a) 1st series.
N672 2 ch. Type **316** 50 10
N673 4 ch. Dandelion 50 10
N674 10 ch. Pink convolvulus . . . 75 10
N675 10 ch. Lily-of-the-valley . . . 75 10
N676 40 ch. Catalpa blossom . . . 2·00 20

(b) 2nd series.
N677 2 ch. Polyanthus 50 10
N678 4 ch. Lychnis 50 10
N679 10 ch. Adonis 75 10
N680 10 ch. Orange lily 75 10
N681 90 ch. Rhododendron . . . 3·00 30

1966. 20th Anniv of Land Reform Law. With gum.
N682 **317** 10 ch. multicoloured . . 20 10

318 Troops advancing, Dashahe **319** Silla Bowl

1966. Paintings of Guerrilla Battles, 1937–39. With gum, except No. N684.
N683 **318** 10 ch. red 30 10
N684 – 10 ch. turquoise 30 10
N685 – 10 ch. purple 30 10
DESIGNS AND BATTLES: No. N684, Troops firing from trees, Taehongdan; N685, Troops on hillside, Jiansanfeng.

1966. Art Treasures of Silla Dynasty. With gum.
N686 **319** 2 ch. ochre . . . . . . 1·25 10
N687 – 5 ch. black . . . . . . 1·25 10
N688 – 10 ch. violet . . . . . . 1·25 10
DESIGNS: 5 ch. Earthenware jug. 10 ch. Censer.

320 Hands holding Torch, Rifle and Hammer **321** Torch and Patriots

1966. 80th Anniv of Labour Day. With gum.
N689 **320** 10 ch. multicoloured . . 30 10

1966. 30th Anniv of Association for Restoration of Fatherland.
N690 **321** 10 ch. red and yellow . . 30 10

322 Harvester

1966. Aid for Agriculture. Multicoloured.
N691 5 ch. Type **322** 25 10
N692 10 ch. Labourer 35 10

323 Young Pioneers

1966. 20th Anniv of Korean Children's Union. Without gum.
N693 **323** 10 ch. multicoloured . . . 50 10

324 Kangson Steel Works

1966. Korean Industries. With gum.
N694 **324** 10 ch. grey . . . . . . 3·50 15
N695 – 10 ch. red (Pongung Chemical Works) . . . 3·50 15

325 Pacific Saury

1966. Korean Fishes. With gum except Nos. N699/700.
N696 **325** 2 ch. blue, green & pur 80 10
N697 – 5 ch. purple, green & brn 1·00 10
N698 – 10 ch. blue, buff & green 1·50 15
N699 – 10 ch. purple and green 1·50 15
N700 – 40 ch. green, buff & blue 3·50 60
FISHES: 5 ch. Pacific cod; 10 ch. (N698), Chum salmon, (N699), Yellowfish; 40 ch. Pink salmon.

326 Professor Kim Bong Han

1966. Kyungrak Biological System. With gum.
N701 **326** 2 ch. blue, green & yell 60 10
N702 – 4 ch. multicoloured . . . 60 10
N703 – 5 ch. multicoloured . . . 60 10
N704 – 10 ch. multicoloured . . 60 10
N705 – 10 ch. multicoloured . . 60 10
N706 – 10 ch. multicoloured . . 60 10
N707 – 15 ch. multicoloured . . 60 10
N708 – 40 ch. multicoloured . . 60 10
DESIGNS: No. N704, Kyongrak Institute; N708, Figure of Man; N702/3, 705/7, Diagram of system.
Nos. N701/8 were issued together, se-tenant, forming a composite design.

327 Leonov in Space ("Voskhod 2")

1966. Cosmonauts Day. Multicoloured.
N710 5 ch. Type **327** 20 10
N711 10 ch. "Luna 9" 55 10
N712 40 ch. "Luna 10" . . . . . 1·10 20

328 Footballers

1966. World Cup Football Championship. Mult.
N713 10 ch. Type **328** . . . . . . 1·25 25
N714 10 ch. Jules Rimet Cup, football and boots . . . . 1·25 25
N715 10 ch. Goalkeeper saving goal (vert) . . . . 1·25 25

329 Defence of Seoul

1966. Korean War of 1950–53. With gum.
N716 **329** 10 ch. green 35 10
N717 – 10 ch. purple 35 10
N718 – 10 ch. purple 35 10
DESIGNS: No. N717, Battle on Mt. Napal; N718, Battle for Height 1211.

330 Women in Industry

1966. 20th Anniv of Sex Equality Law.
N719 **330** 10 ch. multicoloured . . 30 10

331 Industrial Workers **332** Water-jar Dance

1966. 20th Anniv of Industrial Nationalization.
N720 **331** 10 ch. multicoloured . . 90 10

1966. Korean Dances. Multicoloured. 5 ch., 40 ch. with or without gum; others without.
N721 5 ch. Type **332** . . . . . . 1·00 10
N722 10 ch. Bell dance . . . . . 1·75 15
N723 10 ch. "Dancer in a Mural Painting" . . . . 1·75 15
N724 15 ch. Sword dance . . . . 1·75 20
N725 40 ch. Gold Cymbal dance . . 3·25 30

333 Korean attacking U.S. Soldier **334** Yakovlev Yak-12M Crop-spraying

1966. Korean Reunification Campaign. With gum.
N726 **333** 10 ch. green 60 10
N727 – 10 ch. purple 60 10
N728 – 10 ch. lilac . . . . . . 3·75 45
DESIGNS: No. N727, Korean with young child; N728, Korean with shovel, industrial scene and electric train.

1966. Industrial Uses of Aircraft. With gum except 2 ch. and 5 ch.
N729 **334** 2 ch. green and purple 50 10
N730 – 5 ch. brown and green 6·00 20
N731 – 10 ch. brown and blue 1·50 10
N732 – 40 ch. brown and blue 1·50 10
DESIGNS: 5 ch. Yakovlev Yak-18U (forest-fire observation); 10 ch. Lisunov Li-2 (geological survey); 40 ch. Lisunov Li-2 (detection of fish shoals).

1966. Korean Revolutionaries (3rd issue). As T **212**. With gum.
N733 10 ch. violet (O Jung Hub)
N734 10 ch. green (Kim Gyong Sok)
N735 10 ch. blue (Li Dong Gol)

335 Kim Il Sung University

1966. 20th Anniv of Kim Il Sung University. With gum.
N736 **335** 10 ch. violet 50 10

336 Judo **337** Hoopoe

1966. Ganefo Games, Phnom-Penh.
N737 **336** 5 ch. black, green & bl 60 10
N738 – 10 ch. black, green and deep green 60 10
N739 – 10 ch. black and red . . 60 10
DESIGNS: No. N738, Basketball; N739, Table tennis.

1966. Korean Birds. Multicoloured. Inscr "1966".
N740 2 ch. Common rosefinch . . 1·40 10
N741 5 ch. Type **337** . . . . . . 1·60 15
N742 10 ch. Black-breasted thrush (blue background) . . . . 1·90 25
N743 10 ch. Crested lark (green background) . . . . . . 1·90 25
N744 40 ch. White-bellied black woodpecker . . . . . . 4·25 70
The 2 ch. and 10 ch. (both) are horiz.

338 Building Construction

1966. "Increased Production with Economy". Multicoloured. Without gum (40 ch.) or with gum (others).
N745 5 ch. Type **338** 25 10
N746 10 ch. Furnaceman and graph 45 10
N747 10 ch. Machine-tool production 45 10
N748 40 ch. Miners and pit-head 1·40 15

339 Parachuting

1966. National Defence Sports. With gum.
N749 **339** 2 ch. brown 75 10
N750 – 5 ch. red 55 10
N751 – 10 ch. blue . . . . . 2·75 30
N752 – 40 ch. green . . . . . 1·60 20
DESIGNS: 5 ch. Show jumping; 10 ch. Motor cycle racing; 40 ch. Radio receiving and transmitting competition.

340 "Samil Wolgan" (Association Magazine) **341** Red Deer

1966. 30th Anniv of "Samil Wolgan" Magazine.
N753 **340** 10 ch. multicoloured . . 90 15

1966. Korean Deer. Multicoloured.
N754 2 ch. Type **341** 30 10
N755 5 ch. Sika deer 50 10
N756 10 ch. Indian muntjac (erect) 90 10
N757 10 ch. Reindeer (grazing) . . 90 10
N758 70 ch. Fallow deer . . . . . 2·25 25

342 Blueberries **343** Onpo Rest Home

1966. Wild Fruit. Multicoloured.
N759 2 ch. Type **342** 50 10
N760 5 ch. Wild pears 70 10
N761 10 ch. Wild raspberries . . . 90 10
N762 10 ch. Schizandra 90 10
N763 10 ch. Wild plums 90 10
N764 40 ch. Jujube . . . . 2·25 15

1966. Korean Rest Homes. With gum.
N765 **343** 2 ch. violet 25 10
N766 – 5 ch. turquoise 35 10
N767 – 10 ch. green 50 10
N768 – 40 ch. black 80 20
REST HOMES: 5 ch. Mt. Myohyang; 10 ch. Songdowon; 40 ch. Hongwon.

344 Soldier

1967. 19th Anniv of Army Day. Without gum.
N769 **344** 10 ch. green, yell & red 25 10

345 Sow

1967. Domestic Animals. Multicoloured. Without gum. 40 ch. also with gum.
N770 5 ch. Type **345** 40 10
N771 10 ch. Goat 50 10
N772 40 ch. Ox . . . . 1·00 25

346 Battle Scene

1967. 30th Anniv of Battle of Pochonbo. With gum.
N773 **346** 10 ch. orange, red & grn 50 10

347 Students

1967. Compulsory Technical Education for Nine Years.
N774 **347** 10 ch. multicoloured . . 25 10

348 Table Tennis Player

1967. 29th International Table Tennis Championships, Pyongyang. Designs showing players in action. 5 ch. with or without gum.
N775 **348** 5 ch. multicoloured . . . 40 10
N776 – 10 ch. multicoloured . . . 70 10
N777 – 40 ch. multicoloured . . 1·10 15

349 Anti-aircraft Defences

1967. Paintings of Guerrilla War against the Japanese. With gum.
N778 **349** 10 ch. blue 35 10
N779 – 10 ch. purple . . . . . 3·00 25
N780 – 10 ch. violet 35 10
PAINTINGS: No. N779, Blowing-up railway bridge; N780, People helping guerrillas in Wangyugou.

1967. War Heroes (2nd series). As T **292**. Designs showing portraits and combat scenes. With gum.
N781 10 ch. slate 40 10
N782 10 ch. violet 40 10
N783 10 ch. blue 75 10
PORTRAITS: No. N781, Li Dae Hun and grenade-throwing; N782, Choe Jong Un and soldiers charging; N783, Kim Hwa Ryong and air dog-fighter aircraft.

350 Workers

1967. Labour Day.
N784 **350** 10 ch. multicoloured . . 25 10

351 Card Game

1967. Korean Children. Multicoloured.
N785 5 ch. Type **351** . . . . . . 1·00 10
N786 10 ch. Children modelling tractor 60 10
N787 40 ch. Children playing with ball . . . . 1·10 20

MINIMUM PRICE

The minimum price quoted is 10p which represents a handling charge rather than a basis for valuing common stamps. For further notes about prices see introductory pages.

352 Victory Monument

1967. Unveiling of Battle of Ponchonbo Monument.
N788 **352** 10 ch. multicoloured . . 30 10

353 Attacking Tank

354 "Polygonatum japonicum"

1967. Monuments to War of 1950–53. 2 ch. with or without gum.
N789 **353** 2 ch. green & turquoise 20 10
N790 – 5 ch. sepia and green . . 85 10
N791 – 10 ch. brown and buff 30 10
N792 – 40 ch. brown and blue 60 15
MONUMENTS: 5 ch. Soldier-musicians; 10 ch. Soldier; 40 ch. Soldier with children.

1967. Medicinal Plants. Multicoloured; background colour of 10 ch. values given to aid identification. Nos. 793/5 and 797 with or without gum.
N793 2 ch. Type **354** . . . . . 1·00 10
N794 5 ch. "Hibiscus manihot" . . 1·00 10
N795 10 ch. "Scutellaria baicalensis" (turquoise) . . . . 1·25 10
N796 10 ch. "Pulsatilla koreana" (blue) . . . . 1·25 10
N797 10 ch. "Rehmannian glutinosa" (yellow) . . . . 1·25 10
N798 40 ch. "Tanacetum boreale" 3·25 35

355 Servicemen

1967. People's Army. Multicoloured. 5 ch. with or without gum.
N799 5 ch. Type **355** 20 10
N800 10 ch. Soldier and farmer . . 25 10
N801 10 ch. Officer decorating soldier 25 10

356 Freighter "Chollima"

1967. With gum.
N802 **356** 10 ch. green . . . . . . 1·10 10

357 "Reclamation of Tideland"

1967. "Heroic Struggle of the Chollima Riders". Paintings. Without gum (5 ch.) or with gum (others).
N803 – 5 ch. brown 40 10
N804 **357** 10 ch. grey 55 10
N805 – 10 ch. green 85 10
DESIGNS—VERT: 5 ch. "Drilling Rock Precipice"; 10 ch. (N805), "Felling Trees".

358 "Erimaculus isenbeckii"

1967. Crabs. Multicoloured.
N806 2 ch. Type **358** 90 15
N807 5 ch. "Neptunus trituberculatus" . . . . . 1·10 15
N808 10 ch. "Paralithodes camtschatica" . . . . . . 1·60 15
N809 40 ch. "Chionoecetes opilio" 2·50 40

359 Electric Train and Hand switching Points

1967. Propaganda for Reunification of Korea.
N810 **359** 10 ch. multicoloured . . 2·25 40

360 Tongrim Waterfall

361 Chollima Flying Horse and Banners

1967. Korean Waterfalls. 2 ch. with or without gum. Multicoloured.
N811 2 ch. Type **360** . . . . . . 2·75 15
N812 10 ch. Sanju waterfall, Mt. Myohyang . . . . 3·25 20
N813 40 ch. Sambang waterfall, Mt. Chonak . . . . 5·00 45

1967. "The Revolutionary Surge Upwards". Various designs incorporating the Chollima Flying Horse.
N814 – 5 ch. blue . . . . 1·40 20
N815 – 10 ch. red 25 10
N816 – 10 ch. green 25 10
N817 – 10 ch. lilac 25 10
N817 **361** 10 ch. red 20 10
DESIGNS—HORIZ: 5 ch. Ship, electric train and lorry (Transport); N815, Bulldozers (Building construction); N816, Tractors (Rural development); N817, Heavy presses (Machine-building industry).

362 Lenin

1967. 50th Anniv of Russian October Revolution.
N819 **362** 10 ch. brown, yell & red 25 10

363 Voters and Banner

1967. Korean Elections. Multicoloured.
N820 10 ch. Type **363** 35 10
N821 10 ch. Woman casting vote (vert) 35 10

364 European Black Vulture

1967. Birds of Prey. Multicoloured. With gum.
N822 2 ch. Type **364** . . . . . . 2·10 35
N823 10 ch. Booted eagle (horiz) 4·00 50
N824 40 ch. White-bellied sea eagle 5·00 80

365 Chongjin

1967. North Korean Cities. With gum.
N825 **365** 5 ch. green 70 10
N826 – 10 ch. lilac 70 10
N827 – 10 ch. violet 70 10
DESIGNS: No. N826, Humhung; N827, Sinuiju.

366 Soldier brandishing Red Book

1967. "Let us carry out the Decisions of the Workers' Party Conference!". Multicoloured.
N828 10 ch. Type **366** 25 10
N829 10 ch. Militiaman holding bayonet 25 10
N830 10 ch. Foundryman and bayonet 25 10

367 Whaler firing Harpoon

1967. With gum.
N831 **367** 10 ch. blue . . . . 2·00 25

368 Airman, Soldier and Sailor

1968. 20th Anniv of People's Army. Mult. With gum.
N832 10 ch. Type **368** 30 10
N833 10 ch. Soldier below attack in snow 30 10
N834 10 ch. Soldier below massed ranks 30 10
N835 10 ch. Soldier holding flag 30 10
N836 10 ch. Soldier holding book 30 10
N837 10 ch. Soldiers and armed workers with flag 30 10
N838 10 ch. Furnaceman and soldier 30 10
N839 10 ch. Soldier saluting . . . 30 10
N840 10 ch. Charging soldiers . . . 30 10
N841 10 ch. Soldier, sailor and airman below flag 30 10

1968. War Heroes (3rd series). As T **292**. With gum.
N842 10 ch. violet 25 10
N843 10 ch. purple 25 10
PORTRAITS: No. N842, Han Gye Ryol firing Bren gun; N843, Li Su Bok charging up hill.

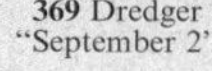

369 Dredger "September 2"

370 Ten-storey Flats, East Pyongyang

371 Palace of Students and Children, Kaesong

1968. With gum.
N844 **369** 5 ch. green 75 10
N845 **370** 10 ch. blue 30 10
N846 **371** 10 ch. blue 30 10

372 Marshal Kim Il Sung

1968. Marshal Kim Il Sung's 56th Birthday. With gum.

N847 **372** 40 ch. multicoloured . . 65 40

373 Kim Il Sung with Mother

1968. Childhood of Kim Il Sung. Multicoloured.

N848 10 ch. Type **373** 35 10
N849 10 ch. Kim Il Sung with his father 35 10
N850 10 ch. Setting out from home, aged 13 . . . . . . 35 10
N851 10 ch. Birthplace at Mangyongdae 35 10
N852 10 ch. Mangyong Hill . . . 35 10

374 Matsu-take Mushroom

1968. Mushrooms. With gum.

N853 **374** 5 ch. brown and green . . 4·25 50
N854 – 10 ch. ochre, brn & grn 6·00 75
N855 – 10 ch. brown and green . 6·00 75

DESIGNS: No. N854, Black mushroom; N855, Cultivated mushroom.

375 Leaping Horseman

1968. 20th Anniv of Korean People's Democratic Republic. Multicoloured. With gum.

N856 10 ch. Type **375** . . . . . . 1·25 10
N857 10 ch. Four servicemen . . . 1·25 10
N858 10 ch. Soldier with bayonet . 1·25 10
N859 10 ch. Advancing with banners 1·25 10
N860 10 ch. Statue . . . . 1·25 10
N861 10 ch. Korean flag . . . . . 1·25 10
N862 10 ch. Soldier and peasant with flag . . . . 1·25 10
N863 10 ch. Machine-gunner with flag . . . . 1·25 10

376 Domestic Products

377 Proclaiming the Ten Points

1968. Development of Light Industries. Multicoloured. With gum.

N864 2 ch. Type **376** 25 10
N865 5 ch. Textiles . . . . 1·00 10
N866 10 ch. Tinned produce . . . 40 10

1968. Kim Il Sung's Ten Point Political Programme. Multicoloured.

N867 2 ch. Type **377** 15 10
N868 5 ch. Soldier and artisan (horiz) 20 10

378 Livestock

1968. Development of Agriculture. Mult. With gum.

N869 5 ch. Type **378** 25 10
N870 10 ch. Fruit-growing 25 10
N871 10 ch. Wheat-harvesting . . . 25 10

379 Yesso Scallop

1968. Shellfish. Multicoloured. With gum.

N872 5 ch. Type **379** . . . . . . 1·10 10
N873 5 ch. Meretrix chione (venus clam) . . . . 1·10 10
N874 10 ch. "Modiolus hanleyi" (mussel) . . . . 1·75 20

380 Kim Il Sung at Head of Columns

1968. Battle of Pochonbo Monument. Detail of Monument. Multicoloured.

N875 10 ch. Type **380** 25 10
N876 10 ch. Head of right-hand column 25 10
N877 10 ch. Tail of right-hand column 25 10
N878 10 ch. Head of left-hand column 25 10
N879 10 ch. Tail of left-hand column 25 10
N880 10 ch. Centre of right-hand column 25 10
N881 10 ch. Centre of left-hand column 25 10

SIZES—HORIZ: Nos. N876/8, 43×28 mm. 880/1, 56×28 mm.

The centrepiece of the Monument is flanked by two columns of soldiers, headed by Kim Il Sung.

381 Museum of the Revolution, Pochonbo

382 Grand Theatre, Pyongyang

1968.

N883 **381** 2 ch. green 20 10
N884 **382** 10 ch. brown 65 10

383 Irrigation

1969. Rural Development. Multicoloured.

N885 3 ch. Type **383** 20 10
N886 5 ch. Agricultural mechanisation 20 10
N887 10 ch. Electrification 40 10
N888 40 ch. Applying fertilisers and spraying trees 60 10

384 Grey Rabbits

1969. Rabbits. Mult. With or without gum.

N889 2 ch. Type **384** 45 10
N890 10 ch. Black rabbits 45 10
N891 10 ch. Brown rabbits 45 10
N892 10 ch. White rabbits 45 10
N893 40 ch. Doe and young . . . 1·40 15

385 "Age and Youth"

1969. Public Health Service.

N894 **385** 2 ch. brown and blue . . 35 10
N895 – 10 ch. blue and red . . . 75 10
N896 – 40 ch. green and yellow 1·50 20

DESIGNS: 10 ch. Nurse with syringe; 40 ch. Auscultation by woman doctor.

386 Sowing Rice Seed

1969. Agricultural Mechanisation.

N897 **386** 10 ch. green 75 10
N898 – 10 ch. orange 75 10
N899 – 10 ch. black 75 10
N900 – 10 ch. brown 75 10

DESIGNS: No. N898, Rice harvester; N899, Weed-spraying machine; N900, Threshing machine.

387 Ponghwa

1969. Revolutionary Historical Sites. Multicoloured.

N901 10 ch. Type **387** 25 10
N902 10 ch. Mangyongdae, birthplace of Kim Il Sung 25 10

388 Kim crosses into Manchuria, 1926, aged 13

1969. Kim Il Sung in Manchuria. Multicoloured. No. N907 with gum.

N903 10 ch. Type **388** 40 10
N904 10 ch. Leading strike of Yuwen Middle School boys, 1927 40 10
N905 10 ch. Leading anti-Japanese demonstration in Kirin, 1928 40 10
N906 10 ch. Presiding at meeting of Young Communist League, 1930 . . . . 40 10
N907 10 ch. Meeting of young revolutionaries 40 10

389 Birthplace at Chilgol

1969. Commemoration of Mrs. Kang Ban Sok, mother of Kim Il Sung. Multicoloured.

N908 10 ch. Type **389** 30 10
N909 10 ch. With members of Women's Association . . . 30 10
N910 10 ch. Resisting Japanese police . . . . 2·50 40

390 Pegaebong Bivouac

1969. Bivouac Sites in the Guerrilla War against the Japanese. Multicoloured.

N911 5 ch. Type **390** 20 10
N912 10 ch. Mupo site (horiz) . . . 30 10
N913 10 ch. Chongbong site . . . 30 10
N914 40 ch. Konchang site (horiz) 1·00 20

391 Chollima Statue

392 Museum of the Revolution, Pyongyang

1969.

N915 **391** 10 ch. blue 25 10
N916 **392** 10 ch. green 25 10

393 Mangyong Chickens

395 Statue of Marshal Kim Il Sung

394 Marshal Kim Il Sung and Children

1969. Korean Poultry.

N917 **393** 10 ch. blue 45 10
N918 – 10 ch. violet . . . . . . 1·25 15

DESIGN: No. N918, Kwangpo ducks.

1969. Kim Il Sung's Educational System. Mult.

N919 2 ch. Type **394** 25 10
N920 10 ch. Worker with books . . 25 10
N921 40 ch. Students with books 50 20

1969. Memorials on Pochonbo Battlefield. Inscr "1937.6.4". Multicoloured.

N922 5 ch. Machine-gun post . . . 25 10
N923 10 ch. Type **395** 25 10
N924 10 ch. "Aspen-tree" monument 25 10
N925 10 ch. Glade Konjang Hill 25 10

396 Teaching at Myongsin School

1969. Commemoration of Kim Hyong Jik, father of Kim Il Sung. Multicoloured.

N926 10 ch. Type **396** 30 10
N927 10 ch. Secret meeting with Korean National Association members . . . 30 10

397 Relay Runner

1969. 20th Anniv of Sports Day.
N928 **397** 10 ch. multicoloured . . 35 10

398 President Nixon attacked by Pens

1969. Anti-U.S. Imperialism Journalists' Conference, Pyongyang.
N929 **398** 10 ch. multicoloured . . 35 10

399 Fighters and Battle

1969. Implementation of Ten-Point Programme of Kim Il Sung. Multicoloured.
N930 5 ch. Type **399** (Reunification of Korea) 30 10
N931 10 ch. Workers upholding slogan (vert) 30 10

400 Bayonet Attack over U.S. Flag

1969. Anti-American Campaign.
N932 **400** 10 ch. multicoloured . . 35 10

401 Armed Workers

1969. Struggle for the Reunification of Korea. Multicoloured.
N933 10 ch. Workers stabbing U.S. soldier (vert) 20 10
N934 10 ch. Kim Il Sung and crowd with flags (vert) 20 10
N935 50 ch. Type **401** 50 20

402 Buri

1969. Korean Fishes. Multicoloured.
N936 5 ch. Type **402** . . . . . . 1·00 10
N937 10 ch. Eastern dace . . . . . 1·75 10
N938 40 ch. Flat-headed grey mullet . . . . 3·00 40

403 Freighter "Taesungsan"

1969.
N939 **403** 10 ch. purple 75 10

405 Dahwangwai (1935)

1970. Guerrilla Conference Places.
N940 **405** 2 ch. blue and green . . 25 10
N941 – 5 ch. brown and green 25 10
N942 – 10 ch. lt green and green 25 10
DESIGNS: 5 ch. Yaoyinggou (barn) (1935); 10 ch. Xiaohaerbaling (tent) (1940).

406 Lake Chon

407 Vietnamese Soldier and Furnaceman

1970. Mt. Paekdu, Home of Revolution (1st issue). Inscr "1970".
N943 **406** 10 ch. black, brn & grn 60 10
N944 – 10 ch. black, grn & yell 60 10
N945 – 10 ch. purple, bl & yell 60 10
N946 – 10 ch. black, blue and pink 60 10
DESIGNS: No. N944, Piryu Peak; N945, Pyongsa (Soldier) Peak; N946, Changgun (General) Peak.
See also Nos. N979/81.

1970. Help for the Vietnamese People.
N947 **407** 10 ch. green, brn & red 20 10

408 Receiving his Father's Revolvers from his Mother

1970. Revolutionary Career of Kim Il Sung. Multicoloured.
N948 10 ch. Type **408** 65 20
N949 10 ch. Receiving smuggled weapons from his mother 65 20
N950 10 ch. Talking to farm workers 65 20
N951 10 ch. At Kalun meeting, 1930 65 20

409 Lenin

410 March of Koreans

1970. Birth Centenary of Lenin.
N952 **409** 10 ch. brn & cinnamon 30 10
N953 – 10 ch. brown and green 30 10
DESIGN: No. N953, Lenin making a speech.

1970. 15th Anniv of Association of Koreans in Japan.
N954 **410** 10 ch. red 20 10
N955 10 ch. purple 20 10

411 Uniformed Factory Worker

412 Students and Newspapers

1970. Workers' Militia.
N956 **411** 10 ch. green, brn & mve 20 10
N957 – 10 ch. green, brown & bl 20 10
DESIGN—HORIZ: No. N957, Militiaman saluting.

1970. Peasant Education. Multicoloured.
N958 2 ch. Type **412** 35 10
N959 5 ch. Peasant with book . . . 20 10
N960 10 ch. Students in class . . . 20 10

413 "Electricity Flows"

1970. Commemoration of Army Electrical Engineers.
N961 **413** 10 ch. brown 40 10

414 Soldier with Rifle

1970. Campaign Month for Withdrawal of U.S. Troops from South Korea.
N962 **414** 5 ch. violet 15 10
N963 – 10 ch. purple 30 10
DESIGN: 10 ch. Soldier and partisan.

415 Rebel wielding Weapons

1970. Struggle in South Korea against U.S. Imperialism.
N964 **415** 10 ch. violet 20 10

416 Labourer ("Fertilisers")

417 Railway Guard

1970. Encouragement of Increased Productivity.
N965 **416** 10 ch. green, pink & brn . 40 10
N966 – 10 ch. green, red & brn . 70 10
N967 – 10 ch. blue, green & brn . 40 10
N968 – 10 ch. bistre, brn & grn 40 10
N969 – 10 ch. violet, grn & brn 50 10
DESIGNS: No. N966, Furnaceman ("Steel"); N967, Operative ("Machines"); N968, Labourer ("Building Construction"); N969, Miner ("Mining").

1970. "Speed the Transport System".
N970 **417** 10 ch. blue, orge & grn 1·25 15

418 Agriculture

1970. Executive Decisions of the Workers' Party Congress. Designs embodying book.
N971 **418** 5 ch. red 20 10
N972 – 10 ch. green . . . . . 1·10 15
N973 – 40 ch. green . . . . . 1·10 15
DESIGNS: 10 ch. Industry; 40 ch. The Armed Forces.

419 Chollima Statue and Workers' Party Banner

421 Emblem of League

1970. 25th Anniv of Korean Workers' Party.
N974 **419** 10 ch. red, brown & buff 20 10

1971. 25th Anniv of League of Socialist Working Youth.
N976 **421** 10 ch. red, brown & blue 20 10

422 Log Cabin, Nanhutou

1971. 35th Anniv of Nanhutou Guerrilla Conference.
N977 **422** 10 ch. multicoloured . . 20 10

423 Tractor Driver

1971. 25th Anniv of Land Reform Law.
N978 **423** 2 ch. red, green & black 20 10

1971. Mt. Paekdu, Home of Revolution (2nd issue). As T **406** but inscr "1971".
N979 2 ch. black, olive and green 35 10
N980 5 ch. pink, black and slate 2·25 15
N981 10 ch. black, red and grey 60 10
DESIGNS—HORIZ: 2 ch. General view; 10 ch. Western peak. VERT: 5 ch. Waterfall.

424 Popyong Museum

1971. Museum of the Revolution.
N982 **424** 10 ch. brown and yellow 20 10
N983 – 10 ch. blue and orange 20 10
N984 – 10 ch. green and orange 20 10
DESIGNS: No. N983, Mangyongdae Museum; N984, Chunggang Museum.

425 Miner

1971. Six Year Plan for Coal Industry.
N985 **425** 10 ch. multicoloured . . 40 10

426 Kim Il Sung

1971. Founding of Anti-Japanese Guerrilla Army. Multicoloured.
N986 10 ch. Type **426** 35 10
N987 10 ch. Kim Il Sung founding Anti-Japanese Guerrilla Army 35 10
N988 10 ch. Kim Il Sung addressing the people 35 10
N989 10 ch. Kim Il Sung and members of Children's Corps 35 10
Nos. N987/9 are horiz.

428 Hands holding Hammer and Rifle

1971. 85th Anniv of Labour Day.
N990 **428** 1 w. red, brown & buff 2·25 40

429 Soldiers and Map

430 Monument

1971. 35th Anniv of Association for Restoration of Fatherland.
N991 **429** 10 ch. red, buff & black 35 10

1971. Battlefields in Musan Area, May 1939. Multicoloured.

N992 5 ch. Type **430** 15 10
N993 10 ch. Machine guns in perspex cases (horiz) 20 10
N994 40 ch. Huts among birch trees (horiz) 55 15

431 Koreans Marching

432 Flame Emblem

1971. Solidarity of Koreans in Japan.

N995 **431** 10 ch. brown 20 10

1971. 25th Anniv of Korean Childrens' Union.

N996 **432** 10 ch. red, yellow and blue 20 10

433 Marchers and Banners

434 Foundryman

1971. 6th Congress of League of Socialist Working Youth.

N997 **433** 5 ch. red, buff and black 10 10
N998 – 10 ch. red, green & black 20 10
DESIGN: 10 c. Marchers and banner under globe.

1971. 25th Anniv of Labour Law.

N999 **434** 5 ch. black, purple & buff 20 10

435 Young Women

1971. 25th Anniv of Sex Equality Law.

N1000 **435** 5 ch. multicoloured 20 10

436 Schoolchildren

1971. 15th Anniv of Compulsory Primary Education.

N1001 **436** 10 ch. multicoloured 50 10

437 Choe Yong Do and Combat Scene

1971. Heroes of the Revolutionary Struggle in South Korea.

N1002 **437** 5 ch. black and green 25 10
N1003 – 10 ch. red and brown 25 10
N1004 – 10 ch. black and red 25 10
DESIGNS: No. N1003, Revolutionary with book; N1004, Kim Jong Tae and scene of triumph.

438 Two Foundrymen

1971. 25th Anniv of Nationalization of Industry Law.

N1005 **438** 5 ch. black, grn & brn 1·50 10

439 Struggle in Korea

1971. The Anti-Imperialist and Anti-U.S. Imperialist Struggles.

N1006 **439** 10 ch. red, black and brown 25 10
N1007 – 10 ch. brown, black and blue 35 10
N1008 – 10 ch. red, black and pink 50 10
N1009 – 10 ch. black, olive and green 25 10
N1010 – 10 ch. orange, black and red 50 10
N1011 – 40 ch. green, black and pink 50 15
DESIGNS: No. N1007, Struggle in Vietnam; N1008, Soldier with rifle and airplane marked "EC"; N1009, Struggle in Africa; N1010, Cuban soldier and Central America; N1011, Bayonetting U.S. soldier.

440 Kim Il Sung University

1971. 25th Anniv of Kim Il Sung University.

N1012 **440** 10 ch. grey, red & yellow 20 10

441 Iron-ore Ladle (Mining)

1971. Tasks of Six Year Plan. Multicoloured.

N1013 10 ch. Type **441** 2·75 15
N1014 10 ch. Workers and text 30 10
N1015 10 ch. Electric train and track (Transport) 2·75 15
N1016 10 ch. Hand and wrench (Industry) 30 10
N1017 10 ch. Mechanical scoop (Construction) 2·75 15
N1018 10 ch. Manufactured goods (Trade) 30 10
N1019 10 ch. Crate on hoists (Exports) 25 10
N1020 10 ch. Lathe (Heavy Industries) 2·75 15
N1021 10 ch. Freighter (Shipping) 60 10
N1022 10 ch. Household equipment (Light Industries) 25 10
N1023 10 ch. Corncob and wheat (Agriculture) 40 10

442 Technicians

1971. Cultural Revolution. Multicoloured.

N1024 2 ch. Type **442** 20 10
N1025 5 ch. Mechanic 25 10
N1026 10 ch. Schoolchildren 30 10
N1027 10 ch. Chemist 50 10
N1028 10 ch. Composer at piano 85 15

443 Workers with Red Books

1971. Ideological Revolution. Multicoloured.

N1029 10 ch. Type **443** 20 10
N1030 10 ch. Workers reading book 20 10
N1031 10 ch. Workers' lecture 20 10
N1032 10 ch. Worker and pneumatic drill 20 10

444 Korean Family

1971. Improvement in Living Standards.

N1033 **444** 10 ch. multicoloured 15 10

445 Furnaceman

1971. Implementation of Decisions of Fifth Workers' Party Conference.

N1034 **445** 10 ch. multicoloured 1·00 10

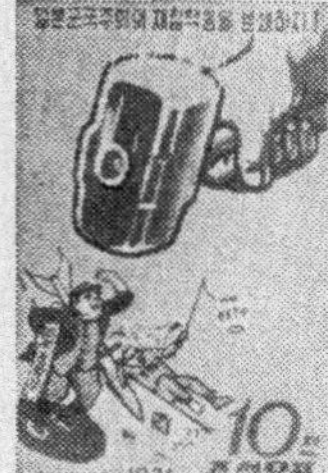
446

447 6000-ton Press

1971. Solidarity with South Korean Revolutionaries.

N1036 **446** 10 ch. brown, blue and black 30 10
N1037 – 10 ch. brown, flesh and red 30 10
N1038 – 10 ch. multicoloured 30 10
N1039 – 10 ch. multicoloured 30 10
DESIGNS—VERT: No. N1037, U.S. soldier attacked by poster boards; N1038, Hands holding rifles aloft. HORIZ: No. N1039, Men advancing with rifles.

1971.

N1040 **447** 2 ch. brown 70 10
N1041 – 5 ch. blue 90 15
N1042 – 10 ch. green 1·10 10
N1043 – 10 ch. green 1·10 10
DESIGNS: No. N1041, Refrigerated freighter "Ponghwasan"; N1042, 300 h.p. bulldozer; N1043, "Sungrisan" lorry.

448 Title-page and Militants

1971. 35th Anniv of "Samil Wolgan" Magazine.

N1044 **448** 10 ch. red, green & blk 45 10

452 Poultry Chicks

1972. Poultry Breeding.

N1051 **452** 5 ch. yellow, black and brown 25 10
N1052 – 10 ch. orange, bistre and brown 35 10
N1053 – 40 ch. blue, orange and deep blue 55 15
DESIGNS: 10 ch. Chickens and battery egg house; 40 ch. Eggs and fowls suspended from hooks.

453 Scene from "Village Shrine"

1972. Films of Guerrilla War.

N1054 **453** 10 ch. grey and green 60 10
N1055 – 10 ch. blue, pur & orge 60 10
N1056 – 10 ch. purple, bl & yell 60 10
DESIGNS: No. N1055, Patriot with pistol ("A Sea of Blood"); N1056, Guerrilla using bayonet ("The Lot of a Self-Defence Corps Member").

454 Kim Il Sung acknowledging Greetings

1972. Kim Il Sung's 60th Birthday. Scenes in the life of Kim Il Sung, dated "1912–1972". Mult.

N1057 5 ch. Type **454** 20 10
N1058 5 ch. In campaign H.Q. 20 10
N1059 5 ch. Military conference (horiz) 20 10
N1060 10 ch. In wheatfield (horiz) 30 10
N1061 10 ch. Directing construction (horiz) 2·00 40
N1062 10 ch. Talking to foundry workers (horiz) 20 10
N1063 10 ch. Aboard whaler (horiz) 55 10
N1064 10 ch. Visiting a hospital (horiz) 75 10
N1065 10 ch. Viewing orchard (horiz) 20 10
N1066 10 ch. With survey party on Haeju–Hasong railway line (horiz) 2·00 40
N1067 10 ch. Meeting female workers at silk factory (horiz) 1·00 15
N1068 10 ch. Village conference (horiz) 20 10
N1069 10 ch. Touring chicken factory (horiz) 35 10
N1070 40 ch. Relaxing with children 45 20
N1071 1 wn. Giant portrait and marchers 70 40

455 Bugler sounding "Charge".

1972. 40th Anniv of Guerrilla Army.

N1073 **455** 10 ch. multicoloured 45 10

456 Pavilion of Ryongpo

1972. Historic Sites of the 1950–53 War. Mult.

N1074 2 ch. Type **456** 15 10
N1075 5 ch. Houses at Onjong 15 10
N1076 10 ch. Headquarters, Kosanjin 15 10
N1077 40 ch. Victory Museum, Chonsung-dong 30 10

457 Volleyball

1972. Olympic Games, Munich. Multicoloured.

N1078 2 ch. Type **457** 35 10
N1079 5 ch. Boxing (horiz) 50 10
N1080 10 ch. Judo 50 10
N1081 10 ch. Wrestling (horiz) 50 10
N1082 40 ch. Rifle-shooting 1·10 20

458 Chollima Street, Pyongyang

1971. Chollima Street, Pyongyang.

N1083 – 5 ch. orange and black . 1·60 15
N1084 **458** 10 ch. yellow and black . 60 15
N1085 – 10 ch. green and black . 60 15

DESIGNS: No. N1083, Bridge and skyscraper blocks; N1085, Another view looking up street.

459 Dredger

1972. Development of Natural Resources. Multicoloured.

N1086 5 ch. Type **459** 35 10
N1087 10 ch. Forestry 50 10
N1088 40 ch. Reclaiming land from the sea 60 15

460 Ferrous Industry

1972. Tasks of the Six-Year Plan. The Metallurgical Industry. Inscr "1971–1976". Multicoloured.

N1089 10 ch. Type **460** . . . . . . 1·40 10
N1090 10 ch. Non-ferrous Industry 40 10

461 Iron Ore Industry

1972. Tasks of the Six-Year Plan. The Mining Industry. Inscr "1971–1976". Multicoloured.

N1091 10 ch. Type **461** 40 10
N1092 10 ch. Coal mining industry 1·50 15

462 Electronic and Automation Industry

1972. Tasks of the Six-Year Plan. The Engineering Industry. Inscr "1971–1976". Multicoloured.

N1093 10 ch. Type **462** 60 10
N1094 10 ch. Single-purpose machines 40 10
N1095 10 ch. Machine tools . . . 40 10

463 Clearing Virgin Soil

1972. Tasks of the Six-Year Plan. Rural Economy. Multicoloured.

N1096 10 ch. Type **463** 45 10
N1097 10 ch. Irrigation 45 10
N1098 10 ch. Harvesting 45 10

464 Automation

1972. Tasks of the Six-Year Plan. Inscr "1971–1976". Multicoloured.

N1099 10 ch. Type **464** . . . . . . 1·60 10
N1100 10 ch. Agricultural mechanisation 50 10
N1101 10 ch. Lightening of household chores 50 10

465 Chemical Fibres and Materials

1972. Tasks of the Six-Year Plan. The Chemical Industry. Inscr "1971–1976". Multicoloured.

N1102 10 ch. Type **465** 60 10
N1103 10 ch. Fertilisers, insecticides and weed killers 60 10

466 Textiles

1972. Tasks of the Six-Year Plan. Consumer Goods. Inscr "1971–1976". Multicoloured.

N1104 10 ch. Type **466** 65 10
N1105 10 ch. Kitchen ware and overalls 45 10
N1106 10 ch. Household goods . . 45 10

467 Fish, Fruit and Vegetables

1972. Tasks of the Six-Year Plan. The Food Industry. Multicoloured.

N1107 10 ch. Type **467** 90 10
N1108 10 ch. Tinned foods 65 10
N1109 10 ch. Food packaging . . . 65 10

468 Electrifying Railway Lines

1972. Tasks of the Six-Year Plan. Transport. Inscr "1971–1976". Multicoloured.

N1110 10 ch. Type **468** 45 10
N1111 10 ch. Laying new railway track 45 10
N1112 10 ch. Freighters 55 10

469 Soldier with Shell

1972. North Korean Armed Forces. Multicoloured.

N1113 10 ch. Type **469** 35 10
N1114 10 ch. Marine 35 10
N1115 10 ch. Air Force pilot . . . 35 10

470 "Revolution of 19 April 1960"

1972. The Struggle for Reunification of Korea. Multicoloured.

N1116 10 ch. Type **470** 15 10
N1117 10 ch. Marchers with banner 15 10
N1118 10 ch. Insurgents with red banner 15 10
N1119 10 ch. Attacking U.S. and South Korean soldiers . . 15 10
N1120 10 ch. Workers with posters 15 10
N1121 10 ch. Workers acclaiming revolution . . . . 3·50 40
N1122 10 ch. Workers and manifesto 15 10

471 Single-spindle Automatic Lathe

1972. Machine Tools.

N1123 **471** 5 ch. green and purple 25 10
N1124 – 10 ch. blue and green 35 10
N1125 – 40 ch. green & brown 80 15

DESIGNS—HORIZ: 10 ch. "Kusong-3" lathe; VERT: 40 ch. 2,000 ton crank press.

472 Casting Vote

1972. National Elections. Multicoloured.

N1126 10 ch. Type **472** 25 10
N1127 10 ch. Election campaigner 25 10

475 Soldier

1973. 25th Anniv of Founding of Korean People's Army. Multicoloured.

N1130 5 ch. Type **475** 20 10
N1131 10 ch. Sailor 30 10
N1132 40 ch. Airman 70 25

476 Wrestling Site

1973. Scenes of Kim Il Sung's Childhood, Mangyongdae. Multicoloured.

N1133 2 ch. Type **476** 15 10
N1134 5 ch. Warship rock 15 10
N1135 10 ch. Swinging site (vert) 20 10
N1136 10 ch. Sliding rock 20 10
N1137 40 ch. Fishing site 60 15

477 Monument to Socialist Revolution and Construction, Mansu Hill

1973. Museum of the Korean Revolution.

N1138 **477** 10 ch. multicoloured . . 25 10
N1139 – 10 ch. multicoloured . . 25 10
N1140 – 40 ch. multicoloured . . 50 15
N1141 – 3 wn. green and yellow 2·50 60

DESIGNS—As Type **477**: 10 ch. (N1139) Similar monument but men in military clothes; 40 ch. Statue of Kim Il Sung. HORIZ—60 × 29 mm: 3 wn. Museum building.

478 Karajibong Camp

1973. Secret Camps by Tuman-Gang in Guerrilla War, 1932. Multicoloured.

N1142 10 ch. Type **478** 15 10
N1143 10 ch. Soksaegol Camp . . 15 10

479

1973. Menace of Japanese Influence in South Korea.

N1144 **479** 10 ch. multicoloured . . 20 10

480 Wrecked U.S. Tanks

1973. Five-point Programme for Reunification of Korea. Multicoloured.

N1145 2 ch. Type **480** 40 10
N1146 5 ch. Electric train and crane lifting tractor . . . . . . 2·50 20
N1147 10 ch. Leaflets falling on crowd 20 10
N1148 10 ch. Hand holding leaflet and map of Korea . . . 40 10
N1149 40 ch. Banner and globe . . 60 20

481 Lorries

482 Volleyball

1973. Lorries and Tractors. Multicoloured.

N1150 10 ch. Type **481** 50 10
N1151 10 ch. Tractors and earth-moving machine 50 10

1973. Socialist Countries' Junior Women's Volleyball Games, Pyongyang.

N1152 **482** 10 ch. multicoloured . . 50 10

483 Battlefield

1973. 20th Anniv of Victory in Korean War.

N1153 **483** 10 ch. green, purple and black 20 10
N1154 – 10 ch. brown, blue and black 20 10

DESIGN: 10 ch. Urban fighting.

484 "The Snow Falls"

1973. Mansudae Art Troupe. Dances. Multicoloured.

N1155 10 ch. Type **484** 60 10
N1156 25 ch. "A Bumper Harvest of Apples" . . . . 1·50 25
N1157 40 ch. "Azalea of the Fatherland" . . . . . . 1·75 30

485 Schoolchildren

1973. Ten Years Compulsory Secondary Education.

N1158 **485** 10 ch. multicoloured . . 25 10

486 "Fervour in the Revolution"

1973. The Works of Kim Il Sung (1st series).
N1159 **486** 10 ch. brown, red and yellow 15 10
N1160 – 10 ch. brown, green and yellow 15 10
N1161 – 10 ch. lake, brown and yellow 15 10
DESIGNS: No. N1160, Selected works; N1161, "Strengthen the Socialist System".
See also Nos. N1217/18.

487 Celebrating Republic

1973. 25th Anniv of People's Republic. Multicoloured.
N1162 5 ch. Type **487** 10 10
N1163 10 ch. Fighting in Korean War 10 10
N1164 40 ch. Peace and reconstruction . . . . . 1·60 40

488 Pobwang Peak

1973. Mt. Myohyang. Multicoloured.
N1165 2 ch. Type **488** 25 10
N1166 5 ch. Inhodae Pavilion . . . 35 10
N1167 10 ch. Taeha Falls (vert) . . 1·75 30
N1168 40 ch. Rongyon Falls (vert) 2·50 30

489 Party Memorial Building

1973. Party Memorial Building.
N1169 **489** 1 wn. brown, grey and buff . . . . 1·25 30

490 Football and Handball

1973. National People's Sports Meeting. Mult.
N1170 2 ch. Type **490** 60 10
N1171 5 ch. High jumper and woman sprinter 40 10
N1172 10 ch. Skaters and skiers . . 50 10
N1173 10 ch. Wrestling and swinging 40 10
N1174 40 ch. Parachutist and motor cyclists . . . . 3·00 25

491 Weightlifting **492** Chongryu Cliff

1973. Junior Weightlifting Championships of Socialist Countries.
N1175 **491** 10 ch. blue, brown and green 50 10

1973. Scenery of Moran Hill, Pyongyang. Multicoloured.
N1176 2 ch. Type **492** 70 15
N1177 5 ch. Moran Waterfall . . . 2·75 40
N1178 10 ch. Pubyok Pavilion . . . 75 10
N1179 40 ch. Ulmil Pavilion . . . 90 15

493 Rainbow Bridge **494** Magnolia Flower

1973. Diamond Mountains Scenery (4th issue). Multicoloured.
N1180 2 ch. Type **493** . . . . . . 1·50 15
N1181 5 ch. Suspension footbridge, Okryudong (horiz) . . . 1·50 15
N1182 10 ch. Chonnyo Peak . . . 75 10
N1183 10 ch. Chilchung Rock and Sonji Peak (horiz) 75 10
N1184 40 ch. Sujong and Pari Peaks (horiz) 85 15

1973.
N1185 **494** 10 ch. multicoloured . . 60 10

495 S. Korean Revolutionaries

1973. South Korean Revolution. Multicoloured
N1186 10 ch. Type **495** 30 10
N1187 10 ch. Marching revolutionaries 30 10

496 Cock sees Butterflies

1973. Scenes from "Cock Chasing Butterflies". Fairy Tale. Multicoloured.
N1188 2 ch. Type **496** . . . . . . 1·50 10
N1189 5 ch. Butterflies discuss how to repel cock . . . . 1·50 10
N1190 10 ch. Cock chasing butterflies with basket . . . . . . 2·00 15
N1191 10 ch. Cock chasing butterfly up cliff . . . . 2·00 20
N1192 40 ch. Cock chasing butterflies over cliff . . . . 2·25 25
N1193 90 ch. Cock falls into sea and butterflies escape . . . . 2·75 30

497 Yonpung

1973. Historical Sites of War and Revolution (40 ch.). Multicoloured.
N1196 2 ch. Type **497** 10 10
N1197 5 ch. Hyangha 10 10
N1198 10 ch. Changgol 15 10
N1199 40 ch. Paeksong 55 10

498 Science Library, Kim Il Sung University

1973. New Buildings in Pyongyang.
N1200 **498** 2 ch. violet 50 10
N1201 – 5 ch. green 15 10
N1202 – 10 ch. brown 25 10
N1203 – 40 ch. brown and buff . . . 55 15
N1204 – 90 ch. buff 95 30
DESIGNS—HORIZ: 10 ch. Victory Museum; 40 ch. People's Palace of Culture; 90 ch. Indoor stadium. VERT: 5 ch. Building No. 2, Kim Il Sung University.

499 Red Book

1973. Socialist Constitution of North Korea. Multicoloured.
N1205 10 ch. Type **499** 15 10
N1206 10 ch. Marchers with red book and banners 15 10
N1207 10 ch. Marchers with red book and emblem 15 10

500 Oriental Great Reed Warbler

1973. Korean Songbirds. Multicoloured.
N1208 5 ch. Type **500** . . . . . . 1·60 25
N1209 10 ch. Grey starling (facing right) . . . . 2·25 45
N1210 10 ch. Daurian starling (facing left) . . . . 2·25 45

503 Chollima Statue

1974. The Works of Kim Il Sung (2nd series). Multicoloured.
N1217 10 ch. Type **503** 65 10
N1218 10 ch. Bayonets threatening U.S. soldier 15 10

504 Train in Station

1974. Opening of Pyongyang Metro. Multicoloured.
N1219 10 ch. Type **504** 45 10
N1220 10 ch. Escalators 45 10
N1221 10 ch. Station hall 45 10

505 Capital Construction Front

1974. Five Fronts of Socialist Construction. Multicoloured.
N1222 10 ch. Type **505** 15 10
N1223 10 ch. Agricultural front . . . 25 10
N1224 10 ch. Transport front . . . 1·25 15
N1225 10 ch. Fisheries front . . . 90 15
N1226 10 ch. Industrial front (vert) 25 10

506 Marchers with Banners

1974. 10th Anniv of Publication of "Theses on the Socialist Rural Question in Our Country". Multicoloured.
N1227 10 ch. Type **506** 15 10
N1228 10 ch. Book and rejoicing crowd 15 10
N1229 10 ch. Tractor & banners . . 15 10
Nos. N1227/9 were issued together, se-tenant, forming a composite design.

507 Manure Spreader

1974. Farm Machinery.
N1230 **507** 2 ch. green, black & red 60 10
N1231 – 5 ch. red, black & blue 60 10
N1232 – 10 ch. red, black & grn 60 10
DESIGNS: 5 ch. "Progress" tractor; 10 ch. "Mount Taedoksan" tractor.

508 Archery (Grenoble)

1974. North Korean Victories at International Sports Meetings. Multicoloured.
N1233 2 ch. Type **508** . . . . . . 1·00 15
N1234 5 ch. Gymnastics (Varna) 25 10
N1235 10 ch. Boxing (Bucharest) 40 10
N1236 20 ch. Volleyball (Pyongyang) 25 10
N1237 30 ch. Rifle shooting (Sofia) 60 10
N1238 40 ch. Judo (Tbilisi) 80 15
N1239 60 ch. Model aircraft flying (Vienna) (horiz) . . . . 1·25 20
N1240 1 wn. 50 Table tennis (Peking) (horiz) . . . . 2·25 30

509 Book and Rejoicing Crowd

1974. The First Country with No Taxes.
N1241 **509** 10 ch. multicoloured . . 20 10

510 Drawing up Programme in Woods

1974. Kim Il Sung during the Anti-Japanese Struggle. Multicoloured.
N1242 10 ch. Type **510** 25 10
N1243 10 ch. Giving directions to Pak Dal 25 10
N1244 10 ch. Presiding over Nanhutou Conference . . 25 10
N1245 10 ch. Supervising creation of strongpoint 25 10

511 Sun Hui loses her Sight

1974. Scenes from "The Flower Girl" (revolutionary opera). Multicoloured.
N1246 2 ch. Type **511** 65 10
N1247 5 ch. Death of Ggot Bun's mother 65 10
N1248 10 ch. Ggot Bun throws boiling water at landlord . 1·40 10
N1249 40 ch. Ggot Bun joins revolutionaries . . . . . 1·75 15

MINIMUM PRICE
The minimum price quoted is 10p which represents a handling charge rather than a basis for valuing common stamps. For further notes about prices see introductory pages.

512 Leopard Cat

1974. 15th Anniv of Pyongyang Zoo. Multicoloured.

N1251 2 ch. Type **512** 60 10
N1252 5 ch. Lynx 60 10
N1253 10 ch. Red fox 60 10
N1254 10 ch. Wild boar 60 10
N1255 20 ch. Dhole 60 15
N1256 40 ch. Brown bear 75 25
N1257 60 ch. Leopard . . . . . . 1·25 25
N1258 70 ch. Tiger . . . . . . 1·75 30
N1259 90 ch. Lion . . . . 2·00 35

513 "Rosa acucularis lindly"

1974. Roses. Multicoloured.

N1261 2 ch. Type **513** 40 10
N1262 5 ch. Yellow sweet briar . . 45 10
N1263 10 ch. Pink aromatic rose . . 55 10
N1264 10 ch. Aronia sweet briar (yellow centres) 55 10
N1265 40 ch. Multi-petal sweet briar 1·40 10

515 Weigela

1974. Flowering Plants of Mt. Paekdu. Mult.

N1267 2 ch. Type **515** 50 10
N1268 5 ch. Amaryllis 50 10
N1269 10 ch. Red lily 50 10
N1270 20 ch. Orange lily 65 10
N1271 40 ch. Azalea 90 10
N1272 60 ch. Yellow lily . . . . . 1·50 10

516 Postwoman and Construction Site

1974. Cent of U.P.U. and Admission of North Korea to Union. Multicoloured.

N1273 10 ch. Type **516** . . . . . 1·50 15
N1274 25 ch. Chollima monument . . 25 10
N1275 40 ch. Globe and Antonov An-12 transport planes . . 1·00 15

517 Common Pond Frog

1974. Amphibians. Multicoloured.

N1276 2 ch. Type **517** . . . . . 1·00 10
N1277 5 ch. Oriental fire-bellied toad 1·25 10
N1278 10 ch. Bullfrog . . . . . . 1·50 15
N1279 40 ch. Common toad . . . 2·00 25

MORE DETAILED LISTS

are given in the Stanley Gibbons Catalogues referred to in the country headings.
For lists of current volumes see Introduction.

518 "Women of Namgang Village"

1974. Korean Paintings. Multicoloured.

N1281 2 ch. Type **518** 60 10
N1282 5 ch. "An Old Man on the Rakdong River" (60 × 49 mm) 75 10
N1283 10 ch. "Morning in the Naekumgang" (bridge) . . . 1·50 10
N1284 20 ch. "Mt. Kumgang" (60 × 49 mm) . . . . . . 1·25 15

519 "Elektron 1" and "Elektron 2", 1964

1974. Cosmonauts Day. Multicoloured.

N1286 10 ch. Type **519** 15 10
N1287 20 ch. "Proton 1", 1965 . . 25 10
N1288 30 ch. "Venera 3", 1966 . . 40 10
N1289 40 ch. "Venera 5" and "Venera 6", 1969 . . . . 50 10

521 Antonov An-2 Biplane

1974. Civil Aviation. Multicoloured

N1292 2 ch. Type **521** 65 10
N1293 5 ch. Lisunov Li-2 . . . . 65 10
N1294 10 ch. Ilyushin Il-14P . . . 90 10
N1295 40 ch. Antonov An-24 . . . 1·25 35
N1296 60 ch. Ilyushin Il-18 . . . . 2·00 50

522 "Rhododendron redowskianum"

1974. Plants of Mt. Paekdu. Multicoloured.

N1298 2 ch. Type **522** 45 10
N1299 5 ch. "Dryas octopetala" . . 45 10
N1300 10 ch. "Potentilla fruticosa" 50 10
N1301 20 ch. "Papaver somniferum" 65 10
N1302 40 ch. "Phyllodoce caerulea" 90 20
N1303 60 ch. "Oxytropis anertii" 1·50 40

523 "Sobaek River in the Morning"

1974. Modern Korean Paintings (1st series). Multicoloured.

N1304 10 ch. Type **523** 60 10
N1305 20 ch. "Combatants of Mt. Laohei" (60 × 40 mm) . . 65 10
N1306 30 ch. "Spring in the Fields" 75 15
N1307 40 ch. "Tideland Night" . . 3·00 30
N1308 60 ch. "Daughter" (60 × 54 mm) . . . . 1·10 40

See also Nos. N1361/5, N1386/96 and N1485/9.

525 Log Cabin, Unha Village

1974. Historic Sites of the Revolution. Multicoloured.

N1310 5 ch. Munmyong 25 10
N1311 10 ch. Type **525** 25 10

526 Sesame

1974. Oil-producing Plants. Multicoloured.

N1312 2 ch. Type **526** 75 10
N1313 5 ch. "Perilla frutescens" . . 80 10
N1314 10 ch. Sunflower 90 10
N1315 40 ch. Castor bean . . . . 1·25 40

527 Kim Il Sung as Guerrilla Leader

1974. Kim Il Sung. Multicoloured.

N1316 10 ch. Type **527** 20 10
N1317 10 ch. Commander of the People's Army (52 × 35 mm) 20 10
N1318 10 ch. "The commander is also a son of the people" (52 × 35 mm) 20 10
N1319 10 ch. Negotiating with the Chinese anti-Japanese unit (52 × 35 mm) 20 10

528

1974. Grand Monument on Mansu Hill. Mult.

N1320 10 ch. Type **528** 15 10
N1321 10 ch. As T **528** but men in civilian clothes 15 10
N1322 10 ch. As T **528** but men facing left 15 10
N1323 10 ch. As No. N1322 but men in civilian clothes 15 10

529 Factory Ship "Chilbosan"

1974. Deep-sea Fishing. Multicoloured.

N1324 2 ch. Type **529** 70 25
N1325 5 ch. Trawler support ship "Paekdusan" 70 25
N1326 10 ch. Freighter "Moranbong" 70 25
N1327 20 ch. Whale-catcher . . . 70 25
N1328 30 ch. Trawler 70 25
N1329 40 ch. Stern trawler 70 25

539 Kim Il Sung crossing River Agrok

1975. 50th Anniv of Kim Il Sung's crossing of River Agrok.

N1349 **539** 10 ch. multicoloured . . 25 10

540 Pak Yong Sun "World Table Tennis Queen"

1975. Pak Yong Sun, Winner of 33rd World Table Tennis Championships, Calcutta.

N1350 **540** 10 ch. multicoloured . . 1·00 10

541 Common Zebra

1975. Pyongyang Zoo. Multicoloured.

N1352 10 ch. Type **541** 30 10
N1353 10 ch. African buffalo . . . 30 10
N1354 20 ch. Giant panda (horiz) 80 10
N1355 25 ch. Bactrian camel . . . 70 15
N1356 30 ch. Indian elephant . . . 1·25 20

542 "Blue Dragon"

1975. 7th-century Mural Paintings from Koguryo Tombs, Kangso.

N1357 10 ch. Type **542** 75 10
N1358 15 ch. "White Tiger" . . . 1·00 10
N1359 25 ch. "Red Phoenix" (vert) 1·25 10
N1360 40 ch. "Snake-turtle" . . . 1·75 25

543 "Spring in the Guerrilla Base" (1968)

1975. Modern Korean Paintings (2nd series). Anti-Japanese struggle. Multicoloured.

N1361 10 ch. Type **543** 35 10
N1362 10 ch. "Revolutionary Army landing at Unggi" (1969) 35 10
N1363 15 ch. "Sewing Team Members" (1961) 55 10
N1364 20 ch. "Girl Watering Horse" (1969) . . . . 1·00 15
N1365 30 ch. "Kim Jong Suk giving Guidance to Children's Corps" (1970) 80 20

544 Cosmonaut

1975. Cosmonauts' Day. Multicoloured.
N1366 10 ch. Type **544** 15 10
N1367 30 ch. "Lunokhod" moon vehicle (horiz) 40 10
N1368 40 ch. "Soyuz" spacecraft and "Salyut" space laboratory (horiz) 55 15

546 The Beacon lit at Pochonbo, 1937

1975. Kim Il Sung during the Guerrilla War against the Japanese. Multicoloured.
N1370 10 ch. Type **546** 25 10
N1371 10 ch. "A Bowl of Parched-rice Powder", 1938 . . . 25 10
N1372 10 ch. Guiding the Nanpaizi meeting, November, 1938 25 10
N1373 10 ch. Welcoming helper . . 25 10
N1374 10 ch. Lecturing the guerrillas 25 10
N1375 15 ch. Advancing into the homeland, May 1939 . . 35 10
N1376 25 ch. By Lake Samji, May 1939 . . . . 45 10
N1377 30 ch. At Sinsadong, May 1939 . . . . 55 10
N1378 40 ch. Xiaohaerbaling meeting, 1940 . . . . . 65 15

547 Vase of Flowers and Kim Il Sung's Birthplace

1975. Kim Il Sung's 63rd Birthday. Multicoloured.
N1379 10 ch. Type **547** 10 10
N1379a 40 ch. Kim Il Sung's birthplace, Mangyongdae 35 10

548 South Korean Insurgent

1975. 15th Anniv of April 19th Rising.
N1380 **548** 10 ch. multicoloured . . 15 10

549 "Kingfisher at a Lotus Pond"

1975. Paintings of Li Dynasty. Multicoloured.
N1381 5 ch. Type **549** . . . . . . 1·50 10
N1382 10 ch. "Crabs" . . . . . . 1·00 10
N1383 15 ch. "Rose of Sharon" . . 1·40 15
N1384 25 ch. "Lotus and Water Cock" . . . . 2·00 30
N1385 30 ch. "Tree Peony and Red Junglefowl" . . . . . . 3·00 30

1975. Modern Korean Paintings (3rd series). Fatherland Liberation War. Dated designs as T **543**. Multicoloured.
N1386 5 ch. "On the Advance Southward" (1966) (vert) . 30 10
N1387 10 ch. "The Assigned Post" (girl sentry) (1968) (vert) . 40 10
N1388 15 ch. "The Heroism of Li Su Bok" (1965) 40 10
N1389 25 ch. "Retaliation" (woman machine-gunner) (1970) . 65 20
N1390 30 ch. "The awaited Troops" (1970) 80 20

1975. Modern Korean Paintings (4th series). Socialist Construction. As T **543**. Multicoloured.
N1391 10 ch. "Pine Tree" (1966) (vert) 90 10
N1392 10 ch. "The Blue Signal Lamp" (1960) (vert) . . . 2·75 10
N1393 15 ch. "A Night of Snowfall" (1963) 90 10
N1394 20 ch. "Smelters" (1968) . . 1·00 15
N1395 25 ch. "Tideland Reclamation" (1961) . . 1·00 15
N1396 30 ch. "Mount Paekgum" (1966) . . . . 1·00 20

550 Flag and Building

552 "Feet first" entry (man)

1975. 20th Anniv of "Chongryon" Association of Koreans in Japan.
N1397 **550** 10 ch. multicoloured . . 15 10
N1398 3 wn. multicoloured . . 2·50 55

1975. Diving. Multicoloured.
N1400 10 ch. Type **552** 25 10
N1401 25 ch. Piked somersault (man) 50 10
N1402 40 ch. "Head first" entry (woman) . . . . 1·00 15

553

1975. Campaign against U.S. Imperialism.
N1403 **553** 10 ch. multicoloured . . 30 10

554 Silver Carp

1975. Fresh-water Fish. Multicoloured.
N1404 10 ch. Type **554** 70 10
N1405 10 ch. Elongate ilisha (swimming to right) . . . 70 10
N1406 15 ch. Banded minnow . . 1·00 15
N1407 25 ch. Bare-headed bagrid . 1·60 20
N1408 30 ch. Amur catfish (swimming to right) . . . 2·00 30
N1409 30 ch. Chevron snakehead (swimming to left) . . . . 2·00 30

555

1975. 10th Socialist Countries' Football Tournament, Pyongyang.
N1410 **555** 5 ch. multicoloured . . 35 10
N1411 – 10 ch. multicoloured . . 35 10
N1412 – 15 ch. multicoloured . . 40 10
N1413 – 20 ch. multicoloured . . 50 15
N1414 – 50 ch. multicoloured . . 90 35
DESIGNS: 10 ch. to 50 ch. Various footballers.

556 Blue and Yellow Macaw

557 Flats

1975. Birds. Multicoloured.
N1416 10 ch. Type **556** . . . . . . 1·25 15
N1417 15 ch. Sulphur-crested cockatoo . . . . 1·50 20
N1418 20 ch. Blyth's parakeet . . . 1·90 30
N1419 25 ch. Rainbow lory . . . . 2·25 35
N1420 30 ch. Budgerigar . . . . . 2·50 40

1975. New Buildings in Pyongyang. Multicoloured.
N1421 90 ch. Saesallim (formerly Sarguson) St. . . . . . . 1·50 40
N1422 1 wn. Type **557** . . . . . . 1·75 45
N1423 2 wn. Potonggang Hotel . . 2·75 60

558 White Peach Blossom

559 Sejongbong

1975. Blossoms of Flowering Trees. Multicoloured.
N1424 10 ch. Type **558** 40 10
N1425 15 ch. Red peach blossom 40 10
N1426 20 ch. Red plum blossom 60 15
N1427 25 ch. Apricot blossom . . 75 15
N1428 30 ch. Cherry blossom . . . 1·00 20

1975. Landscapes in the Diamond Mountains. Multicoloured.
N1429 5 ch. Type **559** 40 10
N1430 10 ch. Chonsondae 65 10
N1431 15 ch. Pisamun 85 10
N1432 25 ch. Manmulsang . . . . 1·10 20
N1433 30 ch. Chaehabong . . . . 1·25 20

560 Azalea

1975. Flowers of the Azalea Family. Multicoloured.
N1434 5 ch. Type **560** 50 10
N1435 10 ch. White azalea 50 10
N1436 15 ch. Wild rhododendron 60 10
N1437 20 ch. White rhododendron 60 15
N1438 25 ch. Rhododendron . . . 80 15
N1439 30 ch. Yellow rhododendron 1·10 20

561 Gliders

1975. Training for National Defence. Mult.
N1440 5 ch. Type **561** 60 10
N1441 5 ch. Radio-controlled model airplane 60 10
N1442 10 ch. "Free fall parachutist" (vert) 75 10
N1443 10 ch. Parachutist landing on target (vert) 75 10
N1444 20 ch. Parachutist with bouquet of flowers (vert) 1·10 15

562 Wild Apple

1975. Fruit Tree Blossom. Multicoloured.
N1446 10 ch. Type **562** 40 10
N1447 15 ch. Wild pear 40 10
N1448 20 ch. Hawthorn 50 15
N1449 25 ch. Chinese quince . . . 70 20
N1450 30 ch. Flowering quince . . 80 20

563 Torch of Juche

1975. 30th Anniv of Korean Workers' Party. Multicoloured.
N1451 2 ch. "Victory" and American graves 10 10
N1452 2 ch. Sunrise over Mt. Paekdu-san 10 10
N1453 5 ch. Type **563** 10 10
N1454 5 ch. Chollima Statue and sunset over Pyongyang 10 10
N1455 10 ch. Korean with Red Book 10 10
N1456 10 ch. Chollima Statue . . . 10 10
N1457 25 ch. Crowds and burning building 35 10
N1458 70 ch. Flowers and map of Korea 95 15

564 Welcoming Crowd

1975. 30th Anniv of Kim Il Sung's Return to Pyongyang.
N1460 **564** 20 ch. multicoloured . . 25 15

565 Workers holding "Juche" Torch

1975. 30th Anniv of "Rodong Simmun" (Journal of the Central Committee of the Worker's Party.)
N1461 **565** 10 ch. multicoloured . . 50 10

566 Hyonmu Gate

1975. Ancient Wall-Gates of Pyongyang. Multicoloured.
N1463 10 ch. Type **566** 10 10
N1464 10 ch. Taedong Gate . . . 10 10
N1465 15 ch. Potong Gate 20 10
N1466 20 ch. Chongum Gate . . . 35 15
N1467 30 ch. Chilsong Gate (vert) 45 25

567

1975. Views of Mt. Chilbo.

N1468	567	10 ch. multicoloured . .	40	10
N1469	–	10 ch. multicoloured . .	40	10
N1470	–	15 ch. multicoloured . .	65	10
N1471	–	20 ch. multicoloured . .	75	15
N1472	–	30 ch. multicoloured . .	85	20

DESIGNS: Nos. N1468/72, Various views.

568 Right-hand Section of Monument

1975. Historic Site of Revolution in Wangjaesan. Multicoloured.

N1473	10 ch. Type **568**	10	10
N1474	15 ch. Left-hand section of monument	20	10
N1475	25 ch. Centre section of monument	30	15
N1476	30 ch. Centre section, close up	40	20

No. N1475 is 38 × 60 mm and No. N1476, 60 × 38 mm.

569 Marchers with Flags

1976. 30th Anniv of Korean League of Socialist Working Youth. Multicoloured.

N1477	2 ch. Flags and Emblem . .	15	10
N1478	70 ch. Type **569**	90	40

570 Geese

1976. Ducks and Geese. Multicoloured.

N1479	10 ch. Type **570**	40	10
N1480	20 ch. "Perennial" duck . .	90	10
N1481	40 ch. Kwangpo duck . . .	1·60	20

571 "Oath"

1976. Korean Peoples Army (sculptural works). Multicoloured.

N1482	5 ch. Type **571**	10	10
N1483	10 ch. "Union of Officers with Men" (horiz)	15	10
N1484	10 ch. "This Flag to the Height"	15	10

572 "Rural Road at Evening"

1976. Modern Korean Paintings (5th series). Social Welfare. Multicoloured.

N1485	10 ch. Type **572**	60	10
N1486	15 ch. "Passing on Technique" (1970) . . .	70	10
N1487	25 ch. "Mother (and Child)" (1965)	85	15
N1488	30 ch. "Medical Examination at School" (1970) (horiz)	1·50	15
N1489	40 ch. "Lady Doctor of Village" (1970) (horiz) . .	1·75	20

573 Worker holding Text of Law

1976. 30th Anniv of Agrarian Reform Law.

N1490	573	10 ch. multicoloured . .	20	10

574 Telephones and Satellite

1976. Centenary of First Telephone Call. Multicoloured. With or without gum.

N1491	2 ch. Type **574**	40	10
N1492	5 ch. Satellite and antenna	40	10
N1493	10 ch. Satellite and telecommunications systems	40	10
N1494	15 ch. Telephone and linesman	1·10	10
N1495	25 ch. Satellite and map of receiving stations	1·50	15
N1496	40 ch. Satellite and cable-laying barge	1·75	20

575 Cosmos

1976. Flowers. Multicoloured.

N1498	5 ch. Type **575**	25	10
N1499	10 ch. Dahlia	25	10
N1500	20 ch. Zinnia	45	15
N1501	40 ch. China aster	70	25

576 Fruit and Products

1976. Pukchong Meeting of Korean Workers' Party Presidium. Multicoloured.

N1502	5 ch. Type **576**	75	10
N1503	10 ch. Fruit and orchard scene	75	10

577 "Pulgungi" Electric Locomotive

1976. Railway Locomotives. Multicoloured.

N1504	5 ch. Type **577**	40	10
N1505	10 ch. "Chaju" underground train	75	10
N1506	15 ch. "Saebyol" diesel locomotive	95	15

GUM. All the following stamps were issued with gum, except where otherwise stated.

578 Satellite

1976. Space Flight. With or without gum.

N1507	578	2 ch. multicoloured . .	15	10
N1508	–	5 ch. multicoloured . .	15	10
N1509	–	10 ch. multicoloured . .	20	10
N1510	–	15 ch. multicoloured . .	30	10
N1511	–	25 ch. multicoloured . .	45	15
N1512	–	40 ch. multicoloured . .	70	20

DESIGNS: 5 ch. to 40 ch. Various satellites and space craft.

579 Kim Il Sung beside Car

1976. Kim Il Sung's 64th Birthday.

N1514	579	10 ch. multicoloured . .	40	10

580 Bat and Ribbon

1976. 3rd Asian Table Tennis Championships. Multicoloured. Without gum.

N1516	5 ch. Type **580**	40	10
N1517	10 ch. Three women players with flowers	40	10
N1518	20 ch. Player defending . .	65	10
N1519	25 ch. Player making attacking shot	1·00	15

581 Kim Il Sung announcing Establishment of Association

1976. 40th Anniv of Association for the Restoration of the Fatherland. Without gum.

N1521	581	10 ch. multicoloured . .	10	10

582 Golden Pheasant

1976. Pheasants. Multicoloured. With or without gum.

N1522	2 ch. Type **582**	75	10
N1523	5 ch. Lady Amherst's pheasant	80	10
N1524	10 ch. Silver pheasant . . .	95	15
N1525	15 ch. Reeves's pheasant . .	1·10	25
N1526	25 ch. Temminck's tragopan	1·40	40
N1527	40 ch. Ringed-necked pheasant (albino)	1·75	65

583 Monument and Map of River

585 Bronze Medal (Hockey, Pakistan)

584 Running

1976. Potong River Monument. Without gum.

N1529	583	10 ch. brown & green	20	10

1976. Olympic Games, Montreal. Multicoloured.

N1530	2 ch. Type **584**	30	10
N1531	5 ch. Diving	30	10
N1532	10 ch. Judo	30	10
N1533	15 ch. Gymnastics	40	10
N1534	25 ch. Gymnastics	80	15
N1535	40 ch. Fencing	3·00	20

1976. Olympic Medal Winners (1st issue). Multicoloured.

N1537	2 ch. Type **585**	75	10
N1538	5 ch. Bronze medal (shooting, Rudolf Dollinger)	25	10
N1539	10 ch. Silver medal (boxing, Li Byong Uk)	25	15
N1540	15 ch. Silver medal (cycling, Daniel Morelon)	2·00	15
N1541	25 ch. Gold medal (marathon, Waldemar Cierpinski) . .	90	20
N1542	40 ch. Gold medal (boxing, Ku Yong Jo)	1·10	25

586 Boxing (Ku Yong Jo)

1976. Olympic Medal Winners (2nd issue). Multicoloured.

N1544	2 ch. Type **586**	25	10
N1545	5 ch. Gymnastics (Nadia Comaneci)	25	10
N1546	10 ch. Pole vaulting (Tadeusz Slusarki)	25	10
N1547	15 ch. Hurdling (Guy Drut)	30	10
N1548	20 ch. Cycling (Bernt Johansson)	2·50	15
N1549	40 ch. Football (East Germany)	1·50	20

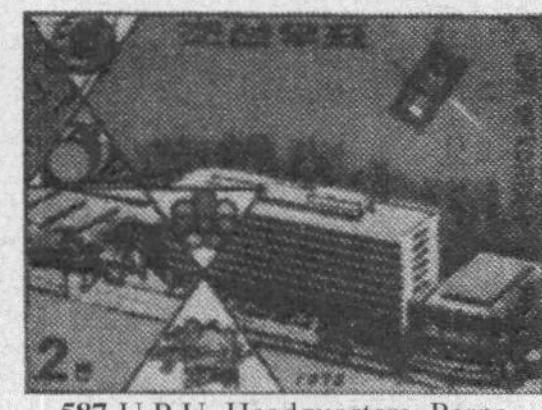
587 U.P.U. Headquarters, Berne

1976. International Festivities. Multicoloured.

N1551	2 ch. Type **587**	40	10
N1552	5 ch. Footballers (World Cup)	40	10
N1553	10 ch. Olympic Stadium	40	10
N1554	15 ch. Olympic Village	40	10
N1555	25 ch. Junk and satellite	70	20
N1556	40 ch. Satellites	75	20

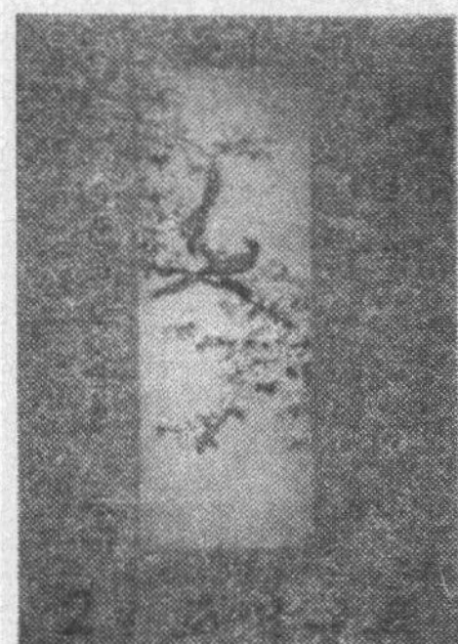
588 Azure-winged Magpies

1976. Embroidery. Multicoloured. With or without gum.

N1558	2 ch. Type **588**	1·25	15
N1559	5 ch. White magpie	90	15
N1560	10 ch. Roe deer	30	10
N1561	15 ch. Black-naped oriole and magnolias	1·40	15
N1562	25 ch. Fairy with flute (horiz)	70	15
N1563	40 ch. Tiger	1·60	40

589 Roman "5" and Flame

1976. 5th Non-aligned States' Summit Conference, Colombo. Without gum.

N1565	**589** 10 ch. multicoloured	10	10

590 Trophy and Certificate

1976. World Model Plane Championships (1975). Multicoloured. Without gum.

N1566	5 ch. Type **590**	20	10
N1567	10 ch. Trophy and medals	30	10
N1568	20 ch. Model airplane and emblem	45	10
N1569	40 ch. Model glider and medals	75	15

591 "Pulgungi" Diesel Shunting Locomotive

1976. Locomotives. Multicoloured.

N1570	2 ch. Type **591**	40	10
N1571	5 ch. "Saebyol" diesel locomotive	55	10
N1572	10 ch. "Saebyol" diesel shunting locomotive	65	10
N1573	15 ch. Electric locomotive	75	10
N1574	25 ch. "Kumsong" diesel locomotive	95	15
N1575	40 ch. "Pulgungi" electric locomotive	1·10	20

592 House of Culture

1976. House of Culture. Without gum.

N1577	**592** 10 ch. brown and black	15	10

593 Kim Il Sung visiting Tosongrang

1976. Revolutionary Activities of Kim Il Sung. Multicoloured.

N1578	2 ch. Type **593**	20	10
N1579	5 ch. Kim Il Sung visits pheasants	20	10
N1580	10 ch. Kim Il Sung on hilltop	25	10
N1581	15 ch. Kim Il Sung giving house to farmhand	30	10
N1582	25 ch. Kim Il Sung near front line	70	10
N1583	40 ch. Kim Il Sung walking in rain	70	15

594 Kim Il Sung with Union Members

1976. 50th Anniv of Down-with-Imperialism Union. Without gum.

N1585	**594** 20 ch. multicoloured	35	15

604 Searchlights and Kim Il Sung's Birthplace

605 Spring Costume

1977. New Year. Without gum.

N1589	**604** 10 ch. multicoloured	10	10

1977. National Costumes of Li Dynasty. Mult.

N1590	10 ch. Type **605** (postage)	45	10
N1591	15 ch. Summer costume	60	10
N1592	20 ch. Autumn costume	70	15
N1593	40 ch. Winter costume (air)	1·10	20

606 Two Deva Kings (Koguryo Dynasty)

1977. Korean Cultural Relics. Multicoloured.

N1594	2 ch. Type **606** (postage)	40	10
N1595	5 ch. Gold-copper decoration, Koguryo Dynasty	40	10
N1596	10 ch. Copper Buddha, Koryo Dynasty	60	10
N1597	15 ch. Gold-copper Buddha, Paekje Dynasty	70	10
N1598	25 ch. Gold crown, Koguryo Dynasty	85	15
N1599	40 ch. Gold-copper sun decoration, Koguryo Dynasty (horiz)	1·00	20
N1600	50 ch. Gold crown, Silla Dynasty (air)	1·10	35

607 Worker with Five-point Programme

1977. Five-point Programme for Remaking Nature. Without gum.

N1601	**607** 10 ch. multicoloured	20	10

608 Pine Branch and Map of Korea

1977. 60th Anniv of Korean National Association. Without gum.

N1602	**608** 10 ch. multicoloured	35	10

609 Championship Emblem and Trophy

1977. 34th World Table Tennis Championships. Multicoloured. Without gum.

N1603	10 ch. Type **609** (postage)	30	10
N1604	15 ch. Pak Yong Sun	40	10
N1605	20 ch. Pak Yong Sun with trophy	70	15
N1606	40 ch. Pak Yong Ok and Yang Ying (air)	1·10	20

610 Kim Il Sung founds Guerrilla Army at Mingyuegou

1977. Kim Il Sung's 65th Birthday. Multicoloured.

N1607	2 ch. Type **610**	10	10
N1608	5 ch. In command of army	10	10
N1609	10 ch. Visiting steel workers in Kangson	25	10
N1610	15 ch. Before battle	20	10
N1611	25 ch. In schoolroom	25	10
N1612	40 ch. Viewing bumper harvest	35	10

611 "Chollima 72" Trolleybus

1977. Trolleybuses. Without gum.

N1614	**611** 5 ch. blue, lilac & black	1·00	10
N1615	– 10 ch. red, green & blk	1·00	10

DESIGN: 10 ch. "Chollima 74" trolleybus.

612 Red Flag and Hand holding Rifle

1977. 45th Anniv of Korean People's Revolutionary Army. Without gum.

N1616	**612** 40 ch. red, yellow & blk	50	20

613 Proclamation and Watchtower

1977. 40th Anniv of Pochonbo Battle. Without gum.

N1617	**613** 10 ch. multicoloured	10	10

614 Koryo White Ware Teapot

1977. Korean Porcelain. Multicoloured.

N1618	10 ch. Type **614** (postage)	70	10
N1619	15 ch. White vase, Li Dynasty	85	10
N1620	20 ch. Celadon vase, Koryo Dynasty	1·00	10
N1621	40 ch. Celadon vase with lotus decoration, Koryo Dynasty (air)	1·50	15

615 Postal Transport

1977. Postal Services. Multicoloured. Without gum.

N1623	2 ch. Type **615**	1·00	15
N1624	10 ch. Postwoman delivering letter	40	10
N1625	30 ch. Mil Mi-8 helicopter	1·00	30
N1626	40 ch. Ilyushin Il-18 airliner and world map	1·10	30

616 "Rapala arata"

1977. Butterflies and Dragonflies. Multicoloured.

N1627	2 ch. Type **616** (postage)	60	10
N1628	5 ch. "Colias aurora"	80	10
N1629	10 ch. Poplar admiral	1·00	10
N1630	15 ch. "Anax partherope" (dragonfly)	1·50	10
N1631	25 ch. "Sympetrum pedemontanum" (dragonfly)	1·75	10
N1632	50 ch. "Papilio maackii" (air)	2·25	20

617 Grey Cat 618

1977. Cats. Multicoloured.

N1634	2 ch. Type **617**	1·25	10
N1635	10 ch. Black and white cat	1·60	15
N1636	25 ch. Ginger cat	2·75	20

1977. Dogs. Multicoloured.

N1638	5 ch. Type **618** (postage)	1·00	10
N1639	15 ch. Chow	1·25	10
N1640	50 ch. Pungsang dog (air)	1·75	15

619 Kim Il Sung and President Tito

1977. Visit of President Tito.

N1642 619 10 ch. multicoloured . . 10 10
N1643 15 ch. multicoloured . . 15 10
N1644 20 ch. multicoloured . . 20 10
N1645 40 vh. multicoloured . . 25 10

620 Girl and Symbols of Education

1977. 5th Anniv of 11-year Compulsory Education. Without gum.

N1646 620 10 ch. multicoloured . . 10 10

621 Chinese Mactra and Cobia
622 Students and "Theses"

1977. Shellfish and Fish. Multicoloured.

N1647 2 ch. Type 621 (postage) . . 45 10
N1648 5 ch. Bladder moon 65 10
N1649 10 ch. "Arca inflata" and pomfret 95 15
N1650 25 ch. Thomas's rapa whelk and grouper . . . . 1·40 40
N1651 50 ch. Thomas's rapa whelk and globefish (air) . . . . 2·10 75

1977. Kim Il Sung's "Theses on Socialist Education". Multicoloured. Without gum.

N1653 10 ch. Type 622 . . . . . . 20 10
N1654 20 ch. Students, crowd and text 30 10

623 "Juche" Torch
624 Jubilant Crowd

1977. Seminar on the Juche Idea. Multicoloured. Without gum.

N1655 2 ch. Type 623 . . . . . . 10 10
N1656 5 ch. Crowd and red book . . 10 10
N1657 10 ch. Chollima Statue and flags 10 10
N1658 15 ch. Handclasp and red flag on world map 10 10
N1659 25 ch. Map of Korea and anti-U.S. slogans 15 10
N1660 40 ch. Crowd and Mt. Paekdu-san 20 10

1977. Election of Deputies to Supreme People's Assembly. Without gum.

N1662 624 10 ch. multicoloured . . 10 10

625 Footballers

1977. World Cup Football Championship, Argentina. Without gum.

N1663 625 10 ch. multicoloured . . 90 15
N1664 – 15 ch. multicoloured . . 1·25 20
N1665 – 40 ch. multicoloured . . 2·00 25

DESIGNS: 15, 40 ch. Different football scenes.

626 Kim Il Sung with Rejoicing Crowds

1977. Re-election of Kim Il Sung. Without gum.

N1667 626 10 ch. multicoloured . . 20 10

627 Chollima Statue and Symbols of Communication

1977. 20th Anniv of Socialist Countries' Communication Organization. Without gum.

N1668 627 10 ch. multicoloured . . 20 10

638 Chollima Statue and City Skyline

1978. New Year. Without gum.

N1687 638 10 ch. multicoloured . . 20 10

639 Skater in 19th-century Costume
640 Post-rider and "Horse-ticket"

1978. Winter Olympic Games, Sapporo and Innsbruck. Multicoloured.

N1688 2 ch. Type 639 (postage) . . 50 10
N1699 5 ch. Skier 50 10
N1690 10 ch. Woman skater . . . 50 10
N1691 15 ch. Hunter on skis . . . 60 10
N1692 20 ch. Woman (in 19th-century costume) on skis . . 60 10
N1693 25 ch. Viking with long-bow . 2·75 15
N1694 40 ch. Skier (air) . . . . . 1·50 15

1978. Postal Progress. Multicoloured.

N1696 2 ch. Type 640 (postage) . . 40 10
N1697 5 ch. Postman on motor cycle 1·75 10
N1698 10 ch. Electric train and post-van . . . . 1·75 15
N1699 15 ch. Mail steamer and Mil Mi-8 helicopter . . . . . 1·00 15
N1700 25 ch. Tupolev Tu-154 jetliner and satellite 90 15
N1701 40 ch. Dove and U.P.U. headquarters (air) 60 15

641 Self-portrait
643 Show Jumping

642 "Chungsong" Tractor

1978. 400th Birth Anniv of Rubens.

N1703 641 2 ch. multicoloured . . 25 10
N1704 5 ch. multicoloured . . 25 10
N1705 40 ch. multicoloured . . 1·50 20

1978. Farm Machines. Without gum.

N1707 642 10 ch. red and black . . 45 10
N1708 – 10 ch. brown and black . 45 10

DESIGN: No. N1708, Sprayer.

1978. Olympic Games, Moscow (1980). Equestrian Events. Multicoloured.

N1709 2 ch. Type 643 . . . . . . 25 10
N1710 5 ch. Jumping bar 35 10
N1711 10 ch. Cross-country . . . 45 10
N1712 15 ch. Dressage 50 10
N1713 25 ch. Water splash 75 15
N1714 40 ch. Dressage (different) . 1·25 15

644 Soldier

1978. Korean People's Army Day. Multicoloured. Without gum.

N1716 5 ch. Type 644 . . . . . . 10 10
N1717 10 ch. Servicemen saluting . 10 10

645 "Mangyongbong" (Freighter)

1978. Korean Ships. Multicoloured.

N1718 2 ch. Type 645 (postage) . . 1·75 45
N1719 5 ch. "Hyoksin" (freighter) . 35 15
N1720 10 ch. "Chongchongang" (gas carrier) 35 15
N1721 30 ch. "Sonbong" (tanker) . 60 20
N1722 50 ch. "Taedonggang" (freighter) (air) . . . . . 1·10 40

646 Uruguayan Footballer

1978. World Cup Football Championship Winners. Multicoloured.

N1724 5 ch. Type 646 (postage) . . 50 10
N1725 10 ch. Italian player 50 10
N1726 15 ch. West German player . 50 10
N1727 25 ch. Brazilian player . . . 50 10
N1728 40 ch. English player . . . 1·00 10
N1729 50 ch. Hands holding World Cup (vert) (air) . . . . . 1·50 15

647 Footballers (1930 Winners, Uruguay)

1978. History of World Cup Football Championship. Multicoloured.

N1731 20 ch. Type 647 (postage) . . 85 15
N1732 20 ch. Italy, 1934 . . . . . 85 15
N1733 20 ch. France, 1938 . . . . 85 15
N1734 20 ch. Brazil, 1950 . . . . 85 15
N1735 20 ch. Switzerland, 1954 . . 85 15
N1736 20 ch. Sweden, 1958 . . . . 85 15
N1737 20 ch. Chile, 1962 . . . . . 85 15
N1738 20 ch. England, 1966 . . . 85 15
N1739 20 ch. Mexico, 1970 . . . . 85 15
N1740 20 ch. West Germany, 1974 . 85 15
N1741 20 ch. Argentina, 1978 . . . 85 15
N1742 50 ch. Footballers and emblem (air) 85 15

648 "Sea of Blood" (opera)

1978. Art from the Period of Anti-Japanese Struggle. Multicoloured.

N1744 10 ch. Type 648 . . . . . . 40 10
N1745 15 ch. Floral kerchief embroidered with map of Korea 50 10
N1746 20 ch. "Tansimjul" (maypole dance) 75 15

649 Red Flag and "7", Electricity and Coal

1978. Second 7 Year Plan. Multicoloured. Without gum.

N1748 5 ch. Type 649 . . . . . . 25 10
N1749 10 ch. Steel and non-ferrous metal 30 10
N1750 15 ch. Engineering and chemical fertilizer 35 10
N1751 30 ch. Cement and fishing . 70 10
N1752 50 ch. Grain and tideland reclamation 75 10

650 Gymnastics (Alfred Flatow)

1978. Olympic Games History and Medal-winners. Multicoloured.

N1753 20 ch. Type 650 . . . . . . 75 15
N1754 20 ch. Runners (Michel Theato) 75 15
N1755 20 ch. Runners (Wyndham Halswelle) 75 15
N1756 20 ch. Rowing (William Kinnear) 75 15
N1757 20 ch. Fencing (Paul Anspach) . . . . 1·50 25
N1758 20 ch. Runners (Ugo Frigerio) 75 15
N1759 20 ch. Runners (Ahmed El Quafi) 75 15
N1760 20 ch. Cycling (Robert Charpentier) . . . . . . 1·75 35
N1761 20 ch. Gymnastics (Josep Stalder) 75 15
N1762 20 ch. Boxing (Lazio Papp) 1·00 20
N1763 20 ch. Runners (Ronald Delany) 75 15
N1764 20 ch. High jump (Jolanda Balas) 75 15
N1765 20 ch. High jump (Valery Brumel) 75 15
N1766 20 ch. Gymnastics (Vera Caslavska) 75 15
N1767 20 ch. Rifle shooting (Li Ho Jun) 75 15

651 Douglas DC-8-63 and Comte Gentleman

1978. Airplanes. Multicoloured.
N1769 2 ch. Type **651** 70 10
N1770 10 ch. Ilyushin Il-62M and Avia BH-25 . . . . . . 80 10
N1771 15 ch. Douglas DC-8-63 and Savoia Marchetti S-71 . . 90 10
N1772 20 ch. Tupolev Tu-144 and Kalinin K-5 . . . . . . 1·10 10
N1773 25 ch. Tupolev Tu-154 and Antonov An-2 biplane . . 1·10 10
N1774 30 ch. Ilyushin Il-18 . . . . 1·10 10
N1775 40 ch. Concorde and Wibault 283 trimotor . . . . . . 2·25 40

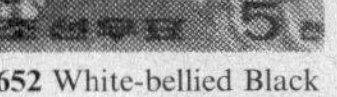

652 White-bellied Black Woodpecker and Map

653 Demonstrators and Korean Map

1978. White-bellied Black Woodpecker Preservation. Multicoloured.
N1777 5 ch. Type **652** 85 10
N1778 10 ch. Woodpecker and eggs 1·00 15
N1779 15 ch. Woodpecker feeding young . . . . 1·25 25
N1780 25 ch. Woodpecker feeding young (different) . . . . 1·60 40
N1781 50 ch. Adult woodpecker on tree trunk . . . . 2·50 80

1978. 30th Anniv of Democratic People's Republic of Korea. Multicoloured. Without gum.
N1783 10 ch. Type **653** 10 10
N1784 10 ch. Flag and soldiers . . 10 10
N1785 10 ch. Flag and "Juche" . . 10 10
N1786 10 ch. Red Flag 10 10
N1787 10 ch. Chollima Statue and city skyline 10 10
N1788 10 ch. "Juche" torch and men of three races 10 10

654 Cat and Pup

668 Red Flag and Pine Branch

655 Footballers

1978. Animal Paintings by Li Am. Multicoloured.
N1789 10 ch. Type **654** . . . . . 2·50 30
N1790 15 ch. Cat up a tree . . . . 2·50 30
N1791 40 ch. Wild geese . . . . . 2·50 30

1978. Argentina's Victory in World Cup Football Championship. Without gum.
N1792 **655** 10 ch. multicoloured . . 75 10
N1793 – 15 ch. multicoloured . . 85 15
N1794 – 25 ch. multicoloured . . 1·10 20
DESIGNS: 15, 25 ch. Different football scenes.

1979. New Year. Without gum.
N1812 **668** 10 ch. multicoloured . . 15 10

669 Kim Il Sung with Children's Corps Members, Maanshan

1979. International Year of the Child (1st issue). Multicoloured.

(a) Paintings of Kim Il Sung and children.
N1813 5 ch. Type **669** 15 10
N1814 10 ch. Kim Il Sung and Children's Corps members in classroom 25 10
N1815 15 ch. New Year gathering 30 10
N1816 20 ch. Kim Il Sung and children in snow 45 10
N1817 30 ch. Kim Il Sung examines children's schoolbooks (vert) 50 10

(b) Designs showing children
N1818 10 ch. Tug-of-war 15 10
N1819 15 ch. Dance "Growing up Fast" 40 15
N1820 20 ch. Children of many races and globe 40 10
N1821 25 ch. Children singing . . . 65 15
N1822 30 ch. Children in toy spaceships 40 10
See also Nos. N1907/17.

670 Rose

1979. Roses. Multicoloured.
N1824 1 wn. Red rose . . . . . .
N1825 3 wn. White rose . . . . .
N1826 5 wn. Type **670** . . . . .
N1827 10 wn. Deep pink rose . . .
See also Nos. N1837/42.

671 Warriors on Horseback

672 Red Guard and Industrial Skyline

1979. "The Story of Two Generals". Multicoloured. Without gum.
N1828 5 ch. Type **671** 20 10
N1829 10 ch. Farm labourer blowing feather 30 10
N1830 10 ch. Generals fighting on foot 30 10
N1831 10 ch. Generals on horseback 30 10

1979. 20th Anniv of Worker-Peasant Red Guards. Without gum.
N1832 **672** 10 ch. multicoloured . . 15 10

673 Clement-Bayard Airship "Fleurus"

1979. Airships. Multicoloured. Without gum.
N1833 10 ch. Type **673** . . . . . 1·25 15
N1834 20 ch. N.1 "Norge" . . . . 1·25 15

674 Crowd of Demonstrators

1979. 60th Anniv of 1st March Popular Uprising. Without gum.
N1836 **674** 10 ch. blue and red . . 15 10

1979. Roses. As Nos. N1824/7. Multicoloured.
N1837 5 ch. Type **670** (postage) . . 40 10
N1838 10 ch. As No. N1827 . . . 45 10
N1839 15 ch. As No. N1824 . . . 50 10
N1840 20 ch. Yellow rose 60 10
N1841 30 ch. As No. 1825 . . . . 70 10
N1842 50 ch. Deep pink rose (different) (air) 90 15

675 Table Tennis Trophy

676 Marchers with Red Flag

1979. 35th World Table Tennis Championship, Pyongyang. Multicoloured. With or without gum.
N1843 5 ch. Type **675** 20 10
N1844 10 ch. Women's doubles . . 20 10
N1845 15 ch. Women's singles . . 40 10
N1846 20 ch. Men's doubles . . . 60 10
N1847 30 ch. Men's singles 80 10

1979. Socialist Construction under Banner of Juche Idea. Multicoloured. Without gum.
N1849 5 ch. Type **676** 10 10
N1850 10 ch. Map of Korea . . . 10 10
N1851 10 ch. Juche torch 10 10

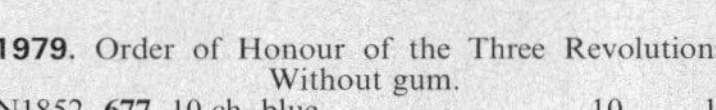

677 Badge

678 Emblem, Satellite orbiting Globe and Aerials

1979. Order of Honour of the Three Revolutions. Without gum.
N1852 **677** 10 ch. blue 10 10

1979. World Telecommunications Day. Without gum.
N1853 **678** 10 ch. multicoloured . . 25 10

679 Advancing Soldiers and Monument

1979. 40th Anniv of Battle in Musan Area. Without gum.
N1854 **679** 10 ch. mauve, light blue and blue 20 10

680 Exhibition Entrance

1979. International Friendship Exhibition. Without gum.
N1855 **680** 10 ch. multicoloured . . 10 10

681 "Peonies"

1979. 450th Death Anniv (1978) of Albrecht Durer (artist) (1st issue). Multicoloured.
N1856 15 ch. Type **681** 75 20
N1857 20 ch. "Columbines" . . . . 1·25 20
N1858 25 ch. "A Great Tuft of Grass" . . . . 1·25 20
N1859 30 ch. "Wing of a Bird" . . 1·75 40
See also No. N2012.

682 Fencing

1979. Olympic Games, Moscow (2nd issue). Multicoloured. With gum (10, 40 ch. only).
N1861 5 ch. Type **682** . . . . . 1·50 10
N1862 10 ch. Gymnastics 40 10
N1863 20 ch. Yachting 75 15
N1864 30 ch. Athletics 60 15
N1865 40 ch. Weightlifting 60 15

683 Hunting

1979. Horse-riding (people of Koguryo Dynasty). Multicoloured.
N1867 5 ch. Type **683** 65 10
N1868 10 ch. Archery contest . . . 65 10
N1869 15 ch. Man beating drum on horseback 25 10
N1870 20 ch. Man blowing horn 25 10
N1871 30 ch. Man and horse, armoured with chainmail 25 10
N1872 50 ch. Hawking (air) . . . . 2·00 15

684 Judo

685 Warrior's Costume

1979. Olympic Games, Moscow (3rd issue). Multicoloured. With gum (5, 15, 20, 30 ch. only).
N1873 5 ch. Type **684** 40 10
N1874 10 ch. Volleyball 40 10
N1875 15 ch. Cycling . . . . . . 1·50 25
N1876 20 ch. Basketball 60 15
N1877 25 ch. Canoeing 60 15
N1878 30 ch. Boxing 90 25
N1879 40 ch. Shooting 85 20

1979. Warrior Costumes of Li Dynasty.
N1881 **685** 5 ch. multicoloured . . 20 10
N1882 – 10 ch. multicoloured . . 20 10
N1883 – 15 ch. multicoloured . . 30 10
N1884 – 20 ch. multicoloured . . 45 10
N1885 – 30 ch. multicoloured . . 60 10
N1886 – 50 ch. multicoloured (air) 90 15
DESIGNS: 10 ch. to 50 ch. Different costumes.

686 Wrestling

687 Monument

1979. Olympic Games, Moscow (4th issue). Multicoloured.
N1887 10 ch. Type **686** 25 10
N1888 15 ch. Handball 30 10
N1889 20 ch. Archery . . . . . . 1·60 25
N1890 25 ch. Hockey . . . . . . 1·60 45
N1891 30 ch. Rowing 75 15
N1892 40 ch. Football . . . . . . 1·50 25

1979. Chongbong Monument. Without gum.
N1894 **687** 10 ch. multicoloured . . 20 10

688 Bottle-feeding Fawn

1979. Sika Deer. Multicoloured.

N1895	5 ch. Type **688** (postage)	20	10
N1896	10 ch. Doe and fawn	20	10
N1897	15 ch. Stag drinking from stream	20	15
N1898	20 ch. Stag	25	15
N1899	30 ch. Stag and doe	35	25
N1900	50 ch. Antlers and deer (air)	50	35

689 Moscovy Ducks

1979. Central Zoo, Pyongyang. Multicoloured.

N1901	5 ch. Type **689** (postage)	25	10
N1902	10 ch. Ostrich	50	10
N1903	15 ch. Common turkey	70	15
N1904	20 ch. Dalmatian pelican	80	20
N1905	30 ch. Vulturine guinea-fowl	95	30
N1906	50 ch. Mandarins (air)	1·50	45

690 Girl with Model Viking Ship

1979. International Year of the Child (2nd issue). Multicoloured.

N1907	20 ch. Type **690**	1·00	20
N1908	20 ch. Boys with model steam railway locomotive	2·50	85
N1909	20 ch. Boy with model biplane	1·25	20
N1910	20 ch. Boy with model spaceman	80	20
N1911	30 ch. Boy with model speedboat	1·50	30
N1912	30 ch. Boy sitting astride toy electric train	2·50	85
N1913	30 ch. Boy and model airplane	1·60	30
N1914	30 ch. Boy and flying spaceman	1·00	30

691 Footballers

1979. International Year of the Child (3rd issue). Multicoloured.

N1916	20 ch. Type **691**	1·25	20
N1917	30 ch. Footballers (different)	1·75	30

692 Japanese Stonefish

1979. Marine Life. Multicoloured.

N1919	20 ch. Type **692**	1·25	10
N1920	30 ch. Schlegel's redfish	1·40	20
N1921	50 ch. Northern sealion	1·75	30

693 Cross-country Skiing (Sergei Saveliev)

1979. Winter Olympic Games, Lake Placid. Multicoloured.

N1922	10 ch. Figure skating (Irina Rodnina and Aleksandr Zaitsev) (horiz)	40	15
N1923	20 ch. Ice hockey (Russian team) (horiz)	65	20
N1924	30 ch. Ladies 5 km relay (horiz)	1·10	25
N1925	40 ch. Type **693**	1·25	30
N1926	50 ch. Ladies' speed skating (Tatiana Averina)	1·50	35

694 The H7oney Bee collecting Nectar

1979. The Honey Bee. Multicoloured.

N1928	20 ch. Type **694**	1·40	10
N1929	30 ch. Bee and flowers	1·75	15
N1930	50 ch. Bee hovering over flower	2·00	25

695 Kim Jong Suk's Birthplace, Heoryong

1979. Historic Revolutionary Sites.

N1931	**695**	10 ch. multicoloured	15	10
N1932	–	10 ch. brown, blue & blk	15	10

DESIGN: No. N1932, Sinpa Revolutionary Museum.

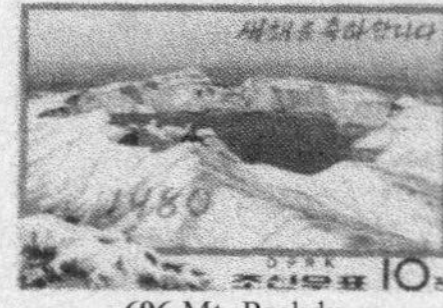
696 Mt. Paekdu

1980. New Year.

N1933	**696**	10 ch. multicoloured	55	10

697 Student and Books

1980. Studying.

N1934	**697**	10 ch. multicoloured	25	10

698 Conveyor Belt

1980. Unryul Mine Conveyor Belt.

N1935	**698**	10 ch. multicoloured	55	10

699 Children of Three Races

1980. International Day of the Child. Multicoloured.

N1936	10 ch. Type **699**	30	10
N1937	10 ch. Girl dancing to accordion	50	10
N1938	10 ch. Children in fairground airplane	40	10
N1939	10 ch. Children as astronauts	30	10
N1940	10 ch. Children on tricycles	1·25	30
N1941	10 ch. Children with toy diesel train	1·75	45
N1942	10 ch. "His loving care for the children, future of the fatherland" ($59\frac{1}{2} \times 38$ mm)	30	10

700 Monument

1980. Chongsan-ri Historic Site. Multicoloured.

N1944	5 ch. Type **700**	10	10
N1945	10 ch. Meeting place of the General Membership	15	10

701 Monument

1980. Monument marking Kim Jong Suk's Return.

N1946	**701**	10 ch. multicoloured	15	10

702 Vasco Nunez de Balboa

1980. Conquerors of the Earth. Multicoloured.

N1947	10 ch. Type **702**	50	10
N1948	20 ch. Francisco de Orellana	75	20
N1949	30 ch. Haroun Tazieff	1·00	35
N1950	40 ch. Edmund Hillary and Sherpa Tenzing	1·50	45

703 Museum

1980. Ryongpo Revolutionary Museum.

N1952	**703**	10 ch. blue and black	20	10

704 Rowland Hill and Stamps

1980. Death Centenary (1979) of Sir Rowland Hill. Multicoloured.

N1953	30 ch. Type **704**	3·50	75
N1954	50 ch. Rowland Hill and stamps (different)	3·50	75

705 North Korean Red Cross Flag

1980. World Red Cross Day. Multicoloured.

N1955	10 ch. Type **705**	70	20
N1956	10 ch. Henri Dunant (founder)	70	20
N1957	10 ch. Nurse and child	70	20
N1958	10 ch. Polikarpov Po-2 biplane and ship	1·00	25
N1959	10 ch. Mil Mi-4 helicopter	1·00	25
N1960	10 ch. Children playing at nurses	70	20
N1961	10 ch. Red Cross Map over Korea and forms of transport	3·50	60

706 Fernando Magellan

1980. Conquerors of the Sea. Multicoloured.

N1963	10 ch. Type **706**	1·75	25
N1964	20 ch. Fridtjof Nansen	1·75	25
N1965	30 ch. Auguste and Jacques Piccard	2·25	25
N1966	40 ch. Jacques-Yves Cousteau	3·00	55

707 Korean Stamps and Penny Black

1980. "London 1980" International Stamp Exhibition. Multicoloured.

N1968	10 ch. Type **707** (postage)	2·00	40
N1969	20 ch. Korean cover and British Guiana 1 c. black and red	2·00	30
N1970	30 ch. Early Korean stamp and modern cover	2·00	40
N1971	50 ch. Korean stamps	2·50	35
N1972	40 ch. Korean stamp and miniature sheet (air)	1·60	35

708 Wright Brothers

1980. Conquerors of Sky and Space. Multicoloured.

N1974	10 ch. Type **708**	75	15
N1975	20 ch. Louis Bleriot	1·00	25
N1976	30 ch. Anthony Fokker	1·50	40
N1977	40 ch. Secondo Campini and Sir Frank Whittle	2·00	45

709 Space Station on Planet   710 Flag and Banners

1980. Conquerors of the Universe. Multicoloured.

N1979 10 ch. Orbiting space station . . 20 10
N1980 20 ch. Type **709** 25 20
N1981 30 ch. Prehistoric animals and spaceships 90 35
N1982 40 ch. Prehistoric animals and birds and spaceship . . . 1·10 45

1980. 25th Anniv of General Association of Korean Residents in Japan (Chongryon).

N1984 **710** 10 ch. multicoloured . . 20 10

711 Hospital

1980. Pyongyang Maternity Hospital.

N1985 **711** 10 ch. blue, pur & blk 45 15

712 Health Centre

1980. Changgangwon Health Centre, Pyongyang.

N1986 **712** 2 ch. black and blue . . 25 10

713 Hand holding Rifle   714 Workers' Hostel, Samjiyon

1980. 50th Anniv of Revolutionary Army.

N1987 **713** 10 ch. multicoloured . . 25 10

1980.

N1988 **714** 10 ch. brown, bl & blk 30 10
N1989 – 10 ch. black and green 50 20
N1990 – 10 ch. black and red . . 50 20
N1991 – 10 ch. black and yellow 50 20
N1992 – 10 ch. multicoloured . . 30 10
N1993 – 10 ch. multicoloured . . 30 10
N1994 – 10 ch. multicoloured . . 1·00 35
N1995 – 10 ch. green and black 75 25
N1996 – 10 ch. grey, blue & blk 3·50 60
N1997 – 10 ch. multicoloured . . 4·00 60

DESIGNS: No. N1989, "Taedonggang" rice transplanter; N1990, "Chongsan-ri" rice harvester; N1991, Maize harvester; N1992, Revolutionary building, Songmun-ri; N1993, Revolutionary building, Samhwa; N1994, Sundial of 1438; N1995, 16th-century "turtle" ship; N1996, Pungsan dog; N1997, Japanese quail.

715 Party Emblem

1980. 6th Korean Workers' Party Congress. Multicoloured.

N1998 10 ch. Type **715** 15 10
N1999 10 ch. Students and Laurel leaf on globe 15 10
N2000 10 ch. Group with accordion 45 15
N2001 10 ch. Group with banner, microscope, book and trophy 25 10
N2002 10 ch. Worker with book and flag 75 25
N2003 10 ch. Worker with spanner and flag 75 25
N2004 10 ch. Marchers with torch and flags 15 10
N2005 10 ch. Emblem, marchers and map 20 10

716 Dribbling Ball

1980. World Cup Football Championship, 1978–1982. Multicoloured.

N2007 20 ch. Type **716** . . . . . . 2·50 60
N2008 30 ch. Tackle . . . . 3·00 80

717 Irina Rodnina and Aleksandr Zaitsev

1980. Winter Olympic Gold Medal Winners.

N2010 **717** 20 ch. multicoloured . . 4·00 1·75

718 "Soldier with Horse"   719 Kepler, Astrolabe and Satellites

1980. 450th Death Anniv (1978) of Albrecht Durer (artist) (2nd issue).

N2012 **718** 20 ch. multicoloured . . 5·00 1·50

1980. 350th Death Anniv of Johannes Kepler (astronomer).

N2014 **719** 20 ch. multicoloured . . 2·50 90

720 German 1 m. and Russian 30 k. Zeppelin Stamps

1980. 3rd International Stamp Fair, Essen. Mult.

N2016 10 ch. Type **720** 85 25
N2017 20 ch. German 2 m. and Russian 35 k. Zeppelin stamps . . . . 1·75 45
N2018 30 ch. German 4 m. and Russian 1 r. Zeppelin stamps . . . . 2·50 65

721 Shooting (Aleksandr Melentev)

1980. Olympic Medal Winners. Multicoloured.

N2020 10 ch. Type **721** 30 15
N2021 20 ch. Cycling (Robert Dill-Bundi) . . . . 3·25 75
N2022 25 ch. Gymnastics (Stoyan Deltchev) 50 25
N2023 30 ch. Wrestling (Chang Se Hong and Li Ho Pyong) 50 25
N2024 35 ch. Weightlifting (Ho Bong Chol) 50 25
N2025 40 ch. Running (Marita Koch) 50 30
N2026 50 ch. Modern Pentathlon (Anatoli Starostin) . . . 70 35

722 Tito   723 Convair CV 340 Airliner

1980. President Tito of Yugoslavia Commemoration.

N2028 **722** 20 ch. multicoloured . . 30 10

1980. 25th Anniv of First Post-War Flight of Lufthansa.

N2029 **723** 20 ch. multicoloured . . 4·75 1·75

724 Early Steam Locomotive

1980. 150th Anniv of Liverpool–Manchester Railway.

N2031 **724** 20 ch. multicoloured . . 5·00 1·75

725 Steam and Electric Locomotives

1980. Centenary of First Electric Train.

N2033 **725** 20 ch. multicoloured . . 5·00 1·75

726 Hammarskjold

1980. 75th Birth Anniv of Dag Hammarskjold (Former Secretary General of United Nations).

N2035 **726** 20 ch. multicoloured . . 2·50 1·25

727 Bobby Fischer and Boris Spassky

1980. World Chess Championship, Merano.

N2037 **727** 20 ch. multicoloured . . 5·50 1·75

728 Stolz

1980. Birth Centenary of Robert Stolz (composer).

N2039 **728** 20 ch. multicoloured . . 2·50 75

729 Chollima Statue   730 Russian Fairy Tale

1981. New Year. Without gum.

N2041 **729** 10 ch. multicoloured . . 25 10

1981. International Year of the Child (1979) (4th issue). Fairy Tales. Multicoloured.

N2042 10 ch. Type **730** . . . . . . 1·10 30
N2043 10 ch. Icelandic tale . . . . 1·10 30
N2044 10 ch. Swedish tale . . . . 1·10 30
N2045 10 ch. Irish tale . . . . . . 1·40 30
N2046 10 ch. Italian tale . . . . . 1·10 30
N2047 10 ch. Japanese tale . . . . 1·10 30
N2048 10 ch. German tale . . . . 1·10 30

731 Changgwang Street

1981. Changgwang Street, Pyongyang.

N2050 **731** 10 ch. multicoloured . . 35 10

732 Footballers

1981. World Cup Football Championship, Spain (1982) (1st issue). Multicoloured.

N2051 10 ch. Type **732** . . . . . . 2·25 45
N2052 20 ch. Hitting ball past defender . . . . 2·25 45
N2053 30 ch. Disputing possession of ball . . . . 2·25 45

See also Nos. N2055/9 and N2201/6.

733 Map, Emblem and World Cup

1981. World Cup Football Championship, Spain (1982) (2nd issue). Multicoloured.

N2055 10 ch. Type **733** . . . . . . 1·50 30
N2056 15 ch. Footballers . . . . . . 1·50 30
N2057 20 ch. Heading ball . . . . 1·50 30
N2058 25 ch. Footballers (different) 1·50 30
N2059 30 ch. Footballers (different) 1·50 30

734 Workers with Book and Marchers with Banner

1981. Implementation of Decision of the 6th Koreans' Party Congress. Multicoloured.

N2061 2 ch. Type **734** 10 10
N2062 10 ch. Worker with book . . 10 10
N2063 10 ch. Workers and industrial plant 25 10
N2064 10 ch. Electricity and coal (horiz) . . . . 1·25 25
N2065 10 ch. Steel and non-ferrous metals (horiz) 25 10

N2066 10 ch. Cement and fertilizers (horiz) 25 10
N2067 30 ch. Fishing and fabrics (horiz) 35 10
N2068 40 ch. Grain and harbour (horiz) 25 10
N2069 70 ch. Clasped hands . . . 20 10
N2070 1 w. Hand holding torch . . 30 15

735 Footballers

1981. Gold Cup Football Championship, Uruguay.
N2071 **735** 20 ch. multicoloured . . 2·50 75

736 Dornier Do-X Flying Boat

1981. "Naposta '81" International Stamp Exhibition, Stuttgart. Multicoloured.
N2073 10 ch. Type **736** . . . . . . 2·75 50
N2074 20 ch. Airship LZ-120 "Bodensee" . . . . . . 2·75 50
N2075 30 ch. "Gotz von Berlichingen" . . . . . 1·50 40

737 Telecommunications Equipment

1981. World Telecommunications Day.
N2077 **737** 10 ch. multicoloured . . . 1·75 20

738 "Iris pseudacorus"

1981. Flowers. Multicoloured.
N2078 10 ch. Type **738** . . . . . . 1·00 15
N2079 20 ch. "Iris pallasii" . . . . 1·25 20
N2080 30 ch. "Gladiolus gandavensis" . . . . . . 1·60 30

739 Austrian "WIPA 1981" and Rudolf Kirchschlager Stamps

1981. "WIPA 1981" International Stamp Exhibition, Vienna. Multicoloured.
N2081 20 ch. Type **739** . . . . . . 1·90 60
N2082 30 ch. Austrian Maria Theresa and Franz Joseph stamps . 2·50 80

MORE DETAILED LISTS
are given in the Stanley Gibbons Catalogues referred to in the country headings.
For lists of current volumes see Introduction.

740 Rings Exercise

741 Armed Workers

1981. Centenary of International Gymnastic Federation. Multicoloured.
N2084 10 ch. Type **740** 50 20
N2085 15 ch. Horse exercise 60 20
N2086 20 ch. Backwards somersault 80 20
N2087 25 ch. Floor exercise 90 25
N2088 30 ch. Exercise with hoop 1·10 25

1981. 50th Anniv of Mingyuehgou Meeting.
N2090 **741** 10 ch. multicoloured . . 20 10

742 Farm Building, Sukchon

1981. 20th Anniv of Agricultural Guidance System and Taean Work System.
N2091 **742** 10 ch. green, black and gold 20 10
N2092 – 10 ch. blue, black and gold 20 10
DESIGN: No. N2092, Taean Revolutionary Museum.

743 Woman and Banner

1981. 55th Anniv of Formation of Women's Anti-Japanese Association.
N2093 **743** 5 wn. multicoloured . . 2·75 75

743a Scene from Opera

1981. 10th Anniv of "Sea of Blood" (opera).
N2094 **743a** 10 wn. multicoloured

744 Joan of Arc

1981. 550th Death Anniv of Joan of Arc. Multicoloured.
N2095 10 ch. Type **744** . . . . . . 2·00 50
N2096 10 ch. Archangel Michael 2·25 50
N2097 70 ch. Joan of Arc in armour 2·25 50

745 Torch, Mountains and Flag

1981. 55th Anniv of Down with Imperialism Union.
N2099 **745** 1 wn. 50 multicoloured 40 20

746 "Young Girl by the Window"

1981. 375th Birth Anniv of Rembrandt (artist). Multicoloured.
N2100 10 ch. Type **746** 70 25
N2101 20 ch. "Rembrandt's Mother" 1·50 45
N2102 30 ch. "Saskia van Uylenburgh" . . . . . . 2·00 70
N2103 40 ch. "Pallas Athene" . . . 2·50 90

747 Emblem and Banners over Pyongyang

1981. Symposium of Non-Aligned Countries on Food Self-Sufficiency, Pyongyang. Multicoloured.
N2105 10 ch. Type **747** 20 10
N2106 50 ch. Harvesting 50 10
N2107 90 ch. Factories, tractors and marchers with banner . . 70 15

748 St. Paul's Cathedral

1981. Wedding of Prince of Wales (1st issue). Multicoloured.
N2108 10 ch. Type **748** . . . . . . 1·40 35
N2109 20 ch. Great Britain Prince of Wales Investiture stamp 1·40 35
N2110 30 ch. Lady Diana Spencer 1·40 35
N2111 40 ch. Prince Charles in military uniform . . . . 1·40 35
See also Nos. N2120/3.

749 "Four Philosophers" (detail)

1981. Paintings by Rubens. Multicoloured.
N2113 10 ch. Type **749** 40 20
N2114 15 ch. "Portrait of Helena Fourment" 60 25
N2115 20 ch. "Portrait of Isabella Brandt" 90 25
N2116 25 ch. "Education of Maria de Medici" . . . . 1·10 30
N2117 30 ch. "Helena Fourment and her Child" . . . . 1·40 35
N2118 40 ch. "Helena Fourment in her Wedding Dress" . . . 1·75 40

750 Royal Couple

1981. Wedding of Prince of Wales (2nd issue). Multicoloured.
N2120 10 ch. Type **750** . . . . . . 1·75 45
N2121 20 ch. Couple on balcony after wedding . . . . 1·75 45
N2122 30 ch. Couple outside St. Paul's Cathedral . . . . 1·75 45
N2123 70 ch. Full-length wedding portrait of couple . . . . 1·75 45

751 Rowland Hill and Stamps

1981. "Philatokyo '81" International Stamp Exhibition. Multicoloured.
N2125 10 ch. Korean 2 ch. Seminar on Juche Idea stamp (41 × 29 mm) 75 20
N2126 10 ch. Korean 10 and 70 ch. stamps (41 × 29 mm) . . . 2·00 75
N2127 10 ch. Type **751** . . . . . . 2·00 75
N2128 20 ch. Korean Fairy Tale stamps . . . . 1·75 40
N2129 30 ch. Japanese stamps . . . 3·00 90

752 League Members and Flag

1981. Seventh League of Socialist Working Youth Congress, Pyongyang.
N2131 **752** 10 ch. multicoloured . . 20 10
N2132 80 ch. multicoloured . . 60 10

753 Government Palace, Sofia, Bulgarian Arms and Khan Asparuch

1981. 1300th Anniv of Bulgarian State.
N2133 **753** 10 ch. multicoloured . . 25 10

754 Dimitrov

1981. Birth Centenary of Georgi Dimitrov (Bulgarian statesman).
N2134 **754** 10 ch. multicoloured . . 25 10

755 Emblem, Boeing 747-200, City Hall and Mercedes "500"

1981. "Philatelia '81" International Stamp Fair, Frankfurt-am-Main.
N2135 **755** 20 ch. multicoloured . . 2·50 35

756 Concorde, Airship "Graf Zeppelin" and Count Ferdinand von Zeppelin

1981. "Philexfrance 82" International Stamp Exhibition, Paris. Multicoloured. (a) As T **756**.
N2136 10 ch. Type **756** . . . . . . 2·75 40
N2137 20 ch. Concorde, Breguet Provence airliner and Santos-Dumont's biplane "14 bis" . . . . . . 3·25 75
N2138 30 ch. "Mona Lisa" (Leonardo da Vinci) and stamps . . . . 1·75 30

(b) Size 32 × 53 mm.
N2140 10 ch. Hotel des Invalides, Paris . . . . 1·00 45
N2141 20 ch. President Mitterrand of France . . . . 1·00 45
N2142 30 ch. International Friendship Exhibition building . . . . 1·00 45
N2143 70 ch. Kim Il Sung . . . . 1·00 45

757 Rising Sun **758** Emblem and Flags

1982. New Year.
N2144 **757** 10 ch. multicoloured . . 30 10

1982. "Prospering Korea". Multicoloured.
N2145 2 ch. Type **758** 15 10
N2146 10 ch. Industry 25 10
N2147 10 ch. Agriculture 25 10
N2148 10 ch. Mining 45 10
N2149 10 ch. Arts 25 10
N2150 10 ch. Al Islet lighthouse, Uam-ri . . . . 2·50 40
N2151 40 ch. Buildings 50 15

759 "The Hair-do"

1982. Birth Centenary of Pablo Picasso (artist). Multicoloured.
N2152 10 ch. Type **759** 75 20
N2153 10 ch. "Paulo on a donkey" 1·75 35
N2154 20 ch. "Woman leaning on Arm" 90 25
N2155 20 ch. "Harlequin" . . . . 1·75 35
N2156 25 ch. "Child with Pigeon" 1·90 50
N2157 25 ch. "Reading a Letter" 1·75 35
N2158 35 ch. "Portrait of Gertrude Stein" . . . . 1·50 30
N2159 35 ch. "Harlequin" (different) 1·75 35
N2160 80 ch. "Minotaur" . . . . 1·75 35
N2161 90 ch. "Mother with Child" 1·75 35

760 Fireworks over Pyongyang

1982. Kim Il Sung's 70th Birthday. Multicoloured.
N2163 10 ch. Kim Il Sung's birthplace, Mangyongdae 20 10
N2164 10 ch. Type **760** 20 10
N2165 10 ch. "The Day will dawn on downtrodden Korea" . . 20 10
N2166 10 ch. Signalling start of Pochonbo Battle 20 10
N2167 10 ch. Kim Il Sung starting Potong River project . . 20 10
N2168 10 ch. Embracing bereaved children 20 10
N2169 10 ch. Kim Il Sung as Supreme Commander 20 10
N2170 10 ch. "On the Road of Advance" 20 10
N2171 10 ch. Kim Il Sung kindling flame of Chollima Movement, Kansong Steel Plant 75 25
N2172 10 ch. Kim Il Sung talking to peasants 20 10
N2173 10 ch. Kim Il Sung fixing site of reservoir 30 10
N2174 20 ch. Kim Il Sung visiting Komdok Valley 75 25
N2175 20 ch. Kim Il Sung visiting Red Flag Company . . . 20 10
N2176 20 ch. Kim Il Sung teaching Juche farming methods 20 10
N2177 20 ch. Kim Il Sung visiting iron works 35 10
N2178 20 ch. Kim Il Sung talking with smelters 35 10
N2179 20 ch. Kim Il Sung at chemical plant 45 10
N2180 20 ch. Kim Il Sung with fishermen 40 10
Nos. 2165/80 are horiz designs.

761 Soldier saluting

1982. 50th Anniv of People's Army.
N2182 **761** 10 ch. multicoloured . . 25 10

762 "The Bagpiper" (Durer) **763** Surveyors

1982. 4th Essen International Stamp Fair.
N2183 **762** 30 ch. multicoloured . . 3·75 40

1982. Implementation of Four Nature-remaking Tasks.
N2184 **763** 10 ch. multicoloured . . 45 10

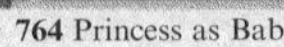
764 Princess as Baby **765** Tower of the Juche Idea, Pyongyang

1982. 21st Birthday of Princess of Wales.
N2185 **764** 10 ch. multicoloured . . 30 20
N2186 – 20 ch. multicoloured . . 65 35
N2187 – 30 ch. multicoloured . . 75 45
N2188 – 50 ch. multicoloured . . 1·00 40
N2189 – 60 ch. multicoloured . . 1·00 40
N2190 – 70 ch. multicoloured . . 1·00 40
N2191 – 80 ch. multicoloured . . 1·00 40
DESIGNS: 20 to 80 ch. Princess at various ages.

1982.
2193 **765** 2 wn. multicoloured . . . 1·25 30
2194 – 3 wn. orange and black . . 1·75 40
DESIGN: (26 × 38 mm) 3 wn. Arch of Triumph.

766 Tiger

1982. Tigers.
N2195 **766** 20 ch. multicoloured . . 1·25 35
N2196 – 30 ch. multicoloured . . 1·90 35
N2197 – 30 ch. mult (horiz) . . . 2·75 45
N2198 – 40 ch. mult (horiz) . . . 2·75 45
N2199 – 80 ch. mult (horiz) . . . 2·75 45
DESIGNS: 30 to 80 ch. Tigers.

767 Group 1 Countries

1982. World Cup Football Championship, Spain (3rd issue). Multicoloured.
N2201 10 ch. Type **767** 45 20
N2202 20 ch. Group 2 countries . . 1·00 25
N2203 30 ch. Group 3 countries . . 1·40 30
N2204 40 ch. Group 4 countries . . 1·75 40
N2205 50 ch. Group 5 countries . . 2·00 50
N2206 60 ch. Group 6 countries . . 2·25 50

768 Rocket Launch **769** Charlotte von Stein

1982. The Universe. Multicoloured.
N2208 10 ch. Type **768** . . . . . . 1·25 40
N2209 20 ch. Spaceship over globe 1·25 40
N2210 80 ch. Spaceship between globe and moon . . . . 1·50 40

1982. 150th Death Anniv of Johann von Goethe (writer). Multicoloured.
N2212 10 ch. Type **769** 50 25
N2213 10 ch. Goethe's mother . . 1·50 45
N2214 20 ch. Goethe's sister . . 75 30
N2215 20 ch. Angelika Kauffmann 1·50 45
N2216 25 ch. Charlotte Buff . . . 90 35
N2217 25 ch. Anna Amalia . . . . 1·50 45
N2218 35 ch. Lili Schonemann . . 1·25 40
N2219 35 ch. Charlotte von Lengefeld . . . . 1·50 45
N2220 80 ch. Goethe . . . . . . 1·60 45

770 Player holding aloft World Cup

1982. World Cup Football Championship Results. Multicoloured.
N2222 20 ch. Type **770** . . . . . . 1·25 30
N2223 30 ch. Group of players with World Cup . . . . . . 1·75 50
N2224 30 ch. Type **770** . . . . . . 2·50 65
N2225 40 ch. As No. N2203 . . . 2·50 65
N2226 80 ch. King Juan Carlos of Spain and two players with World Cup . . . . . . 2·50 65

771 Princess and Prince William of Wales

1982. 1st Wedding Anniv of Prince and Princess of Wales.
N2228 **771** 30 ch. multicoloured . . 2·75 90

772 Royal Couple with Prince William

1982. Birth of Prince William of Wales. Multicoloured.
N2230 10 ch. Couple with Prince William (different) . . . 75 25
N2231 10 ch. Princess of Wales holding bouquet . . . . 1·50 75
N2232 20 ch. Couple with Prince William (different) . . . 90 30
N2233 20 ch. Prince Charles carrying baby, and Princess of Wales 1·50 75
N2234 30 ch. Type **772** . . . . . . 1·00 40
N2235 30 ch. Prince Charles carrying baby, and Princess of Wales (different) . . . . 1·50 75
N2236 40 ch. Princess with baby 1·40 45
N2237 40 ch. Prince and Princess of Wales (horiz) . . . . . . 2·40 95
N2238 50 ch. Princess with baby (different) . . . . 1·75 50
N2239 50 ch. Prince and Princess of Wales in evening dress (horiz) . . . . 2·40 95
N2240 80 ch. Couple with Prince William (different) . . . 1·50 75
N2241 80 ch. Prince Charles holding baby, and Princess of Wales (horiz) . . . . 2·40 95

773 Airship "Nulli Secundus II", 1908

1982. Bicentenary of Manned Flight (1st issue). Multicoloured.
N2243 10 ch. Type **773** . . . . . . 1·25 40
N2244 10 ch. Pauley and Durs Egg's dirigible balloon "The Dolphin", 1818 . . . . . 2·50 60
N2245 20 ch. Tissandier Brothers' airship, 1883 . . . . . . 1·50 50
N2246 20 ch. Guyton de Morveau's balloon with oars, 1784 2·50 60
N2247 30 ch. Parseval airship PL-VII, 1912 . . . . . . 2·00 60
N2248 30 ch. Sir George Cayley's airship design, 1837 . . . 2·50 60
N2249 40 ch. Count de Lennox's balloon "Eagle", 1834 . . 2·25 60
N2250 40 ch. Camille Vert's balloon "Poisson Volant", 1859 . 2·50 60
N2251 80 ch. Dupuy de Lome's airship, 1872 . . . . . . 2·50 60

774 "Utopic Balloon Post" (Balthasar Antoine Dunker)

1982. Bicentenary of Manned Flight (2nd issue). Multicoloured.

N2253 10 ch. Type **774** . . . . . . 1·50 40
N2254 10 ch. Montgolfier balloon at Versailles, 1783 . . . . . 3·00 60
N2255 20 ch. "... and they fly into heaven and have no wings ..." . . . . 2·00 50
N2256 20 ch. Montgolfier Brothers' balloon, 1783 . . . . . 3·00 60
N2257 30 ch. Pierre Testu-Brissy's balloon ascent on horseback, 1798 . . . . 2·50 60
N2258 30 ch. Charles's hydrogen balloon landing at Nesle, 1783 . . . . 3·00 60
N2259 40 ch. Gaston Tissandier's test flight of "Zenith", 1875 . . 3·00 60
N2260 40 ch. Blanchard and Jeffries' balloon flight over English Channel, 1785 . . . . . 3·00 60
N2261 80 ch. Henri Giffard's balloon "Le Grand Ballon Captif" at World Fair, 1878 . . . 3·00 60

775 Turtle with Scroll

1982. Tale of the Hare. Multicoloured.

N2263 10 ch. Type **775** . . . . 1·00 15
N2264 20 ch. Hare riding on turtle 1·50 20
N2265 30 ch. Hare and turtle before Dragon King . . . . . . 1·75 30
N2266 40 ch. Hare back on land 2·25 40

776 Flag, Red Book and City　　**777** Tower of Juche Idea

1982. 10th Anniv of Socialist Constitution.

N2267 **776** 10 ch. multicoloured . . 25 10

1983. New Year.

N2268 **777** 10 ch. multicoloured . . 15 10

778 Children reading "Saenal"

1983. 55th Anniv of "Saenal" Newspaper.

N2269 **778** 10 ch. multicoloured . . 50 10

779 "Man in Oriental Costume"

1983. Paintings by Rembrandt. Multicoloured.

N2270 10 ch. Type **779** 60 20
N2271 10 ch. "Child with dead Peacocks" (detail) . . . . 2·00 40
N2272 20 ch. "The Noble Slav" . . 1·25 30
N2273 20 ch. "Old Man in Fur Hat" 2·00 40
N2274 30 ch. "Dr. Tulp's Anatomy Lesson" (detail) . . . . 3·25 50
N2275 30 ch. "Portrait of a fashionable Couple" . . . 2·00 40
N2276 40 ch. "Two Scholars disputing" . . . . 1·50 35
N2277 40 ch. "Woman with Child" 2·00 40
N2278 80 ch. "Woman holding an Ostrich Feather Fan" . . 2·00 40

780 Airships "Gross Basenach II" and "Graf Zepplin" over Cologne

1983. "Luposta" International Air Mail Exhibition, Cologne. Multicoloured.

N2280 30 ch. Type **780** . . . . . . 3·00 90
N2281 40 ch. Parsevel airship PL-II over Cologne . . . . . . 3·00 90

781 Banner and Monument

1983. 50th Anniv of Wangjaesan Meeting.

N2283 **781** 10 ch. multicoloured . . 20 10

782 Karl Marx

1983. Death Centenary of Karl Marx.

N2284 **782** 10 ch. multicoloured . . 50 25

783 Scholar, Marchers and Map of Journey

1983. 60th Anniv of Thousand-ri Journey for Learning.

N2285 **783** 10 ch. multicoloured . . 1·00 10

784 "Madonna of the Goldfinch"

1983. 500th Birth Anniv of Raphael. Multicoloured.

N2286 10 ch. Type **784** . . . . . . 1·50 40
N2287 20 ch. "The School of Athens" (detail) . . . . 1·50 40
N2288 30 ch. "Madonna of the Grand Duke" . . . . . 1·75 45
N2289 50 ch. "Madonna of the Chair" . . . . 1·90 45
N2290 50 ch. "Madonna of the Lamb" . . . . 1·50 50
N2291 80 ch. "The Beautiful Gardener" . . . . . . 1·50 50

785 Department Store No. 1

1983. Pyongyang Buildings. Multicoloured.

N2293 2 ch. Chongryu Restaurant 20 10
N2294 10 ch. Part of Munsu Street 30 10
N2295 10 ch. Ice Rink 40 10
N2296 40 ch. Type **785** 60 15
N2297 70 ch. Grand People's Study House 75 25

786 Emblem and Crowd　　**788** Satellite, Masts and Dish Aerial

787 Judo

1983. 5th Anniv of International Institute of Juche Idea.

N2298 **786** 10 ch. multicoloured . . 15 10

1983. Olympic Games, Los Angeles (1st issue). Multicoloured.

N2299 20 ch. Type **787** 65 40
N2300 20 ch. Wrestling . . . . . 1·25 40
N2301 30 ch. Judo (different) (value in gold) 65 40
N2302 30 ch. Judo (different) (value in black) . . . . . . 1·25 40
N2303 40 ch. Boxing 65 40
N2304 40 ch. Li Ho Jun (1972 shooting gold medalist) 1·25 40
N2305 50 ch. Weightlifting 65 40
N2306 50 ch. Wrestling (different) 1·25 40
N2307 80 ch. Boxing (different) 1·25 40
See also Nos. N2359/64.

1983. World Communications Year (1st issue).

N2309 **788** 10 ch. multicoloured . . 1·50 20
See also Nos. N2349/53.

789 Emblem, Giant Panda and Stamp

1983. "Tembal 83" International Thematic Stamp Exhibition, Basel. Multicoloured.

N2310 20 ch. Type **789** . . . . . . 1·75 35
N2311 30 ch. Emblem, flag and Basel Town Post stamp . . . . 1·90 35

790 "Colourful Cow" (kogge), 1402

1983. Old Ships. Multicoloured.

N2312 20 ch. Type **790** . . . . . . 1·10 45
N2313 20 ch. "Kwi-Sun" ("turtle" ship), 1592 . . . . . . 2·50 75
N2314 35 ch. "Great Harry" (warship), 1555 . . . . . 1·50 55
N2315 35 ch. Admiral Li Sun Sin and "turtle" ship . . . . . 2·50 75
N2316 50 ch. "Eagle of Lubeck" (galleon), 1567 . . . . . 2·10 70

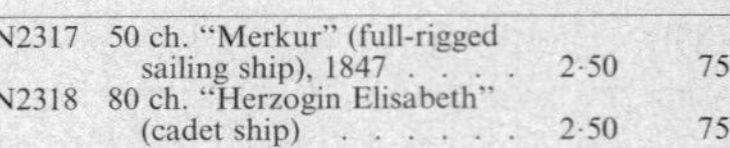
N2317 50 ch. "Merkur" (full-rigged sailing ship), 1847 . . . . 2·50 75
N2318 80 ch. "Herzogin Elisabeth" (cadet ship) . . . . . . 2·50 75

791 "Locomotion", 1825, Great Britain

1983. Railway Locomotives. Multicoloured.

N2320 20 ch. Type **791** . . . . . . 1·50 60
N2321 20 ch. "Drache", 1848, Germany . . . . 4·75 1·00
N2322 35 ch. "Adler", 1835, Germany . . . . 2·00 80
N2323 35 ch. Korean steam locomotive . . . . 4·50 1·00
N2324 50 ch. "Austria", 1837, Austria . . . . 3·25 80
N2325 50 ch. Bristol and Exeter Railway steam locomotive, 1853 . . . . 4·75 1·00
N2326 80 ch. Caledonian Railway locomotive, 1859 . . . . 4·75 1·00

792 Map, Hand and Weapons

1983. 10th Anniv of Publication of Five-point Policy for Korea's Reunification.

N2328 **792** 10 ch. multicoloured . . 25 10

793 Emblem, Tower of Juche Idea and Fireworks

1983. World Conference on Journalists against Imperialism and for Friendship and Peace, Pyongyang. Multicoloured.

N2329 10 ch. Type **793** 20 10
N2330 40 ch. Emblem and rainbow and clasped hands 40 15
N2331 70 ch. Emblem, map and hand with raised forefinger . . 50 20

794 Worker and Banners

1983. "Let's Create the Speed of the 80s".

N2332 **794** 10 ch. multicoloured . . 25 10

795 Soldier and Rejoicing Crowd

1983. 30th Anniv of Victory in Liberation War.

N2333 **795** 10 ch. multicoloured . . 25 10

796 "Gorch Fock" (cadet barque) and Korean 1978 2 ch. Stamp

1983. "Bangkok 1983" International Stamp Exhibition.

N2334 **796** 40 ch. multicoloured . . 3·00 1·25

797 Skiing

1983. Winter Olympic Games, Sarajevo (1984). Multicoloured.

N2336 10 ch. Type **797** 55 25
N2337 20 ch. Figure skating (vert) 2·00 45
N2338 30 ch. Skating (pair) . . . . 1·60 55
N2339 50 ch. Ski jumping . . . . 1·60 55
N2340 50 ch. Ice hockey (vert) . . 2·00 45
N2341 80 ch. Speed skating (vert) 2·00 45

798 Workers and Soldier with Books

1983. 35th Anniv of Korean People's Democratic Republic.

N2343 **798** 10 ch. multicoloured . . 35 10

799 Archery

800 Girls holding Hands

1983. Folk Games. Multicoloured.

N2344 10 ch. Type **799** . . . . . 2·50 40
N2345 10 ch. Flying kites 65 20
N2346 40 ch. See-sawing 65 20
N2347 40 ch. Swinging 65 20

1983. Korean–Chinese Friendship.

N2348 **800** 10 ch. multicoloured . . 50 10

801 Envelopes and Forms of Transport

802 Portrait

1983. World Communications Year (2nd issue). Multicoloured.

N2349 30 ch. Mail van, motorcyclist and hand holding magazines . . . . 4·75 90
N2350 30 ch. Satellite, globe and dish aerial . . . . 1·25 40
N2351 40 ch. Type **801** . . . . . . 4·75 1·10
N2352 40 ch. Television cameraman 1·25 40
N2353 80 ch. Telephone and aerial 1·25 40

1983. Paintings by Rubens. Multicoloured.

N2355 40 ch. Type **802** . . . . . . 1·40 60
N2356 40 ch. Portrait (different) (horiz) . . . . 1·75 75
N2357 80 ch. "The Sentencing of Midas" (horiz) . . . . . 1·75 75

803 Sprinting

1983. Olympic Games, Los Angeles (2nd issue). Multicoloured.

N2359 10 ch. Type **803** 75 20
N2360 20 ch. Show jumping . . . 1·75 45
N2361 30 ch. Cycling . . . . . . 3·00 55
N2362 50 ch. Handball . . . . . . 2·00 60
N2363 50 ch. Fencing . . . . . . 1·75 45
N2364 80 ch. Gymnastics . . . . . 1·75 45

804 "St. Catherine" 805 Kimilsungflower

804a Cat

1983. 450th Death Anniv (1984) of Antonio Correggio (artist). Multicoloured.

N2366 20 ch. Type **804** . . . . . . 1·75 60
N2367 20 ch. "Morning" (detail) 2·50 75
N2368 35 ch. "Madonna" . . . . 1·75 60
N2369 35 ch. "Morning" (different) 2·50 75
N2370 50 ch. "Madonna with St. John" . . . . 1·75 60
N2371 50 ch. "St. Catherine" (different) . . . . 2·50 75
N2372 80 ch. "Madonna and Child" 2·50 75

1983. Cats. Multicoloured, frame colour given.

N2373a **804a** 10 ch. green . . . . 1·25 10
N2373b – 10 ch. gold . . . . 1·25 10
N2373c – 10 ch. blue . . . . 1·25 10
N2373d – 10 ch. red . . . . 1·25 10
N2373e – 10 ch. silver . . . . 1·25 10

DESIGNS: Different cats' heads.

1983. New Year.

N2374 **805** 10 ch. multicoloured . . 85 10

806 Worker and Workers' Party Flag

1984. "Under the Leadership of the Workers' Party". Multicoloured.

N2375 10 ch. Type **806** 25 10
N2376 10 ch. Ore-dressing plant No. 3, Komdok General Mining Enterprise, and Party Flag 40 10

807 Farm Worker, Rice and Maize

1984. 20th Anniv of Publication of "Theses of the Socialist Rural Question in Our Country".

N2377 **807** 10 ch. multicoloured . . 25 10

808 Changdok School, Chilgol

1984. Kim Il Sung's 72nd Birthday.

N2378 **808** 5 ch. green, black & bl 25 10
N2379 – 10 ch. multicoloured . . 25 10

DESIGN: 10 ch. Birthplace, Mangyongdae, and rejoicing crowd.

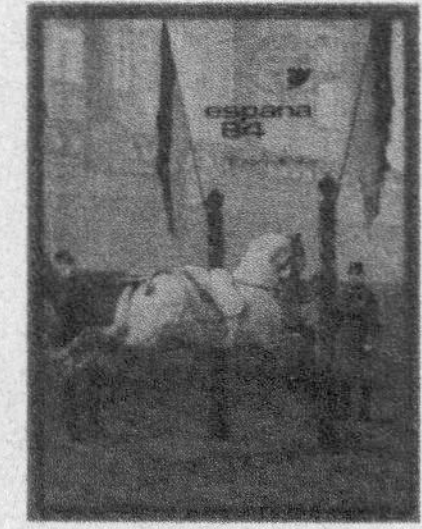

809 "Spanish Riding School" (Julius von Blaas)

1984. "Espana 84" International Stamp Exhibition, Madrid. Multicoloured.

N2380 10 ch. Type **809** . . . . . . 1·75 50
N2381 20 ch. "Ferdinand of Austria" (Rubens) . . . . 1·75 50

810 "La Donna Velata" 812 Construction Site

811 Map and Second Stage Pumping Station

1984. 500th Birth Anniv (1983) of Raphael (artist). Multicoloured.

N2383 10 ch. "Portrait of Agnolo Doni" . . . . 1·50 50
N2384 20 ch. Type **810** . . . . . . 1·50 50
N2385 30 ch. "Portrait of Jeanne d'Aragon" . . . . 1·50 50

1984. 25th Anniv of Kiyang Irrigation System.

N2387 **811** 10 ch. multicoloured . . 50 10

1984. Construction on Five District Fronts.

N2388 **812** 10 ch. red, black & yell 50 10

813 Bobsleighing (East Germany)

1984. Winter Olympic Games Medal Winners. Multicoloured.

N2389 10 ch. Ski jumping (Matti Nykaenen) . . . . 1·75 50
N2390 20 ch. Speed skating (Karin Enke) . . . . 1·50 40
N2391 20 ch. Slalom (Max Julen) 1·75 50
N2392 30 ch. Type **813** . . . . . . 1·50 40
N2393 30 ch. Downhill skiing (Maria Walliser) . . . . 1·75 50
N2394 40 ch. Cross-country skiing (Thomas Wassberg) . . . 2·75 60
N2395 80 ch. Cross-country skiing (Marja-Liisa Hamalainen) 2·75 60

814 Steam Locomotive, 1919

1984. Essen International Stamp Fair. Mult.

N2397 20 ch. Streamlined steam locomotive, 1939 . . . . 4·00 65
N2398 30 ch. Type **814** . . . . . . 4·00 65

815 "Mlle. Fiocre in the Ballet 'La Source' "

1984. 150th Birth Anniv of Edgar Degas (artist). Multicoloured.

N2400 10 ch. Type **815** . . . . . . 1·50 25
N2401 20 ch. "The Dance Foyer at the Rue le Peletier Opera" 2·50 25
N2402 30 ch. "Race Meeting" . . . 3·75 40

816 Map of Pyongnam Irrigation System and Reservoir

1984. Irrigation Experts Meeting, Pyongyang.

N2404 **816** 2 ch. multicoloured . . 40 10

817 Korean Stamp and Building 818 Crowd and Banners

1984. U.P.U. Congress Stamp Exn, Hamburg.

N2405 **817** 20 ch. multicoloured . . 3·00 40

1984. Proposal for Tripartite Talks.

N2407 **818** 10 ch. multicoloured . . 40 10

819 Nobel experimenting

1984. 150th Birth Anniv (1983) of Alfred Bernhard Nobel (inventor). Multicoloured.

N2408 20 ch. Type **819** . . . . . . 3·00 45
N2409 30 ch. Portrait of Nobel . . 3·00 45

820 Drinks, Tinned Food, Clothes and Flats

1984. Improvements of Living Standards.

N2411 **820** 10 ch. multicoloured . . 55 10

821 Sunhwa School, Mangyongdae

1984. School of Kim Hyong Jik (Kim Il Sung's Father).

N2412 **821** 10 ch. multicoloured . . 40 10

822 Armed Crowd with Banners

1984. 65th Anniv of Kuandian Conference.

N2413 **822** 10 ch. multicoloured . . 40 10

823 "Thunia bracteata"

1984. Flowers. Multicoloured.

N2414 10 ch. "Cattleya loddigesii" 1·00 10
N2415 20 ch. Type **823** 1·25 25
N2416 30 ch. "Phalaenopsis amabilis" 1·75 40

824 Swordfish and Trawler

1984. Fishing Industry. Multicoloured.

N2418 5 ch. Type **824** 1·25 15
N2419 10 ch. Blue marlin and trawler 1·75 25
N2420 40 ch. Sailfish and game fishing launch 4·50 1·25

825 Revolutionary Museum, Chilgol

1984.

N2421 **825** 10 ch. multicoloured 40 10

826 Kim Hyok, Cha Gwang Su and Youth

828 Clock Face

827 Inauguration of a French Railway Line, 1860

1984. "Let's All become the Kim Hyoks and Cha Gwang Sus of the '80s".

N2422 **826** 10 ch. multicoloured 60 10

1984. Centenary (1983) of "Orient Express". Multicoloured.

N2423 10 ch. Type **827** 1·40 25
N2424 20 ch. Opening of a British railway line, "1821" 2·50 50
N2425 30 ch. Inauguration of Paris–Rouen line, 1843 3·00 90

1984. Centenary of Greenwich Meridian.

N2427 **828** 10 ch. multicoloured. 2·50 1·00

829 Grand Theatre, Hamburg

830 Turning on Machinery

1984.

N2429 **829** 10 ch. blue 40 10

1984. Automation of Industry.

N2430 **830** 40 ch. multicoloured 60 30

831 "Dragon Angler"

1984. Paintings. Multicoloured.

N2431 10 ch. Type **831** 1·00 10
N2432 20 ch. "Ox Driver" (Kim Du Ryang) (47 × 35 mm) 1·25 25
N2433 30 ch. "Bamboo" (Kim Jin U) (47 × 35 mm) 1·75 40

832 Tsiolkovsky

1984. K. E. Tsiolkovsky (space scientist). Mult.

N2435 20 ch. Type **832** 90 25
N2436 30 ch. "Sputnik" orbiting Earth 1·25 40

833 "Pongdaesan"

1984. Container Ships. Multicoloured.

N2438 10 ch. Type **833** 95 10
N2439 20 ch. "Ryongnamsan" 1·10 35
N2440 30 ch. "Rungrado" 1·50 55

834 Caracal

1984. Animals. Multicoloured.

N2442 10 ch. Spotted hyenas 60 10
N2443 20 ch. Type **834** 90 25
N2444 30 ch. Black-backed jackals 1·25 40
N2445 40 ch. Foxes 1·60 60

835 Marie Curie

836 Chestnut-eared Aracari

1984. 50th Anniv of Marie Curie (physicist).

N2447 **835** 10 ch. multicoloured 2·00 25

1984. Birds. Multicoloured.

N2449 10 ch. Hoopoe 1·10 15
N2450 20 ch. South African crowned cranes 1·50 35
N2451 30 ch. Saddle-bill stork 2·00 50
N2452 40 ch. Type **836** 2·75 65

837 Cosmonaut

1984. Space Exploration. Multicoloured.

N2454 10 ch. Type **837** 50 10
N2455 20 ch. Cosmonaut on space-walk 75 25
N2456 30 ch. Cosmonaut (different) 1·00 40

838 "Arktika"

1984. Russian Ice-breakers. Multicoloured.

N2458 20 ch. Type **838** 1·25 35
N2459 30 ch. "Ermak" 1·75 50

839 Mendeleev

1984. 150th Birth Anniv of Dmitri Mendeleev (chemist).

N2461 **839** 10 ch. multicoloured 95 10

840 Kim Il Sung in U.S.S.R.

1984. Kim Il Sung's Visits to Eastern Europe. Multicoloured.

N2463 10 ch. Type **840** 60 10
N2464 10 ch. In Poland 60 10
N2465 10 ch. In German Democratic Republic 60 10
N2466 10 ch. In Czechoslovakia 60 10
N2467 10 ch. In Hungary 60 10
N2468 10 ch. In Bulgaria 60 10
N2469 10 ch. In Rumania 60 10

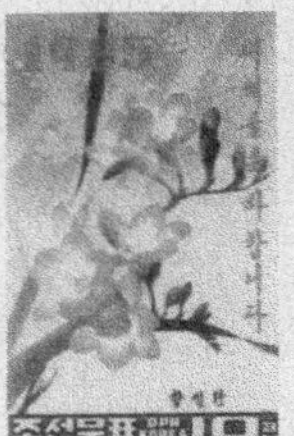

841 Freesia

1985. New Year.

N2471 **841** 10 ch. multicoloured 75 10

842 Journey Route, Steam Locomotive and Memorials

1985. 60th Anniv of 1000 ri Journey by Kim Il Sung. Multicoloured.

N2472 5 ch. Type **842** 1·25 10
N2473 10 ch. Boy trumpeter and schoolchildren following route 50 10

Nos. N2472/3 were issued together, se-tenant, forming a composite design.

843 Cugnot's Steam Car, 1769

844 Camp, Mt. Paekdu

1985. History of the Motor Car (1st series). Multicoloured.

N2474 10 ch. Type **843** 1·40 10
N2475 15 ch. Goldsworthy Gurney steam omnibus, 1825 1·40 15
N2476 20 ch. Gottlieb Daimler diesel car, 1885 1·40 25
N2477 25 ch. Benz three-wheeled diesel car, 1886 1·60 35
N2478 30 ch. Peugeot diesel car, 1891 2·00 40

See also Nos. N2562/6.

1985. Korean Revolution Headquarters.

N2480 **844** 10 ch. multicoloured 40 20

845 Taechodo Lighthouse

846 Hedgehog challenges Tiger

1985. Lighthouses. Multicoloured.

N2481 10 ch. Type **845** 1·75 10
N2482 20 ch. Sodo 1·90 30
N2483 30 ch. Pido 2·25 45
N2484 40 ch. Suundo 2·75 70

1985. "The Hedgehog defeats the Tiger" (fable). Multicoloured.

N2485 10 ch. Type **846** 60 10
N2486 20 ch. Tiger goes to stamp on rolled-up hedgehog 90 25
N2487 30 ch. Hedgehog clings to tiger's nose 1·25 40
N2488 35 ch. Tiger flees 1·40 50
N2489 40 ch. Tiger crawls before hedgehog 1·60 60

847 "Pleurotus cornucopiae"

848 West Germany v. Hungary, 1954

1985. Fungi. Multicoloured.

N2490 10 ch. Type **847** 1·10 10
N2491 20 ch. Oyster fungus 1·40 25
N2492 30 ch. "Catathelasma ventricosum" 1·90 40

1985. World Cup Football Championship Finals.

N2493 **848** 10 ch. black, buff & brn 60 10
N2494 – 10 ch. multicoloured 60 10
N2495 – 20 ch. black, buff & brn 90 25
N2496 – 20 ch. multicoloured 90 25
N2497 – 30 ch. black, buff & brn 1·25 40
N2498 – 30 ch. multicoloured 1·25 40
N2499 – 40 ch. black, buff & brn 1·60 60
N2500 – 40 ch. multicoloured 1·60 60

DESIGNS—VERT: No. N2496 West Germany v. Netherlands, 1974; N2499, England v. West Germany, 1966. HORIZ: No. N2494, Brazil v. Italy, 1970; N2495, Brazil v. Sweden, 1958; N2497, Brazil v. Czechoslovakia, 1962; N2498, Argentina v. Netherlands, 1968; N2500, Italy v. West Germany, 1982.

MINIMUM PRICE

The minimum price quoted is 10p which represents a handling charge rather than a basis for valuing common stamps. For further notes about prices see introductory pages.

849 Date and Kim Il Sung's Birthplace   **850** Horn Player

1985. 73rd Birthday of Kim Il Sung.
N2502 **849** 10 ch. multicoloured . . 40 10

1985. 4th-century Musical Instruments. Mult.
N2503 10 ch. Type **850** . . . . . . 1·40 10
N2504 20 ch. So (pipes) player . . 1·40 25

851 Chongryon Hall, Tokyo   **852** Common Marmoset

1985. 30th Anniv of Chongryon (General Association of Korean Residents in Japan).
N2505 **851** 10 ch. brown 40 10

1985. Mammals. Multicoloured.
N2506 5 ch. Type **852** 85 10
N2507 10 ch. Ring-tailed lemur . . 85 10

854 Buenos Aires and Argentina 1982 Stamp   **855** Dancer and Gymnast

1985. "Argentina '85" International Stamp Exhibition, Buenos Aires. Multicoloured.
N2509 10 ch. Type **854** 75 10
N2510 20 ch. Iguacu Falls and Argentina 1984 and North Korea 1978 stamps (horiz) 2·50 25

1985. 12th World Youth and Students' Festival, Moscow. Multicoloured.
N2512 10 ch. Type **855** 60 10
N2513 20 ch. Spassky Tower, Moscow, and Festival emblem 90 25
N2514 40 ch. Youths of different races . . . . 1·60 60

856 Peace Pavilion, Youth Park   **857** Liberation Celebrations

1985. Pyongyang Buildings.
N2515 **856** 2 ch. black and green 20 10
N2516 – 40 ch. brown and lt brn 45 20
DESIGN: 40 ch. Multi-storey flats, Chollima Street.

1985. 40th Anniv of Liberation.
N2517 – 5 ch. red, black & blue 20 10
N2518 – 10 ch. multicoloured . . 40 10
N2519 – 10 ch. brown, blk & grn 40 10
N2520 – 10 ch. multicoloured . . 40 10
N2521 **857** 10 ch. yellow, blk & red 40 10
N2522 – 10 ch. red, orange & blk 40 10
N2523 – 40 ch. multicoloured . . 60 20
DESIGNS—HORIZ: No. N2517, Soldiers with rifles and flag; N2518, Crowd with banners and Flame of Juche; N2519, Korean and Soviet soldiers raising arms; N2520, Japanese soldiers laying down weapons; N2523, Students bearing banners. VERT: No. N2522, Liberation Tower, Moran Hill, Pyongyang.

858 Halley and Comet

1985. Appearance of Halley's Comet. Multicoloured.
N2525 10 ch. Type **858** 90 10
N2526 20 ch. Diagram of comet's flight and space probe . . 1·25 25

859 "Camellia japonica"   **861** Party Founding Museum

860 "Hunting"

1985. Flowers. Multicoloured.
N2528 10 ch. "Hippeastrum hybridum" 90 10
N2529 20 ch. Type **859** . . . . . . 1·25 25
N2530 30 ch. "Cyclamen persicum" 1·75 40

1985. Koguryo Culture.
N2531 10 ch. "Hero" (vert) 60 10
N2532 15 ch. "Heroine" (vert) . . 75 15
N2533 20 ch. "Flying Fairy" . . . 90 25
N2534 25 ch. Type **860** . . . . . . 1·10 35

1985. 40th Anniv of Korean Workers' Party. Multicoloured.
N2536 5 ch. Type **861** 20 10
N2537 10 ch. Soldier with gun and workers 40 10
N2538 10 ch. Soldiers and flag . . 40 10
N2539 40 ch. Statue of worker, peasant and intellectual holding aloft party emblem 60 20

862 Arch of Triumph, Pyongyang   **863** Colosseum, Rome, and N. Korea 1975 10 ch. Stamp

1985. 40th Anniv of Kim Il Sung's Return.
N2541 **862** 10 ch. brown and green . 40 10

1985. "Italia '85" International Stamp Exhibition, Rome. Multicoloured.
N2542 10 ch. Type **863** 60 10
N2543 20 ch. "The Holy Family" (Raphael) (vert) 90 25
N2544 30 ch. Head of "David" (statue, Michelangelo) (vert) . . . . 1·25 40

864 Mercedes Benz Type "300"

1985. South-West German Stamp Fair, Sindelfingen. Multicoloured.
N2546 10 ch. Type **864** . . . . . . 1·00 10
N2547 15 ch. Mercedes Benz Type "770" . . . . 1·40 15
N2548 20 ch. Mercedes Benz "W 150" . . . . 1·75 25
N2549 30 ch. Mercedes Type "600" 2·00 40

865 Tackle

1985. World Cup Football Championship, Mexico (1st issue). Multicoloured.
N2551 20 ch. Type **865** . . . . . . 1·10 25
N2552 30 ch. Three players . . . . 1·40 40
See also Nos. N2558/9 and N2577/82.

866 Dancers

1985. International Youth Year. Multicoloured.
N2554 10 ch. Type **866** 60 10
N2555 20 ch. Sports activities . . . 90 25
N2556 30 ch. Technology . . . . 1·25 40

867 Players

1985. World Cup Football Championship, Mexico (2nd issue). Multicoloured.
N2558 20 ch. Type **867** . . . . . . 1·25 25
N2559 30 ch. Goalkeeper and players 1·60 40

868 Juche Torch   **869** Amedee Bollee and Limousine, 1901

1986. New Year.
N2561 **868** 10 ch. multicoloured . . 40 10

1986. History of the Motor Car (2nd series). Multicoloured.
N2562 10 ch. Type **869** 75 10
N2563 20 ch. Stewart Rolls, Henry Royce and "Silver Ghost", 1906 . . . . 1·25 25
N2564 25 ch. Giovanni Agnelli and Fiat car, 1912 . . . . . 1·40 35
N2565 30 ch. Ettore Bugatti and "Royal" coupe, 1928 . . 1·60 40
N2566 40 ch. Louis Renault and fiacre, 1906 . . . . . . 2·25 60

870 Gary Kasparov   **872** Tongdu Rock, Songgan

871 Cemetery Gate

1986. World Chess Championship, Moscow.
N2568 **870** 20 ch. multicoloured . . 2·25 25

1986. Revolutionary Martyrs' Cemetery, Pyongyang. Multicoloured.
N2570 5 ch. Type **871** 20 10
N2571 10 ch. Bronze sculpture (detail) 55 10

1986. 37th Anniv of Pres. Kim Il Sung's Visit to Songgan Revolutionary Site.
N2572 **872** 10 ch. multicoloured . . 40 10

873 Buddhist Scriptures Museum

1986. Mt. Myohyang Buildings.
N2573 **873** 10 ch. brown and green 40 10
N2574 – 20 ch. violet and red . . 50 10
DESIGN: 20 ch. Taeung Hall.

874 Tomato Anemonefish

1986. Fishes. Multicoloured.
N2575 10 ch. Pennant coralfish . . 1·50 20
N2576 20 ch. Type **874** . . . . . . 2·25 45

875 Footballers and Flags of Italy, Bulgaria and Argentina

1986. World Cup Football Championship, Mexico (3rd issue). Designs showing footballers and flags of participating countries. Multicoloured.
N2577 10 ch. Type **875** 60 10
N2578 20 ch. Mexico, Belgium, Paraguay and Iraq . . . 90 25
N2579 25 ch. France, Canada, U.S.S.R. and Hungary . . 1·10 35
N2580 30 ch. Brazil, Spain, Algeria and Northern Ireland . . 1·25 40
N2581 35 ch. West Germany, Uruguay, Scotland and Denmark . . . . 1·40 50
N2582 40 ch. Poland, Portugal, Morocco and England . . 1·60 60

876 Singer, Pianist and Emblem

1986. 4th Spring Friendship Art Festival, Pyongyang.
N2584 **876** 1 wn. multicoloured . . 1·25 55

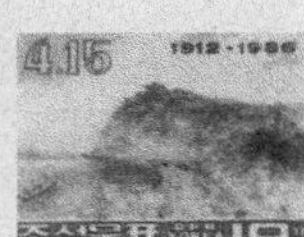

877 Daimler "Motorwagen", 1886   **878** Mangyong Hill

1986. 60th Anniv of Mercedes-Benz (car manufacturers). Multicoloured.
N2585 10 ch. Type **877** 75 10
N2586 10 ch. Benz "velo", 1894 . . 75 10
N2587 20 ch. Mercedes car, 1901 1·00 25
N2588 20 ch. Benz limousine, 1909 1·00 25
N2589 30 ch. Mercedes "tourenwagen", 1914 . . 1·40 40
N2590 30 ch. Mercedes-Benz "170" 6-cylinder, 1931 . . . . . 1·40 40
N2591 40 ch. Mercedes-Benz "380", 1933 . . . . 1·75 60
N2592 40 ch. Mercedes-Benz "540 K", 1936 . . . . . 1·75 60

1986. 74th Birthday of Kim Il Sung.
N2594 **878** 10 ch. multicoloured . . 30 10

879 Crowd

1968. 50th Anniv of Association for the Restoration of the Fatherland.
N2595 **879** 10 ch. multicoloured . . 30 10

880 Dove carrying Letter

881 "Mona Lisa" (Leonardo da Vinci)

1986. International Peace Year. Multicoloured.
N2596 10 ch. Type **880** 50 10
N2597 20 ch. U.N. Headquarters, New York 80 25
N2598 30 ch. Dove, globe and broken missiles . . . . 1·10 40

1986.
N2600 **881** 20 ch. multicoloured . . 90 25

882 Pink Iris

883 Kim Un Suk

1986. Irises. Multicoloured.
N2601 20 ch. Type **882** . . . . . . 1·25 25
N2602 30 ch. Violet iris . . . . . 1·75 40

1986. Tennis Players. Multicoloured.
N2604 10 ch. Type **883** (postage) 2·00 35
N2605 20 ch. Ivan Lendl . . . . . 2·00 35
N2606 30 ch. Steffi Graf . . . . . 2·00 35
N2607 50 ch. Boris Becker (air) . . 2·00 35

884 Sulphur-crested Cockatoo

1986. "Stampex '86" Stamp Exhibition, Adelaide, Australia.
N2608 **884** 10 ch. multicoloured . . 1·50 15

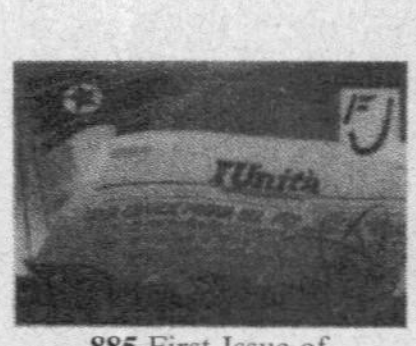
885 First Issue of "L'Unita"

886 "Express II" (icebreaker) and Sweden 1872 20 ore Stamp

1986. National "L'Unita" (Italian Communist Party newspaper) Festival, Milan. Multicoloured.
N2610 10 ch. Type **885** 60 10
N2611 20 ch. Milan Cathedral . . 90 25
N2612 30 ch. "Pieta" (Michelangelo) (vert) . . . . 1·25 40

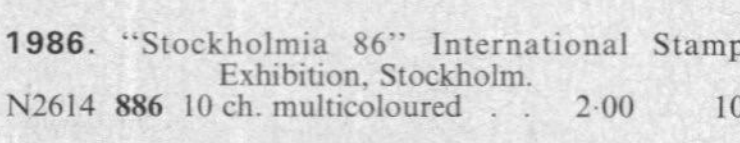
1986. "Stockholmia 86" International Stamp Exhibition, Stockholm.
N2614 **886** 10 ch. multicoloured . . 2·00 10

887 Reprint of First Stamp

1986. 40th Anniv of First North Korean Stamps (1st issue). Multicoloured.
N2616 10 ch. Type **887** (postage) 75 10
N2617 15 ch. Imperforate reprint of first stamp . . . . 1·25 20
N2618 50 ch. 1946 50 ch. violet stamp (air) . . . . 2·00 75
See also Nos. N2619/21.

888 Postal Emblems and 1962 and 1985 Stamps

1986. 40th Anniv of First North Korean Stamps (2nd issue). Multicoloured.
N2619 10 ch. Type **888** (postage) 2·00 25
N2620 15 ch. General Post Office and 1976 and 1978 stamps 2·00 35
N2621 50 ch. Kim Il Sung, first stamp and reprint (vert) (air) . . 1·60 45

1986. World Cup Football Championship Results. Nos. N2577/82 optd **1st: ARG 2nd: FRG 3rd: FRA 4th: BEL**.
N2622 10 ch. multicoloured 80 10
N2623 20 ch. multicoloured . . . . 1·10 25
N2624 25 ch. multicoloured . . . . 1·40 35
N2625 30 ch. multicoloured . . . . 1·50 40
N2626 35 ch. multicoloured . . . . 1·60 50
N2627 40 ch. multicoloured . . . . 1·90 60

890 Flag and Man with raised Fist

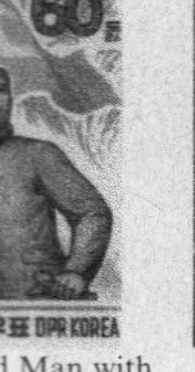
892 Schoolchildren

891 Gift Animals House

1986. 60th Anniv of Down-with-Imperialism Union.
N2629 **890** 10 ch. multicoloured . . 30 10

1986. 1st Anniv of Gift Animals House, Central Zoo, Pyongyang.
N2630 **891** 2 wn. multicoloured . . 3·00 1·10

1986. 40th Anniv of U.N.E.S.C.O. Multicoloured.
N2631 10 ch. Type **892** 60 10
N2632 50 ch. Anniversary emblem, Grand People's Study House and telecommunications (horiz) 1·50 75

893 Communications Satellite

1986. 15th Anniv of Intersputnik.
N2633 **893** 5 wn. multicoloured . . 7·00 3·00

894 Oil tanker leaving Lock

1986. West Sea Barrage.
N2634 **894** 10 ch. multicoloured . . 50 10
N2635 – 40 ch. green, black and gold . . . . 1·25 20
N2636 – 1 wn. 20 multicoloured . 2·75 60
DESIGNS: 20 ch. Aerial view of dam; 1 wn. 20, Aerial view of lock.

895 Common Morel

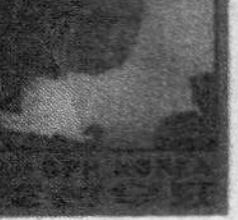
896 Machu Picchu, Peru, and N. Korea Taedong Gate Stamp

1986. Minerals and Fungi. Multicoloured.
N2637 10 ch. Lengenbachite (postage) . . . . 2·00 25
N2638 10 ch. Common funnel cap 2·00 25
N2639 15 ch. Rhodochrosite . . . 2·00 25
N2640 15 ch. Type **895** . . . . . . 2·00 25
N2641 50 ch. Annabergite (air) . . 2·00 25
N2642 50 ch. Blue russula . . . . 2·00 25

1986. North Korean Three-dimensional Photographs and Stamps Exhibition, Lima, Peru.
N2643 **896** 10 ch. multicoloured . . 1·25 20

897 Pine Tree

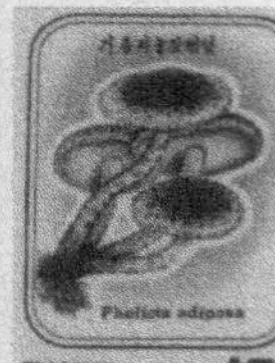
898 "Pholiota adiposa"

1987. New Year. Multicoloured.
N2645 10 ch. Type **897** 75 15
N2646 40 ch. Hare 90 25

1987. Fungi. Multicoloured.
N2647 10 ch. Type **898** . . . . . . 1·50 20
N2648 20 ch. Chanterelle . . . . . 1·75 20
N2649 30 ch. "Boletus impolitus" 2·00 30

899 Kim Ok Song (composer)

901 East Pyongyang Grand Theatre

1987. Musicians' Death Anniversaries. Mult.
N2651 10 ch. Maurice Ravel (composer, 50th anniv) 1·50 20
N2652 10 ch. Type **899** (22nd anniv) 1·50 20
N2653 20 ch. Giovanni Lully (composer, 300th anniv) 1·50 20
N2654 30 ch. Franz Liszt (composer, centenary (1986)) . . . . 1·50 20
N2655 40 ch. Violins (250th anniv of Antonio Stradivari (violin maker) . . . . 1·50 20
N2656 40 ch. Christoph Gluck (composer, bicent) . . . 1·50 20

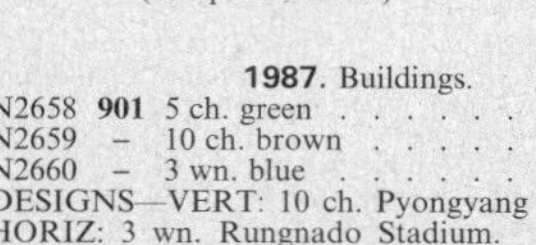
1987. Buildings.
N2658 **901** 5 ch. green 35 10
N2659 – 10 ch. brown 45 10
N2660 – 3 wn. blue . . . . . . 3·00 90
DESIGNS—VERT: 10 ch. Pyongyang Koryo Hotel. HORIZ: 3 wn. Rungnado Stadium.

902 "Gorch Fock" (German cadet barque)

1987. Sailing Ships. Multicoloured.
N2661 20 ch. Type **902** (postage) 70 20
N2662 30 ch. "Tovarishch" (Russian cadet barque) (vert) . . . 1·00 30
N2663 50 ch. "Belle Poule" (cadet schooner) (vert) (air) . . 1·50 50
N2664 50 ch. "Sagres II" (Portuguese cadet barque) (vert) . . . 1·50 50

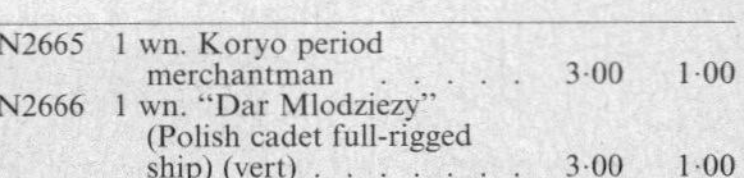
N2665 1 wn. Koryo period merchantman . . . . . 3·00 1·00
N2666 1 wn. "Dar Mlodziezy" (Polish cadet full-rigged ship) (vert) . . . . 3·00 1·00

903 Road Signs

1987. Road Safety.
N2667 **903** 10 ch. blue, red and black (postage) . . . . . . 1·00 10
N2668 – 10 ch. red and black . . 1·00 10
N2669 – 20 ch. blue, red & blk 1·25 20
N2670 – 50 ch. red and black (air) 1·50 50
DESIGNS: Nos. N2668/70, Different road signs.

904 Fire Engine

1987. Fire Engines.
N2671 **904** 10 ch. multicoloured (postage) . . . . . . 1·75 25
N2672 – 20 ch. multicoloured . . 1·90 25
N2673 – 30 ch. multicoloured . . 2·50 30
N2674 – 50 ch. multicoloured (air) 3·25 50
DESIGNS: N2672/4, 20 ch. to 50 ch. Different machines.

905 "Apatura ilia" and Spiraea

1987. Butterflies and Flowers. Multicoloured.
N2675 10 ch. Type **905** 70 10
N2676 10 ch. "Ypthima argus" and fuchsia 70 10
N2677 20 ch. "Neptis philyra" and aquilegia . . . . 1·00 20
N2678 20 ch. "Papilio protenor" and chrysanthemum . . . . . 1·00 20
N2679 40 ch. "Parantica sita" and celosia . . . . 1·60 40
N2680 40 ch. "Vanessa indica" and hibiscus . . . . 1·60 40

906 Association Monument, Pyongyang

907 Doves, Emblem and Tree

1987. 70th Anniv of Korean National Association (independence movement).
N2681 **906** 10 ch. red, silver & blk 25 10

1987. 5th Spring Friendship Art Festival, Pyongyang.
N2682 **907** 10 ch. multicoloured . . 25 10

908 Mangyong Hill

909 Bay

1987. 75th Birthday of Kim Il Sung. Mult.
N2683 10 ch. Type **908** 25 10
N2684 10 ch. Kim Il Sung's birthplace, Mangyongdae (horiz) 25 10
N2685 10 ch. "A Bumper Crop of Pumpkins" (62 × 41 mm) 25 10
N2686 10 ch. "Profound Affection for the Working Class" 25 10

1987. Horses. Multicoloured.

N2687	10 ch. Type **909**	40	10
N2688	10 ch. Bay (different)	40	10
N2689	40 ch. Grey rearing	1·25	40
N2690	40 ch. Grey on beach	1·25	40

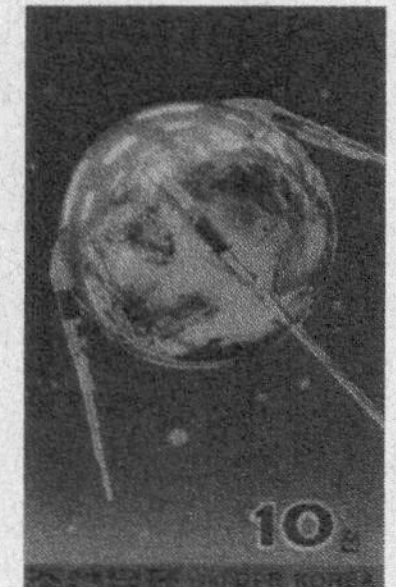

910 "Sputnik 1" (first artificial satellite)

1987. Transport. Multicoloured.

N2691	10 ch. "Juche" high speed train (horiz)	40	10
N2692	10 ch. Electric locomotive "Mangyongdae" (horiz)	40	10
N2693	10 ch. Type **910** (30th anniv of flight)	40	10
N2694	20 ch. Laika (30th anniv of first animal in space)	70	20
N2695	20 ch. Tupolev Tu-144 supersonic airliner (horiz)	70	20
N2696	20 ch. Concorde (11th anniv of first commercial flight) (horiz)	70	20
N2697	30 ch. Count Ferdinand von Zeppelin (70th death anniv) and airship LZ-4 (horiz)	1·00	30
N2698	80 ch. Zeppelin and diagrams and drawings of airships (horiz)	3·00	1·00

911 Musk Ox

1987. "Capex '87" International Stamp Exhibition, Toronto. Multicoloured.

N2699	10 ch. Type **911**	65	10
N2700	40 ch. Jacques Cartier, his ship "Grande Hermine" and "Terry Fox" (ice-breaker) (horiz)	1·75	40
N2701	60 ch. Ice hockey (Winter Olympics, Calgary, 1988) (horiz)	1·75	60

912 Trapeze Artistes

1987. International Circus Festival, Monaco. Multicoloured.

N2702	10 ch. Type **912**	40	10
N2703	10 ch. "Brave Sailors" (North Korean acrobatic act) (vert)	40	10
N2704	20 ch. Clown and elephant (vert)	70	20
N2705	20 ch. North Korean artiste receiving "Golden Clown" award	70	20
N2706	40 ch. Performing horses and cat act	2·10	40
N2707	50 ch. Prince Rainier and his children applauding	1·50	50

913 Attack on Watch Tower

1987. 50th Anniv of Battle of Pochonbo.

N2708 **913**	10 ch. brown, black and ochre	25	10

914 Sports

1987. Angol Sports Village.

N2709 **914**	5 ch. brown and gold	15	10
N2710 –	10 ch. blue and gold	25	10
N2711 –	40 ch. brown and gold	75	25
N2712 –	70 ch. blue and gold	1·25	40
N2713 –	1 wn. red and gold	1·90	60
N2714 –	1 wn. 20 violet	2·25	70

DESIGNS: Exteriors of—10 ch. Indoor swimming pool; 40 ch. Weightlifting gymnasium; 70 ch. Table tennis gymnasium; 1 wn. Football stadium; 1 wn. 20, Handball gymnasium.

915 Mandarins

1987. Mandarins. Multicoloured.

N2715	20 ch. Type **915**	1·10	25
N2716	20 ch. Mandarins on shore	1·10	25
N2717	20 ch. Mandarins on branch	1·10	25
N2718	40 ch. Mandarins in water	1·60	40

916 Exhibition Site and 1987 3 wn. Stamp

1987. "Olymphilex '87" Olympic Stamps Exhibition, Rome.

N2719 **916**	10 ch. multicoloured	90	10

917 Underground Station and Guard

1987. Railway Uniforms. Multicoloured.

N2721	10 ch. Type **917**	40	10
N2722	10 ch. Underground train and station supervisor	40	10
N2723	20 ch. Guard and electric train	60	15
N2724	30 ch. Guard with flag and electric train	85	20
N2725	40 ch. "Orient Express" guard and steam locomotive	1·10	25
N2726	40 ch. German ticket controller and diesel train	1·10	25

918 White Stork

920 Victory Column

919 Ice Skating

1987. "Hafnia 87" International Stamp Exhibition, Copenhagen. Multicoloured.

N2727	40 ch. Type **918**	1·75	40
N2728	60 ch. "Danmark" (cadet full-rigged ship) and "Little Mermaid", Copenhagen	1·75	40

1987. Winter Olympic Games, Calgary (1988). Multicoloured.

N2729	40 ch. Type **919**	1·00	30
N2730	40 ch. Ski jumping	1·00	30
N2731	40 ch. Skiing (value on left) (horiz)	1·00	30
N2732	40 ch. Skiing (value on right) (horiz)	1·00	30

1987. 750th Anniv of Berlin and "Philatelia '87" International Stamp Exhibition, Cologne. Mult.

N2734	10 ch. Type **920**	40	10
N2735	20 ch. Reichstag (horiz)	70	20
N2736	30 ch. Pfaueninsel Castle	1·00	30
N2737	40 ch. Charlottenburg Castle (horiz)	1·25	40

921 Garros and Bleriot XI

1987. Birth Centenary of Roland Garros (aviator) and Tennis as an Olympic Sport. Multicoloured.

N2739	20 ch. Type **921**	1·50	20
N2740	20 ch. Ivan Lendl (tennis player)	2·25	20
N2741	40 ch. Steffi Graf (tennis player)	3·00	40

923 Pyongyang Buildings

1988. New Year. Multicoloured.

N2744	10 ch. Type **923**	20	10
N2745	40 ch. Dragon	75	25

924 Banner and Newspaper

925 Birthplace, Mt. Paekdu

1988. 60th Anniv of "Saenal" Newspaper.

N2746 **924**	10 ch. multicoloured	45	10

1988. Kim Jong Il's Birthday.

N2747 **925**	10 ch. multicoloured	20	10

926 Henry Dunant (founder)

1988. 125th Anniv of International Red Cross. Multicoloured.

N2749	10 ch. Type **926**	75	10
N2750	20 ch. North Korean Red Cross emblem and map	1·00	15
N2751	20 ch. International Committee headquarters, Geneva	1·10	15
N2752	40 ch. Pyongyang Maternity Hospital, doctor and baby	1·25	25

927 "Santa Maria"

1988. 500th Anniv (1992) of Discovery of America by Christopher Columbus. Multicoloured.

N2754	10 ch. Type **927**	1·25	10
N2755	20 ch. "Pinta"	1·25	20
N2756	30 ch. "Nina"	1·25	30

Nos. N2754/6 were issued together, se-tenant, forming a composite design of Columbus's ships leaving Palos.

928 Montgolfier Balloon and Modern Hot-air Balloons

929 Dancers

1988. "Juvalux '88" International Youth Stamp Exhibition, Luxembourg. Multicoloured.

N2758	40 ch. Type **928**	90	25
N2759	60 ch. Steam locomotive and railway map of Luxembourg, 1900	1·60	35

1988. 6th Spring Friendship Art Festival, Pyongyang. Multicoloured.

N2760	10 ch. Singer (poster)	20	10
N2761	1 wn. 20 Type **929**	1·90	75

930 Inaugural Congress Emblem

931 Birthplace, Mangyongdae

1988. 10th Anniv of International Institute of the Juche Idea.

N2762 **930**	10 ch. multicoloured	20	10

1988. 76th Birthday of Kim Il Sung.

N2763 **931**	10 ch. multicoloured	20	10

932 "Urho" (ice-breaker)

1988. "Finlandia 88" International Stamp Exhibition, Helsinki. Multicoloured.

N2765	40 ch. Type **932**	1·40	25
N2766	60 ch. Matti Nykaenen (Olympic Games ski-jumping medallist)	1·10	35

933 Postcard for 1934 Championship

934 Emblem

1988. World Cup Football Championship, Italy (1st issue). Multicoloured.

N2767	10 ch. Football match	50	10
N2768	20 ch. Type **933**	85	15
N2769	30 ch. Player tackling (horiz)	1·25	20

See also Nos. N2924/7.

1988. 13th World Youth and Students' Festival, Pyongyang (1st issue). Multicoloured.

N2771 5 ch. Type **934** 10 10
N2772 10 ch. Dancer 40 10
N2773 10 ch. Gymnast and gymnasium, Angol Sports Village 20 10
N2774 10 ch. Map of Korea, globe and doves 30 10
N2775 10 ch. Finger pointing at shattered nuclear rockets . . 75 10
N2776 1 wn. 20 Three differently coloured hands and dove . . 2·10 75

See also Nos. N2860/3 and N2879/80.

935 Fairy

936 Mallards

1988. "Eight Fairies of Mt. Kumgang" (tale). Multicoloured.

N2777 10 ch. Type **935** 20 10
N2778 15 ch. Fairy at pool and fairies on rainbow 30 10
N2779 20 ch. Fairy and woodman husband 40 15
N2780 25 ch. Couple with baby . . 50 15
N2781 30 ch. Couple with son and daughter 55 20
N2782 35 ch. Family on rainbow . . 65 20

1988. "Praga '88" International Stamp Exhibition, Prague. Multicoloured.

N2783 20 ch. Type **936** . . . . . . 1·10 15
N2784 40 ch. Vladimir Remek (Czechoslovak cosmonaut) . . 75 25

937 Red Crossbill

1988. Birds. Multicoloured.

N2785 10 ch. Type **937** 55 15
N2786 15 ch. Stonechat 75 20
N2787 20 ch. European nuthatch . . 1·10 25
N2788 25 ch. Great spotted woodpecker . . . . . . 1·25 30
N2789 30 ch. Common kingfisher . . 1·50 35
N2790 35 ch. Bohemian waxwing . . 1·60 45

938 Fair Emblem

1988. 40th International Stamp Fair, Riccione.

N2791 **938** 20 ch. multicoloured . . 40 15

939 Emu

1988. Bicentenary of Australian Settlement. Mult.

N2793 10 ch. Type **939** 60 15
N2794 15 ch. Satin bowerbirds . . 85 20
N2795 25 ch. Laughing kookaburra (vert) . . . . . . 1·40 35

MINIMUM PRICE

The minimum price quoted is 10p which represents a handling charge rather than a basis for valuing common stamps. For further notes about prices see introductory pages.

940 Floating Crane "5-28"

1988. Ships. Multicoloured.

N2797 10 ch. Type **940** 40 15
N2798 20 ch. Freighter "Hwanggumsan" 60 20
N2799 30 ch. Freighter "Changjasan Chongnyon-ho" 75 25
N2800 40 ch. Liner "Samjiyon" . . 1·00 30

941 "Hansa"

1988. 150th Birth Anniv of Count Ferdinand von Zeppelin (airship pioneer). Multicoloured.

N2801 10 ch. Type **941** 40 10
N2802 20 ch. "Schwaben" 75 15
N2803 30 ch. "Viktoria Luise" . . 90 20
N2804 40 ch. LZ-3 . . . . . . 1·25 25

942 Kim Il Sung and Jambyn Batmunkh

944 Tower of Juche Idea

943 Hero and Labour Hero of the D.P.R.K. Medals

1988. Kim Il Sung's Visit to Mongolia.

N2806 **942** 10 ch. multicoloured . . 20 10

1988. National Heroes Congress.

N2807 **943** 10 ch. multicoloured . . 20 10

1988. 40th Anniv of Democratic Republic. Multicoloured.

N2808 5 ch. Type **944** 10 10
N2809 10 ch. Smelter and industrial buildings 20 10
N2810 10 ch. Soldier and Mt. Paekdu 20 10
N2811 10 ch. Map of Korea and globe 20 10
N2812 10 ch. Hand holding banner, globe and doves 20 10

945 "Sunflowers" (Vincent van Gogh)

946 Emblem

1988. "Filacept 88" Stamp Exhibition, The Hague. Multicoloured.

N2814 40 ch. Type **945** . . . . . . 1·50 25
N2815 60 ch. "The Chess Game" (Lucas van Leyden) (horiz) 2·50 35

1988. 16th Session of Socialist Countries' Post and Telecommunications Conference, Pyongyang.

N2816 **946** 10 ch. multicoloured . . 20 10

947 Chaju "82" 10-ton Truck

948 "Owl"

1988. Tipper Trucks. Multicoloured.

N2817 20 ch. Type **947** 40 15
N2818 40 ch. Kumsusan-ho 40-ton truck 75 25

1988. Paintings by O Un Byol. Multicoloured.

N2819 10 ch. Type **948** . . . . . . 1·75 20
N2820 15 ch. "Dawn" (red junglefowl) 80 20
N2821 20 ch. "Beautiful Rose received by Kim Il Sung" 60 15
N2822 25 ch. "Sun and Bamboo" 75 15
N2823 30 ch. "Autumn" (fruit tree) 85 20

949 "Chunggi" Steam Locomotive No. 35

1988. Railway Locomotives. Multicoloured.

N2824 10 ch. Type **949** 70 10
N2825 20 ch. "Chunggi" steam locomotive No. 22 . . . 95 15
N2826 30 ch. "Chongiha" electric locomotive No. 3 . . . 1·10 20
N2827 40 ch. "Chunggi" steam locomotive No. 307 . . . 1·40 25

950 Pirmen Zurbriggen (downhill skiing)

1988. Winter Olympic Games, Calgary, Medal Winners. Multicoloured.

N2828 10 ch. Type **950** 20 10
N2829 20 ch. Yvonne van Gennip (speed skating) 40 15
N2830 30 ch. Marjo Matikainen (cross-country skiing) . . 55 20
N2831 40 ch. U.S.S.R. (ice hockey) (horiz) 75 25

951 Yury Gagarin

1988. 1st Man and Woman in Space. Mult.

N2833 20 ch. Type **951** 40 15
N2834 40 ch. Valentina Tereshkova 75 25

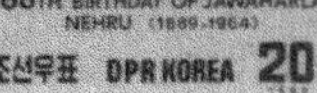

952 Nehru

953 Chollima Statue

1988. Birth Centenary of Jawaharlal Nehru (Indian statesman) and "India 89" International Stamp Exhibition, New Delhi.

N2835 **952** 20 ch. purple, black and gold 60 15

1989. New Year. Multicoloured.

N2837 10 ch. Type **953** 20 10
N2838 20 ch. "The Dragon Angler" (17th-century painting) 60 15
N2839 40 ch. "Tortoise and Serpent" (Kangso tomb painting) (horiz) 90 25

954 Archery

1989. National Defence Training. Multicoloured.

N2840 10 ch. Type **954** 90 10
N2841 15 ch. Rifle shooting 30 10
N2842 20 ch. Pistol shooting . . . 40 15
N2843 25 ch. Parachuting 50 15
N2844 30 ch. Launching model glider 55 20

955 Dobermann Pinscher

957 Agriculture

1989. Animals presented to Kim Il Sung. Mult.

N2845 10 ch. Type **955** 50 10
N2846 20 ch. Labrador 70 15
N2847 25 ch. German shepherd . . 1·00 15
N2848 30 ch. Rough collies (horiz) 1·00 20
N2849 35 ch. Serval (horiz) . . . . 1·25 20

1989. 25th Anniv of Publication of "Theses on the Socialist Rural Question in our Country" by Kim Il Sung.

N2852 **957** 10 ch. multicoloured . . 40 10

958 The Gypsy and Grapes

959 Korean Girl

1989. Fungi and Fruits. Multicoloured.

N2853 10 ch. Type **958** 50 10
N2854 20 ch. Caesar's mushroom and magnolia vine 80 15
N2855 25 ch. "Lactarius hygrophoides" and "Eleagnus crispa" . . . 1·10 15
N2856 30 ch. "Agaricus placomyces" and Chinese gooseberries 1·25 20
N2857 35 ch. Horse mushroom and "Lycium chinense" . . 1·50 20
N2858 40 ch. Elegant boletus and "Juglans cordiformis" . . 1·75 25

1989. 13th World Youth and Students' Festival, Pyongyang (2nd issue). Multicoloured.

N2860 10 ch. Type **959** 20 10
N2861 20 ch. Children of different races 40 15
N2862 30 ch. Fairy and rainbow . . 55 20
N2863 40 ch. Young peoples and Tower of Juche Idea . . . 45 25

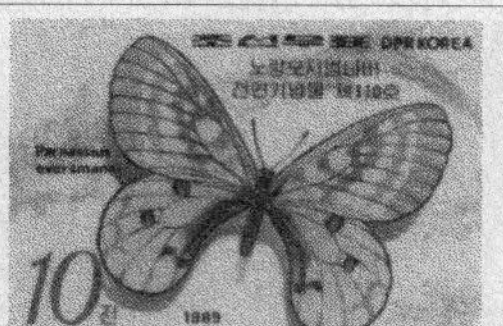
960 "Parnassius eversmanni"

1969. Insects. Multicoloured.

N2864 10 ch. Type **960** 50 15
N2865 15 ch. "Colias heos" 60 15
N2866 20 ch. "Dilipa fenestra" . . 70 15
N2867 25 ch. "Buthus martensis" 80 15
N2868 30 ch. "Trichogramma ostriniae" 95 15
N2869 40 ch. "Damaster constricticollis" . . . . . 1·00 15

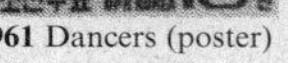

961 Dancers (poster) **962** Birthplace, Mangyongdae

1989. Spring Friendship Art Festival, Pyongyang.
N2871 **961** 10 ch. multicoloured . . 45 10

1989. 77th Birthday of Kim Il Sung.
N2872 **962** 10 ch. multicoloured . . 20 10

963 Battle Plan and Monument to the Victory

1989. 50th Anniv of Battle of the Musan Area.
N2873 **963** 10 ch. blue, flesh & red 60 10

964 Modern Dance

1989. Chamo System of Dance Notation. Multicoloured.
N2874 10 ch. Type **964** 55 10
N2875 20 ch. Ballet 70 15
N2876 25 ch. Modern dance (different) 85 15
N2877 30 ch. Traditional dance . . 1·00 20

965 Hands supporting Torch **966** Victorious Badger

1989. 13th World Youth and Students' Festival, Pyongyang (3rd issue).
N2879 **965** 5 ch. blue 10 10
N2880 – 10 ch. brown 20 10
DESIGN: 10 ch. Youth making speech.

1989. "Badger measures the Height" (cartoon film). Multicoloured.
N2881 10 ch. Cat, bear and badger race to flag pole 80 10
N2882 40 ch. Cat and bear climb pole while badger measures shadow . . . . 1·25 25
N2883 50 ch. Type **966** . . . . . . 1·50 30

MINIMUM PRICE

The minimum price quoted is 10p which represents a handling charge rather than a basis for valuing common stamps. For further notes about prices see introductory pages.

967 Kyongju Observatory and Star Chart **969** Pele (footballer) and 1978 25 ch. Stamp

1989. Astronomy.
N2884 **967** 20 ch. multicoloured . . 1·00 15

1989. "Brasiliana 89" International Stamp Exhibition, Rio de Janeiro.
N2887 **969** 40 ch. multicoloured . . 1·25 25

970 Nurse and Ambulance

1989. Emergency Services. Multicoloured.
N2888 10 ch. Type **970** 20 10
N2889 20 ch. Surgeon and ambulance 30 15
N2890 30 ch. Fireman and fire engine 2·25 20
N2891 40 ch. Fireman and engine (different) . . . . 2·25 25

971 Kaffir Lily **972** Air Mail Letter and Postal Transport

1989. Plants presented to Kim Il Sung. Mult.
N2892 10 ch. Type **971** 40 10
N2893 15 ch. Tulips 50 10
N2894 20 ch. Flamingo lily 75 15
N2895 25 ch. "Rhododendron obtusum" 90 15
N2896 30 ch. Daffodils . . . . . . 1·00 20

1989. 150th Anniv of the Penny Black and "Stamp World London 90" International Stamp Exhibition (1st issue). Multicoloured.
N2898 5 ch. Type **972** 40 10
N2899 10 ch. Post box and letters 55 10
N2900 20 ch. Stamps, tweezers and magnifying glass 60 15
N2901 30 ch. First North Korean stamps 75 20
N2902 40 ch. Universal Postal Union emblem and headquarters, Berne . . . . 1·00 25
N2903 50 ch. Sir Rowland Hill and Penny Black . . . . . . 1·25 30
See also No. N2956.

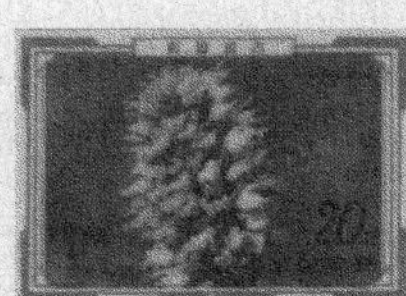
973 "Bistorta incana"

1989. Alpine Flowers. Multicoloured.
N2904 10 ch. "Iris setosa" 50 10
N2905 15 ch. "Aquilegia japonica" 60 10
N2906 20 ch. Type **973** 75 15
N2907 25 ch. "Rodiola elongata" . 90 15
N2908 30 ch. "Sanguisorba sitchensis" 95 20

974 Tree, Mt. Paekdu **975** Skipping

1989. Slogan-bearing Trees (1st series). Mult.
N2910 10 ch. Type **974** 20 10
N2911 3 wn. Tree, Oun-dong, Pyongyang . . . . . . 5·50 1·75
N2912 5 wn. Tree, Mt. Kanbaek . . 9·50 3·25
See also No. N2931.

1989. Children's Games. Multicoloured.
N2913 10 ch. Type **975** 20 10
N2914 20 ch. Windmill . . . . . 1·25 15
N2915 30 ch. Kite 55 20
N2916 40 ch. Whip and top 75 25

977 Diesel Train and Sinpa Youth Station

1989. Railway Locomotives. Multicoloured.
N2918 10 ch. Type **977** 40 10
N2919 20 ch. "Pulgungi" electric locomotive 60 15
N2920 25 ch. Diesel goods train . . 70 15
N2921 30 ch. Diesel train 85 20
N2922 40 ch. Steam locomotive . . 1·00 25
N2923 50 ch. Steam locomotive (different) . . . . 1·10 30

978 Players and Map of Italy

1989. World Cup Football Championship, Italy (2nd issue). Multicoloured.
N2924 10 ch. Type **978** . . . . . . 1·00 10
N2925 20 ch. Free kick 50 15
N2926 30 ch. Goal mouth scrimmage 75 20
N2927 40 ch. Goalkeeper diving for ball 95 25

979 Megellan (navigator) and his Ship "Vitoria"

1989. "Descobrex '89" International Stamp Exhibition, Portugal.
N2928 **979** 30 ch. multicoloured . . 1·25 20

980 Mangyong Hill and Pine Branches **981** Ryukwoli

1990. New Year. Multicoloured.
N2929 10 ch. Type **980** 20 10
N2930 20 ch. Koguryo mounted archers 90 15

1990. Slogan-bearing Trees (2nd series). As T **974**. Multicoloured.
N2931 5 ch. Tree, Mt. Paekdu . . . 25 10

1990. Dogs. Multicoloured.
N2932 20 ch. Type **981** . . . . . . 1·25 20
N2933 30 ch. Palryuki . . . . . . 1·25 20
N2934 40 ch. Komdungi . . . . . 1·25 20
N2935 50 ch. Oulruki . . . . . . 1·25 20

982 Birthplace, Mt. Paekdu **983** Stone Instruments and Primitive Man

1990. Birthday of Kim Jong Il.
N2936 **982** 10 ch. brown 20 10

1990. Evolution of Man. Multicoloured.
N2937 10 ch. Type **983** 45 10
N2938 40 ch. Palaeolithic and Neolithic man 90 25

984 Rungna Bridge, Pyongyang

1990. Bridges. Multicoloured.
N2939 10 ch. Type **984** 45 10
N2940 20 ch. Potong bridge, Pyongyang 60 15
N2941 30 ch. Sinuiji-Ryucho Island Bridge 85 20
N2942 40 ch. Chungsongui Bridge, Pyongyang . . . . . . 1·10 25

985 Infantryman **987** Dancers (poster)

986 "Atergatis subdentatus"

1990. Warriors' Costumes. Multicoloured.
N2943 20 ch. Type **985** 40 15
N2944 30 ch. Archer 55 20
N2945 50 ch. Military commander in armour 95 30
N2946 70 ch. Officer's costume, 10th–14th centuries . . . . . 1·25 40
Nos. N2943/5 depict costumes from the 3rd century B.C. to the 7th century A.D.

1990. Crabs. Multicoloured.
N2947 20 ch. Type **986** 60 15
N2948 30 ch. "Platylambrus validus" 75 20
N2949 50 ch. "Uca arcuata" . . . 1·10 30

1990. Spring Friendship Art Festival, Pyongyang.
N2950 **987** 10 ch. multicoloured . . 30 10

988 Monument at Road Folk, Mangyongdae **989** "Gymnocalycium sp."

1990. 78th Birthday of Kim Il Sung.
N2951 **988** 10 ch. green and gold 20 10

1990. Cacti. Multicoloured.
N2953 10 ch. Type **989** 50 10
N2954 30 ch. "Pyllocactus hybridus" 90 20
N2955 50 ch. "Epiphyllum truncatum" . . . . . . 1·50 30

990 Exhibition Emblem **991** Congo Peafowl

1990. "Stamp World London 90" International Stamp Exhibition (2nd issue).
N2956 **990** 20 ch. red and black . . 40 15

1990. Peafowl. Multicoloured.
N2958 10 ch. Type **991** 50 10
N2959 20 ch. Common peafowl . . 1·00 20

992 Dolphin and Submarine

1990. Bio-engineering. Multicoloured.

N2961	10 ch. Type **992**	1·10	25
N2962	20 ch. Bat and dish aerial	1·10	25
N2963	30 ch. Owl and Tupolev Tu-154 jetliner	1·10	30
N2964	40 ch. Squid, "Soyuz" rocket and Concorde supersonic jetliner	1·10	25

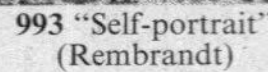

993 "Self-portrait" (Rembrandt)

994 K. H. Rummenigge (footballer)

1990. "Belgica 90" International Stamp Exhibition, Brussels. Multicoloured.

N2965	10 ch. Type **993**	30	10
N2966	20 ch. "Self-portrait" (Raphael)	60	15
N2967	30 ch. "Self-portrait" (Rubens)	75	20

1990. "Dusseldorf '90" International Youth Stamp Exhibition. Multicoloured.

N2968	20 ch. Steffi Graf (tennis player)	85	15
N2969	30 ch. Exhibition emblem	55	20
N2970	70 ch. Type **994**	1·25	40

995 Workers' Stadium, Peking, and Games Mascot

1990. 11th Asian Games, Peking (Nos. N2971/2) and 3rd Asian Winter Games, Samjiyon (N2973). Multicoloured.

N2971	10 ch. Type **995**	30	10
N2972	30 ch. Chollima Statue and sportsmen	75	20
N2973	40 ch. Sportsmen and Games emblem	1·00	25

996 Ball

1990. West Germany, Winners of World Cup Football Championship. Multicoloured.

N2974	15 ch. Emblem of F.I.F.A. (International Federation of Football Associations)	40	10
N2975	20 ch. Jules Rimet	50	15
N2976	25 ch. Type **996**	60	15
N2977	30 ch. Olympic Stadium, Rome (venue of final)	65	20
N2978	35 ch. Goalkeeper	75	20
N2979	40 ch. Emblem of West German Football Association	90	25

997 Kakapo and Map of New Zealand

1990. "New Zealand 1990" International Stamp Exhibition, Auckland.

No.	Type	Description		
N2981	**997**	30 ch. multicoloured	1·25	40

999 Head of Procession

1990. Koguryo Wedding Procession. Mult.

N2983	10 ch. Type **999**	1·00	20
N2984	30 ch. Bridegroom	1·00	20
N2985	50 ch. Bride in carriage	1·00	20
N2986	1 wn. Drummer on horse	1·00	20

Nos. N2983/6 were issued together, se-tenant, forming a composite design.

1000 Marchers descending Mt. Paekdu

1990. Rally for Peace and Reunification of Korea.

No.	Type	Description		
N2987	**1000**	10 ch. multicoloured	20	10

1001 Praying Mantis

1990. Insects. Multicoloured.

N2989	20 ch. Type **1001**	40	15
N2990	30 ch. Ladybird	55	20
N2991	40 ch. "Pheropsophus jessoensis"	75	25
N2992	70 ch. "Phyllium siccifolium"	1·25	40

1002 Footballers

1990. North–South Reunification Football Match, Pyongyang. Multicoloured.

N2993	10 ch. Type **1002**	75	10
N2994	20 ch. Footballers (different)	75	15

1003 Concert Emblem

1004 Ox

1990. National Reunification Concert.

No.	Type	Description		
N2996	**1003**	10 ch. multicoloured	20	10

1990. Farm Animals.

No.	Type	Description		
N2997	**1004**	10 ch. brown & green	20	10
N2998	–	20 ch. lilac & yellow	40	15
N2999	–	30 ch. grey and red	55	20
N3000	–	40 ch. green and yellow	75	25
N3001	–	50 ch. brown and blue	95	30

DESIGNS: 20 ch. Pig; 30 ch. Goat; 40 ch. Sheep; 50 ch. Horse.

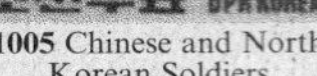

1005 Chinese and North Korean Soldiers

1006 Anniversary Emblem

1990. 40th Anniv of Participation of Chinese Volunteers in Korean War. Multicoloured.

N3002	10 ch. Type **1005**	20	10
N3003	20 ch. Populace welcoming volunteers (horiz)	40	15
N3004	30 ch. Rejoicing soldiers and battle scene (horiz)	50	20
N3005	40 ch. Post-war reconstruction (horiz)	60	25

1990. 40th Anniv of United Nations Development Programme.

No.	Type	Description		
N3007	**1006**	1 wn. blue, silver & blk	1·90	65

1007 Mikado Sturgeon

1008 Sheep

1990. Fishes.

No.	Type	Description		
N3008	**1007**	10 ch. brown & green	25	10
N3009	–	20 ch. green and blue	55	15
N3010	–	30 ch. blue and purple	75	25
N3011	–	40 ch. brown and blue	1·00	30
N3012	–	50 ch. violet and green	1·25	35

DESIGNS: 20 ch. Large-headed seabream; 30 ch. Agoo flyingfish; 40 ch. Fat greenling; 50 ch. Tobiji-ei eagle ray.

1990. New Year.

No.	Type	Description		
N3013	**1008**	40 ch. multicoloured	75	25

1009 Moorhen

1010 Giant Panda

1990. Birds.

No.	Type	Description		
N3014	**1009**	10 ch. blue, grn & blk	45	10
N3015	–	20 ch. brown, bistre and black	70	25
N3016	–	30 ch. green, grey and black	90	35
N3017	–	40 ch. brown, orange and black	1·25	45
N3018	–	50 ch. ochre, brown and black	1·75	55

DESIGNS: 20 ch. Jay; 30 ch. Three-toed woodpecker; 40 ch. Whimbrel; 50 ch. Water rail.

1991. "Phila Nippon '91" International Stamp Exhibition, Tokyo. Multicoloured.

N3019	10 ch. Type **1010**	30	10
N3020	20 ch. Two giant pandas feeding	50	15
N3021	30 ch. Giant panda clambering onto branch	70	20
N3022	40 ch. Giant panda on rock	90	25
N3023	50 ch. Two giant pandas	1·10	30
N3024	60 ch. Giant panda in tree fork	1·25	35

1011 Changsan

1991. Revolutionary Sites.

N3026	5 ch. Type **1011**	10	10
N3027	10 ch. Oun	20	10

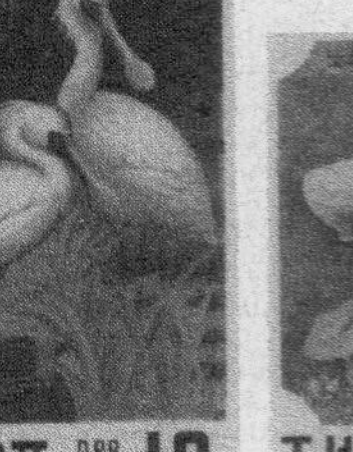

1012 Black-faced Spoonbills

1014 Hedgehog Fungus

1013 "Clossiana angarensis"

1991. Endangered Birds. Multicoloured.

N3028	10 ch. Type **1012**	25	10
N3029	20 ch. Grey herons	50	15
N3030	30 ch. Great egrets	70	25
N3031	40 ch. Manchurian cranes	95	30
N3032	50 ch. Japanese white-necked cranes	1·25	35
N3033	70 ch. White storks	1·75	50

1991. Alpine Butterflies. Multicoloured.

N3034	10 ch. Type **1013**	25	10
N3035	20 ch. "Erebia embla"	40	15
N3036	30 ch. Camberwell beauty	60	20
N3037	40 ch. Comma	75	30
N3038	50 ch. Eastern pale clouded yellow	90	35
N3039	60 ch. "Theela betulae"	1·10	45

1991. Fungi. Multicoloured.

N3040	10 ch. Type **1014**	25	10
N3041	20 ch. "Phylloporus rhodoxanthus"	45	15
N3042	30 ch. "Calvatia craniiformis"	60	20
N3043	40 ch. Cauliflower clavaria	80	30
N3044	50 ch. "Russula integra"	1·00	35

1015 Kumchon

1991. Revolutionary Sites. Multicoloured.

N3045	10 ch. Type **1015**	15	10
N3046	40 ch. Samdung	60	30

1016 Dr. Kye Ung Sang (researcher)

1017 Emblem and Venue

1991. Silkworm Research. Multicoloured.

N3047	10 ch. Type **1016**	15	10
N3048	20 ch. Chinese oak silk moth	30	15
N3049	30 ch. "Attacus ricini"	45	20
N3050	40 ch. "Antheraea yamamai"	60	30
N3051	50 ch. Silkworm moth	75	35
N3052	60 ch. "Aetias artemis"	90	45

1991. 9th Spring Friendship Art Festival, Pyongyang.

No.	Type	Description		
N3053	**1017**	10 ch. multicoloured	10	10

1018 Emperor Penguins

1020 Map and Kim Jong Ho

1019 People's Palace of Culture (venue)

1991. Antarctic Exploration. Multicoloured.

N3054		10 ch. Type **1018**	40	15
N3055		20 ch. Research station	40	15
N3056		30 ch. Elephant seals	75	20
N3057		40 ch. Research ship	1·00	30
N3058		50 ch. Southern black-backed gulls	1·50	35

1991. 85th Interparliamentary Union Conference, Pyongyang.

N3060	**1019**	10 ch. dp green, grn & sil	15	10
N3061	–	1 wn. 50 multicoloured	2·25	1·10

DESIGN: 1 wn. 50, Conference emblem and azalea.

1991. 130th Anniv of Publication of Kim Jong Ho's Map "Taidong Yu Jido".

N3062	**1020**	90 ch. black, brn & sil	1·40	70

1021 Cynognathus

1991. Dinosaurs. Multicoloured.

N3063		10 ch. Type **1021**	25	10
N3064		20 ch. Brontosaurus	40	15
N3065		30 ch. Stegosaurus and allosaurus	55	20
N3066		40 ch. Pterosauria	70	30
N3067		50 ch. Ichthyosaurus	85	35

1022 Sprinting

1991. Olympic Games, Barcelona (1992 (1st issue). Multicoloured.

N3068		10 ch. Type **1022**	15	10
N3069		10 ch. Hurdling	15	10
N3070		20 ch. Long jumping	30	15
N3071		20 ch. Throwing the discus	30	15
N3072		30 ch. Putting the shot	45	20
N3073		30 ch. Pole vaulting	45	20
N3074		40 ch. High jumping	60	30
N3075		40 ch. Throwing the javelin	60	30

See also Nos. N3142/7.

1023 Cats and Tree Sparrows

1991. Cats. Multicoloured.

N3077		10 ch. Type **1023**	40	10
N3078		20 ch. Cat and rat	40	15
N3079		30 ch. Cat and butterfly	55	20
N3080		40 ch. Cats with ball	75	30
N3081		50 ch. Cat and frog	90	35

1025 Wild Horse

1991. Horses. Multicoloured.

N3083		10 ch. Type **1025**	25	10
N3084		20 ch. Hybrid of wild ass and wild horse	40	15
N3085		30 ch. Przewalski's horse	60	20
N3086		40 ch. Wild ass	75	30
N3087		50 ch. Wild horse (different)	90	35

1026 Pennant Coralfish

1991. Fishes. Multicoloured.

N3088		10 ch. Type **1026** (postage)	40	10
N3089		20 ch. Clown triggerfish	75	25
N3090		30 ch. Tomato anemonefish	1·00	30
N3091		40 ch. Palette surgeonfish	1·40	45
N3092		50 ch. Freshwater angelfish (air)	1·60	55

1027 Rhododendrons

1991. Flowers. Multicoloured.

N3094		10 ch. Begonia	25	10
N3095		20 ch. Gerbera	40	15
N3096		30 ch. Type **1027**	55	20
N3097		40 ch. Phalaenopsis	70	30
N3098		50 ch. "Impatiens sultanii"	85	35
N3099		60 ch. Streptocarpus	1·00	45

Nos. N3097/9 commemorate "CANADA '92" international youth stamp exhibition, Montreal.

1028 Panmunjom

1991.

N3100	**1028**	10 ch. multicoloured	15	10

1029 Magnolia **1030** Players

1991. National Flower.

N3101	**1029**	10 ch. multicoloured	40	10

1991. Women's World Football Championship, China. Multicoloured.

N3102		10 ch. Type **1030**	25	10
N3103		20 ch. Dribbling the ball	40	15
N3104		30 ch. Heading the ball	55	20
N3105		40 ch. Overhead kick	70	30
N3106		50 ch. Tackling	85	35
N3107		60 ch. Goalkeeper	1·10	45

1031 Squirrel Monkeys

1992. Monkeys. Multicoloured.

N3108		10 ch. Type **1031**	25	10
N3109		20 ch. Pygmy marmosets	40	15
N3110		30 ch. Red-handed tamarins	60	20

1032 Eagle Owl

1992. Birds of Prey. Multicoloured.

N3112		10 ch. Type **1032**	15	10
N3113		20 ch. Common buzzard	30	15
N3114		30 ch. African fish eagle	1·00	30
N3115		40 ch. Steller's sea eagle	60	30
N3116		50 ch. Golden eagle	75	35

1033 Birthplace, Mt. Paekdu

1992. Birthday of Kim Jong Il. Mt. Paekdu. Multicoloured.

N3118		10 ch. Type **1033**	15	10
N3119		20 ch. Mountain summit	30	15
N3120		30 ch. Lake Chon (crater lake)	45	20
N3121		40 ch. Lake Sarryi	60	30

1034 Service Bus

1992. Transport.

N3123	**1034**	10 ch. multicoloured	25	10
N3124	–	20 ch. multicoloured	40	15
N3125	–	30 ch. multicoloured	60	20
N3126	–	40 ch. multicoloured	75	30
N3127	–	50 ch. multicoloured	90	35
N3128	–	60 ch. multicoloured	1·10	45

DESIGNS: 20 ch. to 60 ch. Different buses and electric trams.

1035 Dancers and Emblem

1992. Spring Friendship Art Festival, Pyongyang.

N3129	**1035**	10 ch. multicoloured	30	10

1036 Birthplace, Mangyongdae

1992. 80th Birthday of Kim Il Sung. Revolutionary Sites. Multicoloured.

N3130		10 ch. Type **1036** (postage)	15	10
N3131		10 ch. Party emblem and Turubong monument	15	10
N3132		10 ch. Map and Ssuksom	15	10
N3133		10 ch. Statue of soldier and Tongchang	15	10
N3134		40 ch. Cogwheels and Taean	60	30
N3135		40 ch. Chollima Statue and Kangson	60	30
N3136		1 wn. 20 Monument and West Sea Barrage (air)	1·75	85

1038 Soldiers on Parade

1992. 60th Anniv of People's Army. Multicoloured.

N3139		10 ch. Type **1038**	15	10
N3140		10 ch. Couple greeting soldier	15	10
N3141		10 ch. Army, air force and navy personnel	15	10

1039 Hurdling

1992. Olympic Games, Barcelona (2nd issue). Multicoloured.

N3142		10 ch. Type **1039**	25	10
N3143		20 ch. High jumping	40	15
N3144		30 ch. Putting the shot	60	20
N3145		40 ch. Sprinting	75	30
N3146		50 ch. Long jumping	90	35
N3147		60 ch. Throwing the javelin	1·10	45

1040 Planting Crops

1992. Evolution of Man. Designs showing life in the New Stone Age (10, 20 ch.) and the Bronze Age (others). Multicoloured.

N3149		10 ch. Type **1040** (postage)	15	10
N3150		20 ch. Family around cooking pot	30	15
N3151		30 ch. Ploughing fields	45	20
N3152		40 ch. Performing domestic chores	60	30
N3153		50 ch. Building a dolmen (air)	75	35

1041 White-bellied Black Woodpecker **1042** Map and Hands holding Text

1992. Birds. Multicoloured.

N3154		10 ch. Type **1041**	15	10
N3155		20 ch. Ring-necked pheasant	30	15
N3156		30 ch. White stork	45	20
N3157		40 ch. Blue-winged pitta	60	30
N3158		50 ch. Pallas's sandgrouse	75	35
N3159		60 ch. Black grouse	90	45

1992. 20th Anniv of Publication of North–South Korea Joint Agreement.

N3161	**1042**	1 wn. 50 multicoloured	90	30

1043 "Bougainvillea spectabilis" **1044** Venus, Earth, Mars and Satellite

1992. Flowers. Multicoloured.

N3163		10 ch. Type **1043**	25	10
N3164		20 ch. "Ixora chinensis"	40	15
N3165		30 ch. "Dendrobium taysuwie"	60	20
N3166		40 ch. "Columnea gloriosa"	75	30
N3167		50 ch. "Crinum"	90	35
N3168		60 ch. "Ranunculus asiaticus"	1·10	45

1992. The Solar System. Multicoloured.

N3169		50 ch. Type **1044**	90	35
N3170		50 ch. Jupiter	90	35
N3171		50 ch. Saturn	90	35
N3172		50 ch. Uranus	90	35
N3173		50 ch. Neptune and Pluto	90	35

Nos. N3169/73 were issued together, se-tenant, forming a composite design.

1045 "470" Dinghy **1046** Moreno Mannini (defender)

1992. "Riccione '92" Stamp Fair. Multicoloured.

N3175		10 ch. Type **1045**	15	10
N3176		20 ch. Sailboard	30	15
N3177		30 ch. Sailing dinghy	45	20
N3178		40 ch. "Finn" dinghy	60	30
N3179		50 ch. "420" dinghy	75	35
N3180		60 ch. Fair emblem	90	45

1992. Sampdoria, Italian Football Champion, 1991. Multicoloured.

N3181		20 ch. Type **1046**	30	15
N3182		30 ch. Gianluca Vialli (forward)	45	30
N3183		40 ch. Pietro Vierchowod (defender)	60	30
N3184		50 ch. Fausto Pari (defender)	75	35
N3185		60 ch. Roberto Mancini (forward)	90	45
N3186		1 wn. Paolo Mantovani (club president)	1·50	75

1047 Black-belts warming up

1992. 8th World Taekwondo Championship, Pyongyang. Multicoloured.
N3188 10 ch. Type **1047** 15 10
N3189 30 ch. "Roundhouse" kick 45 30
N3190 50 ch. High kick 75 35
N3191 70 ch. Flying kick . . . . . 1·00 50
N3192 90 ch. Black-belt breaking tiles with fist . . . . 1·40 70

1048 Common Toad ("Bufo bufo")

1992. Frogs and Toads. Multicoloured.
N3194 40 ch. Type **1048** (postage) . 75 30
N3195 40 ch. Moor frog ("Rana arvalis") 75 30
N3196 40 ch. "Rana chosenica" . . 75 30
N3197 70 ch. Common pond frog ("Rana nigromaculata") 1·25 50
N3198 70 ch. Japanese tree toad ("Hyla japonica") . . . . 1·25 50
N3199 70 ch. "Rana coreana" (air) 1·25 50

1049 "Rhododendron mucronulatum"

1992. World Environment Day. Multicoloured.
N3200 10 ch. Type **1049** (postage) . 15 10
N3201 30 ch. Barn swallow 45 20
N3202 40 ch. "Stewartia koreana" (flower) 60 30
N3203 50 ch. "Dictyoptera aurora" (beetle) 75 35
N3204 70 ch. "Metasequoia glyptostroboides" (tree) 1·00 50
N3205 90 ch. Chinese salamander 1·40 70
N3206 1 wn. 20 "Ginkgo biloba" (tree) (air) . . . . . . 1·75 85
N3207 1 wn. 40 Alpine bullhead . . 3·00 1·25

1050 Fin Whale ("Balaenoptera physalus")

1992. Whales and Dolphins. Multicoloured.
N3208 50 ch. Type **1050** (postage) . 1·00 35
N3209 50 ch. Common dolphin ("Delphinus delphis") . . 1·00 35
N3210 50 ch. Killer Whale ("Orcinus orca") . . . . 1·00 35
N3211 50 ch. Hump-backed whale ("Megaptera nodosa") . . 1·00 35
N3212 50 ch. Bottle-nosed whale ("Berardius bairdii") . . 1·00 35
N3213 50 ch. Sperm whale ("Physeter catadon") (air) . . . . . 1·00 35

1051 Mother and Chicks

1992. New Year. Roosters in various costumes. Multicoloured.
N3214 10 ch. Type **1051** 15 10
N3215 20 ch. Lady 30 15
N3216 30 ch. Warrior 45 20
N3217 40 ch. Courtier 60 30
N3218 50 ch. Queen 75 35
N3219 60 ch. King 90 45

1052 Choe Chol Su (boxing)

1992. Gold Medal Winners at Barcelona Olympics. Multicoloured.
N3221 10 ch. Type **1052** 15 10
N3222 20 ch. Pae Kil Su (gymnastics) 30 15
N3223 50 ch. Ri Hak Son (freestyle wrestling) 75 35
N3224 60 ch. Kim Il (freestyle wrestling) 90 45

1053 Golden Mushroom

1055 League Members and Flag

1054 "Keumkangsania asiatica"

1993. Fungi. Multicoloured.
N3227 10 ch. Type **1053** 15 10
N3228 20 ch. Shaggy caps 30 15
N3229 30 ch. "Ganoderma lucidum" 45 20
N3230 40 ch. Brown mushroom 60 30
N3231 50 ch. "Volvaria bombycina" 75 35
N3232 60 ch. "Sarcodon aspratus" . 90 45

1993. Plants. Multicoloured.
N3234 10 ch. Type **1054** 25 10
N3235 20 ch. "Echinosophora koreensis" 80 15
N3236 30 ch. "Abies koreana" . . 55 20
N3237 40 ch. "Benzoin angustifolium" 75 30
N3238 50 ch. "Abeliophyllum distichum" 85 35
N3239 60 ch. "Abelia mosanensis" 1·00 45

1993. 8th League of Socialist Working Youth Congress. Multicoloured.
N3241 10 ch. Type **1055** 15 10
N3242 40 ch. Flame, League emblem and text 60 30

1056 Phophyong Revolutionary Site Tower and March Corps Emblem

1057 Tower of Juche Idea and Grand Monument, Mt. Wangjae

1993. 70th Anniv of 1000-ri Journey for Learning.
N3243 **1056** 10 ch. multicoloured 15 10

1993. 60th Anniv of Wangjaesan Meeting.
N3244 **1057** 5 ch. multicoloured . . 10 10

1058 "Kimjomgil" (begonia)

1059 Pilot Fish

1993. 51st Birthday of Kim Jong Il.
N3245 **1058** 10 ch. multicoloured 40 10

1993. Fishes. Multicoloured.
N3247 10 ch. Type **1059** 25 10
N3248 20 ch. Japanese stingray . . 55 20
N3249 30 ch. Opah 80 30
N3250 40 ch. Coelacanth . . . . 1·10 45
N3251 50 ch. Moara grouper . . . 1·25 50

MINIMUM PRICE

The minimum price quoted is 10p which represents a handling charge rather than a basis for valuing common stamps. For further notes about prices see introductory pages.

1060/1064 "Spring on the Hill" (½-size illustration)

1993. 18th-century Korean Painting.
N3253 **1060** 40 ch. multicoloured . 60 30
N3254 **1061** 40 ch. multicoloured . 60 30
N3255 **1062** 40 ch. multicoloured . 60 30
N3256 **1063** 40 ch. multicoloured . 60 30
N3257 **1064** 40 ch. multicoloured . 60 30
Nos. N3253/7 were issued together, se-tenant, forming the composite design illustrated.

1065 Violinist, Dancers and Emblem

1993. Spring Friendship Art Festival, Pyongyang.
N3258 **1065** 10 ch. multicoloured 15 10

1066 Books

1993. 81st Birthday of Kim Il Sung and Publication of his Reminiscences "With the Century".
N3259 **1066** 10 ch. multicoloured 15 10

1067 Kwangbok Street

1993. Pyongyang. Multicoloured.
N3261 10 ch. Type **1067** 15 10
N3262 20 ch. Chollima Street . . . 30 15
N3263 30 ch. Munsu Street 45 20
N3264 40 ch. Moranbong Street . . 60 30
N3265 50 ch. Thongil Street . . . 75 35

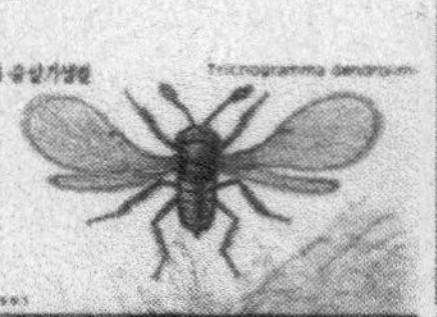
1068 "Trichogramma dendrolimi" (fly)

1069 Ri In Mo

1993. Insects. Multicoloured.
N3267 10 ch. Type **1068** 15 10
N3268 20 ch. "Brachymeria obscurata" (fly) 30 15
N3269 30 ch. "Metrioptera brachyptera" (cricket) . . 45 20
N3270 50 ch. European field cricket 75 35
N3271 70 ch. "Geocoris pallidipennis" (beetle) . . 1·00 50
N3272 90 ch. "Cyphonony x dorsalis" (wasp) fighting spider . . . . 1·40 70

1993. Return from Imprisonment of Ri In Mo (war correspondent).
N3273 **1069** 10 ch. multicoloured 15 10

1070 Footballers

1071 Grey-headed Green Woodpecker

1993. World Cup Football Championship, U.S.A.
N3275 **1070** 10 ch. multicoloured 25 10
N3276 – 20 ch. multicoloured 40 15
N3277 – 30 ch. multicoloured 60 20
N3278 – 50 ch. multicoloured 90 35
N3279 – 70 ch. multicoloured 1·25 50
N3280 – 90 ch. multicoloured 1·75 70
DESIGNS: 20 ch. to 90 ch. Various footballing scenes.

1993. Birds. Multicoloured.
N3281 10 ch. Type **1071** 15 10
N3282 20 ch. King bird of paradise . 30 15
N3283 30 ch. Lesser bird of paradise 45 20
N3284 40 ch. Paradise whydah . . 60 30
N3285 50 ch. Magnificent bird of paradise 75 35
N3286 60 ch. Greater bird of paradise 90 45
Nos. N3283/4 also commemorate "Indopex '93" international stamp exhibition, Surabaya.

1072 Korean Peninsula and Flag (½-size illustration)

1993. Self-adhesive. Roul.
N3287 **1072** 1 w. 50 multicoloured 2·00 30
No. N3287 is for any one of the six stamps which together make up the design illustrated. They are peeled from a card backing.

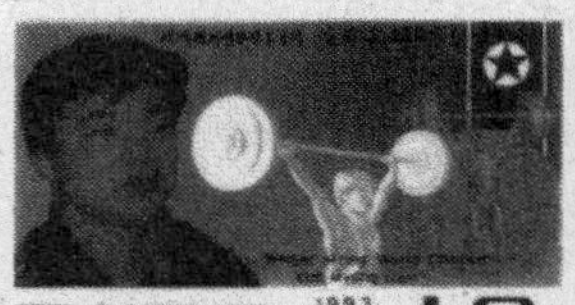
1073 Kim Myong Nam (weightlifting, 1990)

1993. World Champions. Multicoloured.
N3293 10 ch. Type **1073** 15 10
N3294 20 ch. Kim Kwang Suk (gymnastics, 1991) . . . 30 15
N3295 30 ch. Pak Yong Sun (table tennis, 1975, 1977) . . . 45 20
N3296 50 ch. Kim Yong Ok (radio direction-finding, 1990) 75 35
N3297 70 ch. Han Yun Ok (taekwondo, 1987, 1988, 1990) . . . . 1·00 50
N3298 90 ch. Kim Yong Sik (free-style wrestling, 1986, 1989) 1·40 70

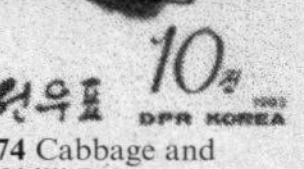
1074 Cabbage and Chilli Peppers

1075 State Arms

1993. Fruits and Vegetables. Multicoloured.
N3299 10 ch. Type **1074** 15 10
N3300 20 ch. Squirrels and horse chestnuts 30 15
N3301 30 ch. Grapes and peach 45 20
N3302 40 ch. Birds and persimmon 60 30
N3303 50 ch. Tomatoes, aubergine and cherries 75 35
N3304 60 ch. Radish, onion and garlic 90 45

1993.
N3305 **1075** 10 ch. red 15 10

1076 Soldiers and Civilians

1993. 40th Anniv of Victory in Liberation War. Multicoloured.
N3306 10 ch. Type **1076** 15 10
N3307 10 ch. Officer and soldier 15 10
N3308 10 ch. Guided missiles on low-loaders on parade 15 10
N3309 10 ch. Anti-aircraft missiles on lorries on parade 15 10

N3310 10 ch. Self-propelled missile launchers (tracked vehicles) on parade 15 10
N3311 10 ch. Machine gun emplacement (30 × 48 mm) 15 10
N3312 10 ch. Soldier holding flag (bronze statue) (30 × 48 mm) 15 10
N3314 10 ch. Kim Il Sung at strategic policy meeting 15 10
N3315 10 ch. Kim Il Sung directing battle for Height 1211 15 10
N3316 10 ch. Kim Il Sung at munitions factory 15 10
N3317 10 ch. Kim Il Sung with tank commanders 15 10
N3318 10 ch. Kim Il Sung with triumphant soldiers . . . 15 10
N3319 20 ch. Kim Il Sung with artillery unit 30 15
N3320 20 ch. Kim Il Sung encouraging machine gun crew 30 15
N3321 20 ch. Kim Il Sung studying map of Second Front . . 30 15
N3322 20 ch. Kim Il Sung with airmen 30 15
N3323 20 ch. Musicians ("Alive is art of Korea") 30 15
N3313 40 ch. Soldiers and flags ("Let us become Kim Jims and Ri Su Boks of the 90s") (30 × 48 mm) 60 30

1077 Choe Yong Do **1078** "Robinia sp."

1993. National Reunification Prize Winners. Multicoloured.
N3325 10 ch. Type **1077** 15 10
N3326 20 ch. Kim Ku 30 15
N3327 30 ch. Hong Myong Hui . . 45 20
N3328 40 ch. Ryo Un Hyong . . . 60 30
N3329 50 ch. Kim Jong Thae . . . 75 35
N3330 60 ch. Kim Chaek 90 45

1993. "Taipei '93" International Stamp Exhibition, Taipeh. Multicoloured.
N3331 20 ch. Type **1078** 40 15
N3332 30 ch. "Hippeastrum" . . . 60 20

1079 Newton

1080 King Tongmyong shooting Bow

1993. 350th Birth Anniv (1992) of Sir Isaac Newton (mathematician and scientist). Multicoloured.
N3334 10 ch. Type **1079** 25 10
N3335 20 ch. Apple tree and formula of law of gravitation . . . 40 15
N3336 30 ch. Satellite, reflecting telescope, dish aerial, globe and rocket 60 20
N3337 50 ch. Formula of binomial theorem 90 35
N3338 70 ch. Newton's works and statue . . . . 1·10 50

1993. Restoration of King Tongmyong of Koguryo's Tomb. Multicoloured.
N3339 10 ch. Type **1080** 15 10
N3340 20 ch. King Tongmyong saluting crowd 30 15
N3341 30 ch. Restoration monument 45 20
N3342 40 ch. Temple of the Tomb of King Tongmyong (horiz) . 60 30
N3343 50 ch. Tomb (horiz) 75 35

1082 "Cytropodium andresoni"

1084 Mao Tse-tung at Yanan, 1944

1993. Orchids. Multicoloured.
N3346 10 ch. Type **1082** 25 10
N3347 20 ch. "Cattleya" 40 15
N3348 30 ch. "Cattleya intermedia" "Oculata" 60 20
N3349 40 ch. Potinaria "Maysedo godensia" 75 30
N3350 50 ch. Kim Il Sung flower . 1·00 35

1993. Birth Centenary of Mao Tse-tung. Multicoloured.
N3352 10 ch. Type **1084** 15 10
N3353 20 ch. Seated portrait (Peking, 1960) 30 15
N3354 30 ch. Casting a vote, 1953 . 45 20
N3355 40 ch. With pupils at Shaoshan Secondary School, 1959 . . . . . . 60 30

1085 Phungsan

1086 Purple Hyosong Flower

1994. New Year. Dogs. Multicoloured.
N3358 10 ch. Type **1085** 15 10
N3359 20 ch. Yorkshire terriers . . 30 15
N3360 30 ch. Gordon setter 45 20
N3361 40 ch. Pomeranian 60 30
N3362 50 ch. Spaniel with pups . . 75 35

1994. 52nd Birthday of Kim Jong Il. Multicoloured.
N3364 10 ch. Type **1086** 25 10
N3365 40 ch. Yellow hyosong flower 80 30

1087 Red and Black Dragon-eyed

1994. Goldfishes. Multicoloured.
N3367 10 ch. Type **1087** 20 10
N3368 30 ch. Red and white bubble-eyed 70 30
N3369 50 ch. Red and white veil-tailed wenyu . . . . 1·10 50
N3370 70 ch. Red and white fringe-tailed . . . . 1·60 75

1088 Crowd with Banners

1089 Wheat, Banner and Woman writing

1994. 20th Anniv of Publication of "Programme for Modelling the Whole Society on the Juche Idea" by Kim Jong Il.
N3371 **1088** 20 ch. multicoloured . 30 15

1994. 30th Anniv of Publication of "Theses on the Socialist Rural Question in Our Country" by Kim Il Sung. Multicoloured.
N3373 10 ch. Type **1089** 15 10
N3374 10 ch. Electricity generating systems and pylon 15 10
N3375 10 ch. Lush fields, grain and tractor 15 10
N3376 40 ch. Modern housing, books, food crops and laboratory technician . . 60 30
N3377 40 ch. Revellers 60 30

1090 "Mangyongbong-92" (ferry)

1091 National Flag

1994. Ships. Multicoloured.
N3379 20 ch. Type **1090** 30 15
N3380 30 ch. "Osandok" (freighter) 45 20
N3381 40 ch. "Ryongaksan" (stern trawler) 60 30
N3382 50 ch. Stern trawler 75 35

1994.
N3384 **1091** 10 ch. red and blue 15 10

1092 Birthplace and Magnolia (national flower)

1093 "Chrysosplenium sphaerospermum"

1994. 82nd Birthday of Kim Il Sung. Multicoloured.
N3385 10 ch. Type **1092** 15 10
N3386 40 ch. Birthplace, Manyongdae, and Kim Il Sung flower 60 30

1994. Alpine Plants on Mt. Paekdu. Multicoloured.
N3388 10 ch. Type **1093** 25 10
N3389 20 ch. "Campanula cephalotes" 40 15
N3390 40 ch. "Trollius macropetalus" 75 30
N3391 40 ch. "Gentiana algida" 75 30
N3392 50 ch. "Sedum kamtschaticum" 90 35

1094 National Olympic Committee Emblem **1095** Red Cross Launch ("Relief on the Sea")

1994. Centenary of International Olympic Committee. Multicoloured.
N3394 10 ch. Type **1094** 15 10
N3395 20 ch. Pierre de Coubertin (founder) 30 15
N3396 30 ch. Olympic flag and flame 45 20
N3397 50 ch. Emblem of Centennial Olympic Congress, Paris . . 75 35

1994. 75th Anniv of International Red Cross and Red Crescent Federation. Multicoloured.
N3399 10 ch. Electric tram, pedestrians on footbridge and traffic lights ("Prevention of Traffic Accident") 45 10
N3400 20 ch. Type **1095** 30 15
N3401 30 ch. Planting tree ("Protection of Environment") 45 20
N3402 40 ch. Dam ("Prevention of Drought Damage") . . . 60 30

1994. No. N3287 surch **160** in circle.
N3403 **1072** 1 wn. 60 on 1 wn. 50 multicoloured . . . 2·10 1·00

1097 Northern Fur Seal

1994. Marine Mammals. Multicoloured.
N3404 10 ch. Type **1097** 25 10
N3405 40 ch. Southern elephant seal 75 30
N3406 60 ch. Southern sealion . . 1·10 45

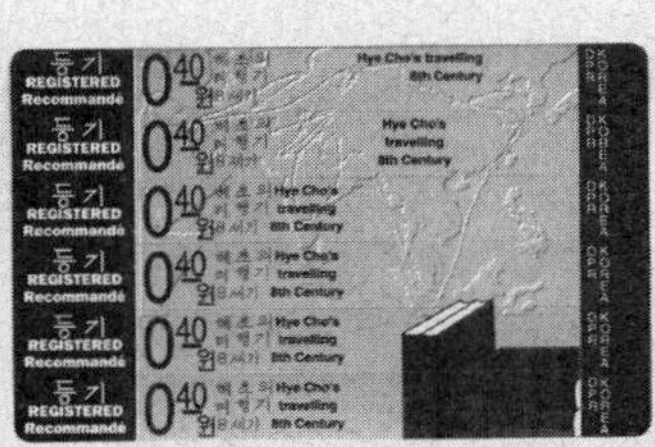
1098 Map of Asia and Books (½-size illustration)

1994. 8th-century Travels of Hye Cho. Self-adhesive. Roul.
N3408 **1098** 40 ch. multicoloured . 55 25
No. N3408 is for any one of the six stamps which together make up the design illustrated. They are peeled from a card backing.

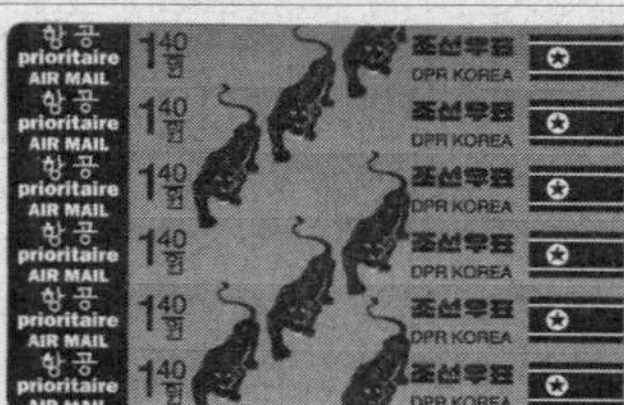
1099 Tigers (½-size illustration)

1994. Self-adhesive. Roul.
N3409 **1099** 1 wn. 40 multicoloured . 1·90 95
No. N3409 is for any one of the six stamps which together make up the design illustrated. They are peeled from a card backing.

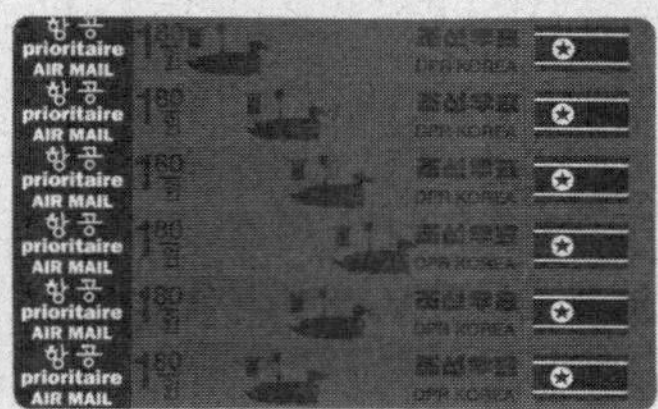
1101 "Turtle" Ships (½-size illustration)

1994. Self-adhesive. Roul.
N3411 **1101** 1 wn. 80 multicoloured . 2·40 1·10
No. N3411 is for any one of the six stamps which together make up the design illustrated. They are peeled from a card backing.

1102 Striped Bonnet **1104** Korean Script and "100"

1103 Trapeze

1994. Molluscs. Multicoloured.
N3412 30 ch. Type **1102** 60 20
N3413 40 ch. Equilateral venus . . 1·00 30

1994. Circus Acrobatics. Multicoloured.
N3416 10 ch. Type **1103** 15 10
N3417 20 ch. Reino (Swedish acrobat) performing rope dance 30 15
N3418 30 ch. Seesaw performer . . 45 20
N3419 40 ch. Unicycle juggler . . . 60 30

1994. Birth Centenary of Kim Hyong Jik (father of Kim Il Sung). Multicoloured.
N3420 **1104** 10 ch. multicoloured . 10 10

1105 Jon Pong Jun and Battle Scene

1994. Centenary of Kabo Peasant War.
N3422 **1105** 10 ch. multicoloured . 15 10

1107 Workers and Banner

1109 "Acorus calamus"

1108 Onsong Fish

1994. Revolutionary Economic Strategy.
N3424 **1107** 10 ch. multicoloured . 15 10

1994. Fossils. Multicoloured.
N3425 40 ch. Type **1108** 90 30
N3426 40 ch. Metasequoia 75 30
N3427 40 ch. Mammoth teeth . . . 75 30
N3428 80 ch. Archaeopteryx . . . 1·50 60

1994. Medicinal Plants. Multicoloured.
N3429 20 ch. Type **1109** 30 15
N3430 30 ch. "Arctium lappa" . . 45 20

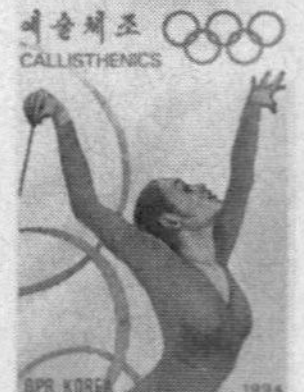
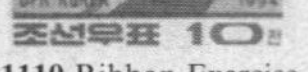
1110 Ribbon Exercise

1111 Chou En-lai at Tianjun, 1919

1994. Callisthenics. Multicoloured.
N3432 10 ch. Type **1110** 15 10
N3433 20 ch. Ball exercise 30 15
N3434 30 ch. Hoop exercise . . . 45 20
N3435 40 ch. Ribbon exercise (different) 60 30
N3436 50 ch. Club exercise 75 35

1994. 96th Birth Anniv of Chou En-lai (Chinese statesman). Multicoloured.
N3437 10 ch. Type **1111** 15 10
N3438 20 ch. Arrival in Northern Shanxi from Long March . 30 15
N3439 30 ch. At Conference of Asian and African Countries, Bandung, Indonesia, 1955 . . . . 45 20
N3440 40 ch. Surrounded by children in Wulumuqi, Xinjiang Province 60 30

1113 Kim Il Sung as Youth, 1927

1994. Kim Il Sung Commemoration (1st issue). (a) As T **1113**. Each red, gold and black.
N3444 40 ch. Type **1113** 60 30
N3445 40 ch. Kim Il Sung and Kim Jong Suk 60 30
N3446 40 ch. Kim Il Sung as young man 60 30

(b) Horiz designs as T **1115**. Each purple, gold and black.
N3447 40 ch. Kim Il Sung making speech, Pyongyang, 1945 . 60 30
N3448 40 ch. Kim Il Sung sitting at desk 60 30
N3449 40 ch. Kim Il Sung at microphone 60 30

See also Nos. N3459/63.

1114 Player No. 4

1994. World Cup Football Championship, U.S.A. Multicoloured.
N3451 10 ch. Type **1114** 15 10
N3452 20 ch. Player No. 5 . . . . 30 15
N3453 30 ch. Player No. 6 . . . . 45 20
N3454 40 ch. Player No. 7 . . . . 60 30
N3455 1 wn. Player No. 8 . . . . 1·50 75
N3456 1 wn. 50 Player No. 9 . . . 2·25 1·10

1115 Kim Il Sung making Radio Broadcast, 1950

1994. Kim Il Sung Commemoration (2nd issue). (a) Each green, gold and black.
N3458 40 ch. Type **1115** 60 30
N3459 40 ch. Kim Il Sung with four soldiers, 1951 . . . . . 60 30
N3460 40 ch. Kim Il Sung and crowd of soldiers, 1953 . . . . 60 30

(b) Multicoloured (N3463) or lilac, gold and black (others).
N3461 40 ch. Kim Il Sung with workers at Chongjin Steel Plant, 1959 . . . . . . 60 30
N3462 40 ch. Kim Il Sung on Onchon Plain 60 30
N3463 40 ch. Kim Il Sung at desk using telephone 60 30

1116 National Flags and Flowers

1117 Ri Myon Sang and Score of "Snow Falls"

1994. Korean–Chinese Friendship.
N3465 **1116** 40 ch. multicoloured . 60 30

1994. Composers. Multicoloured.
N3467 50 ch. Type **1117** . . . . . 1·00 35
N3468 50 ch. Pak Han Kyu and score of "Nobody Knows" . . 1·00 35
N3469 50 ch. Ludwig van Beethoven and score of piano sonata No. 14 . . . . 1·00 35
N3470 50 ch. Wolfgang Amadeus Mozart and score of symphony No. 39 . . . . 1·00 35

1118 National Emblem

1994.
N3471 **1118** 1 wn. green . . . . . 1·50 75
N3472 3 wn. brown . . . . . 4·00 2·00

1119 P. Wiberg (Alpine combined skiing)

1994. Winter Olympic Games, Lillehammer, Gold Medal Winners. Multicoloured.
N3473 10 ch. Type **1119** 15 10
N3474 20 ch. D. Compagnoni (slalom) 30 15
N3475 30 ch. O. Baiul (figure skating) 45 20
N3476 40 ch. D. Jansen (speed skating) 60 30
N3477 1 wn. L. Yegorova (cross-country sking) . . . . . 1·50 75
N3478 1 wn. 50 B. Blair (speed skating) . . . . 2·25 1·10

1120 Pig Couple

1121 Pison Waterfalls, Mt. Myohyang

1995. New Year. Year of the Pig. Multicoloured.
N3480 20 ch. Type **1120** 45 15
N3481 40 ch. Pigs carrying bucket and spade 80 30

1995. 20th Anniv of World Tourism Organization. Multicoloured.
N3483 30 ch. Tower of Juche Idea, Pyongyang 45 20
N3484 30 ch. Type **1121** 45 20
N3485 30 ch. Myogilsang (cliff-face carving of Buddha), Mt. Kumgang 45 20

1122 Mangyongdae, Badaogou and Badge

1123 Monument bearing 50th Birthday Ode, Mt. Paekdu

1995. 70th Anniv of 1000-ri (250 mile) Journey by Kim Il Sung to Restore Fatherland.
N3486 **1122** 40 ch. multicoloured . 60 30

1995. 53rd Birthday of Kim Jong Il.
N3487 **1123** 10 ch. multicoloured . 15 10

1124 Reconstruction Monument

1125 Jamaedo Lighthouse

1995. Completion of Reconstruction of King Tangun's Tomb. Multicoloured.
N3489 10 ch. Type **1124** 15 10
N3490 30 ch. Bronze dagger on plinth 45 20
N3491 50 ch. Monument inscribed with exploits of King Tangun 75 15
N3492 70 ch. Gateway (horiz) . . . 1·00 50

1995. Lighthouses. Multicoloured.
N3494 20 ch. Type **1125** 30 15
N3495 1 wn. Phido Lighthouse, West Sea Barrage . . . . . 1·75 85

1126 Cracked Green Russula

1127 Couple planting Tree

1995. Fungi. Multicoloured.
N3496 20 ch. Type **1126** 50 15
N3497 30 ch. "Russula atropurpurea" 75 20

1995. Tree Planting Day.
N3499 **1127** 10 ch. multicoloured . 30 10

1128 Birthplace, Mangyongdae

1995. 83rd Birth Anniv of Kim Il Sung. Multicoloured.
N3500 10 ch. Type **1128** 15 10
N3501 40 ch. Tower of Juche Idea and Kim Il Sung flower (vert) 60 30

1129 Deng Xiaoping waving

1995. 20th Anniv of Kim Il Sung's Visit to China. Multicoloured.
N3503 10 ch. Type **1129** 15 10
N3504 20 ch. Deng Xiaoping of China sitting in armchair (vert) 30 15

1130 Venue

1995. 40th Anniv of Asian–African Conference, Bandung.
N3506 **1130** 10 ch. black, buff and red 15 10
N3507 – 50 ch. brown, gold and black 75 35

DESIGN: 50 ch. Kim Il Sung receiving honorary Doctorate at Indonesia University.

1131 Emblem

1132 Amethyst

1995. International Sports and Cultural Festival for Peace, Pyongyang. Multicoloured.
N3509 20 ch. Type **1131** 30 15
N3510 40 ch. Dancer 60 30
N3511 40 ch. Inoki Kanji (leader of Sports Peace Party of Japan) 60 30

1995. Minerals.
N3513 **1132** 20 ch. multicoloured . 50 15

1133 Tree Sparrow

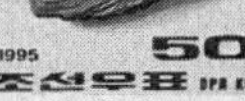
1134 Ostrea

1995. White Animals. Multicoloured.
N3514 40 ch. Type **1133** 60 30
N3515 40 ch. "Stichopus japonicus" (sea slug) 60 30

1995. Fossils. Multicoloured.
N3516 50 ch. Type **1134** . . . . . 1·00 35
N3517 1 wn. Cladophlebis (fern) . . 1·50 75

1135 Chess

1136 National Flag and Korean Hall, Tokyo

1995. Traditional Games. Multicoloured.
N3518 30 ch. Type **1135** 50 20
N3519 60 ch. Taekwondo . . . . 1·00 45
N3520 70 ch. Yut . . . . 1·25 50

1995. 40th Anniv of Association of Koreans in Japan.
N3521 **1136** 1 wn. multicoloured . . 1·50 75

1137 Weightlifting

1138 "Russula citrina"

1995. Olympic Games, Atlanta (1996). Multicoloured.
N3522 50 ch. Type **1137** 90 35
N3523 50 ch. Boxing 90 35

1995. Fungi. Multicoloured.
N3525 40 ch. Type **1138** 75 30
N3526 60 ch. Black trumpets . . . . 1·00 45
N3527 80 ch. Shaggy caps . . . . 1·40 60

1140 Mt. Paekdu and Revolutionaries **1141** Markswoman

1995. 50th Anniv of Liberation. Multicoloured.
N3529 10 ch. Type **1140** 15 10
N3530 30 ch. Map of Korea and family 45 20
N3531 60 ch. Medal 90 45

1995. 1st Military World Games, Rome.
N3534 **1141** 40 ch. multicoloured . 60 30

1143 Emblem and Banner **1144** Arch of Triumph, Pyongyang

1995. 50th Anniv of Korean Workers' Party. Multicoloured.
N3536 10 ch. Type **1143** 15 10
N3537 20 ch. Statue of worker, peasant and intellectual . . 30 15
N3538 30 ch. Party monument . . . 45 20

1995. 50th Anniv of Kim Il Sung's Return to Homeland.
N3540 **1144** 10 ch. multicoloured . 15 10

1145 Tuna **1147** Guinea Pig

1995. Designs as T **1145**. Each brown and black.

(a) Fishes.
N3541 40 ch. Type **1145** 70 30
N3542 50 ch. Pennant coralfish (with two bands) 90 35
N3543 50 ch. Needlefish 90 35
N3544 60 ch. Seascorpion . . . . . 1·00 45
N3545 5 wn. Emperor angelfish . . 6·50 3·25

(b) Buildings on Kwangbok Street, Pyongyang.
N3546 60 ch. Circus 90 45
N3547 70 ch. Flats . . . . 1·00 50
N3548 80 ch. Ryanggang Hotel . . 1·25 60
N3549 90 ch. Tower apartment block (vert) . . . . 1·40 70
N3550 1 wn. Sosan Hotel (vert) . . 1·50 75

(c) Machines.
N3551 10 ch. Kamsusan tipper truck 15 10
N3552 20 ch. Bulldozer 30 15
N3553 30 ch. Excavator 45 20
N3554 40 ch. Earth mover (vert) . . 60 30
N3555 10 wn. "Chollima 80" tractor (vert) . . . . 13·00 6·50

(d) Animals.
N3556 30 ch. Giraffe (vert) 45 20
N3557 40 ch. Ostrich (vert) 60 30
N3558 60 ch. Bluebuck (vert) . . . 90 45
N3559 70 ch. Bactrian camel . . . 1·00 50
N3560 3 wn. Indian rhinoceros . . 4·25 2·00

(e) Sculptures of Children.
N3561 30 ch. Boy holding bird (vert) 45 20
N3562 40 ch. Boy with goose (vert) . 60 30
N3563 60 ch. Girl with geese (vert) . 90 45
N3564 70 ch. Boy and girl with football (vert) . . . . . . 1·00 50
N3565 2 wn. Boy and girl arguing over football (vert) . . . 3·00 1·50

1996. Rodents. Multicoloured.
N3567 20 ch. Type **1147** 50 15
N3568 20 ch. Squirrel 50 15
N3569 30 ch. White mouse 70 20

1148 Emblem, Badge and Flag **1149** Restoration Mounument

1996. 50th Anniv of League of Socialist Working Youth.
N3570 **1148** 10 ch. multicoloured . 15 10

1996. Reconstruction of Tomb of King Wanggon. Multicoloured.
N3571 30 ch. Type **1149** 60 20
N3572 40 ch. Entrance gate . . . 75 30
N3573 50 ch. Tomb 90 35

1152 Jong Il Peak and Kim Jong Il Flower **1153** Pairs Skating

1996. 54th Birthday of Kim Jong Il.
N3576 **1152** 10 ch. multicoloured . 40 10

1996. 5th Paektusan Prize Figure Skating Championships. Multicoloured.
N3578 10 ch. Type **1153** 25 10
N3579 20 ch. Pairs skating (different) 40 15
N3580 30 ch. Pairs skating (different) 60 20
N3581 50 ch. Women's individual skating 90 35

1155 Farm Worker **1156** 1946 20 ch. Stamp and Tower of Juche Idea

1996. 50th Anniv of Agrarian Reform Law.
N3584 **1155** 10 ch. multicoloured . 15 10

1996. 50th Anniv of First North Korean Stamps.
N3585 **1156** 1 wn. multicoloured . . 1·40 70

1158 Birthplace, Mangyongdae

1996. 84th Birth Anniv of Kim Il Sung.
N3587 **1158** 10 ch. multicoloured . 15 10

1159 Gateway

1996. "China '96" Asian International Stamp Exhibition, Peking. Landmarks in Zhejiang. Multicoloured.
N3589 10 ch. Type **1159** 25 10
N3590 10 ch. Haiyin Pool 25 10

1160 Hopscotch **1161** Association Pamphlets

1996. Children's Games. Multicoloured.
N3592 20 ch. Type **1160** 40 15
N3593 40 ch. Shuttlecock 75 30
N3594 50 ch. Sledging 90 35

1996. 60th Anniv of Association for Restoration of the Fatherland.
N3595 **1161** 10 ch. multicoloured . 15 10

1163 Arctic Fox **1164** Boy Saluting

1996. Polar Animals. Multicoloured.
N3597 50 ch. Type **1163** 75 35
N3598 50 ch. Polar bear 75 35
N3599 50 ch. Emperor penguins . . 75 35
N3600 50 ch. Leopard seals 75 35

1996. 50th Anniv of Korean Children's Union.
N3601 **1164** 10 ch. multicoloured . 40 10

1165 Steam Locomotive **1167** Open Book and Characters

1996. Railway Locomotives. Multicoloured.
N3603 50 ch. Type **1165** 75 35
N3604 50 ch. Electric locomotive (green livery) 75 35
N3605 50 ch. Steam locomotive (facing right) 75 35
N3606 50 ch. Diesel locomotive (red and yellow livery) 75 35

1996. 760th Anniv of Publication of "Complete Collection of Buddhist Scriptures printed from 80,000 Wooden Blocks".
N3608 **1167** 40 ch. multicoloured . 60 30

1168 Worker using Microphone

1996. 50th Anniv of Labour Law.
N3609 **1168** 50 ch. multicoloured . 75 35

1171 Kumsusan Memorial Palace

1996. 2nd Death Anniv of Kim Il Sung.
N3612 **1171** 10 ch. multicoloured . 15 10

1172 Kim Il Sung meeting Jiang Zemin of China, 1991 **1173** Football and Ancient Greek Athletes

1996. 35th Anniv of Korean–Chinese Treaty for Friendship, Co-operation and Mutual Assistance.
N3614 **1172** 10 ch. brown, gold and black 15 10
N3615 – 10 ch. green, gold and black 15 10

DESIGN: 10 ch. Kim Il Sung meeting Pres. Mao Tse-tung of China, 1954.

1996. Centenary of Modern Olympic Games and Olympic Games, Atlanta. Multicoloured.
N3617 50 ch. Type **1173** 85 35
N3618 50 ch. Tennis, Olympic Anthem and 1896 5 l. Greek stamp 85 35
N3619 50 ch. Throwing the hammer and advertisement poster for first modern olympics . 85 35
N3620 50 ch. Baseball and Olympic stadium, Atlanta 85 35

1174 Couple **1175** State Arms and Symbols of Industry and Communications

1996. 50th Anniv of Sex Equality Law.
N3621 **1174** 50 ch. multicoloured . 70 35

1996. 50th Anniv of Nationalization of Industries.
N3623 **1175** 50 ch. bistre and brown 65 30

1176 Boy with Ball **1178** University Buildings, Pyongyang

1996. 50th Anniv of U.N.I.C.E.F. Multicoloured.
N3624 10 ch. Type **1176** 25 10
N3625 20 ch. Boy with building blocks 35 15
N3626 50 ch. Boy eating melon . . 75 30
N3627 60 ch. Girl playing accordion 90 40

1996. 50th Anniv of Kim Il Sung University.
N3629 **1178** 10 ch. multicoloured . 15 10

1179 Tiger **1180** Red Flag and Tower of Juche Idea

1996. World Conservation Union Congress, Montreal, Canada. Multicoloured.
N3630 50 ch. Type **1179** 75 30
N3631 50 ch. White spoonbill . . . 75 30

1996. 70th Anniv of Down-with-Imperialism Union
N3633 **1180** 10 ch. multicoloured . . 30 10

1183 Japanese Eel

1996. Freshwater Fishes. Multicoloured.
N3636 20 ch. Type **1183** 70 15
N3637 20 ch. Menada grey mullet ("Liza haematocheila") . 70 15

1184 Soldiers and Supreme Commander's Flag

1996. 5th Anniv of Appointment of Kim Jong Il as Supreme Commander of the People's Army.
N3639 **1184** 20 ch. multicoloured . 50 15

1185 "Ox Driver" (Kim Tu Ryang)

1997. New Year. Year of the Ox. Multicoloured.

N3640 70 ch. Type **1185** . . . . . 2·25 45
N3641 70 ch. Bronze ritual plate of two bulls and a tiger . . . 2·25 45
N3642 70 ch. Boy with bull (ceramic) 2·25 45
N3643 70 ch. Boy flautist sitting on bull (sculpture) . . . . . 2·25 45

1186 Left-hand Detail

1187 Kitten with Dogs in Basket

1997. "Flowers and Butterflies" by Nam Kye U. Multicoloured.

N3645 50 ch. Type **1186** . . . . . 1·25 30
N3646 50 ch. Centre detail . . . . 1·25 30
N3647 50 ch. Right-hand detail . . 1·25 30

Nos. N3645/7 were issued together, se-tenant, forming a composite design of the painting.

1997. Paintings of Cats and Dogs. Multicoloured.

N3648 50 ch. Type **1187** . . . . . 1·25 30
N3649 50 ch. Pup in vine-wreathed basket, kitten and pumpkin . . . . 1·50 30

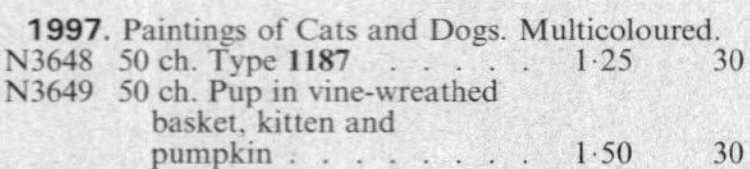

1189 Birthplace, Mt. Paekdu

1997. 55th Birthday of Kim Jong Il.

N3652 **1189** 10 ch. multicoloured . 40 10

1190 Pair

1997. 6th Paektusan Prize International Figure Skating Championships, Pyongyang. Multicoloured.

N3654 50 ch. Type **1190** . . . . . 1·50 30
N3655 50 ch. Pair (mauve) . . . . 1·50 30
N3656 50 ch. Pair (green) . . . . . 1·50 30

1193 "Prunus ansu"

1194 Foundation Monument

1997. Apricots. Multicoloured.

N3659 50 ch. Type **1193** . . . . . 1·40 30
N3660 50 ch. "Prunus mandshurica" . . . . . 1·40 30
N3661 50 ch. Hoeryong white apricot ("Prunus armeniaca") . . 1·40 30
N3662 50 ch. Puksan apricot ("Prunus sibirica") . . . 1·40 30

1997. 80th Anniv of Foundation of Korean National Association.

N3663 **1194** 10 ch. brown and green 50 10

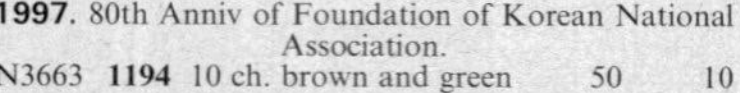

1195 Sapling

1196 Birthplace, Mangyongdae

1997. 50th Anniv of Reforestation Day.

N3664 **1195** 10 ch. multicoloured

1997. 85th Birth Anniv of Kim Il Sung. Multicoloured.

N3666 10 ch. Type **1196** 50 10
N3667 20 ch. Sliding Rock (horiz) . 1·00 10
N3668 40 ch. Warship Rock (horiz) . 1·25 25

1197 Cap Badge and Modern Weapons

1997. 65th Anniv of People's Army.

N3670 **1197** 10 ch. multicoloured . 10 10

1198 Map of Korea

1199 Tower of Juche Idea, People and Flag

1997. 25th Anniv of Publication of North–South Korea Joint Agreement.

N3672 **1198** 10 ch. multicoloured . 10 10

1997. Posters reflecting Joint New Year Newspaper Editorials. Multicoloured.

N3674 10 ch. Type **1199** 10 10
N3675 10 ch. Man with flag 10 10
N3676 10 ch. Soldier, miner, farmer, intellectual and bugler . . 10 10

1201 Memorial Post and Blazing Fortress

1204 "Redlichia chinensis"

1997. 60th Anniv of Battle of Pochonbo.

N3678 **1201** 40 ch. multicoloured . 35 15

1997. Fossils. Multicoloured.

N3681 50 ch. Type **1204** 45 20
N3682 1 wn. "Ptychoparia coreanica" 90 45

1205 Kim Il Sung at Kim Chaek Ironworks, June 1985

1207 Spring

1206 Blindman's Buff

1997. 3rd Death Anniv of Kim Il Sung. Multicoloured.

N3683 50 ch. Kim Il Sung at microphones (party conference, October 1985) 45 20
N3684 50 ch. Type **1205** 45 20
N3685 50 ch. Kim Il Sung and farmers holding wheat (Songsin Co-operative Farm, Sadong District, 1993) 45 20
N3686 50 ch. Performing artists applauding Kim Il Sung, 1986 . . . . 45 20
N3687 50 ch. Kim Il Sung at Jonchon Factory, Jagang Province, 1991 . . . . . 45 20
N3688 50 ch. Kim Il Sung receiving flowers at People's Army Conference, 1989 . . . . 45 20

1997. Children's Games. Multicoloured.

N3689 30 ch. Type **1206** 30 15
N3690 60 ch. Five stones 55 25
N3691 70 ch. Arm wrestling 65 30

1997. Women's National Costumes. Multicoloured.

N3692 10 ch. Type **1207** 10 10
N3693 40 ch. Summer 35 15
N3694 50 ch. Autumn 45 20
N3695 60 ch. Winter 55 25

1208 Aerial View

1997. Chongryu Bridge, Pyongyang. Multicoloured.

N3696 50 ch. Type **1208** 45 20
N3697 50 ch. Chongryu Bridge and birds 45 20

1209 Sun, Magnolias and Balloons

1997. 85th Anniv of Juche Era and Sun Day.

N3698 **1209** 10 ch. multicoloured . 10 10

1210 Korean Text and Kim Il Sung University

1997. 20th Anniv of Publication of Theses on Socialist Education.

N3700 **1210** 10 ch. multicoloured . 10 10

1212 Chonbul Peak

1997. 10th Anniv of Korean Membership of World Tourism Organization. Mt Chilbo. Multicoloured.

N3702 50 ch. Type **1212** 45 20
N3703 50 ch. Sea-Chilbo (coast) . . 45 20
N3704 50 ch. Rojok Peak 45 20

1213 Podok Hermitage

1997. Kumgang Mountains. Multicoloured.

N3705 50 ch. Type **1213** 45 20
N3706 50 ch. Kumgang Gate . . . 45 20

1214 School, Pupil and Mt Paekdu

1997. 50th Anniv of Mangyongdae Revolutionary School.

N3707 **1214** 40 ch. multicoloured . 35 15

1215 Lion

1217 Ten-pin Bowling

1997. Animals presented as Gifts to Kim Il Sung. Multicoloured.

N3708 20 ch. Type **1215** (Ethiopia, 1987) 15 10
N3709 30 ch. Jaguar (Japan, 1992) . 30 15
N3710 50 ch. Barbary sheep (Czechoslovakia, 1992) . . 45 20
N3711 80 ch. Scarlet macaw (Austria, 1979) 70 35

1997. Sports. Multicoloured.

N3713 50 ch. Type **1217** 45 20
N3714 50 ch. Golf 45 20
N3715 50 ch. Fencing 45 20

1218 Snails

1220 "Juche 87" and Temple

1997. Snails. Multicoloured.

N3716 50 ch. Type **1218** 45 20
N3717 50 ch. Two snails on leaf . . 45 20
N3718 50 ch. Snail laying eggs . . . 45 20

1997. New Year. Year of the Tiger. Multicoloured.

N3720 10 ch. Type **1220** 10 10
N3721 50 ch. Tiger in rocket (24 x 34 mm) 45 20
N3722 50 ch. Tiger steering ship (24 x 34 mm) 45 20

1221 Birthplace, Hoeryong

1997. 80th Birth Anniv of Kim Jong Suk (revolutionary).

N3724 **1221** 10 ch. multicoloured . 10 10

1222 Skiing

1223 Birthdate and Celebration Ribbon

1998. Winter Olympic Ganes, Nagano, Japan. Multicoloured.

N3726 20 ch. Type **1222** 15 10
N3727 40 ch. Speed skating 35 15

1998. 56th Birth Anniv of Kim Jong Il.

N3728 **1223** 10 ch. multicoloured . 10 10

MINIMUM PRICE

The minimum price quoted is 10p which represents a handling charge rather than a basis for valuing common stamps. For further notes about prices see introductory pages.

1224 Korean Tigers

1998. Wildlife Paintings. Multicoloured.
N3730 50 ch. Type **1224** 45 20
N3731 50 ch. White cranes 45 20

1225 Route Map, Birthplace at Mangyongdae and Trail Followers

1998. 75th Anniv of 1000-ri (250 mile) Journey by Kim Il Sung.
N3733 **1225** 10 ch. multicoloured . 10 10

1226 Soldiers and Balloons

1998. 5th Anniv of Appointment of Kim Jong Il as Chairman of National Defence Commission.
N3734 **1226** 10 ch. multicoloured . 10 10

1227 Flags and Birthplace, Mangyongdae

1229 United Front Tower and Moranbong Theatre

1998. 86th Birth Anniv of Kim Il Sung.
N3735 **1227** 10 ch. multicoloured . 10 10

1998. 50th Anniv of North–South Conference, Pyongyang.
N3737 **1229** 10 ch. brown, blue and black 10 10

1230 Players and Championship Emblem

1231 Cabbages

1998. World Cup Football Championship, France. Multicoloured.
N3738 30 ch. Type **1230** 30 15
N3739 50 ch. Player winning ball and emblem 45 20

1998. Vegetables. Multicoloured.
N3741 10 ch. Type **1231** 10 10
N3742 40 ch. Radishes 35 15
N3743 50 ch. Spring onions 45 20
N3744 60 ch. Cucumbers 55 25
N3745 70 ch. Pumpkins 65 30
N3746 80 ch. Carrots 70 35
N3747 90 ch. Garlic 80 40
N3748 1 wn. Peppers 90 45

1232 "Countryside in May" (Jong Jong Yo)

1998. Paintings. Multicoloured.
N3749 60 ch. Type **1232** 55 25
N3750 1 wn. 40 "Dance" (Kim Yong Jun) . . . . 1·25 65

1233 Model of Automatic Space Station (from U.S.S.R.)

1998. International Friendship Exhibition, Myohyang Mountains (2nd series). Multicoloured.
N3752 1 wn. Type **1233** 90 45
N3753 1 wn. Ceramic flower vase (from Egypt) 90 45
N3754 1 wn. "Crane" (statuette, from Billy Graham (evangelist)) 90 45

1234 Research Ship, Buoy and Dolphins in Globe and Hydro-meteorological Headquarters

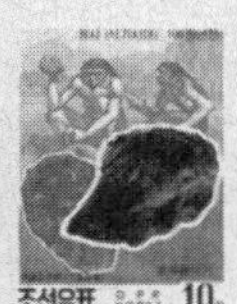
1235 Stone Age Implement

1998. International Year of the Ocean. Multicoloured.
N3756 10 ch. Type **1234** 10 10
N3757 80 ch. Sailing dinghies and mother with child 70 35

1998. Korean Central History Museum, Pyongyang. Multicoloured.
N3759 10 ch. Type **1235** 10 10
N3760 2 wn. 50 Fossil skull of monkey . . . . 2·25 1·10

1236 Commander of Hedgehog Unit and Squirrel

1998. "Squirrels and Hedgehogs" (cartoon film). Multicoloured.
N3762 20 ch. Type **1236** 15 10
N3763 30 ch. Commander of hedgehog unit receiving invitation to banquet . . . 30 15
N3764 60 ch. Weasel ordering mouse to poison bear 55 25
N3765 1 wn. 20 Squirrel with poisoned bear . . . . . . 1·10 55
N3766 2 wn. Weasel and mice invade Flower Village . . . . . 1·75 90
N3767 2 wn. 50 Hedgehog scout rescues squirrel . . . . . 2·25 1·10

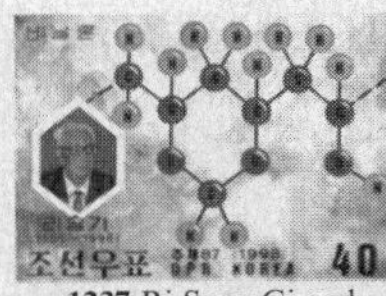
1237 Ri Sung Gi and Molecular Model

1998. 2nd Death Anniv of Ri Sung Gi (inventor of vinalon material).
N3768 **1237** 40 ch. multicoloured . 35 20

1238 Tiger Cub

1239 "Victory" (Liberation War Monument, Pyongyang) and Medal

1998. Young Mammals. Multicoloured.
N3770 10 ch. Type **1238** 10 10
N3771 50 ch. Donkey foal 45 20
N3772 1 wn. 60 Elephant . . . . . 1·50 75
N3773 2 wn. Two lion cubs . . . . 1·75 90

1998. 45th Anniv of Victory in Liberation War.
N3774 **1239** 45 ch. brown and pink 40 20

1240 "White Herons in Forest"

1241 Pouch

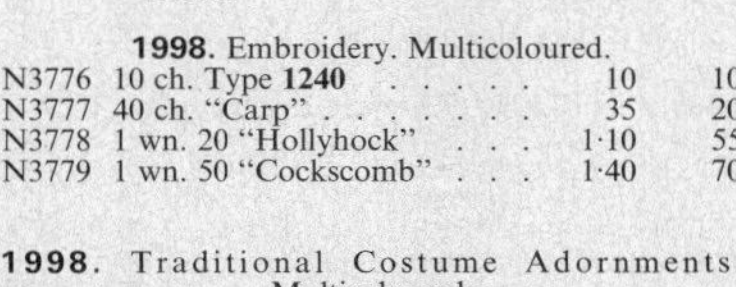

1998. Embroidery. Multicoloured.
N3776 10 ch. Type **1240** 10 10
N3777 40 ch. "Carp" 35 20
N3778 1 wn. 20 "Hollyhock" . . . 1·10 55
N3779 1 wn. 50 "Cockscomb" . . . 1·40 70

1998. Traditional Costume Adornments. Multicoloured.
N3781 10 ch. Type **1241** 10 10
N3782 50 ch. Tassels 45 25
N3783 1 wn. 50 Hairpin . . . . . 1·40 70
N3784 1 wn. 90 Silver knife . . . . 1·75 90

1242 Rocket and State Flag

1243 Kim Jong Il Flower

1998. Launch of First Korean Artificial Satellite "Kwangmyongsong 1".
N3785 **1242** 40 ch. multicoloured . 35 20

1998. Re-election of Kim Jong Il as Chairman of National Defence Commission.
N3787 **1243** 10 ch. multicoloured . 10 10

1244 Tower of Juche Idea, State Arms and Flag

1998. 50th Anniv of Democratic Republic (1st issue). Multicoloured.
N3789 10 ch. Type **1244** 10 10
N3790 1 wn. Painting "The Founding of the Democratic People's Republic of Korea, Our Glorious Fatherland" (Kim Il Sung waving from balcony) (48 x 30 mm) . . 90 45
N3791 1 wn. Painting "Square of Victory" (Kim Il Sung and crowd with banners) (48 x 30 mm) 90 45
N3792 1 wn. Poster "The Sacred Marks of the Great Leader Kim Il Sung will shine on this Land of Socialism" (Kim Il Sung with produce against panoramic background of Korea) (48 x 30 mm) 90 45

1245 "Let Us Push Ahead with the Forced March for Final Victory"

1247 Cycling

1998.
N3793 **1245** 10 ch. multicoloured . 10 10

1998. Olympic Games, Sydney, Australia (2000). Multicoloured.
N3795 20 ch. Type **1247** 15 10
N3796 50 ch. Football 45 25
N3797 80 ch. Show jumping 70 35
N3798 1 wn. 50 Throwing the javelin . . . . 1·40 70

1248 "Cyclamen persicum"

1249 Oral Vaccination

1998. Plants presented as Gifts to Kim Jong Il. Multicoloured.
N3800 20 ch. Type **1248** (France, 1994) 15 10
N3801 2 wn. "Dianthus chinensis" var. "laciniatus" (Japan, 1994) . . . . 1·75 90

1998. National Vaccination Day.
N3802 **1249** 40 ch. multicoloured . 35 20

1250 Leopard

1998. The Leopard. Multicoloured.
N3803 1 wn. Type **1250** 90 45
N3804 1 wn. Leopard in snow . . . 90 45
N3805 1 wn. Leopard looking to left 90 45
N3806 1 wn. Leopard's face 90 45

1251 Canal

1998. Land and Environment Conservation Day. Multicoloured.
N3807 10 ch. Type **1251** 10 10
N3808 40 ch. Motorway, tower blocks and lorry 35 20

APPENDIX

The following stamps have either been issued in excess of postal needs or have not been available to the public in reasonable quantities at face value. Such stamps may later be given full listing if there is evidence of regular postal use.

1976.

Olympic Games, Montreal. Three-dimensional stamps showing Olympic events. 5, 10, 15, 20, 25, 40 ch.

1977.

Olympic Games, Montreal. Three-dimensional stamps showing medals. 5, 10, 15, 20, 25, 40 ch.

Olympic Games, Montreal. 1976 Olympic Games issue optd with winners' names. 5, 10, 15, 20, 25, 40 ch.

1979.

XIII Winter Olympic Games, 1980. Nos. N1688/94 optd. 2, 5, 10, 15, 20, 25, 40 ch.

1981.

Nobel Prizes for Medicine. Nos. N1955/61 optd. 7 × 10 ch.

World Cup Football Championship, Spain (1982). Nos. N1731/41 optd. 12 × 20 ch.

World Cup Football Championship, Spain (1982). Three-dimensional stamps. Air 20, 30 ch.

1982.

21st Birthday of Princess of Wales. Nos. N2108/11 and N2120/3 optd. 10, 20, 30, 40 ch; 10, 20, 30, 70 ch.

Birth of Prince William of Wales. Nos. N2185/91 optd. 10, 20, 30, 50, 60, 70, 80 ch.

World Cup Football Championship, Spain, Results. Nos. N2201/6 optd. 10, 20, 30, 40, 50, 60 ch.

Birth of Prince William of Wales. Three-dimensional stamps. 3 × 30 ch.

1983.

XXIII Olympic Games, Los Angeles, 1984. Nos. N2084/8 optd. 10, 15, 20, 25, 30 ch.

1984.

European Royal History. 81 × 10 ch.

KOUANG TCHEOU (KWANGCHOW) Pt. 17

An area and port of S. China, leased by France from China in April 1898. It was returned to China in February 1943.

1906. 100 centimes = 1 franc.
1919. 100 cents = 1 piastre.

Unless otherwise stated the following are optd or surch on stamps of Indo-China.

1906. Surch **Kouang Tcheou-Wan** and value in Chinese.

1	**8**	1 c. green	1·50	1·50
2		2 c. red on yellow	1·50	1·40
3		4 c. mauve on blue	2·00	1·90
4		5 c. green	2·00	2·00
5		10 c. red	2·00	2·00
6		15 c. brown on blue	5·00	4·75
7		20 c. red on green	2·00	2·00
8		25 c. blue	2·00	2·00
9		30 c. brown on cream	2·50	2·50
10		35 c. black on yellow	3·50	3·25
11		40 c. black on grey	2·50	2·50
12		50 c. brown on cream	10·00	10·00
13	D	75 c. brown on orange	15·00	15·00
14	**8**	1 f. green	18·00	18·00
15		2 f. brown on yellow	18·00	18·00
16	D	5 f. mauve on lilac	£120	£120
17	**8**	10 f. red on green	£150	£150

1908. Native types surch **KOUANG-TCHEOU** and value in Chinese.

18	**10**	1 c. black and brown	40	45
19		2 c. black and brown	40	50
20		4 c. black and blue	45	50
21		5 c. black and green	45	45
22		10 c. black and red	45	45
23		15 c. black and violet	1·10	1·10
24	**11**	20 c. black and violet	2·00	2·00
25		25 c. black and blue	2·50	2·50
26		30 c. black and brown	4·25	4·50
27		35 c. black and green	5·75	6·00
28		40 c. black and brown	6·00	6·00
29		50 c. black and red	6·50	6·50
30	**12**	75 c. black and orange	6·50	6·50
31	–	1 f. black and red	7·50	7·50
32	–	2 f. black and green	20·00	20·00
33	–	5 f. black and blue	40·00	40·00
34	–	10 f. black and violet	60·00	60·00

1919. Nos. 18/34 surch in figures and words.

35	**10**	⅖ on 1 c. black and brown	40	45
36		⅘ c. on 2 c. black and brown	35	45
37		1⅗ c. on 4 c. black and blue	50	55
38		2 c. on 5 c. black and green	55	55
39		4 c. on 10 c. black and red	1·40	85
40		6 c. on 15 c. black & violet	55	45
41	**11**	8 c. on 20 c. black & violet	2·00	1·90
42		10 c. on 25 c. black and blue	5·50	5·00
43		12 c. on 30 c. black & brown	1·10	85
44		14 c. on 35 c. black & green	1·25	1·10
45		16 c. on 40 c. black & brown	90	70
46		20 c. on 50 c. black and red	90	65
47	**12**	30 c. on 75 c. black & orange	3·50	3·50
48	–	40 c. on 1 f. black and red	4·25	4·25
49	–	80 c. on 2 f. black and green	5·00	4·25
50	–	2 p. on 5 f. black and blue	95·00	90·00
51	–	4 p. on 10 f. black & violet	12·00	11·50

1923. Native types optd **KOUANG-TCHEOU** only. (Value in cents and piastres).

52	**10**	⅒ c. red and grey	20	30
53		⅕ c. black and blue	20	30
54		⅖ c. black and brown	25	30
55		⅘ c. black and red	30	35
56		1 c. black and brown	40	35
57		2 c. black and green	65	55
58		3 c. black and violet	65	55
59		4 c. black and orange	65	55
60		5 c. black and red	65	55
61	**11**	6 c. black and red	80	55
62		7 c. black and green	70	70
63		8 c. black on lilac	1·00	55
64		9 c. black & yellow on green	1·00	85
65		10 c. black and blue	1·00	85
66		11 c. black and violet	1·00	85
67		12 c. black and brown	1·00	85
68		15 c. black and orange	2·00	1·40
69		20 c. black and blue on buff	1·00	85
70		40 c. black and red	2·00	1·75
71		1 p. black & green on green	6·00	4·75
72		2 p. black & purple on pink	10·00	7·75

1927. Pictorial types optd **KOUANG-TCHEOU**.

73	**22**	⅒ c. green	20	30
74		⅕ c. yellow	30	30
75		⅖ c. blue	30	35
76		⅘ c. brown	40	35
77		1 c. orange	50	45
78		2 c. green	75	55
79		3 c. blue	75	55
80		4 c. pink	75	55
81		5 c. violet	75	55
82	**23**	6 c. red	75	55
83		7 c. brown	75	55
84		8 c. green	75	55
85		9 c. purple	1·00	65
86		10 c. blue	1·00	65
87		11 c. orange	1·00	70
88		12 c. grey	1·00	65
89	**24**	15 c. brown and red	1·50	1·10
90		20 c. grey and violet	2·00	1·40
91	–	25 c. mauve and brown	2·00	1·40
92	–	30 c. olive and blue	1·50	95
93	–	40 c. blue and red	1·50	85
94	–	50 c. grey and green	2·00	1·00
95	–	1 p. black, yellow and blue	4·00	2·50
96	–	2 p. blue, orange and red	4·50	2·75

1937. 1931 issue optd **KOUANG-TCHEOU**.

98	**33**	⅒ c. blue	20	30
99		⅕ c. lake	30	30
100		⅖ c. red	20	30
101		½ c. brown	25	25
102		⅘ c. violet	40	30
103	**33**	1 c. brown	30	30
104		2 c. green	30	30
126	–	3 c. brown	50	30
105	–	3 c. green	75	45
106	–	4 c. blue	75	55
127	–	4 c. green	50	30
128	–	4 c. yellow	1·75	1·00
107	–	5 c. purple	75	55
129	–	5 c. green	50	35
108	–	6 c. red	50	45
130	–	7 c. black	50	45
131	–	8 c. lake	50	45
132	–	9 c. black on yellow	50	45
109	–	10 c. blue	85	65
133	–	10 c. blue on pink	75	55
110	–	15 c. blue	60	45
134	–	18 c. blue	30	30
111	–	20 c. red	60	45
112	–	21 c. green	60	45
135	–	22 c. green	50	35
113	–	25 c. purple	2·00	1·60
136	–	25 c. blue	70	45
114	–	30 c. brown	50	45
115	**36**	50 c. brown	75	60
116		60 c. purple	80	60
137		70 c. blue	70	45
117		1 p. green	1·10	90
118		2 p. red	1·75	1·00

1939. New York World's Fair. As T **28** of Mauritania.

119		13 c. red	80	55
120		23 c. deep blue and blue	80	55

1939. 150th Anniv of French Revolution. As T **29** of Mauritania.

121		6 c. + 2 c. green	5·00	3·75
122		7 c. + 3 c. brown	5·00	3·75
123		9 c. + 4 c. orange	5·00	3·75
124		13 c. + 10 c. red	5·00	3·75
125		23 c. + 20 c. blue	5·00	3·75

KUWAIT Pt. 1, Pt. 19

An independent Arab Shaikhdom on the N.W. coast of the Persian Gulf with Indian and later British postal administration. On 1 February, 1959, the Kuwait Government assumed responsibility for running its own postal service. In special treaty relations with Great Britain until 19 June 1961 when Kuwait became completely independent.

1923. 12 pies = 1 anna; 16 annas = 1 rupee.
1957. 100 naye paise = 1 rupee.
1961. 1000 fils = 1 dinar.

Stamps of India optd **KUWAIT**.

1923. King George V.

16	**56**	½ a. green	2·50	1·40
16b	**79**	½ a. green	4·50	1·10
2	**57**	1 a. brown	2·50	2·50
17b	**81**	1 a. brown	4·50	85
3	**58**	1½ a. brown (No. 163)	2·00	4·25
4	**59**	2 a. lilac	3·25	2·50
19c		2 a. red	4·50	2·00
18	**70**	2 a. lilac	3·00	90
19		2 a. red	20·00	85·00
5	**61**	2 a. 6 p. blue	2·25	8·00
6	**62**	3 a. orange	4·25	19·00
20		3 a. blue	2·75	1·75
21		3 a. red	5·50	4·25
22a	**63**	4 a. green	5·50	13·00
22	**71**	4 a. green	25·00	80·00
9	**64**	6 a. bistre	8·50	13·00
23	**65**	8 a. mauve	17·00	13·00
11	**66**	12 a. red	14·00	40·00
12	**67**	1 r. brown and green	17·00	23·00
26		2 r. red and orange	10·00	65·00
27		5 r. blue and violet	80·00	£200
28		10 r. green and red	£170	£375
29		15 r. blue and olive	£475	£750

1933. Air.

31	**72**	2 a. green	14·00	27·00
32		3 a. blue	2·75	2·50
33		4 a. olive	85·00	£170
34		6 a. bistre	2·75	4·50

1939. King George VI.

36	**91**	½ a. brown	7·00	1·75
38		1 a. red	7·00	1·50
39	**92**	2 a. red	7·00	2·50
41	–	3 a. green	7·00	2·00
43	–	4 a. brown	35·00	14·00
44	–	6 a. green	25·00	7·50
45	–	8 a. violet	28·00	32·00
46	–	12 a. red	20·00	48·00
47	**93**	1 r. slate and brown	6·50	2·75
48		2 r. purple and brown	3·75	13·00
49		5 r. green and blue	12·00	18·00
50		10 r. purple and red	60·00	75·00
51		15 r. brown and green	£130	£190

1942. King George VI stamps of 1940.

52	**100a**	3 p. slate	1·25	2·50
53		½ a. purple	1·25	2·50
54		9 p. green	2·75	7·50
55		1 a. red	1·50	2·00
56	**101**	1½ a. violet	3·25	7·50
57		2 a. red	3·50	2·75
58	**101**	3 a. violet	3·75	3·50
59		3½ a. blue	4·00	7·50
60	**102**	4 a. brown	3·50	2·50
60a		6 a. green	14·00	8·50
61		8 a. violet	7·00	2·75
62		12 a. purple	7·50	3·25
63	–	14 a. purple (No. 277)	14·00	16·00

From 1948 onwards, for stamps with similar surcharges, but without name of country, see British Postal Agencies in Eastern Arabia.

Stamps of Great Britain surch **KUWAIT** and new values in Indian currency.

1948. King George VI.

64	**128**	½ a. on ½d. green	1·25	1·25
84		½ a. on ½d. orange	1·75	1·50
65		1 a. on 1d. red	1·25	1·25
85		1 a. on 1d. blue	1·75	1·10
66		1½ a. on 1½d. brown	1·75	75
86		1½ a. on 1½d. green	1·75	2·25
67		2 a. on 2d. orange	1·25	90
87		2 a. on 2d. brown	1·75	85
68		2½ a. on 2½d. blue	1·75	1·00
88		2½ a. on 2½d. red	1·75	2·25
69		3 a. on 3d. violet	1·25	30
89	**129**	4 a. on 4d. blue	1·50	90
70		6 a. on 6d. purple	1·25	60
71	**130**	1 r. on 1s. brown	3·00	1·00
72	**131**	2 r. on 2s. 6d. green	3·50	4·50
73		5 r. on 5s. red	5·50	4·50
73a	–	10 r. on 10s. blue (No. 478a)	38·00	6·00

1948. Silver Wedding.

74	**137**	2½ a. on 2½d. blue	1·50	60
75	**138**	15 r. on £1 blue	30·00	30·00

1948. Olympic Games.

76	**139**	2½ a. on 2½d. blue	1·00	1·50
77	**140**	3 a. on 3d. violet	1·00	1·50
78	–	6 a. on 6d. purple	1·25	1·50
79	–	1 r. on 1s. brown	1·25	1·50

1949. U.P.U.

80	**143**	2½ a. on 2½d. blue	90	1·75
81	**144**	3 a. on 3d. violet	1·25	2·25
82	–	6 a. on 6d. purple	1·25	2·25
83	–	1 r. on 1s. brown	1·25	1·25

1951. Pictorial high values.

90	**147**	2 r. on 2s. 6d. green	15·00	4·50
91	–	5 r. on 5s. red (No. 510)	21·00	5·00
92	–	10 r. on 10s. blue (No. 511)	29·00	6·50

1952. Queen Elizabeth II.

93	**154**	½ a. on ½d. orange	20	80
94		1 a. on 1d. blue	20	10
95		1½ a. on 1½d. green	15	40
96		2 a. on 2d. brown	35	10
97	**155**	2½ a. on 2½d. red	15	40
98		3 a. on 3d. lilac	40	10
99		4 a. on 4d. blue	1·25	75
100	**157**	6 a. on 6d. purple	1·25	10
101	**160**	12 a. on 1s. 3d. green	5·00	2·50
102		1 r. on 1s. 6d. blue	4·50	10

1953. Coronation.

103	**161**	2½ a. on 2½d. red	3·00	2·50
104	–	4 a. on 4d. blue	3·00	2·50
105	**163**	12 a. on 1s. 3d. green	4·50	4·00
106	–	1 r. on 1s. 6d. blue	4·00	1·00

1955. Pictorials.

107	**166**	2 r. on 2 s. 6d. brown	7·00	2·00
108	–	5 r. on 5s. red	7·50	4·50
109	–	10 r. on 10s. blue	8·00	4·50

1957. Queen Elizabeth II.

120	**157**	1 n.p. on 5d. brown	10	70
121	**154**	3 n.p. on ½d. orange	60	2·50
122		6 n.p. on 1d. blue	60	1·25
123		9 n.p. on 1½d. green	60	2·00
124		12 n.p. on 2d. brown	60	2·00
125	**155**	15 n.p. on 2½d. red	60	2·00
126		20 n.p. on 3d. lilac	60	30
127		25 n.p. on 4d. blue	2·25	3·25
128	**157**	40 n.p. on 6d. purple	1·00	30
129	**158**	50 n.p. on 9d. olive	5·50	4·00
130	**160**	75 n.p. on 1s. 3d. green	5·50	4·25

20 Shaikh Abdullah

21 Dhow

1958.

131	**20**	5 n.p. green	50	10
132a		10 n.p. red	20	10
133		15 n.p. brown	20	15
134		20 n.p. violet	20	10
135		25 n.p. orange	35	10
136		40 n.p. purple	1·50	55
137	**21**	40 n.p. blue	45	20
138	–	50 n.p. red	40	20
139	–	75 n.p. green	45	30
140	–	1 r. purple	50	35
141	–	2 r. blue and brown	2·50	70
142	–	5 r. green	4·00	1·50
143	–	10 r. lilac	13·00	4·50

DESIGNS—HORIZ: As Type **21**: 50 n.p. Oil pipelines; 75 n.p. Shuwaikh Power Station. 36 × 20 mm: 1 r. Oil rig; 2 r. Single-masted dhow; 5 r. Kuwait Mosque; 10 r. Main Square, Kuwait Town.

22 Shaikh Abdullah and Flag

1960. 10th Anniv of Shaikh's Accession.

144	**22**	40 n.p. red and green	35	10
145		60 n.p. red and blue	45	20

1961. As 1958 issue but currency changed and new designs.

146	**20**	1 f. green	15	10
147		2 f. red	15	10
148		4 f. brown	15	10
149		5 f. violet	15	10
150		8 f. red	20	10
151		15 f. purple	25	10
152	–	20 f. green (as No. 142)	50	10
153	–	25 f. blue	90	10
154	–	30 f. blue and brown (as No. 141)	1·25	10
155	–	35 f. black and red	75	40
156	**21**	40 f. blue (32 × 22 mm)	1·25	15
157	–	45 f. brown	50	10
158	–	75 f. brown & grn (as No. 141)	2·50	60
159	–	90 f. brown and blue	1·75	35
160	–	100 f. red	3·25	10
161	**21**	250 f. green (32 × 22 mm)	8·00	1·50
162	–	1 d. orange	10·00	1·50
163	–	3 d. red (as No. 142)	25·00	18·00

NEW DESIGNS—37 × 20 mm: 25, 100 f. Vickers Viscount 700 airliner over South Pier, Mina al Ahmadi; 35, 90 f. Shuwaikh Secondary School; 45 f., 1 d. Wara Hill.

23 Telegraph Pole

1962. 4th Arab Telecommunications Union Conference.

164	**23**	8 f. blue and black	15	10
165		20 f. red and black	35	20

1962. Arab League Week. As T **76** of Libya.

166		20 f. purple	20	10
167		45 f. brown	50	20

25 Mubarakiya School, Shaikh Abdullah and Shaikh Mubarak

1962. Golden Jubilee of Mubarakiya School.

168	**25**	8 f. multicoloured	20	10
169		20 f. multicoloured	50	20

26 National Flag and Crest

1962. National Day.

170	**26**	8 f. multicoloured	10	10
171		20 f. multicoloured	35	20
172		45 f. multicoloured	80	30
173		90 f. multicoloured	1·25	1·25

1962. Malaria Eradication. As T **26a** of Yemen.

174		4 f. green and turquoise	15	10
175		25 f. grey and green	55	25

28 "Industry and Progress"

1962. Bicentenary of Sabah Dynasty.

176	**28**	8 f. multicoloured	10	10
177		20 f. multicoloured	35	15
178		45 f. multicoloured	75	15
179		75 f. multicoloured	1·25	50

29 Mother and Child **31** "Education from Oil"

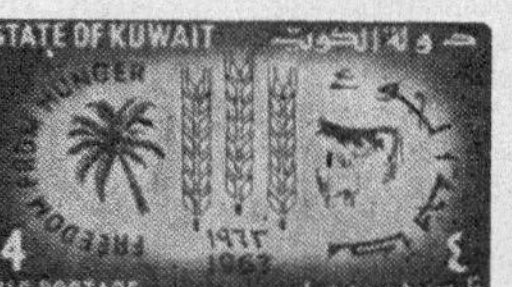

30 Campaign Emblem, Palm and Domestic Animals

1963. Mothers' Day. Centres black and green; value black; country name red.

180 **29** 8 f. yellow 10 10
181 20 f. blue 20 15
182 45 f. olive 50 25
183 75 f. grey 80 40

1963. Freedom from Hunger. Design in brown and green. Background colours given.

184 **30** 4 f. blue 10 10
185 8 f. yellow 25 15
186 20 f. lilac 50 25
187 45 f. pink . . . . 1·10 70

1963. Education Day.

188 **31** 4 f. brown, blue and yellow 10 10
189 20 f. green, blue and yellow 50 15
190 45 f. purple, blue and yellow 90 35

32 Shaikh Abdullah and Flags

1963. 2nd Anniv of National Day. Flags in green, black and red; values in black.

191 **32** 4 f. blue 40 30
192 5 f. ochre 60 55
193 20 f. violet . . . . 3·25 2·25
194 50 f. brown . . . . 6·50 3·75

33 Human Lungs, and Emblems of W.H.O. and Kuwait

1963. W.H.O. "Tuberculosis Control" Campaign. Emblem yellow: arms black, green and red.

195 **33** 2 f. black and stone 10 10
196 4 f. black and green 20 10
197 8 f. black and blue 25 10
198 20 f. black and red . . . . 1·00 35

34 Municipal Hall and Scroll

1963. New Constitution. Centres dull purple; Amir red.

199 **34** 4 f. red 15 10
200 8 f. green 20 10
201 20 f. purple 35 10
202 45 f. brown 60 15
203 75 f. violet . . . . 1·25 50
204 90 f. blue . . . . 1·40 75

35 Football

36 Scales of Justice and Globe

1963. Arab Schools Games. Multicoloured.

205 1 f. Type **35** 10 10
206 4 f. Basketball 10 10
207 5 f. Swimming (horiz) 10 10
208 8 f. Running 15 10
209 15 f. Throwing the javelin (horiz) 30 15
210 20 f. Pole vaulting (horiz) . . . 40 20
211 35 f. Gymnastics (horiz) . . . 90 35
212 45 f. Gymnastics . . . . . . 1·25 75

1963. 15th Anniv of Declaration of Human Rights.

213 **36** 8 f. black, green & violet . . 10 10
214 20 f. black, yellow & grey . . 40 20
215 25 f. black, brown and blue . 60 30

37 Shaikh Abdullah

38 Rameses II in War Chariot

1964. Multicoloured, frame colours given.

216 **37** 1 f. grey 10 10
217 2 f. blue 10 10
218 4 f. brown 15 10
219 5 f. brown 15 10
220 8 f. brown 25 10
221 10 f. green 25 10
222 15 f. green 35 35
223 20 f. blue 35 10
224 25 f. green 40 10
225 30 f. green 50 10
226 40 f. violet 70 15
227 45 f. violet 85 15
228 50 f. yellow 90 20
229 70 f. purple . . . . 1·10 25
230 75 f. red . . . . 1·25 35
231 90 f. blue . . . . 1·60 35
232 100 f. lilac . . . . 1·75 40
233 250 f. brown (25 × 30 mm) . . 5·00 90
234 1 d. purple (25 × 30 mm) . . 14·00 3·75

1964. Nubian Monuments Preservation.

235 **38** 8 f. purple, blue and buff 15 10
236 20 f. violet, blue & lt blue 40 20
237 30 f. violet, blue & turquoise 55 35

39 Mother and Child

1964. Mother's Day.

238 **39** 8 f. blue, green and grey . . 10 10
239 20 f. blue, green and red . . 25 10
240 30 f. blue, green and bistre 40 20
241 45 f. indigo, green and blue 65 30

40 Nurse giving B.C.G. Vaccine to Patient, and Bones of Chest

41 Dhow and Microscope

1964. World Health Day.

242 **40** 8 f. green and brown . . . 30 10
243 20 f. red and green 85 25

1964. Education Day.

244 **41** 8 f. multicoloured 15 10
245 15 f. multicoloured 30 10
246 20 f. multicoloured 35 15
247 30 f. multicoloured 60 25

42 Dhow and Doves

1964. 3rd Anniv of National Day. Badge in blue, brown, black, red and green.

248 **42** 8 f. black and brown . . . 25 15
249 20 f. black and green . . . 40 25
250 30 f. black and grey 60 35
251 45 f. black and blue 85 55

43 A.P.U. Emblem

44 Hawker Siddeley Comet 4C and Douglas DC-3 Airliners

1964. 10th Anniv of Arab Postal Union's Permanent Office, Cairo.

252 **43** 8 f. brown and blue 25 10
253 20 f. blue and yellow . . . 45 20
254 45 f. brown and green . . . 85 50

1964. Air. 10th Anniv of Kuwait Airways. Sky in blue; aircraft blue, red and black.

255 **44** 20 f. black and bistre . . . 45 25
256 25 f. black and brown . . . 60 30
257 30 f. black and green . . . 70 30
258 45 f. black and brown . . . 1·00 40

45 Conference Emblem

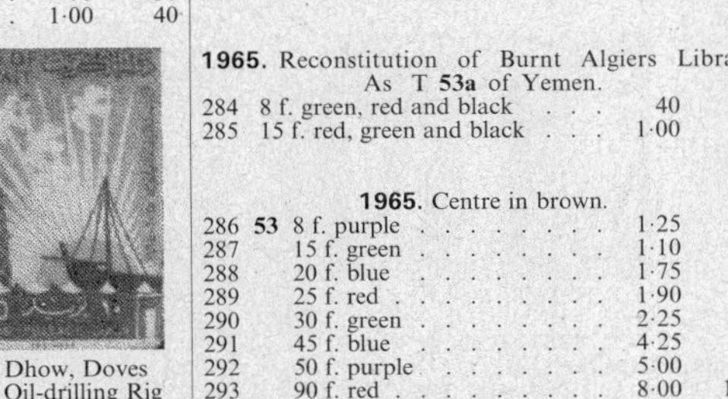

46 Dhow, Doves and Oil-drilling Rig

1965. 1st Arab Journalists' Conference, Kuwait.

259 **45** 8 f. multicoloured 30 10
260 20 f. multicoloured 55 20

1965. 4th Anniv of National Day.

261 **46** 10 f. multicoloured 15 10
262 15 f. multicoloured 35 15
263 20 f. multicoloured 75 20

47 I.C.Y. Emblem

48 Mother and Children

1965. International Co-operation Year.

264 **47** 8 f. black and red 25 10
265 20 f. black and blue 55 25
266 30 f. black and green . . . 1·00 40

The stamps are inscribed "CO-OPERATIVE".

1965. Mothers' Day.

267 **48** 8 f. multicoloured 20 10
268 15 f. multicoloured 40 20
269 20 f. multicoloured 65 25

49 Weather Kite

1965. World Meteorological Day.

270 **49** 4 f. blue and yellow 25 10
271 5 f. blue and orange 25 10
272 20 f. blue and green . . . . 1·10 25

50 Census Graph

1965. Population Census.

273 **50** 8 f. black, brown & blue . . 20 10
274 20 f. black, pink and green . 60 25
275 50 f. black, green and red . . 1·40 60

1965. Deir Yassin Massacre. As T **52a** of Yemen.

276 4 f. red and blue 40 20
277 45 f. red and green . . . . . . 1·90 65

51 Atomic Symbol and Tower of Shuwaikh Secondary School

1965. Education Day.

278 **51** 4 f. multicoloured 15 10
279 20 f. multicoloured 45 15
280 45 f. multicoloured 80 30

52 I.T.U. Emblem and Symbols

53 Saker Falcon

1965. I.T.U. Centenary.

281 **52** 8 f. red and blue 40 25
282 20 f. red and green 80 40
283 45 f. blue and red . . . . . 1·50 70

1965. Reconstitution of Burnt Algiers Library. As T **53a** of Yemen.

284 8 f. green, red and black . . . 40 15
285 15 f. red, green and black . . . 1·00 20

1965. Centre in brown.

286 **53** 8 f. purple . . . . 1·25 15
287 15 f. green . . . . 1·10 15
288 20 f. blue . . . . 1·75 25
289 25 f. red . . . . 1·90 35
290 30 f. green . . . . 2·25 40
291 45 f. blue . . . . 4·25 60
292 50 f. purple . . . . 5·00 70
293 90 f. red . . . . 8·00 1·40

54 Open Book

55 Shaikh Sabah

1966. Education Day.

294 **54** 8 f. multicoloured 20 10
295 20 f. multicoloured 45 10
296 30 f. multicoloured 85 25

1966.

297 **55** 4 f. multicoloured 15 10
298 5 f. multicoloured 15 10
299 20 f. multicoloured 40 15
300 30 f. multicoloured 55 25
301 40 f. multicoloured 70 35
302 45 f. multicoloured 75 40
303 70 f. multicoloured . . . . 1·75 60
304 90 f. multicoloured . . . . 2·00 80

56 Pomfrets and Ears of Wheat

1966. Freedom from Hunger.

305 **56** 20 f. multicoloured . . . . 1·00 50
306 45 f. multicoloured . . . . 2·25 95

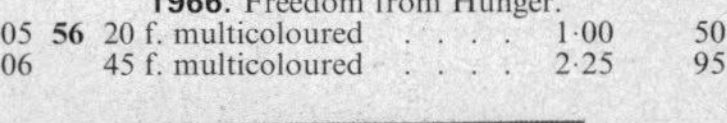

57 Eagle and Scales of Justice

1966. 5th Anniv of National Day.

307 **57** 20 f. multicoloured 80 30
308 25 f. multicoloured 90 30
309 45 f. multicoloured . . . . 1·60 60

58 Cogwheel and Map of Arab States

59 Mother and Children

1966. Arab Countries Industrial Development Conference, Kuwait.

310 **58** 20 f. green black and blue 50 15
311 50 f. green, black & brown 1·00 45

1966. Mothers' Day.

312 **59** 20 f. multicoloured 50 15
313 45 f. multicoloured . . . . 1·00 30

60 Red Crescent and Emblem of Medicine

61 "Man and his Cities"

1966. 5th Arab Medical Conference, Kuwait.

314 **60** 15 f. red and blue 35 15
315 30 f. red, blue and pink . . 80 40

1966. World Health Day.

316 **61** 8 f. multicoloured 50 15
317 10 f. multicoloured 75 20

62 W.H.O. Building

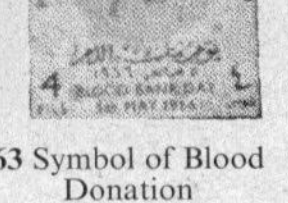

63 Symbol of Blood Donation

1966. Inaug of W.H.O. Headquarters, Geneva.

318 **62** 5 f. green, blue and red . . . 50 10
319 10 f. green, blue & turq . . 90 15

1966. Traffic Day. As T **66** of Yemen.

320		10 f. red, emerald and green	50	10
321		20 f. emerald, red and green	75	25

1966. Blood Bank Day.

322	**63**	4 f. multicoloured	40	10
323		8 f. multicoloured	85	25

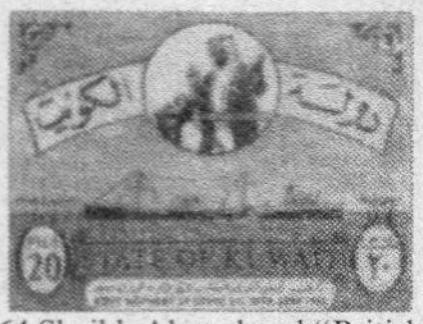

64 Shaikh Ahmad and "British Fusilier" (tanker)

1966. 20th Anniv of 1st Crude Oil Shipment.

324	**64**	20 f. multicoloured	60	25
325		45 f. multicoloured	1·40	55

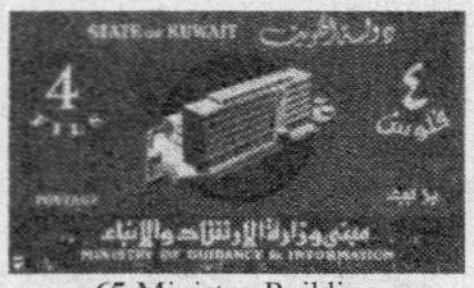

65 Ministry Building

1966. Inauguration of Ministry of Guidance and Information Building.

326	**65**	4 f. red and brown	20	10
327		5 f. brown and green	20	10
328		8 f. green and violet	30	10
329		20 f. orange and blue	65	20

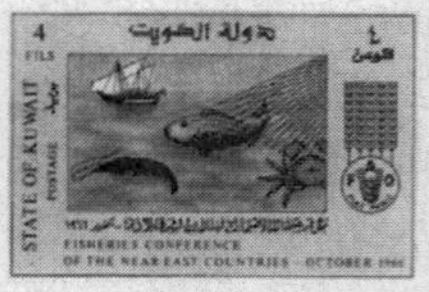

66 Dhow, Lobster, Fish and Crab

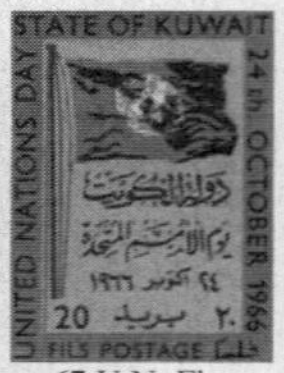

67 U.N. Flag

1966. F.A.O. Near East Countries Fisheries Conference, Kuwait.

330	**66**	4 f. multicoloured	85	25
331		20 f. multicoloured	1·10	50

1966. U.N. Day.

332	**67**	20 f. multicoloured	75	25
333		45 f. multicoloured	1·10	50

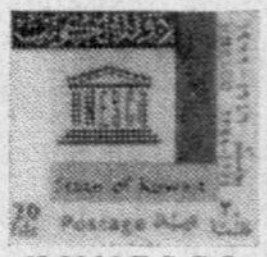

68 U.N.E.S.C.O. Emblem

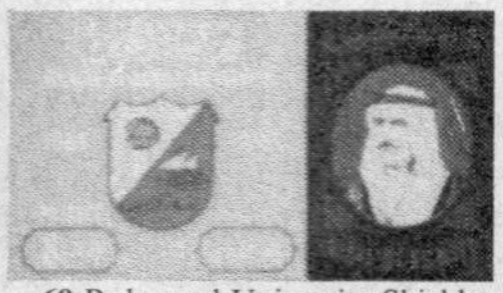

69 Ruler and University Shield

1966. 20th Anniv of U.N.E.S.C.O.

334	**68**	20 f. multicoloured	75	60
335		45 f. multicoloured	1·50	1·25

1966. Opening of Kuwait University.

336	**69**	8 f. multicoloured	25	10
337		10 f. multicoloured	25	15
338		20 f. multicoloured	75	25
339		45 f. multicoloured	1·50	75

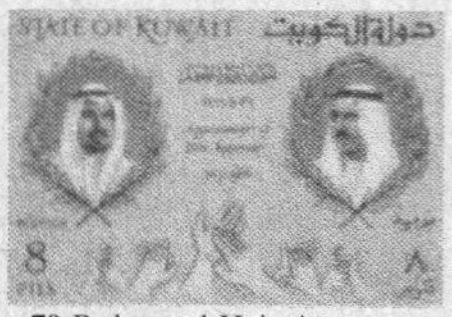

70 Ruler and Heir-Apparent

1966. Appointment of Heir-Apparent.

340	**70**	8 f. multicoloured	25	10
341		20 f. multicoloured	60	30
342		45 f. multicoloured	1·25	70

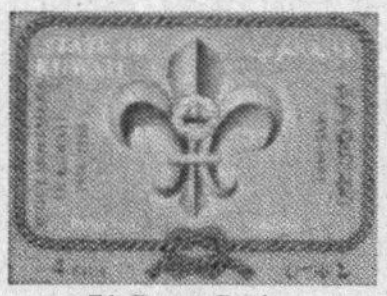

71 Scout Badge

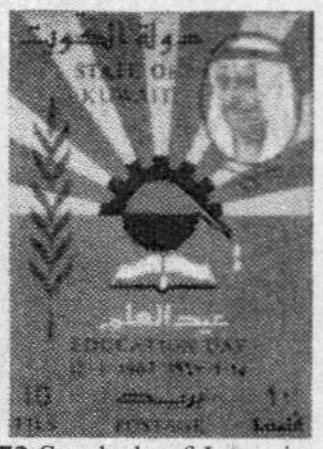

72 Symbols of Learning

1966. 30th Anniv of Kuwait Scouts.

343	**71**	4 f. brown and green	50	15
344		20 f. green and brown	1·75	50

1967. Education Day.

345	**72**	10 f. multicoloured	30	15
346		45 f. multicoloured	80	35

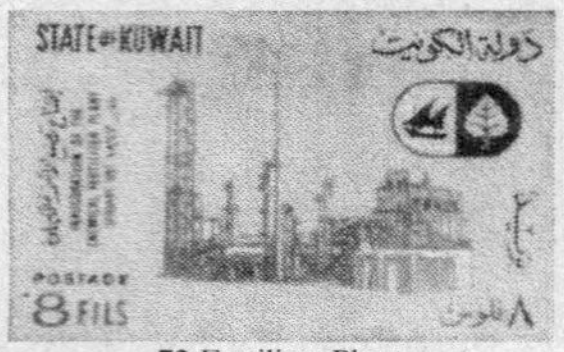

73 Fertiliser Plant

1967. Inauguration of Chemical Fertiliser Plant.

347	**73**	8 f. multicoloured	40	15
348		20 f. multicoloured	1·00	30

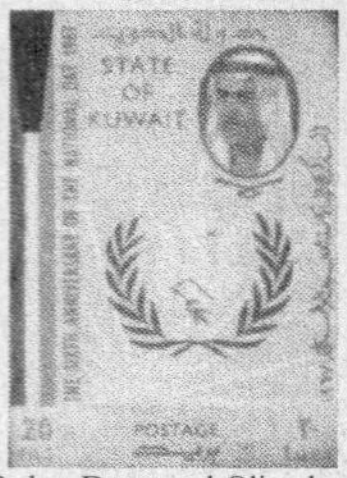

74 Ruler, Dove and Olive-branch

1967. 6th Anniv of National Day.

349	**74**	8 f. multicoloured	30	10
350		20 f. multicoloured	80	30

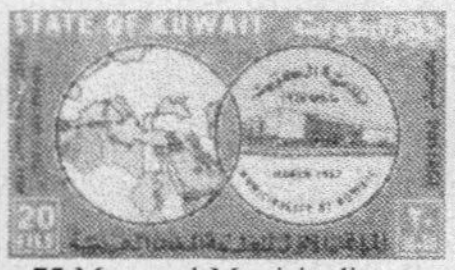

75 Map and Municipality Building

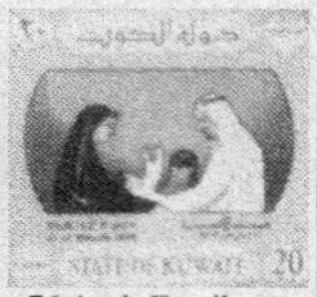

76 Arab Family

1967. 1st Arab Cities Organization Conf, Kuwait.

351	**75**	20 f. multicoloured	1·00	25
352		30 f. multicoloured	1·40	60

1967. Family's Day.

353	**76**	20 f. multicoloured	80	25
354		45 f. multicoloured	1·60	60

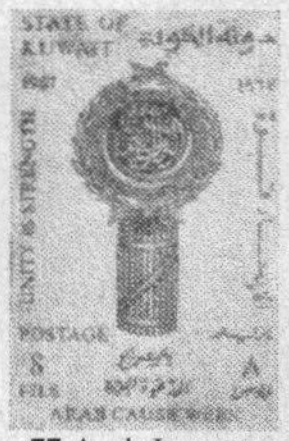

77 Arab League Emblem

78 Sabah Hospital

1967. Arab Cause Week.

355	**77**	8 f. blue and grey	30	10
356		10 f. green and yellow	60	15

1967. World Health Day.

357	**78**	8 f. multicoloured	85	15
358		20 f. multicoloured	1·00	40

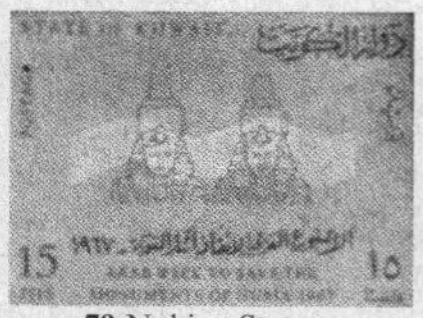

79 Nubian Statues

1967. Arab Week for Nubian Monuments Preservation.

359	**79**	15 f. green, brown & yellow	60	20
360		20 f. green, purple and blue	90	25

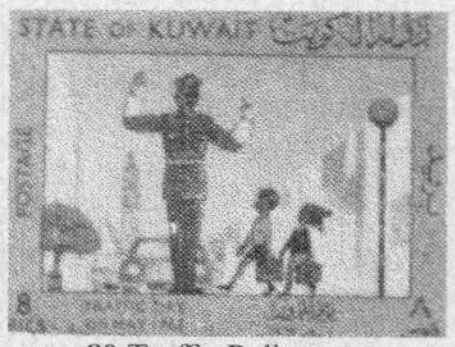

80 Traffic Policeman

1967. Traffic Day.

361	**80**	8 f. multicoloured	80	25
362		20 f. multicoloured	1·75	65

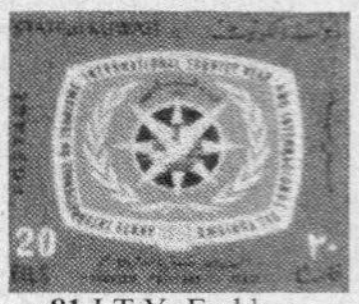

81 I.T.Y. Emblem

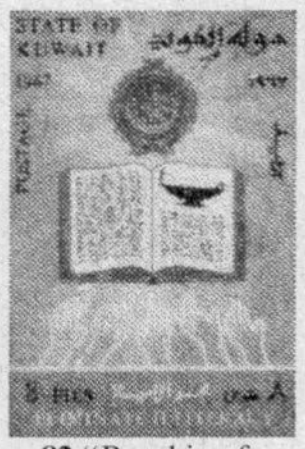

82 "Reaching for Knowledge"

1967. International Tourist Year.

363	**81**	20 f. black, blue & turq	65	40
364		45 f. black, blue and mauve	1·25	85

1967. "Eliminate Illiteracy" Campaign.

365	**82**	8 f. multicoloured	75	10
366		20 f. multicoloured	1·50	35

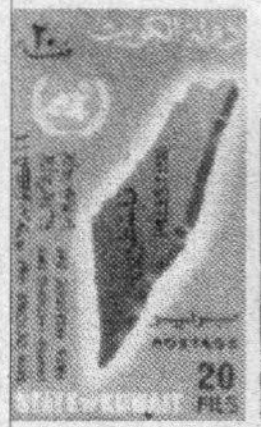

83 Map of Palestine

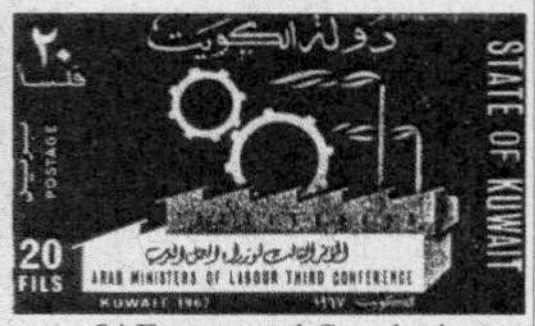

84 Factory and Cogwheels

1967. U.N. Day.

367	**83**	20 f. red and blue	50	20
368		45 f. red and orange	1·10	50

1967. 3rd Arab Labour Ministers' Conference.

369	**84**	20 f. yellow and red	60	20
370		45 f. yellow and grey	1·40	50

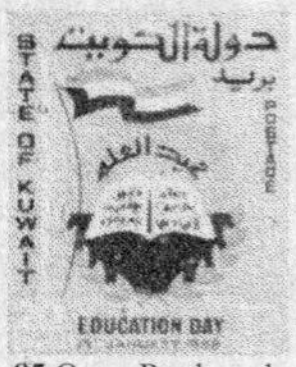

85 Open Book and Kuwaiti Flag

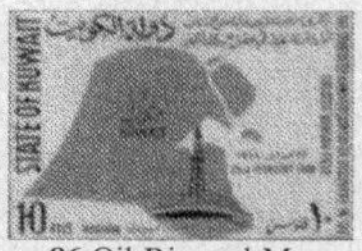

86 Oil Rig and Map

1968. Education Day.

371	**85**	20 f. multicoloured	50	30
372		45 f. multicoloured	1·25	60

1968. 30th Anniv of Oil Discovery in Greater Burgan Field.

373	**86**	10 f. multicoloured	75	40
374		20 f. multicoloured	1·25	70

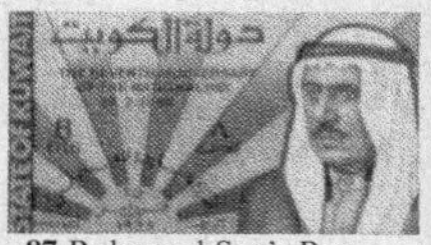

87 Ruler and Sun's Rays

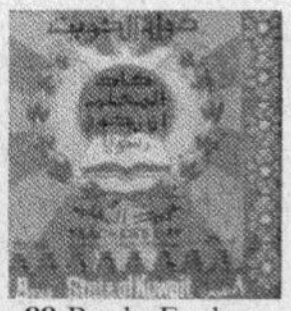

88 Book, Eagle and Sun

1968. 7th Anniv of National Day.

375	**87**	8 f. multicoloured	25	10
376		10 f. multicoloured	25	20
377		15 f. multicoloured	45	25
378		20 f. multicoloured	60	35

1968. Teachers' Day.

379	**88**	8 f. multicoloured	30	10
380		20 f. multicoloured	40	15
381		45 f. multicoloured	75	40

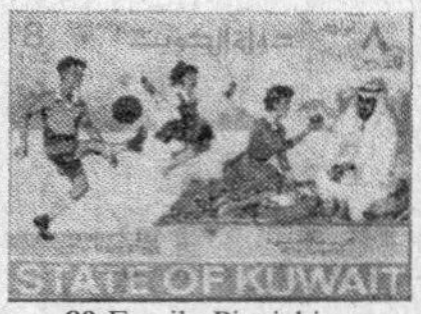

89 Family Picnicking

1968. Family Day.

382	**89**	8 f. multicoloured	20	10
383		10 f. multicoloured	20	10
384		15 f. multicoloured	30	10
385		20 f. multicoloured	45	20

MORE DETAILED LISTS
are given in the Stanley Gibbons Catalogues referred to in the country headings.
For lists of current volumes see Introduction.

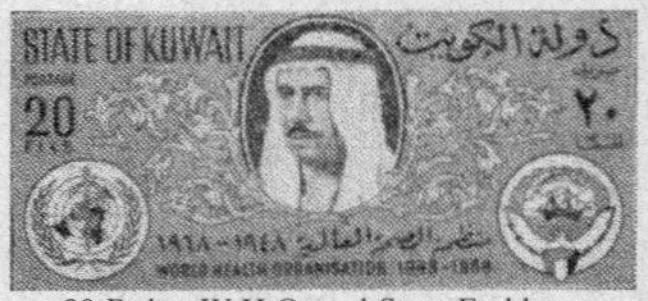

90 Ruler, W.H.O. and State Emblems

1968. World Health Day and 20th Anniv of W.H.O.

386	**90**	20 f. multicoloured	60	50
387		45 f. multicoloured	1·50	1·10

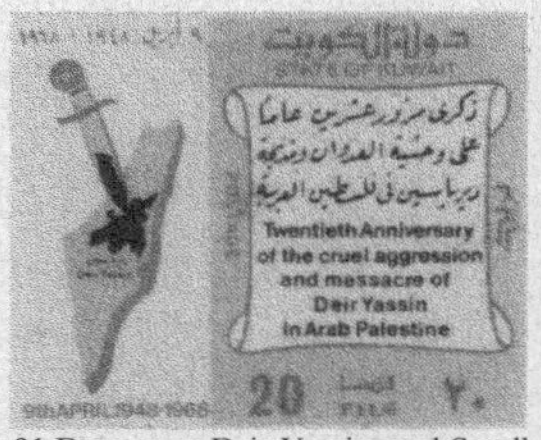

91 Dagger on Deir Yassin, and Scroll

1968. 20th Anniv of Deir Yassin Massacre.

388	**91**	20 f. red and blue	80	25
389		45 f. red and violet	2·75	50

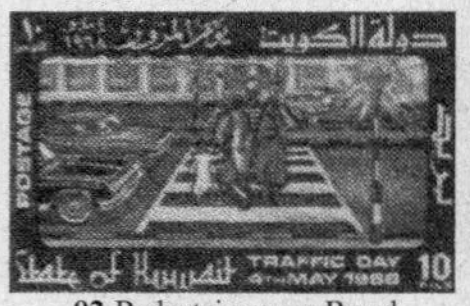

92 Pedestrians on Road Crossing

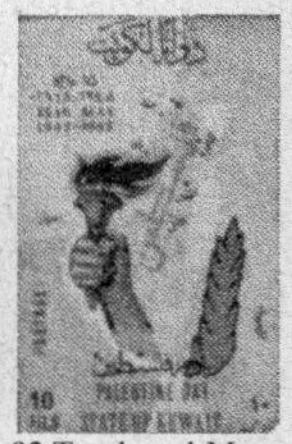

93 Torch and Map

1968. Traffic Day.

390	**92**	10 f. multicoloured	75	60
391		15 f. multicoloured	1·25	85
392		20 f. multicoloured	1·75	1·00

1968. Palestine Day.

393	**93**	10 f. multicoloured	70	10
394		20 f. multicoloured	1·25	25
395		45 f. multicoloured	2·50	50

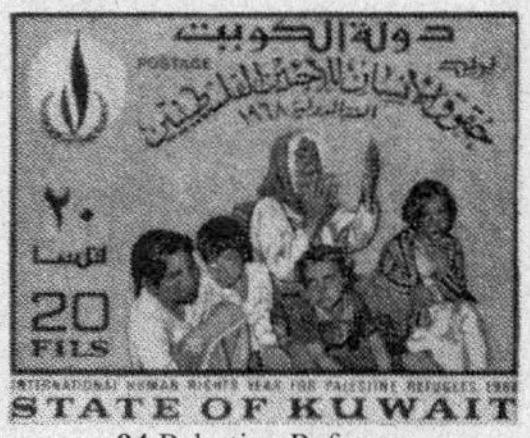

94 Palestine Refugees

1968. Human Rights Year.

396	**94**	20 f. multicoloured	25	15
397		30 f. multicoloured	35	15
398		45 f. multicoloured	65	15
399		90 f. multicoloured	1·25	45

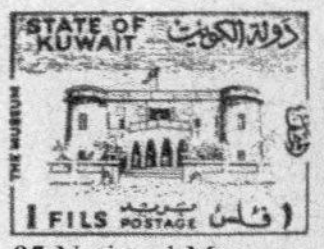

95 National Museum

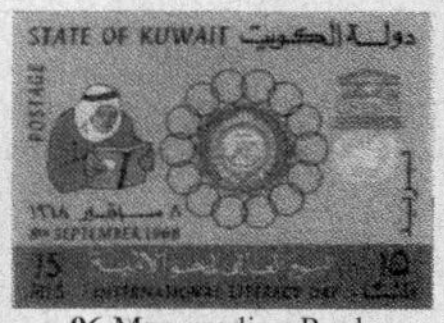

96 Man reading Book

1968.

400	**95**	1 f. green and brown	10	10
401		2 f. green and purple	10	10
402		5 f. red and black	15	10
403		8 f. green and brown	20	10
404		10 f. purple and blue	20	10
405		20 f. blue and brown	45	10
406		25 f. orange and blue	55	10
407		30 f. green and blue	70	20
408		45 f. deep purple and purple	1·10	20
409		50 f. red and green	1·60	45

1968. International Literacy Day.

410	**96**	15 f. multicoloured	30	10
411		20 f. multicoloured	70	15

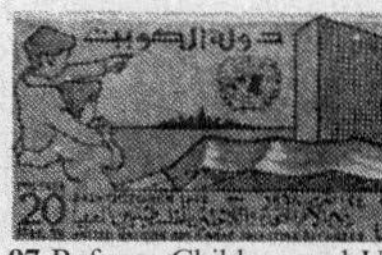

97 Refugee Children and U.N. Headquarters

1968. United Nations Day.

412	**97**	20 f. multicoloured	30	10
413		30 f. multicoloured	40	20
414		45 f. multicoloured	70	25

98 Chamber of Commerce Building

1968. Inauguration of Kuwait Chamber of Commerce and Industry Building.

415 **98** 10 f. purple and orange . . 25 10
416 15 f. blue and mauve . . . 30 15
417 20 f. green and brown . . . 45 15

99 Conference Emblem

1968. 14th Arab Chambers of Commerce, Industry and Agriculture Conference.

418 **99** 10 f. multicoloured 25 10
419 15 f. multicoloured 30 10
420 20 f. multicoloured 40 15
421 30 f. multicoloured 70 30

100 Refinery Plant

101 Holy Koran, Scales and People

1968. Inauguration of Shuaiba Refinery.

422 **100** 10 f. multicoloured 30 15
423 20 f. multicoloured 60 20
424 30 f. multicoloured 95 35
425 45 f. multicoloured . . . . 1·75 45

1968. 1,400th Anniv of the Holy Koran.

426 **101** 8 f. multicoloured 30 15
427 20 f. multicoloured 75 40
428 30 f. multicoloured . . . . 1·25 60
429 45 f. multicoloured . . . . 1·60 85

102 Boeing 707 Airliner

1969. Inauguration of Boeing 707 Aircraft by Kuwait Airways.

430 **102** 10 f. multicoloured 35 20
431 20 f. multicoloured 75 35
432 25 f. multicoloured . . . . 1·10 45
433 45 f. multicoloured . . . . 2·00 65

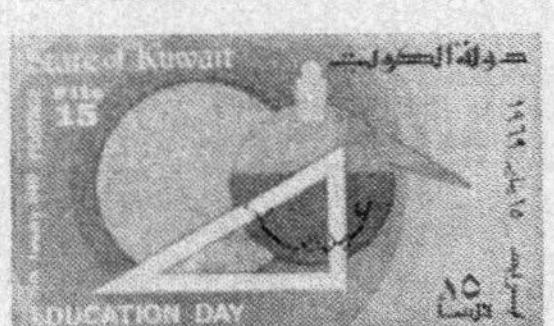

103 Globe and Symbols of Engineering and Science

1969. Education Day.

434 **103** 15 f. multicoloured 35 25
435 20 f. multicoloured 65 30

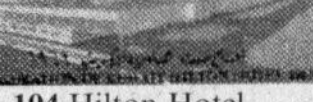

104 Hilton Hotel

105 Family and Teachers' Society Emblem

1969. Inauguration of Kuwait Hilton Hotel.

436 **104** 10 f. multicoloured 35 15
437 20 f. multicoloured 65 15

1969. Education Week.

438 **105** 10 f. multicoloured 35 15
439 20 f. multicoloured 65 15

106 Flags and Laurel

107 Emblem, Teacher and Class

1969. 8th Anniv of National Day.

440 **106** 15 f. multicoloured 25 15
441 20 f. multicoloured 40 20
442 30 f. multicoloured 60 40

1969. Teachers' Day.

443 **107** 10 f. multicoloured 30 15
444 20 f. multicoloured 55 15

108 Kuwaiti Family

1969. Family Day.

445 **108** 10 f. multicoloured 30 15
446 20 f. multicoloured 55 20

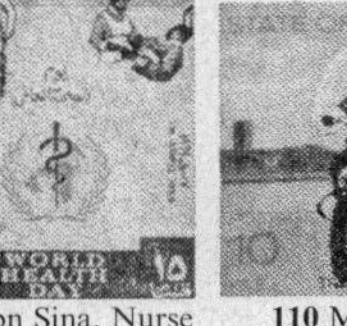

109 Ibn Sina, Nurse with Patient and W.H.O. Emblem

110 Motor-cycle Police

1969. World Health Day.

447 **109** 15 f. multicoloured 70 15
448 20 f. multicoloured 80 20

1969. Traffic Day.

449 **110** 10 f. multicoloured 75 15
450 20 f. multicoloured . . . . 2·00 25

111 I.L.O. Emblem

1969. 50th Anniv of I.L.O.

451 **111** 10 f. gold, black and red 30 10
452 20 f. gold, black and green 50 15

112 Tanker "Al Sabahiah"

1969. 4th Anniv of Kuwait Shipping Company.

453 **112** 20 f. multicoloured 90 35
454 45 f. multicoloured . . . . 1·90 90

113 Woman writing Letter

114 Amir Shaikh Sabah

1969. International Literacy Day.

455 **113** 10 f. multicoloured 25 10
456 20 f. multicoloured 55 20

1969. Portraits multicoloured; background colours given.

457 **114** 8 f. blue 25 10
458 10 f. pink 25 10
459 15 f. grey 35 15
460 20 f. yellow 40 15
461 25 f. lilac 50 20
462 30 f. orange 70 25
463 45 f. grey 95 35
464 **114** 50 f. green . . . . 1·10 40
465 70 f. blue . . . . 1·25 50
466 75 f. blue . . . . 1·40 55
467 90 f. brown . . . . 1·40 70
468 250 f. purple . . . . . . 5·50 2·00
469 500 f. green . . . . . . 10·50 6·50
470 1 d. purple . . . . . . 17·00 11·00

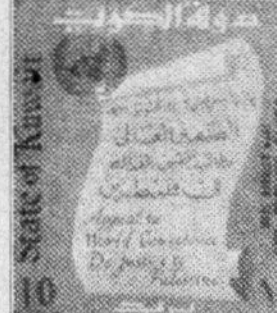

115 "Appeal to World Conscience"

116 Earth Station

1969. United Nations Day.

471 **115** 10 f. blue, black and green 30 10
472 20 f. blue, black and stone 60 15
473 45 f. blue, black and red 1·00 30

1969. Inauguration of Kuwait Satellite Communications Station. Multicoloured.

474 20 Type **116** 90 20
475 45 f. Dish aerial on Globe (vert) 1·90 50

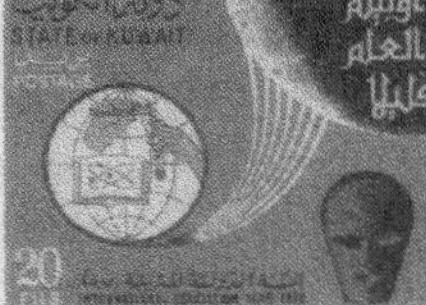

117 Refugee Family

118 Globe, Symbols and I.E.Y. Emblem

1969. Palestinian Refugee Week.

476 **117** 20 f. multicoloured. . . . 1·40 40
477 45 f. multicoloured . . . . 3·00 1·25

1970. International Education Year.

478 **118** 20 f. multicoloured 40 25
479 45 f. multicoloured . . . . 1·00 60

119 Shoue

1970. Kuwait Sailing Dhows. Multicoloured.

480 8 f. Type **119** 40 10
481 10 f. Sambuk 40 10
482 15 f. Baggala 60 20
483 20 f. Battela 75 15
484 25 f. Bum 90 25
485 45 f. Baggala . . . . 1·75 55
486 50 f. Dhow-building . . . . . 2·00 55

120 Kuwaiti Flag

1970. 9th Anniv of National Day.

487 **120** 15 f. multicoloured 65 15
488 20 f. multicoloured 75 15

121 Young Commando and Dome of the Rock, Jerusalem

1970. Support for Palestinian Commandos. Multicoloured.

489 10 f. Type **121** 50 20
490 20 f. Commando in battle-dress 1·00 40
491 45 f. Woman commando . . . 2·50 90

122 Parents with "Children"

1970. Family Day.

492 **122** 20 f. multicoloured 40 15
493 30 f. multicoloured 60 25

123 Arab League Flag, Emblem and Map

1970. 25th Anniv of Arab League.

494 **123** 20 f. brown, green and blue 50 10
495 45 f. violet, green and orange 75 30

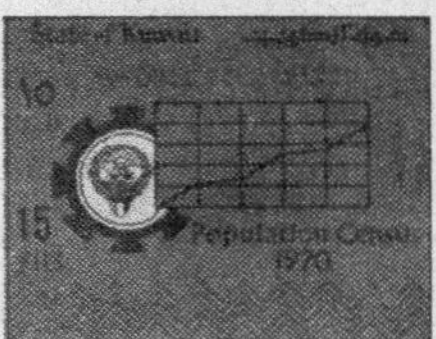

124 Census Emblem and Graph

1970. Population Census.

496 **124** 15 f. multicoloured 20 10
497 20 f. multicoloured 50 10
498 30 f. multicoloured 70 20

125 Cancer the Crab in "Pincers"

126 Traffic Lights and Road Signs

1970. World Health Day.

499 **125** 20 f. multicoloured 45 10
500 30 f. multicoloured 65 20

1970. Traffic Day.

501 **126** 20 f. multicoloured . . . . 1·00 45
502 30 f. multicoloured . . . . 1·50 70

127 Red Crescent

1970. International Red Cross and Crescent Day.

503 **127** 10 f. multicoloured 40 15
504 15 f. multicoloured 60 20
505 30 f. multicoloured . . . . 1·50 50

128 New Headquarters Building

1970. Opening of New U.P.U. Headquarters Building, Berne.

506 **128** 20 f. multicoloured 60 20
507 30 f. multicoloured 90 35

129 Amir Shaikh Sabah

130 U.N. Symbols

1970.

508 **129** 20 f. multicoloured 65 20
509 45 f. multicoloured . . . . 1·60 75

1970. 25th Anniv of United Nations.

511 **130** 20 f. multicoloured 40 15
512 45 f. multicoloured 70 30

131 "Medora" (tanker) at Sea Island Jetty

1970. Oil Shipment Facilities, Kuwait.

513 131 20 f. multicoloured 90 30
514 45 f. multicoloured . . . . 2·10 65

132 Kuwaiti and U.N. Emblems and Hand writing

1970. International Literacy Day.

515 132 10 f. multicoloured 70 15
516 15 f. multicoloured 90 15

133 Guards and Badge

1970. First Graduation of National Guards.

517 133 10 f. multicoloured 55 15
518 20 f. multicoloured . . . . 1·10 20

134 Symbols and Flag

136 Map of Palestine on Globe

135 Dr. C. Best and Sir F. Banting (discoverers of insulin) and Syringe

1971. 10th Anniv of National Day.

519 134 20 f. multicoloured 70 30
520 30 f. multicoloured 95 45

1971. World Health Day, and 50th Anniv of Discovery of Insulin.

521 135 20 f. multicoloured 50 15
522 45 f. multicoloured . . . . 1·10 40

1971. Palestine Week.

523 136 20 f. multicoloured . . . . 1·00 75
524 45 f. multicoloured . . . . 2·25 1·50

137 I.T.U. Emblem

138 "Three Races"

1971. World Telecommunications Day.

525 137 20 f. black, brown & silver 70 20
526 45 f. black, brown & gold 1·60 60

1971. Racial Equality Year.

527 138 15 f. multicoloured 35 20
528 30 f. multicoloured 65 50

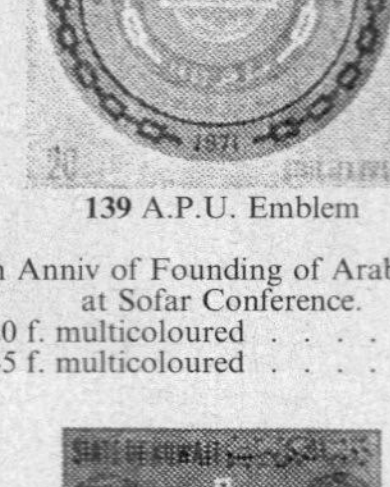

139 A.P.U. Emblem

1971. 25th Anniv of Founding of Arab Postal Union at Sofar Conference.

529 139 20 f. multicoloured 50 25
530 45 f. multicoloured . . . . 1·00 40

140 Book, Pupils, Globes and Pen

1971. International Literacy Day.

531 140 25 f. multicoloured 60 20
532 60 f. multicoloured . . . . 1·50 60

141 Footballers

1971. Regional Sports Tournament, Kuwait. Multicoloured.

533 20 f. Type 141 . . . . 95 35
534 30 f. Footballer blocking attack 1·40 50

142 Emblems of U.N.I.C.E.F. and Kuwait

1971. 25th Anniv of U.N.I.C.E.F.

535 142 25 f. multicoloured 40 25
536 60 f. multicoloured 90 50

143 Book Year Emblem

1972. International Book Year.

537 143 20 f. black and brown . . . 50 30
538 45 f. black and green . . . 1·10 60

144 Crest and Laurel

1972. 11th Anniv of National Day.

539 144 20 f. multicoloured 85 50
540 45 f. multicoloured . . . . 1·40 85

145 Telecommunications Centre

1972. Inauguration of Telecommunications Centre, Kuwait.

541 145 20 f. multicoloured . . . . 1·00 40
542 45 f. multicoloured . . . . 2·50 1·00

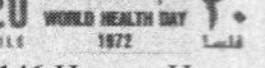

146 Human Heart

147 Nurse and Child

1972. World Health Day and World Heart Month.

543 146 20 f. multicoloured . . . . 1·25 25
544 45 f. multicoloured . . . . 2·75 50

1972. International Red Cross and Crescent Day.

545 147 8 f. multicoloured 75 10
546 40 f. multicoloured . . . . 2·40 75

148 Football

1972. Olympic Games, Munich. Multicoloured.

547 2 f. Type 148 . . . . 10 10
548 4 f. Running 15 10
549 5 f. Swimming 20 10
550 8 f. Gymnastics 30 10
551 10 f. Throwing the discus . . . 35 10
552 15 f. Show jumping 45 15
553 20 f. Basketball 50 20
554 25 f. Volleyball 65 30

149 Produce and Fishing Boat

151 Ancient Capitals

150 Bank Emblem

1972. 11th F.A.O. Near East Regional Conference, Kuwait.

555 149 5 f. multicoloured 40 30
556 10 f. multicoloured . . . . 1·25 75
557 20 f. multicoloured . . . . 2·50 1·40

1972. 20th Anniv of National Bank of Kuwait.

558 150 10 f. multicoloured 30 15
559 35 f. multicoloured . . . . 1·00 70

1972. Archaeological Excavations on Failaka Island. Multicoloured.

560 2 f. Type 151 . . . . 10 15
561 5 f. View of excavations . . . 25 10
562 10 f. "Leaf" capital 45 10
563 15 f. Excavated building . . . 95 20

152 Floral Emblem

153 Interpol Emblem

1973. 12th Anniv of National Day.

564 152 10 f. multicoloured 30 15
565 20 f. multicoloured 65 45
566 30 f. multicoloured 95 65

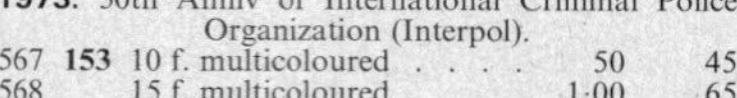

1973. 50th Anniv of International Criminal Police Organization (Interpol).

567 153 10 f. multicoloured 50 45
568 15 f. multicoloured . . . . 1·00 65
569 20 f. multicoloured . . . . 1·50 95

154 C.I.S.M. Badge and Flags

155 Airways Building

1973. 25th Anniv of International Military Sports Council (C.I.S.M.).

570 154 30 f. multicoloured 65 40
571 40 f. multicoloured . . . . 1·00 50

1973. Opening of Kuwait Airways H.Q. Building.

572 155 10 f. multicoloured 35 15
573 15 f. multicoloured 55 25
574 20 f. multicoloured 70 30

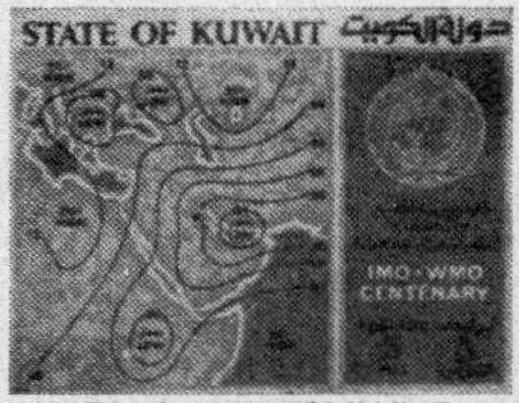

156 Weather Map of Middle East

1973. Centenary of World Meteorological Organization.

575 156 5 f. multicoloured 30 10
576 10 f. multicoloured 50 15
577 15 f. multicoloured 85 25

157 Shaikhs Ahmed and Sabah

1973. 50th Anniv of 1st Kuwait Stamp Issue (overprints on India of 1923).

578 157 10 f. multicoloured 40 15
579 20 f. multicoloured 75 25
580 70 f. multicoloured . . . . 2·50 1·10

158 Mourning Dove

1973. Birds and Hunting Equipment. Multicoloured.

(a) Size 32 × 32 mm.

581 5 f. Type 158 . . . . 50 15
582 5 f. Hoopoe ("Upupa epops") . 50 15
583 5 f. Rock dove ("Columba livia") 50 15
584 5 f. Stone-curlew ("Burhinus oedicnemus") . . 50 15
585 8 f. Great grey shrike ("Lanius excubitor") 70 15
586 8 f. Red-backed shrike ("Lanius collurio") 70 15
587 8 f. Black-headed shrike ("Lanius schach") 70 15
588 8 f. Golden oriole ("Orielus chinensis") 70 15
589 10 f. Willow warbler ("Phylloscopus trochilus") . 70 15
590 10 f. Great reed warbler ("Acrocephalus arundinaceus") 70 15
591 10 f. Blackcap ("Sylvia atricapilla") 70 15
592 10 f. Barn swallow ("Hirundo rustica") 70 15
593 15 f. Rock thrush ("Monticola solitarius") . . 1·10 25
594 15 f. Redstart ("Phoenicurus phoenicurus") . . . . . 1·10 25
595 15 f. Common wheatear ("Oenanthe oenanthe") . . . 1·10 25
596 15 f. Bluethroat ("Luscinia svecica") . . . . 1·10 25
597 20 f. Houbara bustard ("Chlamydotis undulata") . . 1·50 30
598 20 f. Pin-tailed sandgrouse ("Pterocles alchata") . . . . 1·50 30
599 20 f. Giant wood rail ("Aramides ypecaha") . . . 1·50 30
600 20 f. Spotted crake ("Porzana porzana") . . . . 1·50 30

(b) Size 38 × 38 mm.

601 25 f. American kestrel ("Falco sparverius") . . . . 2·00 35
602 25 f. Great black-backed gull ("Larus marinus") . . . . . 2·00 35

No.	Type	Description	Unused	Used
603		25 f. Purple heron ("Ardea purpurea")	2·00	35
604		25 f. Wryneck ("Jynx torquilla")	2·00	35
605		30 f. European bee eater ("Merops apiaster")	2·25	45
606		30 f. Saker falcon ("Accipiter")	2·25	45
607		30 f. Grey wagtail ("Motacilla cinerea")	2·25	45
608		30 f. Pied wagtail ("Motacilla alba")	2·25	45
609		45 f. Bird traps	3·00	80
610		45 f. Driving great grey shrikes into net	3·00	80
611		45 f. Stalking rock dove with hand net	3·00	80
612		45 f. Great grey shrike and disguised lure	3·00	80

159 Flame Emblem

160 Congress Emblem

1973. 25th Anniv of Declaration of Human Rights.

No.	Type	Description	Unused	Used
613	159	10 f. multicoloured	40	10
614		40 f. multicoloured	1·10	35
615		75 f. multicoloured	1·75	60

1974. 4th Congress of Arab Veterinary Union, Kuwait.

No.	Type	Description	Unused	Used
616	160	30 f. multicoloured	60	20
617		40 f. multicoloured	85	35

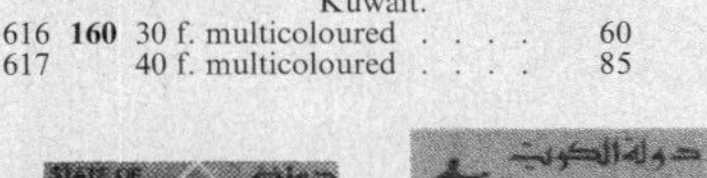

161 Flag and Wheat Ear Symbol

163 Tournament Emblem

162 A.M.U. Emblem

1974. 13th Anniv of National Day.

No.	Type	Description	Unused	Used
618	161	20 f. multicoloured	30	10
619		30 f. multicoloured	50	25
620		70 f. multicoloured	1·40	1·00

1974. 12th Conference of Arab Medical Union and 1st Conference of Kuwait Medical Society.

No.	Type	Description	Unused	Used
621	162	30 f. multicoloured	1·25	30
622		40 f. multicoloured	1·75	80

1974. 3rd Arabian Gulf Trophy Football Tournament, Kuwait.

No.	Type	Description	Unused	Used
623	163	25 f. multicoloured	80	15
624		45 f. multicoloured	1·75	70

164 Institute Buildings

1974. Inauguration of Kuwait Institute for Scientific Research.

No.	Type	Description	Unused	Used
625	164	15 f. multicoloured	70	25
626		20 f. multicoloured	1·40	30

165 Emblems of Kuwait, Arab Postal Union and U.P.U.

1974. Centenary of U.P.U.

No.	Type	Description	Unused	Used
627	165	20 f. multicoloured	25	15
628		30 f. multicoloured	30	30
629		60 f. multicoloured	50	45

166 Symbolic Telephone Dial

167 Council Emblem and Flags of Member States

1974. World Telecommunications Day.

No.	Type	Description	Unused	Used
630	166	10 f. multicoloured	60	20
631		30 f. multicoloured	1·90	75
632		40 f. multicoloured	3·00	1·00

1974. 17th Anniv of Signing Arab Economic Unity Agreement.

No.	Type	Description	Unused	Used
633	167	20 f. green, black and red	60	25
634		30 f. red, black and green	70	40

168 "Population Growth"

1974. World Population Year.

No.	Type	Description	Unused	Used
635	168	30 f. multicoloured	75	30
636		70 f. multicoloured	1·75	70

169 Fund Building

1974. Kuwait Fund for Arab Economic Development.

No.	Type	Description	Unused	Used
637	169	10 f. multicoloured	45	10
638		20 f. multicoloured	75	25

170 Shuaiba Emblem

1974. 10th Anniv of Shuaiba Industrial Area.

No.	Type	Description	Unused	Used
639	170	10 f. multicoloured	40	15
640		20 f. multicoloured	1·00	30
641		30 f. multicoloured	1·40	55

171 Arms of Kuwait and "14"

1975. 14th Anniv of National Day.

No.	Type	Description	Unused	Used
642	171	20 f. multicoloured	40	20
643		70 f. multicoloured	1·25	60
644		75 f. multicoloured	1·60	70

172 Census Symbols

1975. Population Census.

No.	Type	Description	Unused	Used
645	172	8 f. multicoloured	15	10
646		20 f. multicoloured	35	10
647		30 f. multicoloured	50	25
648		70 f. multicoloured	1·40	75
649		100 f. multicoloured	1·75	1·10

173 I.W.Y. and Kuwait Women's Union Emblems

1975. International Women's Year.

No.	Type	Description	Unused	Used
650	173	15 f. multicoloured	50	15
651		20 f. multicoloured	60	30
652		30 f. multicoloured	85	45

174 Classroom within Open Book

1975. International Literacy Day.

No.	Type	Description	Unused	Used
653	174	20 f. multicoloured	50	15
654		30 f. multicoloured	85	45

175 I.S.O. Emblem

176 U.N. Flag, Rifle and Olive-branch

1975. World Standards Day.

No.	Type	Description	Unused	Used
655	175	10 f. multicoloured	30	15
656		20 f. multicoloured	55	25

1975. 30th Anniv of U.N.O.

No.	Type	Description	Unused	Used
657	176	20 f. multicoloured	50	15
658		45 f. multicoloured	1·10	50

177 Shaikh Sabah

1975.

No.	Type	Description	Unused	Used
659	177	8 f. multicoloured	35	15
660		20 f. multicoloured	60	20
661		30 f. multicoloured	70	30
662		50 f. multicoloured	1·25	50
663		90 f. multicoloured	2·40	85
664		100 f. multicoloured	3·00	1·10

178 Kuwait "Skyline"

1976. 15th Anniv of National Day.

No.	Type	Description	Unused	Used
665	178	10 f. multicoloured	50	15
666		20 f. multicoloured	90	15

178a Emblem, Microscope and Operation

179 Early and Modern Telephones

1976. 2nd Annual Conference of Kuwait Medical Association.

No.	Type	Description	Unused	Used
667	178a	5 f. multicoloured	30	15
668		10 f. multicoloured	60	20
669		30 f. multicoloured	1·90	55

1976. Telephone Centenary.

No.	Type	Description	Unused	Used
670	179	5 f. black and orange	20	15
671		15 f. black and blue	65	15

180 Eye

1976. World Health Day.

No.	Type	Description	Unused	Used
672	180	10 f. multicoloured	40	15
673		20 f. multicoloured	75	15
674		30 f. multicoloured	1·25	35

181 Red Crescent Emblem

1976. 10th Anniv of Kuwait Red Crescent Society.

No.	Type	Description	Unused	Used
675	181	20 f. multicoloured	40	15
676		30 f. multicoloured	70	30
677		45 f. multicoloured	1·25	55
678		75 f. multicoloured	2·00	1·40

182 Suburb of Manama

183 Basketball

1976. U.N. Human Settlements Conference.

No.	Type	Description	Unused	Used
679	182	10 f. multicoloured	35	15
680		20 f. multicoloured	65	15

1976. Olympic Games, Montreal. Multicoloured.

No.	Description	Unused	Used
681	4 f. Type **183**	10	10
682	8 f. Running	15	10
683	10 f. Judo	20	10
684	15 f. Handball	30	10
685	20 f. Figure-skating	35	10
686	30 f. Volleyball	55	25
687	45 f. Football	70	35
688	70 f. Swimming	1·10	85

184 Ethnic Heads and Map of Sri Lanka

185 Torch, U.N.E.S.C.O. Emblem and Kuwaiti Arms

1976. Non-Aligned Countries' Congress, Colombo.

No.	Type	Description	Unused	Used
689	184	20 f. multicoloured	35	10
690		30 f. multicoloured	50	30
691		45 f. multicoloured	85	45

1976. 30th Anniv of U.N.E.S.C.O.

No.	Type	Description	Unused	Used
692	185	20 f. multicoloured	45	10
693		45 f. multicoloured	1·00	50

186 Pot-throwing

187 Diseased Knee

1977. Popular Games. Multicoloured.

No.	Description	Unused	Used
694	5 f. Type **186**	20	10
695	5 f. Kite-flying	20	10
696	5 f. Balancing sticks	20	10
697	5 f. Spinning tops	20	10
698	10 f. Blind-man's-buff (horiz)	25	15
699	10 f. Rowing (horiz)	25	15
700	10 f. Rolling hoops (horiz)	25	15
701	10 f. Rope game (horiz)	25	15
702	15 f. Skipping	50	25
703	15 f. Marbles	50	25
704	15 f. Carting	50	25
705	15 f. Teetotum (tops)	50	25
706	20 f. Halma (horiz)	80	40
707	20 f. Model boating (horiz)	80	40
708	20 f. Pot and candle (horiz)	80	40
709	20 f. Hide-and-seek (horiz)	80	40
710	30 f. Knucklebones	90	50
711	30 f. Hiding the stone	90	50
712	30 f. Hopscotch	90	50
713	30 f. Catch-as-catch-can	90	50
714	40 f. Bowls (horiz)	1·60	70
715	40 f. Hockey (horiz)	1·60	70
716	40 f. Guessing which hand (horiz)	1·60	70
717	40 f. Jacks (horiz)	1·60	70
718	60 f. Hiding the cake (horiz)	2·00	1·25
719	60 f. Chess (horiz)	2·00	1·25
720	60 f. Story-telling (horiz)	2·00	1·25
721	60 f. Treasure hunt (horiz)	2·00	1·25
722	70 f. Hobby horses (horiz)	2·25	1·40
723	70 f. Hide-and-seek (horiz)	2·25	1·40
724	70 f. Catch shadow (horiz)	2·25	1·40
725	70 f. Throwing game (horiz)	2·25	1·40

1977. World Rheumatism Year.

No.	Type	Description	Unused	Used
726	187	20 f. multicoloured	40	15
727		30 f. multicoloured	60	30
728		45 f. multicoloured	90	45
729		75 f. multicoloured	1·25	85

188 Shaikh Sabah   189 Kuwait Tower

1977. 16th National Day.

730 **188** 10 f. multicoloured 15 10
731 15 f. multicoloured 30 15
732 30 f. multicoloured 65 20
733 80 f. multicoloured . . . . 1·40 55

1977. Inauguration of Kuwait Tower.

734 **189** 30 f. multicoloured 75 15
735 80 f. multicoloured . . . . 2·00 55

190 A.P.U. Emblem and Flags

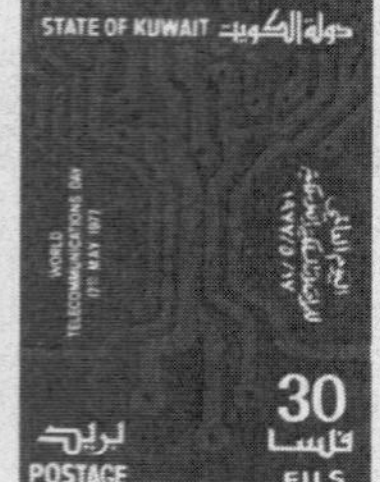

191 Printed Circuit

1977. 25th Anniv of Arab Postal Union.

736 **190** 5 f. multicoloured 20 10
737 15 f. multicoloured 20 10
738 30 f. multicoloured 40 20
739 80 f. multicoloured . . . . 1·10 60

1977. World Telecommunications Day.

740 **191** 30 f. orange and brown . . 60 30
741 80 f. orange and green . . 1·50 70

192 Shaikh Sabah

192a Aerogramme stamp

1977.

742 **192** 15 f. brown, black & blue . 80 35
743 25 f. brown, black & yell . 1·40 35
744 30 f. brown, black & red . 1·75 50
745 80 f. brown, black & lilac . 4·00 1·25
746 100 f. brown, black & orge . 5·00 1·40
747 150 f. brown, black & blue . 9·00 2·25
748 200 f. brown, black & green . 10·00 3·25

1977. Aerogramme stamp. Imperf.

748a **192a** 55 f. red and blue . . .

No. 748a was applied before sale to aerogrammes to uprate the imprinted 25 f. stamp. It was not available separately.

193 Championship Emblem

1977. 4th Asian Youth Basketball Championships.

749 **193** 30 f. multicoloured 50 50
750 80 f. multicoloured . . . . 1·50 1·00

194 "Popular Dancing" (O. Al-Nakeeb)

1977. Children's Paintings. Multicoloured.

751 15 f. Type **194** 35 20
752 15 f. "Al Deirah" (A. M. al-Onizi) 35 20
753 30 f. "Fishing" (M. al-Jasem) 60 45
754 30 f. "Dugg al-Harees" (B. al-Sa'adooni) (vert) . . . 60 45
755 80 f. "Fraisa Dancing" (M. al-Mojaibel) (vert) . . . . 1·50 1·25
756 80 f. "Kuwaiti Girl" (K. Ghazi) (vert) . . . . 1·50 1·25

195 Dome of the Rock and Palestinian Freedom Fighters

1978. Palestinian Freedom Fighters.

757 **195** 30 f. multicoloured . . . . 1·25 70
758 80 f. multicoloured . . . . 2·40 1·50

196 Dentist treating Patient

1978. 10th Arab Dental Union Congress.

759 **196** 30 f. multicoloured 70 55
760 80 f. multicoloured . . . . 1·75 1·10

197 Carrying Water from Dhows

1978. Water Resources. Multicoloured.

761 5 f. Type **197** 25 10
762 5 f. Camel 25 10
763 5 f. Water carrier 25 10
764 5 f. Pushing water in cart . . . 25 10
765 10 f. Irrigation with donkey . . 35 10
766 10 f. Water troughs in desert . . 35 10
767 10 f. Pool by a town 35 10
768 10 f. Watering crops 35 10
769 15 f. Bedouin watering sheep . 50 10
770 15 f. Bedouin women by pool . 50 10
771 15 f. Camels watered by pipeline 50 10
772 15 f. Water skins in Bedouin tent 50 10
773 20 f. Oasis with wells 55 10
774 20 f. Washing and drinking at home 55 10
775 20 f. Water urn 55 10
776 20 f. Filling vessels from taps . 55 10
777 25 f. Desalination plant 65 15
778 25 f. Water tanker 65 15
779 25 f. Filling water tankers . . . 65 15
780 25 f. Modern water tanks . . . 65 15
781 30 f. Catching water during storm (vert) 85 15
782 30 f. Water tank (vert) 85 15
783 30 f. Sheet to catch rain (vert) . 85 15
784 30 f. Trees by water tanks (vert) . 85 15
785 80 f. Carrying water on donkey (vert) . . . . 2·00 60
786 80 f. Woman carrying water-can (vert) . . . . 2·00 60
787 80 f. Woman with water-skins (vert) . . . . 2·00 60
788 80 f. Tanker delivering water to house (vert) . . . . . 2·00 60
789 100 f. Tanker delivering to courtyard tank (vert) . . . . 2·75 90
790 100 f. Household cistern (vert) . 2·75 90
791 100 f. Filling cistern (vert) . . 2·75 90
792 100 f. Drawing water from well (vert) . . . . 2·75 90

198 Symbols of Development

1978. 17th National Day.

793 **198** 30 f. multicoloured 35 25
794 80 f. multicoloured . . . . 1·00 70

199 Face of Smallpox Victim

1978. Global Eradication of Smallpox.

795 **199** 30 f. multicoloured 40 30
796 80 f. multicoloured . . . . 1·10 70

INDEX

Countries can be quickly located by referring to the index at the end of this volume.

200 Microwave Antenna

201 Shaikh Jabir

1978. 10th World Telecommunications Day.

797 **200** 30 f. multicoloured 35 25
798 80 f. multicoloured . . . . 1·10 70

1978. Portrait in brown; background colour given.

799 **201** 15 f. green 40 15
800 30 f. orange 80 35
801 80 f. purple . . . . 1·75 85
802 100 f. green . . . . 2·00 1·00
803 130 f. brown . . . . 3·25 1·40
804 180 f. violet . . . . 4·75 2·00
805 1 d. red . . . . 15·00 9·00
806 4 d. blue . . . . 50·00 22·00

Nos. 805/6 are larger, 24 × 29 mm.

202 Mount Arafat, Pilgrims and Kaaba

1978. Pilgrimage to Mecca.

807 **202** 30 f. multicoloured 50 40
808 80 f. multicoloured . . . . 1·40 1·00

203 U.N. and Anti-Apartheid Emblems

1978. International Anti-Apartheid Year.

809 **203** 30 f. multicoloured 40 25
810 80 f. multicoloured . . . . 1·00 70
811 180 f. multicoloured . . . . 2·10 1·50

204 Refugees

1978. 30th Anniv of Declaration of Human Rights.

812 **204** 30 f. multicoloured 40 30
813 80 f. multicoloured . . . . 1·25 75
814 100 f. multicoloured . . . 1·75 1·00

205 Information Centre

1978. Kuwait Information Centre.

815 **205** 5 f. multicoloured 10 10
816 15 f. multicoloured 20 10
817 30 f. multicoloured 35 20
818 80 f. multicoloured 90 60

206 Kindergarten

207 Kuwaiti Flag and Doves

1979. International Year of the Child.

819 **206** 30 f. multicoloured 40 35
820 80 f. multicoloured . . . . 1·00 85

1979. 18th National Day.

821 **207** 30 f. multicoloured 40 30
822 80 f. multicoloured 95 75

208 Crops and Greenhouse

1979. 4th Arab Agriculture Ministers Congress.

823 **208** 30 f. multicoloured 40 25
824 80 f. multicoloured 95 75

209 World Map, Koran and Symbols of Arab Achievements   210 Children flying Kites

1979. The Arabs.

825 **209** 30 f. multicoloured 40 30
826 80 f. multicoloured 95 75

1979. Children's Paintings. Multicoloured.

827 30 f. Type **210** 40 35
828 30 f. Girl and doves 40 35
829 30 f. Crowd and balloons . . . 40 35
830 80 f. Boys smiling (horiz) . . . 1·00 90
831 80 f. Children in landscape (horiz) . . . . 1·00 90
832 80 f. Tug-of-war (horiz) . . . . 1·00 90

211 Wave Pattern and Television Screen

212 International Military Sports Council Emblem

1979. World Telecommunications Day.

833 **211** 30 f. multicoloured 35 30
834 80 f. multicoloured 95 85

1979. 29th International Military Football Championship.

835 **212** 30 f. multicoloured 45 25
836 80 f. multicoloured . . . . 1·25 85

213 Child and Industrial Landscape

1979. World Environment Day.

837 **213** 30 f. multicoloured 50 40
838 80 f. multicoloured . . . . 1·40 1·10

214 Children supporting Globe

215 Children with Television

1979. 50th Anniv of International Bureau of Education.

839 **214** 30 f. multicoloured 35 25
840 80 f. multicoloured 85 75
841 130 f. multicoloured . . . 1·40 1·25

1979. 25th Anniv of Kuwaiti Kindergartens. Children's Drawings. Multicoloured.

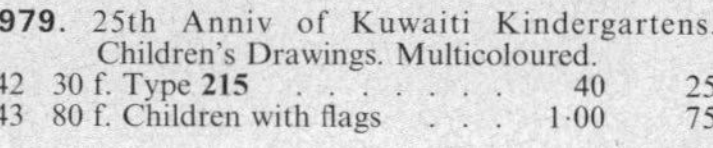

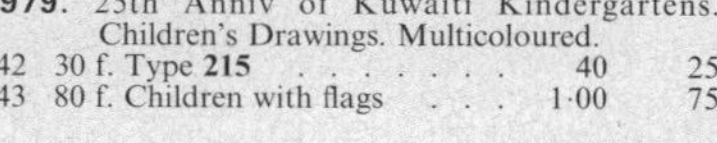

842 30 f. Type **215** 40 25
843 80 f. Children with flags . . . 1·00 75

216 The Kaaba, Mecca

217 Figure, with Dove and Torch, clothed in Palestinian Flag

1979. Pilgrimage to Mecca.

844 **216** 30 f. multicoloured 40 30
845 80 f. multicoloured . . . . 1·50 85

1979. International Day of Solidarity with Palestinians.
846 **217** 30 f. multicoloured . . . . 1·50 65
847 80 f. multicoloured . . . . 3·00 1·25

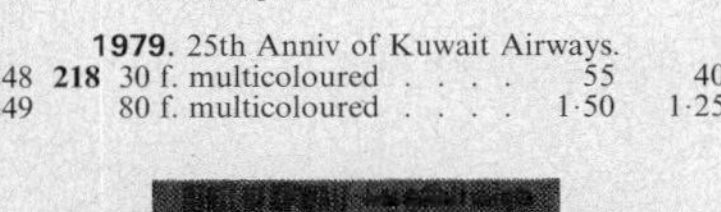

218 Boeing 747 and Douglas DC-3 Airliners

1979. 25th Anniv of Kuwait Airways.
848 **218** 30 f. multicoloured 55 40
849 80 f. multicoloured . . . . 1·50 1·25

219 "Pinctada" Shell bearing Map of Kuwait

1980. 19th National Day.
850 **219** 30 f. multicoloured 40 30
851 80 f. multicoloured . . . . 1·10 75

220 Graph with Human Figures

1980. Population Census.
852 **220** 30 f. black, silver and blue 50 25
853 80 f. black, gold & orange 1·10 60

221 Campaign Emblem

1980. World Health Day. Anti-Smoking Campaign.
854 **221** 30 f. multicoloured 60 35
855 80 f. multicoloured . . . . 1·75 1·10

222 Municipality Building

1980. 50th Anniv of Kuwait Municipality.
856 **222** 15 f. multicoloured 20 10
857 30 f. multicoloured 40 30
858 80 f. multicoloured . . . . 1·25 75

223 "The Future"

1980. Children's Imagination of Future Kuwait. Multicoloured.
859 30 f. Type **223** 50 30
860 80 f. Motorways . . . . 1·50 95

224 Hand blotting-out Factory

1980. World Environment Day.
861 **224** 30 f. multicoloured 55 30
862 80 f. multicoloured . . . . 1·50 60

225 Volleyball

226 O.P.E.C. Emblem and Globe

1980. Olympic Games, Moscow. Multicoloured.
863 15 f. Type **225** 20 20
864 15 f. Tennis 20 20
865 30 f. Swimming 35 25
866 30 f. Weightlifting 35 25
867 30 f. Basketball 35 25
868 30 f. Judo 35 25
869 80 f. Gymnastics 95 60
870 80 f. Badminton 95 60
871 80 f. Fencing 95 60
872 80 f. Football 95 60

1980. 20th Anniv of Organization of Petroleum Exporting Countries.
873 **226** 30 f. multicoloured 50 35
874 80 f. multicoloured . . . . 1·50 55

227 Mosque and Kaaba, Mecca

1980. 1400th Anniv of Hegira.
875 **227** 15 f. multicoloured 25 15
876 30 f. multicoloured 50 30
877 80 f. multicoloured . . . . 1·40 85

228 Dome of the Rock

229 Ibn Sina (Avicenna)

1980. International Day of Solidarity with Palestinian People.
878 **228** 30 f. multicoloured . . . . 1·00 40
879 80 f. multicoloured . . . . 2·50 1·25

1980. Birth Millenary of Ibn Sina (philosopher and physician).
880 **229** 30 f. multicoloured 60 25
881 80 f. multicoloured . . . . 1·25 85

230 Islamic Symbols

231 Person in Wheelchair playing Snooker

1981. 1st Islamic Medicine Conference, Kuwait.
882 **230** 30 f. multicoloured 50 30
883 80 f. multicoloured . . . . 1·50 85

1981. International Year of Disabled Persons. Multicoloured.
884 30 f. Type **231** 50 30
885 80 f. Girl in wheelchair . . . . 1·50 85

232 Symbols of Development and Progress

1981. 20th National Day.
886 **232** 30 f. multicoloured 50 30
887 80 f. multicoloured . . . . 1·50 85

233 Emblem of Kuwait Dental Association

234 "Lamp"

1981. 1st Kuwait Dental Association Conference.
888 **233** 30 f. multicoloured . . . . 1·00 55
889 80 f. multicoloured . . . . 2·50 1·50

1981. World Red Cross and Red Crescent Day.
890 **234** 30 f. multicoloured 90 55
891 80 f. multicoloured . . . . 2·50 1·50

235 Emblems of I.T.U. and W.H.O. and Ribbons forming Caduceus

236 Tanker polluting Sea and Car polluting Atmosphere

1981. World Telecommunications Day.
892 **235** 30 f. multicoloured 70 50
893 70 f. multicoloured . . . . 2·25 1·40

1981. World Environment Day.
894 **236** 30 f. multicoloured 75 50
895 80 f. multicoloured . . . . 2·40 1·25

237 Sief Palace

1981.
896 **237** 5 f. multicoloured 10 10
897 10 f. multicoloured 10 10
898 15 f. multicoloured 10 10
899 25 f. multicoloured 15 15
900 30 f. multicoloured 20 15
901 40 f. multicoloured 25 15
902 60 f. multicoloured 40 20
903 80 f. multicoloured 50 30
904 100 f. multicoloured . . . 65 45
905 115 f. multicoloured . . . 70 50
906 130 f. multicoloured . . . 80 70
907 150 f. multicoloured . . . 1·10 70
908 180 f. multicoloured . . . 1·25 75
909 250 f. multicoloured . . . 1·50 80
910 500 f. multicoloured . . . 3·25 1·10
911 1 d. multicoloured . . . . 6·25 1·50
912 2 d. multicoloured . . . . 12·00 2·25
913 3 d. multicoloured . . . . 16·00 6·75
914 4 d. multicoloured . . . . 25·00 8·50

Nos. 911/14 are larger, 33 × 28 mm and have a different border.

238 Pilgrims

1981. Pilgrimage to Mecca.
915 **238** 30 f. multicoloured 60 50
916 80 f. multicoloured . . . . 2·25 1·25

239 Palm Trees, Sheep, Camel, Goat and F.A.O. Emblem

1981. World Food Day.
917 **239** 30 f. multicoloured 65 45
918 80 f. multicoloured . . . . 2·00 1·25

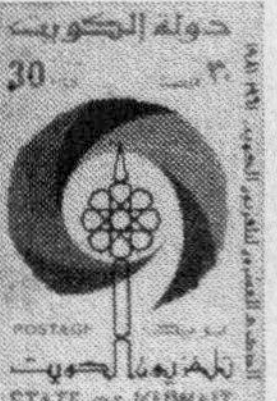

240 Television Emblem

241 Blood Circulation Diagram

1981. 20th Anniv of Kuwait Television.
919 **240** 30 f. multicoloured 70 45
920 80 f. multicoloured . . . . 2·00 1·25

1982. 1st International Symposium on Pharmacology of Human Blood Vessels.
921 **241** 30 f. multicoloured . . . . 1·00 80
922 80 f. multicoloured . . . . 2·25 1·10

242 Symbols of Development, Progress and Peace

1982. 21st National Day.
923 **242** 30 f. multicoloured 50 30
924 80 f. multicoloured . . . . 1·40 85

243 Emblem of Kuwait Boy Scouts Association on Globe

1982. 75th Anniv of Boy Scout Movement.
925 **243** 30 f. multicoloured 60 40
926 80 f. multicoloured . . . . 1·75 1·00

244 Emblem of Arab Pharmacists Union

1982. Arab Pharmacists Day.
927 **244** 30 f. multicoloured 85 60
928 80 f. multicoloured . . . . 2·75 1·75

245 Red Crescent, Arab and W.H.O. Emblem

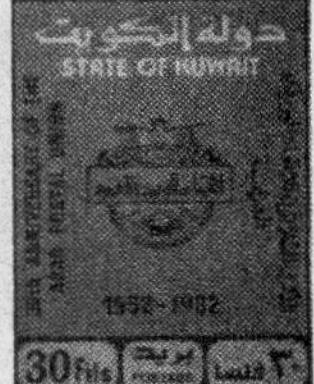

246 A.P.U. Emblem

1982. World Health Day.
929 **245** 30 f. multicoloured . . . . 1·00 65
930 80 f. multicoloured . . . . 3·00 1·75

1982. 30th Anniv of Arab Postal Union.
931 **246** 30 f. black, orange and green 85 60
932 80 f. black, green and orange 2·75 1·50

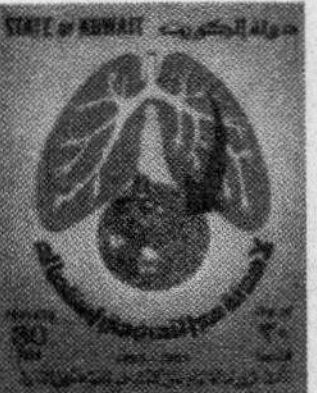

247 Lungs and Microscope

249 Museum Exhibits

248 Crest and Emblems of Kuwait Football Association and Olympic Committee

1982. Centenary of Discovery of Tubercle Bacillus.
933 **247** 30 f. multicoloured . . . . 1·00 60
934 80 f. multicoloured . . . . 2·75 1·60

1982. World Cup Football Championship, Spain.
935 **248** 30 f. multicoloured 75 40
936 80 f. multicoloured . . . . 2·00 1·25

1982. 10th Anniv of Science and Natural History Museum.
937 **249** 30 f. multicoloured . . . . 1·50 1·00
938 80 f. multicoloured . . . . 4·50 3·00

250 "Al-Wattyah" (container ship)

1982. 6th Anniv of United Arab Shipping Company. Multicoloured.
939 30 f. Type **250** 75 35
940 80 f. "Al-Salimiah" (freighter) . 1·75 90

251 Palm Trees

1982. Arab Palm Tree Day.
941 **251** 30 f. multicoloured 50 30
942 80 f. multicoloured . . . . 1·50 90

252 Pilgrims

1982. Pilgrimage to Mecca.
943 **252** 15 f. multicoloured 30 20
944 30 f. multicoloured 70 45
945 80 f. multicoloured . . . . 1·90 1·25

253 Desert Flower

1983. Desert Plants. As T **253**. Multicoloured; background colours given. (a) Vert designs.
946 10 f. green 10 10
947 10 f. violet 10 10
948 10 f. salmon 10 10
949 10 f. pink (blue flowers) 10 10
950 10 f. bistre 10 10
951 10 f. green 10 10
952 10 f. light orange 10 10
953 10 f. red (poppy) 10 10
954 10 f. brown 10 10
955 10 f. blue 10 10
956 15 f. green 15 15
957 15 f. purple 15 15
958 15 f. blue 15 15
959 15 f. blue (iris) 15 15
960 15 f. olive 15 15
961 15 f. red 15 15
962 15 f. brown 15 15
963 15 f. blue (bellflowers) 15 15
964 15 f. mauve 15 15
965 15 f. pink 15 15
966 30 f. brown 40 25
967 30 f. mauve 40 25
968 30 f. blue 40 25
969 30 f. green 40 25
970 30 f. pink 40 25
971 30 f. blue 40 25
972 30 f. green 40 25
973 30 f. mauve 40 25
974 30 f. bistre 40 25
975 30 f. yellow 40 25

(a) Horiz designs.
976 40 f. red (fungi) 75 35
977 40 f. green (fungi) 75 35
978 40 f. violet 50 35
979 40 f. blue 50 35
980 40 f. grey 50 35
981 40 f. green 50 35
982 40 f. mauve 50 35
983 40 f. brown 50 35
984 40 f. blue 50 35
985 40 f. green (daisies) 50 35
986 80 f. violet 90 70
987 80 f. green 90 70
988 80 f. yellow (yellow flowers) . . 90 70
989 80 f. brown (green leaves) . . . 90 70
990 80 f. blue 90 70
991 80 f. yellow 90 70
992 80 f. green 90 70
993 80 f. violet (red berries) . . . 90 70
994 80 f. brown (yellow flowers) . . 90 70
995 80 f. yellow (red and blue flowers) 90 70
DESIGNS: Various plants.

254 Peace Dove on Map of Kuwait

1983. 22nd National Day.
996 **254** 30 f. multicoloured 60 35
997 80 f. multicoloured . . . . 1·50 95

255 I.M.O. Emblem

1983. 25th Anniv of International Maritime Organization.
998 **255** 30 f. multicoloured 35 20
999 80 f. multicoloured . . . . 1·00 60

256 Virus and Map of Africa

1983. 3rd International Conference on Impact of Viral Diseases on Development of Middle East and African Countries.
1000 **256** 15 f. multicoloured . . . 30 15
1001 30 f. multicoloured . . . 60 35
1002 80 f. multicoloured . . . 1·50 95

257 Stylized Figures exercising

1983. World Health Day.
1003 **257** 15 f. multicoloured . . . 30 20
1004 30 f. multicoloured . . . 65 45
1005 80 f. multicoloured . . . 1·90 1·25

258 U.P.U., W.C.Y. and I.T.U. Emblems

1983. World Communications Year.
1006 **258** 15 f. multicoloured . . . 35 20
1007 30 f. multicoloured . . . 65 45
1008 80 f. multicoloured . . . 1·60 1·25

259 Map of Kuwait and Dhow

1983. World Environment Day.
1009 **259** 15 f. multicoloured . . . 45 20
1010 30 f. multicoloured . . . 85 45
1011 80 f. multicoloured . . . 2·00 1·25

260 Walls of Jerusalem

1983. World Heritage Convention.
1012 **260** 15 f. multicoloured . . . 35 20
1013 30 f. multicoloured . . . 65 45
1014 80 f. multicoloured . . . 1·60 1·25

261 Pilgrims in Mozdalipha

1983. Pilgrimage to Mecca.
1015 **261** 15 f. multicoloured . . . 35 20
1016 30 f. multicoloured . . . 65 45
1017 80 f. multicoloured . . . 1·60 1·25

262 Arab within Dove

1983. International Day of Solidarity with Palestinian People.
1018 **262** 15 f. multicoloured . . . 35 20
1019 30 f. multicoloured . . . 65 45
1020 80 f. multicoloured . . . 1·60 1·25

263 Kuwait Medical Association and Congress Emblems

1984. 21st Pan-Arab Medical Congress.
1021 **263** 15 f. multicoloured . . . 35 20
1022 30 f. multicoloured . . . 65 45
1023 80 f. multicoloured . . . 1·60 1·25

264 State Arms within Key

1984. Inauguration of New Health Establishments.
1024 **264** 15 f. multicoloured . . . 35 20
1025 30 f. multicoloured . . . 65 45
1026 80 f. multicoloured . . . 1·60 1·25

265 Dove and Globe

266 Symbols of Medicine within Head

1984. 23rd National Day.
1027 **265** 15 f. multicoloured . . . 35 20
1028 30 f. multicoloured . . . 65 45
1029 80 f. multicoloured . . . 1·60 1·25

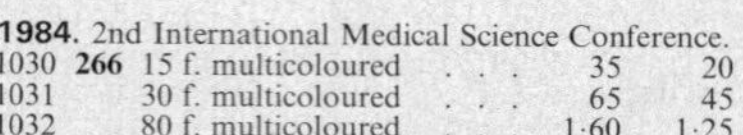

1984. 2nd International Medical Science Conference.
1030 **266** 15 f. multicoloured . . . 35 20
1031 30 f. multicoloured . . . 65 45
1032 80 f. multicoloured . . . 1·60 1·25

267 Douglas DC-3 Airliner

1984. 30th Anniv of Kuwait Airways Corporation.
1033 **267** 30 f. blue, dp blue & yell . 75 60
1034 80 f. blue, dp bl & mve . . 2·00 1·10

268 Magazine Covers

269 Family and Emblems

1984. 25th Anniv of "Al-Arabi" (magazine).
1035 **268** 15 f. multicoloured . . . 30 20
1036 30 f. multicoloured . . . 60 35
1037 80 f. multicoloured . . . 1·50 1·00

1984. World Health Day.
1038 **269** 15 f. multicoloured . . . 30 20
1039 30 f. multicoloured . . . 70 40
1040 80 f. multicoloured . . . 1·90 1·10

270 Sudanese Orphan and Village

1984. Hanan Kuwaiti Village, Sudan.
1041 **270** 15 f. multicoloured . . . 35 20
1042 30 f. multicoloured . . . 75 40
1043 80 f. multicoloured . . . 1·90 1·10

271 I.C.A.O., Kuwait Airport and Kuwait Airways Emblems

1984. 40th Anniv of I.C.A.O.
1044 **271** 15 f. multicoloured . . . 35 20
1045 30 f. multicoloured . . . 75 40
1046 80 f. multicoloured . . . 1·90 1·10

272 Map of Arab Countries and Youths

1984. Arab Youth Day.
1047 **272** 30 f. multicoloured . . . 70 40
1048 80 f. multicoloured . . . 1·90 1·10

273 Swimming

1984. Olympic Games, Los Angeles. Multicoloured.
1049 30 f. Type **273** 40 25
1050 30 f. Hurdling 40 25
1051 80 f. Judo 75 60
1052 80 f. Equestrian 75 60

274 Anniversary Emblem, Camera, Airplane, Al-Aujairy Observatory and Wind Tower

1984. 10th Anniv of Science Club.

1053	**274**	15 f. multicoloured . . .	35	15
1054		30 f. multicoloured . . .	85	40
1055		80 f. multicoloured . . .	2·10	1·10

275 Stoning the Devil

1984. Pilgrimage to Mecca.

1056	**275**	30 f. multicoloured . . .	80	40
1057		80 f. multicoloured . . .	1·75	1·10

276 Anniversary Emblem

1984. 20th Anniv of International Telecommunications Satellite Consortium (Intelsat).

1058	**276**	30 f. multicoloured . . .	80	40
1059		80 f. multicoloured . . .	1·75	1·10

277 Council Emblem

278 Hands breaking Star

1984. 5th Supreme Council Session of Gulf Co-operation Council.

1060	**277**	30 f. multicoloured . . .	70	40
1061		80 f. multicoloured . . .	1·75	1·10

1984. International Day of Solidarity with Palestinian People.

1062	**278**	30 f. multicoloured . . .	70	40
1063		80 f. multicoloured . . .	1·75	1·10

279 Company Emblem as Satellite

280 I.Y.Y. Emblem

1984. 50th Anniv of Kuwait Oil Company.

1064	**279**	30 f. multicoloured . . .	70	40
1965		80 f. multicoloured . . .	1·75	1·10

1985. International Youth Year.

1066	**280**	30 f. multicoloured . . .	40	20
1067		80 f. multicoloured . . .	1·25	75

281 "24", Hand holding Flame and Dove

282 Programme Emblem

1985. 24th National Day.

1068	**281**	30 f. multicoloured . . .	60	30
1069		80 f. multicoloured . . .	1·75	1·10

1985. International Programme for Communications Development.

1070	**282**	30 f. multicoloured . . .	70	40
1071		80 f. multicoloured . . .	1·75	1·10

283 Emblem

284 Molar

1985. 1st Arab Gulf Social Work Week.

1072	**283**	30 f. multicoloured . . .	70	40
1073		80 f. multicoloured . . .	1·75	1·10

1985. 3rd Kuwait Dental Association Conference.

1074	**284**	30 f. multicoloured . . .	70	40
1075		80 f. multicoloured . . .	1·75	1·10

285 Emblem

286 Globe and Figures

1985. Population Census.

1076	**285**	30 f. multicoloured . . .	85	40
1077		80 f. multicoloured . . .	1·75	1·10

1985. World Health Day.

1078	**286**	30 f. multicoloured . . .	85	40
1079		80 f. multicoloured . . .	1·75	1·10

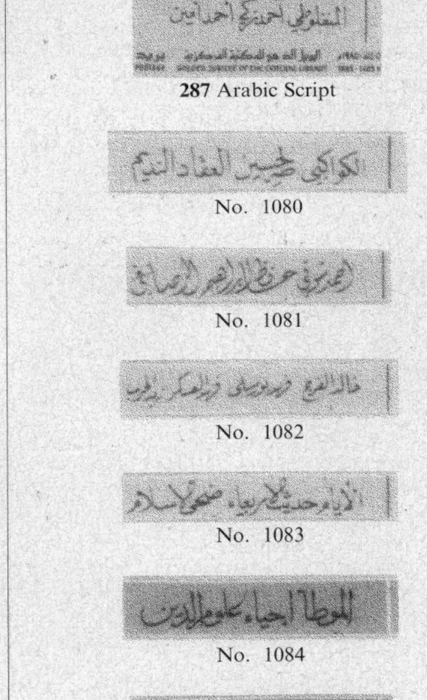

287 Arabic Script

No. 1080

No. 1081

No. 1082

No. 1083

No. 1084

No. 1085

No. 1086

No. 1087

1985. 50th Anniv of Central Library. Designs showing titles of books and names of authors in Arabic script (first line of text illustrated above).

1080	30 f. gold	1·00	45
1081	30 f. gold	1·00	45
1082	30 f. gold	1·00	45
1083	30 f. gold	1·00	45
1084	80 f. black and gold	2·50	1·00
1085	80 f. black and gold	2·50	1·00
1086	80 f. black and gold	2·50	1·00
1087	80 f. black and gold	2·50	1·00

288 Seascape

1985. World Environment Day.

1088	**288**	30 f. multicoloured . . .	1·50	40
1089		80 f. multicoloured . . .	3·00	1·10

289 Anniversary Emblem

1985. 25th Anniv of Organization of Petroleum Exporting Countries.

1090	**289**	30 f. ultram, bl & mve	85	40
1091		80 f. ultram, bl & brn	1·90	1·10

290 Emblem and Heads

1985. Introduction of Civilian Identity Cards.

1092	**290**	30 f. multicoloured . . .	85	40
1093		80 f. multicoloured . . .	1·90	1·10

291 Flag on Globe within Symbolic Design

1985. International Day of Solidarity with Palestinian People.

1094	**291**	15 f. multicoloured . . .	75	30
1095		30 f. multicoloured . . .	1·40	60
1096		80 f. multicoloured . . .	2·50	1·50

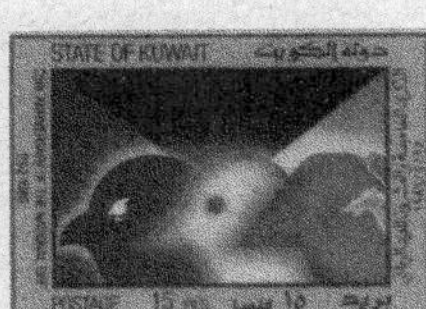

292 Birds

1986. 25th National Day.

1097	**292**	15 f. multicoloured . . .	20	15
1098		30 f. multicoloured . . .	75	35
1099		80 f. multicoloured . . .	2·00	90

293 Emblem

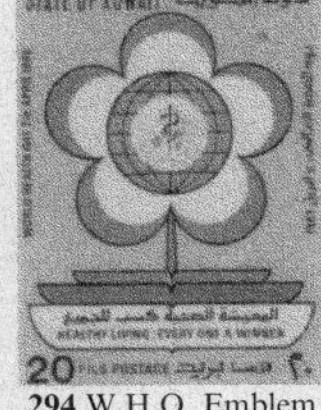

294 W.H.O. Emblem as Flower

1986. 20th Anniv of Kuwait Red Crescent.

1100	**293**	20 f. multicoloured . . .	60	45
1101		25 f. multicoloured . . .	85	70
1102		70 f. multicoloured . . .	2·50	1·90

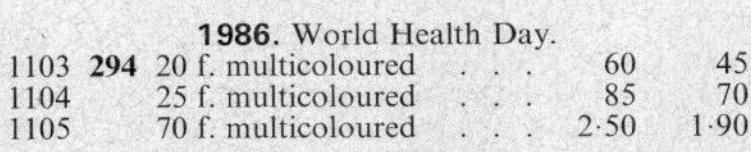

1986. World Health Day.

1103	**294**	20 f. multicoloured . . .	60	45
1104		25 f. multicoloured . . .	85	70
1105		70 f. multicoloured . . .	2·50	1·90

295 I.P.Y. Emblem

1986. International Peace Year.

1106	**295**	20 f. green, blue & black	50	45
1107		25 f. blue, yellow & black	75	50
1108		70 f. blue, mauve & black	2·25	1·40

296 "Al Mirqab"

1986. 10th Anniv of United Arab Shipping Company. Container Ships. Multicoloured.

1109	20 f. Type **296**	1·00	45
1110	70 f. "Al Mubarakiah" . . .	3·50	1·90

297 Bank Emblem on Map

1986. 25th Anniv of Gulf Bank.

1111	**297**	20 f. multicoloured . . .	50	30
1112		25 f. multicoloured . . .	75	40
1113		70 f. multicoloured . . .	2·25	1·50

298 Zig-zags and Diamonds

1986. Sadu Art. Multicoloured.

1114	20 f. Type **298**	50	25
1115	70 f. Triangles and symbols	1·60	95
1116	200 f. Stripes and triangles . .	3·75	2·75

299 Dove on Manacled Hand pointing to Map

1986. International Day of Solidarity with Palestinian People.

1117	**299**	20 f. multicoloured . . .	75	50
1118		25 f. multicoloured . . .	1·00	70
1119		70 f. multicoloured . . .	3·00	2·00

300 Conference Emblem

1987. 5th Islamic Summit Conference.

1120	**300**	25 f. multicoloured . . .	60	30
1121		50 f. multicoloured . . .	1·25	70
1122		150 f. multicoloured . . .	3·25	2·00

301 Map in National Colours and Symbols of Development

1987. 26th National Day.
1123 **301** 50 f. multicoloured . . . 1·25 50
1124 150 f. multicoloured . . . 3·00 1·50

302 Health Science Centre

1987. 3rd Kuwait International Medical Sciences Conference: Infectious Diseases in Developing Countries.
1125 **302** 25 f. multicoloured . . . 75 25
1126 150 f. multicoloured . . . 3·00 1·50

303 Campaign Emblem

1987. World Health Day. Child Immunization Campaign.
1127 **303** 25 f. multicoloured . . . 60 25
1128 50 f. multicoloured . . . 1·00 50
1129 150 f. multicoloured . . . 2·40 1·50

304 Jerusalem

1987. "Jerusalem is an Arab City".
1130 **304** 25 f. multicoloured . . . 60 15
1131 50 f. multicoloured . . . 1·00 40
1132 150 f. multicoloured . . . 2·40 1·25

305 Pilgrims in Miqat Wadi Mihrim

1987. Pilgrimage to Mecca.
1133 **305** 25 f. multicoloured . . . 50 15
1134 50 f. multicoloured . . . 75 40
1135 150 f. multicoloured . . . 2·25 1·00

306 Emblem

308 Project Monument and Site Plan

307 Buoy and Container Ship

1987. Arab Telecommunications Day.
1136 **306** 25 f. multicoloured . . . 50 15
1137 50 f. multicoloured . . . 75 40
1138 150 f. multicoloured . . . 2·25 1·00

1987. World Maritime Day.
1139 **307** 25 f. multicoloured . . . 50 20
1140 50 f. multicoloured . . . 75 40
1141 150 f. multicoloured . . . 2·25 1·00

1987. Al-Qurain Housing Project.
1142 **308** 25 f. multicoloured . . . 50 15
1143 50 f. multicoloured . . . 75 40
1144 150 f. multicoloured . . . 2·25 1·00

309 Unloading Container Ship

1987. 10th Anniv of Ports Public Authority.
1145 **309** 25 f. multicoloured . . . 20 10
1146 50 f. multicoloured . . . 55 25
1147 150 f. multicoloured . . . 2·00 85

310 Symbolic Design

311 Emblem

1987. International Day of Solidarity with Palestinian People.
1148 **310** 25 f. multicoloured . . . 20 10
1149 50 f. multicoloured . . . 60 25
1150 150 f. multicoloured . . . 2·00 85

1988. 25th Anniv of Women's Cultural and Social Society.
1151 **311** 25 f. multicoloured . . . 20 10
1152 50 f. multicoloured . . . 60 25
1153 150 f. multicoloured . . . 2·00 85

312 Emblem

313 Hands holding W.H.O. Emblem

1988. 27th National Day.
1154 **312** 25 f. multicoloured . . . 20 10
1155 50 f. multicoloured . . . 60 25
1156 150 f. multicoloured . . . 2·00 85

1988. World Health Day. 40th Anniv of W.H.O.
1157 **313** 25 f. multicoloured . . . 20 10
1158 50 f. multicoloured . . . 60 25
1159 150 f. multicoloured . . . 2·00 85

314 Regional Maritime Protection Organization Symbol

315 Society Emblem

1988. 10th Anniv of Kuwait Regional Convention for Protection of Marine Environment.
1160 **314** 35 f. ultram, blue & brn . 25 15
1161 50 f. ultram, blue & grn . 60 25
1162 150 f. ultram, blue & pur . 2·00 85

1988. 25th Anniv of Kuwait Teachers' Society.
1163 **315** 25 f. multicoloured . . . 20 10
1164 50 f. multicoloured . . . 60 25
1165 150 f. multicoloured . . . 2·00 75

316 Pilgrims at al-Sail al-Kabir Miqat

1988. Pilgrimage to Mecca.
1166 **316** 25 f. multicoloured . . . 20 10
1167 50 f. multicoloured . . . 60 25
1168 150 f. multicoloured . . . 2·00 75

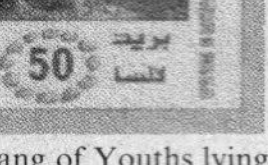
317 Gang of Youths lying in wait for Soldiers

318 Ring of Dwellings around Key

1988. Palestinian "Intifida" Movement.
1169 **317** 50 f. multicoloured . . . 75 40
1170 150 f. multicoloured . . . 3·00 1·50

1988. Arab Housing Day.
1171 **318** 50 f. multicoloured . . . 50 30
1172 100 f. multicoloured . . . 1·00 60
1173 150 f. multicoloured . . . 2·00 75

319 Map of Palestine highlighted on Globe

320 Volunteers embracing Globe

1988. International Day of Solidarity with Palestinian People.
1174 **319** 50 f. multicoloured . . . 40 25
1175 100 f. multicoloured . . . 1·00 60
1176 150 f. multicoloured . . . 2·00 75

1988. International Volunteer Day.
1177 **320** 50 f. multicoloured . . . 50 30
1178 100 f. multicoloured . . . 1·00 60
1179 150 f. multicoloured . . . 2·00 75

321 Conference, Kuwait Society of Engineers and Arab Engineers Union Emblems

1989. 18th Arab Engineering Conference.
1180 **321** 50 f. multicoloured . . . 50 30
1181 100 f. multicoloured . . . 1·00 60
1182 150 f. multicoloured . . . 2·00 75

322 Flags as Figures supporting Map

323 Conference Emblem

1989. 28th National Day.
1183 **322** 50 f. multicoloured . . . 50 30
1184 100 f. multicoloured . . . 1·00 60
1185 150 f. multicoloured . . . 2·00 75

1989. 5th Kuwait Dental Association Conference.
1186 **323** 50 f. multicoloured . . . 50 30
1187 150 f. multicoloured . . . 1·00 70
1188 250 f. multicoloured . . . 1·75 1·10

324 Emblems

325 Anniversary Emblem

1989. World Health Day.
1189 **324** 50 f. multicoloured . . . 50 30
1190 150 f. multicoloured . . . 1·00 70
1191 250 f. multicoloured . . . 1·75 1·10

1989. 10th Anniv of Arab Board for Medical Specializations.
1192 **325** 50 f. multicoloured . . . 50 20
1193 150 f. multicoloured . . . 1·00 55
1194 250 f. multicoloured . . . 1·75 85

326 Torch, Pen and Flag

1989. 25th Anniv of Kuwait Journalists' Association.
1195 **326** 50 f. multicoloured . . . 40 35
1196 200 f. multicoloured . . . 1·50 1·00
1197 250 f. multicoloured . . . 2·00 1·40

327 Attan'eem Miqat, Mecca

1989. Pilgrimage to Mecca.
1198 **327** 50 f. multicoloured . . . 85 55
1199 150 f. multicoloured . . . 2·75 1·75
1200 200 f. multicoloured . . . 3·50 2·25

328 Al-Qurain Housing Project

329 Tree

1989. Arab Housing Day.
1201 **328** 25 f. multicoloured . . . 45 30
1202 50 f. multicoloured . . . 85 55
1203 150 f. multicoloured . . . 2·75 1·75

1989. Greenery Week.
1204 **329** 25 f. multicoloured . . . 45 30
1205 50 f. multicoloured . . . 85 55
1206 150 f. multicoloured . . . 2·75 1·75

330 Dhow

331 Emblem and Map

1989. Coil Stamps.
1207 **330** 50 f. gold and green . . . 1·25 85
1208 100 f. gold and blue . . . 2·50 1·75
1209 200 f. gold and red . . . 5·00 3·50

1989. 5th Anniv of Gulf Investment Corporation.
1210 **331** 25 f. multicoloured . . . 45 30
1211 50 f. multicoloured . . . 85 55
1212 150 f. multicoloured . . . 2·75 1·75

332 Emblem

333 Zakat House

1989. 1st Anniv of "Declaration of Palestine State".
1213 **332** 50 f. multicoloured . . . 85 55
1214 150 f. multicoloured . . . 2·75 1·75
1215 200 f. multicoloured . . . 3·50 2·25

1989. Orphanage Sponsorship Project.
1216 **333** 25 f. multicoloured . . . 45 30
1217 50 f. multicoloured . . . 85 55
1218 150 f. multicoloured . . . 2·75 1·75

334 Shaikh Sabah al-Salem as-Sabah (former Chief) and Officers

335 Globe and Dove

1989. 50th Anniv (1988) of Kuwait Police.

1219	**334**	25 f. multicoloured	45	30
1220		50 f. multicoloured	85	55
1221		150 f. multicoloured	2·75	1·75

1990. 29th National Day.

1222	**335**	25 f. multicoloured	45	30
1223		50 f. multicoloured	85	55
1224		150 f. multicoloured	2·75	1·75

336 Earth, Clouds and Weather Balloon

1990. World Meteorological Day.

1225	**336**	50 f. multicoloured	85	55
1226		100 f. multicoloured	1·75	1·10
1227		150 f. multicoloured	2·75	1·75

337 Map bordered by National Flag

338 Lanner Falcon

1990. World Health Day.

1228	**337**	50 f. multicoloured	85	55
1229		100 f. multicoloured	1·75	1·10
1230		150 f. multicoloured	2·75	1·75

1990.

1231	**338**	50 f. gold and blue	85	55
1232		100 f. gold and red	1·75	1·10
1233		150 f. gold and green	2·75	1·75

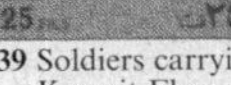

339 Soldiers carrying Kuwait Flag

340 Dove and Map

1991. Liberation (1st issue).

1234	**339**	25 f. multicoloured	40	25
1235		50 f. multicoloured	80	50
1236		150 f. multicoloured	2·40	1·60

See also Nos. 1243/84.

1991. Peace.

1237	**340**	50 f. multicoloured	80	50
1238		100 f. multicoloured	1·60	1·00
1239		150 f. multicoloured	2·40	1·60

341 Flag, Map, Kuwait Towers and Globe

342 Sweden

1991. Reconstruction.

1240	**341**	50 f. multicoloured	80	50
1241		150 f. multicoloured	2·40	1·60
1242		200 f. multicoloured	3·00	1·90

1991. Liberation (2nd issue). Each showing a dove coloured with the flag of one of the assisting nations. Multicoloured.

1243	50 f. Type **342**	45	30
1244	50 f. Soviet Union	45	30
1245	50 f. United States of America	45	30
1246	50 f. Kuwait	45	30
1247	50 f. Saudi Arabia	45	30
1248	50 f. United Nations	45	30
1249	50 f. Singapore	45	30
1250	50 f. France	45	30
1251	50 f. Italy	45	30
1252	50 f. Egypt	45	30
1253	50 f. Morocco	45	30
1254	50 f. United Kingdom	45	30
1255	50 f. Philippines	45	30
1256	50 f. United Arab Emirates	45	30
1257	50 f. Syria	45	30
1258	50 f. Poland	45	30
1259	50 f. Australia	45	30
1260	50 f. Japan	45	30
1261	50 f. Hungary	45	30
1262	50 f. Netherlands	45	30
1263	50 f. Denmark	45	30
1264	50 f. New Zealand	45	30
1265	50 f. Czechoslovakia	45	30
1266	50 f. Bahrain	45	30
1267	50 f. Honduras	45	30
1268	50 f. Turkey	45	30
1269	50 f. Greece	45	30
1270	50 f. Oman	45	30
1271	50 f. Qatar	45	30
1272	50 f. Belgium	45	30
1273	50 f. Sierra Leone	45	30
1274	50 f. Argentina	45	30
1275	50 f. Norway	45	30
1276	50 f. Canada	45	30
1277	50 f. Germany	45	30
1278	50 f. South Korea	45	30
1279	50 f. Bangladesh	45	30
1280	50 f. Bulgaria	45	30
1281	50 f. Senegal	45	30
1282	50 f. Spain	45	30
1283	50 f. Niger	45	30
1284	50 f. Pakistan	45	30

343 "Human Terror"

344 Emblem

1991. 1st Anniv of Iraqi Invasion. Multicoloured.

1286	50 f. Type **343**	80	50
1287	100 f. "Invasion of Kuwait"	1·60	1·00
1288	150 f. "Environmental Terrorism" (horiz)	2·40	1·60

1991. 30th Anniv (1990) of Organization of Petroleum Exporting Countries.

1290	**344**	25 f. multicoloured	45	30
1291		50 f. multicoloured	80	50
1292		150 f. multicoloured	2·40	1·60

345 National Flag, Arabic Script and Broken Chains

1991. Campaign to Free Kuwaiti Prisoners of War. Each black and yellow.

1293	50 f. Type **345**	70	45
1294	150 f. Prison bars, "Don't Forget Our P.O.W.'s" and broken chains	2·00	1·25

346 Names of Member Countries forming Tree

1991. 12th Gulf Co-operation Council Summit Conference, Kuwait. Multicoloured.

1296	25 f. Type **346**	35	25
1297	150 f. National flags as leaves of plant	2·00	1·25

347 I.L.Y. Emblem

1992. International Literacy Year (1990).

1299	**347**	50 f. blue and brown	70	45
1300		100 f. blue and yellow	1·40	90
1301		150 f. blue and mauve	2·00	1·25

348 Doves and National Flag

1992. 31st National Day (1302) and 1st Anniv of Liberation (1303).

1302	**348**	50 f. black, green and red	40	25
1303	–	150 f. multicoloured	1·25	80

DESIGN: 150 f. Assisting nations' flags.

349 Dromedaries

1992.

1305	**349**	25 f. multicoloured	15	10
1306		50 f. multicoloured	30	20
1307		150 f. multicoloured	95	60
1308		200 f. multicoloured	1·25	80
1309		350 f. multicoloured	2·10	1·25

350 Paddle, La Giralda Tower and Kuwaiti Pavilion

1992. "Expo '92" World's Fair, Seville. Multicoloured.

1310	50 f. Type **350**	30	20
1311	50 f. Dhows	30	20
1312	50 f. Dhow	30	20
1313	50 f. Kuwaiti Pavilion and dhow	30	20
1314	150 f. Kuwaiti Pavilion on Spanish flag	90	60
1315	150 f. Paddle and La Giralda Tower on hoist of Kuwaiti flag	90	60
1316	150 f. Paddle, La Giralda Tower and dhow on Spanish flag	90	60
1317	150 f. Kuwaiti Pavilion and dhow on fly of Kuwaiti flag	90	60

351 Snake around Top of Palm Tree

1992. 2nd U.N. Conference on Environment and Development, Rio de Janeiro, Brazil. Mult.

1319	150 f. Type **351**	1·25	80
1320	150 f. Snakes, Kuwait colours on map and palm tree	1·25	80
1321	150 f. Skull, snake around tree trunk and dead fish	1·25	80
1322	150 f. Snake around camel's neck and bird	1·25	80

Nos. 1319/22 were issued together, se-tenant, forming a composite design of the painting "Environmental Terrorism".

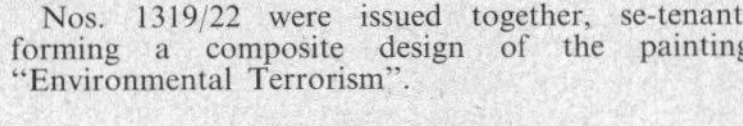

352 Palace of Justice

1992.

1324	**352**	25 f. multicoloured	20	10
1325		50 f. multicoloured	40	25
1326		100 f. multicoloured	80	50
1327		150 f. multicoloured	1·25	80
1328		250 f. multicoloured	2·00	1·25

353 Running and Handball

1992. Olympic Games, Barcelona. Multicoloured.

1329	50 f. Swimming and football	65	40
1330	100 f. Type **353**	1·25	80
1331	150 f. Judo and show jumping	1·90	1·25

Each value also portrays the Olympic flag and Prince Fahed al-Ahmad al-Sabah, President of several sports organizations, who was killed in the Iraqi invasion.

354 Tanks, Demonstrators with Placards and Executed Civilians

1992. 2nd Anniv of Iraqi Invasion. Children's Drawings. Multicoloured.

1332	50 f. Type **354**	30	20
1333	50 f. Soldiers rounding up civilians	30	20
1334	50 f. Military vehicles and Kuwait Towers	30	20
1335	50 f. Battle scene	30	20
1336	150 f. Tanks, bleeding eye and soldiers	95	60
1337	150 f. Battle scene around fortifications	95	60
1338	150 f. Liberation	95	60
1339	150 f. Soldiers and military vehicles	95	60

355 Burning Well

1992. 1st Anniv of Extinguishing of Oil Well Fires. Multicoloured.

1341	25 f. Type **355**	15	10
1342	50 f. Spraying dampener on fire	30	20
1343	150 f. Close-up of spraying	95	60
1344	250 f. Extinguished well (horiz)	1·60	1·00

356 Kuwait Towers

357 Laying Bricks to form "32"

1993.

1345	**356**	25 f. multicoloured	15	10
1346		100 f. multicoloured	70	45
1347		150 f. multicoloured	95	60

1993. 32nd National Day.

1348	**357**	25 f. multicoloured	15	10
1349		50 f. multicoloured	30	20
1350		150 f. multicoloured	95	60

358 Symbols of Oppression and Freedom

359 Hands Signing

1993. 2nd Anniv of Liberation.

1351	**358**	25 f. multicoloured	15	10
1352		50 f. multicoloured	30	20
1353		150 f. multicoloured	95	60

1993. Deaf Child Week.

1354 359 25 f. multicoloured 15 10
1355 50 f. multicoloured 30 20
1356 150 f. multicoloured 95 60
1357 350 f. multicoloured 2·10 1·40

360 Chained Prisoner **361** Hand scratching Map

1993. Campaign to Free Kuwaiti Prisoners of War. Multicoloured.

1358 50 f. Type **360** 35 20
1359 150 f. Chained hand, hoopoe and barred window (horiz) 1·10 70
1360 200 f. Screaming face on wall of empty cell 1·50 1·00

1993. 3rd Anniv of Iraqi Invasion.

1361 361 50 f. multicoloured 30 20
1362 150 f. multicoloured 85 55

362 Emblem

1993. 40th Anniv of Kuwait Air Force.

1363 362 50 f. multicoloured 40 25
1364 150 f. multicoloured 1·10 70

363 Flower and Dove **364** Anniversary Emblem

1994. 33rd National Day.

1365 363 25 f. multicoloured 15 10
1366 50 f. multicoloured 30 20
1367 150 f. multicoloured 90 60

1994. 3rd Anniv of Liberation.

1368 364 25 f. multicoloured 15 10
1369 50 f. multicoloured 30 20
1370 150 f. multicoloured 90 60

365 Anniversary Emblem **366** Stylized Emblems

1994. 25th Anniv of Central Bank of Kuwait.

1371 365 25 f. multicoloured 15 10
1372 50 f. multicoloured 30 20
1373 150 f. multicoloured 90 60

1994. Int Year of the Family. Mult.

1374 50 f. Type **366** 30 20
1375 150 f. Three I.Y.F. emblems 90 60
1376 200 f. Globe, emblem and spheres (horiz) 1·00 65

367 Emblem on Sky **368** Fingerprint in Water

1994. 20th Anniv of Industrial Bank of Kuwait.

1377 367 50 f. multicoloured 25 10
1378 100 f. gold, blue and black 55 35
1379 150 f. multicoloured 80 50

1994. Martyrs' Day. Multicoloured.

1380 50 f. Type **368** 30 10
1381 100 f. Fingerprint in sand 60 40
1382 150 f. Fingerprint in national colours 90 60
1383 250 f. Fingerprint in clouds over Kuwait Towers 1·50 1·00

369 Anniversary Emblem **370** Free and Imprisoned Doves

1994. 75th Anniv of I.L.O.

1385 369 50 f. multicoloured 25 10
1386 150 f. multicoloured 80 50
1387 350 f. gold, blue and black 1·75 1·10

1994. 4th Anniv of Iraqi Invasion.

1388 370 50 f. multicoloured 25 10
1389 150 f. multicoloured 80 50
1390 350 f. multicoloured 1·75 1·10

371 Emblem **372** Anniversary Emblem

1994. Kuwait Ports Authority.

1391 371 50 f. multicoloured 25 10
1392 150 f. multicoloured 80 50
1393 350 f. multicoloured 1·75 1·10

1994. 20th Anniv of Kuwait Science Club.

1394 372 50 f. multicoloured 25 10
1395 100 f. multicoloured 55 35
1396 150 f. multicoloured 75 50

373 Map and Building **374** I.C.A.O. and Kuwait International Airport Emblems

1994. Inauguration of Arab Towns Organization Permanent Headquarters. Multicoloured.

1397 50 f. Type **373** 25 10
1398 100 f. Close-up of arched facade 55 35
1399 150 f. Door 75 50

1994. 50th Anniv of I.C.A.O. Mult.

1400 100 f. Type **374** 55 35
1401 150 f. Emblems and control tower 85 55
1402 350 f. Airplane and "50 years" 1·90 1·25

375 Anniversary Emblem **376** Family

1994. 40th Anniv of Kuwait Airways.

1403 375 50 f. multicoloured 20 10
1404 100 f. multicoloured 50 35
1405 150 f. multicoloured 75 50

1995. Population Census.

1406 376 50 f. multicoloured 25 10
1407 100 f. multicoloured 45 30
1408 150 f. multicoloured 70 45

377 Children waving Flags **378** Falcon dragging Kuwaiti Flag from Snake's Grip

1995. 34th National Day.

1409 377 25 f. multicoloured 10 10
1410 50 f. multicoloured 25 10
1411 150 f. multicoloured 70 45

1995. 4th Anniv of Liberation.

1412 378 25 f. multicoloured 10 10
1413 50 f. multicoloured 25 10
1414 150 f. multicoloured 70 45

379 Conference Venue

1995. International Medical Conference. Mult.

1415 50 f. Type **379** 25 10
1416 100 f. Lecture 45 30
1417 150 f. Emblem on map of Kuwait in national colours 70 45

380 Anniversary Emblem and Flags **381** Emblem

1995. 50th Anniv of Arab League. Multicoloured.

1418 50 f. Type **380** 25 10
1419 100 f. Kuwaiti and League flags and League emblem (horiz) 45 30
1420 150 f. Handshake and League emblem 70 45

1995. World Health Day. "A World without Polio".

1421 381 50 f. multicoloured 25 10
1422 150 f. multicoloured 70 45
1423 200 f. multicoloured 90 60

382 "100" **383** Olive Branch falling from Wounded Dove's Beak

1995. Centenary of Volleyball.

1424 382 50 f. multicoloured 25 10
1425 100 f. multicoloured 45 30
1426 150 f. multicoloured 70 45

1995. 5th Anniv of Iraqi Invasion.

1427 383 50 f. multicoloured 20 10
1428 100 f. multicoloured 40 25
1429 150 f. multicoloured 60 40

384 Doves and Anniversary Emblem **385** Farmer with Animals

1995. 50th Anniv of U.N.O.

1430 384 25 f. multicoloured 10 10
1431 50 f. multicoloured 20 10
1432 150 f. multicoloured 60 40

1995. 50th Anniv of F.A.O. Multicoloured.

1433 50 f. Type **385** 20 10
1434 100 f. Fish market 40 25
1435 150 f. Agriculture 60 40

386 Emblems within Ruler **387** "Onobrychis ptolemaica"

1995. World Standards Day. Multicoloured.

1437 50 f. Type **386** 20 10
1438 100 f. Emblems and aspects of industry (48 × 27 mm) 40 25
1439 150 f. As No. 1438 60 40

1995. Flowers. Multicoloured.

1440 5 f. Type **387** 10 10
1441 15 f. "Convolvulus oxyphyllus" 10 10
1442 25 f. Corn poppy 10 10
1443 50 f. "Moltkiopsis ciliata" 20 10
1444 150 f. "Senecio desfontainei" 60 40

388 Coins forming Map of Kuwait **389** Boy Scout in Watchtower

1996. Money Show.

1445 388 25 f. multicoloured 10 10
1446 100 f. multicoloured 40 25
1447 150 f. multicoloured 60 40

1996. 60th Anniv of Scout Movement in Kuwait. Multicoloured.

1448 50 f. Type **389** 20 10
1449 100 f. Scout drawing water from well 40 25
1450 150 f. Scouts planting sapling 60 40

390 Hands supporting Ear of Wheat **391** Dove trailing National Colours, Falcon and City

1996.

1451 390 50 f. multicoloured 20 10
1452 100 f. multicoloured 40 25
1453 150 f. multicoloured 60 40

1996. 35th National Day.

1454 391 25 f. multicoloured 10 10
1455 50 f. multicoloured 20 10
1456 150 f. multicoloured 60 40

392 Horses **393** View through Gateway

1996. 5th Anniv of Liberation.

1457 392 25 f. multicoloured 10 10
1458 50 f. multicoloured 20 10
1459 150 f. multicoloured 60 40

1996. Arab City Day.

1460 393 50 f. multicoloured 20 10
1461 100 f. multicoloured 40 25
1462 150 f. multicoloured 60 40

394 Emblem **395** Figures holding Open Book within Bird

1996. 7th Kuwait Dental Association Conference.

1463 394 25 f. multicoloured 10 10
1464 50 f. multicoloured 20 10
1465 150 f. multicoloured 60 40

1996. 50th Anniv of U.N.E.S.C.O.

1466 395 25 f. multicoloured 10 10
1467 100 f. multicoloured 40 25
1468 150 f. multicoloured 60 40

396 Flags, Anniversary Emblem and Tanker **397** Shaikh Mubarak al-Sabah

1996. 50th Anniv of First Oil Shipment from Kuwait.
1469 **396** 25 f. multicoloured . . . 10 10
1470 100 f. multicoloured . . . 40 25
1471 150 f. multicoloured . . . 60 40

1996. Centenary of Accession as Emir of Shaikh Mubarak al-Sabah. Multicoloured.
1472 25 f. Type **397** 10 10
1473 50 f. Shaikh Mubarak al-Sabah and ribbons 20 10
1474 150 f. Type **397** 60 40

398 Rifle Shooting

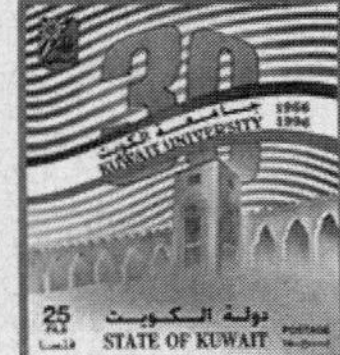

399 Festival Emblem

1996. Olympic Games, Atlanta. Multicoloured.
1475 25 f. Type **398** 10 10
1476 50 f. Running 20 10
1477 100 f. Weightlifting 40 25
1478 150 f. Fencing 60 40

1996. National Council for Culture, Art and Letters. First Children's Cultural Festival.
1479 **399** 25 f. multicoloured . . . 10 10
1480 100 f. multicoloured . . . 40 25
1481 150 f. multicoloured . . . 60 40

400 Emblem

401 University

1996. 3rd Al-Qurain Cultural Festival
1482 **400** 50 f. multicoloured . . . 20 10
1483 100 f. multicoloured . . . 40 25
1484 150 f. multicoloured . . . 60 40

1996. 30th Anniv of Kuwait University.
1485 **401** 25 f. multicoloured . . . 10 10
1486 100 f. multicoloured . . . 40 25
1487 150 f. multicoloured . . . 60 40

402 Liberation Tower

403 Sehel's Grey Mullet

1996.
1488 **402** 5 f. multicoloured 10 10
1489 10 f. multicoloured . . . 10 10
1490 15 f. multicoloured . . . 10 10
1491 25 f. multicoloured . . . 10 10
1492 50 f. multicoloured . . . 20 10
1493 100 f. multicoloured . . . 40 25
1494 150 f. multicoloured . . . 60 40
1495 200 f. multicoloured . . . 80 50
1496 250 f. multicoloured . . . 1·00 65
1497 350 f. multicoloured . . . 1·40 90

1997. Marine Life. Multicoloured. (a) Fishes.
1498 25 f. Type **403** 10 10
1499 50 f. Yellow-finned seabream . 20 10
1500 100 f. Greasy grouper 40 25
1501 150 f. Silver-backed seabream . 60 40
1502 200 f. Silver grunt 80 50
1503 350 f. Silver pomfret . . . . 1·40 90

(b) Shrimps.
1504 25 f. Tail and body segments of shrimps 10 10
1505 25 f. Head and body segments of shrimps 10 10
1506 25 f. Underside of fish and body and legs of shrimp 10 10
1507 25 f. Head of shrimp, fish and body and legs of shrimp . . 10 10
1508 50 f. Tail and body segments of two shrimps 20 10
1509 50 f. Legs and body segments of shrimp 20 10
1510 50 f. Body segments of shrimp and fish 20 10
1511 50 f. Head of shrimp, seaweed and body and legs of shrimp 20 10
1512 100 f. Tail and body segments of two shrimps 40 25
1513 100 f. Head, legs and body segments of shrimps 40 25
1514 100 f. Body of shrimp 40 25
1515 100 f. Part of head, legs, tail and body of three shrimps . . . 40 25
1516 150 f. Body segments of two shrimps and upper half of fish 60 40
1517 150 f. Front part of bodies of two shrimps and tail of fish . 60 40
1518 150 f. Heads of two shrimps, complete shrimp and fish . . 60 40
1519 150 f. Body segments of two shrimps and front part of shrimps head 60 40

Nos. 1504/19 were issued together, se-tenant, forming a composite design of shrimps in a marine environment.

404 Flag, Cupped Hands and Sunflower

1997. 36th National Day.
1520 **404** 25 f. multicoloured . . . 10 10
1521 50 f. multicoloured . . . 20 10
1522 150 f. multicoloured . . . 60 40

405 Flag, rejoicing Crowd and Shaikh Jabir

1997. 6th Anniv of Liberation.
1523 **405** 25 f. multicoloured . . . 10 10
1524 50 f. multicoloured . . . 20 10
1525 150 f. multicoloured . . . 60 40

406 Emblem

407 Emblem

1997. 10th Anniv of Montreal Protocol (on reduction of use of chlorofluorcarbons).
1526 **406** 25 f. multicoloured . . . 10 10
1527 50 f. multicoloured . . . 20 10
1528 150 f. multicoloured . . . 60 40

1997. Kuwait Industries Exhibition.
1529 **407** 25 f. multicoloured . . . 10 10
1530 50 f. multicoloured . . . 20 10
1531 150 f. multicoloured . . . 60 40

408 Signs of Zodiac and Whale

1997. 25th Anniv of Educational Science Museum.
1532 25 f. Type **408** 10 10
1533 50 f. Space shuttle orbiting Earth, whale, astronaut and dinosaur (horiz) 20 10
1534 150 f. Symbols of past, present and future around whale . . 60 40

409 National Council for Culture, Arts and Letters Emblem

1997. 22nd Kuwait Arabic Book Exhbition.
1536 **409** 25 f. multicoloured . . . 10 10
1537 50 f. multicoloured . . . 20 10
1538 150 f. multicoloured . . . 60 40

410 Ink-well and Book (first book fair, 1975)

1997. Kuwait Cultural History.
1539 25 f. Type **410** 10 10
1540 25 f. Front page of "Kuwait Magazine" (1928) 10 10
1541 25 f. Front page "A'lam al-Fikr" (periodical) (1970) . . 10 10
1542 25 f. Pyramids and dhow ("Al'Bitha" magazine, 1946) 10 10
1543 25 f. Rising sun over open book and quill ("Al'am al Ma'rifa" (periodical), 1978) 10 10
1544 25 f. Book with dhow on front cover ("Dalil Almohtar Fi Alaam Al-Bihar", 1923) . . 10 10
1545 25 f. Arabic script and "brick" design ("Al-Arabi" magazine, 1958) 10 10
1546 25 f. Open book (inauguration of first public library, 1923) . 10 10
1547 25 f. Two covers showing Arabic script in boxes and cosmic explosion ("Al Thaqafa Al-Alamiya" (periodical), 1981) 10 10
1548 25 f. Actors and curtain ("The World Theatre" (periodical), 1969) 10 10
1549 50 f. Entrance to Qibliya Girls' School (1937) 20 10
1550 50 f. Scissors cutting ribbon (first Fine Arts Exhibition, 1959) 20 10
1551 50 f. Mubarakiya School (1912) 20 10
1552 50 f. Family entering Kuwait National Museum (1958) . . 20 10
1553 50 f. Shuwaikh Secondary School (1953) 20 10
1554 50 f. Door and three windows (Al-Marsam Al-Hor, 1959) . 20 10
1555 50 f. Decorated screen (Alma'had Aldini, 1947) . . 20 10
1556 50 f. Courtyard of Folklore Centre (1956) 20 10
1557 50 f. Three columns of Arabic script (Al Ma'arif printing press, 1947) 20 10
1558 50 f. Class photograph (Literary Club, 1924) 20 10
1559 150 f. Heads and curtains (Folk Theatre Group, 1956) . . . 60 40
1560 150 f. Musical instruments and notes (Academy of Music, 1972) 60 40
1561 150 f. Film frames, audience and camera (opening of Al-Sharqiya cinema, 1955) . . 60 40
1562 150 f. Curtains around couple at oasis (Theatrical Academy, 1967) 60 40
1563 150 f. Marine views in film frame ("Bas Ya Bahar" (first Kuwaiti feature film), 1970) . 60 40

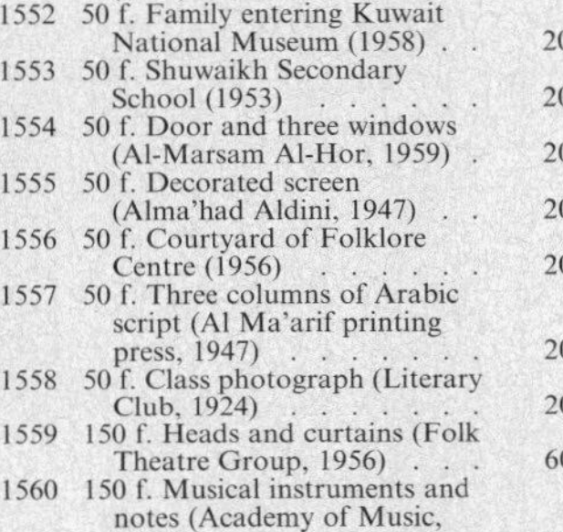

411 Doves flying over Members' Flags

1997. 18th Gulf Co-operation Council Summit, Kuwait. Multicoloured.
1564 25 f. Type **411** 10 10
1565 50 f. Members' flags forming doves wheeling over map (horiz) 20 10
1566 150 f. Doves perched atop wall of members' flags 60 40

412 State Flag

1998. 37th National Day.
1567 **412** 25 f. multicoloured . . . 10 10
1568 50 f. multicoloured . . . 20 10
1569 150 f. multicoloured . . . 60 40

413 Flag, Map and Dove

1998. 7th Anniv of Liberation.
1570 **413** 25 f. multicoloured . . . 10 10
1571 50 f. multicoloured . . . 20 10
1572 150 f. multicoloured . . . 60 40

414 Emblem

415 Text on Open Page with Flowers

1998. Anti-drugs Campaign.
1573 **414** 25 f. multicoloured . . . 10 10
1574 50 f. multicoloured . . . 20 10
1575 150 f. multicoloured . . . 60 40

1998. Martyrs' Day. Multicoloured.
1576 25 f. Type **415** 10 10
1577 50 f. Tree 20 10
1578 150 f. Calligraphy 60 40

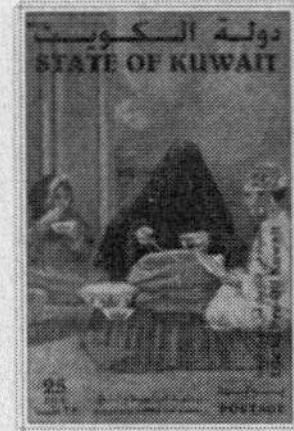

416 Woman selling Cooked Vegetables

417 Child's Face

1998. Life in Pre-Oil Kuwait (1st series). Mult.
1580 25 f. Type **416** 10 10
1581 50 f. Ship-building 20 10
1582 100 f. Sailor strapping his box . 40 25
1583 150 f. Pearl divers wading out to boat 60 40
1584 250 f. Delivering fresh water . 1·00 65
1585 350 f. Pigeon trainer . . . . 1·40 90

See also Nos. 1599/604.

1998. 12th Anniv of Chernobyl Nuclear Disaster.
1586 **417** 25 f. multicoloured . . . 10 10
1587 50 f. multicoloured . . . 20 10
1588 150 f. multicoloured . . . 60 40

418 World Map and Emblem

1998. International Year of the Ocean. Multicoloured.
1589 25 f. Type **418** 10 10
1590 50 f. Motifs as in Type **418** but differently arranged in rectangle (27 × 37 mm) . . 20 10
1591 150 f. Type **418** 60 40

419 Emblem

1998. 25th Anniv of Union of Consumer Co-operative Societies. Multicoloured.
1592 **419** 25 f. multicoloured . . . 10 10
1593 50 f. multicoloured . . . 20 10
1594 150 f. multicoloured . . . 60 40

HAVE YOU READ THE NOTES AT THE BEGINNING OF THIS CATALOGUE?
These often provide answers to the enquiries we receive.

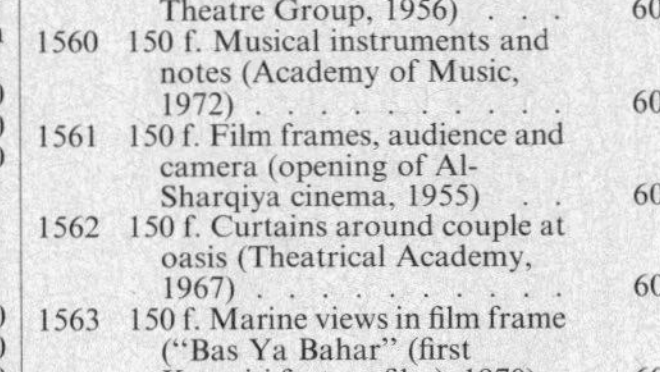

420 Men on Crutches

1998. Anti-landmine Campaign. Details from painting by Jafar Islah. Multicoloured.

1595	25 f. Type **420**	10	10
1596	50 f. Man on crutch	20	10
1597	150 f. Man on crutches and woman helping child	60	40

1998. Life in Pre-Oil Kuwait (2nd series). As T **416**. Multicoloured.

1599	25 f. Hairdresser	10	10
1600	50 f. Hand-grinding	20	10
1601	100 f. Tailor	40	25
1602	150 f. Artist	60	40
1603	250 f. Potter	1·00	65
1604	350 f. Hand-spinning	1·40	90

421 New Postal Emblem

1998.

1605	**421**	25 f. multicoloured	10	10
1606		50 f. multicoloured	20	10
1607		100 f. multicoloured	40	25
1608		150 f. multicoloured	60	40
1609		250 f. multicoloured	1·00	65

422 Child's Painting

1998. Children's Cultural House.

1610	**422**	25 f. multicoloured	10	10
1611		50 f. multicoloured	20	10
1612		150 f. multicoloured	60	40

423 Collage

1998. 50th Anniv of Universal Declaration of Human Rights.

1613	**423**	25 f. multicoloured	10	10
1614		50 f. multicoloured	20	15
1615		150 f. multicoloured	60	40

OFFICIAL STAMPS

1923. Stamps of India (King George V) optd **KUWAIT SERVICE**.

O 1	**56**	½ a. green	1·50	21·00
O 2	**57**	1 a. brown	2·50	11·00
O 3	**58**	1½ a. brown (No. 163)	3·25	28·00
O 4	**59**	2 a. lilac	4·25	23·00
O17	**70**	2 a. lilac	55·00	£150
O 5	**61**	2 a. 6 p. blue	4·25	50·00
O 6	**62**	3 a. orange	3·50	60·00
O19		3 a. blue	4·25	38·00
O 8	**63**	4 a. green	3·50	55·00
O20	**71**	4 a. green	4·25	65·00
O 9	**65**	8 a. mauve	5·50	65·00
O22	**66**	12 a. red	25·00	£150
O10	**67**	1 r. brown and green	14·00	£130
O11		2 r. red and orange	18·00	£180
O12		5 r. blue and violet	60·00	£375
O13		10 r. green and red	£110	£350
O14		15 r. blue	£180	£475

POSTAGE DUE STAMPS

D 34 D 51

1963.

D199	D **34**	1 f. brown and black	10	20
D200		2 f. lilac and black	15	25
D201		5 f. blue and black	25	20
D202		8 f. green and black	50	35
D203		10 f. yellow and black	70	65
D204		25 f. red and black	1·60	2·00

The above stamps were not sold to the public unused until 1st July, 1964.

1965.

D276	D **51**	4 f. pink and yellow	15	20
D277		15 f. red and blue	50	35
D278		40 f. blue and green	1·00	75
D279		50 f. green and mauve	1·40	1·00
D280		100 f. blue and yellow	2·50	2·00

KYRGYZSTAN Pt. 10

Formerly Kirghizia, a constituent republic of the Soviet Union, Kyrgyzstan became independent in 1991. Its capital Frunze reverted to its previous name of Bishkek.

1992. 100 kopeks = 1 rouble.
1993. 100 tyin = 1 som.

1 Sary-C'helek Nature Reserve

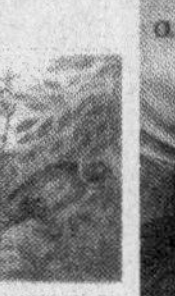
2 Golden Eagle

1992.
1 1 15 k. multicoloured 15 15

1992.
2 2 50 k. multicoloured 25 20

3 "Cattle at Issyk-Kule" (G. A. Aitiev)

1992.
3 3 1 r. multicoloured 25 15

4 Carpet and Samovar

1992.
4 4 1 r. 50 multicoloured 25 15

5 Cave Paintings

1993. National Monuments. Multicoloured.
5 10 k. Type **5** 10 10
6 50 k. 11th-century tower, Burana (vert) 10 10
7 1 r. + 25 k. Mausoleum of Manas, Talas (vert) 10 10
8 2 r. + 50 k. Mausoleum, Uzgen 15 10
9 3 r. Yurt 20 15
10 5 r. + 50 k. Statue of Manas, Bishkek 35 25
11 9 r. Cultural complex, Bishkek 55 35

The premium on Nos. 7/8 and 10 were used for the financing of a Manas museum.

1000 КЫРГЫЗСТАН
(6)

20 т. КЫРГЫЗСТАН
(7)

1993. Nos. 5940, 6073 and 4671 of Russia surch as T **6**.
13 10 k. on 1 k. brown 15 10
14 20 k. on 2 k. brown 40 20
15 30 k. on 3 k. red 60 40

1993. Nos. 4672/3 of Russia surch as T **7**.
16 20 t. on 4 k. red 20 10
17 30 t. on 6 k. blue 40 30

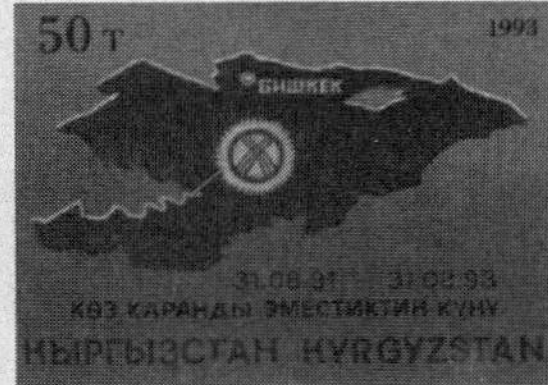
8 Map

1993. 2nd Anniv of Independence (18) and 1st Anniv of Admission to United Nations (19). Multicoloured.
18 50 t. Type **8** 35 25
19 60 t. U.N. emblem, national flag and Government Palace, Bishkek (vert) 45 30

9 Komuz

1993. Music.
20 9 30 t. multicoloured 25 15

10 Dog

12 Mauve Flowers

11 Adult and Cub

1994. New Year. Year of the Dog.
22 10 60 t. multicoloured 20 15

1994. The Snow Leopard. Multicoloured.
23 10 t. Type **11** 15 10
24 20 t. Lying curled-up 35 20
25 30 t. Sitting 45 30
26 40 t. Head 60 40

1994. Flowers. Multicoloured.
27 1 t. Type **12** 10 10
28 3 t. Daisies (horiz) 10 10
29 10 t. Tulip 10 10
30 16 t. Narcissi 10 10
31 20 t. Deep pink flower 15 10
32 30 t. White flower 20 15
33 40 t. Yellow flower 30 25

13 Fluorite
15 Woman with Rug

14 Turkestan Catfish

1994. Minerals. Multicoloured.
36 80 t. Type **13** 20 15
37 90 t. Calcite 20 15
38 100 t. Getchellite 20 15
39 110 t. Barite 25 20
40 120 t. Auripigment 25 20
41 140 t. Antimonite 30 20

1994. Fishes. Multicoloured.
43 110 t. Type **14** 30 20
44 120 t. Schmidt's dace 40 30
45 130 t. Scaleless osman 50 40
46 140 t. Spotted stone loach 60 45

1995. Traditional Costumes. Multicoloured.
48 50 t. Type **15** 10 10
49 50 t. Musician 10 10
50 100 t. Falconer 25 15
51 100 t. Woman with long plaits 25 15

16 Butterfly, Traffic Lights and Emblem

17 Brown Bear

1995. Road Safety Week.
52 16 200 t. multicoloured 30 20

1995. Animals. Multicoloured.
53 110 t. Type **17** 10 10
54 120 t. Snow leopard (horiz) 15 10
55 130 t. Golden eagle 30 15
56 140 t. Menzbier's marmot (horiz) 25 15
57 150 t. Brown harrier eagle (horiz) 35 15
58 160 t. Griffon vulture 40 20
59 190 t. Red fox (horiz) 35 20

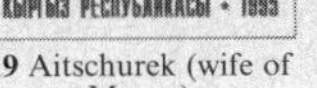
19 Aitschurek (wife of Manas)

20 Osprey

1995. Millenary of "Manas" (epic poem). Each blue and gold.
62 10 t. + 5 t. Type **19** 10 10
63 20 t. + 10 t. Hoopoe on youth's wrist 10 10
64 30 t. + 10 t. Birth of Semetey, son of Manas 10 10
65 30 t. + 10 t. Woman carrying spear and leading horse 10 10
66 40 t. + 15 t. Warrior astride dead dragon 15 10
67 50 t. + 15 t. Jakyp, father of Manas 20 15
68 50 t. + 15 t. Manas on horseback 20 15
69 50 t. + 15 t. Seytek, grandson of Manas 20 15

1995. Birds. Multicoloured.
71 10 t. Type **20** 10 10
72 50 t. Tawny eagle 10 10
73 100 t. Himalayan griffon 20 15
74 140 t. Saker falcon 25 15
75 150 t. Short-toed eagle 25 15
76 200 t. Lammergeier 35 25
77 300 t. Golden eagle 50 30

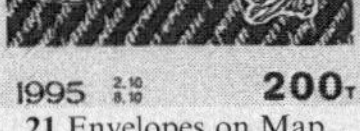
21 Envelopes on Map and U.P.U. Emblem

22 State Arms

1995. Postage Stamp Week.
79 21 200 t. multicoloured 30 20

1995.
80 22 20 t. violet 10 10
81 50 t. blue 10 10
82 100 t. brown 15 10
86 500 t. green 65 50

23 Mare and Foal Galloping

1995. Horses. Multicoloured.
89 10 t. Type **23** 10 10
90 50 t. Palamino mare and foal (vert) 10 10
91 100 t. Brown mare and foal (vert) 20 15
92 140 t. Chestnut mare and foal (vert) 25 15
93 150 t. Chestnut mare and foal 25 15
94 200 t. Grey mare and foal 35 25
95 300 t. Pair of foals 50 30

25 River Nile, Egypt

1995. Natural Wonders of the World. Multicoloured.
98 10 t. Type **25** 10 10
99 50 t. Mt. Kilimanjaro, Tanzania 10 10
100 100 t. Sahara Desert, Algeria 15 10
101 140 t. Amazon River, Brazil (vert) 20 15
102 150 t. Grand Canyon, U.S.A. (vert) 20 15
103 200 t. Victoria Falls, Zimbabwe (vert) 25 20
104 350 t. Mt. Everest, Nepal 50 35
105 400 t. Niagara Falls, Canada 55 40

No. 98 is wrongly inscribed "Egipt".

26 Steppe Ribbon Snake

1996. Reptiles. Multicoloured.
107 20 t. Type **26** 10 10
108 50 t. Fat-tailed panther gecko 10 10
109 50 t. Tessellated water snake 10 10
110 100 t. Central Asian viper 15 10
111 150 t. Arguta 25 20
112 200 t. Dione snake 35 25
113 250 t. "Asyblepharus sp." (wrongly inscr "Asymblepharus") 40 30

28 Show Jumping and Traditional Horse Race

1996. Olympic Games, Atlanta, U.S.A. Multicoloured.
116 100 t. + 20 t. Type **28** 25 15
117 140 t. + 30 t. Boxing and traditional wrestling match 35 25
118 150 t. + 30 t. Archer and mounted archer shooting at eagle 50 40
119 300 t. + 50 t. Judo competitor, ballooning, yachting and water-skiing 85 65

29 Golden Eagle

1997. Animals.
120 600 t. Type **29** 85 60
121 600 t. Markhor ("Capra falconeri") 85 60
122 600 t. Argali ("Ovis ammon") 85 60
123 600 t. Himalayan griffon ("Gyps himalayensis") 85 60
124 600 t. Asiatic wild ass ("Equus hemionus") 85 60
125 600 t. Wolf ("Canis lupus") 85 60
126 600 t. Brown bear ("Ursus arctos") (wrongly inscr "arctor") 85 60
127 600 t. Saiga ("Saiga tatarica") 85 60

30 Tiger

1998. New Year. Year of the Tiger.
128 30 600 t. multicoloured 65 45

31 "Parnassius actius"

1998. Butterflies. Multicoloured.

129	600 t. Type **31** (wrongly inscr "Parnasius")	65	45
130	600 t. "Colias christophi"	65	45
131	600 t. Swallowtail ("Papilio machaon")	65	45
132	600 t. "Colias thisoa"	65	45
133	600 t. "Parnassius delphius"	65	45
134	600 t. "Parnassius tianschanicus"	65	45

32 Roe Deer

1998. Animals. Multicoloured.

135	600 t. Type **32**	60	45
136	600 t. Osprey ("Pandion haliaetus")	60	45
137	600 t. Hoopoe ("Upupa epops")	60	45
138	600 t. White stork ("Ciconia ciconia")	60	45
139	1000 t. Golden oriole ("Oriolus oriolus")	60	45
140	1000 t. Snow leopard	60	45
141	1000 t. Common kingfisher ("Alcedo althis")	60	45
142	1000 t. Common kestrel ("Falco tinnunculus")	60	45

LA AGUERA Pt. 9

An administrative district of Spanish Sahara whose stamps it later used.

1920. Rio de Oro stamps optd **LA AGUERA.**

1 **15** 1 c. green 1·60 1·60
2 2 c. brown 1·60 1·60
3 5 c. green 1·60 1·60
4 10 c. red 1·60 1·60
5 15 c. yellow 1·60 1·60
6 20 c. violet 1·60 1·60
7 25 c. blue 1·60 1·60
8 30 c. brown 1·60 1·60
9 40 c. pink 1·60 1·60
10 50 c. blue 5·25 5·25
11 1 p. red 9·50 9·50
12 4 p. purple 30·00 30·00
13 10 p. orange 60·00 60·00

2

1923.

14 **2** 1 c. blue 70 70
15 2 c. green 70 70
16 5 c. green 70 70
17 10 c. red 70 70
18 15 c. brown 70 70
19 20 c. yellow 70 70
20 25 c. blue 70 70
21 30 c. brown 70 70
22 40 c. red 90 90
23 50 c. purple 3·25 3·25
24 1 p. mauve 6·25 6·25
25 4 p. violet 16·00 16·00
26 10 p. orange 25·00 25·00

LABUAN Pt. 1

An Island off the N. coast of Borneo, ceded to Great Britain in 1846, and a Crown Colony from 1902. Incorporated with Straits Settlements in 1906, it used Straits stamps till it became part of N. Borneo in 1946.

100 cents = 1 dollar

1

18

1879.

17 **1** 2 c. green 13·00 22·00
39 2 c. red 3·25 3·50
6 6 c. orange 85·00 90·00
40 6 c. green 6·50 4·50
7 8 c. red 85·00 85·00
41 8 c. violet 2·50 7·00
43 10 c. brown 8·00 8·00
9 12 c. red £200 £275
45 12 c. blue 3·50 6·50
4 16 c. blue 50·00 £110
46 16 c. grey 4·00 8·50
47 40 c. orange 18·00 32·00

1880. (a) Surch **8**.

11 **1** 8 on 12 c. red £950 £650

(b) Surch **6 6** or **8 8**.

12 **1** 6 on 16 c. blue £1700 £700
13 8 on 12 c. red £1100 £800

1881. Surch **EIGHT CENTS**.

14 **1** 8 c. on 12 c. red £225 £275

1881. Surch **Eight Cents**.

15 **1** 8 c. on 12 c. red £110 £120

1883. Manuscript surch **one Dollar A.S.H.**

22 **1** $1 on 16 c. blue £2750

1885. Surch **2 CENTS** horiz.

23 **1** 2 c. on 8 c. red £160 £350
24 2 c. on 16 c. blue £850 £750

1885. Surch **2 Cents** horiz.

25 **1** 2 c. on 16 c. blue £110 £160

1885. Surch with large **2 Cents** diag.

26 **1** 2 c. on 8 c. red 65·00 £100

1891. Surch **6 Cents**.

35 **1** 6 c. on 8 c. violet 6·50 6·50
37 6 c. on 16 c. blue £1700 £1600
38 6 c. on 40 c. orange £7000 £3750

1892. Surch as **Two CENTS** or **Six CENTS**.

49 **1** 2 c. on 40 c. orange £150 90·00
50 6 c. on 16 c. grey £300 £140

Most issues from 1894 exist cancelled-to-order with black bars. Our prices are for stamps postally used, cancelled-to-order examples being worth considerably less.

1894. Types of North Borneo (different colours) optd **LABUAN**.

62 **24** 1 c. black and mauve 1·50 6·50
63 **25** 2 c. black and blue 2·50 6·50
64a **26** 3 c. black and yellow 6·50 9·00
65a **27** 5 c. black and green 27·00 10·00
67 **28** 6 c. black and red 2·50 11·00
69 **29** 8 c. black and pink 7·00 23·00
70 **30** 12 c. black and orange 23·00 40·00
71 **31** 18 c. black and brown 22·00 45·00
74a **32** 24 c. blue and mauve 13·00 38·00
80 **10** 25 c. green 22·00 26·00
81 – 50 c. purple (as No. 82) 22·00 26·00
82 – $1 blue (as No. 83) 50·00 45·00

1895. No. 83 of North Borneo surch **LABUAN** and value in cents.

75 4 c. on $1 red 1·00 1·75
76 10 c. on $1 red 2·25 1·40
77 20 c. on $1 red 23·00 8·50
78 30 c. on $1 red 25·00 30·00
79 40 c. on $1 red 22·00 24·00

1896. Jubilee of Cession of Labuan to Gt. Britain. Nos. 62/8 optd **1846 JUBILEE 1896**.

83 **24** 1 c. black and mauve 17·00 21·00
84d **25** 2 c. black and blue 30·00 14·00
85 **26** 3 c. black and yellow 30·00 22·00
86 **27** 5 c. black and green 48·00 16·00
87 **28** 6 c. black and red 24·00 20·00
88b **29** 8 c. black and pink 35·00 11·00

1897. Stamps of North Borneo, Nos. 92 to 106 (different colours), optd **LABUAN**. Opt at top of stamp.

89 1 c. black and purple 4·00 4·75
90 2 c. black and blue 11·00 4·25
91b 3 c. black and yellow 8·50 6·50
92a 5 c. black and green 32·00 40·00
93b 6 c. black and red 4·50 19·00
94a 8 c. black and pink 15·00 12·00
95a 12 c. black and orange 25·00 45·00

Overprint at foot of stamp.

98a – 12 c. black and orange (as No. 106) 38·00 42·00

Opt at foot. Inscr "POSTAL REVENUE".

96b – 18 c. black and bistre (as No. 108) 15·00 40·00

Opt at foot. Inscr "POSTAGE AND REVENUE".

99a – 18 c. black and bistre (as No. 110) 75·00 60·00

Opt at top. Inscr "POSTAGE AND REVENUE".

101b – 18 c. black and bistre (as No. 110) 28·00 48·00

Opt at top. "POSTAGE AND REVENUE" omitted.

97a – 24 c. blue and lilac (as No. 109) 10·00 42·00

Opt at top. Inscr "POSTAGE AND REVENUE".

100 – 24 c. blue and mauve (No. 111) 23·00 48·00

1899. Stamps of Labuan surch **4 CENTS**.

102 4 c. on 5 c. blk & grn (92a) 30·00 26·00
103 4 c. on 6 c. blk & red (93b) 19·00 19·00
104a 4 c. on 8 c. black and pink (94a) 22·00 32·00
105 4 c. on 12 c. black and orange (98a) 32·00 35·00
106 4 c. on 18 c. black and olive (101b) 21·00 17·00
107 4 c. on 24 c. blue and mauve (100) 20·00 27·00
108 4 c. on 25 c. green (80) 5·50 7·50
109 4 c. on 50 c. purple (81) 5·50 7·50
110 4 c. on $1 blue (82) 5·50 7·50

1900. Stamps of North Borneo, as Nos. 95 to 107, optd **LABUAN**.

111 2 c. black and green 3·75 2·50
112 4 c. black and brown 6·50 32·00
113a 4 c. black and red 6·50 7·50
114 5 c. black and blue 25·00 18·00
115 10 c. brown and grey 45·00 70·00
116 16 c. green and brown 55·00 95·00

1902.

117 **18** 1 c. black and purple 3·50 6·50
118 2 c. black and green 3·00 4·00
119 3 c. black and brown 3·00 8·00
120 4 c. black and red 3·00 3·50
121 8 c. black and orange 7·50 8·00
122 10 c. brown and blue 3·00 8·50
123 12 c. black and yellow 3·50 10·00
124 16 c. green and brown 4·75 14·00
125 18 c. black and brown 3·25 14·00
126 25 c. green and blue 6·00 15·00
127 50 c. purple and lilac 10·00 40·00
128 $1 red and orange 8·00 45·00

1904. Surch **4 cents**.

129 – 4 c. on 5 c. black and green (92a) 30·00 35·00
130 – 4 c. on 6 c. black and red (93b) 12·00 32·00
131 – 4 c. on 8 c. black and pink (94a) 24·00 35·00
132 – 4 c. on 12 c. black and orange (98a) 19·00 35·00
133 – 4 c. on 18 c. black and olive (101b) 19·00 38·00
134 – 4 c. on 24 c. blue and mauve (100) 16·00 38·00
135 **10** 4 c. on 25 c. green (80) 8·50 21·00
136 4 c. on 50 c. purple (81) 8·50 21·00
137 4 c. on $1 blue (82) 8·50 21·00

POSTAGE DUE STAMPS

1901. Optd **POSTAGE DUE**.

D1 2 c. black and green (111) 11·00 20·00
D2 3 c. black and yellow (91) 16·00 70·00
D3b 4 c. black and red (113) 25·00 70·00
D4 5 c. black and blue (114) 38·00 85·00
D5 6 c. black and red (93b) 18·00 75·00
D6 8 c. black and pink (94a) 45·00 75·00
D7 12 c. black and orange (98a) 65·00 85·00
D8 18 c. black and olive (101b) 17·00 80·00
D9 24 c. blue and mauve (100) 32·00 70·00

LAGOS Pt. 1

A British colony on the southern coast of Nigeria. United with Southern Nigeria in 1906 to form the Colony and Protectorate of Southern Nigeria.

12 pence = 1 shilling;
20 shillings = 1 pound

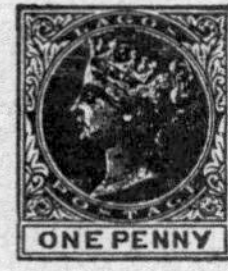

1

3

1874.

21 **1** ½d. green 2·00 80
17 1d. mauve 18·00 10·00
22 1d. red 2·00 80
11 2d. blue 38·00 12·00
23 2d. grey 55·00 5·00
19 3d. brown 14·00 5·00
5 4d. red 65·00 40·00
24 4d. lilac 95·00 8·50
25 6d. green 8·00 35·00
26 1s. orange 7·00 20·00
27 2s. 6d. black £275 £250
28 5s. blue £475 £400
29 10s. brown £1200 £800

1887.

30 **1** 2d. mauve and blue 2·75 2·00
31 2½d. blue 3·50 1·75
32 3d. mauve and brown 2·50 3·25
33 4d. mauve and black 2·25 1·75
34 5d. mauve and green 2·00 11·00
36 6d. mauve 4·75 3·00
35a 6d. mauve and red 4·75 12·00
36 7½d. mauve and red 2·00 26·00
37 10d. mauve and yellow 3·25 13·00
38 1s. green and black 5·00 23·00
39 2s. 6d. green and red 22·00 75·00
40 5s. green and blue 38·00 £140
41 10s. green and brown 65·00 £180

1893. Surch **HALF PENNY** and bars.

42 **1** ½d. on 4d. mauve and black 3·75 2·50

1904.

44 **3** ½d. green 1·50 5·50
45 1d. purple and black on red 1·00 15
56 2d. purple and blue 2·00 1·40
47 2½d. purple and blue on blue 1·00 1·50
48 3d. purple and brown 1·75 1·75
59a 6d. purple and mauve 4·25 1·25
60a 1s. green and black 18·00 2·25
61 2s. 6d. green and red 12·00 38·00
62 5s. green and blue 22·00 90·00
63 10s. green and brown 50·00 £170

LAOS Pt. 21

Previously part of French Indo-China, the Kingdom of Laos was proclaimed in 1947. In 1949 it became an Associated State within the French Union and in 1953 it became fully independent within the Union.

Laos left the French Union in 1956. In 1976 it became a Republic.

1951. 100 cents = 1 piastre.
1955. 100 cents = 1 kip.

1 River Mekong 2 King Sisavang Vong

1951.

1 **1** 10 c. green and turquoise 20 20
2 20 c. red and purple 20 30
3 30 c. blue and indigo 1·00 85
4 – 50 c. brown and deep brown 50 35
5 – 60 c. orange and red 45 50
6 – 70 c. turquoise and blue 45 50
7 – 1 p. violet and deep violet 45 50
8 **2** 1 p. 50 purple and brown 85 65
9 – 2 p. green and turquoise 16·00 4·00
10 – 3 p. red and purple 90 75
11 – 5 p. blue and indigo 1.25 80
12 – 10 p. purple and brown 2·75 1·25

DESIGNS—As Type **1**: 50 c. to 70 c. Luang Prabang; 1 p. and 2 p. to 10 p. Vientiane.

3 Laotian Woman

4 Laotian Woman Weaving

1952.

13 **3** 30 c. violet and blue (post) 40 35
14 80 c. turquoise and green 40 35
15 1 p. 10 red and crimson 90 35
16 1 p. 90 blue and indigo 1·40 80
17 3 p. deep brown and brown 1·40 80
18 – 3 p. 30 violet and deep violet (air) 85 60
19 **4** 10 p. green and blue 1·90 1·25
20 20 p. red and crimson 3·25 2·00
21 30 p. brown and black 4·75 3·50

DESIGN—As Type **4**: 3 p. 30, Vat Pra Keo shrine.

5 King Sisavang Vong and U.P.U. Monument

1952. 1st Anniv of Admission to U.P.U.

22 **5** 80 c. violet, bl & ind (postage) 75 85
23 1 p. brown, red and lake 75 75
24 1 p. 20 blue and violet 75 85
25 1 p. 50 brown, emerald & grn 75 85
26 1 p. 90 turquoise and sepia 1·10 1·25
27 25 p. indigo and blue (air) 4·25 4·75
28 50 p. sepia, purple and brown 5·00 5·50

6 Girl carrying her Brother

7 Court of Love

1953. Red Cross Fund. Cross in red.

29 **6** 1 p. 50 + 1 p. purple & blue 2·75 2·75
30 3 p. + 1 p. 50 red and green 2·50 2·75
31 3 p. 90 + 2 p. 50 pur & brn 2·50 2·75

1953.

32 **7** 4 p. 50 turquoise and blue 1·00 85
33 6 p. brown and slate 1·10 85

8 Buddha

1953. Air. Statues of Buddha.

34 – 4 p. green 95 85
35 – 6 p. 50 green 1·40 1·10
36 – 9 p. green 2·00 1·50
37 **8** 11 p. 50 orange, brown & red 2·75 2·50
38 – 40 p. purple 6·50 2·50
39 – 100 p. green 13·50 10·50

DESIGNS—HORIZ: 4 p. Reclining. VERT: 6 p. 50, Seated; 9 p. Standing (full-face); 40 p. Standing (facing right); 100 p. Buddha and temple dancer.

9 Vientiane

1954. Golden Jubilee of King Sisavang Vong.

40 **9** 2 p. violet and blue (postage) 50·00 35·00
41 3 p. red and brown 45·00 38·00
42 50 p. turquoise & blue (air) £140 £160

10 Ravana

1955. Air. "Ramayana" (dramatic poem).

43 **10** 2 k. blue, emerald and green . 1·00 90
44 – 4 k. red and brown . . . 1·25 1·25
45 – 5 k. green, brown and red . . 2·50 1·75
46 – 10 k. black, orange & brown 4·50 3·00
47 – 20 k. olive, green and violet 5·50 4·25
48 – 30 k. black, brown and blue 7·50 5·50

DESIGNS—HORIZ: 4 k. Hanuman, the white monkey; 5 k. Ninh Laphath, the black monkey. VERT: 10 k. Sita and Rama; 20 k. Luci and Ravana's friend; 30 k. Rama.

11 Buddha and Worshippers

1956. 2500th Anniv of Buddhist Era.

49 **11** 2 k. brown (postage) . . . . 3·50 2·25
50 3 k. black . . . . 3·50 2·25
51 5 k. sepia . . . . 5·50 3·50
52 20 k. carmine and red (air) . 35·00 30·00
53 30 k. green and bistre . . . 35·00 32·00

Nos. 49/53 were wrongly inscribed as commemorating the birth anniversary of Buddha.

12 U.N. Emblem **13**

1956. 1st Anniv of Admission to U.N.

54 **12** 1 k. black (postage) 50 45
55 2 k. blue 65 50
56 4 k. red 90 70
57 6 k. violet . . . . 1·10 90
58 **13** 15 k. blue (air) . . . . . . 4·00 4·00
59 30 k. lake . . . . 5·50 5·50

14 Flute Player

1957. Native Musicians.

60 **14** 2 k. multicoloured (postage) . 1·25 80
61 – 4 k. multicoloured . . . . 1·25 80
62 – 8 k. blue, brown and orange . 2·10 95
63 – 12 k. multicoloured (air) . . 1·90 1·90
64 – 14 k. multicoloured . . . . 2·25 2·25
65 – 20 k. multicoloured . . . . 2·50 2·50

DESIGNS—VERT: 4 k. Piper; 14 k. Violinist; 20 k. Drummer. HORIZ: 8 k. Xylophonist; 12 k. Bells player.

15 Harvesting Rice

1957. Rice Cultivation.

66 **15** 3 k. multicoloured 70 40
67 – 5 k. brown, red and green . . 70 50
68 – 16 k. violet, olive and blue . . 1·50 90
69 – 26 k. chocolate, brown & grn . 1·90 1·50

DESIGNS—VERT: 5 k. Drying rice; 16 k. Winnowing rice. HORIZ: 26 k. Polishing rice.

16 "The Offertory" **18** Mother and Child

17 Carrier Elephants

1957. Air. Buddhism.

70 **16** 10 k. multicoloured 60 60
71 – 15 k. brown, yellow & choc . 90 90
72 – 18 k. yellow and green . . . 1·25 1·25
73 – 24 k. red, black and yellow . 2·40 2·40

DESIGNS—As T **16**: HORIZ: 15 k. "Meditation" (children on river craft). 48 × 36½ mm: 24 k. "The Great Renunciation" (dancers with horse). VERT: 18 k. "Serenity" (head of Buddhist).

1958. Laotian Elephants. Multicoloured.

74 10 c. Type **17** 45 20
75 20 c. Elephant's head with head-dress 45 20
76 30 c. Elephant with howdah (vert) 45 20
77 2 k. Elephant hauling log . . . 65 35
78 5 k. Elephant walking with calf (vert) . . . . 1·90 75
79 10 k. Caparisoned elephant (vert) 2·25 90
80 13 k. Elephant bearing throne (vert) . . . . 3·75 1·50

1958. Air. 3rd Anniv of Laotian Red Cross. Cross in red.

81 **18** 8 k. black and grey 90 90
82 12 k. olive and brown . . . 90 90
83 15 k. turquoise and green . . 1·10 1·10
84 20 k. violet and bistre . . . 1·25 1·25

19

1958. Inauguration of U.N.E.S.C.O. Headquarters Building, Paris.

85 **19** 50 c. blue, orange and red . . 25 20
86 – 60 c. violet, brown and green . 25 20
87 – 70 c. blue, brown and red . . 25 20
88 – 1 k. red, blue and bistre . . 45 25

DESIGNS—VERT: 60 c. Woman, children and part of exterior of U.N.E.S.C.O. building; 70 c. Woman and children hailing U.N.E.S.C.O. building superimposed on globe. HORIZ: 1 k. General view of U.N.E.S.C.O. building and Eiffel Tower.

20 King Sisavang Vong

1959.

89 **20** 4 k. lake 30 30
90 6 k. 50 red 30 30
91 9 k. mauve 30 30
92 13 k. green 30 30

21 Stage Performance **22** Portal of Vat Phou Temple, Pakse

1959. Education and Fine Arts.

93 **21** 1 k. multicoloured 20 15
94 – 2 k. lake, violet and black . . 25 15
95 – 3 k. black, green and purple . 30 20
96 – 5 k. green, yellow and violet . 45 35

DESIGNS—VERT: 2 k. Student and "Lamp of Learning"; 5 k. Stage performers and Buddhist temple. HORIZ: 3 k. Teacher and children with "Key to Education".

1959. Laotian Monuments. Multicoloured.

97 50 c. Type **22** 15 15
98 1 k. 50 That Ing Hang, Savannakhet 15 15
99 2 k. 50 Vat Phou Temple, Pakse 20 20
100 7 k. That Luang, Vientiane . . 30 30
101 11 k. As 7 k., but different view . 30 30
102 12 k. 50 Phou-Si Temple, Luang Prabang 45 45

The 1 k. 50, 2 k. 50 and 11 k. are horiz and the rest vert.

1960. World Refugee Year. Nos. 89 and 79 surch **ANNEE MONDIALE DU REFUGIE 1959–1960** and premium.

103 4 k. + 1 k. lake 50 70
104 10 k. + 1 k. multicoloured . . 50 70

24 Plain of Jars, Xieng Khouang **25** Funeral Urn

1960. Air. Tourism.

105 **24** 9 k. 50 red, bistre and blue . 25 25
106 – 12 k. brown violet and green . 35 30
107 – 15 k. red, green and brown . 50 45
108 – 19 k. brown, orange and green 60 50

DESIGNS—HORIZ: 12 k. Phapheng Falls, Champassak; 15 k. Pair of bullocks with cart. VERT: 19 k. Buddhist monk and village.

1961. Funeral of King Sisavang Vong.

109 **25** 4 k. bistre, black and red . 30 30
110 – 6 k. 50 brown and black . . 30 30
111 – 9 k. brown and black . . . 30 30
112 – 25 k. black 70 70

DESIGNS: 6 k. 50, Urn under canopy; 9 k. Catafalque on dragon carriage; 25 k. King Sisavang Vong.

26 Temples and Statues ("Pou Gneu Nha Gneu") **27** King Savang Vatthana

1962. Air. Festival of Makha Bousa.

113 **26** 11 k. brown, red and green . 30 30
114 – 14 k. blue and orange . . . 30 30
115 – 20 k. green, yellow and mauve 50 50
116 – 25 k. red, blue and green . . 60 60

DESIGNS—As T **26**: 14 k. Bird ("Garuda"); 20 k. Flying deities ("Hanuman"). 36 × 48 mm: 25 k. Warriors ("Nang Teng One").

1962.

117 **27** 1 k. brown, red and blue . . 10 10
118 2 k. brown, red and mauve . 15 15
119 5 k. brown, red and blue . . 25 15
120 10 k. brown, red and bistre . 40 25

28 Laotian Boy **29** Royal Courier

1962. Malaria Eradication.

121 **28** 4 k. olive, black & green . . 20 10
122 – 9 k. brown, black & turq . . 20 20
123 – 10 k. red, yellow & olive . . 40 25

DESIGNS: 9 k. Laotian girl; 10 k. Campaign emblem.

1962. Philatelic Exhibition, Vientiane, and Stamp Day.

124 – 50 c. multicoloured . . . . 1·00 1·00
125 – 70 c. multicoloured 20 20
126 – 1 k. black, green and red . . 35 35
127 **29** 1 k. 50 multicoloured . . . 35 35

DESIGNS—HORIZ: 50 c. Modern mail transport; 70 c. Dancer and globe. VERT: 1 k. Royal courtier on elephant.

30 Fisherman

1963. Freedom from Hunger.

128 **30** 1 k. bistre, violet and green . 20 15
129 – 4 k. blue, brown and green . 20 20
130 – 5 k. blue, bistre and green . 25 25
131 – 9 k. blue, green and brown . 40 40

DESIGNS—VERT: 4 k. Threshing rice; 9 k. Harvesting rice. HORIZ: 5 k. Ploughing paddy field.

31 Queen of Laos **32** Laotian supporting U.N. Emblem

1963. Red Cross Centenary.

132 **31** 4 k. red, blue and brown . . 20 20
133 6 k. multicoloured 25 25
134 10 k. red, blue and brown . . 30 30

1963. 15th Anniv of Declaration of Human Rights.

135 **32** 4 k. purple, blue and red . . 50 30

33 Temple, Map and Rameses II

1964. Nubian Monuments Preservation.

136 **33** 4 k. multicoloured 20 20
137 6 k. multicoloured 30 30
138 10 k. multicoloured 35 35

34 Offertory Vase and Horn

1964. "Constitutional Monarchy". Multicoloured.

139 10 k. Type **34** 20 15
140 15 k. Seated Buddha of Vat Pra Keo 30 20
141 20 k. Laotians walking across map 35 30
142 40 k. Royal Palace, Luang Prabang 70 55

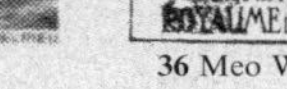

35 Phra Vet and Wife **36** Meo Warrior

1964. Folklore. Phra Vet Legend. Multicoloured.

143 10 k. Type **35** 25 25
144 32 k. "Benediction" 35 35
145 45 k. Phame and wife . . . 40 40
146 55 k. Arrest of Phame . . . 70 70

1964. "People of Laos".

147 – 25 k. black, brown and green (postage) 60 60
148 **36** 5 k. multicoloured (air) . . 25 15
149 – 10 k. flesh, slate and purple . 35 20
150 – 50 k. brown, drab and lilac . 1·40 85

DESIGNS: 10 k. Kha hunter; 25 k. Girls of three races; 50 k. Thai woman.

37 Red Lacewing

1965. Butterflies and Moths.

151 **37** 10 k. chestnut, brown and green (postage) 75 40
152 – 25 k. blue, black & yellow . 1·10 60
153 – 40 k. yellow, brown & grn . 1·90 90
154 – 20 k. red and yellow (air) . 1·10 60

BUTTERFLIES—As Type **37**: 25 k. Yellow pansy. 48 × 27 mm: 20 k. Atlas moth; 40 k. "Dysphania militaris" (moth).

38 Wattay Airport ("French Aid")

1965. Foreign Aid.
155 **38** 25 k. mauve, brown & turq . . . 30 20
156 – 45 k. brown and green . . . 35 30
157 – 55 k. brown and blue . . . 50 40
158 – 75 k. multicoloured 60 50
DESIGNS—VERT: 45 k. Mother bathing child (water resources: "Japanese Aid"); 75 k. School and plants (education and cultivation: "American Aid"). HORIZ: 55 k. Studio of radio station ("British Aid").

39 Hophabang

1965.
159 **39** 10 k. multicoloured 20 15

40 Teleprinter-operator, Globe and Map

1965. I.T.U. Centenary.
160 **40** 5 k. brown, violet & purple . . 20 15
161 – 30 k. brown, blue & green . . 30 30
162 – 50 k. multicoloured 50 35
DESIGNS: 30 k. Globe, map, telephonist and radio operator; 50 k. Globe, radio receiver and mast.

1965. Surch.
163 **20** 1 k. on 4 k. lake 20 15
164 5 k. on 6 k. 50 brown . . . 25 20

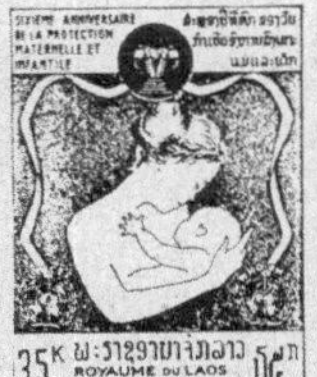

42 Mother and Baby **43** Leopard Cat

1965. 6th Anniv of U.N. "Protection of Mother and Child".
165 **42** 35 k. blue and red 70 30

1965. Air. Laotian Fauna.
166 **43** 22 k. yellow, brown & grn . . 30 25
167 – 55 k. brown, sepia & blue . . 40 30
168 – 75 k. brown and green . . . 65 40
169 – 100 k. brown, black & yell . . 90 60
170 – 200 k. black and red . . . 1·90 1·40
DESIGNS: 55 k. Phayre's flying squirrel; 75 k. Javan mongoose; 100 k. Chinese porcupine; 200 k. Binturong.

44 U.N. Emblem on Map **45** Bulls in Combat

1965. 20th Anniv of U.N.
171 **44** 5 k. blue, grey and green . . 20 15
172 25 k. blue, grey and mauve . . 25 20
173 40 k. blue, grey and turquoise 35 35

1965. Laotian Pastimes.
174 **45** 10 k. brown, black and orange 25 20
175 – 20 k. blue, red and green . . 30 20
176 – 25 k. red, blue and green . . 45 30
177 – 50 k. multicoloured 50 40
DESIGNS: 20 k. Tikhy (form of hockey); 25 k. Pirogue race; 50 k. Rocket festival.

46 Slaty-headed Parakeet

1966. Birds.
178 **46** 5 k. green, brown and red . . 70 20
179 – 15 k. brown, black & turq . . 80 40
180 – 20 k. sepia, ochre and blue . 1·10 60
181 – 45 k. blue, sepia and violet . 3·50 2·10
BIRDS: 15 k. White-crested laughing thrush; 20 k. Osprey; 45 k. Indian roller (or "blue jay").

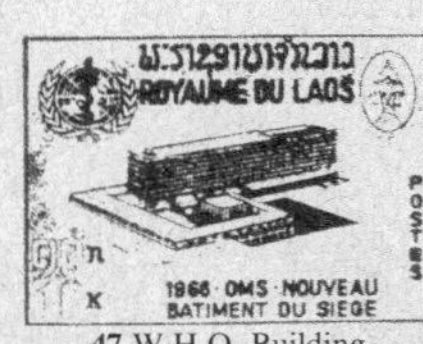

47 W.H.O. Building

1966. Inaug of W.H.O. Headquarters, Geneva.
182 **47** 10 k. blue and turquoise . . 20 20
183 25 k. green and red 25 20
184 50 k. black and blue 45 45

48 Ordination of Priests

1966. Laotian Ceremonies. Multicoloured.
186 10 k. Type **48** 25 15
187 25 k. Sand-hills ceremony . . . 25 20
188 30 k. "Wax pagoda" procession (vert) 35 30
189 40 k. "Sou-Khouan" ceremony (vert) 40 35

49 U.N.E.S.C.O. Emblem

1966. 20th Anniv of U.N.E.S.C.O.
190 **49** 20 k. orange and black . . . 15 15
191 30 k. blue and black 25 20
192 40 k. green and black . . . 30 25
193 60 k. red and black 45 40

50 Letter, Carrier Pigeon and Emblem

1966. International Correspondence Week.
195 **50** 5 k. blue, brown and red . . 20 15
196 20 k. purple, black & green . . 30 20
197 40 k. brown, red and blue . . 40 25
198 45 k. black, green & purple . . 45 30

51 Flooded Village **52** Carving, Siprapouthbat Pagoda

1967. Mekong Delta Flood Relief. Multicoloured.
200 20 k. + 5 k. Type **51** 25 25
201 40 k. + 10 k. Flooded market-place 40 40
202 60 k. + 15 k. Flooded airport . . 1·10 1·10

1967. Buddhist Art.
204 **52** 5 k. green and brown . . . 15 15
205 – 20 k. blue and sepia . . . 25 20
206 – 50 k. purple and sepia . . . 35 35
207 – 70 k. grey and brown . . . 45 35
DESIGNS (carvings in temple pagodas, Luang Prabang): 30 k. Visoun; 50 k. Xiengthong; 70 k. Visoun (different).

53 General Post Office

1967. Opening of New G.P.O. Building, Vientiane.
208 **53** 25 k. brown, green and pur . . 20 20
209 50 k. blue, green and slate . . 30 25
210 70 k. red, green and brown . . 50 35

54 Giant Snakehead **55** "Cassia fistula"

1967. Fishes.
211 **54** 20 k. black, bistre and blue . 35 30
212 – 35 k. slate, bistre and blue . 45 30
213 – 45 k. sepia, ochre and green . 75 35
214 – 60 k. black, bistre and green . 95 45
DESIGNS: 35 k. Giant catfish; 45 k. Tire-track spiny eel; 60 k. Bronze knifefish.

1967. Flowers.
215 **55** 30 k. yellow, green and mauve 25 25
216 – 55 k. red, green and orange . 35 30
217 – 75 k. red, green and blue . . 50 40
218 – 80 k. yellow, mauve and green 60 45
DESIGNS: 55 k. "Cucuma singulario"; 75 k. "Poinciana regia"; 80 k. "Plumeria acutifolia".

56 Harvesting

1967. 10th Anniv of Laotian Red Cross.
219 **56** 20 k. + 5 k. multicoloured . 25 25
220 50 k. + 10 k. multicoloured . 85 35
221 60 k. + 15 k. multicoloured . 55 55

57 Banded Krait

1967. Reptiles.
223 **57** 5 k. blue, yellow and green . 20 15
224 – 40 k. brown, bistre and green 25 20
225 – 100 k. chocolate, brown and green 75 50
226 – 200 k. black, brown and green 1·60 1·25
DESIGNS: 40 k. Marsh crocodile; 100 k. Pit viper; 200 k. Water monitor.

58 Human Rights Emblem

1968. Human Rights Year. Emblem in red and green.
227 **58** 20 k. green 20 20
228 30 k. brown 25 20
229 50 k. blue 50 35

59 Military Parade **60** W.H.O. Emblem

1968. Army Day. Multicoloured.
231 15 k. Type **59** (postage) . . . 20 15
232 20 k. Soldiers and tank in battle 30 15
233 60 k. Soldiers and Laotian flag 50 25
234 200 k. Parade of colours before National Assembly building (air) 75 55
235 300 k. As 200 k. . . . . . 1·25 70

1968. 20th Anniv of W.H.O.
237 **60** 15 k. brown, red & purple . 25 20
238 30 k. brown, green & blue . 30 20
239 70 k. brown, purple & red . 50 30
240 110 k. light brown, purple and brown 70 45
241 250 k. brown, blue & green 1·75 1·00

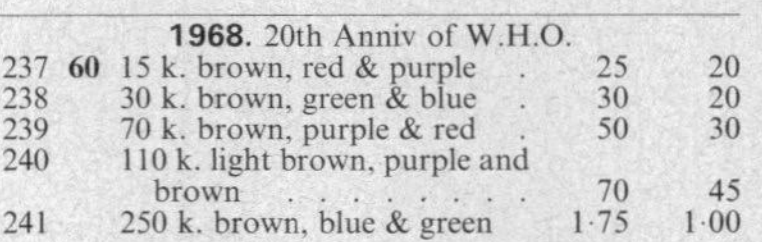

61 "Chrysochroa mnizechi" **62** "Mangifera indica"

1968. Beetles.
243 **61** 30 k. blue, yellow and green (postage) 40 25
244 – 50 k. black, orange & pur . 55 35
245 – 90 k. blue, orange & ochre 1·10 55
246 – 120 k. black & orange (air) 1·10 55
247 – 160 k. multicoloured . . . . 1·40 75
INSECTS—VERT: 50 k. "Aristobia approximator"; 90 k. "Eutaenia corbetti". HORIZ: 120 k. "Dorysthenes walkeri"; 160 k. "Megaloxantha bicolor".

1968. Laotian Fruits.
248 **62** 20 k. green, blue & black . 15 15
249 – 50 k. green, red and blue . 30 25
250 – 180 k. green, brown & orge 80 70
251 – 250 k. green, brown & yell 1·25 90
DESIGNS—VERT: 50 k. "Tamarindus indica". HORIZ: 180 k. "Artocarpus intregrifolia"; 250 k. "Citrullus vulgaris".

63 Hurdling

1968. Olympic Games, Mexico.
252 **63** 15 k. green, blue & brown . 20 15
253 – 80 k. brown, turq & blue . 40 30
254 – 100 k. blue, brown & green . 55 30
255 – 110 k. brown, red and blue . 65 40
DESIGNS: 80 k. Tennis; 100 k. Football; 110 k. High jumping.

64 Oriental Door, Wat Ongtu (detail)

1969. Wat Ongtu Temple.
256 **64** 150 k. gold, black and red . 1·10 60
257 – 200 k. gold, black and red . 1·75 90
DESIGN: 200 k. Central door, Wat Ongtu.

65 "Pharak praying to the Gods"

1969. Laotian "Ballet Royal". Designs showing dance characters. Multicoloured.
258 10 k. Type **65** (postage) 25 15
259 15 k. "Soukhib ordered to attack" 35 20
260 20 k. "Thotsakan reviewing troops" 40 30
261 30 k. "Nang Sida awaiting punishment" 60 35
262 40 k. "Pharam inspecting his troops" 75 35
263 60 k. "Hanuman about to rescue Nang Sida" . . . . . . 1·25 50
264 110 k. "Soudagnou battling with Thotsakan" (air) . . . . 1·75 1·25
265 300 k. "Pharam dancing with Thotsakkan" . . . . 3·75 2·25

66 Handicrafts Workshop, Vientiane

1969. 10th Anniv of I.L.O.
267 **66** 30 k. violet & purple (postage) 25 20
268 60 k. brown and green . . . 60 30
269 – 300 k. black & brown (air) 2·25 1·40
DESIGN: 300 k. Elephants moving logs.

67 Chinese Pangolin

1969. "Wild Animals" (1st series). Multicoloured.
270 15 k. Type **67** (postage) 30 20
271 30 k. Type **67** 30 25
272 70 k. Sun bear (air) 35 30
273 120 k. Common gibbon (vert) 75 50
274 150 k. Tiger 80 60
See also Nos. 300/3 and 331/5.

68 Royal Mausoleum, Luang Prabang

1969. 10th Death Anniv of King Sisavang Vong.
275 **68** 50 k. ochre, blue and green 60 40
276 – 70 k. ochre and lake . . . 70 40
DESIGN: 70 k. King Sisavang Vong (medallion).

69 "Lao Woman being Groomed" (Leguay)

1969. Air. Paintings by Marc Leguay (1st series). Multicoloured.
277 10 k. Type **69** . . . . 1·25 70
278 150 k. "Village Market" (horiz) 1·75 90
See also Nos. 285, 307/9 and 357/61.

70 Carved Capital, Wat Xiengthong

1970. Laotian Pagodas. Multicoloured.
279 70 k. Type **70** (postage) . . . 60 50
280 100 k. Library, Wat Sisaket (air) 90 40
281 120 k. Wat Xiengthong (horiz) 1·50 70

71 "Noon" Drum

1970. Laotian Drums.
282 **71** 30 k. mult (postage) 65 50
283 – 55 k. black, green & brown 1·00 65
284 – 125 k. brown, yellow and flesh (air) . . . . 1·75 1·00
DESIGNS—HORIZ: 55 k. Bronze drum. VERT: 125 k. Wooden drum.

1970. Air. Paintings by Marc Leguay (2nd series). As T **69**. Multicoloured.
285 150 k. "Banks of the Mekong" (horiz) . . . . 1·75 90

72 Franklin D. Roosevelt

1970. Air. 25th Death Anniv of Franklin D. Roosevelt (American statesman).
286 **72** 120 k. slate and green . . . 1·00 70

73 "Lenin explaining Electrification Plan" (L. Shmatko)

1970. Birth Centenary of Lenin.
287 **73** 30 k. multicoloured 35 25
288 70 k. multicoloured 45 40

1970. "Support for War Victims". Nos. 258/65 ("Ballet Royal") surch Soutien aux Victimes de la Guerre and premium.
289 10 k. + 5 k. mult (postage) . . 40 40
290 15 k. + 5 k. multicoloured . . 40 40
291 20 k. + 5 k. multicoloured . . 40 40
292 30 k. + 5 k. multicoloured . . 40 40
293 40 k. + 5 k. multicoloured . . 70 70
294 60 k. + 5 k. multicoloured . . 90 90
295 110 k. + 5 k. mult (air) . . . 1·75 1·75
296 300 k. + 5 k. multicoloured 2·75 2·75

75 Weaving Silk

1970. "EXPO 70" World Fair, Osaka, Japan. Laotian Silk Industry.
297 **75** 30 k. bl, brn & red (postage) 40 25
298 – 70 k. multicoloured 70 45
299 – 125 k. multicoloured (air) 85 70
DESIGNS: 70 k. Silk-spinning; 125 k. Winding ske

76 Wild Boar

77 Buddha, U.N. Emblem and New York H.Q.

1970. Wild Animals (2nd series).
300 **76** 20 k. brown & grn (postage) 45 25
301 – 60 k. brown and olive . . . 75 40
302 – 210 k. brown, red and yellow (air) . . . . 2·00 1·25
303 – 500 k. green, brown & orge 4·00 2·40
ANIMALS: 210 k. Leopard. 500 k. Gaur.

1970. 25th Anniv of U.N.O.
304 **77** 30 k. brown, mauve and blue (postage) 40 30
305 70 k. brown, blue and green . 60 50
306 – 125 k. multicoloured (air) . . 1·25 85
DESIGN—26 × 36 mm: 125 k. Nang Thorani ("Goddess of the Earth") and New York Headquarters.

1970. Air. Paintings by Marc Leguay (3rd series). As T **69**. Multicoloured.
307 100 k. "Village Track" 50 40
308 120 k. "Paddy-field in the Rainy Season" (horiz) 70 50
309 150 k. "Village Elder" 80 60

78 "Nakhanet"

1971. Laotian Mythology (1st series). Frescoes from Triumphal Arch, Vientiane. Multicoloured.
310 **78** 70 k. orange, brown and red (postage) 50 35
311 – 85 k. green, yellow & blue 60 45
312 – 125 k. multicoloured (air) 1·25 65
DESIGNS: As T **78**: 85 k. "Rahu". 49 × 36 mm: 125 k. "Underwater duel between Nang Matsa and Hanuman".
See also Nos. 352/4 and 385/7.

79 Silversmiths

1971. Laotian Traditional Crafts. Multicoloured.
313 30 k. Type **79** 20 20
314 50 k. Potters 40 20
315 70 k. Pirogue-builder (49 × 36 mm) 50 30

80 Laotian and African Children

1971. Racial Equality Year.
316 **80** 30 k. blue, red and green . . 25 15
317 – 60 k. violet, red and yellow 45 30
DESIGN: 60 k. Laotian dancers and musicians.

81 Buddhist Monk at That Luang

1971. 50th Anniv of Vientiane Rotary Club.
318 **81** 30 k. violet, brown & blue 35 20
319 – 70 k. grey, red and blue . . 50 35
DESIGN—VERT: 70 k. Laotian girl on "Dragon" staircase.

82 "Dendrobium agregatum"

83 Dancers from France and Laos

1971. Laotian Orchids. Multicoloured.
320 30 k. Type **82** (postage) 45 25
321 40 k. "Rynchostylis giganterum" 65 40
322 50 k. "Ascocentrum miniatur" (horiz) 70 40
323 60 k. "Paphiopedilum exul" . . 90 50
324 70 k. "Trichoglottis fasciata" (horiz) 95 65
325 80 k. Cattleya (horiz) . . . . . 1·10 65
326 125 k. Brazilian cattleya (horiz) (air) . . . . 1·75 80
327 150 k. "Vanda teres" (horiz) 1·90 1·10
Nos. 321, 323 and 325 are smaller, 22 × 36 or 36 × 22 mm. Nos. 326/7 are larger, 48 × 27 mm.

1971. Air. "Twin Cities" of St. Astier (France) and Keng-Kok (Laos).
328 **83** 30 k. brown and light brown . 20 15
329 70 k. purple and plum . . . 30 20
330 100 k. green & deep green . 55 35

84 Common Palm Civet

1971. Wild Animals (3rd series).
331 **84** 25 k. black, violet and blue (postage) 20 20
332 40 k. black, green and olive 30 30
333 – 50 k. orange and green . . . 45 40
334 – 85 k. brown, green & emerald 70 60
335 – 300 k. brown and green (air) 1·40 1·00
DESIGNS: 50 k. Lesser Malay chevrotain; 85 k. Sambar; 300 k. Javan rhinoceros.

85 Laotian Woman (design from 1952 issue)

1971. 20th Anniv of Laotian Stamps.
336 **85** 30 k. chocolate, brown and violet (postage) 20 20
337 – 40 k. multicoloured 20 20
338 – 50 k. black, flesh and blue . 35 25
339 – 125 k. violet, brn & grn (air) 70 50
DESIGNS—36 × 48 mm: 40 k. Violinist (As No. 64); 50 k. Rama (As No. 48); 125 k. "The Offertory" (As Type **16**).

86 "Sunset on the Mekong"

1971. Air. Paintings by Chamnane Prisayane. Mult.
341 125 k. Type **86** 55 45
342 150 k. "Quiet Morning at Ban Tane Pieo" 75 65

87 Children reading Book

1972. International Book Year.
343 **87** 30 k. green (postage) . . . 20 15
344 – 70 k. brown 30 25
345 – 125 k. violet (air) 70 45
DESIGNS—36 × 22 mm: 70 k. Laotian illustrating manuscript. 48 × 27 mm: 125 k. Father showing manuscripts to children.

88 Nam Ngum Dam and Obelisk

1972. 25th Anniv of U.N. Economic Commission for Asia and the Far East (E.C.A.F.E.). Multicoloured.

346		40 k. Type **88** (postage)	20	20
347		80 k. Type **88**	30	25
348		145 k. Lake and spill-way, Nam Ngum Dam (air)	80	50

89 "The Water-carrier"

1972. 25th Anniv of U.N.I.C.E.F. Drawings by Lao Schoolchildren. Multicoloured.

349		50 k. Type **89** (postage)	25	20
350		80 k. "Teaching Bamboo-weaving"	30	25
351		120 k. "Riding a Water-buffalo" (air)	70	45

90 "Nakharath"

1972. Air. Laotian Mythology (2nd series).

352	**90**	100 k. turquoise	40	30
353	–	120 k. lilac	70	45
354	–	150 k. brown	80	55

DESIGNS: 120 k. "Nang Kinnali"; 150 k. "Norasing".

91 Festival Offerings

1972. Air. That Luang Religious Festival.

355	**91**	110 k. brown	45	35
356	–	125 k. purple	65	50

DESIGN: 125 k. Festival procession.

1972. Air. Paintings by Marc Leguay (4th series). As T **69**. Multicoloured.

357		50 k. "In the Paddy Field" (detail)	25	20
358		50 k. "In the Paddy Field" (different detail)	25	20
359		70 k. "Village in the Rainy Season" (detail)	35	25
360		70 k. "Village in the Rainy Season" (different detail)	35	25
361		120 k. "Laotian Mother"	70	45

Nos. 357/8 and 359/60 when placed together form the complete painting in each case.

92 Attopeu Religious Costume

93 "Lion" Guardian, That Luang

1973. Regional Costumes.

362	**92**	40 k. yellow, mauve & brown (postage)	40	20
363	–	90 k. black, lake & brown	70	30
364	–	120 k. brown, sepia and mauve (air)	70	35
365	–	150 k. ochre, lake & brown	90	45

DESIGNS: 90 k. Phongsaly festival costume; 120 k. Luang Prabang wedding costume; 150 k. Vientiane evening dress.

1973. 55th Anniv of Lions International.

366	**93**	40 k. red, purple and blue	35	20
367		80 k. red, yellow and blue	55	35
368	–	150 k. multicoloured (air)	1·00	70

DESIGN—48 × 27 mm: 150 k. Lions emblems and statue of King Saysetthathirath, Vientiane.

94 Satellite passing Rahu

1973. Traditional and Modern Aspects of Space. Multicoloured.

369		80 k. Type **94**	35	20
370		150 k. Landing module and Laotian festival rocket	80	40

95 Dr. Gerhard Hansen and Map of Laos

1973. Centenary of Identification of Leprosy Bacillus by Hansen.

371	**95**	40 k. purple, dp pur & orge	45	30
372		80 k. purple, brown & yell	70	40

96 "Benediction"

97 "Nang Mekhala". (Goddess of the Sea)

1973. 25th Anniv of Laotian Boy Scouts Association.

373	**96**	70 k. yellow & brn (postage)	55	35
374	–	110 k. violet & orange (air)	55	20
375	–	150 k. blue, drab & brown	75	35

DESIGNS—48 × 27 mm: 110 k. Campfire entertainment; 150 k. Scouts helping flood victims, Vientiane, 1966.

1973. Air. Centenary of World Meteorological Organization.

376	**97**	90 k. lilac, red and brown	55	30
377	–	150 k. brown, red & lt brn	1·00	50

DESIGN—HORIZ: 150 k. "Chariot of the Sun".

99 Interpol H.Q., Paris

1973. 50th Anniv of Int Criminal Police Organization (Interpol).

382	**99**	40 k. blue (postage)	30	20
383		80 k. brown and light brown	35	20
384	–	150 k. violet, red and green (air)	80	35

DESIGN—48 × 27 mm: 150 k. Woman in opium-poppy field.

100 "Phra Sratsvady"

1974. Air. Laotian Mythology (3rd series).

385	**100**	100 k. red, brown & lilac	70	30
386	–	110 k. brown, lilac & red	85	40
387	–	150 k. violet, brown and light brown	1·25	60

DESIGNS: 110 k. "Phra Indra"; 150 k. "Phra Phrom".

101 Boy and Postbox

102 "Eranthemum nervosum"

1974. Centenary of U.P.U.

388	**101**	70 k. brown, green and blue (postage)	40	25
389		80 k. brown, blue & green	50	30
390	–	200 k. brown & red (air)	1·75	1·00

DESIGN—48 × 36 mm: 200 k. Laotian girls with letters, and U.P.U. Monument, Berne (Type **105**).

1974. Laotian Flora.

391	**102**	30 k. violet & grn (postage)	35	25
392	–	50 k. multicoloured	50	30
393	–	80 k. red, green & brown	80	40
394	–	500 k. green & brown (air)	3·50	1·90

DESIGNS—As T **102**: HORIZ: 50 k. Water lily; 80 k. Red silk-cotton. 36 × 36 mm: 500 k. Pitcher plant.

103 Mekong Ferry carrying Bus

1974. Laotian Transport.

395	**103**	25 k. brown & orge (postage)	45	20
396	–	90 k. brown and bistre	1·10	70
397	–	250 k. brown & green (air)	2·00	1·25

DESIGNS—VERT: 90 k. Bicycle rickshaw. HORIZ: 250 k. Mekong house boat.

104 Marconi, and Laotians with Transistor Radio

1974. Birth Centenary of Guglielmo Marconi (radio pioneer).

398	**104**	60 k. grey, green & brown (postage)	30	20
399		90 k. grey, brown & green	45	30
400	–	200 k. blue & brown (air)	1·50	60

DESIGN: 200 k. Communications methods.

105 U.P.U. Monument and Laotian Girls

1974. Air. Centenary of U.P.U.

401	**105**	500 k. lilac and red	2·25	1·75

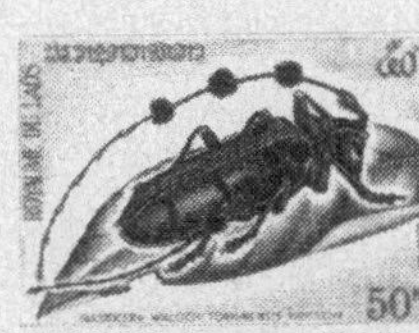
106 "Diastocera wallichi"

1974. Beetles.

403	**106**	50 k. brown, black and green (postage)	55	45
404	–	90 k. black, turq & grn	1·10	60
405	–	100 k. black, orange & brn	1·25	85
406	–	110 k. violet, red & grn (air)	1·25	55

DESIGNS: 90 k. "Macrochenus isabellunus"; 100 k. "Purpuricenus malaccensis"; 110 k. "Sternocera multipunctata".

107 Pagoda and Sapphire

1974. "Mineral Riches".

407	**107**	100 k. brown, green & blue	40	30
408	–	110 k. brown, blue & yellow	50	30

DESIGN: 110 k. Gold-panning and necklace.

108 King Savang Vatthana, Prince Souvanna Phouma and Prince Souvanouvong

1975. 1st Anniv (1974) of Laotian Peace Treaty.

409	**108**	80 k. brown, ochre & grn	30	25
410		300 k. brown, ochre & pur	70	50
411		420 k. brown, ochre and turquoise	80	60

109 Fortune-teller's Chart

1975. Chinese New Year ("Year of the Rabbit").

413	**109**	40 k. brown and green	35	20
414	–	200 k. black, brown and green	1·10	50
415	–	350 k. brown, green and blue	2·00	90

DESIGNS—HORIZ: 200 k. Fortune-teller. VERT: 350 k. Woman riding hare.

110 U.N. Emblem and Frieze

112

1975. International Women's Year.

416	**110**	100 k. blue and turquoise	40	25
417	–	200 k. orange and green	70	35

DESIGN: 200 k. I.W.Y. Emblem.

1975. "Pravet Sandone" Religious Festival.

420	**112**	80 k. multicoloured	35	20
421	–	110 k. multicoloured	45	25
422	–	120 k. multicoloured	55	45
423	–	130 k. multicoloured	90	50

DESIGNS: 110 k. to 130 k. various legends.

113 Buddha and Stupas

1975. U.N.E.S.C.O. Campaign for Preservation of Borobudur Temple (in Indonesia).

424	**113**	100 k. green, blue & brn	30	25
425	–	200 k. ochre, green & brn	55	30

DESIGN: 200 k. Temple sculptures.

114 Laotian Arms

115 Thathiang, Vien-Tran

1976. Multicoloured, background colour given.

427	**114**	1 k. blue	10	10
428		2 k. mauve	10	10
429		5 k. green	15	10
430		10 k. violet	20	20
431		200 k. orange	1·00	1·00

1976. Pagodas. Multicoloured.

433 1 k. Type **115** 10 10
434 2 k. Phonsi, Luang Prabang 10 10
435 30 k. Type **115** 10 10
436 80 k. As 2 k. 40 30
437 100 k. As 2 k. 50 45
438 300 k. Type **115** 1·50 90

116 Silversmith

1977. Laotian Crafts. Multicoloured.

440 1 k. Type **116** 10 10
441 2 k. Weaver 10 10
442 20 k. Potter 25 25
443 50 k. Basket-weaver (vert) 30 25

117 Gubarev, Grechko and "Salyut" Space Station

1977. 60th Anniv of Russian Revolution. Multicoloured.

445 5 k. Type **117** 10 10
446 20 k. Lenin 10 10
447 50 k. As 20 k. 20 20
448 60 k. Type **117** 35 25
449 100 k. Government Palace, Vientiane, and Kremlin, Moscow (horiz) 70 50
450 250 k. As 100 k. 1·60 1·25

118 Laotian Arms **119** Soldiers with Flag

1978.

452 **118** 5 k. yellow and black 10 10
453 10 k. sepia and black 10 10
454 50 k. purple and black 15 10
455 100 k. green and black 50 25
456 250 k. violet and black 1·25 70

1978. Army Day. Multicoloured.

457 20 k. Type **119** 10 10
458 40 k. Soldiers attacking village (horiz) 15 15
459 300 k. Anti-aircraft guns 1·60 75

120 Marchers with Banner **121** Printed Circuit and Map of Laos

1978. National Day. Multicoloured.

460 20 k. Type **120** 10 10
461 50 k. Women with flag 25 15
462 400 k. Dancer 1·75 75

1979. World Telecommunications Day.

464 **121** 30 k. orange, brown & sil 10 10
465 – 250 k. multicoloured 70 50

DESIGN: 250 k. Printed circuit, map of Laos and transmitter tower.

122 Woman posting Letter

1979. 15th Anniv of Asian-Oceanic Postal Union. Multicoloured.

466 5 k. Type **122** 10 10
467 10 k. Post Office counter 10 10
468 80 k. As 10 k. 40 25
469 100 k. Type **122** 50 30

123 Children playing Ball

1979. International Year of the Child (1st issue). Multicoloured. Without gum.

470 20 k. Type **123** 10 10
471 50 k. Children at school (horiz) 25 15
472 200 k. Mother feeding child 1·50 45
473 500 k. Nurse immunising child 4·25 1·10

124 Elephant, Buffalo and Pirogues

1979. Transport. Multicoloured.

475 5 k. Type **124** 15 10
476 10 k. Buffalo carts 15 10
477 70 k. As No. 476 50 15
478 500 k. Type **124** 2·25 1·25

125 Dancing Child

1979. International Year of the Child (2nd issue). Multicoloured. Without gum.

479 100 k. Children playing musical instruments (horiz) 40 25
480 200 k. Child releasing dove 65 40
481 600 k. Type **125** 2·25 1·25

126 Forest and Paddy Field

1980. 5th Anniv of Republic (1st issue) and 25th Anniv of People's Front. Mult. Without gum.

483 30 c. Type **126** 15 10
484 50 c. Classroom and doctor examining baby (horiz) 20 10
485 1 k. Three women 50 20
486 2 k. Dam and electricity pylons (horiz) 1·10 65

127 Lenin Reading

1980. 110th Birth Anniv of Lenin. Multicoloured.

488 1 k. Type **127** 15 10
489 2 k. Lenin writing 35 15
490 3 k. Lenin and Red Flag (vert) 55 20
491 4 k. Lenin making speech (vert) 90 30

MINIMUM PRICE

The minimum price quoted is 10p which represents a handling charge rather than a basis for valuing common stamps. For further notes about prices see introductory pages.

128 Workers in Field

1980. 5th Anniv of Republic (2nd issue). Multicoloured. Without gum.

493 50 c. Type **128** 10 10
494 1 k. 60 Loading logs on lorry and elephant hauling logs 30 15
495 4 k. 60 Veterinary workers tending animals 70 35
496 5 k. 40 Workers in paddy field 1·00 45

129 Emblems of Industry, Technology, Transport, Sport and Art

1981. 26th P.C.U.S. (Communist Party) Congress. Multicoloured.

498 60 c. Type **129** 15 10
499 4 k. 60 Communist star breaking manacles and globe 80 30
500 5 k. Laurel branch and broken bomb 1·00 35

131 Player heading Ball **132** Disabled Person on Telephone

1981. World Cup Football Championship, Spain (1982) (1st issue). Multicoloured.

503 1 k. Type **131** 20 10
504 2 k. Receiving ball 35 10
505 3 k. Passing ball 55 20
506 4 k. Goalkeeper diving for ball (horiz) 80 25
507 5 k. Dribbling 1·10 40
508 6 k. Kicking ball 1·50 50

See also Nos. 545/50.

1981. International Year of Disabled Persons. Multicoloured.

509 3 k. Type **132** 50 20
510 5 k. Disabled teacher 1·10 40
511 12 k. Person in wheelchair mending net 3·00 60

133 Wild Cat

1981. Wild Cats. Multicoloured.

512 10 c. Type **133** 10 10
513 20 c. Fishing cat 10 10
514 30 c. Caracal 10 10
515 40 c. Clouded leopard 15 10
516 50 c. Flat-headed cat 15 10
517 9 k. Jungle cat 3·00 70

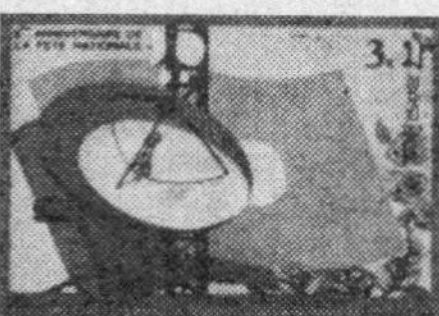

134 Dish Aerial and Flag

1981. 6th National Day Festival. Multicoloured.

518 3 k. Type **134** 50 30
519 4 k. Soldier and flag 65 40
520 5 k. Girls presenting flowers to soldier, flag and map of Laos 95 50

135 Indian Elephant

1982. Indian Elephant. Multicoloured.

521 1 k. Type **135** 20 10
522 2 k. Elephant carrying log 45 15
523 3 k. Elephant with passengers 70 25
524 4 k. Elephant in trap 90 35
525 5 k. Elephant and young 1·25 35
526 5 k. 50 Herd of elephants 1·60 50

136 Laotian Wrestling

1982. Wrestling.

527 **136** 50 c. multicoloured 10 10
528 – 1 k. 20 multicoloured 20 10
529 – 2 k. multicoloured 35 20
530 – 2 k. 50 multicoloured 55 30
531 – 4 k. multicoloured 80 35
532 – 5 k. multicoloured 1·40 45

DESIGNS: 1 k. 20 to 5 k. Various wrestling scenes.

137 "Nymphaea zanzibariensis"

1982. Water Lilies. Multicoloured.

533 30 c. Type **137** 10 10
534 40 c. "Nelumbo nucifera" "Gaertn Rose" 10 10
535 60 c. "Nymphaea rosea" 10 10
536 3 k. "Nymphaea nouchali" 60 35
537 4 k. "Nymphaea" White 95 40
538 7 k. "Nelumbo nucifera" "Gaertn White" 1·90 50

138 Barn Swallow

1982. Birds. Multicoloured.

539 50 c. Type **138** 30 15
540 1 k. Hoopoe 60 40
541 2 k. Common kingfisher 2·25 80
542 3 k. Black-naped blue monarch 1·90 80
543 4 k. Grey wagtail (horiz) 2·10 1·25
544 10 k. Long-tailed tailor bird (horiz) 7·25 2·40

139 Football

1982. World Cup Football Championship, Spain (2nd issue).
545 **139** 1 k. multicoloured 20 10
546 – 2 k. multicoloured 40 10
547 – 3 k. multicoloured 55 20
548 – 4 k. multicoloured 70 25
549 **139** 5 k. multicoloured . . . . 1·10 40
550 – 6 k. multicoloured . . . . 1·40 45
DESIGNS: 2 k. to 6 k. Various football scenes.

140 "Herona marathus"

1982. Butterflies. Multicoloured.
552 1 k. Type **140** 20 10
553 2 k. "Neptis paraka" 40 20
554 3 k. "Euripus halitherses" . . . 70 30
555 4 k. "Lebadea martha" . . . . 1·10 40
556 5 k. "Iton semamora" (42 × 26 mm) . . . . 1·75 75
557 6 k. Common Palm Fly (59 × 41 mm) . . . . 2·00 1·00

142 River Raft

1982. River Craft. Multicoloured.
559 50 c. Type **142** 10 10
560 60 c. River sampan 15 10
561 1 k. River house boat 25 10
562 2 k. River passenger steamer . . 50 25
563 3 k. River ferry 70 30
564 8 k. Self-propelled barge . . . 1·90 70

143 Vat Chanh

1982. Pagodas. Multicoloured.
565 50 c. Type **143** 10 10
566 60 c. Vat Inpeng 15 10
567 1 k. Vat Dong Mieng 25 10
568 2 k. Ho Tay 50 20
569 3 k. Vat Ho Pha Keo 70 25
570 8 k. Vat Sisaket . . . . 1·90 60

1982. Various stamps optd **1982**.
571 **114** 1 k. multicoloured . . . .
572 **116** 1 k. multicoloured . . . .
573 – 2 k. multicoloured (441) . .
574 **117** 5 k. multicoloured . . . .
575 **118** 5 k. yellow and black . . .
576 **122** 5 k. multicoloured . . . .
577 **124** 5 k. multicoloured . . . .
578 – 10 k. multicoloured (467) .
579 – 10 k. multicoloured (476) .
580 – 20 k. multicoloured (446) .
581 **119** 20 k. multicoloured . . . .
582 **121** 30 k. orange, brown and silver . . . .
583 – 40 k. multicoloured (458) .
584 – 50 k. multicoloured (443) .
585 – 70 k. multicoloured (477) .
586 – 80 k. multicoloured (468) .
587 **122** 100 k. multicoloured . . .
588 **114** 200 k. multicoloured . . .
589 **121** 250 k. multicoloured . . .

145 Poodle

1982. Dogs. Multicoloured.
591 50 c. Type **145** 10 10
592 60 c. Samoyed 10 10
593 1 k. Boston terrier 25 10
594 2 k. Cairn terrier 65 20
595 3 k. Chihuahua 90 25
596 8 k. Bulldog . . . . 2·50 60

146 Woman watering Crops

1982. World Food Day. Multicoloured.
597 7 k. Type **146** . . . . 1·40 45
598 8 k. Woman transplanting rice 1·75 55

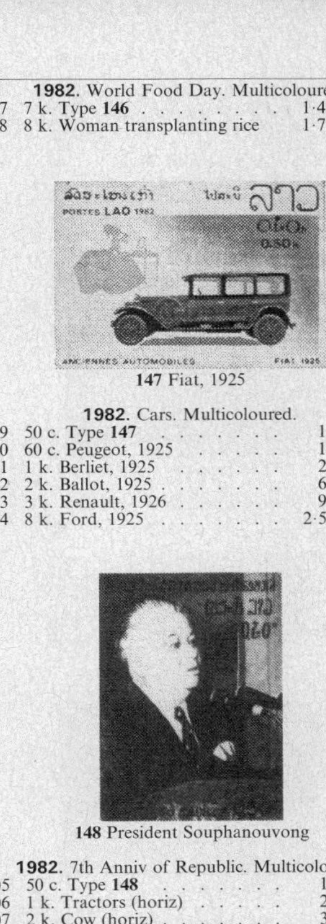

147 Fiat, 1925

1982. Cars. Multicoloured.
599 50 c. Type **147** 10 10
600 60 c. Peugeot, 1925 . . . . . 10 10
601 1 k. Berliet, 1925 . . . . . . 25 10
602 2 k. Ballot, 1925 . . . . . . 65 20
603 3 k. Renault, 1926 . . . . . 90 25
604 8 k. Ford, 1925 . . . . 2·50 60

148 President Souphanouvong

1982. 7th Anniv of Republic. Multicoloured.
605 50 c. Type **148** 10 10
606 1 k. Tractors (horiz) 25 10
607 2 k. Cow (horiz) 35 20
608 3 k. Lorry passing dish aerial (horiz) 50 35
609 4 k. Nurse examining child . . 75 35
610 5 k. Classroom (horiz) 95 45
611 6 k. Dancer . . . . 1·40 50

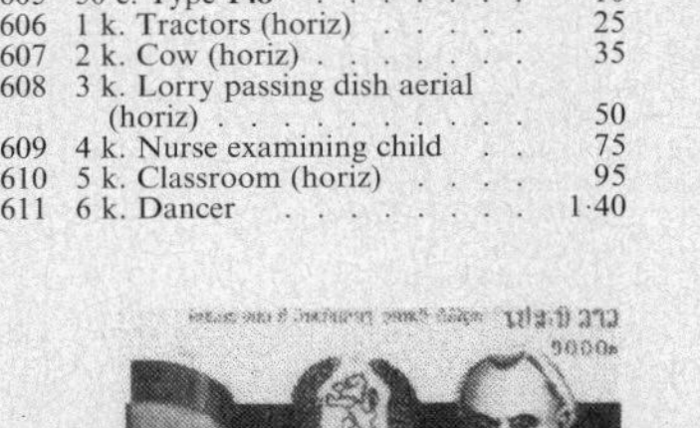

149 Dimitrov, Flag and Arms of Bulgaria

1982. Birth Centenary of Georgi Dimitrov (Bulgarian statesman).
612 **149** 10 k. multicoloured . . . . 1·90 1·25

150 Kremlin and Arms of U.S.S.R.

151 Hurdling

1982. 60th Anniv of U.S.S.R. Multicoloured.
613 3 k. Type **150** 60 40
614 4 k. Doves and maps of U.S.S.R. and Laos 90 70

1983. Olympic Games, Los Angeles (1984) (1st issue). Multicoloured.
616 50 c. Type **151** 10 10
617 1 k. Javelin 20 10
618 2 k. Basketball 40 15
619 3 k. Diving 60 25
620 4 k. Gymnastics 80 40
621 10 k. Weightlifting . . . . . . 2·25 60
See also Nos. 708/14.

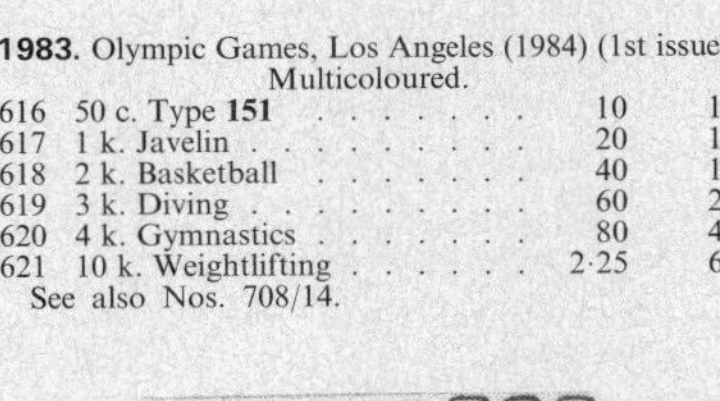

152 Bucking Horse

1983. Horses. Multicoloured.
623 50 c. Type **152** 10 10
624 1 k. Rearing black horse . . . 20 10
625 2 k. Trotting brown horse . . . 40 15
626 3 k. Dappled grey horse . . . 65 25
627 4 k. Wild horse crossing snow . 90 40
628 10 k. Horse in paddock . . . . 2·50 60

153 "St. Catherine of Alexandria"

154 A. Gubarev (Soviet) and V. Remek (Czechoslovak)

1983. 500th Birth Anniv of Raphael (artist). Multicoloured.
629 50 c. Type **153** 10 10
630 1 k. "Adoration of the Kings" . 20 10
631 2 k. "Madonna of the Grand Duke" 40 15
632 3 k. "St. George and the Dragon" 65 25
633 4 k. "The Vision of Ezekiel" . 90 35
634 10 k. "Adoration of the Kings" (different) . . . . 2·50 60

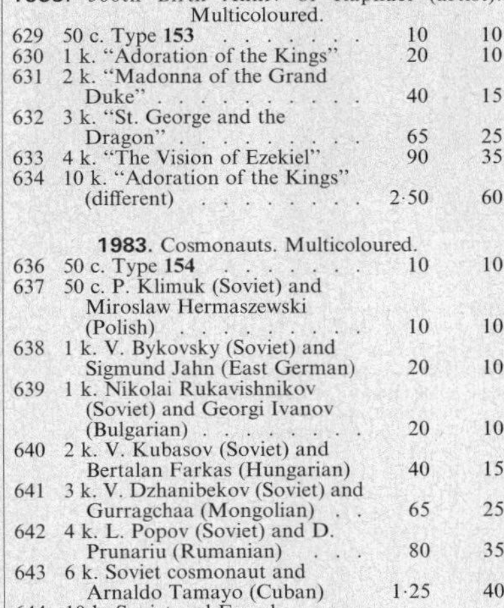

1983. Cosmonauts. Multicoloured.
636 50 c. Type **154** 10 10
637 50 c. P. Klimuk (Soviet) and Miroslaw Hermaszewski (Polish) 10 10
638 1 k. V. Bykovsky (Soviet) and Sigmund Jahn (East German) 20 10
639 1 k. Nikolai Rukavishnikov (Soviet) and Georgi Ivanov (Bulgarian) 20 10
640 2 k. V. Kubasov (Soviet) and Bertalan Farkas (Hungarian) 40 15
641 3 k. V. Dzhanibekov (Soviet) and Gurragchaa (Mongolian) . . 65 25
642 4 k. L. Popov (Soviet) and D. Prunariu (Rumanian) . . . 80 35
643 6 k. Soviet cosmonaut and Arnaldo Tamayo (Cuban) 1·25 40
644 10 k. Soviet and French cosmonauts . . . . 2·40 60

155 Jacques Charles's Hydrogen Balloon, 1783

1983. Bicentenary of Manned Flight. Mult.
646 50 c. Type **155** 10 10
647 1 k. Blanchard and Jeffries' balloon, 1785 . . . . . . 20 10
648 2 k. Vincenzo Lunardi's balloon (London–Ware flight), 1784 . 40 15
649 3 k. Modern hot-air balloon over city 75 25
650 4 k. Massed balloon ascent, 1890 80 30
651 10 k. Auguste Piccard's stratosphere balloon "F.N.R.S.", 1931 . . . . . 2·50 60

157 "Dendrobium sp."

1983. Flowers. Multicoloured.
654 1 k. Type **157** 20 10
655 2 k. "Aerides odoratum" . . . 40 15
656 3 k. "Dendrobium aggregatum" . 70 25
657 4 k. "Dendrobium" 80 30
658 5 k. "Moschatum" . . . . . . 1·00 40
659 6 k. "Dendrobium sp." (different) . . . . 1·25 45

158 Downhill Skiing

1983. Winter Olympic Games, Sarajevo (1984) (1st issue). Multicoloured.
660 50 c. Type **158** 10 10
661 1 k. Slalom 25 10
662 2 k. Ice hockey 50 15
663 3 k. Speed skating 75 25
664 4 k. Ski jumping . . . . . . 1·00 30
665 10 k. Luge . . . . 2·40 80
See also Nos. 696/702.

160 Clown Knifefish

1983. Fishes of Mekong River. Multicoloured.
668 1 k. Type **160** 30 15
669 2 k. Common carp 65 25
670 3 k. Lesser Mekong catfish . . 1·00 45
671 4 k. Giant barb . . . . 1·10 50
672 5 k. Black shark . . . . 1·50 70
673 6 k. Nile mouthbrooder . . . . 2·00 75

161 Magellan and "Vitoria"

1983. Explorers and their Ships. Multicoloured.
674 1 k. Type **161** 50 20
675 2 k. Jacques Cartier and "Grande Hermine" 90 30
676 3 k. Columbus and "Santa Maria" . . . . 1·40 50
677 4 k. Pedro Alvares Cabral and "El Ray" . . . . 1·50 60
678 5 k. Cook and H.M.S. "Resolution" . . . . . . 2·10 80
679 6 k. Charcot and "Pourquoi-pas?" . . . . 2·40 90
No. 679 is wrongly inscribed "Cabot".

162 Tabby Cat

1983. Domestic Cats. Multicoloured.
680 1 k. Type **162** 20 10
681 2 k. Long-haired Persian . . . 40 15
682 3 k. Siamese 65 25
683 4 k. Burmese 75 30
684 5 k. Persian . . . . 1·00 40
685 6 k. Tortoiseshell . . . . . . 1·25 45

1983. Nos. 430 and 466 optd **1983**.
685a **122** 5 k. multicoloured . . . .
685b **114** 10 k. multicoloured . . .

163 Marx, Book, Sun and Signature

1983. Death Centenary of Karl Marx. Mult.
686 1 k. Marx, dove, globe and flags 30 10
687 4 k. Type **163** 90 35
688 6 k. Marx and flags . . . . . 1·60 65

164 Elephant dragging Log

1983. 8th Anniv of Republic. Multicoloured.
689 1 k. Type **164** 30 10
690 4 k. Cattle and pig (horiz) . . . 90 35
691 6 k. Crops . . . . 1·60 65

165 Carrier Pigeon and Telex Machine

1983. World Communications Year. Multicoloured.

692 50 c. Type **165** 10 10
693 1 k. Early telephone, handset and receiver 25 10
694 4 k. Television tube and aerial 80 35
695 6 k. Satellite and dish aerial 1·50 55

166 Ice Skating 167 Tiger

1984. Winter Olympic Games, Sarajevo (2nd issue). Multicoloured.

696 50 c. Type **166** 10 10
697 1 k. Speed skating 30 10
698 2 k. Biathlon 40 15
699 3 k. Luge (horiz) 80 30
700 4 k. Downhill skiing (horiz) 95 35
701 5 k. Ski jumping 1·40 45
702 6 k. Slalom 1·60 55

1984. Endangered Animals. The Tiger. Mult.

704 25 c. Type **167** 10 10
705 25 c. Tigers (horiz) 10 10
706 3 k. Tiger and cubs (horiz) 90 30
707 4 k. Tiger cubs 1·10 40

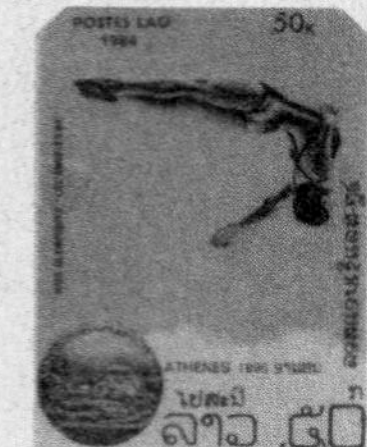

168 Diving

1984. Olympic Games, Los Angeles (2nd issue). Multicoloured.

708 50 c. Type **168** 10 10
709 1 k. Volleyball 25 10
710 2 k. Running 40 15
711 4 k. Basketball 85 25
712 5 k. Judo 1·10 35
713 6 k. Football 1·50 40
714 7 k. Gymnastics 1·75 50

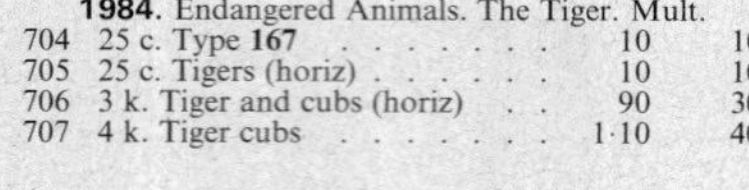

169 Tuned Drums

1984. Musical Instruments. Multicoloured.

716 1 k. Type **169** 20 10
717 2 k. Xylophone 35 15
718 3 k. Pair of drums 70 25
719 4 k. Hand drum 90 25
720 5 k. Barrel drum 1·10 35
721 6 k. Pipes and string instrument 1·75 55

170 National Flag 171 Chess Game

1984. National Day. Multicoloured.

722 60 c. Type **170** 15 10
723 1 k. National arms 35 10
724 2 k. As No. 723 50 20

1984. 60th Anniv of World Chess Federation. Multicoloured.

725 50 c. Type **171** 10 10
726 1 k. Renaissance game from "The Three Ages of Man" (miniature attr. to Estienne Porchier) 25 10
727 2 k. Woman teaching girls 40 15
728 2 k. Margrave Otto IV of Brandenburg playing chess with his wife 40 15
729 3 k. Four men at chessboard 75 30
730 4 k. Two women playing 1·00 35
731 8 k. Two men playing 2·25 55

Nos. 725, 727 and 729/31 show illustrations from King Alfonso X's "Book of Chess, Dice and Tablings".

172 "Cardinal Nino de Guevara" (El Greco) 173 "Adonis aestivalis"

1984. "Espana 84" International Stamp Exhibition, Madrid. Multicoloured.

733 50 c. Type **172** 10 10
734 1 k. "Gaspar de Guzman, Duke of Olivares, on Horseback" (Velazquez) 25 10
735 2 k. "The Annunciation" (Murillo) 40 15
736 2 k. "Portrait of a Lady" (Zurbaran) 40 15
737 3 k. "The Family of Charles IV" (Goya) 75 30
738 4 k. "Two Harlequins" (Picasso) 1·00 35
739 8 k. "Abstract" (Miro) 2·25 55

1984. Woodland Flowers. Multicoloured.

741 50 c. Type **173** 10 10
742 1 k. "Alpinia speciosa" 25 10
743 2 k. "Cassia lechenaultiana" 40 15
744 2 k. "Aeschynanthus speciosus" 40 15
745 3 k. "Datura meteloides" 75 30
746 4 k. "Quamoclit pennata" 95 35
747 8 k. "Commelina benghalensis" 2·25 55

174 Nazzaro

1984. 19th Universal Postal Union Congress Philatelic Salon, Hamburg. Cars. Multicoloured.

748 50 c. Type **174** 10 10
749 1 k. Daimler 25 10
750 2 k. Delage 40 15
751 2 k. Fiat "S 57/14B" 40 15
752 3 k. Bugatti 75 30
753 4 k. Itala 1·10 35
754 8 k. Blitzen Benz 2·25 55

175 "Madonna and Child"

1984. 450th Death Anniv of Correggio (artist). Multicoloured.

756 50 c. Type **175** 10 10
757 1 k. Detail showing horsemen resting 25 10
758 2 k. "Madonna and Child" (different) 40 15
759 2 k. "Mystical Marriage of St. Catherine" 40 15
760 3 k. "Four Saints" 75 30
761 4 k. "Noli me Tangere" 95 35
762 8 k. "Christ bids Farewell to the Virgin May" 1·90 55

176 "Luna 1"

1984. Space Exploration. Multicoloured.

764 50 c. Type **176** 10 10
765 1 k. "Luna 2" 25 10
766 2 k. "Luna 3" 40 15
767 2 k. Kepler and "Sputnik 2" 40 15
768 3 k. Newton & Lunokhod 2 75 30
769 4 k. Jules Verne and "Luna 13" 1·00 35
770 8 k. Copernicus and space station 2·10 60

177 Malaclemys Terrapin

1984. Reptiles. Multicoloured.

771 50 c. Type **177** 10 10
772 1 k. Banded krait 25 10
773 2 k. Indian python (vert) 40 15
774 2 k. Reticulated python 40 15
775 3 k. Tokay gecko 80 30
776 4 k. "Natrix subminiata" (snake) 1·10 40
777 8 k. Dappled ground gecko 2·40 65

178 Greater Glider

1984. "Ausipex 84" International Stamp Exhibition, Melbourne. Marsupials. Multicoloured.

778 50 c. Type **178** 10 10
779 1 k. Platypus 25 10
780 2 k. Southern hairy-nosed wombat ("Lasiorhinus latifrons") 40 15
781 2 k. Tasmanian devil ("Sarcophilus harrisii") 40 15
782 3 k. Thylacine 75 30
783 4 k. Tiger cat 1·00 35
784 8 k. Wallaby 2·10 60

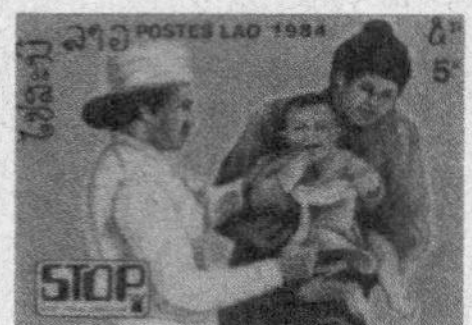

179 Nurse with Mother and Child

1984. Anti-poliomyelitis Campaign. Multicoloured.

786 5 k. Type **179** 1·10 50
787 6 k. Doctor inoculating child 1·40 55

180 Dragon Stair-rail

1984. Laotian Art. Multicoloured.

788 50 c. Type **180** 10 10
789 1 k. Capital of column 25 10
790 2 k. Decorative panel depicting god 40 15
791 2 k. Decorative panel depicting leaves 40 15
792 3 k. Stylized leaves (horiz) 70 30
793 4 k. Triangular flower decoration (horiz) 1·00 35
794 8 k. Circular lotus flower decoration 1·90 60

181 River House Boats

1984. 9th Anniv of Republic. Multicoloured.

795 1 k. Type **181** 45 15
796 2 k. Passengers boarding Fokker Friendship airliner 50 20
797 4 k. Building a bridge 1·10 45
798 10 k. Building a road 2·50 1·00

182 Players with Ball

1985. World Cup Football Championship, Mexico (1986) (1st issue). Multicoloured.

799 50 c. Type **182** 10 10
800 1 k. Heading the ball 25 10
801 2 k. Defending the ball 45 15
802 3 k. Running with ball 70 20
803 4 k. Taking possession of ball 1·10 35
804 5 k. Heading the ball (different) 1·40 45
805 6 k. Saving a goal 1·75 55

See also Nos. 868/74.

183 Motor Cycle

1985. Centenary of Motor Cycle. Multicoloured.

807 50 c. Type **183** 10 10
808 1 k. Gnome Rhone, 1920 25 10
809 2 k. F.N. "M67C", 1928 45 15
810 3 k. Indian "Chief", 1930 70 20
811 4 k. Rudge Multi, 1914 1·10 35
812 5 k. Honda "Benly J", 1953 1·40 45
813 6 k. CZ, 1938 1·75 55

1985. Various stamps optd **1985**.

813a – 40 k. multicoloured (458)
813b – 50 k. multicoloured (443)
813c – 50 k. multicoloured (447)
813d – 70 k. multicoloured (477)
813e – 80 k. multicoloured (468)
813f – 100 k. multicoloured (449)
813g **122** 100 k. multicoloured
813h **114** 200 k. multicoloured
813i – 250 k. multicoloured (450)
813j **118** 250 k. violet and black
813k **121** 250 k. multicoloured
813m – 300 k. multicoloured (459)

184 Fly Agaric

1985. Fungi. Multicoloured.

814 50 c. Type **184** 15 10
815 1 k. Cep 30 10
816 2 k. Shaggy ink cap ("Coprinus comatus") 70 20
817 2 k. The blusher ("Amanita rubescens") 70 20
818 3 k. Downy boletus 1·25 30
819 4 k. Parasol mushroom 2·10 45
820 8 k. Brown roll-rim 3·25 90

184a Battle Plan, Kursk, and Tanks

1985. 40th Anniv of End of Second World War. Multicoloured.

820a 1 k. Type **184a** 30 15
820b 2 k. Monument and military parade, Red Square, Moscow 60 25
820c 4 k. Street battle and battle plan, Stalingrad 1·25 40
820d 5 k. Battle plan and Reichstag, Berlin 1·50 50
820e 6 k. Soviet Memorial, Berlin-Treptow, and military parade at Brandenburg Gate 1·75 60

185 Lenin reading "Pravda"

1985. 115th Birth Anniv of Lenin. Multicoloured.

821 1 k. Type **185** 25 10
822 2 k. Lenin (vert) 45 30
823 10 k. Lenin addressing meeting (vert) 2·40 1·50

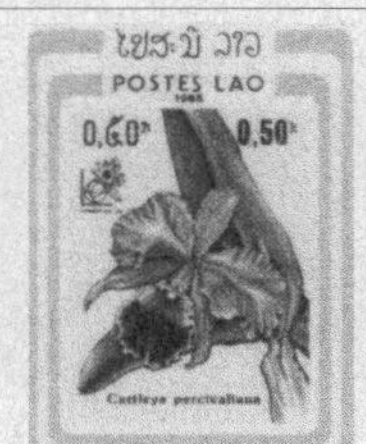

186 "Cattleya percivaliana"

1985. "Argentina '85" International Stamp Exhibition, Buenos Aires. Orchids. Multicoloured.

824 50 c. Type **186** 10 10
825 1 k. "Odontoglossum luteo-purpureum" 25 10
826 2 k. "Cattleya lueddemanniana" 45 15
827 2 k. "Maxillaria sanderiana" 45 15
828 3 k. "Miltonia vexillaria" . . . 70 25
829 4 k. "Oncidium varicosum" . . 1·10 35
830 8 k. "Cattleya dowiana" . . . 2·50 70

187 Rhesus Macaque **188** "Saturn" Rocket on Launch Pad

1985. Mammals. Multicoloured.

832 2 k. Type **187** 45 15
833 3 k. Kouprey 70 25
834 4 k. Porcupine (horiz) . . . . 1·10 35
835 5 k. Asiatic black bear (horiz) 1·40 45
836 10 k. Chinese pangolin . . . . 2·75 90

1985. 10th Anniv of "Soyuz"–"Apollo" Space Link. Multicoloured.

837 50 c. Type **188** 10 10
838 1 k. Soviet rocket on launch pad 25 10
839 2 k. "Apollo" approaching "Soyuz 19" (horiz) 50 15
840 2 k. "Soyuz 19" approaching "Apollo" (horiz) 50 15
841 3 k. "Apollo" and crew T. Stafford, V. Brand and and D. Stayton (horiz) 80 25
842 4 k. "Soyuz 19" and crew A. Leonov and V. Kubasov (horiz) . . . . 1·10 35
843 8 k. "Apollo" and "Soyuz 19" docked (horiz) . . . . . . 2·25 70

189 Fiat Biplane

1985. "Italia '85" International Stamp Exhibition, Rome. Multicoloured. (a) Aircraft. As T **189**.

844 50 c. Type **189** 15 10
845 1 k. Cant Z.501 Gabbiano flying boat 30 10
846 2 k. Marina Fiat MF.5 flying boat 60 15
847 3 k. Macchi Castoldi MC-100 flying boat 90 25
848 4 k. Anzani biplane . . . . . 1·25 35
849 5 k. Ambrosini biplane . . . . 1·50 45
850 6 k. Piaggio P-148 . . . . . . 1·90 55

(b) Columbus and his Ships. Size 40 × 29 mm.

852 1 k. "Pinta" 45 10
853 2 k. "Nina" 60 10
854 3 k. "Santa Maria" 90 25
855 4 k. Christopher Columbus . . 1·25 35
856 5 k. Map of Columbus's first voyage . . . . 1·50 45

190 U.N. and National Flags on Globe **191** Woman feeding Child

1985. 40th Anniv of U.N.O. Multicoloured.

857 2 k. Type **190** 65 40
858 3 k. U.N. emblem and Laotian arms on globe 95 55
859 10 k. Map on globe . . . . . 3·25 1·75

1985. Lao Health Services. Multicoloured.

860 1 k. Type **191** 25 15
861 3 k. Red Cross nurse injecting child (horiz) 90 40
862 4 k. Red Cross nurse tending patient (horiz) . . . . . . 1·10 70
863 10 k. Mother breast-feeding baby 2·50 1·50

192 Soldier, Workers and Symbols of Industry and Agriculture

1985. 10th Anniv of Republic. Multicoloured.

864 3 k. Type **192** 80 50
865 10 k. Soldier, workers and symbols of transport and communications . . . . . . 2·75 1·75

193 Soldier with Flag and Workers

1985. 30th Anniv of Lao People's Revolutionary Party. Multicoloured.

866 2 k. Type **193** 70 40
867 8 k. Soldier with flag and workers (different) . . . . 2·40 1·40

194 Footballers **194a** Cosmonaut, "Mir" Space Complex and Earth

1986. World Cup Football Championship, Mexico (2nd issue).

868 **194** 50 c. multicoloured 10 10
869 – 1 k. multicoloured 25 10
870 – 2 k. multicoloured 50 15
871 – 3 k. multicoloured 75 25
872 – 4 k. multicoloured 90 30
873 – 5 k. multicoloured . . . . 1·10 40
874 – 6 k. multicoloured . . . . 1·40 55

DESIGNS: 1 k. to 6 k. Various football scenes.

1986. 17th Soviet Communist Party Congress. Multicoloured.

875a 4 k. Type **194a** 90 35
875b 20 k. Lenin and Red Flag . . 4·50 95

195 "Pelargonium grandiflorum" **196** "Aporia hippia"

1986. Flowers. Multicoloured.

876 50 c. Type **195** 10 10
877 1 k. Columbine 25 10
878 2 k. "Fuchsia globosa" 50 15
879 3 k. "Crocus aureus" 75 25
880 4 k. Hollyhock 90 30
881 5 k. "Gladiolus purpureo" . . 1·10 45
882 6 k. "Hyacinthus orientalis" . . 1·75 65

1986. Butterflies. Multicoloured.

883 50 c. Type **196** 10 10
884 1 k. "Euthalia irrubescens" . . 25 10
885 2 k. "Japonica lutea" 50 15
886 3 k. "Pratapa ctesia" 75 25
887 4 k. Leaf butterfly 90 30
888 5 k. yellow orange-tip . . . . 1·10 45
889 6 k. Chestnut tiger . . . . . . 1·75 65

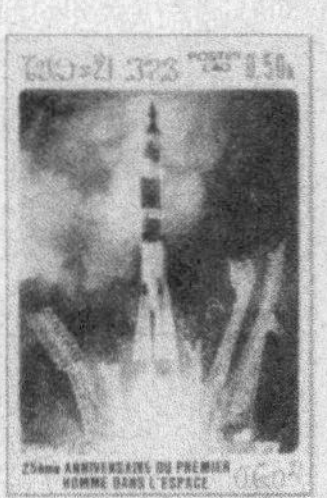

197 Rocket launch at Baikanur Space Centre **198** Giraffe

1986. 25th Anniv of First Man in Space. Multicoloured.

890 50 c. Type **197** 10 10
891 1 k. "Molniya" communications satellite 20 10
892 2 k. "Salyut" space station (horiz) 50 20
893 3 k. Yuri Gargarin, "Sputnik 1" and rocket debris (horiz) . . 70 30
894 4 k. "Luna 3" and moon . . . 95 40
895 5 k. Vladimir Komarov on first space walk . . . . 1·40 50
896 6 k. "Luna 16" lifting off from moon . . . . 1·60 90

1986. Animals. Multicoloured.

898 50 c. Type **198** 10 10
899 1 k. Lion 20 10
900 2 k. African elephant 40 20
901 3 k. Red kangaroo 60 30
902 4 k. Koala 80 40
903 5 k. Greater flamingo . . . . 1·25 50
904 6 k. Giant panda . . . . . . 1·75 90

199 Boeing 747-100

1986. Air. Aircraft. Multicoloured.

906 20 k. Type **199** . . . . 2·50 1·90
907 50 k. Ilyushin Il-86 . . . . . 7·00 5·25

200 Great Argus Pheasant (½-size illustration)

1986. Pheasants. Multicoloured.

908 50 c. Type **200** 10 10
909 1 k. Silver pheasant 25 10
910 2 k. Ring-necked pheasant . . . 50 20
911 3 k. Lady Amherst's pheasant 75 30
912 4 k. Reeves's pheasant 90 40
913 5 k. Golden pheasant . . . . 1·10 50
914 6 k. Copper pheasant . . . . 1·75 90

201 Scarlet King Snake

1986. Snakes. Multicoloured.

915 50 c. Corn snake 10 10
916 1 k. Type **201** 25 10
917 1 k. Richard's blind snake (vert) 25 10
918 2 k. Western ring-necked snake 50 25
919 4 k. Mangrove snake 90 40
920 5 k. Indian python . . . . . 1·10 50
921 6 k. Common cobra (vert) . . 1·75 90

202 Bayeux Tapestry (detail) and Comet Head

1986. Appearance of Halley's Comet. Multicoloured.

922 50 c. Comet over Athens (65 × 21 mm) 10 10
923 1 k. Type **202** 30 10
924 2 k. Edmond Halley (astronomer) and comet tail (20 × 21 mm) . 60 20
925 3 k. "Vega" space probe and comet head 90 30
926 4 k. Galileo and comet tail (20 × 21 mm) . . . . . . 1·10 40
927 5 k. Comet head (20 × 21 mm) 1·40 50
928 6 k. "Giotto" space probe and comet tail . . . . 1·75 90

Nos. 923/4, 925/6 and 927/8 resepctively were issued together, se-tenant, each pair forming a composite design.

203 Keeshond **204** "Mammillaria matudae"

1986. "Stockholmia 86" International Stamp Exhibition. Dogs. Multicoloured.

930 50 c. Type **203** 10 10
931 1 k. Elkhound (horiz) 20 10
932 2 k. Bernese (horiz) 45 25
933 3 k. Pointing griffon (horiz) . . 70 35
934 4 k. Collie (horiz) 90 45
935 5 k. Irish water spaniel (horiz) . 1·10 55
936 6 k. Briard (horiz) . . . . . . 1·60 80

1986. Cacti. Multicoloured.

938 50 c. Type **204** 10 10
939 1 k. "Mammillaria theresae" . . 25 10
940 2 k. "Ariocarpus trigonus" . . 45 20
941 3 k. "Notocactus crassigibbus" 65 30
942 4 k. "Astrophytum asterias" hybrid 80 40
943 5 k. "Melocactus manzanus" . . 1·00 50
944 6 k. "Astrophytum ornatum" hybrid . . . . 1·25 60

205 Arms and Dove on Globe **206** Vat Phu Champasak

1986. International Peace Year.

945 **205** 3 k. multicoloured 85 40
946 – 5 k. black, blue and red . . 1·25 60
947 – 10 k. multicoloured . . . . 2·50 1·25

DESIGNS: 5 k. Dove on smashed bomb; 10 k. People supporting I.P.Y. emblem.

1984. 40th Anniv of U.N.E.S.C.O. Multicoloured.

948 3 k. Type **206** 75 30
949 4 k. Dish aerial and map of Laos on globe . . . . 1·00 40
950 9 k. People reading books (horiz) 2·00 80

207 Speed Skating

1987. Winter Olympic Games, Calgary (1988). (1st issue). Multicoloured.

951 50 c. Type **207** 10 10
952 1 k. Biathlon 25 10
953 2 k. Figure skating (pairs) . . . 50 25
954 3 k. Luge (horiz) 70 35
955 4 k. Four-man bobsleigh (horiz) 90 45
956 5 k. Ice hockey (horiz) . . . . 1·10 55
957 6 k. Ski jumping (horiz) . . . 1·40 70

See also Nos. 1046/51.

208 Gymnast and Urn

1987. Olympic Games, Seoul (1988) (1st issue). Sports and Greek Pottery. Multicoloured.

959 50 c. Type **208** 10 10
960 1 k. Throwing the discus and vase (horiz) 25 10
961 2 k. Running and urn 50 25
962 3 k. Show jumping and bowl (horiz) 70 35
963 4 k. Throwing the javelin and plate 90 45
964 5 k. High jumping and bowl with handles (horiz) . . . . . 1·10 55
965 6 k. Wrestling and urn . . . . 1·40 70

See also Nos. 1053/9.

209 Great Dane

1987. Dogs. Multicoloured.

967 50 c. Type **209** 10 10
968 1 k. Black labrador 25 10
969 2 k. St. Bernard 50 15
970 3 k. Tervuren shepherd dog . . 70 25
971 4 k. German shepherd 90 30
972 5 k. Beagle . . . . 1·10 45
973 6 k. Golden retriever . . . . . 1·50 50

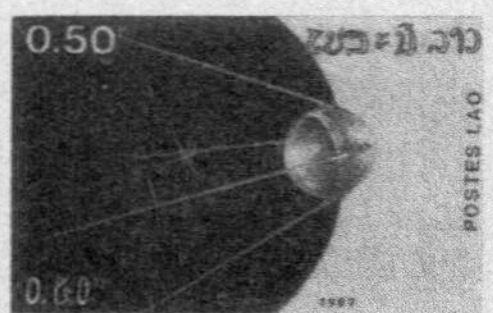

210 "Sputnik 1"

1987. 30th Anniv of Launch of First Artificial Satellite. Multicoloured.

974 50 c. Type **210** 10 10
975 1 k. "Sputnik 2" 20 10
976 2 k. "Cosmos 97" 40 20
977 3 k. "Cosmos" 60 30
978 4 k. "Mars" 75 35
979 5 k. "Luna 1" 95 45
980 9 k. "Luna 3" (vert) . . . . . 1·50 75

211 "MONTREAL" Handstamp on Letter to Quebec and Schooner

1987. "Capex 87" International Stamp Exhibition, Toronto. Ships and Covers. Multicoloured.

981 50 c. Type **211** 25 10
982 1 k. "PAID MONTREAL" on letter and schooner 35 10
983 2 k. Letter from Montreal to London and "William D. Lawrence" (full-rigged ship) . 55 20
984 3 k. 1840 letter to Williamsburgh and "Neptune" (steamer) . . 75 30
985 4 k. 1844 letter to London and "Athabasca" (screw-steamer) 95 40
986 5 k. 1848 letter and "Chicora" (paddle-steamer) . . . . . 1·10 50
987 6 k. 1861 letter and "Passport" (river paddle-steamer) . . . 1·40 60

212 Horse

1987. Horses. Multicoloured.

989 50 c. Type **212** 10 10
990 1 k. Chestnut (vert) 25 15
991 2 k. Black horse with sheepskin noseband (vert) 50 30
992 3 k. Dark chestnut (vert) . . . 75 45
993 4 k. Black horse (vert) . . . . 1·00 60
994 5 k. Chestnut with plaited mane (vert) . . . . 1·40 85
995 6 k. Grey (vert) . . . . 1·75 1·00

213 Volvo "480"

1987. Motor Cars. Multicoloured.

996 50 c. Type **213** 10 10
997 1 k. Alfa Romeo "33" 20 10
998 2 k. Ford "Fiesta" 40 20
999 3 k. Ford "Fiesta" (different) 65 30
1000 4 k. Ford "Granada" 80 40
1001 5 k. Citroen "AX" . . . . . 1·25 60
1002 6 k. Renault "21" . . . . . 1·40 70

214 "Vanda teres"

1987. Orchids. Multicoloured.

1004 3 k. Type **214** 10 10
1005 7 k. "Laeliocattleya" sp. . . . 15 10
1006 10 k. "Paphiopedilum" hybrid 25 10
1007 39 k. "Sobralia" sp. 85 40
1008 44 k. "Paphiopedilum" hybrid (different) 95 45
1009 47 k. "Paphiopedilum" hybrid (different) . . . . 1·10 50
1010 50 k. "Cattleya trianaei" . . . 1·25 60

215 Elephants

1987. "Hafnia 87" International Stamp Exhibition, Copenhagen. Elephants. Multicoloured.

1012 50 c. Type **215** 10 10
1013 1 k. Three elephants 20 10
1014 2 k. Elephant feeding 40 20
1015 3 k. Elephant grazing on grass 60 30
1016 4 k. Adult with calf 80 40
1017 5 k. Elephant walking . . . . 1·10 60
1018 6 k. Elephant (vert) . . . . . 1·40 70

216 Building Bamboo House

1987. International Year of Shelter for the Homeless. Multicoloured.

1020 1 k. Type **216** 10 10
1021 27 k. Building wooden house 60 30
1022 46 k. House on stilts . . . . 1·25 60
1023 70 k. Street of houses on stilts 1·75 90

217 Clown Loach

1987. Fishes. Multicoloured.

1024 3 k. Type **217** 15 10
1025 7 k. Harlequin filefish 25 10
1026 10 k. Silver-spotted squirrelfish 40 15
1027 39 k. Mandarin fish . . . . . 1·40 55
1028 44 k. Coral hind . . . . 1·60 65
1029 47 k. Zebra lionfish . . . . . 1·90 70
1030 50 k. Semicircle angelfish . . . 2·10 85

218 Watering Seedlings

1987. World Food Day. Multicoloured.

1031 1 k. Type **218** 10 10
1032 3 k. Harvesting maize (vert) 10 10
1033 5 k. Harvesting rice 15 10
1034 63 k. Children with fish (vert) 2·00 70
1035 142 k. Tending pigs and poultry 3·50 1·50

219 Wounded Soldiers on Battlefield

1987. 70th Anniv of Russian Revolution. Multicoloured.

1036 1 k. Type **219** 20 10
1037 2 k. Mother and baby 40 20
1038 4 k. Storming the Winter Palace 80 40
1039 8 k. Lenin amongst soldiers and sailors . . . . 1·50 70
1040 10 k. Lenin labouring in Red Square . . . . 1·90 90

220 Hoeing

1987. Rice Culture in Mountain Regions. Mult.

1041 64 k. Type **220** . . . . 1·40 70
1042 100 k. Working in paddy fields 2·25 1·10

221 Laotheung Costume

1987. Ethnic Costumes. Multicoloured.

1043 7 k. Type **221** 25 10
1044 38 k. Laoloum costume . . . 90 40
1045 144 k. Laosoun costume . . . 3·00 1·40

222 Two-man Bobsleigh

1988. Winter Olympic Games, Calgary (2nd issue). Multicoloured.

1046 1 k. Type **222** 10 10
1047 4 k. Biathlon (shooting) . . . 15 10
1048 20 k. Cross-country skiing . . 50 25
1049 42 k. Ice hockey . . . . . . 1·00 50
1050 63 k. Speed skating . . . . . 1·50 75
1051 70 k. Slalom . . . . 1·75 90

223 Throwing the Javelin

1988. Olympic Games, Seoul (2nd issue). Mult.

1053 2 k. Type **223** 10 10
1054 5 k. Triple jumping 15 10
1055 10 k. Men's gymnastics . . . 25 15
1056 12 k. Pirogue racing 30 15
1057 38 k. Women's gymnastics . . 90 45
1058 46 k. Fencing . . . . 1·10 50
1059 100 k. Wrestling . . . . 2·50 1·25

224 Tyrannosaurus

1988. "Juvalux 88" Youth Philately Exhibition, Luxembourg. Prehistoric Animals. Multicoloured.

1061 3 k. Type **224** (wrongly inscr "Trachodon") 10 10
1062 7 k. "Ceratosaurus nasicornis" (vert) 15 10
1063 39 k. "Iguanodon bernissartensis" (vert) . . . 80 35
1064 44 k. Scolosaurus (vert) . . . 1·25 60
1065 47 k. "Phororhacus" sp. (vert) . 1·25 60
1066 50 k. Anatosaurus (wrongly inscr "Tyrannosaurus") . . 1·40 65

225 Adults in Hygiene Class

1988. 40th Anniv of W.H.O. Multicoloured.

1068 5 k. Type **225** 10 10
1069 27 k. Fumigating houses . . . 55 25
1070 164 k. Woman pumping fresh water (vert) . . . . 3·50 1·40

226 "Sans Pareil", 1829 **227** Red Frangipani

1988. "Essen 88" International Stamp Fair. Early Railway Locomotives. Multicoloured.

1071 6 k. Type **226** 15 10
1072 15 k. "Rocket", 1829 . . . . 40 15
1073 20 k. "Royal George", 1827 (horiz) 60 20
1074 25 k. Trevithick's locomotive, 1803 (horiz) 75 25
1075 30 k. "Novelty", 1829 (horiz) . 1·00 30
1076 100 k. "Tom Thumb", 1829 (horiz) . . . . 3·50 1·10

1988. "Finlandia 88" International Stamp Exhibition, Helsinki. Flowers. Multicoloured.

1078 8 k. Type **227** 20 10
1079 9 k. Hollyhock 25 10
1080 15 k. Flame-of-the forest . . . 35 15
1081 33 k. Golden shower 75 35
1082 64 k. "Dahlia coccinea" (red) 1·50 70
1083 69 k. "Dahlia coccinea" (yellow) . . . . 1·75 90

228 Sash Pattern

1988. Decorative Stencil Patterns.

1085 **228** 1 k. multicoloured 10 10
1086 – 2 k. yellow, red and black 10 10
1087 – 3 k. multicoloured 10 10
1088 – 25 k. multicoloured . . . 50 25
1089 – 163 k. multicoloured . . . 3·50 1·25

DESIGNS (stencils for)—VERT: 2 k. Pagoda doors; 3 k. Pagoda walls. HORIZ: 25 k. Pagoda pillars; 163 k. Skirts.

229 Dove and Figures **230** Stork-billed Kingfisher

1988. 125th Anniv of Red Cross Movement. Multicoloured.

1090 4 k. Type **229** 10 10
1091 52 k. Red Cross workers with handicapped people . . . . 1·00 50
1092 144 k. Red Cross worker vaccinating baby (horiz) . . 3·50 1·10

1988. Birds. Multicoloured.

1093 6 k. Type **230** 20 10
1094 10 k. Japanese quail 25 10
1095 13 k. Blossom-headed parakeet . . 35 15
1096 44 k. Orange-breasted green pigeon 80 40
1097 63 k. Black-crested bulbul . . . 1·40 70
1098 64 k. Mountain imperial pigeon 1·60 80

231 Red Cross Workers loading Supplies into Pirogue

1988. Completion of 1st Five Year Plan. Multicoloured.

1099 20 k. Type **231** 50 10
1100 40 k. Library 90 45
1101 50 k. Irrigating fields . . . . 1·25 60
1102 100 k. Improvement in communications . . . . . 2·50 1·40

232 Ruy Lopez Segura

1988. Chess Masters. Multicoloured.

1103 1 k. Type **232** 10 10
1104 2 k Karl Anderssen 10 10
1105 3 k. Paul Morphy (wrongly inscr "Murphy") 15 10
1106 6 k. Wilhelm Steinitz 25 10
1107 7 k. Emanuel Lasker 30 15
1108 12 k. Jose Raul Capablanca . . 50 20
1109 172 k. Aleksandr Alekhine . . 4·25 1·75

233 Tortoiseshell and White

1989. "India 89" International Stamp Exhibition, New Delhi. Cats. Multicoloured.

1110 5 k. Type **233** 10 10
1111 6 k. Brown tabby 15 10
1112 10 k. Black and white 25 10
1113 20 k. Red tabby 50 15
1114 50 k. Black . . . . 1·00 35
1115 172 k. Silver tabby and white . 3·50 1·25

234 Gunboat, Tank, Soldiers and Flags

1989. 40th Anniv of People's Army. Multicoloured.

1117 1 k. Type **234** 10 10
1118 2 k. Soldier teaching mathematics (vert) 10 10
1119 3 k. Army medics vaccinating civilians 15 10
1120 250 k. Peasant, revolutionary, worker and soldiers . . . . 5·50 1·00

235 Footballers

1989. World Cup Football Championship, Italy (1990) (1st issue). Multicoloured.

1121 10 k. Type **235** 15 10
1122 15 k. Footballer looking to pass ball 25 10
1123 20 k. Ball hitting player on chest 40 15
1124 25 k. Tackle 55 20
1125 45 k. Dribbling ball 90 35
1126 105 k. Kicking ball . . . . . 2·25 90
See also Nos. 1168/73.

236 Couple planting Sapling

1989. Preserve Forests Campaign. Multicoloured

1128 4 k. Type **236** 10 10
1129 10 k. Burning and fallen trees . . 20 10
1130 12 k. Man felling tree (vert) . . 25 15
1131 200 k. Trees on map (vert) . . 4·00 2·50

237 Camilo Cienfuegos, Fidel Castro and Flag

238 Skaters

1989. 30th Anniv of Cuban Revolution. Multicoloured.

1132 45 k. Type **237** . . . . 1·25 35
1133 50 d. Cuban and Laotian flags . . 1·25 35

1989. Winter Olympic Games, Albertville (1992) (1st issue). Figure Skating. Multicoloured.

1134 9 k. Type **238** 20 10
1135 10 k. Pair (horiz) 20 10
1136 15 k. Ice dancing 35 15
1137 24 k. Female skater 50 25
1138 29 k. Pair 55 25
1139 114 k. Male skater . . . . . 2·50 1·00
See also Nos. 1196/1201, 1237/41 and 1276/80.

239 High Jumping

241 Sapodillas

240 "Poor on Seashore"

1989. Olympic Games, Barcelona (1992) (1st issue). Multicoloured.

1141 5 k. Type **239** 15 10
1142 15 k. Gymnastics 45 25
1143 20 k. Cycling (horiz) 60 30
1144 25 k. Boxing (horiz) 75 40
1145 70 k. Archery . . . . 1·90 1·00
1146 120 k. Swimming . . . . . . 3·75 2·10
See also Nos. 1179/84, 1231/5 and 1282/6.

1989. "Philexfrance '89" International Stamp Exhibition, Paris. Paintings by Picasso. Mult.

1148 5 k. Type **240** 10 10
1149 7 k. "Motherhood" 15 10
1150 8 k. "Portrait of Jaime S. le Bock" 20 15
1151 9 k. "Harlequins" 25 15
1152 105 k. "Boy with Dog" . . . 2·25 1·00
1153 114 k. "Girl on Ball" . . . . 2·25 1·00

1989. Fruits. Multicoloured.

1155 5 k. Type **241** 10 10
1156 20 k. Sugar-apples 45 20
1157 20 k. Guavas 45 20
1158 30 k. Durians 70 30
1159 50 k. Pomegranates . . . . . 1·10 50
1160 172 k. "Moridica charautia" . . 3·75 1·75

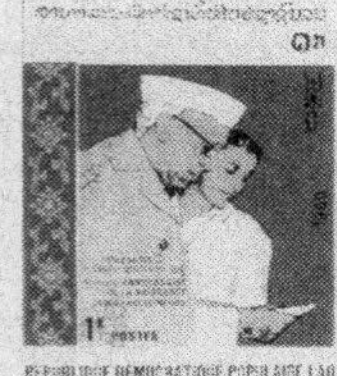

242 Sikhotabong Temple, Khammouane

243 Nehru and Woman

1989. Temples. Multicoloured.

1161 5 k. Type **242** 10 10
1162 15 k. Dam Temple, Vientiane . . 35 20
1163 61 k. Ing Hang Temple, Savannakhet . . . . 1·10 65
1164 161 k. Ho Vay Phra Luang Temple, Vientiane . . . . 3·75 2·10

1989. Birth Centenary of Jawaharlal Nehru (Indian statesman). Multicoloured.

1165 1 k. Type **243** 10 10
1166 60 k. Nehru and group of children (horiz) . . . . . . 1·25 35
1167 200 k. Boy garlanding Nehru . . 4·25 1·25

244 Footballer

1990. World Cup Football Championship, Italy (2nd issue).

1168 **244** 10 k. multicoloured . . . 25 10
1169 – 15 k. multicoloured . . . 35 15
1170 – 20 k. multicoloured . . . 50 25
1171 – 25 k. multicoloured . . . 60 30
1172 – 45 k. multicoloured . . . 1·10 55
1173 – 105 k. multicoloured . . . 2·75 1·25
DESIGNS: 15 to 105 k. Different footballing scenes.

245 Teacher and Adult Class

1990. International Literacy Year. Multicoloured.

1175 10 k. Type **245** 25 10
1176 50 k. Woman teaching child (vert) . . . . 1·40 70
1177 60 k. Monk teaching adults . . 1·50 75
1178 150 k. Group reading and writing under tree . . . . . 3·75 1·75

246 Basketball

1990. Olympic Games, Barcelona (1992) (2nd issue). Multicoloured.

1179 10 k. Type **246** 20 10
1180 30 k. Hurdling 60 25
1181 45 k. High jumping 95 40
1182 50 k. Cycling . . . . 1·10 45
1183 60 k. Throwing the javelin . . 1·25 50
1184 90 k. Tennis . . . . 2·00 80

247 Great Britain 1840 Penny Black and Mail Coach

1990. "Stamp World London 90" International Stamp Exhibition. Multicoloured.

1186 15 k. Type **247** 35 15
1187 20 k. U.S. 1847 5 c. stamp and early steam locomotive . . 1·50 25
1188 40 k. France 1849 20 c. stamp and mail balloons, Paris, 1870 . 90 35
1189 50 k. Sardinia 1851 5 c. stamp and post rider . . . . . . 1·10 45
1190 60 k. Indo-China 1892 1 c. stamp and elephant . . . . 1·40 50
1191 100 k. Spain 1850 6 c. stamp and Spanish galleon . . . . . 2·25 90

248 Ho Chi Minh addressing Crowd

1990. Birth Centenary of Ho Chi Minh. Mult.

1193 40 k. Type **248** 85 35
1194 60 k. Ho Chi Minh and Laotian President . . . . 1·25 50
1195 160 k. Ho Chi Minh and Vietnamese flag (vert) . . . 3·50 1·40

249 Speed Skating

1990. Winter Olympic Games, Albertville (1992) (2nd issue). Multicoloured.

1196 10 k. Type **249** 20 10
1197 25 k. Cross-country skiing (vert) 55 20
1198 30 k. Downhill skiing 65 25
1199 35 k. Tobogganing 75 30
1200 80 k. Figure skating (pairs) (vert) . . . . 1·75 70
1201 90 k. Biathlon . . . . 2·00 80

250 That Luang, 1990

1990. 430th Anniv of That Luang. Multicoloured.

1203 60 k. That Luang, 1867 (horiz) . 1·40 55
1204 70 k. That Luang, 1930 (horiz) . 1·50 60
1205 130 k. Type **250** . . . . . . 2·75 1·10

251 Tui

1990. "New Zealand 1990" International Stamp Exhibition, Auckland. Multicoloured.

1206 10 k. Type **251** 20 10
1207 15 k. Sky lark 30 10
1208 20 k. New Zealand sooty oystercatcher 40 15
1209 50 k. Common cormorant . . . 1·00 40
1210 60 k. Eastern reef heron . . . 1·25 50
1211 100 k. Brown kiwi . . . . . 2·50 1·00

252 Brown-antlered Deer

1990. Mammals. Multicoloured.

1213 10 k. Type **252** 25 10
1214 20 k. Gaur 50 20
1215 40 k. Wild water buffalo . . . 1·00 40
1216 45 k. Kouprey . . . . 1·00 40
1217 120 k. Javan rhinoceros . . . 3·00 1·25

253 Surgeons Operating

1990. 40th Anniv of United Nations Development Programme. Multicoloured.

1218 30 k. Type **253** 60 25
1219 45 k. Fishermen inspecting catch . . . . 1·50 55
1220 80 k. Air-traffic controller (vert) 1·60 65
1221 90 k. Electricity plant workers 1·75 70

254 Rice Ceremony

1990. New Year. Multicoloured.

1222 5 k. Type **254** 10 10
1223 10 k. Elephant in carnival parade 25 10
1224 50 k. Making offerings at temple . . . . 1·25 50
1225 150 k. Family ceremony . . . 3·75 1·50

255 Memorial, Wreath and Eternal Flame

1990. 15th National Day Festival. Multicoloured.

1226 15 k. Type **255** 40 15
1227 20 k. Celebration parade . . . 50 20
1228 80 k. Hospital visit . . . . . 2·00 80
1229 120 k. Girls parading with banner . . . . 2·75 1·10

257 Two-man Kayak

1991. Olympic Games, Barcelona (1992) (3rd issue). Multicoloured.

1231 22 k. Type **257** 10 10
1232 32 k. Canoeing 10 10
1233 285 k. Diving (vert) 95 40
1234 330 k. Racing dinghies (vert) . 1·10 45
1235 1000 k. Swimming . . . . . . 3·25 1·25

258 Bobsleighing

1991. Winter Olympic Games, Albertville (1992) (3rd issue). Multicoloured.

1237 32 k. Type **258** 10 10
1238 135 k. Cross-country skiing (horiz) 45 20
1239 250 k. Ski jumping (horiz) . . 85 35
1240 275 k. Biathlon (horiz) 95 40
1241 900 k. Speed skating (horiz) 3·00 1·25

259 Pha Pheng Falls, Champassak

1991. Tourism. Multicoloured.

1243 155 k. Type **259** 45 15
1244 220 k. Pha Tang mountains, Vangvieng 65 25
1245 235 k. Tat Set waterfall, Saravane (vert) 75 30
1246 1000 k. Plain of Jars, Xieng Khouang (vert) . . . . . . 2·75 1·10

260 Match Scene

1991. World Cup Football Championship, U.S.A. (1994) (1st issue). Multicoloured.

1247 32 k. Type **260** 10 10
1248 330 k. Goalkeeper catching ball 1·10 45
1249 340 k. Player controlling ball (vert) . . . . 1·25 50
1250 400 k. Player dribbling ball . . 1·50 60
1251 500 k. Tackle . . . . 1·90 75
See also Nos. 1292/6, 1370/4 and 1386/90.

261 Planting Saplings

1991. National Tree Planting Day. Multicoloured.

1253 350 k. Type **261** 70 25
1254 700 k. Planting saplings (different) . . . . 2·00 80
1255 800 k. Removing saplings from store . . . . 2·40 95

262 "Mallard", 1938, Great Britain

1991. "Espamer '91" Spain-Latin America Stamp Exhibition, Buenos Aires. Railway Locomotives. Multicoloured.

1256 25 k. Type **262** 10 10
1257 32 k. Class 4500 steam locomotive, France (inscr "Pacific 231") 15 10
1258 285 k. Streamlined steam locomotive, U.S.A. . . . . 1·40 45
1259 650 k. Canadian Pacific Class T1b steam locomotive, 1938 . . . . 3·00 1·00
1260 750 k. East African Railways Class 59 steam locomotive, 1955 . . . . 3·75 1·25

263 Spindle Festival

1991. Traditional Music. Multicoloured.

1262 20 k. Type **263** 10 10
1263 220 k. Mong player (vert) . . 60 25
1264 275 k. Siphandone singer (vert) 70 25
1265 545 k. Khap ngum singer . . 1·60 60
1266 690 k. Phouthaydam dance . . 2·00 80

264 Great Purple

1991. "Phila Nippon '91" International Stamp Exhibition, Tokyo. Butterflies. Multicoloured.

1267 55 k. Type **264** 20 10
1268 90 k. "Luehdorfia puziloi" (wrongly inscr "Luendorfia") 30 10
1269 255 k. "Papilio bianor" . . . 75 30
1270 285 k. Swallowtail 85 35
1271 900 k. Mikado swallowtail . . 2·75 1·10

265 Emblem and Pattern

266 Bobsleighing

1991. International Decade for Cultural Development (1988–97). Multicoloured.

1273 285 k. Type **265** 45 20
1274 330 k. Emblem and drum . . . 55 20
1275 1000 k. Emblem and pipes . . 1·60 65

1992. Winter Olympic Games, Albertville (4th issue). Multicoloured.

1276 200 k. Type **266** 60 25
1277 220 k. Slalom skiing 65 25
1278 250 k. Downhill skiing (horiz) 75 30
1279 500 k. One-man luge . . . . 1·50 60
1280 600 k. Figure skating . . . . 1·75 70

267 Running

269 Argentinian and Italian Players and Flags

268 Pest Control

1992. Olympic Games, Barcelona (4th issue). Multicoloured.

1282 32 k. Type **267** 10 10
1283 245 k. Baseball 75 30
1284 275 k. Tennis 80 30
1285 285 k. Basketball 85 35
1286 900 k. Boxing (horiz) . . . . 2·75 1·10

1992. World Health Day. Multicoloured.

1288 200 k. Type **268** 60 25
1289 255 k. Anti-smoking campaign 75 30
1290 330 k. Donating blood . . . . 1·00 40
1291 1000 k. Vaccinating child (vert) 3·25 1·25

1992. World Cup Football Championship, U.S.A. (1994) (2nd issue). Multicoloured.

1292 260 k. Type **269** 60 25
1293 305 k. German and English players and flags 85 35
1294 310 k. United States flag, ball and trophy 90 35
1295 350 k. Italian and English players and flags . . . . 1·10 45
1296 800 k. German and Argentinian players and flags . . . . . 2·50 1·00

270 Common Cobra

1992. Snakes. Multicoloured.

1298 280 k. Type **270** 75 30
1299 295 k. Common cobra 80 30
1300 420 k. Wagler's pit viper . . . 1·10 45
1301 700 k. King cobra (vert) . . . 2·25 90

271 Doorway and Ruins

1992. Restoration of Wat Phou. Multicoloured.

1302 185 k. Type **271** 50 20
1303 220 k. Doorway (different) . . 60 25
1304 1200 k. Doorway with collapsed porch (horiz) . . . . . . 3·50 1·40

272 "Pinta" and Juan Martinez's Map

1992. "Genova '92" International Thematic Stamp Exhibition. Multicoloured.

1305 100 k. Type **272** 30 10
1306 300 k. Piri Reis's letter and caravelle (vert) 90 35
1307 350 k. Magellan's ship and Paolo del Pozo Toscanelli's world map . . . . 1·10 45
1308 400 k. Gabriel de Vallesca's map and Vasco da Gama's flagship "Sao Gabriel" . . . . . . 1·25 50
1309 455 k. Juan Martinez's map and Portuguese four-masted caravel . . . . 1·40 55

273 Woman in Traditional Costume

274 Boy Drumming

1992. Traditional Costumes of Laotian Mountain Villages.

1311 **273** 25 k. multicoloured . . . 10 10
1312 – 55 k. multicoloured . . . 15 10
1313 – 400 k. multicoloured . . . 1·10 45
1314 – 1200 k. multicoloured . . 3·75 1·25
DESIGNS: 55 to 1200 k. Different costumes.

1992. International Children's Day. Children at Play. Multicoloured.

1315 220 k. Type **274** 75 30
1316 285 k. Girls skipping (horiz) . 1·00 40
1317 330 k. Boys racing on stilts . 1·10 45
1318 400 k. Girls playing "escape" game (horiz) . . . . . . 1·40 55

275 Praying before Buddha

276 Crested Gibbon

1992. National Customs. Multicoloured.

1319 100 k. Type **275** 30 10
1320 140 k. Wedding (horiz) . . . 40 15
1321 160 k. Religious procession (horiz) 50 20
1322 1500 k. Monks receiving alms (horiz) . . . . 4·75 1·90

1992. Climbing Mammals. Multicoloured.

1323 10 k. Type **276** 10 10
1324 100 k. Variegated langur . . . 30 10
1325 250 k. Pileated gibbon 70 30
1326 430 k. Francois's monkey . . 1·25 50
1327 800 k. Lesser slow loris . . . 2·25 90

277 New York

1993. 130th Anniv of Underground Railway Systems. Multicoloured.

1328 15 k. Type **277** 15 10
1329 50 k. West Berlin 25 10
1330 100 k. Paris 50 15
1331 200 k. London . . . . 1·00 30
1332 900 k. Moscow . . . . 4·75 1·40

278 Malayan Bullfrog

1993. Amphibians. Multicoloured.

1334 55 k. Type **278** 20 10
1335 90 k. Muller's clawed frog . . 30 10
1336 100 k. Glass frog (vert) . . . 35 15
1337 185 k. Giant toad 70 30
1338 1200 k. Common tree frog (vert) 4·25 1·75

279 Common Tree-shrew — 280 Noble Scallop

1993. Mammals. Multicoloured.

1339 45 k. Type **279** 15 10
1340 60 k. Philippine flying lemur . 20 10
1341 120 k. Loris 35 15
1342 500 k. Eastern tarsier . . . . 1·50 60
1343 600 k. Giant gibbon . . . . . 1·75 70

1993. Molluscs. Multicoloured.

1344 20 k. Type **280** 10 10
1345 30 k. Precious wentletrap . . 10 10
1346 70 k. Spider conch 25 10
1347 500 k. Aulicus cone . . . . . 1·75 70
1348 1000 k. Milleped spider conch . 3·50 1·40

281 Drugs and Skull smoking

1993. Anti-drugs Campaign. Multicoloured.

1349 200 k. Type **281** 70 30
1350 430 k. Burning seized drugs . 1·50 60
1351 900 k. Instructing on dangers of drugs . . . . 3·00 1·25

282 House — 283 Greater Spotted Eagle

1993. Traditional Houses. Multicoloured.

1352 32 k. Type **282** 10 10
1353 200 k. Thatched house with gable end (horiz) 70 30
1354 650 k. Thatched house (horiz) . 2·25 90
1355 750 k. House with tiled roof (horiz) . . . . 2·50 1·00

1993. Birds of Prey. Multicoloured.

1356 10 k. Type **283** 10 10
1357 100 k. Spotted little owl . . . 35 15
1358 330 k. Pied harrier (horiz) . . 1·10 45
1359 1000 k. Short-toed eagle . . . 3·50 1·40

284 Fighting Forest Fire

1993. Environmental Protection. Multicoloured.

1360 32 k. Type **284** 10 10
1361 40 k. Wildlife on banks of River Mekong 15 10
1362 260 k. Paddy fields 85 35
1363 1100 k. Oxen in river . . . . 1·40 55

285 "Narathura atosia"

1993. "Bangkok 1993" International Stamp Exhibition. Butterflies. Multicoloured.

1364 35 k. Type **285** 10 10
1365 80 k. "Parides philoxenus" . . 25 10
1366 150 k. "Euploea harrisi" . . . 50 20
1367 220 k. Yellow orange-tip . . . 75 30
1368 500 k. Female common palm fly 1·75 70

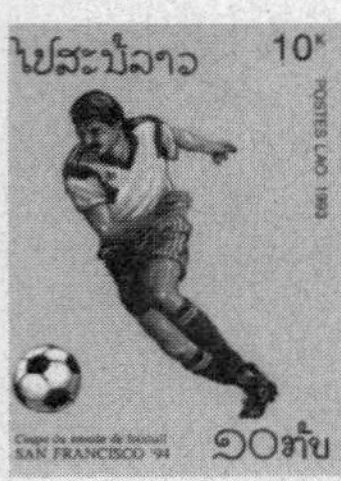

286 Footballer — 287 Hesperornis

1993. World Cup Football Championship, U.S.A. (3rd issue). Multicoloured.

1370 10 k. Type **286** 10 10
1371 20 k. Brazil player 10 10
1372 285 k. Uruguay player 90 35
1373 400 k. Germany player . . . 1·25 50
1374 800 k. Forward challenging goalkeeper . . . . 2·50 1·00

1994. Prehistoric Birds. Multicoloured.

1376 10 k. Type **287** 10 10
1377 20 k. Mauritius dodo 10 10
1378 150 k. Archaeopteryx 50 20
1379 600 k. Phororhachos . . . . . 2·00 80
1380 700 k. Giant moa . . . . . . 2·25 90

288 Olympic Flag and Flame — 289 Bridge and National Flags

1994. Centenary of International Olympic Committee. Multicoloured.

1382 100 k. Type **288** 35 10
1383 250 k. Ancient Greek athletes (horiz) 90 30
1384 1000 k. Pierre de Coubertin (founder) and modern athlete . . . . 3·50 1·10

1994. Opening of Friendship Bridge between Laos and Thailand.

1385 **289** 500 k. multicoloured . . . 70 25

290 World Map and Players

1994. World Cup Football Championship, U.S.A. (4th issue).

1386 **290** 40 k. multicoloured . . . 10 10
1387 – 50 k. multicoloured . . . 10 10
1388 – 60 k. multicoloured . . . 10 10
1389 – 320 k. multicoloured . . . 45 15
1390 – 900 k. multicoloured . . . 1·25 45

DESIGNS: 50 to 900 k. Different players on world map.

291 Pagoda

1994. Pagodas.

1392 **291** 30 k. multicoloured . . . 10 10
1393 – 150 k. multicoloured . . . 20 10
1394 – 380 k. multicoloured . . . 55 20
1395 – 1100 k. multicoloured . . 1·60 55

DESIGNS: 150 to 1100 k. Different gabled roofs.

292 Bear eating

1994. The Malay Bear. Multicoloured.

1396 50 k. Type **292** 10 10
1397 90 k. Bear's head 15 10
1398 200 k. Adult and cub 30 10
1399 220 k. Bear 30 10

293 Grass Snake

1994. Amphibians and Reptiles. Multicoloured.

1400 70 k. Type **293** 10 10
1401 80 k. Tessellated snake . . . 10 10
1402 90 k. Fire salamander 15 10
1403 600 k. Alpine newt 85 30
1404 800 k. Green lizard (vert) . . 1·10 40

294 Phra Xayavoraman 7 — 295 Family supporting Healthy Globe

1994. Buddhas. Multicoloured.

1406 15 k. Type **294** 10 10
1407 280 k. Phra Thong Souk . . . 40 15
1408 390 k. Phra Manolom 55 20
1409 800 k. Phra Ongtu . . . . . 1·10 40

1994. International Year of the Family. Multicoloured.

1410 200 k. Type **295** 30 10
1411 500 k. Mother taking child to school (horiz) 70 25
1412 700 k. Mother and children . . 1·00 35

296 Kong Hang

1994. Traditional Laotian Drums. Multicoloured.

1414 370 k. Type **296** 50 20
1415 440 k. Kong Leng (portable drum) 60 20
1416 450 k. Kong Toum (drum on stand) 65 25
1417 600 k. Kong Phene (hanging drum) 85 30

297 Elephant in Procession

1994. Ceremonial Elephants. Multicoloured.

1418 140 k. Type **297** 20 10
1419 400 k. Elephant in pavilion . . 55 20
1420 890 k. Elephant in street procession (vert) . . . . . 1·25 45

298 Theropodes

1994. Prehistoric Animals. Multicoloured.

1421 50 k. Type **298** 10 10
1422 380 k. Iguanodontides 55 20
1423 420 k. Sauropodes 60 20

299 Playing Musical Instruments

1995. 20th Anniv of World Tourism Organization. Multicoloured.

1424 60 k. Type **299** 10 10
1425 250 k. Women dancing 35 15
1426 400 k. Giving alms to monks . 55 20
1427 650 k. Waterfall (vert) 90 30

300 Trachodon — 302 Children and Emblem

301 Indian Jungle Mynah

1995. Prehistoric Animals. Multicoloured.

1429 50 k. Type **300** 10 10
1430 70 k. Protoceratops 10 10
1431 300 k. Brontosaurus 40 15
1432 400 k. Stegosaurus 55 20
1433 600 k. Tyrannosaurus 85 30

1995. Birds. Multicoloured.

1434 50 k. Type **301** 10 10
1435 150 k. Jerdon's starling . . . 20 10
1436 300 k. Common mynah 40 15
1437 700 k. Southern grackle . . . 1·00 35

1995. 25th Anniv of Francophonie. Multicoloured.

1438 50 k. Type **302** 10 10
1439 380 k. Golden roof decorations 55 20
1440 420 k. Map 60 20

303 Pole Vaulting — 304 Chalice

1995. Olympic Games, Atlanta, U.S.A. (1st Issue). Multicoloured.

1441 60 k. Type **303** 10 10
1442 80 k. Throwing the javelin . . 10 10
1443 200 k. Throwing the hammer . 25 10
1444 350 k. Long jumping 45 15
1445 700 k. High jumping 95 35

See also Nos. 1484/9.

1995. Antique Vessels. Multicoloured.

1447 70 k. Type **304** 10 10
1448 200 k. Resin and silver bowl (horiz) 25 10
1449 450 k. Geometrically-decorated bowl (horiz) 60 20
1450 600 k. Religious chalice (horiz) 80 30

305 Procession

1995. Rocket Festival. Multicoloured.

1451 80 k. Launching rocket (vert) . 10 10
1452 160 k. Type **305** 20 10
1453 500 k. Musicians in procession . 70 25
1454 700 k. Crowds and rockets . . 95 35

INDEX

Countries can be quickly located by referring to the index at the end of this volume.

306 Red Tabby Longhair

1995. Cats. Multicoloured.
1455 40 k. Type **306** 10 10
1456 50 k. Siamese sealpoint 10 10
1457 250 k. Red tabby longhair (different) 35 15
1458 400 k. Tortoiseshell shorthair 55 20
1459 650 k. Head of tortoiseshell shorthair (vert) 90 30

307 "Nepenthes villosa"

1995. Insectivorous Plants. Multicoloured.
1461 90 k. Type **307** 10 10
1462 100 k. "Dionaea muscipula" 15 10
1463 350 k. "Sarracenia flava" 45 15
1464 450 k. "Sarracenia purpurea" 60 20
1465 500 k. "Nepenthes ampullaria" 70 25

308 Stag Beetle

1995. Insects. Multicoloured.
1467 40 k. Type **308** 10 10
1468 50 k. May beetle 10 10
1469 500 k. Blue carpenter beetle 70 25
1470 800 k. Great green grasshopper 1·10 40

309 Cattle grazing

1995. 50th Anniv of F.A.O. Multicoloured.
1471 80 k. Type **309** 10 10
1472 300 k. Working paddy field 40 15
1473 1000 k. Agriculture 1·40 50

310 At Meeting

1995. 50th Anniv of U.N.O. Peoples of Different Races. Multicoloured.
1474 290 k. Type **310** 40 15
1475 310 k. Playing draughts 40 15
1476 440 k. Children playing 60 20

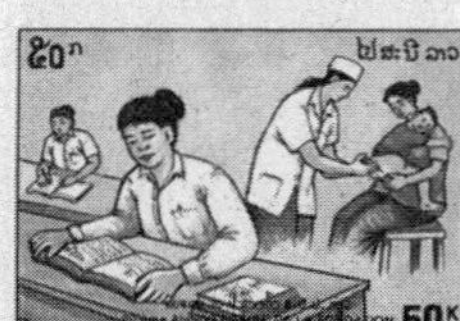

311 Students and Nurse vaccinating Child

1995. 20th Anniv of Republic. Multicoloured.
1477 50 k. Type **311** 10 10
1478 280 k. Agricultural land 40 15
1479 600 k. Bridge 80 30

312 Mong

1996. Traditional New Year Customs. Multicoloured.
1480 50 k. Type **312** 10 10
1481 280 k. Phouthai 40 15
1482 380 k. Ten Xe 55 20
1483 420 k. Lao Loum 60 20

313 Cycling

1996. Olympic Games, Atlanta, U.S.A. (2nd issue). Multicoloured.
1484 30 k. Type **313** 10 10
1485 150 k. Football 20 10
1486 200 k. Basketball (vert) 30 10
1487 300 k. Running (vert) 40 15
1488 500 k. Shooting 70 25

314 Sun Bear

1996. Animals. Multicoloured.
1490 40 k. Type **314** 10 10
1491 60 k. Grey pelican 10 10
1492 200 k. Leopard 30 10
1493 250 k. Swallowtail 35 15
1494 700 k. Indian python 1·00 35

315 Weaving

1996. International Women's Year. Multicoloured.
1495 20 k. Type **315** 10 10
1496 290 k. Physical training instructress 40 15
1497 1000 k. Woman feeding child (vert) 1·40 50

316 Rat

FRANCE ´98
1996
POSTES LAO
20k
317 Players

1996. New Year. Year of the Rat.
1498 **316** 50 k. multicoloured 10 10
1499 – 340 k. multicoloured 50 20
1500 – 350 k. multicoloured 50 20
1501 – 370 k. multicoloured 50 20
DESIGNS: 340 k. to 370 k. Different rats.

1996. World Cup Football Championship, France (1998) (1st issue).
1502 **317** 20 k. multicoloured 10 10
1503 – 50 k. multicoloured 10 10
1504 – 300 k. multicoloured 40 15
1505 – 400 k. multicoloured 55 20
1506 – 500 k. multicoloured 70 25
DESIGNS: 50 k. to 500 k. Different footballing scenes.
See also Nos. 1589/94.

318 Village Women grinding Rice

1996. Children's Drawings. Multicoloured.
1508 180 k. Type **318** 25 10
1509 230 k. Women picking fruit 30 10
1510 310 k. Village women preparing food 45 15
1511 370 k. Women tending vegetable crops 50 20

319 Morane Monoplane

1996. "Capex'96" International Stamp Exhibition, Toronto, Canada. Aircraft. Multicoloured.
1512 25 k. Type **319** 10 10
1513 60 k. Sopwith Camel biplane 10 10
1514 150 k. De Havilland D.H.4 biplane 20 10
1515 250 k. Albatros biplane 35 15
1516 800 k. Caudron biplane 1·10 40

320 Front View

1996. Ox-carts. Multicoloured.
1517 50 k. Type **320** 10 10
1518 100 k. Side view 15 10
1519 440 k. Oxen pulling cart 60 20

321 "Dendrobium secundum"

322 White Horse

1996. Orchids. Multicoloured.
1520 50 k. Type **321** 10 10
1521 200 k. "Ascocentrum miniatum" 30 10
1522 500 k. "Aerides multiflorum" 70 25
1523 520 k. "Dendrobium aggregatum" 75 25

1996. Saddle Horses. Multicoloured.
1524 50 k. Type **322** 10 10
1525 80 k. Horse with red and black bridle 10 10
1526 200 k. Bay horse with white bridle and reins 30 10
1527 400 k. Horse with red and yellow cords braided into mane 55 20
1528 600 k. Chestnut horse with white blaze 85 30

323 Pupils displaying Slates to Teacher

1996. 50th Anniv of U.N.I.C.E.F. Multicoloured.
1530 200 k. Type **323** 30 10
1531 500 k. Mother breastfeeding (vert) 70 25
1532 600 k. Woman drawing water at public well 85 30

324 Leatherback Turtle

1996. 25th Anniv of Greenpeace (environmental organization). Turtles. Multicoloured.
1533 150 k. Type **324** 20 10
1534 250 k. Leatherback turtle at water's edge 35 15
1535 400 k. Hawksbill turtle 55 20
1536 450 k. "Chelonia agassizi" 65 20

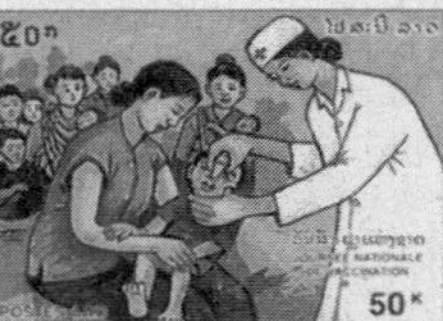

325 Oral Vaccination

1997. National Vaccination Day. Multicoloured.
1537 50 k. Type **325** 10 10
1538 340 k. Nurse injecting child's leg 45 15
1539 370 k. Nurse pushing child in wheelchair 50 15

326 George Stephenson and "Pioneer", 1836

1997. Steam Railway Locomotives. Multicoloured.
1540 100 k. "Kinnaird", 1846 (44 × 27 mm) 10 10
1541 200 k. Type **326** 30 10
1542 300 k. Robert Stephenson and long-boiler express locomotive, 1848 40 15
1543 400 k. Stephenson locomotive "Adler", 1835, Germany 55 20
1544 500 k. "Lord of the Isles", 1851–84 70 25
1545 600 k. "The Columbine", 1845 80 25
The 200 and 300 k. are wrongly inscribed "Stepheson".

327 Pseudoryx lying down

1997. Pseudoryx (Saola). Multicoloured.
1547 350 k. Type **327** 50 15
1548 380 k. Grazing (vert) 50 15
1549 420 k. Scratching with hind leg 60 20

328 Masked Lovebirds ("Agapornis personata")

330 Steaming Rice

329 Signs of the Chinese Zodiac

1997. Lovebirds. Multicoloured.
1550 50 k. Type **328** 10 10
1551 150 k. Grey-headed lovebird ("Agapornis cana") 10 10
1552 200 k. Nyasa lovebirds ("Agapornis lilianae") 30 10
1553 400 k. Fischer's lovebirds ("Agapornis fischeri") 55 20
1554 500 k. Black-cheeked lovebirds ("Agapornis nigregenis") 70 25
1555 800 k. Peach-faced lovebird ("Agapornis roseicollis") 1·10 35

1997. New Year. Year of the Ox. Multicoloured.
1557 50 k. Type **329** 10 10
1558 300 k. Woman riding ox (vert) 40 15
1559 440 k. Ox on float in procession 60 20

1997. Food Preparation. Multicoloured.
1560 50 k. Type **330** 10 10
1561 340 k. Water containers (horiz) 45 15
1562 370 k. Table laid with meal (horiz) 50 15

HAVE YOU READ THE NOTES AT THE BEGINNING OF THIS CATALOGUE?
These often provide answers to the enquiries we receive.

331 "Vanda roeblingiana"

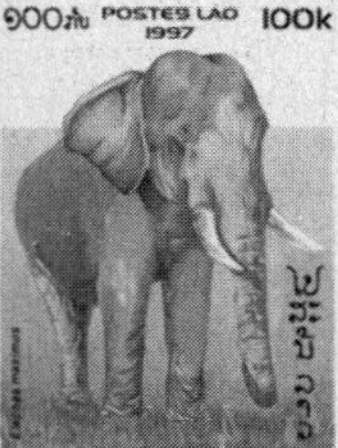

332 Indian Elephant ("Elephas maximus")

1997. Orchids. Multicoloured

1563	50 k. Type **331**	10	10
1564	100 k. "Dendrobium findleyanum"	10	10
1565	150 k. "Dendrobium crepidatum"	10	10
1566	250 k. "Sarcanthus birmanicus"	35	10
1567	400 k. "Cymbidium lowianum"	55	20
1568	1000 k. "Dendrobium gratiosissimum"	1·40	45

1997. Elephants. Multicoloured.

1570	100 k. Type **332**	10	10
1571	250 k. Indian elephant carrying log (horiz)	35	10
1572	300 k. Indian elephant with young (horiz)	40	15
1573	350 k. African elephant ("Loxodonta africana") (horiz)	50	15
1574	450 k. African elephant in water (horiz)	60	20
1575	550 k. African elephant with ears flapping	75	25

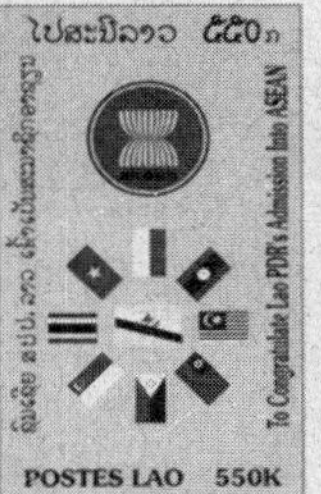

333 Emblem and Brunei Flag

336 Players

335 Headquarters, Djakarta, Indonesia

1997. Admission of Laos into Association of South East Asian Nations. Members' flags, centre flag given.

1577	550 k. Type **333**	75	25
1578	550 k. Indonesia (red and white bands)	75	25
1579	550 k. Laos (red, blue with white circle, red bands)	75	25
1580	550 k. Malaysia (crescent and star on blue quarter, red and white stripes)	75	25
1581	550 k. Myanmar (flower and stars on blue quarter, red)	75	25
1582	550 k. Philippines (sun and stars on white triangle, blue and red bands)	75	25
1583	550 k. Singapore (crescent and five stars on red band, white band)	75	25
1584	550 k. Thailand (red, white, blue, red bands)	75	25
1585	550 k. Vietnam (yellow star on red)	75	25

1997. 30th Anniv of Association of South East Asian Nations. Multicoloured.

1587	150 k. Type **335**	10	10
1588	600 k. Map of Laos and state flag	80	25

1997. World Cup Football Championship, France (1998) (2nd issue).

1589	**336**	100 k. multicoloured	10	10
1590	–	200 k. multicoloured	30	10
1591	–	250 k. multicoloured	35	10
1592	–	300 k. multicoloured	40	15
1593	–	350 k. multicoloured	50	15
1594	–	700 k. multicoloured	1·00	35

DESIGNS: 200 k. to 700 k. Various football scenes.

337 Phoenician Nef

1997. Sailing Ships. Multicoloured.

1596	50 k. Type **337**	10	10
1597	100 k. 13th-century nef	10	10
1598	150 k. 15th-century nef	10	10
1599	200 k. 16th-century Portuguese caravel	30	10
1600	400 k. 17th-century Dutch ship	55	20
1601	900 k. H.M.S. "Victory" (Nelson's flagship)	1·25	40

338 Headdress

1997. Headdresses and Masks. Multicoloured.

1603	50 k. Type **338**	10	10
1604	100 k. Headdress with flower at left	10	10
1605	150 k. Mask with curved tusks (horiz)	10	10
1606	200 k. Mask tipped with headdress decorated with two faces	30	10
1607	350 k. Mask with green face	50	15

339 Two Pirogues

1997. Pirogue Race. Multicoloured.

1608	50 k. Type **339**	10	10
1609	100 k. Crowd cheering competitors from land	10	10
1610	300 k. Side view of two competing pirogues	40	15
1611	500 k. People cheering on spectator boat	70	25

POSTAGE DUE STAMPS

D 5 Vat Sisaket Shrine

D 6 Sampans

D 98 Serpent

1952.

D22	D **5**	10 c. brown	20	35
D23		20 c. violet	20	35
D24		50 c. red	20	30
D25		1 p. green	25	35
D26		2 p. blue	25	35
D27		5 p. purple	70	80
D28	D **6**	10 p. blue	1·10	1·25

1973.

D378	D **98**	10 k. black, brn & yell	10	10
D379		15 k. black, yell & grn	10	10
D380		20 k. black, green & bl	15	15
D381		50 k. black, blue & red	30	30

APPENDIX

The following stamps have either been issued in excess of postal needs or have not been available to the public in reasonable quantities at face value. Such stamps may later be given full listing if there is evidence of regular postal use.

1975.

Centenary of U.P.U. Postage 10, 15, 30, 40 k; Air 1000, 1500 k. On gold foil 2500, 3000 k.

"Apollo-Soyuz" Space Link. Postage 125, 150, 200, 300 k.; Air 450, 700 k.

Bicentenary of American Revolution. Postage 10, 15, 40, 50, 100, 125, 150, 200 k.: Air 1000, 1500 k.

LAS BELA Pt. 1

A state of Baluchistan. Now part of Pakistan.

12 pies = 1 anna; 16 annas = 1 rupee

1

1897.

1	1	½ a. black on white	20·00	13·00
11		½ a. black on blue	10·00	6·50
3		½ a. black on grey	11·00	7·00
12		½ a. black on green	10·00	6·50
8	–	1 a. black on orange	15·00	17·00

The 1 a. has the English inscriptions in a circle with the native inscription across the centre.

LATAKIA Pt. 19

The former state of the Alaouites which changed its name to Latakia in 1930.

Latakia was merged with Syria in 1936.

100 centimes = 1 piastre.

1931. As 1930 stamps of Syria (T **26/7**) optd **LATTAQUIE** in French and Arabic.

65	0 p. 10 mauve	90	60
66	0 p. 20 blue	40	1·40
67	0 p. 20 red	85	1·25
68	0 p. 25 green	40	1·40
69	0 p. 25 violet	1·50	1·75
70	0 p. 50 violet	90	1·60
71	0 p. 75 red	1·75	1·75
72	1 p. green	90	95
73	1 p. 50 brown	2·25	2·25
74	1 p. 50 green	2·25	2·25
75	2 p. violet	2·25	1·40
76	3 p. green	3·25	3·00
77	4 p. orange	3·00	2·25
78	4 p. 50 red	3·00	3·25
79	6 p. green	2·75	3·25
80	7 p. 50 blue	3·00	3·25
81	10 p. brown	4·75	5·00
82	15 p. green	6·25	7·00
83	25 p. purple	14·50	14·50
84	50 p. brown	12·00	12·50
85	100 p. red	35·00	38·00

1931. Air. As 1931 air stamps of Syria optd **LATTAQUIE** in French and Arabic.

86	0 p. 50 yellow	1·40	1·40
87	0 p. 50 brown	1·10	1·60
88	1 p. brown	1·75	1·90
89	2 p. blue	2·25	2·25
90	3 p. green	2·50	2·50
91	5 p. purple	5·25	5·50
92	10 p. blue	6·75	6·75
93	15 p. red	9·00	9·00
94	25 p. orange	17·00	17·00
95	50 p. black	24·00	25·00
96	100 p. mauve	25·00	24·00

POSTAGE DUE STAMPS

1931. Nos. D197/8 of Syria optd **LATTAQUIE** in French and Arabic.

D86	8 p. black on blue	15·00	16·00
D87	15 p. black on pink	11·00	12·50

LATVIA Pt. 10

A country on the Baltic Sea. Previously part of the Russian Empire, Latvia was independent from 1918 to 1940 when it became part of the U.S.S.R. Following the dissolution of the U.S.S.R. in 1991, Latvia once again became an independent republic.

1918. 100 kapeikas = 1 rublis.
1923. 100 santimu = 1 lats.
1991. 100 kopeks = 1 (Russian) rouble.
1992. 100 kopeks = 1 Latvian rouble.
1993. 100 santimu = 1 lats.

1

4

5 Rising Sun

1918. Printed on back of German war maps. Imperf or perf.

15	1	3 k. lilac	10	10
16		5 k. red	10	10
17		10 k. blue	10	10
18		15 k. green	10	10
41		20 k. orange	10	10
20		25 k. grey	50	35
21		35 k. brown	20	20
42		40 k. purple	30	10
22		50 k. violet	20	20
44		75 k. green	25	15
29		3 r. red and blue	1·25	75
30		5 r. red and brown	1·25	60

1919. Liberation of Riga. Imperf.

24	4	5 k. red	20	20
25		15 k. green	20	20
26		35 k. brown	35	45

For stamps of Type **1** and **4** optd with a cross, with or without Russian letters "Z A". see under North-West Russia Nos. 21/42.

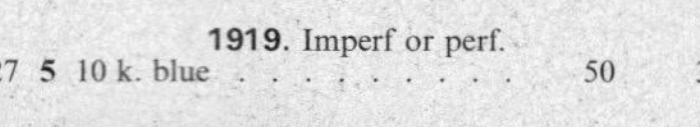

1919. Imperf or perf.

27	5	10 k. blue	50	35

6

7

1919. 1st Anniv of Independence. (a) Size 33 × 45 mm.

32	6	10 k. red and brown	35	35

(b) Size 28 × 38 mm.

33	6	10 k. red and brown	20	20
34		35 k. green and blue	20	20
35		1 r. red and green	75	75

1919. Liberation of Courland.

36	7	10 k. red and brown	10	10
37		25 k. green and blue	20	20
38		35 k. blue and black	30	30
39		1 r. brown and green	55	55

8

1920. Red Cross stamps. (a) On backs of blue Bolshevist notes. Perf.

46	8	20-30 k. red and brown	50	1·50
47		40-55 k. red and blue	50	1·50
48		50-70 k. red and green	50	1·75
49		1 r.-1 r. 30 red and grey	75	2·00

(b) On backs of green Western Army notes. Perf.

50	8	20-30 k. red and brown	40	90
51		40-55 k. red and blue	40	90
52		50-70 k. red and green	60	90
53		1 r.-1 r. 30 red and grey	75	1·75

(c) On backs of red, green and brown Bolshevist notes. Imperf.

54	8	20-30 k. red and brown	1·00	2·75
55		40-55 k. red and blue	1·00	2·75
56		50-70 k. red and green	1·00	2·75
57		1 r.-1 r. 30 red and grey	2·00	4·00

CHARITY PREMIUMS. In the above and later issues where two values are expressed, the lower value represents the franking value and the higher the price charged, the difference being the charity premium.

9

10

1920. Liberation of Latgale.

58	9	50 k. pink and green	20	30
59		1 r. brown and green	30	40

1920. 1st Constituent Assembly.

60	10	50 k. red	50	20
61		1 r. blue	50	15
62		3 r. green and brown	90	70
63		5 r. purple and grey	1·00	80

1920. Surch in white figures on black oval.

64	6	10 r. on 1 r. red and green	2·00	1·10
65		20 r. on 1 r. red and green	3·50	2·50
66		30 r. on 1 r. red and green	4·50	4·00

1920. Surch **2 DIWI RUBLI**. Perf.

67	1	2 r. on 10 k. blue	2·00	1·25
68	4	2 r. on 35 k. brown	50	30

1920. (a) Surch **WEENS** or **DIVI**, value and **RUBLI**.

69	7	1 (WEENS) r. on 35 k. blue and black	30	30
70		2 (DIVI) r. on 10 k. red and brown	45	40
71		2 (DIVI) r. on 25 k. green and blue	70	30

(b) Surch **DIWI RUBLI 2.**

72	6	2 r. on 35 k. green and blue	90	70

(c) Surch **DIVI 2 RUB. 2.**

73	10	2 r. on 50 k. red	25	40

(d) Surch **Desmit rubli.**

74	6	10 r. on 10 r. on 1 r. red and green (No. 64)	1·00	65

1921. Red Cross. Nos. 51/3 surch **RUB 2 RUB**.

75	8	2 r. on 20-30 k. red & brown	2·50	4·50
76		2 r. on 40-55 k. red and blue	2·50	4·50
77		2 r. on 50-70 k. red & green	2·50	4·50
78		2 r. on 1 r.-1 r. 30 k. red and grey	2·50	4·50

1921. Surch in figures and words over thick bar of crossed lines.

79	9	10 r. on 50 k. pink and green	90	70
80		20 r. on 50 k. pink and green	4·25	3·25
81		30 r. on 50 k. pink and green	4·00	3·00
82		50 r. on 50 k. pink and green	7·00	6·50
83		100 r. on 50 k. pink and green	18·00	15·00

19 Bleriot XI

1921. Air. Value in "RUBLU". Imperf or perf.

84	19	10 r. green	5·00	3·00
85		20 r. blue	5·00	1·50

See also Nos. 155/7.

21 Latvian Coat of Arms

22 Great Seal of Latvia

1921. Value in "Kopeks" or "Roubles".

86	21	50 k. violet	25	10
87b		1 r. yellow	25	25
88		2 r. green	20	10
89		3 r. green	30	25
90		5 r. red	80	10
91		6 r. red	1·25	75
92		9 r. orange	90	25
93		10 r. blue	1·10	10
94		15 r. blue	4·50	1·00
95c		20 r. lilac	11·00	1·50
96	22	50 r. brown	20·00	5·00
97		100 r. blue	24·00	4·25

1923. Value in "Santimi" or "Lats".

127	21	1 s. mauve	15	10
129		2 s. yellow	15	10
130		3 s. red	15	10
100		4 s. green	45	10
132		5 s. green	30	10
133		6 s. green and yellow	10	10
134		7 s. green	30	15
103		10 s. red	85	10
136d		10 s. green and yellow	7·00	10
104		12 s. mauve	25	20
105c		15 s. purple and orange	2·75	10
107		20 s. blue	1·50	10
139		20 s. pink	3·00	20
108		25 s. blue	20	10
109		30 s. pink	4·00	15
140		30 s. blue	1·25	10
141		35 s. blue	1·50	10
110		40 s. purple	1·50	15
143		50 s. grey	3·00	15
144	22	1 l. brown and bistre	6·00	15
116		2 l. blue and light blue	14·00	90
117		5 l. green and light green	48·00	3·75
118		10 l. red and light red	6·00	15·00

1923. Charity. War Invalids. Surch **KARA INVALIDIEM S.10S.** and cross.

112	21	1 s. + 10 s. mauve	50	1·00
113		2 s. + 10 s. yellow	50	1·00
114		4 s. + 10 s. green	50	1·00

24 Town Hall

28 Pres. J. Cakste

1925. 300th Anniv of City of Libau.

119	–	6-12 s. blue and red	1·75	4·50
120	24	15-25 s. brown and blue	90	3·50
121	–	25-35 s. green and violet	1·75	3·50
122	–	30-40 s. lake and blue	4·00	14·00
123	–	50-60 s. violet and green	5·00	16·00

DESIGNS—HORIZ: 6-12 s. Harbour and lighthouse; 25-35 s. Spa health pavilion. VERT: 30-40 s. St. Anna's Church; 50-60 s. Arms of Libau.

1927. Surch.

124	1	15 s. on 40 k. purple	50	40
125		15 s. on 50 k. violet	1·10	1·25
126	10	1 l. on 3 r. green & brown	7·50	12·00

1928. Death of President Cakste and Memorial Fund.

150	28	2-12 s. orange	2·50	4·00
151		6-16 s. green	2·50	4·00
152		15-25 s. lake	2·50	4·00
153		25-35 s. blue	2·50	4·00
154		30-40 s. red	2·50	4·00

1928. Air. Value in "SANTIMU" or "SANTIMI".

193	19	10 s. green	1·50	75
156		15 s. red	2·00	1·00
157		25 s. blue	3·50	1·75

29 Ruins at Rezekne

30 Venta

1928. 10th Anniv of Independence. Views.

158	29	6 s. purple and green	50	15
159	–	15 s. green and brown	40	15
160	–	20 s. green and red	90	50
161	–	30 s. brown and blue	1·10	20
162	–	50 s. pink and grey	2·50	2·50
163	–	1 l. sepia and brown	3·00	1·75

DESIGNS: 15 s. Jelgava (Mitau); 20 s. Cesis (Wenden); 30 s. Liepaja (Libau); 50 s. Riga; 1 l. National Theatre, Riga.

1928. Liberty Memorial Fund. Imperf or perf.

164	30	6-16 s. green	2·25	2·25
165	–	10-20 s. red	2·25	2·25
166	–	15-25 s. brown	2·25	2·25
167	–	30-40 s. blue	2·25	2·25
168	–	50-60 s. black	2·25	2·25
169	–	1 l.-1 l. 10 s. purple	3·50	3·50

DESIGNS: 10-20 s. "Latvia" (Woman); 15-25 s. Mitau; 30-40 s. National Theatre, Riga; 50-60 s. Wenden; 1 l.-1 l. 10 s. Trenches, Riga Bridge.

32 Z. A. Meierovics

33 J. Rainis

1929. 3rd Death Anniv of Meierovics (Foreign Minister). Imperf or perf.

170	32	2-4 s. yellow	3·00	3·00
171		6-12 s. green	3·00	3·00
172		15-25 s. purple	3·00	3·00
173		25-35 s. blue	3·00	3·00
174		30-40 s. blue	3·00	3·00

1930. Memorial Fund for J. Rainis (writer and politician). Imperf or perf.

175	33	1-2 s. purple	75	1·75
176		2-4 s. orange	75	1·75
177		4-8 s. green	75	1·75
178		6-12 s. brown and green	75	1·75
179		10-20 s. red	15·00	32·00
180		15-30 s. green and brown	15·00	32·00

34 Klemm KI-20 over Durbe Castle

1930. Air. J. Rainis Memorial Fund. Imperf or perf.

181	34	10-20 s. green and red	10·00	11·50
182		15-30 s. red and green	10·00	11·50

35

36

1930. Anti-T.B. Fund.

183	–	1-2 s. red and purple	50	50
184	–	2-4 s. red and orange	50	50
185	35	4-8 s. red and green	65	80
186	–	5-10 s. brown and green	75	1·10
187	–	6-12 s. yellow and green	75	1·10
188	–	10-20 s. black and red	1·00	1·60
189	–	15-30 s. green and brown	1·50	1·50
190	–	20-40 s. blue and red	1·50	1·75
191	–	25-50 s. lilac, blue and red	2·00	2·50
192	36	30-60 s. lilac, green & blue	2·75	3·00

DESIGNS—VERT: As Type **35**: 1-2 s., 2-4 s. The Crusaders' Cross; 5-10 s. G. Zemgalis; 6-12 s. Tower; 10-20 s. J. Cakste; 15-30 s. Floral design; 20-40 s. A. Kviesis. HORIZ: As Type **36**: 25-50 s. Sanatorium.

1931. Nos. 183/92 surch.

196	9 on 6-12 s. yellow and green	65	1·00
197	16 on 1-2 s. red and purple	10·00	20·00
198	17 s. 2-4 s. red and orange	1·25	2·25
199	19 on 4-8 s. red and green	3·00	7·00
200	20 on 5-10 s. brown and green	2·00	8·00
201	23 on 15-30 s. green & brown	75	1·00
202	25 on 10-20 s. black and red	2·00	3·75
203	35 on 20-40 s blue and red	3·75	4·50
204	45 on 25-50 s. lilac, blue and red	12·00	16·00
205	55 on 30-60 s. lilac, green & bl	13·00	17·00

1931. Air. Charity. Nos. 155/7 surch **LATVIJAS AIZSARGI** and value. Imperf or perf.

206	19	50 on 10 s. green	13·00	18·00
207		1 l. on 15 s. red	13·00	18·00
208		1 l. 50 on 2 s. blue	13·00	18·00

38 Foreign Invasion

1932. Militia Maintenance Fund. Imperf or perf.

209	–	1-11 s. blue and purple	1·90	2·10
210	38	2-17 s. orange and olive	1·90	2·10
211	–	3-23 s. red and brown	1·90	2·10
212	–	4-34 s. green	1·90	2·10
213	–	5-45 s. green	1·90	2·10

DESIGNS: 1-11 s. The Holy Oak and Kriva telling stories; 3-23 s. Lacplesis, the deliverer; 4-34 s. The Black Knight (enemy) slaughtered; 5-45 s. Laimdota, the spirit of Latvia, freed.

39 Infantry Manoeuvres

1932. Militia Maintenance Fund. Imperf or perf.

214	–	6-25 s. purple and brown	4·00	4·50
215	39	7-35 s. blue and green	4·00	4·50
216	–	10-45 s. sepia and green	4·00	4·50
217	–	12-55 s. green and red	4·00	4·50
218	–	15-75 s. violet and red	4·00	4·50

DESIGNS—HORIZ: 6-25 s. Troops on march. VERT: 10-45 s. First aid to soldier; 12-55 s. Army kitchen; 15-75 s. Gen. J. Balodis.

41

1932. Air. Charity. Imperf or perf.

219	41	10-20 s. black and green	12·00	18·00
220		15-30 s. red and grey	12·00	18·00
221		25-50 s. blue and grey	12·00	18·00

1932. Riga Exn of Lettish Products. Optd **Latvijas razojumu izstade Riga. 1932.g.10.-18.IX.**

222	21	3 s. red	50	40
223		10 s. green on yellow	1·50	80
224		20 s. pink	1·50	70
225		35 s. blue	2·40	1·60

43 Leonardo da Vinci

44 "Mourning Mother" Memorial, Riga

1932. Air. Charity. Pioneers of Aviation. Imperf or perf.

226	–	5-25 s. green and brown	10·00	15·00
227	43	10-50 s. green and brown	10·00	15·00
228	–	15-75 s. green and red	13·50	17·00
229	–	20-100 s. mauve and green	13·50	17·00
230	–	25-125 s. blue and brown	13·50	17·00

DESIGNS—VERT: 5 s. Icarus; 15 s. Jacques Charles's hydrogen balloon, 1783 (inscr "Charliers"). HORIZ: 20 s. Wright Type A biplane; 25 s. Bleriot XI monoplane.

1933. Air. Wounded Latvian Airmen Fund. Imperf or perf.

231	–	2-52 s. brown and black	6·00	14·00
232	44	3-53 s. red and black	6·00	14·00
233	–	10-60 s. green and black	6·00	14·00
234	–	20-70 s. red and black	6·00	14·00

DESIGNS: 2 s. Fall of Icarus; 10 s., 20 s. Proposed tombs for airmen.

1933. Air. Charity. Riga–Bathurst Flight. Nos. 155/7 optd **LATVIJA-AFRIKA 1933** or surch also.

235	10 s. green	15·00	50·00
236	15 s. red	15·00	50·00
237	25 s. blue	18·00	50·00
238	50 s. on 15 s. red	£120	£325
239	100 s. on 25 s. blue	£120	£325

In the event the aircraft crashed at Neustettin, Germany, and the mail was forwarded by ordinary post.

46 Biplane under Fire at Riga

1933. Air. Charity. Wounded Latvian Airmen Fund. Imperf or perf.

240	–	3-53 s. blue and orange	20·00	24·00
241	46	7-57 s. brown and blue	20·00	24·00
242	–	35-135 s. black and blue	20·00	24·00

DESIGNS: 3 s. Monoplane taking off; 35 s. Map and aircraft.

47 Glanville Brothers' Gee-Bee Super Sportster

1933. Air. Charity. Wounded Latvian Airmen Fund. Imperf or perf.

243	47	8-68 s. grey and brown	30·00	50·00
244	–	12-112 s. green and purple	30·00	50·00
245	–	30-130 s. grey and blue	30·00	50·00
246	–	40-190 s. blue and purple	30·00	50·00

DESIGNS: 12 s. Supermarine S6B seaplane; 30 s. Airship "Graf Zeppelin" over Riga; 40 s. Dornier Do-X flying boat.

48 President's Palace

50 A. Kronvalds

51

1934. 15th Anniv of New Constitution.

247	48	3 s. red	10	15
248	–	5 s. green	15	10
249	–	10 s. green	1·75	10
250	–	20 s. red	1·75	10
251	–	35 s. blue	10	15
252	48	40 s. brown	20	15

DESIGNS: 5, 10 s. Arms and shield; 20 s. Allegory of Latvia; 35 s. Government Building.

1936. Lettish Intellectuals.

253	50	3 s. red	1·10	4·00
254	–	10 s. green	1·10	4·00
255	–	20 s. mauve	1·10	5·00
256	–	35 s. blue	1·10	5·00

PORTRAITS: 10 s. A. Pumpurs; 20 s. J. Maters; 35 s. Auseklis.

1936. White Cross Fund. Designs incorporating Cross and Stars device as in T **51**.

257	51	3 s. red	1·50	4·00
258	–	10 s. green	1·50	4·00
259	–	20 s. mauve	1·50	5·00
260	–	35 s. blue	1·50	5·00

DESIGNS: 10 s. Oak leaves; 20 s. Doctors and patient; 35 s. Woman holding shield.

53 Independence Monument, Rauna (Ronneburg)

54 President Ulmanis

1937. Monuments.

261	53	3 s. red	35	1·40
262	–	5 s. green	35	60
263	–	10 s. green	35	35
264	–	20 s. red	85	1·00
265	–	30 s. blue	90	1·25
266	–	35 s. blue	1·40	1·50
267	–	40 s. brown	2·25	2·50

DESIGNS—VERT: 10 s. Independence Monument, Jelgava (Mitau); 20 s. War Memorial, Valka (Walk); 30 s. Independence Monument, Iecava (Eckau); 35 s. Independence Monument, Riga; 40 s. Col. Kalpak's Grave, Visagalas Cemetery. HORIZ: 5 s. Cemetery Gate, Riga.

1937. President Ulmanis's 60th Birthday.

268	54	3 s. red and orange	15	10
269		5 s. light green and green	15	15
270		10 s. deep green and green	25	35
271		20 s. purple and red	55	35
272		25 s. grey and blue	85	70
273		30 s. deep blue and blue	85	60
274		35 s. indigo and blue	75	50
275		40 s. lt brown and brown	85	75
276		50 s. green and black	90	80

56 Gaizinkalns, Livonia

57 General J. Balodis

1938. 20th Anniv of Independence.

278	56	3 s. red	10	10
279	–	5 s. green	10	10
280	57	10 s. green	30	10
281	–	20 s. mauve	20	10
282	–	30 s. blue	60	20
283	–	35 s. slate	90	10
284	–	40 s. mauve	80	15

DESIGNS: As Type **56**: 5 s. Latgale landscape; 30 s; City of Riga; 35 s. Rumba waterfall, Courland; 40 s. Zemgale landscape. As Type **57**: 20 s. President Ulmanis.

58 Elementary School, Riga

1939. 5th Anniv of Authoritarian Government.

285	58	3 s. brown	30	60
286	–	5 s. green	30	60
287	–	10 s. green	95	60
288	–	20 s. red	95	65
289	–	30 s. blue	1·40	1·00
290	–	35 s. blue	1·40	1·50
291	–	40 s. purple	1·75	1·00
292	–	50 s. black	2·00	1·25

DESIGNS: 5 s. Jelgava Castle; 10 s. Riga Castle; 2 s. Independence Memorial; 30 s. Eagle and National Flag; 35 s. Town Hall, Daugavpils; 40 s. War Museum and Powder-magazine, Riga; 50 s. Pres. Ulmanis.

59 Reaping

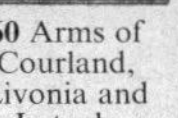

60 Arms of Courland, Livonia and Latgale

61 Arms of Latvian Soviet Socialist Republic

1939. Harvest Festival. Dated "8 X 1939".

294	59	10 s. green	40	40
295	–	20 s. red (Apples)	70	30

1940.

296	60	1 s. violet	25	50
297		2 s. yellow	30	50
298		3 s. red	10	15
299		5 s. brown	10	10
300		7 s. green	10	60
301		10 s. green	75	15
302		20 s. red	75	10
303		30 s. brown	90	40
304		35 s. blue	10	85
305		50 s. green	1·00	50
306		1 l. olive	2·00	60

1940. Incorporation of Latvia in U.S.S.R.

307	61	1 s. violet	15	20
308		2 s. yellow	15	15
309		3 s. red	10	10
310		5 s. olive	10	10
311		7 s. green	10	45
312		10 s. green	30	10
313		20 s. red	65	10
314		30 s. blue	80	30
315		35 s. blue	10	55
316		40 s. brown	60	20
317		50 s. grey	90	25
318		1 l. brown	2·00	35
319		5 l. green	11·00	5·50

63 Latvian Arms 64

1991.

320	63	5 k. silver, brown & lt brn	35	20
321		10 k. silver, brown & drab	15	10
322		15 k. silver, sepia & brown	15	10
323		20 k. silver, blue & lt blue	60	20
324		40 k. silver, green and light green	1·25	40
325		50 k. silver, brown and lilac	1·40	45
326	64	100 k. multicoloured	2·75	80
327		200 k. multicoloured	5·00	1·40

1991. Nos. 6073 and 6077a of Russia surch **LATVIJA** and new value.

332	100 k. on 7 k. blue	10	10
333	300 k. on 2 k. brown	35	25
334	500 k. on 2 k. brown	60	40
335	1000 k. on 2 k. brown	1·25	70

67 Main Statue, Liberty Monument, Riga

68 Olympic Committee Symbol

1991.

336	67	10 k. multicoloured	10	10
337		15 k. multicoloured	10	10
338		20 k. multicoloured	15	10
339		30 k. multicoloured	25	15
340		50 k. multicoloured	40	20
341		100 k. multicoloured	80	45

1992. Recognition of Latvian Olympic Committee.

342	68	50 k. + 25 k. red, silver and drab	40	20
343	–	50 k. + 25 k. red, silver and grey	40	20
344	68	100 k. + 50 k. red, gold and bistre	80	45

DESIGN: No. 343. As T **68** but symbols smaller and inscribed "BERLIN 18.09.91." at left.

69 Vaidelotis

72 Children in Fancy Dress around Christmas Tree

1992. Statues from the base of the Liberty Monument, Riga.

345	–	10 k. black and brown	10	10
346	69	20 k. brown and grey	15	10
347	–	30 k. deep lilac and lilac	25	15
348	69	30 k. deep brown & brown	25	15
349	–	40 k. blue and grey	35	20
350	69	50 k. green and grey	40	25
351	–	50 k. black and grey	40	25
352	–	100 k. purple and mauve	85	45
353	–	200 k. deep blue and blue	1·60	80

DESIGNS: Nos. 345, 347 and 353, Kurzeme (warrior with shield): Nos. 349 and 351/2, Lachplesis (two figures).

1992. Nos. 4672, 6073 and 6077a of Russia surch **LATVIJA** and new value.

354a	1 r. on 7 k. blue	10	10
355	3 r. on 2 k. brown	10	10
356	5 r. on 2 k. brown	20	10
357	10 r. on 2 k. brown	40	20
358	25 r. on 4 k. red	95	45

1992. Birds of the Baltic. As Nos. 506/9 of Lithuania.

359	5 r. black and red	40	25
360	5 r. brown, black and red	40	25
361	5 r. sepia, brown and red	40	25
362	5 r. brown, black and red	40	25

DESIGNS: Nos 359, Osprey ("Pandion haliaetus"); 360, Black-tailed godwit ("Limosa limosa"); 361. Goosander ("Mergus merganser"); 362, Common shelducks ("Tadorna tadorna").

1992. Christmas. Multicoloured.

363	2 r. Type **72**	20	10
364	3 r. Angel choir	30	15
365	10 r. Type **72**	50	20
366	15 r. Adoration of the Kings	65	30

1993. Nos. 4855, 5296 and 5295 of Russia surch **LATVIJA** and new value.

367	50 r. on 6 k. multicoloured	75	35
368	100 r. on 6 k. multicoloured	1·50	75
369	300 r. on 6 k. multicoloured	3·25	1·60

74 Kuldiga Couple

75 Emblem

1993. Traditional Costumes. Multicoloured.

370	5 s. Type **74**	15	10
371	10 s. Alsunga	30	20
372	20 s. Lielvarde	55	35
373	50 s. Rucava	1·40	1·00
374	100 s. Zemgale	3·00	2·00
375	500 s. Ziemellatgale	13·50	9·00

See also Nos. 428, 442, 467 and 491.

1993. National Song Festival.

377	75	3 s. black, gold and brown	15	10
378		5 s. black, gold and lilac	30	15
379	–	15 s. multicoloured	1·00	50

DESIGN: 15 s. Abstract.

76 Pope John Paul II

77 Flags

1993. Papal Visit.
380 **76** 15 s. multicoloured 50 35

1993. 75th Anniv of First Republic.
381 **77** 5 s. multicoloured 15 10
382 15 s. multicoloured 45 35

78 Valters

79 Biathlon

1994. 100th Birthday of Evalds Valters (actor).
383 **78** 15 s. brown, light brown and gold 50 35

1994. Winter Olympic Games, Lillehammer, Norway. Multicoloured.
384 5 s. Type **79** 15 10
385 10 s. Two-man bobsleigh . . . 25 15
386 15 s. One-man luge 50 35
387 100 s. Figure skating . . . . . 2·75 1·50

80 Reed Hut

1994. 70th Anniv of Latvian Ethnological Open-air Museum, Bergi.
389 **80** 5 s. multicoloured 25 10

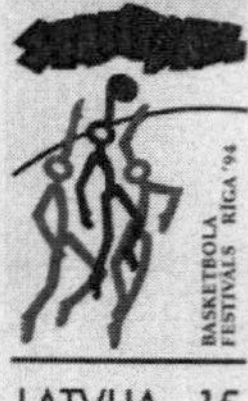

81 Streetball

82 Kurzeme

1994. Basketball Festival, Riga.
390 **81** 15 s. black, grey and orange . 50 35

1994. Arms (1st series). (a) Size 18 × 21 mm.
391 **82** 1 s. red, black and silver . . 10 10
392 – 2 s. multicoloured 10 10
393 – 3 s. silver, black and blue . 10 10
394 – 5 s. silver, black and red . . 10 10
395 – 8 s. silver, black and blue . 20 10
396 – 10 s. silver, black and blue . 25 10
396a – 10 s. multicoloured 20 10
397 – 13 s. black, gold and silver . 30 15
397a – 16 s. multicoloured 35 15
398 – 20 s. silver, black and grey . 50 25
398a – 20 s. multicoloured 45 20
399 – 24 s. green, black and silver . 55 25
399a – 28 s. multicoloured 60 30
400 – 30 s. multicoloured 65 30
401 – 36 s. silver, black and red . 75 35
402 – 50 s. multicoloured . . . . 1·10 55

(b) Size 29 × 23½ mm.
403 – 100 s. multicoloured . . . . 2·10 1·00
404 – 200 s. multicoloured . . . . 4·25 1·10

DESIGNS: 2 s. Auce; 3 s. Zemgale; 5 s. Vidzeme; 8 s. Livani; 10 s. (396) Latgale; 10 s. (396a) Valmiera; 13 s. Preila; 16 s. Ainazi; 20 s. (398) Grobina; 20 s. (398a) Rezekne; 24 s. Tukums; 28 s. Madona; 30, 100 s. Riga; 36 s. Priekule; 50, 200 s. State arms.

See also Nos. 501/6.

83 Emblem

84 Coins in Scales

1994. 75th Anniv of Latvia University.
405 **83** 5 s. gold, blue and green . . 10 10

1994. Europa. Multicoloured.
406 10 s. Type **84** 25 20
407 50 s. Money chest and notes in scales . . . . 1·25 60

85 Eating Cherries

86 Angel

1994. The Fat Dormouse. Multicoloured.
408 5 s. Type **85** 15 10
409 10 s. Eating strawberries . . . 30 15
410 10 s. On leafy branch 30 15
411 15 s. On branch of apple tree . 60 30

1994. Christmas. Multicoloured.
412 3 s. Type **86** 10 10
413 8 s. Angels playing violin and flute 30 15
414 13 s. Angels singing 50 25
415 100 s. Wreath of candles . . . 2·75 1·40

87 Gnome with Candle

88 Emblem

1994. 80th Birthday of Margarita Staraste (children's writer and illustrator). Multicoloured.
416 5 s. Type **87** 15 10
417 10 s. Bear 30 15
418 10 s. Child on sledge 30 15

1994. Roa Safety Year.
419 **88** 10 s. multicoloured 35 10

89 Emblem

90 Bauska Castle (Latvia)

1995. 50th Anniv of U.N.O.
420 **89** 15 s. blue, red and silver . . 50 25

1995. Via Baltica Motorway Project. Multicoloured.
421 **90** 8 s. multicoloured 30 15

91 White-backed Woodpecker

92 Vaivods

1995. European Nature Conservation Year. Birds. Multicoloured.
423 8 s. Type **91** 30 15
424 20 s. Corncrake 75 40
425 24 s. White-winged black tern . 95 50

1995. Birth Centenary of Cardinal Julijans Vaivods.
426 **92** 8 s. multicoloured 20 10

93 Sun and Open Book

1995. 60th Anniv of Karlis Ulmaris Schools Appeal.
427 **93** 8 s. multicoloured 20 10

1995. Traditional Costumes. As T **74**. Multicoloured.
428 8 s. Nica 30 15

94 National Opera House

95 Lacplesis, the Bear Slayer

1995. 800th Anniv of Riga (1st issue). Multicoloured.
430 8 s. Type **94** 25 10
431 16 s. National Theatre 45 20
432 24 s. Art School (44 x 26 mm) . 70 35
433 36 s. Art Museum (44 x 26 mm) . 95 45
See also Nos. 456/9, 479/82, 493/6 and 522/5.

1995. European Peace and Freedom. Multicoloured.
434 16 s. Type **95** 50 25
435 50 s. Spidola . . . . 1·60 80

96 Christmas Tree at Night

97 Stradins

1995. Christmas. Multicoloured.
436 6 s. Type **96** 20 10
437 6 s. Elf flying with candle . . . 20 10
438 15 s. Cottage at night 40 20
439 24 s. Elf with dog and cat . . . 75 35

1996. Birth Centenary of Pauls Stradins (surgeon).
440 **97** 8 s. multicoloured 20 10

98 Zenta Maurina (writer)

100 Cycling

1996. Europa. Famous Women.
441 **98** 36 s. multicoloured . . . . 1·10 50

1996. Traditional Costumes. As T **74**. Multicoloured.
442 8 s. Barta 25 15

1996. Olympic Games, Atlanta. Multicoloured.
445 8 s. Type **100** 20 10
446 16 s. Basketball 40 20
447 24 s. Walking 65 30
448 36 s. Canoeing (horiz) . . . . 1·00 50

101 Swallowtail

1996. Butterflies. Multicoloured.
450 8 s. Type **101** 25 10
451 24 s. Clifden's nonpareil . . . 75 40
452 80 s. Large tiger moth . . . . 2·00 1·00

102 1912 Russo-Balt Fire Engine

103 Apartment Block (E. Laube)

1996. Latvian Car Production. Multicoloured.
453 8 s. Type **102** 25 10
454 24 s. 1899 Leutner-Russia carriage 70 35
455 36 s. 1939 Ford-Vairogs motor car . . . . 1·00 50

1996. 800th Anniv of Riga (2nd issue). Multicoloured.
456 8 s. Type **103** 25 10
457 16 s. Stained glass window (F. Sefels) (30 × 26 mm) . . 45 20
458 24 s. Turreted buildings (E. Laube) (38 × 26 mm) . . 75 35
459 30 s. Couple welcoming charioteer (mural, J. Rozentals) (38 × 26 mm) . 1·00 50

104 Elves and Presents

1996. Christmas. Multicoloured.
460 6 s. Type **104** 15 10
461 14 s. Children with dog and Father Christmas on skis . . 35 20
462 20 s. Child at tree and Father Christmas in armchair . . . 50 25

105 European Nightjar

106 Symbols of Independence

1997. 75th Anniv of Birdlife International (conservation organization). Multicoloured.
463 10 s. Type **105** 30 15
464 20 s. Greater spotted eagle . . 75 35
465 30 s. Aquatic warbler . . . . . 1·10 55

1997. 6th Anniv of Independence.
466 **106** 10 s. multicoloured 30 15

1997. Traditional Costumes. As T **74**. Multicoloured.
467 10 s. Rietumvidzeme 20 10

107 Turaidas Roze

108 "Wappen der Herzogin von Kurland" (galleon)

1997. Europa. Tales and Legends.
469 **107** 32 s. multicoloured 90 45

1997. Baltic Sailing Ships.
470 **108** 10 s. multicoloured 30 15

109 Hermes and Neptune

1997. Centenary of Ventspils International Commercial Port.
472 **109** 20 s. blue, silver & yellow . 60 30

110 Stamp Collecting

1997. Children's Leisure Pursuits. Multicoloured.
473 10 s. Type **110** 25 10
474 12 s. Motor cycle trials (vert) . 40 20
475 20 s. Ice hockey and skiing (vert) 60 30
476 30 s. Tennis, football and basketball . . . . 1·00 50

111 Moricsala

1997. Nature Reserves. Multicoloured.
477 10 s. Type **111** 25 10
478 30 s. Slitere 75 35

112 Woman, Wooden Building and Jewellery (12th century)

1997. 800th Anniv of Riga (3rd issue). 12th–16th Centuries. Multicoloured.
479 10 s. Type **112** 25 10
480 20 s. 13th-century Cathedral cloister, statue (K. Bernevics) and seal of Bishop Albert, rosary beads and writing implement 55 25
481 30 s. Livonian Order's castle, statue of V. von Plettenberg (Order Master) and weapons . 80 40
482 32 s. "Three Brothers" terrace, statue of St. John and seal (27 × 27 mm) 90 45

113 Man and Bear

1997. Christmas. Mummers. Multicoloured.
483 8 s. Type **113** 20 10
484 18 s. Witches 50 25
485 28 s. Horse 70 35

114 Flames

115 Sculpture of Character

1998. Winter Olympic Games, Nagano, Japan.
486 **114** 20 s. multicoloured 55 25

1998. Spridisi Memorial (to Anna Brigadere (writer)) Museum, Tervete.
487 **115** 10 s. multicoloured 25 10

116 Song Festival

1998. Europa. National Festivals.
488 **116** 30 s. multicoloured 65 30

117 Grini

1998. Nature Reserves. Multicoloured.
489 10 s. Type **117** 20 10
490 30 s. Teici 65 30

1998. Traditional Costumes. As T **74**. Multicoloured
491 10 s. Krustpils 20 10

118 Dannenstern House, Wooden Sculpture and Polish and Swedish Coins

1998. 800th Anniv of Riga (4th issue). 16th–20th Centuries. Multicoloured.
493 10 s. Type **118** 20 10
494 20 s. Library, medallion and monument to G. Herder (poet and philosopher) 45 20
495 30 s. Arsenal, Victory column, octant and compass 65 30
496 40 s. Entrance gate to Warrior's Cemetery, "Mother Latvia" (statue) and 5 l. coin 85 40

1998. Arms (2nd series). As T **82**.
500 15 s. multicoloured 30 15
501 15 s. black, blue and silver . . . 30 15
505 30 s. multicoloured 65 30
506 40 s. multicoloured 75 35
DESIGNS: No. 500, Bauska; 501, Ogre; 505, Liepaja; 506, Jelgava.

119 1918 5 k. Stamp

120 Dome Church, Riga

1998. 70th Anniv of First Latvian Stamp.
510 **119** 30 s. red, cream and grey . 65 30

1998. Churches.
511 **120** 10 s. multicoloured 20 10

121 Janis Cakste (1922–27)

122 State Flag

1998. Presidents.
512 **121** 10 s. multicoloured 20 10

1998. 80th Anniv of Declaration of Independence. Multicoloured.
513 10 s. Type **122** 20 10
514 30 s. State arms and flags . . . 65 30

123 Elves building Snowman

1998. Christmas. Multicoloured.
515 10 s. Type **123** 20 10
516 20 s. Elves decorating tree . . . 40 20
517 30 s. Elves sledging 65 30

124 Krustkalnu Nature Reserve

125 Playing Cards and Edgars (from novel "Purva Bridejs")

1999. Europa. Parks and Gardens.
518 30 s. Type **124** 65 30
519 60 s. Gauja National Nature Park . . . . 1·25 60

1999. Latvian Literature. Rudolfs Blaumanis.
520 **125** 110 s. multicoloured . . . 2·25 1·10

126 Council Emblem

1999. 50th Anniv of Council of Europe.
521 **126** 30 s. multicoloured 65 30

127 "Widwud" (schooner)

1999. 800th Anniv of Riga (5th issue). Transport. Multicoloured.
522 10 s. Electric tramcar No. 258 (30 × 26½ mm) 20 10
523 30 s. Type **127** 65 30
524 40 s. Biplane 75 35
525 70 s. Steam locomotive No. Tk-236 . . . . 1·50 75

128 Aglona Basilica

129 Family and State Flag

1999. Churches.
526 **128** 15 s. multicoloured 30 15

1999. 10th Anniv of Baltic Chain (human chain uniting capitals of Latvia, Lithuania and Estonia).
527 **129** 15 s. multicoloured 30 15

130 Rundale Palace

1999. Palaces.
529 **130** 20 s. multicoloured 40 20

131 "Perse"

1999. 90th Death Anniv of Julijs Feders (painter).
530 **131** 15 s. multicoloured 30 15

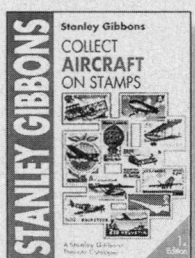

LEBANON Pt. 19

A territory north of the Holy Land, formerly part of the Turkish Empire, Greater Lebanon was given a separate status under French Mandate in 1920. Until September 1923, the French occupation stamps of Syria were used and these were followed by the joint issue of 1923, Nos. 97 etc., of Syria. Independence was proclaimed in 1941, but the country was not evacuated by French troops until 1946.

100 centimes = 1 piastre;
100 piastres = 1 Lebanese pound

1924. Stamps of France surch **GRAND LIBAN** and value. (a) Definitive stamps.
1 **11** 10 c. on 2 c. purple 50 1·00
2 **18** 25 c. on 5 c. orange 55 85
3 50 c. on 10 c. green 70 1·10
4 **15** 75 c. on 15 c. green 90 1·75
5 **18** 1 p. on 20 c. brown 1·25 1·00
6 1,25 p. on 25 c. blue 2·50 2·25
7 1,50 p. on 30 c. orange 1·50 1·75
8 1,50 p. on 30 c. red 95 1·75
9 **15** 2,50 p. on 50 c. blue 1·00 1·25
10 **13** 2 p. on 40 c. red and blue 1·25 2·25
11 3 p. on 60 c. violet and blue 5·00 4·25
12 5 p. on 1 f. red and yellow 5·50 5·75
13 10 p. on 2 f. orange and green 9·00 6·75
14 25 p. on 5 f. blue and buff 12·50 15·00

(b) Pasteur issue.
15 **30** 50 c. on 10 c. green 95 1·40
16 1,50 p. on 30 c. red 1·40 2·00
17 2,50 p. on 50 c. blue 1·00 1·60

(c) Olympic Games issue.
18 **31** 50 c. on 10 c. green and light green 20·00 35·00
19 – 1,25 p. on 25 c. deep red and red 18·00 35·00
20 – 1,50 p. on 30 c. red & black 20·00 35·00
21 – 2,50 p. on 50 c. blue 18·00 35·00

1924. Air. Stamps of France surch **Poste par Avion GRAND LIBAN** and value.
22 **13** 2 p. on 40 c. red and blue 8·25 8·50
23 3 p. on 60 c. violet and blue 8·25 8·50
24 5 p. on 1 f. red and yellow 7·25 8·00
25 10 p. on 2 f. orange and green 8·25 8·25

1924. Stamps of France surch **Grand Liban** (T **13**) or **Gd Liban** (others) and value in French and Arabic. (a) Definitive stamps.
26 **11** 0 p. 10 on 2 c. purple 60 90
27 **18** 0 p. 25 on 5 c. orange 60 85
28 0 p. 50 on 10 c. green 1·25 1·10
29 **15** 0 p. 75 on 15 c. green 1·00 1·50
30 **18** 1 p. on 20 c. brown 50 50
31 1 p. 25 on 25 c. blue 1·50 1·75
32 1 p. 50 on 30 c. red 1·25 1·50
33 1 p. 50 on 30 c. orange 40·00 42·00
34 2 p. on 35 c. violet 1·40 1·90
35 **13** 2 p. on 40 c. red and blue 1·10 85
36 2 p. on 45 c. green and blue 12·00 14·00
37 3 p. on 60 c. violet and blue 1·50 1·40
38 **15** 3 p. on 60 c. violet 1·60 2·00
39 4 p. on 85 c. red 65 1·75
40 **13** 5 p. on 1 f. red and yellow 2·00 2·25
41 10 p. on 2 f. orange & green 4·25 6·75
42 25 p. on 5 f. blue and buff 5·25 9·00

(b) Pasteur issue.
43 **30** 0 p. 50 on 10 c. green 60 30
44 0 p. 75 on 15 c. green 1·25 1·75
45 1 p. 50 on 30 c. red 1·25 1·10
46 2 p. on 45 c. red 2·00 2·25
47 2 p. 50 on 50 c. blue 70 60
48 4 p. on 75 c. blue 1·25 2·25

(c) Olympic Games issue.
49 **31** 0 p. 50 on 10 c. green and light green 20·00 40·00
50 – 1 p. 25 on 25 c. deep red and red 18·00 40·00
51 – 1 p. 50 on 30 c. red & black 18·00 40·00
52 – 2 p. 50 on 50 c. ultramarine and blue 19·00 40·00

(d) Ronsard issue.
53 **35** 4 p. on 75 c. blue on bluish 95 2·25

1924. Air. Stamps of France surch **Gd Liban Avion** and value in French and Arabic.
54 **13** 2 p. on 40 c. red and blue 6·75 8·75
55 3 p. on 60 c. violet and blue 5·00 8·75
56 5 p. on 1 f. red and yellow 4·75 8·75
57 10 p. on 2 f. orange and green 4·75 8·75

5 Cedar of Lebanon

7 Tripoli

6 Beirut

1925. Views.
58 **5** 0 p. 10 violet 25 40
59 **6** 0 p. 25 black 35 85
60 – 0 p. 50 green (Tripoli) 30 95
61 – 0 p. 75 red (Beit ed-Din) 75 1·10
62 – 1 p. purple (Baalbek ruins) 1·10 55
63 – 1 p. 25 green (Mouktara) 1·60 1·75
64 – 1 p. 50 pink (Tyre) 45 50
65 – 2 p. brown (Zahle) 95 35
66 – 2 p. 50 blue (Baalbek) 50 45
67 – 3 p. brown (Deir el-Kamar) 1·25 50
68 – 5 p. violet (Sidon) 8·25 6.00
69 **7** 10 p. purple 8·00 7·25
70 – 25 p. blue (Beirut) 16·00 18·00

1925. Air. Nos. 65 and 67/9 optd **AVION** in French and Arabic.
71 – 2 p. brown 4·00 3·25
72 – 3 p. brown 4·00 3·25
73 – 5 p. violet 4·00 3·25
74 **7** 10 p. purple 4·00 3·25

1926. Air. Nos. 65 and 67/9 optd with Bleriot XI airplane.
75 – 2 p. brown 2·25 3·25
76 – 3 p. brown 2·25 3·25
77 – 5 p. violet 2·25 3·25
78 **7** 10 p. purple 2·25 3·25

1926. War Refugee Charity. Various stamps surch **Secours aux Refugies Afft** and premium in French and Arabic. (a) Postage. Stamps of 1925.
79 **6** 0 p. 25 + 0 p. 25 black 1·75 3·00
80 – 0 p. 50 + 0 p. 25 green 2·50 3·25
81 – 0 p. 75 + 0 p. 25 red 2·00 3·25
82 – 1 p. + 0 p. 50 purple 2·25 3·25
83 – 1 p. 25 + 0 p. 50 green 2·75 4·00
84 – 1 p. 50 + 0 p. 50 pink 2·75 4·00
85 – 2 p. + 0 p. 75 brown 2·75 3·50
86 – 2 p. 50 + 0 p. 75 blue 2·75 4·75
87 – 3 p. + 1 p. brown 2·75 4·50
88 – 5 p. + 1 p. violet 3·75 4·75
89 **7** 10 p. + 2 p. purple 6·25 6·75
90 – 25 p. + 5 p. blue 6·00 8·25

(b) Air. Nos. 75/78 surch.
91 – 2 p. + 1 p. brown 5·50 8·75
92 – 3 p. + 2 p. brown 5·50 8·50
93 – 5 p. + 3 p. violet 5·50 8·75
94 **7** 10 p. + 5 p. purple 5·50 8·50

1926. Stamps of 1925 surch in English and Arabic.
95 – 3 p. 50 on 0 p. 75 red 1·50 1·50
96 **6** 4 p. on 0 p. 25 black 2·00 2·00
98 – 4 p. 50 on 0 p. 75 red 2·10 2·10
99 – 6 p. on 2 p. 50 blue 2·00 2·00
100 – 7 p. 50 on 2 p. 50 blue 2·00 2·00
101 – 12 p. on 1 p. 25 green 1·90 2·00
102 – 15 p. on 25 p. blue 3·00 3·00
103 – 20 p. on 1 p. 25 green 4·75 4·50

1927. Stamps of 1925 and provisional stamps of Lebanon optd **Republique Libanaise.**
104 **5** 0 p. 10 violet 60 70
105 – 0 p. 50 green 20 90
106 – 1 p. purple 50 15
107 – 1 p. 50 pink 70 75
108 – 2 p. brown 1·00 90
109 – 3 p. brown 85 75
110 **6** 4 p. on 0 p. 25 black (No. 96) 65 85
111 – 4 p. 50 on 0 p. 75 red (No. 98) 70 40
112 – 5 p. violet 3·00 3·00
113 – 7 p. 50 on 2 p. 50 blue (No. 100) 1·25 1·00
114 **7** 10 p. purple 4·00 4·00
115 – 15 p. on 25 p. blue (No. 102) 12·50 11·00
117 – 25 p. blue 14·00 15·00

1927. Air. Nos. 75/78 optd **Republique Libanaise.**
118 – 2 p. brown 3·00 3·25
119 – 3 p. brown 3·00 3·25
120 – 5 p. violet 3·00 3·25
121 **7** 10 p. purple 3·00 3·25

الجمهورية اللبنانية
(10)

1928. Nos. 104/117 optd with T **10** or surch also.
145 **5** 05 on 0 p. 10 violet 15 70
124 0 p. 10 violet 80 30
125 – 0 p. 50 green 2·50 2·50
146 – 0 p. 50 on 0 p. 75 red 45 45
126 – 1 p. purple 95 90
127 – 1 p. 50 pink 2·50 2·50
128 – 2 p. brown 2·75 2·75
147 – 2 p. on 1 p. 25 green 1·40 50
129 – 3 p. brown 2·00 1·75
148 **6** 4 p. on 0 p. 25 black 90 30
131 – 4 p. 50 on 0 p. 75 red 2·50 2·50
132a – 5 p. violet 1·75 2·25
149 – 7 p. 50 on 2 p. 50 blue 1·00 45
134 **7** 10 p. purple 7·00 6·00
123 – 15 p. on 25 p. blue 10·00 8·75
136 – 25 p. blue 12·00 12·00

1928. Air. Optd or surch with airplane, **Republique Libanaise** and line of Arabic as T **10**.
151 – 0 p. 50 green 40 1·25
152 – 0 p. 50 on 0 p. 75 red (No. 146) 55 1·25
153 – 1 p. purple 85 1·25
141 – 2 p. brown 2·25 2·75
154 – 2 p. on 1 p. 25 grn (No. 147) 1·10 1·00
142 – 3 p. brown 1·75 2·00
143 – 5 p. violet 2·50 2·75
144 **7** 10 p. purple 2·75 2·50
155 – 15 p. on 25 p. blue (No. 123) £225 £250
156 – 25 p. blue £170 £150

14 Silkworm Larva, Cocoon and Moth

1930. Silk Congress.
157 **14** 4 p. sepia 11·00 12·00
158 4½ p. red 11·00 13·00
159 7½ p. blue 11·00 10·00
160 10 p. violet 11·00 13·00
161 15 p. green 12·00 10·00
162 25 p. purple 11·00 11·00

15 Cedars of Lebanon

16a Baalbek

1930. Views.
163b – 0 p. 10 orange (Beirut) 40 35
164 **15** 0 p. 20 brown 35 60
165 – 0 p. 25 blue (Baalbek) 30 50
166 – 0 p. 50 brown (Bickfaya) 95 60
166b – 0 p. 75 brown (Baalbek) 2·00 2·25
167 – 1 p. green (Saida) 3·25 2·75
167a – 1 p. purple (Saida) 3·25 90
168 – 1 p. 50 purple (Beit ed-Din) 5·00 5·50
168a – 1 p. 50 green (Beit ed-Din) 5·25 90
169 – 2 p. blue (Tripoli) 6·00 5·50
170 – 3 p. sepia (Baalbek) 6·50 5·50
171 – 4 p. brown (Nahr-el-Kalb) 7·00 2·50
172 – 4 p. 50 red (Beaufort) 7·00 4·50
173 – 5 p. green (Beit ed-Din) 2·50 1·50
251 – 5 p. blue (Nahr el-Kalb) 95 20
174 – 6 p. purple (Tyre) 8·00 2·50
175 **16a** 7 p. 50 blue 6·00 1·25
176 – 10 p. green (Hasbaya) 12·00 3·25
177 – 15 p. purple (Afka Falls) 17·00 5·00
178 – 25 p. green (Beirut) 20·00 7·25
179 – 50 p. grn (Deir el-Kamar) 70·00 25·00
180 – 100 p. black (Baalbek) 70·00 28·00

17 Jebeil (Byblos)

1930. Air. Potez 29-4 biplane and views as T **17**.
181 0 p. 50 purple (Rachaya) 35 85
182 1 p. green (Broumana) 30 35
183 2 p. orange (Baalbek) 1·25 90
184 3 p. red (Hasroun) 1·10 95
185 5 p. green (Byblos) 90 70
186 10 p. red (Kadisha) 2·25 1·60
187 15 p. brown (Beirut) 2·50 1·10
188 25 p. violet (Tripoli) 1·75 1·00
189 50 p. lake (Kabelais) 5·50 4·25
190 100 p. brown (Zahle) 9·00 8·25

18 Skiing

1936. Air. Tourist Propaganda.
191 **18** 0 p. 50 green 1·60 2·25
192 – 1 p. orange 2·25 2·50
193 **18** 2 p. violet 1·60 2·75
194 – 3 p. green 1·90 2·50
195 **18** 5 p. red 2·25 2·50
196 – 10 p. brown 2·25 2·50
197 – 15 p. red 48·00 45·00
198 **18** 25 p. green £120 £180
DESIGN: 1, 3, 10, 15 p. Jounieh Bay.

20 Cedar of Lebanon

21 President Edde

22 Lebanese Landscape

1937.
199 **20** 0 p. 10 red 15 20
200 0 p. 20 blue 40 70
201 0 p. 25 lilac 25 1·00
202 0 p. 50 mauve 20 20
203 0 p. 75 brown 60 30
207 **21** 3 p. violet 1·40 60
208 4 p. brown 25 25
209 4 p. 50 red 1·10 30
211 **22** 10 p. red 1·10 35
212 12½ p. blue 95 20
213 15 p. green 1·10 50
214 20 p. brown 1·60 25
215 25 p. red 3·50 75
216 50 p. violet 5·00 2·50
217 100 p. sepia 7·50 2·75

23 Exhibition Pavilion, Paris

1937. Air. Paris International Exhibition.
218 **23** 0 p. 50 black 85 90
219 1 p. green 75 1·60
220 2 p. brown 80 1·60
221 3 p. green 80 1·60
222 5 p. green 1·10 2·00
223 10 p. red 6·25 7·50
224 15 p. purple 6·00 7·50
225 25 p. brown 11·00 12·50

25 Ruins of Baalbek

1937. Air.
226 – 0 p. 50 blue 10 20
227 – 1 p. red 75 60
228 – 2 p. sepia 90 70
229 – 3 p. red 1·60 1·10
230 – 5 p. green 1·10 40
231 **25** 10 p. violet 40 35
232 – 15 p. blue 1·50 1·60
233 – 25 p. violet 3·75 3·00
234 – 50 p. green 8·00 4·00
235 – 100 p. brown 3·50 2·75
DESIGN: 0 p. 50 to 5 p. Beit ed-Din.

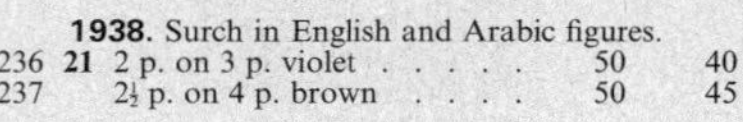

1938. Surch in English and Arabic figures.
236 **21** 2 p. on 3 p. violet 50 40
237 2½ p. on 4 p. brown 50 45

27 Medical College, Beirut

1938. Air. Medical Congress.
238 **27** 2 p. green 1·75 2·25
239 3 p. orange 1·75 2·50
240 5 p. violet 2·75 4·00
241 10 p. red 7·25 9·75

28 Maurice Nogues and Liore et Olivier LeO H.24-3 Flying Boat over Beirut

32 Emir Bechir Chehab

1938. Air. 10th Anniv of 1st Air Service between France and Lebanon.
242 **28** 10 p. purple 2·40 3·25

1938. Surch.
243 **16a** 6 p. on 7 p. 50 blue 1·40 1·00
244 – 7 p. 50 on 50 p. grn (No. 179) 1·40 1·25
245 – 7 p. 50 on 100 p. blk (No. 180) 1·25 1·40
246 **22** 12 p. 50 on 7 p. 50 blue 2·50 2·50
247 12½ on 7 p. 50 blue 45 40

1939. As T **16a**, but with differing figures and Arabic inscriptions in side panels, and imprint at foot "IMP. CATHOLIQUE-BEYROUTH-LIBAN" instead of "HELIO VAUGIRARD".
248 1 p. green 1·10 35
249 1 p. 50 purple 90 60
250 7 p. 50 red 1·60 65
DESIGN: 1 p. to 7 p. 50, Beit ed-Din.

1942. 1st Anniv of Proclamation of Independence.
252 **32** 0 p. 50 green (postage) 2·00 2·00
253 1 p. 50 purple 2·00 2·00
254 6 p. red 2·00 2·00
255 15 p. blue 2·00 2·00
256 – 10 p. purple (air) 3·75 3·75
257 – 50 p. green 3·75 3·75
DESIGN: 10, 50 p. Airplane over mountains.

1943. Surch in English and Arabic and with old values cancelled with ornaments.
258 **21** 2 p. on 4 p. brown 4·25 3·75
261 – 2 p. on 5 p. blue (251) 55 40
262 – 3 p. on 5 p. blue (251) 55 40
259 – 6 p. on 7 p. 50 red (No. 250) 85 55
263 **22** 6 p. on 12½ p. blue 75 55
264 7½ p. on 12½ p. blue 1·25 1·25
260 10 p. on 12½ p. blue 95 65

37 Parliament House

38 Bechamoun

1944. 2nd Anniv of Proclamation of Independence.

No.	Type	Description		
265	**37**	25 p. red (postage)	7·50	7·50
266	–	50 p. blue	7·50	7·50
267	**37**	150 p. blue	7·50	7·50
268	–	200 p. purple	7·50	7·50

DESIGN: 50 p., 200 p. Government House.

No.	Type	Description		
269	**38**	25 p. green (air)	2·25	2·00
270		50 p. orange	3·25	2·50
271	–	100 p. brown	3·50	2·25
272	–	200 p. violet	4·75	3·75
273	–	300 p. green	15·00	12·00
274	–	500 p. brown	35·00	25·00

DESIGNS: 100 p., 200 p. Rachaya Citadel; 300 p., 500 p. Beirut.

38a Beirut Isolation Hospital

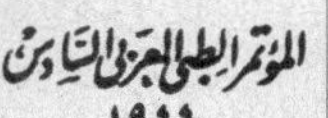

(39)

1944. 6th Medical Congress. Optd with T **39**.

No.	Type	Description		
275	**38a**	10 p. red (postage)	5·00	5·00
276		20 p. blue	5·00	5·00
277	–	20 p. orange (air)	2·25	2·25
278	–	50 p. blue	2·25	2·25
279	–	100 p. purple	3·75	3·75

DESIGN: Nos. 277/9, Bhannes Sanatorium.

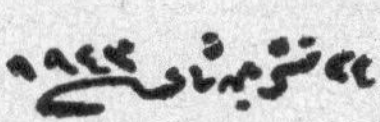

(**40** Trans "Nov. 23, 1943")

1944. 1st Anniv of President's Return to Office. Nos. 265/74 optd with T **40**.

No.	Type	Description		
280	**37**	25 p. red (postage)	10·00	10·00
281	–	50 p. blue	10·00	10·00
282	**37**	150 p. blue	10·00	10·00
283	–	200 p. purple	10·00	10·00
284	**38**	25 p. green (air)	3·75	3·75
285	–	50 p. orange	6·75	6·75
286	–	100 p. brown	8·75	8·75
287	–	200 p. violet	16·00	16·00
288	–	300 p. green	21·00	21·00
289	–	500 p. brown	40·00	40·00

41 Crusader Castle, Byblos

42 Falls of R. Litani

1945.

No.	Type	Description		
397	**41**	7 p. 50 red (postage)	2·40	20
398		10 p. purple	3·75	25
399		12 p. 50 blue	8·75	30
290		15 p. brown	2·50	2·25
291		20 p. green	2·50	2·25
292	–	25 p. blue	2·50	2·25
400	**41**	25 p. violet	16·00	65
293	–	50 p. red	4·75	2·50
401	**41**	50 p. green	38·00	4·25
294	**42**	25 p. brown (air)	1·90	1·25
295		50 p. purple	2·50	1·90
296	–	200 p. violet	8·75	3·25
297	–	300 p. black	18·00	6·25

DESIGNS—HORIZ: Nos. 292, 293, Crusader Castle, Tripoli; Nos. 296/7, Cedar of Lebanon and skier.

43 V(ictory) and National Flag

44 V(ictory) and Lebanese Soldiers at Bir-Hakeim

1946. Victory. "V" in design. (a) Postage.

No.	Type	Description		
298	**43**	7 p. 50 brown, red & pink	70	10
299		10 p. purple, pink and red	1·00	10
300		12 p. 50 purple, blue and red	1·25	15
301		15 p. green, emerald & red	1·25	25
302		20 p. myrtle, green and red	2·00	25
303		25 p. blue, lt blue and red	3·00	45
304		50 p. blue, violet and red	5·75	1·50
305		100 p. black, blue and red	9·50	3·50

(b) Air.

No.	Type	Description		
306	**44**	15 p. blue, yellow and red	50	20
307		20 p. red and blue	50	35
308		25 p. blue, yellow and red	60	35
309		50 p. black, violet and red	1·00	40
310		100 p. violet and red	3·25	90
311		150 p. brown and red	4·00	1·75

1946. As T **43** but without "V" sign.

312	7 p. 50 lake, red and mauve	70	10
313	10 p. violet, mauve and red	1·00	10
314	12 p. 50 brown, green and red	1·25	20
315	15 p. brown, pink and red	2·25	25
316	20 p. blue, orange and red	1·90	25
317	25 p. myrtle, green and red	3·25	40
318	50 p. blue, lt blue and red	7·00	1·50
319	100 p. black, blue and red	11·50	3·50

45 Grey Herons

1946.

No.	Type	Description		
320	**45**	12 p. 50 red (postage)	14·00	50
321		10 p. orange (air)	3·50	65
322		25 p. blue	5·00	30
323		50 p. green	12·00	95
324		100 p. purple	21·00	4·50

46 Cedar of Lebanon

47

1946.

No.	Type	Description		
325	**46**	0 p. 50 c. brown	25	20
326		1 p. purple	35	20
327		2 p. 50 violet	1·25	20
328		5 p. red	1·90	20
329		6 p. grey	2·50	20

1946. Air. Arab Postal Congress.

No.	Type	Description		
330	**47**	25 p. blue	75	50
331		50 p. green	1·10	75
332		75 p. red	1·90	1·25
333		150 p. violet	4·50	2·25

48 Cedar of Lebanon

49 President, Bridge and Tablet

1947.

No.	Type	Description		
333a	**48**	0 p. 50 brown	1·00	10
333b		2 p. 50 green	1·50	10
333c		5 p. red	2·50	20

1947. Air. Evacuation of Foreign Troops from Lebanon.

No.	Type	Description		
334	**49**	25 p. blue	75	65
335		50 p. red	1·10	95
336		75 p. black	2·50	1·25
337		150 p. green	4·50	2·50

50 Crusader Castle, Tripoli

51 Jounieh Bay

1947.

No.	Type	Description		
338	**50**	12 p. 50 red (postage)	6·25	30
339		25 p. blue	7·75	40
340		50 p. green	25·00	75
341		100 p. violet	32·00	5·50
342	**51**	5 p. green (air)	30	10
343		10 p. mauve	40	10
344		15 p. red	60	10
403		15 p. green	7·50	1·00
345		20 p. orange	95	10
345a		20 p. red	1·25	20
346		25 p. blue	1·25	10
347		50 p. red	3·00	25
348	**51**	100 p. purple	6·25	25
349	–	150 p. purple	12·50	1·10
350	–	200 p. slate	19·00	5·00
351	–	300 p. black	30·00	11·50

DESIGN: 150 p. to 300 p. Grand Serail Palace.

54 Phoenician Galley

1947. Air. 12th Congress of U.P.U., Paris.

No.	Type	Description		
352	–	10 p. blue	75	35
353	–	15 p. red	1·10	50
354	–	25 p. blue	1·50	85
355	**54**	50 p. green	3·50	1·00
356	–	75 p. violet	4·50	1·40
357	–	100 p. brown	6·25	3·00

DESIGN—VERT: 10 p. to 25 p. Posthorn.

55 Faraya Bridge and Statue

1947. Air. Red Cross Fund. Cross in red.

No.	Type	Description		
358	**55**	12 p. 50 + 25 p. green	6·25	5·00
359		25 p. + 50 p. blue	7·00	5·75
360	–	50 p. + 100 p. brown	9·50	7·00
361	–	75 p. + 150 p. violet	20·00	14·00
362	–	100 p. + 200 p. grey	35·00	25·00

DESIGN: 50 p. to 100 p. Djounie Bay and statue.

56 Cedar of Lebanon

58 Lebanese Landscape

1948.

No.	Type	Description		
363	**56**	0 p. 50 blue (postage)	15	10
364		1 p. brown	65	10
395		1 p. orange	30	10
365		2 p. 50 mauve	60	10
366		3 p. green	1·40	10
367		5 p. red	2·00	10
368	–	7 p. 50 red	5·00	20
369	–	10 p. purple	3·25	20
370	–	12 p. 50 blue	8·25	25
371	–	25 p. blue	11·00	65
372	–	50 p. green	25·00	5·00
373	**58**	5 p. red (air)	50	10
374		10 p. mauve	1·10	10
375		15 p. brown	2·75	10
376		20 p. slate	4·50	20
377		25 p. blue	8·25	90
378		50 p. black	14·50	1·75

DESIGN—As T **58**: Nos. 368/72, Zebaide Aqueduct.

59 Europa on Bull

61 Apollo on Sun Chariot

1948. 3rd Meeting of U.N.E.S.C.O., Beirut.

No.	Type	Description		
379	**59**	10 p. orange and red (postage)	1·90	1·25
380		12 p. 50 mauve and violet	2·50	1·90
381		25 p. green and light green	3·00	1·90
382	–	30 p. buff and brown	3·75	2·25
383	–	40 p. green and turquoise	5·75	2·25

DESIGN—VERT: 30, 40 p. Avicenna (philosopher and scientist).

No.	Type	Description		
384	**61**	7 p. 50 blue and light blue (air)	1·60	1·25
385		15 p. black and grey	1·90	1·25
386		20 p. brown and pink	3·25	1·90
387	–	35 p. red	5·25	2·50
388	–	75 p. green	10·50	5·50

DESIGN—HORIZ: 35, 75 p. Symbolical figure.

63 Camel

64 Sikorsky S-51 Helicopter

1949. 75th Anniv of U.P.U.

No.	Type	Description		
389	**63**	5 p. violet (postage)	1·00	75
390		7 p. 50 red	1·50	1·25
391		12 p. 50 blue	2·25	1·60
392	**64**	25 p. blue (air)	5·00	2·50
393		50 p. green	7·50	3·75

65 Cedar of Lebanon

66 Nahr el-Kalb Bridge

1950.

No.	Type	Description		
407	**65**	0 p. 50 red	25	10
408		1 p. red	65	10
409		2 p. 50 violet	1·00	10
410		5 p. purple	1·90	10
411	**66**	7 p. 50 red	2·25	10
412		10 p. lilac	2·75	10
413		12 p. 50 blue	4·50	20
414		25 p. blue	8·75	95
415		50 p. green	25·00	5·00

67 Congressional Flags

1950. Lebanese Emigrants' Congress. Inscr "MOIS DES EMIGRES–ETE 1950".

No.	Type	Description		
416	**67**	7 p. 50 green (postage)	65	20
417		12 p. mauve	65	20
418	–	5 p. blue (air)	2·00	50
419	–	15 p. violet	2·50	75
420	–	25 p. brown	1·25	75
421	–	35 p. green	2·50	1·25

DESIGNS: 5, 15 p. House Martins; 25, 35 p. Pres. Bishara al-Khoury and building.

70 Crusader Castle, Sidon

1950. Air.

No.	Type	Description		
422	**70**	10 p. brown	50	20
423		15 p. green	1·00	15
424		20 p. red	2·25	30
425		25 p. blue	5·00	1·25
426		50 p. grey	7·50	2·50

1950. Surch with figures and bars.

No.	Type	Description		
427	**56**	1 p. on 3 p. green	50	20
428	**46**	2 p. 50 on 6 p. grey	75	20

73 Cedar of Lebanon

74 Nahr el-Kalb Bridge

75 Crusader Castle, Sidon

1951.

No.	Type	Description		
429	**73**	0 p. 50 red (postage)	25	10
430		1 p. brown	50	10
431		2 p. 50 grey	2·50	10
432		5 p. purple	2·75	10
433	**74**	7 p. 50 red	3·00	30
434		10 p. purple	3·75	20
435		12 p. 50 turquoise	7·50	35
436		25 p. blue	11·50	1·25
437		50 p. green	25·00	6·75
438	**75**	10 p. turquoise (air)	80	10
439		15 p. brown	1·75	10
440		20 p. red	1·75	20
441		25 p. blue	2·00	20
442		35 p. mauve	5·00	2·50
443		50 p. blue	9·00	2·00

Type **74** is similar to Type **66** but left value tablets differ.

For design as Type **74** but inscr "LIBAN", see Nos. 561/3.

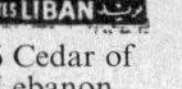

76 Cedar of Lebanon

77 Baalbek

1952.

444	76	0 p. 50 green (postage)	60	10
445		1 p. brown	60	10
446		2 p. 50 blue	90	20
447		5 p. red	1·60	25
448	77	7 p. 50 red	1·90	45
449		10 p. violet	4·50	50
450		12 p. 50 blue	4·50	50
451		25 p. blue	5·75	1·25
452	–	50 p. green	17·00	2·25
453	–	100 p. brown	35·00	7·00
454	–	5 p. red (air)	30	10
455	–	10 p. grey	45	10
456	–	15 p. mauve	80	10
457	–	20 p. orange	1·25	30
458	–	25 p. blue	1·25	40
459	–	35 p. blue	2·10	45
460	–	50 p. green	7·00	50
461	–	100 p. blue	48·00	2·10
462	–	200 p. green	28·00	4·00
463	–	300 p. sepia	38·00	8·75

DESIGNS—As Type **77**: Nos. 452/3, Beaufort Castle; 454/9, Beirut Airport; 460/3, Amphitheatre, Byblos.

78 Cedar of Lebanon **79** General Post Office **80** Douglas DC-4

1953.

559	78	0 p. 50 blue (postage)	20	10
465		1 p. red	70	10
466		2 p. 50 violet	90	20
560		2 p. 50 purple	60	10
467		5 p. green	1·60	25
468	79	7 p. 50 red	2·50	35
469		10 p. green	3·00	50
470		12 p. 50 turquoise	4·25	55
471		25 p. blue	6·25	1·10
472		50 p. brown	11·50	2·50
473	80	5 p. green (air)	30	10
474		10 p. red	55	10
475		15 p. red	80	10
476		20 p. turquoise	1·25	10
477		25 p. blue	3·25	10
478		35 p. brown	4·50	20
479		50 p. blue	6·50	45
480		100 p. sepia	12·00	4·25

For 20 p. green as Type **79** see No. 636.

81 Cedar of Lebanon **82** Beit ed-Din Palace

83 Baalbek

1954.

481	81	0 p. 50 blue (postage)	20	10
482		1 p. orange	35	10
483		2 p. 50 violet	60	20
484		5 p. green	1·10	20
485	82	7 p. 50 red	1·90	45
486		10 p. green	2·75	45
487		12 p. 50 blue	4·50	60
488		25 p. deep blue	6·25	2·25
489		50 p. turquoise	11·00	3·75
490		100 p. sepia	25·00	7·50
491	83	5 p. green (air)	40	10
492		10 p. lilac	70	10
493		15 p. red	80	10
494		20 p. brown	1·10	10
495		25 p. blue	1·25	20
496		35 p. sepia	1·75	25
497	–	50 p. green	5·50	40
498	–	100 p. red	9·00	60
499	–	200 p. sepia	20·00	1·90
500	–	300 p. blue	32·00	3·75

DESIGN—As T **83**: 50 p. to 300 p. Litani Irrigation Canal.

For other values as Nos. 497/500, see Nos. 564/7.

MINIMUM PRICE

The minimum price quoted is 10p which represents a handling charge rather than a basis for valuing common stamps. For further notes about prices see introductory pages.

84 Khalde Airport, Beirut

1954. Air. Opening of Beirut International Airport.

501	84	10 p. red and pink	45	25
502		25 p. blue and ultramarine	1·25	40
503		35 p. brown and sepia	1·75	65
504		65 p. green and turquoise	4·25	2·50

1955. Arab Postal Union. As T **96a** of Syria but smaller, 27×37 mm. Inscr "LIBAN" at top.

505		12 p. 50 green (postage)	50	35
506		25 p. violet	75	35
507		2 p. 50 brown (air)	40	30

85 Rotary Emblem **86** Cedar of Lebanon

87 Jeita Grotto **88** Skiers

1955. Air. 50th Anniv of Rotary International.

508	85	35 p. green	90	65
509		65 p. blue	1·60	95

1955.

510	86	0 p. 50 blue (postage)	20	10
511		1 p. red	25	10
512		2 p. 50 violet	45	10
552		2 p. 50 blue	6·25	25
513		5 p. green	70	10
514	87	7 p. 50 orange	95	10
515		10 p. green	1·60	10
516		12 p. 50 blue	1·60	10
517		25 p. blue	4·00	25
518		50 p. green	5·75	75
519	88	5 p. turquoise (air)	50	35
520		15 p. red	85	20
521		20 p. violet	1·50	20
522		25 p. blue	2·75	30
523		35 p. brown	4·50	50
524		50 p. brown	7·50	70
525		65 p. blue	14·00	2·25

The face value on No. 510 reads "0.50 PIASTRE"; on No. 512 the "2" and "50" are different sizes and the 1 and 5 p. have no dash under "P".

For other colours and new values as Type **88** see Nos. 568/70 and for redrawn Type **86** see Nos. 582/5, 686 and 695/7.

89 Visitor from Abroad **90** Cedar of Lebanon **91** Globe and Columns

92 Oranges

1955. Air. Tourist Propaganda.

526	89	2 p. 50 slate and purple	10	10
527		12 p. 50 blue & ultramarine	30	20
528		25 p. blue and indigo	80	35
529		35 p. blue and green	1·25	50

1955.

530	90	0.50 p. blue (postage)	20	10
531		1 p. orange	20	10
532		2 p. 50 violet	25	10
533		5 p. green	50	10
534	91	7 p. 50 red and orange	65	10
535		10 p. green and brown	75	10
536		12 p. 50 blue and green	95	10
537		25 p. blue and mauve	1·90	20
538		50 p. green and blue	2·75	35
539		100 p. brown and orange	4·50	1·10
540	92	5 p. yellow and green (air)	25	10
541		10 p. orange and green	60	10
542		15 p. orange and green	60	10
543		20 p. orange and brown	1·00	10
544	–	25 p. violet and blue	1·25	10
545	–	35 p. purple and green	2·50	25
546	–	50 p. yellow and black	2·50	25
547	–	65 p. yellow and green	5·00	35
548	–	100 p. orange and green	8·25	1·00
549	–	200 p. red and green	15·00	4·50

DESIGNS—VERT: 25 p. to 50 p. Grapes. HORIZ: 4 p. to 200 p. Quinces.

93 U.N. Emblem **94** Masks, Columns and Gargoyle

1956. Air. 10th Anniv of U.N.

550	93	35 p. blue	4·00	3·25
551		65 p. green	5·25	3·75

1956. Air. Baalbek International Drama Festival. Inscr "FESTIVAL INTERNATIONAL DE BAALBECK".

553	94	2 p. 50 sepia	30	15
554		10 p. green	45	25
555	–	12 p. 50 blue	45	35
556	–	25 p. violet	1·00	45
557	–	35 p. purple	1·90	65
558	–	65 p. slate	3·00	1·90

DESIGNS—HORIZ: 12 p. 50, 25 p. Temple ruins at Baalbek. VERT: 35 p., 65 p. Double bass, masks and columns.

1957. As earlier designs but redrawn. (a) Postage. As T **74** but inscr "LIBAN".

561		7 p. 50 red	1·10	10
562		10 p. brown	1·60	10
563		12 p. 50 blue	1·90	10

(b) Air. Arabic inscription changed. New values and colours.

564	–	10 p. violet	25	10
565	–	15 p. orange	40	10
566	–	20 p. green	50	10
567	–	25 p. blue	60	10
568	88	35 p. green	2·10	20
569		65 p. purple	3·75	55
570		100 p. brown	6·25	1·25

DESIGN: 10 p. to 25 p. As Nos. 497/500.

95 Pres. Chamoun and King Faisal II of Iraq

1957. Air. Arab Leaders' Conference, Beirut.

571	95	15 p. orange	65	40
572	–	15 p. blue	65	40
573	–	15 p. maroon	65	40
574	–	15 p. purple	65	40
575	–	15 p. green	65	40
576	–	25 p. turquoise	65	40
577	–	100 p. brown	4·50	2·25

DESIGNS—As T **95**: 15 p. values show Pres. Chamoun and; King Hussein of Jordan (No. 572), Abdallah Khalil of Sudan (No. 573), Pres. Shukri Bey al-Quwatli of Syria (No. 574) and King Saud of Saudi Arabia (No. 575); 25 p. Map and Pres. Chamoun. 44×44 mm (Diamond shape); 100 p. The six Arab Leaders.

97 Runners **98** Miners

1957. 2nd Pan-Arabian Games, Beirut.

578	97	2 p. 50 sepia (postage)	65	40
579	–	12 p. 50 blue	95	50
580	–	35 p. purple (air)	2·50	1·00
581	–	50 p. green	3·00	1·50

DESIGNS—VERT: 12 p. 50, Footballers. HORIZ: 35 p. Fencers; 50 p. Stadium.

1957.

582	86	0 p. 50 blue (16¼ × 20¼ mm) (postage)	15	10
582a		0 p. 50 violet (17 × 21½ mm)	25	10
583		1 p. brown (16¼ × 20¼ mm)	20	10
583a		1 p. purple (17 × 21½ mm)	25	10
584		2 p. 50 violet (16¼ × 20¼ mm)	35	10
584a		2 p. 50 blue (17 × 21½ mm)	40	10
585		5 p. green (16¼ × 20¼ mm)	50	10
586	98	7½ p. pink	75	10
587		10 p. brown	1·00	10
588		12½ p. blue	1·40	10
589	–	25 p. blue	1·40	10
590	–	50 p. green	2·50	30
591	–	100 p. brown	4·50	90
592	–	5 p. green (air)	20	10
593	–	10 p. orange	25	10
594	–	15 p. brown	25	10
595	–	20 p. purple	40	10
596	–	25 p. blue	50	15
597	–	35 p. purple	80	30
598	–	50 p. green	1·50	45
599	–	65 p. brown	2·50	45
600	–	100 p. grey	3·25	1·25

DESIGNS: POSTAGE—As Type **86**: 50 c. inscr "0 P.50", 2 p. 50, Figures in uniform size; 1 p., 5 p. Short dash under "P". As Type **98**: VERT: 25 p. to 100 p. Potter. AIR—As Type **98**: HORIZ: 5 p. to 25 p. Cedar of Lebanon with signs of the Zodiac, bird and ship. 35 to 100 p. Chamoun Electric Power Station.

99 Cedar of Lebanon **100** Soldier and Flag

101 Douglas DC-6B at Khalde Airport

1959.

601	99	0 p. 50 blue (postage)	15	10
602		1 p. orange	25	10
603		2 p. 50 violet	35	10
604		5 p. green	50	10
605	100	12 p. 50 blue	1·00	10
606		25 p. blue	1·10	10
607		50 p. brown	1·90	25
608		100 p. sepia	3·50	45
609	101	5 p. green (air)	55	10
610		10 p. purple	55	10
611		15 p. violet	80	10
612		20 p. red	1·10	15
613		25 p. violet	1·50	25
614	–	35 p. myrtle	1·10	25
615	–	50 p. turquoise	1·40	25
616	–	65 p. sepia	2·75	45
617	–	100 p. blue	3·25	75

DESIGN—HORIZ: Nos. 614/17, Factory, cogwheel and telegraph pylons.

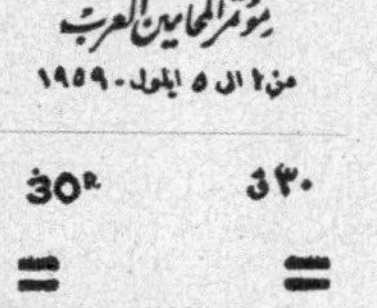

(102)

1959. Lawyers' Conference. Nos. 538 and 546 surch as T **102**.

618		30 p. on 50 p. myrtle and blue (postage)	1·10	65
619		40 p. on 50 p. yellow and black (air)	1·00	65

٣٠ق

مؤتمر الهندسة العربي السابع

من ١٨ الى ٢٢ آب ١٩٥٩

30P

(103)

1959. Air. Engineers' Conference. Nos. 614 and 616 surch as T **103**.

620		30 p. on 35 p. myrtle	65	50
621		40 p. on 65 p. sepia	1·25	75

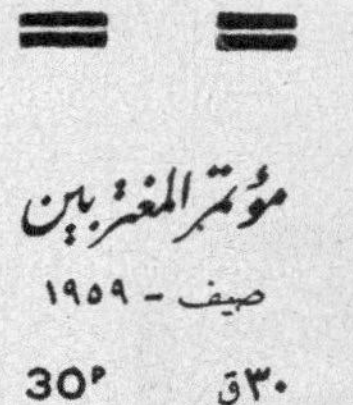

(104) **105** Discus Thrower

1959. Emigrants' Conference. No. 590 surch as T **104**.

622		30 p. on 50 p. green	75	30
623		40 p. on 50 p. green	1·10	60

1959. Air. 3rd Mediterranean Games, Beirut.

624	105	15 p. green	50	25
625	–	30 p. brown	75	40
626	–	40 p. blue	1·60	65

DESIGNS—VERT: 30 p. Weightlifting. HORIZ: 40 p. Games emblem.

106 Soldiers with Standard

108 Planting Tree

1959. Air. 16th Anniv of Independence.
627 106 40 p. red and black 95 65
628 60 p. red and green . . . . 1·25 90

1959. Surch.
629 100 7 p. 50 on 12 p. 50 blue . . 50 10
630 10 p. on 12 p. 50 blue . . . 65 10
631 15 p. on 25 p. blue 75 10
632 – 40 p. on 50 p. green (No. 590) . . . . . . 1·25 90
633 88 40 p. on 65 p. purple (No. 569) (air) . . . . 2·50 60

1960. Air. 25th Anniv of Friends of the Tree Society.
634 108 20 p. purple and green . . 75 50
635 40 p. sepia and green . . . 1·10 75

1960. Air. As T 79 but colours of name and value tablets reversed.
636 20 p. green 70 45

109 Pres. Chehab

1960. Air.
637 109 5 p. green 10 10
638 10 p. blue 10 10
639 15 p. brown 10 10
640 20 p. sepia 15 10
641 30 p. olive 20 10
642 40 p. red 45 15
643 50 p. blue 60 20
644 70 p. purple . . . . 1·10 25
645 100 p. green . . . . 2·25 65

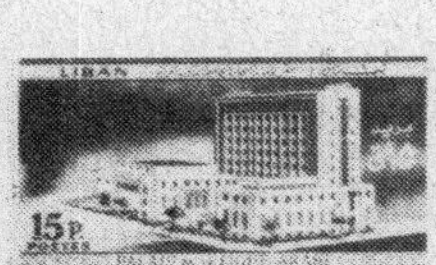
110 Arab League Centre

111 "Uprooted Tree"

1960. Inaug of Arab League Centre, Cairo.
646 110 15 p. turquoise 50 40

1960. Air. World Refugee Year. (a) Size 20¼ × 36½ mm.
647 111 25 p. brown 75 50
648 40 p. green . . . . 1·10 75

(b) Size 19¼ × 35¼ mm.
648b 111 25 p. brown . . . . . . 1·00 1·00
648c 40 p. green . . . . . . 1·25 1·25

112 Martyrs' Monument

1960. Air. Martyrs' Commemoration.
649 112 20 p. purple and green . . 50 30
650 40 p. blue and green . . . 75 50
651 – 70 p. olive and black . . . 1·60 75
DESIGN—VERT: 70 p. Detail of statues on monument.

113 Pres. Chehab and King Mohammed V

114 Pres. Chehab

1960. Air. Visit of King Mohammed V of Morocco.
652 113 30 p. chocolate and brown . 75 50
653 70 p. brown and black . . 1·50 75

1960.
654 114 50 c. green 10 10
655 2 p. 50 olive 10 10
656 5 p. green 15 10
657 7 p. 50 red 30 10
658 15 p. blue 50 25
659 50 p. purple . . . . . . 1·25 30
660 100 p. brown . . . . . . 2·50 50

115 Child

116 Dove, Map and Flags

1960. Air. Mother and Child Days.
661 115 20 p. red and yellow . . . 50 25
662 20 p. + 10 p. red & yellow 75 40
663 – 60 p. blue & light blue . . 1·25 85
664 – 60 p. + 15 p. blue & lt bl 1·90 1·00
DESIGN: Nos. 663/4, Mother and child.

1960. Air. World Lebanese Union Meeting. Beirut. Multicoloured.
665 20 p. Type 116 . . . . 25 20
666 40 p. Cedar of Lebanon and homing pigeons 75 40
667 70 p. Globes and Cedar of Lebanon (horiz) 90 50

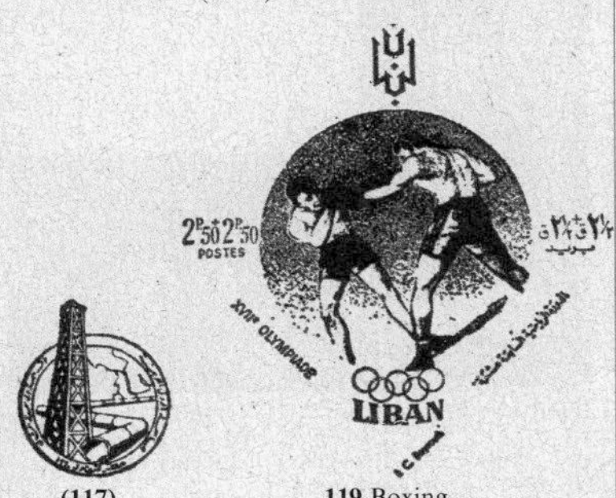

(117) 119 Boxing

1960. Arabian Oil Congress, Beirut. Optd with T 117.
668 86 5 p. green (No. 585) . . . 30 10
669 110 15 p. turquoise 65 40

1960. Air. World Refugee Year. Nos. 648b/c surch in English and Arabic.
669a 111 20 p. + 10 p. on 40 p. grn 7·00 7·00
669b 30 p. + 15 p. on 25 p. brn 10·00 10·00

1961. Olympic Games.
670 119 2 p. 50 + 2 p. 50 brown and blue (postage) 20 20
671 – 5 p. + 5 p. brown and orge 30 25
672 – 7 p. 50 + 7 p. 50 brn & vio 50 40
673 – 15 p. + 15 p. brown & red (air) . . . . 2·50 2·25
674 – 25 p. + 25 p. brown & grn 2·50 2·25
675 – 35 p. + 35 p. brown & bl 2·50 2·25
DESIGNS: 5 p. Wrestling; 7 p. 50, Putting the shot; 15 p. Fencing; 25 p. Cycling; 35 p. Swimming.

120 Pres. Chehab

121 Pres. Chehab and Map of Lebanon

122 U.N. Emblem and Map

1961.
676 120 2 p. 50 ultramarine and blue (postage) 20 10
677 7 p. 50 violet and mauve . 25 10
678 10 p. brown and yellow . . 50 10
679 121 5 p. green & lt green (air) 15 10
680 10 p. brown and ochre . . 45 10
681 70 p. violet and mauve . 1·90 60
682 – 200 p. blue and bistre . . 4·25 2·50
DESIGN—HORIZ: 200 p. Casino, Maameltein.

1961. Air. 15th Anniv of U.N.O.
683 122 20 p. purple and blue . . . 50 25
684 – 30 p. green and brown . . 75 40
685 – 50 p. blue and ultramarine . 1·25 60
DESIGNS—VERT: 30 p. U.N. emblem and Baalbek ruins. HORIZ: 50 p. View of U.N. Headquarters and Manhattan.

123 Cedar of Lebanon

124 Bay of Maameltein

1961. Redrawn version of T 86 (different arrangement at foot). Shaded background.
686 123 2 p. 50 myrtle 50 10
See also Nos. 695/7.

1961. Air.
687 124 15 p. lake 40 20
688 30 p. blue 65 30
689 40 p. sepia 90 45

125 Weaving

1961. Air. Labour Day.
690 – 30 p. red . . . . 1·25 60
691 125 70 p. blue . . . . 2·50 1·25
DESIGN: 30 p. Pottery.

126 Water-skiers

1961. Air. Tourist Month.
692 – 15 p. violet and blue . . . 60 35
693 126 40 p. blue and flesh . . . . 1·25 50
694 – 70 p. olive and flesh . . . 1·90 1·00
DESIGNS—VERT: 15 p. Firework display. HORIZ: 70 p. Tourists in punt.

1961. As T 123 but plain background.
695 2 p. 50 yellow 30 10
696 5 p. lake 40 15
697 10 p. black 65 25

127 G.P.O., Beirut

1961.
698 127 2 p. 50 mauve (postage) . . 30 10
699 5 p. green 50 20
700 15 p. blue . . . . 1·00 35
701 – 35 p. green (air) 60 45
702 – 50 p. brown 90 55
703 – 100 p. black . . . . 1·25 90
DESIGN: 35 p. to 100 p. Motor highway, Dora.

128 Cedars of Lebanon

129 Tyre Waterfront

1961.
704 128 0 p. 50 green (postage) . . 10 10
705 1 p. brown 10 10
706 2 p. 50 blue 10 10
707 5 p. red 25 10
708 7 p. 50 violet 35 10
709 – 10 p. purple 80 10
710 – 15 p. blue . . . . 1·10 20
711 – 50 p. green . . . . 1·25 75
712 – 100 p. black . . . . 3·00 1·10
713 129 5 p. red (air) 20 10
714 10 p. violet 25 10
715 15 p. blue 45 10
716 20 p. orange 45 10
717 30 p. green 50 15
718 – 40 p. purple 75 25
719 – 50 p. blue 90 40
720 – 70 p. green . . . . 1·25 60
721 – 100 p. sepia . . . . 2·25 95
DESIGNS—HORIZ: Nos. 709/12, Zahle. VERT: Nos. 718/21, Afka Falls.
See also Nos. 729/34.

130 U.N.E.S.C.O. Building, Beirut

1961. Air. 15th Anniv of U.N.E.S.C.O. Mult.
722 20 p. Type 130 . . . . 35 25
723 30 p. U.N.E.S.C.O. emblem and cedar (vert) 65 40
724 50 p. U.N.E.S.C.O. Building, Paris . . . . 1·00 60

131 Tomb of Unknown Soldier

132 Scout Bugler

1961. Independence and Evacuation of Foreign Troops Commem. Multicoloured.
725 10 p. Type 131 (postage) . . . 35 10
726 15 p. Soldier and flag 50 10
727 25 p. Cedar emblem (air) . . . 45 25
728 50 p. Emirs Bashir and Fakhreddine 65 50
The 25 p. and 50 p. are horiz.

1962. As Nos. 704/21 but with larger figures of value.
729 128 50 c. green (postage) . . . 20 10
730 1 p. brown 20 10
731 2 p. 50 blue 25 10
732 – 15 p. blue . . . . 3·00 25
733 129 5 p. red (air) 35 10
734 – 40 p. purple . . . . 5·50 75

1962. Lebanese Scout Movement Commemorative.
735 ½ p. black, yell & grn (postage) 10 10
736 1 p. multicoloured 10 10
737 2½ p. green, black and red . . . 10 10
738 6 p. multicoloured 35 10
739 10 p. yellow, black and blue . . 65 10
740 15 p. multicoloured (air) . . . 65 25
741 20 p. yellow, black and violet 75 35
742 25 p. multicoloured . . . . . 1·25 65
DESIGNS—VERT: ½ p. Type 132; 6 p. Lord Baden-Powell; 20 p. Saluting hand. HORIZ: 1 p. Scout with flag, cedar and badge; 2½ p. Stretcher party, badge and laurel; 10 p. Scouts at campfire; 15 p. Cedar and Guide badge; 25 p. Cedar and Scout badge.

133 Arab League Centre, Cairo, and Emblem

134 Blacksmith

1962. Air. Arab League Week.
743 133 20 p. ultramarine and blue 40 25
744 30 p. lake and pink 45 40
745 50 p. geeen and turquoise . 75 65
See also Nos. 792/5.

1962. Air. Labour Day.
746 134 5 p. green and blue 20 10
747 10 p. blue and pink 30 10
748 – 25 p. violet and pink . . . 50 20
749 – 35 p. mauve and blue . . . 65 40
DESIGN—HORIZ: 25 p., 35 p. Tractor.

1962. European Shooting Championships Nos. 670/5 optd **CHAMPIONNAT D'EUROPE DE TIR 2 JUIN 1962** in French and Arabic.
750 119 2 p. 50 + 2 p. 50 (postage) 40 25
751 – 5 p. + 5 p. 65 50
752 – 7 p. 50 + 7 p. 50 . . . . 95 60
753 – 15 p. + 15 p. (air) 95 95
754 – 25 p. + 25 p. . . . . . . 2·25 2·25
755 – 35 p. + 35 p. . . . . . . 2·50 2·50

136 Hand grasping Emblem

137 Rock Temples of Abu Simbel

1962. Air. Malaria Eradication.
756 136 30 p. brown & lt brown . . 75 50
757 – 70 p. violet and lilac . . . 1·25 75
DESIGN: 70 p. Campaign emblem.

1962. Nubian Monuments.
758 137 5 p. bl & ultram (postage) 50 20
759 15 p. lake and brown . . . 75 25
760 – 30 p. yellow and grn (air) 1·25 60
761 – 50 p. olive and grey . . . 2·50 1·25
DESIGNS: 30 p., 50 p. Bas-relief.

138 Playing-card Symbols **139** Schoolboy

1962. Air. European Bridge Championships.
762 **138** 25 p. multicoloured 3·00 1·90
763 40 p. multicoloured 3·25 1·90

1962. Schoolchildren's Day.
764 **139** 30 p. mult (postage) 50 25
765 – 45 p. multicoloured (air) 75 40
DESIGN: 45 p. Teacher.

140 **141** Cherries

1962. Air. 19th Anniv of Independence.
766 **140** 25 p. green, red & turq 75 35
767 25 p. violet, red & turq 75 35
768 25 p. blue, red & turquoise 75 35

1962. Fruits. Multicoloured.
769 0 p. 50 Type **141** (postage) 25 10
770 1 p. Figs 25 10
771 2 p. 50 Type **141** 40 10
772 5 p. Figs 50 10
773 7 p. 50 Type **141** 25 10
774 10 p. Grapes 35 10
775 17 p. 50 Grapes 75 10
776 30 p. Grapes 1·25 25
777 50 p. Oranges 2·25 65
778 100 p. Pomegranates 5·00 140
779 5 p. Apricots (air) 20 10
780 10 p. Plums 25 10
781 20 p. Apples 55 10
782 30 p. Plums 75 25
783 40 p. Apples 90 25
784 50 p. Pears 1·10 40
785 70 p. Medlars 1·90 50
786 100 p. Lemons 3·25 1·10

142 Reaping **143** Nurse tending Baby

1963. Air. Freedom from Hunger.
787 **142** 2 p. 50 yellow and blue 15 10
788 5 p. yellow and green 15 10
789 7 p. 50 yellow & purple 20 10
790 – 15 p. green and red 50 25
791 – 20 p. green and red 65 40
DESIGN—HORIZ: 15 p., 20 p. Three ears of wheat within hand.

1963. Air. Arab League Week. As T **133** but inscr "1963".
792 5 p. violet and blue 10 10
793 10 p. green and blue 20 20
794 15 p. brown and blue 30 25
795 20 p. grey and blue 65 45

1963. Air. Red Cross Centenary.
796 – 5 p. green and red 10 10
797 – 20 p. blue and red 30 10
798 **143** 35 p. red and black 55 25
799 40 p. violet and red 90 45
DESIGN—HORIZ: 5, 20 p. Blood transfusion.

144 Allegory of Music **145** Flag and rising Sun

1963. Air. Baalbek Festival.
800 **144** 35 p. orange and blue 95 50

1963. Air. 20th Anniv of Independence. Flag and sun in red and yellow.
801 **145** 5 p. turquoise 15 10
802 10 p. green 25 25
803 25 p. blue 50 40
804 40 p. drab 75 65

146 Cycling **147** Hyacinth

1964. 4th Mediterranean Games, Naples (1963).
805 **146** 2 p. 50 brown and purple (postage) 20 10
806 – 5 p. orange and blue 25 10
807 – 10 p. brown and violet 40 10
808 – 15 p. orange & green (air) 40 25
809 – 17 p. 50 brown & blue 50 30
810 – 30 p. brown & turq 75 50
DESIGNS—VERT: 5 p. Basketball; 10 p. Running; 15 p. Tennis. HORIZ: 17 p. 50 Swimming; 30 p. Skiing.

1964. Flowers. Multicoloured.
811 0 p. 50 Type **147** (postage) 10 10
812 1 p. Type **147** 10 10
813 2 p. 50 Type **147** 10 10
814 5 p. Cyclamen 10 10
815 7 p. 50 Cyclamen 15 10
816 10 p. Poinsettia 25 10
817 17 p. 50 Anemone 50 10
818 30 p. Iris 1·10 40
819 50 p. Poppy 2·50 65
820 5 p. Lily (air) 25 20
821 10 p. Ranunculus 45 20
822 20 p. Anemone 60 20
823 40 p. Tuberose 1·00 40
824 45 p. Rhododendron 1·10 40
825 50 p. Jasmine 1·25 40
826 70 p. Yellow broom 1·90 65
Nos. 816/26 are vert, size 26½ × 37 mm.

148 Cedar of Lebanon **149**

1964.
827 **148** 0 p. 50 green 25 10
828 **149** 0 p. 50 green 15 10
829 2 p. 50 blue 15 10
830 5 p. mauve 20 10
831 7 p. 50 orange 40 10
832 17 p. 50 purple 70 10

150 Child on Rocking-horse **152** "Flame of Freedom"

151 League Session

1964. Air. Children's Day.
833 – 5 p. red, orange and green 15 10
834 – 10 p. red, orange and brown 25 15
835 **150** 20 p. orange, blue and ultramarine 50 35
836 40 p. yellow, blue and purple 90 65
DESIGN—HORIZ: 5 p., 10 p. Girls skipping.

1964. Air. Arab League Meeting.
837 **151** 5 p. buff, brown and black 25 20
838 10 p. black 35 25
839 15 p. turquoise 65 40
840 20 p. mauve, brn & sepia 1·00 45

1964. Air. 15th Anniv of Declaration of Human Rights.
841 **152** 20 p. red, pink and brown 25 25
842 – 40 p. orange, blue and light blue 50 35
DESIGN: 40 p. Flame on pedestal bearing U.N. emblem.

153 Sick Child **154** Clasped Wrists

1964. Air. "Bal des Petits Lits Blancs" (Ball for children's charity).
843 **153** 2 p. 50 multicoloured 15 10
844 5 p. multicoloured 15 10
845 15 p. multicoloured 25 10
846 – 17 p. 50 multicoloured 40 25
847 – 20 p. multicoloured 50 25
848 – 40 p. multicoloured 80 40
DESIGN—55 × 25½ mm: 17 p. 50 to 40 p. Children in front of palace (venue of ball).

1964. Air. World Lebanese Union Congress, Beirut.
849 **154** 20 p. black, yellow & grn 50 25
850 40 p. black, yellow & pur 90 50

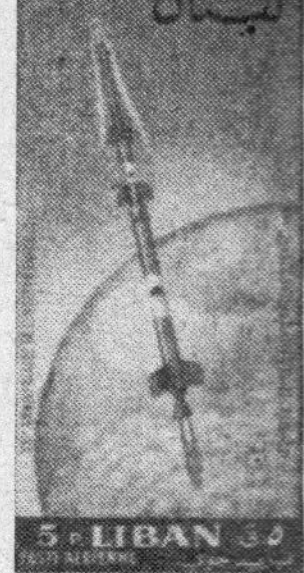

155 Rocket in Flight **156** Temple Columns

1964. Air. 21st Anniv of Independence.
851 **155** 5 p. multicoloured 25 20
852 10 p. multicoloured 25 20
853 – 40 p. blue and black 95 45
854 – 70 p. purple and black 1·40 1·10
DESIGNS—HORIZ: 40 p. to 70 p. "Struggle for Independence" (battle scene).

1965. Baalbek Festival.
855 **156** 2 p. 50 black and orange (postage) 25 20
856 – 7 p.50 black and blue 50 35
857 – 10 p. multicoloured (air) 10 10
858 – 15 p. multicoloured 25 10
859 – 25 p. multicoloured 50 40
860 – 40 p. multicoloured 1·00 50
DESIGNS—28 × 55 mm: 10 p., 15 p. Man in costume; 25 p., 40 p. Woman in costume.

157 Swimming

1965. Olympic Games, Tokyo.
861 **157** 2 p. 50 black, blue and mauve (postage) 20 10
862 – 7 p. 50 purple, green & brn 75 50
863 – 10 p. grey, brown & green 95 60
864 – 15 p. black and green (air) 25 10
865 – 25 p. green and purple 50 25
866 – 40 p. brown and blue 80 40
DESIGNS—HORIZ: 7 p. 50 Fencing; 15 p. Horse-jumping; 40 p. Gymnastics. VERT: 10 p. Basketball; 25 p. Rifle-shooting.

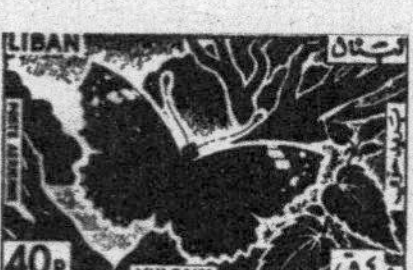

158 Red Admiral

1965. (a) Postage. Birds.
867 – 5 p. multicoloured 40 10
868 – 10 p. multicoloured 55 10
869 – 15 p. chocolate, orge & brn 1·00 10
870 – 17 p. 50 purple, red & blue 1·40 10
871 – 20 p. black, yellow & green 1·60 10
872 – 32 p. 50 yellow, brn & grn 4·00 65

(b) Air. Butterflies.
873 – 30 p. yellow, brown & red 75 10
874 – 35 p. blue, red & bistre 1·10 20
875 **158** 40 p. brown, red & green 1·40 20
876 – 45 p. brown, yellow & blue 1·75 40
877 – 70 p. multicoloured 2·75 50
878 – 85 p. black, orange & green 3·00 65
879 – 100 p. blue and plum 4·50 75
880 – 200 p. brown, blue & pur 8·00 90
881 – 300 p. sepia, yellow & green 12·00 2·50
882 – 500 p. brown, blue and light blue 20·00 5·00
DESIGNS—As T**158**. BIRDS: 5 p. Bullfinch; 10 p. Goldfinch; 15 p. Hoopoe; 17 p. 50, Red-legged partridge; 20 p. Golden oriole; 32 p. 50, European bee eater. BUTTERFLIES: 30 p. Large tiger moth; 35 p. Small postman; 45 p. Common grayling; 70 p. Swallowtail; 85 p. Orange-tip; 100 p. Blue morpho; 200 p. "Erasmia sanguiflua"; 300 p. "Papilio crassus". 35½ × 25 mm: 500 p. Amelia's charakes.

159 Pope Paul and Pres. Helou

1965. Air. Pope Paul's Visit to Lebanon.
883 **159** 45 p. violet and gold 3·25 1·90

160 Sheep

1965.
884 – 50 c. multicoloured 50 10
885 – 1 p. grey, black and mauve 65 10
886 **160** 2 p. 50 yellow, sepia & grn 75 10
DESIGNS: 50 c. Cow and calf; 1 p. Rabbit.

161 "Cedars of Friendship" **162** "Silk Manufacture"

1965. Air.
887 **161** 40 p. multicoloured 1·25 25

1965. Air. World Silk Congress, Beirut. Multicoloured.
888 2 p. 50 Type **162** 20 10
889 5 p. Type **162** 20 10
890 7 p. 50 Type **162** 25 10
891 15 p. Weaver and loom 25 10
892 30 p. As 15 p. 65 25
893 40 p. As 15 p. 1·00 40
894 50 p. As 15 p. 1·25 50

163 Parliament Building

1965. Air. Centenary of Lebanese Parliament.
895 **163** 35 p. brown, ochre & red 40 25
896 40 p. brown, ochre & green 65 40

164 U.N. Emblem and Headquarters **165** Playing-card "King"

1965. Air. 20th Anniv of U.N.O.
897 **164** 2 p. 50 blue 10 10
898 10 p. red 10 10
899 17 p. 50 violet 10 10
900 30 p. green 40 25
901 40 p. brown 50 40

1965. Air. World Bridge Chamipionships, Beirut.
902 **165** 2 p. 50 multicoloured 20 10
903 15 p. multicoloured 45 10
904 17 p. 50 multicoloured 65 25
905 40 p. multicoloured 1·25 50

166 Dagger on Deir Yassin, Palestine — **167** I.T.U. Emblem and Symbols

1965. Air. Deir Yassin Massacre.

No.	Type	Description	Unused	Used
906	166	50 p. multicoloured	2·25	50

1966. Air. Centenary (1965) of I.T.U.

No.	Type	Description	Unused	Used
907	167	2 p. 50 multicoloured	20	10
908		15 p. multicoloured	20	10
909		17 p. 50 multicoloured	45	15
910		25 p. multicoloured	75	30
911		40 p. multicoloured	1·00	40

168 Stage Performance

1966. Air. Baalbek Festival. Multicoloured.

No.	Description	Unused	Used
912	2 p. 50 Type **168**	20	10
913	5 p. Type **168**	20	10
914	7 p. 50 Ballet performance	20	10
915	15 p. Ballet performance	30	10
916	30 p. Concert	65	25
917	40 p. Concert	1·00	40

The 7 p. 50 and 15 p. are vert.

169 Tabarja — **170** W.H.O. Building

1966. Tourism. Multicoloured.

No.	Description	Unused	Used
918	50 c. Hippodrome, Beirut (postage)	10	10
919	1 p. Pigeon Grotto, Beirut	10	10
920	2 p. 50 Type **169**	10	10
921	5 p. Ruins, Beit-Mery	10	10
922	7 p. 50 Ruins, Anjar	10	10
923	10 p. Djezzine Falls (air)	10	10
924	15 p. Sidon Castle	15	10
925	20 p. Amphitheatre, Byblos	25	10
926	30 p. Sun Temple, Baalbek	40	10
927	50 p. Palace, Beit ed-Din	65	10
928	60 p. Nahr-el Kalb	1·50	45
929	70 p. Tripoli	1·25	40

1966. Air. Inauguration of W.H.O. Headquarters, Geneva.

No.	Type	Description	Unused	Used
930	170	7 p. 50 green	25	10
931		17 p. 50 red	35	25
932		25 p. blue	65	35

171 Skiing

1966. Air. International Cedars Festival.

No.	Type	Description	Unused	Used
933	171	2 p. 50 brown, red & green	25	10
934	–	5 p. multicoloured	25	10
935	–	17 p. 50 multicoloured	35	20
936	–	25 p. red, brown & green	1·00	40

DESIGNS: 5 p. Tobogganing; 17 p. 50, Cedar in snow; 25 p. Ski-lift.

172 Inscribed Sarcophagus

1966. Air. Phoenician Invention of the Alphabet.

No.	Type	Description	Unused	Used
937	172	10 p. brown, black & grn	10	10
938	–	15 p. brown, ochre & mve	25	10
939	–	20 p. sepia, blue & ochre	40	25
940	–	30 p. brown, orange & yell	65	40

DESIGNS: 15 p. Phoenician sailing ship; 20 p. Mediterranean route map showing spread of Phoenician alphabet; 30 p. Kadmus with alphabet tablet.

173 Child in Bath — **174** Decade Emblem

1966. Air. Int Children's Day. Multicoloured.

No.	Description	Unused	Used
941	2 p. Type **173**	10	10
942	5 p. Boy and doll in rowing boat	15	10
943	7 p. 50 Girl skiing	25	10
944	15 p. Girl giving food to bird	40	25
945	20 p. Boy doing homework	65	40

1966. Air. International Hydrological Decade.

No.	Type	Description	Unused	Used
947	174	5 p. ultramarine, bl & orge	20	10
948		10 p. red, blue and orange	20	10
949	–	15 p. sepia, green & orange	25	15
950	–	20 p. blue, green & orange	40	25

DESIGN: 15 p., 20 p. Similar "wave" pattern.

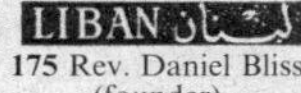

175 Rev. Daniel Bliss (founder) — **176** I.T.Y. Emblem

177 Beit ed-Din Palace

1966. Air. Centenary of American University, Beirut.

No.	Type	Description	Unused	Used
951	175	20 p. brown, yellow & grn	35	15
952	–	30 p. green, brown & blue	45	30

DESIGN: 30 p. University Chapel.

1967. International Tourist Year (1st issue). (a) Postage.

No.	Type	Description	Unused	Used
954	176	50 c. multicoloured	10	10
955		1 p. multicoloured	10	10
956		2 p. 50 multicoloured	10	10
957		5 p. multicoloured	15	10
958		7 p. 50 multicoloured	25	10

(b) Air. Multicoloured.

No.	Description	Unused	Used
959	10 p. Tabarja	20	10
960	15 p. Pigeon Rock, Beirut	25	10
961	17 p. 50 Type **177**	30	10
962	20 p. Sidon	30	10
963	25 p. Tripoli	35	10
964	30 p. Byblos	45	10
965	35 p. Ruins, Tyre	55	10
966	40 p. Temple, Baalbek	75	10

See also Nos. 977/80.

178 Signing Pact, and Flags

1967. Air. 22nd Anniv of Arab League Pact.

No.	Type	Description	Unused	Used
967	178	5 p. multicoloured	10	10
968		10 p. multicoloured	15	10
969		15 p. multicoloured	25	20
970		20 p. multicoloured	35	30

179 Veterans War Memorial Building, San Francisco

1967. Air. San Francisco Pact of 1945. Mult.

No.	Description	Unused	Used
971	2 p. 50 Type **179**	1·00	30
972	5 p. Type **179**	1·00	30
973	7 p. 50 Type **179**	1·00	30
974	10 p. Scroll and flags of U.N. and Lebanon	20	20
975	20 p. As 10 p.	25	20
976	30 p. As 10 p.	50	20

180 Temple Ruins, Baalbek

1967. Air. International Tourist Year (2nd issue). Multicoloured.

No.	Description	Unused	Used
977	5 p. Type **180**	10	10
978	10 p. Ruins, Anjar	15	10
979	15 p. Ancient bridge, Nahr-Ibrahim	25	10
980	20 p. Grotto, Jeita	40	15

181

1967. Air. India Day.

No.	Type	Description	Unused	Used
981	181	2 p. 50 red	10	10
982		5 p. purple	10	10
983		7 p. 50 brown	10	10
984		10 p. blue	20	10
985		15 p. green	45	15

182

1967. Air. 22nd Anniv of Lebanon's Admission to U.N.O.

No.	Type	Description	Unused	Used
986	182	2 p. 50 red	10	10
987		5 p. blue	10	10
988		7 p. 50 green	10	10
989	–	10 p. red	10	10
990	–	20 p. blue	25	10
991	–	30 p. green	45	25

DESIGN: 10, 20, 30 p. U.N. Emblem.

183 Goat and Kid

1967. Animals and Fishes. Multicoloured.

No.	Description	Unused	Used
992	50 c. Type **183** (postage)	20	10
993	1 p. Cattle	20	10
994	2 p. 50 Sheep	20	10
995	5 p. Dromedaries	20	10
996	10 p. Donkey	25	10
997	15 p. Horses	55	10
998	20 p. Basking shark (air)	80	10
999	30 p. Garfish	80	10
1000	40 p. Pollack	1·25	10
1001	50 p. Cuckoo wrasse	1·40	20
1002	70 p. Striped red mullet	3·00	25
1003	100 p. Rainbow trout	4·50	25

184 Ski Jumping

1968. Air. International Ski Congress. Beirut.

No.	Type	Description	Unused	Used
1004	184	2 p. 50 multicoloured	10	10
1005	–	5 p. multicoloured	20	10
1006	–	7 p. 50 multicoloured	20	10
1007	–	10 p. multicoloured	25	20
1008	–	25 p. multicoloured	50	25

DESIGNS: 5 p. to 10 p. Skiing (all different); 25 p. Congress emblem of Cedar and skis.

185 Princess Khaskiah

1968. Air. Emir Fakhreddine II Commem. Mult.

No.	Description	Unused	Used
1009	2 p. 50 Type **185**	10	10
1010	5 p. Emir Fakhreddine II	10	10
1011	10 p. Sidon Citadel	10	10
1012	15 p. Chekif Citadel	25	10
1013	17 p. 50 Beirut Citadel	40	15

The 10 p., 15 p. and 17 p. 50 are horiz designs.

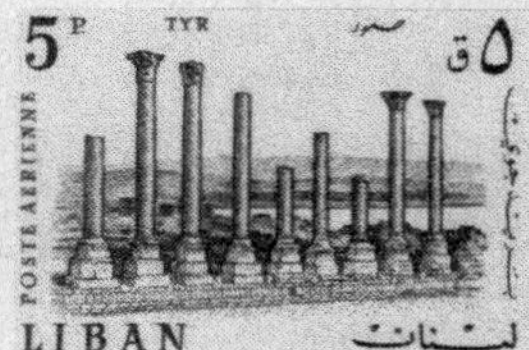

186 Colonnade

1968. Air. Tyre Antiquities.

No.	Type	Description	Unused	Used
1014	–	2 p. 50 brn, cream & pink	20	10
1015	186	5 p. brown, blue & yellow	20	10
1016	–	7 p. 50 brown, buff & grn	25	20
1017	–	10 p. brown, blue & orange	25	20

DESIGNS—VERT: 2 p. 50, Roman bust; 10 p. Bas-relief. HORIZ: 7 p. 50, Arch.

187 Justinian and Mediterranean Map

1968. Air. 1st Anniv of Faculty of Law, Beirut.

No.	Description	Unused	Used
1019	5 p. Justinian (vert)	10	10
1020	10 p. Justinian (vert)	10	10
1021	15 p. Type **187**	20	10
1022	20 p. Type **187**	25	15

188 Arab League Emblem — **190** Jupiter's Temple Ruins, Baalbek

189 Cedar on Globe

1968. Air. Arab Appeal Week.

No.	Type	Description	Unused	Used
1023	188	5 p. multicoloured	10	10
1024		10 p. multicoloured	10	10
1025		15 p. multicoloured	25	15
1026		20 p. multicoloured	40	15

1968. Air. 3rd World Lebanese Union Congress, Beirut.

No.	Type	Description	Unused	Used
1027	189	2 p. 50 multicoloured	10	10
1028		5 p. multicoloured	10	10
1029		7 p. 50 multicoloured	20	10
1030		10 p. multicoloured	20	15

1968. Air. Baalbek Festival. Multicoloured.

No.	Description	Unused	Used
1031	5 p. Type **190**	10	10
1032	10 p. Bacchus's Temple	10	10
1033	15 p. Corniche, Jupiter's Temple	25	15
1034	20 p. Portal, Bacchus's Temple	40	20
1035	25 p. Columns, Bacchus's Temple	50	30

191 Long Jumping and Atlantes

1968. Air. Olympic Games, Mexico.
1036 191 5 p. black, yellow & blue . . . 10 10
1037 – 10 p. black, blue & purple . . 10 10
1038 – 15 p. multicoloured . . . 25 10
1039 – 20 p. multicoloured . . . 40 20
1040 – 25 p. brown 65 40
DESIGNS (each incorporating Aztec relic): 10 p. High jumping; 15 p. Fencing; 20 p. Weightlifting; 25 p. "Sailing boat" with oars.

192 Lebanese driving Tractor ("Work protection") 193 Minshiya Stairs

1968. Air. Human Rights Year. Multicoloured.
1041 10 p. Type 192 . . . . 10 10
1042 15 p. Citizens ("Social Security") 20 10
1043 25 p. Young men of three races ("Unity") 25 20

1968. Air. Centenary of 1st Municipal Council (Deir el-Kamar). Multicoloured.
1044 10 p. Type 193 . . . . 10 10
1045 15 p. Serai kiosk 20 10
1046 25 p. Ancient highway 25 20

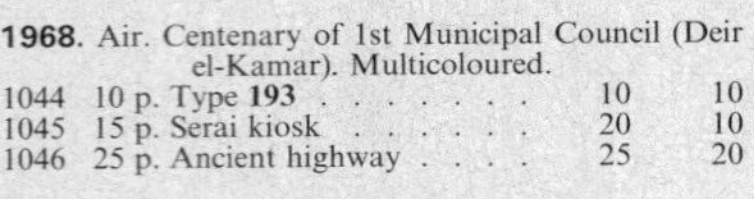
194 Nurse and Child

1969. Air. U.N.I.C.E.F. Multicoloured.
1047 194 5 p. black, brown & blue . . 10 10
1048 – 10 p. black, green & yell . . 10 10
1049 – 15 p. black, red & purple . . 10 10
1050 – 20 p. black, blue & yellow . . 25 20
1051 – 25 p. black, ochre & mve . . 40 20
DESIGNS: 10 p. Produce; 15 p. Mother and child; 20 p. Child with book; 25 p. Children with flowers.

195 Ancient Coin

1969. Air. 20th Anniv of International Museums Council (I.C.O.M.). Exhibits in National Museum, Beirut. Multicoloured.
1052 2 p. 50 Type 195 . . . . . . 10 10
1053 5 p. Gold dagger, Byblos . . . 20 10
1054 7 p. 50 Detail of Ahiram's Sarcophagus 20 10
1055 30 p. Jewelled pectoral 40 25
1056 40 p. Khalde "bird" vase . . . 50 40

196 Water-skiing

1969. Air. Water Sports. Multicoloured.
1057 2 p. 50 Type 196 . . . . . . 10 10
1058 5 p. Water-skiing (group) . . . 10 10
1059 7 p. 50 Paraskiing (vert) . . . 35 10
1060 30 p. Racing dinghies (vert) . . 50 35
1061 40 p. Racing dinghies 75 60

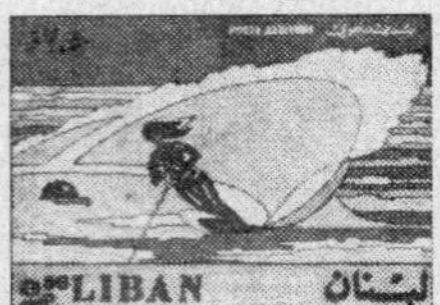

197 Frontier Guard

1969. Air. 25th Anniv of Independence. The Lebanese Army.
1062 2 p. Type 197 . . . . 10 10
1063 5 p. Unknown Soldier's Tomb . . 10 10
1064 7 p. 50 Army Foresters 20 10
1065 15 p. Road-making 20 15
1066 30 p. Military ambulance and Sud Aviation Alouette III helicopter 40 35
1067 40 p. Skiing patrol 60 50

198 Concentric Red Crosses

1971. Air. 25th Anniv of Lebanese Red Cross.
1068 198 15 p. red and black . . . 40 25
1069 – 85 p. red and black . . . 1·50 1·00
DESIGN: 85 p. Red Cross in shape of cedar of Lebanon.

199 Foil and Flags of Arab States

1971. Air. 10th International Fencing Championships. Multicoloured.
1070 10 p. Type 199 . . . . 10 10
1071 15 p. Foil and flags of foreign nations 10 10
1072 35 p. Contest with foils . . . 50 40
1073 40 p. Epee contest 65 40
1074 50 p. Contest with sabres . . 80 50

200 "Farmers at Work" (12th-century Arab painting)

1971. Air. 50th Anniv (1969) of I.L.O.
1075 200 10 p. multicoloured . . . 20 10
1076 40 p. multicoloured . . . 65 40

201 U.P.U. Monument and New H.Q. Building, Berne

1971. Air. New U.P.U. Headquarters Building, Berne.
1077 201 15 p. red, black & yellow . 20 10
1078 35 p. yell, black and orange 65 40

202 "Ravens setting fire to Owls" (14th-century painting)

1971. Air. Children's Day. Multicoloured.
1079 15 p. Type 202 . . . . 35 20
1080 85 p. "The Lion and the Jackal" (13th-century painting), (39 × 29 mm) . . . . 1·60 75

203 Arab League Flag and Map

1971. Air. 25th Anniv of Arab League.
1081 203 30 p. multicoloured . . . 40 15
1082 70 p. multicoloured . . . 75 50

204 Jamhour Electricity Sub-station

1971. Air. Multicoloured.
1083 5 p. Type 204 . . . . 10 10
1084 10 p. Maameltein Bridge . . . 10 10
1085 15 p. Hoteliers' School . . . 10 10
1086 20 p. Litani Dam 20 10
1087 25 p. Interior of T.V. set . . . 25 10
1088 35 p. Bziza Temple 40 10
1089 40 p. Jounieh Harbour 40 15
1090 45 p. Radar scanner, Beirut Airport 55 20
1091 50 p. Hibiscus 75 20
1092 70 p. School of Sciences Building . . . . 1·00 25
1093 85 p. Oranges . . . . 1·25 40
1094 100 p. Satellite Communications Station, Arbanieh . 1·50 65

205 Insignia of Imam al Ouzai (theologian)

1971. Air. Lebanese Celebrities.
1095 205 25 p. brown, gold & grn . . 35 20
1096 – 25 p. brown, gold & yell . . 35 20
1097 – 25 p. brown, gold & yell . . 35 20
1098 – 25 p. brown, gold & grn . . 35 20
PORTRAITS: No. 1096, Bechara el Khoury (poet and writer); 1097, Hassan Kamel el Sabbah (scientist); 1098, Gibran Khalil Gibran (writer).

206 I.E.Y. Emblem and Computer Card

1971. Air. International Education Year.
1099 206 10 p. black, blue and violet 10 10
1100 40 p. black, yellow and red 40 25

207 Dahr-el-Basheq Sanatorium 208 "Solar Wheel" Emblem

1971. Air. Tuberculosis Relief Campaign.
1101 207 50 p. multicoloured . . . 75 40
1102 – 100 p. multicoloured . . . 1·10 65
DESIGN: 100 p. Different view of Sanatorium.

1971. Air. 16th Baalbek Festival.
1103 208 15 p. orange and blue . . 20 10
1104 – 85 p. black, blue & orge . . 80 55
DESIGN: 85 p. Corinthian capital.

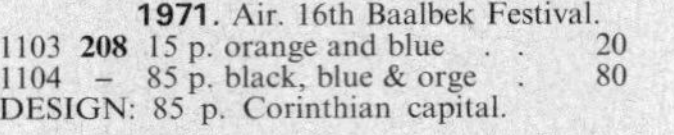

209 Field-gun

1971. Air. Army Day. Multicoloured.
1105 15 p. Type 209 . . . . 25 20
1106 25 p. Dassault Mirage IIICJ jet fighters 80 30
1107 40 p. Army Command H.Q. . . 75 50
1108 70 p. "Tarablous" (naval patrol boat) . . . . 1·50 90

210 Interior Decoration 212 U.N. Emblem

211 Lenin

1971. Air. 2nd Anniv of Burning of Al-Aqsa Mosque, Jerusalem.
1109 210 15 p. brown and deep brown 50 20
1110 35 p. brown and deep brown . . . . 1·00 65

1971. Air. Birth Centenary of Lenin. Mult.
1111 30 p. Type 211 . . . . 50 25
1112 70 p. Lenin in profile . . . . 1·10 65

1971. Air. 25th Anniv of United Nations.
1113 212 15 p. multicoloured . . . 20 10
1114 85 p. multicoloured . . . 95 50

213 "Europa" Mosaic, Byblos

1971. Air. World Lebanese Union.
1115 213 10 p. multicoloured . . . 25 10
1116 40 p. multicoloured . . . 1·00 40

1972. Various stamps surch.
1117 5 p. on 7 p. 50 (No. 922) (postage) 10 10
1118 5 p. on 7 p. 50 (No. 958) . . . 10 10
1119 25 p. on 32 p. 50 (No. 872) 90 10
1120 5 p. on 7 p. 50 (No. 1016) (air) 10 10
1121 100 p. on 300 p. (No. 881) . . 3·25 90
1122 100 p. on 500 p. (No. 882) . . 3·25 90
1123 200 p. on 300 p. (No. 881) . . 4·50 1·75

217 Morning Glory 218 Ornate Arches

1973. Air. Multicoloured.
1124 2 p. 50 Type 217 . . . . . . 10 10
1125 5 p. Roses 20 10
1126 15 p. Tulips 25 10
1127 25 p. Lilies 40 10
1128 40 p. Carnations 50 20
1129 50 p. Iris 75 10
1130 70 p. Apples . . . . 1·25 20
1131 75 p. Grapes . . . . 1·25 20
1132 100 p. Peaches . . . . . . 2·00 60
1133 200 p. Pears . . . . 3·25 45
1134 300 p. Cherries . . . . . . 4·50 85
1135 500 p. Oranges . . . . . . 6·25 1·50

1973. Air. Lebanese Domestic Architecture.
1136 – 35 p. multicoloured . . . 50 25
1137 218 50 p. multicoloured . . . 75 35
1138 – 85 p. multicoloured . . . 1·25 45
1139 – 100 p. multicoloured . . . 1·40 60
DESIGNS: Nos. 1136 and 1138/39, Various Lebanese dwellings.

219 Girl with Lute

1973. Air. Ancient Costumes. Multicoloured.

1140	5 p. Woman with rose	15	10
1141	10 p. Shepherd	25	10
1142	20 p. Horseman	25	20
1143	25 p. Type **219**	40	20

220 Swimming

1973. Air. 5th Pan-Arab Schools' Games, Beirut. Multicoloured.

1144	5 p. Type **220**	10	10
1145	10 p. Running	15	10
1146	15 p. Gymnastics	25	10
1147	20 p. Volleyball	40	10
1148	25 p. Basketball	40	20
1149	50 p. Table-tennis	75	35
1150	75 p. Handball	1·00	45
1151	100 p. Football	2·00	1·10

221 Brasilia

1973. Air. 150th Anniv of Brazil's Independence. Multicoloured.

1153	5 p. Type **221**	10	10
1154	20 p. Salvador (Bahia) in 1823	25	10
1155	25 p. Map and Phoenician galley	40	20
1156	50 p. Emperor Pedro I and Emir Fakhreddine II	85	40

222 Marquetry **223** Cedar of Lebanon

1973. Air. Lebanese Handicrafts. Multicoloured.

1157	10 p. Type **222**	15	10
1158	20 p. Weaving	25	10
1159	35 p. Glass-blowing	40	15
1160	40 p. Pottery	65	20
1161	50 p. Metal-working	75	20
1162	70 p. Cutlery-making	1·00	25
1163	85 p. Lace-making	1·40	40
1164	100 p. Handicrafts Museum	1·75	50

1974.

1165	**223** 50 c. green, brn & orge	20	10

224 Camp Site and Emblems

1974. Air. 11th Arab Scout Jamboree, Smar-Jubeil, Lebanon. Multicoloured.

1166	2 p. 50 Type **224**	10	10
1167	5 p. Scout badge and map	10	10
1168	7 p. 50 Map of Arab countries	20	10
1169	10 p. Lord Baden-Powell and Baalbek	20	10
1170	15 p. Guide and camp	20	10
1171	20 p. Lebanese Guide and Scout badge	30	10
1172	25 p. Scouts around campfire	45	10
1173	30 p. Globe and Scout badge	50	20
1174	35 p. Flags of participating countries	70	20
1175	50 p. Scout chopping wood for old man	1·00	35

225 Mail Train

1974. Centenary of U.P.U. Multicoloured.

1176	5 p 50 Type **225**	75	45
1177	20 p. Container ship	45	10
1178	25 p. Congress building, Lausanne, and U.P.U. H.Q., Berne	45	10
1179	50 p. Mail plane	75	45

226 Congress Building, Sofar

227 "Mountain Road" (O. Onsi)

1974. Air. 25th Anniv of Arab Postal Union. Multicoloured.

1180	5 p. Type **226**	10	10
1181	20 p. View of Sofar	20	10
1182	25 p. A.P.U. H.Q., Cairo	25	10
1183	50 p. Ministry of Posts, Beirut	1·00	55

1974. Air. Lebanese Paintings. Multicoloured.

1184	50 p. Type **227**	65	30
1185	50 p. "Clouds" (M. Farroukh)	65	30
1186	50 p. "Woman" (G. K. Gebran)	65	30
1187	50 p. "Embrace" (C. Gemayel)	65	30
1188	50 p. "Self-portrait" (H. Serour)	65	30
1189	50 p. "Portrait" (D. Corm)	65	30

228 Hunter killing Lion

1974. Air. Hermel Excavations. Multicoloured.

1190	5 p. Type **228**	10	10
1191	10 p. Astarte	15	10
1192	25 p. Dogs hunting boar	40	20
1193	35 p. Greco-Roman tomb	65	40

229 Book Year Emblem

1974. Air. International Book Year (1972).

1194	**229** 5 p. multicoloured	10	10
1195	10 p. multicoloured	15	10
1196	25 p. multicoloured	40	15
1197	35 p. multicoloured	50	60

230 Magnifying Glass

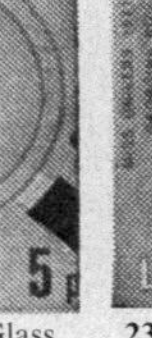
231 Georgina Rizk in Lebanese Costume

1974. Air. Stamp Day. Multicoloured.

1198	5 p. Type **230**	10	10
1199	10 p. Linked posthorns	10	10
1200	15 p. Stamp-printing	20	10
1201	20 p. "Stamp" in mount	35	20

1974. Air. Miss Universe 1971 (Georgina Rizk). Multicoloured.

1202	5 p. Type **231**	10	10
1203	20 p. Head-and-shoulders portrait	15	10
1204	25 p. Type **231**	25	15
1205	50 p. As 20 p.	65	40

232 Winds

234 Discus-throwing

233 U.N.I.C.E.F. Emblem and Sikorsky S-55 Helicopter

1974. Air. U.N. Conference on Human Environment, Stockholm, 1972. Multicoloured.

1207	5 p. Type **232**	10	10
1208	25 p. Mountains and plain	40	10
1209	30 p. Trees and flowers	40	20
1210	10 p. Sea	50	40

1974. Air. 25th Anniv of U.N.I.C.E.F. Multicoloured.

1212	20 p. Type **233**	45	10
1213	25 p. Emblem and child welfare clinic	25	10
1214	35 p. Emblem and kindergarten class	45	20
1215	70 p. Emblem and schoolgirls in laboratory	85	25

1974. Air. Olympic Games, Munich (1972). Mult.

1217	5 p. Type **234**	10	10
1218	10 p. Putting the shot	10	10
1219	15 p. Weight-lifting	15	10
1220	35 p. Running	50	25
1221	50 p. Wrestling	65	25
1222	85 p. Javelin-throwing	1·25	40

235 Symbols of Archaeology

1975. Air. Beirut — "University City". Multicoloured.

1224	20 p. Type **235**	25	10
1225	25 p. Science and medicine	25	10
1226	35 p. Justice and commerce	45	35
1227	70 p. Industry and commerce	90	50

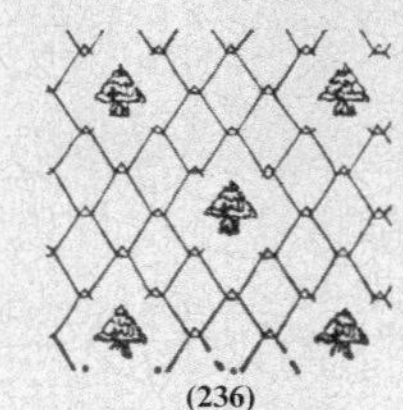
(236)

1978. Air. Various stamps optd with different patterns as T **236**. (a) Tourist Views. Nos. 1090, 1092/3.

1228	45 p. Radar scanner, Beirut Airport	45	20
1229	70 p. School of Sciences Building	90	25
1230	85 p. Oranges	1·00	35

(b) Flowers and Fruits. Nos. 1124/35.

1231	2 p. 50 Type **217**	10	10
1232	5 p. Roses	10	10
1233	15 p. Tulips	25	10
1234	25 p. Lilies	45	10
1235	40 p. Carnations	45	15
1236	50 p. Iris	65	15
1237	70 p. Apples	90	25
1238	75 p. Grapes	1·25	25
1239	100 p. Peaches	1·25	40
1240	200 p. Pears	2·50	1·40
1241	300 p. Cherries	3·75	2·50
1242	500 p. Oranges	6·25	3·75

(c) Lebanese Domestic Architecture. Nos. 1136/9.

1243	– 35 p. multicoloured	55	10
1244	**218** 50 p. multicoloured	65	15
1245	– 85 p. multicoloured	1·00	35
1246	– 100 p. multicoloured	1·25	40

(d) Ancient Costumes. Nos. 1140/3.

1247	5 p. Woman with rose	10	10
1248	10 p. Shepherd	15	10
1249	20 p. Horseman	30	10
1250	25 p. Type **219**	45	10

(e) Lebanese Handicrafts. Nos. 1157/8, 1160/4.

1251	10 p. Type **222**	15	10
1252	20 p. Weaving	30	10
1253	40 p. Pottery	45	15
1254	50 p. Metal-working	75	15
1255	70 p. Cutlery-making	90	25
1256	85 p. Lace-making	1·00	35
1257	100 p. Handicraft Museum	1·25	40

237 Mikhail Naimy (poet) and View of al-Chakroub Baskinta

1978. Air. Mikhail Naimy Festival Week. Mult.

1258	25 p. Mikhail Naimy and Sannine mountains	25	10
1259	50 p. Type **237**	50	25
1260	75 p. Mikhail Naimy (vert)	80	40

238 Heart and Arrow

239 Army Badge

1978. Air. World Health Day. "Down with Blood Pressure".

1261	**238** 50 p. blue, red and black	75	40

1980. Army Day. Multicoloured.

1262	25 p. Type **239** (postage)	40	20
1263	50 p. Statue of Emir Fakhr el Dine on horseback (air)	65	25
1264	75 p. Soldiers with flag (horiz)	95	25

240 13th-century European King

1980. Air. 50th Anniv (1974) of International Chess Federation. Multicoloured.

1265	50 p. Rook, knight and Jubilee emblem (horiz)	75	25
1266	75 p. Type **240**	1·25	40
1267	100 p. Rook and Lebanon Chess Federation emblem	1·90	65
1268	150 p. 18th-century French rook, king and knight	2·50	1·00
1269	200 p. Painted faience rook, queen and bishop	3·25	1·50

241 Congress, U.P.U. and Lebanon Post Emblems

1981. Air. 18th U.P.U. Congress, Rio de Janeiro (1979).

1270	**241** 25 p. blue, brown and black	40	15
1271	50 p. pink, brown & black	65	25
1272	75 p. green, brown & black	1·00	40

242 Children on Raft

243 President Sarkis

1981. Air. International Year of the Child (1979).

1273	**242** 100 p. multicoloured	1·25	65

1981. 5th Anniv of Election of President Sarkis.

1274	**243** 125 p. multicoloured	95	50
1275	300 p. multicoloured	2·75	1·10
1276	500 p. multicoloured	4·50	1·60

244 Society Emblem and Children

1981. Air. Centenary (1978) of Al-Makassed Islamic Welfare Society. Multicoloured.

1277	50 p. Type **244**	50	15
1278	75 p. Institute building	75	20
1279	100 p. Al-Makassed (founder)	95	35

245 Stork carrying Food

1982. World Food Day (1981). Multicoloured.
1280 50 p. Type **245** 50 25
1281 75 p. Ear of wheat and globe 75 40
1282 100 p. Fruit, fish and grain 1·50 65

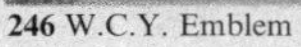

246 W.C.Y. Emblem **247** Phoenician Galley flying Scout Flag

1983. World Communications Year.
1283 **246** 300 p. multicoloured . . . 2·50 1·25

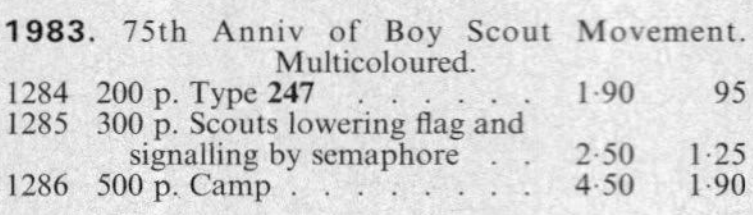

1983. 75th Anniv of Boy Scout Movement. Multicoloured.
1284 200 p. Type **247** . . . . . . 1·90 95
1285 300 p. Scouts lowering flag and signalling by semaphore . . 2·50 1·25
1286 500 p. Camp . . . . 4·50 1·90

248 "The Soul is Back"

1983. Birth Centenary of Gibran (poet and painter). Multicoloured.
1287 200 p. Type **248** . . . . . . 1·90 95
1288 300 p. "The Family" . . . . 2·50 1·25
1288 500 p. "Gibran" . . . . . . 4·50 1·90
1289 1000 p. "The Prophet" . . . 8·75 4·75

249 Cedar of Lebanon **250** Iris

1984.
1292 **249** 5 p. multicoloured 20 10

1984. Flowers. Multicoloured.
1293 10 p. Type **250** 25 10
1294 25 p. Periwinkle 40 25
1295 50 p. Barberry 95 40

251 Dove with Laurel over Buildings

1984. Lebanese Army. Multicoloured.
1296 75 p. Type **251** 70 40
1297 150 p. Cedar and soldier holding rifle . . . . 1·50 90
1298 300 p. Broken chain, hand holding laurel wreath and cedar . . . . 3·25 1·90

252 Temple Ruins, Fakra

1984. Multicoloured.
1299 100 p. Type **252** 95 40
1300 200 p. Temple ruins, Bziza . . 1·90 90
1301 500 p. Roman arches and relief, Tyre . . . . 4·75 1·90

253 President taking Oath

1988. Installation of President Amin Gemayel.
1302 **253** L£25 multicoloured . . . 60 40

254 Map of South America and Cedar of Lebanon

1989. 1st World Festival of Lebanese Youth in Uruguay.
1303 **254** L£5 multicoloured 20 10

255 Satellite, Flags and Earth **256** Children

1988. "Arabsat" Telecommunications Satellite.
1304 **255** L£10 multicoloured . . . 40 25

1988. U.N.I.C.E.F. Child Survival Campaign.
1305 **256** L£15 multicoloured . . . 65 40

257 Arabic "75" and Scout Emblems **258** President, Map and Dove

1988. 75th Anniv (1987) of Arab Scouts Movement.
1306 **257** L£20 multicoloured . . . 65 40

1988. International Peace Year (1986).
1307 **258** L£50 multicoloured . . . 1·25 65

259 Red Cross and Figures **260** Cedar of Lebanon

1988. Red Cross.
1308 **259** L£10 + L£1 red, silver and black 40 25
1309 – L£20 + L£2 multicoloured 65 40
1310 – L£30 + L£3 silver, green and red . . . . 1·00 60
DESIGNS: L£20, Helmeted heads; L£30, Globe, flame, and dove holding map of Lebanon.

1989.
1311 **260** L£50 green and mauve . . 25 15
1312 L£70 green and brown . . 40 20
1313 L£100 green and yellow 65 30
1314 L£200 green and blue . 1·25 65
1315 L£500 dp green and green 3·25 1·60

261 Dining in the Open at Zahle, 1883

1993. 50th Anniv of Independence. Multicoloured.
1316 L£200 Type **261** 40 25
1317 L£300 Castle ruins, Saida (vert) 55 40
1318 L£500 Presidential Palace, Baabda 95 65
1319 L£1000 Sword ceremony (vert) 1·90 1·25
1320 L£3000 Model for the rebuilding of central Beirut . . . . 5·50 3·00
1321 L£5000 President Elias Hrawi and state flag (vert) . . . . 10·00 6·75

262 Protection of Plants **263** Martyrs' Monument, Beirut

1994. Environmental Protection. Multicoloured.
1323 L£100 Type **262** 15 10
1324 L£200 Protection against forest fires 30 20
1325 L£500 Reforesting with cedars . 75 50
1326 L£1000 Creation of urban green zones . . . . 1·50 1·00
1327 L£2000 Trees . . . . . . 2·50 1·60
1328 L£5000 Green tree in town . . 8·00 5·25

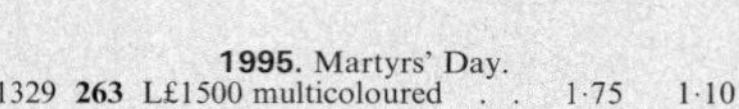

1995. Martyrs' Day.
1329 **263** L£1500 multicoloured . . 1·75 1·10

264 Arabic Script under Magnifying Glass and Headquarters

1996. Anniversaries and Events. Multicoloured.
1330 L£100 Type **264** (inauguration of Postal Museum, Arab League Headquarters, Cairo) . . . 10 10
1331 L£500 Anniversary emblem (50th anniv of U.N.I.C.E.F.) (horiz) 40 25
1332 L£500 Ears of wheat and anniversary emblem (50th anniv (1995) of F.A.O.) . . 40 25
1333 L£1000 U.N. Building (New York) and anniversary emblem (50th anniv (1995) of U.N.O.) 80 55
1334 L£1000 Emblem (International Year of the Family (1994)) (horiz) 80 55
1335 L£2000 Anniversary emblem (75th anniv (1994) of I.L.O.) (horiz) . . . . 1·60 1·10
1336 L£2000 Emblem (50th anniv of Arab League) . . . . . . 1·60 1·10
1337 L£3000 Emblem (75th anniv (1994) of Lebanese Law Society) . . . . 2·40 1·60
1338 L£3000 Rene Moawad (former President, 70th birth anniv (1995)) . . . . 2·40 1·60

265 Commemorative Medallion

1997. 1st Anniv of Shelling of Cana Refugee Camp.
1339 **265** L£1100 multicoloured . . 90 60

INDEX

Countries can be quickly located by referring to the index at the end of this volume.

266 Pope John Paul II and President Hrawi

1998. Papal Visit.
1340 **266** L£10000 multicoloured . . 8·00 5·25

POSTAGE DUE STAMPS

1924. Postage Due stamps of France surch **GRAND LIBAN** and value in "CENTIEMES" or "PIASTRES".
D26 **D 11** 50 c. on 10 c. brown . . 1·90 3·00
D27 1 p. on 20 c. green . . . 2·75 3·75
D28 2 p. on 30 c. red . . . . 1·90 3·75
D29 3 p. on 50 c. purple . . . 1·90 3·75
D30 5 p. on 1 f. purple on yellow . . . . 1·90 3·50

1924. Postage Due stamps of France surch **Gd Liban** and value in French and Arabic.
D58 **D 11** 0 p. 50 on 10 c. brown . 1·00 3·75
D59 1 p. on 20 c. green . . . 1·40 3·75
D60 2 p. on 30 c. red . . . . 1·40 2·75
D61 3 p. on 50 c. purple . . . 1·40 3·50
D62 5 p. on 1 f. purple on yell . 90 3·75

D 7 Nahr el-Kalb

1925.
D75 **D 7** 0 p. 50 brown on yellow . 35 50
D76 – 1 p. red on pink . . . . 40 1·10
D77 – 2 p. black on blue . . . 55 1·75
D78 – 3 p. brown on orange . 1·40 2·50
D79 – 5 p. black on green . . . 1·75 3·25
DESIGNS—HORIZ: 1 p. Pine Forest, Beirut; 2 p. Pigeon Grotto, Beirut; 3 p. Beaufort Castle; 5 p. Baalbeck.

1927. Optd **Republique Libanaise**.
D122 **D 7** 0 p. 50 brown on yellow . 40 1·25
D123 – 1 p. red on pink . . . . 70 1·75
D124 – 2 p. black on blue . . . 1·50 2·00
D125 – 3 p. brown on orange . 2·50 3·00
D126 – 5 p. black on green . . . 3·75 4·25

1928. Nos. D 122/6 optd with T **10**.
D145 **D 7** 0 p. 50 brown on yellow . 1·00 1·90
D146 – 1 p. red on pink . . . . 1·10 2·00
D147 – 2 p. black on blue . . . 2·00 2·50
D148 – 3 p. brown on orange . 3·00 4·25
D149 – 5 p. black on green . . . 3·25 4·50

D 18

D 19 Bas-relief from Sarcophagus of King Ahiram at Byblos

D 32

1931.
D191 **D 18** 0 p. 50 black on pink . 55 55
D192 – 1 p. black on blue . . . 80 75
D193 – 2 p. black on yellow . . 90 1·75
D194 – 3 p. black on green . . 1·75 1·60
D195 **D 32** 5 p. black on orange . . 5·25 6·25
D196 **D 19** 8 p. black on pink . . . 3·75 3·50
D252 **D 32** 10 p. green . . . . . . 5·00 4·50
D197 – 15 p. black . . . . . . 2·50 3·00
DESIGNS: 1 p. Bas-relief of Phoenician galley; 2 p. Arabesque; 3 p. Garland; 15 p. Statuettes.

D 43 National Museum

1945.
D298 **D 43** 2 p. black on lemon . . 2·75 2·75
D299 5 p. blue on pink . . . 3·25 3·25
D300 25 p. blue on green . . 4·75 4·75
D301 50 p. purple on blue . . 5·00 5·00

D 53

1947.
D352 **D 53** 5 p. black on green . . 3·75 1·25
D353 25 p. black on yellow . 38·00 3·25
D354 50 p. black on blue . . 22·00 8·25

D 59 Monument at Hermel

1948.
D379 **D 59** 2 p. black on yellow . . 2·50 65
D380 3 p. black on pink . . 5·75 2·50
D381 10 p. black on blue . . 14·00 5·00

D 67

1950.
D416 **D 67** 1 p. red 95 20
D417 5 p. blue . . . . . . 2·75 75
D418 10 p. green . . . . . . 5·00 1·60

D 78

1952.
D464 **D 78** 1 p. mauve 20 10
D465 2 p. violet 30 20
D466 3 p. green 45 20
D467 5 p. blue 65 25
D468 10 p. brown . . . . . 1·25 50
D469 25 p. black . . . . . 9·75 1·25

D 81 **D 93**

1953.
D481 **D 81** 1 p. red 15 10
D482 2 p. green 15 10
D483 3 p. orange 15 10
D484 5 p. purple 25 20
D485 10 p. brown 65 20
D486 15 p. blue . . . . . . 1·25 65

1955.
D550 **D 93** 1 p. brown 10 10
D551 2 p. green 10 10
D552 3 p. turquoise 10 10
D553 5 p. purple 10 10
D554 10 p. green 30 20
D555 15 p. blue 30 20
D556 25 p. purple 75 50

D 178 **D 184** Emir Fakhreddine II

1967.
D967 **D 178** 1 p. green 10 10
D968 5 p. mauve 10 10
D969 15 p. blue 30 30

1968.
D1004 **D 184** 1 p. slate and grey 10 10
D1005 2 p. turquoise & green 10 10
D1006 3 p. orange & yellow 10 10
D1007 5 p. purple and red 10 10
D1008 10 p. olive & yellow 10 10
D1009 15 p. blue and violet 35 35
D1010 25 p. blue & lt blue 60 60

POSTAL TAX STAMPS

These were issued between 1945 and 1962 for compulsory use on inland mail (and sometimes on mail to Arab countries) to provide funds for various purposes.

T 41 **(T 42)**

1945. Lebanese Army. Fiscal stamp as Type T **41** surch with Type T **42**.
T289 **T 41** 5 p. on 30 c. brown . . £425 1·75

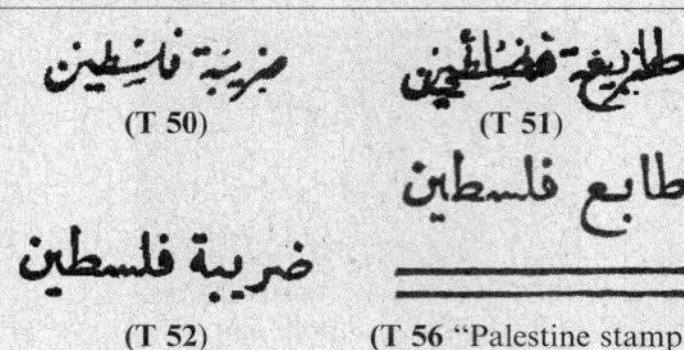

(T 50) (T 51) (T 52) (T 56 "Palestine stamp").

1947. Aid to War in Palestine. Surch as Type T **42** but (a) With top line Type T **50**.
T338 **T 41** 5 p. on 25 c. green . . . 13·00 1·40
T339 5 p. on 30 c. brown . . 18·00 2·75
T340 5 p. on 60 c. blue . . . 27·00 2·00
T341 5 p. on 3 p. pink . . . . 13·50 2·50
T342 5 p. on 15 p. blue . . . 13·50 1·00
(b) With top line Type T **51**.
T343 **T 41** 5 p. on 10 p. red . . . . 60·00 3·00
(c) With top line Type T **52**.
T344 **T 41** 5 p. on 3 p. pink . . . . 13·50 1·75
(d) As No. T344 but with figure "5" at left instead of "0" and without inscr between figures.
T345 **T 41** 5 p. on 3 p. pink . . . . £300 22·00

1948. Palestine Aid. No. T289 optd with Type T **56**.
T363 **T 41** 5 p. on 30 c. brown . . 18·00 2·40

T 95 Family and Ruined House

1956. Earthquake Victims.
T559 **T 95** 2 p. 50 brown . . . . . 2·00 20

T 99 Rebuilding **T 100** Rebuilding

1957. Earthquake Victims.
T601 **T 99** 2 p. 50 brown . . . . 2·00 20
T602 2 p. 50 green . . . . 1·25 20
T603 **T 100** 2 p. 50 brown . . . . 1·25 10

T 132 Rebuilding **T 133** Rebuilding

1961. Earthquake Victims.
T729 **T 132** 2 p. 50 brown . . . . 1·25 10
T730 **T 133** 2 p. 50 blue . . . . . 1·00 10

LEEWARD ISLANDS Pt. 1

A group of islands in the Br. W. Indies, including Antigua, Barbuda, British Virgin Islands, Dominica (till end of 1939), Montserrat, Nevis and St. Christopher (St. Kitts). Stamps of Leeward Islands were used concurrent with the issues for the respective islands until they were withdrawn on the 1 July, 1956.

1890. 12 pence = 1 shilling;
20 shillings = 1 pound.
1951. 100 cents = 1 West Indian dollar.

1 **(3)**

1890.
1 **1** ½d. mauve and green . . . . 3·25 1·25
2 1d. mauve and red . . . . 3·25 20
3 2½d. mauve and blue . . . 3·75 20
4 4d. mauve and orange . . . 4·00 7·00
5 6d. mauve and brown . . . 10·00 11·00
6 7d. mauve and grey . . . . 3·25 11·00
7 1s. green and red . . . . 16·00 40·00
8 5s. green and blue £120 £225

1897. Diamond Jubilee. Optd with T **3**.
9 **1** ½d. mauve and green . . . . 3·00 10·00
10 1d. mauve and red . . . . 3·50 10·00
11 2½d. mauve and blue . . . 4·00 10·00
12 4d. mauve and orange . . 28·00 70·00
13 6d. mauve and brown . . 48·00 90·00
14 7d. mauve and grey . . . 48·00 90·00
15 1s. green and red £120 £190
16 5s. green and blue £450 £750

1902. Surch **One Penny**.
17 **1** 1d. on 4d. mauve and orange . 1·75 4·75
18 1d. on 6d. mauve and brown . 2·50 10·00
19 1d. on 7d. mauve and grey . 2·25 4·50

1902. As T **1**, but portrait of King Edward VII.
29 ½d. purple and green . . . . . 3·00 1·75
21 1d. purple and red . . . . . 5·50 20
22 2d. purple and brown . . . . 2·50 4·25
23 2½d. purple and blue . . . . 4·00 2·25
24 3d. purple and black . . . . 3·25 7·50
25 6d. purple and brown . . . . 2·00 8·00
26 1s. green and red . . . . . . 2·25 18·00
27 2s. 6d. green and black . . . 27·00 65·00
28 5s. green and blue . . . . . 48·00 70·00

1907. As last, colours changed.
36 ¼d. brown . . . . 2·00 1·50
37 ½d. green . . . . 2·25 75
38 1d. red . . . . 7·00 70
39 2d. grey . . . . 2·75 7·50
40 2½d. blue . . . . 4·50 4·00
41 3d. purple and yellow . . . . 3·25 7·50
42 6d. purple . . . . 6·50 7·00
43 1s. black on green . . . . . 3·25 21·00
44 2s. 6d. black and red on blue . 38·00 48·00
45 5s. green and red on yellow . . 40·00 65·00

10 King George V **14** King George VI

1912.
46 **10** ¼d. brown . . . . 1·50 80
59 ½d. green 75 75
60 1d. red . . . . 2·00 55
61 1d. violet . . . . 2·25 1·00
63 1½d. red . . . . 2·75 2·00
64 1½d. brown 75 10
65 2d. grey . . . . 1·50 80
67 2½d. blue . . . . 2·75 1·00
66 2½d. yellow . . . . 6·00 45·00
69 3d. purple on yellow . . . . 85 6·50
68 3d. blue . . . . 4·00 22·00
70 4d. black & red on yellow . . 2·50 20·00
71 5d. purple and green . . . . 2·25 4·25
53 6d. purple . . . . 2·00 8·00
54 1s. black on green . . . . . 2·00 8·00
74a 2s. purple & blue on blue . . 7·00 42·00
75 2s. 6d. black & red on blue . 6·50 23·00
76 3s. green and violet . . . . 12·00 24·00
77 4s. black and red . . . . . 12·00 42·00
57b 5s. green & red on yellow . . 17·00 55·00
Larger type, as T **15** of Malta.
79 **13** 10s. green and red on green . 50·00 75·00
80 £1 purple and black on red . £225 £250

1935. Silver Jubilee. As T **10a** of Gambia.
88 1d. blue and red . . . . . . 1·60 1·25
89 1½d. blue and grey . . . . . 2·25 70
90 2½d. brown and blue . . . . 2·25 3·25
91 1s. grey and purple . . . . . 5·50 14·00

1937. Coronation. As T **10b** of Gambia.
92 1d. red 30 15
93 1½d. brown 40 35
94 2½d. blue 40 45

1938.
95a **14** ¼d. brown . . . . 10 1·25
96 ½d. green 60 60
97 ½d. grey . . . . 30 1·25
99 1d. red . . . . 1·75 1·50
100 1d. green 55 15
101 1½d. brown 90 50
102 1½d. orange and black . . . 60 30
103 2d. grey . . . . 2·50 1·00
104 2d. red . . . . 1·40 90
105a 2½d. blue . . . . 60 1·25
106 2½d. black and purple . . . 55 15
107a 3d. orange 40 85
108 3d. blue 65 15
109a 6d. purple . . . . 4·50 2·25
110b 1s. black on green . . . . 4·25 90
111a 2s. purple & blue on blue . 10·00 1·50
112a 5s. green & red on yellow . 32·00 14·00
113c – 10s. green & red on green . £120 70·00
114b – £1 purple and black on red . 35·00 20·00
Nos. 113b/4b are as Type **15** of Bermuda but with portrait of King George VI.

1946. Victory. As T **11a** of Gambia.
115 1½d. brown 15 30
116 3d. orange 15 30

1949. Silver Wedding. As T **11b/c** of Gambia.
117 2½d. blue 10 10
118 5s. green . . . . 3·75 2·75

1949. U.P.U. As T **11d/g** of Gambia.
119 2½d. black 15 80
120 3d. blue . . . . 1·25 80
121 6d. mauve 30 80
122 1s. turquoise 30 80

1951. Inauguration of B.W.I. University College. As T **43a/b** of Grenada.
123 3 c. orange and black 30 60
124 12 c. red and violet 60 60

1953. Coronation. As T **11h** of Gambia.
125 3 c. black and green . . . . . 40 1·75

1954. As T **14** but portrait of Queen Elizabeth II facing left.
126 ½ c. brown 10 40
127 1 c. grey 50 75
128 2 c. green 50 10
129 3 c. yellow and black . . . . 1·25 75
130 4 c. red . . . . 1·00 10
131 5 c. black and purple . . . . 1·75 75
132 6 c. yellow . . . . 1·75 30
133 8 c. blue . . . . 2·50 10
134 12 c. purple . . . . 1·75 10
135 24 c. black and green . . . . 1·75 20
136 48 c. purple and blue . . . . 6·00 2·75
137 60 c. brown and green . . . 6·00 2·25
138 $1.20 green and red . . . . 5·00 2·75

Larger type as T **15** of Malta, but portrait of Queen Elizabeth II facing left.

139 $2.40 green and red . . . . . 6·50 5·00
140 $4.80 purple and black . . . . 6·50 6·50

LESOTHO Pt. 1

Formerly Basutoland, attained independence on 4 October, 1966 and changed its name to Lesotho.

1966. 100 cents = 1 rand.
1979. 100 lisente = 1 (ma)loti.

33 Moshoeshoe I and Moshoeshoe II

1966. Independence.

106 **33** 2½ c. brown, black & red . . 10 10
107 5 c. brown, black & blue . . 10 10
108 10 c. brown, black & green . 15 10
109 20 c. brown, black & purple 20 15

1966. Nos. 69 etc. of Basutoland optd **LESOTHO**.

110A **8** ½ c. black and sepia . . . 10 10
111A – 1 c. black and green . . 10 10
112A – 2 c. blue and orange . . 60 10
113B **26** 2½ c. sage and red . . . 50 10
114A – 3½ c. indigo and blue . . 30 10
115A – 5 c. brown and green . . 10 10
116A – 10 c. bronze and purple . 10 10
117B – 12½ c. brown & turquoise 30 20
118A 25 c. blue and red . . . 30 20
119B – 50 c. black and red . . 60 50
120B **9** 1 r. black and purple . . 65 75

35 "Education, Culture and Science" **36** Maize

1966. 20th Anniv of U.N.E.S.C.O.

121 **35** 2½ c. yellow and green . . . 10 10
122 5 c. green and olive . . . 15 10
123 12½ c. blue and red . . . 35 10
124 25 c. orange and blue . . . 60 25

1967.

125 **36** ½ c. green and violet . . . 10 10
126 – 1 c. sepia and red . . . 10 10
149 – 2 c. yellow and green . . 10 10
128 – 2½ c. black and ochre . . 10 10
151 – 3 c. chocolate, green & brn . 15 15
152 – 3½ c. blue and yellow . . 15 10
130 – 5 c. bistre and blue . . . 10 10
131 – 10 c. brown and grey . . 10 10
132 – 12½ c. black and orange . 20 10
133 – 25 c. black and blue . . . 55 20
134 – 50 c. black, blue & turquoise 4·50 65
135 – 1 r. multicoloured . . . 65 75
136 – 2 r. black, gold and purple . 1·00 1·75

DESIGNS—HORIZ: 1 c. Cattle; 2 c. Aloes; 2½ c. Basotho hat; 3 c. Sorghum; 3½ c. Merino sheep ("Wool"); 5 c. Basotho pony; 10 c. Wheat; 12½ c. Angora goat ("Mohair"); 25 c. Maletsunyane Falls; 50 c. Diamonds; 1 r. Arms of Lesotho. VERT: 2 r. Moshoeshoe II.

See also Nos. 191/203.

46 Students and University

1967. 1st Conferment of University Degrees.

137 **46** 1 c. sepia, blue and orange . 10 10
138 2½ c. sepia, ultramarine & bl 10 10
139 12½ c. sepia, blue and red . . 10 10
140 25 c. sepia, blue and violet . 15 15

47 Statue of Moshoeshoe I

1967. 1st Anniv of Independence.

141 **47** 2½ c. black and green . . . 10 10
142 – 12½ c. multicoloured . . . 25 15
143 – 25 c. black, green & ochre . 35 25

DESIGNS: 12½ c. National flag; 25 c. Crocodile (national emblem).

50 Lord Baden-Powell and Scout Saluting

1967. 60th Anniv of Scout Movement.

144 **50** 15 c. multicoloured 20 10

51 W.H.O. Emblem and World Map

1968. 20th Anniv of World Health Organization.

145 **51** 2½ c. blue, gold and red . . 15 10
146 – 25 c. multicoloured 45 30

DESIGN: 25 c. Nurse and child.

55 Running Hunters

1968. Rock Paintings.

160 **55** 3 c. brown, turq & grn . . . 25 10
161 – 3½ c. yellow, olive & sepia . 30 10
162 – 5 c. red, ochre & brown . . 35 10
163 – 10 c. yellow, red & purple . 45 10
164 – 15 c. buff, yellow and brown 75 30
165 – 20 c. green, yell & brown . . 90 55
166 – 25 c. yellow, brown & black . 1·00 75

DESIGNS—HORIZ: 3½ c. Baboons; 10 c. Archers; 20 c. Eland; 25 c. Hunting scene. VERT: 5 c. Javelin thrower; 15 c. Blue cranes.

62 Queen Elizabeth II Hospital

1969. Centenary of Maseru (capital). Mult.

167 2½ c. Type **62** 10 10
168 10 c. Lesotho Radio Station . . 10 10
169 12½ c. Leabua Jonathan Airport 35 10
170 25 c. Royal Palace 25 15

66 Rally Car passing Basuto Tribesman

1969. "Roof of Africa" Car Rally.

171 **66** 2½ c. yellow, mve & plum . . 15 10
172 – 12½ c. blue, yellow & grey . . 20 10
173 – 15 c. blue, black & mauve . 20 10
174 – 20 c. black, red and yellow . 20 10

DESIGNS: 12½ c. Rally car on mountain road; 15 c. Chequered flags and "Roof of Africa" Plateau; 20 c. Map of rally route and Independence Trophy.

71 Gryponyx and Footprints

1970. Prehistoric Footprints (1st series).

175 – 3 c. brown and sepia 70 70
176 **71** 5 c. purple, pink & sepia . . 85 30
177 – 10 c. yellow, black & sepia . 1·00 35
178 – 15 c. yellow, black & sepia . 1·60 2·25
179 – 25 c. blue and black . . . . 2·50 2·25

DESIGNS: 3 c. Dinosaur footprints at Moyeni; 10 c. Plateosauravus and footprints; 15 c. Tritylodon and footprints; 25 c. Massospondylus and footprints.

No. 175 is larger, 60 × 23 mm.

See also Nos. 596/8.

75 Moshoeshoe I as a Young Man

1970. Death Centenary of Chief Moshoeshoe I.

180 **75** 2½ c. green and mauve . . . 10 10
181 – 25 c. blue and brown . . . 20 20

DESIGN: 25 c. Moshoeshoe I as an old man.

77 U.N. Emblem and "25"

1970. 25th Anniv of United Nations.

182 **77** 2½ c. pink, blue & purple . . 10 10
183 – 10 c. multicoloured 10 10
184 – 12½ c. red, blue and drab . . 10 15
185 – 25 c. multicoloured 15 30

DESIGNS: 10 c. U.N. Building; 12½ c. "People of the World"; 25 c. Symbolic dove.

78 Gift Shop, Maseru

1970. Tourism. Multicoloured.

186 2½ c. Type **78** 10 10
187 5 c. Trout fishing 20 10
188 10 c. Pony trekking 25 10
189 12½ c. Skiing, Maluti Mountains 50 10
190 20 c. Holiday Inn, Maseru . . 40 50

79 Maize **80** Lammergeier

1971. As Nos. 147/58 but in new format omitting portrait, as in T **79**. New designs for 4 c., 2 r.

191 **79** ½ c. green and violet . . . 10 10
192 – 1 c. brown and red . . . 10 10
193 – 2 c. yellow and green . . 10 10
194 – 2½ c. black, green & yell . 10 10
195 – 3 c. brown, green & yell . 10 10
196 – 3½ c. blue and yellow . . 10 10
196a – 4 c. multicoloured . . . 20 10
197 – 5 c. brown and blue . . 15 10
198 – 10 c. brown and grey . . 15 10
199 – 12½ c. brown and orange . 25 30
200 – 25 c. slate and blue . . . 60 40
201 – 50 c. black, blue & green . 6·00 4·25
202 – 1 r. multicoloured . . . 1·75 2·25
401 – 2 r. brown and blue . . . 70 2·25

DESIGNS—HORIZ: 4 c. National flag. VERT: 2 r. Statue of Moshoeshoe I.

1971. Birds. Multicoloured.

204 2½ c. Type **80** . . . . 2·25 20
205 5 c. Bald ibis . . . . 3·00 2·50
206 10 c. Rufous rockjumper . . . 3·00 2·00
207 12½ c. Blue bustard . . . . . 3·75 3·50
208 15 c. Painted snipe . . . . . 4·25 4·50
209 20 c. Golden-breasted bunting . 4·25 4·50
210 25 c. Ground woodpecker . . . 4·75 4·50

81 Lionel Collett Dam

1971. Soil Conservation. Multicoloured.

211 4 c. Type **81** 10 10
212 10 c. Contour ridges 10 10
213 15 c. Earth dams 25 10
214 25 c. Beaver dams 35 35

82 Diamond Mining

1971. Development. Multicoloured.

215 4 c. Type **82** 75 40
216 10 c. Pottery 30 10
217 15 c. Weaving 45 60
218 20 c. Construction . . . . . 55 1·50

83 Mail Cart

1972. Centenary of Post Office.

219 **83** 5 c. brown and pink 15 20
220 – 10 c. multicoloured 15 10
221 – 15 c. blue, black and brown . 30 15
222 – 20 c. multicoloured 45 90

DESIGNS—HORIZ: 10 c. Postal bus; 20 c. Maseru Post Office. VERT: 15 c. 4d. Cape of Good Hope stamp of 1876.

84 Sprinting

1972. Olympic Games, Munich. Multicoloured.

223 4 c. Type **84** 15 10
224 10 c. Shot putting 20 10
225 15 c. Hurdling 30 10
226 25 c. Long-jumping 35 55

85 "Adoration of the Shepherds" (Matthias Stomer)

1972. Christmas.

227 **85** 4 c. multicoloured 10 10
228 10 c. multicoloured 10 10
229 25 c. multicoloured 15 20

86 W.H.O. Emblem

1973. 25th Anniv of W.H.O.

230 **86** 20 c. yellow and blue . . . 30 30

1973. O.A.U. 10th Anniv Nos. 194 and 196a/8 optd **O.A.U. 10th Anniversary Freedom in Unity**.

231 2½ c. black, green and brown . . 10 10
232 4 c. multicoloured 10 10
233 5 c. brown and blue 10 10
234 10 c. brown and blue 15 15

88 Basotho Hat and W.F.P. Emblem

1973. 10th Anniv of World Food Programme. Multicoloured.

235 4 c. Type **88** 10 10
236 15 c. School feeding 20 15
237 20 c. Infant feeding 20 20
238 25 c. "Food for work" 25 25

89 "Aeropetes tulbaghia"

1973. Butterflies. Multicoloured.

239 4 c. Type **89** 75 10
240 5 c. "Papilio demodocus" . . . 85 50
241 10 c. "Cynthia cardui" . . . . 1·25 50
242 15 c. "Precis hierta" . . . . . 2·25 1·75
243 20 c. "Precis oenone" . . . . 2·25 1·75
244 25 c. "Danaus chrysippus" . . 2·50 2·75
245 30 c. "Colotis evenina" . . . . 2·50 3·75

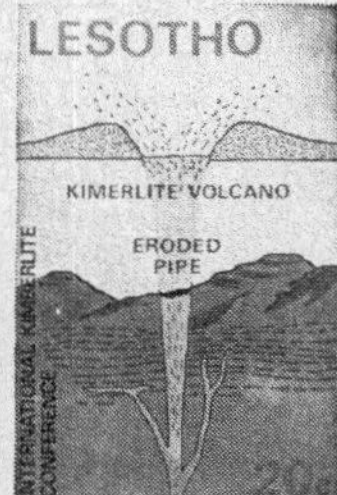

90 Kimberlite Volcano

92 Open Book and Wreath

91 "Health"

1973. International Kimberlite Conference. Mult.

246 10 c. Map of diamond mines (horiz) . . . . 2·00 50
247 15 c. Kimberlite-diamond rock (horiz) . . . . 2·25 2·25
248 20 c. Type **90** . . . . 2·25 2·50
249 30 c. Diamond prospecting . . 3·75 7·00

1974. Youth and Development. Multicoloured.

250 4 c. Type **91** 10 10
251 10 c. "Education" 15 10
252 20 c. "Agriculture" 20 10
253 25 c. "Industry" 30 20
254 30 c. "Service" 30 25

1974. 10th Anniv of U.B.L.S. Multicoloured.

255 10 c. Type **92** 15 10
256 15 c. Flags, mortar-board and scroll 20 20
257 20 c. Map of Africa 25 20
258 25 c. King Moshoeshoe II capping a graduate 25 50

93 Senqunyane River Bridge, Marakabei

1974. Rivers and Bridges. Multicoloured.

259 4 c. Type **93** 10 10
260 5 c. Tsoelike River and bridge . 10 10
261 10 c. Makhaleng River Bridge . 20 10
262 15 c. Seaka Bridge, Orange/Senqu River 35 35
263 20 c. Masianokeng Bridge Phuthiatsana River 40 40
264 25 c. Mahobong Bridge, Hlotse River 45 45

94 U.P.U. Emblem

1974. Centenary of U.P.U.

265 **94** 4 c. green and black 10 10
266 – 10 c. orange, yellow & blk . 15 10
267 – 15 c. multicoloured . . . 20 60
268 – 20 c. multicoloured . . . 45 85

DESIGNS: 10 c. Map of air-mail routes; 15 c. Post Office H.Q., Maseru; 20 c. Horseman taking rural mail.

95 Siege of Thaba-Bosiu

1974. 150th Anniv of Siege of Thaba-Bosiu. Multicoloured.

269 4 c. Type **95** 10 10
270 5 c. The wreath-laying 10 10
271 10 c. Moshoeshoe I (vert) . . . 25 10
272 20 c. Makoanyane, the warrior (vert) 90 55

96 Mamokhorong

1974. Basotho Musical Instruments. Multicoloured.

273 4 c. Type **96** 10 10
274 10 c. Lesiba 10 10
275 15 c. Setolotolo 15 20
276 20 c. Meropa 15 20

97 Horseman in Rock Archway

1975. Sehlabathebe National Park. Mult.

278 4 c. Type **97** 30 10
279 5 c. Mountain view through arch 30 10
280 15 c. Antelope by stream . . . 50 45
281 20 c. Mountains and lake . . . 50 50
282 25c. Tourists by frozen waterfall . 65 75

98 Morena Moshoeshoe I

99 Mokhibo Dance

1975. Leaders of Lesotho.

283 **98** 3 c. black and blue 10 10
284 – 4 c. black and mauve . . . 10 10
285 – 5 c. black and pink 10 10
286 – 6 c. black and brown . . . 10 10
287 – 10 c. black and red 10 10
288 – 15 c. black and red 20 20
289 – 20 c. black and green . . . 25 30
290 – 25 c. black and blue . . . 25 40

DESIGNS: 4 c. King Moshoeshoe II; 5 c. Morena Letsie I; 6 c. Morena Lerotholi; 10 c. Morena Letsie II; 15 c. Morena Griffith; 20 c. Morena Seeiso Griffith Lerotholi; 25 c. Mofumahali Mantsebo Seeiso, O.B.E.

The 25 c. also commemorates International Women's Year.

1975. Traditional Dances. Multicoloured.

291 4 c. Type **99** 15 10
292 10 c. Ndlamo 20 10
293 15 c. Baleseli 35 65
294 20 c. Mohobelo 40 85

100 Enrolment

1976. 25th Anniv of Lesotho Red Cross. Mult.

296 4 c. Type **100** 50 10
297 10 c. Medical aid 70 10
298 15 c. Rural service . . . . . 1·00 1·25
299 25 c. Relief supplies . . . . . 1·40 2·25

101 Tapestry

1976. Multicoloured.

300 2 c. Type **101** 10 30
301 3 c. Mosotho horseman 20 30
302 4 c. Map of Lesotho 65 10
303 5 c. Lesotho Brown diamond . 55 60
304 10 c. Lesotho Bank 30 10
305 15 c. Lesotho and O.A.U. flags 90 65
306 25 c. Sehlabathebe National Park 60 35
307 40 c. Pottery . . . . 60 1·00
308 50 c. Prehistoric rock art . . . 2·00 2·00
309 1 r. King Moshoeshoe II (vert) 75 1·75

102 Football

103 "Rising Sun"

1976. Olympic Games, Montreal. Mult.

310 4 c. Type **102** 15 10
311 10 c. Weightlifting 15 10
312 15 c. Boxing 35 10
313 25 c. Throwing the discus . . . 50 35

1976. 10th Anniv of Independence. Multicoloured.

314 4 c. Type **103** 10 10
315 10 c. Open gates 10 10
316 15 c. Broken chains 40 20
317 25 c. Britten Norman Islander aircraft over hotel 50 35

104 Telephones, 1876 and 1976

1976. Centenary of Telephone. Multicoloured.

318 4 c. Type **104** 10 10
319 10 c. Early handset and telephone-user, 1976 . . . 15 10
320 15 c. Wall telephone and telephone exchange 25 15
321 25 c. Stick telephone and Alexander Graham Bell . . . 45 40

105 "Aloe striatula"

106 Large-toothed Rock Hyrax

1977. Aloes and Succulents. Multicoloured.

322 3 c. Type **105** 25 10
323 4 c. "Aloe aristata" 30 10
324 5 c. "Kniphofia caulescens" . . 35 10
325 10 c. "Euphorbia pulvinata" . . 50 10
326 15 c. "Aloe saponaria" . . . . 1·50 40
327 20 c. "Caralluma lutea" . . . 1·50 65
328 25 c. "Aloe polyphylla" . . . . 1·75 90

See also Nos. 347/54.

1977. Animals. Multicoloured.

329 4 c. Type **106** . . . . 2·50 20
330 5 c. Cape porcupine . . . . . 2·50 30
331 10 c. Zorilla (polecat) . . . . 2·75 20
332 15 c. Klipspringer . . . . . . 10·00 2·25
333 25 c. Chacma baboon . . . . 12·00 3·00

107 "Rheumatic Man"

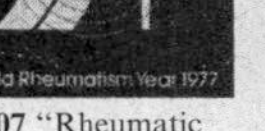

110 Black and White Heads

108 Small-mouthed Yellowfish

1977. World Rheumatism Year.

334 **107** 4 c. yellow and red 10 10
335 – 10 c. blue and deep blue . . 15 10
336 – 15 c. yellow and blue . . . 30 10
337 – 25 c. red and black 40 45

DESIGNS—Each show the "Rheumatic Man" as Type **107**: 10 c. Surrounded by "pain"; 15 c. Surrounded by "chain"; 25 c. Supporting globe.

1977. Fish. Multicoloured.

338 4 c. Type **108** 30 10
339 10 c. Mudfish 45 10
340 15 c. Rainbow trout . . . . . 1·00 35
341 25 c. Barnard's mudfish . . . 1·10 60

1977. No. 198 surch **3**.

342 3 c. on 10 c. brown and blue . . 90 90

1977. Decade for Action to Combat Racism.

343 **110** 4 c. black and mauve . . . 10 10
344 – 10 c. black and blue . . . 10 10
345 – 15 c. black and orange . . 15 15
346 – 25 c. black and green . . . 25 25

DESIGNS: 10 c. Jigsaw pieces; 15 c. Cogwheels; 25 c. Handshake.

1978. Flowers. As T **105**. Multicoloured.

347 2 c. "Papaver aculeatum" . . . 10 20
348 3 c. "Diascia integerrima" . . . 10 20
349 4 c. "Helichrysum trilineatum" 10 10
350 5 c. "Zaluzianskya maritima" . 10 10
351 10 c. "Gladiolus natalensis" . . 20 20
352 15 c. "Chironia krebsii" . . . 30 40
353 25 c. "Wahlenbergia undulata" 50 1·00
354 40 c. "Brunsvigia radulosa" . . 85 2·00

111 Edward Jenner vaccinating Child

112 Tsoloane Falls

1978. Global Eradication of Smallpox. Mult.

355 5 c. Type **111** 20 10
356 25 c. Head of child and W.H.O. emblem 70 75

1978. Waterfalls. Multicoloured.

357 4 c. Type **112** 15 10
358 10 c. Qiloane Falls 25 10
359 15 c. Tsoelikana Falls 45 60
360 25 c. Maletsunyane Falls . . . 75 1·50

113 Wright Flyer III, 1903

1978. 75th Anniv of First Powered Flight. Mult.

361 5 c. Type **113** 15 10
362 25 c. Wilbur and Orville Wright . 40 55

114 "Orthetrum farinosum"

115 Oudehout Branch in Flower

1978. Insects. Multicoloured.

363 4 c. Type **114** 10 10
364 10 c. "Phymateus viridipes" . . 20 10
365 15 c. "Belonogaster lateritis" . 30 40
366 25 c. "Sphodromantis gastrica" 50 80

1979. Trees. Multicoloured.

367 4 c. Type **115** 15 10
368 10 c. Wild olive 20 10
369 15 c. Blinkblaar 35 80
370 25 c. Cape holly . . . . 70 1·50

116 Mampharoane

1979. Reptiles. Multicoloured.

371A 4 s. Type **116** 10 10

372A 10 s. Qoaane 20 10

373A 15 s. Leupa 30 60

374A 25 s. Masumu . . . . 60 1·25

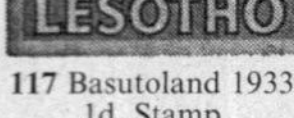

117 Basutoland 1933 1d. Stamp

118 Detail of painting "Children's Games" by Brueghel

1979. Death Centenary of Sir Rowland Hill.

375 **117** 4 s. multicoloured 10 10

376 – 15 s. multicoloured 30 20

377 – 25 s. black, orange & bistre 40 30

DESIGNS: 15 s. Basutoland 1962 ½ c. new currency definitive; 25 s. Penny Black.

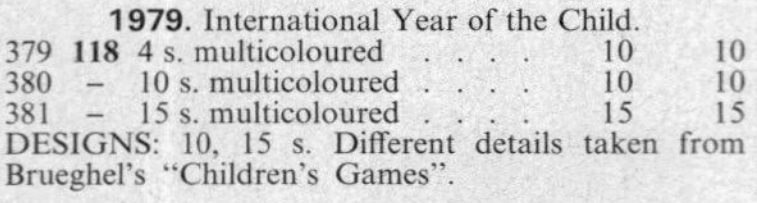

1979. International Year of the Child.

379 **118** 4 s. multicoloured 10 10

380 – 10 s. multicoloured 10 10

381 – 15 s. multicoloured 15 15

DESIGNS: 10, 15 s. Different details taken from Brueghel's "Children's Games".

119 Beer Strainer, Broom and Mat

1980. Grasswork. Multicoloured.

383 4 s. Type **119** 10 10

384 10 s. Winnowing basket 10 10

385 15 s. Basotho hat 20 25

386 25 s. Grain storage 35 40

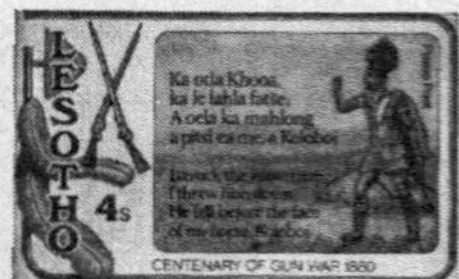

120 Praise Poet

1980. Centenary of Gun War. Multicoloured.

387 4 s. Type **120** 15 10

388 5 s. Lerotholi, Commander of Basotho Army 15 10

389 10 s. Ambush at Qalabane . . 20 10

390 15 s. Snider and Martini-Henry rifles 60 45

391 25 s. Map showing main areas of action 70 55

121 Olympic Flame, Flags and Kremlin

1980. Olympic Games, Moscow. Multicoloured.

392 25 s. Type **121** 25 25

393 25 s. Doves, flame and flags . . 25 25

394 25 s. Football 25 25

395 25 s. Running 25 25

396 25 s. Opening ceremony . . . 25 25

1980. Nos. 203 and 300/9 surch **s** or new value.

402A 2 s. on 2 c. Type **101** 10 10

403A 3 s. on 3 c. Mosotho horseman 20 10

410A 5 s. on 5 c. Lesotho Brown diamond 90 10

404B 6 s. on 4 c. Map of Lesotho . 30 10

411B 10 s. on 10 c. Lesotho Bank . 10 10

412A 25 s. on 25 c. Schlabathebe National Park 25 30

406A 40 s. on 40 c. Pottery . . . 45 50

414A 50 s. on 50 c. Prehistoric rock art . . . . 1·50 55

415B 75 s. on 15 c. Lesotho and O.A.U. flags 70 75

409A 1 m. on 1 r. King Moshoeshoe II . . . . 80 1·00

417A 2 m. on 2 r. Statue of King Moshoeshoe I . . . . . . 80 1·40

123 Beer Mug

124 Queen Elizabeth the Queen Mother with Prince Charles

1980. Pottery. Multicoloured.

418 4 s. Type **123** 10 10

419 10 s. Beer brewing pot 10 10

420 15 s. Water pot 15 15

421 25 s. Pot shapes 25 30

1980. 80th Birthday of The Queen Mother. Mult.

423 5 s. Type **124** 25 25

424 10 s. The Queen Mother . . . 25 25

425 1 m. 1947 Basutoland Royal Visit 2d. stamp (54×43 mm) . . . 90 90

125 Lesotho Evangelical Church, Morija

1980. Christmas. Multicoloured.

426 4 s. Type **125** 10 10

427 15 s. St. Agnes' Anglican Church, Teyateyaneng 10 10

428 25 s. Cathedral of Our Lady of Victories, Maseru 15 10

429 75 s. University Chapel, Roma . 45 50

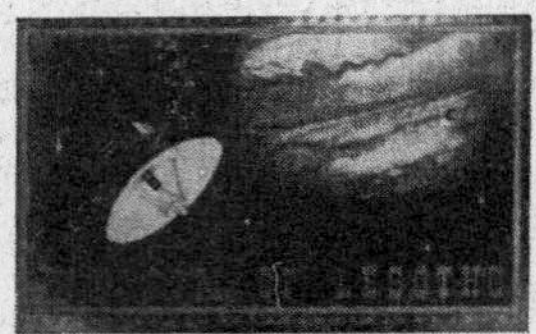

126 "Voyager" Satellite and Jupiter

1981. Space Exploration. Multicoloured.

431 25 c. Type **126** 30 25

432 25 c. "Voyager" and Saturn . . 30 25

433 25 c. "Voyager" passing Saturn 30 25

434 25 c. "Space Shuttle" releasing satellite 30 25

435 25 c. "Space Shuttle" launching into space 30 25

127 Greater Kestrel

1981. Birds. Multicoloured.

437 1 s. Type **127** 15 40

438 2 s. Speckled pigeon (horiz) . . 15 40

439 3 s. South African crowned crane 20 40

440 5 s. Bokmakierie shirike . . . 20 40

504 6 s. Cape robin chat 30 10

505 7 s. Yellow canary 30 10

506 10 s. Red-billed pintail (horiz) . 30 10

507 25 s. Malachite kingfisher . . . 80 30

508 40 s. Yellow-tufted malachite sunbird (horiz) . . . . . 1·00 45

509 60 s. Cape longclaw (horiz) . . 1·25 90

510 75 s. Hoopoe (horiz) . . . . . 1·75 90

448 1 m. Red bishop (horiz) . . . 2·25 75

449 2 m. Egyptian goose (horiz) . . 2·50 1·50

450 5 m. Lilac-breasted roller (horiz) 4·00 4·00

1981. Royal Wedding. As T **116** of Gambia. Multicoloured.

451 25 s. Wedding Bouquet from Lesotho 10 10

452 50 s. Prince Charles riding . . 20 25

453 75 s. Prince Charles and Lady Diana Spencer 30 50

HAVE YOU READ THE NOTES AT THE BEGINNING OF THIS CATALOGUE?
These often provide answers to the enquiries we receive.

130 "Santa planning his Annual Visit"

1981. Christmas. Paintings by Norman Rockwell. Multicoloured.

455 6 s. Type **130** 15 10

456 10 s. "Santa reading his Mail" . 25 10

457 15 s. "The Little Spooners" . . 30 20

458 20 s. "Raleigh Rockwell Travels" 30 25

459 25 s. "Ride 'em Cowboy" . . . 30 30

460 60 s. "The Discovery" . . . . 50 1·00

131 Duke of Edinburgh, Award Scheme Emblem and Flags

1981. 25th Anniv of Duke of Edinburgh Award Scheme. Multicoloured.

462 6 s. Type **131** 10 10

463 7 s. Tree planting 10 10

464 25 s. Gardening 25 20

465 40 s. Mountain climbing . . . 40 40

466 75 s. Award Scheme emblem . . 70 75

132 Wild Cat

1981. Wildlife. Multicoloured.

468 6 s. Type **132** . . . . 1·25 30

469 20 s. Chacma baboon (44×31 mm) . . . . 2·00 70

470 25 s. Cape eland . . . . 2·50 75

471 40 s. Porcupine . . . . 3·25 1·75

472 50 s. Oribi (44×31 mm) . . . 3·25 1·75

133 Scout Bugler

1982. 75th Anniv of Boy Scout Movement. Multicoloured.

474 6 s. Type **133** 50 25

475 30 s. Scouts hiking 70 50

476 40 s. Scout sketching 75 60

477 50 s. Scout with flag 75 65

478 75 s. Scouts saluting 80 80

134 Jules Rimet Trophy with Footballers and Flags of 1930 Finalists (Argentina and Uruguay)

1982. World Cup Football Championship, Spain. Each showing Trophy with Players and Flags from Past Finals. Multicoloured.

480 15 s. Type **134** 25 25

481 15 s. Czechoslovakia and Italy, 1934 . . . . 25 25

482 15 s. Hungary and Italy, 1938 . 25 25

483 15 s. Brazil and Uruguay, 1950 25 25

484 15 s. Hungary and W. Germany, 1954 . . . . 25 25

485 15 s. Sweden and Brazil, 1958 . 25 25

486 15 s. Czechoslovakia and Brazil, 1962 . . . . 25 25

487 15 s. W. Germany and England, 1966 . . . . 25 25

488 15 s. Italy and Brazil, 1970 . . 25 25

489 15 s. Holland and W. Germany, 1974 . . . . 25 25

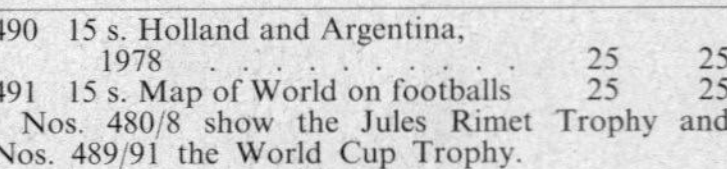

490 15 s. Holland and Argentina, 1978 . . . . 25 25

491 15 s. Map of World on footballs 25 25

Nos. 480/8 show the Jules Rimet Trophy and Nos. 489/91 the World Cup Trophy.

135 Portrait of George Washington

1982. 250th Birth Anniv of George Washington. Mult.

493 6 s. Type **135** 10 10

494 7 s. Washington with step-children and dog 10 10

495 10 s. Washington with Indian chief 15 10

496 25 s. Washington with troops . 30 30

497 40 s. Washington arriving in New York 40 40

498 1 m. Washington on parade . . 1·00 1·10

136 Lady Diana Spencer in Tetbury, May 1981

137 Mosotho reading Sesotho Bible

1982. 21st Birthday of Princess of Wales. Mult.

514a 30 s. Lesotho coat of arms . . 40 40

515 50 s. Type **136** 60 60

516 75 s. Wedding picture at Buckingham Palace . . . . 80 1·00

517 1 m. Formal portrait . . . . 1·25 1·40

1982. Centenary of Sesotho Bible. Multicoloured.

518 6 s. Type **137** 15 20

519 15 s. Sesotho bible and Virgin Mary holding infant Jesus . . 20 25

520 1 m. Sesotho bible and Cathedral (62×42 mm) 50 75

138 Birthday Greetings

1982. Birth of Prince William of Wales. Mult.

521 6 s. Type **138** . . . . 2·25 2·50

522 60 s. Princess Diana and Prince William . . . . 1·00 1·00

139 "A Partridge in a Pear Tree"

1982. Christmas. "The Twelve Days of Christmas". Walt Disney cartoon characters. Multicoloured.

523 2 s. Type **139** 10 10

524 2 s. "Two turtle doves" 10 10

525 3 s. "Three French hens" . . . 10 10

526 3 s. "Four calling birds" . . . 10 10

527 4 s. "Five golden rings" . . . 10 10

528 4 s. "Six geese a-laying" . . . 10 10

529 75 s. "Seven swans a-swimming" 1·40 1·75

530 75 s. "Eight maids a-milking" . 1·40 1·75

140 "Lepista caffrorum"

1983. Fungi. Multicoloured.
532 10 s. Type **140** 15 10
533 30 s. "Broomeia congregata" . 30 40
534 50 s. "Afroboletus luteolus" . . 60 90
535 75 s. "Lentinus tuber-regium" . 90 1·40

141 Ba-Leseli Dance

1983. Commonwealth Day. Multicoloured.
536 5 s. Type **141** 10 10
537 30 s. Tapestry weaving 20 30
538 60 s. Queen Elizabeth II (vert) . 35 65
539 75 s. King Moshoeshoe II (vert) 40 80

142 "Dancers in a Trance" (rock painting from Ntloana Tsoana)

1983. Rock Paintings. Multicoloured.
540 6 s. Type **142** 20 10
541 25 s. "Baboons", Sehonghong . 55 35
542 60 s. "Hunters attacking Mountain Reedbuck", Makhetha . . . . 60 1·10
543 75 s. "Eland", Lehaha la Likhomo . . . . 65 1·60

143 Montgolfier Balloon, 1783

1983. Bicentenary of Manned Flight. Mult.
545 7 s. Type **143** 15 10
546 30 s. Wright brothers and Flyer I 30 40
547 60 s. First airmail flight . . . . 50 1·25
548 1 m. Concorde . . . . 1·75 2·25

144 Rev. Eugene Casalis

1983. 150th Anniv of Arrival of the French Missionaries. Multicoloured.
550 6 s. Type **144** 10 10
551 25 s. The founding of Morija . 10 10
552 40 s. Baptism of Libe 10 15
553 75 s. Map of Lesotho 20 25

145 Mickey Mouse and Pluto greeted by Friends

1983. Christmas. Walt Disney Characters in scenes from "Old Christmas" (Washington Irving's sketchbook). Multicoloured.
554 1 s. Type **145** 10 10
555 2 s. Donald Duck and Pluto . . 10 10
556 3 s. Donald Duck with Huey, Dewey and Louie 10 10
557 4 s. Goofy, Donald Duck and Mickey Mouse 10 10
558 5 s. Goofy holding turkey, Donald Duck and Mickey Mouse 10 10
559 6 s. Goofy and Mickey Mouse 10 10
560 7 s. Donald and Daisy Duck . . 2·00 2·40
561 1 m. Goofy and Clarabell . . . 2·50 2·75

146 "Danaus chrysippus"

1984. Butterflies. Multicoloured.
563 1 s. Type **146** 30 40
564 2 s. "Aeropetes tulbaghia" . . 30 40
565 3 s. "Colotis evenina" 35 40
566 4 s. "Precis oenone" 35 40
567 5 s. "Precis hierta" 35 40
568 6 s. "Catopsilia florella" . . . 35 10
569 7 s. "Phalanta phalantha" . . . 35 10
570 10 s. "Acraea stenobea" . . . 40 10
571 15 s. "Cynthia cardui" 90 10
572 20 s. "Colotis subfasciatus" . . 1·00 10
573 30 s. "Charaxes jasius" . . . . 1·25 30
574 50 s. "Terias brigitta" . . . . 1·50 40
575 60 s. "Pontia helice" . . . . . 1·60 50
576 75 s. "Colotis regina" . . . . 1·75 50
577 1 m. "Hypolimnas misippus" . 2·00 1·50
578 5 m. "Papilio demodocus" . . 4·50 7·50

147 "Thou shalt not have Strange Gods before Me"

1984. Easter. The Ten Commandments. Mult.
579 20 s. Type **147** 30 30
580 20 s. "Thou shalt not take the name of the Lord thy God in vain" 30 30
581 20 s. "Remember thou keep holy the Lord's Day" 30 30
582 20 s. "Honour thy father and mother" 30 30
583 20 s. "Thou shalt not kill" . . 30 30
584 20 s. "Thou shalt not commit adultery" 30 30
585 20 s. "Thou shalt not steal" . . 30 30
586 20 s. "Thou shalt not bear false witness against thy neighbour" 30 30
587 20 s. "Thou shalt not covet thy neighbour's wife" 30 30
588 20 s. "Thou shalt not covet thy neighbour's goods" 30 30

148 Torch Bearer

1984. Olympic Games, Los Angeles. Multicoloured.
590 10 s. Type **148** 10 10
591 30 s. Horse-riding 10 10
592 50 s. Swimming 15 20
593 75 s. Basketball 20 25
594 1 m. Running 25 30

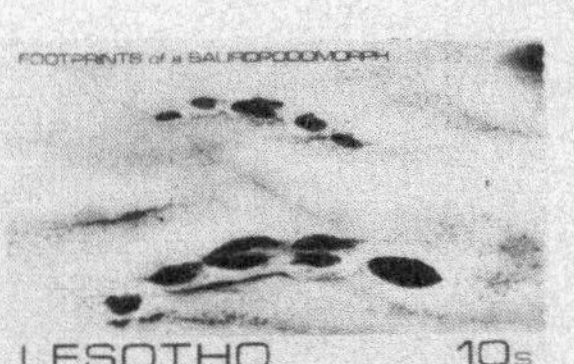

149 Sauropodomorph Footprints

1984. Prehistoric Footprints (2nd series). Mult.
596 10 s. Type **149** 55 30
597 30 s. Lesothosaurus footprints . 75 1·25
598 50 s. Footprint of carnivorous dinosaur . . . . 90 2·00

150 Wells Fargo Coach, 1852

1984. "Ausipex" Int Stamp Exhibition, Melbourne. Bicent of First Mail Coach Run. Mult.
599 6 s. Type **150** 10 10
600 7 s. Basotho mail cart, circa 1900 10 10
601 10 s. Bath mail coach, 1784 . . 10 10
602 30 s. Cobb coach, 1853 . . . . 30 35
603 50 s. Exhibition logo and Royal Exhibition Buildings, Melbourne (82 × 25 mm) . . 50 55

151 "The Orient Express" (1900)

1984. Railways of the World. Multicoloured.
605 6 s. Type **151** 40 15
606 15 s. Class 05 streamlined steam locomotive No. 001, Germany (1935) 40 30
607 30 s. Caledonian Railway steam locomotive "Cardean" (1906) 50 60
608 60 s. Atchison, Topeka & Santa Fe "Super Chief" express (1940) . . . . 60 1·75
609 1 m. L.N.E.R. "Flying Scotsman" (1934) . . . . . 65 2·00

152 Eland Calf

1984. Baby Animals. Multicoloured.
611 15 s. Type **152** 35 20
612 20 s. Young chacma baboons . 40 25
613 30 s. Oribi calf 55 40
614 75 s. Young Natal red hares . . 1·25 1·60
615 1 m. Black-backed jackal pups (46 × 27 mm) . . . . 1·50 2·00

153 Crown of Lesotho

154 Christ condemned to Death

1985. Silver Jubilee of King Moshoeshoe II. Mult.
616 6 s. Type **153** 10 10
617 30 s. King Moshoeshoe in 1960 20 30
618 75 s. King Moshoeshoe in traditional dress, 1985 . . . 50 75
619 1 m. King Moshoeshoe in uniform, 1985 . . . . 70 1·10

1985. Easter. The Stations of the Cross. Mult.
620 20 s. Type **154** 20 25
621 20 s. Christ carrying the Cross 20 25
622 20 s. Falling for the first time 20 25
623 20 s. Christ meets Mary . . . 20 25
624 20 s. Simon of Cyrene helping to carry the Cross 20 25
625 20 s. Veronica wiping the face of Christ 20 25
626 20 s. Christ falling a second time 20 25
627 20 s. Consoling the women of Jerusalem 20 25
628 20 s. Falling for the third time 20 25
629 20 s. Christ being stripped . . . 20 25
630 20 s. Christ nailed to the Cross 20 25
631 20 s. Dying on the Cross . . . 20 25
632 20 s. Christ taken down from the Cross 20 25
633 20 s. Christ being laid in the sepulchre 20 25

155 Duchess of York with Princess Elizabeth, 1931

1985. Life and Times of Queen Elizabeth the Queen Mother. Multicoloured.
635 10 s. Type **155** 15 10
636 30 s. The Queen Mother in 1975 50 50
637 60 s. Queen Mother with Queen Elizabeth and Princess Margaret, 1980 . . . . . . 60 90
638 2 m. Four generations of Royal Family at Prince Henry's christening, 1984 . . . . . 1·25 2·50

156 B.M.W. "732i"

1985. Century of Motoring. Multicoloured.
640 6 s. Type **156** 25 15
641 10 s. Ford "Crown Victoria" . . 35 15
642 30 s. Mercedes-Benz "500SE" . 75 50
643 90 s. Cadillac "Eldorado Biarritz" . . . . 1·50 2·50
644 2 m. Rolls-Royce "Silver Spirit" 2·00 4·00

157 American Cliff Swallow

158 Two Youths Rock-climbing

1985. Birth Bicentenary of John J. Audubon (ornithologist). Designs showing original paintings. Multicoloured.
646 5 s. Type **157** 40 30
647 6 s. Great crested grebe (horiz) 40 30
648 10 s. Vesper sparrow (horiz) . . 55 30
649 30 s. Greenshank (horiz) . . . 1·25 75
650 60 s. Stilt sandpiper (horiz) . . 2·00 2·75
651 2 m. Glossy ibis (horiz) . . . . 3·50 5·50

1985. International Youth Year and 75th Anniv of Girl Guide Movement. Multicoloured.
652 10 s. Type **158** 20 10
653 30 s. Young technician in hospital laboratory 50 40
654 75 s. Three guides on parade . . 1·00 1·25
655 2 m. Guide saluting . . . . . 1·75 3·00

159 U.N. (New York) 1951 1 c. Definitive and U.N. Flag

160 Cosmos

1985. 40th Anniversary of U.N.O.
657 **159** 10 s. multicoloured 25 10
658 – 30 s. multicoloured 60 35
659 – 50 s. multicoloured 95 85
660 – 2 m. black and green . . . 5·00 6·50
DESIGNS—VERT: 30 s. Ha Sofonia Earth Satellite Station; 2 m. Maimonides (physician, philosopher and scholar). HORIZ: 50 s. Lesotho Airways Fokker F.27 Friendship at Maseru Airport.

1985. Wild Flowers. Multicoloured.
661 6 s. Type **160** 40 15
662 10 s. Small agapanthus 55 15
663 30 s. Pink witchweed . . . . . 1·10 70
664 60 s. Small iris . . . . 1·50 2·00
665 90 s. Wild geranium or cranesbill 1·75 3·00
666 1 m. Large spotted orchid . . . 3·00 5·00

1985. 150th Birth Anniv of Mark Twain. Walt Disney cartoon characters illustrating various Mark Twain quotations. As T **145a** of Gambia. Multicoloured.
667 6 s. Mrs Jumbo and baby Dumbo (vert) 40 15
668 50 s. Uncle Scrooge and Goofy reading newspaper (vert) . . 1·25 1·00
669 90 s. Winnie the Pooh, Tigger, Piglet and Owl (vert) . . . . 1·75 2·00
670 1 m. 50 Goofy at ship's wheel (vert) . . . . 2·75 3·00

1985. Birth Bicentenaries of Grimm Brothers (folklorists). Walt Disney cartoon characters in scenes from "The Wishing Table". As T **145b** of Gambia. Multicoloured.
672 10 s. The tailor (Donald Duck) 35 15
673 60 s. The second son (Dewey) with magic donkey and gold coins . . . . 1·25 1·25
674 75 s. The eldest son (Huey) with wishing table laden with food 1·50 1·50
675 1 m. The innkeeper stealing the third son's (Louie) magic cudgel . . . . 2·00 2·50

161 Male Lammergeier on Watch

162 Two Players chasing Ball

1986. Flora and Fauna of Lesotho. Multicoloured.
677 7 s. Type **161** . . . . 1·25 40
678 9 s. Prickly pear 70 20
679 12 s. Stapelia 70 20
680 15 s. Pair of lammergeiers . . . 2·00 50
681 35 s. Pig's ears . . . . 1·10 60
682 50 s. Male lammergeier in flight 3·50 2·50
683 1 m. Adult and juvenile lammergeiers . . . . 3·75 4·50
684 2 m. Columnar cereus . . . . 3·75 6·00

1986. World Cup Football Championship, Mexico. Multicoloured.
686 35 s. Type **162** . . . . . . 1·25 50
687 50 s. Goalkeeper saving goal . . 1·75 1·25
688 1 m. Three players chasing ball 3·00 2·75
689 2 m. Two players competing for ball . . . . 5·00 5·00

1986. Appearance of Halley's Comet. As T **151a** of Gambia. Multicoloured.
691 9 s. Galileo and 200 inch Hale telescope, Mount Palomar Observatory, California . . . 50 15
692 15 s. Halley's Comet and "Pioneer Venus 2" spacecraft 75 20
693 70 s. Halley's Comet of 684 A.D. (from "Nuremberg Chronicle", 1493) . . . . . 1·60 1·40
694 3 m. Comet and landing of William the Conqueror, 1066 4·00 5·50

163 International Year of the Child Gold Coin

1986. First Anniv of New Currency (1980). Multicoloured.
696 30 s. Type **163** . . . . . . 4·00 6·50
697 30 s. Five maloti banknote . . 4·00 6·50
698 30 s. Fifty lisente coin . . . . 4·00 6·50
699 30 s. Ten maloti banknote . . . 4·00 6·50
700 30 s. One sente coin . . . . . 4·00 6·50
These stamps were prepared in 1980, but were not issued at that time.

1986. 60th Birthday of Queen Elizabeth II. As T **151b** of Gambia.
701 90 s. black and yellow 50 60
702 1 m. multicoloured 55 65
703 2 m. multicoloured . . . . . . 90 1·40
DESIGNS: 90 s. Princess Elizabeth in pantomime; 1 m. Queen at Windsor Horse Show, 1971; 2 m. At Royal Festival Hall, 1971.

1986. Centenary of Statue of Liberty. Immigrants to the U.S.A. As T **153a** of Gambia. Multicoloured.
705 15 s. Bela Bartok (composer) . 85 30
706 35 s. Felix Adler (philosopher) 85 30
707 1 m. Victor Herbert (composer) 3·00 2·00
708 3 m. David Niven (actor) . . . 4·25 4·00

1986. "Ameripex" International Stamp Exhibition, Chicago. Walt Disney cartoon characters delivering mail. As T **315a** of Gambia. Multicoloured.
710 15 s. Mickey Mouse and Goofy as Japanese mail runners . . . 55 20
711 35 s. Mickey Mouse and Pluto with mail sledge 90 30
712 1 m. Goofy as postman riding Harley-Davidson motorcycle 1·75 2·00
713 2 m. Donald Duck operating railway mailbag apparatus . 2·25 3·25

1986. Various stamps surch. (a) On Nos. 437 etc (Birds)
729 9 s. on 5 s. Bokmakierie shrike 15 20
715 9 s. on 10 s. Red-billed pintail (horiz) . . . . 3·00 1·25
716 15 s. on 1 s. Type **127** . . . . 7·00 3·00
717 15 s. on 2 s. Speckled pigeon (horiz) . . . . 4·00 4·50
718 15 s. on 5 s. Bokmakierie shrike 1·75 35
719 15 s. on 60 s. Cape longclaw (horiz) 20 10
730 16 s. on 25 s. Malachite kingfisher . . . . 2·25 1·00
731 35 s. on 25 s. Malachite kingfisher 60 60
721 35 s. on 75 s. Hoopoe . . . . 22·00 18·00

(b) On Nos. 563, etc (Butterflies).
722 9 s. on 30 s. "Charaxes jasius" . 15 10
723 9 s. on 60 s. "Pontia helice" . 4·00 4·00
724 15 s. on 1 s. Type **146** . . . . 2·75 2·75
725 15 s. on 2 s. "Aeropetes tulbaghia" 20 20
726 15 s. on 3 s. "Colotis evenina" . 20 20
727 15 s. on 5 s. "Precis hierta" . 20 20
732 20 s. on 4 s. "Precis oenone" . 10 10
728 35 s. on 75 s. "Colotis regina" . 35 35
733 40 s. on 7 s. "Phalanta phalantha" 15 20

(c) No. 722 further surch.
734 3 s. on 9 s. on 30 s. "Charaxes jasius" 15 15
735 7 s. on 9 s. on 30 s. "Charaxes jasius" 25 25

1986. Royal Wedding. As T **153b** of Gambia. Multicoloured.
736 50 s. Prince Andrew and Miss Sarah Ferguson 40 40
737 1 m. Prince Andrew 70 70
738 3 m. Prince Andrew piloting helicopter . . . . 2·25 2·25

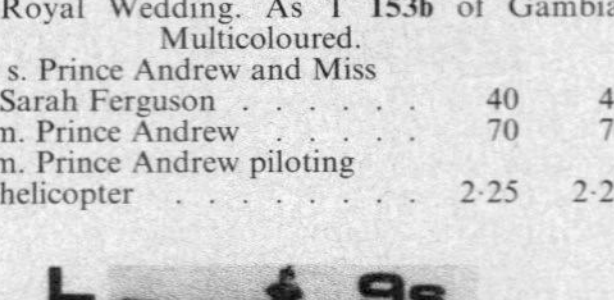

171 Basotho Pony and Rider

1986. 20th Anniv of Independence. Multicoloured.
740 9 s. Type **171** 30 10
741 15 s. Basotho woman spinning mohair 30 15
742 35 s. Crossing river by rowing boat 40 30
743 3 m. Thaba Tseka Post Office . 1·00 3·00

1986. Christmas. Walt Disney cartoon characters. As T **318a** of Grenada. Multicoloured.
745 15 s. Chip'n' Dale pulling Christmas cracker 50 20
746 35 s. Mickey and Minnie Mouse 75 30
747 1 m. Pluto pulling Christmas taffy . . . . 1·50 2·25
748 2 m. Aunt Matilda baking . . 2·00 3·25

172 Rally Car

173 Lawn Tennis

1987. Roof of Africa Motor Rally. Multicoloured.
750 9 s. Type **172** 30 10
751 15 s. Motorcyclist 35 15
752 35 s. Motorcyclist (different) . . 55 35
753 4 m. Rally car (different) . . . 3·00 5·00

1987. Olympic Games, Seoul (1988) (1st issue). Multicoloured.
754 9 s. Type **173** 40 10
755 15 s. Judo 40 15
756 20 s. Athletics 45 20
757 35 s. Boxing 60 30
758 1 m. Diving . . . . 1·00 1·60
759 3 m. Ten-pin bowling . . . . 2·00 4·50
See also Nos. 838/41.

174 Isaac Newton and Reflecting Telescope

1987. Great Scientific Discoveries. Multicoloured.
761 5 s. Type **174** 30 10
762 9 s. Alexander Graham Bell and first telephone 30 15
763 75 s. Robert Goddard and liquid fuel rocket 80 75
764 4 m. Chuck Yeager and Bell XS-1 rocket plane . . . . . . 2·75 4·50

175 Grey Rhebuck

1987. Flora and Fauna. Multicoloured.
766 5 s. Type **175** 40 15
767 9 s. Cape clawless otter 40 15
768 15 s. Cape grey mongoose . . . 55 20
769 20 s. Free State daisy (vert) . . 60 20
770 35 s. River bells (vert) 75 30
771 1 m. Turkey flower (vert) . . . 1·75 2·50
772 2 m. Sweet briar (vert) . . . . 2·25 3·75
773 3 m. Mountain reedbuck . . . 2·75 5·00

176 Scouts hiking

178 "Madonna and Child" (detail)

177 Spotted Trunkfish and Columbus's Fleet

1987. World Scout Jamboree, Australia. Mult.
775 9 s. Type **176** 50 20
776 15 s. Scouts playing football . . 55 20
777 35 s. Kangaroos 70 50
778 75 s. Scout saluting . . . . . 1·50 1·25
779 4 m. Australian scout windsurfing . . . . 3·75 6·00

1987. 500th Anniv (1992) of Discovery of America by Columbus. Multicoloured.
781 9 s. Type **177** 45 20
782 15 s. Green turtle and ships . . 60 20
783 35 s. Columbus watching common dolphins from ship . 80 40
784 5 m. White-tailed tropic bird and fleet at sea . . . . 4·25 6·50
No. 782 is inscribed "Carribbean" in error.

1987. Christmas. Paintings by Raphael. Mult.
786 9 s. Type **178** 30 10
787 15 s. "Marriage of the Virgin" 45 15
788 35 s. "Coronation of the Virgin" (detail) 90 40
789 90 s. "Madonna of the Chair" 2·00 3·50

179 Lesser Pied Kingfisher

1988. Birds. Multicoloured.
791 2 s. Type **179** 20 30
792 3 s. Three-banded plover . . . 20 30
793 5 s. Spur-winged goose 20 30
794 10 s. Clapper lark 20 20
795 12 s. Red-eyed bulbul 30 10
796 16 s. Cape weaver 30 10
797 20 s. Paradise sparrow ("Red-headed Finch") . . . 30 10
798 30 s. Mountain chat 35 20
799 40 s. Stonechat 40 20
800 55 s. Pied barbet 50 25
801 60 s. Red-shouldered glossy starling 55 50
802 75 s. Cape sparrow 65 60
803 1 m. Cattle egret 75 80
804 3 m. Giant kingfisher . . . . 1·50 2·50
805 10 m. Helmet guineafowl . . . 4·00 7·00

1988. Royal Ruby Wedding. Nos. 701/3 optd **40TH WEDDING ANNIVERSARY H.M. QUEEN ELIZABETH II H.R.H. THE DUKE OF EDINBURGH.**
806 90 s. black and yellow 50 65
807 1 m. multicoloured 60 80
808 2 m. multicoloured . . . . . 1·00 1·40

181 Mickey Mouse and Goofy outside Presidential Palace, Helsinki

1988. "Finlandia '88" International Stamp Exhibition, Helsinki. Designs showing Walt Disney cartoon characters in Finland. Mult.
810 1 s. Type **181** 10 10
811 2 s. Goofy and Mickey Mouse in sauna 10 10
812 3 s. Goofy and Mickey Mouse fishing in lake 10 10
813 4 s. Mickey and Minnie Mouse and Finlandia Hall, Helsinki 10 10
814 5 s. Mickey Mouse photographing Goofy at Sibelius Monument, Helsinki 10 10
815 10 s. Mickey Mouse and Goofy pony trekking 10 10
816 3 m. Goofy, Mickey and Minnie Mouse at Helsinki Olympic Stadium . . . . 3·00 3·00
817 5 m. Mickey Mouse and Goofy meeting Santa at Arctic Circle 4·00 4·00

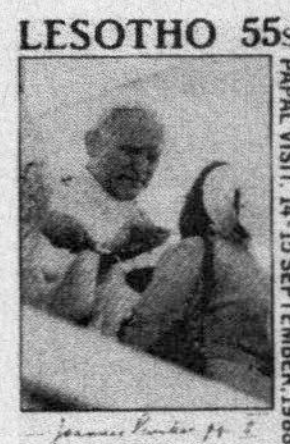

182 Pope John Paul II giving Communion

183 Large-toothed Rock Hyrax

1988. Visit of Pope John Paul II. Mult.
819 55 s. Type **182** 40 25
820 2 m. Pope leading procession . . 1·25 1·50
821 3 m. Pope at airport . . . . . 1·75 2·00
822 4 m. Pope John Paul II . . . . 2·25 2·75

1988. Small Mammals of Lesotho. Mult.
824 16 s. Type **183** 30 15
825 40 s. Ratel and black-throated honey guide (bird) 70 40
826 75 s. Small-spotted genet . . . 90 75
827 3 m. Yellow mongoose . . . . 2·75 3·75

184 "Birth of Venus" (detail) (Botticelli)

1988. Famous Paintings. Multicoloured.
829 15 s. Type **184** 30 15
830 25 s. "View of Toledo" (El Greco) 35 20
831 40 s. "Maids of Honour" (detail) (Velasquez) 45 25
832 50 s. "The Fifer" (Manet) . . . 55 30
833 55 s. "Starry Night" (detail) (Van Gogh) 55 30
834 75 s. "Prima Ballerina" (Degas) 70 70
835 2 m. "Bridge over Water Lilies" (Monet) . . . . 1·75 2·00
836 3 m. "Guernica" (detail) (Picasso) . . . . 1·75 2·50

185 Wrestling

1988. Olympic Games, Seoul (2nd series). Mult.
838 12 s. Type **185** 10 10
839 16 s. Show jumping (vert) . . . 10 10
840 55 s. Shooting 20 30
841 3 m. 50 As 16 s. (vert) . . . . 1·40 2·00

186 Yannick Noah and Eiffel Tower, Paris

1988. 75th Anniv of Int Tennis Federation. Mult.
843 12 s. Type **186** 30 15
844 20 s. Rod Laver and Sydney Harbour Bridge and Opera House 35 20
845 30 s. Ivan Lendl and Prague . . 40 25
846 65 s. Jimmy Connors and Tokyo (vert) 55 40

847 1 m. Arthur Ashe and Barcelona (vert) 80 60
848 1 m. 55 Althea Gibson and New York (vert) 1·00 90
849 2 m. Chris Evert and Vienna (vert) 1·50 1·25
850 2 m. 40 Boris Becker and Houses of Parliament, London (vert) 1·75 1·75
851 3 m. Martina Navratilova and Golden Gate Bridge, San Francisco 1·75 2·00

No. 844 is inscribed "SIDNEY" in error.

1988. Christmas. 500th Birth Anniv of Titian (artist). As T **166a** of Gambia but inscr "CHRISTMAS 1988". Multicoloured.

853 12 s. "The Averoldi Polyptych" (detail) 20 10
854 20 s. "Christ and the Adulteress" (detail) 20 10
855 35 s. "Christ and the Adulteress" (different detail) 30 20
856 45 s. "Angel of the Annunciation" 40 30
857 65 s. "Saint Dominic" 55 50
858 1 m. "The Vendramin Family" (detail) 75 80
859 2 m. "Mary Magdalen" 1·25 1·75
860 3 m. "The Tribute Money" 1·75 2·50

187 Pilatus PC-6 Turbo Porter

1989. 125th Anniv of International Red Cross. Aircraft. Multicoloured.

862 12 s. Type **187** 15 10
863 20 s. Unloading medical supplies from Cessna Caravan I 20 15
864 55 s. De Havilland D.H.C.6 Twin Otter 200/300 40 40
865 3 m. Douglas DC-3 2·00 3·00

1989. Japanese Art. Paintings by Hiroshige. As T **177a** of Gambia, but horiz. Multicoloured.

867 12 s. "Dawn Mist at Mishima" 30 10
868 16 s. "Night Snow at Kambara" 35 10
869 20 s. "Wayside Inn at Mariko Station" 35 10
870 35 s. "Shower at Shono" 55 10
871 55 s. "Snowfall on the Kisokaido near Oi" 65 40
872 1 m. "Autumn Moon at Seba" 85 85
873 3 m. 20 "Evening Moon at Ryogoku Bridge" 2·25 3·00
874 5 m. "Cherry Blossoms at Arashiyama" 2·75 3·75

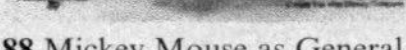

188 Mickey Mouse as General **189** "Paxillus involutus"

1989. "Philexfrance 89" International Stamp Exhibition, Paris. Designs showing Walt Disney cartoon characters in French military uniforms of the Revolutionary period. Multicoloured.

876 1 s. Type **188** 10 10
877 2 s. Ludwig von Drake as infantryman 10 10
878 3 s. Goofy as grenadier 10 10
879 4 s. Horace Horsecollar as cavalryman 10 10
880 5 s. Pete as hussar 10 10
881 10 s. Donald Duck as marine 10 10
882 3 m. Gyro Gearloose as National Guard 3·00 3·25
883 5 m. Scrooge McDuck as admiral 3·75 4·25

1989. Fungi. Multicoloured.

900 12 s. Type **189** 20 10
901 16 s. "Ganoderma applanatum" 20 15
902 55 s. "Suillus granulatus" 45 35
903 5 m. "Stereum hirsutum" 3·25 4·50

190 Sesotho Huts **192** Launch of "Apollo 11"

191 Marsh Sandpiper

1989. Maloti Mountains. Multicoloured.

905 1 m. Type **190** 70 90
906 1 m. American aloe and mountains 70 90
907 1 m. River valley with waterfall 70 90
908 1 m. Sesotho tribesman on ledge 70 90

Nos. 905/8 were printed together, se-tenant, forming a composite design.

1989. Migrant Birds. Multicoloured.

910 12 s. Type **191** 80 30
911 65 s. Little stint 1·50 70
912 1 m. Ringed plover 2·00 1·50
913 4 m. Curlew sandpiper 3·50 5·50

1989. 20th Anniv of First Manned Landing on Moon. Multicoloured.

915 12 s. Type **192** 25 10
916 16 s. Lunar module "Eagle" landing on Moon (horiz) 25 15
917 40 s. Neil Armstrong leaving "Eagle" 45 25
918 55 s. Edwin Aldrin on Moon (horiz) 50 30
919 1 m. Aldrin performing scientific experiment (horiz) 85 85
920 2 m. "Eagle" leaving Moon (horiz) 1·50 1·75
921 3 m. Command module "Columbia" in Moon orbit (horiz) 2·00 2·25
922 4 m. Command module on parachutes 2·50 2·75

193 English Penny Post Paid Mark, 1680

1989. "World Stamp Expo '89" International Stamp Exhibition, Washington. Stamps and Postmarks.

924 **193** 75 s. red, black and stone 60 65
925 – 75 s. black, grey and red 60 65
926 – 75 s. violet, black & brn 60 65
927 – 75 s. brown, black & lt brn 60 65
928 – 75 s. black and yellow 60 65
929 – 75 s. multicoloured 60 65
930 – 75 s. black and lilac 60 65
931 – 75 s. black, red & brown 60 65
932 – 75 s. red, black & yellow 60 65

DESIGNS: No. 925, German postal seal and feather, 1807; 926, British Post Office in Crete 1898 20 pa. stamp; 927, Bermuda 1848 Perot 1d. provisional; 928, U.S.A. Pony Express cancellation, 1860; 929, Finland 1856 5 k. stamp; 930, Fiji 1870 "Fiji Times" 1d. stamp, 1870; 931, Sweden newspaper wrapper handstamp, 1823; 932, Bhor 1879 ½ a. stamp.

193b "The Immaculate Conception"

1989. Christmas. Paintings by Velazquez. Mult.

934 12 s. Type **193b** 10 10
935 20 s. "St. Anthony Abbot and St. Paul the Hermit" 15 10
936 35 s. "St. Thomas the Apostle" 25 25
937 55 s. "Christ in the House of Martha and Mary" 35 35
938 1 m. "St. John writing The Apocalypse on Patmos" 60 75
939 3 m. "The Virgin presenting the Chasuble to St. Ildephonsus" 1·60 2·25
940 4 m. "The Adoration of the Magi" 2·00 2·75

194 Scene from 1966 World Cup Final, England

1989. World Cup Football Championship, Italy. Scenes from past finals. Multicoloured.

942 12 s. Type **194** 40 10
943 16 s. 1970 final, Mexico 40 15
944 55 s. 1974 final, West Germany 85 40
945 5 m. 1982 final, Spain 3·50 5·00

1990. No. 889 and 798/9 surch **16 s.**

948 16 s. on 12 s. Red-eyed bulbul 60 15
948e 16 s. on 30 s. Mountain chat 60 15
948f 16 s. on 40 s. Stonechat 60 15

197 "Byblia anvatara"

1990. Butterflies. Multicoloured.

949 12 s. Type **197** 50 15
950 16 s. "Cynthia cardui" 65 15
951 55 s. "Precis oenone" 90 40
952 65 s. "Pseudacraea boisduvali" 1·00 65
953 1 m. "Precis orithya" 1·50 1·25
954 2 m. "Precis sophia" 2·50 2·50
955 3 m. "Danaus chrysippus" 3·25 3·75
956 4 m. "Druryia antimachus" 4·25 6·00

198 "Satyrium princeps"

1990. "EXPO 90" International Garden and Greenery Exhibition, Osaka. Local Orchids. Multicoloured.

958 12 s. Type **198** 55 15
959 16 s. "Huttonaea pulchra" 60 15
960 55 s. "Herschelia graminifolia" 1·25 30
961 1 m. "Ansellia gigantea" 1·75 75
962 1 m. 55 "Polystachya pubescens" 2·00 1·75
963 2 m. 40 "Penthea filicornis" 2·00 2·25
964 3 m. "Disperis capensis" 2·25 3·25
965 4 m. "Disa uniflora" 3·00 4·00

1990. 90th Birthday of Queen Elizabeth the Queen Mother. As T **99** of Grenada Grenadines.

967 1 m. 50 black and mauve 95 1·00
968 1 m. 50 black and mauve 95 1·00
969 1 m. 50 black and mauve 95 1·00

DESIGNS: No. 967, Lady Elizabeth Bowes-Lyon and brother in fancy dress; 968, Lady Elizabeth Bowes-Lyon in evening dress; 969, Lady Elizabeth Bowes-Lyon wearing hat.

199 King Moshoeshoe II and Prince Mohato wearing Seana-Marena Blankets **200** Filling Truck at No. 1 Quarry

1990. Traditional Blankets. Multicoloured.

971 12 s. Type **199** 10 10
972 16 s. Prince Mohato wearing Seana-Marena blanket 10 10
973 1 m. Pope John Paul II wearing Seana-Marena blanket 1·75 1·10
974 3 m. Basotho horsemen wearing Matlama blankets 2·00 2·75

1990. Lesotho Highlands Water Project. Mult.

976 16 s. Type **200** 35 10
977 20 s. Tanker lorry on Pitseng–Malibamatso road 35 10
978 55 s. Piers for Malibamatso Bridge 55 30
979 2 m. Excavating Mphosong section of Pitseng–Malibamatso road 2·00 3·00

201 Mother breastfeeding Baby **203** "Virgin and Child" (detail, Rubens)

1990. U.N.I.C.E.F. Child Survival Campaign. Multicoloured.

981 12 s. Type **201** 40 10
982 55 s. Baby receiving oral rehydration therapy 70 45
983 1 m. Weight monitoring 1·00 2·00

1990. Olympic Games, Barcelona (1992). As T **195a** of Gambia. Multicoloured.

984 16 s. Men's triple jump 30 10
985 55 s. Men's 200 metres race 50 25
986 1 m. Men's 5000 metres race 80 90
987 4 m. Show jumping 2·75 4·00

1990. Christmas. Paintings by Rubens. Mult.

989 12 s. Type **203** 20 10
990 16 s. "Adoration of the Magi" (detail) 20 10
991 55 s. "Head of One of the Three Kings" 45 25
992 80 s. "Adoration of the Magi" (different detail) 60 60
993 1 m. "Virgin and Child" (different detail) 70 70
994 2 m. "Adoration of the Magi" (different detail) 1·25 1·75
995 3 m. "Virgin and Child" (different detail) 2·00 2·50
996 4 m. "Adoration of the Magi" (different detail) 2·25 3·00

204 Mickey Mouse at Nagasaki Peace Park

1991. "Phila Nippon '91" International Stamp Exhibition, Tokyo. Walt Disney cartoon characters in Japan. Multicoloured.

998 20 s. Type **204** 45 15
999 30 s. Mickey Mouse on Kamakura Beach 50 20
1000 40 s. Mickey and Donald Duck with Bunraku puppet 55 25
1001 50 s. Mickey and Donald eating soba 60 35
1002 75 s. Mickey and Minnie Mouse at tea house 85 70
1003 1 m. Mickey running after "Hikari" express train 1·00 1·00
1004 3 m. Mickey Mouse with deer at Todaiji Temple, Nara 2·50 3·25
1005 4 m. Mickey and Minnie outside Imperial Palace 2·75 3·50

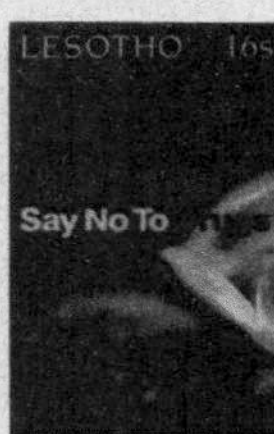

205 Stewart Granger ("King Solomon's Mines") **207** Victim of Drug Abuse

206 "Satyrus aello"

1991. Famous Films with African Themes. Mult.

1007 12 s. Type **205** 35 20
1008 16 s. Johnny Weissmuller ("Tarzan the Ape Man") 35 20
1009 30 s. Clark Gable and Grace Kelly ("Mogambo") 50 35
1010 55 s. Sigourney Weaver and gorilla ("Gorillas in the Mist") 75 55
1011 70 s. Humphrey Bogart and Katharine Hepburn ("The African Queen") 90 80
1012 1 m. John Wayne and capture of rhinoceros ("Hatari!") 1·25 1·00
1013 2 m. Meryl Streep and De Havilland Gipsy Moth light aircraft ("Out of Africa") 2·00 2·25
1014 4 m. Arsenio Hall and Eddie Murphy ("Coming to America") 2·75 3·50

1991. Butterflies. Multicoloured.

1016B 2 s. Type **206** 10 20
1017B 3 s. "Erebia medusa" 10 20
1018A 5 s. "Melanargia galathea" 30 30
1019B 10 s. "Erebia aethiops" 15 10
1020A 20 s. "Coenonympha pamphilus" 35 30
1021B 25 s. "Pyrameis atalanta" 20 10
1022B 30 s. "Charaxes jasius" 20 10
1023B 40 s. "Colias palaeno" 20 10
1024B 50 s. "Colias cliopatra" 30 20
1025B 60 s. "Colias philodice" 30 20
1026B 70 s. "Rhumni gonepterix" 40 25
1027B 1 m. "Colias caesonia" 45 30
1028B 2 m. "Pyrameis cardui" 75 70
1029B 3 m. "Danaus chrysippus" 1·25 1·00
1030B 10 m. "Apatura iris" 3·00 3·25

1991. "Say No To Drugs" Campaign.
1031 **207** 16 s. multicoloured . . . 70 60

208 Wattled Cranes

1991. Southern Africa Development Co-ordination Conference Tourism Promotion. Multicoloured.
1032 12 s. Type **208** 70 70
1033 16 s. Butterfly on flowers . . . 70 70
1034 25 s. Zebra and tourist bus at Mukurub (rock formation), Namibia 85 30

209 De Gaulle in 1939

211 "St. Anne with Mary and the Child Jesus"

1991. Birth Centenary of Charles de Gaulle (French statesman).
1036 **209** 20 s. black and brown . . 40 15
1037 – 40 s. black and purple . . 60 25
1038 – 50 s. black and green . . 60 40
1039 – 60 s. black and blue . . . 70 65
1040 – 4 m. black and red . . . 2·25 3·75
DESIGNS: 40 s. General De Gaulle as Free French leader; 50 s. De Gaulle as provisional President of France, 1944–46; 60 s. Charles de Gaulle in 1958; 4 m. Pres. De Gaulle.

1991. 10th Wedding Anniv of Prince and Princess of Wales. As T **198b** of Gambia. Multicoloured.
1041 50 s. Prince and Princess of Wales 80 25
1042 70 s. Prince Charles at polo and Princess Diana holding Prince Henry 80 45
1043 1 m. Prince Charles with Prince Henry and Princess Diana in evening dress . . . . . . 1·00 65
1044 3 m. Prince William and Prince Henry in school uniform . . 1·75 2·75

1991. Christmas. Drawings by Albrecht Durer.
1046 **211** 20 s. black and mauve . . 25 10
1047 – 30 s. black and blue . . . 35 20
1048 – 50 s. black and green . . 50 25
1049 – 60 s. black and red . . . 55 30
1050 – 70 s. black and yellow . . 60 45
1051 – 1 m. black and orange . . 75 75
1052 – 2 m. black and purple . . 1·50 2·00
1053 – 4 m. black and blue . . 2·25 3·50
DESIGNS: 30 s. "Mary on Grass Bench"; 50 s. "Mary with Crown of Stars"; 60 s. "Mary with Child beside Tree"; 70 s. "Mary with Child beside Wall"; 1 m. "Mary in Halo on Crescent Moon"; 2 m. "Mary breastfeeding Child"; 4 m. "Mary with Infant in Swaddling Clothes".

212 Mickey Mouse and Pluto pinning the Tail on the Donkey

1991. Children's Games. Walt Disney cartoon characters. Multicoloured.
1055 20 s. Type **212** 40 15
1056 30 s. Mickey playing mancala . . 45 20
1057 40 s. Mickey rolling hoop . . . 50 20
1058 50 s. Minnie Mouse hula-hooping 55 25
1059 70 s. Mickey and Pluto throwing a frisbee 75 60
1060 1 m. Donald Duck with a diabolo . . . . 1·00 1·00
1061 2 m. Donald's nephews playing marbles . . . . 2·00 2·50
1062 3 m. Donald with Rubik's cube 2·50 3·25

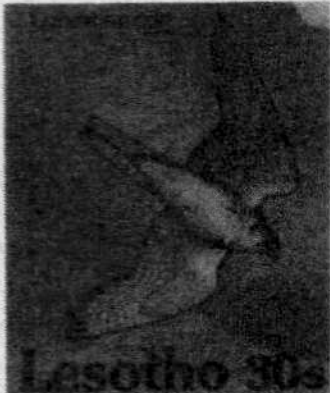

213 Lanner Falcon

1992. Birds. Multicoloured.
1064 30 s. Type **213** 50 50
1065 30 s. Bateleur 50 50
1066 30 s. Paradise sparrow (inscr "Red-headed Finch") . . . 50 50
1067 30 s. Lesser striped swallow . . 50 50
1068 30 s. Alpine swift 50 50
1069 30 s. Didric cuckoo 50 50
1070 30 s. Yellow-tufted malachite sunbird 50 50
1071 30 s. Burchell's gonolek ("Crimson-breasted Shrike") 50 50
1072 30 s. Pin-tailed whydah . . . 50 50
1073 30 s. Lilac-breasted roller . . 50 50
1074 30 s. Little black bustard ("Korhaan") 50 50
1075 30 s. Black-collared barbet . . 50 50
1076 30 s. Secretary bird 50 50
1077 30 s. Red-billed quelea 50 50
1078 30 s. Red bishop 50 50
1079 30 s. Ring-necked dove . . . 50 50
1080 30 s. Yellow canary 50 50
1081 30 s. Cape longclaw 50 50
1082 30 s. Cordon-bleu (inscr "Blue Waxbill") 50 50
1083 30 s. Golden bishop 50 50
Nos. 1064/83 were printed together, se-tenant, forming a composite design.

1992. 40th Anniv of Queen Elizabeth II's Accession. As T **202a** of Gambia. Multicoloured.
1084 20 s. Huts on mountain . . . 20 15
1085 30 s. View from mountains . . 25 20
1086 1 m. Cacti and mountain . . . 65 65
1087 4 m. Thaba-Bosiu . . . . . 2·25 3·00

215 Minnie Mouse as Spanish Lady, 1540–1660

1992. International Stamp Exhibitions. Walt Disney cartoon characters. Multicoloured. (a) "Granada '92", Spain. Traditional Spanish Costumes.
1089 20 s. Type **215** 40 15
1090 50 s. Mickey Mouse as Don Juan at Lepanto, 1571 . . . 55 30
1091 70 s. Donald in Galician costume, 1880 . . . . . . 70 50
1092 2 m. Daisy Duck in Aragonese costume, 1880 . . . . . . 1·75 2·50

(b) "World Columbian Stamp Expo '92". Red Indian Life.
1094 30 s. Donald Duck making arrowheads 30 30
1095 40 s. Goofy playing lacrosse . 40 40
1096 1 m. Mickey Mouse and Donald Duck planting corn 70 80
1097 3 m. Minnie Mouse doing bead work . . . . 1·60 2·50

216 Stegosaurus

1992. Prehistoric Animals. Multicoloured.
1099 20 s. Type **216** 45 30
1100 30 s. Ceratosaurus 55 35
1101 40 s. Procompsognathus . . . 65 45
1102 50 s. Lesothosaurus 75 55
1103 70 s. Plateosaurus . . . . . 1·00 70
1104 1 m. Gasosaurus . . . . . . 1·25 1·00
1105 2 m. Massospondylus . . . . 1·75 2·00
1106 3 m. Archaeopteryx . . . . . 2·00 2·50

217 Men's Discus

LESOTHO 20s
Virgin and Child
CHRISTMAS 1992
218 "Virgin and Child" (Sassetta)

1992. Olympic Games, Albertville and Barcelona. Multicoloured.
1108 20 s. Type **217** 20 15
1109 30 s. Men's long jump 25 15
1110 40 s. Women's 4 × 100 metres relay 30 25
1111 70 s. Women's 100 metres . . 50 50
1112 1 m. Men's parallel bars . . . 70 70
1113 2 m. Men's double luge (horiz) 1·40 1·60
1114 3 m. Women's 30k cross-country skiing (horiz) . . . . . . 1·75 2·25
1115 4 m. Men's biathlon . . . . . 2·00 2·50

1992. Christmas. Religious Paintings. Mult.
1117 20 s. Type **218** 25 15
1118 30 s. "Coronation of the Virgin" (Master of Bonastre) 30 20
1119 40 s. "Virgin and Child" (Master of SS. Cosmas and Damian) 40 25
1120 70 s. "The Virgin of Great Panagia" (detail) (12th-century Russian school) . . 70 55
1121 1 m. "Madonna and Child" (Vincenzo Foppa) 95 95
1122 2 m. "Madonna and Child" (School of Lippo Memmi) . 1·75 2·00
1123 3 m. "Virgin and Child" (Barnaba da Modena) . . . 2·25 2·75
1124 4 m. "Virgin and Child with Saints" (triptych) (Simone dei Crocifissi) . . . . 2·50 3·00

220 Baby Harp Seal (Earth Summit '92, Rio)

1993. Anniversaries and Events. Multicoloured.
1127 20 s. Type **220** 40 30
1128 30 s. Giant panda (Earth Summit '92, Rio) 55 30
1129 40 s. Airship "Graf Zeppelin" over globe (75th death anniv of Count Ferdinand von Zeppelin) 55 30
1130 70 s. Woman grinding maize (International Conference on Nutrition, Rome) 55 45
1131 4 m. Lt. Robinson's Royal Aircraft Factory B.E.2C shooting down Schutte Lanz SL-11 airship (75th death anniv of Count Ferdinand von Zeppelin) . . . . 2·50 2·75
1132 5 m. Valentina Tereshkova and "Vostok 6" (30th anniv of first woman in space) . . . 2·50 2·75

1993. Bicentenary of the Louvre, Paris. Paintings by Poussin. As T **209b** of Gambia. Multicoloured.
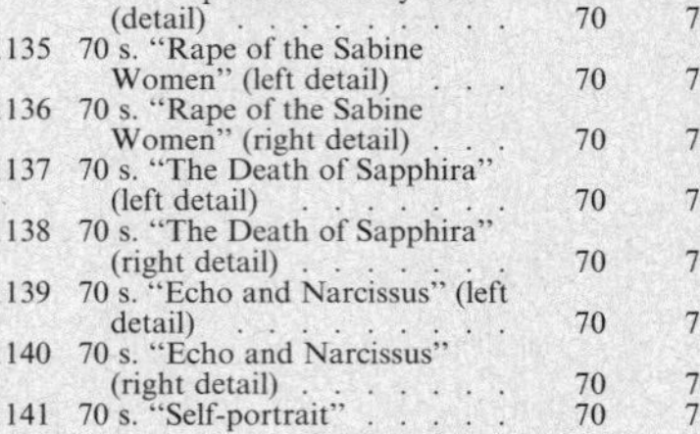
1134 70 s. "Orpheus and Eurydice" (detail) 70 70
1135 70 s. "Rape of the Sabine Women" (left detail) . . . 70 70
1136 70 s. "Rape of the Sabine Women" (right detail) . . . 70 70
1137 70 s. "The Death of Sapphira" (left detail) 70 70
1138 70 s. "The Death of Sapphira" (right detail) 70 70
1139 70 s. "Echo and Narcissus" (left detail) 70 70
1140 70 s. "Echo and Narcissus" (right detail) 70 70
1141 70 s. "Self-portrait" 70 70

222 Aloe

1993. Flowers. Multicoloured.
1143 20 s. Type **222** 25 10
1144 30 s. Calla lily 30 15
1145 40 s. Bird of paradise plant . . 35 15
1146 70 s. Amaryllis 55 40
1147 1 m. Agapanthus 75 60
1148 2 m. Crinum . . . . 1·75 1·50
1149 4 m. Watsonia . . . . 1·90 2·25
1150 5 m. Gazania . . . . 2·00 2·50

223 "Precis westermanni"

1993. Butterflies. Multicoloured.
1152 20 s. Type **223** 40 15
1153 40 s. "Precis sophia" 50 20
1154 70 s. "Precis terea" 65 45
1155 1 m. "Byblia acheloia" . . . 75 75
1156 2 m. "Papilio antimachus" . . 1·25 1·50
1157 5 m. "Pseudacraea boisduvali" . . . . 1·75 2·50
No. 1157 is inscribed "Pesudacraea boisduvali" in error.

1993. 40th Anniv of Coronation. As T **215a** of Gambia.
1159 20 s. multicoloured 30 45
1160 40 s. multicoloured 45 60
1161 1 m. black and green 70 90
1162 5 m. multicoloured . . . . . 3·00 3·25
DESIGNS: 20 s. Queen Elizabeth II at Coronation (photograph by Cecil Beaton); 40 s. St. Edward's Crown and Sceptre; 1 m. Queen Elizabeth the Queen Mother; 5 m. Queen Elizabeth II and family.

225 East African Railways Vulcan Steam Locomotive, 1929

1993. African Railways. Multicoloured.
1164 20 s. Type **225** 40 15
1165 30 s. Beyer-Garratt Class 15A steam locomotive, Zimbabwe Railways, 1952 . . . . . . 50 20
1166 40 s. Class 25 steam locomotive, South African Railways, 1953 60 20
1167 70 s. Class A 58 steam locomotive, East African Railways 75 40
1168 1 m. Class 9E electric locomotives, South African Railways 90 70
1169 2 m. Class 87 diesel-electric locomotive, East African Railways, 1971 . . . . . 1·40 1·25
1170 3 m. Class 92 diesel locomotive, East African Railways, 1971 . . . . 1·75 1·75
1171 5 m. Class 26 steam locomotive No. 3450, South African Railways, 1982 . . . . . 2·00 2·50

226 Court-house

1993. Traditional Houses. Multicoloured.
1173 20 s. Type **226** 25 10
1174 30 s. House with reed fence . . 30 15
1175 70 s. Unmarried girls' house . 55 40
1176 4 m. Hut made from branches . 2·75 3·75

227 Black and White Shorthair

1993. Domestic Cats. Multicoloured.
1178 20 s. Type **227** 30 10
1179 30 s. Shorthair tabby lying down 15 10
1180 70 s. Head of Shorthair tabby . 35 20
1181 5 m. Black and white shorthair with shorthair tabby . . . 2·25 1·10

228 Pluto in Chung Cheng Park, Keelung

1993. "Taipei '93" Asian International Stamp Exhibition, Taiwan. Walt Disney cartoon characters in Taiwan. Multicoloured.
1183 20 s. Type **228** 30 10
1184 30 s. Donald Duck at Chiao-Tienkung Temple Festival . 35 15
1185 40 s. Goofy with lantern figures 40 20
1186 70 s. Minnie Mouse shopping at temple festival 65 40

1187 1 m. Daisy Duck at Queen's Head Rock, Yehliu (vert) 80 70
1188 1 m. 20 Mickey and Minnie at National Concert Hall (vert) 1·00 1·00
1189 2 m. Donald at Chiang Kai-shek Memorial Hall (vert) 1·40 1·50
1190 2 m. 50 Donald and Daisy at the Grand Hotel, Taipei 1·75 2·00

229 Tseliso "Frisco" Khomari (Lesotho)
230 King Letsie III signing Oath of Office

1994. World Cup Football Championship '94, U.S.A. Multicoloured.
1192 20 s. Type **229** 40 10
1193 30 s. Thato "American Spoon" Mohale (Lesotho) 45 15
1194 40 s. Jozic Davor (Yugoslavia) and Freddy Rincorn (Colombia) 55 20
1195 50 s. Lefika "Mzee" Lekhotla (Lesotho) 60 25
1196 70 s. Litsiso "House-on-fire" Khali (Lesotho) 75 55
1197 1 m. Roger Milla (Cameroun) 90 75
1198 1 m. 20 David Platt (England) 1·25 1·50
1199 2 m. Karl Heinz Rummenigge (Germany) and Soren Lerby (Denmark) 1·75 2·25

1994. 1st Anniv of Restoration of Democracy. Multicoloured.
1201 20 s. Type **230** 10 10
1202 30 s. Parliament building (horiz) 10 10
1203 50 s. Swearing-in of Dr. Ntsu Mokhehle as Prime Minister (horiz) 10 10
1204 70 s. Maj-Gen P. Ramaema handing Instruments of Government to Dr. Ntsu Mokhehle (horiz) 15 10

231 Aquatic River Frog

1994. "Philakorea '94" International Stamp Exhibition, Seoul. Frogs and Toads. Mult.
1205 35 s. Type **231** 10 10
1206 50 s. Bubbling kassina 10 10
1207 1 m. Guttural toad 20 10
1208 1 m. 50 Common river frog 30 40

232 De Havilland D.H.C.6 Twin Otter and Emblem

1994. 50th Anniv of I.C.A.O. Multicoloured.
1210 35 s. Type **232** 10 10
1211 50 s. Fokker F.27 Friendship on runway 10 10
1212 1 m. Fokker F.27 Friendship over Moshoeshoe I International Airport 20 15
1213 1 m. 50 Cessna light aircraft over mountains 30 35

1995. No. 1022 surch **20s**.
1214a 20 s. on 30 s. "Charaxes jasius" 40 20

234 "Tagetes minuta"
235 Pius XII College, 1962

1995. Medicinal Plants. Multicoloured.
1215 35 s. Type **234** 10 10
1216 50 s. "Plantago lanceolata" 10 10
1217 1 m. "Amaranthus spinosus" 20 25
1218 1 m. 50 "Taraxacum officinale" 30 35

1995. 50th Anniv of University Studies in Lesotho. Multicoloured.
1220 35 s. Type **235** 10 10
1221 50 s. Campus, University of Basutoland, Bechuanaland and Swaziland, 1966 10 10
1222 70 s. Campus, University of Botswana, Lesotho and Swaziland, 1970 15 20
1223 1 m. Administration Block, University of Botswana, Lesotho and Swaziland, 1975 20 25
1224 1 m. 50 Administration Block, National University of Lesotho, 1988 30 35
1225 2 m. Procession of Vice-Chancellors, National University of Lesotho, 1995 45 50

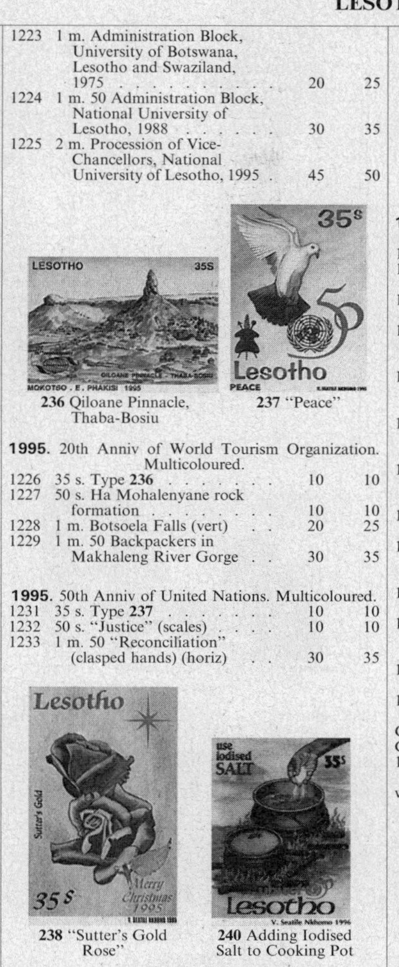

236 Qiloane Pinnacle, Thaba-Bosiu
237 "Peace"

1995. 20th Anniv of World Tourism Organization. Multicoloured.
1226 35 s. Type **236** 10 10
1227 50 s. Ha Mohalenyane rock formation 10 10
1228 1 m. Botsoela Falls (vert) 20 25
1229 1 m. 50 Backpackers in Makhaleng River Gorge 30 35

1995. 50th Anniv of United Nations. Multicoloured.
1231 35 s. Type **237** 10 10
1232 50 s. "Justice" (scales) 10 10
1233 1 m. 50 "Reconciliation" (clasped hands) (horiz) 30 35

238 "Sutter's Gold Rose"
240 Adding Iodised Salt to Cooking Pot

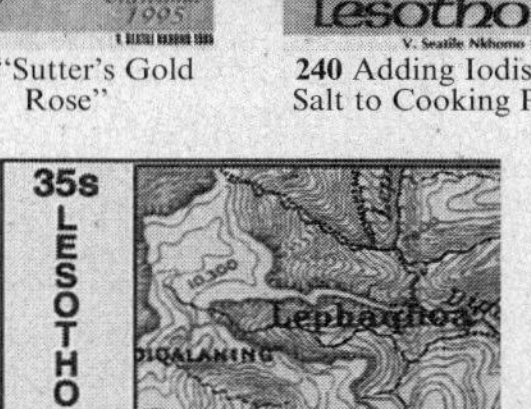

239 Part of 1911 Map showing Lephaqhoa

1995. Christmas. Roses. Multicoloured.
1234 5 s. Type **238** 10 10
1235 50 s. "Michele Meilland" 10 10
1236 1 m. "J. Otto Thilow" 20 25
1237 2 m. "Papa Meilland" 40 45

1996. Completion of New Standard Map of Lesotho (1994). Map Sections of Malibamatso Valley. Multicoloured. (a) 1911 Map.
1238 35 s. Type **239** 10 10
1239 35 s. Boritsa Tsuene 10 10
1240 35 s. Molapo 10 10
1241 35 s. Nkeu 10 10
1242 35 s. Three rivers flowing east 10 10
1243 35 s. Tibedi and Rafanyane 10 10
1244 35 s. Two rivers flowing east 10 10
1245 35 s. Madibatmatso River 10 10
1246 35 s. Bokung River 10 10
1247 35 s. Semena River 10 10

(b) 1978 Map.
1248 35 s. Mountains and river valley 10 10
1249 35 s. Pelaneng and Lepaqoa 10 10
1250 35 s. Mamohau 10 10
1251 35 s. Ha Lejone 10 10
1252 35 s. Ha Thoora 10 10
1253 35 s. Ha Mikia 10 10
1254 35 s. Ha Kosetabole 10 10
1255 35 s. Ha Seshote 10 10
1256 35 s. Ha Rapooane 10 10
1257 35 s. Bokong Ha Kennan 10 10

(c) 1994 Map.
1258 35 s. Mafika-Lisiu Pass 10 10
1259 35 s. Ha Lesaoana 10 10
1260 35 s. Ha Masaballa 10 10
1261 35 s. Ha Nkisi 10 10
1262 35 s. Ha Rafanyane 10 10
1263 35 s. Laitsoka Pass 10 10
1264 35 s. "Katse Reservoir" 10 10
1265 35 s. Seshote 10 10
1266 35 s. Sephareng 10 10
1267 35 s. Katse Dam 10 10
Nos. 1238/47, 1248/57 and 1258/67 respectively were printed together, se-tenant, forming composite designs.

1996. 50th Anniv of U.N.I.C.E.F. Multicoloured.
1268 35 s. Type **240** 10 10
1269 50 s. Herdboys with livestock (horiz) 10 10
1270 70 s. Children in class (horiz) 15 20
1271 1 m. 50 Boys performing traditional dance (horiz) 30 35

241 U.S.A. Basketball Team, 1936

1996. Olympic Games, Atlanta. Previous Gold Medal Winners. Multicoloured.
1272 1 m. Type **241** 20 25
1273 1 m. 50 Brandenburg Gate and stadium, Berlin, 1936 30 35
1274 1 m. 50 Glen Morris (U.S.A.) (decathlon, 1936) (vert) 30 35
1275 1 m. 50 Saidi Aouita (Morocco) (5000m running, 1984) (vert) 30 35
1276 1 m. 50 Arnie Robinson (U.S.A.) (long jump, 1976) (vert) 30 35
1277 1 m. 50 Hans Woellke (Germany) (shot put, 1936) (vert) 30 35
1278 1 m. 50 Renate Stecher (Germany) (100m running, 1972) (vert) 30 35
1279 1 m. 50 Evelyn Ashford (U.S.A.) (100m running, 1984) (vert) 30 35
1280 1 m. 50 Willie Davenport (U.S.A.) (110m hurdles, 1968) (vert) 30 35
1281 1 m. 50 Bob Beamon (U.S.A.) (long jump, 1968) (vert) 30 35
1282 1 m. 50 Heidi Rosendhal (Germany) (long jump, 1972) (vert) 30 35
1283 2 m. Jesse Owens (U.S.A.) (track and field, 1936) (vert) 40 45
1284 3 m. Speed boat racing 60 65
No. 1273 is inscribed "BRANDEBOURG GATE" in error. No. 1274 incorrectly identifies Glen Morris as the gold medal winner in the 1936 long jump.
Nos. 1274/82 were printed together, se-tenant, with the backgrounds forming a composite design.

242 Class WP Steam Locomotive (India)

1996. Trains of the World. Multicoloured.
1286 1 m. 50 Type **242** 30 35
1287 1 m. 50 Canadian Pacific steam locomotive No. 2471 (Canada) 30 35
1288 1 m. 50 The "Caledonian" (Great Britain) 30 35
1289 1 m. 50 Steam locomotive "William Mason" (U.S.A.) 30 35
1290 1 m. 50 "Trans-Siberian Express" (Russia) 30 35
1291 1 m. 50 Steam train (Switzerland) 30 35
1292 1 m. 50 ETR 450 high speed train (Italy) 30 35
1293 1 m. 50 TGV express train (France) 30 35
1294 1 m. 50 XPT high speed train (Australia) 30 35
1295 1 m. 50 "Blue Train" (South Africa) 30 35
1296 1 m. 50 Intercity 225 express train (Great Britain) 30 35
1297 1 m. 50 "Hikari" express train (Japan) 30 35

243 Mother's Union Member, Methodist Church

1996. Christmas. Mothers' Unions. Multicoloured.
1299 35 s. Type **243** 10 10
1300 50 s. Roman Catholic Church 10 10
1301 1 m. Lesotho Evangelical Church 20 25
1302 1 m. 50 Anglican Church 30 35
No. 1302 is inscribed "Anglian" in error.

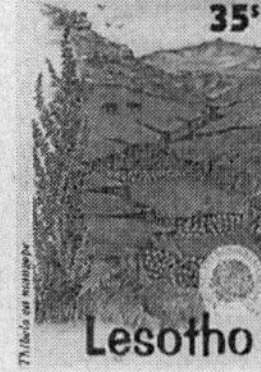

244 Hand Clasp (Co-operation for Development)
245 Land Reclamation

1997. 10th Anniv of Lesotho Highland Water Project (1996). Multicoloured.
1303 35 s. Type **244** 10 10
1304 50 s. Bearded vulture and rock painting (Nature and Heritage) 10 10
1305 1 m. Malibamatso Bridge (Engineering) 20 25
1306 1 m. 50 Katse Valley in 1986 and 1996 (75 × 28 mm) 30 35
No. 1305 is inscribed "Developement" in error.

1997. Environment Protection. Multicoloured.
1307 35 s. Type **245** 10 10
1308 50 s. Throwing rubbish into bin 15 20
1309 1 m. Hands holding globe and tree 25 30
1310 1 m. 20 Recycling symbol and rubbish 30 35
1311 1 m. 50 Collecting rain water 40 45

1997. World Cup Football Championship, France (1998). As T **283a** of Gambia, but vert. Multicoloured.
1312 1 m. Schmeichel, Denmark 20 25
1313 1 m. 50 Bergkamp, Netherlands 30 35
1314 1 m. 50 Argentine players celebrating 30 35
1315 1 m. 50 Argentine and Dutch players competing for ball 30 35
1316 1 m. 50 Players heading ball 30 35
1317 1 m. 50 Goalkeeper deflecting ball 30 35
1318 1 m. 50 Goal-mouth melee 30 35
1319 1 m. 50 Argentine player kicking ball 30 35
1320 2 m. Southgate, England 40 45
1321 2 m. 50 Asprilla, Colombia 50 55
1322 3 m. Gascoigne, England 60 65
1323 4 m. Giggs, Wales 80 85

247 "Spialia spio"

1997. Butterflies. Multicoloured.
1325 1 m. 50 Type **247** 30 35
1326 1 m. 50 "Leptotes pirithous" 30 35
1327 1 m. 50 "Acraea satis" 30 35
1328 1 m. 50 "Belenois aurota" 30 35
1329 1 m. 50 "Spindasis natalensis" 30 35
1330 1 m. 50 "Torynesis orangica" 30 35
1331 1 m. 50 "Lepidochysops variabilis" 30 35
1332 1 m. 50 "Pinacopteryx eriphia" 30 35
1333 1 m. 50 "Anthene butleri livida" 30 35
Nos. 1325/33 were printed together, se-tenant, with the backgrounds forming a composite design.
No. 1326 is inscribed "Cyclyrius pirithous", No. 1332 "Pinacopteryx eriphea", both in error.

248 Rock Paintings and Boy
249 Diana, Princess of Wales

1998. 40th Anniv of Morija Museum and Archives. Multicoloured.
1335 35 s. Type **248** 10 10
1336 45 s. Hippopotamus and lower jaw bone (horiz) 10 15
1337 50 s. Woman and cowhide skirt 15 20
1338 1 m. Drum and "thomo" (musical bow) 25 30
1339 1 m. 50 Warrior with "khau" (gorget awarded for valour) 40 45
1340 2 m. Herders with ox (horiz) 50 55

1998. Diana, Princess of Wales Commemoration. Multicoloured.
1341 3 m. Type **249** 60 65
1342 3 m. Wearing grey jacket 60 65
1343 3 m. Wearing white polo-necked jumper 60 65
1344 3 m. Wearing pearl necklace 60 65
1345 3 m. Wearing white evening dress 60 65
1346 3 m. Wearing pale blue jacket 60 65

250 Atitlan Grebe

1998. Fauna of the World. Multicoloured. (a) Vert designs as T **250**.

1348 1 m. Type **250** 20 25
1349 1 m. Cabot's tragopan 20 25
1350 1 m. Spider monkey 20 25
1351 1 m. Dibatag 20 25
1352 1 m. Right whale 20 25
1353 1 m. Imperial parrot 20 25
1354 1 m. Cheetah 20 25
1355 1 m. Brown-eared pheasant 20 25
1356 1 m. Leatherback turtle 20 25
1357 1 m. Imperial woodpecker 20 25
1358 1 m. Andean condor 20 25
1359 1 m. Barbary deer 20 25
1360 1 m. Grey gentle lemur 20 25
1361 1 m. Cuban parrot 20 25
1362 1 m. Numbat 20 25
1363 1 m. Short-tailed albatross 20 25
1364 1 m. Green turtle 20 25
1365 1 m. White rhinoceros 20 25
1366 1 m. Diademed sifaka 20 25
1367 1 m. Galapagos penguin 20 25

(b) Horiz designs, each 48 × 31 mm.

1368 1 m. 50 Impala 30 35
1369 1 m. 50 Black bear 30 35
1370 1 m. 50 American buffalo 30 35
1371 1 m. 50 African elephant 30 35
1372 1 m. 50 Kangaroo 30 35
1373 1 m. 50 Lion 30 35
1374 1 m. 50 Giant panda 30 35
1375 1 m. 50 Tiger 30 35
1376 1 m. 50 Zebra 30 35

251 Cape Vulture

1998. Endangered Species. Cape Vulture. Mult.

1378 1 m. Type **251** 20 25
1379 1 m. Looking towards ground 20 25
1380 1 m. Looking over shoulder 20 25
1381 1 m. Facing right 20 25

252 Siamese

1998. Cats of the World. Multicoloured.

1382 70 s. Type **252** 15 20
1383 1 m. Chartreux 20 25
1384 2 m. Korat 40 45
1385 2 m. Japanese bobtail 40 45
1386 2 m. British white 40 45
1387 2 m. Bengal 40 45
1388 2 m. Abyssinian 40 45
1389 2 m. Snowshoe 40 45
1390 2 m. Scottish fold 40 45
1391 2 m. Maine coon 40 45
1392 2 m. Balinese 40 45
1393 2 m. Persian 40 45
1394 2 m. Javanese 40 45
1395 2 m. Turkish angora 40 45
1396 2 m. Tiffany 40 45
1397 3 m. Egyptian mau 60 65
1398 4 m. Bombay 80 85
1399 5 m. Burmese 1·00 1·10

Nos. 1385/90 and 1391/6 respectively were printed together, se-tenant, with the backgrounds forming composite designs.

253 "Laccaria laccata"

1998. Fungi of the World. Multicoloured.

1401 70 s. Type **253** 15 20
1402 1 m. "Mutinus caninus" 20 25
1403 1 m. "Hygrophorus psittacinus" 20 25
1404 1 m. "Cortinarius obtusus" 20 25
1405 1 m. "Volvariella bombycina" 20 25
1406 1 m. "Cortinarius caerylescens" 20 25
1407 1 m. "Laccaria amethystina" 20 25
1408 1 m. "Tricholoma aurantium" 20 25
1409 1 m. "Amanita excelsa (spissa)" 20 25
1410 1 m. "Clavaria helvola" 20 25
1411 1 m. Unidentified species (inscr "Cortinarius caerylescens") 20 25
1412 1 m. "Russula queletii" 20 25
1413 1 m. "Amanita phalloides" 20 25
1414 1 m. "Lactarius deliciosus" 20 25
1415 1 m. 50 "Tricholoma lascivum" 30 35
1416 2 m. "Clitocybe geotropa" 40 45
1417 3 m. "Amanita excelsa" 60 65
1418 4 m. Red-capped bolete 80 85

Nos. 1406, 1407, 1414 and 1416 are inscribed "Continarius caerylescens", "Laccaria amethystea", "Lactarius delicious", and "Clitocybe geotrapa", all in error.

254 "Simba"

1998. World Cinema. Multicoloured. (a) Films about Africa.

1420 2 m. Type **254** 40 45
1421 2 m. "Call to Freedom" 40 45
1422 2 m. "Cry the Beloved Country" 40 45
1423 2 m. "King Solomon's Mines" 40 45
1424 2 m. "Flame and the Fire" 40 45
1425 2 m. "Cry Freedom" 40 45
1426 2 m. "Bopha!" 40 45
1427 2 m. "Zulu" 40 45

(b) Japanese Film Stars.

1428 2 m. Takamine Hideko 40 45
1429 2 m. James Shigeta 40 45
1430 2 m. Miyoshi Umeki 40 45
1431 2 m. May Ishimara 40 45
1432 2 m. Sessue Hayakawa 40 45
1433 2 m. Miiko Taka 40 45
1434 2 m. Mori Masayuki 40 45
1435 2 m. Hara Setsuko 40 45
1436 2 m. Kyo Machiko 40 45

Nos. 1420/7 and 1428/36 respectively were printed together, se-tenant, with the backgrounds forming composite designs.

No. 1423 is inscribed "KING SOLOMAN'S MINES" in error.

255 Ceresiosaurus

1998. Prehistoric Animals. Multicoloured.

1438 2 m. Type **255** 40 45
1439 2 m. Rhomaleosaurus 40 45
1440 2 m. Anomalocaris 40 45
1441 2 m. Mixosaurus 40 45
1442 2 m. Stethacanthus 40 45
1443 2 m. Dunklosteus 40 45
1444 2 m. Tommotia 40 45
1445 2 m. Sanctacaris 40 45
1446 2 m. Ammonites 40 45
1447 2 m. Rhamphorhynchus 40 45
1448 2 m. Brachiosaurus 40 45
1449 2 m. Mamenchisaurus hochuanensis 40 45
1450 2 m. Ceratosaurus nasicornis 40 45
1451 2 m. Archaeopteryx 40 45
1452 2 m. Leaellynasaura amicagraphica 40 45
1453 2 m. Chasmosaurus belli 40 45
1454 2 m. Deinonychus and Pachyrhinosaurus 40 45
1455 2 m. Deinonychus 40 45
1456 2 m. Nyctosaurus 40 45
1457 2 m. Volcanoes 40 45
1458 2 m. Eudimorphodon 40 45
1459 2 m. Apatosaurus 40 45
1460 2 m. Peteinosaurus 40 45
1461 2 m. Tropeognathus 40 45
1462 2 m. Pteranodon ingens 40 45
1463 2 m. Ornithodesmus 40 45
1464 2 m. Wuerhosaurus 40 45

Nos. 1438/46, 1447/55 and 1456/64 respectively were printed together, se-tenant, with the backgrounds forming composite designs.

256 Treefish

1998. Year of the Ocean. Fishes. Multicoloured.

1466 1 m. Type **256** 20 25
1467 1 m. Tigerbarb 20 25
1468 1 m. Bandtail puffer 20 25
1469 1 m. Cod 20 25
1470 1 m. 50 Clown loach 30 35
1471 1 m. 50 Christy's lyretail 30 35
1472 1 m. 50 Filefish 30 35
1473 1 m. 50 Sicklefin killie 30 35
1474 2 m. Brook trout 40 45
1475 2 m. Emerald betta 40 45
1476 2 m. Pacific electric ray 40 45
1477 2 m. Bighead searobin 40 45
1478 2 m. Weakfish 40 45
1479 2 m. Red drum 40 45
1480 2 m. Blue marlin 40 45
1481 2 m. Yellowfin tuna 40 45
1482 2 m. Barracuda 40 45
1483 2 m. Striped bass 40 45
1484 2 m. White shark 40 45
1485 2 m. Permit 40 45
1486 2 m. Purple firefish 40 45
1487 2 m. Harlequin sweetlips 40 45
1488 2 m. Clown wrasse 40 45
1489 2 m. Bicolour angelfish 40 45
1490 2 m. False cleanerfish 40 45
1491 2 m. Mandarinfish 40 45
1492 2 m. Regal tang 40 45
1493 2 m. Clownfish 40 45
1494 2 m. Bluegill 40 45
1495 2 m. Grayling 40 45
1496 2 m. Walleye 40 45
1497 2 m. Brown trout 40 45
1498 2 m. Atlantic salmon 40 45
1499 2 m. Northern pike 40 45
1500 2 m. Large-mouth bass 40 45
1501 2 m. Rainbow trout 40 45
1502 2 m. Platy variatus 40 45
1503 2 m. Archerfish 40 45
1504 2 m. Clown knifefish 40 45
1505 2 m. Angelicus 40 45
1506 2 m. Black arowana 40 45
1507 2 m. Spotted scat 40 45
1508 2 m. Kribensis 40 45
1509 2 m. Golden pheasant 40 45
1510 3 m. Harlequin tuskfish 60 65
1511 4 m. Half-moon angelfish 80 85
1512 5 m. Spotted trunkfish 1·00 1·10
1513 6 m. Wolf eel 1·25 1·40
1514 7 m. Cherubfish 1·40 1·50

Nos. 1470/3 show the face value as "M1.5".

257 Crowning of King Letsie III

1998. 1st Anniv of Coronation of King Letsie III. Multicoloured.

1516 1 m. Type **257** 20 25
1517 1 m. King saluting Basotho nation 20 25
1518 1 m. King Letsie in profile 20 25

258 "Pelargonium sidoides"

1998. Flowers. Multicoloured.

1519 10 s. Type **258** 10 10
1520 15 s. "Aponogeton ranunculiflorus" 10 10
1521 20 s. "Sebaea leiostyla" 10 10
1522 40 s. "Sebaea grandis" 10 10
1523 50 s. "Satyrium neglectum" 10 10
1524 60 s. "Massonia jasminiflora" 10 10
1525 70 s. "Ajuga ophrydis" 15 20
1526 80 s. "Nemesia fruticans" 20 25
1527 1 m. "Aloe broomii" 20 25
1528 2 m. "Wahlenbergia androsacea" 40 45
1529 2 m. 50 "Phygelius capensis" 50 55
1530 3 m. "Dianthus basuticus" 60 65
1531 4 m. 50 "Rhodohypoxis baurii" 90 95
1532 5 m. "Turbina oblongata" 1·00 1·10
1533 6 m. "Hibiscus microcarpus" 1·10 1·40
1534 10 m. "Lobelia erinus" ("Moraea stricta") 2·00 2·10

259 Japanese Akita

1999. Dogs. Multicoloured.

1535 70 s. Type **259** 15 20
1536 1 m. Canaan dog 20 25
1537 2 m. Husky ("ESKIMO DOG") 40 45
1538 2 m. Cirneco dell'Etna 40 45
1539 2 m. Afghan hound 40 45
1540 2 m. Finnish spitz 40 45
1541 2 m. Dalmatian 40 45
1542 2 m. Basset hound 40 45
1543 2 m. Shar-pei 40 45
1544 2 m. Boxer 40 45
1545 2 m. Catalan sheepdog 40 45
1546 2 m. English toy spaniel 40 45
1547 2 m. Greyhound 40 45
1548 2 m. Keeshond 40 45
1549 2 m. Bearded collie 40 45
1550 4 m. 50 Norwegian elkhound 90 95

Nos. 1538/43 and 1544/9 were printed together, se-tenant, with the backgrounds forming composite designs.

260 Belted Kingfisher

1999. Birds. Multicoloured.

1552 70 s. Type **260** 15 20
1553 1 m. 50 Palm cockatoo (vert) 30 35
1554 2 m. Red-tailed hawk 40 45
1555 2 m. Evening grosbeak 40 45
1556 2 m. Lesser blue-winged pitta 40 45
1557 2 m. Atlamira oriole 40 45
1558 2 m. Rose-breasted grosbeak 40 45
1559 2 m. Yellow warbler 40 45
1560 2 m. Akiapolaau 40 45
1561 2 m. American goldfinch 40 45
1562 2 m. Northern flicker 40 45
1563 2 m. Western tanager 40 45
1564 2 m. Blue jay (vert) 40 45
1565 2 m. Northern cardinal (vert) 40 45
1566 2 m. Yellow-headed blackbird (vert) 40 45
1567 2 m. Red crossbill (vert) 40 45
1568 2 m. Cedar waxwing (vert) 40 45
1569 2 m. Vermilion flycatcher (vert) 40 45
1570 2 m. Pileated woodpecker (vert) 40 45
1571 2 m. Western meadowlark (vert) 40 45
1572 2 m. Kingfisher (vert) 40 45
1573 3 m. Tufted puffin 60 65
1574 4 m. Reddish egret 80 85
1575 5 m. Hoatzin (vert) 1·00 1·10

No. 1553 shows the face value as "M1.5".

Nos. 1555/63 and 1564/72 were printed together, se-tenant, with the backgrounds forming composite designs.

261 "Cattleya dowiana"

LESOTHO M1.50
266 "Water Lily at Night" (Pan Tianshou)

262 "Austerity" Type Series 52 Steam Locomotive, Frankfurt, 1939

1999. Orchids of the World. Multicoloured.

1577 1 m. 50 Type **261** 30 35
1578 2 m. "Cochleanthes discolor" 40 45
1579 2 m. "Cischweinfia dasyandra" 40 45
1580 2 m. "Ceratostylis retisquama" 40 45
1581 2 m. "Comparettia speciosa" 40 45
1582 2 m. "Cryptostylis subulata" 40 45
1583 2 m. "Cycnoches ventricosum" 40 45
1584 2 m. "Dactylorhiza maculata" 40 45
1585 2 m. "Cypripedium calceolus" 40 45
1586 2 m. "Cymbidium finlaysonianum" 40 45
1587 2 m. "Apasia epidendroides" 40 45
1588 2 m. "Barkaria lindleyana" 40 45
1589 2 m. "Bifrenaria tetragona" 40 45
1590 2 m. "Bulbophyllum graveolens" 40 45
1591 2 m. "Brassavola flagellaris" 40 45
1592 2 m. "Bollea lawrenceana" 40 45
1593 2 m. "Caladenia carnea" 40 45
1594 2 m. "Catasetum macrocarpum" 40 45
1595 2 m. "Cattleya aurantiaca" 40 45
1596 2 m. "Dendrobium bellatulum" 40 45
1597 2 m. "Dendrobium trigonopus" 40 45
1598 2 m. "Dimerandra emarginata" 40 45
1599 2 m. "Dressleria eburnea" 40 45
1600 2 m. "Dracula tubeana" 40 45
1601 2 m. "Disa kirstenbosch" 40 45
1602 2 m. "Encyclia alata" 40 45
1603 2 m. "Epidendrum pseudepidendrum" 40 45
1604 2 m. "Eriopsis biloba" 40 45
1605 3 m. "Diurus behrii" 60 65
1606 4 m. "Ancistrochilus rothchildianus" 80 85
1607 5 m. "Aerangis curnowiana" 1·00 1·10
1608 7 m. "Arachnis flos-aeris" 1·40 1·50
1609 8 m. "Aspasia principissa" 1·60 1·75

No. 1583 was inscribed "Cycnoches ventricsum" in error.

1999. "iBRA '99" International Stamp Exhibition, Nuremburg. Railway Locomotives. Multicoloured.
1611 7 m. Type **262** . . . . 1·40 1·50
1612 8 m. "Adler" and Brandenburg Gate, Berlin, 1835 . . . . . 1·60 1·75

1999. 150th Death Anniv of Katsushika Hokusai (Japanese artist). Horiz designs as T **298b** of Gambia. Multicoloured.
1613 3 m. "View of Sumida River in Snow" 60 65
1614 3 m. "Two Carp" 60 65
1615 3 m. "The Blind" (woman with eyes closed) 60 65
1616 3 m. "The Blind" (woman with one eye open) 60 65
1617 3 m. "Fishing by Torchlight" . 60 65
1618 3 m. "Whaling off the Goto Islands" 60 65
1619 3 m. "Makamaro watching the Moon from a Hill" 60 65
1620 3 m. "Peonies and Butterfly" . 60 65
1621 3 m. "The Blind" (old man with open eyes) 60 65
1622 3 m. "The Blind" (old man with one eye open) 60 65
1623 3 m. "People crossing an Arched Bridge" (four people on bridge) 60 65
1624 3 m. "People crossing an Arched Bridge" (two people on bridge) 60 65

1999. 10th Anniv of United Nations Rights of the Child Convention. As T **298c** of Gambia. Mult.
1626 2 m. African boy 45 50
1627 2 m. Asian girl 45 50
1628 2 m. European boy 45 50
Nos. 1626/8 were printed together, se-tenant, the backgrounds forming a composite design.

1999. 250th Birth Anniv of Johann von Goethe (German writer). As T **298d** of Gambia.
1629 6 m. multicoloured . . . . . 1·25 1·40
1630 6 m. blue, lilac and black . . . 1·25 1·40
1631 6 m. multicoloured . . . . . 1·25 1·40
DESIGNS—HORIZ: No. 1626, Mephistopheles appearing as dog in Faust's study; 1627, Von Goethe and Von Schiller; 1628, Mephistopheles disguised as a dog scorching the Earth.
No. 1626, in addition to the normal country name, shows "GUYANA" twice in violet across the centre of the design.

1999. "China '99" International Stamp Exhibition, Beijing. Paintings of Pan Tianshou (Chinese artist). Multicoloured.
1633 1 m. 50 Type **266** 30 35
1634 1 m. 50 "Hen and Chicks" . . 30 35
1635 1 m. 50 "Plum Blossom and Orchid" 30 35
1636 1 m. 50 "Plum Blossom and Banana Tree" 30 35
1637 1 m. 50 "Crane and Pine" . . 30 35
1638 1 m. 50 "Swallows" 30 35
1639 1 m. 50 "Eagle on the Pine" (bird looking up) 30 35
1640 1 m. 50 "Palm Tree" 30 35
1641 1 m. 50 "Eagle on the Pine" (bird looking down) 30 35
1642 1 m. 50 "Orchids" 30 35

1999. "Queen Elizabeth the Queen Mother's Century". As T **304a** of Gambia.
1644 5 m. black and gold . . . . . 1·00 1·10
1645 5 m. multicoloured . . . . . 1·00 1·10
1646 5 m. black and gold . . . . . 1·00 1·10
1647 5 m. multicoloured . . . . . 1·00 1·10
DESIGNS: No. 1644, Queen Elizabeth, 1938; 1645, King George VI and Queen Elizabeth, 1948; 1646, Queen Mother wearing tiara, 1963; 1647, Queen Mother wearing blue hat, Canada, 1989.

268 Chinese Soldier firing Rocket, 1150

270 King Letsie III and Miss Karabo Anne Motsoeneng

269 U.S.S. "New Jersey" (battleship)

1999. New Millennium. People and Events of Twelfth Century (1150–99). Multicoloured.
1649 1 m. 50 Type **268** 30 35
1650 1 m. 50 Burmese temple guardian, 1150 . . . . 30 35
1651 1 m. 50 Troubadour serenading Lady, 1150 . . . . 30 35
1652 1 m. 50 Abbot Suger (advisor to French Kings), 1150 . . . . 30 35
1653 1 m. 50 Pope Adrian IV, 1154 . 30 35
1654 1 m. 50 Henry II of England, 1154 . . . . 30 35
1655 1 m. 50 Bust of Frederick Barbarossa, King of Germany, and Holy Roman Emperor, 1155 . . . . . . 30 35
1656 1 m. 50 Shogun Yoritomo of Japan, 1156 . . . . 30 35
1657 1 m. 50 Count and Countess of Vaudemont (Crusader monument), 1165 . . . . 30 35
1658 1 m. 50 Ibn Rushd (Arab translator), 1169 . . . . 30 35
1659 1 m. 50 Archbishop Thomas a Becket, 1170 . . . . . . 30 30
1660 1 m. 50 Leaning Tower of Pisa, 1174 . . . . 30 35
1661 1 m. 50 Pivot windmill, 1180 . 30 35
1662 1 m. 50 Saladin (Saracen general), 1187 . . . . 30 35
1663 1 m. 50 King Richard the Lionheart of England, 1189 . 30 35
1664 1 m. 50 Moal (statues), Easter Island, 1150 (59 x 39 mm) . 30 35
1665 1 m. 50 Crusader, 1189 . . . . 30 35

1999. Maritime Developments 1700–2000. Mult.
1666 4 m. Type **269** 80 85
1667 4 m. "Aquila" (Italian aircraft carrier) 80 85
1668 4 m. "De Zeven Provincien" (Dutch cruiser) 80 85
1669 4 m. H.M.S. "Formidable" (aircraft carrier) 80 85
1670 4 m. "Vittorio Veneto" (Italian cruiser) 80 85
1671 4 m. H.M.S. "Hampshire" (destroyer) 80 85
1672 4 m. "France" (French liner) . 80 85
1673 4 m. "Queen Elizabeth 2" (liner) 80 85
1674 4 m. "United States" (American liner) 80 85
1675 4 m. "Queen Elizabeth" (liner) 80 85
1676 4 m. "Michelangelo" (Italian liner) 80 85
1677 4 m. "Mauretania" (British liner) 80 85
1678 4 m. "Shearwater" (British hydrofoil ferry) 80 85
1679 4 m. British Class M submarine 80 85
1680 4 m. SRN 130 hovercraft . . . 80 85
1681 4 m. Italian Second World War submarine 80 85
1682 4 m. SRN 3 hovercraft 80 85
1683 4 m. "Soucoupe Plongeante" (oceanographic submersible) 80 85
1684 4 m. "James Watt" (early steamship) 80 85
1685 4 m. "Savannah" (steam/sail ship), 1819 . . . . 80 85
1686 4 m. "Amistad" (slave schooner) 80 85
1687 4 m. American Navy brig . . . 80 85
1688 4 m. "Great Britain" (liner) . . 80 85
1689 4 m. "Sirius" (paddle steamer) . 80 85
Nos. 1686 and 1687 both have their names wrongly inscribed as "ARMISTAD" and "BRICK" on the sheet margin.

2000. Wedding of King Letsie III. Multicoloured.
1691 1 m. Type **270** 20 25
1692 1 m. Miss Karabo Anne Motsoeneng 20 25
1693 1 m. King Letsie III 20 25
1694 1 m. King Letsie III and Miss Karabo Motsoeneng in traditional dress 20 25

POSTAGE DUE STAMPS

1966. Nos. D9/10 of Basutoland optd **LESOTHO**.
D11 D **2** 1 c. red 30 75
D12 5 c. violet 30 90

D 1

D 2

1967.
D13 D **1** 1 c. blue . . . . 15 3·00
D14 2 c. red . . . . 15 3·50
D15 5 c. green . . . . 20 3·50

1986.
D19 D **2** 2 s. green 15 70
D20 5 s. blue 15 70
D21 35 s. violet . . . . . . 50 1·25

APPENDIX

The following stamps have either been issued in excess of postal needs, or have not been available to the public in reasonable quantities at face value.

1981-83.
15th Anniv of Independence. Classic Stamps of the World. 10 m. × 40, each embossed on gold foil.

LIBERIA Pt. 13

A republic on the W. coast of Africa, founded as a home for freed slaves.

100 cents = 1 dollar.

1

2

1860.

7	1	6 c. red	23·00	32·00
8		12 c. blue	20·00	32·00
9		24 c. green	23·00	32·00

1880.

13	1	1 c. blue	3·25	4·75
14		2 c. red	2·25	3·25
15		6 c. mauve	4·25	5·50
16		12 c. yellow	4·25	6·00
17		24 c. red	5·00	6·75

1881.

18	2	3 c. black	4·25	4·00

3

4

5 "Alligator" (first settlers' ship)

1882.

47	3	8 c. blue	3·25	3·25
20		16 c. red	4·25	3·25

1886.

49	3	1 c. red	95	95
50		2 c. green	95	1·00
23		3 c. mauve	1·00	1·00
52		4 c. brown	1·10	1·00
27		6 c. grey	1·50	1·50
54	4	8 c. grey	2·75	2·75
55		16 c. yellow	4·25	4·25
29	5	32 c. blue	17·00	17·00

7 Liberian Star

8 African Elephant

9 Oil Palm

10 Pres. H. R. W. Johnson

11 Vai Woman

12 Seal

13 Star

15 Hippopotamus

17 President Johnson

1892.

75	7	1 c. red	30	30
76		2 c. blue	30	30
77	8	4 c. black and green	2·10	1·60
78	9	6 c. green	85	75
79	10	8 c. black and brown	60	75
80	11	12 c. red	60	85
81	12	16 c. lilac	2·10	1·60
82	13	24 c. green on yellow	1·50	1·25
83	12	32 c. blue	3·00	2·50
84	15	$1 black and blue	10·00	5·75
85	13	$2 brown on buff	4·25	3·75
86	17	$5 black and red	5·50	5·50

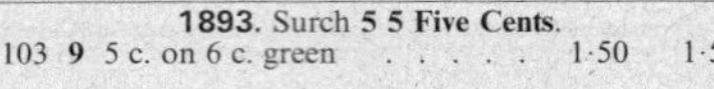
1893. Surch **5 5 Five Cents.**

103	9	5 c. on 6 c. green	1·50	1·50

24

1894. Imperf or roul.

117	24	5 c. black and red	6·25	6·25

35

36

1897.

144	9	1 c. purple	70	35
145		1 c. green	85	50
146	15	2 c. black and bistre	1·50	1·10
147		2 c. black and red	1·60	1·40
148	8	5 c. black and lake	1·60	1·10
149		5 c. black and blue	3·00	2·00
150	10	10 c. blue and yellow	60	50
151	11	15 c. black	60	65
152	12	20 c. red	1·90	1·25
153	13	25 c. green	1·25	85
154	12	30 c. blue	4·25	3·00
155	35	50 c. black and brown	2·10	2·75

The prices in the "used" column of sets marked with a dagger (†) against the date of issue are for stamps "cancelled to order" from remainder stocks. Postally used specimens are worth appreciably more.

†1897.

156	36	3 c. red and green	25	40

1901. Official stamps of 1892–98 optd **ORDINARY.**

175	9	1 c. purple (No. O157)	50·00	35·00
176		1 c. green (O158)	28·00	32·00
177	7	2 c. blue (O120)	75·00	80·00
178	15	2 c. black and brn (O159)	£100	45·00
179		2 c. black & red (O160)	28·00	32·00
180	24	5 c. green and lilac (O130)	£225	£225
181	8	5 c. black and red (O161)	£150	£150
182		5 c. black and bl (O162)	22·00	28·00
183	10	8 c. black and brn (O122)	75·00	
184		10 c. blue and yell (O163)	28·00	32·00
169	11	12 c. red (O92)	£100	£100
185		15 c. black (O164)	28·00	32·00
170	12	16 c. lilac (O93)		
186		16 c. lilac (O124)	£325	£325
187		20 c. red (O165)	32·00	38·00
171	13	24 c. green and yell (O94)	£300	£300
188		24 c. green on yell (O125)	32·00	38·00
189		25 c. green (O166)	32·00	38·00
190	12	30 c. blue (O167)	28·00	32·00
191	13	32 c. blue (O126)	£150	£150
192	35	50 c. black & brn (O168)	38·00	42·00
172	15	$1 black and bl (O96)	£1300	£1300
193		$1 black and bl (O127)	£225	£250
194	13	$2 brown on buff (O128)	£1300	£1300
174	17	$5 black and red (O98)	£3000	£3000
196		$5 black and red (O129)	£1400	£1400

1902. Surch **75 c.** and bar.

206	15	75 c. on $1 black & blue	8·25	7·75

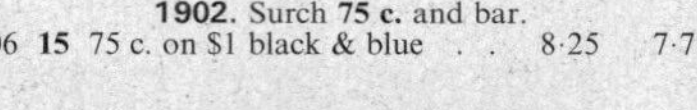

40 Liberty

1903.

209	40	3 c. black	25	15

1903. Surch in words.

216	12	10 c. on 16 c. lilac	2·50	4·50
217	13	15 c. on 24 c. green on yell	3·00	5·00
218	12	20 c. on 32 c. blue	4·25	5·25

1904. Surch

219	9	1 c. on 5 c. on 6 c. green (No. 103)	60	80
220	8	2 c. on 4 c. black and green (No. O89)	2·50	3·25
221	12	2 c. on 30 c. blue (No. 154)	6·25	9·25

50 African Elephant

51 Head of Mercury

52 Mandingo Tribesmen

53 Pres. Barclay and Executive Mansion

†1906.

224	50	1 c. black and green	1·00	50
225	51	2 c. black and red	15	15
226	–	5 c. black and blue	2·00	75
227	–	10 c. black and red	8·00	90
228	–	15 c. green and violet	7·00	2·75
229	–	20 c. black and orange	10·00	2·10
230	–	25 c. grey and blue	75	20
231	–	30 c. violet	70	15
232	–	50 c. black and green	75	20
233	–	75 c. black and brown	7·00	2·10
234	–	$1 black and pink	1·90	25
235	52	$2 black and green	3·00	35
236	53	$5 grey and red	5·75	50

DESIGNS—As Type **50**: 5 c. Chimpanzee; 15 c. Agama lizard; 75 c. Pygmy hippopotamus. As Type **51**: 10 c. Great blue turaco; 20 c. Great egret; 25 c. Head of Liberty on coin; 30 c. Figures "30"; 50 c. Liberian flag. As Type **53**: $1 Head of Liberty.

55 Coffee Plantation

56 Gunboat "Lark"

57 Commerce

†1909. The 10 c. is perf or roul.

250	55	1 c. black and green	25	15
251	–	2 c. black and red	25	15
252	56	5 c. black and blue	1·75	35
254	57	10 c. black and purple	25	20
255	–	15 c. black and blue	1·25	35
256	–	20 c. green and red	2·50	50
257	–	25 c. black and brown	1·75	35
258	–	30 c. brown	1·75	35
259	–	50 c. black and green	2·75	60
260	–	75 c. black and brown	2·25	45

DESIGNS—As Type **55**: 2 c. Pres. Barclay; 15 c. Vai woman spinning cotton; 20 c. Pepper plant; 25 c. Village hut; 30 c. Pres. Barclay (in picture frame). As Type **56**: 50 c. Canoeing; 75 c. Village (design shaped like a book).

1909. No. 227 surch **Inland 3 Cents.**

261	–	3 c. on 10 c. black & red	3·50	5·00

†1910. Surcharged **3 CENTS INLAND POSTAGE.** Perf or rouletted.

274	57	3 c. on 10 c. black & purple	35	25

1913. Various types surch with new value and bars or ornaments.

322	–	1 c. on 2 c. black and red (No. 251)	2·25	3·00
290	57	+ 2 c. on 3 c. on 10 c. blk and purple	60	2·00
323	56	2 c. on 5 c. black & blue	2·25	3·00
292	–	2 c. on 15 c. black and blue (No. 255)	1·25	1·25
279	–	2 c. on 25 c. grey & blue (A) (No. 230)	7·50	3·75
281	–	2 c. on 25 c. black and brown (A) (No. 257)	7·50	3·75
295	–	2 c. on 25 c. black and brown (B) (No. 257)	6·25	6·25
296	–	5 c. on 20 c. green & red (No. 256)	85	4·50
280	–	5 c. on 30 c. violet (C) (No. 231)	7·50	3·75
282	–	5 c. on 30 c. brown (C) (No. 258)	7·50	3·75
297	–	5 c. on 30 c. brown (D) (No. 258)	3·75	3·75
278	36	8 c. on 3 c. red and green	60	30
283	–	10 c. on 50 c. black and green (E) (No. 259)	9·25	5·75
299	–	10 c. on 50 c. black and green (F) (No. 259)	6·75	6·75
303	–	20 c. on 75 c. black and brown (No. 260)	3·25	6·25
304	53	25 c. on $1 black & pink	32·00	32·00
305	–	50 c. on $2 black and green (No. 235)	9·25	9·25
308	–	$1 on $5 grey and red (No. 236)	42·00	42·00

Descriptions of surcharges. (A) **1914 2 CENTS.** (B) **2** over ornaments. (C) **1914 5 CENTS.** (D) **5** over ornaments. (E) **1914 10 CENTS.** (F) **10** and ornaments.

64 House on Providence Is

65 Monrovia Harbour, Providence Is

†1915.

288	64	2 c. red	20	10
289	65	3 c. violet	20	10

1916. Liberian Frontier Force. Surch **LFF 1 C.**

332	9	1 c. on 1 c. green	£120	£120
333	50	1 c. on 1 c. black and grn	£375	£375
334	55	1 c. on 1 c. black and grn	2·75	4·25
335	–	1 c. on 2 c. black and red (No. 251)	2·75	4·25

1916. Surch **1916** over new value.

339	1	3 c. on 6 c. mauve	32·00	32·00
340		5 c. on 12 c. yellow	4·00	4·00
341		10 c. on 24 c. red	3·25	3·75

1917. Surch **1917** and value in words.

342	13	4 c. on 25 c. green	8·25	9·25
343	52	5 c. on 30 c. violet (No. 231)	60·00	65·00

1918. Surch **3 CENTS.**

345	57	3 c. on 10 c. black & purple	2·40	3·75

91 Bongo

93

92 African Palm Civet

94 Traveller's Tree

†1918.

349	91	1 c. black and green	65	25
350	92	2 c. black and red	65	25
351	–	5 c. black and blue	15	10
352	93	10 c. green	20	10
353	–	15 c. green and black	2·50	20
354	–	20 c. black and red	50	15
355	94	25 c. green	3·25	25
356	–	30 c. black and mauve	13·00	70
357	–	50 c. black and blue	13·00	1·10
358	–	75 c. black and olive	1·00	25
359	–	$1 blue and brown	4·25	25
360	–	$2 black and violet	6·00	30
361	–	$5 brown	6·00	40

DESIGNS—As Type **91**: 5 c. Coat of Arms; 15 c. Oil palm; 20 c. Statue of Mercury; 75 c. Heads of Mandingos; $5 "Liberia" seated. As Type **92**: 50 c. West African mudskipper; $1 Coast view; $2 Liberia College. As Type **93**: 30 c. Palm-nut Vulture.

1918. Geneva Red Cross Fund. Surch **TWO CENTS** and red cross.

375	91	1 c. + 2 c. black and green	75	75
376	92	2 c. + 2 c. black and red	75	75
377	–	5 c. + 2 c. black and blue	25	1·00
378	93	10 c. + 2 c. green	50	1·00
379	–	15 c. + 2 c. green & black	2·40	1·75
380	–	20 c. + 2 c. black and red	1·50	3·00
381	94	25 c. + 2 c. green	3·25	3·25
382	–	30 c. + 2 c. black & mve	8·75	4·75
383	–	50 c. + 2 c. black & blue	7·00	5·75
384	–	75 c. + 2 c. black & olive	2·10	5·25
385	–	$1 + 2 c. blue and brown	4·25	7·00
386	–	$2 + 2 c. black and violet	5·75	11·50
387	–	$5 + 2 c. brown	14·00	23·00

1920. Surch **1920** and value and two bars.

393	91	3 c. on 1 c. black & grn	1·50	2·75
394	92	4 c. on 2 c. black & red	1·50	3·00
395	R 42	5 c. on 10 c. black & bl	3·75	4·25
396		5 c. on 10 c. black & red	3·75	4·25
397		5 c. on 10 c. black & grn	3·75	4·25
398		5 c. on 10 c. black & vio	3·75	4·25
399		5 c. on 10 c. black & red	3·75	4·25

100 Cape Mesurado

101 Pres. D. E. Howard

†1921.

402 **100** 1 c. green 20 10
403 **101** 5 c. black and blue 25 10
404 – 10 c. blue and red 80 10
405 – 15 c. green and purple . . 3·00 50
406 – 20 c. green and red . . . . 1·50 25
407 – 25 c. black and yellow . . 2·75 50
408 – 30 c. purple and green . . 1·00 15
409 – 50 c. blue and yellow . . . 1·00 25
410 – 75 c. sepia and red . . . . 1·00 40
411 – $1 black and red . . . . . 17·00 1·00
412 – $2 violet and yellow . . . 30·00 1·75
413 – $5 red and purple . . . . 22·00 1·50

DESIGNS—VERT: 10 c. Arms. HORIZ: 15 c. Crocodile; 20 c. Pepper plant; 25 c. Leopard; 30 c. Village; 50 c. "Kru" boatman; 75 c. St. Paul's River; $1 Bongo (antelope); $2 Great Indian hornbill; $5 African elephant.

†1921. Optd **1921**.

414 **100** 1 c. green . . . . 9·25 50
415 **64** 2 c. red . . . . 9·25 50
416 **65** 3 c. violet . . . . 12·50 50
417 **101** 5 c. black and blue . . . . 2·75 50
418 – 10 c. blue and red . . . . 20·00 50
419 – 15 c. green and purple . . 11·50 1·00
420 – 20 c. green and red . . . . 5·25 60
421 – 25 c. black and yellow . . 11·50 1·00
422 – 30 c. purple and green . . 3·00 50
423 – 50 c. blue and yellow . . . 3·00 70
424 – 75 c. sepia and red . . . . 3·75 50
425 – $1 black and red . . . . . 30·00 1·50
426 – $2 violet and yellow . . . 32·00 2·50
427 – $5 red and purple . . . . 32·00 5·25

107 Arrival of First Settlers in "Alligator"

†1923. Centennial issue.

466 **107** 1 c. black and blue . . . . 14·00 70
467 2 c. brown and red . . . . 17·00 70
468 5 c. blue and olive . . . . 17·00 70
469 10 c. mauve and green . . 4·75 70
470 $1 brown and red . . . . 7·00 70

108 J. J. Roberts Memorial

109 House of Representatives, Monrovia

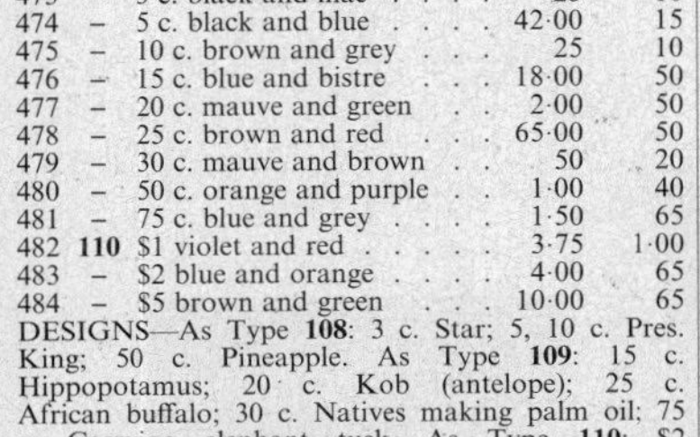
110 Rubber Plantation

†1923.

471 **108** 1 c. green . . . . 3·75 10
472 **109** 2 c. brown and red . . . . 3·75 10
473 – 3 c. black and lilac 25 10
474 – 5 c. black and blue . . . . 42·00 15
475 – 10 c. brown and grey . . . 25 10
476 – 15 c. blue and bistre . . . 18·00 50
477 – 20 c. mauve and green . . 2·00 50
478 – 25 c. brown and red . . . 65·00 50
479 – 30 c. mauve and brown . . 50 20
480 – 50 c. orange and purple . . 1·00 40
481 – 75 c. blue and grey . . . 1·50 65
482 **110** $1 violet and red . . . . . 3·75 1·00
483 – $2 blue and orange . . . . 4·00 65
484 – $5 brown and green . . . 10·00 65

DESIGNS—As Type **108**: 3 c. Star; 5, 10 c. Pres. King; 50 c. Pineapple. As Type **109**: 15 c. Hippopotamus; 20 c. Kob (antelope); 25 c. African buffalo; 30 c. Natives making palm oil; 75 c. Carrying elephant tusk. As Type **110**: $2 Stockton lagoon; $5 Styles of huts.

1926. Surch **Two Cents** and thick bar or wavy lines or ornamental scroll.

504 **91** 2 c. on 1 c. black & green 3·00 3·25

116 Palm Trees

117 Map of Africa

118 President King

1928.

511 **116** 1 c. green 40 15
512 2 c. violet 20 20
513 3 c. brown 35 20
514 **117** 5 c. blue 55 35
515 **118** 10 c. grey 70 35
516 **117** 15 c. purple . . . . 3·75 1·40
517 $1 brown . . . . 42·00 15·00

1936. Nos. O518 and 512/13 surch **AIR MAIL SIX CENTS.**

525 **116** 6 c. on 1 c. green . . . . . £170 90·00
526 6 c. on 2 c. violet . . . . . £170 90·00
527 6 c. on 3 c. brown . . . . . £170 90·00

122 Ford "Tin Goose"

1936. Air. 1st Air Mail Service of 28th February.

530 **122** 1 c. black and green . . . 25 10
531 2 c. black and red 25 10
532 3 c. black and violet . . . 40 10
533 4 c. black and orange . . . 40 15
534 5 c. black and blue 45 15
535 6 c. black and green . . . 45 20

1936. Nos. 350/61 surch **1936** and new values in figures.

536 1 c. on 2 c. black and red . . . 30 50
537 3 c. on 5 c. black and blue . . . 30 45
538 4 c. on 10 c. green 25 40
539 6 c. on 15 c. green and black . . 30 55
540 8 c. on 20 c. black and red . . . 20 60
541 12 c. on 30 c. black and mauve . 1·00 1·25
542 14 c. on 50 c. black and blue . . 1·50 1·75
543 16 c. on 75 c. black and olive . . 50 60
544 18 c. on $1 blue and brown . . 60 80
545 22 c. on $2 black and violet . . 60 95
546 24 c. on $5 brown . . . . . . 75 1·25

1936. Nos. O363/74 optd with Star and **1936** or surch also in figures and words.

547 1 c. on 2 c. black and red . . . 30 50
548 3 c. on 5 c. black and blue . . . 25 50
549 4 c. on 10 c. green 20 45
550 6 c. on 15 c. green & brown . . 25 60
551 8 c. on 20 c. black and lilac . . 30 60
552 12 c. on 30 c. black & violet . . 85 1·10
553 14 c. on 50 c. black & brown . . 1·00 1·50
554 16 c. on 75 c. black & brown . . 45 60
555 18 c. on $1 blue and olive . . . 50 65
556 22 c. on $2 black and olive . . 60 90
557 24 c. on $5 green 75 95
558 25 c. green and brown . . . . 75 1·25

126 Hippopotamus

1937.

559 – 1 c. black and green . . . 1·25 35
560 – 2 c. black and red . . . . 1·00 30
561 – 3 c. black and purple . . . 1·00 35
562 **126** 4 c. black and orange . . . 1·50 60
563 – 5 c. black and blue . . . . 2·75 50
564 – 6 c. black and green . . . 45 20

DESIGNS: 1 c. Black and white casqued hornbill; 2 c. Bushbuck; 3 c. African buffalo; 5 c. Western reef heron; 6 c. Pres. Barclay.

127 Tawny Eagle in Flight

128 Three-engine Flying Boat

129 Little Egrets

1938. Air.

565 **127** 1 c. green 50 10
566 **128** 2 c. red 15 10
567 – 3 c. olive 40 10
568 **129** 4 c. orange 50 10
569 – 5 c. green 60 10
570 **128** 10 c. violet 25 10
571 – 20 c. mauve 30 15
572 – 30 c. grey . . . . 1·40 15
573 **127** 50 c. brown . . . . 3·00 25
574 – $1 blue . . . . 1·40 25

DESIGNS—VERT: 20 c., $1 Sikorsky S-43 amphibian. HORIZ: 3, 30 c. Lesser black-backed gull in flight.

130 Immigrant Ships nearing Liberian Coast

1940. Centenary of Founding of Liberian Commonwealth.

575 **130** 3 c. blue 50 15
576 – 5 c. brown 20 10
577 – 10 c. green 25 15

DESIGNS: 5 c. Seal of Liberia and Flags of original Settlements; 10 c. Thos. Buchanan's house and portrait.

1941. Centenary of First Postage Stamps. Nos. 575/7 optd **POSTAGE STAMP CENTENNIAL 1840-1940** and portrait of Rowland Hill.

578 **130** 3 c. blue (postage) . . . . 1·75 1·75
579 – 5 c. brown . . . . 1·75 1·75
580 – 10 c. green . . . . 1·75 1·75
581 **130** 3 c. blue (air) . . . . . . 1·40 1·40
582 – 5 c. brown . . . . 1·40 1·40
583 – 10 c. green . . . . 1·40 1·40

Nos. 581/3 are additionally optd with airplane and **AIR MAIL**.

1941. Red Cross Fund. Nos. 575/7 surch **RED CROSS** plus Red Cross and **TWO CENTS.**

584 **130** + 2 c. on 3 c. blue (post) 1·40 1·40
585 – + 2 c. on 5 c. brown . . . 1·40 1·40
586 – + 2 c. on 10 c. green . . . 1·40 1·40
587 **130** + 2 c. on 3 c. blue (air) . . 1·40 1·40
588 – + 2 c. on 5 c. brown . . . 1·40 1·40
589 – + 2 c. on 10 c. green . . . 1·40 1·40

Nos. 587/9 are additionally optd with airplane and **AIR MAIL**.

1941. Air. 1st Flight to U.S.A. Nos. 565/74 surch **First Flight LIBERIA-U.S. 1941, 50 c.** and bar.

594 **127** 50 c. on 1 c. £2000 £250
595 **128** 50 c. on 2 c. . . . . £150 75·00
596 – 50 c. on 3 c. . . . . £225 75·00
597 **129** 50 c. on 4 c. . . . . 70·00 35·00
598 50 c. on 5 c. . . . . 70·00 35·00
599 **128** 50 c. on 10 c. . . . . . . 45·00 38·00
600 – 50 c. on 20 c. £1500 £150
601 – 50 c. on 30 c. . . . . . . 80·00 30·00
602 **127** 50 c. brown . . . . 80·00 35·00
603 – $1 blue . . . . 45·00 30·00

The first flight was cancelled and covers were sent by ordinary mail. The flight took place in 1942 and the stamps were reissued but with the date obliterated.

1942. As Nos. 594/601 but with date "1941" obliterated by two bars.

604 **127** 50 c. on 1 c. green . . . . 8·50 8·50
605 **128** 50 c. on 2 c. red . . . . . 6·00 6·75
606 – 50 c. on 3 c. green . . . . 7·50 7·50
607 **129** 50 c. on 4 c. orange . . . . 7·00 7·00
608 50 c. on 5 c. green . . . . 7·00 7·00
609 **128** 50 c. on 10 c. violet . . . . 5·25 6·25
610 – 50 c. on 20 c. mauve . . . 5·25 6·25
611 – 50 c. on 30 c. grey . . . . 7·50 7·50
612 **127** 50 c. brown . . . . 7·50 7·50
613 – $1 blue . . . . 6·25 7·50

138 Miami–Monrovia Air Route

1942. Air.

614 **138** 10 c. red 20 10
615 – 12 c. blue 30 10
616 – 24 c. green 35 10
617 **138** 30 c. green 35 10
618 35 c. lilac 40 15
619 50 c. purple 50 15
620 70 c. olive 55 30
621 $1.40 red 75 50

DESIGN: 12, 24 c. Boeing 247 airliner over Liberian Agricultural and Industrial Fair.

139 Bushbuck

1942.

622 – 1 c. brown and violet . . . 80 20
623 – 2 c. brown and blue . . . 80 20
624 – 3 c. brown and green . . . 1·25 45
625 **139** 4 c. red and black . . . . 2·00 70
626 – 5 c. brown and olive . . . 1·75 70
627 – 10 c. black and red . . . . 3·75 1·10

DESIGNS—HORIZ: 1 c. Royal antelope; 2 c. Water chevrotain; 3 c. Jentink's duiker; 5 c. Banded duiker. VERT: 10 c. Diana monkey.

1944. Stamps of 1928 and 1937 surch.

628 **116** 1 c. on 2 c. violet . . . . . 7·50 7·50
634 **126** 1 c. on 4 c. black & orge 48·00 40·00
629 **118** 1 c. on 10 c. grey . . . . . 10·00 6·25
635 – 2 c. on 3 c. black and purple (No. 561) . . . . 50·00 40·00
630 **117** 2 c. on 5 c. blue . . . . . 3·25 3·25
632 **116** 3 c. on 2 c. violet . . . . . 27·00 30·00
636 – 4 c. on 5 c. black and blue (No. 563) . . . . 28·00 28·00
633 **118** 4 c. on 10 c. grey . . . . . 3·25 3·25
637 – 5 c. on 1 c. black and green (No. 559) . . . . 85·00 55·00
638 – 6 c. on 2 c. black and red (No. 560) . . . . 12·50 12·50
639 – 10 c. on 6 c. black and green (No. 564) . . . . 14·00 12·50

1944. Air stamps of 1936 and 1938 surch.

643 **128** 10 c. on 2 c. red . . . . . 27·00 30·00
644 **129** 10 c. on 5 c. green . . . . 11·50 11·50
640 **122** 30 c. on 1 c. black & grn 80·00 50·00
645 30 c. on 3 c. olive (No. 567) £100 85·00
646 **129** 30 c. on 4 c. orange . . . . 11·50 11·50
641 **122** 50 c. on 3 c. black & vio 20·00 23·00
642 70 c. on 2 c. black & red 50·00 50·00
647 – $1 on 3 c. olive (No. 567) 42·00 42·00
648 **127** $1 on 50 c. brown . . . . 27·00 22·00

150 Pres. Roosevelt reviewing Troops

1945. Pres. Roosevelt Memorial.

650 **150** 3 c. black & pur (postage) 15 15
651 5 c. black and blue 30 25
652 70 c. black & brown (air) 1·00 1·00

151 Opening Monrovia Harbour Project

1946. Opening of Monrovia Harbour Project by Pres. Tubman.

653 **151** 5 c. blue (postage) 25 15
654 24 c. green (air) . . . . . 1·90 2·10

1947. As T **151**, but without inscr at top.

655 5 c. violet (postage) 15 15
656 25 c. red (air) . . . . 1·00 1·10

152 1st Postage Stamps of United States and Liberia

1947. U.S. Postage Stamps Centenary and 87th Anniv of Liberian Postal Issues.

657 **152** 5 c. red (postage) 30 15
658 12 c. green (air) 40 15
659 22 c. violet 50 20
660 50 c. blue 60 25

153 Matilda Newport Firing Canon

1947. 125th Anniv of Defence of Monrovia.
662 **153** 1 c. black & green (post) 15 10
663 3 c. black and violet 20 10
664 5 c. black and blue 20 15
665 10 c. black and yellow 1·50 45
666 25 c. black and red (air) 1·40 35

154 Liberty

156 Douglas DC-3

1947. Centenary of National Independence.
667 – 1 c. green (postage) 20 10
668 **154** 2 c. purple 20 10
669 – 3 c. purple 30 15
670 – 5 c. blue 40 15
671 – 12 c. orange (air) 60 20
672 – 25 c. red 75 35
673 – 50 c. brown 90 70
DESIGNS—VERT: 1 c. Liberian star; 3 c. Arms of Liberia; 4 c. Map of Liberia; 12 c. J. J. Roberts Monument; 25 c. Liberian Flag; 50 c. (26½ × 33 mm) Centenary Monument.

1948. Air. First Liberian International Airways Flight (Monrovia-Dakar).
674 **156** 25 c. red 1·50 1·00
675 50 c. blue 2·40 1·50

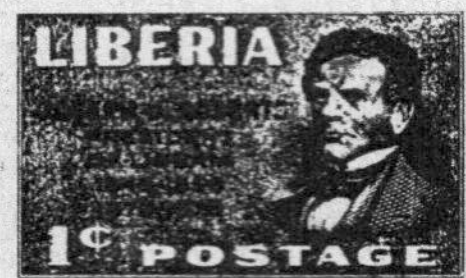

157 Joseph J. Roberts

1949. Liberian Presidents. Portrait and name in black.
(a) Postage.
676 – 1 c. green (Roberts) 1·60 3·25
677 **157** 1 c. green 15 10
678 – 1 c. pink (Roberts) 25 15
679 – 2 c. pink (Benson) 35 35
680 – 2 c. yellow (Benson) 35 15
681 – 3 c. mauve (Warner) 35 35
682 – 4 c. olive (Payne) 35 55
683 – 5 c. blue (Mansion) 45 55
684 – 6 c. orange (Roye) 55 95
685 – 7 c. green (Gardner and Russell) 70 1·25
686 – 8 c. red (Johnson) 70 1·40
687 – 9 c. purple (Cheeseman) 1·10 1·10
688 – 10 c. yellow (Coleman) 75 35
689 – 10 c. grey (Coleman) 40 20
690 – 15 c. orange (Gibson) 85 40
691 – 15 c. blue (Gibson) 25 15
692 – 20 c. grey (A. Barclay) 1·25 70
693 – 20 c. red (A. Barclay) 50 45
694 – 25 c. red (Howard) 1·60 1·10
695 – 25 c. blue (Howard) 50 45
696 – 50 c. turquoise (King) 3·25 95
697 – 50 c. purple (King) 70 60
698 – $1 mauve (E. Barclay) 5·75 70
699 – $1 brown (E. Barclay) 4·00 55
(b) Air.
700 – 25 c. blue (Tubman) 1·00 55
701 – 25 c. green (Tubman) 75 35
Nos. 676 and 678 have a different portrait of Roberts wearing a moustache.

158 Colonists and Map

159 Hand holding Book

1949. Multicoloured.
702 1 c. Settlers approaching village (postage) 50 75
703 2 c. Rubber tapping and planting 50 75
704 3 c. Landing of first colonists in 1822 1·00 1·50
705 5 c. Jehudi Ashmun and Matilda Newport defending stockade 50 75
706 25 c. Type **158** (air) 1·25 1·50
707 50 c. Africans and coat of arms 2·75 3·25

1950. National Literacy Campaign.
708 **159** 5 c. blue (postage) 20 15
709 – 25 c. red (air) 70 70
DESIGN—VERT: 25 c. Open book and rising sun.

160 U.P.U. Monument, Berne

1950. 75th Anniv of U.P.U.
711 **160** 5 c. black and grn (post) 20 15
712 – 10 c. black and mauve 30 30
713 – 25 c. purple & orge (air) 3·25 3·25
DESIGNS—HORIZ: 10 c. Standehaus, Berne. VERT: 25 c. U.P.U. Monument, Berne.

161 Carey, Ashmun and Careysburg

162 U.N. Headquarters

163 Flags and U.N. Emblem

1952. Designs all show portrait of Ashmun.
715 – 1 c. green (postage) 10 10
716 **161** 2 c. blue and red 10 10
717 – 3 c. green and purple 10 10
718 – 4 c. green and brown 15 10
719 – 5 c. red and blue 20 15
720 – 10 c. blue and red 25 20
721 – 25 c. black & pur (air) 35 35
722 – 50 c. red and blue 1·00 45
DESIGNS—VERT: 1 c. Seal of Liberia; 3 c. Harper and Harper City; 5 c. Buchanan and Upper Buchanan. HORIZ: 4 c. Marshall and Marshall City; 10 c. Roberts and Robertsport; 25 c. Monroe and Monrovia; 50 c. Tubman and map.

1952. U.N. Commem.
724 **162** 1 c. blue (postage) 10 10
725 – 4 c. blue and pink 15 10
726 – 10 c. brown and yellow 25 20
727 **163** 25 c. red and blue (air) 55 45
DESIGNS—HORIZ: 4 c. Liberian and U.N. flags and scroll; 10 c. Liberian and U.N. emblems.

164 Modern Road-building

1953. Air. Transport.
729 **164** 12 c. brown 15 15
730 – 25 c. purple 75 30
731 – 35 c. violet 1·60 30
732 – 50 c. orange 65 25
733 – 70 c. green 1·25 40
734 – $1 blue 1·40 55
DESIGNS: 25 c. "African Glen" (freighter) in Monrovia Harbour; 35 c. Diesel locomotive; 50 c. Free Port of Monrovia; 70 c. Roberts Field Airport; $1 Tubman Bridge.

165 Common Bulbul

166 Blue-throated Roller

1953. Imperf or perf.
735 **165** 1 c. red and blue 1·00 20
736 **166** 3 c. blue and salmon 1·00 20
737 – 4 c. brown and yellow 1·50 25
738 – 5 c. turquoise & mauve 1·75 30
739 – 10 c. mauve and green 1·75 30
740 – 12 c. orange and brown 2·75 40
BIRDS: As Type **165**: 4 c. Yellow-casqued hornbill; 5 c. Giant kingfisher. As Type **166**: 10 c. African jacana; 12 c. Broad-tailed paradise whydah.

167 Hospital

1954. Liberian Govt. Hospital Fund.
741 – 5 c. + 5 c. black and purple (postage) 20 15
742 – 10 c. + 5 c. black and red (air) 15 20
743 **167** 20 c. + 5 c. black & grn 25 25
744 – 25 c. + 5 c. black, red and blue 30 20
DESIGNS—As Type **167**: 5 c. Medical research workers; 10 c. Nurses. 46 × 35 mm: 25 c. Doctor examining patient.

168 Children of the World

1954. Air. U.N.I.C.E.F.
745 **168** $5 ultramarine, red & blue 27·00 23·00

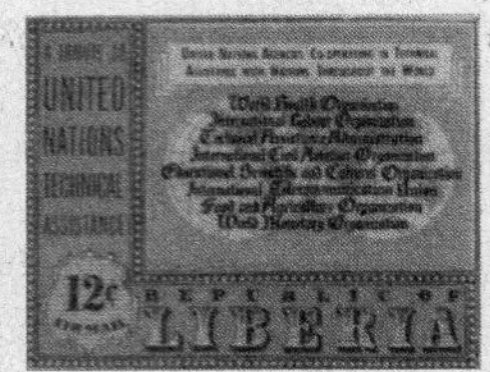

169 U.N. Organizations

1954. Air. U.N. Technical Assistance.
746 **169** 12 c. black and blue 25 15
746 – 15 c. brown and yellow 25 15
747 – 20 c. black and green 30 20
749 – 25 c. blue and red 35 25
DESIGNS: 15 c. Printers; 20 c. Mechanic; 25 c. Teacher and students.

1954. Air. Visit of President Tubman to U.S.A. As Nos. 729/34 but colours changed and inscr "COMMEMORATING PRESIDENTIAL VISIT U.S.A.—1954".
750 12 c. orange 20 20
751 25 c. blue 80 25
752 35 c. red 4·00 1·50
753 50 c. mauve 80 30
754 70 c. brown 1·10 50
755 $1 green 1·60 3·25

170 Football

171 "Callichilia stenosepala"

1955. Sports.
756 – 3 c. red & grn (post) 15 10
757 **170** 5 c. black and orange 15 10
758 – 25 c. violet and yellow 25 20
759 – 10 c. blue & mve (air) 20 15
760 – 12 c. brown and blue 15 15
761 – 25 c. red and green 20 20
DESIGNS—VERT: 3 c. Tennis; 25 c. Boxing (No. 758). HORIZ: 10 c. Baseball; 12 c. Swimming; 25 c. Running (No. 761).

1955. Flowers.
763 **171** 6 c. yellow, salmon & green (postage) 15 10
764 – 7 c. red, yellow & green 15 10
765 – 8 c. buff, blue and green 20 10
766 – 9 c. green and orange 25 15
767 – 20 c. yellow, green and violet (air) 15 15
768 – 25 c. yellow, green & red 20 20
FLOWERS—VERT: 7 c. "Gomphia subcordata"; 8 c. "Listrostachys chudata"; 9 c. "Mussaenda isertiana". HORIZ: 20 s. "Costus"; 25 c. "Barteria nigritiana".

172 U.N. General Assembly

173 Tapping Rubber and Rotary Emblem

1955. Air. 10th Anniv of U.N.
769 – 10 c. blue and red 20 10
770 **172** 15 c. black and violet 25 15
771 – 25 c. brown and green 35 15
772 – 50 c. green and red 1·00 20
DESIGNS—VERT: 10 c. U.N. emblem; 25 c. Liberian Secretary of State signing U.N. Charter. HORIZ: 50 c. Page from U.N. Charter.

1955. 50th Anniv of Rotary International.
773 **173** 5 c. green & yell (postage) 25 15
774 – 10 c. blue and red (air) 15 50
775 – 15 c. brown, yellow & red 20 65
DESIGNS: 10 c. Rotary International H.Q., Evanston; 15 c. View of Monrovia.

174 Coliseum, New York

1956. 5th International Philatelic Exhibition, New York.
777 – 3 c. brown and green (postage) 15 10
778 **174** 4 c. brown and green 10 25
779 – 6 c. purple and black 20 10
780 **174** 10 c. blue and red (air) 25 15
781 – 12 c. violet and orange 20 15
782 – 15 c. purple & turquoise 25 20
DESIGNS—VERT: 3 c., 15 c. Statue of Liberty. HORIZ: 6 c., 12 c. The Globe.

175 Chariot Race

1956. Olympic Games.
784 – 4 c. brown & olive (post) 15 15
785 – 6 c. black and green 15 10
786 – 8 c. brown and blue 20 10
787 **175** 10 c. black and red 25 10
788 – 12 c. purple and grn (air) 20 15
789 – 20 c. multicoloured 30 20
DESIGNS—HORIZ: 4 c. Olympic rings, eastern grey kangaroo and emu; 8 c. Goddess of Victory; 12 c., 20 c. Olympic torch superimposed on map of Australia. VERT: 6 c. Discus thrower.

176 Douglas DC-6B "John Alden" at Idelwild Airport

1957. 1st Anniv of Inauguration of Liberia–U.S. Direct Air Service.
791 **176** 3 c. blue & orge (postage) 15 15
792 – 5 c. black and mauve 20 20
793 **176** 12 c. blue & green (air) 30 25
794 – 15 c. black and brown 30 25
795 **176** 25 c. blue and red 45 25
796 – 50 c. black and blue 85 30
DESIGN: 5, 15, 50 c. President Tubman and "John Alden" at Roberts Field, Liberia.

177 Children's Playground

1957. Inaug of Antoinette Tubman Child Welfare Foundation. Inscr as in T **177**.

797 **177** 4 c. green & red (postage) 10 10
798 – 5 c. brown & turquoise . . 15 10
799 – 6 c. violet and bistre . . 15 10
800 – 10 c. blue and red 20 15
801 – 15 c. brown & blue (air) 20 15
802 – 35 c. purple and grey . . . 35 25

DESIGNS: 5 c. Teacher with pupil; 6 c. National anthem with choristers; 10 c. Children viewing welfare home; 15 c. Nurse inoculating youth; 35 c. Kamara triplets.

178 German Flag and Brandenburg Gate

1958. Pres. Tubman's European Tour. Flags in national colours.

804 **178** 5 c. blue (postage) 15 10
805 – 5 c. brown 15 10
806 – 5 c. red 15 10
807 – 10 c. black (air) 25 15
808 – 15 c. green 25 20
809 – 15 c. blue 25 20
810 – 15 c. violet 25 20

DESIGNS: Flags of: Netherlands and windmill (No. 805); Sweden and Royal Palace, Stockholm (No. 806); Italy and Colosseum (No. 807); France and Arc de Triomphe (No. 808); Switzerland and Alpine chalet (No. 809); Vatican City and St. Peter's Basilica (No. 810).

179 Map of the World

180 Africans and Map

1958. 10th Anniv of Declaration of Human Rights.

811 **179** 3 c. blue and black 25 15
812 – 5 c. brown and blue . . . 20 20
813 – 10 c. orange and black . . 30 75
814 – 12 c. black and red 40 35

DESIGNS: 5 c. U.N. Emblem and H.Q. building; 10 c. U.N. Emblem; 12 c. U.N. Emblem and initials of U.N. agencies.

1959. Africa Freedom Day.

816 **180** 20 c. orge & brn (postage) 30 30
817 – 25 c. brown & blue (air) 35 20

DESIGN: 25 c. Two Africans looking at Pres. Tubman's declaration of Africa Freedom Day.

181

182 Abraham Lincoln

1959. Inaug of U.N.E.S.C.O. Building, Paris.

818 **181** 25 c. pur & grn (postage) 35 40
819 – 25 c. red and blue (air) . . 35 30

DESIGN—HORIZ: No. 819 U.N.E.S.C.O. Headquarters, Paris.

1959. 150th Birth Anniv of Abraham Lincoln.

821 **182** 10 c. blk & blue (postage) 25 30
822 15 c. black and orange . . 30 30
823 25 c. black & grn (air) . . 55 50

183 Presidents Toure, Tubman and Nkrumah at Conference Table

184 "Care of Refugees"

1960. "Big Three" Conf, Saniquellie, Liberia.

825 **183** 25 c. black & red (postage) 35 25
826 – 25 c. black, bl & buff (air) 35 25

DESIGN: No. 826, Medallion portraits of Presidents Toure (Guinea), Tubman (Liberia) and Nkrumah (Ghana).

1960. World Refugee Year.

827 **184** 25 c. green & blk (postage) 35 30
828 25 c. blue & black (air) . . 55 40

185

186 Weightlifting

1960. 10th Anniv of African Technical Co-operation (C.C.T.A.).

830 **185** 25 c. green & blk (postage) 35 50
831 – 25 c. brown and blue (air) . 45 35

DESIGN: No. 831, Map of Africa with symbols showing fields of assistance.

1960. Olympic Games, Rome.

832 **186** 5 c. brn and grn (postage) 20 15
833 – 10 c. brown and purple . . 40 75
834 – 15 c. brown and orange . . 35 30
835 – 25 c. brown & blue (air) 70 80

DESIGNS—HORIZ: 10 c. Rowing; 25 c. Javelin-throwing. VERT: 15 c. Walking.

187 Stamps of 1860 and Map

188 "Guardians of Peace"

1960. Liberian Stamp Centenary. Stamps, etc., in green, red and blue. Colours of map and inscriptions given.

837 **187** 5 c. black (postage) 25 15
838 20 c. brown 40 40
839 25 c. blue (air) 50 40

1961. Membership of U.N. Security Council.

841 **188** 25 c. blue & red (postage) 45 35
842 – 25 c. blue and red (air) . . 45 25

DESIGN—HORIZ: No. 842, Dove of Peace, Globe and U.N. Emblem.

189 Anatomy Class, University of Liberia

190 President Roberts

1961. 15th Anniv of U.N.E.S.C.O.

845 **189** 25 c. brn & grn (postage) 35 35
846 – 25 c. brown & violet (air) 35 25

DESIGN: No. 846, Science class, University of Liberia.

1961. 150th Birth Anniv of Joseph J. Roberts (first President of Liberia).

848 **190** 5 c. sepia & orge (postage) 20 15
849 – 10 c. sepia and blue . . . 35 15
850 – 25 c. sepia & green (air) . . 45 35

DESIGNS—HORIZ: 10 c. Pres. Roberts and old and new presidential mansions; 25 c. Pres. Roberts and Providence Is.

191 Scout and Sports

1961. Liberian Boy Scout Movement.

852 **191** 5 c. sepia & vio (postage) 25 20
853 – 10 c. ochre and blue . . . 30 20
854 – 25 c. sepia & green (air) . . 40 30

DESIGNS—HORIZ: 10 c. Scout badge and scouts in camp. VERT: 25 c. Scout and badge.

192 Hammarskjold and U.N. Emblem

193 Campaign Emblem

1962. Dag Hammarskjold Commem.

856 **192** 20 c. blk & blue (postage) 30 20
857 25 c. black & pur (air) . . 35 25

1962. Malaria Eradication.

859 **193** 25 c. green & red (postage) 35 25
860 – 25 c. orange & violet (air) 35 25

DESIGN—HORIZ: No. 860, Campaign emblem and slogan.

194 Pres. Tubman and New York Skyline

1962. Air. President's Visit to U.S.A.

862 **194** 12 c. multicoloured 25 15
863 25 c. multicoloured 35 30
864 50 c. multicoloured 70 55

195 U.N. Emblem

1962. U.N. Day.

865 **195** 20 c. bistre & grn (postage) 35 30
866 – 25 c. blue & dp blue (air) 45 30

DESIGN: 25 c. U.N. emblem and flags.

196 Treasury Building

197 F.A.O. Emblem, Bowl and Spoon

1962. Liberian Government Buildings.

868 – 1 c. orge & blue (postage) 10 15
869 **196** 5 c. violet and blue 15 10
870 – 10 c. brown and buff . . . 20 15
871 – 15 c. blue and salmon . . . 25 20
872 – 80 c. yellow and brown . . 1·60 1·00
873 – 12 c. lake & green (air) . . 25 15
874 – 50 c. blue and orange . . . 1·00 90
875 – 70 c. blue and mauve . . . 1·40 1·00
876 **196** $1 black and orange . . . 2·00 1·10

BUILDINGS: 1 c., 80 c. Executive; 10 c., 50 c. Information; 12 c., 15 c., 70 c. Capitol.

1963. Freedom from Hunger.

877 **197** 5 c. pur & turq (postage) 15 10
878 – 25 c. yellow & green (air) 35 20

DESIGN: 25 c. F.A.O. emblem and Globe.

198 Rocket

1963. Space Exploration.

880 **198** 10 c. yell & blue (postage) 20 15
881 – 15 c. brown and blue . . . 35 40
882 – 25 c. green & orge (air) . . 45 30

DESIGNS—HORIZ: 15 c. Space capsule. VERT: 25 c. "Telstar" TV satellite.

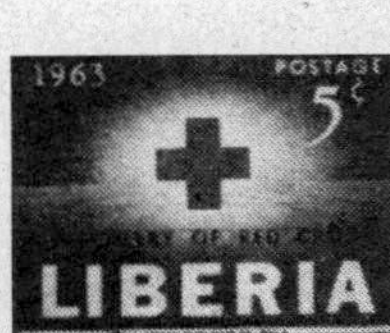

199 Red Cross

200 "Unity" Scroll

1963. Red Cross Centenary.

884 **199** 5 c. green & red (postage) 15 15
885 – 10 c. grey and red 20 20
886 – 25 c. violet & red (air) . . 35 30
887 – 50 c. blue and red . . . . 1·00 85

DESIGNS—VERT: 10 c. Emblem and torch. HORIZ: 25 c. Red Cross and Globe; 50 c. Emblem and Globe.

1963. Conference of African Heads of State, Addis Ababa.

888 **200** 20 c. brn & grn (postage) 40 35
889 – 25 c. red and green (air) 45 30

DESIGN: 25 c. Map of Africa (inscr "AFRICAN SUMMIT CONFERENCE").

201 Ski-jumping

202 President Kennedy

1963. Winter Olympic Games, Innsbruck. (1964).

890 **201** 5 c. blue and red (postage) 20 20
891 – 10 c. red and blue (air) . . 25 25
892 – 25 c. orange and green . . 35 35

DESIGNS—VERT: 10 c. Olympic flame. HORIZ: 25 c. Olympic rings. All have mountain scenery as backgrounds.

1964. President Kennedy Memorial Issue.

894 **202** 20 c. blk & blue (postage) 35 20
895 – 25 c. black & pur (air) . . 45 25

DESIGN—VERT: 25 c. Pres. Kennedy, full face portrait.

203 "Relay I" Satellite

204 Mt. Fuji

1964. Space Communications.

897 – 10 c. orange and green . . 20 15
898 **203** 15 c. blue and mauve . . . 25 20
899 – 25 c. yellow, black & blue 45 25

SATELLITES—HORIZ: 10 c. "Syncom"; 25 c. "Mariner II".

1964. Olympic Games, Tokyo.

901 **204** 10 c. green and yellow . . 15 10
902 – 15 c. purple and red . . . 20 15
903 – 25 c. red and buff 45 20

DESIGNS: 15 c. Japanese arch and Olympic Flame; 25 c. Cherry blossom and stadium.

205 Scout Bugle

206 "The Great Emancipator" (statue)

1965. Liberian Boy Scouts.

905 – 5 c. brown and blue (postage) 25 15
906 **205** 10 c. ochre and green . . . 40 25
907 – 25 c. blue and red (air) . . 50 35

DESIGNS—VERT: 5 c. Scout badge and saluting hand; 25 c. Liberian flag within scout badge.

1965. Death Centenary of Abraham Lincoln.

909 **206** 5 c. brown and sepia . . . 20 25
910 – 20 c. green & lt brown . . 35 30
911 – 25 c. blue and purple . . . 40 40

DESIGNS—HORIZ: 20 c. Bust of Lincoln, and Pres. Kennedy. VERT: 25 c. Lincoln statue, Chicago (after St. Gaudens).

207 I.C.Y. Emblem

1965. International Co-operation Year.

913 **207** 12 c. brown and orange . . 70 25
914 25 c. brown and blue . . . 40 25
915 50 c. brown and green . . 80 70

208 I.T.U. Emblem and Symbols

1965. Centenary of I.T.U.

917 **208** 25 c. brn & grn (post) 40 50
918 35 c. mauve and black 60 50
919 50 blue and red (air) 80 45

209 Pres. Tubman and Flag

210 Sir Winston Churchill

1965. Pres. Tubman's 70th Birthday. Multicoloured.

921 25 c. Type **209** (postage) 35 30
922 25 c. President and Liberian arms (air) 35 25

1966. Churchill Commemoration.

924 **210** 15 c. black & orge (postage) 30 30
925 – 20 c. black and green 35 25
926 – 25 c. black and blue (air) 40 30

DESIGNS—HORIZ: 20 c. Churchill in uniform of Trinity House Elder Brother; 25 c. Churchill and Houses of Parliament.

211 Pres. Roberts

212 Footballers and Hemispheres

1966. Liberian Presidents.

928 **211** 1 c. black & pink (postage) 10 10
929 – 2 c. black and yellow 10 10
930 – 3 c. black and violet 10 10
931 – 4 c. black and yellow 75 50
932 – 5 c. black and orange 10 10
933 – 10 c. black and green 15 10
934 – 25 c. black and blue 35 20
935 – 50 c. black and mauve 70 65
936 – 80 c. black and red 1·25 95
937 – $1 black and brown 1·40 15
938 – $2 black and purple 3·25 2·75
939 – 25 c. black and green (air) 35 25

PRESIDENTS: 2 c. Benson; 3 c. Warner; 4 c. Payne; 5 c. Roye; 10 c. Coleman; 25 c. (postage) Howard; 25 c. (air) Tubman; 50 c. King; 80 c. Johnson; $1 Barclay; $2 Cheesman.

1966. World Cup Football Championships.

940 **212** 10 c. brown & turquoise 15 15
941 – 25 c. brown and mauve 35 30
942 – 35 c. brown and orange 50 45

DESIGNS—VERT: 25 c. Presentation cup, football and boots; 35 c. Footballer.

213 Pres. Kennedy taking Oath

1966. 3rd Death Anniv (Nov. 22nd) of Pres. Kennedy.

944 **213** 15 c. black & red (postage) 25 15
945 – 20 c. purple and blue 35 20
946 – 25 c. blue, black and ochre (air) 45 30
947 – 35 c. blue and pink 85 45

DESIGNS: 20 c. Kennedy stamps of 1964; 25 c. U.N. General Assembly and Pres. Kennedy; 35 c. Pres. Kennedy and rocket on launching pad.

214 Children on See-saw

1966. 20th Anniv of U.N.I.C.E.F.

949 **214** 5 c. blue and red 20 20
950 – 80 c. brown and green 1·50 1·50

DESIGN: 80 c. Child playing "Doctors".

215 Giraffe

216 Scout Emblem and Various Sports

1966. Wild Animals. Multicoloured.

951 2 c. Type **215** 10 10
952 3 c. Lion 20 15
953 5 c. Crocodile (horiz) 15 10
954 10 c. Chimpanzees 40 20
955 15 c. Leopard (horiz) 50 25
956 20 c. Black rhinoceros (horiz) 60 40
957 25 c. African elephant 70 50

1967. World Scout Jamboree, Idaho.

958 – 10 c. purple and green 20 15
959 **216** 25 c. red and blue 35 50
960 – 40 c. brown and green 85 60

DESIGNS—VERT: 10 c. Jamboree emblem. HORIZ: 40 c. Scout by campfire, and Moon landing.

217 Pre-Hispanic Sculpture

218 W.H.O. Building, Brazzaville

1967. Publicity for Olympic Games, Mexico (1968).

962 **217** 10 c. violet and orange 75 85
963 – 25 c. orange, black & blue 35 40
964 – 40 c. red and green 60 65

DESIGNS—VERT: 25 c. Aztec calendar. HORIZ: 40 c. Mexican sombrero, guitar and ceramics.

1967. Inauguration of W.H.O.'s Regional Office, Brazzaville.

966 **218** 5 c. yellow and blue 20 20
967 – 80 c. green and yellow 1·25 1·25

DESIGN—VERT: 80 c. As Type **218** but in vertical format.

219 Boy with Rattle

220 Ice-hockey

1967. Musicians and Instruments. Multicoloured.

968 2 c. Type **219** 15 15
969 3 c. Tomtom and soko violin 20 20
970 5 c. Mang harp 25 25
971 10 c. Alimilim 30 30
972 15 c. Xylophone drums 35 35
973 25 c. Tomtoms 50 40
974 35 c. Oral harp 75 60

The 3 c. and 5 c. are horiz designs.

1967. Publicity for Winter Olympic Games, Grenoble (1968).

975 **220** 10 c. blue and green 15 20
976 – 25 c. violet and blue 35 30
977 – 40 c. brown and orange 85 50

DESIGNS: 25 c. Ski-jumping; 40 c. Tobogganing.

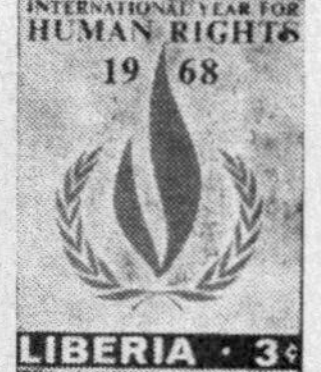

221 Pres. Tubman

222 Human Rights Emblem

1967. Re-election of Pres. Tubman for 6th Term.

979 **221** 25 c. brown and blue 35 25

1968. Human Rights Year.

981 **222** 3 c. blue and red 10 10
982 80 c. green and brown 1·60 1·60

223 Dr. King and Hearse

224 Throwing the Javelin and Statue of Diana

1968. Martin Luther King Commem.

984 **223** 15 c. brown and blue 25 20
985 – 25 c. brown and blue 40 30
986 – 35 c. black and olive 60 65

DESIGNS—VERT: 25 c. Dr. Martin Luther King. HORIZ: Dr. King and Lincoln Monument.

1968. Olympic Games, Mexico.

988 **224** 15 c. violet and brown 25 15
989 – 25 c. blue and red 35 15
990 – 35 c. brown and green 50 30

DESIGNS: 25 c. Throwing the discus and Quetzalcoatl sculpture; 35 c. High-diving and Xochilcalco bas-relief.

225 President Tubman

226 I.L.O. Symbol

1968. 25th Anniv of Pres. Tubman's Administration.

992 **225** 25 c. black, brown & silver 1·10 50

1969. 50th Anniv of I.L.O.

994 **226** 25 c. blue & gold (postage) 35 35
995 – 80 c. green & gold (air) 1·50 1·40

DESIGN: 80 c. As Type **226** but vertical.

227 "Prince Balthasar Carlos" (Velasquez)

228 Bank Emblem on "Tree"

1969. Paintings (1st series). Multicoloured.

996 3 c. Type **227** 10 10
997 5 c. "Red Roofs" (Pissarro) 20 10
998 10 c. "David and Goliath" (Caravaggio) 30 15
999 12 c. "Still Life" (Chardin) 30 15
1000 15 c. "The Last Supper" (Leonardo da Vinci) 35 15
1001 20 c. "Regatta at Argenteuil" (Monet) 50 20
1002 25 c. "Judgement of Solomon" (Giorgione) 45 25
1003 35 c. "The Sistine Madonna" (Raphael) 85 30

Nos. 997/1001 are horiz.
See also Nos. 1010/1017.

1969. 5th Anniv of African Development Bank.

1004 **228** 25 c. brown and blue 45 40
1005 80 c. red and green 1·50 1·10

229 Memorial Plaque

1969. 1st Man on the Moon.

1006 **229** 15 c. blue and ochre 25 15
1007 – 25 c. blue and orange 70 20
1008 – 35 c. red and slate 1·00 25

DESIGNS—VERT: 25 c. Moon landing and Liberian; 35 c. "Kennedy" stamp of 1966; 35 c. Module lifting off from Moon.

1969. Paintings (2nd series). As T **227**. Multicoloured.

1010 3 c. "The Gleaners" (Millet) 15 10
1011 5 c. "View of Toledo" (El Greco) 20 15
1012 10 c. "Heads of Negroes" (Rubens) 30 15
1013 12 c. "The Last Supper" (El Greco) 30 20
1014 15 c. "Peasants Dancing" (Brueghel) 35 20
1015 20 c. "Hunters in the Snow" (Brueghel) 40 25
1016 25 c. "Descent from the Cross" (detail, Weyden) 45 30
1017 35 c. "The Conception" (Murillo) 60 40

Nos. 1010, 1012/15 are horiz.

230 Peace Dove and Emblems

1970. 25th Anniv of United Nations.

1018 **230** 5 c. grn & silver (postage) 15 25
1019 – $1 blue and silver (air) 1·25 1·00

DESIGN: $1, U.N. emblem and olive branch.

231 World Cup "Football" Emblem

1970. World Cup Football Championships, Mexico.

1020 **231** 5 c. brown and blue 20 15
1021 – 10 c. brown and green 25 20
1022 – 25 c. gold and purple 45 30
1023 – 35 c. red and blue 60 45

DESIGN—VERT: 10 c. Tialoc, Mexican Rain God; 25 c. Jules Rimet Cup. HORIZ: 35 c. Football in sombrero.

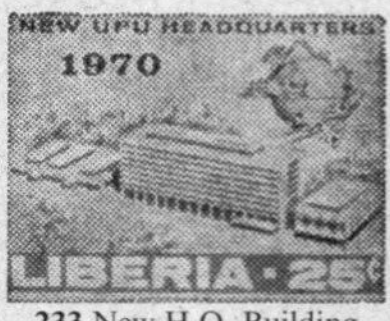

232 Japanese Singer and Festival Plaza

1970. Expo 70. Multicoloured.

1025 2 c. Type **232** 10 10
1026 3 c. Japanese singer and Expo hall 15 10
1027 5 c. Aerial view of "EXPO 70" 30 10
1028 7 c. "Tanabata" Festival 30 10
1029 8 c. "Awa" Dance Festival 30 15
1030 25 c. "Sado-Okesa" Dance Festival 1·10 25

233 New H.Q. Building

1970. Inauguration of New U.P.U. Headquarters Building, Berne.

1032 **233** 25 c. brown and blue 35 35
1033 – 80 c. brown & chestnut 1·50 1·50

DESIGN—VERT: 80 c. Similar to Type **233** but with larger U.P.U. monument.

234 "The First Consul" (Vien)

1970. Birth Bicentenary of Napoleon Bonaparte. Multicoloured.

1034 3 c. Type **234** 20 10
1035 5 c. "Napoleon visiting school" (unknown artist) 30 15
1036 10 c. "Napoleon Bonaparte" (detail, Isabey) 35 15
1037 12 c. "The French Campaign" (Meissonier) 40 20
1038 20 c. "The Abdication" (Bouchot) 80 30
1039 25 c. "Meeting of Napoleon and Pope Pius VII" (Demarne) 1·50 35

Design of 10 c. is incorrectly attributed to Gerard on the stamp.

235 Pres. Tubman

1970. Pres. Tubman's 75th Birthday.

1041	**235**	25 c. multicoloured . . .	75	25

236 "Adoration of the Magi" (Van der Weyden)

1970. Christmas. "The Adoration of the Magi" by artists as below. Multicoloured.

1043		3 c. Type **236**	10	10
1044		5 c. H. Memling	15	10
1045		10 c. S. Lochner	25	15
1046		12 c. A. Altdorfer (vert) . . .	30	15
1047		20 c. H. van der Goes	35	15
1048		25 c. H. Bosch (vert)	40	30

237 Bapende Mask

239 Pres. Tubman and Women at Ballot Box

238 Astronauts on Moon

1971. African Ceremonial Masks. Masks from different tribes. Multicoloured.

1050		2 c. Type **237**	10	10
1051		3 c. Dogon	15	10
1052		5 c. Baoule	15	15
1053		6 c. Dedougou	20	15
1054		9 c. Dan	25	15
1055		15 c. Bamileke	30	20
1056		20 c. Bapende (different) . . .	40	30
1057		25 c. Bamileke costume . . .	60	30

1971. "Apollo 14". Moon Mission. Multicoloured.

1058		3 c. Type **238**	15	10
1059		5 c. Astronaut and Moon vehicle	15	10
1060		10 c. Erecting U.S. flag on Moon	20	10
1061		12 c. Splashdown	40	15
1062		20 c. Astronauts leaving capsule	45	15
1063		25 c. "Apollo 14" crew . . .	60	20

1971. 25th Anniv of Liberian Women's Suffrage.

1065	**239**	3 c. blue and brown . . .	15	30
1066	–	80 c. brown and green . .	1·50	1·50

DESIGN—HORIZ: 80 c. Pres. Tubman, women and map.

240 Hall of Honour, Munich

1971. Olympic Games, Munich (1972) (1st issue). Views of Munich. Multicoloured.

1067		3 c. Type **240**	15	10
1068		5 c. View of central Munich	15	10
1069		10 c. National Museum . . .	20	10
1070		12 c. Max Joseph's Square . .	25	10
1071		20 c. Propylaen, King's Square	40	15
1072		25 c. Liesel-Karistadt Fountain	60	20

241 American Scout

242 Pres. William Tubman

1971. World Scout Jamboree, Asagiri, Japan. Scouts in national uniforms. Multicoloured.

1074		3 c. Type **241**	15	10
1075		5 c. West Germany	15	10
1076		10 c. Australia	20	15
1077		12 c. Great Britain	25	15
1078		20 c. Japan	40	20
1079		25 c. Liberia	60	30

1971. Pres. Tubman Memorial Issue.

1081	**242**	3 c. brown, blue & black	10	10
1082		25 c. brown, pur & blk	35	35

243 Common Zebra and Foal

1971. 25th Anniv of U.N.I.C.E.F. Animals with young. Multicoloured.

1083		5 c. Type **243**	20	10
1084		7 c. Koalas	30	15
1085		8 c. Guanaco	35	15
1086		10 c. Red fox and cubs . . .	45	15
1087		20 c. Savanna monkeys . . .	65	25
1088		25 c. Brown bears	90	35

244 Cross-country Skiing and Sika Deer

1971. Winter Olympic Games, Sapporo, Japan. Sports and Hokkaido Animals. Multicoloured.

1090		2 c. Type **244**	10	10
1091		3 c. Tobogganing and black woodpecker	70	15
1092		5 c. Ski-jumping and Brown bear	15	10
1093		10 c. Bob-sleighing and common guillemots	1·00	15
1094		15 c. Figure-skating and Northern pika	30	20
1095		25 c. Slalom-skiing and Manchurian cranes	2·00	45

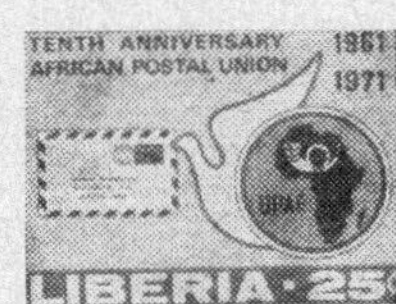

245 A.P.U. Emblem, Dove and Letter

1971. 10th Anniv of African Postal Union.

1097	**245**	25 c. orange and blue . .	35	50
1098		80 c. brown and grey . .	1·10	1·00

246 "Elizabeth" (emigrant ship) at Providence Island

1972. 150th Anniv of Liberia.

1099	**246**	3 c. green and blue . . .	70	50
1100	–	20 c. blue and orange . .	35	20
1101	**246**	25 c. purple & orange . .	2·00	55
1102	–	35 c. purple and green . .	1·10	75

DESIGNS—VERT: 20 c., 35 c. Arms and Founding Fathers Monument, Monrovia.

247 Pres. Tolbert and Map

1972. Inaug of Pres. Wm. R. Tolbert Jnr.

1104	**247**	25 c. brown and green . .	35	25
1105	–	80 c. brown and blue . .	1·60	80

DESIGN—VERT: 80 c. Pres. Tolbert standing by desk.

248 Football

1972. Olympic Games, Munich (2nd issue). Multicoloured.

1106		3 c. Type **248**	10	10
1107		5 c. Swimming	15	10
1108		10 c. Show-jumping	25	10
1109		12 c. Cycling	30	15
1110		20 c. Long-jumping	45	20
1111		25 c. Running	60	25

249 Globe and Emblem

251 Emperor Haile Selassie

250 Astronaut and Moon Rover

1972. 50th Anniv of Int Y's Men's Clubs.

1113	**249**	15 c. violet and gold . . .	40	15
1114	–	90 c. green and blue . . .	1·75	1·75

DESIGN: 90 c. Club emblem on World Map.

1972. Moon Mission of "Apollo 16". Mult.

1115		3 c. Type **250**	10	10
1116		5 c. Reflection on visor . . .	10	10
1117		10 c. Astronauts with cameras	15	10
1118		12 c. Setting up equipment . .	50	15
1119		20 c. "Apollo 16" emblem . .	65	20
1120		25 c. Astronauts in Moon Rover	90	50

1972. Emperor Haile Selassie of Ethiopia's 80th Birthday.

1122	**251**	20 c. green and yellow . .	40	30
1123		25 c. purple & yellow . .	45	40
1124		35 c. brown & yellow . .	85	85

252 H.M.S. "Ajax" (ship of the line), 1809

1972. Famous Ships of the British Royal Navy. Multicoloured.

1125		3 c. Type **252**	35	25
1126		5 c. H.M.S. "Hogue" (screw ship of the line), 1848 . . .	65	25
1127		7 c. H.M.S. "Ariadne" (frigate), 1816	85	30
1128		15 c. H.M.S. "Royal Adelaide" (ship of the line), 1828 . . .	1·00	55
1129		20 c. H.M.S. "Rinaldo" (screw sloop), 1860	1·40	70
1130		25 c. H.M.S. "Nymphe" (screw sloop), 1888	1·90	1·00

253 Pres. Tolbert taking Oath

1972. First Year President Tolbert Presidency.

1132	**253**	15 c. multicoloured . . .	65	55
1133		25 c. multicoloured . . .	95	95

254 Klaus Dibiasi and Italian Flag

1973. Olympic Games, Munich. Gold-medal Winners. Multicoloured.

1135		5 c. Type **254**	10	10
1136		8 c. Borzov and Soviet flag	15	10
1137		10 c. Yanagida and Japanese flag	15	10
1138		12 c. Spitz and U.S. flag . . .	20	15
1139		15 c. Keino and Kenyan flag	25	15
1140		25 c. Meade and Union Jack	35	25

255 Astronaut on Moon

1973. Moon Flight of "Apollo 17". Multicoloured.

1142		2 c. Type **255**	10	10
1143		3 c. Testing lunar rover at Cape Kennedy	10	10
1144		10 c. Collecting Moon rocks	15	10
1145		15 c. Lunar rover on Moon	20	15
1146		20 c. "Apollo 17" crew at Cape Kennedy	30	20
1147		25 c. Astronauts on Moon . .	35	25

256 Steam Locomotive, Great Britain

1973. Historical Railways. Steam locomotives of 1895-1905. Multicoloured.

1149		2 c. Type **256**	25	10
1150		3 c. Netherlands	35	10
1151		10 c. France	65	15
1152		15 c. No. 1800, U.S.A.	95	20
1153		20 c. Class 150 No. 1, Japan .	2·00	25
1154		25 c. Germany	3·00	30

257 O.A.U. Emblem

1973. 10th Anniv of Organization of African Unity.

1156	**257**	3 c. multicoloured	10	10
1157		5 c. multicoloured	10	10
1158		10 c. multicoloured . . .	15	10
1159		15 c. multicoloured . . .	20	15
1160		25 c. multicoloured . . .	35	25
1161		50 c. multicoloured . . .	1·00	1·00

258 Edward Jenner and Roses

1973. 25th Anniv of W.H.O. Multicoloured.

1162	1 c. Type **258**	15	10
1163	4 c. Sigmund Freud and violets	15	10
1164	10 c. Jonas Salk and chrysanthemums	25	10
1165	15 c. Louis Pasteur and scabious	40	15
1166	20 c. Emil von Behring and mallow	45	20
1167	25 c. Sir Alexander Fleming and rhododendrons	85	25

259 Stanley Steamer, 1910

1973. Vintage Cars. Multicoloured.

1169	2 c. Type **259**	10	10
1170	3 c. Cadillac Model A, 1903	10	10
1171	10 c. Clement-Baynard, 1904	15	10
1172	15 c. Rolls-Royce Silver Ghost tourer, 1907	25	15
1173	20 c. Maxwell gentleman's speedster, 1905	35	20
1174	25 c. Chadwick, 1907	50	25

260 Copernicus, Armillary Sphere and Satellite Communications System

1973. 500th Birth Anniv of Copernicus. Mult.

1176	1 c. Type **260**	10	10
1177	4 c. Eudoxus solar system	10	10
1178	10 c. Aristotle, Ptolemy and Copernicus	15	10
1179	15 c. "Saturn" and "Apollo" spacecraft	25	15
1180	20 c. Astronomical observatory satellite	35	20
1181	25 c. Satellite tracking-station	50	25

261 Radio Mast and Map of Africa

1974. 20th Anniv of "Eternal Love Winning Africa". Radio Station. Multicoloured.

1183	13 c. Type **261**	25	25
1184	15 c. Radio Mast and map of Liberia	35	25
1185	17 c. Type **261**	35	50
1186	25 c. As 15 c.	50	40

262 "Thomas Coutts" (full-rigged sailing ship) and "Aureol" (liner)

1974. Cent of U.P.U. Multicoloured.

1187	2 c. Type **262**	20	10
1188	3 c. Boeing 707 airliner and "Brasil" (liner), satellite and Monrovia Post Office	30	10
1189	10 c. U.S. and Soviet Telecommunications satellites	15	10
1190	15 c. Postal runner and Boeing 707 airliner	25	20
1191	20 c. British Advanced Passenger Train (APT) and Liberian mail-van	1·50	25
1192	25 c. American Pony Express rider	50	35

263 Fox Terrier

1974. Dogs. Multicoloured.

1194	5 c. Type **263**	15	10
1195	10 c. Boxer	20	10
1196	16 c. Chihuahua	30	15
1197	19 c. Beagle	35	20
1198	25 c. Golden retriever	40	25
1199	50 c. Collie	1·10	50

264 West Germany v. Chile Match

1974. World Cup Football Championships, West Germany. Scenes from semi-final matches. Multicoloured.

1201	1 c. Type **264**	10	10
1202	2 c. Australia v. East Germany	10	10
1203	5 c. Brazil v. Yugoslavia	15	10
1204	10 c. Zaire v. Scotland	20	10
1205	12 c. Netherlands v. Uruguay	25	15
1206	15 c. Sweden v. Bulgaria	30	15
1207	20 c. Italy v. Haiti	40	20
1208	25 c. Poland v. Argentina	60	25

265 "Chrysiridia madagascariensis"

1974. Tropical Butterflies. Multicoloured.

1210	1 c. Type **265**	10	10
1211	2 c. "Catagramma sorana"	10	10
1212	5 c. "Erasmia pulchella"	20	10
1213	17 c. "Morpho cypris"	50	25
1214	25 c. "Agrias amydon"	70	35
1215	40 c. "Vanessa cardui"	1·40	45

266 Pres. Tolbert and Gold Medallion

1974. "Family of Man" Award to President Tolbert. Multicoloured.

1217	3 c. Type **266**	10	25
1218	$1 Pres. Tolbert, medallion and flag	1·40	1·40

267 Churchill with Troops

1974. Birth Centenary of Sir Winston Churchill. Multicoloured.

1219	3 c. Type **267**	10	10
1220	10 c. Churchill and aerial combat	30	10
1221	15 c. Churchill aboard "Liberty" ship in Channel	55	15
1222	17 c. Churchill reviewing troops in desert	30	15
1223	20 c. Churchill crossing Rhine	40	20
1224	25 c. Churchill with Roosevelt	50	25

268 Marie Curie

1978. International Women's Year. Multicoloured.

1226	2 c. Type **268**	10	10
1227	3 c. Mahalia Jackson	10	10
1228	5 c. Joan of Arc	10	10
1229	10 c. Eleanor Roosevelt	15	10
1230	25 c. Matilda Newport	50	25
1231	50 c. Valentina Tereshkova	70	55

269 Old State House, Boston, and U.S. 2 c. "Liberty Bell" Stamp of 1926

1975. Bicentenary of American Independence.

1233	5 c. Type **269**	15	10
1234	10 c. George Washington and 1928 "Valley Forge" stamp	30	10
1235	15 c. Philadelphia and 1937 "Constitution" stamp	45	15
1236	20 c. Benjamin Franklin and 1938 "Ratification" stamp	50	15
1237	25 c. Paul Revere's Ride and 1925 "Lexington-Concord" stamp	70	20
1238	50 c. "Santa Maria" and 1893 "Columbus' Landing" stamp	2·25	55

270 Dr. Schweitzer, Yellow Baboon and Lambarene Hospital

1975. Birth Centenary of Dr Albert Schweitzer. Multicoloured.

1240	1 c. Type **270**	10	10
1241	3 c. Schweitzer, African elephant and canoe	15	10
1242	5 c. Schweitzer, African buffalo and canoe	1·25	20
1243	6 c. Schweitzer, kob and dancer	30	10
1244	25 c. Schweitzer, lioness and village woman	75	25
1245	50 c. Schweitzer, common zebras and clinic scene	1·40	65

271 "Apollo" Spacecraft

1975. "Apollo-Soyuz" Space Link. Multicoloured.

1247	5 c. Type **271**	10	10
1248	10 c. "Soyuz" spacecraft	15	10
1249	15 c. American-Russian hand-clasp	20	15
1250	20 c. Flags and maps of America and Russia	25	15
1251	25 c. Leonov and Kubasov	35	20
1252	50 c. Slayton, Brand and Stafford	95	50

272 Presidents Tolbert and Stevens, and Signing Ceremony

1975. Liberia–Sierra Leone Mano River Union Agreement.

1254	**272**	2 c. multicoloured	10	10
1255		3 c. multicoloured	10	10
1256		5 c. multicoloured	10	10
1257		10 c. multicoloured	15	10
1258		25 c. multicoloured	35	25
1259		50 c. multicoloured	70	70

273 Figure Skating

1976. Winter Olympic Games, Innsbruck. Multicoloured.

1260	1 c. Type **273**	10	10
1261	4 c. Ski jumping	20	20
1262	10 c. Skiing (slalom)	30	20
1263	25 c. Ice hockey	60	30
1264	35 c. Speed skating	90	40
1265	50 c. Two-man bobsledding	1·25	65

274 Pres. Tolbert taking Oath

1976. Inauguration of President William R. Tolbert, Jr. Multicoloured.

1267	3 c. Type **274**	10	10
1268	25 c. Pres. Tolbert in Presidential Chair (vert)	35	25
1269	$1 Liberian crest, flat and commemorative gold coin	1·90	1·40

275 Weightlifting

1976. Olympic Games, Montreal. Multicoloured.

1270	2 c. Type **275**	10	10
1271	3 c. Pole-vaulting	10	10
1272	10 c. Hammer and shot-put	30	15
1273	25 c. "Tempest" dinghies	65	35
1274	35 c. Gymnastics	90	60
1275	50 c. Hurdling	1·25	65

276 Bell's Telephone and Receiver

1976. Telephone Centenary. Multicoloured.

1277	1 c. Type **276**	10	10
1278	4 c. Mail-coach	10	10
1279	5 c. "Intelsat 4" satellite	15	10
1280	25 c. Cable-ship "Dominia", 1926	1·25	30
1281	40 c. British Advanced Passenger Train (APT)	1·60	50
1282	50 c. Wright Flyer I, airship "Graf Zeppelin" and Concorde	1·75	60

277 Gold Nugget Pendant

1976. Liberian Products (1st series). Multicoloured.

1284	1 c. Mano River Bridge	10	10
1285	3 c. Type **277**	10	10
1286	5 c. "V" ring	10	10
1286a	7 c. As No. 1286	15	25
1287	10 c. Rubber tree and tyre	15	10
1287a	15 c. Combine harvester	20	10
1287b	17 c. As No. 1289	45	10
1287c	20 c. Hydro-electric plant	60	45
1288	25 c. Mesurado shrimp	75	25
1288a	27 c. Dress and woman tie-dying cloth	80	60
1289	55 c. Great barracuda	1·40	35
1289a	$1 Train carrying iron ore	4·50	60

For designs as Type **277** but in a smaller size, see Nos. 1505/8.

278 Black Rhinoceros

1976. Animals. Multicoloured.

1290	2 c. Type **278**	10	10
1291	3 c. Bongo	10	10
1292	5 c. Chimpanzee (vert)	15	10
1293	15 c. Pygmy hippopotamus	40	15
1294	25 c. Leopard	80	40
1295	$1 Gorilla	3·00	90

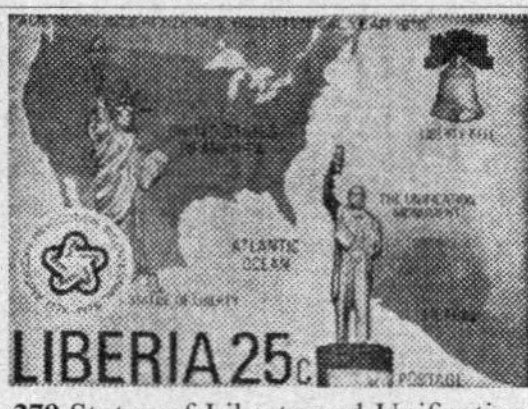

279 Statue of Liberty and Unification Monument on Maps of U.S.A. and Liberia

1976. Bicentenary of American Revolution. Multicoloured.

1297 25 c. Type **279** 35 25
1298 $1 Presidents Washington and Ford (U.S.A.), Roberts and Tolbert (Liberia) . . . . . 1·75 65

280 Baluba Masks

1977. Second World Black and African Festival of Arts and Culture, Lagos (Nigeria). Tribal Masks. Multicoloured.

1300 5 c. Type **280** 10 10
1301 10 c. Bateke 15 10
1302 15 c. Basshilele 20 15
1303 20 c. Igungun 30 15
1304 25 c. Maisi 60 20
1305 50 c. Kifwebe . . . . 1·10 45

281 Latham's Francolin

1977. Liberian Wild Birds. Multicoloured.

1307 5 c. Type **281** 65 10
1308 10 c. Narina trogon 95 15
1309 15 c. Rufous-crowned roller . . . 95 20
1310 20 c. Brown-cheeked hornbill . . . 1·00 25
1311 25 c. Common bulbul . . . . . 1·25 30
1312 50 c. African fish eagle . . . . 2·40 80

282 Alwin Schockemohle (individual jumping)

1977. Olympic Games, Montreal. Equestrian Gold-medal Winners. Multicoloured.

1314 5 c. Edmund Coffin (military dressage) (postage) 15 10
1315 15 c. Type **282** 40 20
1316 20 c. Christine Stuckelberger (dressage) 50 30
1317 25 c. "Nations Prize" (French team) 70 35
1318 55 c. Military dressage (U.S.A. team) (air) . . . . 1·25 70

283 Queen Elizabeth II

1977. Silver Jubilee of Queen Elizabeth II. Multicoloured.

1320 15 c. Type **283** 35 15
1321 25 c. Queen Elizabeth and Prince Philip with President and Mrs. Tubman of Liberia . . 55 25
1322 80 c. Queen Elizabeth, Prince Philip and Royal Arms . . 2·40 70

284 "Blessing the Children"

1977. Christmas. Multicoloured.

1324 20 c. Type **284** 50 25
1325 25 c. "The Good Shepherd" . . . 70 35
1326 $1 "Jesus and the Woman of Samaria at the Well" . . . 2·00 1·00

285 Dornier Do-X Flying Boat

1978. "Progress in Aviation". Multicoloured.

1327 2 c. Type **285** 10 10
1328 3 c. Space shuttle "Enterprise" on Boeing 747 . . . . . . 10 10
1329 5 c. Edward Rickenbacker and Douglas DC-3 . . . . . . 10 10
1330 25 c. Charles Lindbergh and "Spirit of St. Louis" . . . 45 20
1331 35 c. Louis Bleriot and Bleriot XI monoplane 65 35
1332 50 c. Wright Brothers and Flyer I 90 55

286 Santos-Dumont's Airship "Ballon No. 9 La Badaleuse", 1903

1978. 75th Anniv of First Zeppelin Flight. Multicoloured.

1334 2 c. Type **286** 10 10
1335 3 c. Thomas Baldwin's airship "U.S. Military No. 1", 1908 . . 10 10
1336 5 c. Tissandier brothers' airship, 1883 . . . . 10 10
1337 25 c. Parseval airship PL-VII, 1912 . . . . 40 20
1338 40 c. Airship "Nulli Secundus II", 1908 . . . . 75 35
1339 50 c. Beardmore airship R-34, 1919 . . . . 85 55

287 Tackling

288 Coronation Chair

1978. World Cup Football Championship, Argentina.

1341 **287** 2 c. multicoloured 10 10
1342 – 3 c. mult (horiz) 10 10
1343 – 10 c. mult (horiz) 15 10
1344 – 25 c. mult (horiz) 60 20
1345 – 35 c. multicoloured 80 25
1346 – 50 c. mult (horiz) . . . . 1·25 50

DESIGNS: Nos. 1342/6 Different match scenes.

1978. 25th Anniv of Coronation. Multicoloured.

1348 5 c. Type **288** 10 25
1349 25 c. Imperial State Crown . . 35 25
1350 $1 Buckingham Palace (horiz) . . 1·75 1·00

289 Mohammed Ali Jinnah and Flags

1978. Birth Centenary of Mohammed Ali Jinnah (first Governor-General of Pakistan).

1352 **289** 30 c. multicoloured . . . 1·50 1·50

290 Carter and Tolbert Families

1978. Visit of President Carter of U.S.A. Mult.

1353 5 c. Type **290** 10 10
1354 25 c. Presidents Carter and Tolbert with Mrs. Carter at microphones 50 45
1355 $1 Presidents Carter and Tolbert in open car . . . . 2·00 2·00

291 Italy v. France

292 Timber Truck

1978. Argentina's Victory in World Cup Football Championship. Multicoloured.

1356 1 c. Brazil v. Spain (horiz) . . 10 10
1357 2 c. Type **291** 10 10
1358 10 c. Poland v. West Germany (horiz) 15 10
1359 27 c. Peru v. Scotland 65 25
1360 35 c. Austria v. West Germany . 80 55
1361 50 c. Argentinian players with Cup . . . . 1·25 80

1978. 8th World Forestry Congress, Djakarta. Multicoloured.

1363 5 c. Chopping up log (horiz) . . 10 10
1364 10 c. Type **292** 15 10
1365 25 c. Felling trees (horiz) . . . 60 20
1366 50 c. Loggers (horiz) . . . . 1·10 70

293 Presidents Gardner and Tolbert with Monrovia Post Office

1979. Centenary of U.P.U. Membership. Mult.

1367 5 c. Type **293** 10 10
1368 35 c. Presidents Gardner and Tolbert with U.P.U. emblem . 90 90

294 "25" and Radio Waves

1979. 25th Anniv of Radio ELWA. Multicoloured.

1369 35 c. Type **294** 75 75
1370 $1 Radio tower . . . . . . 2·10 2·10

295 I.Y.C., Decade of the African Child and S.O.S. Villages Emblems

1979. International Year of the Child. Multicoloured.

1371 5 c. Type **295** 10 10
1372 25 c. As Type **295** but with UNICEF instead of S.O.S. Villages emblem 25 20
1373 35 c. Type **295** 50 25
1374 $1 As No. 1372 . . . . . . 1·40 1·40

296 Clasped Arms and Torches

1979. Organization for African Unity Summit Conference, Monrovia. Multicoloured.

1375 5 c. Type **296** 10 10
1376 27 c. Masks 40 25
1377 35 c. African animals 50 50
1378 50 c. Thatched huts and common bulbuls . . . . . 1·75 70

297 Sir Rowland Hill and Liberian 15 c. Stamp, 1974

1979. Death Centenary of Sir Rowland Hill. Multicoloured.

1379 3 c. Type **297** 10 10
1380 10 c. Pony Express rider . . . 15 10
1381 15 c. British mail coach . . . 20 35
1382 25 c. "John Penn" (paddle-steamer) 75 55
1383 27 c. Class "Coronation" streamlined steam locomotive No. 6235, Great Britain . . 1·10 25
1384 50 c. Concorde . . . . 1·50 90

298 President Tolbert giving Blood

1979. National Red Cross Blood Donation Campaign. Multicoloured.

1386 30 c. Type **298** 45 25
1387 50 c. President Tolbert and Red Cross . . . . 1·00 1·00

299 "World Peace" (tanker)

1979. 2nd World Maritime Day and 30th Anniv of Liberia Maritime Programme. Multicoloured.

1388 5 c. Type **299** 30 15
1389 $1 "World Peace" (different) . . 2·25 2·00

300 "A Good Turn"

1979. Scout Paintings by Norman Rockwell. Multicoloured.

1390 5 c. Scout giving first aid to pup ("A Good Scout") 20 15
1391 5 c. Type **300** 20 15
1392 5 c. "Good Friends" 20 15
1393 5 c. "Spirit of America" . . . 20 15
1394 5 c. "Scout Memories" . . . 20 15
1395 5 c. "The Adventure Trail" . . 20 15
1396 5 c. "On My Honour" 20 15
1397 5 c. "A Scout is Reverent" . . 20 15
1398 5 c. "The Right Way" 20 15
1399 5 c. "The Scoutmaster" . . . 20 15

1400 10 c. "A Scout is Loyal" . . . 35 20
1401 10 c. "An Army of Friendship" 35 20
1402 10 c. "Carry on" 35 20
1403 10 c. "A Good Scout" 35 20
1404 10 c. "The Campfire Story" 35 20
1405 10 c. "High Adventure" . . . 35 20
1406 10 c. "Mighty Proud" . . . 35 20
1407 10 c. "Tomorrow's Leader" 35 20
1408 10 c. "Ever Onward" 35 20
1409 10 c. "Homecoming" . . . 35 20
1410 15 c. "Scouts of Many Trails" 40 25
1411 15 c. "America builds for Tomorrow" 40 25
1412 15 c. "The Scouting Trail" . . 40 25
1413 15 c. "A Scout is Reverent" 40 25
1414 15 c. "A Scout is Helpful" 40 25
1415 15 c. "Pointing the Way" . . 40 25
1416 15 c. "A Good Sign All Over the World" 40 25
1417 15 c. "To Keep Myself Physically Strong" 40 25
1418 15 c. "A Great Moment" . . 40 25
1419 15 c. "Growth of a Leader" 40 25
1420 25 c. "A Scout is Loyal" . . 60 35
1421 25 c. "A Scout is Friendly" 60 35
1422 25 c. "We Too, Have a Job to Do" 60 35
1423 25 c. "I Will do my Best" . . 60 35
1424 25 c. "A Guiding Hand" . . . 60 35
1425 25 c. "Breakthrough for Freedom" 60 35
1426 25 c. "Scouting is Outing" . . 60 35
1427 25 c. "Beyond the Easel" . . . 60 35
1428 25 c. "Come and Get It" . . . 60 35
1429 25 c. "America's Manpower begins with Boypower" . . 60 35
1430 35 c. "All Together" 80 45
1431 35 c. "Men of Tomorrow" . . 80 45
1432 35 c. "Friend in Need" . . . 80 45
1433 35 c. "Our Heritage" 80 45
1434 35 c. "Forward America" . . 80 45
1435 35 c. "Can't Wait" 80 45
1436 35 c. "From Concord to Tranquility" 80 45
1437 35 c. "We Thank Thee" . . . 80 45
1438 35 c. "So Much Concern" . . . 80 45
1439 35 c. "Spirit of '76" 80 45

301 Mrs. Tolbert and Children

1979. S.O.S. Children's Village, Monrovia. Multicoloured.
1440 25 c. Mrs. Tolbert and children (different) (horiz) 35 50
1441 40 c. Type **301** 90 90

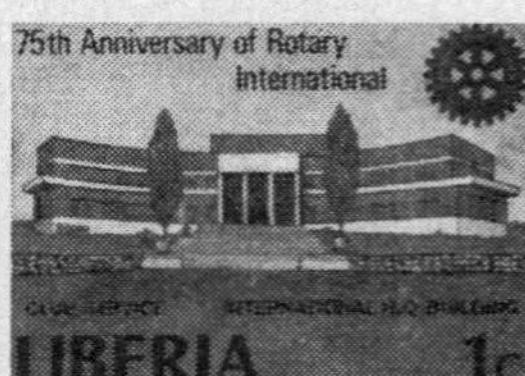

302 International Headquarters, Evanston, Illinois

1979. 75th Anniv of Rotary International. Multicoloured.
1442 1 c. Type **302** 10 10
1443 5 c. Vocational services . . . 10 10
1444 17 c. Wheelchair patient and nurse (community service) (vert) 20 35
1445 27 c. Flags (international service) 40 50
1446 35 c. Different races holding hands around globe (health, hunger and humanity) . . . 50 50
1447 50 c. President Tolbert and map of Africa (17th anniv of Monrovia Rotary Club) (vert) 1·00 1·00

303 Ski Jumping

1980. Winter Olympic Games, Lake Placid. Multicoloured.
1449 1 c. Type **303** 10 10
1450 5 c. Pairs figure skating . . . 10 10
1451 17 c. Bobsleigh 20 35
1452 27 c. Cross-country skiing . . 75 75
1453 35 c. Speed skating 75 75
1454 50 c. Ice hockey . . . . . 1·00 1·00

304 Presidents Tolbert of Liberia and Stevens of Sierra Leone and View of Mano River

1980. 5th Anniv of Mano River Union and 1st Anniv (1979) of Postal Union.
1456 **304** 8 c. multicoloured 15 10
1457 27 c. multicoloured . . . 45 50
1458 35 c. multicoloured . . . 80 75
1459 80 c. multicoloured . . . 1·75 1·75

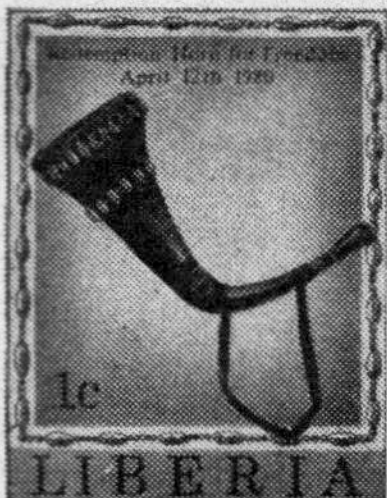

305 Redemption Horn

1981. People's Redemption Council (1st series). Multicoloured.
1460 1 c. Type **305** 10 10
1461 10 c. M/Sgt. Doe and allegory of redemption (horiz) . . . 10 10
1462 14 c. Map, soldier and citizens (horiz) 15 15
1463 $2 M/Sgt. Samuel Doe (chairman of Council) . . . 3·75 3·75
See also Nos. 1475/8.

306 Players and Flags of Argentine, Uruguay, Italy and Czechoslovakia

1981. World Cup Football Championships, Spain (1982). Multicoloured.
1464 3 c. Type **306** 10 10
1465 5 c. Players and flags of Hungary, Italy, Germany, Brazil and Sweden 10 10
1466 20 c. Players and flags of Italy, Germany, Brazil and Sweden 20 20
1467 27 c. Players and flags of Czechoslovakia, Brazil, Great Britain and Germany . . . 25 25
1468 40 c. Players and flags of Italy, Brazil, Germany and Netherlands 60 60
1469 55 c. Players and flags of Netherlands and Uruguay 1·10 1·10

307 M/Sgt. Doe and Crowd

1981. 1st Anniv of People's Redemption Council. Multicoloured.
1471 22 c. Type **307** 20 20
1472 27 c. M/Sgt. Doe and national flag 25 25
1473 30 c. Hands clasping arms, sunrise and map 45 45
1474 $1 M/Sgt. Doe, "Justice" and soldiers . . . . 1·75 1·75

1981. People's Redemption Council (2nd series).
1475 6 c. Type **305** 10 10
1476 23 c. As No. 1461 . . . . . 20 20
1477 31 c. As No. 1462 . . . . . 45 45
1478 41 c. As No. 1463 . . . . . 60 60

MINIMUM PRICE

The minimum price quoted is 10p which represents a handling charge rather than a basis for valuing common stamps. For further notes about prices see introductory pages.

308 John Adams **309** Prince Charles and Lady Diana Spencer

1981. Presidents of the United States (1st series). Multicoloured.
1479 4 c. Type **308** 10 10
1480 5 c. William Henry Harrison 10 10
1481 10 c. Martin Van Buren . . . 15 15
1482 17 c. James Monroe 20 20
1483 20 c. John Quincy Adams . . 25 25
1484 22 c. James Madison 25 25
1485 27 c. Thomas Jefferson . . . 35 30
1486 30 c. Andrew Jackson 55 50
1487 40 c. John Tyler 80 70
1488 80 c. George Washington . . 1·50 1·50
See also Nos. 1494/1503, 1519/27 and 1533/42.

1981. British Royal Wedding. Multicoloured.
1490 31 c. Type **309** 30 30
1491 41 c. Intertwined initials . . . 40 40
1492 62 c. St. Paul's Cathedral . . 1·10 1·10

1981. Presidents of the United States (2nd series). As T **308**. Multicoloured.
1494 6 c. Rutherford B. Hayes . . . 10 10
1495 12 c. Ulysses S. Grant 15 15
1496 14 c. Millard Fillmore 20 15
1497 15 c. Zachary Taylor 20 15
1498 20 c. Abraham Lincoln . . . 25 20
1499 27 c. Andrew Johnson 30 25
1500 31 c. James Buchanan 50 45
1501 41 c. James A. Garfield . . . 70 60
1502 50 c. James K. Polk 80 70
1503 55 c. Franklin Pierce . . . . 1·00 85

1981. Liberian Products (2nd series). As T **277**, but smaller, 33 × 20 mm. Multicoloured.
1504a 1 c. Mano River Bridge . . . 10 10
1505 3 c. Type **277** 10 10
1506 6 c. Rubber tree and tyre . . 10 10
1506a 15 c. Combine harvester . . . 20 15
1507 25 c. Mesurado shrimp . . . 35 35
1508 31 c. Hydro-electric plant . . 70 70
1509 41 c. Dress and woman tie-dying cloth 60 55
1509a 80 Great barracuda . . . . 2·50 1·50
1510 $1 Diesel train carrying iron ore . . . . 5·75 1·60

310 Disabled Children

312 Lady Diana Spencer

311 Examination Room

1982. International Year of Disabled People (1981). Multicoloured.
1515 23 c. Type **310** 35 35
1516 62 c. Child leading blind woman 1·25 95

1982. 30th Anniv of West African Examination Council.
1517 **311** 6 c. multicoloured 10 10
1518 31 c. multicoloured . . . 45 45

1982. Presidents of the United States (3rd series). As T **308**. Multicoloured.
1519 4 c. William Taft 10 25
1520 5 c. Calvin Coolidge 10 10
1521 6 c. Benjamin Harrison . . . 15 15
1522 10 c. Warren Harding 20 25
1523 22 c. Grover Cleveland . . . 45 45
1524 27 c. Chester Arthur 50 70
1525 31 c. Woodrow Wilson . . . 60 60
1526 41 c. William McKinley . . . 70 80
1527 80 c. Theodore Roosevelt . . 1·50 1·60

1982. Princess of Wales. 21st Birthday. Mult.
1529 31 c. Type **312** 70 70
1530 41 c. Lady Diana Spencer (different) 85 85
1531 62 c. Lady Diana accepting flower . . . . 1·25 1·25

1982. Presidents of the United States (4th series). As T **308**. Multicoloured.
1533 4 c. Jimmy Carter 10 10
1534 6 c. Gerald Ford 15 15
1535 14 c. Harry Truman 25 25
1536 17 c. Franklin D. Roosevelt 30 30
1537 23 c. Lyndon B. Johnson . . . 40 40
1538 27 c. Richard Nixon 45 50
1539 31 c. John F. Kennedy 50 60
1540 35 c. Ronald Reagan 60 80
1541 50 c. Herbert Hoover 80 90
1542 55 c. Dwight D. Eisenhower 1·00 1·00

1982. Birth of Prince William of Wales. Nos. 1529/31 optd **ROYAL BABY 21-6-82 PRINCE WILLIAM.**
1544 31 c. Type **312** 45 45
1545 41 c. Lady Diana Spencer (different) 60 60
1546 62 c. Lady Diana accepting flower 95 95

314 Lt. Col. Fallah nGaida Varney

1983. 3rd Anniv of National Redemption Day. Multicoloured.
1548 3 c. Type **314** 10 10
1549 6 c. Commander-in-Chief Samuel Doe 10 10
1550 10 c. Major-General Jlatoh Nicholas Podier 15 15
1551 15 c. Brigadier-General Jeffery Sei Gbatu 20 15
1552 31 c. Brigadier-General Thomas Gunkama Quiwonkpa . . . 50 45
1553 41 c. Colonel Abraham Doward Kollie 60 80

315 National Archives Centre

1983. Opening of National Archives Centre. Multicoloured.
1555 6 c. Type **315** 10 10
1556 31 c. National Archives Centre 50 45

316 "Circumcision of Christ"

1983. Christmas. 500th Birth Anniv of Raphael. Multicoloured.
1557 6 c. Type **316** 10 10
1558 15 c. "Adoration of the Magi" (detail) 20 15
1559 25 c. "The Annunciation" (detail) 40 35
1560 31 c. "Madonna of the Baldachino" 50 45
1561 41 c. "Holy Family" (detail) 60 55
1562 62 c. "Madonna and Child with Five Saints" (detail) 90 85

317 Graduates of M.U.R. Training Programmes

1984. 10th Anniv (1983) of Mano River Union. Multicoloured.

No.	Description	Unused	Used
1564	6 c. Type **317**	10	10
1565	25 c. Map of Africa	40	35
1566	31 c. Presidents and map of member states	50	45
1567	41 c. President of Guinea signing Accession Agreement	70	85

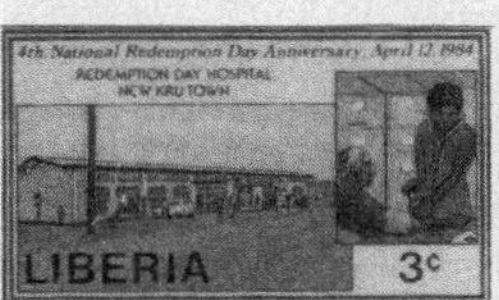

318 Redemption Day Hospital, New Kru Town

1984. 4th Anniv of National Redemption Day. Multicoloured.

No.	Description	Unused	Used
1569	3 c. Type **318**	10	10
1570	10 c. Ganta-Harpa Highway project	15	15
1571	20 c. Opening of Constitution Assembly	35	30
1572	31 c. Commander-in-Chief Doe launching Ganta-Harper Highway project	50	45
1573	41 c. Presentation of Draft Constitution	70	85

319 "Adoration of the Magi"

1984. Rubens Paintings (1st series). Multicoloured.

No.	Description	Unused	Used
1574	6 c. Type **319**	10	10
1575	15 c. "Coronation of Catherine"	25	20
1576	25 c. "Adoration of the Magi"	70	70
1577	31 c. "Madonna and Child with Halo"	85	85
1578	41 c. "Adoration of the Shepherds"	1·10	1·10
1579	62 c. "Madonna and Child with Saints"	1·75	1·75

See also Nos. 1612/17.

320 Jesse Owens

1984. Olympic Games, Los Angeles. Multicoloured.

No.	Description	Unused	Used
1581	3 c. Type **320**	10	10
1582	4 c. Rafer Johnson	10	10
1583	25 c. Miruts Yifter	65	65
1584	41 c. Kipchoge Keino	1·10	1·10
1585	62 c. Muhammad Ali	1·75	1·75

321 Liberian Ducks and Water Birds

1984. Louisiana World Exposition. Multicoloured.

No.	Description	Unused	Used
1587	6 c. Type **321**	1·25	30
1588	31 c. Bulk carrier loading ore at Buchanan Harbour	1·60	75
1589	41 c. Peters' mormyrid, electric catfish, Nile perch, krib and jewel cichlid	1·50	1·10
1590	62 c. Diesel train carrying iron ore	1·75	90

322 Mother and Calf

1984. Pygmy Hippopotami. Multicoloured.

No.	Description	Unused	Used
1591	6 c. Type **322**	20	10
1592	10 c. Pair of hippopotami	80	80
1593	20 c. Close-up of hippopotamus	1·40	1·40
1594	31 c. Hippopotamus and map	2·10	2·10

323 Mrs. Doe and Children

1984. Indigent Children's Home, Bensonville. Multicoloured.

No.	Description	Unused	Used
1595	6 c. Type **323**	10	10
1596	31 c. Mrs. Doe and children (different)	50	50

324 New Soldiers' Barracks

1985. 5th Anniv of National Redemption Day. Multicoloured.

No.	Description	Unused	Used
1597	6 c. Type **324**	10	10
1598	31 c. Pan-African Plaza	50	50

325 Bohemian Waxwing

1985. Birth Bicentenary of John J. Audubon (ornithologist). Multicoloured.

No.	Description	Unused	Used
1599	1 c. Type **325**	15	10
1600	3 c. Bay-breasted warbler	30	10
1601	6 c. White-winged crossbill	35	15
1602	31 c. Grey phalarope	1·90	85
1603	41 c. Eastern bluebird	2·50	1·25
1604	62 c. Common cardinal	3·50	2·00

326 Germany v. Morocco, 1970

1985. World Cup Football Championship, Mexico (1986). Multicoloured.

No.	Description	Unused	Used
1605	6 c. Type **326**	10	10
1606	15 c. Zaire v. Brazil, 1974	20	15
1607	25 c. Tunisia v. Germany, 1978	60	60
1608	31 c. Cameroun v. Peru, 1982 (vert)	75	75
1609	41 c. Algeria v. Germany, 1982	95	95
1610	62 c. Senegal team	1·40	1·40

327 "Mirror of Venus" (detail)

328 Women transplanting Rice

1985. Rubens Paintings (2nd series). Mult.

No.	Description	Unused	Used
1612	6 c. Type **327**	10	10
1613	15 c. "Adam and Eve in Paradise" (detail)	20	15
1614	25 c. "Andromeda" (detail)	60	60
1615	31 c. "The Three Graces" (detail)	75	75
1616	41 c. "Venus and Adonis" (detail)	95	95
1617	62 c. "The Daughters of Leucippus" (detail)	1·40	1·40

1985. World Food Day.

No.	Description	Unused	Used
1619 **328**	25 c. multicoloured	1·25	85
1620	31 c. multicoloured	1·50	1·10

329 Queen Mother in Garter Robes

330 Alamo, San Antonio, Texas

1985. 85th Birthday of Queen Elizabeth the Queen Mother. Multicoloured.

No.	Description	Unused	Used
1621	31 c. Type **329**	35	30
1622	41 c. At the races	80	75
1623	62 c. Waving to the crowds	1·10	1·10

1986. "Ameripex '86" International Stamp Exhibition, Chicago. Multicoloured.

No.	Description	Unused	Used
1625	25 c. Type **330**	60	60
1626	31 c. Liberty Bell, Philadelphia	75	75
1627	80 c. Magnifying glass, emblem and Liberian stamps	1·90	1·90

331 Unveiling Ceremony, 1886 (after E. Moran)

333 Royal Theatre. Gendarmenmarkt

332 Max Julen (Men's Giant Slalom)

1986. Centenary of Statue of Liberty. Multicoloured.

No.	Description	Unused	Used
1628	20 c. Type **331**	30	50
1629	31 c. Frederic-Auguste Bartholdi (sculptor) and statue	75	75
1630	$1 Head of statue	2·40	2·40

1987. Winter Olympic Games, Calgary (1988). 1984 Games Gold Medallists. Multicoloured.

No.	Description	Unused	Used
1631	3 c. Type **332**	10	10
1632	6 c. Debbi Armstrong (women's giant slalom)	10	10
1633	31 c. Peter Angerer (biathlon)	35	55
1634	60 c. Bill Johnson (men's downhill)	1·10	1·10
1635	80 c. East German team (four-man bobsleigh)	1·40	1·40

1987. Liberian–German Friendship. 750th Anniv of Berlin. Multicoloured.

No.	Description	Unused	Used
1637	6 c. Type **333**	10	10
1638	31 c. Kaiser Friedrich Museum, River Spree	35	55
1639	60 c. Charlottenburg Palace	1·10	1·10
1640	80 c. Kaiser Wilhelm Memorial Church	1·40	1·40

334 Othello and Desdemona ("Othello")

1987. William Shakespeare. Multicoloured.

No.	Description	Unused	Used
1642	3 c. Type **334**	10	10
1643	6 c. Romeo and Juliet ("Romeo and Juliet")	10	10
1644	10 c. Falstaff ("The Merry Wives of Windsor")	15	10
1645	15 c. Falstaff, Doll Tearsheet and Prince Hal ("Henry IV", Part 2)	20	15
1646	31 c. Hamlet holding Yorick's skull ("Hamlet")	60	50
1647	60 c. Macbeth and the three witches ("Macbeth")	1·25	1·25
1648	80 c. Lear and companions in the storm ("King Lear")	1·75	1·75
1649	$2 William Shakespeare and Globe Theatre, Southwark	4·00	4·00

335 Emblem

1987. Amateur Radio Week. 25th Anniv of Liberia Radio Amateur Association. Multicoloured.

No.	Description	Unused	Used
1650	10 c. Type **335**	15	10
1651	10 c. Amateur radio enthusiasts	15	10
1652	35 c. Certificate awarded to participants in anniversary "On the Air" activity	80	70
1653	35 c. Globe, flags and banner	80	70

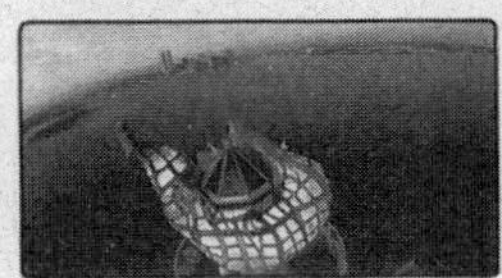

336 Illuminated Torch Flame

1987. Centenary of Statue of Liberty. Multicoloured.

No.	Description	Unused	Used
1654	6 c. Type **336**	10	10
1655	6 c. Scaffolding around statue's head	10	10
1656	6 c. Men working on head	10	10
1657	6 c. Men working on crown	10	10
1658	6 c. Statue's toes	10	10
1659	15 c. Statue behind "Sir Winston Churchill" (cadet schooner)	45	20
1660	15 c. "Bay Queen" (harbour ferry)	45	20
1661	15 c. Posters on buildings and crowd	20	15
1662	15 c. Tug and schooner in bay	45	20
1663	15 c. Decorated statues around building	20	15
1664	31 c. Fireworks display around statue	60	50
1665	31 c. Statue floodlit	60	50
1666	31 c. Statue's head	60	50
1667	31 c. Fireworks display around statue (different)	60	50
1668	31 c. Statue (half-length)	60	50
1669	60 c. Wall poster on building (vert)	1·10	1·00
1670	60 c. Yachts and cabin cruisers on river (vert)	1·50	1·00
1671	60 c. Measuring statue's nose (vert)	1·10	1·00
1672	60 c. Plastering nose (vert)	1·10	1·00
1673	60 c. Finishing off repaired nose (vert)	1·10	1·00

337 Dr. Doe (President), Dr. Moniba (Vice-President), Flags and Hands

1988. 2nd Anniv of Second Republic.

No.	Description	Unused	Used
1674 **337**	10 c. multicoloured	15	10
1675	35 c. multicoloured	65	55

338 Breast-feeding

1988. U.N.I.C.E.F. Child Survival and Development Campaign. Multicoloured.

No.	Description	Unused	Used
1676	3 c. Type **338**	10	10
1677	6 c. Oral rehydration therapy (vert)	10	10
1678	31 c. Immunization	60	50
1679	$1 Growth monitoring (vert)	2·00	2·00

339 Chief Justice Emmanuel N. Gbalazeh swearing-in Dr. Samuel Kanyon Doe

1988. Inauguration of Second Republic.

No.	Description	Unused	Used
1680 **339**	6 c. multicoloured	10	10

340 Footballer and Stadium

1988. 2nd Anniv of Opening of Samuel Kanyon Doe Sports Complex.
1681 **340** 31 c. multicoloured 60 50

341 Child and Volunteer reading

1988. 25th Anniv of U.S. Peace Corps in Liberia.
1682 **341** 10 c. multicoloured 10 10
1683 35 c. multicoloured 70 60

342 Pres. Doe, Farm Workers and Produce

1988. Green Revolution.
1684 **342** 10 c. multicoloured 25 10
1685 35 c. multicoloured 85 35

344 Emblem

345 Type GP10 Diesel Locomotive, Nimba

1988. 25th Anniv of Organization of African Unity.
1687 **344** 10 c. multicoloured 10 10
1688 35 c. multicoloured 70 60
1689 $1 multicoloured 2·00 2·00

1988. Locomotives. Multicoloured.
1690 10 c. Type **345** 25 15
1691 35 c. Triple-headed diesel iron ore train 85 50

346 Helping Boy to Walk

347 Baseball

1988. 25th Anniv of St. Joseph's Catholic Hospital. Multicoloured.
1693 10 c. Type **346** 10 10
1694 10 c. Medical staff and hospital 10 10
1695 35 c. Monk, child, candle and hospital 65 65
1696 $1 Map behind doctor with nurse holding baby 1·90 1·90

1988. Olympic Games, Seoul. Multicoloured.
1697 10 c. Type **347** 10 10
1698 35 c. Hurdling 65 65
1699 45 c. Fencing 80 80
1700 80 c. Synchronised swimming 1·40 1·40
1701 $1 Yachting 1·75 1·75

348 Monkey Bridge

349 Tending Crops

1988.
1703 10 c. Type **348** 10 10
1704 35 c Sasa players (horiz) 40 60
1705 45 c. Snake dancers 70 75

1988. 10th Anniv of International Fund for Agricultural Development. Multicoloured.
1706 10 c. Type **349** 10 10
1707 35 c. Farmers tending livestock and spraying crops 70 60

350 Destruction of Royal Exchange, 1838

1988. 300th Anniv of Lloyd's of London. Multicoloured.
1708 10 c. Type **350** 10 10
1709 35 c. Britten Norman Islander airplane (horiz) 60 60
1710 45 c. "Chevron Antwerp" (tanker) (horiz) 70 75
1711 $1 "Lakonia" (liner) ablaze, 1963 2·00 2·00

351 Honouring Head of Operational Smile Team

1989. 3rd Anniv of Second Republic.
1712 **351** 10 c. black and blue 10 10
1713 35 c. black and red 80 85
1714 – 50 c. black and mauve 1·25 1·25
DESIGN: 50 c. Pres. Samuel Doe at John F. Kennedy Memorial Hospital.

1989. Presidents of United States (5th series). As T **308**. Multicoloured.
1715 $1 George Bush 2·50 2·50

352 "Harmony"

353 Union Glass Factory, Gardersville, Monrovia

1989. Liberia–Japan Friendship. 50th Anniv of Rissho Kosei-Kai (lay Buddhist association). Multicoloured.
1716 10 c. Type **352** 10 10
1717 10 c. Nikkyo Niwano (founder and president of association) 10 10
1718 10 c. Rissho Kosei-Kai headquarters, Tokyo 10 10
1719 50 c. Eternal Buddha, Great Sacred Hall 1·40 1·40

1989. 15th Anniv of Mano River Union. Mult.
1721 10 c. Type **353** 15 10
1722 35 c. Presidents of Guinea, Sierra Leone and Liberia 70 60
1723 45 c. Monrovia–Freetown highway 85 80
1724 50 c. Flags, map and mail van 85 85
1725 $1 Presidents at 1988 Summit 2·00 1·90

354 Symbols of International Co-operation

357 Helicopter Carrier U.S.S. "Okinawa"

1989. World Telecommunications Day.
1726 **354** 50 c. multicoloured 85 85

1989. 20th Anniv of First Manned Landing on Moon. Multicoloured.
1728 10 c. Type **357** 60 15
1729 35 c. Edwin Aldrin, Neil Armstrong and Michael Collins (crew) (28 × 28 mm) 70 60
1730 45 c. "Apollo 11" flight emblem (28 × 28 mm) 1·00 80
1731 $1 Aldrin descending to Moon's surface 2·00 2·00

358 Renovation of Statue of Liberty

360 Nehru and Flag

1989. "Philexfrance '89" International Stamp Exhibition, Paris, and "World Stamp Expo '89" International Stamp Exhibition, Washington D.C. Multicoloured.
1733 25 c. Type **358** 55 45
1734 25 c. French contingent at statue centenary celebrations 55 45
1735 25 c. Statue, officials and commemorative plaque 55 45

1989. Birth Centenary of Jawaharlal Nehru (Indian statesman). Multicoloured.
1737 45 c. Type **360** 85 70
1738 50 c. Nehru 95 80

361 Close View of Station

1990. New Standard A Earth Satellite Station. Multicoloured.
1739 10 c. Type **361** 15 10
1740 35 c. Distant view of station 85 85

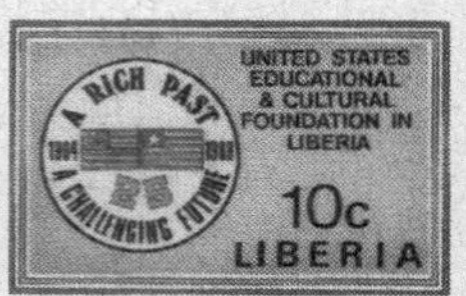

362 Emblem

1990. 25th Anniv of United States Educational and Cultural Foundation in Liberia. Multicoloured.
1741 10 c. Type **362** 15 10
1742 45 c. Similar to Type **362** but differently arranged 85 70

363 Flags, Arms, Map and Union Emblem

364 Bomi County

1990. 10th Anniv of Pan-African Postal Union.
1743 **363** 35 c. multicoloured 70 55

1990. County Flags. Multicoloured.
1744 10 c. Type **364** 10 10
1745 10 c. Bong 10 10
1746 10 c. Grand Bassa 10 10
1747 10 c. Grand Cape Mount 10 10
1748 10 c. Grand Gedeh 10 10
1749 10 c. Grand Kru 10 10
1750 10 c. Lofa 10 10
1751 10 c. Margibi 10 10
1752 10 c. Maryland 10 10
1753 10 c. Montserrado 10 10
1754 10 c. Nimba 10 10
1755 10 c. Rivercress 10 10
1756 10 c. Sinoe 10 10
1757 35 c. Type **364** 65 55
1758 35 c. Bong 65 55
1759 35 c. Grand Bassa 65 55
1760 35 c. Grand Cape Mount 65 55
1761 35 c. Grand Gedeh 65 55
1762 35 c. Grand Kru 65 55
1763 35 c. Lofa 65 55
1764 35 c. Margibi 65 55
1765 35 c. Maryland 65 55
1766 35 c. Montserrado 65 55
1767 35 c. Nimba 65 55
1768 35 c. Rivercress 65 55
1769 35 c. Sinoe 65 55
1770 45 c. Type **364** 85 70
1771 45 c. Bong 85 70
1772 45 c. Grand Bassa 85 70
1773 45 c. Grand Cape Mount 85 70
1774 45 c. Grand Gedeh 85 70
1775 45 c. Grand Kru 85 70
1776 45 c. Lofa 85 70
1777 45 c. Margibi 85 70
1778 45 c. Maryland 85 70
1779 45 c. Montserrado 85 70
1780 45 c. Nimba 85 70
1781 45 c. Rivercress 85 70
1782 45 c. Sinoe 85 70
1783 50 c. Type **364** 1·10 1·10
1784 50 c. Bong 1·10 1·10
1785 50 c. Grand Bassa 1·10 1·10
1786 50 c. Grand Cape Mount 1·10 1·10
1787 50 c. Grand Gedeh 1·10 1·10
1788 50 c. Grand Kru 1·10 1·10
1789 50 c. Lofa 1·10 1·10
1790 50 c. Margibi 1·10 1·10
1791 50 c. Maryland 1·10 1·10
1792 50 c. Montserrado 1·10 1·10
1793 50 c. Nimba 1·10 1·10
1794 50 c. Rivercress 1·10 1·10
1795 50 c. Sinoe 1·10 1·10
1796 $1 Type **364** 2·00 2·00
1797 $1 Bong 2·00 2·00
1798 $1 Grand Bassa 2·00 2·00
1799 $1 Grand Cape Mount 2·00 2·00
1800 $1 Grand Gedeh 2·00 2·00
1801 $1 Grand Kru 2·00 2·00
1802 $1 Lofa 2·00 2·00
1803 $1 Margibi 2·00 2·00
1804 $1 Maryland 2·00 2·00
1805 $1 Montserrado 2·00 2·00
1806 $1 Nimba 2·00 2·00
1807 $1 Rivercress 2·00 2·00
1808 $1 Sinoe 2·00 2·00

365 Lady Elizabeth Bowes-Lyon as Girl

368 Boxing

367 Clasped Hands and Map

1991. 90th Birthday (1990) of Queen Elizabeth the Queen Mother. Multicoloured.
1809 10 c. Type **365** 15 10
1810 $2 As Duchess of York (29 × 36½ mm) 4·00 4·00

1991. National Unity. Multicoloured.
1812 35 c. Type **367** 65 50
1813 45 c. National flag and map of Africa (ECOMOG (West African States Economic Community peace-keeping forces)) 85 65
1814 50 c. Brewer, Konneh and Michael Francis (co-chairmen) and national flag (All-Liberia Conference) 95 75

1992. Olympic Games, Barcelona. Multicoloured.
1815 45 c. Type **368** 85 65
1816 50 c. Football 95 75
1817 $1 Weightlifting 1·90 1·75
1818 $2 Water polo 3·75 3·50

369 "Disarm Today"

1993. Peace and Redevelopment. Multicoloured.
1820 50 c. Type **369** 95 70
1821 $1 "Join your Parents and build Liberia" 1·90 1·40
1822 $2 "Peace must prevail in Liberia" 3·75 2·75

OFFICIAL STAMPS

1892. 1892 stamps optd **OFFICIAL.**

O 87 **7** 1 c. red 30 40
O 88 2 c. blue 30 50
O 89 **8** 4 c. black and green 50 50
O104 **9** 5 c. on 6 c. green (No. 89) 80 80
O 90 6 c. green 60 50
O 91 **10** 8 c. black and brown 45 45
O 92 **11** 12 c. red 1·10 1·10
O 93 **12** 16 c. lilac 1·10 1·10
O 94 **13** 24 c. green on yellow 1·10 1·10
O 95 **12** 32 c. blue 1·10 1·10
O 96 **15** $1 black and blue 22·00 8·75
O 97 **13** $2 brown on buff 9·00 6·25
O 98 **17** $5 black and red 13·50 5·75

1894. 1892 stamps optd **O S.**

O119 **7** 1 c. red 30 20
O120 2 c. blue 60 25
O121 **8** 4 c. black and green 95 35
O122 **10** 8 c. black and brown 80 35
O123 **11** 12 c. red 1·10 40
O124 **12** 16 c. lilac 1·10 40
O125 **13** 24 c. green on yellow 1·10 45
O126 **12** 32 c. blue 1·60 55
O127 $1 black and blue 13·50 13·50
O128 $2 brown on buff 13·50 13·50
O129 $5 black and red 80·00 55·00

1894. 1894 stamp in different colours optd **O S.** Imperf or roul.

O130 **24** 5 c. green and lilac 1·75 2·00

1898. 1897 stamps optd **O S.**

O157 **9** 1 c. purple 35 35
O158 1 c. green 35 35
O159 **15** 2 c. black and bistre 1·00 30
O160 2 c. black and red 1·50 70
O161 **8** 5 c. black and lake 1·50 70
O162 5 c. black and blue 1·90 70
O163 **10** 10 c. blue and yellow 85 80
O164 **11** 15 c. black 85 80
O165 **12** 20 c. red 1·40 95
O166 **13** 25 c. green 85 80
O167 **12** 30 c. blue 2·40 1·40
O168 **35** 50 c. black and brown 2·10 1·40

†1903. Stamp of 1903, but different colour, optd **O S.**

O210 **40** 3 c. green 20 15

1904. Nos. O104 and 167 surch **ONE O.S.** and bars or **OS 2** and bars.

O222 **9** 1 c. on 5 c. on 6 c. green 1·10 1·10
O223 **12** 2 c. on 30 c. blue 7·75 7·50

†1906. Stamps of 1906, but different colours, optd **OS.**

O237 **50** 1 c. black and green 50 50
O238 **51** 2 c. black and red 15 15
O239 – 5 c. black and blue 55 35
O240 – 10 c. black and violet 6·00 60
O241 – 15 c. black and brown 2·00 40
O242 – 20 c. black and green 6·00 75
O243 – 25 c. grey and purple 30 15
O244 – 30 c. brown 50 15
O245 – 50 c. green and brown 50 20
O246 – 75 c. black and blue 1·10 75
O247 – $1 black and green 55 25
O248 **52** $2 black and purple 1·50 25
O249 **53** $5 black and orange 3·75 30

†1909. Stamps of 1909, but different colours, optd **OS.** 10 c. perf or roul.

O262 **55** 1 c. black and green 15 10
O263 – 2 c. brown and red 15 10
O264 **56** 5 c. black and blue 1·00 15
O266 **57** 10 c. blue and black 50 25
O267 – 15 c. black and purple 50 25
O268 – 20 c. green and bistre 75 45
O269 – 25 c. green and blue 70 50
O270 – 30 c. blue 60 40
O271 – 50 c. green and brown 2·25 40
O272 – 75 c. black and violet 1·10 40

1910. No. O266 surch **3 CENTS INLAND POSTAGE.** Perf or roul.

O276 **57** 3 c. on 10 c. blue & black 55 45

1914. Official stamps surch: (A) **1914 2 CENTS.** (B) **+ 2 c.** (C) **5.** (D) **CENTS 20 OFFICIAL.**

O291 **57** + 2 c. on 3 c. on 10 c. blue and black (B) (No. O275) 60 1·60
O284 – 2 c. on 25 c. grey and pur (A) (No. O243) 15·00 6·25
O285 – 5 c. on 30 c. blue (C) (No. O270) 5·25 3·00
O286 – 20 c. on 75 c. black and violet (D) (No. O272) 7·00 3·00

1914. No. 233 surch **CENTS 20 OFFICIAL.**

O287 20 c. on 75 c. black and brown 5·25 3·00

1915. Official stamps of 1906 and 1909 surch in different ways.

O325 – 1 c. on 2 c. brown and red (No. O263) 2·25 2·50
O326 **56** 2 c. on 5 c. black and blue (No. O264) 2·50 3·00
O310 – 2 c. on 15 c. black and purple (No. O267) 65 45
O311 – 2 c. on 25 c. green and blue (No. O269) 3·75 3·75
O312 – 5 c. on 20 c. green and bistre (No. O268) 65 50
O313 – 5 c. on 30 c. green and brown (No. O270) 5·75 5·75
O314 – 10 c. on 50 c. green and brown (No. O271) 6·50 7·50
O316 – 20 c. on 75 c. black and violet (No. O272) 2·00 2·00
O317 – 25 c. on $1 black and green (No. O247) 13·50 13·50
O318 **52** 50 c. on $2 black and purple (No. O248) 15·00 15·00
O320 **53** $1 on $5 black and orange (No. O249) 15·00 15·00

1915. No. O168 surch **10 10** and ornaments and bars.

O321 **35** 10 c. on 50 c. black & brn 9·75 9·75

1915. Military Field Post. Official stamps surch **L E F 1 c.**

O336 **50** 1 c. on 1 c. black and green (No. O237) £325 £325
O337 **55** 1 c. on 1 c. black and green (No. O262) 3·00 3·50
O338 – 1 c. on 2 c. brown and red (No. O263) 2·40 2·50

1917. No. O244 surch **FIVE CENTS 1917** and bars.

O344 – 5 c. on 30 c. brown 15·00 15·00

1918. No. O266 surch **3 CENTS.**

O348 **57** 3 c. on 10 c. blue & black 1·40 1·50

†1918. Stamps of 1918, but in different colours, optd **O S.**

O362 **91** 1 c. brown and green 50 15
O363 **92** 2 c. black and red 50 15
O364 – 5 c. black and blue 75 10
O365 **93** 10 c. blue 35 10
O366 – 15 c. green and brown 1·75 40
O367 – 20 c. black and lilac 55 10
O368 **94** 25 c. green and brown 3·25 45
O369 – 30 c. black and violet 4·00 50
O370 – 50 c. black and brown 5·00 50
O371 – 75 c. black and brown 2·00 15
O372 – $1 blue and olive 3·75 30
O373 – $2 black and olive 6·25 20
O374 – $5 green 8·25 20

1920. Nos. O362/3 surch **1920** and value and two bars.

O400 **91** 3 c. on 1 c. brown & grn 95 50
O401 **92** 4 c. on 2 c. black and red 60 50

†1921. Stamps of 1915 and 1921, in different colours, optd **O S** or **OFFICIAL.**

O428 **100** 1 c. green 70 10
O429 **64** 2 c. red 4·50 10
O430 **65** 3 c. brown 70 10
O431 **101** 5 c. brown and blue 70 10
O432 – 10 c. black and purple 35 15
O433 – 15 c. green and black 2·75 50
O434 – 20 c. blue and brown 1·10 25
O435 – 25 c. green and orange 3·75 50
O436 – 30 c. red and brown 75 15
O437 – 50 c. green and black 75 25
O438 – 75 c. purple and blue 1·90 25
O439 – $1 black and blue 12·50 55
O440 – $2 green and orange 22·00 1·50
O441 – $5 blue and green 17·00 1·75

†1921. Nos. O400/41 optd **1921.**

O442 **100** 1 c. green 4·00 20
O443 **64** 2 c. red 4·00 20
O444 **65** 3 c. brown 4·00 25
O445 **101** 5 c. brown and blue 2·40 25
O446 – 10 c. black and purple 4·00 25
O447 – 15 c. green and black 4·25 15
O448 – 20 c. blue and brown 4·25 35
O449 – 25 c. green and orange 5·00 40
O450 – 30 c. red and brown 4·00 30
O451 – 50 c. green and black 4·75 15
O452 – 75 c. purple and blue 2·75 15
O453 – $1 black and blue 8·75 1·10
O454 – $2 green and orange 21·00 2·50
O455 – $5 blue and green 16·00 3·00

†1923. Stamps of 1923, but different colours, optd **O S.**

O485 **108** 1 c. black and green 5·25 10
O486 **109** 2 c. brown and red 5·25 10
O487 – 3 c. black and blue 5·25 10
O488 – 5 c. green and orange 5·25 10
O489 – 10 c. purple and olive 5·25 10
O490 – 15 c. blue and green 75 40
O491 – 20 c. blue and lilac 75 40
O492 – 25 c. brown 16·00 40
O493 – 30 c. brown and blue 70 20
O494 – 50 c. brown and bistre 70 30
O495 – 75 c. green and grey 70 25
O496 **110** $1 green and red 1·50 40
O497 – $2 red and purple 2·00 50
O498 – $5 brown and blue 3·75 50

1926. No. O362 surch **Two Cents** and thick bar or wavy lines or ornamental scroll or two bars.

O506 **91** 2 c. on 1 c. brown & grn 90 80

1928. Stamps of 1928 optd **OFFICIAL SERVICE.**

O518 **116** 1 c. green 70 35
O519 2 c. violet 1·40 50
O520 3 c. brown 1·40 15
O521 **117** 5 c. blue 80 15
O522 **118** 10 c. grey 2·40 1·00
O523 **117** 15 c. lilac 1·40 60
O524 $1 brown 40·00 16·00

1944. No. O484 surch.

O649 4 c. on 10 c. grey 8·00 8·00

POSTAGE DUE STAMPS

1892. Stamps of 1886 surch **POSTAGE DUE** and value in frame.

D 99 **4** 3 c. on 3 c. mauve 1·25 1·25
D100 6 c. on 6 c. grey 6·25 6·25

D 23

1894.

D110 **D 23** 2 c. black and orange on yellow 95 55
D111 4 c. blk & red on rose 95 55
D112 6 c. blk & brn on buff 95 75
D113 8 c. black & blue on bl 1·00 75
D114 10 c. black and green on mauve 1·25 95
D115 20 c. black and violet on grey 1·25 95
D116 40 c. black and brown on green 2·50 1·75

REGISTRATION STAMPS

R 22

1893.

R105 **R 22** (10 c.) black (Buchanan) £275 £350
R106 (10 c.) black ("Grenville") £1000 £1250
R107 (10 c.) black (Harper) £1000 £1250
R108 (10 c.) black (Monrovia) 40·00 £175
R109 (10 c.) blk (Robertsport) £500 £575

1894. Surch **10 CENTS 10** twice.

R140 **R 22** 10 c. blue on pink (Buchanan) 3·75 3·75
R141 10 c. green on buff (Harper) 3·75 3·75
R142 10 c. red on yellow (Monrovia) 3·75 3·75
R143 10 c. red on blue (Robertsport) 3·75 3·75

R 42 Pres. Gibson

†1904.

R211 **R 42** 10 c. black and blue (Buchanan) 1·50 25
R212 10 c. black and red ("Grenville") 1·50 25
R213 10 c. black and green (Harper) 1·50 25
R214 10 c. black and violet (Monrovia) 1·50 25
R215 10 c. black and purple (Robertsport) 1·50 25

R 96 Patrol Boat "Quail"

1919. Roul or perf.

R388 **R 96** 10 c. blue and black (Buchanan) 90 5·75
R389 10 c. black and brown ("Grenville") 90 7·50
R390 10 c. black and green (Harper) 90 5·25
R391 10 c. blue and violet (Monrovia) 90 5·75
R392 10 c. black and red (Robertsport) 90 7·50

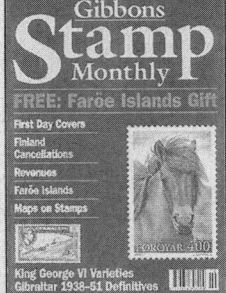

R 106 Gabon Viper

†1921.

R456 **R 106** 10 c. black and red (Buchanan) 23·00 2·50
R457 10 c. black and red (Greenville) 14·00 2·50
R458 10 c. black and blue (Harper) 18·00 2·50
R459 10 c. black and orange (Monrovia) 14·00 2·50
R460 10 c. black and green (Robertsport) 14·00 2·50

†1921. Optd **1921.**

R461 **R 106** 10 c. black and lake 20·00 4·25
R462 10 c. black and red 20·00 4·25
R463 10 c. black and blue 20·00 4·25
R464 10 c. black and orange 20·00 4·25
R465 10 c. black and green 20·00 4·25

R 111 Sailing Skiff (Buchanan)

†1923. Various sea views.

R499 **R 111** 10 c. red and black 8·50 55
R500 – 10 c. green and black 8·50 55
R501 – 10 c. orange and black 8·50 55
R502 – 10 c. blue and black 8·50 55
R503 – 10 c. violet and black 8·50 55

DESIGNS: No. R500, Lighter (Greenville); R501, Full-rigged sailing ship (Harper); R502, "George Washington" (liner) (Monrovia); R503, Canoe (Robertsport).

1941. No. 576 surch **REGISTERED 10 CENTS 10.**

R592 10 c. on 5 c. brown (postage) 1·40 1·40
R593 10 c. on 5 c. brown (air) 1·40 1·40

No. R593 is additionally optd with airplane and **AIR MAIL.**

SPECIAL DELIVERY STAMPS

1941. No. 576 surch with postman and **SPECIAL DELIVERY 10 CENTS 10.**

S590 10 c. on 5 c. brown (postage) 1·40 1·40
S591 10 c. on 5 c. brown (air) 1·40 1·40

No. S591 is additionally optd with airplane and **AIR MAIL.**

LIBYA Pt. 8; Pt. 13

A former Italian colony in N. Africa, comprising the governorates of Cyrenaica and Tripolitania. From the end of 1951 an independent kingdom including the Fezzan also. Following a revolution in 1969 the country became the Libyan Arab Republic.

1912. 100 centesimi = 1 lira.
1952. 1000 milliemes = 1 Libyan pound.
1972. 1000 dirhams = 1 dinar.

A. ITALIAN COLONY.

1912. Stamps of Italy optd **LIBIA** (No. 5) or **Libia** (others).

No.	Type	Description	Unused	Used
1	**30**	1 c. brown	20	60
2	**31**	2 c. brown	20	35
3	**37**	5 c. green	20	30
4		10 c. red	20	20
5	**41**	15 c. grey	18·00	1·50
6	**37**	15 c. grey	2·00	3·50
7	**33**	20 c. orange	30	35
8	**41**	20 c. orange	1·25	3·00
9	**39**	25 c. blue	50	50
10		40 c. brown	80	1·25
11	**33**	45 c. green	7·50	11·00
12	**39**	50 c. violet	2·25	1·00
13		60 c. red	4·25	12·00
14	**34**	1 l. brown and green	24·00	2·00
15		5 l. blue and red	£120	£170
16		10 l. green and pink	9·50	40·00

1915. Red Cross stamps of Italy optd **LIBIA.**

No.	Type	Description	Unused	Used
17	**53**	10 c. + 5 c. red	1·25	3·50
18	**54**	15 c. + 5 c. grey	5·00	8·00
19		20 c. on 15 c. + 5 c. grey	5·00	8·00
20		20 c. + 5 c. orange	2·00	4·75

1916. No. 100 of Italy optd **LIBIA.**

No.	Type	Description	Unused	Used
21	**41**	20 c. on 15 c. grey	18·00	5·00

4 Roman Legionary

5 Goddess of Plenty

6 Roman Galley leaving Tripoli

7 Victory

1921.

No.	Type	Description	Unused	Used
22	**4**	1 c. brown and black	20	90
23		2 c. brown and black	20	90
24		5 c. green and black	40	55
50		7½ c. brown and black	30	1·25
51	**5**	10 c. pink and black	10	10
52		15 c. orange and brown	1·90	60
27		25 c. blue and deep blue	30	15
54	**6**	30 c. brown and black	10	35
55		50 c. green and black	10	10
30		55 c. violet and black	1·90	5·00
57	**7**	75 c. red and purple	10	10
58a		1 l. brown	1·25	10
59	**6**	1 l. 25 blue and indigo	10	10
32	**7**	5 l. blue and black	9·00	7·00
33		10 l. green and blue	40·00	55·00

1922. Victory stamps of Italy optd **LIBIA.**

No.	Type	Description	Unused	Used
34	**62**	5 c. green	50	2·00
35		10 c. red	50	2·00
36		15 c. grey	50	3·25
37		25 c. blue	50	3·00

1922. Nos. 9 and 12 of Libya surch.

No.	Type	Description	Unused	Used
38	**39**	40 c. on 50 c. mauve	1·10	1·40
39		80 c. on 25 c. blue	1·60	5·00

9 "Libyan Sibyl" by Michelangelo

10 Bedouin Woman

1924.

No.	Type	Description	Unused	Used
41	**9**	20 c. green	30	10
42		40 c. brown	1·10	40
43		60 c. blue	30	10
44		1 l. 75 orange	30	10
45		2 l. red	1·60	80
46		2 l. 55 violet	1·60	2·75

1928. Air. Air stamps of Italy optd **Libia.**

No.	Type	Description	Unused	Used
63	**88**	50 c. pink	3·00	4·50
64		80 c. brown and purple	6·00	19·00

1928. Types of Italy optd **LIBIA** (No. 67) or **Libia** (others).

No.	Type	Description	Unused	Used
65	**92**	7½ c. brown	6·00	15·00
66	**34**	1 l. 25 blue	24·00	11·00
67	**91**	1 l. 75 brown	28·00	1·25

1936. 10th Tripoli Trade Fair.

No.	Type	Description	Unused	Used
68	**10**	50 c. violet	70	1·40
69		1 l. 25 blue	90	4·25

1936. Air. Nos. 96 and 99 of Cyrenaica optd **LIBIA.**

No.	Type	Description	Unused	Used
70	–	50 c. violet	80	10
71	**17**	1 l. black	2·75	19·00

1937. Air. Stamps of Tripolitania optd **LIBIA.**

No.	Type	Description	Unused	Used
72	**18**	50 c. red	30	10
73		60 c. red	40	
74		75 c. blue	40	12·00
75		80 c. purple	40	12·00
76	**19**	1 l. blue	1·00	60
77		1 l. 20 brown	40	15·00
78		1 l. 50 orange	40	
79		5 l. green	40	

11 Triumphal Arch

12 Roman Theatre, Sabrata

1937. Inauguration of Coastal Highway.

No.	Type	Description	Unused	Used
80	**11**	50 c. red (postage)	1·50	3·00
81		1 l. 25 blue	1·50	7·00
82	**12**	50 c. purple (air)	1·50	4·00
83		1 l. black	1·50	6·50

1937. 11th Tripoli Trade Fair. Optd **XI FIERA DI TRIPOLI.**

No.	Type	Description	Unused	Used
84	**11**	50 c. red (postage)	5·00	12·00
85		1 l. 25 blue	5·00	12·00
86	**12**	50 c. purple (air)	5·00	12·00
87		1 l. black	5·00	12·00

14 Benghazi Waterfront

1938. 12th Tripoli Trade Fair.

No.	Type	Description	Unused	Used
88	**14**	5 c. brown (postage)	30	50
89	–	10 c. brown	30	50
90	**14**	25 c. green	50	50
91	–	50 c. violet	50	40
92	**14**	75 c. red	60	2·00
93	–	1 l. 25 blue	60	2·00

DESIGN: 10 c., 50 c., 1 l. 25, Fair Buildings.

No.	Type	Description	Unused	Used
94		50 c. brown (air)	1·00	1·00
95		1 l. blue	1·00	3·00

DESIGN—VERT: View of Tripoli.

16 Statue of Augustus

17 Eagle and Serpent

1938. Birth Bimillenary of Augustus the Great.

No.	Type	Description	Unused	Used
96	**16**	5 c. green (postage)	30	85
97	–	10 c. red	30	85
98	**16**	25 c. green	50	65
99	–	50 c. mauve	50	35
100	**16**	75 c. red	75	1·40
101	–	1 l. 25 blue	75	1·40
102	**17**	50 c. brown (air)	50	1·10
103		1 l. mauve	75	2·50

DESIGN: 10, 50 c., 1 l. 25, Statue of Goddess of Plenty.

18 Agricultural Landscape

1939. 13th Tripoli Trade Fair. Inscr "XIII FIERA CAMPIONARIA DE TRIPOLI" etc.

No.	Type	Description	Unused	Used
104	**18**	5 c. green (postage)	20	55
105	–	20 c. red	40	55
106	**18**	50 c. mauve	50	30
107	–	75 c. red	60	90
108	**18**	1 l. 25 blue	60	90

DESIGN: 20, 75 c. View of Ghadames.

No.	Type	Description	Unused	Used
109	–	25 c. green (air)	40	1·10
110	–	50 c. green	50	90
111	–	1 l. mauve	50	1·10

DESIGNS—Fiat G18V airplane over: 25 c., 1 l. Arab and camel in desert; 50 c. Fair entrance.

19 Buildings

1940. Naples Exhibition.

No.	Type	Description	Unused	Used
112	**19**	5 c. brown (postage)	20	35
113	–	10 c. orange	20	35
114	–	25 c. green	60	85
115	**19**	50 c. violet	60	85
116	–	75 c. red	60	1·25
117	–	1 l. 25 blue	60	1·40
118	–	2 l. + 75 c. red	60	2·00

DESIGNS—HORIZ: 10, 75 c., 2 l. Oxen and plough. VERT: 25 c., 1 l. 25, Mosque.

No.	Type	Description	Unused	Used
119	–	50 c. black (air)	40	1·40
120	–	1 l. brown	40	1·40
121	–	2 l. + 75 c. blue	65	2·25
122	–	5 l. + 2 l. 50 brown	65	2·25

DESIGNS—HORIZ: 50 c., 2 l. Savoia Marchetti S.M.75 airplane over city; 1, 5 l. Savoia Marchetti S-73 airplane over oasis.

19a Hitler and Mussolini

1941. Rome-Berlin Axis Commemoration.

No.	Type	Description	Unused	Used
123	**19a**	5 c. orange (postage)	20	3·00
124		10 c. brown	20	3·00
125		20 c. purple	50	3·00
126		25 c. green	50	3·00
127		50 c. violet	50	3·00
128		75 c. red	50	5·00
129		1 l. 25 blue	50	5·00
130		50 c. green (air)	60	10·00

B. INDEPENDENT.

LIBYA (20)

4 MAL. LIBYA (21)

8 FRANCS LIBYA (22)

1951. Stamps of Cyrenaica optd. (a) For use in Cyrenaica, optd as T **20.**

No.	Type	Description	Unused	Used
131	**24**	1 m. brown	15	15
132		2 m. red	20	20
133		3 m. yellow	25	25
134		4 m. green	28·00	19·00
135		5 m. brown	35	35
136		8 m. orange	40	40
137		10 m. violet	60	60
138		12 m. red	1·10	1·10
139		20 m. blue	1·50	1·50
140	**25**	50 m. blue and brown	8·75	8·75
141		100 m. red and black	14·50	14·50
142		200 m. violet and blue	45·00	40·00
143		500 m. yellow and green	£150	£130

(b) For use in Tripolitania. Surch as T **21** in Military Authority lire.

No.	Type	Description	Unused	Used
151	**24**	1 mal. on 2 m. red	25	25
152		2 mal. on 4 m. green	25	25
153		4 mal. on 8 m. orange	25	25
154		5 mal. on 10 m. violet	35	35
155		6 mal. on 12 m. red	35	35
156		10 mal. on 20 m. blue	65	65
157	**25**	24 mal. on 50 m. blue and brown	3·00	3·00
158		48 mal. on 100 m. red	11·00	11·00
159		96 mal. on 200 m. violet and blue	27·00	27·00
160		240 mal. on 500 m. yellow and green	70·00	70·00

(c) For use in the Fezzan. Surch as T **22.**

No.	Type	Description	Unused	Used
166	**24**	2 f. on 2 m. red	20	20
167		4 f. on 4 m. green	30	30
168		8 f. on 8 m. orange	35	40
169		10 f. on 10 m. violet	50	50
170		12 f. on 12 m. red	75	75
171		20 f. on 20 m. blue	2·00	2·00
172	**25**	48 f. on 50 m. blue & brn	38·00	35·00
173		96 f. on 100 m. red and black	40·00	35·00
174		192 f. on 200 m. violet and blue	£110	80·00
175		480 f. on 500 m. yellow and green	£190	£190

23 King Idris

(28)

30

1952.

No.	Type	Description	Unused	Used
176	**23**	2 m. brown	10	10
177		4 m. grey	10	10
178		5 m. green	12·50	35
179		8 m. red	40	25
180	**23**	10 m. violet	12·50	15
181		12 m. red	75	15
182		20 m. blue	13·50	45
183		25 m. brown	13·50	45
184	–	50 m. blue and brown	1·75	65
185	–	100 m. red and black	3·75	1·90
186	–	200 m. violet and blue	6·00	3·50
187	–	500 m. orange and green	25·00	17·00

Nos. 184/7 are larger.

1955. Arab Postal Union. As T **96a** of Syria but inscr "LIBYE" at top.

No.	Type	Description	Unused	Used
200		5 m. brown	1·25	60
201		10 m. green	1·90	90
202		30 m. violet	4·25	2·00

1955. 2nd Arab Postal Congress, Cairo. Nos. 200/2 optd with T **28.**

No.	Type	Description	Unused	Used
203		5 m. brown	40	30
204		10 m. green	95	50
205		30 m. violet	2·25	1·25

1955. No. 177 surch.

No.	Type	Description	Unused	Used
206	**23**	5 m. on 4 m. grey	1·25	45

1955.

No.	Type	Description	Unused	Used
207	**30**	1 m. black on yellow	10	10
208		2 m. bistre	1·40	50
209		2 m. brown	10	10
210		3 m. blue	10	10
211		4 m. black	1·50	50
212		4 m. lake	20	15
213		5 m. green	40	20
214		10 m. lilac	65	25
215		18 m. red	15	10
216		20 m. orange	25	15
217		30 m. blue	50	20
218		35 m. brown	65	25
219		40 m. lake	1·10	40
220		50 m. olive	85	25
221	–	100 m. purple and slate	1·75	50
222	–	200 m. lake and blue	9·25	1·40
223	–	500 m. orange and green	15·00	7·25
224	–	£L1 green, brown on yellow	21·00	11·50

Nos. 221/4 are larger 27 x 32 mm.
See also Nos. 242/57.

33 Immam's Tomb at Djaghboub

34 Map of Libya

1956. Death Centenary of Imam Essayed Mohamed Aly el Senussi.

No.	Type	Description	Unused	Used
225	**33**	5 m. green	20	20
226		10 m. lilac	35	20
227		15 m. red	95	75
228		30 m. blue	1·60	1·25

1956. 1st Anniv of Admission to U.N.

No.	Type	Description	Unused	Used
229	**34**	15 m. buff and blue	30	15
230		35 m. buff, purple & blue	1·00	30

35

36

1957. Arab Postal Congress, Tripoli.

No.	Type	Description	Unused	Used
231	**35**	15 m. blue	1·75	90
232		500 m. brown	12·50	6·50

1958. 10th Anniv of Declaration of Human Rights.

No.	Type	Description	Unused	Used
233	**36**	10 m. violet	20	15
234		15 m. green	25	20
235		30 m. blue	95	50

37 F.A.O. Emblem and Date Palms

39

1959. 1st Int Dates Conf, Tripoli.

No.	Type	Description	Unused	Used
236	**37**	10 m. black and violet	20	15
237		15 m. black and green	50	20
238		45 m. black and blue	1·00	50

1960. Inauguration of Arab League Centre, Cairo. As T **61** of Jordan, but with Arms of Libya and inscr "LIBYA".

239 10 m. black and green 50 20

1960. World Refugee Year.

240 **39** 10 m. black and violet 25 15
241 45 m. black and blue 1·25 75

1960. As Nos. 207 etc. On coloured paper.

242 **30** 1 m. black on grey 10 10
243 2 m. brown on buff 10 10
244 3 m. indigo on blue 10 10
245 4 m. lake on red 10 10
246 5 m. green on green 10 10
247 10 m. lilac on violet 10 10
248 15 m. sepia on buff 10 10
249 20 m. orange on orange 20 10
250 30 m. red on pink 20 15
251 40 m. lake on red 30 20
252 45 m. blue on blue 35 20
253 50 m. olive on bistre 35 20
254 – 100 m. purple & slate on blue 1·25 35
255 – 200 m. lake & blue on blue 3·25 1·40
256 – 500 m. orange and green on green 23·00 5·50
257 – £L1 green & brown on brn 23·00 11·00

40 Palm Tree and Radio Mast  **41** Military Watchtower (medallion)

1960. 3rd Arab Telecommunications Conf, Tripoli.

258 **40** 10 m. violet 15 10
259 15 m. turquoise 20 10
260 45 m. lake 1·40 65

1961. Army Day.

261 **41** 5 m. brown and green 20 10
262 15 m. brown and blue 60 15

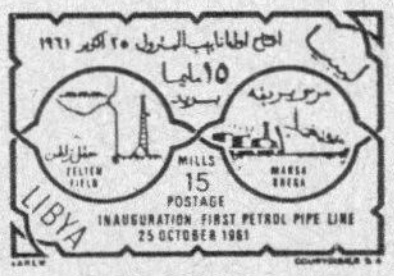

42 Zelten Field and Marsa Brega Port

1961. Inaug of First Libyan Petrol Pipeline.

263 **42** 15 m. green and buff 25 10
264 50 m. brown and lavender 75 40
265 100 m. blue and light blue 2·25 90

43 Broken Chain and Agricultural Scenes

1961. 10th Anniv of Independence.

266 **43** 15 m. sepia, turquoise and green 15 10
267 – 50 m. sepia, brown & buff 45 25
268 – 100 m. sepia, blue & salmon 2·10 80

DESIGNS—(embodying broken chain): 50 m. Modern highway and buildings; 100 m. Industrial machinery.

44 Tuareg Camel Riders

1962. International Fair, Tripoli.

269 **44** 10 m. chestnut and brown 60 10
270 – 15 m. green and purple 75 25
271 – 50 m. blue and green 2·00 1·60

DESIGNS: 15 m. Well; 50 m. Oil derrick.

45 Campaign Emblem  **46** Ahmed Rafik

1962. Malaria Eradication.

273 **45** 15 m. multicoloured 25 20
274 50 m. multicoloured 1·10 90

1962. 1st Death Anniv of Ahmed Rafik el Mehdawi (poet).

276 **46** 15 m. green 15 10
277 20 m. brown 55 20

47 Scout Badge and Handclasp  **48** City within Oildrop

1962. 3rd Boy Scouts' Meeting, Tripoli.

278 **47** 5 m. sepia, red and yellow 10 10
279 – 10 m. sepia, yellow & blue 20 10
280 – 15 m. sepia, yellow & grey 25 20

DESIGNS: 10 m. Scouts and badge; 15 m. Badge and camp.

1962. Inauguration of Essider Terminal, Sidrah Oil Pipeline.

282 **48** 15 m. purple and green 45 15
283 50 m. olive and brown 1·10 45

49 Red Crescent encircling Globe

1963. International Red Cross Centenary.

284 **49** 10 m. multicoloured 20 15
285 15 m. multicoloured 25 20
286 20 m. multicoloured 90 60

50 Rainbow over Map of Tripoli

1963. International Trade Fair, Tripoli.

287 **50** 15 m. multicoloured 25 20
288 30 m. multicoloured 70 20
289 50 m. multicoloured 1·40 60

51 Palm and Well 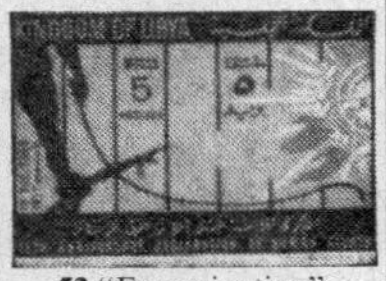 **52** "Emancipation"

1963. Freedom from Hunger.

290 **51** 10 m. green, brown & blue 20 10
291 – 15 m. ochre, purple & grn 25 20
292 – 45 m. sepia, blue & salmon 1·10 75

DESIGNS: 15 m. Camel and sheep; 45 m. Farmer sowing and tractor.

1963. 15th Anniv of Declaration of Human Rights.

293 **52** 5 m. brown and blue 10 10
294 15 m. purple and blue 20 10
295 50 m. green and blue 45 30

54 Map and Fair Entrance  **55** Child playing in Sun

1964. International Fair, Tripoli.

300 **54** 10 m. green, brown and red 75 15
301 15 m. green, brown & purple 1·00 50
302 30 m. green, brown & blue 1·40 75

1964. Children's Day. Sun gold.

303 **55** 5 m. violet, red and pink 10 10
304 – 15 m. brown, bistre & buff 20 15
305 **55** 45 m. violet, blue & lt blue 1·25 65

DESIGN: 15 m. Child in bird's nest.

56 Lungs and Stethoscope

1964. Anti-Tuberculosis Campaign.

307 **56** 20 m. violet 90 25

57 Crown and Map  **58** Libyan Woman, Silk Moth and Cocoon

1964. 1st Anniv of Libyan Union.

308 **57** 5 m. orange and green 15 10
309 50 m. yellow and blue 1·00 50

1964. Emancipation of Libyan Women.

310 **58** 10 m. blue and green 15 10
311 20 m. blue and yellow 55 35
312 35 m. blue and pink 85 80

59 Flags and Scout Salute  **60** Bayonet

1964. Libyan Scouts. Multicoloured.

314 10 m. Type **59** 65 20
315 20 m. Scout badge and saluting hands 1·25 60

1964. Foundation of the Senussi Army.

317 **60** 10 m. brown and green 15 10
318 20 m. black and orange 65 40

61 Ahmed Bahloul (poet)  **62** Football

1964. Ahmed Bahloul El-Sharef Commem.

319 **61** 15 m. purple 20 10
320 20 m. blue 65 20

1964. Olympic Games, Tokyo. Rings in Gold.

321 5 m. black and blue (Type **62**) 25 20
322 10 m. black & purple (Cycling) 25 20
323 20 m. black and red (Boxing) 50 20
324 30 m. black and buff (Runner) 65 50
325 35 m. black and olive (High-diving) 65 50
326 50 m. black & grn (Hurdling) 65 50

Nos. 321/6 were arranged together se-tenant in the sheets, each block of six being superimposed with the Olympic "rings" symbol.

63 A.P.U. Emblem  **64** I.C.Y. Emblem

1964. 10th Anniv of Arab Postal Union.

328 **63** 10 m. blue and yellow 10 10
329 15 m. brown and lilac 20 10
330 30 m. brown and green 95 65

1965. International Co-operation Year.

331 **64** 5 m. gold & blue (postage) 25 10
332 15 m. gold and red 90 25
333 50 m. gold and violet (air) 1·50 35

65 European Bee Eater

1965. Birds. Multicoloured.

335 5 m. Long-legged buzzard 95 20
336 10 m. Type **65** 1·25 20
337 15 m. Black-bellied sandgrouse 1·75 20
338 20 m. Houbara bustard 2·10 30
339 30 m. Spotted sandgrouse 2·75 55
340 40 m. Barbary partridge 3·25 80

The 5 m. and 40 m. are vert.

66 Fair Emblem

1965. International Trade Fair, Tripoli.

341 **66** 50 m. multicoloured 75 50

67 Compass, Rocket and Balloons

1965. World Meteorological Day.

342 **67** 10 m. multicoloured 10 10
343 15 m. multicoloured 20 15
344 50 m. multicoloured 1·00 70

68 I.T.U. Emblem and Symbols

1965. Centenary of I.T.U.

345 **68** 10 m. brown 10 10
346 20 m. purple 15 10
347 50 m. mauve 90 65

69 Lamp and Burning Library  **70** Rose

1965. Reconstitution of Burnt Algiers Library.

348 **69** 15 m. multicoloured 20 10
349 50 m. multicoloured 90 25

1965. Flowers. Multicoloured.

351 1 m. Type **70** 10 10
352 2 m. Iris 10 10
353 3 m. Cactus flower 10 10
354 4 m. Sunflower 50 10

71 Sud Aviation Super Caravelle over Globe  **72** Forum, Cyrene

1965. Inaug of Kingdom of Libya Airlines.

355 **71** 5 m. multicoloured 10 10
356 10 m. multicoloured 20 10
357 15 m. multicoloured 70 10

1965.
358 **72** 50 m. olive and blue 70 25
359 – 100 m. brown and blue . . . 1·25 45
360 – 200 m. blue and purple . . . 3·00 95
361 – 500 m. green and red . . . 6·50 2·75
362 – £L1 brown and green . . . 14·00 6·50
DESIGNS—VERT: 100 m. Trajan's Arch, Leptis Magna; 200 m. Apollo's Temple, Cyrene. HORIZ: 500 m. Antonine Temple, Sabratha; £L1 Theatre, Sabratha.

73 "Helping Hands"

1966. Air. Nubian Monuments Preservation.
363 **73** 10 m. brown and bistre . . 20 10
364 15 m. brown and green . . . 25 10
365 40 m. brown and chestnut 1·10 50

74 Germa Mausoleum

1966.
367 **74** 70 m. violet and brown . . 1·40 75
See also No. E368.

75 Globe and Satellites

1966. International Trade Fair, Tripoli.
369 **75** 15 m. black, gold & green 20 10
370 45 m. black, gold and blue 70 20
371 55 m. black, gold & purple 95 60

76 League Centre, Cairo, and Emblem

77 W.H.O. Building

1966. Arab League Week.
372 **76** 20 m. red, green and black 10 10
373 55 m. blue, red and black 65 50

1966. Air. Inauguration of W.H.O. Headquarters, Geneva.
374 **77** 20 m. black, yellow & blue 20 10
375 50 m. black, green and red 65 25
376 65 m. black, salmon & lake 95 70

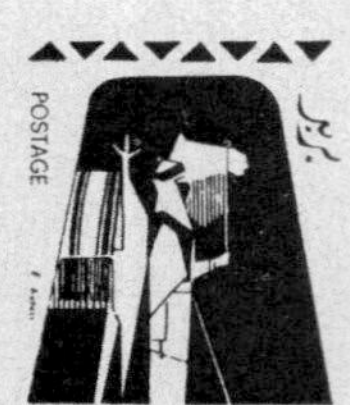
78 Tuareg with Camel

80 Leaping Deer

1966. Tuaregs.
378 **78** 10 m. red 95 65
379 – 20 m. blue . . . . 2·25 1·25
380 – 50 m. multicoloured . . . . 4·50 3·25
DESIGNS—VERT: 20 m. As Type **78** but positions of Tuareg and camel reversed. 62 x 39 mm: 50 m. Tuareg with camel (different).

1966. 1st Arab Girl Scouts Camp (5 m.) and 7th Arab Boy Scouts Camp (25 and 65 m.). Multicoloured.
382 5 m. Type **80** 10 10
383 25 m. Boy scouts 20 10
384 65 m. Camp emblem (vert) . . 1·00 50

81 Airline Emblem

1966. Air. 1st Anniv of Kingdom of Libya Airlines.
385 **81** 25 m. multicoloured 20 15
386 60 m. multicoloured . . . . 1·00 75
387 85 m. multicoloured . . . . 1·40 1·00

82 U.N.E.S.C.O. Emblem

83 Castle of Columns, Tolemaide

1967. 20th Anniv of U.N.E.S.C.O.
388 **82** 15 m. multicoloured 20 10
389 25 m. multicoloured 90 20

1967. Tourism.
390 **83** 25 m. black, brown & violet 20 10
391 – 55 m. brown, violet & black 90 50
DESIGN—HORIZ: 55 m. Sebba Fort.

84 "British Confidence" (tanker) at Oil Terminal

1967. Inaug of Marsa al Hariga Oil Terminal.
392 **84** 60 m. multicoloured . . . . 1·75 65

85 Fair Emblem

86 I.T.Y. Emblem

1967. International Fair, Tripoli.
393 **85** 15 m. multicoloured 50 10
394 55 m. multicoloured 75 50

1967. International Tourist Year.
395 **86** 5 m. black and blue 10 10
396 10 m. blue and black . . . 10 10
397 45 m. black, blue and pink 60 15

87 Running

88 Open Book and Arab League Emblem

1967. Mediterranean Games, Tunisia. Designs showing action "close-ups".
398 **87** 5 m. black, orange and blue 10 10
399 – 10 m. black, brown & blue 10 10
400 – 15 m. black, violet and blue 10 10
401 – 45 m. black, red and blue 30 25
402 – 75 m. black, green and blue 75 30
DESIGNS: 10 m. Throwing the javelin; 15 m. Cycling; 45 m. Football; 75 m. Boxing.

1967. Literacy Campaign.
403 **88** 5 m. orange and violet . . . 10 10
404 10 m. green and violet . . . 10 10
405 15 m. purple and violet . . 15 10
406 25 m. blue and violet . . . 20 15

89 Human Rights Emblem

90 Cameleers, Fokker Friendship, Oil Rig and Map

1968. Human Rights Year.
407 **89** 15 m. red and green 15 10
408 60 m. blue and orange . . . 65 25

1968. International Fair, Tripoli.
409 **90** 55 m. multicoloured 95 30

91 Arab League Emblem

1968. Arab League Week.
410 **91** 10 m. red and blue 10 10
411 45 m. green and orange . . 65 50

92 Children "Wrestling" (statue)

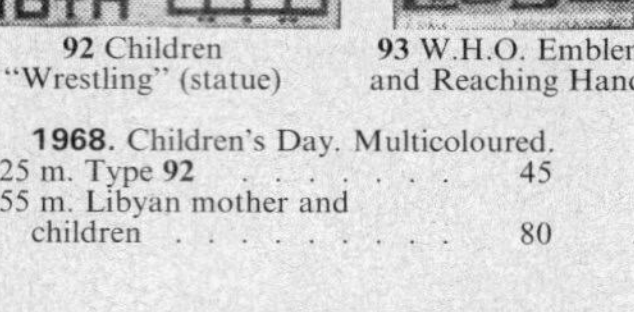
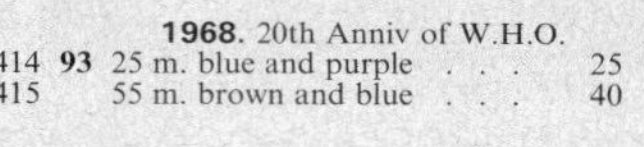
93 W.H.O. Emblem and Reaching Hands

1968. Children's Day. Multicoloured.
412 25 m. Type **92** 45 15
413 55 m. Libyan mother and children 80 55

1968. 20th Anniv of W.H.O.
414 **93** 25 m. blue and purple . . . 25 15
415 55 m. brown and blue . . . 40 25

94 Oil Pipeline Map

1968. Inauguration of Zueitina Oil Terminal.
416 **94** 10 m. multicoloured 20 10
417 60 m. multicoloured . . . . 1·10 65

95 "Teaching the People"

1968. "Eliminate Illiteracy".
418 **95** 5 m. mauve 10 10
419 10 m. orange 10 10
420 15 m. blue 10 10
421 20 m. green 20 20

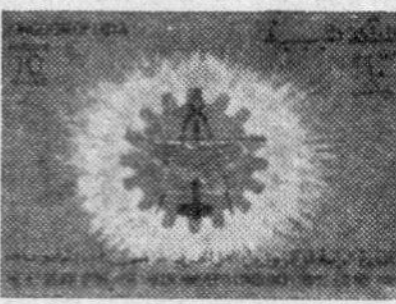
96 Conference Emblem

1968. 4th Session of Arab Labour Ministries Conference, Tripoli.
422 **96** 10 m. multicoloured 10 10
423 15 m. multicoloured 20 10

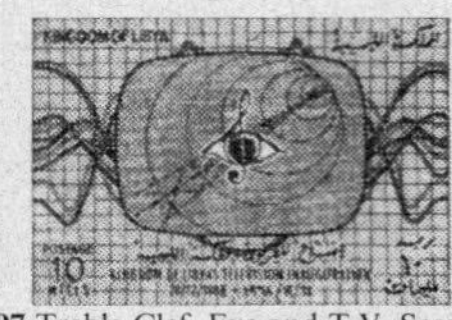
97 Treble Clef, Eye and T.V. Screen

1968. Inauguration of Libyan Television Service.
424 **97** 10 m. multicoloured 10 10
425 30 m. multicoloured 65 20

98 Bridge, Callipers and Road Sign

1968. Opening of Wadi El Kuf Bridge.
426 **98** 25 m. multicoloured 15 15
427 60 m. multicoloured 70 25

99 Melons

100 Fair Emblem

1969. Fruits. Multicoloured.
428 5 m. Type **99** 10 10
429 10 m. Dates 10 10
430 15 m. Lemons 10 10
431 20 m. Oranges 15 10
432 25 m. Peaches 50 15
433 35 m. Pears 90 50

1969. 8th International Trade Fair, Tripoli.
434 **100** 25 m. multicoloured . . . 15 10
435 35 m. multicoloured . . . 25 15
436 40 m. multicoloured . . . 60 20

101 Hoisting Weather Balloon

1969. World Meteorological Day.
437 **101** 60 m. multicoloured . . . 1·10 65

102 Family on Staircase within Cogwheel

103 I.L.O. Emblem

1969. 10th Anniv of Libyan Social Insurance.
438 **102** 15 m. multicoloured . . . 15 10
439 55 m. multicoloured . . . 30 25

1969. 50th Anniv of I.L.O.
440 **103** 10 m. green, black & turq 10 10
441 60 m. green, black and red 70 50

104 Emblem and Desert Scene

1969. African Tourist Year.
442 **104** 15 m. multicoloured . . . 15 10
443 30 m. multicoloured . . . 65 50

105 Members of the Armed Forces and Olive Branch

106 Dish Aerial and Flags

1969. Revolution of 1st September.

444 105 5 m. multicoloured 25 10
445 10 m. multicoloured . . . 35 20
446 15 m. multicoloured . . . 55 25
447 25 m. multicoloured . . . 85 40
448 45 m. multicoloured . . . 1·00 60
449 60 m. multicoloured . . . 2·10 1·00

On Nos. 444/9 the value is in white and the designer's name appears at the foot of design.

1970. 5th Anniv of Arab Satellite Communications Co-operation Agreement.

450 106 15 m. multicoloured . . . 50 15
451 20 m. multicoloured . . . 75 20
452 25 m. multicoloured . . . 1·00 25
453 40 m. multicoloured . . . 1·50 75

107 Arab League Flag, Arms and Map

1970. Silver Jubilee of Arab League.

454 107 10 m. sepia, green & blue 10 10
455 15 m. brown, green & orge 15 15
456 20 m. purple, grn & olive 50 25

1970. Revolution of 1st September. Designs as T **105**, but without imprint "M. A. Siala" at foot, and figures of value differently inscr

457 87 5 m. multicoloured 25 10
458 10 m. multicoloured 35 20
459 15 m. multicoloured 55 25
460 25 m. multicoloured 85 40
461 45 m. multicoloured . . . . 1·00 60
462 60 m. multicoloured . . . . 2·10 1·00

108 New Headquarters Building

109 Arms and Soldiers

1970. New U.P.U. Headquarters Building, Berne.

463 108 10 m. multicoloured . . . 15 10
464 25 m. multicoloured . . . 20 20
465 60 m. multicoloured . . . 95 60

1970. Nos. 358 and 360/2 with "KINGDOM OF LIBYA" inscriptions obliterated.

465a 72 50 m. olive and blue . . .
466 – 200 m. blue and purple . .
467 – 500 m. green and pink . .
468 – £L1 brown and green . . .

These stamps were sold only for use on parcel post items. Other values may exist so overprinted, but were unauthorised.

See also Nos. 518/23.

1970. Evacuation of Foreign Military Bases in Libya.

469 109 15 m. black and red . . . 15 15
470 25 m. yellow, blue & red 45 20
471 45 m. yellow, red & green 1·25 30

110 Soldiers and Libyan Flag

111 U.N. Emblem, Dove and Scales

1970. 1st Anniv of Libyan Arab Republic.

472 110 20 m. multicoloured . . . 55 15
473 25 m. multicoloured . . . 70 15
474 30 m. multicoloured . . . 1·25 75

1970. 25th Anniv of United Nations.

475 111 5 m. brown, red & green 25 10
476 10 m. green, red & emerald 65 15
477 60 m. green, red and blue 1·75 75

112 Map and Flags

113 Dove, U.N. Emblem and Globe

1970. Signing of Tripoli Charter of Co-operation.

478 112 15 m. green, black & red 5·00 1·50

1971. 10th Anniv of U.N. De-colonisation Declaration.

479 113 15 m. multicoloured . . . 50 15
480 20 m. multicoloured . . . 75 20
481 60 m. multicoloured . . . 1·90 75

114 Education Year Emblem

115 Palestinian Guerrilla

1971. International Education Year.

482 114 5 m. brown, red & black 15 10
483 10 m. green, red & black 50 10
484 20 m. blue, red & black 1·10 15

1971. "Al-Fatah" Movement for the Liberation of Palestine.

485 115 5 m. multicoloured 15 10
486 10 m. multicoloured . . . 50 15
487 100 m. multicoloured . . . 1·75 1·00

116 Fair Emblem

117 O.P.E.C. Emblem

1971. 9th International Trade Fair, Tripoli.

488 116 15 m. multicoloured . . . 15 10
489 30 m. multicoloured . . . 65 20

1971. Organization of Petroleum Exporting Countries (O.P.E.C.).

490 117 10 m. brown and yellow 15 10
491 70 m. violet and pink . . . 1·25 65

118 Global Symbol

1971. World Telecommunications Day (Nos. 494/5) and Pan-African Telecommunications Network.

492 – 5 m. multicoloured 10 10
493 – 15 m. multicoloured . . . 10 15
494 118 25 m. multicoloured . . . 20 15
495 35 m. multicoloured . . . 50 25

DESIGN: 5 m., 15 m. Telecommunications map of Africa.

119 Soldier, Torch and Flag

120 Ramadan Suehli

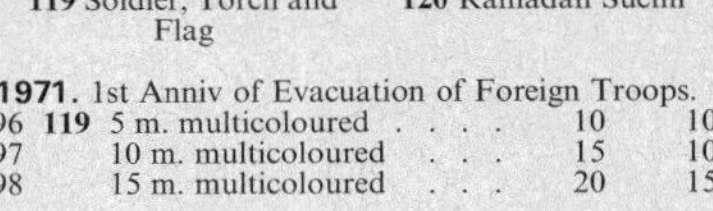

1971. 1st Anniv of Evacuation of Foreign Troops.

496 119 5 m. multicoloured . . . 10 10
497 10 m. multicoloured . . . 15 10
498 15 m. multicoloured . . . 20 15

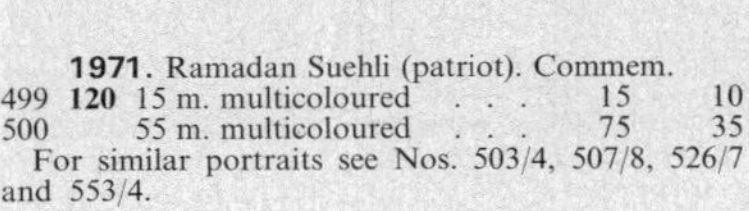

1971. Ramadan Suehli (patriot). Commem.

499 120 15 m. multicoloured . . . 15 10
500 55 m. multicoloured . . . 75 35

For similar portraits see Nos. 503/4, 507/8, 526/7 and 553/4.

121 Palm and Dates

122 Pres. Gamal Nasser

1971. 2nd Anniv of 1st September Revolution.

501 121 5 m. multicoloured 20 10
502 15 m. multicoloured . . . 1·00 15

1971. 40th Death Anniv of Omar el Mukhtar (patriot). As T **120**.

503 5 m. multicoloured 10 10
504 100 m. multicoloured . . . . . 1·75 90

1971. 1st Death Anniv of Pres. Nasser of Egypt.

505 122 5 m. black, green & pur 10 10
506 15 m. black, purple & grn 95 10

1971. 21st Death Anniv of Ibrahim Usta Omar (poet). As T **120**.

507 25 m. multicoloured 25 15
508 30 m. multicoloured 80 20

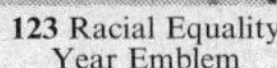

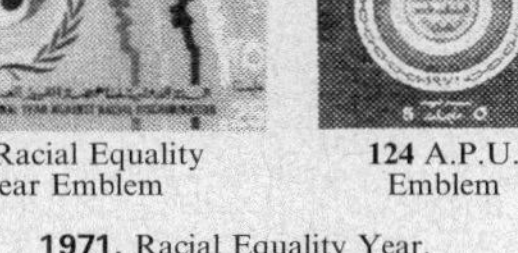

123 Racial Equality Year Emblem

124 A.P.U. Emblem

1971. Racial Equality Year.

509 123 25 m. multicoloured . . . 25 15
510 35 m. multicoloured . . . 70 15

1971. 25th Anniv of Founding of Arab Postal Union at Sofar Conference.

511 124 5 m. multicoloured 10 10
512 10 m. multicoloured . . . 20 10
513 15 m. multicoloured . . . 15 10

125 Arab Postal Union. Emblem and Envelopes

126 Book Year Emblem

1971. 10th Anniv of African Postal Union. Mult.

514 10 m. Type **125** 10 10
515 15 m. Type **125** 15 10
516 25 m. A.P.U. Emblem and dove with letter 25 15
517 55 m. As 25 m. 95 35

1971. Nos. 423/33 with "KINGDOM OF LIBYA" inscriptions obliterated.

518 5 m. Type **99** . . . .
519 10 m. Dates . . . .
520 15 m. Lemons . . . .
521 20 m. Oranges . . . .
522 25 m. Peaches . . . .
523 35 m. Pears . . . .

1972. International Book Year.

524 126 15 m. multicoloured . . . 15 10
525 20 m. multicoloured . . . 25 20

1972. Ahmed Gnaba (poet). Commem. As T **120**.

526 20 m. multicoloured 25 10
527 35 m. multicoloured 65 20

127 Libyan Arms

128 Tombs, Ghirza

1972. Values in Milliemes.

528 127 5 m. multicoloured 10 10
529 10 m. multicoloured . . . 10 10
530 25 m. multicoloured . . . 15 10
531 30 m. multicoloured . . . 20 10
532 35 m. multicoloured . . . 25 10
533 40 m. multicoloured . . . 50 15
534 45 m. multicoloured . . . 60 15
535 55 m. multicoloured . . . 85 20
536 60 m. multicoloured . . . 1·00 35
537 90 m. multicoloured . . . 1·60 90

1972. Libyan Antiquities. Multicoloured.

538 5 m. Type **128** 10 10
539 10 m. Cufic inscription, Ajdabiya 10 10
540 15 m. Marcus Aurelius' Arch, Tripoli (horiz) 15 10
541 25 m. Exchanging Weapons (cave painting, Wadi Zigza) . . . 65 15
542 55 m. Garamantian chariot (wall drawing, Wadi Zigza) . . . 1·40 65
543 70 m. "Libya crowning Cyrene" (Roman relief, Cyrene) . . . 2·50 90

129 Fair Emblem

130 Heart and Skeletal Arm

1972. 10th Int Trade Fair, Tripoli.

544 129 25 m. multicoloured . . . 20 15
545 35 m. multicoloured . . . 25 20
546 50 m. multicoloured . . . 95 25
547 70 m. multicoloured . . . 1·40 35

1972. World Health Day.

548 130 15 m. multicoloured . . . 1·10 25
549 25 m. multicoloured . . . 2·25 75

131 "Unity" Symbol on Map

132

1972. 1st Anniv of Libyan-Egyptian Federation Agreement.

550 131 15 m. yellow, blue & black 10 10
551 20 m. yellow, green & emer 20 10
552 25 m. yellow, red & black 80 20

1972. Birth Centenary (1970) of Suleiman el Baruni (writer). As T **120**.

553 10 m. multicoloured 95 15
554 70 m. multicoloured . . . . . 1·25 75

1972. New Currency (Dirhams and Dinars). As Type **127**. (a) Size 19 x 24 mm.

555 127 15 dh. multicoloured . . . 10 10
556 65 dh. multicoloured . . . 75 50
557 70 dh. multicoloured . . . 90 65
558 80 dh. multicoloured . . . 1·25 65

(b) Size 27 x 32 mm.

559 127 100 dh. multicoloured . . . 1·75 2·00
560 200 dh. multicoloured . . . 3·25 1·60
561 500 dh. multicoloured . . . 7·50 5·00
562 1 D. multicoloured . . . . 13·50 10·00

1972.

563 132 5 m. multicoloured . . . . 1·90 50
564 20 m. multicoloured . . . 7·50 1·40
565 50 m. multicoloured . . . 18·00 3·75

Nos. 563/5 were also issued with the Arabic face values expressed in the new currency.

See also Nos. 657/9.

133 Environmental Emblem

134 Olympic Emblems

1972. U.N. Environmental Conservation Conference, Stockholm.

566 133 15 dh. multicoloured . . . 50 10
567 55 dh. multicoloured . . . 1·10 35

1972. Olympic Games, Munich.

568 134 25 dh. multicoloured . . . 1·50 35
569 35 dh. multicoloured . . . 2·25 90

135 Symbolic Tree and "Fruit"

136 Dome of the Rock

1972. 3rd Anniv of 1st September Revolution.

570 135 15 dh. multicoloured . . . 15 10
571 25 dh. multicoloured . . . 70 15

1973. Dome of the Rock, Jerusalem.

572 136 10 dh. multicoloured . . . 10 10
573 25 dh. multicoloured . . . 50 15

137 Nicolas Copernicus

138 Libyan Eagle and Fair

1973. 500th Birth Anniv of Copernicus. Mult.

574		15 dh. Type **137**	15	10
575		25 dh. "Copernicus in his Observatory" (horiz)	50	15

1973. 11th International Trade Fair, Tripoli.

576	**138**	5 dh. multicoloured	15	10
577		10 dh. multicoloured	50	10
578		15 dh. multicoloured	90	15

139 Blind Persons and Occupations

140 Map and Laurel

1973. Role of the Blind in Society.

579	**139**	20 dh. multicoloured	5·50	1·25
580		25 dh. multicoloured	10·00	2·50

1973. 10th Anniv of Organization of African Unity.

584	**140**	15 dh. multicoloured	20	10
585		25 dh. multicoloured	65	45

141 Interpol H.Q., Paris

1973. 50th Anniv of International Criminal Police Organization (Interpol).

586	**141**	10 dh. multicoloured	10	10
587		15 dh. multicoloured	15	10
588		25 dh. multicoloured	60	20

142 Map and Emblems

143 W.M.O. Emblem

1973. Census.

589	**142**	10 dh. blue, black & red	3·00	65
590		25 dh. green, black & blue	4·25	1·25
591		35 dh. orange, black & grn	8·00	2·50

1973. W.M.O. Centenary.

592	**143**	5 dh. blue, black and red	10	10
593		10 dh. blue, black & green	15	10

144 Footballers

1973. 2nd Palestine Cup Football Championship.

594	**144**	5 dh. brown and green	45	20
595		25 dh. brown and red	80	15

145 Revolutionary Torch

146 "Writing Ability"

1973. 4th Anniv of September 1st Revolution.

596	**145**	15 dh. multicoloured	20	10
597		25 dh. multicoloured	85	10

1973. Literacy Campaign.

598	**146**	25 dh. multicoloured	50	15

147 Doorway of Old City Hall

148 Militiamen and Flag

1973. Cent of Tripoli Municipality. Mult.

599		10 dh. Type **147**	20	10
600		25 dh. Khondok fountain	50	10
601		35 dh. Clock tower	75	40

1973. Libyan Militia.

602	**148**	15 dh. multicoloured	15	10
603		25 dh. multicoloured	55	10

149 Arabic Quotation from Speech of 15 April 1973

1973. Declaration of Cultural Revolution by Col. Gaddafi. Multicoloured.

604		25 dh. Type **149**	20	10
605		70 dh. As Type **149** but text in English	60	30

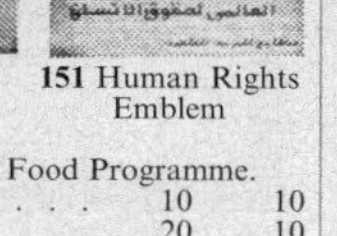

150 Ploughing with Camel

151 Human Rights Emblem

1973. 10th Anniv of World Food Programme.

606	**150**	10 dh. multicoloured	10	10
607		25 dh. multicoloured	20	10
608		35 dh. multicoloured	55	15

1973. 25th Anniv of Declaration of Human Rights.

609	**151**	25 dh. red, purple & blue	20	10
610		70 dh. red, green and blue	1·10	30

152 Flat-headed Grey Mullet

154 Emblem formed with National Flags

153 Lookout Post and Scout Salute

1973. Fishes. Multicoloured.

611		5 dh. Type **152**	15	10
612		10 dh. Zebra seabream	70	10
613		15 dh. Grouper	1·00	15
614		20 dh. Painted comber	1·50	20
615		25 dh. Yellow-finned tunny	2·75	30

1974. 20th Anniv of Scouting in Libya.

616	**153**	5 dh. multicoloured	95	10
617		20 dh. multicoloured	2·50	50
618		25 dh. multicoloured	4·00	1·25

1974. 12th International Trade Fair, Tripoli.

619	**154**	10 dh. multicoloured	50	10
620		25 dh. multicoloured	75	15
621		35 dh. multicoloured	1·25	35

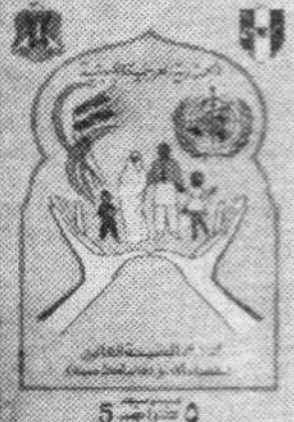

155 Family within Protective Hands

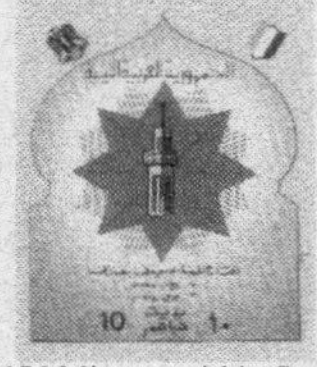

156 Minaret within Star

1974. World Health Day.

622	**155**	5 dh. multicoloured	15	10
623		25 dh. multicoloured	50	20

1974. Inauguration of Benghazi University.

624	**156**	10 dh. multicoloured	20	10
625		25 dh. multicoloured	75	15
626		35 dh. multicoloured	1·10	25

157 U.P.U. Emblem within Star

158 Traffic Lights and Signs

1974. Centenary of U.P.U.

627	**157**	25 dh. multicoloured	5·50	75
628		70 dh. multicoloured	10·00	1·50

1974. Motoring and Touring Club of Libya.

629	**158**	5 dh. multicoloured	10	10
630		10 dh. multicoloured	15	10
631		25 dh. multicoloured	15	10

159 Tank, Refinery and Pipeline

160 W.P.Y. Emblem and People

1974. 5th Anniv of 1st September Revolution.

632	**159**	5 dh. multicoloured	10	10
633		20 dh. multicoloured	15	10
634		25 dh. multicoloured	15	10
635		35 dh. multicoloured	20	15

1974. World Population Year.

637	**160**	25 dh. multicoloured	20	10
638		35 dh. multicoloured	50	20

161

162 Congress Emblem

1975. 13th International Trade Fair, Tripoli. Libyan Costumes.

639	**161**	5 dh. multicoloured	10	10
640	–	10 dh. multicoloured	10	10
641	–	15 dh. multicoloured	10	10
642	–	20 dh. multicoloured	20	10
643	–	25 dh. multicoloured	75	10
644	–	50 dh. multicoloured	1·10	20

DESIGNS: 10 dh. to 50 dh. Various costumes.

1975. Arab Workers' Congress.

645	**162**	10 dh. multicoloured	10	10
646		25 dh. multicoloured	15	15
647		35 dh. multicoloured	50	15

163 Teacher at Blackboard

164 Human Figures, Text and Globe

1975. Teachers' Day.

648	**163**	10 dh. multicoloured	10	10
649		25 dh. multicoloured	20	10

1975. World Health Day.

650	**164**	20 dh. multicoloured	15	10
651		25 dh. multicoloured	20	10

165 Readers and Bookshelves

166 Festival Emblem

1975. Arab Book Exhibition.

652	**165**	10 dh. multicoloured	10	10
653		20 dh. multicoloured	20	10
654		25 dh. multicoloured	50	15

1975. 2nd Arab Youth Festival.

655	**166**	20 dh. multicoloured	15	10
656		25 dh. multicoloured	20	15

1975. As Nos. 563/5 but without "L.A.R.".

657	**132**	5 dh. black, orange & blue	35	10
658		20 dh. black, yellow & bl	75	10
659		50 dh. black, green & blue	1·40	15

167 Games Emblem

168 Dove of Peace

1975. 7th Mediterranean Games, Algiers.

660	**167**	10 dh. multicoloured	10	10
661		25 dh. multicoloured	45	10
662		50 dh. multicoloured	85	20

1975. 6th Anniv of September 1st Revolution. Multicoloured.

663		25 dh. Type **168**	20	10
664		70 dh. Peace dove with different background	95	25

169 Khalil Basha Mosque

170 Arms and Crowds

1975. Mosques. Multicoloured.

666		5 dh. Type **169**	10	10
667		10 dh. Sidi Abdulla El Shaab	10	10
668		15 dh. Sidi Ali El Fergani	10	10
669		20 dh. Al Kharruba (vert)	15	10
670		25 dh. Katiktha (vert)	20	10
671		30 dh. Murad Agha (vert)	45	15
672		35 dh. Maulai Mohamed (vert)	55	15

1976. National People's Congress.

673	**170**	35 dh. multicoloured	20	10
674		40 dh. multicoloured	25	10

171 Dialogue Emblem

172 Woman blowing Bugle

1976. Islamic-Christian Dialogue Seminar.

675	**171**	40 dh. multicoloured	50	15
676		115 dh. multicoloured	1·40	60

1976. International Trade Fair, Tripoli. Mult.

677		10 dh. Type **172**	10	10
678		20 dh. Lancer	15	10
679		30 dh. Drummer	65	10
680		40 dh. Bagpiper	75	20
681		100 dh. Woman with jug on head	1·90	35

173 Early and Modern Telephones

1976. Telephone Centenary. Multicoloured.

682		40 dh. Type **173**	1·60	15
683		70 dh. Alexander Graham Bell	2·75	50

174 Mother and Child   175 Hands supporting Eye

1976. International Children's Day.

685	**174**	85 dh. multicoloured	75	30
686		110 dh. multicoloured	1·10	40

1976. World Health Day.

687	**175**	30 dh. multicoloured	20	10
688		35 dh. multicoloured	20	10
689		40 dh. multicoloured	50	15

176 Little Bittern

1976. Libyan Birds. Multicoloured.

690		5 dh. Type **176**	75	25
691		10 dh. Great grey shrike	1·40	40
692		15 dh. Fulvous babbler	2·00	50
693		20 dh. European bee eater (vert)	2·75	70
694		25 dh. Hoopoe	3·00	95

177 Barabekh Plant   178 Cycling

1976. Natural History Museum. Multicoloured.

695		10 dh. Type **177**	10	10
696		15 dh. Fin whale (horiz)	15	10
697		30 dh. Lizard (horiz)	20	10
698		40 dh. Elephant's skull (horiz)	70	15
699		70 dh. Bonnelli's eagle	3·00	70
700		115 dh. Barbary sheep	2·00	40

1976. Olympic Games, Montreal. Multicoloured.

701		15 dh. Type **178**	10	10
702		25 dh. Boxing	20	10
703		70 dh. Football	95	20

179 Global "Tree"   180 Agricultural and Industrial Symbols

1976. Non-Aligned Countries' Colombo Conference.

705	**179**	115 dh. multicoloured	95	35

1976. 7th Anniv of Revolution.

706	**180**	30 dh. multicoloured	15	10
707		40 dh. multicoloured	45	15
708		100 dh. multicoloured	90	55

181 Various Sports   182 Chessboard and Pieces

1976. 5th Arab Games, Damascus.

710	**181**	15 dh. multicoloured	10	10
711		30 dh. multicoloured	15	10
712		100 dh. multicoloured	1·00	55

1976. Arab Chess Olympiad, Tripoli.

714	**182**	15 dh. multicoloured	95	15
715		30 dh. multicoloured	1·60	60
716		100 dh. multicoloured	5·00	95

183 Ratima   186 Kaaba, Mecca

184 Emblem and Text

1976. Libyan Flora. Multicoloured.

717		15 dh. Type **183**	15	10
718		20 dh. "Sword of Crow"	15	10
719		35 dh. "Lasef"	50	10
720		40 dh. "Yadid"	80	15
721		70 dh. Esparto grass	1·90	25

1976. International Archives Council.

722	**184**	15 dh. multicoloured	10	10
723		35 dh. multicoloured	15	10
724		70 dh. multicoloured	55	20

1976. Pilgrimage to Mecca.

729	**186**	15 dh. multicoloured	10	10
730		30 dh. multicoloured	15	10
731		70 dh. multicoloured	30	20
732		100 dh. multicoloured	75	30

187   188 Basket

1977. Coil Stamps.

733	**187**	5 dh. multicoloured	10	10
734		20 dh. multicoloured	10	10
735		50 dh. multicoloured	55	40

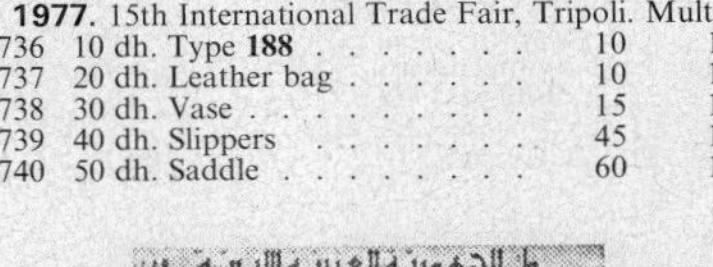
1977. 15th International Trade Fair, Tripoli. Mult.

736		10 dh. Type **188**	10	10
737		20 dh. Leather bag	10	10
738		30 dh. Vase	10	10
739		40 dh. Slippers	45	15
740		50 dh. Saddle	60	15

189 Girl with Flowers

1977. Children's Day. Multicoloured.

742		10 dh. Type **189**	10	10
743		30 dh. Clothes shop	15	10
744		40 dh. Orchard	20	15

190 Fighters and Machine-gun   191 Protected Child

1977. 9th Anniv of Battle of Al-Karamah.

745	**190**	15 dh. multicoloured	10	10
746		25 dh. multicoloured	15	10
747		70 dh. multicoloured	80	25

1977. World Health Day.

748	**191**	15 dh. multicoloured	10	10
749		30 dh. multicoloured	15	10

192 A.P.U. Emblem

1977. 25th Anniv of Arab Postal Union.

750	**192**	15 dh. multicoloured	10	10
751		20 dh. multicoloured	15	10
752		40 dh. multicoloured	20	15

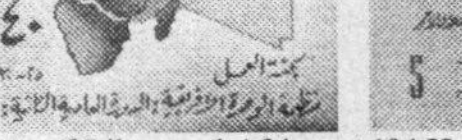
193 Maps of Libya and Africa   194 Heart on Map of Libya

1977. Organization of African Unity Conference, Tripoli.

753	**193**	40 dh. multicoloured	1·00	20
754		70 dh. multicoloured	1·50	30

1977. Red Crescent Commemoration.

755	**194**	5 dh. multicoloured	10	10
756		10 dh. multicoloured	15	10
757		30 dh. multicoloured	65	15

195 Messenger and Jet Fighter

1977. Communications Progress. Multicoloured.

758		20 dh. Type **195**	15	10
759		25 dh. Arab rider and Concorde	30	15
760		60 dh. Satellite and aerial	55	20
761		115 dh. Television relay via satellite	1·10	65
762		150 dh. Camel rider and Boeing 727 airliner loading	1·75	90
763		200 dh. "Apollo-Soyuz" link	2·25	1·10

196 Mosque   197 Archbishop Capucci

1977. Libyan Mosques.

765	**196**	40 dh. multicoloured	20	15
766	–	50 dh. multicoloured	50	15
767	–	70 dh. multicoloured	70	20
768	–	90 dh. multicoloured	85	30
769	–	100 dh. multicoloured	1·00	35
770	–	115 dh. multicoloured	1·25	75

DESIGNS: 50 dh. to 115 dh. Various mosques. The 50 dh. and 100 dh. are vertical.

1977. 3rd Anniv of Archbishop Capucci's Imprisonment.

771	**197**	30 dh. multicoloured	15	10
772		40 dh. multicoloured	20	15
773		115 dh. multicoloured	1·25	60

198 Clasped Hands and Emblems   199 Swimming

1977. 8th Anniv of Revolution.

774	**198**	15 dh. multicoloured	10	10
775		30 dh. multicoloured	15	10
776		85 dh. multicoloured	80	25

1977. Arab School Sports. Multicoloured.

778		5 dh. Type **199**	10	10
779		10 dh. Handball (horiz)	10	10
780		15 dh. Football	15	10
781		25 dh. Table tennis (horiz)	50	20
782		40 dh. Basketball	1·10	65

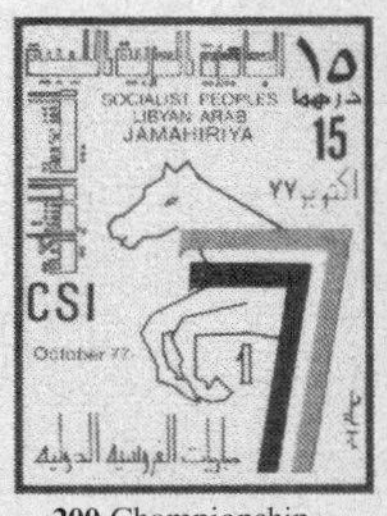

200 Championship Emblem   201 Dome of the Rock

1977. 1st International Turf Championships, Tripoli. Multicoloured.

783		5 dh. Horse jumping (facing left)	10	10
784		10 dh. Arab horseman	10	10
785		15 dh. Type **200**	15	10
786		45 dh. Horse jumping fence (facing right)	55	15
787		115 dh. Arab horseman racing	1·40	80

1977. Palestine Welfare.

789	**201**	5 dh. multicoloured	10	10
790		10 dh. multicoloured	10	10

202 Fort, and Hands writing Arabic Script in Book   203 Emblem

1977. "The Green Book". Multicoloured.

791		35 dh. Type **202**	15	10
792		40 dh. Type **202** (text in English)	20	15
793		115 dh. Dove with "Green Book" and map	1·25	70

1977. World Standards Day.

794	**203**	5 dh. multicoloured	10	10
795		15 dh. multicoloured	10	10
796		30 dh. multicoloured	15	10

204 Giraffe

1978. Rock Drawings from Wadi Mathendous. Multicoloured.

797		10 dh. Crocodiles (horiz)	10	10
798		15 dh. Elephant hunt (horiz)	10	10
799		20 dh. Type **204**	15	10
800		30 dh. Antelope (horiz)	45	15
801		40 dh. Elephant (horiz)	65	20

205 Silver Pendant

206 Compass and Lightning Flash

1978. 16th Tripoli International Fair.

No.	Type	Description	Unused	Used
802	205	5 dh. silver, black and red	10	10
803	–	10 dh. silver, black & violet	10	10
804	–	20 dh. silver, black & green	10	10
805	–	25 dh. silver, black & blue	15	10
806	–	115 dh. silver, black & blue	1·10	70

DESIGNS: 10 dh. Silver ornamental plate; 20 dh. Necklace with three pendants; 25 dh. Crescent-shaped silver brooch; 115 dh. Silver armband.

1978. Arab Cultural Education Organisation.

No.	Type	Description	Unused	Used
807	206	30 dh. multicoloured	20	15
808		115 dh. multicoloured	1·40	65

207 Dancing a Round

1978. Children's Day. Children's Paintings. Multicoloured.

No.	Description	Unused	Used
809	40 dh. Type 207	20	15
810	40 dh. Children with placards	20	15
811	40 dh. Shopping street	20	15
812	40 dh. Playground	20	15
813	40 dh. Wedding ceremony	20	15

208 Brickwork Clenched Fist

1978. The Arabs.

No.	Type	Description	Unused	Used
814	208	30 dh. multicoloured	20	15
815		115 dh. multicoloured	1·10	35

209 Blood Pressure Meter

211 Games Emblem

210 Microwave Antenna

1978. World Hypertension Month.

No.	Type	Description	Unused	Used
816	209	30 dh. multicoloured	15	15
817		115 dh. multicoloured	1·25	35

1978. World Telecommunications Day.

No.	Type	Description	Unused	Used
818	210	30 dh. multicoloured	15	15
819		115 dh. multicoloured	1·00	35

1978. 3rd African Games, Algiers.

No.	Type	Description	Unused	Used
820	211	15 dh. copper, violet & blk	10	10
821		30 dh. silver, lilac & black	15	10
822		115 dh. gold, purple & blk	1·10	35

212 Aerial View of Airport

1978. Inauguration of Tripoli International Airport. Multicoloured.

No.	Description	Unused	Used
823	40 dh. Type 212	30	10
824	115 dh. Terminal building	1·25	65

213 Ankara

1978. Turkish-Libyan Friendship.

No.	Type	Description	Unused	Used
825	213	30 dh. multicoloured	15	10
826		35 dh. multicoloured	15	10
827		115 dh. multicoloured	1·10	35

214 "Armed Forces"

215 Crater

1978. 9th Anniv of 1st September Revolution. Multicoloured.

No.	Description	Unused	Used
828	30 dh. Type 214	60	15
829	35 dh. Tower, Green Book and symbols of progress	15	10
830	115 dh. "Industry"	95	70

1978. 2nd Symposium on Geology of Libya. Multicoloured.

No.	Description	Unused	Used
832	30 dh. Type 215	15	10
833	40 dh. Oasis	20	15
834	115 dh. Crater (different)	1·10	60

216 "Green Book" and Different Races

1978. International Anti-Apartheid Year.

No.	Type	Description	Unused	Used
835	216	30 dh. multicoloured	15	10
836		40 dh. multicoloured	20	15
837		115 dh. multicoloured	85	35

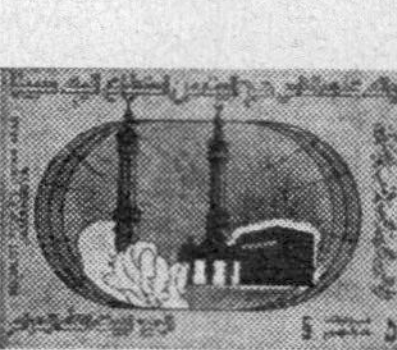

217 Pilgrims, Minarets and Kaaba

218 Clasped Hands and Globe

1978. Pilgrimage to Mecca.

No.	Type	Description	Unused	Used
838	217	5 dh. multicoloured	10	10
839		10 dh. multicoloured	10	10
840		15 dh. multicoloured	10	10
841		20 dh. multicoloured	15	10

1978. U.N. Conference for Technical Co-operation between Developing Countries.

No.	Type	Description	Unused	Used
842	218	30 dh. multicoloured	15	10
843		40 dh. multicoloured	20	15
844		115 dh. multicoloured	85	35

219 Workers, Rifles, Torch and Flag

220 Human Figure and Scales

1978. Arab Countries Summit Conference. Multicoloured.

No.	Description	Unused	Used
845	30 dh. Type 219	15	10
846	40 dh. Map of Middle East, eagle and crowd (horiz)	20	15
847	115 dh. As 40 dh.	85	35
848	145 dh. Type 219	1·00	45

1978. 30th Anniv of Declaration of Human Rights.

No.	Type	Description	Unused	Used
849	220	15 dh. multicoloured	10	10
850		30 dh. multicoloured	20	15
851		115 dh. multicoloured	50	35

221 Horse Racing and Fort

222 Lilienthal's Biplane Glider

1978. Libyan Study Centre.

No.	Type	Description	Unused	Used
852	221	20 dh. multicoloured	15	10
853		40 dh. multicoloured	20	15
854		115 dh. multicoloured	95	60

1978. 75th Anniv of First Powered Flight. Mult.

No.	Description	Unused	Used
855	20 dh. Type 222	10	10
856	25 dh. Lindbergh's "Spirit of St. Louis"	10	10
857	30 dh. Admiral Richard Byrd's Trimotor "Floyd Bennett"	1·25	25
858	50 dh. Bleriot 5190 Santos Dumont flying boat and airship "Graf Zeppelin"	1·50	35
859	115 dh. Wright brothers and Wright Type A	1·10	75

223 Libyans, Torch and Laurel Wreath

224 Mounted Dorcas Gazelle Head

1979.

No.	Type	Description	Unused	Used
861	223	5 dh. multicoloured	10	10
862		10 dh. multicoloured	10	10
863		15 dh. multicoloured	10	10
864		30 dh. multicoloured	20	10
865		50 dh. multicoloured	20	10
866		60 dh. multicoloured	25	15
867		70 dh. multicoloured	30	15
868		100 dh. multicoloured	75	25
869		115 dh. multicoloured	85	30
870		200 dh. multicoloured	1·10	45
871		250 dh. multicoloured	1·90	65
871		500 dh. multicoloured	3·50	65
872		1000 dh. multicoloured	6·75	3·50
872a		1500 dh. multicoloured	12·50	4·25
872b		2500 dh. multicoloured	23·00	7·50

Nos. 861/9 measure 18 x 23 mm and Nos. 870/2b 26 x 32 mm.

1979. Coil Stamps.

No.	Type	Description	Unused	Used
873	224	5 dh. multicoloured	15	10
874		20 dh. multicoloured	25	10
875		50 dh. multicoloured	80	25

225 Tortoise

1979. Libyan Animals. Multicoloured.

No.	Description	Unused	Used
876	5 dh. Type 225	10	10
877	10 dh. Addax (vert)	10	10
878	15 dh. Algerian hedgehog	20	10
879	20 dh. North African crested porcupine	20	10
880	30 dh. Dromedaries	30	15
881	35 dh. Wild cat (vert)	40	15
882	45 dh. Dorcas gazelle (vert)	95	25
883	115 dh. Cheetah	1·90	75

226 Carpet

1979. 17th Tripoli International Trade Fair.

No.	Type	Description	Unused	Used
884	226	10 dh. multicoloured	10	10
885	–	15 dh. multicoloured	10	10
886	–	30 dh. multicoloured	15	10
887	–	45 dh. multicoloured	15	10
888	–	115 dh. multicoloured	85	35

DESIGNS: 15 dh. to 115 dh. Different carpets

227 Aircraft and People

1979. International Year of the Child. Children's Paintings (1st series). Multicoloured.

No.	Description	Unused	Used
889	20 dh. Type 227	10	10
890	20 dh. Shepherd with flock	10	10
891	20 dh. Open air cafe	10	10
892	20 dh. Boat in storm	10	10
893	20 dh. Policeman on traffic duty	10	10

See also Nos. 975/9.

228 World Map, Koran and Symbols of Arab Achievements

229 Radar Tower and Map

1979. The Arabs.

No.	Type	Description	Unused	Used
894	228	45 dh. multicoloured	20	15
895		70 dh. multicoloured	55	20

1979. World Meteorological Day.

No.	Type	Description	Unused	Used
896	229	15 dh. multicoloured	10	10
897		30 dh. multicoloured	15	10
898		50 dh. multicoloured	20	15

230 Medical Care

1979. World Health Day.

No.	Type	Description	Unused	Used
899	230	40 dh. multicoloured	20	15

231 "Carpobrotus acinaciformis"

232 Farmer and Sheep

1979. Libyan Flowers. Multicoloured.

No.	Description	Unused	Used
900	10 dh. Type 231	10	10
901	15 dh. "Caralluma europaea"	10	10
902	20 dh. "Arum cirenaicum"	10	10
903	35 dh. "Lavatera arborea"	50	15
904	40 dh. "Capparis spinosa"	50	15
905	50 dh. "Ranunculus asiaticus"	60	15

1979. 10th Anniv of Revolution. Mult.

No.	Description	Unused	Used
906	15 dh. Type 232	10	10
907	15 dh. Crowd with Green Book	10	10
908	15 dh. Oil field	10	10
909	15 dh. Refinery	10	10
910	30 dh. Dish aerial	15	10
911	30 dh. Hospital	15	10
912	30 dh. Doctor examining patient	15	10
913	30 dh. Surgeon	15	10
914	40 dh. Street, Tripoli	20	15
915	40 dh. Steel mill	20	15
916	40 dh. Tanks	20	15
917	40 dh. Tuareg horsemen	20	15
918	70 dh. Revolutionaries and Green Book	70	20
919	70 dh. Crowd within map of Libya	70	20
920	70 dh. Mullah	70	20
921	70 dh. Student	70	20

233 Volleyball 234 Emblem

1979. "Universiada '79" World University Games, Mexico City. Multicoloured.

923 45 dh. Type **233** 20 15
924 115 dh. Football . . . . . . 1·10 30

1979. 3rd World Telecommunications Exhibition, Geneva.

925 **234** 45 dh. multicoloured . . . 20 15
926 115 dh. multicoloured . . . 1·25 30

235 Seminar Emblem and Crowd

1979. International Seminar on the "Green Book". Multicoloured.

927 10 dh. Type **235** 10 10
928 35 dh. Seminar in progress . . 45 15
929 100 dh. Colonel Gaddafi with "Green Book" . . . . . . 1·00 30

No. 928 is horizontal, 70 x 43 mm.

236 Horsemen in Town

1979. Evacuation of Foreign Forces. Multicoloured.

931 30 dh. Type **236** 15 10
932 40 dh. Tuareg horsemen . . . 20 15

237 Football Match

1979. Mediterranean Games, Split.

934 **237** 15 dh. multicoloured . . . 10 10
935 30 dh. multicoloured . . . 50 10
936 70 dh. multicoloured . . . 1·25 20

238 Cyclist and Emblem

1979. Junior Cycling Championships, Tripoli. Multicoloured.

937 15 dh. Type **238** 10 10
938 30 dh. Cyclists and emblem . . 15 10

239 Horse-jumping

1979. Pre-Olympics. Multicoloured.

939 45 dh. Type **239** 20 15
940 60 dh. Javelin 55 15
941 115 dh. Hurdles . . . . 1·10 55
942 160 dh. Football . . . . . . 1·40 65

Nos. 939/42 exist from sheets on which an overall Moscow Olympics emblem in silver was superimposed on the stamps.

240 Figure clothed in Palestinian Flag 241 Ploughing

1979. Solidarity with Palestinian People.

944 **240** 30 dh. multicoloured . . . 15 10
945 115 dh. multicoloured . . . 1·10 30

1980. World Olive Oil Year.

946 **241** 15 dh. multicoloured . . . 10 10
947 30 dh. multicoloured . . . 15 10
948 45 dh. multicoloured . . . 20 15

242 Hockey (left) 243 Pipes

1980. National Sports. Multicoloured.

949 10 dh. Type **242** 10 10
950 10 dh. Hockey (right) 10 10
951 10 dh. Leap-frog (left) 10 10
952 10 dh. Leap-frog (right) 10 10
953 15 dh. Long jump (left) 10 10
954 15 dh. Long jump (right) . . . 10 10
955 15 dh. Ball catching (left) . . . 10 10
956 15 dh. Ball catching (right) . . 10 10
957 20 dh. Wrestling (left) 10 10
958 20 dh. Wrestling (right) 10 10
959 20 dh. Stone throwing (left) . . 10 10
960 20 dh. Stone throwing (right) 10 10
961 30 dh. Tug-of-war (left) 15 10
962 30 dh. Tug-of-war (right) . . . 15 10
963 30 dh. Jumping (left) 15 10
964 30 dh. Jumping (right) 15 10
965 45 dh. Horsemen (left) 45 15
966 45 dh. Horsemen (right) . . . 45 15
967 45 dh. Horsemen with whips (left) 45 15
968 45 dh. Horsemen with whips (right) 45 15

Nos. 949/68 were issued together, divided into se-tenant blocks of four within the sheet, each horizontal pair forming a composite design.

1980. 18th Tripoli International Fair. Multicoloured.

969 5 dh. Drum (horiz) 10 10
970 10 dh. Drum (different) (horiz) 10 10
971 15 dh. Type **243** 10 10
972 20 dh. Bagpipes (horiz) 10 10
973 25 dh. Stringed instrument and bow (horiz) 15 10

1980. International Year of the Child (1979) (2nd issue). As T **227**. Multicoloured.

975 20 dh. "Horse Riding" 10 10
976 20 dh. "Beach scene" 10 10
977 20 dh. "Fish" 10 10
978 20 dh. "Birthday party" 10 10
979 20 dh. "Sheep Festival" 10 10

244 Mosque and Kaaba

1980. 400th Anniv of Hejira.

980 **244** 50 dh. multicoloured . . . 25 15
981 115 dh. multicoloured . . . 1·10 55

245 Surgical Operation and Hospital

1980. World Health Day.

982 **245** 20 dh. multicoloured . . . 10 10
983 50 dh. multicoloured . . . 50 15

246 Battle of Shoghab "Shahat", 1913

1980. Battles (1st series). Multicoloured.

984 20 dh. Gardabia, 1915 . . . . 20 15
986 20 dh. Type **246** 10 10
988 20 dh. Fundugh al-Shibani "Garian" 10 10
990 20 dh. Yefren 10 10
992 20 dh. Ghira "Brak" 20 15
994 20 dh. El Hani (Shiat) 35 15
996 20 dh. Sebah 20 15
998 20 dh. Sirt 10 10
985 35 dh. Gardabia 10 10
987 35 dh. Shoghab "Shahat" . . . 20 15
989 35 dh. Fundagh al-Shibani "Garian" 20 15
991 35 dh. Yefren 20 15
993 35 dh. Ghira "Brak" 20 15
995 35 dh. El Hani (Shiat) 60 25
997 35 dh. Sebah 20 15
999 35 dh. Sirt 10 10

The two values commemorating each battle were issued in se-tenant pairs, each pair forming a composite design.

See also Nos. 1027/50, 1140/63 and 1257/80.

247 Flame 248 Ghadames

1980. Sheikh Zarruq Festival.

1000 **247** 40 dh. multicoloured . . . 20 15
1001 115 dh. multicoloured . . 1·00 65

1980. Arabian Towns Organization. Mult.

1003 15 dh. Type **248** 10 10
1004 30 dh. Derna 15 10
1005 50 dh. Ahmad Pasha Mosque, Tripoli 50 15

249 Guides on Hike

1980. 14th Pan-Arab Scout Jamboree. Multicoloured.

1006 15 dh. Type **249** 10 10
1007 30 dh. Guides cooking 15 10
1008 50 dh. Cub Scouts cooking . . 25 15
1009 115 dh. Scouts map-reading 1·10 60

250 Oil Refinery

1980. 11th Anniv of Revolution. Multicoloured.

1011 5 dh. Type **250** 10 10
1012 10 dh. Recreation and youth 10 10
1013 15 dh. Agriculture 10 10
1014 25 dh. Boeing 727-200 airplane and liner 60 15
1015 40 dh. Education 20 15
1016 115 dh. Housing 95 30

251 Camels, Map of Libya and Conference Emblem

1980. World Tourism Conference, Manila. Mult.

1018 45 dh. Type **251** 20 15
1019 115 dh. Emblem, map and camel riders 95 30

252 Figures supporting O.P.E.C. Emblem 253a Map of Libya and Science Symbols

253 Death of Omar el Mukhtar

1980. 20th Anniv of Organization of Petroleum Exporting Countries. Multicoloured.

1020 45 dh. O.P.E.C. emblem and globe 20 15
1021 115 dh. Type **252** 95 30

1980. 49th Death Anniv of Omar el Mukhtar (patriot).

1022 **253** 20 dh. multicoloured . . . 10 10
1023 35 dh. multicoloured . . . 20 15

1980. Birth Millenary of Avicenna (philosopher) and School Scientific Exhibition. Multicoloured.

1025 45 dh. Type **253a** 20 15
1026 115 d. Avicenna and Exhibition Emblem . . . . 1·10 30

1981. Battles (2nd series). As T **246**. Mult.

1027 20 dh. Zuara 10 10
1029 20 dh. Tawargha 10 10
1031 20 dh. Dernah 10 10
1033 20 dh. Bir Tagreft 10 10
1035 20 dh. Funduk El Jamel "Misurata" 10 10
1037 20 dh. Sidi El Khemri "Gusbat" 10 10
1039 20 dh. El Khoms 10 10
1041 20 dh. Roghdalin "Menshia" 10 10
1043 20 dh. Ain Zara "Tripoli" . . 10 10
1045 20 dh. Rughbat el Naga "Benina" 10 10
1047 20 dh. Tobruk 10 10
1049 20 dh. Ikshadia "Werfella" 10 10
1028 35 dh. Zuara 15 15
1030 35 dh. Tawargha 15 15
1032 35 dh. Dernah 15 15
1034 35 dh. Bir Tagreft 15 15
1036 35 dh. Funduk El Jamel "Misurata" 15 15
1038 35 dh. Sidi El Khemri "Gusbat" 15 15
1040 35 dh. El khoms 15 15
1042 35 dh. Roghdalin "Menshia" 15 15
1044 35 dh. Ain Zara "Tripoli" . . 15 15
1046 35 dh. Rughbat el Naga "Benina" 15 15
1048 35 dh. Tobruk 15 15
1050 35 dh. Ikshadia "Werfella" 15 15

The two values commemorating each battle were issued in se-tenant pairs, each pair forming a composite design.

254 Tent, Trees and Sun

1981. Children's Day. Children's Paintings. Multicoloured.

1051 20 dh. Type **254** 10 10
1052 20 dh. Women 10 10
1053 20 dh. Picnic 10 10
1054 20 dh. Aeroplane and playing children 10 10
1055 20 dh. Mosque and man with camel 10 10

255 Central Bank

257 Crowd and "Green Book" Stamp of 1977

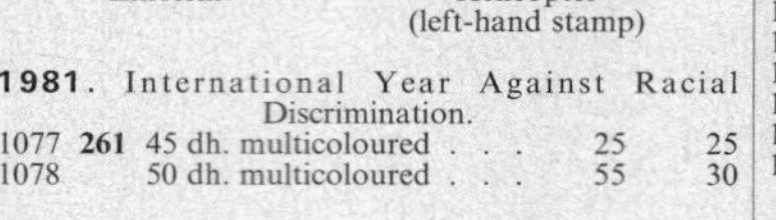
256 Pots

1981. 25th Anniv of Central Bank of Libya.
1056 **255** 45 dh. multicoloured . . . 15 15
1057 115 dh. multicoloured . . 95 35

1981. Tripoli International Fair. Multicoloured.
1059 5 dh. Type **256** 10 10
1060 10 dh. Silver coffee pot (vert) 10 10
1061 15 dh. Long-necked vase (vert) 10 10
1062 45 dh. Round-bellied vase . . 45 15
1063 115 dh. Jug . . . . 1·10 35

1981. People's Authority Declaration.
1064 **257** 50 dh. multicoloured . . . 15 15
1065 115 dh. multicoloured . . 95 35

258 Tajoura Hospital, Medical Complex, Patients receiving Treatment and W.H.O. Emblem

1981. World Health Day.
1066 **258** 45 dh. multicoloured . . . 15 15
1067 115 dh. multicoloured . . 95 35

259 Eye and Man on Crutches

1981. International Year of Disabled People.
1068 **259** 20 dh. green, blue & blk . 10 10
1069 – 45 dh. green, black & bl . 15 15
1070 – 115 dh. blue and green . . 1·00 35
DESIGNS: 45 dh. Globe and I.Y.D.P. emblem; 115 dh. Hands holding shield with I.Y.D.P. emblem, eye and man on crutch.

260 Horse

1981. Libyan Mosaics. Multicoloured.
1071 10 dh. Type **260** 10 10
1072 20 dh. Ship 10 10
1073 30 dh. Birds, fish and flowers 10 10
1074 40 dh. Leopard 40 15
1075 50 dh. Man playing musical instrument 50 15
1076 115 dh. Fishes . . . . 1·10 35

INDEX
Countries can be quickly located by referring to the index at the end of this volume.

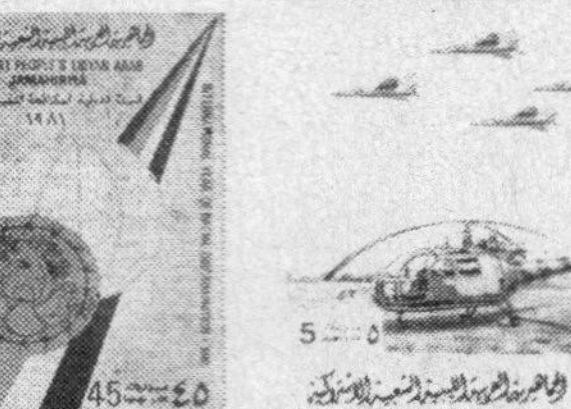
261 Racial Discrimination Emblem

262 Jet Fighters and Sud Aviation Alouette III Helicopter (left-hand stamp)

1981. International Year Against Racial Discrimination.
1077 **261** 45 dh. multicoloured . . . 25 25
1078 50 dh. multicoloured . . . 55 30

1981. 12th Anniv of Revolution.
1079 **262** 5 dh. blue and light blue 15 10
1080 – 5 dh. blue and light blue 15 10
1081 – 5 dh. blue and light blue 10 10
1082 – 5 dh. blue and light blue 10 10
1083 – 10 dh. black and blue . . 10 10
1084 – 10 dh. black and blue . . 10 10
1085 – 10 dh. black and blue . . 10 10
1086 – 10 dh. black and blue . . 10 10
1087 – 15 dh. brown & lt brown 10 10
1088 – 15 dh. brown & lt brown 10 10
1089 – 15 dh. brown & lt brown 10 10
1090 – 15 dh. brown & lt brown 10 10
1091 – 20 dh. blue and green . . 15 15
1092 – 20 dh. blue and green . . 15 15
1093 – 20 dh. blue and green . . 15 15
1094 – 20 dh. blue and green . . 15 15
1095 – 25 dh. brown and yellow 15 15
1096 – 25 dh. brown and yellow 15 15
1097 – 25 dh. brown and yellow 15 15
1098 – 25 dh. brown and yellow 15 15
DESIGNS—VERT: No. 1080, Jet fighter (right-hand stamp); Nos. 1081/2, Parachutists; Nos. 1083/4, Tank parade; Nos. 1085/6, Marching frogmen; Nos. 1087/8, Anti-aircraft rocket trucks; Nos. 1089/90, Missile trucks. HORIZ: Nos. 1091/2, Marching sailors; Nos. 1093/4, Jeeps and anti-aircraft rocket trucks; Nos. 1095/6, Armoured vehicles and landrovers; Nos. 1097/8, Tank parade.
Each pair forms a horizontal composite design, the first number being the left-hand stamp in each instance.

263 Wheat and Plough

1981. World Food Day.
1100 **263** 45 dh. multicoloured . . . 25 25
1101 200 dh. multicoloured . . 1·75 95

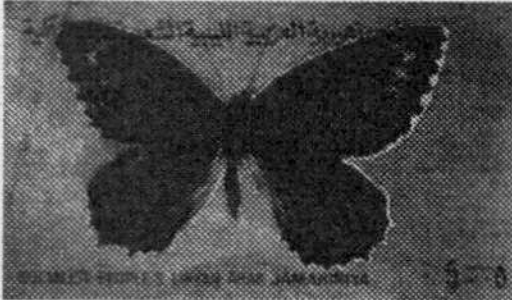
264 "Pseudotergumia fidia"

1981. Butterflies. Multicoloured.
1102 5 dh. Type **264** 15 10
1103 5 dh. "Chazara prieuri" (sun in background) 15 10
1104 5 dh. "Polygonia c-album" (trees in background) . . . 15 10
1105 5 dh. "Colias crocea" (mosque in background) 15 10
1106 10 dh. "Anthocharis bellia" (face value bottom right) 15 10
1107 10 dh. "Pandoriana pandora" (face value bottom left) . . 15 10
1108 10 dh. "Melanargia ines" (face value top right) . . . 15 10
1109 10 dh. "Charaxes jasius" (face value top left) 15 10
1110 15 dh. "Nymphales antiopa" (face value bottom right) 30 30
1111 15 dh. "Eurodryas desfontainii" (face value bottom left) . . 30 30
1112 15 dh. "Iphiclides podalirius" (face value top right) . . . 30 30
1113 15 dh. "Glaucopsyche melanops" (face value top left) 30 30
1114 25 dh. "Spialia sertorius" (face value bottom right) . . . 50 45
1115 25 dh. "Pieris brassicae" (face value bottom left) 50 45
1116 25 dh. "Lysandra albicans" (face value top right) . . . 50 45
1117 25 dh. "Celastrina argiolus" (face value top left) . . . 50 45
The four designs of each value were issued together in small sheets of four, showing composite background designs.

265 Grapes

266 I.Y.D.P. Emblem and Globe

1981. Fruit. Multicoloured.
1119 5 dh. Type **265** 10 10
1120 10 dh. Dates 10 10
1121 15 dh. Lemons 10 10
1122 20 dh. Oranges 15 15
1123 35 dh. Barbary figs 20 20
1124 55 dh. Pomegranate 65 30

1981. International Year of Disabled Persons.
1125 **266** 45 dh. multicoloured . . . 25 25
1126 115 dh. multicoloured . . 90 55

267 Animals (looking right)

1982. Libyan Mosaics. Multicoloured.
1127 45 dh. Type **267** 50 25
1128 45 dh. Orpheus 50 25
1129 45 dh. Animals (looking left) 50 25
1130 45 dh. Fishes 50 25
1131 45 dh. Fishermen 50 25
1132 45 dh. Fishes and ducks . . . 50 25
1133 45 dh. Farm 50 25
1134 45 dh. Birds and fruit 50 25
1135 45 dh. Milking 50 25

268 Koran Texts leading to Ka'aba

269 Grinding Flour

1982. Third Koran Reading Contest. Multicoloured.
1136 10 dh. Type **268** 10 10
1137 35 dh. Koran and formation of the World 20 20
1138 115 dh. Reading the Koran 95 55

1982. Battles (3rd series). As T **246**. Multicoloured.
1140 20 dh. Hun "Gioffra" 15 15
1142 20 dh. Gedabia 15 15
1144 20 dh. El Asaba "Gianduba" 15 15
1146 20 dh. El Habela 15 15
1148 20 dh. Suk El Ahad "Tarhuna" 15 15
1150 20 dh. El Tangi 15 15
1152 20 dh. Sokna 15 15
1154 20 dh. Wadi Smalus "Jabel El Akdar" 15 15
1156 20 dh. Sidi Abuagela "Agelat" 15 15
1158 20 dh. Sidi Surur "Zeliten" 15 15
1160 20 dh. Kuefia 15 15
1162 20 dh. Abunjeim 15 15
1141 35 dh. Hun "Gioffra" 20 20
1143 35 dh. Gedabia 20 20
1145 35 dh. El Asaba "Gianduba" 20 20
1147 35 dh. El Habela 20 20
1149 35 dh. Suk El Ahad "Tarhuna" 20 20
1151 35 dh. El Tangi 20 20
1153 35 dh. Sokna 20 20
1155 35 dh. Wadi Smalus "Jabel El Akdar" 20 20
1157 35 dh. Sidi Abuagela "Agelat" 20 20
1159 35 dh. Sidi Surur "Zeliten" 20 20
1161 35 dh. Kuefia 20 20
1163 35 dh. Abunjeim 20 20
The two values commemorating each battle were issued in se-tenant pairs, each pair forming a composite design.

1982. Tripoli International Fair. Multicoloured.
1164 5 dh. Type **269** 10 10
1165 10 dh. Ploughing 10 10
1166 25 dh. Stacking hay 15 15
1167 35 dh. Weaving 20 20
1168 45 dh. Cooking 50 25
1169 100 dh. Harvesting 95 50

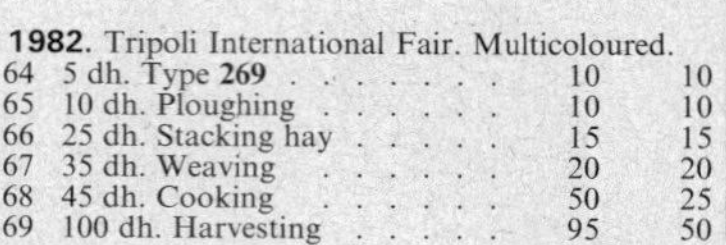

270 "ALFATAH" forming Farm Vehicle

1982. People's Authority Declaration. Multicoloured.
1170 100 dh. Type **270** 75 50
1171 200 dh. Colonel Gaddafi, old man, "Green Book" and guns 1·75 95
1172 300 dh. Rejoicing crowd . . . 2·50 1·40

271 Scout flying Model Airship

272 Map of Africa and A.F.C. Emblem

1982. 75th Anniv of Boy Scout Movement. Mult.
1173 100 dh. Type **271** 75 50
1174 200 dh. Scouts helping injured dog . . . . 1·75 95
1175 300 dh. Scout reading to old man . . . . 1·75 1·40
1176 400 dh. Scout with model rocket 3·75 2·25

1982. African Football Cup Competition.
1178 **272** 100 dh. multicoloured . . 95 50
1179 200 dh. multicoloured . . 1·90 95

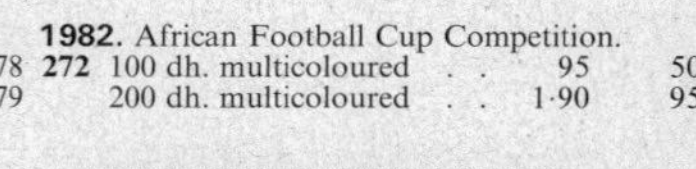

273 Footballer

1982. World Cup Football Championship, Spain. Multicoloured.
1180 45 dh. Type **273** 25 25
1181 100 dh. Footballer (different) 75 50
1182 200 dh. As No. 1173 . . . . 1·60 95
1183 300 dh. Footballer and goalkeeper . . . . 2·25 1·40

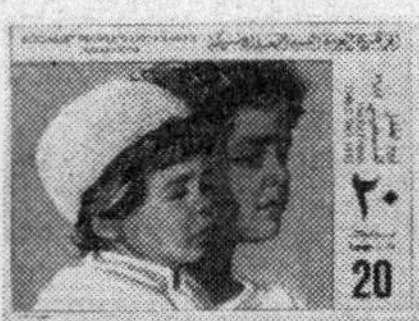
274 Palestinian Children

1982. Palestinian Children's Day. Multicoloured.
1185 20 dh. Type **274** 15 15
1186 20 dh. Girl with dish 15 15
1187 20 dh. Child with turban . . . 15 15
1188 20 dh. Young child 15 15
1189 20 dh. Young boy 15 15

275 Lanner Falcon

277 Map of Libya and A.P.U. Emblem

276 Nurses' Class, Operating Theatre and Doctor examining Child

1982. Birds. Multicoloured.
1190 15 dh. Type **275** 55 35
1191 15 dh. Common swift 55 35
1192 15 dh. Peregrine falcon . . . 55 35
1193 15 dh. Greater flamingo . . . 55 35
1194 25 dh. Whitethroat 90 50
1195 25 dh. Turtle dove 90 50
1196 25 dh. Black-bellied sandgrouse 90 50
1197 25 dh. Egyptian vulture . . . 90 50
1198 45 dh. Golden oriole . . . . 1·50 85
1199 45 dh. European bee eater . . 1·50 85
1200 45 dh. Common kingfisher . . 1·50 85
1201 45 dh. Common roller . . . . 1·50 85
1202 95 dh. Barbary partridge . . . 3·00 1·60
1203 95 dh. Barn owl . . . . . . 3·00 1·60
1204 95 dh. Cream-coloured courser 3·00 1·60
1205 95 dh. Hoopoe . . . . 3·00 1·60

The four designs of each value were printed together in se-tenant blocks of four, forming a composite design.

1982. Teaching Hospitals.
1207 **276** 95 dh. multicoloured . . . 85 50
1208 100 dh. multicoloured . . . 85 50
1209 205 dh. multicoloured . . 2·00 1·10

1982. 30th Anniv of Arab Postal Union.
1210 **277** 100 dh. multicoloured . . 95 50
1211 200 dh. multicoloured . . 1·90 95

278 19th-century Chinese King and Diagram of Fischer v Spassky, 1972

1982. World Chess Championship, Moscow. Mult.
1212 100 dh. Type **278** . . . . . . 1·25 50
1213 100 dh. African king and diagram of Karpov v Korchnoi, 1978 . . . . . 1·25 50
1214 100 dh. Modern bishop and diagram of Smyslov v Karpov, 1971 . . . . . . 1·25 50
1215 100 dh. 19th-century European rook and diagram of Tal v Vadasz, 1977 . . . . . . 1·25 50

Nos. 1212/15 were printed together, se-tenant, forming a composite design.

279 Hexagonal Pattern

1982. World Telecommunications Day.
1217 **279** 100 dh. multicoloured . . 75 50
1218 200 dh. multicoloured . . 1·50 95

280 Map of Libya and "Green Book"

1982. 51st Anniv of International Philatelic Federation (F.I.P.).
1219 **280** 200 dh. multicoloured . . . 1·75 95

281 Family & Flag

283 Palm Tree and Red Crescent

282 Pres. Gaddafi and Jet Aircraft

1982. Organization of African Unity Summit. Multicoloured.
1221 50 dh. Type **281** 30 30
1222 100 dh. Map, dove and symbols of industry and agriculture 75 50
1223 200 dh. Pres. Gaddafi and crowd with "Green Book" (65 x 36 mm.) . . . . 1·90 95

1982. 13th Anniv of Revolution. Multicoloured.
1225 15 dh. Type **282** 15 10
1226 20 dh. Gaddafi, soldiers and rockets 15 10
1227 30 dh. Gaddafi, sailors and naval vessels 50 25
1228 45 dh. Gaddafi, soldiers and tanks 25 25
1229 70 dh. Gaddafi, and armed forces 60 35
1230 100 dh. Gaddafi and women soldiers 90 50

1982. 25th Anniv of Libyan Red Crescent. Multicoloured.
1232 100 dh. Type **283** 95 50
1233 200 dh. "25" within crescents 1·90 95

284 Globe, Dove and Rifle

286 Philadelphus

285 Gaddafi, Crowd, "Green Book" and Emblems

1982. Solidarity with Palestinian People.
1234 **284** 100 dh. black, mauve and green 95 40
1235 200 dh. black, blue and green . . . . 1·90 80

1982. Al Fateh University Symposium on the "Green Book". Multicoloured.
1236 100 dh. Type **285** 95 45
1237 200 dh. Gaddafi, "Green Book", map and emblems . . . . 1·90 95

1983. Flowers. Multicoloured.
1238 25 dh. Type **286** 15 10
1239 25 dh. Hypericum 15 10
1240 25 dh. Antirrhinum 15 10
1241 25 dh. Lily 15 10
1242 25 dh. Capparis 15 10
1243 25 dh. Tropaeolum 15 10
1244 25 dh. Roses 15 10
1245 25 dh. Chrysanthemum . . . 15 10
1246 25 dh. "Nigella damascena" 15 10
1247 25 dh. "Guilladia lanceolata" 15 10
1248 25 dh. Dahlia 15 10
1249 25 dh. "Dianthus caryophyllus" 15 10
1250 25 dh. "Notobasis syriaca" 15 10
1251 25 dh. "Nerium oleander" . . 15 10
1252 25 dh. "Iris histroides" . . . 15 10
1253 25 dh. "Scolymus hispanicus" 15 10

287 Customs Council Building, Brussels, and Warrior on Horseback

288 Camel

1983. 30th Anniv of Customs Co-operation Council. Multicoloured.
1254 25 dh. Type **287** 15 10
1255 50 dh. Customs building . . . 25 20
1256 100 dh. Customs building and warrior with sword 50 45

1983. Battles (4th series). As T **246**. (a) Battle of Ghaser Ahmed.
1257 50 dh. multicoloured 25 20
1258 50 dh. multicoloured 25 20

(b) Battle of Sidi Abuarghub.
1259 50 dh. multicoloured 25 20
1260 50 dh. multicoloured 25 20

(c) Battle of Ghar Yunes.
1261 50 dh. multicoloured 25 20
1262 50 dh. multicoloured 25 20

(d) Battle of Bir Otman.
1263 50 dh. multicoloured 25 20
1264 50 dh. multicoloured 25 20

(e) Battle of Sidi Sajeh.
1265 50 dh. multicoloured 25 20
1266 50 dh. multicoloured 25 20

(f) Battle of Ras el-Hamam.
1267 50 dh. multicoloured 25 20
1268 50 dh. multicoloured 25 20

(g) Battle of Zawiet Ishghefa.
1269 50 dh. multicoloured 25 20
1270 50 dh. multicoloured 25 20

(h) Battle of Wadi Essania.
1271 50 dh. multicoloured 25 20
1272 50 dh. multicoloured 25 20

(i) Battle of El-Meshiashta.
1273 50 dh. multicoloured 25 20
1274 50 dh. multicoloured 25 20

(j) Battle of Gharara.
1275 50 dh. multicoloured 25 20
1276 50 dh. multicoloured 25 20

(k) Battle of Abughelan.
1277 50 dh. multicoloured 20 20
1278 50 dh. multicoloured 20 20

(l) Battle of Mahruka.
1279 50 dh. multicoloured 20 20
1280 50 dh. multicoloured 20 20

The two values for each battle were printed together in se-tenant pairs, forming composite designs.

1983. Farm Animals. Multicoloured.
1281 25 dh. Type **288** 15 10
1282 25 dh. Cow 15 10
1283 25 dh. Horse 15 10
1284 25 dh. Bull 15 10
1285 25 dh. Goat 15 10
1286 25 dh. Sheep dog 15 10
1287 25 dh. Ewe 15 10
1288 25 dh. Ram 15 10
1289 25 dh. Greylag goose 15 10
1290 25 dh. Helmet guineafowl . . 15 10
1291 25 dh. Rabbit 15 10
1292 25 dh. Wood pigeon 15 10
1293 25 dh. Common turkey . . . 15 10
1294 25 dh. Cockerel 15 10
1295 25 dh. Hen 15 10
1296 25 dh. Goose 15 10

289 Musician with Twin-horned Pipe

1983. Tripoli International Fair. Multicoloured.
1297 40 dh. Type **289** 20 15
1298 45 dh. Bagpipes (horiz) . . . 25 20
1299 50 dh. Horn 25 20
1300 55 dh. Flute (horiz) 30 25
1301 75 dh. Pipe 65 35
1302 100 dh. Man and woman at well 90 45

290 Phoenician Galley

1983. 25th Anniv of International Maritime Organization. Multicoloured.
1303 100 dh. Type **290** . . . . . . 1·25 55
1304 100 dh. Ancient Greek galley 1·25 55
1305 100 dh. Ancient Egyptian ship 1·25 55
1306 100 dh. Roman sailing ship 1·25 55
1307 100 dh. Viking longship . . . 1·25 55
1308 100 dh. Libyan xebec . . . . 1·25 55

291 Motorist

1983. Children's Day. Multicoloured.
1309 20 dh. Type **291** 10 10
1310 20 dh. Tractor and trailer . . 10 10
1311 20 dh. Child with dove and globe 10 10
1312 20 dh. Scout camp 10 10
1313 20 dh. Dinosaur 10 10

292 Pres. Gaddafi with Children

1983. World Health Day. Multicoloured.
1314 25 dh. Type **292** 15 10
1315 50 dh. Gaddafi and old man in wheelchair 25 20
1316 100 dh. Gaddafi visiting sick girl (horiz) 80 45

293 Gaddafi, Map and "Green Book"

294 Economic Emblems on Map of Africa

1983. 1st World "Green Book" Symposium. Multicoloured.
1317 50 dh. Type **293** 25 20
1318 70 dh. Syposium in session and emblem (56 x 37 mm) . . . 60 30
1319 80 dh. Gaddafi, "Green Book", emblem and "Jamahiriya" 65 35

1983. 25th Anniv of African Economic Committee.
1321 **294** 50 dh. multicoloured . . . 25 20
1322 100 dh. multicoloured . . 90 45
1323 250 dh. multicoloured . . 1·90 1·10

296 Cuckoo Wrasse ("Labrus bimaculatus")

1983. Fishes. Multicoloured.
1325 25 dh. Type **296** 30 15
1326 25 dh. Streaked gurnard ("Trigoporus lastoviza") . . 30 15
1327 25 dh. Peacock wrasse ("Thalassoma pavo") . . . 30 15
1328 25 dh. Mediterranean cardinal-fish ("Apogon imberbis") . . 30 15
1329 25 dh. Atlantic mackerel ("Scomber scombrus") . . 30 15
1330 25 dh. Black seabream ("Spondyliosoma cantharus") 30 15
1331 25 dh. Greater weaver ("Trachinus draco") . . . 30 15
1332 25 dh. Peacock blenny ("Blennius pavo") 30 15
1333 25 dh. Lesser red scorpionfish ("Scorpaena notata") . . . 30 15
1334 25 dh. Painted comber ("Serranus scriba") . . . 30 15
1335 25 dh. Angler ("Lophius piscatorius") 30 15
1336 25 dh. Stargazer ("Uranoscopus scaber") 30 15
1337 25 dh. Frigate mackerel ("Auxis thazard") 30 15
1338 25 dh. John dory ("Zeus faber") 30 15
1339 25 dh. Flying gurnard ("Dactylopterus volitans") . 30 15
1340 25 dh. Corb ("Umbrina cirrosa") 30 15

297 "Still-life" (Gauguin)

1983. Paintings. Multicoloured.
1341 50 dh. Type **297** 25 20
1342 50 dh. Abstract 25 20
1343 50 dh. "The Conquest of Tunis by Charles V" (Rubens) . . 25 20
1344 50 dh. "Arab Band in Horse-drawn Carriage" 25 20
1345 50 dh. "Apotheosis of Gaddafi" (vert) 25 20
1346 50 dh. Horses (detail of Raphael's "The Triumph of David over the Assyrians") (vert) 25 20

1347 50 dh. "Workers" (vert) . . . 25 20
1348 50 dh. "Sunflowers" (Van Gogh) (vert) 25 20

298 Basketball

1983. Olympic Games, Los Angeles. Mult.
1349 10 dh. Type **298** 10 10
1350 15 dh. High jumping 10 10
1351 25 dh. Running 15 10
1352 50 dh. Gymnastics 25 20
1353 100 dh. Windsurfing 80 45
1354 200 dh. Shot-putting . . . . 1·50 95

299 I.T.U. Building, Antenna and W.C.Y. Emblem

1983. World Communications Year.
1356 **299** 10 dh. multicoloured . . . 10 10
1357 50 dh. multicoloured . . 25 20
1358 100 dh. multicoloured . . 75 45

300 "The House is to be served by its Residents"

1983. Extracts from the Green Book. Mult.
1359 10 dh. Type **300** 10 10
1360 15 dh. "Power, wealth and arms are in the hands of the people" 10 10
1361 20 dh. "Masters in their own castles" (vert) 10 10
1362 35 dh. "No democracy without popular congresses" 20 15
1363 100 dh. "The authority of the people" (vert) 50 45
1364 140 dh. "The Green Book is the guide of humanity for final release" . . . . 1·10 70

301 Handball

1983. 2nd African Youth Festival. Multicoloured.
1366 100 dh. Type **301** 85 45
1367 100 dh. Basketball 85 45
1368 100 dh. High jumping 85 45
1369 100 dh. Running 85 45
1370 100 dh. Football 85 45

302 Marching Soldiers

1983. 14th Anniv of September Revolution. Mult.
1371 65 dh. Type **302** 35 30
1372 75 dh. Weapons and communications training . . 40 35
1373 90 dh. Women with machine-guns and bazookas 70 40
1374 100 dh. Machine-gun training 75 45
1375 150 dh. Bazooka training . . 1·10 70
1376 250 dh. Rifle training . . . . 2·00 1·10

303 Saluting Scouts

1983. Scout Jamborees. Multicoloured.
1378 50 dh. Type **303** 25 20
1379 100 dh. Scouts around camp fire 90 45
EVENTS. 50 dh. Second Islamic Scout Jamboree; 100 dh. 15th Pan Arab Scout Jamboree.

304 Traffic Cadets **305** Saadun

1983. Traffic Day. Multicoloured.
1381 30 dh. Type **304** 40 15
1382 70 dh. Traffic policeman . . . 70 30
1383 200 dh. Police motorcyclists 1·90 1·25

1983. 90th Birth Anniv of Saadun (patriot soldier).
1384 **305** 100 dh. multicoloured . . 90 45

306 Walter Wellman's airship "America", 1910

1983. Bicentenary of Manned Flight. Mult.
1385 100 dh. Type **306** . . . . . . 1·00 55
1386 100 dh. Airship "Nulli Secundus", 1907 . . . . . 1·00 55
1387 100 dh. Jean-Baptiste Meusnier's balloon design, 1784 . . . . 1·00 55
1388 100 dh. Blanchard and Jeffries' Channel crossing, 1785 (vert) 1·00 55
1389 100 dh. Pilatre de Rozier's hydrogen/hot-air balloon flight, 1784 (vert) . . . . 1·00 55
1390 100 dh. First Montgolfier balloon, 1783 (vert) . . . . 1·00 55

307 Globe and Dove

1983. Solidarity with Palestinian People.
1393 **307** 200 dh. green, blue & blk 1·60 95

308 Gladiators fighting

1983. Mosaics. Multicoloured.
1394 50 dh. Type **308** 50 20
1395 50 dh. Gladiators fighting (different) 50 20
1396 50 dh. Gladiators and slave 50 20
1397 50 dh. Two musicians . . . 50 20
1398 50 dh. Three musicians . . . 50 20
1399 50 dh. Two gladiators . . . 50 20
1400 50 dh. Two Romans and bound victim 50 20
1401 50 dh. Leopard and man hunting deer 50 20
1402 50 dh. Deer and man with boar 50 20

309 Traditional Architecture

1983. Achievements of the Revolution. Mult.
1403 10 dh. Type **309** 10 10
1404 15 dh. Camels drinking and mechanization of farming 10 10
1405 20 dh. Computer operator and industrial scene 10 10
1406 35 dh. Modern architecture 15 10
1407 100 dh. Surgeons and nurses treating patients and hospital 90 40
1408 140 dh. Airport and airplane 1·25 75

310 Flooding a River Bed **311** Mahmud Burkis

1983. Colonel Gaddafi–River Builder. Multicoloured.
1410 50 dh. Type **310** 20 15
1411 50 dh. Irrigation pipe and agricultural produce 20 15
1412 100 dh. Colonel Gaddafi, irrigation pipe and farmland (62 x 44 mm) . . . . . . 1·00 40
1413 100 dh. Colonel Gaddafi and map (68 x 32 mm) . . . . 1·00 40
1414 150 dh. Colonel Gaddafi explaining irrigation project (35 x 32 mm) . . . . . . 1·40 65
Nos. 1410/12 were printed together in se-tenant strips of three forming a composite design.

1984. Personalities. Multicoloured.
1416 100 dh. Type **311** . . . . . 1·00 40
1417 100 dh. Ahmed el-Bakbak . . 1·00 40
1418 100 dh. Mohamed el-Misurati 1·00 40
1419 100 dh. Mahmud Ben Musa 1·00 40
1420 100 dh. Abdulhamid el-Sherif 1·00 40
1421 100 dh. Mehdi el-Sherif . . . 1·00 40
1422 100 dh. Mahmud Mustafa Dreza . . . . 1·00 40
1423 100 dh. Hosni Fauzi el-Amir 1·00 40
1424 100 dh. Ali Haidar el-Saati . . 1·00 40
1425 200 dh. Ahmed el-Feghi Hasan 1·50 80
1426 200 dh. Bashir el-Jawab . . 1·50 80
1427 200 dh. Ali el-Gariani . . . 1·50 80
1428 200 dh. Muktar Shakshuki . . 1·50 80
1429 200 dh. Abdurrahman el-Busayri . . . . 1·50 80
1430 200 dh. Ibbrahim Bakir . . . 1·50 80
1431 200 dh. Mahmud el-Janzuri . 1·50 80

312 Windsurfing **313** Col. Gaddafi with Schoolchildren

1984. Water Sports. Multicoloured.
1432 25 dh. Type **312** 30 10
1433 25 dh. Dinghy sailing (orange and red sails) 30 10
1434 25 dh. Dinghy sailing (mauve sails) 30 10
1435 25 dh. Hang-gliding on water skis 20 10
1436 25 dh. Water-skiing 20 10
1437 25 dh. Angling from boat . . 30 10
1438 25 dh. Men in speed boat . . 30 10
1439 25 dh. Water-skiing (different) 20 10
1440 25 dh. Fishing 30 10
1441 25 dh. Canoeing 20 10
1442 25 dh. Surfing 20 10
1443 25 dh. Water-skiing (different) 20 10
1444 25 dh. Scuba diving 30 10
1445 25 dh. Diving 30 10
1446 25 dh. Swimming in snorkel and flippers 30 10
1447 25 dh. Scuba diving for fish 30 10

1984. African Children's Day. Multicoloured.
1448 50 dh. Type **313** 50 15
1449 50 dh. Colonel Gaddafi and children in national dress 50 15
1450 100 dh. Colonel Gaddafi on map and children at various activities (62 x 43 mm) . . . 1·90 60

314 Women in National, Casual and Military Dress

1984. Libyan Women's Emancipation. Multicoloured.
1451 55 dh. Type **314** 50 20
1452 70 dh. Women in traditional, casual and military dress (vert) 75 25
1453 100 dh. Colonel Gaddafi and women in military dress . . 95 40

315 Theatre, Sabratha

1984. Roman Ruins of Cyrenaica. Multicoloured.
1454 50 dh. Type **315** 20 15
1455 60 dh. Temple, Cyrene 50 20
1456 70 dh. Monument, Sabratha (vert) 60 25
1457 100 dh. Amphitheatre, Leptis Magna 90 40
1458 150 dh. Temple, Cyrene (different) . . . . 1·40 65
1459 200 dh. Basilica, Leptis Magna 1·90 80

316 Silver Dirham, 115 h. **318** Muktar Shiaker Murabet

317 Men at Tea Ceremony

1984. Arabic Islamic Coins (1st series).
1460 **316** 200 dh. silver, yellow and black . . . . 1·90 85
1461 – 200 dh. silver, mauve and black . . . . 1·90 85
1462 – 200 dh. silver, green and black . . . . 1·90 85
1463 – 200 dh. silver, orange and black . . . . 1·90 85
1464 – 200 dh. silver, blue and black . . . . 1·90 85
DESIGNS: No. 1461, Silver dirham, 93 h; 1462, Silver dirham, 121 h; 1463, Silver dirham, 49 h; 1464, Silver dirham, 135 h.
See also Nos. 1643/5.

1984. International Trade Fair, Tripoli. Mult.
1465 25 dh. Type **317** 15 10
1466 35 dh. Woman making tea . . 15 15
1467 45 dh. Men taking tea 20 15
1468 55 dh. Family taking tea . . . 50 20
1469 75 dh. Veiled women pouring tea 70 30
1470 100 dh. Robed men taking tea 1·00 40

1984. Musicians. Multicoloured.
1471 100 dh. Type **318** . . . . . 1·25 65
1472 100 dh. El-Aref el-Jamal . . . 1·25 65
1473 100 dh. Ali Shiaalia . . . . . 1·25 65
1474 100 dh. Bashir Fehmi . . . . 1·25 65

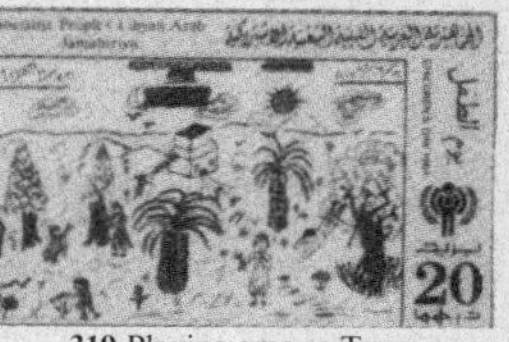

319 Playing among Trees

1984. Children's Day. Designs showing children's paintings. Multicoloured.
1475 20 dh. Type **319** 10 10
1476 20 dh. A rainy day 10 10
1477 20 dh. Weapons of war . . . 10 10
1478 20 dh. Playing on the swing 10 10
1479 20 dh. Playing in the park . . 10 10

320 Crest and "39"

1984. 39th Anniv of Arab League.
1480 **320** 30 dh. multicoloured . . . 15 15
1481 40 dh. multicoloured . . . 20 15
1482 50 dh. multicoloured . . . 55 20

321 Red Four-seater Car

1984. Motor Cars and Steam Locomotives. Mult.
1483 100 dh. Type **321** . . . . . . 1·25 65
1484 100 dh. Red three-seater car 1·25 65
1485 100 dh. Yellow two-seater car with three lamps . . . . . . 1·25 65
1486 100 dh. Covered red four-seater car . . . . 1·25 65
1487 100 dh. Yellow two-seater car with two lamps . . . . . . 1·25 65
1488 100 dh. Cream car with spare wheel at side . . . . 1·25 65
1489 100 dh. Green car with spare wheel at side . . . . 1·25 65
1490 100 dh. Cream four-seater car with spare wheel at back . . 1·25 65
1491 100 dh. Locomotive pulling wagon and coach . . . . . 1·40 45
1492 100 dh. Purple and blue locomotive . . . . 1·40 45
1493 100 dh. Cream locomotive . . 1·40 45
1494 100 dh. Lilac and brown locomotive . . . . 1·40 45
1495 100 dh. Lilac and black locomotive with red wheels 1·40 45
1496 100 dh. Cream and red locomotive . . . . 1·40 45
1497 100 dh. Purple and black locomotive with red wheels 1·40 45
1498 100 dh. Green and orange locomotive . . . . 1·40 45

322 Stylised People and Campaign Emblem

1984. World Health Day. Anti-Polio Campaign. Multicoloured.
1499 20 dh. Type **322** 10 10
1500 30 dh. Stylised people and 1981 20 dh. stamp 15 15
1501 40 dh. Stylised people and Arabic emblem 50 15

323 Man making Slippers

1984. Handicrafts. Multicoloured.
1502 150 dh. Type **323** . . . . . . 1·60 65
1503 150 dh. Man making decorative harness . . . . 1·60 65
1504 150 dh. Women forming cotton into skeins . . . . . . 1·60 65
1505 150 dh. Woman spinning by hand . . . . 1·60 65
1506 150 dh. Man weaving . . . . 1·60 65
1507 150 dh. Women weaving . . . 1·60 65

324 Telephones, Dial and Mail

1984. Postal and Telecommunications Union Congress. Multicoloured.
1508 50 dh. Type **324** 50 20
1509 50 dh. Woman working at computer console, dial and man working on computer 50 20
1510 100 dh. Satellite, map, laurel branches and telephone handset . . . . 1·00 40

325 Armed Soldiers and Civilians **326** Children behind Barbed Wire

1984. Abrogation of 17th May Treaty. Multicoloured.
1511 50 dh. Type **325** 65 20
1512 50 dh. Map, dove and burning banner 65 20
1513 50 dh. Soldiers shaking hands and crowd with banners (30 × 40 mm) 65 20
1514 100 dh. Hands tearing treaty, Gaddafi and crowd (62 × 40 mm) . . . . 1·25 40
1515 100 dh. Gaddafi addressing crowd . . . . 1·25 40
Nos. 1512/14 were printed together in se-tenant strips of three, forming a composite design.

1984. Child Victims of Invasion Day. Multicoloured.
1516 70 dh. Torn flags on barbed wire 70 25
1517 100 dh. Type **326** . . . . . . 1·00 40

327 "The Party System Aborts Democracy" **328** Man in Brown Robes

1984. Quotations from "The Green Book". Multicoloured.
1518 100 dh. Type **327** 95 40
1519 100 dh. Colonel Gaddafi . . . 95 40
1520 100 dh. "Partners not wage-workers" 95 40
1521 100 dh. "No representation in lieu of the people. Representation is falsification" 95 40
1522 100 dh. The Green Book . . . 95 40
1523 100 dh. "Committees everywhere" 95 40
1524 100 dh. "Forming parties splits societies" 95 40
1525 100 dh. Skyscraper and earthmover 95 40
1526 100 dh. "No democracy without popular congresses" 95 40

1984. Costumes. Multicoloured.
1527 100 dh. Type **328** . . . . . . 1·25 65
1528 100 dh. Woman in green dress and red shawl . . . . . . 1·25 65
1529 100 dh. Man in ornate costume and turban . . . . 1·25 65
1530 100 dh. Man in short trousers and plain shirt . . . . . . 1·25 65
1531 100 dh. Woman in shift and trousers with white shawl 1·25 65
1532 100 dh. Man in long white robe and red shawl . . . . . . 1·25 65

329 Footballer tackling

1984. World Cup Football Championship. Multicoloured.
1533 70 dh. Type **329** 70 25
1534 70 dh. Footballers in magenta and green shirts 70 25
1535 70 dh. Footballers in orange and lemon shirts 70 25
1536 70 dh. Goalkeeper failing to save ball 70 25
1537 70 dh. Footballers in yellow and brown shirts 70 25
1538 70 dh. Top of Trophy and footballer in green striped shirt 70 25
1539 70 dh. Top of Trophy and footballers in blue and pink shirts 70 25
1540 70 dh. Footballers in black and white striped and green and red striped shirts 70 25
1541 70 dh. Footballers in green and red striped shirts 70 25
1542 70 dh. Foot of trophy and footballers in orange striped and blue shirts 70 25
1543 70 dh. Foot of trophy and goalkeeper 70 25
1544 70 dh. Goalkeeper saving headed ball 70 25
1545 70 dh. Referee and footballers 70 25
1546 70 dh. Footballers in white with red striped sleeves and orange shirts 70 25
1547 70 dh. Footballers in white and green striped and orange shirts 70 25
1548 70 dh. Footballer in pink shirt 70 25
Nos. 1533/48 were printed in sheetlets of 16 stamps, the backgrounds to the stamps forming an overall design of a stadium.

330 Football **331** Palm Trees

1984. Olympic Games, Los Angeles. Mult.
1549 100 dh. Type **330** . . . . . . 1·25 65
1550 100 dh. Swimming . . . . . 1·25 65
1551 100 dh. Throwing the discus 1·25 65
1552 100 dh. Windsurfing . . . . 1·25 65
1553 100 dh. Basketball . . . . . 1·25 65
1554 100 dh. Running . . . . . . 1·25 65

1984. 9th World Forestry Congress. Mult.
1556 100 dh. Four types of forest 1·10 40
1557 200 dh. Type **331** . . . . . . 2·10 1·10

332 Modern Building

1984. 15th Anniv of Revolution. Multicoloured.
1558 25 dh. Type **332** 15 10
1559 25 dh. Front of building . . . 15 10
1560 25 dh. Building by pool . . . 15 10
1561 25 dh. Col. Gaddafi (three-quarter portrait) 15 10
1562 25 dh. High-rise block 15 10
1563 25 dh. Crane and mosque . . 15 10
1564 25 dh. Motorway interchange 15 10
1565 25 dh. House and garden . . 15 10
1566 25 dh. Shepherd and flock . . 15 10
1567 25 dh. Combine harvester . . 15 10
1568 25 dh. Tractors 15 10
1569 25 dh. Scientific equipment 15 10
1570 25 dh. Col Gaddafi (full face) 15 10
1571 25 dh. Water pipeline 15 10
1572 25 dh. Lighthouse 15 10
1573 25 dh. Liner at quay 45 10

333 Armed Man

334 Soldier flogging Civilian

1984. Evacuation of Foreign Forces. Mult. (a) As T **333.**
1574 50 dh. Type **333** 50 20
1575 50 dh. Armed man (different) 50 20
1576 100 dh. Men on horseback charging (62 x 40 mm) . . . 1·00 40

(b) As T **334.**
1577 100 dh. Type **334** . . . . . . 1·00 40
1578 100 dh. Girl on horse charging soldiers . . . . 1·00 40
1579 100 dh. Mounted soldiers and wounded being tended by women . . . . 1·00 40

335 Woman riding Skewbald Showjumper

1984. Equestrian Events. Multicoloured.
1580 25 dh. Type **335** 15 10
1581 25 dh. Man riding black showjumper (stands in background) 15 10
1582 25 dh. Jockey riding chestnut horse (stands in background) 15 10
1583 25 dh. Man on chestnut horse jumping in cross-country event 15 10
1584 25 dh. Man riding bay horse in showjumping competition 15 10
1585 25 dh. Woman on black horse in dressage competition . . . 15 10
1586 25 dh. Man on black horse in dressage competition . . . 15 10
1587 25 dh. Woman riding chestnut horse in cross-country event 15 10
1588 25 dh. Jockey riding bay horse 15 10
1589 25 dh. Woman on bay horse in dressage competition . . . 15 10
1590 25 dh. Man on grey horse in dressage competition . . . 15 10
1591 25 dh. Jockey riding grey steeplechaser 15 10
1592 25 dh. Woman riding grey showjumper 15 10
1593 25 dh. Woman riding through water in cross-country competition 15 10
1594 25 dh. Woman on chestnut horse in cross-country competition 15 10
1595 25 dh. Man riding dun showjumper 15 10
Nos. 1580/95 were printed together in sheetlets of 16 stamps, the backgrounds of the stamps forming an overall design of an equestrian ring.

336 Man cleaning Corn **337** Map and Pharmaceutical Equipment

1984. Traditional Agriculture. Multicoloured.
1596 100 dh. Type **336** . . . . . . 1·25 65
1597 100 dh. Man using oxen to draw water from well . . . . . 1·25 65
1598 100 dh. Man making straw goods . . . . 1·25 65
1599 100 dh. Shepherd with sheep 1·25 65
1600 100 dh. Man treating animal skin . . . . 1·25 65
1601 100 dh. Man climbing coconut tree . . . . 1·25 65

1984. 9th Conference of Arab Pharmacists Union.
1602 **337** 100 dh. multicoloured . . 1·25 40
1603 200 dh. multicoloured . . 2·50 1·10

338 Crowd with Banner showing Map of North Africa

1984. Arab-African Unity. Multicoloured.

1604 100 dh. Type **338** 1·25 65
1605 100 dh. Crowd and men holding flags 1·25 65

339 1982 and 1983 Solidarity Stamps and Map of Palestine

1984. Solidarity with Palestinian People.

1606 **339** 100 dh. multicoloured 1·25 40
1607 150 dh. multicoloured 1·90 1·00

340 Boeing 747SP, 1975

1984. 40th Anniv of International Civil Aviation Organization. Multicoloured.

1608 70 dh. Type **340** 95 30
1609 70 dh. Concorde, 1969 95 30
1610 70 dh. Lockheed TriStar 500, 1978 95 30
1611 70 dh. Airbus Industrie A310, 1982 95 30
1612 70 dh. Tupolev Tu-134A, 1962 95 30
1613 70 dh. Shorts 360, 1981 95 30
1614 70 dh. Boeing 727-100, 1963 95 30
1615 70 dh. Sud Aviation Caravelle 10R, 1965 95 30
1616 70 dh. Fokker Friendship, 1955 95 30
1617 70 dh. Lockheed Constellation, 1946 95 30
1618 70 dh. Martin M-130 flying boat, 1955 95 30
1619 70 dh. Douglas DC-3, 1936 95 50
1620 70 dh. Junkers Ju-52/3m, 1932 95 30
1621 70 dh. Lindbergh's "Spirit of St. Louis", 1927 95 30
1622 70 dh. De Havilland Moth, 1925 95 30
1623 70 dh. Wright Flyer I, 1903 95 30

Nos. 1608/23 were printed together in sheetlets of 16 stamps, the backgrounds of the stamps forming an overall design of a runway.

341 Coin

342 Mother and Son

1984. 20th Anniv of African Development Bank. Multicoloured.

1624 50 dh. Type **341** 55 20
1625 70 dh. Map of Africa and "20" 1·00 25
1626 100 dh. "20" and symbols of industry and agriculture 1·25 65

1985. U.N.I.C.E.F. Child Survival Campaign. Multicoloured.

1627 70 dh. Type **342** 1·00 50
1628 70 dh. Couple and children 1·00 50
1629 70 dh. Col. Gaddafi and children 1·00 50
1630 70 dh. Boys in uniform 1·00 50

343 Mohamed Hamdi

344 Pipeline, River, Plants and Map

1985. Musicians and Instruments. Multicoloured.

1631 100 dh. Kamel el-Ghadi 1·25 65
1632 100 dh. Fiddle rebab 1·25 65
1633 100 dh. Ahmed el-Khogia 1·25 65
1634 100 dh. Violin 1·25 65
1635 100 dh. Mustafa el-Fallah 1·25 65
1636 100 dh. Zither 1·25 65
1637 100 dh. Type **343** 1·25 65
1638 100 dh. Mask 1·25 65

1985. Col. Gaddafi–River Builder. Multicoloured.

1639 100 dh. Type **344** 1·25 65
1640 100 dh. Water droplet, river and flowers 1·25 65
1641 100 dh. Dead tree with branch thriving in water droplet 1·25 65

345 Gold Dinar, 105 h.

1985. Arabic Islamic Coins (2nd series). Mult.

1643 200 dh. Type **345** 2·50 1·25
1644 200 dh. Gold dinar, 91 h. 2·50 1·25
1645 200 dh. Gold dinar, 77 h. 2·50 1·25

346 Fish

347 Gaddafi in Robes and Hat

1985. Fossils. Multicoloured.

1647 150 dh. Type **346** 3·00 90
1648 150 dh. Frog 1·90 55
1649 150 dh. Mammal 1·90 55

1985. People's Authority Declaration. Mult.

1650 100 dh. Type **347** 1·25 65
1651 100 dh. Gaddafi in black robe holding book 1·25 65
1652 100 dh. Gaddafi in dress uniform without cap 1·25 65
1653 100 dh. Gaddafi in black dress uniform with cap 1·25 65
1654 100 dh. Gaddafi in white dress uniform 1·25 65

348 Cymbal Player

1985. International Trade Fair, Tripoli. Mult.

1655 100 dh. Type **348** 1·25 65
1656 100 dh. Piper and drummer 1·25 65
1657 100 dh. Drummer and bagpipes player 1·25 65
1658 100 dh. Drummer 1·25 65
1659 100 dh. Tambour player 1·25 65

349 Goalkeeper catching Ball

350 Emblem, Radio Transmitter and Satellite

1985. Children's Day. Multicoloured.

1660 20 dh. Type **349** 10 10
1661 20 dh. Child on touchline with ball 10 10
1662 20 dh. Letters of alphabet as players 10 10
1663 20 dh. Goalkeeper saving ball 10 10
1664 20 dh. Player heading ball 10 10

1985. International Communications Development Programme.

1665 **350** 30 dh. multicoloured 15 10
1666 70 dh. multicoloured 75 25
1667 100 dh. multicoloured 1·10 65

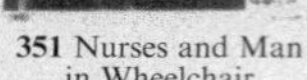

351 Nurses and Man in Wheelchair

352 "Mytilidae"

1985. World Health Day. Multicoloured.

1668 40 dh. Type **351** 50 10
1669 60 dh. Nurses and doctors 75 15
1670 100 dh. Nurse and child 1·25 65

1985. Sea Shells. Multicoloured.

1671 25 dh. Type **352** 40 15
1672 25 dh. Purple dye murex ("Muricidae") 40 15
1673 25 dh. Tuberculate cockle ("Cardiidae") 40 15
1674 25 dh. "Corallophilidae" 40 15
1675 25 dh. Trunculus murex ("Muricidae") 40 15
1676 25 dh. "Muricacea" 40 15
1677 25 dh. "Turridae" 40 15
1678 25 dh. Nodose paper nautilus ("Argonautidae") 40 15
1679 25 dh. Giant tun ("Tonnidae") 40 15
1680 25 dh. Common pelican's-foot ("Aporrhaidae") 40 15
1681 25 dh. "Trochidae" 40 15
1682 25 dh. "Cancellariidae" 40 15
1683 25 dh. "Epitoniidae" 40 15
1684 25 dh. "Turbinidae" 40 15
1685 25 dh. Zoned mitre ("Mitridae") 40 15
1686 25 dh. Cat's-paw scallop ("Pectinidae") 40 15

Nos. 1671/86 were printed se-tenant, the backgrounds forming an overall design of the sea bed.

353 Books and Emblem

354 Girls Skipping

1985. International Book Fair, Tripoli.

1687 **353** 100 dh. multicoloured 1·25 60
1688 200 dh. multicoloured 2·25 1·25

1985. International Youth Year. Multicoloured.

1689 20 dh. Type **354** 10 10
1690 20 dh. Boys playing with stones 10 10
1691 20 dh. Girls playing hopscotch 10 10
1692 20 dh. Boys playing with sticks 10 10
1693 20 dh. Boys playing with spinning top 10 10

355 Abdussalam Lasmar Mosque

356 Jamila Zemerli

1985. Minarets. Multicoloured.

1695 50 dh. Type **355** 50 15
1696 50 dh. Zaoviat Kadria Mosque 50 15
1697 50 dh. Zaoviat Amura Mosque 50 15
1698 50 dh. Gurgi Mosque 50 15
1699 50 dh. Mizran Mosque 50 15
1700 50 dh. Salem Mosque 50 15
1701 50 dh. Ghat Mosque 50 15
1702 50 dh. Ahmed Karamanli Mosque 50 15
1703 50 dh. Atya Mosque 50 15
1704 50 dh. El Kettani Mosque 50 15
1705 50 dh. Benghazi Mosque 50 15
1706 50 dh. Derna Mosque 50 15
1707 50 dh. El Derug Mosque 50 15
1708 50 dh. Ben Moussa Mosque 50 15
1709 50 dh. Ghadames Mosque 50 15
1710 50 dh. Abdulwahab Mosque 50 15

1985. Teachers' Day. Multicoloured.

1711 100 dh. Type **356** 1·25 65
1712 100 dh. Hamida El-Anezi 1·25 65

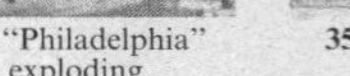

357 "Philadelphia" exploding

358 Gaddafi and Followers

1985. Battle of the "Philadelphia". Multicoloured.

1713 50 dh. Type **357** 60 20
1714 50 dh. Men with swords 60 20
1715 100 dh. Men fighting and ship's rigging (59 x 45 mm) 1·25 45

Nos. 1713/15 were printed together, se-tenant, forming a composite design.

1986. Colonel Gaddafi's Islamic Pilgrimage. Multicoloured.

1716 200 dh. Gaddafi writing 2·50 1·25
1717 200 dh. Gaddafi praying 2·50 1·25
1718 200 dh. Gaddafi, crowds and Kaaba 2·50 1·25
1719 200 dh. Gaddafi and mirror 2·50 1·25
1720 200 dh. Type **358** 2·50 1·25

359 "Leucopaxillus lepistoides"

1985. Mushrooms. Multicoloured.

1722 50 dh. Type **359** 1·10 25
1723 50 dh. "Amanita caesarea" 1·10 25
1724 50 dh. "Coriolus hirsutus" 1·10 25
1725 50 dh. "Cortinarius subfulgens" 1·10 25
1726 50 dh. "Dermocybe pratensis" 1·10 25
1727 50 dh. "Macrolepiota excoriata" 1·10 25
1728 50 dh. "Amanita curtipes" 1·10 25
1729 50 dh. "Trametes ljubarskyi" 1·10 25
1730 50 dh. "Pholiota aurivella" 1·10 25
1731 50 dh. "Boletus edulis" 1·10 25
1732 50 dh. "Geastrum sessile" 1·10 25
1733 50 dh. "Russula sanguinea" 1·10 25
1734 50 dh. "Cortinarius herculeus" 1·10 25
1735 50 dh. "Pholiota lenta" 1·10 25
1736 50 dh. "Amanita rubescens" 1·10 25
1737 50 dh. "Seleroderma polyrhizum" 1·10 25

Nos. 1722/37 were printed together, se-tenant, the backgrounds of the stamps forming an overall design of map of Mediterranean.

360 Woman in Purple Striped Dress

361 "In Need Freedom is Latent"

1985. Traditional Women's Costumes. Multicoloured.

1738 100 dh. Type **360** 1·25 65
1739 100 dh. Woman in robes covering her face 1·25 65
1740 100 dh. Woman in colourful robes with heavy jewellery 1·25 65
1741 100 dh. Woman in long blue striped dress 1·25 65
1742 100 dh. Woman in red dress and trousers 1·25 65

1985. Quotations from "The Green Book".

1743 **361** 100 dh. lt grn, grn & blk 45 35
1744 – 100 dh. multicoloured 45 35
1745 – 100 dh. lt grn, grn & blk 45 35
1746 – 100 dh. lt grn, grn & blk 45 35
1747 – 100 dh. multicoloured 45 35
1748 – 100 dh. lt grn, grn & blk 45 35
1749 – 100 dh. lt grn, grn & blk 45 35
1750 – 100 dh. multicoloured 45 35
1751 – 100 dh. lt grn, grn & blk 45 35

DESIGNS: No. 1744, Gaddafi in uniform reading; 1745, "To make a party you split society"; 1746, "Public sport is for all the masses"; 1747, "Green Books" and doves; 1748, "Wage-workers are a type of slave, however improved their wages may be"; 1749, "People are only harmonious with their own arts and heritages"; 1750, Gaddafi addressing crowd; 1751, "Democracy means popular rule not popular expression".

362 Tree and Citrus Fruits

1985. 16th Anniv of Revolution. Multicoloured.

1752 100 dh. Type **362** . . . . . . 1·25 65
1753 100 dh. Oil pipeline and tanks 1·25 65
1754 100 dh. Capital and olive branch . . . . 1·25 65
1755 100 dh. Mosque and modern buildings . . . . 1·25 65
1756 100 dh. Flag and mountains 1·25 65
1757 100 dh. Telecommunications 1·25 65

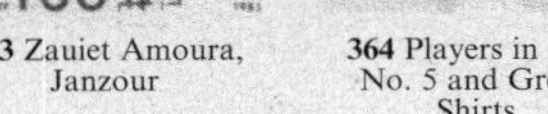

363 Zauiet Amoura, Janzour

364 Players in Red No. 5 and Green Shirts

1985. Mosque Gateways. Multicoloured.

1759 100 dh. Type **363** . . . . . . 1·25 65
1760 100 dh. Shiaieb El-Ain, Tripoli 1·25 65
1761 100 dh. Zauiet Abdussalam El-Asmar, Zliten . . . . . . 1·25 65
1762 100 dh. Karamanli, Tripoli . . 1·25 65
1763 100 dh. Gurgi, Tripoli . . . . 1·25 65

1985. Basketball. Multicoloured.

1764 25 dh. Type **364** 15 10
1765 25 dh. Players in green number 7 and red shirts 15 10
1766 25 dh. Players in green number 8 and red shirts 15 10
1767 25 dh. Players in red number 6 and green shirts 15 10
1768 25 dh. Players in red number 4 and green number 7 shirts 15 10
1769 25 dh. Players in green numbers 6 and 5 and red number 9 shirts 15 10
1770 25 dh. Basket and one player in red and two in green shirts 15 10
1771 25 dh. Players in red number 8 and green number 7 shirts 15 10
1772 25 dh. Two players in green shirts and two in red shirts, one number 4 . . . . . . 15 10
1773 25 dh. Players in red numbers 4 and 7 and green shirts . . . 15 10
1774 25 dh. Players in red numbers 4 and 9 and green numbers 7 and 4 shirts 15 10
1775 25 dh. Players in red number 6 and green shirts 15 10
1776 25 dh. Players in red number 9 and green number 8 shirts 15 10
1777 25 dh. Players in red number 8 and green number 5 shirts 15 10
1778 25 dh. Players in red number 4 and green shirts 15 10
1779 25 dh. Players in red number 5 and green number 10 shirts 15 10

Nos. 1764/79 were printed together se-tenant, the backgrounds of the stamps forming an overall design of baseball court and basket.

365 People in Light Ray

1985. Evacuation of Foreign Forces. Multicoloured.

1780 100 dh. Man on crutches in web and light shining on tree . . 1·25 65
1781 100 dh. Hands pulling web away from man . . . . 1·25 65
1782 100 dh. Type **365** . . . . 1·25 65

MINIMUM PRICE

The minimum price quoted is 10p which represents a handling charge rather than a basis for valuing common stamps. For further notes about prices see introductory pages.

366 Stockbook, Magnifying Glass and Stamps

367 Players

1985. Stamp Day. "Italia '85" International Stamp Exhibition, Rome. Multicoloured.

1783 50 dh. Man and desk on flying stamp above globe 65 15
1784 50 dh. Type **366** 65 15
1785 50 dh. Stamps escaping from wallet 65 15

1986. World Cup Football Championship, Mexico (1st issue). Multicoloured.

1786 100 dh. Type **367** . . . . . . 1·25 65
1787 100 dh. Players in red and white number 10 and yellow shirts 1·25 65
1788 100 dh. Goalkeeper and player defending goal against attack 1·25 65
1789 100 dh. Goalkeeper diving to make save . . . . 1·25 65
1790 100 dh. Goalkeeper jumping to make save . . . . 1·25 65
1791 100 dh. Player in red and white shirt tackling player in lime shirt . . . . 1·25 65

See also Nos. 1824/9.

368 Hands releasing Dove

1985. Solidarity with Palestinian People.

1793 **368** 100 dh. multicoloured . . 95 35
1794 150 dh. multicoloured . . 1·60 75

370 Headquarters and Dish Aerial

371 Paper and Quill in Hand

1986. 1st Anniv of General Posts and Telecommunications Corporation.

1807 **370** 100 dh. multicoloured . . 1·00 30
1808 150 dh. multicoloured . . 1·50 75

1986. Peoples' Authority Declaration. Multicoloured.

1809 50 dh. Type **371** 65 40
1810 50 dh. Paper and globe in hand 65 40
1811 100 dh. "Green Books" and dove (53 x 37 mm) . . . . 1·25 65

372 Flute

1986. International Trade Fair, Tripoli. Mult.

1812 100 dh. Type **372** . . . . . . 1·25 65
1813 100 dh. Drums . . . . 1·25 65
1814 100 dh. Double pipes . . . . 1·25 65
1815 100 dh. Tambourines . . . . 1·25 65
1816 100 dh. Drum hung from shoulder . . . . 1·25 65

373 Boy Scout with Fish on Hook

1986. Children's Day. Multicoloured.

1817 50 dh. Type **373** . . . . . . 1·10 25
1818 50 dh. Boy on camel 65 15
1819 50 dh. Boy catching butterflies 65 15
1820 50 dh. Boy playing drum . . . 65 15
1821 50 dh. Boy and giant goalkeeper on football pitch 65 15

374 Emblem, Man and Skull in Blood Droplet

1986. World Health Day. Multicoloured, background colours given.

1822 **374** 250 dh. silver . . . . . . 2·50 1·25
1823 250 dh. gold . . . . . . 2·50 1·25

375 Footballers

1986. World Cup Football Championship, Mexico (2nd issue). Multicoloured.

1824 50 dh. Type **375** 65 15
1825 50 dh. Player jumping over player on ground 65 15
1826 50 dh. Referee and players . . 65 15
1827 50 dh. Goalkeeper trying to save ball 65 15
1828 50 dh. Player about to tackle 65 15
1829 50 dh. Player jumping over ball 65 15

376 Peas

377 Health Programmes

1986. Vegetables. Multicoloured.

1831 50 dh. Type **376** 45 15
1832 50 dh. Marrow 45 15
1833 50 dh. Beans 45 15
1834 50 dh. Aubergine 45 15
1835 50 dh. Corn on the cob . . . 45 15
1836 50 dh. Tomato 45 15
1837 50 dh. Red pepper 45 15
1838 50 dh. Zucchini 45 15
1839 50 dh. Garlic 45 15
1840 50 dh. Cabbage 45 15
1841 50 dh. Cauliflower 45 15
1842 50 dh. Celery 45 15
1843 50 dh. Onions 45 15
1844 50 dh. Carrots 45 15
1845 50 dh. Potato 45 15
1846 50 dh. Radishes 45 15

Nos. 1831/46 were printed together in sheetlets of 16 stamps, the backgrounds of the stamps forming an overall design of a garden.

1986. Jamahiriya Thought. Multicoloured.

1847 50 dh. Type **377** 50 15
1848 50 dh. Education programmes 50 15
1849 100 dh. "Green Book", agricultural scenes and produce (agriculture programmes) (62 x 41 mm) 1·75 45

378 Gaddafi studying Plane

1986. Colonel Gaddafi, "Great man-made River Builder". Multicoloured.

1850 100 dh. Type **378** 95 30
1851 100 dh. Gaddafi showing planned route on map . . . 95 30
1852 100 dh. Gaddafi and old well 95 30
1853 100 dh. Gaddafi in desert . . 95 30
1854 100 dh. Gaddafi and pipe . . 95 30
1855 100 dh. Gaddafi at pumping station 95 30
1856 100 dh. Gaddafi and storage tank 95 30
1857 100 dh. Workers' hut 95 30
1858 100 dh. Water in cupped hands and irrigation equipment . . 95 30
1859 100 dh. Gaddafi turning wheel at opening ceremony 95 30
1860 100 dh. Laying pipes 95 30
1861 100 dh. Pipe sections on lorries 95 30
1862 100 dh. Gaddafi in robes holding "Green Book" 95 30
1863 100 dh. Boy giving Gaddafi bowl of fruit 95 30
1864 100 dh. Boy drinking from tap 95 30
1865 100 dh. Gaddafi praying . . . 95 30

379 Gaddafi with Children

1986. Colonel Gaddafi, "Man of Peace". Multicoloured.

1866 100 dh. Type **379** . . . . . . 1·10 30
1867 100 dh. Reading book in tent 1·10 30
1868 100 dh. With his mother . . . 1·10 30
1869 100 dh. Praying in tent with his sons . . . . 1·10 30
1870 100 dh. Talking to hospital patient . . . . 1·10 30
1871 100 dh. Driving tractor . . . 1·10 30

380 General Dynamics F-111 Exploding above Man with injured Child

381 Gaddafi, Ruined buildings and Stretcher-bearers

1986. Battle of the U.S.S. "Philadelphia" and American Attack on Libya. Multicoloured.

(a) As T **380**.

1872 50 dh. Type **380** 40 25
1873 50 dh. American aircraft carrier and escaping family 60 25
1874 100 dh. "Philadelphia" exploding (59 x 38 mm) . . 1·25 50

(b) As T **381**.

1875 70 dh. Type **381** 80 20
1876 70 dh. Burning wreckage of car and man and boy in rubble 80 20
1877 70 dh. Woman and child by burning ruin 80 20
1878 70 dh. Men running from bomb strike 80 20
1879 70 dh. Covered body and rescue workers searching ruins . . 80 20
1880 70 dh. Libyans and General Dynamics F-111 airplane tail and wing 80 25
1881 70 dh. Libyans waving fists 80 20
1882 70 dh. Rescue workers lifting child from rubble 80 20
1883 70 dh. Weeping women and soldier carrying baby . . . 80 20
1884 70 dh. Libyans and glare of explosion 80 20
1885 70 dh. Libyans and General Dynamics F-111 airplane wing and nose 80 25
1886 70 dh. Man carrying girl . . . 80 20
1887 70 dh. Coffins held aloft by crowd 80 20
1888 70 dh. Crowd carrying pictures of Gaddafi 80 20
1889 70 dh. Wounded being tended 80 20
1890 70 dh. Hands tending wounded baby 80 20

(c) Size 89 x 32 mm.

1891 100 dh. General Dynamics F-111 bombers, Gaddafi and anti-aircraft rockets . . . . 1·25 35

Nos. 1872/4 were printed together in se-tenant strips of three within the sheet, each strip forming a composite design.

382 "The House must be served by its own Tenant"

1986. Quotations from the "Green Book".

No.	Type	Description	Mint	Used
1892	**382**	100 dh. lt grn, grn & blk	1·00	30
1893	–	100 dh. multicoloured	1·00	30
1894	–	100 dh. lt grn, grn & blk	1·00	30
1895	–	100 dh. lt grn, grn & blk	1·00	30
1896	–	100 dh. multicoloured	1·00	30
1897	–	100 dh. lt grn, grn & blk	1·00	30
1898	–	100 dh. lt grn, grn & blk	1·00	30
1899	–	100 dh. multicoloured	1·00	30
1900	–	100 dh. lt grn, grn & blk	1·00	30

DESIGNS: No. 1893, Gaddafi; 1894, "The Child is raised by his mother"; 1895, "Democracy is the Supervision of the People by the People"; 1896, "Green Books"; 1897, "Representation is a Falsification of Democracy"; 1898, "The Recognition of Profit is an Acknowledgement of Exploitation"; 1899, Vase of roses, iris, lilies and jasmine; 1900, "Knowledge is a Natural Right of every Human Being which Nobody has the Right to deprive him of under any Pretext".

383 Map, Chrysanthemum and Health Services

1986. 17th Anniv of Revolution. Multicoloured.

No.	Type	Description	Mint	Used
1901		200 dh. Type **383**	2·50	95
1902		200 dh. Map, sunflower and agriculture programme	2·50	95
1903		200 dh. "Sunflowers" (Van Gogh)	2·50	95
1904		200 dh. Map, rose and defence programme	2·50	95
1905		200 dh. Map, campanula and oil exploration programme	2·50	95

384 Moroccan and Libyan Women

1986. Arab-African Union. Multicoloured.

No.	Type	Description	Mint	Used
1906		250 dh. Type **384**	2·50	80
1907		250 dh. Libyan and Moroccan horsemen	2·50	80

385 Libyan Horseman

1986. Evacuation of Foreign Forces. Multicoloured.

No.	Type	Description	Mint	Used
1908		50 dh. Type **385**	50	15
1909		100 dh. Libyan horsemen trampling Italian soldiers	1·10	30
1910		150 dh. Italian soldiers charging	1·50	50

386 Globe and Rose

1986. International Peace Year. Multicoloured, background colours given.

No.	Type	Description	Mint	Used
1911	**386**	200 dh. green	1·90	70
1912		200 dh. blue	1·90	70

387 Brick "Fists" and Maps within Laurel Wreath

1986. Solidarity with Palestinian People. Multicoloured, background colours given.

No.	Type	Description	Mint	Used
1913	**387**	250 dh. blue	2·50	80
1914		250 dh. red	2·50	80

388 Drummer

1986. Folk Music. Multicoloured.

No.	Type	Description	Mint	Used
1915		70 dh. Type **388**	95	20
1916		70 dh. Masked stick dancer	95	20
1917		70 dh. Woman dancer with pot headdress	95	20
1918		70 dh. Bagpipe player	95	20
1919		70 dh. Tambour player	95	20

389 Gazelles

1987. Endangered Animals. Sand Gazelle. Multicoloured.

No.	Type	Description	Mint	Used
1920		100 dh. Type **389**	1·25	30
1921		100 dh. Mother and calf	1·25	30
1922		100 dh. Gazelle drinking	1·25	30
1923		100 dh. Gazelle lying down	1·25	30

390 Oil Derricks and Crowd

391 Sheep and Shepherd

1987. People's Authority Declaration. Multicoloured.

No.	Type	Description	Mint	Used
1924		500 dh. Type **390**	4·00	1·75
1925		500 dh. Buildings and crowd	4·00	1·75
1926		1000 dh. Gaddafi addressing crowd and globe (40 x 38 mm)	8·00	3·25

1987. 18th Anniv of Revolution. Multicoloured.

No.	Type	Description	Mint	Used
1927		150 dh. Type **391**	1·50	50
1928		150 dh. Col. Gaddafi in robes	1·50	50
1929		150 dh. Mosque	1·50	50
1930		150 dh. Water flowing from irrigation pipe	1·50	50
1931		150 dh. Combine harvester	1·50	50
1932		150 dh. Col. Gaddafi in army uniform with microphone	1·50	50
1933		150 dh. Harvesting crop	1·50	50
1934		150 dh. Irrigation	1·50	50
1935		150 dh. Soldier with rifle	1·50	50
1936		150 dh. Buildings behind Libyan with rifle	1·50	50
1937		150 dh. Fountain	1·50	50
1938		150 dh. Buildings and beach	1·50	50
1939		150 dh. Fort and girls	1·50	50
1940		150 dh. Children and hand on rifle butt	1·50	50
1941		150 dh. Theatre	1·50	50
1942		150 dh. Couple	1·50	50

392 Omar Abed Anabi al Mansusri

1988. Personalities. Multicoloured.

No.	Type	Description	Mint	Used
1943		100 dh. Type **392**	75	30
1944		200 dh. Ahmed Ali al Emrayd	1·50	70
1945		300 dh. Khalifa Said Ben Asker	2·50	1·00
1946		400 dh. Mohamed Ben Farhat Azawi	3·00	1·10
1947		500 dh. Mohamed Souf al Lafi al Marmori	3·75	1·50

393 Gaddafi and Crowd with Raised Fists around Earthmover Bucket

1988. Freedom Festival Day.

No.	Type	Description	Mint	Used
1948	**393**	100 dh. multicoloured	95	30
1949		150 dh. multicoloured	1·60	75
1950		250 dh. multicoloured	2·50	1·25

394 Woman and Children running

1988. 2nd Anniv of American Attack on Libya. Multicoloured.

No.	Type	Description	Mint	Used
1951		150 dh. Type **394**	1·40	50
1952		150 dh. Gaddafi playing chess with boy	1·40	50
1953		150 dh. Gaddafi and children	1·40	50
1954		150 dh. Gaddafi in robes	1·40	50
1955		150 dh. Gaddafi and boys praying	1·40	50
1956		150 dh. Gaddafi and injured girl	1·40	50
1957		150 dh. Gaddafi in robes with children (horiz)	1·40	50
1958		150 dh. Gaddafi making speech (horiz)	1·40	50
1959		150 dh. Gaddafi and family (horiz)	1·40	50

395 Roses

1988. 19th Anniv of Revolution.

No.	Type	Description	Mint	Used
1961	**395**	100 dh. multicoloured	75	30
1962		250 dh. multicoloured	2·00	80
1963		300 dh. multicoloured	2·25	1·00
1964		500 dh. multicoloured	4·25	1·50

396 Relay

397 Dates

1988. Olympic Games, Seoul. Multicoloured.

No.	Type	Description	Mint	Used
1965		150 dh. Type **396**	1·25	50
1966		150 dh. Cycling	1·25	50
1967		150 dh. Football	1·25	50
1968		150 dh. Tennis	1·25	50
1969		150 dh. Running	1·25	50
1970		150 dh. Showjumping	1·25	50

1988. The Palm Tree. Multicoloured.

No.	Type	Description	Mint	Used
1972		500 dh. Type **397**	4·25	1·50
1973		1000 dh. Tree	8·00	3·75

398 Petrol Bomb, Sling and Map

399 Globe, Declaration and Dove

1988. Palestinian "Intifada" Movement. Mult.

No.	Type	Description	Mint	Used
1974		100 dh. Type **398**	95	30
1975		200 dh. Boy holding stones (45 x 38 mm)	1·60	70
1976		300 dh. Map and flag	2·50	1·00

1989. People's Authority Declaration.

No.	Type	Description	Mint	Used
1977	**399**	260 dh. multicoloured	1·10	65
1978		500 dh. multicoloured	2·00	1·25

400 Crowd and Green Books
(½-size illustration)

1989. 20th Anniv of Revolution. Multicoloured.

No.	Type	Description	Mint	Used
1979		150 dh. Type **400**	1·25	40
1980		150 dh. Soldiers, Colonel Gaddafi and water pipeline	1·25	40
1981		150 dh. Military hardware, Gaddafi in uniform, education, communications and medicine	1·25	40
1982		150 dh. Armed horsemen	1·25	40
1983		150 dh. U.S.S. "Philadelphia" exploding	1·25	55

401 Execution Victims, Soldiers and Colonel Gaddafi

1989. 78th Anniv of Deportation of Libyans to Italy. Multicoloured.

No.	Type	Description	Mint	Used
1985		100 dh. Type **401**	40	25
1986		100 dh. Colonel Gaddafi and Libyans	40	25
1987		100 dh. Soliders, deportees and Gaddafi	40	25
1988		100 dh. Deportees on jetty and in boats	55	25
1989		100 dh. Gaddafi and corpses	40	25

402 Demoliton of Wall

403 Emblem of Committee for supporting "Intifida"

1989. "Demolition of Borders".

No.	Type	Description	Mint	Used
1991	**402**	150 dh. multicoloured	1·60	1·60
1992		200 dh. multicoloured	2·10	2·10

1989. Palestinian "Intifida" Movement. Mult.

No.	Type	Description	Mint	Used
1993		100 dh. Type **403**	1·10	1·10
1994		300 dh. Crowd of youths	3·00	3·00
1995		500 dh. Emblem (1st anniv of declaration of State of Palestine)	4·75	4·75

404 Circulation Diagram and Annafis

1989. Ibn Annafis (physician) Commemorative.

No.	Type	Description	Mint	Used
1996	**404**	100 dh. multicoloured	1·25	1·25
1997		150 dh. multicoloured	1·90	1·90

405 Green Books and Fort

406 Libyan People and Soldier

1990. People's Authority Declaration.

No.	Type	Description	Mint	Used
1998	**405**	300 dh. multicoloured	2·75	2·75
1999		500 dh. multicoloured	5·00	5·00

1990. 20th Anniv of American Forces Evacuation.

No.	Type	Description	Mint	Used
2000	**406**	100 dh. multicoloured	1·00	1·00
2001		400 dh. multicoloured	4·00	4·00

407 Eagle

408 Anniversary Emblem

1990. 21st Anniv of Revolution.

2002	407	100 dh. multicoloured	1·00	1·00
2003		400 dh. multicoloured	4·00	4·00
2004		1000 dh. multicoloured	10·50	10·50

1990. 30th Anniv of Organization of Petroleum Exporting Countries.

2006	408	100 dh. multicoloured	1·00	1·00
2007		400 dh. multicoloured	4·00	4·00

409 I.L.Y. Emblem and Figures

410 Player, Globe and Ball

1990. International Literacy Year.

2008	409	100 dh. multicoloured	1·10	1·10
2009		300 dh. multicoloured	3·00	3·00

1990. World Cup Football Championship, Italy.

2010	410	100 dh. multicoloured	1·00	1·00
2011		400 dh. multicoloured	4·00	4·00
2012		500 dh. multicoloured	5·00	5·00

411 Hand holding Ears of Wheat

412 Members' Flags

1990. World Food Day. Multicoloured.

2014	500 dh. Type **411**	5·00	5·00
2015	2000 dh. Ploughing	20·00	20·00

1991. 2nd Anniv of Union of Arab Maghreb.

2016	412	100 dh. multicoloured	1·10	1·10
2017		300 dh. multicoloured	3·00	3·00

413 Flame, Scroll and Koran

1991. People's Authority Declaration.

2018	413	300 dh. multicoloured	2·75	2·75
2019		400 dh. multicoloured	3·75	3·75

414 Girl and International Year of the Child Emblem

415 World Health Organization Emblem

1991. Children's Day. Multicoloured.

2020	100 dh. Type **414**	95	95
2021	400 dh. Boy and Day of the African Child emblem	3·75	3·75

1991. World Health Day. Multicoloured.

2022	100 dh. Type **415**	95	95
2023	200 dh. As Type **415** but with emblem additionally inscr "W.H.O. O.M.S."	1·90	1·90

416 Wadi el Hayat

417 Digging Riverbed and laying Pipes

1991. Scenes from Libya. Multicoloured.

2024	100 dh. Type **416**	95	95
2025	250 dh. Mourzuk (horiz)	2·50	2·50
2026	500 dh. Ghadames (horiz)	5·00	5·00

1991. Great Man-made River. Multicoloured.

2027	50 dh. Type **417**	25	15
2028	50 dh. Col. Gaddafi, agricultural projects and livestock (59 x 37 mm)	25	15
2029	50 dh. Produce	25	15

Nos. 2027/9 were printed together, se-tenant, forming a composite design.

418 "22", Roses and Broken Chain

1991. 22nd Anniv of Revolution. Multicoloured.

2030	300 dh. Type **418**	2·75	2·75
2031	400 dh. "22" within wheat/ cogwheel wreath and broken chain	3·75	3·75

419 Emblem and Globe

1991. "Telecom 91" International Telecommunications Exhibition, Geneva. Multicoloured.

2033	100 dh. Type **419**	95	95
2034	500 dh. Buldings and dish aerial (horiz)	4·50	4·50

420 Monument and Soldier

1991. 80th Anniv of Deportation of Libyans to Italy. Multicoloured.

2035	100 dh. Type **420**	95	95
2036	400 dh. Naval transport, Libyans and soldiers	3·75	3·75

421 Map

1991. Arab Unity.

2038	421	50 dh. multicoloured	20	10
2039		100 dh. multicoloured	40	20

422 Lorry

424 State Arms

423 Gaddafi and Camels

1991. Paris–Dakar Trans-Sahara Rally. Mult.

2040	50 dh. Type **422**	20	10
2041	50 dh. Blue lorry	20	10
2042	50 dh. African Product lorry	20	10
2043	50 dh. Tomel lorry	20	10
2044	50 dh. All-terrain vehicle No. 173	20	10
2045	50 dh. Mitsusuki all-terrain vehicle	20	10
2046	50 dh. Michedop all-terrain vehicle	20	10
2047	50 dh. All-terrain vehicle No. 401	20	10
2048	50 dh. Motor cycle No. 100	20	10
2049	50 dh. Rider pushing red motor cycle	20	10
2050	50 dh. Rider pushing white motor cycle	20	10
2051	50 dh. Motor cycle No. 98	20	10
2052	50 dh. Motor cycle No. 101	20	10
2053	50 dh. Motor cycle No. 80	20	10
2054	50 dh. Motor cycle No. 12	20	10
2055	50 dh. Motor cycle No. 45	20	10

1992. "Gaddafi, Man of Peace 1992". Multicoloured, colour of frame given.

2056	423	100 dh. green	40	20
2057		100 dh. grey	40	20
2058		100 dh. red	40	20
2059		100 dh. ochre	40	20

1992.

2061	424	100 dh. green, brn & yell	40	20
2062		150 dh. green, brn & grey	60	30
2063		200 dh. green, brown & bl	85	45
2064		250 dh. green, brn & orge	1·10	55
2065		300 dh. green, brn & vio	1·25	65
2066		400 dh. green, brn & mve	1·75	90
2067		450 dh. emerald, brn & grn	1·90	95

425 1991 100 dh. Stamp, Tweezers, Magnifying Glass and Stamps

1992. 3rd Anniv of Union of Arab Maghreb.

2068	425	75 dh. multicoloured	30	15
2069		80 dh. multicoloured	35	20

426 Horse-drawn Carriage

1992. International Trade Fair, Tripoli. Mult.

2070	50 dh. Type **426**	20	10
2071	100 dh. Horse-drawn cart	40	20

427 Emblem

429 Big-eyed Tuna

428 Emblem and Camel Rider

1992. People's Authority Declaration.

2072	427	100 dh. multicoloured	40	20
2073		150 dh. multicoloured	60	30

1992. African Tourism Year.

2074	428	50 dh. multicoloured	20	10
2075		100 dh. multicoloured	40	20

1992. Fishes. Multicoloured.

2076	100 dh. Type **429**	75	30
2077	100 dh. Mackerel scad	75	30
2078	100 dh. Little tuna (seven spines on back)	75	30
2079	100 dh. Seabream (continuous dorsal fin)	75	30
2080	100 dh. Spanish mackerel (four spines on back)	75	30
2081	100 dh. Striped red mullet (with whiskers)	75	30

430 Horsewoman with Rifle

431 Long Jumping

1992. Horse Riders. Multicoloured.

2082	100 dh. Type **430**	40	20
2083	100 dh. Man on rearing white horse	40	20
2084	100 dh. Man on brown horse with ornate bridle	40	20
2085	100 dh. Roman soldier on brown horse	40	20
2086	100 dh. Man in blue coat on brown horse	40	20
2087	100 dh. Arab on white horse	40	20

1992. Olympic Games, Barcelona. Multicoloured.

2089	50 dh. Type **431**	20	10
2090	50 dh. Throwing the discus	20	10
2091	50 dh. Tennis	20	10

432 Palm Trees

1992. Achievements of the Revolution. Mult.

2093	100 dh. Type **432**	40	20
2094	150 dh. Ingots and foundry	60	30
2095	250 dh. Container ship	1·10	55
2096	300 dh. Airplane	1·25	65
2097	400 dh. Assembly hall	1·75	90
2098	500 dh. Water pipes and Gaddafi	2·10	1·10

433 Gaddafi

434 Laurel Wreath, Torch and "23"

1992. Multicoloured, background colours given.

2099	433	500 dh. green	2·50	1·10
2100		1000 dh. pink	5·00	2·50
2101		2000 dh. blue	10·00	5·00
2102		5000 dh. violet	25·00	12·50
2103		6000 dh. orange	32·00	16·00

1992. 23rd Anniv of Revolution. Multicoloured.

2104	50 dh. Type **434**	20	10
2105	100 dh. Laurel wreath, flag, sun and "23"	40	20

435 Antelope drinking

436 Horse and Broken Chain

1992. Oases. Multicoloured.

2107	100 dh. Type **435**	40	20
2108	200 dh. Sun setting behind camel train (vert)	85	45
2109	300 dh. Camel rider	1·25	65

1992. Evacuation of Foreign Forces. Multicoloured.

2110	75 dh. Type **436**	30	15
2111	80 dh. Flag and broken chain	35	20

437 Monument and Dates

1992. 81st Anniv of Deportation of Libyans to Italy.
2112 **437** 100 dh. multicoloured . . 40 20
2113 250 dh. multicoloured . . 1·10 55

438 Dome of the Rock and Palestinian

1992. Palestinian "Intifida" Movement. Mult.
2114 100 dh. Type **438** 40 20
2115 300 dh. Map, Dome of the Rock, flag and fist (vert) . . 1·25 65

439 Red and White Striped Costume
440 Mohamed Ali Imsek

1992. Women's Costumes. Multicoloured.
2116 50 dh. Type **439** 20 10
2117 50 dh. Large red hat with silver decorations, white tunic and red wrap 20 10
2118 50 dh. Brown and orange striped costume with small gold necklace and horseshoe brooch 20 10
2119 50 dh. Purple and white costume 20 10
2120 50 dh. Orange striped costume 20 10

1993. Physicians
2121 **440** 40 dh. black, yellow and silver 15 10
2122 – 60 dh. black, green and gold 20 15
DESIGN: 60 dh. Aref Adhani Arif.

441 Globe, Crops and Spoon-feeding Man

1993. International Nutrition Conference, Rome.
2123 **441** 70 dh. multicoloured . . . 35 25
2124 80 dh. multicoloured . . . 40 30

442 Gaddafi, Eagle and Oil Refinery

1993. People's Authority Declaration.
2125 **442** 60 dh. multicoloured . . . 20 15
2126 65 dh. multicoloured . . . 25 15
2127 75 dh. multicoloured . . . 25 15

MINIMUM PRICE

The minimum price quoted is 10p which represents a handling charge rather than a basis for valuing common stamps. For further notes about prices see introductory pages.

443 Crowd with Tambours
445 Girl

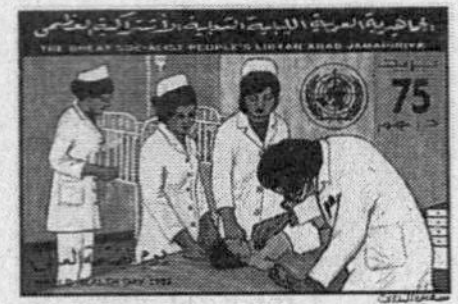

444 Examining Baby

1993. International Trade Fair, Tripoli. Mult.
2128 60 dh. Type **443** 20 15
2129 60 dh. Crowd with camel . . 20 15
2130 60 dh. Dance of veiled men (horiz) 20 15
2131 60 dh. Women preparing food (horiz) 20 15

1993. World Health Day. Multicoloured.
2133 75 dh. Type **444** 25 15
2134 85 dh. Medical staff attending patient 30 20

1993. Children's Day. Multicoloured.
2135 75 dh. Type **445** 25 15
2136 75 dh Girl wearing blue and white veil and gold cuff . . 25 15
2137 75 dh. Girl with white fluted collar and silver veil 25 15
2138 75 dh. Girl with hands clasped 25 15
2139 75 dh. Girl wearing blue scallop-edged veil 25 15

446 Phoenician Ship

1993. Ships. Multicoloured
2140 50 dh. Type **446** 20 15
2141 50 dh. Arab galley 20 15
2142 50 dh. Pharaonic ship 20 15
2143 50 dh. Roman bireme 20 15
2144 50 dh. Carvel 20 15
2145 50 dh. Yacht (globe showing Italy) 20 15
2146 50 dh. Yacht (globe showing Greece) 20 15
2147 50 dh. Galeasse 20 15
2148 50 dh. Nau 20 15
2149 50 dh. Yacht (globe showing left half of Libya) 20 15
2150 50 dh. Yacht (globe showing right half of Libya) 20 15
2151 50 dh. "Santa Maria" 20 15
2152 50 dh. "France" (liner) . . . 20 15
2153 50 dh. Schooner 20 15
2154 50 dh. Sail/steam warship . . 20 15
2155 50 dh. Modern liner 20 15
Nos. 2140/55 were issued together, se-tenant, the centre four stamps forming a composite design.

447 Combine Harvesters
448 Woman tending Youth

1993. 24th Anniv of Revolution. Multicoloured.
2156 50 dh. Type **447** 20 15
2157 50 dh. Col. Gaddafi 20 15
2158 50 dh. Cattle behind men filling sack with grain 20 15
2159 50 dh. Chickens behind shepherd with flock 20 15
2160 50 dh. Oil rig 20 15
2161 50 dh. Eagle and camel . . . 20 15
2162 50 dh. Industrial plant . . . 20 15
2163 50 dh. Water pipeline 20 15
2164 50 dh. Man harvesting dates . 20 15
2165 50 dh. Man in field and boxes of produce 20 15
2166 50 dh. Pile of produce 20 15
2167 50 dh. Man picking courgettes . 20 15
2168 50 dh. Children reading . . . 20 15
2169 50 dh. Typist and laboratory worker 20 15
2170 50 dh. Hand-picking crop and ploughing with tractor . . . 20 15
2171 50 dh. Tractor towing circular harrow 20 15
Nos. 2156/71 were issued together, se-tenant, forming several composite designs.

1993. 82nd Anniv of Deportation of Libyans to Italy. Multicoloured.
2172 50 dh. Type **448** 20 15
2173 50 dh. Soldiers and Libyan family 20 15
2174 50 dh. Col. Gaddafi (in turban) 20 15
2175 50 dh. Libyans in food queue . 20 15
2176 50 dh. Man being flogged . . 20 15
2177 50 dh. Horseman charging between soldiers and Libyans 20 15
2178 50 dh. Soldier with manacled Libyan before court 20 15
2179 50 dh. Libyans gazing at hanged man 20 15
2180 50 dh. Crowd of Libyans and two soldiers 20 15
2181 50 dh. Soldiers guarding procession of Libyans . . . 20 15
2182 50 dh. Soldiers and manacled Libyans on quayside . . . 20 15
2183 50 dh. Deportees in boat . . . 20 15
2184 50 dh. Col. Gaddafi (bare-headed) 20 15
2185 50 dh. Two Libyan families and branch of palm tree 20 15
2186 50 dh. Soldiers in disarray (ruins in background) 20 15
2187 50 dh. Libyan horsemen . . . 20 15
Nos. 2172/87 were issued together, se-tenant, forming several composite designs.

449 Brooch
451 Player and Trophy

450 Gaddafi, Soldiers and Jet Fighters

1994. Silver Jewellery. Multicoloured.
2188 55 dh. Type **449** 20 15
2189 55 dh. Armlet 20 15
2190 55 dh. Pendant 20 15
2191 55 dh. Pendants hanging from oblong 20 15
2192 55 dh. Necklace 20 15
2193 55 dh. Slippers 20 15

1994. 25th Anniv of Revolution. Multicoloured.
2194 100 dh. Type **450** 35 25
2195 100 dh. Libyan tribesmen and Gaddafi in uniform (59 × 38 mm) 35 25
2196 100 dh. Peaceful pursuits and elderly couple 35 25
Nos. 2194/6 were issued together, se-tenant, forming a composite design.

1994. World Cup Football Championship, U.S.A. Multicoloured.
2198 100 dh. Type **451**
2199 100 dh. Kicking ball with inside of foot 35 25
2200 100 dh. Kicking ball in air . . 35 25
2201 100 dh. Goalkeeper 35 25
2202 100 dh. Running with ball . . 35 25
2203 100 dh. Player taking ball on chest 35 25

452 Gaddafi

1994. 83rd Anniv of Deportation of Libyans to Italy. Multicoloured.
2205 95 dh. Type **452** 35 25
2206 95 dh. Light plane over rifleman 35 25
2207 95 dh. Couple running from biplane 35 25
2208 95 dh. Biplane flying over men and boy 35 25
2209 95 dh. Man trapped beneath fallen horse 35 25
2210 95 dh. Soldiers and Libyans fighting (camel's head and neck in foreground) 35 25
2211 95 dh. Soldiers surrounding fallen Libyan 35 25
2212 95 dh. Man carrying boy . . . 35 25
2213 95 dh. Soldier with whip raised 35 25
2214 95 dh. Robed man shouting . . 35 25
2215 95 dh. Tank and battle scene . 35 25
2216 95 dh. Women fleeing mounted soliers 35 25
2217 95 dh. Man being flogged and woman cradling head of fallen Libyan 35 25
2218 95 dh. Soldiers and Libyans fighting (camels in background) 35 25
2219 95 dh. Women and soldiers on quayside 35 25
2220 95 dh. Deportees in two boats . 35 25
Nos. 2205/20 were issued together, se-tenant, forming several composite designs.

453 Darghut
454 Armed Forces

1994. Mosques. Multicoloured.
2221 70 dh. Type **453** 25 15
2222 70 dh. Benghazi 25 15
2223 70 dh. Kabao 25 15
2224 70 dh. Gouzgu 25 15
2225 70 dh. Siala 25 15
2226 70 dh. El Kettani 25 15

1994. People's Authority Declaration. Multicoloured.
2227 80 dh. Type **454** 30 20
2228 80 dh. Truck, hand holding Green Book and ears of wheat 30 20
2229 80 dh. Pipes on trailers, water pipeline and family 30 20
2230 80 dh. Crowd with Green Books 30 20
2231 80 dh. Col. Gaddafi 30 20
2232 80 dh. Youths and produce . . 30 20
Nos. 2227/32 were issued together, se-tenant, forming a composite design.

455 Sun over Cemetery, National Flag, Dove and Footprints
457 Declaration and Flowers

456 Men with Weapons and Troops in Background

1994. Evacuation of Foreign Forces.
2233 **455** 65 dh. multicoloured . . . 25 15
2234 95 dh. multicoloured . . . 35 20

1994. Gaddafi Prize for Human Rights. Multicoloured.
2235 95 dh. Type **456** 35 20
2236 95 dh. Men with weapons . . 35 20
2237 95 dh. President Nelson Mandela of South Africa . . 35 20
2238 95 dh. President Gaddafi . . . 35 20
2239 95 dh. Amerindian meditating . 35 20
2240 95 dh. Warriors on horseback . 35 20
2241 95 dh. Amerindian chief . . . 35 20
2242 95 dh. Amerindian 35 20
2243 95 dh. Riflemen and aircraft . 35 20
2244 95 dh. Bomber, women, fire and left page of book 35 20
2245 95 dh. Right page of book and surgeon operating 35 20
2246 95 dh. Surgeons operating . . 35 20
2247 95 dh. Masked revolutionaries with flag 35 20

2248		95 dh. Revolutionaries raising arms with flag	35	20
2249		95 dh. Young boys with stones	35	20
2250		95 dh. Revolutionaries, fire and troops	35	20

Nos. 2235/50 were issued together, se-tenant, forming a composite design.

1995. People's Authority Declaration. Multicoloured, colour of background given.

2251	457	100 dh. yellow	35	20
2252		100 dh. blue	35	20
2253		100 dh. green	35	20

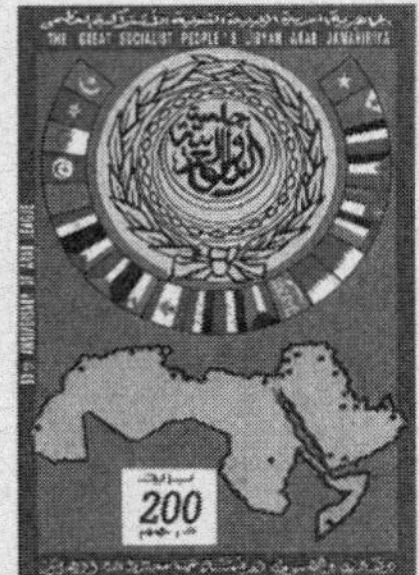

458 Emblem, Members' Flags and Map showing Member Countries

1995. 50th Anniv of Arab League. Multicoloured, frame colour given.

2254	458	200 f. blue	70	45
2255		200 f. green	70	45

459 Messaud Zentuti

1995. 60th Anniv of National Football Team. Designs showing players. Multicoloured.

2257		100 dh. Type **459**	35	20
2258		100 dh. Salem Shermit	35	20
2259		100 dh. Ottoman Marfua	35	20
2260		100 dh. Ghaleb Siala	35	20
2261		100 dh. Team, 1935	35	20
2262		100 dh. Senussi Mresila	35	20

Nos. 2257/62 were issued together, se-tenant, forming a composite design.

460 Dromedary 461 Grapefruit

1995. Libyan Zoo. Multicoloured.

2263		100 dh. Type **460**	35	20
2264		100 dh. Secretary bird	35	20
2265		100 dh. African wild dog	35	20
2266		100 dh. Oryx	35	20
2267		100 dh. Baboon	35	20
2268		100 dh. Golden jackal	35	20
2269		100 dh. Crowned eagle	35	20
2270		100 dh. Eagle owl	35	20
2271		100 dh. Desert hedgehog	35	20
2272		100 dh. Sand gerbil	35	20
2273		100 dh. Addax	35	20
2274		100 dh. Fennec fox	35	20
2275		100 dh. Lanner falcon	35	20
2276		100 dh. Desert wheatear	35	20
2277		100 dh. Pin-tailed sandgrouse	35	20
2278		100 dh. Jerboa	35	20

Nos. 2263/78 were issued together, se-tenant, the backgrounds forming a composite design.

1995. Fruit. Multicoloured.

2279		100 dh. Type **461**	35	20
2280		100 dh. Wild cherry	35	20
2281		100 dh. Mulberry	35	20
2282		100 dh. Strawberry	35	20
2283		100 dh. Plum	35	20
2284		100 dh. Pear	35	20
2285		100 dh. Apricot	35	20
2286		100 dh. Almond	35	20
2287		100 dh. Prickly pear	35	20
2288		100 dh. Lemon	35	20
2289		100 dh. Peach	35	20
2290		100 dh. Dates	35	20
2291		100 dh. Olive	35	20
2292		100 dh. Orange	35	20
2293		100 dh. Fig	35	20
2294		100 dh. Grape	35	20

Nos. 2279/94 were issued together, se-tenant, the backgrounds forming a composite design.

462 Students

1995. 26th Anniv of Revolution. Multicoloured.

2295		100 dh. Type **462**	35	20
2296		100 dh. Mosque, teacher and students	35	20
2297		100 dh. President Gaddafi	35	20
2298		100 dh. Laboratory workers	35	20
2299		100 dh. Hospital patient, doctor examining child and nurse	35	20
2300		100 dh. Surgeons operating	35	20
2301		100 dh. Cobblers and keyboard operator	35	20
2302		100 dh. Sound engineers and musician	35	20
2303		100 dh. Crane and apartment block	35	20
2304		100 dh. Silos	35	20
2305		100 dh. Oil rig platform	35	20
2306		100 dh. Airplane and ships	35	20
2307		100 dh. Animals grazing and farmer	35	20
2308		100 dh. Pipeline	35	20
2309		100 dh. Camels at trough and crops	35	20
2310		100 dh. Crops and farm vehicle	35	20

Nos. 2295/2310 were issued together, se-tenant, forming a composite design.

463 Scout Badge and Wildlife

1995. Scouting. Multicoloured.

2311		250 dh. Type **463**	85	55
2312		250 dh. Badge, butterflies and scouts with animals (59 x 39 mm)	85	55
2313		250 dh. Badge and scouts	85	55

Nos. 2311/13 were issued together, se-tenant, forming a composite design.

464 Warships and Rocket

1995. 9th Anniv of American Attack on Libya. Multicoloured.

2314		100 dh. Type **464**	35	20
2315		100 dh. Bombers, helicopters, warships and Libyans (59 x 49 mm)	35	20
2316		100 dh. Bomber and woman holding baby	35	20

Nos. 2314/16 were issued together, se-tenant, forming a composite design.

465 Gaddafi on Horseback 466 Dromedary and Woman with Water Jars

1995. International Trade Fair, Tripoli. Multicoloured.

2317		100 dh. Type **465**	35	20
2318		100 dh. Horseman	35	20
2319		100 dh. Horseman (horse galloping to right)	35	20
2320		100 dh. Horsemen with whips (horiz)	35	20
2321		100 dh. Horseman holding rifle (horiz)	35	20
2322		100 dh. Horsewoman brandishing rifle in air (horiz)	35	20

1995. City of Ghadames. Multicoloured.

2324		100 dh. Type **466**	35	20
2325		100 dh. Making cheeses	35	20
2326		100 dh. Woman holding jar	35	20
2327		100 dh. Feeding chickens	35	20
2328		100 dh. Spinning wool	35	20
2329		100 dh. Woman in traditional costume	35	20
2330		100 dh. Drying grain	35	20
2331		100 dh. Milking goat	35	20
2332		100 dh. Making shoes	35	20
2333		100 dh. Weaving	35	20
2334		100 dh. Engraving brass tabletops	35	20
2335		100 dh. Harvesting dates	35	20
2336		100 dh. Reading scriptures	35	20
2337		100 dh. Potter	35	20
2338		100 dh. Washing clothes in well	35	20
2339		100 dh. Picking fruit	35	20

467 Family with Torch and National Flag

1995. Evacuation of Foreign Forces.

2340	467	50 dh. multicoloured	20	10
2341		100 dh. multicoloured	35	20
2342		200 dh. multicoloured	70	45

468 Honeycomb and Bees on Flowers

1995. Arab Beekeepers' Association. Multicoloured, colour of border given.

2343	468	100 dh. mauve	35	20
2344		100 dh. lilac	35	20
2345		100 dh. green	35	20

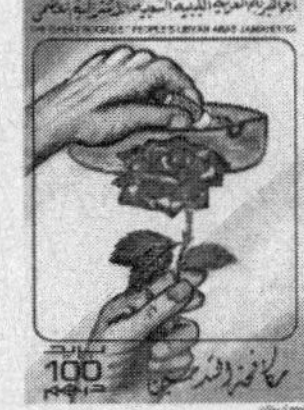

469 Stubbing out Cigarette and holding Rose 470 Dr. Mohamed Feituri

1995. World Health Day. Multicoloured, colour of central band given.

2346	469	100 dh. yellow	35	20
2347		100 dh. orange	35	20

1995.

2348	470	200 dh. multicoloured	70	45

471 Gaddafi and Horsemen

1995. 84th Anniv of Deportation of Libyans to Italy. Multicoloured.

2349		100 dh. Type **471**	35	20
2350		100 dh. Horsemen	35	20
2351		100 dh. Battle scene	35	20
2352		100 dh. Bomber over battle scene	35	20
2353		100 dh. Libyans with rifles	35	20
2354		100 dh. Soldiers fighting with Libyans	35	20
2355		100 dh. Soldiers with weapons and man on ground	35	20
2356		100 dh. Soldiers with rifles and building in background	35	20
2357		100 dh. Libyans	35	20
2358		100 dh. Soldiers charging men on ground	35	20
2359		100 dh. Soldiers shooting at horseman	35	20
2360		100 dh. Soldiers pushing Libyan to ground	35	20
2361		100 dh. Horsemen charging	35	20

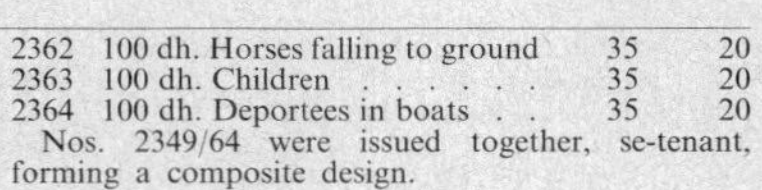

2362		100 dh. Horses falling to ground	35	20
2363		100 dh. Children	35	20
2364		100 dh. Deportees in boats	35	20

Nos. 2349/64 were issued together, se-tenant, forming a composite design.

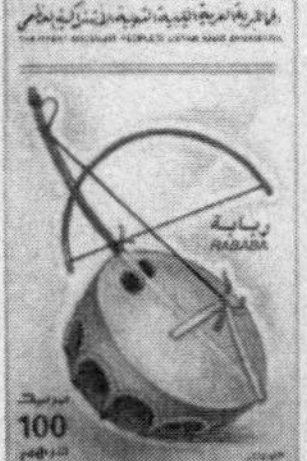

472 Rababa 473 Blue Door

1995. Musical Instruments. Multicoloured.

2365		100 dh. Type **472**	35	20
2366		100 dh. Nouba	35	20
2367		100 dh. Clarinet	35	20
2368		100 dh. Drums	35	20
2369		100 dh. Magruna	35	20
2370		100 dh. Zukra	35	20
2371		100 dh. Zil	35	20
2372		100 dh. Kaman	35	20
2373		100 dh. Guitar	35	20
2374		100 dh. Trumpet	35	20
2375		100 dh. Tapla	35	20
2376		100 dh. Gonga	35	20
2377		100 dh. Saxophone	35	20
2378		100 dh. Piano	35	20
2379		100 dh. Ganoon	35	20
2380		100 dh. Ood	35	20

1995. Doors from Mizda. Multicoloured.

2381		100 dh. Type **473**	35	20
2382		100 dh. Door with arch detail	35	20
2383		100 dh. Door made of logs	35	20
2384		100 dh. Arched door	35	20
2385		100 dh. Wide door with bolts	35	20

474 Sports within Olympic Rings

1995. Centenary of International Olympic Committee. Multicoloured, colour of face value given.

2386	474	100 dh. black	35	20
2387		100 dh. red	35	20

475 Baryonyx

1995. Prehistoric Animals. Multicoloured.

2388		100 dh. Type **475**	35	20
2389		100 dh. Oviraptor	35	20
2390		100 dh. Stenonychosaurus	35	20
2391		100 dh. Tenontosaurus	35	20
2392		100 dh. Yangchuanosaurus	35	20
2393		100 dh. Stegotetrabelodon (facing right)	35	20
2394		100 dh. Stegotetrabelodon (facing left)	35	20
2395		100 dh. Psittacosaurus	35	20
2396		100 dh. Heterodontosaurus	35	20
2397		100 dh. "Loxodonta atlantica"	35	20
2398		100 dh. "Mammuthus africanavus"	35	20
2399		100 dh. Erlikosaurus	35	20
2400		100 dh. Cynognathus	35	20
2401		100 dh. Plateosaurus	35	20
2402		100 dh. Staurikosaurus	35	20
2403		100 dh. Lystrosaurus	35	20

Nos. 2388/2403 were issued together, se-tenant, the backgrounds forming a composite design.

476 Child and Dinosaur walking with Stick

1995. Children's Day. Multicoloured.

2405 100 dh. Type **476** 35 20
2406 100 dh. Child on mammoth's back 35 20
2407 100 dh. Child on way to school and tortoise under mushroom 35 20
2408 100 dh. Dinosaur playing football 35 20
2409 100 dh. Child pointing rifle at pteranodon 35 20

477 Helicopter, Soldier and Stone-thrower

1995. Palestinian "Intifida" Movement. Multicoloured.

2410 100 dh. Type **477** 35 20
2411 100 dh. Dome of the Rock and Palestinian with flag . . 35 20
2412 100 dh. Women with flag . . 35 20

Nos. 2410/12 were issued together, se-tenant, forming a composite design.

478 Airplane, Control Tower and Tailfin

1995. 50th Anniv of I.C.A.O. Multicoloured, colour of face value given.

2413 **478** 100 dh. blue 35 20
2414 100 dh. black 35 20

479 Headquarters, New York

480 "Iris germanica"

1995. 50th Anniv of U.N.O. Multicoloured, colour of background given.

2415 **479** 100 dh. pink 35 20
2416 100 dh. lilac 35 20

1995. Flowers. Multicoloured.

2417 200 dh. Type **480** 35 20
2418 200 dh. "Canna edulis" 35 20
2419 200 dh. "Nerium oleander" . . 35 20
2420 200 dh. Corn poppy ("Papaver rhoeas") 35 20
2421 200 dh. Bird of Paradise flower ("Strelitzia reginae") . . . 35 20
2422 200 dh. "Amygdalus communis" 35 20

481 Open Hand

483 Man holding Fruit

482 Football

1996. People's Authority Declaration. Multicoloured.

2423 **481** 100 dh. multicoloured . . 35 20
2424 150 dh. multicoloured . . 50 30
2425 200 dh. multicoloured . . 65 40

1996. Olympic Games, Atlanta, U.S.A. Multicoloured.

2426 100 dh. Type **482** 35 20
2427 100 dh. Long jumping 35 20
2428 100 dh. Tennis 35 20
2429 100 dh. Cycling 35 20
2430 100 dh. Boxing 35 20
2431 100 dh. Equestrian show jumping 35 20

Nos. 2426/31 were issued together, se-tenant, the background forming a composite design of the Games emblem.

1996. 27th Anniv of Revolution. Multicoloured.

2433 100 dh. Type **483** 35 20
2434 100 dh. Water flowing along chute and out of pipe . . . 35 20
2435 100 dh. Tractor, water and women with flowers 35 20
2436 100 dh. Man working on pipe by water 35 20
2437 100 dh. Man sewing 35 20
2438 100 dh. Woman textile worker . 35 20
2439 100 dh. President Gaddafi in white shirt and red cape . . 35 20
2440 100 dh. Women laboratory workers 35 20
2441 100 dh. Anatomy instruction and man using microscope . 35 20
2442 100 dh. Child holding hand to face 35 20
2443 100 dh. Woman praying before open Koran 35 20
2444 100 dh. Man weaving 35 20
2445 100 dh. Two aircraft 35 20
2446 100 dh. Man on camel, liner and dish aerial 35 20
2447 100 dh. Stern of liner and television camera 35 20
2448 100 dh. Woman using microphone and woman being filmed 35 20

Nos. 2433/48 were issued together, se-tenant, forming a composite design.

484 Bomb Exploding

1996. 10th Anniv of American Attack on Libya. Multicoloured.

2449 100 dh. Type **484** 35 20
2450 100 dh. Man with raised arms . 35 20
2451 100 dh. Woman carrying child . 35 20
2452 100 dh. Injured man on ground and fighter plane 35 20
2453 100 dh. Fireman hosing down burning car 35 20
2454 100 dh. Exploding plane . . . 35 20
2455 100 dh. Head of President Gaddafi 35 20
2456 100 dh. Airplane bombing tented camp 35 20
2457 100 dh. Rescuers helping two women 35 20
2458 100 dh. Man with bandaged head and hand 35 20
2459 100 dh. Woman with hankerchief to mouth . . . 35 20
2460 100 dh. Stretcher bearers . . . 35 20
2461 100 dh. Explosion and man being carried away 35 20
2462 100 dh. Explosion and man with injured hand 35 20
2463 100 dh. Rescuers helping injured mother with baby 35 20
2464 100 dh. Burning car and helpers tending injured boy 35 20

Nos. 2449/64 were issued together, se-tenant, forming a composite design.

485 "Necora puber" (crab)

1996. Crustaceans. Multicoloured.

2465 100 dh. Type **485** 35 20
2466 100 dh. "Lissa chiragra" (crab) 35 20
2467 100 dh. Rock lobster ("Palinurus elephas") . . . 35 20
2468 100 dh. "Scyllarus arctus" . . 35 20
2469 100 dh. Green crab ("Carcinus maenas") 35 20
2470 100 dh. Helmet crab ("Calappa granulata") 35 20
2471 100 dh. "Parapenaeus longirostris" (prawn) 35 20
2472 100 dh. Norway lobster ("Nephrops norvegicus") . . 35 20
2473 100 dh. "Eriphia verrucosa" (crab) 35 20
2474 100 dh. Edible crab ("Cancer pagurus") 35 20
2475 100 dh. "Penaeus kerathurus" (prawn) 35 20
2476 100 dh. Mantis shrimp ("Squilla mantis") 35 20
2477 100 dh. Spider crab ("Maja squinado") 35 20
2478 100 dh. "Pilumnus hirtellus" (crab) 35 20
2479 100 dh. "Pagurus alatus" (crab) 35 20
2480 100 dh. "Macropodia tenuirostris" 35 20

Nos. 2465/80 were issued together, se-tenant, the backgrounds forming a composite design.

486 Mats

487 Woman kneeling over Boy

1996. Maghreb Handicrafts Day. Basketwork. Multicoloured.

2481 100 dh. Type **486** 35 20
2482 100 dh. Lidded storage vessel . 35 20
2483 100 dh. Bowl 35 20
2484 100 dh. Mug and teapot . . . 35 20
2485 100 dh. Box with open lid . . 35 20
2486 100 dh. Bird's-eye view of dish . 35 20
2487 100 dh. Pot with wide base and mouth and narrower neck . . 35 20
2488 100 dh. Lidded pot with carrying handle 35 20
2489 100 dh. Bulbous bottle-shaped carrier 35 20
2490 100 dh. Large dish 35 20
2491 100 dh. Oval dish with well in centre 35 20
2492 100 dh. Straight-sided bottle-shaped carrier 35 20
2493 100 dh. Vessel with double carrying handles and open lid 35 20
2494 100 dh. Dish on stand 35 20
2495 100 dh. Pot with wide base and narrow mouth 35 20
2496 100 dh. Bag with lid 35 20

1996. 85th Anniv of Deportation of Libyans to Italy. Multicoloured.

2497 100 dh. Type **487** 35 20
2498 100 dh. Horseman leading prisoner 35 20
2499 100 dh. President Gaddafi wearing turban 35 20
2500 100 dh. Old man holding stick in camp 35 20
2501 100 dh. Man being flogged . . 35 20
2502 100 dh. Horseman, soldiers and crowd wearing fezzes . . . 35 20
2503 100 dh. Prisoner, advocate and man in tricolour sash . . . 35 20
2504 100 dh. Family and soldier . . 35 20
2505 100 dh. Soldiers guarding prisoners (boy at front) . . 35 20
2506 100 dh. Soldiers escorting woman on camel and man on donkey 35 20
2507 100 dh. Prisoners being escorted through street 35 20
2508 100 dh. Prisoners in boat . . . 35 20
2509 100 dh. President Gaddafi in white embroided shirt with open hand 35 20
2510 100 dh. Group of prisoners including man with raised arm 35 20
2511 100 dh. Horsemen charging and soldiers 35 20
2512 100 dh. Horseman with rifle . . 35 20

Nos. 2497/2512 were issued together, se-tenant, forming several composite designs.

488 Bay

1996. Horses. Multicoloured.

2513 100 dh. Type **488** 35 20
2514 100 dh. Light brown horse under tree (branches at right of stamp) 35 20
2515 100 dh. Light brown horse by lake under tree (branch at left) 35 20
2516 100 dh. Dark brown horse (edge of lake at left) 35 20
2517 100 dh. Black horse with hoof raised 35 20
2518 100 dh. Chestnut horse 35 20
2519 100 dh. Grey horse running . . 35 20
2520 100 dh. Piebald 35 20
2521 100 dh. Head of grey and tail of black horses 35 20
2522 100 dh. Head of black and tail of chestnut horses 35 20
2523 100 dh. Head and rump of chestnut horses 35 20
2524 100 dh. Head of chestnut horse with white mane 35 20
2525 100 dh. Head of black horse and parts of three other horses . 35 20
2526 100 dh. Head of chestnut horse with blond mane and parts of three other horses 35 20
2527 100 dh. Head of dark brown horse and parts of three other horses 35 20
2528 100 dh. Head of dark brown and part of chestnut horses . . 35 20

Nos. 2513/28 were issued together, se-tenant, forming a composite design.

489 Camel

490 Photographer, Newspapers and Computer

1996. Camels. Multicoloured.

2529 200 dh. Type **489** 65 40
2530 200 dh. Head of camel 65 40
2531 200 dh. Dark brown dromedary 65 40
2532 200 dh. Long-haired Bactrian camel 65 40
2533 200 dh. Light brown Bactrian camel 65 40
2534 200 dh. Brown Bactrian camel with white stripe and tail . . 65 40

Nos. 2529/34 were issued together, se-tenant, forming a composite design.

1996. The Press and Information. Multicoloured.

2535 100 dh. Type **490** 35 20
2536 200 dh. Television, control desk, musicians, computer and dish aerial 65 40

491 "Mene rhombea"

492 Palestinian Flag and Hands holding up Stones

1996. Fossils. Multicoloured.

2537 200 dh. Type **491** 65 40
2538 200 dh. "Mesodon macrocephalus" 65 40
2539 200 dh. "Eyron arctiformis" . . 65 40
2540 200 dh. Stegosaurus 65 40
2541 200 dh. Pteranodon 65 40
2542 200 dh. Allosaurus 65 40

1996. Palestinian "Intifida" Movement.

2543 **492** 100 dh. multicoloured . . 35 20
2544 150 dh. multicoloured . . 50 30
2545 200 dh. multicoloured . . 65 40

493 Child

494 Cat

1996. African Child Day. Multicoloured.

2546 50 dh. Type **493** 10 10
2547 150 dh. Type **493** 40 25
2548 200 dh. Mother and child . . . 50 35

1996. Children's Day. Cats. Multicoloured.

2549 100 dh. Type **494** 25 15
2550 100 dh. Tabby (back view with head turned) 25 15
2551 100 dh. Colourpoint (black and white) 25 15
2552 100 dh. Tabby adult and kitten 25 15
2553 100 dh. Tortoiseshell white (sitting) 25 15

495 Family and Tower Block

1996. World Family Day. Multicoloured.

No.	Description	Unused	Used
2554	150 dh. Type **495**	40	25
2555	150 dh. Family and car parked by palm trees	40	25
2556	200 dh. Family, symbolic globe and flowers (45 × 26 mm)	50	35

Nos. 2554/6 were issued together, se-tenant, forming a composite design.

496 Mohamed Kamel el-Hammali

1996. Libyan Teachers. Multicoloured.

No.	Description	Unused	Used
2557	100 dh. Type **496**	25	15
2558	100 dh. Mustafa Abdalla ben-Amer	25	15
2559	100 dh. Mohamed Messaud Fesheka	25	15
2560	100 dh. Kairi Mustafa Serraj	25	15
2561	100 dh. Muftah el-Majri	25	15
2562	100 dh. Mohamed Hadi Arafa	25	15

497 Mohamed Salim

1996. Libyan Singers. Multicoloured.

No.	Description	Unused	Used
2563	100 dh. Type **497**	25	15
2564	100 dh. Mohamed M. Sayed Bumedyen	25	15
2565	100 dh. Otman Najim	25	15
2566	100 dh. Mahmud Sherif	25	15
2567	100 dh. Mohamed Ferjani Marghani	25	15
2568	100 dh. Mohamed Kabazi	25	15

498 Snake

1996. Reptiles. Multicoloured.

No.	Description	Unused	Used
2569	100 dh. Type **498**	25	15
2570	100 dh. Diamond-back snake beside river	25	15
2571	100 dh. Turtle on water (segmented shell and large flippers)	25	15
2572	100 dh. Snake wrapped around tree branch	25	15
2573	100 dh. Brown lizard on tree trunk	25	15
2574	100 dh. Coiled snake with head raised and mouth open	25	15
2575	100 dh. Snake with head raised beside water	25	15
2576	100 dh. Turtle on water (flat shell, pointed snout and small flippers)	25	15
2577	100 dh. Green lizard on tree trunk	25	15
2578	100 dh. Snake with wavy pattern on ground	25	15
2579	100 dh. Snake with horns	25	15
2580	100 dh. Chameleon	25	15
2581	100 dh. Tortoise on ground (facing right)	25	15
2582	100 dh. Snake on rock with head raised	25	15
2583	100 dh. Tortoise on ground (facing left)	25	15
2584	100 dh. Grey lizard on rock	25	15

Nos. 2569/84 were issued together, se-tenant, forming a composite design.

499 Mirror and Clothes Brush

1996. International Trade Fair, Tripoli. Each silver, pink and black.

No.	Description	Unused	Used
2585	100 dh. Type **499**	25	15
2586	100 dh. Decanter on tray	25	15
2587	100 dh. Two round-bottomed flasks	25	15
2588	100 dh. Two long-necked flasks	25	15
2589	100 dh. Covered bowl	25	15
2590	100 dh. Backs of hairbrush and mirror	25	15

500 Gaddafi and Symbolic Scenes

501 Scouts and Stamp Album

1997. People's Authority Declaration.

No.	Type	Description	Unused	Used
2591	**500**	100 dh. multicoloured	25	15
2592		200 dh. multicoloured	25	15
2593		300 dh. multicoloured	25	15

1997. Postal Savings Bank. Multicoloured.

No.	Description	Unused	Used
2594	50 dh. Type **501**	10	10
2595	50 dh. Two Girl Guides and albums	10	10
2596	100 dh. Bank books and butterflies	25	15

Nos. 2594/6 were issued together, se-tenant, forming a composite design.

502 Scientist with Test Tubes

503 Death enveloping Man's Head

1997. World Health Day. Multicoloured.

No.	Description	Unused	Used
2597	50 dh. Type **502**	10	10
2598	50 dh. Scientist at microscope	10	10
2599	100 dh. Doctor and nurse examining baby	25	15

Nos. 2597/9 were issued together, se-tenant, forming a composite design.

1997. Anti-drugs Campaign.

No.	Type	Description	Unused	Used
2600	**503**	100 dh. multicoloured	25	15
2601		150 dh. multicoloured	40	25
2602		200 dh. multicoloured	50	35

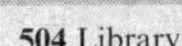

504 Library

1997. Arab National Central Library.

No.	Type	Description	Unused	Used
2603	**504**	100 dh. multicoloured	25	15
2604		200 dh. multicoloured	50	35

505 Dancer and Local Crafts

1997. Arab Tourism Year.

No.	Type	Description	Unused	Used
2606	**505**	100 dh. multicoloured	25	15
2607		200 dh. multicoloured	50	25
2608		250 dh. multicoloured	65	45

CONCESSIONAL LETTER POST

1929. No. CL227 of Italy optd **LIBIA.**

No.	Type	Description	Unused	Used
CL68	CL **93**	10 c. blue	11·00	12·00

1941. No. CL267 of Italy optd **LIBIA.**

No.	Type	Description	Unused	Used
CL123	CL **109**	10 c. brown	5·00	5·00

EXPRESS LETTER STAMPS

A. ITALIAN ISSUES.

1915. Express Letter stamps of Italy optd **Libia.**

No.	Type	Description	Unused	Used
E17	E **35**	25 c. pink	9·00	8·00
E18	E **41**	30 c. blue and pink	6·00	16·00

E **8**

1921.

No.	Type	Description	Unused	Used
E34	E **8**	30 c. red and blue	1·10	2·75
E35		50 c. brown and red	1·60	4·25
E42		60 c. brown and red	2·50	7·00
E43		2 l. red and blue	5·00	15·00

Nos. E34 and E43 are inscribed "EXPRES".

1922. Nos. E17/18 surch.

No.	Type	Description	Unused	Used
E40	E **35**	60 c. on 25 c. pink	3·75	7·00
E41	E **41**	1 l. 60 on 30 c. blue and pink	5·00	17·00

1926. Nos. E42/3 surch.

No.	Type	Description	Unused	Used
E62	E **8**	70 on 60 c. brown and red	3·25	7·00
E64		1 l. 25 on 60 c. brown and red	2·75	1·00
E63		2.50 on 2 l. red and blue	3·75	14·00

B. INDEPENDENT ISSUE

1966. Design similar to T **74** inscr "EXPRES".

No.	Description	Unused	Used
E368	90 m. red and green	2·25	1·25

DESIGN—HORIZ: 90 m. Saracen Castle, Zuela.

OFFICIAL STAMPS

1952. Optd **Official** in English and Arabic.

No.	Type	Description	Unused	Used
O192	**23**	2 m. brown	40	35
O193		4 m. grey	65	50
O194		5 m. green	4·50	1·60
O195		8 m. red	2·50	75
O196		10 m. violet	3·75	1·25
O197		12 m. red	6·75	2·50
O198		20 m. blue	13·50	5·25
O199		25 m. brown	17·00	6·75

PARCEL POST STAMPS

Unused prices are for complete pairs, used prices for a half.

1915. Parcel Post stamps of Italy optd **LIBIA** on each half of the stamp.

No.	Type	Description	Unused	Used
P17	P **53**	5 c. brown	80	30
P18		10 c. blue	80	30
P19		20 c. black	1·00	30
P20		25 c. red	2·00	30
P21		50 c. orange	2·00	30
P22		1 l. violet	1·75	30
P23		2 l. green	2·40	30
P24		3 l. yellow	3·00	30
P25		4 l. grey	3·00	30
P26		10 l. purple	35·00	7·00
P27		12 l. brown	65·00	7·00
P28		15 l. green	65·00	10·00
P29		20 l. purple	65·00	12·00

1927. Parcel Post stamps of Italy optd **LIBIA** on each half of the stamp.

No.	Type	Description	Unused	Used
P62	P **92**	5 c. brown	£8000	
P63		10 c. blue	1·60	35
P64		25 c. red	1·60	35
P65		30 c. blue	50	35
P66		50 c. orange	70·00	10·00
P67		60 c. red	50	35
P68		1 l. violet	24·00	3·50
P69		2 l. green	30·00	3·50
P70		3 l. bistre	1·00	40
P71		4 l. black	1·00	40
P72		10 l. mauve	£160	15·00
P73		20 l. purple	£160	15·00

POSTAGE DUE STAMPS

A. ITALIAN ISSUES.

1915. Postage Due stamps of Italy optd **Libia.**

No.	Type	Description	Unused	Used
D17	D **12**	5 c. mauve and orange	60	1·90
D18		10 c. mauve and orange	1·00	2·00
D19		20 c. mauve and orange	1·40	3·50
D20		30 c. mauve and orange	2·00	3·50
D21		40 c. mauve and orange	2·25	3·50
D22		50 c. mauve and orange	2·00	3·50
D23		60 c. mauve and orange	3·00	5·00
D24		60 c. brown and orange	45·00	80·00
D25		1 l. mauve and blue	2·00	2·00
D26		2 l. mauve and blue	30·00	35·00
D27		5 l. mauve and blue	35·00	50·00

1934. Postage Due stamps of Italy optd **LIBIA.**

No.	Type	Description	Unused	Used
D68	D **141**	5 c. brown	15	70
D69		10 c. blue	15	70
D70		20 c. red	80	55
D71		25 c. green	80	55
D72		30 c. red	80	1·10
D73		40 c. brown	80	1·75
D74		50 c. violet	1·10	20
D75		60 c. blue	1·60	2·75

D76	D 142	1 l. orange	1·40	20
D77		2 l. green	24·00	4·50
D78		5 l. violet	48·00	15·00
D79		10 l. blue	7·00	15·00
D80		20 l. red	7·00	17·00

B. INDEPENDENT ISSUES

1951. Postage Due stamps of Cyrenaica optd. (a) For use in Cyrenaica. Optd as T **20**.

D144	D 26	2 m. brown	5·00	5·00
D145		4 m. green	5·00	5·00
D146		8 m. red	6·75	6·25
D147		10 m. orange	7·50	6·25
D148		20 m. yellow	11·00	10·00
D149		40 m. blue	30·00	20·00
D150		100 m. black	40·00	23·00

(b) For use in Tripolitania. Surch as T **21**.

D161	D 26	1 mal. on 2 m. brown	5·50	5·00
D162		2 mal. on 4 m. green	7·50	5·50
D163		4 mal. on 8 m. red	12·50	10·00
D164		10 mal. on 20 m. yellow	27·00	20·00
D165		20 mal. on 40 m. blue	45·00	35·00

D 25

D 53 Government Building, Tripoli

1952.

D188	D 25	2 m. brown	65	25
D189		5 m. green	95	50
D190		10 m. red	2·25	95
D191		50 m. blue	7·50	2·25

1964.

D296	D 53	2 m. brown	10	10
D297		6 m. green	20	10
D298		10 m. red	70	45
D299		50 m. blue	1·25	85

D 185 Men in Boat

1976. Ancient Mosaics. Multicoloured.

D725	5 dh. Type D **185**	10	10
D726	10 dh. Head of Medusa	10	10
D727	20 dh. Peacock	10	10
D728	50 dh. Fish	80	25

LIECHTENSTEIN Pt. 8

A small independent principality lying between Austria and Switzerland.

1912. 100 heller = 1 krone.
1921. 100 rappen = 1 franc (Swiss).

1 Prince John II

1912.

4	1	5 h. green	11·00	9·75
2		10 h. red	85·00	9·75
3		25 h. blue	85·00	35·00

2

3

1917.

7	2	3 h. violet	1·50	80
8		5 h. green	1·50	80
9	3	10 h. purple	1·50	80
10		15 h. brown	1·50	80
11		20 h. green	1·50	80
12		25 h. blue	1·50	80

1918. 60th Anniv of Prince John's Accession. As T **3** but dated "1858–1918" in upper corners.

13	3	20 h. green	50	90

1920. Optd with a scroll pattern.

14	2	5 h. green	2·00	5·50
15	3	10 h. purple	2·00	5·50
16		25 h. blue	2·00	5·50

1920. Surch.

17	2	40 h. on 3 h. violet	2·00	5·50
18	3	1 k. on 15 h. brown	2·00	5·50
19		2½ k. on 20 h. green	2·00	5·50

7

8 Castle of Vaduz

1920. Imperf.

20	7	5 h. bistre	15	3·50
21		10 h. orange	15	3·50
22		15 h. blue	15	3·50
23		20 h. brown	15	3·50
24		25 h. green	15	3·50
25		30 h. grey	15	3·50
26		40 h. red	15	3·50
27	8	1 k. blue	15	3·50

9 Prince John I

10 Arms

1920. Perf.

28	7	5 h. bistre	15	40
29		10 h. orange	15	40
30		15 h. blue	15	40
31		20 h. brown	15	40
32	–	25 h. green	15	40
33	7	30 h. grey	15	40
34	–	40 h. purple	15	40
35	–	50 h. green	15	40
36	–	60 h. brown	15	40
37	–	80 h. pink	15	40
38	8	1 k. lilac	15	65
39	–	2 k. blue	25	70
40	9	5 k. black	50	90
41	–	7½ k. grey	65	1·10
42	10	10 k. brown	75	1·40

DESIGNS—As Type **8**: 25 h. St. Mamertus Chapel; 40 h. Gutenberg Castle; 50 h. Courtyard, Vaduz Castle; 60 h. Red House, Vaduz; 80 h. Church Tower, Schaan; 2 k. Bendern. As Type **9**: 7½ k. Prince John II.

11 Madonna

14 Arms

15 St. Mamertus Chaple

16 Vaduz

1920. Prince John's 80th Birthday. Imperf or perf.

43	11	50 h. green	55	1·10
44		80 h. red	55	1·10
45		2 k. blue	55	1·10

1921. Surch **2 Rp.** and bars.

47	7	2 r. on 10 h. orge (No. 21)	35	16·00

1921.

47a	14	2 r. yellow	80	6·75
48		2½ r. brown	80	8·25
49		3 r. orange	80	5·50
50		5 r. green	9·00	1·00
51		7½ r. blue	5·25	25·00
65		10 r. green	21·00	3·25
53		13 r. brown	6·50	60·00
54		15 r. violet	13·00	13·00
55	15	20 r. black and violet	60·00	1·00
56	–	25 r. black and red	2·50	1·75
57	–	30 r. black and green	70·00	9·00
66	–	30 r. black and blue	14·00	1·50
58	–	35 r. black and brown	3·75	8·00
59	–	40 r. black and blue	7·00	2·75
60	–	50 r. black and green	6·50	3·00
61	–	80 r. black and grey	23·00	50·00
62	16	1 f. black and red	50·00	32·00

DESIGNS—As Type **15**: 25 r. Vaduz Castle; 30 r. Bendern; 35 r. Prince John II; 40 r. Church Tower at Schaan; 50 r. Gutenberg Castle; 80 r. Red House, Vaduz.

1924. Surch.

63	14	5 on 7½ r. blue	1·00	1·75
64		10 on 13 r. brown	60	1·10

19 Vine-dresser

21 Government Bldg. and Church, Vaduz

1924.

67	19	2½ r. mauve and green	1·00	4·50
68		5 r. blue and brown	1·60	70
69		7½ r. brown and green	1·10	4·50
70	–	10 r. green	9·00	55
71	19	15 r. green and purple	5·25	21·00
72	–	20 r. red	32·00	70
73	21	1½ f. blue	65·00	70·00

DESIGN—As Type **19**: 10, 20 r. Castle of Vaduz.

22 Prince John II

23

1925. 85th Birthday of Prince John.

74	22	10 + 5 r. green	29·00	13·00
75		20 + 5 r. red	24·00	13·00
76		30 + 5 r. blue	5·25	2·75

1927. 87th Birthday of Prince. Arms multicoloured.

77	23	10 + 5 r. green	8·00	16·00
78		20 + 5 r. purple	8·00	16·00
79		30 + 5 r. blue	8·00	15·00

24 Salvage Work by Austrian soldiers

1928. Flood Relief.

80	–	5 r. + 5 r. brown and purple	19·00	21·00
81	–	10 r. + 10 r. brown & green	26·00	22·00
82	24	20 r. + 10 r. brown and red	26·00	22·00
83	–	30 r. + 10 r. brown & blue	16·00	22·00

DESIGNS: 5 r. Railway bridge between Buchs and Schaan; 10 r. Village of Ruggell; 30 r. Salvage work by Swiss soldiers.

26 Prince John II, 1858-1928

1928. 70th Anniv of Accession of Prince John II.

84	–	10 r. green and brown	1·75	1·75
85	–	20 r. green and red	4·25	3·50
86	–	30 r. green and blue	9·25	11·00
87	–	60 r. green and mauve	35·00	55·00
88	26	1 f. 20 blue	45·00	60·00
89		1 f. 50 brown	80·00	£130
90		2 f. red	80·00	£130
91		5 f. green	80·00	£160

DESIGN—VERT: 10 r. to 60 r. Prince John II.

28 Prince Francis I

31 Girl Vintager

32 Prince Francis I and Princess Elsa

34 Monoplane over Vaduz Castle and Rhine Valley

1929. Accession of Prince Francis I.

92	–	10 r. green	50	1·75
93	28	20 r. red	1·00	2·25
94	–	30 r. blue	1·00	11·00
95	–	70 r. brown	16·00	75·00

PORTRAITS: 10 r. Prince Francis I as a boy; 30 r. Princess Elsa; 70 r. Prince Francis and Princess Elsa.

1930.

96	31	3 r. red	55	1·00
97	–	5 r. green	1·10	1·00
98	–	10 r. lilac	1·10	1·00
99	–	20 r. red	24·00	1·10
100	–	25 r. green	5·25	21·00
101	–	30 r. blue	5·75	1·10
102	–	35 r. green	9·25	9·00
103	–	40 r. brown	8·00	4·25
104	–	50 r. black	90·00	11·00
105	–	60 r. green	70·00	14·00
106	–	90 r. purple	80·00	85·00
107	–	1 f. 20 brown	80·00	£170
108	–	1 f. 50 blue	40·00	45·00
109	32	2 f. brown and green	65·00	85·00

DESIGNS—VERT: 5 r. Mt. Three Sisters–Edelweiss; 10 r. Alpine cattle–alpine roses; 20 r. Courtyard of Vaduz Castle; 25 r. Mt. Naafkopf; 30 r. Valley of Samina; 35 r. Rofenberg Chapel; 40 r. St. Mamertus' Chapel; 50 r. Kurhaus at Malbun; 60 r. Gutenberg Castle; 90 r. Schellenberg Monastery; 1 f. 20, Vaduz Castle; 1 f. 50, Pfaelzer club hut.

1930. Air.

110	–	15 r. brown	6·00	10·00
111	–	20 r. green	13·50	15·00
112	–	25 r. brown	7·25	25·00
113	–	35 r. blue	13·50	25·00
114	34	45 r. green	30·00	60·00
115		1 f. purple	50·00	40·00

DESIGNS—VERT: 15, 20 r. Biplane over snowy mountain peak. HORIZ: 25, 35 r. Biplane over Vaduz Castle.

35 Airship "Graf Zeppelin" over Alps

1931. Air.

116	35	1 f. green	40·00	80·00
117	–	2 f. blue	£100	£225

DESIGN: 2 f. Airship "Graf Zeppelin" (different).

37 Princess Elsa

38 Mt. Naafkopf

39 Prince Francis I

1932. Youth Charities.

118	–	10 r. + 5 r. green	18·00	25·00
119	37	20 r. + 5 r. red	18·00	25·00
120	–	30 r. + 10 r. blue	18·00	32·00

DESIGNS—22 × 29 mm: 10 r. Arms of Liechtenstein. As Type **37**: 30 r. Prince Francis.

1933.

121	38	25 r. orange	£160	70·00
122	–	90 r. green	7·50	45·00
123	–	1 f. 20 brown	80·00	£190

DESIGNS: 90 r. Gutenberg Castle; 1 f. 20, Vaduz Castle.

1933. Prince Francis's 80th Birthday.

124	39	10 r. violet	16·00	24·00
125		20 r. red	16·00	24·00
126		30 r. blue	16·00	24·00

40

41 "Three Sisters"

42 Vaduz Castle

44 Prince Francis I

45 Arms of Liechtenstein

46 Golden Eagle

1933.

127	40	3 r. red	15	45
128	41	5 r. green	3·00	75
129	–	10 r. violet	75	50
130	–	15 r. orange	20	85
131	–	20 r. red	50	45
132	–	25 r. brown	17·00	42·00
133	–	30 r. blue	3·25	90
134	–	35 r. green	1·00	4·00
135	–	40 r. brown	90	2·50
136	42	50 r. brown	18·00	14·00
137	–	60 r. purple	1·90	4·50
138	–	90 r. green	6·00	16·00
139	–	1 f. 20 blue	1·75	13·00
140	–	1 f. 50 brown	2·00	19·00
141	–	2 f. brown	45·00	£120
142	44	3 f. blue	65·00	£130
143	45	5 f. purple	£225	£750

DESIGNS—As Type **41**: 10 r. Schaan Church; 15 r. Bendern am Rhein; 20 r. Town Hall, Vaduz; 25 r. Saminatal. As Type **44**: 2 f. Princess Elsa. As Type **42**: 30 r. Saminatal (different); 35 r. Schellenberg ruins; 40 r. Government Building, Vaduz; 60 r. Vaduz Castle (different); 90 r. Gutenberg Castle; 1 f. 20, Pfalzer Hut, Bettlerjoch; 1 f. 50, Valuna.

See also Nos. 174, 225/6 and 258.

1934. Air.

145	46	10 r. violet	8·00	14·00
146	–	15 r. orange	18·00	35·00
147	–	20 r. red	18·00	35·00
148	–	30 r. blue	18·00	35·00
149	–	50 r. green	12·00	26·00

DESIGNS: 10 r. to 20 r. Golden eagles in flight; 30 r. Ospreys in nest; 50 r. Golden eagle on rock.

1935. Air. No. 115 surch **60 Rp.**

150	34	60 r. on 1 f. purple	26·00	38·00

49 "Hindenburg" and Schaan Church

1936. Air.

151	49	1 f. red	32·00	65·00
152	–	2 f. violet	27·00	65·00

DESIGN: 2 f. "Graf Zeppelin" over Schaan Airport.

51 Masescha am Triesenberg

52 Schellenberg Castle

1937.

154	–	3 r. brown	15	50
155	51	5 r. green and buff	15	20
156	–	10 r. violet and buff	15	15

157 – 15 r. black and buff 45 60
158 – 20 r. red and buff 20 30
159 – 25 r. brown and buff . . . . 90 3·00
160 – 30 r. blue and buff . . . . 1·75 60
161 **52** 40 r. green and buff . . . . 1·60 1·50
162 – 50 c. brown and buff . . . 1·40 2·00
163 – 60 r. purple and buff . . . . 1·60 2·00
164 – 90 r. violet and buff . . . . 9·25 11·00
165 – 1 f. purple and buff . . . . 1·60 8·00
166 – 1 f. 20 brown and buff . . . . 8·00 14·00
167 – 1 f. 50 grey and buff . . . . 5·25 14·00

DESIGNS—As Type **51**: 3 r. Schalun ruins; 10 r. Knight and Vaduz Castle; 15 r. Upper Saminatal; 20 r. Church and Bridge at Bendern; 25 r. Steg Chapel and girl. As Type **52**: 30 r. Farmer and orchard, Triesenberg; 50 r. Knight and Gutenberg Castle; 60 r. Baron von Brandis and Vaduz Castle; 90 r. "Three Sisters" mountain; 1 f. Boundary-stone on Luziensteig; 1 f. 20, Minstrel and Gutenberg Castle; 1 f. 50, Lawena (Schwarzhorn).

53 Roadmakers at Triesenberg

1937. Workers' Issue.

168 – 10 r. mauve 80 45
169 **53** 20 r. red . . . . 1·10 90
170 – 30 r. blue . . . . 1·90 1·90
171 – 50 r. brown . . . . 1·00 2·50

DESIGNS: 10 r. Bridge at Malbun; 30 r. Binnen Canal Junction; 50 r. Francis Bridge, near Planken.

1938. Death of Prince Francis I.

174 **44** 3 f. black on yellow . . . . 6·00 55·00

54 Josef Rheinberger 55 Black-headed Gulls

1939. Birth Centenary of Rheinberger (composer).

175 **54** 50 r. grey . . . . 65 3·25

1939. Air.

176 – 10 r. violet (Barn swallows) . 40 40
177 **55** 15 r. orange . . . . 65 1·50
178 – 20 r. red (Herring gull) . . . 1·75 45
179 – 30 r. blue (Common buzzard) 1·60 1·25
180 – 50 r. green (Northern goshawk) . . . . 5·00 2·00
181 – 1 f. red (Lammergeier) . . . 4·25 13·00
182 – 2 f. violet Lammergeier . . . 4·00 13·00

56 Offering Homage to First Prince

1939. Homage to Francis Joseph II.

183 **56** 20 r. red . . . . 1·10 1·60
184 30 r. blue . . . . 1·10 1·60
185 50 r. green . . . . 1·10 1·60

57 Francis Joseph II

1939.

186 – 2 f. green on cream . . . . 5·00 24·00
187 – 3 f. violet on cream . . . . 4·50 24·00
188 **57** 5 f. brown on cream . . . . 11·00 19·00

DESIGNS: 2 f. Cantonal Arms; 3 f. Arms of Principality.

58 Prince John when a Child

1940. Birth Centenary of Prince John II.

189 **58** 20 r. red . . . . 40 1·75
190 – 30 r. blue . . . . 55 2·75
191 – 50 r. green . . . . 1·00 7·00
192 – 1 f. violet . . . . 5·00 45·00
193 – 1 f. 50 black . . . . 4·00 40·00
194 – 3 f. brown . . . . 3·00 17·00

DESIGNS—As Type **58**: Portraits of Prince John in early manhood (30 r.), in middle age (50 r.) and in later life (1 f.), and Memorial tablet (1 f. 50). As Type **44**: 3 f. Framed portrait of Prince John II.

60 Wine Press

1941. Agricultural Propaganda.

195 – 10 r. brown 35 50
196 **60** 20 r. purple . . . . 60 1·00
197 – 30 r. blue . . . . 60 2·00
198 – 50 r. green . . . . 2·25 13·00
199 – 90 r. violet . . . . 2·25 15·00

DESIGNS: 10 r. Harvesting maize; 30 r. Sharpening scythe; 50 r. Milkmaid and cow; 90 r. Girl wearing traditional headdress.

61 Madonna and Child 62 Prince Hans Adam

1941.

200 **61** 10 f. purple on stone . . . . 32·00 80·00

1941. Princes (1st issue).

201 **62** 20 r. red . . . . 30 1·25
202 – 30 r. blue (Wenzel) . . . . 65 2·00
203 – 1 f. grey (Anton Florian) . . . 1·90 12·00
204 – 1 f. 50 green (Joseph) . . . 1·90 12·00

See also Nos. 210/13 and 217/20.

63 St. Lucius preaching

1942. 600th Anniv of Separation from Estate of Montfort.

205 **63** 20 r. red on pink 90 80
206 – 30 r. blue on pink . . . . . 90 2·00
207 – 50 r. green on pink . . . . 1·75 5·50
208 – 1 f. brown on pink . . . . 2·25 11·00
209 – 2 f. violet on pink . . . . 2·50 11·00

DESIGNS: 30 r. Count of Montfort replanning Vaduz; 50 r. Counts of Montfort-Werdenberg and Sargans signing treaty; 1 f. Battle of Gutenberg; 2 f. Homage to Prince of Liechtenstein.

64 Prince John Charles 65 Princess Georgina

1942. Princes (2nd issue).

210 **64** 20 r. pink 30 80
211 – 30 r. blue (Francis Joseph I) 45 1·50
212 – 1 f. purple (Alois I) . . . 1·75 11·00
213 – 1 f. 50 brown (John I) . . . 1·75 11·00

1943. Marriage of Prince Francis Joseph II and Countess Georgina von Wildczek.

214 – 10 r. purple 45 50
215 **65** 20 r. red 45 80
216 – 30 r. blue 45 80

PORTRAITS—VERT: 10 r. Prince Francis Joseph II. HORIZ (44×25 mm): 30 r. Prince and Princess.

66 Alois II 67 Marsh Land

1943. Princes (3rd issue).

217 **66** 20 r. brown 30 65
218 – 30 r. blue . . . . 60 1·25
219 – 1 f. brown . . . . 90 6·50
220 – 1 f. 50 green . . . . 90 6·50

PORTRAITS: 30 r. John II; 1 f. Francis I; 1 f. 50, Francis Joseph II.

1943. Completion of Irrigation Canal.

221 **67** 10 r. violet 20 40
222 – 30 r. blue . . . . 40 1·90
223 – 50 r. green . . . . 75 7·00
224 – 2 f. brown . . . . 1·60 11·00

DESIGNS: 30 r. Draining the canal; 50 r. Ploughing reclaimed land; 2 f. Harvesting crops.

1943. Castles. As T **41**.

225 10 r. grey (Vaduz) 40 35
226 20 r. brown (Gutenberg) . . . 55 80

69 Planken 70 Prince Francis Joseph II

1944. Various designs. Buff backgrounds.

227 **69** 3 r. brown 15 20
228 – 5 r. green (Bendern) 15 10
228a – 5 r. brown (Bendern) . . . 18·00 60
229 – 10 r. grey (Triesen) 20 10
230 – 15 r. grey (Ruggell) 30 85
231 – 20 r. red (Vaduz) 30 20
232 – 25 r. brown (Triesenberg) . . 30 75
233 – 30 r. blue (Schaan) 30 25
234 – 40 r. brown (Balzers) . . . 60 1·10
235 – 50 r. blue (Mauren) . . . . 70 1·50
236 – 60 r. green (Schellenberg) . . 3·75 4·25
237 – 90 r. green (Eschen) . . . 3·75 4·50
238 – 1 f. purple (Vaduz Castle) . . 2·25 3·75
239 – 1 f. 20 brown (Valunatal) . . 2·50 5·00
240 – 1 f. 50 blue (Lawena) . . . 2·50 5·00

1944.

241 **70** 2 f. brown and buff . . . . 4·75 11·00
242 – 3 f. green and buff . . . . 3·00 9·00

DESIGN: 3 f. Princess Georgina.

See also Nos. 302/3.

72 73

1945. Birth of Crown Prince Johann Adam Pius (known as Prince Hans Adam).

243 **72** 20 r. red, yellow and gold . . 60 40
244 30 r. blue, yellow and gold . . 75 1·10
245 100 r. grey, yellow and gold . 2·00 4·00

1945.

246 **73** 5 f. blue on buff . . . . . 15·00 23·00
247 5 f. brown on buff . . . . . 19·00 32·00

74 First Aid 75 St. Lucius

1945. Red Cross. Cross in red.

248 – 10 r. + 10 r. purple and buff 1·40 1·50
249 **74** 20 r. + 20 r. purple and buff . 1·40 2·25
250 – 1 f. + 1 f. 40 blue and buff 6·00 20·00

DESIGNS: 10 r. Mother and children; 1 f. Nurse and invalid.

1946.

251 **75** 10 f. grey on buff . . . . . 29·00 24·00

76 Red Deer Stag 79 Wilbur Wright

1946. Wild Life.

252 **76** 20 r. red . . . . 1·40 1·60
255 – 20 r. red (Chamois) . . . . 2·00 2·25
283 – 20 r. red (Roebuck) . . . . 9·00 2·25
253 – 30 r. blue (Arctic hare) . . . 2·00 3·00
256 – 30 r. blue (Alpine marmot) . 3·00 3·00
284 – 30 r. green (Black grouse) . 19·00 6·00
285 – 80 r. brown (Eurasian badger) 32·00 35·00
254 – 1 f. 50 green (Capercaillie) . 9·50 10·00
257 – 1 f. 50 brown (Golden eagle) . 9·50 16·00

1947. Death of Princess Elsa. As No. 141.

258 – 2 f. black on yellow . . . . 3·00 12·00

1948. Air. Pioneers of Flight.

259 – 10 r. green 65 20
260 – 15 r. violet . . . . 65 1·10
261 – 20 r. brown 80 20
262 – 25 r. red . . . . 1·25 1·60
263 – 40 r. blue . . . . 1·40 1·60
264 – 50 r. blue . . . . 1·75 1·75
265 – 1 f. purple . . . . 2·50 3·00
266 – 2 f. purple . . . . 4·50 4·00
267 **79** 5 f. green . . . . 5·50 5·50
268 – 10 f. black . . . . 30·00 17·00

PORTRAITS: 10 r. Leonardo da Vinci; 15 r. Joseph Montgolfier; 20 r. Jakob Degen; 25 r. Wilhelm Kress; 40 r. Etienne Robertson; 50 r. William Henson; 1 f. Otto Lilienthal; 2 f. Salomon Andree; 10 f. Icarus.

80 "Ginevra de Benci" (Da Vinci)

1949. Paintings.

269 **80** 10 r. green 45 30
270 – 20 r. red . . . . 1·25 60
271 – 30 r. brown . . . . 3·00 1·25
272 – 40 r. blue . . . . 6·00 65
273 – 50 r. violet . . . . 5·00 6·50
274 – 60 r. grey . . . . 11·00 5·50
275 – 80 r. brown . . . . 2·50 4·00
276 – 90 r. green . . . . 11·00 5·00
277 – 120 r. mauve . . . . 2·50 4·75

DESIGNS: 20 r. "Portrait of a Young Girl" (Rubens); 30 r. Self-portrait of Rembrandt in plumed hat; 40 r. "Stephan Gardiner, Bishop of Winchester" (Quentin Massys); 50 r. "Madonna and Child" (Hans Memling); 60 r. "Franz Meister in 1456" (Jehan Fouquet); 80 r. "Lute Player" (Orazio Gentileschi); 90 r. "Portrait of a Man" (Bernhardin Strigel); 120 r. "Portrait of a Man (Duke of Urbino)" (Raphael).

1949. No. 227 surch **5 Rp.** and bars.

278 **69** 5 r. on 3 r. brown and buff . . 60 40

82 Posthorn and Map of World

1949. 75th Anniv of U.P.U.

279 **82** 40 r. blue . . . . 2·50 3·50

83 Rossauer Castle 86 Boy cutting Loaf

1949. 250th Anniv of Acquisition of Domain of Schellenberg.

280 **83** 20 r. purple . . . . 1·25 1·25
281 – 40 r. blue . . . . 5·50 5·50
282 – 1 f. 50 red . . . . 7·00 7·00

DESIGN—HORIZ: 40 r. Bendern Church. VERT: 1 f. 50, Prince Johann Adam I.

1950. Surch **100 100**.

286 **82** 100 r. on 40 r. blue . . . . 20·00 38·00

1951. Agricultural scenes.

287 **86** 5 r. mauve 20 10
288 – 10 r. green 45 10
289 – 15 r. brown . . . . 4·50 5·00
290 – 20 r. brown . . . . 1·00 20
291 – 25 r. purple . . . . 4·50 5·00
292 – 30 r. green . . . . 3·25 55
293 – 40 r. blue . . . . 8·50 4·50
294 – 50 r. purple . . . . 7·50 3·00
295 – 60 r. brown . . . . 7·00 3·00
296 – 80 r. brown . . . . 9·00 8·00
297 – 90 r. green . . . . 14·00 4·75
298 – 1 f. blue . . . . 48·00 6·00

DESIGNS: 10 r. Man whetting scythe; 15 r. Mowing; 20 r. Girl and sweet corn; 25 r. Haywain; 30 r. Gathering grapes; 40 r. Man with scythe; 50 r. Herdsman with cows; 60 r. Ploughing; 80 r. Girl carrying basket of fruit; 90 r. Woman gleaning; 1 f. Tractor hauling corn.

87 "Lock on the Canal" (Aelbert Cuyp) 88 "Willem von Heythuysen, Burgomaster of Haarlem" (Frans Hals)

1951. Paintings.

299 **87** 10 r. + 10 r. green . . . . 8·00 6·00
300 **88** 20 r. + 20 r. brown . . . . 8·00 12·00
301 – 40 r. + 10 r. blue . . . . . 8·00 8·00

DESIGN—As Type **87**: 40 r. "Landscape" (Jacob van Ruysdael).

90 Vaduz Castle   96 Lord Baden-Powell

1951.
302 **70** 2 f. blue . . . . 12·00 25·00
303 – 3 f. brown . . . . £130 75·00
304 **90** 5 f. green £140 £130
DESIGN: 3 f. Princess Georgina.

1952. No. 281 surch **1.20**
308 1 f. 20 on 40 r. blue . . . . . 16·00 42·00

1952. Paintings from Prince's Collection. (a) As T **80** but size 25 × 30 mm.
309 10 r. green 80 80
305 20 r. purple . . . . 32·00 3·00
307 40 r. blue . . . . 12·00 5·00
312 40 r. blue . . . . 27·00 42·00
PAINTINGS: No. 309, "Portrait of a Young Man" (A. G.); 305, "Portrait" (Giovanni Salvoldo); 307, "St. John" (Andrea del Sarto); 312, "Leonhard, Count of Hag" (Hans von Kulmbach).

(b) As T **88** ($22\frac{1}{2} \times 24$ mm).
310 20 r. brown . . . . 12·00 2·25
306 30 r. green . . . . 22·00 7·50
311 30 r. brown . . . . 25·00 6·50
PAINTINGS: No. 310, "St. Nicholas" (Bartholomaus Zeitblom); 306, "Madonna and Child" (Sandro Botticelli); 311, "St. Christopher" (Lucas Cranach the elder).

1953. 14th International Scout Conf.
313 **96** 10 r. green . . . . 1·25 1·00
314 20 r. brown . . . . 10·00 1·75
315 25 r. red . . . . 10·00 17·00
316 40 r. blue . . . . 10·00 3·25

97 Alemannic Ornamental Disc, (c. A. D. 600)   98 Prehistoric Walled Settlement, Borscht

1953. Opening of National Museum, Vaduz.
317 **97** 10 r. brown . . . . 6·50 8·50
318 **98** 20 r. green . . . . 6·50 7·50
319 – 1 f. 20 blue . . . . 38·00 24·00
DESIGN—VERT: 1 f. 20, Rossen jug (3000 B.C.).

99 Footballers   100 Madonna and Child

1954. Football.
320 **99** 10 r. brown and red . . . . 2·00 1·00
321 – 20 r. deep green and green 8·00 1·50
322 – 25 r. deep brown & brown 20·00 25·00
323 – 40 r. violet and grey . . . . 16·00 9·00
DESIGNS: 20 r. Footballer kicking ball; 25 r. Goal-keeper; 40 r. Two footballers.
For stamps in similar designs see Nos. 332/5, 340/3, 351/4 and 363/6.

1954. Nos. 299/301 surch in figures.
324 **87** 35 r. on 10 r. + 10 r. green 3·00 2·00
325 **88** 60 r. on 20 r. + 10 r. brown 12·00 10·00
326 – 65 r. on 40 r. + 10 r. blue 7·50 7·00

1954. Termination of Marian Year.
327 **100** 20 r. brown . . . . 2·50 3·00
328 40 r. black . . . . 12·00 14·00
329 1 f. brown . . . . 13·00 14·00

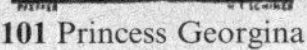

101 Princess Georgina   102 Crown Prince John Adam Pius

1955.
330 – 2 f. brown . . . . 55·00 35·00
331 **101** 3 f. green . . . . 55·00 35·00
PORTRAIT: 2 f. Prince Francis Joseph II.

1955. Mountain Sports. As T **99.**
332 10 r. purple and blue . . . . . 1·50 1·25
333 20 r. green and bistre . . . . . 4·00 1·25
334 25 r. brown and blue . . . . . 14·00 14·00
335 40 r. green and red . . . . . 12·00 4·25
DESIGNS: 10 r. Slalom racer; 20 r. Mountaineer hammering in piton; 25 r. Skier; 40 r. Mountaineer resting on summit.

1955. 10th Anniv of Liechtenstein Red Cross. Cross in red.
336 **102** 10 r. violet . . . . 1·25 60
337 – 20 r. green . . . . 3·50 1·75
338 – 40 r. brown . . . . 6·50 7·00
339 – 60 r. red . . . . 6·50 5·00
PORTRAITS: 20 r. Prince Philip; 40 r. Prince Nicholas; 60 r. Princess Nora.
See also No. 350.

1956. Athletics. As T **99.**
340 10 r. green and brown 80 60
341 20 r. purple and green . . . . 3·00 1·10
342 40 r. brown and blue . . . . 4·50 5·50
343 1 f. brown and red . . . . . . 10·00 10·00
DESIGNS: 10 r. Throwing the javelin; 20 r. Hurdling; 40 r. Pole vaulting; 1 f. Running.

103   104 Prince Francis Joseph II

1956. 150th Anniv of Sovereignty of Liechtenstein.
344 **103** 10 r. purple and gold . . . 2·00 75
345 1 f. 20 blue and gold . . . 8·00 3·50

1956. 50th Birthday of Prince Francis Joseph II.
346 **104** 10 r. green . . . . 1·40 40
347 15 r. blue . . . . 2·00 2·50
348 25 r. purple . . . . 2·00 2·50
349 60 r. brown . . . . 7·00 2·50

1956. 6th Philatelic Exhibition, Vaduz. As T **102** but inscr "6. BRIEFMARKEN-AUSSTELLUNG".
350 20 r. green . . . . 2·50 40

1956. Gymnastics. As T **99.**
351 10 r. green and pink . . . . . 2·50 1·10
352 15 r. purple and green . . . . 5·00 6·00
353 25 r. green and drab . . . . . 6·00 7·00
354 1 f. 50 brown and yellow . . . 13·00 14·00
DESIGNS: 10 r. Somersaulting; 15 r. Vaulting; 25 r. Exercising with rings; 1 f. 50, Somersaulting on parallel bars.

105 Norway Spruce   106 Lord Baden-Powell

1957. Liechtenstein Trees and Bushes.
355 **105** 10 r. purple . . . . 3·00 1·75
356 – 20 r. red . . . . 3·00 70
357 – 1 f. green . . . . 6·00 6·00
DESIGNS: 20 r. Wild rose bush; 1 f. Silver birch.
See also Nos. 369/71, 375/7 and 401/3.

1957. 50th Anniv of Boy Scout Movement and Birth Centenary of Lord Baden-Powell (founder).
358 – 10 r. blue . . . . 1·00 1·25
359 **106** 20 r. brown . . . . 1·00 1·25
DESIGN: 10 r. Torchlight procession.

107 St. Mamertus Chapel   108 Relief Map of Liechtenstein

1957. Christmas.
360 **107** 10 r. brown 70 20
361 – 40 r. blue . . . . 2·00 5·00
362 – 1 f. 50 purple . . . . . . 8·00 8·50
DESIGNS—(from St. Mamertus Chapel): 40 r. Altar shrine; 1 f. 50, "Pieta" (sculpture).
See also Nos. 372/4 and 392/4.

1958. Sports. As T **99.**
363 15 r. violet and blue . . . . . 1·50 1·25
364 30 r. green and purple . . . . 5·00 6·00
365 40 r. green and orange . . . . 5·00 6·00
366 90 r. brown and green . . . . 4·25 4·25
DESIGNS: 15 r. Swimmer; 30 r. Fencers; 40 r. Tennis player; 90 r. Racing cyclists.

1958. Brussels International Exhibition.
367 **108** 25 r. violet, stone and red 50 55
368 40 r. purple, blue and red 60 55

1958. Liechtenstein Trees and Bushes. As T **105.**
369 20 r. brown (Sycamore) . . . . 3·00 60
370 50 r. green (Holly) . . . . . . 12·00 3·50
371 90 r. violet (Yew) . . . . . . 3·00 2·75

1958. Christmas. As T **107.**
372 20 r. green . . . . 2·50 2·25
373 35 r. violet . . . . 2·50 2·25
374 80 r. brown . . . . 2·75 2·25
DESIGNS: 20 r. "St. Maurice and St. Agatha"; 35 r. "St. Peter"; 80 r. St. Peter's Chapel, Mals-Balzers.

1959. Liechtenstein Trees and Bushes. As T **105.**
375 20 r. lilac (Red-berried larch) . 4·50 2·25
376 50 r. red (Red-berried elder) . . 4·00 2·25
377 90 r. green (Linden) . . . . . 3·50 3·00

109   111 Harvester

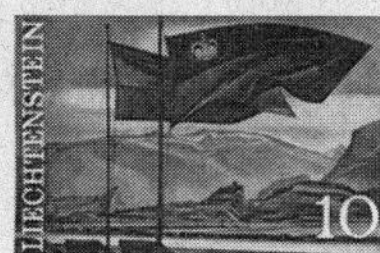
110 Flags of Vaduz Castle and Rhine Valley

1959. Pope Pius XII Mourning.
378 **109** 30 r. purple and gold . . . 65 75

1959. Views.
379 – 5 r. brown 10 10
380 **110** 10 r. purple 10 10
381 – 20 r. mauve 25 10
382 – 30 r. red 30 15
383 – 40 r. green 75 35
384 – 50 r. blue 45 30
385 – 60 r. blue 65 40
386 **111** 75 r. brown . . . . . . 1·00 1·25
387 – 80 r. green 75 55
388 – 90 r. purple 90 65
389 – 1 f. brown 90 80
390 – 1 f. 20 red . . . . 1·25 1·25
390a – 1 f. 30 green . . . . . . 1·40 1·25
391 – 1 f. 50 blue . . . . 1·50 1·50
DESIGNS—HORIZ: 5 r. Bendern Church; 20 r. Rhine Dam; 30 r. Gutenberg Castle; 40 r. View from Schellenberg; 50 r. Vaduz Castle; 60 r. Naafkopf-Falknis Mountains (view from the Bettlerjoch); 1 f. 20, Harvesting apples; 1 f. 30, Farmer and wife; 1 f. 50, Saying grace at table. VERT: 80 r. Alpine haymaker; 90 r. Girl in vineyard; 1 f. Mother in kitchen.

1959. Christmas. As T **107.**
392 5 r. green 50 15
393 60 r. brown . . . . 5·00 4·00
394 1 f. purple . . . . 2·50 2·50
DESIGNS: 5 r. Bendern Church belfry; 60 r. Relief on bell of St. Theodul's Church; 1 f. Sculpture on tower of St. Lucius's Church.

112 Bell 47J Ranger Helicopter

1960. Air. 30th Anniv of 1st Liechtenstein Air Stamps.
395 **112** 30 r. red . . . . 2·00 2·25
396 – 40 r. blue . . . . 5·00 2·25
397 – 50 r. purple . . . . 6·00 5·00
398 – 75 r. green . . . . 2·50 2·50
DESIGNS: 40 r. Boeing 707 jetliner; 50 r. Convair Coronado jetliner; 75 r. Douglas DC-8 jetliner.

1960. World Refugee Year. Nos. 367/8 surch **WELTFLUCHTLINGSJAHR 1960,** uprooted tree and new value.
399 **108** 30 + 10 r. on 40 r. purple, blue and red 60 85
400 50 + 10 r. on 25 r. violet, stone and red . . . . . 80 1·00

1960. Liechtenstein Trees and Bushes. As T **105.**
401 20 r. brown (Beech) . . . . . 5·50 6·50
402 30 r. purple (Juniper) . . . . . 6·00 8·00
403 50 r. turquoise (Mountain pines) 17·00 10·50

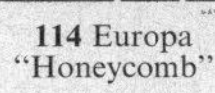

114 Europa "Honeycomb"   115 Princess Gina

1960. Europa.
404 **114** 50 r. multicoloured . . . . 60·00 40·00

1960.
404a – 1 f. 70 violet . . . . . . 1·00 85
405 **115** 2 f. blue . . . . 1·75 1·40
406 – 3 f. brown . . . . 2·25 1·50
PORTRAITS: 1 f. 70, Crown Prince Hans Adam; 3 f. Prince Francis Joseph II.

116 Heinrich von Frauenberg   117 "Power Transmission"

1961. Minnesingers (1st issue). Multicoloured. Reproduction from the Manessian Manuscript of Songs.
407 15 r. Type **116** 30 35
408 25 r. Ulrich von Liechtenstein 50 50
409 35 r. Ulrich von Gutenberg . . 60 70
410 1 f. Konrad von Altstatten . . 1·10 1·10
411 1 f. 50 Walther von der Vogelweide . . . . 5·00 8·00
See also Nos. 415/18 and 428/31.

1961. Europa.
412 **117** 50 r. multicoloured 45 25

118 Clasped Hands   119 Campaign Emblem

1962. Europa.
413 **118** 50 r. red and blue 40 40

1962. Malaria Eradication.
414 **119** 50 r. blue 35 35

1962. Minnesingers (2nd issue). As T **116.** Mult.
415 20 r. King Konradin 20 20
416 30 r. Kraft von Toggenburg . . 60 60
417 40 r. Heinrich von Veldig . . 60 60
418 2 f. Tannhauser . . . . 1·75 1·75

120 Pieta   121 Prince Francis Joseph II

1962. Christmas.
419 **120** 30 r. mauve 40 40
420 – 50 r. red 55 55
421 – 1 f. 20 blue . . . . . . 1·25 1·25
DESIGNS: 50 r. Fresco with angel; 1 f. 20, View of Mauren.
See also Nos. 438/40.

1963. 25th Anniv of Reign of Prince Francis Joseph II.
422 **121** 5 f. green . . . . 4·00 3·25

122 Milk and Bread

1963. Freedom from Hunger.
423 **122** 50 r. brown, purple & red . 35 35

123 "Angel of Annunciation"   124 "Europa"

1963. Red Cross Cent. Cross in red; background grey.
424 **123** 20 r. yellow and green . . 25 25
425 – 80 r. violet and mauve . . 60 60
426 – 1 f. blue and ultramarine . 80 80
DESIGNS: 80 r. "The Epiphany"; 1 f. "Family".

1963. Europa.
427 **124** 50 r. multicoloured 75 65

1963. Minnesingers (3rd issue). As T **116.** Mult.
428 25 r. Heinrich von Sax 25 25
429 30 r. Kristan von Hamle . . . 40 40
430 75 r. Werner von Teufen . . . 75 75
431 1 f. 70 Hartmann von Aue . . 1·75 1·75

125 Olympic Rings and Flags

126 Arms of Counts of Werdenberg, Vaduz

1964. Olympic Games, Tokyo.
432 **125** 50 r. red, black and blue . . . 30 30

1964. Arms (1st issue). Multicoloured.
433 20 f. Type **126** 20 15
434 30 f. Barons of Brandis 30 20
435 80 r. Counts of Sulz 75 65
436 1 f. 50 Counts of Hohenems . . 1·10 90
See also Nos. 443/6.

127 Roman Castle, Schaan

128 P. Kaiser

1964. Europa.
437 **127** 50 f. multicoloured 80 70

1964. Christmas. As T **120.**
438 10 r. purple 10 10
439 40 r. blue 25 25
440 1 f. 30 purple . . . . 1·10 1·10
DESIGNS: 10 r. Masescha Chapel; 40 r. "Mary Magdalene" (altar painting); 1 f. 30, "St. Sebastian, Madonna and Child, and St. Rochus" (altar painting).

1964. Death Centenary of Peter Kaiser (historian).
441 **128** 1 f. green on cream 80 70

129 "Madonna" (wood sculpture, c. 1700)

130 Europa "Links" (ancient belt-buckle)

1965.
442 **129** 10 f. red . . . . 7·00 4·50

1965. Arms (2nd issue). As T **126.** Multicoloured.
443 20 r. Von Schellenberg 20 15
444 30 r. Von Gutenberg 25 20
445 80 r. Von Frauenberg 75 70
446 1 f. Von Ramschwag 75 70

1965. Europa.
447 **130** 50 r. brown, grey and blue . . 30 40

131 "Jesus in the Temple"

1965. Birth Centenary of Ferdinand Nigg (painter).
448 – 10 r. deep green and green . . 10 10
449 – 30 r. brown and orange . . . 15 15
450 **131** 1 f. 20 green and blue . . . 75 75
DESIGNS—VERT: 10 r. "The Annunciation"; 30 r. "The Magi".

132 Princess Gina and Prince Franz (after painting by Pedro Leitao)

133 Telecommunications Symbols

1965. Special Issue.
451 **132** 75 r. multicoloured 65 65
See also No. 457.

1965. Centenary of I.T.U.
452 **133** 25 r. multicoloured 20 20

134 Tree ("Wholesome Earth")

1966. Nature Protection.
453 **134** 10 r. green and yellow . . . 10 10
454 – 20 r. blue and light blue . . 15 15
455 – 30 r. blue and green . . . 15 15
456 – 1 f. 50 red and yellow . . . 1·40 1·40
DESIGNS: 20 r. Bird ("Pure Air"); 30 r. Fish ("Clean Water"); 1 f. 50, Sun ("Protection of Nature").

1966. Prince Franz Joseph II's 60th Birthday. As T **132**, but with portrait of Prince Franz and inscr "1906–1966".
457 – 1 f. multicoloured 80 80

135 Arms of Herren von Richenstein

136 Europa "Ship"

1966. Arms of Triesen Families. Multicoloured.
458 20 r. Type **135** 15 15
459 30 r. Jinker Vaistli 20 20
460 60 r. Edle von Trisun 50 50
461 1 f. 20 Die von Schiel 80 80

1966. Europa.
462 **136** 50 r. multicoloured 30 30

137 Vaduz Parish Church

138 Cogwheels

1966. Restoration of Vaduz Parish Church.
463 **137** 5 r. green and red 10 10
464 – 20 r. purple and bistre . . . 15 10
465 – 30 r. blue and red 20 20
466 – 1 f. 70 brown and green . . 1·10 90
DESIGNS: 20 r. St. Florin; 30 r. Madonna; 1 f. 70, God the Father.

1967. Europa.
467 **138** 50 r. multicoloured 30 30

139 "The Man from Malanser"

141 "Alpha and Omega"

1967. Liechtenstein Sagas (1st series). Multicoloured.
468 20 r. Type **139** 20 10
469 30 r. "The Treasure of Gutenberg" 25 15
470 1 f. 20 "The Giant of Guflina" 65 40
See also Nos. 492/4 and 516/18.

1967. Christian Symbols. Multicoloured.
472 20 r. Type **141** 10 10
473 30 r. "Tropaion" (Cross as victory symbol) 10 10
474 70 r. Christ's monogram . . . 55 55

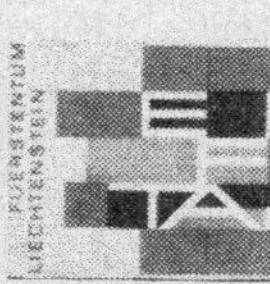

142 Father J. B. Buchel (educator, historian and poet)

143 "E.F.T.A."

1967. Buchel Commemoration.
475 **142** 1 f. red and green 65 35

1967. European Free Trade Association.
476 **143** 50 r. multicoloured 65 25

144 "Peter and Paul", Mauren

145 Campaign Emblem

1967. "Patrons of the Church". Multicoloured.
477 5 r. "St. Joseph", Planken . . 15 10
478 10 r. "St. Lawrence", Schaan . 15 10
479 20 r. Type **144** 20 10
480 30 r. "St. Nicholas", Balzers . 25 10
480a 40 r. "St. Sebastian", Nendeln 50 25
481 50 r. "St. George", Schellenberg 50 20
482 60 r. "St. Martin", Eschen . . 60 30
483 70 r. "St. Fridolin", Ruggell . 65 40
484 80 r. "St. Gallus", Triesen . . 75 45
485 1 f. "St. Theodolus", Triesenberg 85 40
486 1 f. 20 "St. Anna", Vaduz Castle 95 70
487 1 f. 50 "St. Marie", Bendern-Camprin . . . . 1·10 80
488 2 f. "St. Lucius", (patron saint of Liechtenstein) . . . . . 1·50 1·10

1967. "Technical Assistance".
489 **145** 50 r. + 20 r. multicoloured 30 30

146 Europa "Key"

1968. Europa.
490 **146** 50 r. multicoloured 30 25

147 Arms of Liechtenstein and Wilczek

148 Sir Rowland Hill

1968. Silver Wedding Anniv of Prince Francis Joseph II and Princess Gina.
491 **147** 75 r. multicoloured 45 40

1968. Liechtenstein Sagas (2nd series). As T **139.** Multicoloured.
492 30 r. "The Treasure of St. Mamerten" 20 15
493 50 r. "The Hobgoblin in the Bergerwald" 25 25
494 80 r. "The Three Sisters" . . . 65 65

1968. "Pioneers of Philately" (1st series).
495 **148** 20 r. green 15 10
496 – 30 r. brown 20 15
497 – 1 f. black 85 75
PORTRAITS: 30 r. Philippe de Ferrary; 1 f. Maurice Burrus.
See also Nos. 504/5 and 554/6.

150 Arms of Liechtenstein

151 Colonnade

1969.
498 **150** 3 f. 50 brown . . . . . . 2·25 1·50

1969. Europa.
499 **151** 50 r. multicoloured 35 30

152 "Biology"

1969. 250th Anniv of Liechtenstein. Multicoloured.
500 10 r. Type **152** 10 10
501 30 r. "Physics" 20 15
502 50 r. "Astronomy" 40 30
503 80 r. "Art" 60 60

1969. "Pioneers of Philately" (2nd series). As T **148.**
504 80 r. brown 50 40
505 1 f. 20 blue . . . . 1·10 90
PORTRAITS: 80 r. Carl Lindenberg; 1 f. 20, Theodore Champion.

153 Arms of St. Luzi Monastery

154 Symbolic "T"

1969. Arms of Church Patrons. Multicoloured.
506 20 r. St. Johann's Abbey . . . 20 10
507 30 r. Type **153** 25 20
508 30 r. Ladies' Priory, Schanis . 25 20
509 30 r. Knights Hospitallers, Feldkirch 25 20
510 50 r. Pfafers Abbey 35 30
511 50 r. Weingarten Abbey . . . 35 30
512 75 r. St. Gallen Abbey 70 50
513 1 f. 20 Ottobeuren Abbey . . 1·10 80
514 1 f. 50 Chur Episcopate . . . . 1·40 90

1969. Centenary of Liechtenstein Telegraph System.
515 **154** 30 r. multicoloured 15 15

1969. Liechtenstein Sagas (3rd series). As T **139.** Multicoloured.
516 20 r. "The Cheated Devil" . . 20 15
517 50 r. "The Fiery Red Goat" . 45 25
518 60 r. "The Grafenberg Treasure" 65 35

155 Orange Lily

156 "Flaming Sun"

1970. Nature Conservation Year. Multicoloured.
519 20 r. Type **155** 25 15
520 30 r. Wild orchid 45 20
521 50 r. Ranunculus 60 40
522 1 f. 20 Bog bean . . . . . . 1·25 1·00
See also Nos. 532/5 and 548/51.

1970. Europa.
523 **156** 50 r. yellow, blue & green . 35 30

157 Prince Wenzel

158 Prince Francis Joseph II

1970. 25th Anniv of Liechtenstein Red Cross.
524 **157** 1 f. multicoloured 55 45

1970.
526 – 1 f. 70 green . . . . . . 1·10 1·10
526a – 2 f. 50 blue . . . . 1·90 1·50
527 **158** 3 f. black . . . . 2·10 1·75
DESIGNS: 1 f. 70, Prince Hans Adam; 2 f. 50, Princess Gina.

159 "Mother and Child" (R. Schadler)

160 Bronze Boar (La Tene period)

1970. Christmas.
528 **159** 30 r. multicoloured 20 15

1971. National Museum Inauguration
529 **160** 25 r. black, blue & ultram 20 15
530 – 30 r. green and brown . . 30 15
531 – 75 r. multicoloured 60 40
DESIGNS: 30 r. Ornamental peacock (Roman, 2nd-century); 75 r. Engraved bowl (13th-century).

1971. Liechtenstein Flowers (2nd series). As T **155.** Multicoloured.
532 10 r. Cyclamen 20 10
533 20 r. Moonwort 20 15
534 50 r. Superb pink 45 35
535 1 f. 50 Alpine columbine . . . 1·40 1·00

161 Europa Chain

1971. Europa.
536 161 50 r. yellow, blue & black 30 30

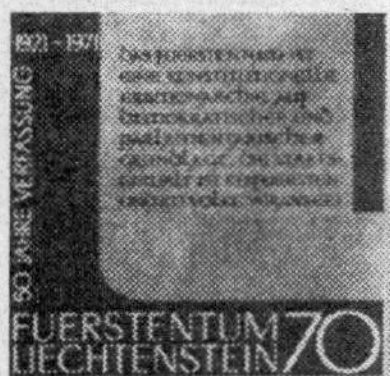

162 Part of Text

163 Cross-country Skiing

1971. 50th Anniv of 1921 Constitution. Mult.
537 70 r. Type **162** 60 50
538 80 r. Princely crown 65 55

1971. Winter Olympic Games, Sapporo, Japan (1972). Multicoloured.
539 15 r. Type **163** 20 10
540 40 r. Ice hockey 35 25
541 65 r. Downhill skiing 55 40
542 1 f. 50 Figure skating 1·40 1·25

164 "Madonna and Child" (sculpture, Andrea della Robbia)

165 Gymnastics

1971. Christmas.
543 164 30 r. multicoloured 20 15

1972. Olympic Games, Munich. Multicoloured.
544 10 r. Type **165** 15 10
545 20 r. High jumping 20 15
546 40 r. Running 40 25
547 60 r. Throwing the discus 50 35

1972. Liechtenstein Flowers (3rd series). As T **155.** Multicoloured.
548 20 r. Sulphur anemone 15 15
549 30 r. Turk's-cap lily 30 20
550 60 r. Alpine centaury 60 40
551 1 f. 20 Reed-mace 1·10 75

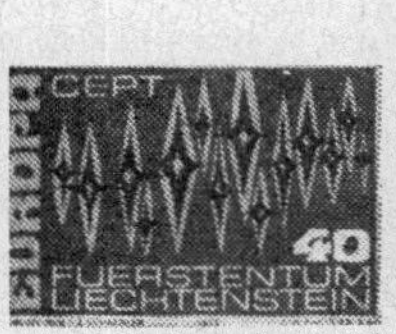

166 "Communications"

168 "Faun"

1972. Europa.
552 166 40 r. multicoloured 30 25

1972. "Pioneers of Philately" (3rd series). As T **148.**
554 30 r. green 25 25
555 40 r. purple 30 30
556 1 f. 30 blue 1·10 85
PORTRAITS: 30 r. Emilio Diena; 40 r. Andre de Cock; 1 f. 30, Theodore E. Steinway.

1972. "Natural Art". Motifs fashioned from roots and branches. Multicoloured.
557 20 r. Type **168** 15 15
558 30 r. "Dancer" 20 20
559 1 f. 10 "Owl" 90 90

169 "Madonna with Angels" (F. Nigg)

170 Lawena Springs

1972. Christmas.
560 169 30 r. multicoloured 25 20

1972. Landscapes.
561 – 5 r. purple and yellow 10 10
562 170 10 r. green and light green 10 10
563 – 15 r. brown and green 10 10
564 – 25 r. purple and blue 25 20
565 – 30 r. purple and brown 30 10
566 – 40 r. purple and brown 40 20
567 – 50 r. blue and lilac 30 20
568 – 60 r. green and yellow 55 30
569 – 70 r. blue and cobalt 60 35
570 – 80 r. green and light green 70 40
571 – 1 f. brown and green 95 45
572 – 1 f. 30 blue and green 1·10 75
573 – 1 f. 50 brown and blue 1·40 75
574 – 1 f. 80 brown & lt brown 1·60 1·10
575 – 2 f. brown and blue 1·90 1·25
DESIGNS: 5 r. Silum; 15 r. Ruggeller Reed; 25 r. Steg Kirchlispitz; 30 r. Feld Schellenberg; 40 r. Rennhof Mauren; 50 r. Tidrufe; 60 r. Eschner Riet; 70 r. Mittagspitz; 80 r. Schaan Forest; 1 f. St. Peter's Chapel, Mals; 1 f. 30, Frommenhaus; 1 f. 50, Ochsenkopf; 1 f. 80, Hehlawangspitz; 2 f. Saminaschlucht.

171 Europa "Posthorn"

1973. Europa.
576 171 30 r. multicoloured 25 20
577 40 r. multicoloured 35 30

172 Chambered Nautilus Goblet

173 Arms of Liechtenstein

1973. Treasures from Prince's Collection (1st issue). Drinking Vessels. Multicoloured.
578 30 r. Type **172** 25 20
579 70 r. Ivory tankard 60 45
580 1 f. 10 Silver cup 80 70
See also Nos. 589/92.

1973.
581 173 5 f. multicoloured 3·50 2·75

174 False Ringlet

175 "Madonna" (Bartolomeo di Tommaso da Foligno)

1973. Small Fauna of Liechtenstein (1st series). Multicoloured.
582 30 r. Type **174** 35 20
583 40 r. Curlew 1·25 30
584 60 r. Edible frog 60 40
585 80 r. Grass snake 80 55
See also Nos. 596/9.

1973. Christmas.
586 175 30 r. multicoloured 25 20

176 "Shouting Horseman" (sculpture, Andrea Riccio)

177 Footballers

1974. Europa. Multicoloured.
587 30 r. Type **176** 25 20
588 40 r. "Squatting Aphrodite" (sculpture, Antonio Susini) 35 30

1974. Treasures from Prince's Collection (2nd issue). Porcelain. As T **172.** Multicoloured.
589 30 r. Vase, 19th century 25 20
590 50 r. Vase, 1740 40 30
591 60 r. Vase, 1830 50 40
592 1 f. Vase, c. 1700 80 75

1974. World Cup Football Championship, West Germany.
593 177 80 f. multicoloured 80 55

178 Posthorn and U.P.U. Emblem

179 Bishop Marxer

1974. Centenary of Universal Postal Union.
594 178 40 r. black, green & gold 30 25
595 60 r. black, red and gold 40 40

1974. Small Fauna of Liechtenstein (2nd series). As T **174.** Multicoloured.
596 15 r. Mountain newt 20 10
597 25 r. Adder 25 15
598 70 r. Cynthia's fritillary (butterfly) 1·75 60
599 1 f. 10 Three-toed woodpecker 2·75 85

1974. Death Centenary of Bishop Franz Marxer.
600 179 1 f. multicoloured 85 85

180 Prince Francis Joseph II and Princess Gina

1974.
601 180 10 f. brown and gold 6·50 4·50

181 "St. Florian"

182 Prince Constantin

1974. Christmas. Glass Paintings. Multicoloured.
602 30 r. Type **181** 20 15
603 50 r. "St. Wendelin" 35 30
604 60 r. "St. Mary, Anna and Joachim" 45 40
605 70 r. "Jesus in Manger" 55 50

1975. Liechtenstein Princes.
606 182 70 r. green and gold 55 50
607 – 80 r. purple and gold 70 60
608 – 1 f. 20 blue and gold 95 85
PORTRAITS: 80 r. Prince Maximilian; 1 f. 20, Prince Alois.

183 "Cold Sun" (M. Frommelt)

184 Imperial Cross

1975. Europa. Paintings. Multicoloured.
609 30 r. Type **183** 25 20
610 60 r. "Village" (L. Jager) 55 45

1975. Imperial Insignia (1st series). Multicoloured.
611 30 r. Type **184** 25 20
612 60 r. Imperial sword 40 35
613 1 f. Imperial orb 80 70
614 1 f. 30 Imperial robe (50 × 32 mm) 2·50 2·50
615 2 f. Imperial crown 2·00 1·75
See also Nos. 670/3.

185 "Red Cross Activities"

186 St. Mamerten, Triesen

1975. 30th Anniv of Liechtenstein Red Cross.
616 185 60 r. multicoloured 45 35

1975. European Architectural Heritage Year. Multicoloured.
617 40 r. Type **186** 25 25
618 50 r. Red House, Vaduz 30 30
619 70 r. Prebendary buildings, Eschen 50 60
620 1 f. Gutenberg Castle, Balzers 75 85

187 Speed Skating

188 "Daniel in the Lions' Den"

1975. Winter Olympic Games, Innsbruck (1976). Multicoloured.
621 20 r. Type **187** 20 10
622 25 r. Ice hockey 25 15
623 70 r. Downhill skiing 70 50
624 1 f. 20 Slalom 1·10 85

1975. Christmas and Holy Year. Capitals in Chur Cathedral.
625 188 30 r. violet and gold 25 20
626 – 60 r. green and gold 50 40
627 – 90 r. red and gold 75 65
DESIGNS: 60 r. "Madonna"; 90 r. "St. Peter".

189 Mouflon

190 Crayfish

1976. Europa. Ceramics by Prince Hans von Liechtenstein. Multicoloured.
628 40 r. Type **189** 50 25
629 80 r. "Ring-necked Pheasant and Brood" 80 60

1976. World Wildlife Fund. Multicoloured.
630 25 r. Type **190** 25 20
631 40 r. Turtle 50 30
632 70 r. European otter 75 65
633 80 r. Lapwing 1·50 90

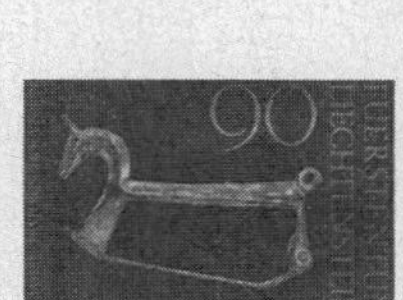

191 Roman Fibula

193 Judo

1976. 75th Anniv of National Historical Society.
634 191 90 r. multicoloured 75 60

1976. Olympic Games, Montreal. Multicoloured.
636 35 r. Type **193** 25 20
637 50 r. Volleyball 35 35
638 80 r. Relay 50 50
639 1 f. 10 Long jumping 70 75

194 "Singing Angels"

195 "Pisces"

1976. 400th Birth Anniv (1977) of Peter Paul Rubens (painter). Multicoloured.
640 50 r. Type **194** 50 60
641 70 r. "Sons of the Artist" 75 85
642 1 f. "Daughters of Cecrops" (49 × 39 mm) 3·00 3·25

1976. Signs of the Zodiac (1st series). Multicoloured.
643 20 r. Type **195** 15 15
644 40 r. "Aries" 30 25
645 80 r. "Taurus" 50 55
646 90 r. "Gemini" 70 75
See also Nos. 666/9 and 710/13.

196 "Child Jesus of Prague"

197 Sarcophagus Statue, Chur Cathedral

1976. Christmas. Monastic Wax Sculptures. Mult.

647 20 r. Type **196** 15 10
648 50 r. "The Flight into Egypt" (vert) 40 35
649 80 r. "Holy Trinity" (vert) . . 60 55
650 1 f. 50 "Holy Family" . . . . 1·10 1·00

1976. Bishop Ortlieb von Brandis of Chur Commemoration.

651 **197** 1 f. 10 brown and gold . . 70 65

199 Map of Liechtenstein, 1721 (J. Heber)

200 Coin of Emperor Constantine II

1977. Europa. Multicoloured.

664 40 r. Type **199** 20 20
665 80 r. "View of Vaduz, 1815" (F. Bachmann) 45 45

1977. Signs of the Zodiac (2nd series). As T **195.** Multicoloured.

666 40 r. "Cancer" 25 20
667 70 r. "Leo" 45 45
668 80 r. "Virgo" 55 55
669 1 f. 10 "Libra" 65 70

1977. Imperial Insignia (2nd series). As T **184.** Multicoloured.

670 40 r. Holy Lance and Reliquary with Particle of the Cross . . 30 25
671 50 r. "St. Matthew" (Imperial Book of Gospels) 35 30
672 80 r. St. Stephen's Purse . . . 55 55
673 90 r. Tabard of Imperial Herald . 75 75

1977. Coins (1st series). Multicoloured.

674 35 r. Type **200** 30 25
675 70 r. Lindau Brakteat 50 50
676 80 r. Coin of Ortlieb von Brandis 60 60
See also Nos. 707/9.

201 Frauenthal Castle, Styria

202 Children in Costume

1977. Castles.

677 **201** 20 r. green and gold . . . 15 15
678 – 50 r. red and gold 30 30
679 – 80 r. lilac and gold 45 50
680 – 90 r. blue and gold 50 60
DESIGNS: 50 r. Gross-Ullersdorf, Moravia; 80 r. Liechtenstein Castle, near Modling, Austria; 90 r. Palais Liechtenstein, Alserbachstrasse, Vienna.

1977. National Costumes. Multicoloured.

681 40 r. Type **202** 25 25
682 70 r. Two girls in traditional costume 40 45
683 1 f. Woman in festive costume 60 65

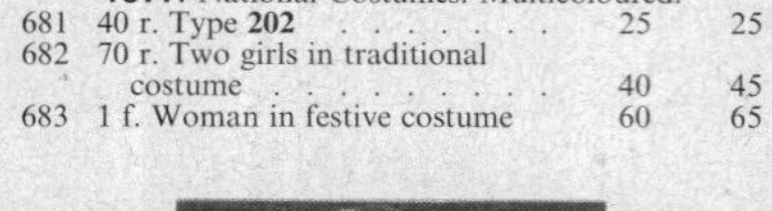

203 Princess Tatjana

1977. Princess Tatjana.

684 **203** 1 f. 10 lt brn, brn & gold 1·00 80

204 "Angel"

205 Palais Liechtenstein, Bankgasse, Vienna

1977. Christmas. Sculptures by Erasmus Kern. Multicoloured.

685 20 r. Type **204** 15 15
686 50 r. "St. Rochus" 30 30
687 80 r. "Madonna" 70 55
688 1 f. 50 "God the Father" . . . 1·10 1·00

1978. Europa.

689 **205** 40 r. blue and gold 30 25
690 – 80 r. red and gold 70 55
DESIGN: 80 r. Feldsberg Castle.

206 Farmhouse, Triesen

207 Vaduz Castle

1978. Buildings. Multicoloured.

691 10 r. Type **206** 10 10
692 20 r. Upper village of Triesen 15 10
693 35 r. Barns at Balzers 30 20
694 40 r. Monastery building, Bendern 30 10
695 50 r. Rectory tower, Balzers-Mals 40 25
696 70 r. Rectory, Mauren 50 30
697 80 r. Farmhouse, Schellenberg 70 45
698 90 r. Rectory, Balzers 75 70
699 1 f. Rheinberger House, Vaduz 80 55
700 1 f. 10 Vaduz Mitteldorf . . . 90 70
701 1 f. 50 Town Hall, Triesenberg 1·25 95
702 2 f. National Museum and Administrator's residence, Vaduz . . . . 1·75 1·10

1978. 40th Anniv of Prince Francis Joseph II's Accession. Royal Residence. Multicoloured.

703 40 r. Type **207** 40 40
704 50 r. Courtyard 40 40
705 70 r. Hall 65 65
706 80 r. High Altar, Castle Chapel 75 75

208 Coin of Prince Charles

209 "Portrait of a Piebald" (J. G. von Hamilton and A. Faistenberger)

1978. Coins (2nd series). Multicoloured.

707 40 r. Type **208** 30 30
708 50 r. Coin of Prince John Adam 40 40
709 80 r. Coin of Prince Joseph Wenzel 65 65

1978. Signs of the Zodiac (3rd series). As T **195.** Multicoloured.

710 40 r. "Scorpio" 30 25
711 50 r. "Sagittarius" 40 35
712 80 r. "Capricorn" 65 60
713 1 f. 50 "Aquarius" . . . . . 1·25 1·10

1978. Paintings. Multicoloured.

714 70 r. Type **209** 50 50
715 80 r. "Portrait of a Blackish-brown Stallion" (J. G. von Hamilton) 65 65
716 1 f. 10 "Golden Carriage of Prince Joseph Wenzel" (Martin von Meytens) ($48\frac{1}{2} \times 38$ mm) 85 85

210 "Adoration of the Shepherds"

211 Comte AC-8 Mail Plane "St. Gallen" over Schaan

1978. Christmas. Church Windows, Triesenberg. Multicoloured.

717 20 r. Type **210** 15 15
718 50 r. "Enthroned Madonna with St. Joseph" 40 30
719 80 r. "Adoration of the Magi" 70 65

1979. Europa. Multicoloured.

720 40 r. Type **211** 50 45
721 80 r. Airship "Graf Zeppelin" over Vaduz Castle 80 70

212 Child Drinking

213 Ordered Wave-field

1979. International Year of the Child. Multicoloured.

722 80 r. Type **212** 40 50
723 90 r. Child eating 50 60
724 1 f. 10 Child reading 85 70

1979. 50th Anniv of International Radio Consultative Committee (CCIR).

725 **213** 50 r. blue and black . . . 40 30

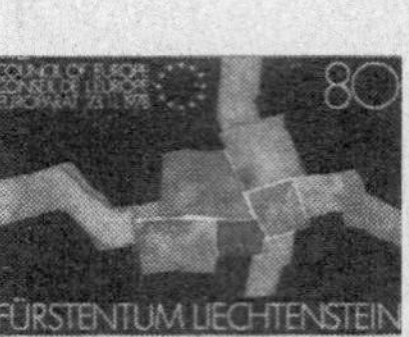

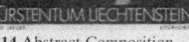

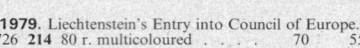

214 Abstract Composition

215 Sun rising over Continents

1979. Liechtenstein's Entry into Council of Europe.

726 **214** 80 r. multicoloured 70 55

1979. Development Aid.

727 **215** 1 f. multicoloured 80 70

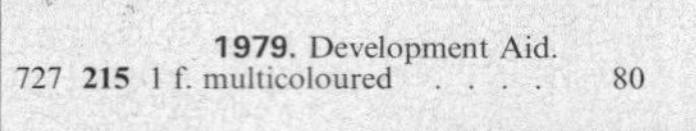

216 Arms of Carl Ludwig von Sulz

217 Sts. Lucius and Florian (fresco, Waltensberg-Vuorz Church)

1979. Heraldic Windows in the Liechtenstein National Museum. Multicoloured.

728 40 r. Type **216** 30 25
729 70 r. Arms of Barbara von Sulz 65 55
730 1 f. 10 Arms of Ulrich von Ramschwag and Barbara von Hallwil 90 80

1979. Patron Saints.

731 **217** 20 f. multicoloured . . . . 13·00 11·00

218 Base of Ski Slope, Valuna

1979. Winter Olympic Games, Lake Placid (1980). Multicoloured.

732 40 r. Type **218** 35 25
733 70 r. Malbun and Ochsenkopf 65 55
734 1 f. 50 Ski-lift, Sareis . . . 1·25 1·00

219 "The Annunciation"

1979. Christmas. Embroideries by Ferdinand Nigg. Multicoloured.

735 20 r. Type **219** 15 10
736 50 r. "Christmas" 40 30
737 80 r. "Blessed are the Peacemakers" 60 50

220 Maria Leopoldine von Esterhazy (bust by Canova)

221 Arms of Andreas Buchel, 1690

1980. Europa.

738 **220** 40 r. green, turq & gold . . 35 35
739 – 80 r. brown, red and gold 50 50
DESIGN: 80 r. Maria Theresia von Liechtenstein (after Martin von Meytens).

1980. Arms of Bailiffs (1st series). Multicoloured.

740 40 r. Type **221** 30 25
741 70 r. Georg Marxer, 1745 . . . 60 55
742 80 r. Luzius Frick, 1503 . . . 70 60
743 1 f. 10 Adam Oehri, 1634 . . . 85 80
See also Nos. 763/6, and 788/91.

222 3 r. Stamp of 1930

223 Milking Pail

1980. 50th Anniv of Postal Museum.

744 **222** 80 r. red, green and grey . . 75 60

1980. Alpine Dairy Farming Implements. Mult.

745 20 r. Type **223** 15 15
746 50 r. Wooden heart dairy herd descent marker 40 30
747 80 r. Butter churn 65 55

224 Crossbow

1980. Hunting Weapons.

748 **224** 80 r. brown and lilac . . . 70 60
749 – 90 r. black and green . . 80 70
750 – 1 f. 10 black and stone . . 90 80
DESIGNS: 90 r. Spear and knife; 1 f. 10, Rifle and powder-horn.

225 Triesenberg Costumes

1980. Costumes. Multicoloured.

751 40 r. Type **225** 30 25
752 70 r. Dancers, Schellenberg . . 65 55
753 80 r. Brass band, Mauren . . . 70 65

226 Beech Trees, Matrula (spring)

227 Angel bringing Shepherds Good Tidings

1980. The Forest in the Four Seasons. Multicoloured.

754 40 r. Type **226** 30 30
755 50 r. Firs in the Valorsch (summer) 45 40
756 80 r. Beech tree, Schaan (autumn) 70 60
757 1 f. 50 Edge of forest at Oberplanken (winter) . . . . 1·25 1·25

1980. Christmas. Multicoloured.

758 20 r. Type **227** 15 15
759 50 r. Crib 40 30
760 80 r. Epiphany 65 60

228 National Day Procession

230 Scout Emblems

1981. Europa. Multicoloured.
761 40 r. Fireworks at Vaduz Castle . . 35 25
762 80 r. Type **228** 75 65

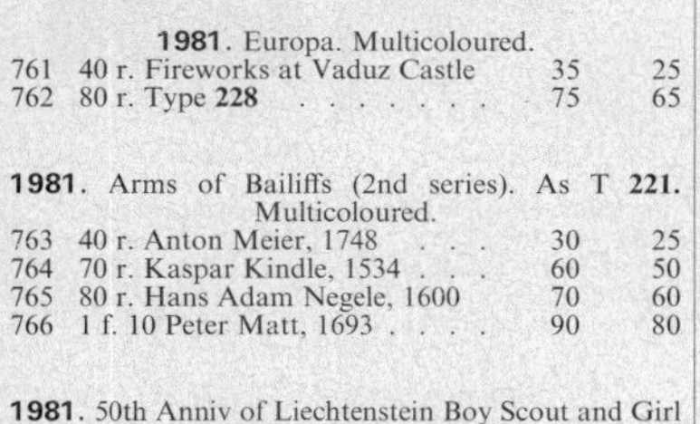

1981. Arms of Bailiffs (2nd series). As T **221.** Multicoloured.
763 40 r. Anton Meier, 1748 . . . 30 25
764 70 r. Kaspar Kindle, 1534 . . . 60 50
765 80 r. Hans Adam Negele, 1600 . 70 60
766 1 f. 10 Peter Matt, 1693 . . . . 90 80

1981. 50th Anniv of Liechtenstein Boy Scout and Girl Guide Movements.
768 **230** 20 r. multicoloured 30 15

231 Symbols of Disability

232 St. Theodul (sculpture)

1981. International Year of Disabled Persons.
769 **231** 40 r. multicoloured 30 25

1981. 1600th Birth Anniv of St. Theodul.
770 **232** 80 r. multicoloured 65 55

233 "Xanthoria parietina"

1981. Mosses and Lichens. Multicoloured.
771 40 r. Type **233** 30 25
772 50 r. "Parmelia physodes" . . . 50 40
773 70 r. "Sphagnum palustre" . . 65 55
774 80 r. "Amblystegium serpens" . 80 65

234 Gutenberg Castle

1981. Gutenberg Castle. Multicoloured.
775 20 r. Type **234** 20 15
776 40 r. Courtyard 30 25
777 50 r. Parlour 40 35
778 1 f. 10 Great Hall 95 85

235 Cardinal Karl Borromaus von Mailand

236 St. Nicholas blessing Children

1981. Famous Visitors to Liechtenstein (1st series). Multicoloured.
779 40 r. Type **235** 30 30
780 70 r. Johann Wolfgang von Goethe (writer) 65 60
781 89 r. Alexander Dumas the younger (writer) 75 65
782 1 f. Hermann Hesse (writer) . . 85 80
See also Nos. 804/7 and 832/5.

1981. Christmas. Multicoloured.
783 20 r. Type **236** 15 15
784 50 r. Adoration of the Kings . . 40 30
785 80 r. Holy Family 70 55

237 Peasant Revolt, 1525

1982. Europa. Multicoloured.
786 40 r. Type **237** 40 30
787 80 r. King Wenceslaus with Counts (Imperial direct rule, 1396) 85 65

1982. Arms of Bailiffs (3rd series). As T **221.** Multicoloured.
788 40 r. Johann Kaiser, 1664 . . . 40 30
789 70 r. Joseph Anton Kaufmann, 1748 . . . . 70 60
790 80 r. Christoph Walser, 1690 . 80 75
791 1 f. 10 Stephan Banzer, 1658 . 1·10 1·00

238 Triesenberg Sports Ground

239 Crown Prince Hans Adam

1982. World Cup Football Championship, Spain. Multicoloured.
792 15 r. Type **238** 20 15
793 25 r. Eschen/Mauren playing fields 25 25
794 1 f. 80 Rheinau playing fields, Balzers . . . . 1·75 1·60

1982. "Liba 82" Stamp Exhibition. Multicoloured.
795 1 f. Type **239** 90 85
796 1 f. Princess Marie Aglae . . . 90 85

240 Tractor (agriculture)

1982. Rural Industries. Multicoloured.
797 30 r. Type **240** 30 25
798 50 r. Cutting flowers (horticulture) 50 40
799 70 r. Workers with logs (forestry) 70 65
800 150 r. Worker and milk (dairy farming) . . . . 1·50 1·40

241 "Neu Schellenberg"

1982. 150th Birth Anniv of Mortiz Menzinger (artist). Multicoloured.
801 40 r. Type **241** 30 25
802 50 r. "Vaduz" 55 40
803 100 r. "Bendern" 90 80

242 Angelika Kauffmann (artist, self-portrait)

243 Angel playing Lute

1982. Famous Visitors to Liechtenstein (2nd series). Multicoloured.
804 40 r. Emperor Maximilian I (after Benhard Strigel) 30 25
805 70 f. Georg Jenatsch (liberator of Grisons) 65 50
806 80 r. Type **242** 75 60
807 1 f. St. Fidelis of Sigmaringen . 1·00 90

1982. Christmas. Details from High Altar by Jakob Russ, Chur Cathedral. Multicoloured.
808 20 r. Type **243** 15 15
809 50 r. Madonna and child . . . 45 35
810 80 r. Angel playing organ . . . 70 60

244 Notker Balbulus of St. Gall

245 Shrove Thursday

1983. Europa. Multicoloured.
811 40 r. Type **244** 30 25
812 80 r. Hildegard of Bingen . . . 70 55

1983. Shrovetide and Lent Customs. Mult.
813 40 r. Type **245** 30 25
814 70 r. Shrovetide carnival . . . 55 50
815 1 f. 80 Lent Sunday bonfire . . 1·40 1·40

246 River Bank

247 "Schaan"

1983. Anniversaries and Events. Multicoloured.
816 20 r. Type **246** 30 20
817 40 r. Montgolfier Brothers' balloon 35 30
818 50 r. Airmail envelope 50 35
819 80 r. Plant and hands holding spade 70 65

EVENTS: 20 r. Council of Europe river and coasts protection campaign; 40 r. Bicentenary of manned flight; 50 r. World Communications Year; 80 r. Overseas aid.

1983. Landscape Paintings by Anton Ender. Mult.
820 40 r. Type **247** 35 25
821 50 r. "Gutenberg Castle" . . . 55 45
822 200 r. "Steg Reservoir" . . . . 2·00 2·00

248 Princess Gina

249 Pope John Paul II

1983. Multicoloured.
823 2 f. 50 Type **248** . . . . . . 2·25 1·40
824 3 f. Prince Francis Joseph II . 2·75 2·00

1983. Holy Year.
825 **249** 80 r. multicoloured 75 60

250 Snowflakes and Stripes

251 Seeking Shelter

1983. Winter Olympic Games, Sarajevo. Mult.
826 40 r. Type **250** 35 25
827 80 r. Snowflake 75 65
828 1 f. 80 Snowflake and rays . . 1·50 1·50

1983. Christmas. Multicoloured.
829 20 r. Type **251** 15 15
830 50 r. Infant Jesus 50 35
831 80 r. Three Kings 75 65

252 Aleksandr Vassilievich Suvorov (Russian general)

253 Bridge

1984. Famous Visitors to Liechtenstein (3rd series). Multicoloured.
832 40 r. Type **252** 40 30
833 70 r. Karl Rudolf von Buol-Schauenstein, Bishop of Chur 65 60
834 80 r. Carl Zuckmayer (dramatist) 75 65
835 1 f. Curt Goetz (actor) 95 90

1984. Europa. 25th Anniv of E.P.T. Conf.
836 **253** 50 r. blue and deep blue . . 50 40
837 80 r. pink and brown . . . 75 70

254 The Warning Messenger

255 Pole Vaulting

1984. Liechtenstein Legends. The Destruction of Trisona. Each brown, grey and blue.
838 35 r. Type **254** 30 25
839 50 r. The buried town 55 40
840 80 r. The spared family 80 70

1984. Olympic Games, Los Angeles. Mult.
841 70 r. Type **255** 60 55
842 80 r. Throwing the discus . . . 70 65
843 1 f. Putting the shot 85 80

256 Currency (trade and banking)

1984. Occupations. Multicoloured.
844 5 r. Type **256** 10 10
845 10 r. Plumber adjusting pipe (building trade) 15 10
846 20 r. Operating machinery (industry–production) . . . 20 15
847 35 r. Draughtswoman (building trade–planning) 35 20
848 45 r. Office worker and world map (industry–sales) 50 35
849 50 r. Cook (tourism) 55 30
850 60 r. Carpenter (building trade–interior decoration) 70 45
851 70 r. Doctor injecting patient (medical services) 75 60
852 80 r. Scientist (industrial research) 80 55
853 100 r. Bricklayer (building trade) 90 65
854 120 r. Flow chart (industry–administration) . . . . . . 1·25 1·10
855 150 r. Handstamping covers (post and communications) . . . 1·60 1·00

257 Princess Marie

258 Annunciation

1984. Multicoloured.
856 1 f. 70 Type **257** . . . . . . 1·50 1·25
857 2 f. Crown Prince Hans Adam . . 1·75 1·50

1984. Christmas. Multicoloured.
858 35 r. Type **258** 30 25
859 50 r. Holy Family 50 40
860 80 r. The Three Kings 80 70

259 Apollo and the Muses playing Music (detail from 18th-century harpsichord lid)

1985. Europa. Music Year. Multicoloured.
861 50 r. Type **259** 60 50
862 80 r. Apollo and the Muses playing music (different) . . 80 75

260 St. Elisabeth Convent, Schaan

1985. Monasteries. Multicoloured.
863 50 r. Type **260** 50 40
864 1 f. Schellenberg Convent . . . 1·00 1·00
865 1 f. 70 Gutenberg Mission, Balzers . . . . 1·50 1·40

261 Princess Gina and handing out of Rations

1985. 40th Anniv of Liechtenstein Red Cross. Multicoloured.
866 20 r. Type **261** 30 30
867 50 r. Princess Gina and Red Cross ambulance 75 75
868 120 r. Princess Gina with refugee children . . . . 1·50 1·50

262 Justice **264** "Portrait of a Canon" (Quentin Massys)

1985. Cardinal Virtues. Multicoloured.
869 35 r. Type **262** 30 30
870 50 r. Temperance 50 50
871 70 r. Prudence 70 70
872 1 f. Fortitude . . . . 1·10 1·10

1985. Paintings in Metropolitan Museum, New York. Multicoloured.
874 50 r. Type **264** 60 60
875 1 f. "Clara Serena Rubens" (Rubens) . . . . 1·10 1·10
876 1 f. 20 "Duke of Urbino" (Raphael) . . . . 1·25 1·25

265 Halberd used by Charles I's Bodyguard

1985. Guards' Weapons and Armour. Mult.
877 35 r. Type **265** 35 30
878 50 r. Morion used by Charles I's bodyguard 45 45
879 80 r. Halberd used by Carl Eusebius's bodyguard . . . 65 65

266 Frankincense **267** Puppets performing Tragedy

1985. Christmas. Multicoloured.
880 35 r. Type **266** 35 25
881 50 r. Gold 60 50
882 80 r. Myrrh 65 65

1985. Theatre. Multicoloured.
883 50 r. Type **267** 70 70
884 80 r. Puppets performing comedy 90 90
885 1 f. 50 Opera . . . . 1·40 1·40

268 Courtyard **269** Barn Swallows

1986. Vaduz Castle. Multicoloured.
886 20 r. Type **268** 20 15
887 25 r. Keep 40 30
888 50 r. Castle 60 45
889 90 r. Inner gate 75 60
890 1 f. 10 Castle from gardens . . 90 60
891 1 f. 40 Courtyard (different) . . 1·10 90

1986. Europa. Birds. Multicoloured.
892 50 r. Type **269** 75 75
893 90 r. European robin . . . . . 1·25 1·25

270 "Offerings" **271** Palm Sunday

1986. Lenten Fast.
894 **270** 1 f. 40 multicoloured . . . 1·25 1·25

1986. Religious Festivals. Multicoloured.
895 35 r. Type **271** 40 30
896 50 r. Wedding 45 35
897 70 r. Rogation Day procession 65 55

272 Karl Freiherr Haus von Hausen **273** Francis Joseph II

1986. 125th Anniv of Liechtenstein Land Bank.
898 **272** 50 r. brown, ochre & buff 55 55

1986. 80th Birthday of Prince Francis Joseph II.
899 **273** 3 f. 50 multicoloured . . . 2·75 2·50

274 Roebuck in Ruggeller Riet **275** Cabbage and Beetroot

1986. Hunting. Multicoloured.
900 35 r. Type **274** 45 45
901 50 r. Chamois at Rappenstein 80 80
902 1 f. 70 Stag in Lawena . . . . 1·75 1·75

1986. Field Crops. Multicoloured.
903 50 r. Type **275** 45 45
904 80 r. Red cabbages 75 75
905 90 r. Potatoes, onions and garlic 90 90

276 Archangel Michael **277** Silver Fir

1986. Christmas. Multicoloured.
906 35 r. Type **276** 35 30
907 50 r. Archangel Gabriel 70 70
908 90 r. Archangel Raphael . . . . 1·00 1·00

1986. Tree Bark. Multicoloured.
909 35 r. Type **277** 30 30
910 90 r. Norway spruce . . . . . 1·00 1·00
911 1 f. 40 Pedunculate oak . . . . 1·50 1·50

278 Gamprin Primary School **280** Niklaus von Flue

1987. Europa. Multicoloured.
912 50 r. Type **278** 60 60
913 90 r. Schellenberg parish church 90 90

1987. 500th Death Anniv of Niklaus von Flue (martyr).
914 **280** 1 f. 10 multicoloured . . . 1·25 1·25

281 Bullhead **282** Princes Alois (frame as in first stamps)

1987. Fishes (1st series). Multicoloured.
915 50 r. Type **281** 70 70
916 90 r. Brown trout . . . . . . 1·25 1·25
917 1 f. 10 European grayling . . . 1·90 1·90
See also Nos. 959/61.

1987. 75th Anniv of First Liechtenstein Stamps.
918 **282** 2 f. multicoloured . . . . 2·10 1·90

283 Staircase **284** Arms

1987. Liechtenstein City Palace, Vienna. Multicoloured.
919 35 r. Type **283** 35 30
920 50 r. Minoritenplatz doorway 70 70
921 90 r. Staircase (different) . . . 1·00 1·00

1987. 275th Anniv of Transfer of County of Vaduz to House of Liechtenstein.
922 **284** 1 f. 40 multicoloured . . . 1·25 1·25

285 Constitution Charter, 1862 **286** St. Matthew

1987. 125th Anniv of Liechtenstein Parliament.
923 **285** 1 f. 70 multicoloured . . . 1·50 1·50

1987. Christmas. Illuminations from Golden Book of Pfafers Abbey. Multicoloured.
924 35 r. Type **286** 35 30
925 50 r. St. Mark 50 50
926 60 r. St. Luke 60 60
927 90 r. St. John . . . . 1·00 1·00

287 "The Toil of the Cross-Country Skier" **288** Dish Aerial

1987. Winter Olympic Games, Calgary (1988). Multicoloured.
928 25 r. Type **287** 30 30
929 90 r. "The Courageous Pioneers of Skiing" . . . . 1·00 1·00
930 1 f. 10 "As our Grandfathers used to ride on a Bobsled" . . . 1·25 1·25

1988. Europa. Transport and Communications. Mult.
931 50 r. Type **288** 50 50
932 90 r. Maglev monorail . . . . 1·40 1·40

289 Agriculture

1988. European Campaign for Rural Areas. Multicoloured.
933 80 r. Type **289** 75 75
934 90 r. Village centre . . . . . . 1·10 1·10
935 1 f. 70 Road . . . . 1·75 1·75

290 Headphones on Books (Radio Broadcasts) **292** St. Barbara's Shrine, Balzers

1988. Costa Rica–Liechtenstein Cultural Co-operation.
936 **290** 50 r. multicoloured 65 65
937 – 1 f. 40 red, brown and green 1·50 1·50
DESIGN: 1 f. 40, Man with pen and radio (Adult education).

1988. Wayside Shrines. Multicoloured.
939 25 r. Type **292** 40 40
940 35 r. Shrine containing statues of Christ, St. Peter and St. Paul at Oberdorf, Vaduz 50 50
941 50 r. St. Anthony of Egypt's shrine, Fallagass, Ruggel . . 60 60

293 Cycling **294** Joseph and Mary

1988. Olympic Games, Seoul. Multicoloured.
942 50 r. Type **293** 45 45
943 80 r. Gymnastics 80 80
944 90 r. Running . . . . 1·00 1·00
945 1 f. 40 Equestrian event . . . . 1·75 1·75

1988. Christmas. Multicoloured.
946 35 r. Type **294** 35 30
947 50 r. Baby Jesus 70 70
948 90 r. Wise Men presenting gifts to Jesus . . . . 1·10 1·10

295 Letter beside Footstool (detail) **296** "Cat and Mouse"

1988. "The Letter" (portrait of Marie-Theresa, Princesse de Lamballe by Anton Hickel). Multicoloured.
949 50 r. Type **295** 65 65
950 90 r. Desk and writing materials (detail) . . . . 1·10 1·10
951 2 f. "The Letter" (complete painting) . . . . 2·00 2·00

1989. Europa. Children's Games. Multicoloured.
952 50 r. Type **296** 55 55
953 90 r. "Hide and Seek" . . . . 1·10 1·10

298 Rheinberger and Score **299** Little Ringed Plover

1989. 150th Birth Anniv of Josef Gabriel Rheinberger (composer).
954 **298** 2 f. 90 black, blue & pur 2·50 2·50

1989. Endangered Animals. Multicoloured.
955 25 r. Type **299** 85 40
956 35 r. Green tree frog 60 50
957 50 r. "Libelloides coccajus" (lace-wing) 80 75
958 90 r. Polecat . . . . 1·60 1·50

300 Northern Pike

1989. Fishes (2nd series). Multicoloured.
959 50 r. Type **300** 60 60
960 1 f. 10 Brown trout . . . . . 1·60 1·60
961 1 f. 40 Stone loach . . . . . . 2·25 2·25

301 Return of Cattle from Alpine Pastures **302** Falknis

1989. Autumn Customs. Multicoloured.
962 35 r. Type **301** 40 40
963 50 r. Peeling corn cobs 65 65
964 80 r. Cattle market 85 85

1989. Mountains. Watercolours by Josef Schadler.

965 – 5 r. multicoloured 10 10
966 – 10 r. multicoloured 10 10
967 – 35 r. multicoloured 30 25
968 – 40 r. multicoloured 35 25
969 – 45 r. multicoloured 40 30
970 **302** 50 r. multicoloured 45 35
971 – 60 r. multicoloured 55 40
972 – 70 r. multicoloured 65 50
973 – 75 r. multicoloured 70 55
974 – 80 r. violet, brown & black 75 60
975 – 1 f. multicoloured 90 70
976 – 1 f. 20 multicoloured 1·10 85
977 – 1 f. 50 multicoloured 1·40 1·00
978 – 1 f. 60 multicoloured 1·50 1·10
979 – 2 f. multicoloured 1·75 1·50

DESIGNS: 5 r. Augstenberg; 10 r. Hahenespiel; 35 r. Nospitz; 40 r. Ochsenkopf; 45 r. Three Sisters; 60 r. Kuhgrat; 70 r. Galinakopf; 75 r. Plassteikopf; 80 pf. Naafkopf; 1 f. Schonberg; 1 f. 20, Bleikaturm; 1 f. 50, Garselliturm; 1 f. 60, Schwarzhorn; 2 f. Scheienkopf.

303 "Melchior and Balthasar" **304** Mace Quartz

1989. Christmas. Details of triptych by Hugo van der Goes. Multicoloured.

981 35 r. Type **303** 50 50
982 50 r. "Kaspar and Holy Family" (27 × 34 mm) 75 70
983 90 r. "St. Stephen" 1·00 1·00

1989. Minerals. Multicoloured.

984 50 r. Type **304** 55 55
985 1 f.10 Globe pyrite 1·25 1·25
986 1 f. 50 Calcite 1·75 1·75

305 Nendeln Forwarding Agency, 1864 **306** Penny Black

1990. Europa. Post Office Buildings. Mult.

987 50 r. Type **305** 70 70
988 90 r. Vaduz post office, 1976 1·10 1·10

1990. 150th Anniv of the Penny Black.

989 **306** 1 f. 50 multicoloured 1·75 1·50

307 Footballers **308** Tureen, Oranges and Grapes

1990. World Cup Football Championship, Italy.

990 **307** 2 f. multicoloured 2·00 1·75

1990. 9th Death Anniv of Benjamin Steck (painter). Multicoloured.

991 50 r. Type **308** 70 70
992 80 r. Apples and pewter bowl 1·00 1·00
993 1 f. 50 Basket, apples, cherries and pewter jug 1·50 1·50

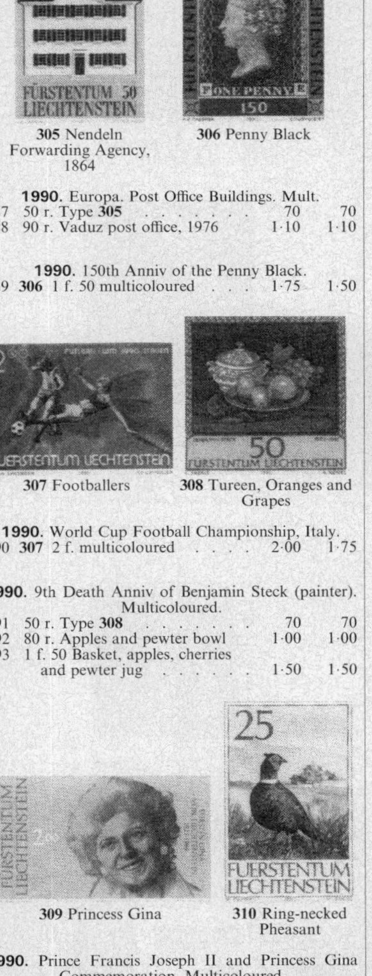

309 Princess Gina **310** Ring-necked Pheasant

1990. Prince Francis Joseph II and Princess Gina Commemoration. Multicoloured.

994 2 f. Type **309** 1·90 1·90
995 3 f. Prince Francis Joseph II 2·75 2·75

1990. Game Birds. Multicoloured.

996 25 r. Type **310** 40 40
997 50 r. Black grouse 70 70
998 2 f. Mallard 2·75 2·75

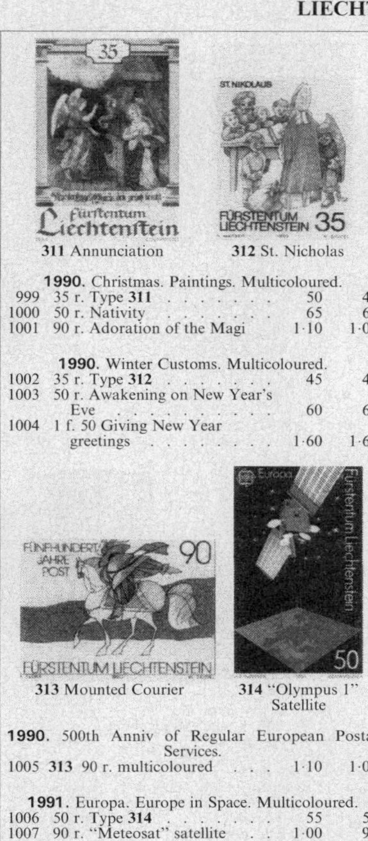

311 Annunciation **312** St. Nicholas

1990. Christmas. Paintings. Multicoloured.

999 35 r. Type **311** 50 45
1000 50 r. Nativity 65 60
1001 90 r. Adoration of the Magi 1·10 1·00

1990. Winter Customs. Multicoloured.

1002 35 r. Type **312** 45 45
1003 50 r. Awakening on New Year's Eve 60 60
1004 1 f. 50 Giving New Year greetings 1·60 1·60

313 Mounted Courier **314** "Olympus 1" Satellite

1990. 500th Anniv of Regular European Postal Services.

1005 **313** 90 r. multicoloured 1·10 1·00

1991. Europa. Europe in Space. Multicoloured.

1006 50 r. Type **314** 55 55
1007 90 r. "Meteosat" satellite 1·00 95

315 St. Ignatius de Loyola (founder of Society of Jesus) **316** U.N. Emblem and Dove

1991. Anniversaries. Multicoloured.

1008 80 r. Type **315** (500th birth anniv) 85 85
1009 90 r. Wolfgang Amadeus Mozart (composer, death bicentenary) 95 95

1991. Admission to U.N. Membership (1990).

1010 **316** 2 f. 50 multicoloured 2·50 2·50

317 Non-Commissioned Officer and Private **318** "Near Maloja" (Giovanni Giacometti)

1991. 125th Anniv of Last Mobilization of Liechtenstein's Military Contingent (to the Tyrol). Multicoloured.

1011 50 r. Type **317** 55 55
1012 70 r. Tunic, chest and portrait 75 55
1013 1 f. Officer and private 1·10 1·10

1991. 700th Anniv of Swiss Confederation. Paintings by Swiss artists. Multicoloured.

1014 50 r. Type **318** 55 55
1015 80 r. "Rhine Valley" (Ferdinand Gehr) 85 85
1016 90 r. "Bergell" (Augusto Giacometti) 95 95
1017 1 f. 10 "Hoher Kasten" (Hedwig Scherrer) 1·25 1·25

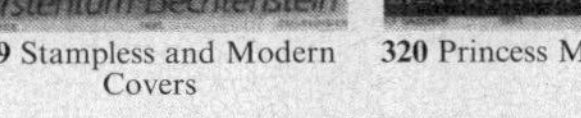

319 Stampless and Modern Covers **320** Princess Marie

1991. "Liba 92" National Stamp Exhibition, Vaduz.

1018 **319** 90 r. multicoloured 90 90

1991. Multicoloured.

1019 3 f. Type **320** 2·50 2·50
1020 3 f. 40 Prince Hans Adam II 3·00 3·00

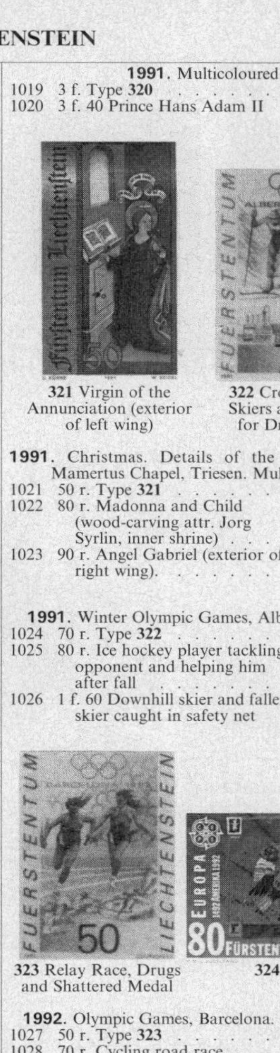

321 Virgin of the Annunciation (exterior of left wing) **322** Cross-country Skiers and Testing for Drug Abuse

1991. Christmas. Details of the altar from St. Mamertus Chapel, Triesen. Multicoloured.

1021 50 r. Type **321** 50 50
1022 80 r. Madonna and Child (wood-carving attr. Jorg Syrlin, inner shrine) 80 80
1023 90 r. Angel Gabriel (exterior of right wing) 90 90

1991. Winter Olympic Games, Albertville. Mult.

1024 70 r. Type **322** 80 70
1025 80 r. Ice hockey player tackling opponent and helping him after fall 90 80
1026 1 f. 60 Downhill skier and fallen skier caught in safety net 1·75 1·60

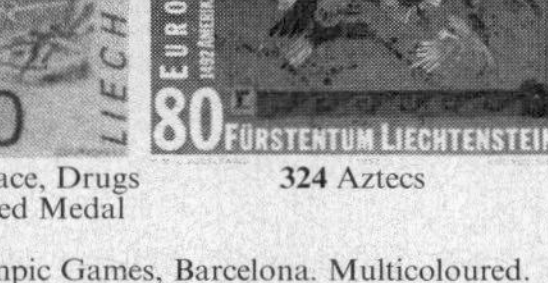

323 Relay Race, Drugs and Shattered Medal **324** Aztecs

1992. Olympic Games, Barcelona. Multicoloured.

1027 50 r. Type **323** 50 45
1028 70 r. Cycling road race 1·00 65
1029 2 f. 50 Judo 2·75 2·25

1992. Europa. 500th Anniv of Discovery of America by Columbus. Multicoloured.

1030 80 r. Type **324** 75 75
1031 90 r. Statue of Liberty and New York skyline 85 85

325 Clown in Envelope ("Good Luck") **327** "Blechnum spicant"

1992. Greetings Stamps. Multicoloured.

1032 50 r. Type **325** 50 45
1033 50 r. Wedding rings in envelope and harlequin violinist 50 45
1034 50 r. Postman blowing horn (31 × 21 mm) 50 45
1035 50 r. Flying postman carrying letter sealed with heart (31 × 21 mm) 50 45

1992. Ferns. Multicoloured.

1037 40 r. Type **327** 40 35
1038 50 r. Maidenhair spleenwort 50 45
1039 70 r. Hart's-tongue 70 65
1040 2 f. 50 "Asplenium ruta-muraria" 2·40 2·25

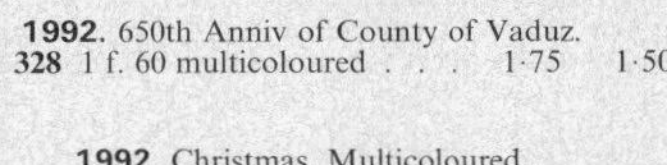

328 Reading Edict **329** Chapel of St. Mamertus, Triesen

1992. 650th Anniv of County of Vaduz.

1041 **328** 1 f. 60 multicoloured 1·75 1·50

1992. Christmas. Multicoloured.

1042 50 r. Type **329** 50 45
1043 90 r. Crib, St. Gallus's Church, Triesen 90 85
1044 1 f. 60 St. Mary's Chapel, Triesen 1·75 1·50

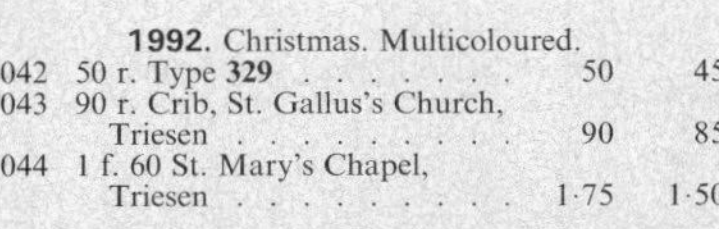

330 Crown Prince Alois **331** "Nafkopf and Huts, Steg"

1992.

1045 **330** 2 f. 50 multicoloured 2·00 2·00

1993. 1400th Birth Anniv of Hans Gantner (painter). Multicoloured.

1046 50 r. Type **331** 50 45
1047 60 r. "Hunting Lodge, Sass" 55 50
1048 1 f. 80 "Red House, Vaduz" 1·75 1·60

332 "910805" (Bruno Kaufmann) **333** "Tale of the Ferryman" (painting)

1993. Europa. Contemporary Art. Multicoloured.

1049 80 r. Type **332** 85 80
1050 1 f. "The Little Blue" (Evi Kliemand) 95 90

1993. Tibetan Collection in the National Museum. Multicoloured.

1051 60 r. Type **333** 70 65
1052 80 r. Religious dance mask 85 80
1053 1 f. "Tale of the Fish" (painting) 1·25 1·25

334 "Tree of Life" **335** "The Black Hatter"

1993. Missionary Work.

1054 **334** 1 f. 80 multicoloured 1·90 1·75

1993. Homage to Liechtenstein.

1055 **335** 2 f. 80 multicoloured 2·75 2·50

337 Origanum **338** Eurasian Badger

1993. Flowers. Illustrations from "Hortus Botanicus Liechtensteinsis". Multicoloured.

1057 50 r. Type **337** 60 55
1058 60 r. Meadow sage 70 65
1059 1 f. "Seseli annuum" 1·10 1·00
1060 2 f. 50 Large self-heal 2·40 2·25

1993. Animals. Multicoloured.

1061 60 r. Type **338** 70 65
1062 80 r. Beech marten 95 90
1063 1 f. Red fox 1·25 1·10

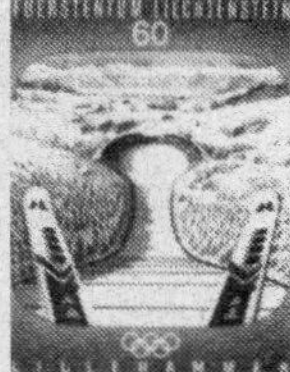

339 "Now that the Quiet Days are Coming..." (Rainer Maria Rilke) **340** Ski Jump

1993. Christmas. Multicoloured.

1064 60 r. Type **339** 60 55
1065 80 r. "Can You See the Light..." (Th. Friedrich) 85 80
1066 1 f. "Christmas, Christmas..." (R. A. Schroder) 95 90

1993. Winter Olympic Games, Lillehammer, Norway (1994). Multicoloured.

1067 60 r. Type **340** 85 80
1068 80 r. Slalom . . . . 1·10 1·00
1069 2 f. 40 Bobsleighing . . . . . 2·40 2·25

341 Seal and Title Page

342 Andean Condor

1994. Anniversaries. Multicoloured.

1070 60 r. Type **341** (275th anniv of Principality) 70 70
1071 1 f. 80 State, Prince's and Olympic flags (centenary of International Olympic Committee) . . . . 1·75 1·75

1994. Europa. Discoveries of Alexander von Humboldt. Multicoloured.

1072 80 r. Type **342** 80 80
1073 1 f. "Rhexia cardinalis" (plant) 90 90

343 Football Pitch and Hopi Indians playing Kickball

344 Elephant with Letter

1994. World Cup Football Championship, U.S.A.

1074 **343** 2 f. 80 multicoloured . . . 2·75 2·75

1994. Greetings Stamps. Multicoloured.

1075 60 r. Type **344** 70 70
1076 60 r. Cherub with flower and hearts 70 70
1077 60 r. Pig with four-leaf clover . 70 70
1078 60 r. Dog holding bunch of tulips 70 70

345 "Eulogy of Madness" (mobile, Jean Tinguely)

1994. Homage to Liechtenstein.

1079 **345** 4 f. black, pink and violet . 3·75 3·75

346 Spring

1994. Seasons of the Vine. Multicoloured.

1080 60 r. Type **346** 70 70
1081 60 r. Vine leaves (Summer) . . 70 70
1082 60 r. Trunk in snowy landscape (Winter) 70 70
1083 60 r. Grapes (Autumn) . . . 70 70

Nos. 1080/3 were issued together, se-tenant, forming a composite design.

347 Strontium

1994. Minerals. Multicoloured.

1084 60 r. Type **347** 70 70
1085 80 r. Quartz 90 90
1086 3 f. 50 Iron dolomite . . . . 3·25 3·00

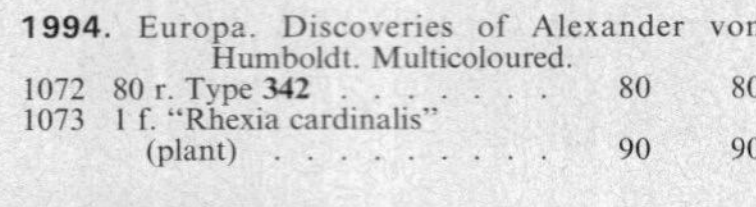

HAVE YOU READ THE NOTES AT THE BEGINNING OF THIS CATALOGUE?
These often provide answers to the enquiries we receive.

348 "The True Light"

349 Earth

1994. Christmas. Multicoloured.

1087 60 r. Type **348** 70 70
1088 80 r. "Peace on Earth" . . . 90 90
1089 1 f. "Behold, the House of God" . . . . 1·10 1·10

1994. The Four Elements. Multicoloured.

1090 60 r. Type **349** 70 70
1091 80 r. Water 90 90
1092 1 f. Fire . . . . 1·10 1·10
1093 2 f. 50 Air . . . . 2·50 2·50

350 "The Theme of all our Affairs must be Peace"

351 U.N. Flag and Bouquet of Flowers

1995. Europa. Peace and Freedom. Quotations of Franz Josef II. Multicoloured.

1094 80 r. Type **350** 85 85
1095 1 f. "Through Unity comes Strength and the Bearing of Sorrows" . . . . 1·10 1·10

1995. Anniversaries and Event. Multicoloured.

1096 60 r. Princess Marie with children (50th anniv of Liechtenstein Red Cross) (horiz) 65 65
1097 1 f. 80 Type **351** (50th anniv of U.N.O.) . . . . 1·75 1·75
1098 3 f. 50 Alps (European Nature Conservation Year) . . . . 3·25 3·25

352 "Falknis Mountains"

353 "One Heart and One Soul"

1995. Birth Centenary of Anton Frommelt (painter). Multicoloured.

1099 60 r. Type **352** 65 65
1100 80 r. "Three Oaks" 85 85
1101 4 f. 10 "The Rhine" . . . . . 4·00 4·00

1995. Greetings Stamps. Multicoloured.

1102 60 r. Type **353** 65 65
1103 60 r. Bandage round sunflower ("Get Well") 65 65
1104 60 r. Baby arriving over rainbow ("Hurrah! Here I am") . . 65 65
1105 60 r. Delivering letter by hot-air balloon ("Write again") . . 65 65

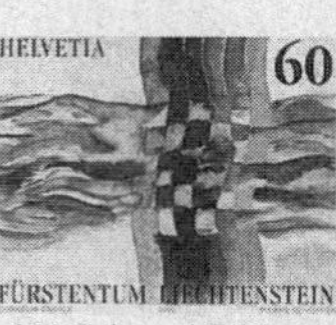

354 Coloured Ribbons woven through River

355 Arnica

1995. Liechtenstein–Switzerland Co-operation.

1106 **354** 60 r. multicoloured . . . 65 65

No. 1106 was valid for use in both Liechtenstein and Switzerland (see No. 1308 of Switzerland).

1995. Medicinal Plants. Multicoloured.

1107 60 r. Type **355** 65 65
1108 80 r. Giant nettle 85 85
1109 1 f. 80 Common valerian . . . 1·75 1·75
1110 3 f. 50 Fig-wort . . . . . . 3·25 3·25

356 Angel (detail of painting)

357 "Lady with Lap-dog" (Paul Wunderlich)

1995. Christmas. Painting by Lorenzo Monaco. Multicoloured.

1111 60 r. Type **356** 50 50
1112 80 r. "Virgin Mary with Infant and Two Angels" 70 70
1113 1 f. Angel facing left (detail of painting) 85 85

1995. Homage to Liechtenstein.

1114 **357** 4 f. multicoloured . . . . 3·75 3·75

358 Eschen

359 Crucible

1996. Scenes. Multicoloured.

1115 10 r. Type **358** 10 10
1116 20 r. Planken 15 10
1118 80 r. Ruggell 65 50
1120 1 f. Nendeln 80 60
1122 1 f. 20 Triesen 95 70
1123 1 f. 30 Triesen . . . . . . 1·10 85
1125 1 f. 70 Schaanwald . . . . 1·50 1·10
1126 2 f. Gamprin . . . . 1·75 1·40
1127 4 f. Triesenberg . . . . . 3·50 2·75
1128 5 f. Vaduz Castle . . . . . 4·25 4·25

1996. Bronze Age in Europe.

1130 **359** 90 r. multicoloured . . . 75 75

360 Kinsky and Diary Extract, 7 March 1917

1996. Europa. Famous Women. Nora, Countess Kinsky (mother of Princess Gina of Liechtenstein)

1131 **360** 90 r. grey, purple and blue . 75 75
1132 – 1 f. 10 grey, blue and purple 95 95

DESIGN: 1 f. 10, Kinsky and diary extract for 28 February 1917.

361 Gymnastics

1996. Centenary of Modern Olympic Games. Multicoloured.

1133 70 r. Type **361** 60 60
1134 90 r. Hurdling 75 75
1135 1 f. 10 Cycling 95 95

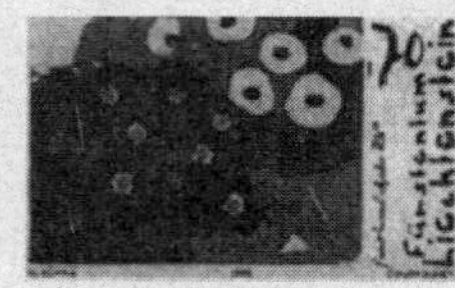

362 "Primroses"

1996. Birth Centenary of Ferdinand Gehr (painter). Multicoloured.

1136 70 r. Type **362** 60 60
1137 90 r. "Daisies" 75 75
1138 1 f. 10 "Poppy" 95 95
1139 1 f. 80 "Buttercups" (33 × 23 mm) . . . . 1·50 1·50

363 State Arms

1996.

1140 **363** 10 f. multicoloured . . . 8·00 8·00

364 Veldkirch, 1550

1996. Millenary of Austria.

1141 **364** 90 r. multicoloured . . . 75 75

365 "Poltava"

366 St. Matthew

1996. 43rd Death Anniv of Eugen Zotow (painter). Multicoloured.

1142 70 r. Type **365** 60 60
1143 1 f. 10 "Three Bathers in a Berlin Park" 95 95
1144 1 f. 40 "Vaduz" . . . . . . 1·25 1·25

1996. Christmas. Illustrations from Illuminated Manuscript "Liber Viventium Fabariensis". Multicoloured.

1145 70 r. Type **366** 60 60
1146 90 r. Emblems of St. Mark . . 75 75
1147 1 f. 10 Emblems of St. Luke . 95 95
1148 1 f. 80 Emblems of St. John . 1·50 1·50

367 Schubert

368 The Wild Gnomes

1997. Birth Bicentenary of Franz Schubert (composer).

1149 **367** 70 r. multicoloured . . . 60 60

1997. Europa. Tales and Legends. Multicoloured.

1150 90 r. Type **368** 75 75
1151 1 f. 10 Man, pumpkin and rabbit (The Foal of Planken) . . . 95 95

369 "Madonna and Child with St. Lucius and St. Florinus" (Gabriel Dreher)

1997. National Patron Saints.

1152 **369** 20 f. multicoloured . . . 17·00 17·00

370 "Phaeolepiota aurea"

1997. Fungi. Multicoloured.

1153 70 r. Type **370** 60 60
1154 90 r. "Helvella silvicola" . . . 75 75
1155 1 f. 10 Orange peel fungus . . 90 90

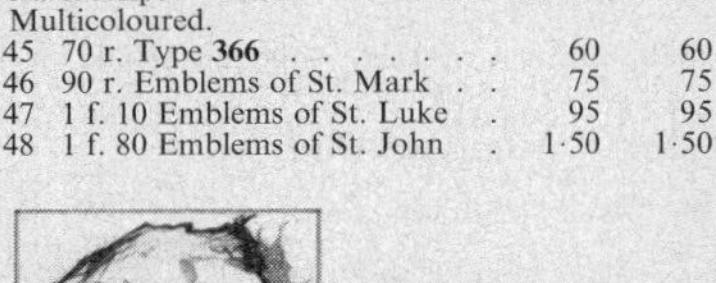

371 Steam Train, Schaanwald Halt

372 "Girl with Flower" (Enrico Baj)

1997. 125th Anniv of Liechtenstein Railways. Multicoloured.
1156 70 r. Type **371** 60 60
1157 90 r. Diesel-electric train, Nendeln station 75 75
1158 1 f. 80 Electric train, Schaan-Vaduz station . . . . . . 1·50 1·50

1997. Homage to Liechtenstein.
1159 **372** 70 r. multicoloured . . . 60 60

373 Basket of Roses **374** Cross-country skiing

1997. Christmas. Glass Tree Decorations. Multicoloured.
1160 70 r. Type **373** 60 60
1161 90 r. Bell 80 80
1162 1 f. 10 Bauble 95 95

1997. Winter Olympic Games, Nagano, Japan (1998). Skiing. Multicoloured.
1163 70 r. Type **374** 60 60
1164 90 r. Slalom 80 80
1165 1 f. 80 Downhill . . . . . . 1·60 1·60

375 "Verano (The Summer)"

1998. Homage to Liechtenstein. Paintings by Heinz Mack. Multicoloured.
1166 70 r. Type **375** 60 60
1167 70 r. "Homage to Liechtenstein" 60 60
1168 70 r. "Between Day and Dream" 60 60
1169 70 r. "Salute Cirico!" 60 60

376 Prince's Festival Procession, Vaduz

1998. Europa. National Festivals. Multicoloured.
1170 90 r. Type **376** 80 80
1171 1 f. 10 Music Societies Festival, Gutenberg Castle, Balzers . 95 95

377 National Flags on Bridge

1998. 75th Anniv of Liechtenstein–Switzerland Customs Treaty.
1172 **377** 1 f. 70 multicoloured . . . 1·50 1·50

378 Goalkeeper

1998. World Cup Football Championship, France.
1173 **378** 1 f. 80 multicoloured . . . 1·60 1·60

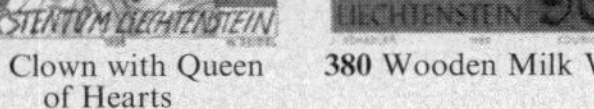

379 Clown with Queen of Hearts **380** Wooden Milk Vat

1998. Greeting Stamps. Clowns. Multicoloured.
1174 70 r. Type **379** 60 60
1175 70 r. Clown holding four-leaf clovers 60 60
1176 70 r. Clown raising hat . . . 60 60
1177 70 r. Clown holding heart . . 60 60

1998. Traditional Crafts. Multicoloured.
1178 90 r. Type **380** 80 80
1179 2 f. 20 Clog . . . . 1·90 1·90
1180 3 f. 50 Wheel . . . . 3·00 3·00

381 Expelling Johann Langer from Liechtenstein

1998. 150th Anniv of 1848 Revolutions in Europe.
1181 **381** 1 f. 80 multicoloured . . . 1·60 1·60

382 Virgin Mary

1998. Christmas. Multicoloured.
1182 70 r. Type **382** 55 55
1183 90 r. "The Nativity" (35 × 26 mm) 70 70
1184 1 f. 10 Joseph 85 85
Nos. 1182 and 1184 show details of the complete relief depicted on No. 1183.

383 Zum Lowen Guest House **384** Automatic and Manual Switchboards

1998. Preservation of Historical Environment. Hinterschellenberg. Multicoloured.
1185 90 r. Type **383** 70 75
1186 1 f. 70 St. George's Chapel (vert) . . . . 1·40 1·40
1187 1 f. 80 Houses . . . . 1·40 1·40

1998. Centenary of Telephone in Liechtenstein.
1188 **384** 2 f. 80 multicoloured . . 2·25 2·25

386 Smooth Snake and Schwabbrunnen-Aescher Nature Park **387** Council Anniversary Emblem and Silhouettes

1999. Europa. Parks and Gardens. Multicoloured.
1190 90 r. Type **386** 70 70
1191 1 f. 10 Corncrake and Ruggell marsh 85 85

1999. Anniversaries and Event. Multicoloured.
1192 70 r. Type **387** (50th anniv of Council of Europe and European Convention on Human Rights) 55 40
1193 70 r. Bird with envelope in beak (125th anniv of U.P.U.) . . 55 40
1194 70 r. Heart in hand (75th anniv of Caritas Liechtenstein (welfare organization)) . . . 55 40

388 Judo

1999. 8th European Small States Games, Liechtenstein. Multicoloured.
1195 70 r. Type **388** 55 40
1196 70 r. Swimming 55 40
1197 70 r. Throwing the javelin . . 55 40
1198 90 r. Cycling 70 50
1199 90 r. Shooting 70 50
1200 90 r. Tennis 70 50
1201 90 r. Squash 70 50
1202 90 r. Table tennis 70 50
1203 90 r. Volleyball 70 50

389 "Herrengasse"

1999. Paintings by Eugen Verling. Multicoloured.
1204 70 r. Type **389** 55 55
1205 2 f. "Old Vaduz with Castle" . 80 80
1206 4 f. "House in Furst-Franz-Josef Street, Vaduz" . . . . 3·25 3·25

390 Scene from "Faust", Act I

1999. 250th Birth Anniv of Johann Wolfgang Goethe (poet and playwright). Multicoloured.
1207 1 f. 40 Type **390** . . . . . . 1·10 1·10
1208 1 f. 70 Faust and the Devil sealing wager . . . . 1·40 1·40

391 "The Annunciation" **392** Identification Mark on Door, Ubersaxen

1999. Christmas. Paintings by Joseph Walser from Chapel of Our Lady of Comfort, Dux. Multicoloured.
1209 70 r. Type **391** 55 55
1210 90 r. "Nativity" 70 70
1211 1 f. 10 "Adoration" 85 85

1999. Walser Identification Marks. Multicoloured.
1212 70 r. Type **392** 55 55
1213 90 r. Mark on mural 70 70
1214 1 f. 80 Mark on axe . . . . . 1·40 1·40

393 Gutenberg

1999. 600th Birth Anniv of Johannes Gutenberg (inventor of printing press).
1215 **393** 3 f. 60 multicoloured . . 1·90 1·90

OFFICIAL STAMPS

1932. Stamps of 1930 optd **REGIERUNGS DIENSTSACHE** under crown.
O118 5 r. green (No. 97) . . . . . 7·00 7·50
O119 10 r. lilac . . . . 50·00 8·00
O120 20 r. red . . . . 55·00 8·00
O121 30 r. blue . . . . 11·00 8·00
O122 35 r. green . . . . 8·00 16·00
O123 50 r. black . . . . 50·00 11·00
O124 60 r. green . . . . 10·50 23·00
O125 1 f. 20 brown £140 £275

1933. Nos. 121 and 123 optd **REGIERUNGS DIENSTSACHE** in circle round crown.
O126 **38** 25 r. orange . . . . . . 28·00 23·00
O127 – 1 f. 20 brown . . . . . 60·00 £225

1934. Nos. 128 etc. optd **REGIERUNGS DIENSTSACHE** in circle round crown.
O150 **41** 5 r. green . . . . 80 1·50
O151 – 10 r. violet . . . . . . 1·10 1·25
O152 – 15 r. orange . . . . . . 35 1·10
O153 – 20 r. red . . . . 40 1·40
O155 – 25 r. brown . . . . . . 2·10 8·50
O156 – 30 r. blue . . . . 3·00 4·50
O157 **42** 50 r. brown . . . . . . 1·00 1·75
O158 – 90 r. green . . . . . . 6·75 28·00
O159 – 1 f. 50 brown . . . . . 38·00 £140

1937. Stamps of 1937 optd **REGIERUNGS DIENSTSACHE** in circle round crown.
O174 **51** 5 r. green and buff . . . 20 50
O175 – 10 r. violet and buff . . . 40 90
O176 – 20 r. red and buff . . . 75 75
O177 – 25 r. brown and buff . . . 30 90
O178 – 30 r. blue and buff . . . 1·00 70
O179 – 50 r. brown and buff . . . 75 90
O180 – 1 f. purple and buff . . . 75 6·50
O181 – 1 f. 50 grey and buff . . . 2·10 7·50

1947. Stamps of 1944 optd **DIENSTMARKE** and crown.
O255 5 r. green . . . . 1·25 60
O256 10 r. violet . . . . 1·25 85
O257 20 r. red . . . . 1·50 85
O258 30 r. blue . . . . 2·00 1·40
O259 50 r. grey . . . . 2·00 2·25
O260 1 f. red . . . . 4·00 6·75
O261 1 f. 50 blue . . . . 4·00 6·75

O 86 **O 198** Government Building, Vaduz

1950. Buff paper.
O287 **O 86** 5 r. purple and grey . . 10 10
O288 10 r. green and mauve . 10 10
O289 20 r. brown and blue . . 15 15
O290 30 r. purple and red . . 30 25
O291 40 r. blue and brown . . 30 30
O292 55 r. green and red . . 1·00 1·00
O293 60 r. grey and mauve . 1·00 1·00
O294 80 r. orange and grey . . 75 75
O295 90 r. brown and blue . . 80 1·40
O296 1 f. 20 turquoise and orange . . . . . . 1·50 1·50

1968. White paper.
O495 **O 86** 5 r. brown and orange . 10 10
O496 10 r. violet and red . . 10 10
O497 20 r. red and green . . 15 15
O498 30 r. green and red . . 25 25
O499 50 r. blue and red . . . 40 40
O500 60 r. orange and blue . . 50 50
O501 70 r. purple and green . 60 60
O502 80 r. green and red . . 70 70
O503 95 r. green and red . . 1·00 1·00
O504 1 f. purple & turquoise . 90 90
O505 1 f. 20 brown & turq . . 1·40 1·40
O506 2 f. brown and orange . 1·60 1·60

1976.
O652 **O 198** 10 r. brown and violet . 10 10
O653 20 r. red and blue . . 15 15
O654 35 r. blue and red . . 20 20
O655 40 r. violet and green . 25 25
O656 50 r. green and mauve . 30 30
O657 70 r. purple and green . 40 40
O658 80 r. green and purple . 50 50
O659 90 r. violet and blue . 60 60
O660 1 f. grey and purple . . 90 90
O661 1 f. 10 brown and blue . 1·00 1·00
O662 1 f. 50 green and red . 1·40 1·40
O663 2 f. orange and blue . 1·75 1·75
O664 5 f. purple and orange . 6·75 6·50

POSTAGE DUE STAMPS

D 11 **D 25** **D 58**

1920.
D43 **D 11** 5 h. red 10 25
D44 10 h. red 10 25
D45 15 h. red 10 25
D46 20 h. red 10 25
D47 25 h. red 15 30
D48 30 h. red 15 30
D49 40 h. red 15 30
D50 **D 11** 50 h. red 15 30
D51 80 h. red 15 30
D52 1 k. blue 20 50
D53 2 k. blue 20 50
D54 5 k. blue 20 50

1928.
D84 **D 25** 5 r. red and violet . . 1·00 2·50
D85 10 r. red and violet . . 1·25 2·50
D86 15 r. red and violet . . 2·50 10·00
D87 20 r. red and violet . . 2·50 2·50
D88 25 r. red and violet . . 2·50 7·00
D89 30 r. red and violet . . 6·50 10·00
D90 40 r. red and violet . . 8·00 11·00
D91 50 r. red and violet . . 8·50 16·00

1940.
D189 **D 58** 5 r. red and blue . . . 1·25 3·00
D190 10 r. red and blue . . . 50 75
D191 15 r. red and blue . . . 75 3·25
D192 20 r. red and blue . . . 80 1·60
D193 25 r. red and blue . . . 1·40 3·25
D194 30 r. red and blue . . . 2·25 5·00
D195 40 r. red and blue . . . 2·25 4·50
D196 50 r. red and blue . . . 2·25 5·50

LITHUANIA Pt.10

A country on the Baltic Sea, under Russian rule until occupied by the Germans in the first World War (see German Eastern Command). It was an independent republic from 1918 to 1940, when it was incorporated into the U.S.S.R.

Lithuania declared its independence in 1990, and the U.S.S.R. formally recognised the republic in 1991.

1918. 100 skatiku = 1 auksinas.
1922. 100 centu = 1 litas.
1990. 100 kopeks = 1 rouble.
1992. Talons.
1993. 100 centu = 1 litas.

1 2

1918.

3	1	10 s. black on buff	40·00	22·00
4		15 s. black on buff	35·00	22·00
5		20 s. black on buff	4·50	3·25
6		30 s. black on buff	4·50	3·25
7		40 s. black on buff	12·00	6·00
8		50 s. black on buff	4·50	3·25

1919.

9	2	10 s. black on buff	5·50	1·90
10		15 s. black on buff	5·50	1·90
11		20 s. black on buff	5·50	1·90
12		30 s. black on buff	5·50	1·90

3 4

1919.

13	3	10 s. black on buff	1·60	1·00
14		15 s. black on buff	1·60	1·00
15		20 s. black on buff	1·60	1·00
16		30 s. black on buff	1·60	1·00
17		40 s. black on buff	1·60	1·00
18		50 s. black on buff	1·60	1·00
19		60 s. black on buff	1·60	1·40

1919.

20	4	10 s. black on buff	2·00	1·00
21		15 s. black on buff	2·00	1·00
22		20 s. black on buff	2·00	1·00
23		30 s. black on buff	2·00	1·00
24		40 s. black on buff	2·00	1·50
25		50 s. black on buff	2·00	1·50
26		60 s. black on buff	2·00	2·00

5 Arms 6 7

1919. "auksinas" in lower case letters on 1 to 5 a.

40	5	10 s. pink	15	15
50		10 s. orange	15	15
51		15 s. violet	15	10
52		20 s. blue	15	10
43		30 s. orange	15	15
53		30 s. bistre	15	10
54		40 s. brown	15	10
55	6	50 s. green	15	10
56		60 s. red and violet	15	10
57		75 s. red and yellow	15	10
37	7	1 a. red and grey	35	20
38		3 a. red and brown	35	20
39		5 a. red and green	40	30

1921. As T **4**, but "AUKSINAS" or "AUKSINAI" in capital letters.

58	7	1 a. red and grey	15	10
59		3 a. red and brown	25	15
60		5 a. red and green	40	25

11 Lithuania receiving Independence

12 Lithuania arises

1920. 2nd Anniv of Independence.

65	11	10 s. lake	1·50	2·00
66		15 s. lilac	1·50	2·00
67		20 s. blue	1·50	2·00
68	12	30 s. brown	1·50	2·00
69	–	40 s. green and brown	1·50	2·00
70	12	50 s. red	1·50	2·00
71		60 s. lilac	1·50	2·00
72	–	80 s. red and violet	1·50	2·00
73	–	1 a. red and green	1·50	2·00
74	–	3 a. red and brown	1·60	2·00
75	–	5 a. red and green	1·60	2·00

DESIGNS—VERT: 40 s., 80 s., 1 a. Lithuania with chains broken; 3, 5 a. (25 × 25 mm) Arms.

16 Arms

17 Vytautas

1920. National Assembly.

76	16	10 s. red	40	30
77		15 s. violet	50	40
78	17	20 s. green	50	40
79	16	30 s. brown	60	50
80	–	40 s. violet and green	60	50
81	17	50 s. brown and orange	60	50
82		60 s. red and orange	60	50
83	–	80 s. red, grey and black	60	60
84	–	1 a. yellow and black	60	60
85	–	3 a. green and black	75	70
86	–	5 a. violet and black	2·00	1·75

DESIGNS—As Type **17**: 40 s., 80 s., 1 a. Gediminas. As Type **16**: 1 a. to 5 a. Sacred Oak and Altar.

20 Sower

21 Kestutis

22 Reaper

23

28 Allegory of Flight

24 Flying Posthorn

25 Junkers F-13 over River Niemen

1921.

87	20	10 s. red	30	1·75
88		15 s. mauve	15	1·00
89		20 s. blue	10	10
90	22	30 s. brown	50	4·25
91	21	40 s. red	15	10
92	22	50 s. olive	10	10
93		60 s. mauve and green	40	5·00
94	21	80 s. red and orange	20	15
95		1 a. green and brown	15	10
96		2 a. red and blue	15	10
97	23	3 a. blue and brown	50	2·00
124	20	4 a. blue and yellow	30	75
98	23	5 a. red and grey	60	3·25
125	20	8 a black and green	35	1·00
99	23	10 a. mauve and red	75	35
100		25 a. green and brown	1·40	1·25
101		100 a. grey and red	6·00	6·00

1921. Air. Inauguration of Kaunas–Konigsberg Air Service.

102	24	20 s. blue	65	55
103		40 s. orange	65	55
104		60 s. green	75	65
105		80 s. red	75	65
106	25	1 a. green and red	2·00	1·25
107	–	2 a. brown and blue	2·00	1·50
108	–	5 a. grey and yellow	2·75	2·75

DESIGNS—As Type **25**: 2 a. Three Junkers F-13 monoplanes; 5 a. Junkers F-13 over Gediminas Castle.

1921. Air. Inauguration of Air Mail Service.

109	28	20 s. lilac and orange	90	1·50
110		40 s. red and blue	90	1·50
111		60 s. olive and blue	1·00	1·60
112		80 s. green and yellow	1·00	1·60
113		1 a. blue and green	90	1·60
114		2 a. red and grey	1·50	1·75
115		5 a. green and purple	1·50	1·75

1922. Surch **4 AUKSINAI** with or without frame.

116	6	4 a. on 75 s. red and yellow	40	40

30 Junkers F-13

1922. Air.

118	30	1 a. red and brown	1·40	2·00
119		3 a. green and violet	1·40	2·00
120		5 a. yellow and blue	1·90	2·75

31 Junkers F-13 over Gediminas Castle

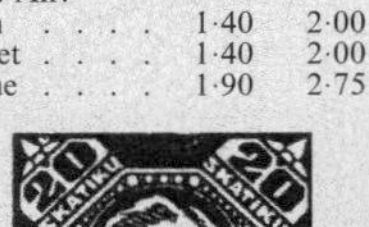
33 Pte. Luksis

1922. Air.

121	31	2 a. red and blue	1·25	1·00
122		4 a. red and brown	1·25	1·00
123		10 a. blue and black	2·00	1·50

1922. "De jure" Recognition of Lithuania by League of Nations. Inscr "LIETUVA DE JURE".

126	33	20 s. red and black	50	50
127	–	40 s. violet and green	40	40
128	–	50 s. blue and purple	40	40
129	–	60 s. orange and violet	40	40
130	–	1 a. blue and red	40	40
131	–	2 a. brown and blue	50	50
132	–	3 a. blue and brown	50	50
133	–	4 a. purple and green	50	50
134	–	5 a. red and brown	50	50
135	–	6 a. blue	60	50
136	–	8 a. yellow and blue	60	50
137	–	10 a. green and violet	90	75

DESIGNS—VERT: 40 s. Lt. Juozapavicius; 50 s. Dr. Basanavicius; 60 s. Mrs. Petkevicaite; 1 a. Prof. Voldemaras; 2 a. Dovidaitis; 3 a. Dr. Slezevicius; 4 a. Dr. Galvanauskas; 5 a. Dr. Grinius; 6 a. Dr. Stulginskis; 8 a. Pres. Smetona. HORIZ: (39 × 27 mm): 10 a. Stauguitis, Pres. Smetona and Silingas.

1922. Surch.

138	5	1 c. on 10 s. orange (postage)	50	5·00
139		1 c. on 15 s. violet	50	5·00
143		1 c. on 20 s. blue	50	4·00
144		1 c. on 30 s. orange	40·00	£100
145		1 c. on 30 s. bistre	20	40
146		1 c. on 40 s. brown	50	4·00
148	22	1 c. on 50 s. olive	10	15
149	6	2 c. on 50 s. green	75	4·00
150		2 c. on 60 s. red and violet	10	10
151		2 c. on 75 s. red and yellow	50	5·00
152	20	3 c. on 10 s. red	1·10	6·00
153		3 c. on 15 s. mauve	15	15
154		3 c. on 20 s. blue	20	3·00
155	22	3 c. on 30 s. brown	90	8·50
156	21	3 c. on 40 s. red	15	15
157	7	3 c. on 1 a. (No. 37)	75·00	£120
158		3 c. on 1 a. (No. 58)	25	1·25
159		3 c. on 3 a. (No. 38)	60·00	£100
160		3 c. on 3 a. (No. 59)	10	65
161		3 c. on 5 a. (No. 39)	32·00	55·00
162		3 c. on 5 a. (No. 60)	20	80
163	22	5 c. on 50 s. olive	10	10
164		5 c. on 60 s. mauve & green	2·75	16·00
165	21	5 c. on 80 s. red & orange	20	40
166	6	5 c. on 4 a. on 75 s. red and yellow	50	11·00
168	21	10 c. on 1 a. green & brown	25	10
169		10 c. on 2 a. red and blue	10	10
170	20	15 c. on 4 a. blue & yellow	20	10
171	23	25 c. on 3 a. blue and green	5·00	24·00
172		25 c. on 5 a. red and grey	3·00	8·50
173		25 c. on 10 a. mauve & red	75	1·60
174	20	30 c. on 8 a. black & green	25	25
175	23	50 c. on 25 a. green & brown	1·10	3·00
176		1 l. on 100 a grey and red	2·00	3·25
177	24	10 c. on 20 s. blue (air)	1·00	3·50
178		10 c. on 40 s. orange	1·25	5·00
179		10 c. on 60 s. green	1·00	5·00
180		10 c. on 80 s. red	1·25	5·00
181	25	20 c. on 1 a. green and red	4·75	12·50
182	–	20 c. on 2 a. (No. 107)	8·00	18·00
183	31	25 c. on 2 a. red and blue	1·00	85
184		30 c. on 4 a. red and brown	1·00	80
185	–	50 c. on 5 a. (No. 108)	1·40	1·25
186	31	50 c. on 10 a. blue & black	65	1·25
187	30	1 l. on 5 a. yellow & blue	12·50	27·00

38 Wayside Cross

39 Ruins of Kaunas Castle

40 Seminary Church

1923.

201	38	2 c. brown	60	30
202		3 c. bistre	85	25
203		5 c. green	85	10
204		10 c. violet	1·50	10
189		15 c. red	1·00	10
190		20 c. green	1·00	15
191		25 c. blue	1·00	10
206		36 c. brown	7·50	65
192	39	50 c. green	1·00	10
193		60 c. red	1·10	15
194	40	1 l. orange and green	5·50	10
195		3 l. red and grey	5·50	55
196		5 l. brown and blue	7·00	90

43 Arms of Memel

44 Ruins of Trakai

1923. Union of Memel with Lithuania.

210	43	1 c. red and green	80	1·25
211	–	2 c. mauve	80	1·25
212	–	3 c. yellow	80	1·25
213	43	5 c. buff and blue	80	1·25
214	–	10 c. red	1·50	1·50
215	–	15 c. green	1·50	1·50
216	44	25 c. violet	2·00	1·75
217	–	30 c. red	2·00	2·50
218	–	60 c. green	4·50	4·75
219	–	1 l. green	3·00	3·00
220	–	2 l. red	5·00	6·00
221	44	3 l. blue	5·50	7·00
222	–	5 l. blue	13·50	14·50

DESIGNS—As Type **43**: 3 c., 2 l. Chapel of Biruta; 10 c., 15 c. War Memorial Kaunas; As Type **44**: 2, 30 c. Arms of Lithuania; 60 c., 5 l. Memel Lighthouse; 1 l. Memel Harbour.

45 Biplane

46 Biplane

1924. Air.

223	45	20 c. yellow	1·40	70
224		40 c. green	1·40	70
225		60 c. red	1·50	75
226	46	1 l. brown	3·25	65

1924. Charity. War Orphans Fund. Surch **KARO NASLAICIAMS** and premium.

227	38	2 c. + 2 c. bistre (postage)	1·00	1·50
228		3 c. + 3 c. bistre	1·00	1·50
229		5 c. + 5 c. green	1·00	1·50
231		10 c. + 10 c. violet	1·00	2·50
232		15 c. + 15 c. red	1·00	2·50
233		20 c. + 20 c. olive	2·00	3·00
235		25 c. + 25 c. blue	4·00	7·00
236		36 c. + 34 c. brown	6·00	9·00
237	39	50 c. + 50 c. green	6·00	9·00
238		60 c. + 60 c. red	7·50	12·00
239	40	1 l. + 1 l. orange and green	7·50	12·00
240		3 l. + 2 l. red and grey	12·00	16·00
241		5 l. + 3 l. brown and blue	18·00	25·00
242	45	20 c. + 20 c. yellow (air)	8·00	10·00
243		40 c. + 40 c. green	8·00	10·00
244		60 c. + 60 c. red	8·00	10·00
245	46	1 l. + 1 l. brown	12·00	14·00

49 Swallow carrying Letter

56

57

1926. Air.

246	49	20 c. red	70	30
247		40 c. orange and mauve	70	30
248		60 c. black and blue	1·50	35

1926. Charity. War Invalids. Nos. 227/39 surch with new values and small ornaments.

249	38	1 c. + 1 c. on 2 c. + 2 c.	1·00	1·25
250		2 c. + 2 c. on 3 c. + 3 c.	1·00	1·25
251		2 c. + 2 c. on 5 c. + 5 c.	1·00	1·25
253		5 c. + 5 c. on 10 c. + 10 c.	1·75	2·00
254		5 c. + 5 c. on 15 c. + 15 c.	1·75	2·00
255		10 c. + 10 c. on 20 c. + 20 c.	1·75	2·00
257		10 c. + 10 c. on 25 c. + 25 c.	4·00	5·00
258		14 c. + 14 c. on 36 c. + 34 c.	6·00	7·00
259	39	20 c. + 20 c. on 50 c. + 50 c.	4·00	5·00
260		25 c. + 25 c. on 60 c. + 60 c.	6·00	9·00
261	40	30 c. + 30 c. on 1 l. + 1 l.	10·00	15·00

1926. Charity. War Orphans. Nos. 227/39 surch **V.P.** and new values in circular ornament.

262	38	1 c. + 1 c. on 2 c. + 2 c.	1·00	1·25
263		2 c. + 2 c. on 3 c. + 3 c.	1·00	1·25
264		2 c. + 2 c. on 5 c. + 5 c.	1·00	1·25
266		5 c. + 5 c. on 10 c. + 10 c.	2·00	2·50
267		10 c. + 10 c. on 15 c. + 15 c.	2·00	2·50
268		15 c. + 15 c. on 20 c. + 20 c.	2·50	2·50
270		15 c. + 15 c. on 25 c. + 25 c.	5·00	5·00
271		19 c. + 19 c. on 36 c. + 34 c.	5·00	6·00
272	39	25 c. + 25 c. on 50 c. + 50 c.	6·00	7·50
273		30 c. + 30 c. on 60 c. + 60 c.	9·00	12·00
274	40	50 c. + 50 c. on 1 l. + 1 l.	12·00	18·00

1927.

275 **56** 2 c. orange 75 10
276 3 c. brown 75 10
277 5 c. green . . . . 1·00 10
278 10 c. violet . . . . 2·00 10
279 15 c. red . . . . 1·75 10
280 25 c. blue . . . . 1·75 10
283 30 c. blue . . . . 12·00 1·00

1927. Dr. Basanavicius Mourning issue.

285 **57** 15 c. red . . . . 90 1·00
286 25 c. blue . . . . 90 1·00
287 50 c. green . . . . 1·10 1·00
288 60 c. violet . . . . 2·00 2·75

58 "Vytis" of the Lithuanian Arms

1927.

289 **58** 1 l. green and grey . . . . 1·25 50
290 3 l. violet and green . . . . 3·25 50
291 5 l. brown and grey . . . . 5·00 1·25

59 President Antanas Smetona 60 Lithuania liberated

1928. 10th Anniv of Independence.

292 **59** 5 c. green and brown . . . 25 10
293 10 c. black and violet . . . 25 10
294 15 c. brown and orange . . 30 10
295 25 c. slate and blue . . . 65 10
296 **60** 50 c. purple and blue . . . 85 20
297 60 c. black and red . . . . 1·10 45
298 – 1 l. brown . . . . 1·75 90

DESIGN—HORIZ: 1 l. Lithuania's resurrection (angel and soldiers). Dated 1918-1928.

62 63

64 J. Tubelis 66 Railway Station, Kaunas

1930. 500th Death Anniv of Grand Duke Vytautas.
(a) Postage.

299 **62** 2 c. brown 25 10
300 3 c. violet and brown . . . 25 10
301 5 c. red and green 25 10
302 10 c. green and violet . . . 25 10
303 15 c. violet and red . . . 25 10
304 30 c. purple and blue . . . 25 10
305 36 c. olive and purple . . . 35 15
306 50 c. blue and green . . . 35 20
307 60 c. red and blue 60 10
308 **63** 1 l. purple, grey and green 1·50 40
309 3 l. violet, pink and mauve 3·25 1·25
310 5 l. red, grey and brown . . 4·00 1·75
311 10 l. black and blue . . . . 13·00 18·00
312 25 l. green and brown . . . 35·00 48·00

(b) Air.

313 **64** 5 c. brown, yellow & black 35 35
314 10 c. black, drab and blue 40 40
315 15 c. blue, grey and purple 40 40
316 – 20 c. red, orange & brown 1·00 55
317 – 40 c. violet, lt blue and blue 1·40 80
318 – 60 c. black, lilac and green 1·60 1·40
319 – 1 l. black, lilac and red . . 3·00 1·50

DESIGNS—HORIZ: 20 c., 40 c. Vytautas and Kaunas; 60 c., 1 l. Vytautas and Smetona.

1932. Orphans' Fund. Imperf or perf.

320 **66** 5 c. blue and brown . . . 1·00 1·00
321 10 c. purple and brown . . 1·00 1·00
322 – 15 c. brown and green . . . 30 30
323 – 25 c. blue and green . . . 45 50
324 – 50 c. grey and olive . . . 70 1·25
325 – 60 c. grey and mauve . . . 1·00 4·25
326 – 1 l. blue and grey . . . . 2·50 3·25
327 – 3 l. purple and green . . . 4·50 5·00

DESIGNS—As Type **66**: 15, 25 c. "The Two Pines" (painting); 50 c. G.P.O. VERT: 60 c., 1, 3 l. Vilnius Cathedral.

68 Map of Lithuania, Memel and Vilna

1932. Air. Orphans' Fund. Imperf or perf.

328 **68** 5 c. red and green 25 25
329 10 c. purple and brown . . 25 25
330 – 15 c. blue and buff 40 40
331 – 20 c. black and brown . . . 2·40 2·00
332 – 40 c. purple and yellow . . 2·00 2·50
333 – 60 c. blue and buff . . . . 3·00 5·50
334 – 1 l. purple and green . . . 3·50 5·50
335 – 2 l. blue and green . . . . 3·75 5·50

DESIGNS: 15, 20 c. Airplane over R. Niemen; 40, 60 c. Town Hall, Kaunas; 1, 2 l. Vytautas Church, Kaunas.

69 Vytautas escapes from Prison

71 Coronation of Mindaugas

1932. 15th Anniv of Independence. Imperf or perf.

336 **69** 5 c. purple and red (postage) 50 50
337 10 c. brown and grey . . . 50 50
338 – 15 c. green and red 50 50
339 – 25 c. brown and purple . . 75 1·25
340 – 50 c. brown and green . . . 1·00 1·25
341 – 60 c. red and green . . . . 2·50 5·00
342 – 1 l. black and blue . . . . 3·25 3·25
343 – 3 l. green and purple . . . 3·50 5·50

344 – 5 c. lilac and green (air) . . 15 20
345 – 10 c. red and green 15 25
346 **71** 15 c. brown and violet . . . 20 30
347 – 20 c. black and red 45 45
348 – 40 c. black and purple . . . 65 1·25
349 – 60 c. black and orange . . . 1·90 6·00
350 – 1 l. green and violet . . . . 3·00 3·50
351 – 2 l. brown and blue . . . . 3·25 6·00

DESIGNS—POSTAGE. As Type **69**: 15, 25 c. Vytautas and Jagello preaching the gospel; 50, 60 c. Battle of Grunewald; 1, 3 l. Proclamation of Independence. AIR. As Type **71**: 5, 10 c. Battle of Saules; 40 c. Gediminas in Council; 60 c. Founding of Vilnius; 1 l. Russians surrendering to Gediminas; 2 l. Algirdas before Moscow.

72 A. Visteliauskas

1933. 50th Anniv of Publication of "Ausra".

352 **72** 5 c. red and green 20 25
353 10 c. red and blue 20 25
354 – 15 c. red and orange 20 25
355 – 25 c. brown and blue . . . 55 75
356 – 50 c. blue and green . . . . 65 1·00
357 – 60 c. deep brown & lt brn 2·00 5·00
358 – 1 l. purple and red . . . . 2·50 3·75
359 – 3 l. purple and blue . . . . 3·50 6·00

PORTRAITS: 15, 25 c. P. Vileisis; 50, 60 c. J. Sliupas; 1, 3 l. J. Basanavicius.

73 Trakai Castle

1933. Air. 550th Death Anniv of Grand Duke Kestutis.

360 **73** 5 c. blue and green 20 35
361 10 c. brown and violet . . . 20 35
362 – 15 c. violet and blue 20 35
363 – 20 c. purple and brown . . . 55 80
364 – 40 c. purple and blue . . . 90 1·60
365 – 60 c. blue and red . . . . 2·25 7·00
366 – 1 l. blue and green . . . . 3·00 4·50
367 – 2 l. green and violet . . . . 3·75 9·00

DESIGNS: 15, 20 c. Kestutis encounters Birute; 40, 60 c. Birute; 1, 2 l. Kestutis and Algirdas.

74 Mother and Child

75 J. Tumas Vaizgantas

1933. Child Welfare. (a) Postage.

373 **74** 5 c. brown and green . . . 15 20
374 10 c. blue and red 15 20
375 – 15 c. purple and green . . . 20 25
376 – 25 c. black and orange . . . 40 75
377 – 50 c. red and green . . . . 55 1·00
378 – 60 c. orange and black . . . 1·90 4·50
379 – 1 l. blue and brown . . . . 2·50 3·50
380 – 3 l. green and purple . . . 3·50 6·00

DESIGNS—VERT: 15, 25 c. Boy reading a book; 50, 60 c. Boy with building bricks; 1, 3 l. Mother and child weaving.

(b) Air. Various medallion portraits in triangular frames.

381 – 5 c. blue and red 15 15
382 – 10 c. green and violet . . . 15 15
383 **75** 15 c. brown and green . . . 15 15
384 20 c. blue and red 25 35
385 – 40 c. green and lake . . . . 85 1·25
386 – 60 c. brown and blue . . . 1·75 3·25
387 – 1 l. blue and yellow . . . . 1·90 2·75
388 – 2 l. lake and green . . . . 3·25 4·00

DESIGNS: 5, 10 c. Maironis; 40, 60 c. Vincas Kudirka; 1, 2 l. Zemaite.

76 Captains S. Darius and S. Girenas

78 "Flight" mourning over Wreckage 81 President A. Smetona

1934. Air. Death of Darius and Girenas (trans-Atlantic airmen).

389 **76** 20 c. red and black 10 10
390 – 40 c. blue and red 10 10
391 **76** 60 c. violet and black . . . 10 10
392 **78** 1 l. black and red 35 15
393 – 3 l. orange and green . . . 1·00 2·00
394 – 5 l. blue and brown . . . . 4·00 4·25

DESIGNS—HORIZ: 40 c. Bellanca monoplane "Lituanica" over Atlantic. VERT: 3 l. "Lituanica" and globe; 5 l. "Lituanica" and Vytis.

1934. President's 60th Birthday.

395 **81** 15 c. red . . . . 3·00 10
396 30 c. green . . . . 5·00 15
397 60 c. blue . . . . 10·00 30

82 83 84 Gleaner

85

1934.

398 **82** 2 c. red and orange 25 10
399 5 c. green 30 10
400 **83** 10 c. brown 75 10
401 **84** 25 c. brown and green . . . 2·00 10
402 **83** 35 c. red . . . . 2·00 10
403 **84** 50 c. blue . . . . 3·50 10
404 **85** 1 l. purple and red . . . . 18·00 10
405 3 l. green 20 10
406 – 5 l. purple and blue 20 20
407 – 10 l. brown and yellow . . . 1·25 1·25

DESIGNS—HORIZ: as Type **85**: 5 l., 10 l. Knight.
For design as Type **82** but smaller, see Nos. 411/12.

1935. Air. Honouring Atlantic Flyer Vaitkus. No. 390 optd **F. VAITKUS nugalejo Atlanta 21-22-IX-1935.**

407a – 40 c. blue and red £190 £300

87 Vaitkus and Air Route 88 President Smetona

1936. Air. Felix Vaitkus's New York–Ireland Flight.

408 **87** 15 c. purple . . . . 1·40 45
409 30 c. green . . . . 1·60 1·10
410 60 c. blue . . . . 2·50 1·10

1936. As T **82** but smaller (18 × 23 mm).

411 **82** 2 c. orange 10 10
412 5 c. green 10 10

1936.

413 **88** 15 c. red . . . . 4·00 10
414 30 c. green . . . . 9·00 10
415 60 c. blue . . . . 7·50 10

89 90 Archer

1937.

416 **89** 10 c. green . . . . 1·10 10
417 25 c. mauve 10 10
418 35 c. red 60 10
419 50 c. brown 30 10
419a 1 l. blue 15 30

1938. 1st National Olympiad Fund.

420 **90** 5 c. + 5 c. green . . . . . 7·00 9·00
421 – 15 c. + 5 c. red . . . . . . 9·00 10·00
422 – 30 c. + 10 c. blue . . . . . 12·00 14·00
423 – 60 c. + 15 c. brown . . . . 18·00 20·00

DESIGNS: 15 c. Throwing the javelin; 30 c. Diving; 60 c. Relay runner breasting tape.

1938. Scouts' and Guides' National Camp Fund. Nos. 420/3 optd **TAUTINE SKAUCIU** (or **SKAUTU**) **STOVYKLA** and badge.

424 **90** 5 c. + 5 c. green . . . . . 7·00 8·50
425 – 15 c. + 5 c. red . . . . . . 9·00 9·50
426 – 30 c. + 10 c. blue . . . . . 12·00 14·00
427 – 60 c. + 15 c. brown . . . . 17·00 19·00

92 President Smetona 93 Scoring a Goal

1939. 20th Anniv of Independence.

428 – 15 c. red 30 10
429 **92** 30 c. green 30 10
430 – 35 c. mauve 55 25
431 **92** 60 c. blue 60 25

DESIGN: 15, 35 c. Dr. Basanavicius proclaiming Lithuanian independence.

1939. 3rd European Basketball Championship and Physical Culture Fund.

432 – 15 c. + 10 c. brown . . . . 7·50 7·50
433 **93** 30 c. + 15 c. green . . . . 7·50 7·50
434 – 60 c. + 40 c. violet . . . . 15·00 17·00

DESIGNS—VERT: 15 c. Scoring a goal. HORIZ: (40½ × 36 mm); 60 c. International flags and ball.

1939. Recovery of Vilnius. Nos. 428/31 optd **VILNIUS 1939-X-10** and trident.

435 – 15 c. red 75 30
436 **92** 30 c. green 75 40
437 – 35 c. mauve . . . . 1·00 55
438 **92** 60 c. blue . . . . 1·40 85

95 Vytis 96 Vilnius

1940. "Liberty" Issue.

439 **95** 5 c. brown 10 10
440 – 10 c. green 40 30
441 – 15 c. orange 10 10
442 – 25 c. brown 10 30
443 – 30 c. green 15 10
444 – 35 c. orange 20 45

DESIGNS: 10 c. Angel; 15 c. Woman releasing a dove; 25 c. Mother and children; 30 c. "Liberty Bell"; 35 c. Mythical animal.

1940. Recovery of Vilnius.
445 **96** 15 c. brown 30 15
446 – 30 c. green 55 25
447 – 60 c. blue . . . . 1·10 90
DESIGNS—VERT: 30 c. Portrait of Gediminas. HORIZ: 60 c. Ruins of Trakai Castle.

1940. Incorporation of Lithuania in U.S.S.R. Optd **LTSR 1940 VII 21**.
448 **82** 2 c. red and orange 15 40
449 **95** 5 c. brown 15 40
450 – 10 c. green (No. 440) . . . 3·25 5·00
451 – 15 c. orange (No. 441) . . . 15 50
452 – 25 c. brown (No. 442) . . . 20 75
453 – 30 c. green (No. 443) . . . 25 80
454 – 35 c. orange (No. 444) . . . 25 1·50
455 **89** 50 c. brown . . . . 25 1·40

From 1940 to 1990 Lithuania used stamps of Russia.

99 Angel and Map

1990. No gum. Imperf.
456 **99** 5 k. green 10 10
457 10 k. lilac 10 10
458 20 k. blue 20 10
459 50 k. red 75 40

1990. No gum. Imperf (simulated perfs).
460 **99** 5 k. green and brown . . . 10 10
461 10 k. purple and brown . . . 10 10
462 20 k. blue and brown . . . 30 20
463 50 k. red and brown 90 45

100 Vytis **101** Hill of Crosses, Siauliai

1991.
464 **100** 10 k. black, gold & brown 10 10
465 15 k. black, gold & green 10 10
466 20 k. black, gold and blue 10 10
467 30 k. black, gold and red 15 10
468 40 k. black and gold . . . 10 10
469 50 k. black, gold & violet . 10 10
470 **101** 50 k. brown, chestnut & blk 10 10
471 **100** 100 k. black, gold & green 10 10
472 – 200 k. brown, chestnut and black 80 40
473 **100** 500 k. black, gold & blue . 40 20
DESIGN: As T **101**–200 k. Lithuanian Liberty Bell.
See also Nos. 482 and 488/9.

102 Liberty Statue, Kaunas **103** Angel with Trumpet

1991. National Day.
480 **102** 20 k. mauve, silver & blk 15 10

1991. 1st Anniv of Declaration of Independence from U.S.S.R.
481 **103** 20 k. dp green & green . . 15 10

1991. No gum. Imperf (simulated perfs).
482 **100** 15 k. green and black . . . 10 10

104 Wayside Crosses

1991.
483 **104** 40 k. green and silver . . . 15 10
484 – 70 k. brown, buff & gold . 30 15
485 – 100 k. brown, yell & silver . 45 20
DESIGNS: 70 k. "Madonna" (icon from Pointed Gate Chapel, Vilnius); 100 k. Towers of St. Anne's Church, Vilnius.

105 Candle

1991. 50th Anniv of Resistance to Soviet and German Occupations.
486 **105** 20 k. yellow, black & bis 10 10
487 – 50 k. rose, black and red 25 10
488 – 70 k. multicoloured 35 15
DESIGNS: 50 k. Shield pierced by swords; 70 k. Sword and wreath.

1991. No gum. Imperf.
489 **100** 25 k. black and brown . . 10 10
490 30 k. black and purple . . 15 10

106 World Map and Games Emblem **107** National Flag in Ice-axe and Mt. Everest

1991. 4th International Lithuanians' Games.
491 **106** 20 k. green, black & yell 20 10
492 – 50 k. + 25 k. green, black and yellow 55 25
DESIGN: 50 k. Symbolic female athlete.

1991. Lithuanian Expedition to Mt. Everest.
493 **107** 20 k. multicoloured 20 10
494 70 k. multicoloured 55 25

108 Trakai Castle **109** Black Storks

1991. 650th Death Anniv of Grand Duke Gediminas. Each brown, ochre and green.
495 30 k. Type **108** 15 10
496 50 k. Gediminas 25 15
497 70 k. Vilnius in 14th century 40 20

1991. Birds in the Red Book. Multicoloured.
498 30 k. + 15 k. Type **109** 50 25
499 50 k. Common cranes 60 30

110 U.N. and National Emblems and National Flag **111** National Team Emblem and Colours

1992. Admission to U.N.O.
500 **110** 100 k. multicoloured . . . 15 10

1992. Winter Olympic Games, Albertville, and Summer Games, Barcelona. Multicoloured.
501 50 k. + 25 k. Type **111** 15 10
502 130 k. Winter Games emblem 30 15
503 280 k. Summer Games emblem 55 25

112 Slipper Orchid **113** Goosander ("Mergus merganser")

1992. Plants in the Red Book. Multicoloured.
504 200 k. Type **112** 30 15
505 300 k. Sea holly 50 25

1992. Birds of the Baltic. No value expressed.
506 **113** B (15 t.) black and green 55 25
507 – B (15 t.) brown, blk & grn 55 25
508 – B (15 t.) sepia, brn & grn 55 25
509 – B (15 t.) brown, blk & grn 55 25
DESIGNS: No. 506, Osprey ("Pandion haliaetus"); 507, Black-tailed godwit ("Limosa limosa"); 509, Common shelduck ("Tadorna tadorna").

114 Kedainiai **115** Couple

1992. Arms. Multicoloured.
510 2 t. Type **114** 10 10
511 3 t. Vilnius 10 10
512 10 t. State arms 30 15
See also Nos. 531/3, 569/71, 594/5, 628/30, 663/5, 682/4 and 712/14.

1992. Costumes of Suvalkija.
513 **115** 2 t. multicoloured 15 10
514 – 5 t. multicoloured 30 15
515 – 7 t. multicoloured 45 20
DESIGNS: 5, 7 t. Different costumes.

116 Zapyskis Church

1993. Churches.
516 **116** 3 t. black and stone . . . 10 10
517 – 10 t. black and blue . . . 25 10
518 – 15 t. black and grey . . . 40 20
DESIGNS: 10 t. Church of St. Peter and St. Paul, Vilnius; 15 t. Church of the Resurrection, Kaunas.

1993. Nos. 467, 490 and 468 surch.
519 **100** 1 t. on 30 k. blk, gold & red 10 10
520 1 t. on 30 k. black & pur 10 10
521 3 t. on 40 k. black & gold 15 10

118 Jonas Basanavicius (statesman)

1993. National Day. No value expressed.
522 **118** A (3 t.) red, cinnamon and brown 10 10
523 – B (15 t.) green, stone and brown 55 25
DESIGN: No. 523, Jonas Vileisis (politician).

119 Vytautas **120** Simonas Daukantas (historian)

1993. 600th Anniv (1987) of Accession of Grand Duke Vytautas.
524 – 5 t. gold, red and black . . 10 10
525 **119** 10 t. green, black and red 25 10
526 – 15 t. black, yellow & red 40 20
DESIGNS: 5 t. Seal; 15 t. "Battle of Grunwald" (Jan Matejka).

1993. Birth Anniversaries. Each brown and yellow.
528 10 t. Type **120** (bicent) 15 10
529 20 t. Vydunas (125th anniv) . . 35 20
530 45 t. Vincas Mykolaitis-Putinas (philosopher, centenary) . . 80 40

1993. Town Arms. As T **114**. Multicoloured.
531 5 c. Skuodas 10 10
532 30 c. Telsiai 20 10
533 50 c. Klaipeda 35 15

121 "Watchtower" (M. K. Ciurlionis) **122** State Arms

1993. World Unity Day (5 c.) and Transatlantic Flight (80 c.). Multicoloured.
534 5 c. Type **121** 10 10
535 80 c. Steponas Dariaus and Stasys Gireno 50 25

1993. No value expressed.
536 **122** A, green, brown and red 10 10
537 B, red, green and bistre 35 20

123 Pope John Paul II and View of Siluva **124** Couple

1993. Papal Visit. Multicoloured.
538 60 c. Type **123** 35 20
539 60 c. Pope and Hill of Crosses 35 20
540 80 c. Pope and Kaunas 50 25
541 80 c. Pope and Ausra Gates, Vilnius 50 25

1993. Costumes of Dzukai.
542 **124** 60 c. multicoloured 25 10
543 – 80 c. multicoloured 40 20
544 – 1 l. multicoloured 55 25
DESIGNS: 80 c. to 1 l. Different costumes.

125 Klaipeda Post Office

1993. 75th Anniv of First Lithuanian Postage Stamps.
545 **125** 60 c. multicoloured 35 15
546 – 60 c. multicoloured 30 15
547 – 80 c. multicoloured 50 25
548 – 1 l. black, brown and green . 60 30
DESIGNS: No. 546, Kaunas post office; 547, Ministry for Post and Information, Vilnius; 548, First Lithuanian stamp.

126 "The Ladle Carver" (A. Gudaitis) **127** European Pond Turtle

1993. Europa. Contemporary Art.
549 **126** 80 c. multicoloured 45 25

1993. Pond Life. Multicoloured.
550 80 c. Type **127** 40 20
551 1 l. Running toad 45 25

128 Games Emblem and Team Colours **130** Kristijonas Donelaitis

129 Antanas Smetona (President 1919–22 and 1926–40)

1994. Winter Olympic Games, Lillehammer, Norway.
552 **128** 1 l. 10 multicoloured . . . 45 20

1994. National Day.
553 **129** 1 l. red and black 30 15
554 – 1 l. brown and black 30 15
DESIGN: No. 554, Aleksandras Stulginskis (President 1922–26).

1994. Writers. Each cream, brown and orange.
555 60 c. Type **130** 25 10
556 80 c. Vincas Kudirka 35 15
557 1 l. Jonas Maciulis Maironis . . 45 20

131 State Arms

132 Rockets by Kazimieras Simonavicius (illus from "Artis Magnae Artilleriae")

1994.

558	131	5 c. brown	10	10
559		10 c. lilac	10	10
560		20 c. green	10	10
612		40 c. purple	15	10
613		50 c. blue	20	10

1994. Europa. Inventions and Discoveries.

561	132	80 c. multicoloured	45	20

133 Couple

134 Music Note, Globe and Flag

1994. 19th-century Costumes of Zemaiciai (Lowlands).

563	133	5 c. multicoloured	10	10
564	–	80 c. multicoloured	35	15
565	–	1 l. multicoloured	45	20

DESIGNS: 80 c., 1 l., Different costumes from Zemaiciai.

1994. Lithuanians of the World Song Festival.

566	134	10 c. multicoloured	10	10

135 State Arms

136 Common Bat

1994.

567	135	2 l. multicoloured	80	40
568		3 l. multicoloured	1·25	60

1994. Town Arms. As T **114** but size 25×32 mm. Multicoloured.

569		10 c. Punia	10	10
570		60 c. Alytus	25	10
571		80 c. Perloja	35	15

1994. Mammals. Multicoloured.

572		20 c. Type **136**	15	10
573		20 c. Fat dormouse	15	10

137 Kaunas Town Hall

1994. Town Halls.

574	137	10 c. black and mauve	10	10
575	–	60 c. black and blue	25	10
576	–	80 c. black and green	35	15

DESIGNS: 60 c. Kedainiai; 80 c. Vilnius.

138 Madonna and Child

1994. Christmas.

577	138	20 c. multicoloured	15	10

139 Steponas Kairys

1995. National Day. Signatories to 1918 Declaration of Independence.

578	139	20 c. lilac, grey and black	10	10
579	–	20 c. blue, grey and black	10	10

DESIGN: No. 579, Pranas Dovydaitis (Head of Government, Mar–Apr 1919).

140 Kaunas (Lithuania)

141 "Lithuanian School, 1864–1904" (P. Rimsa)

1995. Via Baltica Motorway Project.

581	140	20 c. multicoloured	10	10

1995. Europa. Peace and Freedom.

583	141	1 l. multicoloured	40	20

142 Couple

143 Motiejus Valancius (120th death)

1995. Costumes of the Highlands.

584	–	20 c. multicoloured	10	10
585	–	70 c. multicoloured	25	15
586	142	1 l. multicoloured	40	20

DESIGNS: 70 c. to 1 l. Different 19th-century costumes.

1995. Anniversaries.

587	143	30 c. cream, purple and yellow	10	10
588	–	40 c. cream, green and orange	20	10
589	–	70 c. cream, deep blue and pink	30	15

DESIGNS: 40 c. Zemaite (150th birth); 70 c. Kipras Petrauskas (110th birth).

144 Pieta

145 Torch-bearer

1995. Day of Mourning and Hope.

590	144	20 c. multicoloured	10	10

1995. 5th World Lithuanians Games.

591	145	30 c. multicoloured	15	10

146 "Baptria tibiale"

147 "Valerija Mesalina"

1995. Butterflies and Moths in "The Red Book". Multicoloured.

592		30 c. Type **146**	20	10
593		30 c. Cream-spot tiger moth ("Arctia villica")	20	10

1995. Town Arms. As T **114**. Multicoloured.

594		40 c. Virbalis	20	10
595		1 l. Kudirkos Naumiestis (horiz)	40	20

1995. 250th Birth Anniv of Pranciskus Smuglevicius (painter).

596	147	40 c. multicoloured	20	10

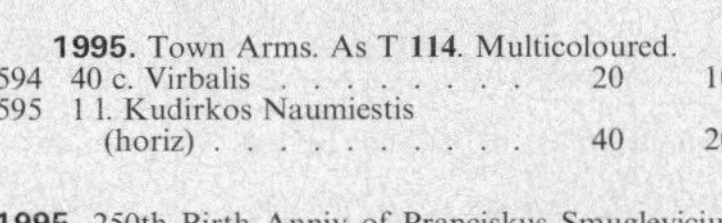

148 Trakai Island Castle

1995. Castles.

597	–	40 c. multicoloured	15	10
598	148	70 c. blue, deep blue and black	30	15
599	–	1 l. multicoloured	35	20

DESIGNS: 40 c. Vilnius Upper Castle; 1 l. Birzai Castle.

149 Star over Winter Scene

150 Bison

1995. Christmas. Multicoloured.

600		40 c. Type **149**	20	10
601		1 l. Churchgoers with lanterns	40	20

1996. The European Bison. Multicoloured.

602		30 c. Type **150**	10	10
603		40 c. Pair of bison	15	10
604		70 c. Adult and calf	25	10
605		1 l. Parents and calf	30	15

151 Kazys Grinius (130th)

1996. Birth Anniversaries.

606	151	40 c. cream, brown and blue	15	10
607	–	1 l. cream, bistre and yellow	40	20
608	–	1 l. cream, blue and red	40	20

DESIGNS: No. 607, Antanas Zmuidzinavicius (120th); 608, Balys Sruoga (centenary).

152 Vladas Mironas

1996. National Day. Signatories to 1918 Declaration of Independence.

609	152	40 c. cream, grey and black	15	10
610	–	40 c. bistre, brown and black	15	10

DESIGN: No. 610, Jurgis Saulys.

153 Barbora Radvilaite

154 Couple

1996. Europa. Famous Women

611	153	1 l. multicoloured	30	15

1996. Costumes of Klaipeda. 19th-century costumes. Multicoloured.

618		40 c. Type **154**	15	10
619		1 l. Woman in red skirt and man in frock-coat	45	20
620		1 l. Woman in black skirt and man in blue waistcoat	45	20

155 Angel

156 "The Discus Thrower"

1996. Day of Mourning and Hope.

621	155	40 c. blue, red and black	20	10
622	–	40 c. green, red and black	20	10

DESIGN: No. 622, Head of crucifix.

1996. Olympic Games, Atlanta. Multicoloured.

623		1 l. Type **156**	35	15
624		1 l. Basketball	35	15

157 "Sacrifice"

159 Angels heralding

1996. 85th Death Anniv of Mikolajus Ciurlionis (artist). Multicoloured.

625		40 c. Type **157**	15	10
626		40 c. "Cemetery"	15	10

1996. Town Arms. As T **114** but size 25 × 32 mm.

628		50 c. multicoloured	20	10
629		90 c. red, black and yellow	40	20
630		1 l. 20 multicoloured	50	25

DESIGN: 50 c. Seduva; 90 c. Panevezys; 1 l. 20, Zarasai.

1996. Christmas. Multicoloured.

632		50 c. Type **159**	20	10
633		1 l. 20 Elf riding on "Pegasus"	40	20

160 Ieva Simonaityte (writer, birth centenary)

161 Title Page

1997. Anniversaries.

634	160	50 c. stone, brown and green	15	10
635	–	90 c. stone, grey and yellow	35	20
636	–	1 l. 20 stone, green and orange	40	20

DESIGNS: 90 c. Jonas Sliupas (physician, 53rd death); 1 l. 20, Vladas Jurgutis (financier, 31st death).

1997. 450th Anniv of Publication of "Catechism of Mazvydas" (first Lithuanian book).

637	161	50 c. brown and grey	20	10

162 Mykolas Birziska

1997. National Day. Signatories to 1918 Declaration of Independence.

639	162	50 c. green, light green and black	20	10
640	–	50 c. purple, stone and black	20	10

DESIGN: No. 640, Kazimieras Saulys.

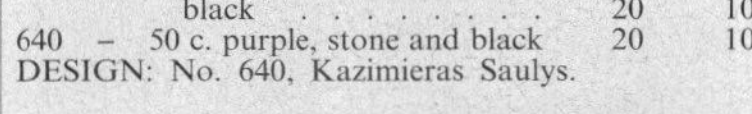

164 "Little Witch" (Jovita Jankeviciute)

165 Lecture

1997. Europa. Tales and Legends. Multicoloured.

642		1 l. 20 Type **164**	45	20
643		1 l. 20 "Rainbow" (Ieva Staseviciute) (horiz)	45	20

1997. 600th Anniv of First Lithuanian School.

644	165	50 c. multicoloured	20	10

166 Kurshes Ship

1997. Baltic Sailing Ships.
645 **166** 50 c. multicoloured 20 10

167 Park

1997. Centenary of Palanga Botanical Park.
647 **167** 50 c. yellow, black and brown 20 10

168 Ship of Flags 169 Elk's-horn Staff, 3000 B.C.

1997. 2nd Baltic Sea Games, Lithuania.
648 **168** 90 c. multicoloured 35 15

1997. Museum Exhibits. Multicoloured.
649 90 c. Type **169** 35 15
650 1 l. 20 Silver coins of Grand Duke Kazimierz IV, 15th century A.D. 45 20

170 Vytis's Cross 171 Black Morel

1997.
651 **170** 5 c. yellow & light yellow . 10 10
652 10 c. yellow and cream . . 10 10
653 20 c. green and brown . . 10 10
654 35 c. purple and lilac . . 10 10
655 50 c. brown & cinnamon . 15 10
656 70 c. yellow and cream . . 20 10

1997. Fungi in the Red Book. Multicoloured.
660 1 l. 20 Type **171** 50 25
661 1 l. 20 Bronze boletus 50 25

172 Letter and Seal 173 Cherub holding Lantern above Town

1997. 674th Anniv of Letters of Invitation for Migrants sent by Grand Duke Gediminas to European Cities.
662 **172** 50 c. multicoloured 20 10

1997. Town Arms. As T **114** but size 25 × 33 mm.
663 50 c. Neringa 15 10
664 90 c. Vilkaviskis 30 15
665 1 l. 20 Pasvalys 40 20

1997. Christmas. Multicoloured.
666 50 c. Type **173** 15 10
667 1 l. 20 Snow-covered trees . . . 40 20

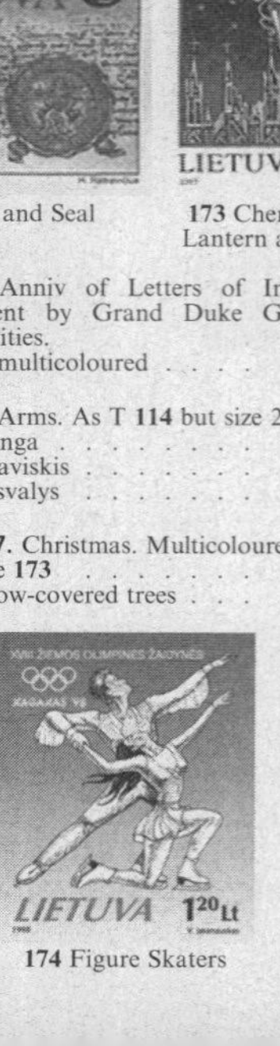

174 Figure Skaters

1998. Winter Olympic Games, Nagano, Japan.
668 **174** 1 l. 20 ultramarine and blue . 35 15

175 Alfonsas Petrulis (priest)

1998. National Day. Signatories to 1918 Declaration of Independence.
669 **175** 50 c. green, grey and black . 15 10
670 – 90 c. brown, light brown and black 30 15
DESIGN: No. 670, Jokubas Sernas (lawyer and politician).

178 Gustaitis and ANBO-41 (reconnaissance plane)

1998. Birth Centenary of Antanas Gustaitis (pilot and aircraft constructor). Multicoloured.
673 2 l. Type **178** 60 30
674 3 l. ANBO-VIII (light bomber) and diagrams 90 45

179 National Song Festival 180 Tadas Ivanauskas (zoologist, 27th death anniv)

1998. Europa. National Festivals.
675 **179** 1 l. 20 multicoloured . . . 35 15

1998. Anniversaries.
676 **180** 50 c. green, light yellow and yellow 15 10
677 – 90 c. red, yellow and orange 30 15
678 – 90 c. green, yellow and orange 30 15
DESIGNS—45 × 25 mm: No. 677, Stasys Lozoraitis (diplomat, birth centenary) and Stasys Lozoraitis (diplomat, 10th death anniv); No. 678, Jurgis Baltrusaitis (writer and diplomat, 125th birth anniv) and Jurgis Baltrusaitis (art historian, 4th death anniv).

181 Long Jumping

1998. 6th World Lithuanian Games and Second National Games.
679 **181** 1 l. 35 multicoloured . . . 40 20

182 Atlantic Salmon

1998. Fishes in the Red Book. Multicoloured.
680 1 l. 40 Type **182** 45 20
681 1 l. 40 Whitefish ("Coregonus lavaretus") 45 20

1998. Town Arms. As T **114** but size 25 × 33 mm. Multicoloured.
682 70 c. Kernave 20 10
683 70 c. Trakai 20 10
684 1 l. 35 Kaunas 40 20

183 Vilnuis–Cracow Postal Service, 1562

1998. Postal History.
685 **183** 70 c. multicoloured 20 10

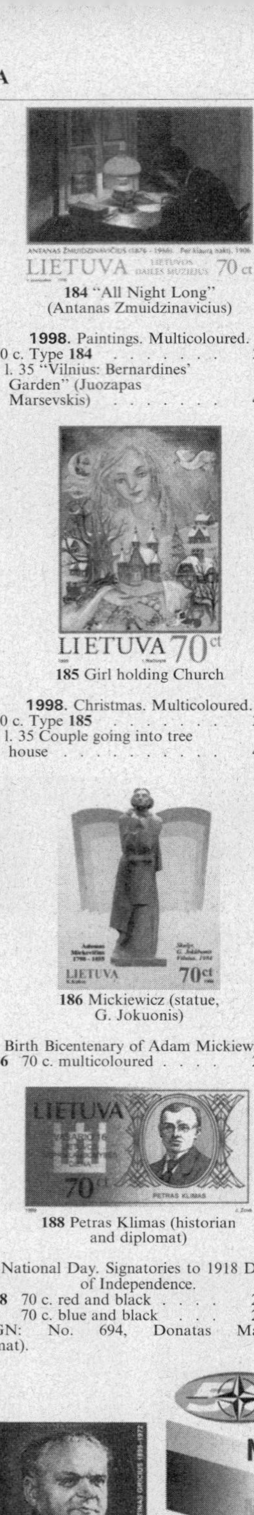

184 "All Night Long" (Antanas Zmuidzinavicius)

1998. Paintings. Multicoloured.
687 70 c. Type **184** 20 10
688 1 l. 35 "Vilnius: Bernardines' Garden" (Juozapas Marsevskis) 40 20

185 Girl holding Church

1998. Christmas. Multicoloured.
689 70 c. Type **185** 20 10
690 1 l. 35 Couple going into tree house 40 20

186 Mickiewicz (statue, G. Jokuonis)

1998. Birth Bicentenary of Adam Mickiewicz (poet).
691 **186** 70 c. multicoloured 20 10

188 Petras Klimas (historian and diplomat)

1999. National Day. Signatories to 1918 Declaration of Independence.
693 **188** 70 c. red and black 20 10
694 – 70 c. blue and black . . . 20 10
DESIGN: No. 694, Donatas Malinauskas (diplomat).

189 Augustinas Gricius (dramatist)

190 Emblem and State Flag

1999. Birth Centenaries.
695 **189** 70 c. black, cream and orange 20 10
696 – 70 c. brown, cream and pink 20 10
697 – 1 l. 35 green, cream amd orange 40 20
DESIGNS: No. 696, Juozas Matulis (chemist); 697, Pranas Skardzius (philologian).

1999. 50th Anniv of North Atlantic Treaty Organization.
698 **190** 70 c. multicoloured 20 10

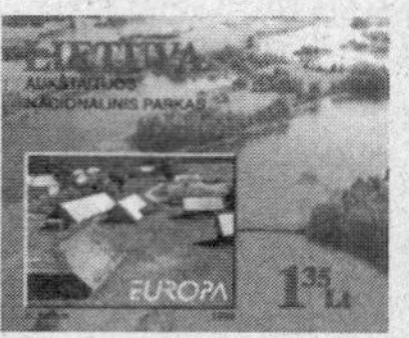

191 Aukstaitija National Park

1999. Europa. Parks and Gardens. Multicoloured.
699 1 l. 35 Type **191** 40 20
700 1 l. 35 Curonian Spit National Park 40 20

192 Council Flag

193 Boarded Clay Windmill, Melniai

1999. 50th Anniv of Council of Europe.
701 **192** 70 c. multicoloured 20 10

1999. Windmills. Multicoloured.
702 70 c. Type **193** 20 10
703 70 c. Red-brick windmill, Pumpenai 20 10

194 "Dasypoda argentata" 195 Sculpture of U.P.U. Emblem, Berne

1999. Bumble Bees. Multicoloured.
704 70 c. Type **194** 20 10
705 2 l. "Bombus pomorum" . . . 60 30

1999. 125th Anniv of Universal Postal Union.
706 **195** 70 c. multicoloured 20 10

196 1918 and 1990 Stamps and Society Emblems

1999. 75th Anniv of Lithuanian Philatelic Society.
707 **196** 1 l. multicoloured 30 15

198 Family and State Flag 199 Emblem

1999. 10th Anniv of the Baltic Chain (human chain uniting the capitals of Lithuania, Estonia and Latvia).
709 **198** 1 l. multicoloured 30 15

1999. 50th Anniv of Establishment of Lithuanian Freedom Fight Movement.
711 **199** 70 c. multicoloured 20 10

1999. Town Arms. Designs as T **114** but size 25 × 33 mm. Multicoloured.
712 70 c. Marijampole 20 10
713 1 l. Siauliai 30 15
714 1 l. 40 Rokiskis 40 20

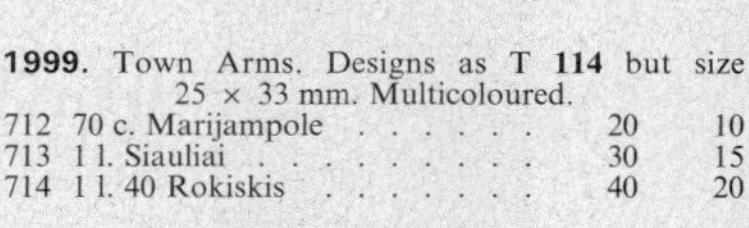

200 Sword of General S. Zukauskas, 1927

201 "Horse and Bear" (fable)

1999. Exhibits in Vytautas Magnus War Museum. Multicoloured.
715 70 c. Type **200** 20 10
716 3 l. 17th-century Hussar's armour 90 45

1999. Birth Bicentenary of Simonas Stanevicius (writer).
717 **201** 70 c. multicoloured 20 10

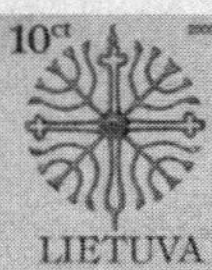

202 "Winter Symphony" **203** Top of Monument

1999. Christmas. Multicoloured.

718		70 c. Type **202**	20	10
719		1 l. 35 Cathedral, candles and bell	40	20

2000. Ironwork.

720	**203**	10 c. blue and brown	10	10
721	–	20 c. blue and stone	10	10
722	–	1 l. blue and pink	30	15
723	–	1 l. 30 blue and green	40	20
724	–	1 l. 70 blue and light blue	50	25

DESIGNS: 20 c. to 1 l. 70, Different examples of ornamental ironwork.

204 Jonas Vailokaitis

2000. National Day. Signatories to 1918 Declaration of Independence.

725	**204**	1 l. 30 orange, stone and black	40	25
726	–	1 l. 70 brown, stone and black	50	25

DESIGN: 1 l. 70, Jonas Smilgevicius.

206 Vincas Pietaris (writer, 150th anniv)

2000. Birth Anniversaries.

728	**206**	1 l. green, black and purple	30	15
729	–	1 l. 30 black, black and brown	40	20
730	–	1 l. 70 brown, black and blue	50	25

DESIGNS: 1 l. 30, Kanutas Ruseckas (painter, bicentenary); 1 l. 70, Povilas Visinskis (literary critic, 125th anniv).

LOMBARDY AND VENETIA Pt. 2

Formerly known as Austrian Italy. Although these provinces used a different currency the following issues were valid throughout Austria. Lombardy was annexed by Sardinia in 1859 and Venetia by Italy in 1866.

1850. 100 centesimi = 1 lira.
1858. 100 soldi = 1 florin.
100 kreuzer = 1 gulden.

1 Arms of Austria

1850. Imperf.

1c 1 5 c. orange . . . . £950 55·00
2c 10 c. black . . . . £1000 42·00
7 15 c. red £325 75
4 30 c. brown . . . . £1300 3·50
5e 45 c. blue . . . . £4250 8·50

1859. As T 4 and 5 of Austria (Emperor Francis Joseph I) but value in soldi. Perf.

16 5 2 s. yellow . . . . £275 50·00
17 4 3 s. black £900 £150
18 3 s. green . . . . £225 50·00
19 5 5 s. red . . . . £120 2·25
20 10 s. brown . . . . £180 23·00
21 15 s. blue . . . . £1100 40·00

3 Emperor Francis Joseph I

4 Arms of Austria

1861.

25 3 5 s. red . . . . £900 1·40
26 10 s. brown . . . . £900 13·00

1863.

27 4 2 s. yellow . . . . 55·00 £110
33 3 s. green . . . . 12·00 9·00
34 5 s. red . . . . 1·75 1·00
35 10 s. blue . . . . 11·00 3·00
36 15 s. brown . . . . 55·00 38·00

JOURNAL STAMPS

J 5

1858. Imperf.

J22 J 5 1 k. black £1100 £3000
J23 2 k. red . . . . £130 40·00
J24 4 k. red £25000 £3000

LOURENCO MARQUES Pt. 9

A Portuguese colony in E. Africa, now part of Mozambique, whose stamps it uses.

1895. 1000 reis = 1 milreis.
1913. 100 centavos = 1 escudo.

1895. "Figures" key-type inscr "LOURENCO MARQUES".

1 R 5 r. yellow 20 15
2 10 r. mauve 25 15
3 15 r. brown 40 35
4 20 r. lilac 40 35
10 25 r. green 30 15
12 50 r. blue 35 15
18 75 r. pink 80 40
14 80 r. green . . . . 1·10 75
7 100 r. brown on yellow . . . 85 50
16 150 r. red on pink 90 75
8 200 r. blue on blue . . . . 1·50 90
9 300 r. blue on brown . . . . 1·50 90

1895. 700th Death Anniv of St. Anthony. Optd **L. MARQUES CENTENARIO DE S. ANTONIO MDCCCXCV** on (a) "Embossed" key-type inscr "PROVINCIA DE MOCAMBIQUE".

19 Q 5 r. black . . . . 4·50 4·00
20 10 r. green . . . . 7·00 4·50
21 20 r. red . . . . 8·00 5·50
22 25 r. purple . . . . 10·00 7·25
23 40 r. brown . . . . 8·00 6·75
27a 50 r. blue . . . . 5·50 4·50
25 100 r. brown . . . . 15·00 11·00
26 200 r. violet . . . . 12·00 11·00
27 300 r. orange . . . . 18·00 16·00

(b) "Figures" key-type inscr "MOCAMBIQUE".

28 R 5 r. orange . . . . 5·25 3·75
29 10 r. mauve . . . . 8·50 7·50
30 50 r. blue . . . . 13·00 7·50
35 75 r. pink . . . . 14·00 9·50
32 80 r. green . . . . 23·00 17·00
33 100 r. brown on yellow . . . 25·00 23·00
35a 150 r. red on pink . . . . 16·00 13·00

1897. No. 9 surch **50 reis**.

36 R 50 r. on 300 r. blue on brown 70·00 50·00

1898. "King Carlos" key-type inscr "LOURENCO MARQUES". Name and value in black.

37 S $2\frac{1}{2}$ r. grey 15 15
38 5 r. orange 15 15
39 10 r. green 15 15
40 15 r. brown 50 45
83 15 r. green 20 15
41 20 r. lilac 30 15
42 25 r. green 35 15
84 25 r. red 20 15
43 50 r. blue 50 25
85 50 r. brown 45 35
86 65 r. blue . . . . 2·25 2·00
44 75 r. pink . . . . 1·00 80
87 75 r. purple 65 60
45 80 r. mauve 95 65
46 100 r. blue on blue 50 25
88 115 r. brown on pink . . . . 2·50 2·00
89 130 r. brown on yellow . . . 2·50 2·00
47 150 r. brown on yellow . . . 85 75
48 200 r. purple on pink . . . . 1·50 75
49 300 r. blue on pink . . . . 1·00 80
90 400 r. blue on yellow . . . . 2·50 2·00
50 500 r. black on blue . . . . 2·10 1·25
51 700 r. mauve on yellow . . . 3·75 2·75

1899. Green and brown fiscal stamps of Mozambique, as T 9 of Macao, bisected and each half surch **Correio de Lourenco Marques** and value. Imperf.

55 – 5 r. on half of 10 r. 60 30
56 – 25 r. on half of 10 r. 60 30
57 – 50 r. on half of 30 r. 60 30
58 – 50 r. on half of 800 r. . . . 90 50

1899. No. 44 surch **50 Reis**.

59 S 50 r. on 75 r. pink . . . . . 1·50 1·10

1902. "Figures" and "Newspaper" key-types surch.

60 V 65 r. on $2\frac{1}{2}$ r. brown . . . . 1·25 1·10
62 R 65 r. on 5 r. yellow . . . . 1·25 1·10
63 65 r. on 15 r. brown . . . . 1·25 1·10
64 65 r. on 20 r. lilac . . . . 1·25 1·10
66 115 r. on 10 r. mauve . . . . 1·25 1·10
67 115 r. on 200 r. blue on bl . . 1·25 1·10
68 115 r. on 300 r. bl on brn . . 1·25 1·10
70 130 r. on 25 r. green . . . . 1·25 1·10
72 130 r. on 80 r. green . . . . 1·25 1·10
73 130 r. on 150 r. red on pink . 1·25 1·10
74 400 r. on 50 r. blue . . . . 4·25 1·90
76 400 r. on 75 r. pink . . . . 3·25 2·10
78 400 r. on 100 r. brown on yellow . . . . 2·10 1·40

1902. "King Carlos" key-type inscr "LOURENCO MARQUES" optd **PROVISORIO**.

79 S 15 r. brown 75 50
80 25 r. green 65 40
81 50 r. blue 80 60
82 75 r. pink . . . . 1·25 75

1905. No. 86 surch **50 REIS**.

91 S 50 r. on 65 r. blue . . . . . 1·00 95

1911. "King Carlos" key-type inscr "LOURENCO MARQUES" optd **REPUBLICA**.

92 S $2\frac{1}{2}$ r. grey 10 10
93 5 r. orange 10 10
94 10 r. green 15 15
95 15 r. green 15 15
96 20 r. lilac 30 20
97 25 r. red 20 15
98 50 r. brown 35 25
99 75 r. purple 35 25
100 100 r. blue on blue 35 25
178 115 r. brown on pink 35 35
102 130 r. brown on yellow . . . 30 25
103 200 r. purple on pink 30 25
104 400 r. blue on yellow 50 35
105 500 r. black on blue 60 50
106 700 r. mauve on yellow . . . 80 50

1913. Surch **REPUBLICA LOURENCO MARQUES** and value on "Vasco da Gama" issues of (a) Portuguese Colonies.

107 $\frac{1}{4}$ c. on $2\frac{1}{2}$ r. green 50 45
108 $\frac{1}{2}$ c. on 5 r. red 50 45
109 1 c. on 10 r. purple 50 45
110 $2\frac{1}{2}$ c. on 25 r. green 50 45
111 5 c. on 50 r. blue 50 45
112 $7\frac{1}{2}$ c. on 75 r. brown . . . . 1·25 85
113 10 c. on 100 r. brown 65 45
114 15 c. on 150 r. brown 65 45

(b) Macao.

115 $\frac{1}{4}$ c. on $\frac{1}{2}$ a. green 60 45
116 $\frac{1}{2}$ c. on 1 a. red 60 45
117 1 c. on 2 a. purple 60 45
118 $2\frac{1}{2}$ c. on 4 a. green 60 45
119 5 c. on 8 a. blue 60 45
120 $7\frac{1}{2}$ c. on 12 a. brown . . . 1·00 85
121 10 c. on 16 a. brown 75 45
122 15 c. on 24 a. brown 75 45

(c) Timor.

123 $\frac{1}{4}$ c. on $\frac{1}{2}$ a. green 60 45
124 $\frac{1}{2}$ c. on 1 a. red 60 45
125 1 c. on 2 a. purple 60 45
126 $2\frac{1}{2}$ c. on 4 a. green 60 45
127 5 c. on 8 a. blue 60 45
128 $7\frac{1}{2}$ c. on 12 a. brown . . . 1·00 90
129 10 c. on 16 a. brown 80 45
130 15 c. on 24 a. brown 80 45

1914. "Ceres" key-type inscr "LOURENCO MARQUES".

147 U $\frac{1}{4}$ c. green 10 10
148 $\frac{1}{2}$ c. black 10 10
149 1 c. green 10 10
150 $1\frac{1}{2}$ c. brown 15 15
151 2 c. red 15 15
152 $2\frac{1}{2}$ c. violet 15 15
153 5 c. blue 15 15
154 $7\frac{1}{2}$ c. brown 15 15
155 U 8 c. grey 15 15
140 10 c. red 80 40
157 15 c. purple 35 35
142 20 c. green 45 35
143 30 c. brown on green . . . 70 50
144 40 c. brown on pink . . . . 2·50 2·00
145 50 c. orange on orange . . . 1·00 90
146 1 e. green on blue . . . . 1·10 90

1914. Provisionals of 1902 overprinted **REPUBLICA**.

166 R 115 r. on 10 r. mauve . . . 30 30
167 115 r. on 200 r. blue on bl . 35 30
168 115 r. on 300 r. blue on brown 30 30
161 130 r. on 25 r. green 50 40
164 130 r. on 80 r. green 50 40
169 130 r. on 150 r. red on pink . 30 30
184 400 r. on 50 r. blue 80 45
185 400 r. on 75 r. pink 80 25

1915. Nos. 93 and 148 perf diagonally and each half surch $\frac{1}{4}$.

170 S $\frac{1}{4}$ on half of 5 r. orange . . . 1·40 1·10
171 U $\frac{1}{4}$ on half of $\frac{1}{2}$ c. black . . . 1·40 1·10

Prices of Nos. 170/1 are for whole stamps.

1915. Surch **Dois centavos**.

172 S 2 c. on 15 r. (No. 83) . . . 45 35
173 2 c. on 15 c. (No. 95) . . . 45 35

1918. Red Cross Fund. "Ceres" key-type inscr "LOURENCO MARQUES", optd **9-3-18** and Red Cross or surch with value in figures and bars also.

188 U $\frac{1}{4}$ c. green 85 85
189 $\frac{1}{2}$ c. black 85 85
190 1 c. green 85 85
191 $2\frac{1}{2}$ c. violet 85 85
192a 5 c. blue 85 85
193 10 c. red . . . . 1·75 85
194 20 c. on $1\frac{1}{2}$ c. brown . . . . 1·75 85
195 30 c. brown on green . . . 1·75 1·50
196 40 c. on 2 c. red . . . . 1·75 1·50
197 50 c. on $7\frac{1}{2}$ c. brown . . . 1·75 1·50
198 70 c. on 8 c. grey . . . . 1·75 1·50
199 1 e. on 15 c. purple . . . 1·75 1·50

1920. No. 166 surch **Um quarto de centavo**.

200 R $\frac{1}{4}$ c. on 115 r. on 10 r. mauve 30 20

1920. No. 152 surch in figures or words.

201 U 1 c. on $2\frac{1}{2}$ c. violet 20 15
202 $1\frac{1}{2}$ c. on $2\frac{1}{2}$ c. violet . . . 20 15
203 4 c. on $2\frac{1}{2}$ c. violet 20 15

For other surcharges on "Ceres" key-type of Lourenco Marques, see Mozambique Nos. 309/10 and Nos. D44 and 46.

NEWSPAPER STAMPS

1893. "Newspaper" key-type inscr "LOURENCO MARQUES".

N1 V $2\frac{1}{2}$ r. brown 15 15

1895. 700th Death Anniv of St. Anthony. "Newspaper" key-type inscr "MOCAMBIQUE" optd **L. MARQUES CENTENARIO DE S. ANTONIO MDCCCXCV**.

N36 V $2\frac{1}{2}$ r. brown . . . . . . 2·25 1·90

LUBECK Pt. 7

Formerly one of the free cities of the Hanseatic League. In 1868 joined the North German Confederation.

16 schilling = 1 mark

1

3

1859. Imperf.

9 1 $\frac{1}{2}$ s. lilac . . . . 12·00 £1400
10 1 s. orange . . . . 27·00 £1400
3 2 s. brown . . . . 14·00 £225
4 $2\frac{1}{2}$ s. red . . . . 38·00 £650
6 4 s. green . . . . 13·00 £350

1863. Rouletted.

11 3 $\frac{1}{2}$ s. green . . . . 35·00 80·00
13 1 s. orange £120 £140
14 2 s. red . . . . 18·00 55·00
16 $2\frac{1}{2}$ s. blue . . . . 45·00 £325
17 4 s. bistre . . . . 32·00 £110

4

5

1864. Imperf.

19 4 $1\frac{1}{4}$ s. brown . . . . 22·00 60·00

1865. Roul.

21 5 $1\frac{1}{2}$ s. mauve . . . . 20·00 80·00

LUXEMBOURG Pt. 4

An independent Grand Duchy lying between Belgium and the Saar District. Under German Occupation from 1940 to 1944.

1852. $12\frac{1}{2}$ centimes = 1 silver groschen.
100 centimes = 1 franc.
1940. 100 pfennig = 1 reichsmark.
1944. 100 centimes = 1 franc (Belgian).

1 Grand Duke William III

3

4

1852. Imperf.

2 1 10 c. black . . . . £1900 40·00
3a 1 s. red . . . . £1200 70·00

1859. Imperf or roul.

23 3 1 c. brown . . . . 35·00 4·50
21 1 c. orange . . . . 30·00 6·00
17 2 c. black . . . . 15·00 13·00
8 4 c. yellow £180 £170
20 4 c. green . . . . 35·00 20·00
10 4 10 c. blue . . . . £190 17·00
24 10 c. purple . . . . £110 2·00
25 10 c. lilac . . . . £120 2·00
28 $12\frac{1}{2}$ c. red . . . . £170 5·00
30 20 c. brown . . . . £120 4·00
12 25 c. brown £375 £250
32 25 c. blue . . . . £750 11·00
13 30 c. purple £300 £200
14 $37\frac{1}{2}$ c. green £300 £170
35 $37\frac{1}{2}$ c. bistre £750 £250
39 40 c. orange . . . . 38·00 80·00

1872. Surch **UN FRANC**. Roul.

37 4 1 f. on $37\frac{1}{2}$ c. bistre . . . . £900 70·00

1874. Perf.

64 3 1 c. brown . . . . 7·50 4·00
65 2 c. black . . . . 7·00 1·25
42 4 c. green . . . . 1·00 8·00
43 5 c. yellow . . . . £170 24·00
67 4 10 c. lilac £160 70
61 $12\frac{1}{2}$ c. red £190 £180
69 20 c. brown . . . . 42·00 15·00
70 25 c. blue . . . . £250 4·00
71 30 c. red . . . . 3·50 19·00
55 40 c. orange . . . . 95 8·00

1879. Surch **Un Franc**. Perf.

56 4 1 f. on $37\frac{1}{2}$ c. bistre . . . . 7·00 24·00

7 Agriculture and Trade

8 Grand Duke Adolf

9

1882.

116 7 1 c. grey 15 25
117 2 c. brown 10 20
118 4 c. bistre . . . . 35 1·90
119 5 c. green 50 20
120 10 c. red . . . . 5·00 20
98 $12\frac{1}{2}$ c. blue . . . . 1·00 25·00
122 20 c. orange . . . . 2·00 2·00
123 25 c. blue . . . . £150 1·60
101 30 c. green . . . . 15·00 12·00
124 50 c. brown . . . . 65 9·00
103 1 f. lilac . . . . 70 25·00
104 5 f. orange . . . . 30·00 £160

1891.

127 8 10 c. red 15 25
145 $12\frac{1}{2}$ c. green 50 50
146 20 c. orange . . . . 10·50 50
147 25 c. blue 40 30
148 30 c. green . . . . 1·00 1·00
149 $37\frac{1}{2}$ c. green . . . . 2·00 2·00
150 50 c. brown . . . . 6·75 2·40
151 1 f. purple . . . . 12·00 5·00
135 $2\frac{1}{2}$ f. black . . . . 1·25 20·00
136 5 f. lake . . . . 32·00 65·00

1895.

152 9 1 c. grey . . . . 1·90 30
153 2 c. brown 10 20
154 4 c. bistre . . . . 15 1·00
155 5 c. green . . . . 1·90 20
156 10 c. red . . . . 6·50 20

10

11 Grand Duke William IV

13 Grand Duchess Adelaide

1906.

157 10 1 c. grey 10 20
158 2 c. brown 10 20
159 4 c. bistre 15 25
160 5 c. green 25 20
231 5 c. mauve 15 20
161 6 c. lilac 10 30
161a $7\frac{1}{2}$ c. orange . . . . 10 3·00

162 **11** 10 c. red 1·10 20
163 12½ slate 1·00 40
164 15 c. brown 1·40 60
165 20 c. orange 1·90 50
166 25 c. blue 50·00 30
166a 30 c. olive 55 50
167 37½ c. green 55 50
168 50 c. brown 3·75 60
169 87½ c. blue 1·40 9·00
170 1 f. purple 4·75 1·50
171 2½ f. red 40·00 80·00
172 5 f. purple 8·00 50·00

1912. Surch **62½ cts.**
173 **11** 62½ c. on 87½ c. blue 1·40 2·00
173a 62½ c. on 2½ f. red 1·90 4·00
173b 62½ c. on 5 f. purple 40 3·00

1914.
174 **13** 10 c. purple 10 20
175 12½ c. green 10 20
176 15 c. brown 10 20
176a 17½ c. brown 10 40
177 25 c. blue 10 20
178 30 c. brown 10 40
179 35 c. blue 10 40
180 37½ c. brown 10 40
181 40 c. red 20 40
182 50 c. grey 20 40
183 62½ c. green 30 3·00
183a 87½ c. orange 30 3·00
184 1 f. brown 2·00 60
185 2½ f. red 40 3·00
186 5 f. violet 8·00 45·00

1916. Surch in figures and bars.
187 **10** 2½ on 5 c. green 10 20
188 3 on 2 c. brown 10 20
212 5 on 1 c. grey 10 20
213 5 on 4 c. bistre 10 40
214 5 on 7½ c. orange 10 20
215 6 on 2 c. brown 20 25
189 **13** 7½ on 10 c. red 10 20
190 17½ on 30 c. brown 10 40
191 20 on 17½ c. brown 10 20
216 25 on 37½ c. sepia 10 20
217 75 on 62½ c. green 10 20
218 80 on 87½ c. orange 10 20
192 87½ on 1 f. brown 50 6·00

17 Grand Duchess Charlotte
18 Vianden Castle

1921. Perf.
194 **17** 2 c. brown 10 20
195 3 c. green 10 20
196 6 c. purple 10 20
197 10 c. green 10 20
193a 15 c. red* 10 20
198 15 c. green 10 20
234 15 c. orange 10 20
199 20 c. orange 10 30
235 20 c. green 10 20
200 25 c. green 10 20
201 30 c. red 10 20
202 40 c. orange 10 20
203 50 c. blue 10 40
236 50 c. red 10 20
204 75 c. red 10 1·10
237 75 c. blue 10 20
205 80 c. black 20 85
206a **18** 1 f. red 10 30
238 1 f. blue 10 50
207 – 2 f. blue 75 50
239 – 2 f. brown 2·25 1·90
208 – 5 f. violet 11·00 8·00
DESIGNS—As Type **18**: 2 f. Factories at Esch; 5 f. Railway viaduct over River Alzette.
*No. 193a was originally issued on the occasion of the birth of Crown Prince Jean.
See also Nos. 219/20.

21 Monastery at Clervaux

1921. War Monument Fund.
209 **21** 10 c. + 5 c. green 15 3·50
210 – 15 c. + 10 c. orange 15 6·00
211 – 25 c. + 10 c. green 15 3·50
DESIGNS—HORIZ: 15 c. Pfaffenthal; 25 c. as Type **26**.

1922. Philatelic Exhibition. Imperf.
219 **17** 25 c. green 1·60 5·50
220 30 c. red 1·60 5·50

26 Luxembourg

28 Echternach

1923.
222a **26** 10 f. black 4·75 12·00

1923. Unveiling of War Memorial by Prince Leopold of Belgium. Nos. 209/11 surch **27 mai 1923** and additional values.
223 **21** 10 + 5 + 25 c. green 1·00 15·00
224 – 15 + 10 + 25 c. orange 1·00 20·00
225 – 25 + 10 + 25 c. green 1·00 15·00

1923.
226a **28** 3 f. blue 60 50

1924. Charity. Death of Grand Duchess Marie Adelaide. Surch **CARITAS** and new value.
227 **13** 12½ c. + 7½ c. green 10 3·00
228 35 c. + 10 c. blue 10 3·00
229 2½ f. + 1 f. red 80 30·00
230 5 f. + 2 f. violet 50 20·00

1925. Surch **5**.
240 **17** 5 on 10 c. green 10 20

31

32 Grand Duchess Charlotte

1925. Anti-T.B. Fund.
241 **31** 5 c. + 5 c. violet 10 60
242 30 c. + 5 c. orange 10 3·00
243 50 c. + 5 c. brown 10 6·00
244 1 f. + 10 c. blue 25 15·00

1926.
245 **32** 5 c. mauve 10 20
246 10 c. olive 10 10
246a 15 c. black 10 20
247 20 c. orange 10 30
248 25 c. green 10 30
248a 25 c. brown 10 30
248b 30 c. green 10 30
248c 30 c. violet 30 20
248d 35 c. violet 1·50 30
248e 35 c. green 10 20
249 40 c. brown 10 20
250 50 c. brown 10 20
250a 60 c. green 1·50 20
251 65 c. brown 15 1·40
251a 70 c. violet 10 10
252 75 c. red 10 50
252a 75 c. brown 10 20
253 80 c. brown 15 1·50
253a 90 c. red 50 1·40
254 1 f. black 40 30
254a 1 f. red 40 25
255 1¼ f. blue 10 50
255a 1¼ f. yellow 5·00 1·25
255b 1¼ f. green 30 20
255c 1¼ f. red 10·00 2·00
255d 1½ f. blue 1·00 1·50
255e 1¾ f. blue 70 25

33 Prince Jean

34 Grand Duchess and Prince Felix

1926. Child Welfare.
256 **33** 5 c. + 5 c. black and mauve 10 50
257 40 c. + 10 c. black & green 10 1·00
258 50 c. + 15 c. black & yellow 10 1·00
259 75 c. + 20 c. black & red 20 12·00
260 1 f. 50 c. + 30 c. blk and bl 20 13·00

1927. International Philatelic Exhibition.
261 **34** 25 c. purple 1·00 11·00
262 50 c. green 1·50 17·00
263 75 c. red 1·00 11·00
264 1 f. black 1·00 11·00
265 1½ f. blue 1·00 11·00

35 Princess Elisabeth

37 Clervaux

1927. Child Welfare.
266 **35** 10 c. + 5 c. black and blue 10 50
267 50 c. + 10 black & brown 10 1·00
268 75 c. + 20 c. black & orge 10 1·50
269 1 f. + 30 c. black and red 20 12·00
270 1½ f. + 50 c. black & blue 20 12·00

1927. Stamps of 1921 and 1926 surch.
270a **32** 10 on 30 c. green 30 40
271 **17** 15 on 20 c. green 10 20
272 **32** 15 on 25 c. green 20 60
273 **17** 35 on 40 c. orange 10 20
274 **32** 60 on 65 c. brown 10 40
275 **17** 60 on 75 c. blue 10 20
276 **32** 60 on 75 c. red 10 40
277 **17** 60 on 80 c. black 20 40

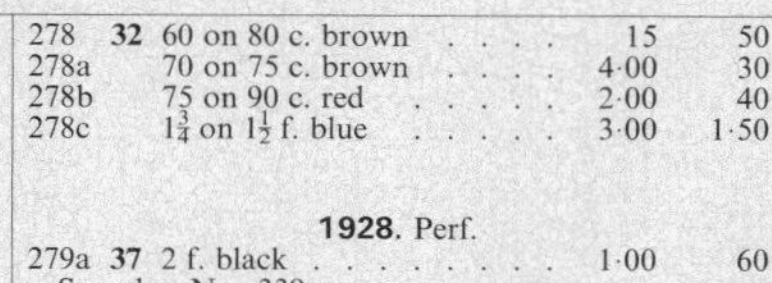
278 **32** 60 on 80 c. brown 15 50
278a 70 on 75 c. brown 4·00 30
278b 75 on 90 c. red 2·00 40
278c 1¾ on 1½ f. blue 3·00 1·50

1928. Perf.
279a **37** 2 f. black 1·00 60
See also No. 339.

38 Princess Marie Adelaide

39 Princess Marie Gabrielle

1928. Child Welfare.
280 **38** 10 c. + 5 c. purple & green 20 1·00
281 60 c. + 10 c. olive & brown 30 3·00
282 75 c. + 15 c. green and red 50 8·00
283 1 f. + 25 c. brown & green 1·50 24·00
284 1½ f. + 50 c. blue & yellow 1·50 24·00

1928. Child Welfare.
285 **39** 10 c. + 10 c. green & brn 20 1·00
286 35 c. + 15 c. brown & grn 1·00 7·00
287 75 c. + 30 c. black and red 1·00 10·00
288 1¼ f. + 50 c. green and red 2·00 24·00
289 1¾ f. + 75 c. black & blue 3·00 30·00

40 Prince Charles

41 Arms of Luxembourg

1930. Child Welfare.
290 **40** 10 c. + 5 c. brown & green 20 1·00
291 75 c. + 10 c. green & brn 1·25 5·00
292 1 f. + 25 c. violet and red 2·50 20·00
293 1¼ f. + 75 c. black & yell 4·00 25·00
294 1¾ f. + 1 f. 50 brown & bl 4·50 25·00

1930.
295 **41** 5 c. red 50 30
296 10 c. green 60 20

42 Biplane over River Alzette
43 Luxembourg, Lower Town

1931. Air.
296a **42** 50 c. green 80 85
297 75 c. brown 75 1·50
298 1 f. red 75 1·50
299 1¼ f. purple 75 1·50
300 1¾ f. blue 75 1·50
300a 3 f. black 1·75 5·75

1931.
301 **43** 20 f. green 3·50 19·00

44 Princess Alix

45 Countess Ermesinde

46 Emperor Henry VII

1931. Child Welfare.
302 **44** 10 c. + 5 c. grey & brown 20 1·00
303 75 c. + 10 c. green and red 4·00 15·00
304 1 f. + 25 c. grey and green 7·00 30·00
305 1¼ f. + 75 c. green & violet 7·00 30·00
306 1¾ f. + 1 f. 50 grey & blue 12·00 55·00

1932. Child Welfare.
307 **45** 10 c. + 5 c. brown 30 80
308 75 c. + 10 c. violet 2·00 15·00
309 1 f. + 25 c. red 10·00 35·00
310 1¼ f. + 75 c. lake 10·00 40·00
311 1¾ f. + 1 f. 50 blue 10·00 40·00

1933. Child Welfare.
312 **46** 10 c. + 5 c. brown 30 80
313 75 c. + 10 c. purple 5·00 15·00
314 1 f. + 25 c. red 12·00 40·00
315 1¼ f. + 75 c. brown 15·00 50·00
316 1¾ f. + 1 f. 50 blue 15·00 55·00

47 Gateway of the Three Towers

48 Arms of John the Blind

1934.
317 **47** 5 f. green 1·00 7·50

1934. Child Welfare.
318 **48** 10 c. + 5 c. violet 10 1·00
319 35 c. + 10 c. green 2·50 10·00
320 75 c. + 15 c. red 2·50 10·00
321 1 f. + 25 c. red 15·00 50·00
322 1¼ f. + 75 c. orange 15·00 50·00
323 1¾ f. + 1½ f. blue 15·00 50·00

50 Surgeon

1935. International Relief Fund for Intellectuals.
324 – 5 c. violet 15 1·40
325 – 10 c. red 30 1·40
326 – 15 c. olive 30 2·00
327 – 20 c. orange 45 2·50
328 – 35 c. green 80 3·50
329 – 50 c. black 90 5·00
330 – 70 c. green 1·50 6·00
331 **50** 1 f. red 2·00 7·00
332 – 1 f. 25 turquoise 8·00 55·00
333 – 1 f. 75 blue 10·00 55·00
334 – 2 f. brown 30·00 £120
335 – 3 f. brown 40·00 £160
336 – 5 f. blue 70·00 £300
337 – 10 f. purple £180 £500
338 **50** 20 f. green £200 £600
DESIGNS — HORIZ: 5 c., 10 f. Schoolteacher; 15 c., 3 f. Journalist; 20 c. 1 f. 75, Engineer; 35 c., 1 f. 25, Chemist. VERT: 10 c., 2 f. "The Arts"; 50 c., 5 f. Barrister; 70 c. University.
This set was sold at the P.O. at double face value.

1935. Esch Philatelic Exhibition. Imperf.
339 **37** 2 f. (+ 50 c.) black 5·00 16·00

52 Vianden

1935.
340 **52** 10 f. green 1·40 12·50

53 Charles I

54 Town Hall

1935. Child Welfare.
341 **53** 10 c. + 5 c. violet 10 40
342 35 c. + 10 c. green 30 60
343 70 c. + 20 c. brown 1·00 1·50
344 1 f. + 25 c. red 14·00 40·00
345 1 f. 25 + 75 c. brown 14·00 40·00
346 1 f. 75 + 1 f. 50 blue 14·00 50·00

1936. 11th Int Philatelic Federation Congress.
347 **54** 10 c. brown 20 50
348 35 c. green 30 1·00
349 70 c. orange 35 1·50
350 1 f. red 1·40 9·00
351 1 f. 25 violet 2·40 12·00
352 1 f. 75 blue 1·40 10·00

55 Wenceslas I

56 Wenceslas II

1936. Child Welfare.
353 **55** 10 c. + 5 c. brown 10 30
354 35 c. + 10 c. green 20 60
355 70 c. + 20 c. slate 40 80
356 1 f. + 25 c. red . . . . . . 2·50 15·00
357 1 f. 25 + 75 c. violet . . . 5·00 30·00
358 1 f. 75 + 1 f. 50 blue . . . 5·00 20·00

1937. Child Welfare.
360 **56** 10 c. + 5 c. black and red . 10 40
361 35 c. + 10 c. green & pur 20 50
362 70 c. + 20 c. red and blue . 20 50
363 1 f. + 25 c. red and green . 1·00 17·00
364 1 f. 25 + 75 c. purple and brown . . . . 1·50 17·00
365 1 f. 75 + 1 f. 50 blue and black . . . . 2·00 20·00

57 St. Willibrord

61 Sigismond of Luxembourg

1938. Echternach Abbey Restoration Fund (1st issue). 1200th Death Anniv of St. Willibrord.
366 **57** 35 c. + 10 c. green 25 50
367 – 70 c. + 10 c. black 70 60
368 – 1 f. 25 + 25 c. red . . . . 90 2·50
369 – 1 f. 75 + 50 c. blue . . . . 2·00 3·00
370 – 3 f. + 2 f. red . . . . . . 6·00 9·00
371 – 5 f. + 5 f. violet . . . . . 6·00 8·00
DESIGNS—As Type **57**: 70 c. Town Hall, Echternach; 1 f. 25, Pavilion, Echternach Municipal Park; 31×51 mm. 1 f. 75, St. Willibrord (from miniature); 42×38 mm: 3 f. Echternach Basilica; 5 f. Whitsuntide dancing procession.
See also Nos. 492/7 and 569/70.

1938. Child Welfare.
372 **61** 10 c. + 5 c. black & mauve 10 40
373 35 c. + 10 c. black & green 20 50
374 70 c. + 20 c. black & brn 30 50
375 1 f. + 25 c. black and red 2·00 16·00
376 1 f. 25 + 75 c. black & grey 2·00 16·00
377 1 f. 75 + 1 f. 50 black and blue . . . . 3·00 24·00

62 Arms of Luxembourg

63 William I

1939. Centenary of Independence.
378 **62** 35 c. green 15 20
379 **63** 50 c. orange 25 20
380 – 70 c. green 10 20
381 – 75 c. olive . . . . 50 1·00
382 – 1 f. red . . . . 1·25 2·00
383 – 1 f. 25 violet 15 20
384 – 1 f. 75 blue 15 20
385 – 3 f. brown 30 50
386 – 5 f. black . . . . 30 8·00
387 – 10 f. red . . . . 1·00 11·00
PORTRAITS—As Type **63**: 70 c. William II; 75 c. William III; 1 f. Prince Henry; 1 f. 25 Grand Duke Adolphe; 1 f. 75 William IV; 3 f. Marie-Anne, wife of William IV; 5 f. Grand Duchess Marie Adelaide; 10 f. Grand Duchess Charlotte.

1939. Surch in figures.
388 **32** 30 c. on 60 c. green . . . . 10 1·50

65 Allegory of Medicinal Spring

66 Prince Jean

1939. Mondorf-les-Bains Propaganda.
389 **65** 2 f. red . . . . 30 3·00

MINIMUM PRICE

The minimum price quoted is 10p which represents a handling charge rather than a basis for valuing common stamps. For further notes about prices see introductory pages.

1939. 20th Anniv of Reign and of Royal Wedding.
390 **66** 10 c. + 5 c. brn on cream 10 30
391 – 35 c. + 10 c. green on cream 20 1·00
392 – 70 c. + 20 c. black on cream 55 1·50
393 **66** 1 f. + 25 c. red on cream 4·00 35·00
394 – 1 f. 25 + 75 c. violet on cream 5·00 55·00
395 – 1 f. 75 + 1 f. 50 blue on cream 6·00 70·00
PORTRAITS: 35 c., 1 f. 25, Prince Felix; 70 c., 1 f. 75, Grand Duchess Charlotte.

1940. Anti-T.B. Fund. Surch with Cross of Lorraine and premium.
396 **65** 2 f. + 50 c. grey . . . . . . 1·00 17·00

1940-44. GERMAN OCCUPATION.

1940. T **94** of Germany optd **Luxemburg**.
397 **94** 3 pf. brown 15 50
398 4 pf. blue 15 60
399 5 pf. green 15 50
400 6 pf. green 15 50
401 8 pf. red 15 50
402 10 pf. brown 15 50
403 12 pf. red 15 20
404 15 pf. purple 50 65
405 20 pf. blue . . . . 50 1·10
406 25 pf. blue . . . . 80 1·00
407 30 pf. green 80 60
408 40 pf. mauve . . . . 80 1·00
409 50 pf. black and green . . . 60 1·50
410 60 pf. black and purple . . 2·00 4·00
411 80 pf. black and blue . . . 7·00 20·00
412 100 pf. black and yellow . . 2·50 4·00

1940. Types of Luxembourg surch.
413 **32** 3 Rpf. on 15 c. black . . . 10 50
414 4 Rpf. on 20 c. orange . . . 10 50
415 5 Rpf. on 35 c. green . . . 10 50
416 6 Rpf. on 10 c. green . . . 10 50
417 8 Rpf. on 25 c. brown . . . 10 50
418 10 Rpf. on 40 c. brown . . . 10 50
419 12 Rpf. on 60 c. green . . . 10 50
420 15 Rpf. on 1 f. red . . . . 40 4·00
421 20 Rpf. on 50 c. brown . . . 10 1·00
422 25 Rpf. on 5 c. mauve . . . 80 4·00
423 30 Rpf. on 70 c. violet . . . 15 1·00
424 40 Rpf. on 75 c. brown . . . 15 1·00
425 50 Rpf. on 1¼ f. greeen . . . 15 1·00
426 **65** 60 Rpf. on 2 f. red . . . . 3·50 24·00
427 **47** 80 Rpf. on 5 f. green . . . 50 3·25
428 **52** 100 Rpf. on 10 f. green . . . 50 3·25

1941. Nos. 739/47 of Germany optd **Luxemburg**.
429 3 pf. + 2 pf. brown 50 75
430 4 pf. + 3 pf. blue 50 75
431 5 pf. + 3 pf. green 50 75
432 6 pf. + 4 pf. green 50 75
433 8 pf. + 4 pf. orange 50 75
434 12 pf. + 6 pf. red 50 75
435 15 pf. + 10 pf. purple . . . . 3·50 9·00
436 25 pf. + 15 pf. blue . . . . . 3·50 9·00
437 40 pf. + 35 pf. purple . . . . 3·50 9·00

1944. INDEPENDENCE REGAINED.

70 Grand Duchess Charlotte

71 "Britannia"

1944.
438 **70** 5 c. brown 10 10
439 10 c. slate 10 10
440 20 c. orange 20 10
441 25 c. brown 10 10
442 30 c. red 30 30
443 35 c. green 15 30
444 40 c. blue 30 30
445 50 c. violet 10 10
445a 60 c. orange . . . . 1·50 15
446 70 c. red 15 20
447 70 c. green . . . . 50 1·00
448 75 c. brown 30 20
449 1 f. olive 10 10
450 1¼ f. orange 20 20
451 1½ f. orange 30 15
452 1¾ f. blue 30 30
453 2 f. red . . . . 3·50 15
454 2½ f. mauve . . . . 5·00 5·00
455 3 f. green 50 50
456 3½ f. blue 60 85
457 5 f. green 20 20
458 10 f. red . . . . 30 1·40
459 20 f. blue . . . . 50 20·00

1945. Liberation.
460 – 60 c. + 1 f. 40 green 10 20
461 – 1 f. 20 + 1 f. 80 red 10 20
462 **71** 2 f. 50 + 3 f. 50 blue 10 20
463 – 4 f. 20 + 4 f. 80 violet . . . 10 20
DESIGNS: 60 c. Ship symbol of Paris between Cross of Lorraine and Arms of Luxembourg; 1 f. 20, Man killing snake between Arms of Russia and Luxembourg; 4 f. 20, Eagle between Arms of U.S.A. and Luxembourg.

72 Statue of the Madonna in Procession

74 Lion of Luxembourg

73 Altar and Shrine of the Madonna

1945. Our Lady of Luxembourg.
464 **72** 60 c. + 40 c. green 20 80
465 – 1 f. 20 + 80 c. red 20 80
466 – 2 f. 50 + 2 f. 50 blue . . . 30 5·00
467 – 5 f. 50 + 6 f. 50 violet . . . 1·25 70·00
468 **73** 20 f. + 20 f. brown . . . . 1·25 70·00
DESIGNS: As Type **72**: 1 f. 20, The Madonna; 2 f. 50, The Madonna and Luxembourg; 5 f. 50, Portal of Notre Dame Cathedral.

1945.
469 **74** 20 c. black 20 20
470 30 c. green 20 20
470a 60 c. violet 30 20
471 75 c. brown 30 20
472 1 f. 20 red 20 20
473 1 f. 50 violet 20 20
474 2 f. 50 blue 30 30

75 Members of the Maquis

76

1945. National War Victims Fund.
475 **75** 20 c. + 30 c. green & buff 20 1·00
476 – 1 f. 50 + 1 f. red and buff 20 1·00
477 – 3 f. 50 + 3 f. 50 blue & buff 40 10·00
478 – 5 f. + 10 f. brown & buff 30 10·00
DESIGNS: 1 f. 50, Mother and children; 3 f. 50, Political prisoner; 5 f. Executed civilian.

1946. Air.
479 – 1 f. green and blue 20 20
480 **76** 2 f. brown and yellow . . . 20 20
481 – 3 f. brown and yellow . . . 20 20
482 – 4 f. violet and grey 30 30
483 **76** 5 f. purple and yellow . . . 25 25
484 – 6 f. purple and blue 30 30
485 – 10 f. brown and yellow . . 1·50 30
486 **76** 20 f. blue and grey . . . . 1·75 1·00
487 – 50 f. green and light green 3·50 1·50
DESIGNS: 1, 4, 10 f. Airplane wheel; 3, 6, 50 f. Airplane engine and castle.

77 John the Blind, King of Bohemia

78 Exterior Ruins of St. Willibrord Basilica

79 St. Willibrord

1946. 600th Death Anniv of John the Blind.
488 **77** 60 c. + 40 c. green & grey 15 1·75
489 1 f. 50 + 50 c. red & buff 25 2·00
490 3 f. 50 + 3 f. 50 blue & grey 2·00 26·00
491 5 f. + 10 f. brown & grey 1·00 22·00

1947. Echternach Abbey Restoration (2nd issue). Inscr "ECHTERNACH".
492 **78** 20 c. + 10 c. black 30 30
493 – 60 c. + 10 c. green 60 50
494 – 75 c. + 25 c. red . . . . 1·00 80
495 – 1 f. 50 c. + 50 c. brown . . 1·25 80
496 – 3 f. 50 c. + 2 f. 50 blue . . 6·00 5·00
497 **79** 25 f. + 25 f. purple . . . . 32·00 25·00
DESIGNS—As Type **78**: 60 c. Statue of Abbot Bertels; 75 c. Echternach Abbey emblem; 1 f. 50, Ruined interior of Basilica; 3 f. 50, St. Irmine and Pepin II carrying model of Abbey.

80 U.S. Military Cemetery, Hamm

82 Michel Lentz (national poet)

1947. Honouring Gen. George S. Patton.
498 **80** 1 f. 50 red and buff 50 20
499 – 3 f. 50 blue and buff . . . 2·50 3·00
500 **80** 5 f. green and grey . . . . 2·50 2·00
501 – 10 f. purple and grey . . . 11·00 40·00
PORTRAIT: 3 f. 50, 10 f. Gen. G. S. Patton.

1947. National Welfare Fund.
502 **82** 60 c. + 40 c. brown & buff 80 1·10
503 1 f. 50 + 50 c. pur & buff 1·10 1·10
504 3 f. 50 + 3 f. 50 blue & grey 6·50 20·00
505 10 f. + 5 f. green and grey 6·00 20·00

83 L'Oesling

85 "Dicks" (Edmund de la Fontaine)

1948. Tourist Propaganda.
505a – 2 f. 50 brown & chocolate 1·90 40
505b – 3 f. violet . . . . 6·00 1·25
505c – 4 f. blue . . . . 4·00 1·25
506 **83** 7 f. brown . . . . 20·00 80
507 – 10 f. green . . . . 2·50 20
508 – 15 f. red . . . . 2·50 40
509 – 20 f. blue . . . . 3·75 55
DESIGNS—HORIZ: 2 f. 50, Television transmitter, Dudelange; 3 f. Radio Luxembourg; 4 f. Victor Hugo's house, Vianden; 10 f. River Moselle; 15 f. Mining district. VERT: 20 f. Luxembourg.

1948. National Welfare Fund.
510 **85** 60 c. + 40 c. brown & bis 45 50
511 1 f. 50 + 50 c. red & pink 60 70
512 3 f. 50 + 3 f. 50 blue & grey 9·50 19·00
513 10 f. + 5 f. green and grey 8·50 19·00

86 Grand Duchess Charlotte

87 Date-stamp and Map

1948.
513a **86** 5 c. orange 10 10
513b 10 c. blue 10 10
514 15 c. olive 15 10
514a 20 c. purple 20 10
515 25 c. grey 20 10
515a 30 c. olive 20 10
515b 40 c. red 30 30
515c 50 c. orange 40 15
516 60 c. bistre 30 20
517 80 c. green 30 20
518 1 f. red . . . . 1·00 10
518a 1 f. 20 black . . . . . . 1·00 30
518b 1 f. 25 brown . . . . . . 1·00 40
519 1 f. 50 turquoise . . . . . 1·00 10
520 1 f. 60 grey . . . . 1·00 1·00
521 2 f. purple . . . . 1·00 10
521a 2 f. 50 red . . . . 1·50 10
521b 3 f. blue . . . . 12·00 40
521c 3 f. 50 red . . . . 3·50 40
522 4 f. blue . . . . 3·50 40
522a 5 f. violet . . . . 9·50 40
523 6 f. purple . . . . 7·00 40
524 8 f. green . . . . 5·00 80

1949. 75th Anniv of U.P.U.
525 **87** 80 c. green, lt green & black . 50 60
526 2 f. 50 red, pink and black . 2·50 1·50
527 4 f. ultramarine, blue & black 5·00 6·00
528 8 f. brown, buff and black 17·00 32·00

88 Michel Rodange

89 Young Girl

1949. National Welfare Fund.
529 **88** 60 c. + 40 c. green & grey 50 50
530 2 f. + 1 f. purple & claret 5·00 4·00
531 4 f. + 2 f. blue and grey . . 9·00 8·00
532 10 f. + 5 f. brown & buff 9·00 20·00

1950. War Orphans Relief Fund.
533 – 60 c. + 15 c. turquoise . . . 2·00 90
534 **89** 1 f. + 20 c. red . . . . . 5·00 1·25
535 – 2 f. + 30 c. brown . . . . 3·00 1·25
536 **89** 4 f. + 75 c. blue . . . . 12·00 15·00
537 – 8 f. + 3 f. black . . . . 32·00 40·00
538 **89** 10 f. + 5 f. purple . . . . 32·00 40·00
DESIGN: 60 c., 2 f., 8 f. Mother and boy.

90 J. A. Zinnen (composer)

91 Ploughman and Factories

1950. National Welfare Week.
539 **90** 60 c. + 10 c. violet & grey 55 30
540 2 f. + 15 c. red and buff 1·00 40
541 4 f. + 15 c. blue and grey 7·00 7·00
542 8 f. + 5 f. brown and buff 20·00 28·00

1951. To Promote United Europe.
543 **91** 80 c. green and light green 10·00 10·00
544 – 1 f. violet and light violet 5·00 50
545 – 2 f. brown and grey . . . . 25·00 50
546 **91** 2 f. 50 red and orange . . . 25·00 20·00
547 – 3 f. brown and yellow . . . 40·00 30·00
548 – 4 f. blue and light blue . . . 60·00 40·00
DESIGNS: 1, 3 f. Map, people and "Rights of Man" Charter; 2, 4 f. Scales balancing "United Europe" and "Peace".

92 L. Menager (composer)

1951. National Welfare Fund.
549 **92** 60 c. + 10 c. black & grey 40 40
550 2 f. + 15 c. green and grey 40 40
551 4 f. + 15 c. blue and grey 5·00 4·00
552 8 f. + 5 f. purple and grey 25·00 32·00

92a T **1** and **86**

92b T **1**

1952. National Philatelic Exhibition ("CENTILUX") and Stamp Centenary.
552a **92a** 80 c. black, purple and green (air) 50 50
552b 2 f. 50 black, pur & red 1·50 1·50
552c 4 f. black, purple & blue 4·00 4·00
552d 8 f. black, purple & red 48·00 55·00
552e 10 f. black, purple & brn 38·00 45·00
552f **92b** 2 f. black and green (postage) . . . . . . 30·00 35·00
552g 4 f. red and green . . . 30·00 35·00

93 Hurdling

1952. 15th Olympic Games, Helsinki.
553 **93** 1 f. black and green . . . 60 30
554 – 2 f. black and light brown (Football) . . . . . . 3·00 30
555 – 2 f. 50 black and pink (Boxing) . . . . 4·00 1·60
556 – 3 f. blk & drab (Water polo) 5·00 2·00
557 – 4 f. black & blue (Cycling) 25·00 7·00
558 – 8 f. black & lilac (Fencing) 16·00 4·50

94 J. B. Fresez (painter)

95 Prince Jean and Princess Josephine Charlotte

1952. National Welfare Fund.
559 **94** 60 c. + 15 c. green & blue 40 40
560 2 f. + 25 c. brown & orange 40 40
561 4 f. + 25 c. violet and grey 4·00 4·00
562 8 f. + 4 f. 75 purple & lt pur 30·00 35·00

1953. Royal Wedding.
563 **95** 80 c. violet & deep mauve 45 35
564 1 f. 20 deep brown & brown 45 35
565 2 f. deep green and green 1·50 35
566 3 f. deep purple and purple 1·50 50
567 4 f. deep blue and blue . . . 7·00 1·00
568 9 f. brown and red . . . . 7·00 1·00

96 Echternach Basilica

97 Pierre D'Aspelt

1953. Echternach Abbey Restoration (3rd issue).
569 **96** 2 f. red . . . . 4·00 35
570 – 2 f. 50 olive . . . . . . 6·00 6·00
DESIGN: 2 f. 50, Interior of Basilica.

1953. 7th Birth Centenary of Pierre D'Aspelt.
571 **97** 4 f. black . . . . 8·00 5·00

98 "Candlemas Singing"

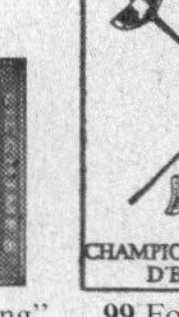

99 Foils, Mask and Gauntlet

1953. National Welfare Fund.
572 **98** 25 c. + 15 c. carmine and red 30 40
573 – 80 c. + 20 c. blue & brown 30 40
574 – 1 f. 20 + 30 c. green & turq 70 80
575 **98** 2 f. + 25 c. brown and red 60 40
576 – 4 f. + 50 c. blue & turquoise 6·00 7·00
577 – 7 f. + 3 f. 35 lilac & violet 19·00 22·00
DESIGNS: 80 c., 4 f. "The Rattles"; 1 f. 20, 7 f. "The Easter-eggs".

1954. World Fencing Championships.
578 **99** 2 f. deep brown and brown on cream . . . . 4·00 80

100 Fair Emblem

101 Earthenware Whistle

1954. Luxembourg International Fair.
579 **100** 4 f. multicoloured . . . . 10·00 4·00

1954. National Welfare Fund.
580 **101** 25 c. + 5 c. red & orange 40 50
581 – 80 c. + 20 c. grey & black 40 50
582 – 1 f. 20 + 30 c. green and cream . . . . 1·50 1·75
583 **101** 2 f. + 25 c. brown & buff 60 60
584 – 4 f. + 50 c. dp blue & blue 7·00 7·00
585 – 7 f. + 3 f. 45 violet & mve 23·00 27·00
DESIGNS: 80 c., 4 f. Sheep and drum; 1 f. 20, 7 f. Merry-go-round horses.

102 Tulips

103

1955. Mondorf-les-Bains Flower Show.
586 **102** 80 c. red, green & brown 30 30
587 – 2 f. yellow, green and red 40 30
588 – 3 f. purple, green & emer 3·50 3·50
589 – 4 f. orange, green & blue 5·50 5·50
FLOWERS: 2 f. Daffodils; 3 f. Hyacinths; 4 f. Parrot tulips.

1955. 1st National Crafts Exhibition.
590 **103** 2 f. black and grey . . . . 1·50 25

104 "Charter"

105 "Christmas Day"

1955. 10th Anniv of U.N.
591 **104** 80 c. blue and black . . . 45 50
592 – 2 f. brown and red . . . . 5·00 15
593 – 4 f. red and blue . . . . . 4·00 4·00
594 – 9 f. green and brown . . . 2·00 1·00
SYMBOLIC DESIGNS: 2 f. "Security"; 4 f. "Justice"; 9 f. "Assistance".

1955. National Welfare Fund.
595 – 25 c. + 5 c. red and pink 30 30
596 **105** 80 c. + 20 c. black & grey 30 30
597 – 1 f. 20 + 30 c. deep green and green 60 80
598 – 2 f. + 25 c. deep brown and brown 60 30
599 **105** 4 f. + 50 c. blue & lt blue 6·00 11·00
600 – 7 f. + 3 f. 45 pur & mve 14·00 16·00
ALLEGORICAL DESIGNS: 25 c., 2 f. "St. Nicholas's Day"; 1 f. 20, 7 f. "Twelfth Night".

1956. Mondorf-les-Bains Flower Show. As T **102** but inscription at top in one line. Multicoloured.
601 2 f. Anemones 65 30
602 3 f. Crocuses . . . . 2·50 2·50

1956. Roses. As T **102** but inscr at top "LUXEMBOURG–VILLE DES ROSES". Multicoloured.
603 2 f. 50 Yellow roses . . . . . 5·50 5·00
604 4 f. Red roses . . . . 2·50 2·50

108 Steel Plant and Girder

109 Blast Furnaces and Map

1956. 50th Anniv of Esch-sur-Alzette.
605 **108** 2 f. red, black and turq . . 2·50 40

1956. European Coal and Steel Community. Inscr as in T **109**.
606 **109** 2 f. red . . . . 30·00 1·40
607 – 3 f. blue . . . . 30·00 24·00
608 – 4 f. green . . . . 6·00 5·00
DESIGNS—VERT: 3 f. Girder supporting City of Luxembourg. HORIZ: 4 f. Chain and miner's lamp.

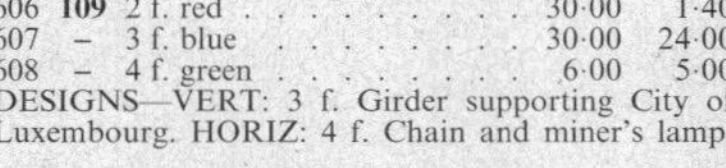

110

111 Luxembourg Central Station

1956. Europa.
609 **110** 2 f. black and brown . . . £225 25
610 3 f. red and orange . . . . 42·00 40·00
611 4 f. deep blue and blue . . 3·00 3·00

1956. Electrification of Luxembourg Railways.
612 **111** 2 f. sepia and black . . . . 3·50 65

112 I. de la Fontaine

113 Arms of Echternach

1956. Council of State Centenary. Inscr as in T **112**.
613 **112** 2 f. sepia . . . . 1·50 30
614 – 7 f. purple . . . . 3·00 80
DESIGN: 7 f. Grand Duchess Charlotte.

1956. National Welfare Fund. Inscr "CARITAS 1956". Arms. Multicoloured.
615 25 c. + 5 c. Type **113** 25 30
616 80 c. + 20 c. Esch-sur-Alzette 25 30
617 1 f. 20 + 30 c. Grevenmacher 30 80
618 2 f. + 25 c. Type **113** 25 30
619 4 f. + 50 c. Esch-sur-Alzette 4·00 5·00
620 7 f. + 3 f. 45 Grevenmacher 8·00 13·00

114 Lord Baden-Powell and Scout Emblems

115 Prince Henri

1957. Birth Centenary of Lord Baden-Powell, and 50th Anniv of Scouting Movement.
621 **114** 2 f. brown and green . . . 1·00 30
622 – 2 f. 50 red and violet . . . 2·50 2·25
DESIGN: 2 f. 50, as Type **114** but showing Girl Guide emblems.

1957. "Prince Jean and Princess Josephine-Charlotte Foundation" Child Welfare Clinic.
623 **115** 2 f. dp brown and brown 1·00 20
624 – 3 f. dp green and green . . 4·00 4·00
625 – 4 f. deep blue and blue . . 3·00 3·00
DESIGNS—HORIZ: 3 f. Children's Clinic Project. VERT: 4 f. Princess Marie-Astrid.

116 "Peace"

117 Fair Entrance and Flags

1957. Europa.
626 **116** 2 f. brown . . . . 2·00 15
627 3 f. red . . . . 35·00 18·00
628 4 f. purple . . . . 30·00 16·00

1957. National Welfare Fund. Arms as T **113** inscr "CARITAS 1957". Multicoloured.
629 25 c. + 5 c. Luxembourg . . . 30 40
630 80 c. + 20 c. Mersch 30 40
631 1 f. 20 + 30 c. Vianden 40 50
632 2 f. + 25 c. Luxembourg . . . 30 30
633 4 f. + 50 c. Mersch . . . . . 4·50 5·50
634 7 f. + 3 f. 45 Vianden . . . . 5·50 8·00

1958. 10th Anniv of Luxembourg Int Fair.
635 **117** 2 f. multicoloured 15 15

118 Luxembourg Pavilion

119 St. Willibrord holding Child (after Puseel)

1958. Brussels Exhibition.
636 **118** 2 f. 50 blue and red 15 15

1958. 1300th Birth Anniv of St. Willibrord.
637 – 1 f. red 20 30
638 **119** 2 f. 50 sepia 25 15
639 – 5 f. blue . . . . 1·00 90
DESIGNS: 1 f. St. Willibrord and St. Irmina holding inscribed plaque; 5 f. St. Willibrord and Suppliant. (Miracle of the wine-cask).

119a Europa

120 Open-air Theatre at Wiltz

1958. Europa.
640 **119a** 2 f. 50 blue and red . . . 15 15
641 3 f. 50 brown and green 20 25
642 5 f. red and blue 80 75

1958. Wiltz Open-air Theatre Commemoration.
643 **120** 2 f. 50 sepia and grey . . . 60 15

121 Vineyard

122 Grand Duchess Charlotte

1958. Bimillenary of Moselle Wine Industry.
644 **121** 2 f. 50 brown and green 60 15

1958. National Welfare Fund. Arms as T **113** inscr "CARITAS 1958". Multicoloured.
645 30 c. + 10 c. Capellen 30 30
646 1 f. + 25 c. Diekirch 30 30
647 1 f. 50 + 25 c. Redange . . . 50 50
648 2 f. 50 + 50 c. Capellen . . . 30 30
649 5 f. + 50 c. Diekirch . . . . 4·50 5·00
650 8 f. 50 + 4 f. 60 Redange . . . 5·00 8·00

1959. 40th Anniv of Accession of Grand Duchess Charlotte.
651 **122** 1 f. 50 dp green and green 80 25
652 2 f. 50 brown and lt brown 80 20
653 5 f. lt blue & ultramarine 1·60 1·25

123 N.A.T.O. Emblem

123a Europa

1959. 10th Anniv of N.A.T.O.
654 **123** 2 f. 50 blue and olive . . . 15 10
655 8 f. 50 blue and brown . . 40 40

1959. Mondorf-les-Bains Flower Show. As T **102** but inscr "1959".
656 1 f. violet, yellow and turquoise 25 30
657 2 f. 50 red, green and blue . . . 55 20
658 3 f. blue, green and purple . . 75 70
FLOWERS: 1 f. Iris; 2 f. 50, Peony; 3 f. Hortensia.

1959. Europa.
659 **123a** 2 f. 50 green 40 15
660 5 f. blue 90 75

124 Steam Locomotive and First Bars of Hymn "De Feierwon"

1959. Railways Centenary.
661 **124** 2 f. 50 blue and red . . . . 2·25 40

1959. National Welfare Fund. Arms as T **113** inscr "CARITAS 1959". Multicoloured.
662 30 c. + 10 c. Clervaux 30 30
663 1 f. + 25 c. Remich 30 30
664 1 f. 50 + 25 c. Wiltz 50 50
665 2 f. 50 + 50 c. Clervaux . . . 30 30
666 5 f. + 50 c. Remich . . . . 1·50 2·00
667 8 f. 50 + 4 f. 60 Wiltz . . . 7·00 12·00

125 Refugees seeking Shelter

126 Steel Worker

1960. World Refugee Year.
668 **125** 2 f. 50 blue and salmon . . 15 15
669 – 5 f. blue and violet . . . 20 35
DESIGN—HORIZ: 5 f. "The Flight into Egypt" (Biblical scene).

1960. 10th Anniv of Schuman Plan.
670 **126** 2 f. 50 lake 20 15

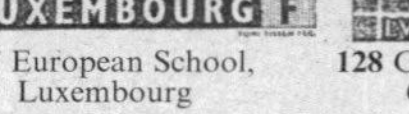

127 European School, Luxembourg

128 Grand Duchess Charlotte

1960. European School Commemoration.
671 **127** 5 f. black and blue . . . . 1·00 1·00

1960.
672 **128** 10 c. red 10 20
673 20 c. red 10 20
673a 25 c. orange 20 20
674 30 c. drab 10 20
675 50 c. green 50 20
676 1 f. violet 50 10
677 1 f. 50 mauve 50 15
678 2 f. turquoise 60 10
679 2 f. 50 purple . . . . . . 1·00 15
680 3 f. dull purple . . . . . . 2·50 10
680a 3 f. 50 turquoise . . . . . 3·00 2·00
681 5 f. brown . . . . 1·50 20
681a 6 f. turquoise . . . . . . 2·50 20

129 Heraldic Lion, and Tools

1960. 2nd National Crafts Exhibition.
682 **129** 2 f. 50 multicoloured . . . 1·60 20

129a Conference Emblem

130 Princess Marie-Astrid

1960. Europa.
683 **129a** 2 f. 50 green and black 20 15
684 5 f. black and red 60 25

1960. National Welfare Fund. Inscr "CARITAS 1960". Centres and inscr in sepia.
685 **130** 30 c. + 10 c. blue 20 20
686 – 1 f. + 25 c. pink 20 20
687 – 1 f. 50 + 25 c. turquoise 40 50
688 **130** 2 f. 50 + 50 c. yellow . . . 35 25
689 – 5 f. + 50 c. lilac . . . . . 1·00 2·50
690 – 8 f. 50 + 4 f. 60 sage . . . 10·00 13·00
DESIGNS: Princess Marie-Astrid standing (1, 5 f.), sitting with book on lap (1 f. 50, 8 f. 50).

131 Great Spotted Woodpecker

132 Patton Monument, Ettelbruck

1961. Animal Protection Campaign. Inscr "PROTECTION DES ANIMAUX".
691 **131** 1 f. multicoloured 50 15
692 – 1 f. 50 buff, blue and black 25 25
693 – 3 f. brown, buff and violet 40 40
694 – 8 f. 50 multicoloured . . . 70 50
DESIGNS—VERT: 8 f. 50, Dachshund. HORIZ: 1 f. 50, Cat; 3 f. Horse.

1961. Tourist Publicity.
695 **132** 2 f. 50 blue and black . . . 60 20
696 – 2 f. 50 green 60 20
DESIGN—VERT: No. 696, Clervaux.

133 Doves

134 Prince Henri

1961. Europa.
697 **133** 2 f. 50 red 10 10
698 5 f. blue 20 20

1961. National Welfare Fund. Inscr "CARITAS 1961". Centres and inscr in sepia.
699 **134** 30 c. + 10 c. mauve . . . 20 20
700 – 1 f. + 25 c. lavender . . . 20 20
701 – 1 f. 50 + 25 c. salmon . . 35 45
702 **134** 2 f. 50 + 50 c. green . . . 35 30
703 – 5 f. + 50 c. yellow . . . . 2·50 3·00
704 – 8 f. 50 + 4 f. 60 grey . . . 4·50 7·00
DESIGNS: Prince Henri when young boy (1, 5 f.); youth in formal dress (1 f. 50, 8 f. 50).

MINIMUM PRICE

The minimum price quoted is 10p which represents a handling charge rather than a basis for valuing common stamps. For further notes about prices see introductory pages.

135 Cyclist carrying Cycle

136 Europa "Tree"

1962. World Cross-country Cycling Championships, Esch-sur-Alzette.
705 **135** 2 f. 50 multicoloured . . . 30 15
706 – 5 f. multicoloured (Emblem) 30 40

1962. Europa.
707 **136** 2 f. 50 multicoloured . . . 15 10
708 5 f. brown, green & purple 15 20

137 St. Laurent's Church, Diekirch

138 Prince Jean and Princess Margaretha as Babies

1962.
709 **137** 2 f. 50 black and brown 55 15

1962. National Welfare Fund. inscr "CARITAS 1962". Centres and inscr in sepia.
710 **138** 30 c. + 10 c. buff 20 20
711 – 1 f. + 25 c. blue 20 20
712 – 1 f. 50 + 25 c. olive . . . 30 40
713 – 2 f. 50 + 50 c. pink . . . 30 25
714 – 5 f. + 50 c. green . . . . 1·60 2·50
715 – 8 f. 50 + 4 f. 60 violet . . 3·50 5·50
PORTRAITS—VERT: 1 f., 2 f. 50, Prince Jean and: 2 f. 50, 5 f. Princess Margaretha, at various stages of childhood. HORIZ: 8 f. 50, The Royal Children.

139 Blackboard

140 Benedictine Abbey, Munster

1963. 10th Anniv of European Schools.
716 **139** 2 f. 50 green, red and grey 10 10

1963. Millenary of City of Luxembourg and International Philatelic Exhibition. (a) Horiz views.
717 – 1 f. blue 15 30
718 **140** 1 f. 50 red 15 30
719 – 2 f. 50 green 15 30
720 – 3 f. brown 40 30
721 – 5 f. violet 15 30
722 – 11 f. blue . . . . 1·50 1·75
VIEWS: 1 f. Bock Rock; 2 f. 50, Rham Towers; 3 f. Grand Ducal Palace; 5 f. Castle Bridge; 11 f. Millenary Buildings.

(b) Vert multicoloured designs.
723 1 f. "Three Towers" Gate . . . 10 10
724 1 f. 50 Great Seal 15 15
725 2 f. 50 "The Black Virgin" (statue), St. John's Church 15 15
726 3 f. Citadel 15 15
727 5 f. Town Hall 35 70

141 Colpach Castle 142 "Human Rights"

1963. Red Cross Centenary.
728 **141** 2 f. 50 red and slate . . . 15 10

1963. 10th Anniv of European "Human Rights" Convention.
729 **142** 2 f. 50 blue on gold 20 10

143 "Co-operation"

144 Brown trout snapping Bait

1963. Europa.
730 **143** 3 f. green, orange & turq 20 10
731 6 f. orange, red & brown 20 25

1963. World Fishing Championships, Wormeldange.
732 **144** 3 f. slate 15 15

145 Telephone Dial

146 St. Roch (patron saint of bakers)

1963. Inauguration of Automatic Telephone System.
733 **145** 3 f. green, black and blue 15 15

1963. National Welfare Fund. Patron Saints of Crafts and Guilds. Inscr "CARITAS 1963". Multicoloured.
734 50 c. + 10 c. Type **146** 15 15
735 1 f. + 25 c. St. Anne (tailors) 15 15
736 2 f. + 25 c. St. Eloi (smiths) 15 40
737 3 f. + 50 c. St. Michel (haberdashers) 15 15
738 6 f. + 50 c. St. Barthelemy (butchers) . . . . 1·25 2·00
739 10 f. + 5 f. 90 St. Thibaut (seven crafts) . . . . 2·00 3·50

147 Power House

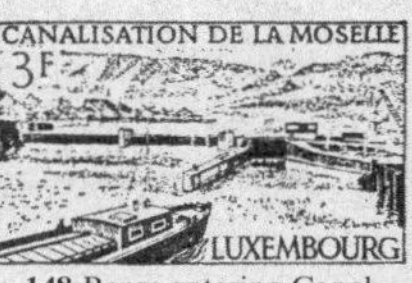

148 Barge entering Canal

1964. Inauguration of Vianden Reservoir.
740 **147** 2 f. blue, brown and red 20 15
741 – 3 f. light blue, turq & red 20 15
742 – 6 f. brown, blue and green 30 15
DESIGNS—HORIZ: 3 f. Upper reservoir. VERT: 6 f. Lohmuhle Dam.

1964. Inauguration of Moselle Canal.
743 **148** 3 f. indigo and blue 30 15

149 Europa "Flower"

150 Students thronging "New Athenaeum"

1964. Europa.
744 **149** 3 f. blue, brown & cream 15 10
745 6 f. sepia, green & yellow 15 20

1964. Opening of "New Athenaeum" (education centre).
746 **150** 3 f. black and green . . . 10 10

150a King Baudouin, Queen Juliana and Grand Duchess Charlotte

1964. 20th Anniversary of "BENELUX".
747 **150a** 3 f. brown, yellow & blue 10 10

151 Grand Duke Jean and Princess Josephine-Charlotte — **152** Three Towers

1964. Accession of Grand Duke Jean.
748 **151** 3 f. deep blue & lt blue . . 30 10
749 6 f. sepia and light brown . 30 20

1964. National Welfare Fund. Inscr "CARITAS 1964". Multicoloured.
750 50 c. + 10 c. Type **152** 15 15
751 1 f. + 25 c. Grand Duke Adolphe Bridge 15 15
752 2 f. + 25 c. Lower Town . . . 15 15
753 3 f. + 50 c. Type **152** 15 15
754 6 f. + 50 c. Grand Duke Adolphe Bridge . . . . 1·00 2·00
755 10 f. + 5 f. 90 Lower Town 1·50 2·50

153 Rotary Emblem and Cogwheels — **154** Grand Duke Jean

1965. 60th Anniv of Rotary International.
756 **153** 3 f. multicoloured 15 10

1965.
757 **154** 25 c. brown 10 10
758 50 c. red 10 10
759 1 f. blue 10 10
760 1 f. 50 purple 10 10
761a 2 f. red 10 10
762 2 f. 50 orange 10 10
763a 3 f. green 20 10
763b 3 f. 50 brown 20 20
764a 4 f. purple 20 10
764ba 5 f. green 50 10
765a 6 f. lilac 30 10
765b 7 f. orange 30 10
765c 8 f. blue 50 10
766 9 f. green 40 20
766a 10 f. black 60 10
767 12 f. red . . . . . . 1·00 10
767a 14 f. blue 50 40
767b 16 f. green . . . . . 1·00 25
767c 18 f. green 80 30
767d 20 f. blue . . . . . 1·10 20
767e 22 f. brown 80 60

155 I.T.U. Emblem and Symbols

1965. Centenary of I.T.U.
768 **155** 3 f. blue, lake and violet 10 10

156 Europa "Sprig" — **157** "The Roman Lady of the Titelberg"

1965. Europa.
769 **156** 3 f. turquoise, red and black 15 10
770 6 f. brown, blue and green 15 20

1965. National Welfare Fund. Fairy Tales. Inscr "CARITAS 1965". Multicoloured.
771 50 c. + 10 c. Type **157** . . . 15 20
772 1 f. + 25 c. "Schappchen, the Huntsman" 15 20
773 2 f. + 25 c. "The Witch of Koerich" 15 20
774 3 f. + 50 c. "The Goblins of Schoendels" 15 20
775 6 f. + 50 c. "Tollchen, Watchman of Hesperange" 30 1·50
776 10 f. + 5 f. 90 "The Old Spinster of Heispelt" . . . . . 1·25 3·00

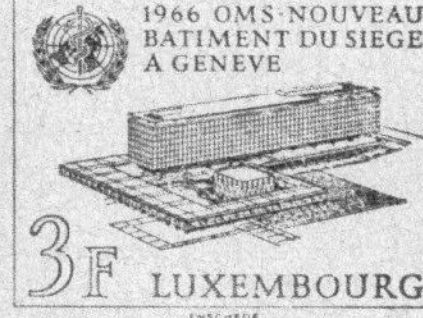

158 "Flag" and Torch — **159** W.H.O. Building

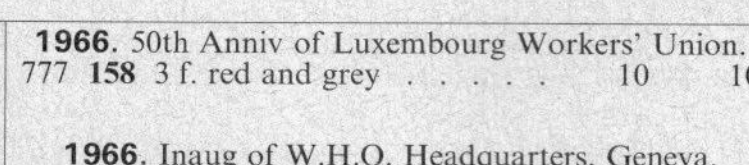

1966. 50th Anniv of Luxembourg Workers' Union.
777 **158** 3 f. red and grey 10 10

1966. Inaug of W.H.O. Headquarters, Geneva.
778 **159** 3 f. green 10 10

160 Golden Key — **161** Europa "Ship"

1966. Tercentenary of Solemn Promise to Our Lady of Luxembourg.
779 **160** 1 f. 50 green 10 20
780 – 2 f. red 10 20
781 – 3 f. blue 10 20
782 – 6 f. brown 20 30
DESIGNS: 2 f. Interior of Luxembourg Cathedral (after painting by J. Martin); 3 f. Our Lady of Luxembourg (after engraving by R. Collin); 6 f. Gallery pillar, Luxembourg Cathedral (after sculpture by D. Muller).

1966. Europa.
783 **161** 3 f. blue and grey 10 10
784 6 f. green and brown . . . 20 20

162 Class 1800 Diesel-electric Locomotive

1966. Luxembourg Railwaymen's Philatelic Exhibition. Multicoloured.
785 1 f. 50 Type **162** 35 30
786 3 f. Class 3600 electric locomotive 40 25

163 Grand Duchess Charlotte Bridge — **164** Kirchberg Building and Railway Viaduct

1966. Tourism.
787 **163** 3 f. lake 10 10
See also Nos. 807/8, 828 and 844/5.

1966. "Luxembourg-European Centre".
788 **164** 1 f. 50 green 30 30
789 – 13 f. blue (Robert Schuman monument) 60 15

165 "Mary, Veiled Matron of Wormeldange" — **166** City of Luxembourg, 1850 (after engraving by N. Liez)

1966. National Welfare Fund. Luxembourg Fairy Tales. Multicoloured.
790 50 c. + 10 c. Type **165** 10 20
791 1 f. 50 + 25 c. "Jekel Warden of the Wark" 10 20
792 2 f. + 25 c. "The Black Gentleman of Vianden" . . 10 20
793 3 f. + 50 c. "The Gracious Fairy of Rosport" 15 20
794 6 f. + 1 f. "The Friendly Shepherd of Donkolz" . . . 35 1·00
795 13 f. + 6 f. 90 "The Little Sisters of Trois-Vierges" . . . . . 70 2·50

1967. Centenary of Treaty of London.
796 **166** 3 f. brown, blue and green 35 15
797 – 6 f. red, brown and blue 20 30
DESIGN—VERT: 6 f. Plan of Luxembourg fortress c. 1850 (after T. de Cederstolpe).

167 Cogwheels — **168** Lion on Globe

1967. Europa.
798 **167** 3 f. purple, grey and buff 15 10
799 6 f. sepia, purple and blue 15 20

1967. 50th Anniv of Lions International.
800 **168** 3 f. yellow, purple & black 10 10

169 European Institutions Building, Luxembourg — **170** Hikers and Hostel

1967. N.A.T.O. Council Meeting, Luxembourg.
801 **169** 3 f. turquoise and green . . 10 10
802 6 f. red and pink 25 35

1967. Luxembourg Youth Hostels.
803 **170** 1 f. 50 multicoloured . . . 10 15

171 Shaving-dish (after Degrotte) — **172** "Gardener"

1967. "200 Years of Luxembourg Pottery".
804 **171** 1 f. 50 multicoloured . . . 10 15
805 – 3 f. multicoloured 20 15
DESIGN—VERT: 3 f. Vase, circa 1820.

1967. "Family Gardens" Congress, Luxembourg.
806 **172** 1 f. 50 orange and green 10 15

1967. Tourism. As T **163**.
807 3 f. indigo and blue 30 15
808 3 f. purple, green and blue . . 50 15
DESIGNS—HORIZ: No. 807, Moselle River and quayside, Mertert. VERT: No. 808, Moselle, Church and vines, Wormeldange.

173 Prince Guillaume — **174** Football

1967. National Welfare Fund. Royal Children and Residence.
809 **173** 50 c. + 10 c. brown & buff 15 20
810 – 1 f. 50 + 25 c. brown & bl 15 20
811 – 2 f. + 25 c. brown & red 15 20
812 – 3 f. + 50 c. brown & yell 80 20
813 – 6 f. + 1 f. brown & lav 40 1·00
814 – 13 f. + 6 f. 90 brn, grn & bl 70 3·50
DESIGNS: 1 f. 50, Princess Margaretha; 2 f. Prince Jean; 3 f. Prince Henri; 6 f. Princess Marie-Astrid; 13 f. Berg Castle.

1968. Olympic Games, Mexico.
815 – 50 c. light blue and blue . . 10 15
816 **174** 1 f. 50 green & emerald . . 10 15
817 – 2 f. yellow and green . . . 10 15
818 – 3 f. lt orange and orange . . 10 10
819 – 6 f. green and blue 15 20
820 – 13 f. red and crimson . . . 30 30
DESIGNS: 50 c. Diving; 2 f. Cycling; 3 f. Running; 6 f. Walking; 13 f. Fencing.

175 Europa "Key"

1968. Europa.
821 **175** 3 f. brown, black & green 10 10
822 6 f. green, black & orange 20 30

176 Thermal Bath Pavilion, Mondorf-les-Bains

1968. Mondorf-les-Bains Thermal Baths.
823 **176** 3 f. multicoloured 15 10

177 Fair Emblem

1968. 20th Anniv of Luxembourg Int Fair.
824 **177** 3 f. multicoloured 15 10

178 Village Project — **179** "Blood Transfusion"

1968. Luxembourg SOS Children's Village.
825 **178** 3 f. purple and green . . . 10 10
826 – 6 f. black, blue and purple 20 30
DESIGN—VERT: 6 f. Orphan with foster-mother.

1968. Blood Donors of Luxembourg Red Cross.
827 **179** 3 f. red and blue 20 10

180 Fokker Friendship over Luxembourg — **181** Cap Institute

1968. Tourism.
828 **180** 50 f. dp blue, brown & bl 3·00 60

1968. National Welfare Fund. Luxembourg Handicapped Children.
829 **181** 50 c. + 10 c. brown and blue 15 20
830 – 1 f. 50 + 25 c. brn and grn 15 20
831 – 2 f. + 25 c. brown & yell 20 30
832 – 3 f. + 50 c. brown & blue 25 20
833 – 6 f. + 1 f. brown & buff 40 1·00
834 – 13 f. + 6 f. 90 brown and pink . . . . 1·50 3·50
DESIGNS: 1 f. 50, Deaf and dumb child; 2 f. Blind child; 3 f. Nurse supporting handicapped child; 6 f. and 13 f. Mentally handicapped children (different).

183 Colonnade

1969. Europa.
836 **183** 3 f. multicoloured 15 10
837 6 f. multicoloured 30 30

184 "The Wooden Horse" (Kutter)

1969. 75th Birth Anniv of Joseph Kutter (painter). Multicoloured.
838 3 f. Type **184** 50 15
839 6 f. "Luxembourg" (Kutter) 50 30

185 ILO Emblem — **186** National Colours

1969. 50th Anniv of Int Labour Organization.
840 **185** 3 f. gold, violet and green 10 10

1969. 25th Anniv of "BENELUX" Customs Union.
841 **186** 3 f. multicoloured 20 10

187 N.A.T.O. Emblem

188 Ear of Wheat and Agrocentre, Mersch

1969. 20th Anniv of N.A.T.O.

842 **187** 3 f. orange and brown . . 20 10

1969. "Modern Agriculture".

843 **188** 3 f. grey and green 10 10

189 Echternach

190 Vianden Castle

1969. Tourism.

844 **189** 3 f. indigo and blue 20 10
845 – 3 f. blue and green 20 10

DESIGN: No. 845, Wiltz.

1969. National Welfare Fund. Castles (1st series). Multicoloured.

846 50 c. + 10 c. Type **190** 15 20
847 1 f. 50 + 25 c. Lucilinburhuc 15 20
848 2 f. + 25 c. Bourglinster . . . 15 20
849 3 f. + 50 c. Hollenfels 15 20
850 6 f. + 1 f. Ansembourg . . . . 45 1·50
851 13 f. + 6 f. 90 Beaufort . . . . 1·00 3·50

See also Nos. 862/7.

191 Pasque Flower

192 Firecrest

1970. Nature Conservation Year. Multicoloured.

852 3 f. Type **191** 20 10
853 6 f. West European hedgehogs 60 40

1970. 50 Years of Bird Protection.

854 **192** 1 f. 50 green, black & orge 20 15

193 "Flaming Sun"

1970. Europa.

855 **193** 3 f. multicoloured 10 10
856 6 f. multicoloured 20 30

194 Road Safety Assoc. Emblem and Traffic

1970. Road Safety.

857 **194** 3 f. black, red and lake . . 30 15

195 "Empress Kunegonde and Emperor Henry II" (stained-glass windows, Luxembourg Cathedral)

1970. Centenary of Luxembourg Diocese.

858 **195** 3 f. multicoloured 15 20

196 Population Pictograph

1970. Population Census.

859 **196** 3 f. red, blue and green 15 10

197 Facade of Town Hall, Luxembourg

1970. 50th Anniv of Union of Four Suburbs with Luxembourg City.

860 **197** 3 f. brown, ochre & blue . 15 10

198 U.N. Emblem

199 Monks in the Scriptorium

1970. 25th Anniv of United Nations.

861 **198** 1 f. 50 violet and blue . . . 10 10

1970. National Welfare Fund. Castles (2nd series). Designs as T **190**.

862 50 c. + 10 c. Clervaux 15 20
863 1 f. 50 + 25 c. Septfontaines 15 20
864 2 f. + 25 c. Bourscheid 15 20
865 3 f. + 50 c. Esch-sur-Sure . . . 15 20
866 6 f. + 1 f. Larochette . . . . 60 1·50
867 13 f. + 6 f. 90 Brandenbourg 1·10 3·50

1971. Medieval Miniatures produced at Echternach. Multicoloured.

868 1 f. 50 Type **199** 10 15
869 3 f. Vine-growers going to work 15 10
870 6 f. Vine-growers at work and returning home 25 20
871 13 f. Workers with spades and hoe 45 55

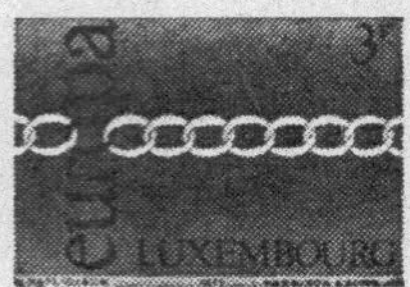

200 Europa Chain

1971.

872 **200** 3 f. black, brown and red 20 15
873 6 f. black, brown & green 60 50

201 Olympic Rings and Arms of Luxembourg

202 "50" and Emblem

1971. Int Olympic Committee Meeting, Luxembourg.

874 **201** 3 f. red, gold and blue . . 10 10

1971. 50th Anniv of Luxembourg's Christian Workers' Union (L.C.G.B.).

875 **202** 3 f. purple, orange & yell 10 10

203 Artificial Lake, Upper Sure Valley

204 Child with Coin

1971. Man-made Landscapes.

876 **203** 3 f. blue, grey and brown 40 20
877 – 3 f. brown, green and blue 40 25
878 – 15 f. black, blue & brown 60 20

DESIGNS: No. 877, Water-processing plant, Esch-sur-Sure; No. 878, ARBED (United Steelworks) Headquarters Building, Luxembourg.

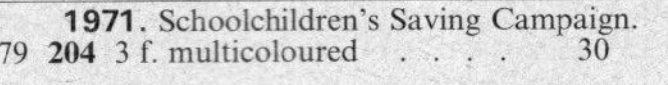

1971. Schoolchildren's Saving Campaign.

879 **204** 3 f. multicoloured 30 10

205 "Bethlehem Children"

206 Coins of Belgium and Luxembourg

1971. National Welfare Fund. "The Nativity"–wood-carvings in Beaufort Church. Multicoloured.

880 1 f. + 25 c. Type **205** 30 20
881 1 f. 50 + 25 c. "Shepherds" 30 20
882 3 f. + 50 c. "Virgin, Child Jesus and St. Joseph" 30 20
883 8 f. + 1 f. "Herdsmen" . . . . 1·00 2·50
884 18 f. + 6 f. 50 "One of the Magi" 2·00 5·50

1972. 50th Anniv of Belgium-Luxembourg Economic Union.

885 **206** 1 f. 50 silver, black & grn 15 15

207 Bronze Mask (1st cent.)

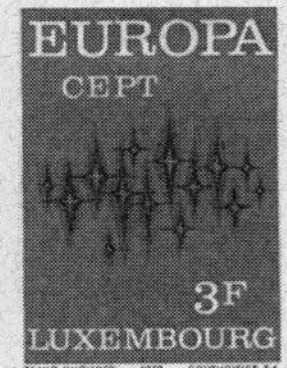

208 "Communications"

1972. Gallo-Roman Exhibits from Luxembourg State Museum. Multicoloured.

886 1 f. Samian bowl (2nd cent) (horiz) 15 15
887 3 f. Type **207** 30 15
888 8 f. Limestone head (2nd/3rd century) 85 80
889 15 f. Glass "head" flagon (4th century) 50 60

1972. Europa.

890 **208** 3 f. multicoloured 40 10
891 8 f. multicoloured 85 85

209 Archer

210 R. Schuman (after bronze by R. Zilli)

1972. 3rd European Archery Championships, Luxembourg.

892 **209** 3 f. multicoloured 30 10

1972. 20th Anniv of Establishment of European Coal and Steel Community in Luxembourg.

893 **210** 3 f. green and grey 40 15

211 National Monument

212 "Renert"

1972. Monuments and Buildings.

894 **211** 3 f. brown, green & violet 50 15
895 – 3 f. brown, green and blue 50 15

DESIGN: No. 895, European Communities' Court of Justice.

1972. Cent of Publication of Michel Rodange's "Renert" (satirical poem).

896 **212** 3 f. multicoloured 30 10

213 "Angel"

214 "Epona on Horseback"

1972. National Welfare Fund. Stained Glass Windows in Luxembourg Cathedral. Multicoloured.

897 1 f. + 25 c. Type **213** 15 20
898 1 f. 50 + 25 c. "St. Joseph" 15 20
899 3 f. + 50 c. "Holy Virgin with Child Jesus" 15 20
900 8 f. + 1 f. "People of Bethlehem" 1·00 2·50
901 18 f. + 6 f. 50 "Angel" (facing left) . . . . 3·00 7·00

1973. Archaeological Relics. Multicoloured.

902 1 f. Type **214** 15 20
903 4 f. "Panther attacking swan" (horiz) 30 10
904 8 f. Celtic gold coin . . . . . 1·10 1·10
905 15 f. Bronze boar (horiz) . . . 90 65

215 Europa "Posthorn"

216 Bee on Honeycomb

1973. Europa.

906 **215** 4 f. orange, blue & violet 35 10
907 8 f. green, yellow & purple 1·25 1·00

1973. Bee-keeping.

908 **216** 4 f. multicoloured 55 10

217 Nurse and Child

218 Capital, Vianden Castle

1973. Day Nurseries in Luxembourg.

909 **217** 4 f. multicoloured 30 10

1973. Romanesque Architecture in Luxembourg.

910 **218** 4 f. purple and green . . . 20 10
911 – 8 f. blue and brown . . . 80 75

DESIGN: 8 f. Detail of altar, St. Irmina's Chapel, Rosport.

219 Labour Emblem

220 J. de Busleyden

1973. 50th Anniv of Luxembourg Board of Labour.

912 **219** 3 f. multicoloured 20 10

1973. 500th Anniv of Great Council of Malines.

913 **220** 4 f. purple and brown . . . 20 10

221 Monument, Wiltz

222 Joachim and St. Anne

1973. National Strike Monument.

914 **221** 4 f. green, brown and grey 20 10

1973. National Welfare Fund. "The Nativity". Details from 16th-century reredos, Hachiville Hermitage. Multicoloured.

915 1 f. + 25 c. Type **222** 15 20
916 3 f. + 25 c. "Mary meets Elizabeth" 15 20
917 4 f. + 50 c. "Magus presenting gift" 20 20
918 8 f. + 1 f. "Shepherds at the manger" . . . . 1·00 2·50
919 15 f. + 7 f. "St. Joseph with Candle" . . . . 3·00 7·00

223 Princess Marie-Astrid, Association President

224 Flame Emblem

1974. Luxembourg Red Cross Youth Association.
920 **223** 4 f. multicoloured . . . . 1·60 15

1974. 50th Anniv of Luxembourg Mutual Insurance Federation.
921 **224** 4 f. multicoloured 50 10

225 Seal of Henry VII, King of the Romans

226 "Hind" (A. Tremont)

1974. Seals in Luxembourg State Archives.
922 **225** 1 f. brown, yellow & pur . 10 10
923 – 3 f. brown, yellow & grn . 20 25
924 – 4 f. dark brown, yell & brn . 30 10
925 – 19 f. brown, yellow & bl . . 1·00 90
DESIGNS: 3 f. Equestrian seal of John the Blind, King of Bohemia; 4 f. Municipal seal of Diekirch; 19 f. Seal of Marienthal Convent.

1974. Europa. Sculptures. Multicoloured.
926 4 f. Type **226** 80 10
927 8 f. "Abstract" (L. Wercollier) . 2·25 1·50

227 Churchill Memorial, Luxembourg

228 Diagram of Fair

1974. Birth Centenary of Sir Winston Churchill.
928 **227** 4 f. multicoloured 30 10

1974. New International Fair, Luxembourg-Kirchberg.
929 **228** 4 f. multicoloured 20 10

229 "Theis the Blind" (artist unknown)

230 "Crowning of St. Cecily and St. Valerien" (Hollenfels Church)

1974. 150th Death Anniv of "Theis the Blind" (Mathias Schou, folk singer).
930 **229** 3 f. multicoloured 20 30

1974. Gothic Architecture.
931 **230** 4 f. brown, green & violet 30 30
932 – 4 f. black, brown & blue 30 20
DESIGN: No. 932, Interior of Septfontaines Church.

231 U.P.U. Emblem on "100"

1974. Centenary of Universal Postal Union.
933 **231** 4 f. multicoloured 20 10
934 8 f. multicoloured 80 70

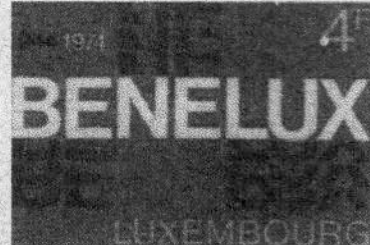

232 "Benelux"

1974. 30th Anniv of Benelux (Customs Union).
935 **232** 4 f. turquoise, green & bl 1·00 15

233 Differdange

1974. Tourism.
936 **233** 4 f. purple . . . . 1·00 15

234 "Annunciation"

236 The Fish Market, Luxembourg

1974. National Welfare Fund. Illustrations from "Codex Aureus Epternacensis". Multicoloured.
937 1 f. + 25 c. Type **234** 15 20
938 3 f. + 25 c. "Visitation" . . . 15 20
939 4 f. + 50 c. "Nativity" . . . 20 20
940 8 f. + 1 f. "Adoration of the Magi" . . . . 1·25 3·00
941 15 f. + 7 f. "Presentation at the Temple" . . . . 2·40 6·00

1975. European Architectural Heritage Year.
943 **236** 1 f. green 70 20
944 – 3 f. brown . . . . 1·25 30
945 – 4 f. lilac . . . . 1·40 15
946 – 19 f. red . . . . 1·50 1·00
DESIGNS—HORIZ: 3 f. Bourglinster Castle; 4 f. Market Square, Echternach. VERT: 19 f. St. Michael's Square, Mersch.

237 "Joseph Kutter" (self-portrait)

238 Dr. Albert Schweitzer

1975. Luxembourg Culture, and Europa. Paintings. Multicoloured.
947 1 f. Type **237** 15 15
948 4 f. "Remich Bridge" (N. Klopp) (horiz) . . . . 1·00 20
949 8 f. "Still Life" (J. Kutter) (horiz) 2·00 1·90
950 20 f. "The Dam" (D. Lang) . . 1·50 45

1975. Birth Centenary of Dr. Albert Schweitzer (medical missionary).
951 **238** 4 f. blue . . . . 1·00 15

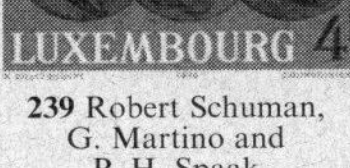

239 Robert Schuman, G. Martino and P.-H. Spaak

240 Civil Defence Emblem

1975. 25th Anniv of Robert Schuman Declaration for European Unity.
952 **239** 4 f. black, gold and green 60 15

1975. 15th Anniv of Civil Defence Reorganization.
953 **240** 4 f. multicoloured 60 10

241 Ice Skating

242 Fly Orchid

1975. Sports. Multicoloured.
954 **241** 3 f. purple, blue and green 45 25
955 – 4 f. brown, grn & dp brn 65 15
956 – 15 f. blue, brown & green 1·40 65
DESIGNS — HORIZ: 4 f. Water-skiing. VERT: 15 f. Rock-climbing.

1975. National Welfare Fund. Protected Plants (1st series). Multicoloured.
957 1 f. + 25 c. Type **242** 20 20
958 3 f. + 25 c. Pyramid orchid . . 40 35
959 4 f. + 50 c. Marsh helleborine 50 15
960 8 f. + 1 f. Pasque flower . . . 1·50 2·00
961 15 f. + 7 f. Bee orchid . . . . 3·50 6·00
See also Nos. 976/80 and 997/1001.

243 Grand Duchess Charlotte (80th)

244 7th-century Disc-shaped Brooch

1976. Royal Birthdays. Multicoloured.
962 6 f. Type **243** . . . . 1·50 20
963 6 f. Prince Henri (21st) . . . . 1·50 20

1976. Luxembourg Culture. Ancient Treasures from Merovingian Tombs. Multicoloured.
964 2 f. Type **244** 15 20
965 5 f. 5th-6th century glass beaker (horiz) 30 30
966 6 f. Ancient pot (horiz) 30 15
967 12 f. 7th cent. gold coin . . . . 1·00 1·00

245 Soup Tureen

1976. Europa. 19th century Pottery. Multicoloured.
968 6 f. Type **245** 75 15
969 12 f. Bowl . . . . 1·90 1·50

246 Independence Hall, Philadelphia

247 Symbol representing "Strength and Impetus"

1976. Bicentenary of American Revolution.
970 **246** 6 f. multicoloured 30 10

1976. Olympic Games, Montreal.
971 **247** 6 f. gold, magenta and mauve 20 10

248 Association Emblem and "Sound Vibrations"

249 "Virgin and Child"

1976. 30th Anniv of "Jeunesses Musicales" (Youth Music Association).
972 **248** 6 f. multicoloured 30 10

1976. Renaissance Art. Multicoloured.
973 6 f. Type **249** 30 10
974 12 f. Bernard de Velbruck, Lord of Beaufort (funeral monument) . . . . 1·00 80

250 Alexander Graham Bell

1976. Telephone Centenary.
975 **250** 6 f. green 30 10

1976. National Welfare Fund. Protected Plants (2nd series). As T **242**. Multicoloured.
976 2 f. + 25 c. Gentian 20 20
977 5 f. + 25 c. Wild daffodil . . . 20 20
978 6 f. + 50 c. Red helleborine (orchid) 40 25
979 12 f. + 1 f. Late spider orchid 1·00 2·00
980 20 f. + 8 f. Twin leaved squill 3·00 6·00

251 Johann von Goethe (poet)

252 Fish Market, Luxembourg

1977. Luxembourg Culture. Famous Visitors to Luxembourg.
981 **251** 2 f. purple 15 10
982 – 5 f. violet 25 20
983 – 6 f. black 60 15
984 – 12 f. violet 70 75
DESIGNS: 5 f. Joseph Mallard William Turner (painter); 6 f. Victor Hugo (writer); 12 f. Franz Liszt (musician).

1977. Europa. Multicoloured.
985 6 f. Type **252** 35 10
986 12 f. Grand Duke Adolphe railway bridge and European Investment Bank . . . . . 1·25 1·00

253 Esch-sur-Sure

254 Marguerite de Busbach (founder)

1977. Tourism.
987 **253** 5 f. blue 50 20
988 – 6 f. brown 40 10
DESIGNS 6 f. Ehnen.

1977. Anniversaries. Multicoloured.
989 6 f. Type **254** 40 15
990 6 f. Louis Braille (after Filippi) 40 15
ANNIVERSARIES: No. 989, 350th anniv of foundation of Notre Dame Congregation; No. 990, 125th death anniv.

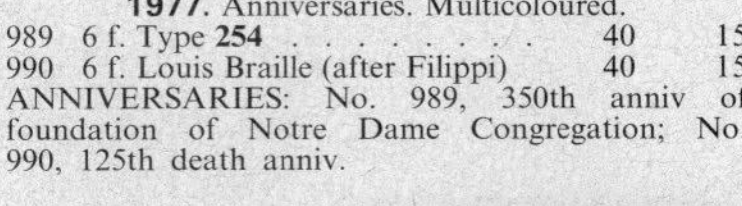

256 St. Gregory the Great

257 Head of Medusa

1977. Baroque Art. Sculpture from Feulen Parish Church pulpit attributed to J.-G. Scholtus.
992 **256** 6 f. purple 40 15
993 – 12 f. grey 80 80
DESIGN: 12 f. St. Augustine.

1977. Roman Mosaic at Diekirch.
994 **257** 6 f. multicoloured 60 20

258 Scene from "Orpheus and Eurydice" (Gluck)

1977. 25th Wiltz International Festival.
995 **258** 6 f. multicoloured 60 15

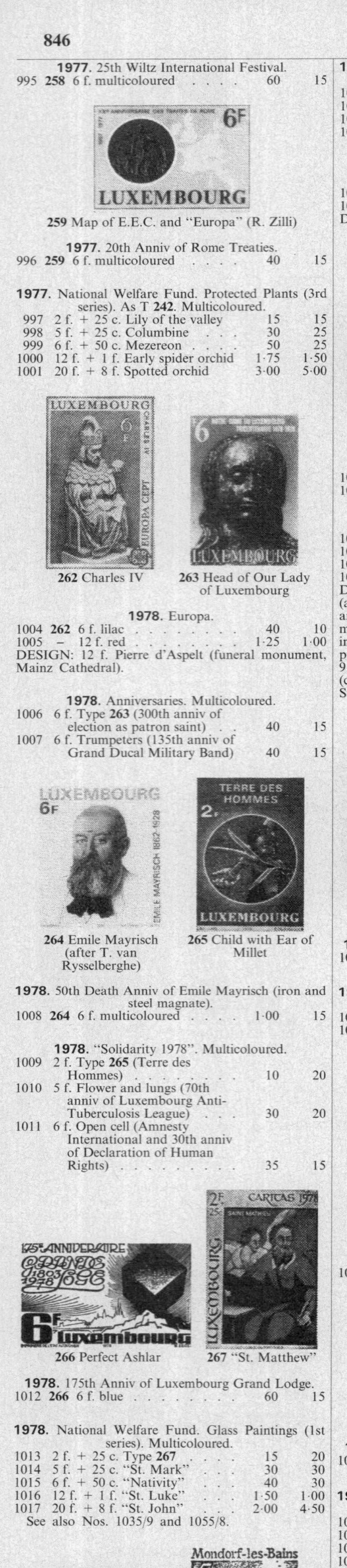

259 Map of E.E.C. and "Europa" (R. Zilli)

1977. 20th Anniv of Rome Treaties.
996 **259** 6 f. multicoloured 40 15

1977. National Welfare Fund. Protected Plants (3rd series). As T **242**. Multicoloured.
997 2 f. + 25 c. Lily of the valley 15 15
998 5 f. + 25 c. Columbine . . . 30 25
999 6 f. + 50 c. Mezereon . . . 50 25
1000 12 f. + 1 f. Early spider orchid 1·75 1·50
1001 20 f. + 8 f. Spotted orchid 3·00 5·00

262 Charles IV **263** Head of Our Lady of Luxembourg

1978. Europa.
1004 **262** 6 f. lilac 40 10
1005 – 12 f. red . . . . 1·25 1·00
DESIGN: 12 f. Pierre d'Aspelt (funeral monument, Mainz Cathedral).

1978. Anniversaries. Multicoloured.
1006 6 f. Type **263** (300th anniv of election as patron saint) . . 40 15
1007 6 f. Trumpeters (135th anniv of Grand Ducal Military Band) 40 15

264 Emile Mayrisch (after T. van Rysselberghe) **265** Child with Ear of Millet

1978. 50th Death Anniv of Emile Mayrisch (iron and steel magnate).
1008 **264** 6 f. multicoloured . . . . 1·00 15

1978. "Solidarity 1978". Multicoloured.
1009 2 f. Type **265** (Terre des Hommes) 10 20
1010 5 f. Flower and lungs (70th anniv of Luxembourg Anti-Tuberculosis League) . . . 30 20
1011 6 f. Open cell (Amnesty International and 30th anniv of Declaration of Human Rights) 35 15

266 Perfect Ashlar **267** "St. Matthew"

1978. 175th Anniv of Luxembourg Grand Lodge.
1012 **266** 6 f. blue 60 15

1978. National Welfare Fund. Glass Paintings (1st series). Multicoloured.
1013 2 f. + 25 c. Type **267** 15 20
1014 5 f. + 25 c. "St. Mark" . . . 30 30
1015 6 f. + 50 c. "Nativity" . . . 40 30
1016 12 f. + 1 f. "St. Luke" . . . 1·50 1·00
1017 20 f. + 8 f. "St. John" . . . 2·00 4·50
See also Nos. 1035/9 and 1055/8.

268 Denarius of Gaius Julius Caesar **269** Mondorf-les-Bains

1979. Luxembourg Culture. Roman Coins in the State Museum. Multicoloured.
1018 5 f. Type **268** 30 15
1019 6 f. Sestertius of Faustina I 50 15
1020 9 f. Follis of Helena 80 50
1021 26 f. Solidus of Valens . . . . 1·75 1·40
See also Nos. 1040/3 and 1060/3.

1979. Tourism.
1022 **269** 5 f. green, brown & blue 60 20
1023 – 6 f. red . . . . 1·25 15
DESIGN: 6 f. Luxembourg Central Station.

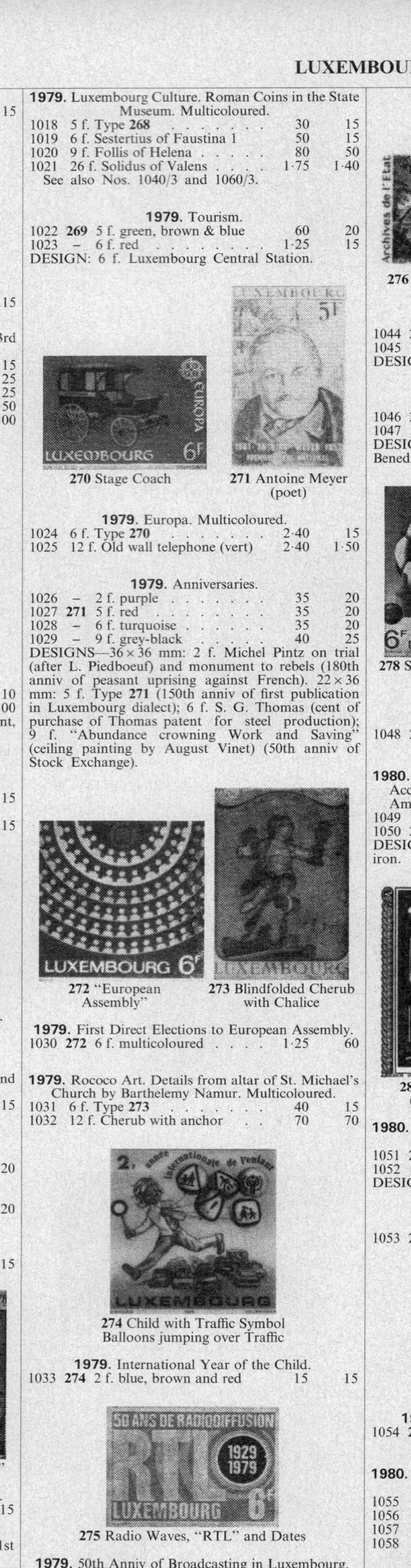

270 Stage Coach **271** Antoine Meyer (poet)

1979. Europa. Multicoloured.
1024 6 f. Type **270** . . . . 2·40 15
1025 12 f. Old wall telephone (vert) 2·40 1·50

1979. Anniversaries.
1026 – 2 f. purple 35 20
1027 **271** 5 f. red 35 20
1028 – 6 f. turquoise 35 20
1029 – 9 f. grey-black 40 25
DESIGNS—36×36 mm: 2 f. Michel Pintz on trial (after L. Piedboeuf) and monument to rebels (180th anniv of peasant uprising against French). 22×36 mm: 5 f. Type **271** (150th anniv of first publication in Luxembourg dialect); 6 f. S. G. Thomas (cent of purchase of Thomas patent for steel production); 9 f. "Abundance crowning Work and Saving" (ceiling painting by August Vinet) (50th anniv of Stock Exchange).

272 "European Assembly" **273** Blindfolded Cherub with Chalice

1979. First Direct Elections to European Assembly.
1030 **272** 6 f. multicoloured . . . . 1·25 60

1979. Rococo Art. Details from altar of St. Michael's Church by Barthelemy Namur. Multicoloured.
1031 6 f. Type **273** 40 15
1032 12 f. Cherub with anchor . . 70 70

274 Child with Traffic Symbol Balloons jumping over Traffic

1979. International Year of the Child.
1033 **274** 2 f. blue, brown and red 15 15

275 Radio Waves, "RTL" and Dates

1979. 50th Anniv of Broadcasting in Luxembourg.
1034 **275** 6 f. blue and red 50 15

1979. National Welfare Fund. Glass Paintings (2nd series). As T **267**. Multicoloured.
1035 2 f. + 25 c. "Spring" 15 15
1036 5 f. + 25 c. "Summer" . . . 30 30
1037 6 f. + 50 c. "Charity" . . . 40 30
1038 12 f. + 1 f. "Autumn" . . . 80 1·50
1039 20 f. + 8 f. "Winter" . . . 1·50 4·50

1980. Luxembourg Culture. Medieval Coins in the State Museum. As T **268**. Multicoloured.
1040 2 f. Grosso of Emperor Henry VII 20 20
1041 5 f. Grosso of John the Blind of Bohemia 20 20
1042 6 f. "Mouton d'or" of Wenceslas I and Jeanne, Duke and Duchess of Brabant 80 15
1043 20 f. Grosso of Wenceslas II, Duke of Luxembourg . . . 2·00 80

276 State Archives Building **277** Jean Monnet (statesman)

1980. Tourism.
1044 **276** 6 f. purple, ultram & bl 50 15
1045 – 6 f. red and brown . . . 60 15
DESIGN—VERT: No. 1045, Ettelbruck Town Hall.

1980. Europa.
1046 **277** 6 f. black 50 15
1047 – 12 f. olive . . . . 1·25 85
DESIGN: 12 f. St. Benedict of Nursia (founder of Benedictine Order) (statue in Echternach Abbey).

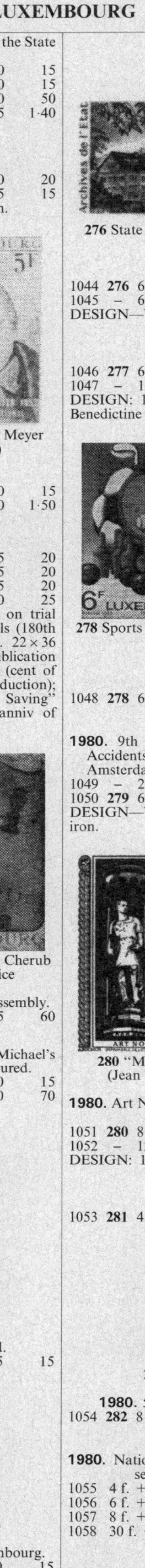

278 Sports Equipment **279** Gloved Hand protecting Worker from Machinery

1980. "Sports for All".
1048 **278** 6 f. black, orange & grn 1·40 30

1980. 9th World Congress on the Prevention of Accidents at Work and Occupational Diseases, Amsterdam.
1049 – 2 f. multicoloured 20 15
1050 **279** 6 f. brown, grey and red 40 15
DESIGN—VERT: 2 f. Worker pouring molten iron.

280 "Mercury" (Jean Mich) **281** Postcoded Letter

1980. Art Nouveau Sculpture. Statues beside entrance to State Savings Bank.
1051 **280** 8 f. lilac 45 15
1052 – 12 f. blue 55 60
DESIGN: 12 f. "Ceres" (Jean Mich).

1980. Postcode Publicity.
1053 **281** 4 f. brown, ochre and red 60 15

282 Policemen and Patrol Car

1980. 50th Anniv of National Police Force.
1054 **282** 8 f. multicoloured 80 20

1980. National Welfare Fund. Glass Paintings (3rd series). As T **267**. Multicoloured.
1055 4 f. + 50 c. "St. Martin" . . 30 20
1056 6 f. + 50 c. "St. Nicholas" 30 25
1057 8 f. + 1 f. "Virgin and child" 40 1·00
1058 30 f. + 10 f. "St. George" . . 2·25 5·00

1981. Luxembourg Culture. Coins in the State Museum. As T **268**.
1060 4 f. Patagon of Philip IV of Spain, 1635 . . . . . . 25 20
1061 6 f. 12 sols coin of Maria Theresa, 1775 . . . . . . 30 20
1062 8 f. 12 sols coin of Emperor Joseph II, 1789 . . . . . . 30 15
1063 30 f. Siege crown of Emperor Francis II, 1795 . . . . . 1·40 80

MINIMUM PRICE

The minimum price quoted is 10p which represents a handling charge rather than a basis for valuing common stamps. For further notes about prices see introductory pages.

284 European Parliament Building, Luxembourg **285** Cock-shaped Whistle sold at Easter Monday Market

1981. Tourism.
1064 **284** 8 f. brown and blue . . . 30 15
1065 – 8 f. red and blue 30 15
DESIGN: No. 1065, National Library.

1981. Europa. Multicoloured.
1066 8 f. Procession of beribboned sheep and town band to local fair 40 15
1067 12 f. Type **285** 60 50

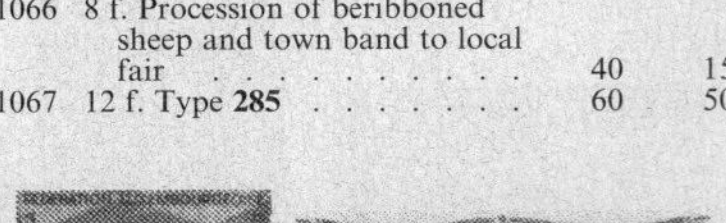

286 Staunton Knight on Chessboard **287** Prince Henri and Princess Maria Teresa

1981. Anniversaries.
1068 **286** 4 f. multicoloured 40 15
1069 – 8 f. ochre, brown & silver 40 15
1070 – 8 f. multicoloured 40 15
DESIGNS—VERT: 4 f. Type **286** (50th anniv of Luxembourg Chess Federation); 8 f. (1070), Passbook and State Savings Bank (125th anniv of State Savings Bank). HORIZ: 8 f. (1069), First Luxembourg banknote (125th anniv of International Bank of Luxembourg's issuing rights).

1981. Royal Wedding.
1071 **287** 8 f. multicoloured 50 40

288 Gliders over Useldange **289** Flame

1981. Aviation. Multicoloured.
1072 8 f. Type **288** 55 25
1073 16 f. Cessna 172F Skyhawk and 182H Skylane sports planes . 80 60
1074 35 f. Boeing 747-200F 182H over Luxembourg-Findel airport terminal . . . . . 1·60 85

1981. Energy Conservation.
1075 **289** 8 f. multicoloured 30 15

290 Arms of Petange **291** "Apple Trees in Blossom" (Frantz Seimetz)

1981. National Welfare Fund. Arms of Local Authorities (1st series). Multicoloured.
1076 4 f. + 50 c. Type **290** . . . 15 15
1077 6 f. + 50 c. Larochette . . . 25 25
1078 8 f. + 1 f. "Adoration of the Magi" (School of Rubens) . 40 30
1079 16 f. + 2 f. Stadtbredimus 80 2·00
1080 35 f. + 12 f. Weiswampach 2·50 5·00
See also Nos. 1097/1101 and 1119/23.

1982. Luxembourg Culture. Landscapes through the Four Seasons. Multicoloured.
1081 4 f. Type **291** 20 15
1082 6 f. "Landscape" (Pierre Blanc) 30 30
1083 8 f. "The Larger Hallerbach" (Guido Oppenheim) 45 15
1084 16 f. "Winter Evening" (Eugene Mousset) . . . . 1·00 70

292 Cross of Hinzert and Statue "Political Prisoner" (Lucien Wercollier)

293 Treaty of London, 1867, and Luxembourg Fortress

1982. National Monument of the Resistance and Deportation, Notre-Dame Cemetery.
1085 **292** 8 f. multicoloured 40 15

1982. Europa. Multicoloured.
1086 8 f. Type **293** 50 15
1087 16 f. Treaty of Paris, 1951, and European Coal and Steel Community Building, Luxembourg 90 75

294 St. Theresa of Avila (wood statue, Carmel Monastery)

295 State Museum

1982. Anniversaries. Multicoloured.
1088 4 f. Type **294** (400th death anniv) 30 15
1089 8 f. Raoul Follereau (social worker for lepers, 5th death anniv) 50 15

1982. Tourism.
1090 **295** 8 f. brown, blue & black 50 15
1091 – 8 f. buff, black and blue 40 15
DESIGN: No. 1091, Luxembourg Synagogue.

296 Bourscheid Castle

297 Key in Lock

1982. Classified Monuments (1st series).
1092 **296** 6 f. blue 30 15
1093 – 8 f. red 50 15
DESIGN—HORIZ: 8 f. Vianden Castle.
See also Nos. 1142/3, and 1165/6.

1982. Anniversaries. Multicoloured.
1094 4 f. Type **297** (50th anniv of International Youth Hostel Federation) 50 15
1095 8 f. Scouts holding hands around globe (75th anniv of Scouting Movement) (vert) 60 15

298 Monument to Civilian and Military Deportation

1982. Civilian and Military Deportation Monument, Hollerich Station.
1096 **298** 8 f. multicoloured 55 25

1982. National Welfare Fund. Arms of Local Authorities (2nd series) and Stained Glass Window (8 f.). As T **290**. Multicoloured.
1097 4 f. + 50 c. Bettembourg 25 20
1098 6 f. + 50 c. Frisange 30 25
1099 8 f. + 1 f. "Adoration of the Shepherds" (Gustav Zanter, Hoscheid parish church) 45 30
1100 16 f. + 2 f. Mamer 90 2·00
1101 35 f. + 12 f. Heinerscheid 2·50 5·00

299 Modern Fire Engine

300 "Mercury" (Auguste Tremont)

1983. Centenary of National Federation of Fire Brigades. Multicoloured.
1102 8 f. Type **299** 65 15
1103 16 f. Hand fire-pump (18th century) 80 65

1983. Anniversaries and Events.
1104 **300** 4 f. multicoloured 20 20
1105 – 6 f. multicoloured 50 30
1106 – 8 f. brown, black and blue 50 15
1107 – 8 f. deep blue and blue 50 15
DESIGNS: No. 1104, Type **300** (25th Congress of International Association of Foreign Exchange Dealers); 1105, N.A.T.O. emblem surrounded by flags of member countries (25th anniv of N.A.T.O.); 1106, Echternach Cross of Justice (30th Congress of International Union of Barristers); 1107, Globe and customs emblem (30th anniv of Customs Co-operation Council).

301 Robbers attacking Traveller

1983. Europa. Miniatures from "Codex Aureus Escorialensis", illustrating Parable of the Good Samaritan. Multicoloured.
1108 8 f. Type **301** 1·25 20
1109 16 f. Good Samaritan helping traveller 2·75 1·10

302 Initial "H" from "Book of Baruch"

303 Despatch Rider and Postcode

1983. Luxembourg Culture. Echternach Abbey Giant Bible. Multicoloured.
1110 8 f. Type **302** 45 20
1111 35 f. Initial "B" from letter of St. Jerome to Pope Damasius I 1·50 1·00

1983. World Communications Year. Mult.
1112 8 f. Type **303** 80 20
1113 8 f. European Communications Satellite (horiz) 2·00 30

304 St. Lawrence's Church, Diekirch

305 Basketball

1983. Tourism.
1114 **304** 7 f. orange, brown and blue 30 15
1115 – 10 f. orange, brown & bl 40 20
DESIGN—HORIZ: 10 f. Dudelange Town Hall.

1983. Anniversaries and Events. Multicoloured.
1116 7 f. Type **305** (50th anniv of Luxembourg basketball Federation) 55 20
1117 10 f. Sheepdog (European Working Dog Championships) 80 20
1118 10 f. City of Luxembourg ("The Green Heart of Europe") 1·25 20

1983. National Welfare Fund. Arms of Local Authorities (3rd series) and Painting. As T **290**. Multicoloured.
1119 4 f. + 1 f. Winseler 30 20
1120 7 f. + 1 f. Beckerich 40 30
1121 10 f. + 1 f. "Adoration of the Shepherds" (Lucas Bosch) 50 35
1122 16 f. + 2 f. Feulen 1·10 2·00
1123 40 f. + 13 f. Mertert 2·50 5·00

306 Lion and First Luxembourg Stamp

307 Pedestrian Precinct

1984. Anniversaries. Each black, red and blue.
1124 10 f. Type **306** 70 30
1125 10 f. Lion and ministry buildings 70 30
1126 10 f. Lion and postman's bag 70 30
1127 10 f. Lion and diesel locomotive 1·25 60
ANNIVERSARIES: No. 1124, 50th anniv of Federation of Luxembourg Philatelic Societies; 1125, 75th anniv of Civil Service Trade Union Movement; 1126, 75th anniv of Luxembourg Postmen's Trade Union; 1127, 125th anniv of Luxembourg Railways.

1984. Environmental Protection. Multicoloured.
1128 7 f. Type **307** 30 30
1129 10 f. City of Luxembourg sewage treatment plant 40 20

308 Hands supporting European Parliament Emblem

309 Bridge

1984. 2nd Direct Elections to European Parliament.
1130 **308** 10 f. multicoloured 60 20

1984. Europa. 25th Anniv of European Post and Telecommunications Conference.
1131 **309** 10 f. green, dp grn & blk 1·75 20
1132 16 f. orange, brown & blk 3·50 1·00

310 "The Smoker" (David Teniers the Younger)

311 "The Race" (Jean Jacoby)

1984. Paintings. Multicoloured.
1133 4 f. Type **310** 50 30
1134 7 f. "Young Turk caressing his Horse" (Eugene Delacroix) (horiz) 70 30
1135 10 f. "Ephiphany" (Jan Steen) (horiz) 1·00 20
1136 50 f. "The Lacemaker" (Pieter van Slingelandt) 4·00 2·50

1984. Olympic Games, Los Angeles.
1137 **311** 10 f. orange, black & bl 65 20

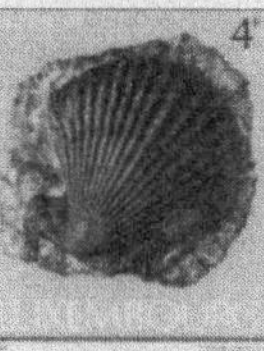

312 "Pecten sp."

313 "American Soldier" (statue by Michel Heitz at Clervaux)

1984. Luxembourg Culture. Fossils in the Natural History Museum. Multicoloured.
1138 4 f. Type **312** 45 20
1139 7 f. Devil's toe-nail 85 35
1140 10 f. "Coeloceras raquinianum" (ammonite) 1·25 15
1141 16 f. Dapedium (fish) 1·60 95

1984. Classified Monuments (2nd series). As T **296**.
1142 7 f. turquoise 35 30
1143 10 f. brown 45 15
DESIGNS: 7 f. Hollenfels Castle; 10 f. Larochette Castle.

1984. 40th Anniv of Liberation.
1144 **313** 10 f. black, red and blue 1·50 20

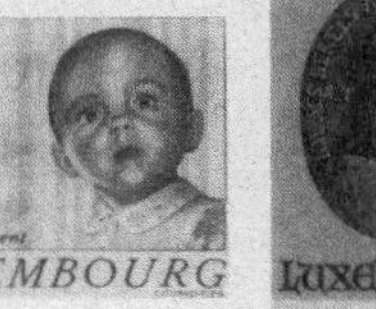

314 Infant astounded by Surroundings

315 Jean Bertels (abbot of Echternach Abbey)

1984. National Welfare Fund. The Child. Mult.
1145 4 f. + 1 f. Type **314** 40 40
1146 7 f. + 1 f. Child dreaming 60 60
1147 10 f. + 1 f. "Nativity (crib, Steinsel church) 1·00 50
1148 16 f. + 2 f. Child sulking 2·50 3·00
1149 40 f. + 13 f. Girl admiring flower 7·00 8·00

1985. Luxembourg Culture. Portrait Medals in State Museum (1st series). Multicoloured.
1150 4 f. Type **315** (steatite medal, 1595) 20 20
1151 7 f. Emperor Charles V (bronze medal, 1537) 30 30
1152 10 f. King Philip II of Spain (silver medal, 1555) 40 20
1153 30 f. Maurice of Orange-Nassau (silver medal, 1615) 1·60 90
See also Nos. 1173/6.

316 Fencing

317 Papal Arms

1985. Anniversaries. Multicoloured.
1154 10 f. Type **316** (50th anniv of Luxembourg Fencing Federation) 60 20
1155 10 f. Benz "Velo" (centenary of automobile) 60 20
1156 10 f. Telephone within concentric circles (centenary of Luxembourg telephone service) 60 20

1985. Visit of Pope John Paul II.
1157 **317** 10 f. multicoloured 60 20

318 Treble Clef within Map of National Anthem

320 Little Owl

1965. Europa. Music Year. Multicoloured.
1158 10 f. Type **318** (Grand Duke Adolphe Union of choral, instrumental and folklore societies) 1·75 30
1159 16 f. Neck of violin, music school and score of Beethoven's Violin Concerto opus 61 3·50 1·25

1985. Endangered Animals. Multicoloured.
1161 4 f. Type **320** 1·75 40
1162 7 f. European wildcat (horiz) 2·00 30
1163 10 f. Red admiral (horiz) 3·00 30
1164 50 f. European tree frog 6·00 2·00

1985. Classified Monuments (3rd series). As T **296**.
1165 7 f. red 50 20
1166 10 f. green 50 15
DESIGNS—HORIZ: 7 f. Echternach orangery. VERT: 10 f. Mohr de Waldt house.

321 Mansfeld Arms (book binding)

322 Application

1985. Luxembourg Culture.
1167 **321** 10 f. multicoloured 50 30

1985. National Welfare Fund. Multicoloured.
1168 4 f. + 1 f. Type **322** 40 30
1169 7 f. + 1 f. Friendship 60 50
1170 10 f. + 1 f. "Adoration of the Magi" (16th century alabaster sculpture) 1·00 50
1171 16 f. + 2 f. Child identifying with his favourite characters 2·50 3·00
1172 40 f. + 13 f. Shame 7·50 10·00

1986. Luxembourg Culture. Portrait Medals in State Museum (2nd series). As T **315**.
1173 10 f. multicoloured 50 30
1174 12 f. multicoloured 60 20
1175 18 f. black, grey and blue 80 50
1176 20 f. multicoloured 1·25 80
DESIGNS: 10 f. Count of Monterey (silver medal, 1675); 12 f. Louis XIV of France (silver medal, 1684); 18 f. Pierre de Weyms (president of Provincial Council) (pewter medal, 1700); 20 f. Duke of Marlborough (silver medal, 1706).

323 Bee on Flower **324** Forest and City

1986. Anniversaries. Multicoloured.

1177 12 f. Type **323** (centenary of Federation of Luxembourg Beekeeper's Association) . . 80 20
1178 12 f. Table tennis player (50th anniv of Luxembourg Table Tennis Federation) 80 20
1179 11 f. Mosaic of woman with water jar (centenary of Mondorf State Spa) 80 20

1986. Europa. Multicoloured.

1180 12 f. Type **324** . . . . 1·25 15
1181 20 f. Mankind, industry and countryside . . . . 2·00 75

325 Fort Thungen **326** Schuman

1986. Luxembourg Town Fortifications. Mult.

1182 15 f. Type **325** . . . . 1·40 50
1183 18 f. Invalids' Gate (vert) . . 1·50 50
1184 50 f. Malakoff Tower (vert) . . 3·00 90

1986. Birth Centenary of Robert Schuman (politician).

1185 **326** 2 f. black and red 10 10
1186 10 f. black and blue . . . 40 30

327 Road through Red Triangle on Map **328** Ascent to Chapel of the Cross, Grevenmacher

1986. European Road Safety Year.

1187 **327** 10 f. multicoloured . . . 75 20

1986. Tourism.

1188 **328** 12 f. multicoloured . . . 70 30
1189 – 12 f. brown, stone & red . . 70 30

DESIGN: No. 1189, Relief from Town Hall facade, Esch-sur-Alzette.

329 Presentation of Letter of Freedom to Echternach (after P. H. Witkamp) **330** Annunciation

1986. 800th Birth Anniv of Countess Ermesinde of Luxembourg.

1190 **329** 12 f. brown and stone . . 50 30
1191 – 30 f. buff, black and grey 1·50 80

DESIGN: 30 f. Seal, 1238.

1986. National Welfare Fund. Illustrations from 15th-century "Book of Hours". Multicoloured.

1192 6 f. + 1 f. Type **330** . . . . . 1·00 30
1193 10 f. + 1 f. Angel appearing to shepherds 50 40
1194 12 f. + 2 f. Nativity . . . . . 1·00 50
1195 18 f. + 2 f. Adoration of the Magi . . . . 3·00 3·50
1196 20 f. + 8 f. Flight into Egypt 5·00 6·50

331 Garden Dormouse **332** Network Emblem

1987. Endangered Animals. Multicoloured.

1197 6 f. Type **331** 80 30
1198 10 f. Banded agrion (vert) . . 1·25 55
1199 12 f. Dipper (vert) . . . . . 2·00 65
1200 25 f. Salamander . . . . . . 2·75 1·40

1987. 50th Anniversaries. Multicoloured.

1201 12 f. Type **332** (Amateur Short Wave Network) 55 30
1202 12 f. Anniversary Emblem (International Fair) 55 30

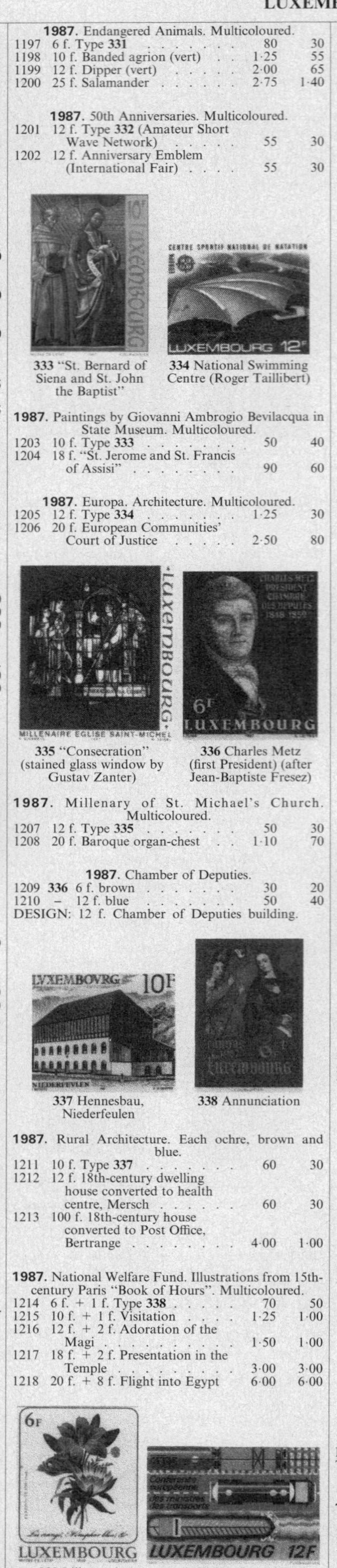
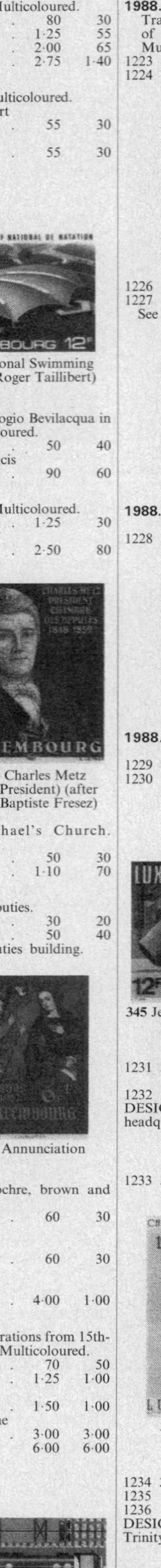

333 "St. Bernard of Siena and St. John the Baptist" **334** National Swimming Centre (Roger Taillibert)

1987. Paintings by Giovanni Ambrogio Bevilacqua in State Museum. Multicoloured.

1203 10 f. Type **333** 50 40
1204 18 f. "St. Jerome and St. Francis of Assisi" 90 60

1987. Europa. Architecture. Multicoloured.

1205 12 f. Type **334** . . . . 1·25 30
1206 20 f. European Communities' Court of Justice . . . . . 2·50 80

335 "Consecration" (stained glass window by Gustav Zanter) **336** Charles Metz (first President) (after Jean-Baptiste Fresez)

1987. Millenary of St. Michael's Church. Multicoloured.

1207 12 f. Type **335** 50 30
1208 20 f. Baroque organ-chest . . 1·10 70

1987. Chamber of Deputies.

1209 **336** 6 f. brown 30 20
1210 – 12 f. blue 50 40

DESIGN: 12 f. Chamber of Deputies building.

337 Hennesbau, Niederfeulen **338** Annunciation

1987. Rural Architecture. Each ochre, brown and blue.

1211 10 f. Type **337** 60 30
1212 12 f. 18th-century dwelling house converted to health centre, Mersch 60 30
1213 100 f. 18th-century house converted to Post Office, Bertrange . . . . 4·00 1·00

1987. National Welfare Fund. Illustrations from 15th-century Paris "Book of Hours". Multicoloured.

1214 6 f. + 1 f. Type **338** 70 50
1215 10 f. + 1 f. Visitation . . . . 1·25 1·00
1216 12 f. + 2 f. Adoration of the Magi . . . . 1·50 1·00
1217 18 f. + 2 f. Presentation in the Temple . . . . 3·00 3·00
1218 20 f. + 8 f. Flight into Egypt 6·00 6·00

339 Lilies and Water-lily **340** Rail, Road and Water Transport

1988. Luxembourg Culture. Flower Illustrations by Pierre-Joseph Redoute. Multicoloured.

1219 6 f. Type **339** 75 30
1220 10 f. Primulas and double narcissus 75 40
1221 12 f. Tulips and chrysanthemums . . . . . 2·00 50
1222 50 f. Irises and gorterias . . . 4·00 2·00

1988. European Conference of Ministers of Transport, Luxembourg (1223) and 25th Anniv of Eurocontrol (air safety organization) (1224). Multicoloured.

1223 12 f. Type **340** 85 45
1224 20 f. Boeing 747 airplane . . . 1·25 80

342 Wiltz Town Hall and Cross of Justice

1988. Tourism. Multicoloured.

1226 10 f. Type **342** 70 30
1227 12 f. Differdange Castle (vert) 70 30

See also Nos. 1254/5 and 1275/6.

343 Athletes

1988. 50th Anniv of League of Luxembourg Student Sports Associations.

1228 **343** 12 f. multicoloured . . . 60 15

344 Automated Mail Sorting

1988. Europa. Transport and Communications. Multicoloured.

1229 12 f. Type **344** . . . . 2·50 20
1230 20 f. Electronic communications . . . . 3·00 1·25

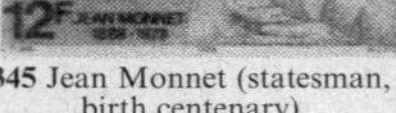

345 Jean Monnet (statesman, birth centenary) **346** Emblem and Flame

1988. European Anniversaries.

1231 **345** 12 f. pink, brown and light brown 75 20
1232 – 12 f. brown and green . . 1·00 20

DESIGN: No. 1232, European Investment Bank headquarters, Kirchberg (30th anniv).

1988. Olympic Games, Seoul.

1233 **346** 12 f. multicoloured . . . 60 15

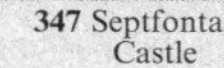

347 Septfontaines Castle **348** Annunciation to Shepherds

1988. Doorways.

1234 **347** 12 f. black and brown . . 70 15
1235 – 25 f. black and green . . . 1·50 80
1236 – 50 f. black and brown . . 2·50 1·50

DESIGNS: 25 f. National Library; 50 f. Holy Trinity Church.

1988. National Welfare Fund. Illustrations from 16th-century "Book of Hours". Multicoloured.

1237 9 f. + 1 f. Type **348** 60 40
1238 12 f. + 2 f. Adoration of the Magi 70 40
1239 18 f. + 2 f. Madonna and Child 2·50 2·50
1240 20 f. + 8 f. Pentecost . . . . 3·00 3·00

349 C. M. Spoo (promoter of Luxembourgish) **350** Grand Ducal Family Vault Bronze (Auguste Tremont)

1989. Anniversaries.

1241 **349** 12 f. black, red & brown 60 25
1242 – 18 f. multicoloured . . . 90 50
1243 – 20 f. red, black and grey 1·25 75

DESIGNS: 12 f. Type **349** (75th death anniv); 18 f. Stylized inking pad (125th anniv of Book Workers' Federation); 20 f. Henri Dunant (founder of International Red Cross) (75th anniv of Luxembourg Red Cross).

1989. 150th Anniv of Independence.

1244 **350** 12 f. multicoloured . . . 60 30

351 "Astra" Satellite and Map on T.V. Screens **352** Cyclist

1989. Launch of 16-channel T.V. Satellite.

1245 **351** 12 f. multicoloured . . . 60 30

1989. Start in Luxembourg of Tour de France Cycling Race.

1246 **352** 9 f. multicoloured 70 30

353 Assembly and Flag **354** Emblem

1989. 40th Anniv of Council of Europe.

1247 **353** 12 f. multicoloured . . . 70 30

1989. Centenary of Interparliamentary Union.

1248 **354** 12 f. yellow, blue & ind 70 30

355 Hands **356** "Three Children in a Park" (anon)

1989. 3rd Direct Elections to European Parliament.

1249 **355** 12 f. multicoloured . . . 70 30

1989. Europa. Children's Games and Toys. Multicoloured.

1250 12 f. Type **356** 75 30
1251 20 f. "Child with Drum" (anon) 1·50 95

357 Grand Duke Jean **358** Charles IV

1989. 25th Anniv of Accession of Grand Duke Jean.

1252 **357** 3 f. black and orange . . 60 60
1253 9 f. black and green . . . 80 80

1989. Tourism. As T **342**. Multicoloured.

1254 12 f. Clervaux Castle 50 30
1255 18 f. 1st-century bronze wild boar, Titelberg 90 65

1989. Luxembourg History. Stained Glass Windows by Joseph Oterberger, Luxembourg Cathedral. Multicoloured.
1256 12 f. Type **358** 75 30
1257 20 f. John the Blind . . . . . 1·00 85
1258 25 f. Wenceslas II . . . . . . 1·00 85

359 St. Lambert and St. Blase, Fennange **360** Funfair (650th anniv of Schueberfouer)

1989. National Welfare Fund. Restored Chapels (1st series). Multicoloured.
1259 9 f. + 1 f. Type **359** 50 30
1260 12 f. + 2 f. St. Quirinus, Luxembourg (horiz) 60 50
1261 18 f. + 3 f. St. Anthony the Hermit, Reisdorf (horiz) . . 2·00 2·00
1262 25 f. + 8 f. The Hermitage, Hachiville . . . . 3·00 3·00
See also Nos. 1280/3 and 1304/7.

1990. Anniversaries.
1263 **360** 9 f. multicoloured 80 30
1264 – 12 f. brown, pink & black 55 30
1265 – 18 f. multicoloured . . . 90 50
DESIGNS: 12 f. Batty Weber (writer, 50th death anniv); 18 f. Dish aerial (125th anniv of International Telecommunications Union).

361 Troops at Fortress

1990. Luxembourg Culture. Etchings of the Fortress by Christoph Wilhelm Selig. Multicoloured.
1266 9 f. Type **361** 60 30
1267 12 f. Soldiers by weir 70 40
1268 20 f. Distant view of fortress 1·50 1·00
1269 25 f. Walls . . . . 2·00 90

362 Paul Eyschen (75th anniv) **363** "Psallus pseudoplatini" (male and female) on Maple

1990. Statesmen's Death Anniversaries.
1270 **362** 9 f. brown and blue . . . 50 30
1271 – 12 f. blue and brown . . . 60 40
DESIGN: 12 f. Emmanuel Servais (centenary).

1990. Centenary of Luxembourg Naturalists' Society.
1272 **363** 12 f. multicoloured . . . 70 40

364 General Post Office, Luxembourg City **365** Hammelsmarsch Fountain (Will Lofy)

1990. Europa. Post Office Buildings.
1273 **364** 12 f. black and brown . . 1·00 30
1274 – 20 f. black and blue . . . 1·75 70
DESIGN—VERT: 20 f. Esch-sur-Alzette Post Office.

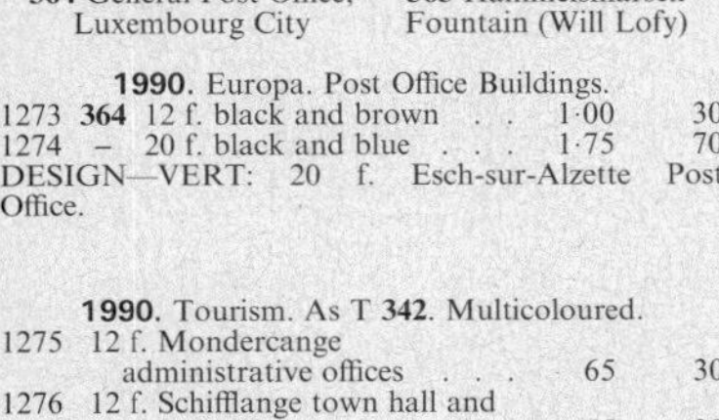

1990. Tourism. As T **342**. Multicoloured.
1275 12 f. Mondercange administrative offices . . 65 30
1276 12 f. Schifflange town hall and church 65 30

1990. Fountains. Multicoloured.
1277 12 f. Type **365** 60 30
1278 25 f. Doves Fountain . . . . 1·25 80
1279 50 f. Maus Ketty Fountain, Mondorf-les-Bains (Will Lofy) . . . . 2·25 1·50

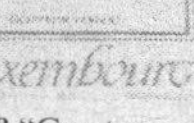

366 Congregation of the Blessed Virgin Mary, Vianden **368** "Geastrum varians"

1990. National Welfare Fund. Restored Chapels (2nd series). Multicoloured.
1280 9 f. + 1 f. Type **366** 60 40
1281 12 f. + 2 f. Notre Dame, Echternach (horiz) 70 50
1282 18 f. + 3 f. Consoler of the Afflicted, Grentzingen (horiz) 1·75 1·75
1283 25 f. + 8 f. St. Pirmin, Kaundorf . . . . 3·00 3·00

1991. Fungi. Illustrations by Pierre-Joseph Redoute. Multicoloured.
1285 14 f. Type **368** . . . . 1·00 40
1286 14 f. "Agaricus (Gymnopus) thiebautii" . . . . 1·00 40
1287 18 f. "Agaricus (Lepiota) lepidocephalus" . . . . . 1·50 75
1288 25 f. "Morchella favosa" . . . 2·00 1·25

369 "View from the Trier Road" **370** Dicks (after Jean Goedert)

1991. Luxembourg Culture. 50th Death Anniv of Sosthene Weis (painter). Multicoloured.
1289 14 f. Type **369** 80 40
1290 18 f. "Vauban Street and the Viaduct" . . . . 1·40 1·25
1291 25 f. "St. Ulric Street" (vert) 1·50 1·00

1991. Death Centenary of Edmond de la Fontaine (pen-name Dicks) (poet).
1292 **370** 14 f. multicoloured . . . 70 40

371 Claw grasping Piece of Metal (after Emile Kirscht) **372** National Miners' Monument, Kayl

1991. 75th Anniv of Trade Union Movement in Luxembourg.
1293 **371** 14 f. multicoloured . . . 70 40

1991. Tourism. Multicoloured.
1294 14 f. Type **372** 75 40
1295 14 f. Magistrates' Court, Redange-sur-Attert (horiz) 75 40

373 Earth and Orbit of "Astra 1A" and "1B" Satellites **374** Telephone

1991. Europa. Europe in Space. Multicoloured.
1296 14 f. Type **373** 90 40
1297 18 f. Betzdorf Earth Station 1·50 85

1991. Posts and Telecommunications.
1298 **374** 4 f. brown . . . . 1·50 1·50
1299 – 14 f. blue 60 50
DESIGN: 14 f. Postbox.

375 1936 International Philatelic Federation Congress Stamp **376** Girl's Head

1991. 50th Stamp Day.
1300 **375** 14 f. multicoloured . . . 60 40
The stamp illustrated on No. 1300 incorrectly shows a face value of 10 f.

1991. Mascarons (stone faces on buildings) (1st series).
1301 **376** 14 f. black, buff & brown 60 40
1302 – 25 f. black, buff and pink 1·00 80
1303 – 50 f. black, buff and blue 2·00 1·60
DESIGNS: 25 f. Woman's head; 50 f. Man's head.
See also Nos. 1320/22.

377 Chapel of St. Donatus, Arsdorf **378** Jean-Pierre Pescatore Foundation

1991. National Welfare Fund. Restored Chapels (3rd series). Multicoloured.
1304 14 f. + 2 f. Type **377** 80 60
1305 14 f. + 2 f. Chapel of Our Lady of Sorrows, Brandenbourg (horiz) 80 60
1306 18 f. + 3 f. Chapel of Our Lady, Luxembourg (horiz) . . . . 1·90 1·90
1307 22 f. + 7 f. Chapel of the Hermitage, Wolwelange . . 3·00 3·00

1992. Buildings. Multicoloured.
1308 14 f. Type **378** 80 35
1309 14 f. Higher Technology Institute, Kirchberg 80 35
1310 14 f. New Fairs and Congress Centre, Kirchberg 80 35

379 Inner Courtyard, Bettembourg Castle

1992. Tourism. Multicoloured.
1311 18 f. Type **379** 75 45
1312 25 f. Walferdange railway station . . . . 1·40 60

380 Athlete (detail of mural, Armand Strainchamps)

1992. Olympic Games, Barcelona.
1313 **380** 14 f. multicoloured . . . 1·50 35

381 Luxembourg Pavilion **382** Lions Emblem

1992. "Expo '92" World's Fair, Seville.
1314 **381** 14 f. multicoloured . . . 55 35

1992. 75th Anniv of Lions International.
1315 **382** 14 f. multicoloured . . . 55 35

383 Memorial Tablet (Lucien Wercollier) **384** Nicholas Gonner (editor)

1992. 50th anniv of General Strike.
1316 **383** 18 f. brown, grey and red 75 70

1992. Europa. 500th anniv of Discovery of America by Columbus. Luxembourg Emigrants to America.
1317 **384** 14 f. brown, black and grn 1·00 35
1318 – 22 f. blue, black & orange 1·50 1·00
DESIGN: 22 f. Nicolas Becker (writer).

385 Star and European Community Emblem **386** Posthorn and Letters

1992. Single European Market.
1319 **385** 14 f. multicoloured . . . 55 35

1992. Mascarons (2nd series). As T **376**.
1320 14 f. black, buff and green . . 55 35
1321 22 f. black, buff and blue . . . 90 1·00
1322 50 f. black, buff and purple 2·00 1·60
DESIGNS: 14 f. Ram's head; 22 f. Lion's head; 50 f. Goat's head.

1992. 150th Anniv of Post and Telecommunications Office. Designs showing stained glass windows by Auguste Tremont. Multicoloured.
1323 14 f. Type **386** 55 35
1324 22 f. Post rider . . . . 1·25 1·25
1325 50 f. Telecommunications . . 2·00 1·60

387 Hazel Grouse **388** Grand Duke Jean

1992. National Welfare Fund. Birds (1st series). Multicoloured.
1326 14 f. + 2 f. Type **387** 65 50
1327 14 f. + 2 f. Golden oriole (vert) 65 50
1328 18 f. + 3 f. Black stork . . . 2·00 2·00
1329 22 f. + 7 f. Red kite (vert) . . 3·00 3·00
See also Nos. 1364/7 and 1383/6.

1993.
1330 **388** 1 f. black and yellow . . 10 10
1331 2 f. black and green . . 10 10
1332 5 f. black and yellow . . 20 10
1334 7 f. black and brown . . 30 20
1334a 8 f. black and green . . 25 15
1335 10 f. black and blue . . 45 30
1337 14 f. black and purple . . 55 35
1338 15 f. black and green . . 55 35
1339 16 f. black and orange . . 70 45
1340 18 f. black and yellow . . 75 45
1341 20 f. black and red . . . 75 45
1343 22 f. black and green . . 90 55
1345 25 f. black and blue . . 1·00 60
1349 100 f. black and brown . . 3·00 2·50

389 Old Ironworks Cultural Centre, Steinfort

1993. Tourism. Multicoloured.
1350 14 f. Type **389** 55 35
1351 14 f. "Children with Grapes" Fountain, Schwebsingen . . 55 35

390 Collage by Maurice Esteve

1993. New Surgical Techniques.
1352 **390** 14 f. multicoloured . . . 55 35

391 Hotel de Bourgogne (Prime Minister's offices)

1993. Historic Houses. Multicoloured.
1353 14 f. Type **391** 55 35
1354 20 f. Simons House (now Ministry of Agriculture) . . 85 50
1355 50 f. Cassal House . . . . . 2·50 1·60

392 "Rezlop" (Fernand Roda)

1993. Europa. Contemporary Art. Multicoloured.

1356 14 f. Type **392** 55 35

1357 22 f. "So Close" (Sonja Roef) 1·25 1·40

393 Monument (detail D. Donzelli), Tetange Cemetery

394 Emblem

1993. 75th Death Anniv of Jean Schortgen (first worker elected to parliament).

1358 **393** 14 f. multicoloured . . . 55 35

1993. Centenary of Artistic Circle of Luxembourg.

1359 **394** 14 f. mauve and violet . . 55 35

395 European Community Ecological Label

396 Tram No. 1 (Transport Museum, Luxembourg)

1993. Protection of Environment.

1360 **395** 14 f. blue, green & emer . 55 35

1993. Museum Exhibits (1st series). Multicoloured.

1361 14 f. Type **396** . . . . 1·10 65

1362 22 f. Iron ore tipper wagon (National Mining Museum, Rumelange) . . . . 1·50 80

1363 60 f. Horse-drawn carriage (Arts and Ancient Crafts Museum, Wiltz) . . . . 2·25 2·00

See also Nos. 1404/6 and 1483/4.

1993. National Welfare Fund. Birds (2nd series). As T **387**. Multicoloured.

1364 14 f. + 2 f. Common snipe ("Becassine") 65 50

1365 14 f. + 2 f. Common kingfisher ("Martin-Pecheur") (vert) . 65 50

1366 18 f. + 3 f. Little ringed plover ("Petit Gravelot") . . . . 1·60 1·50

1367 22 f. + 7 f. Sand martin ("Hirondelle de Rivage") (vert) . . . . 2·50 2·50

397 "Snow-covered Landscape" (Joseph Kutter)

1994. Artists' Birth Centenaries. Multicoloured.

1368 14 f. Type **397** 60 40

1369 14 f. "The Moselle" (Nico Klopp) 60 40

398 Members' Flags

399 17th-Century Herald's Tabard

1994. 4th Direct Elections to European Parliament.

1370 **398** 14 f. multicoloured . . . 60 40

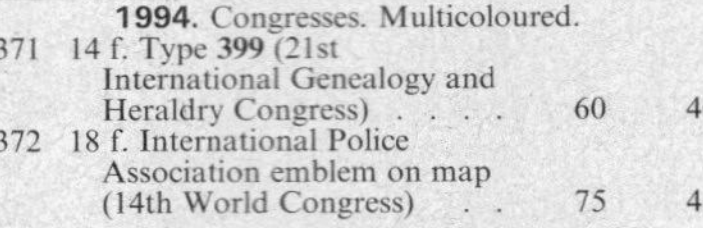

1994. Congresses. Multicoloured.

1371 14 f. Type **399** (21st International Genealogy and Heraldry Congress) 60 40

1372 18 f. International Police Association emblem on map (14th World Congress) . . 75 45

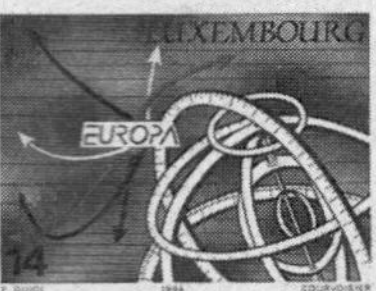

400 Arrows and Terrestrial Globe

1994. Europa. Discoveries. Multicoloured.

1373 14 f. Type **400** 60 40

1374 22 f. Chart, compass rose and sails . . . . 1·25 1·00

401 "Family" (Laura Lammar)

1994. International Year of the Family.

1375 **401** 25 f. multicoloured . . . 1·25 60

402 Crowds cheering American Soldiers

1994. 50th Anniv of Liberation.

1376 **402** 14 f. multicoloured . . . 60 40

403 Western European Union Emblem (40th anniv)

1994. Anniversaries and Campaigns.

1377 **403** 14 f. blue, lilac and ultramarine 85 40

1378 – 14 f. multicoloured . . . 85 40

1379 – 14 f. multicoloured . . . 2·25 65

DESIGNS—No. 1378, Emblem (25th anniv in Luxembourg of European Communities' Office for Official Publications); 1379, 10th-century B.C. ceramic bowl from cremation tomb, Bigelbach (European Bronze Age Campaign).

404 Munster Abbey (General Finance Inspectorate)

1994. Former Refuges now housing Government Offices. Multicoloured.

1380 15 f. Type **404** 65 40

1381 25 f. Holy Spirit Convent (Ministry of Finance) . . . 1·00 1·00

1382 60 f. St. Maximine Abbey of Trier (Ministry of Foreign Affairs) . . . . 2·50 2·00

1994. National Welfare Fund. Birds (3rd series). As T **387**. Multicoloured.

1383 14 f. + 2 f. Stonechat ("Traquet Patre") (vert) 65 50

1384 14 f. + 2 f. Grey partridge ("Perdix Grise") 65 60

1385 18 f. + 3 f. Yellow wagtail ("Bergeronnette Printaniere") . . . . 1·50 1·40

1386 22 f. + 7 f. Great grey shrike ("Pie-Grieche Grise") (vert) . 2·50 2·50

405 "King of the Antipodes"

406/409 Panoramic View of City (½-size illustration)

1995. Luxembourg, European City of Culture.

1387 **405** 16 f. multicoloured . . . 70 45

1388 – 16 f. multicoloured . . . 70 45

1389 – 16 f. multicoloured . . . 70 45

1390 **406** 16 f. multicoloured . . . 70 45

1391 **407** 16 f. multicoloured . . . 70 45

1392 **408** 16 f. multicoloured . . . 70 45

1393 **409** 16 f. multicoloured . . . 2·00 45

1394 – 16 f. multicoloured . . . 70 45

DESIGNS—As T **405**: No. 1388, "House with Arcades and Yellow Tower"; 1389, "Small Path" (maze). 35 × 26 mm: No. 1394, Emblem.

Nos. 1390/3 were issued together, se-tenant, forming the composite design illustrated.

410 Landscape and Slogan

411 Colour Spectrum and Barbed Wire

1995. European Nature Conservation Year.

1395 **410** 16 f. multicoloured . . . 70 45

1995. Europa. Peace and Freedom. 50th Anniv of Liberation of Concentration Camps. Mult.

1396 16 f. Type **411** 70 45

1397 25 f. Wire barbs breaking through symbolic sky and earth . . . . 1·10 70

412 Emblem

1995. Anniversaries and Event. Multicoloured.

1398 16 f. Type **412** (6th Small European States Games, Luxembourg) 70 45

1399 32 f. Diagram of section through Earth (27th anniv of underground Geodynamics Laboratory, Walferdange) (33 × 34 mm) . . . . . . 1·40 85

1400 80 f. Anniversary emblem (50th anniv of U.N.O.) . . . . . 3·25 2·50

413 Boeing 757

1995. 40th Anniv of Luxembourg–Iceland Air Link.

1401 **413** 16 f. multicoloured . . . 70 45

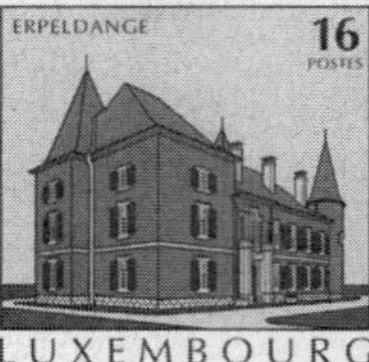

414 Erpeldange Castle

415 Stained Glass Window from Alzingen Church

1995. Tourism. Multicoloured.

1402 16 f. Type **414** 70 45

1403 16 f. Schengen Castle 70 45

1995. Museum Exhibits (2nd series). Vert designs as T **396**. Multicoloured.

1404 16 f. Churn (Country Art Museum, Vianden) 70 45

1405 32 f. Wine-press (Wine Museum, Ehnen) . . . . 1·40 85

1406 80 f. Sculpture of potter (Leon Nosbusch) (Pottery Museum, Nospelt) . . . . 3·25 2·50

1995. Christmas.

1407 **415** 16 f. + 2 f. multicoloured . 80 60

416 Broad-leaved Linden ("Tilia platyphyllos")

417 Mayrisch (after Theo van Rysselberghe)

1995. National Welfare Fund. Trees (1st series). Multicoloured.

1408 16 f. + 2 f. Type **416** 80 60

1409 16 f. + 2 f. Horse chestnut ("Aesculus hippocastanum") (horiz) 80 60

1410 20 f. + 3 f. Pedunculate oak (horiz) . . . . 1·25 1·25

1411 32 f. + 7 f. Silver birch . . . 2·00 2·00

See also Nos. 1432/5 and 1458/61.

1996. 68th Death Anniv of Emile Mayrisch (engineer).

1412 **417** A (16 f.) multicoloured . . 65 40

418 Mounument, Place Clairefontaine (Jean Cardot)

420 "Marie Munchen"

419 Electric Railcar

1996. Birth Centenary of Grand Duchess Charlotte.

1413 **418** 16 f. multicoloured . . . 65 40

1996. 50th Anniv of Luxembourg National Railway Company. Multicoloured.

1414 16 f. Type **419** 65 40

1415 16 f. Linked cars 65 40

1416 16 f. Train (right-hand detail) 65 40

Nos. 1414/16 were issued together, se-tenant, forming a composite design of a Series 2000 electric railcar set.

1996. 96th Death Anniv of Mihaly Munkacsy (painter). Multicoloured.

1417 16 f. Type **420** 65 40

1418 16 f. Munkacsy (after Edouard Charlemont) (horiz) 65 40

421 Workers and Emblem

422 Marie de Bourgogne

1996. Anniversaries.

1419 **421** 16 f. green, orange and black 65 40

1420 – 20 f. multicoloured . . . 80 50

1421 – 25 f. multicoloured . . . 1·00 60

1422 – 32 f. multicoloured . . . 1·25 75

DESIGNS—HORIZ: 16 f. Type **421** (75th anniv of Luxembourg Confederation of Christian Trade Unions); 32 f. Film negative (centenary of motion pictures). VERT: 20 f. Transmitter and radiowaves (centenary of Guglielmo Marconi's patented wireless telegraph); 25 f. Olympic flame and rings (centenary of modern Olympic Games).

1996. Europa. Famous Women. Duchesses of Luxembourg. Multicoloured.

1423 16 f. Type **422** 65 40

1424 25 f. Maria-Theresa of Austria . . . . 1·00 60

423 Handstamp

1996. Bicentenary (1995) of Registration and Property Administration.
1425 **423** 16 f. multicoloured . . . 65 40

424 Children of different Cultures (Michele Dockendorf)

1996. "Let us Live Together". Multicoloured.
1426 16 f. Type **424** 65 40
1427 16 f. "L'Abbraccio" (statue, Marie-Josee Kerschen) (vert) 65 40

425 Eurasian Badger

1996. Mammals. Multicoloured.
1428 16 f. Type **425** 65 40
1429 20 f. Polecat 80 50
1430 80 f. European otter . . . . . 3·25 2·40

426 "The Birth of Christ" (icon, Eva Mathes)

427 John the Blind

1996. Christmas.
1431 **426** 16 f. + 2 f. multicoloured . 70 55

1996. National Welfare Fund. Trees (2nd series). As T **416**. Multicoloured.
1432 16 f. + 2 f. Willow ("Salix sp.") (horiz) 70 55
1433 16 f. + 2 f. Ash ("Fraxinus excelsior") 70 55
1434 20 f. + 3 f. Mountain ash (horiz) 1·25 1·25
1435 32 f. + 7 f. Common beech . . 1·90 1·90

1996. 700th Birth Anniv of John the Blind (King of Bohemia and Count of Luxembourg).
1436 **427** 32 f. multicoloured . . . 1·25 75

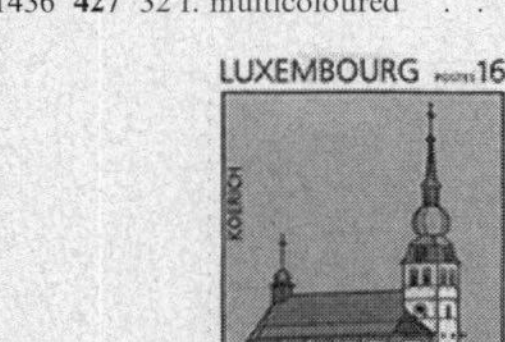

428 Koerich Church

1997. Tourism. Multicoloured.
1437 16 f. Type **428** 55 35
1438 16 f. Servais House, Mersch (horiz) 55 35

429 Birthplace of Robert Schuman (politician), Luxembourg-Clausen

1997. Anniversaries. Multicoloured.
1439 16 f. Type **429** (40th anniv of Treaties of Rome establishing European Economic Community and European Atomic Energy Community) 55 35
1440 20 f. National colours forming wing of Mercury (75th anniv of Belgium–Luxembourg Economic Union) 70 45

430 "Grand Duchess Charlotte"

1997. 11th World Federation of Rose Societies Congress, Belgium, Mondorf (Luxembourg) and the Netherlands. Roses. Multicoloured.
1441 16 f. Type **430** 55 35
1442 20 f. "The Beautiful Sultana" (33 × 26 mm) 70 45
1443 80 f. "In Memory of Jean Soupert" (33 × 26 mm) . . 3·25 2·50

431 Badge, Luxembourg Fortress, Shako and Sword

432 The Beautiful Melusina

1997. Anniversaries.
1444 **431** 16 f. multicoloured . . . 55 35
1445 – 16 f. black, blue and red . 55 35
1446 – 16 f. brown, green and pink 55 35
DESIGNS—As T **431**: No. 1444, Type **431** (bicentenary of Grand Ducal Gendarmerie Corps); 1445, Cock and rabbit (75th anniv of Luxembourg Union of Small Domestic Animals Farming Societies). 33 × 33 mm: 16 f. Bather and attendant, early 1900s (150th anniv of Mondorf spa).

1997. Europa. Tales and Legends. Multicoloured.
1447 16 f. Type **432** 55 35
1448 25 f. The Hunter of Hollenfels . 85 55

433 Face on Globe

1997. "Juvalux 98" Youth Stamp Exhibition. Multicoloured.
1449 16 f. Type **433** 55 35
1450 80 f. Postmen (painting, Michel Engels) . . . . 3·25 2·50

434 Emblem

1997. Sar–Lor–Lux (Saarland–Lorraine–Luxembourg) European Region.
1451 **434** 16 f. multicoloured . . . 55 35

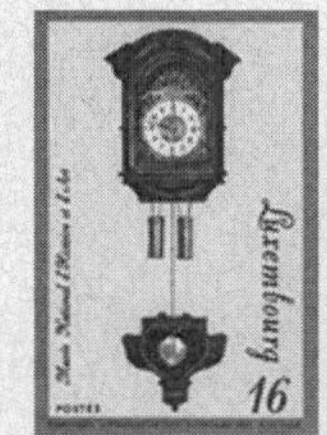

435 Wall Clock by Dominique Nauens, 1816

436 "Kalborn Mill" (Jean-Pierre Gleis)

1997. Clocks. Multicoloured.
1452 16 f. Type **435** 55 35
1453 32 f. Astronomical clock by J. Lebrun, 1850 (26 × 44 mm) . . . . 1·10 70
1454 80 f. Wall clock by Mathias Hebeler, 1815 . . . . . 3·25 2·50

1997. Water Mills. Multicoloured.
1455 16 f. Type **436** 55 35
1456 50 f. Interior of Ramelli mill, 1588 (from book "The Water Wheel" by Wilhelm Wolfel) (vert) . . . . 2·00 1·50

437 Holy Family

438 Count Henri V

1997. Christmas.
1457 **437** 16 f. + 2 f. multicoloured . 95 90

1997. National Welfare Fund. Trees (3rd series). As T **416**. Multicoloured.
1458 16 f. + 2 f. Wych elm ("Ulmus glabra") 60 45
1459 16 f. + 2 f. Norway maple ("Acer platanoides") 60 45
1460 20 f. + 3 f. Wild cherry 80 80
1461 32 f. + 7 f. Walnut (horiz) . . 1·75 1·75

1997. 750th Anniv of Accession of Henri V, Count of Luxembourg.
1462 **438** 32 f. multicoloured . . . 1·40 95

439 Rodange Church

440 Cog and "50"

1998. Tourism. Multicoloured.
1463 16 f. Type **439** 55 35
1464 16 f. Back of local authority building, Hesperange (horiz) 55 35

1998. Anniversaries.
1465 **440** 16 f. multicoloured . . . 55 35
1466 – 16 f. multicoloured . . . 55 35
1467 – 20 f. multicoloured . . . 70 45
1468 – 50 f. black, red and stone . 1·75 1·10
DESIGNS: No. 1465, Type **440** (50th anniv of Independent Luxembourg Trade Union); 1466, Festival poster (Rene Wismer) (50th anniv of Broom Festival, Wiltz); 1467, Memorial (death centenary of Jean Antoine Zinnen (composer of national anthem)); 1468, Typewriter keys and page from first issue of "Luxemburger Wort" (150th anniv of abolition of censorship).

441 Brown Trout

1998. Freshwater Fishes. Multicoloured.
1469 16 f. Type **441** 55 35
1470 25 f. Bullhead 85 55
1471 50 f. Riffle minnow . . . . . 2·00 1·60

442 Henri VII and Flags outside Fair Venue, Kirchberg

1998. 700th Anniv of Granting to Count Henri VII of Right to Hold a Fair. Value indicated by letter.
1472 **442** A (16 f.) multicoloured . . 55 35

443 Fireworks over Adolphe Bridge (National Day)

444 Town Postman, 1880

1998. Europa. National Festivals. Multicoloured.
1473 16 f. Type **443** 55 35
1474 25 f. Stained-glass window and flame (National Remembrance Day) 85 55

1998. "Juvalux '98" Youth Stamp Exhibition. Multicoloured.
1475 16 f. Type **444** 55 35
1476 25 f. Letter, 1590 (horiz) . . . 85 55
1477 50 f. Rural postman, 1880 . . 2·00 1·60

445 Masonic Symbols (Paul Moutschen)

1998. 150th Anniv of St. John of Hope Freemason Lodge.
1479 **445** 16 f. multicoloured . . . 55 35

446 Echternach

1998. 1300th Anniv of Echternach Abbey. Multicoloured.
1480 16 f. Type **446** 55 35
1481 48 f. Buildings in Echternach . 1·60 1·00
1482 60 f. Echternach Abbey . . . 2·40 1·90

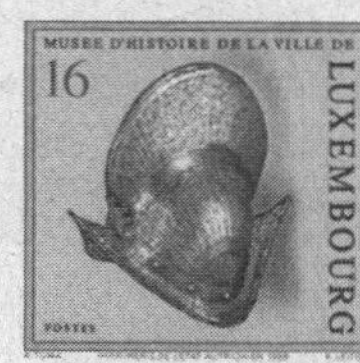

447 Spanish Morion (late 16th century)

1998. Museum Exhibits (3rd series). City of Luxembourg History Museum. Multicoloured.
1483 16 f. Type **447** 55 35
1484 80 f. Wayside Cross from Hollerich (1718) . . . . . 3·25 2·00

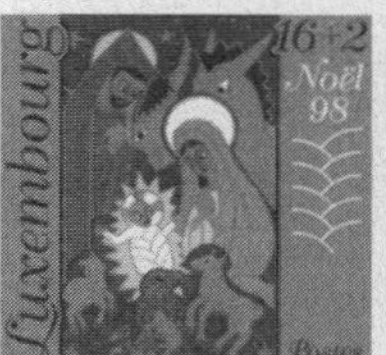

448 "Nativity" (altarpiece by Georges Saget, St. Mauritius Abbey, Clervaux)

1998. Christmas.
1485 **448** 16 f. + 2 f. multicoloured . 60 45

449 "Bech"

1998. National Welfare Fund (1st Series). Villages. 16th-century drawings by Jean Bertels. Multicoloured.
1486 16 f. + 2 f. Type **449** 60 45
1487 16 f. + 2 f. "Ermes Turf" (now Ermsdorf) 60 45
1488 20 f. + 3 f. "Itsich" (now Itzig) 80 80
1489 32 f. + 7 f. "Stein Hem" (now Steinheim) . . . . 1·50 1·50
See also Nos. 1510/13.

450 Globe and Jigsaw

1998. 40th Anniv of North Atlantic Maintenance and Supply Agency.
1490 **450** 36 f. multicoloured . . . 1·25 75

451 Council Building and Emblem

1999. 50th Anniv of Council of Europe.
1491 **451** 16 f. multicoloured . . . 50 30

452 Euro Coin and Map

1999. Introduction of the Euro (European currency). Value expressed by letter.
1492 **452** A (16 f.) multicoloured . . 50 30

453 Tawny Owl

455 Spectacles

454 Globe and Emblem

1999. Owls. Multicoloured.
1493 A (16 f.) Type **453** 50 30
1494 32 f. Eagle owl (horiz) . . . . 1·00 60
1495 60 f. Barn owl (horiz) . . . . 1·90 1·10

1999. 50th Anniv of N.A.T.O.
1496 **454** 80 f. multicoloured . . . 2·50 1·50

1999. International Year of the Elderly.
1497 **455** 16 f. multicoloured . . . 50 30

456 Emblem and Envelopes

1999. 125th Anniv of Universal Postal Union.
1498 **456** 16 f. multicoloured . . . 50 30

457 Haute-Sure National Park

1999. Europa. Parks and Gardens. Multicoloured.
1499 16 f. Type **457** 50 30
1500 25 f. Ardennes-Eifel National Park 40 25

458 Emblem

1999. Anniversaries. Multicoloured.
1501 16 f. Type **458** (75th anniv of National Federation of Mutual Socieites) 50 30
1502 32 f. Camera and roll of film (50th anniv of Luxembourg Federation of Amateur Photographers) . . . . . . 1·00 60
1503 80 f. Gymnasts (centenary of Luxembourg Gymnastics Federation) . . . . 2·50 1·50

459 Cars on Motorway

1999. Communications of the Future. Mult.
1504 16 f. Type **459** 50 30
1505 20 f. Earth and satellite . . . 60 35
1506 80 f. Planets and spacecraft . . 1·50 90

460 Prince Guillaume

461 A. Mayrisch de Saint-Hubert

1999. 18th Birthday (11 November) of Prince Guillaume.
1507 **460** 16 f. multicoloured . . . 50 30

1999. 125th Birth Anniv of Aline Mayrisch de Saint-Hubert (President of Luxembourg Red Cross).
1508 **461** 20 f. multicoloured . . . 60 35

462 Decorated Church Tower

1999. Christmas
1509 **462** 16 f. + 2 f. multicoloured 55 40

1999. National Welfare Fund. Villages (2nd series). As T **449**, showing 6th-century drawings by Jean Bertels. Multicoloured.
1510 16 f. + 2 f. "Oswiler" (now Osweiler) 55 40
1511 16 f. + 2 f. "Bettem Burch" (now Bettembourg) 55 40
1512 20 f. + 3 f. "Cruchte auf der Alset" (now Cruchten) . . . 70 70
1513 32 f. + 7 f. "Berchem" . . . . 1·25 1·25

463 "Gateway" (sketch by Goethe)

1999. 250th Birth Anniv of Johann Wolfgang von Goethe (poet and playwright).
1514 **463** 20 f. chestnut, cream and brown 60 35

464 "2000"

2000. New Millennium. Mult. Self-adhesive.
1515 A (16 f.) Type **464** (blue streaks emanating from bottom right) 50 30
1516 A (16 f.) Blue streaks emanating from bottom left 50 30
1517 A (16 f.) Blue streaks emanating from top right 50 30
1518 A (16 f.) Blue streaks emanating from top left 50 30

OFFICIAL STAMPS

1875. Stamps of 1859–72 optd **OFFICIEL**. Roul.
O79 3 1 c. brown 30·00 40·00
O80 2 c. black 30·00 40·00
O81 4 10 c. lilac £2250 £2500
O82 12½ c. red £500 £600
O83 20 c. brown 40·00 60·00
O84 25 c. blue £275 £150
O85 30 c. purple 35·00 80·00
O88 40 c. orange £180 £250
O87 1 f. on 37½ c. bistre (No. 37) £160 25·00

1875. Stamps of 1874–79 optd **OFFICIEL**. Perf.
O 89 3 1 c. brown 10·00 30·00
O 90 2 c. black 12·00 35·00
O 91 4 c. green £100 £160
O 92 5 c. yellow 70·00 80·00
O 93a 4 10 c. lilac £100 £110
O111 12½ c. red 90·00 £110
O 98 20 c. brown
O 99a 25 c. blue 2·00 2·50
O 96 1 f. on 37½ c. bistre (No. 56) 35·00 60·00

1881. Stamp of 1859 optd **S. P.** Roul.
O116 3 40 c. orange 40·00 70·00

1881. Stamps of 1874–79 optd **S. P.** Perf.
O128 3 1 c. brown 8·75 10·00
O129 2 c. black 10·00 10·00
O118 4 c. green £180 £200
O123 5 c. yellow £150 £200
O124 4 10 c. lilac £150 £200
O131 12½ c. red £180 £225
O132 20 c. brown 70·00 £100
O133 25 c. blue 70·00 £100
O134 30 c. red 80·00 £120
O120 1 f. on 37½ c. bistre (No. 56) 35·00 50·00

1882. Stamps of 1882 optd **S. P.**
O141 7 1 c. grey 25 40
O142 2 c. brown 25 40
O143 4 c. olive 25 50
O144 5 c. green 30 60
O181 10 c. red 12·00 16·00
O158 12½ c. blue 1·50 5·00
O159 20 c. orange 1·50 4·00
O183 25 c. blue 20·00 25·00
O149 30 c. olive 4·00 9·00
O150 50 c. brown 1·00 3·00
O151 1 f. lilac 1·00 3·00
O152 5 f. orange 12·00 40·00

1891. Stamps of 1891 optd **S. P.**
O188 8 10 c. red 25 50
O191 12½ c. green 7·00 7·00
O192 20 c. orange 12·00 9·00
O193 25 c. blue 30 55
O194 30 c. green 7·00 9·00
O195 37½ c. green 7·00 9·00
O196 50 c. brown 6·00 10·00
O197 1 f. purple 6·00 12·00
O198 2½ f. black 40·00 75·00
O199 5 f. lake 35·00 55·00

1898. Stamps of 1895 optd **S. P.**
O213 9 1 c. grey 2·00 2·00
O214 2 c. brown 1·00 1·50
O215 4 c. bistre 1·00 1·50
O216 5 c. green 4·00 5·00
O217 10 c. red 25·00 35·00

1908. Stamps of 1906 optd **Officiel**.
O218 10 1 c. grey 10 30
O219 2 c. brown 10 30
O220 4 c. bistre 10 30
O221 5 c. green 10 30
O271 5 c. mauve 10 30
O222 6 c. lilac 10 30
O223 7½ c. yellow 10 30
O224 10 c. red 20 40
O225 12½ c. slate 20 50
O226 15 c. brown 30 50
O227 20 c. orange 30 60
O228 25 c. blue 30 60
O229 30 c. olive 4·00 7·00
O230 37½ c. green 50 60
O231 50 c. brown 80 1·25
O232 87½ c. blue 2·00 3·50
O233 1 f. purple 3·00 4·00
O234 2½ f. red 70·00 70·00
O235 5 f. purple 60·00 45·00

1915. Stamps of 1914 optd **Officiel**.
O236 13 10 c. purple 20 70
O237 12½ c. green 20 70
O238 15 c. brown 20 70
O239 17½ c. brown 20 70
O240 25 c. blue 20 70
O241 30 c. brown 1·50 5·50
O242 35 c. blue 20 1·25
O243 37½ c. brown 20 1·50
O244 40 c. red 30 1·25
O245 50 c. grey 30 1·00
O246 62½ c. green 30 1·50
O247 87½ c. orange 30 2·00
O248 1 f. brown 30 1·50
O249 2½ f. red 30 3·00
O250 5 f. violet 30 3·50

1922. Stamps of 1921 optd **Officiel**.
O251 17 2 c. brown 10 20
O252 3 c. green 10 20
O253 6 c. purple 10 40
O272 10 c. green 10 30
O273 15 c. green 10 30
O274 15 c. orange 10 30
O256 20 c. orange 10 40
O275 20 c. green 10 30
O257 25 c. green 10 40
O258 30 c. red 10 40
O259 40 c. orange 10 40
O260 50 c. blue 20 60
O276 50 c. red 20 50
O261 75 c. red 20 60
O277 75 c. blue 20 50
O266 80 c. black 20 50
O263 18 1 f. red 30 2·00
O278 1 f. blue 30 1·00
O267 – 2 f. blue 1·40 2·25
O279 – 2 f. brown 2·00 5·50
O269 – 5 f. violet 5·50 10·00

1922. Stamps of 1923 optd **Officiel**.
O268b 28 3 f. blue 40 1·50
O270 26 10 f. black 9·00 24·00

1926. Stamps of 1926 optd **Officiel**.
O280 32 5 c. mauve 10 20
O281 10 c. green 10 20
O298 15 c. black 30 80
O282 20 c. orange 10 20
O283 25 c. green 10 20
O300 25 c. brown 20 60
O301 30 c. green 30 1·40
O302 30 c. violet 30 80
O303 35 c. violet 30 80
O304 35 c. green 30 80
O286 40 c. brown 10 20
O287 50 c. brown 10 20
O307 60 c. green 30 60
O288 65 c. brown 10 20
O308 70 c. violet 3·00 6·25
O289 75 c. red 10 40
O309 75 c. brown 30 60
O291 80 c. brown 10 40
O292 90 c. red 20 60
O293 1 f. black 20 50
O312 1 f. red 40 2·25
O294 1¼ f. blue 10 50
O313 1¼ f. yellow 2·00 6·25
O314 1¼ f. green 1·90 4·50
O315 1½ f. blue 30 1·40
O316 1¾ f. blue 40 1·50

1928. Stamp of 1928 optd **Officiel**.
O317 37 2 f. black 40 1·50

1931. Stamp of 1931 optd **Officiel**.
O318 43 20 f. green 2·00 8·50

1934. Stamp of 1934 optd **Officiel**.
O319 47 5 f. green 1·40 6·00

1935. No. 340 optd **Officiel**.
O341 52 10 f. green 1·50 7·00

POSTAGE DUE STAMPS

D 12 Arms of Luxembourg

D 77

1907.
D173 D 12 5 c. black and green 10 20
D174 10 c. black and green 1·10 20
D175 12½ c. black and green 30 80
D176 20 c. black and green 60 80
D177 25 c. black and green 13·00 1·25
D178 50 c. black and green 50 4·00
D179 1 f. black and green 30 3·50

1920. Surch.
D193 D 12 15 on 12½ c. blk & grn 1·50 8·00
D194 30 on 25 c. blk & grn 1·50 9·00

1922.
D221 D 12 5 c. red and green 20 40
D222 10 c. red and green 20 30
D223 20 c. red and green 20 30
D224 25 c. red and green 20 30
D225 30 c. red and green 40 30
D226 35 c. red and green 40 20
D227 50 c. red and green 40 30
D228 60 c. red and green 30 30
D229 70 c. red and green 40 30
D230 75 c. red and green 40 20
D231 1 f. red and green 20 50
D232 2 f. red and green 40 7·00
D233 3 f. red and green 1·25 13·00

1946.
D488 D 77 5 c. green 30 30
D489 10 c. green 30 30
D490 20 c. green 30 30
D491 30 c. green 30 30
D492 50 c. green 30 30
D493 70 c. green 40 55
D494 75 c. green 1·50 30
D495 1 f. red 30 30
D496 1 f. 50 red 30 30
D497 2 f. red 30 30
D498 3 f. red 80 30
D499 5 f. red 1·25 30
D500 10 f. red 2·00 3·50
D501 20 f. red 4·00 23·00

MACAO Pt. 9

A Portuguese territory in China at the mouth of the Canton River.

1884. 1000 reis = 1 milreis.
1894. 78 avos = 1 rupee.
1913. 100 avos = 1 pataca.

1884. "Crown" key-type inscr "MACAU".
10 P 5 r. black 8·00 5·00
2 10 r. orange 14·00 10·00
21 10 r. green 15·00 10·00
12 20 r. bistre 20·00 13·00
27 20 r. red 20·00 15·00
13 25 r. red 7·50 5·00
22 25 r. lilac 15·00 10·00
14 40 r. blue 40·00 35·00
23 40 r. buff 25·00 15·00
15 50 r. green 50·00 38·00
24 50 r. blue 15·00 12·00
31 80 r. grey 40·00 30·00
16 100 r. lilac 22·00 16·00
17 200 r. orange 24·00 16·00
9 300 r. brown 25·00 18·00

1885. "Crown" key type of Macao surch **80 reis** in circle. No gum.
19 P 80 r. on 100 r. lilac 60·00 38·00

1885. "Crown" key type of Macao surch in Reis. With gum, (43, 44, 45), no gum (others).
32 P 5 r. on 25 r. pink 15·00 10·00
43 5 r. on 80 r. grey 7·50 6·00
46 5 r. on 100 r. lilac 50·00 40·00
33 10 r. on 25 r. pink 25·00 15·00
38 10 r. on 50 r. green 85·00 70·00
44 10 r. on 80 r. grey 20·00 15·00
47 10 r. on 200 r. orange 50·00 40·00
35 20 r. on 50 r. green 18·00 12·00
45 20 r. on 80 r. grey 38·00 20·00
40 40 r. on 50 r. green 75·00 60·00

1885. "Crown" key-type of Macao surch with figure of value only and bar. No gum.
41 P 5 on 25 r. red 40·00 25·00
42a 10 on 50 r. green 30·00 22·00

9

1887. Fiscal stamps as T **9** surch **CORREIO** and new value. No gum.
50 5 r. on 10 r. green and brown £100 80·00
51 5 r. on 20 r. green and brown £100 80·00
52 5 r. on 60 r. green and brown £100 80·00
53 10 r. on 10 r. green and brown £120 90·00
54 10 r. on 60 r. green and brown £120 90·00
55 40 r. on 20 r. green and brown £200 £140

1888. "Embossed" key-type inscr "PROVINCIA DE MACAU".
56 Q 5 r. black 7·50 5·00
57 10 r. green 7·50 5·00
58 20 r. red 12·50 7·50
59 25 r. mauve 14·00 7·50
60 40 r. brown 15·00 8·00
61 50 r. blue 16·00 8·00
62 80 r. grey 20·00 12·00
63 100 r. brown 22·00 14·00
71 200 r. lilac 35·00 12·00
72 300 r. orange 32·00 12·00

1892. No. 71 surch **30 30**.
73 Q 30 on 200 r. lilac 40·00 30·00

1894. "Embossed" key-type of Macao surch **PROVISORIO**, value and Chinese characters. No gum.
75b Q 1 a. on 5 r. black 10·00 5·00
76 3 a. on 20 r. red 12·00 5·00
77 4 a. on 25 r. violet 15·00 8·00
89 5 a. on 30 on 200 r. lilac (No. 73) 75·00 60·00
78 6 a. on 40 r. brown 16·00 8·00
79 8 a. on 50 r. blue 35·00 15·00
80 13 a. on 80 r. grey 15·00 12·00
81 16 a. on 100 r. brown 20·00 10·00
82 31 a. on 200 r. lilac 70·00 35·00
83 47 a. on 300 r. orange 85·00 18·00

1894. "Figures" key-type inscr "MACAU".
91 R 5 r. yellow 6·00 2·50
92 10 r. mauve 6·00 2·50
93 15 r. brown 8·00 5·00
94 20 r. lilac 12·00 6·00
95 25 r. green 20·00 12·00
96 50 r. blue 24·00 12·00
97 75 r. pink 48·00 32·00
98 80 r. green 35·00 18·00
99 100 r. brown on buff 35·00 16·00
100 150 r. red on pink 45·00 16·00
101 200 r. blue on blue 60·00 20·00
102 300 r. blue on brown 75·00 22·00

1898. As Vasco da Gama types of Portugal but inscr "MACAU".
104 ½ a. green 3·00 1·90
105 1 a. red 3·00 1·90
106 2 a. purple 3·00 1·90
107 4 a. green 4·00 1·90
108 8 a. blue 7·50 2·75
109 12 a. brown 8·00 3·25
110 16 a. brown 8·00 2·75
111 24 a. brown 10·00 5·00

1898. "King Carlos" key-type inscr "MACAU". Name and value in black.
112 S ½ a. grey 1·50 60
113 1 a. yellow 1·50 60
114 2 a. green 1·50 60
115 2½ a. brown 2·50 1·50
116 3 a. lilac 2·50 1·50
173 3 a. grey 4·00 2·00
174 4 a. green 5·00 2·75
175 4 a. red 3·75 2·00
176 5 a. brown 5·00 3·00
177 6 a. brown 5·00 3·50
119 8 a. blue 6·00 3·00
178 8 a. brown 6·00 3·75
120 10 a. blue 6·00 3·00
121 12 a. pink 8·00 6·00
179 12 a. purple 20·00 12·50
122 13 a. mauve 10·00 7·00
180 13 a. lilac 10·00 6·50
123 15 a. green 20·00 12·00
124 16 a. blue on blue 10·00 5·00
181 18 a. brown on pink 18·00 15·00
125 20 a. brown on cream 11·00 6·00
126 24 a. brown on yellow 15·00 8·00
127 31 a. purple 18·00 8·00
182 31 a. purple on pink 18·00 15·00
128 47 a. blue on pink 28·00 11·00
183 47 a. blue on yellow 30·00 25·00
129 78 a. black on blue 35·00 16·00

1900. "King Carlos" key-type of Macao surch **PROVISORIO** and new value.
132 S 5 on 13 a. mauve 6·00 3·50
133 10 on 16 a. blue on blue 8·50 4·00
134 15 on 24 a. brown on yell 18·00 4·50
135 20 on 31 a. purple 24·00 5·00

1902. Various types of Macao surch.
138 Q 6 a. on 5 r. black 5·00 2·50
142 R 6 a. on 5 r. yellow 5·00 3·00
136 P 6 a. on 10 r. yellow 15·00 8·00
137 6 a. on 10 r. green 10·00 7·50
139 Q 6 a. on 10 r. green 5·00 3·00
143 R 6 a. on 10 r. mauve 10·00 6·00
144 6 a. on 15 r. brown 10·00 6·00
145 6 a. on 25 r. green 6·00 4·00
140 Q 6 a. on 40 r. brown 5·00 3·00
146 R 6 a. on 80 r. green 6·00 3·50
148 6 a. on 100 r. brn on buff 15·00 4·50
149 6 a. on 200 r. blue on blue 5·00 3·00
151 V 18 a. on 2½ r. brown 6·50 5·00
153 Q 18 a. on 20 r. red 16·00 4·00
162 R 18 a. on 20 r. lilac 15·00 6·00
154 Q 18 a. on 25 r. mauve 75·00 32·00
163 R 18 a. on 50 r. blue 15·00 6·00
165 18 a. on 75 r. pink 15·00 5·00
155 Q 18 a. on 80 r. grey £100 50·00
156 18 a. on 100 r. brown 12·00 7·50
166 R 18 a. on 150 r. red on pink 15·00 6·00
158 Q 18 a. on 200 r. lilac £100 50·00
160 18 a. on 300 r. orange 18·00 6·75
167 R 18 a. on 300 r. blue on brn 15·00 7·50

1902. "King Carlos" type of Macao optd **PROVISORIO**.
168 S 2 a. green 10·00 5·00
169 4 a. green 10·00 5·00
170 8 a. blue 10·00 5·00
171 10 a. blue 10·00 6·00
172 12 a. pink 18·00 7·50

1905. No. 179 surch **10 AVOS** and bar.
184 S 10 a. on 12 a. purple 18·00 10·00

1910. "Due" key-type of Macao, but with words "PORTEADO" and "RECEBER" cancelled.
185 W ½ a. green 10·00 6·00
186 1 a. green 10·00 6·00
187 2 a. grey 10·00 6·00

1911. "King Carlos" key-type of Macao optd **REPUBLICA**.
188 S ½ a. grey 1·00 75
189 1 a. orange 1·00 75
190 2 a. green 1·00 75
191 3 a. grey 1·00 75
192 4 a. red 3·00 2·50
193 5 a. brown 3·00 2·00
194 6 a. brown 3·00 2·00
195 8 a. brown 3·00 2·00
196 10 a. blue 3·00 2·00
197 13 a. lilac 4·50 3·00
198 16 a. blue on blue 4·50 3·00
199 18 a. brown on pink 10·00 7·00
200 20 a. brown on cream 10·00 7·00
201 31 a. purple on pink 10·00 7·00
202 47 a. blue on yellow 15·00 10·00
203 78 a. black on blue 25·00 15·00

30

32

1911. Fiscal stamp surch **POSTAL 1 AVO** and bar.
204 30 1 a. on 5 r. brown, yellow and black 10·00 5·00

1911. Stamps bisected and surch.
205 S 2 a. on half of 4 a. red (No. 175) 30·00 15·00
206 5 a. on half of 10 a. blue (No. 120) 75·00 60·00
207 5 a. on half of 10 a. blue (No. 171) 85·00 75·00

1911.
210 32 1 a. black £350 £300
211 2 a. black £400 £325

1913. Provisionals of 1902 surch in addition with new value and bars over old value and optd **REPUBLICA**.
212 R 2 a. on 18 a. on 20 r. lilac (No. 162) 8·00 3·00
213 2 a. on 18 a. on 50 r. blue (No. 163) 8·00 3·00
215 2 a. on 18 a. on 75 r. pink (No. 165) 10·00 3·00
216 2 a. on 18 a. on 150 r. red on pink (No. 166) 10·00 3·00

1913. Provisionals of 1902 and 1905 optd **REPUBLICA**.
218 Q 6 a. on 5 r. (No. 138) 5·00 3·50
284 R 6 a. on 5 r. (No. 142) 3·00 2·00
217 P 6 a. on 10 r. (No. 137) 15·00 10·00
285 Q 6 a. on 10 r. (No. 139) 3·00 1·50
286 R 6 a. on 10 r. (No. 143) 3·00 2·00
287 6 a. on 15 r. (No. 144) 1·90 1·50
288 6 a. on 25 r. (No. 145) 1·90 1·50
220 Q 6 a. on 40 r. (No. 140) 6·00 5·00
289 R 6 a. on 80 r. (No. 146) 1·90 1·50
291 6 a. on 100 r. (No. 148) 4·00 2·50
292 6 a. on 200 r. (No. 149) 4·00 2·50
281 S 8 a. (No. 170) 2·50 1·50
282 10 a. (No. 171) 2·50 1·50
283 S 10 a. on 12 a. (No. 184) 2·50 1·50
293 V 18 a. on 2½ r. (No. 151) 2·00 2·25
229 Q 18 a. on 20 r. (No. 153) 8·50 6·75
295 R 18 a. on 20 r. (No. 162) 4·00 3·00
296 18 a. on 50 r. (No. 163) 5·00 4·00
298 18 a. on 75 r. (No. 165) 5·00 4·00
230 Q 18 a. on 100 r. (No. 156) 42·00 30·00
299 R 18 a. on 150 r. (No. 166) 5·00 4·00
233 Q 18 a. on 300 r. (No. 160) 20·00 10·00
300 R 18 a. on 300 r. (No. 167) 9·50 6·00

1913. Stamps of 1911 issue surch.
252 S ½ a. on 5 a. brown 5·00 3·00
255 1 a. on 13 a. lilac 6·50 4·00
253 4 a. on 8 a. brown 6·00 4·50

1913. Vasco da Gama stamps of Macao optd **REPUBLICA**, and the 12 a. surch **10 A**.
256 ½ a. green 4·00 1·50
257 1 a. red 6·00 1·50
258 2 a. purple 6·00 1·50
259 4 a. green 5·00 1·50
260 8 a. blue 6·00 2·75
261 10 a. on 12 a. brown 12·00
262 16 a. brown 7·50 3·25
263 24 a. brown 10·00 4·00

1913. "Ceres" key-type inscr "MACAU".
264 U ½ a. green 1·00 60
310 1 a. black 1·75 75
311 1½ a. green 1·10 60
280 2 a. green 2·00 55
313 3 a. orange 4·00 2·00
267 4 a. red 2·25 1·25
315 4 a. yellow 3·00 1·75
268 5 a. brown 3·00 1·90
269 6 a. violet 3·00 2·00
270 8 a. brown 3·25 2·00
271 10 a. blue 3·25 2·25
272 12 a. brown 3·50 2·25
320 14 a. mauve 10·00 7·50
321 16 a. grey 6·00 3·25
274 20 a. red 8·00 5·00
322 24 a. green 8·50 5·00
323 32 a. brown 12·00 9·00
275 40 a. purple 9·00 6·00
324 56 a. pink 20·00 15·00
276 58 a. brown on green 15·00 10·00
325 72 a. brown 35·00 12·00
277 76 a. brown on pink 16·00 11·00
278 1 p. orange on orange 18·00 14·00
326 1 p. orange 50·00 25·00
279 3 p. green on blue 75·00 50·00
327 3 p. turquoise £120 75·00
328 5 p. red £190 £100

1919. Surch.
301 U ½ a. on 5 a. brn (No. 268) 40·00 30·00
330 1 a. on 24 a. grn (No. 322) 3·00 1·60
302 R 2 on 6 a. on 25 r. green (No. 288) £200 £100
303 2 on 6 a. on 80 r. green (No. 289) 20·00 15·00
304 S 2 a. on 6 a. (No. 177) 65·00 40·00
331 U 2 a. on 32 a. (No. 323) 3·00 1·60
332 4 a. on 12 a. (No. 272) 3·00 1·60
329 5 a. on 6 a. vio (No. 269) 4·50 2·50
334 7 a. on 8 a. brn (No. 270) 3·00 2·25
335 12 a. on 14 a. (No. 320) 3·00 2·25
336 15 a. on 16 a. (No. 321) 3·00 2·25
337 20 a. on 56 a. pink (No. 324) 40·00 25·00

50 "Portugal" and Galeasse

1934.
338 **50** ½ a. brown 30 30
339 1 a. brown 30 30
340 2 a. green 75 40
341 3 a. mauve 75 40
342 4 a. black 80 50
343 5 a. grey 80 50
344 6 a. brown 80 50
345 7 a. red 1·00 60
346 8 a. blue 1·00 60
347 10 a. red 1·50 1·00
348 12 a. blue 1·50 1·00
349 14 a. green 1·50 1·10
350 15 a. purple 1·50 1·00
351 20 a. orange 1·50 1·00
352 30 a. green 4·00 1·90
353 40 a. violet 4·00 1·90
354 50 a. brown 7·50 6·00
355 1 p. blue 20·00 10·00
356 2 p. brown 30·00 16·00
357 3 p. green 42·00 22·00
358 5 p. mauve 65·00 35·00

1936. Air. Stamps of 1934 optd **Aviao** and with Greek characters or surch also.
359 **40** 2 a. green 4·00 2·00
360 3 a. mauve 4·00 2·00
361 5 a. on 6 a. brown 4·00 2·00
362 7 a. red 4·00 2·00
363 8 a. blue 6·00 4·00
364 15 a. purple 20·00 10·00

54 Vasco da Gama
56 Airplane over Globe

1938. Name and value in black.
365 **54** 1 a. green (postage) 1·00 60
366 2 a. brown 1·00 60
367 3 a. violet 1·00 60
368 4 a. green 1·00 60
369 – 5 a. red 1·00 60
370 – 6 a. grey 2·00 1·00
371 – 8 a. purple 2·00 1·00
372 – 10 a. mauve 2·50 1·10
373 – 12 a. red 2·50 1·10
374 – 15 a. orange 2·50 1·25
375 – 20 a. blue 4·75 2·00
376 – 40 a. black 8·00 3·00
377 – 50 a. brown 8·00 3·00
378 – 1 p. red 22·00 8·50
379 – 2 p. green 40·00 12·50
380 – 3 p. blue 65·00 16·00
381 – 5 p. brown £110 20·00

382 **56** 1 a. red (air) 35 35
383 2 a. violet 45 35
384 3 a. orange 45 35
385 5 a. blue 1·00 60
386 10 a. red 2·00 95
387 20 a. green 3·25 1·50
388 50 a. brown 6·00 2·25
389 70 a. red 12·00 4·00
390 1 p. mauve 25·00 5·50
DESIGNS: Nos. 369/71, Mousinho de Albuquerque; Nos. 372/4, Henry the Navigator; Nos. 375/7, Dam; Nos. 378/81, Afonso de Albuquerque.

1940. Surch.
391 **50** 1 a. on 6 a. brn (No. 344) 5·00 3·50
394 2 a. on 6 a. brn (No. 344) 2·00 1·60
395 3 a. on 6 a. brn (No. 344) 2·00 1·60
401 – 3 a. on 6 a. grey (No. 370) 60·00 45·00
396 **50** 5 a. on 7 a. red (No. 345) 2·00 1·60
397 5 a. on 8 a. blue (No. 346) 2·00 1·60
398 8 a. on 30 a. (No. 352) 7·50 4·50
399 8 a. on 40 a. (No. 353) 7·50 4·50
400 8 a. on 50 a. (No. 354) 7·50 4·50

61 Mountain Fort
62 Our Lady of Fatima

1948.
410 – 1 a. brown and orange 2·00 50
427 – 1 a. violet and pink 1·00 25
411 **61** 2 a. purple 1·40 50
428 2 a. brown and yellow 1·00 25
412 – 3 a. purple 3·00 1·10
429 – 3 a. orange 1·75 40
413 – 8 a. red 4·00 1·75
430 – 8 a. grey 40 70
414 – 10 a. purple 4·25 1·75
431 – 10 a. brown and orange 6·00 1·00
415 – 20 a. blue 8·50 2·00
416 – 30 a. grey 9·00 2·00
432 – 30 a. blue 14·00 2·50
417 – 50 a. brown and buff 12·50 2·25
433 – 50 a. olive and green 30·00 4·00
418 – 1 p. green 50·00 18·00
419 – 1 p. blue 80·00
434 – 1 p. brown 60·00 7·50
420 – 2 p. red 50·00 12·00
421 – 3 p. green 70·00 15·00
422 – 5 p. violet 85·00 20·00
DESIGNS—HORIZ: 1 a. Macao house; 3 a. Port of Macao; 8 a. Praia Grande Bay; 10 a. Leal Senado Sq; 20 a. Sao Jerome Hill; 30 a. Street scene, Macao; 50 a. Relief of goddess of Ma (allegory); 5 p. Forest road. VERT: 1 p. Cerco Gateway; 2 p. Barra Pagoda, Ma-Cok-Miu; 3 p. Post Office.

1948. Honouring the Statue of Our Lady of Fatima.
423 **62** 8 a. red 20·00 7·50

64 Globe and Letter
65 Bells and Dove

1949. 75th Anniv of U.P.U.
424 **64** 32 a. purple 40·00 12·00

1950. Holy Year.
425 **65** 32 a. black 12·00 5·00
426 – 50 a. red 18·00 7·50
DESIGN: 50 a. Angel holding candelabra.

66 Arms and Dragon

1950.
435 **66** 1 a. yellow on cream 1·00 40
436 2 a. green on green 1·00 40
437 10 a. purple on green 4·00 85
438 10 a. mauve on green 4·00 85

67 F. Mendes Pinto
68 Junk

1951.
439 **67** 1 a. indigo and blue 60 20
440 – 2 a. brown and green 1·25 20
441 – 3 a. green & light green 2·00 25
442 – 6 a. violet and blue 3·50 40
443 – 10 a. brown and orange 6·50 85
444 **67** 20 a. purple & lt purple 14·00 1·40
445 – 30 a. brown and green 22·00 2·10
446 – 50 a. red and orange 35·00 3·25
DESIGNS: 2, 10 a. St. Francis Xavier; 3, 50 a. J. Alvaras; 6, 30 a. L. da Camoens.

1951.
447 – 1 p. ultramarine & blue 15·00 3·00
448 – 3 p. black and blue 75·00 20·00
449 **68** 5 p. brown and orange £100 25·00
DESIGNS—HORIZ: 1 p. Sampan. VERT: 3 p. Junk.

69 Our Lady of Fatima
71 St. Raphael Hospital

1951. Termination of Holy Year.
450 **69** 60 a. mauve and pink 32·00 8·00

1952. 1st Tropical Medicine Congress, Lisbon.
451 **71** 6 a. lilac and black 5·00 1·00

72 St. Francis Xavier Statue
73 The Virgin

1952. 400th Death Anniv of St. Francis Xavier.
452 **72** 3 a. black on cream 1·75 60
453 – 16 a. brown on buff 5·00 2·00
454 – 40 a. black on blue 10·00 3·00
DESIGNS: 16 a. Miraculous Arm of St. Francis; 40 a. Tomb of St. Francis.

1953. Missionary Art Exhibition.
455 **73** 8 a. brown and drab 3·00 60
456 10 a. blue and brown 7·50 2·00
457 50 a. green and drab 18·00 3·00

74 Honeysuckle
75 Portuguese Stamp of 1853 and Arms of Portuguese Overseas Provinces

1953. Indigenous Flowers.
458 **74** 1 a. yellow, green and red 50 10
459 – 3 a. purple, green & yellow 50 10
460 – 5 a. red, green and brown 50 10
461 – 10 a. multicoloured 50 15
462 – 16 a. yellow, green & brown 85 15
463 – 30 a. pink, brown & green 2·00 50
464 – 39 a. multicoloured 2·75 50
465 – 1 p. yellow, green & purple 7·00 85
466 – 3 p. red, brown and grey 20·00 3·00
467 – 5 p. yellow, green and red 30·00 7·50
FLOWERS: 3 a. Myosotis; 5 a. Dragon claw; 10 a. Nunflower; 16 a. Narcissus; 30 a. Peach blossom; 39 a. Lotus blossom; 1 p. Chrysanthemum; 3 p. Plum blossom; 5 p. Tangerine blossom.

1954. Portuguese Stamp Centenary.
468 **75** 10 a. multicoloured 12·00 3·00

76 Father M. de Nobrega and View of Sao Paulo
77 Map of Macao

1954. 4th Centenary of Sao Paulo.
469 **76** 39 a. multicoloured 9·00 3·50

1956. Map multicoloured. Values in red, inscr in brown. Colours given are of the backgrounds.
470 **77** 1 a. drab 25 10
471 3 a. slate 40 10
472 5 a. brown 1·00 10
473 10 a. buff 1·75 40
474 30 a. blue 3·50 75
475 40 a. green 4·00 2·00
476 90 a. grey 10·00 2·50
477 1 p. 50 pink 18·00 4·00

78 Exhibition Emblem and Atomic Emblems
79 "Cinnamomum camphora"

1958. Brussels International Exhibition.
478 **78** 70 a. multicoloured 7·50 2·00

1958. 6th International Congress of Tropical Medicine.
479 **79** 20 a. multicoloured 8·00 2·00

80 Globe girdled by Signs of the Zodiac
81 Boeing 707 over Ermida da Penha

1960. 500th Death Anniv of Prince Henry the Navigator.
480 **80** 2 p. multicoloured 12·00 2·00

1960. Air. Multicoloured.
481 50 a. Praia Grande Bay 3·00 70
482 76 a. Type **81** 5·00 1·25
483 3 p. Macao 10·00 1·50
484 5 p. Mong Ha 22·00 2·00
485 10 p. Shore of Praia Grande Bay 30·00 4·00

82 Hockey
83 "Anopheles hycranus sinensis"

1962. Sports. Multicoloured.
486 10 a. Type **82** 30 10
487 16 a. Wrestling 75 10
488 20 a. Table tennis 85 35
489 50 a. Motor cycle racing 1·50 40
490 1 p. 20 Relay racing 12·00 2·50
491 2 p. 50 Badminton 32·00 6·50

1962. Malaria Eradication.
492 **83** 40 a. multicoloured 8·00 2·00

84 Bank Building

85 I.T.U. Emblem and St. Gabriel

1964. Centenary of National Overseas Bank.
493 **84** 20 a. multicoloured . . . . 12·00 3·00

1965. Centenary of I.T.U.
494 **85** 10 a. multicoloured . . . . 6·00 1·50

86 Infante Dom Henrique Academy and Visconde de Sao Januario Hospital

87 Drummer, 1548

1966. 40th Anniv of Portuguese National Revolution.
495 **86** 10 a. multicoloured . . . . 9·00 1·00

1966. Portuguese Military Uniforms. Multicoloured.
496 10 a. Type **87** . . . . 1·50 30
497 15 a. Soldier, 1548 . . . . . . 3·00 30
498 20 a. Arquebusier, 1649 . . . . 3·00 35
499 40 a. Infantry officer, 1783 . . 5·00 75
500 50 a. Infantryman, 1783 . . . 5·00 1·00
501 60 a. Infantryman, 1902 . . . 8·00 2·00
502 1 p. Infantryman, 1903 . . . . 11·00 3·00
503 3 p. Infantryman, 1904 . . . . 22·00 10·00

88 O. E. Carmo and Patrol Boat "Vega"

89 Arms of Pope Paul VI, and "Golden Rose"

1967. Centenary of Military Naval Assn. Mult.
504 10 a. Type **88** . . . . 2·50 1·00
505 20 a. Silva Junior and sail frigate "Don Fernando" . . . . . 7·50 2·00

1967. 50th Anniv of Fatima Apparitions.
506 **89** 50 a. multicoloured . . . . 6·50 1·50

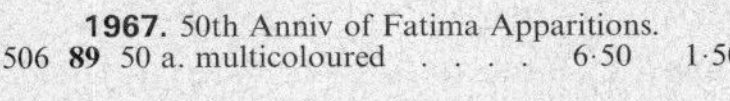

90 Cabral Monument, Lisbon

91 Adm. Gago Coutinho with Sextant

1968. 500th Birth Anniv of Pedro Cabral (explorer). Multicoloured.
507 20 a. Type **90** . . . . 5·00 1·00
508 70 a. Cabral's statue, Belmonte 10·00 1·50

1969. Birth Centenary of Admiral Gago Coutinho.
509 **91** 20 a. multicoloured . . . . 5·00 1·00

92 Church and Convent of Our Lady of the Reliquary, Vidigueira

93 L. A. Rebello da Silva

1969. 500th Birth Anniv of Vasco da Gama (explorer).
510 **92** 1 p. multicoloured . . . . 14·00 2·00

1969. Centenary of Overseas Administrative Reforms.
511 **93** 90 a. multicoloured . . . . 5·00 1·00

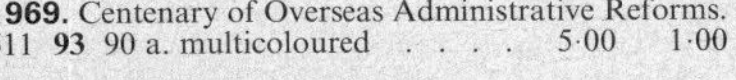

94 Bishop D. Belchoir Carneiro

95 Facade of Mother Church, Golega

1969. 400th Anniv of Misericordia Monastery, Macao.
512 **94** 50 a. multicoloured . . . . 5·00 1·00

1969. 500th Birth Anniv of King Manoel I.
513 **95** 30 a. multicoloured . . . . 9·00 1·00

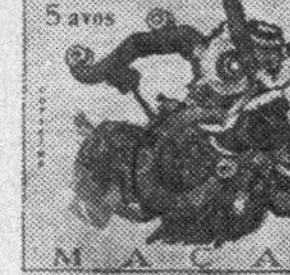

96 Marshal Carmona

97 Dragon Mask

1970. Birth Centenary of Marshal Carmona.
514 **96** 5 a. multicoloured. . . . . 2·50 75

1971. Chinese Carnival Masks. Multicoloured.
515 5 a. Type **97** . . . . 1·50 50
516 10 a. Lion mask . . . . 3·00 75

98 Portuguese Traders at the Chinese Imperial Court

1972. 400th Anniv of Camoens' "The Lusiads" (epic poem).
517 **98** 20 a. multicoloured . . . . 10·00 6·00

99 Hockey

1972. Olympic Games, Munich.
518 **99** 50 a. multicoloured . . . . 3·50 1·00

100 Fairey IIID Seaplane "Santa Cruz" arriving at Rio de Janeiro

1972. 50th Anniv of First Flight from Lisbon to Rio de Janeiro.
519 **100** 5 p. multicoloured . . . . 16·00 2·75

101 Lyre Emblem and Theatre Facade

102 W.M.O. Emblem

1972. Centenary of Pedro V Theatre, Macao.
520 **101** 2 p. multicoloured . . . . 12·00 1·25

1973. Centenary of W.M.O.
521 **102** 20 a. multicoloured . . . . 4·50 1·00

103 Visconde de Sao Januario

104 Chinnery (self-portrait)

1974. Centenary of Visconde de Sao Januario Hospital. Multicoloured.
522 15 a. Type **103** . . . . . . 1·50 50
523 60 a. Hospital buildings of 1874 and 1974 . . . . 3·00 1·00

1974. Birth Bicent of George Chinnery (painter).
524 **104** 30 a. multicoloured . . . . 4·00 1·00

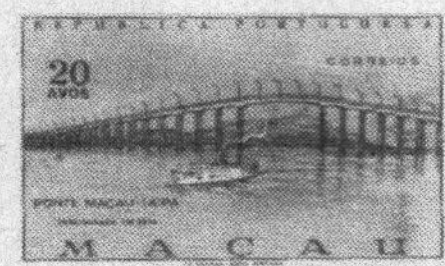

105 Macao–Taipa Bridge

1975. Inauguration of Macao–Taipa Bridge. Multicoloured.
525 20 a. Type **105** . . . . 2·00 50
526 2 p. 20 View of Bridge from below . . . . 12·00 2·00

106 Man waving Banner

1975. 1st Anniv of Portuguese Revolution.
527 **106** 10 a. multicoloured . . . . 3·00 90
528 1 p. multicoloured . . . . 12·00 3·00

107 Pou Chai Pagoda

1976. Pagodas. Multicoloured.
529 10 p. Type **107** . . . . 12·00 1·00
530 20 p. Tin Hau Pagoda . . . . 25·00 3·00

108 Symbolic Figure

1977. Legislative Assembly.
531 **108** 5 a. blue, dp blue & black 3·00 1·00
532 2 p. brown and black . . . 20·00 5·00
533 5 p. yellow, green & black 30·00 6·00

1979. Nos. 462, 464, 469, 482, 523 and 526 surch.
536 – 10 a. on 16 a. yellow, green and brown . . . . 3·00 75
537 – 30 a. on 39 a. multicoloured 5·00 90
538 **76** 30 a. on 39 a. multicoloured 45·00 7·50
539 – 30 a. on 60 a. multicoloured 3·00 1·25
540 **81** 70 a. on 76 a. multicoloured 8·50 2·00
541 – 2 p. on 2 p. 20 multicoloured 7·50 2·00

111 Camoes and Macao Harbour

113 Buddha and Macao Cathedral

1981. 400th Death Anniv (1980) of Camoes (Portuguese poet).
542 **111** 10 a. multicoloured 30 20
543 30 a. multicoloured 30 20
544 1 p. multicoloured . . . . 1·50 1·00
545 3 p. multicoloured . . . . 5·00 2·00

1981. Transcultural Psychiatry Symposium.
547 **113** 15 a. multicoloured 30 10
548 40 a. multicoloured 30 15
549 50 a. multicoloured 70 25
550 60 a. multicoloured 70 30
551 1 p. multicoloured . . . . 1·75 50
552 2 p. 20 multicoloured . . . 3·00 1·50

115 Health Services Buildings

1982. Buildings.
554 – 10 a. grey, blue & yellow . 15 10
555 – 20 a. black, green & lt grn . 15 10
556 **115** 30 a. green, grey & stone . 25 10
557 – 40 a. yellow, lt grn & grn . 25 10
558 – 60 a. orange, chocolate and brown 25 15
559 – 80 a. pink, green & brown . 40 10
560 – 90 a. purple, blue and red . 30 15
561 – 1 p. multicoloured 50 15
562 – 1 p. 50 yellow, brn & grey . 60 15
563 – 2 p. purple, ultramarine and blue . . . . 1·00 30
564 – 2 p. 50 ultramarine, pink and blue . . . . 1·00 30
565 – 3 p. yellow, green and olive . 85 30
566 – 7 p. 50 lilac, blue and red . 2·00 1·00
567 – 10 p. grey, lilac & mauve . 7·00 1·75
568 – 15 p. yellow, brown & red . 3·00 1·00

DESIGNS: 10 a. Social Welfare Institute; 20 a. Holy House of Mercy; 40 a. Guia lighthouse; 60 a. St. Lawrence's Church; 80 a. St. Joseph's Seminary; 90 a. Pedro V Theatre; 1 p. Cerco city gate; 1 p. 50, St. Domenico's Church; 2 p. Luis de Camoes Museum; 2 p. 50, Ruins of St. Paul's Church; 3 p. Palace of St. Sancha (Governor's residence); 7 p. 50, Senate House; 10 p. Schools Welfare Service building; 15 p. Barracks of the Moors (headquarters of Port Captaincy and Maritime Police).

116 Heng Ho (Moon goddess)

1982. Autumn Festival. Multicoloured.
569 40 a. Type **116** 45 40
560 1 p. Decorated gourds . . . . 1·40 60
561 2 p. Paper lantern . . . . . . 2·00 85
562 5 p. Warrior riding lion . . . . 5·00 1·00

117 Aerial View of Macao, Taipa and Coloane Islands

118 "Switchboard Operators" (Lou Sok Man)

1982. Macao's Geographical Situation. Multicoloured.
573 50 a. Type **117** 25 15
574 3 p. Map of South China . . . 3·50 1·50

1983. World Communications Year. Children's Drawings. Multicoloured.
575 60 a. Type **118** 30 10
576 3 p. Postman and pillar box (Lai Sok Pek) . . . . 1·50 60
577 6 p. Globe with methods of communication (Loi Chak Keong) . . . . 5·50 3·00

119 "Asclepias curassavica"

120 Galleon and Map of Macao (left)

1983. Medicinal Plants. Multicoloured.
578 20 a. Type **119** 30 15
579 40 a. "Acanthus ilicifolius" . . 60 25
580 60 a. "Melastoma sanguineum" 1·25 30
581 70 a. Indian lotus ("Nelumbo nucifera") . . . . 1·50 45
582 1 p. 50 "Bombax malabaricum" 3·00 1·00
583 2 p. 50 "Hibiscus mutabilis" 6·00 2·00

1983. 16th Century Portuguese Discoveries. Multicoloured.
585 4 p. Type **120** . . . . 2·00 1·25
586 4 p. Galleon, astrolabe and map of Macao (right) . . . . . 2·00 1·25
Nos. 585/6 were printed together, se-tenant, forming a composite design.

MINIMUM PRICE

The minimum price quoted is 10p which represents a handling charge rather than a basis for valuing common stamps. For further notes about prices see introductory pages.

121 Rat **122** Detail of First Macao Stamp, 1884

1984. New Year. "Year of the Rat".
587 **121** 60 a. multicoloured . . . . 7·50 3·00

1984. Centenary of Macao Stamps.
588 **122** 40 a. black and red . . . . 1·00 30
589 3 p. black and red . . . . 3·00 1·00
590 5 p. black and brown . . . 4·00 2·00

123 Jay

1984. "Ausipex 84" International Stamp Exhibition, Melbourne. Birds. Multicoloured.
592 30 a. White-breasted and common kingfishers . . . . 1·00 40
593 40 a. Type **123** . . . . 1·25 40
594 50 a. Japanese white eye . . . 1·50 60
595 70 a. Hoopoe . . . . 2·00 75
596 2 p. 50 Pekin robin . . . . . 6·00 1·25
597 6 p. Mallard . . . . 12·00 4·00

124 Hok Lou T'eng

1984. "Philakorea 84" International Stamp Exhibition, Seoul. Fishing Boats. Multicoloured.
598 20 a. Type **124** 25 20
599 60 a. Tai Tong 60 30
600 2 p. Tai Mei Chai . . . . . 1·50 70
601 5 p. Ch'at Pong T'o . . . . . 4·00 1·75

125 Ox and Moon **126** Open Hand with Stylized Doves

1985. New Year. Year of the Ox.
602 **125** 1 p. multicoloured . . . . 3·00 1·00

1985. International Youth Year. Multicoloured.
603 2 p. 50 Type **126** . . . . . . 1·50 50
604 3 p. Open hands and plants . . 2·00 75

127 Pres. Eanes

1985. Visit of President Ramalho Eanes of Portugal.
605 **127** 1 p. 50 multicoloured . . . 1·25 50

128 Riverside Scene **129** "Euploea midamus"

1985. 25th Anniv of Luis de Camoes Museum. Paintings by Cheng Chi Yun. Multicoloured.
606 2 p. 50 Type **128** . . . . . . 5·00 1·00
607 2 p. 50 Man on seat and boy filling jar from river . . . . . 5·00 1·00
608 2 p. 50 Playing harp in summerhouse . . . . . . 5·00 1·00
609 2 p. 50 Three men by river . . 5·00 1·00

1985. World Tourism Day. Butterflies. Mult.
610 30 a. Type **129** 50 20
611 50 a. Great orange-tip 50 30
612 70 a. "Lethe confusa" 85 30
613 2 p. Purple sapphire . . . . . 1·75 1·00
614 4 p. "Euthalia phemius seitzi" . . 3·00 1·50
615 7 p. 50 Common birdwing . . . 6·00 3·50

130 Tou (sailing barge) **131** Tiger and Moon

1985. "Italia '85" International Stamp Exhibition, Rome. Cargo Boats. Multicoloured.
617 50 a. Type **130** 50 30
618 70 a. "Veng Seng Lei" (motor junk) 70 30
619 1 p. "Tong Heng Long No. 2" (motor junk) . . . . . . 1·00 40
620 6 p. "Fong Vong San" (container ship) . . . . 5·00 3·00

1986. New Year. Year of the Tiger.
621 **131** 1 p. 50 multicoloured . . . 2·50 1·00

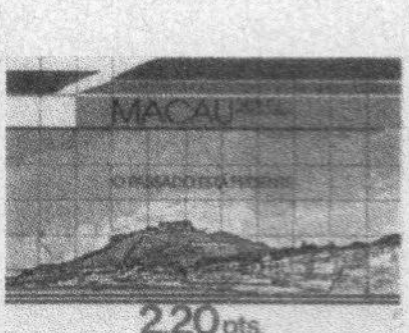
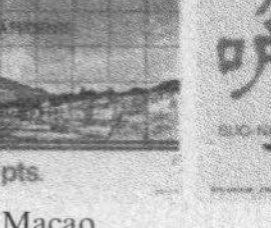

132 View of Macao **133** Suo-na

1986. Macao, "the Past is still Present".
622 **132** 2 p. 20 multicoloured . . . 2·00 75

1986. "Ameripex '86" International Stamp Exn, Chicago. Musical Instruments. Multicoloured.
623 20 a. Type **133** 30 15
624 50 a. Sheng (pipes) 35 25
625 60 a. Er-hu (bowed instrument) . 50 40
626 70 a. Ruan (string instrument) . 75 40
627 5 p. Cheng (harp) . . . . . . 7·50 2·50
628 8 p. Pi-pa (lute) . . . . 12·00 7·50

134 "Flying Albatros" (hydrofoil)

1986. "Stockholmia 86" International Stamp Exhibition. Passenger Ferries. Multicoloured.
630 10 a. Type **134** 25 40
631 40 a. "Tejo" (hovercraft) . . . 30 60
632 3 p. "Tercera" (jetfoil) . . . . 1·25 2·00
633 7 p. 50 "Cheung Kong" (high speed ferry) . . . . 3·50 5·00

135 Taipa Fortress **136** Sun Yat-sen

1986. 10th Anniv of Security Forces. Fortresses. Multicoloured.
634 2 p. Type **135** . . . . 2·50 1·60
635 2 p. St. Paul on the Mount . . 2·50 1·60
636 2 p. St. Francis . . . . 2·50 1·60
637 2 p. Guia . . . . 2·50 1·60
Nos. 634/7 were printed together, se-tenant, forming a composite design.

1986. 120th Birth Anniv of Dr. Sun Yat-sen.
638 **136** 70 a. multicoloured . . . . 2·00 1·00

137 Hare and Moon **138** Wa To (physician)

1987. New Year. Year of the Hare.
640 **137** 1 p. 50 multicoloured . . . 4·00 1·00

1987. Shek Wan Ceramics. Multicoloured.
641 2 p. 20 Type **138** . . . . . . 1·60 1·60
642 2 p. 20 Choi San, God of Fortune 1·60 1·60
643 2 p. 20 Yi, Sun God . . . . . 1·60 1·60
644 2 p. 20 Cung Kuei, Keeper of Demons . . . . 1·60 1·60

139 Boats

1987. Dragon Boat Festival. Multicoloured.
645 50 a. Type **139** 50 10
646 5 p. Dragon boat prow . . . . 3·00 1·50

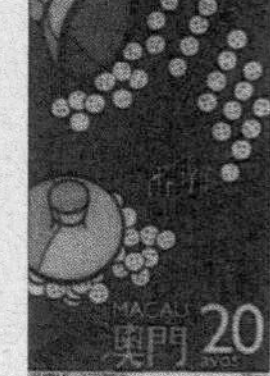

140 Circular Fan **141** Fantan

1987. Fans. Multicoloured.
647 30 a. Type **140** 30 15
648 70 a. Folding fan with tree design 60 25
649 1 p. Square-shaped fan with peacock design . . . . . . 4·00 1·25
650 6 p. Heart-shaped fan with painting of woman and tree 10·00 3·25

1987. Casino Games. Multicoloured.
652 20 a. Type **141** 25 15
653 40 a. Cussec 40 25
654 4 p. Baccarat . . . . 2·50 85
655 7 p. Roulette . . . . 8·00 2·10

142 Goods Hand-cart **143** Dragon and Moon

1987. Traditional Vehicles. Multicoloured.
656 10 a. Type **142** 30 10
657 70 a. Open sedan chair 50 10
658 90 a. Rickshaw . . . . 1·50 65
659 10 p. Cycle rickshaw . . . . . 7·25 1·60

1988. New Year. Year of the Dragon.
661 **143** 2 p. 50 multicoloured . . . 2·50 1·00

144 West European Hedgehog

1988. Protected Mammals. Multicoloured.
662 3 p. Type **144** . . . . 3·00 1·00
663 3 p. Eurasian badger . . . . . 3·00 1·00
664 3 p. European otter . . . . . 3·00 1·00
665 3 p. Chinese pangolin . . . . 3·00 1·00

145 Breastfeeding

1988. 40th Anniv of W.H.O. Multicoloured.
666 60 a. Type **145** 25 10
667 80 a. Vaccinating child 50 25
668 2 p. 40 Donating blood . . . . 2·00 65

146 Bicycles

1988. Transport. Multicoloured.
669 20 a. Type **146** 15 10
670 50 a. Lambretta and Vespa . . 25 10
671 3 p. 30 Open-sided motor car . 1·25 80
672 5 p. Renault delivery truck, 1912 2·50 1·50

147 Hurdling **148** Intelpost (electronic mail)

1988. Olympic Games, Seoul. Multicoloured.
674 40 a. Type **147** 30 10
675 60 a. Basketball 50 15
676 1 p. Football . . . . 1·50 65
677 8 p. Table tennis . . . . . . 4·50 1·60

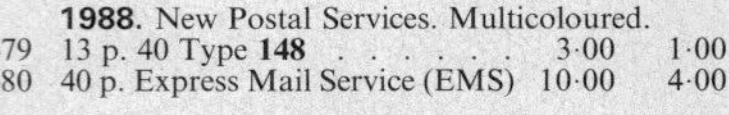

1988. New Postal Services. Multicoloured.
679 13 p. 40 Type **148** . . . . . . 3·00 1·00
680 40 p. Express Mail Service (EMS) 10·00 4·00

149 B.M.W. Saloon Car **150** Snake and Moon

1988. 35th Macao Grand Prix. Multicoloured.
681 80 a. Type **149** 25 15
682 2 p. 80 Motor cycle . . . . . 1·25 65
683 7 p. Formula 3 car . . . . . . 4·00 1·60

1989. New Year. Year of the Snake.
685 **150** 3 p. multicoloured . . . . . 1·75 45

151 Water Carrier **152** White Building

1989. Traditional Occupations (1st series). Multicoloured.
686 50 a. Type **151** 25 10
687 1 p. Tan-kya (boat) woman . . 40 15
688 4 p. Tin-tin man (pedlar) . . . 1·25 85
689 5 p. Tao-fu-fa (soya bean cheese) vendor . . . . 2·50 1·00
See also Nos. 714/17 and 743/6.

1989. Paintings by George Vitalievich Smirnoff in Luis Camoes Museum Multicoloured.
690 2 p. Type **152** 40 40
691 2 p. Building with railings . . . 40 40
692 2 p. Street scene 40 40
693 2 p. White thatched cottage . . 40 40

153 Common Cobra **154** Talu

1989. "Philexfrance 89" International Stamp Exhibition, Paris. Snakes of Macao. Mult.
694 2 p. 50 Type **153** 90 30
695 2 p. 50 Banded krait ("Bungarus fasciatus") 90 30
696 2 p. 50 Bamboo pit viper ("Trimeresurus albolabris") 90 30
697 2 p. 50 Rat snake ("Elaphe radiata") 90 30

1989. Traditional Games. Multicoloured.
698 10 a. Type **154** 15 10
699 60 a. Triol (marbles) 35 10
700 3 p. 30 Chiquia (shuttlecock) . 1·25 30
701 5 p. Chinese chequers . . . . 2·25 1·10

155 Piaggio P-136L Flying Boat **156** Malacca

1989. Aircraft. Multicoloured.

702 50 a. Type **155** 40 25
703 70 a. Martin M-130 flying boat . 40 25
704 2 p. 80 Fairey 111D seaplane . . 75 40
705 4 p. Hawker Osprey seaplane . . 2·00 1·25

1989. "World Stamp Expo '89" International Stamp Exhibition, Washington D.C. Portuguese Presence in Far East. Multicoloured.

707 40 a. Type **156** 15 10
708 70 a. Thailand 25 10
709 90 a. India 40 10
710 2 p. 50 Japan 75 35
711 7 p. 50 China . . . . 2·00 1·50

157 Horse and Moon **159** Long-finned Grouper ("Epinephelus megachir")

1990. New Year. Year of the Horse.

713 **157** 4 p. multicoloured . . . . 1·00 45

1990. Traditional Occupations (2nd series). As T **151**. Multicoloured.

714 30 a. Long-chau singer 15 10
715 70 a. Cobbler 25 10
716 1 p. 50 Travelling penman . . . 75 35
717 7 p. 50 Fisherman with wide nets 2·50 1·40

1990. Fishes. Multicoloured.

719 2 p. 40 Type **159** . . . . . 1·10 45
720 2 p. 40 Malabar snapper ("Lutianus malabaricus") . . 1·10 45
721 2 p. 40 Spotted snakehead ("Ophiocepalus maculatus") 1·10 45
722 2 p. 40 Paradise fish ("Macropodus opercularis") 1·10 45

160 Porcelain

1990. "New Zealand 1990" International Stamp Exhibition, Auckland. Industrial Diversification. Multicoloured.

723 3 p. Type **160** 30 30
724 3 p. Furniture 30 30
725 3 p. Toys . . . . 1·00 75
726 3 p. Artificial flowers 30 30

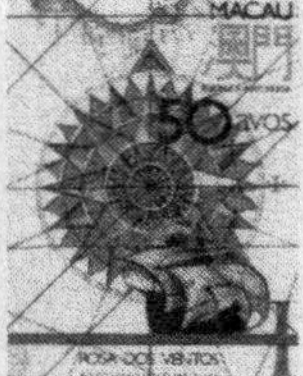

161 Cycling **162** Rose by Lazaro Luis

1990. 11th Asian Games, Peking. Multicoloured.

728 80 a. Type **161** 15 10
729 1 p. Swimming 25 10
730 3 p. Judo 75 30
731 4 p. 20 Shooting . . . . . . 1·75 1·00

1990. Compass Roses. Designs showing roses from ancient charts by cartographer named. Mult.

733 50 a. Type **162** 15 10
734 1 p. Diogo Homem 25 10
735 3 p. 50 Diogo Homem (different) 80 35
736 6 p. 50 Fernao Vaz Dourado . . 2·00 1·00

HAVE YOU READ THE NOTES AT THE BEGINNING OF THIS CATALOGUE?
These often provide answers to the enquiries we receive.

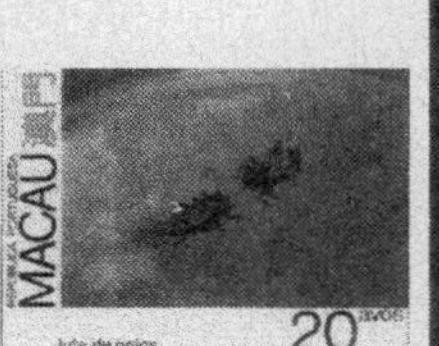

163 Cricket Fight **164** Goat and Moon

1990. Betting on Animals. Multicoloured.

738 20 a. Type **163** 20 10
739 80 a. Hwamei fight 45 15
740 1 p. Greyhound racing 75 25
741 10 p. Horse racing . . . . . 2·50 1·10

1991. New Year. Year of the Goat.

742 **164** 4 p. 50 multicoloured . . . 1·25 40

1991. Traditional Occupations (3rd series). As T **151**. Multicoloured.

743 80 a. Knife-grinder 25 10
744 1 p. 70 Flour-puppets vendor . . 50 25
745 3 p. 50 Street barber . . . . 1·00 50
746 4 p. 20 Fortune-teller . . . . 1·50 85

165 True Harp ("Harpa harpa")

1991. Sea Shells. Multicoloured.

747 3 p. Type **165** . . . . 1·25 40
748 3 p. Oil-lamp tun ("Tonna zonata") . . . . 1·25 40
749 3 p. Bramble murex ("Murex pecten") . . . . 1·25 40
750 3 p. Rose-branch murex ("Chicoreus rosarius") . . . 1·25 40

The Latin names on Nos. 749/50 are incorrect.

166 Character and Backcloth

1991. Chinese Opera. Multicoloured.

751 **166** 60 a. multicoloured 40 35
752 – 80 a. multicoloured 40 35
753 – 1 p. multicoloured 85 65
754 – 10 p. multicoloured . . . . 3·75 2·10

DESIGNS: Nos. 752/4, Different backcloths and costumes.

167 "Delonix regia" and Lou Lim Ioc Garden

1991. Flowers and Gardens (1st series). Mult.

755 1 p. 70 Type **167** 40 25
756 3 p. "Ipomoea cairica" and Sao Francisco Garden 75 50
757 3 p. 50 "Jasminum mesyi" and Sun Yat Sen Park 90 60
758 4 p. 20 "Bauhinia variegata" and Seac Pai Van Park . . . . 1·00 65

See also Nos. 815/18.

168 Portuguese Traders unloading Boats **169** Firework Display

1991. Cultural Exchange. Nambam Paintings attr. Kano Domi. Multicoloured.

760 4 p. 20 Type **168** . . . . . 1·00 55
761 4 p. 20 Portuguese traders displaying goods to buyers . . 1·00 40

1991. Christmas. Multicoloured.

763 1 p. 70 Type **169** 40 20
764 3 p. Father Christmas 60 40
765 3 p. 50 Man dancing 75 45
766 4 p. 20 January 1st celebrations 1·00 55

170 Concertina Door

1992. Doors and Windows. Multicoloured.

767 1 p. 70 Type **170** 40 20
768 3 p. Window with four shutters . 60 40
769 3 p. 50 Window with two shutters 75 45
770 4 p. 20 Louvred door . . . . 1·00 55

171 Monkey and Moon **172** T'it Kuai Lei

1992. New Year. Year of the Monkey.

771 **171** 4 p. 50 multicoloured . . . 1·00 60

1992. Gods of Chinese Mythology (1st series). Multicoloured.

772 3 p. 50 (1) Type **172** . . . . 1·25 1·00
773 3 p. 50 (2) Chong Lei Kun . . 1·25 1·00
774 3 p. 50 (3) Cheong Kuo Lou on donkey . . . . 1·25 1·00
775 3 p. 50 (4) Loi Tong Pan . . . 1·25 1·00

See also Nos. 796/9.

173 Lion Dance **174** High Jumping

1992. "World Columbian Stamp Expo '92", Chicago. Chinese Dances. Multicoloured.

776 1 p. Type **173** 20 10
777 2 p. 70 Lion dance (different) . 75 35
778 6 p. Dragon dance . . . . . 1·60 85

1992. Olympic Games, Barcelona. Multicoloured

779 80 a. Type **174** 20 10
780 4 p. 20 Badminton 80 55
781 4 p. 70 Roller hockey . . . . 1·00 60
782 5 p. Yachting . . . . 1·25 65

175 Na Cha Temple

1992. Temples (1st series). Multicoloured.

784 1 p. Type **175** 20 10
785 1 p. 50 Kun Iam 40 25
786 1 p. 70 Hong Kon 50 30
787 6 p. 50 A Ma . . . . 2·00 1·10

See also Nos. 792/5 and 894/8.

176 Tung Sin Tong Services **177** Rooster and Dragon

1992. Centenary of Tung Sin Tong (medical and educational charity).

788 **176** 1 p. multicoloured 35 20

1992. Portuguese–Chinese Friendship.

789 **177** 10 p. multicoloured . . . . 2·00 1·25

178 Red Junglefowl **179** Children carrying Banners

1992. New Year. Year of the Cock.

791 **178** 5 p. multicoloured . . . . 1·10 65

1993. Temples (2nd series). As T **175**. Mult.

792 50 a. T'am Kong 15 10
793 2 p. T'in Hau 40 25
794 3 p. 50 Lin Fong 75 45
795 8 p. Pau Kong . . . . . . 1·50 1·10

1993. Gods of Chinese Mythology (2nd series). As T **172**. Multicoloured.

796 3 p. 50 (1) Lam Ch'oi Wo flying on crane 75 45
797 3 p. 50 (2) Ho Sin Ku (goddess) on peach blossom 75 45
798 3 p. 50 (3) Hon Seong Chi crossing sea on basket of flowers 75 45
799 3 p. 50 (4) Ch'ou Kuok K'ao crossing river on plank . . . 75 45

1993. Chinese Wedding. Multicoloured.

800 3 p. Type **179** 50 40
801 3 p. Bride 50 40
802 3 p. Bridegroom 50 40
803 3 p. Wedding guests 50 40

Nos. 800/3 were issued together, se-tenant, forming a composite design.

180 Bird perched on Hand **181** Scops Owl

1993. Environmental Protection.

805 **180** 1 p. multicoloured 75 20

1993. Birds of Prey. Multicoloured.

806 3 p. Type **181** . . . . 2·25 40
807 3 p. Barn owl ("Tyto alba") . . 2·25 40
808 3 p. Peregrine falcon ("Falco peregrinus") . . . . 2·25 40
809 3 p. Golden eagle ("Aquila obrysaetos") . . . . 2·25 40

182 Town Hall

1993. Union of Portuguese-speaking Capital Cities.

811 **182** 1 p. 50 green, blue & red . . 50 20

183 Portuguese Missionaries

1993. 450th Anniv of First Portuguese Visit to Japan. Multicoloured.

812 50 a. Japanese man with musket . 20 10
813 3 p. Type **183** 60 40
814 3 p. 50 Traders carrying goods . 75 45

184 "Spathodea campanulata" and Luis de Camoes Garden

1993. Flowers and Gardens (2nd series). Multicoloured.
815 1 p. Type **184** 25 10
816 2 p. "Tithonia diversifolia" and Montanha Russa Garden . . 45 25
817 3 p. "Rhodomyrtus tomentosa" and Cais Garden 75 40
818 8 p. "Passiflora foetida" and Flora Garden . . . . 2·00 1·10

185 Caravel

1993. 16th-century Sailing Ships. Multicoloured.
820 1 p. Type **185** 25 10
821 2 p. Caravel (different) 45 25
822 3 p. 50 Nau 75 45
823 4 p. 50 Galleon . . . . 1·00 60

186 Saloon Car

1993. 40th Anniv of Macao Grand Prix. Multicoloured.
825 1 p. 50 Type **186** 30 20
826 2 p. Motor cycle 40 25
827 4 p. 50 Racing car 80 60

187 Chow-chow and Moon

1994. New Year. Year of the Dog.
828 **187** 5 p. multicoloured . . . . 1·00 65

188 Map and Prince Henry (½-size illustration)

1994. 600th Birth Anniv of Prince Henry the Navigator.
829 **188** 3 p. multicoloured 60 40

189 Lakeside Hut

1994. Birth Bicentenary of George Chinnery (artist). Multicoloured.
830 3 p. 50 Type **189** 60 45
831 3 p. 50 Fisherman on sea wall . . 60 45
832 3 p. 50 Harbour 60 45
833 3 p. 50 Sao Tiago Fortress . . . 60 45

190 Lai Sis Exchange

1994. Spring Festival of Lunar New Year. Multicoloured.
835 1 p. Type **190** 20 10
836 2 p. Flower and tangerine tree decorations 40 25
837 3 p. 50 Preparing family meal . 75 45
838 4 p. 50 Paper decorations bearing good wishes . . . . 1·00 60

191 "Longevity" **192** Footballer

1994. Legends and Myths (1st series). Chinese Gods. Multicoloured.
839 3 p. Type **191** 50 40
840 3 p. "Prosperity" 50 40
841 3 p. "Happiness" 50 40
See also Nos. 884/7, 930/2, 994/7 and 1035/8.

1994. World Cup Football Championship, U.S.A.
843 2 p. Type **192** 40 25
844 3 p. Tackling 60 40
845 3 p. 50 Heading ball 75 45
846 4 p. 50 Goalkeeper saving goal . 95 60

193 Rice Shop **194** Astrolabe

1994. Traditional Chinese Shops. Multicoloured.
848 1 p. Type **193** 20 10
849 1 p. 50 Medicinal tea shop . . 30 20
850 2 p. Salt-fish shop 50 25
851 3 p. 50 Pharmacy 90 45

1994. Nautical Instruments. Multicoloured.
852 3 p. Type **194** 60 40
853 3 p. 50 Quadrant 75 45
854 4 p. 50 Sextant . . . . . . 1·00 65

195 Fencing

1994. 12th Asian Games, Hiroshima, Japan. Multicoloured.
855 1 p. Type **195** 20 10
856 2 p. Gymnastics 45 25
857 3 p. Water-polo 70 40
858 3 p. 50 Pole vaulting 80 45

196 Nobre de Carvalho Bridge

1994. Bridges. Multicoloured.
859 1 p. Type **196** 20 10
860 8 p. Friendship Bridge . . . . 1·75 1·10

197 Carp **199** Pig and Moon

198 Angel's Head (stained glass window, Macao Cathedral)

1994. Good Luck Signs. Multicoloured.
861 3 p. Type **197** 70 40
862 3 p. 50 Peaches 75 45
863 4 p. 50 Water lily . . . . . 1·00 60

1994. Religious Art. Multicoloured.
864 50 a. Type **198** 15 10
865 1 p. Holy Ghost (stained glass window, Macao Cathedral) . 25 10
866 1 p. 50 Silver sacrarium 30 20
867 2 p. Silver salver 50 25
868 3 p. "Escape into Egypt" (ivory statuette) 75 40
869 3 p. 50 Gold and silver cup . . 85 45

1995. New Year. Year of the Pig.
870 **199** 5 p. 50 multicoloured . . . 1·00 70

200 "Lou Lim Iok Garden"

1995. Paintings of Macao by Lio Man Cheong. Multicoloured.
871 50 a. Type **200** 15 10
872 1 p. "Guia Fortress and Lighthouse" 20 10
873 1 p. 50 "Barra Temple" . . . 35 20
874 2 p. "Avenida da Praia, Taipa" . 45 25
875 2 p. 50 "Kun Iam Temple" . . 60 30
876 3 p. "St. Paul's Seminary" . . 70 40
877 3 p. 50 "Penha Hill" 80 45
878 4 p. "Gates of Understanding Monument" 90 50

201 Magnifying Glass over Goods

1995. World Consumer Day.
879 **201** 1 p. multicoloured 25 10

202 Pangolin **203** Kun Sai Iam

1995. Protection of Chinese ("Asian") Pangolin. Multicoloured.
880 1 p. 50 In fork of tree 35 20
881 1 p. 50 Hanging from tree by tail 35 20
882 1 p. 50 On leafy branch 35 20
883 1 p. 50 Type **202** 35 20

1995. Legends and Myths (2nd series). Kun Sai Iam (Buddhist god). Multicoloured.
884 3 p. Type **203** 50 40
885 3 p. Holding baby 50 40
886 3 p. Sitting behind water lily . . 50 40
887 3 p. With water lily and dragon-fish 70 40

204/7 Senado Square (½-size illustration)

1995. Senado Square.
889 **204** 2 p. multicoloured 55 25
890 **205** 2 p. multicoloured 55 25
891 **206** 2 p. multicoloured 55 25
892 **207** 2 p. multicoloured 55 25
Nos. 889/92 were issued together, se-tenant, forming the composite design illustrated.

1995. Temples (3rd series). As T **175**. Multicoloured.
894 50 a. Kuan Tai 10 10
895 1 p. Pak Tai 15 10
896 1 p. 50 Lin K'ai 25 20
897 3 p. Se Kam Tong 50 40
898 3 p. 50 Fok Tak 60 45

208 Pekin Robin ("Leiothrix lutea")

1995. "Singapore'95" International Stamp Exhibition. Birds. Multicoloured.
899 2 p. 50 Type **208** . . . . . . 1·10 30
900 2 p. 50 Japanese white eye ("Zosterops japonica") . . . . 1·10 30
901 2 p. 50 Canary ("Serinus canarius canarius") . . . . 1·10 30
902 2 p. 50 Nightingale ("Gurrulax canonus") . . . . 1·10 30

209 Pipa

1995. International Music Festival. Musical Instruments. Multicoloured.
904 1 p. Type **209** 60 10
905 1 p. Erhu (string instrument) . 60 10
906 1 p. Gong (hand-held drum) . . 60 10
907 1 p. Sheng (string instrument) . 60 10
908 1 p. Xiao (flute) 60 10
909 1 p. Tambor (drum) 60 10

210 Anniversary Emblem, World Map and U.N. Headquarters, New York

1995. 50th Anniv of United Nations Organization.
911 **210** 4 p. 50 multicoloured . . . 75 60

211 Terminal Building

1995. Inauguration of Macao International Airport. Multicoloured.
912 1 p. Type **211** 15 10
913 1 p. 50 Terminal (different) . . 25 20
914 2 p. Loading airplane and cargo building 35 20
915 3 p. Control tower 50 40

212 Rat **213** Cage

1996. New Year. Year of the Rat.
918 **212** 5 p. multicoloured 85 65

1996. Traditional Chinese Cages.
920 **213** 1 p. multicoloured 15 10
921 – 1 p. 50 multicoloured . . . 25 20
922 – 3 p. multicoloured 50 40
923 – 4 p. 50 multicoloured . . . 75 60
DESIGNS: 1 p. 50 to 4 p. 50, Different cages.

214 Street **215** Tou Tei (God of Earth)

1996. Paintings of Macao by Herculano Estorninho. Multicoloured.
925 50 a. Fishing boats (horiz) . . . 10 10
926 1 p. 50 Town square 25 20
927 3 p. Type **214** 50 40
928 5 p. Townscape (horiz) 85 65

1996. Legends and Myths (3rd series). Multicoloured.
930 3 p. 50 Type **215** 60 45
931 3 p. 50 Choi San (God of Fortune) 60 45
932 3 p. 50 Chou Kuan (God of the Kitchen) 60 45

216 Customers

1996. Traditional Chinese Tea Houses. Multicoloured.
934 2 p. Type **216** 35 25
935 2 p. Waiter with tray of steamed stuffed bread 35 25
936 2 p. Newspaper vendor 35 25
937 2 p. Waiter pouring tea at table . 35 25
Nos. 934/7 were issued together, se-tenant, forming a composite design.

217 Get Well Soon

1996. Greetings stamps. Multicoloured.
939 50 a. Type **217** 10 10
940 1 p. 50 Congratulations on new baby 25 20
941 3 p. Happy birthday 50 40
942 4 p. Wedding congratulations . 65 50

218 Swimming

1996. Olympic Games, Atlanta, U.S.A. Multicoloured.
943 2 p. Type **218** 35 25
944 3 p. Football 50 40
945 3 p. 50 Gymnastics 60 45
946 4 p. 50 Sailboarding 75 60

219 Crane (civil, 1st rank)

1996. Civil and Military Insignia of the Mandarins (1st series). Multicoloured.
948 2 p. 50 Type **219** 40 30
949 2 p. 50 Lion (military, 2nd rank) 40 30
950 2 p. 50 Golden pheasant (civil, 2nd rank) 40 30
951 2 p. 50 Leopard (military, 3rd rank) 40 30
See also Nos. 1061/4.

220 Trawler with Multiple Nets

1996. Nautical Sciences: Fishing Nets. Multicoloured.
952 3 p. Type **220** 50 40
953 3 p. Modern trawler with net from stern 50 40
954 3 p. Two sailing junks with common net 50 40
955 3 p. Junk with two square nets at sides 50 40
Nos. 952/5 were issued together, se-tenant, forming a composite design.

221 National Flag and Statue

1996. 20th Anniv of Legislative Assembly.
956 **221** 2 p. 80 multicoloured . . . 45 35

222 Dragonfly

1996. Paper Kites. Multicoloured.
958 3 p. 50 Type **222** 55 45
959 3 p. 50 Butterfly 55 45
960 3 p. 50 Owl 55 45
961 3 p. 50 Swallow 55 45

223 Doll 224 Ox

1996. Traditional Chinese Toys. Multicoloured.
963 50 a. Type **223** 10 10
964 1 p. Fish 20 10
965 3 p. Painted doll 50 40
966 4 p. 50 Dragon 70 55

1997. New Year. Year of the Ox.
967 **224** 5 p. 50 multicoloured . . . 85 65

225 Colourful and Gold Twos

1997. Lucky Numbers. Multicoloured.
969 2 p. Type **225** 30 25
970 2 p. 80 Eights 45 35
971 3 p. Threes 45 35
972 3 p. 90 Nines 65 50

226 "Sail Boats" 227 Elderly Woman

1997. Paintings of Macao by Kwok Se. Multicoloured.
974 2 p. Type **226** 30 25
975 3 p. "Fortress on the Hill" . . 45 35
976 3 p. 50 "Asilum" 55 40
977 4 p. 50 "Portas do Cerco" . . . 70 55

1997. Tan-Ka (boat) People. Multicoloured.
979 1 p. Type **227** 15 10
980 1 p. 50 Elderly woman holding tiller 20 15
981 2 p. 50 Woman with child on back 35 25
982 5 p. 50 Man mending fishing nets 80 60

228 Entrance to Temple 229 Dragon Dancers

1997. A-Ma Temple. Multicoloured.
983 3 p. 50 Type **228** 50 40
984 3 p. 50 Wall and terraces of Temple 50 40
985 3 p. 50 View of incense smoke through gateway 50 40
986 3 p. 50 Incense smoke emanating from pagoda 50 40

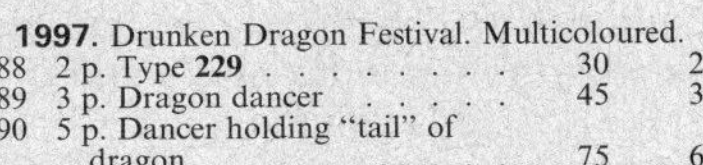

1997. Drunken Dragon Festival. Multicoloured.
988 2 p. Type **229** 30 20
989 3 p. Dragon dancer 45 35
990 5 p. Dancer holding "tail" of dragon 75 60

230 Frois with Japanese Man

1997. 400th Death Anniv of Father Luis Frois (author of "The History of Japan"). Multicoloured.
992 2 p. 50 Type **230** 35 25
993 2 p. 50 Father Frois and church (vert) 35 25

231 Wat Lot

1997. Legends and Myths (4th series). Door Gods. Multicoloured.
994 2 p. 50 Type **231** 35 25
995 2 p. 50 San Su 35 25
996 2 p. 50 Chon Keng 35 25
997 2 p. 50 Wat Chi Kong 35 25

232 Globe and First Aid and Family Health School

1997. 77th Anniv of Macao Red Cross.
999 **232** 1 p. 50 multicoloured . . . 20 15

233 Balconies

1997. Balconies.
1000 **233** 50 a. multicoloured . . . 10 10
1001 – 1 p. multicoloured . . . 15 10
1002 – 1 p. 50 multicoloured . . . 20 15
1003 – 2 p. multicoloured . . . 30 20
1004 – 2 p. 50 multicoloured . . . 35 25
1005 – 3 p. multicoloured . . . 45 35
DESIGNS: 1 p. to 3 p. Various balcony styles.

234 Plant Leaf Fan

1997. Fans. Multicoloured.
1007 50 a. Type **234** 10 10
1008 1 p. Paper fan 15 10
1009 3 p. 50 Silk fan 50 40
1010 4 p. Feather fan 60 45

235 Wood 236 Kung Fu

1997. Feng Shui. The Five Elements. Multicoloured.
1012 50 a. Type **235** 10 10
1013 1 p. Fire 15 10
1014 1 p. 50 Earth 20 15
1015 2 p. Metal 30 20
1016 2 p. 50 Water 35 25

1997. Martial Arts. Multicoloured.
1018 1 p. 50 Type **236** 20 15
1019 3 p. 50 Judo 50 40
1020 4 p. Karate 60 45

237 Tiger

1998. New Year. Year of the Tiger.
1021 **237** 5 p. 50 multicoloured . . 80 65

238 Soup Stall

1998. Street Traders. Multicoloured.
1023 1 p. Type **238** 15 10
1024 1 p. 50 Snack stall 25 20
1025 2 p. Clothes stall 30 20
1026 2 p. 50 Balloon stall 40 30
1027 3 p. Flower stall 45 35
1028 3 p. 50 Fruit stall 55 40

239 Beco da Se

1998. Gateways. Multicoloured.
1030 50 a. Type **239** 10 10
1031 1 p. Patio da Ilusao 15 10
1032 3 p. 50 Travessa das galinhas . 55 40
1033 4 p. Beco das Felicidades . . . 60 45

240 Woman and Child

1998. Legends and Myths (5th series). Gods of Ma Chou. Multicoloured.
1035 4 p. Type **240** 60 45
1036 4 p. Woman and man's face in smoke 60 45
1037 4 p. Woman with children playing instruments 60 45
1038 4 p. Goddess and sailing barges 60 45

241 "Sao Gabriel" (flagship)

1998. 500th Anniv of Vasco da Gama's Voyage to India via Cape of Good Hope. Multicoloured. (a) Wrongly dated "1598 1998".
1040 1 p. Type **241** 15 10
1041 1 p. 50 Vasco da Gama . . . 25 20
1042 2 p. "Sao Gabriel" and map of India 30 20

(b) Correctly dated "1498 1998".
1044 1 p. Type **241** 15 10
1045 1 p. 50 As No. 1041 . . . . . 25 20
1046 2 p. As No. 1042 . . . . . . 30 20

242 Mermaid and Caravel

1998. International Year of the Ocean. Multicoloured.
1048 2 p. 50 Type **242** 40 30
1049 3 p. Whale and oil-rig 45 35

243 Players

1998. World Cup Football Championship, France. Multicoloured.

1051 3 p. Type **243** 45 35
1052 3 p. 50 Players competing for ball 55 40
1053 4 p. Player kicking ball clear while being tackled 60 45
1054 4 p. 50 Player beating another to ball 70 55

244 Lio Seak Chong Mask

1998. Chinese Opera Masks. Multicoloured.

1056 1 p. 50 Type **244** 25 20
1057 2 p. Wat Chi Kong 30 20
1058 3 p. Kam Chin Pao 45 35
1059 5 p. Lei Kwai 75 60

1998. Civil and Military Insignia of the Mandarins (2nd series). As T **219**. Multicoloured.

1061 50 a. Lion (military, 2nd rank) 10 10
1062 1 p. Bear (military, 5th rank) 15 10
1063 1 p. 50 Golden pheasant (civil, 2nd rank) 25 20
1064 2 p. Silver pheasant (civil, 5th rank) 30 20

245 Smiling Buddha

1998. Kun Iam Temple. Multicoloured.

1066 3 p. 50 Type **245** 55 40
1067 3 p. 50 Pavilion and temple gardens 55 40
1068 3 p. 50 Temple gateway 55 40
1069 3 p. 50 Pagoda, stream and gardens 55 40

Nos. 1066/9 were issued together, se-tenant, forming a composite design.

246 Carriage in Street

1998. Paintings of Macao by Didier Rafael Bayle. Multicoloured.

1071 2 p. Type **246** 30 20
1072 3 p. Street (horiz) 45 35
1073 3 p. 50 Building (horiz) 55 40
1074 4 p. 50 Kiosk in square 70 55

247 Dragon

1998. Tiles by Eduardo Nery (from panel at Departure Lounge of Macao Airport). Multicoloured.

1076 1 p. Type **247** 15 10
1077 1 p. 50 Galleon 25 20
1078 2 p. 50 Junk 40 30
1079 5 p. 50 Phoenix 85 65

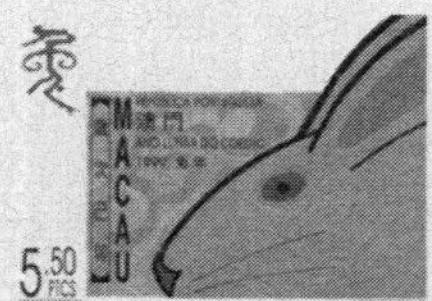

248 Rabbit

1999. New Year. Year of the Rabbit.

1081 **248** 5 p. 50 multicoloured 85 65

249 Jia Bao Yu

1999. Literature. Characters from "A Dream of Red Mansions" by Cao Xue Qin. Multicoloured.

1083 2 p. Type **249** 30 25
1084 2 p. Lin Dai Yu holding pole and cherry blossom 30 25
1085 2 p. Bao Chai holding fan 30 25
1086 2 p. Wang Xi Feng sitting in chair 30 25
1087 2 p. You San Jie holding sword 30 25
1088 2 p. Qing Wen sewing "pea-cock" cloak 30 25

250 Sailing Ships

1999. "Australia'99" International Stamp Exhibition, Melbourne. Oceans and Maritime Heritage. Multicoloured.

1090 1 p. 50 Type **250** 25 20
1091 2 p. 50 Marine life 40 30

251 De Havilland D.H.9 Biplane

1999. 75th Anniv of Sarmento de Beires and Brito Pais's Portugal–Macao Flight. Multicoloured.

1093 3 p. Breguet 16 Bn2 Patria 45 35
1094 3 p. Type **251** 45 35

252 Carrying Containers on Yoke

1999. The Water Carrier. Multicoloured.

1096 1 p. Type **252** 10 10
1097 1 p. 50 Filling containers from pump 10 10
1098 2 p. Lowering bucket down well 30 25
1099 2 p. 50 Filling containers from tap 40 30

253 "Sea-Me-We-3" Undersea Fibre Optic Cable

1999. Telecommunications Services. Multicoloured.

1101 50 a. Type **253** 10 10
1102 1 p. Dish aerial at Satellite Earth Station 10 10
1103 3 p. 50 Analogue mobile phone 55 45
1104 4 p. Televisions 60 50
1105 4 p. 50 Internet and e-mail 70 55

254 Macao Cultural Centre

1999. Modern Buildings. Multicoloured.

1107 1 p. Type **254** 10 10
1108 1 p. 50 Museum of Macao 25 20
1109 2 p. Macao Maritime Museum 30 25
1110 2 p. 50 Ferry Terminal 40 30
1111 3 p. Macao University 45 35
1112 3 p. 50 Public Administration building (vert) 55 45
1113 4 p. 50 Macao World Trade Centre (vert) 70 55
1114 5 p. Coloane kart-racing track (vert) 75 60
1115 8 p. Bank of China (vert) 1·25 1·00
1116 12 p. National Overseas Bank (vert) 1·90 1·50

255 Health Department

1999. Classified Buildings in Tap Seac District. Multicoloured.

1117 1 p. 50 Type **255** 25 20
1118 1 p. 50 Central Library (face value in salmon) 25 20
1119 1 p. 50 Centre of Modern Art of the Orient Foundation (face value in yellow) 25 20
1120 1 p. 50 Portuguese Institute of the Orient (face value in light blue) 25 20

Nos. 1117/20 were issued together, se-tenant, forming a composite design.

256 Teapot and Plate of Food

258 Chinese and Portuguese Ships, Christ's Cross and Yin Yang

257 "Portuguese Sailor and Chinese Woman" (Lagoa Henriques), Company of Jesus Square

1999. Dim Sum. Multicoloured.

1122 2 p. 50 Type **256** 40 30
1123 2 p. 50 Plates of food, chop-sticks and left half of bowls 40 30
1124 2 p. 50 Plates of food, glass, cups and right half of bowls 40 30
1125 2 p. 50 Plates of food and large teapot 40 30

Nos. 1122/5 were issued together, se-tenant, forming a composite design.

1999. Contemporary Sculptures. Multicoloured.

1127 1 p. Type **257** 10 10
1128 1 p. 50 "The Gate of Understanding" (Charters de Almeida), Praia Grande Bay (vert) 25 20
1129 2 p. 50 "Statue of the Goddess Kun Iam" (Cristina Leiria), Macao Cultural Centre (vert) 40 30
1130 3 p. 50 " Taipa Viewing Point" (Dorita Castel-Branco), Nobre de Carvalho Bridge, Taipa 55 45

1999. Portuguese–Chinese Cultural Mix. Mult.

1132 1 p. Type **258** 10 10
1133 1 p. 50 Ah Mah Temple and Portuguese and Macanese architecture 25 20
1134 2 p. Bridge, steps and Chinese architecture 30 25
1135 3 p. Macanese architecture and Portuguese terrace 45 35

Nos. 1132/5 were issued together, se-tenant, forming a composite design.

INDEX
Countries can be quickly located by referring to the index at the end of this volume.

259 Globe

1999. Macao Retrospective. Multicoloured.

1137 1 p. Type **259** 10 10
1138 1 p. 50 Roof terrace 25 20
1139 2 p. Portuguese and Chinese people 30 25
1140 3 p. 50 Modern Macao 55 45

CHARITY TAX STAMPS

The notes under this heading in Portugal also apply here.

43

C 48 Our Lady of Charity (altarpiece, Macao Cathedral)

1919. Fiscal stamp optd **TAXA DE GUERRA**

C305 **43** 2 a. green 7·50 5·00
C306 11 a. green 10·00 7·50

The above was for use in Timor as well as Macao.

1925. As Marquis de Pombal issue of Portugal but inscr "MACAU".

C329 C **73** 2 a. red 2·00 1·00
C330 – 2 a. red 2·00 1·25
C331 C **75** 2 a. red 2·00 1·75

1930. No gum.

C332 C **48** 5 a. brown and buff 40·00 30·00

1945. As Type C **48** but values in Arabic and Chinese numerals left and right, at bottom of design. No gum.

C486 1 a. olive and green 1·00 25
C487 2 a. purple and grey 1·00 25
C415 5 a. brown and yellow 30·00 30·00
C416 5 a. blue and light blue 42·00 38·00
C417 10 a. green and light green 28·00 18·00
C488 10 a. blue and green 1·75 25
C418 15 a. orange & lt orange 28·00 18·00
C419 20 a. red and orange 42·00 35·00
C489 20 a. brown and yellow 3·00 40
C420 50 a. lilac and buff 42·00 35·00
C472 50 a. red and pink 30·00 10·00

1981. No. C487 and similar higher (fiscal) values surch **20 avos** and Chinese characters.

C546 20 a. on 2 a. purple on grey 4·00 2·00
C534 20 a. on 1 p. green & lt grn 4·00 1·25
C535 20 a. on 3 p. black and pink 4·00 1·25
C536 20 a. on 5 p. brown & yellow

1981. No. C418 surch **10 avos** and Chinese characters.

C553 10 a. on 15 a. orange and light orange 4·00 2·50

NEWSPAPER STAMPS

1892. "Embossed" key-type of Macao surch **JORNAES** and value. No gum.

N73 Q $2\frac{1}{2}$ r. on 10 r. green 15·00 5·00
N74 $2\frac{1}{2}$ r. on 40 r. brown 15·00 5·00
N75 $2\frac{1}{2}$ r. on 80 r. grey 15·00 5·00

1893. "Newspaper" key-type inscr "Macau".

N80 V $2\frac{1}{2}$ r. brown 4·00 3·00

1894. "Newspaper" key-type of Macao surch $\frac{1}{2}$ **avo PROVISORIO** and Chinese characters.

N82 V $\frac{1}{2}$ a. on $2\frac{1}{2}$ r. brown 8·00 6·00

POSTAGE DUE STAMPS

1904. "Due" key-type inscr "MACAU". No gum (12 a. to 1p.), with or without gum (others).

D184 W $\frac{1}{2}$ a. green 1·25 1·00
D185 1 a. green 1·25 1·00
D186 2 a. grey 1·25 1·00
D187 4 a. brown 1·25 1·00
D188 5 a. orange 2·50 1·50
D189 8 a. brown 2·50 1·50
D190 12 a. brown 3·00 2·00
D191 20 a. blue 7·50 5·00
D192 40 a. red 8·00 5·50
D193 50 a. orange 18·00 12·00
D194 1 p. lilac 35·00 20·00

1911. "Due" key-types of Macao optd **REPUBLICA**.

D204 W $\frac{1}{2}$ a. green 1·00 90
D205 1 a. green 1·00 90
D206 2 a. grey 1·00 90
D207 4 a. brown 1·00 90
D208 5 a. orange 1·00 90
D209 8 a. brown 1·00 90
D287 12 a. brown 3·00 1·50
D211 20 a. blue 5·00 2·50
D212 40 a. red 10·00 5·00
D290 50 a. orange 15·00 7·00
D291 1 p. lilac 12·00 10·00

1925. Marquis de Pombal issue, as Nos. C329/31 optd **MULTA**.

D329	C **73**	4 a. red	2·00	1·50
D330	–	4 a. red	2·00	1·50
D331	C **75**	4 a. red	2·00	1·50

1947. As Type D **1** of Portuguese Colonies, but inscr "MACAU".

D410	D **1**	1 a. black and purple	45	20
D411		2 a. black and violet	45	20
D412		4 a. black and blue	80	45
D413		5 a. black and brown	80	45
D414		8 a. black and purple	1·25	80
D415		12 a. black and brown	2·10	1·60
D416		20 a. black and green	4·00	2·50
D417		40 a. black and red	6·75	3·25
D418		50 a. black and yellow	9·25	3·25
D419		1 p. black and blue	18·00	3·25

1949. Postage stamps of 1934 surch **PORTEADO** and new value.

D424	**50**	1 a. on 4 a. black	2·00	85
D425		2 a. on 6 a. brown	2·00	85
D426		4 a. on 8 a. blue	2·00	85
D427		5 a. on 10 a. red	2·00	85
D428		8 a. on 12 a. blue	4·00	1·25
D429		12 a. on 30 a. green	6·00	3·00
D430		20 a. on 40 a. violet	10·00	5·75

1951. Optd **PORTEADO** or surch also.

D439	**66**	1 a. yellow on cream	1·75	40
D440		2 a. green on green	1·75	85
D441		7 a. on 10 a. mauve on green	1·75	85

D **70**

1952. Numerals in red. Name in black.

D451	D **70**	1 a. blue and green	40	15
D452		3 a. brown and salmon	40	15
D453		5 a. slate and blue	40	15
D454		10 a. red and blue	85	85
D455		30 a. blue and brown	1·60	1·25
D456		1 p. brown & grey	3·25	1·60

MACEDONIA Pt. 3

Part of Austro-Hungarian Empire until 1918 when it became part of Yugoslavia. Separate stamps were issued during German Occupation in the Second World War.

In 1991 Macedonia became an independent republic.

A. GERMAN OCCUPATION

100 stotinki = 1 lev

Македония
8. IX. 1944
1 лв.
(G 1)

1944. Stamps of Bulgaria, 1940-44. (a) Surch as Type G 1.

G1 1 l. on 10 st. orange . . . . . . 3·50 14·00
G2 3 l. on 15 st. blue . . . . . . 3·50 14·00

(b) Surch similar to Type G 1 but larger.

G3 6 l. on 10 st. blue . . . . . . 4·00 18·00
G4 9 l. on 15 st. green . . . . . . 4·00 18·00
G5 9 l. on 15 st. green . . . . . . 5·00 24·00
G6 15 l. on 4 l. black . . . . . . 12·00 50·00
G7 20 l. on 7 l. blue . . . . . . 12·00 50·00
G8 30 l. on 14 l. brown . . . . . 20·00 50·00

B. INDEPENDENT REPUBLIC

1991. 100 paras = 1 dinar
1992. 100 deni (de.) = 1 denar (d.)

1 Trumpeters

2 Emblems and Inscriptions

1991. Obligatory Tax. Independence.
1 **1** 2 d. 50 black and orange . . . 35 35

1992. Obligatory Tax. Anti-cancer Week. (a) T **2** showing Red Cross symbol at bottom left.

2 **2** 5 d. mauve, black and blue . . 55 55
3 – 5 d. multicoloured 55 55
4 – 5 d. multicoloured 55 55
5 – 5 d. multicoloured 55 55

DESIGNS: No. 3, Flowers, columns and scanner; 4, Scanner and couch; 5, Computer cabinet.

(b) As T **2** but with right-hand inscr reading down instead of up and without Red Cross symbol.

6 5 d. mauve, black & blue (as No. 2) 25 25
7 5 d. multicoloured (as No. 3) . . 25 25
8 5 d. multicoloured (as No. 4) . . 25 25
9 5 d. multicoloured (as No. 5) . . 25 25

3 Red Cross Aircraft dropping Supplies

1992. Obligatory Tax. Red Cross Week. Multicoloured.

10 10 d. Red Cross slogans (dated "08–15 MAJ 1992" 15 15
11 10 d. Type **3** 15 15
12 10 d. Treating road accident victim 15 15
13 10 d. Evacuating casualties from ruined building 15 15

The three pictoral designs are taken from children's paintings.

4 "Skopje Earthquake"

6 Nurse with Baby

5 "Wood-carvers Petar and Makarie" (icon), St. Joven Bigorsk Monastery, Debar

1992. Obligatory Tax. Solidarity Week.

14 **4** 20 d. black and mauve . . . 15 15
15 – 20 d. multicoloured 15 15
16 – 20 d. multicoloured 15 15
17 – 20 d. multicoloured 15 15

DESIGNS: No. 15, Red Cross nurse with child; 16, Mothers carrying toddlers at airport; 17, Family at airport.

1992. 1st Anniv of Independence.

18 **5** 30 d. multicoloured 35 35

For 40 d. in same design see No. 33.

1992. Obligatory Tax. Anti-tuberculosis Week. Multicoloured.

19 20 d. Anti-tuberculosis slogans (dated "14–21.IX.1992") . . . 10 10
20 20 d. Type **6** 10 10
21 20 d. Nurse giving oxygen . . . 10 10
22 20 d. Baby in cot 10 10

7 "The Nativity" (fresco, Slepce Monastery)

9 Radiography Equipment

8 Mixed Bouquet

1992. Christmas. Multicoloured.

23 100 d. Type **7** 50 50
24 500 d. "Madonna and Child" (fresco), Zrze Monastery . . . 1·75 1·75

1993. Obligatory Tax. Red Cross Fund. Multicoloured.

25 20 d. Red Cross slogans 10 10
26 20 d. Marguerites 10 10
27 20 d. Carnations 10 10
28 20 d. Type **8** 10 10

1993. Obligatory Tax. Anti-cancer Week. Multicoloured.

29 20 d. Anti-cancer slogans (dated "1–8 MART 1993") 10 10
30 20 d. Type **9** 10 10
31 20 d. Overhead treatment unit . 10 10
32 20 d. Scanner 10 10

1993. As No. 18 but changed value.

33 **5** 40 d. multicoloured 40 40

10 Macedonian Flag

1993.

34 **10** 10 d. multicoloured 10 10
35 40 d. multicoloured 45 45
36 50 d. multicoloured 55 55

11 Macedonian Roach

1993. Fishes from Lake Ohrid. Multicoloured.

37 50 d. Type **11** 15 15
38 100 d. Lake Ohrid salmon . . . 20 20
39 1000 d. Type **11** . . . . . 2·00 2·00
40 2000 d. As No. 38 . . . . . 3·00 3·00

12 Crucifix, St. George's Monastery

1993. Easter.

41 **12** 300 d. multicoloured 70 70

13 Diagram of Telecommunications Cable and Map

1993. Opening of Trans-Balkan Telecommunications Line.

42 **13** 500 d. multicoloured 70 70

14 Red Cross Worker with Baby

1993. Obligatory Tax. Red Cross Week. Multicoloured.

43 50 d. Red Cross inscriptions (dated "08–15 MAJ 1993") 10 10
44 50 d. Type **14** 10 10
45 50 d. Physiotherapist and child in wheelchair 10 10
46 50 d. Stretcher party 10 10

See also No. 73.

15 Unloading U.N.I.C.E.F. Supplies from Lorry

1993. Obligatory Tax. Solidarity Week.

47 – 50 de. black, mauve and silver 10 10
48 **15** 50 de. multicoloured 10 10
49 – 50 de. multicoloured 10 10
50 – 50 de. multicoloured 10 10

DESIGNS: No. 47, "Skopje Earthquake"; 49, Labelling parcels in warehouse; 50, Consignment of parcels on fork-lift truck.

See also No. 72.

16 U.N. Emblem and Rainbow

1993. Admission to United Nations Organization.

51 **16** 10 d. multicoloured . . . . 1·00 1·00

17 "Insurrection" (detail) (B. Lazeski)

19 Tapestry

18 Children in Meadow

1993. 90th Anniv of Macedonian Insurrection.

52 **17** 10 d. multicoloured . . . . 1·00 1·00

1993. Obligatory Tax. Anti-tuberculosis Week. Multicoloured.

54 50 de. Anti-tuberculosis slogans (dated "14–21.09.1993") . . 10 10
55 50 de. Type **18** 10 10
56 50 de. Bee on flower 10 10
57 50 de. Goat behind boulder . . 10 10

See also No. 71.

1993. Centenary of Founding of Inner Macedonia Revolutionary Organization.

58 **19** 4 d. multicoloured 30 30

20 "The Nativity" (fresco from St. George's Monastery, Rajcica)

1993. Christmas. Multicoloured.

60 2 d. Type **20** 25 25
61 20 d. "The Three Kings" (fresco from Slepce Monastery) . . . 1·00 1·00

21 Lily

1994. Obligatory Tax. Anti-cancer Week. Multicoloured.

62 1 d. Red Cross and anti-cancer emblems 10 10
63 1 d. Type **21** 10 10
64 1 d. Caesar's mushroom 20 20
65 1 d. Mute swans on lake 20 20

1994. Nos. 1, 18 and 34 surch.

66 **5** 2 d. on 30 d. multicoloured . . 15 15
67 **1** 8 d. on 2 d. 50 black and orange 40 40
68 **6** 15 d. on 10 d. multicoloured . 70 70

23 Decorated Eggs

24 Kosta Racin (writer)

1994. Easter.

69 **23** 2 d. multicoloured 25 25

1994. Obligatory Tax. Red Cross Week. As previous designs but values, and date (70), changed. Multicoloured.

70 1 d. Red Cross inscriptions (dated "8–15 MAJ 1994") 10 10
71 1 d. Type **18** 10 10
72 1 d. As No. 50 . . . . 10 10
73 1 d. Type **14** 10 10

1994. Revolutionaries. Portraits by Dimitar Kondovski. Multicoloured.

74 8 d. Type **24** 45 45
75 15 d. Grigor Prlicev (writer) . . 1·00 1·00
76 20 d. Nikola Vaptsarov (Bulgarian poet) . . . . . . 1·75 1·75
77 50 d. Goce Delcev (founder of Internal Macedonian–Odrin Revolutionary Organization) . 2·40 2·40

25 "Skopje Earthquake"

26 Tree and Family

1994. Obligatory Tax. Solidarity Week.

78 **25** 1 d. black, red and silver . . 10 10

1994. Census.

79 **26** 2 d. multicoloured 25 25

27 St. Prohor Pcinski Monastery (venue)

28 Swimmer

1994. 50th Anniv of Macedonian National Liberation Council.

80 **27** 5 d. multicoloured 30 30

1994. Swimming Marathon, Ohrid.

82 **28** 8 d. multicoloured 45 45

29 Turkish Cancellation and 1992 30 d. Stamp on Cover

1994. 150th Anniv (1993) of Postal Service in Macedonia.
83 **29** 2 d. multicoloured 20 20

30 Mastheads

1994. 50th Anniversaries of "Nova Makedonija", "Mlad Borec" and "Makedonka" (newspapers).
84 **30** 2 d. multicoloured 25 25

31 Open Book

1994. 50th Anniv of St. Clement of Ohrid Library. Multicoloured.
85 2 d. Type **31** 15 15
86 10 d. Page of manuscript (vert) . 50 50

32 Globe

33 Wireless and Gramophone Record

1994. Obligatory Tax. Anti-AIDS Week.
87 – 2 d. red and black 10 10
88 **32** 2 d. black, red and blue . . . 10 10
89 – 2 d. black, yellow and red . . 10 10
90 – 2 d. black and red 10 10
DESIGNS: No. 87, Inscriptions in Cyrillic (dated "01-08.12.1994"); 89, Exclamation mark in warning triangle; 90, Safe sex campaign emblem.

1994. 50th Anniv of Macedonian Radio.
91 **33** 2 d. multicoloured 20 20

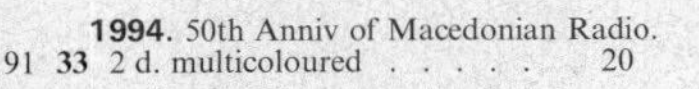

34 Macedonian Pine

1994. Flora and Fauna. Multicoloured.
92 5 d. Type **34** 35 35
93 10 d. Lynx 80 80

1995. Nos. 35 and 33 surch.
94 **10** 2 d. on 40 d. multicoloured . 35 35
96 **5** 5 d. on 40 d. multicoloured . 35 35

36 Emblems and Inscriptions

38 Voluntary Workers

37 Fresco

1995. Obligatory Tax. Anti-Cancer Week. Multicoloured.
97 1 d. Type **36** 10 10
98 1 d. White lilies 10 10
99 1 d. Red lilies 10 10
100 1 d. Red roses 10 10

1995. Easter.
101 **37** 4 d. multicoloured 30 30

1995. Obligatory Tax. Red Cross. Multicoloured.
102 1 d. Cross and inscriptions in Cyrillic (dated "8–15 MAJ 1995") 10 10
103 1 d. Type **38** 10 10
104 1 d. Volunteers in t-shirts . . . 10 10
105 1 d. Globe, red cross and red crescent 10 10

39 Troops on Battlefield

1995. 50th Anniv of End of Second World War.
106 **39** 2 d. multicoloured 25 25

40 Anniversary Emblem

1995. 50th Anniv of Macedonian Red Cross.
107 **40** 2 d. multicoloured 20 20

41 Rontgen and X-Ray Lamp

1995. Centenary of Discovery of X-Rays by Wilhelm Rontgen.
108 **41** 2 d. multicoloured 20 20

42 "Skopje Earthquake"

1995. Obligatory Tax. Solidarity Week.
109 **42** 1 d. black, red and gold . . 10 10

43 Cernodrinski (dramatist)

1995. 50th Anniv of Vojdan Cernodrinski Theatre Festival.
110 **43** 10 d. multicoloured 50 50

44 Kraljevic (fresco, Markov Monastery, Skopje)

1995. 600th Death Anniv of Marko Kraljevic (Serbian Prince).
111 **44** 20 d. multicoloured . . . . 1·00 1·00

45 Puleski

1995. Death Centenary of Gorgi Puleski (linguist and revolutionary).
112 **45** 2 d. multicoloured 20 20

46 Manuscript, Bridge and Emblem

1995. Writers' Festival, Struga.
113 **46** 2 d. multicoloured 25 25

47 Robert Koch (discoverer of tubercule bacillus)

48 Child holding Parents' Hands

1995. Obligatory Tax. Anti-tuberculosis Week.
114 **47** 1 d. brown, black and red . 10 10

1995. Obligatory Tax. Childrens' Week. self-adhesive. Imperf.
115 **48** 2 d. blue 10 10

49 Maleshevija

50 Interior of Mosque

1995. Buildings. Multicoloured.
116 2 d. Type **49** 15 15
117 20 d. Krakornica . . . . 1·10 1·10

1995. Tetovo Mosque.
118 **50** 15 d. multicoloured 90 90

51 Lumiere Brothers (inventors of cine-camera)

1995. Centenary of Motion Pictures. Multicoloured.
119 10 d. Type **51** 55 55
120 10 d. Milton and Janaki Manaki (Macedonian cinematographers) 55 55
Nos. 119/20 were issued together, se-tenant, forming a composite design.

52 Globe in Nest within Frame

1995. 50th Anniv of U.N.O. Multicoloured.
121 20 d. Type **52** 80 80
122 50 d. Sun within frame . . . . 2·50 2·50

53 Male and Female Symbols

1995. Obligatory Tax. Anti-AIDS Week.
123 **53** 1 d. multicoloured 10 10

54 Madonna and Child

1995. Christmas.
124 **54** 15 d. multicoloured 75 75

55 Dalmatian Pelican

1995. Birds. Multicoloured.
125 15 d. Type **55** 75 75
126 40 d. Lammergeier . . . . . . 2·00 2·00

56 Letters of Alphabet and Jigsaw Pieces

1995. 50th Anniv of Alphabet Reform.
127 **56** 5 d. multicoloured 35 35

57 St. Clement of Ohrid (detail of fresco)

1995. 700th Anniv of Fresco, St. Bogorodica's Church, Ohrid.
128 **57** 8 d. multicoloured 45 45

58 Postal Headquarters, Skopje

59 Zip joining Flags

1995. 2nd Anniv of Membership of U.P.U.
130 **58** 10 d. multicoloured 60 60

1995. Entry to Council of Europe and Organization for Security and Co-operation in Europe.
131 **59** 20 d. multicoloured . . . . 1·10 1·10

60 Hand holding out Apple

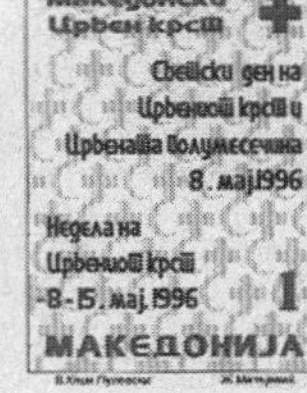

61 Inscriptions

1996. Obligatory Tax. Anti-cancer Week.
132 **60** 1 d. multicoloured 10 10

1996. Obligatory Tax. Red Cross Week. Each red, black and yellow.
133 1 d. Type **61** 10 10
134 1 d. Red Cross principles in Macedonian 10 10
135 1 d. Red Cross principles in English 10 10
136 1 d. Red Cross principles in French 10 10
137 1 d. Red Cross principles in Spanish 10 10

62 Canoeing **63** "Skopje Earthquake"

1996. Olympic Games, Atlanta. Designs showing statue of discus thrower and sport. Multicoloured.
138 2 d. Type **62** 10 10
139 8 d. Basketball (vert) 40 40
140 15 d. Swimming 75 75
141 20 d. Wrestling 95 95
142 40 d. Boxing (vert) . . . . . 1·75 1·75
143 50 d. Running (vert) . . . . . 2·25 2·25

1996. Obligatory Tax. Solidarity Week.
144 **63** 1 d. gold, red and black . . 10 10

64 Scarecrow Drug Addict **65** Boy

1996. United Nations Anti-drugs Decade.
145 **64** 20 d. multicoloured 75 75

1996. Children's Week. Children's Drawings. Multicoloured.
146 2 d. Type **65** 10 10
147 8 d. Girl 35 35

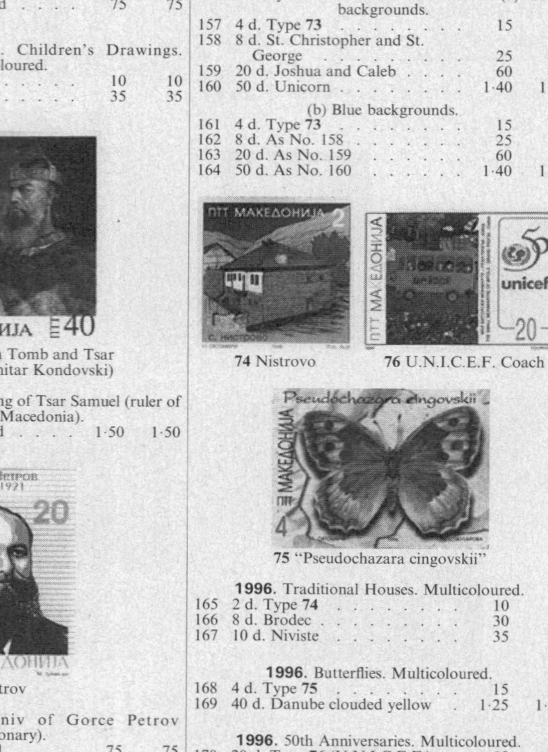

66 Fragment from Tomb and Tsar Samuel (after Dimitar Kondovski)

1996. Millenary of Crowning of Tsar Samuel (ruler of Bulgaria and Macedonia).
148 **66** 40 d. multicoloured . . . . 1·50 1·50

67 Petrov

1996. 75th Death Anniv of Gorce Petrov (revolutionary).
149 **67** 20 d. multicoloured 75 75

68 Ohrid Seal, 1903, and State Flag

1996. 5th Anniv of Independence.
150 **68** 10 d. multicoloured 40 40

69 Lungs on Globe **70** Vera Ciriviri-Trena (freedom fighter)

1996. Obligatory Tax. Anti-tuberculosis Week.
151 **69** 1 d. red, blue and black . . 10 10

1996. Europa. Famous Women. Multicoloured.
152 20 d. Type **70** 65 65
153 40 d. Mother Teresa (Nobel Peace Prize winner and founder of Missionaries of Charity) . . . . 1·25 1·25

71 Hand holding Syringe

1996. Obligatory Tax. Anti-AIDS Week.
154 **71** 1 d. black, red and yellow . 10 10

72 Candle, Nuts and Fruit **73** "Daniel in the Lions' Den"

1996. Christmas. Multicoloured.
155 10 d. Type **72** 35 35
156 10 d. Tree and carol singers . . 35 35

1996. Early Christian Terracotta Reliefs. (a) Green backgrounds.
157 4 d. Type **73** 15 15
158 8 d. St. Christopher and St. George 25 25
159 20 d. Joshua and Caleb 60 60
160 50 d. Unicorn . . . . 1·40 1·40

(b) Blue backgrounds.
161 4 d. Type **73** 15 15
162 8 d. As No. 158 . . . . 25 25
163 20 d. As No. 159 . . . . 60 60
164 50 d. As No. 160 . . . . 1·40 1·40

74 Nistrovo **76** U.N.I.C.E.F. Coach

75 "Pseudochazara cingovskii"

1996. Traditional Houses. Multicoloured.
165 2 d. Type **74** 10 10
166 8 d. Brodec 30 30
167 10 d. Niviste 35 35

1996. Butterflies. Multicoloured.
168 4 d. Type **75** 15 15
169 40 d. Danube clouded yellow . 1·25 1·25

1996. 50th Anniversaries. Multicoloured.
170 20 d. Type **76** (U.N.I.C.E.F.) . 65 65
171 40 d. Church in Mtskheta, Georgia (U.N.E.S.C.O.) . . 1·40 1·40

77 Skier

1997. 50 Years of Ski Championships at Sar Planina.
172 **77** 20 d. multicoloured 70 70

78 Bell

1997. 150th Birth Anniv of Alexander Graham Bell (telephone pioneer).
173 **78** 40 d. multicoloured . . . . 1·40 1·40

79 Family and Healthy Foodstuffs **81** Red Cross on Globe

80 Hound

1997. Obligatory Tax. Anti-cancer Week.
174 **79** 1 d. multicoloured 10 10

1997. Roman Mosaics from Heraklia. Multicoloured.
175 2 d. Type **80** 10 10
176 8 d. Steer 25 25
177 20 d. Lion 70 70
178 40 d. Leopard with prey . . . 1·25 1·25

1997. Obligatory Tax. Red Cross Week.
180 **81** 1 d. multicoloured 10 10

82 Gold Plate

1997. 1100th Anniv of Cyrillic Alphabet. Multicoloured.
181 10 d. Type **82** 30 30
182 10 d. Sts. Cyril and Methodius . 30 30

83 School-children **84** Mountain Flowers

1997. Obligatory Tax. Solidarity Week.
183 **83** 1 d. multicoloured 10 10

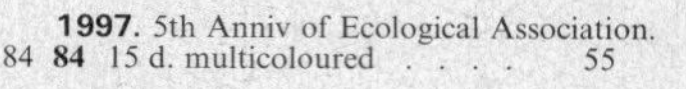

1997. 5th Anniv of Ecological Association.
184 **84** 15 d. multicoloured 55 55

85 Itar Pejo **86** St. Naum and St. Naum's Church, Ohrid

1997. Europa. Tales and Legends. Multicoloured.
185 20 d. Type **85** 70 70
186 40 d. Stork-men . . . . 1·25 1·25

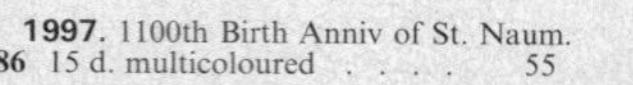

1997. 1100th Birth Anniv of St. Naum.
187 **86** 15 d. multicoloured 55 55

87 Diseased Lungs **88** Stibnite

1997. Obligatory Tax. Anti-tuberculosis Week.
188 **87** 1 d. multicoloured 10 10

1997. Minerals. Multicoloured.
189 27 d. Type **88** 95 95
190 40 d. Lorandite . . . . 1·40 1·40

89 Dove and Sun above Child in Open Hand

1997. International Children's Day.
191 **89** 27 d. multicoloured 95 95

90 Chanterelle

1997. Fungi. Multicoloured.
192 2 d. Type **90** 10 10
193 15 d. Bronze boletus 50 50
194 27 d. Caesar's mushroom . . . 95 95
195 50 d. "Morchella conica" . . . 1·75 1·75

91 Group of Children **92** Gandhi

1998. Obligatory Tax. Anti-AIDS Week.
196 **91** 1 d. multicoloured 10 10

1998. 50th Death Anniv of Mahatma Gandhi (Indian independence campaigner).
197 **92** 30 d. multicoloured . . . . 1·00 1·00

93 Formula of Pythagoras's Theory

1998. 2500th Death Anniv of Pythagoras (philosopher and mathematician).
198 **93** 16 d. multicoloured 55 55

94 Alpine Skiing

1998. Winter Olympic Games, Nagano, Japan. Multicoloured.
199 4 d. Type **94** 15 15
200 30 d. Cross-country skiing . . 1·00 1·00

95 Novo Selo

1998. Traditional Houses. Multicoloured.

201 2 d. Type **95** 10 10
202 4 d. Jablanica 15 15
202a 4 d. Svekani 10 10
202b 5 d. Teovo 10 10
203 16 d. Kiselica 35 35
204 20 d. Konopnica 70 70
205 30 d. Ambar . . . . 1·00 1·00
206 50 d. Galicnik . . . . 1·75 1·75

96 "Exodus" (Kole Manev)

1998. 50th Anniv of Exodus of Children during Greek Civil War.

215 **96** 30 d. multicoloured . . . . 1·00 1·00

97 "Proportions of Man" (Leonardo da Vinci)

1998. Obligatory Tax. Anti-cancer Week.

216 **97** 1 d. multicoloured 10 10

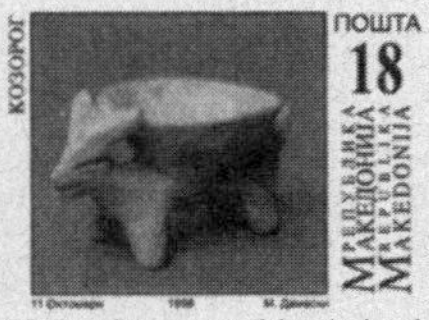

98 Bowl supported by Animal

1998. Archaeological Finds from Nedit. Multicoloured.

217 4 d. Carafes 15 15
218 18 d. Type **98** 60 60
219 30 d. Sacred female figurine . . 1·00 1·00
220 60 d. Stemmed cup . . . . . 2·10 2·10

99 Football Pitch

1998. World Cup Football Championship, France. Multicoloured.

221 4 d. Type **99** 15 15
222 30 d. Globe and football pitch . 1·00 1·00

100 Folk Dance

1998. Europa. National Festivals. Multicoloured.

223 30 d. Type **100** . . . . 1·00 1·00
224 40 d. Carnival . . . . 1·40 1·40

101 Profiles

1998. Obligatory Tax. Red Cross Week.

225 **101** 2 d. multicoloured . . . 10 10

102 Carnival Procession

103 Hands and Red Cross

1998. 18th Congress of Carnival Towns, Strumica.

226 **102** 30 d. multicoloured . . . 1·00 1·00

1998. Obligatory Tax. Solidarity Week.

227 **103** 2 d. multicoloured . . . 10 10

104 Flower

105 Cupovski

1998. Environmental Protection. Multicoloured.

228 4 d. Type **104** 15 15
229 30 d. Polluting chimney uprooting tree . . . . . . 1·00 1·00

1998. 120th Birth Anniv of Dimitrija Cupovski.

230 **105** 16 d. multicoloured . . . 55 55

106 Steam Locomotive and Station

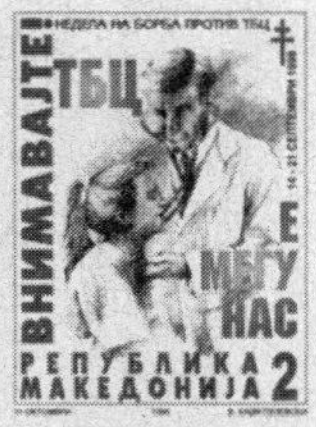

107 Doctor and Patient

1997. 150th Anniv of Railways in Macedonia. Multicoloured.

231 30 d. Type **106** . . . . 1·00 1·00
232 60 d. Steam locomotive, 1873 (horiz) . . . . 2·10 2·10

1998. Obligatory Tax. Anti-tuberculosis Week.

233 **107** 2 d. multicoloured 10 10

108 "Ursus spelaeus"

1998. Fossilized Skulls. Multicoloured.

234 4 d. Type **108** 10 10
235 8 d. "Mesopithecus pentelici" . 15 15
236 18 d. "Tragoceros" 40 40
237 30 d. "Aceratherium incsivum" . 65 65

109 Atanos Badev (composer) and Score

1998. Centenary of "Zlatoustova Liturgy".

238 **109** 25 d. multicoloured . . . 50 50

110 Child with Kite

1998. Children's Day.

239 **110** 30 d. multicoloured . . . 65 65

111 "Cerambyx cerdo" (longhorn beetle)

1998. Insects. Multicoloured.

240 4 d. Type **111** 10 10
241 8 d. Alpine longhorn beetle . . 15 15
242 20 d. European rhinoceros beetle 40 40
243 40 d. Stag beetle 85 85

112 Reindeer and Snowflakes

1998. Christmas and New Year. Multicoloured.

244 4 d. Type **112** 10 10
245 30 d. Bread and oak leaves . . . 65 65

113 Ribbon and Gender Symbols

1998. Obligatory Tax. Anti-AIDS Week.

246 **113** 2 d. multicoloured 10 10

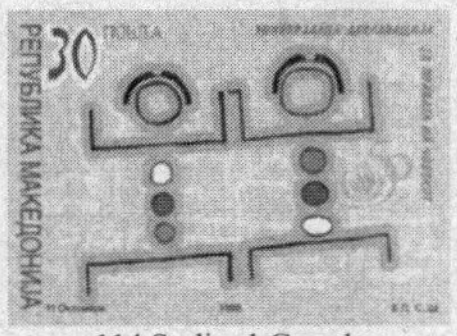

114 Stylized Couple

1998. 50th Anniv of Universal Declaration of Human Rights.

247 **114** 30 d. multicoloured . . . 65 65

115 Sharplaninec

1999. Dogs.

248 **115** 15 d. multicoloured . . . 30 30

116 Girl's Face

117 "The Annunciation" (Demir Hisar, Slepce Monastery)

1999. Obligatory Tax. Anti-cancer Week.

249 **116** 2 d. multicoloured 10 10

1999. Icons. Multicoloured.

250 4 d. Type **117** 10 10
251 8 d. "Saints" (St. Nicholas's Church, Ohrid) 15 15
252 18 d. "Madonna and Child" (Demir Hisar, Slepce Monastery) 40 40
253 30 d. "Christ the Redeemer" (Zrze Monastery, Prilep) . . 65 65

118 Pandilov and "Hay Harvest"

1999. Birth Centenary of Dimitar Pandilov (painter).

255 **118** 4 d. multicoloured 10 10

119 Telegraph Apparatus

1999. Centenary of the Telegraph in Macedonia.

256 **119** 4 d. multicoloured 10 10

120 University and Sts. Cyril and Methodius

1999. 50th Anniv of Sts. Cyril and Methodius University.

257 **120** 8 d. multicoloured 15 15

121 Anniversary Emblem and Map of Europe

1999. 50th Anniv of Council of Europe.

258 **121** 30 d. multicoloured . . . 65 65

122 Pelister National Park

1999. Europa. Parks and Gardens. Multicoloured.

259 30 d. Type **122** 65 65
260 40 d. Mavrovo National Park . 85 85

123 Figures linking Raised Arms

1999. Obligatory Tax. Red Cross Week.

261 **123** 2 d. multicoloured 10 10

124 People running round Globe

125 Tree

1999. Obligatory Tax. Solidarity Week.

262 **124** 2 d. multicoloured 10 10

1999. Environmental Protection.

263 **125** 30 d. multicoloured . . . 65 65

126 Tsar Petur Delyan

1999. Medieval Rulers of Macedonia. Mult.

264 4 d. Type **126** 10 10
265 8 d. Prince Gjorgji Vojteh . . . 15 15
266 18 d. Prince Dobromir Hrs . . 40 40
267 30 d. Prince Strez 65 65

Nos. 264/7 were issued together, se-tenant, forming a composite design.

127 Kuzman Shaikarev (author)

1999. 125th Anniv of First Macedonian Language Primer.

268 **127** 4 d. multicoloured . . . 10 10

128 Faces in Outline of Lungs

129 "Crocus scardicus"

1999. Obligatory Tax. Anti-tuberculosis Week.

269	**128**	2 d. multicoloured	10	10

1999. Flowers. Multicoloured.

270	4 d. Type **129**	10	10
271	8 d. "Astragalus mayeri"	15	15
272	18 d. "Campanula formanekiana"	40	40
273	30 d. "Viola kosaninii"	65	65

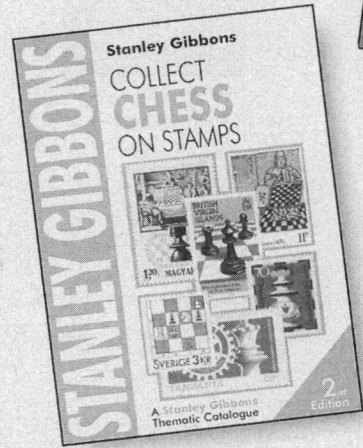

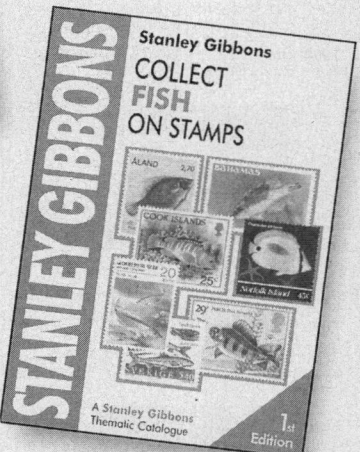

MADAGASCAR Pt. 6

A large island in the Indian Ocean off the east coast of Africa. French Post Offices operated there from 1885.

In 1896 the island was declared a French colony, absorbing Diego-Suarez and Ste. Marie de Madagascar in 1898 and Nossi-Be in 1901.

Madagascar became autonomous as the Malagasy Republic in 1958; it reverted to the name of Madagascar in 1992.

100 centimes = 1 franc.

A. FRENCH POST OFFICES

1889. Stamps of French Colonies "Commerce" type surch with value in figures.

1 J 05 on 10 c. black on lilac £475 £150
2 05 on 25 c. black on red £475 £140
4 05 on 40 c. red on yellow £110 70·00
5 5 on 10 c. black on lilac £160 90·00
6 5 on 25 c. black on red £160 95·00
7 15 on 25 c. black on red £110 70·00
3 25 on 40 c. red on yellow £425 £120

5

1891. No gum. Imperf.

9 5 5 c. black on green £100 17·00
10 10 c. black on blue 70·00 22·00
11 15 c. blue on blue 75·00 24·00
12 25 c. brown on buff 14·00 8·50
13 1 f. black on yellow £800 £200
14 5 f. black and lilac on lilac £1500 £900

1895. Stamps of France optd **POSTE FRANCAISE Madagascar**.

15 10 5 c. green 4·75 3·75
16 10 c. black on lilac 30·00 19·00
17 15 c. blue 40·00 7·00
18 25 c. black on red 55·00 6·00
19 40 c. red on yellow 45·00 12·00
20 50 c. red 65·00 12·00
21 75 c. brown on orange 60·00 27·00
22 1 f. olive 85·00 18·00
23 5 f. mauve on lilac £110 50·00

1896. Stamps of France surch with value in figures in oval.

29 10 5 c. on 1 c. black on blue £4000 £1500
30 15 c. on 2 c. brown on yell £1500 £750
31 25 c. on 3 c. grey £1700 £750
32 25 c. on 4 c. red on grey £4250 £1400
33 25 c. on 40 c. red on yellow £900 £550

B. FRENCH COLONY OF MADAGASCAR AND DEPENDENCIES

1896. "Tablet" key-type inscr "MADAGASCAR ET DEPENDANCES".

1 D 1 c. black & red on blue 50 50
2 2 c. brown & blue on buff 60 60
2a 2 c. brown & blk on buff 2·75 2·75
3 4 c. brown & bl on grey 85 40
17 5 c. green and red 75 30
6 10 c. black & blue on lilac 4·75 60
18 10 c. red and blue 1·00 25
7 15 c. blue and red 6·00 55
19 15 c. grey and red 1·10 30
8 20 c. red & blue on green 3·50 85
9 25 c. black & red on pink 4·75 40
20 25 c. blue and red 12·50 14·00
10 30 c. brown & bl on drab 4·75 1·50
21 35 c. black & red on yell 28·00 3·50
11 40 c. red & blue on yellow 5·25 1·00
12 50 c. red & blue on pink 6·75 85
22 50 c. brown & red on blue 20·00 16·00
13 75 c. violet & red on orge 2·25 1·50
14 1 f. green and red 7·00 1·90
15 1 f. green and blue 12·50 8·00
16 5 f. mauve & blue on lilac 25·00 16·00

1902. "Tablet" key-type stamps as above surch.

27 D 0,01 on 2 c. brown and blue on buff 4·50 3·00
27a 0,01 on 2 c. brown and black on buff 2·50 4·00
29 0,05 on 30 c. brown and blue on drab 3·50 3·50
23 05 on 50 c. red and blue on pink 2·00 1·50
31 0,10 on 50 c. red and blue on pink 3·00 3·50
24 10 on 5 f. mauve and blue on lilac 14·00 12·00
32 0,15 on 75 c. violet and red on orange 1·75 1·75
33 0,15 on 1 f. green & red 1·75 2·50
25 15 on 1 f. green and red 3·50 1·75

1902. Nos. 59 and 61 of Diego-Suarez surch.

35 D 0,05 on 30 c. brown and blue on drab 85·00 £100
36 0,10 on 50 c. red and blue on pink £3250 £3000

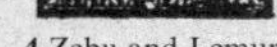
4 Zebu and Lemur

5 Transport in Madagascar

1903.

38 4 1 c. purple 55 30
39 2 c. brown 50 50
40 4 c. brown 55 55
41 5 c. green 4·75 55
42 10 c. red 5·00 50
43 15 c. red 5·00 65
44 20 c. orange 3·00 1·25
45 25 c. blue 20·00 1·50
46 30 c. red 22·00 8·00
47 40 c. lilac 20·00 3·25
48 50 c. brown 35·00 13·50
49 75 c. yellow 38·00 14·50
50 1 f. green 38·00 23·00
51 2 f. blue 50·00 24·00
52 5 f. black 50·00 55·00

1908.

53a 5 1 c. green and violet 10 20
54 2 c. green and red 10 20
55 4 c. brown and green 10 25
56 5 c. olive and green 45 15
90 5 c. red and black 30 15
57 10 c. brown and pink 30 15
91 10 c. olive and green 30 30
92 10 c. purple and brown 45 30
58 15 c. red and lilac 35 20
93 15 c. green and olive 35 65
94 15 c. red and blue 1·40 1·60
59 20 c. brown and orange 30 30
60 25 c. black and blue 1·60 25
95 25 c. black and violet 60 25
61 30 c. black and brown 1·60 1·40
96 30 c. brown and red 65 65
97 30 c. purple and green 75 45
98 30 c. light green and green 1·10 1·25
62 35 c. black and red 1·10 60
63 40 c. black and brown 80 60
64 45 c. black and green 60 50
99 45 c. red and scarlet 75 1·25
100 45 c. purple and lilac 1·25 1·40
65 50 c. black and violet 60 45
101 50 c. black and blue 65 30
102 50 c. yellow and black 85 40
103 60 c. violet on pink 75 1·10
104 65 c. blue and black 1·10 1·25
66 75 c. black and red 55 35
105 85 c. red and green 1·25 2·00
67 1 f. green and brown 55 30
106 1 f. blue 95 1·25
107 1 f. green and mauve 5·50 6·00
108 1 f. 10 green and brown 1·25 1·60
68 2 f. green and blue 3·00 95
69 5 f. brown and violet 9·50 3·75

1912. "Tablet" key-type surch.

70 D 05 on 15 c. grey and red 35 30
71 05 on 20 c. red and blue on green 40 65
72 05 on 30 c. brown and blue on drab 40 65
73 10 on 75 c. violet and red on orange 3·00 6·00
81 0.60 on 75 c. violet and red on orange 4·50 4·50
82 1 f. on 5 f. mauve and blue on lilac 45 85

1912. Surch.

74 4 05 on 2 c. brown 25 45
75 05 on 20 c. orange 35 50
76 05 on 30 c. red 35 80
77 10 on 40 c. lilac 50 95
78 10 on 50 c. brown 85 2·00
79 10 on 75 c. brown 2·50 4·50
83 1 f. on 5 f. black 20·00 20·00

1915. Surch 5c and red cross.

80 5 10 c. + 5 c. brown and pink 35 90

1921. Surch **1 cent**.

84 5 1 c. on 15 c. red and lilac 50 70

1921. Type **5** (some colours changed) surch.

109 5 25 c. on 15 c. red and lilac 40 45
85 0,25 on 35 c. black and red 4·00 3·25
86 0,25 on 40 c. black & brown 3·50 3·50
87 0,25 on 45 c. black & green 2·50 2·75
110 25 c. on 2 f. green and blue 40 40
112 25 c. on 5 f. brown & violet 65 80
88 0,30 on 40 c. black & brown 1·40 1·40
113 50 c. on 1 f. green & brown 1·25 25
89 0,60 on 75 c. black and red 1·90 2·00
114 60 on 75 c. violet on pink 40 40
115 65 c. on 75 c. black and red 1·10 2·75
116 85 c. on 45 c. black & green 1·10 2·75
117 90 c. on 75 c. pink and red 60 80
118 1 f. 25 on 1 f. blue 50 50
119 1 f. 50 on 1 f. lt blue & blue 80 20
120 3 f. on 5 f. violet and green 3·25 1·60
121 10 f. on 5 f. mauve and red 7·50 3·25
122 20 f. on 5 f. blue and mauve 5·75 4·00

14 Sakalava Chief

15 Zebus

17 Betsileo Woman

18 General Gallieni

1930.

123 18 1 c. blue 20 40
124 15 1 c. green and blue 20 25
125 14 2 c. brown and red 10 10
177 18 3 c. blue 15 25
126 14 4 c. mauve and brown 15 35
127 15 5 c. red and green 15 15
128 – 10 c. green and red 10 10
129 17 15 c. red 10 10
130 15 20 c. blue and brown 20 20
131 – 25 c. brown and lilac 20 10
132 17 30 c. green 40 30
133 14 40 c. red and green 30 35
134 17 45 c. lilac 55 50
178 18 45 c. green 35 40
179 50 c. brown 20 10
180 60 c. mauve 15 30
136 15 65 c. mauve and brown 55 25
181 18 70 c. red 35 35
137 17 75 c. brown 50 25
138 15 90 c. red 85 80
182 18 90 c. brown 30 15
139 – 1 f. blue and brown 1·00 90
140 – 1 f. red and scarlet 45 45
140a – 1 f. 25 brown and blue 95 75
183 18 1 f. 40 orange 50 35
141 14 1 f. 50 ultramarine & blue 4·50 1·25
142 1 f. 50 red and brown 50 55
278 1 f. 50 brown and red 20 50
184 18 1 f. 60 violet 50 40
143 14 1 f. 75 red and brown 2·50 1·00
185 18 2 f. red 35 20
186a 3 f. green 55 60
146 14 5 f. brown and mauve 70 40
147 18 10 f. orange 2·75 1·90
148 14 20 f. blue and brown 1·40 1·40

DESIGN—VERT. 10 c., 25 c., 1 f., 1 f. 25, Hova girl.

1931. "Colonial Exhibition" key-types inscr "MADAGASCAR".

149 E 40 c. black and green 55 55
150 F 50 c. black and mauve 1·25 70
151 G 90 c. black and red 85 90
152 H 1 f. 50 black and blue 1·40 1·00

19 Bloch 120 over Madagascar

20 J. Laborde and Tananarivo Palace

1935. Air.

153 19 50 c. red and green 50 55
154 90 c. red and green 35 40
155 1 f. 25 red and lake 35 40
156 1 f. 50 red and blue 40 45
157 1 f. 60 red and blue 20 25
158 1 f. 75 red and orange 5·25 3·25
159 2 f. red and blue 50 30
160 3 f. red and orange 35 30
161 3 f. 65 red and black 35 40
162 3 f. 90 red and green 35 30
163 4 f. red and carmine 35·00 1·90
164 4 f. 50 red and black 18·00 80
165 5 f. 50 red and green 45 40
166 6 f. red and mauve 45 40
167 6 f. 90 red and purple 45 50
168 8 f. red and mauve 70 90
169 8 f. 50 red and green 80 95
170 9 f. red and green 45 50
171 12 f. red and brown 55 65
172 12 f. 50 red and violet 1·25 95
173 15 f. red and orange 60 60
174 16 f. red and green 1·25 1·25
175 20 f. red and brown 1·90 1·40
176 50 f. red and blue 3·25 3·00

1937. International Exhibition, Paris. As T **58a** of Guadeloupe.

187 20 c. violet 60 75
188 30 c. green 75 85
189 40 c. red 50 50
190 50 c. brown and agate 45 60
191 90 c. red 45 60
192 1 f. 50 blue 45 90

1938. 60th Death Anniv of Jean Laborde (explorer).

193 20 35 c. green 35 45
194 55 c. violet 40 45
195 65 c. red 35 50
196 80 c. purple 45 40
197 1 f. red 35 30
198 1 f. 25 red 45 40
199 1 f. 75 blue 90 35
200 2 f. 15 brown 1·75 1·25
201 2 f. 25 blue 75 75
202 2 f. 50 brown 40 45
203 10 f. green 60 60

1938. Int Anti-Cancer Fund. As T **58b** of Guadeloupe.

204 1 f. 75 + 50 c. blue 3·75 6·00

1939. New York World's Fair. As T **58c** of Guadeloupe.

205 1 f. 25 red 75 80
206 2 f. 25 blue 80 85

1939. 150th Anniv of French Revolution. As T **58d** of Guadeloupe.

207 45 c. + 25 c. green and black (postage) 4·75 5·75
208 70 c. + 30 c. brown and black 5·25 5·75
209 90 c. + 35 c. orange and black 4·75 5·75
210 1 f. 25 + 1 f. red and black 4·75 5·75
211 2 f. 25 + 2 f. blue and black 5·00 5·75
212 4 f. 50 + 4 f. black and orange (air) 9·00 10·00

1942. Surch **50** and bars.

213 15 50 on 65 c. mauve & brown 95 35

1942. Free French Administration. Optd **FRANCE LIBRE** or surch also.

214 14 2 c. brown and red (postage) 65 65
215 18 3 c. blue 85·00 90·00
216 15 0,05 on 1 c. green and blue 50 60
217 20 0,10 on 55 c. violet 75 90
218 17 15 c. red 6·25 6·25
219 20 0,30 on 65 c. red 50 60
220 15 0 f. 50 on 0,05 on 1 c. green and blue 50 65
221 50 on 65 c. mauve & brown 55 25
222 18 50 on 90 c. brown 40 20
223 15 65 c. mauve and brown 65 65
224 18 70 c. red 55 60
225 20 80 c. purple 1·40 1·40
226 – 1,00 on 1 f. 25 brown and blue (No. 140a) 1·40 1·40
227 20 1,00 on 1 f. 25 red 5·00 5·00
228 18 1 f. 40 orange 60 60
229 5 1 f. 50 on 1 f. blue 1·75 1·75
230 14 1 f. 50 ultramarine & blue 90 90
231 1 f. 50 red and brown 90 90
232 18 1,50 on 1 f. 60 violet 55 55
233 14 1,50 on 1 f. 75 red & brown 55 50
234 20 1,50 on 1 f. 75 blue 55 55
235 18 1 f. 60 violet 50 60
236 20 2,00 on 2 f. 15 brown 50 50
237 2 f. 25 blue 55 50
238 – 2 f. 25 blue (No. 206) 55 55
239 20 2 f. 50 brown 2·00 2·25
240 5 10 f. on 5 f. mauve & red 15·00 11·00
241 20 10 f. green 2·75 3·00
242 5 20 f. on 5 f. blue & mauve 9·00 9·50
243 14 20 f. blue and brown £550 £650
244 19 1,00 on 1 f. 25 red and lake (air) 3·00 3·25
245 1 f. 50 red and blue 3·75 3·75
246 1 f. 75 red and orange 55·00 60·00
247 3,00 on 3 f. 65 red & black 65 25
248 8 f. red and purple 80 75
249 8,00 on 8 f. 50 red & green 60 30
250 12 f. red and brown 1·75 1·60
251 12 f. 50 red and violet 90 85
252 16 f. red and green 3·25 3·25
253 50 f. red and blue 2·75 2·75

24 Traveller's Tree

29 Gen. Gallieni

1943. Free French Issue.

254 24 5 c. brown 10 25
255 10 c. mauve 10 10
256 25 c. green 10 20
257 30 c. orange 10 10
258 40 c. blue 20 20
259 80 c. purple 10 10
260 1 f. blue 15 15
261 1 f. 50 c. red 20 15
262 2 f. yellow 15 10
263 2 f. 50 c. blue 20 25
264 4 f. blue and red 20 10
265 5 f. green and black 45 15
266 10 f. red and blue 60 20
267 20 f. violet and brown 40 40

1943. Free French Administration. Air. As T **63a** of Guadeloupe, but inscr "MADAGASCAR".

268 1 f. orange 40 40
269 1 f. 50 c. red 40 40
270 5 f. purple 40 40
271 10 f. black 40 40
272 25 f. blue 85 45
273 50 f. green 1·40 70
274 100 f. red 50 80

1944. Mutual Aid and Red Cross Funds. As T **58e** of Guadeloupe.

275 5 f. + 20 f. green 50 80

1944. Surch **1 f. 50.**

276 **24** 1 f. 50 on 5 c. brown . . . 35 55
277 1 f. 50 on 10 c. mauve . . . 50 80

1945. Ebouc. As T **58f** of Guadeloupe.

279 2 f. black 20 35
280 25 f. green 50 85

1946. Air. Victory. As T **63b** of Guadeloupe.

281 8 f. red 40 40

1945. Surch with new value.

282 **24** 50 c. on 5 c. brown 35 35
283 60 c. on 5 c. brown 40 45
284 70 c. on 5 c. brown 35 40
285 1 f. 20 on 5 c. brown 35 35
286 2 f. 40 on 25 c. green 35 45
287 3 f. on 25 c. green 30 30
288 4 f. 50 on 25 c. green 45 50
289 15 f. on 2 f. 50 blue 35 45

1946. Air. From Chad to the Rhine. As T **63c** of Guadeloupe.

290 5 f. blue 75 85
291 10 f. red 80 90
292 15 f. green 80 90
293 20 f. brown . . . . 1·00 1·10
294 25 f. violet . . . . 1·25 1·40
295 50 f. red . . . . 1·10 1·40

1946.

296 – 10 c. green (postage) 10 25
297 – 30 c. orange 10 25
298 – 40 c. olive 10 25
299 – 50 c. purple 10 10
300 – 60 c. blue 10 25
301 – 80 c. green 10 25
302 – 1 f. sepia 10 10
303 – 1 f. 20 green 20 20
304 **29** 1 f. 50 red 10 10
305 – 2 f. black 10 10
306 – 3 f. purple 10 10
307 – 3 f. 60 red 60 60
308 – 4 f. blue 25 20
309 – 5 f. orange 35 15
310 – 6 f. blue 20 10
311 – 10 f. lake 25 25
312 – 15 f. brown 35 20
313 – 20 f. blue 45 35
314 – 25 f. brown 80 45
315 – 50 f. blue and red (air) . . . 90 45
316 – 100 f. brown and red . . . 1·75 85
317 – 200 f. brown and green . . . 3·50 2·00

DESIGNS—As T **29**. VERT: 10 to 50 c. Native with spear; 6, 10 f. Gen. Duchesne; 15, 20, 25 f. Lt.-Col. Joffre. HORIZ: 60, 80 c. Zebus; 1 f., 1 f. 20, Sakalava man and woman; 3 f. 60, 4, 5 f. Betsimisaraka mother and child. 49 × 28 mm: 50 f. Aerial view of Port of Tamatave. 28 × 51 mm: 100 f. Allegory of flight. 51 × 28 mm: Douglas DC-2 airplane and map of Madagascar.

36 Gen. Gallieni and View

1946. 50th Anniv of French Protectorate.

318 **36** 10 f. + 5 f. purple 35 45

1948. Air. Discovery of Adelie Land, Antarctic. No. 316 optd **TERRE ADELIE DUMONT D'URVILLE 1840.**

319 – 100 f. brown and red . . . . 35·00 50·00

1949. Air. 75th Anniv of U.P.U. As T **38** of New Caledonia.

320 25 f. multicoloured . . . . . 2·75 1·90

1950. Colonial Welfare Fund. As T **39** of New Caledonia.

321 10 f. + 2 f. purple and green . . . 3·50 4·00

38 Cacti and Succulents

39 Long-tailed Ground Roller

40 Woman and Forest Road

1952.

322 **38** 7 f. 50 green & blue (postage) 70 35
323 **39** 8 f. lake . . . . 1·75 35
324 15 f. blue and green . . . . 3·00 30
325 – 50 f. green and blue (air) . . 2·25 40
326 – 100 f. black, brown & blue . . 8·50 1·50
327 – 200 f. brown and green . . . 12·50 4·50
328 **40** 500 f. brown, sepia & green . 21·00 5·00

DESIGNS—As Type **40**: 50 f. Palm trees; 100 f. Antsirabe Viaduct; 200 f. Ring-tailed lemurs.

1952. Military Medal Centenary As T **40** of New Caledonia.

329 15 f. turquoise, yellow & green . 1·50 1·90

1954. Air. 10th Anniv of Liberation. As T **42** of New Caledonia.

330 15 f. purple and violet . . . . 2·00 1·50

41 Marshal Lyautey

1954. Birth Centenary of Marshal Lyautey.

331 **41** 10 f. indigo, blue & ultram . . 65 10
332 40 f. lake, grey and black . . 1·00 10

42 Gallieni School

43 Cassava

1956. Economic and Social Development Fund.

333 – 3 f. brown and grey 20 10
334 **42** 5 f. brown and chestnut . . 15 10
335 – 10 f. blue and grey 50 15
336 – 15 f. green and turquoise . . 40 15

DESIGNS: 3 f. Tamatave and tractor; 10 f. Dredging canal; 15 f. Irrigation.

1956. Coffee. As T **44** of New Caledonia.

337 20 f. sepia and brown 40 15

1957. Plants.

338 **43** 2 f. green, brown and blue . . 25 10
339 – 4 f. red, brown and green . . 25 15
340 – 12 f. green, brown & violet . 45 15

DESIGNS: 4 f. Cloves; 12 f. Vanilla.

Issues of 1958–92. For issues between these dates, see under MALAGASY REPUBLIC.

362 Children with Mascot

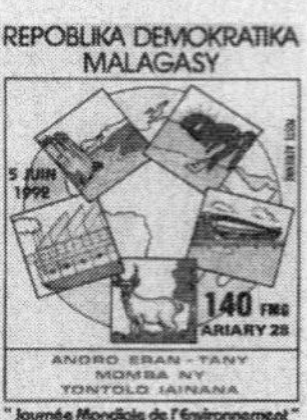

363 Environmental Projects

1992. School Sports Festival (1990).

910 **362** 140 f. multicoloured 35 10

1992. Air. World Environment Day.

911 **363** 140 f. multicoloured 10 10

364 Post Box and Globe

365 Basenji

1992. Air. World Post Day.

912 **364** 500 f. multicoloured 75 25

1992. Domestic Animals. Multicoloured.

913 140 f. Type **365** 10 10
914 500 f. Anglo-Arab horse . . . 90 25
915 640 f. Tortoiseshell cat and kitten . . . . 1·10 30
916 1025 f. Siamese and colour-point (cats) . . . . 1·60 50
917 1140 f. Holstein horse . . . . 2·25 60
918 5000 f. German shepherd dogs . 6·50 75

366 Foodstuffs

1992. International Nutrition Conference, Rome.

920 **366** 500 f. multicoloured . . . . 1·10 25

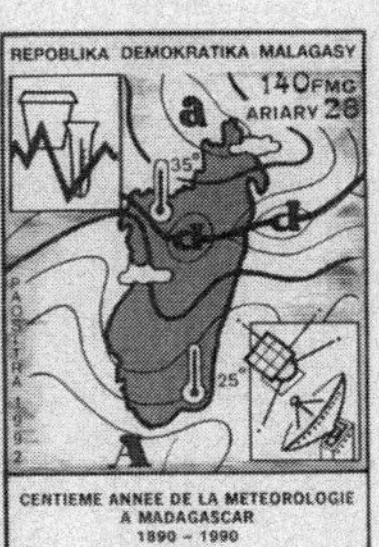

367 Weather Map

1992. Centenary of Meteorological Service.

921 **367** 140 f. multicoloured 35 10

368 "Eusemia bisma"

1992. Butterflies and Moths. Multicoloured.

922 15 f. Type **368** 10 10
923 35 f. Tailed comet moth (vert) . 10 10
924 65 f. "Alcides aurora" 10 10
925 140 f. "Agarista agricola" . . . 35 10
926 600 f. "Trogonoptera croesus" . 1·40 30
927 850 f. "Trogonodtera priamus" . 1·75 45
928 1300 f. "Pereute leucodrosime" . 2·25 70

369 Barn Swallow

1992. Birds. Multicoloured.

930 40 f. Type **369** 10 10
931 55 f. Pied harrier (vert) 10 10
932 60 f. European cuckoo (vert) . . 10 10
933 140 f. Sacred ibis 10 10
934 210 f. Purple swamphen 45 10
935 500 f. Common roller . . . . 1·10 25
936 2000 f. Golden oriole . . . . . 4·00 1·10

370 Gymnastics

1992. Olympic Games, Barcelona. Multicoloured.

938 65 f. Type **370** 10 10
939 70 f. High jumping 10 10
940 120 f. Archery 10 10
941 140 f. Cycling 35 10
942 675 f. Weightlifting . . . . . 1·10 30
943 720 f. Boxing . . . . 1·40 35
944 1200 f. Two-man kayak . . . . 1·75 60

371 Pusher-tug, Pangalanes Canal

1993.

946 **371** 140 f. multicoloured . . . 35 10

372 BMW **373** Hyacinth Macaw

1993. Motor Cars. Multicoloured.

947 20 f. Type **372** 10 10
948 40 f. Toyota "Carina" 10 10
949 60 f. Cadillac 10 10
950 65 f. Volvo 10 10
951 140 f. Mercedes-Benz 10 10
952 640 f. Ford "Sierra" . . . . . 1·00 30
953 3000 f. Honda "Concerto" . . . 4·50 90

1993. Parrot Family. Multicoloured.

955 50 f. Type **373** 10 10
956 60 f. Cockatiel 10 10
957 140 f. Budgerigar 10 10
958 500 f. Jandaya conure 60 25
959 675 f. Budgerigar (different) . . 1·10 35
960 800 f. Red-fronted parakeet . . 1·40 45
961 1750 f. Kea . . . . 2·75 65

375 Albert Einstein (physics, 1921) and Niels Bohr (physics, 1922)

1993. Nobel Prize Winners. Multicoloured.

964 500 f. Type **375** 60 25
965 500 f. Wolfgang Pauli (physics, 1945) and Max Born (physics, 1954) 60 25
966 500 f. Joseph Thomson (physics, 1906) and Johannes Stark (physics, 1919) 60 25
967 500 f. Otto Hahn (physics, 1944) and Hideki Yukawa (physics, 1949) 60 25
968 500 f. Owen Richardson (physics, 1928) and William Shockley (physics, 1956) 60 25
969 500 f. Albert Michelson (physics, 1907) and Charles Townes (physics, 1964) 60 25
970 500 f. Wilhelm Wien (physics, 1911) and Lev Landau (physics, 1962) 60 25
971 500 f. Carl Braun (physics, 1909) and Sir Edward Appleton (physics, 1947) 60 25
972 500 f. Percy Bridgman (physics, 1946) and Nikolai Semyonov (physics, 1956) 60 25
973 500 f. Sir William Ramsay (chemistry, 1904) and Glenn Seaborg (chemistry, 1951) . . 60 25
974 500 f. Otto Wallach (chemistry, 1910) and Hermann Staudinger (chemistry, 1953) . 60 25
975 500 f. Richard Synge (chemistry, 1952) and Axel Theorell (chemistry, 1955) 60 25
976 500 f. Thomas Morgan (medicine, 1933) and Hermann Muller (medicine, 1946) 60 25
977 500 f. Allvar Gullstrand (medicine, 1911) and Willem Einthoven (Medicine, 1924) . 60 25
978 500 f. Sir Charles Sherrington (medicine, 1932) and Otto Loewi (medicine, 1936) . . . 60 25
979 500 f. Jules Bordet (medicine, 1936) and Sir Alexander Fleming (medicine, 1945) . . 60 25

376 1956 Bugatti

1993. Racing Cars and Railway Locomotives. Multicoloured.

980 20 f. Type **376** 10 10
981 20 f. 1968 Ferrari 10 10
982 20 f. 1948 Class C62 steam locomotive, 1948, Japan . . 10 10

983 20 f. Electric train, 1975, Russia 10 10
984 140 f. 1962 Lotus Mk 25 10 10
985 140 f. 1970 Matra 10 10
986 140 f. Diesel locomotive, 1954, Norway 10 10
987 140 f. Class 26 steam locomotive, 1982, South Africa 10 10
988 1250 f. 1963 Porsche 90 65
989 1250 f. 1980 Ligier JS 11 90 65
990 1250 f. Metroliner electric train, 1967, U.S.A. 90 65
991 1250 f. Diesel train, 1982, Canada 90 65
992 3000 f. 1967 Honda 2·10 1·50
993 3000 f. 1992 Benetton B 192 2·10 1·50
994 3000 f. Union Pacific Railroad diesel-electric locomotive, 1969, U.S.A. 2·10 2·10
995 3000 f. TGV Atlantique express train, 1990, France 2·10 2·10

377 Pharaonic Ship

1993. Ships. Multicoloured.
996 5 f. Type **377** 10 10
997 5 f. Mediterranean carrack 10 10
998 5 f. "Great Western" (sail paddle-steamer), 1837 10 10
999 5 f. "Mississippi" (paddle-steamer), 1850 10 10
1000 15 f. Phoenician bireme 10 10
1001 15 f. Viking ship 10 10
1002 15 f. "Clermont" (first commercial paddle-steamer), 1806 10 10
1003 15 f. "Pourquoi Pas?" (Charcot's ship), 1936 10 10
1004 140 f. "Santa Maria" (Columbus's ship), 1492 10 10
1005 140 f. H.M.S. "Victory" (ship of the line), 1765 10 10
1006 140 f. Motor yacht 10 10
1007 140 f. "Bremen" (liner), 1950 10 10
1008 10000 f. "Sovereign of the Seas" (galleon), 1637 9·25 80
1009 10000 f. "Cutty Sark" (clipper) 9·25 80
1010 10000 f. "Savannah" (nuclear-powered freighter) 9·25 80
1011 10000 f. "Condor" (hydrofoil) 9·25 80
No. 999 is wrongly inscribed "Mississipi".

378 Johannes Gutenberg and Printing Press

1993. Inventors. Multicoloured.
1012 500 f. Type **378** 60 25
1013 500 f. Sir Isaac Newton and telescope 60 25
1014 500 f. John Dalton and atomic theory 60 25
1015 500 f. Louis Jacques Daguerre and camera 60 25
1016 500 f. Michael Faraday and electric motor 60 25
1017 500 f. Wright brothers and "Flyer" 60 25
1018 500 f. Alexander Bell and telephone 60 25
1019 500 f. Thomas Edison and telegraph 60 25
1020 500 f. Karl Benz and motor vehicle 60 25
1021 500 f. Sir Charles Parsons and "Turbina" 60 25
1022 500 f. Rudolf Diesel and diesel locomotive 60 35
1023 500 f. Guglielmo Marconi and early radio 60 25
1024 500 f. Lumiere brothers and cine-camera 60 35
1025 500 f. Herman Oberth and space rocket 60 25
1026 500 f. John Mauchly, J. Prosper Eckert and computer 60 25
1027 500 f. Arthur Shawlow, compact disc and laser 60 25

379 Leonardo da Vinci and "Virgin of the Rocks"

1993. Painters. Multicoloured.
1028 50 f. Type **379** 10 10
1029 50 f. Titian and "Sacred and Profane Love" 10 10
1030 50 f. Rembrandt and "Jeremiah crying" 10 10
1031 50 f. J. M. W. Turner and "Ulysses" 10 10
1032 640 f. Michelangelo and the Doni Tondo 70 30
1033 640 f. Peter Paul Rubens and "Self-portrait" 70 30
1034 640 f. Francisco Goya and "Don Manuel Osorio de Zuniga" 70 30
1035 640 f. Eugene Delacroix and "Christ on Lake Gennesaret" 70 30
1036 1000 f. Claude Monet and "Poppyfield" 95 50
1037 1000 f. Paul Gauguin and "Two Tahitians" 95 50
1038 1000 f. Henri Marie de Toulouse-Lautrec and "Woman with a Black Boa" 95 50
1039 1000 f. Salvador Dali and "St. James of Compostela" 95 50
1040 2500 f. Pierre Auguste Renoir and "Child carrying Flowers" 2·75 90
1041 2500 f. Vincent Van Gogh and "Dr. Paul Gachet" 2·75 90
1042 2500 f. Pablo Picasso and "Crying Woman" 2·75 90
1043 2500 f. Andy Warhol and "Portrait of Elvis" 2·75 90

380 Sunset Moth ("Chrysiridia madagascariensis")

1993. Butterflies, Moths and Birds. Multicoloured.
1044 45 f. Type **380** 10 10
1045 45 f. African monarch ("Hypolimnas misippus") 10 10
1046 45 f. Southern crested Madagascar coucal ("Coua verreauxi") 10 10
1047 45 f. African marsh owl ("Asio helvola") 10 10
1048 60 f. "Charaxes antamboulou" 10 10
1049 60 f. "Papilio antenor" 10 10
1050 60 f. Crested Madagascar coucal ("Coua cristata") 10 10
1051 60 f. Helmet bird ("Euryceros prevostii") 10 10
1052 140 f. "Hypolimnas dexithea" 10 10
1053 140 f. "Charaxes andronodorus" 10 10
1054 140 f. Giant Madagascar coucal ("Couca gigas") 10 10
1055 140 f. Madagascar red fody ("Foudia madagascarensis") 10 10
1056 3000 f. "Euxanthe madagascarensis" 3·25 45
1057 3000 f. "Papilio grosesmithi" 3·25 45
1058 3000 f. Sicklebill ("Falculea palliata") 3·25 45
1059 3000 f. Madagascar serpent eagle ("Eutriorchis astur") 3·25 45
Nos. 1044/59 were issued together, se-tenant, the butterfly and bird designs respectively forming composite designs.

381 Henri Dunant and Volunteers unloading Red Cross Lorry

1993. Anniversaries and Events. Multicoloured.
1060 500 f. Type **381** (award of first Nobel Peace Prize, 1901) 35 25
1061 640 f. Charles de Gaulle and battlefield (50th anniv of Battle of Bir-Hakeim (1992)) 45 30
1062 1025 f. Crowd at Brandenburg Gate (bicentenary (1991) and fourth anniv of breach of Berlin Wall) 1·10 55
1063 1500 f. Doctors giving health instruction to women (Rotary International and Lions International) 1·60 55
1064 3000 f. Konrad Adenauer (German chancellor 1949–63, 24th death anniv (1991)) 3·25 60
1065 3500 f. "LZ-4" (airship), 1908, and Count Ferdinand von Zeppelin (75th death anniv (1992)) 4·00 60

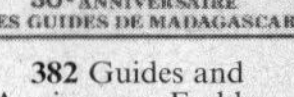

382 Guides and Anniversary Emblem

383 Player, Trophy and Ficklin Home, Macon

1993. Air. 50th Anniv of Madagascan Girl Guides.
1067 **382** 140 f. multicoloured 10 10

1993. World Cup Football Championship, United States (1992). Multicoloured.
1068 140 f. Type **383** 10 10
1069 640 f. Player, trophy and Herndon Home, Atlanta 65 35
1070 1025 f. Player, trophy and Cultural Centre, Augusta 1·40 55
1071 5000 f. Player, trophy and Old Governor's Mansion, Milledgeville 6·00 1·00

1993. Various stamps optd with emblem and inscription. (a) Germany, World Cup Football Champion, 1990. Nos. 778/81 optd **VAINQUEUR:ALLEMAGNE**.
1073 **328** 350 f. multicoloured 25 15
1074 – 1000 f. multicoloured 90 50
1075 – 1500 f. multicoloured 1·50 80
1076 – 2500 f. multicoloured 2·75 1·00

(b) Gold Medallists at Winter Olympic Games, Albertville (1992). Nos. 812/15 optd with olympic rings, "**MEDAILLE D'OR**" and further inscr as below.
1077 350 f. **BOB A QUATRE (AUT) INGO APPELT HARALD WINKLER GERHARD HAIDACHER THOMAS SCROLL** 25 15
1078 1000 f. **1000 M. - OLAF ZINKE (GER)** 90 50
1079 1500 f. **50 KM LIBRE BJOERN DAEHLIE (NOR)** 1·50 80
1080 2500 f. **SUPER G MESSIEURS KJETIL-ANDRE AAMODT (NOR)** 2·75 1·25

(c) Anniversaries. Nos. 1060, 675 and 707 optd as listed below.
1082 500 f. Red Cross and **130e ANNIVERSAIRE DE LA CREATION DE LA CROIX-ROUGE 1863-1993** 2·25 1·10
1083 550 f. Lions emblem and **75eme ANNIVERSAIRE LIONS** 2·25 1·10
1084 1500 f. Guitar and **THE ELVIS'S GUITAR 15TH ANNIVERSARY OF HIS DEATH 1977-1992** 1·75 80
1085 1500 f. Guitar and **GUITARE ELVIS 15eme ANNIVERSAIRE DE SA MORT 1977-1992** 1·75 80

(d) 50th Death Anniv of Robert Baden-Powell (founder of Boy Scouts). Optd **50eme ANNIVERSAIRE DE LA MORT DE BADEN POWEL** and emblem. (i) On Nos. 870/5 with scout badge in wreath.
1086 **354** 140 f. multicoloured 10 10
1087 – 500 f. multicoloured 35 25
1088 – 640 f. multicoloured 45 30
1089 – 1025 f. multicoloured 1·10 30
1090 – 1140 f. multicoloured 1·10 35
1091 – 3500 f. multicoloured 3·25 1·10

(ii) On No. 676 with profile of Baden-Powell.
1093 1500 f. multicoloured 1·75 80

(e) Bicentenary of French Republic. Nos. 761/5 optd **Republique Francaise** and emblem within oval and **BICENTENAIRE DE L'AN I DE LA REPUBLIQUE FRANCAISE**.
1094 250 f. multicoloured 20 15
1095 350 f. multicoloured 25 15
1096 1000 f. multicoloured 1·10 50
1097 1500 f. multicoloured 1·75 50
1098 2500 f. multicoloured 2·75 90

385 Great Green Turban

1993. Molluscs. Multicoloured.
1100 40 f. Type **385** 10 10
1101 60 f. Episcopal mitre 10 10
1102 65 f. Common paper nautilis 10 10
1103 140 f. Textile cone 10 10
1104 500 f. European sea hare 90 25
1105 675 f. "Harpa amouretta" 1·10 35
1106 2500 f. Tiger cowrie 3·50 70

386 Tiger Shark

1993. Sharks. Multicoloured.
1108 10 f. Type **386** 10 10
1109 45 f. Japanese sawshark 10 10
1110 140 f. Whale shark 15 10
1111 270 f. Smooth hammerhead 30 20
1112 600 f. Oceanic white-tipped shark 65 35
1113 1200 f. Zebra shark 1·25 80
1114 1500 f. Goblin shark 1·90 1·10

387 Map of Africa and Industry

1993. Air. African Industrialization Day.
1116 **387** 500 f. red, yellow and blue 80 50

388 "Superviem Odoriko" Express Train

389 "Paphiopedilum siamense"

1993. Locomotives. Multicoloured.
1117 5 f. Type **388** 10 10
1118 15 f. Morrison Knudsen diesel locomotive No. 801 10 10
1119 140 f. ER-200 diesel train, Russia 10 10
1120 265 f. General Motors GP60 diesel-electric locomotive No. EKD-5, U.S.A. 20 15
1121 300 f. New Jersey Transit diesel locomotive, U.S.A. 20 15
1122 575 f. ICE high speed train, Germany 40 30
1123 2500 f. X2000 high speed train, Sweden 1·75 1·25

1993. Orchids. Multicoloured.
1125 50 f. Type **389** (wrongly inscr "Paphpiopedilum") 10 10
1126 65 f. "Cypripedium calceolus" 10 10
1127 70 f. "Ophrys oestrifera" 10 10
1128 140 f. "Cephalanthera rubra" 10 10
1129 300 f. "Cypripedium macranthon" 20 15
1130 640 f. "Calanthe vestita" 80 30
1131 2500 f. "Cypripedium guttatum" 3·25 90

390 "Necrophorus tomentosus"

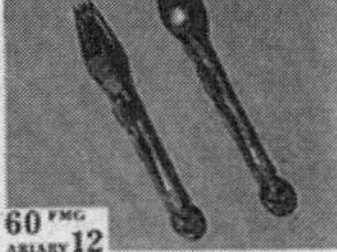

392 Fork and Spoon, Sakalava

391 Lufthansa Airliner, Germany

1994. Beetles. Multicoloured.
1133 20 f. Type **390** 10 10
1134 60 f. "Dynastes tityus" 10 10
1135 140 f. "Megaloxanta bicolor" 10 10
1136 605 f. Searcher 40 10
1137 720 f. "Chrysochroa mirabilis" 50 15
1138 1000 f. "Crioceris asparaqi" 70 25
1139 1500 f. Rose chafer 1·10 35

1994. Aircraft. Multicoloured.
1141 10 f. Type **391** 10 10
1142 10 f. British Aerospace/Aerospatiale Concorde supersonic jetliner of Air France 10 10
1143 10 f. Air Canada airliner 10 10
1144 10 f. ANA airliner, Japan 10 10
1145 60 f. Boeing 747 jetliner of British Airways 10 10
1146 60 f. Dornier Do-X flying boat, Germany 10 10

1147 60 f. Shinmeiwa flying boat, Japan 10 10
1148 60 f. Royal Jordanian airliner 10 10
1149 640 f. Alitalia airliner 45 15
1150 640 f. French–European Development Project Hydro 2000 flying boat 45 15
1151 640 f. Boeing 314 flying boat 45 15
1152 640 f. Air Madagascar airliner . 45 15
1153 5000 f. Emirates Airlines airliner, United Arab Emirates . . . . 3·50 1·10
1154 5000 f. Scandinavian Airways airliner . . . . 3·50 1·10
1155 5000 f. KLM airliner, Netherlands . . . . . . 3·50 1·10
1156 5000 f. Air Caledonie airliner, New Caledonia . . . . . 3·50 1·10

Nos. 1141/56 were issued together, se-tenant, Nos. 1146/7 and 1150/1 forming a composite design.

1994. Traditional Crafts. Multicoloured.

1157 30 f. Silver jewellery, Mahafaly 10 10
1158 60 f. Type **392** 10 10
1159 140 f. Silver jewellery, Antandroy 10 10
1160 430 f. Silver jewellery on table, Sakalava 30 10
1161 580 f. Frames of decorated paper, Ambalavao . . . 40 10
1162 1250 f. Silver jewellery, Sakalava 90 30
1163 1500 f. Marquetry table, Ambositra . . . . . . 1·10 35

393 "Chicoreus torrefactus" (shell)

1994. Marine Life. Multicoloured.

1165 15 f. Type **393** 10 10
1166 15 f. "Fasciolaria filamentosa" (shell) 10 10
1167 15 f. Regal angelfish ("Pigopytes diacanthus") 10 10
1168 15 f. Coelacanth ("Latimeria chalumnae") 10 10
1169 30 f. "Stellaria solaris" (shell) 10 10
1170 30 f. Ventral harp ("Harpa ventricosa") 10 10
1171 30 f. Blue-tailed boxfish ("Ostracion cyanurus") . 10 10
1172 30 f. Clown wrasse ("Coris gaimardi") 10 10
1173 1250 f. Lobster ("Panulirus sp.") 90 30
1174 1250 f. "Stenopus hispidus" (crustacean) 90 30
1175 1250 f. Undulate triggerfish ("Balistapus undulatus") . 90 30
1176 1250 f. Forceps butterflyfish ("Forcipiger longirostris") 90 30
1177 1500 f. Hermit crab ("Pagure") . . . . . . 1·10 35
1178 1500 f. Hermit crab ("Bernard l'Hermite") . . . . . 1·10 35
1179 1500 f. Diadem squirrelfish ("Adioryx diadema") . . . 1·10 35
1180 1500 f. Lunulate lionfish ("Pterois lunulata") . . . 1·10 35

Nos. 1165/80 were issued together, se-tenant, the backgrounds forming a composite design.

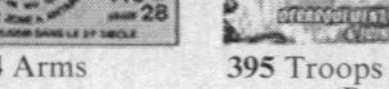

394 Arms **395** Troops landing on Beach

1994. Air. Junior Economic Chamber Zone A (Africa, Middle East and Indian Ocean) Conference, Antananarivo. Multicoloured.

1181 140 f. Type **394** 10 10
1182 500 f. Arms as in Type **394** but with inscriptions differently arranged (vert) 70 20

1994. 50th Anniv of Allied Landings at Normandy. Multicoloured.

1183 1500 f. Type **395** . . . . . 1·10 35
1184 3000 f. German troops defending ridge and allied troops (as T **397**) . . . . 2·25 75
1185 3000 f. Airplanes over battle scene, trooper with U.S. flag and German officer (as T **397**) 2·25 75

Nos. 1183/5 were issued together, se-tenant, forming a composite design.

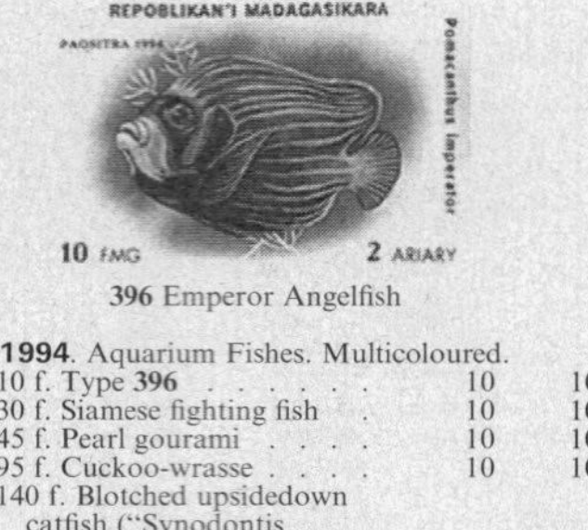

396 Emperor Angelfish

1994. Aquarium Fishes. Multicoloured.

1186 10 f. Type **396** 10 10
1187 30 f. Siamese fighting fish . 10 10
1188 45 f. Pearl gourami 10 10
1189 95 f. Cuckoo-wrasse 10 10
1190 140 f. Blotched upsidedown catfish ("Synodontis nigreventris") 10 10
1191 140 f. Jack Dempsey ("Cichlasoma biocellatum") 10 10
1192 3500 f. Mummichog . . . . 2·50 80

397 Notre Dame Cathedral, Armed Resistance Fighters and Rejoicing Crowd

1994. 50th Anniv of Liberation of Paris by Allied Forces. Multicoloured.

1194 1500 f. Crowd and Arc de Triomphe (as T **395**) . . 55 15
1195 3000 f. Type **397** . . . . . 1·10 35
1196 3000 f. Eiffel Tower and tank convoy . . . . 1·10 35

Nos. 1194/6 were issued together, se-tenant, forming a composite design.

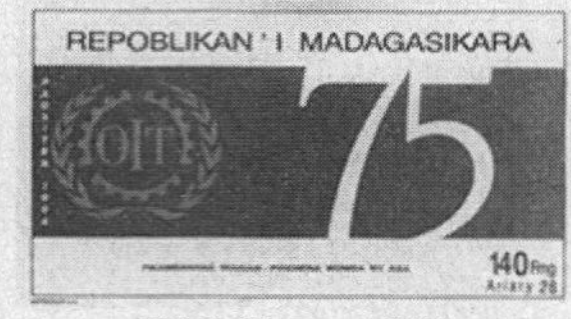

398 Emblem and "75"

1994. 75th Anniv of I.L.O.

1197 **398** 140 f. multicoloured . . 10 10

399 Biathlon

1994. Winter Olympic Games, Lillehammer, Norway. Multicoloured. (a) Without overprints.

1198 140 f. Type **399** 10 10
1199 1250 f. Ice hockey 45 15
1200 2000 f. Figure skating . . . 75 25
1201 2500 f. Skiing (downhill) . . 95 30

(b) Gold Medal Winners. Nos. 1198/1201 optd.

1203 140 f. Optd **M. BEDARD CANADA** 10 10
1204 1250 f. Optd **MEDAILLE D'OR SUEDE** 45 15
1205 2000 f. Optd **O. BAYUL UKRAINE** 75 25
1206 2500 f. Optd **M. WASMEIER ALLEMAGNE** 95 30

401 Majestic performing Dressage Exercise and Windsor Hotel, 1892

1994. Olympic Games, Atlanta, U.S.A. Mult.

1208 640 f. Type **401** 25 10
1209 1000 f. Covington Courthouse, 1884, and putting the shot 35 10
1210 1500 f. Table tennis and Carolton Community Activities Centre 55 15
1211 3000 f. Newman Commercial Court Square, 1800, and footballer . . . . . . 1·10 35

402 Spider on Map of Madagascar **403** "Oceonia oncidiflora"

1994. "Archaea workmani" (spider).

1213 **402** 500 f. multicoloured . . 20 15

1994. Flowers, Fruit, Fungi and Vegetables. Multicoloured.

1214 45 f. Type **403** 10 10
1215 45 f. Breadfruit ("Artocarpus altilis") 10 10
1216 45 f. "Russula annulata" . . 10 10
1217 45 f. Sweet potato 10 10
1218 60 f. "Cymbidella rhodochica" 10 10
1219 60 f. "Eugenia malaceensis" 10 10
1220 60 f. "Lactarius claricolor" . 10 10
1221 60 f. Yam 10 10
1222 140 f. Vanilla orchid ("Vanilla planifolia") 10 10
1223 140 f. "Jambosa domestica" 10 10
1224 140 f. "Russula tuberculosa" 10 10
1225 140 f. Avocado 10 10
1226 3000 f. "Phaius humblotii" . 1·10 35
1227 3000 f. Papaya . . . . . . 1·10 35
1228 3000 f. "Russula fistulosa" . 1·10 35
1229 3000 f. Manioc . . . . . . 1·10 35

Nos. 1214/29 were issued together, se-tenant, the backgrounds forming a composite design.

PARCEL POST STAMPS

1919. Receipt stamp of France surch **MADAGASCAR ET DEPENDANCES 0fr.10 COLIS POSTAUX**.

P81 0 f. 10 on 10 c. grey . . . . . 2·75 2·75

1919. Fiscal stamp of Madagascar surch **COLIS POSTAUX 0f.10**.

P82 0 f. 10 on 1 f. pink . . . . . 70·00 42·00

1919. Fiscal stamps surch **Madagascar et Dependances** (in capitals on No. P83) **COLIS POSTAUX 0f.10.**

P83 0 f. 10 pink . . . . 6·25 4·75
P84 0 f. 10 red and green . . . . 1·50 1·25
P85 0 f. 10 black and green . . . . 1·75 1·25

POSTAGE DUE STAMPS

1896. Postage Due stamps of Fr. Colonies optd **Madagascar et DEPENDANCES.**

D17 U 5 c. blue . . . . 5·00 4·75
D18 10 c. brown . . . . 5·00 4·25
D19 20 c. yellow . . . . 4·50 5·00
D20 30 c. red . . . . 5·50 5·00
D21 40 c. mauve . . . . 50·00 30·00
D22 50 c. violet . . . . 6·00 5·00
D23 1 f. green . . . . 55·00 35·00

D 6 Governor's Palace, Tananarive **D 37**

1908.

D70 D 6 2 c. red 10 10
D71 4 c. violet 10 15
D72 5 c. green 10 20
D73 10 c. red 10 20
D74 20 c. olive 10 30
D75 40 c. brown on cream . . 15 30
D76 50 c. brown on blue . . 15 25
D77 60 c. red 20 45
D78 1 f. blue 25 55

1924. Surch in figures.

D123 D 6 60 c. on 1 f. red . . . . 1·00 1·40
D124 2 f. on 1 f. purple . . . 45 60
D125 3 f. on 1 f. blue 45 60

1942. Free French Administration. Optd **FRANCE LIBRE** or surch also.

D254 D 6 10 c. red 55 65
D255 20 c. green 55 65
D256 0,30 on 5 c. green . . . 55 65
D257 40 c. brown on cream . . 55 65
D258 50 c. brown and blue . . 55 65
D259 60 c. red 55 65
D260 1 f. blue 55 65
D261 1 f. on 2 c. purple . . . 3·00 3·50
D262 2 f. on 4 c. violet . . . 1·25 1·50
D263 2 f. on 1 f. mauve . . . 55 65
D264 3 f. on 1 f. blue 55 65

1947.

D319 D 37 10 c. mauve 10 25
D320 30 c. brown 10 25
D321 50 c. green 10 25
D322 1 f. brown 10 25
D323 2 f. red 20 30
D324 3 f. brown 15 30
D325 4 f. blue 15 40
D326 5 f. red 25 45
D327 10 f. green 35 55
D328 20 f. blue . . . . . . 40 1·00

APPENDIX

The following stamps have either been issued in excess of postal needs or have not been available to the public in reasonable quantities at face value.

1992.

Olympic Games, Barcelona. 500 f. (on gold foil).

1993.

Bicentenary of French Republic. 1989 "Philexfrance 89" issue optd. 5000 f.

1994.

Elvis Presley (entertainer). 10000 f. (on gold foil).

World Cup Football Championship, U.S.A. 10000 f. (on gold foil).

Winter Olympic Games, Lillehammer, Norway. 10000 f. (on gold foil).

Olympic Games, Atlanta, U.S.A. 5000 f. (on gold foil).

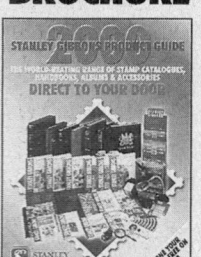

MADEIRA Pt. 9

A Portuguese island in the Atlantic Ocean off the N.W. coast of Africa. From 1868 to 1929 and from 1980 separate issues were made.

1868. 1000 reis = 1 milreis.
1912. 100 centavos = 1 escudo.

Nos. 1/78b are stamps of Portugal optd **MADEIRA**.

1868. With curved value label. Imperf.

No.	Type	Description	Unused	Used
1	14	20 r. bistre	£180	£140
2		50 r. green	£180	£140
3		80 r. orange	£190	£140
4		100 r. lilac	£100	£140

1868. With curved value label. Perf.

No.	Type	Description	Unused	Used
10	14	5 r. black	50·00	35·00
13		10 r. yellow	85·00	75·00
14		20 r. bistre	£130	£100
15		25 r. red	50·00	11·00
16		50 r. green	£160	£140
17		80 r. orange	£160	£140
19		100 r. mauve	£160	£140
20		120 r. blue	£100	80·00
21		240 r. mauve	£450	£400

1871. With straight value label.

No.	Type	Description	Unused	Used
30	15	5 r. black	8·25	5·75
47		10 r. yellow	26·00	20·00
72a		10 r. green	60·00	50·00
48		15 r. brown	18·00	11·00
49		20 r. bistre	29·00	20·00
34		25 r. pink	10·50	4·00
51		50 r. green	60·00	27·00
71		50 r. blue	£110	55·00
36		80 r. orange	£100	75·00
53		100 r. mauve	80·00	48·00
38		120 r. blue	£100	80·00
55		150 r. blue	£160	£130
74		150 r. yellow	£250	£225
39		240 r. lilac	£650	£500
67		300 r. lilac	70·00	65·00

1880. Stamps of 1880.

No.	Type	Description	Unused	Used
79	16	5 r. black	24·00	20·00
78		25 r. grey	26·00	20·00
78b		25 r. brown	26·00	20·00
77	17	25 r. grey	26·00	20·00

1898. Vasco da Gama. As Nos. 378/85 of Portugal.

No.	Type	Description	Unused	Used
134		2½ r. green	2·25	1·25
135		5 r. red	2·25	1·25
136		10 r. purple	3·00	1·50
137		25 r. green	2·50	1·25
138		50 r. blue	8·25	3·25
139		75 r. brown	10·00	6·75
140		100 r. brown	10·00	6·75
141		150 r. brown	13·50	11·00

For Nos. 134/41 with **REPUBLICA** overprint, see Nos. 455/62 of Portugal.

6 Ceres

7 20 r. Stamp, 1868

1929. Funchal Museum Fund. Value in black.

No.	Type	Description	Unused	Used
148	6	3 c. violet	60	60
149		4 c. yellow	60	60
150		5 c. blue	60	60
151		6 c. brown	75	75
152		10 c. red	75	75
153		15 c. green	75	75
154		16 c. brown	75	75
155		25 c. purple	80	80
156		32 c. green	80	80
157		40 c. brown	80	80
158		50 c. grey	80	80
159		64 c. blue	80	80
160		80 c. brown	80	80
161		96 c. red	3·25	3·25
162		1 e. black	70	70
163		1 e. 20 pink	70	70
164		1 e. 60 blue	70	70
165		2 e. 40 yellow	1·00	1·00
166		3 e. 36 green	1·25	1·25
167		4 e. 50 red	1·25	1·25
168		7 e. blue	2·50	2·50

1980. 112th Anniv of First Overprinted Madeira Stamps.

No.	Type	Description	Unused	Used
169	7	6 e. 50 black, bistre & green	20	10
170	–	19 e. 50 black, purple & red	75	50

DESIGN: 19 e. 50, 100 r. stamp, 1868.

8 Ox Sledge

1980. World Tourism Conference, Manila, Philippines. Multicoloured.

No.	Type	Description	Unused	Used
172		50 c. Type **8**	10	10
173		1 e. Wine and grapes	10	10
174		5 e. Map of Madeira	40	10
175		6 e. 50 Basketwork	40	10
176		8 e. Orchid	65	25
177		30 e. Fishing boat	1·60	50

9 O Bailinho (folk dance)

1981. Europa.

No.	Type	Description	Unused	Used
178	9	22 e. multicoloured	1·10	60

10 Portuguese Caravel approaching Madeira

11 "Dactylorhiza foliosa"

1981. 560th Anniv (1980) of Discovery of Madeira. Multicoloured.

No.	Type	Description	Unused	Used
180		8 e. 50 Type **10**	35	10
181		33 e. 50 Prince Henry the Navigator and map of Atlantic Ocean	1·60	50

1981. Regional Flowers. Multicoloured.

No.	Type	Description	Unused	Used
182		7 e. Type **11**	25	10
183		8 e. 50 "Geranium maderense"	35	10
184		9 e. "Goodyera macrophylla"	35	10
185		10 e. "Armeria maderensis"	35	10
186		12 e. 50 "Matthiola maderensis"	15	10
187		20 e. "Isoplexis sceptrum"	50	35
188		27 e. "Viola paradoxa"	1·00	45
189		30 e. "Erica maderensis"	60	25
190		33 e. 50 "Scilla maderensis"	1·10	70
191		37 e. 50 "Cirsium latifolium"	75	45
192		50 e. "Echium candicans"	1·25	65
193		100 e. "Clethra arborea"	2·10	80

12 First Sugar Mill

13 Dancer holding Dolls on Staff

1982. Europa.

No.	Type	Description	Unused	Used
199	12	33 e. 50 multicoloured	1·75	70

1982. O Brinco Dancing Dolls. Multicoloured.

No.	Type	Description	Unused	Used
201		27 e. Type **13**	1·00	55
202		33 e. 50 Dancers	1·50	75

14 Los Levadas Irrigation Channels

1983. Europa.

No.	Type	Description	Unused	Used
203	14	37 e. 50 multicoloured	1·25	55

15 Flag of Madeira

16 Rally Car

1983. Flag.

No.	Type	Description	Unused	Used
205	15	12 e. 50 multicoloured	65	10

1984. Europa. As T **398** of Portugal but additionally inscr "MADEIRA".

No.	Type	Description	Unused	Used
206		51 e. multicoloured	1·60	95

1984. 25th Anniv of Madeira Rally. Multicoloured.

No.	Type	Description	Unused	Used
208		16 e. Type **16**	40	10
209		51 e. Rally car (different)	1·50	55

MINIMUM PRICE

The minimum price quoted is 10p which represents a handling charge rather than a basis for valuing common stamps. For further notes about prices see introductory pages.

17 Basket Sledge

18 Braguinha Player

1984. Transport (1st series). Multicoloured.

No.	Type	Description	Unused	Used
210		16 e. Type **17**	25	10
211		35 e. Hammock	90	50
212		40 e. Borracheiros (wine carriers)	1·10	50
213		51 e. Carreira local sailing boat	1·40	50

See also Nos. 218/21.

1985. Europa.

No.	Type	Description	Unused	Used
214	18	60 e. multicoloured	1·75	75

19 Black Scabbardfish

1985. Fishes (1st series). Multicoloured.

No.	Type	Description	Unused	Used
216		40 e. Type **19**	1·25	50
217		60 e. Opah	1·50	75

See also Nos. 222/3 and 250/3.

1985. Transport (2nd series). As T **17**. Multicoloured.

No.	Type	Description	Unused	Used
218		20 e. Ox sledge	30	10
219		40 e. Mountain railway	95	50
220		46 e. Fishing boat and basket used by pesquitos (itinerant fish sellers)	1·40	75
221		60 e. Coastal ferry	1·25	90

1986. Fishes (2nd series). As T **19**. Multicoloured.

No.	Type	Description	Unused	Used
222		20 e. Big-eyed tuna	75	15
223		75 e. Alfonsino	2·50	95

20 Cory's Shearwater and Tanker

1986. Europa.

No.	Type	Description	Unused	Used
224	20	68 e. 50 multicoloured	1·75	80

21 Sao Lourenco Fort, Funchal

1986. Fortresses. Multicoloured.

No.	Type	Description	Unused	Used
226		22 e. 50 Type **21**	50	10
227		52 e. 50 Sao Joao do Pico Fort, Funchal	1·25	60
228		68 e. 50 Sao Tiago Fort, Funchal	1·75	70
229		100 e. Nossa Senhora do Amparo Fort, Machico	2·50	85

22 Firecrest 24 Funchal Cathedral

23 Social Services Centre, Funchal (Raul Chorao Ramalho)

1987. Birds (1st series). Multicoloured.

No.	Type	Description	Unused	Used
230		25 e. Type **22**	50	15
231		57 e. Trocaz pigeon	1·25	65
232		74 e. 50 Barn owl	1·75	90
233		125 e. Soft-plumaged petrel	2·50	1·25

See also Nos. 240/3.

1987. Europa. Architecture.

No.	Type	Description	Unused	Used
234	23	74 e. 50 multicoloured	1·60	85

1987. Historic Buildings. Multicoloured.

No.	Type	Description	Unused	Used
236		51 e. Type **24**	1·10	60
237		74 e. 50 Old Town Hall, Santa Cruz	1·50	65

25 "Maria Cristina" (mail boat)

1988. Europa. Transport and Communications.

No.	Type	Description	Unused	Used
238	25	80 e. multicoloured	1·60	65

1988. Birds (2nd series). As T **22** but horiz. Multicoloured.

No.	Type	Description	Unused	Used
240		27 e. European robin	40	15
241		60 e. Rock sparrow	1·10	60
242		80 e. Chaffinch	1·50	70
243		100 e. European sparrow hawk	2·00	80

26 Columbus and Funchal House

27 Child flying Kite

1988. Christopher Columbus's Houses in Madeira. Multicoloured.

No.	Type	Description	Unused	Used
244		55 e. Type **26**	1·10	60
245		80 e. Columbus and Porto Santo house (horiz)	1·50	60

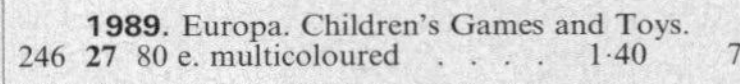

1989. Europa. Children's Games and Toys.

No.	Type	Description	Unused	Used
246	27	80 e. multicoloured	1·40	70

28 Church of St. John the Evangelist

29 Spiny Hatchetfish

1989. "Brasiliana 89" Stamp Exhibition, Rio de Janeiro. Madeiran Churches. Multicoloured.

No.	Type	Description	Unused	Used
248		29 e. Type **28**	45	10
249		87 e. St. Clara's Church and Convent	1·40	85

1989. Fishes (3rd series). Multicoloured.

No.	Type	Description	Unused	Used
250		29 e. Type **29**	35	15
251		60 e. Dog wrasse	1·10	60
252		87 e. Rainbow wrasse	1·90	90
253		100 e. Madeiran scorpionfish	2·25	1·40

30 Zarco Post Office 31 Bananas

1990. Europa. Post Office Buildings.

No.	Type	Description	Unused	Used
254	30	80 e. multicoloured	1·10	60

1990. Sub-tropical Fruits. Multicoloured.

No.	Type	Description	Unused	Used
256		5 e. Type **31**	10	10
257		10 e. Thorn apple	10	10
258		32 e. Avocado	40	15
259		35 e. Mangoes	35	10
260		38 e. Tomatoes	40	15
261		60 e. Sugar apple	95	45
262		65 e. Surinam cherries	80	45
263		70 e. Brazilian guavas	90	50
264		85 e. Delicious fruits	90	50
265		100 e. Passion fruit	1·50	80
266		110 e. Papayas	1·40	55
267		125 e. Guava	1·40	65

32 Tunny Boat

1990. Boats. Multicoloured.

270	32 e. Type **32**	35	15
271	60 e. Desert Islands boat	85	45
272	70 e. Maneiro	1·00	50
273	95 e. Chavelha	1·50	85

33 Trocaz Pigeon

1991. The Trocaz Pigeon. Multicoloured.

274	35 e. Type **33**	55	25
275	35 e. Two pigeons	55	25
276	35 e. Pigeon on nest	55	25
277	35 e. Pigeon alighting on twig	55	25

Nos. 264/7 were issued together, se-tenant, forming a composite design.

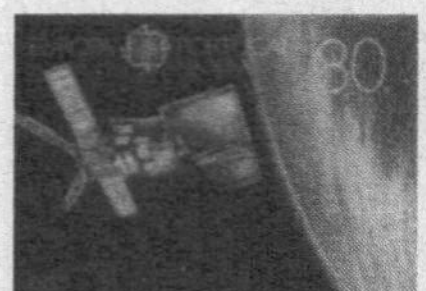

34 European Remote Sensing ("ERS1") Satellite

1991. Europa. Europe in Space.

278	**34**	80 e. multicoloured	1·00	60

35 Columbus and Funchal House

1992. Europa. 500th Anniv of Discovery of America by Columbus.

280	**35**	85 e. multicoloured	80	50

36 "Gaviao" (ferry)

1992. Inter-island Ships. Multicoloured.

281	38 e. Type **36**	35	15
282	65 e. "Independencia" (catamaran ferry)	60	35
283	85 e. "Madeirense" (car ferry)	80	45
284	120 e. "Funchalense" (freighter)	1·25	60

37 "Shadow thrown by Christa Maar" (Lourdes Castro)

39 Window of St. Francis's Convent, Funchal

38 Seals Swimming

1993. Europa. Contemporary Art.

285	**37**	90 e. multicoloured	1·00	50

1993. Mediterranean Monk Seal. Multicoloured.

287	42 e. Type **38**	45	20
288	42 e. Seal basking	45	20
289	42 e. Two seals on rocks	45	20
290	42 e. Mother suckling young	45	20

Nos. 287/90 were issued together, se-tenant, forming a composite design.

1993. Regional Architecture. Multicoloured.

291	42 e. Type **39**	40	20
292	130 e. Window of Mercy, Old Hospital, Funchal	1·25	60

40 Native of Cape of Good Hope and Explorer with Model Caravel

1994. Europa. Discoveries.

293	**40**	100 e. multicoloured	90	50

41 Embroidery

1994. Traditional Crafts (1st series). Multicoloured.

295	45 e. Type **41**	35	20
296	75 e. Tapestry	65	35
297	100 e. Boots	90	45
298	140 e. Wicker chair back	1·25	60

See also Nos. 301/4.

42 Funchal

43 Bread Dough Figures

1994. District Arms. Multicoloured.

299	45 e. Type **42**	35	20
300	140 e. Porto Santo	1·10	55

1995. Traditional Crafts (2nd series). Multicoloured.

301	45 e. Type **43**	35	20
302	80 e. Inlaid wooden box	65	35
303	95 e. Bamboo cage	75	40
304	135 e. Woollen bonnet	1·10	55

44 Guiomar Vilhena (entrepreneur)

1996. Europa. Famous Women.

305	**44**	98 e. multicoloured	80	40

45 "Adoration of the Magi"

1996. Religious Paintings by Flemish Artists. Multicoloured.

307	47 e. Type **45**	40	20
308	78 e. "St. Mary Magdalene"	65	35
309	98 e. "The Annunciation" (horiz)	80	40
310	140 e. "Saints Peter, Paul and Andrew" (horiz)	1·10	55

46 "Eumichtis albostigmata" (moth)

1997. Butterflies and Moths. Multicoloured.

311	49 e. Type **46**	35	20
312	80 e. Menophra maderae (moth)	60	30
313	100 e. Painted lady	70	35
314	140 e. Large white	1·00	55

47 Robert Achim and Anne of Arfet (Legend of Machico)

1997. Europa. Tales and Legends.

315	**47**	100 e. multicoloured	70	35

48 New Year's Eve Fireworks Display, Funchal

1998. Europa. National Festivals.

317	**48**	100 e. multicoloured	70	35

49 "Gonepteryx cleopatra"

1998. Butterflies and Moths. Multicoloured.

319	50 e. Type **49**	35	20
320	85 e. "Xanthorhoe rupicola"	60	30
321	100 e. "Noctua teixeirai"	70	35
322	140 e. "Xenochlorodes nubigena"	95	50

50 Madeira Island Nature Park

1999. Europa. Parks and Gardens.

323	**50**	100 e. multicoloured	65	35

51 Medieval Floor Tile

1999. Tiles from Frederico de Freitas Collection, Funchal. Multicoloured.

325	51 e. Type **51**	35	20
326	80 e. English art-nouveau tile (19–20th century)	55	30
327	95 e. Persian tile (14th century)	65	35
328	100 e. Spanish Moor tile (13th century)	65	35
329	140 e. Dutch Delft tile (18th century)	95	50
330	210 e. Syrian tile (13–14th century)	1·50	75

CHARITY TAX STAMPS

The note under this heading in Portugal also applies here.

1925. As Marquis de Pombal stamps of Portugal but inscr "MADEIRA".

C142	C **73**	15 c. grey	1·25	1·25
C143	–	15 c. grey	1·25	1·25
C144	C **75**	15 c. grey	1·25	1·25

NEWSPAPER STAMP

1876. Newspaper stamp of Portugal optd **MADEIRA**.

N69	N **17**	$2\frac{1}{2}$ r. green	8·00	3·25

POSTAGE DUE STAMPS

1925. Marquis de Pombal stamps as Nos. C1/3 optd **MULTA**.

D145	C **73**	30 c. grey	1·25	1·25
D146	–	30 c. grey	1·25	1·25
D147	C **75**	30 c. grey	1·25	1·25

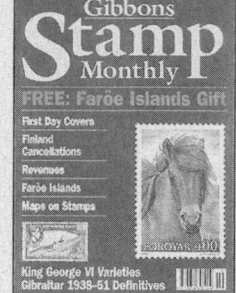

MAFEKING Pt. 1

A town in the Cape of Good Hope. Special stamps issued by British garrison during Boer War.

12 pence = 1 shilling;
20 shillings = 1 pound

1900. Surch **MAFEKING, BESIEGED.** and value.

(a) On Cape of Good Hope stamps.

1 **6** 1d. on ½d. green . . . . . . £170 55·00
2 **17** 1d. on ½d. green . . . . . . £225 65·00
3 3d. on 1d. red . . . . . . £170 50·00
4 **6** 6d. on 3d. mauve £25000 £250
5 1s. on 4d. olive £5500 £325

(b) On stamps of Bechuanaland Protectorate (opts on Great Britain).

6 **71** 1d. on ½d. red (No. 59) . . . £170 55·00
7 **57** 3d. on 1d. lilac (No. 61) . . . £850 85·00
13 **73** 6d. on 2d. green and red (No. 62) . . . . £1100 70·00
9 **75** 6d. on 3d. purple on yell (No. 63) £4000 £250
14 **79** 1s. on 6d. purple on red (No. 65) . . . . £3750 85·00

(c) On stamps of British Bechuanaland (opts on Great Britain).

10 **3** 6d. on 3d. lilac and black (No. 12) . . . . £350 60·00
11 **76** 1s. on 4d. green and brown (No. 35) . . . . £1200 70·00
15 **79** 1s. on 6d. purple on red (No. 36) £13000 £650
16 **82** 2s. on 1s. green (No. 37) . . £7000 £325

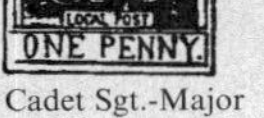

3 Cadet Sgt.-Major Goodyear

4 General Baden-Powell

1900.

17 **3** 1d. blue on blue £800 £275
19 **4** 3d. blue on blue £1200 £400

MALACCA Pt. 1

A British Settlement on the Malay Peninsula which became a state of the Federation of Malaya, incorporated in Malaysia in 1963.

100 cents = 1 dollar (Malayan)

1948. Silver Wedding. As T **11b/c** of Gambia.

1 10 c. violet 30 70
2 $5 brown . . . . 26·00 35·00

1949. As T **58** of Straits Settlements.

3 1 c. black 30 70
4 2 c. orange 70 45
5 3 c. green . . . . 30 1·75
6 4 c. brown 20 10
6a 5 c. purple . . . . 45 1·50
7 6 c. grey 60 85
8 8 c. red . . . . 30 5·50
8a 8 c. green . . . . 85 4·50
9 10 c. mauve 20 10
9a 12 c. red . . . . 95 4·25
10 15 c. blue 70 60
11 20 c. black and green . . . . . 30 6·00
11a 20 c. blue . . . . 1·75 2·50
12 25 c. purple and orange 30 70
12a 35 c. red and purple . . . . . 1·00 3·00
13 40 c. red and purple . . . . . 1·25 11·00
14 50 c. black and blue . . . . . 75 1·25
15 $1 blue and purple . . . . . . 7·00 19·00
16 $2 green and red . . . . . . 20·00 21·00
17 $5 green and brown . . . . . 42·00 35·00

1949. U.P.U. As T **11d/g** of Gambia.

18 10 c. purple 20 45
19 15 c. blue . . . . 1·40 1·75
20 25 c. orange . . . . 45 3·75
21 50 c. black . . . . 1·00 4·00

1953. Coronation. As T **11h** of Gambia.

22 10 c. black and purple 55 75

1 Queen Elizabeth II

1954.

23 **1** 1 c. black 10 60
24 2 c. orange . . . . 30 1·00
25 4 c. brown 40 10
26 5 c. mauve . . . . 30 2·00
27 6 c. grey 10 30
28 8 c. green . . . . 30 2·00
29 10 c. purple 50 10
30 12 c. red . . . . 20 2·25
31 20 c. blue . . . . 20 1·00
32 25 c. purple and orange . . . . 20 1·00
33 30 c. red and purple 20 30
34 35 c. red and purple 20 80
35 **1** 50 c. black and blue . . . . . 30 1·75
36 $1 blue and purple . . . . . . 5·00 6·00
37 $2 green and red . . . . . . 22·00 30·00
38 $5 green and brown . . . . . 23·00 38·00

1957. As Nos. 92/102 of Kedah but inset portrait of Queen Elizabeth II.

39 1 c. black 10 40
40 2 c. red 10 40
41 4 c. sepia 10 10
42 5 c. lake 10 10
43 8 c. green . . . . 1·25 2·50
44 10 c. sepia 30 10
45 20 c. blue 30 40
46 50 c. black and blue 30 50
47 $1 blue and purple . . . . . . 2·25 2·50
48 $2 green and red . . . . . . 11·00 17·00
49 $5 brown and green . . . . . . 14·00 29·00

2 Copra

1960. As Nos. 39/49 but with inset picture of Melaka tree and Pelandok (mouse-deer) as in T **2**.

50 1 c. black 10 30
51 2 c. red 10 40
52 4 c. sepia 10 10
53 5 c. lake 10 10
54 8 c. green . . . . 2·50 2·50
55 10 c. purple 30 10
56 20 c. blue 50 60
57 50 c. black and blue 40 60
58 $1 blue and purple . . . . . . 1·75 2·50
59 $2 green and red . . . . . . 4·50 6·50
60 $5 brown and green . . . . . . 9·00 12·00

3 "Vanda hookeriana"

1965. As Nos. 115/21 of Kedah but with Arms of Malacca inset and inscr "MELAKA" as in T **3**.

61 **3** 1 c. multicoloured 10 90
62 – 2 c. multicoloured 10 90
63 – 5 c. multicoloured 10 10
64 – 6 c. multicoloured 30 55
65 – 10 c. multicoloured 20 10
66 – 15 c. multicoloured . . . . . 1·75 40
67 – 20 c. multicoloured . . . . . 2·25 90

The higher values used in Malacca were Nos. 20/7 of Malaysia.

4 "Papilio demoleus"

1971. Butterflies. As Nos. 124/30 of Kedah but with Arms of Malacca as in T **4**. Inscr "melaka".

70 – 1 c. multicoloured . . . . . . 40 1·50
71 – 2 c. multicoloured . . . . . . 60 1·50
72 – 5 c. multicoloured . . . . . . 1·00 60
73 **4** 6 c. multicoloured . . . . . . 1·00 2·25
74 – 10 c. multicoloured . . . . . 1·00 50
75 – 15 c. multicoloured . . . . . 1·75 20
76 – 20 c. multicoloured . . . . . 1·75 1·75

The higher values in use with this issue were Malaysia Nos. 64/71.

5 "Durio zibethinus"

6 Rubber

1979. Flowers. As Nos. 135/41 of Kedah but with Arms of Malacca and inscr "melaka" as in T **5**.

82 1 c. "Rafflesia hasseltii" 10 80
83 2 c. "Pterocarpus indicus" . . . 10 80
84 5 c. "Lagerstroemia speciosa" . . 15 70
85 10 c. Type **5** 20 20
86 15 c. "Hibiscus rosa-sinesis" . . 20 10
87 20 c. "Rhododendron scortechinii" 25 10
88 25 c. "Etlingera elatior" (inscr "Phaeomeria speciosa") . . . 45 60

1986. As Nos. 152/8 of Kedah but with Arms of Malacca and inscr "MELAKA" as in T **6**.

96 1 c. Coffee 10 10
97 2 c. Coconuts 10 10
98 5 c. Cocoa 10 10
99 10 c. Black pepper 10 10
100 15 c. Type **6** 10 10
101 20 c. Oil palm 10 10
102 30 c. Rice 15 20

MALAGASY REPUBLIC Pt. 6; Pt. 13

The former areas covered by Madagascar and Dependencies were renamed the Malagasy Republic within the French Community on 14 October 1958. It became independent on 26 June 1960. In 1992 it reverted to the name of Madagascar.

1958. 100 centimes = 1 franc.
1976. 5 francs = 1 ariary.

1958. 10th Anniv of Declaration of Human Rights. As T **48** of New Caledonia.
1 10 f. brown and blue 65 45

1959. Tropical Flora. As T **47** of New Caledonia.
2 6 f. green, brown and yellow . . 15 10
3 25 f. multicoloured 80 15
DESIGNS—HORIZ: 6 f. "Datura"; 25 f. Poinsettia.

1 Malagasy Flag and Assembly Hall

1959. Proclamation of Malagasy Republic and "French Community" Commemorative (60 f.).
4 **1** 20 f. red, green and purple . . 30 20
5 – 25 f. red, green and grey . . . 40 25
6 – 60 f. multicoloured . . . . . . 1·10 45
DESIGNS—VERT: 25 f. Malagasy flag on map of Madagascar; 60 f. Natives holding French and Malagasy flags.

2 "Chionaema pauliani" (butterfly)

3 Reafforestation

1960.
7 – 30 c. multicoloured (postage) 15 10
8 – 40 c. brown, choc & green . . 15 10
9 – 50 c. turquoise and purple . . 15 10
10 **2** 1 f. red, purple and black . . . 20 15
11 – 3 f. black, red and olive . . . 35 20
12 – 5 f. green, brown and red . . . 10 10
13 – 6 f. yellow and green 10 10
14 – 8 f. black, green and red . . . 15 10
15 – 10 f. green, brown & turq . . 45 10
16 – 15 f. green and brown 55 15
17 – 30 f. multicoloured (air) . . . 1·60 40
18 – 40 f. brown and turquoise . . 1·40 30
19 – 50 f. multicoloured . . . . . 2·75 50
20 – 100 f. multicoloured . . . . . 4·50 85
21 – 200 f. yellow and violet . . . 7·50 1·50
22 – 500 f. brown, blue and green 10·50 2·50
BUTTERFLIES—As Type **2**: 30 c. Purple-tip; 40 c. "Acraea hova"; 50 c. Clouded mother-of-pearl; 3 f. "Hypolimnas dexithea". 48 × 27 mm: 50 f. "Charaxes antamboulou"; 100 f. Sunset moth. 27 × 48 mm: 200 f. Tailed comet moth.
OTHER DESIGNS—As Type **2**: HORIZ: 5 f. Sisal; 8 f. Pepper; 15 f. Cotton. VERT: 6 f. Ylang ylang (flower); 10 f. Rice. $48\frac{1}{2} \times 27$ mm: 30 f. Sugar cane trucks; 40 f. Tobacco plantation; 500 f. Mandrare Bridge.

1960. Trees Festival.
23 **3** 20 f. brown, green and ochre 35 25

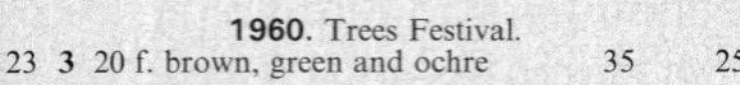

4

5 Pres. Philibert Tsiranana

1960. 10th Anniv of African Technical Co-operation Commission.
24 **4** 25 f. lake and green 45 35

1960.
25 **5** 20 f. brown and green 60 35

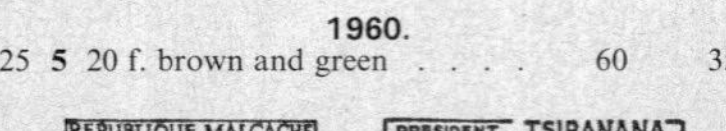

6 Young Athletes

7 Pres. Tsiranana

1960. 1st Youth Games, Tananarive.
26 **6** 25 f. brown, chestnut & blue 50 30

1960.
27 **7** 20 f. black, red and green . . 25 10

1960. Independence. Surch + **10 F FETES DE L'INDEPENDANCE**.
28 **7** 20 f. + 10 f. black, red & grn 55 35

9 Ruffed Lemur

1961. Lemurs.
29 – 2 f. purple & turq (postage) 15 15
30 **9** 4 f. black, brown and myrtle 20 15
31 – 12 f. brown and green 50 30
32 – 65 f. brown, sepia and myrtle (air) . . . . 2·25 65
33 – 85 f. black, sepia and green 2·25 1·00
34 – 250 f. purple, black and turq 6·50 2·75
LEMURS—VERT: As Type **9**: 2 f. Grey gentle lemur; 12 f. Mongoose-lemur. 48 × 27 mm: 65 f. Diadem sifaka; 85 f. Indris; 250 f. Verreaux's sifaka.

10 Diesel Train

11 U.N. and Malagasy Flags, and Govt. Building, Tananarive

1962.
35 **10** 20 f. myrtle . . . . 1·50 45
36 – 25 f. blue 35 15
DESIGN: 25 f. President Tsiranana Bridge.

1962. Admission into U.N.O.
37 **11** 25 f. multicoloured 35 20
38 85 f. multicoloured . . . . . 1·40 55

1962. Malaria Eradication. As T **43** of Mauritania.
39 25 f. + 5 f. green 80 80

12 Ranomafana

1962. Tourist Publicity.
40 **12** 10 f. purple, myrtle and blue (postage) 20 15
41 – 30 f. purple, blue and myrtle 40 15
42 – 50 f. blue, myrtle and purple 60 25
43 – 60 f. myrtle, purple and blue 80 35
44 – 100 f. brown, myrtle and blue (air) . . . . 1·75 95
DESIGNS—As Type **12**: 30 f. Tritriva Lake; 50 f. Foulpointe; 60 f. Fort Dauphin. $27 \times 47\frac{1}{2}$ mm: 100 f. Boeing 707 airliner over Nossi-Be.

13 G.P.O., Tamatave

1962. Stamp Day.
45 **13** 25 f. + 5 f. brown, myrtle and blue 35 40

14 Malagasy and U.N.E.S.C.O. Emblems

15 Hydro-electric Station

1962. U.N.E.S.C.O. Conference on Higher Education in Africa, Tananarive.
46 **14** 20 f. black, green and red . . 35 25

1962. 1st Anniv of Union of African and Malagasy States. As T **45** of Mauritania.
47 30 f. green 45 35

1962. Malagasy Industrialisation.
48 **15** 5 f. multicoloured 10 10
49 – 8 f. multicoloured 15 10
50 – 10 f. multicoloured 20 10
51 – 15 f. brown, black and blue 35 15
52 – 20 f. multicoloured 35 20
DESIGNS—HORIZ: 8 f. Atomic plant; 15 f. "Esso Gasikara" (tanker); 20 f. Hertzian aerials at Tananarive-Fianarantsoa. VERT: 10 f. Oilwell.

16 Globe and Factory

1963. International Fair, Tamatave.
53 **16** 25 f. orange and black . . . 30 20

1963. Freedom from Hunger. As T **51** of Mauritania.
54 25 f. + 5 f. lake, brown & red 60 60

17 Douglas DC-8 Airliner

1963. Air. Malagasy Commercial Aviation.
55 **17** 500 f. blue, red and green . . 8·50 3·25

18 Central Post Office, Tananarive

19 Madagascar Blue Pigeon

1963. Stamp Day.
56 **18** 20 f. + 5 f. brown & turq 55 35

1963. Malagasy Birds and Orchids (8 f. to 12 f.). Multicoloured. (a) Postage as T **19**.
57 1 f. Type **19** 75 30
58 2 f. Blue Madagascar coucal . . 75 30
59 3 f. Madagascar red fody . . . 75 30
60 6 f. Madagascar pygmy kingfisher 90 30
61 8 f. "Gastrorchis humblotii" . . 20 15
62 10 f. "Eulophiella roempleriana" 65 25
63 12 f. "Angraceum sesquipedale" 65 25
(b) Air. Horiz: $49\frac{1}{2} \times 28$ mm.
64 40 f. Helmet bird . . . . . . 3·25 45
65 100 f. Pitta-like Ground roller 8·00 1·25
66 200 f. Crested wood ibis . . . . 17·00 3·50

20 Centenary Emblem and Map

21 U.P.U. Monument, Berne, and Map of Malagasy

1963. Red Cross Centenary.
67 **20** 30 f. multicoloured 80 60

1963. Air. African and Malagasy Posts and Telecommunications Union. As T **56** of Mauritania.
68 85 f. multicoloured . . . . . . 1·40 90

1963. Air. 2nd Anniv of Malagasy's admission to U.P.U.
69 **21** 45 f. blue, red and turquoise 50 25
70 85 f. blue, red and violet . . 90 50

22 Arms of Fianarantsoa

23 Flame, Globe and Hands

1963. Town Arms (1st series). Multicoloured.
71 1 f. 50 Antsirabe 10 10
72 5 f. Antalaha 15 10
73 10 f. Tulear 20 10
74 15 f. Majunga 30 15
75 20 f. Type **22** 40 15
75a 20 f. Manajary 25 10
76 25 f. Tananarive 45 15
76a 30 f. Nossi Be 35 15
77 50 f. Diego-Suarez 85 50
77a 90 f. Antsohihy . . . . 1·40 55
See also Nos. 174/7 and 208/9.

1963. 15th Anniv of Declaration of Human Rights.
78 **23** 60 f. ochre, bronze & mauve 55 45

24 Met Station, Tananarive

1964. Air. World Meteorological Day.
79 **24** 90 f. brown, blue and grey 1·50 1·25

25 Postal Cheques and Savings Bank Building, Tananarive

26 Scouts beside Campfire

1964. Stamp Day.
80 **25** 25 f. + 5 f. brown, bl & grn 50 60

1964. 40th Anniv of Malagasy Scout Movement.
81 **26** 20 f. multicoloured 55 25

27 Symbolic Bird and Globe within "Egg"

28 Statuette of Woman

1964. "Europafrique".
82 **27** 45 f. brown and green . . . 45 35

1964. Malagasy Art.
83 **28** 6 f. brown, blue and indigo (postage) 25 15
84 – 30 f. brown, bistre & green 45 20
85 – 100 f. brown, red & vio (air) 1·50 95
DESIGNS: 30 f. Statuette of squatting vendor. $27 \times 48\frac{1}{2}$ mm: 100 f. Statuary of peasant family, ox and calf.

1964. French, African and Malagasy Co-operation. As T **68** of Mauritania.
86 25 f. brown, chestnut and black 40 25

29 Tree on Globe

30 Cithern

1964. University of Malagasy Republic.
87 **29** 65 f. black, red and green 50 25

1965. Malagasy Musical Instruments.
88 – 3 f. brown, blue and mauve (postage) 20 10
89 **30** 6 f. sepia, purple and green 25 10
90 – 8 f. brown, black and green 35 10
91 – 25 f. multicoloured 90 50
92 – 200 f. brown, orange and green (air) . . . . 4·00 2·25
DESIGNS—As Type **30**: 3 f. Kabosa (lute); 8 f. Hazolahy (sacred drum). LARGER–VERT: $35\frac{1}{2} \times 48$ mm: 25 f. "Valiha Player" (after E. Ralambo). 27 × 48 mm: 200 f. Bara violin.

31 Foulpointe Post Office

1965. Stamp Day.
93 **31** 20 f. brown, green & orange . . . 20 15

32 I.T.U. Emblem

33 J.-J. Rabearivelo (poet)

1965. I.T.U. Centenary.
94 **32** 50 f. green, blue and red . . 1·00 45

1965. Rabearivelo Commemorative.
95 **33** 40 f. brown and orange . . . 40 25

34 Nurse weighing Baby

1965. Air. International Co-operation Year.
96 **34** 50 f. black, bistre and blue . . 60 35
97 – 100 f. purple, brown & blue . . 1·25 60
DESIGN: 100 f. Boy and girl.

35 Pres. Tsiranana

36 Bearer

1965. Pres. Tsiranana's 55th Birthday.
98 **35** 20 f. multicoloured 25 15
99 25 f. multicoloured 30 20

1965. Postal Transport.
102 – 3 f. violet, blue and brown . . 30 15
103 – 4 f. blue, brown and green . . 25 15
104 **36** 10 f. multicoloured 25 15
105 – 12 f. multicoloured 30 20
106 – 20 f. multicoloured 90 20
107 – 25 f. multicoloured 80 20
108 – 30 f. red, brown and blue . . 2·25 1·60
109 – 65 f. brown, blue & violet . . 1·50 50
DESIGNS—HORIZ: 3 f. Early car; 4 f. Filanzane (litter); 12 f. Pirogue; 20 f. Horse-drawn mail-cart; 25 f. Bullock cart; 30 f. Early railway postal carriage; 65 f. Hydrofoil, "Porthos", Betsiboka.

37 Diseased Hands

1966. World Leprosy Day.
110 **37** 20 f. purple, red and green . . 35 20

38 Planting Trees

1966. Reafforestation Campaign.
111 **38** 20 f. violet, brown & turq . . 35 20

39 "Cicindelidae chaetodera andriana"

1966. Malagasy Insects. Multicoloured.
112 1 f. Type **39** 10 10
113 6 f. "Mantodea tisma freiji" . . 20 10
114 12 f. "Cerambycini mastododera nodicollis" 45 20
115 45 f. "Trachelophoru giraffa" . . 85 30

40 Madagascar 1 c. Stamp of 1903

41 Betsileo Dance

1966. Stamp Day.
116 **40** 25 f. bistre and red 35 25

1966. Folk Dances. Multicoloured.
117 2 f. Bilo Sakalava dance (vert) (postage) 15 10
118 5 f. Type **41** 25 15
119 30 f. Antandroy dance (vert) . . 55 20
120 200 f. Southern Malagasy dancer (air) . . . . 3·50 1·50
121 250 f. Sakalava Net Dance . . 4·00 2·25
Nos. 120/1 are size 27 × 48 mm.

43 "Tree" of Emblems

1966. O.C.A.M. Conference, Tananarive.
122 **43** 25 f. multicoloured 30 15
The above was issued with "Janvier 1966" obliterated by bars, and optd "**JUIN 1966**".

44 Singing Anthem

45 U.N.E.S.C.O. Emblem

1966. National Anthem.
123 **44** 20 f. brn, mauve and green . . 25 10

1966. 20th Anniv of U.N.E.S.C.O.
124 **45** 30 f. blue, bistre and red . . 35 20

46 Lions Emblem

47 Harvesting Rice

1967. 50th Anniv of Lions Int.
125 **46** 30 f. multicoloured 40 20

1967. International Rice Year.
126 **47** 20 f. multicoloured 30 15

48 Adventist Temple, Tanambao-Tamatave

1967. Religious Buildings (1st series).
127 **48** 3 f. ochre, blue and green . . 10 10
128 – 5 f. lilac, purple and green . . 10 10
129 – 10 f. purple, blue and green . . 25 10
BUILDINGS—VERT: 5 f. Catholic Cathedral, Tananarive. HORIZ: 10 f. Mosque, Tamatave.
See also Nos. 148/50.

49 Raharisoa at Piano

1967. 4th Death Anniv of Norbert Raharisoa (composer).
130 **49** 40 f. multicoloured 55 20

50 Jean Raoult's Bleriot XI, 1911

1967. "History of Malagasy Aviation".
131 **50** 5 f. brown, blue and green (postage) 35 15
132 – 45 f. black, blue & brown . . 90 35
133 – 500 f. black, blue and ochre (air) . . . . 8·75 3·75
DESIGNS: 45 f. Bernard Bougault and flying boat, 1926. 48 × 27 mm: 500 f. Jean Dagnaux and Breguet 19A2 biplane, 1927.

51 Ministry of Communications, Tananarive

52 Church, Torch and Map

1967. Stamp Day.
134 **51** 20 f. green, blue & orange . . 25 15

1967. Air. 5th Anniv of U.A.M.P.T. As T **101** of Mauritania.
135 100 f. mauve, bistre and red . . 1·25 60

1967. Centenary of Malagasy Lutheran Church.
136 **52** 20 f. multicoloured 30 15

53 Map and Decade Emblem

54 Woman's Face and Scales of Justice

1967. Int Hydrological Decade.
137 **53** 90 f. brown, red and blue . . 85 45

1967. Women's Rights Commission.
138 **54** 50 f. blue, ochre and green . . 50 25

55 Human Rights Emblem

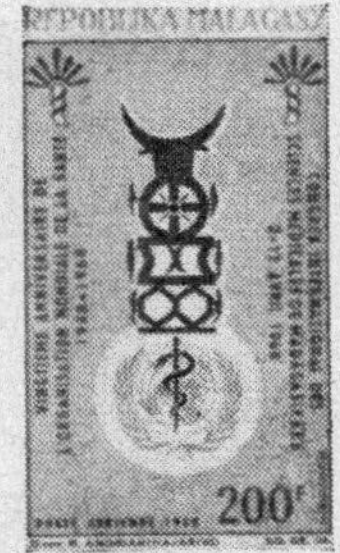

56 Congress and W.H.O. Emblems

1968. Human Rights Year.
139 **55** 50 f. red, green and black . . 40 25

1968. Air. 20th Anniv of W.H.O. and Int Medical Sciences Congress, Tananarive.
140 **56** 200 f. red, blue and ochre . . 2·40 1·25

57 International Airport, Tananarive-Ivato

1968. Air. Stamp Day.
141 **57** 500 f. blue, green & brown . . 6·75 3·25

1968. Nos. 33 and 38 surch.
142 **11** 20 f. on 85 f. (postage) . . . 40 30
143 – 20 f. on 85 f. (No. 33) (air) . . 50 30

59 "Industry and Construction"

61 Isotry Protestant Church, Fitiavana, Tananarive

60 Church and Open Bible

1968. Five-Year Plan (1st issue).
144 **59** 10 f. plum, red and green . . 15 10
145 – 20 f. black, red and green . . 20 15
146 – 40 f. blue, brown & ultram . . 2·10 60
DESIGNS—VERT: 20 f. "Agriculture". HORIZ: 40 f. "Transport".
See also Nos. 156/7.

1968. 150th Anniv of Christianity in Madagascar.
147 **60** 20 f. multicoloured 25 10

1968. Religious Buildings (2nd series).
148 **61** 4 f. brown, green and red . . 10 10
149 – 12 f. brown, blue and violet . . 20 10
150 – 50 f. indigo, blue and green . . 45 25
DESIGNS: 12 f. Catholic Cathedral, Fianarantsoa; 50 f. Aga Khan Mosque, Tananarive.

62 President Tsiranana and Wife

63 Cornucopia, Coins and Map

1968. 10th Anniv of Republic.
151 **62** 20 f. brown, red and yellow . . 20 10
152 30 f. brown, red and blue . . 25 15

1968. 50th Anniv of Malagasy Savings Bank.
154 **63** 20 f. multicoloured 25 10

64 "Dance of the Whirlwind"

1968. Air.
155 **64** 100 f. multicoloured . . . . 1·50 65

65 Malagasy Family

1968. Five Year Plan (2nd issue).
156 **65** 15 f. red, yellow and blue . . 15 10
157 – 45 f. multicoloured 40 25
DESIGN—VERT: 45 f. Allegory of "Achievement".

1968. Air. "Philexafrique" Stamp Exn., Abidjan (1969) (1st issue). As T **113a** of Mauritania.
158 100 f. multicoloured . . . . . 2·75 80
DESIGN: 100 f. "Young Woman sealing a Letter". (J. B. Santerre).

1969. Air. "Philexafrique" Stamp Exn., Abidjan, Ivory Coast (2nd issue). As T **114a** of Mauritania.
159 50 f. red, green and drab . . . 1·60 90
DESIGN: 50 f. Malagasy Arms, map and Madagascar stamp of 1946.

68 "Queen Adelaide receiving Malagasy Mission, London" (1836-37)

1969.

160 **68** 250 f. multicoloured . . . . 4·50 3·25

69 Hand with Spanner, Cogwheels and I.L.O. Emblem

1969. 50th Anniv of I.L.O.

161 **69** 20 f. multicoloured 25 15

70 Post and Telecommunications Building, Tananarive

1969. Stamp Day.

162 **70** 30 f. multicoloured 35 20

71 Map, Steering Wheel and Vehicles

72 President Tsiranana making Speech

1969. 20th Anniv of Malagasy Motor Club.

163 **71** 65 f. multicoloured 60 35

1969. 10th Anniv of President Tsiranana's Assumption of Office.

164 **72** 20 f. multicoloured 20 10

73 Bananas

74 Start of Race and Olympic Flame

1969. Fruits.

165 **73** 5 f. green, brown and blue 15 10
166 – 15 f. red, myrtle and green 30 10

DESIGN: 15 f. Lychees.

1969. Olympic Games, Mexico (1968).

167 **74** 15 f. brown, red and green 25 20

75 "Malagasy Seashore, East Coast" (A. Razafinjohany)

1969. Air. Paintings by Malagasy Artists. Multicoloured.

168 100 f. Type **75** . . . . 1·25 80
169 150 f. "Sunset on the High Plateaux" (H. Ratovo) . . . 2·50 1·40

76 Imerino House, High Plateaux

77 Ambalavao Arms

1969. Malagasy Traditional Dwellings (1st series).

170 – 20 f. red, blue and green . . 20 10
171 – 20 f. brown, red and blue 20 10
172 **76** 40 f. red, blue and indigo 40 20
173 – 60 f. purple, green & blue 60 25

HOUSES—HORIZ: 20 f. (No. 170), Tsimihety hut, East Coast; 60 f. Betsimisaraka dwellings, East Coast. VERT: 20 f. (No. 171), Betsileo house, High Plateaux.

See also Nos. 205/6.

1970. Town Arms (2nd series). Multicoloured.

174 10 f. Type **77** 20 10
175 25 f. Morondava 35 15
176 25 f. Ambatondrazaka 35 15
177 80 f. Tamatave 90 35

See also Nos. 208/9.

78 Agate

80 U.N. Emblem and Symbols

1970. Semi-precious Stones. Multicoloured.

178 5 f. Type **78** . . . . 1·60 55
179 20 f. Ammonite . . . . 3·25 1·10

1970. New U.P.U. Headquarters Building, Berne. As T **81** of New Caledonia.

180 20 f. blue, brown and mauve 30 20

1970. 25th Anniv of United Nations.

181 **80** 50 f. black, blue & orange 65 25

81 Astronaut and Module on Moon

1970. Air. 1st Anniv of "Apollo 11" Moon-landing.

182 **81** 75 f. green, slate and blue 1·10 40

82 Malagasy Fruits

1970.

183 **82** 20 f. multicoloured 30 15

83 Delessert's Lyria

1970. Sea Shells (1st series). Multicoloured.

184 5 f. Type **83** 50 15
185 10 f. Bramble murex 65 25
186 20 f. Thorny oyster . . . . . 1·40 50

84 Aye-aye

1970. International Nature Conservation Conference, Tananarive.

187 **84** 20 f. multicoloured 40 30

85 Boeing 737 in Flight

1970. Air.

188 **85** 200 f. red, green and blue 2·40 1·25

86 Pres. Tsiranana

87 Calcite

1970. Pres. Tsiranana's 60th Birthday.

189 **86** 30 f. brown and green . . . 30 15

1971. Minerals Multicoloured.

190 12 f. Type **87** . . . . 1·60 45
191 15 f. Quartz . . . . 2·25 65

88 Soap Works, Tananarive

1971. Malagasy Industries.

192 **88** 5 f. multicoloured 15 10
193 – 15 f. black, brown and blue 25 10
194 – 50 f. multicoloured 55 15

DESIGNS: 15 f. Chrome works, Comina-Andriamena; 50 f. Textile complex, Sotema-Majunga.

89 Globe and Emblems

1971. Council Meeting of Common Market Countries with African and Malagasy Associated States, Tananarive.

195 **89** 5 f. multicoloured 15 15

90 Rural Mobile Post Office

91 Gen. De Gaulle

1971. Stamp Day.

196 **90** 25 f. multicoloured 35 15

1971. Death (1970) of Gen. Charles de Gaulle.

197 **91** 30 f. black, red and blue . . 70 35

92 Palm Beach Hotel, Nossi-Be

93 Forestry Emblem

1971. Malagasy Hotels.

198 **92** 25 f. multicoloured 30 20
199 – 65 f. brown, blue & green 60 30

DESIGN: 65 f. Hilton Hotel, Tananarive.

1971. Forest Preservation Campaign.

200 **93** 3 f. multicoloured 15 10

MINIMUM PRICE

The minimum price quoted is 10p which represents a handling charge rather than a basis for valuing common stamps. For further notes about prices see introductory pages.

94 Jean Ralaimongo

96 Vezo Dwellings, South-east Coast

1971. Air. Malagasy Celebrities.

201 **94** 25 f. brown, red & orange 30 15
202 – 65 f. brown, myrtle & green 40 25
203 – 100 f. brown, ultram & bl 90 40

CELEBRITIES: 65 f. Albert Sylla; 100 f. Joseph Ravoahangy Andrianavalona.

1971. Air. 10th Anniv of African and Malagasy Posts and Telecommunications Union. As T **139a** of Mauritania.

204 100 f. U.A.M.P.T. H.Q. Brazzaville, and painting "Mpisikidy" (G. Rakotovao) 1·00 60

1971. Malagasy Traditional Dwellings (2nd series). Multicoloured.

205 5 f. Type **96** 15 10
206 10 f. Antandroy hut, South coast 20 10

97 "Children and Cattle in Meadow" (G. Rasoaharijaona)

1971. 25th Anniv of U.N.I.C.E.F.

207 **97** 50 f. multicoloured 65 30

1972. Town Arms (3rd series). As T **77**. Mult.

208 1 f. Maintirano Arms 10 10
209 25 f. Fenerive-Est 35 20

99 Cable-laying train

1972. Co-axial Cable Link, Tananarive–Tamatave.

210 **99** 45 f. brown, green and red 2·75 1·25

100 Telecommunications Station

1972. Inauguration of Philibert Tsiranana Satellite Communications Station.

211 **100** 85 f. multicoloured 75 45

101 Pres. Tsiranana and Voters

102 "Moped" Postman

1972. Presidential Elections.

212 **101** 25 f. multicoloured 40 35

1972. Stamp Day.

213 **102** 10 f. multicoloured 40 20

1972. De Gaulle Memorial. No. 197 surch **MEMORIAL +20F.**

214 **91** 30 f. + 20 f. blk, red & bl 60 60

104 Exhibition Emblem and Stamps   105 Road and Monument

1972. 2nd National Stamp Exn, Antanarive.
215 **104** 25 f. multicoloured 35 30
216 40 f. multicoloured 60 35
217 100 f. multicoloured . . . 1·25 75

1972. Opening of Andapa-Sambava Highway.
219 **105** 50 f. multicoloured 35 25

106 Petroleum Refinery, Tamatave   107 R. Rakotobe

1972. Malagasy Economic Development.
220 **106** 2 f. blue, green and yellow 20 10
221 – 100 f. multicoloured . . . 3·00 30
DESIGN: 100 f. 3600 CV diesel locomotive.

1972. Air. 1st Death Anniv of Rene Rakotobe (poet).
222 **107** 40 f. brown, purple & orge 40 20

108 College Buildings

1972. 150th Anniv of Razafindrahety College, Tananarive.
223 **108** 10 f. purple, brown & blue 15 10

109 Volleyball

1972. African Volleyball Championships.
224 **109** 12 f. black, orange & brn 40 15

110 Runners breasting Tape

1972. Air. Olympic Games, Munich. Multicoloured.
225 100 f. Type **110** . . . . 1·40 60
226 200 f. Judo . . . . 2·25 90

111 Hospital Complex

1972. Inauguration of Ravoahangy Andrianavalona Hospital.
227 **111** 6 f. multicoloured 20 15

112 Mohair Goat

1972. Air. Malagasy Wool Production.
228 **112** 250 f. multicoloured . . . 3·75 2·25

113 Ploughing with Oxen

1972. Agricultural Expansion.
229 **113** 25 f. multicoloured 25 15

114 "Virgin and Child" (15th-cent. Florentine School)

1972. Air. Christmas. Religious Paintings. Mult.
230 85 f. Type **114** 85 55
231 150 f. "Adoration of the Magi" (A. Mantegna) (horiz) . . . 2·00 85

115 Betsimisarka Women

1972. Traditional Costumes. Multicoloured.
232 10 f. Type **115** 20 10
233 15 f. Merina mother and child 30 20

116 Astronauts on Moon   117 "Natural Produce"

1973. Air. Moon Flight of "Apollo 17".
234 **116** 300 f. purple, brown & grey 3·25 1·75

1973. 10th Anniv of Malagasy Freedom from Hunger Campaign Committee.
235 **117** 25 f. multicoloured 30 15

118 "The Entombment" (Grunewald)

1973. Air. Easter. Multicoloured.
236 100 f. Type **118** . . . . . . 1·00 55
237 200 f. "The Resurrection" (Grunewald) (vert) . . . . 2·25 1·10

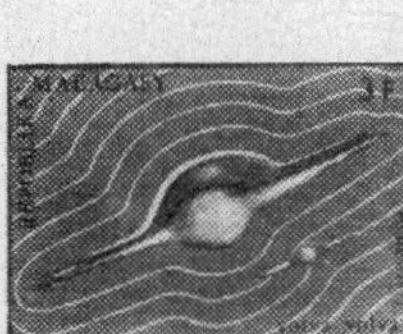

119 Shuttlecock Volva   120 Postal Courier, Tsimandoa

1973. Sea Shells (2nd series). Multicoloured.
238 3 f. Type **119** 15 10
239 10 f. Arthritic spider conch . . 25 20
240 15 f. Common harp 50 30
241 25 f. Type **119** 70 45
242 40 f. As 15 f. . . . . 1·10 50
243 50 f. As 10 f. . . . . 2·25 60

1973. Stamp Day.
244 **120** 50 f. blue, green & brown 45 20

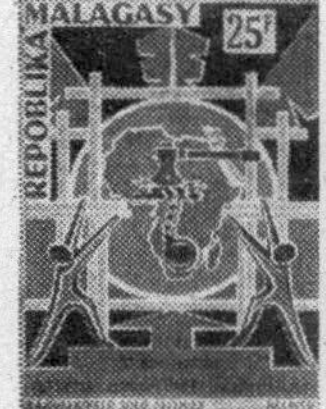

121 "Africa" within Scaffolding   122 "Cameleon campani"

1973. 10th Anniv of Organization of African Unity.
245 **121** 25 f. multicoloured 30 15

1973. Malagasy Chameleons. Multicoloured.
246 1 f. Type **122** 10 10
247 5 f. "Cameleon nasutus" (male) 10 10
248 10 f. "Cameleon nasutus" (female) 15 10
249 40 f. As 5 f. 55 25
250 60 f. Type **122** 85 35
251 85 f. As 10 f. . . . . 1·25 65

123 Excursion Carriage

1973. Air. Early Malagasy Railways. Multicoloured.
252 100 f. Type **123** . . . . . . 1·75 85
253 150 f. Mallet steam locomotive No. 24, 1907 . . . . . . 2·50 1·40

124 "Cypripedium"

1973. Orchids. Multicoloured.
254 10 f. Type **124** 30 15
255 25 f. "Nepenthes pervillei" . . 50 20
256 40 f. As 25 f. . . . . 1·00 35
257 100 f. Type **124** . . . . . . 2·25 85

1973. Pan African Drought Relief. No. 235 surch **SECHERESSE SOLIDARITE AFRICAINE** and value.
258 **117** 100 f. on 25 f. multicoloured 1·10 60

126 Dish Aerial and Met. Station   128 Greater Dwarf Lemur

1973. Air. W.M.O. Centenary.
259 **126** 100 f. orange, blue & blk 1·25 65

1973. 12th Anniv of African and Malagasy Posts and Telecommunications. As T **155a** of Mauritania.
260 100 f. red, violet and green . . 90 45

1973. Malagasy Lemurs.
261 **128** 5 f. brown, green & pur (postage) 55 15
262 – 25 f. brown, sepia & green 1·10 65
263 – 150 f. brn, grn & sepia (air) 2·75 1·25
264 **128** 200 f. brown, turq & blue 4·00 1·75
DESIGN—VERT: 25 f., 150 f. Weasel-lemur.

129 Pres. Kennedy

1973. Air. 10th Death Anniv of Pres. John Kennedy.
265 **129** 300 f. multicoloured . . . 3·25 1·75

130 Footballers

1973. Air. World Cup Football Championships. West Germany.
266 **130** 500 f. mauve, brown and light brown . . . . . . 5·50 2·50

CURRENCY. Issues from No. 267 to No. 389 have face values shown as "Fmg". This abbreviation denotes the Malagasy Franc which was introduced in 1966.

131 Copernicus, Satellite and Diagram

1974. Air. 500th Birth Anniv of Copernicus.
267 **131** 250 f. blue, brown & green 3·25 1·50

1974. No. 76a surch.
268 25 f. on 30 f. multicoloured . . 25 15

133 Agricultural Training   135 Family and House

134 Male Player, and Hummingbird on Hibiscus

1974. 25th World Scouting Conference, Nairobi, Kenya.
269 **133** 4 f. grey, blue and green (postage) 10 10
270 – 15 f. purple, green & blue 20 15
271 – 100 f. ochre, red & blue (air) 80 45
272 – 300 f. brown, blue & black 3·50 1·75
DESIGNS—VERT: 15 f. Building construction. HORIZ: 100 f. First Aid training; 300 f. Fishing.

1974. Air. Asia, Africa and Latin America Table-Tennis Championships, Peking.
273 **134** 50 f. red, blue and brown 80 30
274 – 100 f. red, blue and violet 1·60 70
DESIGN: 100 f. Female player, and stylised bird.

1974. World Population Year.
275 **135** 25 f. red, orange and blue 25 10

INDEX

Countries can be quickly located by referring to the index at the end of this volume.

136 Micheline Railcar

1974. Air. Malagasy Railway Locomotives.
276 **136** 50 f. green, red & brown . . . 75 25
277 – 85 f. red, blue and green . . . 1·25 30
278 – 200 f. blue, lt blue & brn . . . 3·25 80
DESIGNS: 85 f. Track-inspection trolley; 200 f. Garratt steam locomotive, 1926.

137 U.P.U. Emblem and Letters

1974. Air. Centenary of U.P.U.
279 **137** 250 f. red, blue and violet . . . 3·00 1·40

138 Rainibetsimisaraka

1974. Rainibetsimisaraka Commemoration.
280 **138** 25 f. multicoloured 35 20

1974. Air. West Germany's Victory in World Cup Football Championships. No. 266 optd **R.F.A. 2 HOLLANDE 1**.
281 **130** 500 f. mauve, brown and light brown . . . . . . 5·00 2·75

140 "Apollo" and "Soyuz" spacecraft

1974. Air. Soviet–U.S. Space Co-operation.
282 **140** 150 f. orange, green & blue . . . 1·10 60
283 – 250 f. green, blue & brn . . . 2·00 1·00
DESIGN: No. 283, As Type **140** but different view.

141 Marble Slabs 143 Faces and Maps

1974. Marble Industry. Multicoloured.
284 4 f. Type **141** 55 15
285 25 f. Quarrying . . . . 1·40 25

1974. Air. Universal Postal Union. Centenary (2nd issue). No. 279 optd **100 ANS COLLABORATION INTERNATIONALE**.
286 **137** 250 f. red, blue and violet . . . 1·75 1·00

1974. Europafrique.
287 **143** 150 f. brown, red & orange . . . 1·40 70

144 "Food in Hand"

1974. "Freedom from Hunger".
288 **144** 80 f. blue, brown & grey . . . 65 35

145 "Coton" 146 Malagasy People

1974. Malagasy Dogs. Multicoloured.
289 50 f. Type **145** . . . . 1·40 45
290 100 f. Hunting dog . . . . . . 2·25 1·10

1974. Founding of "Fokonolona" Commune.
291 **146** 5 f. multicoloured 15 10
292 10 f. multicoloured 15 10
293 20 f. multicoloured 20 10
294 60 f. multicoloured 60 30

147 "Discovering Talent"

1974. National Development Council.
295 **147** 25 f. multicoloured 20 10
296 35 f. multicoloured 30 15

148 "Adoration of the Magi" (David) 149 Malagasy Girl and Rose

1974. Air. Christmas. Multicoloured.
297 200 f. Type **148** . . . . 2·25 95
298 300 f. "Virgin of the Cherries and Child" (Metzys) . . . . . . 3·25 1·25

1975. International Women's Year.
299 **149** 100 f. brown, orange & grn . . . 85 40

150 Colonel Richard Ratsimandrava (Head of Government)

1975.
300 **150** 15 f. brown, black & yell . . . 15 10
301 25 f. brown, black & blue . . . 20 15
302 100 f. brown, black & grn . . . 80 35

151 Sofia Bridge

1975.
303 **151** 45 f. multicoloured 50 20

152 U.N. Emblem and Part of Globe

1975. Air. 30th Anniv of U.N. Charter.
304 **152** 300 f. multicoloured . . . 2·75 1·25

153 De Grasse (after Mauzaisse) and "Randolph"

1975. Bicentenary of American Revolution (1st issue). Multicoloured.
305 40 f. Type **153** (postage) . . . 85 25
306 50 f. Lafayette, "Lexington" and H.M.S. "Edward" 95 30
307 100 f. D'Estaing and "Languedoc" (air) . . . . . 1·75 50
308 200 f. Paul Jones, "Bonhomme Richard" and H.M.S. "Serapis" . . . . 2·50 1·10
309 300 f. Benjamin Franklin, "Millern" and "Montgomery" . . . 3·50 1·60

154 "Euphorbia viguieri"

1975. Malagasy Flora. Multicoloured.
311 15 f. Type **154** (postage) . . . 25 15
312 25 f. "Hibiscus rosesinensis" . . . 40 20
313 30 f. "Plumeria rubra acutitolia" . . . 55 20
314 40 f. "Pachypodium rosulatum" . . . 1·00 30
315 85 f. "Turraea sericea" (air) . . 1·75 1·00

1975. Air. "Apollo" - "Soyuz" Space Link Nos. 282/3 optd **JONCTION 17 JUILLET 1975**.
316 **140** 150 f. orange, grn & blue . . . 1·00 60
317 – 250 f. green, blue & brown . . . 2·25 1·00

156 Temple Frieze

1975. Air. "Save Borobudur Temple" (in Indonesia) Campaign.
318 **156** 50 f. red, orange and blue . . . 1·00 50

157 "Racial Unity" 159 Lily Waterfall

158 Pryer's Woodpecker

1975. Namibia Day.
319 **157** 50 f. multicoloured 45 20

1975. International Exposition, Okinawa. Fauna. Multicoloured.
320 25 f. Type **158** (postage) . . . 3·00 45
321 40 f. Ryukyu rabbit 50 20
322 50 f. Toad 70 30
323 75 f. Tortoise . . . . 1·40 40
324 125 f. Sika deer (air) . . . . 1·50 55

1975. Lily Waterfall. Multicoloured.
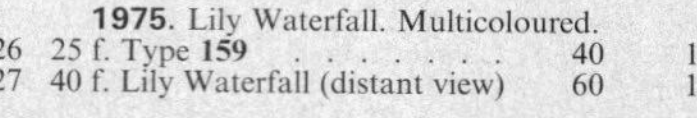
326 25 f. Type **159** 40 15
327 40 f. Lily Waterfall (distant view) . . 60 15

160 Hurdling

1975. Air. "Pre-Olympic Year". Olympic Games, Montreal (1976). Multicoloured.
328 75 f. Type **160** 60 35
329 200 f. Weightlifting (vert) . . . 2·00 75

161 Bobsleigh "Fours"

1975. Winter Olympic Games, Innsbruck. Multicoloured.
330 75 f. Type **161** (postage) . . . 50 25
331 100 f. Ski-jumping 80 35
332 140 f. Speed-skating . . . . . 1·25 50
333 200 f. Cross-country skiing (air) . . 2·00 75
334 245 f. Downhill skiing . . . . 2·25 90

162 Pirogue

1975. Malagasy Sailing-vessels. Multicoloured.
336 8 f. Type **162** 55 15
337 45 f. Malagasy schooner . . . 1·10 25

163 Canoeing

1976. Olympic Games, Montreal. Multicoloured.
338 40 f. Type **163** (postage) . . . 25 15
339 50 f. Sprinting and hurdling . . . 35 20
340 100 f. Putting the shot, and long-jumping (air) 90 35
341 200 f. Gymnastics-horse and parallel bars . . . . 1·75 75
342 300 f. Trampoline-jumping and high-diving . . . . 2·40 1·00

164 "Apollo 14" Lunar Module and Flight Badge

1976. Air. 5th Anniv of "Apollo 14" Mission.
344 **164** 150 f. blue, red and green . . . 1·25 65

1976. Air. 5th Anniv of "Apollo 14" Mission. No. 344 optd **5e Anniversaire de la mission APOLLO XIV**.
345 **164** 150 f. blue, red and green . . . 1·25 75

166 "Graf Zeppelin" over Fujiyama

1976. 75th Anniv of Zeppelin. Multicoloured.
346 40 f. Type **166** (postage) . . . 35 15
347 50 f. "Graf Zeppelin" over Rio de Janeiro 40 15
348 75 f. "Graf Zeppelin" over New York 80 25
349 100 f. "Graf Zeppelin" over Sphinx and pyramids 95 35
350 200 f. "Graf Zeppelin" over Berlin (air) . . . . 2·25 75
351 300 f. "Graf Zeppelin" over London . . . . 4·00 1·00

167 "Prevention of Blindness"

1976. World Health Day.
353 **167** 100 f. multicoloured . . . 1·25 55

168 Aragonite

1976. Minerals and Fossils. Multicoloured.
354 25 f. Type **168** 50 15
355 50 f. Fossilised wood . . . . . 1·10 55
356 150 f. Celestyte . . . . 3·25 1·60

169 Alexander Graham Bell and Early Telephone

1976. Telephone Centenary. Multicoloured.
357 25 f. Type **169** 15 10
358 50 f. Cable maintenance, 1911 . 30 15
359 100 f. Telephone operator and switchboard, 1895 . . . . . 60 25
360 200 f. "Emile Baudot" cable ship 2·25 90
361 300 f. Man with radio-telephone 2·25 80

170 Children reading Book

1976. Children's Books Promotion. Multicoloured.
363 10 f. Type **170** 15 10
364 25 f. Children reading book (vert) 35 15

1976. Medal winners, Winter Olympic Games, Innsbruck. Nos. 330/4 optd **VAINQUEUR** and medal winner.
365 75 f. Type **161** (postage) . . . 50 25
366 100 f. Ski-jumping 80 40
367 140 f. Skating . . . . 1·25 50
368 200 f. Cross-country skiing (air) 1·40 75
369 245 f. Downhill skiing . . . . . 1·90 1·00
OPTS: 75 f. **ALLEMAGNE FEDERALE**; 100 f. **KARL SCHNABL, AUTRICHE**; 140 f. **SHEILA YOUNG, ETATS-UNIS**; 200 f. **IVAR FORMO, NORVEGE**; 245 f. **ROSI MITTERMAIER, ALLEMAGNE DE L'OUEST**.
The subject depicted on No. 367 is speed-skating, an event in which the gold medal was won by J. E. Storholt, Norway.

1976. Bicentenary of American Revolution (2nd issue). Nos. 305/9 optd **"4 JUILLET 1776-1976"**.
371 **153** 40 f. multicoloured (postage) 35 25
372 – 50 f. multicoloured 40 30
373 – 100 f. multicoloured (air) . . 75 50
374 – 200 f. multicoloured . . . 1·50 85
375 – 300 f. multicoloured . . . 2·25 1·25

173 Descent Trajectory

1976. "Viking" Landing on Mars. Multicoloured.
377 75 f. Type **173** 40 20
378 100 f. "Viking" landing module separation 60 25
379 200 f. "Viking" on Martian surface . . . . 1·25 55
380 300 f. "Viking" orbiting Mars 2·00 80

174 Rainandriamampandry
175 Doves over Globe

1976. 30th Anniv of Treaties signed by Rainandriamampandry (Foreign Minister).
382 **174** 25 f. multicoloured 30 20

1976. Indian Ocean – "Zone of Peace". Multicoloured.
383 60 f. Type **175** 35 20
384 160 f. Doves flying across Indian Ocean (horiz) . . . . 1·10 55

1976. Olympic Games Medal – winners. Nos. 338/342 optd with names of two winners on each stamp.
385 **163** 40 f. multicoloured (postage) 25 15
386 – 50 f. multicoloured 35 25
387 – 100 f. multicoloured (air) . . 70 40
388 – 200 f. multicoloured . . . 1·40 65
389 – 300 f. multicoloured . . . 2·00 1·00
OVERPRINTS: 40 f. **V. DIBA, A. ROGOV**; 50 f. **H. CRAWFORD, J. SCHALLER**; 100 f. **U. BEYER, A. ROBINSON**; 200 f. **N. COMANECI, N. ANDRIANOV**; 300 f. **K. DIBIASI, E. VAYTSEKHOVSKAIA**.

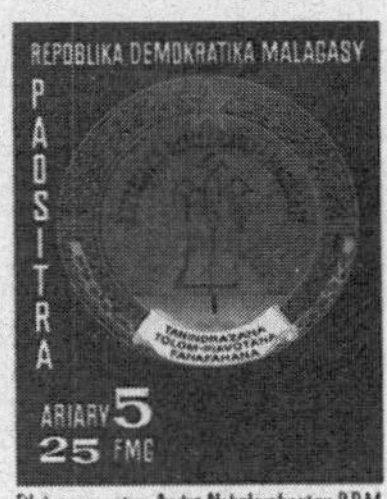

177 Malagasy Arms

1976. 1st Anniv of Malagasy Democratic Republic.
391 **177** 25 f. multicoloured 20 10

178 Rabezavana (Independence Movement leader)

1977. National Heroes. Multicoloured.
392 25 f. Type **178** 20 10
393 25 f. Lt. Albert Randriamaromanana 20 10
394 25 f. Ny Avana Ramanantoanina (politician) 20 10
395 100 f. Fasam-Pirenena National Mausoleum, Tananarive (horiz) 75 40

179 Family

1977. World Health Day.
396 **179** 5 f. multicoloured 15 10

180 Medical School, Antananarivo

1977. 80th Anniv of Medical School Antananarivo.
397 **180** 250 f. multicoloured . . . 2·00 95

181 Rural Post Van

1977. Rural Mail.
398 **181** 35 f. multicoloured 30 15

182 Morse Key and Man with Headphones

1977. 90th Anniv of Antananarivo–Tamatave Telegraph.
399 **182** 15 f. multicoloured 15 10

183 Academy Emblem

1977. 75th Anniv of Malagasy Academy.
400 **183** 10 f. multicoloured 15 10

184 Lenin and Russian Flag

1977. 60th Anniv of Russian Revolution.
401 **184** 25 f. multicoloured . . . . 1·10 10

185 Raoul Follereau

1978. 25th Anniv of World Leprosy Day.
402 **185** 5 f. multicoloured 90 10

186 Microwave Antenna
187 "Co-operation"

1978. World Telecommunications Day.
403 **186** 20 f. multicoloured 15 10

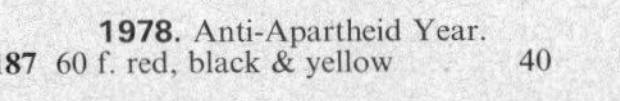
1978. Anti-Apartheid Year.
404 **187** 60 f. red, black & yellow . . 40 25

188 Children with Instruments of Revolution
189 Tractor, Factory and Labourers

1978. "Youth–Pillar of the Revolution".
405 **188** 25 f. multicoloured 75 45

1978. Socialist Co-operatives.
406 **189** 25 f. multicoloured 15 10

190 Women at Work
191 Children with Books, Instruments and Fruit

1979. "Women, Pillar of the Revolution".
407 **190** 40 f. multicoloured 25 15

1979. International Year of the Child.
408 **191** 10 f. multicoloured 20 10

192 Ring-tailed Lemur
193 J. V. S. Razakandraina

1979. Animals. Multicoloured.
409 25 f. Type **192** (postage) . . . 25 15
410 125 f. Black lemur . . . . . . 1·40 30
411 1000 f. Malagasy civet . . . . 8·50 2·25
412 20 f. Tortoise (air) 20 20
413 95 f. Black lemur (different) . . 1·00 40

1979. J. V. S. Razakandraina (poet) Commem.
414 **193** 25 f. multicoloured 15 10

194 "Centella asiatica"

1979. Medicinal Plant.
415 **194** 25 f. multicoloured 15 10

195 Map of Malagasy and Ste. Marie Telecommunications Station

1979. Telecommunications.
416 **195** 25 f. multicoloured 20 10

196 Post Office, Antsirabe

1979. Stamp Day.
417 **196** 500 f. multicoloured . . . 3·25 1·10

197 Palestinians with Flag

1979. Air. Palestinian Solidarity.
418 **197** 60 f. multicoloured 50 20

198 Concorde and Map of Africa

1979. 20th Anniv of ASECNA (African Air Safety Organization).
419 **198** 50 f. multicoloured 60 20

199 Lenin addressing Meeting

1980. 110th Birth Anniv of Lenin.
420 **199** 25 f. multicoloured 45 10

200 Taxi-Bus **201** Map illuminated by Sun

1980. 5th Anniv of Socialist Revolution.
421 **200** 30 f. multicoloured 20 10

1980. 20th Anniv of Independence.
422 **201** 75 f. multicoloured 50 30

202 Military Parade

1980. 20th Anniv of Army.
423 **202** 50 f. multicoloured 35 15

203 Joseph Raseta

1980. Dr. Joseph Raseta Commemoration.
424 **203** 30 f. multicoloured 20 10

204 Anatirova Temple

1980. Anatirova Temple Centenary.
425 **204** 30 f. multicoloured 20 10

205 Boxing

1980. Olympic Games, Moscow. Multicoloured.
426 30 f. Hurdling 45 10
427 75 f. Type **205** 90 25
428 250 f. Judo . . . . 1·75 75
429 500 f. Swimming . . . . . . 3·25 1·50

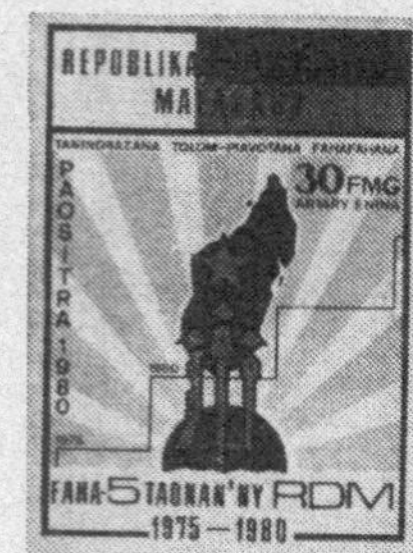

206 Emblem, Map and Sun

1980. 5th Anniv of Malagasy Democratic Republic.
430 **206** 30 f. multicoloured 20 10

207 Skier

1981. Winter Olympic Games, Lake Placid (1980).
431 **207** 175 f. multicoloured . . . 1·10 55

208 "Angraecum leonis" **209** Handicapped Student

1981. Flowers. Multicoloured.
432 5 f. Type **208** 10 10
433 80 f. "Angraecum famosum" 60 25
434 170 f. "Angraecum sesquipedale" 1·25 55

1981. International Year of Disabled People. Multicoloured.
435 25 f. Type **209** 20 10
436 80 f. Disabled carpenter . . . 55 25

210 Ribbons forming Caduceus, I.T.U. and W.H.O. Emblems

1981. World Telecommunications Day.
437 **210** 15 f. blue, black & yellow 15 10
438 45 f. multicoloured 35 15

211 Valentina Tereshkova (first woman in space)

1981. Space Achievements. Multicoloured.
439 30 f. Type **211** 15 10
440 80 f. Astronaut on Moon . . . 55 25
441 90 f. Yury Gagarin (first man in space) 65 30

212 Raphael-Louis Rafiringa

1981. Raphael-Louis Rafiringa Commemoration.
442 **212** 30 f. multicoloured 20 10

213 Child writing Alphabet

1981. World Literary Day.
443 **213** 30 f. multicoloured 20 10

214 Ploughing and Sowing

1981. World Food Day.
444 **214** 200 f. multicoloured . . . 1·25 60

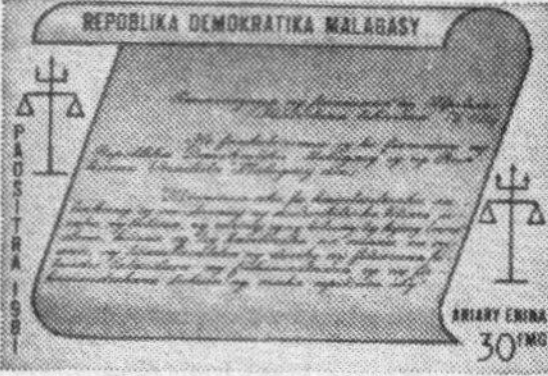

215 Magistrates' Oath

1981. Renewal of Magistrates' Oath.
445 **215** 30 f. mauve and black . . 20 10

216 "Dove"

1981. Birth Centenary of Pablo Picasso.
446 **216** 80 f. multicoloured 60 25

217 U.P.U. Emblem and Malagasy Stamps

1981. 20th Anniv of Admission to U.P.U.
447 **217** 5 f. multicoloured 10 10
448 30 f. multicoloured 20 10

218 Stamps forming Map of Malagasy

1981. Stamp Day.
449 **218** 90 f. multicoloured 65 30

219 Hook-billed Vanga

1982. Birds. Multicoloured.
450 25 f. Type **219** . . . . 1·40 55
451 30 f. Courol . . . . 1·40 55
452 200 f. Madagascar fish eagle (vert) . . . . 8·25 3·25

220 Vaccination **221** Jeannettee Mpihira

1982. Centenary of Discovery of Tubercule Bacillus.
453 **220** 30 f. multicoloured 30 15

1982. Jeannette Mpihira Commemoration.
454 **221** 30 f. multicoloured 20 10

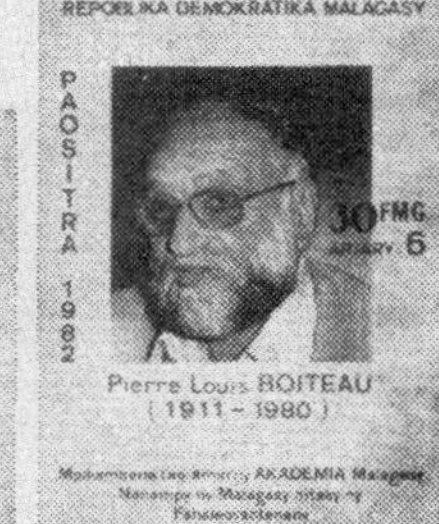

222 Woman's Head formed from Map of Africa **223** Pierre Louis Boiteau

1982. Air. 20th Anniv of Panafrican Women's Organization.
455 **222** 80 f. multicoloured 60 30

1982. Pierre Louis Boiteau Commemoration.
456 **223** 30 f. multicoloured 20 15

224 Andekaleka Dam

1982. Air. Andekaleka Hydro-electric Complex.
457 **224** 80 f. multicoloured 60 30

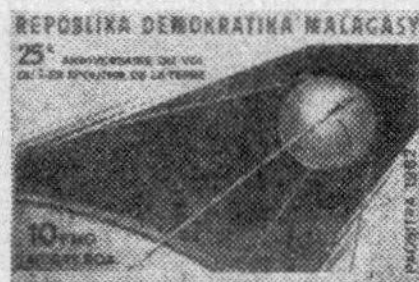

225 "Sputnik I"

1982. 25th Anniv of First Artificial Satellite. Multicoloured.

458 10 f. Type **225** 10 10
459 80 f. Yuri Gagarin 60 30
460 100 f. "Soyuz-Salyut" space station 75 35

226 Heading Ball

1982. World Cup Football Championship, Spain. Multicoloured.

461 30 f. Type **226** 20 10
462 40 f. Running with ball 30 15
463 80 f. Tackle 60 30

227 Ploughing, Sowing and F.A.O. Emblem

1982. World Food Day.

465 **227** 80 f. multicoloured 50 30

228 Bar Scene

1982. 150th Anniv of Edouard Manet (artist). Multicoloured.

466 5 f. Type **228** 45 15
467 30 f. Woman in white 65 10
468 170 f. Man with pipe . . . . . 2·75 65

229 Emperor Snapper

1982. Fishes. Multicoloured.

470 5 f. Type **229** 20 20
471 20 f. Sailfish 30 20
472 30 f. Lionfish 40 20
473 50 f. Yellow-finned tuna . . . 65 20
474 200 f. Black-tipped grouper . . 3·00 85

230 Fort Mahavelona

1982. Landscapes. Multicoloured.

476 10 f. Type **230** (postage) . . . 10 10
477 30 f. Ramena coast 20 10
478 400 f. Jacarandas in flower (air) 2·75 1·50

231 Flags of Russia and Malagasy, Clasped Hands and Tractors

1982. 60th Anniv of U.S.S.R. Multicoloured.

479 10 f. Type **231** 10 10
480 15 f. Flags, clasped hands and radio antenna 10 10
481 30 f. Map of Russia, Kremlin and Lenin 15 10
482 150 f. Flags, clasped hands, statue and arms of Malagasy . . . 1·00 45

232 Television, Drums, Envelope and Telephone

1983. World Communications Year. Multicoloured.

483 30 f. Type **232** 15 10
484 80 f. Stylized figures holding cogwheel . . . . 2·75 60

233 Axe breaking Chain on Map of Africa

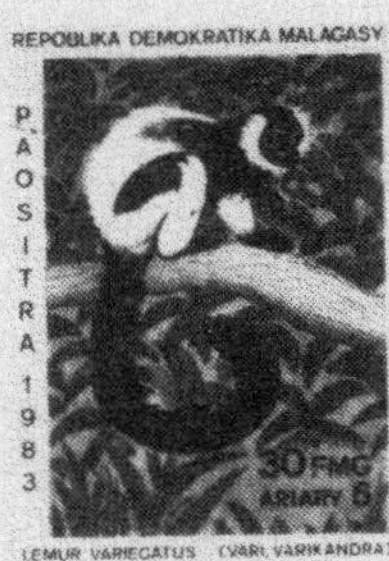
234 Henri Douzon

1983. 20th Anniv of Organization of African Unity.

485 **233** 30 f. multicoloured 20 10

1983. Henri Douzon (lawyer) Commemorative.

486 **234** 30 f. multicoloured 20 10

237 Ruffed Lemur

1984. Lemurs. Multicoloured.

489 30 f. Type **237** 35 20
490 30 f. Verreaux's sifaka 35 20
491 30 f. Lesser mouse-lemur (horiz) 35 20
492 30 f. Aye-aye (horiz) 35 20
493 200 f. Indri (horiz) . . . . . 2·75 1·10

238 Ski Jumping

1984. Winter Olympic Games, Sarajevo. Mult.

495 20 f. Type **238** 15 10
496 30 f. Ice hockey 20 10
497 30 f. Downhill skiing 20 10
498 30 f. Speed skating 20 10
499 200 f. Ice dancing . . . . . . 1·40 70

239 Renault, 1907

1984. Early Motor Cars. Multicoloured.

501 15 f. Type **239** 20 10
502 30 f. Benz, 1896 . . . . 30 15
503 30 f. Baker, 1901 . . . . . . 30 15
504 30 f. Blake, 1901 . . . . . . 30 15
505 200 f. F.I.A.L., 1908 . . . . . 2·00 75

240 Pastor Ravelojaona

241 "Noli me Tangere"

1984. Pastor Ravelojaona (encylopedist) Commemoration.

507 **240** 30 f. multicoloured 20 15

1984. 450th Death Anniv of Correggio. Paintings by Artist.

508 **241** 5 f. multicoloured 10 10
509 – 20 f. multicoloured 15 10
510 – 30 f. multicoloured 25 15
511 – 80 f. multicoloured 45 25
512 – 200 f. multicoloured . . . 1·40 65

242 Paris Landmarks and Emblem

243 Football

1984. 60th Anniv of International Chess Federation. Multicoloured.

514 5 f. Type **242** 15 15
515 20 f. Wilhelm Steinitz and stylized king 20 15
516 30 f. Vera Menchik and stylized queen 35 15
517 30 f. Anatoly Karpov and trophy 35 15
518 215 f. Nona Gaprindashvili and trophy . . . . 2·75 90

1984. Olympic Games, Los Angeles.

520 **243** 100 f. multicoloured . . . 45 30

244 "Eudaphaenura splendens"

245 Ralaimongo

1984. Butterflies. Multicoloured.

521 15 f. Type **244** 20 15
522 50 f. "Acraea hova" 60 20
523 50 f. "Othreis boesae" 60 20
524 50 f. "Pharmocophagus antenor" 60 20
525 200 f. "Epicausis smithii" . . . 2·25 1·00

1984. Birth Centenary of Jean Ralaimongo (politician).

527 **245** 50 f. multicoloured 30 15

246 Children in Brief-case

247 "Disa incarnata"

1984. 25th Anniv of Children's Rights Legislation.

528 **246** 50 f. multicoloured 40 15

1984. Orchids. Multicoloured.

529 20 f. Type **247** (postage) . . . 20 10
530 235 f. "Eulophiella roempleriana" . . . . . . 2·25 85
531 50 f. "Eulophiella roempleriana" (horiz) (air) 60 25
532 50 f. "Grammangis ellisii" (horiz) 60 25
533 50 f. "Grammangis spectabilis" 60 25

248 U.N. Emblem and Cotton Plant

249 "Sun Princess" (Sadio Diouf)

1984. 20th Anniv of United Nations Conference on Commerce and Development.

535 **248** 100 f. multicoloured . . . 60 30

1984. 40th Anniv of International Civil Aviation Organization.

536 **249** 100 f. multicoloured . . . 65 30

250 Bible, Map and Gothic Letters

1985. 150th Anniv of First Bible in Malagasy Language.

537 **250** 50 f. brown, pink and black 30 15

251 Farming Scenes, Census-taker and Farmer

252 Lap-dog

1985. Agricultural Census.

538 **251** 50 f. grey, black and mauve 30 15

1985. Cats and Dogs. Multicoloured.

539 20 f. Type **252** 20 15
540 20 f. Siamese cat 20 15
541 50 f. Abyssinian cat (vert) . . . 60 20
542 100 f. Cocker spaniel (vert) . . 1·25 35
543 235 f. Poodle . . . . 2·50 90

253 Russian Soldiers in Berlin

1985. 40th Anniv of Victory in Second World War.

545 20 f. Type **253** 15 10
546 50 f. Arms of French squadron and fighter planes 40 15
547 100 f. Victory parade, Red Square, Moscow 75 30
548 100 f. French troops entering Paris (vert) . . . . 1·25 30

254 Parade in Stadium

1985. 10th Anniv of Malagasy Democratic Republic.
549 **254** 50 f. multicoloured 40 15

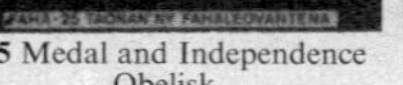

255 Medal and Independence Obelisk — **256** Peace Dove and Stylised People

1985. 25th Anniv of Independence.
550 **255** 50 f. multicoloured 40 15

1985. 12th World Youth and Students' Festival, Moscow.
551 **256** 50 f. multicoloured 40 15

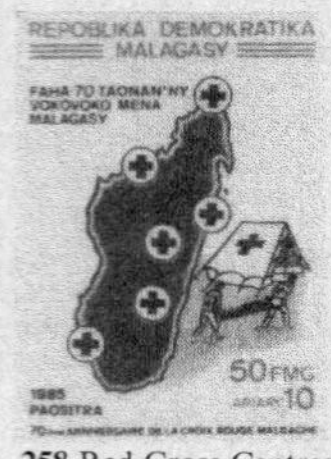

257 I.Y.Y. Emblem and Map of Madagascar — **258** Red Cross Centres and First Aid Post

1985. International Youth Year.
552 **257** 100 f. multicoloured 60 25

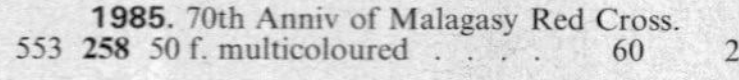

1985. 70th Anniv of Malagasy Red Cross.
553 **258** 50 f. multicoloured 60 25

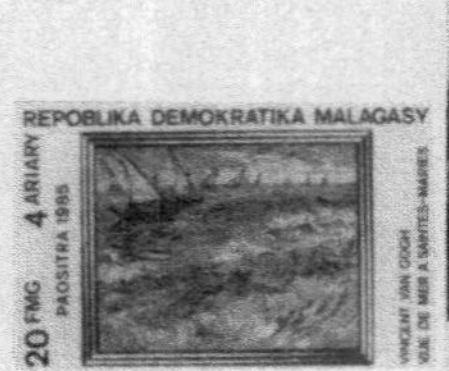

259 "View of Sea at Saintes-Maries" (Vincent van Gogh) — **260** Indira Gandhi

1985. Impressionist Paintings. Multicoloured.
554 20 f. Type **259** 45 10
555 20 f. "Rouen Cathedral in the Evening" (Claude Monet) (vert) 45 10
556 45 f. "Young Girls in Black" (Pierre-Auguste Renoir) (vert) 80 20
557 50 f. "Red Vineyard at Arles" (van Gogh) 80 20
558 100 f. "Boulevard des Capucines, Paris" (Monet) 1·40 40

1985. Indira Gandhi (Indian Prime Minister) Commemoration.
560 **260** 100 f. multicoloured 80 30

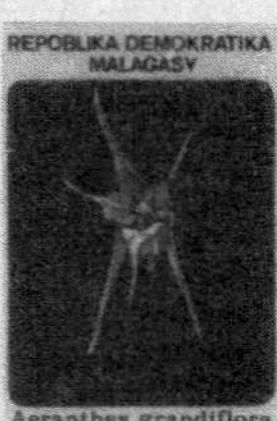

261 Figures and Dove on Globe and Flag — **262** "Aeranthes grandiflora"

1985. 40th Anniv of U.N.O.
561 **261** 100 f. multicoloured 65 25

1985. Orchids. Multicoloured.
562 20 f. Type **262** 20 10
563 45 f. "Angraecum magdalenae" and "Nephele oenopion" (insect) (horiz) 35 15
564 50 f. "Aerangis stylosa" 35 15
565 100 f. "Angraecum eburneum longicalcar" and "Hippotion batschi" (insect) 80 35
566 100 f. "Angraecum sesquipedale" and "Xanthopan morganipredicta" (insect) 80 35

263 Russian and Czechoslovakian Cosmonauts

1985. Russian "Interkosmos" Space Programme. Multicoloured.
568 20 f. Type **263** 15 10
569 20 f. Russian and American flags and "Apollo"–"Soyuz" link 15 10
570 50 f. Russian and Indian cosmonauts 30 15
571 100 f. Russian and Cuban cosmonauts 50 25
572 200 f. Russian and French cosmonauts 1·25 60

264 Emblem in "10" — **265** Headquarters

1985. 10th Anniv of Malagasy Democratic Republic.
574 **264** 50 f. multicoloured 30 15

1986. 10th Anniv of ARO (State insurance system).
575 **265** 50 f. yellow and brown 30 15

266 "David and Uriah" (Rembrandt) — **268** Sombrero, Football and Player

267 Comet

1986. Foreign Paintings in Hermitage Museum, Leningrad. Multicoloured.
576 20 f. Type **266** 20 10
577 50 f. "Portrait of Old Man in Red" (Rembrandt) 50 30
578 50 f. "Danae" (Rembrandt) (horiz) 50 30
579 50 f. "Marriage of Earth and Water" (Rubens) 50 30
580 50 f. "Portrait of Infanta Isabella's Maid" (Rubens) 50 30

1986. Air. Appearance of Halley's Comet.
582 **267** 150 f. multicoloured 1·00 50

1986. Russian Paintings in the Tretyakov Gallery, Moscow. As T **266**. Multicoloured.
583 20 f. "Fruit and Flowers" (I. Khroutsky) (horiz) 15 10
584 50 f. "The Rooks have Returned" (A. Savrasov) 30 20
585 50 f. "Unknown Woman" (I. Kramskoi) (horiz) 30 20
586 50 f. "Aleksandr Pushkin" (O. Kiprenski) 30 20
587 100 f. "March, 1895" (I. Levitan) (horiz) 90 40

1986. World Cup Football Championship, Mexico.
589 **268** 150 f. multicoloured 1·10 30

269 Child Care — **270** Jungle Cat

1986. U.N.I.C.E.F. Child Survival Campaign.
590 **269** 60 f. multicoloured 40 15

1986. Wild Cats. Multicoloured.
591 10 f. Type **270** 20 10
592 10 f. Wild cat 20 10
593 60 f. Caracal 45 20
594 60 f. Leopard cat 45 20
595 60 f. Serval 45 20

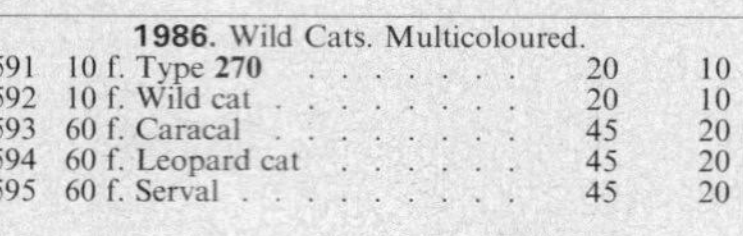

271 Dove above Hands holding Globe

1986. International Peace Year. Multicoloured.
597 60 f. Type **271** 40 15
598 150 f. Doves above emblem and map 1·00 45

272 U.P.U. Emblem on Dove — **273** U.P.U. Emblem on Globe

1986. World Post Day.
599 **272** 60 f. multicoloured (postage) 40 15
600 150 f. blue, black and red (air) 1·10 50

1986. Air. 25th Anniv of Admission to U.P.U.
601 **273** 150 f. multicoloured 1·10 50

274 Giant Madagascar Coucal

1986. Birds. Multicoloured.
602 60 f. Type **274** 1·60 60
603 60 f. Crested Madagascar coucal 1·60 60
604 60 f. Rufous vangas (vert) 1·60 60
605 60 f. Red-tailed vangas (vert) 1·60 60
606 60 f. Sicklebill 1·60 60

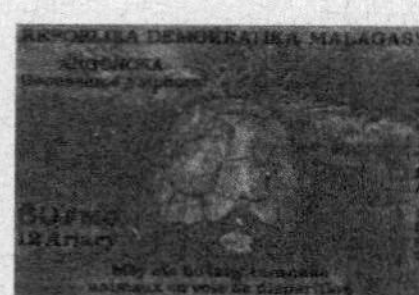

275 Tortoise

1987. Endangered Animals. Multicoloured.
608 60 f. Type **275** 50 20
609 60 f. Crocodile 50 20
610 60 f. Crested wood ibis (vert) 50 20
611 60 f. Vasa parrot 50 20

276 Crowd in "40"

1987. 40th Anniv of Anti-Colonial Uprising.
613 **276** 60 f. brown, red & yellow 35 15
614 – 60 f. multicoloured 35 15
DESIGN: No. 614, Hands in broken manacles, map, rifleman and spearman.

277 Emblems, Map and Pictogram

1987. 1st Indian Ocean Towns Games.
615 **277** 60 f. multicoloured 35 15
616 150 f. multicoloured 1·10 35

278 "Sarimanok"

1987. The "Sarimanok" (replica of early dhow). Multicoloured.
617 60 f. Type **278** 50 20
618 150 f. "Sarimanok" (different) 1·25 40

279 Coffee Plant — **280** Rifle Shooting and Satellite

1987. 25th Anniv of African and Malagasy Coffee Producers Organization. Multicoloured.
619 60 f. Type **279** 35 15
620 150 f. Map showing member countries 1·10 35

1987. Winter Olympic Games, Calgary (1988). Multicoloured.
621 60 f. Type **280** 25 10
622 150 f. Slalom 60 20
623 250 f. Luge 1·25 40
624 350 f. Speed skating 1·40 50
625 400 f. Ice hockey 1·60 60
626 450 f. Ice skating (pairs) 2·00 70

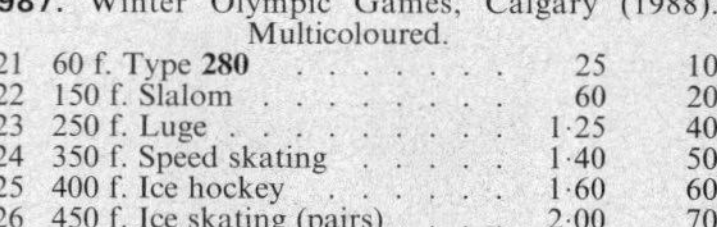

281 "Giotto" Space Probe

1987. Appearance of Halley's Comet (1986). Space Probes. Multicoloured.
628 60 f. Type **281** 25 10
629 150 f. "Vega 1" 60 20
630 250 f. "Vega 2" 1·25 40
631 350 f. "Planet A 1" 1·40 50
632 400 f. "Planet B 1" 1·60 60
633 450 f. "I.C.E." 2·00 70

282 Piper Aztec — **283** Rabearivelo

1987. Air. 25th Anniv of Air Madagascar. Multicoloured.
635 60 f. Type **282** 40 20
636 60 f. De Havilland Twin Otter 40 20
637 150 f. Boeing 747-200 1·00 40

1987. 50th Death Anniv of Jean-Joseph Rabearivelo (poet).
638 **283** 60 f. multicoloured 30 15

284 Communications Equipment Robot and Print-out Paper — **285** Emblem

1987. National Telecommunications Research Laboratory.
639 **284** 60 f. green, black and red 30 15

1987. 150th Anniv of Execution of Rafaravavy Rasalama (Christian martyr).
640 **285** 60 f. black, deep blue and blue 30 15

286 Hand using Key and Telegraphist

1987. Centenary of Antananarivo–Tamatave Telegraph.

641	286	60 f. multicoloured	30	15

287 Bartholomeu Dias and Departure from Palos, 1492

1987. 500th Anniv (1992) of Discovery of America by Columbus. Multicoloured.

642	60 f. Type **287**	30	20
643	150 f. Route around Samana Cay and Henry the Navigator	60	25
644	250 f. Columbus and crew disembarking, 1492, and A. de Marchena	75	30
645	350 f. Building Fort Navidad and Paolo del Pozzo Toscanelli	1·10	40
646	400 f. Columbus in Barcelona, 1493, and Queen Isabella of Spain	1·25	50
647	450 f. Columbus and "Nina"	1·75	70

288 Showjumping and "Harlequin" (Picasso)

1987. Olympic Games, Barcelona (1992). Multicoloured.

649	60 f. Type **288** (postage)	15	10
650	150 f. Weightlifting and Barcelona Cathedral	40	20
651	250 f. Hurdling and Canaletas Fountain	70	30
652	350 f. High jumping and Parc d'Attractions	1·00	40
653	400 f. Gymnast on bar and church (air)	1·40	50
654	450 f. Gymnast with ribbon and Triumphal Arch	1·75	50

289 Anniversary Emblem, T.V. Tower and Interhotel "Berlin"

290 Musician and Dancers

1987. 750th Anniv of Berlin.

656	289	150 f. multicoloured	25	15

1987. Schools Festival.

657	290	60 f. multicoloured	15	10

291 Madagascar Pasteur Institute and Pasteur

1987. Centenary of Pasteur Institute, Paris.

658	291	250 f. multicoloured	60	25

292 "After the Shipwreck" (Eugene Delacroix)

1987. Paintings in Pushkin Museum of Fine Arts, Moscow. Multicoloured.

659	10 f. Type **292**	15	10
660	60 f. "Jupiter and Callisto" (Francois Boucher) (vert)	15	10
661	60 f. "Still Life with Swan" (Frans Snyders)	15	10
662	60 f. "Chalet in the Mountains" (Gustave Courbet)	15	10
663	150 f. "At the Market" (Joachim Bueckelaer)	40	15

293 Emblem

294 Family and House on Globe

1987. 10th Anniv of Pan-African Telecommunications Union.

665	293	250 f. multicoloured	40	20

1988. International Year of Shelter for the Homeless (1987). Multicoloured.

666	80 f. Type **294**	15	10
667	250 f. Hands forming house protecting family from rain	35	20

295 Lenin addressing Crowd

1988. 70th Anniv of Russian Revolution. Mult.

668	60 f. Type **295**	15	10
669	60 f. Revolutionaries	15	10
670	150 f. Lenin in crowd	25	15

296 Broad-nosed Gentle Lemur

1988. Endangered Species. Multicoloured.

671	60 f. Type **296**	15	10
672	150 f. Diadem sifaka	20	15
673	250 f. Indri	35	15
674	350 f. Ruffed lemur	60	25
675	550 f. Purple herons (horiz)	1·25	70
676	1500 f. Nossi-be chameleon (horiz)	2·40	1·25

297 Ice Skating

1988. Winter Olympic Games, Calgary. Mult.

678	20 f. Type **297**	10	10
679	60 f. Speed-skating	10	10
680	60 f. Slalom	10	10
681	100 f. Cross-country skiing	20	10
682	250 f. Ice hockey	45	20

298 Dove, Axe breaking Chain and Map

1988. 25th Anniv of Organization of African Unity.

684	298	80 f. multicoloured	15	10

299 Institute Building

1988. 20th Anniv of National Posts and Telecommunications Institute.

685	299	80 f. multicoloured	15	10

300 College

1988. Centenary of St. Michael's College.

686	300	250 f. multicoloured	30	20

301 Pierre and Marie Curie in Laboratory

302 Emblem

1988. 90th Anniv of Discovery of Radium.

687	301	150 f. brown and mauve	40	15

1988. 10th Anniv of Alma-Ata Declaration (on health and social care).

688	302	60 f. multicoloured	15	10

303 Emblem

304 Ring-tailed Lemurs on Island

1988. 40th Anniv of W.H.O.

689	303	150 f. brown, blue and black	20	15

1988. 50th Anniv of Tsimbazaza Botanical and Zoological Park. Multicoloured.

690	20 f. Type **304**	15	10
691	80 f. Ring-tailed lemur with young (25 × 37 mm)	20	10
692	250 f. Palm tree and ring-tailed lemur within "Zoo" (47 × 32 mm)	40	20

305 Hoopoe and Blue Madagascar Coucal

306 Cattle grazing

1988. Scouts, Birds and Butterflies. Multicoloured.

694	80 f. Type **305**	60	30
695	250 f. "Chrysiridia croesus" (butterfly)	40	20
696	270 f. Nelicourvi weaver and red forest fody	1·25	50
697	350 f. "Papilio dardanus" (butterflies)	60	40
698	550 f. Crested Madagascar coucal	2·25	1·00
699	1500 f. "Argema mittrei" (butterfly)	2·50	2·00

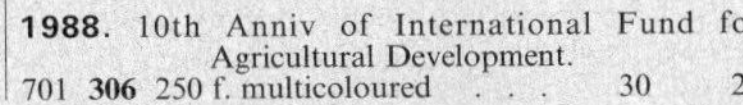

1988. 10th Anniv of International Fund for Agricultural Development.

701	306	250 f. multicoloured	30	20

307 Karl Bach and Clavier

308 Books

1988. Musicians' Anniversaries. Multicoloured.

702	80 f. Type **307** (death bicentenary)	15	10
703	250 f. Franz Schubert and piano (160th death)	40	15
704	270 f. Georges Bizet and scene from "Carmen" (150th birth)	40	20
705	350 f. Claude Debussy and scene from "Pelleas et Melisande" (70th death)	50	25
706	550 f. George Gershwin at piano writing score of "Rhapsody in Blue" (90th birth)	75	45
707	1500 f. Elvis Presley (10th death (1987))	2·75	1·25

1988. "Ecole en Fete" Schools Festival.

709	308	80 f. multicoloured	15	10

309 "Black Sea Fleet at Feodosiya" (Ivan Aivazovski)

310 "Tragocephala crassicornis"

1988. Paintings of Sailing Ships. Multicoloured.

710	20 f. Type **309**	40	15
711	80 f. "Lesnoie" (N. Semenov)	40	15
712	80 f. "Seascape with Sailing Ships" (Simon de Vlieger)	40	15
713	100 f. "Orel" (N. Golitsine) (horiz)	45	15
714	250 f. "Naval Battle Exercises" (Adam Silo)	90	25

1988. Endangered Beetles. Multicoloured.

716	20 f. Type **310**	15	10
717	80 f. "Polybothris symptuosa-gema"	55	25
718	250 f. "Euchroea auripigmenta"	1·25	60
719	350 f. "Stellognata maculata"	1·60	80

311 Stretcher Bearers and Anniversary Emblem

312 Symbols of Human Rights

1988. 125th Anniv of International Red Cross. Multicoloured.

720	80 f. Type **311**	15	10
721	250 f. Red Cross services, emblem and Henri Dunant (founder)	35	20

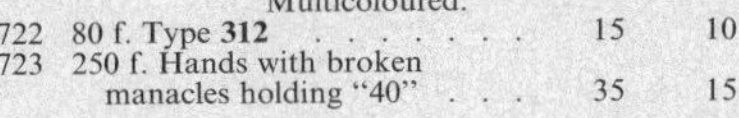

1988. 40th Anniv of Declaration of Human Rights. Multicoloured.

722	80 f. Type **312**	15	10
723	250 f. Hands with broken manacles holding "40"	35	15

313 Mercedes-Benz "Blitzen-Benz", 1909

1989. Cars and Trains. Multicoloured.
724 80 f. Type **313** 15 10
725 250 f. Micheline diesel railcar "Tsikirity", 1952, Tananarive–Moramanga line . . . . . . 1·50 15
726 270 f. Bugatti coupe binder, "41" 40 20
727 350 f. Class 1020 electric locomotive, Germany . . . 1·90 25
728 1500 f. Souleze 701 diesel train, Malagasy . . . . 4·75 1·25
729 2500 f. Opel racing car, 1913 3·50 2·00

314 Tyrannosaurus

1989. Prehistoric Animals. Multicoloured.
731 20 f. Type **314** 15 10
732 80 f. Stegosaurus 20 10
733 250 f. Arsinoitherium 40 15
734 450 f. Triceratops 80 30

315 "Tahitian Girls"

1989. Woman in Art. Multicoloured.
736 20 f. Type **315** 10 10
737 80 f. "Portrait of a Girl" (Jean-Baptiste Greuze) 15 10
738 80 f. "Portrait of a Young Woman" (Titian) 15 10
739 100 f. "Woman in Black" (Auguste Renoir) 20 10
740 250 f. "The Lace-maker" (Vasily Tropinine) 35 15

316 "Sobennikoffia robusta" **317** Nehru

1989. Orchids. Multicoloured.
742 5 f. Type **316** 15 10
743 10 f. "Grammangis fallax" (horiz) 15 10
744 80 f. "Angraecum sororium" 20 10
745 80 f. "Cymbidiella humblotii" 20 10
746 250 f. "Oenia oncidiiflora" . . 60 20

1989. Birth Centenary of Jawaharlal Nehru (Indian statesman).
748 **317** 250 f. multicoloured . . . 45 15

318 Mahamasina Sports Complex, Lake Anosy and Ampefiloha Quarter

1989. Antananarivo. Multicoloured.
749 5 f. Type **318** 10 10
750 20 f. Andravoahangy and Anjanahary Quarters 10 10
751 80 f. Zoma market and Faravohitra Quarter 15 10
752 80 f. Andohan' Analekely Quarter and 29 March Column 15 10
753 250 f. Avenue de l'Independance and Jean Ralaimongo Column 35 15
754 550 f. Lake Anosy, Queen's Palace and Andohalo School 70 35

MORE DETAILED LISTS
are given in the Stanley Gibbons Catalogues referred to in the country headings.
For lists of current volumes see Introduction.

319 Rose Quartz

1989. Ornamental Minerals. Multicoloured.
755 80 f. Type **319** 20 10
756 250 f. Fossilized wood 60 20

320 Pope and Rasoamanarivo **321** Map and Runner with Torch

1989. Visit of Pope John Paul II and Beatification of Victoire Rasoamanarivo. Multicoloured.
757 80 f. Type **320** 20 10
758 250 f. Map and Pope 55 20

1989. Town Games.
759 **321** 80 f. + 20 f. multicoloured 15 15

322 "Storming the Bastille"

1989. Bicentenary of French Revolution (1st issue).
760 **322** 250 f. multicoloured . . . 35 15
See also Nos. 773/5.

323 Mirabeau and Gabriel Riqueti at Meeting of States General

1989. "Philexfrance 89" International Stamp Exhibition, Paris. Multicoloured.
761 250 f. Type **323** 30 15
762 350 f. Camille Desmoulins' call to arms 45 20
763 1000 f. Lafayette and crowd demanding bread . . . . . 1·25 60
764 1500 f. Trial of King Louis XVI 2·00 80
765 2500 f. Assassination of Marat 3·25 1·25

324 "Mars 1"

1989. Space Probes. Multicoloured.
767 20 f. Type **324** 10 10
768 80 f. "Mars 3" 15 10
769 80 f. "Zond 2" 15 10
770 250 f. "Mariner 9" 35 15
771 270 f. "Viking 2" 40 20

325 "Liberty guiding the People" (Eugene Delacroix)

1989. Bicentenary of French Revolution (2nd issue). Multicoloured.
773 5 f. Type **325** (postage) 10 10
774 80 f. "La Marseillaise" (Francois Rude) 15 10
775 250 f. "Oath of the Tennis Court" (Jacques Louis David) (air) . 35 15

326 Rene Cassin (founder) **327** Mother and Young on Bamboo

1989. 25th Anniv of International Human Rights Institute for French Speaking Countries.
776 **326** 250 f. multicoloured . . . 30 15

1989. Golden Gentle Lemur.
777 **327** 250 f. multicoloured . . . 40 20

328 Footballer and Cavour Monument, Turin **330** Long Jumping

329 Pennant Coralfish

1989. World Cup Football Championship, Italy. Multicoloured.
778 350 f. Type **328** 50 20
779 1000 f. Footballer and Christopher Columbus monument, Genoa . . . . . 1·40 50
780 1500 f. Florentine footballer, 1530, and "David" (sculpture, Michelangelo) . . . . 2·00 75
781 2500 f. Footballer and "Rape of Proserpina" (sculpture, Bernini), Rome . . . . . . 3·25 1·40

1990. Fishes. Multicoloured.
783 5 f. Type **329** 10 10
784 20 f. Snub-nosed parasitic eel (vert) 20 10
785 80 f. Manta ray (vert) 35 15
786 250 f. Black-tipped grouper . . 90 30
787 320 f. Smooth hammerhead . . 1·25 45

1990. Olympic Games, Barcelona (1992). Mult.
789 80 f. Type **330** 10 10
790 250 f. Pole vaulting 35 15
791 550 f. Hurdling 65 25
792 1500 f. Cycling . . . . 2·00 60
793 2000 f. Baseball . . . . 2·50 80
794 2500 f. Tennis . . . . 3·25 1·25

331 "Queen of the Isalo" (rock)

1990. Natural Features. Multicoloured.
796 70 f. Type **331** 15 10
797 150 f. Lonjy Island (as T **332**) 25 15

332 Pipe

1990. Sakalava Craft. Multicoloured.
798 70 f. Type **332** 15 10
799 150 f. Combs (as T **331**) . . . 25 15

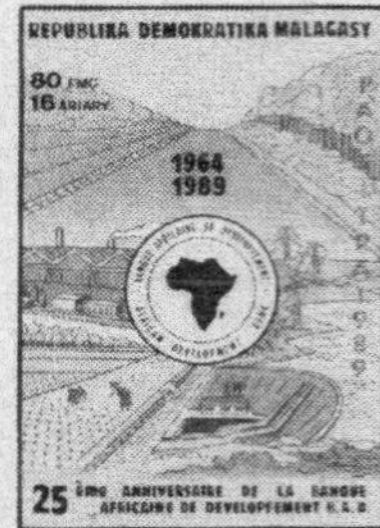

333 Emblem and Projects

1990. 25th Anniv of African Development Bank.
800 **333** 80 f. multicoloured 15 10

334 "Voyager II" and Neptune

1990. 20th Anniv of First Manned Landing on Moon. Multicoloured.
801 80 f. Type **334** 15 10
802 250 f. Hughes Hercules flying boat, Boeing 747 airliner and flying boat "of the future" . 40 15
803 550 f. "Noah" satellite tracking elephants 70 25
804 1500 f. Venus and "Magellan" space probe . . . . 1·25 55
805 2000 f. Halley's Comet and Concorde . . . . 2·25 90
806 2500 f. "Apollo 11" landing capsule and crew . . . . 3·25 1·00

335 Liner on Globe **336** Maps showing Development between 1975 and 1990

1990. 30th Anniv of International Maritime Organization.
808 **335** 250 f. ultramarine, bl & blk 55 15

1990. Air. 15th Anniv of Malagasy Socialist Revolution.
809 **336** 100 f. multicoloured . . . 15 10
810 – 350 f. black and grey . . . 45 25
DESIGN: 350 f. Presidential Palaces, 1975 and 1990.

337 Oral Vaccination **338** Four-man Bobsleigh

1990. Anti-Polio Campaign.
811 **337** 150 f. multicoloured . . . 30 15

1990. Winter Olympic Games, Albertville (1992) (1st issue). Multicoloured.
812 350 f. Type **338** 40 20
813 1000 f. Speed skating . . . . . 1·25 40
814 1500 f. Cross-country skiing . . 2·00 65
815 2500 f. Super G . . . . 3·00 1·10
See also Nos. 862/8.

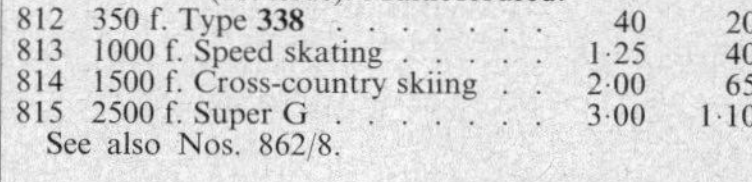

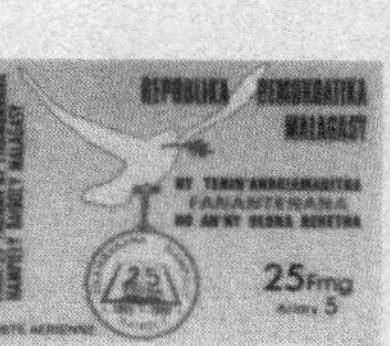

339 Society Emblem **340** Mascot

1990. Air. 25th Anniv of Malagasy Bible Society.
817 **339** 25 f. multicoloured 10 10
818 – 100 f. blue, black & green 15 10
DESIGN—VERT: 100 f. Society emblem.

1990. 3rd Indian Ocean Island Games, Malagasy (1st issue).
819 **340** 100 f. + 20 f. on 80 f. + 20 f. multicoloured . . . 15 15
820 350 f. + 20 f. on 250 f. + 20 f. multicoloured . . . 75 40

The games were originally to be held in 1989 and the stamps were printed for release then. The issued stamps are handstamped with the correct date and new value.

See also Nos. 822/3.

341 Symbols of Agriculture and Industry

342 Torch

1990. 30th Anniv of Independence.
821 **341** 100 f. multicoloured . . . 15 10

1990. 3rd Indian Ocean Island Games, Malagasy (2nd issue).
822 **342** 100 f. multicoloured . . . 15 10
823 350 f. multicoloured . . . 45 20

343 Envelopes forming Map and Mail Transportation

1990. Air. World Post Day.
824 **343** 350 f. multicoloured . . . 2·00 55

344 Ho Chi Minh

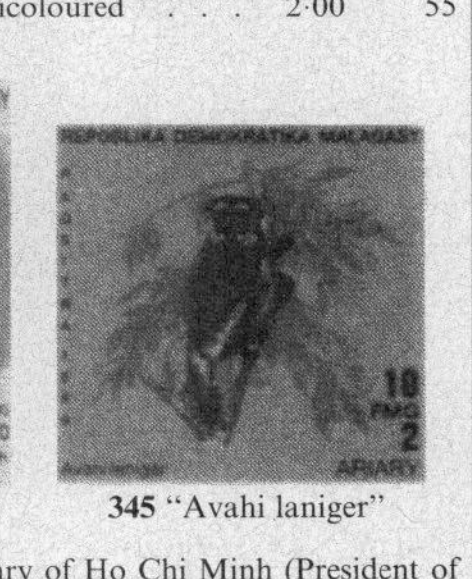

345 "Avahi laniger"

1990. Birth Centenary of Ho Chi Minh (President of North Vietnam, 1945–69).
825 **344** 350 f. multicoloured . . . 40 20

1990. Lemurs. Multicoloured.
826 10 f. Type **345** 10 10
827 20 f. "Lemur fulvus albifrons" 10 10
828 20 f. "Lemur fulvus sanfordi" 10 10
829 100 f. "Lemur fulvus collaris" 25 15
830 100 f. "Lepulemur ruficaudatus" 25 15

346 Fluted Giant Clam

347 Letters in Book

1990. Shells. Multicoloured.
832 40 f. Type **346** 25 15
833 50 f. Dimidiate and subulate augers 35 15

1990. International Literacy Year. Multicoloured.
834 20 f. Type **347** 10 10
835 100 f. Open book and hand holding pen (horiz) 20 15

348 Cep

349 De Gaulle, Leclerc and Parod under Arc de Triomphe, 1944

1991. Fungi. Multicoloured.
836 25 f. Type **348** 10 10
837 100 f. Butter mushroom . . . 35 10
838 350 f. Fly agaric 55 20
839 450 f. Scarlet-stemmed boletus 75 25
840 680 f. Flaky-stemmed witches' mushroom . . . . 1·10 40
841 800 f. Brown birch bolete . . . 1·25 45
842 900 f. Orange birch bolete . . . 1·40 55

1991. Multicoloured.
844 100 f. Type **349** 10 10
845 350 f. "Galileo" space probe near Jupiter 55 10
846 800 f. Crew of "Apollo 11" on moon . . . . 1·10 25
847 900 f. De Gaulle and Free French emblem, 1942 . . . . . 1·40 30
848 1250 f. Concorde aircraft and German ICE high speed train . . . . 3·25 80
849 2500 f. Gen. Charles de Gaulle (French statesman) . . . . 3·25 95

350 Industrial and Agricultural Symbols and Arms

351 Baobab Tree

1991. 15th Anniv (1990) of Republic.
851 **350** 100 f. multicoloured . . . 10 10

1991. Trees. Multicoloured.
852 140 f. Type **351** 55 10
853 500 f. "Dideria madagascariensis" . . . . . 1·10 45

352 Whippet

353 Cross-country Skiing

1991. Dogs. Multicoloured.
854 30 f. Type **352** 35 10
855 50 f. Japanese spaniel 45 10
856 140 f. Toy terrier 90 10
857 350 f. Chow-chow 65 10
858 500 f. Chihuahua 90 15
859 800 f. Afghan hound . . . . . 1·10 25
860 1140 f. Papillon . . . . . . 1·75 65

1991. Winter Olympic Games, Albertville (2nd issue). Multicoloured.
862 5 f. Type **353** 10 10
863 15 f. Biathlon 10 10
864 60 f. Ice hockey 35 10
865 140 f. Skiing 45 10
866 640 f. Ice skating 45 30
867 1000 f. Ski jumping . . . . . 1·90 50
868 1140 f. Speed skating . . . . . 2·75 60

354 "Helictopleurus splendidicollis"

1992. Scouts, Insects and Fungi. Multicoloured.
870 140 f. Type **354** 10 10
871 500 f. "Russula radicans" (mushroom) 90 25
872 640 f. "Cocles contemplator" (insect) . . . . 1·10 30
873 1025 f. "Russula singeri" (mushroom) . . . . 1·60 50
874 1140 f. "Euchroea oberthurii" (beetle) . . . . 1·75 60
875 3500 f. "Lactariopsis pandani" (mushroom) . . . . 5·50 2·00

355 Former and Present Buildings

1992. 90th Anniv (1991) of Paul Minault College.
877 **355** 140 f. multicoloured . . . 45 10

356 Repairing Space Telescope

1992. Space. Multicoloured.
878 140 f. Type **356** 10 10
879 500 f. "Soho" sun probe . . . 65 25
880 640 f. "Topex-Poseidon" oceanic survey satellite 90 30
881 1025 f. "Hipparcos" planetary survey satellite . . . . . . 1·25 50
882 1140 f. "Voyager 2" Neptune probe . . . . 1·40 60
883 5000 f. "ETS-VI" Japanese test communications satellite . . 6·75 1·25

357 Ryuichi Sakamoto

1992. Entertainers. Multicoloured.
885 100 f. Type **357** 10 10
886 350 f. John Lennon 55 15
887 800 f. Bruce Lee . . . . 1·40 40
888 900 f. Sammy Davis jun . . . 1·60 45
889 1250 f. John Wayne . . . . . 1·60 60
890 2500 f. James Dean . . . . . 3·25 1·25

358 Lychees

1992. Fruits. Multicoloured.
892 10 f. Type **358** 10 10
893 50 f. Oranges 10 10
894 60 f. Apples 10 10
895 140 f. Peaches 35 10
896 555 f. Bananas (vert) . . . . . 1·10 30
897 800 f. Avocados (vert) . . . . 1·40 40
898 1400 f. Mangoes (vert) . . . . 2·40 75

359 9th-century Galley

360 Couple in Heart

1992. Sailing Ships. Multicoloured.
900 15 f. Type **359** 10 10
901 65 f. Full-rigged sailing ship, 1878 . . . . 10 10
902 140 f. "Golden Hind" (Drake's flagship) 45 10
903 500 f. 18th-century dhow . . . 1·00 25
904 640 f. "Ostrust" (galleon), 1721 (vert) . . . . 1·10 30
905 800 f. Dutch caravel, 1599 (vert) . . . . 1·40 40
906 1025 f. "Santa Maria" (Columbus's flagship), 1492 . 1·75 50

1992. Anti-AIDS Campaign.
908 **360** 140 f. black and mauve . . 35 10

361 Tending Trees

1992. Reforestation.
909 **361** 140 f. dp green, blk & grn . 10 10

POSTAGE DUE STAMPS

D **13** Independence Obelisk

1962.
D45 **D 13** 1 f. green 10 10
D46 2 f. brown 10 10
D47 3 f. violet 10 10
D48 4 f. slate 10 10
D49 5 f. red 10 10
D50 10 f. green 15 15
D51 20 f. purple 20 20
D52 40 f. blue 50 45
D53 50 f. red 75 70
D54 100 f. black . . . . . . 1·40 1·25

APPENDIX

The following stamps have either been issued in excess of postal needs or have not been available to the public in reasonable quantities at face value.

1987.
Winter Olympic Games, Calgary (1988). 1500 f. (on gold foil).

1989.
Scout and Butterfly. 5000 f. (on gold foil).

"Philexfrance 89" Int. Stamp Exhibition, Paris. 5000 f. (on gold foil).

World Cup Football Championship, Italy. 5000 f. (on gold foil).

1990.
Winter Olympic Games, Albertville (1992). 5000 f. (on gold foil).

1991.
Birth Centenary of De Gaulle. 5000 f. (on gold foil).

1992.
Olympic Games, Barcelona. 500 f. (on gold foil).

1993.
Bicentenary of French Republic. 1989 "Philexfrance 89" issue optd. 5000 f.

1994.
Elvis Presley (entertainer). 10000 f. (on gold foil).

World Cup Football Championship, U.S.A. 10000 f. (on gold foil).

Winter Olympic Games, Lillehammer, Norway. 10000 f. (on gold foil).

Olympic Games, Atlanta, U.S.A. 5000 f. (on gold foil).

For further issues see under MADAGASCAR.

MALAWI Pt. 1

Formerly Nyasaland, became an independent Republic within the Commonwealth on 6 July 1966.

1964. 12 pence = 1 shilling;
20 shillings = 1 pound.
1970. 100 tambalas = 1 kwacha.

44 Dr. H. Banda (Prime Minister) and Independence Monument

1964. Independence.

211 **44** 3d. olive and sepia 10 10
212 – 6d. multicoloured 10 10
213 – 1s. 3d. multicoloured . . . 35 10
214 – 2s. 6d. multicoloured . . . 45 1·25

DESIGNS—each with Dr. Hastings Banda: 6d. Rising sun; 1s. 3d. National flag; 2s. 6d. Coat of arms.

48 Tung Tree

1964. As Nos. 199/210 of Nyasaland but inscr "MALAWI" as in T **48**. The 9d., 1s. 6d. and £2 are new values and designs.

252 ½d. violet 10 10
216 1d. black and green 10 10
217 2d. brown 10 10
218 3d. brown, green & bistre . . 15 10
219 4d. blue and yellow 60 15
220 6d. purple, green and blue . . 75 10
221 9d. brown, green & yellow . . 30 15
258 1s. brown, blue and yellow . . 25 10
223 1s. 3d. green and brown . . . 50 60
259 1s. 6d. brown and green . . . 30 10
224 2s. 6d. brown and blue . . . 1·10 1·00
225 5s. multicoloured (I) . . . . 65 2·25
225a 5s. multicoloured (II) . . . 5·00 90
226 10s. green, salmon & black . . 1·50 2·00
227 £1 brown and yellow . . . . 7·00 5·50
262 £2 multicoloured . . . . . . 25·00 24·00

DESIGNS (New): 1s. 6d. Burley tobacco; £2 "Cyrestis camillus" (butterfly).

Two types of 5s. I, inscr "LAKE NYASA". II, inscr "LAKE MALAWI".

49 Christmas Star and Globe

1964. Christmas.

228 **49** 3d. green and gold 10 10
229 6d. mauve and gold 10 10
230 1s. 3d. violet and gold . . . 10 10
231 2s. 6d. blue and gold 20 40

50 Coins

1964. Malawi's First Coinage. Coins in black and silver.

232 **50** 3d. green 10 10
233 9d. mauve 20 10
234 1s. 6d. purple 25 10
235 3s. blue 35 70

1965. Nos. 223/4 surch.

236 1s. 6d. on 1s. 3d. green & brown 10 10
237 3s. on 2s. 6d. brown & blue . . 20 20

52 Chilembwe leading Rebels

1965. 50th Anniv of 1915 Rising.

238 **52** 3d. violet and green 10 10
239 9d. olive and orange 10 10
240 1s. 6d. brown and blue 15 10
241 3s. turquoise and blue 20 25

53 "Learning and Scholarship"

1965. Opening of Malawi University.

242 **53** 3d. black and green 10 10
243 9d. black and mauve 10 10
244 1s. 6d. black and violet . . . 10 10
245 3s. black and blue 15 40

54 "Papilio ophidicephalus"

1966. Malawi Butterflies. Multicoloured.

247 4d. Type **54** 80 10
248 9d. "Papilio desmondi" (magdae) 1·25 10
249 1s. 6d. "Epamera handmani" . 1·75 30
250 3s. "Amauris crawshayi" . . . 2·75 6·00

58 British Central Africa 6d. Stamp of 1891 **59** President Banda

1966. 75th Anniv of Postal Services.

263 **58** 4d. blue and green 10 10
264 9d. blue and red 15 10
265 1s. 6d. blue and lilac 20 10
266 3s. grey and blue 30 70

1966. Republic Day.

268 **59** 4d. brown, silver & green . . 10 10
269 9d. brown, silver & mauve . . 10 10
270 1s. 6d. brown, silver & vio . . 15 10
271 3s. brown, silver and blue . . 25 15

60 Bethlehem

1966. Christmas.

273 **60** 4d. green and gold 10 10
274 9d. purple and gold 10 10
275 1s. 6d. red and gold 15 10
276 3s. blue and gold 40 70

61 "Ilala I"

1967. Lake Malawi Steamers.

277 **61** 4d. black, yellow & green . . 40 10
278 – 9d. black, yellow & mauve . . 45 10
279 – 1s. 6d. black, red & violet . 65 20
280 – 3s. black, red and blue . . . 1·25 1·75

DESIGNS: 9d. "Dove"; 1s. 9d. "Chauncy Maples I" (wrongly inscr "Chauncey"); 3s. "Gwendolen".

62 Golden Mbuna (female)

1967. Lake Malawi Cichlids. Multicoloured.

281 4d. Type **62** 20 10
282 9d. Scraped-mouthed mbuna . . 30 10
283 1s. 6d. Zebra mbuna 40 20
284 3s. Orange mbuna . . . . . . 1·25 1·75

63 Rising Sun and Gearwheel

1967. Industrial Development.

285 **63** 4d. black and green 10 10
286 9d. black and red 10 10
287 1s. 6d. black and violet . . . 10 10
288 3s. black and blue 15 15

64 Mary and Joseph beside Crib

1967. Christmas.

290 **64** 4d. blue and green 10 10
291 9d. blue and red 10 10
292 1s. 6d. blue and yellow . . . 10 10
293 3s. deep blue and blue 15 15

65 "Calotropis procera"

1968. Wild Flowers. Multicoloured.

295 4d. Type **65** 15 10
296 9d. "Borreria dibrachiata" . . 15 10
297 1s. 6d. "Hibiscus rhodanthus" . 15 10
298 3s. "Bidens pinnatipartita" . . 20 95

66 Bagnall Steam Locomotive, No. 1 "Thistle"

1968. Malawi Locomotives.

300 **66** 4d. green, blue and red . . . 40 10
301 – 9d. red, blue and green . . . 50 15
302 – 1s. 6d. multicoloured 75 30
303 – 3s. multicoloured . . . . . 1·40 3·00

DESIGNS: 9d. Class G steam locomotive No. 49; 1s. 6d. Class "Zambesi" diesel locomotive No. 202; 3s. Diesel railcar No. DR1.

67 "The Nativity" (Piero della Francesca)

1968. Christmas. Multicoloured.

305 4d. Type **67** 10 10
306 9d. "The Adoration of the Shepherds" (Murillo) 10 10
307 1s. 6d. "The Adoration of the Shepherds" (Reni) 10 10
308 3s. "Nativity, with God the Father and Holy Ghost" (Pittoni) 15 15

69 Nyassa Lovebird **70** Carmine Bee Eater

1968. Birds (1st series). Multicoloured.

310 1d. Scarlet-chested sunbird (horiz) 15 10
311 2d. Violet starling (horiz) . . . 15 10
312 3d. White-browed robin chat (horiz) 20 10
313 4d. Red-billed fire finch (horiz) 35 40
314 6d. Type **69** 45 15
315 9d. Yellow-rumped bishop . . 50 60
316 1s. Type **70** 60 15
317 1s. 6d. Grey-headed bush shrike 5·00 8·00
318 2s. Paradise whydah . . . . . 5·00 8·00
319 3s. African paradise flycatcher (vert) . . . . 4·50 4·25
320 5s. Bateleur (vert) . . . . . . 7·00 4·25
321 10s. Saddle-bill stork (vert) . . 5·50 7·50
322 £1 Purple heron (vert) . . . . 10·00 18·00
323 £2 Knysna turaco ("Livingstone's Loerie") . . . . 42·00 48·00

SIZES: 1d. to 9d. as Type **69**; 1s. 6d. to £2 as Type **70**.

See also Nos. 473/85.

71 I.L.O. Emblem

1969. 50th Anniv of Int Labour Organization.

324 **71** 4d. gold and green 10 10
325 9d. gold and brown 10 10
326 1s. 6d. gold and brown . . . 10 10
327 3s. gold and blue 15 15

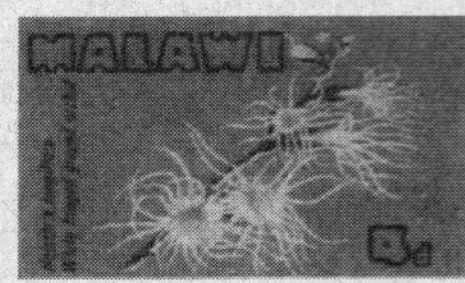

72 White-fringed Ground Orchid

1969. Orchids of Malawi. Multicoloured.

329 4d. Type **72** 15 10
330 9d. Red ground orchid 20 10
331 1s. 6d. Leopard tree orchid . . 30 20
332 3s. Blue ground orchid . . . . 60 2·00

73 African Development Bank Emblem **74** Dove over Bethlehem

1969. 5th Anniv of African Development Bank.

334 **73** 4d. yellow, brown & ochre . 10 10
335 9d. yellow, ochre & green . . 10 10
336 1s. 6d. yellow, ochre & brn . 10 10
337 3s. yellow, ochre and blue . . 15 15

1969. Christmas.

339 **74** 2d. black and yellow 10 10
340 4d. black and turquoise . . . 10 10
341 9d. black and red 10 10
342 1s. 6d. black and violet . . . 10 10
343 3s. black and blue 15 15

75 "Zonocerus elegans" (grasshopper) **77** Runner

1970. Insects of Malawi. Multicoloured.

345 4d. Type **75** 15 10
346 9d. "Mylabris dicincta" (beetle) 15 10
347 1s. 6d. "Henosepilachna elaterii" (ladybird) 20 10
348 3s. "Sphodromantis speculabunda" (mantid) . . 35 45

1970. Rand Easter Show. No. 317 optd **Rand Easter Show 1970**.

350 1s. 6d. multicoloured . . . . . 50 1·75

1970. 9th Commonwealth Games, Edinburgh.

351 **77** 4d. blue and green 10 10
352 9d. blue and red 10 10
353 1s. 6d. blue and yellow . . . 10 10
354 3s. deep blue and blue 15 15

1970. Decimal Currency. Nos. 316 and 318 surch.

356 10 t. on 1s. multicoloured . . . 1·75 25
357 20 t. on 2s. multicoloured . . . 2·25 2·50

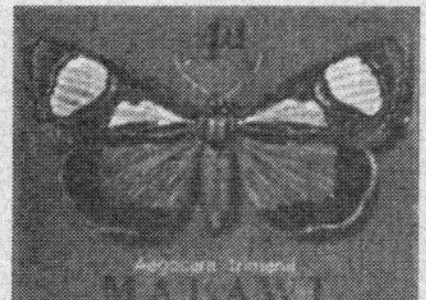

79 "Aegocera trimeni"

1970. Moths. Multicoloured.

358 4d. Type **79** 20 10
359 9d. "Faidherbia bauhiniae" . . 30 10
360 1s. 6d. "Parasa karschi" . . . 50 20
361 3s. "Teracotona euprepia" . . 1·25 3·25

80 Mother and Child

1970. Christmas.
363 **80** 2d. black and yellow 10 10
364 4d. black and green 10 10
365 9d. black and red 10 10
366 1s. 6d. black and purple . . 10 10
367 3s. black and blue 15 15

1971. No. 319 surch **30t Special United Kingdom Delivery Service**.
369 30 t. on 3s. multicoloured . . . 50 2·00
No. 369 was issued for use on letters carried by an emergency airmail service from Malawi to Great Britain during the British postal strike. The fee of 30 t. was to cover the charge for delivery by a private service, and ordinary stamps to pay the normal airmail postage had to be affixed as well. These stamps were in use from 8 February to 8 March.

82 Decimal Coinage and Cockerel
83 Greater Kudu

1971. Decimal Coinage.
370 **82** 3 t. multicoloured 15 10
371 8 t. multicoloured 20 10
372 15 t. multicoloured 25 20
373 30 t. multicoloured . . . . 35 1·50

1971. Decimal Currency. Antelopes. Mult.
375 1 t. Type **83** 10 10
376 2 t. Nyala 15 10
377 3 t. Mountain reedbuck 20 50
378 5 t. Puku 40 75
379 8 t. Impala 45 60
380 10 t. Eland 60 10
381 15 t. Klipspringer . . . . . . 1·00 20
382 20 t. Suni . . . . 1·50 90
383 30 t. Roan antelope . . . . . 8·00 90
384 50 t. Waterbuck 90 65
385 1 k. Bushbuck . . . . 1·50 85
386 2 k. Red forest duiker . . . . 2·75 1·50
387 4 k. Common duiker . . . . . 20·00 18·00
Nos. 380/7 are larger, size 25 × 42 mm.
No. 387 is incorrectly inscr "Gray Duiker".

85 Christ on the Cross
87 "Holarrhena febrifuga"

1971. Easter. Multicoloured.
388 **85** 3 t. black and green 10 20
389 – 3 t. black and green 10 20
390 **85** 8 t. black and red 10 20
391 – 8 t. black and red 10 20
392 **85** 15 t. black and violet . . . 20 30
393 – 15 t. black and violet . . . 20 30
394 **85** 30 t. black and blue 25 45
395 – 30 t. black and blue 25 45
DESIGN: Nos. 389, 391, 393, 395, The Resurrection.
Both designs from "The Small Passion" (Durer).

1971. Flowering Shrubs and Trees. Mult.
397 3 t. Type **87** 10 10
398 8 t. "Brachystegia spiciformis" 15 10
399 15 t. "Securidaca longepedunculata" 25 10
400 30 t. "Pterocarpus rotundifolius" 40 50

88 Drum Major
89 "Madonna and Child" (William Dyce)

1971. 50th Anniv of Malawi Police Force.
402 **88** 30 t. multicoloured . . . . 65 1·25

1971. Christmas. Multicoloured.
403 3 t. Type **89** 10 10
404 8 t. "The Holy Family" (M. Schongauer) 15 10
405 15 t. "The Holy Family with St. John" (Raphael) 20 20
406 30 t. "The Holy Family" (Bronzino) . . . . 50 1·40

90 Vickers Viscount 700

1972. Air. Malawi Aircraft. Multicoloured.
408 3 t. Type **90** 30 10
409 8 t. Hawker Siddeley H.S.748 . 50 10
410 15 t. Britten Norman Islander . 75 30
411 30 t. B.A.C. One Eleven . . . 1·25 2·25

91 Figures (Chencherere Hill)

1972. Rock Paintings.
413 **91** 3 t. green and black 35 10
414 – 8 t. red, grey and black . . . 45 10
415 – 15 t. multicoloured 55 30
416 – 30 t. multicoloured . . . . 65 1·00
DESIGNS: 8 t. Lizard and cat (Chencherere Hill); 15 t. Schematics (Diwa Hill); 30 t. Sun through rain (Mikolongwe Hill).

92 Boxing

1972. Olympic Games, Munich.
418 **92** 3 t. multicoloured 10 10
419 8 t. multicoloured 15 10
420 15 t. multicoloured 20 10
421 30 t. multicoloured 35 45

93 Arms of Malawi
94 "Adoration of the Kings" (Orcagna)

1972. Commonwealth Parliamentary Conf.
423 **93** 15 t. multicoloured 30 35

1972. Christmas. Multicoloured.
424 3 t. Type **94** 10 10
425 8 t. "Madonna and Child Enthroned" (Florentine School) 10 10
426 15 t. "Virgin and Child" (Crivelli) 20 10
427 30 t. "Virgin and Child with St. Anne" (Flemish School) . . 45 70

95 "Charaxes bohemani"

1973. Butterflies. Multicoloured.
429 3 t. Type **95** 30 10
430 8 t. "Uranothauma crawshayi" 55 10
431 15 t. "Charaxes acuminatus" . 75 30
432 30 t. "Amauris ansorgei" (inscr in error "EUPHAEDRA ZADDACHI") . . . . . . 3·50 7·50
433 30 t. "Amauris ansorgei" (inscr corrected) . . . . . . 3·00 7·50

96 Livingstone and Map

1973. Death Cent of David Livingstone (1st issue).
435 **96** 3 t. multicoloured 10 10
436 8 t. multicoloured 15 10
437 15 t. multicoloured 20 10
438 30 t. multicoloured 35 60
See also No. 450.

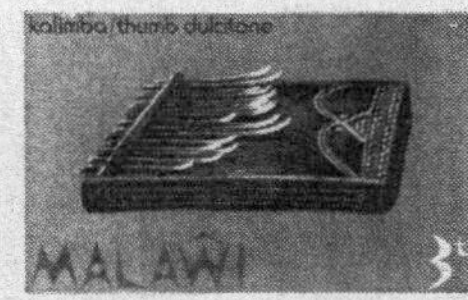

97 Thumb Dulcitone

1973. Musical Instruments. Multicoloured.
440 3 t. Type **97** 10 10
441 8 t. Hand zither (vert) 15 10
442 15 t. Hand drum (vert) 25 10
443 30 t. One-stringed fiddle . . . 45 60

98 The Magi

1973. Christmas.
445 **98** 3 t. blue, lilac & ultramarine 10 10
446 8 t. red, lilac and brown . . 10 10
447 15 t. mauve, blue & dp mve 15 10
448 30 t. yellow, lilac & brown . 30 70

99 Stained-glass Window, Livingstonia Mission

1973. Death Cent of David Livingstone (2nd issue).
450 **99** 50 t. multicoloured . . . . 45 1·00

100 Large-mouthed Black Bass

1973. 35th Anniv of Malawi Angling Society. Multicoloured.
452 3 t. Type **100** 25 10
453 8 t. Rainbow trout 30 10
454 15 t. Silver alestes ("Lake salmon") 55 20
455 30 t. Tigerfish . . . . 85 1·25

101 U.P.U. Monument and Map of Africa

1974. Centenary of U.P.U.
457 **101** 3 t. green and brown . . . 10 10
458 8 t. red and brown 10 10
459 15 t. violet and brown . . 15 10
460 30 t. blue and brown . . . 30 70

102 Capital Hill, Lilongwe

1974. 10th Anniv of Independence.
462 **102** 3 t. multicoloured 10 10
463 8 t. multicoloured 10 10
464 15 t. multicoloured 10 10
465 30 t. multicoloured 25 35

103 "Madonna of the Meadow" (Bellini)

1974. Christmas. Multicoloured.
467 3 t. Type **103** 10 10
468 8 t. "The Holy Family with Sts. John and Elizabeth" (Jordaens) 10 10
469 15 t. "The Nativity" (Pieter de Grebber) 15 10
470 30 t. "Adoration of the Shepherds" (Lorenzo di Credi) 30 50

104 Arms of Malawi
105 African Snipe

106 Spur-winged Goose

1975.
472 **104** 1 t. blue 20 40
472a 5 t. red . . . . 50 1·40

1975. Birds (2nd series). Mult. (a) As T **105**.
473 1 t. Type **105** . . . . 30 1·50
474 2 t. Double-banded sandgrouse (horiz) . . . . 50 1·50
475 3 t. Blue quail (horiz) . . . . 1·50 1·50
476 5 t. Bare-throated francolin . . 3·50 1·25
477 8 t. Harlequin quail (horiz) . . 4·75 1·00
(b) As T **106**.
502 10 t. Type **106** . . . . 2·00 1·25
503 15 t. Barrow's bustard . . . . 2·00 1·75
480 20 t. Comb duck . . . . . . 1·00 2·25
481 30 t. Helmet guineafowl . . . 1·25 70
482 50 t. African pygmy goose (horiz) 2·00 1·60
483 1 k. Garganey . . . . 3·00 7·50
504 2 k. White-faced whistling duck 5·00 9·50
485 4 k. African green pigeon . . . 13·00 16·00

107 M.V. "Mpasa"

1975. Ships of Lake Malawi. Multicoloured.
486 3 t. Type **107** 30 10
487 8 t. M.V. "Ilala II" 40 10
488 15 t. M.V. "Chauncy Maples II" 75 30
489 30 t. M.V. "Nkwazi" . . . . . 1·00 2·50

108 "Habenaria splendens"
109 Thick-tailed Bushbaby

1975. Malawi Orchids. Multicoloured.
491 3 t. Type **108** 40 10
492 10 t. "Eulophia cucullata" . . 50 10
493 20 t. "Disa welwitschii" 80 25
494 40 t. "Angraecum conchiferum" 1·10 1·50

1976. Malawi Animals. Multicoloured.
496 3 t. Type **109** 10 10
497 10 t. Leopard 35 10
498 20 t. Roan antelope 55 35
499 40 t. Common zebra . . . . . 1·00 2·75

1975. 10th Africa, Caribbean and Pacific Ministerial Conference. No. 482 optd **10th ACP Ministerial Conference 1975.**
514 50 t. African pygmy goose . . 1·00 2·00

111 "A Castle with the Adoration of the Magi"

1975. Christmas. Religious Medallions. Mult.
515 3 t. Type **111** 10 10
516 10 t. "The Nativity" 15 10
517 20 t. "Adoration of the Magi" (different) 20 10
518 40 t. "Angel appearing to Shepherds" . . . . 50 1·90

112 Alexander Graham Bell

113 President Banda

1976. Centenary of Telephone.
520 **112** 3 t. green and black 10 10
521 10 t. purple and black . . . 10 10
522 20 t. violet and black . . . 20 10
523 40 t. blue and black . . . 50 90

1976. 10th Anniv of Republic. Multicoloured.
525 **113** 3 t. green 10 10
526 10 t. purple 10 10
527 20 t. blue 20 10
528 40 t. blue 50 90

114 Bagnall Diesel Shunter No. 100

1976. Malawi Locomotives. Multicoloured.
530 3 t. Type **114** 40 10
531 10 t. Class "Shire" diesel locomotive No. 503 . . . . 70 10
532 20 t. Nippon Sharyo diesel-hydraulic locomotive No. 301 . . . . 1·40 45
533 40 t. Hunslet diesel-hydraulic locomotive No. 110 . . . . 2·10 4·75

1976. Centenary of Blantyre Mission. Nos. 479 and 481 optd **Blantyre Mission Centenary 1876–1976.**
535 15 t. Barrow's bustard . . . . 1·25 1·00
536 30 t. Helmet guineafowl . . . . 1·50 2·50

116 Child on Bed of Straw

117 Man and Woman

1976. Christmas.
537 **116** 3 t. multicoloured 10 10
538 10 t. multicoloured 10 10
539 20 t. multicoloured 20 10
540 40 t. multicoloured 40 60

1977. Handicrafts. Wood-carvings. Mult.
542 4 t. Type **117** 10 10
543 10 t. Elephant (horiz) 15 10
544 20 t. Rhinoceros (horiz) 20 10
545 40 t. Antelope 50 70

118 Chileka Airport

1977. Transport. Multicoloured.
547 4 t. Type **118** 40 10
548 10 t. Blantyre–Lilongwe Road . . 40 10
549 20 t. M.V. "Ilala II" . . . . . 1·25 35
550 40 t. Blantyre–Nacala rail line . 2·00 4·00

119 Blue-grey Mbuna

1977. Fish of Lake Malawi. Multicoloured.
552B 4 t. Type **119** 30 10
553B 10 t. Livingston mbuna . . . 40 20
554A 20 t. Zebra mbuna . . . . . 1·40 30
555B 40 t. Malawi scale-eater . . . 1·25 95

120 "Madonna and Child with St. Catherine and the Blessed Stefano Maconi" (Borgognone)

121 "Entry of Christ into Jerusalem" (Giotto)

1977. Christmas.
557 **120** 4 t. multicoloured 10 10
558 – 10 t. multicoloured 10 10
559 – 20 t. multicoloured 20 10
560 – 40 t. multicoloured 50 70

DESIGNS: 10 t. "Madonna and Child with the Eternal Father and Angels" (Borgognone); 20 t. Bottigella altarpiece (detail, Foppa); 40 t. "Madonna of the Fountain" (van Eyck).

1978. Easter. Paintingss by Giotto. Multicoloured.
562 4 t. Type **121** 10 10
563 10 t. "The Crucifixion" 15 10
564 20 t. "Descent from the Cross" . 30 10
565 40 t. "Jesus appears before Mary" 50 55

122 Nyala

124 "Vanilla polylepis"

123 Malamulo Seventh Day Adventist Church

1978. Wildlife. Multicoloured.
567 4 t. Type **122** . . . . 1·25 10
568 10 t. Lion (horiz) . . . . . . 3·50 30
569 20 t. Common zebra (horiz) . . 6·50 80
570 40 t. Mountain reedbuck . . . 8·00 5·50

1978. Christmas. Multicoloured.
572 4 t. Type **123** 10 10
573 10 t. Likoma Cathedral 10 10
574 20 t. St. Michael's and All Angels', Blantyre 20 10
575 40 t. Zomba Catholic Cathedral 40 60

1979. Orchids. Multicoloured.
577 1 t. Type **124** 50 30
578 2 t. "Cirrhopetalum umbellatum" 50 30
579 5 t. "Calanthe natalensis" . . . 50 10
580 7 t. "Ansellia gigantea" 50 50
581 8 t. "Tridactyle bicaudata" . . . 50 30
582 10 t. "Acampe pachyglossa" . . . 50 10
583 15 t. "Eulophia quartiniana" . . 50 15
584 20 t. "Cyrtorchis arcuata" . . . 50 50
585 30 t. "Eulophia tricristata" . . 1·25 30
586 50 t. "Disa hamatopetala" . . . 85 50
587 75 t. "Cynorchis glandulosa" . . 2·00 4·25
588 1 k. "Aerangis kotschyana" . . 1·60 1·25
589 1 k. 50 "Polystachya dendrobiiflora" . . . . . . 1·75 2·75
590 2 k. "Disa ornithantha" . . . . 1·75 2·00
591 4 k. "Cyrtorchis praetermissa" . 3·00 3·50

125 Tsamba

1979. National Tree Planting Day. Mult.
592 5 t. Type **125** 20 10
593 10 t. Mulanje cedar 25 10
594 20 t. Mlombwa 40 20
595 40 t. Mbawa . . . . 70 2·25

126 Train crossing Viaduct

1979. Opening of Salima–Lilongwe Railway Line. Multicoloured.
597 5 t. Type **126** 25 10
598 10 t. Diesel railcar at station . . 40 10
599 20 t. Diesel train rounding bend . 60 30
600 40 t. Diesel train passing through cutting . . . . 85 1·25

127 Young Child

1979. International Year of the Child. Designs showing young children. Multicoloured; background colours given.
602 **127** 5 t. green 10 10
603 – 10 t. red 10 10
604 – 20 t. mauve 25 10
605 – 40 t. blue 45 80

128 1964 3d. Independence Commemorative Stamp

1979. Death Centenary of Sir Rowland Hill. Designs showing 1964 Independence Commemorative Stamps. Multicoloured.
606 5 t. Type **128** 10 10
607 10 t. 6d. value 10 10
608 20 t. 1s. 3d. value 20 10
609 40 t. 2s. 6d. value 35 60

129 River Landscape

1979. Christmas. Multicoloured.
611 5 t. Type **129** 10 10
612 10 t. Sunset 10 10
613 20 t. Forest and hill 25 15
614 40 t. Plain and mountains . . . 50 2·00

130 Limbe Rotary Club Emblem

132 Agate Nodule

131 Mangochi District Post Office

1980. 75th Anniv of Rotary International.
615 **130** 5 t. multicoloured 10 10
616 – 10 t. multicoloured 10 10
617 – 20 t. blue, gold and red . . 30 15
618 – 40 t. gold and blue . . . . 75 1·60

DESIGNS: 10 t. Blantyre Rotary Club pennant; 20 t. Lilongwe Rotary Club pennant; 40 t. Rotary International emblem.

1980. "London 1980" International Stamp Exhibition.
620 **131** 5 t. black and green . . . 10 10
621 – 10 t. black and red 10 10
622 – 20 t. black and violet . . . 15 10
623 – 1 k. black and blue . . . . 65 1·10

DESIGNS: 10 t. New Blantyre Sorting Office; 20 t. Mail transfer hut, Walala; 1 k. First Nyasaland Post Office, Chiromo.

1980. Gemstones. Multicoloured.
625 5 t. Type **132** 60 10
626 10 t. Sunstone 80 10
627 20 t. Smoky quartz . . . . . 1·40 30
628 1 k. Kyanite crystal . . . . . 3·50 6·00

133 Elephants

1980. Christmas. Children's Paintings. Multicoloured.
629 5 t. Type **133** 40 10
630 10 t. Flowers 30 10
631 20 t. Class "Shire" diesel train 75 20
632 1 k. Malachite kingfisher . . . 1·60 2·00

134 Suni

1981. Wildlife. Multicoloured.
633 7 t. Type **134** 15 10
634 10 t. Blue duiker 20 10
635 20 t. African buffalo 30 15
636 1 k. Lichtenstein's hartebeest . . 1·25 1·60

135 "Kanjedza II" Standard "A" Earth Station

1981. International Communications. Mult.
637 7 t. Type **135** 10 10
638 10 t. Blantyre International Gateway Exchange 15 10
639 20 t. "Kanjedza I" standard "B" earth station 25 15
640 1 k. "Satellite communications" 1·50 1·90

136 Maize

1981. World Food Day. Agricultural Produce. Multicoloured.
642 7 t. Type **136** 15 10
643 10 t. Rice 20 10
644 20 t. Finger-millet 30 20
645 1 k. Wheat . . . . 1·00 1·40

137 "The Adoration of the Shepherds" (Murillo) **138** Impala Herd

1981. Christmas. Paintings. Multicoloured.
646 7 t. Type **137** 20 10
647 10 t. "The Holy Family" (Lippi) (horiz) 25 10
648 20 t. "The Adoration of the Shepherds" (Louis le Nain) (horiz) 45 15
649 1 k. "The Virgin and Child, St. John the Baptist and an Angel" (Paolo Morando) . . . . 1·10 1·75

1982. National Parks. Wildlife. Multicoloured.
650 7 t. Type **138** 20 10
651 10 t. Lions 35 10
652 20 t. Greater kudu 50 20
653 1 k. Greater flamingoes . . . . 2·25 4·25

139 Kamuzu Academy

1982. Kamuzu Academy.
654 **139** 7 t. multicoloured 15 10
655 – 20 t. multicoloured 20 10
656 – 30 t. multicoloured 30 45
657 – 1 k. multicoloured . . . . 1·00 2·75
DESIGNS: 20 t. to 1 k. Various views of the Academy.

140 Attacker challenging Goalkeeper

1982. World Cup Football Championship, Spain. Multicoloured.
658 7 t. Type **140** 75 10
659 20 t. FIFA World Cup trophy . . 1·60 1·10
660 30 t. Football stadium . . . . 1·90 3·25

141 Blantyre War Memorial, St. Paul's Church

1982. Remembrance Day. Multicoloured.
662 7 t. Type **141** 10 10
663 20 t. Zomba war memorial . . 15 10
664 30 t. Chichiri war memorial . . 20 30
665 1 k. Lilongwe war memorial . . 65 3·25

142 Kwacha International Conference Centre

1983. Commonwealth Day. Multicoloured.
666 7 t. Type **142** 10 10
667 20 t. Tea-picking, Mulanje . . 20 10
668 30 t. World map showing position of Malawi 25 30
669 1 k. Pres. Dr. H. Kamuzu Banda . . 60 1·50

143 "Christ and St. Peter" **144** Pair by Lake

1983. 500th Birth Anniv of Raphael. Details from the cartoon for "The Miraculous Draught of Fishes" Tapestry. Multicoloured.
670 7 t. Type **143** 35 10
671 20 t. "Hauling in the Catch" . . 75 80
672 30 t. "Fishing Village" (horiz) . . 90 2·50

1983. African Fish Eagle. Multicoloured.
674 30 t. Type **144** . . . . 1·60 1·90
675 30 t. Making gull-like call . . 1·60 1·90
676 30 t. Diving on prey . . . . 1·60 1·90
677 30 t. Carrying fish . . . . 1·60 1·90
678 30 t. Feeding on catch . . . . 1·60 1·90

145 Kamuzu International Airport

1983. Bicentenary of Manned Flight. Mult.
679 7 t. Type **145** 10 10
680 20 t. Kamuzu International Airport (different) 25 15
681 30 t. B.A.C. One Eleven 40 45
682 1 k. Short Empire "C" Class flying boat at Cape Maclear . . 1·10 2·25

146 "Clerodendrum myricoides" **147** Golden Mbuna

1983. Christmas. Flowers. Multicoloured.
684 7 t. Type **146** 40 10
685 20 t. "Gloriosa superba" . . 90 15
686 30 t. "Gladiolus laxiflorus" . . 1·25 60
687 1 k. "Aframomum angustifolium" . . . . 3·00 6·50

1984. Fishes. Multicoloured.
688 1 t. Type **147** 30 60
689 2 t. Malawi eyebiter 30 60
690 5 t. Blue mbuna 30 50
691 7 t. Lombardo's mbuna 30 10
692 8 t. Golden zebra mbuna 30 10
693 10 t. Fairy cichlid 30 10
694 15 t. Crabro mbuna 30 10
695 20 t. Marbled zebra mbuna . . 30 10
696 30 t. Sky-blue mbuna 40 20
697 40 t. Venustus cichlid 60 30
698 50 t. Thumbi emperor cichlid . . 1·75 2·25
699 75 t. Purple mbuna . . . . 2·25 3·50
700 1 k. Zebra mbuna . . . . 2·50 3·50
701 2 k. Fairy cichlid (different) . . 3·50 5·00
702 4 k. Mbenje emperor cichlid . . 4·75 8·00
Nos. 688 and 691/7 exist with different imprint dates at foot.

148 Smith's Red Hare

1984. Small Mammals. Multicoloured.
703 7 t. Type **148** 40 10
704 20 t. Gambian sun squirrel . . 65 50
705 30 t. South African hedgehog . . 75 1·10
706 1 k. Large-spotted genet . . 90 5·50

149 Running **150** "Euphaedra neophron"

1984. Olympic Games, Los Angeles. Mult.
707 7 t. Type **149** 15 10
708 20 t. Boxing 35 20
709 30 t. Cycling 75 70
710 1 k. Long jumping . . . . 1·40 3·50

1984. Butterflies.
712 **150** 7 t. multicoloured 95 30
713 – 20 t. yellow, brown and red . 2·25 45
714 – 30 t. multicoloured . . . . 2·50 1·10
715 – 1 k. multicoloured . . . . 4·25 9·00
DESIGNS: 20 t. "Papilio dardanus"; 30 t. "Antanartia schaeneia"; 1 k. "Spindasis nyassae".

151 "Virgin and Child" (Duccio) **152** "Leucopaxillus gracillimus"

1984. Christmas. Religious Paintings. Multicoloured.
716 7 t. Type **151** 45 10
717 20 t. "Madonna and Child" (Raphael) . . . . 1·25 20
718 30 t. "Virgin and Child" (ascr to Lippi) . . . . 1·75 70
719 1 k. "The Wilton Diptych" . . 3·25 7·50

1985. Fungi. Multicoloured.
720 7 t. Type **152** . . . . 1·25 30
721 20 t. "Limacella guttata" . . 2·50 45
722 30 t. "Termitomyces eurrhizus" . . 3·00 1·25
723 1 k. "Xerulina asprata" . . . . 5·50 9·50

153 Map showing Member States and Lumberjack (Forestry)

1985. 5th Anniv of Southern African Development Co-ordination Conference. Designs showing map and aspects of development.
724 **153** 7 t. black, green and light green 75 10
725 – 15 t. black, red and pink . 1·25 20
726 – 20 t. black, violet and mauve 4·00 1·75
727 – 1 k. black, blue and light blue . . . . 4·50 9·00
DESIGNS: 15 t. Radio mast (Communications); 20 t. Diesel locomotive (Transport); 1 k. Trawler and net (Fishing).

154 M.V. "Ufulu"

1985 Ships of Lake Malawi (2nd series). Mult.
728 7 t. Type **154** 90 10
729 15 t. M.V. "Chauncy Maples II" 1·75 20
730 20 t. M.V. "Mtendere" . . . . 2·25 65
731 1 k. M.V. "Ilala II" . . . . 4·50 6·00

155 Stierling's Woodpecker **156** "The Virgin of Humility" (Jaime Serra)

1985. Birth Bicentenary of John J. Audubon (ornithologist). Multicoloured.
733 7 t. Type **155** . . . . 1·25 30
734 15 t. Lesser seedcracker . . . . 2·25 30
735 20 t. East coast akelat . . . . 2·25 65
736 1 k. Boehm's bee eater . . . . 4·25 6·00

1985. Christmas. Nativity Paintings. Mult.
738 7 t. Type **156** 30 10
739 15 t. "The Adoration of the Magi" (Stefano da Zevio) . . 75 15
740 20 t. "Madonna and Child" (Gerard van Honthorst) . . 85 25
741 1 k. "Virgin of Zbraslav" (Master of Vissy Brod) . . . . 2·25 3·75

157 Halley's Comet and Path of "Giotto" Spacecraft

1986. Appearance of Halley's Comet. Mult.
742 8 t. Type **157** 60 10
743 15 t. Halley's Comet above Earth 65 15
744 20 t. Comet and dish aerial, Malawi . . . . 1·00 30
745 1 k. "Giotto" spacecraft . . . . 2·00 4·00

158 Two Players competing for Ball

1986. World Cup Football Championship, Mexico. Multicoloured.
746 8 t. Type **158** 70 10
747 15 t. Goalkeeper saving goal . . 95 20
748 20 t. Two players competing for ball (different) . . . . 1·10 35
749 1 k. Player kicking ball . . . . 4·00 3·50

159 President Banda **160** "Virgin and Child" (Botticelli)

1986. 20th Anniv of Republic. Multicoloured.
751 8 t. Type **159** . . . . 1·50 2·25
752 15 t. National flag 80 15
753 20 t. Malawi coat of arms . . 85 25
754 1 k. Kamuzu International Airport and emblem of national airline . . . . 3·50 4·50

1986. Christmas. Multicoloured.
755 8 t. Type **160** 45 10
756 15 t. "Adoration of the Shepherds" (Guido Reni) . . 80 15
757 20 t. "Madonna of the Veil" (Carlo Dolci) . . . . 1·25 35
758 1 k. "Adoration of the Magi" (Jean Bourdichon) . . . . 3·75 7·50

161 Wattled Crane

1987. Wattled Crane. Multicoloured.
759 8 t. Type **161** . . . . 1·25 30
760 15 t. Two cranes . . . . 2·00 40
761 20 t. Cranes at nest . . . . 2·25 75
762 75 t. Crane in lake . . . . 4·50 9·00

162 Bagnall Steam Locomotive No. 2 "Shamrock"

1987. Steam Locomotives. Multicoloured.

767 10 t. Type **162** . . . . 1·75 30
768 25 t. Class D steam locomotive No. 8, 1914 . . . . 2·50 40
769 30 t. Bagnall steam locomotive No. 1 "Thistle" . . . . . . 2·75 85
770 1 k. Kitson steam locomotive No. 6, 1903 . . . . 5·00 9·00

163 Hippopotamus grazing

164 "Stathmostelma spectabile"

1987. Hippopotamus. Multicoloured.

771 10 t. Type **163** . . . . 1·25 30
772 25 t. Hippopotami in water . . 2·00 40
773 30 t. Female and calf in water 2·00 75
774 1 k. Hippopotami and cattle egret . . . . 5·50 9·00

1987. Christmas. Wild Flowers. Multicoloured.

776 10 t. Type **164** 65 10
777 25 t. "Pentanisia schweinfurthii" 1·50 25
778 30 t. "Chironia krebsii" . . . . 1·75 55
779 1 k. "Ochna macrocalyx" . . . 3·00 7·50

165 African and Staunton Knights

166 High Jumping

1988. Chess. Local and Staunton chess pieces. Multicoloured.

780 15 t. Type **165** . . . . 1·00 20
781 35 t. Bishops . . . . 1·50 70
782 50 t. Rooks . . . . 1·75 1·50
783 2 k. Queens . . . . 5·50 8·50

1988. Olympic Games, Seoul. Multicoloured.

784 15 t. Type **166** 30 10
785 35 t. Javelin throwing 50 20
786 50 t. Tennis 75 50
787 2 k. Shot-putting . . . . . . 1·60 3·00

167 Scrub Warbler

168 "Madonna in the Church" (Jan van Eyck)

1988. Birds. Multicoloured.

789 1 t. Type **167** 10 10
790 2 t. Yellow-throated woodland warbler 10 10
791 5 t. Moustached green tinkerbird 10 10
792 7 t. Waller's red-winged starling 10 10
793 8 t. Oriole-finch 10 10
794 10 t. Starred robin . . . . . 1·75 30
795 15 t. Bar-tailed trogon 10 10
796 20 t. Green-backed twin-spot . 10 10
797 30 t. African grey cuckoo shrike 10 10
798 40 t. Black-fronted bush shrike 10 10
799 50 t. White-tailed crested flycatcher . . . . 2·25 60
800 75 t. Green barbet 10 10
801 1 k. Lemon dove ("Cinnamon Dove") 10 10
802 2 k. Silvery-cheeked hornbill . 10 15
803 4 k. Crowned eagle 10 15
804 10 k. Anchieta's sunbird . . . 5·00 5·50
804a 10 k. As 10 t. 30 35

167a Rebuilt Royal Exchange, 1844

1988. 300th Anniv of Lloyd's of London. Mult.

805 15 t. Type **167a** 30 10
806 35 t. Opening ceremony, Nkula Falls Hydro-electric Power Station (horiz) 60 20
807 50 t. Air Malawi B.A.C. One Eleven airliner (horiz) . . . 1·75 60
808 2 k. "Seawise University" (formerly "Queen Elizabeth") on fire, Hong Kong, 1972 . . 3·50 3·25

1988. Christmas. Multicoloured.

809 15 t. Type **168** 60 10
810 35 t. "Virgin, Infant Jesus and St. Anna" (da Vinci) 90 25
811 50 t. "Virgin and Angels" (Cimabue) . . . . 1·25 70
812 2 k. "Virgin and Child" (Baldovinetti Apenio) . . . 3·00 5·00

169 Robust Cichlid

1989. 50th Anniv of Malawi Angling Society. Multicoloured.

813 15 t. Type **169** 50 10
814 35 t. Small-scaled minnow ("Mpasa") 95 30
815 50 t. Long-scaled yellowfish . . 1·40 1·40
816 2 k. Tigerfish . . . . 3·75 7·50

170 Independence Arch, Blantyre

1989. 25th Anniv of Independence. Multicoloured.

817 15 t. Type **170** 70 10
818 35 t. Grain silos . . . . 1·25 30
819 50 t. Capital Hill, Lilongwe . . 1·75 1·50
820 2 k. Reserve Bank Headquarters 4·50 8·00

171 Blantyre Digital Telex Exchange

1989. 25th Anniv of African Development Bank. Multicoloured.

821 15 t. Type **171** 70 10
822 40 t. Dzalanyama steer . . . . 1·25 30
823 50 t. Mikolongwe heifer . . . 1·75 1·50
824 2 k. Zebu bull . . . . 4·50 8·00

172 Rural House with Verandah

1989. 25th Anniv of Malawi–United Nations Co-operation. Multicoloured.

825 15 t. Type **172** 70 10
826 40 t. Rural house . . . . . . 1·25 30
827 50 t. Traditional hut and modern houses . . . . 1·75 1·50
828 2 k. Tea plantation . . . . . 4·50 8·00

173 St. Michael and All Angels Church

1989. Christmas. Churches of Malawi. Mult.

829 15 t. Type **173** 70 10
830 40 t. Catholic Cathedral, Limbe 1·25 30
831 50 t. C.C.A.P. Church, Nkhoma 1·75 1·50
832 2 k. Cathedral, Likoma Island . 4·50 8·00

174 Ford "Sedan", 1915

175 Player heading Ball into Net

1990. Vintage Vehicles. Multicoloured.

833 15 t. Type **174** 80 10
834 40 t. Two-seater Ford, 1915 . . 1·25 30
835 50 t. Ford pick-up, 1915 . . . 1·75 1·50
836 1 k. Chevrolet bus, 1930 . . . 4·50 8·00

1990. World Cup Football Championship, Italy. Multicoloured.

838 15 t. Type **175** 90 10
839 40 t. Player tackling . . . . . 1·40 30
840 50 t. Player scoring goal . . . 1·90 1·50
841 2 k. World Cup . . . . 4·75 8·00

176 Anniversary Emblem on Map

1990. 10th Anniv of Southern Africa Development Co-ordination Conference. Multicoloured.

843 15 t. Type **176** 85 10
844 40 t. Tilapia . . . . 1·40 40
845 50 t. Cedar plantation . . . . 1·75 1·50
846 2 k. Male nyala (antelope) . . 4·25 8·00

177 "Aerangis kotschyana"

178 "The Virgin and the Child Jesus" (Raphael)

1990. Orchids. Multicoloured.

848 15 t. Type **177** . . . . 1·50 20
849 40 t. "Angraecum eburneum" . . 2·50 70
850 50 t. "Aerangis luteo-alba rhodostica" . . . . 2·50 1·60
851 2 k. "Cyrtorchis arcuata whytei" 5·50 8·00

1990. Christmas. Paintings by Raphael. Mult.

853 15 t. Type **178** 80 10
854 40 t. "Transfiguration" (detail) 1·50 30
855 50 t. "St. Catherine of Alexandrie" (detail) . . . . 1·60 90
856 2 k. "Transfiguration" . . . . 4·50 8·00

179 Buffalo

1991. Wildlife. Multicoloured.

858 20 t. Type **179** 80 15
859 60 t. Cheetah . . . . 2·00 1·00
860 75 t. Greater kudu . . . . . . 2·00 1·00
861 2 k. Black rhinoceros . . . . . 7·50 9·00

180 Chiromo Post Office, 1891

1991. Centenary of Postal Services. Mult.

863 20 t. Type **180** 70 10
864 60 t. Re-constructed mail exchange hut at Walala . . . 1·40 85
865 75 t. Mangochi post office . . . 1·50 95
866 2 k. Satellite Earth station . . . 4·75 8·00

181 Red Locust

182 Child in a Manger

1991. Insects. Multicoloured.

868 20 t. Type **181** 85 20
869 60 t. Weevil . . . . 2·00 1·10
870 75 t. Cotton stainer bug . . . 2·00 1·40
871 2 k. Pollen beetle . . . . . . 5·50 8·50

1991. Christmas. Multicoloured.

872 20 t. Type **182** 65 10
873 60 t. Adoration of the Kings and Shepherds . . . . 1·60 45
874 75 t. Nativity . . . . 1·75 75
875 2 k. Virgin and Child . . . . . 4·25 8·00

183 Red Bishop

1992. Birds. Multicoloured.

876 75 t. Type **183** . . . . 1·25 1·25
877 75 t. Lesser striped swallow . . 1·25 1·25
878 75 t. Long-crested eagle . . . . 1·25 1·25
879 75 t. Lilac-breasted roller . . . 1·25 1·25
880 75 t. African paradise flycatcher 1·25 1·25
881 75 t. White-fronted bee eater . 1·25 1·25
882 75 t. White-winged black tern . 1·25 1·25
883 75 t. African fire finch . . . . 1·25 1·25
884 75 t. White-browed robin chat 1·25 1·25
885 75 t. African fish eagle . . . . 1·25 1·25
886 75 t. Malachite kingfisher . . . 1·25 1·25
887 75 t. Lesser masked weaver . . 1·25 1·25
888 75 t. Barn owl . . . . 1·25 1·25
889 75 t. Variable sunbird . . . . 1·25 1·25
890 75 t. Lesser flamingo . . . . . 1·25 1·25
891 75 t. South African crowned crane . . . . 1·25 1·25
892 75 t. African pitta . . . . . . 1·25 1·25
893 75 t. African darter . . . . . 1·25 1·25
894 75 t. White-faced whistling duck 1·25 1·25
895 75 t. African pied wagtail . . . 1·25 1·25

184 Long Jumping

1992. Olympic Games, Barcelona. Multicoloured.

896 20 t. Type **184** 70 10
897 60 t. High jumping . . . . . . 1·10 60
898 75 t. Javelin . . . . 1·40 90
899 2 k. Running . . . . 2·75 4·50

185 "The Angel Gabriel" (detail, "The Annunciation") (Philippe de Champaigne)

186 "Voyager 2" passing Saturn

1992. Christmas. Religious Paintings. Mult.

901 20 t. Type **185** 60 10
902 75 t. "Virgin and Child" (Bernandino Luini) . . . . . 1·25 50
903 95 t. "Virgin and Child" (Sassoferrato) . . . . 1·60 90
904 2 k. "Virgin Mary" (detail, "The Annunciation") (De Champaigne) . . . . 4·00 6·00

1992. International Space Year. Multicoloured.

905 20 t. Type **186** 85 30
906 75 t. Centre of galaxy . . . . 1·75 90
907 95 t. Kanjedza II Standard A Earth Station . . . . 1·90 1·00
908 2 k. Communications satellite . 4·00 5·50

187 "Strychnos spinosa"

188 "Apaturopsis cleocharis

1993. World Forestry Day. Indigenous Fruit Trees. Multicoloured.

909 20 t. Type **187** 60 15
910 75 t. "Adansonia digitata" . . 1·40 80
911 95 t. "Ximenia caffra" . . . . 1·50 1·00
912 2 k. "Uapaca kirkiana" . . . . 2·75 4·50

1993. Butterflies. Multicoloured.

913 20 t. Type **188** 90 30
914 75 t. "Euryphura achlys" . . . 1·75 85
915 95 t. "Cooksonia aliciae" . . . 2·00 1·25
916 2 k. "Charaxes protoclea azota" 3·00 4·25

189 The Holy Family

190 Kentrosaurus

1993. Christmas. Multicoloured.

917 20 t. Type **189** 10 10
918 75 t. Shepherds and star . . . 20 20
919 95 t. Three Kings 25 30
920 2 k. Adoration of the Kings . . 65 1·50

1993. Prehistoric Animals. Multicoloured.

921 20 t. Type **190** 45 30
922 75 t. Stegosaurus 80 90
923 95 t. Sauropod . . . . 85 1·00

191 Socolof's mbuna

1994. Fishes. Multicoloured.

925 20 t. Type **191** 20 10
926 75 t. Golden mbuna 50 30
927 95 t. Lombardo's mbuna . . . 55 35
928 1 k. Scraper-mouthed mbuna . 60 70
929 2 k. Zebra mbuna . . . . . . 1·25 1·75
930 4 k. Elongate mbuna . . . . . 2·00 3·25

192 "Ilala II" (lake vessel)

1994. Ships of Lake Malawi. Multicoloured.

931 20 t. Type **192** 20 10
932 75 t. "Ufulu" (tanker) 30 25
933 95 t. "Pioneer" (steam launch) . 35 30
934 2 k. "Dove" (paddle-steamer) . . 60 1·25

193 "Virgin and Child" (detail) (Durer)

194 Pres. Bakili Muluzi (C.O.M.E.S.A. chairman, 1994–95)

1994. Christmas. Religious Paintings. Multicoloured.

936 20 t. Type **193** 15 10
937 75 t. "Wise Men present Gifts" (Franco-Flemish Book of Hours) 30 15
938 95 t. "The Nativity" (detail) (Fra Filippo Lippi) (horiz) . . . 35 15
939 2 k. "Nativity Scene with Wise Men" (Rogier van der Weyden) (horiz) . . . . . . 1·00 1·50

1995. Establishment of C.O.M.E.S.A. (Common Market for Eastern and Southern African States).

940 **194** 40 t. multicoloured 10 10
941 1 k. 40 multicoloured . . . 20 20
942 1 k. 80 multicoloured . . . 25 30
943 2 k. multicoloured 30 50

195 Telecommunications Training

1995. 50th Anniv of the United Nations. Mult.

944 40 t. Type **195** 10 10
945 1 k. 40 Village women collecting water 35 20
946 1 k. 80 Mt. Mulanje 30 40
947 2 k. Villagers in field 40 55

196 Teacher and Class

1995. Christmas. Multicoloured.

949 40 t. Type **196** 10 10
950 1 k. 40 Dispensing medicine . . 25 20
951 1 k. 80 Crowd at water pump . 30 35
952 2 k. Refugees on ferries 30 45

197 "Precis tugela"

1996. Butterflies. Multicoloured.

953 60 t. Type **197** 15 10
954 3 k. "Papilio pelodorus" . . . 35 30
955 4 k. "Acrea acrita" 40 35
956 10 k. "Melanitis leda" . . . . 90 1·50

198 Children's Party

199 Map of Malawi

1996. Christmas. Multicoloured.

957 10 t. Type **198** 15 10
958 20 t. Nativity play 20 10
959 30 t. Children wearing party hats 25 15
960 60 t. Mother and child 40 60

1997. 50th Death Anniv of Paul Harris (founder of Rotary International). Multicoloured.

961 60 t. Type **199** 15 10
962 3 k. African fish eagle 30 75
963 4 k. 40 Leopard 40 50
964 5 k. Rotary International emblem 50 65

200 Mother and Child

201 The Nativity

1997. 50th Anniv of U.N.I.C.E.F. Multicoloured.

965 60 t. Type **200** 15 10
966 3 k. Children in class 30 25
967 4 k. 40 Boy with fish 40 50
968 5 k. Nurse inoculating child . . 50 65

1997. Christmas. Multicoloured.

969 60 t. Type **201** 15 10
970 3 k. The Nativity (different) . . 30 20
971 4 k. 40 Adoration of the Magi . 40 50
972 5 k. The Holy Family 50 70

1998. Diana, Princess of Wales Commemoration. As T **91** of Kiribati. Multicoloured.

973 60 t. Wearing red dress 15 10
974 6 k. Wearing lilac jacket . . . 20 20
975 7 k. With head scarf 25 30
976 8 k. Wearing blue evening dress . 35 45

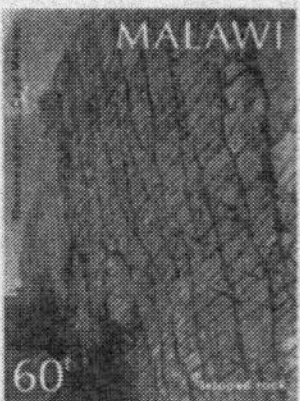

202 Tattooed Rock, Mwalawamphini, Cape Maclear

1998. Monuments. Multicoloured.

978 60 t. Type **202** 10 10
979 6 k. War Memorial Tower, Zomba 20 20
980 7 k. Mtengatenga Postal Hut, Walala (horiz) 25 25
981 8 k. P.I.M. Church, Chiradzulu (horiz) 30 30

No. 978 is inscribed "tatooed" and No. 979 "Memoral", both in error.

203 Woman voting

1998. 50th Anniv of Declaration of Human Rights. Multicoloured.

982 60 t. Type **203** 10 10
983 6 k. Books, pens and pencils ("Education") 20 20
984 7 k. Man and woman on scales ("Justice") 25 25
985 8 k. Person hugging house and land ("Property") 30 30

POSTAGE DUE STAMPS

D 2

1967.

D 6 **D 2** 1d. red . . . . 15 3·00
D 7 2d. brown . . . . 20 3·00
D 8 4d. violet . . . . 25 3·25
D 9 6d. blue . . . . 25 3·50
D10 8d. green . . . . 35 3·75
D11 1s. black . . . . 45 4·00

1971. Values in tambalas. No accent over "W" of "MALAWI".

D12 **D 2** 2 t. brown . . . . 30 3·00
D13 4 t. mauve . . . . 50 3·00
D14 6 t. blue . . . . 50 3·25
D15 8 t. green . . . . 50 3·25
D16 10 t. brown . . . . . . 60 3·25

1975. With circumflex over "W" of "MALAWI".

D27 **D 2** 2 t. brown . . . . 60 1·00
D28 4 t. purple . . . . 60 1·00
D29 6 t. blue . . . . 60 1·00
D21 8 t. green . . . . 1·50 2·25
D31 10 t. black . . . . 60 1·00

MALAYA (BRITISH MILITARY ADMINISTRATION) Pt. 1

The following stamps were for use throughout the Malayan States and in Singapore during the period of the British Military Administration and were gradually replaced by individual issues for each state.

100 cents = 1 dollar

1945. Straits Settlements stamps optd **B M A MALAYA**.

1a	58	1 c. black	10	30
2a		2 c. orange	20	10
4		3 c. green	30	50
5		5 c. brown	70	90
6a		6 c. grey	30	20
7		8 c. red	30	10
8a		10 c. purple	40	10
10		12 c. blue	1·75	4·50
12a		15 c. blue	75	20
13a		25 c. purple and red	1·40	30
14a		50 c. black on green	60	10
15		$1 black and red	2·00	10
16		$2 green and red	2·75	75
17		$5 green and red on green	85·00	80·00
18		$5 purple and orange	3·75	3·00

For stamps inscribed "MALAYA" at top and with Arabic characters at foot see under Kelantan, Negri Sembilan, Pahang, Perak, Selangor or Trengganu.

MALAYA (JAPANESE OCCUPATION OF) Pt. 1

Japanese forces invaded Malaya on 8 December 1941 and the conquest of the Malay peninsula was completed by the capture of Singapore on 15 February.

The following stamps were used in Malaya until the defeat of Japan in 1945.

100 cents = 1 dollar

(a) JOHORE

POSTAGE DUE STAMPS

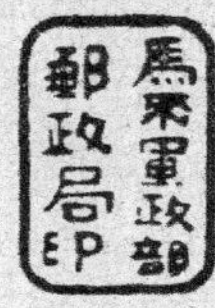
(1)

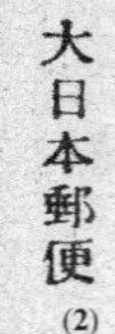

(2)

1942. Nos. D1/5 of Johore optd with T **1**.

JD1a	D 1	1 c. red	25·00	70·00
JD2a		4 c. green	65·00	80·00
JD3a		8 c. orange	75·00	90·00
JD4a		10 c. brown	16·00	50·00
JD5a		12 c. purple	29·00	50·00

1943. Postage Due stamps of Johore optd with T **2**.

JD 6	D 1	1 c. red	4·50	20·00
JD 7		4 c. green	4·75	21·00
JD 8		8 c. orange	5·00	22·00
JD 9		10 c. brown	4·50	26·00
JD10		12 c. purple	6·00	38·00

(b) KEDAH

1942. Stamps of Kedah optd **DAI NIPPON 2602**.

J 1	1	1 c. black	3·50	5·50
J 2		2 c. green	24·00	30·00
J 3		4 c. violet	3·50	4·00
J 4		5 c. yellow	3·00	3·50
J 5		6 c. red	2·25	8·50
J 6		8 c. black	2·75	1·75
J 7	6	10 c. blue and brown	8·00	8·00
J 8		12 c. black and violet	22·00	28·00
J 9		25 c. blue and purple	7·00	9·50
J10		30 c. green and red	65·00	75·00
J11		40 c. black and purple	28·00	40·00
J12		50 c. brown and blue	30·00	42·00
J13		$1 black and green	£140	£150
J14		$2 green and brown	£170	£170
J15		$5 black and red	65·00	75·00

(c) KELANTAN

(**5**) Sunagawa Seal

(**6**) Handa Seal

1942. Stamps of Kelantan surch. (a) With T **5**. (i) New value in **CENTS**.

J16	4	1 c. on 50 c. green & orge	£225	£180
J17		2 c. on 40 c. orange & grn	£450	£275
J18		4 c. on 30 c. violet & red	£1700	£1200
J19		5 c. on 12 c. blue	£225	£180
J20		6 c. on 25 c. red & violet	£275	£190
J21		8 c. on 5 c. brown	£325	£140
J22		10 c. on 6 c. red	75·00	£120
J23		12 c. on 8 c. green	48·00	£110
J24		25 c. on 10 c. purple	£1200	£1300
J25		30 c. on 4 c. red	£1800	£2000
J26		40 c. on 2 c. green	55·00	85·00
J27		50 c. on 1 c. green & yell	£1300	£1200
J28		$1 on 4 c. black and red	50·00	75·00
J29		$2 on 5 c. green & red on yell	50·00	75·00
J30		$5 on 6 c. red	50·00	75·00

(ii) New Value in **Cents**.

J32	4	1 c. on 50 c. green & orge	£130	85·00
J33		2 c. on 40 c. orange & grn	£110	90·00
J34		5 c. on 12 c. blue	£110	£110
J35	4	8 c. on 5 c. brown	£100	70·00
J36		10 c. on 6 c. red	£250	£275
J37		12 c. on 8 c. green	£425	£450
J38		30 c. on 4 c. red	£2000	£2250
J39		40 c. on 2 c. green	£450	£475
J40		50 c. on 1 c. green & yell	£1100	£1100

(b) With T **6** and new value.

J41	4	1 c. on 50 c. green & orge	90·00	£130
J42		2 c. on 40 c. orange & grn	95·00	£140
J43		8 c. on 5 c. brown	65·00	£120
J44		10 c. on 6 c. red	85·00	£140
J31		12 c. on 8 c. green	£140	£200

(d) PENANG

(**11**) Okugawa Seal

(**12**) Ochiburi Seal

1942. Straits Settlements stamps optd. (a) As T **11**.

J56	58	1 c. black	9·50	11·00
J57		2 c. orange	24·00	22·00
J58		3 c. green	20·00	22·00
J59		5 c. brown	24·00	24·00
J60		8 c. grey	26·00	27·00
J61		10 c. purple	50·00	50·00
J62		12 c. blue	27·00	38·00
J63		15 c. blue	38·00	45·00
J64		40 c. red and purple	90·00	£100
J65		50 c. black/green	£190	£200
J66		$1 black and red on blue	£200	£225
J67		$2 green and red	£500	£500
J68		$5 green and red on green	£1500	£1400

(b) With T **12**.

J69	58	1 c. black	£120	£110
J70		2 c. orange	£110	85·00
J71		3 c. green	90·00	95·00
J72		5 c. brown	£1400	£1400
J73		8 c. grey	65·00	80·00
J74		10 c. purple	95·00	£110
J75		12 c. blue	90·00	£100
J76		15 c. blue	90·00	£100

1942. Stamps of Straits Settlements optd **DAI NIPPON 2602 PENANG**.

J77	58	1 c. black	2·50	2·00
J78		2 c. orange	4·25	3·00
J79		3 c. green	3·75	2·25
J80		5 c. brown	2·25	4·00
J81		8 c. grey	2·25	1·40
J82		10 c. purple	1·50	2·00
J83		12 c. blue	3·00	10·00
J84		15 c. blue	1·75	2·25
J85		40 c. red and purple	4·25	10·00
J86		50 c. black and green	3·75	18·00
J87		$1 black and red on blue	6·00	25·00
J88		$2 green and red	42·00	75·00
J89		$5 green and red on green	£450	£550

(e) SELANGOR.

1942. Agri-horticultural Exhibition. Stamps of Straits Settlements optd **SELANGOR EXHIBITION DAI NIPPON 2602 MALAYA**.

J90	58	2 c. orange	12·00	24·00
J91		8 c. grey	13·00	24·00

(f) SINGAPORE

(**15**) "Malay Military Government Division Postal Services Bureau Seal"

1942. Stamps of Straits Settlements optd with T **15**.

J92	58	1 c. black	13·00	17·00
J93		2 c. orange	13·00	13·00
J94		3 c. green	50·00	70·00
J95		8 c. grey	22·00	18·00
J96		15 c. blue	15·00	15·00

(g) TRENGGANU

1942. Stamps of Trengganu optd with T **1**.

J 97	4	1 c. black	95·00	90·00
J 98		2 c. green	£140	£140
J 99a		2 c. on 5 c. purple on yellow (No. 59)	45·00	70·00
J100		3 c. brown	80·00	80·00
J101		4 c. red	£140	£140
J102		5 c. purple on yellow	10·00	19·00
J103		6 c. orange	8·50	25·00
J104		8 c. grey	9·00	13·00
J105		8 c. on 10 c. blue (No. 60)	13·00	38·00
J106		10 c. blue	16·00	28·00
J107		12 c. blue	8·00	29·00
J108		20 c. purple and orange	8·50	26·00
J109		25 c. green and purple	7·50	32·00
J110		30 c. purple and black	8·00	26·00
J111		35 c. red on yellow	22·00	38·00
J112		50 c. green and red	65·00	75·00
J113		$1 purple and blue on blue	£2500	£2500
J114		$3 green and red on green	50·00	85·00
J115	–	$5 green and red on yellow (No. 31)	£130	£180
J116	–	$25 purple and blue (No. 40)	£1000	
J117	–	$50 green and yellow (No. 41)	£8500	
J118	–	$100 green and red (No. 42)	£1100	

1942. Stamps of Trengganu optd **DAI NIPPON 2602 MALAYA**.

J119	4	1 c. black	12·00	10·00
J120		2 c. green	£160	£180
J121		2 c. on 5 c. purple on yellow (No. 59)	6·00	8·00
J122		3 c. brown	9·00	17·00
J123		4 c. red	9·00	11·00
J124		5 c. purple on yellow	5·50	12·00
J125		6 c. orange	5·00	12·00
J126		8 c. grey	70·00	25·00
J127		8 c. on 10 c. blue (No. 60)	5·50	10·00
J128		12 c. blue	5·00	20·00
J129		20 c. purple and orange	10·00	13·00
J130		25 c. green and purple	7·00	27·00
J131		30 c. purple and black	7·50	24·00
J132		$3 green and red on green	60·00	£110

1942. Stamps of Trengganu optd with T **2**.

J133	4	1 c. black	9·00	16·00
J134		2 c. green	8·00	24·00
J135		2 c. on 5 c. purple on yellow (No. 59)	6·00	18·00
J136		5 c. purple on yellow	6·50	24·00
J137		6 c. orange	8·00	27·00
J138		8 c. grey	55·00	80·00
J139		8 c. on 10 c. blue (No. 60)	19·00	40·00
J140		10 c. blue	80·00	£180
J141		12 c. blue	13·00	35·00
J142		20 c. purple and orange	15·00	35·00
J143		25 c. green and purple	13·00	38·00
J144		30 c. purple and black	16·00	40·00
J145		35 c. red on yellow	16·00	42·00

1942. Postage Due stamps of Trengganu optd with T **2**.

JD17	D 1	1 c. red	50·00	80·00
JD18a		4 c. green	50·00	85·00
JD19		8 c. yellow	14·00	50·00
JD20		10 c. brown	14·00	50·00

(h) GENERAL ISSUES

1942. Stamps of various states optd with T **1**. (a) Straits Settlements.

J146	58	1 c. black	3·25	3·25
J147		2 c. green	£1700	£1700
J148		2 c. orange	3·00	2·25
J149		3 c. green	2·75	2·25
J150		5 c. brown	22·00	28·00
J151		8 c. grey	3·75	2·25
J152		10 c. purple	42·00	42·00
J153		12 c. blue	75·00	95·00
J154		15 c. blue	3·50	3·75
J155		30 c. purple and orange	£1500	£1600
J156		40 c. red and purple	80·00	90·00
J157		50 c. black and green	45·00	48·00
J158		$1 black & red on blue	75·00	75·00
J159		$2 green and red	£130	£140
J160		$5 green & red on green	£170	£180

There also exists a similar overprint with double-lined frame.

(b) Negri Sembilan

J161b	6	1 c. black	15·00	16·00
J162		2 c. orange	20·00	16·00
J163		3 c. green	27·00	20·00
J164c		5 c. brown	15·00	11·00
J165		6 c. grey	£140	£120
J166		8 c. red	85·00	75·00
J167		10 c. purple	£130	£130
J168		12 c. blue	£1100	£1100
J169		15 c. blue	18·00	8·00
J170		25 c. purple and red	28·00	38·00
J171		30 c. purple and orange	£180	£150
J172		40 c. red and purple	£850	£850
J173		50 c. black on green	£550	£550
J174a		$1 black and red on blue	£180	£190
J175		$5 green and red on green	£450	£475

(c) Pahang

J176	15	1 c. black	45·00	40·00
J177		3 c. green	£225	£225
J178		5 c. brown	12·00	9·00
J179		8 c. grey	£475	£425
J180		8 c. red	22·00	10·00
J181		10 c. purple	£180	£120
J182a		12 c. blue	£1200	£1200
J183		15 c. blue	£100	£100
J184		25 c. purple and red	19·00	29·00
J185		30 c. purple and orange	12·00	28·00
J186		40 c. red and purple	17·00	32·00
J187		50 c. black on green	£550	£550
J188		$1 black and red on blue	£110	£130
J189		$5 green & red on green	£600	£700

(d) Perak

J190	51	1 c. black	50·00	32·00
J191		2 c. orange	29·00	20·00
J192		3 c. green	26·00	28·00
J193		5 c. brown	7·00	6·00
J194		8 c. grey	50·00	42·00
J195		8 c. red	28·00	35·00
J196		10 c. purple	26·00	24·00
J197		12 c. blue	£225	£225
J198		15 c. blue	24·00	30·00
J199		25 c. purple and red	14·00	25·00
J200		30 c. purple and orange	17·00	32·00
J201		40 c. red and purple	£325	£325
J202		50 c. black on green	38·00	50·00
J203		$1 black & red on blue	£400	£400
J204		$2 green and red	£2000	£2000
J205		$5 green & red on green	£475	

(e) Selangor

J206	46	1 c. black	12·00	22·00
J207		2 c. green	£900	£900
J208		2 c. orange	80·00	50·00
J210a		3 c. green	18·00	18·00
J211		5 c. brown	6·00	5·50
J212a		6 c. red	£200	£250
J213		8 c. grey	17·00	17·00
J214		10 c. purple	13·00	21·00
J215		12 c. blue	60·00	60·00
J216		15 c. blue	16·00	22·00
J217a		25 c. purple and red	60·00	80·00
J218		30 c. purple and orange	11·00	24·00
J219		40 c. red and purple	£130	£130
J220a		50 c. black on green	85·00	90·00
J221	48	$1 black & red on blue	30·00	42·00
J222		$2 green and red	35·00	60·00
J223		$5 green and red on green	65·00	85·00

1942. Various stamps optd **DAI NIPPON 2602 MALAYA**. (a) Stamps of Straits Settlements.

J224	58	2 c. orange	85	50
J225		3 c. green	50·00	65·00
J226		8 c. grey	3·50	2·00
J227		15 c. blue	9·00	6·50

(b) Stamps of Negri Sembilan

J228	6	1 c. black	1·50	60
J229		2 c. orange	4·00	50
J230		3 c. green	3·00	45
J231		5 c. brown	60	1·00
J232		6 c. grey	2·50	1·00
J233		8 c. red	3·25	1·25
J234		10 c. purple	3·00	2·50
J235		15 c. blue	10·00	2·50
J236		25 c. purple and red	3·00	9·50
J237		30 c. purple and orange	5·00	3·00
J238		$1 black and red on blue	£100	£110

(c) Stamps of Pahang

J239	15	1 c. black	1·50	1·50
J240		5 c. brown	1·00	70
J241		8 c. red	25·00	2·50
J242		10 c. purple	9·00	6·50
J243		12 c. blue	1·25	8·00
J244		25 c. purple and red	3·75	14·00
J245		30 c. purple and orange	1·90	7·00

(d) Stamps of Perak

J246	51	2 c. orange	1·75	1·00
J247		3 c. green	60	75
J248		8 c. red	60	40
J249		10 c. purple	9·00	5·50
J250		15 c. blue	4·00	2·00
J251		50 c. black on green	2·00	3·00
J252		$1 black and red on blue	£350	£400
J253		$5 green and red on green	32·00	65·00

(e) Stamps of Selangor

J254	46	3 c. green	60	2·00
J255		12 c. blue	1·10	9·00
J256		15 c. blue	3·50	1·50
J257		40 c. red and purple	2·00	3·00
J258	48	$2 green and red	10·00	30·00

1942. No. 108 of Perak surch **DAI NIPPON 2602 MALAYA 2 Cents**.

J259	88	2 c. on 5 c. brown	1·25	1·75

1942. Stamps of Perak optd **DAI NIPPON YUBIN** ("Japanese Postal Service") or surch also in figures and words.

J260	51	1 c. black	3·00	6·50
J261		2 c. on 5 c. brown	2·00	6·50
J262		8 c. red	3·50	2·25

1943. Various stamps optd vert or horiz with T **2** or surch in figures and words. (a) Stamps of Straits Settlements.

J263	58	8 c. grey	1·40	50
J264		12 c. blue	65	6·50
J265		40 c. red and purple	75	3·00

(b) Stamps of Negri Sembilan.

J266	6	1 c. black	30	85
J267		2 c. on 5 c. brown	50	50
J268		6 c. on 5 c. brown	40	95
J269		25 c. purple and red	1·10	9·50

(c) Stamp of Pahang

J270	7	6 c. on 5 c. brown	50	75

(d) Stamps of Perak

J272	51	1 c. black	80	60
J274		2 c. on 5 c. brown	45	45
J275		5 c. brown	45	40
J276		8 c. red	55	70
J277		10 c. purple	60	50
J278		30 c. purple and orange	1·75	3·00
J279		50 c. black on green	3·00	13·00
J280		$5 green & red on green	50·00	80·00

(e) Stamps of Selangor

J288	46	1 c. black	35	50
J289		2 c. on 5 c. brown	30	50
J282		3 c. green	40	45
J290		3 c. on 5 c. brown	30	3·00
J291		5 c. brown	50	3·00
J293		6 c. on 5 c. brown	30	70
J283		12 c. blue	45	1·60
J284		15 c. blue	2·75	3·00
J285	48	$1 black and red on blue	3·00	16·00
J295	46	$1 on 10 c. purple	30	1·00
J296		$1.50 on 30 c. purple and orange	30	1·00
J286	48	$2 green and red	10·00	38·00
J287		$5 green & red on green	22·00	70·00

25 Tapping Rubber

27 Japanese Shrine, Singapore

1943.

J297	25	1 c. green	30	55
J298	–	2 c. green	30	15
J299	25	3 c. grey	15	15
J300	–	4 c. red	65	15
J301	–	8 c. blue	15	15
J302	–	10 c. purple	15	15
J303	27	15 c. violet	35	2·25
J304	–	30 c. olive	35	35
J305	–	50 c. blue	1·75	2·25
J306	–	70 c. blue	16·00	10·00

DESIGNS—VERT: 2 c. Fruit; 4 c. Tin dredger; 8 c. War Memorial, Bukit Batok, Singapore; 10 c. Fishing village; 30 c. Sago palms; 50 c. Straits of Johore. HORIZ: 70 c. Malay Mosque, Kuala Lumpur.

28 Ploughman

29 Rice-planting

1943. Savings Campaign.

J307	**28**	8 c. violet	7·50	2·75
J308		15 c. red	6·00	2·75

1944. "Re-birth of Malaya".

J309	**29**	8 c. red	10·00	2·75
J310		15 c. mauve	4·00	3·00

大日本

マライ郵便

50 セント

(30)

1944. Stamps intended for use on Red Cross letters. Surch with T **30**. (a) On Straits Settlements.

J311	**58**	50 c. on 50 c. black on grn	11·00	24·00
J312		$1 on $1 black and red on bl	20·00	35·00
J313		$1.50 on $2 grn on red	32·00	70·00

(b) On Johore

J314	**24**	50 c. on 50 c. pur & red	8·00	20·00
J315		$1.50 on $2 green & red	5·50	14·00

(c) On Selangor

J316	**48**	$1 on $2 black & red on bl	4·00	14·00
J317		$1.50 on $2 green & red	6·50	20·00

POSTAGE DUE STAMPS

1942. Postage Due stamps of Malayan Postal Union optd with T **1**.

JD21	D **1**	1 c. violet	12·00	20·00
JD22		3 c. green	48·00	50·00
JD23		4 c. green	32·00	26·00
JD24		8 c. red	65·00	55·00
JD25		10 c. orange	20·00	30·00
JD26		12 c. blue	20·00	38·00
JD27		50 c. black	50·00	65·00

1942. Postage Due stamps of Malayan Postal Union optd **DAI NIPPON 2602 MALAYA**.

JD28	D **1**	1 c. violet	1·60	8·00
JD29		3 c. green	9·50	15·00
JD30		4 c. green	8·50	10·00
JD31		8 c. red	12·00	14·00
JD32		10 c. orange	1·60	10·00
JD33		12 c. blue	1·60	23·00

1943. Postage Due stamps of Malayan Postal Union optd with T **2**.

JD34	D **1**	1 c. violet	80	2·75
JD35		3 c. green	80	2·75
JD36		4 c. green	38·00	38·00
JD37		5 c. red	70	3·25
JD38		9 c. orange	60	4·75
JD39		10 c. orange	70	4·50
JD40		12 c. blue	90	9·50
JD41		15 c. blue	90	5·00

MALAYA (THAI OCCUPATION OF) Pt. 1

Stamps issued for use in the four Malay states of Kedah, Kelantan, Perlis and Trengganu ceded by Japan to Thailand on 19 October 1943 and restored to British rule on the defeat of the Japanese.

100 cents = 1 dollar

TM **1** War Memorial

1943.

TM1	TM **1**	1 c. yellow	30·00	32·00
TM2		2 c. brown	12·00	20·00
TM3		3 c. green	20·00	38·00
TM4		4 c. purple	14·00	28·00
TM5		8 c. red	14·00	20·00
TM6		15 c. blue	38·00	60·00

MALAYAN FEDERATION Pt. 1

An independent country within the British Commonwealth, comprising all the Malay States (except Singapore) and the Settlements of Malacca and Penang. The component units retained their individual stamps. In 1963 the Federation became part of Malaysia (q.v).

100 cents (sen) = 1 Malayan dollar

1 Tapping Rubber

1957.

1	**1**	6 c. blue, red and yellow	50	10
2	–	12 c. multicoloured	85	40
3	–	25 c. multicoloured	2·25	10
4	–	30 c. red and lake	80	20

DESIGNS—HORIZ: 12 c. Federation coat of arms; 25 c. Tin dredge. VERT: 30 c. Map of the Federation.

5 Prime Minister Tunku Abdul Rahman and Populace greeting Independence

1957. Independence Day.

5	**5**	10 c. brown	10	10

6 United Nations Emblem **8** Merdeka Stadium, Kuala Lumpur

1958. U.N. Economic Commission for Asia and Far East Conference, Kuala Lumpur.

6	**6**	12 c. red	30	55
7	–	30 c. purple	40	55

DESIGN: 30 c. As Type **6** but vert.

1958. 1st Anniv of Independence.

8	**8**	10 c. multicoloured	15	10
9	–	30 c. multicoloured	40	60

DESIGN—VERT: 30 c. Portrait of the Yang di-Pertuan Agong (Tuanku Abdul Rahman).

11 Malayan with "Torch of Freedom" **12** Mace and Malayan Peoples

1958. 10th Anniv of Declaration of Human Rights.

10	–	10 c. multicoloured	15	10
11	**11**	30 c. green	45	50

DESIGN—VERT: 10 c. "Human Rights".

1959. Inauguration of Parliament.

12	**12**	4 c. red	10	10
13		10 c. violet	10	10
14		25 c. green	35	20

14 **15** Seedling Rubber Tree and Map

1960. World Refugee Year.

15	–	12 c. purple	10	50
16	**14**	30 c. green	10	10

DESIGN: 12 c. As Type **14** but horiz.

1960. Natural Rubber Research Conf and 15th Int Rubber Study Group Meeting, Kuala Lumpur.

17	**15**	6 c. multicoloured	20	1·00
18		30 c. multicoloured	50	60

No. 18 is inscr "INTERNATIONAL RUBBER STUDY GROUP 15th MEETING KUALA LUMPUR" at foot.

16 The Yang di-Pertuan Agong (Tuanku Syed Putra)

1961. Installation of Yang di-Pertuan Agong, Tuanku Syed Putra.

19	**16**	10 c. black and blue	10	10

17 Colombo Plan Emblem **18** Malaria Eradication Emblem

1961. Colombo Plan Conf, Kuala Lumpur.

20	**17**	12 c. black and mauve	35	2·00
21		25 c. black and green	80	2·00
22		30 c. black and blue	70	30

1962. Malaria Eradication.

23	**18**	25 c. brown	20	35
24		30 c. lilac	20	15
25		50 c. blue	40	30

19 Palmyra Palm Leaf

1962. National Language Month.

26	**19**	10 c. brown and violet	15	10
27		20 c. brown and green	30	35
28		50 c. brown and mauve	90	90

20 "Shadows of the Future"

1962. Introduction of Free Primary Education.

29	**20**	10 c. purple	10	10
30		25 c. ochre	30	40
31		30 c. green	1·75	10

21 Harvester and Fisherman

1963. Freedom from Hunger.

32	**21**	25 c. pink and green	1·00	2·50
33		30 c. pink and lake	1·75	1·00
34		50 c. pink and blue	1·75	2·50

22 Dam and Pylon

1963. Cameron Highlands Hydro-Electric Scheme.

35	**22**	20 c. green and violet	45	10
36		30 c. turquoise and blue	55	80

MALAYAN POSTAL UNION Pt. 1

In 1936 postage due stamps were issued in Type D **1** for use in Negri Sembilan, Pahang, Perak, Selangor and Straits Settlements but later their use was extended to the whole of the Federation and Singapore, and from 1963 throughout Malaysia.

POSTAGE DUE STAMPS

D 1

1936.

D 7	D **1**	1 c. purple	2·75	1·75
D14		1 c. violet	30	1·25
D15		2 c. slate	80	2·00
D 8		3 c. green	6·00	10·00
D 2		4 c. green	12·00	1·00
D17		4 c. sepia	45	4·25
D 9		5 c. red	6·00	7·50
D 3		8 c. red	6·00	3·50
D19		8 c. orange	2·00	4·00
D11		9 c. orange	50·00	48·00
D 4		10 c. orange	8·00	30
D 5		12 c. blue	9·00	14·00
D20		12 c. mauve	1·00	5·50
D12		15 c. blue	£140	35·00
D21		20 c. blue	4·00	6·50
D 6		50 c. black	28·00	6·00

1965. Surch **10 cents**.

D29	D **1**	10 c. on 8 c. orange	30	2·00

MALAYSIA Pt. 1

Issues for use by the new Federation comprising the old Malayan Federation (Johore ("JOHOR"), Kedah, Kelantan, Malacca ("MELAKA"), Negri Sembilan ("NEGERI SEMBILAN"), Pahang, Penang ("PULAU PINANG"), Perak, Perlis, Selangor and Trengganu), Sabah (North Borneo), Sarawak and Singapore, until the latter became an independent state on 9 August, 1965.

Stamps inscr "MALAYSIA" and state name are listed under the various states, as above.

100 cents (sen) = 1 Malaysian dollar

A. NATIONAL SERIES

General issues for use throughout the Federation.

1 Federation Map **2** Bouquet of Orchids

1963. Inauguration of Federation.

1	**1**	10 c. yellow and violet	40	10
2		12 c. yellow and green	1·00	60
3		50 c. yellow and brown	1·40	10

1963. 4th World Orchid Congress, Singapore.

4	**2**	6 c. multicoloured	1·25	1·25
5		25 c. multicoloured	1·25	25

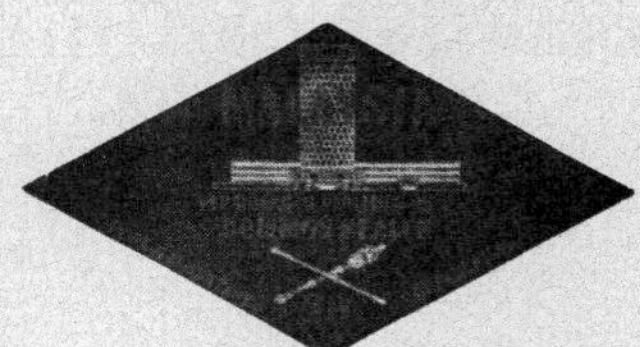

4 Parliament House, Kuala Lumpur

1963. 9th Commonwealth Parliamentary Conference, Kuala Lumpur.

7	**4**	20 c. mauve and gold	65	40
8		30 c. green and gold	65	15

5 "Flame of Freedom" and Emblems of Goodwill, Health and Charity

1964. Eleanor Roosevelt Commemoration.

9	**5**	25 c. black, red & turquoise	20	10
10		30 c. black, red and lilac	20	15
11		50 c. black, red & yellow	20	10

6 Microwave Tower and I.T.U. Emblem

1965. Centenary of I.T.U.

12	**6**	2 c. multicoloured	15	80
13		25 c. multicoloured	1·25	50
14		50 c. multicoloured	1·75	10

7 National Mosque

1965. Opening of National Mosque, Kuala Lumpur.

15	**7**	6 c. red	10	10
16		15 c. brown	20	10
17		20 c. green	20	15

8 Air Terminal

1965. Opening of Int Airport, Kuala Lumpur.

18	**8**	15 c. black, green and blue	30	10
19		30 c. black, green & mauve	60	20

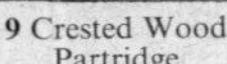

9 Crested Wood Partridge

17 Sepak Raga (ball game) and Football

1965. Birds. Multicoloured.
20 25 c. Type **9** 50 10
21 30 c. Blue-backed fairy bluebird . . 60 10
22 50 c. Black-naped oriole 80 10
23 75 c. Rhinoceros hornbill . . . 90 10
24 $1 Zebra dove . . . . 1·50 10
25 $2 Great argus pheasant . . . . 3·50 30
26 $5 Asiatic paradise flycatcher . . 18·00 2·50
27 $10 Blue-tailed pitta . . . . . 48·00 11·00
For the lower values see the individual sets listed under each of the states which form Malaysia.

1965. 3rd South East Asian Peninsular Games.
28 **17** 25 c. black and green 40 90
29 – 30 c. black and purple . . . 40 20
30 – 50 c. black and blue 70 30
DESIGNS: 30 c. Running; 50 c. Diving.

20 National Monument

21 The Yang di-Pertuan Agong (Tuanku Ismail Nasiruddin Shah)

1966. National Monument, Kuala Lumpur.
31 **20** 10 c. multicoloured 20 10
32 20 c. multicoloured 30 40

1966. Installation of Yang di-Pertuan Agong, Tuanku Ismail Nasiruddin Shah.
33 **21** 15 c. black and yellow . . . 10 10
34 50 c. black and blue 20 20

22 School Building

1966. 150th Anniv of Penang Free School.
35 **22** 20 c. multicoloured 55 10
36 50 c. multicoloured 70 10

23 "Agriculture"

1966. 1st Malaysia Plan. Multicoloured.
37 15 c. Type **23** 20 10
38 15 c. "Rural Health" 20 10
39 15 c. "Communications" . . . . 1·25 15
40 15 c. "Education" 20 10
41 15 c. "Irrigation" 20 10

28 Cable Route Maps (½-size illustration)

1967. Completion of Malaysia–Hong Kong Link of SEACOM Telephone Cable.
42 **28** 30 c. multicoloured 80 30
43 75 c. multicoloured . . . . . 2·50 3·25

29 Hibiscus and Paramount Rulers

1967. 10th Anniv of Independence.
44 **29** 15 c. multicoloured 20 10
45 50 c. multicoloured 80 80

30 Mace and Shield

1967. Centenary of Sarawak Council.
46 **30** 15 c. multicoloured 10 10
47 50 c. multicoloured 30 50

31 Straits Settlements 1867 8 c. Stamp and Malaysian 1965 25 c. Stamp

1967. Stamp Centenary.
48 **31** 25 c. multicoloured . . . . . 1·40 2·25
49 – 30 c. multicoloured . . . . . 1·40 1·75
50 – 50 c. multicoloured . . . . . 2·25 2·50
DESIGNS: 30 c. Straits Settlements 1867 24 c. stamp and Malaysian 1965 30 c. stamp; 50 c. Straits Settlements 1867 32 c. stamp and Malaysian 1965 50 c. stamp.

34 Tapping Rubber, and Molecular Unit

1968. Natural Rubber Conf, Kuala Lumpur. Multicoloured.
51 25 c. Type **34** 25 10
52 30 c. Tapping rubber and export consignment 40 20
53 50 c. Tapping rubber and aircraft tyres 40 10

37 Mexican Sombrero and Blanket with Olympic Rings

39 Tunku Abdul Rahman against background of Pandanus Weave

1968. Olympic Games, Mexico. Multicoloured.
54 30 c. Type **37** 20 10
55 75 c. Olympic Rings and Mexican Embroidery 55 20

1969. Solidarity Week.
56 **39** 15 c. multicoloured 15 10
57 – 20 c. multicoloured . . . . . 40 1·00
58 – 50 c. multicoloured 40 20
DESIGNS—VERT: 20 c. As Type **39** (different). HORIZ: 50 c. Tunku Abdul Rahman with pandanus pattern.

42 Peasant Girl with Sheaves of Paddy

1969. National Rice Year.
59 **42** 15 c. multicoloured 15 10
60 75 c. multicoloured 55 85

43 Satellite-tracking Aerial

1970. Satellite Earth Station.
61 **43** 15 c. drab, black and blue . . 95 15
62 – 30 c. multicoloured . . . . . 95 1·75
63 – 30 c. multicoloured . . . . . 95 1·75
DESIGN—40 × 27 mm: Nos. 62/3, "Intelstat III" in Orbit.
No. 62 has inscriptions and value in white and No. 63 has them in gold.

45 "Euploea leucostictus"

46 Emblem

1970. Butterflies. Multicoloured.
64 25 c. Type **45** . . . . 1·00 10
65 30 c. "Zeuxidia amethystus" . . 1·50 10
66 50 c. "Polyura athamas" . . . . 1·75 10
67 75 c. "Papilio memnon" . . . . 2·00 10
68 $1 "Appias nero" . . . . . . 2·50 10
69 $2 "Trogonoptera brookiana" . 3·50 10
70 $5 "Narathura centaurus" . . . 5·00 2·75
71 $10 "Terinos terpander" . . . . 17·00 5·00
Lower values were issued for use in the individual States.

1970. 50th Anniv of Int Labour Organization.
72 **46** 30 c. grey and blue 10 20
73 75 c. pink and blue 20 30

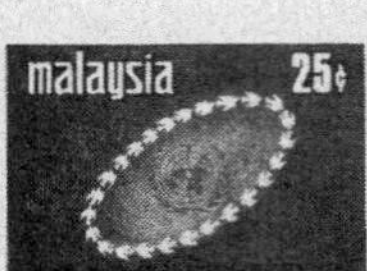

47 U.N. Emblem encircled by Doves

50 The Yang di-Pertuan Agong (Tuanku Abdul Halim Shah)

1970. 25th Anniv of United Nations.
74 **47** 25 c. gold, black and brown . 30 40
75 – 30 c. multicoloured 30 35
76 – 50 c. black and green 40 75
DESIGNS: 30 c. Line of doves and U.N. emblem; 50 c. Doves looping U.N. emblem.

1971. Installation of Yang di-Pertuan Agong (Paramount Ruler of Malaysia).
77 **50** 10 c. black, gold & yellow . . 20 30
78 15 c. black, gold & mauve . . 20 30
79 50 c. black, gold and blue . . 60 1·60

51 Bank Negara Complex

1971. Opening of Bank Negara Building.
80 **51** 25 c. black and silver 90 90
81 50 c. black and gold . . . . 90 1·10

52 Aerial View of Parliament Buildings

1971. 17th Commonwealth Parliamentary Association Conference, Kuala Lumpur. Multicoloured.
82 25 c. Type **52** . . . . 1·25 50
83 75 c. Ground view of Parliament Buildings (horiz 73 × 23½ mm) 2·75 1·75

53 54 55
Malaysian Carnival

1971. Visit ASEAN Year.
84 **53** 30 c. multicoloured . . . . . 1·50 55
85 **54** 30 c. multicoloured . . . . . 1·50 55
86 **55** 30 c. multicoloured . . . . . 1·50 55
ASEAN = Association of South East Asian Nations.
Nos. 84/6 form a composite design of a Malaysian Carnival, as Types **53/5**.

56 Trees, Elephant and Tiger

1971. 25th Anniv of U.N.I.C.E.F. Multicoloured.
87 15 c. Type **56** . . . . 1·90 45
88 15 c. Cat and kittens . . . . . 1·90 45
89 15 c. Sun, flower and bird (22 × 29 mm) . . . . 1·90 45
90 15 c. Monkey, elephant and lion in jungle . . . . 1·90 45
91 15 c. Spider and butterflies . . . 1·90 45

57 Athletics

1971. 6th S.E.A.P. Games, Kuala Lumpur. Mult.
92 25 c. Type **57** 45 40
93 30 c. Sepak Raga players . . . 60 50
94 50 c. Hockey . . . . 1·50 95
S.E.A.P. = South East Asian Peninsula.

58 59 60
Map and Tourist Attractions

1971. Pacific Area Tourist Association Conference.
95 **58** 30 c. multicoloured . . . . . 2·25 70
96 **59** 30 c. multicoloured . . . . . 2·25 70
97 **60** 30 c. multicoloured . . . . . 2·25 70
Nos. 95/7 form a composite design of a map showing tourist attractions, as Types **58/60**.

BANDARAYA KUALA LUMPUR 1972
61 Kuala Lumpur City Hall

1972. City Status for Kuala Lumpur. Multicoloured.
98 25 c. Type **61** . . . . 1·25 1·25
99 50 c. City Hall in floodlights . . 2·00 1·25

62 SOCSO Emblem

64 Fireworks, National Flag and Flower

63 W.H.O. Emblem

1973. Social Security Organization.
100 **62** 10 c. multicoloured 15 15
101 15 c. multicoloured 25 10
102 50 c. multicoloured . . . . 60 1·40

1973. 25th Anniv of W.H.O.
103 **63** 30 c. multicoloured 65 25
104 – 75 c. multicoloured . . . . 1·60 1·75
The 75 c. is similar to Type **63**, but vertical.

1973. 10th Anniv of Malaysia.
105 **64** 10 c. multicoloured 40 25
106 15 c. multicoloured 55 15
107 50 c. multicoloured . . . . 1·90 1·60

65 Emblems of Interpol and Royal Malaysian Police

1973. 50th Anniv of Interpol. Multicoloured.
108 25 c. Type **65** . . . . 1·00 50
109 75 c. Emblems within "50" . . 2·25 2·00

66 Boeing 737 and M.A.S. Emblem

1973. Foundation of Malaysian Airline System..
110 **66** 15 c. multicoloured 35 10
111 30 c. multicoloured 65 60
112 50 c. multicoloured . . . . 95 1·60

67 Kuala Lumpur

1974. Establishment of Kuala Lumpur as Federal Territory.
113 **67** 25 c. multicoloured 50 85
114 50 c. multicoloured . . . . 1·00 1·75

68 Development Projects

1974. 7th Annual Meeting of Asian Development Bank's Board of Governors, Kuala Lumpur.
115 **68** 30 c. multicoloured 25 50
116 75 c. multicoloured . . . . 80 1·75

69 Scout Badge and Map

1974. Malaysian Scout Jamboree. Multicoloured.
117 10 c. Type **69** 55 30
118 15 c. Scouts saluting and flags (46×24 mm) 70 30
119 50 c. Scout badge . . . . . . 1·75 2·25

70 Coat of Arms and Power Installations

1974. 25th Anniv of National Electricity Board. Multicoloured.
120 30 c. Type **70** 30 50
121 75 c. National Electricity Board Building (37×27 mm) . . . 1·00 2·00

71 U.P.U. and Post Office Emblems within "100"

1974. Centenary of U.P.U.
122 **71** 25 c. green, yellow & red . . 20 35
123 30 c. blue, yellow and red . . 25 35
124 75 c. orange, yellow & red . . 65 1·75

72 Gravel Pump in Tin Mine

1974. 4th World Tin Conf, Kuala Lumpur. Mult.
125 15 c. Type **72** . . . . 1·75 20
126 20 c. Open-cast mine . . . . . 2·00 1·25
127 50 c. Dredger within "ingot" . 3·75 4·50

73 Hockey-players, World Cup and Federation Emblem

74 Congress Emblem

1975. 3rd World Cup Hockey Championships.
128 **73** 30 c. multicoloured 90 60
129 75 c. multicoloured . . . . 2·10 2·25

1975. 25th Anniv of Malaysian Trade Union Congress.
130 **74** 20 c. multicoloured 20 25
131 25 c. multicoloured 30 30
132 30 c. multicoloured 45 60

75 Emblem of M.K.P.W. (Malayan Women's Organization)

76 Ubudiah Mosque, Kuala Kangsar

1975. International Women's Year.
133 **75** 10 c. multicoloured 15 25
134 15 c. multicoloured 30 25
135 50 c. multicoloured . . . . 1·25 2·25

1975. Koran Reading Competition. Multicoloured.
136 15 c. Type **76** . . . . 1·60 40
137 15 c. Zahir Mosque, Alor Star 1·60 40
138 15 c. National Mosque, Kuala Lumpur . . . . 1·60 40
139 15 c. Sultan Abu Bakar Mosque, Johore Bahru . . . . 1·60 40
140 15 c. Kuching State Mosque, Sarawak . . . . 1·60 40

77 Plantation and Emblem

1975. 50th Anniv of Malaysian Rubber Research Institute. Multicoloured.
141 10 c. Type **77** 40 15
142 30 c. Latex cup and emblem . . 1·10 70
143 75 c. Natural rubber in test-tubes 2·25 2·25

77a "Hebomoia glaucippe"

1976. Multicoloured.
144 10 c. Type **77a** . . . . 2·50 6·00
145 15 c. "Precis orithya" . . . . 2·50 6·00

78 Scrub Typhus

79 The Yang di-Pertuan Agong (Tuanku Yahya Petra)

1976. 75th Anniv of Institute of Medical Research. Multicoloured.
146 20 c. Type **78** 25 15
147 25 c. Malaria diagnosis 40 20
148 $1 Beri-beri . . . . 1·60 2·50

1976. Installation of Yang di-Pertuan Agong.
149 **79** 10 c. black, brown & yell . . 25 10
150 15 c. black, brown & mve . . 40 10
151 50 c. black, brown & blue . 2·25 2·50

80 State Council Complex

1976. Opening of State Council Complex and Administrative Building, Sarawak.
152 **80** 15 c. green and yellow . . . 35 10
153 20 c. green and mauve . . . 45 40
154 50 c. green and blue . . . . 1·00 1·40

81 E.P.F. Building

82 Blind People at Work

1976. 25th Anniv of Employees' Provident Fund. Multicoloured.
155 10 c. Type **81** 15 10
156 25 c. E.P.F. emblems (27×27 mm) 25 50
157 50 c. E.P.F. Building at night . 60 1·25

1976. 25th Anniv of Malayan Assn for the Blind. Multicoloured.
158 10 c. Type **82** 15 15
159 75 c. Blind man and shadow . . 1·25 2·40

83 Independence Celebrations, 1957

84 F.E.L.D.A. Village Scheme

1977. 1st Death Anniv of Tun Abdul Razak (Prime Minister).
160 15 c. Type **83** . . . . 1·50 40
161 15 c. "Education" . . . . . . 1·50 40
162 15 c. Tun Razak and map ("Development") . . . . . 1·50 40
163 15 c. "Rukunegara" (National Philosophy) . . . . 1·50 40
164 15 c. ASEAN meeting . . . . 1·50 40

1977. 21st Anniv of Federal Land Development Authority (F.E.L.D.A.). Multicoloured.
165 15 c. Type **84** 30 10
166 30 c. Oil palm settlement . . . 80 1·50

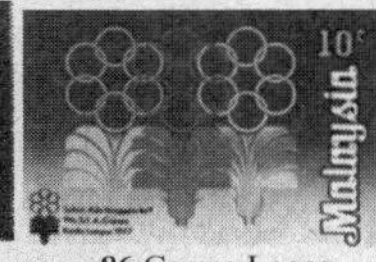

85 Figure "10"

86 Games Logos

1977. 10th Anniv of Association of South East Asian Nations (A.S.E.A.N.). Multicoloured.
167 10 c. Type **85** 10 10
168 75 c. Flags of members . . . . 1·25 65

1977. Ninth South East Asia Games, Kuala Lumpur. Multicoloured.
169 10 c. Type **86** 15 15
170 20 c. "Ball" 20 15
171 75 c. Symbolic athletes . . . . 75 1·50

87 Islamic Development Bank Emblem

1978. Islamic Development Bank Board of Governors' Meeting, Kuala Lumpur.
172 **87** 30 c. multicoloured 25 15
173 75 c. multicoloured 65 70

88 Mobile Post Office

1978. Fourth Commonwealth Postal Administrations Conference, Kuala Lumpur. Multicoloured.
174 10 c. Type **88** 30 10
175 25 c. G.P.O., Kuala Lumpur . . 75 1·25
176 50 c. Rural delivery by motorcycle . . . . 2·00 2·50

89 Boy Scout Emblem

1978. Fourth Malaysian Scout Jamboree, Sarawak. Multicoloured.
177 15 c. Type **89** 50 10
178 $1 Bees and honeycomb . . . 2·50 2·50

90 Dome of the Rock, Jerusalem

1978. Palestinian Welfare.
179 **90** 15 c. multicoloured 50 10
180 30 c. multicoloured . . . . 1·25 1·50

91 Globe and Emblems

1978. Global Eradication of Smallpox.
181 **91** 15 c. black, red and blue . . 25 20
182 30 c. black, red and green . 40 10
183 50 c. black, red and pink . . 70 55

92 "Seratus Tahun Getah Asli" and Tapping Knives Symbol

1978. Centenary of Rubber Industry.
184 **92** 10 c. gold and green 10 10
185 – 20 c. blue, brown & green . 10 10
186 – 75 c. gold and green 45 65

DESIGNS: 20 c. Rubber tree seedling and part of "maxi stump"; 75 c. Graphic design of rubber tree, latex cup and globe arranged to form "100".

93 Sultan of Selangor's New Palace

1978. Inaug of Shah Alam New Town as State Capital of Selangor. Multicoloured.
187 10 c. Type **93** 10 10
188 30 c. Aerial view of Shah Alam 20 15
189 75 c. Shah Alam . . . . 55 1·50

94 Tiger

1979. Animals. Multicoloured.
190 30 c. Type **94** . . . . 1·75 10
191 40 c. Malayan flying lemur . . 80 10
192 50 c. Lesser Malay chevrotain . 1·75 10
193 75 c. Leathery pangolin . . . . 1·00 10
194 $1 Malayan turtle . . . . . . 1·50 10
195 $2 Malayan tapir . . . . . . 1·50 10
196 $5 Gaur . . . . 4·50 1·75
197 $10 Orang-utang (vert) . . . . 7·00 3·25

96 View of Central Bank of Malaysia

97 I.Y.C. Emblem

1979. 20th Anniv of Central Bank of Malaysia. Multicoloured.
198 10 c. Type **96** 10 10
199 75 c. Central Bank (vert) . . . 40 75

1979. International Year of the Child.
200 **97** 10 c. gold, blue and salmon 30 10
201 – 15 c. multicoloured 40 10
202 – $1 multicoloured . . . . . 2·50 3·25
DESIGNS: 15 c. Children holding hands in front of globe; $1 Children playing.

98 Dam and Power Station

1979. Opening of Hydro-Electric Power Station, Temengor.
203 **98** 15 c. multicoloured 20 15
204 – 25 c. multicoloured 35 60
205 – 50 c. multicoloured . . . . 55 1·25
DESIGNS: 25 c., 50 c. Different views of Dam.

99 Exhibition Emblem **100** Tuanku Haji Ahmad Shah

1979. 3rd World Telecommunications Exhibition, Geneva.
206 **99** 10 c. orange, blue & silver . 10 30
207 – 15 c. multicoloured 15 10
208 – 50 c. multicoloured . . . . 40 1·75
DESIGNS—34 × 24 mm: 15 c. Telephone receiver joining the one half of World to the other. 39 × 28 mm: 50 c. Communications equipment.

1980. Installation of Tuanku Haji Ahmad Shah as Yang di-Pertuan Agong.
209 **100** 10 c. black, gold & yellow . 10 20
210 15 c. black, gold & purple . 15 10
211 50 c. black, gold and blue . 40 1·50

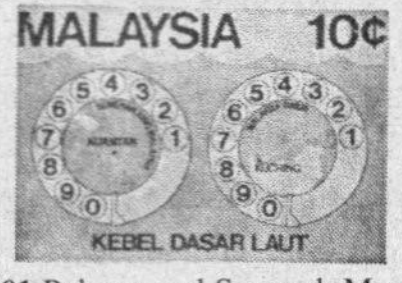

101 Pahang and Sarawak Maps within Telephone Dials

1980. Kuantan–Kuching Submarine Cable Project. Multicoloured.
212 10 c. Type **101** 10 30
213 15 c. Kuantan and Kuching views within telephone dials . . . 15 10
214 50 c. Pahang and Sarawak maps within telephone receiver . . 35 1·40

102 Bangi Campus

1980. 10th Anniv of National University of Malaysia. Multicoloured.
215 10 c. Type **102** 15 20
216 15 c. Jalan Pantai Baru campus 20 10
217 75 c. Great Hall . . . . 65 2·50

103 Mecca

1980. Moslem Year 1400 A.H. Commemoration.
218 **103** 15 c. multicoloured 10 10
219 50 c. multicoloured . . . . 30 1·25
No. 219 is inscribed in Roman lettering.

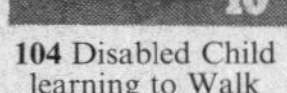
104 Disabled Child learning to Walk **105** Industrial Scene

1981. International Year for Disabled Persons. Multicoloured.
220 10 c. Type **104** 30 30
221 15 c. Girl sewing 55 10
222 75 c. Disabled athlete . . . . 1·50 3·25

1981. Expo "81" Industrial Training Exposition, Kuala Lumpur and Seminar, Genting Highlands. Multicoloured.
223 10 c. Type **105** 10 10
224 15 c. Worker and bulldozer . . 15 10
225 30 c. Workers at shipbuilding plant 25 35
226 75 c. Agriculture and fishing produce, workers and machinery . . . . 65 2·00

106 "25"

1981. 25th Anniv of Malaysian National Committee for World Energy Conferences. Multicoloured.
227 10 c. Type **106** 15 20
228 15 c. Drawings showing importance of energy sources in industry 30 10
229 75 c. Symbols of various energy sources . . . . 1·50 2·75

107 Drawing showing development of Sabah from Village to Urbanised Area

1981. Centenary of Sabah. Multicoloured.
230 15 c. Type **107** 50 15
231 80 c. Drawing showing traditional and modern methods of agriculture . . . 2·00 4·00

108 "Samanea saman"

1981. Trees. Multicoloured.
232 15 c. Type **108** 55 10
233 50 c. "Dyera costulata" (vert) . 1·75 1·40
234 80 c. "Dryobalanops aromatica" (vert) . . . . 2·00 4·00

109 Jamboree Emblem

1982. 5th Malaysian/7th Asia-Pacific Boy Scout Jamboree. Multicoloured.
235 15 c. Type **109** 35 10
236 50 c. Malaysian flag and scout emblem 80 85
237 80 c. Malaysian and Asia-Pacific scout emblem . . . . 1·25 4·00

110 A.S.E.A.N. Building and Emblem

1982. 15th Anniv of Ministerial Meeting of A.S.E.A.N. (Association of South East Asian Nations). Multicoloured.
238 15 c. Type **110** 15 10
239 $1 Flags of members . . . . . 80 2·50

111 Dome of the Rock, Jerusalem

1982. "Freedom for Palestine".
240 **111** 15 c. gold, green and blk . 75 15
241 $1 silver, green and black . 3·25 4·00

112 Views of Kuala Lumpur in 1957 and 1982

1982. 25th Anniv of Independence. Multicoloured.
242 10 c. Type **112** 10 10
243 15 c. Malaysian industries . . . 15 15
244 50 c. Soldiers on parade . . . 40 55
245 80 c. Independence ceremony 70 2·25

113 Shadow Play

1982. Traditional Games. Multicoloured.
247 10 c. Type **113** 55 30
248 15 c. Cross Top 55 15
249 75 c. Kite flying . . . . 2·25 4·00

114 Sabah Hats

1982. Malaysian Handicrafts. Multicoloured.
250 10 c. Type **114** 25 30
251 15 c. Gold-threaded cloth . . . 25 20
252 75 c. Sarawak pottery . . . . 1·25 3·00

115 Gas Exploitation Logo

1983. Export of Liquefied Natural Gas from Bintulu Field, Sarawak. Multicoloured.
253 15 c. Type **115** 75 15
254 20 c. "Tenaga Satu" (liquid gas tanker) . . . . 1·50 70
255 $1 Gas drilling equipment . . . 3·50 5·50

116 Flag of Malaysia

1983. Commonwealth Day. Multicoloured.
256 15 c. Type **116** 10 10
257 20 c. The King of Malaysia . . 15 20
258 40 c. Oil palm tree and refinery 25 45
259 $1 Satellite view of earth . . . 60 2·00

117 Nile Mouthbrooder

1983. Freshwater Fishes. Multicoloured.
260 20 c. Type **117** . . . . 1·50 1·75
261 20 c. Common carp . . . . . 1·50 1·75
262 40 c. Lampan barb . . . . . 2·25 2·75
263 40 c. Grass carp . . . . 2·25 2·75

118 Lower Pergau River Bridge

1983. Opening of East-West Highway. Mult.
264 15 c. Type **118** 80 15
265 20 c. Perak river reservoir bridge 1·00 75
266 $1 Map showing East–West highway . . . . 3·75 5·50

119 Northrop Tiger II Fighter

1983. 50th Anniv of Malaysian Armed Forces. Multicoloured.
267 15 c. Type **119** . . . . 1·25 15
268 20 c. Missile boat . . . . . . 1·75 45
269 40 c. Battle of Pasir Panjang . . 2·25 2·50
270 80 c. Trooping the Colour . . . 3·25 5·00

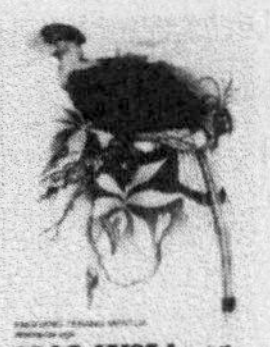

120 Helmeted Hornbill **122** Sky-scraper and Mosque, Kuala Lumpur

121 Bank Building, Ipoh

1983. Hornbills of Malaysia. Multicoloured.
280 15 c. Type **120** . . . . 1·00 15
281 20 c. Wrinkled hornbill . . . . 1·25 50
282 50 c. Long-crested hornbill . . 2·00 2·00
283 $1 Rhinoceros hornbill . . . . 3·25 5·00

1984. 25th Anniv of Bank Negara. Multicoloured.
284 20 c. Type **121** 40 30
285 $1 Bank building, Alor Setar . 2·00 3·50

1984. 10th Anniv of Federal Territory of Kuala Lumpur. Multicoloured.
286 20 c. Type **122** 80 20
287 40 c. Aerial view . . . . 1·60 1·40
288 80 c. Gardens and clock-tower (horiz) . . . . 2·50 4·50

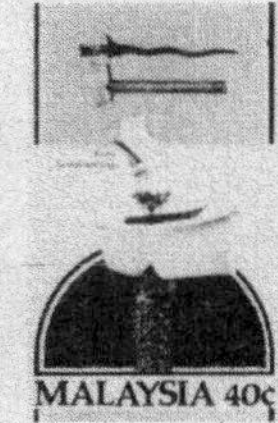

123 Map showing Industries **124** Semenanjung Keris

1984. Formation of Labuan Federal Territory. Multicoloured.
289 20 c. Type **123** 75 25
290 $1 Flag and map of Labuan . . 3·75 4·50

1984. Traditional Malay Weapons. Multicoloured.
291 40 c. Type **124** . . . . 1·25 1·75
292 40 c. Pekakak keris . . . . . 1·25 1·75
293 40 c. Jawa keris . . . . 1·25 1·75
294 40 c. Lada tumbuk . . . . . . 1·25 1·75

125 Map of World and Transmitter

1984. 20th Anniv of Asia–Pacific Broadcasting Union. Multicoloured.
295 20 c. Type **125** 40 25
296 $1 Clasped hands within "20" . 2·00 3·75

126 Facsimile Service **127** Yang di-Pertuan Agong (Tuanku Mahmood)

1984. Opening of New General Post Office, Kuala Lumpur. Multicoloured.

297	15 c. Type **126**	35	20
298	20 c. New G.P.O. building	45	45
299	$1 Mailbag conveyor	2·00	3·75

1984. Installation of Yang di-Pertuan Agong (Tuanku Mahmood).

300	**127**	15 c. multicoloured	40	20
301		20 c. multicoloured	45	20
302	–	40 c. multicoloured	85	1·00
303	–	80 c. multicoloured	2·00	4·25

DESIGN—HORIZ: 40 c., 80 c. Yang di-Pertuan Agong and federal crest.

128 White Hibiscus

129 Parliament Building

1984. Hibiscus. Multicoloured.

304	10 c. Type **128**	50	30
305	20 c. Red hibiscus	1·00	20
306	40 c. Pink hibiscus	1·75	2·00
307	$1 Orange hibiscus	2·75	4·75

1985. 25th Anniv of Federal Parliament. Mult.

308	20 c. Type **129**	30	15
309	$1 Parliament Building (different) (horiz)	1·75	2·25

130 Banded Linsang

1985. Protected Animals of Malaysia (1st series). Multicoloured.

310	10 c. Type **130**	60	10
311	40 c. Slow loris (vert)	2·00	1·40
312	$1 Spotted giant flying squirrel (vert)	4·00	5·00

See also Nos. 383/6.

131 Stylised Figures

1985. International Youth Year. Multicoloured.

313	20 c. Type **131**	30	15
314	$1 Young workers	3·25	4·50

132 Steam Locomotive No. 1, 1885

1985. Centenary of Malayan Railways.

315	**132**	15 c. black, red and orange	1·40	40
316	–	20 c. multicoloured	1·60	50
317	–	$1 multicoloured	3·75	5·00

DESIGNS: 20 c. Class 20 diesel-electric locomotive, 1957; $1 Hitachi Class 23 diesel-electric locomotive, 1983.

133 Blue Proton "Saga 1.3s" Car

1985. Production of Proton "Saga" (Malaysian national car). Multicoloured.

319	20 c. Type **133**	80	15
320	40 c. White Proton "Saga 1.3s"	1·40	1·00
321	$1 Red Proton "Saga 1.5s"	2·50	4·00

134 Penang Bridge

135 Offshore Oil Rig

1985. Opening of Penang Bridge. Multicoloured.

322	20 c. Type **134**	90	15
323	40 c. Penang Bridge and location map	1·75	90
324	$1 Symbolic bridge linking Penang to mainland (40 × 24 mm)	3·50	4·25

1985. Malaysian Petroleum Production. Mult.

325	15 c. Type **135**	1·00	20
326	20 c. Malaysia's first oil refinery (horiz)	1·10	50
327	$1 Map of Malaysian offshore oil and gas fields (horiz)	3·50	4·50

136 Sultan Azlan Shah and Perak Royal Crest

137 Crested Fireback Pheasant

1985. Installation of the Sultan of Perak.

328	**136**	15 c. multicoloured	35	10
329		20 c. multicoloured	45	25
330		$1 multicoloured	2·50	4·00

1986. Protected Birds of Malaysia (1st series). Multicoloured.

331	20 c. Type **137**	2·50	3·00
332	20 c. Malay peacock-pheasant	2·50	3·00
333b	40 c. Bulwer's pheasant (horiz)	2·00	3·25
334b	40 c. Great argus pheasant (horiz)	2·00	3·25

See also Nos. 394/7.

139 Two Kadazan Dancers, Sabah

140 Stylised Competitors

1986. Pacific Area Travel Association Conference, Malaysia. Multicoloured.

335	20 c. Type **139**	75	95
336	20 c. Dyak dancer and longhouse, Sarawak	75	95
337	20 c. Dancers and fortress, Malacca	75	95
338	40 c. Malay dancer and Kuala Lumpur	1·10	1·40
339	40 c. Chinese opera dancer and Penang Bridge	1·10	1·40
340	40 c. Indian dancer and Batu Caves	1·10	1·40

1986. Malaysia Games. Multicoloured.

341	20 c. Type **140**	1·25	20
342	40 c. Games emblems (vert)	2·25	2·00
343	$1 National and state flags (vert)	6·00	7·25

141 Rambutan

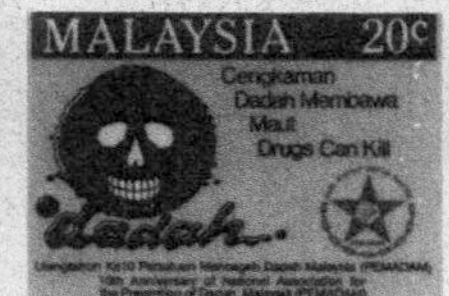

142 Skull and Slogan "Drugs Can Kill"

1986. Fruits of Malaysia. Multicoloured.

344	40 c. Type **141**	15	20
345	50 c. Pineapple	15	20
346	80 c. Durian	25	30
347	$1 Mangosteen	30	35
348	$2 Star fruit	60	65
349	$5 Banana	1·60	1·75
350	$10 Mango	3·25	3·50
351	$20 Papaya	6·25	6·50

1986. 10th Anniv of National Association for Prevention of Drug Addiction. Multicoloured.

352	20 c. Type **142**	1·00	30
353	40 c. Bird and slogan "Stay Free From Drugs"	1·40	1·10
354	$1 Addict and slogan "Drugs Can Destroy" (vert)	2·25	3·75

143 MAS Logo and Map showing Routes

144 Building Construction

1986. Inaugural Flight of Malaysian Airlines Kuala Lumpur–Los Angeles Service. Multicoloured.

355	20 c. Type **143**	1·10	15
356	40 c. Logo, stylized aircraft and route diagram	1·75	65
357	$1 Logo and stylized aircraft	3·00	2·50

1986. 20th Anniv of National Productivity Council and 25th Anniv of Asian Productivity Organization (40 c., $1). Multicoloured.

358	20 c. Type **144**	85	25
359	40 c. Planning and design (horiz)	1·40	1·25
360	$1 Computer-controlled car assembly line (horiz)	3·75	5·50

145 Old Seri Menanti Palace, Negri Sembilan

1986. Historic Buildings of Malaysia (1st series). Multicoloured.

361	15 c. Type **145**	50	20
362	20 c. Old Kenangan Palace, Perak	55	20
363	40 c. Old Town Hall, Malacca	1·00	70
364	$1 Astana, Kuching, Sarawak	2·25	3·50

See also Nos. 465/8.

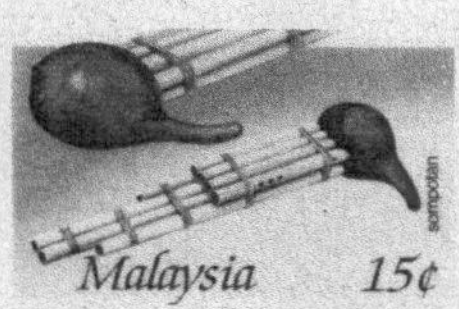

146 Sompotan (bamboo pipes)

1987. Malaysian Musical Instruments. Multicoloured.

365	15 c. Type **146**	55	10
366	20 c. Sapih (four-stringed chordophone)	65	20
367	50 c. Serunai (pipes) (vert)	1·40	40
368	80 c. Rebab (three-stringed fiddle) (vert)	1·90	1·25

147 Modern Housing Estate

1987. International Year of Shelter for the Homeless. Multicoloured.

369	20 c. Type **147**	40	15
370	$1 Stylised families and houses	1·50	1·00

148 Drug Addict and Family

1987. International Conference on Drug Abuse, Vienna. Multicoloured.

371	20 c. Type **148**	1·00	65
372	20 c. Hands holding drugs and damaged internal organs	1·00	65
373	40 c. Healthy boy and broken drug capsule	1·50	90
374	40 c. Drugs and healthy internal organs	1·50	90

Nos. 371/2 and 373/4 were printed together, se-tenant, forming composite designs.

149 Spillway and Power Station

1987. Opening of Sultan Mahmud Hydro-electric Scheme, Kenyir, Trengganu. Multicoloured.

375	20 c. Type **149**	50	10
376	$1 Dam, spillway and reservoir	2·50	1·50

150 Crossed Maces and Parliament Building, Kuala Lumpur

1987. 33rd Commonwealth Parliamentary Conference. Multicoloured.

377	20 c. Type **150**	25	10
378	$1 Parliament building and crossed mace emblem	1·00	1·00

151 Dish Aerial, Satellite and Globe

1987. Asia/Pacific Transport and Communications Decade. Multicoloured.

379	15 c. Type **151**	40	10
380	20 c. Diesel train and car	1·25	65
381	40 c. Container ships and lorry	1·50	1·25
382	$1 Malaysian Airlines Boeing 747, Kuala Lumpur Airport	2·75	4·00

152 Temminck's Golden Cat

1987. Protected Animals of Malaysia (2nd series). Multicoloured.

383	15 c. Type **152**	1·50	40
384	20 c. Flatheaded cat	1·50	40
385	40 c. Marbled cat	2·50	1·75
386	$1 Clouded leopard	4·50	5·50

153 Flags of Member Nations and "20"

1987. 20th Anniv of Association of South East Asian Nations. Multicoloured.

387	20 c. Type **153**	20	10
388	$1 Flags of member nations and globe	80	1·00

154 Mosque and Portico

1988. Opening of Sultan Salahuddin Abdul Aziz Shah Mosque. Multicoloured.

389	15 c. Type **154**	20	10
390	20 c. Dome, minarets and Sultan of Selangor	20	20
391	$1 Interior and dome (vert)	70	1·25

155 Aerial View

1988. Sultan Ismail Hydro-electric Power Station, Paka, Trengganu. Multicoloured.

392	20 c. Type **155**	20	10
393	$1 Power-station and pylons	80	90

156 Black-naped Blue Monarch

157 Outline Map and Products of Sabah

1988. Protected Birds of Malaysia (2nd series). Multicoloured.

394	20 c. Type **156**	1·75	1·75
395	20 c. Scarlet-backed flowerpecker	1·75	1·75
396	50 c. Yellow-backed sunbird	2·50	2·50
397	50 c. Black and red broadbill	2·50	2·50

1988. 25th Anniv of Sabah and Sarawak as States of Malaysia. Multicoloured.

398	20 c. Type **157**	40	50
399	20 c. Outline map and products of Sarawak	40	50
400	$1 Flags of Malaysia, Sabah and Sarawak (30 × 40 mm)	1·00	1·50

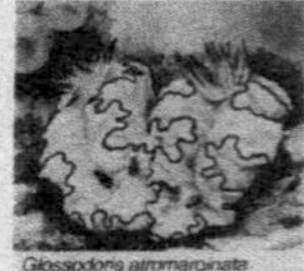

158 "Glossodoris atromarginata"

159 Sultan's Palace, Malacca

1988. Marine Life (1st series). Multicoloured.
401 20 c. Type **158** 85 90
402 20 c. Ocellate nudibranch . . . 85 90
403 20 c. "Chromodoris annae" . . 85 90
404 20 c. "Flabellina macassarana" 85 90
405 20 c. Ruppell's nudibranch . . 85 90
Nos. 401/5 were printed together, se-tenant, forming a composite background design.
See also Nos. 410/13, 450/3, 492/6 and 559/62.

1989. Declaration of Malacca as Historic City. Multicoloured.
407 20 c. Type **159** 20 15
408 20 c. Independence Memorial Building 20 15
409 $1 Porta De Santiago Fortress (vert) . . . . 1·00 1·40

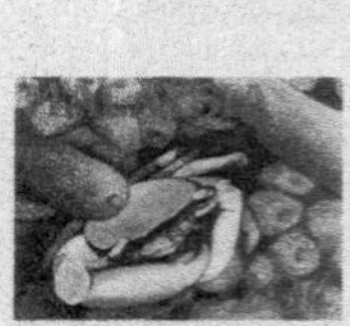

160 "Tetralia nigrolineata"

161 Map of Malaysia and Scout Badge

1989. Marine Life (2nd series). Crustaceans. Multicoloured.
410 20 c. Type **160** 45 65
411 20 c. "Neopetrolisthes maculatus" (crab) 45 65
412 40 c. "Periclimenes holthuisi" (shrimp) 55 90
413 40 c. "Synalpheus neomeris" (shrimp) 55 90

1989. 7th National Scout Jamboree. Multicoloured.
414 10 c. Type **161** 25 10
415 20 c. Saluting national flag . . 40 25
416 80 c. Scouts around camp fire (horiz) . . . . 1·25 2·50

162 Cycling

163 Sultan Azlan Shah

1989. 15th South East Asian Games, Kuala Lumpur. Multicoloured.
417 10 c. Type **162** 40 20
418 20 c. Athletics 30 20
419 50 c. Swimming (vert) 60 85
420 $1 Torch bearer (vert) . . . . 95 2·25

1989. Installation of Sultan Azlan Shah as Yang di-Pertuan Agong.
421 **163** 20 c. multicoloured 20 15
422 40 c. multicoloured 30 35
423 $1 multicoloured . . . . . 70 1·75

164 Putra World Trade Centre and Pan-Pacific Hotel

1989. Commonwealth Heads of Government Meeting, Kuala Lumpur. Multicoloured.
424 20 c. Type **164** 20 10
425 50 c. Traditional dancers (vert) 65 75
426 $1 National flag and map showing Commonwealth countries . . . . 1·25 2·25

165 Clock Tower, Kuala Lumpur City Hall and Big Ben

166 Sloth and Map of Park

1989. Inaugural Malaysia Airlines "747" Non-stop Flight to London. Each showing Malaysia Airlines Boeing "747-400". Multicoloured.
427 20 c. Type **165** . . . . 1·00 1·40
428 20 c. Parliament Buildings, Kuala Lumpur, and Palace of Westminster . . . . 1·00 1·40
429 $1 World map showing route . 2·50 2·75

1989. 50th Anniv of National Park. Multicoloured.
430 20 c. Type **166** 50 20
431 $1 Pair of Malay ocellated pheasants . . . . 1·75 2·75

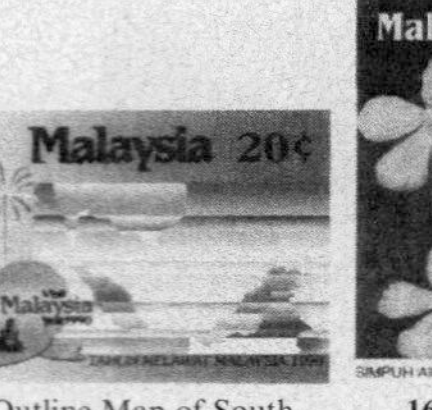

167 Outline Map of South-east Asia and Logo

168 "Dillenia suffruticosa"

1990. "Visit Malaysia Year". Multicoloured.
432 20 c. Type **167** 40 15
433 50 c. Traditional drums 75 90
434 $1 Scuba diving, windsurfing and yachting . . . . 1·25 2·25

1990. Wildflowers (1st series). Multicoloured.
435 15 c. Type **168** 25 15
436 20 c. "Mimosa pudica" 30 20
437 50 c. "Ipmoea carnea" 60 70
438 $1 "Nymphaea pubescens" . . 80 1·75
See also Nos. 505/8.

169 Monument and Rainbow

171 Alor Setar

170 Seri Negara Building

1990. Kuala Lumpur, Garden City of Lights. Multicoloured.
439 20 c. Type **169** 20 20
440 40 c. Mosque and skyscrapers at night (horiz) 40 55
441 $1 Kuala Lumpur skyline (horiz) 95 2·00

1990. 1st Summit Meeting of South–South Consultation and Co-operation Group, Kuala Lumpur. Multicoloured.
442 20 c. Type **170** 20 15
443 80 c. Summit logo . . . . . . 80 1·75

1990. 250th Anniv of Alor Setar. Multicoloured.
444 20 c. Type **171** 20 20
445 40 c. Musicians and monument (vert) 30 35
446 $1 Zahir Mosque (vert) . . . . 85 1·75

172 Sign Language Letters

1990. International Literacy Year. Multicoloured.
447 20 c. Type **172** 15 10
448 40 c. People reading 30 35
449 $1 Symbolic person reading (vert) . . . . 90 2·00

173 Leatherback Turtle

1990. Marine Life (3rd series). Sea Turtles. Mult.
450 15 c. Type **173** 60 10
451 20 c. Common green turtle . . 60 15
452 40 c. Olive Ridley turtle . . . . 1·25 80
453 $1 Hawksbill turtle . . . . . 2·25 3·00

174 Safety Helmet, Dividers and Industrial Skyline

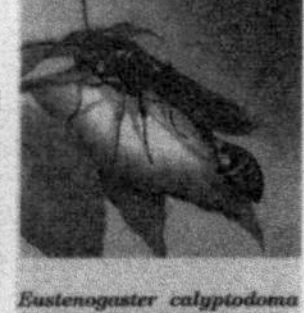

175 "Eustenogaster calyptodoma"

1991. 25th Anniv of MARA (Council of the Indigenous People). Multicoloured.
454 20 c. Type **174** 15 10
455 40 c. Documents and graph . . 30 35
456 $1 25th Anniversary logo . . . 75 1·75

1991. Insects. Wasps. Multicoloured.
457 15 c. Type **175** 25 30
458 20 c. "Vespa affinis indonensis" 25 20
459 50 c. "Sceliphorn javanum" . . 60 70
460 $1 "Ampulex compressa" . . . 1·00 1·75

176 Tunku Abdul Rahman Putra and Independence Rally

1991. Former Prime Ministers of Malaysia. Multicoloured.
462 $1 Type **176** . . . . 70 1·00
463 $1 Tun Abdul Razak Hussein and jungle village . . . . 70 1·00
464 $1 Tun Hussein Onn and standard-bearers . . . . . 70 1·00

177 Maziah Palace, Trengganu

1991. Historic Buildings of Malaysia (2nd series). Multicoloured.
465 15 c. Type **177** 20 10
466 20 c. Grand Palace, Johore . . 20 15
467 40 c. Town Palace, Kuala Langat, Selangor 45 50
468 $1 Jahar Palace, Kelantan . . . 90 1·75

178 Museum Building in 1891, Brass Lamp and Fabric

179 Rural Postman on Cycle

1991. Centenary of Sarawak Museum. Mult.
469 30 c. Type **178** 20 15
470 $1 Museum building in 1991, vase and fabric . . . . 80 1·25

1992. Inauguration of Post Office Corporation. Multicoloured.
471 30 c. Type **179** 50 65
472 30 c. Urban postman on motorcycle 50 65
473 30 c. Inner city post van . . . 50 65
474 30 c. Industrial post van . . . 50 65
475 30 c. Malaysian Airlines Boeing 747 and globe 50 65

180 Hill Forest and Jelutong Tree

1992. Tropical Forests. Multicoloured.
476 20 c. Type **180** 20 10
477 50 c. Mangrove swamp and Bakau Minyak tree 45 50
478 $1 Lowland forest and Chengal tree . . . . 90 1·50

MALAYSIA $1

181 Tuanku Ja'afar and Coat of Arms

182 Badminton Players

1992. 25th Anniv of Installation of Tuanku Ja'afar as Yang di-Pertuan Besar of Negri Sembilan. Multicoloured.
479 30 c. Type **181** 20 20
480 $1 Palace, Negri Sembilan . . . 80 1·60

1992. Malaysian Victory in Thomas Cup Badminton Championship. Multicoloured.
481 $1 Type **182** 55 75
482 $1 Thomas Cup and Malaysian flag 55 75

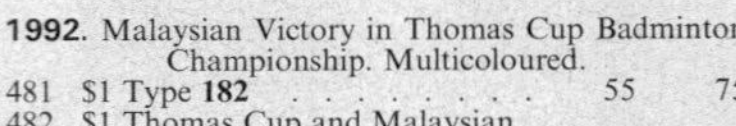

183 Women in National Costumes

1992. 25th Anniv of A.S.E.A.N. (Association of South East Asian Nations). Multicoloured.
484 30 c. Type **183** 40 30
485 50 c. Regional flowers 65 75
486 $1 Traditional architecture . . 1·25 2·25

184 Straits Settlements 1867 1½ c. and Malaysian Federation 1957 10 c. Stamps

1992. 125th Anniv of Postage Stamps and "Kuala Lumpur '92" Int Stamp Exn. Multicoloured.
487 30 c. Type **184** 35 50
488 30 c. Straits Settlements 1867 2 c. and Malaysia 1963 Federation Inauguration 12 c. 35 50
489 50 c. Straits Settlements 1868 4 c. and Malaysia 1990 Kuala Lumpur 40 c. 65 80
490 50 c. Straits Settlements 1867 12 c. and Malaysia "Kuala Lumpur '92" $2 . . . . . 65 80

185 "Acropora"

186 Girls smiling

1992. Marine Life (4th series). Corals. Multicoloured.
492 30 c. Type **185** 70 85
493 30 c. "Dendronephthya" . . . 70 85
494 30 c. "Dendrophyllia" 70 85
495 30 c. "Sinularia" 70 85
496 30 c. "Melithaea" 70 85

1993. 16th Asian–Pacific Dental Congress. Multicoloured.
498 30 c. Type **186** 50 65
499 30 c. Girls smiling with koala bear 50 65
500 50 c. Dentists with Japanese, Malaysian and South Korean flags . . . . 80 1·00
501 $1 Dentists with New Zealand, Thai, Chinese and Indonesian flags . . . . 1·00 1·25

187 View of Golf Course

188 "Alpinia rafflesiana"

1993. Cent of Royal Selangor Golf Club. Mult.
502 30 c. Type **187** 60 20
503 50 c. Old and new club houses 90 80
504 $1 Bunker on course (horiz) . . 1·75 2·00

1993. Wildflowers (2nd series). Gingers. Mult.

505 20 c. Type **188** 35 10
506 30 c. "Achasma megalocheilos" 45 20
507 50 c. "Zingiber spectabile" . . 80 80
508 $1 "Costus speciosus" . . . . 1·60 2·00

189 Forest under Magnifying Glass

190 White-breasted Kingfisher

1993. 14th Commonwealth Forestry Conference, Kuala Lumpur. Multicoloured.

509 30 c. Type **189** 40 20
510 50 c. Hand holding forest . . . 65 70
511 $1 Forest in glass dome (vert) . 1·40 2·25

1993. Kingfishers. Multicoloured

512 30 c. Type **190** 60 80
513 30 c. Pair of blue-eared kingfishers 60 80
514 50 c. Chestnut-collared kingfisher . . . . 80 1·00
515 50 c. Pair of three-toed kingfishers . . . . 80 1·00

191 SME MD3-160m Light Aircraft

1993. Langkawi International Maritime and Aerospace Exhibition '93. Multicoloured.

516 30 c. Type **191** 35 20
517 50 c. Eagle X-TS light aircraft . 65 75
518 $1 "Kasturi" (frigate) . . . . 1·25 2·00

192 Jeriau Waterfalls

1994. Visit Malaysia. Multicoloured.

520 20 c. Type **192** 25 10
521 30 c. Flowers 30 25
522 50 c. Turtle and fishes 45 55
523 $1 Orang-utan and other wildlife 90 1·50

193 Planetarium and Planets

1994. National Planetarium, Kuala Lumpur. Mult.

524 30 c. Type **193** 50 20
525 50 c. Static displays 65 75
526 $1 Planetarium auditorium . . 1·50 2·00

194 "Spathoglottis aurea"

195 Decorative Bowl

1994. Orchids. Multicoloured.

527 20 c. Type **194** 35 10
528 30 c. "Paphiopedilum barbatum" 45 25
529 50 c. "Bulbophyllum lobbii" . . 75 85
530 $1 "Aerides odorata" . . . . 1·25 1·75

1994. World Islamic Civilisation Festival '94, Kuala Lumpur. Multicoloured.

532 20 c. Type **195** 15 10
533 30 c. Celestial globe 25 20
534 50 c. Dinar coins 40 55
535 $1 Decorative tile . . . . . . 75 1·25

196 Flock of Chickens and Vet examining Cat

197 Workers laying Electric Cable

1994. Centenary of Veterinary Services. Mult.

536 30 c. Type **196** 35 20
537 50 c. Vet in abattoir 60 50
538 $1 Herd of cows and veterinary equipment . . . . 1·00 1·50

1994. Centenary of Electricity Supply. Multicoloured.

539 30 c. Type **197** 25 45
540 30 c. Illuminated city 25 45
541 $1 City of the future . . . . . 70 1·10

198 Expressway from the Air

199 Sultan Tuanku Ja'afar

1994. Opening of North–South Expressway. Mult.

542 30 c. Type **198** 20 20
543 50 c. Expressway junction . . . 35 50
544 $1 Expressway bridge . . . . 80 1·25

1994. Installation of Sultan Tuanku Ja'afar as Yang di-Pertuan Agong.

545 **199** 30 c. multicoloured 20 20
546 50 c. multicoloured 40 50
547 $1 multicoloured . . . . . 80 1·25

200 Map of Malaysia and Logo

201 Tunku Abdul Rahman Putra and National Flag

1994. 16th Commonwealth Games, Kuala Lumpur (1998) (1st issue). Multicoloured.

548 $1 Type **200** . . . . 80 1·00
549 $1 Wira (games mascot) holding national flag . . . . 80 1·00

See also Nos. 575/6, 627/30, 668/71 and 693/708.

1994. 5th Death Anniv of Tunku Abdul Rahman Putra (former Prime Minister). Multicoloured.

550 30 c. Type **201** 25 20
551 $1 The Residency, Kuala Lumpur . . . . 75 1·00

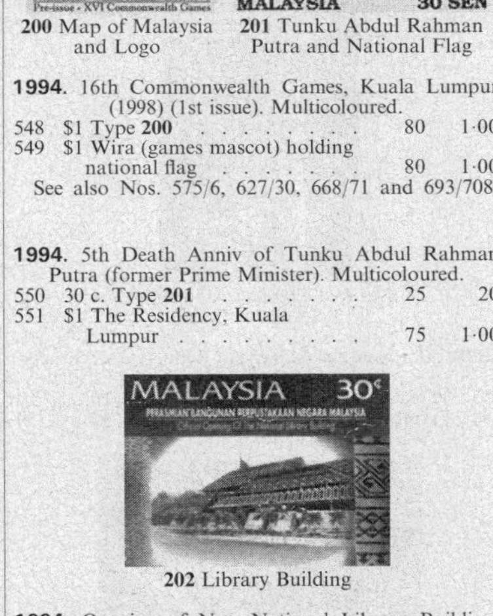

202 Library Building

1994. Opening of New National Library Building. Multicoloured.

552 30 c. Type **202** 20 25
553 50 c. Computer plan on screen . 45 50
554 $1 Ancient Koran . . . . . . 1·00 1·40

203 "Microporus xanthopus"

1995. Fungi. Multicoloured.

555 20 c. Type **203** 15 10
556 30 c. "Cookeina tricholoma" . . 25 20
557 50 c. "Phallus indusiatus" ("Dictyophora phalloidea") . 45 55
558 $1 "Ramaria sp." . . . . . . 90 1·50

204 Seafans

1995. Marine Life (5th series). Corals. Multicoloured.

559 20 c. Type **204** 50 65
560 20 c. Feather stars 50 65
561 30 c. Cup coral 50 65
562 30 c. Soft coral 50 65

205 Clouded Leopard on Branch

1995. Endangered Species. Clouded Leopard. Mult.

563 20 c. Type **205** 25 25
564 30 c. With cubs 30 30
565 50 c. Crouched on branch . . . 45 50
566 $1 Climbing tree . . . . . . 70 1·00

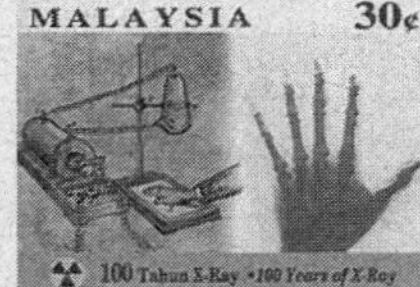

206 Early X-Ray Equipment and X-Ray of Hand

1995. Centenary of Discovery of X-Rays by Wilhelm Conrad Rontgen. Multicoloured.

567 30 c. Type **206** 30 50
568 30 c. Body scanner and brain scan 30 50
569 $1 Chest X-rays . . . . 95 1·25

207 Jembiah (curved dagger)

1995. "Singapore '95" International Stamp Exhibition. Traditional Malay Weapons. Mult.

570 20 c. Type **207** 15 10
571 30 c. Keris panjang (sword) . . 25 20
572 50 c. Kerambit (curved dagger) . 40 50
573 $1 Keris sundang (sword) . . . 80 1·50

208 Badminton, Cricket, Shooting, Tennis, Hurdling, Hockey and Weightlifting

1995. 16th Commonwealth Games, Kuala Lumpur (1998) (2nd issue). Multicoloured.

575 $1 Type **208** . . . . 1·25 1·40
576 $1 Cycling, bowls, boxing, basketball, rugby, gymnastics and swimming . . . . . . 1·25 1·40

209 Leatherback Turtle ("Dermochelys coriacea")

1995. Turtles. Multicoloured.

577 30 c. Type **209** 50 70
578 30 c. Green turtle ("Chelonia mydas") 50 70

210 Anniversary Emblem and Symbolic People around Globe

1995. 50th Anniv of United Nations. Multicoloured.

579 30 c. Type **210** 15 20
580 $1 United Nations emblem . . 60 80

211 Boeing 747, Globe, Emblem and Malaysian Scenes

212 Proton "Saga 1.5" Saloon, 1985

1995. 50th Anniv of International Air Transport Association. Designs each showing Boeing 747 and Globe. Multicoloured.

581 30 c. Type **211** 30 40
582 30 c. Asian and Australasian scenes 30 40
583 50 c. European and African scenes 45 65
584 50 c. North and South American scenes 45 65

1995. 10th Anniv of Proton Cars. Multicoloured.

585 30 c. Type **212** 25 30
586 30 c. "Iswara 1.5" aeroback, 1992 . . . . 25 30
587 30 c. "Iswara 1.5" saloon, 1992 . 25 30
588 30 c. "Wira 1.6" saloon, 1993 . 25 30
589 30 c. "Wira 1.6" aeroback, 1993 . . . . 25 30
590 30 c. Proton rally car, 1994 . . 25 30
591 30 c. "Satria 1.6" hatchback, 1994 . . . . 25 30
592 30 c. "Perdana 2.0" saloon, 1995 25 30
593 30 c. "Wira 1.6" aeroback, 1995 . . . . 25 30
594 30 c. "Wira 1.8" saloon, 1995 . 25 30

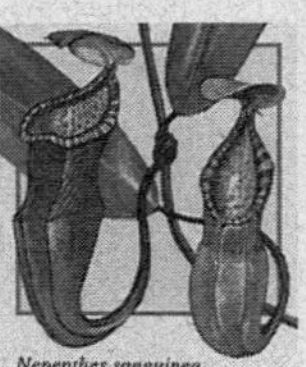

213 "Ariane 4" Launch Rocket

214 "Nepenthes sanguinea"

1996. Launch of MEASAT I (Malaysia East Asia Satellite). Multicoloured.

595 30 c. Type **213** 25 20
596 50 c. Satellite over Eastern Asia 40 45
597 $1 Satellite Earth station, Langkawi . . . . 90 1·40

1996. Pitcher Plants. Multicoloured.

599 30 c. Type **214** 25 35
600 30 c. "Nepenthes macfarlanei" . 25 35
601 50 c. "Nepenthes rajah" . . . 35 50
602 50 c. "Nepenthes lowii" . . . 35 50

215 Brahminy Kite

1996. Birds of Prey. Multicoloured.

603 20 c. Type **215** 20 15
604 30 c. Crested serpent eagle . . 30 25
605 50 c. White-bellied sea eagle . . 45 55
606 $1 Crested hawk eagle . . . . 90 1·50

216 Family, Globe and Burning Drugs

1996. International Day against Drug Abuse and Illicit Trafficking. Multicoloured.

608 30 c. Type **216** 25 35
609 30 c. Sporting activities 25 35
610 $1 Family and rainbow 60 80

217 "Graphium sarpedon"

218 Kuala Lumpur Tower

1996. "ISTANBUL '96" International Stamp Exhibition. Butterflies. Multicoloured.
611 30 c. Type **217** 40 50
612 30 c. "Terinos terpander" . . . 40 50
613 30 c. "Melanocyma faunula" . 40 50
614 30 c. "Trogonoptera brookiana" 40 50
615 30 c. "Delias hyparete" 40 50

1996. Opening of Kuala Lumpur Telecommunications Tower. Multicoloured.
616 30 c. Type **218** 20 20
617 50 c. Diagram of top of tower . 30 35
618 $1 Kuala Lumpur Tower at night . . . . 80 1·00

219 C.A.P.A. Logo on Kite

1996. 14th Conference of the Confederation of Asian and Pacific Accountants. Multicoloured.
620 30 c. Type **219** 20 20
621 $1 Globe and C.A.P.A. logo . . 60 70

220 Model of D.N.A. Molecule

1996. Opening of National Science Centre, Kuala Lumpur. Multicoloured.
623 30 c. Type **220** 25 20
624 50 c. Planetary model and Science Centre 40 40
625 $1 National Science Centre . . 90 1·25

222 Running

1996. 16th Commonwealth Games, Kuala Lumpur (1998) (3rd issue). Multicoloured.
627 30 c. Type **222** 20 30
628 30 c. Hurdling 20 30
629 50 c. High jumping 30 50
630 50 c. Javelin 30 50

223 Pygmy Blue Flycatcher

224 Transit Train leaving Station

1997. Highland Birds. Multicoloured.
631 20 c. Type **223** 25 10
632 30 c. Silver-eared mesia 30 20
633 50 c. Black-sided flower-pecker . 40 45
634 $1 Scarlet sunbird . . . . . . 70 1·25

1997. Opening of Kuala Lumpur Light Rail Transit System. Multicoloured.
636 30 c. Type **224** 40 55
637 30 c. Trains in central Kuala Lumpur 40 55

225 Bowler

1997. International Cricket Council Trophy, Kuala Lumpur. Multicoloured.
638 30 c. Type **225** 30 15
639 50 c. Batsman 45 40
640 $1 Wicket-keeper . . . . . . 80 1·00

226 Boeing 747-400 over World Map

1997. 50th Anniv of Aviation in Malaysia. Mult.
641 30 c. Type **226** 40 15
642 50 c. Boeing 747-400 over Kuala Lumpur 50 40
643 $1 Tail fins of four airliners . . 80 1·10

227 "Schima wallichii"

228 World Youth Football Championship Mascot

1997. Highland Flowers. Multicoloured.
644 30 c. Type **227** 30 40
645 30 c. "Aeschynanthus longicalyx" 30 40
646 30 c. "Aeschynanthus speciosa" 30 40
647 30 c. "Phyllagathis tuberculata" 30 40
648 30 c. "Didymocarpus quinquevulnerus" 30 40

1997. 9th World Youth Football Championship, Malaysia. Multicoloured.
649 30 c. Type **228** 15 10
650 50 c. Football and players . . 25 30
651 $1 Map of Malaysia and football 50 70

229 Members of First Conference, 1897

1997. Centenary of Rulers' Conference. Mult.
652 30 c. Type **229** 15 10
653 50 c. State emblem 25 25
654 $1 Seal and press 50 55

230 A.S.E.A.N. Logo and Ribbons

1997. 30th Anniv of Association of South-east Asian Nations. Multicoloured.
655 30 c. Type **230** 20 10
656 50 c. "30" enclosing logo . . . 35 35
657 $1 Chevrons and logo 65 90

231 "Tubastrea sp."

232 Women Athletes, Scientist and Politician

1997. International Year of the Coral Reefs. Multicoloured.
658 20 c. Type **231** 15 10
659 30 c. "Melithaea sp." 15 10
660 50 c. "Aulostomus chinensis" . 30 30
661 $1 "Symphillia sp." 45 70

1997. 20th International Pan-Pacific and South-east Asia Women's Association Conference, Kuala Lumpur. Multicoloured.
663 30 c. Type **232** 20 30
664 30 c. Family and house 20 30

234 Group of 15 Emblem

237 Kundang

235 Hockey

1997. 7th Summit Conference of the Group of 15, Kuala Lumpur. Multicoloured.
666 30 c. Type **234** 10 10
667 $1 Flags of member countries . 70 85

1997. 16th Commonwealth Games, Kuala Lumpur (1998) (4th issue). Multicoloured.
668 30 c. Type **235** 20 30
669 30 c. Netball 20 30
670 50 c. Cricket 30 40
671 50 c. Rugby 30 40

1998. Fruit. Multicoloured.
674 20 c. Type **237** 10 10
675 30 c. Sentul 10 10
676 50 c. Pulasan 15 20
677 $1 Asam gelugur 60 75

239 Mas (coin) from Trengganu, 1793–1808

1998. Gold coins. Multicoloured.
679 20 c. Type **239** 10 10
680 30 c. Kupang from Kedah, 1661–1687 . . . . 15 10
681 50 c. Kupang from Johore, 1597–1615 . . . . 30 30
682 $1 Kupang from Kelantan, 1400–1780 . . . . 40 70

240 Red Crescent Ambulance Boat and Emblem

1998. 50th Anniv of Malaysian Red Crescent Society. Multicoloured.
683 30 c. Type **240** 10 10
684 1 Ambulance and casualty . . 40 50

241 Transit Train and Boeing 747-400 at Airport

1998. Opening of Kuala Lumpur International Airport. Designs showing control tower. Mult.
685 30 c. Type **241** 20 10
686 50 c. Airport Terminals 40 30
687 $1 Airliner in flight . . . . . 80 1·00

242 "Solanum torvum"

243 Weightlifting

1998. Medicinal Plants. Multicoloured.
689 20 c. Type **242** 10 10
690 30 c. "Tinospora crispa" . . . 15 10
691 50 c. "Jatropha podagrica" . . 25 25
692 $1 "Hibiscus rosa-sinensis" . . 40 70

1998. 16th Commonwealth Games, Kuala Lumpur, Malaysia (5th issue). (Sports). Multicoloured.
693 20 c. Type **243** 10 10
694 20 c. Badminton 10 10
695 20 c. Netball 10 10
696 20 c. Shooting 10 10
697 30 c. Men's hockey 10 10
698 30 c. Women's hockey 10 10
699 30 c. Cycling 10 10
700 30 c. Bowls 10 10
701 50 c. Gymnastics 15 20
702 50 c. Cricket 15 20
703 50 c. Rugby 15 20
704 50 c. Running 15 20
705 $1 Swimming 30 35
706 $1 Squash 30 35
707 $1 Boxing 30 35
708 $1 Ten-pin bowling 30 35

244 L.R.T. "Putra" Type Train

1998. Modern Kuala Lumpur Rail Transport. Multicoloured.
709b 30 c. Type **244** 30 10
710b 50 c. L.R.T. "Star" type train . 35 20
711 $1 K.T.M commuter train . . 40 55

245 Globe and A.P.E.C. Logo

1998. Asia–Pacific Econmic Co-operation Conference. Multicoloured.
712b 30 c. Type **245** 30 10
713 $1 Business meeting and computer office 40 50

248 Profile of Elderly Couple, World Map and Emblem

1999. International Year of the Older Person. Multicoloured.
717 $1 Type **248** 30 35
718 $1 Four silhouettes of elderly people, world map and emblem 30 35

249 "Syzygium malaccense"

250 Kucing Malaysia Cat

1999. Rare Fruits of Malaysia. Multicoloured.
719 20 c. Type **249** 10 15
720 30 c. "Garcinia prainiana" . . . 10 15
721 50 c. "Mangifera caesia" . . . 15 20
722 $1 "Salacca glabrescens" . . . 30 35

1999. Malaysian Cats. Multicoloured.
727 30 c. Type **250** 10 15
728 50 c. Siamese 15 20
729 $1 Abyssinian 30 35

251 Sumatran Rhinoceros

1999. Protected Mammals of Malaysia. Mult.
731 20 c. Type **251** 10 15
732 30 c. Panther 10 15
733 50 c. Sun bear 15 20
734 $1 Indian elephant 30 35
739 $2 Orang-utan 60 65

252 Hearts and AIDS Ribbons

1999. 5th International Conference on AIDS in Asia and the Pacific. Each red, blue and black.

741	30 c. Type **252**	10	15
742	50 c. Fragmenting and stylised AIDS ribbons	15	20
743	$1 Two AIDS ribbons	30	35

253 P. Ramlee in Traditional Dress

1999. 70th Birth Anniv of P. Ramlee (actor and film director) Commemoration. (a) Multicoloured.

744	20 c. Type **253**	10	15
745	30 c. Receiving an award	10	15
746	50 c. Playing part of soldier in film	15	20
747	$1 Using film camera	30	35
	(b) Each brown, light brown and black.		
749	30 c. In traditional dress	10	15
750	30 c. With hands raised	10	15
751	30 c. Singing into microphone	10	15
752	30 c. Wearing army uniform	10	15

B. FEDERAL TERRITORY ISSUES

For use in the Federal Territories of Kuala Lumpur and (from 1984) Labuan.

K **1** "Rafflesia hasseltii"

K **2** Coffee

1979. Flowers. Multicoloured.

K1	1 c. Type K **1**	10	30
K2	2 c. "Pterocarpus indicus"	10	30
K3	5 c. "Lagerstroemia speciosa"	10	30
K4	10 c. "Durio zibethinus"	10	10
K5	15 c. "Hibiscus rosa-sinensis"	20	10
K6	20 c. "Rhododendron scortechinii"	20	10
K7	25 c. "Etlingera elatior" (inscr "Phaeomeria speciosa")	40	10

1986. Agricultural Products of Malaysia. Mult.

K15	1 c. Type K **2**	10	10
K16	2 c. Coconuts	10	10
K17	5 c. Cocoa	10	10
K18	10 c. Black pepper	10	10
K19	15 c. Rubber	10	10
K20	20 c. Oil palm	10	10
K21	30 c. Rice	15	20

POSTAGE DUE STAMPS

Until 15 August, 1966, the postage due stamps of Malaysian Postal Union were in use throughout Malaysia.

D 1

D 2

1966.

D 1	D **1**	1 c. red	20	2·50
D 2		2 c. blue	25	2·50
D 3		4 c. green	85	5·00
D18		8 c. green	45	3·25
D19		10 c. blue	45	2·25
D 6		12 c. violet	60	4·50
D20		20 c. brown	55	2·75
D21		50 c. bistre	90	3·50

1986.

D22	D **2**	5 c. mauve and lilac	10	10
D23		10 c. black and grey	10	10
D24		20 c. red and brown	10	10
D25		50 c. green and blue	15	20
D26		$1 blue and cobalt	55	70

MALDIVE ISLANDS Pt. 1

A group of islands W. of Ceylon. A republic from 1 Jan., 1953, but reverted to a sultanate in 1954. Became independent on 26 July, 1965 and left the British Commonwealth, but was re-admitted as an Associate Member on 9 July, 1982.

1906. 100 cents = 1 rupee.
1951. 100 larees = 1 rupee.

1906. Nos. 268, 277/9 and 283/4 of Ceylon optd MALDIVES.

1	44	2 c. brown	14·00	30·00
2	48	3 c. green	18·00	30·00
3		4 c. orange and blue	32·00	70·00
4	–	5 c. purple	4·50	6·50
5	48	15 c. blue	60·00	£120
6		25 c. brown	70·00	£130

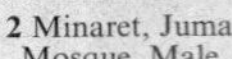

2 Minaret, Juma Mosque, Male **5** Palm Tree and Dhow

1909.

7a	2	2 c. brown	2·50	90
11A		2 c. grey	2·75	2·00
8		3 c. green	40	70
12A		3 c. brown	70	2·25
9		5 c. purple	40	35
15A		6 c. red	1·50	5·00
10		10 c. red	7·50	80
16A		10 c. green	85	55
17A		15 c. black	6·50	12·00
18A		25 c. brown	6·50	12·00
19A		50 c. purple	6·50	12·00
20B		1 r. blue	12·00	2·75

1950.

21	5	2 l. olive	1·50	40
22		3 l. blue	8·50	40
23		5 l. green	8·50	50
24		6 l. brown	70	30
25		10 l. red	70	30
26		15 l. orange	70	30
27		25 l. purple	70	30
28		50 l. violet	70	30
29		1 r. brown	8·50	25·00

8 Native Products

1952.

30	–	3 l. blue (Fish)	1·00	30
31	8	5 l. green	50	1·40

9 Male Harbour

10 Fort and Building

1956.

32	9	2 l. purple	10	10
33		3 l. slate	10	10
34		5 l. brown	10	10
35		6 l. violet	10	10
36		10 l. green	10	10
37		15 l. brown	10	60
38		25 l. red	10	10
39		50 l. orange	10	10
40	10	1 r. green	15	10
41		5 r. blue	60	30
42		10 r. mauve	1·50	85

11 Cycling

1960. Olympic Games.

43	11	2 l. purple and green	15	10
44		3 l. slate and purple	15	10
45		5 l. brown and blue	15	10
46		10 l. green and brown	15	10
47		15 l. sepia and blue	15	25
48	–	25 l. red and olive	15	25
49	–	50 l. orange and violet	20	40
50	–	1 r. green and purple	40	1·25

DESIGN—VERT: 25 l. to 1 r. Basketball.

13 Tomb of Sultan

1960.

51	13	2 l. purple	10	10
52	–	3 l. green	10	10
53	–	5 l. brown	2·75	2·75
54	–	6 l. blue	10	10
55	–	10 l. red	10	10
56	–	15 l. sepia	10	10
57	–	25 l. violet	10	10
58	–	50 l. grey	10	10
59	–	1 r. orange	15	10
60	–	5 r. blue	3·00	60
61	–	10 r. green	7·50	1·25

DESIGNS: 3 l. Custom House; 5 l. Cowrie shells; 6 l. Old Royal Palace; 10 l. Road to Juma Mosque, Male; 15 l. Council House; 25 l. New Government Secretariat; 50 l. Prime Minister's Office; 1 r. Old Ruler's Tomb; 5 r. Old Ruler's Tomb (distant view); 10 r. Maldivian port.

Higher values were also issued, intended mainly for fiscal use.

24 "Care of Refugees"

1960. World Refugee Year.

62	24	2 l. violet, orange & green	10	10
63		3 l. brown, green and red	10	10
64		5 l. green, sepia and red	10	10
65		10 l. green, violet and red	10	10
66		15 l. violet, green and red	10	10
67		25 l. blue, brown and green	10	10
68		50 l. olive, red and blue	10	10
69		1 r. red, slate and violet	15	35

25 Coconuts **26** Map of Male

1961.

70	25	2 l. brown and green	10	10
71		3 l. brown and blue	10	10
72		5 l. brown and mauve	10	10
73		10 l. brown and orange	10	10
74		15 l. brown and black	10	15
75	26	25 l. multicoloured	15	20
76		50 l. multicoloured	15	30
77		1 r. multicoloured	20	45

27 5 c. Stamp of 1906

1961. 55th Anniv of First Maldivian Stamp.

78	27	2 l. purple, blue and green	10	10
79		3 l. purple, blue and green	10	10
80		5 l. purple, blue and green	10	10
81		6 l. purple, blue and green	10	10
82	–	10 l. green, red and purple	10	10
83	–	15 l. green, red and purple	15	15
84	–	20 l. green, red and purple	15	20
85	–	25 l. red, green and black	15	20
86	–	50 l. red, green and black	25	80
87	–	1 r. red. green and black	40	1·75

DESIGNS: 10 l. to 20 l. Posthorn and 3 c. stamp of 1906; 25 l. to 1 r. Olive sprig and 2 c. stamp of 1906.

30 Malaria Eradication Emblem **31** Children of Europe and America

1962. Malaria Eradication.

88	30	2 l. brown	10	10
89		3 l. green	10	10
90		5 l. turquoise	10	10
91		10 l. red	10	10
92	–	15 l. sepia	15	10
93	–	25 l. blue	20	15
94	–	50 l. myrtle	25	40
95	–	1 r. purple	55	60

Nos. 92/5 are as Type **30**, but have English inscriptions at the side.

1962. 15th Anniv of U.N.I.C.E.F.

96	31	2 l. multicoloured	10	10
97		6 l. multicoloured	10	10
98		10 l. multicoloured	10	10
99		15 l. multicoloured	10	10
100	–	25 l. multicoloured	10	10
101	–	50 l. multicoloured	10	10
102	–	1 r. multicoloured	15	20
103	–	5 r. multicoloured	80	3·00

DESIGN: Nos. 100/3, Children of Middle East and Far East.

33 Sultan Mohamed Farid Didi **39** Fishes in Net

34 Royal Angelfish

1962. 9th Anniv of Enthronement of Sultan.

104	33	3 l. brown and green	10	10
105		5 l. brown and blue	10	10
106		10 l. brown and blue	15	10
107		20 l. brown and olive	20	20
108		50 l. brown and mauve	25	40
109		1 r. brown and violet	35	55

1963. Tropical Fish. Multicoloured.

110		2 l. Type **34**	10	15
111		3 l. Type **34**	10	15
112		5 l. Type **34**	15	15
113		10 l. Moorish idol (fish)	25	15
114		25 l. As 10 l.	65	20
115		50 l. Diadem soldierfish	90	40
116		1 r. Powder-blue surgeonfish	1·25	55
117		5 r. Racoon butterflyfish	6·25	9·50

1963. Freedom from Hunger.

118	39	2 l. brown and green	30	80
119	–	5 l. brown and red	50	70
120	39	7 l. brown and turquoise	70	70
121	–	10 l. brown and blue	85	70
122	39	25 l. brown and red	3·00	3·25
123	–	50 l. brown and violet	4·75	7·00
124	39	1 r. brown and mauve	7·50	11·00

DESIGN—VERT: 5 l., 10 l., 50 l. Handful of grain.

41 Centenary Emblem **42** Maldivian Scout Badge

1963. Centenary of Red Cross.

125	41	2 l. red and purple	30	1·25
126		15 l. red and green	65	80
127		50 l. red and brown	1·50	1·75
128		1 r. red and blue	2·25	2·00
129		4 r. red and olive	7·00	20·00

1964. World Scout Jamboree, Marathon (1963).

130	42	2 l. green and violet	10	10
131		3 l. green and brown	10	10
132		25 l. green and blue	15	15
133		1 r. green and red	55	1·50

43 Mosque, Male

1964. "Maldives Embrace Islam".

134	43	2 l. purple	10	10
135		3 l. green	10	10
136		10 l. red	10	10
137		40 l. purple	30	15
138		60 l. blue	50	15
139		85 l. brown	60	20

44 Putting the Shot

1964. Olympic Games, Tokyo.

140	44	2 l. purple and blue	10	10
141		3 l. red and brown	10	10
142		5 l. bronze and green	15	10
143		10 l. violet and purple	20	10
144	–	15 l. sepia and brown	30	10
145	–	25 l. indigo and blue	50	10
146	–	50 l. bronze and olive	75	25
147	–	1 r. purple and grey	1·25	50

DESIGN: 15 l. to 1 r. Running.

46 Telecommunications Satellite

1965. International Quiet Sun Years.

148	46	5 l. blue	15	15
149		10 l. brown	20	15
150		25 l. green	40	15
151		1 r. mauve	90	55

47 Isis (wall carving, Abu Simbel) **49** "XX" and U.N. Flag

48 Pres. Kennedy and Doves

1965. Nubian Monuments Preservation.

152	47	2 l. green and purple	10	10
153	–	3 l. lake and green	10	10
154	47	5 l. green and purple	15	10
155	–	10 l. blue and orange	20	10
156	47	15 l. brown and violet	35	15
157	–	25 l. purple and blue	60	15
158	47	50 l. green and sepia	75	35
159	–	1 r. ochre and green	1·10	55

DESIGN: 3, 10, 25 l., 1 r. Rameses II on throne (wall carving, Abu Simbel).

1965. 2nd Death Anniv of Pres. Kennedy.

160	48	2 l. black and mauve	10	10
161		5 l. brown and mauve	10	10
162		25 l. blue and mauve	10	10
163	–	1 r. purple, yellow & green	25	25
164	–	2 r. bronze, yellow & green	40	40

DESIGN: 1 r., 2 r. Pres. Kennedy and hands holding olive-branch.

1965. 20th Anniv of U.N.

165	49	3 l. blue and brown	10	10
166		10 l. blue and violet	15	10
167		1 r. blue and green	65	35

50 I.C.Y. Emblem

1965. International Co-operation Year.

168	50	5 l. brown and bistre	15	10
169		15 l. brown and lilac	20	10
170		50 l. brown and olive	45	30
171		1 r. brown and red	1·25	1·50
172		2 r. brown and blue	1·75	3·00

INDEX

Countries can be quickly located by referring to the index at the end of this volume.

51 Princely Cone Shells

1966. Multicoloured.
174 2 l. Type **51** 20 40
175 3 l. Yellow flowers 20 40
176 5 l. Reticulate distorsio and leopard shells 30 15
177 7 l. Camellias 30 15
178 10 l. Type **51** 60 15
179 15 l. Crab plover and seagull 2·50 30
180 20 l. As 3 l. 80 30
181 30 l. Type **51** 2·00 35
182 50 l. As 15 l. 4·50 55
183 1 r. Type **51** 3·00 55
184 1 r. As 7 l. 3·00 55
185 1 r. 50 As 3 l. 3·50 2·00
186 2 r. As 7 l. 4·75 2·50
187 5 r. As 15 l. 17·00 10·00
188 10 r. As 5 l. 17·00 14·00
The 3 l., 7 l., 20 l., 1 r. (No. 184), 1 r. 50 and 2 r. are DIAMOND (43½×43½ mm).

52 Maldivian Flag

1966. 1st Anniv of Independence.
189 **52** 10 l. green, red & turquoise 40 10
190 1 r. multicoloured 1·60 40

53 "Luna 9" on Moon

1966. Space Rendezvous and Moon Landing.
191 **53** 10 l. brown, indigo & blue 20 10
192 – 25 l. green and red 30 10
193 **53** 50 l. brown and green 40 15
194 – 1 r. turquoise and brown 70 35
195 – 2 r. green and violet 1·50 65
196 – 5 r. pink and turquoise 2·25 1·60
DESIGNS: 25 l., 1 r., 5 r. "Gemini 6" and "7" rendezvous in space; 2 r. "Gemini" spaceship as seen from the other spaceship.

54 U.N.E.S.C.O. Emblem and Owl on Book

1966. 20th Anniv of U.N.E.S.C.O. Multicoloured.
198 2 l. Type **54** 10 50
199 3 l. U.N.E.S.C.O. emblem and globe and microscope 10 50
200 5 l. U.N.E.S.C.O. emblem and mask, violin and palette 30 15
201 50 l. Type **54** 1·75 45
202 1 r. Design as 3 l. 2·50 75
203 5 r. Design as 5 l. 8·75 13·00

55 Sir Winston Churchill and Cortege

1966. Churchill Commem. Flag in red and blue.
204 **55** 2 l. brown 15 40
205 – 10 l. turquoise 65 10
206 **55** 15 l. green 1·00 10
207 – 25 l. violet 1·60 15
208 – 1 r. brown 4·00 75
209 **55** 2 r. 50 red 9·50 9·50
DESIGN: 10 l., 25 l., 1 r. Churchill and catafalque.

56 Footballers and Jules Rimet Cup

1967. England's Victory in World Cup Football Championship. Multicoloured.
210 2 l. Type **56** 10 40
211 3 l. Player in red shirt kicking ball 10 40
212 5 l. Scoring goal 10 10
213 25 l. As 3 l. 60 10
214 50 l. Making a tackle 1·00 20
215 1 r. Type **56** 2·00 55
216 2 r. Emblem on Union Jack 3·25 3·00

57 Ornate Butterflyfish

1967. Tropical Fishes. Multicoloured.
218 2 l. Type **57** 10 30
219 3 l. Black-saddled pufferfish 15 30
220 5 l. Blue boxfish 20 10
221 6 l. Picasso triggerfish 20 20
222 50 l. Semicircle angelfish 3·25 30
223 1 r. As 3 l. 4·50 75
224 As 50 l. 8·50 8·00

58 Hawker Siddeley H.S.748 over Hulule Airport Building

1967. Inauguration of Hulule Airport.
225 **58** 2 l. violet and olive 15 40
226 – 5 l green and lavender 20 10
227 **58** 10 l. violet and green 25 10
228 – 15 l. green and ochre 40 10
229 **58** 30 l. ultramarine & blue 90 10
230 – 50 l. brown and mauve 1·50 20
231 **58** 5 r. blue and orange 5·00 5·50
232 – 10 r. brown and blue 7·00 9·00
DESIGN: 5, 15, 50 l., 10 r. Airport building and Hawker Siddeley H.S.748.

59 "Man and Music" Pavilion

1967. World Fair, Montreal. Multicoloured.
233 2 l. Type **59** 10 10
234 5 l. "Man and His Community" Pavilion 10 10
235 10 l. Type **59** 10 10
236 50 l. As 5 l. 30 20
237 1 r. Type **59** 65 40
238 2 r. As 5 l. 1·25 90

1968. Int Tourist Year (1967). Nos. 225/32 optd **International Tourist Year 1967**.
240 **58** 2 l. violet and olive 10 30
241 – 5 l. green and lavender 15 15
242 **58** 10 l. violet and green 20 15
243 – 15 l. green and ochre 15 15
244 **58** 30 l. ultramarine & blue 30 20
245 – 50 l. brown and mauve 30 25
246 **58** 5 r. blue and orange 3·50 3·75
247 – 10 r. brown and blue 5·00 6·00

61 Cub signalling and Lord Baden-Powell

63 Putting the Shot

62 French Satellite "A 1"

1968. Maldivian Scouts and Cubs.
248 **61** 2 l. brown, green & yellow 10 30
249 – 3 l. red, blue and lt blue 10 30
250 **61** 25 l. violet, lake and red 1·50 30
251 – 1 r. green, brown and light green 3·50 1·60
DESIGN: 3 l. and 1 r. Scouts and Lord Baden-Powell.

1968. Space Martyrs.
252 **62** 2 l. mauve and blue 10 30
253 – 3 l. violet and brown 10 30
254 – 7 l. brown and lake 15 30
255 – 10 l. blue, drab and black 15 15
256 – 25 l. green and violet 40 15
257 **62** 50 l. blue and brown 75 30
258 – 1 r. purple and green 1·10 50
259 – 2 r. brown, blue and black 1·75 1·75
260 – 5 r. mauve, drab & black 2·75 3·00
DESIGNS: 3 l., 25 l. "Luna 10"; 7 l., 1 r. "Orbiter" and "Mariner"; 10 l., 2 r. Astronauts White, Grissom and Chaffee; 5 r. Cosmonaut V. M. Komarov.

1968. Olympic Games, Mexico (1st Issue). Multicoloured.
262 2 l. Type **63** 10 15
263 6 l. Throwing the discus 10 15
264 10 l. Type **63** 10 10
265 25 l. As 6 l. 15 10
266 1 r. Type **63** 50 35
267 2 r. 50 As 6 l. 1·25 1·50
See also Nos. 294/7.

64 "Adriatic Seascape" (Bonington)

1968. Paintings. Multicoloured.
268 50 l. Type **64** 75 30
269 1 r. "Ulysses deriding Polyphemus" (Turner) 1·25 45
270 2 r. "Sailing Boat at Argenteuil" (Monet) 2·00 1·75
271 5 r. "Fishing Boat at Les Saintes-Maries" (Van Gogh) 4·25 4·25

65 LZ-130 "Graf Zeppelin II" and Montgolfier's Balloon

1968. Development of Civil Aviation.
272 **65** 2 l. brown, green and blue 15 40
273 – 3 l. blue, violet and brown 15 40
274 – 5 l. green, red and blue 15 15
275 – 7 l. blue, purple & orange 90 55
276 **65** 10 l. brown, blue & purple 35 15
277 – 50 l. red, green and olive 1·50 20
278 – 1 r. green, blue and red 2·25 50
279 – 2 r. purple, bistre and blue 14·00 10·00
DESIGNS: 3 l., 1 r. Boeing 707-420 and Douglas DC-3; 5 l., 50 l. Wright Type A and Lilienthal's glider; 7 l., 2 r. Projected Boeing 733 and Concorde.

66 W.H.O. Building, Geneva

1968. 20th Anniv of World Health Organization.
280 **66** 10 l. violet, turquoise & blue 60 10
281 25 l. green, brown & yellow 1·00 15
282 1 r. brown, emerald & grn 3·25 90
283 2 r. violet, purple & mauve 5·25 5·50

1968. 1st Anniv of Scout Jamboree, Idaho. Nos. 248/51 optd **International Boy Scout Jamboree, Farragut Park, Idaho, U.S.A. August 1–9, 1967.**
284 **61** 2 l. brown, green & yellow 10 40
285 – 3 l. red, blue and lt blue 10 40
286 **61** 25 l. violet, lake and red 1·50 40
287 – 1 r. green, brown and light green 4·50 2·10

68 Curlew and Redshank

1968. Multicoloured.
288 2 l. Type **68** 50 60
289 10 l. Pacific grinning tun and Papal mitre shells 1·25 20
290 25 l. Oriental angel wing and tapestry turban shells 1·75 25
291 50 l. Type **68** 6·00 90
292 1 r. As 10 l. 4·50 95
293 2 r. As 25 l. 4·75 4·50

69 Throwing the Discus
71 "The Thinker" (Rodin)

70 Fishing Dhow

1968. Olympic Games, Mexico (2nd issue). Multicoloured.
294 10 l. Type **69** 10 10
295 50 l. Running 20 10
296 1 r. Cycling 2·00 35
297 2 r. Basketball 2·75 1·25

1968. Republic Day.
298 **70** 10 l. brown, blue & green 75 20
299 – 1 r. green, red and blue 3·00 80
DESIGN: 1 r. National flag, crest and map.

1969. U.N.E.S.C.O. "Human Rights". Designs showing sculptures by Rodin. Multicoloured.
300 6 l. Type **71** 30 15
301 10 l. "Hands" 30 15
302 1 r. 50 "Eve" 2·00 2·25
303 2 r. 50 "Adam" 2·50 3·00

72 Module nearing Moon's Surface

1969. First Man on the Moon. Multicoloured.
305 6 l. Type **72** 15 15
306 10 l. Astronaut with hatchet 15 15
307 1 r. 50 Astronaut and module 2·25 1·40
308 2 r. 50 Astronaut using camera 2·50 2·00

1969. Gold Medal Winner, Olympic Games, Mexico (1968). Nos. 295/6 optd **Gold Medal Winner Mohamed Gammoudi 5000 m. run Tunisia REPUBLIC OF MALDIVES** or similar opt.
310 50 l. multicoloured 60 60
311 1 r. multicoloured 1·40 90
The inscription on No. 310 honours P. Trentin (cycling, France).

74 Racoon Butterflyfish

1970. Tropical Fishes. Multicoloured.
312 2 l. Type **74** 40 70
313 5 l. Clown triggerfish 65 40
314 25 l. Broad-barred lionfish 2·25 40
315 50 l. Long-nosed butterflyfish 3·00 1·00
316 1 r. Emperor angelfish 4·00 1·00
317 2 r. Royal angelfish 5·50 6·50

75 Columbia Dauman Victoria, 1899

1970. "75 Years of the Automobile". Multicoloured.

318	2 l. Type **75**	20	30
319	5 l. Duryea phaeton, 1902	25	30
320	7 l. Packard S-24, 1906	30	30
321	10 l. Autocar Runabout, 1907	35	30
322	25 l. Type **75**	1·50	30
323	50 l. As 5 l.	2·75	55
324	1 r. As 7 l.	3·50	90
325	2 r. As 10 l.	4·50	5·50

76 U.N. Headquarters, New York

1970. 25th Anniv of United Nations. Mult.

327	2 l. Type **76**	10	50
328	10 l. Surgical operation (W.H.O.)	95	15
329	25 l. Student, actress and musician (U.N.E.S.C.O.)	2·00	30
330	50 l. Children at work and play (U.N.I.C.E.F.)	2·00	60
331	1 r. Fish, corn and farm animals (F.A.O.)	2·00	90
332	2 r. Miner hewing coal (I.L.O.)	5·00	5·50

77 Ship and Light Buoy

78 "Guitar-player and Masqueraders" (A. Watteau)

1970. 10th Anniv of I.M.C.O. Multicoloured.

333	50 l. Type **77**	50	40
334	1 r. Ship and lighthouse	3·25	85

1970. Famous Paintings showing the Guitar. Multicoloured.

335	3 l. Type **78**	10	30
336	7 l. "Spanish Guitarist" (Manet)	10	30
337	50 l. "Costumed Player" (Watteau)	50	35
338	1 r. "Mandoline-player" (Roberti)	85	55
339	2 r. 50 "Guitar-player and Lady" (Watteau)	2·25	2·75
340	5 r. "Mandoline-player" (Frans Hals)	4·00	4·50

79 Australian Pavilion

82 Footballers

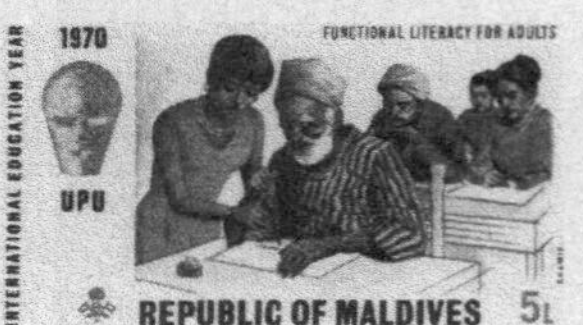

80 Learning the Alphabet

1970. "EXPO 70" World Fair, Osaka, Japan. Multicoloured.

342	2 l. Type **79**	10	40
343	3 l. West German Pavilion	10	40
344	10 l. U.S. Pavilion	30	10
345	25 l. British Pavilion	80	15
346	50 l. Soviet Pavilion	1·40	35
347	1 r. Japanese Pavilion	1·90	65

1970. Int Education Year. Multicoloured.

348	5 l. Type **80**	20	15
349	10 l. Training teachers	25	10
350	25 l. Geography lesson	60	15
351	50 l. School inspector	80	45
352	1 r. Education by television	1·25	75

1970. "Philympia 1970" Stamp Exn, London. Nos. 306/8 optd **Philympia London 1970**.

353	10 l. multicoloured	10	10
354	1 r. 50 multicoloured	65	75
355	2 r. 50 multicoloured	1·00	1·50

1970. World Cup Football Championships, Mexico.

357	**82** 3 l. multicoloured	15	40
358	– 6 l. multicoloured	20	40
359	– 7 l. multicoloured	20	30
360	– 25 l. multicoloured	90	20
361	– 1 r. multicoloured	2·50	90

DESIGNS: 6 l. to 1 r. Different designs showing footballers in action.

83 Little Boy and U.N.I.C.E.F. Flag

84 Astronauts Lovell, Haise and Swigert

1970. 25th Anniv of U.N.I.C.E.F. Multicoloured.

362	5 l. Type **83**	10	15
363	10 l. Little girl with U.N.I.C.E.F. "balloon"	10	15
364	1 r. Type **83**	1·75	85
365	2 r. As 10 l.	2·75	3·00

1971. Safe Return of "Apollo 13". Multicoloured.

366	5 l. Type **84**	20	15
367	20 l. Explosion in Space	40	15
368	1 r. Splashdown	1·10	50

85 "Multiracial Flower"

86 "Mme. Charpentier and her Children" (Renoir)

1971. Racial Equality Year.

369	**85** 10 l. multicoloured	10	15
370	25 l. multicoloured	20	15

1971. Famous Paintings showing "Mother and Child". Multicoloured.

371	5 l. Type **86**	25	20
372	7 l. "Susanna van Collen and her Daughter" (Rembrandt)	30	20
373	10 l. "Madonna nursing the Child" (Titian)	40	20
374	20 l. "Baroness Belleli and her Children" (Degas)	1·00	20
375	25 l. "The Cradle" (Morisot)	1·00	20
376	1 r. "Helena Fourment and her Children" (Reubens)	3·00	85
377	3 r. "On the Terrace" (Renoir)	5·50	6·50

87 Alan Shepard

1971. Moon Flight of "Apollo 14". Multicoloured.

378	6 l. Type **87**	30	20
379	10 l. Stuart Roosa	35	20
380	1 r. 50 Edgar Mitchell	4·50	3·00
381	5 r. Mission insignia	9·50	9·50

88 "Ballerina" (Degas)

1971. Famous Paintings showing "Dancers". Multicoloured.

382	5 l. Type **88**	20	20
383	10 l. "Dancing Couple" (Renoir)	25	20
384	2 r. "Spanish Dancer" (Manet)	2·75	2·50
385	5 r. "Ballerinas" (Degas)	5·00	5·00
386	10 r. "La Goulue at the Moulin Rouge" (Toulouse-Lautrec)	7·50	8·00

1972. Visit of Queen Elizabeth II and Prince Philip. Nos. 382/6 optd **ROYAL VISIT 1972**.

387	**88** 5 l. multicoloured	15	10
388	– 10 l. multicoloured	20	10
389	– 2 r. multicoloured	4·50	4·00
390	– 5 r. multicoloured	8·00	8·00
391	– 10 r. multicoloured	9·50	10·00

90 Book Year Emblem

1972. International Book Year.

392	**90** 25 l. multicoloured	15	10
393	5 r. multicoloured	1·60	2·00

91 Scottish Costume

1972. National Costumes of the World. Mult.

394	10 l. Type **91**	50	10
395	15 l. Netherlands	55	15
396	25 l. Norway	90	15
397	50 l. Hungary	1·75	55
398	1 r. Austria	2·25	80
399	2 r. Spain	4·00	3·25

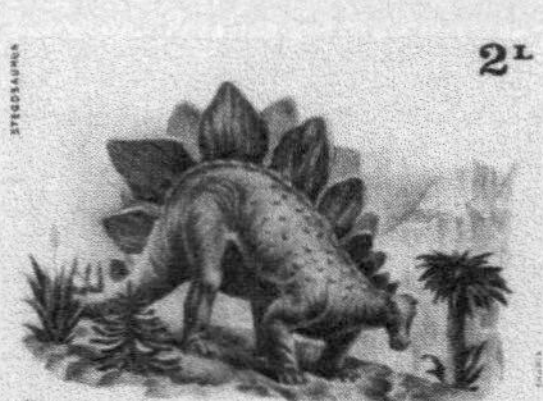

92 Stegosaurus

1972. Prehistoric Animals. Multicoloured.

400	2 l. Type **92**	50	50
401	7 l. Dimetrodon (inscr "Edaphosaurus")	90	40
402	25 l. Diplodocus	1·75	40
403	50 l. Triceratops	2·00	75
404	2 r. Pteranodon	5·00	5·00
405	5 r. Tyrannosaurus	9·00	9·50

93 Cross-country Skiing

1972. Winter Olympic Games, Sapporo, Japan. Multicoloured.

406	3 l. Type **93**	10	30
407	6 l. Bobsleighing	10	30
408	15 l. Speed skating	20	20
409	50 l. Ski jumping	1·00	45
410	1 r. Figure skating (pair)	1·75	70
411	2 r. 50 Ice hockey	5·50	3·25

94 Scout Saluting

95 Cycling

1972. 13th Boy Scout Jamboree, Asagiri, Japan (1971). Multicoloured.

412	10 l. Type **94**	75	20
413	15 l. Scout signalling	95	20
414	50 l. Scout blowing bugle	3·25	1·25
415	1 r. Scout playing drum	4·50	2·25

1972. Olympic Games, Munich. Multicoloured.

416	5 l. Type **95**	50	20
417	10 l. Running	20	20
418	25 l. Wrestling	30	20
419	50 l. Hurdling	50	35
420	2 r. Boxing	1·25	1·75
421	5 r. Volleyball	2·75	3·25

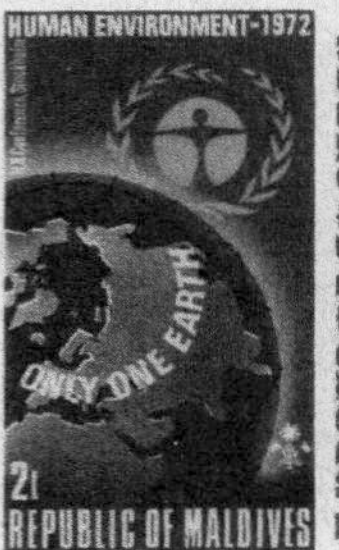

96 Globe and Conference Emblem

97 "Flowers" (Van Gogh)

1972. U.N. Environmental Conservation Conf, Stockholm.

423	**96** 2 l. multicoloured	10	30
424	3 l. multicoloured	10	30
425	15 l. multicoloured	30	15
426	50 l. multicoloured	75	45
427	2 r. 50 multicoloured	3·25	4·00

1973. Floral Paintings. Multicoloured.

428	1 l. Type **97**	10	30
429	2 l. "Flowers in Jug" (Renoir)	10	30
430	3 l. "Chrysanthemums" (Renoir)	10	30
431	50 l. "Mixed Bouquet" (Bosschaert)	1·25	20
432	1 r. As 3 l.	1·75	40
433	5 r. As 2 l.	3·50	5·00

1973. Gold-medal Winners, Munich Olympic Games. Nos. 420/1 optd as listed below.

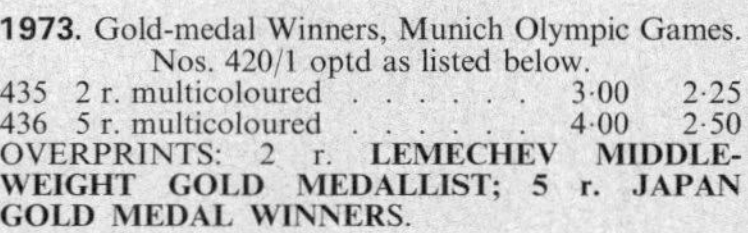

435	2 r. multicoloured	3·00	2·25
436	5 r. multicoloured	4·00	2·50

OVERPRINTS: 2 r. **LEMECHEV MIDDLE-WEIGHT GOLD MEDALLIST**; 5 r. **JAPAN GOLD MEDAL WINNERS**.

99 Animal Care

1973. International Scouting Congress, Nairobi and Addis Ababa. Multicoloured.

438	1 l. Type **99**	10	20
439	2 l. Lifesaving	10	20
440	3 l. Agricultural training	10	20
441	4 l. Carpentry	10	20
442	5 l. Playing leapfrog	10	20
443	1 r. As 2 l.	2·75	75
444	2 r. As 4 l.	4·00	4·75
445	3 r. Type **99**	4·50	7·00

100 Blue Marlin

1973. Fishes. Multicoloured.

447 1 l. Type **100** 10 30
448 2 l. Skipjack tuna 10 30
449 3 l. Blue-finned tuna 10 30
450 5 l. Dolphin (fish) 10 30
451 60 l. Humpbacked snapper . . 80 40
452 75 l. As 60 l. . . . . 1·00 40
453 1 r. 50 Yellow-edged lyretail . . 1·75 1·75
454 2 r. 50 As 5 l. . . . . 2·25 2·75
455 3 r. Spotted coral grouper . . . 2·25 3·00
456 10 r. Spanish mackerel . . . . 4·75 8·00
Nos. 451/2 are smaller, size 29 × 22 mm.

101 Golden-fronted Leafbird

1973. Fauna. Multicoloured.

458 1 l. Type **101** 10 30
459 2 l. Indian flying fox 10 30
460 3 l. Land tortoise 10 30
461 4 l. Butterfly ("Kallima inachus") 30 30
462 50 l. As 3 l. 60 35
463 2 r. Type **101** . . . . 4·00 4·00
464 3 r. As 2 l. . . . . 3·50 4·00

102 "Lantana camara"

1973. Flowers of the Maldive Islands. Mult.

466 1 l. Type **102** 10 20
467 2 l. "Nerium oleander" 10 20
468 3 l. "Rosa polyantha" 10 20
469 4 l. "Hibiscus manihot" 10 20
470 5 l. "Bougainvillea glabra" . . 10 20
471 10 l. "Plumera alba" 10 20
472 50 l. "Poinsettia pulcherrima" . 55 30
473 5 r. "Ononis natrix" . . . . . 3·25 5·00

103 "Tiros" Weather Satellite

1974. Centenary of World Meteorological Organization. Multicoloured.

475 1 l. Type **103** 10 10
476 2 l. "Nimbus" satellite 10 10
477 3 l. "Nomad" (weather ship) . . 10 10
478 4 l. Scanner, A.P.T. Instant Weather Picture equipment . 10 10
479 5 l. Richard's wind-speed recorder 10 10
480 2 r. Type **103** . . . . 3·00 3·50
481 3 r. As 3 l. . . . . 3·25 3·75

104 "Apollo" Spacecraft and Pres. Kennedy

1974. American and Russian Space Exploration Projects. Multicoloured.

483 1 l. Type **104** 10 15
484 2 l. "Mercury" capsule and John Glenn 10 15
485 3 l. "Vostok 1" and Yuri Gagarin 10 20
486 4 l. "Vostok 6" and Valentina Tereshkova 10 20
487 5 l. "Soyuz 11" and "Salyut" space-station 10 20
488 2 r. "Skylab" space laboratory 3·50 3·50
489 3 r. As 2 l. . . . . 4·00 4·00

MINIMUM PRICE

The minimum price quoted is 10p which represents a handling charge rather than a basis for valuing common stamps. For further notes about prices see introductory pages.

105 Copernicus and "Skylab" Space Laboratory
106 "Maternity" (Picasso)

1974. 500th Birth Anniv of Nicholas Copernicus (astronomer). Multicoloured.

491 1 l. Type **105** 10 15
492 2 l. Orbital space-station of the future 10 15
493 3 l. Proposed "Space-shuttle" craft 10 15
494 4 l. "Mariner 2" Venus probe . . 10 20
495 5 l. "Mariner 4" Mars probe . . 10 20
496 25 l. Type **105** 90 20
497 1 r. 50 As 2 l. . . . . 2·50 3·25
498 5 r. As 3 l. . . . . 4·00 10·00

1974. Paintings by Picasso. Multicoloured.

500 1 l. Type **106** 10 10
501 2 l. "Harlequin and Friend" . . 10 10
502 3 l. "Pierrot Sitting" 10 10
503 20 l. "Three Musicians" . . . 25 15
504 75 l. "L'Aficionado" 55 40
505 5 r. "Still Life" . . . . 3·50 4·75

107 U.P.U. Emblem, Steam and Diesel Locomotives

1974. Cent of Universal Postal Union. Mult.

507 1 l. Type **107** 10 10
508 2 l. Paddle-steamer and modern mailboat 10 10
509 3 l. Airship "Graf Zeppelin" and Boeing 747 airliner . . . 10 10
510 1 r. 50 Mailcoach and motor van 85 85
511 2 r. 50 As 2 l. . . . . 1·10 1·60
512 5 r. Type **107** . . . . 1·75 3·00

108 Footballers
109 "Capricorn"

1974. World Cup Football Championships, West Germany.

514 **108** 1 l. multicoloured 15 10
515 – 2 l. multicoloured 15 10
516 – 3 l. multicoloured 15 10
517 – 4 l. multicoloured 15 10
518 – 75 l. multicoloured . . . . 1·25 75
519 – 4 r. multicoloured . . . . 2·50 4·00
520 – 5 r. multicoloured . . . . 2·50 4·00
DESIGNS: Nos. 515/20 show football scenes similar to Type **108**.

1974. Signs of the Zodiac. Multicoloured.

522 1 l. Type **109** 20 30
523 2 l. "Aquarius" 20 30
524 3 l. "Pisces" 20 30
525 4 l. "Aries" 20 30
526 5 l. "Taurus" 20 30
527 6 l. "Gemini" 20 30
528 7 l. "Cancer" 20 30
529 10 l. "Leo" 30 30
530 15 l. "Virgo" 30 30
531 20 l. "Libra" 30 30
532 25 l. "Scorpio" 30 30
533 5 r. "Sagittarius" . . . . . . 6·50 12·00

110 Churchill and Avro Type 683 Lancaster
111 Bullmouth Helmet

1974. Birth Cent of Sir Winston Churchill. Mult.

535 1 l. Type **110** 15 30
536 2 l. Churchill as pilot 15 30
537 3 l. Churchill as First Lord of the Admiralty 20 30
538 4 l. Churchill and H.M.S. "Eagle" (aircraft carrier) . . 20 30
539 5 l. Churchill and De Havilland Mosquito bombers 20 30
540 60 l. Churchill and anti-aircraft battery . . . . 2·75 1·50
541 75 l. Churchill and tank in desert 3·00 1·50
542 5 r. Churchill and Short S.25 Sunderland flying boat . . . 11·00 12·00

1975. Sea Shells and Cowries. Multicoloured.

544 1 l. Type **111** 10 30
545 2 l. Venus comb murex 10 30
546 3 l. Common or major harp . . 10 30
547 4 l. Chiragra spider conch . . . 10 30
548 5 l. Geography cone 10 30
549 60 l. Dawn cowrie (22 × 30 mm) . 3·00 2·00
550 75 l. Purplish clanculus (22 × 30 mm) . . . . 3·50 2·00
551 5 r. Ramose murex . . . . . 8·50 11·00

112 Royal Throne
113 Guavas

1975. Historical Relics and Monuments. Multicoloured.

553 1 l. Type **112** 10 10
554 10 l. Candlesticks 10 10
555 25 l. Lamp-tree 15 10
556 60 l. Royal umbrellas 30 30
557 75 l. Eid-Miskith Mosque (horiz) 35 35
558 3 r. Tomb of Al-Hafiz Abu-al Barakath-al Barubari (horiz) 1·60 2·75

1975. Exotic Fruits. Multicoloured.

559 2 l. Type **113** 10 30
560 4 l. Maldive mulberry 15 30
561 5 l. Mountain apples 15 30
562 10 l. Bananas 20 15
563 20 l. Mangoes 40 25
564 50 l. Papaya . . . . 1·00 60
565 1 r. Pomegranates . . . . . . 1·75 70
566 5 r. Coconut . . . . 5·50 11·00

114 "Phyllangia"

1975. Marine Life. Corals, Urchins and Sea Stars. Multicoloured.

568 1 l. Type **114** 10 10
569 2 l. "Madrepora oculata" . . . 10 10
570 3 l. "Acropora gravida" . . . 10 10
571 4 l. "Stylotella" 10 10
572 5 l. "Acrophora cervicornis" . . 10 10
573 60 l. "Strongylocentrotus purpuratus" 75 65
574 75 l. "Pisaster ochraceus" . . . 85 75
575 5 r. "Marthasterias glacialis" . . 5·00 6·50

115 Clock Tower and Customs Building within "10"

1975. 10th Anniv of Independence. Multicoloured.

577 4 l. Type **115** 10 10
578 5 l. Government offices 10 10
579 7 l. Waterfront 10 10
580 15 l. Mosque and minaret . . . 10 10
581 10 r. Sultan Park and museum 2·25 6·00

1975. "Nordjamb 75" World Scout Jamboree, Norway. Nos. 443/5 optd **14th Boy Scout Jamboree July 29–August 7, 1975**.

582 – 1 r. multicoloured 40 40
583 – 2 r. multicoloured 60 60
584 **99** 3 r. multicoloured . . . . 1·25 1·25

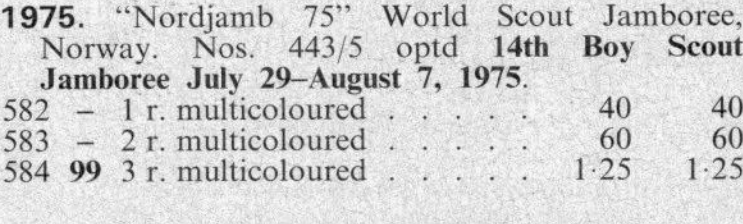

117 Madura Prau

1975. Ships. Multicoloured.

586 1 l. Type **117** 10 10
587 2 l. Ganges patela 10 10
588 3 l. Indian palla (vert) 10 10
589 4 l. Odhi (dhow) (vert) 10 10
590 5 l. Maldivian schooner 10 10
591 25 l. "Cutty Sark" (British tea clipper) 90 40
592 1 r. Maldivian baggala (vert) . 1·50 70
593 5 r. "Maldive Courage" (freighter) . . . . 3·00 6·00

118 "Brahmophthalma wallichi" (moth)

1975. Butterflies and Moth. Multicoloured.

595 1 l. Type **118** 15 30
596 2 l. "Teinopalpus imperialis" . 15 30
597 3 l. "Cethosia biblis" 15 30
598 4 l. "Idea jasonia" 15 30
599 5 l. "Apatura ilia" 15 30
600 25 l. "Kallima horsfieldi" . . . 1·25 35
601 1 r. 50 "Hebomoia leucippe" . 3·50 3·75
602 5 r. "Papilio memnon" . . . . 8·00 10·00

119 "The Dying Captive"
120 Beaker and Vase

1975. 500th Birth Anniv of Michelangelo. Multicoloured.

604 1 l. Type **119** 10 10
605 2 l. Detail of "The Last Judgement" 10 10
606 3 l. "Apollo" 10 10
607 4 l. Detail of Sistine Chapel ceiling 10 10
608 5 l. "Bacchus" 10 10
609 1 r. Detail of "The Last Judgement" (different) . . . 1·25 30
610 2 r. "David" . . . . 1·50 2·00
611 5 r. "Cumaean Sibyl" . . . . . 2·25 5·00

1975. Maldivian Lacquerware. Multicoloured.

613 2 l. Type **120** 10 30
614 4 l. Boxes 10 30
615 50 l. Jar with lid 30 20
616 75 l. Bowls with covers 40 30
617 1 r. Craftsman at work 50 40

121 Map of Maldives

1975. Tourism. Multicoloured.

618 4 l. Type **121** 20 20
619 5 l. Motor launch and small craft 20 20
620 7 l. Sailing-boats 20 20
621 15 l. Underwater fishing . . . 20 20
622 3 r. Hulule Airport . . . . . 2·50 2·50
623 10 r. Motor cruisers . . . . . 4·50 6·50

122 Cross-country Skiing
123 "General Burgoyne" (Reynolds)

1976. Winter Olympic Games, Innsbruck. Multicoloured.

624 1 l. Type **122** 10 10
625 2 l. Speed-skating (pairs) . . . 10 10
626 3 l. Figure-skating (pairs) . . . 10 10
627 4 l. Four-man bobsleighing . . . 10 10
628 5 l. Ski-jumping 10 10
629 25 l. Figure-skating (women's) . 35 10
630 1 r. 15 Skiing (slalom) . . . . 90 1·25
631 4 r. Ice-hockey . . . . 1·50 4·00

1976. Bicent of American Revolution. Mult.

633 1 l. Type **123** 10 10
634 2 l. "John Hancock" (Copley) . 10 10
635 3 l. "Death of Gen. Montgomery" (Trumbull) (horiz) 10 10

636 4 l. "Paul Revere" (Copley) 10 10
637 5 l. "Battle of Bunker Hill" (Trumbull) (horiz) 10 10
638 2 r. "The Crossing of the Delaware" (Sully) (horiz) 2·00 2·50
639 3 r. "Samuel Adams" (Copley) 2·50 3·00
640 5 r. "Surrender of Cornwallis" (Trumbull) (horiz) 3·00 3·25

124 Thomas Edison

1976. Centenary of Telephone. Multicoloured.
642 1 l. Type **124** 10 20
643 2 l. Alexander Graham Bell 10 20
644 3 l. Telephone of 1919, 1937 and 1972 10 20
645 10 l. Cable entrance into station 20 20
646 20 l. Equaliser circuit assembly 30 20
647 1 r. "Salernum" (cable ship) 1·75 55
648 10 r. "Intelsat IV-A" and Earth Station 4·75 7·50

1976. "Interphil 76" International Stamp Exhibition, Philadelphia. Nos. 638/40 optd **MAY 29TH-JUNE 6TH "INTERPHIL" 1976.**
650 2 r. multicoloured 1·50 1·75
651 3 r. multicoloured 2·00 2·25
652 5 r. multicoloured 2·50 2·75

126 Wrestling

127 "Dolichos lablab"

1976. Olympic Games, Montreal. Multicoloured.
654 1 l. Type **126** 10 10
655 2 l. Putting the shot 10 10
656 3 l. Hurdling 10 10
657 4 l. Hockey 10 10
658 5 l. Running 10 10
659 6 l. Javelin-throwing 10 10
660 1 r. 50 Discus-throwing 1·25 1·75
661 5 r. Volleyball 2·75 5·25

1976. Vegetables. Multicoloured.
663 2 l. Type **127** 10 20
664 4 l. "Moringa pterygosperma" 10 20
665 10 l. "Solanum melongena" 10 10
666 20 l. "Moringa pterygosperma" 1·25 1·50
667 50 l. "Cucumis sativus" 50 65
668 75 l. "Trichosanthes anguina" 55 75
669 1 r. "Momordica charantia" 65 85
670 2 r. "Trichosanthes anguina" 2·75 6·00

128 "Viking" approaching Mars

1977. "Viking" Space Mission.
671 **128** 5 r. multicoloured 2·25 2·75

129 Coronation Ceremony

1977. Silver Jubilee of Queen Elizabeth II. Multicoloured.
673 1 l. Type **129** 10 10
674 2 l. Queen and Prince Philip 10 10
675 3 l. Royal couple with Princes Andrew and Edward 10 10
676 1 r. 15 Queen with Archbishops 35 35
677 3 r. State coach in procession 60 55
678 4 r. Royal couple with Prince Charles and Princess Anne 60 90

130 Beethoven and Organ

1977. 150th Death Anniv of Ludwig van Beethoven. Multicoloured.
680 1 l. Type **130** 15 20
681 2 l. Portrait and manuscript of "Moonlight Sonata" 15 20
682 3 l. With Goethe at Teplitz 15 20
683 4 l. Beethoven and string instruments 15 20
684 5 l. Beethoven's home, Heiligenstadt 15 20
685 25 l. Hands and gold medals 85 20
686 2 r. Portrait and "Missa solemnis" 2·75 3·00
687 5 r. Composer's hearing-aids 4·75 5·00

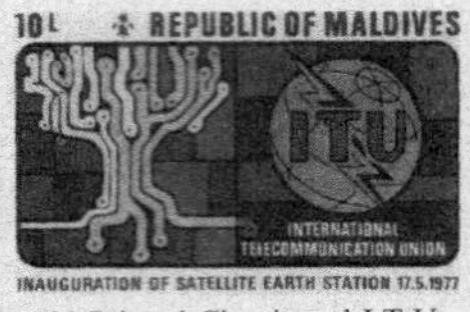

131 Printed Circuit and I.T.U. Emblem

1977. Inauguration of Satellite Earth Station. Multicoloured.
689 10 l. Type **131** 10 10
690 90 l. Central Telegraph Office 45 45
691 10 r. Satellite Earth Station 3·00 6·00

132 "Miss Anne Ford" (Gainsborough)

133 Lesser Frigate Birds

1977. Artists' Birth Anniversaries. Multicoloured.
693 1 l. Type **132** (250th anniv) 10 10
694 2 l. Group painting by Rubens (400th anniv) 10 10
695 3 l. "Girl with Dog" (Titian) (500th Anniv) 10 10
696 4 l. "Mrs. Thomas Graham" (Gainsborough) 10 10
697 5 l. "Artist with Isabella Brant" (Rubens) 10 10
698 95 l. Portrait by Titian 75 40
699 1 r. Portrait by Gainsborough 75 40
700 10 r. "Isabella Brant" (Rubens) 3·75 7·00

1977. Birds. Multicoloured.
702 1 l. Type **133** 20 30
703 2 l. Crab plover 20 30
704 3 l. White-tailed tropic bird 20 30
705 4 l. Wedge-tailed shearwater 20 30
706 5 l. Grey heron 20 30
707 20 l. White tern 90 30
708 95 l. Cattle egret 2·25 1·60
709 1 r. 25 Black-naped tern 2·50 2·50
710 5 r. Pheasant coucal 6·50 8·00

134 Charles Lindbergh

136 Rheumatic Heart

135 Boat Building

1977. 50th Anniv of Lindbergh's Transatlantic Flight and 75th Anniv of First Navigable Airships. Multicoloured.
712 1 l. Type **134** 10 10
713 2 l. Lindbergh and "Spirit of St. Louis" 10 10
714 3 l. Lindbergh's Miles Mohawk aircraft (horiz) 10 10
715 4 l. Lebaudy-Juillot airship "Morning Post" (horiz) 10 10
716 5 l. Airship "Graf Zeppelin" and portrait of Zeppelin 10 10
717 1 r. Airship "Los Angeles" (horiz) 60 30
718 3 r. Lindbergh and Henry Ford 1·40 1·75
719 10 r. Vickers airship R-23 rigid airship 2·50 5·50

No. 715 is inscr "Lebaudy I built by H. Juillot 1902".

1977. Occupations. Multicoloured.
721 6 l. Type **135** 35 20
722 15 l. Fishing 55 20
723 20 l. Cadjan weaving 65 20
724 90 l. Mat-weaving 2·00 1·40
725 2 r. Lace-making (vert) 3·50 4·00

1977. World Rheumatism Year. Multicoloured.
726 1 l. Type **136** 10 30
727 50 l. Rheumatic shoulder 40 20
728 2 r. Rheumatic hands 75 1·25
729 3 r. Rheumatic knees 85 1·40

137 Lilienthal's Biplane Glider

1978. 75th Anniv of First Powered Aircraft. Multicoloured.
730 1 l. Type **137** 20 30
731 2 l. Chanute's glider 20 30
732 3 l. Wright glider No. II, 1901 20 30
733 4 l. A. V. Roe's Triplane I 20 30
734 5 l. Wilbur Wright demonstrating Wright Type A for King Alfonso of Spain 20 30
735 10 l. A. V. Roe's Avro Type D biplane 50 30
736 20 l. Wright Brothers and A. G. Bell at Washington 1·25 30
737 95 l. Hadley's triplane 3·00 2·25
738 5 r. Royal Aircraft Factory B.E.2A biplanes at Upavon, 1914 8·50 10·00

No. 732 is wrongly dated "1900".

138 Newgate Prison

139 Television Set

1978. World Eradication of Smallpox. Mult.
740 15 l. Foundling Hospital, London (horiz) 50 30
741 50 l. Type **138** 1·25 60
742 2 r. Edward Jenner (discoverer of smallpox vaccine) 2·25 4·00

1978. Inaug of Television in Maldive Islands. Mult.
743 15 l. Type **139** 40 30
744 25 l. Television aerials 55 30
745 1 r. 50 Control desk (horiz) 2·25 2·75

140 Mas Odi

1978. Ships. Multicoloured.
746 1 l. Type **140** 10 15
747 2 l. Battela 10 15
748 3 l. Bandu odi (vert) 10 15
749 5 l. "Maldive Trader" (freighter) 20 20
750 1 r. "Fath-hul Baaree" (brigantine) 65 30
751 1 r. 25 Mas dhoni 85 1·00
752 3 r. Baggala (vert) 1·10 1·75
753 4 r. As 1 r. 25 1·10 1·75

141 Ampulla

142 Capt. Cook

1978. 25th Anniv of Coronation. Multicoloured.
755 1 l. Type **141** 10 10
756 2 l. Sceptre with Dove 10 10
757 3 l. Golden Orb 10 10
758 1 r. 15 St. Edward's Crown 15 15
759 2 r. Sceptre with Cross 20 25
760 5 r. Queen Elizabeth II 55 70

1978. 250th Birth Anniv of Capt. James Cook and Bicent of Discovery of Hawaiian Islands. Mult.
762 1 l. Type **142** 10 15
763 2 l. Statue of Kamehameha I of Hawaii 10 15
764 3 l. H.M.S. "Endeavour" 10 15
765 25 l. Route of third voyage 45 45
766 75 l. H.M.S. "Discovery" H.M.S. "Resolution" and map of Hawaiian Islands (horiz) 1·25 1·25
767 1 r. 50 Cook meeting Hawaiian islanders (horiz) 2·00 2·25
768 10 r. Death of Capt. Cook (horiz) 5·00 10·00

143 "Schizophrys aspera"

1978. Crustaceans. Multicoloured.
770 1 l. Type **143** 10 10
771 2 l. "Atergatis floridus" 10 10
772 3 l. "Perenon planissimum" 10 10
773 90 l. "Portunus granulatus" 50 40
774 1 r. "Carpilius maculatus" 50 40
775 2 r. "Huenia proteus" 1·00 1·40
776 25 r. "Etisus laevimanus" 7·00 13·00

144 "Four Apostles"

145 T.V. Tower and Building

1978. 450th Death Anniv of Albrecht Durer (artist).
778 **144** 10 l. multicoloured 10 10
779 – 20 l. multicoloured 15 10
780 – 55 l. multicoloured 20 20
781 – 1 r. black, brown and buff 30 30
782 – 1 r. 80 multicoloured 45 60
783 – 3 r. multicoloured 70 1·25

DESIGNS—VERT: 20 l. "Self-portrait at 27"; 55 l. "Madonna and Child with a Pear"; 1 r. 80, "Hare"; 3 r. "Great Piece of Turf". HORIZ: 1 r. "Rhinoceros".

1978. 10th Anniv of Republic. Multicoloured.
785 1 l. Fishing boat 10 10
786 5 l. Montessori School 10 10
787 10 l. Type **145** 10 10
788 25 l. Islet 15 15
789 50 l. Boeing 737 aircraft 40 15
790 95 l. Beach scene 40 30
791 1 r. 25 Dhow at night 65 55
792 3 r. President's residence 75 1·25
793 5 r. Masjidh Afeefuddin Mosque 90 2·50

The 1, 5, 25 to 95 l., 1 r. 25 and 3, 5 r. are horiz designs.

146 Human Rights Emblem

1978. 30th Anniv of Declaration of Human Rights.
795 **146** 30 l. pink, lilac and green 15 15
796 90 l. yellow, brown and green 40 60
797 1 r. 80 blue, deep blue and green 70 1·00

147 Great Spotted or Rare Spotted Cowrie

148 Delivery by Bellman

1979. Shells. Multicoloured.
798 1 l. Type **147** 10 10
799 2 l. Imperial cone 10 10
800 3 l. Great green turban 10 10
801 10 l. Giant spider conch 45 10
802 1 r. White-toothed cowrie 2·00 40
803 1 r. 80 Fig cone 3·00 2·50
804 3 r. Glory of the sea cone 4·50 3·75

1979. Death Cent of Sir Rowland Hill. Mult.
806 1 l. Type **148** 10 10
807 2 l. Mail coach, 1840 (horiz) 10 10
808 3 l. First London letter box, 1855 10 10
809 1 r. 55 Penny Black 30 50
810 5 r. First Maldive Islands stamp 70 1·25

149 Girl with Teddy Bear

151 Sari with Overdress

150 "White Feathers"

1979. Int Year of the Child (1st issue). Mult.
812 5 l. Type **149** 10 10
813 1 r. 25 Boy with sailing boat 40 50
814 2 r. Boy with toy rocket 45 55
815 3 r. Boy with toy airship 60 75
See also Nos. 838/46.

1979. 25th Death Anniv of Henri Matisse (artist). Multicoloured.
817 20 l. Type **150** 15 15
818 25 l. "Joy of Life" 15 15
819 30 l. "Eggplants" 15 15
820 1 r. 50 "Harmony in Red" 45 65
821 5 r. "Still-life" 70 2·25

1979. National Costumes. Multicoloured.
823 50 l. Type **151** 15 15
824 75 l. Sashed apron dress 20 20
825 90 l. Serape 25 25
826 95 l. Ankle-length printed dress 30 30

152 "Gloriosa superba"

1979. Flowers. Multicoloured.
827 1 l. Type **152** 10 10
828 3 l. "Hibiscus tiliaceus" 10 10
829 50 l. "Barringtonia asiatica" 20 15
830 1 r. "Abutilon indicum" 40 25
831 5 r. "Guettarda speciosa" 1·00 2·00

153 Weaving

1979. Handicraft Exhibition. Multicoloured.
833 5 l. Type **153** 10 10
834 10 l. Lacquerwork 10 10
835 1 r. 30 Tortoiseshell jewellery 35 45
836 2 r. Carved woodwork 50 80

154 Mickey Mouse attacked by Bird

1979. International Year of the Child (2nd issue). Disney Characters. Multicoloured.
838 1 l. Goofy delivering parcel on motor-scooter (vert) 10 10
839 2 l. Type **154** 10 10
840 3 l. Goofy half-covered with letters 10 10
841 4 l. Pluto licking Minnie Mouse's envelopes 10 10
842 5 l. Mickey Mouse delivering letters on roller skates (vert) 10 10
843 10 l. Donald Duck placing letter in mail-box 10 10
844 15 l. Chip and Dale carrying letter 10 10
845 1 r. 50 Donald Duck on monocycle (vert) 75 95
846 5 r. Donald Duck with ostrich in crate (vert) 2·25 3·25

155 Post-Ramadan Dancing

1980. National Day. Multicoloured.
848 5 l. Type **155** 10 10
849 15 l. Musicians and dancer, Eeduu Festival 10 10
850 95 l. Sultan's ceremonial band 30 30
851 2 r. Dancer and drummers Circumcision Festival 55 85

156 Leatherback Turtle

1980. Turtle Conservation Campaign. Mult.
853 1 l. Type **156** 10 20
854 2 l. Flatback turtle 10 20
855 5 l. Hawksbill turtle 15 20
856 10 l. Loggerhead turtle 20 20
857 75 l. Olive ridley turtle 80 45
858 10 r. Atlantic ridley turtle 3·00 4·25

157 Paul Harris (founder)

1980. 75th Anniv of Rotary Int. Mult.
860 75 l. Type **157** 35 10
861 90 l. Humanity 40 20
862 1 r. Hunger 40 25
863 10 r. Health 2·50 4·50

1980. "London 1980" International Stamp Exhibition. Nos. 809/10 optd **LONDON 1980**.
865 1 r. 55 Penny Black 1·75 1·00
866 5 r. First Maldives stamp 3·25 2·75

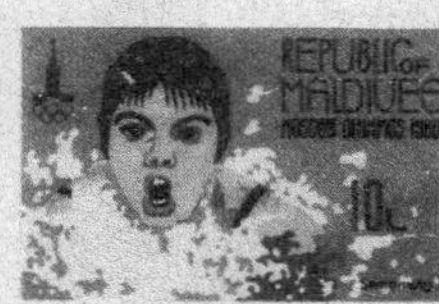

159 Swimming

1980. Olympic Games, Moscow. Multicoloured.
868 10 l. Type **159** 10 10
869 50 l. Running 20 20
870 3 r. Putting the shot 70 1·10
871 4 r. High jumping 80 1·40

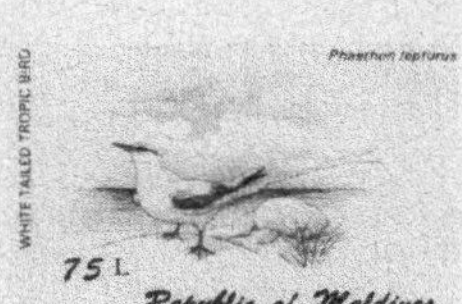

160 White-tailed Tropic Bird

1980. Birds. Multicoloured.
873 75 l. Type **160** 25 15
874 95 l. Sooty tern 35 30
875 1 r. Common noddy 35 30
876 1 r. 55 Curlew 50 70
877 2 r. Wilson's petrel 60 85
878 4 r. Caspian tern 1·10 1·60

161 Seal of Ibrahim II

1980. Seals of the Sultans.
880 **161** 1 l. brown and black 10 10
881 – 2 l. brown and black 10 10
882 – 5 l. brown and black 10 10
883 – 1 r. brown and black 30 30
884 – 2 r. brown and black 50 70
DESIGNS: 2 l. Mohammed Imadudeen II; 5 l. Bin Haji Ali; 1 r. Kuda Mohammed Rasgefaanu; 2 r. Ibrahim Iskander I.

162 Queen Elizabeth the Queen Mother

1980. 80th Birthday of the Queen Mother.
886 **162** 4 r. multicoloured 1·00 1·25

163 Munnaru

1980. 1400th Anniv of Hegira. Multicoloured.
888 5 l. Type **163** 15 10
889 10 l. Hukuru Miskiiy mosque 15 10
890 30 l. Medhuziyaaraiy (shrine of saint) 20 30
891 55 l. Writing tablets with verses of Koran 25 35
892 90 l. Mother teaching child Koran 45 70

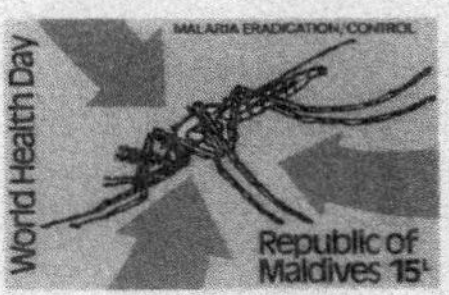

164 Malaria Eradication

1980. World Health Day. Multicoloured.
894 15 l. Type **164** 10 10
895 25 l. Nutrition 10 10
896 1 r. 50 Dental health 1·25 1·00
897 5 r. Clinics 2·50 2·75

165 White Rabbit

1980. Walt Disney's "Alice in Wonderland". Multicoloured.
899 1 l. Type **165** 10 10
900 2 l. Alice falling into Wonderland 10 10
901 3 l. Alice too big to go through door 10 10
902 4 l. Alice with Tweedledum and Tweedledee 10 10
903 5 l. Alice and caterpillar 10 10
904 10 l. The Cheshire cat 10 10
905 15 l. Alice painting the roses 10 10
906 2 r. 50 Alice and the Queen of Hearts 2·50 2·25
907 4 r. Alice on trial 2·75 2·50

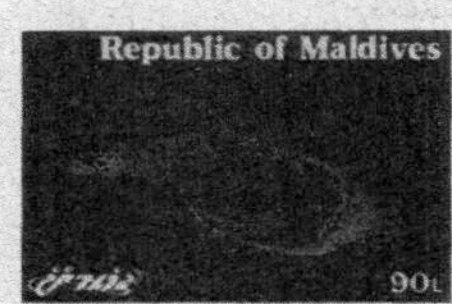

166 Indian Ocean Ridley Turtle

1980. Marine Animals. Multicoloured.
909 90 l. Type **166** 2·00 60
910 1 r. 25 Pennant coralfish 2·50 1·25
911 2 r. Spiny lobster 3·25 1·75

167 Pendant Lamp

168 Prince Charles and Lady Diana Spencer

1981. National Day. Multicoloured.
913 10 l. Tomb of Ghaazee Muhammad Thakurufaan (horiz) 10 10
914 20 l. Type **167** 15 10
915 30 l. Chair used by Muhammad Thakurufaan 20 10
916 95 l. Muhammad Thakurufaan's palace (horiz) 45 30
917 10 r. Cushioned divan 2·25 4·00

1981. British Royal Wedding. Multicoloured.
918 1 r. Type **168** 15 15
919 2 r. Buckingham Palace 25 25
920 5 r. Prince Charle, polo player 40 50

169 First Majlis Chamber

1981. 50th Anniv of Citizens' Majlis (grievance rights). Multicoloured.
922 95 l. Type **169** 30 30
923 1 r. Sultan Muhammed Shamsuddin III 35 35

170 "Self-portrait with a Palette"

171 Airmail Envelope

1981. Birth Centenary of Pablo Picasso. Mult.
925 5 l. Type **170** 15 10
926 10 l. "Woman in Blue" 20 10
927 25 l. "Boy with Pipe" 35 10
928 30 l. "Card Player" 35 10
929 90 l. "Sailor" 65 40
930 3 r. "Self-portrait" 1·25 1·25
931 5 r. "Harlequin" 1·75 1·75

1981. 75th Anniv of Postal Service.
933 **171** 25 l. multicoloured 10 10
934 75 l. multicoloured 20 25
935 5 r. multicoloured 70 1·25

172 Boeing 737 taking off

1981. Male International Airport. Multicoloured.
936 5 l. Type **172** 20 20
937 20 l. Passengers leaving Boeing 737 40 20
938 1 r. 80 Refuelling 75 1·00
939 4 r. Plan of airport 1·00 2·00

173 Homer

174 Preparation of Maldive Fish

1981. International Year of Disabled People. Multicoloured.
941 2 l. Type **173** 10 10
942 5 l. Miguel Cervantes 10 10
943 1 r. Beethoven 2·00 85
944 5 r. Van Gogh 3·00 5·00

1981. Decade for Women. Multicoloured.
946 20 l. Type **174** 10 10
947 90 l. 16th-century Maldive women 25 25
948 1 r. Farming 30 30
949 2 r. Coir rope-making 55 1·10

MINIMUM PRICE

The minimum price quoted is 10p which represents a handling charge rather than a basis for valuing common stamps. For further notes about prices see introductory pages.

175 Collecting Bait

1982. Fishermen's Day. Multicoloured.

950 5 l. Type **175** . . . 35 15
951 15 l. Fishing boats . . . 65 25
952 90 l. Fisherman with catch . . 1·25 60
953 1 r. 30 Sorting fish . . . 1·75 1·10

176 Bread Fruit

1981. World Food Day. Multicoloured.

955 10 l. Type **176** . . . 25 10
956 25 l. Hen with chicks . . . 60 15
957 30 l. Maize . . . 60 20
958 75 l. Skipjack tuna . . . 1·75 65
959 1 r. Pumpkin . . . 2·00 70
960 2 r. Coconuts . . . 2·25 2·75

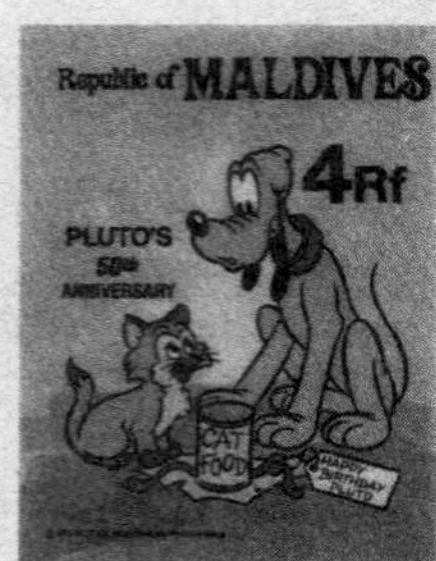

177 Pluto and Cat

1982. 50th Anniv of Pluto (Walt Disney Cartoon Character).

962 **177** 4 r. multicoloured . . . 3·00 2·75

1982. 21st Birthday of Princess of Wales. As T **278** of Grenada. Multicoloured.

964 95 l. Balmoral . . . 20 20
965 3 r. Prince and Princess of Wales 60 65
966 5 r. Princess on aircraft steps . 1·00 95

179 Scout saluting and Camp-site

1983. 75th Anniv of Boy Scout Movement. Multicoloured.

968 1 r. 30 Type **179** . . . 40 45
969 1 r. 80 Lighting a fire . . . 50 60
970 4 r. Life-saving . . . 1·10 1·40
971 5 r. Map-reading . . . 1·40 1·75

180 Footballer

1982. World Cup Football Championship, Spain.

973 **180** 90 l. multicoloured . . . 1·25 60
974 – 1 r. 50 multicoloured . . 1·75 1·10
975 – 3 r. multicoloured . . . 2·50 1·75
976 – 5 r. multicoloured . . . 3·25 2·50

DESIGNS: 1 r. 50 to 5 r. Various footballers.

1982. Birth of Prince William of Wales. Nos. 964/6 optd **ROYAL BABY 21.6.82.**

978 95 l. Type **178** . . . 15 20
979 3 r. Prince and Princess of Wales 45 65
980 5 r. Princess on aircraft steps . 70 95

181 Basic Education Scheme

1983. National Education. Multicoloured.

982 90 l. Type **181** . . . 15 25
983 95 l. Primary education . . . 15 25
984 1 r. 30 Teacher training . . . 20 30
985 2 r. 50 Printing educational material . . . 40 60

182 Koch isolates the Bacillus

183 Blohm and Voss Seaplane "Nordsee"

1983. Centenary of Robert Koch's Discovery of Tubercle Bacillus. Multicoloured.

987 5 l. Type **182** . . . 10 15
988 15 l. Micro-organism and microscope . . . 15 15
989 95 l. Dr. Robert Koch in 1905 35 45
990 3 r. Dr. Koch and plates from publication . . . 85 1·50

1983. Bicentenary of Manned Flight. Mult.

992 90 l. Type **183** . . . 2·25 70
993 1 r. 45 Macchi Castoldi MC.72 seaplane . . . 2·75 1·75
994 4 r. Boeing F4B-3 biplane fighter 4·50 3·25
995 5 r. Renard and Krebs airship "La France" . . . 4·50 3·50

184 "Curved Dash" Oldsmobile, 1902

1983. Classic Motor Cars. Multicoloured.

997 5 l. Type **184** . . . 20 40
998 30 l. Aston Martin "Tourer", 1932 . . . 60 40
999 40 l. Lamborghini "Muira", 1966 . . . 60 45
1000 1 r. Mercedes-Benz "300SL", 1945 . . . 1·00 70
1001 1 r. 40 Stutz "Bearcat", 1913 1·25 2·00
1002 5 r. Lotus "Elite", 1958 . . 2·00 4·25

185 Rough-toothed Dolphin

1983. Marine Mammals. Multicoloured.

1004 30 l. Type **185** . . . 1·60 60
1005 40 l. Indo-Pacific hump-backed dolphin . . . 1·60 65
1006 4 r. Finless porpoise . . . 5·00 4·00
1007 6 r. Pygmy sperm whale . . 10·00 7·00

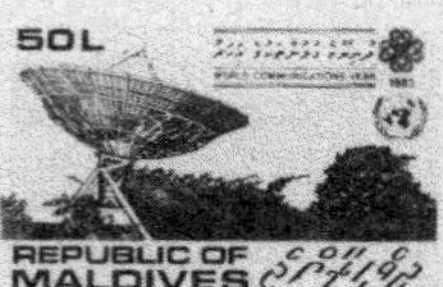

186 Dish Aerial

1983. World Communications Year. Multicoloured.

1009 50 l. Type **186** . . . 40 20
1010 1 r. Land, sea and air communications . . . 1·00 60
1011 2 r. Ship-to-shore communications . . . 1·40 1·50
1012 10 r. Air traffic controller . . 3·75 6·50

187 "La Donna Gravida"

1983. 500th Birth Anniv of Raphael. Mult.

1014 90 l. Type **187** . . . 25 25
1015 3 r. "Giovanna d'Aragona" (detail) . . . 75 1·25
1016 4 r. "Woman with Unicorn" . 75 1·75
1017 6 r. "La Muta" . . . 1·00 2·25

188 Refugee Camp

1983. Solidarity with the Palestinian People. Multicoloured.

1019 4 r. Type **188** . . . 1·50 2·00
1020 5 r. Refugee holding dead child 1·60 2·00
1021 6 r. Child carrying food . . 1·90 2·50

189 Education Facilities

1983. National Development Programme. Multicoloured.

1022 7 l. Type **189** . . . 20 10
1023 10 l. Health service and education . . . 30 10
1024 5 r. Growing more food . . 1·50 1·25
1025 6 r. Fisheries development . . 2·00 1·50

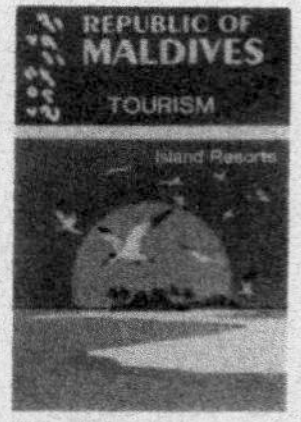

190 Baseball

194 Island Resort and Common Terns

193 Hands breaking Manacles

1984. Olympic Games, Los Angeles. Multicoloured.

1027 50 l. Type **190** . . . 25 15
1028 1 r. 55 Backstroke swimming . 55 40
1029 3 r. Judo . . . 1·25 90
1030 4 r. Shot-putting . . . 1·40 1·40

1984. U.P.U. Congress, Hamburg. Nos. 994/5 optd **19th UPU CONGRESS HAMBURG**.

1032 4 r. Boeing "F4B-3" . . . 1·40 1·40
1033 5 r. "La France" airship . . 1·60 1·60

1984. Surch **RF1.45**. (a) Nos. 964/6.

1035 1 r. 45 on 95 l. Type **178** . . 2·00 1·50
1036 1 r. 45 on 3 r. Prince and Princess of Wales . . . 2·00 1·50
1037 1 r. 45 on 5 r. Princess on aircraft steps . . . 2·00 1·50

(b) Nos. 978/80.

1039 1 r. 45 on 95 l. Type **178** . . 2·00 1·50
1040 1 r. 45 on 3 r. Prince and Princess of Wales . . . 2·00 1·50
1041 1 r. 45 on 5 r. Princess on aircraft steps . . . 2·00 1·50

1984. Namibia Day. Multicoloured.

1043 6 r. Type **193** . . . 1·10 1·25
1044 8 r. Namibian family . . . 1·40 1·75

1984. Tourism. Multicoloured.

1046 7 l. Type **194** . . . 30 10
1047 15 l. Dhow . . . 30 10
1048 20 l. Snorkelling . . . 30 10
1049 2 r. Wind-surfing . . . 75 40
1050 4 r. Aqualung diving . . . 1·25 75
1051 6 r. Night fishing . . . 2·00 1·25
1052 8 r. Game fishing . . . 2·25 1·50
1053 10 r. Turtle on beach . . . 2·50 1·75

195 Frangipani

1984. "Ausipex" International Stamp Exhibition, Melbourne. Multicoloured.

1054 5 r. Type **195** . . . 2·25 1·75
1055 10 r. Cooktown orchid . . . 4·75 3·75

196 Facade of Male Mosque

1984. Opening of Islamic Centre. Multicoloured.

1057 2 r. Type **196** . . . 45 50
1058 5 r. Male Mosque and minaret (vert) . . . 1·10 1·25

197 Air Maldives Boeing 737

1984. 40th Anniv of I.C.A.O. Multicoloured.

1059 7 l. Type **197** . . . 40 15
1060 4 r. Air Lanka Lockheed L-1011 Tristar . . . 2·25 1·25
1061 6 r. Alitalia Douglas DC-10-30 . . . 2·75 1·60
1062 8 r. L.T.U. Lockheed L-1011 Tristar . . . 3·00 2·25

198 Daisy Duck

1984. 50th Birthday of Donald Duck. Walt Disney Cartoon Characters. Multicoloured.

1064 3 l. Type **198** . . . 10 10
1065 4 l. Huey, Dewey and Louie . 10 10
1066 5 l. Ludwig von Drake . . . 10 10
1067 10 l. Gyro Gearloose . . . 10 10
1068 15 l. Uncle Scrooge painting self-portrait . . . 15 10
1069 25 l. Donald Duck with camera 15 10
1070 5 r. Donald Duck and Gus Goose . . . 2·25 1·25
1071 8 r. Gladstone Gander . . . 2·50 2·00
1072 10 r. Grandma Duck . . . 3·00 2·50

199 "The Day" (detail)

200 "Edmond Iduranty" (Degas)

1984. 450th Death Anniv of Correggio (artist). Mult.

1075 5 r. Type **199** . . . 1·00 1·50
1076 10 r. "The Night" (detail) . . 1·50 1·75

1984. 150th Birth Anniv of Edgar Degas (artist). Multicoloured.

1078 75 l. Type **200** . . . 20 20
1079 2 r. "James Tissot" . . . 50 50
1080 5 r. "Achille de Gas in Uniform" . . . 1·00 1·00
1081 10 r. "Lady with Chrysanthemums" . . . 1·75 2·00

201 Pale-footed Shearwater

204 Queen Elizabeth the Queen Mother, 1981

202 Squad Drilling

1985. Birth Bicentenary of John J. Audubon (ornithologist) (1st issue). Designs showing original paintings. Multicoloured.

1083 3 r. Type **201** . . . . 1·75 80
1084 3 r. 50 Little grebe (horiz) . . 2·00 90
1085 4 r. Common cormorant . . . 2·00 1·00
1086 4 r. 50 White-faced storm petrel (horiz) . . . . 2·00 1·10

See also Nos. 1192/9.

1985. National Security Service. Multicoloured.

1088 15 l. Type **202** 40 10
1089 20 l. Combat patrol 40 10
1090 1 r. Fire fighting . . . . . . 1·75 40
1091 2 r. Coastguard cutter . . . . 2·25 1·00
1092 10 r. Independence Day Parade (vert) . . . . 3·00 3·50

1985. Olympic Games Gold Medal Winners, Los Angeles. Nos. 1027/30 optd.

1094 50 l. Type **190** (optd **JAPAN**) 20 10
1095 1 r. 55 Backstroke swimming (optd **GOLD MEDALIST THERESA ANDREWS USA**) 40 40
1096 3 r. Judo (optd **GOLD MEDALIST FRANK WIENEKE USA**) 85 75
1097 4 r. Shot-putting (optd **GOLD MEDALIST CLAUDIA LOCH WEST GERMANY**) 1·00 95

1985. Life and Times of Queen Elizabeth the Queen Mother. Multicoloured.

1099 3 r. Type **204** 45 60
1100 5 r. Visiting the Middlesex Hospital (horiz) . . . . . 65 1·00
1101 7 r. The Queen Mother . . . 85 1·25

Stamps as Nos. 1099/1101 but with face values of 1 r., 4 r. and 10 r. exist from additional sheetlets with changed background colours.

1985. 300th Birth Anniversary of Johann Sebastian Bach (composer). As T **309a** of Grenada. Mult.

1103 15 l. Lira da braccio 10 10
1104 2 r. Tenor oboe 50 45
1105 4 r. Serpent 90 85
1106 10 r. Table organ . . . . . . 1·90 2·25

205 Mas Odi (fishing boat)

1985. Maldives Ships and Boats. Multicoloured.

1108 5 l. Type **205** 10 10
1109 5 l. Battela (dhow) 10 10
1110 10 l. Addu odi (dhow) 10 10
1111 2 r. 60 Modern dhoni (fishing boat) . . . . 1·25 1·50
1112 2 r. 70 Mas dhoni (fishing boat) 1·25 1·50
1113 3 r. Baththeli dhoni . . . . . 1·40 1·60
1114 5 r. "Inter I" (inter-island vessel) . . . . 2·25 2·75
1115 10 r. Dhoni-style yacht . . . 4·00 6·00

206 Windsurfing

207 United Nations Building, New York

1985. 10th Anniv of World Tourism Organization. Multicoloured.

1116 6 r. Type **206** . . . . 1·75 1·75
1117 8 r. Scuba diving . . . . . . 2·00 2·00

1985. 40th Anniv of U.N.O. and International Peace Year. Multicoloured.

1119 15 l. Type **207** 10 10
1120 2 r. Hands releasing peace dove 40 45
1121 4 r. U.N. Security Council meeting (horiz) 70 85
1122 10 r. Lion and lamb . . . . . 1·25 2·00

208 Maldivian Delegate voting in U.N. General Assembly

1985. 20th Anniv of United Nations Membership. Multicoloured.

1124 20 l. Type **208** 10 10
1125 15 r. U.N. and Maldivian flags, and U.N. Building, New York . . . . 2·00 3·00

209 Youths playing Drums

1985. International Youth Year. Multicoloured.

1126 90 l. Type **209** 15 20
1127 6 r. Tug-of-war . . . . 80 1·10
1128 10 r. Community service (vert) 1·25 2·00

210 Quotation and Flags of Member Nations

1985. 1st Summit Meeting of South Asian Association for Regional Co-operation, Dhaka, Bangladesh.

1130 **210** 3 r. multicoloured . . . . 1·50 1·25

211 Mackerel Frigate

1985. Fishermen's Day. Species of Tuna. Multicoloured.

1131 25 l. Type **211** 35 10
1132 75 l. Kawakawa ("Little tuna") 65 15
1133 3 r. Dog-toothed tuna . . . . 2·00 75
1134 5 r. Yellow-finned tuna . . . 2·50 1·25

1985. 150th Birth Anniv of Mark Twain. Designs as T **145a** of Gambia, showing Walt Disney cartoon characters illustrating various Mark Twain quotations. Multicoloured.

1136 2 l. Winnie the Pooh (vert) . . 10 10
1137 3 l. Gepetto and Figaro the cat (vert) 10 10
1138 4 l. Goofy and basket of broken eggs (vert) 10 10
1139 20 l. Goofy as doctor scolding Donald Duck (vert) 25 10
1140 4 r. Mowgli and King Louis (vert) . . . . 1·40 1·75
1141 13 r. The wicked Queen and mirror (vert) . . . . 5·00 7·00

1985. Birth Bicentenaries of Grimm Brothers (folklorists). Designs as T **145b** of Gambia, showing Walt Disney cartoon characters in scenes from "Dr. Knowall". Multicoloured.

1143 1 l. Donald Duck as Crabb driving oxcart (horiz) . . . 10 10
1144 5 l. Donald Duck as Dr. Knowall (horiz) 10 10
1145 10 l. Dr. Knowall in surgery (horiz) 10 10
1146 15 l. Dr. Knowall with Uncle Scrooge as a lord (horiz) . . . 10 10
1147 3 r. Dr. and Mrs. Knowall in pony and trap (horiz) . . . 1·10 1·50
1148 15 r. Dr. Knowall and thief (horiz) . . . . 5·50 7·00

1986. Appearance of Halley's Comet (1st issue). As T **151a** of Gambia. Multicoloured.

1150 20 l. N.A.S.A. space telescope and Comet 50 25
1151 1 r. 50 E.S.A. "Giotto" spacecraft and Comet . . . 1·25 1·50
1152 2 r. Japanese "Planet A" spacecraft and Comet . . . 1·50 1·75
1153 4 r. Edmond Halley and Stonehenge . . . . 2·25 2·75
1154 5 r. Russian "Vega" spacecraft and Comet . . . . 2·25 2·75

See also Nos. 1206/10.

1986. Centenary of Statue of Liberty. Multicoloured. As T **153a** of Gambia, showing the Statue of Liberty and immigrants to the U.S.A.

1156 50 l. Walter Gropius (architect) 40 30
1157 70 l. John Lennon (musician) 1·50 1·00
1158 1 r. George Balanchine (choreographer) . . . . . 1·50 1·00
1159 10 r. Franz Werfel (writer) . . 3·75 6·50

1986. "Ameripex" International Stamp Exhibition, Chicago. As T **315a** of Grenada, showing Walt Disney cartoon characters and U.S.A. stamps. Multicoloured.

1161 3 l. Johnny Appleseed and 1966 Johnny Appleseed stamp . . 10 10
1162 4 l. Paul Bunyan and 1958 Forest Conservation stamp . 10 10
1163 5 l. Casey and 1969 Professional Baseball Centenary stamp . 10 10
1164 10 l. Ichabod Crane and 1974 "Legend of Sleepy Hollow" stamp 10 10
1165 15 l. John Henry and 1944 75th Anniv of completion of First Transcontinental Railroad stamp 15 15
1166 20 l. Windwagon Smith and 1954 Kansas Territory Centenary stamp 15 15
1167 13 r. Mike Fink and 1970 Great Northwest stamp . . . . . 6·50 6·50
1168 14 r. Casey Jones and 1950 Railroad Engineers stamp . 7·50 7·50

1986. 60th Birthday of Queen Elizabeth II. As T **151b** of Gambia.

1170 1 r. black and yellow 30 25
1171 2 r. multicoloured 40 55
1172 12 r. multicoloured . . . . . 1·50 2·50

DESIGNS: 1 r. Royal Family at Girl Guides Rally, 1938; 2 r. Queen in Canada; 12 r. At Sandringham, 1970.

212 Player running with Ball

1986. World Cup Football Championship, Mexico. Multicoloured.

1174 15 l. Type **212** 75 30
1175 2 r. Player gaining control of ball . . . . 2·50 1·75
1176 4 r. Two players competing for ball . . . . 4·00 3·50
1177 10 r. Player bouncing ball on knee . . . . 7·50 8·00

1986. Royal Wedding. As T **153b** of Gambia. Multicoloured.

1179 10 l. Prince Andrew and Miss Sarah Ferguson 15 10
1180 2 r. Prince Andrew 75 70
1181 12 r. Prince Andrew in naval uniform . . . . 3·25 3·75

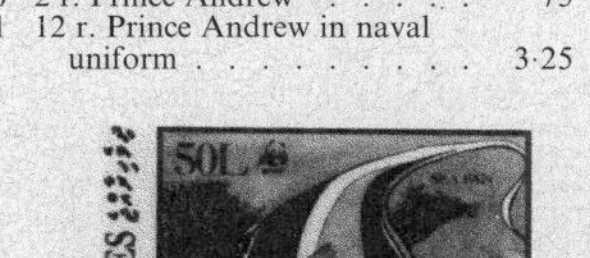

213 Moorish Idol and Sea Fan

1986. Marine Wildlife. Multicoloured.

1183 50 l. Type **213** . . . . 1·25 40
1184 90 l. Regal angelfish . . . . . 1·75 55
1185 1 r. Maldive anemonefish . . 1·75 55
1186 2 r. Tiger cowrie and stinging coral . . . . 2·25 1·60
1187 3 r. Emperor angelfish and staghorn coral . . . . . . 2·50 2·00
1188 4 r. Black-naped tern . . . . 2·50 2·75
1189 5 r. Fiddler crab and staghorn coral . . . . 2·50 2·75
1190 10 r. Hawksbill turtle . . . . 3·00 5·00

1986. Birth Bicentenary (1985) of John J. Audubon (ornithologist) (2nd issue). As T **201** showing original paintings. Multicoloured.

1192 3 l. Little blue heron (horiz) . 30 40
1193 4 l. White-tailed kite 30 40
1194 5 l. Greater shearwater (horiz) 30 40
1195 10 l. Magnificent frigate bird . 40 40
1196 15 l. Black-necked grebe . . . 70 40
1197 20 l. Goosander 70 40
1198 13 r. Peregrine falcon (horiz) . 5·50 6·50
1199 14 r. Prairie chicken (horiz) . . 5·50 6·50

1986. World Cup Football Championship Winners, Mexico. Nos. 1174/7 optd **WINNERS Argentina 3 W. Germany 2**.

1201 15 l. Type **212** 40 30
1202 2 r. Player gaining control of ball . . . . 1·25 1·10
1203 4 r. Two players competing for ball . . . . 2·00 2·00
1204 10 r. Player bouncing ball on knee . . . . 3·25 4·25

1986. Appearance of Halley's Comet (2nd issue). Nos. 1150/4 optd as T **447a** of Ghana.

1206 20 l. N.A.S.A. space telescope and Comet 65 40
1207 1 r. 50 E.S.A. "Giotto" spacecraft and Comet . . . 1·25 1·00
1208 2 r. Japanese "Planet A" spacecraft and Comet . . . 1·50 1·50
1209 4 r. Edmond Halley and Stonehenge . . . . 2·00 2·25
1210 5 r. Russia "Vega" spacecraft and Comet . . . . 2·00 2·25

214 Servicing Aircraft

216 Ixora

215 "Hypholoma fasciculare"

1986. 40th Anniv of U.N.E.S.C.O. Multicoloured.

1212 1 r. Type **214** 60 30
1213 2 r. Boat building 70 90
1214 3 r. Children in classroom . . 80 1·25
1215 5 r. Student in laboratory . . 90 2·00

1986. Fungi of the Maldives. Multicoloured.

1217 15 l. Type **215** 80 25
1218 50 l. "Kuehneromyces mutabilis" (vert) . . . . . 1·50 45
1219 1 r. "Amanita muscaria" (vert) 1·75 60
1220 2 r. "Agaricus campestris" . . 2·50 1·50
1221 3 r. "Amanita pantherina" (vert) 2·50 1·75
1222 4 r. "Coprinus comatus" (vert) 2·50 2·25
1223 5 r. "Gymnopilus junonius" ("Pholiota spectabilis") . . 2·50 2·75
1224 10 r. "Pluteus cervinus" . . . 3·75 4·50

1987. Flowers. Multicoloured.

1226 10 l. Type **216** 10 10
1227 20 l. Frangipani 10 10
1228 50 l. Crinum 90 50
1229 2 r. Pink rose 40 80
1230 4 r. Flamboyant flower . . . 60 1·50
1231 10 r. Ground orchid . . . . . 4·00 6·00

218 "Thespesia populnea"

219 "Precis octavia"

217 Guides studying Wild Flowers

1987. 75th Anniv (1985) of Girl Guide Movement. Multicoloured.

1233 15 l. Type **217** 20 20
1234 2 r. Guides with pet rabbits . . 55 80
1235 4 r. Guide observing white spoonbill . . . . 1·75 2·00
1236 12 r. Lady Baden-Powell and Guide flag . . . . 2·00 4·50

1987. Trees and Plants. Multicoloured.

1238 50 l. Type **218** 10 10
1239 1 r. "Cocos nucifera" 15 20
1240 2 r. "Calophyllum mophyllum" 30 40
1241 3 r. "Xanthosoma indica" (horiz) 45 60
1242 5 r. "Ipomoea batatas" (horiz) 80 1·10
1243 7 r. "Artocarpus altilis" . . . 1·10 1·75

No. 1241 is inscr "Xanthosomaindica" in error.

1987. America's Cup Yachting Championship. As T **321b** of Grenada. Multicoloured.

1245 15 l. "Intrepid", 1970 . . . . 10 10
1246 1 r. "France II", 1974 . . . . 20 20
1247 2 r. "Gretel", 1962 . . . . . 40 60
1248 12 r. "Volunteer", 1887 . . . 2·00 3·00

1987. Butterflies. Multicoloured.

1250 15 l. Type **219** 45 30
1251 20 l. "Atrophaneura hector" . . 45 30
1252 50 l. "Teinopalpus imperialis" 75 40
1253 1 r. "Kallima horsfieldi" . . . 1·00 45

1254 2 r. "Cethosia biblis" . . . . 1·60 1·25
1255 4 r. "Idea jasonia" . . . . 2·50 2·25
1256 7 r. "Papilio memnon" . . . 3·50 4·00
1257 10 r. "Aeropetes tulbaghia" . . 4·00 5·00

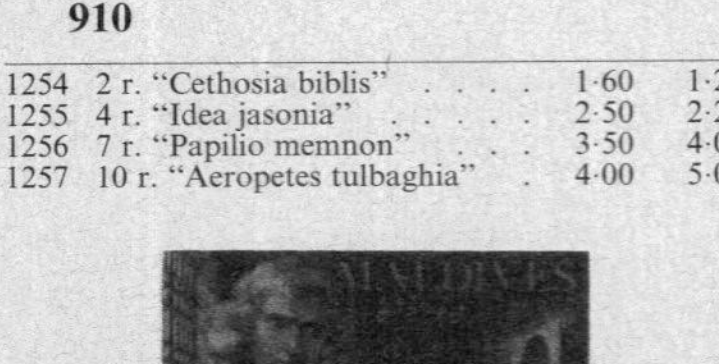

220 Isaac Newton experimenting with Spectrum

1988. Great Scientific Discoveries. Multicoloured.
1259 1 r. 50 Type **220** . . . . . . 1·25 1·00
1260 3 r. Euclid composing "Principles of Geometry" (vert) . . . . 1·60 1·75
1261 4 r. Mendel formulating theory of Genetic Evolution (vert) 1·75 2·00
1262 5 r. Galileo and moons of Jupiter . . . . 3·00 3·00

221 Donald Duck and Weather Satellite

1988. Space Exploration. Walt Disney cartoon characters. Multicoloured.
1264 3 l. Type **221** 10 10
1265 4 l. Minnie Mouse and navigation satellite 10 10
1266 5 l. Mickey Mouse's nephews talking via communication satellite 10 10
1267 10 l. Goofy in lunar rover (vert) 10 10
1268 20 l. Minnie Mouse delivering pizza to flying saucer (vert) 10 10
1269 13 r. Mickey Mouse directing spacecraft docking (vert) . . 5·00 5·00
1270 14 r. Mickey Mouse and "Voyager 2" . . . . 5·00 5·00

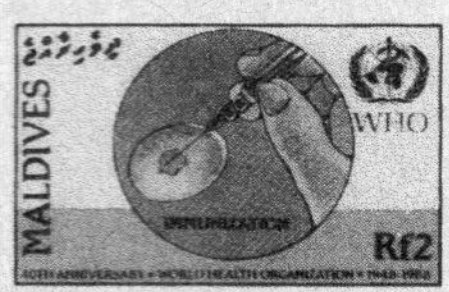

222 Syringe and Bacterium ("Immunization")

1988. 40th Anniv of W.H.O. Multicoloured.
1272 2 r. Type **222** 35 40
1273 4 r. Tap ("Clean Water") . . 60 85

223 Water Droplet and Atoll

1988. World Environment Day (1987). Mult.
1274 15 l. Type **223** 10 10
1275 75 l. Coral reef 20 30
1276 2 r. Audubon's shearwaters in flight . . . . 75 1·25

224 Globe, Carrier Pigeon and Letter
226 Discus-throwing

1988. Transport and Telecommunications Decade. Each showing central globe. Multicoloured.
1278 2 r. Type **224** 60 65
1279 3 r. Dish aerial and girl using telephone . . . . 1·00 1·10
1280 5 r. Satellite, television, telephone and antenna tower 1·75 2·00
1281 10 r. Car, ship and Lockheed Tristar airliner . . . . . . 5·00 5·50

1988. Royal Ruby Wedding. Nos. 1170/2 optd **40TH WEDDING ANNIVERSARY H.M. QUEEN ELIZABETH II H.R.H. THE DUKE OF EDINBURGH.**
1282 1 r. black and yellow 35 25
1283 2 r. multicoloured 50 60
1284 12 r. multicoloured . . . . . 2·50 3·50

1988. Olympic Games, Seoul. Multicoloured.
1286 15 l. Type **226** 10 10
1287 2 r. 100 metres race 40 40
1288 4 r. Gymnastics (horiz) . . . 70 80
1289 12 r. Three-day equestrian event (horiz) . . . . 2·25 3·25

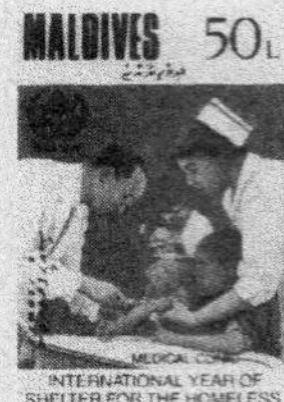

227 Immunization at Clinic
230 Pres. Kennedy and Launch of "Apollo" Spacecraft

228 Breadfruit

1988. Int Year of Shelter for the Homeless. Mult.
1291 50 l. Type **227** 30 30
1292 3 r. Prefab housing estate . . 1·10 1·40

1988. 10th Anniv of International Fund for Agricultural Development. Multicoloured.
1294 7 r. Type **228** . . . . 1·00 1·40
1295 10 r. Mangoes (vert) . . . . 1·50 1·90

1988. World Aids Day. Nos. 1272/3 optd **WORLD AIDS DAY** and emblem.
1297 2 r. Type **222** 35 45
1298 4 r. "Tap" ("Clean Water") . 65 80

1989. 25th Death Anniv (1988) of John F. Kennedy (American statesman). U.S. Space Achievements. Multicoloured.
1299 5 r. Type **230** . . . . 1·75 1·90
1300 5 r. Lunar module and astronaut on Moon . . . . 1·75 1·90
1301 5 r. Astronaut and buggy on Moon . . . . 1·75 1·90
1302 5 r. President Kennedy and spacecraft . . . . 1·75 1·90

1989. Olympic Medal Winners, Seoul. Nos. 1286/9 optd.
1304 15 l. Type **226** (optd **J. SCHULT DDR**) 20 20
1305 2 r. 100 metres race (optd **C. LEWIS USA**) 65 65
1306 4 r. Gymnastics (horiz) (optd **MEN'S ALL AROUND V. ARTEMOV USSR**) . . . . 1·25 1·25
1307 12 r. Three-day equestrian event (horiz) (optd **TEAM SHOW JUMPING W. GERMANY**) 3·00 3·50

1989. 500th Birth Anniv of Titian (artist). As T **166a** of Gambia, showing paintings. Multicoloured.
1309 15 l. "Benedetto Varchi" . . . 10 10
1310 1 r. "Portrait of a Young Man" 20 15
1311 2 r. "King Francis I of France" 40 40
1312 5 r. "Pietro Aretino" . . . . 1·10 1·25
1313 15 r. "The Bravo" . . . . . 4·00 5·00
1314 20 r. "The Concert" (detail) . 4·00 5·50

1989. 10th Anniversary of Asia–Pacific Telecommunity. Nos. 1279/80 optd **ASIA-PACIFIC TELECOMMUNITY 10 YEARS** and emblem. Multicoloured.
1316 3 r. Dish aerial and girl using telephone . . . . 1·25 1·50
1317 5 r. Satellite, television, telephone and antenna tower 1·75 2·00

1989. Japanese Art. Paintings by Hokusai. As T **177a** of Gambia. Multicoloured.
1318 15 l. "Fuji from Hodogaya" (horiz) 10 10
1319 50 l. "Fuji from Lake Kawaguchi" (horiz) 15 15
1320 1 r. "Fuji from Owari" (horiz) . 25 15
1321 2 r. "Fuji from Tsukudajima in Edo" (horiz) 50 40
1322 4 r. "Fuji from a Teahouse at Yoshida" (horiz) 80 90
1323 6 r. "Fuji from Tagonoura" (horiz) . . . . 90 1·25
1324 10 r. "Fuji from Mishima-goe" (horiz) . . . . 2·25 2·75
1325 12 r. "Fuji from the Sumida River in Edo" (horiz) . . . 2·25 2·75

233 Clown Triggerfish

1989. Tropical Fishes. Multicoloured.
1327 20 l. Type **233** 25 20
1328 50 l. Blue-striped snapper . . 35 25
1329 1 r. Powder-blue surgeonfish . 45 30
1330 2 r. Oriental sweetlips 75 65
1331 3 r. Six-barred wrasse . . . . 1·00 85
1332 8 r. Thread-finned butterflyfish . . . . 2·00 2·50
1333 10 r. Bicoloured parrotfish . . 2·40 2·75
1334 12 r. Scarlet-finned squirrelfish . . . . 2·40 2·75

234 Goofy, Mickey and Minnie Mouse with Takuri "Type 3", 1907

1989. "World Stamp Expo '89" International Stamp Exhibition, Washington (1st issue). Designs showing Walt Disney cartoon characters with Japanese cars. Multicoloured.
1336 15 l. Type **234** 20 15
1337 50 l. Donald and Daisy Duck in Mitsubishi "Model A", 1917 40 30
1338 1 r. Goofy in Datsun "Roadstar", 1935 . . . . . 70 50
1339 2 r. Donald and Daisy Duck with Mazda, 1940 . . . . 1·00 75
1340 4 r. Donald Duck with Nissan "Bluebird 310", 1959 . . . 1·50 1·25
1341 6 r. Donald and Daisy Duck with Subaru "360", 1958 . . 1·75 1·75
1342 10 r. Mickey Mouse and Pluto in Honda "5800", 1966 . . . 3·25 3·75
1343 12 r. Mickey Mouse and Goofy in Daihatsu "Fellow", 1966 3·75 4·25

235 Lunar Module "Eagle"

1989. 20th Anniv of First Manned Landing on Moon. Multicoloured.
1346 1 r. Type **235** 30 20
1347 2 r. Astronaut Aldrin collecting dust samples 50 60
1348 6 r. Aldrin setting up seismometer . . . . 1·25 1·75
1349 10 r. Pres. Nixon congratulating "Apollo 11" astronauts . . 1·90 2·50

236 Jawaharlal Nehru with Mahatma Gandhi

1989. Anniversaries and Events. Multicoloured.
1351 20 l. Type **236** (birth cent) . . 90 45
1352 50 l. Opium poppies and logo (anti-drugs campaign) (vert) 90 45
1353 1 r. William Shakespeare (425th birth anniv) 90 45
1354 2 r. Storming the Bastille (bicent of French Revolution) (vert) 90 90
1355 3 r. Concorde (20th anniv of first flight) . . . . 2·50 1·75
1356 8 r. George Washington (bicent of inauguration) . . . . . 2·00 2·50
1357 10 r. William Bligh (bicent of mutiny on the "Bounty") . 4·00 4·00
1358 12 r. Hamburg harbour (800th anniv) (vert) . . . . 3·50 4·00

237 Sir William van Horne (Chairman of Canadian Pacific), Locomotive and Map, 1894
239 "Louis XVI in Coronation Robes" (Duplesis)

238 Bodu Thakurufaanu Memorial Centre, Utheemu

1989. Railway Pioneers. Multicoloured.
1360 10 l. Type **237** 15 15
1361 25 l. Matthew Murray (engineer) with Blenkinsop and Murray's rack locomotive, 1810 . . . . 20 20
1362 50 l. Louis Favre (railway engineer) and steam locomotive entering tunnel . 25 25
1363 2 r. George Stephenson (engineer) and "Locomotion", 1825 . . . 55 55
1364 6 r. Richard Trevithick and "Catch-Me-Who-Can", 1808 . . . . 1·50 1·50
1365 8 r. George Nagelmackers and "Orient Express" dining car . 1·75 1·75
1366 10 r. William Jessop and horse-drawn wagon, Surrey Iron Railway, 1770 . . . . . . 2·50 2·50
1367 12 r. Isambard Brunel (engineer) and GWR steam locomotive, 1833 . . . . 3·00 3·00

1990. 25th Anniv of Independence. Multicoloured.
1369 20 l. Type **238** 10 10
1370 25 l. Islamic Centre, Male . . 10 10
1371 50 l. National flag and logos of international organizations . 10 10
1372 2 r. Presidential Palace, Male . 30 40
1373 5 r. National Security Service 85 1·25

1990. Bicentenary of French Revolution and "Philexfrance '89" International Stamp Exhibition, Paris. French Paintings. Multicoloured.
1375 15 l. Type **239** 15 15
1376 50 l. "Monsieur Lavoisier and his Wife" (David) 25 25
1377 1 r. "Madame Pastoret" (David) 35 35
1378 2 r. "Oath of Lafayette, 14 July 1790" (anon) 55 70
1379 4 r. "Madame Trudaine" (David) . . . . 1·00 1·50
1380 6 r. "Chenard celebrating the Liberation of Savoy" (Boilly) 1·40 1·90
1381 10 r. "An Officer swears Allegiance to the Constitution" (anon) . . . 2·75 3·50
1382 12 r. "Self Portrait" (David) . 3·00 3·50

1990. "Stamp World London '90" International Stamp Exhibition. As T **193** of Gambia, showing Walt Disney cartoon characters playing British sports. Multicoloured.
1384 15 l. Donald Duck, Mickey Mouse and Goofy playing rugby 30 15
1385 50 l. Donald Duck and Chip-n-Dale curling 35 25
1386 1 r. Goofy playing polo . . . 55 40
1387 2 r. Mickey Mouse and nephews playing soccer 80 70
1388 4 r. Mickey Mouse playing cricket . . . . 1·50 1·50
1389 6 r. Minnie and Mickey Mouse at Ascot races . . . . . . 1·90 1·90
1390 10 r. Mickey Mouse and Goofy playing tennis . . . . . . 3·25 3·50
1391 12 r. Donald Duck and Mickey Mouse playing bowls . . . 3·25 3·50

240 Silhouettes of Queen Elizabeth II and Queen Victoria

1990. 150th Anniv of the Penny Black.
1393 **240** 8 r. black and green . . . 2·25 2·50
1394 – 12 r. black and blue . . . 2·75 3·00
DESIGN: 12 r. As Type **240**, but with position of silhouettes reversed.

1990. 90th Birthday of Queen Elizabeth the Queen Mother. As T **103** of Grenada Grenadines.
1396 6 r. black, mauve and blue . . 80 1·10
1397 6 r. black, mauve and blue . . 80 1·10
1398 6 r. black, mauve and blue . . 80 1·10
DESIGNS: No. 1396, Lady Elizabeth Bowes-Lyon; 1397, Lady Elizabeth Bowes-Lyon wearing headband; 1398, Lady Elizabeth Bowes-Lyon leaving for her wedding.

241 Sultan's Tomb

1990. Islamic Heritage Year. Each black and blue.
1400 1 r. Type **241** 25 35
1401 1 r. Thakurufaan's Palace 25 35
1402 1 r. Male Mosque 25 35
1403 2 r. Veranda of Friday Mosque 25 35
1404 2 r. Interior of Friday Mosque 25 35
1405 2 r. Friday Mosque and Monument 25 35

1990. 50th Anniv of Second World War. As T **101** of Grenada Grenadines. Multicoloured.
1406 15 l. Defence of Wake Island, 1941 15 15
1407 25 l. Stilwell's army in Burma, 1944 20 20
1408 50 l. Normandy offensive, 1944 25 25
1409 1 r. Capture of Saipan, 1944 40 40
1410 2 r. 50 D-Day landings, 1944 70 70
1411 3 r. 50 Allied landings in Norway, 1940 90 90
1412 4 r. Lord Mountbatten, Head of Combined Operations, 1943 1·10 1·10
1413 6 r. Japanese surrender, Tokyo Bay, 1945 1·50 1·50
1414 10 r. Potsdam Conference, 1945 2·50 2·50
1415 12 r. Allied invasion of Sicily, 1943 2·75 2·75

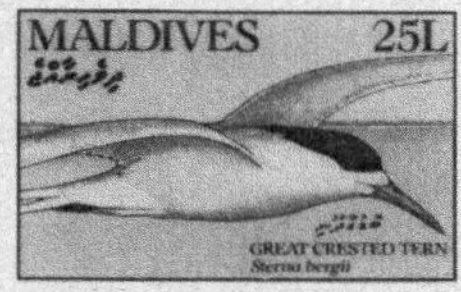

243 Crested Tern

1990. Birds. Multicoloured.
1417 25 l. Type **243** 15 15
1418 50 l. Koel 25 25
1419 1 r. White tern 35 35
1420 3 r. 50 Cinnamon bittern 90 1·00
1421 6 r. Sooty tern 1·40 1·60
1422 8 r. Audubon's shearwater 1·60 2·00
1423 12 r. Common noddy 2·50 3·00
1424 15 r. Lesser frigate bird 2·75 3·25

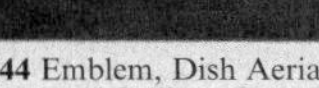
244 Emblem, Dish Aerial and Sailboards

245 "Spathoglottis plicata"

1990. 5th South Asian Association for Regional Co-operation Summit.
1426 **244** 75 l. black and orange 20 25
1427 – 3 r. 50 multicoloured 90 1·25
DESIGN: 3 r. 50, Flags of member nations.

1990. "EXPO '90" International Garden and Greenery Exhibition, Osaka. Flowers. Multicoloured.
1429 20 l. Type **245** 50 30
1430 75 l. "Hippeastrum puniceum" 70 40
1431 2 r. "Tecoma stans" (horiz) 1·00 90
1432 3 r. 50 "Catharanthus roseus" (horiz) 1·25 1·50
1433 10 r. "Ixora coccinea" (horiz) 2·50 2·75
1434 12 r. "Clitorea ternatea" (horiz) 2·75 3·00
1435 15 r. "Caesalpinia pulcherrima" 2·75 3·00

1990. International Literacy Year. As T **198d** of Gambia, showing Walt Disney cartoon characters illustrating fables by Aesop. Multicoloured.
1437 15 l. "The Hare and the Tortoise" 30 15
1438 50 l. "The Town Mouse and the Country Mouse" 50 25
1439 1 r. "The Fox and the Crow" 80 35
1440 3 r. 50 "The Travellers and the Bear" 1·60 1·60
1441 4 r. "The Fox and the Lion" 1·75 1·75
1442 6 r. "The Mice Meeting" 2·25 2·25
1443 10 r. "The Fox and the Goat" 2·75 3·00
1444 12 r. "The Dog in the Manger" 2·75 3·25

247 East African Railways Class 31 Steam Locomotive

248 Ruud Gullit of Holland

1990. Railway Steam Locomotives. Multicoloured.
1446 20 l. Type **247** 55 30
1447 50 l. Steam locomotive, Sudan 75 45
1448 1 r. Class GM Garratt, South Africa 1·00 60
1449 3 r. 7th Class, Rhodesia 2·00 2·00
1450 5 r. Central Pacific Class No. 229, U.S.A. 2·25 2·25
1451 8 r. Reading Railroad No. 415, U.S.A. 2·50 2·75
1452 10 r. Porter narrow gauge, Canada 2·50 2·75
1453 12 r. Great Northern Railway No. 515, U.S.A. 2·50 3·00

1990. World Cup Football Championship, Italy. Multicoloured.
1455 1 r. Type **248** 75 50
1456 2 r. 50 Paul Gascoigne of England 1·25 1·25
1457 3 r. 50 Brazilian challenging Argentine player 1·60 1·60
1458 5 r. Brazilian taking control of ball 2·00 2·00
1459 7 r. Italian and Austrian jumping for header 2·50 2·50
1460 10 r. Russian being chased by Turkish player 2·75 3·00
1461 15 r. Andres Brehme of West Germany 3·00 3·25

249 Winged Euonymus

251 Greek Messenger from Marathon, 490 BC (2480th Anniv)

250 "Summer" (Rubens)

1991. Bonsai Trees and Shrubs. Multicoloured.
1463 20 l. Type **249** 30 20
1464 50 l. Japanese black pine 45 35
1465 1 r. Japanese five needle pine 70 55
1466 3 r. 50 Flowering quince 1·60 1·60
1467 5 r. Chinese elm 2·00 2·00
1468 8 r. Japanese persimmon 2·25 2·50
1469 10 r. Japanese wisteria 2·25 2·50
1470 12 r. Satsuki azalea 2·50 2·75

1991. 350th Death Anniv of Rubens. Mult.
1472 20 l. Type **250** 20 15
1473 50 l. "Landscape with Rainbow" (detail) 35 25
1474 1 r. "Wreck of Aeneas" 55 40
1475 2 r. 50 "Chateau de Steen" (detail) 1·00 1·00
1476 3 r. 50 "Landscape with Herd of Cows" 1·25 1·25
1477 7 r. "Ruins on the Palantine" 2·00 2·50
1478 10 r. "Landscape with Peasants and Cows" 2·25 2·50
1479 12 r. "Wagon fording Stream" 2·50 2·75

1991. Anniversaries and Events (1990). Mult.
1481 50 l. Type **251** 45 25
1482 1 r. Anthony Fokker in Haarlem Spin monoplane (birth centenary) 80 45
1483 3 r. 50 "Early Bird" satellite (25th anniv) 1·50 1·50
1484 7 r. Signing Reunification of Germany agreement (horiz) 1·75 2·50
1485 8 r. King John signing Magna Carta (775th anniv) 2·25 2·50
1486 10 r. Dwight D. Eisenhower (birth centenary) 2·25 2·50
1487 12 r. Sir Winston Churchill (25th death anniv) 3·25 3·50
1488 15 r. Pres. Reagan at Berlin Wall (German reunification) (horiz) 2·75 3·50

252 Arctic Iceberg and Maldives Dhoni

1991. Global Warming. Multicoloured.
1490 3 r. 50 Type **252** 1·25 1·25
1491 7 r. Antarctic iceberg and "Maldive Trader" (freighter) 2·75 2·75

253 S.A.A.R.C. Emblem and Medal

1991. Year of the Girl Child.
1492 **253** 7 r. multicoloured 1·75 1·75

254 Children on Beach

1991. Year of the Maldivian Child. Children's Paintings. Multicoloured.
1493 3 r. 50 Type **254** 1·50 1·25
1494 5 r. Children in a park 2·00 1·75
1495 10 r. Hungry child dreaming of food 3·00 3·50
1496 25 r. Scuba diver 5·50 8·00

1991. Death Centenary (1990) of Vincent van Gogh (artist). As T **200b** of Gambia. Multicoloured.
1497 15 l. "Still Life: Japanese Vase with Roses and Anemones" (vert) 30 20
1498 20 l. "Still Life: Red Poppies and Daisies" (vert) 30 20
1499 2 r. "Vincent's Bedroom in Arles" 90 80
1500 3 r. 50 "The Mulberry Tree" 1·25 1·00
1501 7 r. "Blossoming Chestnut Branches" 2·00 2·25
1502 10 r. "Peasant Couple going to Work" 2·50 2·75
1503 12 r. "Still Life: Pink Roses" 2·75 3·00
1504 15 r. "Child with Orange" (vert) 3·00 3·25

1991. 65th Birthday of Queen Elizabeth II. As T **198a** of Gambia. Multicoloured.
1506 2 r. Queen at Trooping the Colour, 1990 75 60
1507 5 r. Queen with Queen Mother and Princess Margaret, 1973 1·50 1·50
1508 8 r. Queen and Prince Philip in open carriage, 1986 2·25 2·50
1509 12 r. Queen at Royal Estates Ball 2·75 3·25

1991. 10th Wedding Anniv of Prince and Princess of Wales. As T **198b** of Gambia. Multicoloured.
1511 1 r. Prince and Princess skiing, 1986 45 20
1512 3 r. 50 Separate photographs of Prince, Princess and sons 1·25 90
1513 7 r. Prince Henry in Christmas play and Prince William watching polo 1·50 1·75
1514 15 r. Princess Diana at Ipswich, 1990, and Prince Charles playing polo 3·00 3·00

257 Class C57 Steam Locomotive

1991. Hummel Figurines. As T **200a** of Gambia. Multicoloured.
1516 10 l. Boy painting 15 10
1517 25 l. Boy reading at table 20 15
1518 50 l. Boy with school satchel 30 30
1519 2 r. Girl with basket 70 60
1520 3 r. 50 Boy reading 1·00 1·00
1521 8 r. Girl and young child reading 2·00 2·25
1522 10 r. School girls 2·00 2·50
1523 25 r. School boys 4·25 5·50

1991. "Phila Nippon '91" Int Stamp Exn, Tokyo. Japanese Steam Locomotives. Mult.
1525 15 l. Type **257** 25 15
1526 25 l. Class 6250 locomotive, 1915 (horiz) 35 25
1527 1 r. Class D51 locomotive, 1936 60 40
1528 3 r. 50 Class 8620 locomotive, 1914 (horiz) 1·25 1·10
1529 5 r. Class 10 locomotive, 1889 (horiz) 1·50 1·50
1530 7 r. Class C61 locomotive, 1947 1·75 2·25
1531 10 r. Class 9600 locomotive, 1913 (horiz) 2·00 2·50
1532 12 r. Class D52 locomotive, 1943 (horiz) 2·40 3·00

258 "Salamis temora" and "Vanda caerulea"

1991. Butterflies and Flowers. Multicoloured.
1534 10 l. Type **258** 40 40
1535 25 l. "Meneris tulbaghia" and "Incarvillea younghusbandii" 55 30
1536 50 l. "Polyommatus icarus" and "Campsis grandiflora" 75 40
1537 2 r. "Danaus plexippus" and "Thunbergia grandiflora" 1·25 90
1538 3 r. 50 "Colias interior" and "Medinilla magnifica" 1·75 1·75
1539 5 r. "Ascalapha ordorata" and "Meconopsis horridula" 2·00 2·00
1540 8 r. "Papilio memnon" and "Dillenia obovata" 2·50 3·00
1541 10 r. "Precis octavia" and "Thespesia populnea" 2·50 3·00

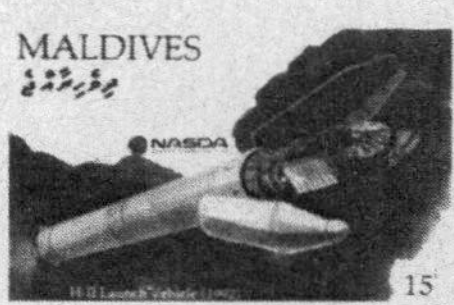
259 "H-II" Rocket

1991. Japanese Space Programme. Multicoloured.
1543 15 l. Type **259** 40 20
1544 20 l. Projected "H-II" orbiting plane 40 20
1545 2 r. Satellite "GMS-5" 1·00 75
1546 3 r. 50 Satellite "MOMO-1" 1·40 1·40
1547 7 r. Satellite "CS-3" 2·25 2·50
1548 10 r. Satellite "BS-2a, 2b" 2·50 2·75
1549 12 r. "H-I" Rocket (vert) 2·75 3·00
1550 15 r. Space Flier unit and U.S. Space shuttle 2·75 3·00

260 Williams "FW-07"

1991. Formula 1 Racing Cars. Multicoloured.
1552 20 l. Type **260** 30 20
1553 50 l. Brabham/BMW "BT50" turbo 40 30
1554 1 r. Williams/Honda "FW-11" 60 45
1555 3 r. 50 Ferrari "312 T3" 1·25 1·25
1556 5 r. Lotus/Honda "99T" 1·75 1·75
1557 7 r. Benetton/Ford "B188" 2·00 2·25
1558 10 r. Tyrrell "P34" six-wheeler 2·25 2·50
1559 21 r. Renault "RE-30B" turbo 4·00 5·00

261 "Testa Rossa", 1957

1991. Ferrari Cars. Multicoloured.
1561 5 r. Type **261** 1·50 1·75
1562 5 r. "275GTB", 1966 1·50 1·75
1563 5 r. "Aspirarta", 1951 1·50 1·75
1564 5 r. "Testarossa" 1·50 1·75
1565 5 r. Enzo Ferrari 1·50 1·75
1566 5 r. "Dino 246", 1958 1·50 1·75
1567 5 r. "Type 375", 1952 1·50 1·75
1568 5 r. Nigel Mansell's Formula 1 racing car 1·50 1·75
1569 5 r. "312T", 1975 1·50 1·75

262 Franklin D. Roosevelt

1991. 50th Anniv of Japanese Attack on Pearl Harbor. American War Leaders. Multicoloured.
1570 3 r. 50 Type **262** 1·25 1·40
1571 3 r. 50 Douglas MacArthur and map of Philippines 1·25 1·40
1572 3 r. 50 Chester Nimitz and Pacific island 1·25 1·40
1573 3 r. 50 Jonathan Wainwright and barbed wire 1·25 1·40
1574 3 r. 50 Ernest King and U.S.S. "Hornet" (aircraft carrier) 1·25 1·40
1575 3 r. 50 Claire Chennault and Curtiss Tomahawk II fighters 1·25 1·40
1576 3 r. 50 William Halsey and U.S.S. "Enterprise" (aircraft carrier) 1·25 1·40

1577 3 r. 50 Marc Mitscher and U.S.S. "Hornet" (aircraft carrier) 1·25 1·40
1578 3 r. 50 James Doolittle and North American B-25 Mitchell bomber 1·25 1·40
1579 3 r. 50 Raymond Spruance and Douglas Dauntless dive bomber 1·25 1·40

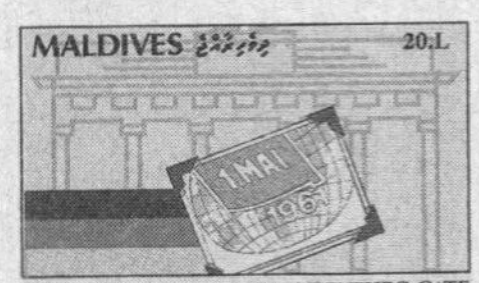

263 Brandenburg Gate and Postcard Commemorating Berlin Wall

1992. Anniversaries and Events. Multicoloured.
1580 20 l. Type **263** 10 10
1581 50 l. Schwarzenburg Palace 15 10
1582 1 r. Spa at Baden 20 15
1583 1 r. 75 Berlin Wall and man holding child 30 30
1584 2 r. Royal Palace, Berlin 35 35
1585 4 r. Demonstrator and border guards 75 75
1586 5 r. Viennese masonic seal 2·00 1·50
1587 6 r. De Gaulle and Normandy landings, 1944 (vert) 2·00 1·75
1588 6 r. Lilienthal's signature and "Flugzeug Nr. 16" 2·00 1·75
1589 7 r. St. Marx 2·00 1·75
1590 7 r. Trans-Siberian Railway Class VL80T electric locomotive No. 1406 (vert) 2·00 1·75
1591 8 r. Kurt Schwitters (artist) and Landesmuseum 2·00 1·75
1592 9 r. Map of Switzerland and man in Uri traditional costume 2·00 1·75
1593 10 r. De Gaulle in Madagascar, 1958 2·00 1·75
1594 10 r. Scouts exploring coral reef 2·00 2·00
1595 11 r. Scout salute and badge (vert) 2·00 2·00
1596 12 r. Trans-Siberian Railway steam locomotive 2·25 2·25
1597 15 r. Imperial German badges 2·00 2·00
1598 20 r. Josepsplatz, Vienna 2·75 2·75

ANNIVERSARIES AND EVENTS: Nos. 1580, 1583, 1585, 1597, Bicentenary of Brandenburg Gate, Berlin; Nos. 1581/2, 1584, 1586, 1589, 1598, Death bicentenary of Mozart (1991); Nos. 1587, 1593, Birth centenary of Charles de Gaulle (French statesman) (1990); No. 1588, Centenary of Otto Lilienthal's first gliding experiments; Nos. 1590, 1596, Centenary of Trans-Siberian Railway; No. 1591, 750th anniv of Hannover; No. 1592, 700th anniv of Swiss Confederation; Nos. 1594/5, 17th World Scout Jamboree, Korea.

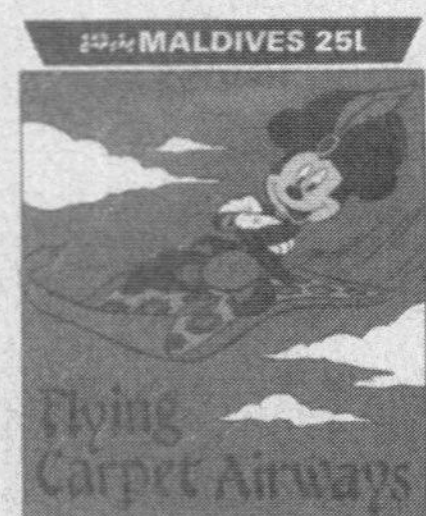

264 Mickey Mouse on Flying Carpet, Arabia

1992. Mickey's World Tour. Designs showing Walt Disney cartoon characters in different countries. Multicoloured.
1600 25 l. Type **264** 30 20
1601 50 l. Goofy and Big Ben, Great Britain 40 25
1602 1 r. Mickey wearing clogs, Netherlands 50 35
1603 2 r. Pluto eating pasta, Italy 85 65
1604 3 r. Mickey and Donald doing Mexican hat dance 1·10 1·10
1605 3 r. 50 Mickey, Goofy and Donald as tiki, New Zealand 1·25 1·25
1606 5 r. Goofy skiing in Austrian Alps 1·50 1·50
1607 7 r. Mickey and city gate, Germany 1·75 2·00
1608 10 r. Donald as samurai, Japan 2·00 2·25
1609 12 r. Mickey as heroic statue, Russia 2·25 2·50
1610 15 r. Mickey, Donald, Goofy and Pluto as German band 2·50 2·75

265 Whimbrel

266 Powder-blue Surgeonfish

1992. Birds. Multicoloured.
1612 10 l. Type **265** 10 10
1613 25 l. Great egret 10 10
1614 50 l. Grey heron 10 10
1615 2 r. Shag 20 25
1616 3 r. 50 Roseate tern 35 40
1617 5 r. Greenshank 50 55
1617a 6 r. 50 + 50 l. Egyptian vulture 70 75
1618 8 r. Hoopoe 80 85
1619 10 r. Black-shouldered kite 1·00 1·10
1620 25 r. Scarlet ibis 2·50 2·75
1620a 30 r. Peregrine falcon 3·00 3·25
1620b 40 r. Black kite 4·00 4·25
1621 50 r. Grey plover 5·00 5·50
1621a 100 r. Common shoveler 10·00 10·50

Nos. 1617a, 1620a/b and 1621a are larger, 23 × 32 mm.

1992. 40th Anniv of Queen Elizabeth II's Accession. As T **202a** of Gambia. Multicoloured.
1622 1 r. Palm trees on beach 40 25
1623 3 r. 50 Path leading to jetty 1·25 1·00
1624 7 r. Tropical plant 2·00 2·50
1625 10 r. Palm trees on beach (different) 2·40 3·00

1992. Fishes. Multicoloured.
1627 7 l. Type **266** 30 20
1628 20 l. Catalufa 40 25
1629 50 l. Yellow-finned tuna 55 30
1630 1 r. Twin-spotted red snapper 75 35
1631 3 r. 50 Hawaiian squirrelfish 1·50 1·25
1632 5 r. Picasso triggerfish 2·00 2·00
1633 8 r. Bennet's butterflyfish 2·25 2·50
1634 10 r. Parrotfish 2·50 2·75
1635 12 r. Coral hind 2·75 3·00
1636 15 r. Skipjack tuna 2·75 3·00

1992. International Stamp Exhibitions. As T **215** of Lesotho showing Walt Disney cartoon characters. Multicoloured. (a) "Granada '92", Spain. The Alhambra.
1638 2 r. Minnie Mouse in Court of the Lions 90 60
1639 5 r. Goofy in Lions Fountain 1·75 1·50
1640 8 r. Mickey Mouse at the Gate of Justice 2·25 2·50
1641 12 r. Donald Duck serenading Daisy at the Vermilion Towers 2·75 3·00

(b) "World Columbian Stamp Expo '92". Chicago Landmarks
1643 1 r. Mickey meeting Jean Baptiste du Sable (founder) 60 35
1644 3 r. 50 Donald Duck at Old Chicago Post Office 1·50 1·00
1645 7 r. Donald at Old Fort Dearborn 2·25 2·50
1646 15 r. Goofy in Museum of Science and Industry 3·00 3·50

On No. 1646 the design is wrongly captioned as the Science and Industry Museum.

267 Coastguard Patrol Boats

1992. Cent of National Security Service. Mult.
1648 3 r. 50 Type **267** 1·50 1·25
1649 5 r. Infantry in training 2·00 1·75
1650 10 r. Aakoatey fort 2·25 2·50
1651 15 r. Fire Service 5·00 5·00

268 Flowers of the United States of America

269 "Laetiporus sulphureus"

1992. National Flowers. Multicoloured.
1653 25 l. Type **268** 40 20
1654 50 l. Australia 60 30
1655 2 r. England 1·10 75
1656 3 r. 50 Brazil 1·50 1·25
1657 5 r. Holland 2·00 2·00
1658 8 r. France 2·25 2·50
1659 10 r. Japan 2·50 2·75
1660 15 r. Africa 2·75 3·00

1992. Fungi. Multicoloured.
1662 10 l. Type **269** 30 30
1663 25 l. "Coprinus atramentarius" 40 30
1664 50 l. "Ganoderma lucidum" 60 40
1665 3 r. 50 "Russula aurata" 1·25 1·00
1666 5 r. "Grifola umbellata" ("Polyporus umbellatus") 1·75 1·75
1667 8 r. "Suillus grevillei" 2·25 2·50
1668 10 r. "Clavaria zollingeri" 2·50 2·50
1669 25 r. "Boletus edulis" 5·00 6·00

1992. Olympic Games, Albertville and Barcelona (1st issue). As T **216** of Lesotho. Multicoloured.
1671 10 l. Pole vault 20 10
1672 25 l. Men's pommel horse (horiz) 25 15
1673 50 l. Men's shot put 30 25
1674 1 r. Men's horizontal bar (horiz) 35 30
1675 2 r. Men's triple jump (horiz) 80 65
1676 3 r. 50 Table tennis 1·10 1·10
1677 5 r. Two-man bobsled 1·40 1·40
1678 7 r. Freestyle wrestling (horiz) 1·75 2·00
1679 8 r. Freestyle ski-jump 1·75 2·00
1680 9 r. Baseball 2·00 2·25
1681 10 r. Women's cross-country Nordic skiing 2·00 2·25
1682 12 r. Men's 200 metres backstroke (horiz) 2·00 2·25

See also Nos. 1684/91.

270 Hurdling

271 Deinonychus

1992. Olympic Games, Barcelona (2nd issue). Multicoloured.
1684 10 l. Type **270** 10 10
1685 1 r. Boxing 30 30
1686 3 r. 50 Women's sprinting 80 70
1687 5 r. Discus 1·25 1·25
1688 7 r. Basketball 2·50 2·25
1689 10 r. Long-distance running 2·00 2·25
1690 12 r. Aerobic gymnastics 2·25 2·50
1691 20 r. Fencing 3·00 3·75

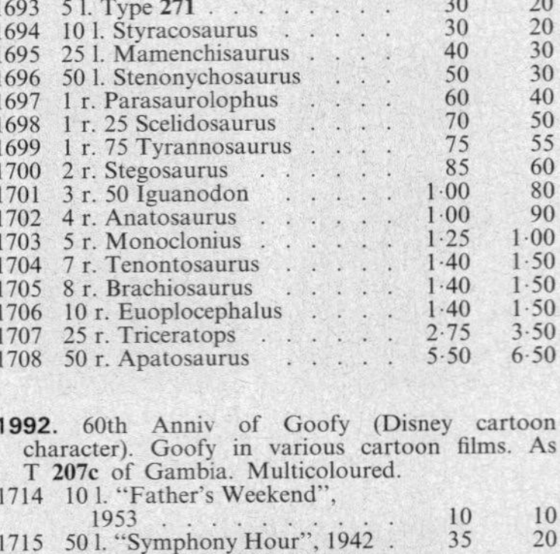

1992. "Genova '92" International Thematic Stamp Exhibition. Prehistoric Animals. Multicoloured.
1693 5 l. Type **271** 30 20
1694 10 l. Styracosaurus 30 20
1695 25 l. Mamenchisaurus 40 30
1696 50 l. Stenonychosaurus 50 30
1697 1 r. Parasaurolophus 60 40
1698 1 r. 25 Scelidosaurus 70 50
1699 1 r. 75 Tyrannosaurus 75 55
1700 2 r. Stegosaurus 85 60
1701 3 r. 50 Iguanodon 1·00 80
1702 4 r. Anatosaurus 1·00 90
1703 5 r. Monoclonius 1·25 1·00
1704 7 r. Tenontosaurus 1·40 1·50
1705 8 r. Brachiosaurus 1·40 1·50
1706 10 r. Euoplocephalus 1·40 1·50
1707 25 r. Triceratops 2·75 3·50
1708 50 r. Apatosaurus 5·50 6·50

1992. 60th Anniv of Goofy (Disney cartoon character). Goofy in various cartoon films. As T **207c** of Gambia. Multicoloured.
1714 10 l. "Father's Weekend", 1953 10 10
1715 50 l. "Symphony Hour", 1942 35 20
1716 75 l. "Frank Duck Brings 'Em Back Alive", 1946 45 20
1717 1 r. "Crazy with the Heat", 1947 45 20
1718 2 r. "The Big Wash", 1948 70 60
1719 3 r. 50 "How to Ride a Horse", 1950 1·25 1·25
1720 5 r. "Two Gun Goofy", 1952 1·50 1·50
1721 8 r. "Saludos Amigos", 1943 (vert) 2·00 2·25
1722 10 r. "How to be a Detective", 1952 2·00 2·25
1723 12 r. "For Whom the Bulls Toil", 1953 2·25 2·50
1724 15 r. "Double Dribble", 1946 (vert) 2·25 2·50

276 Minnie Mouse in "Le Missioner" (Toulouse-Lautrec)

1992. Opening of Euro-Disney Resort, France. Disney cartoon characters superimposed on Impressionist paintings. Multicoloured.
1726 5 r. Type **276** 1·40 1·50
1727 5 r. Goofy in "The Card Players" (Cezanne) 1·40 1·50
1728 5 r. Mickey and Minnie Mouse in "The Cafe Terrace, Place du Forum" (Van Gogh) 1·40 1·50
1729 5 r. Mickey in "The Bridge at Langlois" (Van Gogh) 1·40 1·50
1730 5 r. Goofy in "Chocolate Dancing" (Toulouse-Lautrec) 1·40 1·50
1731 5 r. Mickey and Minnie in "The Seine at Asnieres" (Renoir) 1·40 1·50
1732 5 r. Minnie in "Ball at the Moulin Rouge" (Toulouse-Lautrec) 1·40 1·50
1733 5 r. Mickey in "Wheatfield with Cypresses" (Van Gogh) 1·40 1·50
1734 5 r. Minnie in "When will you Marry?" (Gauguin) 1·40 1·50

277 Rivers

1992. South Asian Association for Regional Co-operation Year of the Environment. Natural and Polluted Environments. Multicoloured.
1736 25 l. Type **277** 15 10
1737 50 l. Beaches 25 10
1738 5 r. Oceans 80 1·00
1739 10 r. Weather 1·50 2·00

278 Jurgen Klinsmann (Germany)

1993. World Cup Football Championship, U.S.A. (1994) (1st issue). German Players and Officials. Multicoloured.
1740 10 l. Type **278** 15 20
1741 25 l. Pierre Littbarski 20 20
1742 50 l. Lothar Matthaus 30 20
1743 1 r. Rudi Voller 35 25
1744 2 r. Thomas Hassler 60 60
1745 3 r. 50 Thomas Berthold 1·00 1·00
1746 4 r. Jurgen Kohler 1·25 1·25
1747 5 r. Berti Vogts 1·40 1·40
1748 6 r. Bodo Illgner 1·60 1·90
1749 7 r. Klaus Augenthaler 1·75 2·00
1750 8 r. Franz Beckenbauer 1·75 2·00
1751 10 r. Andreas Brehme 2·00 2·25
1752 12 r. Guido Buchwald 2·00 2·50

See also Nos. 1990/7 and 2089/2100.

279 German Navy Airship L-13 bombing London, 1914–18

1993. Anniversaries and Events. Mult.
1754 1 r. Type **279** 55 30
1755 3 r. 50 Radio telescope 70 70
1756 3 r. 50 Chancellor Adenauer and Pres. de Gaulle 70 70
1757 6 r. Indian rhinoceros 2·00 1·50
1758 6 r. Columbus and globe 1·50 1·25
1759 7 r. Conference emblems 1·00 1·00
1760 8 r. Green seaturtle 1·40 1·40
1761 10 r. "America" (yacht), 1851 1·75 1·75
1762 10 r. Melvin Jones (founder) and emblem 1·75 1·75
1763 12 r. Columbus landing on San Salvador 2·00 2·00
1764 15 r. "Voyager I" approaching Saturn 3·50 3·50
1765 15 r. Adenauer, N.A.T.O. flag and Lockheed Starfighter aircraft 3·50 3·50
1766 20 r. "Graf Zeppelin" over New York, 1929 3·50 3·50

ANNIVERSARIES AND EVENTS: Nos. 1754, 1766, 75th death anniv of Count Ferdinand von Zeppelin; Nos. 1755, 1764, International Space Year; Nos. 1756, 1765, 25th death anniv of Konrad Adenauer; Nos. 1757, 1760, Earth Summit '92, Rio; Nos. 1758, 1763, 500th anniv of discovery of America by Columbus; No. 1759, International Conference on Nutrition, Rome; No. 1761, Americas Cup Yachting Championship; No. 1762, 75th anniv of International Association of Lions Clubs.

1993. 15th Death Anniv of Elvis Presley (singer). As T **209a** of Gambia. Multicoloured.
1768 3 r. 50 Elvis Presley 70 70
1769 3 r. 50 Elvis with guitar 70 70
1770 3 r. 50 Elvis with microphone 70 70

1993. Bicentenary of the Louvre, Paris. As T **209b** of Gambia. Multicoloured.
1771 8 r. "The Study" (Fragonard) 90 95
1772 8 r. "Denis Diderot" (Fragonard) 90 95
1773 8 r. "Marie-Madelaine Guimard" (Fragonard) 90 95
1774 8 r. "Inspiration" (Fragonard) 90 95
1775 8 r. "Waterfalls, Tivoli" (Fragonard) 90 95
1776 8 r. "The Music Lesson" (Fragonard) 90 95
1777 8 r. "The Bolt" (Fragonard) 90 95
1778 8 r. "Blind-man's Buff" (Fragonard) 90 95
1779 8 r. "Self-portrait" (Corot) 90 95
1780 8 r. "Woman in Blue" (Corot) 90 95
1781 8 r. "Woman with a Pearl" (Corot) 90 95
1782 8 r. "Young Girl at her Toilet" (Corot) 90 95
1783 8 r. "Haydee" (Corot) 90 95
1784 8 r. "Chartres Cathedral" (Corot) 90 95
1785 8 r. "The Belfry of Douai" (Corot) 90 95
1786 8 r. "The Bridge of Mantes" (Corot) 90 95
1787 8 r. "Madame Seriziat" (David) 90 95
1788 8 r. "Pierre Seriziat" (David) 90 95
1789 8 r. "Madame De Verninac" (David) 90 95
1790 8 r. "Madame Recamier" (David) 90 95
1791 8 r. "Self-portrait" (David) 90 95
1792 8 r. "General Bonaparte" (David) 90 95

1793 8 r. "The Lictors bringing Brutus his Son's Body" (David) (left detail) 90 95
1794 8 r. "The Lictors bringing Brutus his Son's Body" (David) (right detail) 90 95

281 James Stewart and Marlene Dietrich ("Destry Rides Again")

1993. Famous Western Films. Multicoloured.
1796 5 r. Type **281** 80 80
1797 5 r. Gary Cooper ("The Westerner") 80 80
1798 5 r. Henry Fonda ("My Darling Clementine") 80 80
1799 5 r. Alan Ladd ("Shane") 80 80
1800 5 r. Kirk Douglas and Burt Lancaster ("Gunfight at the O.K. Corral") 80 80
1801 5 r. Steve McQueen ("The Magnificent Seven") 80 80
1802 5 r. Robert Redford and Paul Newman ("Butch Cassidy and The Sundance Kid") 80 80
1803 5 r. Jack Nicholson and Randy Quaid ("The Missouri Breaks") 80 80

1993. 40th Anniv of Coronation. As T **215a** of Gambia.
1805 3 r. 50 multicoloured 1·00 1·10
1806 5 r. multicoloured 1·25 1·40
1807 10 r. blue and black 1·50 1·75
1808 10 r. blue and black 1·50 1·75
DESIGNS: No. 1805, Queen Elizabeth II at Coronation (photograph by Cecil Beaton); No. 1806, St. Edward's Crown; No. 1807, Guests in the Abbey; No. 1808, Queen Elizabeth II and Prince Philip.

282 Blue Goatfish

1993. Fishes. Multicoloured.
1809 3 r. 50 Type **282** 60 70
1810 3 r. 50 Emperor angelfish 60 70
1811 3 r. 50 Madagascar butterflyfish 60 70
1812 3 r. 50 Regal angelfish 60 70
1813 3 r. 50 Forceps fish ("Longnose butterflyfish") 60 70
1814 3 r. 50 Racoon butterflyfish 60 70
1815 3 r. 50 Harlequin filefish 60 70
1816 3 r. 50 Rectangle triggerfish 60 70
1817 3 r. 50 Yellow-tailed anemonefish 60 70
1818 3 r. 50 Clown triggerfish 60 70
1819 3 r. 50 Zebra lionfish 60 70
1820 3 r. 50 Maldive anemonefish ("Clownfish") 60 70
1821 3 r. 50 Black-faced butterflyfish 60 70
1822 3 r. 50 Bird wrasse 60 70
1823 3 r. 50 Checkerboard wrasse 60 70
1824 3 r. 50 Yellow-faced angelfish 60 70
1825 3 r. 50 Masked bannerfish 60 70
1826 3 r. 50 Thread-finned butterflyfish 60 70
1827 3 r. 50 Painted triggerfish 60 70
1828 3 r. 50 Coral hind 60 70
1829 3 r. 50 Pennant coralfish 60 70
1830 3 r. 50 Black-backed butterflyfish 60 70
1831 3 r. 50 Red-toothed triggerfish 60 70
1832 3 r. 50 Melon butterflyfish 60 70
Nos. 1809/20 and 1821/32 were printed together, se-tenant, with the backgrounds forming composite designs.

283 Gull-billed Tern

1993. Birds. Multicoloured.
1834 3 r. 50 Type **283** 60 70
1835 3 r. 50 White-tailed tropic bird 60 70
1836 3 r. 50 Great frigate bird 60 70
1837 3 r. 50 Wilson's petrel 60 70
1838 3 r. 50 White tern 60 70
1839 3 r. 50 Brown booby 60 70
1840 3 r. 50 Marsh harrier 60 70
1841 3 r. 50 Common noddy 60 70
1842 3 r. 50 Green heron ("Little Heron") 60 70
1843 3 r. 50 Turnstone 60 70
1844 3 r. 50 Curlew 60 70
1845 3 r. 50 Crab plover 60 70
1846 3 r. 50 Pallid harrier (vert) 60 70
1847 3 r. 50 Cattle egret (vert) 60 70
1848 3 r. 50 Koel (vert) 60 70
1849 3 r. 50 Tree pipit (vert) 60 70
1850 3 r. 50 Short-eared owl (vert) 60 70
1851 3 r. 50 Common kestrel ("European Kestrel") (vert) 60 70
1852 3 r. 50 Yellow wagtail (vert) 60 70
1853 3 r. 50 Grey heron ("Common Heron") (vert) 60 70
1854 3 r. 50 Black bittern (vert) 60 70
1855 3 r. 50 Common snipe (vert) 60 70
1856 3 r. 50 Little egret (vert) 60 70
1857 3 r. 50 Little stint (vert) 60 70
Nos. 1834/45 and 1846/57 were printed together, se-tenant, with the backgrounds forming composite designs.

284 Precious Wentletrap

285 Sifaka Lemur

1993. Shells. Multicoloured.
1859 7 l. Type **284** 20 20
1860 15 l. Common purple janthina 25 20
1861 50 l. Asiatic arabian cowrie 40 20
1862 3 r. 50 Common or major harp 1·25 1·00
1863 4 r. Amplustre or royal paper bubble 1·50 1·25
1864 5 r. Sieve cowrie 1·75 1·40
1865 6 r. Episcopal mitre 1·90 1·75
1866 7 r. Camp pitar venus 2·00 2·00
1867 8 r. Spotted or eyed auger 2·00 2·25
1868 10 r. Exposed cowrie 2·00 2·25
1869 12 r. Geographic map cowrie 2·25 2·75
1870 20 r. Bramble murex 2·50 3·50

1993. Endangered Species. Multicoloured.
1872 7 l. Type **285** 30 20
1873 10 l. Snow leopard 30 20
1874 15 l. Numbat 30 20
1875 25 l. Gorilla 50 30
1876 2 r. Koala 70 55
1877 3 r. 50 Cheetah 90 90
1878 5 r. Yellow-footed rock wallaby 1·25 1·25
1879 7 r. Orang-utan 1·75 2·00
1880 8 r. Black lemur 1·75 2·00
1881 10 r. Black rhinoceros 2·00 2·25
1882 15 r. Humpback whale 2·25 2·50
1883 20 r. Mauritius parakeet 2·75 3·00

286 Symbolic Heads and Arrows

287 Early Astronomical Equipment

1993. Productivity Year. Multicoloured.
1885 7 r. Type **286** 1·25 1·40
1886 10 r. Abstract 1·60 1·75

1993. Anniversaries and Events. Mult.
1887 3 r. 50 Type **287** 70 70
1888 3 r. 50 "Still Life with Pitcher and Apples" (Picasso) 70 70
1889 3 r. 50 "Zolte Roze" (Menasze Seidenbeurel) 70 70
1890 3 r. 50 Prince Naruhito and engagement photographs (horiz) 70 70
1891 5 r. "Bowls and Jug" (Picasso) 80 80
1892 5 r. Krysztofory Palace, Cracow 80 80
1893 8 r. "Jabtka i Kotara" (Waclaw Borowski) 1·40 1·40
1894 8 r. Marina Kiehl (Germany) (women's downhill skiing) 1·40 1·40
1895 10 r. "Bowls of Fruit and Loaves on a Table" (Picasso) 1·60 1·60
1896 10 r. Masako Owada and engagement photographs (horiz) 1·60 1·60
1897 15 r. American astronaut in space 2·25 2·25
1898 15 r. Vegard Ulvang (Norway) (30km cross-country skiing) 2·25 2·25
ANNIVERSARIES AND EVENTS: Nos. 1887, 1897, 450th death anniv of Copernicus (astronomer); Nos. 1888, 1891, 1895, 20th death anniv of Picasso (artist); Nos. 1889, 1892/3, "Polska '93" International Stamp Exhibition, Poznan; Nos. 1890, 1896, Marriage of Crown Prince Naruhito of Japan; Nos. 1894, 1898, Winter Olympic Games '94, Lillehammer.

288 "Limenitis procris" and "Mussaenda"

1993. Butterflies and Flowers. Multicoloured.
1900 7 l. Type **288** 30 20
1901 20 l. "Danaus limniace" and "Thevetia neriifolia" 45 20
1902 25 l. "Amblypodia centaurus" and "Clitoria ternatea" 45 20
1903 50 l. "Papilio crino" and "Crossandra infundibuliformis" 60 20
1904 5 r. "Mycalesis patnia" and "Thespesia populnia" 1·75 1·40
1905 6 r. 50 + 50 l. "Idea jasonia" and "Cassia glauca" 2·00 2·25
1906 7 r. "Catopsilia pomona" and "Calotropis" 2·00 2·25
1907 10 r. "Precis orithyia" and "Thunbergia grandiflora" 2·25 2·50
1908 12 r. "Vanessa cardui" and "Caesalpinia pulcherrima" 2·50 3·00
1909 15 r. "Papilio polymnestor" and "Nerium oleander" 2·75 3·25
1910 18 r. "Cirrochroa thais" and "Vinca rosea" 3·00 3·50
1911 20 r. "Pachliopta hector" and "Ixora coccinea" 3·00 3·50

289 Airship "Graf Zeppelin" in Searchlights

1993. Aviation Anniversaries. Multicoloured.
1913 3 r. 50 Type **289** 80 55
1914 5 r. Homing pigeon and message from Santa Catalina mail service, 1894 1·00 90
1915 10 r. Eckener and airship "Graf Zeppelin" 1·75 1·75
1916 15 r. Pilot's badge and loading Philadelphia–Washington mail, 1918 2·50 3·00
1917 20 r. U.S.S. "Macon" (airship) and mooring mast, 1933 2·50 3·00
ANNIVERSARIES: Nos. 1913, 1915, 1917, 125th birth anniv of Hugo Eckener (airship pioneer); Nos. 1914, 1916, Bicent of first airmail flight.

290 Ford Model "T"

1993. Centenaries of Henry Ford's First Petrol Engine (Nos. 1919/30) and Karl Benz's First Four-wheeled Car (others).
1919 **290** 3 r. 50 multicoloured 70 70
1920 – 3 r. 50 multicoloured 70 70
1921 – 3 r. 50 black and violet 70 70
1922 – 3 r. 50 multicoloured 70 70
1923 – 3 r. 50 multicoloured 70 70
1924 – 3 r. 50 multicoloured 70 70
1925 – 3 r. 50 multicoloured 70 70
1926 – 3 r. 50 multicoloured 70 70
1927 – 3 r. 50 multicoloured 70 70
1928 – 3 r. 50 multicoloured 70 70
1929 – 3 r. 50 multicoloured 70 70
1930 – 3 r. 50 black, brown and violet 70 70
1931 – 3 r. 50 multicoloured 70 70
1932 – 3 r. 50 multicoloured 70 70
1933 – 3 r. 50 green, black and violet 70 70
1934 – 3 r. 50 multicoloured 70 70
1935 – 3 r. 50 multicoloured 70 70
1936 – 3 r. 50 multicoloured 70 70
1937 – 3 r. 50 multicoloured 70 70
1938 – 3 r. 50 multicoloured 70 70
1939 – 3 r. 50 multicoloured 70 70
1940 – 3 r. 50 multicoloured 70 70
1941 – 3 r. 50 multicoloured 70 70
1942 – 3 r. 50 black, brown and violet 70 70
DESIGNS: No. 1920, Henry Ford; No. 1921, Plans of first petrol engine; No. 1922, Ford "Probe GT", 1993; No. 1923, Front of Ford "Sportsman", 1947; No. 1924, Back of Ford "Sportsman"; No. 1925, Advertisement of 1915; No. 1926, Ford "Thunderbird", 1955; No. 1927, Ford logo; No. 1928, Ford "Edsel Citation", 1958; No. 1929, Ford half-ton pickup, 1941; No. 1930, Silhouette of early Ford car; No. 1931, Daimler-Benz "Straight 8", 1937; No. 1932, Karl Benz; No. 1933, Mercedes-Benz poster; No. 1934, Mercedes "38-250SS", 1929; No. 1935, Benz "Viktoria", 1893; No. 1936, Benz logo; No. 1937, Plan of Mercedes engine; No. 1938, Mercedes-Benz "300SL Gullwing", 1952; No. 1939, Mercedes-Benz "SL", 1993; No. 1940, Front of Benz 4-cylinder car, 1906; No. 1941, Back of Benz 4-cylinder car and advertisement; No. 1942, Silhouette of early Benz car.
Nos. 1919/30 and 1931/42 were printed together, se-tenant, forming a composite design.

INDEX
Countries can be quickly located by referring to the index at the end of this volume.

291 Ivan, Sonia, Sasha and Peter in the Snow

1993. "Peter and the Wolf". Scenes from Walt Disney's cartoon film. Multicoloured.
1944 7 l. Type **291** 15 15
1945 15 l. Grandpa and Peter 20 20
1946 20 l. Peter on bridge 20 20
1947 25 l. Yascha, Vladimir and Mischa 20 20
1948 50 l. Sasha on lookout 30 20
1949 1 r. The Wolf 35 25
1950 3 r. 50 Peter dreaming 60 60
1951 3 r. 50 Peter taking gun 60 60
1952 3 r. 50 Peter with gun in snow 60 60
1953 3 r. 50 Sasha and Peter 60 60
1954 3 r. 50 Sonia and Peter 60 60
1955 3 r. 50 Peter with Ivan and Sasha 60 60
1956 3 r. 50 Ivan warning Peter of the wolf 60 60
1957 3 r. 50 Ivan, Peter and Sasha in tree 60 60
1958 3 r. 50 Wolf below tree 60 60
1959 3 r. 50 Wolf and Sonia 60 60
1960 3 r. 50 Sasha attacking the wolf 60 60
1961 3 r. 50 Sasha walking into wolf's mouth 60 60
1962 3 r. 50 Peter firing pop gun at wolf 60 60
1963 3 r. 50 Wolf chasing Sonia 60 60
1964 3 r. 50 Ivan tying rope to wolf's tail 60 60
1965 3 r. 50 Peter and Ivan hoisting wolf 60 60
1966 3 r. 50 Sasha and the hunters 60 60
1967 3 r. 50 Ivan and Peter on wolf hanging from tree 60 60

1994. Famous Paintings by Rembrandt and Matisse. As T **221c** of Gambia. Multicoloured.
1969 50 l. "Girl with a Broom" (Rembrandt) 30 15
1970 2 r. "Girl with Tulips" (Matisse) 65 50
1971 3 r. 50 "Young Girl at half-open Door" (Rembrandt) 1·00 90
1972 3 r. 50 "Portrait of Greta Moll" (Matisse) 1·00 90
1973 5 r. "The Prophetess Hannah" (Rembrandt) 1·25 1·00
1974 6 r. 50 "The Idol" (Matisse) 1·50 1·50
1975 7 r. "Woman with a Pink Flower" (Rembrandt) 1·50 1·50
1976 9 r. "Mme Matisse in a Japanese Robe" (Matisse) 1·75 2·00
1977 10 r. "Portrait of Mme Matisse" (Matisse) 1·75 2·00
1978 12 r. "Lucretia" (Rembrandt) 2·00 2·25
1979 15 r. "Lady with a Ostrich Feather Fan" (Rembrandt) 2·00 2·50
1980 15 r. "The Woman with the Hat" (Matisse) 2·00 2·50
No. 1979 is inscribed "The Lady with an Ostich Feather Fan" in error.

1994. "Hong Kong '94" International Stamp Exn (1st issue). As T **222a** of Gambia. Multicoloured.
1982 4 r. Hong Kong 1983 $1 Space Museum stamp and Moon-lantern festival 50 70
1983 4 r. Maldive Islands 1976 5 r. "Viking" space mission stamp and Moon-lantern festival 50 70
Nos. 1982/3 were printed together, se-tenant, forming a composite design.

1994. "Hong Kong '94" International Stamp Exhibition (2nd issue). Ching Dynasty Cloisonne Enamelware. As T **222b** of Gambia. Mult.
1984 2 r. Vase 35 35
1985 2 r. Flower holder 35 35
1986 2 r. Elephant with vase on back 35 35
1987 2 r. Tibetan style lama's teapot 35 35
1988 2 r. Fo-Dog 35 35
1989 2 r. Teapot with swing handle 35 35

295 Windischmann (U.S.A.) and Giannini (Italy)

297 Dome of the Rock, Jerusalem

1994. World Cup Football Championship, U.S.A. (2nd issue). Multicoloured.
1990 7 l. Type **295** 20 15
1991 20 l. Carnevale (Italy) and Gascoigne (England) 30 20
1992 25 l. England players congratulating Platt 30 20
1993 3 r. 50 Koeman (Holland) and Klinsmann (Germany) 85 70

1994 5 r. Quinn (Ireland) and Maldini (Italy) . . . . 1·10 90
1995 7 r. Lineker (England) . . . . 1·50 1·50
1996 15 r. Hassam (Egypt) and Moran (Ireland) . . . . . 2·50 3·00
1997 18 r. Canniggia (Argentina) . . 2·75 3·00

1994. Centenary (1992) of Sierra Club (environmental protection society). Endangered Species. As T **224a** of Gambia. Multicoloured.

2000 6 r. 50 Humpback whale . . . 1·25 1·25
1999 6 r. 50 Humpback whale . . . 1·25 1·25
2000 6 r. 50 Ocelot crouched in grass 1·25 1·25
2001 6 r. 50 Ocelot sitting . . . . 1·25 1·25
2002 6 r. 50 Snow monkey . . . . 1·25 1·25
2003 6 r. 50 Prairie dog . . . . . 1·25 1·25
2004 6 r. 50 Golden lion tamarin . . 1·25 1·25
2005 6 r. 50 Prairie dog eating (horiz) 1·25 1·25
2006 6 r. 50 Prairie dog outside burrow (horiz) . . . . . . 1·25 1·25
2007 6 r. 50 Herd of woodland caribou (horiz) . . . . . . 1·25 1·25
2008 6 r. 50 Woodland caribou facing left (horiz) . . . . . . 1·25 1·25
2009 6 r. 50 Woodland caribou facing right (horiz) . . . . . . 1·25 1·25
2010 6 r. 50 Pair of Galapagos penguins (horiz) . . . . . 1·25 1·25
2011 6 r. 50 Galapagos penguin facing right . . . . 1·25 1·25
2012 6 r. 50 Galapagos penguin looking straight ahead . . . 1·25 1·25
2013 6 r. 50 Bengal tiger looking straight ahead . . . . . 1·25 1·25
2014 6 r. 50 Bengal tiger looking right . . . . 1·25 1·25
2015 6 r. 50 Philippine tarsier with tree trunk at left . . . . 1·25 1·25
2016 6 r. 50 Philippine tarsier with tree trunk at right . . . 1·25 1·25
2017 6 r. 50 Head of Phillippine tarsier 1·25 1·25
2018 6 r. 50 Sierra Club centennial emblem (black, buff and green) . . . . 1·25 1·25
2019 6 r. 50 Golden lion tamarin between two branches (horiz) . . . . 1·25 1·25
2020 6 r. 50 Golden lion tamarin on tree trunk (horiz) . . . . 1·25 1·25
2021 6 r. 50 Tail fin of humpback whale and coastline (horiz) . 1·25 1·25
2022 6 r. 50 Tail fin of humpback whale at night (horiz) . . 1·25 1·25
2023 6 r. 50 Bengal tiger (horiz) . . 1·25 1·25
2024 5 r. 50 Ocelot (horiz) . . . . 1·25 1·25
2025 6 r. 50 Snow monkey in water climbing out of pool (horiz) . 1·25 1·25
2026 6 r. 50 Snow monkey swimming (horiz) . . . . 1·25 1·25

1994. Solidarity with the Palestinians.

2027 **297** 8 r. multicoloured . . . . 1·40 1·50

298 Elasmosaurus

1994. Prehistoric Animals. Multicoloured.

2028/59 25 l., 50 l., 1 r., 3 r. × 24, 5 r., 8 r., 10 r., 15 r., 20 r. Set of 32 . . . . 26·00 26·00

Nos. 2031/42 and 2043/54 respectively were printed together, se-tenant, forming composite designs. The species depicted are, in addition to Type **298**, Dilophosaurus, Avimimus, Dimorphodon, Megalosaurus, Kuehneosaurus, Dryosaurus, Kentrosaurus, Baraposaurus, Tenontosaurus, Elaphrosaurus, Maiasaura, Huayangosaurus, Rutiodon, Pianitzkysaurus, Quetzalcoatlus, Daspletosaurus, Pleurocoelus, Baryonyx, Pentaceratops, Kritosaurus, Microvenator, Nodosaurus, Montanaceratops, Dromiceiomimus, Dryptosaurus, Parkosaurus, Chasmosaurus, Edmontonia, Anatosaurus, Velociraptor and Spinosaurus.

299 Mallet Steam Locomotive, Indonesia

1994. Railway Locomotives of Asia. Multicoloured.

2061 25 l. Type **299** 20 20
2062 50 l. Class C62 steam locomotive, Japan, 1948 . . 25 20
2063 1 r. Class D51 steam locomotive, Japan, 1936 (horiz) 30 20
2064 5 r. Steam locomotive, India (horiz) 90 90
2065 6 r. 50 + 50 l. Class W steam locomotive, India (horiz) . . 1·25 1·50
2066 6 r. 50 + 50 l. Class C53 steam locomotive, Indonesia (horiz) . . . . 1·25 1·50
2067 6 r. 50 + 50 l. Class C10 steam locomotive, Japan (horiz) . 1·25 1·50
2068 6 r. 50 + 50 l. Hanomag steam locomotive, India (horiz) . . 1·25 1·50
2069 6 r. 50 + 50 l. "Hikari" express train, Japan (horiz) . . . . 1·25 1·50
2070 6 r. 50 + 50 l. Class C55 steam locomotive, Japan, 1935 (horiz) . . . . 1·25 1·50
2071 8 r. Class 485 electric locomotive, Japan (horiz) . 1·50 1·75
2072 10 r. Class WP steam locomotive, India (horiz) . . 1·75 2·00
2073 15 r. Class RM steam locomotive, China (horiz) . 2·00 2·25
2074 20 r. Class C57 steam locomotive, Japan, 1937 . . 2·25 2·50

No. 2069 is inscribed "Hakari" in error.

300 Japanese Bobtail

1994. Cats. Multicoloured.

2076 7 l. Type **300** 20 20
2077 20 l. Siamese (vert) 35 20
2078 25 l. Persian longhair 35 20
2079 50 l. Somali (vert) 40 20
2080 3 r. 50 Oriental shorthair . . . 1·00 80
2081 5 r. Burmese . . . . 1·25 1·00
2082 7 r. Bombay carrying kitten . . 1·50 1·50
2083 10 r. Turkish van (vert) . . . 1·50 1·75
2084 12 r. Javanese (vert) . . . . 1·75 2·00
2085 15 r. Singapura . . . . 2·00 2·50
2086 18 r. Turkish angora (vert) . . 2·25 2·75
2087 20 r. Egyptian mau (vert) . . . 2·25 2·75

301 Franco Baresi (Italy) and Stuart McCall (Scotland)

1994. World Cup Football Championship, U.S.A. (3rd issue). Multicoloured. (a) Horiz designs.

2089 10 l. Type **301** 40 40
2090 25 l. Mick McCarthy (Ireland) and Gary Lineker (England) 50 50
2091 50 l. J. Helt (Denmark) and R. Gordillo (Spain) 50 50
2092 5 r. Martin Vasquez (Spain) and Enzo Scifo (Belgium) . . . 1·00 1·00
2093 10 r. Championship emblem . . 1·40 1·40
2094 12 r. Tomas Brolin (Sweden) and Gordon Durie (Scotland) 1·60 1·60

(b) Vert designs.

2095 6 r. 50 Bebeto (Brazil) . . . . 1·10 1·10
2096 6 r. 50 Lothar Matthaus (Germany) . . . . 1·10 1·10
2097 6 r. 50 Diego Maradona (Argentina) . . . . 1·10 1·10
2098 6 r. 50 Stephane Chapuasti (Switzerland) . . . . . . 1·10 1·10
2099 6 r. 50 George Hagi (Rumania) . . . . 1·10 1·10
2100 6 r. 50 Carlos Valderama (Colombia) . . . . 1·10 1·10

1994. 25th Anniv of First Manned Moon Landing. As T **227a** of Gambia. Multicoloured.

2102 5 r. Crew of "Apollo 11" . . . 90 90
2103 5 r. "Apollo 11" mission logo . 90 90
2104 5 r. Edwin Aldrin (astronaut) and "Eagle" 90 90
2105 5 r. Crew of "Apollo 12" . . . 90 90
2106 5 r. "Apollo 12" mission logo . 90 90
2107 5 r. Alan Bean (astronaut) and equipment 90 90
2108 5 r. Crew of "Apollo 16" . . . 90 90
2109 5 r. "Apollo 16" mission logo . 90 90
2110 5 r. Astronauts with U.S. flag . 90 90
2111 5 r. Crew of "Apollo 17" . . . 90 90
2112 5 r. "Apollo 17" mission logo . 90 90
2113 5 r. Launch of "Apollo 17" . . 90 90

1994. Centenary of International Olympic Committee. Gold Medal Winners. As T **227b** of Gambia. Multicoloured.

2115 7 r. Linford Christie (Great Britain) (100 metres), 1992 (vert) . . . . 1·50 1·25
2116 12 r. Koji Gushiken (Japan) (gymnastics), 1984 (vert) . . 1·75 2·00

1994. 50th Anniv of D-Day. As T **227c** of Gambia. Multicoloured.

2118 2 r. U.S. amphibious DUKW . 45 30
2119 4 r. Tank landing craft unloading at Sword Beach . 75 60
2120 18 r. Infantry landing craft at Omaha Beach . . . . . 3·00 4·00

305 Duckpond, Suwan Folk Village

1994. "Philakorea '94" International Stamp Exn, Seoul. Multicoloured.

2122 50 l. Type **305** 15 15
2123 3 r. Pear-shaped bottle (vert) . 45 45
2124 3 r. Vase with dragon decoration (vert) 45 45
2125 3 r. Vase with repaired lip (vert) 45 45
2126 3 r. Stoneware vase with floral decoration (vert) 45 45
2127 3 r. Celadon-glazed vase (vert) . 45 45
2128 3 r. Unglazed stone vase (vert) . 45 45
2129 3 r. Ritual water sprinkler (vert) 45 45
2130 3 r. Long-necked celadon-glazed vase (vert) 45 45
2131 3 r. 50 Yongduson Park . . . 50 50
2132 20 r. Ploughing with ox, Hahoe . . . . 3·00 3·75

306 U.S. "Voyager 2" Satellite

1994. Space Exploration. Multicoloured.

2134 5 r. Type **306** 85 85
2135 5 r. Russian "Sputnik" satellite 85 85
2136 5 r. "Apollo-Soyuz" mission . 85 85
2137 5 r. "Apollo 10" on parachutes 85 85
2138 5 r. "Apollo 11" mission flag . 85 85
2139 5 r. Hubble space telescope . . 85 85
2140 5 r. Edwin "Buzz" Aldrin (astronaut) 85 85
2141 5 r. RCA lunar camera . . . 85 85
2142 5 r. Lunar Rover (space buggy) 85 85
2143 5 r. Jim Irwin (astronaut) . . 85 85
2144 5 r. "Apollo 12" lunar module . 85 85
2145 5 r. Astronaut holding equipment 85 85

307 Mother, Child, Old Man and Town Skyline

1994. United Nations Development Programme. Multicoloured.

2147 1 r. Type **307** 15 10
2148 8 r. Fisherman with son and island . . . . 1·40 1·50

308 School Band

1994. 50th Anniv of Aminiya School. Children's Paintings. Multicoloured.

2149 15 l. Type **308** 10 10
2150 50 l. Classroom 20 15
2151 1 r. School emblem and hand holding book (vert) 30 15
2152 8 r. School girls holding books (vert) . . . . 1·75 2·00
2153 10 r. Sporting activities . . . 1·75 2·00
2154 11 r. School girls holding crown (vert) . . . . 1·90 2·25
2155 13 r. Science lesson . . . . . 1·90 2·25

309 Boeing 747

1994. 50th Anniv of I.C.A.O. Multicoloured.

2156 50 l. Type **309** 30 15
2157 1 r. Hawker Siddeley ("de Havilland") Comet 4 . . . 35 20
2158 2 r. Male International Airport 60 50
2159 3 r. Lockheed L.1649 Super Star 75 75
2160 8 r. European Airbus . . . . 1·40 1·50
2161 10 r. Dornier Do-228 . . . . 1·50 1·60

310 Pintail ("Northern Pintail")

1995. Ducks. Multicoloured.

2163 5 r. Type **310** 75 75
2164 5 r. Comb duck 75 75
2165 5 r. Ruddy shelduck 75 75
2166 5 r. Garganey 75 75
2167 5 r. Indian whistling duck ("Lesser whistling duck") . 75 75
2168 5 r. Green-winged teal 75 75
2169 5 r. Fulvous whistling duck . . 75 75
2170 5 r. Common shoveler ("Northern shoveler") . . . 75 75
2171 5 r. Cotton pygmy goose . . . 75 75
2172 6 r. 50 + 50 l. European pochard (vert) 85 85
2173 6 r. 50 + 50 l. Mallard (vert) . 85 85
2174 6 r. 50 + 50 l. European wigeon (vert) 85 85
2175 6 r. 50 + 50 l. Common shoveler ("Northern shoveler") (vert) 85 85
2176 6 r. 50 + 50 l. Pintail (vert) . 85 85
2177 6 r. 50 + 50 l. Garganey (vert) . 85 85
2178 6 r. 50 + 50 l. Tufted duck (vert) 85 85
2179 6 r. 50 + 50 l. Red-crested pochard ("Ferruginous duck") (vert) 85 85
2180 6 r. 50 + 50 l. Ferruginous duck ("Red-crested pochard") (vert) 85 85

Nos. 2163/71 and 2172/80 were printed together, se-tenant, forming composite designs.

311 Taj Mahal, India

1995. Famous Monuments of the World. Multicoloured.

2182 7 l. Type **311** 10 10
2183 10 l. Washington Monument, U.S.A. 10 10
2184 15 l. Mount Rushmore, U.S.A. 10 10
2185 25 l. Arc de Triomphe, Paris (vert) 10 10
2186 50 l. Sphinx, Egypt (vert) . . . 20 20
2187 5 r. El Castillo, Toltec pyramid, Yucatan 70 70
2188 8 r. Toltec statue, Tula, Mexico (vert) . . . . 1·00 1·25
2189 12 r. Victory Column, Berlin (vert) . . . . 1·40 1·75

312 Donald Duck driving Chariot

1995. History of Wheeled Transport. Scenes from Disney cartoon film "Donald and the Wheel". Multicoloured.

2191 3 l. Type **312** 10 10
2192 4 l. Donald with log 10 10
2193 5 l. Donald driving Stephenson's "Rocket" 10 10
2194 10 l. Donald pondering over circle (vert) 10 10
2195 20 l. Donald in crashed car (vert) 10 10
2196 25 l. Donald listening to early grammaphone 10 10
2197 5 r. Donald on mammoth . . 75 75
2198 20 r. Donald pushing early car . 2·75 3·25

313 Donald Duck playing Saxophone

1995. 60th Birthday of Donald Duck. Walt Disney Cartoon Characters. Multicoloured.

2199 5 r. Type **313** 80 80
2200 5 r. Moby Duck playing fiddle . 80 80
2201 5 r. Feathry Duck with banjo and drum 80 80
2202 5 r. Daisy Duck playing harp . 80 80
2203 5 r. Gladstone Gander with clarinet 80 80
2204 5 r. Huey, Dewey and Louie with bassoon 80 80
2205 5 r. Gus Goose playing flute . 80 80
2206 5 r. Prof. Ludwig von Drake playing trombone 80 80
2207 5 r. Daisy picking flowers . . 80 80
2208 5 r. Donald with backpack . . 80 80
2209 5 r. Grandma Duck with kitten 80 80

2210 5 r. Gus Goose and pie . . . 80 80
2211 5 r. Gyro Gearloose in space . 80 80
2212 5 r. Huey, Dewey and Louie photographing porcupine . 80 80
2213 5 r. Prof. Ludwig von Drake . 80 80
2214 5 r. Scrooge McDuck with money 80 80

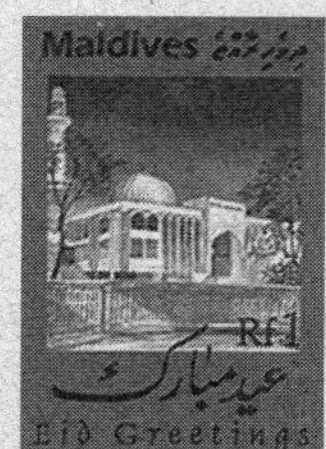

314 Islamic Centre, Male

1995. Eid Greetings. Multicoloured.
2216 1 r. Type **314** 15 15
2217 1 r. Rose 15 15
2218 8 r. Orchid . . . . 1·25 1·25
2219 10 r. Orchid (different) . . . . 1·25 1·25

315 Killer Whale

1995. "Singapore '95" International Stamp Exhibition (1st issue). Whales, Dolphins and Porpoises. Multicoloured.
2220 1 r. Type **315** 20 30
2221 2 r. Bottlenose dolphins . . . 35 35
2222 3 r. Right whale 50 50
2223 3 r. Pair of killer whales . . . 50 50
2224 3 r. Humpback whale 50 50
2225 3 r. Pair of belugas 50 50
2226 3 r. Narwhal 50 50
2227 3 r. Head of blue whale . . . 50 50
2228 3 r. Bowhead whale 50 50
2229 3 r. Head of fin whale 50 50
2230 3 r. Pair of pilot whales . . . 50 50
2231 3 r. Grey whale 50 50
2232 3 r. Sperm whale 50 50
2233 3 r. Pair of goosebeaked whales 50 50
2234 3 r. Hourglass dolphin 50 50
2235 3 r. Bottlenose dolphin (different) 50 50
2236 3 r. Dusky dolphin 50 50
2237 3 r. Spectacled porpoise . . . 50 50
2238 3 r. Fraser's dolphin 50 50
2239 3 r. Camerson's dolphin . . . 50 50
2240 3 r. Pair of spinner dolphins . . 50 50
2241 3 r. Pair of Dalls dolphins . . 50 50
2242 3 r. Spotted dolphin 50 50
2243 3 r. Indus River dolphin . . . 50 50
2244 3 r. Hector's dolphin 50 50
2245 3 r. Amazon River dolphin . . 50 50
2246 8 r. Humpback whale and calf . 1·00 1·00
2247 10 r. Common dolphin . . . 1·25 1·25
See also Nos. 2302/10.

316 Scout Camp and National Flag

1995. 18th World Scout Jamboree, Netherlands. Multicoloured.
2249 10 r. Type **316** . . . . 1·40 1·50
2250 12 r. Campfire cooking . . . 1·50 1·60
2251 15 r. Scouts erecting tent . . . 1·60 1·75
Nos. 2249/51 were printed together, se-tenant, forming a composite design.

317 Soviet Heavy Howitzer Battery

1995. 50th Anniv of End of Second World War in Europe. Multicoloured.
2253 5 r. Type **317** 75 75
2254 5 r. Ruins of Berchtesgaden . 75 75
2255 5 r. U.S. Boeing B-17 Flying Fortress dropping food over the Netherlands 75 75
2256 5 r. Soviet Ilyushin Il-1 bomber 75 75
2257 5 r. Liberation of Belsen . . . 75 75
2258 5 r. Supermarine Spitfire and V-1 flying bomb 75 75
2259 5 r. U.S. tanks advancing through Cologne 75 75
2260 5 r. Reichstag in ruins 75 75

318 Asian Child and Dove

320 Asian Child eating Rice

319 United Nations Emblem

1995. 50th Anniv of United Nations (1st issue). Multicoloured.
2262 6 r. 50 + 50 l. Type **318** . . . 90 1·00
2263 8 r. Globe and dove . . . . . 1·00 1·10
2264 10 r. African child and dove . 1·10 1·25
Nos. 2262/4 were printed together, se-tenant, forming a composite design.

1995. 50th Anniv of United Nations (2nd issue).
2266 **319** 30 l. black, blue and green 10 10
2267 – 8 r. multicoloured . . . 1·00 1·10
2268 – 11 r. multicoloured . . . 1·25 1·40
2269 – 13 r. black, grey and red . 1·60 1·75
DESIGNS: 8 r. Symbolic women, flag and map; 11 r. U.N. soldier and symbolic dove; 13 r. Gun barrels, atomic explosion and bomb sight.

1995. 50th Anniv of F.A.O. (1st issue). Multicoloured.
2270 6 r. 50 + 50 l. Type **320** . . . 90 1·00
2271 8 r. F.A.O. emblem . . . . 1·00 1·10
2272 10 r. African mother and child . 1·10 1·25
See also Nos. 2311/12.

1995. 95th Birthday of Queen Elizabeth the Queen Mother. As T **239a** of Gambia. Multicoloured.
2274 5 r. brown, light brown and black 80 85
2275 5 r. multicoloured 80 85
2276 5 r. multicoloured 80 85
2277 5 r. multicoloured 80 85
DESIGNS: No. 2274, Queen Elizabeth the Queen Mother (pastel drawing); 2275, Without hat; 2276, At desk (oil painting); 2277, Queen Elizabeth the Queen Mother.

1995. 50th Anniv of End of Second World War in the Pacific. As T **239b** of Gambia. Multicoloured.
2279 6 r. 50 + 50 l. Grumman F6F-3 Hellcat aircraft . . . . . . 1·00 1·00
2280 6 r. 50 + 50 l. F4-U1 fighter aircraft attacking beach . . 1·00 1·00
2281 6 r. 50 + 50 l. Douglas SBD Dauntless aircraft . . . . . 1·00 1·00
2282 6 r. 50 + 50 l. American troops in landing craft, Guadalcanal . . . . 1·00 1·00
2283 6 r. 50 + 50 l. U.S. marines in Alligator tanks . . . . . 1·00 1·00
2284 6 r. 50 + 50 l. U.S. landing ship . . . . 1·00 1·00

322 Students using Library

1995. 50th Anniv of National Library. Multicoloured.
2286 2 r. Type **322** 25 25
2287 8 r. Students using library (different) . . . . 1·00 1·25

323 Spur-thighed Tortoise

1995. Turtles and Tortoises. Multicoloured.
2289 3 r. Type **323** 50 50
2290 3 r. Aldabra turtle 50 50
2291 3 r. Loggerhead turtle 50 50
2292 3 r. Olive Ridley turtle . . . 50 50
2293 3 r. Leatherback turtle 50 50
2294 3 r. Green turtle 50 50
2295 3 r. Atlantic ridley turtle . . . 50 50
2296 3 r. Hawksbill turtle 50 50
2297 10 r. Hawksbill turtle on beach . . . . 1·40 1·40
2298 10 r. Pair of hawksbill turtles . 1·40 1·40
2299 10 r. Hawksbill turtle climbing out of water . . . . . 1·40 1·40
2300 10 r. Hawksbill turtle swimming . . . . 1·40 1·40
Nos. 2289/96 were printed together, se-tenant, forming a composite design.
Nos. 2297/2300 include the W.W.F. Panda emblem.

324 "Russula aurata" (fungi) and "Papilio demodocus" (butterfly)

1995. "Singapore '95" International Stamp Exhibition. Butterflies and Fungi. Multicoloured.
2302 2 r. Type **324** 35 35
2303 2 r. "Lepista saeva" and "Kallimoides rumia" . . . 35 35
2304 2 r. "Lepista nuda" and "Hypolimnas salmacis" . . 35 35
2305 2 r. "Xerocomus subtomentosus" ("Boletus subtomentosus" and "Precis octavia") 35 35
2306 5 r. "Gyroporus castaneus" and "Hypolimnas salmacis" . . 85 95
2307 8 r. "Gomphidius glutinosus" and "Papilio dardanus" . . 1·10 1·25
2308 10 r. "Russula olivacea" and "Precis octavia" . . . . . 1·25 1·40
2309 12 r. "Boletus edulis" and "Prepona praeneste" . . . 1·25 1·40
Nos. 2302/5 and 2306/9 respectively were printed together, se-tenant, forming composite designs.
No. 2304 is inscribed "Lapista" in error.

325 Planting Kaashi

1995. 50th Anniv of F.A.O. (2nd issue). Mult.
2311 7 r. Type **325** 90 90
2312 8 r. Fishing boat . . . . . . 1·10 1·10

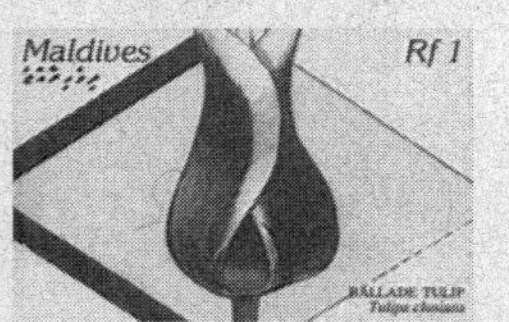

326 Ballade Tulip

1995. Flowers. Multicoloured.
2313 1 r. Type **326** 20 15
2314 3 r. White mallow 50 50
2315 5 r. Regale trumpet lily . . . 75 75
2316 5 r. "Dendrobium Waipahu Beauty" 75 75
2317 5 r. "Brassocattleya Jean Murray" 75 75
2318 5 r. "Cymbidium Fort George" 75 75
2319 5 r. "Paphiopedilum malipoense" 75 75
2320 5 r. "Cycnoches chlorochilon" . 75 75
2321 5 r. "Rhyncholaelia digbgana" 75 75
2322 5 r. "Lycaste deppei" 75 75
2323 5 r. "Masdevallia constricta" . 75 75
2324 5 r. "Paphiopedilum Clair de Lune" 75 75
2325 7 r. "Lilactime dahlia" . . . . 1·00 1·00
2326 8 r. Blue ideal iris . . . . . . 1·10 1·10
2327 10 r. Red crown imperial . . . 1·25 1·25

327 John Lennon with Microphone

329 Johannes van der Waals (1919 Physics)

1995. 15th Death Anniv of John Lennon (musician). Multicoloured.
2329 5 r. Type **327** . . . . 1·25 1·25
2330 5 r. With glasses and moustache . . . . 1·25 1·25
2331 5 r. With guitar . . . . . . 1·25 1·25
2332 5 r. With guitar and wearing glasses . . . . 1·25 1·25
2333 5 r. Wearing sun glasses and red jacket . . . . 1·25 1·25
2334 5 r. Wearing headphones . . . 1·25 1·25

1995. 60th Birth Anniv of Elvis Presley (entertainer). As T **411** of Grenada. Multicoloured.
2337 5 r. Elvis Presley with microphone 75 75
2338 5 r. Wearing red jacket . . . 75 75
2339 5 r. Wearing blue jacket . . . 75 75
2340 5 r. With microphone and wearing blue jacket 75 75
2341 5 r. In army uniform 75 75
2342 5 r. Wearing yellow bow tie . . 75 75
2343 5 r. In yellow shirt 75 75
2344 5 r. In light blue shirt 75 75
2345 5 r. Wearing red and white high-collared jacket 75 75

1995. Cent of Nobel Prize Trust Fund. Mult.
2347/55 5 r. × 9 (Type **329**; Charles Guillaume (1920 Physics); Sir James Chadwick (1935 Physics); Willem Einthoven (1924 Medicine); Henrik Dam (1943 Medicine); Sir Alexander Fleming (1945 Medicine); Hermann Muller (1946 Medicine); Rodney Porter (1972 Medicine); Werner Arber (1978 Medicine))
2356/64 5 r. × 9 (Niels Bohr (1922 Physics); Ben Mottelson (1975 Physics); Patrick White (1973 Literature); Elias Canetti (1981 Literature); Theodor Kocher (1909 Medicine); August Krogh (1920 Medicine); William Murphy (1934 Medicine); John Northrop (1946 Chemistry); Luis Leloir (1970 Chemistry))
2365/73 5 r. × 9 (Dag Hammarskjold (1961 Peace); Alva Myrdal (1982 Peace); Archbishop Desmond Tutu (1984 Peace); Rudolf Eucken (1908 Literature); Aleksandr Solzhenitsyn (1970 Literature); Gabriel Marquez (1982 Literature); Chen Yang (1957 Physics); Karl Muller (1987 Physics); Melvin Schwartz (1988 Physics))
2374/82 5 r. × 9 (Robert Millikan (1923 Physics); Louis de Broglie (1929 Physics); Ernest Walton (1951 Physics); Richard Willstatter (1915 Chemistry); Lars Onsager (1968 Chemistry); Gerhard Herzberg (1971 Chemistry); William B. Yeats (1923 Literature); George Bernard Shaw (1925 Literature); Eugene O'Neill (1936 Literature))
2383/91 5 r. × 9 (Bernardo Houssay (1947 Medicine); Paul Muller (1948 Medicine); Walter Hess (1949 Medicine); Sir MacFarlane Burnet (1960 Medicine); Baruch Blumberg (1976 Medicine); Daniel Nathans (1978 Medicine); Glenn Seaborg (1951 Chemistry); Ilya Prigogine (1977 Chemistry); Kenichi Fukui (1981 Chemistry))
2392/2400 5 r. × 9 (Carl Spitteler (1919 Literature); Henri Bergson (1927 Literature); Johannes Jensen (1944 Literature); Antoine-Henri Becquerel (1903 Physics); Sir William H. Bragg (1915 Physics); Sir William L. Bragg (1915 Physics); Frederik Bajer (1908 Peace); Leon Bourgeois (1920 Peace); Karl Benning (1921 Peace))
Set of 54 . . . . . . 27·00 29·00

330 Rythmic Gymnast and Japanese Fan

1996. Olympic Games, Atlanta (1st issue). Mult.
2402 1 r. Type **330** 20 15
2403 3 r. Archer and Moscow Olympics logo 50 50
2404 5 r. Diver and Swedish flag . . 75 75
2405 5 r. Canadian Maple Leaf . . 75 75
2406 5 r. Shot putting (decathlon) . 75 75
2407 5 r. Moscow Olympic medal and ribbon 75 75
2408 5 r. Fencer 75 75
2409 5 r. Gold medal 75 75
2410 5 r. Equestrian competitor . . 75 75
2411 5 r. Sydney Opera House . . . 75 75

2412 5 r. Athlete on starting blocks . 75 75
2413 5 r. South Korean flag 75 75
2414 7 r. High jumper and Tower Bridge, London . . . . . 1·00 1·00
2415 10 r. Athlete on starting blocks and Brandenburg Gate, Germany . . . . . . 1·10 1·10
2416 12 r. Hurdler and Amsterdam Olympic logo . . . . . . 1·25 1·40

See also Nos. 2469/87.

1996. 125th Anniv of Metropolitan Museum of Art, New York. As T **251** of Gambia. Multicoloured.

2418/25 4 r. × 8 ("Self-Portrait" (Degas); "Andromache and Astyanax" (Prud'hon); "Rene Grenier" (Toulouse-Lautrec); "The Banks of the Bievre near Bicetre" (Rousseau); "The Repast of the Lion" (Rousseau); "Portrait of Yves Gobillard-Morisot" (Degas); "Sunflowers" (Van Gogh); "The Singer in Green" (Degas))
2426/33 4 r. × 8 ("Still Life" (Fantin-Latour); "Portrait of a Lady in Grey" (Degas); "Apples and Grapes" (Monet); "The Englishman" (Toulouse-Lautrec); "Cypresses" (Van Gogh); "Flowers in a Chinese Vase" (Redon); "The Gardener" (Seurat); "Large Sunflowers I" (Nølde))
2434/41 4 r. × 8 (All by Manet: "The Spanish Singer"; "Young Man in Costume of Majo"; "Mademoiselle Victorine"; "Boating"; "Peonies"; "Woman with a Parrot"; "George Moore"; "The Monet Family in their Garden")
2442/9 4 r. × 8 ("Goldfish" (Matisse); "Spanish Woman: Harmony in Blue" (Matisse); "Nasturtiums and the "Dance" II" (Matisse); "The House behind Trees" (Braque); "Mada Primavesi" (Klimt); "Head of a Woman" (Picasso); "Woman in White" (Picasso); "Harlequin" (Picasso))
2418/49 Set of 32 . . . . 16·00 17·00

332 Mickey Mouse on Great Wall of China

1996. "CHINA '96" 9th Asian International Stamp Exhibition, Peking. Walt Disney Cartoon Characters in China. Multicoloured.

2451 2 r. Type **332** 55 55
2452 2 r. Pluto with temple guardian 55 55
2453 2 r. Minnie Mouse with pandas 55 55
2454 2 r. Mickey windsurfing near junks 55 55
2455 2 r. Goofy cleaning grotto statue 55 55
2456 2 r. Donald and Daisy Duck at Marble Boat 55 55
2457 2 r. Mickey with terracotta warriors 55 55
2458 2 r. Goofy with geese and masks 55 55
2459 2 r. Donald and Goofy on traditional fishing boat . . 55 55
2460 2 r. Mickey and Minnie in dragon boat 55 55
2461 2 r. Donald at Peking opera . . 55 55
2462 2 r. Mickey and Minnie in Chinese garden 55 55
2463 3 r. Mickey and Minnie at the Ice Pagoda (vert) 65 65
2464 3 r. Donald and Mickey flying Chinese kites (vert) 65 65
2465 3 r. Goofy playing anyiwu (vert) 65 65
2466 3 r. Paper cutouts of Mickey and Goofy (vert) 65 65
2467 3 r. Donald and Mickey in dragon dance (vert) 65 65

333 Stella Walsh (Poland) (100m sprint, 1932) on Medal

1996. Olympic Games, Atlanta (2nd issue). Previous Gold Medal Winners. Multicoloured.

2469 1 r. Type **333** 10 10
2470 3 r. Emile Zatopek (Czechoslovakia) (10,000m running, 1952) and Olympic torch (vert) 30 35
2471 5 r. Yanko Rousseu (Bulgaria) (lightweight, 1980) (vert) . . 50 55
2472 5 r. Peter Baczako (Hungary) (middle heavyweight, 1980) (vert) 50 55
2473 5 r. Leonid Taranenko (Russia) (heavyweight, 1980) (vert) . 50 55
2474 5 r. Aleksandr Kurlovich (Russia) (heavyweight, 1988) (vert) 50 55
2475 5 r. Assen Zlateu (Bulgaria) (middleweight, 1980) (vert) . 50 55
2476 5 r. Zeng Guoqiang (China) (flyweight, 1984) (vert) . . . 50 55
2477 5 r. Yurik Vardanyan (Russia) (heavyweight, 1980) (vert) . 50 55
2478 5 r. Sultan Rakhmanov (Russia) (super heavyweight, 1980) (vert) 50 55
2479 5 r. Vassily Alexeev (Russia) (super heavyweight, 1972) (vert) 50 55
2480 5 r. Ethel Catherwood (Canada) (high jump, 1928) 50 55
2481 5 r. Mildred Didrikson (U.S.A.) (javelin, 1932) 50 55
2482 5 r. Francina Blankers-Koen (Netherlands) (80m hurdles, 1948) 50 55
2483 5 r. Tamara Press (Russia) (shot put, 1960) 50 55
2484 5 r. Lia Manoliu (Rumania) (discus, 1968) 50 55
2485 5 r. Rosa Mota (Portugal) (marathon, 1988) 50 55
2486 10 r. Olga Fikotova (Czechoslovakia) (discus, 1956) on medal . . . . . 1·00 1·10
2487 12 r. Joan Benoit (U.S.A.) (marathon, 1984) on medal . 1·25 1·40

1996. 70th Birthday of Queen Elizabeth II. As T **255a** of Gambia. Multicoloured.

2489 8 r. Queen Elizabeth II . . . 80 85
2490 8 r. Wearing hat 80 85
2491 8 r. At desk 80 85

335 African Child

1996. 50th Anniv of U.N.I.C.E.F. Multicoloured.

2493 5 r. Type **335** 50 55
2494 7 r. European girl 70 75
2495 7 r. Maldivian boy 70 75
2496 10 r. Asian girl . . . . 1·00 1·10

336 "Sputnik 1" Satellite

1996. Space Exploration. Multicoloured.

2498 6 r. Type **336** 60 65
2499 6 r. "Apollo 11" command module 60 65
2500 6 r. "Skylab" 60 65
2501 6 r. Astronaut Edward White walking in space 60 65
2502 6 r. "Mariner 9" 60 65
2503 6 r. "Apollo" and "Soyuz" docking 60 65

337 "Epiphora albida"

1996. Butterflies. Multicoloured.

2505 7 r. Type **337** 70 75
2506 7 r. "Satyrus dryas" 70 75
2507 7 r. "Satyrus lena" 70 75
2508 7 r. "Papilio tynderaeus" . . . 70 75
2509 7 r. "Urota suraka" 70 75
2510 7 r. "Satyrus nercis" 70 75
2511 7 r. "Papilio troilus" (vert) . . 70 75
2512 7 r. "Papilio cresphontes" (vert) 70 75
2513 7 r. Lime swallowtail caterpillar (vert) 70 75
2514 7 r. "Cynthia virginiensis" (vert) 70 75
2515 7 r. Monarch caterpillar (vert) . 70 75
2516 7 r. "Danaus plexippus" (vert) . 70 75
2517 7 r. Monarch caterpillar and pupa (vert) 70 75
2518 7 r. "Chlosyne harrisii" (vert) . 70 75
2519 7 r. "Cymothoe coccinata" (vert) 70 75
2520 7 r. "Morpho rhetenor" (vert) . 70 75
2521 7 r. "Callicore lidwina" (vert) . 70 75
2522 7 r. "Heliconius erato reductimacula" (vert) . . . 70 75

338 Amtrak F40H Diesel-electric Locomotive, U.S.A.

1996. Trains of the World. Multicoloured.

2524 3 r. Type **338** 30 35
2525 3 r. Stephenson's "Experiment" . 30 35
2526 3 r. Indian-Pacific Intercontinental, Australia . 30 35
2527 3 r. Stephenson's Killingworth type steam locomotive, 1815 30 35
2528 3 r. George Stephenson . . . 30 35
2529 3 r. Stephenson's "Rocket", 1829 . . . . 30 35
2530 3 r. High Speed Train 125, Great Britain 30 35
2531 3 r. First rail passenger coach "Experiment", 1825 . . . . 30 35
2532 3 r. Union Pacific Class U25B diesel locomotive (inscr "Tofac"), U.S.A. 30 35
2533 3 r. Southern Pacific's "Daylight" express, 1952, U.S.A. 30 35
2534 3 r. Timothy Hackworth's "Sans Pareil", 1829 . . . . . . 30 35
2535 3 r. Chicago and North Western diesel locomotive, U.S.A. . 30 35
2536 3 r. Richard Trevithick's "Pen-y-Darren" locomotive, 1804 30 35
2537 3 r. Isambard Kingdom Brunel 30 35
2538 3 r. Great Western locomotive, 1838 . . . . 30 35
2539 3 r. Vistadome observation car, Canada 30 35
2540 3 r. Mohawk and Hudson Railroad "Experiment", 1832 30 35
2541 3 r. ICE high speed train, Germany 30 35
2542 3 r. Electric container locomotive, Germany . . . 30 35
2543 3 r. John Blenkinsop's rack locomotive, 1811 . . . . . 30 35
2544 3 r. Diesel-electric locomotive, Western Australia . . . 30 35
2545 3 r. Timothy Hackworth's "Royal George", 1827 . . . 30 35
2546 3 r. Robert Stephenson . . . 30 35
2547 3 r. Trevithick's "Newcastle" . 30 35
2548 3 r. Deltic diesel-electric locomotive, Great Britain . 30 35
2549 3 r. Stockton and Darlington Railway locomotive No. 5 "Stockton", 1826 . . . . . 30 35
2550 3 r. Channel Tunnel "Le Shuttle" train 30 35

339 Bongo

1996. Wildlife of the World. Multicoloured.

2552 5 r. Type **339** 50 55
2553 5 r. Bushbuck 50 55
2554 5 r. Namaqua dove 50 55
2555 5 r. Hoopoe 50 55
2556 5 r. African fish eagle 50 55
2557 5 r. Egyptian goose 50 55
2558 5 r. Saddle-bill stork 50 55
2559 5 r. Blue-breasted kingfisher . 50 55
2560 5 r. Yellow baboon 50 55
2561 5 r. Banded duiker ("Zebra Duiker") 50 55
2562 5 r. Yellow-backed duiker . . 50 55
2563 5 r. Pygmy hippopotamus . . 50 55
2564 5 r. Large-spotted genet . . . 50 55
2565 5 r. African spoonbill 50 55
2566 5 r. White-faced whistling duck 50 55
2567 5 r. Helmet guineafowl . . . 50 55
2568 7 r. Cotton-headed tamarin (horiz) 70 75
2569 7 r. European bison (horiz) . . 70 75
2570 7 r. Tiger (horiz) 70 75
2571 7 r. Capercaillie (horiz) . . . 70 75
2572 7 r. Giant panda (horiz) . . . 70 75
2573 7 r. "Trogonoptera brookiana" (butterfly) (horiz) 70 75
2574 7 r. American beaver (horiz) . 70 75
2575 7 r. "Leiopelma hamiltoni" (frog) (horiz) 70 75
2576 7 r. Manatee (horiz) 70 75

Nos. 2552/9, 2560/7 and 2568/76 respectively were printed together, se-tenant, with the backgrounds forming composite designs.

No. 2553 is inscribed "BUSHBACK" in error.

340 Giant Panda

1996. Endangered Species. Multicoloured.

2578 5 r. Type **340** 50 55
2579 5 r. Indian elephant 50 55
2580 5 r. Arrow-poison frog . . . 50 55
2581 5 r. Mandrill 50 55
2582 5 r. Snow leopard 50 55
2583 5 r. California condor 50 55
2584 5 r. Whale-headed stork ("Shoebill Stork") 50 55
2585 5 r. Red-billed hornbill . . . 50 55
2586 5 r. Hippopotamus 50 55
2587 5 r. Gorilla 50 55
2588 5 r. Lion 50 55
2589 5 r. South African crowned crane 50 55

341 Mickey Mouse climbing out of Puddle

1996. Centenary of the Cinema. Cartoon Frames from "The Little Whirlwind" (Nos. 2591/2607) or "Pluto and the Flypaper (Nos. 2608/24). Mult.

2591 4 r. Type **341** 90 90
2592 4 r. Frame 2 . . . . 90 90
2593 4 r. Frame 3 . . . . 90 90
2594 4 r. Frame 4 . . . . 90 90
2595 4 r. Frame 5 . . . . 90 90
2596 4 r. Frame 6 . . . . 90 90
2597 4 r. Frame 7 . . . . 90 90
2598 4 r. Frame 8 . . . . 90 90
2599 4 r. Frame 9 . . . . 90 90
2600 4 r. Frame 10 . . . . 90 90
2601 4 r. Frame 11 . . . . 90 90
2602 4 r. Frame 12 . . . . 90 90
2603 4 r. Frame 13 . . . . 90 90
2604 4 r. Frame 14 . . . . 90 90
2605 4 r. Frame 15 . . . . 90 90
2606 4 r. Frame 16 (Mickey holding fish above head) 90 90
2607 4 r. Frame 17 (Mickey throwing fish into pool) 90 90
2608 4 r. Frame 1 (Pluto) 90 90
2609 4 r. Frame 2 . . . . 90 90
2610 4 r. Frame 3 . . . . 90 90
2611 4 r. Frame 4 . . . . 90 90
2612 4 r. Frame 5 . . . . 90 90
2613 4 r. Frame 6 . . . . 90 90
2614 4 r. Frame 7 . . . . 90 90
2615 4 r. Frame 8 . . . . 90 90
2616 4 r. Frame 9 . . . . 90 90
2617 4 r. Frame 10 . . . . 90 90
2618 4 r. Frame 11 . . . . 90 90
2619 4 r. Frame 12 . . . . 90 90
2620 4 r. Frame 13 . . . . 90 90
2621 4 r. Frame 14 . . . . 90 90
2622 4 r. Frame 15 . . . . 90 90
2623 4 r. Frame 16 . . . . 90 90
2624 4 r. Frame 17 . . . . 90 90

342 Letter "O" with Chinese Character

1997. "HONG KONG '97" International Stamp Exhibition. Multicoloured.

2626 5 r. Letter "H" and Chinese couple 50 55
2627 5 r. Type **342** 50 55
2628 5 r. Letter "N" and Chinese dragon 50 55
2629 5 r. Letter "G" and carnival dragon 50 55
2630 5 r. Letter "K" and modern office block 50 55
2631 5 r. Letter "O" and Chinese character (different) . . . 50 55
2632 5 r. Letter "N" and Chinese fan cases 50 55
2633 5 r. Letter "G" and Chinese junk 50 55

343 California Condor

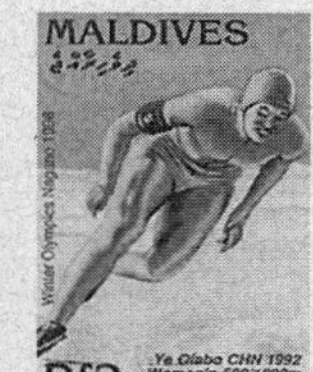

344 Ye Qiabo (China) (women's 500/1000m speed skating, 1992)

1997. Birds of the World. Multicoloured.

2635	5 r. Type **343**	50	55
2636	5 r. Audouin's gull	50	55
2637	5 r. Atlantic puffin	50	55
2638	5 r. Resplendent quetzal	50	55
2639	5 r. Puerto Rican amazon	50	55
2640	5 r. Lesser bird of paradise	50	55
2641	5 r. Japanese crested ibis	50	55
2642	5 r. Mauritius kestrel	50	55
2643	5 r. Kakapo	50	55

Nos. 2635/43 were printed together, se-tenant, with the backgrounds forming a composite design.

1997. Winter Olympic Games, Nagano, Japan (1998). Multicoloured.

2645	2 r. Type **344**	20	25
2646	3 r. Leonhard Stock (Austria) (downhill skiing, 1980)	30	35
2647	5 r. Herma von Szabo-Planck (Austria) (figure skating, 1924)	50	55
2648	5 r. Katarina Witt (Germany) (figure skating, 1988)	50	55
2649	5 r. Natalia Bestemianova and Andrei Bukin (Russia) (pairs ice dancing, 1988)	50	55
2650	5 r. Jayne Torvill and Christopher Dean (Great Britain) (pairs ice dancing, 1984)	50	55
2651	8 r. Bjorn Daehlie (Norway) (cross-country skiing, 1992)	80	85
2652	12 r. Wolfgang Hoppe (Germany) (bobsleigh, 1984)	1·25	1·40

345 Crowned Solitary Eagle

1997. Eagles. Multicoloured.

2654	1 r. Type **345**	10	15
2655	2 r. African hawk eagle (horiz)	20	25
2656	3 r. Lesser spotted eagle	30	35
2657	5 r. Stellar's sea eagle	50	55
2658	5 r. Bald eagle attacking	50	55
2659	5 r. Bald eagle on branch	50	55
2660	5 r. Bald eagle looking left	50	55
2661	5 r. Bald eagle looking right	50	55
2662	5 r. Bald eagle sitting on branch with leaves	50	55
2663	5 r. Bald eagle soaring	50	55
2664	8 r. Spanish imperial eagle (horiz)	80	85
2665	10 r. Harpy eagle	1·00	1·10
2666	12 r. Crested serpent eagle (horiz)	1·25	1·40

346 Blitzer Benz, 1911

1997. Classic Cars. Multicoloured.

2668	5 r. Type **346**	50	55
2669	5 r. Datsun, 1917	50	55
2670	5 r. Auburn 8-120, 1929	50	55
2671	5 r. Mercedes-Benz C280, 1996	50	55
2672	5 r. Suzuki UR-1	50	55
2673	5 r. Chrysler Atlantic	50	55
2674	5 r. Mercedes-Benz 190SL, 1961	50	55
2675	5 r. Kwaishinha D.A.T., 1916	50	55
2676	5 r. Rolls-Royce Roadster 20/25	50	55
2677	5 r. Mercedes-Benz SLK, 1997	50	55
2678	5 r. Toyota Camry, 1996	50	55
2679	5 r. Jaguar MK 2, 1959	50	55

347 "Patris II", Greece (1926)

1997. Passenger Ships. Multicoloured.

2681	1 r. Type **347**	10	15
2682	2 r. "Infanta Beatriz", Spain (1928)	20	25
2683	3 r. "Vasilefs Constantinos", Greece (1914)	30	35
2684	3 r. "Cunene", Portugal (1911)	30	35
2685	3 r. "Selandia", Denmark (1912)	30	35
2686	3 r. "President Harding", U.S.A. (1921)	30	35
2687	3 r. "Ulster Monarch", Great Britain (1929)	30	35
2688	3 r. "Matsonia", U.S.A. (1913)	30	35
2689	3 r. "France", France (1911)	30	35
2690	3 r. "Campania", Great Britain (1893)	30	35
2691	3 r. "Klipfontein", Holland (1922)	30	35
2692	3 r. "Eridan", France (1929)	30	35
2693	3 r. "Mount Clinton", U.S.A. (1921)	30	35
2694	3 r. "Infanta Isabel", Spain (1912)	30	35
2695	3 r. "Suwa Maru", Japan (1914)	30	35
2696	3 r. "Yorkshire", Great Britain (1920)	30	35
2697	3 r. "Highland Chieftain", Great Britain (1929)	30	35
2698	3 r. "Sardinia", Norway (1920)	30	35
2699	3 r. "San Guglielmo", Italy (1911)	30	35
2700	3 r. "Avila", Great Britain (1927)	30	35
2701	8 r. "Stavangerfjord", Norway (1918	80	85
2702	12 r. "Baloeran", Netherlands (1929)	1·25	1·40

1997. 50th Anniv of U.N.E.S.C.O. As T **273a** of Gambia. Multicoloured.

2704	1 r. Prayer wheels, Lhasa (vert)	10	15
2705	2 r. Ruins of Roman Temple of Diana, Portugal	20	25
2706	3 r. Santa Maria Cathedral, Hildesheim, Germany	30	35
2707	5 r. Vivunga National Park, Zaire (vert)	50	55
2708	5 r. Valley of Mai Nature Reserve, Seychelles (vert)	50	55
2709	5 r. Kandy, Sri Lanka (vert)	50	55
2710	5 r. Taj Mahal, India (vert)	50	55
2711	5 r. Istanbul, Turkey (vert)	50	55
2712	5 r. Sana'a, Yemen (vert)	50	55
2713	5 r. Bleinheim Palace, England (vert)	50	55
2714	5 r. Grand Canyon National Park, U.S.A. (vert)	50	55
2715	5 r. Tombs, Gondar, Ethiopia (vert)	50	55
2716	5 r. Bwindi National Park, Uganda (vert)	50	55
2717	5 r. Bemaraha National Reserve, Madagascar (vert)	50	55
2718	5 r. Buddhist ruins at Takht-I-Bahi, Pakistan (vert)	50	55
2719	5 r. Anuradhapura, Sri Lanka (vert)	50	55
2720	5 r. Cairo, Egypt (vert)	50	55
2721	5 r. Ruins, Petra, Jordan (vert)	50	55
2722	5 r. Volcano, Ujung Kulon National Park, Indonesia (vert)	50	55
2723	5 r. Terrace, Mount Taishan, China (vert)	50	55
2724	5 r. Temple, Mount Taishan, China (vert)	50	55
2725	5 r. Temple turret, Mount Taishan, China (vert)	50	55
2726	5 r. Standing stones, Mount Taishan, China (vert)	50	55
2727	5 r. Courtyard, Mount Taishan, China (vert)	50	55
2728	5 r. Staircase, Mount Taishan, China (vert)	50	55
2729	5 r. Terracotta Warriors, China (vert)	50	55
2730	5 r. Head of Terracota Warrior, China (vert)	50	55
2731	7 r. Doorway, Abu Simbel, Egypt (vert)	70	75
2732	8 r. Mandraki, Rhodes, Greece	80	85
2733	8 r. Agios Stefanos Monastery, Meteora, Greece	80	85
2734	8 r. Taj Mahal, India	80	85
2735	8 r. Cistercian Abbey of Fontenay, France	80	85
2736	8 r. Yarushima, Japan	80	85
2737	8 r. Cloisters, San Gonzalo Convent, Portugal	80	85
2738	8 r. Olympic National Park, U.S.A.	80	85
2739	8 r. Waterfall, Nahanni National Park, Canada	80	85
2740	8 r. Mountains, National Park, Argentina	80	85
2741	8 r. Bonfin Salvador Church, Brazil	80	85
2742	8 r. Convent of the Companions of Jesus, Morelia, Mexico	80	85
2743	8 r. Two-storey temple, Horyu Temple, Japan	80	85
2744	8 r. Summer house, Horyu Temple, Japan	80	85
2745	8 r. Temple and cloister, Horyu Temple, Japan	80	85
2746	8 r. Single storey temple, Horyu Temple, Japan	80	85
2747	8 r. Well, Horyu Temple, Japan	80	85
2748	10 r. Scandola Nature Reserve, France	1·00	1·10
2749	12 r. Temple on the Lake, China	1·25	1·40

No. 2717 is inscribed "MADAGASGAR" and 2737 "COVENT", both in error.

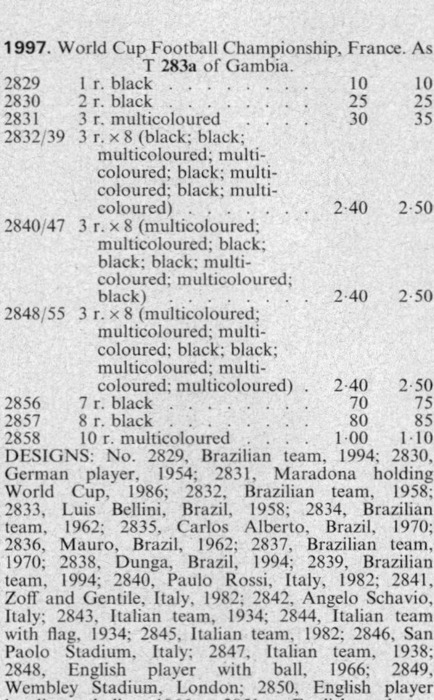

349 White Doves and S.A.A.R.C. Logo

1997. 9th South Asian Association for Regional Cooperation Summit, Male. Multicoloured.

2751	3 r. Type **349**	30	35
2752	5 r. Flags of member countries	50	55

1997. Golden Wedding of Queen Elizabeth and Prince Philip. As T **276c** of Gambia. Multicoloured.

2753	5 r. Queen Elizabeth II	50	55
2754	5 r. Royal coat of arms	50	55
2755	5 r. Queen Elizabeth and Prince Philip at opening of Parliament	50	55
2756	5 r. Queen Elizabeth and Prince Philip with Prince Charles, 1948	50	55
2757	5 r. Buckingham Palace from the garden	50	55
2758	5 r. Prince Philip	50	55

1997. "Pacific '97" International Stamp Exhibition, San Francisco. Death Centenary of Heinrich von Stephan (founder of the U.P.U.). As T **276d** of Gambia.

2760	2 r. green and black	20	25
2761	2 r. brown and black	20	25
2762	2 r. violet	20	25

DESIGNS: No. 2760, Early Indian Mail Messenger; 2761, Von Stephan and Mercury; 2762, Autogyro, Washington.

1997. Birth Bicentenary of Hiroshige (Japanese painter). "One Hundred Famous Views of Edo". As T **541a** of Ghana. Multicoloured.

2763	8 r. "Dawn at Kanda Myojn Shrine"	80	85
2764	8 r. "Kiyomizu Hall and Shinobazu Pond at Ueno"	80	85
2765	8 r. "Ueno Yamashita"	80	85
2766	8 r. "Moon Pine, Ueno"	80	85
2767	8 r. "Flower Pavilion, Dango Slope, Sendagi"	80	85
2768	8 r. "Shitaya Hirokoji"	80	85

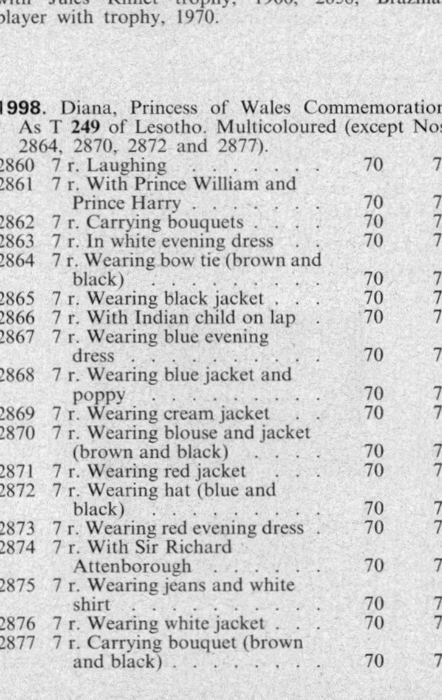

353 Common Noddy

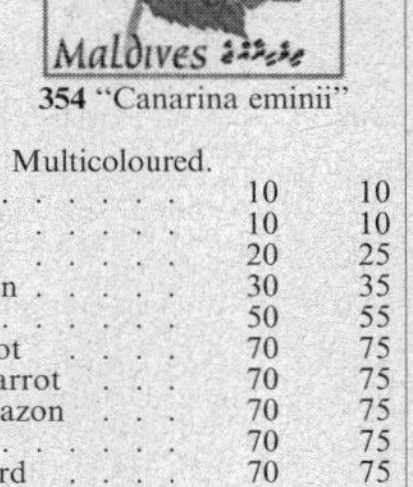

354 "Canarina eminii"

1997. Birds. Multicoloured.

2770	30 l. Type **353**	10	10
2771	1 r. Spectacled owl	10	10
2772	2 r. Malay fish owl	20	25
2773	3 r. Peregrine falcon	30	35
2774	5 r. Golden eagle	50	55
2775	7 r. Ruppell's parrot	70	75
2776	7 r. Blue-headed parrot	70	75
2777	7 r. St. Vincent amazon	70	75
2778	7 r. Grey parrot	70	75
2779	7 r. Masked lovebird	70	75
2780	7 r. Sun conure	70	75
2781	8 r. Bateleur	80	85
2782	10 r. Whiskered tern with chicks	1·00	1·10
2783	10 r. Common caracara	1·00	1·10
2784	15 r. Red-footed booby	1·50	1·60

1997. Flowers. Multicoloured

2786	1 r. Type **354**	10	10
2787	2 r. "Delphinium macrocentron"	20	25
2788	3 r. "Leucadendron discolor"	30	35
2789	5 r. "Nymphaea caerulea"	50	55
2790	7 r. "Rosa multiflora polyantha" (20 × 23 mm)	70	75
2791	8 r. "Bulbophyllum barbigerum"	80	85
2792	8 r. "Acacia seyal" (horiz)	80	85
2793	8 r. "Gloriosa superba" (horiz)	80	85
2794	8 r. "Gnidia subcordata" (horiz)	80	85
2795	8 r. "Platycelyphium voense" (horiz)	80	85
2796	8 r. "Aspilia mossambicensis" (horiz)	80	85
2797	8 r. "Adenium obesum" (horiz)	80	85
2798	12 r. "Hibiscus vitifolius"	1·25	1·40

Nos. 2792/7 were printed together, se-tenant, with the backgrounds forming a composite design.

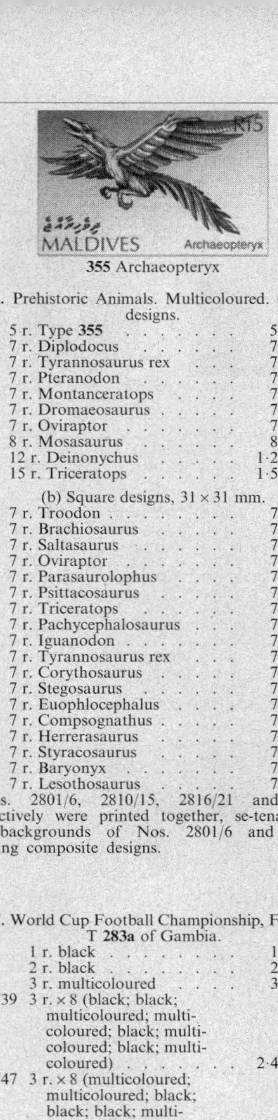

355 Archaeopteryx

1997. Prehistoric Animals. Multicoloured. (a) Horiz designs.

2800	5 r. Type **355**	50	55
2801	7 r. Diplodocus	70	75
2802	7 r. Tyrannosaurus rex	70	75
2803	7 r. Pteranodon	70	75
2804	7 r. Montanceratops	70	75
2805	7 r. Dromaeosaurus	70	75
2806	7 r. Oviraptor	70	75
2807	8 r. Mosasaurus	80	85
2808	12 r. Deinonychus	1·25	1·40
2809	15 r. Triceratops	1·50	1·60

(b) Square designs, 31 × 31 mm.

2810	7 r. Troodon	70	75
2811	7 r. Brachiosaurus	70	75
2812	7 r. Saltasaurus	70	75
2813	7 r. Oviraptor	70	75
2814	7 r. Parasaurolophus	70	75
2815	7 r. Psittacosaurus	70	75
2816	7 r. Triceratops	70	75
2817	7 r. Pachycephalosaurus	70	75
2818	7 r. Iguanodon	70	75
2819	7 r. Tyrannosaurus rex	70	75
2820	7 r. Corythosaurus	70	75
2821	7 r. Stegosaurus	70	75
2822	7 r. Euophlocephalus	70	75
2823	7 r. Compsognathus	70	75
2824	7 r. Herrerasaurus	70	75
2825	7 r. Styracosaurus	70	75
2826	7 r. Baryonyx	70	75
2827	7 r. Lesothosaurus	70	75

Nos. 2801/6, 2810/15, 2816/21 and 2822/7 respectively were printed together, se-tenant, with the backgrounds of Nos. 2801/6 and 2810/15 forming composite designs.

1997. World Cup Football Championship, France. As T **283a** of Gambia.

2829	1 r. black	10	10
2830	2 r. black	25	25
2831	3 r. multicoloured	30	35
2832/39	3 r. × 8 (black; black; multicoloured; multi-coloured; black; multi-coloured; black; multi-coloured)	2·40	2·50
2840/47	3 r. × 8 (multicoloured; multicoloured; black; black; black; multi-coloured; multicoloured; black)	2·40	2·50
2848/55	3 r. × 8 (multicoloured; multicoloured; multi-coloured; black; black; multicoloured; multi-coloured; multicoloured)	2·40	2·50
2856	7 r. black	70	75
2857	8 r. black	80	85
2858	10 r. multicoloured	1·00	1·10

DESIGNS: No. 2829, Brazilian team, 1994; 2830, German player, 1954; 2831, Maradona holding World Cup, 1986; 2832, Brazilian team, 1958; 2833, Luis Bellini, Brazil, 1958; 2834, Brazilian team, 1962; 2835, Carlos Alberto, Brazil, 1970; 2836, Mauro, Brazil, 1962; 2837, Brazilian team, 1970; 2838, Dunga, Brazil, 1994; 2839, Brazilian team, 1994; 2840, Paulo Rossi, Italy, 1982; 2841, Zoff and Gentile, Italy, 1982; 2842, Angelo Schavio, Italy; 2843, Italian team, 1934; 2844, Italian team with flag, 1934; 2845, Italian team, 1982; 2846, San Paolo Stadium, Italy; 2847, Italian team, 1938; 2848, English player with ball, 1966; 2849, Wembley Stadium, London; 2850, English player heading ball, 1966; 2851, English players celebrating, 1966; 2852, English and German players chasing ball, 1966; 2853, English player wearing No. 21 shirt, 1966; 2854, English team with Jules Rimet trophy, 1966; 2855, German player wearing No. 5 shirt, 1966; 2856, Argentine player holding trophy, 1978; 2857, English players with Jules Rimet trophy, 1966; 2858, Brazilian player with trophy, 1970.

1998. Diana, Princess of Wales Commemoration. As T **249** of Lesotho. Multicoloured (except Nos. 2864, 2870, 2872 and 2877).

2860	7 r. Laughing	70	75
2861	7 r. With Prince William and Prince Harry	70	75
2862	7 r. Carrying bouquets	70	75
2863	7 r. In white evening dress	70	75
2864	7 r. Wearing bow tie (brown and black)	70	75
2865	7 r. Wearing black jacket	70	75
2866	7 r. With Indian child on lap	70	75
2867	7 r. Wearing blue evening dress	70	75
2868	7 r. Wearing blue jacket and poppy	70	75
2869	7 r. Wearing cream jacket	70	75
2870	7 r. Wearing blouse and jacket (brown and black)	70	75
2871	7 r. Wearing red jacket	70	75
2872	7 r. Wearing hat (blue and black)	70	75
2873	7 r. Wearing red evening dress	70	75
2874	7 r. With Sir Richard Attenborough	70	75
2875	7 r. Wearing jeans and white shirt	70	75
2876	7 r. Wearing white jacket	70	75
2877	7 r. Carrying bouquet (brown and black)	70	75

356 Pres. Nelson Mandela

357 Pres. John F. Kennedy

1998. 80th Birthday of Nelson Mandela (President of South Africa).

2879 **356** 7 r. multicoloured 70 75

1998. Pres. John F. Kennedy Commemoration. Multicoloured, background colours given.

2880 **357** 5 r. green 50 55
2881 – 5 r. green 50 55
2882 – 5 r. brown (inscr at right) . 50 55
2883 – 5 r. yellow 50 55
2884 – 5 r. violet 50 55
2885 – 5 r. blue 50 55
2886 – 5 r. grey 50 55
2887 – 5 r. brown (inscr at left) . 50 55
2888 – 5 r. blue (value at bottom right) 50 55

DESIGNS: Nos. 2881/8, Various portraits.

358 Yakovlev Yak-18 (from 1947)

1998. Aircraft in Longest Continuous Production. Multicoloured.

2889 5 r. Type **358** 50 55
2890 5 r. Beechcraft Bonanza (from 1947) 50 55
2891 5 r. Piper Cub (1937–82) . . . 50 55
2892 5 r. Tupolev Tu-95 (1954–90) . 50 55
2893 5 r. Lockheed C-130 Hercules (from 1954) 50 55
2894 5 r. Piper PA-28 Cherokee (from 1961) 50 55
2895 5 r. Mikoyan Gurevich MiG-21 (from 1959) 50 55
2896 5 r. Pilatus PC-6 Turbo Porter (from 1960) 50 55
2897 5 r. Antonov An-2 (from 1949) 50 55

359 White American Shorthair

1998. Cats. Multicoloured.

2899 5 r. Type **359** 50 55
2900 7 r. American curl and Maine coon (horiz) 70 75
2901 7 r. Maine coon (horiz) . . . 70 75
2902 7 r. Siberian (horiz) 70 75
2903 7 r. Somali (horiz) 70 75
2904 7 r. European Burmese (horiz) . 70 75
2905 7 r. Nebelung (horiz) 70 75
2906 7 r. Bicolor British shorthair (horiz) 70 75
2907 7 r. Manx (horiz) 70 75
2908 7 r. Tabby American shorthair (horiz) 70 75
2909 7 r. Silver tabby Persian (horiz) 70 75
2910 7 r. Oriental white (horiz) . . 70 75
2911 7 r. Norwegian forest cat (horiz) 70 75
2912 8 r. Sphynx cat 80 85
2913 10 r. Tabby American shorthair 1·00 1·10
2914 12 r. Scottish fold . . . . . . 1·25 1·25

Nos. 2900/5 and 2906/11 respectively were printed together, se-tenant, forming composite designs.

360 Boeing 737 HS

1998. Aircraft. Multicoloured.

2916 2 r. Type **360** 20 25
2917 5 r. CL-215 (flying boat) . . . 50 55
2918 5 r. Orion 50 55
2919 5 r. Yakolev Yak-54 . . . . . 50 55
2920 5 r. Cessna sea plane 50 55
2921 5 r. CL-215 (amphibian) . . . 50 55
2922 5 r. CL-215 SAR (amphibian) . 50 55
2923 5 r. Twin Otter 50 55
2924 5 r. Rockwell Quail 50 55
2925 5 r. F.S.W. fighter 50 55
2926 5 r. V-Jet II 50 55
2927 5 r. Pilatus PC-12 . . . . . . 50 55
2928 5 r. Citation Exel 50 55
2929 5 r. Stutz Bearcat 50 55
2930 5 r. Cessna T-37 (B) 50 55
2931 5 r. Peregrine Business Jet . . 50 55
2932 5 r. Beech 58 Baron 50 55
2933 7 r. Boeing 727 . . . . 70 75
2934 8 r. Boeing 747-400 . . . . . 80 85
2935 10 r. Boeing 737 . . . . . . 1·00 1·10

361 Captain Edward Smith's Cap

1998. "Titanic" Commemoration. Multicoloured.

2937 7 r. Type **361** 70 75
2938 7 r. Deck chair 70 75
2939 7 r. Fifth Officer Harold Lowe's coat button 70 75
2940 7 r. Lifeboat 70 75
2941 7 r. "Titanic's" wheel 70 75
2942 7 r. Passenger's lifejacket . . . 70 75

362 Guava Tree

1998. 20th Anniv of International Fund of Agriculture. Multicoloured.

2944 1 r. Type **362** 10 15
2945 5 r. Selection of fruit 50 55
2946 7 r. Fishing boat 70 75
2947 8 r. Papaya tree 80 85
2948 10 r. Vegetable produce . . . 1·00 1·10

363 Thread-finned Butterflyfish

1998. Fish. Multicoloured.

2949 50 l. Type **363** 10 10
2950 50 l. Queen angelfish 10 10
2951 1 r. Oriental sweetlips 10 15
2952 3 r. Mandarin fish 30 35
2953 3 r. Copper-banded butterflyfish 30 35
2954 3 r. Harlequin tuskfish 30 35
2955 3 r. Yellow-tailed demoiselle . 30 35
2956 3 r. Wimplefish 30 35
2957 3 r. Red emperor snapper . . 30 35
2958 3 r. Clown triggerfish 30 35
2959 3 r. Common clown 30 35
2960 3 r. Palette surgeonfish ("Regal Tang") 30 35
2961 5 r. Emperor angelfish 50 55
2962 5 r. Common squirrelfish ("Diadem Squirrelfish") . . 50 55
2963 5 r. Lemon-peel angelfish . . 50 55
2964 5 r. Powder-blue surgeonfish . 50 55
2965 5 r. Moorish idol 50 55
2966 5 r. Bicolor angelfish ("Bicolor Cherub") 50 55
2967 5 r. Duboulay's angelfish ("Scribbled Angelfish") . . 50 55
2968 5 r. Two-banded anemonefish . 50 55
2969 5 r. Yellow tang 50 55
2970 7 r. Red-tailed surgeonfish ("Achilles Tang") 70 75
2971 7 r. Bandit angelfish 70 75
2972 8 r. Hooded butterflyfish ("Red-headed Butterflyfish") . . 80 85
2973 50 r. Blue-striped butterflyfish . 5·00 5·25

364 Baden-Powell inspecting Scouts, Amesbury, 1909

1998. 19th World Scout Jamboree, Chile. Multicoloured.

2975 12 r. Type **364** . . . . 1·25 1·40
2976 12 r. Sir Robert and Lady Baden-Powell with children, 1927 . . . . 1·25 1·40
2977 12 r. Sir Robert Baden-Powell awarding merit badges, Chicago, 1926 . . . . . . 1·25 1·40

365 Diana, Princess of Wales

1998. 1st Death Anniv of Diana, Princess of Wales.

2978 **365** 10 r. multicoloured . . . 1·00 1·10

366 Triton Shell

1999. International Year of the Ocean. Marine Life. Multicoloured.

2979 25 l. Type **366** 10 10
2980 50 l. Napoleon wrasse 10 10
2981 1 r. Whale shark 10 15
2982 3 r. Grey reef shark 30 35
2983 5 r. Harp seal 50 55
2984 5 r. Killer whale 50 55
2985 5 r. Sea otter 50 55
2986 5 r. Beluga 50 55
2987 5 r. Narwhal 50 55
2988 5 r. Walrus 50 55
2989 5 r. Sea lion 50 55
2990 5 r. Humpback salmon 50 55
2991 5 r. Emperor penguin 50 55
2992 7 r. Blue whale 70 75
2993 7 r. Skipjack tuna 70 75
2994 8 r. Ocean sunfish 80 85
2995 8 r. Opalescent squid 80 85
2996 8 r. Electric ray 80 85
2997 8 r. Corded neptune 80 85

Nos. 2983/91 were printed together, se-tenant, with the backgrounds forming a composite design.

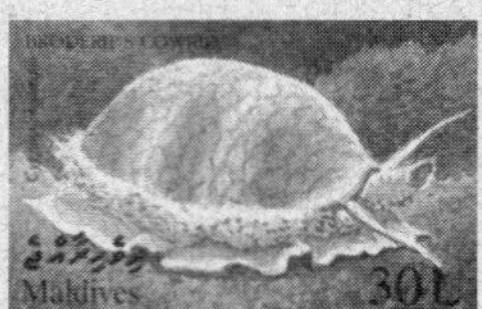

367 Broderip's Cowrie

1999. Marine Life. Multicoloured.

2999 30 l. Type **367** 10 10
3000 1 r. White tern 10 15
3001 3 r. Green heron 30 35
3002 5 r. Manta ray 50 55
3003 5 r. Green turtle 50 55
3004 5 r. Spotted dolphins 50 55
3005 5 r. Moorish idols 50 55
3006 5 r. Threadfin anthias 50 55
3007 5 r. Goldbar wrasse 50 55
3008 5 r. Palette surgeonfish . . . 50 55
3009 5 r. Three-spotted angelfish . 50 55
3010 5 r. Oriental sweetlips 50 55
3011 5 r. Brown booby 50 55
3012 5 r. Red-tailed tropic bird . . 50 55
3013 5 r. Sooty tern 50 55
3014 5 r. Striped dolphin 50 55
3015 5 r. Spinner dolphin 50 55
3016 5 r. Crab plover 50 55
3017 5 r. Hawksbill turtle 50 55
3018 5 r. Indo-Pacific sergeant . . 50 55
3019 5 r. Yellow-finned tuna . . . 50 55
3020 7 r. Blackflag sandperch . . . 70 75
3021 8 r. Coral hind 80 85
3022 10 r. Olive Ridley turtle . . . 1·00 1·10

Nos. 3002/10 and 3011/19 were each printed together, se-tenant, with the backgrounds forming composite designs.

368 Mickey Mouse

1999. 70th Anniv of Mickey Mouse (Disney cartoon character). Multicoloured.

3024/9 5 r. × 6 (Mickey Mouse: Type **368**; laughing; looking tired; frowning; smiling; winking) . . . . 3·00 3·75
3030/5 5 r. × 6 (Minnie Mouse: facing left and smiling; with eyes closed; with hand on head; looking surprised; smiling; looking cross) . . . . 3·00 3·75
3036/41 7 r. × 6 (Donald Duck: facing left and smiling; laughing; looking tired; looking cross; smiling; winking) . 4·25 5·00
3042/7 7 r. × 6 (Daisy Duck: with half closed eyes; laughing; looking shocked; looking cross; facing forwards; with head on one side) . . 4·25 5·00
3048/53 7 r. × 6 (Goofy: facing right and smiling; with eyes closed; with half closed eyes; looking shocked; looking puzzled; looking thoughtful) . . . . . . 4·25 5·00
3054/9 7 r. × 6 (Pluto: looking shocked; with eyes closed; smiling; scowling; with tongue out (orange background); with tongue out (green background) . . . 4·25 5·00

369 Great Orange Tip

1999. Butterflies. Multicoloured.

3061 50 l. Type **369** 10 10
3062 1 r. Large green aporandria . . 10 15
3063 2 r. Common mormon 20 25
3064 3 r. African migrant 30 35
3065 5 r. Common pierrot 50 55
3066 7 r. Crimson tip (vert) 70 75
3067 7 r. Tawny rajah (vert) 70 75
3068 7 r. Leafwing butterfly (vert) . . 70 75
3069 7 r. Great egg-fly (vert) . . . 70 75
3070 7 r. Blue admiral (vert) 70 75
3071 7 r. African migrant (vert) . . 70 75
3072 7 r. Common red flash (vert) . 70 75
3073 7 r. Burmese lascar (vert) . . . 70 75
3074 7 r. Common perriot (vert) . . 70 75
3075 7 r. Baron (vert) 70 75
3076 7 r. Leaf blue (vert) 70 75
3077 7 r. Great orange tip (vert) . . 70 75
3078 10 r. Giant red-eye . . . . . 1·00 1·10

Nos. 3066/71 and 3072/7 were each printed together, se-tenant, with the backgrounds forming composite designs.

370 Scelidosaurus

1999. Prehistoric Animals. Multicoloured.

3080 1 r. Type **370** 10 15
3081 3 r. Yansudaurus 30 35
3082 5 r. Ornitholestes 50 55
3083 7 r. Dimorphodon (vert) . . . 70 75
3084 7 r. Rhamphorhynchus (vert) . 70 75
3085 7 r. Allosaurus (vert) 70 75
3086 7 r. Leaellynasaura (vert) . . . 70 75
3087 7 r. Troodon (vert) 70 75
3088 7 r. Syntarsus (vert) 70 75
3089 7 r. Anchisaurus (vert) 70 75
3090 7 r. Pterenodon (vert) 70 75
3091 7 r. Barosaurus (vert) 70 75
3092 7 r. Iguanodon (vert) 70 75
3093 7 r. Archaeopteryx (vert) . . . 70 75
3094 7 r. Ceratosaurus (vert) . . . 70 75
3095 7 r. Stegosaurus 70 75
3096 7 r. Corythosaurus 70 75
3097 7 r. Cetiosaurus 70 75
3098 7 r. Avimimus 70 75
3099 7 r. Styracosaurus 70 75
3100 7 r. Massospondylus 70 75
3101 8 r. Astrodon 80 85

Nos. 3083/8, 3089/94 and 3095/100 were each printed together, se-tenant, forming composite designs.

371 Express Locomotive, Egypt, 1856

1999. Trains of the World. Multicoloured.

3103 50 l. Type **371** 10 10
3104 1 r. Channel Tunnel Le Shuttle, France, 1994 . . . . . . 10 15
3105 2 r. Gowan and Marx locomotive, U.S.A., 1839 . . . . 20 25
3106 3 r. TGV train, France, 1981 . . 30 35
3107 5 r. "Ae 6/6" electric locomotive, Switzerland, 1954 . . 50 55
3108 7 r. Stephenson's long-boilered locomotive, Great Britain, 1846 (red livery) 70 75
3109 7 r. "Cornwall", Great Britain, 1847 . . . . 70 75
3110 7 r. First locomotive, Germany, 1848 . . . . 70 75
3111 7 r. Great Western locomotive, Great Britain, 1846 . . . . 70 75

3112 7 r. Standard Stephenson locomotive, France, 1837 70 75
3113 7 r. "Meteor", Great Britain, 1843 70 75
3114 7 r. Class 4T diesel-electric locomotive, Great Britain, 1940–65 70 75
3115 7 r. Mainline diesel-electric locomotive No. 20101, Malaya, 1940–65 70 75
3116 7 r. Class 7000 high-speed electric locomotive, France, 1949 70 75
3117 7 r. Diesel hydraulic express locomotive, Thailand, 1940–65 70 75
3118 7 r. Diesel hydraulic locomotive, Burma, 1940–65 70 75
3119 7 r. "Hikari" super express train, Japan, 1940–65 70 75
3120 8 r. Stephenson's long-boilered locomotive, Great Britain, 1846 (orange and green livery) 80 85
3121 10 r. "Philadelphia", Austria, 1838 1·00 1·10
3122 15 r. S.E. and C.R. Class E steam locomotive, Great Britain, 1940 1·50 1·60

1999. "Queen Elizabeth the Queen Mother's Century". As T **304a** of Gambia.

3124 7 r. black and gold 70 75
3125 7 r. black and gold 70 75
3126 7 r. multicoloured 70 75
3127 7 r. multicoloured 70 75

DESIGNS: No. 3124, King George VI and Queen Elizabeth, 1936; 3125, Queen Elizabeth, 1941; 3126, Queen Elizabeth in evening dress, 1960; 3127, Queen Mother at Ascot, 1981.

1999. "iBRA '99" International Stamp Exhibition, Nuremberg. As T **262** of Lesotho. Multicoloured.

3129 12 r. "Adler" (first German railway locomotive), 1833 1·25 1·40
3130 15 r. "Drache" (Henshell and Sohn's first locomotive), 1848 1·50 1·60

The captions on Nos. 3129/30 are transposed.

1999. 150th Death Anniv of Katsushika Hokusai (Japanese artist). As T **298b** of Gambia. Multicoloured (except No. 3133).

3131 7 r. "Haunted House" 70 75
3132 7 r. "Juniso Shrine at Yotsuya" 70 75
3133 7 r. Drawing of bird (black, green and gold) 70 75
3134 7 r. Drawing of two women 70 75
3135 7 r. "Lover in the Snow" 70 75
3136 7 r. "Mountain Tea House" 70 75
3137 7 r. "A Coastal View" 70 75
3138 7 r. "Bath House by a Lake" 70 75
3139 7 r. Drawing of a horse 70 75
3140 7 r. Drawing of two birds on branch 70 75
3141 7 r. "Evening Cool at Ryogoku" 70 75
3142 7 r. "Girls boating" 70 75

1999. 10th Anniv of United Nations Rights of the Child Convention. As T **298c** of Gambia. Multicoloured.

3144 10 r. Baby boy and young mother 1·00 1·10
3145 10 r. Young girl laughing 1·00 1·10
3146 10 r. Three children 1·00 1·10

373 Phobos and Demos (Martian Moons)

2000. Future Colonisation of Mars. Multicoloured.

3149 5 r. Type **373** 50 55
3150 5 r. Improved Hubble Telescope 50 55
3151 5 r. Passenger shuttle 50 55
3152 5 r. Skyscrapers on Mars 50 55
3153 5 r. Martian taxi 50 55
3154 5 r. Martian landing facilities 50 55
3155 5 r. Vegetation in Martian biosphere 50 55
3156 5 r. Walking on Mars and biosphere 50 55
3157 5 r. Mars rover 50 55
3158 5 r. Russian Phobos 25 satellite 50 55
3159 5 r. Earth and Moon 50 55
3160 5 r. Space shuttle leaving Earth 50 55
3161 5 r. Lighthouse on Mars 50 55
3162 5 r. Mars excursion space liner 50 55
3163 5 r. Mars shuttle and skyscrapers 50 55
3164 5 r. Viking Lander 50 55
3165 5 r. Mars air and water purification plant 50 55
3166 5 r. Family picnic on Mars 50 55

Nos. 3149/57 and 3158/66 were each printed together, se-tenant, with the backgrounds forming composite designs.

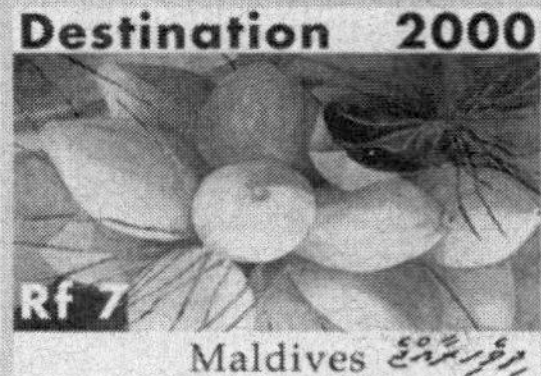

374 Coconuts

2000. "Destination 2000 - Maldives" Campaign. Multicoloured.

3168 7 r. Type **374** 70 75
3169 7 r. Shoal of skipjack tuna 70 75
3170 7 r. Sea plane and traditional dhow 70 75
3171 7 r. "Plumeria alba" 70 75
3172 7 r. Lionfish 70 75
3173 7 r. Windsurfers 70 75

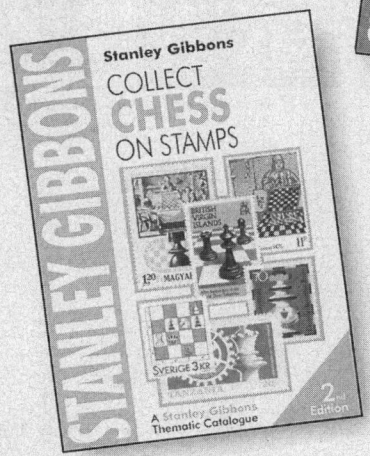

MALI Pt. 6; Pt. 13

Federation of French Sudan and Senegal, formed in 1959 as an autonomous republic within the French Community. In August 1960 the Federation was split up and the French Sudan part became the independent Mali Republic.

100 centimes = 1 franc

A. FEDERATION.

1 Map, Flag, Mali and Torch

1959. Establishment of Mali Federation.
1 **1** 25 f. multicoloured 50 50

2

1959. Air. 300th Anniv of St. Louis, Senegal.
2 **2** 85 f. multicoloured . . . . . . 1·50 1·25

3 West African Parrotfish 4 Violet Starling

1960. (a) Postage. Fish as T **3**.
3 **3** 5 f. orange, blue and bronze . . 40 15
4 – 10 f. black, brown & turquoise 40 25
5 – 15 f. brown, slate and blue . . 55 25
6 – 20 f. black, bistre and green 65 35
7 – 25 f. yellow, sepia and green 80 40
8 – 30 f. red, purple and blue . . 1·00 50
9 – 85 f. red, blue and green . . 3·00 1·75

(b) Air. Birds as T **4**.
10 **4** 100 f. multicoloured . . . . . 6·75 1·75
11 – 200 f. multicoloured . . . . . 15·00 5·50
12 – 500 f. multicoloured . . . . . 40·00 15·00

DESIGNS—HORIZ: 10 f. West African triggerfish; 15 f. Guinean fingerfish; 20 f. Threadfish; 25 f. Shining butterflyfish; 30 f. Monrovian surgeonfish; 85 f. Pink dentex; 200 f. Bateleur. VERT: 500 f. Common gonolek.

1960. 10th Anniv of African Technical Co-operation Commission. As T **4** of Malagasy Republic.
13 25 f. purple and violet . . . . 1·00 75

B. REPUBLIC.

1960. Nos. 6, 7, 9 and 10/12 optd **REPUBLIQUE DU MALI** and bar or bars or surch also.
14 20 f. black, bistre and green (postage) . . . . 1·50 60
15 25 f. red, purple and blue . . . 2·00 60
16 85 f. red, blue and green . . . . 3·75 1·50
17 100 f. multicoloured (air) . . . 5·50 1·50
18 200 f. multicoloured . . . . . 8·50 3·50
19 300 f. on 500 f. multicoloured 14·00 6·00
20 500 f. multicoloured . . . . . 28·00 17·00

7 Pres. Mamadou Konate

1961.
21 **7** 20 f. sepia & green (postage) 25 15
22 – 25 f. black and purple . . . 35 15
23 **7** 200 f. sepia and red (air) . . 3·00 1·00
24 – 300 f. black and green . . . 4·25 1·25

DESIGN: 25, 300 f. President Keita. Nos. 23/4 are larger 27 × 38 mm.

8 U.N. Emblem, Flag and Map

1961. Air. Proclamation of Independence and Admission into U.N.
25 **8** 100 f. multicoloured . . . . . 1·40 90

9 Sankore Mosque, Timbuktu

1961. Air.
26 **9** 100 f. brown, blue and sepia 1·75 55
27 – 200 f. brown, red and green 4·50 1·50
28 – 500 f. green, brown and blue 13·00 3·25

DESIGN: 200 f. View of Timbuktu; 500 f. Arms and view of Bamako.

10 Africans learning Vowels

1961. 1st Anniv of Independence.
29 **10** 25 f. multicoloured 60 30

11 Sheep at Pool 12 African Map and King Mohammed V of Morocco

1961.
30 **11** 50 c. sepia, myrtle and red . . 15 15
31 A 1 f. bistre, green and blue . . 15 15
32 B 2 f. red, green and blue . . . 15 15
33 C 3 f. brown, green and blue . . 15 15
34 D 4 f. blue, green and bistre . . 15 15
35 **11** 5 f. purple, green and blue . . 20 15
36 A 10 f. brown, myrtle & blue . . 20 15
37 B 15 f. brown, green & blue . . 20 15
38 C 20 f. red, green and blue . . 30 25
39 D 25 f. brown and blue 40 20
40 **11** 30 f. brown, green & violet 55 30
41 A 40 f. brown, green & blue . . 1·25 30
42 B 50 f. lake, green and blue . . 50 30
43 C 60 f. brown, green and blue . . 15 15
44 D 85 f. brown, bistre & blue . . 1·75 35

DESIGNS: A, Oxen at pool; B, House of Arts, Mali; C, Land tillage; D, Combine-harvester in rice field.

1962. 1st Anniv of African Conf, Casablanca.
45 **12** 25 f. multicoloured 25 15
46 50 f. multicoloured 50 20

13 Patrice Lumumba

1962. 1st Death Anniv of Patrice Lumumba (Congo leader).
47 **13** 25 f. brown and bistre . . . 20 20
48 100 f. brown and green . . . 75 50

1962. Malaria Eradication. As T **43** of Mauritania.
49 25 f. + 5 f. blue 50 60

14 Pegasus and U.P.U. Emblem

1962. 1st Anniv of Admission into U.P.U.
50 **14** 85 f. multicoloured . . . . . 1·00 65

14a Posthorn on Map of Africa 15 Sansanding Dam

1962. African Postal Union Commem.
51 **14a** 25 f. green and brown . . . 25 20
52 85 f. orange and green . . . 75 50

1962.
53 **15** 25 f. black, green and blue 40 20
54 – 45 f. multicoloured . . . . . 1·25 50

DESIGN—HORIZ: 45 f. Cotton plant.

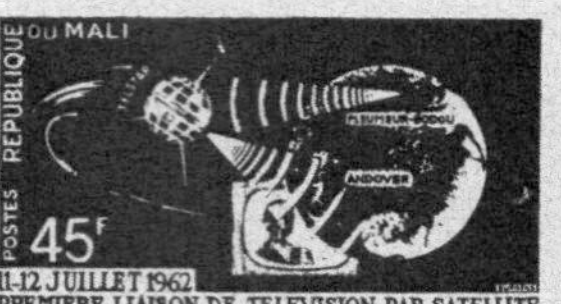

16 "Telstar" Satellite, Globe and Television Receiver

1962. 1st Trans-Atlantic Telecommunications Satellite Link.
55 **16** 45 f. brown, violet and lake . 80 40
56 55 f. violet, olive and green 95 60

17 Soldier and Family 18 Bull's Head, Laboratory Equipment and Chicks

1962. Mali–Algerian Solidarity.
57 **17** 25 f. + 5 f. multicoloured . . 30 30

1963. Zoological Research Centre, Sobuta.
58 **18** 25 f. turq & brn (postage) . . 35 25
59 – 200 f. turquoise, purple and bistre (air) . . . . 3·50 1·25

DESIGN: 200 f. As Type **18** but horiz 47 × 27 mm.

19 Tractor and Campaign Emblem

1963. Freedom from Hunger.
60 **19** 25 f. purple, black and blue 45 20
61 45 f. brown, green & turq . . 80 35

20 Balloon and W.M.O. Emblem

1963. Atmospheric Research.
62 **20** 25 f. multicoloured 40 20
63 45 f. multicoloured 70 35
64 60 f. multicoloured 95 50

21 Race Winners 22 Centenary Emblem and Globe

1963. Youth Week. Multicoloured.
65 5 f. Type **21** 15 10
66 10 f. Type **21** 20 15
67 20 f. Acrobatic dance 35 20
68 85 f. Football . . . . 1·60 55

Nos. 67/8 are horiz.

1963. Red Cross Centenary. Inscr in black.
69 **22** 5 f. multicoloured 30 15
70 10 f. red, yellow and grey . . 40 20
71 85 f. red, yellow and grey . . 1·25 60

23 Stretcher case entering Aero 145 Ambulance Airplane

1963. Air.
72 **23** 25 f. brown, blue and green 45 20
73 – 55 f. blue, ochre and brown 1·25 40
74 – 100 f. blue, brown and green 2·00 75

DESIGNS: 55 f. Douglas DC-3 airliner on tarmac; 100 f. Illyushin Il-18 airliner taking off.

24 South African Crowned Crane standing on Giant Tortoise 26 "Kaempferia aethiopica"

REPUBLIQUE DU MALI POSTE AERIENNE 50F
15e ANNIVERSAIRE DE LA DECLARATION UNIVERSELLE DES DROITS DE L'HOMME

25 U.N. Emblem, Doves and Banner

1963. Air. Fauna Protection.
75 **24** 25 f. brown, red and orange 2·00 50
76 200 f. multicoloured . . . . . 6·00 2·25

1963. Air. 15th Anniv of Declaration of Human Rights.
77 **25** 50 f. yellow, red and green 75 40

1963. Tropical Flora. Multicoloured.
78 30 f. Type **26** 60 25
79 70 f. "Bombax costatum" . . . 1·75 50
80 100 f. "Adenium honghel" . . . 3·00 65

27 Pharaoh and Cleopatra, Philae 28 Locust on Map of Africa

1964. Air. Nubian Monuments Preservation.
81 **27** 25 f. brown and purple . . . 75 25
82 55 f. olive and purple . . . . 1·60 50

1964. Anti-Locust Campaign.
83 **28** 5 f. brown, green and purple 20 15
84 – 10 f. brown, green and olive 30 20
85 – 20 f. brown, green and bistre 75 25
DESIGNS—VERT: 10 f. Locust and map. HORIZ: 20 f. Air-spraying, locust and village.

29 Football

1964. Olympic Games, Tokyo.
86 **29** 5 f. purple, green and red 15 10
87 – 10 f. brown, blue and sepia 30 20
88 – 15 f. red and violet 40 20
89 – 85 f. green, brown & violet 1·25 70
DESIGNS—VERT: 10 f. Boxing; 15 f. Running and Olympic Flame. HORIZ: 85 f. Hurdling. Each design has a stadium in the background.

30 Solar Flares **32** Map of Vietnam

31 President Kennedy

1964. Int Quiet Sun Years.
90 **30** 45 f. olive, red and blue 1·00 35

1964. Air. 1st Death Anniv of Pres. Kennedy.
91 **31** 100 f. multicoloured 1·75 1·25

1964. Mali–South Vietnam Workers' Solidarity Campaign.
92 **32** 30 f. multicoloured 30 20

33 Knysna Turacos

1965. Air. Birds.
93 **33** 100 f. green, blue and red 5·50 1·75
94 – 200 f. black, red and blue 13·50 3·75
95 – 300 f. black, ochre and green 19·00 5·00
96 – 500 f. red, brown and green 29·00 9·50
BIRDS—VERT: 200 f. Abyssinian ground hornbills; 300 f. Egyptian vultures. HORIZ: 500 f. Goliath herons.

34 I.C.Y. Emblem and U.N. Headquarters **36** Abraham Lincoln

35 African Buffalo

1965. Air. International Co-operation Year.
97 **34** 55 f. ochre, purple and blue 75 40

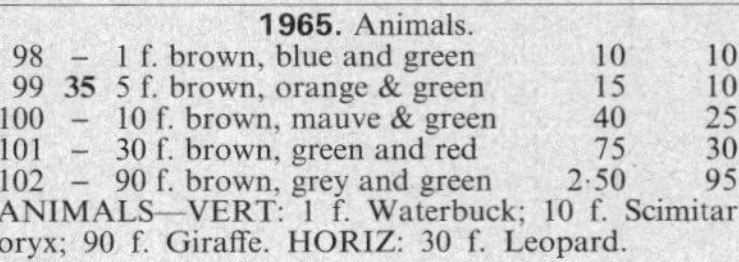

1965. Animals.
98 – 1 f. brown, blue and green 10 10
99 **35** 5 f. brown, orange & green 15 10
100 – 10 f. brown, mauve & green 40 25
101 – 30 f. brown, green and red 75 30
102 – 90 f. brown, grey and green 2·50 95
ANIMALS—VERT: 1 f. Waterbuck; 10 f. Scimitar oryx; 90 f. Giraffe. HORIZ: 30 f. Leopard.

1965. Death Centenary of Abraham Lincoln.
103 **36** 45 f. multicoloured 60 40
104 55 f. multicoloured 65 50

37 Hughes' Telegraph **38** "Lungs" and Mobile X-Ray Unit (Anti-T.B.)

1965. Centenary of I.T.U.
105 – 20 f. black, blue & orange 30 25
106 **37** 30 f. green, brn & orange 60 25
107 – 50 f. green, brown & orge 90 45
DESIGNS—VERT: 20 f. Denis's Pneumatic tube; 50 f. Lescurre's heliograph.

1965. Mali Health Service.
108 **38** 5 f. violet, red and crimson 15 15
109 – 10 f. green, bistre and red 25 15
110 – 25 f. green and brown 40 20
111 – 45 f. green and brown 75 40
DESIGNS: 10 f. Mother and children (Maternal and Child Care); 25 f. Examining patient (Marchoux Institute); 45 f. Nurse (Biological Laboratory).

39 Diving

1965. 1st African Games, Brazzaville, Congo.
112 **39** 5 f. red, brown and blue 25 10
113 – 15 f. turquoise, brown and red (Judo) 75 30

40 Pope John XXIII **41** Sir Winston Churchill

1965. Air. Pope John Commemoration.
114 **40** 100 f. multicoloured 1·90 75

1965. Air. Churchill Commemoration.
115 **41** 100 f. blue and brown 2·00 75

42 Dr. Schweitzer and Young African

1965. Air. Dr. Albert Schweitzer Commemoration.
116 **42** 100 f. multicoloured 2·00 75

43 Leonov

1966. International Astronautic Conference, Athens (1965). Multicoloured.
117 100 f. Type **43** 1·75 60
118 100 f. White 1·75 60
119 300 f. Cooper, Conrad, Leonov and Beliaiev (vert) 4·50 2·00

44 Vase, Quill and Cornet

1966. World Festival of Negro Arts, Dakar, Cameroun.
120 **44** 30 f. black, red and ochre 30 20
121 – 55 f. red, black and green 75 35
122 – 90 f. brown, orange & blue 1·25 60
DESIGNS: 55 f. Mask, brushes and palette, microphones; 90 f. Dancers, Mask, patterned cloth.

45 W.H.O. Building

1966. Inaug of W.H.O. Headquarters, Geneva.
123 **45** 30 f. green, blue and yellow 40 20
124 45 f. red, blue and yellow 60 35

46 Fisherman with Net

1966. River Fishing.
125 **46** 3 f. brown and blue 15 15
126 – 4 f. purple, blue and brown 20 15
127 – 20 f. purple, green and blue 35 15
128 **46** 25 f. purple, blue and green 75 20
129 – 60 f. purple, lake and green 1·50 45
130 – 85 f. plum, green and blue 1·50 50
DESIGNS: 4 f., 60 f. Collective shore fishing; 20 f., 85 f. Fishing pirogue.

47 Papal Arms, U.N. and Peace Emblems

1966. Air. Pope Paul's Visit to U.N.
131 **47** 200 f. blue, green & turq 2·75 1·10

48 Initiation Ceremony **49** People and U.N.E.S.C.O. Emblem

1966. Mali Pioneers. Multicoloured.
132 5 f. Type **48** 25 15
133 25 f. Pioneers dancing 75 20

1966. Air. 20th Anniv of U.N.E.S.C.O.
134 **49** 100 f. red, green and blue 1·75 70

50 Footballers, Globe, Cup and Football

1966. Air. World Cup Football Championships, England.
135 **50** 100 f. multicoloured 1·75 70

51 Cancer ("The Crab") **52** U.N.I.C.E.F. Emblem and Children

1966. Air. 9th International Cancer Congress, Tokyo.
136 **51** 100 f. multicoloured 1·75 55

1966. 20th Anniv of U.N.I.C.E.F.
137 **52** 45 f. blue, purple & brown 60 25

53 Inoculating Cattle

1967. Campaign for Preventing Cattle Plague.
138 **53** 10 f. multicoloured 25 10
139 30 f. multicoloured 50 20

54 Desert Vehicles in Pass

1967. Air. Crossing of the Hoggar (1924).
140 **54** 200 f. green, brown & vio 4·75 2·25

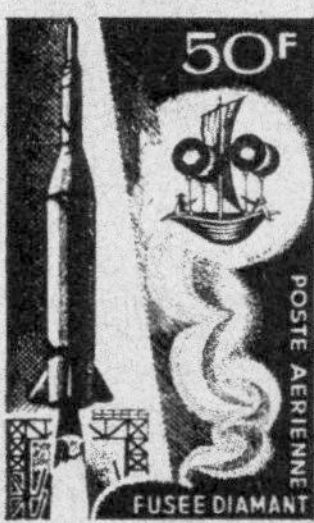

55 "Diamant" Rocket and Francesco de Lana-Terzis's "Aerial Ship" **56** Ancient City

1967. Air. French Space Rockets and Satellites.
141 **55** 50 f. blue, turquoise & pur 85 30
142 – 100 f. lake, purple & turq 1·60 50
143 – 200 f. purple, olive and blue 2·60 1·00
DESIGNS: 100 f. Satellite "A 1" and Jules Verne's "rocket"; 200 f. Satellite "D 1" and Da Vinci's "bird-powered" flying machine.

1967. International Tourist Year.
144 **56** 25 f. orange, blue and violet 30 20

57 Amelia Earhart and Mail Route-map

1967. Air. 30th Anniv of Amelia Earhart's Flight, via Gao.
145 **57** 500 f. multicoloured 7·50 3·25

58 "The Bird Cage" 59 Scout Emblems and Rope Knots

1967. Air. Picasso Commemoration. Designs showing paintings. Multicoloured.
146 50 f. Type **58** . . . . 1·25 30
147 100 f. "Paul as Harlequin" . . 2·00 70
148 250 f. "The Pipes of Pan" . . . 4·00 1·50
See also Nos. 158/9 and 164/7.

1967. Air. World Scout Jamboree, Idaho.
149 **59** 70 f. red and green . . . . 1·00 30
150 – 100 f. black, lake and green 1·25 45
DESIGN: 100 f. Scout with "walkie-talkie" radio.

60 "Chelorrhina polyphemus" 61 School Class

1967. Insects.
151 **60** 5 f. green, brown and blue 40 20
152 – 15 f. purple, brown & green 75 25
153 – 50 f. red, brown and green 1·25 55
INSECTS—HORIZ: 15 f. "Ugada grandicollis"; 50 f. "Phymateus cinctus".

1967. International Literacy Day.
154 **61** 50 f. black, red and green 60 20

62 "Europafrique" 63 Lions Emblem and Crocodile

1967. Europafrique.
155 **62** 45 f. multicoloured 85 25

1967. 50th Anniv of Lions International.
156 **63** 90 f. multicoloured . . . . 1·10 55

64 "Water Resources" 65 Block of Flats, Grenoble

1967. International Hydrological Decade.
157 **64** 25 f. black, blue and bistre 70 20

1967. Air. Toulouse-Lautrec Commemoration. Paintings as T **58**. Multicoloured.
158 100 f. "Gazelle" (horse's head) (horiz) . . . . 2·50 1·10
159 300 f. "Gig drawn by Cob" (vert) 5·50 2·25

1968. Air. Winter Olympic Games, Grenoble.
160 **65** 50 f. brown, green and blue 85 35
161 – 150 f. brown, blue and ultramarine . . . . . . 1·75 65
DESIGN: 150 f. Bob-sleigh course, Huez mountain.

66 W.H.O. Emblem

1968. 20th Anniv of W.H.O.
162 **66** 90 f. blue, lake and green 85 30

67 Human Figures and Entwined Hearts

1968. World "Twin Towns" Day.
163 **67** 50 f. red, violet and green 40 15

1968. Air. Flower Paintings. As T **58**. Mult.
164 50 f. "Roses and Anemones" (Van Gogh) 75 25
165 150 f. "Vase of Flowers" (Manet) 1·75 55
166 300 f. "Bouquet of Flowers" (Delacroix) . . . . 3·25 1·10
167 500 f. "Marguerites" (Millet) 5·00 2·00
SIZES: 50 f., 300 f. 40 × 41½ mm: 150 f. 36 × 47½ mm: 500 f. 50 × 36 mm.

68 Dr. Martin Luther King 69 "Draisienne" Bicycle, 1809

1968. Air. Martin Luther King Commemoration.
168 **68** 100 f. black, pink & purple 85 35

1968. Veteran Bicycles and Motor Cars.
169 **69** 2 f. brown, mauve and green (postage) 35 15
170 – 5 f. red, blue and bistre . . 75 20
171 – 10 f. blue, brown and green 1·25 25
172 – 45 f. black, green & brown 2·00 40
173 – 50 f. red, green & brn (air) 1·00 25
174 – 100 f. blue, mauve & bistre 2·00 60
DESIGNS—HORIZ: 5 f. De Dion-Bouton, 1894; 45 f. Panhard-Levassor, 1914; 100 f. Mercedes-Benz, 1927. VERT: 10 f. Michaux Bicycle, 1861; 50 f. "Bicyclette, 1918".

70 Books, Graph and A.D.B.A. Emblem

1968. 10th Anniv of International African Libraries and Archives Development Association.
175 **70** 100 f. red, black and brown 65 30

71 Football

1968. Air. Olympic Games, Mexico. Multicoloured.
176 100 f. Type **71** . . . . 1·00 40
177 150 f. Long-jumping (vert) . . 1·50 60

1968. Air. "Philexafrique" Stamp Exhibition, Abidjan, Ivory Coast, 1969 (1st issue). As T **113a** of Mauritania. Multicoloured.
178 200 f. "The Editors" (F. M. Granet) . . . . 2·00 1·50

1969. Air. "Philexafrique" Stamp Exn., Abidjan, Ivory Coast (2nd issue). As T **114a** of Mauritania.
179 100 f. purple, red and violet 1·50 1·25
DESIGN: 100 f. Carved animal and French Sudan stamp of 1931.

1969. Air. Birth Bicentenary of Napoleon Bonaparte. Multicoloured. As T **114b** of Mauritania.
180 150 f. "Napoleon Bonaparte, First Consul" (Gros) . . . . 2·50 1·25
181 200 f. "The Bivouac–Battle of Austerlitz" (Lejeune) (horiz) 4·25 1·75

73 Montgolfier Balloon

1969. Air. Aviation History. Multicoloured.
182 50 f. Type **73** 50 20
183 150 f. Ferdinand Ferber's Glider No. 5 1·75 40
184 300 f. Concorde . . . . 3·50 1·40

74 African Tourist Emblem

1969. African Tourist Year.
185 **74** 50 f. red, green and blue 25 20

75 "O.I.T." and I.L.O. Emblem

1969. 50th Anniv of I.L.O.
186 **75** 50 f. violet, blue and green 30 20
187 60 f. slate, red and brown 35 20

76 Panhard of 1897 and Model "24-CT"

1969. French Motor Industry.
188 **76** 25 f. lake, black and bistre (postage) 50 20
189 – 30 f. green and black . . . 75 20
190 – 55 f. red, black and purple (air) . . . . 1·25 35
191 – 90 f. blue, black and red 1·75 45
DESIGNS: 30 f. Citroen of 1923 and Model "DS-21"; 55 f. Renault of 1898 and Model "16"; 90 f. Peugeot of 1893 and Model "404".

77 Clarke (Australia), 10,000 metres (1965)

1969. Air. World Athletics Records.
192 **77** 60 f. brown and blue . . . 30 25
193 – 90 f. brown and red 45 25
194 – 120 f. brown and green . . . 55 35
195 – 140 f. brown and slate . . . 70 35
196 – 150 f. black and red . . . 85 50
DESIGNS: 90 f. Lusis (Russia), Javelin (1968); 120 f. Miyake (Japan), Weightlifting (1967); 140 f. Matson (U.S.A.), Shot-putting (1968); 150 f. Keino (Kenya), 3,000 metres (1965).

78 Hollow Blocks

1969. International Toy Fair, Nuremberg.
197 **78** 5 f. red, yellow and grey . . 15 10
198 – 10 f. multicoloured 15 10
199 – 15 f. green, red and pink . . 30 10
200 – 20 f. orange, blue and red . 35 15
DESIGNS: 10 f. Toy donkey on wheels; 15 f. "Ducks"; 20 f. Model car and race-track.

79 "Apollo 8", Earth and Moon

1969. Air. Moon Flight of "Apollo 8".
201 **79** 2,000 f. gold . . . . 14·00 14·00
This stamp is embossed on gold foil.

1969. Air. 1st Man on the Moon. Nos. 182/4 optd **L'HOMME SUR LA LUNE JUILLET 1969** and Apollo 11.
202 50 f. multicoloured 95 65
203 150 f. multicoloured . . . . . 2·00 1·25
204 300 f. multicoloured . . . . . 3·25 2·50

81 Sheep

1969. Domestic Animals.
205 **81** 1 f. olive, brown and green 10 10
206 – 2 f. brown, grey and red . . 10 10
207 – 10 f. olive, brown and blue 20 10
208 – 35 f. slate and red 60 30
209 – 90 f. brown and blue . . . 1·25 55
ANIMALS: 2 f. Goat; 10 f. Donkey; 35 f. Horse; 90 f. Dromedary.

1969. 5th Anniv of African Development Bank. As T **122a** of Mauritania.
210 50 f. brown, green and purple 25 20
211 90 f. orange, green and brown 45 20

83 "Mona Lisa" (Leonardo da Vinci)

1969. Air. 450th Death Anniv of Leonardo da Vinci.
212 **83** 500 f. multicoloured . . . . 4·50 3·25

84 Vaccination 85 Mahatma Gandhi

1969. Campaign against Smallpox and Measles.
213 **84** 50 f. slate, brown & green 40 15

1969. Air. Birth Centenary of Mahatma Gandhi.
214 **85** 150 f. brown and green . . . 1·75 55

1969. 10th Anniv of Aerial Navigation Security Agency for Africa and Madagascar (A.S.E.C.N.A.). As T **94a** of Niger.
215 100 f. green 75 25

87 West African Map and Posthorns

1970. Air. 11th Anniv of West African Postal Union (C.A.P.T.E.A.O.).
216 **87** 100 f. multicoloured 60 35

1970. Air. Religious Paintings. As T **83**. Mult.
217 100 f. "Virgin and Child" (Van der Weydan School) 70 40
218 150 f. "The Nativity" (The Master of Flamalle) . . . . 1·10 65
219 250 f. "Virgin, Child and St. John the Baptist" (Low Countries School) . . . . 2·40 1·40

89 Franklin D. Roosevelt

91 Lenin

90 Women of Mali and Japan

1970. Air. 25th Death Anniv of Franklin D. Roosevelt.
220 **89** 500 f. black, red and blue 3·50 2·00

1970. "EXPO 70" World Fair, Osaka, Japan.
221 **90** 100 f. orange, brown & blue 60 20
222 – 150 f. red, green & yellow 80 30
DESIGN: 150 f. Flags and maps of Mali and Japan.

1970. Air. Birth Centenary of Lenin.
223 **91** 300 f. black, green & flesh 2·25 1·00

92 Verne and Moon Rockets

1970. Air. Jules Verne "Prophet of Space Travel". Multicoloured.
224 50 f. Type **92** 75 25
225 150 f. Moon orbit . . . . . . 1·75 50
226 300 f. Splashdown . . . . . . 2·50 1·10

93 I.T.U. Emblem and Map

1970. World Telecommunications Day.
227 **93** 90 f. red, brown and sepia 75 25

1970. New U.P.U. Headquarters Building, Berne. As Type **81** of New Caledonia.
228 50 f. brown, green and red . . 40 20
229 60 f. brown, blue and mauve 60 20

1970. Air. Space Flight of "Apollo 13". Nos. 224/6 optd **APOLLO XIII EPOPEE SPATIALE 11-17 AVRIL 1970** in three lines.
230 50 f. multicoloured 50 25
231 150 f. multicoloured . . . . . 1·25 45
232 300 f. multicoloured . . . . . 2·25 1·25

96 "Intelstat 3" Satellite

1970. Air. Space Telecommunications.
233 **96** 100 f. indigo, blue & orange 75 35
234 – 200 f. purple, grey and blue 1·40 50
235 – 300 f. brown, orge & slate 2·50 1·10
236 – 500 f. brown, blue & indigo 3·75 1·60
DESIGNS: 200 f. "Molnya I" satellite; 300 f. Dish aerial, Type PB **2**; 500 f. "Symphony Project" satellite.

97 Auguste and Louis Lumiere, Jean Harlow and Marilyn Monroe

1970. Air. Lumiere Brothers (inventors of the cine camera). Commemoration.
237 **97** 250 f. multicoloured . . . . 2·50 1·25

98 Footballers

1970. Air. World Cup Football Championships, Mexico.
238 **98** 80 f. green, brown and red 50 25
239 200 f. red, brown and blue 1·25 55

99 Rotary Emblem, Map and Antelope

100 "Supporting United Nations"

1970. Air. Rotary International.
240 **99** 200 f. multicoloured . . . . 1·75 60

1970. Air. 25th Anniv of U.N.O.
241 **100** 100 f. blue, brown & violet 70 35

101 Page from 11th century Baghdad Koran

1970. Air. Ancient Muslim Art. Multicoloured.
242 50 f. Type **101** 50 25
243 200 f. "Tree and wild Animals" (Jordanian mosaic, c.730) . . 1·25 55
244 250 f. "The Scribe" (Baghdad miniature, 1287) . . . . . . 2·00 90

1970. Air. Moon Landing of "Luna 16". Nos. 234/5 surch **LUNA 16 PREMIERS PRELEVEMENTS AUTOMATIQUES SUR LA LUNE SEPTEMBRE 1970** and new values.
245 150 f. on 200 f. purple, grey and blue . . . . 1·25 40
246 250 f. on 300 f. brown, orange and grey . . . . 1·75 60

103 G.P.O., Bamako

1970. Public Buildings.
247 **103** 30 f. olive, green & brown 20 20
248 – 40 f. purple, brown & grn 30 20
249 – 60 f. grey, green and red 40 20
250 – 80 f. brown, green and grey 50 25
BUILDINGS: 40 f. Chamber of Commerce, Bamako; 60 f. Ministry of Public Works, Bamako; 80 f. Town Hall, Segou.

104 Pres. Nasser

106 Gallet Steam Locomotive, 1882

105 "The Nativity" (Antwerp School 1530)

1970. Air. Pres. Gamal Nasser of Egypt. Commemoration.
251 **104** 1000 f. gold . . . . 7·50 7·50

1970. Air. Christmas. Paintings. Multicoloured.
252 100 f. Type **105** 70 40
253 250 f. "Adoration of the Shepherds" (Memling) . . . 1·60 95
254 300 f. "Adoration of the Magi" (17th century Flemish school) 2·25 1·25

1970. Mali Railway Locomotives from the Steam Era (1st series).
255 **106** 20 f. black, red and green 1·60 1·40
256 – 40 f. black, green & brown 2·40 1·75
257 – 50 f. black, green & brown 2·75 2·10
258 – 80 f. black, red and green 4·00 3·00
259 – 100 f. black, green & brn 4·75 4·00
LOCOMOTIVES: 40 f. Felou, 1882; 50 f. Bechevel, 1882; 80 f. Series 1100, 1930 (inscr "Type 23"); 100 f. Class 40, 1927 (incr "Type 141" and "vers 1930").
See also Nos. 367/70.

107 Scouts crossing Log-bridge

108 Bambara de San Mask

1970. Scouting in Mali. Multicoloured.
260 5 f. Type **107** 20 15
261 30 f. Bugler and scout camp (vert) 35 15
262 100 f. Scouts canoeing 90 35

1971. Mali Masks and Ideograms. Multicoloured.
263 29 f. Type **108** 15 10
264 25 f. Dogon de Bandiagara mask 20 10
265 59 f. Kanaga ideogram 45 15
266 89 f. Bambara ideogram . . . 60 25

109 General De Gaulle

1971. Air. Charles De Gaulle Commem. Die-stamped on gold foil.
267 **109** 2000 f. gold, red and blue 30·00 30·00

110 Alfred Nobel

111 Tennis Player (Davis Cup)

1971. Air. 75th Death Anniv of Alfred Nobel (philanthropist).
268 **110** 300 f. red, brown & green 2·50 1·25

1971. Air. World Sporting Events.
269 **111** 100 f. slate, purple & blue 75 25
270 – 150 f. olive, brown & grn 1·40 40
271 – 200 f. brown, olive & blue 2·00 60
DESIGNS—HORIZ: 150 f. Steeplechase (inscr "Derby at Epsom" but probably represents the Grand National). VERT: 200 f. Yacht (America Cup).

112 Youth, Sun and Microscope

1971. 50th Anniv of 1st B.C.G. Vaccine Innoculation.
272 **112** 100 f. brown, green & red 85 40

113 "The Thousand and One Nights"

1971. Air. "Tales of the Arabian Nights". Mult.
273 120 f. Type **113** 70 30
274 180 f. "Ali Baba and the Forty Thieves" . . . . 1·00 40
275 200 f. "Aladdin's Lamp" . . . 1·40 50

114 Scouts, Japanese Horseman and Mt. Fuji

1971. 13th World Scout Jamboree, Asagiri, Japan.
276 **114** 80 f. plum, green and blue 75 20

115 Rose between Hands **116** Rural Costume

1971. 25th Anniv of U.N.I.C.E.F.
277 **115** 50 f. brown, red and orge 30 20
278 – 60 f. blue, green & brown 40 20
DESIGN—VERT: 60 f. Nurses and children.

1971. National Costumes. Multicoloured.
279 5 f. Type **116** 15 10
280 10 f. Rural costume (female) 20 15
281 15 f. Tuareg 20 15
282 60 f. Embroidered "boubou" 45 20
283 80 f. Women's ceremonial costume 60 25

117 Olympic Rings and Events

1971. Air. Olympic Games Publicity.
284 **117** 80 f. blue, purple & green 40 20

118 Telecommunications Map

1971. Pan-African Telecommunications Network Year.
285 **118** 50 f. multicoloured 25 20

119 "Mariner 4" and Mars

1971. Air. Exploration of Outer Space.
286 **119** 200 f. green, blue & brown 1·25 50
287 – 300 f. blue, plum & purple 1·75 60
DESIGN: 300 f. "Venera 5" and Venus.

120 "Santa Maria" (1492)

1971. Air. Famous Ships.
288 **120** 100 f. brown, violet & blue 70 35
289 – 150 f. violet, brown & grn 1·25 45
290 – 200 f. green, blue and red 1·60 75
291 – 250 f. red, blue and black 2·25 90
DESIGNS: 150 f. "Mayflower" (1620); 200 f. Battleship "Potemkin" (1905); 250 f. Liner "Normandie" (1935).

121 "Hibiscus rose-sinensis"

1971. Flowers. Multicoloured.
292 20 f. Type **121** 20 10
293 50 f. "Euphorbia pulcherrima" 55 15
294 60 f. "Adenium obesum" . . . 80 20
295 80 f. "Allamanda cathartica" 1·25 25
296 100 f. "Satanocrater berhautii" 1·50 35

122 Allegory of Justice

1971. 25th Anniv of Int Court of Justice, The Hague.
297 **122** 160 f. chocolate, red & brn 80 35

123 Nat King Cole **124** Statue of Olympic Zeus (by Phidias)

1971. Air. Famous Negro Musicians. Multicoloured.
298 130 f. Type **123** . . . . . . 1·25 25
299 150 f. Erroll Garner . . . . . 1·25 30
300 270 f. Louis Armstrong . . . . 1·75 45

1971. Air. "The Seven Wonders of the Ancient World".
301 **124** 70 f. blue, brown & purple 35 20
302 – 80 f. black, brown & blue 40 20
303 – 100 f. blue, red and violet 50 25
304 – 130 f. black, purple & blue 75 30
305 – 150 f. brown, green & bl 1·10 35
306 – 270 f. blue, brown & pur 1·60 75
307 – 280 f. blue, purple & brn 2·00 85
DESIGNS—VERT: 80 f. Pyramid of Cheops, Egypt; 130 f. Pharos of Alexandria; 270 f. Mausoleum of Halicarnassos; 280 f. Colossus of Rhodes. HORIZ: 100 f. Temple of Artemis, Ephesus; 150 f. Hanging Gardens of Babylon.

125 "Family Life" (carving)

1971. 15th Anniv of Social Security Service.
308 **125** 70 f. brown, green and red 40 20

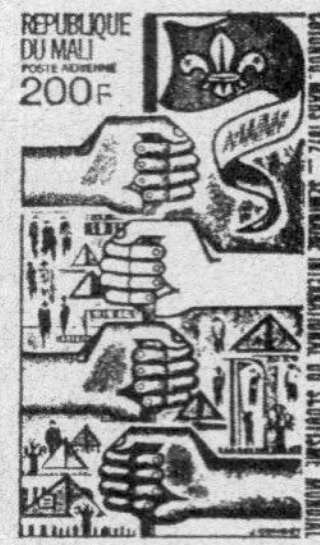

126 Slalom-skiing and Japanese Girl **128** Hands clasping Flagpole

127 "Santa Maria della Salute" (Caffi)

1972. Air. Winter Olympic Games, Sapporo, Japan.
309 **126** 150 f. brown, green & orge 1·00 35
310 – 200 f. green, brown & red 1·50 55
DESIGN: 200 f. Ice-hockey and Japanese actor.

1972. Air. U.N.E.S.C.O. "Save Venice" Campaign. Multicoloured.
312 130 f. Type **127** 80 35
313 270 f. "Rialto Bridge" . . . . 1·50 60
314 280 f. "St. Mark's Square" (vert) 1·75 70

1972. Air. Int Scout Seminar, Cotonou, Dahomey.
315 **128** 200 f. green, orange & brn 1·75 55

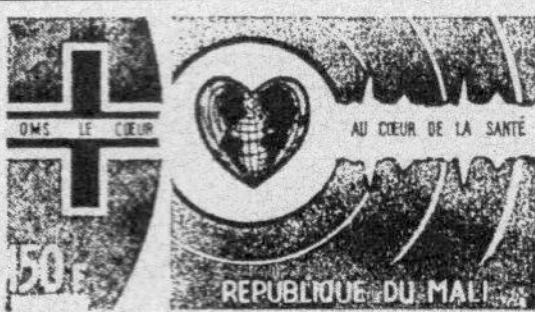

129 Heart and Red Cross Emblems

1972. Air. World Heart Month.
316 **129** 150 f. red and blue . . . . 1·00 40

130 Football

1972. Air. Olympic Games, Munich (1st issue). Sports and Munich Buildings.
317 **130** 50 f. blue, brown & green 25 20
318 – 150 f. blue, brown & green 70 30
319 – 200 f. blue, brown & green 80 50
320 – 300 f. blue, brown & green 1·25 70
DESIGNS—VERT: 150 f. Judo; 200 f. Hurdling. HORIZ: 300 f. Running.
See also Nos. 357/62.

131 "Apollo 15" and Lunar Rover

1972. Air. History of Transport Development.
322 **131** 150 f. red, green and lake 80 40
323 – 250 f. red, blue and green 2·00 1·00
DESIGN: 250 f. Montgolfier's balloon and Cugnot's steam car.

132 "UIT" on T.V. Screen

1972. World Telecommunications Day.
324 **132** 70 f. black, blue and red 40 20

133 Clay Funerary Statue **134** Samuel Morse and Early Telegraph

1972. Mali Archaeology. Multicoloured.
325 30 f. Type **133** 20 15
326 40 f. Female Figure (wood-carving) 30 20
327 50 f. "Warrior" (stone-painting) 40 20
328 100 f. Wrought-iron ritual figures 1·00 35

1972. Death Centenary of Samuel Morse (inventor of telegraph).
329 **134** 80 f. purple, green and red 45 20

135 "Cinderella" **136** Weather Balloon

1972. Air. Charles Perrault's Fairy Tales.
330 **135** 70 f. green, red and brown 45 20
331 – 80 f. brown, red and green 50 25
332 – 150 f. violet, purple & blue 1·10 35
DESIGNS: 80 f. "Puss in Boots"; 150 f. "The Sleeping Beauty".

1972. World Meteorological Day.
333 **136** 130 f. multicoloured . . . 60 30

137 Astronauts and Lunar Rover

1972. Air. Moon Flight of "Apollo 16".
334 **137** 500 f. brown, violet & grn 3·00 1·25

138 Book Year Emblem

1972. Air. International Book Year.
335 **138** 80 f. gold, green and blue 40 25

139 Sarakole Dance, Kayes **140** Learning the Alphabet

1972. Traditional Dances. Multicoloured.
336 10 f. Type **139** 25 15
337 20 f. Malinke dance, Bamako 30 15
338 50 f. Hunter's dance, Bougouni 55 20
339 70 f. Bambara dance, Segou . . 70 20
340 80 f. Dogon dance, Sanga . . . 80 30
341 120 f. Targuie dance, Timbukto 1·40 45

1972. International Literacy Day.
342 **140** 80 f. black and green . . . 40 15

141 Statue and Musical Instruments **142** Club Banner

1972. 1st Anthology of Malinenne Music.
343 **141** 100 f. multicoloured . . . 85 30

1972. Air. 10th Anniv of Bamako Rotary Club.
344 **142** 170 f. purple, blue and red 1·00 40

143 Aries the Ram

1972. Signs of the Zodiac.
345 **143** 15 f. brown and purple 30 20
346 – 15 f. black and brown . . . 30 20
347 – 35 f. blue and red 50 25
348 – 35 f. red and green 50 25
349 – 40 f. brown and blue . . . 60 30
350 – 40 f. brown and purple . . 60 30
351 – 45 f. red and blue 70 35
352 – 45 f. green and red 70 35
353 – 65 f. blue and violet . . . 1·00 35
354 – 65 f. brown and violet . . 1·00 35
355 – 90 f. blue and mauve . . . 1·60 65
356 – 90 f. green and mauve . . 1·60 65
DESIGNS: No. 346, Taurus the Bull; No. 347, Gemini the Twins; No. 348, Cancer the Crab; No. 349, Leo the Lion; No. 350, Virgo the Virgin; No. 351, Libra the Scales; No. 352, Scorpio the Scorpion; No. 353, Sagittarius the Archer; No. 354, Capricornus the Goat; No. 355, Aquarius the Water-carrier; No. 356, Pisces the Fish.

1972. Air. Olympic Games, Munich (2nd issue). Sports and Locations of Games since 1952. As Type **130**.
357 70 f. blue, brown and red . . . 1·75 40
358 90 f. green, red and blue . . . 35 20
359 140 f. olive, green and brown 60 20

360 150 f. brown, green and red . . 65 25
361 170 f. blue, brown and purple 75 30
362 210 f. blue, red and green . . . 90 40
DESIGNS—VERT: 70 f. Boxing, Helsinki Games (1952); 150 f. Weightlifting, Tokyo Games (1964). HORIZ: 90 f. Hurdling, Melbourne Games (1956); 140 f. 200 metres, Rome Games (1960); 170 f. Swimming, Mexico Games (1968); 210 f. Throwing the javelin, Munich Games (1972).

1972. Medal Winners, Munich Olympic Games. Nos. 318/20 and 362 optd with events and names, etc.
363 150 f. blue, brown and green 70 30
364 200 f. blue, brown and green 90 40
365 210 f. blue, red and green . . . 90 40
366 300 f. blue, brown and green 1·25 70
OVERPRINTS: 150 f. **JUDO RUSKA 2 MEDAILLES D'OR**; 200 f. **STEEPLE KEINO MEDAILLE D'OR**; 210 f. **MEDAILLE D'OR 90 m. 48**; 300 f. **100 m.-200m BORZOV 2 MEDAILLES D'OR**

1972. Mali Locomotives (2nd series). As T **106.**
367 10 f. blue, green and red . . . 1·60 1·25
368 30 f. blue, green and brown 3·25 2·50
369 60 f. blue, brown and green 4·00 3·25
370 120 f. purple, green and black 6·75 5·25
LOCOMOTIVES: 10 f. First Locomotive to arrive at Bamako, 1906; 30 f. Steam locomotive, Thies–Bamako line, 1920; 60 f. Class 40 steam locomotive, Thies–Bamako line, 1927 (inscr "141");. 120 f. Alsthom series BB 100 coupled diesel, Dakar–Bamako line, 1947.

146 Emperor Haile Selassie

1972. Air. 80th Birth Anniv of Emperor Haile Selassie.
371 **146** 70 f. multicoloured 30 20

147 Balloon, Breguet 14T Biplane and Map

1972. Air. First Mali Airmail Flight by Balloon, Bamako to Timbuktu. Multicoloured.
372 200 f. Type **147** . . . . . . 1·00 45
373 300 f. Balloon, Concorde and map . . . . 1·40 60

148 High Jumping

1973. 2nd African Games, Lagos, Nigeria. Mult.
374 70 f. Type **148** 30 20
375 270 f. Throwing the discus . . 1·25 60
376 280 f. Football . . . . 1·40 65

149 14th-century German Bishop

150 Interpol Headquarters, Paris

1973. Air. World Chess Championship, Reykjavik, Iceland.
377 **149** 100 f. lt blue, blue & brn 1·25 35
378 – 200 f. red, lt red & black 2·50 75
DESIGN: 200 f. 18th-century Indian knight (elephant).

1973. 50th Anniv of International Criminal Police Organization (Interpol).
379 **150** 80 f. multicoloured 65 20

151 Emblem and Dove with letter

152 "Fauna Protection" Stamp of 1963

1973. 10th Anniv (1971) of African Postal Union.
380 **151** 70 f. multicoloured 35 20

1973. Air. Stamp Day.
381 **152** 70 f. orange, red & brown 1·25 30

153 Astronauts on Moon

155 Handicapped Africans

154 Copernicus

1973. Moon Mission of "Apollo" 17.
382 **153** 250 f. brown and blue . . . 1·75 65

1973. 500th Birth Anniv of Copernicus.
384 **154** 300 f. purple and blue . . . 2·25 1·10

1973. "Help the Handicapped".
385 **155** 70 f. orange, black and red 35 20

156 Dr. G. A. Hansen

1973. Centenary of Hansen's Identification of the Leprosy Bacillus.
386 **156** 200 f. green, black and red 1·60 60

157 Bentley and Alfa Romeo, 1930

1973. 50th Anniv of Le Mans 24 hour Endurance Race.
387 **157** 50 f. green, orange & blue 50 15
388 – 100 f. green, blue and red 1·00 25
389 – 200 f. blue, green and red 2·00 50
DESIGNS: 100 f. Jaguar and Talbot, 1953; 200 f. Matra and Porsche, 1952.

158 Scouts around Campfire

1973. International Scouting Congress, Addis Ababa and Nairobi.
390 **158** 50 f. brown, red and blue 30 15
391 – 70 f. brown, red and blue 50 20
392 – 80 f. red, brown and green 60 20
393 – 130 f. green, blue & brown 85 30
394 – 270 f. red, violet and grey 1·75 60
DESIGNS—VERT: 70 f. Scouts saluting flag; 130 f. Lord Baden-Powell. HORIZ: 80 f. Standard-bearers; 270 f. Map of Africa and Scouts and Guides in ring.

159 Swimming and National Flags

1973. 1st Afro-American Sports Meeting, Bamako.
395 **159** 70 f. green, red and blue 30 20
396 – 80 f. green, red and blue 35 25
397 – 330 f. blue and red . . . . 1·50 70
DESIGNS—VERT: 80 f. Throwing the discus and javelin. HORIZ: 330 f. Running.

1973. Pan-African Drought Relief. No. 296 surch **SECHERESSE SOLIDARITE AFRICAINE** and value.
398 200 f. on 100 f. multicoloured 1·10 65

1973. Air. African Fortnight, Brussels. As T **168a** of Niger.
399 70 f. violet, blue and brown 30 20

162 "Perseus" (Cellini)

164 "Apollo 11" First Landing

163 Stephenson's "Rocket" (1829) and French Buddicom Locomotive

1973. Air. Famous Sculptures.
400 **162** 100 f. green and red . . . 55 25
401 – 150 f. purple and red . . . 85 35
402 – 250 f. green and red . . . 1·50 65
DESIGNS: 150 f. "Pieta" (Michelangelo); 250 f. "Victory of Samothrace".

1973. Air. Famous Locomotives.
403 **163** 100 f. black, blue & brown 1·50 45
404 – 150 f. multicoloured . . . 1·90 50
405 – 200 f. blue, slate and brown 3·25 80
DESIGNS: 150 f. Union Pacific steam locomotive No. 119 (1890) and Santa Fe Railroad steam locomotive "Blue Goose" (1937), U.S.A.; 200 f. "Mistral" express (France) and "Hikari" express train (Japan).

1973. Conquest of the Moon.
406 **164** 50 f. purple, red & brown 25 20
407 – 75 f. grey, blue and red . . 30 20
408 – 100 f. slate, brown and blue 75 30
409 – 280 f. blue, green and red 1·40 65
410 – 300 f. blue, red and green 1·75 80
DESIGNS: 75 f. "Apollo 13" Recovery capsule; 100 f. "Apollo 14" Lunar trolley; 280 f. "Apollo 15" Lunar rover; 300 f. "Apollo 17" lift off from Moon.

165 Picasso

166 Pres. John Kennedy

1973. Air. Pablo Picasso (artist). Commem.
411 **165** 500 f. multicoloured . . . 3·00 1·25

1973. Air. 10th Death Anniv of Pres. Kennedy.
412 **166** 500 f. black, purple & gold 2·50 1·25

1973. Air. Christmas. As T **105** but dated "1973". Multicoloured.
413 100 f. "The Annunciation" (V. Carpaccio) (horiz) 50 25
414 200 f. "Virgin of St. Simon" (F. Baroccio) . . . . 1·25 50
415 250 f. "Flight into Egypt" (A. Solario) . . . . 1·60 70

167 Player and Football

168 Cora

1973. Air. World Football Cup Championships, West Germany.
416 **167** 150 f. red, brown & green 90 35
417 – 250 f. green, brown & violet 1·75 60
DESIGN: 250 f. Goalkeeper and ball.

1973. Musical Instruments.
419 **168** 5 f. brown, red and green 20 10
420 – 10 f. brown and blue . . . 25 10
421 – 15 f. brown, red & yellow . 35 15
422 – 20 f. brown and red . . . 40 15
423 – 25 f. brown, red & yellow 45 15
424 – 30 f. black and blue . . . 60 20
425 – 35 f. sepia, brown and red 70 20
426 – 40 f. brown and red . . . 75 30
DESIGNS—HORIZ: 10 f. Balafon. VERT: 15 f. Djembe; 20 f. Guitar; 25 f. N'Djarka; 30 f. M'Bolon; 35 f. Dozo N'Goni; 40 f. N'Tamani.

169 "Musicians" (mosaic)

1974. Roman Frescoes and Mosaics from Pompeii.
427 **169** 150 f. red, brown and grey 75 35
428 – 250 f. brown, red & orange 1·25 60
429 – 350 f. brown, orange and olive . . . . 1·75 75
DESIGNS—VERT: 250 f. "Alexander the Great" (mosaic); 350 f. "Bacchante" (fresco).

170 Corncob, Worker and "Kibaru" Newspaper

171 Sir Winston Churchill

1974. 2nd Anniv of Rural Press.
430 **170** 70 f. brown and green . . . 35 20

1974. Air. Birth Cent of Sir Winston Churchill.
431 **171** 500 f. black . . . . 2·50 1·50

172 Chess-pieces on Board

1974. Air. 21st Chess Olympiad, Nice.
432 **172** 250 f. indigo, red and blue 3·50 75

173 "The Crucifixion" (Alsace School c. 1380)

1974. Air. Easter. Multicoloured.
433 400 f. Type **173** . . . . 1·60 1·00
434 500 f. "The Entombment" (Titian) (horiz) . . . . . . 2·25 1·25

174 Lenin

1974. Air. 50th Death Anniv of Lenin.
435 **174** 150 f. purple and violet . . 70 30

175 Goalkeeper and Globe
177 Full-rigged Sailing Ship and Modern Liner

176 Horse-jumping Scenes

1974. World Cup Football Championships, West Germany.
436 **175** 270 f. red, green and lilac 1·25 80
437 – 280 f. blue, brown and red 1·60 80
DESIGN: 280 f. World Cup emblem on football.

1974. Air. World Equestrian Championships, La Baule.
438 **176** 130 f. brown, lilac and blue 1·50 60

1974. Centenary of Universal Postal Union.
439 **177** 80 f. purple, lilac & brown 55 25
440 – 90 f. orange, grey and& blue 40 30
441 – 270 f. purple, olive & grn 2·75 1·10
DESIGNS: 90 f. Breguet 14T biplane and Douglas DC-8; 270 f. Steam and electric mail trains.
See also Nos. 463/4.

178 "Skylab" over Africa

1974. Air. Survey of Africa by "Skylab" Space Station.
442 **178** 200 f. indigo, blue & orge 1·00 40
443 – 250 f. blue, purple & orge 1·25 60
DESIGN: 250 f. Astronaut servicing cameras.

1974. Air. 11th Arab Scout Jamboree, Lebanon. Nos. 391/2 surch **130 f. 11e JAMBOREE ARABE AOUT 1974 LIBAN** or **170 f. CONGRES PAN-ARABE LIBAN AOUT 1974**.
444 130 f. on 70 f. brown, red & bl 70 40
445 170 f. on 80 f. blue, grn & red 75 50

1974. Air. 5th Anniv of First landing on Moon. Nos. 408/9 surch **130 f. 1er DEBARQUEMENT SUR LA LUNE 20-VII-69** or **300 f. 1er PAS SUR LA LUNE 21-VII-69**.
446 130 f. on 100 f. slate, brown and blue 70 45
447 300 f. on 280 f. blue, grn & red 1·40 70

1974. West Germany's Victory in World Cup Football Championships. Nos. 436/7 surch **R.F.A. 2 HOLLANDE 1** and value.
448 **175** 300 f. on 270 f. red, green and lilac . . . . 1·40 80
449 – 330 f. on 280 f. blue, brown and red . . . . . . 1·60 80

182 Weaver

183 River Niger near Gao

1974. Crafts and Craftsmen. Multicoloured.
450 50 f. Type **182** 25 15
451 60 f. Potter 30 15
452 70 f. Smith 40 20
453 80 f. Wood-carver 55 20

1974. Mali Views. Multicoloured.
454 10 f. Type **183** 15 10
455 20 f. "The Hand of Fatma" (rock formation, Hombori) (vert) 15 10
456 40 f. Waterfall, Gouina 35 15
457 70 f. Hill-dwellings, Dogon (vert) 60 20

184 Class C No. 3 (1906) and Class P (1939) Steam Locomotives, France

1974. Air. Steam Locomotives.
458 **184** 90 f. indigo, red and blue 1·25 50
459 – 120 f. brown, orange & bl 1·40 60
460 – 210 f. brown, orange & bl 2·75 90
461 – 330 f. black, green & blue 4·00 1·90
DESIGNS: 120 f. Baldwin (1870) and Pacific (1920) steam locomotives, U.S.A.; 210 f. Class A1 (1925) and Buddicom (1847) steam locomotives; 330 f. Hudson steam locomotive, 1938 (U.S.A.) and steam locomotive "Gironde", 1839.

185 Skiing

1974. Air. 50th Anniv of Winter Olympics.
462 **185** 300 f. red, blue and green 1·40 80

1974. Berne Postal Convention. Cent. Nos. 439 and 441 surch **9 OCTOBRE 1974** and value.
463 **177** 250 f. on 80 f. purple, lilac and brown . . . . . . 1·40 80
464 – 300 f. on 270 f. purple, olive and green . . . . . . 3·00 1·25

187 Mao Tse-tung and Great Wall of China

188 "The Nativity" (Memling)

1974. 25th Anniv of Chinese People's Republic.
465 **187** 100 f. blue, red and green 50 30

1974. Air. Christmas. Multicoloured.
466 290 f. Type **188** . . . . . . 1·25 70
467 310 f. "Virgin and Child" (Bourgogne School) . . . . 1·50 75
468 400 f. "Adoration of the Magi" (Schongauer) . . . . . . 1·90 1·10

189 Raoul Follereau (missionary)

191 Dr. Schweitzer

190 Electric Train and Boeing 707

1974. Air. Raoul Follereau, "Apostle of the Lepers".
469 **189** 200 f. blue . . . . . . 1·25 55
469a 200 f. brown . . . . . . 1·75 1·10

1974. Air. Europafrique.
470 **190** 100 f. green, brown & bl 2·75 70
471 110 f. blue, violet & brn 3·00 70

1975. Birth Centenary of Dr Albert Schweitzer.
472 **191** 150 f. turquoise, grn & blue 90 40

192 Patients making Handicrafts and Lions International Emblem

1975. 5th Anniv of Samanko (Leprosy rehabilitation village). Multicoloured.
473 90 f. Type **192** 50 20
474 100 f. View of Samanko . . . 60 25

193 "The Pilgrims at Emmaus" (Champaigne)

1975. Air. Easter. Multicoloured.
475 200 f. Type **193** 90 45
476 300 f. "The Pilgrims at Emmaus" (Veronese) . . . . 1·25 60
477 500 f. "Christ in Majesty" (Limoges enamel) (vert) . . . 2·25 1·25

194 "Journey to the Centre of the Earth"

1975. Air. 70th Death Anniv of Jules Verne.
478 **194** 100 f. green, blue & brn 45 25
479 – 170 f. brown, bl & lt brn 75 35
480 – 190 f. blue, turquoise & brn 1·25 55
481 – 220 f. brown, purple & bl 1·50 60
DESIGNS: 170 f. Jules Verne and "From the Earth to the Moon"; 190 f. Giant octopus–"Twenty Thousand Leagues Under the Sea"; 220 f. "A Floating City".

195 Head of "Dawn" (Tomb of the Medici)

197 Astronaut

196 Nile Pufferfish

1975. Air. 500th Birth Anniv of Michelangelo (artist). Multicoloured.
482 400 f. Type **195** . . . . . . 1·75 1·10
483 500 f. "Moses" (marble statue, Rome) . . . . 2·25 1·25

1975. Fishes (1st series).
484 **196** 60 f. brown, yellow & grn 80 25
485 – 70 f. black, brown & grey 90 35
486 – 80 f. multicoloured . . . . 1·10 40
487 – 90 f. blue, grey and green 1·60 50
488 – 110 f. black and blue . . . 2·25 70
DESIGNS: 70 f. Electric catfish; 80 f. Deep-sided citharinid; 90 f. Lesser tigerfish; 110 f. Nile perch.
See also Nos. 544/8.

1975. Air. Soviet–U.S. Space Co-operation.
489 **197** 290 f. red, blue and black 1·10 50
490 – 300 f. red, blue and black 1·10 60
491 – 370 f. green, purple & blk 1·40 80
DESIGNS: 300 f. "America and Russia"; 370 f. New York and Moscow landmarks.

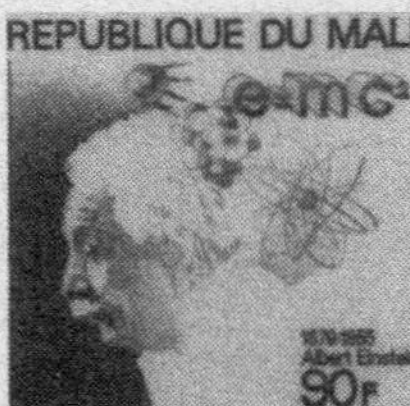

198 Einstein and Equation

199 Woman with Bouquet

1975. Air. 20th Death Anniv of Albert Einstein.
492 **198** 90 f. blue, purple & brown 55 30
See also Nos. 504, 507 and 519.

1975. International Women's Year.
493 **199** 150 f. red and green . . . 70 35

200 Morris "Oxford", 1913

1975. Early Motor-cars.
494 **200** 90 f. violet, brown & blue 60 20
495 – 130 f. red, grey and blue 95 25
496 – 190 f. deep blue, green and blue . . . . 1·40 40
497 – 230 f. brown, blue and red 1·75 45
DESIGNS—MOTOR-CARS: 130 f. Franklin "E", 1907; 190 f. Daimler, 1900; 230 f. Panhard & Levassor, 1895.

201

1975. Air. "Nordjamb 75" World Scout Jamboree, Norway.
498 **201** 100 f. blue, brown & lake 55 25
499 – 150 f. green, brown & bl 75 30
500 – 290 f. lake, brown & blue 1·40 75
DESIGNS: 150 f., 290 f. Scouts and emblem (different).

202 Lafayette and Battle Scene

1975. Air. Bicentenary of American Revolution. Mult.
501 290 f. Type **202** . . . . . . 1·50 65
502 300 f. Washington and battle scene . . . . 1·50 65
503 370 f. De Grasse and Battle of the Chesapeake, 1781 . . . . . 1·90 95

1975. 20th Death Anniv of Sir Alexander Fleming (scientist). As T **198**.
504 150 f. brown, purple and blue 80 35

204 Olympic Rings

1975. Air. "Pre-Olympic Year".
505 **204** 350 f. violet and blue . . . 1·00 65
506 – 400 f. blue . . . . . . 1·10 80
DESIGNS: 400 f. Emblem of Montreal Olympics (1976).

1975. Birth Bicentenary of Andre-Marie Ampere. As T **198**.
507 90 f. brown, red and violet . . 45 20

205 Tristater of Carthage

1975. Ancient Coins.
508 **205** 130 f. black, blue & purple 50 25
509 – 170 f. black, green & brn 70 35
510 – 190 f. black, green & red 1·00 65
511 – 260 f. black, blue & orange 1·75 1·25
COINS: 170 f. Decadrachm of Syracuse; 190 f. Tetradrachm of Acanthe; 260 f. Didrachm of Eretrie.

1975. Air. "Apollo–Soyuz" Space Link. Nos. 489/91 optd **ARRIMAGE 17 Juil. 1975**.
512 **197** 290 f. red, blue and black 1·25 65
513 – 300 f. red, blue and black 1·25 65
514 – 370 f. green, purple & blk 1·50 95

207 U.N. Emblem and Names of Agencies forming "ONU"

1975. 30th Anniv of United Nations Charter.
515 **207** 200 f. blue and green . . . 70 45

208 "The Visitation" (Ghirlandaio)

1975. Air. Christmas. Religious Paintings.
516 290 f. Type **208** . . . . 1·40 55
517 300 f. "Nativity" (Fra Filippo Lippi School) . . . . 1·40 65
518 370 f. "Adoration of the Magi" (Velasquez) . . . . 1·60 1·10

1975. Air. 50th Death Anniv of Clement Ader (aviation pioneer). As T **198**.
519 100 f. purple, red and blue . . 55 20

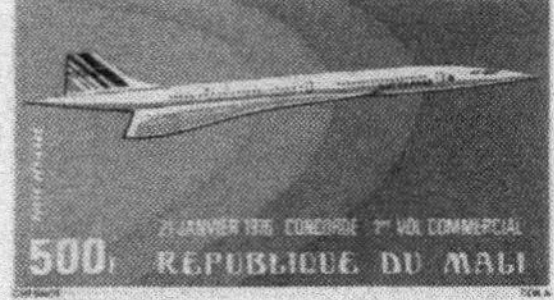

209 Concorde in Flight

1976. Air. Concorde's First Commercial Flight.
520 **209** 500 f. multicoloured . . . 3·75 1·50

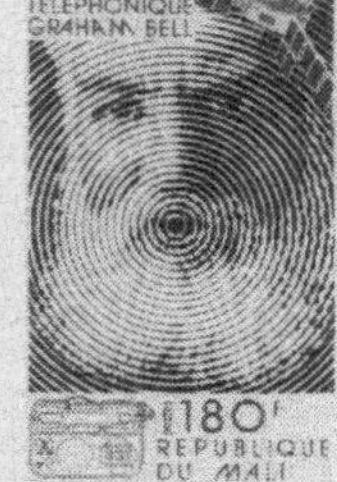

210 Figure-Skating **211** Alexander Graham Bell

1976. Air. Winter Olympic Games, Innsbruck. Multicoloured.
521 120 f. Type **210** 50 25
522 420 f. Ski-jumping . . . . . . 1·50 65
523 430 f. Skiing (slalom) . . . . . 1·50 75

1976. Telephone Centenary.
524 **211** 180 f. blue, brown and light brown 65 35

212 Chameleon

1976. Reptiles. Multicoloured.
525 20 f. Type **212** 20 15
526 30 f. Lizard 30 15
527 40 f. Tortoise 35 20
528 90 f. Python 75 25
529 120 f. Crocodile . . . . 1·25 50

213 Nurse and Patient **215** Constructing Orbital Space Station

214 Dr. Adenauer and Cologne Cathedral

1976. Air. World Health Day.
530 **213** 130 f. multicoloured . . . 55 25

1976. Birth Centenary Dr. Konrad Adenauer.
531 **214** 180 f. purple and brown 90 40

1976. Air. "The Future in Space".
532 **215** 300 f. deep blue, blue and orange . . . . 1·25 60
533 – 400 f. blue, red and purple 1·90 90
DESIGN: 400 f. Sun and space-ship with solar batteries.

216 American Bald Eagle and Liberty Bell

1976. Air. American Revolution Bicentenary and "Interphil '76" Int Stamp Exn, Philadelphia.
534 **216** 100 f. blue, purple & black 1·00 20
535 – 400 f. brown, blue & blk 3·50 85
536 – 440 f. violet, green & blk 2·75 85
DESIGNS—HORIZ: 400 f. Warships and American bald eagle. VERT: 440 f. Red Indians and American bald eagle.

217 Running **218** Scouts marching

1976. Air. Olympic Games, Montreal.
537 **217** 200 f. black, brown & red 70 40
538 – 250 f. brown, green & bl 80 50
539 – 300 f. black, blue & green 1·25 60
540 – 400 f. black, blue & green 1·60 90
DESIGNS: 250 f. Swimming; 300 f. Handball; 440 f. Football.

1976. Air. 1st All-African Scout Jamboree, Nigeria.
541 **218** 140 f. brown, blue & green 70 35
542 – 180 f. brown, green & grey 1·00 40
543 – 200 f. violet and brown . . 1·10 50
DESIGNS—HORIZ: 180 f. Scouts tending calf. VERT: 200 f. Scout surveying camp at dusk.

1976. Fishes (2nd series). As T **196**.
544 100 f. black and blue 80 25
545 120 f. yellow, brown & green 90 35
546 130 f. turquoise, brown & blk 1·10 35
547 150 f. yellow, drab and green 1·25 45
548 220 f. black, green and brown 2·10 80
DESIGNS: 100 f. African bonytongue; 120 f. Budgett's upsidedown catfish; 130 f. Double-dorsal catfish; 150 f. Monod's tilapia; 220 f. Big-scaled tetra.

220 Scenes from Children's Book **221** "Roi de L'Air"

1976. Literature for Children.
549 **220** 130 f. grey, green and red 45 25

1976. 1st Issue of "L'Essor" Newspaper.
550 **221** 120 f. multicoloured . . . 1·00 30

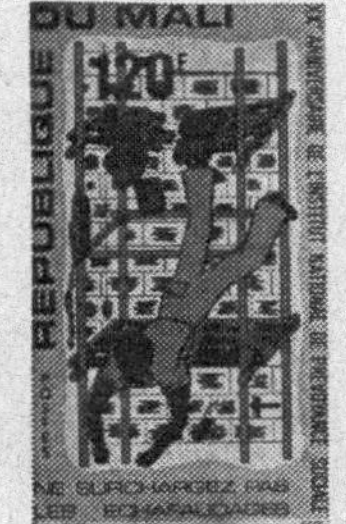

222 Fall from Scaffolding

1976. 20th Anniv of National Social Insurance.
551 **222** 120 f. multicoloured . . . 35 25

223 Moenjodaro

1976. Air. U.N.E.S.C.O. "Save Moenjodaro" (Pakistan) Campaign.
552 **223** 400 f. purple, blue & black 1·75 80
553 – 500 f. red, yellow and blue 2·00 1·25
DESIGN: 500 f. Effigy, animals and remains.

224 Freighter, Vickers Viscount 800 and Map

1976. Air. Europafrique.
554 **224** 200 f. purple and blue . . . 1·10 45

225 Cascade of Letters

1976. 25th Anniv of U.N. Postal Administration.
555 **225** 120 f. orange, green & lilac 45 25

226 Moto Guzzi "254" (Italy)

1976. Motorcycling.
556 **226** 90 f. red, grey and brown 45 20
557 – 120 f. violet, blue & black 55 25
558 – 130 f. red, grey and green 70 25
559 – 140 f. blue, green and grey 90 30
DESIGNS: 120 f. B.M.W. "900" (Germany); 130 f. Honda "Egli" (Japan); 140 f. Motobecane "LT3" (France).

227 "The Nativity" (Taddeo Gaddi)

1976. Air. Christmas. Religious Paintings. Mult.
560 280 f. Type **227** . . . . 1·25 50
561 300 f. "Adoration of the Magi" (Hans Memling) . . . . . . 1·40 60
562 320 f. "The Nativity" (Carlo Crivelli) . . . . 1·50 75

228 Muscat Fishing Boat

1976. Ships.
563 **228** 160 f. purple, green & blue 75 30
564 – 180 f. green, red and blue 75 35
565 – 190 f. purple, blue & green 80 40
566 – 200 f. green, red and blue 85 40
DESIGNS: 180 f. Cochin Chinese junk; 190 f. Dunkirk lightship "Ruytingen"; 200 f. Nile felucca.

229 Rocket in Flight

1976. Air. Operation "Viking".
567 **229** 500 f. blue, red and lake 1·75 1·25
568 – 1000 f. lake, blue and deep blue . . . . 3·00 1·90
DESIGN: 1000 f. Spacecraft on Mars.

230 Pres. Giscard d'Estaing and Sankore Mosque, Timbuktu

1977. Air. Visit of Pres. Giscard d'Estaing of France.
570 **230** 430 f. multicoloured . . . 2·00 80

231 Rocket on Launch-pad, Newton and Apple

1977. Air. 250th Death Anniv of Isaac Newton.
571 **231** 400 f. purple, red & green 2·00 75

232 Prince Philip and Queen Elizabeth II

1977. Air. "Personalities of Decolonisation". Mult.
572 180 f. Type **232** 65 35
573 200 f. General De Gaulle (vert) 1·10 50
574 250 f. Queen Wilhelmina of the Netherlands (vert) 75 55
575 300 f. King Baudouin and Queen Fabiola of Belgium . . . . 1·10 70
576 480 f. Crowning of Queen Elizabeth II (vert) . . . . . 2·00 1·25

233 Lindbergh and "Spirit of St. Louis"

1977. Air. 50th Anniv of Lindbergh's Transatlantic Flight.

577 **233** 420 f. orange and violet . . 1·90 85
578 – 430 f. blue, orange & green 1·90 85
DESIGN: 430 f. "Spirit of St. Louis" crossing the Atlantic.

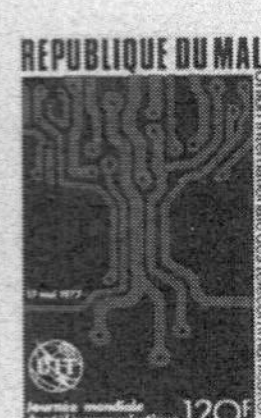

234 Village Indigobird **236** Printed Circuit

235 Louis Braille and Hands reading Book

1977. Mali Birds. Multicoloured.

579 15 f. Type **234** 50 15
580 25 f. Yellow-breasted barbet 80 15
581 30 f. Vitelline masked weaver 80 55
582 40 f. Carmine bee eater . . . . 1·00 60
583 50 f. Senegal parrot . . . . 1·10 60

1977. 125th Death Anniv of Louis Braille (inventor of "Braille" system of reading and writing for the blind".

584 **235** 200 f. blue, red and green . 1·10 45

1977. World Telecommunications Day.

585 **236** 120 f. red and brown . . . 35 20

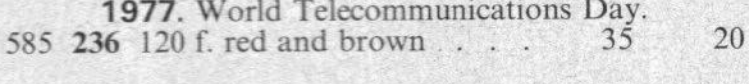

236a Chateau Sassenage, Grenoble

1977. Air. 10th Anniv of International French Language Council.

586 **236a** 300 f. multicoloured . . . 1·00 50

237 Airship LZ-1 over Lake Constance

1977. Air. History of the Zeppelin.

587 **237** 120 f. green, brown & blue 55 25
588 – 130 f. deep blue, brown and blue 65 25
589 – 350 f. red, blue and deep blue 1·75 75
590 – 500 f. deep blue, green and blue . . . . 2·50 95
DESIGNS: 130 f. "Graf Zeppelin" over Atlantic; 350 f. Burning of "Hindenburg" at Lakehurst; 500 f. Count Ferdinand von Zeppelin and "Graf Zeppelin" at mooring mast.

238 "Anaz imperator"

1977. Insects. Multicoloured.

591 5 f. Type **238** 20 15
592 10 f. "Sphadromantis viridis" 25 15
593 20 f. "Vespa tropica" 25 15
594 35 f. "Melolontha melolantha" 30 15
595 60 f. Stag beetle 55 20

239 Knight and Rook **240** Henri Dunant

1977. Chess Pieces.

596 **239** 120 f. black, green & brn 1·10 30
597 – 130 f. green, red and black 1·25 30
598 – 300 f. green, red and blue 2·75 75
DESIGNS—VERT: 130 f. Pawn and Bishop. HORIZ: 300 f. King and Queen.

1977. Air. Nobel Peace Prize Winners. Multicoloured.

599 600 f. Type **240** (founder of Red Cross) . . . . 2·00 1·00
600 700 f. Martin Luther King . . 2·25 1·10

241 Ship **242** "Head of Horse"

1977. Europafrique.

601 **241** 400 f. multicoloured . . . 1·25 75

1977. 525th Birth Anniv of Leonardo da Vinci.

602 **242** 200 f. brown and black . . 75 50
603 – 300 f. brown . . . . . . 1·10 60
604 – 500 f. red . . . . 2·00 85
DESIGNS: 300 f. "Head of Young Girl"; 500 f. Self-portrait.

243 Footballers **245** Dome of the Rock

244 Friendship Hotel

1977. Air. Football Cup Elimination Rounds.

605 – 180 f. brown, green & orge 50 30
606 **243** 200 f. brown, green & orge 60 35
607 – 420 f. grey, green and lilac 1·25 70
DESIGNS—HORIZ: 180 f. Two footballers; 420 f. Tackling.

1977. Inauguration of Friendship Hotel, Bamako.

608 **244** 120 f. multicoloured . . . 35 25

1977. Palestinian Welfare.

609 **245** 120 f. multicoloured . . . 55 20
610 180 f. multicoloured . . . 70 30

246 Mao Tse-tung and "Comatex" Hall, Bamako

1977. Air. Mao Tse-tung Memorial.

611 **246** 300 f. red . . . . 1·25 50

1977. Air. First Commercial Paris–New York Flight by Concorde. Optd **PARIS-NEW YORK 22.11.77.**

612 **209** 500 f. multicoloured . . . 7·00 4·50

248 "Adoration of the Magi" (Rubens)

1977. Air. Christmas. Details from "Adoration of the Magi" by Rubens.

613 **248** 400 f. multicoloured . . . 1·25 75
614 – 500 f. multicoloured . . . 1·60 95
615 – 600 f. multicoloured . . . 2·00 1·10
The 600 f. is a horizontal design.

249 "Hercules and the Nemean Lion"

1978. 400th Birth Anniv of Peter Paul Rubens. Multicoloured.

616 200 f. "Battle of the Amazons" (horiz) 70 35
617 300 f. "Return from Labour in the Fields" (horiz) . . . 1·00 55
618 500 f. Type **249** . . . . . . 1·75 95

250 Schubert and Mute Swans

1978. Air. 150th Death Anniv of Franz Schubert (composer). Multicoloured.

619 300 f. Schubert and bars of music (vert) . . . . 1·75 60
620 420 f. Type **250** . . . . . . 4·25 70

251 Cook and Shipboard Scene

1978. Air. 250th Birth Anniv of Captain James Cook.

621 **251** 200 f. blue, red and violet 1·50 40
622 – 300 f. brown, blue & green 3·00 70
DESIGN: 300 f. Capt. Cook meeting natives.

252 African and Chained Building

1978. World Anti-Apartheid Year.

623 **252** 120 f. violet, brown & blue 40 20
624 – 130 f. violet, blue & orge 40 20
625 – 180 f. brown, pur & orge 60 30
DESIGNS: 130 f. Statue of Liberty and Africans walking to open door; 180 f. African children and mule in fenced enclosure.

253 Players and Ball **254** "Head of Christ"

1978. Air. World Cup Football Championship, Argentina.

626 **253** 150 f. red, green & brown 60 30
627 – 250 f. red, brown & green 1·25 45
628 – 300 f. red, brown and blue 1·50 50
DESIGNS—VERT: 250 f. HORIZ: 300 f. Different football scenes.

1978. Air. Easter. Works by Durer.

630 **254** 420 f. green and brown . . 1·60 75
631 – 430 f. blue and brown . . . 1·60 75
DESIGN: 430 f. "The Resurrection".

255 Red-cheeked Cordon-bleu

1978. Birds. Multicoloured.

632 20 f. Type **255** 20 15
633 30 f. Black-faced fire finch . . 50 20
634 50 f. Red-billed fire finch . . 60 40
635 70 f. African collared dove . . 1·10 40
636 80 f. White-billed buffalo weaver 1·50 50

256 C-3 "Trefle"

1978. Air. Birth Centenary of Andre Citroen (automobile pioneer).

637 **256** 120 f. brown, lake & green 70 20
638 – 130 f. grey, orange & blue 85 25
639 – 180 f. blue, green and red 1·25 30
640 – 200 f. black, red and lake 1·50 40
DESIGNS: 130 f. B-2 "Croisiere Noir" track-laying vehicle, 1924; 180 f. B-14 G Saloon, 1927; 200 f. Model-11 front-wheel drive car, 1934.

1978. 20th Anniv of Bamako Lions Club. Nos. 473/4 surch **XXe ANNIVERSAIRE DU LIONS CLUB DE BAMAKO 1958-1978** and value.

641 120 f. on 90 f. Type **192** . . 45 20
642 130 f. on 100 f. View of Samanko 55 30

258 Names of 1978 U.P.U. members forming Map of the World

1978. Centenary of U.P.U. Foundation Congress, Paris.

643 **258** 120 f. green, orange & mve 45 20
644 – 130 f. yellow, red & green 45 20
DESIGN: 130 f. Names of 1878 member states across globe.

259 Desert Scene

1978. Campaign against Desertification.

645 **259** 200 f. multicoloured . . . 70 35

260 Mahatma Gandhi   262 Dominoes

261 "Dermestes bromius"

1978. 30th Anniv of Gandhi's Assassination.
646 **260** 140 f. brown, red & black . . . 85 30

1978. Insects. Multicoloured.
647 15 f. Type **261** 20 15
648 25 f. "Calosoma sp." 25 15
649 90 f. "Lopocerus variegatus" 45 20
650 120 f. "Coccinella septempunctata" 55 25
651 140 f. "Goliathus giganteus" 70 30

1978. Social Games.
652 **262** 100 f. black, green and red 40 20
653 – 130 f. red, black and blue . 85 25
DESIGN: 130 f. Bridge hand.

263 Ostrich on Nest (Syrian Manuscript)

1978. Air. Europafrique. Multicoloured.
654 100 f. Type **263** . . . . 1·25 20
655 110 f. Common zebra (Mansur miniature) 50 30

1978. Air. World Cup Football Championship Finalists. Nos. 626/8 optd with results.
656 **253** 150 f. red, green & brown 60 25
657 – 250 f. red, brown & green 1·00 45
658 – 300 f. red, brown & blue 1·25 60
OPTS: 150 f. **CHAMPION 1978 ARGENTINE**; 250 f. **2e HOLLANDE**: 300 f. **3e BRESIL 4e ITALIE**.

265 Coronation Coach

1978. Air. 25th Anniv of Coronation of Queen Elizabeth II. Multicoloured.
660 500 f. Type **265** . . . . 1·50 70
661 1000 f. Queen Elizabeth II . . 2·75 1·40

266 Aristotle and African Animals   267 Douglas DC-3 and U.S.A. 1918 24 c. stamp

1978. 2300th Death Anniv of Aristotle (Greek philosopher).
662 **266** 200 f. brow red and grn 90 35

1978. Air. History of Aviation.
663 **267** 80 f. deep blue, red & blue 35 15
664 – 100 f. multicoloured . . . 50 20
665 – 120 f. black, blue and red 60 25
666 – 130 f. green, red & black 65 30
667 – 320 f. violet, blue & red . . 1·50 65
DESIGNS: 100 f. Stampe and Renard SV-4 and Belgium Balloon stamp of 1932; 120 f. Clement Ader's Avion III and France Concorde stamp of 1976; 130 f. Junkers Ju–52/3m and Germany Biplane stamp of 1919; 320 f. Mitsubishi A6M Zero-Sen and Japan Pagoda stamp of 1951.

268 "The Annunciation"

1978. Air. Christmas. Works by Durer.
668 **268** 420 f. brown and black . . 1·25 60
669 – 430 f. brown and green . . 1·25 60
670 – 500 f. black and brown . . 1·60 75
DESIGNS: 430 f. "Virgin and Child"; 500 f. "Adoration of the Magi".

269 Launch of "Apollo 8" and Moon

1978. Air. 10th Anniv of First Manned Flight around the Moon.
671 **269** 200 f. red, green and violet 60 30
672 – 300 f. violet, green and red 1·10 50
DESIGN: 300 f. "Apollo 8" in orbit around the Moon.

270 U.N. and Human Rights Emblems

1978. 30th Anniv of Declaration of Human Rights.
673 **270** 180 f. red, blue and brown 60 35

271 Concorde and Clement Ader's "Eole"

1979. Air. 3rd Anniv of First Commercial Concorde Flight. Multicoloured.
674 120 f. Type **271** 70 25
675 130 f. Concorde and Wright Flyer I 85 30
676 200 f. Concorde and "Spirit of St. Louis" . . . . 1·40 45

1979. Air. "Philexafrique" Stamp Exhibition, Libreville, Gabon (1st issue) and International Stamp Fair, Essen, West Germany. As T **262** of Niger. Multicoloured.
677 200 f. Ruff (bird) and Lubeck 1859 ½ s. stamp . . . . . 1·10 75
678 200 f. Dromedary and Mali 1965 200 f. stamp . . . . 1·90 1·25
See also Nos. 704/5.

1979. Air. Birth Centenary of Albert Einstein (physicist). No. 492 surch **"1879–1979" 130F**.
679 **198** 130 f. on 90 f. blue, purple and brown 55 30

273 "Christ carrying the Cross"

1979. Air. Easter. Works by Durer.
680 **273** 400 f. black and turquoise 1·40 60
681 – 430 f. black and red . . . 1·40 60
682 – 480 f. black and blue . . . 1·60 1·00
DESIGNS: 430 f. "Christ on the Cross"; 480 f. "The Great Lamentation".

274 Basketball and St. Basil's Cathedral, Moscow   275 African Manatee

1979. Air. Pre-Olympic Year. Multicoloured.
683 420 f. Type **274** . . . . . . 1·50 75
684 430 f. Footballer and Kremlin 1·50 75

1979. Endangered Animals. Multicoloured.
685 100 f. Type **275** 45 20
686 120 f. Chimpanzee 65 30
687 130 f. Topi 75 35
688 180 f. Gemsbok 90 40
689 200 f. Giant eland . . . . . . 1·00 55

276 Child and I.Y.C. Emblem

1979. International Year of the Child.
690 **276** 120 f. green, red & brown 40 20
691 – 200 f. purple and green . . 70 35
692 – 300 f. brown, mauve and deep brown . . . . . . 1·00 50
DESIGNS: 200 f. Girl and scout with birds; 300 f. Children with calf.

277 Judo

1979. World Judo Championships, Paris.
693 **277** 200 f. sepia, red and ochre 80 40

278 Wave Pattern and Human Figures   279 Goat's Head and Lizard Fetishes

1979. World Telecommunications Day.
694 **278** 120 f. multicoloured . . . 35 20

1979. World Museums Day. Multicoloured.
695 90 f. Type **279** 30 15
696 120 f. Seated figures (wood carving) 40 20
697 130 f. Two animal heads and figurine (wood carving) . . . 50 25

280 Rowland Hill and Mali 1961 25 f. stamp   281 Cora Players

1979. Death Centenary of Sir Rowland Hill.
698 **280** 120 f. multicoloured . . . 40 20
699 – 130 f. red, blue and green 40 20
700 – 180 f. black, green & blue 60 30
701 – 200 f. black, red & purple 70 35
702 – 300 f. blue, deep blue and red 1·25 50
DESIGNS: 130 f. Airship "Graf Zeppelin" and Saxony stamp of 1850; 180 f. Concorde and France stamp of 1849; 200 f. Stage coach and U.S.A. stamp of 1849; 300 f. U.P.U. emblem and Penny Black.

1979.
703 **281** 200 f. multicoloured . . . 1·00 40

282 Sankore Mosque and "Adenium obesum"

1979. "Philexafrique" Exhibition, Libreville, Gabon (2nd issue).
704 **282** 120 f. multicoloured . . . 90 55
705 – 300 f. red, blue and orange 1·90 1·25
DESIGN: 300 f. Horseman and satellite.

283 Map of Mali showing Conquest of Desert

1979. Operation "Sahel Vert". Multicoloured.
706 200 f. Type **283** 70 30
707 300 f. Planting a tree . . . . . 1·10 50

284 Lemons   285 Sigmund Freud

1979. Fruit (1st series). Multicoloured.
708 10 f. Type **284** 15 10
709 60 f. Pineapple 30 15
710 100 f. Papaw 50 15
711 120 f. Sweet-sops 55 20
712 130 f. Mangoes 65 25
See also Nos. 777/81.

1979. 40th Death Anniv of Sigmund Freud (psychologist).
713 **285** 300 f. sepia and violet . . . 1·25 60

286 Caillie and Camel approaching Fort

1979. 180th Birth Anniv of Rene Caillie (explorer).
714 **286** 120 f. sepia, brown & blue 50 20
715 – 130 f. blue, green & brown 60 25
DESIGN: 130 f. Rene Caillie and map of route across Sahara.

287 "Eurema brigitta"

1979. Butterflies and Moths (1st series). Mult.
716 100 f. Type **287** 60 20
717 120 f. "Papilio pylades" . . . 75 20
718 130 f. "Melanitis leda satyridae" 90 40
719 180 f. "Gonimbrasis belina occidentalis" . . . . 1·50 45
720 200 f. "Bunaea alcinoe" . . . 1·75 50
See also Nos. 800/4.

288 Mali 1970 300 f. Stamp and Modules orbiting Moon

1979. Air. 10th Anniv of First Moon Landing.

721	430 f. Type **288**	1·40	60
722	500 f. 1973 250 f. stamp and rocket launch	1·60	95

289 Capt. Cook and H.M.S. "Resolution" off Kerguelen Islands

1979. Air. Death Bicent of Captain James Cook.

723	300 f. Type **289**	1·75	80
724	400 f. Capt. Cook and H.M.S. "Resolution" off Hawaii	2·50	1·10

290 Menaka Greyhound

1979. Dogs. Multicoloured.

725	20 f. Type **290**	30	15
726	50 f. Water spaniel	45	15
727	70 f. Beagle	60	15
728	80 f. Newfoundland	70	20
729	90 f. Sheepdog	85	20

291 David Janowski

1979. Air. Chess Grand-masters.

730	**291**	100 f. red and brown	85	30
731	–	140 f. red, brown and blue	1·25	30
732	–	200 f. blue, violet & green	1·75	50
733	–	300 f. brown, ochre & red	2·25	70

DESIGNS: 140 f. Alexander Alekhine; 200 f. Willi Schlage; 300 f. Efim Bogoljubow.

292 "The Adoration of the Magi" 1511 (detail, Durer)

1979. Air. Christmas. Works by Durer.

734	**292**	300 f. brown and orange	1·00	50
735	–	400 f. brown and blue	1·25	75
736	–	500 f. brown and green	1·60	95

DESIGNS: 400 f. "Adoration of the Magi" (1503); 500 f. "Adoration of the Magi" (1511, different).

1979. Air. 20th Anniv of ASECNA (African Air Safety Organization). As T **198** of Malagasy but 36 × 27 mm.

737	120 f. multicoloured	40	20

293 Globe, Rotary Emblem and Diesel-electric Train

294 African Ass

1980. Air. 75th Anniv of Rotary International. Multicoloured.

738	220 f. Type **293**	2·75	80
739	250 f. Globe, Rotary emblem and Douglas DC-10 airliner	1·00	45
740	430 f. Bamako Rotary Club and emblem	1·40	75

1980. Protected Animals. Multicoloured.

741	90 f. Type **294**	50	20
742	120 f. Addax	60	20
743	130 f. Cheetahs	75	35
744	140 f. Barbary sheep	80	45
745	180 f. African buffalo	1·00	50

295 Speed Skating

1980. Air. Winter Olympics Game, Lake Placid. Multicoloured.

746	200 f. Type **295**	70	30
747	300 f. Ski jump	1·10	60

296 Stephenson's "Rocket" (1829) and Mali 30 f. Stamp, 1972

1980. Air. 150th Anniv of Liverpool and Manchester Railway.

749	**296**	200 f. blue, brown & green	1·25	45
750	–	300 f. black, brown & turq	2·00	80

DESIGN: 300 f. "Rocket" (1829) and Mali 50 f. railway stamp, 1970.

297 Horse Jumping

1980. Air. Olympic Games, Moscow.

751	**297**	200 f. green, brown & blue	70	30
752	–	300 f. blue, brown & green	1·00	50
753	–	400 f. red, green & lt green	1·50	75

DESIGN: 300 f. Sailing. 400 f. Football.

298 Solar Pumping Station, Koni

1980. Solar Energy. Multicoloured.

755	90 f. Type **298**	30	15
756	100 f. Solar capture tables, Dire	35	15
757	120 f. Solar energy cooker	50	20
758	130 f. Solar generating station, Dire	55	25

299 Nioro Horse

1980. Horses. Multicoloured.

759	100 f. Mopti	50	15
760	120 f. Type **299**	65	15
761	130 f. Koro	75	20
762	180 f. Lake zone horse	90	35
763	200 f. Banamba	1·10	40

300 "Head of Christ" (Maurice Denis)

1980. Air. Easter.

764	**300**	480 f. red and brown	1·60	95
765	–	500 f. brown and red	1·60	95

DESIGN: 500 f. "Christ before Pilate" (Durer).

301 Kepler and Diagram of Earth's Orbit

1980. Air. 350th Death Anniv of J. Kepler (astronomer).

766	**301**	200 f. lt blue, blue & red	80	35
767	–	300 f. mauve, violet & grn	1·25	55

DESIGN: 300 f. Kepler, Copernicus and diagram of solar system.

302 Pluto and Diagram of Orbit

1980. Air. 50th Anniv of Discovery of Planet Pluto.

768	**302**	402 f. blue, grey & mauve	1·90	85

303 "Lunokhod 1" (10th Anniv)

1980. Air. Space Events.

769	**303**	480 f. black, red and blue	1·75	85
770	–	500 f. grey, blue and red	1·75	85

DESIGN: 500 f. "Apollo" - "Soyuz" link-up.

304 Fleming and Laboratory

1980. Sir Alexander Fleming (discoverer of penicillin). Commemoration.

771	**304**	200 f. green, sepia & brn	1·00	35

305 Avicenna, Medical Instruments and Herbs

306 Pilgrim at Mecca

1980. Birth Millenary of Avicenna (Arab physician and philosopher).

772	**305**	120 f. blue, red and brown	40	20
773	–	180 f. dp brn, turq & brn	60	25

DESIGN: 180 f. Avicenna as teacher.

1980. 1400th Anniv of Hegira. Multicoloured.

774	120 f. Type **306**	40	15
775	130 f. Praying hands	40	20
776	180 f. Pilgrims (horiz)	60	30

1980. Fruit (2nd series). As T **284**. Multicoloured.

777	90 f. Guavas	45	20
778	120 f. Cashews	50	20
779	130 f. Oranges	65	25
780	140 f. Bananas	75	25
781	180 f. Grapefruit	90	35

307 Rochambeau and French Fleet at Rhode Island, 1780

1980. Air. French Support for American Independence.

782	**307**	420 f. brown, turq & red	1·75	75
783	–	430 f. black, blue and red	1·75	80

DESIGN: 430 f. Rochambeau, Washington and Eagle.

308 Dove and U.N. Emblem

1980. 60th Anniv of League of Nations.

784	**308**	200 f. blue, red and violet	60	35

309 Scene from "Around the World in 80 Days"

1980. Air. 75th Death Anniv of Jules Verne (writer).

785	**309**	100 f. red, green & brown	10·00	2·75
786	–	100 f. brown, chestnut and turquoise	1·75	30
787	–	150 f. green, brn & dp brn	1·25	40
788	–	150 f. blue, violet & dp bl	1·25	40

DESIGNS: No. 786, Concorde; No. 787, "From the Earth to the Moon"; No. 788, Astronaut on Moon.

310 Xylophone, Mask and Emblem

1980. 6th Arts and Cultural Festival, Bamako.

789	**310**	120 f. multicoloured	40	20

311 Map of Africa and Asia

313 Conference Emblem

1980. 25th Anniv of Afro-Asian Bandung Conference.
790 **311** 300 f. green, red and blue . . . 90 55

1980. Air. Olympic Medal Winners. Nos. 751/3 optd
791 200 f. green, brown and blue . . . 70 35
792 300 f. blue, brown and green . . . 1·00 55
793 400 f. red, green & light green . . . 1·40 75
OVERPRINTS: 200 f. **CONCOURS COMPLET INDIVIDUEL ROMAN (It.) BLINOV (Urss) SALNIKOV (Urss)**; 300 f. **FINN RECHARDT (Fin.) MAYRHOFER (Autr.) BALACHOV (Urss)**; 400 f. **TCHECOSLOVAQUIE ALLEMAGNE DE L'EST URSS**.

1980. World Tourism Conference, Manila. Mult.
795 120 f. Type **313** 35 15
796 180 f. Encampment outside fort and Conference emblem . . . 50 30

314 Dam and Rural Scene

1980. 20th Anniv of Independence. Multicoloured.
797 100 f. Type **314** 40 15
798 120 f. National Assembly Building 40 20
799 130 f. Independence Monument (vert) 45 25

1980. Butterflies. (2nd series). As T **287** but dated "1980". Multicoloured.
800 50 f. "Uterheisa pulchella" (postage) 40 20
801 60 f. "Mylothis chloris pieridae" . . 50 20
802 70 f. "Hypolimnas mishippus" . . 60 20
803 80 f. "Papilio demodocus" . . . 75 20
804 420 f. "Denaus chrysippus" (48 × 36 mm) (air) . . . . . 2·50 1·25

315 Pistol firing Cigarette and Target over Lungs

1980. Anti-Smoking Campaign.
805 **315** 200 f. multicoloured . . . 75 35

316 Electric Train, Boeing 737 and Globe

1980. Europafrique.
806 **316** 300 f. multicoloured . . . 3·75 85

317 Map of West Africa and Agricultural Symbols
318 Gen. de Gaulle and Map of France

1980. 5th Anniv of West African Economic Council. Multicoloured.
807 100 f. Type **317** 35 15
808 120 f. "Transport" . . . . 2·50 85
809 130 f. "Industry" 45 25
810 140 f. "Energy" 50 25

1980. Air. 10th Death Anniv of Gen. Charles de Gaulle. Multicoloured.
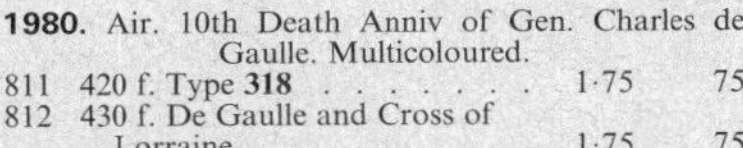
811 420 f. Type **318** . . . . 1·75 75
812 430 f. De Gaulle and Cross of Lorraine . . . . 1·75 75

319 "Hikari" Express Train (Japan) and Mali 1972 10 f. Stamp

1980. Air. Locomotives.
813 **319** 120 f. blue, green and red . . . 95 20
814 – 130 f. green, blue and red . . . 1·25 25
815 – 200 f. orange, black & grn . . . 1·60 40
816 – 480 f. black, red and green . . . 4·25 95
DESIGNS—HORIZ: 130 f. RTG train, U.S.A. and 20 f. locomotive stamp of 1970; 200 f. "Rembrandt" express, Germany, and 100 f. locomotive stamp of 1970. VERT: 480 f. TGV 001 turbotrain, France, and 80 f. locomotive stamp of 1970.

320 "Flight into Egypt" (Rembrandt)
321 Nomo Dogon

1980. Air. Christmas. Multicoloured.
817 300 f. "St. Joseph showing the infant Jesus to St. Catherine" (Lorenzo Lotto) (horiz) . . . 1·00 55
818 400 f. Type **320** . . . . 1·40 80
819 500 f. "Christmas Night" (Gauguin) (horiz) . . . . . 1·60 90

1980. 5th Anniv of African Posts and Telecommunications Union. As T **292** of Niger.
820 130 f. multicoloured 40 20

1981. Statuettes. Multicoloured.
821 60 f. Type **321** 20 15
822 70 f. Senoufo fertility symbol . . 25 15
823 90 f. Bamanan fertility statuette . . 35 15
824 100 f. Senoufo captives snuff-box . . 40 15
825 120 f. Dogon fertility statuette . . 50 20

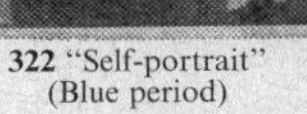

322 "Self-portrait" (Blue period)
323 Mambie Sidibe

1981. Birth Bicentenary of Pablo Picasso (artist).
826 **322** 1000 f. multicoloured . . . 3·50 1·75

1981. Mali Thinkers and Savants.
827 **323** 120 f. brown, buff and red . . . 40 20
828 – 130 f. brown, buff & black . . . 40 25
DESIGN: 130 f. Amadou Hampate Ba.

324 Mosque and Ka'aba
325 Tackle

1981. 1400th Anniv of Hejira.
829 **324** 120 f. multicoloured . . . 40 20
830 180 f. multicoloured . . . 60 30

1981. Air. World Cup Football Championship Eliminators. Multicoloured.
831 100 f. Type **325** 40 20
832 200 f. Heading the ball 85 35
833 300 f. Running for ball . . . . 1·40 50

326 Kaarta Zeba
327 Crinum de Moore "Crinum moorei"

1981. Cattle. Multicoloured.
835 20 f. Type **326** 15 15
836 30 f. Peul du Macina sebu . . . 15 15
837 40 f. Maure zebu 25 15
838 80 f. Touareg zebu 50 15
839 100 f. N'Dama cow 60 20

1981. Flowers. Multicoloured.
840 50 f. Type **327** 30 15
841 100 f. Double rose hibiscus "Hibiscus rosa-sinensis" . . . 80 15
842 120 f. Pervenche "Catharanthus roseus" 90 20
843 130 f. Frangipani "Plumeria rubra" 90 25
844 180 f. Orgueil de Chine "Caesalpinia pulcherrima" . . 1·40 40

328 Mozart and Musical Instruments

1981. Air. 225th Birth Anniv of Mozart. Mult.
845 420 f. Type **328** . . . . 2·00 85
846 430 f. Mozart and musical instruments (different) . . . 2·00 85

329 "The Fall on the Way to Calvary" (Raphael)
330 Yury Gagarin

1981. Air. Easter.
847 500 f. Type **329** . . . . 1·50 85
848 600 f. "Ecce Homo" (Rembrandt) . . . . 2·00 1·25

1981. Air. Space Anniversaries and Events.
849 **330** 200 f. blue, black and red . . . 85 30
850 – 200 f. blue, black & lt blue . . . 85 30
851 – 380 f. multicoloured . . . 1·40 55
852 – 430 f. violet, black & blue . . . 1·60 70
DESIGNS—VERT: No. 849, Type **330**: first man in space (20th anniv); No. 850, Alan Shepard, first American in space (20th anniv); No. 851, Saturn and moons (exploration of Saturn). HORIZ: No. 852, Sir William Herschel, and diagram of Uranus, (Discovery bicentenary)

331 Blind and Sighted Faces
332 Caduceus (Telecommunications and Health)

1981. International Year of Disabled People.
853 **331** 100 f. light brown, brown and green 35 15
854 – 120 f. violet, blue and purple . . 45 20
DESIGN: 120 f. Mechanical hand and human hand with spanner.

1981. World Telecommunications Day.
855 **332** 130 f. multicoloured . . . 40 25

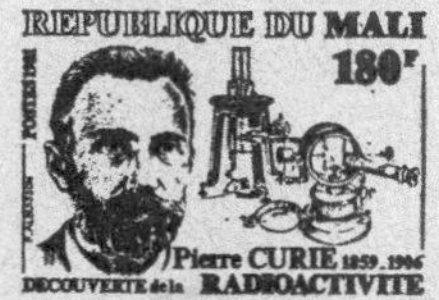

333 Pierre Curie and Instruments

1981. 75th Death Anniv of Pierre Curie (discoverer of radioactivity).
856 **333** 180 f. blue, black & orange . . . 90 30

334 Scouts at Well and Dorcas Gazelle

1981. 4th African Scouting Conference, Abidjan. Multicoloured.
857 110 f. Type **334** 70 30
858 160 f. Scouts signalling and patas monkey . . . . 1·25 60
859 300 f. Scouts saluting and cheetah (vert) . . . . 1·75 85

1981. Air. World Railway Speed Record. No. 816 optd **26 fevrier 1981/Record du monde de vitesse–380 km/h**.
861 480 f. black, red and blue . . . 3·00 90

336 Columbus, Fleet and U.S. Columbus Stamp of 1892

1981. Air. 475th Death Anniv of Christopher Columbus.
862 **336** 180 f. brown, black & bl . . . 90 40
863 – 200 f. green, blue & brown . . . 1·10 40
864 – 260 f. black, violet and red . . . 1·60 60
865 – 300 f. lilac, red and green . . . 1·75 70
DESIGNS—VERT: 200 f. "Nina" and 1 c. Columbus stamp of Spain; 260 f. "Pinta" and 5 c. Columbus stamp of Spain. HORIZ: 300 f. "Santa Maria" and U.S. 3 c. Columbus stamp.

1981. 23rd World Scouting Conference, Dakar. Nos. 857/9 optd **"DAKAR 8 AOUT 1981/28e CONFERENCE MOUNDIALE DU SCOUTISME"**.
866 **334** 110 f. multicoloured . . . 40 20
867 – 160 f. multicoloured . . . 50 30
868 – 300 f. multicoloured . . . 1·25 55

338 Space Shuttle after Launching

1981. Air. Space Shuttle. Multicoloured.
870 200 f. Type **338** 90 30
871 500 f. Space Shuttle in orbit . . 2·25 75
872 600 f. Space Shuttle landing . . 2·50 1·25

339 "Harlequin on a Horse"

1981. Air. Birth Centenary of Pablo Picasso. Mult.
874 600 f. Type **339** . . . . 2·75 1·25
875 750 f. "Child with Pigeon" . . . 3·25 1·40

340 Prince Charles, Lady Diana Spencer and St. Paul's Cathedral

1981. Air. British Royal Wedding. Multicoloured.
876 500 f. Type **340** . . . . 1·25 75
877 700 f. Prince Charles, Lady Diana Spencer and coach . . . . . 1·75 1·10

342 Maure Sheep

343 Heinrich von Stephan (founder of U.P.U.), Latecoere 28 and Concorde

1981. Sheep. Multicoloured.
886 10 f. Type **342** 15 10
887 25 f. Peul sheep 20 10
888 140 f. Sahael sheep 50 25
889 180 f. Touareg sheep 75 35
890 200 f. Djallonke ram 85 35

1981. Universal Postal Union Day.
891 **343** 400 f. red and green . . . . 1·60 70

344 Woman drinking from Bowl

1981. World Food Day.
892 **344** 200 f. brown, orge & mve 65 30

345 "The Incarnation of the Son of God" (detail, Grunewald)

1981. Air. Christmas. Multicoloured.
893 500 f. Type **345** . . . . 1·75 75
894 700 f. "The Campori Madonna" (Correggio) . . . . 2·25 1·25

347 Transport and Hands holding Map of Europe and Africa

1981. Europafrique.
896 **347** 700 f. blue, brown & orge 4·75 1·40

348 Guerin, Calmette, Syringe and Bacillus

1981. 60th Anniv of First B.C.G. Innoculation.
897 **348** 200 f. brown, violet & blk 85 40

1982. Air. World Chess Championship, Merano. Nos. 731 and 733 optd.
898 140 f. red, brown and blue . . 1·25 50
899 300 f. brown, ochre and red . . 2·25 75
OPTS: 140 f. **ANATOLI KARPOV VICTOR KORTCHNOI MERANO (ITALIE) (Octobre-Novembre 1981**; 300 f. **Octobre-Novembre 1981 ANATOLI KARPOV Champion du Monde 1981**.

350 "Nymphaea lotus"

1982. Flowers. Multicoloured.
900 170 f. Type **350** 85 35
901 180 f. "Bombax costatum" . . 90 35
902 200 f. "Parkia biglobosa" . . . 1·00 40
903 220 f. "Gloriosa simplex" . . . 1·25 45
904 270 f. "Satanocrater berhautii" 1·40 50

351 Lewis Carroll and Characters from "Alice" Books

1982. Air. 150th Birth Anniv of Lewis Carroll (Revd. Charles Dodgson).
905 110 f. Type **351** . . . . 1·00 25
906 130 f. Characters from "Alice" books 75 30
907 140 f. Characters from "Alice" books (different) 90 30

352 "George Washington" (Gilbert Stuart)

353 Ciwara Bamanan

1982. Air. 250th Birth Anniv of George Washington.
908 **352** 700 f. multicoloured . . . 2·00 1·25

1982. Masks. Multicoloured.
909 5 f. Type **353** 10 10
910 35 f. Kanga Dogon 15 10
911 180 f. N Domo Bamanan . . . 1·00 40
912 200 f. Cimier (Sogoninkum Bamanan . . . . 1·00 40
913 250 f. Kpelie Senoufo . . . . 1·10 45

354 Football

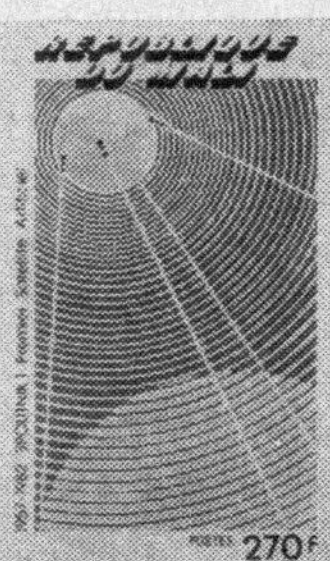

355 "Sputnik 1"

1982. Air. World Cup Football Championship, Spain.
914 **354** 220 f. multicoloured . . . 80 45
915 – 420 f. multicoloured . . . 1·50 90
916 – 500 f. multicoloured . . . 1·75 90
DESIGNS: 420 f., 500 f. Football scenes.

1982. 25th Anniv of First Artificial Satellite.
918 **355** 270 f. violet, blue and red 1·25 50

356 Lord Baden-Powell, Tent and Scout Badge

1982. Air. 125th Birth Anniv of Lord Baden-Powell.
919 300 f. Type **356** . . . . 1·50 50
920 500 f. Saluting scout . . . . . 2·25 90

357 "The Transfiguration" (Fra Angelico)

1982. Air. Easter. Multicoloured.
921 680 f. Type **357** . . . . 2·00 1·25
922 1000 f. "Pieta" (Giovanni Bellini) 3·00 1·90

358 Doctor giving Child Oral Vaccine

360 "En Bon Ami" (N'Teri)

359 Lions Emblem and Blind Person

1982. Anti-Polio Campaign.
923 **358** 180 f. multicoloured . . . 80 35

1982. Lions Club Blind Day.
924 **359** 260 f. orange, blue and red 1·25 50

1982. Hairstyles. Multicoloured.
925 140 f. Type **360** 35 30
926 150 f. Tucked-in pony tail . . . 60 35
927 160 f. "Pour l'Art" 70 45
928 180 f. "Bozo Kun" 75 50
929 270 f. "Fulaw Kun" . . . . . 1·25 60

361 Arms Stamp of Mali and France

1982. Air. "Philexfrance 82" International Stamp Exhibition, Paris. Multicoloured.
930 180 f. Type **361** 60 35
931 200 f. Dromedary caravan and 1979 "Philexafrique II" stamp 1·00 70

362 Fire-engine, 1850

1982. Fire-engines. Multicoloured.
932 180 f. Type **362** 95 35
933 200 f. Fire-engine, 1921 . . . . 1·40 40
934 270 f. Fire-engine, 1982 . . . . 1·60 50

363 Gobra

1982. Zebu. Cattle. Multicoloured.
935 10 f. Type **363** 10 10
936 60 f. Azaouak 25 15
937 110 f. Maure 35 25
938 180 f. Toronke 65 35
939 200 f. Peul Sambourou 75 40

1982. Air. World Cup Football Championship Winners. Nos. 914/16 optd.
940 **354** 220 f. multicoloured . . . 75 45
941 – 420 f. multicoloured . . . 1·50 90
942 – 500 f. multicoloured . . . 1·75 90
OPTS: 220 f. **1 ITALIE 2 RFA 3 POLOGNE**; 420 f. **POLOGNE FRANCE 3-2**; 500 f. **ITALIE RFA 3-1**.

365 "Urchin with Cherries"

1982. Air. 150th Birth Anniv of Edouard Manet (painter).
944 **365** 680 f. multicoloured . . . 2·75 1·25

366 "Virgin and Child" (detail) (Titian)

367 Wind-surfing

1982. Air. Christmas. Multicoloured.
945 500 f. Type **366** . . . . 1·50 90
946 1000 f. "Virgin and Child" (Giovanni Bellini) . . . . . 2·75 1·90

1982. Introduction of Wind-surfing as Olympic Event. Multicoloured.
947 200 f. Type **367** 80 45
948 270 f. Wind-surfer . . . . . . 1·25 55
949 300 f. Wind-surfer (different) 1·40 55

368 Goethe

1982. Air. 150th Death Anniv of Goethe (poet).
950 **368** 500 f. brown, light brown and black . . . . 2·00 90

369 Valentina Tereshkova

370 Transatlantic Balloon "Double Eagle II"

1983. Air. 20th Anniv of Launching of Vostok VI.
951 **369** 400 f. multicoloured . . . 1·25 75

1983. Air. Bicentenary of Manned Flight. Mult.
952 500 f. Type **370** . . . . . . 2·00 90
953 700 f. Montgolfier balloon . . 2·50 1·25

371 Football

1983. Air. Olympic Games, Los Angeles. Mult.
954 180 f. Type **371** 50 30
955 270 f. Hurdles 75 40
956 300 f. Windsurfing . . . . . . 1·10 55

372 "The Transfiguration" (detail)

373 Martin Luther King

1983. Air. Easter. Multicoloured.
957 400 f. Type **372** . . . . 1·25 75
958 600 f. "The Entombment" (detail from Baglioni Retable) . . . 2·00 1·10

1983. Celebrities.
959 **373** 800 f. brown, blue & pur 2·50 1·40
960 – 800 f. brown, red & dp red 2·50 1·40
DESIGN: No. 960, President Kennedy.

374 Oua Hairstyle

375 "Family of Acrobats with Monkey"

1983. Hairstyles. Multicoloured.
961 180 f. Type **374** 60 30
962 200 f. Nation (Diamani) . . . 70 30
963 270 f. Rond Point 90 40
964 300 f. Naamu-Naamu . . . . 1·00 45
965 500 f. Bamba-Bamba . . . . . 2·50 1·40

1983. Air. 10th Death Anniv of Picasso.
966 **375** 680 f. multicoloured . . . 2·00 1·25

376 Lions Club Emblem and Lions

1983. Air. Lions and Rotary Clubs. Mult.
967 700 f. Type **376** . . . . 2·25 2·00
968 700 f. Rotary Club emblem, container ship, diesel railcar and Boeing 737 airliner . . . 6·75 2·25

377 Satellite, Antenna and Telephone

1983. World Communications Year.
969 **377** 180 f. multicoloured . . . 55 30

378 Lavoisier and Apparatus

379 Banzoumana Sissoko

1983. Bicent of Lavoisier's Analysis of Water.
970 **378** 300 f. green, brown & blue 1·10 50

1983. Mali Musicians. Multicoloured.
971 200 f. Type **379** . . . . 1·00 30
972 300 f. Batourou Sekou Kouyate 1·50 45

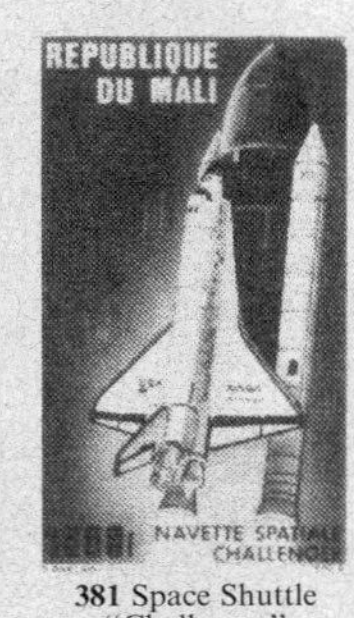

380 Nicephore Niepce and Camera

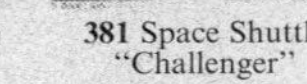

381 Space Shuttle "Challenger"

1983. 150th Death Anniv of Nicephore Niepce (pioneer of photography).
973 **380** 400 f. blue, green & dp grn 1·75 65

1983. Air. Space Shuttle.
974 **381** 1000 f. multicoloured . . . 3·25 1·75

382 Young People and Map of Africa

1983. 2nd Panafrican Youth Festival. Mult.
975 240 f. Type **382** 75 40
976 270 f. Hands reaching for map of Africa 75 40

383 Mercedes, 1914

1983. Air. Paris–Dakar Rally. Multicoloured.
977 240 f. Type **383** . . . . 1·40 40
978 270 f. Mercedes SSK, 1929 . . 1·50 50
979 500 f. Mercedes W 196, 1954 2·50 80

384 Liner and U.P.U. Emblem

385 Pawn and Bishop

1983. U.P.U. Day.
981 **384** 240 f. red, black and blue 1·50 50

1983. Air. Chess Pieces.
982 **385** 300 f. grey, violet and green 2·00 60
983 – 420 f. green, pink and grey 2·50 85
984 – 500 f. blue, dp blue & green 3·25 1·00
DESIGNS: 420 f. Rook and knight; 500 f. King and queen.

386 "Canigiani Madonna"

1983. Air. Christmas. 500th Birth Anniv of Raphael. Multicoloured.
986 700 f. Type **386** . . . . 2·00 1·00
987 800 f. "Madonna of the Lamb" 2·25 1·25

387 Sahara Goat

1984. Goats. Multicoloured.
988 20 f. Type **387** 15 10
989 30 f. Billy goat 20 10
990 50 f. Billy goat (different) . . . 25 15
991 240 f. Kaarta goat . . . . . . 1·00 40
992 350 f. Southern goat . . . . . 1·40 75

388 "Leopold Zborowski" (Modigliani)

389 Henri Dunant (founder of Red Cross)

1984. Air. Birth Centenary of Modigliani (painter).
993 **388** 700 f. multicoloured . . . 2·75 1·25

1984. Air. Celebrities.
994 **389** 400 f. dp blue, red & blue 1·50 65
995 – 540 f. dp blue, red & blue 1·60 85
DESIGN: 540 f. Abraham Lincoln.

390 Sidney Bechet

1984. Air. Jazz Musicians. Multicoloured.
996 470 f. Type **390** . . . . 2·50 75
997 500 f. Duke Ellington . . . . 2·50 80

391 Microlight Aircraft

1984. Air. Microlight Aircraft. Multicoloured.
998 270 f. Type **391** . . . . 1·10 40
999 350 f. Lazor Gemini motorized hang-glider . . . . 1·40 55

392 Weightlifting

1984. Air. Olympic Games, Los Angeles. Multicoloured.
1000 265 f. Type **392** 75 40
1001 440 f. Show jumping 90 70
1002 500 f. Hurdles . . . . 1·10 80

393 "Crucifixion" (Rubens)

1984. Air. Easter.
1004 **393** 940 f. brown & dp brown 3·00 1·50
1005 – 970 f. brown and red . . 3·00 1·50
DESIGN—HORIZ: 970 f. "The Resurrection" (Mantegna).

1984. Currency revaluation. Various stamps surch. (i) U.P.U. Day (No. 981).
1006 **384** 120 f. on 240 f. red, black and blue (postage) . . . 1·10 50

(ii) Goats (Nos. 988/92)
1007 **387** 10 f. on 20 f. mult 10 10
1008 – 15 f. on 30 f. mult 15 10
1009 – 25 f. on 50 f. mult 20 15
1010 – 125 f. on 240 f. mult . . . 95 40
1011 – 175 f. on 350 f. mult . . . 1·75 65

(iii) Paris–Dakar Rally (No. 977)
1012 **383** 120 f. on 240 f. mult (air) 1·25 40

395 Mercedes "Simplex"

1984. Air. 150th Birth Anniv of Gottlieb Daimler (motor car designer).
1035 **395** 350 f. olive, blue and mauve 2·50 1·10
1036 – 470 f. green, violet and plum . . . . 3·25 1·50
1037 – 485 f. blue, violet and plum 3·50 1·75
DESIGNS: 470 f. Mercedes-Benz Type "370 S"; 485 f. Mercedes-Benz "500 S EC".

396 Farm Workers

1984. Progress in Countryside and Protected Essences. Multicoloured.
1038 5 f. Type **396** 10 10
1039 90 f. Carpentry 60 30
1040 100 f. Tapestry making . . . 70 35
1041 135 f. Metal work 80 40
1042 515 f. "Borassus flabelifer" 3·25 1·90
1043 1225 f. "Vitelaria paradoxa" 7·50 3·75

397 Emblem and Child

1984. United Nations Children's Fund.
1044 **397** 120 f. red, brown and green 80 40
1045 – 135 f. red, blue and brown 90 50
DESIGN: 135 f. Emblem and two children.

398 U.P.U. Emblem, Anchor and Hamburg

1984. Universal Postal Union Congress, Hamburg.
1046 **398** 135 f. mauve, green and blue 80 40

1984. Air. Olympic Winners, Los Angeles. No. 1000/1002 optd.

1047 135 f. on 265 f. Optd **HALTERES 56 KGS / 1. WU (CHINE). 2. LAI (CHINE). 3. KOTAKA (JAPON)** . . . 80 40

1048 220 f. on 440 f. Optd **DRESSAGE / PAR EQUIPES / 1. RFA 2. SUISSE / 3. SUEDE** . . . 1·10 75

1049 250 f. on 500 f. Optd **ATHLETISME 3000 METRES STEEPLE / 1. KORIR (KENYA). / 2. MAHMOUD (FRANCE). / 3. DIEMER (E-U)**. . . . . 1·40 1·00

400 Emblem

1984. 10th Anniv of Economic Community of West Africa.

1051 **400** 350 f. multicoloured . . . 1·75 1·10

401 Dimetrodon

1984. Prehistoric Animals. Multicoloured.

1052 10 f. Type **401** 15 15
1053 25 f. Iguanodon (vert) 25 15
1054 30 f. Archaeopteryx (vert) . . . 70 45
1055 120 f. Type **401** . . . . 1·50 45
1056 175 f. As No. 1053 . . . . . 1·75 70
1057 350 f. As No. 1054 . . . . . 4·50 2·75
1058 470 f. Triceratops . . . . . . 5·00 2·50

402 "Virgin and Child between St. Joseph and St. Jerome" (detail, Lorenzo Lotto)

1984. Air. Christmas.

1059 **402** 500 f. multicoloured . . . 3·00 1·60

1984. Drought Aid. No. 758 surch.

1060 **298** 470 f. on 130 f. mult . . . 2·75 1·75

404 Horse Galloping

405 "Clitocybe nebularis"

1985. Horses. Multicoloured.

1061 90 f. Type **404** 70 35
1062 135 f. Beledougou horse . . . 1·25 40
1063 190 f. Nara horse . . . . . . 1·50 70
1064 530 f. Trait horse . . . . . . 4·50 2·00

1985. Fungi. Multicoloured.

1065 120 f. Type **405** . . . . 1·75 65
1066 200 f. "Lepiota cortinarius" . . 2·40 1·00
1067 485 f. "Agaricus semotus" . . 6·00 2·40
1068 525 f. "Lepiota procera" . . . 6·50 2·75

406 Emile Marchoux and Marchoux Institute

1985. Health. Multicoloured.

1069 120 f. Type **406** (World Lepers' Day and 40th anniv of Marchoux Institute) (postage) 80 30
1070 135 f. Lions' emblem and Samanto Village (15th anniv) 85 35
1071 470 f. Laboratory technicians and polio victim (anti-polio campaign) (air) . . . . . 3·50 1·50

407 Profiles and Emblem

1985. 15th Anniv of Technical and Cultural Co-operation Agency.

1072 **407** 540 f. green and brown 3·50 1·90

408 Common Kingfisher

1985. Air. Birth Bicentenary of John J. Audubon (ornithologist). Multicoloured.

1073 180 f. Type **408** . . . . 1·75 90
1074 300 f. Great bustard (vert) . . 2·75 1·40
1075 470 f. Ostrich (vert) . . . . . 4·25 2·40
1076 540 f. Ruppell's griffon . . . 4·50 3·00

409 National Pioneers Movement Emblem

1985. International Youth Year. Multicoloured.

1077 120 f. Type **409** 80 40
1078 190 f. Boy leading oxen . . . 1·40 70
1079 500 f. Sports motifs and I.Y.Y. emblem . . . . 3·50 1·75

410 Sud Aviation Caravelle, Boeing 727-200 and Agency Emblem

1985. Air. 25th Anniv of Aerial Navigation Security Agency for Africa and Madagascar (ASECNA).

1080 **410** 700 f. multicoloured . . . 4·50 2·50

411 Lion, and Scouts collecting Wood

1985. Air. "Philexafrique" Stamp Exhibition, Lome. Multicoloured.

1081 200 f. Type **411** . . . . 1·75 1·25
1082 200 f. Satellite, dish aerial and globe . . . . 1·75 1·25

412 U.P.U. Emblem, Computer and Reservoir (Development)

1985. "Philexafrique" Stamp Exhibition, Lome, Togo (2nd issue). Multicoloured.

1083 250 f. Type **412** . . . . . . 1·75 1·25
1084 250 f. Satellite, girls writing and children learning from television (Youth) . . . . 1·75 1·25

413 Grey Cat

1986. Cats. Multicoloured.

1085 150 f. Type **413** . . . . 1·50 60
1086 200 f. White cat . . . . . . 2·25 80
1087 300 f. Tabby cat . . . . . . 2·50 1·10

414 Hands releasing Doves and Globe

1986. Anti-apartheid Campaign. Multicoloured.

1088 100 f. Type **414** 65 40
1089 120 f. People breaking chain around world 85 50

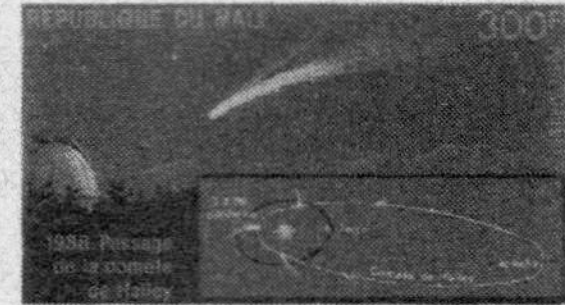

415 Comet and Diagram of Orbit

1986. Air. Appearance of Halley's Comet.

1090 **415** 300 f. multicoloured . . . 2·25 1·25

416 Internal Combustion Engine

1986. Air. Centenaries of First Motor Car with Internal Combustion Engine and Statue of Liberty. Multicoloured.

1091 400 f. Type **416** . . . . 3·00 1·50
1092 600 f. Head of statue, and French and American flags 4·00 2·25

417 Robeson

1986. Air. 10th Death Anniv of Paul Robeson (singer).

1093 **417** 500 f. multicoloured . . . 4·00 2·00

418 Women tending Crop

1986. World Communications Day.

1094 **418** 200 f. multicoloured . . . 1·50 80

419 Players

1986. World Cup Football Championship, Mexico. Multicoloured.

1095 160 f. Type **419** . . . . 1·40 65
1096 225 f. Player capturing ball 1·90 90

420 Watt

1986. 250th Birth Anniv of James Watt (inventor).

1098 **420** 110 f. multicoloured . . . 8·00 3·50

421 Eberth and Microscope

422 Chess Pieces on Board

1986. Air. 60th Death Anniv of Karl Eberth (discoverer of typhoid bacillus).

1099 **421** 550 f. multicoloured . . . 4·00 1·90

1986. Air. World Chess Championship, London and Leningrad. Multicoloured.

1100 400 f. Type **422** . . . . 3·75 1·75
1101 500 f. Knight and board . . . 4·75 2·25

1986. World Cup Winners. Nos. 1095/6 optd **ARGENTINE 3 R.F.A. 2**.

1102 160 f. multicoloured . . . . . 1·25 85
1103 225 f. multicoloured . . . . . 1·60 1·00

424 Head

1986. Endangered Animals. Giant Eland. Mult.

1105 5 f. Type **424** 20 10
1106 20 f. Standing by dead tree 40 10
1107 25 f. Stepping over fallen branch 40 10
1108 200 f. Mother and calf . . . . 2·25 95

425 Mermoz and "Croix du Sud"

1986. Air. 50th Anniv of Disappearance of Jean Mermoz (aviator). Multicoloured.

1109 150 f. Type **425** . . . . 1·25 60
1110 600 f. CAMS 53 flying boat and monoplane . . . . 4·25 2·25
1111 625 f. Map and seaplane "Comte de la Vaulx" . . . 4·50 2·50

1986. 10th Anniv of Concorde's First Commercial Flight. Nos. 674/6 surch **1986–10e Anniversaire du 1er Vol Commercial Supersonique**.

1112 175 f. on 120 f. Type **271** . . . 1·40 80
1113 225 f. on 130 f. Concorde and Wright Flyer I . . . . . . 1·75 1·00
1114 300 f. on 200 f. Concorde and Lindbergh's "Spirit of St. Louis" . . . . 2·75 1·50

427 Hansen and Follereau

1987. Air. 75th Death Anniv of Gerhard Hansen (discoverer of bacillus) and 10th Death Anniv of Raoul Follereau (leprosy pioneer).

1115 **427** 500 f. multicoloured . . . 3·50 1·90

428 Model "A", 1903

1987. 40th Death Anniv of Henry Ford (motor car manufacturer). Multicoloured.
1116 150 f. Type **428** . . . . 1·50 55
1117 200 f. Model "T", 1923 . . . 2·00 75
1118 225 f. "Thunderbird", 1968 . . 2·00 95
1119 300 f. "Continental", 1963 . . 2·25 1·25

429 Konrad Adenauer

431 Scenes from "The Jazz Singer"

430 Runners and Buddha's Head

1987. Air. 20th Death Anniv of Konrad Adenauer (German statesman).
1120 **429** 625 f. stone, brown and red 4·00 2·25

1987. Air. Olympic Games, Seoul (1988) (1st issue).
1121 **430** 400 f. black and brown 2·00 1·40
1122 – 500 f. dp green, grn & red 2·75 1·75
DESIGN: 500 f. Footballers.
See also Nos. 1133/4.

1987. Air. 60th Anniv of First Talking Picture.
1123 **431** 550 f. red, brn & dp brn 4·00 2·25

432 "Apis florea"

1987. Bees. Multicoloured.
1124 100 f. Type **432** 80 50
1125 150 f. "Apis dorsata" . . . . 1·40 70
1126 175 f. "Apis adonsonii" . . . 1·60 80
1127 200 f. "Apis mellifera" . . . . 1·75 1·00

433 Map, Dove and Luthuli

1987. Air. 20th Death Anniv of Albert John Luthuli (Nobel Peace Prize winner).
1128 **433** 400 f. mauve, blue & brn 2·50 1·50

434 Profiles and Lions Emblem

1987. Air. Lions International and Rotary International. Multicoloured.
1129 500 f. Type **434** . . . . 3·00 1·75
1130 500 f. Clasped hands and Rotary emblem . . . . 3·00 1·75

435 Anniversary Emblem and Symbols of Activities

1988. 30th Anniv of Lions International in Mali.
1131 **435** 200 f. multicoloured . . . 1·25 75

436 Emblem and Doctor examining Boy

1988. 40th Anniv of W.H.O.
1132 **436** 150 f. multicoloured . . . 1·10 60

437 Coubertin and Ancient and Modern Athletes

1988. Air. Olympic Games, Seoul (2nd issue). 125th Birth Anniv of Pierre de Coubertin (founder of modern games). Multicoloured.
1133 240 f. Type **437** . . . . 1·10 90
1134 400 f. Stadium, Olympic rings and sports pictograms . . . 1·90 1·40

438 "Harlequin"

1988. Air. 15th Death Anniv of Pablo Picasso (painter).
1135 **438** 600 f. multicoloured . . . 4·25 2·25

439 Concorde and Globe

1988. Air. 15th Anniv of First North Atlantic Crossing by Concorde.
1136 **439** 500 f. multicoloured . . . 4·00 2·00

440 Pres. Kennedy

442 Map

1988. 25th Death Anniv of John Fitzgerald Kennedy (American President).
1137 **440** 640 f. multicoloured . . . 4·00 2·40

1988. Mali Mission Hospital, Mopti. No. 1132 surch **MISSION MALI HOPITAL de MOPTI 300F** and **MEDECINS DU MONDE** emblem.
1138 **436** 300 f. on 150 f. mult . . 2·40 1·75

1988. 25th Anniv of Organization of African Unity.
1139 **442** 400 f. multicoloured . . . 2·50 1·25

443 Map, Leaf and Stove

1989. Air. "Improved Stoves: For a Green Mali". Multicoloured.
1140 5 f. Type **443** 10 10
1141 10 f. Tree and stove 10 10
1142 25 f. Type **443** 15 10
1143 100 f. As No. 1141 . . . . . 60 35

444 Astronauts on Moon

1989. Air. 20th Anniv of First Manned Moon Landing.
1144 **444** 300 f. blue, purple & grn 2·00 1·25
1145 – 500 f. purple, blue & brn 3·25 1·75
DESIGN: 500 f. Astronauts on moon (diff).

445 Emblem and Crossed Syringes

1989. Vaccination Programme. Multicoloured.
1146 20 f. Type **445** 15 10
1147 30 f. Doctor vaccinating woman 20 10
1148 50 f. Emblem and syringes . . 40 15
1149 175 f. Doctor vaccinating child 1·40 65

446 Emblem

1989. 25th Anniv of International Law Institute of French-speaking Countries.
1150 **446** 150 f. multicoloured . . . 1·10 55
1151 200 f. multicoloured . . . 1·40 70

447 Crowd

448 U.P.U. Emblem and Hands holding Envelopes

1989. Air. Bicentenary of French Revolution and "Philexfrance 89" International Stamp Exn, Paris.
1152 **447** 400 f. red, blue & purple 2·50 1·25
1153 – 600 f. violet, pur & mve 3·50 2·00
DESIGN: 600 f. Marianne and Storming of Bastille.

1989. World Post Day.
1154 **448** 625 f. multicoloured . . . 3·50 2·25

449 Pope and Cathedral

1990. Visit of Pope John Paul II.
1155 **449** 200 f. multicoloured . . . 1·60 80

450 Envelopes on Map

1990. 20th Anniv of Multinational Postal Training School, Abidjan.
1156 **450** 150 f. multicoloured . . . 1·25 55

451 Footballers

1990. Air. World Cup Football Championship, Italy. Multicoloured.
1157 200 f. Type **451** . . . . 1·50 75
1158 225 f. Footballers (different) 1·75 85

1990. World Cup Result. Nos. 1157/8 optd. Mult.
1160 200 f. **ITALIE : 2 / ANGLETERRE : 1** . . . . 1·50 85
1161 225 f. **R.F.A. : 1 / ARGENTINE : 0** . . . . 1·75 85

453 Pres. Moussa Traore and Bamako Bridge

1990. 30th Anniv of Independence.
1163 **453** 400 f. multicoloured . . . 2·50 1·50

454 Man writing and Adults learning to Read

455 Woman carrying Water and Cattle at Well

1990. International Literacy Year.
1164 **454** 150 f. multicoloured . . . 1·25 55
1165 200 f. multicoloured . . . 1·50 75

1991. Lions Club (1166) and Rotary International (1167) Projects. Multicoloured.
1166 200 f. Type **455** (6th anniv of wells project) . . . . . . 1·40 75
1167 200 f. Bamako branch emblem and hand (30th anniv of anti-polio campaign) . . . . . 1·40 75

456 Sonrai Dance, Takamba

457 Bank Emblem and Map of France

1991. Dances. Multicoloured.
1168 50 f. Type **456** 30 15
1169 100 f. Malinke dance, Mandiani 60 30
1170 150 f. Bamanan dance, Kono 90 50
1171 200 f. Dogon dance, Songho 1·10 75

1991. 50th Anniv of Central Economic Co-operation Bank.
1172 **457** 200 f. multicoloured . . . 1·25 75

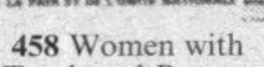

458 Women with Torch and Banner
461 Map of Africa

1992. National Women's Movement for the Safeguarding of Peace and National Unity.
1173 **458** 150 f. multicoloured . . . 75 40

1992. Various stamps surch.
1174 – 25 f. on 470 f. mult (No. 1058) (postage) 15 10
1175 **420** 30 f. on 110 f. mult . . . 18·00 4·50
1176 – 50 f. on 300 f. mult (No. 1087) 25 15
1177 – 50 f. on 1225 f. mult (No. 1043) 25 15
1178 – 150 f. on 135 f. mult (No. 1070) 75 40
1179 – 150 f. on 190 f. mult (No. 1063) 75 40
1180 – 150 f. on 190 f. mult (No. 1078) 75 40
1181 **400** 150 f. on 350 f. mult . . . 75 40
1182 – 150 f. on 485 f. mult (No. 1067) . . . . 1·25 50
1183 – 150 f. on 525 f. mult (No. 1068) . . . . 1·25 50
1184 – 150 f. on 530 f. mult (No. 1064) 75 40
1185 **440** 200 f. on 640 f. mult . . . 1·00 50
1186 – 240 f. on 350 f. mult (No. 1057) . . . . 1·25 65
1187 **448** 240 f. on 625 f. mult . . . 1·25 65
1188 **410** 20 f. on 700 f. mult (air) 10 10
1189 **415** 20 f. on 300 f. mult . . . 10 10
1190 – 25 f. on 470 f. mult (No. 1071) 15 10
1191 **408** 30 f. on 180 f. mult . . . 15 10
1192 – 30 f. on 500 f. purple, blue and brown (No. 1145) 15 10
1193 – 100 f. on 540 f. mult (No. 1076) 50 25
1194 **438** 100 f. on 600 f. mult . . . 50 25
1195 **444** 150 f. on 300 f. blue, purple and green 75 40
1196 **447** 150 f. on 400 f. red, blue and purple 75 40
1197 – 200 f. on 300 f. mult (No. 1074) . . . . 1·00 50
1198 – 240 f. on 600 f. violet, purple & mve (No. 1153) 1·25 65

1992. (a) Postage. No. 1095 surch **150 f "Euro 92"**.
1199 **419** 150 f. on 160 f. mult . . . 75 40

(b) Air. No. 1134 surch **150F "Barcelone 92"**.
1200 150 f. on 400 f. multicoloured 75 40

1993. 1st Anniv of Third Republic.
1201 **461** 150 f. multicoloured . . . 2·00 80

462 Blood, Memorial and Martyrs
463 Polio Victims

1993. 2nd Anniv of Martyrs' Day.
1203 **462** 150 f. multicoloured . . . 70 35
1204 160 f. multicoloured . . . 75 40

1993. Vaccination Campaign.
1205 **463** 150 f. multicoloured . . . 2·00 1·00

464 Lecture on Problem Issues

1993. 35th Anniv of Lions International in Mali.
1207 **464** 200 f. multicoloured . . . 90 45
1208 225 f. multicoloured . . . 1·00 50

465 Place de la Liberte
466 Figure Skating

1993. Multicoloured, background colour of top panel given.
1210 **465** 25 f. yellow 10 10
1211 50 f. green 30 20
1216 225 f. orange . . . . . 1·25 60
1217 240 f. mauve . . . . . . 1·50 60

1994. Winter Olympic Games, Lillehammer. Multicoloured.
1219 150 f. Type **466** 35 20
1220 200 f. Giant slalom 50 25
1221 225 f. Ski jumping 55 30
1222 750 f. Speed skating . . . . . 1·75 90

467 Juan Schiaffino (Uruguay)
468 Scaphonyx

1994. World Cup Football Championship, U.S.A. Players from Different Teams. Multicoloured.
1224 200 f. Type **467** 50 25
1225 240 f. Diego Maradona (Argentine Republic) . . . 60 30
1226 260 f. Paolo Rossi (Italy) . . . 65 35
1227 1000 f. Franz Beckenbauer (Germany) . . . . 2·40 1·25

1994. Prehistoric Animals. Multicoloured.
1229 5 f. Type **468** 10 10
1230 10 f. Cynognathus 10 10
1231 15 f. Lesothosaurus 10 10
1232 20 f. Scutellosaurus 10 10
1233 25 f. Ceratosaurus 10 10
1234 30 f. Dilophosaurus 10 10
1235 40 f. Dryosaurus 10 10
1236 50 f. Heterodontosaurus . . . 10 10
1237 60 f. Anatosaurus 15 10
1238 70 f. Saurornithoides 15 10
1239 80 f. Avimimus 20 10
1240 90 f. Saltasaurus 20 10
1241 300 f. Dromaeosaurus 75 40
1242 400 f. Tsintaosaurus 95 50
1243 600 f. Velociraptor . . . . 1·50 75
1244 700 f. Ouranosaurus . . . . 1·75 90

Nos. 1229/44 were issued together, se-tenant, forming a composite design.

469 "Sternuera castanea"

1994. Insects. Multicoloured.
1246 40 f. Type **469** 20 10
1247 50 f. "Eudicella gralli" (horiz) 20 10
1248 100 f. "Homoderus mellyi" . . 35 15
1249 200 f. "Kraussaria angulifera" (horiz) 60 25

470 Vaccinating Child

1994. Vaccination Campaign.
1250 **470** 150 f. green and black . . 35 20
1251 200 f. blue and black . . 50 25

471 Rock Doves

1994. Birds. Multicoloured.
1252 25 f. Type **471** 10 10
1253 30 f. Helmet guineafowl . . . 10 10
1254 150 f. Crowned cranes (vert) . . 35 20
1255 200 f. Red junglefowl (vert) . . 50 25

472 Family
473 Kirk Douglas in "Spartacus"

1994. International Year of the Family.
1256 **472** 200 f. multicoloured . . 50 25

1994. Film Stars. Multicoloured.
1257 100 f. Type **473** (postage) . . 50 15
1258 150 f. Elizabeth Taylor in "Cleopatra" 70 20
1259 225 f. Marilyn Monroe in "The River of No Return" . . 1·10 30
1260 500 f. Arnold Swarzenegger in "Conan the Barbarian" . 2·50 65
1261 1000 f. Elvis Presley in "Loving You" . . . . 5·25 1·25
1263 200 f. Clint Eastwood in "A Mule for Sister Sara" (inscr "SIERRA TORRIDE") (air) 1·00 25

474 Ella Fitzgerald

1994. Jazz Singers. Multicoloured.
1264 200 f. Type **474** 50 25
1265 225 f. Lionel Hampton . . . 65 30
1266 240 f. Sarah Vaughan 75 30
1267 300 f. Count Basie 90 40
1268 400 f. Duke Ellington . . . . 1·10 50
1269 600 f. Miles Davis . . . . . 1·75 75

475 Soldiers caught in Explosion

1994. 50th Anniv of Second World War D-Day Landings. Multicoloured. (a) Villers-Bocage.
1271 200 f. Type **475** 75 50
1272 200 f. Tank (29 × 47 mm) . . 75 50
1273 200 f. Troops beside tank . . 75 50

(b) Beaumont-sur-Sarthe.
1274 300 f. Bombers and troops under fire . . . . 1·25 75
1275 300 f. Bombers and tanks (29 × 47 mm) . . . . 1·25 75
1276 300 f. Tank and soldier with machine gun . . . . . 1·25 75

(c) Utah Beach (wrongly inscr "Utha").
1277 300 f. Wounded troops and bow of boat . . . . 1·25 75
1278 300 f. Troops in boat (29 × 47 mm) . . . . 1·25 75
1279 300 f. Troops in boats . . . . 1·25 75

(d) Air Battle.
1280 400 f. Bombers . . . . . . 1·25 75
1281 400 f. Aircraft (29 × 47 mm) . 1·25 75
1282 400 f. Airplane on fire . . . 1·25 75

(e) Sainte-Mere-Eglise.
1283 400 f. Troops firing at paratrooper . . . . 1·25 75
1284 400 f. Church and soldier (29 × 47 mm) . . . . 1·25 75
1285 400 f. Paratroopers and German troops . . . . 1·25 75

Nos. 1271/3, 1274/6, 1277/9, 1280/2 and 1283/5 respectively were issued together, se-tenant, forming composite designs.

476 Olympic Rings on National Flag

1994. Centenary of International Olympic Committee (1st issue).
1286 **476** 150 f. multicoloured . . 75 20
1287 200 f. multicoloured . . 1·25 25

See also Nos. 1342/5.

477 Couple holding Condoms

1994. Anti-AIDS Campaign. Multicoloured.
1288 150 f. Type **477** 50 20
1289 225 f. Nurse treating patient and laboratory worker 75 30

478 "Venus of Brassempoury"

1994. Ancient Art. Multicoloured.
1290 15 f. Type **478** 10 10
1291 25 f. Cave paintings, Tanum . 10 10
1292 45 f. Prehistoric men painting mural 10 10
1293 50 f. Cave paintings, Lascaux (horiz) 10 10
1294 55 f. Painting from tomb of Amonherkhopeshef 15 10
1295 65 f. God Anubis laying out Pharoah (horiz) 15 10
1296 75 f. Sphinx and pyramid, Mycerinus (horiz) 20 10
1297 85 f. Bust of Nefertiti . . . 20 10
1298 95 f. Statue of Shibum . . . 25 15
1299 100 f. Cavalry of Ur (horiz) . . 25 15
1300 130 f. Head of Mesopotamian harp 30 15
1301 135 f. Mesopotamian tablet (horiz) 35 20
1302 140 f. Assyrian dignitary . . . 35 20
1303 180 f. Enamel relief from Babylon (horiz) 45 25
1304 190 f. Assyrians hunting . . . 45 25
1305 200 f. "Mona Lisa of Nimrod" 60 25
1306 225 f. Phoenician coins (horiz) . 65 30
1307 250 f. Phoenician sphinx . . . 70 30
1308 275 f. Persian archer 75 35
1309 280 f. Glass paste mask . . . 80 35

479 "Polyptychus roseus"

1994. Multicoloured. (a) Butterflies and Moths.
1310 20 f. Type **479** 10 10
1311 30 f. "Elymniopsis bammakoo" 10 10
1312 40 f. Silver-striped hawk moth . 20 10
1313 150 f. Crimson-speckled moth . 50 20
1314 180 f. Foxy charaxes 60 25
1315 200 f. Common dotted border . 75 25

(b) Plants.
1316 25 f. "Disa kewensis" 10 10
1317 50 f. "Angraecum eburneum" . 10 10
1318 100 f. "Ansellia africana" . . . 25 15
1319 140 f. Sorghum 35 20
1320 150 f. Onion 35 20
1321 190 f. Maize 45 25
1322 200 f. Clouded agaric 70 25
1323 225 f. Parasol mushroom . . . 75 30
1324 500 f. "Lepiota aspera" . . . 1·40 65

(c) Insects.
1325 225 f. Goliath beetle 70 30
1326 240 f. Cricket 75 30
1327 350 f. Praying mantis . . . . 1·00 45

1994. Winter Olympic Games Medal Winners, Lillehammer. Nos. 1219/22 optd.
1328 150 f. **O GRISHSHUK Y. PLATOV RUSSIE** 35 20
1329 150 f. **Y. GORDEYEVA S. GRINKOV RUSSIE** 35 20
1330 200 f. **M. WASMEIER ALLEMAGNE** 50 25
1331 200 f. **D. COMPAGNONI ITALIE** 50 25
1332 225 f. **T. WEISSFLOG ALLEMAGNE** 55 30

1333 225 f. **E. BREDESEN NORVEGE** . . . 55 30
1334 750 f. **J.O. KOSS NORVEGE** . 1·75 90
1335 750 f. **B. BLAIR U.S.A.** . . . 1·75 90

A sheetlet also exists containing Nos. 1219/22 each optd with both of the inscriptions for that value.

1994. Results of World Cup Football Championship. Nos. 1224/27 optd **1. BRESIL 2. ITALIE 3. SUEDE.**

1337 200 f. multicoloured 80 25
1338 240 f. multicoloured 90 30
1339 260 f. multicoloured 95 35
1340 1000 f. multicoloured . . . . 3·00 1·25

482 Pierre de Coubertin (founder) and Torchbearer

483 Statue and Village

1994. Centenary of International Olympic Committee (2nd issue). Multicoloured.

1342 225 f. Type **482** . . . . . . 1·00 30
1343 240 f. Coubertin designing Olympic rings . . . . . . 1·10 30
1344 300 f. Athlete bearing torch and Coubertin (horiz) . . . . . 1·40 40
1345 500 f. Olympic rings and Coubertin at desk (horiz) . 2·00 65

1994. 20th International Tourism Day. Multicoloured.

1347 150 f. Type **483** 75 20
1348 200 f. Sphinx, pyramids and Abu Simbel temple (horiz) . 1·00 25

484 Reiner Klimker (dressage)

1995. Olympic Games, Atlanta (1996). Multicoloured.

1349 25 f. Type **484** 10 10
1350 50 f. Kristin Otto (swimming) . 10 10
1351 100 f. Gunther Winkler (show jumping) 30 10
1352 150 f. Birgit Fischer-Schmidt (single kayak) 40 10
1353 200 f. Nicole Uphoff (dressage) (vert) 60 20
1354 225 f. Renate Stecher (athletics) (vert) 60 20
1355 230 f. Michael Gross (swimming) 70 20
1356 240 f. Karin Janz (gymnastics) . 85 20
1357 550 f. Anja Fichtel (fencing) (vert) . . . . 2·00 50
1358 700 f. Heide Rosendahl-Ecker (long jump) (vert) . . . . . 2·50 80

485 Ernst Opik, "Galileo" Probe, Shoemaker-Levy Comet and Jupiter

1995. Anniversaries and Events. Multicoloured.

1359 150 f. Type **485** 40 10
1360 200 f. Clyde Tombaugh (discoverer of Pluto, 1930) and "Pluto" probe 75 20
1361 500 f. Henri Dunant (founder of Red Cross) . . . . 1·50 40
1362 650 f. Astronauts and lunar rover (first manned moon landing, 1969) . . . . . . 2·00 40
1363 700 f. Emblems of Lions International and Rotary International and child drinking from pump . . . 3·00 40
1364 800 f. Gary Kasparov (world chess champion, 1993) . . . 4·50 50

486 Agriculture and Fishing (regional integration)

1995. 20th Anniv of Economic Community of West African States. Multicoloured.

1365 150 f. Type **486** 50 20
1366 200 f. Emblem and handshake (co-operation) (vert) 75 20
1367 220 f. Emblem and banknotes (proposed common currency) 90 30
1368 225 f. Emblem and doves (peace and security) . . . . 1·10 30

487 Emblems of Alliance for Democracy in Mali and Sudanese Union-RDA

1995. 3rd Anniv of New Constitution. Multicoloured.

1369 150 f. Type **487** (second round of Presidential election) 40 20
1370 200 f. President Alpha Oumar Konare (vert) 50 20
1371 225 f. Emblems of competing parties (first round of Presidential election) . . . 60 30
1372 240 f. Map, flag and initials of parties (multi-party democracy) (vert) 70 30

488 Scout and Viennese Emperor Moth

1995. Scout Jamboree, Netherlands. Designs showing scouts and insects or fungi. Multicoloured.

1373 150 f. Type **488** 40 10
1374 225 f. Brimstone 60 20
1375 240 f. Fig-tree blue 70 20
1376 500 f. Clouded agaric . . . . 1·75 40
1377 650 f. "Agaricus semotus" . . 2·00 50
1378 725 f. Parasol mushroom . . . 2·25 60

489 Paul Harris (founder) and Emblem

490 Imperial Woodpecker ("Campephilus imperialis")

1995. 90th Anniv of Rotary International.

1380 **489** 1000 f. multicoloured . . 5·00 1·25

1995. Birds and Butterflies. Multicoloured.

1382 50 f. Type **490** 10 10
1383 50 f. Blue-crowned motmot ("Momotus momota") . . 10 10
1384 50 f. Keel-billed toucan ("Ramphastos sulfuratus") . 10 10
1385 50 f. Blue-breasted kingfisher ("Halycon malimbica") . . 10 10
1386 50 f. Streamertail ("Trochilus polytmus") 10 10
1387 50 f. Common cardinal ("Cardinalis cardinalis") . . 10 10
1388 50 f. Resplendent quetzal ("Pharomachrus mocinno") 10 10
1389 50 f. Sun conure ("Aratinga solstitialis") 10 10
1390 50 f. Red-necked amazon ("Amazona arausiaca") . . 10 10
1391 50 f. Scarlet ibis ("Eudocimus ruber") 10 10
1392 50 f. Red siskin ("Carduelis cucullatus") 10 10
1393 50 f. Hyacinth macaw ("Anodorhynchus hyacinthinus") 10 10
1394 50 f. Orange-breasted bunting ("Passerina leclancherii") . 10 10
1395 50 f. Red-capped manakin ("Pipra mentalis") 10 10
1396 50 f. Guianan cock of the rock ("Rupicola rupicola") . . 10 10
1397 50 f. Saffron finch ("Sicalis flaveola") 10 10
1398 100 f. Black-spotted barbet ("Capito niger") 40 10
1399 100 f. Amazon kingfisher ("Chloroceryle amazona") . 40 10
1400 100 f. Swallow tanager ("Tersina viridis") 40 10
1401 100 f. Blue-crowned motmot ("Momotus momota") . . 40 10
1402 100 f. Crimson-crested woodpecker ("Campephilus melanoleucos") 40 10
1403 100 f. Red-breasted blackbird ("Leistes militaris") 40 10
1404 100 f. King vulture ("Sarcorhamphus papa") . 40 10
1405 100 f. Capped heron ("Pilherodius pileatus") . . 40 10
1406 100 f. Black-tailed tityra ("Tityra cayana") 40 10
1407 100 f. Paradise tanager ("Tangara chilinsis") . . . 40 10
1408 100 f. Yellow-crowned amazon ("Amazona ochrocephala") 40 10
1409 100 f. Buff-throated saltator ("Saltator maximus") . . . 40 10
1410 100 f. Red-cowled cardinal ("Paroaria dominicana") . . 40 10
1411 100 f. Louisiana heron ("Egretta tricolor") 40 10
1412 100 f. Black-bellied cuckoo ("Piaya melanogaster") . . 40 10
1413 100 f. Barred antshrike ("Thamnophilus doliatus") . 40 10
1414 150 f. Paradise whydah . . . 70 10
1415 150 f. Red-necked francolin . 70 10
1416 150 f. Whale-headed stork (inscr "Stock") 70 10
1417 150 f. Ruff 70 10
1418 150 f. Marabou stork 70 10
1419 150 f. White pelican 70 10
1420 150 f. Western curlew 70 10
1421 150 f. Scarlet ibis 70 10
1422 150 f. Great crested grebe (inscr "Crebe") 70 10
1423 150 f. White spoonbill 70 10
1424 150 f. African jacana 70 10
1425 150 f. African pygmy goose . . 70 10
1426 200 f. Ruby-throated hummingbird 85 15
1427 200 f. Grape shoemaker and blue morpho butterflies . . 85 15
1428 200 f. Northern hobby 85 15
1429 200 f. Cuvier toucan 85 15
1430 200 f. Black-necked red cotinga 85 15
1431 200 f. Green-winged macaws . 85 15
1432 200 f. Flamingo 85 15
1433 200 f. Malachite kingfisher . . 85 15
1434 200 f. Bushy-crested hornbill . 85 15
1435 200 f. Purple swamphen . . . 85 15
1436 200 f. Striped body 85 15
1437 200 f. Painted lady 85 15

Stamps of the same value were issued together, in se-tenant sheetlets, each sheetlet forming a composite design.

491 Emblem and Scales of Justice

1995. 50th Anniv of U.N.O. Multicoloured.

1439 20 f. Type **491** 10 10
1440 170 f. Type **491** 70 30
1441 225 f. Emblem, doves and men with linked arms (horiz) . . 80 30
1442 240 f. As No. 1441 . . . . . 1·00 50

492 Food Jar

1995. Cooking Utensils. Multicoloured.

1443 5 f. Type **492** 20 10
1444 50 f. Pestle and mortar . . . 20 10
1445 150 f. Bowl (horiz) . . . . . 1·00 10
1446 200 f. Grain sack . . . . . . 1·10 15

493 Lennon

1995. 15th Death Anniv of John Lennon (musician).

1448 **493** 150 f. multicoloured . . 2·50 10

494 George Barnes

1995. 40th Anniv of Rock Music (1461/6) and Centenary of Motion Pictures (others). Multicoloured. (a) Actors in Western Films.

1449 150 f. Type **494** 80 40
1450 150 f. William S. Hart 80 40
1451 150 f. Tom Mix 80 40
1452 150 f. Wallace Berry 80 40
1453 150 f. Gary Cooper 80 40
1454 150 f. John Wayne 80 40

(b) Leading Ladies and their Directors.

1455 200 f. Marlene Dietrich and Josef von Sternberg ("The Blue Angel") . . . . . . 1·00 70
1456 200 f. Jean Harlow and George Cukor ("Dinner at Eight") . 1·00 70
1457 200 f. Mary Astor and John Houston ("The Maltese Falcon") . . . . 1·00 70
1458 200 f. Ingrid Bergman and Alfred Hitchcock ("Spellbound") . . . . . . 1·00 70
1459 200 f. Claudette Colbert and Cecil B. de Mille ("Cleopatra") . . . . . . 1·00 70
1460 200 f. Marilyn Monroe and Billy Wilder ("Some Like it Hot") . . . . 1·00 70

(c) Female Singers.

1461 225 f. Connie Francis . . . . 1·25 70
1462 225 f. The Ronettes . . . . . 1·25 70
1463 225 f. Janis Joplin . . . . . 1·25 70
1464 225 f. Debbie Harry . . . . . 1·25 70
1465 225 f. Cyndi Lauper . . . . . 1·25 70
1466 225 f. Carly Simon . . . . . 1·25 70

(d) Musicals.

1467 240 f. Gene Kelly in "Singin' in the Rain" . . . . 1·25 70
1468 240 f. Cyd Charisse and Fred Astaire in "The Bandwagon" . . . . . . 1·25 70
1469 240 f. Liza Minelli in "Cabaret" . . . . 1·25 70
1470 240 f. Julie Andrews in "The Sound of Music" . . . . . 1·25 70
1471 240 f. Ginger Rogers and Fred Astaire in "Top Hat" . . . 1·25 70
1472 240 f. John Travolta and Karen Lynn Gorney in "Saturday Night Fever" . . . . . . 1·25 70

495 Charles de Gaulle (French statesman, 25th death anniv)

1995. Anniversaries. Multicoloured.

1474 150 f. Type **495** 50 20
1475 200 f. General de Gaulle (50th anniv of liberation of France) 70 20
1476 240 f. Enzo Ferrari (car designer, 7th death anniv) . 75 30
1477 500 f. Ayrton Senna (racing driver, 1st death anniv) . . 1·50 20
1478 650 f. Paul Emile Victor (explorer, 88th birthday) . . 2·25 30
1479 725 f. Paul Harris (founder, 90th anniv of Rotary International) . . . . . . 3·50 40
1480 740 f. Michael Schumacher (racing driver, 26th birth anniv) (wrongly dated "1970") . . . . 3·50 40
1481 1000 f. Jerry Garcia (popular singer, death commemoration) . . . . . 4·00 50

OFFICIAL STAMPS

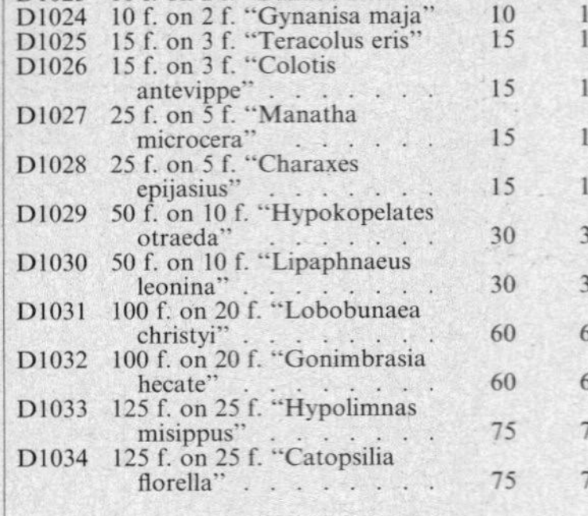

O 9 Dogon Mask — O 30 Mali Flag and Emblems

1961.

O26	O 9	1 f. violet	10	10
O27		2 f. red	10	10
O28		3 f. slate	10	10
O29		5 f. turquoise	15	15
O30		10 f. brown	20	15
O31		25 f. blue	35	15
O32		30 f. red	40	20
O33		50 f. myrtle	70	25
O34		85 f. purple	1·10	65
O35		100 f. green	1·40	65
O36		200 f. purple	2·75	1·40

1964. Centre and flag multicoloured; frame colour given.

O 90	O 30	1 f. green	10	10
O 91		2 f. lavender	10	10
O 92		3 f. slate	10	10
O 93		5 f. purple	10	10
O 94		10 f. blue	15	10
O 95		25 f. ochre	20	15
O 96		30 f. green	25	15
O 97		50 f. orange	35	15
O 98		85 f. brown	50	20
O 99		100 f. red	65	30
O100		200 f. blue	1·50	60

O 341 Arms of Gao

1981. Town Arms. Multicoloured.

O878	5 f. Type O 341	10	10
O879	15 f. Tombouctou	10	10
O880	50 f. Mopti	20	10
O881	180 f. Segou	60	30
O882	200 f. Sikasso	80	30
O883	680 f. Koulikoro	2·50	95
O884	700 f. Kayes	2·75	1·25
O885	1000 f. Bamako	4·00	1·50

1984. Nos. O878/85 surch.

O1013	15 f. on 5 f. Type O 341	15	10
O1014	50 f. on 15 f. Tombouctou	30	15
O1015	120 f. on 50 f. Mopti	70	25
O1016	295 f. on 180 f. Segou	2·00	90
O1017	470 f. on 200 f. Sikasso	3·00	1·50
O1018	515 f. on 680 f. Koulikoro	3·50	1·90
O1019	845 f. on 700 f. Kayes	6·00	2·50
O1020	1225 f. on 1000 f. Bamako	7·50	3·75

POSTAGE DUE STAMPS

D 9 Bambara Mask

1961.

D26	D 9	1 f. black	10	10
D27		2 f. blue	10	10
D28		5 f. mauve	20	10
D29		10 f. orange	25	15
D30		20 f. turquoise	50	25
D31		25 f. purple	65	30

D 28 "Polyptychus roseus"

1964. Butterflies and Moths. Multicoloured.

D83	1 f. Type D 28	10	10
D84	1 f. "Deilephila nerii"	10	10
D85	2 f. "Bunaea alcinoe"	15	15
D86	2 f. "Gynanisa maja"	15	15
D87	3 f. "Teracolus eris"	35	30
D88	3 f. "Colotis antevippe"	35	30
D89	5 f. "Manatha microcera"	35	30
D90	5 f. "Charaxes epijasius"	35	30
D91	10 f. "Hypokopelates otraeda"	45	35
D92	10 f. "Lipaphnaeus leonina"	45	35
D93	20 f. "Lobobunaea christyi"	75	70
D94	20 f. "Gonimbrasia hecate"	75	70
D95	25 f. "Hypolimnas misippus"	1·10	90
D96	25 f. "Castopsilia florella"	1·10	90

1984. Nos. D83/96 surch.

D1021	5 f. on 1 f. Type D 28	10	10
D1022	5 f. on 1 f. "Deilephila nerii"	10	10
D1023	10 f. on 2 f. "Bunaea alcinoe"	10	10
D1024	10 f. on 2 f. "Gynanisa maja"	10	10
D1025	15 f. on 3 f. "Teracolus eris"	15	10
D1026	15 f. on 3 f. "Colotis antevippe"	15	10
D1027	25 f. on 5 f. "Manatha microcera"	15	15
D1028	25 f. on 5 f. "Charaxes epijasius"	15	15
D1029	50 f. on 10 f. "Hypokopelates otraeda"	30	30
D1030	50 f. on 10 f. "Lipaphnaeus leonina"	30	30
D1031	100 f. on 20 f. "Lobobunaea christyi"	60	60
D1032	100 f. on 20 f. "Gonimbrasia hecate"	60	60
D1033	125 f. on 25 f. "Hypolimnas misippus"	75	75
D1034	125 f. on 25 f. "Catopsilia florella"	75	75

APPENDIX

The following stamps have either been issued in excess of postal needs or have not been available to the public in reasonable quantities at face value. Such stamps may later be given full listing if there is evidence of regular postal use.

All on gold foil.

1994.

World Cup Football Championship, U.S.A. Air. 3000 f.

Film Stars. Air. 3000 f.

MALTA Pt. 1

An island in the Mediterranean Sea, south of Italy. After a period of self-government under various Constitutions, independence was attained on 21 September 1964. The island became a republic on 13 December 1974.

1860. 12 pence = 1 shilling;
20 shillings = 1 pound.
1972. 10 mils = 1 cent;
100 cents = M£1.

1

5

1860. Various frames.

18	1	½d. yellow	27·00	35·00
20		½d. green	1·90	50
22	–	1d. red	2·25	35
23	–	2d. grey	5·00	1·40
26	–	2½d. blue	35·00	90
27	–	4d. brown	11·00	3·00
28	–	1s. violet	35·00	9·00
30	5	5s. red	£110	80·00

6 Harbour of Valletta

7 Gozo Fishing Boat

8 Ancient Maltese Galley

9 Emblematic Figure of Malta

10 Shipwreck of St. Paul

12

1899.

31a	6	¼d. brown	1·25	40
79		4d. black	14·00	3·00
32	7	4½d. brown	14·00	10·00
58		4½d. orange	4·25	3·50
59	8	5d. red	26·00	5·00
60		5d. green	4·00	3·50
34	9	2s. 6d. olive	40·00	12·00
35	10	10s. black	85·00	60·00

1902. No. 26 surch **One Penny**.

36	1d. on 2½d. blue	90	1·25

1903.

47b	12	½d. green	3·25	10
48		1d. black and red	11·00	20
49		1d. red	1·75	10
50		2d. purple and grey	7·50	1·75
51		2d. grey	3·00	5·00
52		2½d. purple and blue	15·00	50
53		2½d. blue	5·00	2·50
42		3d. grey and purple	1·75	50
54		4d. black and brown	10·00	5·50
55		4d. black & red on yellow	3·75	3·25
44		1s. grey and violet	14·00	7·00
62		1s. black on green	6·50	2·50
63		5s. green & red on yellow	65·00	70·00

13

15

17

18

1914.

69	13	¼d. brown	70	10
71		½d. green	2·00	30
73		1d. red	1·25	10
75		2d. grey	6·00	3·00
77		2½d. blue	2·00	50
78		3d. purple on yellow	2·50	8·00
80		6d. purple	10·00	16·00
81a		1s. black on green	11·00	14·00
86	15	2s. purple & blue on blue	50·00	29·00
88		5s. green & red on yellow	80·00	95·00
104	17	10s. black	£300	£550

1918. Optd **WAR TAX**.

92	13	½d. green	70	15
93	12	3d. grey and purple	1·40	7·50

1921.

100	18	2d. grey	2·50	1·75

1922. Optd **SELF-GOVERNMENT**.

114	13	¼d. brown	20	75
106		½d. green	70	1·50
116		1d. red	70	15
117	18	2d. grey	2·00	45
118	13	2½d. blue	85	80
108		3d. purple on yellow	2·00	14·00
109		6d. purple	2·00	14·00
110		1s. black on green	3·00	13·00
120	15	2s. purple & blue on blue	40·00	75·00
112	9	2s. 6d. olive	22·00	40·00
113	15	5s. green & red on yellow	50·00	75·00
105	10	10s. black	£180	£275
121	17	10s. black	£110	£160

1922. Surch **One Farthing**.

122	18	¼d. on 2d. grey	40	30

22

23

1922.

123	22	¼d. brown	1·75	60
124		½d. green	1·75	10
125		1d. orange and purple	2·50	15
126		1d. violet	2·50	65
127		1½d. red	2·50	10
128		2d. brown and blue	2·50	90
129		2½d. blue	2·00	6·50
130		3d. blue	2·75	90
131		3d. black on yellow	2·50	9·00
132		4d. yellow and blue	1·25	2·00
133		6d. green and violet	2·75	1·75
134	23	1s. blue and brown	4·75	2·50
135		2s. brown and blue	8·00	8·50
136		2s. 6d. purple and black	9·50	15·00
137		5s. orange and blue	21·00	32·00
138		10s. grey and brown	55·00	£130
140	22	£1 black and red	90·00	£250

1925. Surch **Two pence halfpenny**.

141	22	2½d. on 3d. blue	1·50	2·50

1926. Optd **POSTAGE**.

143	22	¼d. brown	45	2·50
144		½d. green	50	15
145		1d. violet	75	25
146		1½d. red	75	50
147		2d. brown and blue	60	40
148		2½d. blue	1·00	70
149		3d. black on yellow	60	70
150		4d. yellow and blue	4·25	13·00
151		6d. green and violet	2·75	2·50
152	23	1s. blue and brown	4·75	9·00
153		2s. brown and blue	48·00	£130
154		2s. 6d. purple and black	9·50	25·00
155		5s. orange and blue	8·50	27·00
156		10s. grey and brown	7·00	15·00

26

27 Valletta Harbour

28 St. Publius

1926. Inscr "POSTAGE".

157	26	¼d. brown	80	15
158		½d. green	50	15
159		1d. red	2·75	90
160		1½d. brown	1·75	10
161		2d. grey	4·25	8·50
162		2½d. blue	3·75	45
162a		3d. violet	4·00	2·25
163		4d. black and red	2·75	8·00
164		4½d. violet and yellow	3·25	2·50
165		6d. violet and red	4·00	2·50
166	27	1s. black	6·50	3·25
167	28	1s. 6d. black and green	6·50	13·00
168	–	2s. black and purple	6·50	15·00
169	–	2s. 6d. black and red	15·00	42·00
170	–	3s. black and blue	17·00	28·00
171	–	5s. black and green	22·00	60·00
172	–	10s. black and red	55·00	£100

DESIGNS—As Type **27**: 2s. Mdina (Notabile); 5s. Neolithic temple, Mnajdra. As Type **28**: 2s. 6d. Gozo boat; 3s. Neptune; 10s. St. Paul.

1928. Air. Optd **AIR MAIL**.

173	26	6d. violet and red	1·50	90

1928. Optd **POSTAGE AND REVENUE**.

174	26	¼d. brown	1·50	10
175		½d. green	1·50	10
176		1d. red	1·75	3·00
177		1d. brown	4·50	10
178		1½d. brown	1·75	50
179		1½d. red	4·25	10
180		2d. grey	4·00	8·50
181		2½d. blue	1·75	10
182		3d. violet	1·75	40
183		4d. black and red	1·75	1·50
184		4½d. violet and yellow	2·25	1·00
185		6d. violet and red	2·25	1·25
186	27	1s. black	4·75	2·50
187	28	1s. 6d. black and green	5·50	9·50
188	–	2s. black and purple	22·00	50·00
189	–	2s. 6d. black and red	17·00	23·00
190	–	3s. black and blue	19·00	30·00
191	–	5s. black and green	27·00	65·00
192	–	10s. black and red	55·00	90·00

1930. As Nos. 157/72, but inscr "POSTAGE & REVENUE".

193	¼d. brown	50	10
194	½d. green	50	10
195	1d. brown	60	10
196	1½d. red	70	10
197	2d. grey	1·00	30
198	2½d. blue	2·00	10
199	3d. violet	1·50	20
200	4d. black and red	1·25	3·50
201	4½d. violet and yellow	3·00	1·00
202	6d. violet and red	2·25	1·00
203	1s. black	9·50	11·00
204	1s. 6d. black and green	7·50	18·00
205	2s. black and purple	9·50	18·00
206	2s. 6d. black and red	17·00	48·00
207	3s. black and blue	24·00	55·00
208	5s. black and green	30·00	65·00
209	10s. black and red	65·00	£120

1935. Silver Jubilee. As T **10a** of Gambia.

210	½d. black and green	40	50
211	2½d. brown and blue	2·50	4·00
212	6d. blue and olive	7·00	4·00
213	1s. grey and purple	11·00	16·00

1937. Coronation. As T **10b** of Gambia.

214	½d. green	10	10
215	1½d. red	50	20
216	2½d. blue	50	40

37 Grand Harbour, Valletta

38 H.M.S. "St. Angelo"

39 Verdala Palace

1938. Various designs with medallion King George VI.

217	37	¼d. brown	10	10
218	38	½d. green	1·75	30
218a		½d. brown	55	30
219	39	1d. brown	4·25	30
219a		1d. green	60	10
220	–	1½d. red	1·00	30
220b	–	1½d. black	30	15
221	–	2d. black	40	1·75
221a	–	2d. red	40	20
222	–	2½d. blue	75	45
222a	–	2½d. violet	60	10
223	–	3d. violet	45	80
223a	–	3d. blue	30	10
224	–	4½d. olive and brown	50	10
225	–	6d. olive and red	75	30
226	–	1s. black	75	30
227	–	1s. 6d. black and olive	7·00	3·75
228	–	2s. green and blue	4·00	3·75
229	–	2s. 6d. black and red	7·50	5·00
230	–	5s. black and green	4·50	5·50
231	–	10s. black and red	15·00	15·00

DESIGNS—As Types **38/9**. VERT: 1½d. Hypogeum, Hal Saflieni; 3d. St. John's Co-Cathedral; 6d. Statue of Manoel de Vilhena; 1s. Maltese girl wearing faldetta; 5s. Palace Square, Valletta; 10s. St. Paul. HORIZ: 2d. Victoria and Citadel, Gozo; 2½d. De l'Isle Adam entering Mdina; 4½d. Ruins at Mnajdra; 1s. 6d. St. Publius; 2s. Mdina Cathedral; 2s. 6d. Statue of Neptune.

1946. Victory. As T **11a** of Gambia.

232	1d. green	15	10
233	3d. blue	20	40

1948. Self-Government. As 1938 issue optd **SELF-GOVERNMENT 1947**.

234	¼d. brown	20	20
235	½d. brown	20	10
236	1d. green	20	10
236a	1d. grey	20	10
237	1½d. black	75	10
237b	1½d. green	30	10
238	2d. red	85	10
238a	2d. yellow	30	10
239	2½d. violet	80	10
239a	2½d. red	30	85
240	3d. blue	45	15
240a	3d. violet	35	15
241	4½d. olive and brown	2·00	1·50
241a	4½d. olive and blue	50	90
242	6d. olive and red	1·75	15
243	1s. black	2·25	40
244	1s. 6d. black and olive	2·50	45
245	2s. green and blue	5·00	1·50
246	2s. 6d. black and red	12·00	2·50
247	5s. black and green	17·00	3·50
248	10s. black and red	17·00	21·00

1949. Silver Wedding. As T **11b/c** of Gambia.

249	1d. green	50	10
250	£1 blue	38·00	35·00

1949. U.P.U. As T **11d/g** of Gambia.

251	2½d. violet	30	10
252	3d. blue	3·25	50
253	6d. red	1·00	50
254	1s. black	1·00	1·75

53 Queen Elizabeth II when Princess

54 "Our Lady of Mount Carmel" (attrib Palladino)

1950. Visit of Princess Elizabeth.

255	53	1d. green	10	10
256		3d. blue	20	10
257		1s. black	55	60

1951. 7th Centenary of the Scapular.

258	54	1d. green	10	10
259		3d. violet	20	10
260		1s. black	60	40

1953. Coronation. As T **11h** of Gambia.

261	1½d. black and green	30	10

55 St. John's Co-Cathedral

56 "Immaculate Conception" (Caruana) (altar-piece, Cospicua)

1954. Royal Visit.

262	55	3d. violet	30	10

1954. Centenary of Dogma of the Immaculate Conception.

263	56	1½d. green	10	10
264		3d. blue	10	10
265		1s. grey	35	20

57 Monument of the Great Siege, 1565

74 "Defence of Malta"

1956.

266	57	¼d. violet	20	10
267	–	½d. orange	50	10
314	–	1d. black	50	30
269	–	1½d. green	30	10
270	–	2d. sepia	1·25	10
271	–	2½d. brown	55	30
272	–	3d. red	75	10
273	–	4½d. blue	1·00	20

274 – 6d. blue 50 10
275 – 8d. ochre . . . . 1·50 1·00
276 – 1s. violet 50 10
277 – 1s. 6d. turquoise . . . . . 9·50 20
278 – 2s. olive . . . . 11·00 80
279 – 2s. 6d. brown . . . . . . 7·50 2·25
280 – 5s. green . . . . 13·00 2·75
281 – 10s. red . . . . 35·00 9·50
282 – £1 brown . . . . 35·00 22·00

DESIGNS—VERT: ½d. Wignacourt aqueduct horsetrough; 1d. Victory church; 1½d. Second World War memorial; 2d. Mosta Church; 3d. The King's Scroll; 4½d. Roosevelt's Scroll; 8d. Vedette (tower); 1s. Mdina Gate; 1s. 6d. "Les Gavroches" (statue); 2s. Monument of Christ the King; 2s. 6d. Monument of Grand Master Cottoner; 5s. Grand Master Perellos's monument; 10s. St. Paul (statue); £1 Baptism of Christ (statue). HORIZ: 2½d. Auberge de Castile; 6d. Neolithic Temples at Tarxien.

1957. George Cross Commem. Cross in Silver.

283 **74** 1½d. green 15 10
284 – 3d. red 15 10
285 – 1s. brown 15 10

DESIGNS—HORIZ: 3d. Searchlights over Malta. VERT: 1s. Bombed buildings.

77 Design

81 Sea Raid on Grand Harbour, Valletta

1958. Technical Education in Malta. Inscr "TECHNICAL EDUCATION".

286 **77** 1½d. black and green 10 10
287 – 3d. black, red and grey . . . 10 10
288 – 1s. grey, purple and black . . 15 10

DESIGNS—VERT: 3d. "Construction". HORIZ: 1s. Technical School, Paola.

1958. George Cross Commem. Cross in first colour outlined in silver.

289 – 1½d. green and black 15 10
290 **81** 3d. red and black 15 10
291 – 1s. mauve and black 15 10

DESIGNS—HORIZ: 1½d. Bombed-out family; 1s. Searchlight crew.

83 Air Raid Casualties

86 Shipwreck of St. Paul (after Palombi)

87 Statue of St. Paul, Rabat, Malta

1959. George Cross Commemoration.

292 **83** 1½d. green, black & gold . . 20 10
293 – 3d. mauve, black & gold . . 20 10
294 – 1s. grey, black and gold . . 70 80

DESIGNS—HORIZ: 3d. "For Gallantry". VERT: 1s. Maltese under bombardment.

1960. 19th Centenary of the Shipwreck of St. Paul. Inscr as in T **86/7**.

295 **86** 1½d. blue, gold & brown . . 15 10
296 – 3d. purple, gold and blue . . 15 10
297 – 6d. red, gold and grey . . . 25 10
298 **87** 8d. black and gold 30 50
299 – 1s. purple and gold 25 10
300 – 2s. 6d. blue, green & gold . . 1·00 2·00

DESIGNS—As Type **88**: 3d. Consecration of St. Publius, First Bishop of Malta; 6d. Departure of St. Paul (after Palombi). As Type **87**: 1s. Angel with the "Acts of the Apostles"; 2s. 6d. St. Paul with the "Second Epistle to the Corinthians".

92 Stamp of 1860

1960. Centenary of Malta Stamps. Stamp in buff and blue.

301 **92** 1½d. green 25 10
302 3d. red 30 10
303 6d. blue . . . . 40 1·00

93 George Cross

1961. George Cross Commemoration.

304 **93** 1½d. black, cream & bistre . 15 10
305 – 3d. brown and blue 30 10
306 – 1s. green, lilac and violet . . 75 1·40

DESIGNS: 3d. and 1s. show George Cross as Type **93** over backgrounds with different patterns.

96 "Madonna Damascena"

100 Bruce, Zammit and Microscope

1962. Great Siege Commemoration.

307 **96** 2d. blue 10 10
308 – 3d. red 10 10
309 – 6d. bronze 25 10
310 – 1s. purple 25 40

DESIGNS: 3d. Great Siege Monument; 6d. Grand Master La Valette; 1s. Assault on Fort St. Elmo.

1963. Freedom from Hunger. As T **20a** of Gambia.

311 1s. 6d. sepia . . . . 2·25 2·50

1963. Cent of Red Cross. As T **20b** of Gambia.

312 2d. red on black 25 15
313 1s. 6d. red and blue . . . . . 3·00 3·75

1964. Anti-Brucellosis Congress.

316 **100** 2d. brown, black & green . 10 10
317 – 1s. 6d. black and purple . . 90 30

DESIGN: 1s. 6d. Goat and laboratory equipment.

102 "Nicola Cotoner tending Sick Man" (M. Preti)

1964. 1st European Catholic Doctors' Congress, Valletta. Multicoloured.

318 2d. Type **102** 20 10
319 6d. St. Luke and hospital . . . 50 15
320 1s. 6d. Sacra Infermeria, Valletta 1·10 1·90

106 Dove and British Crown

110 Neolithic Era

109 "The Nativity"

1964. Independence.

321 **106** 2d. olive, red and gold . . 30 10
322 – 3d. brown, red and gold . . 30 10
323 – 6d. slate, red and gold . . 70 15
324 **106** 1s. blue, red and gold . . . 70 15
325 – 1s. 6d. blue, red & gold . . 2·00 1·00
326 – 2s. 6d. blue, red & gold . . 2·00 2·25

DESIGNS: 3d., 1s. 6d. Dove and Pope's Tiara; 6d., 2s. 6d. Dove and U.N. emblem.

1964. Christmas.

327 **109** 2d. purple and gold 10 10
328 4d. blue and gold 20 15
329 8d. green and gold 45 45

1965. Multicoloured.

330 ½d. Type **110** 10 10
331 1d. Punic era 10 10
332 1½d. Roman era 30 10
333 2d. Proto Christian era . . . 10 10
334 2½d. Saracenic era 55 10
335 3d. Siculo Norman era . . . 10 10
336 4d. Knights of Malta 40 10
337 4½d. Maltese Navy . . . . . 1·00 40
337b 5d. Fortifications 30 20
338 6d. French occupation 20 10
339 8d. British rule 50 10
339c 10d. Naval Arsenal . . . . . 45 1·60
340 1s. Maltese Corps of the British Army 30 10
341 1s. 3d. International Eucharistic Congress, 1913 . . . . . . 2·00 1·40
342 1s. 6d. Self-Government, 1921 60 10
343 2s. Gozo Civic Council . . . 70 10
344 2s. 6d. State of Malta 70 50
345 3s. Independence, 1964 . . . 1·50 75
346 5s. HAFMED (Allied Forces, Mediterranean) . . . . . . 6·00 1·00
347 10s. The Maltese Islands (map) 3·00 3·00
348 £1 Patron Saints . . . . . . 3·75 5·00

Nos. 339/48 are larger, 41 × 29 mm from perf to perf and include portrait of Queen Elizabeth II.

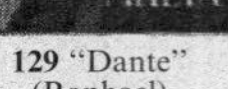

129 "Dante" (Raphael)

131 Turkish Fleet

1965. 700th Birth Anniv of Dante.

349 **129** 2d. blue 10 10
350 6d. green 25 10
351 2s. brown . . . . 1·10 1·50

1965. 400th Anniv of Great Siege. Multicoloured.

352 2d. Turkish camp 30 10
353 3d. Battle scene 30 10
354 6d. Type **131** 50 10
355 8d. Arrival of relief force . . . 90 90
356 1s. Grand Master J. de La Valette's arms 50 10
357 1s. 6d. "Allegory of Victory" (from mural by M. Preti) . . 1·50 30
358 2s. 6d. Victory medal . . . . . 1·75 3·25

SIZES—As Type **131**: 1s. SQUARE (32½ × 32½ mm): others.

137 "The Three Kings"

1965. Christmas.

359 **137** 1d. purple and red 10 10
360 4d. purple and blue 30 25
361 1s. 3d. slate and purple . . 30 30

138 Sir Winston Churchill

1966. Churchill Commemoration.

362 **138** 2d. black, red and gold . . 20 10
363 – 3d. green, olive and gold . . 20 10
364 **138** 1s. purple, red and gold . . 25 10
365 – 1s. 6d. blue, ultram & gold . 35 40

DESIGN: 3d., 1s. 6d. Sir Winston Churchill and George Cross.

140 Grand Master La Valette

145 Pres. Kennedy and Memorial

1966. 400th Anniv of Valletta. Multicoloured.

366 2d. Type **140** 10 10
367 3d. Pope Pius V 10 10
368 6d. Map of Valletta 15 10
369 1s. F. Laparelli (architect) . . . 15 10
370 2s. 6d. G. Cassar (architect) . . 35 50

1966. Pres. Kennedy Commemoration.

371 **145** 3d. olive, gold and black . 10 10
372 1s. 6d. blue, gold & black . 10 10

146 "Trade"

147 "The Child in the Manger"

1966. 10th Malta Trade Fair.

373 **146** 2d. multicoloured 10 10
374 8d. multicoloured 30 25
375 2s. 6d. multicoloured . . . 30 25

1966. Christmas.

376 **147** 1d. multicoloured 10 10
377 4d. multicoloured 10 10
378 1s. 3d. multicoloured . . . 10 10

148 George Cross

149 Crucifixion of St. Peter

1967. 25th Anniv of George Cross Award to Malta.

379 **148** 2d. multicoloured 10 10
380 4d. multicoloured 10 10
381 3s. multicoloured 15 15

1967. 1,900th Anniv of Martyrdom of Saints Peter and Paul.

382 **149** 2d. brown, orange and blk 10 10
383 – 8d. olive, gold and black . 15 10
384 – 3s. blue and black . . . 20 15

DESIGNS—As Type **149**: 3s. Beheading of St. Paul. HORIZ (47 × 25 mm): 8d. Open Bible and episcopal emblems.

152 "St. Catherine of Siena"

156 Temple Ruins, Tarxien

1967. 300th Death Anniv of Melchior Gafa (sculptor). Multicoloured.

385 2d. Type **152** 10 10
386 4d. "St. Thomas of Villanova" 10 10
387 1s. 6d. "Baptism of Christ" (detail) 15 10
388 2s. 6d. "St. John the Baptist" (from "Baptism of Christ") . 15 10

1967. 15th Int Historical Architecture Congress, Valletta. Multicoloured.

389 2d. Type **156** 10 10
390 6d. Facade of Palazzo Falzon, Notabile 10 10
391 1s. Parish Church, Birkirkara . 10 10
392 3s. Portal, Auberge de Castille 25 25

160 "Angels"

166 Human Rights Emblem and People

163 Queen Elizabeth II and Arms of Malta

1967. Christmas. Multicoloured.

393 1d. Type **160** 10 10
394 8d. "Crib" 20 10
395 1s. 4d. "Angels" 20 10

1967. Royal Visit.

396 **163** 2d. multicoloured 10 10
397 – 4d. black, purple and gold 10 10
398 – 3s. multicoloured 20 25
DESIGNS—VERT: 4d. Queen in Robes of Order of St. Michael and St. George. HORIZ: 3s. Queen and outline of Malta.

1968. Human Rights Year. Multicoloured.

399 2d. Type **166** 10 10
400 6d. Human Rights emblem and people (different) 10 10
401 2s. Type **166** (reversed) 10 10

169 Fair "Products"   **170** Arms of the Order of St. John and La Valette

1968. Malta International Trade Fair.

402 **169** 4d. multicoloured 10 10
403 8d. multicoloured 10 10
404 3s. multicoloured 15 10

1968. 4th Death Cent of Grand Master La Valette. Multicoloured.

405 1d. Type **170** 10 10
406 8d. "La Valette" (A. de Favray) 15 10
407 1s. 6d. La Valette's tomb (28 × 23 mm) 15 10
408 2s. 6d. Angels and scroll bearing date of death 20 20
The 8d., 2s. 6d. are vert.

174 Star of Bethlehem and Angel waking Shepherds   **177** "Agriculture"

1968. Christmas. Multicoloured.

409 1d. Type **174** 10 10
410 8d. Mary and Joseph with shepherd watching over Cradle 15 10
411 1s. 4d. Three Wise Men and Star of Bethlehem 15 20

1968. 6th Food and Agricultural Organization Regional Conference for Europe. Mult.

412 4d. Type **177** 10 10
413 1s. F.A.O. emblem and coin . . 10 10
414 2s. 6d. "Agriculture" sowing Seeds 10 15

180 Mahatma Gandhi   **181** ILO Emblem

1969. Birth Centenary of Mahatma Gandhi.

415 **180** 1s. 6d. brown, blk & gold . 15 10

1969. 50th Anniv of Int Labour Organization.

416 **181** 2d. blue, gold and turq . . 10 10
417 6d. sepia, gold & brown . . 10 10

182 Robert Samut

1969. Birth Centenary of Robert Samut (composer of Maltese National Anthem).

418 **182** 2d. multicoloured 10 10

183 Dove of Peace, U.N. Emblem and Sea-Bed

1969. United Nations Resolution on Oceanic Resources.

419 **183** 5d. multicoloured 10 10

184 "Swallows" returning to Malta

1969. Maltese Migrants' Convention.

420 **184** 10d. black, gold and olive . 10 10

185 University Arms and Grand Master de Fonseca (founder)

1969. Bicentenary of University of Malta.

421 **185** 2s. multicoloured 15 20

187 Flag of Malta and Birds

1969. 5th Anniv of Independence.

422 – 2d. multicoloured 10 10
423 **187** 5d. black, red and gold . . 10 10
424 – 10d. black, blue & gold . . 10 10
425 – 1s. 6d. multicoloured . . . 20 35
426 – 2s. 6d. black, brn & gold . 25 45
DESIGNS—SQUARE (31 × 31 mm): 2d. 1919 War Monument. VERT: 10d. "Tourism"; 1s. 6d. U.N. and Council of Europe emblems; 2s. 6d. "Trade and Industry".

191 Peasants playing Tambourine and Bagpipes

1969. Christmas. Children's Welfare Fund. Multicoloured.

427 1d. + 1d. Type **191** 10 20
428 5d. + 1d. Angels playing trumpet and harp 15 20
429 1s. 6d. + 3d. Choir boys singing 15 45

194 "The Beheading of St. John" (Caravaggio)

1970. 13th Council of Europe Art Exn. Mult.

430 1d. Type **194** 10 10
431 2d. "St. John the Baptist" (M. Preti) 10 10
432 5d. Interior of St. John's Co-Cathedral, Valletta 10 10
433 6d. "Allegory of the Order" (Neapolitan school) 15 10
434 8d. "St. Jerome" (Caravaggio) 15 30
435 10d. Articles from the Order of St. John in Malta 15 10
436 1s. 6d. "The Blessed Gerard receiving Godfrey de Bouillon" (A. de Favray) 25 35
437 2s. Cape and Stolone (16th cent) 25 45
SIZES—HORIZ: 1d., 8d. 56 × 30 mm; 2d., 6d. 45 × 32 mm; 10d. 2s. 63 × 21 mm; 1s. 6d. 45 × 34 mm. SQUARE: 5d. 39 × 39 mm.

202 Artist's Impression of Fujiyama

1970. World Fair, Osaka.

438 **202** 2d. multicoloured 10 10
439 5d. multicoloured 10 10
440 3s. multicoloured 15 15

203 "Peace and Justice"   **204** Carol-singers, Church and Star

1970. 25th Anniv of United Nations.

441 **203** 2d. multicoloured 10 10
442 5d. multicoloured 10 10
443 2s. 6d. multicoloured . . . 15 15

1970. Christmas. Multicoloured.

444 1d. + ½d. Type **204** 10 10
445 10d. + 2d. Church, star and angels with Infant 15 20
446 1s. 6d. + 3d. Church, star and nativity scene 20 35

207 Books and Quill

1971. Literary Anniversaries. Multicoloured.

447 1s. 6d. Type **207** (De Soldanis (historian) death bicent) . . 10 10
448 2s. Dun Karm (poet), books, pens and lamp (birth cent) 10 15

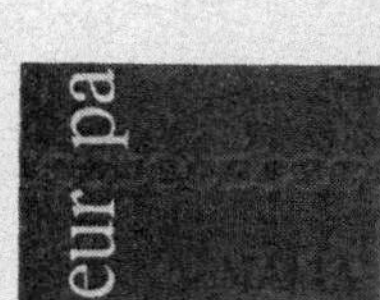

209 Europa "Chain"   **211** "Centaurea spathulata"

210 "St. Joseph, Patron of the Universal Church" (G. Cali)

1971. Europa.

449 **209** 2d. orange, black & olive . 10 10
450 5d. orange, black and red . 10 10
451 1s. 6d. orange, blk & slate 45 90

1971. Cent of Proclamation of St. Joseph as Patron Saint of Catholic Church, and 50th Anniv of Coronation of the Statue of "Our Lady of Victories". Multicoloured.

452 2d. Type **210** 10 10
453 5d. Statue of "Our Lady of Victories" and galley 10 10
454 10d. Type **210** 15 10
455 1s. 6d. As 5d. 30 40

1971. National Plant and Bird of Malta. Multicoloured.

456 2s. Type **211** 10 10
457 5d. Blue rock thrush (horiz) . . 20 10
458 10d. As 5d. 30 15
459 1s. 6d. Type **211** . . . . . . 30 1·25

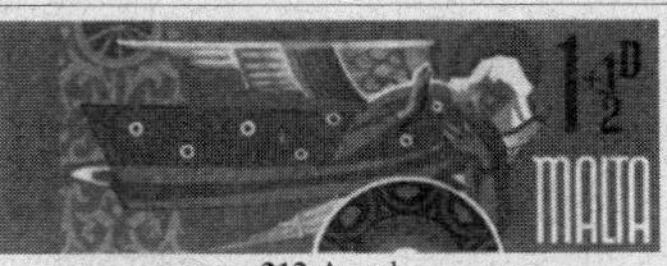

212 Angel

1971. Christmas. Multicoloured.

460 1d. + ½d. Type **212** 10 10
461 10d. + 2d. Mary and the Child Jesus 15 20
462 1s. 6d. + 3d. Joseph lying awake 20 30

213 Heart and W.H.O. Emblem

1972. World Health Day.

464 **213** 2d. multicoloured 10 10
465 10d. multicoloured 15 10
466 2s. 6d. multicoloured . . . 40 80

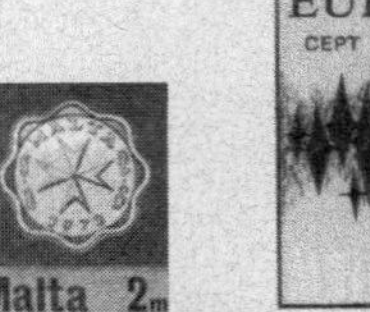

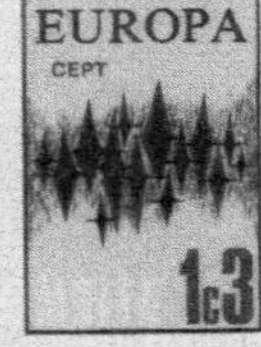

214 Maltese Cross   **216** "Communications"

1972. Decimal Currency. Coins. Multicoloured.

467 2 m. Type **214** 10 10
468 3 m. Bee on honeycomb . . . 10 10
469 5 m. Earthen lampstand . . . 10 10
470 1 c. George Cross 10 10
471 2 c. Classical head 10 10
472 5 c. Ritual altar 10 10
473 10 c. Grandmaster's galley . . 20 10
474 50 c. Great Siege Monument . 1·25 1·25
SIZES: 3 m., 2 c. As Type **214**: 5 m., 1 c., 5 c. 25 × 30 mm; 10 c., 50 c. 31 × 38 mm.

1972. Nos. 337a, 339 and 341 surch.

475 1 c. 3 on 5d. multicoloured . . 10 10
476 3 c. on 8d. multicoloured . . . 15 10
477 5 c. on 1s. 3d. multicoloured . . 15 20

1972. Europa.

478 **216** 1 c. 3 multicoloured . . . 10 10
479 3 c. multicoloured 10 10
480 5 c. multicoloured 15 35
481 7 c. 5 multicoloured . . . 20 75

217 Angel

1972. Christmas.

482 **217** 8 m. + 2 m. brown, grey and gold 10 10
483 – 3 c. + 1 c. purple, violet and gold 15 40
484 – 7 c. 5 + 1 c. 5 indigo, blue and gold 20 50
DESIGNS: No. 483, Angel with tambourine; No. 484, Singing angel.
See also Nos. 507/9.

218 Archaeology   **219** Europa "Posthorn"

1973. Multicoloured.

486 2 m. Type **218** 10 10
487 4 m. History 10 10
488 5 m. Folklore 10 10
489 8 m. Industry 10 10
490 1 c. Fishing industry 10 10
491 1 c. 3 Pottery 10 10
492 2 c. Agriculture 10 10
493 3 c. Sport 10 10
494 4 c. Yacht marina 15 10
495 5 c. Fiesta 15 10
496 7 c. 5 Regatta 25 10
497 10 c. Voluntary service . . . 25 10
498 50 c. Education . . . . 75 1·00
499 £1 Religion . . . . 2·25 2·75
500 £2 Coat of arms (32 × 27 mm) 12·00 17·00
500b £2 National Emblem (32 × 27 mm) . . . . 7·50 14·00

1973. Europa.

501 **219** 3 c. multicoloured 15 10
502 5 c. multicoloured 15 35
503 7 c. 5 multicoloured . . . 25 60

220 Emblem, and Woman holding Corn

221 Girolamo Cassar (architect)

1973. Anniversaries.

504 **220** 1 c. 3 multicoloured . . . 10 10
505 – 7 c. 5 multicoloured . . . 25 40
506 – 10 c. multicoloured . . . 30 50

ANNIVERSARIES: 1 c. 3, 10th anniv of World Food Programme; 7 c. 5, 25th anniv of W.H.O.; 10 c. 25th anniv of Universal Declaration of Human Rights.

1973. Christmas. As T **217**. Multicoloured.

507 8 m. + 2 m. Angels and organ pipes . . . 15 10
508 3 c. + 1 c. Madonna and Child 25 55
509 7 c. 5 + 1 c. 5 Buildings and Star 45 1·00

1973. Prominent Maltese.

511 **221** 1 c. 3 deep green, green and gold . . . 10 10
512 – 3 c. green, blue & gold . . 15 10
513 – 5 c. brown, grn & gold . . 20 15
514 – 7 c. 5 blue, lt bl & gold . . 20 30
515 – 10 c. deep purple, purple and gold . . . 20 40

DESIGNS: 3 c. Giuseppe Barth (ophthalmologist); 5 c. Nicolo' Isouard (composer); 7 c. 5, John Borg (botanist); 10 c. Antonio Sciortino (sculptor).

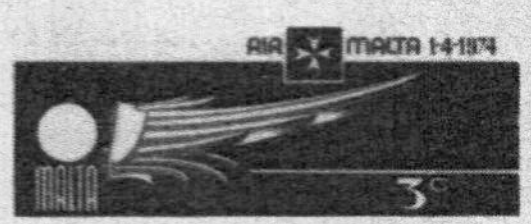

222 "Air Malta" Emblem

1974. Air. Multicoloured.

516 3 c. Type **222** . . . 15 10
517 4 c. Boeing 720B . . . 15 10
518 5 c. Type **222** . . . 20 10
519 7 c. 5 As 4 c. . . . 25 10
520 20 c. Type **222** . . . 80 60
521 25 c. As 4 c. . . . 80 60
522 35 c. Type **222** . . . 1·10 1·40

223 Prehistoric Sculpture

1974. Europa.

523 **223** 1 c. 3 blue, black & gold . . 15 10
524 – 3 c. brown, black & gold . 20 15
525 – 5 c. purple, black & gold . 25 50
526 – 7 c. 5 green, black & gold . 35 1·00

DESIGNS—VERT: 3 c. Old Cathedral Door, Mdina; 7 c. 5, "Vetlina" (sculpture by A. Sciortino). HORIZ: 5 c. Silver monstrance.

224 Heinrich von Stephan (founder) and Land Transport

225 Decorative Star and Nativity Scene

1974. Centenary of U.P.U.

527 **224** 1 c. 3 green, blue & orge . . 30 10
528 – 5 c. brown, red & green . . 30 10
529 – 7 c. 5 blue, violet & grn . . 35 20
530 – 50 c. purple, red & orge . . 1·00 1·25

DESIGNS (each containing portrait as Type **224**): 5 c. "Washington" (paddle-steamer) and "Royal Viking Star" (liner); 7 c. 5, Balloon and Boeing 747-100; 50 c. U.P.U. Buildings, 1874 and 1974.

1974. Christmas. Multicoloured.

532 8 m. + 2 m. Type **225** . . . 10 10
533 3 c. + 1 c. "Shepherds" . . . 15 20
534 5 c. + 1 c. "Shepherds with gifts" 20 35
535 7 c. 5 + 1 c. 5 "The Magi" . . 30 40

226 Swearing-in of Prime Minister

1975. Inauguration of Republic.

536 **226** 1 c. 3 multicoloured . . . 10 10
537 – 5 c. red and black . . . 20 10
538 – 25 c. multicoloured . . . 60 1·00

DESIGNS: 5 c. National flag; 25 c. Minister of Justice, President and Prime Minister.

227 Mother and Child ("Family Life")

1975. International Women's Year.

539 **227** 1 c. 3 violet and gold . . . 15 10
540 – 3 c. blue and gold . . . 20 10
541 **227** 5 c. brown and gold . . . 30 20
542 – 20 c. brown and gold . . . 1·10 2·75

DESIGN: 3 c., 20 c. Office secretary ("Public Life").

228 "Allegory of Malta" (Francesco de Mura)

1975. Europa. Multicoloured.

543 5 c. Type **228** . . . 30 10
544 15 c. "Judith and Holofernes" (Valentin de Boulogne) . . . 50 75

The 15 c. is similar: 47 × 23 mm.

229 Plan of Ggantija Temple

1975. European Architectural Heritage Year.

545 **229** 1 c. 3 black and red . . . 10 10
546 – 3 c. purple, red & brown . . 20 10
547 – 5 c. brown and red . . . 30 25
548 – 25 c. green, red & black . . 1·10 3·00

DESIGNS: 3 c. Mdina skyline; 5 c. View of Victoria, Gozo; 25 c. Silhouette of Fort St. Angelo.

230 Farm Animals

231 "The Right to Work"

1975. Christmas. Multicoloured.

549 8 m. + 2 m. Type **230** . . . 30 25
550 3 c. + 1 c. Nativity scene (50 × 23 mm) . . . 50 75
551 7 c. 5 + 1 c. 5 Approach of the Magi . . . 60 1·40

1975. 1st Anniv of Republic.

552 **231** 1 c. 3 multicoloured . . . 10 10
553 – 5 c. multicoloured . . . 20 10
554 – 25 c. red, blue and black . . 70 1·10

DESIGNS: 5 c. "Safeguarding the Environment"; 25 c. National flag.

232 "Festa Tar-Rahal"

233 Water Polo

1976. Maltese Folklore. Multicoloured.

555 1 c. 3 Type **232** . . . 10 10
556 5 c. "L-Imnarja" (horiz) . . . 15 10
557 7 c. 5 "Il-Karnival" (horiz) . . 35 70
558 10 c. "Il-Gimgha L-Kbira" . . 55 1·40

1976. Olympic Games, Montreal. Multicoloured.

559 1 c. 7 Type **233** . . . 10 10
560 5 c. Sailing . . . 25 10
561 30 c. Athletics . . . 85 1·50

234 Lace-making

1976. Europa. Multicoloured.

562 7 c. Type **234** . . . 20 35
563 15 c. Stone carving . . . 25 60

235 Nicola Cotoner

1976. 300th Anniv of School of Anatomy and Surgery. Multicoloured.

564 2 c. Type **235** . . . 10 10
565 5 c. Arm . . . 15 10
566 7 c. Giuseppe Zammit . . . 20 10
567 11 c. Sacra Infermeria . . . 35 65

236 St. John the Baptist and St. Michael

237 Jean de la Valette's Armour

1976. Christmas. Multicoloured.

568 1 c. + 5 m. Type **236** . . . 15 20
569 5 c. + 1 c. Madonna and Child 20 60
570 7 c. + 1 c. 5 St. Christopher and St. Nicholas . . . 30 80
571 10 c. + 2 c. Complete painting (32 × 27 mm) . . . 40 1·25

Nos. 568/71 show portions of "Madonna and Saints" by Domenico di Michelino.

1977. Suits of Armour. Multicoloured.

572 2 c. Type **237** . . . 10 10
573 7 c. Aloph de Wignacourt's armour . . . 20 10
574 11 c. Jean Jacques de Verdelin's armour . . . 25 50

1977. No. 336 surch **1c7**.

575 1 c. 7 on 4d. multicoloured . . 25 25

239 "Annunciation"

1977. 400th Birth Anniv of Rubens. Flemish Tapestries. Multicoloured.

576 2 c. Type **239** . . . 10 10
577 7 c. "Four Evangelists" . . . 25 10
578 11 c. "Nativity" . . . 45 45
579 20 c. "Adoration of the Magi" 80 1·00

See also Nos. 592/5, 615/18 and 638/9.

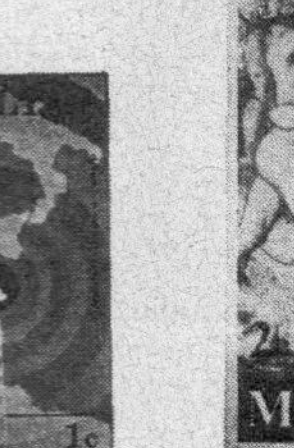

240 Map and Radio Aerial

242 "Aid to Handicapped Workers" (detail from Workers' Monument)

241 Ta' L-Isperanza

1977. World Telecommunications Day.

580 **240** 1 c. black, green and red . . 10 10
581 6 c. black, blue and red . . 20 10
582 – 8 c. black, brn and red . . 30 10
583 – 17 c. black, mauve & red . . 60 40

DESIGN—HORIZ: 8, 17 c. Map, aerial and airplane tail-fin.

1977. Europa. Multicoloured.

584 7 c. Type **241** . . . 30 15
585 20 c. Is-Salini . . . 35 1·00

1977. Maltese Worker Commemoration.

586 **242** 2 c. orange and brown . . 10 10
587 – 7 c. light brown & brown . . 15 10
588 – 20 c. multicoloured . . . 40 60

DESIGNS—VERT: 7 c. "Stoneworker, modern industry and ship-building" (monument detail). HORIZ: 20 c. "Mother with Dead Son" and Service Medal.

243 The Shepherds

1977. Christmas. Multicoloured.

589 1 c. + 5 m. Type **243** . . . 10 20
590 7 c. + 1 c. The Nativity . . . 15 30
591 11 c. + 1 c. 5 The Flight into Egypt . . . 20 45

1978. Flemish Tapestries. (2nd series). As T **239**. Multicoloured.

592 2 c. "The Entry into Jerusalem" 10 10
593 7 c. "The Last Supper" (after Poussin) . . . 25 10
594 11 c. "The Raising of the Cross" (after Rubens) . . . 30 25
595 25 c. "The Resurrection" (after Rubens) . . . 70 80

244 "Young Lady on Horseback and Trooper"

1978. 450th Death Anniv of Albrecht Durer.

596 **244** 1 c. 7 black, red and blue . . 10 10
597 – 8 c. black, red and grey . . 15 10
598 – 17 c. black, red and grey . . 40 45

DESIGNS: 8 c. "The Bagpiper"; 17 c. "The Virgin and Child with a Monkey".

245 Monument to Grand Master Nicola Cotoner (Foggini)

246 Goalkeeper

1978. Europa. Monuments. Multicoloured.

599 7 c. Type **245** . . . 15 10
600 25 c. Monument to Grand Master Ramon Perellos (Mazzuoli) . 35 90

1978. World Cup Football Championship, Argentina. Multicoloured.

601 2 c. Type **246** . . . 10 10
602 11 c. Players heading ball . . . 15 10
603 15 c. Tackling . . . 25 35

247 Boeing 707 over Megalithic Temple

1978. Air. Multicoloured.

605 5 c. Type **247** . . . 20 10
606 7 c. Air Malta Boeing 720B . . 20 10
607 11 c. Boeing 747 taking off from Luqa Airport . . . 35 10
608 17 c. Type **247** . . . 45 30
609 20 c. As 7 c. . . . 60 40
610 75 c. As 11 c. . . . 1·75 2·75

248 Folk Musicians and Village Church

249 Fishing Boat and Aircraft Carrier

1978. Christmas. Multicoloured.

611 1 c. + 5 m. Type **248** . . . 10 10
612 5 c. + 1 c. Choir of Angels . . 15 20
613 7 c. + 1 c. 5 Carol singers . . 20 35
614 11 c. + 3 c. Folk musicians, church, angels and carol singers (58 × 22 mm) . . . 25 45

1979. Flemish Tapestries (3rd series) showing paintings by Rubens. As T **239**. Multicoloured.

615 2 c. "The Triumph of the Catholic Church" 10 10
616 7 c. "The Triumph of Charity" 20 10
617 11 c. "The Triumph of Faith" . 30 25
618 25 c. "The Triumph of Truth" 95 80

1979. End of Military Facilities Agreement. Multicoloured.

619 2 c. Type **249** 10 10
620 5 c. Raising the flag ceremony 10 10
621 7 c. Departing soldier and olive sprig 15 10
622 8 c. Type **249** 40 40
623 17 c. As 5 c. 55 60
624 20 c. As 7 c. 55 60

250 Speronara (fishing boat) and Tail of Air Malta Airliner

251 Children on Globe

1979. Europa. Communications. Multicoloured.

625 7 c. Type **250** 20 10
626 25 c. Coastal watch tower and radio link towers 40 75

1979. International Year of the Child. Multicoloured.

627 2 c. Type **251** 10 10
628 7 c. Children flying kites (27 × 33 mm) 15 10
629 11 c. Children in circle (27 × 33 mm) 20 35

252 Shells

1979. Marine Life. Multicoloured.

630 2 c. Type **252** 10 10
631 5 c. Loggerhead turtle 20 10
632 7 c. Dolphin (fish) 25 10
633 25 c. Noble pen shell . . . . . 90 1·25

253 "The Nativity" (detail)

1979. Christmas. Paintings by Giuseppe Cali. Multicoloured.

634 1 c. + 5 m. Type **253** 10 10
635 5 c. + 1 c. "The Flight into Egypt" (detail) 10 15
636 7 c. + 1 c. 5 "The Nativity" 15 20
637 11 c. + 3 c. "The Flight into Egypt" 25 50

1980. Flemish Tapestries (4th series). As T **239**. Multicoloured.

638 2 c. "The Institution of Corpus Domini" (Rubens) 10 10
639 8 c. "The Destruction of Idolatry" (Rubens) 20 20

254 Hal Saflieni Hypogeum, Paola

255 Dun Gorg Preca

1980 Int Restoration of Monuments Campaign. Multicoloured.

641 2 c. 5 Type **254** 10 15
642 6 c. Vilhena Palace, Mdina . . 25 20
643 8 c. Citadel of Victoria, Gozo (horiz) 30 40
644 12 c. Fort St. Elmo, Valletta (horiz) 40 60

1980. Birth Centenary of Dun Gorg Preca (founder of Society of Christian Doctrine).

645 **255** 2 c. 5 grey and black . . . 10 10

256 Ruzar Briffa (poet)

1980. Europa.

646 **256** 8 c. yellow, brown & grn . 20 10
647 – 30 c. green, brown & lake . 55 1·25

DESIGN: 30 c. Nikiol Anton Vassalli (scholar and patriot).

257 "Annunciation"

258 Rook and Pawn

1980. Christmas. Paintings by A. Inglott. Multicoloured.

648 2 c. + 5 m. Type **257** 10 10
649 6 c. + 1 c. "Conception" . . . 20 20
650 8 c. + 1 c. 5 "Nativity" . . . 25 40
651 12 c. + 3 c. "Annunciation", "Conception" and "Nativity" (47 × 38 mm) 30 70

1980. 24th Chess Olympiad and International Chess Federation Congress. Multicoloured.

652 2 c. 5 Type **258** 25 20
653 8 c. Bishop and pawn 65 20
654 30 c. King, queen and pawn (vert) . . . . 1·00 1·50

259 Barn Owl

260 Traditional Horse Race

1981. Birds. Multicoloured.

655 3 c. Type **259** 30 25
656 8 c. Sardinian warbler 50 25
657 12 c. Woodchat shrike 60 80
658 23 c. British storm petrel . . . 1·10 1·75

1981. Europa. Folklore. Multicoloured.

659 8 c. Type **260** 20 10
660 30 c. Attempting to retrieve flag from end of "gostra" (greasy pole) 40 65

261 Stylised "25"

262 Disabled Artist at Work

1981. 25th Maltese International Trade Fair.

661 **261** 4 c. multicoloured 15 15
662 25 c. multicoloured 50 60

1981. International Year for Disabled Persons. Multicoloured.

663 3 c. Type **262** 20 10
664 35 c. Disabled child playing football 90 75

263 Wheat Ear in Conical Flask

264 Megalithic Building

1981. World Food Day.

665 **263** 8 c. multicoloured 15 15
666 23 c. multicoloured 60 50

1981. History of Maltese Industry. Multicoloured.

667 5 m. Type **264** 10 50
668 1 c. Cotton production 10 10
669 2 c. Early ship-building 70 10
670 3 c. Currency minting 30 10
671 5 c. "Art" 30 25
672 6 c. Fishing 90 25
673 7 c. Agriculture 30 90
674 8 c. Stone quarrying 45 35
675 10 c. Grape pressing 35 50
676 12 c. Modern ship-building . . 1·50 1·50
677 15 c. Energy . . . . 70 1·25
678 20 c. Telecommunications . . . 70 75
679 25 c. "Industry" . . . . 90 1·60
680 50 c. Drilling for Water . . . . 2·00 2·50
681 £1 Sea transport . . . . 6·50 7·00
682 £3 Air transport . . . . 11·00 17·00

265 Children and Nativity Scene

266 Shipbuilding

1981. Christmas. Multicoloured.

683 2 c. + 1 c. Type **265** 20 10
684 8 c. + 2 c. Christmas Eve procession (horiz) 30 20
685 20 c. + 3 c. Preaching midnight sermon 55 75

1982. Shipbuilding Industry.

686 **266** 3 c. multicoloured 15 10
687 – 8 c. multicoloured 30 30
688 – 13 c. multicoloured 55 55
689 – 27 c. multicoloured . . . . 1·25 1·25

DESIGNS: 8 c. to 27 c. Differing shipyard scenes.

267 Elderly Man and Has-Serh (home for elderly)

1982. Care of Elderly. Multicoloured.

690 8 c. Type **267** 40 20
691 30 c. Elderly woman and Has-Zmien (hospital for elderly) . 1·40 1·40

268 Redemption of Islands by Maltese, 1428

1982. Europa. Historical Events. Multicoloured.

692 8 c. Type **268** 40 20
693 30 c. Declaration of rights by Maltese, 1802 . . . . 1·00 1·40

269 Stylised Footballer

1982. World Cup Football Championship, Spain.

694 **269** 3 c. multicoloured 20 10
695 – 12 c. multicoloured 60 55
696 – 15 c. multicoloured 70 65

DESIGNS: 12 c., 15 c. Various stylised footballers.

270 Angel appearing to Shepherds

1982. Christmas. Multicoloured.

698 2 c. + 1 c. Type **270** 15 15
699 8 c. + 2 c. Nativity and Three Wise Men bearing gifts . . . 50 50
700 20 c. + 3 c. Nativity scene (45 × 37 mm) . . . . 1·00 1·00

MINIMUM PRICE

The minimum price quoted is 10p which represents a handling charge rather than a basis for valuing common stamps. For further notes about prices see introductory pages.

271 "Ta Salvo Serafino" (oared brigantine), 1531

1982. Maltese Ships (1st series). Multicoloured.

701 3 c. Type **271** 40 10
702 8 c. "La Madonna del Rosaria" (tartane), 1740 . . . . . . 80 30
703 12 c. "San Paulo" (xebec), 1743 1·25 55
704 20 c. "Ta' Pietro Saliba" (xprunara), 1798 . . . . . 1·60 90

See also Nos. 725/8, 772/5, 792/5 and 809/12.

272 Locomotive "Manning Wardle", 1883

1983. Centenary of Malta Railway. Multicoloured.

705 3 c. Type **272** 45 15
706 13 c. Locomotive "Black Hawthorn", 1884 . . . . . 1·00 1·00
707 27 c. Beyer Peacock locomotive, 1895 . . . . 2·00 3·25

273 Peace Doves leaving Malta

1983. Commonwealth Day. Multicoloured.

708 8 c. Type **273** 25 30
709 12 c. Tourist landmarks 40 60
710 15 c. Holiday beach (vert) . . . 45 75
711 23 c. Ship-building (vert) . . . 70 1·00

274 Ggantija Megalithic Temples, Gozo

1983. Europa. Multicoloured.

712 8 c. Type **274** 40 40
713 30 c. Fort St. Angelo . . . . . 1·00 2·40

275 Dish Aerials (World Communications Year)

1983. Anniversaries and Events. Multicoloured.

714 3 c. Type **275** 45 15
715 7 c. Ships' prows and badge (25th anniv of I.M.O. Convention) 70 55
716 13 c. Container lorries and badge (30th anniv of Customs Co-operation Council) 90 90
717 20 c. Stadium and emblem (9th Mediterranean Games) . . . 1·00 2·25

276 Monsignor Giuseppe de Piro

277 Annunciation

1983. 50th Death Anniv of Monsignor Giuseppe de Piro.

718 **276** 3 c. multicoloured 15 15

1983. Christmas. Multicoloured.

719 2 c. + 1 c. Type **277** 30 15
720 8 c. + 2 c. The Nativity . . . 75 60
721 20 c. + 3 c. Adoration of the Magi . . . . 1·40 2·25

278 Workers at Meeting

1983. 40th Anniv of General Workers' Union. Multicoloured.

722 3 c. Type **278** 25 10
723 8 c. Worker with family . . . 50 40
724 27 c. Union H.Q. Building . . 1·50 1·75

1983. Maltese Ships (2nd series). As T **271**. Multicoloured.

725 2 c. "Strangier" (full-rigged ship), 1813 . . . . 30 25
726 12 c. "Tigre" (topsail schooner), 1839 . . . . 1·25 1·25
727 13 c. "La Speranza" (brig), 1844 1·25 1·25
728 20 c. "Wignacourt" (barque), 1844 . . . . 1·75 2·75

279 Boeing 737

1984. Air. Multicoloured.

729 7 c. Type **279** 50 30
730 8 c. Boeing 720B 60 35
731 16 c. Vickers Vanguard . . . . 1·25 70
732 23 c. Vickers Viscount . . . . 1·50 70
733 27 c. Douglas DC-3 . . . . . 1·75 80
734 38 c. Armstrong Whitworth Atalanta "Artemis" . . . . 2·25 2·75
735 75 c. "Marina" Fiat MF.5 flying boat . . . . 3·25 5·00

280 Bridge

1984. Europa. 25th Anniv of C.E.P.T.

736 **280** 8 c. green, black & yell . . 35 35
737 30 c. red, black & yellow . 1·25 1·25

281 Early Policeman **282** Running

1984. 170th Anniv of Malta Police Force. Multicoloured.

738 3 c. Type **281** 65 15
739 8 c. Mounted police . . . . . 1·50 65
740 11 c. Motorcycle policeman . . 1·75 2·00
741 25 c. Policeman and firemen . . 2·75 3·75

1984. Olympic Games, Los Angeles. Multicoloured.

742 7 c. Type **282** 25 30
743 12 c. Gymnastics 50 70
744 23 c. Swimming . . . . 85 1·25

283 "The Visitation" (Pietru Caruana) **284** Dove on Map

1984. Christmas. Paintings from Church of Our Lady of Porto Salvo, Valletta. Multicoloured.

745 2 c. + 1 c. Type **283** 55 55
746 8 c. + 2 c. "The Epiphany" (Rafel Caruana) (horiz) . . . 1·00 1·25
747 20 c. + 3 c. "Jesus among the Doctors" (Rafel Caruana) (horiz) . . . . 2·00 3·75

1984. 10th Anniv of Republic. Multicoloured.

748 3 c. Type **284** 40 20
749 8 c. Fort St. Angelo 75 65
750 30 c. Hands . . . . 2·50 4·75

285 1885 ½d. Green Stamp **287** Nicolo Baldacchino (tenor)

286 Boy, and Hands planting Vine

1985. Centenary of Malta Post Office. Mult.

751 3 c. Type **285** 45 15
752 8 c. 1885 1d. rose 65 45
753 12 c. 1885 2½d. blue . . . . . 90 1·40
754 20 c. 1885 4d. brown . . . . 1·40 3·00

1985. International Youth Year. Multicoloured.

756 2 c. Type **286** 15 15
757 13 c. Young people and flowers (vert) 85 60
758 27 c. Girl holding flame in hand 1·75 1·40

1985. Europa. European Music Year. Mult.

759 8 c. Type **287** . . . . 2·00 50
760 30 c. Francesco Azopardi (composer) . . . . 3·50 5·00

288 Guzeppi Bajada and Manwel Attard (victims)

1985. 66th Anniv of 7 June 1919 Demonstrations. Multicoloured.

761 3 c. Type **288** 35 15
762 7 c. Karmnu Abela and Wenzu Dyer (victims) 75 40
763 35 c. Model of projected Demonstration monument by Anton Agius (vert) . . . . 2·50 2·75

289 Stylized Birds

1985. 40th Anniv of United Nations Organization. Multicoloured.

764 4 c. Type **289** 25 15
765 11 c. Arrow-headed ribbons . . 85 1·25
766 31 c. Stylized figures . . . . 2·00 3·25

290 Giorgio Mitrovich (nationalist) (death centenary) **291** The Three Wise Men

1985. Celebrities' Anniversaries. Multicoloured.

767 8 c. Type **290** 80 35
768 12 c. Pietru Caxaru (poet and administrator) (400th death anniversary) . . . . 1·60 2·50

1985. Christmas. Designs showing details of terracotta relief by Ganni Bonnici. Multicoloured.

769 2 c. + 1 c. Type **291** 55 75
770 8 c. + 2 c. Virgin and Child . . 1·25 1·75
771 20 c. + 3 c. Angels . . . . . 2·50 4·00

1985. Maltese Ships (3rd series). Steamships. As T **271**. Multicoloured.

772 3 c. "Scotia" (paddle-steamer), 1844 . . . . 75 20
773 7 c. "Tagliaferro" (screw-steamer), 1822 . . . . . 1·40 1·00
774 15 c. "Gleneagles" (screw-steamer), 1885 . . . . . 2·00 3·25
775 23 c. "L'Isle Adam" (screw-steamer), 1886 . . . . . 2·75 4·00

292 John XXIII Peace Laboratory and Statue of St. Francis of Assisi

1986. International Peace Year. Multicoloured.

776 8 c. Type **292** . . . . 1·25 50
777 11 c. Dove and hands holding olive branch (40 × 19 mm) . . 1·50 2·50
778 27 c. Map of Africa, dove and two heads . . . . 3·25 4·75

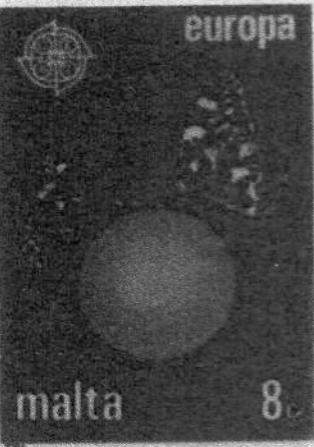

293 Symbolic Plant and "Cynthia cardui", "Vanessa atalanta" and "Polyommatus icarus" **294** Heading the Ball

1986. Europa. Environmental Conservation. Multicoloured.

779 8 c. Type **293** . . . . 1·75 50
780 35 c. Island, Neolithic frieze, sea and sun . . . . 3·25 6·00

1986. World Cup Football Championship, Mexico. Multicoloured.

781 3 c. Type **294** 60 20
782 7 c. Saving a goal . . . . . . 1·25 1·00
783 23 c. Controlling the ball . . . 4·00 6·50

295 Father Diegu

1986. Maltese Philanthropists. Multicoloured.

785 2 c. Type **295** 40 30
786 3 c. Adelaide Cini 50 30
787 8 c. Alfonso Maria Galea . . . 1·25 60
788 27 c. Vincenzo Bugeja . . . . 3·25 6·00

296 "Nativity"

1986. Christmas. Paintings by Giuseppe D'Arena. Multicoloured.

789 2 c. + 1 c. Type **296** . . . . 90 1·00
790 8 c. + 2 c. "Nativity" (detail) (vert) . . . . 2·50 3·00
791 20 c. + 3 c. "Epiphany" . . . 3·75 5·50

1986. Maltese Ships (4th series). As T **271**. Multicoloured.

792 7 c. "San Paul" (freighter), 1921 1·25 50
793 10 c. "Knight of Malta" (mail steamer), 1930 . . . . . 1·50 1·75
794 12 c. "Valetta City" (freighter), 1948 . . . . 1·75 2·75
795 20 c. "Saver" (freighter), 1959 3·00 4·50

297 European Robin

1987. 25th Anniv of Malta Ornithological Society. Multicoloured.

796 3 c. Type **297** . . . . 1·00 50
797 8 c. Peregrine falcon (vert) . . 2·25 1·00
798 13 c. Hoopoe (vert) . . . . . 3·00 4·00
799 23 c. Coy's shearwater . . . . 3·50 6·00

298 Aquasun Lido **299** 16th-century Pikeman

1987. Europa. Modern Architecture. Multicoloured.

800 8 c. Type **298** . . . . 1·25 75
801 35 c. Church of St. Joseph, Manikata . . . . 3·50 6·25

1987. Maltese Uniforms (1st series). Multicoloured.

802 3 c. Type **299** 65 40
803 7 c. 16th-century officer . . . 1·25 90
804 10 c. 18th-century standard bearer . . . . 1·50 2·25
805 27 c. 18th-century General of the Galleys . . . . 3·25 4·75

See also Nos. 832/5, 851/4, 880/3 and 893/6.

300 Maltese Scenes, Wheat Ears and Sun

1987. Anniversaries and Events. Multicoloured.

806 5 c. Type **300** (European Environment Year) . . . . 1·00 50
807 8 c. Esperanto star as comet (Centenary of Esperanto) . . 1·25 60
808 23 c. Family at house door (International Year of Shelter for the Homeless) . . . . . 3·00 3·00

1987. Maltese Ships (5th series). As T **271**. Multicoloured.

809 2 c. "Medina" (freighter), 1969 60 60
810 11 c. "Rabat" (container ship), 1974 . . . . 2·25 2·50
811 13 c. "Ghawdex" (passenger ferry), 1979 . . . . 2·50 2·75
812 20 c. "Pinto" (car ferry), 1987 3·50 4·00

301 "The Visitation"

1987. Christmas. Illuminated illustrations, score and text from 16th-century choral manuscript. Multicoloured.

813 2 c. + 1 c. Type **301** 50 50
814 8 c. + 2 c. "The Nativity" . . 2·00 2·75
815 20 c. + 3 c. "The Adoration of the Magi" . . . . 3·25 4·50

302 Dr. Arvid Pardo (U.N. representative)

1987. 20th Anniv of United Nations Resolution on Peaceful Use of the Seabed. Multicoloured.

816 8 c. Type **302** . . . . 1·00 75
817 12 c. U.N. emblem and sea . . 1·75 3·00

303 Ven. Nazju Falzon (Catholic catechist) **304** "St. John Bosco with Youth" (statue)

1988. Maltese Personalities. Multicoloured.

819 2 c. Type **303** 25 30
820 3 c. Mgr. Sidor Formosa (philanthropist) 25 30
821 4 c. Sir Luigi Preziosi (ophthalmologist) 40 30
822 10 c. Fr. Anastasju Cuschieri (poet) 80 85
823 25 c. Mgr. Pietru Pawl Saydon (Bible translator) . . . . . 2·25 3·25

1988. Religious Anniversaries. Multicoloured.

824 10 c. Type **304** (death centenary) 1·00 1·00
825 12 c. "Assumption of Our Lady" (altarpiece by Perugino, Ta' Pinu, Gozo) (Marian Year) . 1·25 1·50
826 14 c. "Christ the King" (statue by Sciortino) (75th anniv of International Eucharistic Congress, Valletta) . . . . . 1·75 2·50

305 Bus, Ferry and Aircraft **306** Globe and Red Cross Emblems

1988. Europa. Transport and Communications. Multicoloured.

827 10 c. Type **305** . . . . 1·25 75
828 35 c. Control panel, dish aerial and pylons . . . . 2·75 4·50

1988. Anniversaries and Events. Multicoloured.

829 4 c. Type **306** (125th anniv of Int Red Cross) 40 50
830 18 c. Divided globe (Campaign for North–South Interdependence and Solidarity) . 1·75 2·50
831 19 c. Globe and symbol (40th anniv of W.H.O.) . . . . . 1·75 2·50

1988. Maltese Uniforms (2nd series). As T **299**. Multicoloured.

832 3 c. Private, Maltese Light Infantry, 1800 . . . . . . 30 30
833 4 c. Gunner, Malta Coast Artillery, 1802 . . . . . . 35 35
834 10 c. Field Officer, 1st Maltese Provincial Battalion, 1805 . . 85 1·25
835 25 c. Subaltern, Royal Malta Regiment, 1809 . . . . . . 2·25 4·25

307 Athletics **308** Shepherd with Flock

1988. Olympic Games, Seoul. Multicoloured.

836 4 c. Type **307** 30 30
837 10 c. Diving 70 80
838 35 c. Basketball . . . . 2·00 3·00

1988. Christmas. Multicoloured.

839 3 c. + 1 c. Type **308** 30 30
840 10 c. + 2 c. The Nativity . . . 70 1·25
841 25 c. + 3 c. Three Wise Men . 1·75 2·75

309 Commonwealth Emblem **311** Two Boys flying Kite

310 New State Arms

1989. 25th Anniv of Independence. Multicoloured.

842 2 c. Type **309** 25 35
843 3 c. Council of Europe flag . . 25 35
844 4 c. U.N. flag 30 35
845 10 c. Workers, hands gripping ring and national flag . . . 75 95
846 12 c. Scales and allegorical figure of Justice . . . . 90 1·40
847 25 c. Prime Minister Borg Olivier with Independence constitution (42 × 28 mm) . . 1·90 3·25

1989.

848 **310** £1 multicoloured . . . . . 4·00 4·50

1989. Europa. Children's Games. Multicoloured.

849 10 c. Type **311** . . . . 1·25 75
850 35 c. Two girls with dolls . . . 3·25 4·50

1989. Maltese Uniforms (3rd series). As T **299**. Multicoloured.

851 3 c. Officer, Maltese Veterans, 1815 . . . . 45 45
852 4 c. Subaltern, Royal Malta Fencibles, 1839 . . . . . . 50 50
853 10 c. Private, Malta Militia, 1856 1·50 1·50
854 25 c. Colonel, Royal Malta Fencible Artillery, 1875 . . . 2·75 3·75

312 Human Figures and Buildings

1989. Anniversaries and Commemorations. Designs showing logo and stylized human figures. Multicoloured.

855 3 c. Type **312** (20th anniv of U.N. Declaration on Social Progress and Development) 30 30
856 4 c. Workers and figure in wheelchair (Malta's Ratification of European Social Charter) 35 35
857 10 c. Family (40th anniv of Council of Europe) . . . . 80 1·25
858 14 c. Teacher and children (70th anniv of Malta Union of Teachers) . . . . 1·00 1·75
859 25 c. Symbolic knights (Knights of the Sovereign Military Order of Malta Assembly) . 2·25 3·50

313 Angel and Cherub **315** General Post Office, Auberge d'Italie, Valletta

314 Presidents Bush and Gorbachev

1989. Christmas. Vault paintings by Mattia Preti from St. John's Co-Cathedral, Valletta.

860 3 c. + 1 c. Type **313** 60 50
861 10 c. + 2 c. Two angels . . . 1·50 1·75
862 20 c. + 3 c. Angel blowing trumpet . . . . 2·00 3·25

1989. U.S.A.–U.S.S.R. Summit Meeting, Malta.

863 **314** 10 c. multicoloured . . . . 1·00 1·25

1990. Europa. Post Office Buildings. Multicoloured.

864 10 c. Type **315** 75 50
865 35 c. Branch Post Office, Zebbug (horiz) . . . . 2·25 3·50

316 Open Book and Letters from Different Alphabets (International Literacy Year) **318** St. Paul

317 Samuel Taylor Coleridge (poet) and Government House

1990. Anniversaries and Events. Multicoloured.

866 3 c. Type **316** 25 25
867 4 c. Count Roger of Sicily and Norman soldiers (900th anniv of Sicilian rule) (horiz) . . . 45 30
868 19 c. Communications satellite (25th anniv of I.T.U.) (horiz) 1·75 2·50
869 20 c. Football and map of Malta (Union of European Football Association 20th Ordinary Congress, Malta) . . . . . 1·75 2·50

1990. British Authors. Multicoloured.

870 4 c. Type **317** 35 30
871 10 c. Lord Byron (poet) and map of Valletta 70 70
872 12 c. Sir Walter Scott (novelist) and Great Siege 80 95
873 25 c. William Makepeace Thackeray (novelist) and Naval Arsenal . . . . 1·50 2·25

1990. Visit of Pope John Paul II. Bronze Bas-reliefs.

874 **318** 4 c. black, flesh and red . . 50 1·50
875 – 25 c. black, flesh & red . . 1·50 1·75

DESIGN: 25 c. Pope John Paul II.

319 Flags and Football

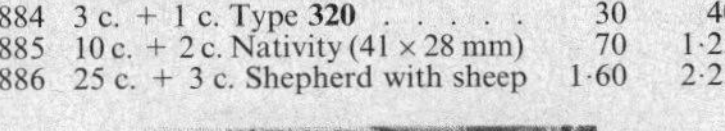

320 Innkeeper

1990. World Cup Football Championship, Italy. Multicoloured.

876 5 c. Type **319** 35 30
877 10 c. Football in net . . . . . 65 1·00
878 14 c. Scoreboard and football . 1·00 1·75

1990. Maltese Uniforms (4th series). As T **299**. Multicoloured.

880 3 c. Captain, Royal Malta Militia, 1889 . . . . 65 55
881 4 c. Field officer, Royal Malta Artillery, 1905 . . . . . . 70 60
882 10 c. Labourer, Malta Labour Corps, 1915 . . . . 1·75 1·50
883 25 c. Lieutenant, King's Own Malta Regiment of Militia, 1918 . . . . 2·75 3·00

1990. Christmas. Figures from Crib by Austin Galea, Marco Bartolo and Rosario Zammit. Multicoloured.

884 3 c. + 1 c. Type **320** 30 40
885 10 c. + 2 c. Nativity (41 × 28 mm) 70 1·25
886 25 c. + 3 c. Shepherd with sheep 1·60 2·25

321 1919 10s. Stamp under Magnifying Glass

1991. 25th Anniv of Philatelic Society of Malta.

887 **321** 10 c. multicoloured 60 70

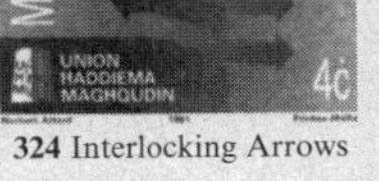

322 "Eurostar" Satellite and V.D.U. Screen **324** Interlocking Arrows

323 St. Ignatius Loyola (founder of Jesuits) (500th birth anniv)

1991. Europa. Europe in Space. Multicoloured.

888 10 c. Type **322** . . . . 1·00 70
889 35 c. "Ariane 4" rocket and projected HOTOL aerospace-plane . . . . 2·00 2·75

1991. Religious Commemorations. Multicoloured.

890 3 c. Type **323** 30 20
891 4 c. Abbess Venerable Maria Adeodata Pisani (185th birth anniversary) (vert) 35 25
892 30 c. St. John of the Cross (400th death anniversary) . . . . . 2·00 2·25

1991. Maltese Uniforms (5th series). As T **299**. Multicoloured.

893 3 c. Officer with colour, Royal Malta Fencibles, 1860 . . . 30 25
894 10 c. Officer with colours, Royal Malta Regiment of Militia, 1903 . . . . 70 60
895 19 c. Officer with Queen's colour, King's Own Malta Regiment, 1968 . . . . 1·40 1·75
896 25 c. Officer with colour, Malta Armed Forces, 1991 . . . . 1·75 2·00

1991. 25th Anniv of Union Haddiema Maghqudin (public services union).

897 **324** 4 c. multicoloured 30 30

325 Honey Buzzard **326** Three Wise Men

1991. Endangered Species. Birds. Multicoloured.

898 4 c. Type **325** . . . . 1·75 2·00
899 4 c. Marsh harrier . . . . . . 1·75 2·00
900 10 c. Eleonora's falcon . . . . 1·75 2·00
901 10 c. Lesser kestrel . . . . . . 1·75 2·00

1991. Christmas. Multicoloured.

902 3 c. + 1 c. Type **326** 30 30
903 10 c. + 2 c. Holy Family . . . 75 90
904 25 c. + 3 c. Two shepherds . . 1·50 2·50

327 Ta' Hagrat Neolithic Temple

1991. National Heritage of the Maltese Islands. Multicoloured.

905 1 c. Type **327** 15 10
906 2 c. Cottoner Gate 20 10
907 3 c. St. Michael's Bastion, Valletta 20 10
908 4 c. Spinola Palace, St. Julian's 30 20
909 5 c. Birkirkara Church 30 20
910 10 c. Mellieha Bay 50 35
911 12 c. Wied iz-Zurrieq 65 45
912 14 c. Mgarr harbour, Gozo . . 75 50
913 20 c. Yacht marina . . . . . 1·25 65
914 50 c. Gozo Channel . . . . . 2·25 1·60
915 £1 "Arab Horses" (sculpture by Antonio Sciortino) . . . . . 3·75 3·50
916 £2 Independence Monument (Ganni Bonnici) (vert) . . . 7·00 7·00

328 Aircraft Tailfins and Terminal

1992. Opening of Int Air Terminal. Mult.

917 4 c. Type **328** 45 30
918 10 c. National flags and terminal 65 65

329 Ships of Columbus

1992. Europa. 500th Anniv of Discovery of America by Columbus. Multicoloured.

919 10 c. Type **329** 75 55
920 35 c. Columbus and map of Americas 2·00 2·25

330 George Cross and Anti-aircraft Gun Crew

332 Church of the Flight into Egypt

331 Running

1992. 50th Anniv of Award of George Cross to Malta. Multicoloured.

921 4 c. Type **330** 65 30
922 10 c. George Cross and memorial bell 1·25 1·00
923 50 c. Tanker "Ohio" entering Grand Harbour 5·00 6·50

1992. Olympic Games, Barcelona. Multicoloured.

924 3 c. Type **331** 45 20
925 10 c. High jumping 95 80
926 30 c. Swimming 2·25 3·75

1992. Rehabilitation of Historical Buildings.

927 **332** 3 c. black, stone & grey 30 20
928 – 4 c. black, stone & pink 35 20
929 – 19 c. black, stone & lilac 1·75 2·25
930 – 25 c. black, stone & green 2·00 2·25

DESIGNS—HORIZ: 4 c. St. John's Co-Cathedral; 25 c. Auberge de Provence. VERT: 19 c. Church of Madonna del Pillar.

333 "The Nativity" (Giuseppe Cali)

1992. Christmas. Religious Paintings by Giuseppe Cali from Mosta Church. Multicoloured.

931 3 c. + 1 c. Type **333** 60 60
932 10 c. + 2 c. "Adoration of the Magi" 1·50 1·50
933 25 c. + 3 c. "Christ with the Elders in the Temple" 2·75 3·25

334 Malta College Building, Valletta

335 Lions Club Emblem

1992. 400th Anniv of University of Malta. Multicoloured.

934 4 c. Type **334** 50 25
935 30 c. Modern University complex, Tal-Qroqq (horiz) 2·25 3·25

1993. 75th Anniv of International Association of Lions Club. Multicoloured.

936 4 c. Type **335** 50 25
937 50 c. Eye (Sight First Campaign) 2·75 3·50

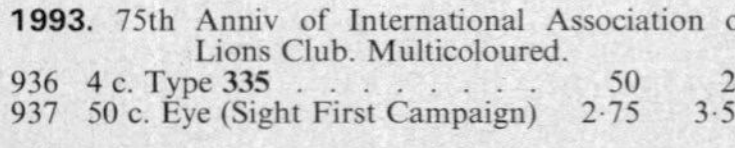

336 Untitled Painting by Paul Carbonaro

1993. Europa. Contemporary Art. Mult.

938 10 c. Type **336** 1·00 50
939 35 c. Untitled painting by Alfred Chircop (horiz) 2·50 4·00

337 Mascot holding Flame

1993. 5th Small States of Europe Games. Multicoloured.

940 3 c. Type **337** 20 20
941 4 c. Cycling 60 30
942 10 c. Tennis 1·25 1·00
943 35 c. Yachting 2·50 3·50

338 Learning First Aid

339 "Papilio machaon"

1993. 50th Anniv of Award of Bronze Cross to Maltese Scouts and Guides. Multicoloured.

945 3 c. Type **338** 30 15
946 4 c. Bronze Cross 30 20
947 10 c. Scout building camp fire 80 80
948 35 c. Governor Lord Gort presenting Bronze Cross, 1943 2·25 3·25

1993. European Year of the Elderly. Butterflies. Multicoloured.

949 5 c. Type **339** 35 20
950 35 c. "Vanessa atalanta" 1·75 2·25

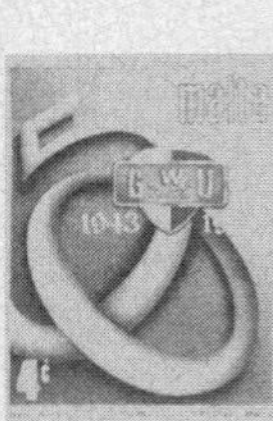

340 G.W.U. Badge and Interlocking "50"

341 Child Jesus and Star

1993. 50th Anniv of General Workers Union.

951 **340** 4 c. multicoloured 35 40

1993. Christmas. Multicoloured.

952 3 c. + 1 c. Type **341** 30 30
953 10 c. + 2 c. Christmas tree 85 95
954 25 c. + 3 c. Star in traditional window 1·60 2·25

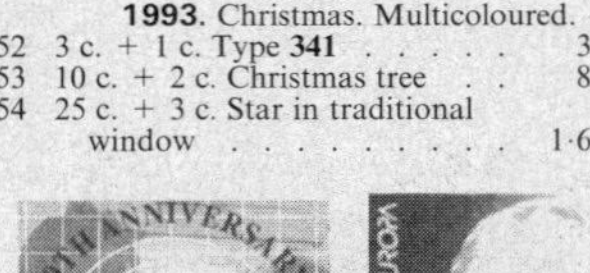

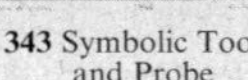

343 Symbolic Tooth and Probe

344 Sir Themistocles Zammit (discoverer of Brucella microbe)

1994. 50th Anniv of Maltese Dental Association. Multicoloured.

956 5 c. Type **343** 35 30
957 44 c. Symbolic mouth and dental mirror 3·00 3·00

1994. Europa. Discoveries. Multicoloured.

958 14 c. Type **344** 50 30
959 30 c. Bi-lingually inscribed candelabrum of 2nd century B.C. (deciphering of ancient Phoenician language) 1·90 3·00

345 Family in Silhouette (International Year of the Family)

346 Football and Map

1994. Anniversaries and Events. Multicoloured.

960 5 c. Type **345** 30 20
961 9 c. Stylised Red Cross (International recognition of Malta Red Cross Society) 60 50
962 14 c. Animals and crops (150th anniv of Agrarian Society) 90 80
963 20 c. Worker in silhouette (75th anniv of I.L.O.) 1·25 1·60
964 25 c. St. Paul's Anglican Cathedral (155th anniv) (vert) 1·40 1·75

1994. World Cup Football Championship, U.S.A. Multicoloured.

965 5 c. Type **346** 40 20
966 14 c. Ball and goal 1·00 80
967 30 c. Ball and pitch superimposed on map 2·50 3·00

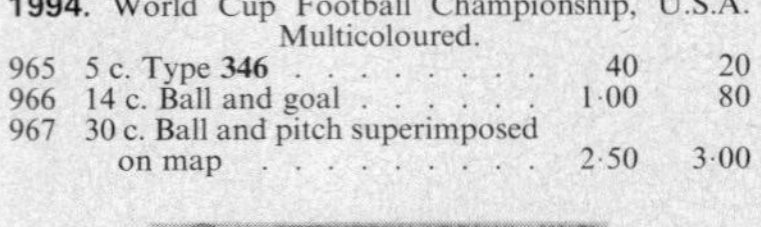

347 Falcon Trophy, Twin Comanche and Auster (25th anniv of Malta International Rally)

1994. Aviation Anniversaries and Events. Multicoloured.

969 5 c. Type **347** 50 20
970 14 c. Alouette helicopter, display teams and logo (Malta International Airshow) 1·75 85
971 20 c. De Havilland Dove "City of Valetta" and Avro York aircraft with logo (50th anniv of I.C.A.O.) 1·90 1·75
972 25 c. Airbus 320 "Nicolas Cottoner" and De Havilland Comet aircraft with logo (50th anniv of I.C.A.O.) 1·90 1·90

348 National Flags and Astronaut on Moon

350 Helmet-shaped Ewer

349 Virgin Mary and Child with Angels

1994. 25th Anniv of First Manned Moon Landing.

973 **348** 14 c. multicoloured 1·10 95

1994. Christmas. Multicoloured.

974 5 c. Type **349** 25 10
975 9 c. + 2 c. Angel in pink (vert) 65 60
976 14 c. + 3 c. Virgin Mary and Child (vert) 90 1·25
977 20 c. + 3 c. Angel in green (vert) 1·60 2·25

Nos. 975/7 are larger, 28 × 41 mm, and depict details from Type **349**.

1994. Maltese Antique Silver Exhibition. Multicoloured.

978 5 c. Type **350** 25 20
979 14 c. Balsamina 70 80
980 20 c. Coffee pot 1·25 1·40
981 25 c. Sugar box 1·50 1·75

351 "60 plus" and Hands touching

352 Hand holding Leaf and Rainbow

1995. Anniversaries and Events. Multicoloured.

982 2 c. Type **351** (25th anniv of National Association of Pensioners) 15 15
983 5 c. Child's drawing (10th anniv of National Youth Council) 25 20
984 14 c. Conference emblem (4th World Conference on Women, Peking, China) 70 80
985 20 c. Nurse and thermometer (50th anniv of Malta Memorial District Nursing Association) 1·25 1·40
986 25 c. Louis Pasteur (biologist) (death centenary) 1·50 1·75

1995. Europa. Peace and Freedom. Multicoloured.

987 14 c. Type **352** 75 55
988 30 c. Peace doves (horiz) 1·50 2·00

353 Junkers Ju 87B "Stuka" Dive Bombers over Valletta and Anti-aircraft Gun

1995. Anniversaries. Multicoloured.

989 5 c. Type **353** (50th anniv of end of Second World War) 25 25
990 14 c. Silhouetted people holding hands (50th anniv of United Nations) 70 80
991 35 c. Hands holding bowl of wheat (50th anniv of F.A.O) (vert) 2·00 2·25

354 Light Bulb

356 Pinto's Turret Clock

355 Rock Wall and Girna

1995. Maltese Electricity and Telecommunications. Multicoloured.

992 2 c. Type **354** 15 15
993 5 c. Symbolic owl and binary codes 25 25
994 9 c. Dish aerial 45 50
995 14 c. Sun and rainbow over trees 70 80
996 20 c. Early telephone, satellite and Moon's surface 1·25 1·50

1995. European Nature Conservation Year. Multicoloured.

997 5 c. Type **355** 35 25
998 14 c. Maltese wall lizards 1·00 80
999 44 c. Aleppo pine 3·00 3·00

1995. Treasures of Malta. Antique Maltese Clocks. Multicoloured.

1000 1 c. Type **356** 10 10
1001 5 c. Michelangelo Sapiano (horologist) and clocks 30 25
1002 14 c. Arlogg tal-lira clock 90 80
1003 25 c. Sundials 1·75 2·50

357 Children's Christmas Eve Procession

1995. Christmas. Multicoloured.

1004 5 c. Type **357** 25 10
1005 5 c. + 2 c. Children with crib (vert) 30 40
1006 14 c. + 3 c. Children with lanterns (vert) 85 90
1007 25 c. + 3 c. Boy with lantern and balustrade (vert) 1·60 1·75

Nos. 1005/7 are 27 × 32 mm and depict details from Type **357**.

358 Silhouetted Children and President's Palace, San Anton

1996. Anniversaries. Multicoloured.

1008 5 c. Type **358** (35th anniv of the President's Award) 25 25
1009 14 c. Nazzareno Camilleri (priest) and St. Patrick's Church, Salesjani (90th birth anniv) 65 65
1010 20 c. St. Mary Euphrasia and convent (birth bicentenary) 1·00 1·10
1011 25 c. Silhouetted children and fountain (50th anniv of U.N.I.C.E.F.) 1·25 1·40

359 Carved Figures from Skorba

1996. Maltese Prehistoric Art Exhibition. Multicoloured.

1012 5 c. Type **359** 30 20
1013 14 c. Temple carving, Gozo 80 85
1014 20 c. Carved figure of a woman, Skorba (vert) 1·10 1·25
1015 35 c. Ghar Dalam pot (vert) 1·90 2·25

360 Mabel Strickland (politician and journalist)

361 Face and Emblem (United Nations Decade against Drug Abuse)

1996. Europa. Famous Women. Multicoloured.

1016 14 c. Type **360** 70 55
1017 30 c. Inez Soler (artist, musician and writer) 1·75 2·00

1996. Anniversaries and Events. Multicoloured.

1018 5 c. Type **361** 25 25
1019 5 c. "Fi" and emblem (50th anniv of Malta Federation of Industry) 25 25
1020 14 c. Commemorative plaque and national flag (75th anniv of self-government) 80 80
1021 44 c. Guglielmo Marconi and early radio equipment (centenary of radio) 2·25 2·50

362 Judo

1996. Olympic Games, Atlanta. Multicoloured.

1022 2 c. Type **362** 10 10
1023 5 c. Athletics 30 25
1024 14 c. Diving 80 80
1025 25 c. Rifle-shooting 1·40 1·60

363 "Harvest Time" (Cali)

1996. 150th Birth Anniv of Guiseppe Cali (painter). Multicoloured.

1026 5 c. Type **363** 30 25
1027 14 c. "Dog" (Cali) 80 70
1028 20 c. "Countrywoman in a Field" (Cali) (vert) 1·10 1·10
1029 25 c. "Cali at his Easel" (Edward Dingli) (vert) 1·25 1·25

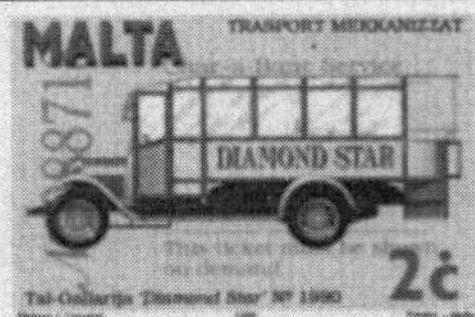

364 Bus No. 1990 "Diamond Star", 1920s

1996. Buses. Multicoloured.

1030 2 c. Type **364** 25 10
1031 5 c. No. 434 "Tom Mix", 1930s 50 25
1032 14 c. No. 1764 "Verdala", 1940s 1·00 80
1033 30 c. No. 3495, 1960s 1·75 2·00

365 Stained Glass Window

1996. Christmas. Multicoloured.

1034 5 c. Type **365** 35 10
1035 5 c.+2 c. Madonna and Child (29 × 35 mm) 40 45
1036 14 c.+3 c. Angel facing right (29 × 35 mm) 80 85
1037 25 c.+3 c. Angel facing left (29 × 35 mm) 1·25 1·40

Nos. 1035/7 show details from Type **365**.

366 Hompesch Arch and Arms, Zabbar

368 Gahan carrying Door

367 Captain-General of the Galleys' Sedan Chair

1997. Bicentenary of Maltese Cities. Multicoloured.

1038 6 c. Type **366** 30 25
1039 16 c. Statue, church and arms, Siggiewi 70 70
1040 26 c. Seated statue and arms, Zejtun 1·10 1·10

1997. Treasures of Malta. Sedan Chairs. Multicoloured.

1042 2 c. Type **367** 15 15
1043 6 c. Cotoner Grandmasters' chair 30 30
1044 16 c. Chair from Cathedral Museum, Mdina (vert) 70 70
1045 27 c. Chevalier D'Arezzo's chair (vert) 1·10 1·10

1997. Europa. Tales and Legends. Multicoloured.

1046 16 c. Type **368** 75 75
1047 35 c. St. Dimitrius appearing from painting 1·25 1·50

369 Modern Sculpture (Antonio Sciortino)

370 Dr. Albert Laferla

1997. Anniversaries. Multicoloured.

1048 1 c. Type **369** 10 15
1049 6 c. Joseph Calleia and film reel (horiz) 40 40
1050 6 c. Gozo Cathedral (horiz) 40 40
1051 11 c. City of Gozo (horiz) 60 50
1052 16 c. Sculpture of head (Sciortino) 80 70
1053 22 c. Joseph Calleia and film camera (horiz) 1·00 1·00

ANNIVERSARIES: 1, 16 c. 50th death anniv of Antonio Sciortino (sculptor); 6 (No. 1049), 22 c. Birth centenary of Joseph Calleia (actor); 6 (No. 1050), 11 c. 300th anniv of construction of Gozo Cathedral.

1997. Pioneers of Education. Multicoloured.

1054 6 c. Type **370** 30 25
1055 16 c. Sister Emilie de Vialar 70 70
1056 19 c. Mgr. Paolo Pullicino 80 80
1057 26 c. Mgr. Tommaso Gargallo 1·00 1·10

371 The Nativity

1997. Christmas. Multicoloured.

1058 6 c. Type **371** 30 10
1059 6 c. + 2 c. Mary and baby Jesus (vert) 35 40
1060 16 c. + 3 c. Joseph with donkey (vert) 80 85
1061 26 c. + 3 c. Shepherd with lamb (vert) 1·25 1·60

Nos. 1059/61 show details from Type **371**.

372 Plan of Fort and Soldiers in Victoria Lines

1997. Anniversaries. Multicoloured (except 6 c.).

1062 2 c. Type **372** 20 10
1063 6 c. Sir Paul Boffa making speech (black and red) 30 25
1064 16 c. Plan of fort and gun crew 90 65
1065 37 c. Queue of voters 1·50 2·00

ANNIVERSARIES: 2, 16 c. Centenary of Victoria Lines; 6, 37 c. 50th anniv of 1947 Self-Government Constitution.

373 "Maria Amelia Grognet" (Antonine de Favray)

1998. Treasures of Malta. Costumes and Paintings.

1066 6 c. Type **373** 40 40
1067 6 c. Gentleman's waistcoat, c. 1790–1810 40 40
1068 16 c. Lady's dinner dress, c. 1880 70 80
1069 16 c. "Veneranda, Baroness Abela, and her Grandson" (De Favray) 70 80

374 Grand Master Ferdinand von Hompesch

1998. Bicentenary of Napoleon's Capture of Malta. Multicoloured.

1071 6 c. Type **374** 30 40
1072 6 c. French fleet 30 40
1073 16 c. French landing 75 90
1074 16 c. General Napoleon Bonaparte 75 90

375 Racing Two-man Luzzus

376 Dolphin and Diver

1998. Europa. Sailing Regatta, Grand Harbour. Multicoloured.

1075 16 c. Type **375** 85 55
1076 35 c. Racing four-man luzzus 1·40 1·75

1998. International Year of the Ocean. Multicoloured.

1077 2 c. Type **376** 20 15
1078 6 c. Diver and sea-urchin 40 25
1079 16 c. Jacques Cousteau and diver (horiz) 85 70
1080 27 c. Two divers (horiz) 1·25 1·50

377 Goalkeeper saving Goal

378 Ships' Wheels (50th anniv of Int Maritime Organization)

1998. World Cup Football Championship, France. Players and flags. Multicoloured.

1081 6 c. Type **377** 40 25
1082 16 c. Two players and referee 85 70
1083 22 c. Two footballers 1·25 1·40

1998. Anniversaries. Multicoloured.

1085 1 c. Type **378** 10 10
1086 6 c. Symbolic family (50th anniv of Universal Declaration of Human Rights) 30 25
1087 11 c. "GRTU" and cogwheels (50th anniv of General Retailers and Traders Union) 45 40
1088 19 c. Mercury (50th anniv of Chamber of Commerce) 70 75
1089 26 c. Aircraft tailfins (25th anniv of Air Malta) 1·10 1·25

379 "Rest on the Flight to Egypt"

1998. Christmas. Paintings by Mattia Preti. Mult.

1090 6 c. Type **379** 30 10
1091 6 c. + 2 c. "Virgin and Child with Sts. Anthony and John the Baptist" 35 40
1092 16 c. + 3 c. "Virgin and Child with Sts. Raphael, Nicholas and Gregory" 80 85
1093 26 c. + 3 c. "Virgin and Child with Sts. John the Baptist and Nicholas" 1·25 1·40

380 Fort St. Angelo

1999. 900th Anniv of the Sovereign Military Order of Malta. Multicoloured.

1094 2 c. Type **380** 15 10
1095 6 c. Grand Master De l'Isle Adam (vert) 30 25
1096 16 c. Grand Master La Valette (vert) 65 55
1097 27 c. Auberge de Castille 1·00 1·40

381 Little Ringed Plover, Ghadira Nature Reserve

1999. Europa. Parks and Gardens. Multicoloured.

1098 16 c. Type **381** 75 55
1099 35 c. Common kingfisher, Simar Nature Reserve 1·25 1·50

382 Council of Europe Assembly

1999. 50th Anniv of Council of Europe. Mult.

1100	6 c. Type **382**	30	25
1101	16 c. Council of Europe Headquarters, Strasbourg	70	55

383 U.P.U. Emblem and Marsamxett Harbour, Valletta

1999. 125th Anniv of Universal Postal Union. Multicoloured.

1102	6 c. Type **383**	40	45
1103	16 c. Nuremberg and "iBRA '99" International Stamp Exhibition emblem	75	80
1104	22 c. Paris and "Philexfrance '99" International Stamp Exhibition emblem	90	1·00
1105	27 c. Peking and "China '99" International Stamp Exhibition emblem	1·00	1·10
1106	37 c. Melbourne and "Australia '99" International Stamp Exhibition emblem	1·10	1·25

384 Couple in Luzzu

1999. Tourism. Multicoloured.

1107	6 c. Type **384**	30	25
1108	16 c. Tourist taking photograph	65	55
1109	22 c. Man sunbathing (horiz)	85	90
1110	27 c. Couple with horse-drawn carriage (horiz)	95	1·00
1111	37 c. Caveman at Ta' Hagrat Neolithic temple (horiz)	1·25	1·50

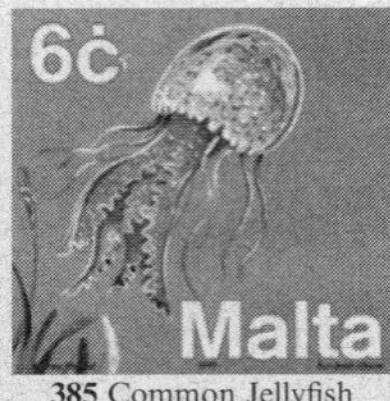

385 Common Jellyfish

1999. Marine Life of the Mediterranean. Mult.

1112	6 c. Type **385**	35	35
1113	6 c. Peacock wrasse	35	35
1114	6 c. Common cuttlefish	35	35
1115	6 c. Violet sea-urchin	35	35
1116	6 c. Dusky grouper	35	35
1117	6 c. Common two-banded seabream	35	35
1118	6 c. Star-coral	35	35
1119	6 c. Spiny spider crab	35	35
1120	6 c. Rainbow wrasse	35	35
1121	6 c. Octopus	35	35
1122	6 c. Atlantic trumpet triton	35	35
1123	6 c. Mediterranean parrotfish	35	35
1124	6 c. Long-snouted seahorse	35	35
1125	6 c. Deep-water hermit crab	35	35
1126	6 c. Mediterranean moray	35	35
1127	6 c. Common starfish	35	35

Nos. 1112/27 were printed together, se-tenant, forming a composite design.

386 Father Mikiel Scerri

1999. Bicentenary of Maltese Uprising against the French. Multicoloured.

1128	6 c. Type **386**	20	25
1129	6 c. "L-Eroj Maltin" (statue)	20	25
1130	16 c. General Belgrand de Vaubois (French commander)	50	55
1131	16 c. Captain Alexander Ball R.N.	50	55

387 "Wolfgang Philip Guttenberg interceding with The Virgin" (votive painting)

1999. Mellieha Sanctuary Commemoration. Mult.

1132	**387**	35 c. multicoloured	1·00	1·10

388 "Pancratium maritimum"

1999. Maltese Flowers. Multicoloured.

1134	2 c. Type **388**	10	10
1135	4 c. "Iris pseudopumila"	10	15
1136	6 c. "Narcissus tazetta"	20	25
1137	16 c. "Crocus longiflorus"	50	55
1138	25 c. "Ornithogalum arabicum"	75	80
1139	46 c. "Tulipa sylvestris"	1·40	1·50

389 Madonna and Child

1999. Christmas. Multicoloured.

1146	6 c. Type **389**	20	25
1147	6 c. + 3 c. Carol singers	25	30
1148	16 c. + 3 c. Santa Claus	60	65
1149	26 c. + 3 c. Christmas decorations	90	95

390 Parliament Chamber and Symbolic Luzzu

1999. 25th Anniv of Republic. Multicoloured.

1150	6 c. Type **390**	20	25
1151	11 c. Parliament in session and Council of Europe emblem	30	35
1152	16 c. Church and Central Bank of Malta building	50	55
1153	19 c. Aerial view of Gozo and emblems	60	65
1154	26 c. Computer and shipyard	75	80

391 Gift and Flowers

2000. Greetings Stamps. Multicoloured.

1155	3 c. Type **391**	10	15
1156	6 c. Photograph, envelope and rose	20	25
1157	16 c. Flowers and silver heart	50	55
1158	20 c. Champagne and pocket watch	60	65
1159	22 c. Wedding rings and roses	65	70

392 Luzzu and Cruise Liner

2000. Malta during the 20th Century. Multicoloured.

1160	6 c. Type **392**	20	25
1161	16 c. Street musicians and modern street carnival	50	55
1162	22 c. Family in 1900 and illuminated quayside	65	70
1163	27 c. Rural occupations and Citadel, Victoria	80	85

393 Footballers and Trophy (Centenary of Malta Football Association)

2000. Sporting Events. Multicoloured.

1164	6 c. Type **393**	20	25
1165	16 c. Swimming and sailing (Olympic Games, Sydney)	50	55
1166	26 c. Judo, shooting and running (Olympic Games, Sydney)	75	80
1167	37 c. Football (European Championship)	1·00	1·10

POSTAGE DUE STAMPS

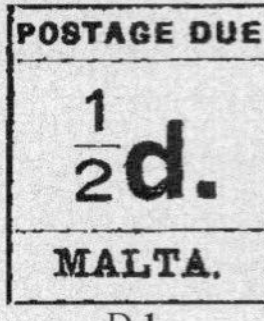

D 1

D 2

1925. Imperf.

D 1	D 1	$\frac{1}{2}$d. black	1·25	4·50
D 2		1d. black	3·00	2·50
D 3		$1\frac{1}{2}$d. black	3·00	3·50
D 4		2d. black	5·50	9·50
D 5		$2\frac{1}{2}$d. black	2·75	2·75
D 6		3d. black on grey	9·00	11·00
D 7		4d. black on yellow	5·00	9·00
D 8		6d. black on yellow	5·00	13·00
D 9		1s. black on yellow	7·50	17·00
D10		1s. 6d. black on yellow	13·00	50·00

1925. Perf.

D32	D 2	$\frac{1}{2}$d. green	35	1·50
D33		1d. violet	30	1·00
D13		$1\frac{1}{2}$d. brown	1·50	80
D14		2d. grey	11·00	1·00
D35		2d. brown	85	70
D36		$2\frac{1}{2}$d. orange	60	70
D37		3d. blue	60	60
D38		4d. green	1·00	80
D39		6d. purple	75	1·00
D40		1s. black	90	1·50
D41		1s. 6d. red	2·25	5·50

D 3 Maltese Lace

D 4

1973.

D42	D 3	2 m. brown and red	10	10
D43		3 m. orange and red	10	15
D44		5m. pink and red	15	20
D45		1 c. blue and green	30	35
D46		2 c. grey and black	30	35
D47		3 c. lt brown and brn	30	35
D48		5 c. dull blue and blue	55	70
D49		10 c. lilac and plum	75	1·00

1993.

D50	D 4	1 c. magenta & mauve	10	10
D51		2 c. blue and light blue	15	15
D52		5 c. green & turquoise	20	20
D53		10 c. orange & yellow	35	35

MANAMA Pt. 19

A dependency of Ajman.

100 dirhams = 1 riyal

1966. Nos. 10, 12, 14 and 18 of Ajman surch **Manama** in English and Arabic and new value.
1 40 d. on 40 n.p. multicoloured . . 25 15
2 70 d. on 70 n.p. multicoloured . . 50 15
3 1 r. 50 on 1 r. 50 multicoloured . 1·40 45
4 10 r. on 10 r. multicoloured . . . 6·50 6·00

1967. Nos. 140/8 of Ajman optd **MANAMA** in English and Arabic. (a) Postage.
5 15 d. blue and brown 10 10
6 30 d. brown and black 15 15
7 50 d. black and brown 35 35
8 70 d. violet and black 60 50

(b) Air.
9 1 r. green and brown 40 25
10 2 r. mauve and black 70 50
11 3 r. black and brown . . . . . 1·10 1·75
12 5 r. brown and black . . . . . 3·50 3·50
13 10 r. blue and brown . . . . . 6·50 6·50

APPENDIX

The following stamps have either been issued in excess of postal needs or have not been available to the public in reasonable quantities at face value. Such stamps may later be given full listing if there is evidence of regular postal use.

1966.

New Currency Surcharges. Stamps of Ajman surch **Manama** in English and Arabic and new value.

(a) Nos. 19/20 and 22/4 (Kennedy). 10 d. on 10 n.p., 15 d. on 15 n.p., 1 r. on 1 r., 2 r. on 2 r., 3 r. on 3 r.

(b) Nos. 27, 30 and 35/6 (Olympics). 5 d. on 5 n.p., 25 d. on 25 n.p., 3 r. on 3 r., 5 r. on 5 r.

(c) Nos. 80/2 and 85 (Churchill). 50 d. on 50 n.p., 75 d. on 75 n.p., 1 r. on 1 r., 5 r. on 5 r.

(d) Nos. 95/8 (Space). Air 50 d. on 50 n.p., 1 r. on 1 r., 3 r. on 3 r., 5 r. on 5 r.

1967.

World Scout Jamboree, Idaho. Postage 30, 70 d., 1 r.; Air 2, 3, 4 r.

Olympic Games, Mexico (1968). Postage 35, 65, 75 d., 1 r.; Air 1 r. 25, 2, 3, 4 r.

Winter Olympic Games, Grenoble (1968). Postage 5, 35, 60, 75 d.; Air 1, 1 r. 25, 2, 3 r.

Paintings by Renoir and Terbrugghen. Air 35, 65 d., 1, 2 r. × 3.

1968.

Paintings by Velazquez. Air 1 r. × 2, 2 r. × 2.

Costumes. Air 30 d. × 2, 70 d. × 2, 1 r. × 2, 2 r. × 2.

Olympic Games, Mexico. Postage 1 r. × 4; Air 2 r. x 4.

Satellites and Spacecraft. Air 30 d. × 2, 70 d. × 2, 1 r. × 2, 2 r. × 2, 3 r. × 2.

Human Rights Year. Kennedy Brothers and Martin Luther King. Air 1 r. × 3, 2 r. × 3.

Sports Champions, Famous Footballers. Postage 15, 20, 50, 75 d., 1 r.; Air 10 r.

Heroes of Humanity. Circular designs on gold or silver foil. 60 d. × 12.

Olympic Games, Mexico. Circular designs on gold or silver foil. Air 3 r. × 8.

Mothers' Day. Paintings. Postage 1 r. × 6.

Kennedy Brothers Commem. Postage 2 r.; Air 5 r.

Cats (1st series). Postage 1, 2, 3 d.; Air 2, 3 r.

5th Death Anniv of Pres. Kennedy. Air 10 r.

Space Exploration. Postage 5, 10, 15, 20, 25 d.; Air 15 r.

Olympic Games, Mexico. Gold Medals. Postage 2 r. × 4; Air 5 r. × 4.

Christmas. Air 5 r.

1969.

Sports Champions. Cyclists. Postage 1, 2, 5, 10, 15, 20 d.; Air 12 r.

Sports Champions. German Footballers. Postage 5, 10, 15, 20, 25 d.; Air 10 r.

Sports Champions. Motor-racing Drivers. Postage 1, 5, 10, 15, 25 d.; Air 10 r.

Motor-racing Cars. Postage 1, 5, 10, 15, 25 d.; Air 10 r.

Sports Champions. Boxers. Postage 5, 10, 15, 20 d.; Air 10 r.

Sports Champions. Baseball Players. Postage 1, 2, 5, 10, 15 d.; Air 10 r.

Birds. Air 1 r. × 11.

Roses. Postage 1 r. × 6.

Animals. Air 1 r. × 6.

Paintings by Italian Artists. 5, 10, 15, 20 d., 10 r.

Great Composers. Air 5, 10, 25 d., 10 r.

Paintings by French Artists. 1 r. × 4.

Nude Paintings. Air 2 r. × 4.

Kennedy Brothers. Air 2, 3, 10 r.

Olympic Games, Mexico. Gold Medal Winners. Postage 1, 2, 10 r.; Air 10 d., 5, 10 r.

Paintings of the Madonna. Postage 10 d.; Air 10 r.

Space Flight of "Apollo 9". Optd on 1968 Space Exploration issue. Air 15 r.

Space Flight of "Apollo 10". Optd on 1968 Space Exploration issue. Air 15 r.

1st Death Anniv of Gagarin. Optd on 1968 Space Exploration issue. 5 d.

2nd Death Anniv of Edward White (astronaut). Optd on 1968 Space Exploration issue. 10 d.

1st Death Anniv of Robert Kennedy. Optd on 1969 Kennedy Brothers issue. Air 2 r.

Olympic Games, Munich (1972). Optd on 1969 Mexico Gold Medal Winners issue. Air 10 d., 5, 10 r.

Moon Mission of "Apollo 11". Air 1, 2, 3 r.

Christmas. Paintings by Brueghel. Postage 1, 2, 4, 5, 10 d.; Air 6 r.

1970.

"Soyuz" and "Apollo" Space Programmes. Postage 1, 2, 4, 5, 10 d.; Air 3, 5 r.

Kennedy and Eisenhower Commem. Embossed on gold foil. Air 20 r.

Lord Baden-Powell Commem. Embossed on gold foil. Air 20 r.

World Cup Football Championship, Mexico. Postage 20, 40, 60, 80 d., 1 r.; Air 3 r.

Brazil's Victory in World Cup Football Championship. Optd on 1970 World Cup issue. Postage 20, 40, 60, 80 d., 1 r.; Air 3 r.

Paintings by Michelangelo. Postage 1, 2, 4, 5, 10 d.; Air 6 r.

World Fair "Expo 70", Osaka, Japan. Air 25, 50, 75 d., 1, 2, 3, 12 r.

Paintings by Renoir. Postage 1, 2, 5, 6, 10 d.; Air 5, 12 r.

Olympic Games, Rome, Tokyo, Mexico and Munich. Postage 15, 30, 50, 70 d.; Air 2, 5 r.

Winter Olympic Games, Sapporo (1972) (1st issue). Postage 2, 3, 4, 10 d.; Air 2, 5 r.

Christmas. Flower Paintings by Brueghel. Postage 5, 20, 25, 30, 50 d.; Air 60 d., 1, 2 r.

1971.

Winter Olympic Games, Sapporo (2nd issue). Postage 1, 2, 3, 4, 5, 6, 8, 10, 12, 15, 20, 25, 30, 35, 40, 50 d.; Air 75 d, 1, 2, 2 r. 50.

Roses. Postage 5, 20, 25, 30, 50 d.; Air 60 d., 1, 2 r.

Birds. Postage 5, 20, 25, 30, 50 d.; Air 60 d., 1, 2 r.

Paintings by Modigliani. Air 25, 50, 60, 75 d., 1 r. 50, 3 r.

Paintings by Rubens. Postage 1, 2, 3, 4, 5, 10 d.; Air 2, 3 r.

"Philatokyo '71" Stamp Exhibition, Paintings by Hokusai and Hiroshige. Postage 10, 15, 20, 25, 50, 75 d.; Air 1, 2 r.

25th Anniv of United Nations. Optd on 1970 Christmas issue. Postage 5, 20, 25, 30, 50 d.; Air 60 d., 1, 2 r.

British Military Uniforms. Postage 5, 20, 25, 30, 50 d.; Air 60 d., 1, 2 r.

Space Flight of "Apollo 14". Postage 15, 25, 50, 60, 70 d.; Air 5 r.

Space Flight of "Apollo 15". Postage 25, 40, 50, 60 d.; Air 1, 6 r.

13th World Scout Jamboree, Asagiri, Japan (1st issue). Postage 1, 2, 3, 5, 7, 10, 12, 15, 20, 25, 30, 35, 40, 50, 65, 80 d.; Air 1, 1 r. 25, 1 r. 50, 2 r.

World Wild Life Conservation. Postage 1, 2, 3, 5, 7, 10, 12, 15, 20, 25, 30, 35, 40, 50, 65, 80 d.; Air 1 r., 1 r. 25, 1 r. 50, 2 r.

13th World Scout Jamboree, Asagiri, Japan (2nd issue). Stamps. Postage 10, 15, 20, 25, 50, 75 d.; Air 1, 2 r.

Winter Olympic Games, Sapporo (3rd issue). Postage 1, 2, 3, 4, 5, 10 d.; Air 2, 3 r.

Cats (2nd series). Postage 15, 25, 40, 60 d.; Air 3, 10 r.

Lions International Clubs. Optd on 1971 Uniforms issue. Postage 5, 20, 25, 30, 50 d.; Air 60 d., 1, 2 r.

Paintings of Ships. Postage 15, 20, 25, 30, 50 d.; Air 60 d., 1, 2 r.

Great Olympic Champions. Postage 25, 50, 75 d., 1 r.; Air 5 r.

Prehistoric Animals. Postage 15, 20, 25, 30, 50, 60 d.; Air 1, 2 r.

Footballers. Postage 5, 10, 15, 20, 40 d.; Air 5 r.

Royal Visit of Queen Elizabeth II to Japan. Postage 10, 20, 30, 40, 50 d.; Air 2, 3 r.

Fairy Tales. Stories by Hans Andersen. Postage 1, 2, 4, 5, 10 d.; Air 3 r.

World Fair, Philadelphia (1976). American Paintings. Postage 20, 25, 50, 60, 75 d.; Air 3 r.

Fairy Tales. Well-known stories. Postage 1, 2, 4, 5, 10 d.; Air 3 r.

Space Flight of "Apollo 16". Postage 20, 30, 40, 50, 60 d.; Air 3, 4 r.

Tropical Fishes. Postage 1, 2, 3, 4, 5, 10 d.; Air 2, 3 r.

European Tour of Emperor Hirohito of Japan. Postage 1, 2, 4, 5, 10 d.; Air 6 r.

Meeting of Pres. Nixon and Emperor Hirohito of Japan in Alaska. Optd on 1971 Emperor's Tour issue. Air 6 r.

2500th Anniv of Persian Empire. Postage 10, 20, 30, 40, 50 d.; Air 3 r.

Space Flight of "Apollo 15" and Future Developments in Space. Postage 10, 15, 20, 25, 50 d.; Air 1, 2 r.

1972.

150th Death Anniv (1971) of Napoleon. Postage 10, 20, 30, 40 d.; Air 1, 2, 3, 4 r.

1st Death Anniv of Gen. de Gaulle. Postage 10, 20, 30, 40 d.; Air 1, 2, 3, 4 r.

Paintings from the "Alte Pinakothek", Munich. Postage 5, 10, 15, 20, 25 d.; Air 5 r.

"Tour de France" Cycle Race. Postage 5, 10, 15, 20, 25, 30, 35, 40, 45, 50, 55, 60 d.; Air 65, 70, 75, 80, 85, 90, 95 d., 1 r.

Cats and Dogs. Postage 10, 20, 30, 40, 50 d.; Air 1 r.

25th Anniv of U.N.I.C.E.F. Optd on 1971 World Scout Jamboree, Asagiri (2nd issue). Postage 10, 15, 20, 25, 50, 75 d.; Air 1, 2 r.

Past and Present Motorcars. Postage 10, 20, 30, 40, 50 d.; Air 1 r.

Military Uniforms. 1 r. × 11.

The United Arab Emirates Ministry of Communications took over the Manama postal service on 1 August 1972. Further stamps inscribed "Manama" issued after that date were released without authority and had no validity.

MANCHUKUO Pt. 17

Issues for the Japanese puppet Government set up in 1932 under President (later Emperor) Pu Yi.

100 fen = 1 yuan

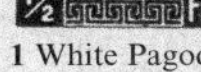

1 White Pagoda, Liaoyang

2 Pu Yi, later Emperor Kang-teh

1932. (a) With five characters in top panel as T **1** and **2**.
1 **1** ½ f. brown 75 25
2 1 f. red 75 10
24 1 f. brown 75 10
25 1½ f. violet . . . . 1·50 75
4 2 f. grey . . . . 2·25 20
26 2 f. blue . . . . 3·50 50
27 3 f. brown . . . . 2·50 10
6 4 f. green 50 10
28 4 f. brown . . . . 18·00 75
7 5 f. green 75 15
8 6 f. red . . . . 3·50 40
9 7 f. grey . . . . 1·25 20
10 8 f. brown . . . . 9·00 6·00
11 10 f. orange . . . . 1·50 15
12 **2** 13 f. brown . . . . 4·50 4·25
13 15 f. red . . . . 15·00 75
14 16 f. blue . . . . 14·00 2·25
15 20 f. brown . . . . 2·75 40
16 30 f. orange . . . . 3·25 1·25
17 50 f. green . . . . 3·75 70
31 1 y. violet . . . . 8·00 5·50

(b) With six characters in top panel.
40 **1** ½ f. brown 25 10
41 1 f. brown 25 10
42 1½ f. violet 65 40
43 3 f. brown 40 10
44 5 f. blue . . . . 8·50 60
45 5 f. slate . . . . 3·50 40
46 6 f. red . . . . 1·00 15
47 7 f. grey . . . . 1·25 40
48 9 f. orange . . . . 1·25 20
55 10 f. blue . . . . 4·25 10
56 **2** 13 f. brown . . . . 3·75 4·25
49 15 f. red . . . . 2·00 25
50 18 f. green . . . . 12·00 3·50
51 20 f. brown . . . . 2·25 20
52 30 f. brown . . . . 3·35 35
53 50 f. green . . . . 3·75 30
54 1 y. violet . . . . 10·00 3·50

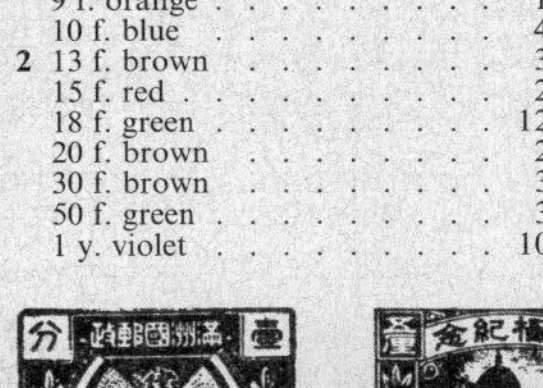

3 Map and Flags

6 Emperor's Palace

1933. 1st Anniv of Republic.
19 **3** 1 f. orange . . . . 1·25 1·00
20 – 2 f. green . . . . 8·50 7·50
21 **3** 4 f. red . . . . 1·25 50
22 – 10 f. blue . . . . 13·00 11·00
DESIGN: 2, 10 f. Council Hall, Hsinking.

1934. Enthronement of Emperor.
32 **6** 1½ f. brown . . . . 1·25 40
33 – 3 f. red . . . . 1·75 20
34 **6** 6 f. green . . . . 5·00 3·75
35 – 10 f. blue . . . . 7·50 3·75
DESIGN: 3 f., 10 f. Phoenixes.

1934. Stamps of 1932 surch with four Japanese characters.
36 **1** 1 f. on 4 f. green (No. 6) . . . 3·50 2·25
37 3 f. on 4 f. green . . . . . 22·00 18·00
38 3 f. on 4 f. brown (No. 28) . . 4·25 2·50
39 **2** 3 f. on 16 f. blue (No. 14) . . 6·50 6·50

In No. 38 the left hand upper character of the surcharge consists of three horizontal lines.

12 Orchid Crest of Manchukuo

13 Changpai Mountain and Sacred Lake

1935. China Mail.
64 **12** 2 f. green 45 15
65 2½ f. violet 35 15
66 **13** 4 f. green . . . . 1·00 30
67 5 f. blue 25 10
68 **12** 8 f. yellow . . . . 2·25 30
60 **13** 12 f. red . . . . 4·50 2·25
70 13 f. brown 50 15

15 Mt. Fuji

16 Phoenixes

1935. Visit of Emperor Kang-teh to Japan.
71 **15** 1½ f. green . . . . 1·00 80
72 **16** 3 f. orange . . . . 1·50 25
73 **15** 6 f. red . . . . 3·25 3·25
74 **16** 10 f. blue . . . . 5·00 2·50

17 Symbolic of Accord

19 State Council Building, Hsinking

20 Chengte Palace, Jehol

1936. Japan–Manchukuo Postal Agreement.
75 **17** 1½ f. brown . . . . 1·75 1·50
76 – 3 f. purple . . . . 1·50 25
77 **17** 6 f. red . . . . 6·50 6·50
78 – 10 f. blue . . . . 5·50 3·50
DESIGN—HORIZ: 3 f., 10 f. Department of Communications.

1936.
79 **19** ½ f. brown 25 15
80 1 f. red 25 10
81 1½ f. lilac . . . . 2·50 2·00
82 A 2 f. green 20 10
83 **19** 3 f. brown 25 15
84 B 4 f. green 20 10
149 **19** 5 f. black . . . . 10 1·00
86 A 6 f. red 75 10
87 B 7 f. black . . . . 1·00 10
88 9 f. red 75 20
89 **20** 10 f. blue 40 10
90 B 12 f. orange 25 10
91 13 f. brown . . . . 10·00 20·00
92 15 f. red . . . . 1·25 30
93 C 18 f. green . . . . 7·50 7·50
94 19 f. green . . . . 3·50 1·50
95 A 20 f. brown . . . . 1·50 35
96 **20** 30 f. brown . . . . 1·75 30
97 D 38 f. blue . . . . 13·00 14·00
98 39 f. blue . . . . 1·00 1·00
99 A 50 f. green . . . . 2·25 30
154 **20** 1 y. purple . . . . 45 2·75
DESIGNS: A, Carting soya-beans; B. Peiling Mausoleum; C, Airplane and grazing sheep (domestic and China air mail); D, Nakajima-built Fokker F.VIIb/3m airplane over Sungari River railway bridge (air mail to Japan).

21 Sun rising over Fields

22 Shadowgraph of old and new Hsinking

1937. 5th Anniv of Founding of State.
101 **21** 1½ f. red . . . . 5·00 6·00
102 **22** 3 f. green . . . . 1·50 1·75

1937. China Mail. Surch in Chinese characters.
108 **12** 2½ f. on 2 f. green . . . . . 2·75 2·00
110 **13** 5 f. on 4 f. green . . . . . 2·75 2·50
111 13 f. on 12 f. brown . . . . 9·50 7·00

27 Pouter Pigeon and Hsinking

1937. Completion of Five Year Reconstruction Plan for Hsinking.
112 **27** 2 f. purple . . . . 2·00 1·00
113 – 4 f. red . . . . 2·00 25
114 **27** 10 f. green . . . . 6·50 4·00
115 – 20 f. blue . . . . 7·50 5·00
DESIGN: 4, 20 f. Flag over Imperial Palace.

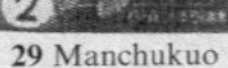

29 Manchukuo **30** Japanese Residents Assn. Building

1937. Japan's Relinquishment of Extra-territorial Rights.

116 **29** 2 f. red . . . . 1·00 25
117 **30** 4 f. green . . . . 2·75 75
118 8 f. orange . . . . 3·25 2·00
119 – 10 f. blue . . . . 2·75 50
120 – 12 f. violet . . . . 3·50 3·00
121 – 20 f. brown . . . . 4·75 2·75

DESIGNS—As Type **30**: 10, 20 f. Dept. of Communications Bldg. HORIZ: 12 f. Ministry of Justice.

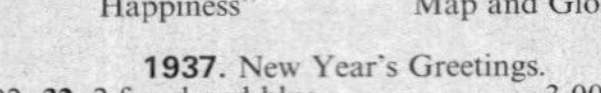

32 "Twofold Happiness" **33** Red Cross on Map and Globe

1937. New Year's Greetings.

122 **32** 2 f. red and blue . . . . . 3·00 30

1938. Inaug of Manchukuo Red Cross Society.

123 **33** 2 f. red . . . . 1·00 1·25
124 4 f. green . . . . 1·00 25

34 Map of Railway Lines **35** "Asia" Express

1939. Completion of 10,000 Kilometres of Manchurian Railways.

125 **34** 2 f. blue and orange . . . . 2·75 1·60
126 **35** 4 f. deep blue and blue . . . 2·75 1·90

36 Manchurian Cranes over Shipmast **37** Census Official and Manchukuo **38** Census Slogans in Chinese and Mongolian

1940. 2nd Visit of Emperor Kang-teh to Japan.

127 **36** 2 f. purple . . . . 1·25 1·50
128 4 f. green . . . . 1·25 1·50

1940. National Census.

129 **37** 2 f. brown and yellow . . . 60 1·50
130 **38** 4 f. deep green and green . . 60 1·50

39 Message of Congratulation **40** Dragon Dance

1940. 2600th Anniv of Founding of Japanese Empire.

131 **39** 2 f. red . . . . 15 1·50
132 **40** 4 f. blue . . . . 15 1·50

紀念新嘉坡
復師我東亞
康德九年

41 Recruit **42**

1941. Enactment of Conscription Law.

133 **41** 2 f. red . . . . 75 1·50
134 4 f. blue . . . . 75 1·50

1942. Fall of Singapore. Stamps of 1936 optd with T **42**.

135 A 2 f. green . . . . 1·00 2·00
136 B 4 f. green . . . . 1·00 2·00

43 Kenkoku Shrine **44** Achievement of Fine Crops

45 Women of Five Races Dancing **46** Map of Manchukuo

1942. 10th Anniv of Founding of State.

137 **43** 2 f. red 25 75
138 **44** 3 f. orange . . . . 2·25 2·25
139 **43** 4 f. lilac 40 75
140 **45** 6 f. green . . . . 2·25 2·50
141 **46** 10 f. red on yellow . . . . 75 1·50
142 – 20 f. blue on yellow . . . . 1·00 1·50

DESIGN—HORIZ: 20 f. Flag of Manchukuo.

1942. 1st Anniv of "Greater East Asia War". Stamps of 1936 optd with native characters above date **8.12.8**.

143 **19** 3 f. brown . . . . 1·00 1·75
144 A 6 f. red . . . . 1·00 1·75

1943. Labour Service Law Proclamation. Stamps of 1936 optd with native characters above heads of pick and shovel.

145 **19** 3 f. brown . . . . 1·00 1·75
146 A 6 f. red . . . . 1·00 1·75

49 Nurse and Stretcher **50** Furnace at Anshan Plant

1943. 5th Anniv of Manchukuo Red Cross Society.

147 **49** 6 f. green . . . . 75 2·50

1943. 2nd Anniv of "Greater East Asia War".

148 **50** 6 f. red . . . . 75 2·50

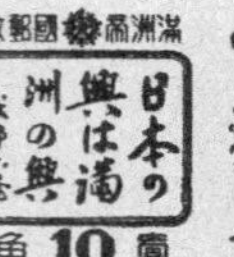
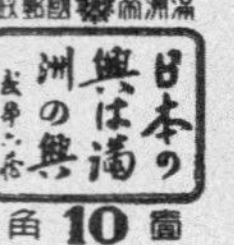

51 Chinese characters **52** Japanese characters **53** "One Heart One Soul"

1944. Friendship with Japan. (a) Chinese characters

155 **51** 10 f. red 25 75
156 40 f. green . . . . 75 1·00

(b) Japanese characters.

157 **52** 10 f. red 25 75
158 40 f. green . . . . 75 1·00

1945. 10th Anniv of Emperor's Edict.

159 **53** 10 f. red . . . . 1·25 4·50

MARIANA ISLANDS Pt. 7

A group of Spanish Islands in the Pacific Ocean of which Guam was ceded to the U.S.A. and the others to Germany. The latter are now under U.S. Trusteeship.

100 pfennig = 1 mark

1899. German stamps optd **Marianen**.

7 **8** 3 pf. brown . . . . 12·00 32·00
8 5 pf. green . . . . 14·00 32·00
9 **9** 10 pf. red . . . . 18·00 38·00
10 20 pf. blue . . . . 22·00 £110
11 25 pf. orange . . . . 60·00 £160
12 50 pf. brown . . . . 60·00 £190

1901. "Yacht" key-type inscr "MARIANEN".

13 N 3 pf. brown 70 90
14 5 pf. green 70 90
15 10 pf. red . . . . 70 2·75
16 20 pf. blue . . . . 1·00 6·00
17 25 pf. black & red on yell . . 1·25 13·00
18 30 pf. black & orge on buff . . 1·25 13·00
19 40 pf. black and red . . . . 1·25 13·00
20 50 pf. black & pur on buff . . 1·40 15·00
21 80 pf. black & red on rose . . 2·00 24·00
22 O 1 m. red . . . . 2·75 70·00
23 2 m. blue . . . . 4·50 90·00
24 3 m. black . . . . 6·50 £130
25 5 m. red and black £130 £500

MARIENWERDER Pt. 7

A district of E. Prussia where a plebiscite was held in 1920. As a result the district remained part of Germany. After the War of 1939-45 it was returned to Poland and reverted to its original name of Kwidzyn.

100 pfennig = 1 mark

1

1920.

1 **1** 5 pf. green 35 35
2 10 pf. red 25 20
3 15 pf. grey 35 35
4 20 pf. brown 30 20
5 25 pf. blue 50 45
6 30 pf. orange 85 65
7 40 pf. brown 50 45
8 50 pf. violet 50 40
9 60 pf. brown . . . . 3·50 2·50
10 75 pf. brown 70 75
11 1 m. brown and green 60 55
12 2 m. purple . . . . 4·75 2·40
13 3 m. red . . . . 4·50 3·25
14 5 m. blue and red . . . . . 10·00 17·00

1920. Stamps of Germany inscr "DEUTSCHES REICH" optd or surch **Commission Interalliee Marienwerder**.

15 **10** 5 pf. green . . . . 12·00 25·00
16 20 pf. blue . . . . 5·00 16·00
17 50 pf. black & pur on buff . . £350 £650
18 75 pf. black and green . . . 3·50 6·00
19 80 pf. black and red on rose . 70·00 £110
25 **12** 1 m. red . . . . 2·75 4·50
21 **24** 1 m. on 2 pf. grey . . . . 20·00 35·00
26 **12** 1 m. 25 green . . . . . . 3·50 5·00
27 1 m. 50 brown . . . . . . 4·00 7·00
22 **24** 2 m. on 2½ pf. grey . . . . 8·00 12·00
28 **13** 2 m. 50 purple . . . . . . 2·40 4·50
23 **10** 3 m. on 3 pf. brown . . . . 12·00 14·00
24 **24** 5 m. on 7½ pf. orange . . . 8·50 14·00

1920. As T **1**, with inscription at top changed to "PLEBISCITE".

29 5 pf. green . . . . 2·75 2·50
30 10 pf. red . . . . 2·75 2·50
31 15 pf. grey . . . . 12·00 12·00
32 20 pf. brown . . . . 1·50 1·60
33 25 pf. blue . . . . 14·00 13·00
34 30 pf. orange . . . . 1·40 1·00
35 40 pf. brown . . . . 1·00 70
36 50 pf. violet . . . . 1·75 1·25
37 60 pf. brown . . . . 5·25 4·00
38 75 pf. brown . . . . 6·50 5·50
39 1 m. brown and green . . . . 1·00 1·00
40 2 m. purple . . . . 1·40 1·10
41 3 m. red . . . . 1·75 1·25
42 5 m. blue and red . . . . . 2·75 1·40

MARSHALL ISLANDS Pts. 7, 22

A group of islands in the Pacific Ocean, a German protectorate from 1885. From 1920 to 1947 it was a Japanese mandated territory and from 1947 part of the United States Trust Territory of the Pacific Islands, using United States stamps. In 1984 it assumed control of its postal services.

A. GERMAN PROTECTORATE

100 pfennig = 1 mark

1897. Stamps of Germany (a) optd **Marschall-Inseln.**

G1 **8** 3 pf. brown £120 £450
G2 5 pf. green £100 £400
G3 **9** 10 pf. red . . . . 30·00 £110
G4 20 pf. blue . . . . 30·00 £110

(b) optd **Marshall-Inseln.**

G 5 **8** 3 pf. brown . . . . 3·00 5·00
G 6 5 pf. green . . . . 7·50 5·50
G 7 **9** 10 pf. red . . . . 10·00 14·00
G 8 20 pf. blue . . . . 13·00 23·00
G 9 25 pf. orange . . . . 17·00 40·00
G10 50 pf. brown . . . . 27·00 48·00

1901. "Yacht" key-type inscr "MARSHALL INSELN".

G11 N 3 pf. brown . . . . 60 1·00
G12 5 pf. green . . . . 60 1·10
G13 10 pf. red . . . . 60 4·00
G14 20 pf. blue . . . . 75 9·00
G15 25 pf. black & red on yell . . 80 15·00
G16 30 pf. blk & orge on buff . . 80 15·00
G17 40 pf. black and red . . . . 80 15·00
G18 50 pf. blk & pur on buff . . 1·10 20·00
G19 80 pf. blk & red on rose . . 2·00 32·00
G20 O 1 m. red . . . . 3·25 75·00
G21 2 m. blue . . . . 4·50 £120
G22 3 m. black . . . . 7·00 £200
G23 5 m. red and black £110 £500

B. REPUBLIC

100 cents = 1 dollar

1 Canoe

1984. Inauguration of Postal Independence. Multicoloured.

1 20 c. Type **1** 55 30
2 20 c. Fishes and net 55 30
3 20 c. Navigational stick-chart . . 55 30
4 20 c. Islet with coconut palms . . 55 30

2 Mili Atoll **3** German Marshall Islands 1900 3 pf. Optd Stamp

1984. Maps. Multicoloured.

5 1 c. Type **2** 10 10
6 3 c. Likiep Atoll 10 10
7 5 c. Ebon Atoll 15 10
8 10 c. Jaluit Atoll 15 10
9 13 c. Ailinginae Atoll 25 15
10 14 c. Wotho Atoll 25 15
11 20 c. Kwajalein and Ebeye Atolls 30 20
12 22 c. Enewetak Atoll 30 20
13 28 c. Ailinglaplap Atoll 45 35
14 30 c. Majuro Atoll 45 25
15 33 c. Namu Atoll 50 40
16 37 c. Rongelap Atoll 55 45
16a 39 c. Taka and Utirik Atolls . . 55 45
16b 44 c. Ujelang Atoll 65 50
16c 50 c. Aur and Maloclap Atolls . . 80 65
17 $1 Arno Atoll . . . . 1·75 75
18 $2 Wotje and Erikub Atolls . . 3·25 2·50
19 $5 Bikini Atoll . . . . 7·50 6·50
20 $10 Mashallese stick chart (31 × 31 mm) . . . . 12·00 10·50

1984. 19th Universal Postal Union Congress Philatelic Salon, Hamburg.

21 **3** 40 c. brown, black & yellow . . 70 50
22 – 40 c. brown, black & yellow . . 70 50
23 – 40 c. blue, black and yellow . . 70 50
24 – 40 c. multicoloured 70 50

DESIGNS: No. 22, German Marshall Islands 1901 3 pf. "Yacht" stamp; 23, German Marshall Islands 1897 20 pf. stamp; 24, German Marshall Islands 1901 5 m. "Yacht" stamp.

4 Common Dolphin

1984. "Ausipex 84" International Stamp Exhibition, Melbourne. Dolphins. Multicoloured.

25 20 c. Type **4** 50 35
26 20 c. Risso's dolphin 50 35
27 20 c. Spotter dolphins 50 35
28 20 c. Bottle-nosed dolphin . . . 50 35

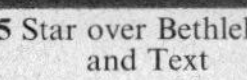

5 Star over Bethlehem and Text **6** Traditional Chief and German and Marshallese Flags

1984. Christmas. Multicoloured.

29 20 c. Type **5** 50 30
30 20 c. Desert landscape 50 30
31 20 c. Two kings on camels . . . 50 30
32 20 c. Third king on camel . . . 50 30

1984. 5th Anniv of Constitution. Multicoloured.

33 20 c. Type **6** 50 30
34 20 c. Pres. Amata Kabua and American and Marshallese flags 50 30
35 20 c. Admiral Chester W. Nimitz and Japanese and Marshallese flags 50 30
36 20 c. Trygve H. Lie (first Secretary-General of United Nations) and U.N. and Marshallese flags . . 50 30

7 Leach's Storm Petrel

1985. Birth Bicentenary of John J. Audubon (ornithologist). Multicoloured.

37 22 c. Type **7** (inscr "Fork-tailed Petrel") (postage) 65 30
38 22 c. Pectoral sandpiper 65 30
39 44 c. Brown booby (inscr "Booby Gannet") (air) . . . . 1·25 80
40 44 c. Whimbrel (inscr "Great Esquimaux Curlew") . . . . 1·25 80

8 Black-spotted Triton

1985. Sea Shells (1st series). Multicoloured.

41 22 c. Type **8** 50 35
42 22 c. Monodon murex 50 35
43 22 c. Diana conch 50 35
44 22 c. Great green turban 50 35
45 22 c. Rose-branch murex 50 35

See also Nos. 85/9, 131/5 and 220/4.

9 Woman as Encourager and Drum

1985. International Decade for Women. Mult.

46 22 c. Type **9** 40 30
47 22 c. Woman as Peacemaker and palm branches 40 30
48 22 c. Woman as Nurturer and pounding stone 40 30
49 22 c. Woman as Benefactress and lesser frigate bird 50 30

Nos. 46/9 were printed together in se-tenant blocks of four within the sheet, each block forming a composite design.

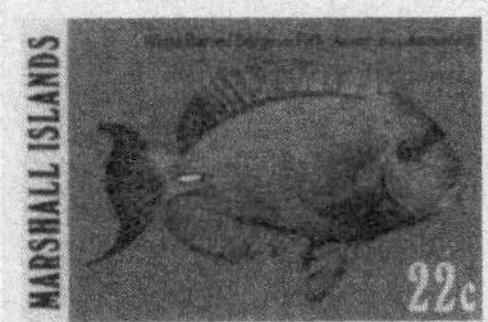
10 Palani ("White Barred Surgeon Fish")

1985. Lagoon Fishes. Multicoloured.

50 22 c. Type **10** 60 40
51 22 c. Silver-spotted squirrelfish ("White Blotched Squirrel Fish") 60 40
52 22 c. Spotted boxfish 60 40
53 22 c. Saddle butterflyfish 60 40

11 Basketball

1985. International Youth Year. Multicoloured.

54 22 c. Type **11** 40 30
55 22 c. Elderly woman recording for oral history project 40 30
56 22 c. Islander explaining navigational stick charts . . . 40 30
57 22 c. Dancers at inter-atoll music and dance competition . . . 40 30

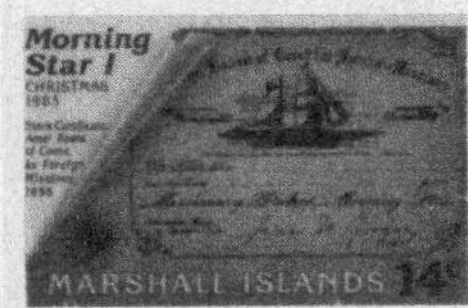
12 American Board of Commissions for Foreign Missions Stock Certificate

1985. Christmas. "Morning Star I" (first Christian missionary ship to visit Marshall Islands). Multicoloured.

58 14 c. Type **12** 15 30
59 22 c. Launching of "Morning Star I", 1856 . . . . 45 30
60 33 c. Departure from Honolulu, 1857 . . . . 70 50
61 44 c. Entering Ebon Lagoon, 1857 80 60

13 "Giotto" and Section of Comet Tail

1985. Appearance of Halley's Comet. Designs showing comet over Roi-Namur Island. Multicoloured.

62 22 c. Space shuttle and comet 1·00 55
63 22 c. "Planet A" space probe and dish aerial . . . . 1·00 55
64 22 c. Type **13** . . . . 1·00 55
65 22 c. "Vega" satellite and buildings on island . . . . 1·00 55
66 22 c. Sir Edmund Halley, satellite communications ship and airplane . . . . 1·00 55

Nos. 62/6 were printed together, se-tenant, forming a composite design.

14 Mallow

1985. Medicinal Plants. Multicoloured.

67 22 c. Type **14** 45 35
68 22 c. Half-flower 45 35
69 22 c. "Guettarda speciosa" . . . 45 35
70 22 c. Love-vine 45 35

15 Trumpet Triton

1986. World Wildlife Fund. Marine Life. Mult.

71 14 c. Type **15** 40 30
72 14 c. Giant clam 40 30
73 14 c. Small giant clam 40 30
74 14 c. Coconut crab 40 30

16 Consolidated PBY-5A Catalina Amphibian

1986. Air. "Ameripex 86" International Stamp Exhibition, Chicago. Mail Planes. Multicoloured.

75 44 c. Type **16** 85 65
76 44 c. Grumman SA-16 Albatross . 85 65
77 44 c. Douglas DC-6B 85 65
78 44 c. Boeing 727-100 . . . . . 85 65

17 Islanders in Outrigger Canoe

1986. 40th Anniv of Operation Crossroads (atomic bomb tests on Bikini Atoll). Multicoloured.

80 22 c. Type **17** 55 35
81 22 c. Advance landing of amphibious DUKW from U.S.S. "Sumner" 55 35
82 22 c. Loading "LST 1108" (tank landing ship) for islanders' departure 55 35
83 22 c. Man planting coconuts as part of reclamation programme 55 35

1986. Sea Shells (2nd series). As T **8**. Multicoloured.

85 22 c. Ramose ("Rose") murex . 50 35
86 22 c. Orange spider conch . . . 50 35
87 22 c. Red-mouth frog shell . . . 50 35
88 22 c. Laciniate conch 50 35
89 22 c. Giant frog shell 50 35

18 Blue Marlin

1986. Game Fishes. Multicoloured.

90 22 c. Type **18** 50 40
91 22 c. Wahoo 50 40
92 22 c. Dolphin 50 40
93 22 c. Yellow-finned tuna 50 40

19 Flowers (top left)

1986. International Peace Year. Multicoloured.

94 22 c. Type **19** (Christmas) (postage) 50 35
95 22 c. Flowers (top right) 50 35
96 22 c. Flowers (bottom left) . . . 50 35
97 22 c. Flowers (bottom right) . . 50 35
98 44 c. Head of Statue crowned with flowers (24 × 39 mm) (cent of Statue of Liberty) (air) . . . 1·00 70

Nos. 94/7 were issued together, se-tenant, in blocks of four within the sheet, each block forming a composite design of mixed flower arrangement.

20 Girl Scout giving Plant to Patient

1986. Air. 20th Anniv of Marshall Island Girl Scouts and 75th Anniv (1987) of United States Girl Scout Movement. Multicoloured.

99 44 c. Type **20** 75 55
100 44 c. Giving salute 75 55
101 44 c. Girl scouts holding hands in circle 75 55
102 44 c. Weaving pandana and palm branch mats 75 55

21 Wedge-tailed Shearwater

1987. Air. Sea Birds. Multicoloured.

103 44 c. Type **21** 95 70
104 44 c. Red-footed booby 95 70
105 44 c. Red-tailed tropic bird . . 95 70
106 44 c. Lesser frigate bird 95 70

22 "James T. Arnold", 1854

1987. Whaling Ships. Multicoloured.

107 22 c. Type **22** 60 45
108 22 c. "General Scott", 1859 . . 60 45
109 22 c. "Charles W. Morgan", 1865 60 45
110 22 c. "Lucretia", 1884 . . . . 60 45

23 Lindbergh's "Spirit of St. Louis" and Congressional Medal of Honour, 1927

1987. Aviators. Multicoloured.

111 33 c. Type **23** 70 45
112 33 c. Charles Lindbergh and Chance Vought F4U Corsair fighter, Marshall Islands, 1944 . . . . 70 45
113 39 c. William Bridgeman and Consolidated B-24 Liberator bomber, Kwajalein, 1944 . . 80 60
114 39 c. Bridgeman and Douglas Skyrocket, 1951 . . . . . . 80 60
115 44 c. John Glenn and Chance Vought F4U Corsair fighters, Marshall Islands, 1944 . . . 1·00 75
116 44 c. Glenn and "Friendship 7" space capsule . . . . 1·00 75

24 Earhart's Lockheed 10E Electra taking off from Lae, New Guinea

1987. Air. "Capex '87" International Stamp Exhibition, Toronto. 50th Anniv of Amelia Earhart's Round the World Flight Attempt. Multicoloured.

117 44 c. Type **24** 90 65
118 44 c. U.S. Coastguard cutter "Itasca" waiting off Howland Island for Electra 90 65
119 44 c. Islanders and crashed Electra on Mili Atoll 90 65
120 44 c. Japanese patrol boat "Koshu" recovering Electra 90 65

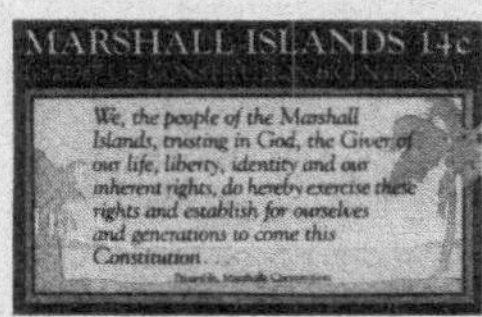

25 "We, the people of the Marshall Islands ..."

1987. Bicentenary of United States of America Constitution. Multicoloured.

122 14 c. Type **25** 30 25
123 14 c. Marshall Is. and U.S.A. emblems 30 25
124 14 c. "We the people of the United States..." 30 25
125 22 c. "All we have and are today as a people..." 45 25
126 22 c. Marshall Is. and U.S.A. flags 45 25
127 22 c. "... to establish Justice..." 45 25
128 44 c. "With this Constitution..." 85 75
129 44 c. Marshall Is. stick chart and U.S. Liberty Bell 85 75
130 44 c. "... to promote the general Welfare..." 85 75

The three designs of each value were printed together, se-tenant, the left hand stamp of each strip bearing quotations from the preamble to the Marshall Islands Constitution and the right hand stamp, quotations from the United States Constitution preamble.

1987. Sea Shells (3rd series). As T **8**. Multicoloured.

131 22 c. Magnificent cone 50 35
132 22 c. Pacific partridge tun . . . 50 35
133 22 c. Scorpion spider conch . . 50 35
134 22 c. Common hairy triton . . 50 35
135 22 c. Arthritic ("Chiragra") spider conch 50 35

26 Planting Coconut

1987. Copra Industry. Multicoloured.

136 44 c. Type **26** 70 55
137 44 c. Making copra 70 55
138 44 c. Bottling extracted coconut oil 70 55

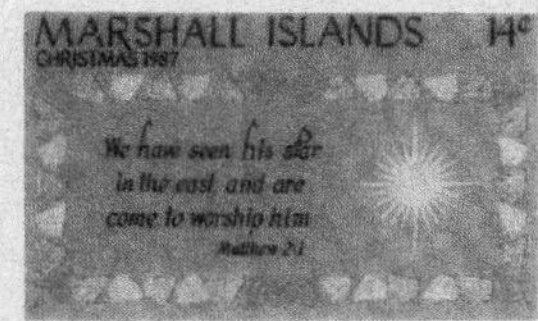

27 "We have seen his star in the east..."

1987. Christmas. Multicoloured.

139 14 c. Type **27** 30 25
140 22 c. "Glory to God in the highest;..." 40 30
141 33 c. "Sing unto the Lord a new song..." 60 40
142 44 c. "Praise him in the cymbals and dances;..." 80 65

28 Eastern Reef Heron

1988. Shore and Water Birds. Multicoloured.

143 44 c. Type **28** 75 50
144 44 c. Bar-tailed godwit 75 50
145 44 c. Blue-faced booby 75 50
146 44 c. Common shoveler 75 50

29 Maroon Anemonefish ("Damselfish")

30 Javelin Thrower

1988. Fishes. Multicoloured.

147 1 c. Type **29** 10 10
148 3 c. Black-faced butterflyfish 10 10
149 14 c. Stocky hawkfish 20 10
150 15 c. White-spotted puffer ("Balloonfish") 20 10
151 17 c. Starry pufferfish ("Trunk Fish") 25 15
152 22 c. Moon ("Lyretail") wrasse 30 20
153 25 c. Six-banded parrotfish 30 20
154 33 c. Spotted ("White-spotted") boxfish 40 25
155 36 c. Yellow ("Spotted") boxfish 45 30
156 39 c. Red-tailed surgeonfish 50 40
157 44 c. Forceps ("Long-snouted") butterflyfish 55 45
158 45 c. Oriental trumpetfish 55 45
159 56 c. False-eyed pufferfish ("Sharp-nosed Puffer") 70 50
160 $1 Yellow seahorse 1·50 70
161 $2 Ghost pipefish 3·50 1·50
162 $5 Clown triggerfish ("Big-spotted Triggerfish") 7·50 5·50
163 $10 Blue-finned trevally ("Blue Jack") (50 × 28 mm) 15·00 11·00

1988. Olympic Games, Seoul. Multicoloured.

166 15 c. Type **30** 35 15
167 15 c. Drawing javelin back and star 35 15
168 15 c. Javelin drawn back fully (value at left) 35 15
169 15 c. Commencing throw (value at right) 35 15
170 15 c. Releasing javelin 35 15
171 25 c. Runner and star (left half) 45 25
172 25 c. Runner and star (right half) 45 25
173 25 c. Runner (value at left) 45 25
174 25 c. Runner (value at right) 45 25
175 25 c. Finish of race 45 25

Nos. 166/70 were printed together, se-tenant, forming a composite design of a javelin throw with background of the Marshallese flag. Nos. 171/5 were similarly arranged forming a composite design of a runner and flag.

31 "Casco" sailing through Golden Gate of San Francisco

1988. Centenary of Robert Louis Stevenson's Pacific Voyages. Multicoloured.

176 25 c. Type **31** 60 40
177 25 c. "Casco" at the Needles of Ua-Pu, Marquesas 60 40
178 25 c. "Equator" leaving Honolulu 60 40
179 25 c. Chieftain's canoe, Majuro Lagoon 60 40
180 25 c. Bronze medallion depicting Stevenson by Augustus St. Gaudens, 1887 60 40
181 25 c. "Janet Nicoll" (inter-island steamer), Majuro Lagoon 60 40
182 25 c. Stevenson's visit to maniap of King Tembinoka of Gilbert Islands 60 40
183 25 c. Stevenson in Samoan canoe, Apia Harbour 60 40
184 25 c. Stevenson on horse Jack at Valima (Samoan home) 60 40

32 Spanish Ragged Cross Ensign (1516-1785) and Magellan's Ship "Vitoria"

1988. Exploration Ships and Flags. Multicoloured.

185 25 c. Type **32** 50 35
186 25 c. British red ensign (1707–1800), "Charlotte" and "Scarborough" (transports) 50 35
187 25 c. American flag and ensign (1837–45), U.S.S. "Flying Fish" (schooner) and U.S.S. "Peacock" (sloop) 50 35
188 25 c. German flag and ensign (1867–1919) and "Planet" (auxiliary schooner) 50 35

33 Father Christmas in Sleigh

34 Nuclear Test on Bikini Atoll

1988. Christmas. Multicoloured.

189 25 c. Type **33** 45 30
190 25 c. Reindeer over island with palm huts and trees 45 30
191 25 c. Reindeer over island with palm trees 45 30
192 25 c. Reindeer and billfish 45 30
193 25 c. Reindeer over island with outrigger canoe 45 30

1988. 25th Anniv of Assassination of John F. Kennedy (American President). Multicoloured.

194 25 c. Type **34** 50 30
195 25 c. Kennedy signing Test Ban Treaty 50 30
196 25 c. Kennedy 50 30
197 25 c. Kennedy using hot-line between Washington and Moscow 50 30
198 25 c. Peace Corps volunteers 50 30

35 "SV-5D PRIME" Vehicle Launch from Vandenberg Air Force Base

1988. Kwajalein Space Shuttle Tracking Station. Multicoloured.

199 25 c. Type **35** (postage) 45 30
200 25 c. Re-entry of "SV-5D" 45 30
201 25 c. Recovery of "SV-5D" off Kwajalein 45 30
202 25 c. Space shuttle "Discovery" over Kwajalein 45 30
203 45 c. Shuttle and astronaut over Rongelap (air) 75 55

Nos. 199/202 were printed together, se-tenant, forming a composite design.

36 1918 Typhoon Monument, Majuro

1989. Links with Japan. Multicoloured.

204 45 c. Type **36** 80 55
205 45 c. Japanese seaplane base and railway, Djarret Islet, 1940s 1·25 90
206 45 c. Japanese fishing boats 1·25 90
207 45 c. Japanese skin-divers 80 55

37 "Island Woman"

1989. Links with Alaska. Oil Paintings by Claire Fejes. Multicoloured.

208 45 c. Type **37** 75 55
209 45 c. "Kotzebue, Alaska" 75 55
210 45 c. "Marshallese Madonna" 75 55

38 Dornier Do-228

1989. Air. Airplanes. Multicoloured.

211 12 c. Type **38** 30 20
212 36 c. Boeing 737 55 40
213 39 c. Hawker Siddeley H.S.748 65 45
214 45 c. Boeing 727 75 55

1989. Sea Shells (4th series). As T **8**. Mult.

220 25 c. Pontifical mitre 55 35
221 25 c. Tapestry turban 55 35
222 25 c. Flame mouthed ("Bull-mouth") helmet 55 35
223 25 c. Prickly Pacific drupe 55 35
224 25 c. Blood-mouth conch 55 35

40 Wandering Tattler

1989. Birds. Multicoloured.

226 45 c. Type **40** 85 60
227 45 c. Turnstone 85 60
228 45 c. Pacific golden plover 85 60
229 45 c. Sanderling 85 60

41 "Bussard" (German cruiser) and 1897 Ship's Post Cancellation

1989. "Philexfrance 89" International Stamp Exhibition, Paris. Marshall Islands Postal History. Multicoloured.

230 25 c. Type **41** 1·50 50
231 25 c. First Day Cover bearing first Marshall Islands stamps and U.S. 10 c. stamp 1·50 50
232 25 c. Consolidated PBY-5 Catalina flying boats, floating Fleet Post Office ("L.S.T. 119"), Majuro, and 1944 U.S. Navy cancellation 1·50 50
233 25 c. Nakajima A6M2 "Rufe" seaplane, mailboat off Mili Island and Japanese cancellation 1·50 50
234 25 c. Majuro Post Office 1·50 50
235 25 c. Consolidated PBY-5A Catalina amphibian, outrigger canoe and 1951 U.S. civilian mail cancellation 1·50 50
236 45 c. "Morning Star V" (missionary ship) and 1905 Jaluit cancellation 1·75 55
237 45 c. 1906 registered cover with Jaluit cancellation 1·75 55
238 45 c. "Prinz Eitel Freiderich" (auxiliary cruiser) and 1914 German ship's post cancellation 1·75 55
239 45 c. "Scharnhorst" (cruiser) leading German Asiatic Squadron and 1914 ship's post cancellation 1·75 55

Nos. 230/5 were printed together, se-tenant, Nos. 231 and 234 forming a composite design to commemorate the 5th anniversary of Marshall Islands Independent Postal Service.

42 Launch of Apollo "11"

1989. 20th Anniv of First Manned Moon Landing. Multicoloured.

241 25 c. Type **42** 1·00 75
242 25 c. Neil Armstrong 1·00 75
243 25 c. Descent of lunar module to moon's surface 1·00 75
244 25 c. Michael Collins 1·00 75
245 25 c. Planting flag on Moon 1·00 75
246 25 c. Edwin "Buzz" Aldrin 1·00 75

43 Polish Cavalry and German Tanks

1989. History of Second World War. Multicoloured. (a) 1st issue. Invasion of Poland, 1939.

248 25 c. Type **43** 45 35

(b) 2nd issue. Sinking of H.M.S. "Royal Oak", 1939.

249 45 c. U-boat and burning battleship 75 55

(c) 3rd issue. Invasion of Finland, 1939.

250 45 c. Troops on skis and tanks 75 55

(d) 4th issue. Battle of the River Plate, 1939.

251 45 c. H.M.S. "Exeter" (cruiser) 75 55
252 45 c. H.M.S. "Ajax" (cruiser) 75 55
253 45 c. "Admiral Graf Spee" (German battleship) 75 55
254 45 c. H.M.N.Z.S. "Achilles" (cruiser) 75 55

See also Nos. 320/44, 359/84, 409/40, 458/77, 523/48 and 575/95.

44 Angel with Horn

45 Dr. Robert Goddard

1989. Christmas. Multicoloured.

255 25 c. Type **44** 70 50
256 25 c. Angel singing 70 50
257 25 c. Angel with lute 70 50
258 25 c. Angel with lyre 70 50

1989. Milestones in Space Exploration. Multicoloured.

259 45 c. Type **45** (first liquid fuel rocket launch, 1926) 90 55
260 45 c. "Sputnik 1" (first man-made satellite, 1957) 90 55
261 45 c. Rocket lifting off (first American satellite, 1958) 90 55
262 45 c. Yury Gagarin (first man in space, 1961) 90 55
263 45 c. John Glenn (first American in Earth orbit, 1962) 90 55
264 45 c. Valentina Tereshkova (first woman in space, 1963) 90 55
265 45 c. Aleksei Leonov (first space walk, 1965) 90 55
266 45 c. Edward White (first American space walk, 1965) 90 55
267 45 c. "Gemini 6" and "7" (first rendezvous in space, 1965) 90 55
268 45 c. "Luna 9" (first soft landing on the Moon, 1966) 90 55
269 45 c. "Gemini 8" (first docking in space, 1966) 90 55
270 45 c. "Venera 4" (first successful Venus probe, 1967) 90 55
271 45 c. Moon seen from "Apollo 8" (first manned orbit of Moon, 1968) 90 55
272 45 c. Neil Armstrong and U.S. flag (first man on Moon, 1969) 90 55
273 45 c. "Soyuz 11" and "Salyut 1" space station (first space station crew, 1971) 90 55
274 45 c. Lunar rover of "Apollo 15" (first manned lunar vehicle, 1971) 90 55
275 45 c. "Skylab 1" (first American space station, 1973) 90 55
276 45 c. "Pioneer 10" and Jupiter (first flight past Jupiter, 1973) 90 55
277 45 c. "Apollo" and "Soyuz" craft approaching each other (first international joint space flight, 1975) 90 55
278 45 c. "Viking 1" on Mars (first landing on Mars, 1976) 90 55
279 45 c. "Voyager 1" and Saturn's rings (first flight past Saturn, 1979) 90 55
280 45 c. "Columbia" (first space shuttle flight, 1981) 90 55
281 45 c. Satellite in outer space (first probe beyond the solar system, 1983) 90 55
282 45 c. Astronaut (first untethered space walk, 1984) 90 55
283 45 c. Launch of space shuttle "Discovery", 1988 90 55

46 White-capped Noddy

1990. Birds. Multicoloured.

284 1 c. Red-tailed tropic bird 15 10
285 5 c. Type **46** 15 10
286 9 c. Whimbrel 15 10
287 10 c. Sanderling 20 15
288 12 c. Black-naped tern 20 15
289 15 c. Wandering tattler 25 20
290 20 c. Bristle-thighed curlew 30 25
291 22 c. Greater scaup 35 30
292 23 c. Common (inscr "Northern") shoveler 35 30
293 25 c. Common (inscr "Brown") noddy 40 35
294 27 c. Sooty tern 40 35
295 28 c. Sharp-tailed sandpiper 40 35

296 29 c. Wedge-tailed shearwater 45 40
297 30 c. American (inscr "Pacific") golden plover 45 40
298 35 c. Brown booby 50 45
299 36 c. Red-footed booby 55 50
300 40 c. White tern 60 55
301 45 c. Green-winged (inscr "Common") teal 70 60
302 50 c. Great frigate bird 75 65
303 52 c. Crested tern (inscr "Great Crested Tern") 90 70
304 65 c. Mongolian (inscr "Lesser Sand") plover 1·00 85
305 75 c. Little tern 1·25 1·00
306 $1 Eastern (inscr "Pacific") reef heron 1·75 1·40
307 $2 Blue-faced (inscr "Masked") booby 3·50 2·50

47 Lodidean (coconut-palm leaf windmill)

1990. Children's Games. Multicoloured.
309 25 c. Type **47** 70 55
310 25 c. Lejonjon (juggling green coconuts) 70 55
311 25 c. Etobobo (coconut leaf musical instrument) 70 55
312 25 c. Didmakol (pandanus leaf flying-toy) 70 55

48 Penny Black

1990. 150th Anniv of the Penny Black. Multicoloured.
313 25 c. Type **48** 75 75
314 25 c. Essay of James Chalmers's cancellation 75 75
315 25 c. Stamp essay by Robert Sievier 75 75
316 25 c. Stamp essay by Charles Whiting 75 75
317 25 c. Stamp essay by George Dickinson 75 75
318 25 c. "City" medal by William Wyon (struck to commemorate Queen Victoria's first visit to City of London) 75 75

1990. History of Second World War. As T **43**. Multicoloured. (a) 5th issue. Invasions of Denmark and Norway, 1940.
320 25 c. German soldier and "Stuka" dive bombers in Copenhagen 45 35
321 25 c. Norwegian soldiers, burning building and German column 45 35

(b) 6th issue. Katyn Forest Massacre of Polish Prisoners, 1940.
322 25 c. Bound hands and grave (vert) 45 35

(c) 7th issue. Appointment of Winston Churchill as Prime Minister of Great Britain, 1940.
323 45 c. Union Jack, Churchill and war scenes 70 50

(d) 8th issue. Invasion of Low Countries, 1940.
324 25 c. Bombing of Rotterdam 45 35
325 25 c. Invasion of Belgium 45 35

(e) 9th issue. Evacuation at Dunkirk, 1940.
326 45 c. British bren-gunner on beach 70 50
327 45 c. Soldiers queueing for boats 70 50
Nos. 326/7 were issued together, se-tenant, forming a composite design.

(f) 10th issue. German Occupation of Paris, 1940.
328 45 c. German soldiers marching through Arc de Triomphe (vert) 70 50

(g) 11th issue. Battle of Mers-el-Kebir, 1940.
329 25 c. Vice-Admiral Sir James Somerville, Vice-Admiral Marcel Gensoul and British and French battleships 45 35

(h) 12th issue. The Burma Road, 1940.
330 25 c. Allied and Japanese forces (vert) 45 35

(i) 13th issue. British Bases and American Destroyers Lend-lease Agreement, 1940.
331 45 c. H.M.S. "Georgetown" (formerly U.S.S. "Maddox") 70 50
332 45 c. H.M.S. "Banff" (formerly U.S.C.G.C. "Saranac") 70 50
333 45 c. H.M.S. "Buxton" (formerly U.S.S. "Edwards") 70 50
334 45 c. H.M.S. "Rockingham" (formerly U.S.S. "Swasey") 70 50

(j) 14th issue. Battle of Britain, 1940.
335 45 c. Supermarine Spitfire Mk 1A fighters 70 50
336 45 c. Hawker Hurricane Mk 1 and Spitfire fighters 70 50
337 45 c. Messerschmitt Bf 109E fighters 70 50
338 45 c. Junkers Ju 87B-2 "Stuka" dive bomber 70 50
Nos. 335/8 were issued together, se-tenant, forming a composite design.

(k) 15th issue. Tripartite Pact, 1940.
339 45 c. Officers' caps of Germany, Italy and Japan (vert) 70 50

(l) 16th issue. Election of Franklin D. Roosevelt for Third United States Presidential Term, 1940.
340 25 c. Roosevelt (vert) 45 35

(m) 17th issue. Battle of Taranto, 1940.
341 25 c. H.M.S. "Illustrious" (aircraft carrier) 45 35
342 25 c. Fairey Swordfish bomber 45 35
343 25 c. "Andrea Doria" (Italian battleship) 45 35
344 25 c. "Conte di Cavour" (Italian battleship) 45 35
Nos. 341/4 were issued together, se-tenant, forming a composite design.

49 Pacific Green Turtles

1990. Endangered Turtles. Multicoloured.
345 25 c. Type **49** 1·10 75
346 25 c. Pacific green turtle swimming 1·10 75
347 25 c. Hawksbill turtle hatching 1·10 75
348 25 c. Hawksbill turtle swimming 1·10 75

50 Stick Chart, Outrigger Canoe and Flag

1990. 4th Anniv of Ratification of Compact of Free Association with United States.
349 **50** 25 c. multicoloured 75 45

51 Brandenburg Gate, Berlin

1990. Re-unification of Germany.
350 **51** 45 c. multicoloured 1·00 70

52 Outrigger Canoe and Stick Chart

1990. Christmas. Multicoloured.
351 25 c. Type **52** 70 50
352 25 c. Missionary preaching and "Morning Star" (missionary ship) 70 50
353 25 c. British sailors dancing 70 50
354 25 c. Electric guitar and couple dancing 70 50

53 Harvesting Breadfruit

1990. Breadfruit. Multicoloured.
355 25 c. Type **53** 70 50
356 25 c. Peeling breadfruit 70 50
357 25 c. Soaking breadfruit 70 50
358 25 c. Kneading dough 70 50

1991. History of Second World War. As T **43**. Multicoloured. (a) 18th issue. Four Freedoms Speech to U.S. Congress by President Franklin Roosevelt, 1941.
359 30 c. Freedom of Speech 50 40
360 30 c. Freedom from Want 50 40
361 30 c. Freedom of Worship 50 40
362 30 c. Freedom from Fear 50 40

(b) 19th issue. Battle of Beda Fomm, 1941.
363 30 c. Tank battle 50 40

(c) 20th issue. German Invasion of Balkans, 1941.
364 29 c. German Dornier DO-17Z bombers over Acropolis, Athens (Greece) (vert) 50 40
365 29 c. German tank and Yugoslavian Parliament building (vert) 50 40

(d) 21st issue. Sinking of the "Bismarck" (German battleship), 1941.
366 50 c. H.M.S. "Prince of Wales" (battleship) 75 60
367 50 c. H.M.S. "Hood" (battle cruiser) 75 60
368 50 c. "Bismarck" 75 60
369 50 c. Fairey Swordfish torpedo bombers 75 60

(e) 22nd issue. German Invasion of Russia, 1941.
370 30 c. German tanks 50 40

(f) 23rd issue. Declaration of Atlantic Charter by United States and Great Britain, 1941.
371 29 c. U.S.S. "Augusta" (cruiser) and Pres. Roosevelt of United States (vert) 50 40
372 29 c. H.M.S. "Prince of Wales" (battleship) and Winston Churchill (vert) 50 40
Nos. 371/2 were issued together, se-tenant, forming a composite design.

(g) 24th issue. Siege of Moscow, 1941.
373 29 c. German tanks crossing snow-covered plain 50 40

(h) 25th issue. Sinking of U.S.S. "Reuben James", 1941.
374 30 c. U.S.S. "Reuben James" (destroyer) 50 40
375 30 c. German U-boat 562 (submarine) 50 40
Nos. 374/5 were issued together, se-tenant, forming a composite design.

(i) 26th issue. Japanese Attack on Pearl Harbor, 1941.
376 50 c. American airplanes (inscr "Peal Harbor") (vert) 75 60
376b As No. 376 but inscr "Pearl Harbor" 75 60
377 50 c. Japanese dive bombers (vert) 75 60
378 50 c. U.S.S. "Arizona" (battleship) (vert) 75 60
379 50 c. "Akagi" (Japanese aircraft carrier) (vert) 75 60
Nos. 376/9 were issued together, se-tenant, forming a composite design.

(j) 27th issue. Japanese Capture of Guam, 1941.
380 29 c. Japanese troops (vert) 50 40

(k) 28th issue. Fall of Singapore to Japan, 1941.
381 29 c. Japanese soldiers with Japanese flag, Union Jack and white flag 50 40

(l) 29th issue. Formation of "Flying Tigers" (American volunteer group), 1941.
382 50 c. American Curtiss Tomahawk fighters 75 60
383 50 c. Japanese Mitsubishi Ki-21 "Sally" bombers 75 60
Nos. 382/3 were issued together, se-tenant, forming a composite design.

(m) 30th issue. Fall of Wake Island to Japan, 1941.
384 29 c. American Grumman Wildcat fighters and Japanese Mitsubishi G3M "Nell" bombers over Wake Island 50 40

54 Boeing 747 carrying "Columbia" to Launch Site

1991. Ten Years of Space Shuttle Flights. Multicoloured.
385 50 c. Type **54** 90 70
386 50 c. Orbital release of Long Duration Exposure Facility from "Challenger", 1984 90 70
387 50 c. Shuttle launch at Cape Canaveral 90 70
388 50 c. Shuttle landing at Edwards Air Force Base 90 70
Nos. 385/8 were issued together, se-tenant, the backgrounds forming a composite design.

55 "Ixora carolinensis"

1991. Native Flowers. Multicoloured.
389 52 c. Type **55** 90 70
390 52 c. Glory-bower ("Clerodendum inerme") 90 70
391 52 c. "Messerschmidia argentea" 90 70
392 52 c. "Vigna marina" 90 70

56 American Bald Eagle and Marshall Islands and U.S. Flags

1991. United States Participation in Operation Desert Storm (campaign to liberate Kuwait).
394 **56** 29 c. multicoloured 60 45

57 Red-footed Booby

1991. Birds. Multicoloured.
395 29 c. Type **57** 90 40
396 29 c. Great frigate bird (facing right) 90 40
397 29 c. Brown booby 90 40
398 29 c. White tern 90 40
399 29 c. Great frigate bird (facing left) 90 40
400 29 c. White-capped ("Black") noddy 90 40

58 Dornier Do-228

1991. Passenger Aircraft. Multicoloured.
402 12 c. Type **58** 35 20
403 29 c. Douglas DC-8 jetliner 75 50
404 50 c. Hawker Siddeley H.S.748 airliner 1·25 90
405 50 c. Saab 2000 1·25 90

59 U.N. and State Emblems and Outrigger Canoe

1991. Admission of Marshall Islands to the United Nations.
406 **59** 29 c. multicoloured 60 45

60 Dove and Glory-bower Flowers

1991. Christmas.
407 **60** 30 c. multicoloured 65 50

61 State Flag and Dove

1991. 25th Anniv of Peace Corps in Marshall Islands.
408 **61** 29 c. multicoloured 55 45

1992. History of Second World War. As T **43**. Multicoloured. (a) 31st issue. Arcadia Conference, Washington D.C., 1942.
409 29 c. Pres. Franklin Roosevelt of U.S.A., Winston Churchill of Great Britain, White House and United Nations emblem 50 40

(b) 32nd issue. Fall of Manila to Japan, 1942.
410 50 c. Japanese tank moving through Manila 75 60

(c) 33rd issue. Capture of Rabaul by Japan, 1942.
411 29 c. Japanese flag, Admiral Yamamoto, General Douglas MacArthur and U.S. flag 50 40

(d) 34th issue. Battle of the Java Sea, 1942.
412 29 c. Sinking of the "De Ruyter" (Dutch cruiser) 50 40

(e) 35th issue. Capture of Rangoon by Japan, 1942.

413 50 c. Japanese tank and soldiers in Rangoon (vert) 75 60

(f) 36th issue. Japanese Landing on New Guinea, 1942.

414 29 c. Japanese soldiers coming ashore 50 40

(g) 37th issue. Evacuation of General Douglas MacArthur from Corregidor, 1942.

415 29 c. MacArthur 50 40

(h) 38th issue. British Raid on Saint Nazaire, 1942.

416 29 c. H.M.S. "Campbeltown" (destroyer) and motor torpedo boat 50 40

(i) 39th issue. Surrender of Bataan, 1942.

417 29 c. Prisoners on "death" march (vert) 50 40

(j) 40th issue. Doolittle Raid on Tokyo, 1942.

418 50 c. North American B-25 Mitchell bomber taking off from U.S.S. "Hornet" (aircraft carrier) (vert) 75 60

(k) 41st issue. Fall of Corregidor to Japan, 1942.

419 29 c. Lt.-Gen. Jonathan Wainwright 50 40

(l) 42nd issue. Battle of the Coral Sea, 1942.

420 50 c. U.S.S. "Lexington" (aircraft carrier) and Grumman F4F-3 Wildcat fighter (inscr "U.S.S. Lexington") 75 60

420b As No. 420 but additionally inscr with aircraft name 75 60

421 50 c. Japanese Aichi D3A 1 "Val" and Nakajima B5N2 "Kate" dive bombers (wrongly inscr 'Mitsubishi A6M2 "Zero" ') 75 60

421a As No. 421 but inscr corrected 75 60

422 50 c. American Douglas TBD-1 Devastator torpedo bombers (wrongly inscr "U.S. Douglas SBD Dauntless") 75 60

422a As No. 422 but with inscr corrected 75 60

423 50 c. "Shoho" (Japanese aircraft carrier) and Mitsubishi A6M2 Zero-Sen fighters (inscr "Japanese carrier Shoho") 75 60

423a As No. 423 but additionally inscr with aircraft name 75 60

The four designs were issued together, se-tenant, each pair forming a composite design.

(m) 43rd issue. Battle of Midway, 1942.

424 50 c. "Akagi" (Japanese aircraft carrier) 75 60

425 50 c. U.S.S. "Yorktown" (aircraft carrier) 75 60

426 50 c. American Douglas SBD Dauntless dive bombers 75 60

427 50 c. Japanese Nakajima B5N2 "Kate" dive bombers 75 60

Nos. 424/7 were issued together, se-tenant, forming a composite design.

(n) 44th issue. Destruction of Lidice (Czechoslovakian village), 1942.

428 29 c. Cross and memorial at Lidice 50 40

(o) 45th issue. German Capture of Sevastopol, 1942.

429 29 c. German siege gun "Dora" (vert) 50 40

(p) 46th issue. Destruction of Convoy PQ-17, 1942.

430 29 c. British merchant ship 50 40

431 29 c. German U-boat 50 40

(q) 47th issue. Marine Landing on Guadalcanal, 1942.

432 29 c. American marines landing on beach 50 40

(r) 48th issue. Battle of Savo Island, 1942.

433 29 c. Admiral Mikawa of Japan (vert) 50 40

(s) 49th issue. Dieppe Raid, 1942.

434 29 c. Soldiers landing at Dieppe 50 40

(t) 50th issue. Battle of Stalingrad, 1942.

435 50 c. Heroes monument and burning buildings (vert) 75 60

(u) 51st issue. Battle of Eastern Solomon Islands, 1942.

436 29 c. Aircraft over U.S.S. "Enterprise" (aircraft carrier) 50 40

(v) 52nd issue. Battle of Cape Esperance, 1942.

437 50 c. American cruiser firing guns at night 75 60

(w) 53rd issue. Battle of El Alamein, 1942.

438 29 c. Gen. Bernard Montgomery of Great Britain and Gen. Erwin Rommel of Germany 50 40

(x) 54th issue. Battle of Barents Sea, 1942.

439 29 c. H.M.S. "Sheffield" (cruiser) 50 40

440 29 c. "Admiral Hipper" (German cruiser) 50 40

62 "Emlain" (bulk carrier) **63** Northern Pintail

1992. Ships flying the Marshall Islands Flag. Multicoloured.

441 29 c. Type **62** 70 50

442 29 c. "CSK Valiant" (tanker) 70 50

443 29 c. "Ionmeto" (fisheries protection vessel) 70 50

444 29 c. "Micro Pilot" (inter-island freighter) 70 50

1992. Nature Protection.

445 **63** 29 c. multicoloured 60 45

64 Tipnol (outrigger canoe) **65** Basket Making

1992. Legends of Discovery. Multicoloured.

446 50 c. Type **64** 75 75

447 50 c. "Santa Maria" (reconstruction of Columbus's flagship) 75 75

448 50 c. Constellation Argo Navis 75 75

449 50 c. Sailor and tipnol 75 75

450 50 c. Christopher Columbus and "Santa Maria" 75 75

451 50 c. Astronaut and Argo Navis constellation 75 75

1992. Handicrafts. Multicoloured.

453 29 c. Type **65** 50 40

454 29 c. Boy holding model outrigger canoe 50 40

455 29 c. Man carving boat 50 40

456 29 c. Fan making 50 40

66 Christmas Offering

1992. Christmas.

457 **66** 29 c. multicoloured 50 40

1993. History of Second World War. As T **43**. Multicoloured. (a) 55th issue. Casablanca Conference, 1943.

458 29 c. Pres. Franklin Roosevelt and Winston Churchill 50 40

(b) 56th issue. Liberation of Kharkov, 1943.

459 29 c. Russian tank in Kharkov 50 40

(c) 57th issue. Battle of the Bismarck Sea, 1943.

460 50 c. Japanese Mitsubishi A6M Zero-Sen fighters and "Arashio" (Japanese destroyer) 75 60

461 50 c. American Lockheed P-38 Lightnings and Australian Bristol Beaufighter fighters 75 60

462 50 c. "Shirayuki" (Japanese destroyer) 75 60

463 50 c. American A-20 Havoc and North American B-52 Mitchell bombers 75 60

Nos 460/63 were issued together, se-tenant, forming a composite design.

(d) 58th issue. Interception of Yamamoto, 1943.

464 50 c. Admiral Yamamoto 75 60

(e) 59th issue. Battle of Kursk, 1943.

465 29 c. German "Tiger 1" tank 50 40

466 29 c. Soviet "T-34" tank 50 40

Nos. 465/6 were issued together, se-tenant, forming a composite design.

(f) 60th issue. Allied Invasion of Sicily, 1943.

467 52 c. Gen. George Patton, Jr 85 60

468 52 c. Gen. Bernard Montgomery 85 65

469 52 c. Americans landing at Licata 85 65

470 52 c. British landing south of Syracuse 85 65

(g) 61st issue. Raids on Schweinfurt, 1943.

471 50 c. American Boeing B-17F Flying Fortress bombers and German Messerschmitt Bf 109 fighter 75 60

(h) 62nd issue. Liberation of Smolensk, 1943.

472 29 c. Russian soldier and burning buildings (vert) 50 40

(i) 63rd issue. Landing at Bougainville, 1943.

473 29 c. American Marines on beach at Empress Augusta Bay 50 40

(j) 64th issue. U.S. Invasion of Tarawa, 1943.

474 50 c. American Marines 75 60

(k) 65th issue. Teheran Allied Conference, 1943.

475 52 c. Winston Churchill of Great Britain, Pres. Franklin Roosevelt of U.S.A. and Iosif Stalin of Russia (vert) 85 65

(l) 66th issue. Battle of North Cape, 1943.

476 29 c. H.M.S. "Duke of York" (British battleship) 50 40

477 29 c. "Scharnhorst" (German battleship) 50 40

67 Atoll Butterflyfish

1993. Reef Life. Multicoloured.

478 50 c. Type **67** 90 60

479 50 c. Brick soldierfish 90 60

480 50 c. Caerulean damselfish 90 60

481 50 c. Japanese inflator-filefish 90 60

482 50 c. Arc-eyed hawkfish 90 60

483 50 c. Powder-blue surgeonfish 90 60

68 "Britannia" (full-rigged ship)

1993. Ships. Multicoloured. (a) Size 35 × 20 mm.

485 10 c. "San Jeronimo" (Spanish galleon) 10 10

486 14 c. U.S.C.G. "Cape Corwin" (fisheries patrol vessel) 15 10

487 15 c. Type **68** 20 15

488 19 c. "Micro Palm" (inter-island freighter) 25 15

489 20 c. "Eendracht" (Dirk Hartog's ship) 30 15

490 23 c. H.M.S. "Cornwallis" (sail frigate) 35 20

491 24 c. U.S.S. "Dolphin" (schooner) 40 20

492 29 c. "Morning Star I" (missionary brigantine) 45 25

493 30 c. "Rurik" (Otto von Kotzebue's brig) (inscr "Rurick") 50 25

494 32 c. "Vitoria" (Magellan's flagship) 55 25

669 32 c. As Type **68** 50 40

670 32 c. U.S.S. "Dolphin" (schooner) 50 40

671 32 c. "Morning Star I" (missionary brigantine) 50 40

672 32 c. U.S.S. "Lexington" (aircraft carrier) 50 40

673 32 c. "Micro Palm" (inter-island freighter) 50 40

674 32 c. H.M.S. "Cornwallis" (sail frigate) 50 40

675 32 c. H.M.S. "Serpent" (brig) 50 40

676 32 c. "Scarborough" (transport) 50 40

677 32 c. "San Jeronimo" (Spanish galleon) 50 40

678 32 c. "Rurik" (Otto van Kotzebue's brig) (inscr "Rurick") 50 40

679 32 c. "Nautilus" (German gunboat) 50 40

680 32 c. Fishing vessels 50 40

681 32 c. Malmel outrigger canoe 50 40

682 32 c. "Eendracht" (Dirk Hartog's ship) 50 40

683 32 c. "Nautilus" (brig) 50 40

684 32 c. "Nagara" and "Isuzu" (Japanese cruisers) 50 40

685 32 c. "Potomac" (whaling ship) 50 40

687 32 c. U.S.C.G. "Assateague" (cutter) 50 40

688 32 c. "Charles W. Morgan" (whaling ship) 50 40

689 32 c. "Victoria" (whaling ship) 50 40

690 32 c. U.S.C.G. "Cape Corwin" (fisheries patrol vessel) 50 40

691 32 c. "Equator" (schooner) 50 40

692 32 c. "Tanager" (inter-island steamer) 50 40

693 32 c. "Tole Mour" (hospital schooner) 50 40

495 35 c. "Nautilus" (German gunboat) 60 30

496 40 c. "Nautilus" (British brig) 65 30

497 45 c. "Nagara" and "Isuzu" (Japanese cruisers) 70 35

498 46 c. "Equator" (schooner) 75 35

499 50 c. U.S.S. "Lexington" (aircraft carrier) 80 40

500 52 c. H.M.S. "Serpent" (brig) 85 45

501 55 c. "Potomac" (whaling ship) 90 50

502 60 c. U.S.C.G. "Assateague" (cutter) 1·00 70

503 75 c. "Scarborough" (transport) 1·10 75

504 78 c. "Charles W. Morgan" (whaling ship) 1·25 90

505 95 c. "Tanager" (inter-island steamer) 1·40 1·00

506 $1 "Tole Mour" (hospital schooner) 1·50 1·10

507 $2.90 Fishing vessels 4·25 2·75

508 $3.00 "Victoria" (whaling ship) 4·50 3·00

(b) Size 46 × 26 mm.

509 $1 Enewetak outrigger canoe 1·50 1·00

510 $2 Jaluit outrigger canoe 4·00 3·00

511 $5 Ailuk outrigger canoe 7·00 5·00

512 $10 Racing outrigger canoes 14·00 10·00

69 Capitol Complex

1993. Inauguration of New Capitol Complex, Majuro. Multicoloured.

513 29 c. Type **69** 40 25

514 29 c. Parliament building 40 25

515 29 c. National seal (vert) 40 25

516 29 c. National flag (vert) 40 25

71 Woman with Breadfruit

1993. Marshallese Life in the 1800s. Designs adapted from sketches by Louis Choris. Multicoloured.

518 29 c. Type **71** 50 35

519 29 c. Canoes and warrior 50 35

520 29 c. Chief and islanders 50 35

521 29 c. Drummer and dancers 50 35

72 Singing Silent Night

1993. Christmas.

522 **72** 29 c. multicoloured 50 35

1994. History of Second World War. As T **43**. Multicoloured.

(a) 67th issue. Appointment of Gen. Dwight D. Eisenhower as Commander of Supreme Headquarters, Allied Expeditionary Force, 1944.

523 29 c. Eisenhower 50 40

(b) 68th issue. Invasion of Anzio, 1944.

524 50 c. Troops landing 70 60

(c) 69th issue. Lifting of Siege of Leningrad, 1944.

525 52 c. St. Isaac's Cathedral and soldier with Soviet flag 85 65

(d) 70th issue. U.S. Liberation of Marshall Islands, 1944.

526 29 c. Douglas SBD Dauntless dive bombers 50 40

(e) 71st issue. Japanese Defeat at Truk, 1944.

527 29 c. Admirals Spruance and Marc Mitscher (vert) 50 40

(f) 72nd issue. U.S. Bombing of Germany, 1944.

528 52 c. Boeing B-17 Flying Fortress bombers 85 65

(g) 73rd issue. Allied Liberation of Rome, 1944.

529 50 c. Lt.-Gen. Mark Clark and flowers in gun barrel (vert) 75 60

(h) 74th issue. Allied Landings in Normandy, 1944.

530 75 c. Airspeed A.S.51 Horsa gliders (inscr "Horsa Gliders") 1·10 80

530b As No. 530 but inscr "Horsa Gliders, Parachute Troops" 1·10 80

531 75 c. Hawker Typhoon 1B and North American P-51B Mustang fighters (wrongly inscr "U.S. P51B Mustangs, British Hurricanes") 1·10 80

531a As No. 531 but inscr corrected 1·10 80

532 75 c. German gun defences (inscr "German Gun Defenses") 1·10 80

532a As No. 523 but inscr "German Gun Defenses, Pointe du Hoc" 1·10 80

533 75 c. Allied amphibious landing 1·10 80

The four designs were issued together, se-tenant, forming a composite design.

(i) 75th issue. V-1 Bombardment of England, 1944.

534 50 c. V-1 flying bomb over River Thames 75 60

(j) 76th issue. U.S. Marines Land on Saipan, 1944.

535 29 c. U.S. and Japanese troops 50 40

(k) 77th issue. First Battle of the Philippine Sea, 1944.

536 50 c. Grumman F6F-3 Hellcat fighter 75 60

(l) 78th issue. U.S. Liberation of Guam, 1944.

537 29 c. Naval bombardment 50 40

(m) 79th issue. Warsaw Uprising, 1944.

538 50 c. Polish Home Army fighter 75 60

(n) 80th issue. Liberation of Paris, 1944.

539 50 c. Allied troops marching along Champs Elysee 75 60

(o) 81st issue. U.S. Marines Land on Peleliu, 1944.

540 29 c. Amphibious armoured tracked vehicle 50 40

(p) 82nd issue. General Douglas MacArthur's Return to Philippines, 1944.

541 52 c. McArthur and soldiers 85 65

(q) 83rd issue. Battle of Leyte Gulf, 1944.

542 52 c. American motor torpedo boat and Japanese warships 85 65

(r) 84th issue. Sinking of the "Tirpitz" (German battleship), 1944.

543 50 c. Avro Lancaster bombers 75 60

544 50 c. Tirpitz burning 75 60

(s) 85th issue. Battle of the Bulge, 1944.

545 50 c. Infantrymen 75 60

546 50 c. Tank driver and tanks 75 60

547 50 c. Pilot and aircraft 75 60

548 50 c. Lt.-Col. Creighton Abrams and Brig.-Gen. Anthony McAuliffe shaking hands 75 60

75 Footballers 76 Neil Armstrong stepping onto Moon

1994. World Cup Football Championship, U.S.A. Multicoloured.

552 50 c. Type **75** . . . . 1·40 60
553 50 c. Footballers (different) . . 1·40 60
Nos. 552/53 were issued together, se-tenant, forming a composite design.

1994. 25th Anniv of First Manned Moon Landing. Multicoloured.

554 75 c. Type **76** 95 70
555 75 c. Planting U.S. flag on Moon 95 70
556 75 c. Astronauts saluting . . . 95 70
557 75 c. Pres. John F. Kennedy and Armstrong 95 70

77 Solar System

1994. The Solar System. Multicoloured.

559 50 c. Type **77** 85 65
560 50 c. Sun 85 65
561 50 c. Moon 85 65
562 50 c. Mercury 85 65
563 50 c. Venus 85 65
564 50 c. Earth 85 65
565 50 c. Mars 85 65
566 50 c. Jupiter 85 65
567 50 c. Saturn 85 65
568 50 c. Uranus 85 65
569 50 c. Neptune 85 65
570 50 c. Pluto 85 65

79 Church and Christmas Tree (Ringo Baso)

1994. Christmas.

573 **79** 29 c. multicoloured 50 40

1995. History of Second World War. As T **43**. Multicoloured.

(a) 86th issue. Yalta Conference, 1945.

575 32 c. Iosif Stalin of U.S.S.R., Winston Churchill of Great Britain and Franklin Roosevelt of U.S.A. (vert) 55 45

(b) 87th issue. Allied Bombing of Dresden, 1945.

576 55 c. "Europe" (Meissen porcelain statuette), flames and bombers (vert) 90 70

(c) 88th issue. U.S. Marine Invasion of Iwo Jima, 1945.

577 $1 Marines planting flag on Mt. Suribachi (vert) . . . . . . 1·60 1·25

(d) 89th issue. U.S. Capture of Remagen Bridge, Germany, 1945.

578 32 c. Troops and tanks crossing bridge (vert) 55 45

(e) 90th issue. U.S. Invasion of Okinawa, 1945.

579 55 c. Soldiers throwing grenades (vert) 90 70

(f) 91st issue. Death of Franklin D. Roosevelt, 1945.

580 50 c. Funeral cortege 75 60

(g) 92nd issue. U.S. and U.S.S.R. Troops meet at Elbe, 1945.

581 32 c. American and Soviet troops 55 45

(h) 93rd issue. Capture of Berlin by Soviet Troops, 1945.

582 60 c. Soviet Marshal Georgi Zhukov and Berlin landmarks 95 75

(i) 94th issue. Allied Liberation of Concentration Camps, 1945.

583 55 c. Inmates and soldier cutting barbed-wire fence 90 70

(j) 95th issue. V-E (Victory in Europe) Day, 1945.

584 75 c. Signing of German surrender, Rheims . . . . . 1·10 80
585 75 c. Soldier kissing girl, Times Square, New York . . . . . 1·10 80
586 75 c. Victory Parade, Red Square, Moscow . . . . 1·10 80
587 75 c. Royal Family and Churchill on balcony of Buckingham Palace, London . . . . . . 1·10 80

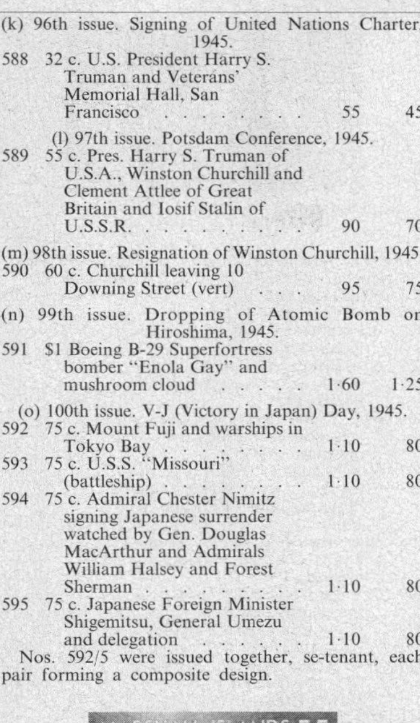

(k) 96th issue. Signing of United Nations Charter, 1945.

588 32 c. U.S. President Harry S. Truman and Veterans' Memorial Hall, San Francisco 55 45

(l) 97th issue. Potsdam Conference, 1945.

589 55 c. Pres. Harry S. Truman of U.S.A., Winston Churchill and Clement Attlee of Great Britain and Iosif Stalin of U.S.S.R. 90 70

(m) 98th issue. Resignation of Winston Churchill, 1945.

590 60 c. Churchill leaving 10 Downing Street (vert) 95 75

(n) 99th issue. Dropping of Atomic Bomb on Hiroshima, 1945.

591 $1 Boeing B-29 Superfortress bomber "Enola Gay" and mushroom cloud . . . . . 1·60 1·25

(o) 100th issue. V-J (Victory in Japan) Day, 1945.

592 75 c. Mount Fuji and warships in Tokyo Bay . . . . 1·10 80
593 75 c. U.S.S. "Missouri" (battleship) . . . . 1·10 80
594 75 c. Admiral Chester Nimitz signing Japanese surrender watched by Gen. Douglas MacArthur and Admirals William Halsey and Forest Sherman . . . . 1·10 80
595 75 c. Japanese Foreign Minister Shigemitsu, General Umezu and delegation . . . . . . 1·10 80
Nos. 592/5 were issued together, se-tenant, each pair forming a composite design.

81 Scuba Diver, Meyer's Butterflyfish and Red-tailed Surgeonfish ("Achilles Tang")

1995. Undersea World (1st series). Multicoloured.

596 55 c. Type **81** 90 70
597 55 c. Moorish idols and scuba diver 90 70
598 55 c. Pacific green turtle and anthias ("Fairy Basslet") . . 90 70
599 55 c. Anthias ("Fairy Basslet"), emperor angelfish and orange-finned anemonefish 90 70
Nos. 596/9 were issued together, se-tenant, forming a composite design.
See also Nos. 865/8.

82 U.S.S. "PT 109" (motor torpedo boat) 83 Marilyn Monroe

1995. 35th Anniv of Election of John F. Kennedy as U.S. President. Multicoloured.

600 55 c. Type **82** (Second World War command) 80 65
601 55 c. Presidential inauguration . 80 65
602 55 c. Peace corps on agricultural project in Marshall Islands . 80 65
603 55 c. U.S. airplane and warships superintending removal of Soviet missiles from Cuba . . 80 65
604 55 c. Kennedy signing Nuclear Test Ban Treaty, 1963 . . . 80 65
605 55 c. Eternal flame on Kennedy's grave, Arlington National Cemetery, Washington D.C. . 80 65

1995. 69th Birth Anniv of Marilyn Monroe (actress). Multicoloured.

606 75 c. Type **83** . . . . 1·10 80
607 75 c. Monroe (face value top right) . . . . 1·10 80
608 75 c. Monroe (face value bottom left) . . . . 1·10 80
609 75 c. Monroe (face value bottom right) . . . . 1·10 80

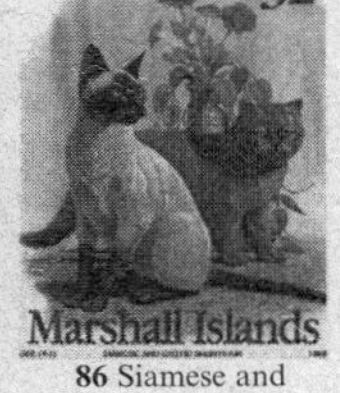

85 "Mir" (Soviet space station) 86 Siamese and Exotic Shorthair

1995. Docking of Atlantis with "Mir" Space Station (611/12) and 20th Anniv of "Apollo"–"Soyuz" Space Link (613/14). Multicoloured.

611 75 c. Type **85** . . . . 1·10 80
612 75 c. "Atlantis" (U.S. space shuttle) . . . . 1·10 80
613 75 c. "Apollo" (U.S. spacecraft) . . . . 1·10 80
614 75 c. "Soyuz" (Soviet spacecraft) 1·10 80
Nos. 611/14 were issued together, se-tenant, forming a composite design.

1995. Cats. Multicoloured.

615 32 c. Type **86** 55 45
616 32 c. American shorthair tabby and red Persian 55 45
617 32 c. Maine coon and Burmese . 55 45
618 32 c. Himalayan and Abyssinian 55 45

87 Sailfish and Tuna

1995. Pacific Game Fish. Multicoloured.

619 60 c. Type **87** . . . . 1·00 75
620 60 c. Albacores . . . . 1·00 75
621 60 c. Wahoo . . . . 1·00 75
622 60 c. Blue marlin . . . . . . 1·00 75
623 60 c. Yellow-finned tunas . . . 1·00 75
624 60 c. Giant trevally . . . . . 1·00 75
625 60 c. Dolphin (fish) . . . . . 1·00 75
626 60 c. Short-finned mako . . . 1·00 75
Nos. 619/26 were issued together, se-tenant, forming a composite design.

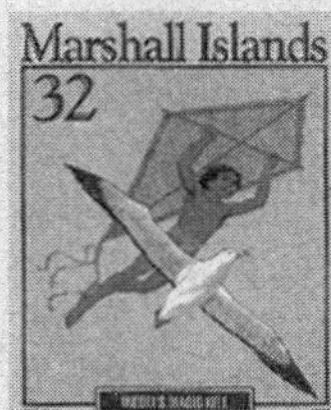

88 Inedel's Magic Kite 91 Shepherds gazing at Sky

1995. Folk Legends (1st series). Multicoloured.

627 32 c. Type **88** 60 45
628 32 c. Lijebake rescues her granddaughter 60 45
629 32 c. Jebro's mother invents the sail 60 45
630 32 c. Limajnon escapes to the moon 60 45
See also Nos. 727/30 and 861/4.

1995. Christmas.

633 **91** 32 c. multicoloured 45 25

92 Messerschmit Me 262-Ia Schwalbe 93 Rabin

1995. Jet Fighters. Multicoloured.

634 32 c. Type **92** 50 40
635 32 c. Gloster Meteor F Mk 8 . . 50 40
636 32 c. Lockheed F-80 Shooting Star 50 40
637 32 c. North American F-86 Sabre 50 40
638 32 c. F9F-2 Panther 50 40
639 32 c. Mikoyan Gurevich MiG-15 50 40
640 32 c. North American F-100 Super Sabre 50 40
641 32 c. Convair TF-102A Delta Dagger 50 40
642 32 c. Lockheed F-104 Starfighter 50 40
643 32 c. Mikoyan Gurevich MiG-21 MT 50 40
644 32 c. F8U Crusader 50 40
645 32 c. Republic F-105 Thunderchief 50 40
646 32 c. Saab J35 Draken 50 40
647 32 c. Fiat G-91Y 50 40
648 32 c. McDonnell Douglas F-4 Phantom II 50 40
649 32 c. Saab JA 37 Viggen . . . 50 40
650 32 c. Dassault Mirage F1C . . 50 40
651 32 c. Grumman F-14 Tomcat . . 50 40
652 32 c. F-15 Eagle 50 40
653 32 c. General Dynamics F-16 Fighting Falcon 50 40
654 32 c. Panavia Tornado F Mk 3 . 50 40
655 32 c. Sukhoi Su-27UB 50 40
656 32 c. Dassault Mirage 2000C . . 50 40
657 32 c. Hawker Siddeley Sea Harrier FRS.MK1 . . . . . 50 40
658 32 c. F-117 Nighthawk 50 40

1995. Yitzhak Rabin (Israeli Prime Minister) Commemoration.

659 **93** 32 c. multicoloured 45 35

95 Blue-grey Noddy

1996. Birds. Multicoloured.

661 32 c. Type **95** 70 55
662 32 c. Spectacled ("Gray-backed") tern 70 55
663 32 c. Blue-faced ("Masked") booby 70 55
664 32 c. Black-footed albatross . . 70 55

96 Cheetah

1996. Big Cats. Multicoloured.

665 55 c. Type **96** 90 70
666 55 c. Tiger 90 70
667 55 c. Lion 90 70
668 55 c. Jaguar 90 70

97 5 l. Stamp

1996. Centenary of Modern Olympic Games. Designs reproducing 1896 Greek Olympic stamps. Multicoloured.

694 60 c. Type **97** 90 70
695 60 c. 60 l. stamp 90 70
696 60 c. 40 l. stamp 90 70
697 60 c. 1 d. stamp 90 70

98 Undersea Eruptions form Islands 99 Presley

1996. History of Marshall Islands. Multicoloured.

698 55 c. Type **98** 75 60
699 55 c. Coral reefs grow around islands 75 60
700 55 c. Storm-driven birds carry seeds to atolls 75 60
701 55 c. First human inhabitants arrive, 1500 B.C. 75 60
702 55 c. Spanish explorers discover islands, 1527 . . . . . . 75 60
703 55 c. John Marshall charts islands, 1788 . . . . 75 60
704 55 c. German Protectorate, 1885 . . . . 75 60
705 55 c. Japanese soldier on beach, 1914 . . . . 75 60
706 55 c. American soldiers liberate islands, 1944 . . . . . . 75 60
707 55 c. Evacuation of Bikini Atoll for nuclear testing, 1946 . . 75 60
708 55 c. Marshall Islands becomes United Nations Trust Territory, 1947 . . . . . 75 60
709 55 c. People and national flag (independence, 1986) . . . 75 60

1996. 40th Anniv of Elvis Presley's First Number One Hit Record "Heartbreak Hotel".

710 **99** 32 c. multicoloured 50 40

101 Dean 102 1896 Quadricycle

1996. 65th Birth Anniv of James Dean (actor).
712 **101** 32 c. multicoloured 50 40

1996. Centenary of Ford Motor Vehicle Production. Multicoloured.
713 60 c. Type **102** 80 60
714 60 c. 1903 Model A Roadster . . 80 60
715 60 c. 1909 Model T touring car . 80 60
716 60 c. 1929 Model A station wagon 80 60
717 60 c. 1955 "Thunderbird" . . . 80 60
718 60 c. 1964 "Mustang" convertible 80 60
719 60 c. 1995 "Explorer" 80 60
720 60 c. 1996 "Taurus" 80 60

103 Evacuees boarding "L.S.T. 1108" (tank landing ship)

1996. 50th Anniv of Operation Crossroads (nuclear testing) at Bikini Atoll. Multicoloured.
721 32 c. + 8 c. Type **103** 60 60
722 32 c. + 8 c. U.S. Navy preparation of site 60 60
723 32 c. + 8 c. Explosion of "Able" (first test) 60 60
724 32 c. + 8 c. Explosion of "Baker" (first underwater test) . . . 60 60
725 32 c. + 8 c. Ghost fleet (targets) 60 60
726 32 c. + 8 c. Bikinian family . . 60 60

1996. Folk Legends (2nd series). As T **88**. Multicoloured.
727 32 c. Letao gives gift of fire . . 50 40
728 32 c. Mennin Jobwodda flying on giant bird 50 40
729 32 c. Koko chasing Letao in canoe 50 40
730 32 c. Mother and girl catching Kouj (octopus) to cook . . . 50 40

104 Pennsylvania Railroad Class K4, U.S.A.

1996. Steam Railway Locomotives. Multicoloured.
731 55 c. Type **104** 75 75
732 55 c. Big Boy, U.S.A. 75 75
733 55 c. Class A4 "Mallard", Great Britain 75 75
734 55 c. Class 242, Spain 75 75
735 55 c. Class 01 No. 052, Germany 75 75
736 55 c. Class 691 No. 031, Italy . 75 75
737 55 c. "Royal Hudson", Canada . 75 75
738 55 c. "Evening Star", Great Britain 75 75
739 55 c. Class 520, South Australia . 75 75
740 55 c. Class 232.U.2, France . . 75 75
741 55 c. Class QJ "Advance Forward", China 75 75
742 55 c. Class C62 "Swallow", Japan 75 75

105 Stick Chart, Outrigger Canoe and Flag

1996. 10th Anniv of Ratification of Compact of Free Association with U.S.A.
744 **105** $3 multicoloured . . . . . 4·50 3·50

106 "Madonna and Child with Four Saints" (detail, Rosso Fiorentino)

1996. Christmas.
745 **106** 32 c. multicoloured 50 40

MINIMUM PRICE

The minimum price quoted is 10p which represents a handling charge rather than a basis for valuing common stamps. For further notes about prices see introductory pages.

107 Curtiss JN-4 "Jenny"

1996. Biplanes. Multicoloured.
746 32 c. Type **107** 50 40
747 32 c. SPAD XIII 50 40
748 32 c. Albatros 50 40
749 32 c. De Havilland D.H.4 Liberty 50 40
750 32 c. Fokker Dr-1 . . . . . . 50 40
751 32 c. Sopwith Camel 50 40
752 32 c. Martin MB-2 . . . . . . 50 40
753 32 c. Martin MB-3A Tommy . . 50 40
754 32 c. Curtiss TS-1 . . . . . . 50 40
755 32 c. P-1 Hawk 50 40
756 32 c. Boeing PW-9 . . . . . . 50 40
757 32 c. Douglas O-2-H 50 40
758 32 c. LB-5 Pirate 50 40
759 32 c. O2U-1 Corsair 50 40
760 32 c. Curtiss F8C Helldiver . . 50 40
761 32 c. Boeing F4B-4 . . . . . . 50 40
762 32 c. J6B Gerfalcon 50 40
763 32 c. Martin BM 50 40
764 32 c. FF-1 Fifi 50 40
765 32 c. C.R.32 Cricket 50 40
766 32 c. Polikarpov I-15 Gull . . . 50 40
767 32 c. Fairey Swordfish 50 40
768 32 c. Aichi D1A2 . . . . 50 40
769 32 c. Grumman F3F 50 40
770 32 c. SOC-3 Seagull 50 40

108 Fan-making

1996. Traditional Crafts. Multicoloured. Self-adhesive gum (780, 782); ordinary or self-adhesive gum (others).
771 32 c. Type **108** 50 40
772 32 c. Boys sailing model outrigger canoes (country name at right) 50 40
773 32 c. Carving canoes 50 40
774 32 c. Weaving baskets (country name at right) 50 40
780 32 c. As No. 772 but with country name at left 55 45
782 32 c. As No. 774 but with country name at left 55 45

110 "Rocking '50s"

1997. 20th Death Anniv of Elvis Presley (entertainer). Different portraits. Multicoloured.
784 32 c. Type **110** 55 45
785 32 c. "Soaring '60s" 55 45
786 32 c. "Sensational '70s" 55 45

111 Kabua **113** St. Andrew

1997. President Amata Kabua Commemoration. Multicoloured.
787 32 c. Type **111** 50 40
788 60 c. As Type **111** but inscr in English at left and right and in Marshallese at foot . . . . 1·00 75

1997. Easter. 140th Anniv of Introduction of Christianity to the Marshall Islands. The Twelve Disciples. Multicoloured.
790 60 c. Type **113** 90 70
791 60 c. St. Matthew 90 70
792 60 c. St. Philip 90 70
793 60 c. St. Simon 90 70
794 60 c. St. Thaddeus 90 70
795 60 c. St. Thomas 90 70
796 60 c. St. Bartholomew 90 70
797 60 c. St. John 90 70
798 60 c. St. James the Lesser . . . 90 70
799 60 c. St. James the Greater . . 90 70
800 60 c. St. Paul 90 70
801 60 c. St. Peter 90 70

114 Immigrants arriving at Ellis Island, New York, 1900

1997. The Twentieth Century (1st series). "Decade of New Possibilities, 1900–1909". Multicoloured.
803 60 c. Type **114** 90 70
804 60 c. Chinese and Dowager Empress Ci Xi, 1900 (Boxer Rebellion) 90 70
805 60 c. George Eastman (inventor of box camera) photographing family, 1900 . . . . . . 90 70
806 60 c. Walter Reed (discoverer of yellow fever transmission by mosquito), 1900 . . . . . 90 70
807 60 c. Sigmund Freud (pioneer of psychoanalysis) (publication of "Interpretation of Dreams", 1900) 90 70
808 60 c. Guglielmo Marconi sending first transatlantic wireless message, 1901 . . . . . . 90 70
809 60 c. Enrico Caruso (opera singer) (first award of Gold Disc for one million record sales, 1903) 90 70
810 60 c. Wright Brothers' Flyer I (first powered flight, Kitty Hawk, 1903) 90 70
811 60 c. Albert Einstein and formula (development of Theory of Relativity, 1905) 90 70
812 60 c. White ensign and H.M.S. "Dreadnought" (battleship), 1906 . . . . 90 70
813 60 c. San Francisco earthquake, 1906 . . . . 90 70
814 60 c. Mohandas Gandhi and protestors, Johannesburg, South Africa, 1906 . . . . . 90 70
815 60 c. Pablo Picasso and "Les Demoiselles d'Avignon", 1907 . . . . 90 70
816 60 c. First Paris–Peking motor car race, 1907 . . . . 90 70
817 60 c. Masjik-i-Salaman oil field, Persia, 1908 . . . . 90 70

See also Nos. 872/86, 948/62 and 975//89.

115 Deng Xiaoping

1997. Deng Xiaoping (Chinese statesman) Commemoration.
818 **115** 60 c. multicoloured 85 65

116 German Marshall Islands 1899 3 pf. Stamp

1997. "Pacific 97" International Stamp Exhibition, San Francisco. Centenary of Marshall Islands Postage Stamps. Multicoloured.
819 50 c. Type **116** 70 70
820 50 c. German Marshall Islands 1899 5 pf. stamp 70 70
821 50 c. German Marshall Islands 1897 10 pf. stamp 70 70
822 50 c. German Marshall Islands 1897 20 pf. stamp 70 70
823 50 c. Unissued German Marshall Islands 25 pf. stamp 70 70
824 50 c. Unissued German Marshall Islands 50 pf. stamp 70 70

117 Curlew on Seashore

1997. The Bristle-thighed Curlew. Multicoloured.
826 16 c. Type **117** 30 20
827 16 c. Flying 30 20
828 16 c. Running 30 20
829 16 c. Standing on branch . . . 30 20

119 Pacific Arts Festival Canoe, Enewetak

1997. Traditional Outrigger Canoes. Multicoloured.
831 32 c. Type **119** 55 45
832 32 c. Kor Kor racing canoes . . 55 45
833 32 c. Large voyaging canoe, Jaluit 55 45
834 32 c. Sailing canoe, Ailuk . . . 55 45

120 Douglas C-54 Skymaster Transport

1997. Aircraft of United States Air Force. Multicoloured.
835 32 c. Type **120** 50 40
836 32 c. Boeing B-36 Peacemaker . 50 40
837 32 c. North American F-86 Sabre jet fighter 50 40
838 32 c. Boeing B-47 Stratojet jet bomber 50 40
839 32 c. Douglas C-124 Globemaster II transport 50 40
840 32 c. Lockheed C-121 Constellation 50 40
841 32 c. Boeing B-52 Stratofortress jet bomber 50 40
842 32 c. North American F-100 Super Sabre jet fighter . . . 50 40
843 32 c. Lockheed F-104 Starfighter jet fighter 50 40
844 32 c. Lockheed C-130 Hercules transport 50 40
845 32 c. Republic F-105 Thunderchief jet fighter . . . 50 40
846 32 c. KC-135 Stratotanker . . . 50 40
847 32 c. Convair B-58 Hustler jet bomber 50 40
848 32 c. McDonnell Douglas F-4 Phantom II jet fighter . . . 50 40
849 32 c. Northrop T-38 Talon trainer 50 40
850 32 c. Lockheed C-141 StarLifter jet transport 50 40
851 32 c. General Dynamics F-111 Aardvark jet fighter 50 40
852 32 c. SR-71 "Blackbird" 50 40
853 32 c. Lockheed C-5 Galaxy jet transport 50 40
854 32 c. A-10 Thunderbolt II bomber 50 40
855 32 c. F-15 Eagle fighter 50 40
856 32 c. General Dynamics F-16 Fighting Falcon jet fighter . . 50 40
857 32 c. Lockheed F-117 "Nighthawk" Stealth bomber 50 40
858 32 c. B-2 Spirit 50 40
859 32 c. C-17 Globemaster III transport 50 40

121 U.S.S. "Constitution"

1997. Bicentenary of Launch of U.S.S. "Constitution" (frigate).
860 **121** 32 c. multicoloured 50 40

1997. Folk Legends (3rd series). As T **88**. Multicoloured.
861 32 c. The Large Pool of Mejit . 55 45
862 32 c. The Beautiful Woman of Kwajalein 55 45
863 32 c. Sharks and Lowakalle Reef 55 45
864 32 c. The Demon of Adrie . . . 55 45

1997. Undersea World (2nd series). As T **81**. Multicoloured.
865 60 c. Watanabe's angelfish, blue-finned trevallys ("Bluefin Jack"), grey reef shark and scuba diver 95 75
866 60 c. Scuba diver, anchor and racoon butterflyfish 95 75
867 60 c. Lionfish and flame angelfish 95 75
868 60 c. Square-spotted anthias ("Fairy Basslet"), anchor, scuba diver with torch and orange-finned anemonefish . 95 75

Nos. 865/8 were issued together, se-tenant, forming a composite design.

122 Diana, Princess of Wales, aged 20

1997. Diana, Princess of Wales Commemoration. Multicoloured.

869 60 c. Type **122** . . . . 1·00 75
870 60 c. Wearing pearl drop earrings (aged 27) . . . . 1·00 75
871 60 c. Wearing pearl choker (aged 36) . . . . 1·00 75

123 Flags and Suffragettes

1997. The Twentieth Century (2nd series). "Decade of Revolution and Great War, 1910–1919". Mult.

872 60 c. Type **123** 75 55
873 60 c. Nobel Prize medal, Ernest Rutherford and diagram of atom, 1911 . . . . 75 55
874 60 c. Sun Yat-Sen (Chinese Revolution, 1911–12) 75 55
875 60 c. Sinking of the "Titanic" (liner), 1912 . . . . 75 55
876 60 c. Igor Stravinsky (composer) and score of "The Rite of Spring", 1913 . . . . 75 55
877 60 c. Building motor car (introduction of assembly line construction of motor vehicles by Ford Motor Company), 1913 . . . . 75 55
878 60 c. Countess Sophie Chotek and Archduke Franz Ferdinand of Austria, 1914 (assassination in Sarajevo leads to First World War) 75 55
879 60 c. Torpedo striking "Lusitania" (liner), 1915 . . 75 55
880 60 c. Battle of Verdun, 1916 . . 75 55
881 60 c. Patrick Pearse and proclamation of Irish Republic (Easter Rebellion, 1916) . . 75 55
882 60 c. Western wall, Jerusalem (Balfour Declaration of Jewish Homeland, 1917) 75 55
883 60 c. "Aurora" (cruiser) signals start of Russian Revolution, 1917 . . . . 75 55
884 60 c. Biplanes and "Red" Baron Manfred von Richthofen (fighter pilot), 1918 . . . . 75 55
885 60 c. Armed revolutionaries, Berlin, 1918 . . . . 75 55
886 60 c. Meeting of heads of state (Treaty of Versailles, 1919) . 75 55

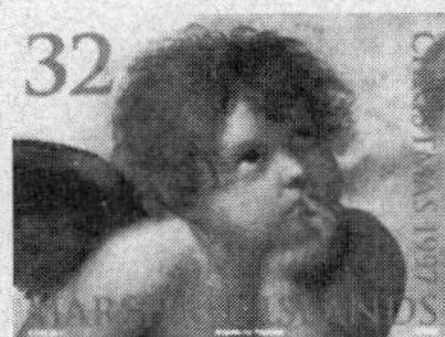

124 Cherub

1997. Christmas. Details of "Sistine Madonna" by Raphael. Multicoloured.

887 32 c. Type **124** 45 35
888 32 c. Cherub resting head on folded arms 45 35

125 U.S.S. "Alabama" (battleship), 1942

1997. Ships named after U.S. States. Multicoloured.

889 20 c. Type **125** 30 20
890 20 c. U.S.S. "Alaska" (cruiser), 1869, and junk 30 20
891 20 c. U.S.S. "Arizona" (battleship), 1916 . . . . . 30 20
892 20 c. U.S.S. "Arkansas" (battleship), 1912 . . . . . 30 20
893 20 c. U.S.S. "California" (cruiser), 1974 . . . . . . 30 20
894 20 c. U.S.S. "Colorado" (battleship), 1921, and landing craft 30 20
895 20 c. U.S.S. "Connecticut" (gunboat), 1776, with fleet . . 30 20
896 20 c. U.S.S. "Delaware" (ship of the line), 1828 . . . . . . 30 20
897 20 c. U.S.S. "Florida" (cruiser), 1967 . . . . 30 20
898 20 c. U.S.S. "Georgia" (battleship), 1906 . . . . . 30 20
899 20 c. U.S.S. "Honolulu" (cruiser), 1938 . . . . 30 20
900 20 c. U.S.S. "Idaho" (battleship), 1919 . . . . 30 20
901 20 c. U.S.S. "Illinois" (battleship), 1901 . . . . . 30 20
902 20 c. U.S.S. "Indiana" (battleship), 1895 . . . . . 30 20
903 20 c. U.S.S. "Iowa" (battleship), 1943 . . . . 30 20
904 20 c. U.S.S. "Kansas" (battleship), 1907 . . . . . 30 20
905 20 c. U.S.S. "Kentucky" (battleship), 1900 . . . . . 30 20
906 20 c. U.S.S. "Louisiana" (frigate), 1812 . . . . . . 30 20
907 20 c. U.S.S. "Maine" (battleship), 1895 . . . . 30 20
908 20 c. U.S.S. "Maryland" (frigate), 1799 . . . . . . 30 20
909 20 c. U.S.S. "Massachusetts" (battleship), 1942 . . . . . 30 20
910 20 c. U.S.S. "Michigan" (paddle gunboat), 1843 . . . . . . 30 20
911 20 c. U.S.S. "Minnesota" (corvette), 1857 . . . . . . 30 20
912 20 c. U.S.S. "Mississippi" (paddle gunboat), 1841, and junk . . 30 20
913 20 c. U.S.S. "Missouri" (battleship), 1944, in Tokyo Bay 30 20
914 20 c. U.S.S. "Montana" (battleship), 1908 . . . . . 30 20
915 20 c. U.S.S. "Nebraska" (battleship), 1907 . . . . . 30 20
916 20 c. U.S.S. "Nevada" (battleship), 1916, at Pearl Harbor 30 20
917 20 c. U.S.S. "New Hampshire" (battleship), 1908, and Statue of Liberty 30 20
918 20 c. U.S.S. "New Jersey" (battleship), 1943 . . . . . 30 20
919 20 c. U.S.S. "New Mexico" (battleship), 1918, in Tokyo Bay 30 20
920 20 c. U.S.S. "New York" (frigate), 1800, and felucca . 30 20
921 20 c. U.S.S. "North Carolina" (battleship), 1941 . . . . . 30 20
922 20 c. U.S.S. "North Dakota" (battleship), 1910 . . . . . 30 20
923 20 c. U.S.S. "Ohio" (ship of the line), 1838 . . . . 30 20
924 20 c. U.S.S. "Oklahoma" (battleship), 1916 . . . . . 30 20
925 20 c. U.S.S. "Oregon" (battleship), 1896 . . . . . 30 20
926 20 c. U.S.S. "Pennsylvania" (battleship), 1905 . . . . . 30 20
927 20 c. U.S.S. "Rhode Island" (paddle gunboat), 1861 . . . 30 20
928 20 c. U.S.S. "South Carolina" (frigate), 1783 . . . . . . 30 20
929 20 c. U.S.S. "South Dakota" (battleship), 1942 . . . . . 30 20
930 20 c. U.S.S. "Tennessee" (battleship), 1906 . . . . . 30 20
931 20 c. U.S.S. "Texas" (battleship), 1914 . . . . 30 20
932 20 c. U.S.S. "Utah" (battleship), 1911 . . . . 30 20
933 20 c. U.S.S. "Vermont" (battleship), 1907 . . . . . 30 20
934 20 c. U.S.S. "Virginia" (schooner), 1798 . . . . . . 30 20
935 20 c. U.S.S. "Washington" (battleship), 1941 . . . . . 30 20
936 20 c. U.S.S. "West Virginia" (battleship), 1923 . . . . . 30 20
937 20 c. U.S.S. "Wisconsin" (battleship), 1944 . . . . . 30 20
938 20 c. U.S.S. "Wyoming" (monitor), 1902 . . . . . . 30 20

Dates given are those of either launch or commission.

128 Presley

1998. 30th Anniv of First Television Special by Elvis Presley (entertainer). Multicoloured.

941 32 c. Type **128** 45 35
942 32 c. Presley in black leather jacket 45 35
943 32 c. Presley in white suit in front of "ELVIS" in lights 45 35

129 Chiragra Spider Conch ("Lambis chiragra")

1998. Sea Shells. Multicoloured.

944 32 c. Type **129** 50 40
945 32 c. Fluted giant clam ("Tridacna squamosa") . . . 50 40
946 32 c. Adusta murex ("Chicoreus brunneus") 50 40
947 32 c. Golden cowrie ("Cypraea aurantium") 50 40

130 Family listening to Radio

1998. The Twentieth Century (3rd series). "Decade of Optimism and Disillusionment, 1920–1929". Multicoloured.

948 60 c. Type **130** 75 55
949 60 c. Leaders from Japan, United States, France, Great Britain and Italy (Washington Conference, 1920) 75 55
950 60 c. Ludwig Mies van der Rohe (architect), 1922 . . . . . . 75 55
951 60 c. Mummiform coffin of Tutankhamun (discovery of tomb, 1922) 75 55
952 60 c. Workers from U.S.S.R., 1923 (emergence of U.S.S.R. as communist state) 75 55
953 60 c. Kemal Ataturk (first president of modern Turkey, 1923) (break-up of Turkish Empire) 75 55
954 60 c. Bix Beiderbecke (trumpeter) and flappers (dancers), 1924 (Jazz Age) 75 55
955 60 c. Robert Goddard demonstrates first liquid-propelled rocket, 1926 . . . 75 55
956 60 c. Poster for "The Jazz Singer" (second talking picture, 1926) 75 55
957 60 c. Benito Mussolini assumes total power in Italy, 1926 . . 75 55
958 60 c. Explosive glare and Leonardo da Vinci's "Proportion of Man" (Big Bang Theory of beginning of Universe, 1927) 75 55
959 60 c. Sir Alexander Fleming discovers penicillin, 1928 . . 75 55
960 60 c. John Logie Baird invents television, 1926 . . . . . 75 55
961 60 c. Airship "Graf Zeppelin" above Mt. Fuji, Japan (first round the world flight, 1929) . 75 55
962 60 c. U.S. stock market crash, 1929 (economic depression) . 75 55

131 Pahi Sailing Canoe, Tuamotu Archipelago

1998. Canoes of the Pacific. Multicoloured.

963 32 c. Type **131** 45 35
964 32 c. Maori war canoe, New Zealand 45 35
965 32 c. Wa'a Kaukahi fishing canoe, Hawaii 45 35
966 32 c. Amatasi sailing canoe, Samoa 45 35
967 32 c. Ndrua sailing canoe, Fiji Islands 45 35
968 32 c. Tongiaki voyaging canoe, Tonga 45 35
969 32 c. Tipairua travelling canoe, Tahiti 45 35
970 32 c. Walap sailing canoe, Marshall Islands 45 35

132 Douglas C-54 Skymaster Transport

1998. 50th Anniv of Berlin Airlift (relief of Berlin during Soviet blockade). Multicoloured.

971 60 c. Type **132** 75 55
972 60 c. Avro Type 685 York transport 75 55
973 60 c. Crowd and building . . . 75 55
974 60 c. Crowd 75 55

Nos. 971/4 were issued together, se-tenant, forming a composite design.

133 Soup Kitchens, 1930 (depression)

1998. The Twentieth Century (4th series). "Decade of the Great Depression, 1930–1939". Multicoloured.

975 60 c. Type **133** 75 55
976 60 c. Ernest Lawrence and first cyclotron, 1931 (splitting of atom) 75 55
977 60 c. Forced collectivization of farms in Soviet Union, 1932 (Stalin era) 75 55
978 60 c. Torchlight Parade celebrates rise of Hitler to power, 1933 (fascism) 75 55
979 60 c. Dneproges Dam on Dnepr River, 1933 (harnessing of nature) 75 55
980 60 c. Streamlined locomotive "Zephyr" (record-breaking run, Denver to Chicago, 1934) 75 55
981 60 c. Douglas DC-3 airliner (first all-metal airliner, 1936) . . . 75 55
982 60 c. Pablo Picasso (artist) and "Guernica" (German bombing during Spanish Civil War, 1937) 75 55
983 60 c. "Hindenburg" (airship disaster), 1937 (media reporting) 75 55
984 60 c. Families fleeing ruins (Japanese assault on Nanjing, 1937) 75 55
985 60 c. Neville Chamberlain declares "Peace in our Time", 1938 (appeasement) 75 55
986 60 c. Chester Carlson (invention of xerography, 1938) 75 55
987 60 c. Jew and Star of David (Kristallnacht (Nazi violence against Jews), 1938) 75 55
988 60 c. Junkers "Stuka" bombers over Poland, 1939 (start of Second World War) 75 55
989 60 c. Audience (premiere of "Gone with the Wind", 1939) (movies) 75 55

134 Coronation of Tsar Nicholas II, 1896

1998. 80th Death Anniv of Tsar Nicholas II and his Family. Multicoloured.

990 60 c. Type **134** 75 55
991 60 c. "Varyag" (cruiser) and Tsar (Russo–Japanese war, 1904–05) 75 55
992 60 c. Troops firing on crowd, Tsar and October manifesto, 1905 . 75 55
993 60 c. Peasant sowing, Tsar and Rasputin, 1905 . . . . . . 75 55
994 60 c. Mounted troops, Tsar and Nicholas II at strategy meeting, 1915 . . . . 75 55
995 60 c. Abdication, Tsar and Ipateva House, Ekaterinburg, 1917 . . . . 75 55

135 Babe Ruth

1998. 50th Death Anniv of Babe Ruth (baseball player).

997 **135** 132 c. multicoloured . . . 50 40

136 NC-4

1998. Aircraft of United States Navy. Mult.

998 32 c. Type **136** 45 35
999 32 c. Consolidated PBY-5 Catalina flying boat 45 35
1000 32 c. TBD Devastator 45 35
1001 32 c. SB2U Vindicator 45 35
1002 32 c. Grumman F4F Wildcat fighter 45 35
1003 32 c. Vought-Sikorsky OS2U Kingfisher seaplane 45 35
1004 32 c. Douglas SBD Dauntless bomber 45 35
1005 32 c. Chance Vought F4U Corsair fighter 45 35
1006 32 c. Curtiss SB2C Helldiver bomber 45 35
1007 32 c. Lockheed PV-1 Ventura bomber 45 35
1008 32 c. Grumman TBM Avenger bomber 45 35
1009 32 c. Grumman F6F Hellcat fighter 45 35
1010 32 c. PB4Y-2 Privateer 45 35
1011 32 c. A-1J Skyraider 45 35
1012 32 c. McDonnell F2H-2P Banshee 45 35
1013 32 c. F9F-2B Panther 45 35
1014 32 c. P5M Marlin 45 35
1015 32 c. F-8 Crusader 45 35
1016 32 c. McDonnell Douglas F-4 Phantom II fighter 45 35
1017 32 c. A-6 Intruder 45 35
1018 32 c. Lockheed P-3 Orion reconnaissance 45 35
1019 32 c. Vought A-70 Corsair II . 45 35
1020 32 c. Douglas A-4 Skyhawk bomber 45 35
1021 32 c. S-3 Viking 45 35
1022 32 c. F/A-18 Hornet 45 35

137 Classic Six, 1912

1998. Chevrolet Vehicles. Multicoloured.

1023 60 c. Type **137** 75 55
1024 60 c. Sport Roadster, 1931 . . 75 55
1025 60 c. Special Deluxe, 1941 . . 75 55
1026 60 c. Cameo Carrier Fleetside, 1955 . . . . 75 55
1027 60 c. Corvette, 1957 . . . . . 75 55
1028 60 c. Bel Air, 1957 . . . . . . 75 55
1029 60 c. Camaro, 1967 . . . . . . 75 55
1030 60 c. Chevelle SS 454, 1970 . . 75 55

138 Letter "A" and Pres. Amata Kabua

1998. Marshallese Alphabet and Language. Mult.

1031 33 c. Type **138** 45 35
1032 33 c. Letter "A" and woman weaving 45 35
1033 33 c. Letter "B" and butterfly . 45 35
1034 33 c. Letter "D" and woman wearing garland of flowers . 45 35
1035 33 c. Letter "E" and fish . . . 45 35
1036 33 c. Letter "I" and couple in front of rainbow 45 35
1037 33 c. Letter "J" and woven mat 45 35
1038 33 c. Letter "K" and Government House 45 35
1039 33 c. Letter "L" and night sky . 45 35
1040 33 c. Letter "L" and red-tailed tropicbird 45 35
1041 33 c. Letter "M" and bread-fruit 45 35
1042 33 c. Letter "M" and arrowroot plant 45 35
1043 33 c. Letter "N" and coconut tree 45 35
1044 33 c. Letter "N" and wave . . 45 35
1045 33 c. Letter "N" and shark . . 45 35
1046 33 c. Letter "O" and fisherman 45 35
1047 33 c. Letter "O" and tattooed woman 45 35
1048 33 c. Letter "O" and lionfish . 45 35
1049 33 c. Letter "P" and visitor's hut 45 35
1050 33 c. Letter "R" and whale . . 45 35
1051 33 c. Letter "T" and outrigger sailing canoe 45 35
1052 33 c. Letter "U" and fire . . . 45 35
1053 33 c. Letter "U" and whale's fin 45 35
1054 33 c. Letter "W" and woven leaf sail 45 35

139 Trust Company of the Marshall Islands Offices, 1998

1998. New Buildings. Multicoloured.

1055 33 c. Type **139** 45 35
1056 33 c. Embassy of the People's Republic of China, 1996 . . 45 35
1057 33 c. Outrigger Marshall Islands Resort, 1996 . . . . 45 35

140 Midnight Angel

1998. Christmas.

1058 **140** 33 c. multicoloured . . . 45 35

141 Launch of "Friendship 7", 1962

1998. John Glenn's (astronaut) Return to Space. Multicoloured.

1059 60 c. Type **141** 75 55
1060 60 c. John Glenn, 1962, and Earth 75 55
1061 60 c. "Friendship 7" orbiting Earth 75 55
1062 60 c. Launch of space shuttle "Discovery", 1998 . . . . 75 55
1063 60 c. John Glenn, 1998, and flag 75 55
1064 60 c. "Discovery" orbiting Earth, 1998 . . . . 75 55

143 British and German Planes over St. Paul's Cathedral (Battle of Britain, 1940)

1998. The Twentieth Century (5th series). "Decade of War and Peace, 1940–1949". Multicoloured.

1067 60 c. Type **143** 75 55
1068 60 c. Japanese aircraft attack American battleship (Pearl Harbor, 1941) (global warfare) 75 55
1069 60 c. Wernher von Braun and missiles (first surface to surface guided missile, 1942) 75 55
1070 60 c. The Dorsey Brothers (Big Bands, 1942) 75 55
1071 60 c. Soviet worker building weaponry (fight for survival against Germans, 1943) . . 75 55
1072 60 c. Concentration camp prisoners (the Holocaust, 1945) . 75 55
1073 60 c. Mushroom cloud and skull (first atomic bomb tested, Alamogordo, New Mexico, 1945) 75 55
1074 60 c. Families reunited (end of war, 1945) 75 55
1075 60 c. Eniac computer and worker (first electronic digital computer goes into operation, 1946) 75 55
1076 60 c. American delegate (United Nations, 1946) 75 55
1077 60 c. Nuremberg Tribunal (trials of Germans for war crimes 1946) 75 55
1078 60 c. George Marshall (U.S. Secretary of State) and Europeans (Marshall Plan, 1947) 75 55
1079 60 c. William Shockley, John Bardeen and Walter Brattain (development of transistor, 1948) 75 55
1080 60 c. Berlin Airlift, 1948–49 (Cold War) 75 55
1081 60 c. Mao Tse-tung proclaiming People's Republic of China, 1949 . . . . 75 55

144 Trireme

1998. Warships. Multicoloured.

1082 33 c. Type **144** 45 35
1083 33 c. Roman galley ("Trireme Romano") 45 35
1084 33 c. Viking longship 45 35
1085 33 c. Ming treasure ship . . . 45 35
1086 33 c. "Mary Rose" (English galleon) 45 35
1087 33 c. "Nuestra Senora del Rosario" (Spanish galleon) . 45 35
1088 33 c. Korean "turtle" ship . . 45 35
1089 33 c. "Brederode" (Dutch ship of the line) 45 35
1090 33 c. Venetian galley 45 35
1091 33 c. "Santissima Trinidad" (Spanish ship of the line) . . 45 35
1092 33 c. "Ville de Paris" (French ship of the line) 45 35
1093 33 c. H.M.S. "Victory" (ship of the line) 45 35
1094 33 c. "Bonhomme Richard" (American sail frigate) . . . 45 35
1095 33 c. U.S.S. "Constellation" (sail frigate) 45 35
1096 33 c. U.S.S. "Hartford" (steam frigate) 45 35
1097 33 c. Fijian Ndrua canoe . . . 45 35
1098 33 c. H.M.S. "Dreadnought" (battleship) 45 35
1099 33 c. H.M.A.S. "Australia" (battle cruiser) 45 35
1100 33 c. H.M.S. "Dorsetshire" (cruiser) 45 35
1101 33 c. "Admiral Graf Spee" (German battleship) 45 35
1102 33 c. "Yamato" (Japanese battleship) 45 35
1103 33 c. U.S.S. "Tautog" (submarine) 45 35
1104 33 c. "Bismarck" (German battleship) 45 35
1105 33 c. U.S.S. "Hornet" (aircraft carrier) 45 35
1106 33 c. U.S.S. "Missouri" (battleship) 45 35

146 American ("Lesser") Golden Plover **147** Tecumseh

1999. Birds. Multicoloured.

1108 1 c. Type **146** 10 10
1109 3 c. Grey-rumped sandpiper ("Siberian (gray-tailed) Tattler") 10 10
1110 5 c. Black-tailed godwit . . . 10 10
1113 20 c. Common ("Brown") noddy 25 20
1114 22 c. White ("Common fairy-") tern 30 25
1116 33 c. Micronesian pigeon . . . 40 30
1117 40 c. Franklin's gull 50 40
1118 45 c. Rufous-necked sandpiper ("Stint") 55 40
1119 55 c. Long-tailed cuckoo . . . 70 55
1121 75 c. Kermadec petrel 95 70
1122 $1 Christmas Island shearwater ("Christmas Shearwater") . 1·25 95
1123 $1.20 Purple-capped fruit dove 1·50 1·25
1124 $2 Mongolian plover . . . . 2·50 1·90
1125 $3.20 Cattle egret . . . . . . 4·00 3·00
1127 $5 Dunlin . . . . 6·25 4·75
1129 $10 Eurasian tree sparrow . . 12·50 9·50

1999. Canoes of the Pacific. Multicoloured. (a) Size 49 × 30 mm.

1130 33 c. Type **131** 40 30
1131 33 c. As No. 964 . . . . . . 40 30
1132 33 c. As No. 965 . . . . . . 40 30
1133 33 c. As No. 966 but inscr changed to "Tongiaki voyaging canoe, Tonga" . . 40 30
1134 33 c. As No. 967 . . . . . . 40 30
1135 33 c. As No. 968 but inscr changed to "Amatasi sailing canoe, Samoa" 40 30
1136 33 c. As No. 969 . . . . . . 40 30
1137 33 c. As No. 970 . . . . . . 40 30

(b) Size 39 × 24 mm.

1138 33 c. Type **131** 40 30
1139 33 c. As No. 1131 . . . . . . 40 30
1140 33 c. As No. 1132 . . . . . . 40 30
1141 33 c. As No. 1133 . . . . . . 40 30
1142 33 c. As No. 1134 . . . . . . 40 30
1143 33 c. As No. 1135 . . . . . . 40 30
1144 33 c. As No. 1136 . . . . . . 40 30
1145 33 c. As No. 1137 . . . . . . 40 30

Nos. 1138/45 were self-adhesive.

1999. Great American Indian Chiefs. Multicoloured.

1146 60 c. Type **147** 75 55
1147 60 c. Powhatan 75 55
1148 60 c. Hiawatha 75 55
1149 60 c. Dull Knife 75 55
1150 60 c. Sequoyah 75 55
1151 60 c. Sitting Bull 75 55
1152 60 c. Cochise 75 55
1153 60 c. Red Cloud 75 55
1154 60 c. Geronimo 75 55
1155 60 c. Chief Joseph 75 55
1156 60 c. Pontiac 75 55
1157 60 c. Crazy Horse 75 55

148 State Flag

1999.

1158 **148** 33 c. multicoloured . . . 40 30

149 Plumeria

1999. Flowers of the Pacific. Multicoloured.

1159 33 c. Type **149** 40 30
1160 33 c. Vanda 40 30
1161 33 c. Ilima 40 30
1162 33 c. Tiare 40 30
1163 33 c. White ginger 40 30
1164 33 c. Hibiscus 40 30

150 Family watching Television

1999. The Twentieth Century (6th series). "Decade of Peril and Progress, 1950–1959". Multicoloured.

1165 60 c. Type **150** 75 55
1166 60 c. U.N. landing at Inchon, Korea, 1950 (Cold War) . . 75 55
1167 60 c. Vaccination against polio, 1952 . . . . 75 55
1168 60 c. American hydrogen bomb test, Enewetak Atoll, 1952 (Arms race) 75 55
1169 60 c. James Watson and Francis Crick (scientists) and DNA double helix, 1953 (unravelling of genetic code) 75 55
1170 60 c. Sir Edmund Hillary, Tenzing Norgay and Mt. Everest, 1953 . . . . 75 55
1171 60 c. Coronation of Queen Elizabeth II, Westminster Abbey, 1953 . . . . 75 55
1172 60 c. Singer and dancers, 1954 (rock 'n' roll music) 75 55
1173 60 c. Ho Chi Minh and Vietnamese troops celebrating victory over French garrison at Dien Bien Phu, 1954 (end of colonial empires) 75 55
1174 60 c. People of different races on bus, 1955 (condemnation of racial discrimination) . . 75 55
1175 60 c. Hungarians firing on Russian tanks, Budapest, 1956 (challenge to Communism) 75 55
1176 60 c. Signing of Treaty of Rome, 1957 (European union) 75 55
1177 60 c. Launch of Russian sputnik, 1957 (space race) . . 75 55
1178 60 c. De Havilland Comet (first commercial jet airline service, 1958) 75 55
1179 60 c. Jack Kilby (inventor) and first microchip, 1959 . . . . 75 55

152 Presley

1999. Elvis Presley, "Artist of the Century".

1181 **152** 33 c. multicoloured . . . 40 30

153 5 m. Stamp

1999. "iBRA '99" International Stamp Exhibition, Nuremberg, Germany. Multicoloured.

1182 60 c. Type **153** 75 55
1183 60 c. 3 m. stamp 75 55
1184 60 c. 2 m. stamp 75 55
1185 60 c. 1 m. stamp 75 55

154 Magnifying Glass over Committee Members

1999. 20th Anniv of Marshall Islands Constitution.

1186 **154** 33 c. multicoloured 40 30

155 Marshall Island Stamps

1999. 15th Anniv of Marshall Islands Postal Service. Multicoloured.

1187 33 c. Type **155** 40 30
1188 33 c. Butterfly, fish, canoe and flower stamps 40 30
1189 33 c. Pres. Amata Kabua, flower and legend stamps 40 30
1190 33 c. Stamps and magnifying glass 40 30

Nos. 1187/90 were issued together, se-tenant, forming a composite design.

156 B-10 B

1999. Legendary Aircraft. Multicoloured.

1191 33 c. Type **156** 40 30
1192 33 c. A-17A Nomad 40 30
1193 33 c. Douglas B-18 Bolo bomber 40 30
1194 33 c. Boeing B-17F Flying Fortress bomber 40 30
1195 33 c. A-20 Havoc 40 30
1196 33 c. North American B-25B Mitchell bomber 40 30
1197 33 c. Consolidated B-24D Liberator bomber 40 30
1198 33 c. North American P-51B Mustang fighter 40 30
1199 33 c. Martin B-26 Marauder bomber 40 30
1200 33 c. A-26B Invader 40 30
1201 33 c. P-59 Airacomet 40 30
1202 33 c. KC-97 Stratofreighter 40 30
1203 33 c. A-1J Skyraider 40 30
1204 33 c. P2V-7 Neptune 40 30
1205 33 c. B-45 Tornado 40 30
1206 33 c. Boeing B-50 Superfortress 40 30
1207 33 c. AJ-2 Savage 40 30
1208 33 c. F9F Cougar 40 30
1209 33 c. Douglas A-3 Skywarrior jet bomber 40 30
1210 33 c. English Electric B-57E Canberra jet bomber 40 30
1211 33 c. EB-66 Destroyer 40 30
1212 33 c. E-2A Hawkeye 40 30
1213 33 c. Northrop F-5E Tiger II jet fighter 40 30
1214 33 c. AV-8B Harrier II 40 30
1215 33 c. B-1B Lancer 40 30

159 T. H. Maiman and Ruby Crystal Laser, 1960

1999. The Twentieth Century (7th series). "Decade of Upheaval and Exploration 1960–1969". Mult.

1218 60 c. Type **159** 75 55
1219 60 c. Young couple (birth control pill, 1960) 75 55
1220 60 c. Yury Gagarin (first man in space, 1961) 75 55
1221 60 c. John F. Kennedy (President of U.S.A., 1960–63) making speech in Berlin, 1961 (failures of Communism) 75 55
1222 60 c. Rachel Carson and endangered species (publication of "Silent Spring", 1962) 75 55
1223 60 c. John F. Kennedy and Russian President Nikita Khrushchev (Cuban missile crisis, 1962) 75 55
1224 60 c. Pope John XXIII and crowds (Spirit of Ecumenism) 75 55
1225 60 c. "Hikari" express train, Japan (new railway record speeds, 1964) 75 55
1226 60 c. Chinese workers waving banners (Chinese cultural revolution, 1965) 75 55
1227 60 c. Soldier with gun (Arab–Israeli six-day war, 1967) 75 55
1228 60 c. Surgeons (first human heart transplants, 1967) 75 55
1229 60 c. American soldiers in jungle (Vietnam war) 75 55
1230 60 c. Robert F. Kennedy (U.S. presidential candidate) and statue of Abraham Lincoln (political assassinations) 75 55
1231 60 c. British Aerospace/Aerospatiale Concorde supersonic jetliner (maiden flight, 1969) 75 55
1232 60 c. Neil Armstrong and Buzz Aldrin planting American flag (first men on Moon, 1969) 75 55

161 "Los Reyes" (Alvarao de Menana de Neyra's galleon, 1568)

1999. European Exploration of Marshall Islands. Multicoloured.

1234 33 c. Type **161** 40 30
1235 33 c. H.M.S. "Dolphin" (Samuel Wallis's frigate, 1767) 40 30
1236 33 c. "Scarborough" (John Marshall's transport, 1788) 40 30
1237 33 c. "Rurik" (Otto van Kotzebue's brig, 1817) 40 30

No. 1236 is wrongly inscribed "Scarsborough" and No. 1237 "Rurick".

162 Nativity

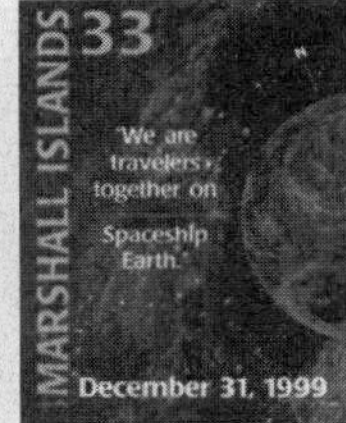

164 Earth in Darkness, December 31, 1999

163 First Scheduled Transatlantic Flight of Boeing 747 Jetliner, 1970

1999. Christmas.

1238 **162** 33 c. multicoloured 40 30

1999. The Twentieth Century (8th series). "Decade of Detente and Discovery 1970–1979". Multicoloured.

1239 60 c. Type **163** 75 55
1240 60 c. Mao Tse Tung and U.S. President Richard Nixon (visit to China, 1972) 75 55
1241 60 c. Terrorist with gun (murder of Israeli athletes at Munich Olympics, 1972) 75 55
1242 60 c. U.S. "Skylab" and U.S.S.R. "Salyut" space stations orbiting Earth 75 55
1243 60 c. Cars queueing for petrol (oil crisis, 1973) 75 55
1244 60 c. Terracotta warriors (discovery of Qin Shi Huang's tomb at Xian, China, 1974) 75 55
1245 60 c. Skulls and Cambodians in paddy fields 75 55
1246 60 c. "Apollo"–"Soyuz" link-up, 1975 (era of detente) 75 55
1247 60 c. "Eagle" (cadet ship) in New York Harbour (bicentenary of U.S. Independence, 1976) 75 55
1248 60 c. Computer and family (personal computers reach markets, 1977) 75 55
1249 60 c. Scanner and scanned images (diagnostic tools revolutionize medicine, 1977) 75 55
1250 60 c. Volkswagen Beetle motor car, 1978 75 55
1251 60 c. Pres. Anwar Sadat of Egypt, U.S. President Jimmy Carter and Israeli Prime Minister Menachim Begin, 1978 (peace in Middle East) 75 55
1252 60 c. Compact disc, 1979 75 55
1253 60 c. Ayatollah Khomeini becomes Iran's leader, 1979 75 55

1999. Year 2000. Multicoloured.

1254 33 c. Type **164** 40 30
1255 33 c. Earth in sunlight, January 1, 2000 40 30

Nos. 1254/5 were issued together, se-tenant, forming a composite design.

MARTINIQUE Pt. 6

An island in the West Indies, now an overseas department using the stamps of France.

100 centimes = 1 franc

1886. Stamp of French Colonies, "Commerce" type.
(a) Surch **MARTINIQUE** and new value.

3 J 01 on 20 c. red on green . . . 8·75 9·00
1 5 on 20 c. red on green . . . . 30·00 26·00
4 05 on 20 c. red on green . . . 7·00 4·50
2 5 c. on 20 c. red on green . . £10000 £10000
6 015 on 20 c. red on green . . . 35·00 35·00
5 15 on 20 c. red on green . . . £130 £110

(b) Surch **MQE 15 c.**

7 J 15 c. on 20 c. red on green . . 60·00 55·00

1888. Stamps of French Colonies, "Commerce" type, surch **MARTINIQUE** and value, thus **01 c.**

10 01 c. on 4 c. brn on grey . . . 7·00 1·75
11 05 c. on 4 c. brn on grey . . . £800 £675
12 05 c. on 10 c. black & lilac . . 60·00 30·00
13 05 c. on 20 c. red on green . . 12·50 9·25
14 05 c. on 30 c. brn on drab . . 16·00 14·50
15a 05 c. on 35 c. blk on yell . . . 10·00 7·75
16 05 c. on 40 c. red on yell . . . 32·00 25·00
17 15 c. on 4 c. brn on grey . . . £7000 £6000
18 15 c. on 20 c. red on green . . 70·00 50·00
19 15 c. on 25 c. blk on pink . . . 9·25 8·00
20 15 c. on 75 c. red on pink . . . £110 90·00

1891. Postage Due stamps of French Colonies surch **TIMBRE-POSTE MARTINIQUE** and value in figures.

21 U 05 c. on 5 c. black . . . . . 7·75 7·00
25 05 c. on 10 c. black . . . . 4·25 5·00
22 05 c. on 15 c. black . . . . 5·50 4·00
23 15 c. on 20 c. black . . . . 8·00 5·50
24 15 c. on 30 c. black . . . . 8·00 6·50

1891. Stamp of French Colonies, "Commerce" type, surch **TIMBRE-POSTE 01c. MARTINIQUE**.

1892. Stamp of French Colonies, "Commerce" type, surch **1892 MARTINIQUE** and new value.

31 15 c. on 25 c. black on pink . . . 15·00 15·00

1892. "Tablet" key-type inscr "MARTINIQUE", in red (1, 5, 15, 25, 75 c., 1 f.) or blue (others).

33 D 1 c. black on blue 80 80
34 2 c. brown on buff 90 85
35 4 c. brown on grey 90 85
36 5 c. green on green . . . . 1·25 45
37 10 c. black on lilac . . . . 5·50 70
47 10 c. red . . . . 1·75 50
38 15 c. blue . . . . 21·00 3·50
48 15 c. grey . . . . 6·25 70
39 20 c. red on green . . . . . 10·00 4·00
40 25 c. black on pink . . . . . 11·50 1·00
49 25 c. blue . . . . 8·50 7·50
41 30 c. brown on drab . . . . 21·00 7·75
50 35 c. black on yellow . . . . 9·50 4·75
42 40 c. red on yellow . . . . . 21·00 7·50
43 50 c. red on pink . . . . . 20·00 9·75
51 50 c. brown on blue . . . . 21·00 15·00
44 75 c. brown on orange . . . 20·00 10·00
45 1 f. green . . . . 16·00 8·25
52 2 f. violet on pink . . . . . 65·00 50·00
53 5 f. mauve on lilac . . . . . 75·00 60·00

1903. Postage Due stamp of French Colonies surch **TIMBRE POSTE 5 F. MARTINIQUE COLIS POSTAUX**.

53a U 5 f. on 60 c. brown on buff . £400 £425

Despite the surcharge Nos. 53a was for use on letters as well as parcels.

1904. Surch **10 c.**

55 10 c. on 5 f. mve on lilac . . . 6·25 6·25

1904. Surch **1904 0f10**.

57 0 f. 10 on 40 c. red on yell . . . 10·50 10·50
58 0 f. 10 on 50 c. red on pink . . . 10·50 10·50
59 0 f. 10 on 75 c. brown on orange 9·75 9·75
60 0 f. 10 on 1 f. green . . . . . 10·50 10·50
61 0 f. 10 on 5 f. mve on lilac . . . £140 £140

13 Martinique Woman

15 Woman and Sugar Cane

14 Fort-de-France

1908.

62 13 1 c. chocolate and brown 15 20
63 2 c. brown and green . . . 15 25
64 4 c. brown and purple . . . 15 25
65 5 c. brown and green . . . 25 15
87 5 c. brown and orange . . . 15 15
66 10 c. brown and red 45 25
88 10 c. olive and green . . . 20 30
89 10 c. red and purple . . . 20 25
67 15 c. red and purple . . . 15 30
90 15 c. olive and green . . . 20 30
91 13 15 c. red and blue 50 70
68 20 c. brown and lilac . . . 50 55
69 14 25 c. brown and blue 75 20
92 25 c. brown and orange . . 25 15
93 30 c. brown and red 35 35
94 30 c. red and carmine . . . 20 35
95 30 c. brown and lt brown . . 20 25
96 30 c. green and blue 70 75
71 35 c. brown and lilac . . . 30 45
72 40 c. brown and green . . . 30 40
73 45 c. chocolate and brown . . 35 45
74 50 c. brown and red 75 45
97 50 c. brown and blue 70 75
98 50 c. green and red 30 20
99 60 c. pink and blue 20 30
100 65 c. brown and violet . . . 90 95
75 75 c. brown and black . . . 70 60
101 75 c. blue and deep blue . . . 20 30
102 75 c. blue and brown . . . 1·40 1·50
103 90 c. carmine and red . . . 3·25 3·25
76 15 1 f. brown and red 40 40
104 1 f. blue 30 40
105 1 f. green and red . . . . 95 1·25
106 1 f. 10 brown and violet . . 2·00 2·00
107 1 f. 50 light blue and blue . . 3·50 3·50
77 2 f. brown and grey . . . . 1·90 1·00
108 3 f. mauve on pink . . . . 5·25 5·25
78 5 f. brown and red . . . . 6·25 6·00

1912. Stamps of 1892 surch.

79 05 on 15 c. grey 50 45
80 05 on 25 c. black on pink . . . 75 85
81 10 on 40 c. red on yellow . . . 90 1·00
82 10 on 5 f. mauve on lilac . . . 1·25 1·40

1915. Surch **5c** and red cross.

83 13 10 c. + 5 c. brown and red . . 1·00 1·00

1920. Surch in figures.

115 13 0,01 on 2 c. brown and grn . . 1·10 1·40
109 0,01 on 15 c. red and purple 25 35
110 0,02 on 15 c. red and purple 15 35
84 05 on 1 c. chocolate & brn 1·00 1·00
111 0,05 on 15 c. red and pur . . 25 35
116 0,05 on 20 c. brown & lilac 1·25 1·40
85 10 on 2 c. brown and green 85 90
117 14 0,15 on 30 c. brown & red . . 6·50 7·00
86 13 25 on 15 c. red and purple 65 70
121 25 c. on 15 c. red & purple 25 35
119 14 0,25 on 50 c. brown and red £170 £170
120 0,25 on 50 c. brown & blue 2·75 3·00
122 15 25 c. on 2 f. brown & grey . . 20 35
123 25 c. on 5 f. brown and red 95 60
112 14 60 on 75 c. pink and blue . . 20 35
113 65 on 45 c. brown & lt brn 60 70
114 85 on 75 c. brown & black 65 80
124 90 c. on 75 c. carmine and red 1·90 2·00
125 15 1 f. 25 on 1 f. blue 20 30
126 1 f. 50 on 1 f. ultramarine and blue 70 80
127 3 f. on 5 f. green and red . . 1·25 1·40
128 10 f. on 5 f. red and green 6·00 6·25
129 20 f. on 5 f. violet & brown 9·25 9·00

1931. "Colonial Exhibition" key-types inscr "MARTINIQUE".

130 E 40 c. black and green . . . 2·25 2·25
131 F 50 c. black and mauve . . . 2·00 2·00
132 G 90 c. black and red . . . 2·25 2·25
133 H 1 f. 50 black and blue . . . 2·25 2·25

26 Basse Pointe Village

27 Government House, Fort-de-France

28 Martinique Woman

1933.

134 26 1 c. red on pink 15 25
135 27 2 c. blue 15 30
136 3 c. purple 20 30
137 26 4 c. green 15 30
138 27 5 c. purple 15 25
139 26 10 c. black on pink 15 20
140 27 15 c. black on red 15 25
141 28 20 c. brown 15 25
142 26 25 c. purple 20 35
143 27 30 c. green 25 25
144 30 c. blue 25 30
145 28 35 c. green 25 35
146 40 c. brown 25 20
147 27 45 c. brown . . . . 1·00 1·10
148 45 c. green 30 45
149 50 c. red 20 15
150 26 55 c. red 45 55
151 60 c. blue 25 35
152 28 65 c. red on blue 25 30
153 70 c. purple 35 35
154 26 75 c. brown 50 50
155 27 80 c. violet 35 35
156 26 90 c. red . . . . 1·10 95
157 90 c. purple 35 40
158 27 1 f. black on green . . . . . 1·10 30
159 27 1 f. red 40 40
160 28 1 f. 25 violet 45 45
161 1 f. 25 red 45 40
162 1 f. 40 blue 40 40
163 27 1 f. 50 blue 35 35
164 1 f. 60 brown 45 45
165 28 1 f. 75 green . . . . 5·50 2·50
166 1 f. 75 blue 40 35
167 26 2 f. blue on green 40 30
168 28 2 f. 25 blue 50 45
169 26 2 f. 50 purple 55 60
170 28 3 f. purple 25 25
171 5 f. red on pink 70 40
172 26 10 f. blue on blue 45 30
173 27 20 f. red on yellow 85 65

30 Belain d'Esnambuc, 1635

31 Schoelcher and Abolition of Slavery, 1848

1935. West Indies Tercentenary.

174 30 40 c. brown . . . . 1·10 1·00
175 50 c. red . . . . 1·10 1·00
176 1 f. 50 blue . . . . 8·00 8·00
177 31 1 f. 75 red . . . . 7·25 7·50
178 5 f. brown . . . . 7·25 7·50
179 10 f. green . . . . 5·25 5·50

1937. International Exhibition, Paris. As T **58a** of Guadeloupe.

180 20 c. violet 85 95
181 30 c. green 85 95
182 40 c. red 85 95
183 50 c. brown and agate . . . . 80 1·10
184 90 c. red . . . . 90 1·10
185 1 f. 50 blue . . . . 1·00 1·10

1938. Int Anti-Cancer Fund. As T **58b** of Guadeloupe.

186 1 f. 75 + 50 c. blue . . . . . 6·50 6·50

1939. New York World's Fair. As T **58c** of Guadeloupe.

187 1 f. 25 red 70 70
188 2 f. 25 blue 70 70

1939. 150th Anniv of French Revolution. As T **58d** of Guadeloupe.

189 45 c. + 25 c. green and black 4·50 4·50
190 70 c. + 30 c. brown and black 4·50 4·50
191 90 c. + 35 c. orange and black 4·50 4·50
192 1 f. 25 + 1 f. red and black . . 4·50 4·50
193 2 f. 25 + 2 f. blue and black 4·50 4·50

1944. Mutual Aid and Red Cross Funds. As T **58e** of Guadeloupe.

194 5 f. + 20 f. violet 65 80

1945. Eboue. As T **58f** of Guadeloupe.

195 2 f. black 20 35
196 25 f. green 55 65

1945. Surch.

197 27 1 f. on 2 c. blue 40 40
198 26 2 f. on 4 c. olive 40 40
199 27 3 f. on 2 c. blue 40 40
200 28 5 f. on 65 c. red on blue . . . 60 60
201 10 f. (DIX f.) on 65 c. red on blue 60 60
202 27 20 f. (VINGT f.) on 3 c. purple 75 75

33 Victor Schoelcher

1945.

203 33 10 c. blue and violet 15 30
204 30 c. brown and red 20 30
205 40 c. blue and light blue . . 25 35
206 50 c. red and purple 30 30
207 60 c. orange and yellow . . 30 40
208 70 c. purple and brown . . 30 40
209 80 c. green and light green 30 40
210 1 f. blue and light blue . . . 30 40
211 1 f. 20 violet and purple . . 30 40
212 1 f. 50 red and orange . . . 30 40
213 2 f. black and grey 30 40
214 2 f. 40 red and pink 75 90
215 3 f. pink and light pink . . . 30 20
216 4 f. ultramarine and blue . . 35 25
217 4 f. 50 turquoise and green 50 35
218 5 f. light brown and brown 40 30
219 10 f. purple and mauve . . . 50 30
220 15 f. red and pink 60 45
221 20 f. olive and green 80 75

1945. Air. As T **63a** of Guadeloupe.

222 50 f. green 50 35
223 100 f. red 55 45

1946. Air. Victory. As T **63b** of Guadeloupe.

224 8 f. blue 50 75

1946. Air. From Chad to the Rhine. As T **63c** of Guadeloupe.

225 5 f. orange 40 50
226 10 f. green 40 50
227 15 f. red 50 60
228 20 f. brown 50 60
229 25 f. blue 60 70
230 50 f. grey 80 90

34 Martinique Woman

39 Mountains and Palms

35 Local Fishing Boats and Rocks

40 West Indians and Flying Boat

1947.

231 34 10 c. lake (postage) 20 30
232 30 c. blue 15 25
233 50 c. brown 15 30
234 35 60 c. green 25 35
235 1 f. lake 25 35
236 1 f. 50 violet 25 35
237 – 2 f. green 60 45
238 – 2 f. 50 brown 60 50
239 – 3 f. blue 45 45
240 – 4 f. brown 45 45
241 – 5 f. green 40 45
242 – 6 f. mauve 45 45
243 – 10 f. blue 75 65
244 – 15 f. lake 90 85
245 – 20 f. brown . . . . 1·25 1·00
246 39 25 f. violet . . . . 1·40 1·25
247 40 f. green . . . . 1·50 1·40
248 40 50 f. purple (air) . . . . . 2·50 2·00
249 – 100 f. green . . . . 3·75 2·50
250 – 200 f. violet . . . . . . 48·00 17·00

DESIGNS—HORIZ: As Type **35**: 2 f. to 3 f. Gathering sugar cane; 4 f. to 6 f. Mount Pele; 10 f. to 20 f. Fruit products. As Type **40**—VERT: 100 f. Aeroplane over landscape. HORIZ: 200 f. Wandering albatross in flight.

POSTAGE DUE STAMPS

1927. Postage Due stamps of France optd **MARTINIQUE**.

D130 D 11 5 c. blue 50 85
D131 10 c. brown . . . . . . 80 1·00
D132 20 c. olive . . . . . . 90 1·00
D133 25 c. red . . . . 1·25 1·50
D134 30 c. red . . . . 1·60 1·75
D135 45 c. green . . . . . . 1·75 1·75
D136 50 c. purple . . . . . . 3·50 3·75
D137 60 c. green . . . . . . 4·25 4·25
D138 1 f. red on yellow . . . 5·25 5·25
D139 2 f. mauve . . . . . . 7·25 7·25
D140 3 f. red . . . . 8·25 8·25

D 29 Fruit

D 43 Map of Martinique

1933.

D174 D 29 5 c. blue on green . . . 15 40
D175 10 c. brown 20 40
D176 20 c. blue 60 65
D177 25 c. red on pink 60 65
D178 30 c. purple 40 45
D179 45 c. red on yellow . . . 30 35
D180 50 c. brown 45 75
D181 60 c. green 45 75
D182 1 f. black on red 65 90
D183 2 f. purple 55 75
D184 3 f. blue on blue 70 85

1947.

D251 D 43 10 c. blue 15 20
D252 30 c. green 15 30
D253 50 c. blue 15 30
D254 1 f. orange 20 35
D255 2 f. purple 45 60
D256 3 f. purple 45 60
D257 4 f. brown 55 70
D258 5 f. red 60 70
D259 10 f. black . . . . . . 90 1·25
D260 20 f. green . . . . . . 90 1·25

MAURITANIA Pt. 6; Pt. 13

A French colony extending inland to the Sahara, incorporated in French West Africa from 1945 to 1959. In 1960 Mauritania became an independent Islamic republic.

1906. 100 centimes = 1 franc.
1973. 100 cents = 1 ouguiya (um).

1906. "Faidherbe", "Palms" and "Balay" key-types inscr "MAURITANIE" in blue (10, 40 c., 5 f.) or red (others).

1 I 1 c. grey 25 30
2 2 c. brown 50 40
3 4 c. brown on blue 75 50
4 5 c. green 1·25 50
5 10 c. pink 6·50 3·00
6 J 20 c. black on blue 11·00 8·50
7 25 c. blue 4·50 3·25
8 30 c. brown on pink 70·00 40·00
9 35 c. black on yellow 4·25 3·00
10 40 c. red on blue 4·50 3·50
11 45 c. brown on green 4·25 3·50
12 50 c. violet 4·50 3·50
13 75 c. green on orange 4·00 3·50
14 K 1 f. black on blue 9·50 8·00
15 2 f. blue on pink 35·00 30·00
16 5 f. red on yellow £100 85·00

6 Merchants crossing Desert

1913.

18 6 1 c. brown and lilac 10 20
19 2 c. blue and black 10 20
20 4 c. black and violet 15 25
21 5 c. green and light green 25 40
37 5 c. red and purple 10 25
22 10 c. orange and pink 55 75
38 10 c. green and light green 10 25
39 10 c. pink on blue 15 30
23 15 c. black and brown 30 40
24 20 c. orange and brown 20 45
25 25 c. ultramarine and blue 80 85
40 25 c. red and green 40 65
26 30 c. pink and green 50 80
41 30 c. orange and red 50 70
42 30 c. yellow and black 15 35
43 30 c. light green and green 70 95
27 35 c. violet and brown 25 45
44 35 c. light green and green 25 50
28 40 c. green and brown 70 1·10
29 45 c. brown and orange 35 55
30 50 c. pink and lilac 35 50
45 50 c. ultramarine and blue 40 50
46 50 c. blue and green 40 60
47 60 c. violet on pink 15 35
48 65 c. blue and brown 50 70
31 75 c. brown and blue 40 70
49 85 c. brown and green 40 60
50 90 c. pink and red 85 90
32 1 f. black and red 40 65
51 1 f. 10 red and mauve 6·50 6·75
52 1 f. 25 brown and blue 1·10 1·25
53 1 f. 50 blue and light blue 70 75
54 1 f. 75 red and green 70 75
55 1 f. 75 ultramarine and blue 75 70
33 2 f. violet and orange 1·00 1·40
56 3 f. mauve on pink 1·00 1·40
34 5 f. blue and violet 1·40 1·50

1915. Surch **5c** and red cross.

35 6 10 c. + 5 c. orange and pink 40 70
36 15 c. + 5 c. black and brown 40 75

1922. Surch in figures and bars (some colours changed).

60 6 25 c. on 2 f. violet and orange 60 60
57 60 on 75 c. violet on pink 50 70
58 65 on 15 c. black and brown 1·00 1·40
59 85 on 75 c. brown and blue 75 1·10
61 90 c. on 75 c. pink and red 1·40 1·40
62 1 f. 25 on 1 f. ultram and blue 55 75
63 1 f. 50 on 1 f. blue and lt blue 65 80
64 3 f. on 5 f. mauve and brown 5·00 5·00
65 10 f. on 5 f. green and mauve 4·25 4·50
66 20 f. on 5 f. orange and blue 4·25 4·50

1931. "Colonial Exhibition" key-types inscr "MAURITANIE".

67 E 40 c. green and black 5·00 5·25
68 F 50 c. purple and black 2·50 2·50
69 G 90 c. red and black 2·50 2·50
70 H 1 f. 50 blue and black 2·50 2·50

1937. International Exhibition, Paris. As T **58a** of Guadeloupe.

71 20 c. violet 60 75
72 30 c. green 60 80
73 40 c. red 50 75
74 50 c. brown 50 70
75 90 c. red 50 80
76 1 f. 50 blue 55 80

1938. International Anti-Cancer Fund. As T **58b** of Guadeloupe.

76b 1 f. 75 + 50 c. blue 3·50 5·00

23 Man on Camel

24 Warriors

25 Encampment

26 Mauritanians

1938.

77 23 2 c. purple 15 30
78 3 c. blue 10 30
79 4 c. lilac 10 30
80 5 c. red 10 30
81 10 c. red 20 35
82 15 c. violet 15 30
83 24 20 c. red 10 30
84 25 c. blue 30 55
85 30 c. purple 20 30
86 35 c. green 35 55
87 40 c. red 35 50
88 45 c. green 35 45
89 50 c. violet 35 55
90 25 55 c. lilac 55 70
91 60 c. violet 40 50
92 65 c. green 40 55
93 70 c. red 50 60
94 80 c. blue 95 1·00
95 90 c. lilac 40 55
96 1 f. red 90 1·10
97 1 f. green 25 45
98 1 f. 25 red 50 90
99 1 f. 40 blue 50 65
100 1 f. 50 violet 45 70
101 1 f. 60 brown 90 1·00
102 26 1 f. 75 blue 75 70
103 2 f. lilac 60 75
104 2 f. 25 blue 45 65
105 2 f. 50 brown 65 80
106 3 f. green 50 70
107 5 f. red 60 90
108 10 f. purple 95 1·40
109 20 f. red 95 1·40

27 Rene Caillie (explorer)

1939. Caillie.

110 27 90 c. orange 50 80
111 2 f. violet 50 80
112 2 f. 25 blue 50 80

1939. New York World's Fair. As T **58c** of Guadeloupe.

113 1 f. 25 red 45 65
114 2 f. 25 blue 45 65

1939. 150th Anniv of French Revolution. As T **58d** of Guadeloupe.

115 45 c. + 25 c. green & black 4·75 5·00
116 70 c. + 30 c. brown & black 4·75 5·00
117 90 c. + 35 c. orange & black 4·75 5·00
118 1 f. 25 + 1 f. red and black 4·75 5·00
119 2 f. 25 + 2 f. blue & black 4·75 5·00

30 Twin-engine Airliner over Jungle

1940. Air.

120 30 1 f. 90 blue 45 60
121 2 f. 90 red 45 60
122 4 f. 50 green 45 60
123 4 f. 90 olive 60 75
124 6 f. 90 orange 65 85

1941. National Defence Fund. Surch **SECOURS NATIONAL** and value.

124a + 1 f. on 50 c. (No. 89) 2·00 2·00
124b + 2 f. on 80 c. (No. 94) 4·00 4·00
124c + 2 f. on 1 f. 50 (No. 100) 4·00 4·00
124d + 3 f. on 2 f. (No. 103) 4·00 4·00

31a Ox Caravan

1942. Marshal Petain issue.

124e 31a 1 f. green 20 1·25
124f 2 f. 50 blue 15 1·25

1942. Air. Colonial Child Welfare Fund. As Nos. 98g/i of Niger.

124g 1 f. 50 + 3 f. 50 green 15
124h 2 f. + 6 f. brown 15
124i 3 f. + 9 f. red 15

1942. Air. Imperial Fortnight. As No. 98j of Niger.

124j 1 f. 20 + 1 f. 80 blue and red 15

32 Twin-engine Airliner over Camel Caravan

1942. Air. T **32** inscr "MAURITANIE" at foot.

124k 32 50 f. orange and yellow 75 1·10

1944. Surch.

125 25 3 f. 50 on 65 c. green 25 20
126 4 f. on 65 c. green 30 35
127 5 f. on 65 c. green 40 60
128 10 f. on 65 c. green 40 50
129 27 15 f. on 90 c. orange 65 70

ISLAMIC REPUBLIC.

35 Flag of Republic

37 Well

38 Slender-billed Gull

1960. Inauguration of Islamic Republic.

130 35 25 f. bistre, green and brown on rose 40 35

1960. 10th Anniv of African Technical Co-operation Commission. As T **4** of Malagasy Republic.

131 25 f. blue and turquoise 40 35

1960.

132 37 50 c. purple & brn (postage) 10 10
133 – 1 f. bistre, brown and green 10 10
134 – 2 f. brown, green and blue 15 10
135 – 3 f. red, sepia and turquoise 20 20
136 – 4 f. buff and green 20 20
137 – 5 f. chocolate, brown & red 15 10
138 – 10 f. blue, black & brown 20 15
139 – 15 f. multicoloured 40 15
140 – 20 f. brown and green 30 15
141 – 25 f. blue and green 50 15
142 – 30 f. blue, violet & bistre 50 15
143 – 50 f. brown and green 80 40
144 – 60 f. purple, red and green 1·25 40
145 – 85 f. brown, sepia & blue 3·50 1·50
146 – 100 f. brown, chocolate and blue (air) 8·00 3·00
147 – 200 f. myrtle, brn and sepia 17·00 6·25
148 38 500 f. sepia, blue & brn 35·00 13·00

DESIGNS—VERT: (As Type **37**) 2 f. Harvesting dates; 5 f. Harvesting millet; 25, 30 f. Seated dance; 50 f. "Telmidi" (symbolic figure); 60 f. Metalsmith; 85 f. Scimitar oryx; 100 f. Greater flamingo; 200 f. African spoonbill. HORIZ: 3 f. Barbary sheep; 4 f. Fennec foxes; 10 f. Cordwainer; 15 f. Fishing-boat; 20 f. Nomad school.

39 Flag and Map

43 Campaign Emblem

42 European, African and Boeing 707 Airliners

1960. Proclamation of Independence.

149 39 25 f. green, brown and chest 50 50

1962. Air. Air Afrique Airline.

150 42 100 f. green, brown & bistre 1·75 1·10

1962. Malaria Eradication.

151 43 25 f. + 5 f. olive 50 50

44 U.N. Headquarters and View of Nouakchott

1962. Admission to U.N.O.

152 44 15 f. brown, black and blue 20 20
153 25 f. brown, myrtle and blue 35 35
154 85 f. brown, purple and blue 1·00 1·00

45 Union Flag

1962. 1st Anniv of Union of African and Malagasy States.

155 45 30 f. blue 45 45

46 Eagle and Crescent over Nouakchott

1962. 8th Endemic Diseases Eradication Conference, Nouakchott.

156 46 30 f. green, brown and blue 45 35

47 Diesel Mineral Train

1962.

157 47 50 f. multicoloured 3·75 1·25

1962. Air. 1st Anniv of Admission to U.N.O. As T **44** but views from different angles and inscr "1 er ANNIVERSAIRE 27 OCTOBRE 1962".

158 100 f. blue, brown & turquoise 1·10 90

49 Map and Agriculture

1962. 2nd Anniv of Independence.

159 49 30 f. green and purple 45 30

50 Congress Representatives

1962. 1st Anniv of Unity Congress.

160 50 25 f. brown, myrtle & blue 45 40

51 Globe and Emblem

1962. Freedom from Hunger.

161 51 25 f. + 5 f. blue, brown & pur 55 55

52 Douglas DC-3 Airliner over Nouakchott Airport

1963. Air. Creation of National Airline.

162 52 500 f. myrtle, brown & blue 12·00 4·50

53 Open-cast Mining, Zouerate

1963. Air. Mining Development. Multicoloured.

163		100 f. Type **53**	2·50	60
164		200 f. Port-Etienne	5·25	2·50

54 Striped Hyena — 56 "Posts and Telecommunications"

1963. Animals.

165	**54**	50 c. black, brown & myrtle	10	10
166	–	1 f. black, blue and buff	10	10
167	–	1 f. 50 brown, olive & pur	20	15
168	–	2 f. purple, green and red	15	15
169	–	5 f. bistre, blue and ochre	25	20
170	–	10 f. black and ochre	50	20
171	–	15 f. purple and blue	50	20
172	–	20 f. bistre, purple and blue	60	20
173	–	25 f. ochre, brown & turq	85	25
174	–	30 f. bistre, brown and blue	1·50	30
175	–	50 f. bistre, brown & green	2·00	60
176	–	60 f. bistre, brown & turq	2·50	90

ANIMALS—HORIZ: 1 f. Spotted hyena; 2 f. Guinea baboons; 10 f. Leopard; 15 f. Bongos; 20 f. Aardvark; 30 f. North African crested porcupine; 60 f. Chameleon. VERT: 1 f. 50, Cheetah; 5 f. Dromedaries; 25 f. Patas monkeys; 50 f. Dorcas gazelle.

1963. Air. African and Malagasy Posts and Telecommunications Union.

177	**56**	85 f. multicoloured	1·00	65

57 "Telstar" Satellite

1963. Air. Space Telecommunications.

178	**57**	50 f. brown, purple & green	65	45
179	–	100 f. blue, brown and red	1·25	80
180	–	150 f. turquoise and brown	2·25	1·50

DESIGNS: 100 f. "Syncom" satellite; 150 f. "Relay" satellite.

58 "Tiros" Satellite — 60 U.N. Emblem, Sun and Birds

59 Airline Emblem

1963. Air. World Meteorological Day.

181	**58**	200 f. brown, blue & green	3·50	1·75

1963. Air. 1st Anniv of "Air Afrique" and DC-8 Service Inauguration.

182	**59**	25 f. multicoloured	50	25

1963. Air. 15th Anniv of Declaration of Human Rights.

183	**60**	100 f. blue, violet & purple	1·25	85

61 Cogwheels and Wheat — 62 Lichtenstein's Sandgrouse

1964. Air. European–African Economic Convention.

184	**61**	50 f. multicoloured	1·10	70

1964. Air. Birds.

185	**62**	100 f. ochre, brown & green	10·00	2·00
186	–	200 f. black, brown & blue	16·00	4·50
187	–	500 f. slate, red and green	35·00	12·50

DESIGNS: 200 f. Reed cormorant; 500 f. Dark chanting goshawk.

63 Temple, Philae

1964. Air. Nubian Monuments Preservation.

188	**63**	10 f. brown, black and blue	45	30
189		25 f. slate, brown and blue	70	60
190		60 f. chocolate, brown & bl	1·50	1·10

64 W.M.O. Emblem, Sun and Lightning — 65 Radar Antennae and Sun Emblem

1964. World Meteorological Day.

191	**64**	85 f. blue, orange & brown	1·25	80

1964. International Quiet Sun Years.

192	**65**	25 f. red, green and blue	35	25

66 Bowl depicting Horse-racing

1964. Air. Olympic Games, Tokyo.

193	**66**	15 f. brown and bistre	30	25
194	–	50 f. brown and blue	60	50
195	–	85 f. brown and red	1·10	1·00
196	–	100 f. brown and green	1·50	1·25

DESIGNS—VERT: 50 f. Running (vase); 85 f. Wrestling (vase). HORIZ: 100 f. Chariot-racing (bowl).

67 Flat-headed Grey Mullet — 68 "Co-operation"

1964. Marine Fauna.

197	**67**	1 f. green, blue and brown	25	15
198	–	5 f. purple, green & brown	40	15
199	–	10 f. green, ochre and blue	50	20
200	–	60 f. slate, green and brown	3·50	1·10

DESIGNS—VERT: 5 f. Lobster ("Panulirus mauritanicus"); 10 f. Lobster ("Panulirus regius"). HORIZ: 60 f. Meagre.

1964. French, African and Malagasy Co-operation.

201	**68**	25 f. brown, green & mauve	40	30

69 Pres. Kennedy — 70 "Nymphaea lotus"

1964. Air. 1st Death Anniv of Pres. Kennedy.

202	**69**	100 f. multicoloured	1·75	1·00

1965. Mauritanian Flowers.

203	**70**	5 f. green, red and blue	25	15
204	–	10 f. green, ochre & purple	40	15
205	–	20 f. brown, red and sepia	60	20
206	–	45 f. turquoise, purple & grn	1·25	60

FLOWERS—VERT: 10 f. "Acacia gommier"; 45 f. "Caralluma retrospiciens". HORIZ: 20 f. "Adenium obesum".

71 "Hardine" — 72 Abraham Lincoln

1965. Musical Instruments and Musicians.

207	**71**	2 f. brown, bistre and blue	25	15
208	–	8 f. brown, bistre and red	50	15
209	–	25 f. brown, black & green	85	20
210	–	40 f. black, blue and violet	1·10	35

DESIGNS: 8 f. "Tobol" (drums); 25 f. "Tidinit" ("Violins"); 40 f. Native band.

1965. Death Centenary of Abraham Lincoln.

211	**72**	50 f. multicoloured	70	35

73 Early Telegraph and Relay Satellite

1965. Air. Centenary of I.T.U.

212	**73**	250 f. green, mauve & blue	4·25	3·25

74 Palms in the Adrar

1965. "Tourism and Archaeology" (1st series).

213	**74**	1 f. green, brown and blue	10	10
214	–	4 f. brown, red and blue	15	10
215	–	15 f. multicoloured	30	20
216	–	60 f. sepia, brown and green	90	45

DESIGNS—VERT: 4 f. Chinguetti Mosque. HORIZ: 15 f. Clay-pits; 60 f. Carved doorway, Qualata.

See also Nos. 255/8.

75 "Attack on Cancer" (the Crab) — 76 Wooden Tea Service

1965. Air. Campaign against Cancer.

217	**75**	100 f. red, blue and ochre	1·50	60

1965. Native Handicrafts.

218	**76**	3 f. brown, ochre and slate	15	15
219	–	7 f. purple, orange and blue	20	20
220	–	25 f. brown, black and red	35	20
221	–	50 f. red, green and orange	75	35

DESIGNS—VERT: 7 f. Snuff-box and pipe; 25 f. Damasquine dagger. HORIZ: 50 f. Mederdra chest.

77 Nouakchott Wharf — 78 Sir Winston Churchill

1965. Mauritanian Development.

222	–	5 f. green and brown	1·75	90
223	**77**	10 f. red, turquoise and blue	15	10
224	–	30 f. red, brown and purple	3·50	1·10
225	–	85 f. violet, lake and blue	1·25	55

DESIGNS—VERT: 5 f., 30 f. Choum Tunnel. HORIZ: 85 f. Nouakchott Hospital.

1965. Air. Churchill Commem.

226	**78**	200 f. multicoloured	2·50	1·25

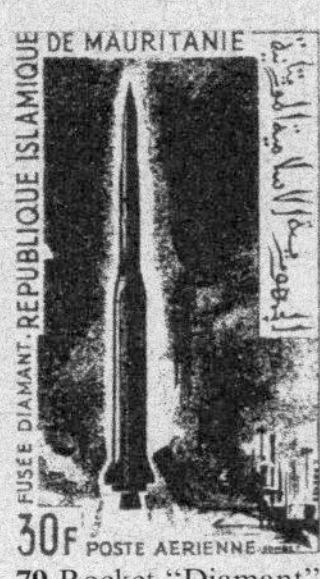

79 Rocket "Diamant"

1966. Air. French Satellites.

227	**79**	30 f. green, red and blue	50	25
228	–	60 f. purple, blue & turquoise	1·00	45
229	–	90 f. lake, violet and blue	1·50	75

DESIGNS—HORIZ: 60 f. Satellite "A 1" and Globe; 90 f. Rocket "Scout" and satellite "FR 1".

80 Dr. Schweitzer and Hospital Scene

1966. Air. Schweitzer Commem.

230	**80**	50 f. multicoloured	1·10	50

81 Stafford, Schirra and "Gemini 6"

1966. Air. Space Flights. Multicoloured.

231		50 f. Type **81**	60	25
232		100 f. Borman, Lovell and "Gemini 7"	1·25	60
233		200 f. Beliaiev, Leonov and "Voskhod 2"	2·50	1·25

82 African Woman and Carved Head

1966. World Festival of Negro Arts, Dakar.

234	**82**	10 f. black, brown & grn	20	10
235	–	30 f. purple, black and blue	35	20
236	–	60 f. purple, red and orange	75	45

DESIGNS: 30 f. Dancers and hands playing cornet; 60 f. Cine-camera and village huts.

83 "Dove" over Map of Africa — **84** Satellite "D 1"

1966. Air. Organization of African Unity (O.A.U.).

237	**83**	100 f. multicoloured	1·00	50

1966. Air. Launching of Satellite "D 1".

238	**84**	100 f. plum, brown & blue . .	1·10	75

85 Breguet 14T2 Salon

1966. Air. Early Aircraft.

239	**85**	50 f. indigo, blue and bistre	1·00	25
240	–	100 f. green, purple & blue	2·00	50
241	–	150 f. turquoise, brn & blue	3·00	75
242	–	200 f. indigo, blue & purple	4·00	1·25

AIRCRAFT: 100 f. Farman Goliath; 150 f. Couzinet "Arc en Ciel"; 200 f. Latecoere 28-3 seaplane "Comte de la Vaulx".

86 "Acacia ehrenbergiana"

1966. Mauritanian Flowers. Multicoloured.

243	10 f. Type **86**	25	15
244	15 f. "Schouwia purpurea" . .	50	15
245	20 f. "Ipomaea asarifolia" . .	65	20
246	25 f. "Grewia bicolor"	75	25
247	30 f. "Pancratium trianthum"	1·10	25
248	60 f. "Blepharis linariifolia" . .	1·75	55

87 DC-8F and "Air Afrique" Emblem

1966. Air. Inauguration of Douglas DC-8F Air Services.

249	**87**	30 f. grey, black and red . .	75	15

88 "Raft of the Medusa" (after Gericault)

1966. Air. 150th Anniv of Shipwreck of the "Medusa".

250	**88**	500 f. multicoloured	9·00	6·50

89 "Myrina silenus" — **90** "Hunting" (petroglyph from Tenses, Adrar)

1966. Butterflies. Multicoloured.

251	5 f. Type **89**	50	20
252	30 f. "Colotis danae"	1·25	40
253	45 f. "Hypolimnas misippus"	2·00	60
254	60 f. "Danaus chrysippus" . .	2·75	85

1966. Tourism and Archaeology (2nd series).

255	**90**	2 f. chestnut and brown . .	15	15
256	–	3 f. brown and blue	20	20
257	–	30 f. green and red	55	25
258	–	50 f. brown, green & pur . .	1·25	80

DESIGNS: 3 f. "Fighting" (petroglyph from Tenses, Adrar); 30 f. Copper jug (from Le Mreyer, Adrar); 50 f. Camel and caravan.

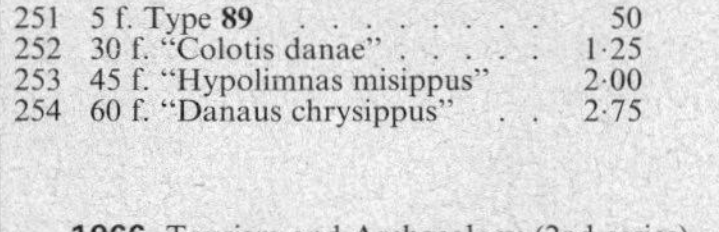

91 Cogwheels and Ears of Wheat

1966. Air. Europafrique.

259	**91**	50 f. multicoloured	70	40

92 U.N.E.S.C.O. Emblem

1966. 20th Anniv of U.N.E.S.C.O.

260	**92**	30 f. multicoloured	45	20

93 Olympic Village, Grenoble

1967. Publicity for Olympic Games (1968).

261	–	20 f. brown, blue and green	30	20
262	**93**	30 f. brown, green and blue	40	30
263	–	40 f. brown, purple & blue	60	40
264	–	100 f. brown, green & blk	1·10	70

DESIGNS—VERT: 20 f. Old and new buildings, Mexico City; 40 f. Ice rink, Grenoble and Olympic torch. HORIZ: 100 f. Olympic stadium, Mexico City.

94 South African Crowned Crane — **95** Globe, Rockets and Eye

1967. Air. Birds. Multicoloured.

265	100 f. Type **94**	4·50	1·60
266	200 f. Great egret	9·00	2·25
267	500 f. Ostrich	20·00	7·25

1967. Air. World Fair, Montreal.

268	**95**	250 f. brown, blue & black .	2·25	1·25

96 Prosopis — **97** Jamboree Emblem and Scout Kit

1967. Trees.

269	**96**	10 f. green, blue and brown	20	10
270	–	15 f. green, blue and purple	25	15
271	–	20 f. green, purple and blue	30	15
272	–	25 f. brown and green . . .	40	20
273	–	30 f. brown, green and red	55	25

TREES: 15 f. Jujube; 20 f. Date palm; 25 f. Peltophorum; 30 f. Baobab.

1967. World Scout Jamboree, Idaho.

274	**97**	60 f. blue, green and brown .	85	35
275	–	90 f. blue, green and red . .	1·40	50

DESIGN—HORIZ: 90 f. Jamboree emblem and scouts.

98 Weaving — **99** Atomic Symbol

1967. Advancement of Mauritanian Women.

276	**98**	5 f. red, black and violet . .	15	10
277	–	10 f. black, violet and green	20	10
278	–	20 f. black, purple and blue	35	15
279	–	30 f. blue, black and brown	45	25
280	–	50 f. black, violet & indigo	70	30

DESIGNS—VERT: 10 f. Needlework; 30 f. Laundering. HORIZ: 20 f. Nursing; 50 f. Sewing (with machines).

1967. Air. International Atomic Energy Agency.

281	**99**	200 f. blue, green and red . .	2·25	1·10

100 Cattle

1967. Campaign for Prevention of Cattle Plague.

282	**100**	30 f. red, blue and green . .	35	25

101 Map of Africa, Letters and Pylons

1967. Air. 5th Anniv of U.A.M.P.T.

283	**101**	100 f. green, brown & pur	1·00	60

102 "Francois of Rimini" (Ingres) — **103** Currency Tokens

1967. Air. Death Centenary of Jean Ingres (painter). Multicoloured.

284	90 f. Type **102**	1·25	60
285	200 f. "Ingres in his Studio" (Alaux)	2·50	1·25

See also Nos. 306/8.

1967. 5th Anniv of West African Monetary Union.

286	**103**	30 f. grey and orange . . .	35	15

104 "Hyphaene thebaica" — **105** Human Rights Emblem

1967. Mauritanian Fruits.

287	**104**	1 f. brown, green & purple	15	10
288	–	2 f. yellow, green & brown	15	10
289	–	3 f. olive, green and violet	15	10
290	–	4 f. red, green and brown	15	10
291	–	5 f. orange, brown & green	20	10

FRUITS—HORIZ: 2 f. "Balanites aegyptiaca"; 4 f. "Ziziphus lotus". VERT: 3 f. "Adansonia digitata"; 5 f. "Phoenix dactylifera".

1968. Human Rights Year.

292	**105**	30 f. yellow, green & black	30	20
293		50 f. yellow, brown & black .	55	35

106 Chancellor Adenauer — **108** Mosque, Nouakchott

107 Skiing

1968. Air. Adenauer Commemoration.

294	**106**	100 f. sepia, brown & blue	1·25	60

1968. Air. Olympic Games, Grenoble and Mexico.

296	**107**	20 f. purple, indigo & blue	30	10
297	–	30 f. brown, green & plum	35	15
298	–	50 f. green, blue and ochre	55	25
299	–	100 f. green, red & brown	1·00	50

DESIGNS—VERT: 30 f. Horse-vaulting; 50 f. Ski-jumping. HORIZ: 100 f. Hurdling.

1968. Tourism. Multicoloured.

300	30 f. Type **108**	25	20
301	45 f. Amogjar Pass	35	20
302	90 f. Cavaliers' Tower, Boutilimit	65	35

109 Man and W.H.O. Emblem

1968. Air. 20th Anniv of W.H.O.

303	**109**	150 f. blue, purple & brn .	1·50	75

110 U.N.E.S.C.O. Emblem and "Movement of Water"

1968. International Hydrological Decade.

304	**110**	90 f. green and lake . . .	70	40

111 U.P.U. Building, Berne

1968. Admission of Mauritania to U.P.U.

305	**111**	30 f. brown and red . . .	35	20

1968. Air. Paintings by Ingres. As T **102**. Mult.

306	100 f. "Man's Torso"	1·10	65
307	150 f. "The Iliad"	1·75	95
308	250 f. "The Odyssey"	2·75	1·60

112 Land-yachts crossing Desert

113 Dr. Martin Luther King

1968. Land-yacht Racing.

309 **112** 30 f. blue, yellow & orange . . 45 25
310 – 40 f. purple, blue & orange . . 55 30
311 – 60 f. green, yellow & orge . . 85 50

DESIGNS—HORIZ: 40 f. Racing on shore. VERT: 60 f. Crew making repairs.

1968. Air. "Apostles of Peace".

312 **113** 50 f. brown, blue and olive . 1·00 40
313 – 50 f. brown and blue . . . 60 25

DESIGN: No. 313, Mahatma Gandhi.

113a "Surprise Letter" (C. A. Coypel)

114 Donkey and Foal

1968. Air. "Philexafrique" Stamp Exn Abidjan, Ivory Coast, (1969) (1st issue).

315 **113a** 100 f. multicoloured . . . 1·75 1·75

1968. Domestic Animals. Multicoloured.

316 5 f. Type **114** 15 10
317 10 f. Ewe and lamb 20 15
318 15 f. Dromedary and calf . . . 25 15
319 30 f. Mare and foal 45 25
320 50 f. Cow and calf 70 35
321 90 f. Goat and kid . . . . . . 1·40 50

114a Forest Scene and Stamp of 1938

1969. Air. "Philexafrique" Stamp Exhibition, Abidjan, Ivory Coast (2nd issue).

322 **114a** 50 f. purple, green & brown 1·10 1·10

114b "Napoleon at Council of Five Hundred" (Bouchot)

115 Map and I.L.O. Emblem

1969. Air. Birth Bicentenary of Napoleon Bonaparte. Multicoloured.

323 50 f. **114b** . . . . 1·50 90
324 90 f. "Napoleon's Installation by the Council of State" (Conder) 2·00 1·25
325 250 f. "The Farewell of Fontainebleau" (Vernet) . . 5·00 3·25

1969. 50th Anniv of I.L.O.

326 **115** 50 f. multicoloured 50 25

116 Monitor Lizard

117 Date Palm, "Parlatoria blanchardi" and "Pharoscymus anchorage"

1969. Reptiles. Multicoloured.

327 5 f. Type **116** 35 20
328 10 f. Horned viper 55 30
329 30 f. Black-collared cobra . . . 1·25 35
330 60 f. Rock python . . . . . . 2·00 1·10
331 85 f. Nile crocodile . . . . . 3·00 1·40

1969. Date-palms. Protection Campaign.

332 **117** 30 f. blue, red and green . . 30 15

118 Camel and Emblem

1969. Air. African Tourist Year.

333 **118** 50 f. purple, blue & orange 85 35

119 Dancers and Baalbek Columns

1969. Baalbek Festival, Lebanon.

334 **119** 100 f. brown, red and blue 1·50 55

120 "Apollo 8" and Moon

1969. Air. Moon Flight of "Apollo 8". Embossed on gold foil.

335 **120** 1,000 f. gold . . . . . . 14·00 14·00

121 Wolde (marathon)

122a Bank Emblem

122 London–Istanbul Route-Map

1969. Air. Gold Medal Winners, Mexico Olympic Games.

336 **121** 30 f. red, brown and blue 25 15
337 – 70 f. red, brown and green 50 30
338 – 150 f. green, bistre and red 1·25 70

DESIGNS: 70 f. Beamon (athletics); 150 f. Vera Caslavska (gymnastics).

1969. Air. London–Sydney Motor Rally.

339 **122** 10 f. brown, blue & purple 25 10
340 – 20 f. brown, blue & purple 50 15
341 – 50 f. brown, blue & purple 85 25
342 – 70 f. brown, blue & purple 1·10 30

ROUTE-MAPS: 20 f. Ankara-Teheran; 50 f. Kandahar–Bombay; 70 f. Perth-Sydney.

1969. 5th Anniv of African Development Bank. Multicoloured.

344 **122a** 30 f. brown, green & blue 30 15

123 Pendant

124 Sea-water Desalination Plant, Nouakchott

1969. Native Handicrafts.

345 **123** 10 f. brown and purple . . 20 15
346 – 20 f. red, black and blue . . 40 20

DESIGN—HORIZ: 20 f. Rahla headdress.

1969. Economic Development.

347 **124** 10 f. blue, purple and red . 20 15
348 – 15 f. black, lake and blue . 25 15
349 – 30 f. black, purple & blue . 30 20

DESIGNS: 15 f. Fishing quay, Nouadhibou; 30 f. Meat-processing plant, Kaedi.

125 Lenin

126 "Sternocera interrupta"

1970. Birth Centenary of Lenin.

350 **125** 30 f. black, red and blue . . 30 20

1970. Insects.

351 **126** 5 f. black, buff and brown 25 15
352 – 10 f. brown, yellow & lake 35 15
353 – 20 f. olive, purple & brown 50 25
354 – 30 f. violet, green & brn 80 45
355 – 40 f. brown, blue and lake 1·50 70

INSECTS: 10 f. "Anoplocnemis curvipes"; 20 f. "Julodis aequinoctialis"; 30 f. "Thermophilum sexmaculatum marginatum"; 40 f. "Plocaederus denticornis".

127 Footballers and Hemispheres

128 Japanese Musician, Emblem and Map on Palette

1970. World Cup Football Championships, Mexico.

356 **127** 25 f. multicoloured 30 20
357 – 30 f. multicoloured 35 20
358 – 70 f. multicoloured 70 30
359 – 150 f. multicoloured . . . 1·60 75

DESIGNS: 30, 70, 150 f. As Type **127**, but with different players.

1970. New U.P.U. Headquarters Building. As T **81** of New Caledonia.

360 30 f. red, brown and green . . 35 20

1970. Air. "EXPO 70" World Fair, Osaka, Japan. Multicoloured.

361 50 f. Type **128** 50 20
362 75 f. Japanese fan 75 35
363 150 f. Stylised bird, map and boat . . . . 1·40 80

129 U.N. Emblem and Examples of Progress

1970. Air. 25th Anniv of U.N.O.

364 **129** 100 f. green, brown & blue 1·25 60

130 Vladimir Komarov

131 Descent of "Apollo 13"

1970. Air. "Lost Heroes of Space" (1st series).

365 **130** 150 f. brown, orge & slate . 1·50 70
366 – 150 f. brown, blue and slate 1·50 70
367 – 150 f. brown, orge & slate . 1·50 70

HEROES: No. 366, Elliott See; 367, Yuri Gagarin. See also Nos. 376/8.

1970. Air. Space Flight of "Apollo 13".

369 **131** 500 f. red, blue and gold . . 5·00 5·00

132 Woman in Traditional Costume

133 Arms and State House

1970. Traditional Costumes. As T **132**.

370 **132** 10 f. orange and brown . . 20 15
371 – 30 f. blue, red and brown 40 20
372 – 40 f. brown, purple & red 50 30
373 – 50 f. blue and brown . . . 70 35
374 – 70 f. brown, choc & bl . . . 90 45

1970. Air. 10th Anniv of Independence.

375 **133** 100 f. multicoloured . . . 1·00 45

1970. Air. "Lost Heroes of Space" (2nd series). As T **130**.

376 150 f. brown, blue & turquoise 1·50 70
377 150 f. brown, blue & turquoise 1·50 70
378 150 f. brown, blue and orange 1·50 70

HEROES: No. 376, Roger Chaffee; No. 377, Virgil Grissom; No. 378, Edward White.

134 Greek Wrestling

1971. Air. "Pre-Olympics Year".

380 **134** 100 f. brown, purple & bl 1·10 75

135 People of Different Races

1971. Racial Equality Year.

381 **135** 30 f. plum, blue & brown 30 15
382 – 40 f. black, red and blue 35 20

DESIGN—VERT: 40 f. European and African hands.

136 Pres. Nasser

1971. Air. Pres. Gamal Nasser of Egypt Commemoration.

383 **136** 100 f. multicoloured . . . 85 40

137 Gen. De Gaulle in Uniform

138 Scout Badge, Scout and Map

1971. De Gaulle Commem. Multicoloured.
384 40 f. Type **137** . . . . 1·25 60
385 100 f. De Gaulle as President of France . . . . 2·75 1·40

1971. Air. 13th World Scout Jamboree, Asagiri, Japan.
387 **138** 35 f. multicoloured 40 20
388 40 f. multicoloured 50 20
389 100 f. multicoloured . . . 1·25 45

139 Diesel Locomotive

1971. Miferma Iron-ore Mines. Multicoloured.
390 35 f. Iron ore train . . . . . . 2·25 1·00
391 100 f. Type **139** . . . . 5·00 2·50
Nos. 390/1 were issued together, se-tenant, forming a composite design.

139a Headquarters, Brazzaville, and Ardin Musicians

1971. Air. 10th Anniv of African and Malagasy Posts and Telecommunications Union.
392 **139a** 100 f. multicoloured . . . 1·10 60

140 A.P.U. Emblem and Airmail Envelope

1971. Air. 10th Anniv of African Postal Union.
393 **140** 35 f. multicoloured 40 25

141 U.N.I.C.E.F. Emblem and Child

1971. 25th Anniv of U.N.I.C.E.F.
394 **141** 35 f. black, brown & blue 35 20

142 "Moslem King" (c. 1218)

1972. Air. Moslem Miniatures. Multicoloured.
395 35 f. Type **142** 45 20
396 40 f. "Enthroned Prince" (Egypt, c. 1334) 60 25
397 100 f. "Pilgrims' Caravan" (Maquamat, Baghdad 1237) 1·50 70

1972. Air. U.N.E.S.C.O. "Save Venice" Campaign. As T **127** of Mali. Multicoloured.
398 45 f. "Quay and Ducal Palace" (Carlevaris) (vert) 60 25
399 100 f. "Grand Canal" (Canaletto) . . . . 1·40 60
400 250 f. "Santa Maria della Salute" (Canaletto) . . . . 3·00 1·50

143 Hurdling

1972. Air. Olympic Games, Munich.
401 **143** 75 f. purple, orange & grn 55 30
402 100 f. purple, blue & brn 75 40
403 200 f. purple, lake & green 1·60 70

144 Nurse tending Baby

145 Samuel Morse and Morse Key

1972. Mauritanian Red Crescent Fund.
405 **144** 35 f. + 5 f. multicoloured . 60 60

1972. World Telecommunications Day. Mult.
406 35 f. Type **145** 35 20
407 40 f. "Relay" satellite and hemispheres 45 20
408 75 f. Alexander Graham Bell and early telephone 70 35

146 Spirifer Shell

1972. Fossil Shells. Multicoloured.
409 25 f. Type **146** . . . . 1·00 35
410 75 f. Trilobite . . . . 2·75 1·10

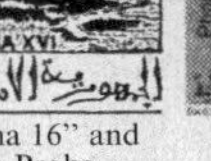

147 "Luna 16" and Moon Probe

151 Mediterranean Monk Seal with Young

149 Africans and 500 f. Coin

1972. Air. Russian Exploration of the Moon.
411 **147** 75 f. brown, blue & green . 60 30
412 – 100 f. brown, grey & violet 90 50
DESIGN—HORIZ: 100 f. "Lunokhod 1".

1972. Air. Gold Medal-Winners, Munich. Nos. 401/3 optd as listed below.
413 **143** 75 f. purple, orange & grn 60 30
414 100 f. purple, blue & brn 80 50
415 200 f. purple, lake & green 1·60 1·00
OVERPRINTS: 75 f. **110m. HAIES MILBURN MEDAILLE D'OR**; 100 f. **400m. HAIES AKII-BUA MEDAILLE D'OR**; 200 f. **3,000m. STEEPLE KEINO MEDAILLE D'OR**.

1972. 10th Anniv of West African Monetary Union.
416 **149** 35 f. grey, brown & green 30 20

1973. Air. Moon Flight of "Apollo 17". No. 267 surch **Apollo XVII Decembre 1972** and value.
417 250 f. on 500 f. multicoloured . 4·00 2·00

1973. Seals. Multicoloured.
418 40 f. Type **151** (postage) . . . 1·50 50
419 135 f. Head of Mediterranean monk seal (air) . . . . . . 4·00 2·00

152 "Lion and Crocodile" (Delacroix)

1973. Air. Paintings by Delacroix. Mult.
420 100 f. Type **152** . . . . 1·50 75
421 250 f. "Lion attacking Forest Hog" . . . . 3·25 2·00

153 "Horns of Plenty"

1973. 10th Anniv of World Food Programme.
422 **153** 35 f. multicoloured 30 20

154 U.P.U. Monument, Berne, and Globe

1973. World U.P.U. Day.
423 **154** 100 f. blue, orange & grn 1·00 65

155 Nomad Encampment and Eclipse

1973. Total Eclipse of the Sun.
424 **155** 35 f. purple and green . . . 35 20
425 – 40 f. purple, red and blue 45 20
426 – 140 f. purple and red . . . 1·60 75
DESIGNS—VERT: 40 f. Rocket and Concorde. HORIZ: 140 f. Observation team.

1973. "Drought Relief". African Solidarity. No. 320 surch **SECHERESSE SOLIDARITE AFRICAINE** and value.
428 20 um. on 50 f. multicoloured . 65 45

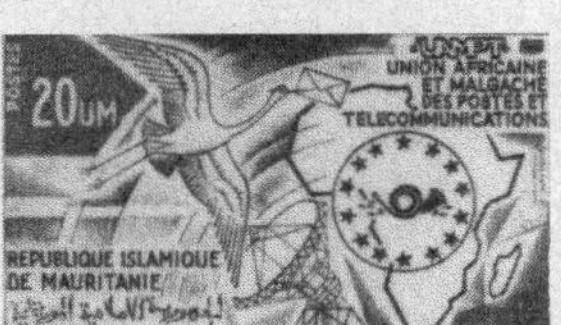

155a Crane with Letter and Union Emblem

1973. 12th Anniv of African and Malagasy Posts and Telecommunications Union.
429 **155a** 20 um. brown, lt brn & orge 1·00 45

157 Detective making Arrest and Fingerprint

1973. 50th Anniv of International Criminal Police Organization (Interpol).
430 **157** 15 um. violet, red & brown . 1·10 45

1974. Various stamps surch with values in new currency. (a) Postage.

(i) Nos. 345/6.
431 **123** 27 um. on 10 f. brown and purple . . . . 1·50 70
432 – 28 um. on 20 f. red, black and blue . . . . 1·75 90

(ii) Nos. 351/5.
433 **126** 5 um. on 5 f. black, buff and brown 70 50
434 – 7 um. on 10 f. brown, yellow and lake 60 30
435 – 8 um. on 20 f. olive, purple and brown 70 35
436 – 10 um. on 30 f. violet, purple and brown . . . . . 1·00 45
437 – 20 um. on 4 f. brown, blue and lake . . . . 2·00 1·10

(iii) Nos. 409/10.
438 **146** 5 um. on 25 f. mult 60 40
439 – 15 um. on 75 f. mult . . . 1·75 1·00

(iv) No. 418.
440 **151** 8 um. on 40 f. multicoloured 90 45

(b) Air.
(i) Nos. 395/7.
441 **142** 7 um. on 35 f. mult 40 20
442 – 8 um. on 40 f. mult 40 20
443 – 20 um. on 100 f. mult . . . 1·50 70

(ii) No. 419.
444 – 27 um. on 135 f. multicoloured . . . . . . 2·25 85

(iii) Nos. 420/1.
445 **152** 20 um. on 100 f. mult . . . 1·60 70
446 – 50 um. on 250 f. mult . . . 3·75 2·00

(iv) Nos. 424/6.
447 **155** 7 um. on 35 f. purple and green 45 20
448 – 8 um. on 40 f. purple, red and blue 45 20
449 – 28 um. on 140 f. purple and red . . . . 1·90 70

159 Footballers

161 Sir Winston Churchill

160 Jules Verne and Scenes from Books

1974. Air. World Cup Football Championships, West Germany.
450 **159** 7 um. multicoloured . . . 40 20
451 8 um. multicoloured . . . 40 20
452 20 um. multicoloured . . . 1·10 50

1974. Air. Jules Verne "Prophet of Space Travel" and "Skylab" Flights Commemoration.
454 **160** 70 um. silver . . . . . . 4·50 4·50
455 – 70 um. silver . . . . . . 4·50 4·50
456 **160** 250 um. gold . . . . . . 12·00 12·00
457 – 250 um. gold . . . . . . 12·00 12·00
DESIGNS: Nos. 455, 457, "Skylab" in Space.

1974. Air. Birth Centenary of Sir Winston Churchill.
458 **161** 40 um. red and purple . . 1·75 95

162 U.P.U. Monument and Globes

1974. Centenary of U.P.U.
459 **162** 30 um. red, green and deep green . . . . 1·25 75
460 50 um. red, light blue and blue . . . . 2·00 1·25

163 5 Ouguiya Coin and Banknote

1974. 1st Anniv of Introduction of Ouguiya Currency.
461 **163** 7 um. black, green and blue 35 20
462 – 8 um. black, mauve and green 40 20
463 – 20 um. black, blue and red . . . . 1·00 50
DESIGNS: 8 u. 10 ouguiya coin and banknote; 20 um. 20 ouguiya coin and banknote.

164 Lenin

166 Two Hunters

1974. Air. 50th Death Anniv of Lenin.
464 **164** 40 um. green and red . . . 2·00 95

1974. Treaty of Berne Centenary. Nos. 459/60 optd **9 OCTOBRE 100 ANS D'UNION POSTALE INTERNATIONALE**.
465 **162** 30 um. red, green and deep green . . . . 1·60 80
466 50 um. red, light blue and blue . . . . 2·00 1·25

1975. Nos. 287/91 surch in new currency.
467 – 1 um. on 5 f. orange, brown and green 10 10
468 – 2 um. on 4 f. red, green and brown 15 15
469 – 3 um. on 2 f. yellow, green and brown 20 15
470 **104** 10 um. on 1 f. brown, green and purple 60 20
471 – 12 um. on 3 f. olive, green and violet 75 30

1975. Rock-carvings, Zemmour.
472 **166** 4 um. red and brown . . . 40 15
473 – 5 um. purple 45 25
474 – 10 um. blue and light blue . . 80 35
DESIGNS—VERT: 5 um. Ostrich. HORIZ: 10 um. Elephant.

167 Mauritanian Women

1975. Air. International Women's Year.
475 **167** 12 um. purple, brown & bl 50 25
476 – 40 um. purple, brown & bl 1·75 85
DESIGNS: 40 um. Head of Mauritanian woman.

168 Combined European and African Heads

169 Dr. Schweitzer

1975. Europafrique.
477 **168** 40 um. brown, red & bistre . 1·60 95

1975. Birth Centenary of Dr. Albert Schweitzer.
478 **169** 60 um. olive, brown & green 2·50 1·50

1975. Pan-African Drought Relief. Nos. 301/2 surch **SECHERESSE SOLIDARITE AFRICAINE** and value.
479 15 um. on 45 f. multicoloured . 1·00 50
480 25 um. on 90 f. multicoloured . 1·40 75

171 Akoujt Plant and Man with Camel

172 Fair Emblem

1975. Mining Industry.
481 **171** 10 um. brown, blue & orge 1·25 30
482 – 12 um. blue, red and brown 1·50 40
DESIGN: 12 um. Mining operations.

1975. Nouakchott National Fair.
483 **172** 10 um. multicoloured . . . 40 25

173 Throwing the Javelin

1975. Air. "Pre-Olympic Year". Olympic Games, Montreal (1976).
484 **173** 50 um. red, green & brown 1·60 1·40
485 – 52 um. blue, brown and red 1·75 1·40
DESIGN: 52 um. Running.

174 Commemorative Medal

1975. 15th Anniv of Independence. Multicoloured.
486 10 um. Type **174** 50 30
487 12 um. Map of Mauritania . . 1·60 60

175 "Soyuz" Cosmonauts Leonov and Kubasov

1975. "Apollo-Soyz" Space Link. Multicoloured.
488 8 um. Type **175** (postage) . . . 45 20
489 10 um. "Soyuz" on launch-pad 55 25
490 20 um. "Apollo" on launch-pad (air) 70 45
491 50 um. Cosmonauts meeting astronauts . . . . 2·00 1·00
492 60 um. Parachute splashdown . 2·25 1·25

176 Foot-soldier of Lauzun's Legion

1976. Bicentenary of American Independence. Multicoloured.
494 8 um. Type **176** (postage) . . . 60 20
495 10 um. "Green Mountain" infantryman 70 20
496 20 um. Lauzun Hussar's officer (air) 90 40
497 50 um. Artillery officer of 3rd Continental Regiment . . . 2·40 1·00
498 60 um. Grenadier of Gatinais' Regiment . . . . 3·00 1·25

1976. 10th Anniv of Arab Labour Charter. No. 408 surch **10e ANNIVERSAIRE DE LA CHARTE ARABE DU TRAVAIL** in French and Arabic.
500 12 um. on 75 f. blue, blk & grn 55 30

178 Commemorative Text on Map

1976. Reunification of Mauritania.
501 **178** 10 um. green, lilac and deep green 45 30

181 Running

1976. Air. Olympic Games, Montreal.
514 **181** 10 um. brown, green and violet 40 25
515 – 12 um. brown, green and violet 50 35
516 – 52 um. brown, green and violet . . . . 1·75 1·25
DESIGNS: 12 um. Vaulting (gymnastics); 52 um. Fencing.

182 LZ-4 at Friedrichshafen

1976. 75th Anniv of Zeppelin Airship. Mult.
517 5 um. Type **182** (postage) . . . 25 15
518 10 um. "Schwaben" over German Landscape 40 20
519 12 um. "Hansa" over Heligoland 50 25
520 20 um. "Bodensee" and Doctor H. Durr . . . . 2·50 75
521 50 um. "Graf Zeppelin" over Capitol, Washington (air) . . 2·25 90
522 60 um. "Graf Zeppelin II" crossing Swiss Alps . . . . 3·00 1·25

183 Temple and Bas-relief

1976. U.N.E.S.C.O. "Save Moenjodaro" (Pakistan) Campaign.
524 **183** 15 um. multicoloured . . . 80 40

184 Sacred Ibis and Yellow-billed Stork

185 Alexander Graham Bell, Early Telephone and Satellite

1976. Air. Mauritanian Birds. Multicoloured.
525 50 um. Type **184** . . . . . . 5·00 1·90
526 100 um. Marabou storks (horiz) . . . . 8·50 4·25
527 200 um. Long-crested and Martial eagles . . . . 18·00 7·25

1976. Telephone Centenary.
528 **185** 10 um. blue, lake and red . 50 25

186 Mohammed Ali Jinnah

1976. Birth Centenary of Mohammed Ali Jinnah (first Governor-General of Pakistan).
529 **186** 10 um. multicoloured . . . 35 20

187 Capsule Assembly

1977. "Viking" Space Mission. Multicoloured.
530 10 um. Misson Control (horiz) . 50 15
531 12 um. Type **187** 55 20
532 20 um. "Viking" in flight (horiz) (air) 80 25
533 50 um. "Viking" over Mars (horiz) . . . . 2·00 60
534 60 um. Parachute descent . . . 2·25 65

188 Bush Hare

1977. Mauritanian Animals. Multicoloured.
536 5 um. Type **188** 30 15
537 10 um. Golden jackals 65 30
538 12 um. Warthogs 90 40
539 14 um. Lion and lioness . . . 1·00 50
540 15 um. African elephants . . . 1·90 80

189 Frederic and Irene Joliot-Curie (Chemistry, 1935)

1977. Nobel Prize-winners. Multicoloured.
541 12 um. Type **189** (postage) . . 75 15
542 15 um. Emil von Behring and nurse inoculating patient (1901) 75 20
543 14 um. George Bernard Shaw and scene from "Androcles and the Lion" (1925) (air) 75 30
544 55 um. Thomas Mann and scene from "Joseph and his Brethren" (1929) . . . . . 1·90 60
545 60 um. International Red Cross and scene on Western Front (Peace Prize) (1917) . . . . . 2·25 70

190 A.P.U. Emblem

1977. 25th Anniv of Arab Postal Union.
547 **190** 12 um. multicoloured . . . 45 30

191 Oil Lamp

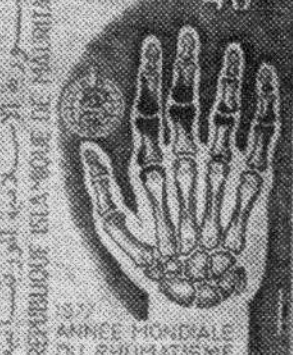

192 Skeleton of Hand

1977. Pottery from Tegdaoust.

548 **191** 1 um. olive, brown and blue . . . 10 10
549 – 2 um. mauve, brown & blue . . . 15 10
550 – 5 um. orange, brown & blue . . . 25 10
551 – 12 um. brown, green and red . . 55 20

DESIGNS: 2 um. Four-handled tureen; 5 um. Large jar; 12 um. Narrow-necked jug.

1977. World Rheumatism Year.

552 **192** 40 um. orange, brown & grn 2·00 1·25

193 Holy Kaaba, Mecca

1977. Air. Pilgrimage to Mecca.

553 **193** 12 um. multicoloured . . . 60 40

194 Charles Lindbergh and "Spirit of St. Louis"

1977. History of Aviation. Multicoloured.

554 12 um. Type **194** 60 15
555 14 um. Clement Ader and "Eole" 70 25
556 15 um. Louis Bleriot and Bleriot XI 85 25
557 55 um. General Italo Balbo and Savoia Marchetti S-55X flying boats . . . . 2·50 70
558 60 um. Concorde . . . . . . 2·75 85

195 Dome of the Rock

197 "Helene Fourment and Her Children" (Rubens)

196 Two Players

1977. Palestinian Welfare.

560 **195** 12 um. multicoloured . . . 70 30
561 14 um. multicoloured . . . 80 35

1977. World Cup Football Championships–Elimination Rounds. Multicoloured.

562 12 um. Type **196** (postage) . . 40 15
563 14 um. Sir Alf Ramsey and Wembley Stadium 50 20
564 15 um. A "throw-in" 60 20
565 50 um. Football and emblems (air) . . . . 2·00 60
566 60 um. Eusebio Ferreira . . . 2·40 1·00

1977. 400th Birth Anniv of Rubens. Paintings. Multicoloured.

568 12 um. Type **197** 50 15
569 14 um. "The Marquis of Spinola" 60 20
570 67 um. "The Four Philosophers" 2·25 75
571 69 um. "Steen Castle and Park" (horiz) . . . . 2·50 85

198 Addra Gazelles

1978. Endangered Animals. Multicoloured.

573 5 um. Scimitar oryx (horiz) . . 35 15
574 12 um. Type **198** 65 25
575 14 um. African manatee (horiz) . 80 35
576 55 um. Barbary sheep . . . . 3·00 1·00
577 60 um. African elephant (horiz) . 3·25 1·25
578 100 um. Ostrich . . . . 4·50 1·75

199 Clasped Hands and President Giscard d'Estaing of France

1978. Air. Franco-African Co-operation. Embossed on foil.

579 **199** 250 um. silver . . . . . . 7·00 7·00
580 500 um. gold . . . . . . 14·00 14·00

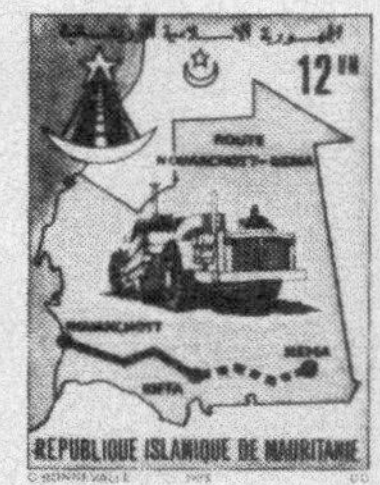

199a Earth-mover and Route Map

200 Footballers

1978. Nouakchott–Nema Highway. Mult.

580a 12 um. Type **199a** . . . . . . 2·00 1·50
580b 14 um. Bulldozer and route map 2·25 1·75

1978. World Cup Football Championship, Argentina. Multicoloured.

581 12 um. Type **200** 40 20
582 14 um. World Cup 50 25
583 20 um. F.I.F.A. flag and football 85 35

201 Raoul Follereau and St. George fighting Dragon

1978. 25th Anniv of Raoul Follereau Foundation.

585 **201** 12 um. brown and green . . 70 40

202 Emblem and People holding Hands

203 Charles de Gaulle

1978. International Anti-Apartheid Year.

586 – 25 um. brown, blue and red 90 60
587 **202** 30 um. brown, blue & green 1·10 70

DESIGN—HORIZ: 25 um. Emblem and people behind fence.

1978. Personalities. Multicoloured.

588 12 um. Type **203** 90 30
589 14 um. King Baudouin of Belgium 90 30
590 55 um. Queen Elizabeth II (25th anniv of Coronation) . . . . 2·00 90

1978. Air. "Philexafrique" Stamp Exhibition, Libreville (Gabon) (1st issue), and 2nd International Stamp Fair, Essen (West Germany). As T **262** of Niger. Multicoloured.

591 20 um. Water rail and Hamburg 1859 ½ s. stamp . . . . . . 1·00 65
592 20 um. Spotted hyena and Mauritania 1967 100 f. South African crowned crane stamp 1·00 65

See also Nos. 619/20.

1978. Argentina's Victory in World Cup Football Championship. Nos. 562/6 optd **ARGENTINE–PAYS BAS 3-1** in English and Arabic.

593 **196** 12 um. mult (postage) . . . 50 25
594 – 14 um. multicoloured . . . 55 30
595 – 15 um. multicoloured . . . 65 30
596 – 50 um. multicoloured (air) . 1·75 1·10
597 – 60 um. multicoloured . . . 2·25 1·40

205 View of Nouakchott

1978. 20th Anniv of Nouakchott.

599 **205** 12 um. multicoloured . . . 45 30

206 Human Rights Emblem

208 Key Chain

207 Wright Flyer I and Clement Ader's Avion III

1978. 30th Anniv of Declaration of Human Rights.

600 **206** 55 um. red and blue . . . 1·60 1·25

1979. Air. 75th Anniv of First Powered Flight.

601 **207** 15 um. grey, red and blue . 1·00 35
602 – 40 um. violet, blue & brn 2·00 1·10

DESIGN: 40 um. Concorde and Wright Flyer I.

1979. Handicrafts. Multicoloured.

603 5 um. Type **208** 25 15
604 7 um. Tooth-brush case 30 20
605 10 um. Knife sheath 45 25

209 "Market Peasant and Wife"

210 Seated Buddha, Temple of Borobudur

1979. 450th Birth Anniv of Albrecht Durer (artist).

606 **209** 12 um. black and red . . . 70 30
607 – 14 um. black and red . . . 60 25
608 – 55 um. black and red . . . 1·60 75
609 – 60 um. black and red . . . 1·90 1·00

DESIGNS: 14 um. "Young Peasant and his Wife"; 55 um. "Mercenary with Banner"; 60 um. "St. George and the Dragon".

1979. U.N.E.S.C.O. Campaign for Preservation of Historic Monuments. Multicoloured.

611 12 um. Type **210** 50 30
612 14 um. Carthaginian warrior and hunting dog 60 30
613 55 um. Erechtheum Caryatid, Acropolis . . . . 1·75 1·25

211 Rowland Hill and Paddle-steamer "Sirius"

1979. Death Centenary of Sir Rowland Hill. Multicoloured.

614 12 um. Type **211** 50 25
615 14 um. Hill and "Great Republic" (paddle-steamer) . 65 25
616 55 um. Hill and "Mauretania I" (liner) . . . . 2·00 60
617 60 um. Hill and "Stirling Castle" (liner) . . . . 2·50 85

212 Satellite over Earth

1979. "Philexafrique" Exhibition, Libreville (2nd issue).

619 – 12 um. multicoloured . . . 60 50
620 **212** 30 um. red, blue and lilac . 1·40 1·25

DESIGN—HORIZ: 12 um. Embossed leather cushion cover.

213 Mother and Children

215 Sprinter on Starting-blocks

1979. International Year of the Child. Multicoloured.

621 12 um. Type **213** 45 25
622 14 um. Mother with sleeping baby 55 35
623 40 um. Children playing with ball 1·50 90

1979. 10th Anniv of "Apollo 11" Moon Landing. Nos. 530/4 optd **ALUNISSAGE APOLLO XI JUILLET 1969**, with Lunar module, or surch also.

624 10 um. Mission Control (horiz) (postage) 40 25
625 12 um. Type **187** 45 30
626 14 um. on 20 u. "Viking" in flight (horiz) (air) 60 25
627 50 um. "Viking" over Mars (horiz) . . . . 1·60 1·00
628 60 um. Parachute descent . . . 1·90 1·10

1979. Pre-Olympic Year. Multicoloured.

630 12 um. Type **215** 35 15
631 14 um. Female runner 40 15
632 55 um. Male runner leaving start 1·50 60
633 60 um. Hurdling . . . . . . 1·60 60

215a Skipper

1979. Fishes. Multicoloured.

634a 1 um. Type **215a** 10 10
634b 2 um. Swordfish 25 15
634c 5 um. Tub gurnard 40 20

216 Ice Hockey

1979. Winter Olympic Games, Lake Placid (1980). Ice Hockey. Multicoloured.

635 10 um. Type **216** 40 20
636 12 um. Saving a goal 45 25
637 14 um. Goalkeeper and player . . 55 25
638 55 um. Two players . . . . . 2·00 60
639 60 um. Goalkeeper . . . . . 2·25 65
640 100 um. Tackle . . . . 3·50 1·25

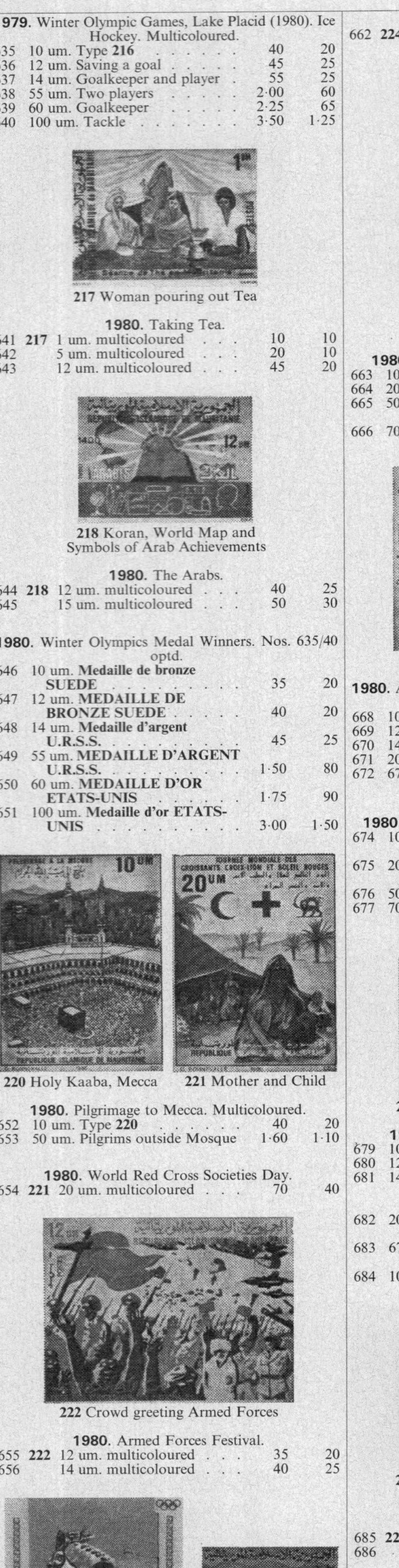

217 Woman pouring out Tea

1980. Taking Tea.

641 **217** 1 um. multicoloured . . . 10 10
642 5 um. multicoloured . . . 20 10
643 12 um. multicoloured . . . 45 20

218 Koran, World Map and Symbols of Arab Achievements

1980. The Arabs.

644 **218** 12 um. multicoloured . . . 40 25
645 15 um. multicoloured . . . 50 30

1980. Winter Olympics Medal Winners. Nos. 635/40 optd.

646 10 um. **Medaille de bronze SUEDE** 35 20
647 12 um. **MEDAILLE DE BRONZE SUEDE** 40 20
648 14 um. **Medaille d'argent U.R.S.S.** 45 25
649 55 um. **MEDAILLE D'ARGENT U.R.S.S.** . . . . . . 1·50 80
650 60 um. **MEDAILLE D'OR ETATS-UNIS** . . . . . . 1·75 90
651 100 um. **Medaille d'or ETATS-UNIS** . . . . 3·00 1·50

220 Holy Kaaba, Mecca **221** Mother and Child

1980. Pilgrimage to Mecca. Multicoloured.

652 10 um. Type **220** 40 20
653 50 um. Pilgrims outside Mosque 1·60 1·10

1980. World Red Cross Societies Day.

654 **221** 20 um. multicoloured . . . 70 40

222 Crowd greeting Armed Forces

1980. Armed Forces Festival.

655 **222** 12 um. multicoloured . . . 35 20
656 14 um. multicoloured . . . 40 25

223 Horse jumping Bar **224** Trees on Map of Mauritania

1980. Olympic Games, Moscow. Multicoloured.

657 10 um. Type **223** 30 20
658 20 um. Water polo 55 30
659 50 um. Horse jumping brick wall (horiz) . . . . 1·40 55
660 70 um. Horse jumping stone wall 1·90 75

1980. Tree Day.

662 **224** 12 um. multicoloured . . . 35 20

225 "Rembrandt's Mother"

1980. Paintings by Rembrandt. Multicoloured.

663 10 um. "Self-portrait" 30 20
664 20 um. Type **225** 75 30
665 50 um. "Portrait of a Man in Oriental Costume" . . . . . 1·75 55
666 70 um. "Titus Lisant" . . . . 2·25 75

226 Footballers

1980. Air. World Cup Football Championship, Spain (1982). Multicoloured.

668 10 um. Type **226** 30 20
669 12 um. Goalkeeper and players . 35 20
670 14 um. Goalkeeper catching ball 40 25
671 20 um. Fighting for possession . 55 30
672 67 um. Tackle . . . . 1·90 75

1980. Olympic Medal Winners. Nos. 657/60 optd.

674 10 um. **VAINQUEUR KOWALLZYK (POL)** . . . 30 20
675 20 um. **VAINQUEUR THEURER (AUTR)** 55 30
676 50 um. **VAINQUEUR URSS** 1·40 55
677 70 um. **VAINQUEUR ROMAN (IT)** . . . . 1·90 75

228 "Mastodonte del Giovi", 1853, Italy

1980. Steam Locomotives. Multicoloured.

679 10 um. Type **228** 55 15
680 12 um. Diesel ore train 60 15
681 14 um. Chicago, Milwaukee and St. Paul Railway locomotive No. 810, U.S.A. 75 20
682 20 um. Bury steam locomotive, 1837, Great Britain . . . . 1·00 25
683 67 um. Locomotive No. 170, France . . . . 3·50 55
684 100 um. Berlin–Potsdam line, Germany . . . . 5·25 95

229 Palm Tree, Crescent and Star, Maize and Map

1980. 20th Anniv of Independence.

685 **229** 12 um. multicoloured . . . 40 20
686 15 um. multicoloured . . . 50 30

230 El Haram Mosque

1981. 15th Century of Hegira. Multicoloured.

687 2 um. Type **230** 10 10
688 12 um. Medine Mosque 40 20
689 14 um. Chinguetti Mosque . . . 50 30

231 Space Shuttle in Orbit

1981. Air. Space Shuttle. Multicoloured.

690 12 um. Type **231** 40 20
691 20 um. Shuttle and space station 85 30
692 50 um. Shuttle performing experiment . . . . 1·75 75
693 70 um. Shuttle landing . . . . 2·50 1·00

232 "The Harlequin"

1981. Air. Birth Centenary of Pablo Picasso. Multicoloured.

695 12 um. Type **232** 50 20
696 20 um. "Vase of Flowers" . . . 75 30
697 50 um. "Three Women at a Fountain" (horiz) . . . . . 1·40 75
698 70 um. "Dinard Landscape" (horiz) . . . . 2·25 1·00
699 100 um. "Le Dejeuner sur l'Herbe" (horiz) . . . . . . 3·00 1·50

233 I.Y.D.P. Emblem

1981. International Year of Disabled People.

700 **233** 12 um. violet, gold & blue 45 30

234 Open Landau

1981. British Royal Wedding. Multicoloured.

701 14 um. Type **234** 40 20
702 18 um. Light carriage 45 20
703 77 um. Closed coupe . . . . . 1·40 1·10

235 George Washington

1981. Bicentenary of Battles of Yorktown and Chesapeake Bay. Multicoloured.

705 14 um. Type **235** 45 25
706 18 um. Admiral de Grasse . . 55 25
707 63 um. Surrender of Cornwallis at Yorktown (horiz) . . . . 1·75 95
708 81 um. Battle of Chesapeake Bay (horiz) . . . . 2·25 1·50

236 Columbus and "Pinta"

1981. 450th Death Anniv of Christopher Columbus. Multicoloured.

709 19 um. Type **236** . . . . . . 1·00 40
710 55 um. Columbus and "Santa Maria" . . . . 2·75 1·10

237 Wheat and F.A.O. Emblem **238** Kemal Ataturk

1981. World Food Day.

711 **237** 19 um. multicoloured . . . 60 40

1981. Birth Centenary of Kemal Ataturk (Turkish statesman).

712 **238** 63 um. multicoloured . . . 2·00 1·25

239 Eastern White Pelicans

1981. Birds of the Arguin. Multicoloured.

713 2 um. Type **239** 40 15
714 18 um. Greater flamingoes . . 1·60 70

240 Hand holding Torn Flag

1981. Battle of Karameh Commemoration.

715 **240** 14 um. multicoloured . . . 45 30

241 "Dermochelys coiacer"

1981. Turtles. Multicoloured.

716 1 um. Type **241** 30 15
717 3 um. "Chelonia mydas" . . . 40 15
718 4 um. "Eretmochelys imbricata" 50 15

242 Sea Scouts

1982. 75th Anniv of Boy Scout Movement. Multicoloured.

719 14 um. Type **242** 55 25
720 19 um. Scouts boarding rowing boat 90 35
721 22 um. Scouts in rowing boat . 1·00 40
722 92 um. Scouts in yacht . . . . 3·00 1·25

243 Deusenberg, 1921

1982. 75th Anniv of French Grand Prix Motor Race. Multicoloured.

724 7 um. Type **243** 50 20
725 12 um. Alfa Romeo, 1932 . . . 60 20
726 14 um. Juan Fangio 75 35
727 18 um. Renault, 1979 . . . . 1·00 40
728 19 um. Niki Lauda . . . . . 1·00 45

244 A.P.U. Emblem **245** Hexagonal Pattern

1982. 30th Anniv of Arab Postal Union.
730 **244** 14 um. orange and brown 45 30

1982. World Telecommunications Day.
731 **245** 21 um. multicoloured . . . 65 45

246 Environmental Emblem on Map

1982. 10th Anniv of U.N. Environmental Programme.
732 **246** 14 um. blue and light blue 45 30

247 Princess of Wales

1982. 21st Birthday of Princess of Wales. Mult.
733 21 um. Type **247** 75 35
734 77 um. Princess of Wales (different) . . . . 2·40 1·10

248 Straw Hut

1982. Traditional Houses. Multicoloured.
736 14 um. Type **248** 45 30
737 18 um. Thatched hut 55 45
738 19 um. Tent 60 45

1982. Birth of Prince William of Wales. Nos. 701/3 surch **NAISSANCE ROYALE 1982**.
739 14 um. Type **234** 45 35
740 18 um. Light carriage 55 40
741 77 um. Closed coupe . . . . . 2·40 1·25

1982. Air. World Cup Football Championship Results. Nos. 668/72 optd **ITALIE 3 ALLEMAGNE (R.F.A.) 1**.
743 10 um. Type **226** 40 25
744 12 um. Goalkeeper punching ball 40 30
745 14 um. Goalkeeper catching ball 45 30
746 20 um. Three players 70 40
747 67 um. Tackle . . . . . . 2·25 1·40

251 Cattle at Collinaire Dam, Hodh El Gharbi

1992. Agricultural Development.
749 14 um. Type **251** . . . . . 1·25 1·10
750 18 um. Irrigation canal, Gorgol 1·75 1·25

252 Desert Rose

1982. Desert Rose.
751 **252** 21 um. multicoloured . . . 1·50 1·00

253 Montgolfier Balloon, 1783

1983. Bicent of Manned Flight. Multicoloured.
752 14 um. Type **253** 65 20
753 18 um. Charles's hydrogen balloon ascent, 1783 (horiz) . 65 30
754 19 um. Goodyear Aerospace airship 65 30
755 55 um. Nieuport 11 "Bebe" biplane (horiz) . . . . . 1·75 70
756 63 um. Concorde (horiz) . . . 3·00 1·00
757 77 um. "Apollo 11" on Moon . 2·50 1·00
No. 754 is wrongly inscribed "Zeppelin".

254 Ouadane

1983. Protection of Ancient Sites. Multicoloured.
758 14 um. Type **254** 40 25
759 18 um. Chinguetti 50 30
760 24 um. Oualata 70 45
761 30 um. Tichitt . . . . . . 1·00 55

255 Manuscript **256** I.M.O. Emblem

1983. Ancient Manuscripts. Multicoloured.
762 2 um. Type **255** 10 10
763 5 um. Decorated manuscript . . 15 15
764 7 um. Shield-shaped patterned manuscript 25 20

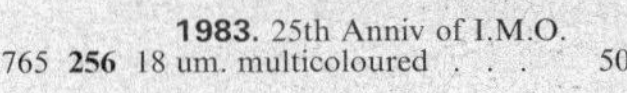

1983. 25th Anniv of I.M.O.
765 **256** 18 um. multicoloured . . . 50 30

257 W.C.Y. Emblem

1983. World Communications Year.
766 **257** 14 um. multicoloured . . . 55 30

258 Customs Emblems

1983. 30th Anniv of Customs Co-operation Council.
767 **258** 14 um. multicoloured . . . 45 30

259 Pilatre de Rozier and Montgolfier Balloon **260** Grinding Stone

1983. Bicentenary of Manned Flight. Mult.
768 10 um. Type **259** (postage) . . 40 20
769 14 um. John Wise and balloon "Atlantic" 50 30
770 25 um. Charles Renard and Renard and Krebs' airship "La France" (horiz) 85 35
771 100 um. Henri Juillot and Lebaudy-Juillot airship "Patrie" (air) (horiz) . . . . 3·75 1·25

1983. Prehistoric Grindstones. Multicoloured.
773 10 um. Type **260** 50 30
774 14 um. Pestle and mortar . . . 75 40
775 18 um. Grinding dish . . . . . 1·00 60

261 Basketball

1983. Pre-Olympic Year. Multicoloured.
776 1 um. Type **261** (postage) . . . 10 10
777 20 um. Wrestling 60 25
778 50 um. Show-jumping . . . . 1·50 80
779 77 um. Running (air) . . . . . 2·25 1·25

262 Lord Baden-Powell (founder of Scout Movement)

1984. Celebrities. Multicoloured.
781 5 um. Type **262** (postage) . . . 15 10
782 14 um. Goethe (poet) 45 20
783 25 um. Rubens and detail of painting "The Virgin and Child" 75 45
784 100 um. P. Harris (founder of Rotary International) (air) . 3·00 1·40

263 Blue-finned Tuna

1984. Fishing Resources. Multicoloured.
786 1 um. Type **263** 10 10
787 2 um. Atlantic mackerel . . . 15 10
788 5 um. European hake 40 15
789 14 um. Atlantic horse-mackerel . 1·10 45
790 18 um. Building a fishing boat 1·25 55

264 Durer and "Madonna and Child"

1984. Multicoloured.
791 10 um. Type **264** (postage) . . 35 20
792 12 um. "Apollo 11" and astronaut (15th anniv of first manned Moon landing) . . . 40 25
793 50 um. Chess pieces and globe 2·00 80
794 77 um. Prince and Princess of Wales (air) . . . . 2·25 1·40

265 Start of Race

1984. Olympic Games, Los Angeles. Multicoloured.
796 14 um. Type **265** 40 25
797 18 um. Putting the shot (vert) 55 25
798 19 um. Hurdling (vert) 55 25
799 44 um. Throwing the javelin (vert) . . . . 1·25 65
800 77 um. High jumping . . . . . 2·00 1·25

266 Feeding Dehydrated Child from Glass **267** Aerial View of Complex

1984. Infant Survival Campaign. Multicoloured.
802 1 um. Type **266** 10 10
803 4 um. Breast-feeding baby . . . 15 10
804 10 um. Vaccinating baby . . . 30 20
805 14 um. Weighing baby 45 30

1984. Nouakchott Olympic Complex.
806 **267** 14 um. multicoloured . . . 50 40

268 Tents and Mosque Courtyard

1984. Pilgrimage to Mecca. Multicoloured.
807 14 um. Type **268** 50 30
808 18 um. Tents and courtyard (different) 75 40

269 Emblem

1984. 10th Anniv of West African Economic Community.
809 **269** 14 um. multicoloured . . . 45 30

270 S. van den Berg (windsurfing)

1984. Air. Olympic Games Sailing Gold Medallists. Multicoloured.
810 14 um. Type **270** 55 25
811 18 um. R. Coutts ("Finn" class) 75 25
812 19 um. Spain ("470" class) . . 1·00 25
813 44 um. U.S.A. ("Soling" class) 1·90 60

1984. Drought Relief. No. 537 surch **Aide au Sahel 84.**
815 18 um. on 10 um. multicoloured 70 50

272 Profiles and Emblem

1985. 15th Anniv of Technical and Cultural Co-operation Agency.
816 **272** 18 um. blue, deep blue and red 60 45

273 Animal drinking in Water Droplet and Skeletons
274 Replanting Trees

1985. Campaign against Drought. Multicoloured.
817 14 um. Type **273** . . . . . . 1·10 50
818 18 um. Lush trees by river in water droplet and dead trees . 1·10 50

1985. Anti-desertification Campaign. Multicoloured.
819 10 um. Type **274** 35 25
820 14 um. Animals fleeing from forest fire 55 30
821 18 um. Planting grass to hold sand dunes 65 50

275 Emblem

1985. 30th Anniv (1984) of Arab League.
822 **275** 14 um. green and black . . 45 30

276 Map, I.Y.Y. Emblem and Youths

1985. Air. "Philexafrique" Stamp Exhibition, Lome. Multicoloured.
823 40 um. Type **276** (International Youth Year) . . . . 1·50 1·25
824 40 um. Nouadhibou oil refinery 1·50 1·25

277 Bonaparte's Gulls

1985. Air. Birth Bicentenary of John J. Audubon (ornithologist). Multicoloured.
825 14 um. Wester tanager and scarlet tanager . . . . 1·10 45
826 18 um. Type **277** . . . . . . 1·40 50
827 19 um. Blue jays . . . . . . 1·50 75
828 44 um. Black skimmer . . . . 4·25 2·50

278 Locomotive "Adler", 1835

1985. Anniversaries. Multicoloured.
830 12 um. Type **278** (150th anniv of German railways) . . . . . 2·25 60
831 18 um. Class 10 steam locomotive, 1956 (150th anniv of German railways) . . . . 2·50 60
832 44 um. Johann Sebastian Bach (composer, 300th birth anniv European Music Year) . . . 1·60 70
833 77 um. Georg Frederick Handel (composer, 300th birth anniv European Music Year) . . . 2·75 1·25
834 90 um. Statue of Liberty (centenary) (vert) . . . . . 2·75 1·40

279 Globe and Emblem

1985. World Food Day.
836 **279** 18 um. multicoloured . . . 55 35

280 Tending Sheep and reading Book

1985. Air. "Philexafrique" Stamp Exhibition, Lome, Togo (2nd issue). Multicoloured.
837 50 um. Type **280** . . . . 2·00 1·50
838 50 um. Dock, iron ore mine and diesel train . . . . 3·50 90

281 Map showing Industries

1985. 25th Anniv of Independence.
839 **281** 18 um. multicoloured . . . 60 40

282 Development

1986. International Youth Year. Multicoloured.
840 18 um. Type **282** 60 30
841 22 um. Re-afforestation (voluntary work) 70 40
842 25 um. Hands reaching from globe to dove (peace) (vert) . 75 50

283 Latecoere Seaplane "Comte de la Vaulx" and Map

1986. Air. 55th Anniv (1985) of First Commercial South Atlantic Flight. Multicoloured.
843 18 um. Type **283** 75 35
844 50 um. Piper Twin Commanche airplanes crossing between maps of Africa and South America . . . . 2·00 1·25

284 Toujounine Earth Receiving Station

1986.
845 **284** 25 um. multicoloured . . . 90 50

285 Heads of Mother and Pup

1986. World Wildlife Fund. Mediterranean Monk Seal. Multicoloured.
846 2 um. Type **285** 50 30
847 5 um. Mother and pup on land 75 50
848 10 um. Mother and pup swimming . . . . 1·00 75
849 18 um. Seal family . . . . . . 2·00 1·00

286 Player and 1970 25 f. Stamp

1986. Air. World Cup Football Championship, Mexico. Multicoloured.
851 8 um. Type **286** 25 10
852 18 um. Player and 1970 30 f. stamp 60 20
853 22 um. Player and 1970 70 f. stamp 70 30
854 25 um. Player and 1970 150 f. stamp 85 35
855 40 um. Player and World Cup trophy on "stamp" . . . . 1·25 60

287 Weaving

1986.
857 **287** 18 um. multicoloured . . . 60 35

288 Emblem, Boeing 737, Douglas DC-10 and Map

1986. Air. 25th Anniv of Air Afrique.
858 **288** 26 um. multicoloured . . . 1·00 40

289 Indian, "Santa Maria" and Route Map

1987. 500th Anniv (1992) of Discovery of America by Christopher Columbus. Multicoloured.
859 2 um. Type **289** (postage) . . . 10 10
860 22 um. Indian, "Nina" and map 65 30
861 35 um. Indian, "Pinta" and map 1·10 50
862 150 um. Indian, map and Christopher Columbus (air) 4·50 1·60

290 J. H. Dort, Comet Picture and Space Probe "Giotto"

1986. Appearance of Halley's Comet. Multicoloured.
864 5 um. Type **290** (postage) . . . 15 10
865 18 um. William Huggins (astronomer) and "Ariane" space rocket 60 20
866 26 um. E. J. Opik and space probes "Giotto" and "Vega" 80 30
867 80 um. F. L. Whipple and "Planet A" space probe (air) 2·75 1·25

291 Astronauts

1986. "Challenger" Astronauts Commemoration. Multicoloured.
869 7 um. Type **291** (postage) . . . 20 10
870 22 um. Judith Resnik and astronaut 60 30
871 32 um. Ellison Onizuka and Ronald McNair . . . . . . 1·00 45
872 43 um. Christa Corrigan McAuliffe (air) . . . . . . 1·50 60

292 Red Seabream

1986. Fishes and Birds. Multicoloured.
874 4 um. Type **292** 30 15
875 22 um. White spoonbills . . . . 2·25 80
876 32 um. Bridled terns . . . . . 2·50 1·10
877 98 um. Sea-trout . . . . . . 5·50 3·00
See also Nos. 896/900.

293 Arrow through Victim
294 Fisherman

1986. 4th Anniv of Massacre of Palestinian Refugees in Sabra and Shatila Camps, Lebanon.
878 **293** 22 um. black, gold & red . 80 40

1986. World Food Day.
879 **294** 22 um. multicoloured . . . 1·25 40

295 Dome of the Rock

1987. "Arab Jerusalem".
880 **295** 22 um. multicoloured . . . 80 40

296 Boxing

1987. Air. Olympic Games, Seoul (1988) (1st issue). Multicoloured.
881 30 um. Type **296** 80 40
882 40 um. Judo . . . . 1·00 55
883 50 um. Fencing . . . . 1·25 70
884 75 um. Wrestling . . . . . . 2·00 1·10
See also Nos. 902/5.

297 Cordoue Mosque

1987. 1200th Anniv of Cordoue Mosque.
886 **297** 30 um. multicoloured . . . 1·00 50

298 Women's Slalom

1987. Air. Winter Olympic Games, Calgary (1988). Multicoloured.
887 30 um. Type **298** . . . . . . 1·10 40
888 40 um. Men's speed skating . . 1·40 55
889 50 um. Ice hockey . . . . . . 1·60 75
890 75 um. Women's downhill skiing 2·50 1·10

299 Adults at Desk

1987. Literacy Campaign. Multicoloured.
892 18 um. Type **299** 60 40
893 20 um. Adults and children reading 80 50

300 People queueing for Treatment

1987. World Health Day.
894 **300** 18 um. multicoloured . . . 70 40

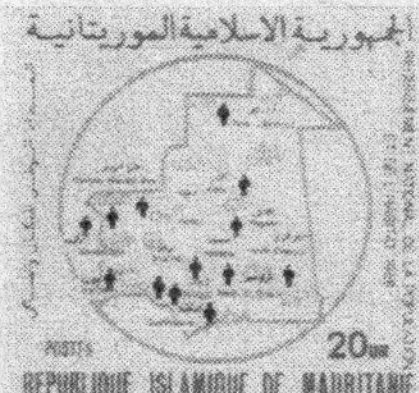

301 Map within Circle

1988. National Population and Housing Census.
895 **301** 20 um. multicoloured . . . 60 35

1988. Fishes and Birds. Horiz designs as T **292**. Multicoloured.
896 1 um. Small-horned blenny . . 10 10
897 7 um. Grey triggerfish 40 15
898 15 um. Skipjack tuna 70 30
899 18 um. Common cormorants . . 70 40
900 80 um. Royal terns . . . . . 3·00 2·00

302 People with Candles

303 Hammer Throwing

1988. 40th Anniv of W.H.O.
901 **302** 30 um. multicoloured . . . 1·00 40

1988. Air. Olympic Games, Seoul (2nd issue). Multicoloured.
902 20 um. Type **303** 50 25
903 24 um. Discus 60 30
904 30 um. Putting the shot 80 40
905 150 um. Javelin throwing . . . 4·00 2·10

1988. Winter Olympic Games Gold Medal Winners. Nos. 887/90 optd.
907 30 um. Optd **Medaille d'or/Vreni Schneider (Suisse)** . . . . . . 1·00 50
908 40 um. Optd **Medaille d'or/1500 m./Andre Hoffman (R.D.A.)** . 1·10 75
909 50 um. Optd **Medaille d'or/U.R.S.S.** . . . . 1·50 1·00
910 75 um. Optd **Medaille d'or/Marina Kiehl (R.F.A.)** . . . 2·25 1·50

305 Flags and Globe

1988. 75th Anniv of Arab Scout Movement.
912 **305** 35 um. multicoloured . . . 1·50 55

306 Men at Ballot Box

1988. 1st Municipal Elections. Multicoloured.
913 20 um. Type **306** 60 30
914 24 um. Woman at ballot box . 80 40

307 Emblem 308 Ploughing with Oxen

1988. 25th Anniv of Organization of African Unity.
915 **307** 40 um. multicoloured . . . 1·25 60

1988. 10th Anniv of International Agricultural Development Fund.
916 **308** 35 um. multicoloured . . . 1·10 70

309 Port Activities

1989. 1st Anniv of Nouakchott Free Port.
917 **309** 24 um. multicoloured . . . 1·25 65

310 "Heliothis armigera" 311 "Nomadacris septemfasciata"

1989. Plant Pests. Multicoloured.
918 2 um. Type **310** 15 15
919 6 um. "Aphis gossypii" 20 15
920 10 um. "Agrotis ypsilon" . . . 35 15
921 20 um. "Chilo sp." 75 30
922 24 um. "Plitella xylostella" . . 85 40
923 30 um. "Henosepilachna elaterii" 1·25 55
924 42 um. "Trichoplusia ni" . . . 1·50 70

1989. Locusts. Multicoloured.
925 5 um. Type **311** 15 10
926 20 um. Locusts mating 60 30
927 24 um. Locusts emerging from chrysallis 70 40
928 40 um. Locusts flying . . . . 1·25 75
929 88 um. Locust (different) . . . 3·00 1·25

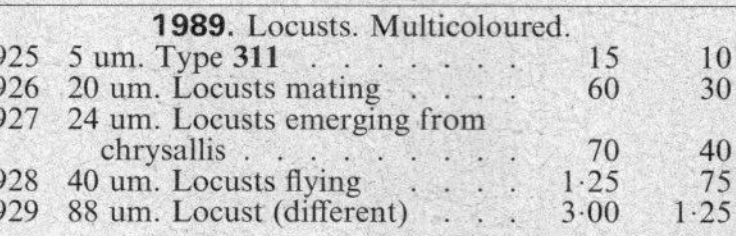

312 Men of Different Races embracing 313 Footballers

1989. "Philexfrance '89" Int Stamp Exn, Paris, and Bicent of French Revolution.
930 **312** 35 um. multicoloured . . . 1·10 60

1989. World Cup Football Championship, Italy (1990) (1st issue).
931 **313** 20 um. multicoloured . . . 1·00 40
See also Nos. 937/41.

314 Attan'eem Migat, Mecca

1989. Pilgrimage to Mecca.
932 **314** 20 um. multicoloured . . . 75 30

315 Emblem 317 Youths

316 Carpet

1989. 25th Anniv of African Development Bank.
933 **315** 37 um. black and mauve . 1·00 50

1989.
934 **316** 50 um. multicoloured . . . 1·50 80

1989. 2nd Anniv of Palestinian "Intifida" Movement.
935 **317** 35 um. multicoloured . . . 1·25 50

318 Member Countries' Leaders (½-size illustration)

1990. 1st Anniv of Arab Maghreb Union.
936 **318** 50 um. multicoloured . . . 1·50 70

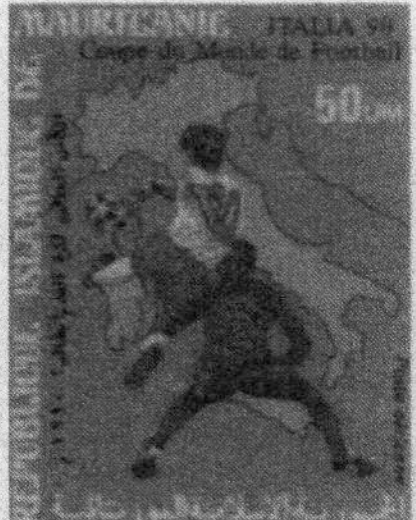

319 Players 320 Envelopes on Map

1990. Air. World Cup Football Championship, Italy (2nd issue).
937 **319** 50 um. multicoloured . . . 1·50 50
938 – 60 um. multicoloured . . . 1·90 60
939 – 70 um. multicoloured . . . 2·00 75
940 – 90 um. multicoloured . . . 2·75 75
941 – 150 um. multicoloured . . 4·50 1·25
DESIGNS: 60 to 150 um. Show footballers.

1990. 20th Anniv of Multinational Postal Training School, Abidjan.
942 **320** 50 um. multicoloured . . . 1·10 50

321 Books and Desk

1990. International Literacy Year.
943 **321** 60 um. multicoloured . . . 1·75 1·00

322 Maps and Earth-moving Vehicles

1990. Mineral Resources.
944 **322** 60 um. multicoloured . . . 2·75 1·25

323 Dressage 324 Emblem

1990. Olympic Games, Barcelona (1992). Mult.
945 5 um. Type **323** (postage) . . . 20 15
946 50 um. Archery . . . . 1·40 40
947 60 um. Throwing the hammer . 1·50 50
948 75 um. Football . . . . 2·00 50
949 90 um. Basketball . . . . . . 2·75 65
950 220 um. Table tennis (air) . . . 6·00 1·40

1990. 2nd Anniv of Declaration of State of Palestine.
952 **324** 85 um. multicoloured . . . 1·75 1·10

325 Camp

1990. Integration of Repatriates from Senegal. Multicoloured.
953 50 um. Type **325** 90 60
954 75 um. Women's sewing group 1·25 1·00
955 85 um. Water collection . . . 1·40 1·00

326 Map, Dove and Mandela

1990. Release from South African Prison of Nelson Mandela.
956 **326** 85 um. multicoloured . . . 1·60 1·10

327 Downhill skiing

1990. Winter Olympic Games, Albertville (1992). Multicoloured.
957 60 um. Type **327** (postage) . . 1·00 60
958 75 um. Cross-country skiing . . 1·50 75
959 90 um. Ice hockey . . . . . . 1·75 95
960 220 um. Figure skating (pairs) (air) . . . . 3·75 2·25

328 Blue Leg

1991. Scouts, Fungi and Butterflies. Multicoloured.
962 5 um. Type **328** (postage) . . . 40 20
963 50 um. "Agaricus bitorquis edulis" . . . . 2·50 80
964 60 um. "Bunea alcinoe" (butterfly) . . . . 2·25 75
965 90 um. "Salamis cytora" (butterfly) . . . . 2·75 1·10
966 220 um. "Bronze boletus" . . . 6·50 3·00
967 75 um. "Cyrestis camillus" (butterfly) (air) . . . . . . 2·50 85

329 Dish Aerials and Transmitting Tower

330 Woman carrying Bucket of Water

1991. 30th Anniv of Independence. Multicoloured.
968 50 um. Type **329** . . . . . . 1·00 65
969 60 um. Container ship in dock 2·00 85
970 100 um. Workers in field . . . 1·75 1·00

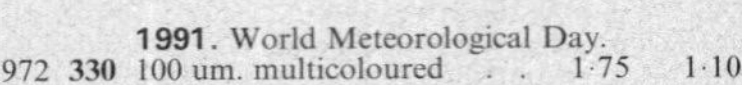

1991. World Meteorological Day.
972 **330** 100 um. multicoloured . . 1·75 1·10

331 Health Centre

1991. 20th Anniv of Medecins sans Frontieres (international medical relief organization).
973 **331** 60 um. multicoloured . . . 70 45

332 Cats

1991. Domestic Animals. Multicoloured.
974 50 um. Type **332** 75 35
975 60 um. Basenji dog . . . . . 1·00 45

333 Globe and Stylized Figures

1991. World Population Day.
976 **333** 90 um. multicoloured . . . 1·00 60

334 Blind Woman with Sight restored

1991. Anti-blindness Campaign.
977 **334** 50 um. multicoloured . . . 55 35

335 Nouakchott Electricity Station

1991. 2nd Anniv of Nouakchott Electricity Station.
978 **335** 50 um. multicoloured . . . 55 35

336 Quarrying

1993. Mineral Exploitation, Haoudat. Multicoloured.
979 50 um. Type **336** 75 35
980 60 um. Dry land 85 40

337 Camel Train

338 Palestinians

1993.
981 **337** 50 um. multicoloured . . . 55 35
982 60 um. multicoloured . . . 65 40

1993. Palestinian "Intifida" Movement. Multicoloured.
983 50 um. Type **338** 55 35
984 60 um. Palestinian children by fire (horiz) 65 40

339 Four-man Bobsleighing

340 Soldier Field, Chicago

1993. Winter Olympic Games, Lillehammer. Multicoloured.
985 10 um. Type **339** 10 10
986 50 um. Luge 55 35
987 60 um. Figure skating 65 40
988 80 um. Skiing 85 55
989 220 um. Cross-country skiing . 2·40 1·50

1994. World Cup Football Championship, U.S.A. Players and Stadiums. Multicoloured.
991 10 um. Type **340** 10 10
992 50 um. Foxboro Stadium, Boston 50 30
993 60 um. Robert F. Kennedy Stadium, Washington D.C. . 65 40
994 90 um. Stanford Stadium, San Francisco 95 60
995 220 um. Giant Stadium, New York . . . . 2·25 1·40

341 Anniversary Emblem and 1962 15 f. Stamp

1995. 50th Anniv of U.N.O.
997 **341** 60 um. multicoloured . . . 60 40

342 Stabilising Desert **345** Weaving

1995. 50th Anniv of F.A.O. Multicoloured.
998 50 um. Type **342** 50 30
999 60 um. Fishermen launching boat 60 40
1000 90 um. Planting crops 85 55

1995. Crafts. Multicoloured.
1006 50 um. Type **345** 30 15
1007 60 um. Metalwork 35 20

346 Door **347** Start of Race

1995. Tourism. Re-vitalization of Ancient Towns. Multicoloured.
1008 10 um. Type **346** 10 10
1009 20 um. Arch and rubble . . . 10 10
1010 40 um. Town in desert 25 15
1011 50 um. Door in ornate wall . . 30 15

1996. Olympic Games, Atlanta, U.S.A. Mult.
1012 20 um. Type **347** 10 10
1013 30 um. Start of race (horiz) . . 15 10
1014 40 um. Running in lane . . . 25 15
1015 50 um. Long-distance race (horiz) 30 15

348 Beaded Locks and Headdress

349 Ball-in-Pot Game

1996. Traditional Hairstyles. Multicoloured.
1016 50 um. Type **348** 30 15
1017 60 um. Woman with hair adornments 35 20

1996. Traditional Games. Multicoloured.
1018 50 um. Type **349** 30 15
1019 60 um. Strategy game with spherical and conical pieces (horiz) 35 20
1020 90 um. Pegs-in-board game (horiz) 50 30

350 Family

1996. 50th Anniv of United Nations Children's Fund. The Rights of the Child. Showing children's drawings. Multicoloured.
1021 50 um. Type **350** 30 15
1022 60 um. Boy in wheelchair . . 35 20

MINIMUM PRICE

The minimum price quoted is 10p which represents a handling charge rather than a basis for valuing common stamps. For further notes about prices see introductory pages.

OFFICIAL STAMPS

O 41 Cross of Trarza

O 179

1961.
O150 **O 41** 1 f. purple and blue . . 10 10
O151 3 f. myrtle and red . . 10 10
O152 5 f. brown and green 10 10
O153 10 f. blue and turquoise 20 10
O154 15 f. orange and blue 30 15
O155 20 f. green and myrtle 35 20
O156 25 f. red and orange . . 40 30
O157 30 f. green and purple 45 30
O158 50 f. sepia and red . . . 1·00 45
O159 100 f. blue and orange 1·60 75
O160 200 f. red and green . . 3·00 1·60

1976.
O502 **O 179** 1 u. multicoloured . . 10 10
O503 2 u. multicoloured . . 15 10
O504 5 u. multicoloured . . 20 15
O505 10 u. multicoloured 40 20
O506 12 u. multicoloured 55 30
O507 40 u. multicoloured 1·75 1·00
O508 50 u. multicoloured 2·25 1·25

POSTAGE DUE STAMPS

1906. Stamps of 1906 optd **T** in a triangle.
D18 I 5 c. green and red . . . . — 27·00
D19 10 c. pink and blue . . . . — 27·00
D20 J 20 c. black & red on blue . — 40·00
D21 25 c. blue and red . . . . — 40·00
D22 30 c. brown & red on pink — £110
D23 50 c. violet and red . . . — £110
D24 K 1 f. black & red on blue . . — £160

1906. "Natives" key-type inscr "MAURITANIE" in blue (10, 30 c.) or red (others).
D25 L 5 c. green . . . . 1·25 1·25
D26 10 c. purple . . . . . . 1·75 1·75
D27 15 c. blue on blue . . . . 4·00 3·25
D28 20 c. black on yellow . . . 6·00 6·00
D29 30 c. red on cream . . . . 6·00 6·75
D30 50 c. violet . . . . . . 9·25 9·25
D31 60 c. black on buff . . . . 6·50 6·75
D32 1 f. black on pink . . . . 11·50 9·25

1914. "Figure" key-type inscr "MAURITANIE".
D35 M 5 c. green 10 25
D36 10 c. red 15 25
D37 15 c. grey 15 30
D38 20 brown 15 30
D39 30 c. blue 25 40
D40 50 c. black 50 95
D41 60 c. orange 40 50
D42 1 f. violet 60 80

1927. Surch in figures.
D67 M 2 f. on 1 f. purple . . . . 1·25 1·75
D68 3 f. on 1 f. brown . . . . 1·25 2·00

D 40 Qualata Motif

D 55 Ruppell's Griffon

1961.
D150 **D 40** 1 f. yellow and purple 10 10
D151 2 f. grey and red . . . 10 10
D152 5 f. pink and red . . . 20 15
D153 10 f. green and myrtle . 25 15
D154 15 f. brown and drab 30 15
D155 20 f. blue and red . . . 35 20
D156 25 f. red and green . . 55 35

1963. Birds. Multicoloured.
D177 50 c. Type **D 55** 60 20
D178 50 c. Common crane 60 20
D179 1 f. Eastern white pelican . . 70 25
D180 1 f. Garganey 70 25
D181 2 f. Golden oriole 85 30
D182 2 f. Variable sunbird 85 30
D183 5 f. Great snipe 95 60
D184 5 f. Common shoveler . . . 95 60
D185 10 f. Vulturine guineafowl . . 1·75 1·10
D186 10 f. Black stork . . . . . 1·75 1·10
D187 15 f. Grey heron . . . . . . 2·00 1·50
D188 15 f. White stork . . . . . 2·00 1·50
D189 20 f. Paradise whydah . . . 2·40 1·75
D190 20 f. Red-legged partridge . . 2·40 1·75
D191 25 f. Little stint . . . . . 3·00 2·10
D192 25 f. Arabian bustard . . . . 3·00 2·10

D 180

1976.

D509	D **180**	1 u. multicoloured . .	10	10
D510		3 u. multicoloured . .	15	15
D511		10 u. multicoloured	35	35
D512		12 u. multicoloured	40	40
D513		20 u. multicoloured	70	70

APPENDIX

The following stamps have either been issued in excess of postal needs or have not been available to the public in a reasonable quantities at face value. Such stamps may later be given full listing if there is evidence of regular postal use.

1962.

World Refugee Year (1960). Optd on 1960–61 Definitive issue, 30, 50, 60 f.

Olympic Games in Rome (1960) and Tokyo (1964). Surch on 1960–61 Definitive issue 75 f. on 15 f., 75 f. on 20 f.

European Steel and Coal Community and Exploration of Iron-ore in Mauritania. Optd on 1960–61 Definitive issue. Air 500 f.

Malaria Eradication. Optd on 1960–61 Definitive issue. Air. 100, 200 f.

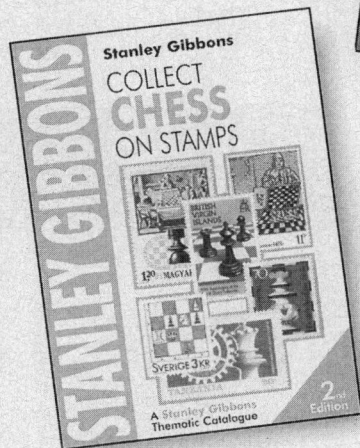

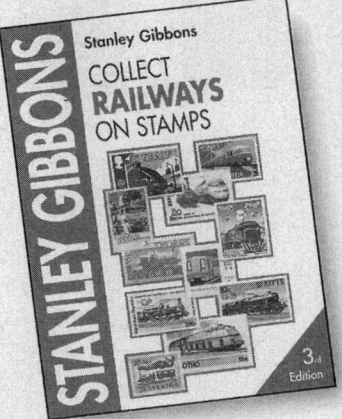

MAURITIUS Pt. 1

An island in the Indian Ocean, east of Madagascar. Attained self-government on 1 September 1967, and became independent on 12 March 1968.

1847. 12 pence = 1 shilling;
20 shillings = 1 pound.
1878. 100 cents = 1 rupee.

1 ("POST OFFICE") 2 ("POST PAID")

1847. Imperf.
1 1 1d. red . . . . — £450000
2 2d. blue . . . . — £550000

1848. Imperf.
23 2 1d. red £1400 £375
25 2d. blue £1900 £500

3 5

1854. Surch **FOUR-PENCE**. Imperf.
26 3 4d. green £750 £375

1858. No value on stamps. Imperf.
27 3 (4d.) green £425 £200
28 (6d.) red . . . . 26·00 45·00
29 (9d.) purple £550 £200

1859. Imperf.
32 5 6d. blue . . . . £550 32·00
33 6d. black . . . . 20·00 32·00
34 1s. red . . . . £2000 45·00
35 1s. green . . . . £425 95·00

6 8

1859. Imperf.
39 6 2d. blue £1100 £400

1859. Imperf.
42 8 1d. red £3000 £750
44 2d. blue £1500 £375

9 10

1860.
56 9 1d. purple . . . . 50·00 9·00
57 1d. brown . . . . 65·00 5·50
60 2d. blue . . . . 65·00 7·50
61a 3d. red . . . . 40·00 9·00
62 4d. red . . . . 80·00 3·00
65 6d. green . . . . 95·00 4·00
50 6d. grey . . . . £180 75·00
63 6d. violet . . . . £160 24·00
51 9d. purple . . . . 85·00 38·00
66 9d. green £100 £170
67 10 10d. red . . . . £180 30·00
70 9 1s. yellow . . . . £140 12·00
53 1s. green £550 £150
69 1s. blue . . . . £130 18·00
71 5s. mauve . . . . £150 48·00

1862. Perf.
54 5 6d. black . . . . 17·00 45·00
55 1s. green £1800 £325

HALF PENNY (11) HALF PENNY (13)

1876. Surcharged with T **11**.
76 9 ½d. on 9d. purple . . . . . 6·50 9·50
77 10 ½d. on 10d. red . . . . . . 1·75 14·00

1877. Surch with T **13**.
79 10 ½d. on 10d. red . . . . . . 3·00 26·00

1877. Surch in words.
80 9 1d. on 4d. red . . . . 7·50 12·00
82 1s. on 5s. mauve £200 £100

1878. Surch.
83 10 2 c. red . . . . 5·50 4·50
84 9 4 c. on 1d. brown . . . . . 7·50 4·50
85 8 c. on 2d. blue . . . . . . 65·00 1·50
86 13 c. on 3d. red . . . . . . 7·50 24·00
87 17 c. on 4d. red . . . . . . £140 2·00
88 25 c. on 6d. blue . . . . . £170 4·75
89 38 c. on 9d. purple . . . . 18·00 48·00
90 50 c. on 1s. green . . . . . 85·00 2·50
91 2 r. 50 on 5s. mauve . . . . 12·00 14·00

18 19

1879. Various frames.
101 18 1 c. violet . . . . 1·75 45
102 2 c. red . . . . 30·00 4·75
103 2 c. green . . . . 2·25 60
104 19 4 c. orange . . . . 65·00 2·50
105 4 c. red . . . . 2·75 60
106 – 8 c. blue . . . . 2·00 90
95 – 13 c. grey £120 £160
107 – 15 c. brown . . . . 4·00 1·25
108 – 15 c. blue . . . . 5·50 90
109 – 16 c. brown . . . . 4·00 1·00
96 – 17 c. red . . . . 50·00 4·75
110 – 25 c. olive . . . . 4·50 1·75
98 – 38 c. purple £150 £190
99 – 50 c. green . . . . 3·75 2·75
111 – 50 c. orange . . . . . . 28·00 8·00
100 – 2 r. 50 purple . . . . . . 30·00 55·00

1883. No. 96 surch **16 CENTS**.
112 16 c. on 17 c. red . . . . . . £130 50·00

1883. No. 96 surch **SIXTEEN CENTS**.
115 16 c. on 17 c. red . . . . . . 60·00 1·00

1885. No. 98 surch **2 CENTS** with bar.
116 2 c. on 38 c. purple . . . . . 85·00 32·00

1887. No. 95 surch **2 CENTS** without bar.
117 2 c. on 13 c. grey . . . . . . 38·00 70·00

1891. Surch in words with or without bar.
123 18 1 c. on 2 c. violet . . . . . 1·25 50
124 – 1 c. on 16 c. brown (No. 109) 1·25 2·75
118 19 2 c. on 4 c. red . . . . . . 1·50 60
119 – 2 c. on 17 c. red (No. 96) . . 90·00 90·00
120 9 2 c. on 38 c. on 9d. purple (No. 89) . . . . 1·90 3·50
121 – 2 c. on 38 c. purple (No. 98) 2·50 3·75

36 37

1895.
127 36 1 c. purple and blue . . . . 75 1·25
128 2 c. purple and orange . . . 2·00 50
129 3 c. purple 60 50
130 4 c. purple and green . . . 3·75 70
131 6 c. green and red . . . . 4·00 4·00
132 18 c. green and blue . . . . 6·50 5·00

1898. Diamond Jubilee.
133 37 36 c. orange and blue . . . 10·00 15·00

1899. Surch in figures and words.
137 – 4 c. on 16 c. brown (No. 109) 2·50 8·00
134 36 6 c. on 18 c. (No. 132) . . . 1·00 1·00
156 12 c. on 18 c. (No. 132) . . 1·75 5·00
163 37 12 c. on 36 c. (No. 133) . . 1·25 1·25
135 15 c. on 36 c. (No. 133) . . 1·40 1·75

40 Admiral Mahe de Labourdonnais, Governor of Mauritius 1735–46

42

1899. Birth Bicentenary of Labourdonnais.
136 40 15 c. blue . . . . 10·00 3·25

1900.
138 36 1 c. grey and black 50 10
139 2 c. purple 75 20
140 3 c. green & red on yellow . 3·50 1·25
141 4 c. purple & red on yellow 1·50 40
142 4 c. green and violet . . . 60 2·00
167a 4 c. black & red on blue . . 1·75 10
144 5 c. purple on buff . . . . 6·00 50·00
145 5 c. purple & blk on buff . 2·50 2·50
168a 6 c. purple & red on red . 1·75 10
147 8 c. green & blk on buff . . 1·75 6·00
148 12 c. black and red . . . . 1·75 2·25
149 15 c. green and orange . . . 10·00 6·00
171 15 c. black & blue on blue . 4·00 35
151a 36 25 c. green & red on grn . . 2·75 11·00
174 50 c. green on yellow . . . 1·50 2·25
175 42 1 r. grey and red . . . . . 20·00 45·00
154 2 r. 50 green & blk on bl . 16·00 75·00
155 5 r. purple & red on red . . 55·00 75·00

1902. Optd **Postage & Revenue.**
157 36 4 c. purple and red on yellow 75 20
158 6 c. green and red . . . . . 75 2·50
159 15 c. green and orange . . . 2·00 30
160 – 25 c. olive (No. 110) . . . . 2·00 2·50
161 – 50 c. green (No. 99) . . . . 3·75 2·50
162 – 2 r. 50 purple (No. 100) . . 75·00 95·00

46 47

1910.
205 46 1 c. black . . . . 1·00 90
206 2 c. brown . . . . 1·00 10
207 2 c. purple on yellow . . . 60 20
183 3 c. green . . . . 2·75 10
184 4 c. green and red . . . . 3·25 10
210 4 c. green . . . . 1·00 10
211 4 c. brown . . . . 2·75 1·25
186 6 c. red . . . . 2·00 20
213 6 c. mauve . . . . 1·25 10
187 8 c. orange . . . . 2·75 1·25
215 10 c. grey . . . . 2·00 3·25
216 10 c. red . . . . 3·75 1·25
217 12 c. red . . . . 1·50 40
218 12 c. grey . . . . 1·75 3·00
219b 15 c. blue 75 25
220 20 c. blue . . . . 2·00 80
221 20 c. purple . . . . 8·50 10·00

1910.
185 47 5 c. grey and red . . . . . 2·50 2·75
188 12 c. grey . . . . 1·75 2·50
190 25 c. black & red on yell . . 1·75 11·00
191 50 c. purple and black . . . 1·75 17·00
192 1 r. black on green . . . . 6·00 11·00
193 2 r. 50 black & red on blue 10·00 60·00
194 5 r. green & red on yellow . 26·00 85·00
195 10 r. green & red on green 85·00 £170

48 51

1913.
223 48 1 c. black . . . . 80 1·00
224 2 c. brown 70 10
225 3 c. green 70 30
226 4 c. green and red 60 30
226c 4 c. green . . . . 4·50 45
227 5 c. grey and red 90 10
228 6 c. brown . . . . 1·00 60
229 8 c. orange . . . . 75 9·00
230 10 c. red . . . . 1·00 20
232b 12 c. grey . . . . 4·25 20
232 12 c. red . . . . 30 3·00
233 15 c. blue 80 20
234 20 c. purple 55 40
235 20 c. blue . . . . 9·50 80
236 25 c. black & red on yell . 30 15
237 50 c. purple and black . . 7·50 3·50
238 1 r. black on green . . . . 3·50 40
239 2 r. 50 black & red on bl . 19·00 6·00
240 5 r. green & red on yell . . 27·00 60·00
204d 10 r. green & red on grn . . 26·00 90·00

1924. As T **42** but Arms similar to T **46**.
222 50 r. purple and green £700 £1300

1925. Surch with figures, words and bar.
242 46 3 c. on 4 c. green . . . . . 2·50 3·75
243 10 c. on 12 c. red 30 30
244 15 c. on 20 c. blue 55 20

1935. Silver Jubilee. As T **10a** of Gambia.
245 5 c. blue and grey 50 10
246 12 c. green and blue . . . . 4·50 10
247 20 c. brown and blue . . . . 4·50 20
248 1 r. grey and purple . . . . 29·00 40·00

1937. Coronation. As T **10b** of Gambia.
249 5 c. violet 40 10
250 12 c. red . . . . 40 1·50
251 20 c. blue 40 10

1938.
252 51 2 c. grey 30 10
253 3 c. purple and red . . . . 2·00 1·75
254b 4 c. green . . . . 1·00 1·75
255a 5 c. violet . . . . 2·25 20
256b 10 c. red . . . . 2·25 10
257 12 c. orange . . . . 1·00 20
258 20 c. blue . . . . 1·00 10
259b 25 c. purple . . . . 5·00 10
260b 1 r. brown . . . . 16·00 90
261a 2 r. 50 violet . . . . 27·00 10·00
262a 5 r. olive . . . . 27·00 22·00
263a 10 r. purple . . . . 11·00 22·00

1946. Victory. As T **11a** of Gambia.
264 5 c. violet 10 10
265 20 c. blue 10 10

52 1d. "Post Office" Mauritius and King George VI

1948. Cent of First British Colonial Stamp.
266 52 5 c. orange and mauve . . . 10 30
267 12 c. orange and green . . . 10 10
268 – 20 c. blue 10 10
269 – 1 r. blue and brown 15 30
DESIGN: 20 c., 1 r. As Type **52**, but showing 2d. "Post Office" Mauritius.

1948. Silver Wedding. As T **11b/c** of Gambia.
270 5 c. violet 10 10
271 10 r. mauve . . . . 9·50 22·00

1949. U.P.U. As T **11d/g** of Gambia.
272 12 c. red 40 65
273 20 c. blue . . . . 1·75 1·50
274 35 c. purple 40 65
275 1 r. brown 40 20

55 Aloe Plant 60 Legend of Paul and Virginie

67 Arms of Mauritius 69 Historical Museum, Mahebourg

1950.
276 – 1 c. purple 10 50
277 – 2 c. red 15 10
278 55 3 c. green . . . . 60 2·50
279 – 4 c. green . . . . 20 1·25
280 – 5 c. blue 15 10
281 – 10 c. red 30 75
282 – 12 c. green . . . . 1·25 2·00
283 60 20 c. blue 60 15
284 – 25 c. red . . . . 1·25 40
285 – 35 c. violet 30 10
286 – 50 c. green . . . . 2·00 50
287 – 1 r. brown . . . . 4·25 10
288 – 2 r. 50 orange . . . . . . 12·00 6·50
289 – 5 r. brown . . . . 14·00 14·00
290 67 10 r. blue . . . . 14·00 18·00
DESIGNS—HORIZ: 1 c. Labourdonnais sugar factory; 2 c. Grand Port; 5 c. Rempart Mountain; 10 c. Transporting cane; 12 c. Mauritius dodo and map; 35 c. Government House, Reduit; 1 r. Timor deer; 2 r. 50, Port Louis; 5 r. Beach scene. VERT: 4 c. Tamarind Falls; 25 c. Labourdonnais statue; 50 c. Pieter Both Mountain.

1953. Coronation. As T **11h** of Gambia.
291 10 c. black and green 70 15

1953. As 1950 but portrait of Queen Elizabeth II. Designs as for corresponding values except where stated.
293 – 2 c. red 10 10
294 – 3 c. green 30 40
295 – 4 c. purple (as 1 c.) 10 60
296 – 5 c. blue 10 10
314 – 10 c. green (as 4 c.) . . . 15 10
298 69 15 c. red 10 10
299 – 20 c. red (as 25 c.) 15 20
300 – 25 c. blue (as 20 c.) . . . 1·50 10
301 – 35 c. violet 20 10
302 – 50 c. green 55 75
315 – 60 c. green (as 12 c.) . . . 1·75 10
303 – 1 r. sepia 30 10
316 – 2 r. 50 orange . . . . . . 5·50 8·50
305 – 5 r. brown . . . . 14·00 9·00
306 – 10 r. blue . . . . 13·00 1·00

70 Queen Elizabeth II and King George III (after Lawrence)

1961. 150th Anniv of British Post Office in Mauritius.
307 70 10 c. black and red 10 10
308 20 c. ultramarine and blue . 30 25
309 35 c. black and yellow . . . 40 25
310 1 r. purple and green . . . 60 25

1963. Freedom from Hunger. As T **20a** of Gambia.
311 60 c. violet 40 10

1963. Cent of Red Cross. As T **20b** of Gambia.
312 10 c. red and black 15 10
313 60 c. red and blue 60 20

71 Bourbon White Eye

1965. Birds. Multicoloured.

317 2 c. Type **71** (yellow background) 40 15
318 3 c. Rodriguez fody (brown background) 1·00 15
319 4 c. Mauritius olive white eye 30 15
340 5 c. Mascarene paradise flycatcher 40 15
321 10 c. Mauritius fody 30 10
322 15 c. Mauritius parakeet (grey background) 2·00 40
323 20 c. Mauritius greybird (yellow background) 2·00 10
324 25 c. Mauritius kestrel 2·00 30
341 35 c. Pink pigeon 30 15
326 50 c. Reunion bulbul 50 40
327 60 c. Mauritius blue pigeon (extinct) (yellow background) 60 10
328 1 r. Mauritius dodo (extinct) (olive background) 5·50 10
329 2 r. 50 Rodriguez solitaire (extinct) 5·00 6·00
330 5 r. Mauritius red rail (extinct) 14·00 9·50
331 10 r. Broad-billed parrot (extinct) 26·00 19·00

For some values with background colours changed see Nos. 370/5.

1965. Centenary of I.T.U. As T **44** of Gibraltar.

332 10 c. orange and green 15 10
333 60 c. yellow and violet 60 20

1965. I.C.Y. As T **45** of Gibraltar.

334 10 c. purple and turquoise 15 10
335 60 c. green and violet 30 20

1966. Churchill Commem. As T **46** of Gibraltar.

336 2 c. blue 10 2·25
337 10 c. green 25 10
338 60 c. brown 1·10 20
339 1 r. violet 1·25 20

1966. 20th Anniv of U.N.E.S.C.O. As T **56a/c** of Gibraltar.

342 5 c. multicoloured 15 20
343 10 c. yellow, violet & green 25 10
344 60 c. black, purple & orange 95 15

86 Red-tailed Tropic Bird

1967. Self-Government. Multicoloured.

345 2 c. Type **86** 20 1·25
346 10 c. Rodriguez brush warbler 60 10
347 60 c. Rose-ringed parakeet (extinct) 70 10
348 1 r. Grey-rumped swiftlet 70 10

1967. Self-Government. Nos. 317/31 optd **SELF GOVERNMENT 1967**.

349 **71** 2 c. multicoloured 10 50
350 – 3 c. multicoloured 10 50
351 – 4 c. multicoloured 10 50
352 – 5 c. multicoloured 10 10
353 – 10 c. multicoloured 10 10
354 – 15 c. multicoloured 10 30
355 – 20 c. multicoloured 15 10
356 – 25 c. multicoloured 15 10
357 – 35 c. multicoloured 20 10
358 – 50 c. multicoloured 30 15
359 – 60 c. multicoloured 30 10
360 – 1 r. multicoloured 50 10
361 – 2 r. 50 multicoloured 1·00 2·25
362 – 5 r. multicoloured 6·00 3·25
363 – 10 r. multicoloured 8·00 14·00

91 Flag of Mauritius

1968. Independence. Multicoloured.

364 2 c. Type **91** 10 1·50
365 3 c. Arms and Mauritius dodo emblem 15 1·50
366 15 c. Type **91** 20 10
367 20 c. As 3 c. 50 10
368 60 c. Type **91** 60 10
369 1 r. As 3 c. 95 10

1968. As Nos. 317/8, 322/3 and 327/8 but background colours changed as below.

370 **71** 2 c. olive 20 1·75
371 – 3 c. blue 1·75 3·75
372 – 15 c. brown 55 20
373 – 20 c. buff 3·50 3·00
374 – 60 c. red 1·50 15
375 – 1 r. purple 2·50 1·25

93 Dominique rescues Paul and Virginie

1968. Bicentenary of Bernardin de St. Pierre's Visit to Mauritius. Multicoloured.

376 2 c. Type **93** 10 80
377 15 c. Paul and Virginie crossing the river 25 10
378 50 c. Visit of Labourdonnais to Madame de la Tour 40 10
379 60 c. Meeting of Paul and Virginie in Confidence 40 10
380 1 r. Departure of Virginie for Europe 50 20
381 2 r. 50 Bernardin de St. Pierre 1·50 3·50

Nos. 377, 379 and 381 are vert.

99 Black-spotted Emperor

1969. Multicoloured (except 10, 15, 25, 60 c.).

382 2 c. Type **99** 10 1·75
383 3 c. Red reef crab 10 2·50
384 4 c. Episcopal mitre 1·40 2·75
385 5 c. Black-saddled pufferfish ("Bourse") 30 10
386 10 c. Starfish (red, black and flesh) 1·00 10
387 15 c. Sea urchin (brown, black and blue) 30 10
480 20 c. Fiddler crab 70 30
389 25 c. Spiny shrimp (red, black and green) 30 2·00
390 30 c. Single harp shells and double harp shell 1·50 1·50
483 35 c. Common paper nautilus 1·00 15
484 40 c. Spanish dancer 1·00 60
448 50 c. Orange spider conch and violet spider conch 45 10
449b 60 c. Blue marlin (black, pink and blue) 65 10
487 75 c. "Conus clytospira" 1·25 1·50
396 1 r. Dolphin (fish) 60 10
452 2 r. 50 Spiny lobster 2·00 4·00
453 5 r. Ruby snapper ("Sacre chien rouge") 3·00 2·00
399w 10 r. Yellow-edged lyretail ("Croissant queue jaune") 2·50 3·00

117 Gandhi as Law Student

1969. Birth Cent of Mahatma Gandhi. Mult.

400 2 c. Type **117** 10 10
401 15 c. Gandhi as stretcher-bearer during Zulu Revolt 25 10
402 50 c. Gandhi as Satyagrahi in South Africa 30 40
403 60 c. Gandhi at No. 10 Downing Street, London 30 10
404 1 r. Gandhi in Mauritius, 1901 40 10
405 2 r. 50 Gandhi, the "Apostle of Truth and Non-Violence" 90 1·75

124 Frangourinier Cane-crusher (18th cent)

1969. 150th Anniv of Telfair's Improvements to the Sugar Industry. Multicoloured.

407 2 c. Three-roller Vertical Mill 10 20
408 15 c. Type **124** 10 10
409 60 c. Beau Rivage Factory, 1867 10 10
410 1 r. Mon Desert-Alma Factory, 1969 10 10
411 2 r. 50 Dr. Charles Telfair (vert) 25 1·00

1970. Expo '70. Nos. 394 and 396 optd **EXPO '70' OSAKA**.

413 60 c. black, red and blue 10 10
414 1 r. multicoloured 10 10

129 Morne Plage, Mountain and Boeing 707

1970. Inauguration of Lufthansa Flight, Mauritius–Frankfurt. Multicoloured.

415 25 c. Type **129** 10 10
416 50 c. Boeing 707 and map (vert) 10 10

131 Lenin as a Student

1970. Birth Centenary of Lenin.

417 **131** 15 c. green and silver 10 10
418 – 75 c. brown 20 20

DESIGN: 75 c. Lenin as founder of U.S.S.R.

133 2d. "Post Office" Mauritius and original Post Office

1970. Port Louis, Old and New. Multicoloured.

419 5 c. Type **133** 10 10
420 15 c. G.P.O. Building (built 1870) 10 10
421 50 c. Mail coach (c. 1870) 40 10
422 75 c. Port Louis Harbour (1970) 55 10
423 2 r. 50 Arrival of Pierre A. de Suffren (1783) 70 70

138 U.N. Emblem and Symbols

1970. 25th Anniv of U.N.

425 **138** 10 c. multicoloured 10 10
426 60 c. multicoloured 40 10

139 Rainbow over Waterfall

1971. Tourism. Multicoloured.

427 10 c. Type **139** 35 10
428 15 c. Trois Mamelles Mountains 35 10
429 60 c. Beach scene 55 10
430 2 r. 50 Marine life 1·50 1·50

Nos. 427/30 have inscriptions on the reverse.

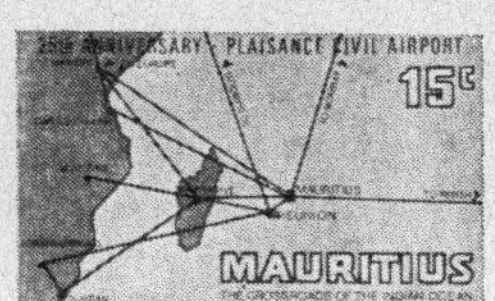

140 "Crossroads" of Indian Ocean

1971. 25th Anniv of Plaisance Airport. Multicoloured.

431 15 c. Type **140** 20 10
432 60 c. Boeing 707 and Terminal buildings 40 10
433 1 r. Air hostesses on gangway 45 10
434 2 r. 50 Farman F.190, "Roland Garros" airplane, Choisy Airfield, 1937 1·75 3·75

141 Princess Margaret Orthopaedic Centre

1971. 3rd Commonwealth Medical Conference. Multicoloured.

435 10 c. Type **141** 10 10
436 75 c. Operating theatre in National Hospital 20 20

142 Queen Elizabeth II and Prince Philip

1972. Royal Visit. Multicoloured.

455 15 c. Type **142** 15 10
456 2 r. 50 Queen Elizabeth II (vert) 2·50 2·50

143 Theatre Facade

1972. 150th Anniv of Port Louis Theatre. Multicoloured.

457 10 c. Type **143** 10 10
458 1 r. Theatre auditorium 40 20

144 Pirate Dhow

1972. Pirates and Privateers. Multicoloured.

459 15 c. Type **144** 65 15
460 60 c. Treasure chest (vert) 1·00 20
461 1 r. Lemene and "L'Hirondelle" (vert) 1·25 20
462 2 r. 50 Robert Surcouf 4·50 7·50

145 Mauritius University

1973. 5th Anniv of Independence. Multicoloured.

463 15 c. Type **145** 10 10
464 60 c. Tea development 15 15
465 1 r. Bank of Mauritius 15 15

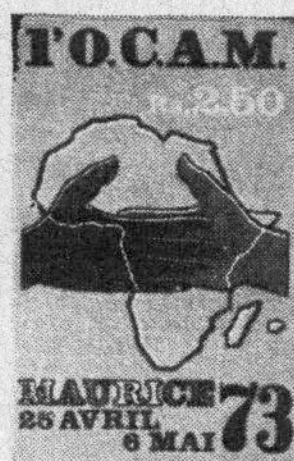

146 Map and Hands

1973. O.C.A.M. Conference. Multicoloured.

466 10 c. O.C.A.M. emblem (horiz) 10 10
467 2 r. 50 Type **146** 40 45

O.C.A.M. = Organisation Commune Africaine Malgache et Mauricienne.

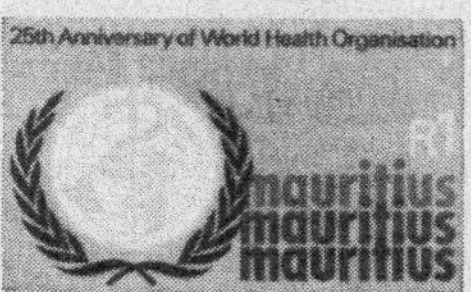

147 W.H.O. Emblem

1973. 25th Anniv of W.H.O.

468 **147** 1 r. multicoloured 10 10

148 Meteorological Station, Vacoas

1973. Centenary of I.M.O./W.M.O.

469 **148** 75 c. multicoloured 30 60

149 Capture of the "Kent" 1800

1973. Birth Bicentenary of Robert Surcouf (privateer).

470 **149** 60 c. multicoloured 50 85

150 P. Commerson

1974. Death Bicentenary (1973) of Philibert Commerson (naturalist).

471 **150** 2 r. 50 multicoloured . . . 30 40

151 Cow being Milked

1974. Eighth F.A.O. Regional Conf for Africa, Mauritius.

472 **151** 60 c. multicoloured 20 20

152 Mail Train

1974. Centenary of U.P.U. Multicoloured.

473 15 c. Type **152** 40 15
474 1 r. New G.P.O., Port Louis . . 40 20

153 "Cottage Life" (F. Leroy)

1975. Aspects of Mauritian Life. Paintings. Multicoloured.

493 15 c. Type **153** 10 10
494 60 c. "Milk Seller" (A. Richard) (vert) 35 10
495 1 r. "Entrance of Port Louis Market" (Thuillier) 35 10
496 2 r. 50 "Washerwoman" (Max Boullee) (vert) 95 80

154 Mace across Map

1975. French-speaking Parliamentary Assemblies Conference, Port Louis.

497 **154** 75 c. multicoloured . . . . 30 1·00

155 Woman with Lamp ("The Light of the World")

1976. International Women's Year.

498 **155** 2 r. 50 multicoloured . . . 35 1·25

156 Parched Landscape

1976. Drought in Africa. Multicoloured.

499 50 c. Type **156** 15 15
500 60 c. Map of Africa and carcass (vert) 15 15

157 "Pierre Loti", 1953–70

1976. Mail Carriers to Mauritius. Multicoloured.

501 10 c. Type **157** 55 10
502 15 c. "Secunder", 1907 . . . . 80 10
503 50 c. "Hindoostan", 1842 . . . 1·25 15
504 60 c. "St. Geran", 1740 . . . . 1·40 15
505 2 r. 50 "Maen", 1638 . . . . . 3·25 6·50

158 "The Flame of Hindi carried across the Seas"

1976. 2nd World Hindi Convention. Multicoloured.

507 10 c. Type **158** 10 10
508 75 c. Type **158** 10 15
509 1 r. 20 Hindi script 20 70

159 Conference Logo and Map of Mauritius

160 King Priest and Breastplate

1976. 22nd Commonwealth Parliamentary Association Conf. Multicoloured.

510 1 r. Type **159** 25 10
511 2 r. 50 Conference logo . . . . 50 1·25

1976. Moenjodaro Excavations, Pakistan. Multicoloured.

512 60 c. Type **160** 30 10
513 1 r. House with well and goblet 50 10
514 2 r. 50 Terracotta figurine and necklace . . . . 1·25 80

161 Sega Scene

1977. 2nd World Black and African Festival of Arts and Culture, Nigeria.

515 **161** 1 r. multicoloured 30 15

162 The Queen with Sceptre and Rod

1977. Silver Jubilee. Multicoloured.

516 50 c. The Queen at Mauritius Legislative Assembly, 1972 . 15 10
517 75 c. Type **162** 20 10
518 5 r. Presentation of Sceptre and Rod 55 75

163 "Hugonia tomentosa"

1977. Indigenous Flowers. Multicoloured.

519 20 c. Type **163** 20 10
520 1 r. "Ochna mauritiana" (vert) . 40 10
521 1 r. 50 "Dombeya acutangula" . 50 20
522 5 r. "Trochetia blackburniana" (vert) . . . . 1·10 1·25

164 De Havilland Twin Otter 200/300

1977. Inaugural Int Flight of Air Mauritius. Multicoloured.

524 25 c. Type **164** 60 10
525 50 c. De Havilland Twin Otter 200/300 and Air Mauritius emblem 80 10
526 75 c. Piper Navajo and Boeing 747-100 . . . . 95 15
527 5 r. Boeing 707 . . . . 3·00 3·25

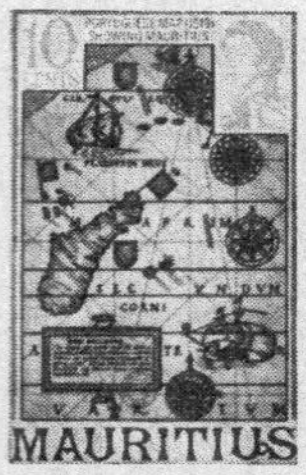

165 Portuguese Map of Mauritius, 1519

166 Mauritius Dodo

1978.

529B **165** 10 c. multicoloured . . 75 90
530A – 15 c. multicoloured . . 1·50 2·25
531A – 20 c. multicoloured . . 80 2·25
532A – 25 c. multicoloured . . 60 75
533B – 35 c. multicoloured . . 1·00 20
534A – 50 c. multicoloured . . 50 60
535A – 60 c. multicoloured . . 60 2·00
536A – 70 c. multicoloured . . 2·75 3·00
537B – 75 c. multicoloured . . 1·75 2·25
538A – 90 c. multicoloured . . 2·75 3·00
539A – 1 r. multicoloured . . . 60 50
540A – 1 r. 20 multicoloured . . 1·75 2·75
541B – 1 r. 25 multicoloured . . 1·50 20
542A – 1 r. 50 multicoloured . . 1·00 1·50
543A – 2 r. multicoloured . . . 60 40
544A – 3 r. multicoloured . . . 60 40
545A – 5 r. multicoloured . . . 60 1·00
546A – 10 r. multicoloured . . . 1·00 1·00
547A – 15 r. multicoloured . . . 1·50 2·25
548A – 25 r. green, black & brn . 2·00 3·00

DESIGNS—HORIZ: 15 c. Dutch Occupation, 1638-1710; 20 c. Map by Van Keulen, c. 1700; 50 c. Construction of Port Louis, c. 1736; 70 c. Map by Bellin, 1763; 90 c. Battle of Grand Port, 1810; 1 r. Landing of the British, 1810; 1 r. 20, Government House, c. 1840; 1 r. 50, Indian immigration, 1835; 2 r. Race Course, c. 1870; 3 r. Place d'Armes, c. 1880; 5 r. Royal Visit postcard, 1901; 10 r. Royal College, 1914; 25 r. First Mauritian Governor-General and Prime Minister. VERT: 25 c. Settlement on Rodriguez, 1691; 35 c. French settlers Charter, 1715; 60 c. Pierre Poivre, c. 1767; 75 c. First coinage, 1794; 1 r. 25 Lady Gomm's Ball, 1847; 15 r. Unfurling of Mauritian flag.

1978. 25th Anniv of Coronation.

549 – 3 r. grey, black and blue . . 25 45
550 – 3 r. multicoloured 25 45
551 **166** 3 r. grey, black and blue . . 25 45

DESIGNS: No. 549, Antelope of Bohun; No. 550, Queen Elizabeth II.

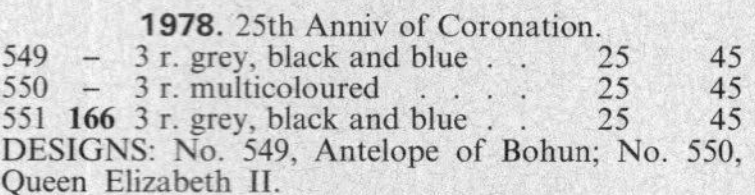

167 Problem of Infection, World War I

1978. 50th Anniv of Discovery of Penicillin.

552 **167** 20 c. multicoloured 50 10
553 – 1 r. multicoloured . . . . 1·10 10
554 – 1 r. 50 black, brn & grn . . 1·50 1·40
555 – 5 r. multicoloured . . . . 2·25 5·50

DESIGNS: 1 r. First mould growth, 1928; 1 r. 50, "Penicillium chrysogenum" ("notatum"); 5 r. Sir Alexander Fleming.

168 "Papilio manlius" (butterfly)

1978. World Wildlife. Multicoloured.

557 20 c. Type **168** . . . . 1·50 10
558 1 r. Geckos 90 10
559 1 r. 50 Greater Mascarene flying fox . . . . 1·25 75
560 5 r. Mauritius kestrel . . . . . 11·00 6·50

169 Ornate Table

171 Father Laval and Crucifix

170 Whitcomb Diesel Locomotive 65H.P., 1949

1978. Bicentenary of Reconstruction of Chateau Le Reduit. Multicoloured.

562 15 c. Type **169** 10 10
563 75 c. Chateau Le Reduit . . . 10 10
564 3 r. Le Reduit gardens 30 45

1979. Railway Locomotives. Multicoloured.

565 20 c. Type **170** 20 10
566 1 r. "Sir William", 1922 . . . 40 10
567 1 r. 50 Kitson type 1930 . . . 60 45
568 2 r. Garratt type, 1927 . . . . 75 85

1979. Beatification of Father Laval (missionary). Multicoloured.

570 20 c. Type **171** 10 10
571 1 r. 50 Father Laval 10 10
572 5 r. Father Laval's tomb (horiz) 35 50

172 Astronaut descending from Lunar Module

173 Great Britain 1855 4d. Stamp and Sir Rowland Hill

1979. 10th Anniv of Moon Landing. Multicoloured. Self-adhesive.

574 20 c. Type **172** 25 30
575 3 r. Astronaut performing experiment on Moon 70 90
576 5 r. Astronaut on Moon . . . 2·50 4·50

1979. Death Cent of Sir Rowland Hill. Mult.

577 25 c. Type **173** 10 10
578 2 r. 1954 60 c. definitive . . . 55 50
579 5 r. 1847 1d. "POST OFFICE" 1·00 1·25

174 Young Child being Vaccinated

1979. International Year of the Child.

581 **174** 15 c. multicoloured 10 10
582 – 25 c. multicoloured 10 10
583 – 1 r. black, blue and light blue 15 10
584 – 1 r. 50 multicoloured 30 20
585 – 3 r. multicoloured 50 50

DESIGNS—HORIZ: 25 c. Children playing; 1 r. 50, Girls in Chemistry laboratory; 3 r. Boy operating lathe. VERT: 1 r. I.Y.C. emblem.

175 The Lienard Obelisk

1980. Pamplemousses Botanical Gardens. Multicoloured.

586 20 c. Type **175** 10 10
587 25 c. Poivre Avenue 10 10
588 1 r. Varieties of Vacoas 20 10
589 2 r. Giant water lilies 45 55
590 5 r. Mon Plaisir (mansion) . . 80 2·25

176 "Emirne" (French steam packet)

1980. "London 1980" International Stamp Exhibition. Mail-carrying Ships. Multicoloured.

592 25 c. Type **176** 30 10
593 1 r. "Boissevain" (cargo liner) . 50 10
594 2 r. "La Boudeuse" (Bougainville's ship) . . . 70 60
595 5 r. "Sea Breeze" (English clipper) . . . . 95 2·00

177 Blind Person Basket-making 178 Prime Minister Sir Seewoosagur Ramgoolam

1980. Birth Centenary of Helen Keller (campaigner for the handicapped). Multicoloured.

596 25 c. Type **177** 20 10
597 1 r. Deaf child under instruction 45 10
598 2 r. 50 Helen reading braille . . 70 35
599 5 r. Helen at graduation, 1904 . 1·25 1·25

1980. 80th Birthday and 40th Year in Parliament of Prime Minister Sir Seewoosagur Ramgoolam.

600 **178** 15 r. multicoloured . . . . 1·00 1·40

179 Headquarters, Mauritius Institute

1980. Centenary of Mauritius Institute. Mult.

601 25 c. Type **179** 15 10
602 2 r. Rare copy of Veda 40 20
603 2 r. Glory of India cone shell . . 55 25
604 5 r. "Le Torrent" (painting by Harpignies) 65 90

180 "Hibiscus liliiflorus" 181 Beau-Bassin/Rose Hill

1981. Flowers. Multicoloured.

605 25 c. Type **180** 20 10
606 2 r. "Erythrospermum monticolum" 70 65
607 2 r. 50 "Chasalia boryana" . . 80 1·25
608 5 r. "Hibiscus columnaris" . . 1·40 2·75

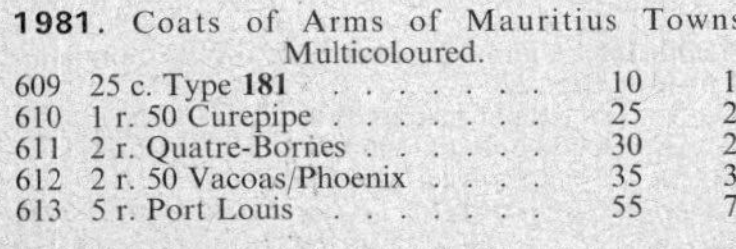

1981. Coats of Arms of Mauritius Towns. Multicoloured.

609 25 c. Type **181** 10 10
610 1 r. 50 Curepipe 25 20
611 2 r. Quatre-Bornes 30 25
612 2 r. 50 Vacoas/Phoenix 35 30
613 5 r. Port Louis 55 75

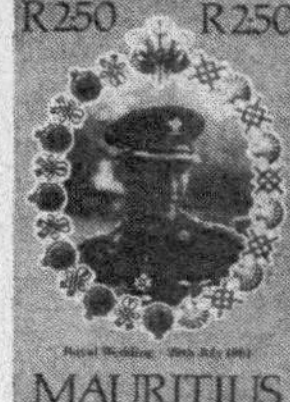

182 Prince Charles as Colonel-in-Chief, Royal Regiment of Wales 184 Drummer and Piper

183 Emmanuel Anquetil and Guy Rozemont

1981. Royal Wedding. Multicoloured

615 25 c. Wedding bouquet from Mauritius 10 10
616 2 r. 50 Type **182** 40 15
617 10 r. Prince Charles and Lady Diana Spencer 80 90

1981. Famous Politicians and Physician.

618 **183** 20 c. black and red 10 10
619 – 25 c. black and yellow . . . 10 10
620 – 1 r. 25 black and green . . 30 25
621 – 1 r. 50 black and red . . . 35 15
622 – 2 r. black and blue 45 20
623 – 2 r. 50 black and brown . . 50 30
624 – 5 r. black and blue . . . . 1·25 90

DESIGNS: 25 c. Remy Ollier and Sookdeo Bissoondoyal; 1 r. 25, Maurice Cure and Barthelemy Ohsan; 1 r. 50, Sir Guy Forget and Renganaden Seeneevassen; 2 r. Sir Abdul Razak Mohamed and Jules Koenig; 2 r. 50, Abdoollatiff Mahomed Osman and Dazzi Rama (Pandit Sahadeo); 5 r. Sir Thomas Lewis (physician) and electrocardiogram.

1981. Religion and Culture. Multicoloured.

625 20 c. Type **184** 10 10
626 2 r. Swami Sivananda (vert) . . 1·00 1·00
627 5 r. Chinese Pagoda . . . . . 1·25 3·00

The 20 c. value commemorates the World Tamil Culture Conference (1980).

185 "Skills" 186 Ka'aba (sacred shrine, Great Mosque of Mecca)

1981. 25th Anniv of Duke of Edinburgh Award Scheme. Multicoloured.

628 25 c. Type **185** 10 10
629 1 r. 25 "Service" 10 10
630 5 r. "Expeditions" 20 30
631 10 r. Duke of Edinburgh . . . 40 70

1981. Moslem Year 1400 A.H Commemoration. Multicoloured.

632 25 c. Type **186** 30 10
633 2 r. Mecca 80 80
634 5 r. Mecca and Ka'aba . . . . 1·40 2·75

187 Scout Emblem 189 Bride and Groom at Buckingham Palace

188 Charles Darwin

1982. 75th Anniv of Boy Scout Movement and 70th Anniv of Scouting in Mauritius.

635 **187** 25 c. lilac and green . . . 10 10
636 – 2 r. brown and ochre . . . 40 30
637 – 5 r. green and olive . . . . 85 1·00
638 – 10 r. green and blue . . . 1·25 2·00

DESIGNS: 2 r. Lord Baden-Powell and Baden-Powell House; 5 r. Grand Howl; 10 r. Ascent of Pieter Both.

1982. 150th Anniv of Charles Darwin's Voyage. Multicoloured.

639 25 c. Type **188** 10 10
640 2 r. Darwin's telescope 30 45
641 2 r. 50 Darwin's elephant ride . 35 55
642 10 r. H.M.S. "Beagle" beached for repairs . . . . 1·40 2·75

1982. 21st Birthday of Princess of Wales. Mult.

643 25 c. Mauritius coat of arms . . 10 10
644 2 r. 50 Princess Diana in Chesterfield, November, 1981 60 35
645 5 r. Type **189** 75 90
646 10 r. Formal portrait . . . . . 2·50 2·50

190 Prince and Princess of Wales with Prince William

1982. Birth of Prince William of Wales.

647 **190** 2 r. 50 multicoloured . . . 75 30

191 Bois Fandamane Plant 193 Early Wall-mounted Telephone

192 Arms and Flag of Mauritius

1982. Centenary of Robert Koch's Discovery of Tubercle Bacillus. Multicoloured.

648 25 c. Type **191** 10 10
649 1 r. 25 Central market, Port Louis 40 40
650 2 r. Bois Banane plant 65 75
651 5 r. Platte de Lezard plant . . . 75 2·25
652 10 r. Dr. Robert Koch . . . . 1·25 3·75

1983. Commonwealth Day. Multicoloured.

653 25 c. Type **192** 10 10
654 2 r. 50 Satellite view of Mauritius 20 30
655 5 r. Harvesting sugar cane . . . 30 75
656 10 r. Port Louis harbour . . . 95 1·50

1983. World Communications Year. Mult.

657 25 c. Type **193** 10 10
658 1 r. 25 Early telegraph apparatus (horiz) 35 20
659 2 r. Earth satellite station . . . 45 50
660 10 r. First hot-air balloon in Mauritius, 1784 (horiz) . . . 80 2·75

194 Map of Nambia 195 Fish Trap

1983. Namibia Day. Multicoloured.

661 25 c. Type **194** 45 10
662 2 r. 50 Hand breaking chains . 1·50 75
663 5 r. Family and settlement . . 2·00 2·25
664 10 r. Diamond mining . . . . 4·75 3·75

1983. Fishery Resources. Multicoloured.

665 25 c. Type **195** 15 10
666 1 r. Fishing boat (horiz) 40 15
667 5 r. Game fishing . . . . . . 75 2·25
668 10 r. Octopus drying (horiz) . . 1·00 4·00

196 Swami Dayananda 197 Adolf von Plevitz

1983. Death Centenary of Swami Dayananda. Multicoloured.

669 25 c. Type **196** 10 10
670 35 c. Last meeting with father . 10 10
671 2 r. Receiving religious instruction 50 65
672 5 r. Swami demonstrating strength . . . . 90 2·50
673 10 r. At a religious gathering . 1·40 3·75

1983. 125th Anniv of Arrival in Mauritius of Adolf von Plevitz (social reformer). Multicoloured.

674 25 c. Type **197** 10 10
675 1 r. 25 La Laura, Government school 30 30
676 5 r. Von Plevitz addressing Commission of Enquiry, 1872 1·00 2·50
677 10 r. Von Plevitz with Indian farm workers . . . . . . 1·75 3·75

198 Courtship Chase

1984. The Mauritius Kestrel. Multicoloured.

678 25 c. Type **198** 85 30
679 2 r. Kestrel in tree (vert) . . . 2·00 1·25
680 2 r. 50 Young kestrel . . . . . 2·25 2·25
681 10 r. Head (vert) . . . . 3·25 8·00

199 Wreck of S.S "Tayeb" 200 Blue Latan Palm

1984. 250th Anniv of "Lloyd's List" (newspaper). Multicoloured.

682 25 c. Type **199** 30 10
683 1 r. S.S. "Taher" 95 15
684 5 r. East Indiaman "Triton" . . 3·00 3·25
685 10 r. M.S. "Astor" . . . . . . 3·50 6·50

1984. Palm Trees. Multicoloured.

686 25 c. Type **200** 10 10
687 50 c. "Hyophorbe vaughanii" . . 20 20
688 2 r. 50 "Tectiphiala ferox" . . 1·25 1·50
689 5 r. Round Island bottle-palm . 2·00 3·00
690 10 r. "Hyophorbe amaricaulis" . 3·25 5·25

201 Slave Girl 203 The Queen Mother on Clarence House Balcony, 1980

202 75th Anniversary Production of "Faust" and Leoville L'Homme

1984. 150th Anniv of Abolition of Slavery and Introduction of Indian Immigrants.

691 **201** 25 c. purple, lilac and brown 15 10
692 – 1 r. purple, lilac and brown 70 10
693 – 2 r. purple and lilac . . . . 1·50 1·00
694 – 10 r. purple and lilac . . . 5·00 8·00

DESIGNS—VERT: 1 r. Slave market. HORIZ: 2 r. Indian immigrant family; 10 r. Arrival of Indian immigrants.

1984. Centenary of Alliance Francaise (cultural organization). Multicoloured.
695 25 c. Type **202** 20 10
696 1 r. 25 Prize-giving ceremony and Aunauth Beejadhur 70 50
697 5 r. First headquarters and Hector Clarenc . . . . . . 2·00 3·00
698 10 r. Lion Mountain and Labourdonnais . . . . . . 2·50 5·00

1985. Life and Times of Queen Elizabeth the Queen Mother. Multicoloured.
699 25 c. The Queen Mother in 1926 20 10
700 2 r. With Princess Margaret at Trooping the Colour 60 30
701 5 r. Type **203** . . . . 75 1·40
702 10 r. With Prince Henry at his christening (from photo by Lord Snowdon) . . . . . . 1·25 2·75

204 High Jumping **205** Adult and Fledgling Pink Pigeons

1985. 2nd Indian Ocean Islands Games. Multicoloured.
704 25 c. Type **204** 20 10
705 50 c. Javelin-throwing 50 30
706 1 r. 25 Cycling . . . . 2·75 1·60
707 10 r. Wind surfing . . . . . . 6·00 8·50

1985. Pink Pigeon. Multicoloured.
708 25 c. Type **205** . . . . 2·00 30
709 2 r. Pink pigeon displaying at nest . . . . 4·25 1·75
710 2 r. 50 On nest . . . . 4·75 3·50
711 5 r. Pair preening . . . . . . 9·00 10·00

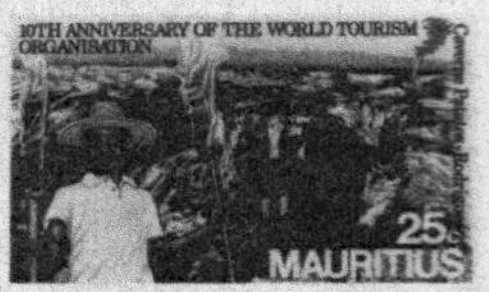

206 Caverne Patates, Rodrigues

1985. 10th Anniv of World Tourism Organization. Multicoloured.
712 25 c. Type **206** 50 10
713 35 c. Coloured soils, Chamarel 50 30
714 5 r. Serpent Island . . . . . . 4·00 4·50
715 10 r. Coin de Mire Island . . . 6·00 8·50

207 Old Town Hall, Port Louis

1985. 250th Anniv of Port Louis. Multicoloured.
716 25 c. Type **207** 10 10
717 1 r. Al-Aqsa Mosque (180th anniv) . . . . 1·00 10
718 2 r. 50 Vase and trees (250th anniv of settlememt of Tamil-speaking Indians) . . . . . 1·25 1·50
719 10 r. Port Louis Harbour . . . 6·50 8·50

208 Edmond Halley and Diagram

1986. Appearance of Halley's Comet. Mult.
720 25 c. Type **208** 40 10
721 1 r. 25 Halley's Comet (1682) and Newton's Reflector . . . . 1·10 50
722 3 r. Halley's Comet passing Earth 1·60 2·00
723 10 r. "Giotto" spacecraft . . . 3·50 6·00

1986. 60th Birthday of Queen Elizabeth II. As T **120a** of Hong Kong. Multicoloured.
724 25 c. Princess Elizabeth wearing badge of Grenadier Guards, 1942 . . . . 10 10
725 75 c. Investiture of Prince of Wales, 1969 . . . . 10 10
726 2 r. With Prime Minister of Mauritius, 1972 . . . . . . 20 25
727 3 r. In Germany, 1978 . . . . 30 40
728 15 r. At Crown Agents Head Office, London, 1983 . . . . 1·25 2·00

209 Maize (World Food Day) **210** "Cryptopus elatus"

1986. International Events. Multicoloured.
729 25 c. Type **209** 10 10
730 1 r. African Regional Industrial Property Organization emblem (10th anniv) 30 10
731 1 r. 25 International Peace Year emblem 65 50
732 10 r. Footballer and Mauritius Football Association emblem (World Cup Football Championship, Mexico) . . 5·50 7·50

1986. Orchids. Multicoloured.
733 25 c. Type **210** 40 10
734 2 r. "Jumellea recta" . . . . . 1·10 45
735 2 r. 50 "Angraecum mauritianum" . . . . 1·25 60
736 10 r. "Bulbophyllum longiflorum" . . . . 2·25 3·00

211 Hesketh Bell Bridge

1987. Mauritius Bridges. Multicoloured.
758 25 c. Type **211** 25 10
759 50 c. Sir Colville Deverell Bridge 35 20
760 2 r. 50 Cavendish Bridge . . . 70 75
761 5 r. Tamarin Bridge . . . . . 90 2·00
762 10 r. Grand River North West Bridge . . . . 1·25 2·50

212 Supreme Court, Port Louis **213** Mauritius Dodo Mascot

1987. Bicentenary of the Mauritius Bar. Mult.
763 25 c. Type **212** 10 10
764 1 r. District Court, Flacq . . . 40 10
765 1 r. 25 Statue of Justice 50 20
766 10 r. Barristers of 1787 and 1987 2·00 2·25

1987. International Festival of the Sea. Mult.
767 25 c. Type **213** 20 10
768 1 r. 50 Yacht regatta (horiz) . . 1·00 90
769 3 r. Water skiing (horiz) . . . 2·00 2·75
770 5 r. "Svanen" (barquentine) . . 2·75 4·25

214 Toys

1987. Industrialisation. Multicoloured.
771 20 c. Type **214** 10 10
772 35 c. Spinning factory 10 10
773 50 c. Rattan furniture 10 10
774 2 r. 50 Spectacle factory . . . 85 80
775 10 r. Stone carving . . . . . . 2·50 2·75

215 Maison Ouvriere (Int Year of Shelter for the Homeless)

1987. Art and Architecture.
776 **215** 25 c. multicoloured 10 10
777 – 1 r. black and grey 25 10
778 – 1 r. 25 multicoloured . . . 30 30
779 – 2 r. multicoloured 55 55
780 – 5 r. multicoloured . . . . 1·00 1·25
DESIGNS: 1 r. "Paul et Virginie" (lithograph); 1 r. 25, Chateau de Rosnay; 2 r. "Vielle Ferme" (Boulle); 5 r. "Trois Mamelles".

216 University of Mauritius

1988. 20th Anniv of Independence. Mult.
781 25 c. Type **216** 10 10
782 75 c. Anniversary gymnastic display 20 10
783 2 r. 50 Hurdlers and aerial view of Sir Maurice Rault Stadium 70 55
784 5 r. Air Mauritius aircraft at Sir Seewoosagur Ramgoolam International Airport . . . . 1·40 1·60
785 10 r. Governor-General Sir Veerasamy Ringadoo and Prime Minister Anerood Jugnauth . . . . 2·25 2·75

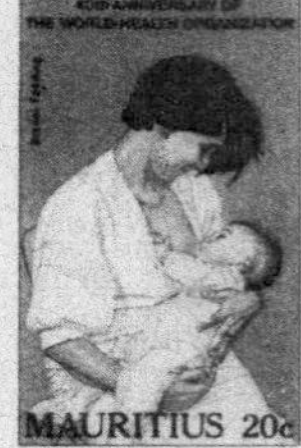

217 Breast Feeding **218** Modern Bank Building

1988. 40th Anniv of W.H.O. Multicoloured.
786 20 c. Type **217** 15 10
787 2 r. Baby under vaccination umbrella and germ droplets . 1·25 70
788 3 r. Nutritious food . . . . . 1·40 1·25
789 10 r. W.H.O logo . . . . . . 2·75 3·25

1988. 150th Anniv of Mauritius Commercial Bank Ltd.
790 **218** 25 c. black, green & blue . 10 10
791 – 1 r. black and red 15 10
792 – 1 r. 25 multicoloured . . . 30 30
793 – 25 r. multicoloured . . . . 6·00 7·00
DESIGNS—HORIZ: 1 r. Mauritius Commercial Bank, 1897; 25 r. Fifteen dollar bank note of 1838. VERT: 1 r. 25, Bank arms.

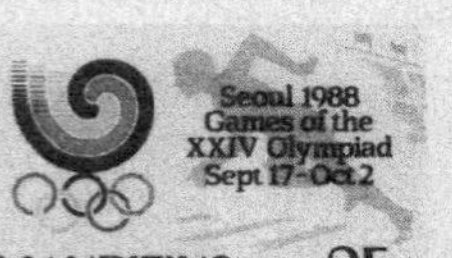

219 Olympic Rings and Athlete

1988. Olympic Games, Seoul. Multicoloured.
794 25 c. Type **219** 10 10
795 35 c. Wrestling 15 15
796 1 r. 50 Long distance running . 75 60
797 10 r. Swimming . . . . 2·50 3·75

220 Nature Park

1989. Protection of the Environment. Mult.
798B 15 c. Underwater view . . . 10 10
799B 20 c. As 15 c. 10 10
800B 30 c. Greenshank 10 10
801B 40 c. Type **220** 10 10
810A 50 c. Round Island (vert) . . 10 10
801cB 60 c. As 50 c. 10 10
811A 75 c. Bassin Blanc 10 10
812A 1 r. Mangrove (vert) 10 10
802A 1 r. 50 Whimbrel 10 10
813A 2 r. Le Morne 10 15
803A 3 r. Marine life 15 20
804B 4 r. Fern tree (vert) 20 25
814A 5 r. Riviere du Poste estuary . 30 35
805A 6 r. Ecological scenery (vert) . 35 40
806B 10 r. "Phelsuma ornata" (gecko) on plant (vert) . . 55 60
806aB 15 r. Benares waves 80 85
807B 25 r. Migratory birds and map (vert) . . . . 1·40 1·50

221 La Tour Sumeire, Port Louis **222** Cardinal Jean Margeot

1989. Bicentenary of the French Revolution.
818 **221** 30 c. black, green & yell . . 10 10
819 – 1 r. black, brown and light brown 20 10
820 – 8 r. multicoloured . . . . 1·50 1·50
821 – 15 r. multicoloured . . . . 2·00 2·25
DESIGNS: 1 r. Salle de Spectacle du Jardin; 8 r. Portrait of Comte de Malartic; 15 r. Bicentenary logo.

1989. Visit of Pope John Paul II. Multicoloured.
822 30 c. Type **222** 30 10
823 40 c. Pope John Paul II and Prime Minister Jugnauth, Vatican, 1988 . . . . 70 25
824 3 r. Mere Marie Magdeleine de la Croix and Chapelle des Filles de Marie, Port Louis, 1864 . 1·25 1·25
825 6 r. St. Francois d'Assise Church, Pamplemousses, 1756 . . . 2·00 2·25
826 10 r. Pope John Paul II . . . . 4·50 5·00

223 Nehru

1989. Birth Centenary of Jawaharlal Nehru (Indian statesman). Multicoloured.
827 40 c. Type **223** 70 20
828 1 r. 50 Nehru with daughter, Indira, and grandsons . . . 1·50 70
829 3 r. Nehru and Gandhi . . . . 2·50 2·50
830 4 r. Nehru with Presidents Nasser and Tito . . . . 2·50 2·75
831 10 r. Nehru with children . . . 4·50 6·00

224 Cane Cutting

1990. 350th Anniv of Introduction of Sugar Cane to Mauritius. Multicoloured.
832 30 c. Type **224** 10 10
833 40 c. Sugar factory, 1867 . . . 15 10
834 1 r. Mechanical loading of cane 30 10
835 25 r. Modern sugar factory . . 8·00 9·00

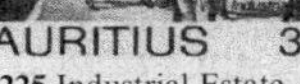

225 Industrial Estate **226** Desjardins (naturalist) (150th death anniv)

1990. 60th Birthday of Prime Minister Sir Anerood Jugnauth. Multicoloured.
836 35 c. Type **225** 10 10
837 40 c. Sir Anerood Jugnauth at desk 10 10
838 1 r. 50 Mauritius Stock Exchange symbol 30 30
839 4 r. Jugnauth with Governor-General Sir Seewoosagur Ramgoolam . . . . 1·50 2·25
840 10 r. Jugnauth greeting Pope John Paul II . . . . 5·50 7·00

1990. Anniversaries. Multicoloured.
841 30 c. Type **226** 20 10
842 35 c. Logo on TV screen (25th anniv of Mauritius Broadcasting Corporation) (horiz) 20 10
843 6 r. Line Barracks (now Police Headquarters) (250th anniv) 3·50 3·75
844 8 r. Town Hall, Curepipe (centenary of municipality) (horiz) . . . . 3·50 4·00

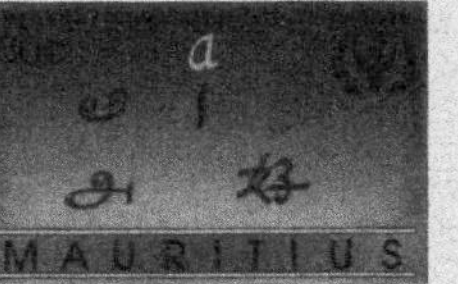

227 Letters from Alphabets

1990. International Literacy Year. Multicoloured.
845 30 c. Type **227** 15 10
846 1 r. Blind child reading Braille 85 15
847 3 r. Open book and globe . . . 1·75 1·75
848 10 r. Book showing world map with quill pen . . . . . . 4·50 6·50

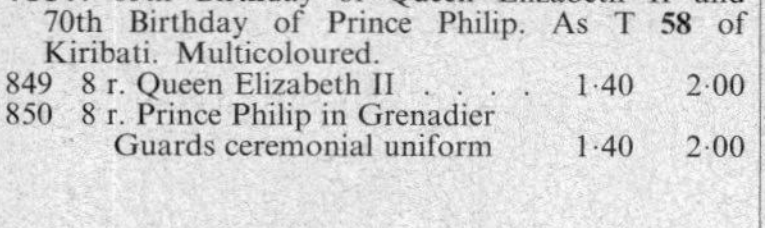

1991. 65th Birthday of Queen Elizabeth II and 70th Birthday of Prince Philip. As T **58** of Kiribati. Multicoloured.

849 8 r. Queen Elizabeth II 1·40 2·00
850 8 r. Prince Philip in Grenadier Guards ceremonial uniform 1·40 2·00

228 City Hall, Port Louis (25th anniv of City status)

1991. Anniversaries and Events. Multicoloured.

851 40 c. Type **228** 10 10
852 4 r. Colonel Draper (race course founder) (150th death anniv) (vert) 1·75 1·75
853 6 r. Joseph Barnard (engraver) and "POST PAID" 2d. stamp (175th birth anniv) (vert) 2·00 2·25
854 10 r. Supermarine Spitfire "Mauritius II" (50th anniv of Second World War) 4·50 6·00

229 "Euploea euphon"

1991. "Phila Nippon '91" International Stamp Exn, Tokyo. Butterflies. Multicoloured.

855 40 c. Type **229** 60 20
856 3 r. "Hypolimnas misippus" (female) 1·90 1·00
857 8 r. "Papilio manlius" 3·50 4·00
858 10 r. "Hypolimnas misippus" (male) 3·50 4·25

230 Green Turtle, Tromelin

1991. Indian Ocean Islands. Multicoloured.

859 40 c. Type **230** 50 20
860 1 r. Glossy ibis, Agalega 1·50 40
861 2 r. Takamaka flowers, Chagos Archipelago 1·60 1·10
862 15 r. Violet spider conch sea shell, St. Brandon 7·00 8·50

231 Pres. Veerasamy Ringadoo and President's Residence

1992. Proclamation of Republic. Multicoloured.

863 40 c. Type **231** 10 10
864 4 r. Prime Minister Anerood Jugnauth and Government House 80 1·25
865 8 r. Children and rainbow 1·75 2·75
866 10 r. Presidential flag 2·00 3·00

232 Ticolo (mascot) **233** Bouquet (25th anniv of Fleurir Maurice)

1992. 8th African Athletics Championships, Port Louis. Multicoloured.

867 40 c. Type **232** 10 10
868 4 r. Sir Anerood Jugnauth Stadium (horiz) 65 95
869 5 r. High jumping (horiz) 75 1·10
870 6 r. Championships emblem 90 1·60

1992. Local Events and Anniversaries. Mult.

871 40 c. Type **233** 10 10
872 1 r. Swami Krishnanandji Maharaj (25th anniv of arrival) 40 10
873 2 r. Boy with dog (humane education) (horiz) 1·10 75
874 3 r. Commission Headquarters (10th anniv of Indian Ocean Commission) (horiz) 1·10 1·00
875 15 r. Radio telescope antenna, Bras d'Eau (project inauguration) (horiz) 4·50 6·00

234 Bank of Mauritius Headquarters **235** Housing Development

1992. 25th Anniv of Bank of Mauritius. Mult.

876 40 c. Type **234** 10 10
877 4 r. Dodo gold coin (horiz) 1·50 90
878 8 r. First bank note issue (horiz) 2·25 2·75
879 15 r. Graph of foreign exchange reserves, 1967–92 (horiz) 4·00 5·50

1993. 25th Anniv of National Day. Multicoloured.

880 30 c. Type **235** 10 10
881 40 c. Gross domestic product graph on computer screen 10 10
882 3 r. National colours on map of Mauritius 40 50
883 4 r. Ballot box 45 60
884 15 r. Grand Commander's insignia for Order of Star and Key of the Indian Ocean 1·75 3·00

236 Bell 206 B JetRanger Helicopter

1993. 25th Anniv of Air Mauritius Ltd. Mult.

885 40 c. Type **236** 60 30
886 3 r. Boeing 747SP 1·00 1·00
887 4 r. Aerospatiale/Aeritalia ATR 42 1·25 1·25
888 10 r. Boeing 767-200ER 2·50 4·00

1993. No. 811 surch **40cs**.

890 40 c. on 75 c. Bassin Blanc 30 30

238 French Royal Charter, 1715, and Act of Capitulation, 1810 **239** "Scotia" (cable ship) and Map of Cable Route

1993. 5th Summit of French-speaking Nations. Multicoloured.

891 1 r. Type **238** 30 10
892 5 r. Road signs 1·75 1·50
893 6 r. Code Napoleon 1·75 2·00
894 7 r. Early Mauritius newspapers 1·75 2·25

1993. Cent of Telecommunications. Mult.

895 40 c. Type **239** 30 10
896 3 r. Morse key and code 70 70
897 4 r. Signal Mountain Earth station 85 1·00
898 8 r. Communications satellite 1·60 2·50

240 Indian Mongoose

1994. Mammals. Multicoloured.

899 40 c. Type **240** 30 10
900 2 r. Indian black-naped hare 60 40
901 8 r. Pair of crab-eating macaque 1·75 2·50
902 10 r. Adult and infant common tenrec 2·00 2·75

241 Dr Edouard Brown-Sequard (physiologist) (death cent)

1994. Anniversaries and Events. Multicoloured.

903 40 c. Type **241** 10 10
904 4 r. Family in silhouette (International Year of the Family) 45 55
905 8 r. World Cup and map of U.S.A. (World Cup Football Championship, U.S.A.) 1·00 1·50
906 10 r. Control tower, SSR International Airport (50th anniv of Civil Aviation Organization) 1·25 1·75

242 "St. Geran" leaving L'Orient for Isle de France, 1744

1994. 250th Anniv of Wreck of "St. Geran" (sailing packet). Multicoloured.

907 40 c. Type **242** 20 10
908 5 r. In rough seas off Isle de France 65 70
909 6 r. Bell and main mast 75 1·00
910 10 r. Artifacts from wreck 1·25 2·25

243 Ring-a-ring-a-roses

1994. Children's Games and Pastimes. Children's paintings. Multicoloured.

912 30 c. Type **243** 10 10
913 40 c. Skipping and ball games 10 10
914 8 r. Water sports 1·25 1·75
915 10 r. Blind man's buff 1·25 1·75

244 Nutmeg **245** Mare Longue Reservoir

1995. Spices. Multicoloured.

916 40 c. Type **244** 10 10
917 4 r. Coriander 55 65
918 5 r. Cloves 65 75
919 10 r. Cardamom 1·25 2·25

1995. 50th Anniv of End of Second World War. As T **75** of Kiribati, but 35 × 28 mm. Mult.

920 5 r. H.M.S. "Mauritius" (cruiser) 1·00 1·40
921 5 r. Mauritian soldiers and map of North Africa 1·00 1·40
922 5 r. Consolidated PBY-5 Catalina flying boat, Tombeau Bay 1·00 1·40

1995. Anniversaries. Multicoloured.

923 40 c. Type **245** (50th anniv of construction) 10 10
924 4 r. Mahebourg to Curepipe road (bicentenary of construction) 60 70
925 10 r. Buildings on fire (centenary of Great Fire of Port Louis) 1·25 2·00

246 Ile Plate Lighthouse **247** Symbolic Children under U.N.I.C.E.F. Umbrella

1995. Lighthouses. Multicoloured.

926 30 c. Type **246** 40 20
927 40 c. Pointe aux Caves 40 20
928 8 r. Ile aux Fouquets 1·75 2·25
929 10 r. Pointe aux Canonniers 2·00 2·25

1995. 50th Anniv of United Nations. Multicoloured.

931 40 c. Type **247** 10 10
932 4 r. Hard hat and building construction (I.L.O.) 35 45
933 8 r. Satellite picture of cyclone (W.M.O.) 70 1·10
934 10 r. Bread and grain (F.A.O.) 90 1·40

248 C.O.M.E.S.A. Emblem

1995. Inauguration of Common Market for Eastern and Southern Africa.

935 **248** 60 c. black and pink 10 10
936 4 r. black and blue 35 45
937 8 r. black and yellow 70 1·10
938 10 r. black and green 90 1·40

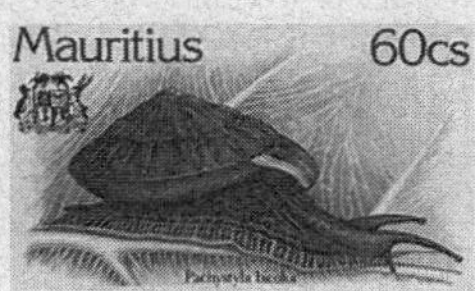

249 "Pachystyla bicolor"

1996. Snails. Multicoloured.

939 60 c. Type **249** 15 10
940 4 r. "Gonidomus pagodus" 45 50
941 5 r. "Harmogenanina implicata" 45 60
942 10 r. "Tropidophora eugeniae" 85 1·60

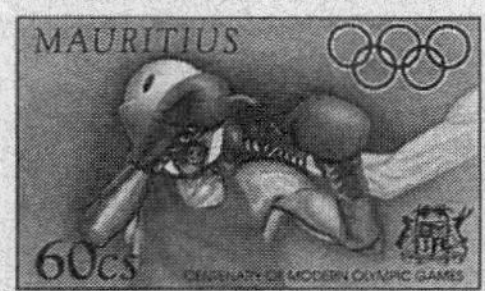

250 Boxing

1996. Centenary of Modern Olympic Games. Multicoloured.

943 60 c. Type **250** 10 10
944 4 r. Badminton 45 50
945 5 r. Basketball 60 65
946 10 r. Table tennis 1·00 1·50

251 "Zambezia" (freighter)

1996. Ships. Multicoloured.

947 60 c. Type **251** 15 10
948 4 r. "Sir Jules" (coastal freighter) 45 50
949 5 r. "Mauritius" (cargo liner) 50 60
950 10 r. "Mauritius Pride" (container ship) 1·00 1·50

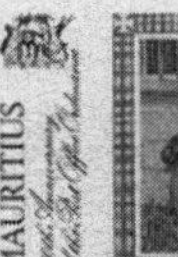

252 Posting a Letter

1996. 150th Anniv of the Post Office Ordinance. Multicoloured.

952 60 c. Type **252** 10 10
953 4 r. "B53" duplex postmark . . 45 50
954 5 r. Modern mobile post office . . 55 60
955 10 r. Carriole (19th-century horse-drawn postal carriage) . . . . 1·00 1·50

253 Vavang

1997. Fruits. Multicoloured.

956 60 c. Type **253** 10 10
957 4 r. Pom zako 45 50
958 5 r. Zambos 55 60
959 10 r. Sapot negro . . . . . . 1·00 1·50

254 Governor Mahe de la Bourdonnais and Map

1997. Aspects of Mauritius History. Multicoloured.

960 60 c. Type **254** 20 15
961 1 r. La Perouse and map of Pacific 30 15
962 4 r. Governor Sir William Gomm and Lady Gomm's Ball, 1847 . . . . 55 50
963 6 r. George Clark discovering skeleton of dodo, 1865 . . . 80 80
964 10 r. Professor Brian Abel-Smith and Social Policies report of 1960 . . . . 1·00 1·50

255 1d. "POST OFFICE" Mauritius

1997. 150th Anniv of "POST OFFICE" Stamps. Multicoloured.

965 60 c. Type **255** 20 10
966 4 r. 2d. "POST OFFICE" Mauritius 40 40
967 5 r. "POST OFFICE" 1d. and 2d. on gold background 50 50
968 10 r. "POST OFFICE" 2d. and 1d. on silver background . . 90 1·40

256 Wheelwright

1997. Small Businesses. Multicoloured.

970 60 c. Type **256** 10 10
971 4 r. Laundryman 30 30
972 5 r. Shipwright 40 40
973 15 r. Quarryman . . . . . . 1·25 1·75

257 "Phelsuma guentheri" (gecko)

1998. Geckos. Multicoloured.

974 1 r. Type **257** 15 10
975 6 r. "Nactus serpensinsula durrelli" 45 50
976 7 r. "Nactus coindemirensis" . . 55 65
977 8 r. "Phelsuma edwardnewtonii" 65 80

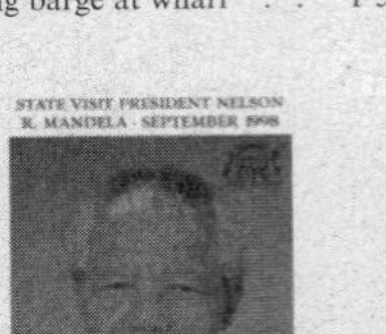

258 Steam Train on Viaduct

1998. Inland Transport. Multicoloured.

978 40 c. Type **258** 15 10
979 5 r. Early lorry 45 45
980 6 r. Bus in town street 50 60
981 10 r. Sailing barge at wharf . . 1·50 2·00

259 President Nelson Mandela

1998. State Visit of President Nelson Mandela of South Africa.

982 **259** 25 r. multicoloured . . . 1·60 2·00

260 Count Maurice of Nassau and Dutch Landing

1998. 400th Anniv of Dutch Landing on Mauritius. Multicoloured.

983 50 c. Type **260** 10 10
984 1 r. Fort Frederik Hendrik and sugar cane 10 10
985 7 r. Dutch map of Mauritius (1670) 65 75
986 8 r. Diagram of landing 70 80

261 Cascade Balfour

1998. Waterfalls. Multicoloured.

988 1 r. Type **261** 10 10
989 5 r. Rochester Falls 30 35
990 6 r. Cascade G.R.S.E. (vert) . . 35 40
991 10 r. 500 ft. Cascade (vert) . . 55 75

262 Plan of Le Reduit

1998. 250th Anniv of Chateau Le Reduit. Multicoloured.

992 1 r. Type **262** 10 10
993 4 r. "Le Chateau du Reduit, 1814" (P. Thuillier) 20 25
994 5 r. "Le Reduit, 1998" (Hassen Edun) 30 35
995 15 r. Commemorative monument 80 1·25

263 Governor Mahe de la Bourdonnais on 15 c. Stamp of 1899

1999. 300th Birth Anniv of Governor Mahe de la Bourdonnais.

996 **263** 7 r. blue, black and red . . 45 55

264 "Clerodendron laciniatum"

1999. Local Plants. Multicoloured.

997 1 r. Type **264** 10 10
998 2 r. "Senecio lamarckianus" . 10 15
999 5 r. "Cylindrocline commersonii" 35 35
1000 9 r. "Psiadia pollicina" . . . 60 75

265 "The Washerwomen" (Herve Masson)

1999. Mauritius through Local Artists' Eyes. Multicoloured.

1001 1 r. Type **265** 10 10
1002 3 r. "The Casino" (Gaetan de Rosnay) 25 25
1003 4 r. "The Four Elements" (Andree Poilly) 30 30
1004 6 r. "Going to Mass" (Xavier Le Juge de Segrais) 45 50

266 Old Chimney, Alma

1999. Old Sugar Mill Chimneys. Multicoloured.

1005 1 r. Type **266** 10 10
1006 2 r. Antoinette 15 15
1007 5 r. Belle Mare 40 40
1008 7 r. Grande Rosalie 50 60

267 Mosquito and Sprayer (Eradication of Malaria)

1999. 20th-century Achievements. Multicoloured.

1010 1 r. Type **267** 10 10
1011 2 r. Judge's robes, silhouette and airliner (emancipation of women) 15 15
1012 5 r. Conference room (international conference centre) . 40 40
1013 9 r. Spoons full of sugar (development of sugar industry) . . 75 85

268 Crest

2000. 150th Anniv of Mauritius Chamber of Commerce and Industry. Multicoloured.

1014 1 r. Type **268** 10 10
1015 2 r. Unity, Vision and Service logos 10 15
1016 7 r. Francis Channell (First Secretary, 1850–72) 40 45
1017 15 r. Louis Lechelle (First President, 1850) 80 85

269 "Cratopus striga" (beetle)

2000. Beetles. Multicoloured.

1018 1 r. Type **269** 10 10
1019 2 r. "Cratopus armatus" . . . 10 15
1020 3 r. "Cratopus chrysochlorus" . 15 20
1021 15 r. "Cratopus nigrogranatus" 80 85

EXPRESS DELIVERY STAMPS

1903. No. 136 surch **EXPRESS DELIVERY 15 c.**

E1 **40** 15 c. on 15 c. blue . . . . . 6·50 18·00

1903. No. 136 surch **EXPRESS DELIVERY (INLAND) 15 c.**

E3 **40** 15 c. on 15 c. blue . . . . . 7·50 2·50

1904. T **42** without value in label (a) Surch **(FOREIGN) EXPRESS DELIVERY 18 CENTS**.

E5 **42** 18 c. green . . . . 1·50 20·00

(b) Surch **EXPRESS DELIVERY (INLAND) 15 c.**

E6 **42** 15 c. green . . . . 3·50 3·50

POSTAGE DUE STAMPS

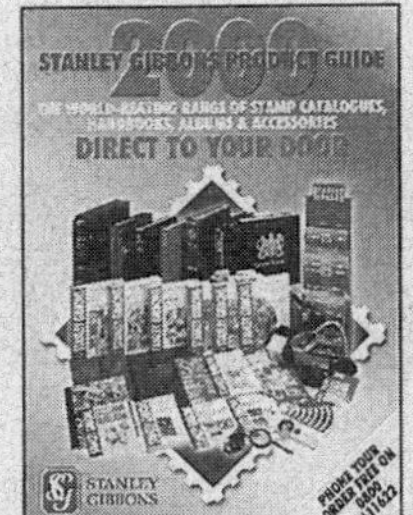

D 1

1933.

D 1 **D 1** 2 c. black . . . . 1·25 50
D 2 4 c. violet 40 65
D 3 6 c. red 40 80
D 4 10 c. green 60 70
D 5 20 c. blue . . . . 50 1·00
D13 50 c. purple . . . . . . 75 12·00
D 7 1 r. orange . . . . . . 70 15·00

1982. Nos. 530/1, 535, 540, 542 and 547 surch **POSTAGE DUE** and value.

D14 10 c. on 15 c. Dutch Occupation, 1638–1710 . . . . 20 30
D15 20 c. on 20 c. Van Keulen's map, c. 1700 . . . . 30 30
D16 50 c. on 60 c. Pierre Poivre, c. 1767 (vert) 30 30
D17 1 r. on 1 r. 20 Government House, c. 1840 . . . . . . 40 30
D18 1 r. 50 on 1 r. 50 Indian immigration, 1835 . . . . 50 75
D19 5 r. on 15 r. Unfurling Mauritian flag, 1968 . . . . 1·00 2·00

MAYOTTE Pt. 6

One of the Comoro Islands adjacent to Madagascar.

In 1974 (when the other islands became an independent state) Mayotte was made an Overseas Department of France, using French stamps. From 1997 it again had its own issues.

100 centimes = 1 franc

1892. "Tablet" key-type inscr "MAYOTTE".

No.	Type	Description		
1	D	1 c. black and red on blue	40	40
2		2 c. brown & blue on buff	50	50
3		4 c. brown & blue on grey	70	60
4		5 c. green & red on green	1·50	1·00
5		10 c. black & blue on lilac	2·00	2·00
15		10 c. red and blue	26·00	20·00
6		15 c. blue and red	6·00	4·00
16		15 c. grey and red	60·00	45·00
7		20 c. red & blue on green	5·25	4·50
8		25 c. black & red on pink	3·75	2·50
17		25 c. blue and red	4·00	3·50
9		30 c. brown & bl on drab	8·25	5·75
18		35 c. black & red on yellow	2·50	2·50
10		40 c. red & blue on yellow	6·75	5·75
19		45 c. black on green	7·50	6·00
11		50 c. red and blue on pink	12·50	8·00
20		50 c. brown & red on blue	6·25	8·25
12		75 c. brown & red on orge	14·00	9·00
13		1 f. green and red	10·50	8·00
14		5 f. mauve & blue on lilac	70·00	60·00

1912. Surch in figures.

No.	Type	Description		
21	D	05 on 20 c. brown and blue on buff	90	90
22		05 on 4 c. brown and blue on grey	35	30
23		05 on 15 c. blue and red	50	50
24		05 on 20 c. red and blue on green	50	60
25		05 on 25 c. black and red on pink	50	60
26		05 on 30 c. brown and blue on drab	60	65
27		10 on 40 c. red and blue on yellow	50	70
28		10 on 45 c. black and red on green	55	55
29		10 on 50 c. red and blue on pink	1·50	1·75
30		10 on 75 c. brown and red on orange	85	1·00
31		10 on 1 f. green and red	1·00	1·10

1997. Stamps of France optd **MAYOTTE.** (a) Nos. 2907/10, 2911a, 2916b, 2919a, 2924 and 2928.

No.	Type	Description		
40	1118	10 c. brown	10	10
41		20 c. green	10	10
42		50 c. violet	10	10
43		1 f. orange	20	10
44		2 f. blue	40	25
45		2 f. 70 green	55	35
46		3 f. 80 blue	75	45
47		5 f. blue	1·00	60
48		10 f. violet	2·00	1·25

(b) No value expressed. No. 3121.

No.	Type	Description		
49	1118	(–) red	75	45

No. 49 was sold at 3 f.

6 Ylang Ylang

1997.

50 **6** 2 f. 70 multicoloured 55 35

7 Arms

1997.

51 **7** 3 f. multicoloured 60 35

8 Terminal Building and Airplane

1997. Air. Inauguration of New Airport.

52 **8** 20 f. indigo, red and blue . . . 4·00 2·40

9 Le Banga

1997.

53 **9** 3 f. 80 multicoloured 75 45

10 Dzen-dze (musical instrument)

1997.

54 **10** 5 f. 20 multicoloured . . . . 1·00 60

1997. Stamps of France optd **MAYOTTE**. (a) On Nos. 3415/20, 3425, 3430 and 3432.

55	10 c. brown	10	10
56	20 c. green	10	10
57	50 c. violet	10	10
58	1 f. orange	20	10
59	2 f. blue	40	25
60	2 f. 70 green	50	30
62	3 f. 80 blue	75	45
66	5 f. blue	95	55
68	10 f. violet	1·90	1·10

(b) On No. 3407. No value expressed. Ordinary or self-adhesive gum.

69 (3 f.) red 60 35

11 Lemur

1997.

71 **11** 3 f. brown and red 65 40

12 Woman's Face

1997.

72 **12** 3 f. 50 multicoloured 75 45

13 Fishes and Corals

1997. Marine Life.

73 **13** 3 f. multicoloured 65 40

14 Reunion, Maps and Airplane

1997. Air. 20th Anniv of First Mayotte–Reunion Air Flight.

74 **14** 5 f. black, blue and green . . 1·10 65

15 Longoni Port

1998.

75 **15** 2 f. 70 multicoloured 55 35

16 Indian Ocean Green Turtle

1998.

76 **16** 3 f. multicoloured 65 40

17 Family on Island

18 Cattle Egret on Zebu's Head

1998. Family Planning.

77 **17** 1 f. multicoloured 20 10

1998. Air.

78 **18** 30 f. multicoloured . . . . . 6·00 3·50

19 Children in Costume

1998. Children's Carnival.

79 **19** 3 f. multicoloured 60 35

20 "Salama Djema II" (ferry)

1998. Mamoudzou–Dzaoudzi Ferry.

80 **20** 3 f. 80 multicoloured 75 45

21 Tsingoni Mosque

22 Mariama Salim

1998.

81 **21** 3 f. multicoloured 60 35

1998. 2nd Death Anniv of Mariama Salim (women's rights activist).

82 **22** 2 f. 70 multicoloured 50 30

23 Spreading Nets

1998. Traditional Fishing, Djarifa.

83 **23** 2 f. multicoloured 40 25

24 Emperor Angelfish

1998.

84 **24** 3 f. multicoloured 60 35

25 Chombos and Workers

1998. The Chombo (agricultural tool).

85 **25** 3 f. multicoloured 60 35

26 Map of Mayotte

1999.

86 **26** 3 f. multicoloured 60 35

27 Reservoir, Combani

1999.

87 **27** 8 f. multicoloured . . . . . 1·50 90

28 Coral Hind

1999. Lagoon Fishes. Multicoloured.

88	2 f. 70 Type **28**	50	30
89	3 f. Lionfish (horiz)	60	35
90	5 f. 20 Regal angelfish (horiz)	1·00	60
91	10 f. Powder-blue surgeonfish (horiz)	1·90	1·10

1999. The Euro (European currency). No. 3553 of France optd **MAYOTTE**.

92 3 f. red and blue 60 35

29 Genet

1999.

93 **29** 5 f. 40 orge, blk & stone . . 1·00 60

30 Baobab Tree

1999.

94 **30** 8 f. multicoloured . . . . . . 1·60 95

31 Prefecture Building

1999. Dzaoudzi Prefecture.

96 **31** 3 f. multicoloured 60 35

33 Vanilla

1999.

98 **33** 4 f. 50 multicoloured 85 50

34 "Le Deba"

1999. Air.

99 **34** 10 f. multicoloured . . . . . . 1·90 1·10

35 Map of Mayotte, Arrow and "2000"

1999. Year 2000.

100 **35** 3 f. multicoloured 60 35

36 Soulou Waterfall

1999.

101 **36** 10 f. multicoloured . . . . 1·90 1·10

MECKLENBURG-SCHWERIN Pt. 7

In northern Germany. Formerly a Grand Duchy, Mecklenburg-Schwerin joined the North German Confederation in 1868.

48 schilling = 1 thaler

1

2

1856. Imperf.

1a 1 ¼ s. red 10·00 10·00
1 ¼ s. red £130 £110
3 2 3 s. yellow 75·00 50·00
4 5 s. blue £200 £275
See note below No. 7.

1864. Roul.

5a 1 ¼ s. red £120 £140
6a ¼ s. red 6·00 6·00
5 ¼ s. red £2250 £1800
6 ¼ s. red 48·00 48·00
11 2 2 s. purple £200 £225
9 3 s. yellow £150 95·00
7 5 s. bistre £130 £225

Nos. 1, 1a, 5, 5a have a dotted background, Nos 6 and 6a a plain background. Prices for Nos. 1a, 5a and 6a are for quarter stamps; prices for Nos. 1, 5 and 6 are for the complete stamp (four quarters) as illustrated in Type **1**.

MECKLENBURG-STRELITZ Pt. 7

In northern Germany. Formerly a Grand Duchy, Mecklenburg-Strelitz joined the North German Confederation in 1868.

30 silbergroschen = 1 thaler

1

2

1864. Roul. Various frames.

2 1 ¼ sgr. orange £150 £2250
3 ⅓ sgr. green 50·00 £1200
6 1 sch. mauve £275 £3500
7 2 1 sgr. red £130 £190
9 2 sgr. blue 28·00 £750
11 3 sgr. bistre 28·00 £1200

MEMEL Pt. 7

A seaport and district on the Baltic Sea, formerly part of Germany. Under Allied control after the 1914–18 war, it was captured and absorbed by Lithuania in 1923 and returned to Germany in 1939. From 1945 the area has been part of Lithuania.

1920. 100 pfennig = 1 mark.
16.4.23. 100 centu = 1 litas.

1920. Stamps of France surch **MEMEL** and **pfennig** or **mark** with figure of value.

1 18 5 pf. on 5 c. green 10 30
2 10 pf. on 10 c. red 10 20
3 20 pf. on 25 c. blue 10 20
4 30 pf. on 30 c. orange 10 20
5 40 pf. on 20 c. brown 10 20
6 50 pf. on 35 c. violet 10 35
7 13 60 pf. on 40 c. red & blue 20 55
8 80 pf. on 45 c. green & blue 15 35
9 1 m. on 50 c. brown & lilac 10 20
10 1 m. 25 on 60 c. violet & bl 70 1·75
11 2 m. on 1 f. red and green 15 25
12 3 m. on 2 f. orange & green 10·00 22·00
13 3 m. on 5 f. blue and buff 11·00 22·00
14 4 m. on 2 f. orange & green 15 35
15 10 m. on 5 f. blue & buff 1·50 5·00
16 20 m. on 5 f. blue & buff 30·00 65·00

1920. Stamps of Germany inscr "DEUTSCHES REICH" optd **Memel- gebiet** or **Memelgebiet**.

17 10 5 pf. green 25 40
18 10 pf. red 2·40 7·00
19 10 pf. orange 15 35
20 24 15 pf. brown 2·25 6·50
21 10 20 pf. blue 15 15
22 30 pf. black & orge on buff 1·25 2·00
23 30 pf. blue 15 35
24 40 pf. black and red 10 15
25 50 pf. black & pur on buff 10 15
26 60 pf. green 45 2·25
27 75 pf. black and green 2·00 5·00
28 80 pf. blue 90 2·75
29 12 1 m. red 20 45
30 1 m. 25 green 12·50 26·00
31 2 m. 50 brown 4·00 7·00
32 13 2 m. blue 1·50 3·25
33 2 m. 50 purple 9·50 22·00

1921. Nos. 2/3, 5/6, 9, 11 and 41 further surch in large figures.

34 18 15 on 10 pf. on 10 c. red 20 35
35 15 on 20 pf. on 25 c. blue 20 55
36 15 on 50 pf. on 35 c. violet 15 45
37 60 on 40 pf. on 20 c. brown 15 15
38 13 75 on 60 pf. on 40 c. red and blue (41) 40 1·00
39 1,25 on 1 m. on 50 c. brown and lilac 15 40
40 5,00 on 2 m. on 1 f. red and green 45 1·25

1921. Surch **MEMEL** and **Pfennig** or **Mark** with figure of value.

54 18 5 pf. on 5 c. orange 10 20
55 10 pf. on 10 c. red 40 1·10
56 10 pf. on 10 c. green 10 20
57 15 pf. on 10 c. green 10 30
58 20 pf. on 20 c. brown 2·75 8·50
59 20 pf. on 25 c. blue 2·75 8·50
60 25 pf. on 5 c. orange 10 15
61 30 pf. on 30 c. red 40 1·75
86 35 pf. on 35 c. violet 10 20
64 13 40 pf. on 40 c. red and blue 10 15
62 15 50 pf. on 50 c. blue 10 15
41 13 60 pf. on 40 c. red and blue 3·00 7·00
87 15 75 pf. on 15 c. green 10 15
63 18 75 pf. on 35 c. violet 10 15
65 13 80 pf. on 45 c. green & blue 10 15
88 18 1 m. on 25 c. blue 10 10
66 13 1 m. on 40 c. red and blue 10 15
89 18 1¼ m. on 30 c. red 10 20
67 13 1 m. 25 on 60 c. violet & bl 10 20
68 1 m. 50 on 45 c. green & bl 10 25
90 2 m. on 45 c. green & blue 10 15
69 2 m. on 1 f. red and green 10 20
91 2¼ m. on 40 c. red and blue 10 20
92 2½ m. on 60 c. violet & blue 20 45
113 18 3 m. on 5 c. orange 10 1·10
70 13 3 m. on 60 c. violet & blue 45 85
93 4 m. on 45 c. green & blue 10 15
71 5 m. on 1 f. red and green 15 45
114 15 6 m. on 15 c. green 15 80
94 13 6 m. on 60 c. violet & blue 10 15
72 6 m. on 2 f. orange & green 15 45
115 18 8 m. on 30 c. red 35 2·25
95 13 9 m. on 1 f. red and green 15 30
73 9 m. on 5 f. blue and buff 20 60
116 10 m. on 45 c. green & blue 35 1·00
43 10 m. on 5 f. blue and buff 65 1·50
96 12 m. on 40 c. red and blue 15 30
117 20 m. on 40 c. red and blue 35 1·60
44 20 m. on 45 c. green & blue 3·75 10·00
97 20 m. on 2 f. orange & grn 15 40
118 30 m. on 60 c. violet & blue 35 1·50
98 30 m. on 5 f. blue and buff 2·25 6·50
119 40 m. on 1 f. red and green 35 1·75
99 50 m. on 2 f. orange & grn 7·00 18·00
120 80 m. on 2 f. orange & grn 35 1·75
121 100 m. on 5 f. blue & buff 45 3·00

1921. Air. Nos. 7/9, 11, 14, 41 and 70 optd **FLUGPOST** in double-lined letters.

47 13 60 pf. on 40 c. red and blue 25·00 70·00
48 60 pf. on 40 c. red and blue (No. 41) 2·00 7·00
49 80 pf. on 45 c. green & blue 2·00 6·00
50 1 m. on 50 c. brown & lilac 1·40 4·50
51 2 m. on 1 f. red and green 2·00 4·50
52 3 m. on 60 c. violet and blue (No. 70) 2·00 6·50
53 4 m. on 2 f. orange & green 2·25 10·00

1922. Air. Optd **Flugpost** in script letters.

74 13 40 pf. on 40 c. red and blue (No. 64) 25 1·00
75 80 pf. on 45 c. green and blue (No. 65) 25 1·00
76 1 m. on 40 c. red and blue (No. 66) 25 1·00
77 1 m. 25 on 60 c. violet and blue (No. 67) 40 1·75
78 1 m. 50 on 45 c. green and blue (No. 68) 40 1·75
79 2 m. on 1 f. red and green (No. 69) 40 1·75
80 3 m. on 60 c. violet and blue (No. 70) 40 1·75
82 4 m. on 2 f. orange and green (No. 14) 40 1·75
83 5 m. on 1 f. red and green (No. 71) 45 2·00
84 6 m. on 2 f. orange and green (No. 72) 45 2·00
85 9 m. on 5 f. blue and buff (No. 73) 55 2·00

1922. Air. Surch as in 1921 and optd **FLUGPOST** in ordinary capitals.

100 13 40 pf. on 40 c. red and blue 1·00 6·00
101 1 m. on 40 c. red and blue 1·00 6·00
102 1 m. 25 on 60 c. violet and blue 1·00 6·00
103 1 m. 50 on 45 c. green and blue 1·00 6·00
104 2 m. on 1 f. red & green 1·00 6·00
105 3 m. on 60 c. violet & blue 1·00 6·00
106 4 m. on 2 f. orange & green 1·00 6·00
107 5 m. on 1 f. red & green 1·00 6·00
108 6 m. on 2 f. orange & green 1·00 6·00
109 9 m. on 5 f. blue & buff 1·00 6·00

1922. Surch as in 1921 but with additional surch **Mark** obliterating **Pfennig**.

110 18 10 m. on 10 pf. on 10 c. green (No. 56) 50 2·50
111 20 m. on 20 pf. on 20 c. brown (No. 58) 40 85
112 15 50 m. on 50 pf. on 50 c. blue (No. 62) 1·25 5·50

1923. Nos. 64 and 67 with additional surch.

122 13 "Mark" on 40 pf. on 40 c. red and blue 50 1·50
123 13 "80—" on 1 m. 25 on 60 c. violet and blue 50 2·00

1923. Nos. 90 and 88 surch with large figures.

124 13 "10" on 2 m. on 45 c. green and blue 1·00 3·50
125 18 "25" on 1 m. on 25 c. blue 1·00 3·50

LITHUANIAN OCCUPATION

The port and district of Memel was captured by Lithuanian forces in 1923 and incorporated in Lithuania.

1

5

1923. (a) Surch **KLAIPEDA (MEMEL)** and value over curved line and **MARKIU**.

1 1 10 m. on 5 c. blue 35 75
2 25 m. on 5 c. blue 35 75
3 50 m. on 25 c. red 35 75
4 100 m. on 25 c. red 50 1·40
5 400 m. on 1 l. brown 1·25 2·50

(b) **Klaipeda (Memel)** and value over two straight lines and **Markiu**.

6 1 10 m. on 5 c. blue 65 1·75
7 25 m. on 5 c. blue 65 1·75
8 50 m. on 25 c. red 65 1·75
9 100 m. on 25 c. red 65 1·75
10 400 m. on 1 l. brown 70 2·25
11 500 m. on 1 l. brown 70 2·25

(c) **KLAIPEDA (Memel)** and value over four stars and **MARKIU**.

12 1 10 m. on 5 c. blue 55 1·75
13 20 m. on 5 c. blue 55 1·75
14 25 m. on 25 c. red 55 1·75
15 50 m. on 25 c. red 65 2·25
16 100 m. on 1 l. brown 80 2·75
17 200 m. on 1 l. brown 80 2·75

1923.

18 5 10 m. brown 20 45
19 20 m. yellow 20 45
20 25 m. orange 20 45
21 40 m. violet 20 45
22 50 m. green 75 85
23 100 m. red 40 40
24 300 m. green 2·50 45·00
25 400 m. brown 45 65
26 500 m. purple 2·50 45·00
27 1,000 m. blue 65 80

7 Liner, Memel Port

8 Memel Arms

9 Memel Lighthouse

1923. Uniting of Memel with Lithuania and Amalgamation of Memel Harbours.

28 7 40 m. green 2·50 12·00
29 50 m. brown 2·50 12·00
30 80 m. green 2·50 12·00
31 100 m. red 2·50 12·00
32 8 200 m. blue 2·50 12·00
33 300 m. brown 2·50 12·00
34 400 m. purple 2·50 12·00
35 500 m. orange 2·50 12·00
36 600 m. green 2·50 12·00
37 9 800 m. blue 2·50 12·00
38 1000 m. purple 2·50 12·00
39 2000 m. red 2·50 12·00
40 3000 m. green 2·50 12·00

1923. No. 123 of Memel surch **Klaipeda**, value and large **M** between bars, sideways.

41 100 m. on 80 on 1 m. 25 on 60 c. 4·00 12·00
42 400 m. on 80 on 1 m. 25 on 60 c. 4·00 12·00
43 500 m. on 80 on 1 m. 25 on 60 c. 4·00 12·00

1923. Surch (thin or thick figures) in **CENT.** or **LITAS**.

60 5 2 c. on 10 m. brown 1·25 5·50
44 2 c. on 20 m. yellow 2·25 3·25
45 2 c. on 50 m. green 2·25 3·25
63 3 c. on 10 m. brown 2·00 5·50
46 3 c. on 40 m. violet 2·50 3·50
47 3 c. on 300 m. green 2·50 3·50
48 5 c. on 100 m. red 2·50 3·50
49 5 c. on 300 m. green 3·00 4·25
50 10 c. on 400 m. brown 5·00 7·00
67 15 c. on 25 m. orange 70·00 £350
51 30 c. on 500 m. purple 3·00 3·50
68 50 c. on 1000 m. blue 1·50 4·75
69 1 l. on 1000 m. blue 3·25 9·00

1923. Surch in **CENTU**.

53 5 2 c. on 300 m. green 3·75 6·25
54 3 c. on 300 m. green 3·75 6·25
55 10 c. on 25 m. orange 3·75 6·25
56 15 c. on 25 m. orange 3·75 6·25
57 20 c. on 500 m. purple 4·50 7·75
58 30 c. on 500 m. purple 3·75 6·25
59 50 c. on 500 m. purple 10·00 17·00

1923. Surch in **CENT.** or **LITAS**.

70 7 15 c. on 40 m. green 3·25 12·00
71 7 30 c. on 50 m. brown 2·50 6·50
72 30 c. on 80 m. green 3·25 10·00
73 30 c. on 100 m. red 2·50 6·50
74 8 50 c. on 200 m. blue 3·25 10·00
75 50 c. on 300 m. brown 2·50 6·50
76 50 c. on 400 m. purple 3·25 11·00
77 50 c. on 500 m. orange 2·50 6·50
78 1 l. on 600 m. green 3·25 11·00
79 9 1 l. on 800 m. blue 3·25 11·00
80 1 l. on 1000 m. purple 3·25 11·00
81 1 l. on 2000 m. red 3·25 11·00
82 1 l. on 3000 m. green 3·25 11·00

1923. Surch in large figures and **Centu** and bars reading upwards.

83 1 10 c. on 25 m. on 5 c. blue (No. 2) 17·00 40·00
84 15 c. on 100 m. on 25 c. red (No. 4) 20·00 £110
85 30 c. on 400 m. on 1 l. brown (No. 5) 4·00 16·00
86 60 c. on 50 m. on 25 c. red (No. 8) 20·00 £130

1923. Surch in large figures and **CENT.** and bars.

87 7 15 c. on 50 m. brown £225 £1400
88 25 c. on 100 m. red £110 £900
89 8 30 c. on 300 m. brown £180 £1000
90 60 c. on 500 m. orange £110 £900

1923. Surch in **Centu** or **Centai** (25 c.) between bars.

91 5 15 c. on 10 m. brown 5·00 20·00
92 15 c. on 20 m. yellow 2·25 10·00
93 15 c. on 25 m. orange 2·75 12·00
94 15 c. on 40 m. violet 2·25 10·00
95 15 c. on 50 m. green 1·50 8·00
96 15 c. on 100 m. red 1·50 8·00
97 15 c. on 400 m. brown 1·25 6·00
98 15 c. on 1000 m. blue 45·00 £250
99 25 c. on 10 m. brown 3·25 16·00
100 25 c. on 20 m. yellow 2·25 9·50
101 25 c. on 25 m. orange 2·75 12·00
102 25 c. on 40 m. violet 2·25 10·00
103 25 c. on 50 m. green 1·40 7·50
104 25 c. on 100 m. red 1·40 7·50
105 25 c. on 400 m. brown 1·25 6·00
106 25 c. on 1000 m. blue 50·00 £275
107 30 c. on 10 m. brown 4·50 19·00
108 30 c. on 20 m. yellow 2·50 10·00
109 30 c. on 25 m. orange 3·25 12·00
110 30 c. on 40 m. violet 2·50 10·00
111 30 c. on 50 m. green 1·40 6·50
112 30 c. on 100 m. red 1·40 7·00
113 30 c. on 400 m. brown 1·25 6·00
114 30 c. on 1000 m. blue 45·00 £250

MEXICO Pt. 15

A republic of Central America. From 1864–67 an Empire under Maximilian of Austria.

8 reales = 100 centavos = 1 peso

1 Miguel Hidalgo y Costilla 2

1856. With or without optd district name. Imperf.

1c 1 ½ r. blue 12·50 14·00
8c ½ r. black on buff 12·50 17·00
6 1 r. orange 11·00 1·60
9b 1 r. black on green 2·50 2·75
7b 2 r. green 10·50 1·60
10c 2 r. black on red 1·40 3·25
4b 4 r. red 55·00 75·00
11b 4 r. black on yellow 22·00 35·00
12a 4 r. red on yellow 50·00 60·00
5c 8 r. lilac 75·00 95·00
13a 8 r. black on brown 48·00 95·00
14a 8 r. green on brown 60·00 80·00

1864. Perf.

15a 2 1 r. red 10
16a 2 r. blue 15
17a 4 r. brown 25
18a 1 p. black 95

3 Arms of Mexico

4 Emperor Maximilian

1864. Imperf.

30 3 3 c. brown £600 £1200
19a ½ r. brown 85·00 £225
31 ½ r. purple 35·00 28·00
31c ½ r. grey 40·00 40·00
32b 1 r. blue 8·25 5·00
33 2 r. orange 2·50 1·60
34 4 r. green 55·00 32·00
35b 8 r. red 80·00 48·00

1864. Imperf.

40 4 7 c. purple £225 £2500
36c 7 c. grey 32·00 60·00
41 13 c. blue 3·75 5·50
42 25 c. orange 3·25 5·00
39c 50 c. green 11·50 11·50

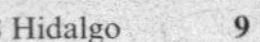

7 Hidalgo 8 Hidalgo 9 Hidalgo

10 Hidalgo 15 Benito Juarez 16

1868. Imperf or perf.

No.	Type	Description	Mint	Used
67	7	6 c. black on brown	4·50	2·50
68		12 c. black on green	1·90	60
69		25 c. blue on pink	3·50	45
70b		50 c. black on yellow	60·00	7·50
71		100 c. black on brown	60·00	22·00
76		100 c. brown on brown	95·00	28·00

1872. Imperf or perf.

No.	Type	Description	Mint	Used
87	8	6 c. green	6·25	6·25
88		12 c. blue	80	65
94		25 c. red	3·50	75
90		50 c. yellow	70·00	16·00
91		100 c. lilac	48·00	25·00

1874. Various frames. Perf.

No.	Type	Description	Mint	Used
102a	9	4 c. orange	3·50	6·25
97	10	5 c. brown	2·10	1·40
98	9	10 c. black	85	50
105		10 c. orange	85	50
99	10	25 c. blue	35	30
107	9	50 c. green	7·00	6·25
108		100 c. red	9·50	8·25

1879.

No.	Type	Description	Mint	Used
115	15	1 c. brown	1·90	1·75
116		2 c. violet	1·75	1·50
117		5 c. orange	1·25	60
118		10 c. blue	1·60	1·25
127a		10 c. brown	1·25	
128		12 c. brown	3·25	3·25
129		18 c. brown	3·75	3·25
130		24 c. mauve	3·75	3·25
119		25 c. red	4·00	4·75
132		25 c. brown	2·10	
120		50 c. green	6·25	6·00
134		50 c. yellow	35·00	38·00
121		85 c. violet	11·00	9·50
122		100 c. black	12·50	11·00
137		100 c. orange	40·00	48·00

1882.

No.	Type	Description	Mint	Used
138	16	2 c. green	3·25	2·50
139		3 c. red	3·25	2·50
140		6 c. blue	2·50	1·90

17 Hidalgo 18

1884.

No.	Type	Description	Mint	Used
141	17	1 c. green	1·25	15
142		2 c. green	1·90	25
157		2 c. red	6·25	1·40
143		3 c. green	3·75	80
158		3 c. brown	8·75	2·50
144		4 c. green	5·00	80
159		4 c. red	12·50	7·50
145		5 c. green	5·00	60
160		5 c. blue	8·75	1·60
146		6 c. green	4·50	45
161		6 c. brown	10·00	2·50
147		10 c. green	4·75	15
162		10 c. orange	7·50	45
148		12 c. green	8·75	1·25
163		12 c. brown	16·00	3·75
149		20 c. green	25·00	95
150		25 c. green	45·00	1·90
164		25 c. blue	55·00	8·75
151		50 c. green	40	1·25
152		1 p. blue	40	4·75
153		2 p. blue	40	8·75
154		5 p. blue	£120	80·00
155		10 p. blue	£170	95·00

1886.

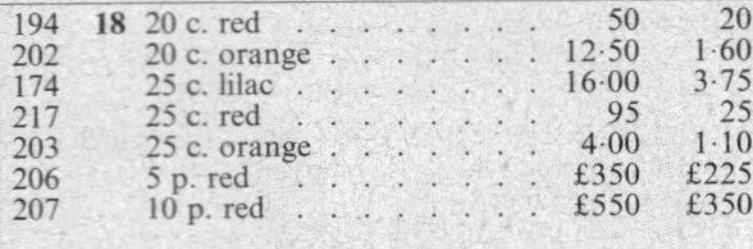

No.	Type	Description	Mint	Used
196	18	1 c. green	30	10
209		2 c. red	35	10
167		3 c. lilac	2·50	1·25
189		3 c. red	30	10
198		3 c. orange	95	35
168		4 c. lilac	4·50	95
211		4 c. red	75	50
199		4 c. orange	1·10	50
191		5 c. blue	20	10
170		6 c. lilac	5·00	60
213		6 c. red	95	60
200		6 c. orange	1·40	35
171		10 c. lilac	5·00	15
193		10 c. red	10	10
185a		10 c. brown	8·75	1·90
201		10 c. orange	7·50	35
172		12 c. lilac	5·00	3·25
215		12 c. red	3·25	3·75
173		20 c. lilac	40·00	22·00
194	18	20 c. red	50	20
202		20 c. orange	12·50	1·60
174		25 c. lilac	16·00	3·75
217		25 c. red	95	25
203		25 c. orange	4·00	1·10
206		5 p. red	£350	£225
207		10 p. red	£550	£350

19 Foot Postman 20 Mounted Postman and Pack Mules 21 Statue of Cuauhtemoc

22 Mailcoach 23 Steam Mail Train

1895.

No.	Type	Description	Mint	Used
253	19	1 c. green	20	10
219		2 c. red	30	10
220		3 c. brown	30	10
221	20	4 c. orange	1·50	25
257	21	5 c. blue	35	10
223	22	10 c. purple	50	10
224	20	12 c. olive	8·25	3·75
225	22	15 c. blue	4·00	80
226		20 c. red	4·00	40
227		50 c. mauve	12·00	4·75
228	23	1 p. brown	32·00	10·00
229		5 p. red	£150	60·00
230		10 p. blue	£190	90·00

27 28 Juanacatlan Falls

29 Popocatepetl 30 Cathedral, Mexico

1899. Various frames for T 27.

No.	Type	Description	Mint	Used
266	27	1 c. green	80	10
276		1 c. purple	60	10
267		2 c. red	2·40	10
277		2 c. green	80	10
268		3 c. brown	1·60	10
278		4 c. red	2·50	20
269		5 c. blue	2·50	10
279		5 c. orange	45	10
270		10 c. brown and purple	3·25	15
280		10 c. orange and blue	2·50	10
271		15 c. purple and lavender	4·25	10
272		20 c. blue and lake	4·75	15
273a	28	50 c. black and purple	19·00	1·25
281		50 c. black and red	40·00	3·50
274	29	1 p. black and blue	42·00	1·90
275	30	5 p. black and red	£130	6·25

32 Josefa Ortiz 40 Hidalgo at Dolores

1910. Centenary of First Independence Movement.

No.	Type	Description	Mint	Used
282	32	1 c. purple	10	10
283	–	2 c. green	10	10
284	–	3 c. brown	25	10
285	–	4 c. red	1·25	20
286	–	5 c. orange	10	10
287	–	10 c. orange and blue	80	10
288	–	15 c. lake and slate	4·50	20
289	–	20 c. blue and lake	2·50	10
290	40	50 c. black and brown	6·25	95
291	–	1 p. black and blue	7·50	1·10
292	–	5 p. black and red	28·00	2·75

DESIGNS: As Type **32**: 2 c. L. Vicario; 3 c. L. Rayon; 4 c. J. Aldama; 5 c. M. Hidalgo; 10 c. I. Allende; 15 c. E. Gonzalez; 20 c. M. Abasolo. As Type **40**: 1 p. Mass on Mt. of Crosses; 5 p. Capture of Granaditas.

REVOLUTIONARY PROVISIONALS

For full list of the provisional issues made during the Civil War from 1913 onwards, see the Stanley Gibbons Part 15 (Central America) Catalogue.

CONSTITUTIONALIST GENERAL ISSUES.

CT 1

1914. "Transitorio".

No.	Type	Description	Mint	Used
CT1	CT 1	1 c. blue	20	15
CT2		2 c. green	30	15
CT3		4 c. blue	7·00	1·60
CT4		5 c. green	7·00	1·90
CT9		5 c. green	10	10
CT5		10 c. red	15	15
CT6		20 c. brown	25	25
CT7		50 c. red	1·60	2·10
CT8		1 p. violet	8·75	10·00

The words of value on No. CT4, are 2×14 mm and on No. CT9 are 2½×16 mm.

1914. Victory of Torreon. Nos. CT1/7 optd **Victoria de TORREON ABRIL 2 - 1914**.

No.	Type	Description	Mint	Used
CT10	CT 1	1 c. blue	95·00	80·00
CT11		2 c. green	£110	95·00
CT12		4 c. blue	£130	£160
CT13		5 c. green	11·50	12·50
CT14		10 c. red	60·00	60·00
CT15		20 c. brown	£1100	£1100
CT16		50 c. red	£1200	£1200

CT 3 CT 4

1914. Handstamped with Type CT 3.

(a) Nos. D282/6.

No.	Type	Description	Mint	Used
CT17	D 32	1 c. blue	8·75	10·00
CT18		2 c. blue	8·75	10·00
CT19		4 c. blue	8·75	10·00
CT20		5 c. blue	8·75	10·00
CT21		10 c. blue	8·75	10·00

(b) Nos. 282/92.

No.	Type	Description	Mint	Used
CT22	32	1 c. purple	35	30
CT23	–	2 c. green	95	80
CT24	–	3 c. brown	95	80
CT25	–	4 c. red	1·60	1·25
CT26	–	5 c. orange	20	10
CT27	–	10 c. orange and blue	1·90	1·25
CT28	–	15 c. lake and slate	3·25	1·90
CT29	–	20 c. blue and lake	6·25	3·75
CT30	40	50 c. black and brown	7·50	5·00
CT31	–	1 p. black and blue	16·00	6·25
CT32	–	5 p. black and red	£100	95·00

1914.

No.	Type	Description	Mint	Used
CT33	CT 4	1 c. pink	80	12·50
CT34		2 c. green	80	11·50
CT35		3 c. orange	80	12·50
CT36		5 c. red	60	5·00
CT37		10 c. green	60	22·00
CT38		25 c. blue	10·00	

CT 5

1914. "Denver" issue.

No.	Type	Description	Mint	Used
CT39	CT 5	1 c. blue	15	20
CT40		2 c. green	15	15
CT41		3 c. orange	25	15
CT42		5 c. red	25	15
CT43		10 c. red	35	40
CT44		15 c. mauve	60	1·10
CT45		50 c. yellow	1·25	1·60
CT46		1 p. violet	5·25	7·50

1914. Optd **GOBIERNO CONSTITUCIONALISTA**.

(a) Nos. 279 and 271/2.

No.	Type	Description	Mint	Used
CT50	–	5 c. orange	48·00	35·00
CT51	–	15 c. purple and lavender	95·00	95·00
CT52	–	20 c. blue and red	£300	£250

(b) Nos. D282/6.

No.	Type	Description	Mint	Used
CT53	D 32	1 c. blue	1·10	1·10
CT54		2 c. blue	1·25	1·25
CT55		4 c. blue	9·50	9·50
CT56		5 c. blue	9·50	9·50
CT57		10 c. blue	1·60	1·60

(c) Nos. 282/92.

No.	Type	Description	Mint	Used
CT58	32	1 c. purple	10	10
CT59	–	2 c. green	10	10
CT60	–	3 c. brown	20	20
CT61	–	4 c. red	25	25
CT62	–	5 c. orange	10	10
CT63	–	10 c. orange and blue	10	10
CT64	–	15 c. lake and slate	35	30
CT65	–	20 c. blue and lake	35	35
CT66	40	50 c. black and brown	1·10	75
CT67	–	1 p. black and blue	4·75	3·25
CT68	–	5 p. black and red	25·00	19·00

CONVENTIONIST ISSUES

(CV 1) Villa-Zapata Monogram

1914. Optd with Type CV 1. (a) Nos. 266/75.

No.	Type	Description	Mint	Used
CV 1	27	1 c. green	60·00	
CV 2		2 c. red	60·00	
CV 3		3 c. brown	32·00	
CV 4		5 c. blue	60·00	
CV 5		10 c. brown and purple	60·00	
CV 6		15 c. purple and lavender	60·00	
CV 7		20 c. blue and red	60·00	
CV 8	28	50 c. black and red	£160	
CV 9	29	1 p. black and blue	£160	
CV10	30	5 p. black and red	£300	

(b) Nos. 276/80.

No.	Type	Description	Mint	Used
CV11	27	1 c. purple	60·00	
CV12		2 c. green	60·00	
CV13		4 c. red	60·00	
CV14		5 c. orange	7·75	
CV15		10 c. orange and blue	48·00	

(c) Nos. D282/6.

No.	Type	Description	Mint	Used
CV16	D 32	1 c. blue	6·00	6·25
CV17		2 c. blue	6·00	6·25
CV18		4 c. blue	6·00	6·25
CV19		5 c. blue	6·00	6·25
CV20		10 c. blue	60·00	6·25

(d) Nos. 282/92.

No.	Type	Description	Mint	Used
CV21	32	1 c. purple	40	40
CV22	–	2 c. green	45	20
CV23	–	3 c. brown	30	30
CV24	–	4 c. red	1·25	1·25
CV25	–	5 c. orange	10	10
CV26	–	10 c. orange and blue	95	95
CV27	–	15 c. lake and slate	95	95
CV28	–	20 c. blue and lake	95	95
CV29	40	50 c. black and brown	6·25	6·25
CV30	–	1 p. black and blue	9·50	9·50
CV31	–	5 p. black and red	95·00	95·00

CONSTITUTIONALIST PROVISIONAL ISSUES

CT 10 CT 11 Carranza Monogram

1914. Nos. 282/92 handstamped with Type CT **10**.

No.	Type	Description	Mint	Used
CT69	32	1 c. purple	6·00	5·50
CT70	–	2 c. green	6·00	5·50
CT71	–	3 c. brown	6·00	5·50
CT72	–	4 c. red	7·50	7·00
CT73	–	5 c. orange	90	90
CT74	–	10 c. orange and blue	7·00	6·25
CT75	–	15 c. lake and slate	7·00	6·25
CT76	–	20 c. blue and lake	8·75	5·75
CT77	40	50 c. black and brown	19·00	19·00
CT78	–	1 p. black and blue	28·00	
CT79	–	5 p. black and red	£100	

1915. Optd with Type CT **11**. (a) No. 271.

No.	Type	Description	Mint	Used
CT80	–	15 c. purple and lavender	50·00	50·00

(b) No. 279.

No.	Type	Description	Mint	Used
CT81	–	5 c. orange	12·50	12·50

(c) Nos. D282/6.

No.	Type	Description	Mint	Used
CT82	D 32	1 c. blue	7·00	
CT83		2 c. blue	7·00	
CT84		4 c. blue	7·00	
CT85		5 c. blue	7·00	
CT86		10 c. blue	7·00	

(d) Nos. 282/92.

No.	Type	Description	Mint	Used
CT87	32	1 c. purple	35	35
CT88	–	2 c. green	35	30
CT89	–	3 c. brown	35	35
CT90	–	4 c. red	1·25	1·25
CT91	–	5 c. orange	10	10
CT92	–	10 c. orange and blue	75	75
CT93	–	15 c. lake and slate	75	75
CT94	–	20 c. blue and lake	75	75
CT95	40	50 c. black and brown	6·25	6·25
CT96	–	1 p. black and blue	9·50	9·50
CT97	–	5 p. black and red	95·00	95·00

GENERAL ISSUES.

43 Coat of Arms 44 Statue of Cuauhtemoc 45 Ignacio Zaragoza

1915. Portraits as T **45**. Roul or perf.

No.	Type	Description	Mint	Used
293	43	1 c. violet	10	10
294	44	2 c. green	20	15
304	45	3 c. brown	20	15
305		4 c. red (Morelos)	20	20
306		5 c. orange (Madero)	25	15
307		10 c. blue (Juarez)	15	10

46 Map of Mexico

47 Lighthouse, Veracruz

48 Post Office, Mexico City

1915.
299 **46** 40 c. grey . . . . 2·25 70
433 40 c. mauve . . . . 1·75 25
300 **47** 1 p. grey and brown 35 60
411 1 p. grey and blue . . . . . 22·00 60
301 **48** 5 p. blue and lake . . . . . 5·00 5·50
412 5 p. grey and green . . . . 1·25 1·50

(49)

50 V. Carranza

1916. Silver Currency. Optd with T **49**. (a) No. 271.
309 – 15 c. purple and lavender . . £250 £250

(b) No. 279.
309a – 5 c. orange . . . . 55·00 55·00

(c) Nos. 282/92.
310 **32** 1 c. purple . . . . 2·10 3·25
311 – 2 c. green 25 15
312 – 3 c. brown 25 15
313 – 4 c. red . . . . 3·75 5·00
314 – 5 c. orange 10 10
315 – 10 c. orange and blue . . . 60 95
316 – 15 c. lake and slate . . . . 1·10 1·90
317 – 20 c. blue and lake . . . . 1·10 1·90
318 **40** 50 c. black and brown . . . 5·25 3·25
319 – 1 p. black and blue . . . . 9·50 4·00
320 – 5 p. black and red . . . . . 95·00 80·00

(d) Nos. CT1/3 and CT5/8.
320b CT **1** 1 c. blue . . . . 15·00
320c 2 c. green . . . . 7·50
320d 4 c. blue £160
320e 10 c. red . . . . 1·40
320f 20 c. brown . . . . . . 1·90
320g 50 c. red . . . . 9·50
320h 1 p. violet . . . . . . 15·00

(e) Nos. CT39/46.
321 CT **5** 1 c. blue . . . . 2·40 12·00
322 2 c. green . . . . 2·40 7·00
323 3 c. orange . . . . 45 7·00
324 5 c. red . . . . 45 7·00
325 10 c. red . . . . 45 3·25
326 15 c. mauve . . . . . . 45 7·00
327 50 c. yellow . . . . . . 70 8·00
328 1 p. violet . . . . 6·00 15·00

(f) Nos. CT58/68.
329 **32** 1 c. purple . . . . 1·60 2·50
330 – 2 c. green 35 30
331 – 3 c. brown 30 30
332 – 4 c. red 30 30
333 – 5 c. orange 50 15
334 – 10 c. orange and blue . . . 35 30
335 – 15 c. lake and slate 40 40
336 – 20 c. blue and lake 40 40
337 **40** 50 c. black and brown . . . 4·75 3·75
338 – 1 p. black and blue . . . . 10·00 10·00
339 – 5 p. black and red . . . . . 95·00 85·00

(g) Nos. CV22/9.
340 **32** 1 c. purple . . . . 7·00 9·50
341 – 2 c. green 75 45
342 – 3 c. brown . . . . 2·00 2·75
343 – 4 c. red . . . . 8·25 9·50
344 – 5 c. orange . . . . 2·75 3·75
345 – 10 c. orange and blue . . . 7·50 8·75
346 – 15 c. lake and slate . . . . 7·50 8·75
347 – 20 c. blue and lake . . . . 7·50 8·75

(h) Nos. CT87/97.
348 **32** 1 c. purple . . . . 1·60 2·10
349 – 2 c. green 30 30
350 – 3 c. brown 25 20
351 – 4 c. red . . . . 3·25 3·75
352 – 5 c. orange 40 10
353 – 10 c. orange and blue . . . 75 1·25
354 – 15 c. lake and slate 60 30
355 – 20 c. blue and red 60 55
356 **40** 50 c. black and brown . . . 4·75 5·50
357 – 1 p. black and blue . . . . 7·00 7·50

1916. Carranza's Triumphal Entry into Mexico City.
358 **50** 10 c. brown . . . . 7·50 8·25
359 10 c. blue 60 30

(51)

1916. Optd with T **51**. (a) Nos. D282/6.
360 D **32** 5 c. on 1 c. blue . . . . 1·60 1·60
361 10 c. on 2 c. blue . . . . 1·60 1·60
362 20 c. on 4 c. blue . . . . 1·60 1·60
363 25 c. on 5 c. blue . . . . 1·60 1·60
364 60 c. on 10 c. blue . . . 75 75
365 1 p. on 1 c. blue 75 75
366 1 p. on 2 c. blue 75 75
367 1 p. on 4 c. blue 40 40
368 1 p. on 5 c. blue . . . . 1·60 1·60
369 1 p. on 10 c. blue . . . . 1·60 1·60

(b) Nos. 282, 286 and 283.
370 **32** 5 c. on 1 c. purple 10 10
371 10 c. on 1 c. purple 10 10
372 – 20 c. on 5 c. orange 10 10
373 – 25 c. on 5 c. orange 15 15
374 – 60 c. on 2 c. green . . . . 10·50 12·50

(c) Nos. CT39/40.
375 CT **5** 60 c. on 1 c. blue . . . . 1·90 3·75
376 60 c. on 2 c. green . . . 1·90 3·75

(d) Nos. CT58, CT62 and CT59.
377 **32** 5 c. on 1 c. purple 10 10
378 – 10 c. on 1 c. purple . . . 60 60
379 – 25 c. on 5 c. purple . . . 15 15
380 – 60 c. on 2 c. green £130 £170

(e) No. CV25.
381 – 25 c. on 5 c. orange 15 10

(f) Nos. CT87, CT91 and CT88.
382 **32** 5 c. on 1 c. purple . . . . 9·50 12·50
383 – 10 c. on 1 c. purple . . . 3·25 4·75
385 – 25 c. on 5 c. orange . . . 50 95
386 – 60 c. on 2 c. green £140

1916. Nos. D282/6 surch **GPM** and value.
387 D **32** $2.50 on 1 c. blue 60 60
388 $2.50 on 2 c. blue . . . 6·25 6·25
389 $2.50 on 4 c. blue . . . 6·25 6·25
390 $2.50 on 5 c. blue . . . 6·25 6·25
391 $2.50 on 10 c. blue . . . 6·25 6·25

52a Arms

53 Zaragoza

1916.
392 **52a** 1 c. purple 15 15

1917. Portraits. Roul or perf.
393 **53** 1 c. violet 25 10
393a 1 c. grey 70 20
394 – 2 c. green (Vazquez) . . . 35 10
395 – 3 c. brown (Suarez) . . . 35 10
396 – 4 c. red (Carranza) 60 20
397 – 5 c. blue (Herrera) 85 10
398 – 10 c. blue (Madero) . . . 1·40 10
399 – 20 c. lake (Dominguez) . . 14·00 35
400 – 30 c. purple (Serdan) . . . 38·00 60
401 – 30 c. black (Serdan) . . . 45·00 60

1919. Red Cross Fund. Surch with cross and premium.
413 5 c. + 3 c. blue (No. 397) . . . 9·00 9·50
414 10 c. + 5 c. blue (No. 398) . . 11·00 9·50

56 Meeting of Iturbide and Guerrero

1921. Centenary of Declaration of Independence.
415 **56** 10 c. brown and blue . . . 9·50 1·90
416 – 10 p. black and brown . . . 9·50 22·00
DESIGN: 10 p. Entry into Mexico City.

58 Golden Eagle

1922. Air.
454 **58** 25 c. sepia and lake 90 20
455 25 c. sepia and green 95 25
456 50 c. red and blue . . . . . 1·25 35

59 Morelos Monument

60 Fountain and Aqueduct

61 Pyramid of the Sun, Teotihuacan

62 Castle of Chapultepec

63 Columbus Monument

74 Benito Juarez

64 Juarez Colonnade

65 Monument to Dona Josefa Ortiz de Dominguez

66 Cuauhtemoc Monument

68 Ministry of Communications

69 National Theatre and Palace of Fine Arts

1923. Roul or perf.
436 **59** 1 c. brown 25 10
437 **60** 2 c. red 15 10
438 **61** 3 c. brown 10 10
429 **62** 4 c. red 60 10
440 **63** 4 c. green 15 10
441 5 c. orange 10 10
453 **74** 8 c. orange 15 10
423 **64** 10 c. brown . . . . 4·75 10
442 **66** 10 c. lake 15 10
443 **65** 20 c. blue 35 10
426 **66** 30 c. green . . . . 35·00 2·50
432 **64** 30 c. green 45 10
434 **68** 50 c. brown 30 10
435 **69** 1 p. blue and lake 50 25

70

72 Sr. Francisco Garcia y Santos

73 Post Office, Mexico City

1926. 2nd Pan-American Postal Congress. Inscr as in T **70/3**.
445 **70** 2 c. red . . . . 1·25 35
446 – 4 c. green . . . . 1·25 40
447 **70** 5 c. orange . . . . 1·25 25
448 – 10 c. red . . . . 1·90 25
449 **72** 20 c. blue . . . . 1·90 50
450 30 c. green . . . . 3·25 1·90
451 40 c. mauve . . . . 6·25 1·60
452 **73** 1 p. blue and brown . . . . 17·00 3·75
DESIGN—As Type **70**: 4 c., 10 c. Map of North and South America.

1929. Child Welfare. Optd **Protection a la Infancia**.
457 **59** 1 c. brown 25 15

77

79 Capt. Emilio Carranza

1929. Obligatory Tax. Child Welfare.
459 **77** 1 c. violet 10 10
461 2 c. green 20 10
462 5 c. brown 15 10

1929. Air. 1st Death Anniv of Carranza (airman).
463 **79** 5 c. sepia and green 55 30
464 10 c. red and sepia 65 35
465 15 c. green and violet . . . 1·90 60
466 20 c. black and sepia . . . 60 35
467 50 c. black and red . . . . 3·75 1·25
468 1 p. sepia and black . . . . 7·75 1·75

80

1929. Air. Perf or roul (10, 15, 20, 50 c.), roul (5, 25 c.), perf (others).
476a **80** 5 c. blue 10 10
477 10 c. violet 10 10
478 15 c. red 15 10
479 20 c. brown 75 10
480 25 c. purple 45 40
472 30 c. black 10 10
473 35 c. blue 15 10
481 50 c. red 45 35
474 1 p. blue and black 60 30
475 5 p. blue and red . . . . . 2·50 2·10
476 10 p. brown and violet . . 3·75 4·50

81

87

1929. Air. Aviation Week.
482 **81** 20 c. violet 60 50
483 40 c. green . . . . 55·00 48·00

1930. 2nd Pan-American Postal Congress issue optd **HABILITADO 1930**.
484 **70** 2 c. red . . . . 2·10 1·40
485 – 4 c. green . . . . 2·10 1·25
486 **70** 5 c. orange . . . . 2·10 1·10
487 – 10 c. red . . . . 3·75 1·25
488 **72** 20 c. blue . . . . 5·00 1·90
489 30 c. green . . . . 4·50 2·10
490 40 c. mauve . . . . 6·25 4·50
491 **73** 1 p. blue and brown . . . . 5·50 3·75

1930. Air. National Tourist Congress. Optd **Primer Congreso Nacional de Turismo. Mexico. Abril 20-27 de 1930.**
492 **80** 10 c. violet (No. 477) . . . 1·25 60

1930. Obligatory Tax. Child Welfare. Surch **HABILITADO $0.01**.
494 **77** 1 c. on 2 c. green 30 15
495 1 c. on 5 c. brown 60 15

1930. Air. Optd **HABILITADO 1930**.
496 **79** 5 c. sepia and green . . . . 3·50 2·75
497 15 c. green and violet . . . 5·50 4·75

1930. Air. Optd **HABILITADO Aereo 1930-1931**.
498 **79** 5 c. sepia and green . . . . 3·75 4·00
499 10 c. red and sepia . . . . 2·10 2·50
500 15 c. green and violet . . . 4·00 4·50
501 20 c. black and sepia . . . 4·50 3·50
502 50 c. black and red . . . . 8·75 6·25
503 1 p. sepia and black . . . . 2·50 1·75

1931. Obligatory Tax. Child Welfare. No. CT58 optd **PRO INFANCIA**.
504 **32** 1 c. purple 20 15

1931. Fourth Centenary of Puebla.
505 **87** 10 c. brown and blue . . . 1·60 25

88

92 Fray Bartolome de las Casas

1931. Air. Aeronautic Exhibition.
506 **88** 25 c. lake . . . . 2·00 1·60

1931. Nos. 446/52 optd **HABILITADO 1931**.
508 – 4 c. green . . . . 35·00
509 **70** 5 c. orange . . . . 6·25
510 – 10 c. red . . . . 6·25
511 **72** 20 c. blue . . . . 6·25
512 30 c. green . . . . 11·00
513 40 c. mauve . . . . 16·00
514 **73** 1 p. blue and brown . . . . . 19·00

1931. Air. Surch **HABILITADO Quince centavos**. Perf or rouletted.
516 **80** 15 c. on 20 c. sepia 20 10

1932. Air. Surch in words and figures. Perf. or roul.
517 **88** 20 c. on 25 c. lake 30 15
521 **80** 30 c. on 20 c. sepia 15 10
519 **58** 40 c. on 25 c. sepia & lake . . . 90 65
520 40 c. on 25 c. sepia & green . . 25·00 25·00
522 **80** 80 c. on 25 c. (No. 480) . . . 90 60

1932. Air. 4th Death Anniv of Emilio Carranza. Optd **HABILITADO AEREO–1932**.
523 **79** 5 c. sepia and green . . . . 3·75 3·25
524 10 c. red and sepia . . . . 3·25 1·90
525 15 c. green and violet . . . 3·75 2·50
526 20 c. black and sepia . . . 3·25 1·75
527 50 c. black and red . . . . 22·00 22·00

1933. Roul.
528 **92** 15 c. blue 15 10

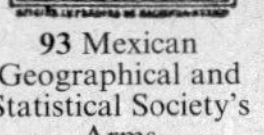

93 Mexican Geographical and Statistical Society's Arms
94 National Theatre and Palace of Fine Arts

1933. 21st Int Statistical Congress and Centenary of Mexican Geographical and Statistical Society.
529 **93** 2 c. green (postage) 75 20
530 5 c. brown . . . . 1·10 25
531 10 c. blue 35 10
532 1 p. violet . . . . 32·00 38·00
533 **94** 20 c. violet and red (air) . . . 2·10 85
534 30 c. violet and brown . . . 4·25 3·75
535 1 p. violet and green . . . . 42·00 45·00

95 Mother and Child
98 Nevada de Toluca

1934. National University. Inscr "PRO-UNIVERSIDAD".
543 **95** 1 c. orange (postage) . . . 10 10
544 – 5 c. green . . . . 1·00 15
545 – 10 c. lake . . . . 1·25 30
546 – 20 c. blue . . . . 5·00 3·25
547 – 30 c. black . . . . 8·75 7·50
548 – 40 c. brown . . . . 15·00 10·00
549 – 50 c. blue . . . . 28·00 32·00
550 – 1 p. black and red . . . . 32·00 30·00
551 – 5 p. brown and black £120 £160
552 – 10 p. violet and brown . . . £500 £650
DESIGNS: 5 c. Archer; 10 c. Festive headdress; 20 c. Woman decorating pot; 30 c. Indian and Inca Lily; 40 c. Potter; 50 c. Sculptor; 1 p. Gold craftsman; 5 p. Girl offering fruit; 10 p. Youth burning incense.
553 **98** 20 c. orange (air) . . . . . 1·75 1·75
554 – 30 c. purple and mauve . . . 3·50 4·25
555 – 50 c. brown and green . . . 4·00 6·25
556 – 75 c. green and black . . . 4·75 8·75
557 – 1 p. blue and green . . . . 5·00 6·25
558 – 5 p. blue and brown . . . . 26·00 60·00
559 – 10 p. red and blue . . . . 80·00 £130
560 – 20 p. red and brown £475 £750
DESIGNS—Airplane over: 30 c. Pyramids of the Sun and Moon, Teotihuacan; 50 c. Mt. Ajusco; 75 c. Mts. Ixtaccihuatl and Popocatepetl; 1 p. Bridge over R. Papagallo; 5 p. Chapultepec Castle entrance; 10 p. Orizaba Peak, Mt. Citlaltepetl; 20 p. Girl and Aztec calendar stone.

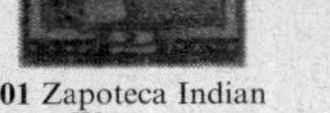

101 Zapoteca Indian Woman
110 Coat of Arms

1934. Pres. Cardenas' Assumption of Office. Designs as Type **101** and **110**. Imprint "OFICINA IMPRESORA DE HACIENDA-MEXICO" at foot of stamp. (a) Postage.
561 – 1 c. orange 30 10
562 **101** 2 c. green 30 10
563 – 4 c. red 45 15
564 – 5 c. brown 30 10
565 – 10 c. blue 40 10
565a – 10 c. violet 80 10
566 – 15 c. blue . . . . 2·50 15
567 – 20 c. green . . . . 1·25 10
567a – 20 c. blue 85 10
568 – 30 c. red 35 10
653 – 30 c. blue 40 10
569 – 40 c. brown 40 10
570 – 50 c. black 45 10
571 **110** 1 p. red and brown . . . . 1·60 10
572 – 5 p. violet and orange . . . 4·75 55
DESIGNS: 1 c. Yalalteca Indian; 4 c. Revolution Monument; 5 c. Los Remedios Tower; 10 c. Cross of Palenque; 15 c. Independence Monument, Mexico City; 20 c. Independence Monument, Puebla; 30 c. "Heroic Children" Monument, Mexico City; 40 c. Sacrificial Stone; 50 c. Ruins of Mitla, Oaxaca; 5 p. Mexican "Charro" (Horseman).

112 Mictlantecuhtli
120 "Peasant admiration"

(b) Air.
573 **112** 5 c. black 20 10
574 – 10 c. brown 45 10
575 – 15 c. green 90 10
576 – 20 c. red . . . . 1·90 10
577 – 30 c. olive 35 10
577a – 40 c. blue 60 10
578 – 50 c. green . . . . 1·60 10
579 – 1 p. red and green . . . . 2·50 10
580 **120** 5 p. black and red . . . . 4·50 25
DESIGNS—HORIZ: 10 c. Temple at Quetzalcoatl; 15 c. Aeroplane over Citlaltepetl; 20 c. Popocatepetl; 30 c. Pegasus; 50 c. Uruapan pottery; 1 p. "Warrior Eagle". VERT: 40 c. Aztec idol.

121 Tractor
122 Arms of Chiapas

1935. Industrial Census.
581 **121** 10 c. violet . . . . 2·50 25

1935. Air. Amelia Earhart Flight to Mexico. No. 576 optd **AMELIA EARHART VUELO DE BUENA VOLUNTAD MEXICO 1935**.
581a 20 c. red £1900 £2500

1935. Annexation of Chiapas Centenary.
582 **122** 10 c. blue 35 15

123 E. Zapata
124 Francisco Madero

1935. 25th Anniv of Revolutionary Plans of Ayala and San Luis Potosi.
583 **123** 10 c. violet (postage) . . . 35 10
584 **124** 20 c. red (air) 20 10

129 Nuevo Laredo Road
131 Rio Corona Bridge

1936. Opening of Nuevo Laredo Highway (Mexico City-U.S.A.).
591 – 5 c. red & green (postage) . . 15 10
592 – 10 c. grey 25 10
593 **129** 20 c. green and brown . . . 75 50
DESIGNS: As Type **129**: 5 c. Symbolical Map of Mexico–U.S.A. road; 10 c. Matalote Bridge.
594 – 10 c. blue (air) 30 10
595 **131** 20 c. orange and violet . . . 30 10
596 – 40 c. green and blue . . . 40 30
DESIGNS: As Type **131**: 10 c. Tasquillo Bridge over Rio Tula; 40 c. Guayalejo Bridge.

1936. 1st Congress of Industrial Medicine and Hygiene. Optd **PRIMER CONGRESO NAL DE HIGIENE V. MED. DEL TRABAJO**.
597 – 10 c. violet (No. 565a) . . . 30 20

1937. As Nos. 561/4, 565a and 576, but smaller. Imprint at foot changed to "TALLERES DE IMP.(RESION) DE EST.(AMPILLAS) Y VALORES-MEXICO".
708 1 c. orange (postage) 25 10
709 2 c. green 25 10
600 4 c. red 40 10
601 5 c. brown 35 10
602 10 c. violet 25 10
603 20 c. red (air) 80 10

134 Blacksmith

1938. Carranza's "Plan of Guadelupe". 25th Anniv Inscr "CONMEMORATIVO PLAN DE GUADALUPE", etc.
604 **134** 5 c. brown & blk (postage) . . 30 10
605 – 10 c. brown 10 10
606 – 20 c. orange and brown . . 3·25 50
607 – 20 c. blue and red (air) . . 20 10
608 – 40 c. red and blue 45 15
609 – 1 p. blue and yellow . . . . 3·00 1·40
DESIGNS—VERT: 10 c. Peasant revolutionary; 20 c. Preaching revolt. HORIZ: 20 c. Horseman; 40 c. Biplane; 1 p. Mounted horseman.

140 Arch of the Revolution
141 Cathedral and Constitution Square

1938. 16th Int Town Planning and Housing Congress, Mexico City. Inscr as in T **140/1**.
610 **140** 5 c. brown (postage) . . . 80 30
611 – 5 c. olive . . . . 1·60 1·40
612 – 10 c. orange . . . . 8·75 7·00
613 – 10 c. brown 30 10
614 – 20 c. black . . . . 2·10 2·50
615 – 20 c. lake . . . . 11·50 9·50
DESIGNS: As Type **140**: 10 c. National Theatre; 20 c. Independence Column.
616 **141** 20 c. red (air) 15 10
617 – 20 c. violet . . . . 8·75 6·25
619 – 40 c. green . . . . 4·50 3·25
620 – 1 p. slate . . . . 4·50 3·25
621 – 1 p. light blue . . . . . . 4·50 3·25
DESIGNS: As Type **141**: 40 c. Chichen Itza Ruins (Yucatan); 1 p. Acapulco Beach.

142 Mosquito and Malaria Victim

1939. Obligatory Tax. Anti-Malaria Campaign.
622 **142** 1 c. blue 95 10

143 Statue of an Indian
144 Statue of Woman Pioneer and Child

1939. Tulsa Philatelic Convention, Oklahoma.
623 **143** 10 c. red (postage) 20 10
624 **144** 20 c. brown (air) 50 20
625 40 c. green . . . . 1·25 60
626 1 p. violet 80 45

145 Mexican Pavilion, World's Fair
146 Morelos Statue on Mexican Pavilion

1939. Air. F. Sarabia non-stop Flight to New York. Optd **SARABIA Vuela MEXICO-NUEVA YORK**.
626a **146** 20 c. blue and red £160 £300

1939. New York World's Fair.
627 **145** 10 c. green & bl (postage) . . 30 10
628 **146** 20 c. green (air) 60 25
629 40 c. purple . . . . 1·60 60
630 1 p. brown and red . . . . 1·00 50

147 J. de Zumarraga
152 "Building"

154 "Transport"

1939. 400th Anniv of Printing in Mexico.
631 **147** 2 c. black (postage) 35 10
632 – 5 c. green 35 10
633 – 10 c. red 10 10
634 – 20 c. blue (air) 10 10
635 – 40 c. green 30 10
636 – 1 p. red and brown 55 35
DESIGNS: 5 c. First printing works in Mexico; 10 c. Antonio D. Mendoza; 20 c. Book frontispiece; 40 c. Title page of first law book printed in America; 1 p. Oldest Mexican Colophon.

1939. National Census. Inscr "CENSOS 1939 1940".
637 **152** 2 c. red (postage) 60 10
638 – 5 c. green 10 10
639 – 10 c. brown 10 10
640 **154** 20 c. blue (air) . . . . . . 2·50 40
641 – 40 c. orange 35 10
642 – 1 p. violet and blue . . . . 1·75 35
DESIGNS: As Type **152**: 5 c. "Agriculture"; 10 c. "Commerce". As Type **154**: 40 c. "Industry"; 1 p. "Seven Censuses".

155 "Penny Black"
156 Roadside Monument

1940. Centenary of First Adhesive Postage Stamps.
643 **155** 5 c. yellow & black (postage) . 45 25
644 10 c. purple 10 10
645 20 c. red and blue 15 10
646 1 p. red and grey . . . . . 4·50 2·50
647 5 p. blue and black . . . . 23·00 19·00
648 5 c. green and black (air) . . 45 30
649 10 c. blue and brown . . . 35 10
650 20 c. violet and red 25 10
651 1 p. brown and red . . . . 2·10 3·25
652 5 p. brown and green . . . 25·00 35·00

1940. Opening of Highway from Mexico City to Guadalajara.
654 **156** 6 c. green 35 10

159 Original College at Patzcuaro

1940. 4th Centenary of National College of St. Nicholas de Hidalgo.
655 – 2 c. violet (postage) 65 25
656 – 5 c. red 40 10
657 – 10 c. olive 40 10
658 **159** 20 c. green (air) 20 10
659 – 40 c. orange 25 10
660 – 1 p. violet, brown & orange . 60 45
DESIGNS—VERT: 2 c. V. de Quiroga; 5 c. M. Ocampo; 10 c. St. Nicholas College Arms; 40 c. Former College at Morelia. HORIZ: 1 p. Present College at Morelia.

163 Pirate Galleon

1940. 400th Anniv of Campeche. Inscr as in T **163**.
661 – 10 c. red & brown (postage) 1·90 60
662 **163** 20 c. brown and red (air) 90 35
663 – 40 c. green and black 75 25
664 – 1 p. black and blue 3·25 1·90
DESIGNS: 10 c. Campeche City Arms; 40 c. St. Miguel Castel; 1 p. Temple of San Francisco.

165 Helmsman **166** Miguel Hidalgo y Costilla

1940. Inauguration of Pres. Camacho.
665 **165** 2 c. orange & black (postage) 1·00 30
666 5 c. blue and brown 3·75 2·10
667 10 c. olive and brown 1·40 40
668 20 c. grey & orange (air) 1·25 60
669 40 c. brown and green 1·25 95
670 1 p. purple and red 2·10 1·25

1940. Compulsory Tax. Dolores Hidalgo Memorial Fund.
671 **166** 1 c. red 30 10

168 Javelin throwing **169** Dark Nebula in Orion

1941. National Athletic Meeting.
675 **168** 10 c. green 2·10 25

1942. Inauguration of Astro-physical Observatory at Tonanzintla, Puebla.
676 **169** 2 c. blue & violet (postage) 80 50
677 – 5 c. blue 5·50 1·25
678 – 10 c. blue and orange 5·50 25
679 – 20 c. blue and green (air) 7·75 1·90
680 – 40 c. blue and red 7·00 2·50
681 – 1 p. black and orange 7·00 2·75
DESIGNS: 5 c. Solar Eclipse; 10 c. Spiral Galaxy of the "Hunting Dog"; 20 c. Extra-Galactic Nebula in Virgo; 40 c. Ring Nebula in Lyra; 1 p. Russell Diagram.

171 Ruins of Chichen-Itza **172** Merida Nunnery

1942. 400th Anniv of Merida. Inscr as in T **171/2**.
682 **171** 2 c. brown (postage) 70 30
683 – 5 c. red 1·40 30
684 – 10 c. violet 80 10
685 **172** 20 c. blue (air) 95 25
686 – 40 c. green 1·40 1·25
687 – 1 p. red 1·60 1·25
DESIGNS—VERT: 5 c. Mayan sculpture; 10 c. Arms of Merida; 40 c. Montejo University Gateway. HORIZ: 1 p. Campanile of Merida Cathedral.

173 "Mother Earth" **175** Hidalgo Monument

1942. 2nd Inter-American Agricultural Conference.
688 **173** 2 c. brown (postage) 40 20
689 – 5 c. blue 1·90 55
690 – 10 c. orange 60 25
691 – 20 c. green (air) 1·25 25
692 – 40 c. brown 75 25
693 – 1 p. violet 1·60 1·25
DESIGNS: 5 c. Sowing wheat; 10 c. Western Hemisphere carrying torch; 20 c. Corn; 40 c. Coffee; 1 p. Bananas.

1942. 400th Anniv of Guadalajara.
694 **175** 2 c. brown & bl (postage) 15 15
695 – 5 c. red and black 60 25
696 – 10 c. blue and red 60 20
697 – 20 c. black and green (air) 80 35
698 – 40 c. green and olive 1·10 50
699 – 1 p. violet and brown 80 60
DESIGNS—VERT: 5 c. Government Palace; 10 c. Guadalajara. HORIZ: 20 c. St. Paul's Church, Zapopan; 40 c. Sanctuary of Our Lady of Guadalupe; 1 p. Arms of Guadalajara.

186 Saltillo Athenaeum, Coahuila

1942. 75th Anniv of Saltillo Athenaeum.
700 **186** 10 c. black 90 20

189 Birthplace of Allende

1943. 400th Anniv of San Miguel de Allende.
701 – 2 c. blue (postage) 50 15
702 – 5 c. brown 55 15
703 – 10 c. black 2·10 50
704 – 20 c. green (air) 45 30
705 **189** 40 c. purple 60 30
706 – 1 p. red 1·75 1·60
DESIGNS—VERT: 2 c. Cupola de las Monjas; 5 c. Gothic Church; 10 c. Gen. de Allende. HORIZ: 20 c. San Miguel de Allende; 1 p. Church seen through cloisters.

190 "Liberty" **192** Dr. de Castorena **194** "Flight"

1944.
707 **190** 12 c. brown 20 10

1944. 3rd National Book Fair.
732 **192** 12 c. brown (postage) 40 10
733 – 25 c. green (air) 45 10
DESIGN: 25 c. Microphone, book and camera.

1944. Air.
734 **194** 25 c. brown 30 10

195 Hands clasping Globe

1945. Inter-American Conference.
735 **195** 12 c. red (postage) 25 10
736 1 p. green 45 10
737 5 p. brown 3·50 2·75
738 10 p. black 6·25 5·00
739 25 c. orange (air) 10 10
740 1 p. green 15 10
741 5 p. blue 1·50 1·10
742 10 p. red 4·00 3·25
743 20 p. blue 8·75 8·00

196 La Paz Theatre, San Luis Potosi

1945. Reconstruction of La Paz Theatre, San Luis Potosi.
744 **196** 12 c. pur & blk (postage) 20 10
745 1 p. blue and black 30 10
746 5 p. red and black 3·75 3·25
747 10 p. green and black 8·25 7·50
748 30 c. green (air) 10 10
749 1 p. purple and green 15 10
750 5 p. black and green 1·40 1·25
751 10 p. blue and black 2·75 2·10
752 20 p. green and black 6·00 5·25

197 Fountain of Diana the Huntress **198** Removing Bandage

1945.
753 **197** 3 c. violet 40 10

1945. Literacy Campaign.
754 **198** 2 c. blue (postage) 15 10
755 6 c. orange 20 10
756 12 c. blue 20 10
757 1 p. olive 25 10
758 5 p. red and black 2·40 1·90
759 10 p. green and blue 13·00 12·50
760 30 c. green (air) 10 10
761 1 p. red 15 10
762 5 p. blue 1·60 1·40
763 10 p. red 2·75 2·75
764 20 p. brown and green 13·00 12·50

199 Founder of National Post Office **200** O.N.U., Olive Branch and Globe

201 O.N.U. and Flags of United Nations

1946. Foundation of Posts in Mexico in 1580.
765 **199** 8 c. black 60 10

1946. United Nations.
766 **200** 2 c. olive (postage) 15 10
767 6 c. brown 15 10
768 12 c. blue 10 10
769 1 p. green 30 10
770 5 p. red 3·25 3·25
771 10 p. blue 14·00 12·50
772 **201** 3 c. brown (air) 10 10
773 1 p. grey 10 10
774 5 p. green and brown 70 50
775 10 p. brown and sepia 2·75 2·50
776 20 p. red and slate 6·75 4·75

202 Zacatecas City Arms **205** Don Genaro Codina and Zacatecas

1946. 400th Anniv of Zacatecas.
777 **202** 2 c. brown (postage) 25 10
778 – 12 c. blue 15 10
779 – 1 p. mauve 30 10
780 – 5 p. red 3·50 1·90
781 – 10 p. black and blue 20·00 6·25
DESIGNS: 1 p. Statue of Gen. Ortega; 5 p. R. L. Velarde (poet); 10 p. F. G. Salinas.
782 – 30 c. grey (air) 10 10
783 **205** 1 p. green and brown 15 10
784 – 5 p. green and red 1·90 1·60
785 – 10 p. brown and green 7·50 2·75
PORTRAITS: 30 c. Fr. Margil de Jesus; 5 p. Gen. Enrique Estrada; 10 p. D. Fernando Villalpando.

207 Learning Vowels **208** Postman

1946. Education Plan.
786 **207** 1 c. sepia 20 10

1947.
787 **208** 15 c. blue 15 10

209 Roosevelt and First Mexican Stamp **210** 10 c. U.S.A. 1847 and Mexican Eagle

1947. U.S.A. Postage Stamp Centenary.
788 **209** 10 c. brown (postage) 1·10 60
789 – 15 c. green 10 10
790 – 25 c. blue (air) 35 20
791 **210** 30 c. black 25 10
792 – 1 p. blue and red 80 15
DESIGNS: 15 c. as Type **209** but vert, 25 c., 1 p. as Type **210** but horiz.

213 Justo Sierra **214** Ministry of Communications

212 Douglas DC-4

1947.
795 **213** 10 p. green and brown (postage) 65·00 8·50
796 **214** 20 p. mauve and green 1·10 90
793 – 10 p. red and brown (air) 75 80
794 **212** 20 p. red and blue 1·50 1·25
DESIGN—HORIZ: 10 p. E. Carranza.

215 Manuel Rincon **217** Vicente Suarez

1947. Battle Centenaries. Portraits of "Child Heroes" etc. Inscr "1er CENTENARIO CHAPULTEPEC ("CHURUBUSCO" or "MOLINO DEL REY") 1847 1947".
797 – 2 c. black (postage) 30 10
798 – 5 c. red 15 10
799 – 10 c. brown 15 10
800 – 15 c. green 15 10
801 **215** 30 c. olive 20 10
802 – 1 p. blue 30 15
803 – 5 p. red and blue . . . . 1·25 1·25
DESIGNS—VERT: 2 c. Francisco Marquez; 5 c. Fernando Montes de Oca; 10 c. Juan Escutin; 15 c. Agustin Melgar; 1 p. Lucas Balderas; 5 p. Flag of San Blas Battalion.

804 **217** 25 c. violet (air) 15 10
805 – 30 c. blue 15 10
806 – 50 c. green 25 10
807 – 1 p. violet 30 10
808 – 5 p. brown and blue . . . 1·25 1·25
DESIGNS—HORIZ: 30 c. Juan de la Barrera; 50 c. Military Academy; 1 p. Pedro Maria Anaya; 5 p. Antonio de Leon.

218 Puebla Cathedral

221 Dance of the Half Moons, Puebla

1950. (a) Postage. As T **218**.
835 – 3 c. blue 15 10
874 – 5 c. brown 25 10
875a – 10 c. green 40 10
876a – 15 c. green 20 10
877e **218** 20 c. blue 30 10
840 – 30 c. red 25 10
879 – 30 c. brown 35 10
880b – 40 c. orange 95 10
1346b – 50 c. blue 10 10
1327b – 80 c. green 35 10
843 – 1 p. brown . . . . . . 2·75 10
1346f – 1 p. green 10 10
1011ab – 1 p. grey 30 10
1327d – 3 p. red 55 10
1012a – 5 p. blue and green . . 1·50 60
1013ab – 10 p. black and blue . . 2·50 1·25
846 – 20 p. violet and green . . 6·25 6·25
1014 – 20 p. violet and black . . 5·75 4·50
1327e – 50 p. orange and green . . 6·25 4·75
DESIGNS: 3 c, 3 p. La Purisima Church, Monterrey; 5 c. Modern building, Mexico City; 10 c. Convent of the Nativity, Tepoztlan; 15 c. 50 p. Benito Juarez; 30 c., 80 c. Indian dancer, Michoacan; 40 c. Sculpture, Tabasco; 50 c. Carved head, Veracruz; 1 p. Actopan Convent and carved head; 5 p. Galleon, Campeche; 10 p. Francisco Madero; 20 p. Modern building, Mexico City.

(b) Air. As T **221**.
897 – 5 c. blue 15 10
898a – 10 c. brown 25 15
899a – 20 c. red 35 10
850 – 25 c. brown 60 10
851 – 30 c. olive 15 10
902 – 35 c. violet 55 10
1327f – 40 c. blue 10 10
904c – 50 c. green 35 10
1056 – 80 c. red 60 70
906a **221** 1 p. grey 45 10
1327h – 1 p. 60 red 60 10
1327i – 1 p. 90 red 35 10
907ab – 2 p. brown 65 25
908 – 2 p. 25 purple 60 45
1327j – 4 p. 30 blue 45 10
1017a – 5 p. orange and brown . . 2·75 35
1327k – 5 p. 20 lilac 70 25
1327l – 5 p. 60 green . . . . . 1·40 30
895 – 10 p. blue and black . . 3·75 60
859a – 20 p. blue and red . . . 5·25 5·75
DESIGNS: 5 c., 1 p. 90 Bay of Acapulco; 10 c., 4 p. 30, Dance of the Plumes, Oaxaca; 20 c. Mayan frescoes, Chiapas; 25 c., 2 p. 25, 5 p. 60, Masks, Michoacan; 30 c. Cuauhtemoc; 35 c., 2 p., 5 p. 20, Taxco, Guerrero; 40 c. Sculpture, San Luis Potosi; 50 c., 1 p. 60, Ancient carvings, Chiapas; 80 c. University City, Mexico City; 5 p. Architecture, Queretaro; 10 p. Hidalgo; 20 p. National Music Conservatoire, Mexico City.

222 Arterial Road

224 Diesel Locomotive and Map

1950. Opening of Mexican Section of Pan-American Highway. Inscr "CARRETERA INTER-NACIONAL 1950".
860 – 15 c. violet (postage) . . . 30 10
861 **222** 20 c. blue 20 10
862 – 25 c. pink (air) . . . . . 1·60 20
863 – 35 c. green 10 10
DESIGNS—HORIZ: 15 c. Bridge; 25 c. Pres. M. Aleman, bridge and map; 35 c. B. Juarez and map.

1950. Inauguration of Mexico–Yucatan Railway.
864 – 15 c. purple (postage) . . . 1·75 30
865 **224** 20 c. red 70 35
866 – 25 c. green (air) 70 35
867 – 35 c. blue 70 40
DESIGNS—VERT: 15 c. Rail-laying. HORIZ: 25 c. Diesel trains crossing Isthmus of Tehuantepec; 35 c. M. Aleman and railway bridge at Coatzacoalcos.

227 Hands and Globe

1950. 75th Anniv of U.P.U.
868 – 50 c. violet (postage) . . . 25 10
869 – 25 c. red (air) 55 25
870 **227** 80 c. blue 30 20
DESIGNS—HORIZ: 25 c. Aztec runner. VERT: 50 c. Letters "U.P.U.".

228

Miguel Hidalgo **229**

1953. Birth Bicentenary of Hidalgo.
871 **228** 20 c. sepia & blue (postage) 1·10 10
872 – 25 c. lake and blue (air) . . 35 10
873 **229** 35 c. green 35 10
DESIGN: As Type **229**: 25 c. Full face portrait.

231 Aztec Athlete

232 View and Mayan Bas-relief

1954. 7th Central American and Caribbean Games.
918 **231** 20 c. blue & pink (postage) 55 10
919 **232** 25 c. brown and green (air) 35 15
920 – 35 c. turquoise and purple 30 10
DESIGN: 35 c. Stadium.

233

234

1954. Mexican National Anthem Centenary.
921 **233** 5 c. lilac & blue (postage) 45 15
922 20 c. brown and purple . . 55 10
923 1 p. green and red 30 20
924 **234** 25 c. blue and lake (air) 45 15
925 35 c. purple and blue . . . 20 10
926 80 c. green and blue . . . 25 15

235 Torchbearer and Stadium

236 Aztec God and Map

1955. 2nd Pan-American Games, Mexico City. Inscr "II JUEGOS DEPORTIVOS PANAMER-ICANOS".
927 **235** 20 c. green & brn (postage) 40 10
928 **236** 25 c. blue and brown (air) 30 10
929 – 35 c. brown and red . . . 30 10
DESIGN: As Type **236**: 35 c. Stadium and map.

237 Olin Design

238 Feathered Serpent and Mask

1956. Mexican Stamp Centenary.
930 **237** 5 c. green & brn (postage) 30 10
931 – 10 c. blue and grey . . . 30 10
932 – 30 c. purple and red . . . 20 10
933 – 50 c. brown and blue . . . 25 10
934 – 1 p. black and green . . . 35 10
935 – 5 p. sepia and bistre . . . 1·60 1·40
DESIGNS: As Type **237**: 10 c. Tohtli bird; 30 c. Zochitl flower; 50 c. Centli corn; 1 p. Mazatl deer; 5 p. Teheutli man's head.

937 **238** 5 c. black (air) 15 10
938 – 10 c. blue 15 10
939 – 50 c. purple 10 10
940 – 1 p. violet 15 10
941 – 1 p. 20 mauve 15 10
942 – 5 p. turquoise 80 80
DESIGNS: As Type **238**: 10 c. Bell tower, coach and Viceroy Enriquez de Almanza; 50 c. Morelos and cannon; 1 p. Mother, child and mounted horseman; 1 p. 20, Sombrero and spurs; 5 p. Emblems of food and education and pointing hand.

239 Stamp of 1856

1956. Centenary Int Philatelic Exn, Mexico City.
944 **239** 30 c. blue and brown . . . 45 15

240 F. Zarco

241 V. Gomez Farias and M. Ocampo

1956. Inscr "CONSTITUYENTE(S) DE 1857".
945 – 25 c. brown (postage) . . 35 10
946 – 45 c. blue 15 10
947 – 60 c. purple 15 10
1346d **240** 70 c. blue 20 10
1327c – 2 p. 30 blue 55 10
949 **241** 15 c. blue (air) 20 10
1327g – 60 c. green 15 15
950 – 1 p. 20 violet and green . 35 15
951 **241** 2 p. 75 purple 50 30
PORTRAITS: As T **240** (postage): 25, 45 c., 2 p. 30, G. Prieto; 60 c. P. Arriagan. As T **41** (air): 60 c., 1 p. 20, L. Guzman and I. Ramirez.

242 Paricutin Volcano

1956. Air. 20th International Geological Congress.
952 **242** 50 c. violet 30 10

243 Map of Central America and the Caribbean

1956. Air. 4th Inter-American Congress of Caribbean Tourism.
953 **243** 25 c. blue and grey 20 10

244 Assembly of 1857

245 Mexican Eagle and Scales

1957. Centenary of 1857 Constitution.
958 – 30 c. gold & lake (postage) 35 10
959 **244** 1 p. green and sepia . . . 25 10
960 **245** 50 c. brown & green (air) 20 10
961 – 1 p. lilac and blue 30 15
DESIGNS—VERT: 30 c. Emblem of Constitution. HORIZ: 1 p. (Air), "Mexico" drafting the Constitution.

246 Globe, Weights and Dials

1957. Air. Centenary of Adoption of Metric System in Mexico.
962 **246** 50 c. black and silver . . . 30 10

247 Train Disaster

248 Oil Derrick

1957. Air. 50th Anniv of Heroic Death of Jesus Garcia (engine driver) at Nacozari.
963 **247** 50 c. purple and red . . . 90 25

1958. 20th Anniv of Nationalization of Oil Industry.
964 **248** 30 c. black & bl (postage) 25 10
965 – 5 p. red and blue . . . . . 3·50 2·50
966 – 50 c. green and black (air) 10 10
967 – 1 p. black and red 20 10
DESIGNS—HORIZ: 50 c. Oil storage tank and "AL SERVICIO DE LA PATRIA" ("At the service of the Fatherland"); 1 p. Oil refinery at night. VERT: 5 p. Map of Mexico and silhouette of oil refinery.

249 Angel, Independence Monument, Mexico City

250 U.N.E.S.C.O. Headquarters, Paris

1958. Air. 10th Anniv of Declaration of Human Rights.
968 **249** 50 c. blue 20 10

1959. Inauguration of U.N.E.S.C.O. Headquarters Building, Paris.
969 **250** 30 c. black and purple . . . 30 10

251 U.N. Headquarters, New York

252 President Carranza

1959. U.N. Economic and Social Council Meeting, Mexico City.
970 **251** 30 c. blue and yellow . . . 30 10

1960. "President Carranza Year" (1959) and his Birth Centenary.
971 **252** 30 c. pur & grn (postage) 20 10
972 – 50 c. violet & salmon (air) 20 10
DESIGN—HORIZ: 50 c. Inscription "Plan de Guadalupe Constitucion de 1917" and portrait as Type **252**.

253 Alexander von Humboldt (statue)

254 Alberto Braniff's Voisin "Boxkite" and Bristol Britannia

1960. Death Centenary of Alexander von Humboldt (naturalist).
973 **253** 40 c. green and brown . . 20 10

1960. Air. 50th Anniv of Mexican Aviation.
974 **254** 50 c. brown and violet . . 40 10
975 1 p. brown and green . . . 40 15

255 Francisco I. Madero **257** Dolores Bell **259** Children at Desk, University and School Buildings

1960. Visit to Mexico of Members of Elmhurst Philatelic Society (American Society of Mexican Specialists). Inscr "HOMENAJE AL COLECCIONISTA".
976 **255** 10 p. sepia, green and purple (postage) . . . . . . 27·00 45·00
977 – 20 p. sepia, green and purple (air) . . . . 38·00 50·00
DESIGN: As No. 1019a 20 p. National Music Conservatoire inscr "MEX. D.F.".

1960. 150th Anniv of Independence.
978 **257** 30 c. red & grn (postage) 60 10
979 – 1 p. sepia and green . . . 25 10
980 – 5 p. blue and purple . . . 3·25 3·25
981 – 50 c. red and green (air) 15 10
982 – 1 p. 20 sepia and blue . . . 20 10
983 – 5 p. sepia and green . . . 3·50 1·40
DESIGNS—VERT: No. 979, Independence Column; No. 980, Hidalgo, Dolores Bell and Mexican Eagle. HORIZ: No. 981, Mexican Flag; No. 982, Eagle breaking chain and bell tolling; No. 983, Dolores Church.

1960. 50th Anniv of Mexican Revolution.
984 – 10 c. multicoloured (postage) 30 10
985 – 15 c. brown and green . . 1·75 10
986 – 20 c. blue and brown . . . 50 10
987 – 30 c. violet and sepia . . 20 10
988 **259** 1 p. slate and purple . . . 25 10
989 – 5 p. grey and purple . . . 2·10 2·10
990 – 50 c. black and blue (air) 20 10
991 – 1 p. green and red 20 10
992 – 1 p. 20 sepia and green . . 20 10
993 – 5 p. lt blue, blue & mauve 2·00 90
DESIGNS: No. 984, Pastoral scene (35½ × 45½ mm). As Type **259** VERT: No. 985, Worker and hospital buildings; No. 986, Peasant, soldier and marine; No. 987, Power lines and pylons; No. 989, Coins, banknotes and bank entrance. HORIZ: No. 990, Douglas DC-8 airliner; No. 991, Riggers on oil derrick; No. 992, Main highway and map; No. 993, Barrage.

261 Count S. de Revillagigedo **262** Railway Tunnel **263** Mosquito Globe and Instruments

1960. Air. National Census.
994 **261** 60 c. black and lake . . . 35 10

1961. Opening of Chihuahua State Railway.
995 **262** 40 c. black & grn (postage) 75 30
996 – 60 c. blue and black (air) 75 30
997 – 70 c. black and blue . . . 75 30
DESIGNS—HORIZ: 60 c. Railway tracks and map of railway; 70 c. Railway viaduct.

1962. Malaria Eradication.
998 **263** 40 c. brown and blue . . . 25 10

264 Pres. Goulart of Brazil **265** Soldier and Memorial Stone

1962. Visit of President of Brazil.
999 **264** 40 c. bistre 65 10

1962. Centenary of Battle of Puebla.
1000 **265** 40 c. sepia and green (postage) 25 10
1001 – 1 p. olive and green (air) 35 10
DESIGN—HORIZ: 1 p. Statue of Gen. Zaragoza.

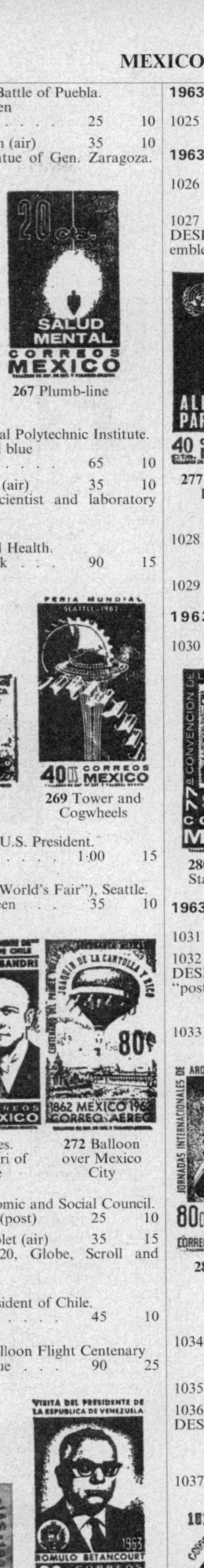

266 Draughtsman and Surveyor **267** Plumb-line

1962. 25th Anniv of National Polytechnic Institute.
1002 **266** 40 c. turquoise and blue (postage) 65 10
1003 – 1 p. olive and blue (air) 35 10
DESIGN—HORIZ: 1 p. Scientist and laboratory assistant.

1962. Mental Health.
1004 **267** 20 c. blue and black . . . 90 15

268 Pres. J. F. Kennedy **269** Tower and Cogwheels

1962. Air. Visit of U.S. President.
1005 **268** 80 c. blue and red . . . . 1·00 15

1962. "Century 21" Exn ("World's Fair"), Seattle.
1006 **269** 40 c. black and green . . 35 10

270 Globe and O.E.A. Emblem **271** Pres. Alessandri of Chile **272** Balloon over Mexico City

1962. Inter-American Economic and Social Council.
1007 **270** 40 c. sepia & grey (post) 25 10
1008 – 1 p. 20 sepia & violet (air) 35 15
DESIGN—HORIZ: 1 p. 20, Globe, Scroll and O.E.A. emblem.

1962. Visit of President of Chile.
1009 **271** 20 c. brown 45 10

1962. Air. 1st Mexican Balloon Flight Centenary
1010 **272** 80 c. black and blue . . . 90 25

273 "ALALC" Emblem **274** Pres. Betancourt of Venezuela

1963. Air. 2nd "ALALC" Session.
1023 **273** 80 c. purple and orange 65 20

1963. Visit of President of Venezuela.
1024 **274** 20 c. blue 35 10

275 Petroleum Refinery **276** Congress Emblem

1963. Air. 25th Anniv of Nationalization of Mexican Petroleum Industry.
1025 **275** 80 c. slate and orange . . 35 10

1963. 19th International Chamber of Commerce Congress, Mexico City.
1026 **276** 40 c. brown and black (postage) 45 10
1027 – 80 c. black and blue (air) 55 20
DESIGN—HORIZ: 80 c. World map and "C.I.C." emblem.

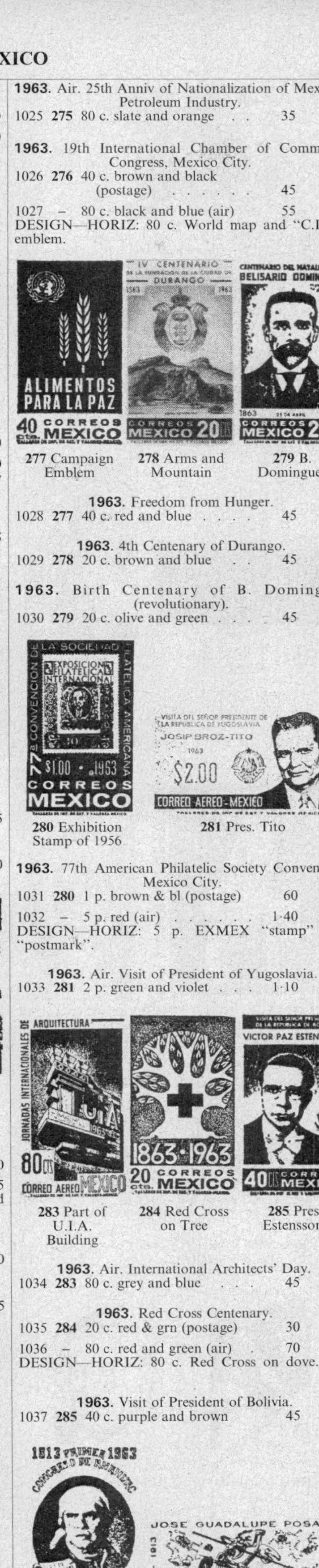

277 Campaign Emblem **278** Arms and Mountain **279** B. Dominguez

1963. Freedom from Hunger.
1028 **277** 40 c. red and blue 45 15

1963. 4th Centenary of Durango.
1029 **278** 20 c. brown and blue . . 45 15

1963. Birth Centenary of B. Dominguez (revolutionary).
1030 **279** 20 c. olive and green . . . 45 15

280 Exhibition Stamp of 1956 **281** Pres. Tito

1963. 77th American Philatelic Society Convention, Mexico City.
1031 **280** 1 p. brown & bl (postage) 60 45
1032 – 5 p. red (air) . . . . . 1·40 1·00
DESIGN—HORIZ: 5 p. EXMEX "stamp" and "postmark".

1963. Air. Visit of President of Yugoslavia.
1033 **281** 2 p. green and violet . . . 1·10 30

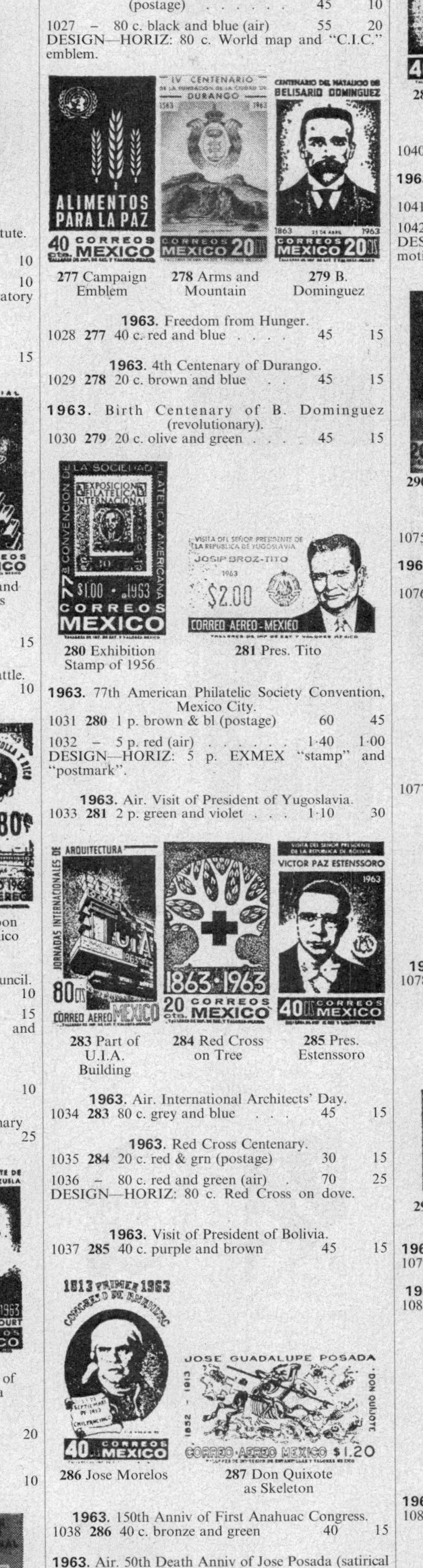

283 Part of U.I.A. Building **284** Red Cross on Tree **285** Pres. Estenssoro

1963. Air. International Architects' Day.
1034 **283** 80 c. grey and blue . . . 45 15

1963. Red Cross Centenary.
1035 **284** 20 c. red & grn (postage) 30 15
1036 – 80 c. red and green (air) 70 25
DESIGN—HORIZ: 80 c. Red Cross on dove.

1963. Visit of President of Bolivia.
1037 **285** 40 c. purple and brown 45 15

286 Jose Morelos **287** Don Quixote as Skeleton

1963. 150th Anniv of First Anahuac Congress.
1038 **286** 40 c. bronze and green 40 15

1963. Air. 50th Death Anniv of Jose Posada (satirical artist).
1039 **287** 1 p. 20 black 75 20

288 University Arms **289** Diesel-electric Train

1963. 90th Anniv of Sinaloa University.
1040 **288** 40 c. bistre and green . . 45 15

1963. 11th Pan-American Railways Congress, Mexico City.
1041 **289** 20 c. brn & blk (postage) 1·25 70
1042 – 1 p. 20 blue and violet (air) 1·25 55
DESIGN: 1 p. 20, Steam and diesel-electric locomotives and horse-drawn tramcar.

290 "F.S.T.S.E." Emblem **291** Mrs. Roosevelt, Flame and U.N. Emblem

1964. 25th Anniv of Workers' Statute.
1075 **290** 20 c. sepia and orange . . 30 10

1964. Air. 15th Anniv of Declaration of Human Rights.
1076 **291** 80 c. blue and orange . . 50 10

292 Pres. De Gaulle

1964. Air. Visit of President of France.
1077 **292** 2 p. blue and brown . . . 1·25 35

293 Pres. Kennedy and Pres. A. Lopez Mateos

1964. Air. Ratification of Chamizal Treaty (1963).
1078 **293** 80 c. black and blue . . . 55 15

294 Queen Juliana and Arms **295** Academy Emblem

1964. Air. Visit of Queen Juliana of the Netherlands.
1079 **294** 20 c. bistre and blue . . . 70 15

1964. Centenary of National Academy of Medicine.
1080 **295** 20 c. gold and black . . . 30 10

296 Lieut. Jose Azueto and Cadet Virgillo Uribe

1964. Air. 50th Anniv of Heroic Defence of Veracruz.
1081 **296** 40 c. green and brown . . 30 10

297 Arms and World Map

1964. Air. International Bar Assn Conf, Mexico City.
1082 **297** 40 c. blue and brown . . 45 10

298 Colonel G. Mendez   299 Dr. Jose Rizal   300 Zacatecas

1964. Centenary of Battle of the Jahuactal Tabasco.
1083 **298** 40 c. olive and brown . . 35 10

1964. 400 Years of Mexican–Philippine Friendship. Inscr "1564 AMISTAD MEXICANO–FILIPINA 1964".
1084 **299** 20 c. blue & grn (postage) 35 10
1085 – 40 c. blue and violet . . . 40 10
1086 – 80 c. blue & lt blue (air) 1·75 25
1087 – 2 p. 75 black and yellow 1·75 70
DESIGNS—As Type **299**: VERT: 40 c. Legaspi. HORIZ: 80 c. "San Pedro" (16th-century Spanish galleon). LARGER (44 × 36 mm): 2 p. 75, Ancient map of Pacific Ocean.

1964. 50th Anniv of Conquest of Zacatecas.
1088 **300** 40 c. green and red . . . 40 10

301 Morelos Theatre, Aguascalientes   302 Andres Manuel del Rio

1965. 50th Anniv of Aguascalientes Convention.
1089 **301** 20 c. purple and grey . . 30 10

1965. Andres M. del Rio Commemoration.
1090 **302** 30 c. black 35 10

303 Netzahualcoyotl Dam   304 J. Morelos (statue)

1965. Air. Inauguration of Netzahualcoyotl Dam.
1091 **303** 80 c. slate and purple . . 30 10

1965. 150th Anniv (1964) of First Constitution.
1092 **304** 40 c. brown and green . . 40 10

305 Microwave Tower   306 Fir Trees

1965. Air. Centenary of I.T.U.
1093 **305** 80 c. blue and indigo . . . 40 20
1094 – 1 p. 20 green and black 45 20
DESIGN: 1 p. 20, Radio-electric station.

1965. Forest Conservation.
1095 **306** 20 c. green and blue . . . 30 10
The inscription "¡CUIDALOS!" means "CARE FOR THEM!".

307 I.C.Y. Emblem

1965. International Co-operation Year.
1096 **307** 40 c. brown and green . . 25 10

308 Camp Fire and Tent

1965. Air. World Scout Conference, Mexico City.
1097 **308** 30 c. ultramarine & blue 40 20

309 King Baudouin and Queen Fabiola

1965. Air. Visit of Belgian King and Queen.
1098 **309** 2 p. blue and green . . . 75 20

310 Mexican Antiquities and Unisphere   311 Dante (after R. Sanzio)

1965. Air. New York World's Fair.
1099 **310** 80 c. green and yellow . . 30 15

1965. Air. Dante's 700th Birth Anniv.
1100 **311** 2 p. red . . . . 1·00 55

312 Sling-thrower   313 Jose M. Morelos y Pavon (leader of independence movement)

1965. Olympic Games (1968) Propaganda (1st series). Museum pieces.
1101 **312** 20 c. blue & olive (postage) 45 10
1102 – 40 c. sepia and red . . . 15 10
1103 – 80 c. slate and red (air) 35 10
1104 – 1 p. 20 indigo and blue 45 15
1105 – 2 p. brown and blue . . . 35 10
DESIGNS—As Type **312**: VERT: 40 c. Batsman. HORIZ: 2 p. Ball game. HORIZ (36 × 20 mm): 80 c. Fieldsman. 1 p. 20, Scoreboard.

1965. 150th Anniv of Morelos's Execution.
1108 **313** 20 c. black and blue . . . 30 10

314 Agricultural Produce   315 Ruben Dario

1966. Centenary of Agrarian Reform Law.
1109 **314** 20 c. red 30 10
1110 – 40 c. black 40 10
DESIGN: 40 c. Emilio Zapata, pioneer of agrarian reform.

1966. Air. 50th Death Anniv of Ruben Dario (Nicaraguan poet).
1111 **315** 1 p. 20 sepia 55 20

316 Father Andres de Urdaneta and Compass Rose   317 Flag and Postal Emblem

1966. Air. 400th Anniv of Father Andres de Urdaneta's Return from the Philippines.
1112 **316** 2 p. 75 black 85 45

1966. 9th Postal Union of Americas and Spain Congress (U.P.A.E.), Mexico City.
1113 **317** 40 c. blk & grn (postage) 35 10
1114 – 80 c. black & mauve (air) 30 15
1115 – 1 p. 20 black and blue . . 35 15
DESIGNS—VERT: 80 c. Flag and posthorn. HORIZ: 1 p. 20, U.P.A.E. emblem and flag.

318 Friar B. de Las Casas   319 E.S.I.M.E. Emblem and Diagram

1966. 400th Death Anniv of Friar Bartolome de Las Casas ("Apostle of the Indies").
1116 **318** 20 c. black on buff . . . 35 10

1966. 50th Anniv of Higher School of Mechanical and Electrical Engineering.
1117 **319** 20 c. green and grey . . . 30 10

320 U Thant and U.N. Emblem   321 "1966 Friendship Year"

1966. Air. U.N. Secretary-General U Thant's Visit to Mexico.
1118 **320** 80 c. black and blue . . . 30 15

1966. Air. "Year of Friendship" with Central American States.
1119 **321** 80 c. green and red . . . 25 10

322 F.A.O. Emblem   323 Running and Jumping

1966. International Rice Year.
1120 **322** 40 c. green 30 10

1966. Olympic Games (1968) Propaganda (2nd series).
1121 **323** 20 c. black & bl (postage) 55 10
1122 – 40 c. black and lake . . . 25 10
1124 – 80 c. black & brown (air) 35 10
1125 – 2 p. 25 black and green 55 25
1126 – 2 p. 75 black and violet 60 35
DESIGNS: 40 c. Wrestling. LARGER (57 × 20 mm): 80 c. Obstacle race; 2 p. 25, American football; 2 p. 75, Lighting Olympic flame.

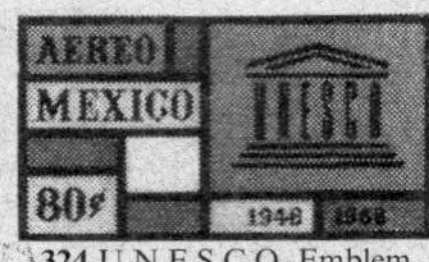

324 U.N.E.S.C.O. Emblem

1966. Air. 20th Anniv of U.N.E.S.C.O.
1128 **324** 80 c. multicoloured . . . 30 10

325 Constitution of 1917   326 Earth and Satellite   327 Oil Refinery

1967. 50th Anniv of Mexican Constitution.
1129 **325** 40 c. black (postage) . . . 45 10
1130 – 80 c. brown & ochre (air) 35 10
DESIGN: 80 c. President V. Carranza.

1967. Air. World Meteorological Day.
1131 **326** 80 c. blue and black . . . 30 20

1967. 7th World Petroleum Congress, Mexico City.
1132 **327** 40 c. black and blue . . . 30 10

328 Nayarit Indian   329 Degollado Theatre

1967. 50th Anniv of Nayarit State.
1133 **328** 20 c. black and green . . 30 10

1967. Cent of Degollado Theatre, Guadalajara.
1134 **329** 40 c. brown and mauve 10 10

330 Mexican Eagle and Crown   331 School Emblem

1967. Centenary of Triumph over the Empire.
1135 **330** 20 c. black and ochre . . 30 10

1967. Air. 50th Anniv of Military Medical School.
1136 **331** 80 c. green and yellow . . 35 15

332 Capt. H. Ruiz Gavino   333 Marco Polo

1967. Air. 50th Anniv of 1st Mexican Airmail Flight. Pachuca–Mexico City.
1137 **332** 80 c. brown and black . . 30 10
1138 – 2 p. brown and black . . 70 20
DESIGN—HORIZ: 2 p. De Havilland D.H.6A biplane.

1967. Air. International Tourist Year.
1139 **333** 80 c. red and black . . . 20 10

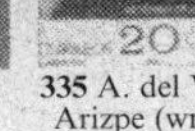

334 Canoeing   335 A. del Valle-Arizpe (writer)

1967. Olympic Games (1968) Propaganda (3rd series).
1140 **334** 20 c. black & bl (postage) 20 10
1141 – 40 c. black and red . . 15 10
1142 – 50 c. black and green . . 15 10
1143 – 80 c. black and violet . . 25 10
1144 – 2 p. black and orange . . 40 15
1146 – 80 c. black & mauve (air) 15 10
1147 – 1 p. 20 black and green 15 10
1148 – 2 p. black and lemon . . 60 20
1149 – 5 p. black and yellow . . 1·00 35
DESIGNS: 40 c. Basketball; 50 c. Hockey; 80 c. (No. 1143), Cycling; 80 c. (No. 1146), Diving; 1 p. 20, Running; 2 p. (No. 1144), Fencing; 2 p. (No. 1148), Weightlifting; 5 p. Football.

1967. Centenary of Fuente Athenaeum, Saltillo.
1151 **335** 20 c. slate and brown . . 30 10

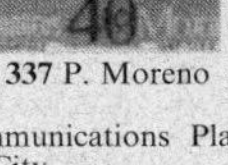

336 Hertz and Clark Maxwell   337 P. Moreno

1967. Air. International Telecommunications Plan Conference, Mexico City.
1152 **336** 80 c. green and black . . 30 10

1967. 150th Death Anniv of Pedro Moreno (revolutionary).

1153 **337** 40 c. black and blue . . . 30 15

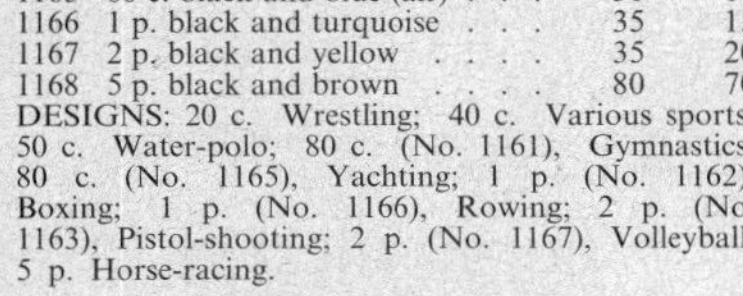

338 Gabino Berreda (founder of Preparatory School)

339 Exhibition Emblem

1968. Centenary of National Preparatory and Engineering Schools.

1154 **338** 40 c. red and blue 35 10
1155 – 40 c. blue and black . . . 35 10

DESIGN: No. 1155, Staircase, Palace of Mining.

1968. Air. "Efimex '68" International Stamp Exn, Mexico City.

1156 **339** 80 c. green and black . . 25 30
1157 2 p. red and black 25 30

The emblem reproduces the "Hidalgo" Official stamp design of 1884.

1968. Olympic Games (1968) Propaganda (4th series). Designs as T **334**, but inscr "1968".

1158 20 c. black & olive (postage) 25 10
1159 40 c. black and purple 25 10
1160 50 c. black and green 25 10
1161 80 c. black and mauve 25 10
1162 1 p. black and brown . . . 1·50 25
1163 2 p. black and grey . . . . 1·75 95

1165 80 c. black and blue (air) . . . 30 10
1166 1 p. black and turquoise . . . 35 15
1167 2 p. black and yellow 35 20
1168 5 p. black and brown 80 70

DESIGNS: 20 c. Wrestling; 40 c. Various sports; 50 c. Water-polo; 80 c. (No. 1161), Gymnastics; 80 c. (No. 1165), Yachting; 1 p. (No. 1162), Boxing; 1 p. (No. 1166), Rowing; 2 p. (No. 1163), Pistol-shooting; 2 p. (No. 1167), Volleyball; 5 p. Horse-racing.

340 Dr. Martin Luther King

1968. Air. Martin Luther King Commemorative.

1170 **340** 80 c. black and grey . . . 35 15

341 Olympic Flame

342 Emblems of Games

1968. Olympic Games, Mexico. (i) Inaug Issue.

1171 **341** 10 p. multicoloured . . . . 2·00 1·25

(ii) Games Issue. Multicoloured designs as T **341**. (20, 40, 50 c. postage and 80 c., 1, 2 p. air) or as T **342** (others).

1172 20 c. Dove of Peace on map (postage) 25 10
1173 40 c. Stadium 30 10
1174 50 c. Telecommunications Tower, Mexico City 30 10
1175 2 p. Palace of Sport, Mexico City . . . . 1·40 25
1176 5 p. Cultural symbols of Games 2·75 80
1178 80 c. Dove and Olympic rings (air) 15 10
1179 1 p. "The Discus-thrower" . . 15 10
1180 2 p. Olympic medals 45 25
1181 5 p. Type **342** . . . . . . 1·75 85
1182 10 p. Line-pattern based on "Mexico 68" & rings . . . 1·50 95

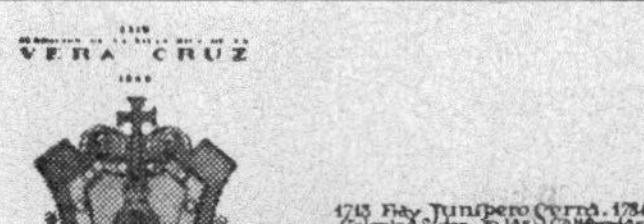

343 Arms of Vera Cruz

344 "Father Palou" (M. Guerrero)

1969. 450th Anniv of Vera Cruz.

1185 **343** 40 c. multicoloured . . . 30 10

1969. Air. 220th Anniv of Arrival in Mexico of Father Serra (coloniser of California).

1186 **344** 80 c. multicoloured . . . 35 10

It was intended to depict Father Serra in this design, but the wrong detail of the painting by Guerrero, which showed both priests, was used.

345 Football and Spectators

1969. Air. World Cup Football Championship (1st issue). Multicoloured.

1187 80 c. Type **345** 25 10
1188 2 p. Foot kicking ball 35 10

See also Nos. 1209/10.

346 Underground Train

1969. Inauguration of Mexico City Underground Railway System.

1189 **346** 40 c. multicoloured . . . 60 20

347 Mahatma Gandhi

348 Footprint on Moon

1969. Air. Birth Centenary of Mahatma Gandhi.

1190 **347** 80 c. multicoloured . . . 30 10

1969. Air. 1st Man on the Moon.

1191 **348** 2 p. black 30 25

349 Bee and Honeycomb

350 "Flying" Dancers and Los Nichos Pyramid, El Tajin

1969. 50th Anniv of I.L.O.

1192 **349** 40 c. brown, blue & yell 20 10

1969. Tourism (1st series). Multicoloured.

1193 40 c. Type **350** 25 10
1193a 40 c. Puerto Vallarta, Jalisco (vert) 25 10
1194 80 c. Acapulco (air) 80 15
1195 80 c. Pyramid, Teotihuacan 60 15
1196 80 c. "El Caracol" (Maya ruin), Yucatan 60 15

See also Nos. 1200/2 and 1274/7.

351 Red Crosses and Sun

352 "General Allende" (D. Rivera)

1969. Air. 50th Anniv of League of Red Cross Societies.

1197 **351** 80 c. multicoloured . . . 30 10

1969. Birth Bicent of General Ignacio Allende ("Father of Mexican Independence").

1198 **352** 40 c. multicoloured . . . 20 10

353 Dish Aerial

354 Question Marks

1969. Air. Inauguration of Satellite Communications Station, Tulancingo.

1199 **353** 80 c. multicoloured . . . 35 10

1969. Tourism (2nd series). As T **350** but dated "1970". Multicoloured.

1200 40 c. Puebla Cathedral 40 10
1201 40 c. Anthropological Museum, Mexico City 40 10
1202 40 c. Belaunzaran Street, Guanajuato 40 10

1970. 9th National and 5th Agricultural Census. Multicoloured.

1204 20 c. Type **354** 30 10
1205 40 c. Horse's head and agricultural symbols 25 10

355 Diagram of Human Eye

1970. 21st International Opthalmological Congress, Mexico City.

1206 **355** 40 c. multicoloured . . . 25 10

356 Cadet Ceremonial Helmet and Kepi

357 Jose Pino Suarez

1970. 50th Anniv of Military College Reorganization.

1207 **356** 40 c. multicoloured . . . 20 10

1970. Birth Centenary (1969) of Jose Maria Pino Suarez (statesman).

1208 **357** 40 c. multicoloured . . . 20 10

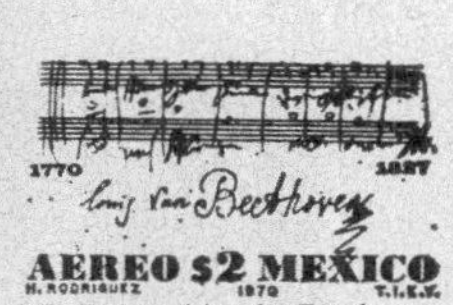

358 Football and Masks

360 Composition by Beethoven

1970. Air. World Cup Football Championship (2nd issue). Multicoloured.

1209 80 c. Type **358** 30 15
1210 2 p. Football and Mexican idols 25 25

1970. Air. Birth Bicentenary of Beethoven.

1212 **360** 2 p. multicoloured 50 25

361 Arms of Celaya

362 "General Assembly"

1970. 400th Anniv of Celaya.

1213 **361** 40 c. multicoloured . . . 20 10

1970. Air. 25th Anniv of U.N.O.

1214 **362** 80 c. multicoloured . . . 30 10

363 "Eclipse de Sol"

364 "Galileo" (Susterman)

1970. Total Eclipse of the Sun (7.3.70).

1215 **363** 40 c. black 20 10

1971. Air. Conquest of Space. Early Astronomers. Multicoloured.

1216 2 p. Type **364** 25 10
1217 2 p. "Kepler" (unknown artist) 25 10
1218 2 p. "Sir Isaac Newton" (Kneller) 25 10

365 "Sister Juana" (M. Cabrera)

1971. Air. Mexican Arts and Sciences (1st series). Paintings. Multicoloured.

1219 80 c. Type **365** 40 15
1220 80 c. "El Paricutin" (volcano) (G. Murillo) 40 15
1221 80 c. "Men of Flames" (J. C. Orozco) 40 15
1222 80 c. "Self-portrait" (J. M. Velasco) 40 15
1223 80 c. "Mayan Warriors" ("Dresden Codex") 40 15

See also Nos. 1243/7, 1284/8, 1323/7, 1351/5, 1390/4, 1417/21, 1523/7, 1540/4, 1650/4, 1688/92, 1834 and 1845.

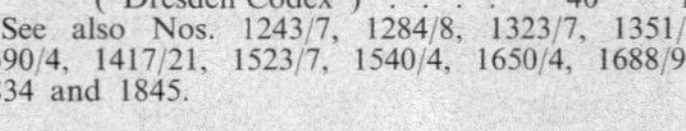

366 Stamps from Venezuela, Mexico and Colombia

1971. Air. "Philately for Peace". Latin-American Stamp Exhibitions 1968–70.

1224 **366** 80 c. multicoloured . . . 35 15

367 Lottery Balls

1971. Bicentenary of National Lottery.

1225 **367** 40 c. black and green . . . 25 10

368 "Francisco Clavijero" (P. Carlin)

1971. Air. Return of the Remains of Francisco Javier Clavijero (historian) to Mexico (1970).

1226 **368** 2 p. brown and green . . 50 25

369 Vasco de Quiroga and "Utopia" (O'Gorman)

370 "Amado Nervo" (artist unknown)

1971. 500th Birth Anniv of Vasco de Quiroga, Archbishop of Michoacan.

1227 **369** 40 c. multicoloured . . . 20 10

1971. Birth Centenary of Amado Nervo (writer).
1228 **370** 80 c. multicoloured . . . 20 10

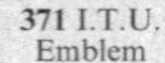

371 I.T.U. Emblem

372 "Mariano Matamoros" (D. Rivera)

1971. Air. World Telecommunications Day.
1229 **371** 80 c. multicoloured . . . 25 10

1971. Air. Birth Bicentenary of Mariano Matamoros (patriot).
1230 **372** 2 p. multicoloured 45 25

373 "General Guerrero" (O'Gorman)

374 Loudspeaker and Sound Waves

1971. Air. 150th Anniv of Independence from Spain.
1231 **373** 2 p. multicoloured 45 25

1971. 50th Anniv of Radio Broadcasting in Mexico.
1232 **374** 40 c. black, blue & green 25 10

375 Pres. Cardenas and Banners

376 Stamps of Venezuela, Mexico, Colombia and Peru

1971. 1st Death Anniv of General Lazaro Cardenas.
1233 **375** 40 c. black and lilac . . . 25 10

1971. Air. "EXFILIMA 71" Stamp Exhibition Lima, Peru.
1234 **376** 80 c. multicoloured . . . 45 15

377 Abstract of Circles

378 Piano Keyboard

1971. Air. 25th Anniv of U.N.E.S.C.O.
1235 **377** 80 c. multicoloured . . . 30 15

1971. 1st Death Anniv of Agustin Lara (composer).
1236 **378** 40 c. black, blue & yellow 30 10

379 "Mental Patients"

380 City Arms of Monterrey

1971. Air. 5th World Psychiatric Congress, Mexico City.
1237 **379** 2 p. multicoloured 25 20

1971. 375th Anniv of Monterrey.
1238 **380** 40 c. multicoloured . . . 10 10

381 Durer's Bookplate

1971. Air. 500th Anniv of Albrecht Durer (artist).
1239 **381** 2 p. black and brown . . 40 25

382 Scientific Symbols

383 Emblem of Mexican Cardiological Institute

1972. Air. 1st Anniv of National Council of Science and Technology.
1240 **382** 2 p. multicoloured 20 10

1972. World Health Month. Multicoloured.
1241 40 c. Type **383** (postage) . . . 10 10
1242 80 c. Heart specialists (air) . . 10 10

1972. Air. Mexican Arts and Sciences (2nd series). Portraits. As T **365**.
1243 80 c. brown and black 75 15
1244 80 c. green and black 75 15
1245 80 c. brown and black 75 15
1246 80 c. blue and black 75 15
1247 80 c. red and black 75 15
PORTRAITS: Nos. 1243, King Netzahualcoyotl of Texcoco (patron of the arts); No. 1244, J. R. de Alarcon (lawyer); No. 1245, J. J. Fernandez de Lizardi (writer); No. 1246, E. G. Martinez (poet); No. 1247, R. L. Velardo (author).

384 Rotary Emblems

385 Indian Laurel and Fruit

1972. Air. 50th Anniv of Rotary Movement in Mexico.
1248 **384** 80 c. multicoloured . . . 10 10

1972. Centenary of Chilpancingo as Capital of Guerrero State.
1249 **385** 40 c. black, gold & green 10 10

386 Track of Car Tyre

1972. Air. 74th Assembly of International Tourist Alliance, Mexico City.
1250 **386** 80 c. black and grey . . . 10 10

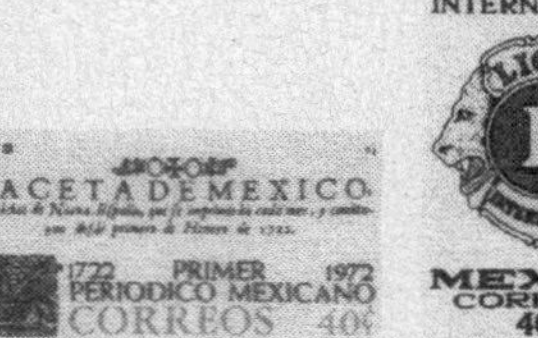

387 First issue of "Gaceta De Mexico"

388 Emblem of Lions Organization

1972. 250th Anniv of Publication of "Gaceta De Mexico" (1st newspaper to be published in Latin America).
1251 **387** 40 c. multicoloured . . . 10 10

1972. Lions' Clubs Convention, Mexico City.
1252 **388** 40 c. multicoloured . . . 10 10

389 "Zaragoza" (cadet sail corvette)

390 "Margarita Maza de Juarez" (artist unknown)

1972. 75th Anniv of Naval Academy, Veracruz.
1253 **389** 40 c. multicoloured . . . 60 10

1972. Death Centenary of Pres. Benito Juarez.
1254 **390** 20 c. mult (postage) . . . 35 10
1255 – 40 c. multicoloured . . . 35 10
1256 – 80 c. black and blue (air) 10 10
1257 – 1 p. 20 multicoloured . . 15 10
1258 – 2 p. multicoloured 20 10
DESIGNS: 40 c. "Benito Juarez" (D. Rivera); 80 c. Page of Civil Register with Juarez signature; 1 p. 20, "Benito Juarez" (P. Clave); 2 p. "Benito Juarez" (J. C. Orozco).

391 "Emperor Justinian I" (mosaic)

392 Atomic Emblem

1972. 50th Anniv of Mexican Bar Association.
1259 **391** 40 c. multicoloured . . . 55 10

1972. Air. 16th General Conference of Int Atomic Energy Organization, Mexico City.
1260 **392** 2 p. black, blue and grey 15 10

393 Caravel on "Stamp"

394 "Sobre las Olas" (sheet-music cover by O'Brandstetter)

1972. Stamp Day of the Americas.
1261 **393** 80 c. violet and brown . . 15 10

1972. Air. 28th International Authors' and Composers' Society Congress, Mexico City.
1262 **394** 80 c. brown 15 10

395 "Mother and Child" (G. Galvin)

1972. Air. 25th Anniv of U.N.I.C.E.F.
1263 **395** 80 c. multicoloured . . . 50 10

396 "Father Pedro de Gante" (Rodriguez y Arangorti)

397 Olympic Emblems

1972. Air. 400th Death Anniv of Father Pedro de Gante (founder of first school in Mexico).
1264 **396** 2 p. multicoloured 25 10

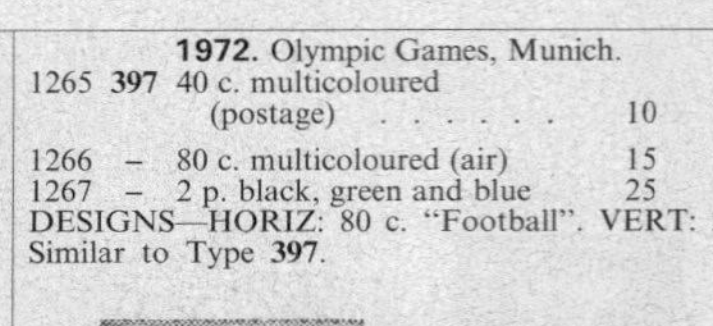

1972. Olympic Games, Munich.
1265 **397** 40 c. multicoloured (postage) 10 10
1266 – 80 c. multicoloured (air) 15 10
1267 – 2 p. black, green and blue 25 10
DESIGNS—HORIZ: 80 c. "Football". VERT: 2 p. Similar to Type **397**.

398 Books on Shelves

400 "Footprints on the Americas"

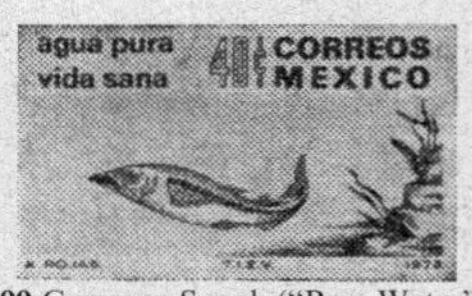

399 Common Snook ("Pure Water")

1972. Int Book Year.
1268 **398** 40 c. multicoloured . . . 10 10

1972. Anti-Pollution Campaign.
1269 **399** 40 c. black & bl (postage) 20 10
1270 – 80 c. black and blue (air) 15 10
DESIGN–VERT: 80 c. Pigeon on cornice ("Pure Air").

1972. Air. Tourist Year of the Americas.
1271 **400** 80 c. multicoloured . . . 15 10

401 Stamps of Mexico, Colombia, Venezuela, Peru and Brazil

1973. Air. "EXFILBRA 72" Stamp Exhibition, Rio de Janeiro, Brazil.
1272 **401** 80 c. multicoloured . . . 15 10

402 "Metlac Viaduct" (J. M. Velasco)

1973. Centenary of Mexican Railways.
1273 **402** 40 c. multicoloured . . . 1·25 25

403 Ocotlan Abbey

1973. Tourism (3rd series). Multicoloured.
1274 40 c. Type **403** (postage) . . . 20 10
1275 40 c. Indian hunting dance, Sonora (vert) 20 10
1276 80 c. Girl in local costume (vert) (air) 35 15
1277 80 c. Sport fishing, Lower California 35 10

404 "God of the Winds"

1973. Air. Centenary of W.M.O.
1278 **404** 80 c. black, blue & mauve . . . 35 10

405 Copernicus

406 Cadet

1973. Air. 500th Birth Anniv of Copernicus (astronomer).
1279 **405** 80 c. green 15 10

1973. 150th Anniv of Military College.
1280 **406** 40 c. multicoloured . . . 10 10

407 "Francisco Madero" (D. Rivera)

408 Antonio Narro (founder)

1973. Birth Centenary of Pres. Francisco Madero.
1281 **407** 40 c. multicoloured . . . 10 10

1973. 50th Anniv of "Antonio Narro" Agricultural School, Saltillo.
1282 **408** 40 c. grey 10 10

409 San Martin Statue

410 Caryon Molecules

1973. Air. Argentina's Gift of San Martin Statue to Mexico City.
1283 **409** 80 c. multicoloured . . . 15 10

1973. Air. "Mexican Arts and Sciences" (3rd series). Astronomers. As T **365** but dated "1973".
1284 80 c. green and red 10 10
1285 80 c. multicoloured 10 10
1286 80 c. multicoloured 10 10
1287 80 c. multicoloured 10 10
1288 80 c. multicoloured 10 10
DESIGNS: No. 1284, Aztec "Sun" stone; No. 1285, Carlos de Siguenza y Gongora; No. 1286, Francisco Diaz Covarrubias; No. 1287, Joaquin Gallo; No. 1288, Luis Enrique Erro.

1973. 25th Anniv of Chemical Engineering School.
1289 **410** 40 c. black, yellow & red . . 10 10

411 Fist with Pointing Finger

412 "EXMEX 73" Emblem

1974. Promotion of Exports.
1294 **411** 40 c. black and green . . 10 10

1974. "EXMEX 73" National Stamp Exhibition, Cuernavaca.
1295 **412** 40 c. black (postage) . . . 10 10
1296 – 80 c. multicoloured (air) . . 15 10
DESIGN: 80 c. Cortes' Palace, Cuernavaca.

413 Manuel Ponce

1974. 25th Death Anniv (1973) of Manuel M. Ponce (composer).
1297 **413** 40 c. multicoloured . . . 10 10

414 Gold Brooch, Mochica Culture

1974. Air. Exhibition of Peruvian Gold Treasures, Mexico City.
1298 **414** 80 c. multicoloured . . . 15 10

415 C.E.P.A.L. Emblem and Flags

416 Baggage

1974. Air. 25th Anniv of U.N. Economic Commission for Latin America (C.E.P.A.L.).
1299 **415** 80 c. multicoloured . . . 15 10

1974. Air. 16th Confederation of Latin American Tourist Organizations (C.O.T.A.L.) Convention, Acapulco.
1300 **416** 80 c. multicoloured . . . 15 10

417 Silver Statuette

419 "Dancing Dogs" (Indian statuette)

418 "The Enamelled Saucepan" (Picasso)

1974. 1st International Silver Fair, Mexico City.
1301 **417** 40 c. multicoloured . . . 10 10

1974. Air. 1st Death Anniv of Pablo Picasso (artist).
1302 **418** 80 c. multicoloured . . . 15 10

1974. 6th Season of Dog Shows.
1303 **419** 40 c. multicoloured . . . 10 10

420 Mariano Azuela

1974. Birth Cent (1973) of Mariano Azuela (writer).
1304 **420** 40 c. multicoloured . . . 10 10

421 Tepotzotlan Viaduct

1974. National Engineers' Day.
1305 **421** 40 c. black and blue . . . 55 15

422 R. Robles (surgeon)

1974. 25th Anniv of W.H.O.
1306 **422** 40 c. brown and green . . 10 10

423 U.P.U. Emblem

1974. "Exfilmex 74" Inter-American Stamp Exhibition, Mexico City.
1307 **423** 40 c. black and green on yellow (postage) . . . 10 10
1308 80 c. black and brown on yellow (air) 15 10

424 Demosthenes

426 Map and Indian Head

425 Lincoln Standard Biplane

1974. 2nd Spanish-American Reading and Writing Studies Congress, Mexico City.
1309 **424** 20 c. green and brown . . . 35 10

1974. Air. 50th Anniv of "Mexicana" (Mexican Airlines). Multicoloured.
1310 80 c. Type **425** 15 10
1311 2 p. Boeing 727-200 jetliner . . 40 10

1974. 150th Anniv of Union with Chiapas.
1312 **426** 20 c. green and brown . . 10 10

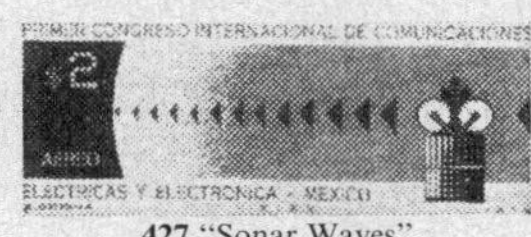

427 "Sonar Waves"

1974. Air. 1st International Electrical and Electronic Communications Congress, Mexico City.
1313 **427** 2 p. multicoloured 15 10

428 S. Lerdo de Tejada

429 Manuscript of Constitution

1974. Centenary of Restoration of Senate.
1314 **428** 40 c. black and blue . . . 10 10

1974. 150th Anniv of Federal Republic.
1315 **429** 40 c. black and green . . 10 10

430 Ball in Play

1974. Air. 8th World Volleyball Championships, Mexico City.
1316 **430** 2 p. black, brown & orge . . 15 10

432 F. C. Puerto

433 Mask, Bat and Catcher's Glove

1974. Air. Birth Centenary of Felipe Carrillo Puerto (politician and journalist).
1318 **432** 80 c. brown and green . . 10 10

1974. Air. 50th Anniv of Mexican Baseball League.
1319 **433** 80 c. brown and green . . 10 10

434 U.P.U. Monument

1974. Centenary of U.P.U.
1320 **434** 40 c. brown and blue (postage) 10 10
1321 – 80 c. multicoloured (air) . . 10 10
1322 – 2 p. brown and green . . . 20 10
DESIGNS: 80 c. Man's face as letter-box, Colonial period; 2 p. Heinrich von Stephan, founder of U.P.U.

1974. Air. Mexican Arts and Sciences (4th series). Music and Musicians. As T **365** but dated "1974". Multicoloured.
1323 80 c. "Musicians" – Mayan painting, Bonampak . . . 15 10
1324 80 c. First Mexican-printed score, 1556 . . . . 15 10
1325 80 c. Angela Peralta (soprano and composer) 15 10
1326 80 c. "Miguel Lerdo de Tejada" (composer) 15 10
1327 80 c. "Silvestre Revueltas" (composer) (bronze by Carlos Bracho) 15 10

435 I.W.Y. Emblem

436 Economic Charter

1975. Air. International Women's Year.
1328 **435** 1 p. 60 black and red 15 10

1975. Air. U.N. Declaration of Nations' Economic Rights and Duties.
1329 **436** 1 p. 60 multicoloured 15 10

437 Jose Maria Mora **439** Dr. M. Jimenez

438 Trans-Altantic Balsa Raft "Acali"

1975. 150th Anniv of Federal Republic.
1330 **437** 20 c. multicoloured 10 10

1975. Air. Trans-Atlantic Voyage of "Acali". Canary Islands to Yucatan (1973).
1331 **438** 80 c. multicoloured 50 10

1975. Air. 5th World Gastroenterological Congress.
1332 **439** 2 p. multicoloured 15 10

440 Aztec Merchants with Goods ("Codex Florentino")

1975. Centenary (1974) of Mexican Chamber of Commerce.
1333 **440** 80 c. multicoloured 10 10

441 Miguel de Cervantes Saavedra (Spanish author) **443** Salvador Novo

442 4-reales Coin of 1675

1975. Air. 3rd International Cervantes Festival, Guanajuato.
1334 **441** 1 p. 60 red and black 15 10

1975. Air. International Numismatics Convention "Mexico 74".
1335 **442** 1 p. 60 bronze and blue 15 10

1975. Air. 1st Death Anniv of Salvador Novo (poet and writer).
1336 **443** 1 p. 60 multicoloured 15 10

444 "Self-portrait" (Siqueiros)

1975. Air. 1st Death Anniv of David Alfaro Siqueiros (painter).
1337 **444** 1 p. 60 multicoloured 15 10

445 General Juan Aldama (detail from mural by Diego Rivera)

1975. Birth Bicentenary (1974) of General Aldama.
1338 **445** 80 c. multicoloured 10 10

446 U.N. and I.W.Y. Emblems

1975. Air. International Women's Year and World Conference.
1339 **446** 1 p. 60 blue and pink 15 10

447 Eagle and Snake ("Codex Duran")

1975. 650th Anniv of Tenochtitlan (now Mexico City). Multicoloured.
1340 80 c. Type **447** (postage) 10 10
1341 1 p. 60 Arms of Mexico City (air) 15 10

448 Domingo F. Sarmiento (educator and statesman)

449 Teachers' Monument, Mexico City

1975. Air. 1st International Congress of "Third World" Educators, Acapulco.
1342 **448** 1 p. 60 green and brown 15 10

1975. Air. Mexican–Lebanese Friendship.
1343 **449** 4 p. 30 green and brown 25 10

450 Games' Emblem

1975. Air. 7th Pan-American Games, Mexico City.
1344 **450** 1 p. 60 multicoloured 15 10

INDEX

Countries can be quickly located by referring to the index at the end of this volume.

451 Julian Carrillo (composer)

452 Academy Emblem

1975. Birth Centenary of J. Carrillo.
1345 **451** 80 c. brown and green 10 10

1975. Cent of Mexican Languages Academy.
1346 **452** 80 c. yellow and brown 10 10

453 University Building

1975. 50th Anniv of Guadalajara University.
1347 **453** 80 c. black, brown & pink 10 10

454 Dr. Atl

455 Road Builders

1975. Air. Atl (Gerardo Murillo-painter and writer). Birth Centenary.
1348 **454** 4 p. 30 multicoloured 25 10

1975. "50 Years of Road Construction" and 15th World Road Congress, Mexico City.
1349 **455** 80 c. black & green (post) 10 10
1350 – 1 p. 60 black & blue (air) 15 10
DESIGN: 1 p. 60, Congress emblem.

1975. Air. Mexican Arts and Sciences (5th series). As T **365**, but dated "1975". Multicoloured.
1351 1 p. 60 Title page, F. Hernandez' "History of New Spain" 15 10
1352 1 p. 60 A. L. Herrera (naturalist) 15 10
1353 1 p. 60 Page from "Badiano Codex" (Aztec herbal) 15 10
1354 1 p. 60 A. Rosenblueth Stearns (neurophysiologist) 15 10
1355 1 p. 60 A. A. Duges (botanist and zoologist) 15 10

456 Car Engine Parts

457 Aguascalientes Cathedral

1975. Mexican Exports. Multicoloured.
1356 – 5 c. blue (postage) 35 10
1471 – 20 c. black 35 10
1356b – 40 c. brown 30 10
1356c **456** 50 c. blue 35 10
1472 50 c. black 35 10
1473 – 80 c. red 10 10
1474 – 1 p. violet and yellow 10 10
1358a – 1 p. black and orange 10 10
1475 – 2 p. blue and turquoise 55 10
1476 – 3 p. brown 25 10
1359b – 4 p. red and brown 25 10
1359e – 5 p. brown 10 10
1359ed – 6 p. red 10 10
1359ee – 6 p. grey 10 10
1359f – 7 p. blue 10 10
1359g – 8 p. brown 10 10
1359h – 9 p. blue 10 10
1479 – 10 p. lt green and green 95 45
1360ac – 10 p. red 10 10
1360ad – 15 p. orange and brown 15 10
1360b – 20 p. black 15 10
1360bc – 20 p. black and red 10 10
1360be – 25 p. brown 25 10
1360bh – 35 p. yellow and mauve 25 10
1360bk – 40 p. yellow and brown 25 10
1360bl – 40 p. gold and green 25 10
1360bm – 40 p. black 10 10
1360c – 50 p. multicoloured 1·25 35
1360d – 50 p. yellow and blue 35 20
1360da – 50 p. red and green 35 20
1360db – 60 p. brown 30 15
1360dc – 70 p. brown 35 20
1360de – 80 p. gold and mauve 20 50
1360df – 80 p. blue 80 50
1360dg – 90 p. blue and green 1·25 55
1360e – 100 p. red, green and grey 70 35
1360ea – 100 p. brown 10 10
1360f – 200 p. yellow, green and grey 1·90 30
1360fb – 200 p. yellow and green 10 10
1360g – 300 p. blue, red and grey 60 60
1360gb – 300 p. blue and red 15 10
1360h – 400 p. bistre, brown and grey 95 35
1360hb – 450 p. brown & mauve 20 10
1360i – 500 p. green, orange and grey 1·90 30
1360ib – 500 p. grey and blue 20 10
1360j – 600 p. multicoloured 30 10
1360k – 700 p. black, red and green 35 10
1360kb – 750 p. black, red and green 30 10
1360l – 800 p. brown & dp brown 40 10
1360m **456** 900 p. black 50 10
1360n – 950 p. blue 40 20
1481a – 1000 p. black, red and grey 50 20
1360pa – 1000 p. red and black 40 8
1360q – 1100 p. grey 60 30
1360r – 1300 p. red, green and grey 60 30
1360rb – 1300 p. red and green 50 25
1360rg – 1400 p. black 50 20
1360s – 1500 p. brown 55 45
1360t – 1600 p. orange 65 30
1360u – 1700 p. green and deep green 70 30
1360w – 1900 p. blue and green 2·25 75
1481b – 2000 p. black and grey 1·25 50
1360xa – 2000 p. black 80 55
1360y – 2100 p. black, orange and grey 80 55
1360ya – 2100 p. black and red 80 55
1360yb – 2200 p. red 90 60
1360z – 2500 p. blue and grey 95 65
1360za – 2500 p. blue 95 65
1630zc – 2800 p. black 1·10 75
1481c – 3000 p. green, grey and orange 1·75 75
1360zf **456** 3600 p. black and grey 1·50 1·00
1360zg – 3900 p. grey and blue 1·60 1·10
1481d – 4000 p. yellow, grey and red 2·40 1·25
1360zj – 4800 p. red, green and grey 1·90 1·25
1481e – 5000 p. grey, green and orange 3·00 1·50
1360zn – 6000 p. green, yellow and grey 2·40 1·60
1360zq – 7200 p. multicoloured 3·00 2·00
1361 – 30 c. bronze (air) 30 10
1482 – 50 c. green and brown 10 10
1361a – 80 c. blue 10 10
1483 – 1 p. 60 black & orange 10 10
1484 – 1 p. 90 red and green 15 10
1361d – 2 p. gold and blue 25 10
1485 – 2 p. 50 red and green 10 10
1361e – 4 p. yellow and brown 25 10
1361f – 4 p. 30 mauve & green 10 20
1361g – 5 p. blue and yellow 95 20
1361h – 5 p. 20 black and red 25 25
1361i – 5 p. 60 green & yellow 10 30
1488 – 10 p. green and light green 55 40
1361j – 20 p. black, red and green 2·75 85
1361k – 50 p. multicoloured 1·60 95

DESIGNS—POSTAGE. 5 c., 6, 1600 p. Steel tubes; 20 c., 40 (1360bm), 1400, 2800 p. Laboratory flasks; 40 c., 100 p. (1360ea) Cup of coffee; 80 c., 10 (1360ac), 2200 p. Steer marked with beef cuts; 1, 3000 p. Electric cable; 2, 90, 1900 p. Abalone shell; 3, 60 p. Men's shoes; 4 p. Ceramic tiles; 5, 1100 p. Chemical formulae; 7, 8, 9, 80 (1360df), 2500 p. Textiles; 10 (1479), 1700 p. Tequila; 15 p. Honeycomb; 20 (1360b), 2000 p. Wrought iron; 20 (1360bc), 2100 p. Bicycles; 25, 70, 1500 p. Hammered copper vase; 35, 40 (1360bk/bl), 50 (1360d), 80 p. (1360de) Books; 50 (1360c), 600 p. Jewellery; 50 (1360da), 4800 p. Tomato; 100 (1360e), 1300 p. Strawberries; 200, 6000 p. Citrus fruit; 300 p. Motor vehicles; 400, 450 p. Printed circuit; 500 (1360i), 5000 p. Cotton boll; 500 (1360ib), 3900 p. Valves (petroleum) industry; 700, 750, 7200 p. Film; 800 p. Construction materials; 1000 p. Farm machinery; 4000 p. Bee and honeycomb. AIR. 30 c. Hammered copper vase; 50 c. Electronic components; 80 c. Textiles; 1 p. 60, Bicycles; 1 p. 90, Valves (petroleum) industry; 2 p. Books; 2 p. 50, Tomato; 4 p. Bee and honeycomb; 4 p. 30, Strawberry; 5 p. Motor vehicles; 5 p. 20, Farm machinery; 5 p. 60, Cotton boll; 10 p. Citrus fruit; 20 p. Film; 50 p. Cotton.

1975. 400th Anniv of Aguascalientes.
1362 **457** 50 c. black and green 35 10

458 J. T. Bodet

460 "Death of Cuautemoc" (Chavez Morado)

459 "Fresco" (J. C. Orozco)

1975. 1st Death Anniv of Jaime T. Bodet (author and late Director-General of U.N.E.S.C.O.).
1363 **458** 80 c. brown and blue . . 10 10

1975. 150th Anniv of Mexican Supreme Court of Justice.
1364 **459** 80 c. multicoloured . . . 10 10

1975. 450th Death Anniv of Emperor Cuautemoc.
1365 **460** 80 c. multicoloured . . . 10 10

461 Allegory of Irrigation

1976. 50th Anniv of Nat Irrigation Commission.
1366 **461** 80 c. deep blue and blue 10 10

462 City Gateway

1976. 400th Anniv of Leon de los Aldamas, Guanajuato.
1367 **462** 80 c. yellow and purple 10 10

463 Early Telephone **464** Gold Coin

1976. Air. Telephone Centenary.
1368 **463** 1 p. 60 black and grey . . 10 10

1976. Air. 4th Int Numismatics Convention.
1369 **464** 1 p. 60 gold, brown & blk 10 10

465 Tlaloc (Aztec god of rain) and Calles Dam

1976. Air. 12th Int Great Dams Congress.
1370 **465** 1 p. 60 purple and green 20 10

466 Perforation Gauge

1976. Air. "Interphil '76" International Stamp Exhibition, Philadelphia.
1371 **466** 1 p. 60 black, red & blue 20 10

467 Rainbow over Industrial Skyline **470** Liberty Bell

1976. Air. U.N. Conf on Human Settlements.
1372 **467** 1 p. 60 multicoloured . . 20 10

1976. Air. Bicentenary of American War of Independence.
1378 **470** 1 p. 60 blue and mauve 20 10

471 Forest Fire

1976. Fire Prevention Campaign.
1379 **471** 80 c. multicoloured 10 10

472 Peace Texts **473** Children on TV Screen

1976. Air. 30th International Asian and North American Science and Humanities Congress, Mexico City.
1380 **472** 1 p. 60 multicoloured . . 15 10

1976. Air. 1st Latin-American Forum on Children's Television.
1381 **473** 1 p. 60 multicoloured . . 20 10

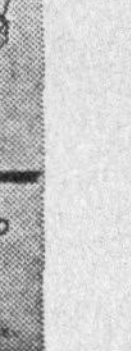

474 Scout's Hat **475** Exhibition Emblem

1976. 50th Anniv of Mexican Boy Scout Movement.
1382 **474** 80 c. olive and brown . . 10 10

1976. "Mexico Today and Tomorrow" Exhibition.
1383 **475** 80 c. black, red & turq . . 10 10

476 New Buildings **477** Dr. R. Vertiz

1976. Inaug of New Military College Buildings.
1384 **476** 50 c. brown and ochre . . 10 10

1976. Centenary of Opthalmological Hospital of Our Lady of the Light.
1385 **477** 80 c. brown and black . . 10 10

478 Guadalupe Basilica

1976. Inauguration of Guadalupe Basilica.
1386 **478** 50 c. bistre and black . . 10 10

479 "40" and Emblem

1976. 40th Anniv of National Polytechnic Institute.
1387 **479** 80 c. black, red and green 10 10

480 Blast Furnace

1976. Inauguration of Lazaro Cardenas Steel Mill, Las Truchas.
1388 **480** 50 c. multicoloured . . . 10 10

481 Natural Elements

1976. Air. World Urbanisation Day.
1389 **481** 1 p. 60 multicoloured . . 10 10

1976. Air. Mexican Arts and Sciences (6th series). As T **365** but dated "1976". Multicoloured.
1390 1 p. 60 black and red 10 10
1391 1 p. 60 multicoloured 10 10
1392 1 p. 60 black and yellow . . . 10 10
1393 1 p. 60 multicoloured 10 10
1394 1 p. 60 brown and black . . . 10 10
DESIGNS: No. 1390, "The Signal" (Angela Gurria); No. 1391, "The God of Today" (L. Ortiz Monasterio); No. 1392, "The God Coatlicue" (traditional Mexican sculpture); No. 1393, "Tiahuicole" (Manuel Vilar); No. 1394, "The Horseman" (Manuel Tolsa).

482 Score of "El Pesebre"

1977. Air. Birth Centenary of Pablo Casals (cellist).
1395 **482** 4 p. 30 blue and brown 15 10

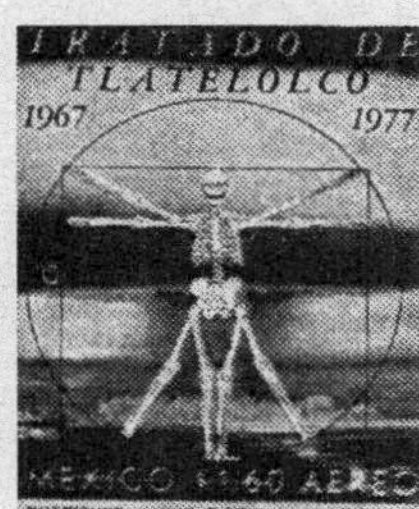

483 "Man's Destruction"

1977. Air. 10th Anniv of Treaty of Tlatelolco.
1396 **483** 1 p. 60 multicoloured . . 10 10

484 Saltillo Cathedral **485** Light Switch, Pylon and Engineers

1977. 400th Anniv of Founding of Saltillo.
1397 **484** 80 c. brown and yellow 10 10

1977. 40 years of Development in Mexico. Federal Electricity Commission.
1398 **485** 80 c. multicoloured . . . 10 10

486 Footballers

1977. Air. 50th Anniv of Mexican Football Federation.
1399 **486** 1 p. 60 multicoloured . . 10 10
1400 – 4 p. 30 yellow, blue & blk 15 10
DESIGN: 4 p. 30, Football emblem.

487 Hands and Scales

1977. Air. 50th Anniv of Federal Council of Reconciliation and Arbitration.
1401 **487** 1 p. 60 orange, brn & blk 10 10

MORE DETAILED LISTS
are given in the Stanley Gibbons Catalogues referred to in the country headings.
For lists of current volumes see Introduction.

488 Flags of Spain and Mexico **489** Tlaloc (weather god)

1977. Resumption of Diplomatic Relations with Spain.
1402 **488** 50 c. multicoloured (postage) 10 10
1403 80 c. multicoloured . . . 10 10
1404 – 1 p. 60 black & grey (air) 10 10
1405 – 1 p. 90 red, grn & lt grn 10 10
1406 – 4 p. 30 grey, brown & grn 15 10
DESIGNS: 1 p. 60, Arms of Mexico and Spain; 1 p. 90, Maps of Mexico and Spain; 4 p. 30, President Jose Lopez Portillo and King Juan Carlos.

1977. Air. Centenary of Central Meterological Observatory.
1407 **489** 1 p. 60 multicoloured . . 10 10

490 Ludwig van Beethoven **491** A. Serdan

1977. Air. 150th Death Anniv of Beethoven.
1408 **490** 1 p. 60 green and brown 10 10
1409 4 p. 30 red and blue . . . 15 10

1977. Birth Centenary of Aquiles Serdan (revolutionary martyr).
1410 **491** 80 c. black, turq & grn 10 10

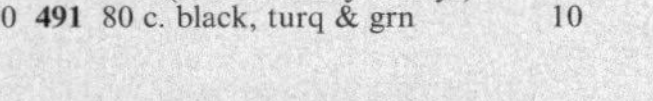

492 Mexico City–Guernavaca Highway

1977. Air. 25th Anniv of First National Highway.
1411 **492** 1 p. 60 multicoloured . . 10 10

493 Poinsettia **494** Arms of Campeche

1977. Christmas.
1412 **493** 50 c. multicoloured . . . 10 10

1977. Air. Bicentenary of Naming of Campeche.
1413 **494** 1 p. 60 multicoloured . . 10 10

495 Tractor and Dam

1977. Air. U.N. Desertification Conference, Mexico City.
1414 **495** 1 p. 60 multicoloured . . 10 10

496 Congress Emblem

1977. Air. 20th World Education, Hygiene and Recreation Congress.
1415 **496** 1 p. 60 multicoloured . . 10 10

497 Freighter "Rio Yaqui" 498 Mayan Dancer

1977. Air. 60th Anniv of National Merchant Marine.
1416 **497** 1 p. 60 multicoloured . . 60 10

1977. Air. Mexican Arts and Sciences (7th series). Pre-colonial statuettes.
1417 **498** 1 p. 60 red, black & pink 10 10
1418 – 1 p. 60 blue, black and lt blue 10 10
1419 – 1 p. 60 grey, black and yellow 10 10
1420 – 1 p. 60 green, black and turquoise 10 10
1421 – 1 p. 60 red, black and grey 10 10
DESIGNS: No. 1418, Aztec god of dance; No. 1419, Snake dance; No. 1420, Dancer, Monte Alban; No. 1421, Dancer, Totonaca.

499 Hospital Scene

1978. Air. 35th Anniv of Mexican Social Insurance Institute. Multicoloured.
1422 1 p. 60 Type **499** 10 10
1423 4 p. 30 Workers drawing benefits 15 10

500 Moorish Fountain

1978. Air. 450th Anniv of Chiapa de Corzo, Chiapas.
1424 **500** 1 p. 60 multicoloured . . 10 10

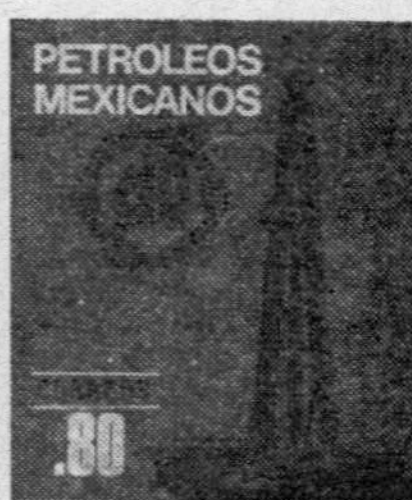

501 Telephones, 1878 and 1978 502 Oilwell

1978. Centenary of Mexican Telephone.
1425 **501** 80 c. red and salmon . . . 10 10

1978. 40th Anniv of Nationalization of Oil Resources.
1426 **502** 80 c. red and salmon (postage) 10 10
1427 – 1 p. 60 blue and red (air) 10 10
1428 – 4 p. 30 black, light blue and blue 55 20
DESIGNS: 1 p. 60, General I. Cardenas (President, 1938); 4 p. 30, Oil rig, Gulf of Mexico.

503 Arms of San Cristobal de las Casas

1978. Air. 450th Anniv of San Cristobal de las Casas, Chiapas.
1429 **503** 1 p. 60 purple, pink and black 10 10

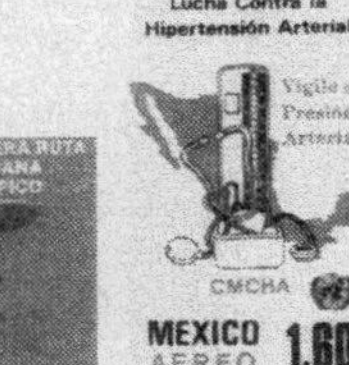

504 Fairchild FC-71 Mail Plane 506 Blood Pressure Gauge and Map of Mexico

505 Globe and Cogwheel

1978. Air. 50th Anniv of First Mexican Airmail Route.
1430 **504** 1 p. 60 multicoloured . . 20 10
1431 4 p. 30 multicoloured . . 30 10

1978. Air. World Conference on Technical Co-operation between Underdeveloped Countries. Multicoloured.
1432 1 p. 60 Type **505** 10 10
1433 4 p. 30 Globe and cogwheel joined by flags 15 10

1978. Air. World Hypertension Month and World Health Day.
1434 **506** 1 p. 60 blue and red . . . 10 10
1435 – 4 p. 30 salmon and blue 15 10
DESIGN: 4 p. 30, Hand with stethoscope.

507 Kicking Ball 508 Francisco (Pancho) Villa

1978. Air. World Cup Football Championship, Argentina.
1436 **507** 1 p. 60 bl, lt orge & orge 10 10
1437 – 1 p. 90 blue, brn & orge 10 10
1438 – 4 p. 30 blue, grn & orge 15 10
DESIGNS: 1 p. 90, Saving a goal; 4 p. 30, Footballer.

1978. Air. Birth Centenary of Francisco Villa (revolutionary leader).
1439 **508** 1 p. 60 multicoloured . . 10 10

509 Emilio Carranza Stamp of 1929 510 Woman and Calendar Stone

1978. Air. 50th Anniv of Mexico–Washington Flight by Emilio Carranza.
1440 **509** 1 p. 60 red and brown . . 10 10

1978. Air. Miss Universe Contest, Acapulco.
1441 **510** 1 p. 60 black, brn & red 10 10
1442 1 p. 90 black, brn & grn 10 10
1443 4 p. 30 black, brn & red 15 10

511 Alvaro Obregon (J. Romero)

1978. Air. 50th Death Anniv of Alvaro Obregon (statesman).
1444 **511** 1 p. 60 multicoloured . . 10 10

512 Institute Emblem

1978. 50th Anniv of Pan-American Institute for Geography and History.
1445 **512** 80 c. blue and black (postage) 10 10
1446 – 1 p. 60 green & blk (air) 10 10
1447 – 4 p. 30 brown and black 15 10
DESIGNS: 1 p. 60, 4 p. 30, Designs as Type **512**, showing emblem.

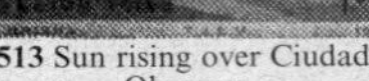
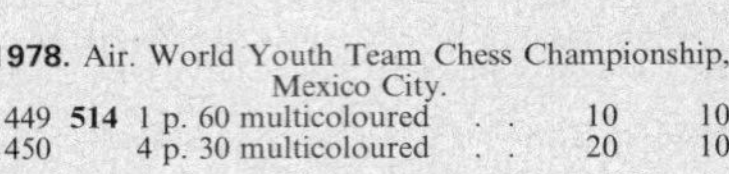
513 Sun rising over Ciudad Obregon 514 Mayan Statue, Rook and Pawn

1978. Air. 50th Anniv of Ciudad Obregon.
1448 **513** 1 p. 60 multicoloured . . 10 10

1978. Air. World Youth Team Chess Championship, Mexico City.
1449 **514** 1 p. 60 multicoloured . . 10 10
1450 4 p. 30 multicoloured . . 20 10

515 Aristotle 516 Mule Deer

1978. Air. 2300th Death Anniv of Aristotle.
1451 **515** 1 p. 60 grey, blue and yellow 10 10
1452 – 4 p. 30 grey, red and yellow 20 10
DESIGN: 4 p. 30, Statue of Aristotle.

1978. Air. World Youth Team Chess Championship, Mexico City.
1453 1 p. 60 Type **516** 20 10
1454 1 p. 60 Ocelot 20 10
See also Nos. 1548/9, 1591/2, 1638/9 and 1683/4.

517 Man's Head and Dove 518 "Dahlia coccinea". ("Dalia" on stamp)

1978. Air. International Anti-Apartheid Year.
1455 **517** 1 p. 60 grey, red and black 10 10
1456 – 4 p. 30 grey, lilac and black 15 10
DESIGN: 4 p. 30, Woman's head and dove.

1978. Mexican Flowers (1st series). Multicoloured.
1457 50 c. Type **518** 10 10
1458 80 c. "Plumeria rubra" . . . 10 10
See also Nos. 1550/1, 1593/4, 1645/6, 1681/2, 1791/2 and 1913/14.

519 Emblem 520 Dr. Rafael Lucio

1978. Air. 12th World Architects' Congress.
1459 **519** 1 p. 60 red, black and orange 10 10

1978. Air. 11th International Leprosy Congress.
1460 **520** 1 p. 60 green 10 10

521 Franz Schubert and "Death and the Maiden" 522 Decorations and Candles

1978. Air. 150th Death Anniv of Franz Schubert (composer).
1461 **521** 4 p. 30 brown, black and green 15 10

1978. Christmas. Multicoloured.
1462 50 c. Type **522** (postage) . . . 10 10
1463 1 p. 60 Children and decoration (air) 10 10

523 Antonio Vivaldi 524 Wright Flyer III

1978. Air. 300th Birth Anniv of Antonio Vivaldi (composer).
1464 **523** 4 p. 30 red, stone and brown 15 10

1978. Air. 75th Anniv of First Powered Flight.
1465 **524** 1 p. 60 orge, yell & mve 15 10
1466 – 4 p. 30 yellow, red & flesh 30 10
DESIGN: 4 p. 30, Side view of Wright Flyer I.

525 Albert Einstein and Equation

1979. Air. Birth Centenary of Albert Einstein (physicist).
1467 **525** 1 p. 60 multicoloured . . 10 10

526 Arms of Hermosillo 527 Sir Rowland Hill

1979. Centenary of Hermosillo, Sonora.
1468 **526** 80 c. multicoloured . . . 10 10

1979. Air. Death Centenary of Sir Rowland Hill.
1469 **527** 1 p. 60 multicoloured . . 10 10

528 "Children" (Adriana Blas Casas)

1979. Air. International Year of the Child.
1470 **528** 1 p. 60 multicoloured . . 10 10

529 Registered Letter from Mexico to Rome, 1880

1979. Air. "Mepsipex 79", Third International Exhibition of Elmhurst Philatelic Society, Mexico City.
1499 **529** 1 p. 60 multicoloured . . 10 10

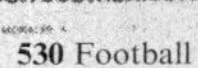

530 Football **531** Josefa Ortiz de Dominguez

1979. "Universiada 79", 10th World University Games, Mexico City (1st issue).
1500 **530** 50 c. grey, black and blue (postage) 10 10
1501 – 80 c. multicoloured . . . 10 10
1502 – 1 p. multicoloured 10 10
1504 – 1 p. 60 multicoloured (air) 10 10
1505 – 4 p. 30 multicoloured . . 15 10
DESIGNS—VERT: 80 c. Aztec ball player; 1 p. Wall painting of athletes; 1 p. 60, Games emblem; 4 p. 30, Flame and doves.
See also Nos. 1514/19.

1979. 150th Death Anniv of Josefa Ortiz de Dominguez (Mayor of Queretaro).
1507 **531** 80 c. pink, black and bright pink 10 10

532 "Allegory of National Culture" (Alfaro Siqueiros)

1979. 50th Anniv of National University's Autonomy. Multicoloured.
1508 80 c. Type **532** (postage) . . . 10 10
1509 3 p. "The Conquest of Energy" (Chavez Morado) 20 10
1510 1 p. 60 "The Return of Quetzalcoatl" (Chavez Morado) (air) 10 10
1511 4 p. 30 "Students reaching for Culture" (Alfaro Siqueiros) 15 10

533 Messenger and U.P.U. Emblem **534** Emiliano Zapata (after Diego Rivera)

1979. Air. Centenary of Mexico's Admission to U.P.U.
1512 **533** 1 p. 60 yellow, black and brown 10 10

1979. Birth Centenary of Emiliano Zapata (revolutionary).
1513 **534** 80 c. multicoloured . . . 10 10

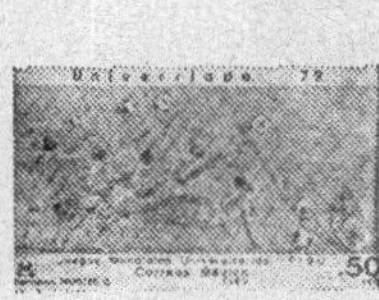

535 Football **536** Tepoztlan, Morelos

1979. "Universiada '79", 10th World University Games, Mexico City (2nd issue). Multicoloured.
1514 50 c. Type **535** (postage) . . . 10 10
1515 80 c. Volleyball 10 10
1516 1 p. Basketball 10 10
1518 1 p. 60 Tennis (air) 10 10
1519 5 p. 50 Swimming 30 20

1979. Tourism (1st series). Multicoloured.
1526 80 c. Type **536** (postage) . . . 10 10
1527 80 c. Mexcaltitan, Nayarit 10 10
1528 1 p. 60 Agua Azul waterfall, Chipas (air) 10 10
1529 1 p. 60 King Coliman statue, Colima 10 10
See also Nos. 1631/4 and 1675/8.

537 Congress Emblem **538** Edison Lamp

1979. Air. 11th Congress and Assembly of International Industrial Design Council.
1530 **537** 1 p. 60 black, mauve and turquoise 10 10

1979. Air. Centenary of Electric Light.
1531 **538** 1 p. 60 multicoloured . . 10 10

539 Martin de Olivares (postmaster) **540** Assembly Emblem

1979. 400th Anniv of Royal Proclamation of Mail Services in the New World. Multicoloured.
1532 80 c. Type **539** (postage) . . . 10 10
1533 1 p. 60 Martin Enriquez de Almanza (viceroy of New Spain) (air) 10 10
1534 5 p. 50 King Philip II of Spain 35 20

1979. Air. 8th General Assembly of Latin American Universities Union.
1536 **540** 1 p. 60 multicoloured . . 10 10

541 Shepherd **542** Moon Symbol from Mexican Codex

1979. Christmas. Multicoloured.
1537 50 c. Type **541** (postage) . . . 10 10
1538 1 p. 60 Girl and Christmas tree (air) 10 10

1979. Air. 10th Anniv of First Man on Moon.
1539 **542** 2 p. 50 multicoloured . . 15 10

543 Church, Yanhuitlan

1980. Air. Mexican Arts and Sciences (8th series). Multicoloured.
1540 1 p. 60 Type **543** 10 10
1541 1 p. 60 Monastery, Yuriria . . 10 10
1542 1 p. 60 Church, Tlayacapan 10 10
1543 1 p. 60 Church, Actopan . . . 10 10
1544 1 p. 60 Church, Acolman . . . 10 10

544 Steps and Snake's Head

1980. National Pre-Hispanic Monuments (1st series). Multicoloured.
1545 80 c. Type **544** (postage) . . . 10 10
1546 1 p. 60 Doble Tlaloc (rain god) (air) 10 10
1547 5 p. 50 Coyolzauhqui (moon goddess) 35 20
See also Nos. 1565/7 and 1605/7.

1980. Mexican Fauna (2nd series). As T **516**. Multicoloured.
1548 80 c. Common turkey (postage) 50 10
1549 1 p. 60 Greater flamingo (air) 50 25

1980. Mexican Flowers (2nd series). As T **518**. Multicoloured.
1550 80 c. "Tajetes erecta" (postage) 15 10
1551 1 p. 60 "Vanilla planifolia" (air) 25 10

545 Jules Verne

1980. Air. 75th Death Anniv of Jules Verne (author).
1552 **545** 5 p. 50 brown and black 35 20

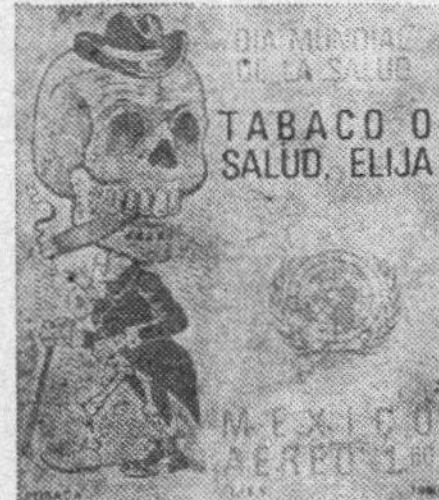

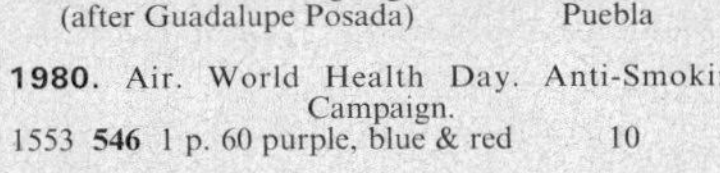

546 Skeleton smoking Cigar (after Guadalupe Posada) **547** China Poblana, Puebla

1980. Air. World Health Day. Anti-Smoking Campaign.
1553 **546** 1 p. 60 purple, blue & red 10 10

1980. National Costumes (1st series). Multicoloured.
1554 50 c. Type **547** (postage) . . . 10 10
1555 80 c. Jarocha, Veracruz . . . 10 10
1556 1 p. 60 Chiapaneca, Chiapas (air) 10 10
See also Nos. 1588/90.

548 Family **549** Cuauhtemoc (last Aztec Emperor)

1980. 10th Population and Housing Census.
1557 **548** 3 p. black and silver . . . 20 10

1980. Pre-Hispanic Personages (1st series). Multicoloured.
1558 80 c. Type **549** 10 10
1559 1 p. 60 Nezahualcoyotl (governor of Tetzcoco) . . 10 10
1560 5 p. 50 Eight Deer Tiger's Claw (11th Mixtec king) 35 20
See also Nos. 1642/4 and 1846/8.

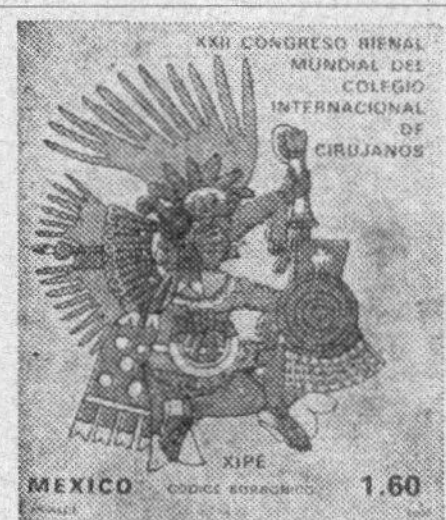

550 Xipe (Aztec god of medicine) **551** Bronze Medal

1980. 22nd World Biennial Congress of International College of Surgeons, Mexico City.
1561 **550** 1 p. 60 multicoloured . . 10 10

1980. Olympic Games, Moscow.
1562 **551** 1 p. 60 bronze, black and turquoise 10 10
1563 – 3 p. silver, black and blue 20 10
1564 – 5 p. 50 gold, black & red 35 20
DESIGNS: 3 p. Silver medal; 5 p. 50, Gold medal.

1980. National Pre-Hispanic Monuments (2nd series). As T **554**. Multicoloured.
1565 80 c. Sacred glass 10 10
1566 1 p. 60 Stone snail 10 10
1567 5 p. 50 Chac Mool (god) . . . 35 20

552 Sacromonte Sanctuary, Amecameca

1980. Colonial Architecture (1st series).
1568 **552** 2 p. 50 grey and black . . 20 10
1569 – 2 p. 50 grey and black . . 20 10
1570 – 3 p. grey and black . . . 25 10
1571 – 3 p. grey and black . . . 25 10
DESIGNS—HORIZ: No. 1552, St. Catherine's Convent, Patzcuaro; No. 1554, Hermitage, Cuernavaca. VERT: No. 1553, Basilica, Culiapan.
See also Nos. 1617/20, 1660/3, 1695/8 and 1784/7.

553 Quetzalcoatl (god) **554** Arms of Sinaloa

1980. World Tourism Conference, Manila, Philippines.
1572 **553** 2 p. 50 multicoloured . . 15 10

1980. 150th Anniv of Sinaloa State.
1573 **554** 1 p. 60 multicoloured . . 10 10

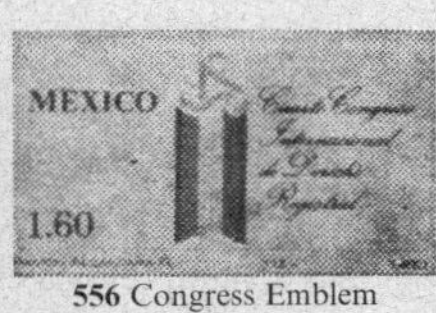

555 Straw Angel **556** Congress Emblem

1980. Christmas. Multicoloured.
1574 50 c. Type **555** 10 10
1575 1 p. 60 Poinsettia in a jug . . 10 10

1980. 4th International Civil Justice Congress.
1576 **556** 1 p. 60 multicoloured . . 10 10

557 Glass Demijohn and Animals **558** "Simon Bolivar" (after Paulin Guerin)

1980. Mexican Crafts (1st series). Multicoloured.

1577 50 c. Type **557** 10 10

1578 1 p. Poncho 10 10

1579 3 p. Wooden mask 20 15

See also Nos. 1624/6.

1980. 150th Death Anniv of Simon Bolivar.

1580 **558** 4 p. multicoloured 30 20

559 Vicente Guerrero

560 Valentin Gomez Farias

1981. 150th Death Anniv of Vicente Guerrero (liberator).

1581 **559** 80 c. multicoloured . . . 10 10

1981. Birth Bicentenary of Valentin Gomez Farias.

1582 **560** 80 c. black and green . . 10 10

561 Table Tennis Balls in Flight

1981. 1st Latin-American Table Tennis Cup.

1583 **561** 4 p. multicoloured 30 20

562 Jesus Gonzalez Ortega

563 Gabino Barreda

1981. Death Centenary of Jesus Gonzalez Ortega.

1584 **562** 80 c. lt brown & brown 10 10

1981. Death Centenary of Gabino Barreda (politician).

1585 **563** 80 c. pink, black & green 10 10

564 Benito Juarez

565 Foundation Monument

1981. 175th Birth Anniv of Benito Juarez (patriot).

1586 **564** 1 p. 60 grn, brn & lt brn . 15 10

1981. 450th Anniv of Puebla City.

1587 **565** 80 c. multicoloured . . . 10 10

1981. National Costumes (2nd series). Vert designs as T **547**. Multicoloured.

1588 50 c. Purepecha, Michoacan 10 10

1589 80 c. Charra, Jalisco 10 10

1590 1 p. 60 Mestiza, Yucatan . . . 15 10

1981. Mexican Fauna (3rd series). Vert designs as T **516**. Multicoloured.

1591 80 c. Northern Mockingbird 65 15

1592 1 p. 60 Mountain Trogon . . 65 35

1981. Mexican Flowers (3rd series). Vert designs as T **518**. Multicoloured.

1593 80 c. Avocado 10 10

1594 1 p. 60 Cacao 15 10

566 "Martyrs of Cananea" (David A. Siqueiros)

1981. 75th Anniv of Martyrs of Cananea.

1595 **566** 1 p. 60 multicoloured . . 15 10

567 Toy Drummer with One Arm

568 Arms of Queretaro

1981. International Year of Disabled People.

1596 **567** 4 p. multicoloured 30 20

1981. 450th Anniv of Queretaro City.

1597 **568** 80 c. multicoloured . . . 10 10

569 Mexican Stamp of 1856 and Postal Service Emblem

1981. 125th Anniv of First Mexican Stamp.

1598 **569** 4 p. multicoloured 30 20

570 Sir Alexander Fleming

572 St. Francisco Xavier Claver

571 Union Congress Building and Emblem

1981. Birth Centenary of Sir Alexander Fleming (discoverer of penicillin).

1599 **570** 5 p. blue and orange . . . 35 10

1981. Opening of New Union Congress Building.

1600 **571** 1 p. 60 green and red . . 10 10

1981. 250th Birth Anniv of St. Francis Xavier Claver.

1601 **572** 80 c. multicoloured . . . 10 10

573 "Desislava" (detail of Bulgarian Fresco)

1981. 1300th Anniv of Bulgarian State. Mult.

1602 1 p. 60 Type **573** 10 10

1603 4 p. Horse-headed cup from Thrace 25 20

1604 7 p. Madara Horseman (relief) 45 30

1981. Pre-Hispanic Monuments. As T **544**. Multicoloured.

1605 80 c. Seated God 10 10

1606 1 p. 60 Alabaster deer's head 15 10

1607 4 p. Jade fish 45 20

574 Pablo Picasso

1981. Birth Centenary of Pablo Picasso (artist).

1608 **574** 5 p. deep green & green 35 20

575 Shepherd

576 Wheatsheaf

1981. Christmas. Multicoloured.

1609 50 c. Type **575** 10 10

1610 1 p. 60 Praying girl 15 10

1981. World Food Day.

1611 **576** 4 p. multicoloured 25 15

577 Thomas Edison, Lightbulb and Gramophone

1981. 50th Death Anniv of Thomas Edison (inventor).

1612 **577** 4 p. stone, brown & green 25 15

578 Co-operation Emblem and Wheat

1981. International Meeting on Co-operation and Development, Cancun.

1613 **578** 4 p. blue, grey and black 25 20

579 Globe and Diesel Locomotive

1981. 15th Pan-American Railway Congress.

1614 **579** 1 p. 60 multicoloured . . 50 25

580 Film Frame

1981. 50th Anniv of Mexican Sound Movies.

1615 **580** 4 p. grey, black and green 25 20

581 Postcode and Bird delivering Letter

1981. Inauguration of Postcodes.

1616 **581** 80 c. multicoloured . . . 10 10

1981. Colonial Architecture (2nd series). As T **522**. Multicoloured.

1617 4 p. Mascarones House . . . 25 15

1618 4 p. La Merced Convent . . . 25 15

1619 5 p. Chapel of the Third Order, Texcoco 30 20

1620 5 p. Father Tembleque Aqueduct, Otumba 30 20

582 "Martyrs of Rio Blanco" (Orozco)

1982. 75th Anniv of Martyrs of Rio Blanco.

1621 **582** 80 c. multicoloured . . . 10 10

583 Ignacio Lopez Rayon

1982. 150th Death Anniv of Ignacio Lopez Rayon.

1622 **583** 1 p. 60 green, red & black 10 10

584 Postal Headquarters

1982. 75th Anniv of Postal Headquarters.

1623 **584** 4 p. pink and green . . . 25 20

1982. Mexican Crafts (2nd series). As T **557**. Multicoloured.

1624 50 c. "God's Eye" (Huichol art) 10 10

1625 1 p. Ceramic snail 10 10

1626 3 p. Tiger mask 20 15

585 Postcoded Letter and Bird

1982. Postcode Publicity.

1627 **585** 80 c. multicoloured . . . 10 10

586 Dr. Robert Koch and Cross of Lorraine

1982. Centenary of Discovery of Tubercle Bacillus.
1628 **586** 4 p. multicoloured 15 10

587 Military Academy 588 Arms of Oaxaca

1982. 50th Anniv of Military Academy.
1629 **587** 80 c. yellow, black & gold 10 10

1982. 450th Anniv of Oaxaca City.
1630 **588** 1 p. 60 multicoloured . . 10 10

1982. Tourism (2nd series). As T **563**. Multicoloured.
1631 80 c. Basaseachic Falls, Chihuahua 10 10
1632 80 c. Natural rock formation, Pueblo Nuevo, Durango . . 10 10
1633 1 p. 60 Mayan City of Edzna, Campeche 10 10
1634 1 p. 60 La Venta (Olmeca sculpture, Tabasco) 10 10

589 Footballers

1982. World Cup Football Championship, Spain. Multicoloured.
1635 1 p. 60 Type **589** 10 10
1636 4 p. Dribbling 15 10
1637 7 p. Tackling 25 15

590 Hawksbill Turtles

1982. Mexican Fauna. Multicoloured.
1638 1 p. 60 Type **590** 10 10
1639 4 p. Grey Whales 15 30

591 Vicente Guerrero

1982. Birth Bicentenary of Vicente Guerrero (independence fighter).
1640 **591** 80 c. multicoloured . . . 10 10

592 Symbols of Peace and Communication

1982. Second U.N. Conference on the Exploration and Peaceful Uses of Outer Space, Vienna.
1641 **592** 4 p. multicoloured 10 10

1982. Pre-Hispanic Personalities (2nd series). As T **549**. Multicoloured.
1642 80 c. Tariacuri 10 10
1643 1 p. 60 Acamapichtli 10 10
1644 4 p. Ten Deer Tiger's breastplate 10 10

593 Pawpaw ("Carica papaya")

1982. Mexican Flora. Multicoloured.
1645 80 c. Type **593** 10 10
1646 1 p. 60 Maize ("Zea mays") 10 10

594 Astrologer

1982. Native Mexican Codices. Florentine Codex. Multicoloured.
1647 80 c. Type **594** 10 10
1648 1 p. 60 Arriving at School . . 10 10
1649 4 p. Musicians 10 10

595 Manuel Gamio (anthropologist)

1982. Mexican Arts and Scientists. Multicoloured.
1650 1 p. 60 Type **595** 10 10
1651 1 p. 60 Isaac Ochoterena (biologist) 10 10
1652 1 p. 60 Angel Maria Garibay (philologist) 10 10
1653 1 p. 60 Manuel Sandoval Vallarta (nuclear physicist) 10 10
1654 1 p. 60 Guillermo Gonzalez Camarena (electronics engineer) 10 10

596 State Archives Building

1982. Inaug of State Archives Building.
1655 **596** 1 p. 60 black and green 10 10

597 Dove and Peace Text

1982. Christmas. Multicoloured.
1656 50 c. Type **597** 10 10
1657 1 p. 60 Dove and Peace text (different) 10 10

598 Hands holding Food

1982. Mexican Food System.
1658 **598** 1 p. 60 multicoloured . . 20 10

MINIMUM PRICE

The minimum price quoted is 10p which represents a handling charge rather than a basis for valuing common stamps. For further notes about prices see introductory pages.

599 "Revolutionary Mexico" Stamp, 1956

1982. Inauguration of Revolution Museum, Chihuahua.
1659 **599** 1 p. 60 grey and green . . 10 10

1982. Colonial Architecture (3rd series). As T **552**. Multicoloured.
1660 1 p. 60 College of Sts. Peter and Paul, Mexico City 10 10
1661 8 p. Convent of Jesus Maria, Mexico City 15 10
1662 10 p. Open Chapel, Tlalmanalco 20 15
1663 14 p. Convent, Actopan . . . 25 20

600 Alfonso Garcia Robles and Laurel 601 Jose Vasconcelos

1982. Alfonso Garcia Robles (Nobel Peace Prize Winner) Commemoration.
1664 **600** 1 p. 60 grey, black & gold 10 10
1665 – 14 p. pink, black & gold 25 20
DESIGN: 14 p. Robles and medal.

1982. Birth Centenary of Jose Vasconcelos (philosopher).
1666 **601** 1 p. 60 black and blue . . 10 10

602 W.C.Y. Emblem and Methods of Communication

1983. World Communications Year.
1667 **602** 16 p. multicoloured . . . 20 15

603 Sonora State Civil War Stamp, 1913

1983. "Herfilex 83" Mexican Revolution Stamp Exhibition.
1668 **603** 6 p. brown, black & green 10 10

604 "Nauticas Mexico" (container ship), World Map and I.M.O. Emblem

1983. 25th Anniv of International Maritime Organization.
1669 **604** 16 p. multicoloured . . . 1·25 30

605 Doctor treating Patient

1983. Constitutional Right to Health Protection.
1670 **605** 6 p. green and red 10 10

606 Valentin Gomez Farias (founder) and Arms of Society

1983. 150th Anniv of Mexican Geographical and Statistical Society.
1671 **606** 6 p. multicoloured 10 10

607 Football

1983. Second World Youth Football Championship, Mexico.
1672 **607** 6 p. black and green . . . 10 10
1673 13 p. black and red . . . 15 10
1674 14 p. black and blue . . . 20 15

1983. Tourism. As T **536**. Multicoloured.
1675 6 p. Federal Palace, Queretaro 10 10
1676 6 p. Water tank, San Luis Potosi 10 10
1677 13 p. Cable car, Zacatecas . . 15 10
1678 14 p. Carved head of Kohunlich, Quintana Roo 20 15

608 Bolivar on Horseback

1983. Birth Bicentenary of Simon Bolivar.
1679 **608** 21 p. multicoloured . . . 25 15

609 Angela Peralta 610 Agave

1983. Death Centenary of Angela Peralta (opera singer).
1680 **609** 9 p. light brown & brown 10 10

1983. Mexican Flora and Fauna (5th series). Multicoloured.
1681 9 p. Type **610** 10 10
1682 9 p. Sapodilla 10 10
1683 9 p. Swallowtail 30 10
1684 9 p. Boa constrictor 10 10

611 Two Candles

1983. Christmas. Multicoloured.
1685 9 p. Type **611** 10 10
1686 20 p. Three candles 25 15

612 S.C.T. Emblem

1983. Integral Communications and Transport System.
1687 **612** 13 p. blue and black . . . 15 10

613 Carlos Chavez (musician)

1983. Mexican Arts and Sciences (10th series). Contemporary Artists. Multicoloured.
1688 **613** 9 p. brown, light brown and deep brown 10 10
1689 – 9 p. brown, light brown and deep brown 10 10
1690 – 9 p. deep brown, light brown and brown . . . 10 10
1691 – 9 p. light brown, deep brown and brown . . . 10 10
1692 – 9 p. deep brown, stone and brown 10 10
DESIGNS: No. 1689, Francisco Goitia (painter); No. 1690, S. Diaz Miron (poet); No. 1691, Carlos Bracho (sculptor); No. 1692, Fanny Anitua (singer).

614 Orozco (self-portrait)

1983. Birth Centenary of Jose Clemente Orozco (artist).
1693 **614** 9 p. multicoloured 10 10

615 Human Rights Emblem

1983. 35th Anniv of Human Rights Declaration.
1694 **615** 20 p. deep blue, yellow and blue 25 15

1983. Colonial Architecture (4th series). As T **552**. Each grey and black.
1695 9 p. Convent, Malinalco . . . 10 10
1696 20 p. Cathedral, Cuernavaca 25 15
1697 21 p. Convent, Tepeji del Rio 25 15
1698 24 p. Convent, Atlatlahucan 30 20

616 Antonio Caso and Books

1983. Birth Centenary of Antonio Caso (philospher).
1699 **616** 9 p. blue, lilac and red . . 10 10

617 Joaquin Velazquez

1983. Bicentenary of Royal Legislation on Mining.
1700 **617** 9 p. multicoloured 10 10

618 Book and Envelopes

1984. Centenary of First Postal Laws.
1701 **618** 12 p. multicoloured . . . 15 10

619 Children dancing around Drops of Anti-Polio Serum

1984. World Anti-Polio Campaign.
1702 **619** 12 p. multicoloured . . . 15 10

620 Muscovy Duck

1984. Mexican Fauna (6th series). Multicoloured.
1703 12 p. Type **620** 65 20
1704 20 p. Red-billed whistling duck 1·10 30

621 Xoloitzcuintle Dog

1984. World Dog Show.
1705 **621** 12 p. multicoloured . . . 15 10

622 Bank Headquarters

1984. Centenary of National Bank.
1706 **622** 12 p. multicoloured . . . 15 10

623 Hands holding Trees 624 Putting the Shot

1984. Protection of Forest Resources.
1707 **623** 20 p. multicoloured . . . 20 15

1984. Olympic Games, Los Angeles. Multicoloured.
1708 14 p. Type **624** 15 15
1709 20 p. Show jumping 20 15
1710 23 p. Gymnastics (floor exercise) 25 20
1711 24 p. Diving 25 20
1712 25 p. Boxing 25 20
1713 26 p. Fencing 25 20

625 Mexican and Russian Flags

1984. 60th Anniv of Diplomatic Relations with U.S.S.R.
1715 **625** 23 p. multicoloured . . . 25 20

626 Hand holding U.N. emblem

1984. International Population Conference.
1716 **626** 20 p. multicoloured . . . 20 15

627 Gen. Mugica

1984. Birth Centenary of General Francisco Mugica (politician).
1717 **627** 14 p. brown and black . . 15 15

628 Emblem and Dates 629 Airline Emblem

1984. 50th Anniv of Economic Culture Fund.
1718 **628** 14 p. brown, black and red 15 15

1984. 50th Anniv of Aeromexico (state airline).
1719 – 14 p. multicoloured . . . 15 15
1720 **629** 20 p. black and red . . . 20 15
DESIGN—36 × 44 mm: 14 p. "Red Cactus" (sculpture, Sebastian).

630 Palace of Fine Arts

1984. 50th Anniv of Palace of Fine Arts.
1721 **630** 14 p. blue, black and brown 15 15

631 Metropolitan Cathedral (detail of facade) 633 Dove and Hand holding Flame

632 Coatzacoalcos Bridge

1984. 275th Anniv of Chihuahua City.
1722 **631** 14 p. brown and black . . 15 15

1984. Inaug of Coatzacoalcos Bridge.
1723 **632** 14 p. multicoloured . . . 15 15

1984. World Disarmament Week.
1724 **633** 20 p. multicoloured . . . 20 15

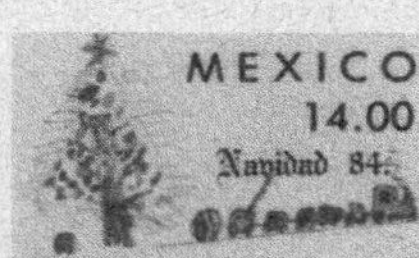

634 Christmas Tree and Toy Train

1984. Christmas. Multicoloured.
1725 14 p. Type **634** 50 25
1726 20 p. Breaking the pinata (balloon filled with gifts) (vert) 20 15

635 Ignacio Manuel Altamirano

1984. 150th Birth Anniv of Ignacio Manuel Altamirano (politician and journalist).
1727 **635** 14 p. red and black . . . 15 15

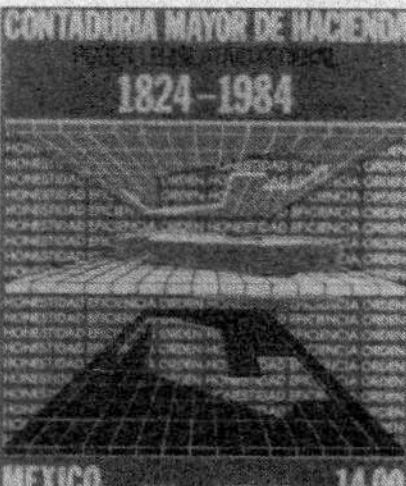

636 Maps, Graph and Text

1984. 160th Anniv of State Audit Office.
1728 **636** 14 p. multicoloured . . . 15 15

637 Half a Football and Mexican Colours

1984. Mexico, Site of 1986 World Cup Football Championship. Multicoloured.

1729 20 p. Type **637** 20 15
1730 24 p. Football and Mexican colours 25 20

638 Romulo Gallegos **639** State Arms and Open Register

1984. Birth Centenary of Romul Gallegos.

1731 **638** 20 p. black and blue . . . 20 15

1984. 125th Anniv of Mexican Civil Register.

1732 **639** 24 p. blue 25 20

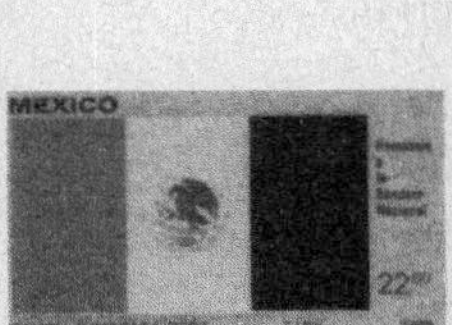

640 Mexican Flag **641** Johann Sebastian Bach

1985. 50th Anniv of National Flag.

1733 **640** 22 p. multicoloured . . . 25 20

1985. 300th Birth Anniv of Johann Sebastian Bach (composer).

1734 **641** 35 p. red and black . . . 15 30

642 I.Y.Y. Emblem **643** Children and Fruit within Book

1985. International Youth Year.

1735 **642** 35 p. purple, gold and black 15 30

1985. Child Survival Campaign.

1736 **643** 36 p. multicoloured . . . 15 10

644 Commemorative Medallion

1985. 450th Anniv of State Mint.

1737 **644** 35 p. gold, mauve & blue 15 10

645 Victor Hugo, Text and Gateway

1985. Death Centenary of Victor Hugo (novelist).

1738 **645** 35 p. grey 15 10

646 Hidalgo 8 r. Stamp, 1856

1985. "Mexifil 85" Stamp Exhibition.

1739 **646** 22 p. grey, black and purple 10 10
1740 – 35 p. grey, black and blue 15 10
1741 – 36 p. multicoloured . . . 15 10

DESIGNS: 35 p. Carranza 10 c. stamp, 1916; 36 p. Juarez 50 p. stamp, 1975.

647 Rockets, Satellite, Nurse and Computer Operator

1985. Launching of First Morelos Satellite. Multicoloured.

1743 22 p. Type **647** 10 10
1744 36 p. Camera, dish aerial, satellite and computers . . 15 10
1745 90 p. Camera, dish aerial, satellite, television and couple telephoning 25 20

Nos. 1743/5 were printed together, se-tenant, forming a composite design.

648 Conifer

1985. 9th World Forestry Congress, Mexico.

1747 **648** 22 p. brown, black and green 10 10
1748 – 35 p. brown, black and green 15 10
1749 – 36 p. brown, black and green 15 10

DESIGNS: 35 p. Silk-cotton trees; 36 p. Mahogany tree.

649 Martin Luis Guzman

1985. Mexican Arts and Sciences (11th series). Contemporary Writers.

1750 **649** 22 p. grey and blue . . . 10 10
1751 – 22 p. grey and blue . . . 10 10
1752 – 22 p. grey and blue . . . 10 10
1753 – 22 p. grey and blue . . . 10 10
1754 – 22 p. grey and blue . . . 10 10

DESIGNS: No. 1751, Augustin Yanez; 1752, Alfonso Reyes; 1753, Jose Ruben Romero; 1754, Artemio de Valle-Arizpe.

650 Miguel Hidalgo

1985. 175th Anniv of Independence Movement. Each green, black and red.

1755 22 p. Type **650** 10 10
1756 35 p. Jose Ma. Morelos . . . 10 10
1757 35 p. Ignacio Allende 10 10
1758 36 p. Leona Vigario 10 10
1759 110 p. Vicente Guerrero . . . 20 15

651 San Ildefonso

1985. 75th Anniv of National University. Mult.

1761 26 p. Type **651** 10 10
1762 26 p. Emblem 10 10
1763 40 p. Modern building 10 10
1764 45 p. 1910 crest and Justo Sierra (founder) 10 10
1765 90 p. University crest 15 10

652 Rural and Industrial Landscapes

1985. 25th Anniv of Inter-American Development Bank.

1766 **652** 26 p. multicoloured . . . 10 10

653 Guns and Doves **654** Hands and Dove

1985. United Nations Disarmament Week.

1767 **653** 36 p. multicoloured . . . 10 10

1985. 40th Anniv of U.N.O.

1768 **654** 26 p. multicoloured . . . 10 10

655 "Girls Skipping" (Mishinoya K. Maki)

1985. Christmas. Children's Paintings. Mult.

1769 26 p. Disabled and able-bodied children playing (Margarita Salazar) 10 10
1770 35 p. Type **655** 10 10

656 Soldadera

1985. 75th Anniv of 1910 Revolution. Each red, black and green.

1771 26 p. Type **656** 10 10
1772 35 p. Pancho Villa 10 10
1773 40 p. Emiliano Zapata 10 10
1774 45 p. Ve

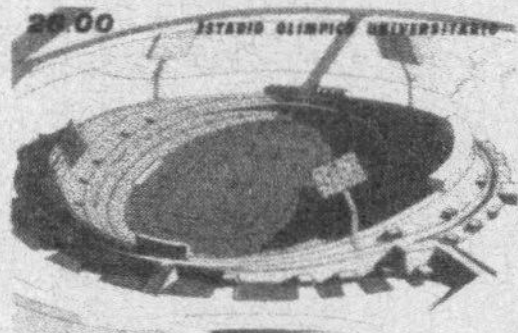

657 "Vigilante" (Federico Silva)

1985. 2nd "Morelos" Telecommunications Satellite Launch.

1777 – 26 p. black and blue . . . 10 10
1778 **657** 35 p. grey, pink and black 10 10
1779 – 45 p. multicoloured . . . 10 10

DESIGNS—VERT: 26 p. "Cosmonaut" (sculpture by Sebastian). HORIZ: 45 p. "Mexican Astronaut" (painting by Cauduro).

658 "Mexico" holding Book

1985. 25th Anniv of Free Textbooks National Commission.

1781 **658** 26 p. multicoloured . . . 10 10

659 Olympic Stadium, University City

1985. World Cup Football Championship, Mexico. Each grey and black.

1782 26 p. Type **659** 10 10
1783 45 p. Azteca Stadium 10 10

1985. Colonial Architecture (5th series). Vert designs as T **552**. Each brown and black.

1784 26 p. Vizcayan College, Mexico City 10 10
1785 35 p. Counts of Heras y Soto Palace, Mexico City 10 10
1786 40 p. Counts of Calimaya Palace, Mexico City 10 10
1787 45 p. St. Carlos Academy, Mexico City 10 10

MEXICO $40

PLANETARIO LUIS ENRIQUE ERRO 50 ANIVERSARIO

661 Luis Enrique Erro Planetarium

1986. 50th Anniv of National Polytechnic Institute. Multicoloured.

1788 40 p. Type **661** 10 10
1789 65 p. National School of Arts and Crafts 10 10
1790 75 p. Founders, emblem and "50" 10 10

1985. Mexican Flowers (6th series). As T **518**. Multicoloured.

1791 40 p. Calabash 10 10
1792 65 p. "Nopalea coccinellifera" (cactus) 10 10

DIA MUNDIAL DE LA SALUD MEXICO
$65

663 Doll

1986. World Health Day.

1793 **663** 65 p. multicoloured . . . 10 10

664 Halley and Comet

1986. Appearance of Halley's Comet.
1794 **664** 90 p. multicoloured . . . 15 10

665 Emblem

1986. Centenary of Geological Institute.
1795 **665** 40 p. multicoloured . . . 10 10

666 "Three Footballers with Berets"

1986. World Cup Football Championship, Mexico (2nd issue). Paintings by Angel Zarraga. Multicoloured.
1796 30 p. Type **666** 10 10
1797 40 p. "Portrait of Ramon Novaro" 10 10
1798 65 p. "Sunday" 10 10
1799 70 p. "Portrait of Ernest Charles Gimpel" 10 10
1800 90 p. "Three Footballers" . . 15 10

667 Ignacio Allende

1986. 175th Death Annivs of Independence Heroes. Multicoloured.
1802 40 p. Type **667** 10 10
1803 40 p. Miguel Hidalgo (after J. C. Orozco) 10 10
1804 65 p. Juan Aldama 10 10
1805 75 p. Mariano Jimenez . . . 10 10

668 Mexican Arms over "FTF"

669 Nicolas Bravo

1986. 50th Anniv of Fiscal Tribunal.
1806 **668** 40 p. black, blue & grey 10 10

1986. Birth Bicentenary of Nicolas Bravo (independence fighter).
1807 **669** 40 p. multicoloured . . . 10 10

670 "Zapata Landscape"

1986. Paintings by Diego Rivera. Multicoloured.
1808 50 p. Type **670** 10 10
1809 80 p. "Nude with Arum Lilies" 10 10
1810 110 p. "Vision of a Sunday Afternoon Walk on Central Avenue" (horiz) 20 15

671 Guadalupe Victoria

1986. Birth Bicentenary of Guadalupe Victoria (first President).
1811 **671** 50 p. multicoloured . . . 10 10

672 People depositing Produce

1986. 50th Anniv of National Depositories.
1812 **672** 40 p. multicoloured . . . 10 10

673 Pigeon above Hands holding Posthorn

674 Emblem

1986. World Post Day.
1813 **673** 120 p. multicoloured . . . 20 15

1986. Foundation of National Commission to Mark 500th Anniv (1992) of Discovery of America.
1814 **674** 50 p. black and red . . . 10 10

675 Ministry of Mines

676 Liszt

1986. 15th Pan-American Roads Congress.
1815 **675** 80 p. grey and black . . . 10 10

1986. 175th Birth Anniv of Franz Liszt (composer).
1816 **676** 100 p. brown and black 15 10

677 U.N. and "Pax Cultura" Emblems

1986. International Peace Year.
1817 **677** 80 p. blue, red and black 10 10

678 Jose Maria Pino Suarez (1st Vice-President of Revolutionary Govt.)

1986. Famous Mexicans buried in The Rotunda of Illustrious Men (1st series).
1818 **678** 50 p. multicoloured . . . 10 10
See also Nos. 1823/4, 1838 and 1899.

679 King

680 "Self-portrait"

1986. Christmas. Multicoloured.
1819 50 p. Type **679** 10 10
1820 80 p. Angel 10 10

1986. Birth Centenary of Diego Rivera (artist).
1821 **680** 80 p. multicoloured . . . 10 10

681 Baby receiving Vaccination

682 Perez de Leon College

1987. National Days for Poliomyelitis Vaccination.
1822 **681** 50 p. multicoloured . . . 10 10

1987. Famous Mexicans buried in The Rotunda of Illustrious Men (2nd series). As T **678**. Mult.
1823 100 p. Jose Maria Iglesias . . 10 10
1824 100 p. Pedro Sainz de Baranda 10 10

1987. Centenary of Higher Education.
1825 **682** 100 p. multicoloured . . . 10 10

683 Kino and Map

1987. 300th Anniv of Father Eusebio Francisco Kino's Mission to Pimeria Alta.
1826 **683** 100 p. multicoloured . . . 10 10

684 Baby's Head

1987. Child Immunization Campaign.
1827 **684** 100 p. deep blue & blue 10 10

685 Staircase

686 "5th of May, 1862, and the Siege of Puebla" Exhibition Poster, 1887

1987. 50th Anniv of Puebla Independent University.
1828 **685** 200 p. grey, pink and black 10 10

1987. 125th Anniv of Battle of Puebla.
1829 **686** 100 p. multicoloured . . . 10 10

687 Stylized City

1987. "Metropolis 87" World Association of Large Cities Congress.
1830 **687** 310 p. red, black and green 45 30

688 Lacquerware Tray, Uruapan, Michoacan

689 Genaro Estrada (author and pioneer of democracy)

1987. Handicrafts. Multicoloured.
1831 100 p. Type **688** 10 10
1832 200 p. Woven blanket, Santa Ana Chiautempan, Tlaxcala 10 10
1833 230 p. Ceramic jar with lid, Puebla, Puebla 15 10

1987. Mexican Arts and Sciences (12th series).
1834 **689** 100 p. brown, black and pink 10 10
See also Nos. 1845, 1880 and 1904/5.

690 "Native Traders" (mural, P. O'Higgins)

1987. 50th Anniv of National Foreign Trade Bank.
1835 **690** 100 p. multicoloured . . . 10 10

691 Diagram of Longitudinal Section through Ship's Hull

1987. 400th Anniv of Publication of First Shipbuilding Manual in America, Diego Garcia de Palacio's "Instrucion Nautica".
1836 **691** 100 p. green, blue & brn 10 10

692 Man carrying Sack of Maize Flour

1987. 50th Anniv of National Food Programme.
1837 **692** 100 p. multicoloured . . . 10 10

1987. Mexicans in Rotunda of Illustrious Men (3rd series). As T **678**. Multicoloured.
1838 100 p. Leandro Valle 10 10

693 "Self-portrait with Skull"

1987. Paintings by Saturnino Herran.
1839 **693** 100 p. brown and black 15 10
1840 – 100 p. multicoloured . . . 15 10
1841 – 400 p. multicoloured . . 60 50
DESIGNS: No. 1840, "The Offering"; 1841, "Creole with Shawl".

694 Flags of Competing Countries

1987. 10th Pan-American Games, Indianapolis.
1842 **694** 100 p. multicoloured . . . 10 10
1843 – 200 p. black, red and green 10 10
DESIGN: 200 p. Running.

695 Electricity Pylon

1987. 50th Anniv of Federal Electricity Commission.
1844 **695** 200 p. multicoloured . . . 10 10

1987. Mexican Arts and Sciences (13th series). As T **689**. Multicoloured.
1845 100 p. J. E. Hernandez y Davalos (author) 10 10

1987. Pre-Hispanic Personages (3rd series). As T **549**. Multicoloured.
1846 100 p. Xolotl (Chichimeca commander) 10 10
1847 200 p. Nezahualpilli (leader of Tezcoco tribe) 10 10
1848 400 p. Motecuhzoma Ilhuicamina (leader of Tenochtitlan tribe) 45 10

696 Stylized Racing Car

1987. Mexico Formula One Grand Prix.
1849 **696** 100 p. multicoloured . . . 10 10

697 Mexican Cultural Centre, Mexico City **698** "Santa Maria" and 1922 Mexican Festival Emblem

1987. Mexican Tourism.
1850 **697** 100 p. multicoloured . . . 10 10

1987. 500th Anniv of "Meeting of Two Worlds" (discovery of America by Columbus) (1st issue).
1851 **698** 150 p. multicoloured . . . 65 20
See also Nos. 1902, 1941, 1979, 2038 and 2062/6.

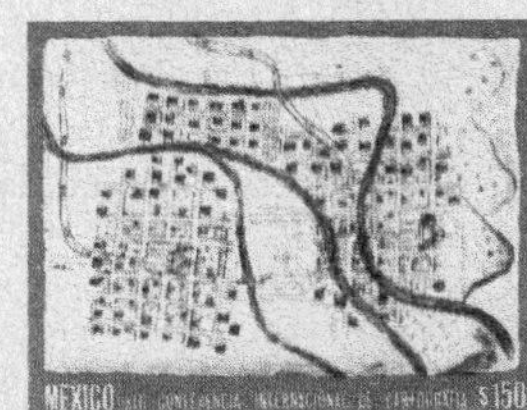

699 16th-century Spanish Map of Mexico City

1987. 13th International Cartography Conference.
1852 **699** 150 p. multicoloured . . . 10 10

1987. Mexican Tourism. As T **697**. Multicoloured.
1853 150 p. Michoacan 30 10
1854 150 p. Garcia Caves, Nuevo Leon 10 10
1855 150 p. View of Mazatlan, Sinaloa 10 10

700 Pre-Hispanic Wedding Ceremony

1987. Native Codices. Mendocino Codex. Mult.
1856 150 p. Type **700** 10 10
1857 150 p. Moctezuma's council chamber 10 10
1858 150 p. Foundation of Tenochtitlan 10 10

701 Dove with Olive Twig

1987. Christmas.
1859 **701** 150 p. mauve 10 10
1860 – 150 p. blue 10 10
DESIGN: No. 1860, As T **701** but dove facing left.

702 "Royal Ordinance for the Carriage of Maritime Mail" Title Page

1987. World Post Day.
1861 **702** 150 p. green and grey . . 10 10

703 Circle of Flags

1987. 1st Meeting of Eight Latin-American Presidents, Acapulco. Multicoloured.
1863 250 p. Type **703** 10 10
1864 500 p. Flags and doves . . . 25 10

TAMAYO 70 años de creación
MEXICO $150

704 "Dualidad 1964"

1987. Rufino Tamayo (painter). "70 Years of Creativity".
1865 **704** 150 p. multicoloured . . . 10 10

705 Train on Metlac Viaduct

1987. 50th Anniv of Railway Nationalization.
1866 **705** 150 p. multicoloured . . . 40 15

706 Stradivarius at Work (detail, 19th-century engraving)

1987. 250th Death Anniv of Antonio Stradivarius (violin-maker).
1867 **706** 150 p. light violet and violet 10 10

707 Statue of Manuel Crescensio Rejon (promulgator of Yucatan State Constitution)

1988. Constitutional Tribunal, Supreme Court of Justice.
1868 **707** 300 p. multicoloured . . . 15 10

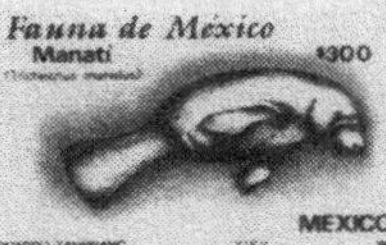

708 American Manatee

1988. Animals. Multicoloured.
1869 300 p. Type **708** 15 10
1870 300 p. Mexican mole salamander 15 10

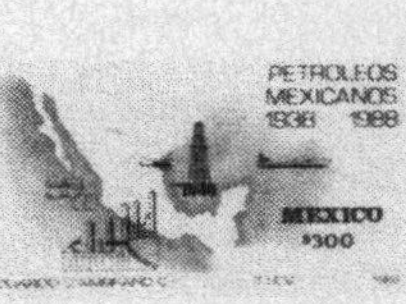

709 Map and Oil Industry Symbols **710** "The Vaccination"

1988. 50th Anniv of Pemex (Nationalized Petroleum Industry).
1871 **709** 300 p. blue and black . . 40 10
1872 – 300 p. multicoloured . . . 15 10
1873 – 500 p. multicoloured . . . 25 10
DESIGNS:—36 × 43 mm: No. 1872, PEMEX emblem. 43 × 36 mm: No. 1873, "50" and oil exploration platform.

1988. World Health Day (1874) and 40th Anniv of W.H.O. (1875). Paintings by Diego Rivera.
1874 **710** 300 p. brown and green 15 10
1875 – 300 p. multicoloured . . . 15 10
DESIGN:—43 × 36 mm: No. 1875, "The People demand Health".

711 "Death Portrait" (Victor Delfin)

1988. 50th Death Anniv of Cesar Vallejo (painter and poet). Multicoloured.
1876 300 p. Type **711** 15 10
1877 300 p. Portrait by Arnold Belkin and "Hoy me palpo..." . . 15 10
1878 300 p. Portrait as in T **711** but larger (30 × 35 mm) 15 10
1879 300 p. Portrait as in No. 1877 but larger (23 × 35 mm) . . 15 10

1988. Mexican Arts and Sciences (14th series). As T **689**.
1880 300 p. brown, black and violet 15 10
DESIGN: 300 p. Carlos Pellicer (poet).

712 Girl and Boy holding Stamp in Tweezers

1988. "Mepsirrey '88" Stamp Exhibition, Monterrey. Multicoloured.
1881 300 p. Type **712** 15 10
1882 300 p. Envelope with "Monterrey" hand-stamp 15 10
1883 500 p. Exhibition emblem . . 25 10

713 Hernandos Rodriguez Racing Circuit, Mexico City

1988. Mexico Formula One Grand Prix.
1884 **713** 500 p. multicoloured . . . 25 10

714 Lopez Verlarde and Rose **715** Emblem

1988. Birth Centenary of Ramon Lopez Verlarde (poet). Multicoloured.
1885 300 p. Type **714** 15 10
1886 300 p. Abstract 15 10

1988. 50th Anniv of Military Sports.
1887 **715** 300 p. multicoloured . . . 15 10

MORE DETAILED LISTS
are given in the Stanley Gibbons Catalogues referred to in the country headings.
For lists of current volumes see Introduction.

716 Chrysanthemum, Container Ship and Flags

1988. Centenary of Mexico–Japan Friendship, Trade and Navigation Treaty.
1888 **716** 500 p. multicoloured . . . 45 10

717 Map **718** Runners

1988. Oceanographical Assembly.
1889 **717** 500 p. multicoloured . . . 25 10

1988. Olympic Games Seoul.
1890 **718** 500 p. multicoloured . . . 25 10

719 Boxer and Flags

1988. 25th Anniv of World Boxing Council.
1892 **719** 500 p. multicoloured . . . 25 10

720 Hospital and Emblem

1988. 125th Anniv of Red Cross.
1893 **720** 300 p. grey, red and black 15 10

721 Posada

1988. 75th Death Anniv of Jose Guadalupe Posada (painter).
1894 **721** 300 p. black and silver . . 15 10

722 "Danaus plexippus"

1988. Endangered Insects. The Monarch Butterfly. Multicoloured.
1895 300 p. Type **722** . . . . . . 1·00 10
1896 300 p. Butterflies on wall . . . 1·00 10
1897 300 p. Butterflies on leaves . . 1·00 10
1898 300 p. Caterpillar, butterfly and chrysalis . . . . 1·00 10

1988. Mexicans in Rotunda of Illustrious Persons (4th series). As T **678**. Multicoloured.
1899 300 p. Manuel Sandoval Vallarta 15 10

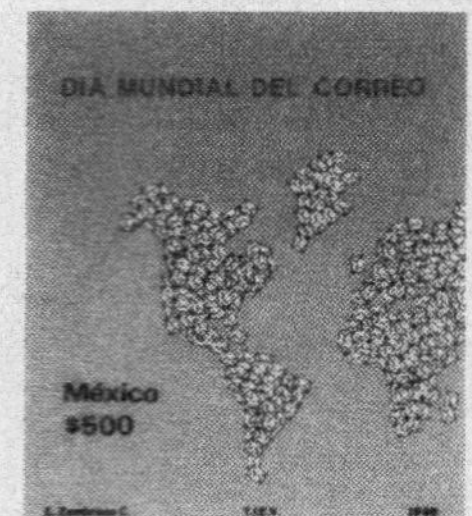

723 Envelopes forming Map

1988. World Post Day.
1900 **723** 500 p. black and blue . . 20 10

724 Indian and Monk writing

1988. 500th Anniv of "Meeting of Two Worlds" (2nd issue). Yanhuitian Codex.
1902 **724** 500 p. multicoloured . . . 20 10

725 Man watering Plant

1988. World Food Day. "Rural Youth".
1903 **725** 500 p. multicoloured . . . 20 10

1988. Mexican Arts and Sciences (15th series). As T **689**.
1904 300 p. black and grey 15 10
1905 300 p. brown, black & yellow 15 10
DESIGNS: No. 1904, Alfonso Caso; 1905, Vito Alessio Robles.

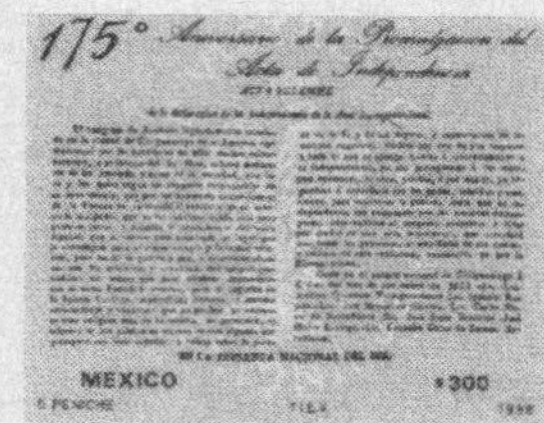

726 Act

1988. 175th Anniv of Promulgation of Act of Independence.
1906 **726** 300 p. flesh and brown 15 10

727 "Self-portrait 1925" **728** Children and Kites

1988. 25th Death Anniv of Antonio Ruiz (painter). Multicoloured.
1907 300 p. Type **727** 15 10
1908 300 p. "La Malinche" 15 10
1909 300 p. "March Past" 15 10

1988. Christmas. Multicoloured.
1910 300 p. Type **728** 15 10
1911 300 p. Food (horiz) 15 10

729 Emblem

1988. 50th Anniv of Municipal Workers Trade Union.
1912 **729** 300 p. black and brown 15 10

1988. Mexican Flowers (7th series). As T **518**. Multicoloured.
1913 300 p. "Mimosa tenuiflora" 15 10
1914 300 p. "Ustilago maydis" . . 30 10

731 "50" and Emblem

1989. 50th Anniv of State Printing Works.
1915 **731** 450 p. brown, grey & red 20 10

732 Arms and Score of National Anthem

1989. 145th Anniv of Dominican Independence.
1916 **732** 450 p. multicoloured . . . 20 10

733 Emblem

1989. Centenary of International Boundary and Water Commission.
1917 **733** 1100 p. multicoloured . . 50 50

734 Emblem

1989. 10th International Book Fair, Mineria.
1918 **734** 450 p. multicoloured . . . 20 10

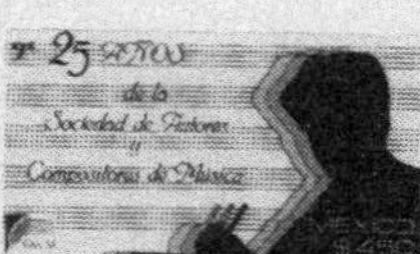
735 Composer at Work

1989. 25th Anniv of Society of Authors and Composers.
1919 **735** 450 p. multicoloured . . . 20 10

736 People

1989. Anti-Aids Campaign.
1920 **736** 450 p. multicoloured . . . 20 10

737 Vicario **738** Statue of Reyes

1989. Birth Bicentenary of Leona Vicario (Independence fighter).
1921 **737** 450 p. brown, deep brown and black 20 10

1989. Birth Centenary of Alfonso Reyes (writer).
1922 **738** 450 p. multicoloured . . . 20 10

739 Speeding Cars

1989. Mexico Formula One Grand Prix.
1923 **739** 450 p. multicoloured . . . 20 10

740 Sea and Mountains **741** Huehuetcotl (god)

1989. 14th Travel Agents' Meeting, Acapulco.
1924 **740** 1100 p. multicoloured . . 50 50

1989. 14th International Congress on Ageing.
1925 **741** 450 p. pink, black and stone 20 10

742 Revolutionary and Battle Site

1989. 75th Anniv of Battle of Zacatecas.
1926 **742** 450 p. black 20 10

743 Catchers

1989. Baseball Professionals' Hall of Fame. Multicoloured.
1927 550 p. Type **743** 20 10
1928 550 p. Striker 20 10
Nos. 1927/8 were printed together, se-tenant, forming a composite design.

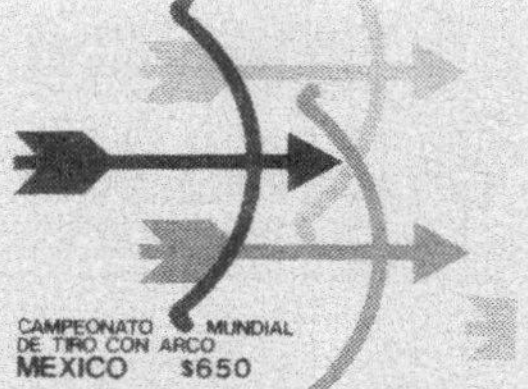

744 Bows and Arrows

1989. World Archery Championships, Switzerland. Multicoloured.
1929 650 p. Type **744** 25 10
1920 650 p. Arrows and target . . . 25 10
Nos. 1929/30 were printed together, se-tenant, forming a composite design.

745 Arms

1989. Centenary of Tijuana.
1931 **745** 1100 p. multicoloured . . 50 20

746 Storming the Bastille

1989. Bicentenary of French Revolution.
1932 **746** 1300 p. multicoloured . . 60 50

747 Mina

1989. Birth Bicentenary of Francisco Xavier Mina (independence fighter).
1933 **747** 450 p. multicoloured . . . 20 10

748 Cave Paintings

1989. 25th Anniv of National Anthropological Museum, Chapultepec.
1934 **748** 450 p. multicoloured . . . 20 10

749 Runners

1989. 7th Mexico City Marathon.
1935 **749** 450 p. multicoloured . . . 20 10

750 Printed Page

1989. 450th Anniv of First American and Mexican Printed Work.
1936 **750** 450 p. multicoloured . . . 20 10

751 Posthorn and Cancellations

1989. World Post Day.
1937 **751** 1100 p. multicoloured . . 50 20

752 "Aguascalientes in History" (Osvaldo Barra)

1989. 75th Anniv of Aguascalientes Revolutionary Convention.
1936 **752** 450 p. multicoloured . . . 20 10

753 Patterns

1989. America. Pre-Columbian Culture.
1939 450 p. Type **753** 20 10
1940 450 p. Traditional writing . . . 20 10

754 Old and New World Symbols **755** Cross of Lorraine

1989. 500th Anniv of "Meeting of Two Worlds" (3rd issue).
1941 **754** 1300 p. multicoloured . . 60 25

1989. 50th Anniv of Anti-tuberculosis National Committee.
1942 **755** 450 p. multicoloured . . . 20 10

756 Mask of God Murcielago

1989.
1943 **756** 450 p. green, black & mve 20 10

757 Bank

1989. 125th Anniv of Serfin Commercial Bank.
1944 **757** 450 p. blue, gold & black 20 10

758 Cortines **759** Man with Sparkler

1989. Birth Centenary of Adolfo Ruiz Cortines (President, 1952–58).
1945 **758** 450 p. multicoloured . . . 20 10

1989. Christmas. Multicoloured.
1946 450 p. Type **759** 20 10
1947 450 p. People holding candles (horiz) 20 10

760 Emblem

1989. 50th Anniv of National Institute of Anthropology and History.
1948 **760** 450 p. gold, red & black 20 10

761 Steam Locomotive, Diesel Train and Felipe Pescador

1989. 80th Anniv of Nationalization of Railways.
1949 **761** 450 p. multicoloured . . . 50 15

762 Bridge

1990. Opening of Tampico Bridge.
1950 **762** 600 p. black, gold & red 20 10

763 Smiling Children

1990. Child Vaccination Campaign.
1951 **763** 700 p. multicoloured . . . 25 10

764 People in Houses

1990. 11th General Population and Housing Census.
1952 **764** 700 p. green, yell & lt grn 25 10

765 Stamp under Magnifying Glass

1990. 10th Anniv of Mexican Philatelic Association.
1953 **765** 700 p. multicoloured . . . 25 10

766 Archive

1990. Bicentenary of National Archive.
1954 **766** 700 p. blue 25 10

767 Emblem and "90"

1990. 1st International Poster Biennale.
1955 **767** 700 p. multicoloured . . . 25 10

768 Messenger, 1790

1990. "Stamp World London 90" International Stamp Exhibition.
1956 **768** 700 p. yellow, red & black 25 10

769 Penny Black

1990. 150th Anniv of the Penny Black.
1957 **769** 700 p. black, red & gold 25 10

770 National Colours and Pope John Paul II

1990. Papal Visit.
1958 **770** 700 p. multicoloured . . . 25 10

771 Church 772 Mother and Child

1990. 15th Travel Agents' Congress.
1959 **771** 700 p. multicoloured . . . 25 10

1990. Mother and Child Health Campaign.
1960 **772** 700 p. multicoloured . . . 25 10

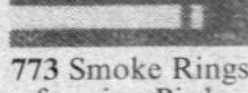

773 Smoke Rings forming Birds 774 Globe as Tree

1990. World Anti-Smoking Day.
1961 **773** 700 p. multicoloured . . . 25 10

1990. World Environment Day.
1962 **774** 700 p. multicoloured . . . 25 10

775 Racing Car and Chequered Flag

1990. Mexico Formula One Grand Prix.
1963 **775** 700 p. black, red & green 25 10

776 Aircraft Tailfin

1990. 25th Anniv of Airports and Auxiliary Services.
1964 **776** 700 p. multicoloured . . . 25 10

777 Family

1990. United Nations Anti-drugs Decade.
1965 **777** 700 p. multicoloured . . . 25 10

778 Tree Trunk

1990. Forest Conservation.
1966 **778** 700 p. multicoloured . . . 25 10

779 Emblem

1990. "Solidarity".
1967 **779** 700 p. multicoloured . . . 25 10
See also No. 2047.

780 Columns and Native Decoration

1990. World Heritage Site. Oaxaca.
1968 **780** 700 p. multicoloured . . . 25 10

781 Elegant Tern

1990. Conservation of Rasa Island, Gulf of California.
1969 **781** 700 p. grey, black & red 80 30

782 Institute Activities

1990. 25th Anniv of Mexican Petroleum Institute.
1970 **782** 700 p. blue and black . . 25 10

783 National Colours, City Monuments and Runners

1990. 18th International Mexico City Marathon.
1971 **783** 700 p. black, red & green 25 10

784 Facade

1990. 50th Anniv of Colima University.
1972 **784** 700 p. multicoloured . . . 25 10

785 Abstract

1990. Mexico City Consultative Council.
1973 **785** 700 p. multicoloured . . . 25 10

786 Electricity Worker

1990. 30th Anniv of Nationalization of Electricity Industry.
1974 **786** 700 p. multicoloured . . . 25 10

787 Violin and Bow

1990. 50th Death Anniv of Silvestre Revueltas (violinist).
1975 **787** 700 p. multicoloured . . . 25 10

788 Building

1990. 450th Anniv of Campeche.
1976 **788** 700 p. multicoloured . . . 25 15

789 Crossed Rifle and Pen 790 Emblem

1990. 80th Anniv of San Luis Plan.
1977 **789** 700 p. multicoloured . . . 25 15

1990. 14th World Supreme Councils Conference.
1978 **790** 1500 p. multicoloured . . 55 35

791 Spanish Tower and Mexican Pyramid

1990. 500th Anniv of "Meeting of Two Worlds" (4th issue).
1979 **791** 700 p. multicoloured . . . 25 15

792 Glass of Beer, Ear of Barley and Hop 793 Carving

1990. Centenary of Brewing Industry.
1980 **792** 700 p. multicoloured . . . 25 15

1990. Bicentenary of Archaeology in Mexico.
1981 **793** 1500 p. multicoloured . . 55 35

794 Ball-game Field 795 Globe and Poinsettia

1990. 16th Central American and Caribbean Games. Multicoloured.
1982 750 p. Type **794** . . . . . . 1·10 20
1983 750 p. Amerindian ball-game player . . . . 1·10 20
1984 750 p. Amerindian ball-game player (different) (horiz) . . 1·10 20
1985 750 p. Yutsil and Balam (mascots) (horiz) . . . . . 1·10 20

1990. Christmas. Multicoloured.
1986 700 p. Type **795** 25 15
1987 700 p. Fireworks and candles 25 15

796 Dog (statuette)

1990. 50th Anniv of Mexican Canine Federation.
1988 **796** 700 p. multicoloured . . . 25 15

797 Microscope, Dolphin and Hand holding Map

1991. 50th Anniv of Naval Secretariat.
1989 **797** 1000 p. gold, black & bl 40 25

798 Means of Transport

1991. Accident Prevention.
1990 **798** 700 p. multicoloured . . . 65 20

799 Products in Bags 800 "In order to Decide, Register"

1991. 15th Anniv of National Consumer Institute.
1991 **799** 1000 p. multicoloured . . 40 25

1991. Electoral Register.
1992 **800** 1000 p. orange, grn & blk 40 25

801 Basketball Player **802** Flowers and Caravel

1991. Olympic Games, Barcelona (1992) (1st issue).
1993 **801** 1000 p. black and yellow . . 40 25
See also Nos. 2050, 2057 and 2080/9.

1991. America (1990). Natural World. Mult.
1994 700 p. Type **802** 75 20
1995 700 p. Right half of caravel, blue and yellow macaw and flowers 75 20
Nos. 1994/5 were issued together, se-tenant, forming a composite design.

803 Children in Droplet

1991. Children's Month. Vaccination Campaign.
1996 **803** 1000 p. multicoloured . . 40 25

804 Map **805** Dove and Children

1991. World Post Day (1990).
1997 **804** 1500 p. multicoloured . . 55 35

1991. Children's Days for Peace and Development.
1998 **805** 1000 p. multicoloured . . 40 25

806 Dove **807** Mining

1991. Family Health and Unity.
1999 **806** 1000 p. multicoloured . . 40 25

1991. 500th Anniv of Mining.
2000 **807** 1000 p. multicoloured . . 40 25

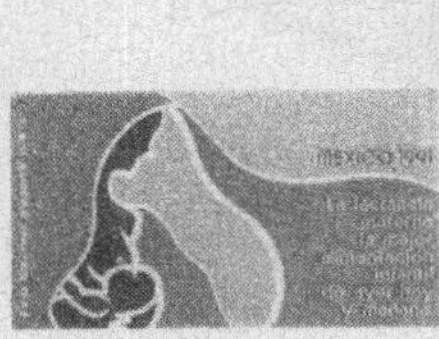

808 Mother feeding Baby **809** Emblem

1991. Breastfeeding Campaign.
2001 **808** 1000 p. buff, blue & brn . . 40 25

1991. 16th Tourism Fair, Acapulco.
2002 **809** 1000 p. green & dp green . . 40 25

810 Rotary Emblem and Independence Monument, Mexico City **811** "Communication"

1991. Rotary International Convention. "Let us Preserve the Planet Earth".
2003 **810** 1000 p. gold and blue . . 40 25

1991. Centenary of Ministry of Transport and Communications (S.C.T.). Multicoloured.
2004 1000 p. Type **811** . . . . . . 1·25 50
2005 1000 p. Boeing 737 landing . . 65 25
2006 1000 p. Facsimile machine . . 65 25
2007 1000 p. Van 65 25
2008 1000 p. Satellites and Earth . . 65 25
2009 1000 p. Railway freight wagons on bridge . . . . 1·25 35
2010 1000 p. Telephone users . . . 65 25
2011 1000 p. Road bridge over road . 65 25
2012 1000 p. Road bridge and cliffs . 65 25
2013 1000 p. Stern of container ship and dockyard . . . . . . 1·25 35
2014 1000 p. Television camera and presenter 65 25
2015 1000 p. Front of truck at toll gate 65 25
2016 1000 p. Roadbuilding ("Solidarity") 65 25
2017 1500 p. Boeing 737 and control tower 80 35
2018 1500 p. Part of fax machine, transmitters and dish aerials on S.C.T. building 80 35
2019 1500 p. Satellite (horiz) 80 35
2020 1500 p. Diesel and electric trains 1·25 50
2021 1500 p. S.C.T. building . . . 80 35
2022 1500 p. Road bridge over ravine . 80 35
2023 1500 p. Bow of container ship and dockyard . . . . . . 1·25 50
2024 1500 p. Bus at toll gate . . . 80 35
2025 1500 p. Rear of truck and trailer at toll gate 80 35
Nos. 2005/25 were issued together, se-tenant, each block containing several composite designs.

812 Jaguar

1991. Lacandona Jungle Conservation.
2026 **812** 1000 p. black, orge & red . . 40 25

813 Driver and Car **814** Emblem and Left-hand Sections of Sun and Earth

1991. Mexico Formula 1 Grand Prix.
2027 **813** 1000 p. multicoloured . . 40 25

1991. Total Eclipse of the Sun. Multicoloured.
2028 1000 p. Type **814** . . . . . . 1·00 25
2029 1000 p. Emblem and right-hand sections of sun and Earth . 1·00 25
2030 1500 p. Emblem and centre of sun and Earth showing north and central America . . . . 1·50 35
Nos. 2028/30 were issued together, se-tenant, forming a composite design.

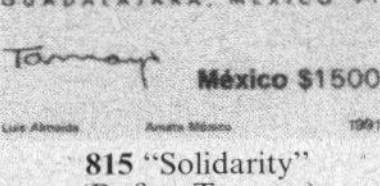

815 "Solidarity" (Rufino Tamayo) **816** Bridge

1991. 1st Latin American Presidential Summit, Guadalajara.
2031 **815** 1500 p. black, orge & yell . . 55 35

1991. Solidarity between Nuevo Leon and Texas.
2032 **816** 2000 p. multicoloured . . 1·10 75

817 Runners **819** Emblem

818 Cogwheel

1991. 9th Mexico City Marathon.
2033 **817** 1000 p. multicoloured . . 40 25

1991. 50th Anniv (1990) of National Chambers of Industry and Commerce.
2034 **818** 1500 p. multicoloured . . 55 35

1991. 55th Anniv of Federation Fiscal Tribunal.
2035 **819** 1000 p. silver and blue . . 40 25

820 National Colours forming Emblem

1991. "Solidarity–Let us Unite in order to Progress".
2036 **820** 1000 p. multicoloured . . 40 25

821 Dove with Letter **822** World Map

1991. World Post Day.
2037 **821** 1000 p. multicoloured . . 40 25

1991. 500th Anniv of "Meeting of Two Worlds" (5th issue).
2038 **822** 1000 p. multicoloured . . 95 25

823 Caravel, Sun and Trees

1991. America. Voyages of Discovery. Mult.
2039 1000 p. Type **823** 75 25
2040 1000 p. Storm cloud, caravel and broken snake 75 25

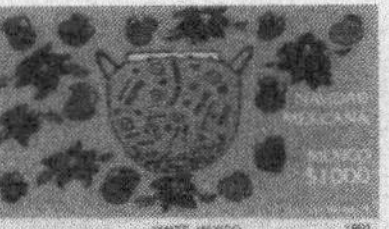

824 Flowers and Pots

1991. Christmas. Multicoloured.
2041 1000 p. Type **824** 40 25
2042 1000 p. Children with decoration 40 25

825 Abstract

1991. Carlos Merida (artist) Commemoration.
2043 **825** 1000 p. multicoloured . . 40 25

826 Score and Portrait

1991. Death Bicentenary of Wolfgang Amadeus Mozart (composer).
2044 **826** 1000 p. multicoloured . . 40 25

827 Kidney Beans and Maize

1991. Self-sufficiency in Kidney Beans and Maize.
2045 **827** 1000 p. multicoloured . . 40 25

828 City Plan

1991. 450th Anniv of Morelia.
2046 **828** 1000 p. brown, stone and red 40 25

1991. "Solidarity". As No. 1967 but new value.
2047 **779** 1000 p. multicoloured . . 40 25

829 Merida

1992. 450th Anniv of Merida.
2048 **829** 1300 p. multicoloured . . 60 40

830 Colonnade

1992. Bicentenary of Engineering Training in Mexico.
2049 **830** 1300 p. blue and red . . . 60 40

831 Horse Rider

1992. Olympic Games, Barcelona (2nd issue).
2050 **831** 2000 p. multicoloured . . 90 60

MINIMUM PRICE

The minimum price quoted is 10p which represents a handling charge rather than a basis for valuing common stamps. For further notes about prices see introductory pages.

832 City Arms

1992. 450th Anniv of Guadalajara. Multicoloured.
2051 1300 p. Type **832** . . . . . . 1·10 40
2052 1300 p. "Guadalajara Town Hall" (Jorge Navarro) . . . 1·10 40
2053 1300 p. "Guadalajara Cathedral" (Gabriel Flores) 1·10 40
2054 1900 p. "Founding of Guadalajara" (Rafael Zamarripa) . . . . 1·60 55
2055 1900 p. Anniversary emblem (Ignacio Vazquez) . . . . 1·60 55

833 Children and Height Gauge

834 Olympic Torch and Rings

1992. Child Health Campaign.
2056 **833** 2000 p. multicoloured . . 90 60

1992. Olympic Games, Barcelona (3rd issue).
2057 **834** 2000 p. multicoloured . . 90 60

835 Horse and Racing Car

1992. "500th Anniv of the Wheel and the Horse in America". Mexico Formula 1 Grand Prix.
2058 **835** 1300 p. multicoloured . . 60 40

836 Satellite and Map of Americas

837 Human Figure and Cardiograph

1992. "Americas Telecom '92" Telecommunications Exhibition.
2059 **836** 1300 p. multicoloured . . 60 40

1992. World Health Day.
2060 **837** 1300 p. black, red & blue 60 40

838 Emblem

1992. 60th Anniv of Military Academy.
2061 **838** 1300 p. red, yellow & blk 60 40

839 "Inspiration of Christopher Columbus" (Jose Maria Obregon)

840 Complex

1992. 500th Anniv of "Meeting of Two Worlds" (6th issue). "Granada 92" International Stamp Exhibition.
2062 1300 p. Type **839** . . . . . . 1·00 40
2063 1300 p. "Racial Encounter" (Jorge Gonazalez Camarena) 1·00 40
2064 2000 p. "Origin of the Sky" (Selden Codex) . . . . . 1·75 60
2065 2000 p. "Quetzalcoatl and Tezcatlipoca" (Borhomico Codex) . . . . 1·75 60
2066 2000 p. "From Spaniard and Indian, mestizo" . . . . . 1·75 60

1992. National Medical Centre.
2068 **840** 1300 p. multicoloured . . 60 40

841 Children, Dove and Globe 842 New-born Baby

1992. Children's Rights.
2069 **841** 1300 p. multicoloured . . 60 40

1992. Traditional Childbirth.
2070 **842** 1300 p. multicoloured . . 60 40

1992. "World Columbian Stamp Expo '92", Chicago. Nos. 2062/6 optd **WORLD COLUMBIAN STAMP EXPO '92 MAY 22-31, 1992 - CHICAGO** and emblem.
2071 1300 p. mult (No. 2062) . . . 2·00 2·00
2072 1300 p. mult (No. 2063) . . . 2·00 2·00
2073 2000 p. mult (No. 2064) . . . 5·00 5·00
2074 2000 p. mult (No. 2065) . . . 5·00 5·00
2075 2000 p. mult (No. 2066) . . . 5·00 5·00

845 Arms of Colleges

1992. Bicentenary of Mexico Notary College.
2078 **845** 1300 p. multicoloured . . 50 35

846 Trees and Cacti

1992. Tree Day.
2079 **846** 1300 p. multicoloured . . 50 35

847 Boxing

848 Athlete

1992. Olympic Games, Barcelona (4th issue). Mult.
2080 1300 p. Type **847** 80 35
2081 1300 p. High jumping 80 35
2082 1300 p. Fencing 80 35
2083 1300 p. Shooting 80 35
2084 1300 p. Gymnastics 80 35
2085 1900 p. Rowing . . . . . . 1·60 50
2086 1900 p. Running . . . . . . 1·60 50
2087 1900 p. Football . . . . . . 1·60 50
2088 1900 p. Swimming . . . . . 1·60 50
2089 2000 p. Equestrian . . . . . 1·60 55

1992. 10th Mexico City Marathon.
2091 **848** 1300 p. multicoloured . . 50 35

849 Emblem

1992. "Solidarity".
2092 **849** 1300 p. multicoloured . . 50 35

851 Television, Map and Radio

1992. 50th Anniv of National Chamber of Television and Radio Industry.
2094 **851** 1300 p. multicoloured . . 50 35

852 Letter orbiting Globe

1992. World Post Day.
2095 **852** 1300 p. multicoloured . . 50 35

853 Satellite above South and Central America and Flags

1992. American Cadena Communications System.
2096 **853** 2000 p. multicoloured . . 1·10 55

854 Gold Compass Rose

1992. America. 500th Anniv of Discovery of America by Columbus. Multicoloured.
2097 2000 p. Type **854** . . . . . . 1·25 55
2098 2000 p. Compass rose (different) and fish . . . . 1·25 55
Nos. 2097/8 were issued together, se-tenant, forming a composite design.

855 Scroll

1992. 400th Anniv of San Luis Potosi.
2099 **855** 1300 p. black and mauve 50 35

856 Berrendos Deer

1992. Conservation.
2100 **856** 1300 p. multicoloured . . 50 35

857 Schooner, Landing Ship, Emblem and Sailors 858 Christmas Tree, Children and Crib

1992. Navy Day.
2101 **857** 1300 p. multicoloured . . 50 35

1992. Christmas. Children's Drawings. Mult.
2102 1300 p. Type **858** 50 35
2103 2000 p. Street celebration (horiz) . . . . 1·25 55

Currency Reform. 1 (new) peso = 1000 (old) pesos.

859 Anniversary Emblem 860 Emblem

1993. 50th Anniv of Mexican Social Security Institute (1st issue).
2104 **859** 1 p. 50 green, gold & blk 60 40
See also Nos. 2110 and 2152/3.

1993. Centenary of Mexican Opthalmological Society.
2105 **860** 1 p. 30 multicoloured . . 50 35

861 Children

862 Society Arms and Founders

1993. Children's Month.
2106 **861** 1 p. 30 multicoloured . . 50 35

1993. 160th Anniv of Mexican Geographical and Statistical Society.
2107 **862** 1 p. 30 multicoloured . . 50 35

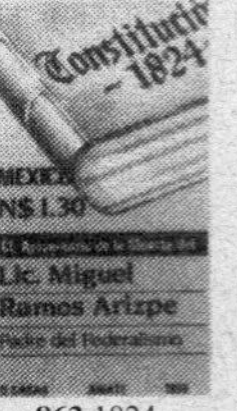

863 1824 Constitution

864 Gomez, Children and Hospital

1993. 150th Death Anniv of Miguel Ramos Arizpe, "Father of Federalism".
2108 **863** 1 p. 30 multicoloured . . 50 35

1993. 50th Anniv of Federico Gomez Children's Hospital.
2109 **864** 1 p. 30 multicoloured . . 50 35

865 Doctor with Child

1993. 50th Anniv of Mexican Social Security Institute (2nd issue). Medical Services.
2110 **865** 1 p. 30 multicoloured . . 50 35

866 Mother feeding Baby

1993. "Health begins at Home".
2111 **866** 1 p. 30 multicoloured . . 50 35

867 Seal and Map

1993. Upper Gulf of California Nature Reserve.
2112 **867** 1 p. 30 multicoloured . . 50 35

HAVE YOU READ THE NOTES AT THE BEGINNING OF THIS CATALOGUE?
These often provide answers to the enquiries we receive.

868 Cantinflas

1993. Mexican Film Stars. Mario Moreno (Cantinflas).
2113 **868** 1 p. 30 black and blue . . 50 35
See also Nos. 2156/60.

869 Campeche

1993. Tourism. Value expressed as "NS". Mult.
2114 90 c. Type **869** 65 25
2115 1 p. Guanajuato 70 25
2263 1 p. 10 As No. 2115 . . . . . 70 10
2116 1 p. 30 Colima 80 35
2264 1 p. 80 As No. 2124 . . . . . 55 20
2265 1 p. 80 As No. 2118 . . . . . 65 20
2266 1 p. 80 As No. 2116 . . . . . 55 20
2267 1 p. 80 As Type **869** 55 20
2117 1 p. 90 Michoacan (vert) . . . 1·25 50
2118 2 p. Coahuila . . . . 1·25 55
2269 2 p. As No. 2266 . . . . . . 90 20
2119 2 p. 20 Queretaro . . . . . . 1·60 60
2271 2 p. 30 As No. 2122 . . . . . 70 25
2272 2 p. 40 As No. 2123 . . . . . 80 25
2120 2 p. 50 Sonora . . . . 2·00 65
2274 2 p. 70 As No. 2145 . . . . . 1·25 25
2121 2 p. 80 Zacatecas (vert) . . . 2·25 75
2276 3 p. Type **869** . . . . . . 1·40 30
2278 3 p. 40 as No. 2271 . . . . . 1·40 35
2122 3 p. 70 Sinaloa . . . . 3·25 1·25
2280 3 p. 80 As No. 2272 . . . . . 1·25 40
2123 4 p. 40 Yucatan . . . . 3·50 1·50
2124 4 p. 80 Chiapas . . . . 3·75 1·60
2145 6 p. Mexico City . . . . . . 4·00 2·00
2290 6 p. 80 As No. 2120 . . . . . 2·50 90
See also Nos. 2410/29.

870 Dr. Maximiliano Ruiz Castaneda

1993. 50th Anniv of Health Service. Multicoloured.
2126 1 p. 30 Type **870** 50 35
2127 1 p. 30 Dr. Bernardo Sepulveda Gutierrez 50 35
2128 1 p. 30 Dr. Ignacio Chavez Sanchez 50 35
2129 1 p. 30 Dr. Mario Salazar Mallen 50 35
2130 1 p. 30 Dr. Gustavo Baz Prada . . 50 35

871 Brazil 30 r. "Bull's Eye" Stamp

872 Runners

1993. 150th Anniv of First Brazilian Stamps.
2131 **871** 2 p. multicoloured 80 55

1993. 11th Mexico City Marathon.
2132 **872** 1 p. 30 multicoloured . . 1·40 55

873 Emblem

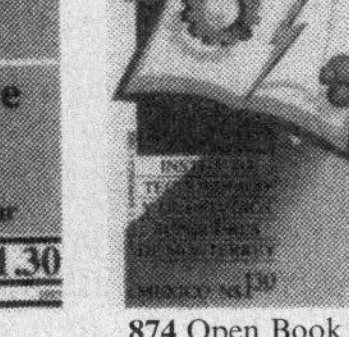

874 Open Book and Symbols

1993. "Solidarity".
2133 **873** 1 p. 30 multicoloured . . 50 35

1993. 50th Anniv of Monterrey Institute of Technology and Higher Education. Multicoloured.
2134 1 p. 30 Type **874** 50 35
2135 2 p. Buildings and mountains . 80 55
Nos. 2134/5 were issued together, se-tenant, forming a composite design.

875 Cogwheels and Emblem

876 Torreon

1993. 75th Anniv of Concamin.
2136 **875** 1 p. 30 multicoloured . . 50 35

1993. Centenary of Torreon.
2137 **876** 1 p. 30 multicoloured . . 50 35

877 Emblem

1993. "Europalia 93 Mexico" Festival.
2138 **877** 2 p. multicoloured 80 55

878 Globe in Envelope

879 Gen. Guadalupe Victoria

1993. World Post Day.
2139 **878** 2 p. multicoloured 80 55

1993. 150th Death Anniv of General Manuel Guadalupe Victoria (first President, 1824–28).
2140 **879** 1 p. 30 multicoloured . . 50 35

880 Emblem

881 Hands protecting Foetus

1993. National Civil Protection System and International Day for Reduction of Natural Disasters.
2141 **880** 1 p. 30 red, blk and yell . 50 35

1993. United Nations Decade of International Law.
2142 **881** 2 p. multicoloured 80 55

882 Torch Carrier

1993. 20th National Wheelchair Games.
2143 **882** 1 p. 30 multicoloured . . 50 35

883 Peon y Contreras

1993. 150th Birth Anniv of Jose Peon y Contreras (poet, dramatist and founder of National Romantic Theatre).
2144 **883** 1 p. 30 violet and black . 50 35

884 Horned Guan

885 Presents around Trees

1993. America. Endangered Birds. Multicoloured.
2145 2 p. Type **884** . . . . 1·25 80
2146 2 p. Resplendent quetzal on branch (horiz) . . . . . . 1·25 80

1993. Christmas. Multicoloured.
2147 1 p. 30 Type **885** 50 35
2148 1 p. 30 Three wise men (horiz) . 50 35

886 Satellites orbiting Earth

1993. "Solidarity".
2149 **886** 1 p. 30 multicoloured . . 50 35

887 School and Arms

1993. 125th Anniv of National Preparatory School.
2150 **887** 1 p. 30 multicoloured . . 50 35

888 Emblem on Map

1993. 55th Anniv of Municipal Workers Trade Union.
2151 **888** 1 p. 30 multicoloured . . 50 35

889 Hands

1993. 50th Anniv of Mexican Social Security Institute (3rd issue). Multicoloured.
2152 1 p. 30 Type **889** (social security) 50 35
2153 1 p. 30 Ball, building blocks, child's painting and dummy (day nurseries) 50 35

890 Mezcala Solidarity Bridge

1993. Tourism. Multicoloured.
2154 1 p. 30 Type **890** 50 35
2155 1 p. 30 Mexico City–Acapulco motorway 50 35

1993. Mexican Film Stars. As T **868**.
2156 1 p. 30 black and blue 50 35
2157 1 p. 30 black and orange . . . 50 35
2158 1 p. 30 black and green . . . 50 35
2159 1 p. 30 black and violet . . . 50 35
2160 1 p. 30 black and pink 50 35
DESIGNS:—No, 2156, Pedro Armendariz in "Juan Charrasqueado"; 2157, Maria Felix in "The Lover"; 2158, Pedro Infante in "Necesito dinero"; 2159, Jorge Negrete in "It is not enough to be a Peasant"; 2160, Dolores del Rio in "Flor Silvestre".

891 Estefania Castaneda Nunez

1994. 72nd Anniv of Secretariat of Public Education. Educationists. Multicoloured.
2161 1 p. 30 Type **891** 50 35
2162 1 p. 30 Lauro Aguirre Espinosa 50 35
2163 1 p. 30 Rafael Ramirez Castaneda 50 35
2164 1 p. 30 Moises Saenz Garza . 50 35
2165 1 p. 30 Gregorio Torres Quintero 50 35
2166 1 p. 30 Jose Vasconcelos . . . 50 35
2167 1 p. 30 Rosaura Zapato Cano . 50 35

892 Zapata (after H. Velarde)

893 Emblem and Worker

1994. 75th Death Anniv of Emiliano Zapata (revolutionary).
2168 **892** 1 p. 30 multicoloured . . 50 35

1994. 75th Anniv of I.L.O.
2169 **893** 2 p. multicoloured 80 50

894 Map and Emblem

895 "Earth and Communication" (frieze, detail)

1994. 50th Anniv of National Schools Building Programme Committee.
2170 **894** 1 p. 30 multicoloured . . 50 35

1994. 3rd Death Anniv of Francisco Zuniga (sculptor).
2171 **895** 1 p. 30 multicoloured . . 50 35

896 Flower and Children

1994. Children's Organization for Peace and Development.
2172 **896** 1 p. 30 multicoloured . . 50 35

897 Greater Flamingo

1994. DUMAC Nature Protection Organization.
2173 **897** 1 p. 30 multicoloured . . 75 60

898 Children and Silhouette of Absentee

1994. Care and Control of Minors.
2174 **898** 1 p. 30 black and green . . 50 35

899 Man and Letters

900 Route Map

1994. 34th World Advertising Congress, Cancun.

2175 **899** 2 p. multicoloured 80 35

1994. 50th Anniv of National Association of Importers and Exporters.

2176 **900** 1 p. 30 multicoloured . . 50 35

901 Head and Emblem

1994. International Telecommunications Day.

2177 **901** 2 p. multicoloured 80 55

902 Animals

1994. Yumka Wildlife Centre, Villahermosa.

2178 **902** 1 p. 30 multicoloured . . 75 60

903 Town Centre

904 Mother and Baby

1994. U.N.E.S.C.O. World Heritage Site, Zacatecas.

2179 **903** 1 p. 30 multicoloured . . 50 35

1994. Friendship Hospital. Mother and Child Health Month.

2180 **904** 1 p. 30 multicoloured . . 55 45

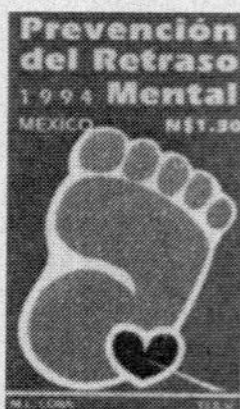

905 Foot and Heart

906 Song and Ornamental Birds

1994. Prevention of Mental Retardation.

2181 **905** 1 p. 30 multicoloured . . 55 45

1994. Nature Conservation. Multicoloured.

2182 1 p. 30 Type **906** . . . . . . 1·00 60
2183 1 p. 30 Game birds (silhouettes) 1·00 60
2184 1 p. 30 Threatened animals (silhouettes) . . . . 1·00 60
2185 1 p. 30 Animals in danger of extinction (silhouettes) . . . 1·00 60
2186 1 p. 30 Orange-fronted conures . . . . 1·00 60
2187 1 p. 30 Yellow-tailed oriole . . 1·00 60
2188 1 p. 30 Pyrrhuloxias . . . . . 1·00 60
2189 1 p. 30 Loggerhead shrike . . 1·00 60
2190 1 p. 30 Northern mockingbird . 1·00 60
2191 1 p. 30 Common turkey . . . 1·00 60
2192 1 p. 30 White-winged dove . . 1·00 60
2193 1 p. 30 Red-billed whistling duck . . . . 1·00 60
2194 1 p. 30 Snow goose . . . . . 1·00 60
2195 1 p. 30 Gambel's quail . . . . 1·00 60
2196 1 p. 30 Peregrine falcon . . . 1·00 60
2197 1 p. 30 Jaguar 80 50
2198 1 p. 30 Jaguarundi 80 50
2199 1 p. 30 Mantled howler monkey 80 50
2200 1 p. 30 Californian sealions . . 80 50
2201 1 p. 30 Pronghorn 80 50
2202 1 p. 30 Scarlet macaw . . . . 1·00 60
2203 1 p. 30 Mexican prairie dogs . 80 50
2204 1 p. 30 Wolf 80 50
2205 1 p. 30 American manatee . . 80 50

907 Player

908 Fish

1994. World Cup Football Championship, U.S.A. Multicoloured.

2206 2 p. Type **907** . . . . 1·00 70
2207 2 p. Goalkeeper . . . . . . 1·00 70

Nos. 2206/7 were issued together, se-tenant, forming a composite design.

1994. International Fishing Festival, Veracruz.

2208 **908** 1 p. 30 multicoloured . . 55 45

909 Stylized Figure and Emblem

910 "Butterflies" (Carmen Parra)

1994. 25th Anniv of Juvenile Integration Centres.

2209 **909** 1 p. 30 multicoloured . . 55 45

1994. 50th Aniv of Diplomatic Relations with Canada.

2210 **910** 2 p. multicoloured 90 65

911 Emblems

912 Emblem and Family

1994. 20th Anniv of National Population Council.

2211 **911** 1 p. 30 multicoloured . . 55 45

1994. International Year of the Family.

2212 **912** 2 p. multicoloured 90 60

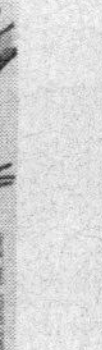

913 Runner breasting Tape

914 Giant Panda

1994. 12th Mexico City International Marathon.

2213 **913** 1 p. 30 multicoloured . . 55 45

1994. Chapultepec Zoo.

2214 **914** 1 p. 30 multicoloured . . 80 45

915 Tree

916 Anniversary Emblem

1994. Tree Day.

2215 **915** 1 p. 30 brown and green . 55 45

1994. 60th Anniv of Economic Culture Fund.

2216 **916** 1 p. 30 multicoloured . . 55 45

917 Statue and Light Rail Transit Train

918 Cathedral and Gardens

1994. 25th Anniv of Mexico City Transport System.

2217 **917** 1 p. 30 multicoloured . . 65 45

1994. 350th Anniv of Salvatierra City, Guanajuato.

2218 **918** 1 p. 30 purple, grey and black 55 45

919 State Flag and National Anthem

1994. National Symbols Week.

2219 **919** 1 p. 30 multicoloured . . 55 45

920 Building and Anniversary Emblem

921 Figures with Flags

1994. 40th Anniv of University City.

2220 **920** 1 p. 30 multicoloured . . 55 45

1994. 5th Solidarity Week.

2221 **921** 1 p. 30 black, red and green 55 45

922 Lopez Mateos

923 Palace Facade

1994. 25th Death Anniv of Adolfo Lopez Mateos (President, 1958–64).

2222 **922** 1 p. 30 multicoloured . . 55 45

1994. 60th Anniv of Palace of Fine Arts.

2223 **923** 1 p. 30 black and grey . . 55 45

924 Rings and "100"

1994. Centenary of International Olympic Committee.

2224 **924** 2 p. multicoloured 90 60

925 Quarter Horse (Juan Rayas)

1994. Horses. Paintings by artists named. Multicoloured.

2225 1 p. 30 Aztec horse (Heladio Velarde) 80 45
2226 1 p. 30 Type **925** 80 45
2227 1 p. 30 Quarter horse (Rayas) (different) 80 45
2228 1 p. 30 Vaquero on horseback (Velarde) 80 45
2229 1 p. 30 Aztec horse (Velarde) . 80 45
2230 1 p. 30 Rider with lance (Velarde) 80 45

926 Emblem

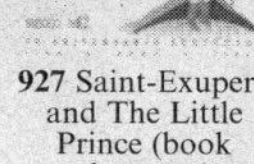

927 Saint-Exupery and The Little Prince (book character)

1994. Inauguration of 20th November National Medical Centre.

2231 **926** 1 p. 30 multicoloured . . 55 45

1994. 50th Death Anniv of Antoine de Saint-Exupery (pilot and writer).

2232 **927** 2 p. multicoloured 90 60

928 Man writing Letters to Woman

929 Urban Postman on Bicycle

1994. World Post Day.

2233 **928** 2 p. multicoloured 90 60

1994. America. Postal Transport. Multicoloured.

2234 2 p. Type **929** 85 50
2235 2 p. Rural postman on rail tricycle . . . . 1·40 75

Nos. 2234/5 were issued together, se-tenant, forming a composite design.

930 Couple (Sofia Bassi)

1994. Ancestors' Day.

2236 **930** 1 p. 30 multicoloured . . 55 45

931 Water Drop and Hand

932 Dr. Mora

1994. National Clean Water Programme.

2237 **931** 1 p. 30 multicoloured . . 55 45

1994. Birth Bicentenary of Dr. Jose Maria Luis Mora (journalist and politician).

2238 **932** 1 p. 30 multicoloured . . 55 45

933 Theatre and Soler (actor)

1994. 15th Anniv of Fernando Soler Theatre, Saltillo, Coahuila.

2239 **933** 1 p. 30 multicoloured . . 55 45

MINIMUM PRICE

The minimum price quoted is 10p which represents a handling charge rather than a basis for valuing common stamps. For further notes about prices see introductory pages.

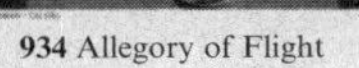

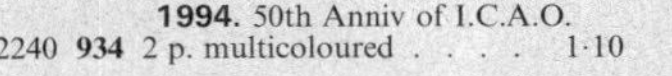

934 Allegory of Flight　**935** Museum's Central Pillar

1994. 50th Anniv of I.C.A.O.
2240 **934** 2 p. multicoloured . . . . 1·10 60

1994. 30th Anniv of National Anthropological Museum.
2241 **935** 1 p. 30 multicoloured . . 55 45

936 Theatrical Masks　**937** Allende

1994. 60th Anniv of National Association of Actors.
2242 **936** 1 p. 30 multicoloured . . 55 45

1994. 225th Birth Anniv of Ignacio Allende (independence hero).
2243 **937** 1 p. 30 multicoloured . . 55 45

938 Chapultepec Castle

1994. 50th Anniv of National History Museum.
2244 **938** 1 p. 30 multicoloured . . 55 45

939 Dome　**940** Anniversary Emblem

1994. Centenary of Coahuila School.
2245 **939** 1 p. 30 multicoloured . . 55 45

1994. 40th Anniv of Pumas University Football Club.
2246 **940** 1 p. 30 blue and gold . . 55 45

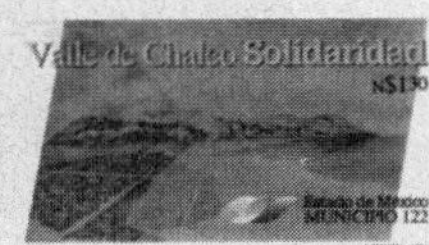

941 Decorated Tree　**942** Valley

1994. Christmas. Multicoloured.
2247 2 p. Type **941** 80 60
2248 2 p. Couple watching shooting star (horiz) 80 60

1994. "Solidarity". Chalco Valley.
2249 **942** 1 p. 30 multicoloured . . 20 15

943 Ines de la Cruz (after Miguel de Cabrera)　**944** X-Ray of Hand and Rontgen

1995. 300th Birth Anniv of Juana Ines de la Cruz (mystic poet).
2250 **943** 1 p. 80 multicoloured . . 30 20

1995. Centenary of Discovery of X-Rays by Wilhelm Rontgen.
2251 **944** 2 p. multicoloured . . . 35 25

945 Ignacio Altamirano　**946** Emblem

1995. Teachers' Day.
2252 **945** 1 p. 80 black, grn & bl . 30 20

1995. World Telecommunications Day. "Telecommunications and the Environment".
2253 **946** 2 p. 70 multicoloured . . 70 55

947 Anniversary Emblem　**948** Marti

1995. 40th Anniv of National Institute of Public Administration.
2254 **947** 1 p. 80 grn, mve & lilac . 30 20

1995. Death Centenary of Jose Marti (Cuban writer and revolutionary).
2255 **948** 2 p. 70 multicoloured . . 70 55

949 Carranza　**950** Kite

1995.. 75th Death Anniv of Venustiano Carranza (President 1914–20).
2256 **949** 1 p. 80 multicoloured . . 30 20

1995.. 20th Anniv of National Tourist Organization.
2257 **950** 2 p. 70 multicoloured . . 70 55

951 Drugs, Skull and Unhappy Face　**952** Cardenas del Rio

1995.. International Day against Drug Abuse and Trafficking. Multicoloured.
2258 1 p. 80 Type **951** 85 20
2259 1 p. 80 Drug addict on swing . 85 20
2260 1 p. 80 Faces behind bars . . 85 20

1995. Birth Centenary of Gen. Lazaro Cardenas del Rio (President 1934–40).
2261 **952** 1 p. 80 black 30 20

953 Man with White Stick and Hand reading Braille

1995. 125th Anniv of National Blind School. Mult.
2262 **953** 1 p. 30 brown and black . 20 15

954 Pintails

1995. Animals. Multicoloured.
2295 2 p. 70 Type **954** 90 50
2296 2 p. 70 Belted kingfisher . . . 90 50
2297 2 p. 70 Orange tiger 90 50
2298 2 p. 70 Hoary bat 90 50

955 Runners　**956** Envelopes

1995. 13th International Marathon, Mexico City.
2299 **955** 2 p. 70 multicoloured . . 40 25

1995. 16th Congress of Postal Union of the Americas, Spain and Portugal, Mexico City.
2300 **956** 2 p. 70 multicoloured . . 40 25

957 Pasteur　**958** Hands holding Envelopes

1995. Death Centenary of Louis Pasteur (chemist).
2301 **957** 2 p. 70 blue, black and green 40 25

1995. World Post Day.
2302 **958** 2 p. 70 multicoloured . . 40 25

959 Basket of Shopping　**960** Anniversary Emblem

1995. World Food Day.
2303 **959** 1 p. 80 multicoloured . . 30 20

1995. 50th Anniv of F.A.O.
2304 **960** 2 p. 70 multicoloured . . 40 25

961 Elias Calles　**962** Cuauhtemoc

1995. 50th Death Anniv of General Plutarco Elias Calles (President 1924–28).
2305 **961** 1 p. 80 multicoloured . . 30 20

1995. 500th Birth Anniv of Cuauhtemoc (Aztec Emperor of Tenochtitlan).
2306 **962** 1 p. 80 multicoloured . . 30 20

963 National Flag, National Anthem and Constitution　**964** Flags as Tail of Dove

1995. National Constitution and Patriotic Symbols Day.
2307 **963** 1 p. 80 multicoloured . . 30 20

1995. 50th Anniv of U.N.O.
2308 **964** 2 p. 70 multicoloured . . 40 25

965 Airplane, Streamlined Train and Motor Vehicle

1995. International Passenger Travel Year.
2309 **965** 2 p. 70 multicoloured . . 80 25

966 "The Holy Family" (Andres de Concha)

1995.. 30th Anniv of Museum of Mexican Art in the Vice-regency Period.
2310 **966** 1 p. 80 multicoloured . . 30 20

967 Pedro Maria Anaya

1995. Generals in Mexican History. Each black, yellow and gold.
2311 1 p. 80 Type **967** 30 20
2312 1 p. 80 Felipe Berriozabal . . 30 20
2313 1 p. 80 Santos Degollado . . 30 20
2314 1 p. 80 Sostenes Rocha . . . 30 20
2315 1 p. 80 Leandro Valle 30 20
2316 1 p. 80 Ignacio Zaragoza . . . 30 20

968 Children playing in Garden (Pablo Osorio Gomez)　**969** Emblem

1995. Christmas. Children's Drawings. Multicoloured.
2317 1 p. 80 Type **968** 30 20
2318 2 p. 70 Adoration of the Wise Men (Oscar Enrique Carrillo) 40 25

1995. 10th Anniv of Mexican Health Foundation.
2319 **969** 1 p. 80 multicoloured . . 30 20

970 Ocelot　**971** Louis Lumiere and Cine-camera

1995. Nature Conservation.
2320 **970** 1 p. 80 multicoloured . . 30 20

1995. Centenary of Motion Pictures.
2321 **971** 1 p. 80 black, mauve and blue 30 20

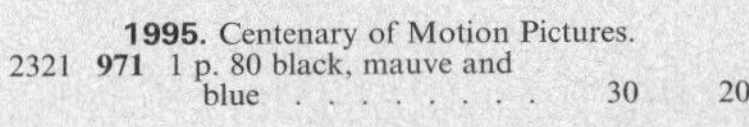

972 Library

1995. National Education Library, Mexico City.
2322 **972** 1 p. 80 green, blue and yellow 30 20

973 "Proportions of Man" (Leonardo da Vinci)   **974** Pedro Vargas

1995. 50th Anniv of National Science and Arts Prize.
2323 **973** 1 p. 80 multicoloured . . 30 20

1995. Radio Personalities. Multicoloured.
2324 1 p. 80 Type **974** 85 20
2325 1 p. 80 Agustin Lara 85 20
2326 1 p. 80 Aguila Sisters 85 20
2327 1 p. 80 Tona "La Negra" . . 85 20
2328 1 p. 80 F. Gabilondo Soler "Cri-Cri" 85 20
2329 1 p. 80 Emilio Teuro 85 20
2330 1 p. 80 Gonzalo Curiel . . . 85 20
2331 1 p. 80 Lola Beltran 85 20

975 Robot Hand holding Optic Fibres

1995. 25th Anniv of Science and Technology Council.
2332 **975** 1 p. 80 multicoloured . . 30 20

976 Airplane

1996. National Aviation Day. Multicoloured.
2333 1 p. 80 Type **976** 70 20
2334 1 p. 80 Squadron 201, 1945 . . 70 20
2335 2 p. 70 Ley Airport 90 25
2336 2 p. 70 Modern jetliner and biplane 90 25

977 Child and Caso

1996. Birth Centenary of Dr. Alfonso Caso (anthropologist).
2337 **977** 1 p. 80 multicoloured . . 30 20

978 Silverio Perez, Carlos Arruza and Manolo Martinez

1996. 50th Anniv of Plaza Mexico (bullring). Matadors. Multicoloured.
2338 1 p. 80 Type **978** 30 20
2339 2 p. 70 Roldolfo Gaona, Fermin Espinosa and Lorenzo Garza 40 25

Nos. 2338/9 were issued together, se-tenant, forming a composite design of the bullring.

979 Bag of Groceries

1996. 20th Anniv of Federal Consumer Council.
2340 **979** 1 p. 80 multicoloured . . 30 20

980 "Treatment of Fracture" (from Sahagun Codex)

1996. 50th Anniv of Mexican Society of Orthopaedics.
2341 **980** 1 p. 80 multicoloured . . 30 20

981 Rulfo

1996. 10th Death Anniv of Juan Rulfo (writer).
2342 **981** 1 p. 80 multicoloured . . 30 20

982 Anniversary Emblem and Map of Mexico   **983** Healthy Hand reaching for Sick Hand

1996. 60th Anniv of National Polytechnic Institute.
2343 **982** 1 p. 80 grey, black and red 30 20

1996. United Nations Decade against the Abuse and Illicit Trafficking of Drugs. Multicoloured.
2344 1 p. 80 Type **983** 60 15
2345 1 p. 80 Man helping addict out of dark hole 60 15
2346 2 p. 70 Stylized figures 90 25

984 Gymnastics   **985** Cameraman and Film Frames of Couples

1996. Olympic Games, Atlanta, U.S.A. Multicoloured.
2347 1 p. 80 Type **984** 45 15
2348 1 p. 80 Hurdling 45 15
2349 2 p. 70 Football 65 25
2350 2 p. 70 Running 65 25
2351 2 p. 70 Show jumping 65 25

1996. Centenary of Mexican Films. Multicoloured.
2352 1 p. 80 Type **985** 25 15
2353 1 p. 80 Camera and film frames of individuals 25 15

986 Scales

1996. 60th Anniv of Fiscal Tribunal.
2354 **986** 1 p. 80 multicoloured . . 25 15

987 Runners' Feet

1996. 14th Mexico City International Marathon.
2355 **987** 2 p. 70 multicoloured . . 40 25

988 Flask, Open Books, Atomic Model and Microscope

1996. Science.
2356 **988** 1 p. 80 multicoloured . . 25 15

989 "Allegory of Foundation of Zacatecas" (anon)

1996. 450th Anniv of Zacatecas.
2357 **989** 1 p. 80 multicoloured . . 25 15

990 Rural Education   **992** Emblem

1996. 25th Anniv of National Council for the Improvement of Education.
2358 **990** 1 p. 80 multicoloured . . 25 15

1996. Family Planning Month.
2360 **992** 1 p. 80 green, mauve and blue 25 15

993 Flag of the "Three Guarantees", 1821

1996. 175th Anniv of Declaration of Independence.
2361 **993** 1 p. 80 multicoloured . . 25 15

994 Blue Morpho, Monkey, Harpy Eagle and other Birds

1996. Nature Conservation. Multicoloured.
2362 1 p. 80 Type **994** 55 15
2363 1 p. 80 Turtle dove, yellow grosbeak with chicks in nest, trogon and hummingbird . 55 15
2364 1 p. 80 Mountains, monarchs (butterflies) in air and American black bear with cub 55 15
2365 1 p. 80 Fishing buzzard, mule deer, lupins and monarchs (butterflies) on plant . . . 55 15
2366 1 p. 80 Scarlet macaws, monarchs, toucan, peafowl and spider monkey hanging from tree 55 15
2367 1 p. 80 Resplendent quetzal, emerald toucanet, bromeliads and tiger-cat 55 15
2368 1 p. 80 Parrots, white-tailed deer and rabbit by river 55 15
2369 1 p. 80 Snake, wolf, puma and lizard on rock and blue-capped bird 55 15
2370 1 p. 80 Coyote, prairie dogs at burrow, quail on branch, deer, horned viper and caracara on cactus 55 15
2371 1 p. 80 Jaguar, euphonias, long-tailed bird, crested bird and bat 55 15
2372 1 p. 80 "Martucha", peacock, porcupine, butterfly and green snake 55 15
2373 1 p. 80 Blue magpie, green-headed bird, owl, woodpecker and hummingbird by river . 55 15
2374 1 p. 80 Cinnamon cuckoo in tree, fox by river and green macaws in tree 55 15
2375 1 p. 80 Wild sheep by rocks, bird on ocotillo plant, bats, owl, lynx and woodpecker on cactus 55 15
2376 1 p. 80 Ant-eater climbing sloping tree, jaguarundi, bat, orchid and ocellated turkey in undergrowth 55 15
2377 1 p. 80 Ocelot, "grison", coral snake, "temazate", paca and otter by river 55 15
2378 1 p. 80 Grey squirrel in tree, salamander, beaver, bird, shrew-mole, mountain hen and racoon by river 55 15
2379 1 p. 80 Butterfly, trogon in red tree, "chachalaca", crested magpie and "tejon" 55 15
2380 1 p. 80 Bat, "tlalcoyote", "rata neotoma", "chichimoco", hare, cardinal (bird), lizard, kangaroo rat and tortoise . 55 15
2381 1 p. 80 Beetle on leaf, tapir, tree frog and "tunpache" . . . 55 15
2382 1 p. 80 Crocodile, insect, cup fungus, boa constrictor and butterfly 55 15
2383 1 p. 80 Armadillo, "tlacuache", iguana, turkey and butterfly . 55 15
2384 1 p. 80 Turkey, collared peccary, zorilla, lizard, rattlesnake and mouse 55 15
2385 1 p. 80 Cacomistle, "matraca", lark, collared lizard and cacti 55 15

Nos. 2362/85 were issued together, se-tenant, forming a composite design of habitats and wildlife under threat.

995 Bird with Letter in Beak   **996** Institute

1996. World Post Day.
2386 **995** 2 p. 70 multicoloured . . 40 25

1996. 50th Anniv of Salvador Zubiran National Nutrition Institute.
2387 **996** 1 p. 80 multicoloured . . 25 15

997 Constantino de Tarnava   **998** "Portrait of a Womam" (Baltasar de Echave Ibia)

1996. 75th Anniv of Radio Broadcasting in Mexico.
2388 **997** 1 p. 80 multicoloured . . 25 15

1996. Virreinal Art Gallery. Multicoloured.
2389 1 p. 80 Type **998** 50 15
2390 1 p. 80 "Portrait of the Child Joaquin Manuel Fernandez de Santa Cruz" (Nicolas Rodriguez Xuarez) 50 15
2391 1 p. 80 "Portrait of Dona Maria Luisa Gonzaga Foncerrada y Labarrieta" (Jose Maria Vazquez) 50 15
2392 1 p. 80 "Archangel Michael" (Luis Juarez) 50 15
2393 2 p. 70 "Virgin of the Apocalypse" (Miguel Cabrera) 65 25

999 Isidro Fabela and Genaro Estrada   **1000** Maize

1996. "Precursors of Foreign Policy".
2394 **999** 1 p. 80 multicoloured . . 25 15

1996. World Food Day.
2395 **1000** 2p. 70 multicoloured . . 40 25

1001 Underground Train around Globe

1996. International Metros Conference.
2396 **1001** 2 p. 70 multicoloured . . 40 25

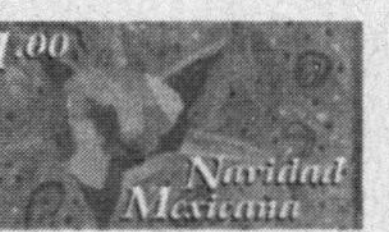

1002 Star (Elias Martin del Campo)

1996. Christmas. Multicoloured.
2397 1 p. Type **1002** 15 10
2398 1 p. 80 Man with star-shaped bundles on stick (Ehecatl Cabrera Franco) (vert) . . 25 15

1003 Henestrosa

1996. Andres Henestrosa (writer) Commemoration.
2399 **1003** 1 p. 80 multicoloured . . 25 15

1004 Old and New Institute Buildings

1005 Emblem

1996. 50th Anniv of National Cancer Institute.
2400 **1004** 1 p. 80 multicoloured . . 25 15

1996. Paisano Programme.
2401 **1005** 2 p. 70 multicoloured . . 40 25

1006 Painting

1996. Birth Centenary of David Alfaro Siqueiros (painter).
2402 **1006** 1 p. 80 multicoloured . . 25 15

1007 Dr. Jose Maria Barcelo de Villagran

1996. 32nd National Assembly of Surgeons.
2403 **1007** 1 p. 80 multicoloured . . 25 15

1008 Black Bears

1996. Nature Conservation.
2404 **1008** 1 p. 80 multicoloured . . 25 15

1009 Smiling Sun

1010 Library

1996. 50th Anniv of U.N.I.C.E.F.
2405 **1009** 1 p. 80 multicoloured . . 25 15

1996. 350th Anniv of Palafoxiana Library, Puebla.
2406 **1010** 1 p. 80 multicoloured . . 25 15

1011 Sphere and Atomic Symbol

1012 Sun's Rays and Earth

1996. National Institute for Nuclear Research.
2407 **1011** 1 p. 80 multicoloured . . 25 15

1996. World Day for the Preservation of the Ozone Layer.
2408 **1012** 1 p. 80 multicoloured . . 25 15

1013 Sculpture

1014 Pellicer (after D. Rivera)

1996. 30 Years of Work by Sebastian (sculptor).
2409 **1013** 1 p. 80 multicoloured . . 25 15

1997. Tourism. As Nos. 2263 etc but with value expressed as "$".

2410	1 p. Colima	15	10
2411	1 p. 80 Chiapas	25	15
2412	2 p. Colima	30	20
2413	2 p. Guanajuato	30	20
2414	2 p. 30 Chiapas	35	25
2415	2 p. 50 Queretaro	35	25
2416	2 p. 60 Colima	40	25
2417	2 p. 70 Mexico City	40	25
2418	3 p. Type **869**	45	30
2419	3 p. 10 Coahuila	45	30
2420	3 p. 40 Sinaloa	50	35
2421	3 p. 50 Mexico City	50	35
2421a	3 p. 60 Sonora	50	35
2421b	3 p. 60 Coahuila	50	35
2421c	3 p. 70 Campeche	50	35
2422	4 p. Michoacan (vert)	60	40
2422a	4 p. 20 Guanajuato	55	35
2423	4 p. 40 Yucatan	65	45
2424	4 p. 90 Sonora	70	45
2425	5 p. Queretaro	70	45
2426	5 p. Colima	65	45
2426a	5 p. 30 Michoacan (vert)	70	45
2426b	5 p. 90 Queretaro	80	55
2427	6 p. Zacatacas (vert)	85	55
2427a	6 p. 50 Sinaloa	85	50
2428	7 p. Sonora	1·00	65
2428a	8 p. Zacatecas (vert)	1·10	75
2429	8 p. 50 Mexico City	1·25	85

1997. Birth Centenary of Carlos Pellicer (lyricist).
2435 **1014** 2 p. 30 multicoloured . . 35 25

1015 Eloy Blanco (after Oswaldo)

1997. Birth Centenary (1996) of Andres Eloy Blanco (poet).
2436 **1015** 3 p. 40 multicoloured . . 50 35

1016 Book, Inkwell and Pencil

1017 Tree, Globe and Atomic Cloud

1997. Confederation of American Educationalists' International Summit Conference.
2437 **1016** 3 p. 40 multicoloured . . 50 35

1997. 30th Anniv of Tlatelolco Treaty (Latin American and Caribbean treaty banning nuclear weapons).
2438 **1017** 3 p. 40 multicoloured . . 50 35

1019 Felipe Angeles

1020 Woman dancing

1997. Noted Generals. Multicoloured.
2440 2 p. 30 Type **1019** 35 25
2441 2 p. 30 Joaquin Amaro Dominguez 35 25
2442 2 p. 30 Mariano Escobedo . . 35 25
2443 2 p. 30 Jacinto Trevino Glez . 35 25
2444 2 p. 30 Candido Aguilar Vargas 35 25
2445 2 p. 30 Francisco Urquizo . . 35 25

1997. International Women's Day.
2446 **1020** 2 p. 30 multicoloured . . 35 25

1021 "Grammar" (Juan Correa)

1997. 1st International Spanish Language Congress.
2447 **1021** 3 p. 40 multicoloured . . 50 35

1022 Chavez

1997. Birth Centenary of Dr. Ignacio Chavez.
2448 **1022** 2 p. 30 multicoloured . . 35 25

1023 State Emblem and Venustiano Carranza (President 1915–20)

1997. 80th Anniv of 1917 Constitution.
2449 **1023** 2 p. 30 multicoloured . . 35 25

1024 Yanez

1997. 50th Anniv of First Edition of "At the Water's Edge" by Agustin Yanez.
2450 **1024** 2 p. 30 multicoloured . . 35 25

1025 Mexican Mythological Figures (Luis Nishizawa)

1997. Centenary of Japanese Immigration.
2451 **1025** 3 p. 40 red, gold and black 50 35

1026 Rafael Ramirez

1027 University

1997. Teachers' Day.
2452 **1026** 2 p. 30 green and black . 35 25

1997. 40th Anniv of Autonomous University of Lower California.
2453 **1027** 2 p. 30 multicoloured . . 35 25

1028 Dove flying Free

1029 Freud

1997. International Day against Illegal Use and Illicit Trafficking of Drugs. Multicoloured.
2454 2 p. 30 Type **1028** 35 25
2455 3 p. 40 Dove imprisoned behind bars 50 35
2456 3 p. 40 Man opening cage . . 50 35
Nos. 2454/6 were issued together, se-tenant, forming a composite design.

1997. 58th Death Anniv of Sigmund Freud (pioneer of psychoanalysis).
2457 **1029** 2 p. 30 blue, green and violet 35 25

1030 School Arms

1031 Emblem

1997. Centenary of Naval School.
2458 **1030** 2 p. 30 multicoloured . . 35 25

1997. Introduction of New Social Security Law.
2459 **1031** 2 p. 30 multicoloured . . 30 20

1032 Globes and Anniversary Emblem

1997. 60th Anniv of National Bank of Foreign Commerce.
2460 **1032** 3 p. 40 multicoloured . . 40 25

1033 Common Porpoises

1997. Nature Conservation.
2461 **1033** 2 p. 30 multicoloured . . 30 20

1034 Passenger Airliners, 1947 and 1997

1997. 50th Anniv of Mexican Air Pilots' College.
2462 **1034** 2 p. 30 multicoloured . . 30 20

1035 Runners

1997. 15th Mexico City Marathon.
2463 **1035** 3 p. 40 multicoloured . . 40 25

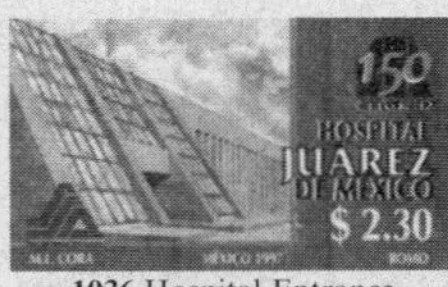

1036 Hospital Entrance

1997. 150th Anniv of Juarez Hospital.
2464 **1036** 2 p. 30 multicoloured . . 30 20

1037 Battle of Padierna

1997. 150th Anniversaries of Battles. Multicoloured.
2465 2 p. 30 Type **1037** 30 20
2466 2 p. 30 Battle of Churubusco . 30 20
2467 2 p. 30 Battle of Molino del Rey 30 20
2468 2 p. 30 Defence of Chapultepec Fort 30 20

1038 Prieto  **1039** Commemorative Cross

1997. Death Centenary of Guillermo Prieto (writer).
2469 **1038** 2 p. 30 blue 30 20

1997. 150th Anniv of Mexican St. Patrick's Battalion.
2470 **1039** 3 p. 40 multicoloured . . 40 25

1040 Emblem  **1041** Bird carrying Letter

1997. Adolescent Reproductive Health Month.
2471 **1040** 2 p. 30 multicoloured . . 30 20

1997. World Post Day. Multicoloured.
2472 3 p. 40 Type **1041** 40 25
2473 3 p. 40 Heinrich von Stephan (founder of U.P.U.) (horiz) . 40 25

1042 Gomez Morin  **1043** Hospital

1997. Birth Centenary of Manuel Gomez Morin (politician).
2474 **1042** 2 p. 30 multicoloured . . 30 20

1997. 50th Anniv of Dr. Manuel Gea Gonzalez General Hospital.
2475 **1043** 2 p. 30 multicoloured . . 30 20

1044 Emblem  **1045** Children celebrating Christmas (Ana Botello)

1997. 75th Anniv of Mexican Bar College of Law.
2476 **1044** 2 p. 30 red and black . . 30 20

1997. Christmas. Children's Paintings. Multicoloured.
2477 2 p. 30 Type **1045** 30 20
2478 2 p. 30 Children playing blind-man's-buff (Adrian Laris) . 30 20

1046 Emblem and Hospital Facade

1997. Centenary of Central University Hospital, Chihuahua.
2479 **1046** 2 p. 30 multicoloured . . 30 20

1047 Molina and Nobel Medal

1997. Dr. Mario Molina (winner of Nobel Prize for Chemistry, 1995).
2480 **1047** 3 p. 40 multicoloured . . 40 25

1048 Products and Storage Shelves  **1049** "Buildings" (Jose Chavez Morado)

1997. National Chamber of Baking Industry. Multicoloured.
2481 2 p. 30 Type **1048** 30 20
2482 2 p. 30 Baker putting loaves in oven 30 20
2483 2 p. 30 Wedding cake, ingredients and baker . . . 30 20
Nos. 2481/3 were issued together, se-tenant, forming a composite design.

1997. 25th Cervantes Festival, Guanajuato.
2484 **1049** 2 p. 30 multicoloured . . 30 20

1050 Galleon and Map of Loreto, California  **1051** Sword and Rifle

1997. 300th Anniv of Loreto.
2485 **1050** 2 p. 30 multicoloured . . 30 20

1998. 50th Anniv of Military Academy, Puebla.
2486 **1051** 2 p. 30 multicoloured . . 30 20

1052 Hands holding Children on Heart  **1053** Dancers (5th of May Festival)

1998. International Women's Day.
2487 **1052** 2 p. 30 multicoloured . . 30 20

1998. Festivals.
2488 **1053** 3 p. 50 multicoloured . . 45 30

1054 Eiffel Tower, Player and Flag  **1055** Sierra

1998. World Cup Football Championship, France. Multicoloured.
2489 2 p. 30 Type **1054** 30 20
2490 2 p. 30 Mascot, Eiffel Tower and flag 30 20

1998. 150th Birth Anniv of Justo Sierra (educationist).
2492 **1055** 2 p. 30 multicoloured . . 30 20

1056 Zubiran

1998. Birth Centenary of Salvador Zubiran (physician).
2493 **1056** 2 p. 30 multicoloured . . 30 20

1057 Emblem

1998. 50th Anniv of Organization of American States.
2494 **1057** 3 p. 40 multicoloured . . 40 25

1058 University Emblem 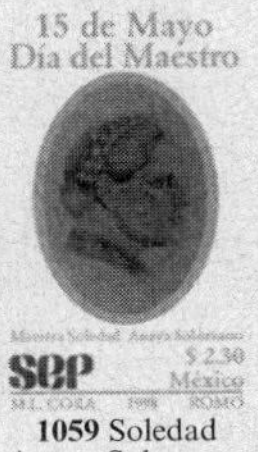 **1059** Soledad Anaya Solorzano

1998. 25th Anniv of People's Autonomous University of Puebla State.
2495 **1058** 2 p. 30 red, silver and black 30 20

1998. Teachers' Day.
2496 **1059** 2 p. 30 bistre, black and cream 30 20

1060 Crops

1998. 250th Anniv of Tamaulipas (formerly New Santander) (1st issue).
2497 **1060** 2 p. 30 multicoloured . . 30 20
See also Nos. 2548.

1061 Macuilxochitl

1998. 20th Anniv of Sports Lottery.
2498 **1061** 2 p. 30 multicoloured . . 30 20

1062 Manila Galleon

1998. Centenary of Philippine Independence.
2499 **1062** 3 p. 40 multicoloured . . 45 30

1063 Garcia Lorca

1998. Birth Centenary of Federico Garcia Lorca (poet).
2501 **1063** 3 p. 40 multicoloured . . 40 25

1064 Emblems

1998. 50th Anniv of Universal Declaration of Human Rights.
2502 **1064** 3 p. 40 green and black . 45 30

1065 Open Book and Dove  **1067** Tree

1066 Alfonso Herrera (founder) and Leopard

1998. International Day against the Use and Illegal Trafficking of Drugs.
2503 **1065** 2 p. 30 multicoloured . . 30 20

1998. 75th Anniv of Chapultepec Zoo.
2504 **1066** 2 p. 30 multicoloured . . 30 20

1998. Tree Day.
2505 **1067** 2 p. 30 multicoloured . . 30 20

1068 St. Peter and St. Paul's Monastery, Teposcolula

1998. Inauguration of Philatelic Museum, Oaxaca. Multicoloured.
2506 2 p. 30 Type **1068** 30 20
2507 2 p. 30 Clay pot, San Bartolo Coyotepec 30 20
2508 2 p. 30 "The Road" (painting, Francisco Toledo) 30 20
2509 2 p. 30 Gold pectoral from Tomb 7, Monte Alban . . . 30 20

1069 Juarez

1998. 126th Death Anniv of Benito Juarez (President 1859–64 and 1867–72).
2510 **1069** 2 p. 30 stone, black and brown 30 20

1070 Cultural Museum

1998. St. Dominic's Cultural Centre, Oaxaca. Multicoloured.
2511 2 p. 30 Type **1070** 30 20
2512 2 p. 30 Francisco de Burgoa Library 30 20
2513 2 p. 30 Historical botanic garden 30 20
2514 3 p. 40 St. Dominic's Monastery (after Teodoro Velasco) 45 30

1071 Frigate Bird, Blue-footed Booby, Whales and Cacti

1998. Marine Life. Multicoloured.
2515 2 p. 30 Type **1071** 30 20
2516 2 p. 30 Albatross, humpback whale and seagulls 30 20
2517 2 p. 30 Tail of whale and swordfish 30 20
2518 2 p. 30 Fish eagle, flamingo, herons and dolphins 30 20
2519 2 p. 30 Turtles, flamingoes, cormorant and palm tree . . 30 20
2520 2 p. 30 Oystercatcher, turn-stone, elephant seal and sealions 30 20
2521 2 p. 30 Dolphin, turtle, seagulls and swallows 30 20
2522 2 p. 30 Killer whale, dolphins and ray 30 20
2523 2 p. 30 Flamingoes, pelican, kingfishers and spider . . . 30 20
2524 2 p. 30 Crocodile, roseate spoonbill and tiger heron . . 30 20
2525 2 p. 30 Schools of sardines and anchovies 30 20

2526 2 p. 30 Turtle, squid, gold-finned tunnyfish and shark . 30 20
2527 2 p. 30 Jellyfish, dolphins and fishes 30 20
2528 2 p. 30 Dolphin (fish), barracudas and haddock . . 30 20
2529 2 p. 30 Manatee, fishes, anemone and coral 30 20
2530 2 p. 30 Seaweed, starfish, coral and fishes 30 20
2531 2 p. 30 Hammerhead shark, angelfish, gudgeon, eels and coral 30 20
2532 2 p. 30 Shrimps, ray and other fishes 30 20
2533 2 p. 30 Octopus, bass, crayfish and other fishes 30 20
2534 2 p. 30 Turtle, porcupinefish, coral, angelfish and other fishes 30 20
2535 2 p. 30 Abalone, clams, razor clam, crayfish and anemone . 30 20
2536 2 p. 30 Seahorses, angelfishes, coral and shells 30 20
2537 2 p. 30 Octopus, turtle, crab and moray eel 30 20
2538 2 p. 30 Butterflyfishes and other fishes 30 20
2539 2 p. 30 Reef shark, angelfish and corals 30 20

Nos. 2515/39 were issued together, se-tenant, forming a composite design.

1072 Runners

1998. 16th International Marathon, Mexico City.
2540 **1072** 3 p. 40 multicoloured . . 45 30

1073 Aztec Deity

1998. World Tourism Day.
2541 **1073** 3 p. 40 multicoloured . . 45 30

1074 Lucas Alaman (founder)

1998. 175th Anniv of National Archives.
2542 **1074** 2 p. 30 green, red and black 30 20

1075 Emblem **1076** Stylised Couple

1998. 75th Anniv of Interpol.
2543 **1075** 3 p. 40 multicoloured . . 45 30

1998. Healthy Pregnancy Month.
2544 **1076** 2 p. 30 multicoloured . . 30 20

1077 Painting by Luis Nishizawa

1998.
2545 **1077** 2 p. 30 multicoloured . . 30 20

1078 Key and Globe

1998. World Post Day.
2546 **1078** 3 p. 40 multicoloured . . 45 30

1079 College Campus

1998. 175th Anniv of Military College.
2547 **1079** 2 p. 30 multicoloured . . 30 20

1080 Map

1998. 250th Anniv of Tamaulipas (formerly New Santander) (2nd issue).
2548 **1080** 2 p. 30 multicoloured . . 30 20

1081 Golden Eagle

1998. Nature Conservation.
2549 **1081** 2 p. 30 multicoloured . . 30 20

1082 Woman and Potatoes

1998. World Food Day.
2550 **1082** 3 p. 30 multicoloured . . 45 30

1083 Mexico arrowed on Globe

1998. National Migration Week.
2551 **1083** 2 p. 30 multicoloured . . 30 20

1084 Jimenez

1998. 25th Death Anniv of Jose Alfredo Jimenez (writer).
2552 **1084** 2 p. 30 multicoloured . . 30 20

1085 Oil Rig and Emblem **1087** Franciscan Monastery, Colima

1086 Mexican Stone Carving and Eiffel Tower

1998. 25th Anniv of Mexican Petroleum Engineers' Association.
2553 **1085** 3 p. 40 multicoloured . . 45 30

1998. Mexican–French Economic and Cultural Co-operation.
2554 **1086** 3 p. 40 multicoloured . . 45 30

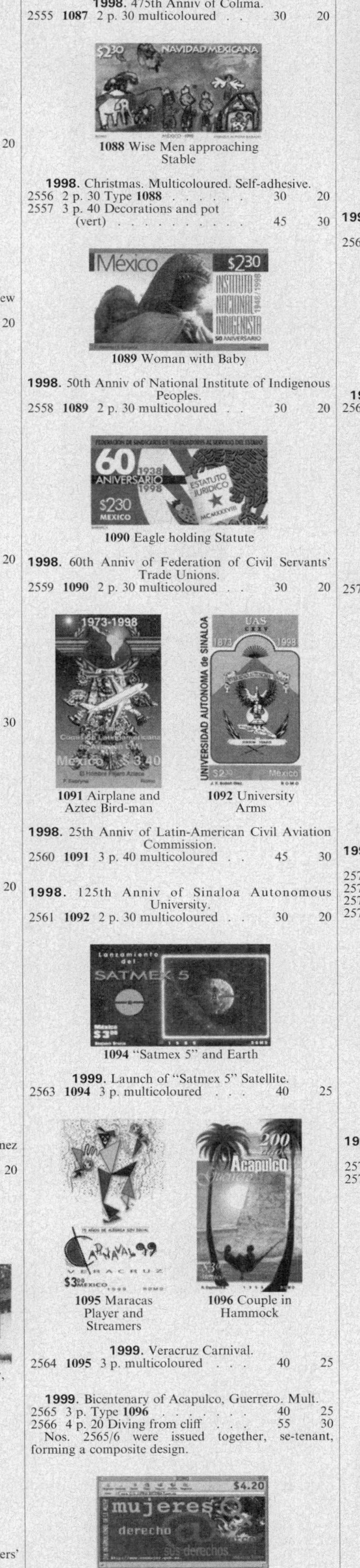

1998. 475th Anniv of Colima.
2555 **1087** 2 p. 30 multicoloured . . 30 20

1088 Wise Men approaching Stable

1998. Christmas. Multicoloured. Self-adhesive.
2556 2 p. 30 Type **1088** 30 20
2557 3 p. 40 Decorations and pot (vert) 45 30

1089 Woman with Baby

1998. 50th Anniv of National Institute of Indigenous Peoples.
2558 **1089** 2 p. 30 multicoloured . . 30 20

1090 Eagle holding Statute

1998. 60th Anniv of Federation of Civil Servants' Trade Unions.
2559 **1090** 2 p. 30 multicoloured . . 30 20

1091 Airplane and Aztec Bird-man **1092** University Arms

1998. 25th Anniv of Latin-American Civil Aviation Commission.
2560 **1091** 3 p. 40 multicoloured . . 45 30

1998. 125th Anniv of Sinaloa Autonomous University.
2561 **1092** 2 p. 30 multicoloured . . 30 20

1094 "Satmex 5" and Earth

1999. Launch of "Satmex 5" Satellite.
2563 **1094** 3 p. multicoloured . . . 40 25

1095 Maracas Player and Streamers **1096** Couple in Hammock

1999. Veracruz Carnival.
2564 **1095** 3 p. multicoloured . . . 40 25

1999. Bicentenary of Acapulco, Guerrero. Mult.
2565 3 p. Type **1096** 40 25
2566 4 p. 20 Diving from cliff . . . 55 30

Nos. 2565/6 were issued together, se-tenant, forming a composite design.

1097 Internet Website

1999. International Women's Day.
2567 **1097** 4 p. 20 multicoloured . . 55 30

1098 "Mexico" (Jorge Gonzalez Camarena)

1999. 40th Anniv of National Commission for Free Textbooks.
2568 **1098** 3 p. multicoloured . . . 40 25

1099 Family Members

1999. 25th Anniv of National Population Council.
2569 **1099** 3 p. multicoloured . . . 40 25

1101 Guadalupe Ceniceros de Perez

1999. Teachers' Day.
2571 **1101** 3 p. multicoloured . . . 40 25

1102 Pitcher

1999. 75th Anniv of Mexican Baseball League. Each black and grey.
2572 3 p. Type **1102** 40 25
2573 3 p. Catcher 40 25
2574 3 p. Skeletal pitcher 40 25
2575 3 p. Pitcher (different) 40 25

1103 10 p. Banknote

1999. 115th Anniv of National Bank of Mexico. Multicoloured.
2576 3 p. Type **1103** 40 25
2577 3 p. Former and current head-quarters 40 25

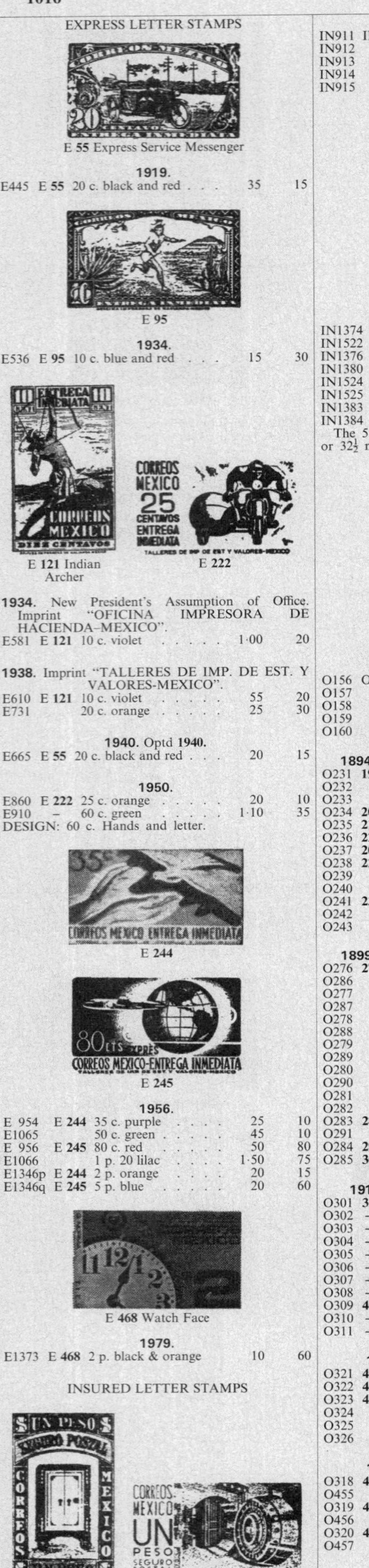

EXPRESS LETTER STAMPS

E 55 Express Service Messenger

1919.
E445 E **55** 20 c. black and red . . . 35 15

E 95

1934.
E536 E **95** 10 c. blue and red . . . 15 30

E **121** Indian Archer

E **222**

1934. New President's Assumption of Office. Imprint "OFICINA IMPRESORA DE HACIENDA–MEXICO".
E581 E **121** 10 c. violet . . . . . 1·00 20

1938. Imprint "TALLERES DE IMP. DE EST. Y VALORES-MEXICO".
E610 E **121** 10 c. violet 55 20
E731 20 c. orange 25 30

1940. Optd **1940.**
E665 E **55** 20 c. black and red . . . 20 15

1950.
E860 E **222** 25 c. orange 20 10
E910 – 60 c. green . . . . . 1·10 35
DESIGN: 60 c. Hands and letter.

E **244**

E **245**

1956.
E 954 E **244** 35 c. purple 25 10
E1065 50 c. green 45 10
E 956 E **245** 80 c. red 50 80
E1066 1 p. 20 lilac . . . . 1·50 75
E1346p E **244** 2 p. orange 20 15
E1346q E **245** 5 p. blue 20 60

E **468** Watch Face

1979.
E1373 E **468** 2 p. black & orange 10 60

INSURED LETTER STAMPS

IN **125** Safe

IN **222** P.O. Treasury Vault

1935. Inscr as in Type IN **125**.
IN583 – 10 c. red . . . . . 1·10 30
IN733 – 50 c. blue 75 25
IN734 IN **125** 1 p. green 75 35
DESIGNS: 10 c. Bundle of insured letters; 50 c. Registered mailbag.

1950.
IN911 IN **222** 20 c. blue 15 10
IN912 40 c. purple 15 10
IN913 1 p. green 20 10
IN914 5 p. green and blue . . . 65 60
IN915 10 p. blue and red . . . 3·00 1·50

IN **469** Padlock

1976.
IN1374 IN **469** 40 c. black & turq 10 10
IN1522 1 p. black & turq 10 10
IN1376 2 p. black and blue 10 10
IN1380 5 p. black & turq 10 10
IN1524 10 p. black & turq 10 10
IN1525 20 p. black & turq 10 10
IN1383 50 p. black & turq 95 95
IN1384 100 p. black & turq 60 60
The 5, 10, 20 p. exist with the padlock either 31 or 32½ mm high.

OFFICIAL STAMPS

O **18** Hidalgo

1884. No value shown.
O156 O **18** Red 30 20
O157 Brown 15 10
O158 Orange 80 15
O159 Green 30 15
O160 Blue 45 35

1894. Stamps of 1895 handstamped **OFICIAL**.
O231 **19** 1 c. green . . . . 3·75 1·25
O232 2 c. red . . . . 4·50 1·25
O233 3 c. brown . . . . 3·75 1·25
O234 **20** 4 c. orange . . . . 5·50 2·50
O235 **21** 5 c. blue . . . . 7·50 2·50
O236 **22** 10 c. purple . . . . 7·00 50
O237 **20** 12 c. olive . . . . 15·00 6·25
O238 **22** 15 c. blue . . . . 8·75 3·75
O239 20 c. red . . . . 8·75 3·75
O240 50 c. mauve . . . . 19·00 9·50
O241 **23** 1 p. brown . . . . 48·00 19·00
O242 5 p. red . . . . £200 95·00
O243 10 p. blue £275 £150

1899. Stamps of 1899 handstamped **OFICIAL**.
O276 **27** 1 c. green . . . . . . 9·50 60
O286 1 c. purple . . . . . . 8·75 95
O277 2 c. red . . . . . . 12·50 95
O287 2 c. green . . . . . . 8·75 95
O278 3 c. brown . . . . . . 12·50 60
O288 4 c. red . . . . . . 16·00 45
O279 5 c. blue . . . . . . 12·50 1·10
O289 5 c. orange . . . . . . 16·00 3·25
O280 10 c. brown and purple 16·00 1·40
O290 10 c. orange and blue 19·00 95
O281 15 c. purple and lavender 16·00 1·40
O282 20 c. blue and red . . . 19·00 45
O283 **28** 50 c. black and purple . . 38·00 6·25
O291 50 c. black and red . . 48·00 6·25
O284 **29** 1 p. black and blue . . 80·00 6·25
O285 **30** 5 p. black and red . . . 50·00 19·00

1911. Independence stamps optd **OFICIAL**.
O301 **32** 1 c. purple . . . . . . 1·25 1·25
O302 – 2 c. green 75 45
O303 – 3 c. brown . . . . . . 1·25 45
O304 – 4 c. red . . . . . . 1·90 45
O305 – 5 c. orange . . . . . . 3·25 1·75
O306 – 10 c. orange and blue . 1·90 45
O307 – 15 c. lake and slate . . 3·25 2·00
O308 – 20 c. blue and lake . . . 2·50 45
O309 **40** 50 c. black and brown . . 8·75 3·75
O310 – 1 p. black and blue . . 15·00 6·25
O311 – 5 p. black and red . . . 55·00 32·00

1915. Stamps of 1915 optd **OFICIAL**.
O321 **43** 1 c. violet 30 55
O322 **44** 2 c. green 30 55
O323 **45** 3 c. brown 30 55
O324 4 c. red 30 55
O325 5 c. orange 30 55
O326 10 c. blue 30 55

1915. Stamps of 1915 optd **OFICIAL**.
O318 **46** 40 c. grey . . . . . . 4·75 3·25
O455 40 c. mauve . . . . . . 3·75 1·90
O319 **47** 1 p. grey and brown . . . 3·25 3·75
O456 1 p. grey and blue . . . 9·50 6·25
O320 **48** 5 p. blue and lake . . . 19·00 16·00
O457 5 p. grey and green . . . 55·00 95·00

1916. Nos. O301/11 optd with T **49**.
O358 **32** 1 c. purple . . . . . . 1·90
O359 – 2 c. green 30
O360 – 3 c. brown 35
O361 – 4 c. red . . . . . . 2·00
O362 – 5 c. orange 35
O363 – 10 c. orange and blue . . 35
O364 – 15 c. lake and slate . . 35
O365 – 20 c. blue and lake . . . 40
O366 **40** 50 c. black and brown . . 55·00
O367 – 1 p. black and blue . . . 3·25
O368 – 5 p. black and red . . . £1600

1918. Stamps of 1917 optd **OFICIAL**.
O424 **53** 1 c. violet . . . . 1·25 60
O446 1 c. grey 30 20
O447 – 2 c. green 20 20
O448 – 3 c. brown 25 20
O449 – 4 c. red . . . . 3·75 45
O450 – 5 c. blue 20 20
O451 – 10 c. blue 30 15
O452 – 20 c. lake . . . . 2·50 2·50
O454 – 30 c. black . . . . 3·75 1·40

1923. No. 416 optd **OFICIAL**.
O485 10 p. black and brown . . . 60·00 95·00

1923. Stamps of 1923 optd **OFICIAL**.
O471 **59** 1 c. brown 20 20
O473 **60** 2 c. red 25 25
O475 **61** 3 c. brown 55 40
O461 **62** 4 c. green . . . . 1·90 1·90
O476 **63** 4 c. green 40 40
O477 5 c. orange 70 65
O489 **74** 8 c. orange . . . . 3·75 2·50
O479 **66** 10 c. lake 55 55
O480 **65** 20 c. blue . . . . 3·25 2·50
O464 **64** 30 c. green 35 25
O467 **68** 50 c. brown 55 55
O469 **69** 1 p. blue and lake . . . . 4·75 4·75

1929. Air. Optd **OFICIAL**.
O501 **80** 5 c. blue (roul) 45 25
O502 **81** 20 c. violet 55 55
O492 **58** 25 c. sepia and lake . . . 3·50 2·75
O490 25 c. sepia and green . . . 1·75 1·25

1929. Air. As 1926 Postal Congress stamp optd **HABILITADO Servicio Oficial Aereo.**
O493 **70** 2 c. black . . . . 26·00 26·00
O494 – 4 c. black . . . . 26·00 26·00
O495 **70** 5 c. black . . . . 26·00 26·00
O496 – 10 c. black . . . . 26·00 26·00
O497 **72** 20 c. black . . . . 26·00 26·00
O498 30 c. black . . . . 26·00 26·00
O499 40 c. black . . . . 26·00 26·00
O500 **73** 1 p. black £950 £950

O 85

1930. Air.
O503 O **85** 20 c. grey . . . . . . 2·75 2·75
O504 35 c. violet 40 95
O505 40 c. blue and brown 50 90
O506 70 c. sepia and violet 50 95

1931. Air. Surch **HABILITADO Quince centavos.**
O515 O **85** 15 c. on 20 c. grey . . . 45 45

1932. Air. Optd **SERVICIO OFICIAL** in one line.
O532 **80** 10 c. violet (perf or roul) . 30 30
O533 15 c. red (perf or roul) . . 85 85
O534 20 c. sepia (roul) 85 85
O531 **58** 50 c. red and blue 90 70

1932. Stamps of 1923 optd **SERVICIO OFICIAL** in two lines.
O535 **59** 1 c. brown 15 15
O536 **60** 2 c. red 10 10
O537 **61** 3 c. brown 95 95
O538 **63** 4 c. green . . . . 3·25 2·50
O539 5 c. red . . . . 3·75 2·50
O540 **66** 10 c. lake . . . . 1·10 75
O541 **65** 20 c. blue . . . . 4·75 3·25
O544 **64** 30 c. green . . . . 2·50 95
O545 **46** 40 c. mauve . . . . 4·75 3·25
O546 **68** 50 c. brown 80 95
O547 **69** 1 p. blue and lake 95 95

1933. Air. Optd **SERVICIO OFICIAL** in two lines.
O553 **58** 50 c. red and blue . . . . 1·00 70

1933. Air. Optd **SERVICIO OFICIAL** in two lines.
O548 **80** 5 c. blue (No. 476a) . . . 30 30
O549 10 c. violet (No. 477) . . 30 30
O550 20 c. sepia (No. 479) . . 30 60
O551 50 c. lake (No. 481) . . . 40 95

1934. Optd **OFICIAL**.
O565 **92** 15 c. blue 35 35

1938. Nos. 561/71 optd **OFICIAL**.
O622 1 c. orange . . . . 70 1·25
O623 2 c. green 45 45
O624 4 c. red 45 45
O625 10 c. violet 45 80
O626 20 c. blue 55 80
O627 30 c. red . . . . 70 1·25
O628 40 c. brown . . . . 70 1·25
O629 50 c. black . . . . 1·00 1·00
O630 1 p. red and brown . . . . 2·50 3·75

PARCEL POST STAMPS

P **167** Steam Mail Train

1941.
P732 P **167** 10 c. red . . . . . . 2·25 55
P733 20 c. violet . . . . . . 2·75 70

P **228** Class DE-10 Diesel-electric Locomotive

1951.
P916 P **228** 10 c. pink . . . . . . 1·50 20
P917 20 c. violet . . . . . . 2·00 40

POSTAGE DUE STAMPS

D **32**

1908.
D282 D **32** 1 c. blue . . . . 1·00 1·00
D283 2 c. blue . . . . 1·00 1·00
D284 4 c. blue . . . . 1·00 1·00
D285 5 c. blue . . . . 1·00 1·100
D286 10 c. blue . . . . 1·00 1·00

MICRONESIA Pt. 22

A group of islands in the Pacific, from 1899 to 1914 part of the German Caroline Islands. Occupied by the Japanese in 1914 the islands were from 1920 a Japanese mandated territory, and from 1947 part of the United States Trust Territory of the Pacific Islands, using United States stamps. Micronesia assumed control of its postal services in 1984.

100 cents = 1 dollar

1 Yap

1984. Inauguration of Postal Independence. Maps. Multicoloured.
1 20 c. Type **1** 50 40
2 20 c. Truk 50 40
3 20 c. Pohnpei 50 40
4 20 c. Kosrae 50 40

2 Fernandez de Quiros

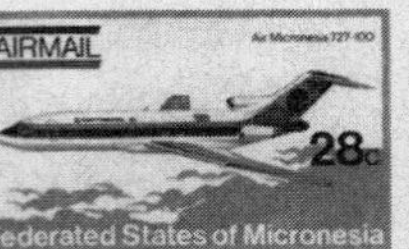

3 Boeing 727-100

1984.
5 **2** 1 c. blue 10 10
6 – 2 c. brown 10 10
7 – 3 c. blue 10 10
8 – 4 c. green 10 10
9 – 5 c. brown and olive 10 10
10 – 10 c. purple 15 10
11 – 13 c. blue 20 10
11a – 15 c. red 20 10
12 – 17 c. brown 25 10
13 **2** 19 c. purple 30 10
14 – 20 c. green 30 10
14a – 22 c. green 30 15
14b – 25 c. orange 30 15
15 – 30 c. red 45 15
15a – 36 c. blue 50 20
16 – 37 c. violet 50 20
16a – 45 c. green 60 30
17 – 50 c. brown and sepia 80 35
18 – $1 olive . . . . 1·25 85
19 – $2 blue . . . . 2·50 1·50
20 – $5 brown . . . . 6·00 4·50
20a – $10 blue . . . . 12·50 11·00
DESIGNS: 2, 20 c. Louis Duperrey; 3, 30 c. Fyodor Lutke; 4, 37 c. Jules Dumont d'Urville; 5 c. Men's house, Yap; 10, 45 c. Sleeping Lady (mountains), Kosrae; 13, 15 c. Liduduhriap waterfall, Pohnpei; 17, 25 c. Tonachau Peak, Truk; 22, 36 c. "Senyavin" (full-rigged sailing ship); 50 c. Devil mask, Truk; $1 Sokehs Rock, Pohnpei; $2 Outrigger canoes, Kosrae; $5 Stone money, Yap; $10 Official seal.

1984. Air. Multicoloured.
21 28 c. Type **3** 55 30
22 35 c. Grumman SA-16 Albatros flying boat 70 50
23 40 c. Consolidated PBY-5A Catalina amphibian 95 60

4 Truk Post Office

1984. "Ausipex 84" International Stamp Exhibition, Melbourne. Multicoloured.
24 20 c. Type **4** (postage) 50 20
25 28 c. German Caroline Islands 1919 3 pf. yacht stamp (air) 60 40
26 35 c. German 1900 20 pf. stamp optd for Caroline Islands . . 70 50
27 40 c. German Caroline Islands 1915 5 m. yacht stamp . . . 80 65

5 Baby in Basket

1984. Christmas. Multicoloured.
28 20 c. Type **5** (postage) 55 25
29 28 c. Open book showing Christmas scenes (air) 65 40
30 35 c. Palm tree decorated with lights 85 50
31 40 c. Women preparing food . . 1·00 65

6 U.S.S. "Jamestown" (warship)

1985. Ships.
32 **6** 22 c. black & brn (postage) . . 65 35
33 – 33 c. black and lilac (air) . . . 85 50
34 – 39 c. black and green . . . . 1·00 75
35 – 44 c. black and red . . . . . 1·40 90
DESIGNS: 33 c. "L'Astrolabe" (D'Urville's ship); 39 c. "La Coquille" (Duperrey's ship); 44 c. "Shenandoah" (Confederate warship).

7 Lelu Protestant Church, Kosrae

1985. Christmas.
36 **7** 22 c black and orange (postage) 55 30
37 – 33 c. black and violet (air) . . 80 50
38 – 44 c. black and green . . . . 1·10 70
DESIGNS: 33 c. Dublon Protestant Church; 44 c. Pohnpei Catholic Church.

8 "Noddy Tern"

1985. Birth Bicentenary of John J. Audubon (ornithologist). Multicoloured.
39 22 c. Type **8** (postage) 70 50
40 22 c. "Turnstone" 70 50
41 22 c. "Golden Plover" 70 50
42 22 c. "Black-bellied Plover" . . 70 50
43 44 c. "Sooty Tern" (air) . . . . 1·25 80

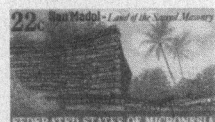

9 Land of Sacred Masonry

1985. Nan Madol, Pohnpei. Multicoloured.
44 22 c. Type **9** (postage) 45 25
45 33 c. Nan Tauas inner courtyard (air) 60 45
46 39 c. Nan Tauas outer wall . . . 75 60
47 44 c. Nan Tauas burial vault . . 90 70

10 Doves, "LOVE" and Hands — 12 Bully Hayes

1986. Anniversaries and Events. Multicoloured.
48 22 c. Type **10** (Interntional Peace Year) 50 35
49 44 c. Halley's comet . . . . . . 1·25 80
50 44 c. "Trienza" (cargo liner) arriving at jetty (40th anniv of return of Nauruans from Truk) 1·25 80

1986. Nos. 1/4 surch.
51 22 c. on 20 c. Type **1** 45 45
52 22 c. on 20 c. Truk 45 45
53 22 c. on 20 c. Pohnpei 45 45
54 22 c. on 20 c. Kosrae 45 45

1986. "Ameripex 86" International Stamp Exhibition, Chicago. Bully Hayes (buccaneer). Multicoloured.
55 22 c. Type **12** (postage) 50 30
56 33 c. Angelo (crew member) forging Hawaii 5 c. blue stamp (air) 65 50
57 39 c. "Leonora" sinking off Kosrae 75 60
58 44 c. Hayes escaping capture on Kosrae 95 75
59 75 c. Cover of book "Bully Hayes, Buccaneer" by Louis Becke 1·50 1·25

13 "Madonna and Child"

1986. Christmas. "Madonna and Child" Paintings.
61 – 5 c. multicoloured (postage) 15 10
62 – 22 c. multicoloured 70 30
63 – 33 c. multicoloured (air) . . . 95 65
64 **13** 44 c. multicoloured . . . . . 1·25 1·00

14 Passports on Globe

1986. 1st Micronesian Passport.
65 **14** 22 c. blue, black and yellow 50 35

15 Emblem (International Year of Shelter for the Homeless)

1987. Anniversaries and Events.
66 **15** 22 c. blue, red and black (postage) 50 40
67 – 33 c. green, red and black (air) 75 50
68 – 39 c. blue, black and red . . 90 60
69 – 44 c. blue, red and black . . 1·25 75
DESIGNS: 33 c. Dollar sign (bicentenary of dollar currency); 39 c. Space capsule (25th anniv of first American to orbit Earth); 44 c. "200 USA" (bicentenary of US constitution).

16 Archangel Gabriel appearing to Mary

1987. Christmas. Multicoloured.
71 22 c. Type **16** (postage) 40 30
72 33 c. Joseph praying and Mary with baby Jesus (air) 60 45
73 39 c. Shepherds with their sheep 75 60
74 44 c. Wise men 90 75

17 Spanish Missionary and Flag

1988. Micronesian History. Multicoloured.
75 22 c. Type **17** (postage) 50 35
76 22 c. Natives producing copra and German flag 50 35
77 22 c. School pupils and Japanese flag 50 35
78 22 c. General store and U.S. flag 50 35
79 44 c. Traditional boatbuilding and fishing skills (air) . . . . . . 1·00 75
80 44 c. Welcoming tourists from Douglas DC-10 airliner and divers investigating World War II wreckage . . . . 1·00 75

18 Ponape White Eye — 19 Marathon

1988. Birds. Multicoloured.
81 3 c. Type **18** (postage) 10 10
82 14 c. Truk monarch 25 10
83 22 c. Ponape starling 35 20
84 33 c. Truk white eye (air) . . . 55 35
85 44 c. Blue-faced parrot finch . . 75 65
86 $1 Yap monarch . . . . 1·50 1·40

1988. Olympic Games, Seoul. Multicoloured.
87 25 c. Type **19** 45 25
88 25 c. Hurdling 45 25
89 45 c. Basketball 70 55
90 45 c. Volleyball 70 55

20 Girls decorating Tree

1988. Christmas. Multicoloured.
91 25 c. Type **20** 45 30
92 25 c. Dove with mistletoe in beak and children holding decorations 45 30
93 25 c. Boy in native clothing and girl in floral dress sitting at base of tree 45 30
94 25 c. Boy in T-shirt and shorts and girl in native clothing sitting at base of tree 45 30
Nos. 91/4 were printed together in blocks of four, se-tenant, forming a composite design.

21 Blue-girdled Angelfish

1988. Truk Lagoon, "Micronesia's Living War Memorial". Multicoloured.
95 25 c. Type **21** 50 40
96 25 c. Jellyfish and shoal of small fishes 50 40
97 25 c. Snorkel divers 50 40
98 25 c. Two golden trevally (black-striped fishes facing left) . . . 50 40
99 25 c. Blackfinned reef shark . . 50 40
100 25 c. Deck railings of wreck and fishes 50 40
101 25 c. Soldierfish (red fish) and damselfish 50 40
102 25 c. Damselfish, narrow-banded batfish and aircraft cockpit . . 50 40
103 25 c. Three Moorish idols (fishes with long dorsal fins) 50 40
104 25 c. Four pickhandle barracuda and shoal 50 40
105 25 c. Spot-banded butterflyfish and damselfish (facing alternate directions) 50 40
106 25 c. Three-spotted dascyllus and aircraft propeller 50 40
107 25 c. Fox-faced rabbitfish and shoal 50 40
108 25 c. Lionfish (fish with spines) 50 40
109 25 c. Scuba diver and white-tailed damselfish 50 40
110 25 c. Tubular corals 50 40
111 25 c. White-tailed damselfish, ornate butterflyfish and brain coral 50 40
112 25 c. Pink anemonefish, giant clam and sea plants 50 40
Nos. 95/112 were printed together, se-tenant, in sheetlets of 18 stamps, the backgrounds of the stamps forming an overall design of the remains of a Japanese ship and "Zero" fighter plane on the Lagoon bed colonized by marine life.

22 Flag of Pohnpei

1989. Air. State Flags. Multicoloured.
113 45 c. Type **22** 65 50
114 45 c. Truk 65 50
115 45 c. Kosrae 65 50
116 45 c. Yap 65 50

23 Plumeria and Headdress

1989. Mwarmwarms (floral decorations). Multicoloured.
117 45 c. Type **23** 65 50
118 45 c. Hibiscus and lei 65 50
119 45 c. Jasmine and Yap religious mwarmwarm 65 50
120 45 c. Bougainvillea and Truk dance mwarmwarm 65 50

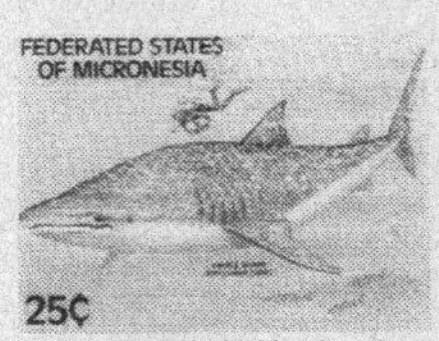

24 Whale Shark

1989. Sharks. Multicoloured.
121 25 c. Type **24** 70 40
122 25 c. Smooth hammerhead . . 70 40
123 45 c. Tiger shark (vert) . . . . 1·10 75
124 45 c. Great white shark (vert) . 1·10 75

26 "Explorer 1" Satellite over North America

1989. 20th Anniv of First Manned Landing on the Moon. Multicoloured.
126 25 c. Bell XS-15 rocket plane . 40 30
127 25 c. Type **26** 40 30
128 25 c. Ed White on space walk during "Gemini 4" mission 40 30
129 25 c. "Apollo 18" spacecraft 40 30
130 25 c. "Gemini 4" space capsule over South America 40 30
131 25 c. Space shuttle "Challenger" 40 30
132 25 c. Italian "San Marco 2" satellite 40 30
133 25 c. Russian "Soyuz 19" spacecraft 40 30
134 25 c. Neil Armstrong descending ladder to Moon's surface during "Apollo 11" mission 40 30
135 $2.40 Lunar module "Eagle" on Moon (34 × 46 mm) . . . . 3·50 2·75
Nos. 126/34 were printed together in se-tenant sheetlets of nine stamps, the backgrounds of the stamps forming an overall design of Earth as viewed from the Moon.

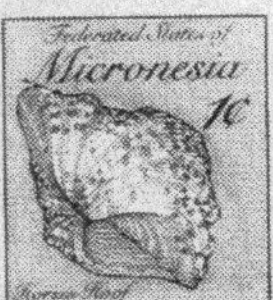

27 Horse's Hoof

1989. Sea Shells. Multicoloured.
136 1 c. Type **27** 10 10
137 3 c. Rare spotted cowrie . . . 10 10
138 15 c. Commercial trochus . . . 20 10
139 20 c. General cone 25 10
140 25 c. Trumpet triton 30 20
141 30 c. Laciniate conch 35 25
142 36 c. Red-mouth olive 45 35
143 45 c. All-red map cowrie 55 45
144 50 c. Textile cone 60 50
145 $1 Orange spider conch . . . . 1·40 1·00
146 $2 Golden cowrie . . . . . . 2·75 2·00
147 $5 Episcopal mitre . . . . . . 6·50 4·50

28 Oranges

1989. "World Stamp Expo '89" International Stamp Exhibition, Washington D.C. "Kosrae–The Garden State". Multicoloured.

155	25 c. Type **28**	40	30
156	25 c. Limes	40	30
157	25 c. Tangerines	40	30
158	25 c. Mangoes	40	30
159	25 c. Coconuts	40	30
160	25 c. Breadfruit	40	30
161	25 c. Sugar cane	40	30
162	25 c. Kosrae house	40	30
163	25 c. Bananas	40	30
164	25 c. Children with fruit and flowers	40	30
165	25 c. Pineapples	40	30
166	25 c. Taro	40	30
167	25 c. Hibiscus	40	30
168	25 c. Ylang ylang	40	30
169	25 c. White ginger	40	30
170	25 c. Plumeria	40	30
171	25 c. Royal poinciana	40	30
172	25 c. Yellow allamanda	40	30

29 Angel over Micronesian Village

1989. Christmas. Multicoloured.

173	25 c. Type **29**	30	20
174	45 c. Truk children dressed as Three Kings	65	50

30 Young Kingfisher and Sokehs Rock, Pohnpei

1990. World Wide Fund for Nature. Micronesian Kingfisher and Micronesian Pigeon.

175	10 c. Type **30**	20	10
176	15 c. Adult kingfisher and rain forest, Pohnpei	30	15
177	20 c. Pigeon flying over lake at Sleeping Lady, Kosrae	45	30
178	25 c. Pigeon perched on leaf, Tol Island, Truk	60	45

31 Wooden Whale Stamp and "Lyra"

1990. "Stamp World London 90" International Stamp Exhibition. 19th-century British Whaling Ships. Multicoloured.

179	45 c. Type **31**	65	45
180	45 c. Harpoon heads and "Prudent"	65	45
181	45 c. Carved whale bone and "Rhone"	65	45
182	45 c. Carved whale tooth and "Sussex"	65	45

33 Beech 18 over Kosrae Airport

34 School Building

1990. Air. Aircraft. Multicoloured.

185	22 c. Type **33**	30	15
186	36 c. Boeing 727 landing at Truk	50	30
187	39 c. Britten Norman Islander over Pohnpei	50	30
188	45 c. Beech Queen Air over Yap	60	35

1990. 25th Anniv of Pohnpei Agriculture and Trade School. Multicoloured.

190	25 c. Type **34**	30	20
191	25 c. Fr. Costigan (founder) and students	30	20
192	25 c. Fr. Hugh Costigan	30	20
193	25 c. Ispahu Samuel Hadley (Metelanim chief) and Fr. Costigan	30	20
194	25 c. Statue of Liberty, New York City Police Department badge and Empire State Building	30	20

36 Loading Mail Plane at Pohnpei Airport

1990. Pacific Postal Transport. Multicoloured.

196	25 c. Type **36**	35	20
197	45 c. Launch meeting "Nantaku" (inter-island freighter) in Truk Lagoon to exchange mail, 1940	65	40

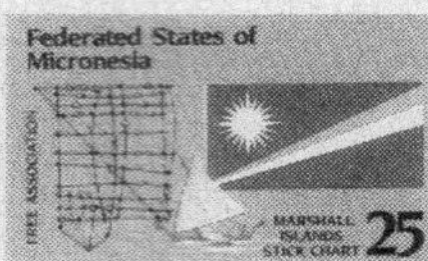

37 Marshallese Stick Chart, Outrigger Canoe and Flag

1990. 4th Anniv of Ratification of Micronesia and Marshall Islands Compacts of Free Association. Multicoloured.

198	25 c. Type **37**	45	20
199	25 c. Great frigate bird, U.S.S. "Constitution" (frigate), U.S. flag and American bald eagle	45	20
200	25 c. Micronesian outrigger canoe and flag	45	20

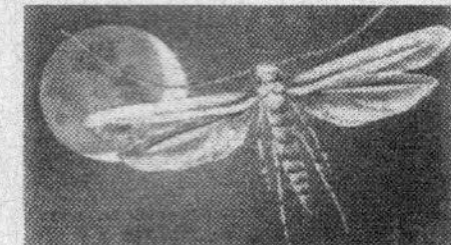

38 "Caloptilia sp." and New Moon

1990. Moths. Multicoloured.

201	45 c. Type **38**	60	50
202	45 c. "Anticrates sp." (inscr "Yponomeatidae") and waxing moon	60	50
203	45 c. "Cosmopterigidae" family and full moon	60	50
204	45 c. "Cosmopteridigae" family and waning moon	60	50

39 Cherub above Roof

41 Hawksbill Turtle returning to Sea

1990. Christmas. "Micronesian Holy Night". Multicoloured.

205	25 c. Type **39**	30	20
206	25 c. Two cherubs and Star of Bethlehem	30	20
207	25 c. Cherub blowing horn	30	20
208	25 c. Lambs, goat, pig and chickens	30	20
209	25 c. Native wise men offering gifts to Child	30	20
210	25 c. Children and dog beside lake	30	20
211	25 c. Man blowing trumpet triton	30	20
212	25 c. Adults and children on path	30	20
213	25 c. Man and children carrying gifts	30	20

Nos. 205/13 were printed together, se-tenant, forming a composite design.

1991. Sea Turtles. Multicoloured.

215	29 c. Type **41**	50	30
216	29 c. Green turtles swimming underwater	50	30
217	50 c. Hawksbill turtle swimming underwater	90	50
218	50 c. Leatherback turtle swimming underwater	90	50

42 Boeing E-3 Sentry

1991. Operations Desert Shield and Desert Storm (liberation of Kuwait). Multicoloured.

219	29 c. Type **42**	40	25
220	29 c. Grumman F-14 Tomcat fighter	40	25
221	29 c. U.S.S. "Missouri" (battleship)	40	25
222	29 c. Multiple Launch Rocket System	40	25
223	$2.90 Great frigate bird with yellow ribbon and flag of Micronesia (50 × 37 mm)	3·75	2·75

43 "Evening Flowers, Toloas, Truk"

1991. "Phila Nippon '91" International Stamp Exhibition, Tokyo. 90th Birth Anniv (1992) of Paul Jacoulet (artist). Micronesian Ukiyo-e Prints by Jacoulet. Multicoloured.

225	29 c. Type **43**	40	25
226	29 c. "The Chief's Daughter, Mogomog"	40	25
227	29 c. "Yagourouh and Mio, Yap"	40	25
228	50 c. "Yap Beauty and Orchids"	70	45
229	50 c. "The Yellow-Eyed Boys, Ohlol"	70	45
230	50 c. "Violet Flowers, Tomil, Yap"	70	45

44 Sheep and Holy Family

1991. Christmas. Shell Cribs. Multicoloured.

232	29 c. Type **44**	40	25
233	40 c. Three Kings arriving at Bethlehem	55	35
234	50 c. Sheep around manger	65	45

45 Pohnpei Fruit Bat

1991. Pohnpei Rain Forest. Multicoloured.

235	29 c. Type **45**	50	35
236	29 c. Purple-capped fruit dove	50	35
237	29 c. Micronesian kingfisher	50	35
238	29 c. Birdnest fern	50	35
239	29 c. Carolines ("Island") swiftlets	50	35
240	29 c. Ponape ("Long-billed") white eye	50	35
241	29 c. Common ("Brown") noddy	50	35
242	29 c. Ponape lory	50	35
243	29 c. Ponape myiagra flycatcher	50	35
244	29 c. Truk Island ("Caroline") ground dove	50	35
245	29 c. White-tailed tropic bird	50	35
246	29 c. Cardinal ("Micronesian") honeyeater	50	35
247	29 c. Ixora	50	35
248	29 c. Rufous ("Pohnpei") fantail	50	35
249	29 c. Grey-brown ("Gray") white eye	50	35
250	29 c. Blue-faced parrot finch	50	35
251	29 c. Slender-billed grey bird ("Cicadabird")	50	35
252	29 c. Green skink	50	35

Nos. 235/52 were issued together, se-tenant, forming a composite design.

46 Britten Norman Islander and Outrigger Canoe

47 Volunteers learning Crop Planting

1992. Air. Multicoloured.

253	40 c. Type **46**	55	35
254	50 c. Boeing 727-200 airliner and outrigger canoe (different)	65	45

1992. 25th Anniv of Presence of United States Peace Corps in Micronesia. Multicoloured.

255	29 c. Type **47**	40	25
256	29 c. Education	40	25
257	29 c. Pres. John Kennedy announcing formation of Peace Corps	40	25
258	29 c. Public health nurses	40	25
259	29 c. Recreation	40	25

48 Queen Isabella of Spain

1992. 500th Anniv of Discovery of America by Christopher Columbus. Multicoloured.

260	29 c. Type **48**	1·10	50
261	29 c. "Santa Maria"	1·10	50
262	29 c. Christopher Columbus	1·10	50

49 Flags

1992. 1st Anniv of U.N. Membership.

264 **49**	29 c. multicoloured	40	25
265	50 c. multicoloured	65	45

50 Bouquet

1992. Christmas.

266 **50**	29 c. multicoloured	40	25

51 Edward Rickenbacker (fighter pilot)

1993. Pioneers of Flight (1st series). Pioneers and aircraft. Multicoloured.

267	29 c. Type **51**	45	30
268	29 c. Manfred von Richthofen (fighter pilot)	45	30
269	29 c. Andrei Tupolev (aeronautical engineer)	45	30
270	29 c. John Macready (first non-stop crossing of U.S.A.)	45	30
271	29 c. Sir Charles Kingsford-Smith (first trans-Pacific flight)	45	30
272	29 c. Igor Sikorsky (aeronautical engineer)	45	30
273	29 c. Lord Trenchard ("Father of the Royal Air Force")	45	30
274	29 c. Glenn Curtiss (builder of U.S. Navy's first aircraft)	45	30

See also Nos. 322/9, 364/71, 395/402, 418/25, 441/8, 453/60 and 514/21.

52 Big-scaled Soldierfish

1993. Fishes. Multicoloured.

275 10 c. Type **52** 15 10
276 19 c. Bennett's butterflyfish . . 25 15
277 20 c. Peacock hind ("Peacock Grouper") 25 15
278 22 c. Great barracuda 30 20
278a 23 c. Yellow-finned tuna . . . 30 20
279 25 c. Coral hind ("Coral Grouper") 30 20
280 29 c. Regal angelfish 40 25
281 30 c. Bleeker's parrotfish . . . 40 25
282 32 c. Saddle butterflyfish (dated "1995") 40 25
283 35 c. Picasso triggerfish ("Picassofish") 45 30
284 40 c. Mandarin fish 50 35
285 45 c. Clown ("Bluebanded") surgeonfish 60 40
285a 46 c. Red-tailed surgeonfish ("Achilles Tang") 60 40
286 50 c. Undulate ("Orange-striped") triggerfish 65 45
287 52 c. Palette surgeonfish . . . 70 45
288 55 c. Moorish idol 70 45
288a 60 c. Skipjack tuna 80 55
289 75 c. Oriental sweetlips . . . 95 65
290 78 c. Square-spotted anthias ("Square-spot Fairy Basslet") 1·00 65
290a 95 c. Blue-striped ("Blue-lined") snapper . . . . 1·25 85
291 $1 Zebra moray . . . . . . 1·25 85
292 $2 Fox-faced rabbitfish . . . 2·50 1·60
293 $2.90 Masked ("Orangespine") unicornfish . . . . 3·75 2·50
294 $3 Flame angelfish . . . . . 3·75 2·50
295 $5 Six-blotched hind ("Cave Grouper") . . . . 6·50 4·25

See also Nos. 465/89 and 522/5.

53 "Great Republic" 54 Jefferson

1993. American Clipper Ships. Multicoloured.

301 29 c. Type **53** 50 35
302 29 c. "Benjamin F. Packard" . 50 35
303 29 c. "Stag Hound" 50 35
304 29 c. "Herald of the Morning" . 50 35
305 29 c. "Rainbow" and junk . . 50 35
306 29 c. "Flying Cloud" 50 35
307 29 c. "Lightning" 50 35
308 29 c. "Sea Witch" 50 35
309 29 c. "Columbia" 50 35
310 29 c. "New World" 50 35
311 29 c. "Young America" . . . 50 35
312 29 c. "Courier" 50 35

1993. 250th Birth Anniv of Thomas Jefferson (U.S. President, 1801–09).

313 **54** 29 c. multicoloured 45 25

55 Yap Outrigger Canoe

1993. Traditional Canoes. Multicoloured.

314 29 c. Type **55** 50 35
315 29 c. Kosrae outrigger canoe . 50 35
316 29 c. Pohnpei lagoon outrigger canoe 50 35
317 29 c. Chuuk war canoe 50 35

56 Ambilos Iehsi 57 Kepirohi Falls

1993. Local Leaders (1st series). Multicoloured.

318 29 c. Type **56** (Pohnpei) 45 25
319 29 c. Andrew Roboman (Yap) . 45 25
320 29 c. Joab Sigrah (Kosrae) . . 45 25
321 29 c. Petrus Mailo (Chuuk) . . 45 25

See also Nos. 409/12.

1993. Pioneers of Flight (2nd series). As T **51**. Multicoloured.

322 50 c. Lawrence Sperry (inventor of the gyro) 75 50
323 50 c. Alberto Santos-Dumont (first powered flight in Europe) 75 50
324 50 c. Hugh Dryden (developer of first guided missile) 75 50
325 50 c. Theodore von Karman (space pioneer) 75 50
326 50 c. Orville Wright (first powered flight) 75 50
327 50 c. Wilbur Wright (second powered flight) 75 50
328 50 c. Otto Lilienthal (first heavier-than-air flight) 75 50
329 50 c. Sir Thomas Sopwith (aircraft designer) 75 50

1993. Pohnpei Tourist Sites. Multicoloured.

330 29 c. Type **57** 40 25
331 50 c. Spanish Wall 65 45

See also Nos. 357/9.

58 Female Common ("Great") Eggfly 59 "We Three Kings"

1993. Butterflies. Multicoloured.

333 29 c. Type **58** 50 30
334 29 c. Female common ("great") eggfly (variant) 50 30
335 50 c. Male monarch 90 50
336 50 c. Male common ("great") eggfly 90 50

See also Nos. 360/3.

1993. Christmas. Carols. Multicoloured.

337 29 c. Type **59** 40 25
338 50 c. "Silent Night, Holy Night" 65 45

60 Baby Basket

1993. Yap. Multicoloured.

339 29 c. Type **60** 40 25
340 29 c. Bamboo raft 40 25
341 29 c. Basketry 40 25
342 29 c. Fruit bat 40 25
343 29 c. Forest 40 25
344 29 c. Outrigger canoes 40 25
345 29 c. Dioscorea yams 40 25
346 29 c. Mangroves 40 25
347 29 c. Manta ray 40 25
348 29 c. "Cyrtosperma taro" . . . 40 25
349 29 c. Fish weir 40 25
350 29 c. Seagrass, golden rabbitfish and masked rabbitfish . . . 40 25
351 29 c. Taro bowl 40 25
352 29 c. Thatched house 40 25
353 29 c. Coral reef 40 25
354 29 c. Lavalava 40 25
355 29 c. Dancers 40 25
356 29 c. Stone money 40 25

1994. Kosrae Tourist Sites. As T **57** but horiz. Multicoloured.

357 29 c. Sleeping Lady (mountains) 40 25
358 40 c. Walung 50 35
359 50 c. Lelu Ruins 65 45

1994. "Hong Kong '94" International Stamp Exhibition. Designs as Nos. 333/6 but with inscriptions in brown and additionally inscribed "Hong Kong '94 Stamp Exhibition" in English (361/2) or Chinese (others).

360 29 c. As No. 333 . . . . . . 50 25
361 29 c. As No. 334 . . . . . . 50 25
362 50 c. As No. 335 . . . . . . 75 50
363 50 c. As No. 336 . . . . . . 75 50

1994. Pioneers of Flight (3rd series). As T **51**. Multicoloured.

364 29 c. Octave Chanute (early glider designer) 45 25
365 29 c. T. Claude Ryan (founder of first commercial airline) . . . 45 25
366 29 c. Edwin (Buzz) Aldrin ("Apollo 11" crew member and second man to step onto moon) 45 25
367 29 c. Neil Armstrong (commander of "Apollo 11" and first man on moon) . . . 45 25
368 29 c. Frank Whittle (developer of jet engine) 45 25
369 29 c. Waldo Waterman (aircraft designer) 45 25
370 29 c. Michael Collins ("Apollo 11" crew member) 45 25
371 29 c. Wernher von Braun (rocket designer) 45 25

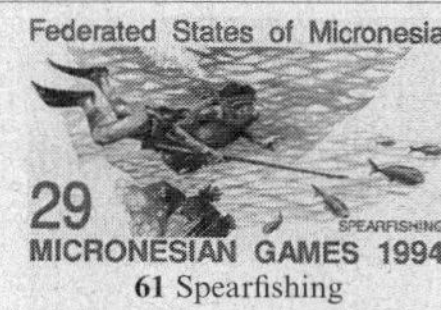

61 Spearfishing

1994. 3rd Micronesian Games. Multicoloured.

372 29 c. Type **61** 45 25
373 29 c. Basketball 45 25
374 29 c. Coconut husking 45 25
375 29 c. Tree climbing 45 25

62 Pohnpei 64 "Fagraea berteriana" (Kosrae)

63 People

1994. Traditional Costumes. Multicoloured.

376 29 c. Type **62** 45 25
377 29 c. Kosrae 45 25
378 29 c. Chuuk 45 25
379 29 c. Yap 45 25

1994. 15th Anniv of Constitution.

380 **63** 29 c. multicoloured 45 25

1994. Native Flowers. Multicoloured.

381 29 c. Type **64** 45 25
382 29 c. "Pangium edule" (Yap) . 45 25
383 29 c. "Pittosporum ferrugineum" (Chuuk) 45 25
384 29 c. "Sonneratia caseolaris" (Pohnpei) 45 25

Nos. 381/4 were issued together, se-tenant, forming a composite design.

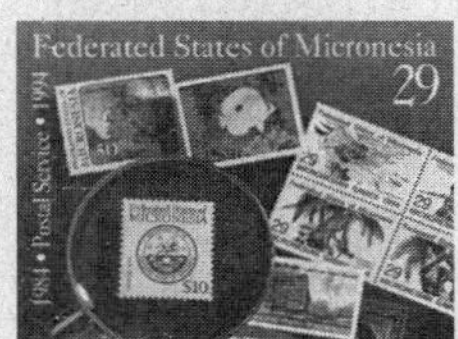

65 1985 $10 Definitive under Magnifying Glass

1994. 10th Anniv of Postal Independence. Multicoloured.

385 29 c. Type **65** 50 30
386 29 c. 1993 traditional canoes block 50 30
387 29 c. 1984 postal independence block 50 30
388 29 c. 1994 native costumes block 50 30

Nos. 385/8 were issued together, se-tenant, forming a composite design of various Micronesian stamps. Nos. 386/8 are identified by the block in the centre of the design.

66 Players 69 Oriental Cuckoo

68 Iguanodons

1994. World Cup Football Championship, U.S.A. Multicoloured.

389 50 c. Type **66** 70 45
390 50 c. Ball and players 70 45

Nos. 389/90 were issued together, se-tenant, forming a composite design.

1994. "Philakorea 1994" International Stamp Exhibition, Seoul. Prehistoric Animals. Multicoloured.

392 29 c. Type **68** 50 30
393 52 c. Iguanodons and coelurosaurs 90 60
394 $1 Camarasaurus . . . . . . 1·60 1·00

Nos. 392/4 were issued together, se-tenant, forming a composite design.

1994. Pioneers of Flight (4th series). As T **51**. Multicoloured.

395 50 c. Yury Gagarin (first man in space) 75 50
396 50 c. Alan Shepard Jr. (first American in space) 75 50
397 50 c. William Bishop (fighter pilot) 75 50
398 50 c. "Atlas" (first U.S. intercontinental ballistic missile) and Karel Bossart (aerospace engineer) 75 50
399 50 c. John Towers (world endurance record, 1912) . . 75 50
400 50 c. Hermann Oberth (space flight pioneer) 75 50
401 50 c. Marcel Dassault (aircraft producer) 75 50
402 50 c. Geoffrey de Havilland (aircraft designer) 75 50

1994. Migratory Birds. Multicoloured.

403 29 c. Type **69** 60 40
404 29 c. Long-tailed koel ("Cuckoo") 60 40
405 29 c. Short-eared owl 60 40
406 29 c. Eastern broad-billed roller ("Dollarbird") 60 40

70 Doves

1994. Christmas. Multicoloured.

407 29 c. Type **70** 50 30
408 50 c. Angels 90 60

1994. Local Leaders (2nd series). As T **56**. Multicoloured.

409 32 c. Anron Ring Buas 55 35
410 32 c. Belarmino Hatheylul . . . 55 35
411 32 c. Johnny Moses 55 35
412 32 c. Paliknoa Sigrah (King John) 55 35

72 Diver, Coral, Clown Triggerfish and Black-backed Butterflyfish

1995. Chuuk Lagoon. Multicoloured.

414 32 c. Type **72** 55 35
415 32 c. Black-backed butterflyfish, lionfish, regal angelfish and damselfishes 55 35
416 32 c. Diver, thread-finned butterflyfish and damselfishes 55 35
417 32 c. Pink anemonefish and damselfishes amongst anemone tentacles 55 35

Nos. 414/17 were issued together, se-tenant, forming a composite design.

1995. Pioneers of Flight (5th series). As T **51**. Multicoloured.

418 32 c. Robert Goddard (first liquid-fuelled rocket) 50 30
419 32 c. Leroy Grumman (first fighter with retractable landing gear) 50 30
420 32 c. Louis-Charles Breguet (aeronautics engineer) . . . 50 30
421 32 c. Juan de la Cierva (inventor of autogyro) 50 30
422 32 c. Hugo Junkers (aircraft engineer) 50 30
423 32 c. James Lovell Jr. (astronaut) 50 30
424 32 c. Donald Douglas (aircraft designer) 50 30
425 32 c. Reginald Mitchell (designer of Spitfire fighter) 50 30

73 West Highland White Terrier

1995. Dogs. Multicoloured.

426 32 c. Type **73** 55 35
427 32 c. Welsh springer spaniel . . 55 35
428 32 c. Irish setter 55 35
429 32 c. Old English sheepdog . . 55 35

74 "Hibiscus tiliaceus"

1995. Hibiscus. Multicoloured.

430 32 c. Type **74** 50 30
431 32 c. "Hibiscus huegelii" . . . 50 30
432 32 c. "Hibiscus trionum" . . . 50 30
433 32 c. "Hibiscus splendens" . . . 50 30
Nos. 430/3 were issued together, se-tenant, forming a composite design.

77 U.S.S. "Portland" (cruiser)

1995. 50th Anniv of End of Second World War. Liberation of Micronesia. Multicoloured.

436 60 c. Type **77** (liberation of Chuuk) . . . . 1·00 70
437 60 c. U.S.S. "Tillman" (destroyer) (Yap) . . . . 1·00 70
438 60 c. U.S.S. "Soley" (destroyer) (Kosrae) . . . . 1·00 70
439 60 c. U.S.S. "Hyman" (destroyer) (Pohnpei) . . . . 1·00 70

1995. Pioneers of Flight (6th series). As T **51**. Multicoloured.

441 60 c. Frederick Rohr (devoloper of mass-production techniques) 90 60
442 60 c. Juan Trippe (founder of Pan-American Airways) . . 90 60
443 60 c. Konstantin Tsiolkovsky (rocket pioneer) 90 60
444 60 c. Count Ferdinand von Zeppelin (airship inventor) . 90 60
445 60 c. Air Chief Marshal Hugh Dowding (commander of R.A.F. Fighter Command, 1940) 90 60
446 60 c. William Mitchell (pioneer of aerial bombing) 90 60
447 60 c. John Northrop (aircraft designer) 90 60
448 60 c. Frederick Handley Page (producer of first twin-engine bomber) 90 60

79 Poinsettia 80 Rabin

1995. Christmas.

449 **79** 32 c. multicoloured 40 25
450 60 c. multicoloured 80 55

1995. Yitzhak Rabin (Israeli Prime Minister) Commemoration.

451 **80** 32 c. multicoloured 55 35

1995. Pioneers of Flight (7th series). As T **51**. Multicoloured.

453 32 c. James Doolittle (leader of America's Second World War bomb raid on Japan) 50 30
454 32 c. Claude Dornier (aircraft designer) 50 30
455 32 c. Ira Eaker (leader of air effort against occupied Europe during Second World War) . 50 30
456 32 c. Jacob Ellehammer (first European manned flight) . . 50 30
457 32 c. Henry Arnold (Commander of U.S. air operations during Second World War) 50 30
458 32 c. Louis Bleriot (first flight across the English Channel) . 50 30
459 32 c. William Boeing (founder of Boeing Corporation) 50 30
460 32 c. Sydney Camm (aircraft designer) 50 30

82 Meeting House

1995. Tourism in Yap. Multicoloured.

461 32 c. Type **82** 50 30
462 32 c. Stone money 50 30
463 32 c. Churu dancing 50 30
464 32 c. Traditional canoe 50 30

1995. Fishes. As Nos. 275/95 but face values changed. Multicoloured.

465 32 c. Bennett's butterflyfish . . 55 25
466 32 c. Regal angelfish 55 25
467 32 c. Undulate ("Orange-striped") triggerfish 55 25
468 32 c. Zebra moray 55 25
469 32 c. Great barracuda 55 25
470 32 c. Bleeker's parrotfish 55 25
471 32 c. Mandarin fish 55 25
472 32 c. Clown ("Blue-banded") surgeonfish 55 25
473 32 c. Big-scaled soldierfish . . . 55 25
474 32 c. Peacock hind ("Peacock Grouper") 55 25
475 32 c. Picasso triggerfish ("Picassofish") 55 25
476 32 c. Masked ("Orangespine") unicornfish 55 25
477 32 c. Red-tailed surgeonfish . . 55 25
478 32 c. Coral hind ("Coral Grouper") 55 25
479 32 c. Palette surgeonfish 55 25
480 32 c. Oriental sweetlips 55 25
481 32 c. Fox-faced rabbitfish . . . 55 25
482 32 c. Saddle butterflyfish (dated "1996") 55 25
483 32 c. Moorish idol 55 25
484 32 c. Square-spotted anthias ("Square-spot Fairy Basslet") 55 25
485 32 c. Flame angelfish 55 25
486 32 c. Yellow-finned tuna . . . 55 25
487 32 c. Skipjack tuna 55 25
488 32 c. Blue-striped ("Blue-lined") snapper 55 25
489 32 c. Six-blotched hind ("Cave Grouper") 55 25
See also Nos. 522/5.

83 Necklace Sea Star

1996. Starfishes. Multicoloured.

490 55 c. Type **83** 85 55
491 55 c. Rhinoceros sea star . . . 85 55
492 55 c. Blue sea star 85 55
493 55 c. Thick-skinned sea star . . 85 55
Nos. 490/3 were issued together, se-tenant, forming a composite design.

84 10 l. Stamp

1996. Centenary of Modern Olympic Games. Designs reproducing 1896 Greek Olympic Issue. Multicoloured.

494 60 c. Type **84** . . . . 1·10 70
495 60 c. 25 l. stamp . . . . 1·10 70
496 60 c. 20 l. stamp . . . . 1·10 70
497 60 c. 10 d. stamp . . . . 1·10 70

85 "Palikir"

1996. Patrol Boats. Multicoloured.

498 32 c. Type **85** 45 25
499 32 c. "Micronesia" 45 25
Nos. 498/9 were issued together, se-tenant, forming a composite design.

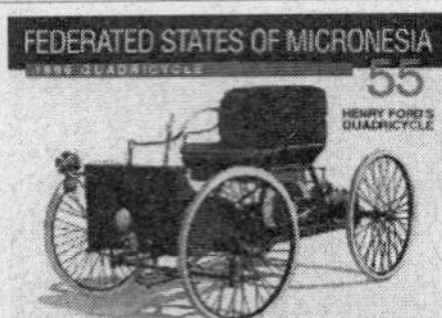

87 1896 Quadricycle

1996. Centenary of Ford Motor Vehicle Production. Multicoloured.

501 55 c. Type **87** 90 60
502 55 c. 1917 Model T Truck . . . 90 60
503 55 c. 1928 Model A Tudor Sedan 90 60
504 55 c. 1932 V-8 Sport Roadster . 90 60
505 55 c. 1941 Lincoln Continental . 90 60
506 55 c. 1953 F-100 Truck 90 60
507 55 c. 1958 Thunderbird convertible 90 60
508 55 c. 1996 Mercury Sable . . . 90 60

88 Reza 89 Oranges

1996. Reza (National Police Drug Enforcement Unit's dog).

509 **88** 32 c. multicoloured 50 30

1996. Citrus Fruits. Multicoloured.

510 50 c. Type **89** 90 60
511 50 c. Limes 90 60
512 50 c. Lemons 90 60
513 50 c. Tangerines 90 60
Nos. 510/13 were issued together, se-tenant, forming a composite design.

1996. Pioneers of Flight (8th series). As T **51**. Multicoloured.

514 60 c. Curtis LeMay (commander of Strategic Air Command) . 90 60
515 60 c. Grover Loening (first American graduate in aeronautical engineering) . . 90 60
516 60 c. Gianni Caproni (aircraft producer) 90 60
517 60 c. Henri Farman (founder of Farman Airlines) 90 60
518 60 c. Glenn Martin (aircraft producer) 90 60
519 60 c. Alliot Verdon Roe (aircraft designer) 90 60
520 60 c. Sergei Korolyov (rocket scientist) 90 60
521 60 c. Isaac Laddon (aircraft designer) 90 60

1996. 10th Asian International Stamp Exhibition, Taipeh. Fishes. As previous designs but additionally inscr for the exhibition in English (522, 525) or Chinese (523/4).

522 32 c. As No. 465 . . . . . . 55 35
523 32 c. As No. 468 . . . . . . 55 35
524 32 c. As No. 475 . . . . . . 55 35
525 32 c. As No. 483 . . . . . . 55 35

90 Wise Men following Star

1996. Christmas.

526 **90** 32 c. multicoloured 50 35
527 60 c. multicoloured 90 60

91 Outrigger Canoe and State Flag

1996. 10th Anniv of Ratification of Compact of Free Association with U.S.A.

528 **91** $3 multicoloured . . . . . 4·50 3·25

92 Water Buffalo

1997. New Year. Year of the Ox.

529 **92** 32 c. multicoloured 50 35

93 Walutahanga, Melanesia 94 Deng Xiaoping

1997. "Pacific 97" International Stamp Exhibition, San Francisco. Sea Goddesses of the Pacific. Multicoloured.

531 32 c. Type **93** 50 30
532 32 c. Tien-Hou holding lantern, China 50 30
533 32 c. Lorop diving in ocean, Micronesia 50 30
534 32 c. Oto-Hime with fisherman, Japan 50 30
535 32 c. Nomoi holding shell, Micronesia 50 30
536 32 c. Junkgowa Sisters in canoe, Australia 50 30

1997. Deng Xiaoping (Chinese statesman) Commemoration. Multicoloured.

537 60 c. Type **94** 85 50
538 60 c. Facing left (bare-headed) . 85 50
539 60 c. Facing right 85 50
540 60 c. Facing left wearing cap . . 85 50

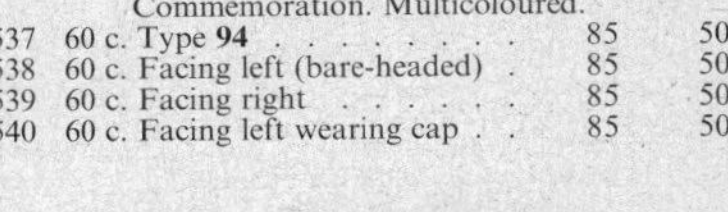

95 "Melia azedarach"

1997. Return of Hong Kong to China. Multicoloured.

542 60 c. Type **95** 85 50
543 60 c. Victoria Peak 85 50
544 60 c. "Dendrobium chrysotoxum" 85 50
545 60 c. "Bauhinia blakeana" . . . 85 50
546 60 c. "Cassia surattensis" . . . 85 50
547 60 c. Sacred lotus ("Nelumbo nucifera") 85 50

96 Tennis

1997. 2nd National Games. Multicoloured.

549 32 c. Type **96** 50 30
550 32 c. Throwing the discus . . . 50 30
551 32 c. Swimming 50 30
552 32 c. Canoeing 50 30

97 Rapids

1997. Birth Bicentenary of Hiroshige Ando (painter). Designs depicting details from "Whirlpools at Naruto in Awa Province" (Nos. 533/5), "Tail of Genji: Viewing the Plum Blossoms" (Nos. 556/8) and "Snow on the Sumida River" (Nos. 559/61). Multicoloured.

553 20 c. Type **97** 30 20
554 20 c. Whirlpools (rocky island at left) 30 20
555 20 c. Whirlpools (rocky island at right) 30 20
556 50 c. Woman on stepping stones 65 40
557 50 c. Woman 65 40
558 50 c. Woman on balcony of house 65 40
559 60 c. House and junks . . . . 1·00 60
560 60 c. Two women . . . . . . 1·00 60
561 60 c. Woman alighting from junk . . . . 1·00 60
Nos. 553/5, 556/8 and 559/61 respectively, were issued, se-tenant, forming composite designs of the paintings depicted.

98 Presley from High School Graduation Yearbook

1997. 20th Death Anniv of Elvis Presley (entertainer). Multicoloured.

563 50 c. Type **98** 85 55
564 50 c. With hound dog Nipper (R.C.A. Records mascot) . . 85 55
565 50 c. Wearing red striped shirt in publicity photograph for "Loving You" (film), 1957 . 85 55
566 50 c. Wearing sailor's cap in scene from "Girls, Girls, Girls!" (film), 1963 . . . . 85 55
567 50 c. Wearing knitted jacket with collar turned up, 1957 . . . 85 55
568 50 c. Wearing stetson in scene from "Flaming Star" (film), 1960 . . . . 85 55

99 Simon Lake and his Submarine "Argonaut", 1897

1997. Ocean Exploration: Pioneers of the Deep. Multicoloured.

569 32 c. Type **99** 40 25
570 32 c. William Beebe and Otis Barton's bathysphere (record depth, 1934) 40 25
571 32 c. Auguste Piccard and his bathyscaphe, 1954 . . . . . 40 25
572 32 c. Harold Edgerton and his deep sea camera, 1954 . . . 40 25
573 32 c. Jacques Piccard and U.S. Navy bathyscaphe "Trieste" (designed by Auguste Piccard) (record depth with Don Walsh, 1960) 40 25
574 32 c. Edwin Link and diving chamber ("Man-in-Sea" projects, 1962) 40 25
575 32 c. Melvin Fisher and diver (discovery of "Atocha" and "Santa Margarita" (Spanish galleons), 1971) 40 25
576 32 c. Robert Ballard and submersible "Alvin", 1978 . 40 25
577 32 c. Sylvia Earle and submersible "Deep Rover" (record dive in armoured suit, 1979) 40 25

100 Black-backed Butterflyfish

1997. Butterflyfishes. Multicoloured.

579 50 c. Type **100** 75 50
580 50 c. Saddle butterflyfish . . . 75 50
581 50 c. Thread-finned butterflyfish 75 50
582 50 c. Bennett's butterflyfish . . 75 50

101 "Christ Glorified in the Court of Heaven" (Fra Angelico) (left detail)

102 Diana, Princess of Wales

1997. Christmas. Multicoloured.

583 32 c. Type **101** 50 35
584 32 c. "Christ Glorified in the Court of Heaven" (right detail) 50 35
585 60 c. "A Choir of Angels" (detail, Simon Marmion) 75 50
586 60 c. "A Choir of Angels" (different detail) 75 50

1997. Diana, Princess of Wales Commemoration.

587 **102** 60 c. multicoloured 75 50

105 Rabbit

1998. Children's Libraries. The Hundred Acre Wood. Featuring characters from the Winnie the Pooh children's books. Multicoloured.

590 32 c. Type **105** 55 35
591 32 c. Owl 55 35
592 32 c. Eeyore 55 35
593 32 c. Kanga and Roo 55 35
594 32 c. Piglet 55 35
595 32 c. Tigger 55 35
596 32 c. Pooh 55 35
597 32 c. Christopher Robin . . . 55 35

Nos. 590/7 were issued together, se-tenant, forming a composite design.

106 Player celebrating Goal

1998. World Cup Football Championship, France. Multicoloured.

599 32 c. Type **106** 50 30
600 32 c. Player in green shirt kicking ball 50 30
601 32 c. Player in yellow shirt tackling another player . . . 50 30
602 32 c. Goalkeeper throwing ball . 50 30
603 32 c. Player in yellow shirt kicking ball overhead 50 30
604 32 c. Goalkeeper in red shirt . . 50 30
605 32 c. Player in yellow shirt with ball between legs 50 30
606 32 c. Player in red shirt and player on ground 50 30

Nos. 599/606 were issued together, se-tenant, forming a composite deisgn of a pitch.

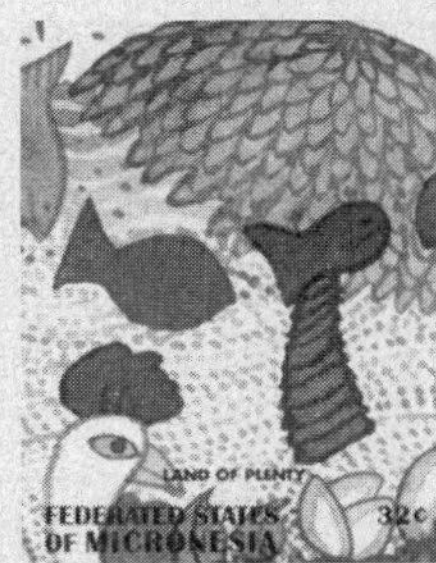

108 Land of Plenty

1998. Old Testament Stories. Multicoloured.

609 32 c. Type **108** 50 30
610 32 c. Adam and Eve 50 30
611 32 c. Serpent of Temptation . . 50 30
612 40 c. Three of Joseph's brothers . 60 40
613 40 c. Joseph and merchants . . 60 40
614 40 c. Ishmaelites 60 40
615 60 c. Rebekah in front of well . 80 50
616 60 c. Eliezer, Abraham's servant 80 50
617 60 c. Angel 80 50

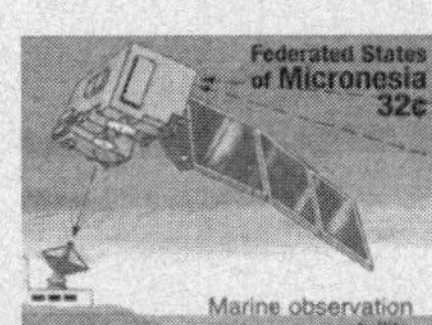

109 Marine Observation Satellite

1998. International Year of the Ocean. Deep Sea Research. Multicoloured.

619 32 c. Type **109** 55 35
620 32 c. "Natsushima" (support vessel) 55 35
621 32 c. "Kaiyo" (research vessel) . 55 35
622 32 c. Anemone 55 35
623 32 c. "Shinkai 2000" (deep-sea research vessel) 55 35
624 32 c. Deep-towed research vessel 55 35
625 32 c. Tripod fish 55 35
626 32 c. Towed deep-survey system 55 35
627 32 c. Black smokers 55 35

Nos. 619/27 were issued together, se-tenant, forming a composite design.

INDEX

Countries can be quickly located by referring to the index at the end of this volume.

110 Grey-brown ("Kosrae") White Eye

111 Ribbon-striped ("White-tipped") Soldierfish

1998. Birds. Multicoloured.

629 50 c. Type **110** 60 40
630 50 c. Truk ("Chuuk") monarch . 60 40
631 50 c. Yap monarch 60 40
632 50 c. Ponape lory 60 40

1998. Fishes. Multicoloured.

634 1 c. Type **111** 10 10
635 2 c. Red-breasted wrasse . . . 10 10
636 3 c. Bicoloured ("Bicolor") angelfish 10 10
637 4 c. Falco hawkfish 10 10
638 5 c. Convict tang 10 10
639 10 c. Square-spotted anthias ("Square-spot Fairy Basslet") 10 10
640 13 c. Orange-spotted ("Orangeband") surgeonfish . 15 10
641 15 c. Multibarred goatfish . . . 20 15
642 17 c. Masked rabbitfish 20 15
643 20 c. White-spotted surgeonfish . 25 15
644 22 c. Blue-girdled angelfish . . 30 20
645 32 c. Rectangle triggerfish ("Wedge Picassofish") . . . 40 25
646 33 c. Black jack 40 25
647 39 c. Red parrotfish 50 35
648 40 c. Lemon-peel angelfish . . 50 35
649 50 c. White-cheeked ("Whitecheek") surgeonfish . 60 40
650 55 c. Scarlet-finned ("Long-jawed") squirrelfish 65 45
651 60 c. Hump-headed ("Humphead") wrasse . . . 75 50
652 77 c. Onespot snapper 95 65
653 78 c. Blue ("Sapphire") damselfish 95 65
654 $1 Blue-finned ("Bluefin") trevally . . . . 1·25 85
655 $3 Whitespot hawkfish . . . . 3·75 2·25
656 $3.20 Tan-faced parrotfish . . . 4·00 2·75
657 $5 Spotted boxfish ("Trunkfish") . . . . 6·25 4·25
658 $10.75 Pink-tailed ("Pinktail") triggerfish . . . . 13·50 9·00
659 $11.75 Yellow-faced angelfish (48 × 25 mm) . . . . 14·50 9·75

112 Fala being stroked

1998. Fala (scottish terrier owned by Franklin D. Roosevelt). Multicoloured.

665 32 c. Type **112** 40 25
666 32 c. Fala and left half of wireless 40 25
667 32 c. Fala and right half of wireless 40 25
668 32 c. Fala and Roosevelt in car . 40 25
669 32 c. Fala's seal 40 25
670 32 c. Fala 40 25

113 "Eskimo Madonna" (Claire Fejes)

1998. Christmas. Works of Art. Multicoloured.

671 32 c. Type **113** 40 25
672 32 c. "Madonna" (Man Ray) . . 40 25
673 32 c. "Peasant Mother" (David Siquerios) 40 25
674 60 c. "Mother and Child" (Pablo Picasso) 40 25
675 60 c. "Gypsy Woman with Baby" (Amedeo Modigliani) . 40 25
676 60 c. "Mother and Child" (Jose Orozco) 40 25

114 Glenn

115 "Sputnik 1"

1998. John Glenn's (first American to orbit Earth) Return to Space. Multicoloured.

678 60 c. Type **114** 75 50
679 60 c. Launch of "Friendship 7" . 75 50
680 60 c. Glenn (bare-headed and in spacesuit) and United States flag on spaceship 75 50
681 60 c. Glenn (in spacesuit) and "Friendship" space capsule . 75 50
682 60 c. Glenn (in spacesuit) and United States flag on pole . . 75 50
683 60 c. Head and shoulders of Glenn in civilian clothes and stars (dated "1992") 75 50
684 60 c. "Friendship 7" 75 50
685 60 c. John Glenn with President Kennedy 75 50
686 60 c. Glenn in overalls 75 50
687 60 c. Launch of "Discovery" (space shuttle) 75 50
688 60 c. Glenn in cockpit 75 50
689 60 c. Head of Glenn in civilian suit 75 50
690 60 c. Glenn fastening inner helmet 75 50
691 60 c. Glenn with full helmet on . 75 50
692 60 c. Model of "Discovery" . . 75 50
693 60 c. Head of Glenn smiling (bare-headed) in spacesuit . . 75 50

1999. Exploration of the Solar System. Multicoloured.

(a) Space Achievements of Russia.

695 33 c. Type **115** (first artificial satellite, 1957) 40 25
696 33 c. Space dog Laika (first animal in space, 1957) (wrongly inscr "Leika") . . . 40 25
697 33 c. "Luna 1", 1959 . . . . . 40 25
698 33 c. "Luna 3", 1959 . . . . . 40 25
699 33 c. Yury Gagarin (first man in space, 1961) 40 25
700 33 c. "Venera 1" probe, 1961 . . 40 25
701 33 c. "Mars 1" probe, 1962 . . 40 25
702 33 c. Valentina Tereshkova (first woman in space, 1963) . . . 40 25
703 33 c. "Voskhod 1", 1964 . . . 40 25
704 33 c. Aleksei Leonov and "Voskhod 2" (first space walk, 1965) 40 25
705 33 c. "Venera 3" probe, 1966 . . 40 25
706 33 c. "Luna 10", 1966 . . . . 40 25
707 33 c. "Luna 9" (first landing on moon, 1966) 40 25
708 33 c. "Lunokhod 1" moon-vehicle from "Luna 17" (first roving vehicle on Moon, 1970) (wrongly inscr "First robot mission....Luna 16") . . 40 25
709 33 c. "Luna 16" on Moon's surface (first robot mission, 1970) (wrongly inscr "First roving vehicle...Luna 17") . . 40 25
710 33 c. "Mars 3", 1971 . . . . . 40 25
711 33 c. Leonid Popov, "Soyuz 35" and Valery Ryumin (first long manned space mission, 1980) . 40 25
712 33 c. Balloon ("Vega 1" Venus–Halley's Comet probe, 1985–86) 40 25
713 33 c. "Vega 1" and Halley's Comet, 1986 . . . . 40 25
714 33 c. "Mir" space station . . . 40 25

The captions on Nos. 708/9 have been transposed.

(b) Achievements of the United States of America

715 33 c. "Explorer 1", 1958 . . . . 40 25
716 33 c. Space observatory "OSO-1", 1962 . . . . 40 25
717 33 c. "Mariner 2" Venus probe, 1962 (first scientifically successful planetary mission) . 40 25
718 33 c. "Mariner 2" Venus probe, 1962 (first scientific interplanetary space discovery) 40 25
719 33 c. "Apollo 8" above Moon's surface 40 25
720 33 c. Astronaut descending ladder on "Apollo 11" mission (first manned Moon landing, 1969) 40 25
721 33 c. Astronaut taking Moon samples, 1969 . . . . . . 40 25
722 33 c. Lunar Rover of "Apollo 15", 1971 . . . . 40 25
723 33 c. "Mariner 9" Mars probe, 1971 . . . . 40 25
724 33 c. "Pioneer 10" passing Jupiter, 1973 . . . . 40 25
725 33 c. "Mariner 10" passing Mercury, 1974 . . . . . . 40 25
726 33 c. "Viking 1" on Mars, 1976 . 40 25
727 33 c. "Pioneer 11" passing Saturn, 1979 . . . . 40 25
728 33 c. "STS-1" (first re-usable spacecraft, 1981) 40 25
729 33 c. "Pioneer 10" (first man-made object to leave solar system, 1983) 40 25
730 33 c. Solar Maximum Mission, 1984 . . . . 40 25
731 33 c. "Cometary Explorer", 1985 . . . . 40 25
732 33 c. "Voyager 2" passing Neptune, 1989 . . . . 40 25
733 33 c. "Galileo" space probe, 1992 . . . . 40 25
734 33 c. "Sojourner" (Mars rover), 1997 . . . . 40 25

116 Map of the Pacific Ocean

1999. Voyages of the Pacific. Multicoloured.

736 33 c. Type **116** 40 25
737 33 c. Parrot 40 25
738 33 c. Red-tailed tropic bird 40 25
739 33 c. Plan of ship's hull 40 25
740 33 c. Sketches of winches 40 25
741 33 c. Yellow flowers 40 25
742 33 c. Full-rigged sailing ship 40 25
743 33 c. Three flowers growing from seeds and top of compass rose 40 25
744 33 c. Fish (background of ship's planking) 40 25
745 33 c. Flag of Yap 40 25
746 33 c. Flag of Truk (palm tree) 40 25
747 33 c. Flag of Kosrae (four stars) and bottom of compass rose 40 25
748 33 c. Sketches of fruit 40 25
749 33 c. Three plants and leaves 40 25
750 33 c. Fish (leaves at left) 40 25
751 33 c. Flag of Pohnpei and equator 40 25
752 33 c. Sextant 40 25
753 33 c. Red plant 40 25
754 33 c. Fish and left side of compass rose 40 25
755 33 c. Right side of compass rose and full-rigged sailing ship 40 25

Nos. 736/55 were issued together, se-tenant, forming a composite design.

117 Couple Meeting

1999. "Romance of the Three Kingdoms" (Chinese novel by Luo Guanzhong). Multicoloured.

756 33 c. Type **117** 40 25
757 33 c. Four men (one with lance) in room 40 25
758 33 c. Two riders in combat 40 25
759 33 c. Four men watching fifth man walking through room 40 25
760 33 c. Captives before man on wheeled throne 40 25
761 50 c. Riders approaching castle 40 25
762 50 c. Warrior pointing at fire 40 25
763 50 c. Opposing warriors riding through thick smoke 40 25
764 50 c. Couple kneeling before man on dais 40 25
765 50 c. Cauldron on fire 40 25

118 Carriage of Leipzig–Dresden Railway and Caroline Islands 1900 20 pf. Stamp

1999. "iBRA" International Stamp Fair, Nuremberg, Germany. Multicoloured.

767 55 c. Type **118** 65 45
768 55 c. Golsdorf steam railway locomotive and Caroline Islands 1 m. "Yacht" stamp 65 45

119 Black Rhinoceros

121 Deep-drilling for Brine Salt

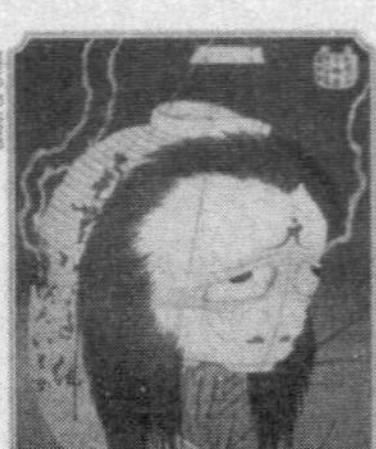

120 "Ghost of O-Iwa"

1999. Earth Day. Multicoloured.

770 33 c. Type **119** 40 25
771 33 c. Cheetah 40 25
772 33 c. Jackass penguin 40 25
773 33 c. Blue whale 40 25
774 33 c. Red-headed woodpecker 40 25
775 33 c. African elephant 40 25
776 33 c. Aurrochs 40 25
777 33 c. Dodo 40 25
778 33 c. Tasmanian wolf 40 25
779 33 c. Giant lemur 40 25
780 33 c. Quagga 40 25
781 33 c. Steller's sea cow 40 25
782 33 c. Pteranodon 40 25
783 33 c. Shonisaurus 40 25
784 33 c. Stegosaurus 40 25
785 33 c. Gallimimus 40 25
786 33 c. Tyrannosaurus 40 25
787 33 c. Archelon 40 25
788 33 c. Brachiosaurus 40 25
789 33 c. Triceratops 40 25

1999. 150th Death Anniv of Hokusai Katsushika (Japanese artist). Multicoloured.

791 33 c. Type **120** 40 25
792 33 c. Spotted horse with head lowered 40 25
793 33 c. "Abe Nakamaro" 40 25
794 33 c. "Ghost of Kasane" 40 25
795 33 c. Bay horse with head held up 40 25
796 33 c. "The Ghost of Kiku and the Priest Mitazuki" 40 25
797 33 c. "Belly Band Float" 40 25
798 33 c. Woman washing herself 40 25
799 33 c. "Swimmers" 40 25
800 33 c. "Eel Climb" 40 25
801 33 c. Woman playing lute 40 25
802 33 c. "Kimo Ga Imo ni Naru" 40 25

Nos. 792 and 795 are inscribed "Hores Drawings".

1999. New Millennium. Multicoloured. (a) Science and Technology of Ancient China.

804 33 c. Type **121** 40 25
805 33 c. Chain pump 40 25
806 33 c. Magic lantern 40 25
807 33 c. Chang Heng's seismograph 40 25
808 33 c. Dial and pointer devices 40 25
809 33 c. Page of Lui Hui's mathematics treatise (value of Pi) 40 25
810 33 c. Porcelain production 40 25
811 33 c. Water mill 40 25
812 33 c. Relief of horse from tomb of Tang Tai-Tsung (the stirrup) 40 25
813 33 c. Page of Lu Yu's tea treatise and detail of Liu Songnian's painting of tea-making 40 25
814 33 c. Umbrella 40 25
815 33 c. Brandy and whisky production 40 25
816 33 c. Page from oldest surviving printed book, woodblock and its print (printing) 40 25
817 33 c. Copper plate and its print (paper money) 40 25
818 33 c. Woodcut showing gunpowder demonstration 40 25
819 33 c. Anji Bridge (segmented arch) (56½ × 36 mm) 40 25
820 33 c. Mercator's star map and star diagram on bronze mirror 40 25

(b) People and Events of the Twelfth Century (1100–1150)

821 20 c. Holy Roman Emperor Henry IV (death, 1106) 30 20
822 20 c. Chastisement of monks of Enryakuji Temple, Kyoto, 1108 30 20
823 20 c. Founding of Knights of the Hospital of St. John, 1113 30 20
824 20 c. Invention of nautical compass, 1117 30 20
825 20 c. Drowning of Prince William, heir of King Henry I of England, 1120 30 20
826 20 c. Pope Callixtus II (Treaty of Worms, 1122, between Papacy and Holy Roman Emperor Henry V) 30 20
827 20 c. Death of Omar Khayyam (Persian poet), 1126 30 20
828 20 c. Death of Duke Guilhem IX, Count of Poitiers and Duke of Aquitaine (earliest known troubadour, 1127) 30 20
829 20 c. Coronation of King Roger II of Sicily, 1130 30 20
830 20 c. King Stephen and Queen Matilda (start of English civil war, 1135) 30 20
831 20 C. Moses Maimonides (philosopher, birth, 1138) 30 20
832 20 c. Abelard and Heloise (Church's censure of Abelard, 1140) 30 20
833 20 c. Defeat of French and German crusaders at Damascus, 1148 30 20
834 20 c. Fall of Mexican city of Tula, 1150s 30 20
835 20 c. Completion of Angkor Vat, Cambodia, 1150 30 20
836 20 c. Rise of Kingdom of Chimu, Peru, 1150s (56½ × 36 mm) 30 20
837 20 c. Honen (Buddhist monk) becomes hermit, 1150 30 20

122 Flowers

1999. Faces of the Millennium: Diana, Princess of Wales. Showing collage of miniature flower photographs. Multicoloured, country panel at left (a) or right (b).

838 50 c. Deep red shades (a) 60 40
839 50 c. Deep red shades (b) 60 40
840 50 c. Deep red shades with violet shades at bottom left (a) 60 40
841 50 c. Blackish shades in bottom left corner (b) 60 40
842 50 c. Violet shades at left and bottom, pinkish shades at right (a) 60 40
843 50 c. Lemon and pink shades (b) 60 40
844 50 c. Violet shades (a) 60 40
845 50 c. Type **122** (rose in bottom row) (b) 60 40

Nos. 838/45 were issued together, se-tenant, and when viewed as a whole, form a portrait of Diana, Princess of Wales.

123 Face of Woman

1999. Costumes of the World. Multicoloured.

846 33 c. Type **123** 30 20
847 33 c. Tools for fabric making 30 20
848 33 c. Head of African Masai warrior and textile pattern 30 20
849 33 c. Head of woman and textile pattern (inscr "French Renaissance costume") 30 20
850 33 c. Head of woman in hat with black feathers ("French princess gown 1900–1910") 30 20
851 33 c. Head of Micronesian woman in wedding costume 30 20
852 33 c. Body of African Masai warrior and head of woman 30 20
853 33 c. Body of woman ("Textile patterns of French Renaissance costume") 30 20
854 33 c. Body of woman ("1900–1910 French princess gown") 30 20
855 33 c. Body and head of two Micronesian women in wedding costumes 30 20
856 33 c. Hem of costume and body of woman ("Details of woman costume from African fabrics") 30 20
857 33 c. Lower part of dress and head of woman ("French Renaissance costume") 30 20
858 33 c. Hem of dress and furled umbrella 30 20
859 33 c. Body and legs of two Micronesian women in wedding costumes 30 20
860 33 c. Head of woman in Japanese Kabuki costume 30 20
861 33 c. Rulers for tailoring 30 20
862 33 c. Scissors 30 20
863 33 c. Japanese fabrics 30 20
864 33 c. Head and body of two women in Japanese Kabuki costumes 30 20
865 33 c. Iron 30 20

Nos. 846/65 were issued together, se-tenant, forming several composite designs.

124 "Holy Family with St. John"

1999. Christmas. Paintings by Anthony van Dyck. Multicoloured.

866 33 c. Type **124** 30 20
867 60 c. "Madonna and Child" 75 50
868 $2 "Virgin and Child with Two Donors" (detail) 2·50 1·60

125 Wright "Flyer I"

1999. Man's First Century of Flight. Multicoloured.

870 33 c. Type **125** 30 20
871 33 c. Bleriot XI and Notre Dame Cathedral, Paris 30 20
872 33 c. Fokker D.VII biplane and Brandenburg Gate, Berlin 30 20
873 33 c. Dornier Komet I (numbered B 240) and Amsterdam 30 20
874 33 c. Charles Lindbergh's Ryan NYP Special "Spirit of St. Louis" and steeple 30 20
875 33 c. Mitsubishi A6M Zero-Sen fighter and Mt. Fuji 30 20
876 33 c. Boeing B-29 Superfortress bomber and roof of building 30 20
877 33 c. Messerschmitt Me 262A jet fighter (swastika on tail) 30 20
878 33 c. Chuck Yeager's Bell X-1 rocket plane and Grand Canyon 30 20
879 33 c. Mikoyan Gurevich MiG-19 over Russian church 30 20
880 33 c. Lockheed U-2 reconnaissance plane over building at night 30 20
881 33 c. Boeing 707 jetliner and head of Statue of Liberty, New York 30 20
882 33 c. British Aerospace/Aerospatiale Concorde supersonic jetliner and top of Eiffel Tower, Paris 30 20
883 33 c. McDonnell Douglas DC-10 jetliner and Sydney Opera House 30 20
884 33 c. B-2 Spirit stealth bomber and globe 30 20

Nos. 870/84 were issued together, se-tenant, forming a composite design of the globe.

MIDDLE CONGO Pt. 6

One of three colonies into which Fr. Congo was divided in 1906. Became part of Fr. Equatorial Africa in 1937. Became part of the Congo Republic within the French Community on 28th November, 1958.

100 centimes = 1 franc

1 Leopard in Ambush

2 Bakalois Woman

3 Coconut Palms, Libreville

1907.

1	1	1 c. olive and brown	10	10
2		2 c. violet and brown	10	10
3		4 c. blue and brown	10	10
4		5 c. green and blue	10	10
21		5 c. yellow and blue	35	45
5		10 c. red and blue	15	10
22		10 c. green and light green	1·25	1·25
6		15 c. purple and pink	85	55
7		20 c. brown and blue	1·25	1·00
8	2	25 c. blue and green	45	35
23		25 c. green and grey	35	45
9		30 c. pink and green	55	45
24		30 c. red	75	75
10		35 c. brown and blue	55	55
11		40 c. green and brown	55	55
12		45 c. violet and orange	2·10	1·90
13		50 c. green and orange	75	70
25		50 c. blue and green	85	85
14		75 c. brown and blue	3·50	2·50
15	3	1 f. green and violet	6·00	4·50
16		2 f. violet and green	5·00	3·25
17		5 f. blue and pink	18·00	16·00

1916. Surch **5c** and red cross.

20	1	10 c. + 5 c. red and blue	45	55

1924. Surch **AFRIQUE EQUATORIALE FRANCAISE** and new value.

26	3	25 c. on 2 f. green and violet	35	35
27		25 c. on 5 f. pink and blue	35	35
28		65 on 1 f. brown and orange	45	55
29		85 on 1 f. brown and orange	55	55
30	2	90 on 75 c. scarlet and red	65	55
31		1 f. 25 on 1 f. ultramarine & bl	25	25
32		1 f. 50 on 1 f. blue & ultram	85	65
33		3 f. on 5 f. pink and brown	1·10	85
34		10 f. on 5 f. green and red	5·50	4·00
35		20 f. on 5 f. purple and brown	8·00	5·50

1924. Optd **AFRIQUE EQUATORIALE FRANCAISE.**

36	1	1 c. olive and brown	15	20
37		2 c. violet and brown	20	20
38		4 c. blue and brown	20	20
39		5 c. yellow and blue	20	20
40		10 c. green and light green	20	20
41		10 c. red and grey	20	20
42		15 c. purple and pink	25	25
43		20 c. brown and blue	25	25
44		20 c. green and light green	25	25
45		20 c. brown and mauve	45	25
46	2	25 c. green and grey	25	25
47		30 c. red	45	25
48		30 c. grey and mauve	20	10
49		30 c. deep green and green	25	25
50		35 c. brown and blue	25	25
51		40 c. green and brown	40	25
52		45 c. violet and orange	75	45
53		50 c. blue and green	50	25
54		50 c. yellow and black	25	15
55		65 c. brown and blue	1·10	90
56		75 c. brown and blue	35	25
57		90 c. red and pink	2·25	1·60
58	3	1 f. green and violet	75	55
59		1 f. 10 mauve and brown	1·75	1·10
60		1 f. 50 ultramarine and blue	3·25	2·40
61		2 f. violet and green	85	65
62		3 f. mauve on pink	3·50	3·00
63		5 f. blue and pink	2·50	1·25

1931. "Colonial Exhibition" key-types inscr "MOYEN CONGO".

65	E	40 c. green and black	2·00	1·90
66	F	50 c. mauve and black	1·10	1·00
67	G	90 c. red and black	1·40	1·10
68	H	1 f. 50 blue and black	2·00	1·10

15 Mindouli Viaduct

1933.

69	15	1 c. brown	10	50
70		2 c. blue	10	50
71		4 c. olive	15	50
72		5 c. red	45	45
73		10 c. green	65	65
74		15 c. purple	1·10	1·25
75		20 c. red on rose	5·50	3·00
76		25 c. orange	1·10	75
77		30 c. green	2·00	1·75
78	–	40 c. brown	85	55
79	–	45 c. black on green	90	65
80	–	50 c. purple	55	35
81	–	65 c. red on green	55	45
82	–	75 c. black on red	5·50	3·50
83	–	90 c. red	55	55
84	–	1 f. red	55	45
85	–	1 f. 25 green	90	60
86	–	1 f. 50 blue	3·25	1·50
87	–	1 f. 75 violet	1·00	75
88	–	2 f. olive	85	65
89	–	3 f. black on red	1·75	1·60
90	–	5 f. grey	8·00	6·50
91	–	10 f. black	35·00	18·00
92	–	20 f. brown	22·00	14·00

DESIGNS: 40 c. to 1 f. 50 Pasteur Institute, Brazzaville; 1 f. 75 to 20 f. Government Building, Brazzaville.

POSTAGE DUE STAMPS

1928. Postage Due type of France optd **MOYEN-CONGO A. E. F.**

D64	D 11	5 c. blue	25	25
D65		10 c. brown	25	25
D66		20 c. olive	55	55
D67		25 c. red	55	55
D68		30 c. red	55	55
D69		45 c. green	55	55
D70		50 c. purple	65	75
D71		60 c. brown on cream	95	95
D72		1 f. red on cream	1·00	1·00
D73		2 f. red	1·75	1·90
D74		3 f. violet	3·25	3·25

D 13 Village

1930.

D75	D 13	5 c. olive and blue	35	45
D76		10 c. brown and red	55	55
D77		20 c. brown and green	1·50	1·50
D78		25 c. brown and blue	2·00	2·25
D79		30 c. green and brown	3·00	3·25
D80		45 c. olive and green	3·00	3·25
D81		50 c. brown and mauve	3·00	3·25
D82		60 c. black and violet	3·50	3·50
D83	–	1 f. black and brown	6·00	6·00
D84	–	2 f. brown and mauve	6·50	6·50
D85	–	3 f. brown and red	6·50	6·50

DESIGN: 1 to 3 f. "William Guinet" (steamer) on the River Congo.

D 17 "Le Djoue"

1933.

D 93	D 17	5 c. green	40	45
D 94		10 c. blue on blue	45	45
D 95		20 c. red on yellow	55	55
D 96		25 c. red	55	55
D 97		30 c. red	65	75
D 98		45 c. purple	65	75
D 99		50 c. black	1·25	1·25
D100		60 c. black on red	1·75	1·75
D101		1 f. red	2·50	2·50
D102		2 f. orange	3·75	3·75
D103		3 f. blue	6·25	6·25

For later issues see **FRENCH EQUATORIAL AFRICA.**

MODENA Pt. 8

A state in Upper Italy, formerly a duchy and now part of Italy. Used stamps of Sardinia after the cessation of its own issues in 1860. Now uses Italian stamps.

100 centesimi = 1 lira

1 Arms of Este

5 Cross of Savoy

1852. Imperf.

9	1	5 c. black on green	10·00	23·00
3		10 c. black on pink	£200	55·00
4		15 c. black on yellow	15·00	12·00
5		25 c. black on buff	18·00	12·00
12		40 c. black on blue	19·00	85·00
13		1 l. black on white	35·00	£1600

1859. Imperf.

18	5	5 c. green	£500	£475
19		15 c. brown	£800	£2250
20		15 c. grey	£100	
21		20 c. black	£800	75·00
22		20 c. lilac	26·00	£400
23		40 c. red	80·00	£700
24		80 c. brown	85·00	£12000

NEWSPAPER STAMPS

1853. As T **1** but in the value tablet inscr "B.G. CEN" and value. Imperf.

N15	1	9 c. black on mauve	£140	40·00
N16		10 c. black on lilac	20·00	£160

N 4

1859. Imperf.

N17	N 4	10 c. black	£400	£1800

MOHELI Pt. 6

An island in the Comoro Archipelago adjacent to Madagascar. A separate French dependency until 1914 when the whole archipelago was placed under Madagascar whose stamps were used until 1950. Now part of the Comoro Islands.

100 centimes = 1 franc

1906. "Tablet" key-type inscr "MOHELI" in blue (2, 4, 10, 20, 30, 40 c., 5 f.) or red (others).

1	D	1 c. black on blue	85	80
2		2 c. brown on buff	85	60
3		4 c. brown on grey	90	1·10
4		5 c. green	1·25	1·00
5		10 c. red	1·60	1·00
6		20 c. red on green	6·00	4·00
7		25 c. blue	6·25	3·00
8		30 c. brown on drab	9·50	7·00
9		35 c. black on yellow	4·75	2·25
10		40 c. red on yellow	7·00	4·25
11		45 c. black on green	45·00	30·00
12		50 c. brown on blue	13·00	8·00
13		75 c. brown on orange	13·00	11·50
14		1 f. green	8·50	8·25
15		2 f. violet on pink	21·00	19·00
16		5 f. mauve on lilac	90·00	75·00

1912. Surch in figures.

17	D	05 on 4 c. brown and blue on grey	55	70
18		05 on 20 c. red and blue on green	90	2·00
19		05 on 30 c. brown and blue on drab	80	1·00
20		10 on 40 c. red and blue on yellow	80	1·00
21		10 on 45 c. black and red on green	60	80
22		10 on 50 c. brown and red on blue	90	1·25

MOLDOVA Pt. 10

Formerly Moldavia, a constituent republic of the Soviet Union. Moldova declared its sovereignty within the Union in 1990 and became independent in 1991.

1991. 100 kopeks = 1 rouble.
1993. Kupon (temporary currency).
1993. 100 bani = 1 leu.

1 Arms

2 Codrii Nature Reserve

1991. 1st Anniv of Declaration of Sovereignty. Multicoloured. Imperf.

1		7 k. Type **1**	10	10
2		13 k. Type **1**	10	10
3		30 k. Flag (35 × 23 mm)	15	10

1992.

4	2	25 k. multicoloured	25	10

3 Arms

4 Tupolev Tu-144

1992.

5	3	35 k. green	10	10
6		50 k. red	10	10
7		65 k. brown	10	10
8		1 r. purple	15	10
9		1 r. 50 blue	25	10

1992. Air.

15	4	1 r. 75 red	10	10
16		2 r. 50 mauve	15	10
17		7 r. 75 violet	60	30
18		8 r. 50 green	80	40

See also Nos. 70/3.

5 European Bee Eater

6 St. Panteleimon's Church

1992. Birds. Multicoloured.

19		50 k. Type **5**	10	10
20		65 k. Golden oriole	10	10
21		2 r. 50 Green woodpecker	20	10
22		6 r. Common roller	50	25
23		7 r. 50 Hoopoe	65	30
24		15 r. European cuckoo	1·25	65

See also Nos. 63/9.

1992. Centenary (1991) of St. Panteleimon's Church, Chisinau.

25	6	1 r. 50 multicoloured	15	10

7 Wolf suckling Romulus and Remus

9 High Jumping

1992. Trajan Memorial, Chisinau.

26	7	5 r. multicoloured	15	10

1992. Various stamps of Russia surch **MOLDOVA** and value.

27		2 r. 50 on 4 k. red (No. 4672)	10	10
28		6 r. on 3 k. red (No. 4671)	10	10
29		8 r. 50 on 4 k. red (No. 4672)	30	15
30		10 r. on 3 k. green (No. 6074)	50	25

1992. Olympic Games, Barcelona. Multicoloured.

31		35 k. Type **9**	10	10
32		65 k. Wrestling	10	10
33		1 r. Archery	10	10
34		2 r. 50 Swimming	30	15
35		10 r. Show jumping	1·10	55

1992. Nos. 4669/71 of Russia surch **MOLDOVA**, new value and bunch of grapes.

37	–	45 k. on 2 k. mauve	10	10
38	–	46 k. on 2 k. mauve	10	10
39	1753	63 k. on 1 k. green	10	10
40	–	63 k. on 3 k. red	10	10
41	1753	70 k. on 1 k. green	10	10
42		4 r. on 1 k. green	30	15

1992. Moldovan Olympic Games Medal Winners. Nos. 33/4 optd.

43		1 r. Archery (optd **NATALIA VALEEV / bronz** and emblem)	40	20
44		2 r. 50 Swimming (optd **IURIE BASCATOV / argint** and emblem)	1·10	55

13 Moldovan Flag, Statue of Liberty and U.N. Emblem and Building

1992. Admission of Moldova to U.N.O. Mult.

46		1 r. 30 Type **13**	10	10
47		12 r. As Type **13** but with motifs differently arranged	40	20

14 Moldovan Flag and Prague Castle

1992. Admission of Moldova to European Security and Co-operation Conference. Multicoloured.

48		2 r. 50 Type **14**	15	10
49		25 r. Helsinki Cathedral and Moldovan flag	50	25

15 Carpet and Pottery 16 Galleon

1992. Folk Art.
50 15 7 r. 50 multicoloured 25 15

1992. 500th Anniv of Discovery of America by Columbus. Multicoloured.
51 1 r. Type **16** 15 10
52 6 r. Carrack 80 40
53 6 r. Caravel 80 40

17 Letter Sorter, Diesel Train, State Flag and U.P.U. Emblem

1992. Admission to U.P.U. Multicoloured.
55 5 r. Type **17** 75 40
56 10 r. Douglas DC-10 jetliner, computerized letter sorting equipment, state flag and U.P.U. emblem 95 50

18 Aesculapius Snake

1993. Protected Animals. Snakes. Multicoloured.
57 3 r. Type **18** 20 10
58 3 r. Aesculapius in tree 20 10
59 3 r. Aesculapius on path 20 10
60 3 r. Aesculapius on rock 20 10
61 15 r. Grass snake 75 40
62 25 r. Adder . . . . 1·25 60
Nos. 57/60 were issued together, se-tenant, forming a composite design.

1993. Birds. As Nos. 19/24 but with values changed and additional design. Multicoloured.
63 2 r. Type **5** 10 10
64 3 r. As No. 20 . . . . 10 10
65 5 r. As No. 21 . . . . 10 10
66 10 r. As No. 22 . . . . 15 10
67 15 r. As No. 23 . . . . 20 10
68 50 r. As No. 24 . . . . 75 35
69 100 r. Barn swallow . . . . . . 1·50 75

1993. Air.
70 4 25 r. red 20 10
71 45 r. brown 35 20
72 50 r. green 40 20
73 90 r. blue 70 35

19 Arms 20

1993.
74 19 2 k. blue 10 10
75 3 k. purple 10 10
76 6 k. green 10 10
77 – 10 k. violet and green 10 10
78 – 15 k. violet and green 10 10
79 – 20 k. violet and grey 10 10
80 – 30 k. violet and yellow . . . 15 10
81 – 50 k. violet and red 20 10
82 20 100 k. multicoloured 40 20
83 250 k. multicoloured 90 45
DESIGN: 10 to 50 k. Similar to Type **19** but with inscription and value at foot differently arranged.

21 Red Admiral 22 "Tulipa bibersteiniana"

1993. Butterflies and Moths. Multicoloured.
94 6 b. Type **21** 10 10
95 10 b. Swallowtail 10 10
96 50 b. Peacock 35 20
97 250 b. Emperor moth . . . . . 1·90 80

1993. Flowers. Multicoloured.
98 6 b. Type **22** 10 10
99 15 b. Lily of the valley 10 10
100 25 b. Snowdrop 15 10
101 30 b. Peony 20 10
102 50 b. Snowdrop 30 15
103 90 b. Pasque flower 60 30

23 Dragos Voda (1352–53) 24 "Story of One Life" (M. Grecu)

1993. 14th-century Princes of Moldavia. Multicoloured.
105 6 b. Type **23** 10 10
106 25 b. Bogdan Voda I (1359–65) . 10 10
107 50 b. Latcu Voda (1365–75) . . 20 10
108 100 b. Petru I Musat (1375–91) . 45 25
109 150 b. Roman Voda Musat (1391–94) 65 35
110 200 b. Stefan I (1394–99) . . . 90 45

1993. Europa. Contemporary Art. Multicoloured.
111 3 b. Type **24** 10 10
112 150 b. "Coming of Spring" (I. Vieru) . . . . 1·60 80

25 Biathletes 27 State Arms

1994. Winter Olympic Games, Lillehammer, Norway. Multicoloured.
113 3 b. Type **25** 10 10
114 150 b. Close-up of biathlete shooting . . . . 1·25 60

1994. No. 4669 of Russia surch **MOLDOVA**, grapes and value.
115 1753 3 b. on 1 k. green 10 10
116 25 b. on 1 k. green 10 10
117 50 b. on 1 k. green 15 10

1994.
118 27 1 b. multicoloured 10 10
119 10 b. multicoloured 10 10
120 30 b. multicoloured 10 10
121 38 b. multicoloured 15 10
122 45 b. multicoloured 15 10
123 75 b. multicoloured 30 15
124 1 l. 50 multicoloured 60 30
125 1 l. 80 multicoloured 70 35
126 2 l. 50 mult (24 × 29 mm) . . 95 50
127 4 l. 50 multicoloured . . . . 1·75 1·25
128 5 l. 40 multicoloured . . . . 2·00 1·40
129 6 l. 90 multicoloured . . . . 2·50 1·50
130 7 l. 20 mult (24 × 29 mm) . . 2·75 1·75
131 13 l. mult (24 × 29 mm) . . 5·25 3·50
132 24 l. mult (24 × 29 mm) . . 9·25 6·00

28 Launch of "Titan II" Rocket 29 Maria Cibotari (singer)

1994. Europa. Inventions and Discoveries. 25th Anniv of First Manned Moon Landing. Multicoloured.
136 1 b. Type **28** 10 10
137 45 b. Ed White (astronaut) on space walk ("Gemini 4" flight, 1965) 65 35
138 2 l. 50 Lunar module landing, 1969 . . . . 2·25 1·25

1994. Entertainers' Death Anniversaries. Mult.
139 3 b. Type **29** (45th) 10 10
140 90 b. Dumitru Caraciobanu (actor, 14th) 40 20
141 150 b. Eugeniu Coca (composer, 40th) 70 35
142 250 b. Igor Vieru (actor, 11th) . 1·10 55

30 Preparing Stamp Design

1994. Stamp Day.
143 30 10 b. black, blue and mauve . 10 10
144 – 45 b. black, mauve and yellow 30 15
145 – 2 l. multicoloured . . . . . 1·25 65
DESIGNS: 45 b. Printing stamps; 2 l. Checking finished sheets.

31 Pierre de Coubertin (founder) 32 Map

1994. Centenary of International Olympic Committee. Multicoloured.
146 60 b. Type **31** 20 10
147 1 l. 50 Rings and "Paris 1994" centenary congress emblem . 65 35

1994. Partnership for Peace Programme (co-operation of N.A.T.O. and Warsaw Pact members).
148 – 60 b. black, ultramarine and blue 20 20
149 32 2 l. 50 multicoloured 30 30
DESIGN: 60 b. Manfred Worner (Secretary-General of N.A.T.O.) and President Mircea Snegur of Moldova.

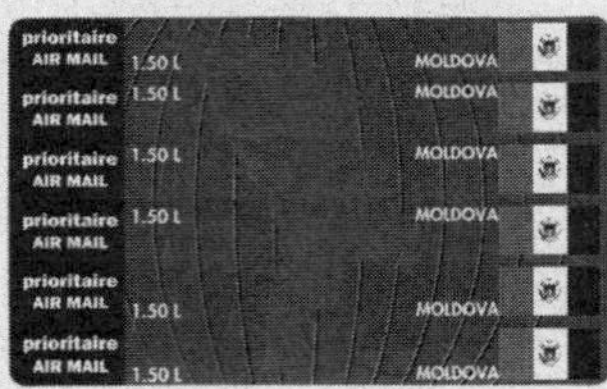

34 Map
(½-size illustration)

1994. Air. Self-adhesive. Roul.
152 34 1 l. 50 multicoloured 50 25
153 4 l. 50 multicoloured . . . . 1·50 75
The individual stamps are peeled directly from the card backing. Each card contains six different designs with the same face value forming the composite design illustrated. Each stamp is a horizontal strip with a label indicating the main class of mail covered by the rate at the left, separated by a vertical line of rouletting. The outer edges of the cards are imperforate.

35 Family 36 Handshake

1994. International Year of the Family. Multicoloured.
154 30 b. Type **35** 20 10
155 60 b. Mother breastfeeding baby 40 20
156 1 l. 50 Child drawing . . . . . 1·50 90

1994. Preliminary Rounds of European Cup Football Championship, England (1996). Multicoloured.
157 10 b. Type **36** 10 10
158 40 b. Players competing for ball 25 15
159 2 l. 40 Goalkeeper making save . 1·50 90

37 "Birth of Jesus Christ" (anon) 38 Cracked Green Russula

1994. Christmas. Multicoloured.
161 20 b. Type **37** 15 10
162 3 l. 60 "Birth of Jesus Christ" (Gherasim) . . . . 1·90 1·00

1995. Fungi. Multicoloured.
163 4 b. Type **38** 10 10
164 10 b. Oak mushroom 25 15
165 20 b. Chanterelle 45 25
166 90 b. Red-capped scaber stalk . 2·10 1·10
167 1 l. 80 "Leccinum duriusculum" . . . . 4·25 2·25

39 Booted Eagle

1995. European Nature Conservation Year. Multicoloured.
168 4 b. Type **39** 40 20
169 45 b. Roe deer . . . . 1·00 50
170 90 b. Wild boar . . . . 2·00 1·10

40 Earthenware Urns and Necklace

1995. National Museum Exhibits. Multicoloured.
171 4 b. Type **40** 10 10
172 10 b. + 2 b. Representation and skeleton of "Dinotherium gigantissimum" 25 15
173 1 l. 80 + 30 b. Silver coins . . 2·75 1·75

41 "May 1945" (Igor Vieru)

1995. Europa. Peace and Freedom. Paintings. Multicoloured.
174 10 b. Type **41** 15 10
175 40 b. "Peace" (Sergiu Cuciuc) . 35 20
176 2 l. 20 "Spring 1944" (Cuciuc) . 2·00 1·10

42 Constantin Stere (writer, 130th birth) 43 Alexandru cel Bun (1400–32)

1995. Anniversaries.
177 42 9 b. brown and grey 15 10
178 – 10 b. purple and grey . . . 15 10
179 – 40 b. lilac and grey 55 30
180 – 1 l. 80 green and grey . . . 2·50 1·50
DESIGNS: 10 b. Tamara Ceban (singer, 5th death); 40 b. Alexandru Plamadeala (sculptor, 55th death); 1 l. 80, Lucian Blaga (philosopher, birth centenary).

1995. 15th–16th Century Princes of Moldavia. Multicoloured.
181 10 b. Type **43** 15 10
182 10 b. Petru Aron (1451–52 and 1454–57) 15 10
183 10 b. Stefan cel Mare (1457–1504) 15 10
184 45 b. Petru Rares (1527–38 and 1541–46) 65 35
185 90 b. Alexandru Lapusneanu (1552–61 and 1564–68) 1·40 70
186 1 l. 80 Ioan Voda cel Cumplit (1572–74) 3·00 1·50

44 Soroca Castle

1995. Castles. Multicoloured.
188 10 b. Type **44** 15 10
189 20 b. Tighina Castle 35 15
190 60 b. Alba Castle 1·00 60
191 1 l. 30 Hotin Castle 2·40 1·60

45 Seal in Eye

46 "50" and Emblem

1995. 50th Anniv of U.N.O. Multicoloured. (a) Ordinary gum. Perf.
192 10 b. Type **45** 20 10
193 10 b. Airplane in eye 20 10
194 1 l. 50 Child's face and barbed wire in eye 3·25 2·00

(b) Self-adhesive. Rouletted.
195 90 b. Type **46** 30 15
196 1 l. 50 Type **46** 45 25

47 "Last Moon of Autumn" 48 Fly Agaric

1995. Centenary of Motion Pictures.
197 **47** 10 b. red and black 15 10
198 – 40 b. green and black 50 25
199 – 2 l. 40 blue and black 3·00 2·00
DESIGNS: 40 b. "Lautarii"; 2 l. 40, "Dimitrie Cantemir".

1996. Fungi. Multicoloured.
200 10 b. Type **48** 10 10
201 10 b. Satan's mushroom 10 10
202 65 b. Death cap 65 35
203 1 l. 30 Clustered woodlover 1·25 70
204 2 l. 40 Destroying angel 2·40 1·25

49 Weightlifting 50 Rudi Monastery

1996. Olympic Games, Atlanta, U.S.A. Multicoloured.
205 10 b. Type **49** 10 10
206 20 b. + 5 b. Judo 35 15
207 45 b. + 10 b. Running 65 35
208 2 l. 40 + 30 b. Kayaking 3·00 1·75

1996. Monasteries. Multicoloured.
210 10 b. Type **50** 10 10
211 90 b. Japca 40 20
212 1 l. 30 Curchi 60 30
213 2 l. 80 Saharna 1·25 70
214 4 l. 40 Capriana 2·10 1·25

51 Moorhens 52 Elena Alistar (president of Women's League)

1996. Birds. Multicoloured.
215 9 b. Type **51** 15 10
216 10 b. Greylag geese 15 10
217 2 l. 20 Turtle doves 1·75 1·10
218 4 l. 40 Mallard 3·50 2·10

1996. Europa. Famous Women. Multicoloured.
220 10 b. Type **52** 15 10
221 3 l. 70 Marie Sklodowska-Curie (physicist) 2·75 1·90

53 Mihail Eminescu (poet) (146th birth anniv) 54 Town Hall

1996. Birth Anniversaries.
223 **53** 10 b. brown and deep brown 10 10
224 – 10 b. sepia and brown 10 10
225 – 2 l. 20 green and brown 90 45
226 – 3 l. 30 green and deep brown 1·40 75
227 – 5 l. 40 brown and deep brown 2·25 1·40
DESIGNS: 10 b. Gavriil Banulescu-Bodoni (Metropolitan of Chisinau, 250th); 2 l. 20, Ion Creanga (writer, 159th); 3 l. 30, Vasile Alecsandri (writer, 172nd); 5 l. 40, Petru Movila and printing press (400th).

1996. 560th Anniv of Chisinau. Multicoloured.
229 10 b. Type **54** 10 10
230 1 l. 30 Cultural Palace 1·25 60
231 2 l. 40 Mazarache Church 2·25 1·40

55 Carol Singers with Star 57 Feteasca

1996. Christmas. Multicoloured.
232 10 b. Type **55** 10 10
233 2 l. 20 + 30 b. Mother and child at centre of star 1·25 60
234 2 l. 80 + 50 b. Children decorating Christmas tree 1·60 1·00

1997. Moldovan Wines. Each showing a grape variety and bottle of wine. Multicoloured.
236 10 b. Type **57** 10 10
237 45 b. Cabernet-Sauvignon 30 15
238 65 b. Sauvignon 45 25
239 3 l. 70 Rara Neagra 2·50 1·50

58 Franz Schubert

1997. Composers. Each green and grey.
240 10 b. Type **58** (birth bicentenary) 10 10
241 10 b. Gavriil Musicescu (150th birth anniv) 10 10
242 45 b. Sergei Rachmaninov 40 20
243 4 l. 40 Georges Enesco 3·75 2·40

59 Girl with Eggs

1997. Easter. Multicoloured.
244 10 b. Type **59** 10 10
245 3 l. 3o0 Easter dish 1·75 1·10

60 Stork flying over Battlements 61 Praying Mantis

1997. Europa. Tales and Legends. Multicoloured.
247 10 b. Type **60** 10 10
248 2 l. 80 Master Manole 1·25 75

1997. Insects in the Red Book. Multicoloured.
250 25 b. Type **61** 10 10
251 80 b. "Ascalaphus macaroniusn" (owl-fly) 45 20
252 1 l. Searcher 55 30
253 2 l. 20 "Liometopum microcephalum" (ant) 1·25 70

62 Post Office No. 12, Chisinau 63 Nicolai Zelinski School, Tiraspol

1997. World Post Day.
255 **62** 10 b. green and olive 10 10
256 – 2 l. 20 green and brown 1·60 80
257 – 3 l. 30 olive and green 2·40 1·40
DESIGNS—HORIZ: 2 l. 20, District Head Post and Telegraph Office, Chisinau. VERT: 3 l. 30, Heinrich von Stephan (founder of U.P.U.) (death centenary).

1997. Protection of Buildings.
258 **63** 7 b. black and violet 10 10
259 – 10 b. black and purple 10 10
260 – 10 b. black and blue 10 10
261 – 90 b. black and yellow 50 25
262 – 1 l. 30 black and blue 75 40
263 – 3 l. 30 black and grey 1·90 90
DESIGNS: No. 259, Railway station, Tighina; 260, Sts. Constantine and Elena Cathedral, Balti; 261, Church, Causeni; 262, Archangel Michael Cathedral, Cahul; 263, Academy of Art, Chisinau.

64 Noul Neamt Monastery, Chitcani 65 Petru Schiopul (1574–77, 1578–79 and 1582–91)

1997. Christmas. Multicoloured.
264 10 b. Type **64** 10 10
265 45 b. "Birth of Our Lord Jesus Christ" 25 15
266 5 l. "Birth of Jesus Christ" (different) 2·75 1·75

1997. 16th–17th Century Princes of Moldavia. Multicoloured.
267 10 b. Type **65** 10 10
268 10 b. Ieremia Movila (1595–1606) 10 10
269 45 b. Stefan Tomsa (1611–15 and 1621–23) 25 15
270 1 l. 80 Radu Mihnea (1616–19 and 1623–26) 95 55
271 2 l. 20 Miron Barnovschi Movila (1626–29 and 1633) 1·10 70
272 2 l. 80 Bogdan Orbul (1504–1517) 1·50 90

66 Skiing

1998. Winter Olympic Games, Nagano, Japan. Multicoloured.
274 10 b. Type **66** 10 10
275 45 b. Pairs figure skating 35 15
276 2 l. 20 Biathlon 1·75 1·10

67 Alexei Mateeici 68 Statue of Stefan cel Mare (Alexandru Plamadeala), Chisinau

1998. Anniversaries. Multicoloured.
277 10 b. Type **67** (110th birth anniv) 10 10
278 40 b. Pantelimon Halippa (115th birth anniv) 20 10
279 60 b. Stefan Ciobanu (115th birth anniv) 35 20
280 2 l. Constantin Stamati-Ciurea (death centenary) 90 45

1998. Art. Multicoloured.
282 10 b. Type **68** 10 10
283 60 b. "The Resurrection of Christ" (icon) 35 20
284 1 l. Modern sculpture (Constantin Brancusi), Targu-Jiu 55 30
285 2 l. 60 Trajan's Column, Rome 1·25 65

69 Masks and Eye 70 Cherries

1998. Europa. National Festivals. Multicoloured.
286 10 b. Type **69** (Eugene Ionescu Theatre Festival) 10 10
287 2 l. 20 Medallion showing potter (Cermanics Fair) 1·10 55

1998. Fruits. Multicoloured.
289 7 b. Type **70** 10 10
290 10 b. Plums 10 10
291 1 l. Apples 55 30
292 2 l. Pears 90 45

72 Chilia

1998. Medieval Towns.
294 **72** 10 b. grey and black 10 10
295 – 60 b. brown and black 35 20
296 – 1 l. red and black 50 25
297 – 2 l. blue and black 95 50
DESIGNS: 60 b. Orhei; 1 l. Suceava; 2 l. Ismail.

73 1858 Moldavia Stamps

1998. 140th Anniv of Stamp Issues of Moldavia. Multicoloured.
298 10 b. Type **73** 10 10
299 90 b. 1858 Moldavia 54 p. and 1928 Rumania 1 and 5 l. stamps 40 20
300 2 l. 20 1858 Moldavia 81 p. and Russian stamps 1·10 55
301 2 l. 40 1858 Moldavia 108 p. and Moldova 1996 10 b. and 1994 45 b. stamps 1·25 65

74 Eagle Owl 75 Couple from Vara

1998. Birds. Multicoloured.
302 25 b. Type **74** 30 15
303 2 l. Demoiselle crane (horiz) 1·25 65

1998. Regional Costumes. Multicoloured.
304 25 b. Type **75** 15 10
305 90 b. Couple from Vara (different) 60 30
306 1 l. 80 Couple from Iarna 1·25 65
307 2 l. Couple from Iarna (different) 1·40 70

76 Anniversary Emblem and "Proportions of Man" (Leonardo da Vinci)

1998. 50th Anniv of Universal Declaration of Human Rights.

308 **76** 2 l. 40 multicoloured . . . 1·60 80

77 Conference Members

1998. 80th Anniv of Union of Bessarabia and Rumania.

309 **77** 90 b. brown, blue and black . 60 30

78 Mail Coach

1999. Anniversaries. Multicoloured.

310 25 b. Type **78** (125th anniv of U.P.U.) 15 10
311 2 l. 20 Map of Europe and Council of Europe emblem (50th anniv) . . . . 1·50 75

79 Prutul de Jos Park

1999. Europa. Parks and Gardens. Multicoloured.

312 25 b. Type **79** 15 10
313 2 l. 40 Padurea Domneasca Park . . . . 1·60 80

80 Balzac

81 "Aleksandr Pushkin and Constantin Stamati" (B. Lebedev)

1999. Birth Bicentenary of Honore de Balzac (writer).

315 **80** 90 b. multicoloured 60 30

1999. Birth Bicentenary of Aleksandr Pushkin (poet).

316 **81** 65 b. brown, deep brown and black 45 25

82 Tranta

1999. National Sports.

317 **82** 25 b. green and light green . 15 10
318 – 1 l. 80 green and yellow . . 1·25 60

DESIGN: 1 l. 80, Oina.

83 Neil Armstrong (first man on Moon)

1999. 30th Anniv of First Manned Moon Landing. Multicoloured.

319 25 b. Type **83** 15 10
320 25 b. Michael Collins (pilot of Command Module) 15 10
321 5 l. Edwin Aldrin (pilot of Lunar Module) . . . . 3·25 1·75

84 Military Merit

85 Embroidered Shirt

1999. Orders and Medals. Multicoloured.

322 25 b. Type **84** 15 10
323 25 b. For Valour 15 10
324 25 b. Civil Merit 15 10
325 90 b. Mihai Eminescu Medal . . 60 30
326 1 l. 10 Order of Gloria Muncii . . 75 40
327 2 l. 40 Order of Stefan al Mare . 1·60 80

1999. Crafts. Multicoloured.

329 5 b. Inlaid wine flask 10 10
330 25 b. Type **85** 15 10
331 95 b. Ceramic jugs 60 30
332 1 l. 80 Wicker table and chairs . 1·25 60

86 Goethe

1999. 250th Birth Anniv of Johann Wolfgang von Goethe (poet).

333 **86** 1 l. 10 multicoloured . . . 40 20

87 Emblem

88 Metropolitan Varlaam

1999. 10th Anniv of Adoption of Latin Alphabet.

334 **87** 25 b. multicoloured 10 10

1999. Patriarchs of the Orthodox Church. Mult.

335 25 b. Type **88** 10 10
336 2 l. 40 Metropolitan Gurie Grosu 80 40

89 Bogdan II (1449–51)

91 Player and Chessboard

90 European Otter ("Lutra lutra")

1999. 15th–17th Century Princes of Moldavia. Multicoloured.

337 25 b. Type **89** 10 10
338 25 b. Bogdan IV (1568–72) . . . 10 10
339 25 b. Constantin Cantemir (1685–93) 10 10
340 1 l. 50 Simon Movila (1606–07) . 55 25
341 3 l. Gheorghe III Duca (1665–66, 1668–72 and 1678–84) . . . 1·00 50
342 3 l. 90 Ilias Alexandru (1666–68) . . . . 1·25 65

1999. Animals in the Red Book. Multicoloured.

344 25 b. Type **90** 10 10
345 1 l. 80 Beluga ("Huso huso") . . 65 30
346 3 l. 60 Greater horseshoe bat ("Rhinolophus ferrumequinum") . . . . 1·10 55

1999. World Women's Chess Championship, Chisinau. Multicoloured.

347 25 b. Type **91** 10 10
348 2 l. 20 + 30 b. Championship venue and emblem 85 40

92 4th-century B.C. Bronze Helmet and Candle Holder

95 Henri Coanda (aeronautical engineer)

94 Ileana Cosinzeana

1999. National History Museum Exhibits. Mult.

349 25 b. Type **92** 10 10
350 1 l. 80 10th-century B.C. ceramic pot 65 30
351 3 l. 60 Gospel, 1855 . . . . . 1·10 55

2000. Folk Heroes. Multicoloured.

353 25 b. Type **94** 10 10
354 1 l. 50 Fat-Frumos 55 25
355 1 l. 80 Harap Alb 65 30

2000. Birth Anniversaries. Each pink and black.

356 25 b. Type **95** (114th anniv) . . 10 10
357 25 b. Toma Ciorba (physician, 136th) 10 10
358 2 l. Guglielmo Marconi (physicist, 126th) 70 35
359 3 l. 60 Norbert Wiener (mathematician, 106th) . . . . . . 1·10 55

POSTAGE DUE STAMPS

D 33 Postal Emblems

1994.

D150 **D 33** 30 b. brown and green . 50 50
D151 40 b. green and lilac . . 65 65

One stamp in the pair was put on insufficiently franked mail, the other stamp on associated documents.

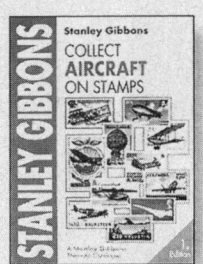

MONACO Pt. 6

A principality on the S. coast of France including the town of Monte Carlo.

100 centimes = 1 French franc

1 Prince Charles III 2 Prince Albert 4 War Widow and Monaco

1885.

1 1 1 c. olive . . . 19·00 16·00
2 2 c. lilac . . . 55·00 27·00
3 5 c. blue . . . 75·00 35·00
4 10 c. brown on yellow . . . 85·00 35·00
5 15 c. red . . . £375 16·00
6 25 c. green . . . £750 65·00
7 40 c. blue on red . . . 85·00 42·00
8 75 c. black on red . . . £275 £110
9 1 f. black on yellow . . . £1900 £500
10 5 f. red on green . . . £3250 £2000

1891.

11 2 1 c. green . . . 75 75
12 2 c. purple . . . 85 85
13 5 c. blue . . . 60·00 5·50
22 5 c. green . . . 45 25
14 10 c. brown on yellow . . . £140 14·00
23 10 c. red . . . 4·50 60
15 15 c. pink . . . £225 6·75
24 15 c. brown on yellow . . . 2·50 60
25 15 c. green . . . 1·75 2·50
16 25 c. green . . . £375 32·00
26 25 c. blue . . . 14·00 4·25
17 40 c. black on pink . . . 4·50 2·50
18 50 c. brown on orange . . . 8·75 4·25
19 75 c. brown on buff . . . 15·00 21·00
20 1 f. black on yellow . . . 25·00 8·75
21 5 f. red on green . . . £130 80·00
28 5 f. mauve . . . £250 £250
29 5 f. green . . . 20·00 26·00

1914. Surcharged **+5c.**

30 2 10 c. + 5 c. red . . . 7·50 6·25

1919. War Orphans Fund.

31 4 2 c. + 3 c. mauve . . . 28·00 30·00
32 5 c. + 5 c. green . . . 15·00 18·00
33 15 c. + 10 c. red . . . 15·00 18·00
34 25 c. + 15 c. blue . . . 40·00 45·00
35 50 c. + 50 c. brown on orge . . . £180 £160
36 1 f. + 1 f. black on yellow . . . £300 £375
37 5 f. + 5 f. red . . . £1000 £1100

1920. Princess Charlotte's Marriage. Nos. 33/7 optd **20 mars 1920** or surch also.

38 4 2 c. + 3 c. on 15 c. + 10 c. . . . 40·00 40·00
39 2 c. + 3 c. on 25 c. + 15 c. . . . 40·00 40·00
40 2 c. + 3 c. on 50 c. + 50 c. . . . 40·00 40·00
41 5 c. + 5 c. on 1 f. + 1 f. . . . 40·00 40·00
42 5 c. + 5 c. on 5 f. + 5 f. . . . 40·00 40·00
43 15 c. + 10 c. red . . . 28·00 28·00
44 25 c. + 15 c. blue . . . 12·50 12·50
45 50 c. + 50 c. brown on orge . . . 55·00 55·00
46 1 f. + 1 f. black on yellow . . . 75·00 75·00
47 5 f. + 5 f. red . . . £6500 £6500

1921. Princess Antoinette's Baptism. Optd **28 DECEMBRE 1920** or surch also.

48 2 5 c. green . . . 45 50
49 75 c. brown on buff . . . 4·50 6·25
50 2 f. on 5 f. mauve . . . 38·00 55·00

1922. Surch.

51 2 20 c. on 15 c. green . . . 1·25 1·50
52 25 c. on 10 c. red . . . 75 1·00
53 50 c. on 1 f. black on yellow . . . 5·50 6·25

8 Prince Albert I 9 St. Devote Viaduct

1922.

54 8 25 c. brown . . . 3·00 4·25
55 – 30 c. green . . . 65 1·10
56 – 30 c. red . . . 40 45
57 9 40 c. brown . . . 65 65
58 – 50 c. blue . . . 3·25 4·00
59 – 60 c. grey . . . 20 25
60 – 1 f. black on yellow . . . 20 20
61a – 2 f. red . . . 40 35
62 – 5 f. brown . . . 32·00 32·00
63 – 5 f. green on blue . . . 7·50 38·00
64 – 10 f. red . . . 12·50 9·25

DESIGNS: As Type **9**: 30 c., 50 c. Oceanographic Museum; 60 c., 1 f., 2 f. The Rock; 5 f., 10 f. Prince's Palace, Monaco.

12 Prince Louis 13 Prince Louis and Palace

1923.

65 12 10 c. green . . . 35 35
66 15 c. red . . . 50 75
67 20 c. brown . . . 30 30
68 25 c. purple . . . 25 30
69 13 50 c. blue . . . 25 30

1924. Surch with new value and bars.

70 2 45 c. on 50 c. brown on orge . . . 50 75
71 75 c. on 1 f. black on yellow . . . 30 30
72 85 c. on 5 f. green . . . 30 30

14 15 16

17 St. Devote Viaduct

1924.

73 14 1 c. grey . . . 10 10
74 2 c. brown . . . 10 10
75 3 c. mauve . . . 2·75 1·90
76 5 c. orange . . . 20 20
77 10 c. blue . . . 10 10
78 15 15 c. green . . . 10 10
79 15 c. violet . . . 2·50 1·50
80 20 c. mauve . . . 15 10
81 20 c. pink . . . 20 10
82 25 c. pink . . . 10 10
83 25 c. red on yellow . . . 15 15
84 30 c. orange . . . 10 10
85 40 c. brown . . . 15 10
86 40 c. blue on blue . . . 15 10
87 45 c. black . . . 70 40
88 16 50 c. green . . . 15 15
89 15 50 c. brown on yellow . . . 10 10
90 16 60 c. brown . . . 10 15
91 15 60 c. green on green . . . 10 10
92 75 c. green on green . . . 20 15
93 75 c. red on yellow . . . 15 10
94 75 c. black . . . 40 50
95 80 c. red on yellow . . . 25 20
96 90 c. red on yellow . . . 2·00 1·25
97 17 1 f. black on yellow . . . 30 25
98 1 f. 05 mauve . . . 70 70
99 1 f. 10 green . . . 8·00 6·25
100 15 1 f. 25 blue on blue . . . 15 15
101 1 f. 50 blue on blue . . . 3·75 1·50
102 – 2 f. brown and mauve . . . 95 60
103 – 3 f. lilac and red on yellow . . . 17·00 10·00
104 – 5 f. red and green . . . 7·00 5·00
105 – 10 f. blue and brown . . . 18·00 17·00

DESIGN—As Type **17**: 2 f. to 10 f. Monaco.

1926. Surch.

106 15 30 c. on 25 c. pink . . . 20 10
107 50 c. on 60 c. green on grn . . . 1·25 15
108 17 50 c. on 1 f. 05 mauve . . . 90 60
109 50 c. on 1 f. 10 green . . . 8·75 6·25
110 15 50 c. on 1 f. 25 blue on blue . . . 1·40 30
111 1 f. 25 on 1 f. blue on blue . . . 65 20
112 – 1 f. 50 on 2 f. brown and mauve (No. 102) . . . 5·00 4·75

20 Prince Charles III, Louis II and Albert I

1928. International Philatelic Exn, Monte Carlo.

113 20 50 c. red . . . 2·10 3·75
114 1 f. 50 blue . . . 2·10 3·75
115 3 f. violet . . . 2·10 3·75

20a 21 Palace Entrance

22 St. Devote's Church 23 Prince Louis II

1933.

116 20a 1 c. plum . . . 10 10
117 2 c. green . . . 10 10
118 3 c. purple . . . 10 10
119 5 c. red . . . 10 10
120 10 c. blue . . . 10 10
121 15 c. violet . . . 75 70
122 21 15 c. red . . . 85 10
123 20 c. brown . . . 85 10
124 A 25 c. sepia . . . 1·25 30
125 22 30 c. green . . . 1·50 30
126 23 40 c. sepia . . . 3·75 1·60
127 B 45 c. brown . . . 3·25 1·25
128 23 50 c. violet . . . 3·00 85
129 C 65 c. green . . . 3·25 65
130 D 75 c. blue . . . 4·25 2·50
131 23 90 c. red . . . 2·75 2·50
132 22 1 f. brown . . . 27·00 6·75
133 D 1 f. 25 red . . . 6·25 3·75
134 23 1 f. 50 blue . . . 32·00 8·75
135 A 1 f. 75 red . . . 32·00 8·75
136 1 f. 75 red . . . 20·00 12·50
137 B 2 f. blue . . . 11·00 4·25
138 21 3 f. violet . . . 18·00 7·50
139 A 3 f. 50 orange . . . 45·00 30·00
140 22 5 f. purple . . . 25·00 17·00
141 A 10 f. blue . . . £120 65·00
142 C 20 f. black . . . £160 £130

DESIGNS—As Type **21**—HORIZ: A, The Prince's Residence; B, The Rock of Monaco; C, Palace Gardens; D, Fortifications and Harbour.

For other stamps in Type **20a** see Nos. 249, etc.

1933. Air. Surch with Bleriot XI airplane and **1f50.**

143 – 1 f. 50 on 5 f. red and green (No. 104) . . . 22·00 23·00

28 Palace Gardens

1937. Charity.

144 28 50 c. + 50 c. green . . . 2·50 2·50
145 – 90 c. + 90 c. red . . . 2·50 2·50
146 – 1 f. 50 + 1 f. 50 blue . . . 5·00 5·00
147 – 2 f. + 2 f. violet . . . 11·00 11·00
148 – 5 f. + 5 f. red . . . 85·00 85·00

DESIGNS—HORIZ: 90 c. Exotic gardens; 1 f. 50, The Bay of Monaco. VERT: 2, 5 f. Prince Louis II.

1937. Postage Due stamps optd **POSTES** or surch also.

149 D 18 5 on 10 c. violet . . . 70 70
150 10 c. violet . . . 70 70
151 15 on 30 c. bistre . . . 70 70
152 20 on 30 c. bistre . . . 70 70
153 25 on 60 c. red . . . 1·25 1·25
154 30 c. bistre . . . 2·25 2·00
155 40 on 60 c. red . . . 2·00 1·90
156 50 on 60 c. red . . . 2·25 2·50
157 65 on 1 f. blue . . . 2·25 2·25
158 85 on 1 f. blue . . . 5·25 4·75
159 1 f. blue . . . 6·50 6·50
160 2 f. 15 on 2 f. red . . . 7·25 7·25
161 2 f. 25 on 2 f. red . . . 17·00 17·00
162 2 f. 50 on 2 f. red . . . 27·00 25·00

31 Prince Louis II 33 Monaco Hospital

1938.

164 31 55 c. brown . . . 3·25 1·50
165 65 c. violet . . . 26·00 12·50
166 70 c. brown . . . 15 15
167 90 c. violet . . . 15 15
168 1 f. red . . . 10·50 6·25
169 1 f. 25 red . . . 20 15
170 1 f. 75 blue . . . 15·00 8·00
171 2 f. 25 blue . . . 20 15

1938. Anti-Cancer Fund. 40th Anniv of Discovery of Radium.

172 – 65 c. + 25 c. green . . . 8·75 8·75
173 33 1 f. 75 + 50 c. blue . . . 11·00 11·00

DESIGN—VERT: 65 c. Pierre and Marie Curie.

34 The Cathedral 38 Monaco Harbour

1939.

174 34 20 c. mauve . . . 15 15
175 – 25 c. brown . . . 30 20
176 – 30 c. green . . . 20 20
177 – 40 c. red . . . 20 20
178 – 45 c. purple . . . 35 20
179 – 50 c. green . . . 25 15
180 – 60 c. red . . . 20 20
181 – 60 c. green . . . 20 50
182 38 70 c. lilac . . . 35 20
183 75 c. green . . . 35 20
184 – 1 f. black . . . 20 20
185 – 1 f. 30 brown . . . 20 20

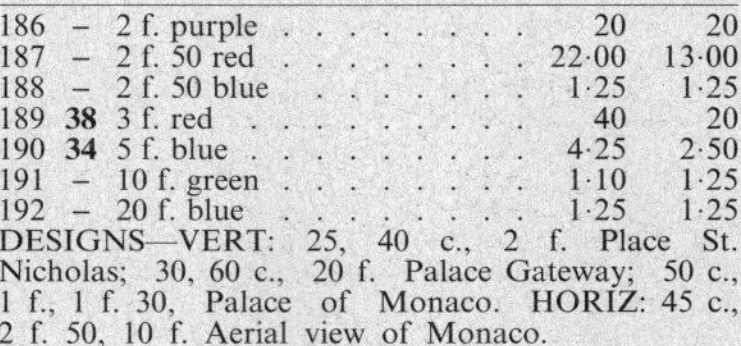

186 – 2 f. purple . . . 20 20
187 – 2 f. 50 red . . . 22·00 13·00
188 – 2 f. 50 blue . . . 1·25 1·25
189 38 3 f. red . . . 40 20
190 34 5 f. blue . . . 4·25 2·50
191 – 10 f. green . . . 1·10 1·25
192 – 20 f. blue . . . 1·25 1·25

DESIGNS—VERT: 25, 40 c., 2 f. Place St. Nicholas; 30, 60 c., 20 f. Palace Gateway; 50 c., 1 f., 1 f. 30, Palace of Monaco. HORIZ: 45 c., 2 f. 50, 10 f. Aerial view of Monaco.

40 Louis II Stadium 41 Lucien

1939. Inauguration of Louis II Stadium, Monaco.

198 40 10 f. green . . . £110 £110

1939. National Relief. XVI–XVIII-century portrait designs and view.

199 41 5 c. + 5 c. black . . . 1·75 1·25
200 – 10 c. + 10 c. purple . . . 1·75 1·25
201 – 45 c. + 15 c. green . . . 5·00 4·25
202 – 70 c. + 30 c. mauve . . . 8·75 8·00
203 – 90 c. + 35 c. violet . . . 9·25 9·25
204 – 1 f. + 1 f. blue . . . 23·00 22·00
205 – 2 f. + 2 f. red . . . 22·00 23·00
206 – 2 f. 25 + 1 f. 25 blue . . . 30·00 25·00
207 – 3 f. + 3 f. red . . . 40·00 42·00
208 – 5 f. + 5 f. red . . . 75·00 85·00

DESIGNS—VERT: 10 c. Honore II; 45 c. Louis I; 70 c. Charlotte de Gramont; 90 c. Antoine I; 1 f. Marie de Lorraine; 2 f. Jacques I; 2 f. 25, Louise-Hippolyte; 3 f. Honore III. HORIZ: 5 f. The Rock of Monaco.

1939. 8th International University Games. As T **40** but inscr "VIIIeme JEUX UNIVERSITAIRES INTERNATIONAUX 1939".

209 40 c. green . . . 1·25 1·25
210 70 c. brown . . . 1·75 1·75
211 90 c. violet . . . 2·00 2·00
212 1 f. 25 red . . . 3·00 3·00
213 2 f. 25 blue . . . 4·25 4·25

1940. Red Cross Ambulance Fund. As Nos. 174/92 in new colours surch with Red Cross and premium.

214 34 20 c. + 1 f. violet . . . 3·25 3·25
215 – 25 c. + 1 f. green . . . 3·25 3·25
216 – 30 c. + 1 f. red . . . 3·25 3·25
217 – 40 c. + 1 f. blue . . . 3·25 3·25
218 – 45 c. + 1 f. red . . . 3·50 3·50
219 – 50 c. + 1 f. brown . . . 3·50 3·50
220 – 60 c. + 1 f. green . . . 3·50 3·50
221 38 75 c. + 1 f. black . . . 3·50 3·50
222 – 1 f. + 1 f. red . . . 4·25 4·25
223 – 2 f. + 1 f. slate . . . 4·25 4·25
224 – 2 f. 50 + 1 f. green . . . 10·00 10·00
225 38 3 f. + 1 f. blue . . . 11·00 11·00
226 34 5 f. + 1 f. black . . . 13·50 13·50
227 – 10 f. + 5 f. blue . . . 22·00 22·00
228 – 20 f. + 5 f. purple . . . 25·00 25·00

44 Prince Louis II

1941.

229 44 40 c. red . . . 20 50
230 80 c. green . . . 20 50
231 1 f. violet . . . 10 10
232 1 f. 20 green . . . 10 10
233 1 f. 50 red . . . 10 10
234 1 f. 50 violet . . . 10 10
235 2 f. green . . . 10 10
236 2 f. 40 red . . . 10 10
237 2 f. 50 blue . . . 60 1·25
238 4 f. blue . . . 10 10

45 46

1941. National Relief Fund.

239 45 25 c. + 25 c. purple . . . 1·40 1·40
240 46 50 c. + 25 c. brown . . . 1·40 1·40
241 75 c. + 50 c. purple . . . 2·10 2·10
242 45 1 f. + 1 f. blue . . . 2·10 2·10
243 46 1 f. 50 + 1 f. 50 red . . . 3·00 3·00
244 45 2 f. + 2 f. green . . . 3·00 3·00
245 46 2 f. 50 + 2 f. blue . . . 3·75 3·75
246 45 3 f. + 3 f. brown . . . 3·75 3·75
247 46 5 f. + 5 f. green . . . 6·25 6·25
248 45 10 f. + 8 f. sepia . . . 10·50 10·50

1941. New values and colours.

249	20a	10 c. black	10	10
250	–	30 c. red (as No. 176)	20	15
251	20a	30 c. green	10	10
252		40 c. red	10	10
253		50 c. violet	10	10
362	34	50 c. brown	10	10
254	20a	60 c. blue	10	10
363	–	60 c. pink (as No. 175)	10	15
255	20a	70 c. brown	10	10
256	34	80 c. green	10	10
257	–	1 f. brown (as Nos. 178)	10	25
258	38	1 f. 20 blue	15	15
259	–	1 f. 50 blue (as Nos. 175)	15	15
260	38	2 f. blue	10	10
261	–	2 f. green (as No. 179)	10	10
262	–	3 f. black (as No. 175)	10	10
364	–	3 f. purple (as No. 176)	20	20
391	–	3 f. green (as No. 175)	40	20
263	34	4 f. mauve	50	20
365	–	4 f. green (as No. 175)	20	20
264	–	4 f. 50 violet (as No. 179)	10	10
265	–	5 f. green (as No. 176)	10	10
392	–	5 f. green (as No. 178)	35	15
393	–	5 f. red (as No. 176)	35	35
266	–	6 f. violet (as No. 179)	60	30
368	–	8 f. brown (as No. 179)	1·75	1·90
267	34	10 f. blue	10	10
370	–	10 f. brown (as No. 179)	1·75	1·25
394	38	10 f. yellow	60	20
268		15 f. red	20	15
269	–	20 f. brown (as No. 178)	40	25
373	–	20 f. red (as No. 178)	75	80
270	38	25 f. green	1·25	85
374		25 f. black	15·00	14·00
397	–	25 f. blue (as No. 176)	23·00	14·00
398	–	25 f. red (as No. 179)	1·75	55
399	–	30 f. blue (as No. 176)	5·25	4·00
400	–	35 f. blue (as No. 179)	3·75	2·00
401	34	40 f. red	3·00	3·75
402		50 f. violet	2·50	65
403	–	65 f. violet (as No. 178)	6·25	6·25
404	34	70 f. yellow	6·25	7·50
405	–	75 f. green (as No. 175)	13·50	8·00
406	–	85 f. red (as No. 175)	8·75	8·00
407	–	100 f. turquoise (as No. 178)	8·75	8·00

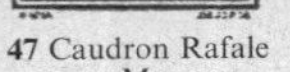

47 Caudron Rafale over Monaco
48 Propeller and Palace

49 Arms, Airplane and Globe
50 Charles II

1942. Air.

271	47	5 f. green	20	30
272		10 f. blue	45	45
273	48	15 f. brown	55	35
274	–	20 f. brown	55	45
275	–	50 f. purple	3·00	1·75
276	49	100 f. red and purple	3·00	1·75

DESIGNS—VERT: 20 f. Pegasus. HORIZ: 50 f. Common gull over Bay of Monaco.

1942. National Relief Fund. Royal Personnages.

277	–	2 c. + 3 c. blue	10	50
278	50	5 c. + 5 c. red	10	50
279	–	10 c. + 5 c. black	10	50
280	–	20 c. + 10 c. green	10	50
281	–	30 c. + 30 c. purple	10	50
282	–	40 c. + 40 c. red	10	50
283	–	50 c. + 50 c. violet	10	50
284	–	75 c. + 75 c. purple	10	50
285	–	1 f. + 1 f. green	10	50
286	–	1 f. 50 + 1 f. red	10	50
287	–	2 f. 50 + 2 f. 50 violet	3·00	5·00
288	–	3 f. + 3 f. blue	3·00	5·00
289	–	5 f. + 5 f. sepia	3·75	6·25
290	–	10 f. + 5 f. purple	3·75	6·75
291	–	20 f. + 5 f. blue	3·75	6·75

PORTRAITS: 2 c. Rainier Grimaldi; 10 c. Jeanne Grimaldi; 20 c. Charles Auguste, Goyon de Matignon; 30 c. Jacques I; 40 c. Louise-Hippolyte; 50 c. Charlotte Grimaldi; 75 c. Marie Charles Grimaldi; 1 f. Honore III; 1 f. 50, Honore IV; 2 f. 50, Honore V; 3 f. Florestan I; 5 f. Charles III; 10 f. Albert I; 20 f. Princess Marie-Victoire.

52 Prince Louis II

1943.

292	52	50 f. violet	85	85

53 St. Devote
54 Blessing the Sea

55 Arrival of St. Devote at Monaco

1944. Charity. Festival of St. Devote.

293	53	50 c. + 50 c. brown	15	15
294	–	70 c. + 80 c. blue	15	15
295	–	80 c. + 70 c. green	15	15
296	–	1 f. + 1 f. purple	25	25
297	–	1 f. 50 + 1 f. 50 red	40	40
298	54	2 f. + 2 f. purple	50	80
299	–	5 f. + 2 f. violet	50	80
300	–	10 f. + 40 f. blue	35	75
301	55	20 f. + 60 f. blue	3·00	5·50

DESIGNS—VERT: 70 c., 1 f. Various processional scenes; 1 f. 50, Burning the boat; 10 f. Trial scene. HORIZ: 80 c. Procession; 5 f. St. Devote's Church.

1945. Air. For War Dead and Deported Workers. As Nos. 272/6 (colours changed) surch.

302	1 f. + 4 f. on 10 f. red	45	45
303	1 f. + 4 f. on 15 f. brown	35	35
304	1 f. + 4 f. on 20 f. brown	35	35
305	1 f. + 4 f. on 50 f. blue	35	35
306	1 f. + 4 f. on 100 f. purple	35	35

57 Prince Louis II 58

1946.

361	57	30 c. black	10	10
389		50 c. olive	10	10
390		1 f. violet	10	10
307		2 f. 50 green	15	10
308		3 f. mauve	15	10
366		5 f. brown	20	15
309		6 f. red	15	10
367		6 f. purple	1·00	1·75
310		10 f. blue	15	10
369		10 f. orange	10	10
371		12 f. red	3·00	2·50
395		12 f. slate	4·25	5·50
396		15 f. lake	4·25	3·75
372		18 f. blue	5·00	6·25
311	58	50 f. grey	1·50	1·75
312		100 f. red	2·10	2·25

59 Child Praying
60 Nurse and Baby

1946. Child Welfare Fund.

313	59	1 f. + 3 f. green	20	20
314		2 f. + 4 f. red	20	20
315		4 f. + 6 f. blue	20	20
316		5 f. + 40 f. mauve	55	55
317		10 f. + 60 f. red	55	55
318		15 f. + 100 f. blue	90	90

1946. Anti-tuberculosis Fund.

319	60	2 f. + 8 f. blue	35	35

1946. Air. Optd **POSTE AERIENNE** over Sud Ouest Cassiopees airplane.

320	58	50 f. grey	3·00	2·75
321		100 f. red	5·00	4·25

INDEX
Countries can be quickly located by referring to the index at the end of this volume.

62 Steamship and Chart

1946. Stamp Day.

322	62	3 f. + 2 f. blue	20	20

63

1946. Air.

323	63	40 f. red	60	85
324		50 f. brown	70	90
325		100 f. green	1·40	1·60
326		200 f. violet	1·50	2·50
326a		300 f. blue & ultramarine	35·00	60·00
326b		500 f. green & deep green	25·00	35·00
326c		1000 f. violet and brown	35·00	60·00

64 Pres. Roosevelt and Palace of Monaco

66 Pres. Roosevelt

1946. President Roosevelt Commemorative.

327	66	10 c. mauve (postage)	10	10
328	–	30 c. blue	15	15
329	64	60 c. green	15	15
330	–	1 f. sepia	30	75
331	–	2 f. + 3 f. green	55	1·10
332	–	3 f. violet	1·00	1·40
333	–	5 f. red (air)	30	60
334	–	10 f. black	60	40
335	66	15 f. + 10 f. orange	1·90	1·40

DESIGNS—HORIZ: 30 c., 5 f. Rock of Monaco; 2 f. Viaduct and St. Devote. VERT: 1 f., 3 f., 10 f. Map of Monaco.

67 Prince Louis II
68 Pres. Roosevelt as a Philatelist

69 Statue of Liberty and New York Harbour
70 Prince Charles III

1947. Participation in the Centenary International Philatelic Exhibition, New York. (a) Postage.

336	67	10 f. blue	2·00	3·75

(b) Air. Dated "1847 1947"

337	68	50 c. violet	40	1·00
338	–	1 f. 50 mauve	30	25
339	–	3 f. orange	30	50
340	–	10 f. blue	2·00	3·75
341	69	15 f. red	3·00	5·00

DESIGNS—HORIZ: As Type **68**: 1 f. 50, G.P.O., New York; 3 f. Oceanographic Museum, Monte Carlo. As Type **69**: 10 f. Bay of Monaco.

1948. Stamp Day.

342	70	6 f. + 4 f. green on blue	20	50

71 Diving
72 Tennis

1948. Olympic Games, Wembley. Inscr "JEUX OLYMPIQUES 1948".

343	–	50 c. green (postage)	15	15
344	–	1 f. red	15	15
345	–	2 f. blue	85	85
346	–	2 f. 50 red	1·75	1·75
347	71	4 f. slate	2·50	2·50
348	–	5 f. + 5 f. brown (air)	6·25	10·50
349	–	6 f. + 9 f. violet	9·25	16·00
350	72	10 f. + 15 f. red	13·50	22·00
351	–	15 f. + 25 f. blue	20·00	32·00

DESIGNS—HORIZ: 50 c. Hurdling; 15 f. Yachting. VERT: 1 f. Running; 2 f. Throwing the discus; 2 f. 50, Basketball; 5 f. Rowing; 6 f. Skiing.

75 The Salmacis Nymph
77 F. J. Bosio (wrongly inscr. "J. F.")

1948. Death Centenary of Francois Joseph Bosio (sculptor).

352	75	50 c. green (postage)	10	10
353	–	1 f. red	20	20
354	–	2 f. blue	60	75
355	–	2 f. 50 violet	1·10	1·50
356	77	4 f. mauve	1·40	2·10
357	–	5 f. + 5 f. blue (air)	7·50	13·50
358	–	6 f. + 9 f. green	8·00	14·50
359	–	10 f. + 15 f. red	10·50	17·00
360	–	15 f. + 25 f. brown	15·00	23·00

DESIGNS—VERT: 1, 5 f. Hercules struggling with Achelous; 2, 6 f. Aristaeus (Garden God); 15 f. The Salmacis Nymph (36 × 48 mm). HORIZ: 2 f. 50, 10 f. Hyacinthus awaiting his turn to throw a quoit.

79 Exotic Gardens
80 "Princess Alice II"

1949. Birth Centenary of Prince Albert I.

375	–	2 f. blue (postage)	25	20
376	79	3 f. green	10	10
377	–	4 f. brown and blue	20	20
378	80	5 f. red	1·25	1·25
379	–	6 f. violet	45	45
380	–	10 f. sepia	80	1·50
381	–	12 f. pink	1·25	2·00
382	–	18 f. orange and brown	2·50	3·50
383	–	20 f. brown (air)	30	55
384	–	25 f. blue	30	55
385	–	40 f. green	1·00	1·90
386	–	50 f. green, brown & black	1·40	2·50
387	–	100 f. red	14·50	8·50
388	–	200 f. orange	8·00	13·50

DESIGNS—HORIZ: 2 f. Yacht "Hirondelle I" (1870); 4 f. Oceanographic Museum, Monaco; 10 f. "Hirondelle II" (1914); 12 f. Albert harpooning whale; 18 f. Buffalo (Palaeolithic mural); 20 f. Constitution Day, 1911; 25 f. Paris Institute of Palaeontology; 200 f. Coin with effigy of Albert. VERT: 6 f. Statue of Albert at tiller; 40 f. Anthropological Museum; 50 f. Prince Albert I; 100 f. Oceanographic Institute, Paris.

83 Palace of Monaco and Globe

1949. 75th Anniv of U.P.U.

410	83	5 f. green (postage)	10	10
411		10 f. orange	5·75	5·75
412		15 f. red	20	25
413		25 f. blue (air)	55	45
414		40 f. sepia and brown	1·25	2·00
415		50 f. blue and green	1·60	2·75
416		100 f. blue and red	2·75	4·50

84 Prince Rainier III and Monaco Palace **85** Prince Rainier III

1950. Accession of Prince Rainier III.

417 **84** 10 c. purple & red (postage) . . . 10 10
418 50 c. brown, light brown and orange . . . 10 10
419 1 f. violet . . . 10 10
420 5 f. deep green and green . . . 1·10 1·90
421 15 f. carmine and red . . . 2·25 3·75
422 25 f. blue, green and ultramarine . . . 3·75 6·25
423 50 f. brown and black (air) . . . 3·00 5·50
424 100 f. blue, deep brown and brown . . . 5·50 10·00

1950.

425 **85** 50 c. violet . . . 10 10
426 1 f. brown . . . 10 10
434 5 f. green . . . 8·75 5·00
427 6 f. green . . . 65 85
428 8 f. green . . . 2·25 2·00
429 8 f. orange . . . 90 35
435 10 f. orange . . . 11·00 7·50
430 12 f. blue . . . 1·25 25
431 15 f. red . . . 1·75 35
432 15 f. blue . . . 1·10 50
433 18 f. red . . . 3·00 1·50

86 Prince Albert I **87** Edmond and Jules de Goncourt

1951. Unveiling of Prince Albert Statue.

436 **86** 15 f. blue . . . 10·50 8·00

1951. 50th Anniv of Goncourt Academy.

437 **87** 15 f. purple . . . 10·50 7·50

88 St. Vincent de Paul **90** St. Peter's Keys and Papal Bull

89 Judgement of St. Devote

1951. Holy Year.

438 **88** 10 c. blue, ultram & red . . . 15 15
439 – 50 c. violet and red . . . 15 15
440 **89** 1 f. green and brown . . . 20 20
441 **90** 2 f. red and purple . . . 30 30
442 – 5 f. green . . . 30 30
443 – 12 f. violet . . . 40 40
444 – 15 f. red . . . 5·25 3·00
445 – 20 f. brown . . . 7·50 4·25
446 – 25 f. blue . . . 10·00 6·25
447 – 40 f. violet and mauve . . . 11·00 6·75
448 – 50 f. brown and olive . . . 15·00 9·25
449 – 100 f. brown . . . 30·00 19·00

DESIGNS—TRIANGULAR: 50 c. Pope Pius XII. As Type **90**—HORIZ: 5 f. Mosaic. VERT: 12 f. Prince Rainier III in St. Peter's; 15 f. St. Nicholas of Patara; 20 f. St. Romain; 25 f. St. Charles Borromeo; 40 f. Coliseum; 50 f. Chapel of St. Devote. As Type **89**: VERT: 100 f. Rainier of Westphalia.

93 Wireless Mast and Monaco **94** Seal of Prince Rainier III

1951. Monte Carlo Radio Station.

450 **93** 1 f. orange, red and blue . . . 55 20
451 15 f. purple, red and violet . . . 3·00 1·25
452 30 f. brown and blue . . . 11·00 6·25

1951.

453 **94** 1 f. violet . . . 1·00 65
454 5 f. black . . . 6·75 2·50
512 5 f. violet . . . 3·75 1·25
513 6 f. red . . . 3·00 1·75
455 8 f. red . . . 6·75 4·25
514 8 f. brown . . . 5·50 3·75
456 15 f. green . . . 11·00 8·00
515 15 f. blue . . . 21·00 5·00
457 30 f. blue . . . 20·00 12·50
516 30 f. green . . . 20·00 16·00

95 Gallery of Hercules

1952. Monaco Postal Museum.

460 **95** 5 f. chestnut and brown . . . 30 30
461 15 f. violet and purple . . . 55 30
462 30 f. indigo and blue . . . 2·25 1·00

96 Football

1953. 15th Olympic Games, Helsinki. Inscr "HELSINKI 1952".

463 – 1 f. mauve & violet (postage) . . . 20 15
464 **96** 2 f. blue and green . . . 20 20
465 – 3 f. pale and deep blue . . . 25 20
466 – 5 f. green and brown . . . 70 30
467 – 8 f. red and lake . . . 2·25 1·10
468 – 15 f. brown, green and blue . . . 1·50 1·10
469 – 40 f. black (air) . . . 11·00 9·25
470 – 50 f. violet . . . 12·50 9·25
471 – 100 f. green . . . 18·00 15·00
472 – 200 f. red . . . 23·00 11·00

DESIGNS: 1 f. Basketball; 3 f. Sailing; 5 f. Cycling; 8 f. Gymnastics; 15 f. Louis II Stadium, Monaco; 40 f. Running; 50 f. Fencing; 100 f. Rifle target and Arms of Monaco; 200 f. Olympic torch.

97 "Journal Inedit"

1953. Centenary of Publication of Journal by E. and J. de Goncourt.

473 **97** 5 f. green . . . 75 50
474 15 f. brown . . . 3·00 75

98 Physalia, Yacht "Princess Alice", Prince Albert, Richet and Portier

1953. 50th Anniv of Discovery of Anaphylaxis.

475 **98** 2 f. violet, green and brown . . . 10 10
476 5 f. red, lake and green . . . 1·00 25
477 15 f. lilac, blue and green . . . 3·00 1·60

99 F. Ozanam **100** St. Jean-Baptiste de la Salle

1954. Death Centenary of Ozanam (founder of St. Vincent de Paul Conferences).

478 **99** 1 f. red . . . 10 10
479 – 5 f. blue . . . 25 60
480 **99** 15 f. black . . . 2·10 2·00

DESIGN: 5 f. Outline drawing of Sister of Charity.

1954. St. J.-B. de la Salle (educationist).

481 **100** 1 f. red . . . 10 10
482 – 5 f. sepia . . . 25 60
483 **100** 15 f. blue . . . 2·10 2·00

DESIGN: 5 f. Outline drawing of De la Salle and two children.

101 **102** **103**

1954. Arms.

484 – 50 c. red, black and mauve . . . 10 10
485 – 70 c. red, black and blue . . . 10 10
486 **101** 80 c. red, black and green . . . 10 10
487 – 1 f. red, black and blue . . . 10 10
488 **102** 2 f. red, black and orange . . . 10 10
489 – 3 f. red, black and green . . . 10 10
490 **103** 5 f. multicoloured . . . 10 10

DESIGNS—HORIZ: 50 c. as Type **101**. VERT: 70 c., 1, 3 f. as Type **102**.

104 Seal of Prince Rainier III

1954. Precancelled.

491 **104** 4 f. red . . . 65 20
492 5 f. blue . . . 20 10
493 8 f. green . . . 65 90
494 8 f. purple . . . 55 20
495 10 f. green . . . 20 10
496 12 f. violet . . . 5·00 1·90
497 15 f. orange . . . 1·25 1·00
498 20 f. green . . . 1·60 1·50
499 24 f. brown . . . 9·25 5·25
500 30 f. blue . . . 1·75 1·00
501 40 f. brown . . . 3·00 1·25
502 45 f. red . . . 2·75 1·40
503 55 f. blue . . . 5·75 3·00

See also Nos. 680/3.

105 Lambarene **106** Dr. Albert Schweitzer

1955. 80th Birthday of Dr. Schweitzer (humanitarian).

504 **105** 2 f. green, turquoise and blue (postage) . . . 10 10
505 **106** 5 f. blue and green . . . 1·40 1·40
506 – 15 f. purple, black and green . . . 3·25 3·25
507 – 200 f. slate, green and blue (air) . . . 40·00 32·00

DESIGNS—As Type **106**: 15 f. Lambarene Hospital. HORIZ—(48 × 27 mm): 200 f. Schweitzer and jungle scene.

107 Common Cormorants

1955. Air.

508a – 100 f. indigo and blue . . . 15·00 12·00
509 – 200 f. black and blue . . . 18·00 9·50
510 – 500 f. grey and green . . . 30·00 16·00
511a **107** 1,000 f. black, turquoise and green . . . 75·00 45·00

DESIGNS—As Type **107**: 100 f. Roseate tern; 200 f. Herring gull; 500 f. Wandering albatrosses.

108 Eight Starting Points **109** Prince Rainier III

1955. 25th Monte Carlo Car Rally.

517 **108** 100 f. red and brown . . . 75·00 50·00

1955.

518 **109** 6 f. purple and green . . . 10 10
519 8 f. violet and red . . . 10 10
520 12 f. green and red . . . 20 10
521 15 f. blue and purple . . . 75 15
522 18 f. blue and orange . . . 2·50 20
523 20 f. turquoise . . . 1·50 30
524 25 f. black and orange . . . 1·25 60
525 30 f. sepia and blue . . . 16·00 7·50
526 30 f. violet . . . 4·25 2·25
527 35 f. brown . . . 4·25 2·25
528 50 f. lake and green . . . 3·75 2·50

See also Nos. 627/41.

110 "La Maison a Vapeur"

111 "The 500 Millions of the Begum" **113** U.S.S. "Nautilus"

112 "Round the World in Eighty Days"

1955. 50th Death Anniv of Jules Verne (author). Designs illustrating his works.

529 – 1 f. blue & brown (postage) . . . 10 10
530 – 2 f. sepia, indigo and blue . . . 10 10
531 **110** 3 f. blue, black and brown . . . 10 10
532 – 5 f. sepia and red . . . 10 10
533 **111** 6 f. grey and sepia . . . 25 25
534 – 8 f. turquoise and olive . . . 35 35
535 – 10 f. sepia, turquoise & ind . . . 1·25 1·10
536 **112** 15 f. red and brown . . . 1·10 85
537 – 25 f. black and green . . . 2·50 1·90
538 **113** 30 f. black, purple & turq . . . 6·25 5·25

539 – 200 f. indigo & blue (air) 24·00 22·00
DESIGNS—As Type **111**—VERT: 1 f. "Five Weeks in a Balloon". HORIZ: 5 f. "Michael Strogoff"; 8 f. "Le Superbe Orenoque". As Type **110**: HORIZ: 2 f. "A Floating Island"; 10 f. "Journey to the Centre of the Earth"; 25 f. "20,000 Leagues under the Sea"; 200 f. "From Earth to Moon".

114 "The Immaculate Virgin" (F. Brea)

1955. Marian Year.
540 **114** 5 f. green, grey and brown 20 20
541 – 10 f. green, grey & brown 30 30
542 – 15 f. brown and sepia 40 40
DESIGNS—As Type **114**: 10 f. "Madonna" (L. Brea). As Type **113**: 15 f. Bienheureux Rainier.

115 Rotary Emblem

1955. 50th Anniv of Rotary International.
543 **115** 30 f. blue and yellow 1·10 1·10

116 George Washington **118** President Eisenhower

117 Abraham Lincoln

1956. 5th International Stamp Exhibition, New York.
544 **116** 1 f. violet and lilac 10 10
545 – 2 f. lilac and purple 10 10
546 **117** 3 f. blue and violet 10 10
547 **118** 5 f. red 20 20
548 – 15 f. brown and chocolate 45 45
549 – 30 f. black, indigo & blue 3·50 2·25
550 – 40 f. brown 4·25 1·90
551 – 50 f. red 4·25 2·50
552 – 100 f. green 5·00 3·00
DESIGNS—As Type **117**: 2 f. F. D. Roosevelt. As Type **116**—HORIZ: 15 f. Monaco Palace in the 18th century; 30 f. Landing of Columbus. LARGER (48 × 36 mm): 50 f. Aerial view of Monaco Palace in the 18th century; 100 f. Louisiana landscape in the 18th century. As Type **118**: 40 f. Prince Rainier III.

120

1956. 7th Winter Olympic Games, Cortina d'Ampezzo and 16th Olympic Games, Melbourne.
553 – 15 f. brown, green & pur 1·25 55
554 **120** 30 f. red 2·50 1·75
DESIGN: 15 f. "Italia" ski-jump.

1956. Nos. D482/95 with "TIMBRE TAXE" barred out and some surch also. (a) Postage.
555 2 f. on 4 f. slate and brown 30 30
556 2 f. on 4 f. brown and slate 30 30
557 3 f. lake and green 35 35
558 3 f. green and lake 35 35
559 5 f. on 4 f. slate and brown 75 30
560 5 f. on 4 f. brown and slate 75 30
561 10 f. on 4 f. slate and brown 1·10 55
562 10 f. on 4 f. brown and slate 1·10 55
563 15 f. on 5 f. violet and blue 2·00 1·00
564 15 f. on 5 f. blue and violet 2·00 1·00
565 20 f. violet and blue 3·00 1·75
566 20 f. blue and violet 3·00 1·75
567 25 f. on 20 f. violet and blue 5·25 3·00
568 25 f. on 20 f. blue and violet 5·25 3·00
569 30 f. on 10 f. indigo and blue 7·25 4·50
570 30 f. on 10 f. blue and indigo 7·25 4·50
571 40 f. on 50 f. brown and red 10·00 6·75
572 40 f. on 50 f. red and brown 10·00 6·75
573 50 f. on 100 f. green and purple 13·50 9·25
574 50 f. on 100 f. purple and green 13·50 10·00

(b) Air. Optd **POSTE AERIENNE** also.
575 100 f. on 20 f. violet and blue 10·50 10·50
576 100 f. on 20 f. blue and violet 10·50 10·50

121 Route Map from Glasgow

1956. 26th Monte Carlo Car Rally.
577 **121** 100 f. brown and red 25·00 16·00

122 Princess Grace and Prince Rainier III

1956. Royal Wedding.
578 **122** 1 f. black & grn (postage) 10 10
579 2 f. black and red 10 10
580 3 f. black and blue 20 15
581 5 f. black and green 55 25
582 15 f. black and brown 80 40
583 100 f. brown & purple (air) 1·10 60
584 200 f. brown and red 1·75 1·00
585 500 f. brown and grey 4·00 2·50

123 Princess Grace **124** Princess Grace with Princess Caroline

1957. Birth of Princess Caroline.
586 **123** 1 f. grey 10 10
587 2 f. olive 10 10
588 3 f. brown 10 10
589 5 f. red 10 10
590 15 f. pink 10 10
591 25 f. blue 1·10 10
592 30 f. violet 1·10 10
593 50 f. red 2·10 75
594 75 f. orange 3·00 2·10

1958. Birth of Prince Albert.
595 **124** 100 f. black 8·00 6·25

125 Order of St. Charles **126** Route Map from Munich

1958. Centenary of Creation of National Order of St. Charles.
596 **125** 100 f. multicoloured 2·50 2·25

1958. 27th Monte Carlo Rally.
597 **126** 100 f. multicoloured 9·25 7·50

127 Statue of the Holy Virgin and Popes Pius IX and Pius XII

1958. Centenary of Apparition of Virgin Mary at Lourdes.
598 **127** 1 f. grey & brown (postage) 10 10
599 – 2 f. violet and blue 10 10
600 – 3 f. sepia and green 10 10
601 – 5 f. blue and sepia 10 10
602 – 8 f. multicoloured 15 15
603 – 10 f. multicoloured 15 10
604 – 12 f. multicoloured 20 15
605 – 20 f. myrtle and purple 30 20
606 – 35 f. myrtle, bistre and brown 40 30
607 – 50 f. blue, green and lake 65 55
608 – 65 f. turquoise and blue 90 70
609 – 100 f. grey, myrtle and blue (air) 1·75 1·50
610 – 200 f. brown and chestnut 2·50 2·50
DESIGNS—VERT: ($26\frac{1}{2} \times 36$ mm): 2 f. St. Bernadette; 3 f. St. Bernadette at Bartres; 5 f. The Miracle of Bourriette; 20 f. St. Bernadette at prayer; 35 f. St. Bernadette's canonization. (22 × 36 mm): 8 f. Stained-glass window. As Type **127**: 50 f. St. Bernadette, Pope Pius XI, Mgr. Laurence and Abbe Peyramale. HORIZ: (48 × 36 mm): 10 f. Lourdes grotto; 12 f. Interior of Lourdes grotto. ($36 \times 26\frac{1}{2}$ mm): 65 f. Shrine of St. Bernadette; (48 × 27 mm): 100 f. Lourdes Basilica; 200 f. Pope Pius X and subterranean interior of Basilica.

128 Princess Grace and Clinic

1959. Opening of new hospital block in "Princess Grace" Clinic, Monaco.
611 **128** 100 f. grey, brown & green 3·00 1·75

129 U.N.E.S.C.O. Headquarters, Paris, and Cultural Emblems

1959. Inaug of U.N.E.S.C.O. Headquarters Building.
612 **129** 25 f. multicoloured 15 10
613 – 50 f. turquoise, black & ol 35 30
DESIGN: 50 f. As Type **129** but with heads of children and letters of various alphabets in place of the emblems.

130 Route Map from Athens **131** Prince Rainier and Princess Grace

1959. 28th Monte Carlo Rally.
614 **130** 100 f. blue, red & grn on blue 6·25 3·75

1959. Air.
615 **131** 300 f. violet 12·50 10·50
616 500 f. blue 21·00 17·00
See also Nos. 642/3.

132 "Princess Caroline" Carnation

1959. Flowers.
617 **132** 5 f. mve, grn and brn 10 10
618 – 10 f. on 3 f. pink, green and brown 10 10
619 – 15 f. on 1 f. yellow & green 15 10
620 – 20 f. purple and green 1·00 60
621 – 25 f. on 6 f. red, yellow and green 1·25 85
622 – 35 f. pink and green 2·50 2·00
623 – 50 f. green and sepia 3·00 2·00
624 – 85 f. on 65 f. lavender, bronze and green 4·00 3·25
625 – 100 f. red and green 5·25 5·00
FLOWERS—As Type **132**: 10 f. "Princess Grace" carnation; 100 f. "Grace of Monaco" rose. VERT: (22 × 36 mm): 15 f. Mimosa; 25 f. Geranium. HORIZ: (36 × 22 mm): 20 f. Bougainvillea; 35 f. "Laurier" rose; 50 f. Jasmine; 85 f. Lavender.

(New currency. 100 (old) francs = 1 (new franc.)

133 "Uprooted Tree" **134** Oceanographic Museum

1960. World Refugee Year.
626 **133** 25 c. green, blue and black 15 15

1960. Prince Rainier types with values in new currency.
627 **109** 25 c. blk & orge (postage) 50 10
628 30 c. violet 20 10
629 40 c. red and brown 85 10
630 45 c. brown and grey 30 10
631 50 c. red and green 40 20
632 50 c. red and brown 40 10
633 60 c. brown and green 1·60 50
634 60 c. brown and purple 1·60 50
635 65 c. blue and brown 11·00 5·00
636 70 c. blue and plum 80 40
637 85 c. green and violet 1·60 1·25
638 95 c. blue 1·50 1·25
639 1 f. 10 blue and brown 3·00 1·75
640 1 f. 30 brown and red 2·75 2·25
641 2 f. 30 purple and orange 3·00 1·00
642 **131** 3 f. violet (air) 48·00 23·00
643 5 f. blue 48·00 32·00

1960.
644 – 5 c. green, black and blue 10 10
645 **134** 10 c. brown and blue 80 10
646 – 10 c. blue, violet and green 10 10
647 – 40 c. purple, grn & dp grn 85 10
648 – 45 c. brown, green & blue 5·00 75
649 – 70 c. brown, red and green 75 20
650 – 80 c. red, green and blue 1·60 1·25
651 – 85 c. black, brown & grey 8·00 2·25
652 – 90 c. red, blue and black 1·00 40
653 – 1 f. multicoloured 1·25 25
654 – 1 f. 15 black, red and blue 2·25 1·75
655 – 1 f. 30 brown, green & bl 2·50 2·25
656 – 1 f. 40 orange, green & vio 8·25 2·75
DESIGNS—HORIZ: 5 c. Palace of Monaco; 10 c. (No. 646), Aquatic Stadium; 40, 45, 80 c., 1 f. 40, Aerial view of Palace; 70, 85, 90 c., 1 f. 15, 1 f. 30, Court of Honour, Monaco Palace; 1 f. Palace floodlit.

134a St. Devote

1960. Air.
668 **134a** 2 f. violet, blue and green 1·40 75
669 3 f. brown, green and blue 2·25 1·10
670 5 f. red 5·00 2·25
671 10 f. brown, grey and green 8·75 2·25

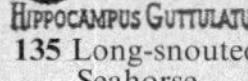

135 Long-snouted Seahorse

136 Route Map from Lisbon

1960. Marine Life and Plants. (a) Marine Life.

672	–	1 c. red and turquoise	10	10
673	–	12 c. brown and blue	55	10
674	**135**	15 c. green and red	65	10
675	–	20 c. multicoloured	60	10

DESIGNS—HORIZ: 1 c. "Macrocheira kampferi" (crab); 20 c. Lionfish. VERT: 12 c. Trapezium horse conch.

(b) Plants.

676	–	2 c. multicoloured	10	10
677	–	15 c. orange, brown & olive	65	10
678	–	18 c. multicoloured	55	10
679	–	20 c. red, olive and brown	55	10

PLANTS—VERT: 2 c. "Selenicereus sp."; 15 c. "Cereus sp."; 18 c. "Aloe ciliaris"; 20 c. "Nopalea dejecta".

1960. Prince Rainier Seal type with values in new currency. Precancelled.

680	**104**	8 c. purple	1·40	60
681		20 c. green	2·75	60
682		40 c. brown	4·50	1·25
683		55 c. blue	6·75	1·90

1960. 29th Monte Carlo Rally.

684	**136**	25 c. black, red and blue on blue	1·90	1·90

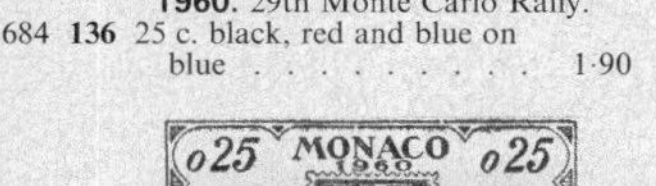

137 Stamps of Monaco 1885, France and Sardinia, 1860

1960. 75th Anniv of 1st Stamp.

685	**137**	25 c. bistre, blue and violet	70	70

138 Aquarium

1960. 50th Anniv of Oceanographic Museum, Monaco.

686	–	5 c. black, blue and purple	20	15
687	**138**	10 c. grey, brown and grn	35	35
688	–	15 c. black, bistre and blue	20	15
689	–	20 c. black, blue & mauve	85	50
690	–	25 c. turquoise	2·00	1·25
691	–	50 c. brown and blue	2·50	1·90

DESIGNS—VERT: 5 c. Oceanographic Museum (similar to Type **134**). HORIZ: 15 c. Conference Hall; 20 c. Hauling-in catch; 25 c. Museum, aquarium and under-water research equipment; 50 c. Prince Albert, "Hirondelle I" (schooner) and "Princess Alice" (steam yacht).

139 Horse-jumping

1960. Olympic Games.

692	**139**	5 c. brown, red and green	10	10
693	–	10 c. brown, blue & green	20	20
694	–	15 c. red, brown & purple	20	20
695	–	20 c. black, blue and green	3·00	3·00
696	–	25 c. purple, turq & grn	1·00	1·00
697	–	50 c. purple, blue & turq	1·25	1·25

DESIGNS: 10 c. Swimming; 15 c. Long jumping; 20 c. Throwing the javelin; 25 c. Free-skating; 50 c. Skiing.

MORE DETAILED LISTS
are given in the Stanley Gibbons Catalogues referred to in the country headings.
For lists of current volumes see Introduction.

140 Rally Badge, Old and Modern Cars

1961. 50th Anniv of Monte Carlo Rally.

698	**140**	1 f. violet, red and brown	1·90	1·90

141 Route Map from Stockholm

142 Marine Life

1961. 30th Monte Carlo Rally.

699	**141**	1 f. multicoloured	1·10	1·10

1961. World Aquariological Congress. Orange network background.

700	**142**	25 c. red, sepia and violet	15	15

143 Leper in Town of Middle Ages

145 Insect within Protective Hand

144 Semi-submerged Sphinx of Ouadi-es-Saboua

1961. Sovereign Order of Malta.

701	**143**	25 c. black, red and brown	15	15

1961. U.N.E.S.C.O. Campaign for Preservation of Nubian Monuments.

702	**144**	50 purple, blue and brown	1·00	1·00

1962. Nature Preservation.

703	**145**	25 c. mauve and purple	15	15

146 Chevrolet, 1912

1961. Veteran Motor Cars.

704		1 c. brown, green and chestnut	10	10
705		2 c. blue, purple and red	10	10
706		3 c. purple, black and mauve	10	10
707		4 c. blue, brown and violet	10	10
708		5 c. green, red and olive	10	10
709		10 c. brown, red and blue	10	10
710		15 c. green and turquoise	15	15
711		20 c. brown, red and violet	20	20
712		25 c. violet, red and brown	35	35
713		30 c. lilac and green	1·10	1·10
714		45 c. green, purple and brown	2·25	2·25
715		50 c. blue, red and brown	2·50	2·50
716		65 c. brown, red and grey	3·00	3·00
717		1 f. blue, red and violet	4·00	4·00

MOTOR CARS: 1 c. Type **146**: 2 c. Peugeot, 1898; 3 c. Fiat, 1901; 4 c. Mercedes, 1901; 5 c. Rolls Royce, 1903;. 10 c. Panhard-Lavassor, 1899; 15 c. Renault, 1898; 20 c. Ford "N", 1906 (wrongly inscr "FORD-S-1908"); 25 c. Rochet-Schneider, 1894; 30 c. FN-Herstal, 1901; 45 c. De Dion Bouton, 1900; 50 c. Buick, 1910; 65 c. Delahaye, 1901; 1 f. Cadillac, 1906.

147 Racing Car and Race Route

1962. 20th Monaco Motor Grand Prix.

718	**147**	1 f. purple	1·75	1·75

148 Route Map from Oslo

1962. 31st Monte Carlo Rally.

719	**148**	1 f. multicoloured	1·10	1·25

149 Louis XII and Lucien Grimaldi

1962. 450th Anniv of Recognition of Monegasque Sovereignty by Louis XII.

720	**149**	25 c. black, red and blue	20	20
721	–	50 c. brown, lake and blue	20	20
722	–	1 f. red, green and brown	55	55

DESIGNS: 50 c. Parchment bearing declaration of sovereignty; 1 f. Seals of two Sovereigns.

150 Mosquito and Swamp

1962. Malaria Eradication.

723	**150**	1 f. green and olive	50	60

151 Sun, Bouquet and "Hope Chest"

1962. National Multiple Sclerosis Society, New York.

724	**151**	20 c. multicoloured	15	10

152 Harvest Scene

1962. Europa.

725	**152**	25 c. brown, green and blue (postage)	15	15
726		50 c. olive and turquoise	25	25
727		1 f. olive and purple	55	55
728	–	2 f. slate, brown and green (air)	1·25	1·25

DESIGN: 2 f. Mercury in flight over Europe.

153 Atomic Symbol and Scientific Centre, Monaco

1962. Air. Scientific Centre, Monaco.

729	**153**	10 f. violet, brown & blue	5·50	5·50

154 Yellow Wagtails

155 Galeazzi's Diving Turret

1962. Protection of Birds useful to Agriculture.

730	**154**	5 c. yellow, brown & green	10	10
731	–	10 c. red, bistre and purple	10	10
732	–	15 c. multicoloured	15	10
733	–	20 c. sepia, green & mauve	50	10
734	–	25 c. multicoloured	60	50
735	–	30 c. brown, blue & myrtle	70	40
736	–	45 c. brown and violet	1·40	1·00
737	–	50 c. black, olive & turq	2·00	1·25
738	–	85 c. multicoloured	2·25	1·90
739	–	1 f. sepia, red and green	3·00	2·25

BIRDS: 10 c. European robins; 15 c. Goldfinches; 20 c. Blackcaps; 25 c. Greater spotted woodpeckers; 30 c. Nightingale; 45 c. Barn owls; 50 c. Common starlings; 85 c. Red crossbills; 1 f. White storks.

1962. Underwater Exploration.

740	–	5 c. black, violet and blue	10	10
741	**155**	10 c. blue, violet & brown	10	10
742	–	25 c. bistre, green and blue	10	10
743	–	45 c. black, blue and green	35	25
744	–	50 c. green, bistre and blue	75	75
745	–	85 c. blue and turquoise	1·25	1·25
746	–	1 f. brown, green and blue	1·90	1·90

DESIGNS—HORIZ: 5 c. Divers; 25 c. Williamson's photosphere (1914) and bathyscaphe "Trieste"; 45 c. Klingert's diving-suit (1797) and modern diving-suit; 50 c. Diving saucer; 85 c. Fulton's "Nautilus" (1800) and modern submarine; 1 f. Alexander the Great's diving bell and Beebe's bathysphere.

156 Donor's Arm and Globe

158 Feeding Chicks in Nest

157 "Ring-a-ring o' Roses"

1962. 3rd Int Blood Donors' Congress' Monaco.

747	**156**	1 f. red, sepia and orange	40	40

1963. U.N. Children's Charter.

748	**157**	5 c. red, blue and ochre	10	10
749	**158**	10 c. green, sepia and blue	10	10
750	–	15 c. blue, red and green	10	10
751	–	20 c. multicoloured	10	10
752	–	25 c. blue, purple & brown	20	20
753	–	50 c. multicoloured	75	30
754	–	95 c. multicoloured	1·40	75
755	–	1 f. purple, red & turq	2·00	1·50

DESIGNS—As Type **157**: 1 f. Prince Albert and Princess Caroline; Children's paintings as Type **158**: HORIZ: 15 c. Children on scales; 50 c. House and child. VERT: 20 c. Sun's rays and children of three races; 25 c. Mother and child; 95 c. Negress and child.

159 Ship's Figurehead

160 Racing Cars

1963. International Red Cross Centenary.

756	**159**	50 c. red, brown & turquoise	50	50
757	–	1 f. multicoloured	80	80

DESIGN—HORIZ: 1 f. Moynier, Dunant and Dufour.

1963. European Motor Grand Prix.

758	**160**	50 c. multicoloured	75	35

161 Emblem and Charter

1963. Founding of Lions Club of Monaco.
759 **161** 50 c. blue, bistre and violet 40 40

162 Hotel des Postes and U.P.U. Monument, Berne

1963. Paris Postal Conference Centenary.
760 **162** 50 c. lake, green & yellow 60 60

163 "Telstar" Satellite and Globe

1963. 1st Link Trans-Atlantic T.V. Satellite.
761 **163** 50 c. brown, green & pur . 40 40

164 Route Map from Warsaw

1963. 32nd Monte Carlo Rally.
762 **164** 1 f. multicoloured . . . . 1·40 1·40

165 Feeding Chicks

1963. Freedom from Hunger.
763 **165** 1 f. multicoloured 75 75

166 Allegory

1963. 2nd Ecumenical Council, Vatican City.
764 **166** 1 f. turquoise, green and red 40 40

167 Henry Ford and Ford "A" Car of 1903

1963. Birth Centenary of Henry Ford (motor pioneer).
765 **167** 20 c. green and purple . . 20 20

168 H. Garin (winner of 1903 race) cycling through Village

1963. 50th "Tour de France" Cycle Race.
766 **168** 25 c. green, brown & blue 20 20
767 – 50 c. sepia, green & blue 25 25
DESIGN: 50 c. Cyclist passing Desgrange Monument, Col du Galibier, 1963.

169 P. de Coubertin and Discus-thrower

1963. Birth Centenary of Pierre de Coubertin (reviver of Olympic Games).
768 **169** 1 f. brown, red and lake . . 75 75

170 Roland Garros and Morane Saulnier Type I

1963. Air. 50th Anniv of 1st Aerial Crossing of Mediterranean Sea.
769 **170** 2 f. sepia and blue . . . . 1·10 1·25

171 Route Map from Paris **173** "Europa"

172 Children with Stamp Album

1963. 33rd Monte Carlo Rally.
770 **171** 1 f. red, turquoise and blue 1·25 1·25

1963. "Scolatex" International Stamp Exn, Monaco.
771 **172** 50 c. blue, violet and red 20 20

1963. Europa.
772 **173** 25 c. brown, red and green 20 20
773 50 c. sepia, red and& blue 60 30

174 Wembley Stadium

1963. Cent of (English) Football Association.
774 **174** 1 c. violet, green and red 10 10
775 – 2 c. red, black and green 10 10
776 – 3 c. orange, olive and red 10 10
777 – 4 c. multicoloured 10 10
Multicoloured horiz designs depicting (a) "Football through the Centuries".
778 10 c. "Calcio", Florence (16th cent) 10 10
779 15 c. "Soule", Brittany (19th cent) 10 10
780 20 c. English military college (after Cruickshank, 1827) . . 10 10
781 25 c. English game (after Overend, 1890) 10 10
(b) "Modern Football".
782 30 c. Tackling 50 50
783 50 c. Saving goal 55 55
784 95 c. Heading ball . . . . . . 1·10 1·10
785 1 f. Corner kick . . . . 1·40 1·40
DESIGNS—As Type **174**: 4 c. Louis II Stadium, Monaco. This stamp is optd in commemoration of the Association Sportive de Monaco football teams in the French Championships and in the Coupe de France, 1962–63. HORIZ: (36 × 22 mm): 2 c. Footballer making return kick; 3 c. Goalkeeper saving ball.
Nos. 778/81 and 782/5 were respectively issued together in sheets and arranged in blocks of 4 with a football in the centre of each block.

175 Communications in Ancient Egypt, and Rocket

1964. "PHILATEC 1964" Int Stamp Exn, Paris.
786 **175** 1 f. brown, indigo & blue . 75 75

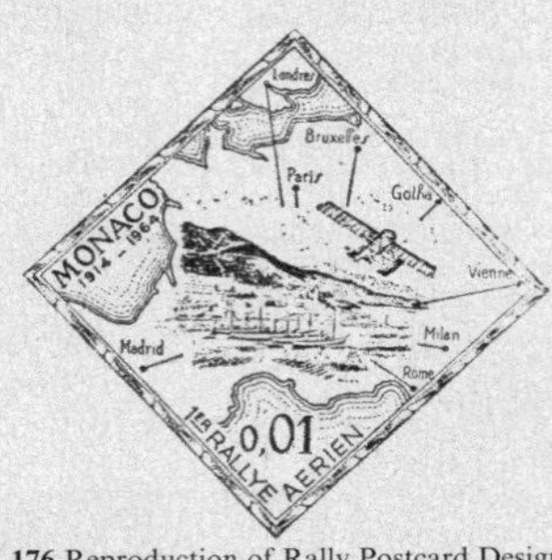

176 Reproduction of Rally Postcard Design

1964. 50th Anniv of 1st Aerial Rally, Monte Carlo.
787 1 c. olive, blue & grn (postage) . 10 10
788 2 c. bistre, brown and blue . . 10 10
789 3 c. brown, blue and green . . 10 10
790 4 c. red, turquoise and blue . . 10 10
791 5 c. brown, red and violet . . . 10 10
792 10 c. violet, brown and blue . . 10 10
793 15 c. orange, brown and blue . . 10 10
794 20 c. sepia, green and blue . . 20 10
795 25 c. brown, blue and red . . . 30 35
796 30 c. myrtle, purple and blue . . 40 50
797 45 c. sepia, turquoise & brn . . 85 60
798 50 c. ochre, olive and violet . . 1·00 85
799 65 c. red, slate and turquoise . 1·40 1·10
800 95 c. turquoise, red and bistre 1·90 1·50
801 1 f. brown, blue and turquoise 2·50 1·90
802 5 f. sepia, blue & brown (air) 3·75 3·75
DESIGNS: 1 c. Type **176**. 48 × 27 mm—Rally planes: 2 c. Renaux's Farman M.F.7 floatplane; 3 c. Espanet's Nieuport 4 seaplane; 4 c. Moineau's Breguet HU-3 seaplane; 5 c. Roland Garros' Morane Saulnier Type I seaplane; 10 c. Hirth's WDD Albatros seaplane; 15 c. Prevost's Deperdussin Monocoque Racer. Famous planes and flights: 20 c. Vickers-Vimy (Ross Smith: London–Port Darwin, 1919); 25 c. Douglas World Cruiser seaplane (U.S. World Flight, 1924); 30 c. Savoia Marchetti S-55M flying boat "Santa Maria" (De Pinedo's World Flight, 1925); 45 c. Fokker F. VIIa/3m "Josephine Ford" (Flight over North Pole, Byrd and Bennett, 1925); 50 c. Ryan NYP Special "Spirit of St. Louis" (1st solo crossing of N. Atlantic, Lindbergh, 1927); 65 c. Breguet 19 "Point d'Interrogation" (Paris–New York, Coste and Bellonte, 1930); 95 c. Latecoere 28-3 seaplane "Comte de la Vaulx" (Dakar–Natal, first S. Atlantic airmail flight, Mermoz, 1930); 1 f. Dornier Do-X flying boat (Germany–Rio de Janeiro, Christiansen, 1930); 5 f. Convair B-58 Hustler (New York–Paris in 3 hours, 19"41" Major Payne, U.S.A.F., 1961).

177 Aquatic Stadium **178** Europa "Flower"

1964. Precancelled.
803 **177** 10 c. multicoloured . . . 2·00 20
803a 15 c. multicoloured . . . 75 20
804 25 c. turquoise, blue & blk 75 20
805 50 c. violet, turq & blk . . 2·00 1·10
The "1962" date has been obliterated with two bars.
See also Nos. 949/51a and 1227/1230.

1964. Europa.
806 **178** 25 c. red, green and blue 20 20
807 50 c. brown, bistre and bl 40 40

179 Weightlifting

1964. Olympic Games, Tokyo and Innsbruck.
808 **179** 1 c. red, brown and blue (postage) 10 10
809 – 2 c. red, green and olive . . 10 10
810 – 3 c. blue, brown and red . . 10 10
811 – 4 c. green, olive and red . . 10 10
812 – 5 f. red, brown and blue (air) 3·00 3·00
DESIGNS: 2 c. Judo; 3 c. Pole vaulting; 4 c. Archery; 5 f. Bobsleighing.

180 Pres. Kennedy and Space Capsule

1964. Pres. Kennedy Commemoration.
813 **180** 50 c. indigo and blue . . . 75 75

181 Monaco and Television Set

1964. 5th Int Television Festival, Monte Carlo.
814 **181** 50 c. brown, blue and red . 30 30

182 F. Mistral and Statue

1964. 50th Death Anniv of Frederic Mistral (poet).
815 **182** 1 f. brown and olive . . . 60 60

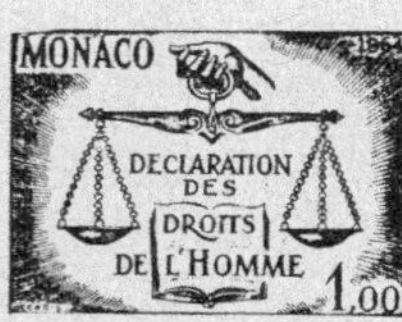

183 Scales of Justice

1964. 15th Anniv of Declaration of Human Rights.
816 **183** 1 f. green and brown . . . 40 40

184 Route Map from Minsk

1964. 34th Monte Carlo Rally.
817 **184** 1 f. brown, turq & ochre 85 85

185 FIFA Emblem

1964. 60th Anniv of Federation Internationale de Football Association (FIFA).
818 **185** 1 f. bistre, blue and red . . 60 60

186 "Syncom 2" and Globe

1965. Cent of I.T.U.
819 **186** 5 c. green & ultra (postage) 10 10
820 – 10 c. chestnut, brown & bl 10 10
821 – 12 c. purple, red and grey 10 10
822 – 18 c. blue, red and purple 10 10
823 – 25 c. violet, bistre & purple 10 10
824 – 30 c. bistre, brown & sepia . 20 20
825 – 50 c. blue and green . . . 25 25
826 – 60 c. blue and brown . . . 75 75
827 – 70 c. sepia, orange & blue . 1·00 1·00
828 – 95 c. black, indigo & blue . 1·10 1·10
829 – 1 f. brown and blue . . . 1·60 1·60
830 – 10 f. green, blue and brown (air) . . . . 5·00 5·00
DESIGNS—As Type **186**: HORIZ: 10 c. "Echo 2"; 18 c. "Lunik 3"; 30 c. A. G. Bell and telephone; 50 c. S. Morse and telegraph; 60 c. E. Belin and "belinograph". VERT: 12 c. "Relay"; 10 f. Monte Carlo television transmitter. LARGER (48½ × 27 mm): 25 c. "Telstar" and Pleumeur-Bodou Station; 70 c. Roman beacon and Chappe's telegraph; 95 c. Cable ships "Great Eastern" and "Alsace"; 1 f. E. Branly, G. Marconi and English Channel.

187 Europa "Sprig"

1965. Europa.
831 **187** 30 c. brown and green . . 50 15
832 60 c. violet and red 75 30

188 Monaco Palace (18th cent)

1966. 750th Anniv of Monaco Palace.
833 **188** 10 c. violet, green and blue 10 10
834 – 12 c. bistre, blue and black 10 10
835 – 18 c. green, black & blue 15 15
836 – 30 c. brown, black & blue 20 20
837 – 60 c. green, blue & bistre 75 75
838 – 1 f. 30 brown and green 1·40 1·40
DESIGNS: (Different views of Palace): 12 c. 17th century; 18 c. 18th century; 30 c. 19th century; 60 c. 19th century; 1 f. 30, 20th century.

189 Dante

1966. 700th Anniv of Dante's Birth.
839 **189** 30 c. green, deep green and red 20 20
840 – 60 c. blue, turquoise & grn 75 75
841 – 70 c. black, green and red . 55 55
842 – 95 c. blue, violet & purple . 80 80
843 – 1 f. turquoise, blue & dp bl 80 80
DESIGNS: (Scenes from Dante's works): 60 c. Dante harassed by the panther (envy); 70 c. Crossing the 5th circle; 95 c. Punishment of the arrogant; 1 f. Invocation of St. Bernard.

190 "The Nativity"

1966. World Association of Children's Friends (A.M.A.D.E.).
844 **190** 30 c. brown 20 20

191 Route Map from London

1966. 35th Monte Carlo Rally.
845 **191** 1 f. blue, purple and red . . 1·00 1·00

192 Princess Grace with Children

1966. Air. Princess Stephanie's 1st Birthday.
846 **192** 3 f. brown, blue and violet 3·00 2·50

193 Casino in 19th Century 194 Europa "Ship"

1966. Centenary of Monte Carlo.
847 – 12 c. black, red and blue (postage) 10 10
848 **193** 25 c. multicoloured 10 10
849 – 30 c. multicoloured 10 10
850 – 40 c. multicoloured 20 20
851 – 60 c. multicoloured 30 30
852 – 70 c. blue and lake 30 30
853 – 95 c. black and purple . . 65 65
854 – 1 f. 30 purple, brown and chestnut . . . . 1·25 1·25
855 – 5 f. lake, ochre and blue (air) 2·25 2·25
DESIGNS—VERT: 12 c. Prince Charles III. HORIZ: 40 c. Charles III Monument; 95 c. Massenet and Saint-Saens; 1 f. 30, Faure and Ravel. LARGER (48 × 27 mm): 30 c. F. Blanc, originator of Monte Carlo, and view of 1860; 60 c. Prince Rainier III and projected esplanade; 70 c. Rene Blum and Diaghilev, ballet character from "Petrouchka". (36 × 36 mm): 5 f. Interior of Opera House, 1879.

1966. Europa.
856 **194** 30 c. orange 15 15
857 60 c. green 50 50

195 Prince Rainier and Princess Grace 197 "Learning to Write"

196 Prince Albert I and Yachts "Hirondelle I" and "Princess Alice"

1966. Air.
858 **195** 2 f. slate and red . . . . 1·25 40
859 3 f. slate and green . . . 2·50 1·00
860 5 f. slate and blue . . . 3·00 1·40
860a 10 f. slate and bistre . . . 6·25 4·00
860b 20 f. brown and orange . . 55·00 42·00

1966. 1st International Oceanographic History Congress, Monaco.
861 **196** 1 f. lilac and blue . . . . 1·40 1·00

1966. 20th Anniv of U.N.E.S.C.O.
862 **197** 30 c. purple and mauve . . 10 10
863 60 c. brown and blue . . . 25 25

198 T.V. Screen, Cross and Monaco Harbour 200 W.H.O. Building

199 "Precontinent III"

1966. 10th Meeting of International Catholic Television Association (U.N.D.A.), Monaco.
864 **198** 60 c. red, purple & crimson 20 15

1966. 1st Anniv of Underwater Research Craft "Precontinent III".
865 **199** 1 f. yellow, brown & blue . 35 30

1966. Inaug of W.H.O. Headquarters, Geneva.
866 **200** 30 c. brown, grn and blue 10 10
867 60 c. brown, red and green 20 20

201 Bugatti, 1931 202 Dog (Egyptian bronze)

1967. 25th Motor Grand Prix, Monaco. Multicoloured. (a) Postage.
868 1 c. Type **201** 10 10
869 2 c. Alfa-Romeo, 1932 . . . . 10 10
870 5 c. Mercedes, 1936 . . . . 10 10
871 10 c. Maserati, 1948 . . . . 10 10
872 18 c. Ferrari, 1955 . . . . . 50 10
873 20 c. Alfa-Romeo, 1950 . . . 10 10
874 25 c. Maserati, 1957 . . . . 15 15
875 30 c. Cooper-Climax, 1958 . . 50 15
876 40 c. Lotus-Climax, 1960 . . 60 50
877 50 c. Lotus-Climax, 1961 . . 85 50
878 60 c. Cooper-Climax, 1962 . 1·10 60
879 70 c. B.R.M., 1963-6 . . . . 1·50 1·10
880 1 f. Walter Christie, 1907 . . 1·75 1·25
881 2 f. 30 Peugeot, 1910 . . . . 3·00 2·50
(b) Air. Diamond. 50 × 50 mm.
882 3 f. black and blue . . . . . 2·50 2·50
DESIGN: 3 f. Panhard-Phenix, 1895.

1967. Int Cynological Federation Congress, Monaco.
883 **202** 30 c. black, purple & green 25 25

203 View of Monte Carlo

1967. International Tourist Year.
884 **203** 30 c. brown, green & blue . 15 10

204 Pieces on Chessboard

1967. Int Chess Grand Prix, Monaco.
885 **204** 60 c. black, plum and blue 65 50

205 Melvin Jones (founder), Lions Emblem and Monte Carlo

1967. 50th Anniv of Lions International.
886 **205** 60 c. blue, ultramarine and brown 30 20

206 Rotary Emblem and Monte Carlo

1967. Rotary International Convention.
887 **206** 1 f. bistre, blue and green 75 30

207 Fair Buildings

1967. World Fair, Montreal.
888 **207** 1 f. red, slate and blue . . 30 30

208 Squiggle on Map of Europe 209 Cogwheels

1967. European Migration Committee (C.I.M.E.).
889 **208** 1 f. brown, bistre and blue 30 25

1967. Europa.
890 **209** 30 c. violet, purple and red 20 20
891 60 c. green, turq & emerald 30 30

210 Dredger and Coastal Chart

1967. 9th Int Hydrographic Congress, Monaco.
892 **210** 1 f. brown, blue and green 60 30

211 Marie Curie and Scientific Equipment

1967. Birth Centenary of Marie Curie.
893 **211** 1 f. blue, olive & brown . . 1·00 60

212 Skiing

1967. Winter Olympic Games, Grenoble.
894 **212** 2 f. 30 brown, blue & slate 1·40 1·25

213 "Prince Rainier I" (E. Charpentier)

1967. Paintings. "Princes and Princesses of Monaco". Multicoloured.

895 1 f. Type **213** 85 85
896 1 f. "Lucien Grimaldi" (A. di Predis) 85 85

See also Nos. 932/3, 958/9, 1005/6, 1023/4, 1070/1, 1108/9, 1213/14, 1271/2, 1325, 1380/1, 1405/6, 1460/1 and 1531/2.

214 Putting the Shot

1968. Olympic Games, Mexico.

897 **214** 20 c. blue, brown and green (postage) 10 10
898 – 30 c. brown, blue & plum 10 10
899 – 60 c. blue, purple and red 20 20
900 – 70 c. red, blue and ochre 25 25
901 – 1 f. blue, brown and orange 50 50
902 – 2 f. 30 olive, blue and lake 1·10 1·10
903 – 3 f. blue, violet & grn (air) 1·90 1·90

DESIGNS: 30 c. High-jumping; 60 c. Gymnastics; 70 c. Water-polo; 1 f. Greco-Roman wrestling; 2 f. 30, Gymnastics (different); 3 f. Hockey.

215 "St. Martin"

1968. 20th Anniv of Monaco Red Cross.

904 **215** 2 f. 30 blue and brown . . 1·40 1·25

216 "Anemones" (after Raoul Dufy)

217 Insignia of Prince Charles III and Pope Pius IX

1968. Monte Carlo Floral Exhibitions.

905 **216** 1 f. multicoloured 55 55

1968. Centenary of "Nullius Diocesis" Abbey.

906 **217** 10 c. brown and red 10 10
907 – 20 c. red, green and brown 10 10
908 – 30 c. brown and blue . . . 20 20
909 – 60 c. brown, blue & green 25 25
910 – 1 f. indigo, bistre and blue 40 40

DESIGNS—VERT: 20 c. "St. Nicholas" (after Louis Brea); 30 c. "St. Benedict" (after Simone Martini); 60 c. Subiaco Abbey. HORIZ: 1 f. Old St. Nicholas' Church (on site of present cathedral).

218 Europa "Key"

1968. Europa.

911 **218** 30 c. red and orange . . . 20 20
912 60 c. blue and red . . . 75 30
913 1 f. brown and green . . . 1·75 1·10

219 First Locomotive on Monaco Line, 1868

1968. Centenary of Nice–Monaco Railway.

914 **219** 20 c. black, blue & purple 30 25
915 – 30 c. black, blue and olive 75 60
916 – 60 c. black, blue and ochre 90 1·10
917 – 70 c. black, violet & brown 2·00 1·60
918 – 1 f. black, blue and red . . 3·00 2·75
919 – 2 f. 30 blue, black and red 5·25 4·00

DESIGNS: 30 c. Class 220-C steam locomotive, 1898; 60 c. Class 230-C steam locomotive, 1910; 70 c. Class 231-F steam locomotive, 1925; 1 f. Class 241-A steam locomotive, 1932; 2 f. 30, Class BB 25200 electric locomotive, 1968.

220 Chateaubriand and Combourg Castle

1968. Birth Centenary of Chateaubriand (novelist).

920 **220** 10 c. plum, green & myrtle 10 10
921 – 20 c. violet, purple & blue . 10 10
922 – 25 c. brown, violet & blue . 10 10
923 – 30 c. violet, choc & brn . . 15 15
924 – 60 c. brown, grn & red . . 25 25
925 – 2 f. 30 brown, mve & blue 1·25 1·25

Scenes from Chateaubriand's novels: 20 c. "Le Genie du Christianisme"; 25 c. "Rene"; 30 c. "Le Dernier Abencerage"; 60 c. "Les Martyrs"; 2 f. 30, "Atala".

221 Law Courts, Paris, and statues—"La France et la Fidelite"

1968. Birth Centenary of J. F. Bosio (Monegasque sculptor).

926 **221** 20 c. brown and purple . . 10 10
927 – 25 c. brown and red . . . 10 10
928 – 30 c. blue and green . . . 10 10
929 – 60 c. green and myrtle . . 60 20
930 – 2 f. 30 black and slate . . . 1·10 1·00

DESIGNS—VERT: (26×36 mm): 25 c. "Henry IV as a Child"; 30 c. "J. F. Bosio" (lithograph); 60 c. "Louis XIV". HORIZ: As Type **221**: 2 f. 30, "Napoleon I, Louis XVIII and Charles X".

222 W.H.O. Emblem

1968. 20th Anniv of W.H.O.

931 **222** 60 c. multicoloured 25 20

1968. Paintings. "Princes and Princesses of Monaco". As T **213**. Multicoloured.

932 1 f. "Prince Charles II" (Mimault) 30 30
933 2 f. 30 "Princess Jeanne Grimaldi" (Mimault) . . . . 1·25 1·25

223 The Hungarian March

1969. Death Centenary of Hector Berlioz (composer).

934 **223** 10 c. brown, violet and green (postage) 10 10
935 – 20 c. brown, olive & mauve 10 10
936 – 25 c. brown, blue & mauve 10 10
937 – 30 c. black, green & black 10 10
938 – 40 c. red, black and slate 10 10
939 – 50 c. brown, slate & purple 15 15
940 – 70 c. brown, slate & green 25 20
941 – 1 f. black, mauve & brown 35 50
942 – 1 f. 15 black, blue & turq 75 75
943 – 2 f. black, blue & grn (air) 1·40 1·25

DESIGNS—HORIZ: 20 c. Mephistopheles appears to Faust; 25 c. Auerbach's tavern; 30 c. Sylphs' ballet; 40 c. Minuet of the goblins; 50 c. Marguerite's bedroom; 70 c. "Forests and caverns"; 1 f. The journey to Hell; 1 f. 15, Heaven; All scenes from Berlioz's "The Damnation of Faust". VERT: 2 f. Bust of Berlioz.

224 "St. Elisabeth of Hungary"

1969. Monaco Red Cross.

944 **224** 3 f. blue, brown and red . . 1·90 1·50

225 "Napoleon I" (P. Delaroche)

1969. Birth Bicentenary of Napoleon Bonaparte.

945 **225** 3 f. multicoloured . . . . 1·90 1·60

226 Colonnade

227 "Head of Woman" (Da Vinci)

1969. Europa.

946 **226** 40 c. red and purple . . . 30 10
947 70 c. blue, brown & black . 1·40 1·00
948 1 f. ochre, brown and blue 1·90 1·25

1969. Precancelled. As T **177**. No date.

949 22 c. brown, blue and black . 35 10
949a 26 c. violet, blue and black . . 40 15
949b 30 c. multicoloured 65 15
950 35 c. multicoloured 45 10
950a 45 c. multicoloured . . . . . 1·00 35
951 70 c. black and blue . . . . . 1·00 35
951a 90 c. green, blue and black . . 1·60 60

1969. 450th Death Anniv of Leonardo da Vinci.

952 **227** 30 c. brown 10 10
953 – 40 c. red and brown . . . 15 10
954 – 70 c. green 25 20
955 – 80 c. sepia 35 25
956 – 1 f. 15 brown 85 45
957 – 3 f. brown . . . . 2·00 1·40

DRAWINGS: 40 c. Self-portrait; 70 c. "Head of an Old Man"; 80 c. "Head of St. Madeleine"; 1 f. 15, "Man's Head"; 3 f. "The Condottiere".

1969. Paintings. "Princes and Princesses of Monaco". As T **213**. Multicoloured.

958 1 f. "Prince Honore II" (Champaigne) 35 35
959 3 f. "Princess Louise-Hippolyte" (Champaigne) . . . . 1·50 1·50

228 Marine Fauna, King Alfonso XIII of Spain and Prince Albert I of Monaco

229 I.L.O. Emblem

1969. 50th Anniv of Int Commission for Scientific Exploration of the Mediterranean, Madrid.

960 **228** 40 c. blue and black . . . 50 50

1969. 50th Anniv of I.L.O.

961 **229** 40 c. multicoloured 20 20

230 Aerial View of Monaco and T.V. Camera

1969. 10th International Television Festival.

962 **230** 40 c. purple, lake and blue 15 15

231 J.C.C. Emblem

1969. 25th Anniv of Junior Chamber of Commerce.

963 **231** 40 c. violet, bistre and blue 15 15

232 Alphonse Daudet and Scenes from "Lettres"

1969. Centenary of Daudet's "Lettres de Mon Moulin".

964 **232** 30 c. lake, violet and green 10 10
965 – 40 c. green, brown & blue 20 20
966 – 70 c. multicoloured 30 25
967 – 80 c. violet, brown & grn 60 30
968 – 1 f. 15 brown, orange & bl 75 75

DESIGNS: (Scenes from the book): 40 c. "Installation" (Daudet writing); 70 c. "Mule, Goat and Wolf"; 80 c. "Gaucher's Elixir" and "The Three Low Masses"; 1 f. 15, Daudet drinking, "The Old Man" and "The Country Sub-Prefect".

233 Conference Building, Albert I and Rainier III

1970. Interparliamentary Union's Spring Meeting, Monaco.

969 **233** 40 c. black, red and purple 15 10

234 Baby Common Seal

1970. Protection of Baby Seals.

970 **234** 40 c. drab, blue and purple 1·00 60

235 Japanese Print **236** Dobermann

1970. Expo 70.
971 **235** 20 c. brown, green and red . . 10 10
972 – 30 c. brown, buff & green . 25 20
973 – 40 c. bistre and violet . . . 15 15
974 – 70 c. grey and red 75 75
975 – 1 f. 15 red, green & purple . 85 85
DESIGNS—VERT: 30 c. Manchurian Cranes (birds); 40 c. Shinto temple gateway. HORIZ: 70 c. Cherry blossom; 1 f. 15, Monaco Palace and Osaka Castle.

1970. International Dog Show, Monte Carlo.
976 **236** 40 c. black and brown . . . 1·10 85

237 Apollo

1970. 20th Anniv of World Federation for Protection of Animals.
977 **237** 30 c. black, red and blue . 40 20
978 – 40 c. brown, blue & green . 40 20
979 – 50 c. brown, ochre & blue . 85 40
980 – 80 c. brown, blue & green . 10·00 1·00
981 – 1 f. brown, bistre and slate . 2·50 2·25
982 – 1 f. 15 brown, green & brown . 3·00 2·50
DESIGNS—HORIZ: 40 c. Basque ponies; 50 c. Common seal. VERT: 80 c. Chamois; 1 f. White-tailed sea eagles; 1 f. 15, European otter.

238 "St. Louis" (King of France)

1970. Monaco Red Cross.
983 **238** 3 f. green, brown and slate . 1·90 1·90
See also Nos. 1022, 1041, 1114, 1189 and 1270.

239 "Roses and Anemones" (Van Gogh)

1970. Monte Carlo Flower Show.
984 **239** 3 f. multicoloured . . . . 2·75 2·50
See also Nos. 1042 and 1073.

240 Moon Plaque, Presidents Kennedy and Nixon

1970. 1st Man on the Moon (1969). Multicoloured.
985 40 c. Type **240** 60 35
986 80 c. Astronauts on Moon . . 1·10 75

241 New U.P.U. Building and Monument **242** "Flaming Sun"

1970. New U.P.U. Headquarters Building.
987 **241** 40 c. brown, black & green 15 10

1970. Europa.
988 **242** 40 c. purple 50 10
989 80 c. green . . . . 1·10 1·00
990 1 f. blue . . . . 1·90 1·50

243 Camargue Horse

1970. Horses.
991 **243** 10 c. slate, olive and blue (postage) 10 10
992 – 20 c. brown, olive and blue 20 10
993 – 30 c. brown, green & blue 50 15
994 – 40 c. grey, brown & slate 85 60
995 – 50 c. brown, olive & blue 1·25 85
996 – 70 c. brown, orange & grn 2·00 1·50
997 – 85 c. blue, green and olive 2·25 1·90
998 – 1 f. 15 black, green & blue 2·75 2·50
999 – 3 f. multicoloured (air) . . 2·25 2·25
HORSES—HORIZ: 20 c. Anglo-Arab; 30 c. French saddle-horse; 40 c. Lippizaner; 50 c. Trotter; 70 c. English thoroughbred; 85 c. Arab; 1 f. 15, Barbary. DIAMOND (50 × 50 mm): 3 f. Rock-drawings of horses in Lascaux grotto.

244 Dumas, D'Artagnan and the Three Musketeers

1970. Death Centenary of Alexandre Dumas (pere) (author).
1000 **244** 30 c. slate, brown & blue 10 10

245 Henri Rougier and Voisin "Boxkite"

1970. 60th Anniv of First Mediterranean Flight.
1001 **245** 40 c. brown, blue & slate 20 10

246 De Lamartine and scene from "Meditations Poetiques"

1970. 150th Anniv of "Meditations Poetiques" by Alphonse de Lamartine (writer).
1002 **246** 80 c. brown, blue & turq 30 15

247 Beethoven

1970. Birth Bicentenary of Beethoven.
1003 **247** 1 f. 30 brown and red . . 2·10 1·25

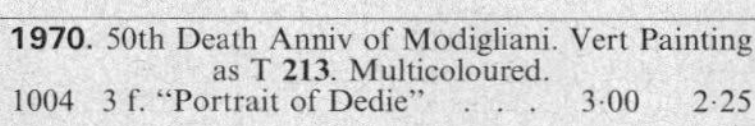

1970. 50th Death Anniv of Modigliani. Vert Painting as T **213**. Multicoloured.
1004 3 f. "Portrait of Dedie" . . . 3·00 2·25

1970. Paintings. "Princes and Princesses of Monaco". As T **213**.
1005 1 f. red and black 30 30
1006 3 f. multicoloured . . . . . . 1·50 1·40
PORTRAITS: 1 f. "Prince Louis I" (F. de Troy); 3 f. "Princess Charlotte de Gramont" (S. Bourdon).

248 Cocker Spaniel **249** Razorbill

1971. International Dog Show, Monte Carlo.
1007 **248** 50 c. multicoloured . . . 2·50 1·90
See also Nos. 1036, 1082, 1119, 1218 and 1239.

1971. Campaign Against Pollution of the Sea.
1008 **249** 50 c. indigo and blue 65 35

250 Hand holding Emblem

1971. 7th Int Blood-Donors Federation Congress.
1009 **250** 80 c. red, violet and grey . 75 30

251 Sextant, Scroll and Underwater Scene

1971. 50th Anniv of Int Hydrographic Bureau.
1010 **251** 80 c. brown, grn & slate . 40 30

252 Detail of Michelangelo Painting ("The Arts")

1971. 25th Anniv of U.N.E.S.C.O.
1011 **252** 30 c. brown, blue & vio 10 10
1012 – 50 c. blue and brown . . 20 10
1013 – 80 c. brown and green . . 30 35
1014 – 1 f. 30 green 75 40
DESIGNS—VERT: 50 c. Alchemist and dish aerial ("Sciences"); 1 f. 30, Prince Pierre of Monaco (National U.N.E.S.C.O. Commission). HORIZ: 80 c. Ancient scribe, book and T.V. screen ("Culture").

253 Europa Chain

1971. Europa.
1015 **253** 50 c. red 85 50
1016 80 c. blue . . . . 1·50 1·10
1017 1 f. 30 green . . . . . . 2·75 2·10

254 Old Bridge, Sospel

1971. Protection of Historic Monuments.
1018 **254** 50 c. brown, blue & green 15 10
1019 – 80 c. brown, green & grey 50 15
1020 – 1 f. 30 red, green & brn 55 40
1021 – 3 f. slate, blue and olive 1·75 1·25
DESIGNS—HORIZ: 80 c. Roquebrune Chateau; 1 f. 30, Grimaldi Chateau, Cagnes-sur-Mer. VERT: 3 f. Roman "Trophy of the Alps", La Turbie.

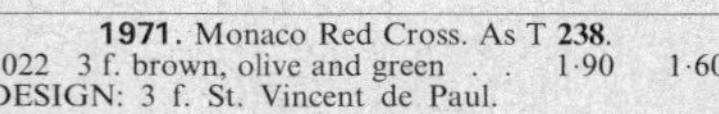

1971. Monaco Red Cross. As T **238**.
1022 3 f. brown, olive and green . . 1·90 1·60
DESIGN: 3 f. St. Vincent de Paul.

1972. Paintings. "Princes and Princesses of Monaco". As T **213**. Multicoloured.
1023 1 f. "Prince Antoine I" (Rigaud) 40 50
1024 3 f. "Princess Marie de Lorraine" (18th-century French School) . . . . . . 1·75 1·60

255 La Fontaine and Animal Fables (350th)

1972. Birth Anniversaries (1971).
1025 **255** 50 c. brown, emer & grn . 30 20
1026 – 1 f. 30 purple, blk & red . 1·10 85
DESIGNS: 1 f. 30, Baudelaire, nudes and cats (150th).

256 Saint-Saens and scene from Opera, "Samson and Delilah"

1972. 50th Death Anniv (1971) of Camile Saint-Saens.
1027 **256** 90 c. brown and sepia . . 40 50

257 Battle Scene

1972. 400th Anniv (1971) of Battle of Lepanto.
1028 **257** 1 f. blue, brown and red 60 40

258 "Christ before Pilate" (engraving by Durer)

1972. 500th Birth Anniv (1971) of Albrecht Durer.
1029 **258** 2 f. black and brown . . . 1·60 1·25

259 "The Cradle" (B. Morisot)

1972. 25th Anniv (1971) of U.N.I.C.E.F.
1030 **259** 2 f. multicoloured . . . . 1·60 1·10

INDEX

Countries can be quickly located by referring to the index at the end of this volume.

260 "Gilles" (Watteau)

1972. 250th Death Anniv (1971) of Watteau.
1031 **260** 3 f. multicoloured . . . . 2·50 1·90

261 Santa Claus

1972. Christmas (1971).
1032 **261** 30 c. red, blue and brown 15 15
1033 50 c. red, green & orange 45 15
1034 90 c. red, blue and brown 80 40

262 Class 743 Steam Locomotive, Italy, and TGV 001 Turbotrain, France

1972. 50th Anniv of International Railway Union.
1035 **262** 50 c. purple, lilac and red 1·00 75

1972. Int Dog Show, Monte Carlo. As T **248**.
1036 60 c. multicoloured . . . . . 2·50 1·90
DESIGN: 60 c. Great Dane.

263 "Pollution Kills"

1972. Anti-Pollution Campaign.
1037 **263** 90 c. brown, green & blk . 50 30

264 Ski-jumping

1972. Winter Olympic Games, Sapporo, Japan.
1038 **264** 90 c. black, red and green 40 30

265 "Communications" 266 "SS. Giovanni e Paolo" (detail, Canaletto)

1972. Europa.
1039 **265** 50 c. blue and orange . . 1·10 75
1040 90 c. blue and green . . . 2·00 1·75

1972. Monaco Red Cross. As T **238**.
1041 3 f. brown and purple . . . . 2·00 1·60
DESIGN: 3 f. St. Francis of Assisi.

1972. Monte Carlo Flower Show. As T **239**.
1042 3 f. multicoloured . . . . . . 3·50 3·00
DESIGN: 3 f. "Vase of Flowers" (Cezanne).

1972. U.N.E.S.C.O. "Save Venice" Campaign.
1043 **266** 30 c. red 25 20
1044 – 60 c. violet 35 25
1045 – 2 f. blue . . . . 2·00 1·60
DESIGNS—27 × 48 mm: 60 c. "S. Pietro di Castello" (F. Guradi). As Type **266**: 2 f. "Piazzetta S. Marco" (B. Bellotto).

267 Dressage

1972. Olympic Games, Munich. Equestrian Events.
1046 **267** 60 c. brown, blue & lake . 40 40
1047 – 90 c. lake, brown & blue . 1·25 1·25
1048 – 1 f. 10 blue, lake & brown 1·90 1·90
1049 – 1 f. 40 brown, lake & blue 3·00 3·00
DESIGNS: 90 c. Cross country; 1 f. 10, Show jumping (wall); 1 f. 40, Show jumping (parallel bars).

268 Escoffier and Birthplace

1972. 125th Birth Anniv of Auguste Escoffier (master chef).
1050 **268** 45 c. black and brown . . 25 15

269 Drug Addiction 270 Globe, Birds and Animals

1972. Campaign Against Drugs.
1051 **269** 50 c. red, brown & orange 50 20
1052 90 c. green, brown & blue 60 30
See also Nos. 1088/91 and 1280/1.

1972. 17th Int Congress of Zoology, Monaco.
1053 **270** 30 c. green, brown & red 15 10
1054 – 50 c. brown, purple and red 30 10
1055 – 90 c. blue, brown & red 40 20
DESIGNS—HORIZ: 50 c. VERT: 90 c. Similar symbolic design.

271 Bouquet 272 "The Nativity" and Child's face

1972. Monte Carlo Flower Show, 1973 (1st issue). Multicoloured.
1056 30 c. Lilies in vase 60 35
1057 50 c. Type **271** . . . . . . 1·00 60
1058 90 c. Flowers in Vase . . . . 1·90 1·25
See also Nos. 1073, 1105/7, 1143/4, 1225/6, 1244, 1282/3 and 1316/17.

1972. Christmas.
1059 **272** 30 c. grey, blue & purple 10 10
1060 50 c. red, purple & brown 20 10
1061 90 c. violet, plum & pur 40 20

273 Louis Bleriot and Bleriot XI

1972. Birth Anniversaries.
1062 **273** 30 c. blue and brown . . 15 10
1063 – 50 c. blue, turquoise and new blue . . . . . 1·10 75
1064 – 90 c. brown and buff . . . 2·50 1·90
DESIGNS AND ANNIVERSARIES: 30 c. (birth centenary); 50 c. Amundsen and polar scene (birth centenary); 90 c. Pasteur and laboratory scene (150th birth anniv).

274 "Gethsemane"

1972. Protection of Historical Monuments. Frescoes by J. Canavesio. Chapel of Notre-Dame des Fontaines, La Brigue.
1065 **274** 30 c. red 10 10
1066 – 50 c. grey 20 15
1067 – 90 c. green 40 50
1068 – 1 f. 40 red 55 75
1069 – 2 f. purple . . . . 1·10 1·10
DESIGNS: 50 c. "Christ Outraged"; 90 c. "Ascent to Calvary"; 1 f. 40, "The Resurrection"; 2 f. "The Crucifixion".

1972. Paintings. "Princes and Princesses of Monaco". As T **213**. Multicoloured.
1070 1 f. "Prince Jacques 1" (N. Largilliere) 40 50
1071 3 f. "Princess Louise-Hippolyte" (J. B. Vanloo) . . . . . . 1·90 1·75

1973. Monte Carlo Flower Show (2nd issue). As T **239**.
1073 3 f. 50 multicoloured . . . . 5·50 4·25
DESIGN: 3 f. 50, "Bouquet of Flowers".

276 Europa "Posthorn"

1973. Europa.
1074 **276** 50 c. orange . . . . . . 2·50 1·25
1075 90 c. green . . . . 3·75 2·50

277 Moliere and Characters from "Le Malade Imaginaire" 278 Colette, Cat and Books

1973. 300th Death Anniv of Moliere.
1076 **277** 20 c. red, brown and blue 30 20

1973. Birth Anniversaries.
1077 **278** 30 c. black, blue and red 1·00 50
1078 – 45 c. multicoloured . . . 2·25 1·40
1079 – 50 c. lilac, purple & blue 30 20
1080 – 90 c. multicoloured . . . 75 60
DESIGNS AND ANNIVERSARIES—HORIZ: 30 c., Type **278** (nature writer, birth cent); 45 c. J.-H. Fabre and insects (entomologist, 150th birth anniv); 90 c. Sir George Cayley and his "convertiplane" (aviation pioneer, birth bicent). VERT: 50 c. Blaise Pascal (philosopher and writer, 350th birth anniv).

279 E. Ducretet, "Les Invalides" and Eiffel Tower

1973. 75th Anniv of Eugene Ducretet's First Hertzian Radio Link.
1081 **279** 30 c. purple and brown . . 20 15

1973. International Dog Show, Monte Carlo. As T **248**. Inscr "1973". Multicoloured.
1082 45 c. Alsatian . . . . 6·25 4·25

280 C. Peguy and Chartres Cathedral

1973. Birth Bicentenary of Charles Peguy (writer).
1083 **280** 50 c. brown, mauve & grey 30 25

281 Telecommunications Equipment 282 Stage Characters

1973. 5th World Telecommunications Day.
1084 **281** 60 c. violet, blue & brown 30 20

1973. 5th World Amateur Theatre Festival.
1085 **282** 60 c. lilac, blue and red . . 60 50

283 Ellis and Rugby Tackle

1973. 150th Anniv of Founding of Rugby Football by William Web Ellis.
1086 **283** 90 c. red, lake and brown 85 60

284 St. Theresa

1973. Birth Centenary of St. Theresa of Lisieux.
1087 **284** 1 f. 40 multicoloured . . . 65 75

285 Drug Addiction

1973. Campaign Against Drugs.
1088 **285** 50 c. red, green and blue 20 15
1089 – 50 c. multicoloured . . . 20 15
1090 **285** 90 c. violet, green and red 75 30
1091 – 90 c. multicoloured . . . 60 40
DESIGN: Nos. 1089, 1091, Children, syringes and addicts.

286 "Institution of the Creche" (Giotto)

1973. 750th Anniv of St. Francis of Assisi Creche.

1092	**286**	30 c. purple (postage)	30	20
1093	–	45 c. red	1·00	75
1094	–	50 c. brown	80	85
1095	–	1 f. green	2·10	1·50
1096	–	2 f. brown	4·00	3·25
1097	–	3 f. blue (air)	3·75	3·00

DESIGN—HORIZ: 45 c. "The Nativity" (School of F. Lippi); 50 c. "The Birth of Jesus Christ" (Giotto). VERT: 1 f. "The Nativity" (15th century miniature); 2 f. "The Birth of Jesus" (Fra Angelico); 3 f. "The Nativity" (Flemish school).

287 Country Picnic

1973. 50th Anniv of National Committee for Monegasque Traditions.

1098	**287**	10 c. blue, green & brown	10	10
1099	–	20 c. violet, blue & green	10	10
1100	–	30 c. sepia, brown & grn	15	15
1101	–	45 c. red, violet & purple	50	50
1102	–	50 c. black, red & brown	60	60
1103	–	60 c. red, violet and blue	75	75
1104	–	1 f. violet, blue & brown	1·25	1·25

DESIGNS—VERT: 20 c. Maypole dance. HORIZ: 30 c. "U Bradi" (local dance); 45 c. St. Jean fire-dance; 50 c. Blessing the Christmas loaf; 60 c. Blessing the sea Festival of St. Devote; 1 f. Corpus Christi procession.

1973. Monte Carlo Flower Show, 1974. As T **271**. Multicoloured.

1105	45 c. Roses and Strelitzia	1·25	75
1106	60 c. Mimosa and myosotis	1·75	1·10
1107	1 f. "Vase of Flowers" (Odilon Redon)	3·25	1·90

1973. Paintings. "Princes and Princesses of Monaco". As T **213**. Multicoloured.

1108	2 f. "Charlotte Grimaldi" (in day dress, P. Gobert)	2·10	1·90
1109	2 f. "Charlotte Grimaldi" (in evening dress, P. Gobert)	2·10	1·90

289 U.P.U. Emblem and Symbolic Heads

290 Farman, Farman F.60 Goliath and Farman H.F.III

1974. Centenary of Universal Postal Union.

1111	**289**	50 c. purple and brown	25	10
1112	–	70 c. multicoloured	35	20
1113	–	1 f. 10 multicoloured	80	55

DESIGNS: 70 c. Hands holding letters; 1 f. 10, "Countries of the World" (famous buildings).

1974. Monaco Red Cross. As T **238**.

1114	3 f. blue, green and purple	1·90	1·75

DESIGN: 3 f. St. Bernard of Menthon.

1974. Birth Centenary of Henry Farman (aviation pioneer).

1115	**290**	30 c. brown, purple & bl	10	10

291 Marconi, Circuit Plan and Destroyer

1974. Birth Centenary of Guglielmo Marconi (radio pioneer).

1116	**291**	40 c. red, dp blue & blue	20	10

292 Duchesne and "Penicillium glaucum"

1974. Birth Centenary of Ernest Duchesne (microbiologist).

1117	**292**	45 c. black, blue & purple	30	10

293 Forest and Engine

1974. 60th Death Anniv of Fernand Forest (motor engineer and inventor).

1118	**293**	50 c. purple, red & black	20	10

1974. International Dog Show, Monte Carlo. As T **248**, inscr "1974".

1119	60 c. multicoloured	3·75	3·00

DESIGN: 60 c. Schnauzer.

294 Ronsard and Characters from "Sonnet to Helene"

1974. 450th Birth Anniv of Pierre de Ronsard (poet).

1120	**294**	70 c. brown and red	40	35

295 Sir Winston Churchill (after bust by O. Nemon)

297 "The King of Rome" (Bosio)

296 Interpol Emblem, and Views of Monaco and Vienna

1974. Birth Centenary of Sir Winston Churchill.

1121	**295**	1 f. brown and grey	50	30

1974. 60th Anniv of 1st International Police Judiciary Congress and 50th Anniv of International Criminal Police Organization (Interpol).

1122	**296**	2 f. blue, brown & green	1·25	80

1974. Europa. Sculptures by J. F. Bosio.

1123	**297**	45 c. green and brown	1·10	1·10
1124	–	1 f. 10 bistre and brown	2·00	1·75

DESIGN: 1 f. 10, "Madame Elizabeth".

298 "The Box" (A. Renoir)

1974. "The Impressionists". Multicoloured.

1126	1 f. Type **298**	2·00	2·00
1127	1 f. "The Dance Class" (E. Degas)	2·00	2·00
1128	2 f. "Impression-Sunrise" (C. Monet) (horiz)	4·00	3·25
1129	2 f. "Entrance to Voisins Village" (C. Pissarro) (horiz)	4·00	3·25
1130	2 f. "The Hanged Man's House" (P. Cezanne) (horiz)	4·00	3·25
1131	2 f. "Floods at Port Marly" (A. Sisley) (horiz)	4·00	3·25

299 Tigers and Trainer

1974. 1st International Circus Festival, Monaco.

1132	**299**	2 c. brown, green & blue	10	10
1133	–	3 c. brown and purple	10	10
1134	–	5 c. blue, brown and red	10	10
1135	–	45 c. brown, black & red	40	20
1136	–	70 c. multicoloured	90	75
1137	–	1 f. 10 brown, grn & red	1·60	1·25
1138	–	5 f. green, blue & brown	5·75	4·75

DESIGNS—VERT: 3 c. Performing horse; 45 c. Equestrian act; 1 f. 10, Acrobats; 5 f. Trapeze act. HORIZ: 5 c. Performing elephants; 70 c. Clowns.

300 Honore II on Medal

1974. 350th Anniv of Monegasque Numismatic Art.

1139	**300**	60 c. green and red	50	35

301 Marine Flora and Fauna

1974. 24th Congress of the International Commission for the Scientific Exploration of the Mediterranean. Multicoloured.

1140	45 c. Type **301**	1·25	85
1141	70 c. Sea-bed flora and fauna	1·60	1·25
1142	1 f. 10 Sea-bed flora and fauna (different)	2·75	2·25

Nos. 1141/2 are larger, size 52 × 31 mm.

1974. Monte Carlo Flower Show. As T **271**. Multicoloured.

1143	70 c. Honeysuckle and violets	1·10	85
1144	1 f. 10 Iris and chrysanthemums	1·60	1·40

302 Prince Rainier III (F. Messina)

303

1974.

1145	**302**	60 c. green (postage)	60	15
1146		80 c. red	75	25
1147		80 c. green	40	10
1148		1 f. brown	1·40	60
1149		1 f. red	75	10
1149a		1 f. green	40	10
1149b		1 f. 10 green	40	10
1150		1 f. 20 violet	4·75	2·50
1150a		1 f. 20 red	65	10
1150b		1 f. 20 green	1·00	10
1151		1 f. 25 blue	1·50	1·10
1151a		1 f. 30 red	65	15
1152		1 f. 40 red	1·10	10
1152a		1 f. 50 black	1·00	40
1153		1 f. 60 grey	1·10	50
1153a		1 f. 70 blue	90	75
1153b		1 f. 80 blue	1·75	1·50
1154		2 f. mauve	2·50	1·60
1154a		2 f. 10 brown	1·60	1·25
1155		2 f. 30 violet	2·25	1·50
1156		2 f. 50 black	2·25	1·90
1157		9 f. violet	6·25	4·00
1158	**303**	10 f. violet (air)	7·50	3·00
1159		15 f. red	10·50	7·50
1160		20 f. blue	16·00	10·00

304 Coastline, Monte Carlo

305 "Haagocereus chosicensis"

1974.

1161	**304**	25 c. blue, green & brown	1·50	60
1162	–	25 c. brown, green & blue	20	20
1163	–	50 c. brown and blue	85	60
1164	**304**	65 c. blue, brown & green	30	20
1165	–	70 c. multicoloured	75	60
1166	**304**	1 f. 10 brown, green & bl	2·25	1·25
1167	–	1 f. 10 black, brown & bl	85	60
1168	–	1 f. 30 brown, green & bl	65	30
1169	–	1 f. 40 green, grey & brn	2·25	1·25
1170	–	1 f. 50 green, blue & blk	1·50	1·25
1171	–	1 f. 70 brown, green & bl	3·75	2·50
1172	–	1 f. 80 brown, green & bl	1·50	1·10
1173	–	2 f. 30 brown, grey & bl	2·50	1·90
1174	–	3 f. brown, grey & green	4·75	1·90
1175	–	5 f. 50 brown, green & blue	9·25	4·25
1176	–	6 f. 50 brown, blue & grn	4·25	3·25

DESIGNS—VERT: 50 c. Palace clock tower; 70 c. Botanical gardens; 1 f. 30, Monaco Cathedral; 1 f. 40, 1 f. 50, Prince Albert I statue and Museum; 3 f. Fort Antoine. HORIZ: 25 c. (1162), 1 f. 70, "All Saints" Tower; 1 f. 10, (1167), Palais de Justice; 1 f. 80, 5 f. 50, La Condamine; 2 f. 30, North Galleries of Palace; 6 f. 50, Aerial view of hotels and harbour.

1975. Plants. Multicoloured.

1180	10 c. Type **305**	10	10
1181	20 c. "Matucana madisoniarum"	35	10
1182	30 c. "Parodia scopaioides"	65	35
1183	85 c. "Mediolobivia arachnacantha"	2·50	1·25
1184	1 f. 90 "Matucana yanganucensis"	4·25	2·75
1185	4 f. "Echinocereus marksianus"	6·75	5·00

306 "Portrait of a Sailor" (P. Florence)

308 "Prologue"

307 "St. Bernardin de Sienne"

1975. Europa.

1186	**306**	80 c. purple	1·10	1·00
1187	–	1 f. 20 blue	1·90	1·50

DESIGN: 1 f. 20, "St. Devote" (Ludovic Brea).

1975. Monaco Red Cross.

1189	**307**	4 f. blue and purple	3·00	2·50

1975. Centenary of "Carmen" (opera by Georges Bizet).

1190	**308**	30 c. violet, brown & blk	10	10
1191	–	60 c. grey, green and red	20	10
1192	–	80 c. green, brown & blk	75	50
1193	–	1 f. 40 purple, brown and ochre	1·25	1·00

DESIGNS—HORIZ: 60 c. Lilla Pastia's tavern; 80 c. "The Smuggler's Den"; 1 f. 40, "Confrontation at Seville".

309 Saint-Simon

310 Dr. Albert Schweitzer

1975. 300th Birth Anniv of Louis de Saint-Simon (writer).

1194	**309**	40 c. blue	25	15

1975. Birth Centenary of Dr. Schweitzer (Nobel Peace Prize Winner).

1195	**310**	60 c. red and brown	75	20

311 "Stamp" and Calligraphy

1975. "Arphila 75" International Stamp Exhibition, Paris.

1196	**311**	80 c. brown and orange	50	35

312 Seagull and Sunrise

1975. International Exposition, Okinawa.

1197	**312**	85 c. blue, green & orange	1·00	75

313 Pike smashing Crab

1975. Anti-Cancer Campaign.
1198 **313** 1 f. multicoloured 65 60

314 Christ with Crown of Thorns

1975. Holy Year.
1199 **314** 1 f. 15 black, brn & pur 1·00 75

315 Villa Sauber, Monte Carlo

1975. European Architectural Heritage Year.
1200 **315** 1 f. 20 green, brown & bl 90 85

316 Woman's Head and Globe

1975. International Women's Year.
1201 **316** 1 f. 20 multicoloured . . . 90 85

317 Rolls-Royce "Silver Ghost" (1907)

1975. Evolution of the Motor Car.

1202	**317**	5 c. blue, green & brown .	10	10
1203	–	10 c. indigo and blue . . .	10	10
1204	–	20 c. blue, ultram & blk	20	10
1205	–	30 c. purple and mauve . .	40	20
1206	–	50 c. blue, purple & mve .	80	75
1207	–	60 c. red and green . . .	1·10	65
1208	–	80 c. indigo and blue . .	2·00	1·50
1209	–	85 c. brown, orge & grn	2·50	2·25
1210	–	1 f. 20 blue, red and green	3·75	3·00
1211	–	1 f. 40 green and blue . .	5·00	3·25
1212	–	5 f. 50 blue, emerald and green	15·00	10·50

MOTOR CARS: 10 c. Hispano-Suiza "H.6B" (1926); 20 c. Isotta Fraschini "8A" (1928); 30 c. Cord "L.29"; 50 c. Voisin "V12" (1930); 60 c. Duesenberg "SJ" (1933); 80 c. Bugatti "57 C" (1938); 85 c. Delahaye "135 M" (1940); 1 f. 20, Cisitalia "Pininfarina" (1945); 1 f. 40, Mercedes-Benz "300 SL" (1955); 5 f. 50, Lamborghini "Countach" (1974).

1975. Paintings. "Princes and Princesses of Monaco". As T **213**. Multicoloured.

1213	2 f. "Prince Honore III" . . .	1·90	1·25
1214	4 f. "Princess Catherine de Brignole"	3·75	3·00

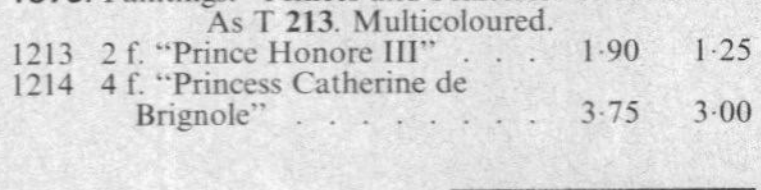

318 Dog behind Bars 319 Maurice Ravel

1975. 125th Birth Anniv of Gen. J. P. Delmas de Grammont (author of Animal Protection Code).

1215	**318**	60 c. black and brown . .	1·10	75
1216	–	80 c. black and brown . .	1·60	1·10
1217	–	1 f. 20 green and purple .	2·25	1·90

DESIGNS—VERT: 80 c. Cat chased up tree. HORIZ: 1 f. 20, Horse being ill-treated.

1975. International Dog Show, Monte Carlo. As T **248**, but inscr "1975". Multicoloured.
1218 60 c. black and purple . . . . 3·75 3·00
DESIGN: 60 c. French poodle.

1975. Birth Centenaries of Musicians.

1219	**319**	60 c. brown and purple . .	1·10	60
1220	–	1 f. 20 black and purple .	2·25	1·60

DESIGN: 1 f. 20, Johann Strauss (the younger).

320 Circus Clown 322 Andre Ampere with Electrical Meter

321 Monaco Florin Coin, 1640

1975. 2nd International Circus Festival.
1221 **320** 80 c. multicoloured . . . 1·25 40

1975. Monaco Numismatics.
1222 **321** 80 c. brown and blue . . 75 30
See also Nos. 1275, 1320 and 1448.

1975. Birth Centenary of Andre Ampere (physicist).
1223 **322** 85 c. indigo and blue . . . 60 60

323 "Lamentations for the Dead Christ"

1975. 500th Birth Anniv of Michelangelo.
1224 **323** 1 f. 40 olive and black . . 1·10 60

1975. Monte Carlo Flower Show (1976). As T **271**. Multicoloured.

1225	60 c. Bouquet of wild flowers	90	60
1226	80 c. Ikebana flower arrangement	1·60	1·00

1975. Precancelled. Surch.

1227	42 c. on 26 c. violet, blue and black (No. 949a)	2·50	1·25
1228	48 c. on 30 c. red, blue, lilac & black (No. 949b)	3·00	1·90
1229	70 c. on 45 c. blue, violet, turq & black (No. 950a)	5·00	2·50
1230	1 f. 35 on 90 c. green, blue and black (No. 951a)	6·25	3·00

325 Prince Pierre de Monaco

1976. 25th Anniv of Literary Council of Monaco.

1231	**325**	10 c. black	10	10
1232	–	20 c. blue and red	20	10
1233	–	25 c. blue and red	20	10
1234	–	30 c. brown	20	15
1235	–	50 c. blue, red and purple	30	20
1236	–	60 c. brown, grn & lt brn	40	50
1237	–	80 c. purple and blue . .	1·00	75
1238	–	1 f. 20 violet, blue & mve	1·60	1·40

COUNCIL MEMBERS—HORIZ: 20 c. A. Maurois and Colette; 25 c. Jean and Jerome Tharaud; 30 c. E. Henriot, M. Pagnol and G. Duhamel; 50 c. Ph. Heriat, J. Supervielle and L. Pierard; 60 c. R. Dorgeles, M. Achard and G. Bauer; 80 c. F. Hellens, A. Billy and Mgr. Grente; 1 f. 20, J. Giono, L. Pasteur Vallery-Radot and M. Garcon.

326 Dachshunds

1976. International Dog Show, Monte Carlo.
1239 **326** 60 c. multicoloured . . . 5·00 3·75

327 Bridge Table and Monte Carlo Coast

1976. 5th Bridge Olympiad, Monte Carlo.
1240 **327** 60 c. brown, green & red 55 30

328 Alexander Graham Bell and Early Telephone

1976. Telephone Centenary.
1241 **328** 80 c. brown, light brown and grey 50 30

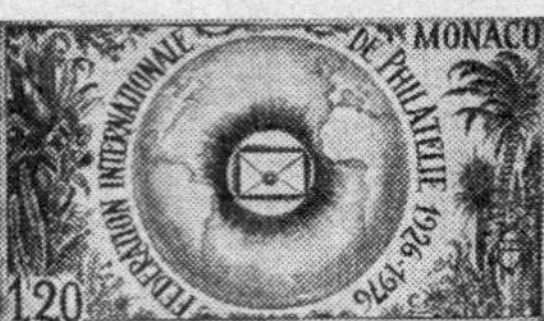

329 Federation Emblem on Globe

1976. 50th Anniv of International Philatelic Federation.
1242 **329** 1 f. 20 red, blue & green . 80 60

330 U.S.A. 2 c. Stamp, 1926

1976. Bicent of American Revolution.
1243 **330** 1 f. 70 black and purple . 1·10 1·10

331 "The Fritillaries" (Van Gogh)

1976. Monte Carlo Flower Show.
1244 **331** 3 f. multicoloured . . . . 7·50 6·25

332 Diving 333 Decorative Plate

1976. Olympic Games, Montreal.

1245	**332**	60 c. brown and blue . .	25	20
1246	–	80 c. blue, brown & green	40	30
1247	–	85 c. blue, green & brown	50	40
1248	–	1 f. 20 brown, green & bl	80	60
1249	–	1 f. 70 brown, blue & grn	1·40	1·25

DESIGNS—VERT: 80 c. Gymnastics; 85 c. Hammer-throwing. HORIZ: 1 f. 20, Rowing; 1 f. 70, Boxing.

1976. Europa. Monegasque Ceramics. Multicoloured.

1251	80 c. Type **333**	80	60
1252	1 f. 20 Grape-harvester (statuette)	1·50	1·10

334 Palace Clock Tower 335 "St. Louise de Marillac" (altar painting)

1976. Precancelled.

1254	**334**	50 c. red	60	30
1255		52 c. orange	30	15
1256		54 c. green	40	20
1257		60 c. green	60	40
1258		62 c. mauve	40	50
1259		68 c. yellow	60	30
1260		90 c. violet	90	65
1261		95 c. red	1·00	60
1262		1 f. 05 brown	85	60
1263		1 f. 60 blue	1·50	90
1264		1 f. 70 turquoise	1·50	1·10
1265		1 f. 85 brown	1·75	1·10

1976. Monaco Red Cross.
1270 **335** 4 f. black, purple & green 2·75 2·50

1976. Paintings. "Princes and Princesses of Monaco". As T **213**.

1271	2 f. purple	2·50	1·90
1272	4 f. multicoloured	4·25	3·00

DESIGNS: 2 f. "Prince Honore IV"; 4 f. "Princess Louise d'Aumont-Mazarin".

336 St. Vincent-de-Paul 337 Marie de Rabutin Chantal

1976. Centenary of St. Vincent-de-Paul Conference, Monaco.
1273 **336** 60 c. black, brown & blue 30 20

1976. 350th Birth Anniv of Marquise de Sevigne (writer).
1274 **337** 80 c. black, violet and red 40 25

338 Monaco 2 g. "Honore II" Coin, 1640

1976. Monaco Numismatics.
1275 **338** 80 c. blue and green . . . 55 30

339 Richard Byrd, "Josephine Ford", Airship "Norge" and Roald Amundsen

1976. 50th Anniv of First Flights over North Pole.
1276 **339** 85 c. black, blue & green . 1·90 1·25

340 Gulliver and Lilliputians 341 Girl's Head and Christmas Decorations

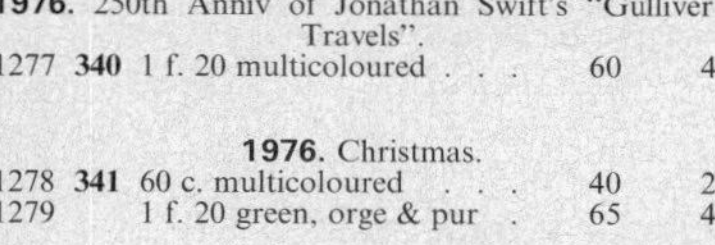

1976. 250th Anniv of Jonathan Swift's "Gulliver's Travels".
1277 **340** 1 f. 20 multicoloured . . . 60 45

1976. Christmas.
1278 **341** 60 c. multicoloured 40 20
1279 1 f. 20 green, orge & pur . 65 40

342 "Drug" Dagger piercing Man and Woman

343 Circus Clown

1976. Campaign against Drug Abuse.
1280 **342** 80 c. blue, orge & bronze 50 30
1281 1 f. 20 lilac, purple & brn 1·00 40

1976. Monte Carlo Flower Show (1977). As T **271**. Multicoloured.
1282 80 c. Flower arrangement . . 1·50 1·00
1283 1 f. Bouquet of flowers . . . 2·25 1·75

1976. 3rd International Circus Festival, Monte Carlo.
1284 **343** 1 f. multicoloured . . . . 1·90 1·10

344 Schooner "Hirondelle I"

1977. 75th Anniv of Publication of "Career of a Navigator" by Prince Albert I (1st issue). Illustrations by L. Tinayre.
1285 **344** 10 c. brown, blue & turq 10 10
1286 – 20 c. black, brown & lake 10 10
1287 – 30 c. green, blue & orge 15 15
1288 – 80 c. black, blue and red 35 50
1289 – 1 f. black and brown . . . 55 60
1290 – 1 f. 25 olive, green & vio 1·25 1·00
1291 – 1 f. 40 brown, olive & grn 1·90 1·50
1292 – 1 f. 90 blue, lt blue & red 3·00 2·50
1293 – 2 f. 50 brown, blue and turquoise . . . . . . 4·25 3·25

DESIGNS—VERT: 20 c. Prince Albert I; 1 f. Helmsman; 1 f. 90, Bringing in the trawl. HORIZ: 30 c. Crew-members; 80 c. "Hirondelle" in a gale; 1 f. 25, Securing the lifeboat; 1 f. 40, Shrimp fishing; 2 f. 50, Capture of an oceanic sunfish.
See also Nos. 1305/13.

345 Pyrenean Sheep and Mountain Dogs

1977. International Dog Show, Monte Carlo.
1294 **345** 80 c. multicoloured . . . 5·00 3·75

346 "Maternity" (M. Cassatt)

1977. World Association of the "Friends of Children".
1295 **346** 80 c. deep brown, brown and black . . . . . . 1·10 75

347 Archers

1977. 10th International Archery Championships.
1296 **347** 1 f. 10 black, brown & bl 60 40

INDEX

Countries can be quickly located by referring to the index at the end of this volume.

348 Charles Lindbergh and "Spirit of St. Louis"

1977. 50th Anniv of Lindbergh's Transatlantic Flight.
1297 **348** 1 f. 90 light blue, blue and brown . . . . 2·00 1·40

349 "Harbour, Deauville"

1977. Birth Centenary of Raoul Dufy (painter).
1298 **349** 2 f. multicoloured . . . . 4·25 3·00

350 "Portrait of a Young Girl"

351 "L'Oreillon" Tower

1977. 400th Birth Anniv of Peter Paul Rubens (painter).
1299 **350** 80 c. orange, brn & blk . . 85 60
1300 – 1 f. red . . . . 1·25 75
1301 – 1 f. 40 orange and red . . 2·25 1·50

DESIGNS: 1 f. "Duke of Buckingham"; 1 f. 40, "Portrait of a Child".

1977. Europa. Views.
1302 **351** 1 f. brown and blue . . . 90 60
1303 – 1 f. 40 blue, brown and bistre . . . . 1·40 1·40

DESIGN: 1 f. 40, St. Michael's Church, Menton.

1977. 75th Anniv of Publication of "Career of a Navigator" by Prince Albert I (2nd issue). Illustrations by L. Tinayre. As T **344**.
1305 10 c. black and blue 10 10
1306 20 c. blue 10 10
1307 30 c. blue, light blue and green 20 20
1308 80 c. brown, black and green 60 30
1309 1 f. grey and green 75 60
1310 1 f. 25 black, brown and lilac 1·10 85
1311 1 f. 40 purple, blue & brown 1·90 1·50
1312 1 f. 90 black, blue and light blue 3·00 2·50
1313 3 f. blue, brown and green . . 4·25 3·50

DESIGNS—HORIZ: 10 c. "Princess Alice" (steam yacht) at Kiel; 20 c. Ship's laboratory; 30 c. "Princess Alice" in ice floes; 1 f. Polar scene; 1 f. 25, Bridge of "Princess Alice" during snowstorm; 1 f. 40, Arctic camp; 1 f. 90, Ship's steam launch in floating ice; 3 f. "Princess Alice" passing iceberg. VERT: 80 c. Crewmen in Arctic dress.

352 Santa Claus & Sledge

353 Face, Poppy and Syringe

1977. Christmas.
1314 **352** 80 c. red, green and blue . 35 25
1315 1 f. 40 multicoloured . . . 65 35

1977. Monte Carlo Flower Show. As T **271**. Mult.
1316 80 c. Snapdragons and campanula 80 75
1317 1 f. Ikebana . . . . 1·50 1·25

1977. Campaign Against Drug Abuse.
1318 **353** 1 f. black, red and violet . 55 30

354 Clown and Flags

1977. 4th International Festival of Circus, Monaco.
1319 **354** 1 f. multicoloured . . . . 1·90 1·10

355 Gold Coin of Honore II

1977. Monaco Numismatics.
1320 **355** 80 c. brown and red . . . 50 35

356 Mediterranean divided by Industry

1977. Protection of the Mediterranean Environment.
1321 **356** 1 f. black, green and blue 60 35

357 Dr. Guglielminetti and Road Tarrers

1977. 75th Anniv of First Experiments at Road Tarring in Monaco.
1322 **357** 1 f. 10 black, bistre and brown 75 60

358 F.M.L.T. Badge and Monte Carlo

1977. 50th Anniv of Monaco Lawn Tennis Federation.
1323 **358** 1 f. blue, red and brown 1·25 60

359 Wimbledon and First Championships

1977. Centenary of Wimbledon Lawn Tennis Championships.
1324 **359** 1 f. 40 grey, green & brown 1·75 1·00

1977. Paintings. "Princes and Princesses of Monaco". As T **213**. Multicoloured.
1325 6 f. "Prince Honore V" . . . 5·00 3·75

360 St. Jean Bosco

1977. Monaco Red Cross. Monegasque Art.
1326 **360** 4 f. green, brown & blue 2·50 2·25

1978. Precancelled. Surch.
1327 **334** 58 c. on 54 c. green . . . 60 30
1328 73 c. on 68 c. yellow . . . 1·00 40
1329 1 f. 15 on 1 f. 05 brown 1·50 1·00
1330 2 f. on 1 f. 85 brown . . . 2·50 1·60

362 Aerial Shipwreck from "L'Ile Mysterieuse"

1978. 150th Birth Anniv of Jules Verne.
1331 **362** 5 c. brown, red and olive 10 10
1332 – 25 c. turquoise, blue & red 10 10
1333 – 30 c. blue, brown & lt blue 15 10
1334 – 80 c. black, green & orge 35 50
1335 – 1 f. brown, lake and blue 85 60
1336 – 1 f. 40 bistre, brown and green . . . . 1·10 65
1337 – 1 f. 70 brown, lt blue and blue . . . . 1·60 1·50
1338 – 5 f. 50 violet and blue . . 4·00 3·50

DESIGNS: 25 c. The abandoned ship from "L'Ile Mysterieuse"; 30 c. The secret of the island from "L'Ile Mysterieuse"; 80 c. "Robur the Conqueror"; 1 f. "Master Zacharius"; 1 f. 40, "The Castle in the Carpathians"; 1 f. 70, "The Children of Captain Grant"; 5 f. 50, Jules Verne and allegories.

363 Aerial View of Congress Centre

1978. Inauguration of Monaco Congress Centre.
1339 **363** 1 f. brown, blue and green 40 30
1340 – 1 f. 40 blue, brown & grn 65 40

DESIGN: 1 f. 40, View of Congress Centre from sea.

364 Footballers and Globe

1978. World Cup Football Championship, Argentina.
1341 **364** 1 f. blue, slate and green 65 55

365 Antonio Vivaldi

366 "Ramoge" (research vessel) and Grimaldi Palace

1978. 300th Birth Anniv of Antonio Vivaldi (composer).
1342 **365** 1 f. brown and red . . . 1·00 85

1978. Environment Protection. "RAMOGE" Agreement.
1343 **366** 80 c. multicoloured . . . 40 50
1344 – 1 f. red, blue and green 65 40

DESIGN—HORIZ: (48 × 27 mm): 1 f. Map of coastline between St. Raphael and Genes.

367 Monaco Cathedral

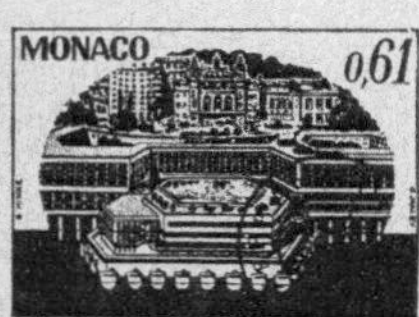

368 Monaco Congress Centre

1978. Europa. Monaco Views.
1345 **367** 1 f. green, brown & blue 80 45
1346 – 1 f. 40 brown, green & bl 1·25 1·10

DESIGN: 1 f. 40, View of Monaco from the east.

1978. Precancelled.
1348 **368** 61 c. orange 30 10
1349 64 c. green 30 10
1350 68 c. blue 30 10
1351 78 c. purple 40 20
1352 83 c. violet 40 20
1353 88 c. orange 40 20
1354 1 f. 25 brown . . . . . 1·00 60
1355 1 f. 30 red 65 40
1356 1 f. 40 green . . . . . 1·00 40
1357 2 f. 10 blue . . . . . . 1·50 1·00
1358 2 f. 25 orange . . . . . 1·40 80
1359 2 f. 35 mauve . . . . . 1·60 80

369 "Cinderella"

1978. 350th Birth Anniv of Charles Perrault (writer).
1360 **369** 5 c. red, olive and violet . . . 10 10
1361 – 25 c. black, brown & mve . . . 10 10
1362 – 30 c. green, lake & brown . . . 15 10
1363 – 80 c. multicoloured . . . 60 50
1364 – 1 f. red, brown and olive . . . 75 60
1365 – 1 f. 40 mauve, ultram & blue . . . 1·00 65
1366 – 1 f. 70 green, blue & grey . . . 1·40 1·10
1367 – 1 f. 90 multicoloured . . . 1·90 1·40
1368 – 2 f. 50 blue, orange & grn . . . 2·50 1·90
DESIGNS: 25 c. "Puss in Boots"; 30 c. "The Sleeping Beauty"; 80 c. "Donkey's Skin"; 1 f. "Little Red Riding Hood"; 1 f. 40, "Bluebeard"; 1 f. 70, "Tom Thumb"; 1 f. 90, "Riquet with a Tuft"; 2 f. 50, "The Fairies".

370 "The Sunflowers" (Van Gogh) **371** Afghan Hound

1978. Monte Carlo Flower Show (1979) and 125th Birth Anniv of Vincent Van Gogh. Multicoloured.
1369 1 f. Type **370** . . . 2·50 1·90
1370 1 f. 70 "The Iris" (Van Gogh) . . . 3·75 2·50

1978. International Dog Show, Monte Carlo. Multicoloured.
1371 1 f. Type **371** . . . 3·00 2·50
1372 1 f. 20 Borzoi . . . 4·25 3·00

372 Girl with Letter **374** Juggling Seals

373 Catherine and William Booth

1978. Christmas.
1373 **372** 1 f. brown, blue and red . . . 1·25 65

1978. Centenary of Salvation Army.
1374 **373** 1 f. 70 multicoloured . . . 1·40 1·25

1978. 5th International Circus Festival, Monaco.
1375 **374** 80 c. orange, black & blue . . . 40 50
1376 – 1 f. multicoloured . . . 65 75
1377 – 1 f. 40 brown, mauve and bistre . . . 1·40 1·10
1378 – 1 f. 90 blue, lilac and mauve . . . 2·10 2·00
1379 – 2 f. 40 multicoloured . . . 3·00 2·50
DESIGNS—HORIZ: 1 f. 40, Horseback acrobatics; 1 f. 90, Musical monkeys; 2 f. 40, Trapeze. VERT: 1 f. Lion tamer.

1978. Paintings. "Princes and Princesses of Monaco". As T **213**. Multicoloured.
1380 2 f. "Prince Florestan I" (G. Dauphin) . . . 2·50 1·90
1381 4 f. "Princess Caroline Gilbert de la Metz" (Marie Verroust) . . . 4·25 3·75

377 "Jongleur de Notre-Dame" (Massenet)

1979. Centenary of "Salle Garnier" (Opera House) (1st issue).
1384 **377** 1 f. blue, orange & mauve . . . 40 20
1385 – 1 f. 20 violet, blk & turq . . . 65 30
1386 – 1 f. 50 maroon, grn & turq . . . 80 65
1387 – 1 f. 70 multicoloured . . . 1·75 1·40
1388 – 2 f. 10 turquoise & violet . . . 2·25 2·00
1389 – 3 f. multicoloured . . . 3·00 2·50
DESIGNS—HORIZ: 1 f. 20, "Hans the Flute Player" (L. Ganne); 1 f. 50, "Don Quixote" (J. Massenet); 2 f. 10, "The Child and the Sorcerer" (M. Ravel); 3 f. Charles Garnier (architect) and south facade of Opera House. VERT: 1 f. 70, "L'Aiglon" (A. Honegger and J. Ibert).
See also Nos. 1399/1404.

378 Flower, Bird and Butterfly

1979. International Year of the Child. Children's Paintings.
1390 **378** 50 c. pink, green & black . . . 20 15
1391 – 1 f. slate, green & orange . . . 45 50
1392 – 1 f. 20 slate, orange & mve . . . 65 75
1393 – 1 f. 50 yellow, brown & bl . . . 1·25 1·10
1394 – 1 f. 70 multicoloured . . . 1·75 1·60
DESIGNS: 1 f. Horse and Child; 1 f. 20, "The Gift of Love"; 1 f. 50, "Peace in the World"; 1 f. 70, "Down with Pollution".

379 Armed Foot Messenger

1979. Europa.
1395 **379** 1 f. 20 brown, green & bl . . . 65 30
1396 – 1 f. 50 brown, turq & bl . . . 80 40
1397 – 1 f. 70 brown, green & bl . . . 1·10 70
DESIGNS: 1 f. 50, 18th cent felucca; 1 f. 70, Arrival of first train at Monaco.

380 "Instrumental Music" (G. Boulanger) (detail of Opera House interior)

1979. Centenary of "Salle Garnier" (Opera House) (2nd issue).
1399 – 1 f. brown, orange & turq . . . 55 20
1400 – 1 f. 20 multicoloured . . . 65 40
1401 – 1 f. 50 multicoloured . . . 1·25 1·00
1402 – 1 f. 70 blue, brown & red . . . 1·75 1·40
1403 – 2 f. 10 red, violet & black . . . 2·25 2·00
1404 **380** 3 f. green, brown and light green . . . 3·00 2·50
DESIGNS: As Type **377**. HORIZ: 1 f. "Les Biches" (F. Poulenc); 1 f. 20, "The Sailors" (G. Auric); 1 f. 70, "Gaiete Parisienne" (J. Offenbach). VERT: 1 f. 50, "La Spectre de la Rose" (C. M. Weber) (after poster by Jean Cocteau); 2 f. 10, "Salome" (R. Strauss).

1979. Paintings. "Princes and Princesses of Monaco". As T **213**. Multicoloured.
1405 3 f. "Prince Charles III" (B. Biard) . . . 2·50 1·90
1406 4 f. "Antoinette de Merode" . . . 3·75 2·50

381 St. Pierre Claver **382** "Princess Grace" Orchid

1979. Monaco Red Cross.
1407 **381** 5 f. multicoloured . . . 3·00 2·75

1979. Monte Carlo Flora 1980.
1408 **382** 1 f. multicoloured . . . 2·50 1·90

383 "Princess Grace" Rose **384** Clown balancing on Ball

1979. Monte Carlo Flower Show.
1409 **383** 1 f. 20 multicoloured . . . 2·50 1·90

1979. 6th International Circus Festival.
1410 **384** 1 f. 20 multicoloured . . . 2·10 1·40

385 Sir Rowland Hill and Penny Black **386** Albert Einstein

1979. Death Centenary of Sir Rowland Hill.
1411 **385** 1 f. 70 brown, blue & blk . . . 65 45

1979. Birth Centenary of Albert Einstein (physicist).
1412 **386** 1 f. 70 brown, grey & red . . . 1·00 75

387 St. Patrick's Cathedral **388** Nativity Scene

1979. Centenary of St. Patrick's Cathedral, New York.
1413 **387** 2 f. 10 black, blue & brn . . . 1·00 60

1979. Christmas.
1414 **388** 1 f. 20 blue, orange & mve . . . 85 60

389 Early Racing Cars

1979. 50th Anniv of Grand Prix Motor Racing.
1415 **389** 1 f. multicoloured . . . 1·10 75

390 Arms of Charles V and Monaco

1979. 450th Anniv of Visit of Emperor Charles V.
1416 **390** 1 f. 50 brown, blue & blk . . . 60 40

391 Setter and Pointer

1979. International Dog Show, Monte Carlo.
1417 **391** 1 f. 20 multicoloured . . . 3·75 3·00

392 Spring

1980. Precancels. The Seasons.
1418 **392** 76 c. brown and green . . . 35 20
1419 – 88 c. olive, emerald & grn . . . 35 20
1420 – 99 c. green and brown . . . 75 60
1421 – 1 f. 14 green, emer & brn . . . 75 60
1422 – 1 f. 60 brown, grey & deep brown . . . 1·25 65
1423 – 1 f. 84 lake, grey & brown . . . 1·25 85
1424 – 2 f. 65 brown, lt blue & bl . . . 1·90 1·25
1425 – 3 f. 05, brown, bl & slate . . . 1·90 1·50
DESIGNS: 99 c., 1 f. 14, Summer; 1 f. 60, 1 f. 84, Autumn; 2 f. 65, 3 f. 05, Winter.

394 Paul P. Harris (founder) and View of Chicago

1980. 75th Anniv of Rotary International.
1434 **394** 1 f. 80 olive, blue & turq . . . 90 65

395 Gymnastics

1980. Olympic Games, Moscow and Lake Placid.
1435 **395** 1 f. 10 blue, brn & grey . . . 30 20
1436 – 1 f. 30 red, brown & blue . . . 40 30
1437 – 1 f. 60 red, blue & brown . . . 55 40
1438 – 1 f. 80 brown, bis & grn . . . 65 40
1439 – 2 f. 30 grey, violet & mve . . . 1·00 65
1440 – 4 f. green, blue & brown . . . 1·40 1·25
DESIGNS: 1 f. 30, Handball; 1 f. 60, Pistol shooting; 1 f. 80, Volleyball; 2 f. 30, Ice hockey; 4 f. Skiing.

396 Colette (novelist) **397** "La Source"

1980. Europa. Each black, green and red.
1441 1 f. 30 Type **396** . . . 35 25
1442 1 f. 80 Marcel Pagnol (writer) . . . 45 30

1980. Birth Bicentenary of Jean Ingres (artist).
1444 **397** 4 f. multicoloured . . . 6·25 5·00

398 Montaigne **399** Guillaume Apollinaire (after G. Pieret)

1980. 400th Anniv of Publication of Montaigne's "Essays".
1445 **398** 1 f. 30 black, red and blue . . . 75 60

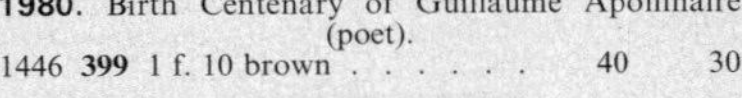

1980. Birth Centenary of Guillaume Apollinaire (poet).
1446 **399** 1 f. 10 brown . . . 40 30

400 Congress Centre

1980. Kiwanis International European Convention.
1447 **400** 1 f. 30 black, blue and red . . . 75 50

401 Honore II Silver Ecu, 1649

1980. Numismatics.
1448 **401** 1 f. 50 black and blue . . . 65 40

MINIMUM PRICE

The minimum price quoted is 10p which represents a handling charge rather than a basis for valuing common stamps. For further notes about prices see introductory pages.

402 Lhassa Apso and Shih Tzu

1980. International Dog Show, Monte Carlo.
1449 **402** 1 f. 30 multicoloured . . . 4·00 3·00

403 "The Princess and the Pea"

1980. 175th Birth Anniv of Hans Christian Andersen.
1450 **403** 70 c. sepia, red & brown 25 20
1451 – 1 f. 30 blue, turq & red 75 60
1452 – 1 f. 50 black, blue & turq 1·00 1·00
1453 – 1 f. 60 red, black & brn 1·40 1·00
1454 – 1 f. 80 yellow, brn & turq 1·50 1·25
1455 – 2 f. 30 brown, pur & vio 1·90 1·50
DESIGNS: 1 f. 30, "The Little Mermaid"; 1 f. 50, "The Chimneysweep and Shepherdess"; 1 f. 60, "The Brave Little Lead Soldier"; 1 f. 80, "The Little Match Girl"; 2 f. 30, "The Nightingale".

404 "The Road" (M. Vlaminck)

1980. 75th Anniv of 1905 Autumn Art Exhibition. Multicoloured.
1456 2 f. Type **404** . . . . 2·50 1·90
1457 3 f. "Woman at Balustrade" (Van Dongen) . . . . . . 3·75 2·50
1458 4 f. "The Reader" (Henri Matisse) . . . . 5·00 4·25
1459 5 f. "Three Figures in a Meadow" (A. Derain) . . . 6·25 5·00

1980. Paintings. "Princes and Princesses of Monaco". As T **213**. Multicoloured.
1460 4 f. "Prince Albert I" (L. Bonnat) . . . . 3·00 2·50
1461 4 f. "Princess Marie Alice Heine" (. Maeterlinck) . . . 3·00 2·50

405 "Sunbirds"

1980. Monaco Red Cross.
1462 **405** 6 f. red, bistre and brown 3·75 3·00

406 "MONACO" balanced on Tightrope

1980. Seventh International Circus Festival, Monaco.
1463 **406** 1 f. 30 red, turquoise & blue 1·90 1·25

407 Children and Nativity

1980. Christmas.
1464 **407** 1 f. 10 blue, carmine and red 35 25
1465 2 f. 30 violet, orange and pink . . . . 1·10 55

1980. Monte Carlo Flower Show, 1981. As T **383**. Multicoloured.
1466 1 f. 30 "Princess Stephanie" Rose . . . . 1·25 85
1467 1 f. 80 Ikebana . . . . . . 2·10 1·25

408 "Alcyonium" 409 Fish with Hand for Tail

1980. Marine Fauna. Multicoloured.
1468 5 c. "Spirographis spallanzanli" 10 10
1469 10 c. "Anemonia sulcata" . . 10 10
1470 15 c. "Leptopsammia pruvoit" 10 10
1471 20 c. "Pteroides" 10 10
1472 30 c. "Paramuricea clavata" (horiz) 30 10
1473 40 c. Type **408** 30 10
1474 50 c. "Corallium rubrum" . . 40 20
1475 60 c. Trunculus murex ("Calliactis parasitica") (horiz) . . . . 1·00 75
1476 70 c. "Cerianthus membranaceus" (horiz) . . 1·25 85
1477 1 f. "Actinia equina" (horiz) . 1·40 85
1478 2 f. "Protula" (horiz) . . . . 2·75 1·10

1981. "Respect the Sea".
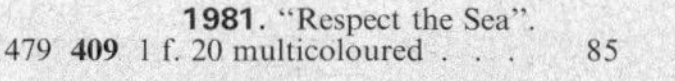
1479 **409** 1 f. 20 multicoloured . . . 85 40

410 Prince Rainier and Princess Grace

1981. Royal Silver Wedding.
1480 **410** 1 f. 20 black and green . . 1·50 1·00
1481 1 f. 40 black and red . . 2·00 1·50
1482 1 f. 70 black and green . . 2·50 1·90
1483 1 f. 80 black and brown . 2·75 2·25
1484 2 f. black and blue . . . 3·75 2·75

411 Mozart (after Lorenz Vogel) 412 Palm Cross

1981. 225th Birth Anniv of Wolfgang Amadeus Mozart (composer).
1485 **411** 2 f. brown, dp brn & bl 1·40 1·00
1486 – 2 f. 50 blue, brn & dp brn 2·10 1·75
1487 – 3 f. 50 dp brown, bl & brn 2·75 2·25
DESIGNS—HORIZ: 2 f. 50, "Mozart at 7 with his Father and Sister" (engraving by Delafoose after drawing by Carmontelle); 3 f. 50 ,"Mozart directing Requiem two Days before his Death" (painting by Baude).

1981. Europa. Multicoloured.
1488 **412** 1 f. 40 green, brown & red 35 25
1489 – 2 f. multicoloured 60 40
DESIGN: 2 f. Children carrying palm crosses.

413 Paris Football Stadium, Cup and Footballer

1981. 25th Anniv of European Football Cup.
1491 **413** 2 f. black and blue . . . 1·25 85

414 I.Y.D.P. Emblem and Girl in Wheelchair

1981. International Year of Disabled Persons.
1492 **414** 1 f. 40 blue and green . . 1·00 40

415 Palace flying Old Flag, National Flag and Monte Carlo

1981. Centenary of National Flag.
1493 **415** 2 f. red, blue and brown . 1·50 1·00

416 Oceanographic Institute, Paris and Oceanographic Museum, Monaco

1981. 75th Anniv of Oceanographic Institute.
1494 **416** 1 f. 20 blue, black & brn 1·00 75

417 Bureau Building and "Faddey Bellingshausen" (hydrographic research ship)

1981. 50th Anniv of Int Hydrographic Bureau.
1495 **417** 2 f. 50 sepia, brown and light brown . . . . . 1·90 1·50

418 Rough Collies and Shetland Sheepdogs

1981. International Dog Show, Monte Carlo.
1496 **418** 1 f. 40 multicoloured . . . 4·25 3·00

419 Rainier III and Prince Albert 421 Arctic Scene and Map

1981. (a) 23 × 28 mm.
1497 **419** 1 f. 40 green (postage) . . 1·00 10
1498 1 f. 60 red . . . . . . 1·50 10
1499 1 f. 60 green 85 10
1500 1 f. 70 green . . . . . 1·10 10
1501 1 f. 80 red . . . . . . 1·00 10
1502 1 f. 80 green . . . . . 1·00 10
1503 1 f. 90 green . . . . . 2·25 40
1504 2 f. red . . . . 1·00 10
1505 2 f. green . . . . . . 1·25 10
1506 2 f. 10 red . . . . . . 1·25 10
1507 2 f. 20 red . . . . . . 1·00 10
1508 2 f. 30 blue . . . . . 3·50 3·00
1509 2 f. 50 brown . . . . . 1·75 85
1510 2 f. 60 blue . . . . . 2·75 2·50
1511 2 f. 80 blue . . . . . 2·75 2·00
1512 3 f. blue . . . . . . 3·25 2·50
1513 3 f. 20 blue . . . . . 3·00 2·50
1514 3 f. 40 blue . . . . . 4·00 2·50
1515 3 f. 60 blue . . . . . 2·75 1·60
1516 4 f. brown . . . . . . 1·60 85
1517 5 f. 50 black . . . . . 2·25 1·75
1518 10 f. purple . . . . . 3·75 1·10
1519 15 f. green . . . . . . 10·00 2·50
1520 20 f. blue . . . . . . 10·00 3·00

(b) 36 × 27 mm.
1521 – 5 f. violet (air) . . . . . 1·75 60
1522 – 10 f. red . . . . 6·25 1·25
1523 – 15 f. green . . . . . . 6·75 1·75
1524 – 20 f. blue . . . . . . 8·00 2·50
1525 – 30 f. brown . . . . . . 12·50 5·00
DESIGN: Nos. 1521/5, Double portrait and monograms.

1981. 1st International Congress on Discovery and History of Northern Polar Regions, Rome.
1530 **421** 1 f. 50 multicoloured . . . 1·75 1·25

1981. Paintings. "Princes and Princesses of Monaco". Vert designs as T **213**. Multicoloured.
1531 3 f. "Prince Louis II" (P.-A. de Laszlo) . . . . . 2·50 1·25
1532 5 f. "Princess Charlotte" (P.-A. de Laszlo) . . . . . 3·75 2·50

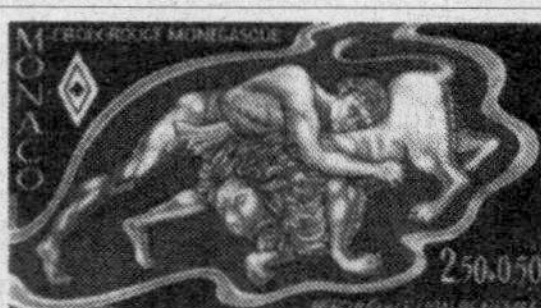
422 Hercules fighting the Nemean Lion

1981. Monaco Red Cross. The Twelve Labours of Hercules (1st series).
1533 **422** 2 f. 50 + 50 c. green, brown and red . . . . 1·50 1·50
1534 – 3 f. 50 + 50 c. blue, green and red . . . . 1·90 1·90
DESIGN: 3 f. 50, Slaying the Hydra of Lerna.
See also Nos. 1584/5, 1631/2, 1699/1700, 1761/2 and 1794/5.

423 Ettore Bugatti (racing car designer) (Cent) 424 Eglantines and Morning Glory

1981. Birth Anniversaries.
1535 **423** 1 f. indigo, blue and red . 1·25 85
1536 – 2 f. black, blue & brown . 1·10 85
1537 – 2 f. 50 brown, black and red 1·40 1·10
1538 – 4 f. multicoloured . . . . 3·75 3·25
1539 – 4 f. multicoloured . . . . 3·75 3·25
DESIGNS: No. 1536, George Bernard Shaw (dramatist, 125th anniv); 1537, Fernand Leger (painter, centenary). LARGER: 37 × 48 mm: 1538, Pablo Picasso (self-portrait) (centenary); 1539, Rembrandt (self-portrait) (375th anniv).

1981. Monte Carlo Flower Show (1982). Mult.
1540 1 f. 40 Type **424** . . . . . . 1·50 1·00
1541 2 f. "Ikebana" (painting by Ikenobo) . . . . 2·25 1·75

425 "Catherine Deneuve" 426 Tiger, Clown, Acrobat and Elephants

1981. 1st International Rose Show, Monte Carlo.
1542 **425** 1 f. 80 multicoloured . . . 3·75 2·50

1981. 8th International Circus Festival, Monaco.
1543 **426** 1 f. 40 violet, mve & blk 2·50 1·50

427 Praying Children and Nativity

1981. Christmas.
1544 **427** 1 f. 20 blue, mauve & brn 85 60

428 "Lancia-Stratos" Rally Car

1981. 50th Monte Carlo Rally (1982).
1545 **428** 1 f. blue, red & turquoise 1·40 1·00

430 "Hoya bella" 431 Spring

1981. Plants in Exotic Garden. Multicoloured.

1547 1 f. 40 Type **430** . . . . . . 3·75 1·50
1548 1 f. 60 "Bolivicereus samaipatanus" . . . . . . 2·25 1·25
1549 1 f. 80 "Trichocereus grandiflorus" (horiz) . . . 2·75 1·25
1550 2 f. "Argyroderma roseum" . 1·90 60
1551 2 f. 30 "Euphorbia milii" . . 2·25 2·00
1552 2 f. 60 "Echinocereus fitchii" (horiz) . . . . 2·25 2·00
1553 2 f. 90 "Rebutia heliosa" (horiz) 2·50 2·25
1554 4 f. 10 "Echinopsis multiplex cristata" (horiz) . . . . . 4·50 3·50

1982. Precancels. The Seasons of the Peach Tree.

1555 **431** 97 c. mauve and green . . 40 25
1556 – 1 f. 25 green, orge & mve 75 60
1557 – 2 f. 03 brown . . . . . . 1·25 65
1558 – 3 f. 36 brown and blue . . 1·90 1·50

DESIGNS: 1 f. 25, Summer; 2 f. 03, Autumn; 3 f. 36, Winter.

432 Nutcracker 433 Capture of Monaco Fortress, 1297

1982. Birds from Mercantour National Park.

1559 **432** 60 c. black, brown & grn 1·00 85
1560 – 70 c. black and mauve . . 1·25 1·00
1561 – 80 c. red, black & orange 1·25 1·10
1562 – 90 c. black, red and blue 1·90 1·60
1563 – 1 f. 40 brown, blk & red . 2·75 2·25
1564 – 1 f. 60 brown, black & blue 3·75 2·50

DESIGNS—VERT: 70 c. Black grouse; 80 c. Rock partridge; 1 f. 60, Golden eagle. HORIZ: 90 c. Wallcreeper; 1 f. 40, Rock ptarmigan.

1982. Europa.

1565 **433** 1 f. 60 blue, brown and red 50 30
1566 – 2 f. 30 blue, brown and red 75 45

DESIGN: 2 f. 30, Signing the Treaty of Peronne, 1641.

434 Old Quarter

1982. Fontvieille.

1568 **434** 1 f. 40 blue, brown & grn 1·00 50
1569 – 1 f. 60 light brown, brown and red . . . . 1·10 60
1570 – 2 f. 30 purple . . . . . . 1·60 1·10

DESIGNS: 1 f. 60, Land reclamation; 2 f. 30, Urban development.

435 Stadium

1982. Fontvieille Sports Stadium (1st series).

1571 **435** 2 f. 30 green, brown & blue 1·50 1·25

See also No. 1616.

436 Arms of Paris

1982. "Philexfrance" International Stamp Exhibition, Paris.

1572 **436** 1 f. 40 red, grey and deep red . . . . 1·00 75

437 Old English Sheepdog

1982. International Dog Show, Monte Carlo. Multicoloured.

1573 60 c. Type **437** . . . . 2·50 1·90
1574 1 f. Briard . . . . 3·00 1·90

438 Monaco Cathedral and Arms

1982. Creation of Archbishopric of Monaco (1981).

1575 **438** 1 f. 60 black, blue and red 90 75

439 St. Francis of Assisi 440 Dr. Robert Koch

1982. 800th Birth Anniv of St. Francis of Assisi.

1576 **439** 1 f. 40 grey and light grey 85 75

1982. Centenary of Discovery of Tubercle Bacillus.

1577 **440** 1 f. 40 purple and lilac . . 1·25 1·00

441 Lord Baden-Powell 443 St. Hubert (18th-century medallion)

1982. 125th Birth Anniv of Lord Baden-Powell (founder of Boy Scout Movement).

1578 **441** 1 f. 60 brown and black . 1·50 1·25

1982. 29th Meeting of International Hunting Council, Monte Carlo.

1580 **443** 1 f. 60 multicoloured . . . 1·40 1·10

444 Books, Reader and Globe

1982. International Bibliophile Association General Assembly, Monte Carlo.

1581 **444** 1 f. 60 blue, purple & red 90 75

445 "Casino, 1870"

1982. Monaco in the "Belle Epoque" (1st series). Paintings by Hubert Clerissi. Multicoloured.

1582 3 f. Type **445** . . . . 1·90 1·40
1583 5 f. "Porte d'Honneur, Royal Palace, 1893" . . . . . . 3·75 2·00

See also Nos. 1629/30, 1701/2, 1763/4, 1801/2, 1851/2, 1889/90 and 1965/6.

1982. Monaco Red Cross. The Twelve Labours of Hercules (2nd series). As T **422**.

1584 2 f. 50 + 50 c. green, red and bright red . . . . 1·50 1·50
1585 3 f. 50 + 50 c. brown, blue and red . . . . 1·90 1·90

DESIGNS: 2 f. 50, Capturing the Erymanthine Boar. 3 f. 50, Shooting the Stymphalian Birds.

446 Nicolo Paganini (violinist and composer, bicent) 447 Vase of Flowers

1982. Birth Anniversaries.

1586 **446** 1 f. 60 brown and purple 1·25 1·00
1587 – 1 f. 80 red, mauve & brn 1·75 1·25
1588 – 2 f. 60 green and red . . . 2·00 1·50
1589 – 4 f. multicoloured . . . . 3·75 3·00
1590 – 4 f. multicoloured . . . . 3·75 3·00

DESIGNS—VERT: No. 1587, Anna Pavlova (ballerina, centenary); 1588, Igor Stravinsky (composer, centenary). HORIZ: (47×36 mm): 1589, "In a Boat" (Edouard Manet, 150th anniv); 1590, "The Black Fish" (Georges Braque, centenary).

1982. Monte Carlo Flower Show (1983). Mult.

1591 1 f. 60 Type **447** . . . . . . 1·90 1·40
1592 2 f. 60 Ikebana arrangement . 2·50 1·90

448 Bowl of Flowers 449 The Three Kings

1982.

1593 **448** 1 f. 60 multicoloured . . . 1·90 1·40

1982. Christmas.

1594 **449** 1 f. 60 green, blue & orge 55 30
1595 – 1 f. 80 green, blue & orge 65 30
1596 – 2 f. 60 green, blue & orge 1·00 55

DESIGNS: 1 f. 80, The Holy Family; 2 f. 60, Shepherds and angels.

450 Prince Albert I and Polar Scene

1982. Centenary of First International Polar Year.

1598 **450** 1 f. 60 brown, green & bl 2·00 1·75

451 Viking Longships off Greenland

1982. Millenary of Discovery of Greenland by Erik the Red.

1599 **451** 1 f. 60 blue, brown & blk 2·00 1·75

452 Julius Caesar in the Port of Monaco ("Aeneid", Book VI)

1982. 2000th Death Anniv of Virgil (poet).

1600 **452** 1 f. 80 deep blue, blue and brown . . . . 2·00 1·75

453 Spring 454 Tourism

1983. Precancels. The Seasons of the Apple Tree.

1601 **453** 1 f. 05 purple, green and yellow 75 30
1602 – 1 f. 35 lt green, deep green and turquoise 85 40
1603 – 2 f. 19 red, brown & grey . 1·50 1·00
1604 – 3 f. 63 yellow and brn . . 2·10 1·60

DESIGNS: 1 f. 35, Summer; 2 f. 19, Autumn; 3 f. 63, Winter.

1983. 50th Anniv of Exotic Garden. Mult.

1605 1 f. 80 Type **454** . . . . . . 1·50 1·10
1606 2 f. Cactus plants (botanical collections) . . . . 1·75 1·25
1607 2 f. 30 Cactus plants (international flower shows) 2·00 1·75
1608 2 f. 60 Observatory grotto (horiz) . . . . 2·50 1·90
1609 3 f. 30 Museum of Prehistoric Anthropology (horiz) . . . 3·50 2·75

455 Alaskan Malamute 457 St. Charles Borromee and Church

1983. International Dog Show, Monte Carlo.

1610 **455** 1 f. 80 multicoloured . . . 5·00 3·75

1983. Centenary of St. Charles Church, Monte Carlo.

1612 **457** 2 f. 60 deep blue, blue and green . . . . 1·25 1·00

458 Montgolfier Balloon, 1783 459 Franciscan College

1983. Europa.

1613 **458** 1 f. 80 blue, brown & grey 55 30
1614 – 2 f. 60 grey, blue & brown 1·00 40

DESIGN: 2 f. 60, Space shuttle.

1983. Centenary of Franciscan College, Monte Carlo.

1616 **459** 2 f. grey, brown and red 90 75

460 Stadium

1983. Fontvieille Sports Stadium (2nd series).

1617 **460** 2 f. green, blue & brown 1·00 40

461 Early and Modern Cars

1983. Centenary of Petrol-driven Motor Car.

1618 **461** 2 f. 90 blue, brown & green 3·00 1·90

462 Blue Whale

1983. International Commission for the Protection of Whales.

1619 **462** 3 f. 30 blue, light blue and grey . . . . 3·75 3·00

463 Dish Aerial, Pigeon, W.C.Y. Emblem and Satellite

1983. World Communications Year.
1620 **463** 4 f. lilac and mauve . . . 1·90 1·40

464 Smoking Moor

1983. Nineteenth Century Automata from the Galea Collection. Multicoloured.
1621 50 c. Type **464** 15 10
1622 60 c. Clown with diabolo 20 10
1623 70 c. Smoking monkey 20 15
1624 80 c. Peasant with pig 60 60
1625 90 c. Buffalo Bill smoking 75 60
1626 1 f. Snake charmer 75 60
1627 1 f. 50 Pianist 1·10 85
1628 2 f. Young girl powdering herself 1·75 1·25

1983. Monaco in the "Belle Epoque" (2nd series). As T **445**. Multicoloured.
1629 3 f. "The Beach, 1902" 3·00 2·50
1630 5 f. "Cafe de Paris, 1905" 4·25 3·75

1983. Monaco Red Cross. The Twelve Labours of Hercules (3rd series). As T **422**.
1631 2 f. 50 + 50 c. brn, bl & red 1·75 1·75
1632 3 f. 50 + 50 c. vio, mauve & red 1·90 1·90
DESIGNS: 2 f. 50, Capturing the Hind of Ceryneia; 3 f. 50, Cleaning the Augean stables.

465 Johannes Brahms (composer)

1983. Birth Anniversaries.
1633 **465** 3 f. deep brown, brown and green 1·50 1·25
1634 – 3 f. black, brown and red 1·60 1·25
1635 – 4 f. multicoloured 3·00 2·50
1635 – 4 f. multicoloured 3·00 2·50
DESIGNS—HORIZ: No. 1633, Type **465** (150th anniv); 1634, Giacomo Puccini (composer) and scene from "Madame Butterfly" (125th anniv). VERT: (37×48 mm): 1635, "Portrait of a Young Man" (Raphael (artist), 500th anniv); 1636, "Cottin Passage" (Utrillo (artist), centenary).

466 Circus Performers **467** Bouquet

1983. 9th International Circus Festival, Monaco.
1637 **466** 2 f. blue, red and green 1·90 1·50

1983. Monte Carlo Flower Show (1984). Mult.
1638 1 f. 60 Type **467** 1·50 1·00
1639 2 f. 60 Arrangement of poppies 2·25 1·50

468 Provencale Creche

1983. Christmas.
1640 **468** 2 f. multicoloured 1·90 1·25

469 Nobel Literature Prize Medal

1983. 150th Birth Anniv of Alfred Nobel (inventor of dynamite and founder of Nobel Prizes).
1641 **469** 2 f. black, grey and red 1·40 1·10

470 O. F. Ozanam (founder) and Paris Headquarters **471** "Tazerka" (oil rig)

1983. 150th Anniv of Society of St. Vincent de Paul.
1642 **470** 1 f. 80 violet and purple 1·00 40

1983. Oil Industry.
1643 **471** 5 f. blue, brown & turq 2·10 1·40

474 Skater and Stadium

1984. Winter Olympic Games, Sarajevo.
1646 **474** 2 f. blue, green and turquoise 65 55
1647 – 4 f. blue, violet & purple 1·40 1·25
DESIGN: 4 f. Skater and snowflake.

475 Bridge **476** Balkan Fritillary

1984. Europa. 25th Anniv of European Post and Telecommunications Conference.
1648 **475** 2 f. blue 1·00 30
1649 3 f. green 1·25 1·00

1984. Butterflies and Moths in Mercantour National Park. Multicoloured.
1651 1 f. 60 Type **476** 1·50 1·10
1652 2 f. "Zygaena vesubiana" 1·90 1·25
1653 2 f. 80 False mnestra ringlet 2·00 1·75
1654 3 f. Small apollo (horiz) 2·75 2·10
1655 3 f. 60 Southern swallowtail (horiz) 3·75 2·50

477 Auvergne Pointer **478** Sanctuary and Statue of Virgin

1984. International Dog Show, Monte Carlo.
1656 **477** 1 f. 60 multicoloured 2·50 1·90

1984. Our Lady of Laghet Sanctuary.
1657 **478** 2 f. blue, brown and green 90 40

479 Piccard's Stratosphere Balloon "F.N.R.S." **480** Concert

1984. Birth Centenary of Auguste Piccard (physicist).
1658 **479** 2 f. 80 black, green & bl 90 55
1659 – 4 f. blue, green & turq 1·60 1·00
DESIGN: 4 f. Bathyscaphe.

1984. 25th Anniv of Palace Concerts.
1660 **480** 3 f. 60 blue and deep blue 1·40 1·00

481 Place de la Visitation **482** Spring

1984. Bygone Monaco (1st series). Paintings by Hubert Clerissi.
1661 **481** 5 c. brown 15 50
1662 – 10 c. red 10 10
1663 – 15 c. violet 10 10
1664 – 20 c. blue 10 10
1665 – 30 c. blue 15 10
1666 – 40 c. green 75 10
1667 – 50 c. red 20 10
1668 – 60 c. blue 10 10
1669 – 70 c. orange 1·25 35
1670 – 80 c. green 20 10
1671 – 90 c. mauve 25 20
1672 – 1 f. blue 30 15
1673 – 2 f. black 85 50
1674 – 3 f. red 2·50 1·00
1675 – 4 f. blue 2·00 1·25
1676 – 5 f. green 1·10 65
1677 – 6 f. green 1·50 1·25
DESIGNS: 10 c. Town Hall; 15 c. Rue Basse; 20 c. Place Saint-Nicolas; 30 c. Quai du Commerce; 40 c. Rue des Iris; 50 c. Ships in harbour; 60 c. St. Charles's Church; 70 c. Religious procession; 80 c. Olive tree overlooking harbour; 90 c. Quayside; 1 f. Palace Square; 2 f. Fishing boats in harbour; 3 f. Bandstand; 4 f. Railway station; 5 f. Mail coach; 6 f. Monte Carlo Opera House.
See also Nos. 2015/27.

1984. Precancels. The Seasons of the Quince.
1678 **482** 1 f. 14 red and green 75 30
1679 – 1 f. 47 dp green & green 85 40
1680 – 2 f. 38 olive, turquoise & green 1·50 1·00
1681 – 3 f. 95 green 2·10 1·60
DESIGNS: 1 f. 47, Summer; 2 f. 38, Autumn; 3 f. 95, Winter.

483 Shepherd **485** Bowl of Mixed Flowers

484 Gargantua and Cattle

1984. Christmas. Crib Figures from Provence. Multicoloured.
1682 70 c. Type **483** 25 15
1683 1 f. Blind man 35 50
1684 1 f. 70 Happy man 1·10 1·00
1685 2 f. Spinner 1·25 1·10
1686 2 f. 10 Angel playing trumpet 1·40 1·25
1687 2 f. 40 Garlic seller 1·60 1·50
1688 3 f. Drummer 1·90 1·60
1689 3 f. 70 Knife grinder 2·25 2·00
1690 4 f. Elderly couple 2·75 2·50

1984. 450th Anniv of First Edition of "Gargantua" by Francois Rabelais.
1691 **484** 2 f. black, red and brown 1·00 40
1692 – 2 f. black, red and blue 1·10 40
1693 – 4 f. green 2·25 1·25
DESIGNS:—As T **484**: No. 1692, Panurge's sheep. 36×48 mm: 1693, Francois Rabelais.

1984. Monte Carlo Flower Show (1985). Mult.
1694 2 f. 10 Type **485** 1·50 1·00
1695 3 f. Ikebana arrangement 2·25 1·50

486 Television Lights and Emblem

1984. 25th International Television Festival, Monte Carlo.
1696 **486** 2 f. 10 blue, grey and mauve 1·00 40
1697 – 3 f. grey, blue and red 1·25 65
DESIGN: 3 f. "Golden Nymph" (Grand Prix).

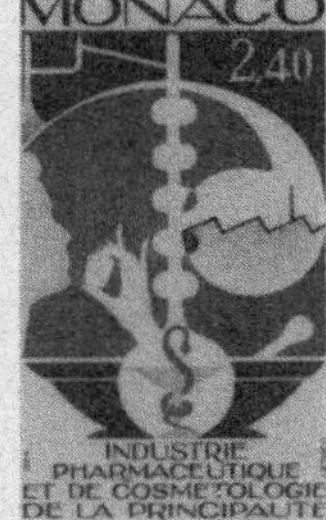

487 Chemical Equipment

1984. Pharmaceutical and Cosmetics Industry.
1698 **487** 2 f. 40 blue, deep blue and green 75 35

1984. Monaco Red Cross. The Twelve Labours of Hercules (4th series). As T **422**.
1699 3 f. + 50 c. brown, light brown and red 1·40 1·40
1700 4 f. + 50 c. green, brown and red 1·75 1·75
DESIGNS: 3 f. Killing the Cretan bull; 4 f. Capturing the Mares of Diomedes.

1984. Monaco in the "Belle Epoque" (3rd series). Paintings by Hubert Clerissi. As T **445**. Mult.
1701 4 f. "Grimaldi Street, 1908" (vert) 3·25 2·50
1702 5 f. "Railway Station, 1910" (vert) 5·25 3·75

489 "Woman with Chinese Vase"

1984. 150th Birth Anniv of Edgar Degas (artist).
1704 **489** 6 f. multicoloured 5·00 3·00

490 Spring

1985. Precancels. Seasons of the Cherry.
1705 **490** 1 f. 22 olive, green and blue 75 30
1706 – 1 f. 57 red, green and yellow 85 40
1707 – 2 f. 55 orange and brown 1·50 1·00
1708 – 4 f. 23 purple, green and blue 2·25 1·90
DESIGNS: 1 f. 57, Summer; 2 f. 55, Autumn; 4 f. 23, Winter.

491 First Stamp

1985. Centenary of First Monaco Stamps.
1709 **491** 1 f. 70 green 65 30
1710 2 f. 10 red 80 10
1711 3 f. blue 1·40 85

493 "Berardia subacaulis" **495** Nadia Boulanger (composer)

1985. Flowers in Mercantour National Park. Mult.
1724 1 f. 70 Type **493** 65 75
1725 2 f. 10 "Saxifraga florulenta" (vert) . . . . 1·00 85
1726 2 f. 40 "Fritillaria moggridgei" (vert) . . . . 1·25 1·00
1727 3 f. "Sempervivum allionii" (vert) . . . . 1·60 1·25
1728 3 f. 60 "Silene cordifolia" (vert) 2·50 1·60
1729 4 f. "Primula allionii" . . . . 2·75 2·00

1985. 25th Anniv of First Musical Composition Competition.
1731 **495** 1 f. 70 brown . . . . . . 1·00 60
1732 – 2 f. 10 blue . . . . 1·25 85
DESIGN: 2 f. 10, Georges Auric (composer).

496 Stadium and Runners

1985. Inauguration of Louis II Stadium, Fontvieille, and Athletics and Swimming Championships.
1733 **496** 1 f. 70 brown, red and violet 55 40
1734 – 2 f. 10 blue, brown and green . . . . 1·00 40
DESIGN: 2 f. 10, Stadium and swimmers.

497 Prince Antoine I

1985. Europa.
1735 **497** 2 f. 10 blue 65 30
1736 – 3 f. red . . . . 1·25 85
DESIGN: 3 f. John-Baptiste Lully (composer).

498 Museum, "Hirondelle I" (schooner) and "Denise" (midget submarine)

1985. 75th Anniv of Oceanographic Museum.
1738 **498** 2 f. 10 black, green and blue 1·10 75

499 Boxer

1985. International Dog Show, Monte Carlo.
1739 **499** 2 f. 10 multicoloured . . . 2·50 1·90

500 Scientific Motifs

1985. 25th Anniv of Scientific Centre.
1740 **500** 3 f. blue, black and violet 1·25 55

501 Children and Hands holding Seedling and Emblem
502 Regal Angelfish

1985. International Youth Year.
1741 **501** 3 f. brown, green and light brown . . . . 1·25 55

1985. Fishes in Oceanographic Museum Aquarium (1st series). Multicoloured.
1742 1 f. 80 Type **502** . . . . . . 1·50 1·25
1743 1 f. 90 Type **502** . . . . . . 2·25 1·00
1744 2 f. 20 Powder blue surgeonfish . . . . 1·50 1·00
1745 3 f. 20 Red-tailed butterflyfish . 2·00 1·90
1746 3 f. 40 As No. 1745 . . . . . 4·00 2·50
1747 3 f. 90 Clown triggerfish . . . 2·50 2·10
1748 7 f. Fishes in aquarium (36 × 48 mm) . . . . 5·00 3·75
See also Nos. 1857/62.

504 Rome Buildings and Emblem

1985. "Italia '85" International Stamp Exhibition, Rome.
1750 **504** 4 f. black, green and red 1·75 1·10

505 Clown **506** Decorations

1985. 11th International Circus Festival, Monaco.
1751 **505** 1 f. 80 multicoloured . . . 1·50 1·10

1985. Christmas.
1752 **506** 2 f. 20 multicoloured . . . 1·25 40

507 Ship and Marine Life **508** Arrangement of Roses, Tulips and Jonquil

1985. Fish Processing Industry.
1753 **507** 2 f. 20 blue, turquoise and brown . . . . 1·25 40

1985. Monte Carlo Flower Show (1986). Mult.
1754 2 f. 20 Type **508** . . . . . . 1·50 1·25
1755 3 f. 20 Arrangement of chrysanthemums and heather 2·25 1·90

509 Globe and Satellite

1985. European Telecommunications Satellite Organization.
1756 **509** 3 f. black, blue and violet 1·50 1·00

510 Sacha Guitry (actor, centenary)

1985. Birth Anniversaries.
1757 **510** 3 f. orange and brown 1·40 1·00
1758 – 4 f. blue, brown and mauve 1·75 1·25
1759 – 5 f. turquoise, blue and grey 2·25 1·75
1760 – 6 f. blue, brown and black 2·75 2·25
DESIGNS: 4 f. Wilhelm and Jacob Grimm (folklorists, bicentenaries); 5 f. Frederic Chopin and Robert Schumann (composers, 175th annivs); 6 f. Johann Sebastian Bach and Georg Friedrich Handel (composers, 300th annivs).

1985. Monaco Red Cross. The Twelve Labours of Hercules (5th series). As T **422**.
1761 3 f. + 70 c. green, deep red and red . . . . 1·40 1·40
1762 4 f. + 80 c. brown, bl & red 1·75 1·75
DESIGNS: 3 f. The Cattle of Geryon; 4 f. The Girdle of Hippolyte.

1985. Monaco in the "Belle Epoque" (4th series). As T **445**, showing paintings by Hubert Clerissi. Multicoloured.
1763 4 f. "Port of Monaco, 1912" . 3·00 1·90
1764 6 f. "Avenue de la Gare 1920" 3·75 3·00

512 Spring

1986. Precancels. Seasons of the Hazel Tree.
1766 **512** 1 f. 28 brown, green & bl 75 30
1767 – 1 f. 65 green, brn & yell 85 40
1768 – 2 f. 67 grey, brown and deep brown . . . . 1·50 1·00
1769 – 4 f. 44 green and brown 2·25 1·90
DESIGNS: 1 f. 65, Summer; 2 f. 67, Autumn; 4 f. 44, Winter.

513 Ancient Monaco

1986. 10th Anniv of "Annales Monegasques" (historical review).
1770 **513** 2 f. 20 grey, blue and brown 1·10 35

514 Scotch Terriers

1986. International Dog Show, Monte Carlo.
1771 **514** 1 f. 80 multicoloured . . . 4·25 3·00

515 Mouflon **516** Research Vessel "Ramoge"

1986. Mammals in Mercantour National Park. Multicoloured.
1772 2 f. 20 Type **515** . . . . . . 1·10 60
1773 2 f. 50 Ibex . . . . 1·40 1·00
1774 3 f. 20 Chamois . . . . . . 1·90 1·60
1775 3 f. 90 Alpine marmot (vert) . 2·75 2·00
1776 5 f. Arctic hare (vert) . . . . 3·50 2·75
1777 7 f. 20 Stoat (vert) . . . . . 4·25 3·25

1986. Europa. Each green, blue and red.
1778 2 f. 20 Type **516** 80 40
1779 3 f. 20 Underwater nature reserve, Larvotto beach . . 1·60 90

517 Prince Albert I and National Council Building

1986. Anniversaries and Events.
1781 **517** 2 f. 50 brown and green . 1·25 85
1782 – 3 f. 20 brown, red and black 2·50 2·25
1783 – 3 f. 90 purple and red . . 3·00 2·50
1784 – 5 f. green, red and blue . . 1·75 1·25
DESIGNS—HORIZ: 2 f. 50, Type **517** (75th anniv of First Constitution); 3 f. 20, Serge Diaghilev and dancers (creation of new Monte Carlo ballet company); 3 f. 90, Henri Rougier and Turcat-Mery car (75th Anniv of first Monte Carlo Rally). VERT: 5 f. Flags and Statue of Liberty (centenary).

518 Chicago and Flags

1986. "Ameripex '86" International Stamp Exhibition, Chicago.
1785 **518** 5 f. black, red and blue 1·75 1·00

520 Comet, Telescopes and 1532 Chart by Apian

1986. Appearance of Halley's Comet.
1787 **520** 10 f. blue, brown & green 4·25 3·00

521 Monte Carlo and Congress Centre

1986. 30th International Insurance Congress.
1788 **521** 3 f. 20 blue, brown & grn 1·75 1·10

522 Christmas Tree Branch and Holly **523** Clown's Face and Elephant on Ball

1986. Christmas. Multicoloured.
1789 1 f. 80 Type **522** 65 25
1790 2 f. 50 Christmas tree branch and poinsettia 90 35

1986. 12th International Circus Festival, Monaco.
1791 **523** 2 f. 20 multicoloured . . . 1·75 1·00

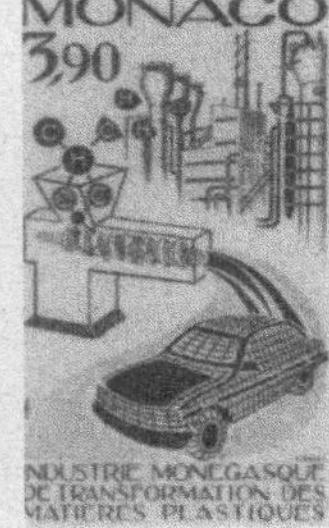

524 Posy of Roses and Acidanthera **525** Making Plastic Mouldings for Car Bodies

1986. Monte Carlo Flower Show (1987). Mult.
1792 2 f. 20 Type **524** . . . . . . 1·50 75
1793 3 f. 90 Lilies and beech in vase 2·50 1·75

1986. Monaco Red Cross. The Twelve Labours of Hercules (6th series). As T **422**.
1794 3 f. + 70 c. green, yell & red . 1·50 1·50
1795 4 f. + 80 c. blue, brn & red . 1·90 1·90
DESIGNS: 3 f. The Golden Apples of the Hesperides; 4 f. Capturing Cerberus.

1986. Plastics Industry.
1796 **525** 3 f. 90 turquoise, red and grey . . . . 1·40 55

526 Scenes from "Le Cid" (Pierre Corneille)

1986. Anniversaries.
1797 **526** 4 f. dp brown and brown 1·40 90
1798 – 5 f. brown and blue . . . 1·75 1·40
DESIGNS: 4 f. Type **526** (350th anniv of first performance); 5 f. Franz Liszt (composer) and bible (175th birth anniv).

527 Horace de Saussure, Mont Blanc and Climbers

1986. Bicentenary of First Ascent of Mont Blanc by Dr. Paccard and Jacques Balmat.
1799 **527** 5 f. 80 blue, red & black . . . 2·25 1·75

528 "The Olympic Diver" (Emma de Sigaldi)

1986. 25th Anniv of Unveiling of "The Olympic Diver" (statue).
1800 **528** 6 f. multicoloured . . . 2·25 1·40

1986. Monaco in the "Belle Epoque" (5th series). Paintings by Hubert Clerissi. As T **445**. Mult.
1801 6 f. "Bandstand and Casino, 1920" (vert) . . . . 3·75 2·50
1802 7 f. "Avenue du Beau Rivage, 1925" (vert) . . . . 5·50 3·50

530 Spring

1987. Precancels. Seasons of the Chestnut.
1804 **530** 1 f. 31 green, yell & brn . . 75 30
1805 – 1 f. 69 green and brown . . 1·00 75
1806 – 2 f. 74 brown, yell & bl . . 1·60 1·25
1807 – 4 f. 56 brown, grn & grey . . 2·25 1·90
DESIGNS: 1 f. 69, Summer; 2 f. 74, Autumn; 4 f. 56, Winter.

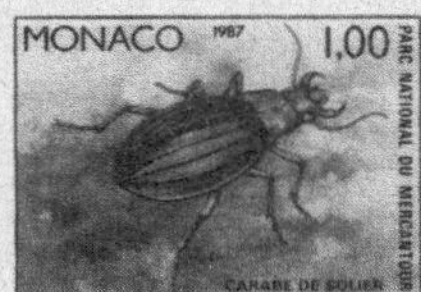

531 Golden Hunter

1987. Insects in Mercantour National Park. Multicoloured.
1808 1 f. Type **531** 40 50
1809 1 f. 90 Golden wasp (vert) . . 1·00 75
1810 2 f. Green tiger beetle . . . . 1·25 1·00
1811 2 f. 20 Brown aeshna (vert) . . 1·60 8·50
1812 3 f. Leaf beetle . . . . 2·50 1·60
1813 3 f. 40 Grasshopper (vert) . . 3·00 2·10

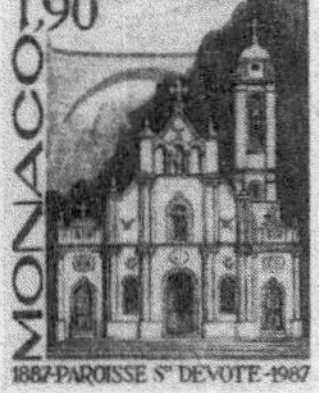

532 St. Devote Church

533 Dogs

1987. Centenary of St. Devote Parish Church.
1814 **532** 1 f. 90 brown 85 25

1987. International Dog Show, Monte Carlo.
1815 **533** 1 f. 90 grey, black & brn . . 1·90 1·25
1816 – 2 f. 70 black and green . . 3·00 1·90
DESIGN: 2 f. 70, Poodle.

534 Stamp Album

1987. Stamp Day.
1817 **534** 2 f. 20 red, purple and mauve . . . . 1·00 50

535 Louis II Stadium, Fontvieille **536** Cathedral

1987. Europa. Each blue, green and red.
1818 2 f. 20 Type **535** . . . . . . 1·00 30
1819 3 f. 40 Crown Prince Albert Olympic swimming pool . . 1·50 85

1987. Centenary of Monaco Diocese.
1821 **536** 2 f. 50 green 80 30

538 Lawn Tennis

1987. 2nd European Small States Games, Monaco.
1823 **538** 3 f. black, red and purple . . 2·25 1·75
1824 – 5 f. blue and black . . . 2·75 2·00
DESIGN: 5 f. Sailing dinghies and windsurfer.

539 "Red Curly Tail" (Alexander Calder)

1987. "Monte Carlo Sculpture 1987" Exhibition.
1825 **539** 3 f. 70 multicoloured . . . 2·00 1·25

MONACO 1,90
540 Prince Rainier III **541** Swallowtail on Stamp

1987. 50th Anniv of Monaco Stamp Issuing Office.
1826 **540** 4 f. blue . . . . 1·40 1·40
1827 – 4 f. red . . . . 1·40 1·40
1828 – 8 f. black . . . . 3·25 3·25
DESIGNS: No. 1827, Prince Louis II. (47×37 mm): 1829, Villa Miraflores.

1987. International Stamp Exhibition.
1829 **541** 1 f. 90 deep green and green 55 25
1830 2 f. 20 purple and red . . 65 45
1831 2 f. 50 purple and mauve . 90 60
1832 3 f. 40 deep blue and blue 1·60 90

542 Festival Poster (J. Ramel) **543** Christmas Scenes

1987. 13th International Circus Festival, Monaco (1988).
1833 **542** 2 f. 20 multicoloured . . . 2·00 1·00

1987. Christmas.
1834 **543** 2 f. 20 red 85 20

544 Strawberry Plants and Campanulas in Bowl **545** Obverse and Reverse of Honore V 5 f. Silver Coin

1987. Monte Carlo Flower Show (1988). Mult.
1835 2 f. 20 Type **544** . . . . . . 1·25 60
1836 3 f. 40 Ikebana arrangement of water lilies and dog roses (horiz) . . . . 1·90 1·25

1987. 150th Anniv of Revival of Monaco Coinage.
1837 **545** 2 f. 50 black and red . . . 1·10 40

546 Graph, Factory, Electron Microscope and Printed Circuit

1987. Electro-Mechanical Industry.
1838 **546** 2 f. 50 blue, green and red 1·00 40

547 St. Devote

1987. Monaco Red Cross. St. Devote, Patron Saint of Monaco (1st series). Multicoloured.
1839 4 f. Type **547** . . . . 1·40 65
1840 5 f. St. Devote and her nurse . 1·75 1·25
See also Nos. 1898/9, 1956/7, 1980/1, 2062/3 and 2101/2.

548 Oceanographic Museum and I.A.E.A. Headquarters, Vienna

1987. 25th Anniv of International Marine Radioactivity Laboratory, Monaco.
1842 **548** 5 f. black, brown and blue 2·10 1·40

549 Jouvet

1987. Birth Centenary of Louis Jouvet (actor).
1843 **549** 3 f. black . . . . 1·10 65

550 River Crossing

1987. Bicentenary of First Edition of "Paul and Virginia" by Bernardin de Saint-Pierre.
1844 **550** 3 f. green, orange and blue 1·25 65

551 Marc Chagall (painter)

1987. Anniversaries.
1845 **551** 4 f. black and red . . . . 1·75 1·00
1846 – 4 f. purple, red and brown 1·75 1·00
1847 – 4 f. red, blue and brown . 1·75 1·00
1848 – 4 f. green, brown & pur . 1·75 1·00
1849 – 5 f. blue, brown and green 2·25 1·25
1850 – 5 f. brown, green and blue 2·25 1·25
DESIGNS: No. 1845, Type **551** (birth centenary); 1846, Chapel of Ronchamp and Charles Edouard Jeanneret (Le Corbusier) (architect, birth centenary); 1847, Sir Isaac Newton (mathematician) and diagram (300th anniv of publication of "Principia Mathematica"); 1848, Key and Samuel Morse (inventor, 150th Anniv of Morse telegraph); 1849, Wolfgang Amadeus Mozart and scene from "Don Juan" (opera, bicentenary of composition); 1850, Hector Berlioz (composer) and scene from "Mass for the Dead" (150th anniv of composition).

1987. Monaco in the "Belle Epoque" (6th series). As T **445** showing paintings by Hubert Clerissi. Multicoloured.
1851 6 f. "Main Ramp to Palace Square, 1925" (vert) . . . . 3·75 2·50
1852 7 f. "Monte Carlo Railway Station, 1925" (vert) . . . 5·00 3·75

552 Coat of Arms **553** Spanish Hogfish

1987.
1853 **552** 2 f. multicoloured 85 30
1854 2 f. 20 multicoloured . . . 65 60

1988. Fishes in Oceanographic Museum Aquarium (2nd series). Multicoloured.
1857 2 f. Type **553** . . . . 1·25 75
1858 2 f. 20 Copper-banded butterflyfish . . . . 1·75 30
1859 2 f. 50 Harlequin filefish . . . 2·00 1·10
1860 3 f. Blue boxfish . . . . . . 1·40 75
1861 3 f. 70 Lionfish . . . . 2·75 2·10
1862 7 f. Moon wrasse (horiz) . . . 3·25 2·25

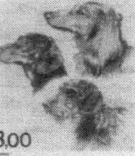

554 Spring **556** Dachshunds

1988. Precancels. Seasons of the Pear Tree. Multicoloured.
1863 1 f. 36 Type **554** 75 30
1864 1 f. 75 Summer . . . . 1·00 75
1865 2 f. 83 Autumn . . . . 1·60 1·25
1866 4 f. 72 Winter . . . . 2·25 1·90
See also Nos. 1952/5.

1988. European Dachshunds Show, Monte Carlo.
1868 **556** 3 f. multicoloured . . . . 2·50 1·90

557 Children of different Races around Globe **558** Satellite Camera above Man with World as Brain

1988. 25th Anniv of World Association of Friends of Children.
1869 **557** 5 f. green, brown & blue . 2·50 1·90

1988. Europa. Transport and Communications. Each black, brown and red.
1870 2 f. 20 Type **558** . . . . . . 1·25 75
1871 3 f. 60 Altantique high speed mail train and aircraft propeller . . . . 2·25 1·75

559 Coxless Four

1988. Centenary of Monaco Nautical Society (formerly Regatta Society).
1873 **559** 2 f. blue, green and red . . 1·00 60

560 Jean Monnet (statesman) **561** "Leccinum rotundifoliae"

1988. Birth Centenaries.
1874 **560** 2 f. black, brown & blue . 2·50 1·60
1875 – 2 f. black and blue . . . 2·50 1·60
DESIGN: No. 1875, Maurice Chevalier (entertainer).

1988. Fungi in Mercantour National Park. Multicoloured.
1876 2 f. Type **561** 70 30
1877 2 f. 20 Crimson wax cap . . . 80 30
1878 2 f. 50 "Pholiota flammans" . . 95 55
1879 2 f. 70 "Lactarius lignyotus" . 1·10 75
1880 3 f. Goaty smell (vert) . . . . 1·25 75
1881 7 f. "Russula olivacea" (vert) . 3·00 1·75

562 Nansen

563 Church and "Miraculous Virgin"

1988. Centenary of First Crossing of Greenland by Fridtjof Nansen (Norwegian explorer).
1882 **562** 4 f. violet . . . . 2·50 1·90

1988. Restoration of Sanctuary of Our Lady of Laghet.
1883 **563** 5 f. multicoloured . . . . 2·10 1·50

564 Anniversary Emblem

1988. 40th Anniv of W.H.O.
1884 **564** 6 f. red and blue . . . . 2·50 1·50

565 Anniversary Emblem

1988. 125th Anniv of Red Cross.
1885 **565** 6 f. red, grey and black . . 2·50 1·50

566 Congress Centre

1988. 10th Anniv of Monte Carlo Congress Centre.
1886 **566** 2 f. green . . . . 1·00 1·00
1887 – 3 f. red . . . . 1·25 1·25
DESIGN: 3 f. Auditorium.

1988. Monaco in the "Belle Epoque" (7th series). Paintings by Hubert Clerissi. As T **445**. Mult.
1889 6 f. "Steam packet in Monte Carlo Harbour, 1910" . . . 3·75 2·50
1890 7 f. "Place de la Gare, 1910" . 4·25 3·00

568 Festival Poster (J. Ramel)

569 Star Decoration

1988. 14th International Circus Festival, Monaco (1989).
1891 **568** 2 f. multicoloured . . . . 1·50 85

1988. Christmas.
1892 **569** 2 f. multicoloured . . . . 1·10 60

570 Arrangement of Fuchsias, Irises, Roses and Petunias

571 Models

1988. Monte Carlo Flower Show (1989).
1893 **570** 3 f. multicoloured . . . . 2·00 1·25

1988. Ready-to-Wear Clothing Industry.
1894 **571** 3 f. green, orange & black 1·25 85

572 Lord Byron (bicentenary)

574 "Le Nain and his Brothers" (Antoine Le Nain)

1988. Writers' Birth Anniversaries.
1895 **572** 3 f. black, brown and blue 1·50 85
1896 – 3 f. purple and blue . . . 1·50 90
DESIGN: No. 1896, Pierre de Marivaux (300th anniv).

1988. Monaco Red Cross. St. Devote, Patron Saint of Monaco (2nd series). As T **547**. Multicoloured.
1898 4 f. Roman governor Barbarus arriving at Corsica . . . . 1·90 1·00
1899 5 f. St. Devote at the Roman senator Eutychius's house . 2·50 1·50

1988. Artists' Birth Anniversaries.
1900 **574** 5 f. brown olive and red 2·75 1·90
1901 – 5 f. black, green and blue 2·75 1·90
DESIGNS: No. 1912, Type **574** (400th anniv): 1913, "The Great Archaeologists" (bronze statue, Giorgio de Chirico) (centenary).

575 Sorcerer

1989. Rock Carvings in Mercantour National Park. Multicoloured.
1902 2 f. Type **575** 85 75
1903 2 f. 20 Oxen in yoke . . . . . 1·00 75
1904 3 f. Hunting implements . . . 1·40 1·25
1905 3 f. 60 Tribal chief . . . . . 2·10 1·60
1906 4 f. Puppet (vert) . . . . . 2·50 1·75
1907 5 f. Jesus Christ (vert) . . . . 2·75 2·00

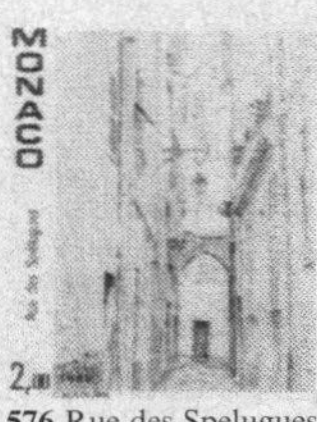

576 Rue des Spelugues

577 Prince Rainier

1989. Old Monaco (1st series). Multicoloured.
1908 2 f. Type **576** 90 40
1909 2 f. 20 Place Saint Nicolas . . 1·00 45
See also Nos. 1969/70 and 2090/1.

1989.
1910 **577** 2 f. blue and azure . . . 1·10 10
1911 2 f. 10 blue and azure . . 1·25 10
1912 2 f. 20 brown and pink . . 1·40 10
1913 2 f. 20 blue and azure . . 1·00 10
1914 2 f. 30 brown and pink . . 1·25 10
1915 2 f. 40 blue and azure . . 85 10
1916 2 f. 50 brown and pink . . 1·00 10
1917 2 f. 70 blue 65 40
1918 2 f. 80 brown and pink . . 1·00 10
1919 3 f. brown and pink . . . 75 45
1920 3 f. 20 blue and cobalt . . 1·50 1·00
1922 3 f. 40 blue and cobalt . . 2·00 1·10
1923 3 f. 60 blue and cobalt . . 2·50 1·25
1924 3 f. 70 blue and cobalt . . 1·25 85
1925 3 f. 80 purple and lilac . . 2·00 60
1926 3 f. 80 blue and cobalt . . 90 55
1927 4 f. purple and lilac . . . 1·00 50
1930 5 f. brown and pink . . . 1·10 40
1932 10 f. dp green and green . 2·50 1·00
1934 **577** 15 f. blue and grey . . . 3·75 1·50
1936 20 f. red and pink . . . . 5·00 1·90
1938 25 f. black and grey . . . 6·25 2·50
1940 40 f. brown and pink . . 10·00 6·25
See also Nos. 2388/90.

578 Yorkshire Terrier

1989. International Dog Show, Monte Carlo.
1941 **578** 2 f. 20 multicoloured . . . 1·25 55

579 Magician, Dove and Cards

1989. 5th Grand Prix of Magic, Monte Carlo.
1942 **579** 2 f. 20 black, blue & red . 1·50 75

580 Nuns and Monks around "Our Lady of Misericorde"

1989. 350th Anniv of Archiconfrerie de la Misericorde.
1943 **580** 3 f. brown, black and red 1·10 75

581 Charlie Chaplin (actor) and Film Scenes

1989. Birth Centenaries.
1944 – 3 f. green, blue & mauve 1·50 1·10
1945 **581** 4 f. purple, green and red 2·25 1·75
DESIGN: 3 f. Jean Cocteau (writer and painter), scene from "The Double-headed Eagle" and frescoes in Villefrance-sur-Mer chapel.

583 Boys playing Marbles

586 "Artist's Mother" (Philibert Florence)

1989. Europa. Children's Games. Each mauve, brown and grey.
1947 2 f. 20 Type **583** . . . . . 1·00 60
1948 3 f. 60 Girls skipping . . . . 1·50 1·10

1989. Precancels. As Nos. 1863/6 but values changed. Multicoloured.
1952 1 f. 39 Type **554** 75 50
1953 1 f. 79 Summer . . . . . . 1·00 75
1954 2 f. 90 Autumn . . . . . . 1·60 1·25
1955 4 f. 84 Winter . . . . 2·25 1·90

1989. Monaco Red Cross. St. Devote, Patron Saint of Monaco (3rd series). As T **547**. Multicoloured.
1956 4 f. St. Devote beside the dying Eutychius . . . . 1·90 1·25
1957 5 f. Barbarus condemns St. Devote to torture for refusing to make a sacrifice to the gods 2·50 1·50

1989. Artists' 150th Birth Anniversaries.
1958 **586** 4 f. brown . . . . 2·25 1·60
1959 – 6 f. multicoloured . . . . 3·25 2·10
1960 – 8 f. multicoloured . . . . 4·25 3·00
DESIGNS—HORIZ: 6 f. "Molesey Regatta" (Alfred Sisley). VERT: 8 f. "Farmyard at Auvers" (Paul Cezanne).

587 Poinsettia, Christmas Roses and Holly

1989. Christmas.
1961 **587** 2 f. multicoloured . . . . 2·50 75

588 Map and Emblem

1989. Centenary of Interparliamentary Union.
1962 **588** 4 f. black, green and red . 1·90 1·00

590 Monaco Palace, White House, Washington, and Emblem

1989. 20th U.P.U. Congress, Washington D.C.
1964 **590** 6 f. blue, brown and black 2·50 1·75

1989. Monaco in the "Belle Epoque" (8th series). Paintings by Hubert Clerissi. As T **445**. Mult.
1965 7 f. "Barque in Monte Carlo Harbour, 1915" (vert) . . . 3·75 2·50
1966 8 f. "Gaming Tables, Casino, 1915" (vert) . . . . 4·25 3·00

591 World Map

592 Clown and Horses

1989. 10th Anniv of Monaco Aide et Presence (welfare organization).
1967 **591** 2 f. 20 brown and red . . 1·75 85

1989. 15th International Circus Festival, Monte Carlo.
1968 **592** 2 f. 20 multicoloured . . . 2·50 1·00

1990. Old Monaco (2nd series). Paintings by Claude Rosticher. As T **576**. Multicoloured.
1969 2 f. 10 La Rampe Major . . . 75 40
1970 2 f. 30 Town Hall Courtyard . 90 45

593 Phalaenopsis "Princess Grace"

594 Bearded Collie

1990. International Garden and Greenery Exposition, Osaka, Japan. Multicoloured.
1971 2 f. Type **593** 55 60
1972 3 f. Iris "Grace Patricia" . . 1·25 85
1973 3 f. "Paphiopedilum" "Prince Rainier III" . . . . 1·25 75
1974 4 f. "Cattleya" "Principessa Grace" . . . . 1·50 1·00
1975 5 f. Rose "Caroline of Monaco" 2·75 1·75

1990. International Dog Show, Monte Carlo.
1976 **594** 2 f. 30 multicoloured . . . 1·60 1·10

595 Noghes and Racing Car

1990. Birth Centenary of Antony Noghes (founder of Monaco Grand Prix and Monte Carlo Rally).

1977 **595** 3 f. red, lilac and black . . 1·50 1·00

596 Cyclist and Lancia Rally Car

1990. Centenary of Automobile Club of Monaco (founded as Cycling Racing Club).

1978 **596** 4 f. blue, brown & purple 2·25 1·75

597 Telephone, Satellite and Dish Aerial

1990. 125th Anniv of I.T.U.

1979 **597** 4 f. lilac, mauve and blue 1·90 1·25

1990. Monaco Red Cross. St. Devote, Patron Saint of Monaco (4th series). As T **547**. Multicoloured.

1980 4 f. St. Devote being flogged . 1·90 1·25
1981 5 f. Placing body of St. Devote in fishing boat . . . . 2·50 1·75

598 Sir Rowland Hill and Penny Black

1990. 150th Anniv of Penny Black.

1982 **598** 5 f. blue and black . . . 3·00 2·00

599 "Post Office, Place de la Mairie"

601 Anatase

1990. Europa. Post Office Buildings. Paintings by Hubert Clerissi. Multicoloured.

1983 2 f. 30 Type **599** . . . . . . 1·00 30
1984 3 f. 70 "Post Office, Avenue d'Ostende" . . . . 1·50 85

1990. Minerals in Mercantour National Park. Mult.

1987 2 f. 10 Type **601** 85 50
1988 2 f. 30 Albite . . . . 1·00 50
1989 3 f. 20 Rutile . . . . 1·40 1·10
1990 3 f. 80 Chlorite . . . . . . 2·00 1·25
1991 4 f. Brookite (vert) . . . . . 2·50 1·90
1992 6 f. Quartz (vert) . . . . . 3·50 2·75

602 Powerboat

603 Pierrot writing (mechanical toy)

1990. World Offshore Powerboat Racing Championship.

1993 **602** 2 f. 30 brown, red & blue 1·25 75

1990. Philatelic Round Table.

1994 **603** 3 f. blue . . . . 1·60 75

604 Christian Samuel Hahnemann (founding of homeopathy)

1990. Bicentenaries.

1995 **604** 3 f. purple, green & black 1·40 85
1996 – 5 f. chestnut, brown & bl 2·00 1·40

DESIGN: 5 f. Jean-Francois Champollion (Egyptologist) and hieroglyphics (birth bicentenary).

605 Monaco Heliport, Fontvieille

606 Petanque Player

1990. 30th International Civil Airports Association Congress, Monte Carlo.

1997 **605** 3 f. black, red and brown 1·25 60
1998 – 5 f. black, blue & brown 2·10 1·25

DESIGN: 5 f. Aerospatiale Ecureuil helicopters over Monte Carlo Congress Centre.

1990. 26th World Petanque Championship.

1999 **606** 6 f. blue, brown & orange 2·75 1·60

607 Spring

608 Miller on Donkey

1990. Precancels. Seasons of the Plum Tree. Multicoloured.

2000 1 f. 46 Type **607** 75 50
2001 1 f. 89 Summer . . . . 1·00 75
2002 3 f. 06 Autumn . . . . 1·60 1·25
2003 5 f. 10 Winter . . . . 2·25 1·90

1990. Christmas. Crib figures from Provence. Multicoloured.

2004 2 f. 30 Type **608** . . . . . . 1·10 50
2005 3 f. 20 Woman carrying faggots 1·40 75
2006 3 f. 80 Baker . . . . 1·90 1·00

See also Nos. 2052/4, 2097/9, 2146/8 and 2191/3.

610 Pyotr Ilich Tchaikovsky (composer)

611 Clown playing Concertina

1990. 150th Birth Anniversaries.

2008 **610** 5 f. blue and green . . . 2·00 1·25
2009 – 5 f. bistre and blue . . . 2·00 1·25
2010 – 7 f. multicoloured . . . . 5·25 3·75

DESIGNS:—As T **610**: No. 2009, "Cathedral" (Auguste Rodin, sculptor). 48 × 37 mm: "The Magpie" (Claude Monet, painter).

1991. 16th International Circus Festival, Monte Carlo.

2011 **611** 2 f. 30 multicoloured . . . 1·40 75

See also No. 2069.

1991. Bygone Monaco (2nd series). Paintings by Hubert Clerissi. As T **481**.

2015 20 c. purple 10 10
2017 40 c. green 10 10
2018 50 c. red 30 30
2019 60 c. blue 15 10
2020 70 c. green 15 10
2021 80 c. blue 45 30
2022 90 c. lilac 30 15
2023 1 f. blue 30 15
2024 2 f. red 75 30
2025 3 f. black 75 35
2027 7 f. grey and black . . . . . 1·75 1·10

DESIGNS: 20 c. Rock of Monaco and Fontvieille; 40 c. Place du Casino; 50 c. Place de la Cremaillere and railway station; 60 c. National Council building; 70 c. Palace and Rampe Major; 80 c. Avenue du Beau Rivage; 90 c. Fishing boats, Fontvieille; 1 f. Place d'Armes; 2 f. Marche de la Condamine; 3 f. Yacht; 7 f. Oceanographic Museum.

612 Abdim's Stork

613 Phytoplankton

1991. International Symposium on Bird Migration. Multicoloured.

2029 2 f. Type **612** . . . . 1·00 40
2030 3 f. Broad-tailed humming birds 1·25 1·00
2031 4 f. Garganeys . . . . . . 2·00 1·40
2032 5 f. Eastern broad-billed roller 2·50 2·00
2033 6 f. European bee eaters . . . 3·25 2·50

1991. Oceanographic Museum (1st series).

2034 **613** 2 f. 10 multicoloured . . . 1·40 75

See also Nos. 2095/6.

614 Schnauzer

615 Cyclamen, Lily-of-the-Valley and Pine Twig in Fir-cone

1991. International Dog Show, Monte Carlo.

2035 **614** 2 f. 50 multicoloured . . . 1·40 1·00

1991. Monte Carlo Flower Show.

2036 **615** 3 f. multicoloured . . . . 1·50 85

616 Corals

617 Control Room, "Eutelsat" Satellite and Globe

1991. "Joys of the Sea" Exhibition. Multicoloured.

2037 2 f. 20 Type **616** . . . . . . 1·50 75
2038 2 f. 40 Coral necklace . . . . 1·25 85

1991. Europa. Europe in Space. Each blue, black and green.

2039 2 f. 30 Type **617** . . . . . . 1·10 30
2040 3 f. 20 Computer terminal, "Inmarsat" satellite, research ship transmitting signal and man with receiving equipment 1·40 60

618 Cross-country Skiers and Statue of Skiers by Emma de Sigaldi

1991. 1992 Olympic Games. (a) Winter Olympics, Albertville.

2042 **618** 3 f. green, blue and olive . 1·50 1·25
2043 – 4 f. green, blue and olive . 2·00 1·60

(b) Olympic Games, Barcelona.

2044 – 3 f. green, lt brown & brown 1·50 1·25
2045 – 5 f. black, brown and green 2·50 2·10

DESIGNS: No. 2043, Right-hand part of statue and cross-country skiers; 2044, Track, relay runners and left part of statue of relay runners by Emma de Sigaldi; 2045, Right part of statue, view of Barcelona and track.

619 Head of "David" (Michelangelo), Computer Image and Artist at Work

620 Prince Pierre, Open Book and Lyre

1991. 25th International Contemporary Art Prize.

2046 **619** 4 f. green, dp green & lilac 1·60 1·10

1991. 25th Anniv of Prince Pierre Foundation.

2047 **620** 5 f. black, blue & brown . 2·00 1·50

621 Tortoises

1991. Hermann's Tortoise. Multicoloured.

2048 1 f. 25 Type **621** . . . . . . 1·25 75
2049 1 f. 25 Head of tortoise . . . 1·25 75
2050 1 f. 25 Tortoise in grass . . . 1·25 75
2051 1 f. 25 Tortoise emerging from among plants . . . . . . 1·25 75

1991. Christmas. As T **608** showing crib figures from Provence. Multicoloured.

2052 2 f. 50 Consul . . . . 1·25 50
2053 3 f. 50 Arlesian woman . . . 1·75 1·10
2054 4 f. Mayor . . . . 2·00 1·50

622 Norway Spruce

1991. Conifers in Mercantour National Park. Multicoloured.

2055 2 f. 50 Type **622** . . . . . . 1·00 20
2056 3 f. 50 Silver fir . . . . . . 1·25 75
2057 4 f. "Pinus uncinata" . . . . 1·50 1·00
2058 5 f. Scots pine (vert) . . . . 2·00 1·25
2059 6 f. Arolla pine . . . . . . 2·50 1·60
2060 7 f. European larch (vert) . . 3·00 1·90

1991. Monaco Red Cross. St. Devote, Patron Saint of Monaco (5th series). As T **547**. Multicoloured.

2062 4 f. 50 Fishing boat carrying body caught in storm . . . 1·90 90
2063 5 f. 50 Dove guiding boat-man to port of Monaco . . . . 2·50 1·50

624 "Portrait of Claude Monet"

1991. 150th Birth Anniv of Auguste Renoir (painter).

2064 **624** 5 f. multicoloured . . . . 2·50 1·90

625 Prince Honore II of Monaco

1991. 350th Anniv of Treaty of Peronne (giving French recognition of sovereignty of Monaco). Paintings by Philippe de Champaigne. Mult.

2065 6 f. Type **625** . . . . 3·00 2·50
2066 7 f. King Louis XIII of France 3·75 2·50

626 Princess Grace (after R. Samini)

1991. 10th Anniv of Princess Grace Theatre.
2067 **626** 8 f. multicoloured . . . . 4·25 3·75

1992. 16th International Circus Festival, Monte Carlo. As No. 2011 but value and dates changed.
2069 **611** 2 f. 50 multicoloured . . . 1·25 85
The 1991 Festival was cancelled.

628 Two-man Bobsleighs

1992. Winter Olympic Games, Albertville (7 f.), and Summer Games, Barcelona (8 f.).
2070 **628** 7 f. blue, turquoise & blk 2·75 1·60
2071 – 8 f. purple, blue and green 3·25 2·10
DESIGN: 8 f. Football.

630 Spring

1992. Precancels. Seasons of the Walnut Tree. Mult.
2073 1 f. 60 Type **630** 85 50
2074 2 f. 08 Summer . . . . 1·00 75
2075 2 f. 98 Autumn . . . . 1·50 1·25
2076 5 f. 28 Winter . . . . 2·25 1·90

631 Golden Labrador

1992. International Dog Show, Monte Carlo.
2077 **631** 2 f. 20 multicoloured . . . 1·25 75

632 Racing along Seafront **633** Mixed Bouquet

1992. 50th Monaco Grand Prix.
2078 **632** 2 f. 50 black, purple & bl 1·10 75

1992. 25th Monte Carlo Flower Show.
2079 **633** 3 f. 40 multicoloured . . . 1·50 1·25

634 Ford Sierra Rally Car

1992. 60th Monte Carlo Car Rally.
2080 **634** 4 f. black, green and red . 1·90 1·25

636 "Pinta" off Palos

1992. Europa. 500th Anniv of Discovery of America by Columbus. Multicoloured.
2082 2 f. 50 Type **636** . . . . . . 1·10 40
2083 3 f. 40 "Santa Maria" in the Antilles . . . . 1·60 1·00
2084 4 f. "Nina" off Lisbon . . . . 2·00 1·50

637 Produce

1992. "Ameriflora" Horticultural Show, Columbus, Ohio. Multicoloured.
2086 4 f. Type **637** . . . . 1·90 1·25
2087 5 f. Vase of mixed flowers . . 2·50 1·90

638 Prince Rainier I and Fleet (detail of fresco by E. Charpentier, Spinola Palace, Genoa)

1992. Columbus Exhibition, Genoa (6 f.), and "Expo '92" World's Fair, Seville (7 f.).
2088 **638** 6 f. brown, red and blue . 2·50 1·60
2089 – 7 f. brown, red and blue . 2·75 2·00
DESIGN: 7 f. Monaco pavilion.

1992. Old Monaco (3rd series). Paintings by Claude Rosticher. As T **576**. Multicoloured.
2090 2 f. 20 La Porte Neuve (horiz) 1·00 30
2091 2 f. 50 La Placette Bosio (horiz) 1·00 35

639 "Christopher Columbus"

1992. "Genova '92" International Thematic Stamp Exhibition. Roses. Multicoloured.
2092 3 f. Type **639** . . . . 1·40 1·00
2093 4 f. "Prince of Monaco" . . . 1·75 1·25

640 Lammergeier

1992.
2094 **640** 2 f. 20 orange, blk & grn . 1·00 75

1992. Oceanographic Museum (2nd series). As T **613**. Multicoloured.
2095 2 f. 20 "Ceratium ranipes" . . 1·10 75
2096 2 f. 50 "Ceratium hexacanthum" . . . . . . 1·40 35

1992. Christmas. As T **608** showing crib figures from Provence. Multicoloured.
2097 2 f. 50 Basket-maker . . . . 1·25 35
2098 3 f. 40 Fishwife . . . . . . 1·75 45
2099 5 f. Rural constable . . . . . 2·25 1·50

641 "Seabus" (projected tourist submarine)

1992.
2100 **641** 4 f. blue, red and brown 1·50 1·25

642 Burning Boat Ceremony, St. Devote's Eve

1992. Monaco Red Cross. St. Devote, Patron Saint of Monaco (6th series).
2101 **642** 6 f. red, blue and brown . 2·50 1·90
2102 – 8 f. purple, orange & red . 3·00 2·50
DESIGN: 8 f. Procession of reliquary, St. Devote's Day.

643 Athletes, Sorbonne University and Coubertin

1992. Centenary of Pierre de Coubertin's Proposal for Revival of Olympic Games.
2103 **643** 10 f. blue . . . . 3·75 2·50

644 Baux de Provence and St. Catherine's Chapel

1992. Titles of Princes of Monaco. Marquis of Baux de Provence.
2104 **644** 15 f. multicoloured . . . 5·50 3·75

646 Clown and Tiger **647** Short-toed Eagles

1993. 17th Int Circus Festival, Monte Carlo.
2106 **646** 2 f. 50 multicoloured . . . 1·10 35

1993. Birds of Prey in Mercantour National Park.
2107 **647** 2 f. chestnut, brown and orange 75 30
2108 – 3 f. indigo, orange & blue 1·25 75
2109 – 4 f. brown, ochre & blue 1·60 1·10
2110 – 5 f. brown, chestnut and green . . . . 2·00 1·40
2111 – 6 f. brown, mauve & grn 2·50 2·00
DESIGNS—HORIZ: 3 f. Peregrine falcon. VERT: 4 f. Eagle owl; 5 f. Honey buzzard; 6 f. Tengmalm's owl.

650 Mixed Bouquet **652** Fire Fighting and Rescue

651 Pennants, Auditorium and Masks

1993. Monte Carlo Flower Show.
2114 **650** 3 f. 40 multicoloured . . . 1·40 85

1993. 10th International Amateur Theatre Festival.
2115 **651** 4 f. 20 multicoloured . . . 1·60 60

1993. World Civil Protection Day.
2116 **652** 6 f. black, red and green . 3·00 1·90

653 Newfoundland **654** Golfer

1993. International Dog Show, Monte Carlo.
2117 **653** 2 f. 20 multicoloured . . . 1·00 75

1993. 10th Monte Carlo Open Golf Tournament.
2118 **654** 2 f. 20 multicoloured . . . 1·00 75

655 Princess Grace **656** Mirror and Candelabra

1993. 10th Death Anniv (1992) of Princess Grace.
2119 **655** 5 f. blue . . . . 1·10 1·25

1993. 10th Antiques Biennale.
2120 **656** 7 f. multicoloured . . . . 2·75 1·75

657 "Echinopsis multiplex" **658** Monte Carlo Ballets

1993. Cacti.
2121 **657** 2 f. 50 green, pur & yell 60 35
2122 – 2 f. 50 green and purple 60 35
2123 – 2 f. 50 green, pur & yell 60 35
2124 – 2 f. 50 green and yellow 60 35
DESIGNS: No. 2122, "Zygocactus truncatus"; 2123, "Echinocereus procumbens"; 2124, "Euphorbia virosa".
See also Nos. 2154/66.

1993. Europa. Contemporary Art.
2125 **658** 2 f. 50 black, brn & pink 1·00 35
2126 – 4 f. 20 grey and brown 1·60 1·00
DESIGN: 4 f. 20, "Evolution" (sculpture, Emma de Sigaldi).

660 State Arms and Olympic Rings

1993. 110th International Olympic Committee Session, Monaco.
2129 **660** 2 f. 80 red, brown & blue 65 75
2130 – 2 f. 80 blue, lt blue & red 60 75
2131 – 2 f. 80 brown, blue & red 65 75
2132 – 2 f. 80 blue, lt blue & red 65 75
2133 – 2 f. 80 brown, blue & red 65 75
2134 – 2 f. 80 blue, lt blue & red 65 75
2135 – 2 f. 80 brown, blue & red 65 75
2136 – 2 f. 80 blue, lt blue & red 65 75
2137 – 4 f. 50 multicoloured . . . 1·00 1·10
2138 – 4 f. 50 black, yellow & bl 1·00 1·10
2139 – 4 f. 50 red, yellow & blue 1·00 1·10
2140 – 4 f. 50 black, yellow & bl 1·00 1·10
2141 – 4 f. 50 red, yellow & blue 1·00 1·10
2142 – 4 f. 50 black, yellow & bl 1·00 1·10
2143 – 4 f. 50 red, yellow & blue 1·00 1·10
2144 – 4 f. 50 red, yellow & blue 1·00 1·10
DESIGNS: Nos. 2129, 2137, Type **660** 2130, Bobsleighing; 2131, Skiing; 2132, Yachting; 2133, Rowing; 2134, Swimming; 2135, Cycling; 2136, 2144, Commemorative inscription; 2138, Gymnastics (rings exercise); 2139, Judo; 2140, Fencing; 2141, Hurdling; 2142, Archery; 2143, Weightlifting.

661 Examining 1891 1 c. Stamp

1993. Centenary of Monaco Philatelic Union.
2145 **661** 2 f. 40 multicoloured . . . 85 35

1993. Christmas. Crib figures from Provence. As T **608**. Multicoloured.
2146 2 f. 80 Donkey 65 40
2147 3 f. 70 Shepherd holding lamb 1·25 85
2148 4 f. 40 Ox lying down in barn 1·60 1·25

662 Grieg, Music and Trolls

1993. 150th Birth Anniv of Edvard Grieg (composer).
2149 **662** 4 f. blue . . . . 2·00 1·25

663 Abstract Lithograph

664 Monaco Red Cross Emblem

1993. Birth Centenary of Joan Miro (painter and sculptor).
2150 **663** 5 f. multicoloured . . . . 2·00 1·75

1993. Monaco Red Cross.
2151 **664** 5 f. red, yellow and black 1·90 1·25
2152 – 6 f. red and black . . . . 2·50 1·90
DESIGN: 6 f. Crosses inscribed with fundamental principles of the International Red Cross.

665 "St. Joseph the Carpenter"

1993. 400th Birth Anniv of Georges de la Tour (painter).
2153 **665** 6 f. multicoloured . . . . 2·50 1·75

1994. Cacti. As Nos. 2121/4 but values changed and additional designs.
2153a 10 c. green, orange and red . 10 10
2154 20 c. green, purple & yell . 10 10
2155 30 c. green and purple . . 10 10
2156 40 c. green and yellow . . 10 10
2157 50 c. green, red and olive . 15 10
2158 60 c. green, red and yellow . 15 10
2159 70 c. green, red and blue . 15 10
2160 80 c. green, orange and red . 20 15
2162 1 f. green, brown and yellow . 25 15
2164 2 f. green, red and yellow . 50 35
2165 2 f. 70 green, red and yellow . 55 25
2166 4 f. green, purple and yellow . 95 85
2166a 4 f. green, red and yellow . 85 55
2167 5 f. green, mauve and brown . 1·25 75
2167a 6 f. brown, green and red . 1·25 75
2167b 7 f. green, brown and red . 1·50 90
DESIGNS: 10 c. "Bromelia brevifolia"; 20 c. Type **657**; 30 c. "Zygocactus truncatus"; 40 c. "Euphorbia virosa"; 50 c. "Selenicereus grandiflorus"; 60 c. "Opuntia basilaris"; 70 c. "Aloe plicatilis"; 80 c. "Opuntia hybride"; 1 f. "Stapelia flavirostris"; 2 f. "Aporocactus flagelliformis"; 2 f. 70, "Opuntia dejecta"; 4 f. (2166), "Echinocereus procumbens"; 4 f. (2166a), "Echinocereus blanckii"; 5 f. "Cereus peruvianus"; 6 f. "Euphorbia milii; 7 f. "Stapelia variegata.

666 Festival Poster

667 Artist/Poet

1994. 18th Int Circus Festival, Monte Carlo.
2168 **666** 2 f. 80 multicoloured . . . 1·10 40

1994. Mechanical Toys.
2169 **667** 2 f. 80 blue 65 40
2170 – 2 f. 80 red 65 40
2171 – 2 f. 80 purple 65 40
2172 – 2 f. 80 green 65 40
DESIGNS: No. 2170, Bust of Japanese woman; 2171, Shepherdess with sheep; 2172, Young Parisienne.

669 King Charles Spaniels

1994. International Dog Show, Monte Carlo.
2175 **669** 2 f. 40 multicoloured . . . 1·00 40

670 Couple, Leaves and Pollution

671 Iris

1994. Monaco Committee of Anti-tuberculosis and Respiratory Diseases Campaign.
2176 **670** 2 f. 40 + 60 c. mult . . . 1·10 85

1994. Monte Carlo Flower Show.
2177 **671** 4 f. 40 multicoloured . . . 1·60 1·00

672 Levitation Trick

1994. 10th Monte Carlo Magic Grand Prix.
2178 **672** 5 f. blue, black and red . . 1·90 1·25

673 Ingredients and Dining Table overlooking Harbour

1994. 35th Anniv of Brotherhood of Cordon d'Or French Chefs.
2179 **673** 6 f. multicoloured . . . . 2·50 1·50

674 Isfjord, Prince Albert I, Map of Spitzbergen and "Princess Alice II"

1994. Europa. Discoveries made by Prince Albert I. Each black, blue and red.
2180 2 f. 80 Type **674** . . . . . . 1·00 45
2181 4 f. 50 Oceanographic Museum, Grimaldi's spookfish and "Eryoneicus alberti" (crustacean) . . . . 1·75 1·00

675 Olympic Flag and Sorbonne University

676 Dolphins through Porthole

1994. Centenary of International Olympic Committee.
2183 **675** 3 f. multicoloured . . . . 1·10 75

1994. Economic Institute of the Rights of the Sea Conference, Monaco.
2184 **676** 6 f. multicoloured . . . . 2·50 1·90

677 Family around Tree of Hearts

678 Footballer's Legs and Ball

1994. International Year of the Family.
2185 **677** 7 f. green, orange and blue . . . . 2·50 1·75

1994. World Cup Football Championship, U.S.A.
2186 **678** 8 f. red and black . . . . 3·00 2·10

679 Athletes and Villa Miraflores

1994. Inauguration of New Seat of International Amateur Athletics Federation.
2187 **679** 8 f. blue, purple and bistre . 3·00 2·10

680 De Dion Bouton, 1903

1994. Vintage Car Collection of Prince Rainier III.
2188 **680** 2 f. 80 black, brown and mauve . . . . 1·10 45

681 Emblem and Monte Carlo

682 Emblem and Korean Scene

1994. 1st Association of Postage Stamp Catalogue Editors and Philatelic Publications Grand Prix.
2189 **681** 3 f. multicoloured . . . . 1·10 45

1994. 21st Universal Postal Union Congress, Seoul.
2190 **682** 4 f. 40 black, blue and red . 1·60 1·10

1994. Christmas. As T **608** showing crib figures from Provence. Multicoloured.
2191 2 f. 80 Virgin Mary . . . . . 1·00 45
2192 4 f. 50 Baby Jesus . . . . . 1·50 70
2193 6 f. Joseph . . . . 1·90 90

683 Prince Albert I

684 Three Ages of Voltaire (writer, 300th anniv)

1994. Inaug of Stamp and Coin Museum (1st issue). Coins.
2194 **683** 3 f. stone, brown and red . 1·25 85
2195 – 4 f. grey, brown and red . 1·60 1·40
2196 – 7 f. stone, brown and red . 2·75 2·10
DESIGNS: 4 f. Arms of House of Grimaldi; 7 f. Prince Rainier III.
See also Nos. 2265/7 and 2283/5.

1994. Birth Anniversaries.
2198 **684** 5 f. green . . . . 1·90 1·50
2199 – 6 f. brown and purple . . 2·25 1·75
DESIGN—HORIZ: 6 f. Sarah Bernhardt (actress, 150th anniv).

685 Heliport and Helicopter

1994. 50th Anniv of International Civil Aviation Organization.
2200 **685** 5 f. green, black and blue . 1·90 1·25
2201 – 7 f. brown, black and red . 2·50 1·90
DESIGN: 7 f. Harbour and helicopter.

687 Blood Vessels on Woman (anti-cancer)

1994. Monaco Red Cross. Health Campaigns.
2203 **687** 6 f. blue, black and red . . 2·25 1·75
2204 – 8 f. green, black and red . 3·00 2·25
DESIGN: 8 f. Tree and woman (anti-AIDS).

688 Robinson Crusoe and Friday

1994. Anniversaries. Multicoloured.
2205 7 f. Type **688** (275th anniv of publication of "Robinson Crusoe" by Daniel Defoe) . 2·50 1·90
2206 9 f. "The Snake Charmer" (150th birth anniv of Henri Rousseau, painter) . . . . 3·00 2·10

689 Clown playing Trombone

690 Crown Prince Albert

1995. 19th Int Circus Festival, Monte Carlo.
2207 **689** 2 f. 80 multicoloured . . . 1·00 45

1995. 35th Television Festival, Monte Carlo.
2208 **690** 8 f. brown . . . . 3·00 1·90

691 Fontvieille

1995. European Nature Conservation Year.
2209 **691** 2 f. 40 multicoloured . . . 85 40

692 American Cocker Spaniel

1995. International Dog Show, Monte Carlo.
2210 **692** 4 f. multicoloured . . . . 1·50 1·00

693 Parrot Tulips

1995. Monte Carlo Flower Show.
2211 **693** 5 f. multicoloured . . . . 1·90 1·10

694 "Acer palmatum"

1995. European Bonsai Congress.
2212 **694** 6 f. multicoloured . . . . 2·25 1·50

695 Alfred Nobel (founder of Nobel Prizes) and Dove

1995. Europa. Peace and Freedom. Multicoloured.
2213 2 f. 80 Type **695** . . . . 1·00 45
2214 5 f. Roses, broken chain and watchtower . . . . 1·90 1·25

696 Emblem of Monagasque Disabled Children Association

1995. International Special Olympics, New Haven, U.S.A.
2215 **696** 3 f. multicoloured . . . . 1·10 75

697 Emblem

1995. Rotary International Convention, Nice.
2216 **697** 4 f. blue . . . . 1·50 1·00

699 Jean Giono

701 Princess Caroline (President)

700 Saint Hubert (patron saint of hunting)

1995. Writers' Birth Centenaries.
2218 **699** 5 f. lilac, brown and green 1·90 1·10
2219 – 6 f. brown, violet and green . . . . 2·25 1·50
DESIGN: 6 f. Marcel Pagnol.

1995. General Assembly of International Council for Hunting and Conservation of Game.
2220 **700** 6 f. blue . . . . 2·25 1·25

1995. World Association of Friends of Children General Assembly, Monaco.
2221 **701** 7 f. blue . . . . 2·50 1·90

702 Athletes and Medal

1995. International Amateur Athletics Federation Grand Prix, Monaco.
2222 **702** 7 f. mauve, purple and grey 2·50 1·50

703 "Trophee des Alpes" (Hubert Clerissi)

1995. 2000th Anniv of Emperor Augustus Monument, La Turbie.
2223 **703** 8 f. multicoloured . . . . 3·00 1·90

704 Prince Pierre (after Philip Laszlo de Lombos)

706 St. Antony (wooden statue)

1995. Birth Centenary of Prince Pierre of Monaco.
2224 **704** 10 f. purple . . . . . . 3·75 2·50

1995. 800th Birth Anniv of St. Antony of Padua.
2226 **706** 2 f. 80 multicoloured . . . 1·00 45

707 United Nations Charter and Peacekeeping Soldiers

1995. 50th Anniv of U.N.O.
2227 **707** 2 f. 50 multicoloured . . . 90 40
2228 – 2 f. 50 multicoloured . . . 90 40
2229 – 2 f. 50 multicoloured . . . 90 40
2230 – 2 f. 50 blue, black and brown 90 40
2231 – 3 f. black, brown and blue . 1·10 75
2232 – 3 f. multicoloured . . . . 1·10 75
2233 – 3 f. multicoloured . . . . 1·10 75
2234 – 3 f. multicoloured . . . . 1·10 75
DESIGNS: No. 2228, Wheat ears, boy and arid ground; 2229, Children from different nationalities; 2230, Head of Colossus, Abu Simbel Temple; 2231, United Nations meeting; 2232, Growing crops and hand holding seeds; 2233, Figures and alphabetic characters; 2234, Lute and U.N.E.S.C.O. headquarters, Paris.
Nos. 2228 and 2232 commemorate the F.A.O., Nos. 2229 and 2233 International Year of Tolerance, Nos. 2230 and 2234 U.N.E.S.C.O.

708 Rose "Grace de Monaco"

709 Balthazar

1995. Flowers. Multicoloured.
2236 3 f. Type **708** 80 50
2237 3 f. Fuchsia "Lakeland Princess" 80 50
2238 3 f. Carnation "Centenaire de Monte-Carlo" 80 50
2239 3 f. Fuchsia "Grace" 80 50
2240 3 f. Rose "Princesse de Monaco" 80 50
2241 3 f. Alstroemeria "Gracia" . . 80 50
2242 3 f. Lily "Princess Gracia" . . 80 50
2243 3 f. Carnation "Princesse Caroline" 80 50
2244 3 f. Rose "Stephanie de Monaco" 80 50
2245 3 f. Carnation "Prince Albert" . 80 50
2246 3 f. Sweet pea "Grace de Monaco" 80 50
2247 3 f. Gerbera "Gracia" 80 50

1995. Christmas. Crib Figures from Provence of the Three Wise Men. Multicoloured.
2248 3 f. Type **709** 80 50
2249 5 f. Gaspard . . . . 1·25 75
2250 6 f. Melchior . . . . 1·60 1·00

710 Tree, Bird, Seahorse and Association Emblem

1995. 20th Anniv of Monaco Association for Nature Protection.
2251 **710** 4 f. green, black and red . 1·75 75

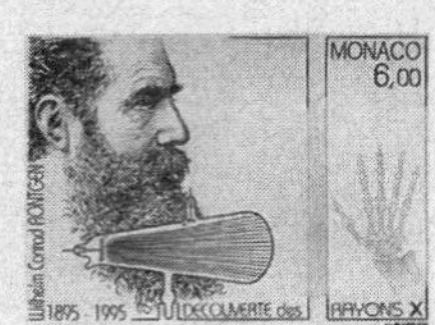

711 Rontgen and X-Ray of Hand

1995. Centenary of Discovery of X-Rays by Wilhelm Rontgen.
2252 **711** 6 f. black, yellow and green . . . . 2·25 1·25

712 First Screening to Paying Public, Paris, December 1895

1995. Centenary of Motion Pictures.
2253 **712** 7 f. blue . . . . 2·50 1·90

713 Allegory of Anti-Leprosy Campaign

1995. Monaco Red Cross. Multicoloured.
2254 7 f. Type **713** . . . . 2·25 1·50
2255 8 f. Doctors Prakash and Mandakini Amte (anti-leprosy campaign in India) . 2·75 1·90

714 First Car with Tyres

1995. Centenary of Invention of Inflatable Tyres.
2256 **714** 8 f. purple and claret . . . 2·75 1·90

715 "Spring"

1995. 550th Birth Anniv of Sandro Botticelli (artist).
2257 **715** 15 f. blue . . . . 5·25 3·75

716 Poster

718 Rhododendron

717 Illusion

1996. 20th International Circus Festival, Monte Carlo.
2258 **716** 2 f. 40 multicoloured . . 60 40

1996. Magic Festival, Monte Carlo.
2259 **717** 2 f. 80 black 70 45

1996. Monte Carlo Flower Show.
2260 **718** 3 f. multicoloured . . . 75 45

719 Wire-haired Fox Terrier

1996. International Dog Show, Monte Carlo.
2261 **719** 4 f. multicoloured . . . 95 60

720 "Chapel" (Hubert Clerissi)

1996. 300th Anniv of Chapel of Our Lady of Mercy.
2262 **720** 6 f. multicoloured . . . 1·50 90

721 Prince Albert I of Monaco ($\frac{1}{2}$-size illustration)

1996. Centenary of Oceanographic Expeditions. Multicoloured.
2263 3 f. Type **721** 75 45
2264 4 f. 50 King Carlos I of Portugal . . . . 1·10 70

722 Prince Rainier III (after F. Messina) **723** Princess Grace

1996. Inauguration of Stamp and Coin Museum (2nd issue). 1974 Prince Rainier design.
2265 **722** 10 f. violet . . . . . . 2·40 1·50
2266 15 f. brown . . . . . . 3·75 2·25
2267 20 f. blue . . . . 4·75 3·00

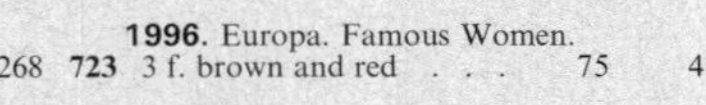

1996. Europa. Famous Women.
2268 **723** 3 f. brown and red . . . 75 45

724 Fishes, Sea and Coastline

1996. 20th Anniv of Ramoge Agreement on Environmental Protection of Mediterranean.
2269 **724** 3 f. multicoloured . . . 75 45

727 Code and Monaco **728** Throwing the Javelin

1996. Introduction of International Dialling Code "377".
2272 **727** 3 f. blue 75 45
2273 3 f. 80 red 90 55

1996. Olympic Games, Atlanta. Multicoloured.
2274 3 f. Type **728** 75 45
2275 3 f. Baseball 75 45
2276 4 f. 50 Running . . . . . . 1·10 70
2277 4 f. 50 Cycling . . . . . . 1·10 70

729 Children of Different Races with Balloon **730** Angel and Star

1996. 50th Anniv of U.N.I.C.E.F.
2278 **729** 3 f. brown, blue and lilac . 75 45

1996. Christmas. Multicoloured.
2279 3 f. Type **730** 75 45
2280 6 f. Angels heralding . . . . 1·50 90

731 Planet and Neptune, God of the Sea (after Roman mosaic, Sousse)

1996. Anniversaries.
2281 **731** 4 f. red, blue and black . 95 60
2282 – 5 f. blue and red . . . 1·25 75
DESIGNS—4 f. Type **731** (150th anniv of discovery of planet Neptune by Johann Galle); 5 f. Rene Descartes (after Franz Hals) (philosopher and scientist, 400th birth anniv).

732 Coins and Press

1996. Inauguaration of Stamp and Coin Museum (3rd issue).
2283 **732** 5 f. brown and blue . . . 1·25 75
2284 – 5 f. brown and purple . . 1·25 75
2285 – 10 f. blue and brown . . 2·40 1·50
DESIGNS—As T **733**: 5 f. Stamp press and engraver. 48 × 37 mm: 10 f. Museum entrance.

733 Camille Corot (bicentenary)

1996. Artists' Birth Anniversaries. Self-portraits. Multicoloured.
2287 6 f. Type **733** . . . . 1·50 90
2288 7 f. Francisco Goya (250th anniv) . . . . 1·75 1·10

734 Allegory

1996. Monaco Red Cross. Anti-Tuberculosis Campaign. Multicoloured.
2289 7 f. Type **734** . . . . 1·75 1·10
2290 8 f. Camille Guerin and Albert Calmette (developers of vaccine) . . . . 1·90 1·25

736 "Gloria" (cadet barque), Club, Motorboat and "Tuiga" (royal yacht)

1996. Monaco Yacht Club.
2292 **736** 3 f. multicoloured . . . 70 45

737 Seal of Prince Ranier III **738** Clown

1996. 700th Anniv of Grimaldi Dynasty (1st issue).
2293 **737** 2 f. 70 red, brown and blue 60 40
See also Nos. 2302/14 and 2326/38.

1996. 21st International Circus Festival, Monte Carlo (1997).
2294 **738** 3 f. multicoloured . . . 70 45

739 Old and New Racing and Rally Cars

1996. Motor Sport.
2295 **739** 3 f. multicoloured . . . 70 45

740 Pictures, Engraving Tools and "Stamps"

1996. 60th Anniv of Stamp Issuing Office (2296) and "Monaco 97" International Stamp Exhibition, Monte Carlo (2297). Each brown, mauve and blue.
2296 3 f. Type **740** 70 45
2297 3 f. Stamp, magnifying glass and letters 70 45
Nos. 2296/7 were issued together, se-tenant, forming a composite design featuring the Grand Staircase of the Prince's Palace.

741 Double Red Camellia

1996. Monte Carlo Flower Show (1997).
2298 **741** 3 f. 80 multicoloured . 85 55

742 Afghan Hound

1996. International Dog Show, Monte Carlo.
2299 **742** 4 f. 40 multicoloured . 1·00 60

743 Award **744** Giant Bellflower and Carob Pods and Leaves

1996. 37th Television Festival, Monto Carlo (1997).
2300 **743** 4 f. 90 multicoloured . 1·10 70

1996.
2301 **744** 5 f. multicoloured . . 1·10 70

745 Rainier I, Battle of Zerikzee, Arms of his wife Andriola Grillo and Chateau de Cagnes

1997. 700th Anniv of Grimaldi Dynasty (2nd issue). The Seigneurs. Multicoloured.
2302 1 f. Type **745** 25 15
2303 1 f. Seal of Charles I, Battle of Crecy, Chateau de Roquebrune and Rocher fortifications 25 15
2304 1 f. Siege of Rocher by Boccanegra, seal of Rainier II, arms of his two wives Ilaria del Caretto and Isabelle Asinari, Vatican and Papal Palace, Avignon 25 15
2305 2 f. Defeat of combined fleets of Venice and Florence and Jean I on horseback and with his wife Pomelline Fregoso . 45 30
2306 2 f. Claudine, acclamation by crowd of her husband Lambert, seals of Lambert and his father Nicolas and strengthening of Monaco Castle 45 30
2307 7 f. Statue of Franois Grimaldi disguised as Franciscan monk and clashes between Ghibellines and Guelphs at Genoa . . . . 1·60 1·00
2308 7 f. Honore I flanked by Pope Paul III and Duke of Savoy and Battle of Lepanto . . 1·60 1·00
2309 7 f. Charles II, flags of Genoa and Savoy and attack on Rocher by Capt. Cartier . . 1·60 1·00

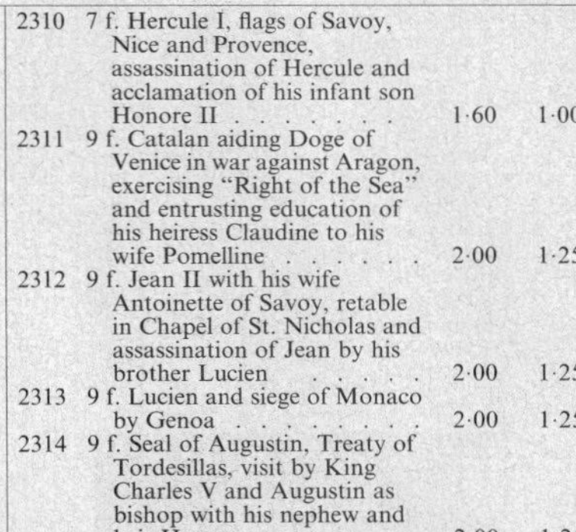
2310 7 f. Hercule I, flags of Savoy, Nice and Provence, assassination of Hercule and acclamation of his infant son Honore II . . . . 1·60 1·00
2311 9 f. Catalan aiding Doge of Venice in war against Aragon, exercising "Right of the Sea" and entrusting education of his heiress Claudine to his wife Pomelline . . . . . . 2·00 1·25
2312 9 f. Jean II with his wife Antoinette of Savoy, retable in Chapel of St. Nicholas and assassination of Jean by his brother Lucien . . . . . 2·00 1·25
2313 9 f. Lucien and siege of Monaco by Genoa . . . . 2·00 1·25
2314 9 f. Seal of Augustin, Treaty of Tordesillas, visit by King Charles V and Augustin as bishop with his nephew and heir Honore . . . . . . 2·00 1·25

746 Tennis Match and Players

1997. Centenary of Monaco Tennis Championships.
2316 **746** 4 f. 60 multicoloured . 1·00 60

747 Prince Rainier, Trophy and Stamp and Coin Museum

1997. Award to Prince Rainier of International Philately Grand Prix (made to "Person who has Contributed Most to Philately") by Association of Catalogue Editors.
2317 **747** 4 f. 60 multicoloured . 1·00 60

748 Images of St. Devote (patron saint) **749** Syringe and Drug Addicts

1997. Europa. Tales and Legends.
2318 **748** 3 f. orange and brown . 65 40
2319 – 3 f. blue 65 40
DESIGN: No. 2319, Hercules.

1997. Monaco Red Cross. Anti-drugs Campaign.
2320 **749** 7 f. black, blue and red 1·50 90

750 First Stamps of United States and Monaco 1996 15 f. Stamp

1997. "Pacific 97" International Stamp Exhibiton, San Francisco. 150th Anniv of First United States Stamps.
2321 **750** 4 f. 90 multicoloured . . 1·00 60

751 Winter and Summer Uniforms, 1997

1997. The Palace Guard. Multicoloured.
2322 3 f. Type **751** 65 40
2323 3 f. 50 Uniforms of 1750, 1815, 1818, 1830 and 1853 . . 75 45
2324 5 f. 20 Uniforms of 1865, 1870, 1904, 1916 and 1935 . . 1·10 70

1997. Victory of Marcelo M. Rios at Monaco Tennis Championships. No. 2316 optd **M. RIOS**.
2325 **746** 4 f. 60 multicoloured . . 1·00 60

1997. 700th Anniv of Grimaldi Dynasty (3rd issue). The Princes. As T **745**. Multicoloured.
2326 1 f. Honore II 20 15
2327 1 f. Louis I 20 15
2328 1 f. Antoine I 20 15
2329 2 f. Jacques I 40 25
2330 7 f. Charles III . . . . . . 1·40 85
2331 7 f. Albert I . . . . . . 1·40 85
2332 7 f. Louis II . . . . . . 1·40 85
2333 7 f. Rainier III . . . . . . 1·40 85
2334 9 f. Louise-Hippolyte . . . 1·75 1·10
2335 9 f. Honore IV (wrongly inscr "Honore III") . . . . . . 1·75 1·10
2336 9 f. Honore III (wrongly inscr "Honore IV") . . . . . 1·75 1·10
2337 9 f. Honore V . . . . . . 1·75 1·10
2338 9 f. Florestan I . . . . . 1·75 1·10

753 Club Badge, Ball as Globe and Stadium

1997. Monaco, Football Champion of France, 1996–97.
2339 **753** 3 f. multicoloured . . 60 40

754 Magic Wand, Hands and Stars

1997. 13th Magic Grand Prix, Monte Carlo.
2340 **754** 4 f. 40 black and gold . 90 55

755 "Francois Grimaldi" (Ernando Venanzi)

1997. Paintings. Multicoloured.
2341 8 f. Type **755** . . . . . . 1·60 1·00
2342 9 f. "St. Peter and St. Paul" (Peter Paul Rubens) . . . . 1·75 1·10

757 Map of Europe and Blue Whales

1997. 49th Session of International Whaling Commission, Monaco.
2344 **757** 6 f. 70 multicoloured . . 1·40 85

758 Princess Charlotte

1997. 20th Death Anniv of Princess Charlotte.
2346 **758** 3 f. 80 brown 80 50

759 Dancer of Russian Ballet and Kremlin, Moscow

761 Diamond-Man (Ribeiro)

760 Trees in Monaco

1997. "Moskva 97" International Stamp Exhbition, Moscow.
2347 **759** 5 f. multicoloured . . . 1·10 70

1997. 10th Anniv of Marcel Korenlein Arboretum.
2348 **760** 9 f. multicoloured . . . 1·90 1·25

1997. Winning Entries in Schoolchildren's Drawing Competition.
2349 **761** 4 f. multicoloured . . . 85 55
2350 – 4 f. 50 blue, ultramarine and red 95 60
DESIGN—HORIZ: 4 f. 50, Flying diamonds (Testa).

762 Four-man Bobsleighing, Speed and Figure Skating and Ice Hockey

1997. Winter Olympic Games, Nagano, Japan (1998). Multicoloured.
2351 4 f. 90 Type **762** . . . . . . 1·00 60
2352 4 f. 90 Alpine skiing, biathlon, two-man bobsleighing and ski jumpimg . . . . 1·00 60
Nos. 2351/2 were issued together, se-tenant, forming a composite design.

763 Albert I (statue) (½-size illustration)

1997. 150th Birth Anniv of Prince Albert I (1st issue).
2353 **763** 8 f. multicoloured . . . 1·75 1·10
See also No. 2368.

764 Clown and Horse

765 Pink Campanula and Carob Plant

1997. 22nd International Circus Festival, Monte Carlo (1998).
2354 **764** 3 f. multicoloured . . . 65 40

1997. Monte Carlo Flower Show (1998).
2355 **765** 4 f. 40 multicoloured . . 95 60

766 "The Departure of Marcus Attilius Regulus for Carthage"

768 Baseball Hat, Television Controller, Ballet Shoe and Football Boot

767 Pope Innocent IV

1997. 250th Birth Anniv of Louis David (painter).
2356 **766** 5 f. 20 green and red . . 1·10 70

1997. 750th Anniv of Creation of Parish of Monaco by Papal Bull.
2357 **767** 7 f. 50 brown and blue . 1·60 1·00

1998. 38th Television Festival.
2358 **768** 4 f. 50 multicoloured . . 95 60

769 Past and Present Presidents

1998. 50th Anniv of Monaco Red Cross.
2359 **769** 5 f. brown and red . . . 1·10 70

770 Boxer and Dobermann

1998. International Dog Show, Monte Carlo.
2360 **770** 2 f. 70 multicoloured . . 55 35

771 White Doves and Laurel Wreath

1998. 30th Meeting of Academy of Peace and International Security.
2361 **771** 3 f. green and blue . . . 65 40

772 Ballet Dancer, Piano Keys, Music Score and Violin

1998. 15th Spring Arts Festival.
2362 **772** 4 f. multicoloured . . . 85 55

773 Pierre and Marie Curie

1998. Centenary of Discovery of Radium.
2363 **773** 6 f. blue and mauve . . . 1·25 75

774 Caravel and Globe

1998. "Expo '98" World's Fair, Lisbon. International Year of the Ocean.
2364 **774** 2 f. 70 multicoloured . . 55 35

775 St. Devote (stained glass window, Palace Chapel) (½-size illustration)

1998. Europa (1st issue). National Festivals.
2365 **775** 3 f. multicoloured . . . 65 40
See also No. 2372.

776 Monte Carlo

777 Kessel

1998. Junior Chamber of Commerce European Conference, Monte Carlo.
2366 **776** 3 f. multicoloured . . . 65 40

1998. Birth Centenary of Joseph Kessel (writer).
2367 **777** 3 f. 90 multicoloured . . 80 50

778 Prince Albert I at different Ages (½-size illustration)

1998. 150th Birth Anniv of Prince Albert I (2nd issue).
2368 **778** 7 f. brown . . . . . . 1·50 90

779 Garnier and Monte Carlo Casino

780 Trophy and Monte Carlo

1998. Death Centenary of Charles Garnier (architect).
2369 **779** 10 f. multicoloured . . . 2·10 1·40

1998. 10th World Music Awards, Monte Carlo.
2370 **780** 10 f. multicoloured . . . 2·10 1·40

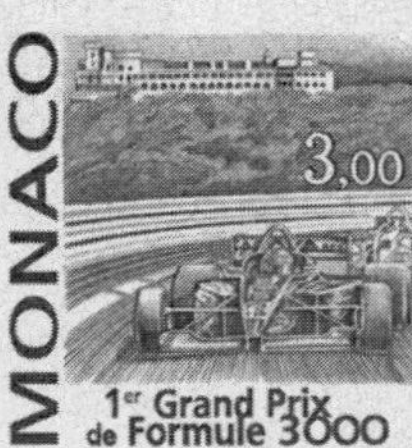

781 Racing Cars

1998. 1st Formula 3000 Grand Prix, Monte Carlo.
2371 **781** 3 f. red and black . . . 65 40

782 Prince Rainier III, Prince Albert and Royal Palace (½-size illustration)

1998. Europa (2nd issue). National Festivals.
2372 **782** 3 f. multicoloured . . . 65 40

783 Porcelain Teapot and Figure of Francois Grimaldi

1998. Fine Arts. Multicoloured.
2373 8 f. Type **783** . . . . 1·75 1·10
2374 9 f. Fine-bound books and illustration . . . . 1·90 1·25

784 Player on Map of France

1998. World Cup Football Championship, France.
2375 **784** 15 f. multicoloured . . . 3·25 2·00

785 Modern and Old Motor Cars and Ferrari

1998. Birth Centenary of Enzio Ferrari (motor manufacturer).
2376 **785** 7 f. multicoloured . . . 1·50 90

786 Gershwin, Trumpeter, Dancers and Opening Bars of "Rhapsody in Blue"

1998. Birth Centenary of George Gershwin (composer).
2377 **786** 7 f. 50 ultramarine, blue and black . . . . 1·60 1·00

787 International Marine Pollution College and Marine Environment Laboratory

1998. International Marine Pollution Conference, Monaco.
2378 **787** 4 f. 50 multicoloured . . 95 60

788 Venue

1998. Post Europ (successor to C.E.P.T.) Plenary Assembly, Monaco.
2379 **788** 5 f. multicoloured . . . 1·10 70

789 Belem Tower, Lisbon, and Palace, Monaco

1998. "Expo '98" World's Fair and Stamp Exhibition, Lisbon.
2380 **789** 6 f. 70 multicoloured . . 1·40 85

790 Sportsmen

1998. 30th Anniv of International Association against Violence in Sport.
2381 **790** 4 f. 20 multicoloured . . 90 55

791 Magician

1998. "Magic Stars" Magic Festival, Monte Carlo.
2382 **791** 3 f. 50 gold and red . . . 75 45

792 Statue and Vatican Colonnade

1998. 400th Birth Anniv of Giovanni Lorenzo Bernini (architect and sculptor).
2383 **792** 11 f. 50 blue and brown . 2·40 1·50

793 Milan Cathedral

794 Christmas Tree Decoration

1998. "Italia 98" International Stamp Exhibition, Milan.
2384 **793** 4 f. 90 green and red . . 1·00 60

1998. Christmas. Multicoloured.
2385 3 f. Type **794** 65 40
2386 6 f. 70 "The Nativity" (detail of icon) (horiz) . . . . 1·40 85

1998. As Nos. 1910 etc but no value expressed.
2388 **577** (2 f. 70) turquoise & blue . 55 35
2389 (3 f.) red and pink . . . 65 40
2390 (3 f. 80) blue and cobalt . 80 50

795 Lion

1998. 23rd International Circus Festival, Monte Carlo (1999).
2391 **795** 2 f. 70 multicoloured . . 55 35

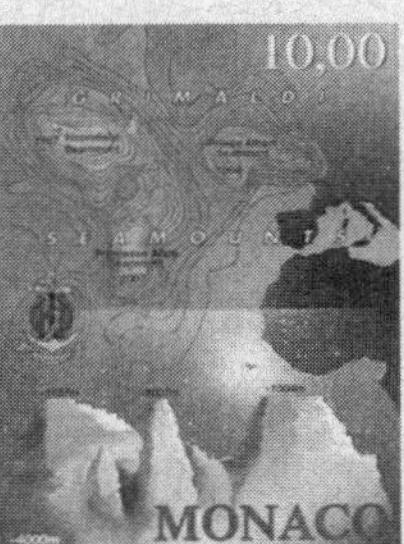

796 Map and Elevation of Seamounts

1998. Grimaldi Seamounts.
2392 **796** 10 f. multicoloured . . . 2·10 1·40

798 1860 Cover and Stamp and Coin Museum

1999. "Monaco 99" International Stamp Exhibition.
2394 **798** 3 f. multicoloured 60 35

799 Festival Poster

1999. 39th Television Festival.
2396 **799** 3 f. 80 multicoloured . . 65 35

800 Cocker Spaniel and American Cocker

1999. International Dog Show, Fontvieille.
2397 **800** 4 f. multicoloured 80 50

801 World Map

1999. 50th Anniv of Geneva Conventions.
2398 **801** 4 f. 40 red, brown and black 85 50

802 Arrangement of Flowers named after Grimaldi Family Members

1999. Monte Carlo Flower Show.
2399 **802** 4 f. 50 multicoloured . . 85 50

803 Children and Heart

1999. 20th Anniv of Monaco Aid and Presence.
2400 **803** 6 f. 70 multicoloured . . 1·25 75
No. 2400 is also denominated in euros.

804 Palace and Centre

1999. 20th Anniv of Congress Centre Auditorium.
2401 **804** 2 f. 70 multicoloured . . 50 30

DENOMINATION. From No. 2402 Monaco stamps are denominated both in francs and in euros. As no cash for the latter is in circulation, the catalogue continues to use the franc value.

805 Globe and Piano Keys

1999. 10th Piano Masters, Monte Carlo.
2402 **805** 4 f. 60 multicoloured . . 90 55

806 Rose "Jubile du Prince de Monaco"

808 Olympic Rings and Trophy

807 Williams's Bugatti (winner of first race) and Michael Schumacher's Car (winner of 1999 race)

1999. Flowers. Multicoloured.
2403 4 f. 90 Type **806** 95 55
2404 6 f. Rose "Prince de Monaco", rose "Grimaldi" and orchid "Prince Rainier III" . . . . 1·10 65

1999. 70th Anniv of Monaco Motor Racing Grand Prix.
2405 **807** 3 f. multicoloured 60 35

1999. 3rd Association of Postage Stamp Catalogue Editors and Philatelic Publications Grand Prix.
2406 **808** 4 f. 40 multicoloured . . 85 50

809 Riders jumping over Monte Carlo (½-size illustration)

1999. 5th International Show Jumping Competition, Monte Carlo.
2407 **809** 5 f. 20 red, black and blue 1·00 60

810 Footballer, Runner and Palace (½-size illustration)

1999. 75th Anniv of Monaco Sports Association. Multicoloured.
2408 7 f. Type **810** . . . . 1·40 85
2409 7 f. Boxer, footballer, harbour, runner and handballer . . . 1·40 85

811 Architect's Drawing of Forum

1999. Construction of Grimaldi Forum (congress and exhibition centre).
2410 **811** 3 f. multicoloured . . . 60 35

812 Facade and Construction

1999. Centenary of Laying of First Stone of Oceanographic Museum.
2411 **812** 5 f. multicoloured . . . . . 1·00 60

813 Eiffel Tower on Map of France, 1849 20 c. "Ceres" Stamp and Emblem

814 Casino and Rock

1999. "Philexfrance 99" International Stamp Exhibition, Paris (1st issue). 150th Anniv of First French Stamps.
2412 **813** 2 f. 70 multicoloured . . 50 30
See also No. 2423.

1999. Europa. Parks and Gardens. Multicoloured.
2413 3 f. Type **814** 60 35
2414 3 f. Fontvieille (48 × 27 mm) . 60 35

815 Fontvieille in 1949, Line Graph and Underground Station in 1999

1999. 50 Years of the Economy. Multicoloured.
2415 5 f. Type **815** (second sector) . 1·00 60
2416 5 f. Le Larvotto in 1949, line graph and Grimaldi Forum in 1999 (third sector) . . . . 1·00 60

817 Honore de Balzac

818 Emblem and Chinese Drawing

1999. Writers' Birth Bicentenaries.
2418 **817** 4 f. 50 blue and scarlet . . 85 50
2419 – 5 f. 20 brown, blue and red . . . . 1·00 60
DESIGN: 5 f. 20, Sophie Rostopchine, Comtesse de Segur.

1999. 125th Anniv of Universal Postal Union.
2420 **818** 3 f. blue, red and yellow . 60 35

819 Iris "Rainier III" and Rose "Rainier III"

821 Emblem and Monaco 1885 and French 1878 Stamps

820 Anniversary Emblem

1999. Flowers.
2421 **819** 4 f. multicoloured 80 50

1999. 50th Anniv of Monaco's Admission to United Nations Educational, Scientific and Educational Organization.
2422 **820** 4 f. 20 multicloured . . . 80 50

1999. "Philexfrance 99" International Stamp Exhibition, Paris (2nd issue).
2423 **821** 7 f. black, blue and mauve . . . . 1·40 85

822 Athletes

1999. 10th Sportel (sport and television) Congress, Fontvieille.
2424 **822** 10 f. multicoloured . . . 1·90 1·10

823 Maltese Cross, Knights and Valletta

1999. 900th Anniv of Sovereign Military Order of Malta and 25th Anniv of National Association of the Order.
2425 **823** 11 f. 50 red, brown and blue . . . . 2·25 1·40

824 1999 Postcard of Monaco, 1989 Definitive Design and Obverse of Jubilee Coin

1999. Postcard, Coin and Stamp Exhibition, Fontvieille (1st issue).
2426 **824** 3 f. multicoloured 60 35
See also No. 2429.

1999. "Magic Stars" Magic Festival, Monte Carlo. As No. 2382 but face value and date changed.
2427 **791** 4 f. 50 gold and red . . . 85 50

826 1949 Postcard of Monaco, Reverse of Jubilee Coin and 1949 Definitive

1999. Postcard, Coin and Stamp Exhibition, Fontvieille (2nd issue).
2429 **826** 6 f. 50 multicoloured . . 1·25 75

827 Pierrot juggling "2000"

828 "Madonna and Child" (Simone Cantarini)

1999. 24th International Circus Festival, Monte Carlo (2000).
2430 **827** 2 f. 70 multicoloured . . 50 30

1999. Christmas.
2431 **828** 3 f. multicoloured 60 35

829 Blessing and Holy Door, St. Peter's Cathedral, Rome

1999. Holy Year 2000.
2432 **829** 3 f. 50 multicoloured . . 70 40

830 Mixed Arrangement

831 Emblem

1999. 33rd Monte Carlo Flower Show.
2433 **830** 4 f. 50 multicoloured . . 85 50

1999. "Monaco 2000" International Stamp Exhibitions.
2434 **831** 3 f. multicoloured 60 35

832 Bust of Napoleon (Antonio Canova)

833 Festival Emblem

2000. 30th Anniv of Napoleonic Museum.
2435 **832** 4 f. 20 multicoloured . . 80 50

2000. 40th Television Festival, Monte Carlo.
2436 **833** 4 f. 90 multicoloured . . 95 55

834 St. Peter and St. James the Major

2000. The Twelve Apostles. Multicoloured.
2437 **834** 4 f. blue, orange and gold 80 50
2438 – 5 f. red and gold . . . . 1·00 60
2439 – 6 f. violet and gold . . . 1·10 65
2440 – 7 f. brown and gold . . . 1·40 85
2441 – 8 f. green and gold . . . 1·60 95
2442 – 9 f. red, orange and gold . 1·75 1·10
DESIGNS: 5 f. St. John and St. Andrew; 6 f. St. Philip and St. Bartholomew; 7 f. St. Matthew and St. Thomas; 8 f. St. James the Minor and St. Jude; 9 f. St. Simon and St. Mathias.

835 Golden Labrador and Golden Retriever

2000. International Dog Show, Monte Carlo.
2443 **835** 6 f. 50 multicoloured . . 1·25 75

POSTAGE DUE STAMPS

D 3 D 4

D 18

1906.
D 29a **D 3** 1 c. green 50 60
D 30 5 c. green 35 45
D 31a 10 c. red 25 60
D 32 10 c. brown £325 £120
D 33 15 c. purple on cream . 2·50 1·25
D113 20 c. bistre on buff . . 50 15
D 34 30 c. blue 30 35
D114 40 c. mauve 15 15
D 35 50 c. brown on buff . . 6·25 3·75
D115 50 c. green 15 15
D116 60 c. black 40 40
D117 60 c. mauve . . . . . 15·00 25·00
D118 1 f. purple on cream . . 50 10
D119 2 f. red . . . . 1·10 1·90
D120 3 f. red . . . . 1·10 1·60
D121 5 f. blue 60 85

1910.
D36 **D 4** 1 c. olive 20 50
D37 10 c. lilac 30 60
D38 30 c. bistre £180 £160

1919. Surch.
D39 **D 4** 20 c. on 10 c. lilac . . . . 6·75 6·75
D40 40 c. on 30 c. bistre . . . 6·75 6·75

1925.
D106 **D 18** 1 c. olive 60 50
D107 10 c. violet 60 60
D108 30 c. bistre 50 75
D109 60 c. red 60 85
D110 1 f. blue . . . . 60·00 60·00
D111 2 f. red . . . . £160 85·00

1925. Surch **1 franc a percevoir**.
D112 **D 3** 1 f. on 50 c. brown on buff 65 65

D 64

D 65

1946.
D327 **D 64** 10 c. black 10 10
D328 30 c. violet 10 10
D329 50 c. blue 10 10
D330 1 f. green 15 15
D331 2 f. brown 15 15
D332 3 f. mauve 20 20
D333 4 f. red 30 35
D334 **D 65** 5 f. brown 20 20
D335 10 f. blue 30 60
D336 20 f. turquoise 40 45
D337 50 f. red and mauve . . 32·00 60·00
D338 100 f. red and green . . 7·50 12·50

D 99 Buddicom Locomotive, 1843

1953.
D478 – 1 f. red and green . . . 10 10
D479 – 1 f. green and red . . . 10 10
D480 – 2 f. turquoise and blue 10 10
D481 – 2 f. blue and turquoise 10 10
D482 **D 99** 3 f. lake and green . . 20 20
D483 – 3 f. green and lake . . 20 20
D484 – 4 f. slate and brown . . 15 15
D485 – 4 f. brown and slate . . 15 15
D486 – 5 f. violet and blue . . 40 40
D487 – 5 f. blue and violet . . 40 40
D488 – 10 f. indigo and blue . . 5·50 9·25
D489 – 10 f. blue and indigo . . 5·50 9·25
D490 – 20 f. violet and blue . . 3·00 5·00
D491 – 20 f. blue and violet . . 3·00 5·00
D492 – 50 f. brown and red . . 6·75 11·00
D493 – 50 f. red and brown . . 6·75 11·00
D494 – 100 f. green and purple 12·50 20·00
D495 – 100 f. purple and green 12·50 20·00
TRIANGULAR DESIGNS: Nos. D478, Pigeons released from mobile loft; D479, Sikorsky S-51 helicopter; D480, Brig; D481, "United States" (liner); D483, Streamlined steam locomotive; D484, Santos-Dumont's monoplane No. 20 Demoiselle; D485, De Havilland Comet 1 airliner; D486, Old motor car; D487, "Sabre" racing-car; D488, Leonardo da Vinci's flying machine; D489, Postal rocket; D490, Mail balloon, Paris, 1870; D491, Airship "Graf Zeppelin"; D492, Postilion; D493, Motor cycle messenger; D494, Mail coach; D495, Railway mail van.

D 140 18th-Century Felucca

1960.

D698	D **140**	1 c. brown, grn & bl	10	10
D699	–	2 c. sepia, bl & grn	15	15
D700	–	5 c. purple, blk & turq	15	25
D701	–	10 c. black, grn & bl	10	10
D702	–	20 c. purple, grn & bl	1·50	1·50
D703	–	30 c. brown, bl & grn	90	90
D704	–	50 c. blue, brn & myrtle	2·10	2·10
D705	–	1 f. brown, myrtle & bl	2·75	2·75

DESIGNS: 2 c. Paddle-steamer "La Palmaria"; 5 c. Arrival of first railway train at Monaco; 10 c. 15th-16th-century armed messenger; 20 c. 18th-century postman; 30 c. "Charles III" (paddle-steamer); 50 c. 17th-century courier; 1 f. Mail coach (19th-century).

D **393** Prince's Seal

D **492** Coat of Arms

1980.

D1426	D **393**	5 c. red and brown	10	10
D1427		10 c. orange and red	10	10
D1428		15 c. violet and red	10	10
D1429		20 c. green and red	10	10
D1430		30 c. blue and red	15	15
D1431		40 c. bistre and red	20	20
D1432		50 c. violet and red	50	50
D1433		1 f. grey and blue	1·00	1·00
D1434		2 f. brown & black	1·25	1·25
D1435		3 f. red and green	1·90	1·90
D1436		4 f. green and red	2·50	2·50
D1437		5 f. brown & mauve	3·00	3·00

1985.

D1712	D **492**	5 c. multicoloured	10	10
D1713		10 c. multicoloured	10	10
D1714		15 c. multicoloured	10	10
D1715		20 c. multicoloured	10	10
D1716		30 c. multicoloured	10	10
D1717		40 c. multicoloured	10	10
D1718		50 c. multicoloured	10	10
D1719		1 f. multicoloured	30	30
D1720		2 f. multicoloured	65	65
D1721		3 f. multicoloured	1·50	1·50
D1722		4 f. multicoloured	1·90	1·90
D1723		5 f. multicoloured	2·50	2·50

MONGOLIA Pt. 10

A republic in Central Asia between China and Russia, independent since 1921.

1924. 100 cents = 1 dollar (Chinese).
1926. 100 mung = 1 tugrik.

1 Eldev-Otchir Symbol

2 Soyombo Symbol

1924. Inscr in black.
1 1 1 c. brown, pink and grey on bistre . . . 4·00 4·00
2 2 c. brown, blue and red on brown . . . 5·00 3·50
3 5 c. grey, red and yellow . . . 25·00 20·00
4 10 c. blue and brown on blue . . 9·00 7·00
5 20 c. grey, blue and white on blue 18·00 10·00
6 50 c. red and orange on pink . . 30·00 18·00
7 $1 bistre, red and white on yellow 45·00 28·00
Stamps vary in size according to the face value.

1926. Fiscal stamps as T **2** optd **POSTAGE** in frame in English and Mongolian.
8 2 1 c. blue . . . . . 10·00 10·00
9 2 c. buff . . . . . 10·00 10·00
10 5 c. purple . . . . . 14·00 12·00
11 10 c. green . . . . . 18·00 15·00
12 20 c. brown . . . . . 20·00 17·00
13 50 c. brown and yellow . . . £175 £160
14 $1 brown and pink . . . £400 £325
15 $5 red and olive . . . £600 —
Stamps vary in size according to the face value.

4 State Emblem: Soyombo Symbol 5

1926. New Currency.
16 4 5 m. black and lilac . . . 4·50 4·50
17 20 m. black and blue . . . 4·00 4·00

1926.
18 5 1 m. black and yellow . . . 1·40 80
19 2 m. black and brown . . . 1·60 90
20 5 m. black and lilac (A) . . . 2·50 1·40
28 5 m. black and lilac (B) . . . 13·00 9·50
21 10 m. black and blue . . . 1·60 1·10
30 20 m. black and blue . . . 14·00 8·00
22 25 m. black and green . . . 4·00 1·75
23 40 m. black and yellow . . . 5·75 2·00
24 50 m. black and brown . . . 7·00 3·25
25 1 t. black, green and brown . . 18·00 6·50
26 3 t. black, yellow and red . . 38·00 30·00
27 5 t. black, red and purple . . 60·00 48·00
In (A) the Mongolian numerals are in the upper and in (B) in the lower value tablets.
These stamps vary in size according to the face value.

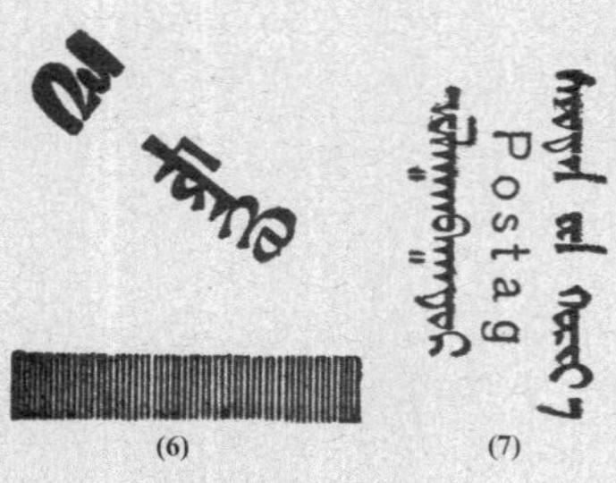

(6) (7)

1930. Surch as T **6**.
32 5 10 m. on 1 m. black & yellow . 25·00 25·00
33 20 m. on 2 m. black & brown . 35·00 30·00
34 25 m. on 40 m. black & yell . . 40·00 35·00

1931. Optd with T **7**.
35 2 1 c. blue . . . . . 17·00 8·00
36 2 c. buff . . . . . 18·00 6·00
37 5 c. purple . . . . . 25·00 6·00
38 10 c. green . . . . . 20·00 6·00
39 20 c. brown . . . . . 32·00 8·50
40 50 c. brown and yellow . . . — —
41 $1 brown and pink . . . — —

1931. Surch **Postage** and value in "Menge".
43 2 5 m. on 5 c. purple . . . 25·00 8·00
44 10 m. on 10 c. green . . . 38·00 20·00
45 20 m. on 20 c. brown . . . 50·00 25·00

9 Govt Building, Ulan Bator

11 Sukhe Bator

12 Lake and Mountain Scenery

1932.
46 – 1 m. brown . . . . . 1·75 1·00
47 – 2 m. red . . . . . 1·75 1·00
48 – 5 m. blue 50 30
49 9 10 m. green 50 30
50 – 15 m. brown 50 30
51 – 20 m. red 50 30
52 – 25 m. violet 75 30
53 11 40 m. black 75 40
54 – 50 m. blue 50 30
55 12 1 t. green 90 50
56 – 3 t. violet . . . . . 2·00 1·25
57 – 5 t. brown . . . . . 12·00 7·50
58 – 10 t. blue . . . . . 20·00 13·00
DESIGNS—As Type **9**: 1 m. Weavers; 5 m. Machinist. As Type **11**: 2 m. Telegraphist; 15 m. Revolutionary soldier carrying flag; 20 m. Mongols learning Latin alphabet; 25 m. Soldier; 50 m. Sukhe Bator's monument. As Type **12**: 3 t. Sheep-shearing; 5 t. Camel caravan; 10 t. Lassoing wild horses (after painting by Sampilon).

13 Mongol Man

14 Camel Caravan

1943. Network background in similar colour to stamps.
59 13 5 m. green . . . . . 3·50 3·50
60 – 10 m. blue . . . . . 6·00 3·75
61 – 15 m. red . . . . . 7·00 5·00
62 14 20 m. brown . . . . . 11·00 9·00
63 – 25 m. brown . . . . . 11·00 11·00
64 – 30 m. red . . . . . 12·00 12·00
65 – 45 m. purple . . . . . 17·00 17·00
66 – 60 m. green . . . . . 28·00 28·00
DESIGNS—VERT: 10 m. Mongol woman; 15 m. Soldier; 30 m. Arms of the Republic; 45 m. Portrait of Sukhe Bator, dated 1894–1923. HORIZ: 25 m. Secondary school; 60 m. Pastoral scene.

15 Marshal Kharloin Choibalsan

17 Victory Medal

16 Choibalsan and Sukhe Bator

1945. 50th Birthday of Choibalsan.
67 15 1 t. black . . . . . 9·00 8·00

1946. 25th Anniv of Independence. As T **16/17**.
68 – 30 m. bistre . . . . . 4·50 3·50
69 16 50 m. purple . . . . . 5·50 4·00
70 – 60 m. brown . . . . . 5·50 5·50
71 – 60 m. black . . . . . 8·00 5·50
72 17 80 m. brown . . . . . 7·50 7·50
73 – 1 t. blue . . . . . 11·00 12·00
74 – 2 t. brown . . . . . 14·00 16·00
DESIGNS—VERT: ($21\frac{1}{2}\times32$ mm): 30 m. Choibalsan, aged four. As Type **17**: 60 m. (No. 71), Choibalsan when young man; 1 t. 25th Anniversary Medal; 2 t. Sukhe Bator. HORIZ: As Type **16**: 60 m. (No. 70), Choibalsan University.

17a Flags of Communist Bloc

1951. Struggle for Peace.
75 17a 1 t. multicoloured . . . . . 7·50 7·50

17b Lenin (after P. Vasilev)

19 Sukhe Bator

18 State Shop

1951. Honouring Lenin.
76 17b 3 t. multicoloured . . . . . 17·00 17·00

1951. 30th Anniv of Independence.
77 – 15 m. green on azure . . . 3·25 3·25
78 18 20 m. orange . . . . . 3·25 3·25
79 – 20 m. multicoloured . . . 3·75 3·75
80 – 25 m. blue on azure . . . 3·75 3·75
81 – 30 m. multicoloured . . . 4·25 4·25
82 – 40 m. violet on pink . . . 4·50 4·50
83 – 50 m. brown on azure . . . 9·00 9·00
84 – 60 m. black on pink . . . 8·00 8·00
85 19 2 t. brown . . . . . 15·00 15·00
DESIGNS—HORIZ: (As Type **18**): 15 m. Altai Hotel; 40 m. State Theatre, Ulan Bator; 50 m. Pedagogical Institute. $55\frac{1}{2}\times26$ mm: 25 m. Choibalsan University. VERT: (As Type **19**): 20 m. (No. 79); 30 m. Arms and flag; 60 m. Sukhe Bator Monument.

20 School-children

1952. Culture.
86 – 5 m. brown on pink . . . 2·00 1·75
87 20 10 m. blue on pink . . . 2·50 2·50
DESIGN: 5 m. New houses.

21 Choibalsan in National Costume

22 Choibalsan and Farm Worker

1953. 1st Death Anniv of Marshal Choibalsan. As T **21/22**.
88 21 15 m. blue . . . . . 2·50 2·75
89 22 15 m. green . . . . . 2·50 2·75
90 21 20 m. green . . . . . 5·00 6·00
91 22 20 m. sepia . . . . . 2·50 2·50
92 – 20 m. blue . . . . . 2·50 2·50
93 – 30 m. sepia . . . . . 3·25 3·25
94 – 50 m. brown . . . . . 3·25 3·25
95 – 1 t. red . . . . . 4·00 4·00
96 – 1 t. purple . . . . . 4·00 4·00
97 – 2 t. red . . . . . 4·00 4·00
98 – 3 t. purple . . . . . 5·00 5·00
99 – 5 t. red . . . . . 19·00 19·00
DESIGNS: As Type **21**: 1 t. (96); 2 t. Choibalsan in uniform. 33×48 mm: 3, 5 t. Busts of Choibalsan and Sukhe Bator. 33×46 mm: 50 m., 1 t. (95), Choibalsan and young pioneer. 48×33 mm: 20 m. (92); 30 m. Choibalsan and factory hand.

23 Arms of the Republic

23a Lenin

1954.
100 23 10 m. red . . . . . 6·50 4·00
101 20 m. red . . . . . 13·00 5·00
102 30 m. red . . . . . 6·00 4·50
103 40 m. red . . . . . 7·00 4·50
104 60 m. red . . . . . 6·50 4·50

1955. 85th Birth Anniv of Lenin.
105 23a 2 t. blue . . . . . 3·75 2·00

23b Flags of the Communist Bloc

24 Sukhe Bator and Choibalsan

1955. Struggle for Peace.
106 23b 60 m. multicoloured . . . 1·25 65

1955.
107 24 30 m. green 30 20
108 – 30 m. blue 50 20
109 – 30 m. red 40 20
110 – 40 m. purple . . . . . 1·00 40
111 – 50 m. brown . . . . . 1·00 45
112 – 1 t. multicoloured . . . . 2·75 1·25
DESIGNS—HORIZ: 30 m. blue, Lake Khobsogol; 50 m. Choibalsan University. VERT: 30 m. red, Lenin Statue, Ulan Bator; 40 m. Sukhe Bator and dog; 1 t. Arms and flag of the Republic.

24a Steam Train linking Ulan Bator and Moscow

25 Arms of the Republic

1956. Mongol–Soviet Friendship. Multicoloured.
113 1 t. Type **24a** . . . . . 25·00 13·00
114 2 t. Flags of Mongolia and Russia . . . . . 4·50 2·75

1956.
115 25 20 m. brown 50 30
116 30 m. brown 65 35
117 40 m. blue 80 45
118 60 m. green . . . . . 1·00 65
119 1 t. red . . . . . 1·60 80

26 Hunter and Golden Eagle

27 Arms

27a Wrestlers

1956. 35th Anniv of Independence.
120 26 30 m. brown . . . . . 38·00 16·00
121 27 30 m. blue . . . . . 5·00 4·00
122 27a 60 m. green . . . . . 15·00 15·00
123 – 60 m. orange . . . . . 15·00 15·00
DESIGN: As Type **26**: 60 m. (No. 123), Children. Also inscr "xxxv".

28

29

1958. With or without gum.
124 28 20 m. red . . . . . 1·50 1·00

1958. 13th Mongol People's Revolutionary Party Congress. With or without gum.
125 **29** 30 m. red and salmon . . . 3·00 2·25

1958. As T **27a** but without "xxxv". With or without gum.
126 50 m. brown on pink . . . . . 5·00 3·75

30 Dove and Globe

1958. 4th Congress of International Women's Federation, Vienna. With or without gum.
127 **30** 60 m. blue . . . . 3·25 2·00

31 Ibex **32** Yak

1958. Mongolian Animals. As T **31/2**.
128 – 30 m. pale blue . . . . . . 15·00 2·50
129 – 30 m. turquoise . . . . . . 15·00 2·50
130 **31** 30 m. green . . . . 3·00 1·50
131 30 m. turquoise . . . . . . 3·00 1·00
132 **32** 60 m. bistre . . . . 3·50 2·00
133 60 m. orange . . . . 3·50 1·25
134 – 1 t. blue . . . . 5·00 2·50
135 – 1 t. light blue . . . . . . 4·00 1·75
136 – 1 t. red . . . . 5·00 3·25
137 – 1 t. red . . . . 4·00 2·00
DESIGNS—VERT: 30 m. (Nos. 128/9), Dalmatian pelicans. HORIZ: 1 t. (Nos. 134/5), Yak, facing right; 1 t. (Nos. 136/7), Bactrian camels.

33 Goat **34** "Tulaga"

1958. Mongolian Animals.
138 **33** 5 m. sepia and yellow . . . 15 10
139 – 10 m. sepia and green . . . 20 10
140 – 15 m. sepia and lilac 35 10
141 – 20 m. sepia and blue 35 10
142 – 25 m. sepia and red 40 10
143 – 30 m. purple and mauve . . 50 10
144 **33** 40 m. green 50 10
145 – 50 m. brown and salmon . . 60 20
146 – 60 m. blue 80 20
147 – 1 t. bistre and yellow . . . 1·75 50
ANIMALS: 10, 30 m. Ram; 15, 60 m. Stallion; 20, 50 m. Bull; 25 m., 1 t. Bactrian camel.

1959.
148 **34** 1 t. multicoloured . . . . . 3·25 1·10

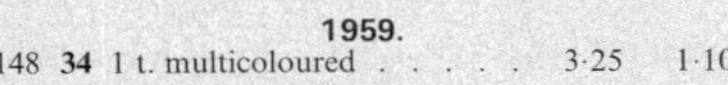

35 Taming a Wild Horse

1959. Mongolian Sports. Centres and inscriptions multicoloured: frame colours given below.
149 **35** 5 m. yellow and orange . . 20 10
150 – 10 m. purple 20 10
151 – 15 m. yellow and green . . . 20 10
152 – 20 m. lake and red 25 10
153 – 25 m. blue 40 15
154 – 30 m. yellow, green & turq 55 15
155 – 70 m. red and yellow . . . 70 30
156 – 80 m. purple . . . . 1·10 60
DESIGNS: 10 m. Wrestlers; 15 m. Introducing young rider; 20 m. Archer; 25 m. Galloping horseman; 30 m. Archery contest; 70 m. Hunting a wild horse; 80 m. Proclaiming a champion.

36 Child Musician

1959. Mongolian Youth Festival (1st issue).
157 **36** 5 m. purple and blue . . . 20 10
158 – 10 m. brown and green . . . 25 10
159 – 20 m. green and purple . . . 25 10
160 – 25 m. blue and green . . . 50 25
161 – 40 m. violet and myrtle . . 95 40
DESIGNS—VERT: 10 m. Young wrestlers; 20 m. Youth on horse; 25 m. Artists in national costume. HORIZ: 40 m. Festival parade.

37 Festival Badge **38** Kalmuck Script

1959. Mongolian Youth Festival (2nd issue).
162 **37** 30 m. purple and blue . . . 30 20

1959. Mongolists' Congress. Designs as T **38** incorporating "MONGOL" in various scripts.
163 – 30 m. multicoloured . . . . 5·00 5·00
164 – 40 m. red, blue and yellow . 5·00 5·00
165 **38** 50 m. multicoloured . . . . 7·00 7·00
166 – 60 m. red, blue and yellow . 11·00 11·00
167 – 1 t. yellow, turquoise & orge 14·00 14·00
SCRIPTS ($29\frac{1}{2} \times 42\frac{1}{2}$ mm): 30 m. Stylized Ulghur; 40 m. Soyombo; 60 m. Square (Pagspa). ($21\frac{1}{2} \times 31$ mm): 1 t. Cyrillic.

39 Military Monument **40** Herdswoman and Lamb

1959. 20th Anniv of Battle of Khalka River.
168 – 40 m. red, brown & yellow 55 15
169 **39** 50 m. multicoloured 55 15
DESIGN: 40 m. Mounted horseman with flag (emblem), inscr "AUGUST 1959 HALHIN GOL".

1959. 2nd Meeting of Rural Economy Co-operatives.
170 **40** 30 m. green . . . . 3·50 3·50

41 Sable

1959. Mongolian Fauna.
171 **41** 5 m. purple, yellow & blue . 15 10
172 – 10 m. multicoloured 90 10
173 – 15 m. black, green and red . 45 10
174 – 20 m. purple, blue and red . 55 15
175 – 30 m. myrtle, purple & grn . 50 15
176 – 50 m. black, blue and green . 1·10 30
177 – 1 t. black, green and red . . 1·75 40
ANIMALS—HORIZ: (58 × 21 mm): 10 m. Ring-necked pheasants; 20 m. European otter; 50 m. Saiga; 1 t. Siberian musk deer. As Type **41**: 15 m. Muskrat; 30 m. Argali.

42 "Lunik 3" in Flight **44** "Flower" Emblem

43 Motherhood Badge

1959. Launching of "Lunik 3" Rocket.
178 **42** 30 m. yellow and violet . . 65 25
179 – 50 m. red, green and blue . . 80 35
DESIGN—HORIZ: 50 m. Trajectory of "Lunik 3" around the Moon.

1960. International Women's Day.
180 **43** 40 m. bistre and blue . . . 40 15
181 **44** 50 m. yellow, green & blue . 70 20

45 Lenin **46** Larkspur

1960. 90th Birth Anniv of Lenin.
182 **45** 40 m. red 40 15
183 50 m. violet 60 30

1960. Flowers.
184 **46** 5 m. blue, green and bistre . 10 10
185 – 10 m. red, green and orange . 10 10
186 – 15 m. violet, green & bistre . 10 10
187 – 20 m. yellow, green & olive . 15 10
188 – 30 m. violet, green & emer . 15 10
189 – 40 m. orange, green & violet . 35 15
190 – 50 m. violet, green and blue . 45 20
191 – 1 t. mauve, green & lt green . 80 40
FLOWERS: 10 m. Tulip; 15 m. Jacob's ladder; 20 m. Asiatic globe flower; 30 m. Clustered bellflower; 40 m. Grass of Parnassus; 50 m. Meadow cranes-bill; 1 t. "Begonia vansiana".

47 Horse-jumping

1960. Olympic Games. Inscr "ROMA 1960" or "ROMA MCMLX". Centres in greenish grey.
192 **47** 5 m. red, black & turquoise 10 10
193 – 10 m. violet and yellow . . 10 10
194 – 15 m. turquoise, black & red 10 10
195 – 20 m. red and blue 10 10
196 – 30 m. ochre, black & green . 10 10
197 – 50 m. blue and turquoise . . 15 10
198 – 70 m. green, black & violet . 25 20
199 – 1 t. mauve and green . . . 35 25
DESIGNS—DIAMOND SHAPED: 10 m. Running; 20 m. Wrestling; 50 m. Gymnastics; 1 t. Throwing the discus. As Type **47**: 15 m. Diving; 30 m. Hurdling; 70 m. High jumping.

48

1960. Red Cross.
200 **48** 20 m. red, yellow and blue . 70 25

49 Newspapers

1960. 40th Anniv of Mongolian Newspaper "Unen" ("Truth").
201 **49** 20 m. buff, green and red . . 15 10
202 30 m. red, yellow and green . 20 15

50 Hoopoe

1961. Mongolian Song-birds.
203 – 5 m. mauve, black and grn . 75 10
204 **50** 10 m. red, black and green . 85 10
205 – 15 m. yellow, black & green . 1·00 15
206 – 20 m. green, black & bistre . 1·25 25
207 – 50 m. blue, black and red . . 1·75 55
208 – 70 m. yellow, black & mve . 2·00 80
209 – 1 t. mauve, orange & black . 2·40 1·10
BIRDS: As Type **50**: 15 m. Golden oriole; 20 m. Siberian capercaillie. Inverted triangulars: 5 m. Rose-coloured starling; 50 m. Eastern broad-billed roller; 70 m. Tibetan sandgrouse; 1 t. Mandarin.

51 Foundry Worker **52** Patrice Lumumba

1961. 15th Anniv of World Federation of Trade Unions.
210 **51** 30 m. red and black 15 10
211 – 50 m. red and violet 20 10
DESIGN—HORIZ: 50 m. Hemispheres.

1961. Patrice Lumumba (Congolese politician) Commemoration.
212 **52** 30 m. brown . . . . 1·50 1·00
213 50 m. purple . . . . 2·00 1·25

53 Bridge **54** Gagarin with Capsule

1961. 40th Anniv of Independence (1st issue). Mongolian Modernization.
214 **53** 5 m. green 10 10
215 – 10 m. blue 10 10
216 – 15 m. red 10 10
217 – 20 m. brown 10 10
218 – 30 m. blue 15 15
219 – 50 m. green 25 15
220 – 1 t. violet 50 30
DESIGNS: 10 m. Shoe-maker; 15 m. Store at Ulan Bator; 30 m. Government Building, Ulan Bator; 50 m. Machinist; 1 t. Ancient and modern houses. ($59 \times 20\frac{1}{2}$ mm): 20 m. Choibalsan University.
See also Nos. 225/32, 233/41, 242/8 and 249/56.

1961. World's First Manned Space Flight. Mult.
221 20 m. Type **54** 15 10
222 30 m. Gagarin and globe (horiz) 30 10
223 50 m. Gagarin in capsule making parachute descent 30 20
224 1 t. Globe and Gagarin (horiz) . 50 35

55 Postman with Reindeer

1961. 40th Anniv of Independence (2nd issue). Mongolian Postal Service.
225 **55** 5 m. red, brown and blue (postage) 15 10
226 – 15 m. violet, brown & bistre . 30 10
227 – 20 m. blue, black and green . 20 10
228 – 25 m. violet, bistre & green . 30 15
229 – 30 m. green, black & lav . . 5·00 1·25
230 – 10 m. orange, black and green (air) 35 10
231 – 50 m. black, pink and green . 1·00 25
232 – 1 t. multicoloured . . . . . 1·10 35
DESIGNS: Postman with—10 m. Horses; 15 m. Camels; 20 m. Yaks; 25 m. "Sukhe Bator" (lake steamer); 30 m. Diesel mail train; 50 m. Ilyushin Il-14M mail plane over map; 1 t. Postal emblem.

56 Rams

1961. 40th Anniv of Independence (3rd issue). Animal Husbandry.

233	**56**	5 m. black, red and blue	10	10
234	–	10 m. black, green & purple	10	10
235	–	15 m. black, red and green	10	10
236	–	20 m. sepia, blue & brown	10	10
237	–	25 m. black, yellow & green	15	10
238	–	30 m. black, red and violet	15	10
239	–	40 m. black, green and red	25	15
240	–	50 m. black, brown & blue	30	25
241	–	1 t. black, violet and olive	55	40

DESIGNS: 10 m. Oxen; 15 m. Camels; 20 m. Pigs and poultry; 25 m. Angora goats; 30 m. Mongolian horses; 40 m. Ewes; 50 m. Cows; 1 t. Combine-harvester.

57 Children Wrestling

1961. 40th Anniv of Independence (5th issue). Mongolian Sports.

242	**57**	5 m. multicoloured	10	10
243	–	10 m. sepia, red and green	10	10
244	–	15 m. purple blue & yellow	10	10
245	–	20 m. red, black and green	55	25
246	–	30 m. purple, green & lav	15	10
247	–	50 m. indigo, orange & blue	30	20
248	–	1 t. purple, blue and grey	35	20

DESIGNS: 10 m. Horse-riding; 15 m. Children on camel and pony; 20 m. Falconry; 30 m. Skiing; 50 m. Archery; 1 t. Dancing.

58 Young Mongol

1961. 40th Anniv of Independence (6th issue). Mongolian Culture.

249	**58**	5 m. purple and green	10	10
250	–	10 m. blue and red	10	10
251	–	15 m. brown and blue	10	10
252	–	20 m. green and violet	15	10
253	–	30 m. red and blue	20	15
254	–	50 m. violet and bistre	40	20
255	–	70 m. green and mauve	45	25
256	–	1 t. red and blue	65	60

DESIGNS—HORIZ: 10 m. Mongol chief; 70 m. Orchestra; 1 t. Gymnast. VERT: 15 m. Sukhe Bator Monument; 20 m. Young singer; 30 m. Young dancer; 50 m. Dombra-player.

59 Mongol Arms 60 Congress Emblem

1961. Arms multicoloured; inscr in blue; background colours given.

257	**59**	5 m. salmon	10	10
258		10 m. lilac	10	10
259		15 m. brown	10	10
260		20 m. turquoise	10	10
261		30 m. ochre	10	10
262		50 m. mauve	15	10
263		70 m. olive	20	10
264		1 t. orange	30	15

1961. 5th World Federation of Trade Unions Congress, Moscow.

265	**60**	30 m. red, yellow and blue	15	10
266		50 m. red, yellow and sepia	20	10

MORE DETAILED LISTS
are given in the Stanley Gibbons Catalogues referred to in the country headings.
For lists of current volumes see Introduction.

61 Dove, Map and Globe

1962. Admission of Mongolia to U.N.O.

267	**61**	10 m. multicoloured	10	10
268	–	30 m. multicoloured	15	10
269	–	50 m. multicoloured	20	15
270	–	60 m. multicoloured	30	20
271	–	70 m. multicoloured	35	30

DESIGNS: 30 m. U.N. Emblem and Mongol Arms; 50 m. U.N. and Mongol flags; 60 m. U.N. Headquarters and Mongolian Parliament building; 70 m. U.N. and Mongol flags, and Assembly.

62 Football, Globe and Flags

1962. World Cup Football Championship, Chile. Multicoloured.

272	10 m. Type **62**	10	10
273	30 m. Footballers, globe and ball	10	10
274	50 m. Footballers playing in stadium	20	15
275	60 m. Goalkeeper saving goal	25	20
276	70 m. Stadium	50	30

63 D. Natsagdorj 64 Torch and Handclasp

1962. 3rd Congress of Mongolian Writers.

277	**63**	30 m. brown	15	10
278		50 m. green	20	10

1962. Afro-Asian People's Solidarity.

279	**64**	20 m. multicoloured	15	10
280		30 m. multicoloured	20	10

65 Flags of Mongolia and U.S.S.R 67 Victory Banner

1962. Mongol-Soviet Friendship.

281	**65**	30 m. multicoloured	15	10
282		50 m. multicoloured	20	10

1962. Malaria Eradication. Nos. 1849/91 optd with Campaign emblem and **LUTTE CONTRE LE PALUDISME.**

283	**46**	5 m.	20	20
284	–	10 m.	20	20
285	–	15 m.	20	20
286	–	20 m.	20	20
287	–	30 m.	30	30
288	–	40 m.	30	30
289	–	50 m.	50	50
290	–	1 t.	80	80

1962. 800th Birth Anniv of Genghis Khan.

291	**67**	20 m. multicoloured	5·50	5·50
292	–	30 m. multicoloured	5·50	5·50
293	–	50 m. black, brown and red	12·00	12·00
294	–	60 m. buff, blue and brown	12·00	12·00

DESIGNS: 30 m. Engraved lacquer tablets; 50 m. Obelisk; 60 m. Genghis Khan.

68 Eurasian Perch

1962. Fishes. Multicoloured.

295	5 m. Type **68**	10	10
296	10 m. Burbot	20	10
297	15 m. Arctic grayling	30	10
298	20 m. Short-spined seascorpion	40	15
299	30 m. Estuarine zander	60	20
300	50 m. Siberian sturgeon	95	30
301	70 m. Waleck's dace	1·25	45
302	1 t. 50 Yellow-winged bullhead	2·25	70

69 Sukhe Bator

1963. 70th Birth Anniv of Sukhe Bator.

303	**69**	30 m. blue	15	10
304		60 m. lake	20	10

70 Dog "Laika" and "Sputnik 2"

1963. Space Flights. Multicoloured.

305	5 m. Type **70**	10	10
306	15 m. Rocket blasting off	15	10
307	25 m. "Lunik 2" (1959)	15	10
308	70 m. Nikolaev and Popovich	30	25
309	1 t. Rocket "Mars" (1962)	40	35

SIZES: As Type **70**: 70 m., 1 t. VERT: (21 × 70 mm): 15 m., 25 m.

71 Children packing Red Cross Parcels

1963. Red Cross Centenary Multicoloured.

310	20 m. Type **71**	10	10
311	30 m. Blood transfusion	15	10
312	50 m. Doctor treating child	20	15
313	60 m. Ambulance at street accident	25	15
314	1 t. 30 Centenary emblem	40	20

72 Karl Marx 73 Woman

1963. 145th Birth Anniv of Karl Marx.

315	**72**	30 m. blue	15	10
316		60 m. lake	20	10

1963. 5th World Congress of Democratic Women, Moscow.

317	**73**	30 m. multicoloured	15	10

74 Peacock

1963. Mongolian Butterflies. Multicoloured.

318	5 m. Type **74**	30	10
319	10 m. Brimstone	35	10
320	15 m. Small tortoiseshell	35	15
321	20 m. Apollo	55	20
322	30 m. Swallowtail	85	25
323	60 m. Damon blue	1·25	50
324	1 t. Poplar admiral	1·75	65

75 Globe and Scales of Justice

1963. 15th Anniv of Declaration of Human Rights.

325	**75**	30 m. red, blue and brown	15	20
326		60 m. black, blue & yellow	25	10

76 Shaggy Ink Cap

1964. Fungi. Multicoloured.

327	5 m. Type **76**	25	10
328	10 m. Woolly milk cap	35	10
329	15 m. Field mushroom	45	15
330	20 m. Milk-white russula	50	20
331	30 m. Granulated boletus	75	30
332	50 m. "Lactarius scrobiculatus"	1·00	45
333	70 m. Saffron milk cap	1·40	65
334	1 t. Variegated boletus	1·90	85

77 Lenin when a Young Man

1964. 60th Anniv of London Bolshevik (Communist) Party.

335	**77**	30 m. red and brown	45	10
336		50 m. ultramarine and blue	50	10

78 Gymnastics

1964. Olympic Games, Tokyo. Multicoloured.

337	5 m. Type **78**	10	10
338	10 m. Throwing the javelin	10	10
339	15 m. Wrestling	10	10
340	20 m. Running	10	10
341	30 m. Horse-jumping	10	10
342	50 m. High-diving	20	15
343	60 m. Cycling	25	20
344	1 t. Emblem of Tokyo Games	40	30

79 Congress Emblem

1964. 4th Mongolian Women's Congress.

345	79	30 m. multicoloured	20	10

80 "Lunik 1"

1964. Space Research. Multicoloured.

346	5 m. Type **80**	10	10
347	10 m. "Vostoks 1 and 2" . . .	10	10
348	15 m. "Tiros" (vert)	10	10
349	20 m. "Cosmos" (vert) . . .	10	10
350	30 m. "Mars Probe" (vert) . .	10	10
351	60 m. "Luna 4" (vert)	20	15
352	80 m. "Echo 2"	30	20
353	1 t. Radio telescope	35	25

81 Horseman and Flag

1964. 40th Anniv of Mongolian Constitution.

354	81	25 m. multicoloured	20	10
355		50 m. multicoloured	30	10

82 Marine Exploration

1965. International Quiet Sun Year. Multicoloured.

356	5 m. Type **82** (postage)	40	10
357	10 m. Weather balloon	15	10
358	60 m. Northern Lights	60	20
359	80 m. Geomagnetic emblems . .	70	25
360	1 t. Globe and I.Q.S.Y. emblem	1·10	50
361	15 m. Weather satellite (air) . .	40	10
362	20 m. Antarctic exploration . .	3·00	55
363	30 m. Space exploration . . .	55	15

83 Horses Grazing

1965. Mongolian Horses. Multicoloured.

364	5 m. Type **83**	15	10
365	10 m. Hunting with golden eagles	1·25	15
366	15 m. Breaking-in wild horse .	20	10
367	20 m. Horses racing	20	10
368	30 m. Horses jumping	25	10
369	60 m. Hunting wolves	30	25
370	80 m. Milking a mare	40	30
371	1 t. Mare and colt	70	40

84 Farm Girl with Lambs

1965. 40th Anniv of Mongolian Youth Movement.

372	84	5 m. orange, bistre & green	10	10
373	–	10 m. bistre, blue and red	10	10
374	–	20 m. ochre, red and violet	20	15
375	–	30 m. lilac, brown & green	30	20
376	–	50 m. orange, buff and blue	55	35

DESIGNS: 10 m. Young drummers; 20 m. Children around campfire; 30 m. Young wrestlers; 50 m. Emblem.

85 Chinese Perch

1965. Mongolian Fishes. Multicoloured.

377	5 m. Type **85**	25	10
378	10 m. Lenok	25	10
379	15 m. Siberian sturgeon	30	15
380	20 m. Taimen	45	15
381	30 m. Banded catfish	75	20
382	60 m. Amur catfish	1·10	20
383	80 m. Northern pike	1·25	40
384	1 t. Eurasian perch	1·75	60

86 Marx and Lenin

87 I.T.U. Emblem and Symbols

1965. Organization of Socialist Countries' Postal Administrations Conference, Peking.

385	86	10 m. black and red	15	10

1965. Air. I.T.U. Centenary.

386	87	30 m. blue and bistre . . .	15	10
387		50 m. red, bistre and blue	20	10

88 Sable

1966. Mongolian Fur Industry.

388	88	5 m. purple, black & yellow .	10	10
389	–	10 m. brown, black & grey .	10	10
390	–	15 m. brown, black & blue .	35	10
391	–	20 m. multicoloured	20	10
392	–	30 m. brown, black & mve .	25	10
393	–	60 m. brown, black & green .	40	25
394	–	80 m. multicoloured	60	40
395	–	1 t. blue, black and olive .	1·40	50

DESIGNS (Fur animals): HORIZ: 10 m. Red fox; 30 m. Pallas's cat; 60 m. Beech marten. VERT: 15 m. European otter; 20 m. Cheetah; 80 m. Stoat; 1 t. Woman in fur coat.

89 W.H.O. Building

1966. Inauguration of W.H.O. Headquarters, Geneva.

396	89	30 m. blue, gold and green .	15	10
397		50 m. blue, gold and red . .	25	10

90 Footballers

1966. World Cup Football Championships. Multicoloured.

398	10 m. Type **90**	10	10
399	30 m. Footballers (different) . .	10	10
400	60 m. Goalkeeper saving goal .	15	15
401	80 m. Footballers (different) . .	30	20
402	1 t. World Cup flag	50	35

92 Sukhe Bator and Parliament Buildings, Ulan Bator

1966. 15th Mongolian Communist Party Congress.

404	92	30 m. multicoloured	20	10

93 Wrestling

95 State Emblem

1966. World Wrestling Championships Toledo (Spain). Similar wrestling designs.

405	93	10 m. black, mauve & pur .	10	10
406	–	30 m. black, mauve & grey .	10	15
407	–	60 m. black, mauve & brn .	20	15
408	–	80 m. black, mauve & lilac .	30	20
409	–	1 t. black, mauve and turq .	40	20

1966. 45th Anniv of Independence. Mult.

411	30 m. Type **95**	1·25	50
412	50 m. Sukhe Bator, emblems of agriculture and industry (horiz)	2·75	75

96 "Physochlaena physaloides"

1966. Flowers. Multicoloured.

413	5 m. Type **96**	10	10
414	10 m. Onion	15	10
415	15 m. Red lily	20	10
416	20 m. "Thermopsis lanceolata"	25	10
417	30 m. "Amygdalus mongolica"	40	20
418	60 m. Bluebeard	50	30
419	80 m. "Piptanthus mongolicus"	60	40
420	1 t. "Iris bungei"	85	55

1966. 60th Birth Anniv of D. Natsagdorj. Nos. 277/8 optd **1906 1966.**

420a	63	30 m. brown	6·50	6·50
420b		50 m. green	6·50	6·50

97 Child with Dove

1966. Children's Day. Multicoloured.

421	10 m. Type **97**	10	10
422	15 m. Children with reindeer . .	10	10
423	20 m. Boys wrestling	10	10
424	30 m. Boy riding horse	20	10
425	60 m. Children on camel . . .	30	15
426	80 m. Shepherd boy with sheep	35	15
427	1 t. Boy archer	70	40

The 15 m., 30 m. and 80 m. are horiz.

98 "Proton 1"

1966. Space Satellites. Multicoloured.

428	5 m. "Vostok 2" (vert)	10	10
429	10 m. Type **98**	10	10
430	15 m. "Telstar 1" (vert) . . .	10	10
431	20 m. "Molniya 1" (vert) . . .	10	10
432	30 m. "Syncom 3" (vert) . . .	10	10
433	60 m. "Luna 9" (vert)	20	15
434	80 m. "Luna 12" (vert)	30	20
435	1 t. Mars and photographs taken by "Mariner 4"	35	25

99 Tarbosaurus

1966. Prehistoric Animals. Multicoloured.

436	5 m. Type **99**	20	10
437	10 m. Talararus	20	10
438	15 m. Protoceratops	30	15
439	20 m. Indricotherium	30	15
440	30 m. Saurolophus	50	20
441	60 m. Mastodon	75	30
442	80 m. Mongolotherium	90	45
443	1 t. Mammuthus	1·00	70

100 Congress Emblem

101 Sukhe Bator and Mongolian and Soviet Soldiers

1967. 9th International Students' Union Congress.

444	100	30 m. ultramarine and blue .	15	10
445		50 m. blue and pink . . .	25	15

1967. 50th Anniv of October Revolution.

446	101	40 m. multicoloured . . .	25	20
447	–	60 m. multicoloured . . .	35	25

DESIGN: 60 m. Lenin, and soldiers with sword.

102 Vietnamese Mother and Child

1967. Help for Vietnam.

448	102	30 m. + 20 m. brown, red and blue	20	10
449		50 m. + 30 m. brown, blue and red	30	15

103 Figure Skating

1967. Winter Olympic Games, Grenoble. Mult.

450 5 m. Type **103** 10 10
451 10 m. Speed skating 10 10
452 15 m. Ice hockey 10 10
453 20 m. Skijumping 15 10
454 30 m. Bob sleighing 15 10
455 60 m. Figure skating (pairs) . . 30 25
456 80 m. Downhill skiing 40 30

104 Bactrian Camel and Calf

1968. Young Animals. Multicoloured.

458 5 m. Type **104** 15 10
459 10 m. Yak 15 10
460 15 m. Lamb 20 10
461 20 m. Foal 30 10
462 30 m. Calf 30 10
463 60 m. Bison 40 15
464 80 m. Roe deer 55 30
465 1 t. Reindeer 80 40

105 Prickly Rose

ДЭХБ
20 ЖИЛ
WHO
(106)

1968. Mongolian Berries.

466 **105** 5 m. ultramarine on blue . 15 10
467 – 10 m. brown on buff . . . 15 10
468 – 15 m. emerald on green . . 20 10
469 – 20 m. red on cream 20 10
470 – 30 m. red on pink 25 10
471 – 60 m. brown on orange . . 45 20
472 – 80 m. turquoise on blue . . 60 25
473 – 1 t. red on cream 80 40

DESIGNS: 10 m. Blackcurrant; 15 m. Gooseberry; 20 m. Crabapple; 30 m. Strawberry; 60 m. Redcurrant; 80 m. Cowberry; 1 t. Sea buckthorn.

1968. 20th Anniv of World Health Organization. Nos. 396/7 optd with T **106**.

474 **89** 30 m. blue, gold and green 2·50 2·50
475 50 m. blue, gold and red . . 2·50 2·50

107 Human Rights Emblem

109 "Portrait of Artist Sharab" (A. Sangatzohyo)

108 "Das Kapital"

1968. Human Rights Year.

476 **107** 30 m. green and blue . . . 15 10

1968. 150th Birth Anniv of Karl Marx. Mult.

477 30 m. Type **108** 15 10
478 50 m. Karl Marx 25 15

1968. Mongolian Paintings. Multicoloured.

479 5 m. Type **109** 15 10
480 10 m. "On Remote Roads" (A. Sangatzohyo) 20 10
481 15 m. "Camel Calf" (B. Avarzad) 30 10
482 20 m. "The Milk" (B. Avarzad) 40 15
483 30 m. "The Bowman" (B. Gombosuren) 55 30
484 80 m. "Girl Sitting on a Yak" (A. Sangatzohyo) 95 55
485 1 t. 40 "Cagan Dara Ekke" (Janaivajara) . . . . 1·90 1·00

110 Volleyball

1968. Olympic Games, Mexico. Multicoloured.

487 5 m. Type **110** 10 10
488 10 m. Wrestling 10 10
489 15 m. Cycling 10 10
490 20 m. Throwing the javelin . . 10 10
491 30 m. Football 10 10
492 60 m. Running 20 15
493 80 m. Gymnastics 30 20
494 1 t. Weightlifting 35 25

111 Hammer and Spade

1968. 7th Anniv of Darkhan Town.

496 **111** 50 m. orange and blue . . 15 10

112 Gorky

113 "Madonna and Child" (Boltraffio)

1968. Birth Centenary of Maksim Gorky (writer).

497 **112** 60 m. ochre and blue . . . 15 10

1968. 20th Anniv (1966) of U.N.E.S.C.O. Paintings by European Masters in National Gallery, Budapest. Multicoloured.

498 5 m. Type **113** 20 10
499 10 m. "St. Roch healed by an angel" (Moretto of Brescia) . 25 10
500 15 m. "Madonna and Child with St. Anne" (Macchietti) . . . 35 10
501 20 m. "St. John on Patmos" (Cano) 45 15
502 30 m. "Young lady with viola da gamba" (Kupetzky) 50 15
503 80 m. "Study of a head" (Amerling) 80 50
504 1 t. 40 "The death of Adonis" (Furini) . . . . 1·60 75

114 Paavo Nurmi (running)

1969. Olympic Games' Gold-medal Winners. Multicoloured.

506 5 m. Type **114** 10 10
507 10 m. Jesse Owens (running) . . 10 10
508 15 m. F. Blankers-Koen (hurdling) 10 10
509 20 m. Laszlo Papp (boxing) . . 10 10
510 30 m. Wilma Rudolph (running) 10 10
511 60 m. Boris Sahlin (gymnastics) 20 10
512 80 m. D. Schollander (swimming) 25 15
513 1 t. A. Nakayama (ring exercises) 35 25

115 Bayit Costume (woman)

1969. Mongolian Costumes. Multicoloured.

515 5 m. Type **115** 10 10
516 10 m. Torgut (man) 15 10
517 15 m. Sakhchin (woman) . . . 20 10
518 20 m. Khalka (woman) 30 10
519 30 m. Daringanga (woman) . . 35 15
520 60 m. Mingat (woman) 50 20
521 80 m. Khalka (man) 65 25
522 1 t. Barga (woman) . . . . . 1·10 40

116 Emblem and Helicopter Rescue

1969. 30th Anniv of Mongolian Red Cross.

523 **116** 30 m. red and blue 60 20
524 – 50 m. red and violet . . . 50 25

DESIGN: 50 m. Shepherd and ambulance.

117 Yellow Lion's-foot

1969. Landscapes and Flowers. Multicoloured.

525 5 m. Type **117** 15 10
526 10 m. Variegated pink 15 10
527 15 m. Superb pink 25 10
528 20 m. Meadow cranesbill . . . 25 10
529 30 m. Mongolian pink 45 15
530 60 m. Asiatic globe flower . . . 50 15
531 80 m. Long-lipped larkspur . . 70 30
532 1 t. Saxaul 85 40

118 "Bullfight" (O. Tsewegdjaw)

1969. 10th Anniv of Co-operative Movement. Paintings in National Gallery, Ulan Bator. Mult.

533 5 m. Type **118** 10 10
534 10 m. "Colts Fighting" (O. Tsewegdjaw) 10 10
535 15 m. "Horse-herd" (A. Sengetsohyo) 20 10
536 20 m. "Camel Caravan" (D. Damdinsuren) 20 10
537 30 m. "On the Steppe" (N. Tsultem) 35 15
538 60 m. "Milking Mares" (O. Tsewegdjaw) 40 15
539 80 m. "Off to School" (B. Avarzad) 50 30
540 1 t. "After Work" (G. Odon) . 80 40

120 Army Crest

БНМАУ-ыг
тунхагласны
45
жилийн ой
1969—XI—26
(121)

1969. 30th Anniv of Battle of Khalka River.

543 **120** 50 m. multicoloured . . . 15 10

1969. 45th Anniv of Mongolian People's Republic. Nos. 411/12 optd with T **121**.

544 **95** 30 m. multicoloured . . . . 3·75 3·75
545 – 50 m. multicoloured . . . . 5·25 5·25

122 "Sputnik 3"

1969. Exploration of Space. Multicoloured.

546 5 m. Type **122** 10 10
547 10 m. "Vostok 1" 10 10
548 15 m. "Mercury 7" 10 10
549 20 m. Space-walk from "Voskhod 2" 10 10
550 30 m. "Apollo 8" in Moon orbit 15 10
551 60 m. Space-walk from "Soyuz 5" 30 20
552 80 m. "Apollo 12" and Moon landing 40 30

123 Wolf

1970. Wild Animals. Multicoloured.

554 5 m. Type **123** 20 10
555 10 m. Brown bear 40 10
556 15 m. Lynx 50 10
557 20 m. Wild Boar 50 10
558 30 m. Elk 55 20
559 60 m. Bobak marmot 65 20
560 80 m. Argali 75 35
561 1 t. "Hun Hunter and Hound" (tapestry) 90 50

124 "Lenin Centenary" (silk panel, Cerenhuu)

1970. Birth Centenary of Lenin. Multicoloured.

562 20 m. Type **124** 15 10
563 50 m. "Mongolians meeting Lenin" (Sangatzohyo) (horiz) 20 10
564 1 t. "Lenin" (Mazhig) 35 15

125 "Fairy Tale" Pavilion

1970. "EXPO 70" World Fair, Osaka, Japan.

565 **125** 1 t. 50 multicoloured . . . 50 45

126 Footballers

1970. World Cup Football Championships, Mexico.

567 **126** 10 m. multicoloured . . . 10 10
568 – 20 m. multicoloured . . . 10 10
569 – 30 m. multicoloured . . . 10 10
570 – 50 m. multicoloured . . . 10 10
571 – 60 m. multicoloured . . . 15 10
572 – 1 t. multicoloured 30 20
573 – 1 t. 30 multicoloured . . . 35 25

DESIGNS: Nos. 568/73, Different football scenes.

127 Common Buzzard

1970. Birds of Prey. Multicoloured.

575	10 m. Type **127**	70	10
576	20 m. Tawny owls	90	10
577	30 m. Northern goshawk	1·10	15
578	50 m. White-tailed sea eagle	1·75	20
579	60 m. Peregrine falcon	1·75	40
580	1 t. Common kestrels	2·00	45
581	1 t. 30 Black kite	2·40	55

128 Soviet Memorial, Treptow, Berlin

129 Mongol Archery

1970. 25th Anniv of Victory in Second World War.

582 **128**	60 m. multicoloured	15	10

1970. Mongolian Traditional Life. Multicoloured.

583	10 m. Type **129**	30	15
584	20 m. Bodg-gegeen's Palace, Ulan Bator	30	15
585	30 m. Mongol horsemen	30	20
586	40 m. "The White Goddess-Mother"	30	25
587	50 m. Girl in National costume	65	45
588	60 m. "Lion's Head" (statue)	75	45
589	70 m. Dancer's mask	85	65
590	80 m. Gateway, Bogd-gegeen's Palace	1·00	1·00

131 I.E.Y. and U.N. Emblems with Flag

1970. International Education Year.

592 **131**	60 m. multicoloured	35	15

132 Horseman, "50" and Sunrise

1970. 50th Anniv of National Press.

593 **132**	30 m. multicoloured	25	10

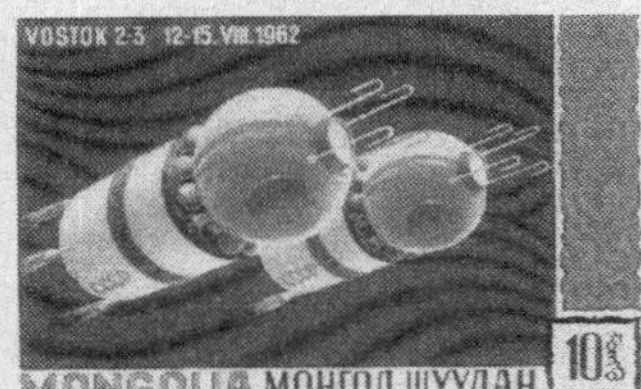

133 "Vostok 3" and "4"

1971. Space Research. Multicoloured.

594	10 m. Type **133**	10	10
595	20 m. Space-walk from "Voskhod 2"	10	10
596	30 m. "Gemini 6" and "7"	10	10
597	50 m. Docking of "Soyuz 4" and "5"	10	10
598	60 m. "Soyuz 6", "7" and "8"	15	10
599	80 m. "Apollo 11" and lunar module	20	15
600	1 t. "Apollo 13" damaged	25	20
601	1 t. 30 "Luna 16"	30	25

No. 594 is incorrectly inscribed "Vostok 2–3". The date refers to flight of "Vostoks 3" and "4".

134 Sukhe Bator addressing Meeting

1971. 50th Anniv of Revolutionary Party. Mult.

603	30 m. Type **134**	10	10
604	60 m. Horseman with flag	15	10
605	90 m. Sukhe Bator with Lenin	25	15
606	1 t. 20 Mongolians with banner	40	25

136 Tsam Mask

1971. Mongol Tsam Masks.

608 **136**	10 m. multicoloured	15	10
609 –	20 m. multicoloured	25	10
610 –	30 m. multicoloured	30	10
611 –	50 m. multicoloured	35	15
612 –	60 m. multicoloured	45	20
613 –	1 t. multicoloured	80	30
614 –	1 t. 30 multicoloured	1·00	50

DESIGNS: Nos. 609/14, Different dance masks.

137 Banner and Party Emblems

1971. 16th Revolutionary Party Congress.

615 **137**	60 m. multicoloured	15	10

138 Steam Locomotive

1971. "50 Years of Transport Development". Multicoloured.

616	20 m. Type **138**	70	10
617	30 m. Diesel locomotive	70	10
618	40 m. Russian "Urals" lorry	65	15
619	50 m. Russian "Moskovich 412" car	75	15
620	60 m. Polikarpov Po-2 biplane	90	25
621	80 m. Antonov An-24B airliner	1·10	40
622	1 t. Lake steamer "Sukhe Bator"	2·00	70

139 Soldier

140 Emblem and Red Flag

1971. 50th Anniv of People's Army and Police. Multicoloured.

623	60 m. Type **139**	10	10
624	1 t. 50 Policeman and child	40	15

1971. 50th Anniv of Revolutionary Youth Organization.

625 **140**	60 m. multicoloured	20	10

141 Mongolian Flag and Year Emblem

1971. Racial Equality Year.

626 **141**	60 m. multicoloured	15	10

142 "The Old Man and the Tiger"

1971. Mongolian Folk Tales. Multicoloured.

627	10 m. Type **142**	20	10
628	20 m. "The Boy Giant-killer"	20	10
629	30 m. Cat and mice	20	10
630	50 m. Mongolians riding on eagle	25	10
631	60 m. Girl on horseback ("The Wise Bride")	40	15
632	80 m. King and courtiers with donkey	55	20
633	1 t. Couple kneeling before empty throne ("Story of the Throne")	80	25
634	1 t. 30 "The Wise Bird"	95	40

143 Yaks

1971. Livestock Breeding. Multicoloured.

635	20 m. Type **143**	20	10
636	30 m. Bactrian camels	20	10
637	40 m. Sheep	25	10
638	50 m. Goats	40	10
639	60 m. Cattle	50	20
640	80 m. Horses	60	25
641	1 t. Pony	95	45

144 Cross-country Skiing

1972. Winter Olympic Games, Sapporo, Japan. Multicoloured.

642	10 m. Type **144**	10	10
643	20 m. Bobsleighing	10	10
644	30 m. Figure skating	10	10
645	50 m. Slalom skiing	10	10
646	60 m. Speed skating	15	10
647	80 m. Downhill skiing	20	15
648	1 t. Ice hockey	25	15
649	1 t. 30 Pairs figure skating	30	20

145 "Horse-breaking" (A. Sengatzohyo)

1972. Paintings by Contemporary Artists from the National Gallery, Ulan Bator. Multicoloured.

651	10 m. Type **145**	15	10
652	20 m. "Black Camel" (A. Sengatzohyo)	20	10
653	30 m. "Jousting" (A. Sengatzohyo)	25	10
654	50 m. "Wrestling Match" (A. Sengatzohyo)	30	10
655	60 m. "Waterfall" (A. Sengatzohyo)	40	10
656	80 m. "Old Musician" (U. Yadamsuren)	50	20
657	1 t. "Young Musician" (U. Yadamsuren)	60	25
658	1 t. 30 "Ancient Prophet" (B. Avarzad)	85	40

147 "Calosoma fischeri" (ground beetle)

1972. Beetles. Multicoloured.

660	10 m. Type **147**	20	10
661	20 m. "Mylabris mongolica" (blister beetle)	25	10
662	30 m. "Sternoplax zichyi" (mealworm beetle)	30	10
663	50 m. "Rhaebus komarovi" (snout weevil)	40	15
664	60 m. "Meloe centripubens" (oil beetle)	55	15
665	80 m. "Eodorcadion mongolicum" (longhorn beetle)	75	25
666	1 t. "Platyope maongolica" (mealworm beetle)	90	30
667	1 t. 30 "Lixus nigrolineatus" (weevil)	1·40	50

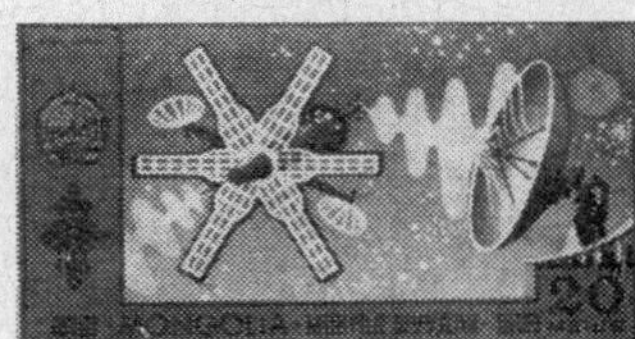

149 Satellite and Dish Aerial ("Telecommunications")

1972. Air. National Achievements. Multicoloured.

669	20 m. Type **149**	10	10
670	30 m. Horse-herd ("Livestock Breeding")	20	10
671	40 m. Diesel train and Tupolev Tu-144 jetliner ("Transport")	95	10
672	50 m. Corncob and farm ("Agriculture")	25	15
673	60 m. Ambulance and hospital ("Public Health")	60	15
674	80 m. Actors ("Culture")	60	20
675	1 t. Factory ("Industry")	65	30

150 Globe, Flag and Dish Aerial

1972. Air. World Telecommunications Day.

676 **150**	60 m. multicoloured	25	15

151 Running

1972. Olympic Games, Munich. Multicoloured.

677	10 m. Type **151**	10	10
678	15 m. Boxing	10	10
679	20 m. Judo	10	10
680	25 m. High jumping	10	10
681	30 m. Rifle-shooting	10	10
682	60 m. Wrestling	20	15
683	80 m. Weightlifting	25	20
684	1 t. Mongolian flag and Olympic emblems	35	25

152 E.C.A.F.E. Emblem

1972. 25th Anniv of E.C.A.F.E.
686 **152** 60 m. blue, gold and red . . 20 10

153 Mongolian Racerunner

1972. Reptiles. Multicoloured.
687 10 m. Type **153** 20 10
688 15 m. Radde's toad 25 10
689 20 m. Halys viper 35 10
690 25 m. Toad-headed agama . . 40 15
691 30 m. Asiatic grass frog . . . 55 15
692 60 m. Plate-tailed geckol . . . 70 25
693 80 m. Steppe ribbon snake . . 85 35
694 1 t. Mongolian agama . . . . 1·25 55

154 "Technical Knowledge"

1972. 30th Anniv of Mongolian State University. Multicoloured.
695 50 m. Type **154** 15 10
696 60 m. University building . . . 20 10

155 "Madonna and Child with St. John the Baptist and a Holy Woman" (Bellini)

1972. Air. U.N.E.S.C.O. "Save Venice" Campaign. Paintings. Multicoloured.
697 10 m. Type **155** 15 10
698 20 m. "The Transfiguration" (Bellini) (vert) 20 10
699 30 m. "Blessed Virgin with the Child" (Bellini) (vert) . . . 25 10
700 50 m. "Presentation of the Christ in the Temple" (Bellini) . . . 40 15
701 60 m. "St. George" (Bellini) (vert) 50 20
702 80 m. "Departure of Ursula" (detail, Carpaccio) (vert) . . 65 35
703 1 t. "Departure of Ursula" (different detail, Carpaccio) . 85 45

156 Manlay-Bator Damdinsuren

157 Spassky Tower, Moscow Kremlin

1972. National Heroes. Multicoloured.
705 10 m. Type **156** 10 10
706 20 m. Ard Ayus in chains (horiz) 20 10
707 50 m. Hatan-Bator Magsarzhav 30 15
708 60 m. Has-Bator on the march (horiz) 40 20
709 1 t. Sukhe Bator 70 30

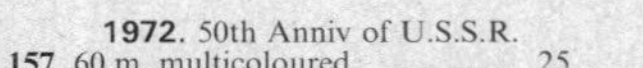

1972. 50th Anniv of U.S.S.R.
710 **157** 60 m. multicoloured . . . 25 15

158 Snake and "Mars 1"

1972. Air. Animal Signs of the Mongolian Calendar and Progress in Space Exploration. Multicoloured.
711 60 m. Type **158** 70 25
712 60 m. Horse and "Apollo 8" (square) 70 25
713 60 m. Sheep and "Electron 2" (square) 70 25
714 60 m. Monkey and "Explorer 6" 70 25
715 60 m. Dragon and "Mariner 2" . 70 25
716 60 m. Pig and "Cosmos 110" (square) 70 25
717 60 m. Dog and "Ariel 2" (square) 70 25
718 60 m. Cockerel and "Venus 1" . 70 25
719 60 m. Hare and "Soyuz 5" . . 70 25
720 60 m. Tiger and "Gemini 7" (square) 70 25
721 60 m. Ox and "Venus 4" (square) 70 25
722 60 m. Rat and "Apollo 15" lunar rover 70 25
The square designs are size 40 × 40 mm.

159 Swimming Gold Medal (Mark Spitz, U.S.A.)

1972. Gold Medal Winners, Munich Olympic Games. Multicoloured.
723 5 m. Type **159** 10 10
724 10 m. High jumping (Ulrike Meyfarth, West Germany) . . 10 10
725 20 m. Gymnastics (Savao Kato, Japan) 10 10
726 30 m. Show jumping (Andras Balczo, Hungary) 10 10
727 60 m. Running (Lasse Viren, Finland) 25 15
728 80 m. Swimming (Shane Gould, Australia) 35 20
729 1 t. Putting the shot (Anatoli Bondarchuk, U.S.S.R.) . . . 40 25

160 Monkey on Cycle

1973. Mongolian Circus (1st series). Mult.
731 5 m. Type **160** 10 10
732 10 m. Seal with ball 15 10
733 15 m. Bear on mono-wheel . . . 20 10
734 20 m. Acrobat on camel . . . 25 10
735 30 m. Acrobat on horse 40 10
736 50 m. Clown playing flute . . . 50 20
737 60 m. Contortionist 60 25
738 1 t. New Circus Hall, Ulan Bator 80 40
See also Nos. 824/30.

161 Mounted Postman

162 Sukhe Bator receiving Traditional Gifts

1973.
739 **161** 50 m. brown (postage) . . 60 10
740 – 60 m. green . . . . 2·50 15
741 – 1 t. purple . . . . 1·00 20
742 – 1 t. 50 blue (air) . . . . . 1·75 25
DESIGNS: 60 m. Diesel train; 1 t. Mail truck; 1 t. 50, Antonov An-24 airliner.

1973. 80th Birth Anniv of Sukhe Bator. Mult.
743 10 m. Type **162** 10 10
744 20 m. Holding reception . . . 10 10
745 50 m. Leading army 20 10
746 60 m. Addressing council . . . 25 10
747 1 t. Giving audience (horiz) . . 45 20

163 W.M.O. Emblem and Meteorological Symbols

1973. Air. Centenary of World Meteorological Organization.
748 **163** 60 m. multicoloured . . . 30 10

164 "Copernicus" (anon)

167 Marx and Lenin

Нэгдлийн Холбооны IV Их
Хурал 1973—6—11
(166)

1973. 500th Birth Anniv of Nicholas Copernicus (astronomer). Multicoloured.
749 50 m. Type **164** 15 10
750 60 m. "Copernicus in his Observatory" (J. Matejko) (55 × 35 mm) 25 10
751 1 t. "Copernicus" (Jan Matejko) 35 15

1973. 4th Agricultural Co-operative Congress, Ulan Bator. No. 538 optd with T **166**.
754 60 m. multicoloured . . . . .

1973. 9th Organization of Socialist States Postal Ministers Congress, Ulan Bator.
755 **167** 60 m. multicoloured . . . 30 10

168 Russian Stamp and Emblems

1973. Air. Council for Mutual Economic Aid Posts and Telecommunications Conference, Ulan Bator. Multicoloured.
756 30 m. Type **168** . . . . 1·25 30
757 30 m. Mongolia 45 20
758 30 m. Bulgaria 45 20
759 30 m. Hungary 45 20
760 30 m. Czechoslovakia 45 20
761 30 m. German Democratic Republic 45 20
762 30 m. Cuba 45 20
763 30 m. Rumania 45 20
764 30 m. Poland . . . . 1·25 30

169 Common Shelduck

1973. Aquatic Birds. Multicoloured.
765 5 m. Type **169** 45 10
766 10 m. Black-throated diver . . 65 10
767 15 m. Bar-headed geese . . . . 1·00 15
768 30 m. Great crested grebe . . . 1·25 20
769 50 m. Mallard . . . . 1·90 40
770 60 m. Mute swan . . . . . . 2·25 40
771 1 t. Greater scaups . . . . . 2·50 60

170 Siberian Weasel

1973. Small Fur Animals. Multicoloured.
772 5 m. Type **170** 20 10
773 10 m. Siberian chipmunk . . . 20 10
774 15 m. Siberian flying squirrel . 20 10
775 20 m. Eurasian badger 25 15
776 30 m. Eurasian red squirrel . . 35 15
777 60 m. Wolverine 70 30
778 80 m. American mink 85 45
779 1 t. Arctic hare . . . . 1·25 60

171 Launching "Soyuz" Spacecraft

1973. Air. "Apollo" and "Soyuz" Space Programmes. Multicoloured.
780 5 m. Type **171** 10 10
781 10 m. "Apollo 8" 10 10
782 15 m. "Soyuz 4" and "5" linked 10 10
783 20 m. "Apollo 11" module on Moon 10 10
784 30 m. "Apollo 14" after splash-down 10 10
785 50 m. Triple flight by "Soyuz 6", "7" and "8" 20 15
786 60 m. "Apollo 16" lunar rover . 25 15
787 1 t "Lunokhod 1" 40 30

172 Global Emblem

1973. 15th Anniv of Review "Problems of Peace and Socialism".
789 **172** 60 m. red, gold and blue . . 25 10

173 Alpine Aster

1973. Mongolian Flowers. Multicoloured.
790 5 m. Type **173** 10 10
791 10 m. Mongolian catchfly . . . 20 10
792 15 m. "Rosa davurica" 25 10
793 20 m. Mongolian dandelion . . 30 15
794 30 m. "Rhododendron dahuricum" 45 25
795 50 m. "Clematis tangutica" . . 55 40
796 60 m. Siberian primrose . . . 65 45
797 1 t. Pasque flower 85 75

174 Poplar Admiral

1974. Butterflies and Moths. Multicoloured.
798 5 m. Type **174** 30 10
799 10 m. Hebe tiger moth 35 10
800 15 m. Purple tiger moth . . . 40 10
801 20 m. Rosy underwing 55 10
802 30 m. "Isoceras kaszabi" (moth) 70 15
803 50 m. Spurge hawk moth . . . 1·00 30
804 60 m. Garden tiger moth . . 1·10 40
805 1 t. Clouded buff . . . . . . 1·50 50

175 "Hebe Namshil" (L. Merdorsh)
176 Comecon Headquarters, Moscow

1974. Mongolian Opera and Drama. Multicoloured.
806 15 m. Type **175** 15 10
807 20 m. "Sive Hiagt" (D. Luvsansharav) (horiz) . . 15 10
808 25 m. "Edre" (D. Namdag) . . 20 10
809 30 m. "The Three Khans of Sara-gol" (horiz) 25 15
810 60 m. "Amarsana" (B. Damdinsuren) 40 20
811 80 m. "Edre" (different scene) . 55 25
812 1 t. "Edre" (different scene) . . 85 55

1974. Air. 25th Anniv of Communist Council for Mutual Economic Aid ("Comecon").
813 **176** 60 m. multicoloured . . . 30 20

177 Government Building and Sukhe Bator Monument, Ulan Bator

1974. 50th Anniv of Renaming of Capital as Ulan Bator.
814 **177** 60 m. multicoloured . . . 20 10

179 Mounted Courier

1974. Air. Centenary of U.P.U. Multicoloured.
816 50 m. Type **179** . . . . . . 1·50 40
817 50 m. Reindeer mail sledge . . 1·50 40
818 50 m. Mail coach . . . . . . 1·50 40
819 50 m. Balloon post . . . . . 2·00 40
820 50 m. Lake steamer "Sukhe Bator" and Polikarpov Po-2 biplane . . . . 2·25 40
821 50 m. Diesel train and P.O. truck 2·25 40
822 50 m. Rocket in orbit . . . . 1·50 40

MINIMUM PRICE
The minimum price quoted is 10p which represents a handling charge rather than a basis for valuing common stamps. For further notes about prices see introductory pages.

180 Performing Horses

1974. Mongolian Circus (2nd series). Multicoloured.
824 10 m. Type **180** (postage) . . . 10 10
825 20 m. Juggler (vert) 15 10
826 30 m. Elephant on ball (vert) . . 20 10
827 40 m. Performing yak 30 15
828 60 m. Acrobats (vert) 45 20
829 80 m. Trick cyclist (vert) . . . 60 25
830 1 t. Contortionist (vert) (air) . . 70 35

181 "Training a Young Horse"

1974. Int Children's Day. Drawings by Lhamsurem. Multicoloured.
831 10 m. Type **181** 10 10
832 20 m. "Boy with Calf" 15 10
833 30 m. "Riding untamed Horse" 20 10
834 40 m. "Boy with Foal" 25 10
835 60 m. "Girl dancing with Doves" 30 15
836 80 m. "Wrestling" 35 25
837 1 t. "Hobby-horse Dance" . . 60 30

182 Archer on Foot

1974. "Nadam" Sports Festival. Multicoloured.
838 10 m. Type **182** 10 10
839 20 m. "Kazlodanie" (Kazakh mounted game) 15 10
840 30 m. Mounted archer 20 10
841 40 m. Horse-racing 25 10
842 60 m. Bucking horse-riding . . 30 15
843 80 m. Capturing wild horse . . 35 25
844 1 t. Wrestling 60 30

183 Giant Panda

1974. Bears. Multicoloured.
845 10 m. Brown bear 25 10
846 20 m. Type **183** 25 10
847 30 m. Giant Panda 45 15
848 40 m. Brown bear 45 20
849 60 m. Sloth bear 70 30
850 80 m. Asiatic black bear . . . 80 50
851 1 t. Brown bear . . . . . . 1·50 65

184 Red Deer

1974. Games Reserves. Fauna. Multicoloured.
852 10 m. Type **184** 15 10
853 20 m. Eurasian beaver 30 10
854 30 m. Leopard 40 15
855 40 m. Herring gull . . . . . . 1·25 30
856 60 m. Roe deer 80 30
857 80 m. Argali 85 35
858 1 t. Siberian musk deer . . . . 1·25 55

185 Detail of Buddhist Temple, Palace of Bogdo Gegen

1974. Mongolian Architecture. Multicoloured.
859 10 m. Type **185** 10 10
860 15 m. Buddhist temple (now museum) 10 10
861 30 m. "Charity" Temple, Ulan Bator 20 10
862 50 m. Yurt (tent) 30 20
863 80 m. Arbour in court-yard . . 50 30

186 Spassky Tower, Moscow, and Sukhe Bator Statue, Ulan Bator
187 Proclamation of the Republic

1974. Brezhnev's Visit to Mongolia.
864 **186** 60 m. multicoloured . . . 30 10

1974. 50th Anniv of Mongolian People's Republic. Multicoloured.
865 60 m. Type **187** 30 10
866 60 m. "First Constitution" (embroidery) 30 10
867 60 m. Mongolian flag 30 10

188 Gold Decanter

1974. Goldsmiths' Treasures of the 19th Century. Multicoloured.
868 10 m. Type **188** 15 10
869 20 m. Silver jug 20 10
870 30 m. Night lamp 25 10
871 40 m. Tea jug 35 20
872 60 m. Candelabra 45 20
873 80 m. Teapot 60 30
874 1 t. Silver bowl on stand . . . 80 40

189 Lapwing

1974. Protection of Water and Nature Conservation. Multicoloured.
875 10 m. Type **189** (postage) . . . 80 15
876 20 m. Lenok (fish) 45 10
877 30 m. Marsh marigolds 40 15
878 40 m. Dalmatian pelican . . . 1·40 20
879 60 m. Eurasian perch 75 25
880 80 m. Sable 75 25
881 1 t. Hydrologist with jar of water (air) 80 30

190 U.S. Mail Coach

1974. Centenary of U.P.U. Multicoloured.
883 10 m. Type **190** 15 10
884 20 m. French postal cart . . . 20 10
885 30 m. Changing horses, Russian mail and passenger carriage . 35 15
886 40 m. Swedish postal coach with caterpillar tracks 45 20
887 50 m. First Hungarian mail van 50 25
888 60 m. German Daimler-Benz mail van and trailer 65 40
889 1 t. Mongolian postal courier . 95 55

191 Red Flag
193 Mongolian Woman

192 "Zygophyllum xanthoxylon" (½-size illustration)

1975. 30th Anniv of Victory.
891 **191** 60 m. multicoloured . . . 30 10

1975. 12th International Botanical Conference. Rare Medicinal Plants. Multicoloured.
892 10 m. Type **192** 20 10
893 20 m. "Incarvillea potaninii" . . 30 10
894 30 m. "Lancea tibetica" . . . 45 15
895 40 m. "Jurinea mongolica" . . 45 20
896 50 m. "Saussurea involucrata" . 55 20
897 60 m. "Allium mongolicum" . . 65 30
898 1 t. "Adonis mongolica" . . . 1·25 40

1975. International Women's Year.
899 **193** 60 m. multicoloured . . . 30 10

194 "Soyuz" on Launch-pad

1975. Air. Joint Soviet–American Space Project. Multicoloured.
900 10 m. Type **194** 20 10
901 20 m. Launch of "Apollo" . . . 15 10
902 30 m. "Apollo" and "Soyuz" spacecraft 30 10
903 40 m. Docking manoeuvre . . . 35 20
904 50 m. Spacecraft docked together 50 20
905 60 m. "Soyuz" in orbit 60 30
906 1 t. "Apollo" and "Soyuz" spacecraft and communications satellite . . 95 40

195 Child and Lamb

1975. International Children's Day. Multicoloured.
908 10 m. Type **195** 10 10
909 20 m. Child riding horse . . . 20 10
910 30 m. Child with calf 20 10
911 40 m. Child and "orphan camel" 25 15
912 50 m. "The Obedient Yak" . . 30 20
913 60 m. Child riding on swan . . 35 25
914 1 t. Two children singing . . . 55 40
See also Nos. 979/85.

196 Pioneers tending Tree

Тээвэр—50
1975—7—15.

(197)

1975. 50th Anniv of Mongolian Pioneer Organization. Multicoloured.

915 50 m. Type **196** 20 10
916 60 m. Children's study circle 30 10
917 1 t. New emblem of Mongolian pioneers 40 20

1975. 50th Anniv of Public Transport. Nos. 616/22 optd with T **197**.

918 **138** 20 m. multicoloured 2·50 2·50
919 – 30 m. multicoloured 2·50 2·50
920 – 40 m. multicoloured 1·90 1·90
921 – 50 m. multicoloured 1·90 1·90
922 – 60 m. multicoloured 2·50 2·50
923 – 80 m. multicoloured 3·00 3·00
924 – 1 t. multicoloured 3·75 3·75

198 Argali

1975. Air. South Asia Tourist Year.

925 **198** 1 t. 50 multicoloured 90 40

199 Golden Eagle attacking Red Fox

1975. Hunting Scenes. Multicoloured.

926 10 m. Type **199** 90 15
927 20 m. Lynx-hunting (vert) 45 10
928 30 m. Hunter stalking bobak marmots 50 15
929 40 m. Hunter riding on reindeer (vert) 60 20
930 50 m. Shooting wild boar 60 25
931 60 m. Wolf in trap (vert) 75 35
932 1 t. Hunters with brown bear 1·00 50

200 Haite's Bullhead

1975. Fishes. Multicoloured.

933 10 m. Type **200** 25 10
934 20 m. Flat-headed asp 40 10
935 30 m. Altai osman 45 15
936 40 m. Tench 55 20
937 50 m. Hump-backed whitefish 80 25
938 60 m. Mongolian redfin 95 30
939 1 t. Goldfish 1·60 60

201 "Morin Hur" (musical instrument)

202 Revolutionary with Banner

1975. Mongolian Handicrafts. Multicoloured.

940 10 m. Type **201** 10 10
941 20 m. Saddle 15 10
942 30 m. Headdress 20 10
943 40 m. Boots 30 15
944 50 m. Cap 40 15
945 60 m. Pipe and tobacco pouch 45 20
946 1 t. Fur hat 75 30

1975. 70th Anniv of 1905 Russian Revolution.

947 **202** 60 m. multicoloured 25 10

203 "Taming a Wild Horse"

1975. Mongolian Paintings. Multicoloured.

948 10 m. Type **203** 10 10
949 20 m. "Camel Caravan" (horiz) 25 10
950 30 m. "Man playing Lute" 35 10
951 40 m. "Woman adjusting Headdress" (horiz) 40 15
952 50 m. "Woman in ceremonial Costume" 40 25
953 60 m. "Woman fetching Water" 50 30
954 1 t. "Woman playing Yaga" (musical instrument) 75 40

204 Ski Jumping

205 "House of Young Technicians"

1975. Winter Olympic Games, Innsbruck. Multicoloured.

956 10 m. Type **204** 10 10
957 20 m. Ice hockey 10 10
958 30 m. Slalom skiing 10 10
959 40 m. Bobsleighing 15 10
960 50 m. Rifle shooting (biathlon) 20 10
961 60 m. Speed skating 20 15
962 1 t. Figure skating 35 25

1975. Public Buildings.

964 **205** 50 m. blue 40 10
965 – 60 m. green 50 15
966 – 1 t. brown 70 25

DESIGNS: 60 m. Hotel, Ulan Bator; 1 t. "Museum of the Revolution".

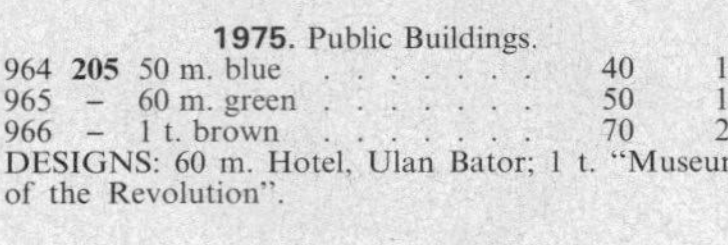

206 "Molniya" Satellite

1976. Air. 40th Anniv of Mongolian Meteorological Office.

967 **206** 60 m. blue and yellow 40 15

209 "National Economy" Star

1976. 17th Mongolian People's Revolutionary Party Congress, Ulan Bator.

970 **209** 60 m. multicoloured 30 10

210 Archery

1976. Olympic Games, Montreal. Multicoloured.

971 10 m. Type **210** 10 10
972 20 m. Judo 10 10
973 30 m. Boxing 10 10
974 40 m. Gymnastics 15 10
975 60 m. Weightlifting 20 15
976 80 m. High jumping 25 20
977 1 t. Rifle shooting 35 25

1976. Int Children's Day. As T **195**. Mult.

979 10 m. Gobi Desert landscape 15 10
980 20 m. Horse-taming 20 10
981 30 m. Horse-riding 25 10
982 40 m. Pioneers' camp 35 10
983 60 m. Young musician 50 20
984 80 m. Children's party 70 25
985 1 t. Mongolian wrestling 90 30

211 Cavalry Charge

1976. 55th Anniv of Revolution. Multicoloured.

986 60 m. Type **211** (postage) 40 10
987 60 m. Man and emblem (vert) 40 10
988 60 m. "Industry and Agriculture" (air) 40 10

213 Osprey

1976. Protected Birds. Multicoloured.

990 10 m. Type **213** 1·50 30
991 20 m. Griffon vulture 1·00 15
992 30 m. Lammergeier 1·40 20
993 40 m. Marsh harrier 1·75 20
994 60 m. European black vulture 2·00 30
995 80 m. Golden eagle 2·50 35
996 1 t. Tawny eagle 2·75 40

214 "Rider on Wild Horse"

1976. Paintings by O. Tsewegdjaw. Multicoloured.

997 10 m. Type **214** 15 10
998 20 m. "The First Nadam" (game on horse-back) (horiz) 20 10
999 30 m. "Harbour on Khobsogol Lake" (horiz) 55 15
1000 40 m. "Awakening the Steppe" (horiz) 45 20
1001 80 m. "Wrestling" (horiz) 60 25
1002 1 t. "The Descent" (yak hauling timber) 1·10 50

215 "Industrial Development"

1976. Mongolian–Soviet Friendship.

1003 **215** 60 m. multicoloured 1·25 20

216 John Naber of U.S.A. (Swimming)

217 Tablet on Tortoise

1976. Olympic Games, Montreal. Gold Medal Winners. Multicoloured.

1004 10 m. Type **216** 10 10
1005 20 m. Nadia Comaneci of Rumania (gymnastics) 10 10
1006 30 m. Kornelia Ender of East Germany (swimming) 10 10
1007 40 m. Mitsuo Tsukahara of Japan (gymnastics) 15 10
1008 60 m. Gregor Braun of West Germany (cycling) 20 15
1009 80 m. Lasse Viren of Finland (running) 25 20
1010 1 t. Nikolai Andrianov of U.S.S.R. (gymnastics) 35 25

1976. Archaeology.

1012 **217** 50 m. brown and blue 80 15
1013 – 60 m. black and green 1·10 15

DESIGN: 60 m. 6th-century stele.

218 R-1 Biplane

1976. Aircraft. Multicoloured.

1014 10 m. Type **218** 20 10
1015 20 m. Polikarpov R-5 biplane 30 10
1016 30 m. Kalinin K-5 monoplane 40 10
1017 40 m. Polikarpov Po-2 biplane 45 15
1018 60 m. Polikarpov I-16 jet fighter 60 25
1019 80 m. Yakovlev Ya-6 Air 6 monoplane 75 35
1020 1 t. Junkers F-13 monoplane 95 40

219 Dancers in Folk Costume

1977. Mongolian Folk Dances. Multicoloured.

1021 10 m. Type **219** 25 10
1022 20 m. Dancing girls in 13th-century costume 35 10
1023 30 m. West Mongolian dance 45 10
1024 40 m. "Ekachi" dance 50 15
1025 60 m. "Bielge" ("Trunk") dance 80 20
1026 80 m. "Hodak" dance 95 30
1027 1 t. "Dojarka" dance 1·10 45

220 Gravitational Effects on "Pioneer"

1977. 250th Death Anniv of Sir Isaac Newton (mathematician). Multicoloured.

1028 60 m. Type **220** (postage) . . 25 15
1029 60 m. Apple tree (25 × 32 mm) . . 25 15
1030 60 m. Planetary motion and sextant 25 15
1031 60 m. Sir Isaac Newton (25 × 32 mm) 25 15
1032 60 m. Spectrum of light . . . 25 15
1033 60 m. Attraction of Earth . . . 25 15
1034 60 m. Laws of motion of celestial bodies (25 × 32 mm) 25 15
1035 60 m. Space-walking (air) . . 25 15
1036 60 m. "Pioneer 10" and Jupiter 25 15

221 Natsagdorj, Mongolian Scenes and Extract from poem "Mother"

1977. Natsagdorj (poet) Commem. Mult.

1037 60 m. Type **221** 40 25
1038 60 m. Border stone, landscape and extract from poem "My Homeland" 40 25

222 Horse Race

1977. Horses. Multicoloured.

1039 10 m. Type **222** 25 10
1040 20 m. Girl on white horse . . . 30 10
1041 30 m. Rangeman on brown horse 40 10
1042 40 m. Tethered horses 55 20
1043 60 m. White mare with foal . . 70 20
1044 80 m. Brown horse with shepherd . . . . 1·00 30
1045 1 t. White horse . . . . . . 1·25 45

223 "Mongolemys elegans"

1977. Prehistoric Animals. Multicoloured.

1046 10 m. Type **223** 30 10
1047 20 m. "Embolotherium ergiliense" 45 10
1048 30 m. "Psittacosaurus mongoliensis" 55 15
1049 40 m. Enthelodon 70 20
1050 60 m. "Spirocerus kiakhtensis" 1·00 25
1051 80 m. Hipparion . . . . . . 1·40 40
1052 1 t. "Bos primigenius" . . . . 1·60 55

225 Child feeding Lambs **226** Industrial Plant and Transport

1977. Children's Day and 1st Balloon Flight in Mongolia. Multicoloured.

1054 10 m. + 5 m. Type **225** . . . 30 15
1055 20 m. + 5 m. Boy playing flute and girl dancing 45 15
1056 30 m. + 5 m. Girl chasing butterflies 55 20
1057 40 m. + 5 m. Girl with ribbon . 60 25
1058 60 m. + 5 m. Girl with flowers . 70 40
1059 80 m. + 5 m. Girl with bucket . 90 50
1060 1 t. + 5 m. Boy going to school 1·25 60

1977. Erdenet (New Town).

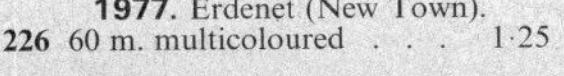

1062 **226** 60 m. multicoloured . . . 1·25 20

227 Trade Unions Emblem

1977. Air. 11th Mongolian Trade Unions Congress.

1063 **227** 60 m. multicoloured . . . 1·00 15

228 Mounting Bell-shaped Gear on Rocket (⅔-size illustration)

1977. Air. 11th Anniv of "Intercosmos" Co-operation. Multicoloured.

1064 10 m. Type **228** 10 10
1065 20 m. Launch of "Intercosmos 3" 10 10
1066 30 m. Research ship "Kosmonavt Yury Gargarin" 40 15
1067 40 m. Observation of lunar eclipse 15 10
1068 60 m. Earth station's multiple antennae 15 15
1069 80 m. Magnetosphere examination, Van Allen Zone 20 20
1070 1 t. Meteorological satellites . 30 25

229 Fire-fighters' Bucket Chain

1977. Mongolian Fire-fighting Services. Multicoloured.

1072 10 m. Type **229** 10 10
1073 20 m. Horse-drawn hand pump 10 10
1074 30 m. Horse-drawn steam pump 10 10
1075 40 m. Fighting forest fire . . . 15 10
1076 60 m. Mobile foam extinguisher 20 15
1077 80 m. Modern fire engine . . 25 20
1078 1 t. Mil Mi-8 helicopter spraying fire 35 25

230 "Molniya" Satellite and Dish Aerial on TV Screen

1977. 40th Anniv of Technical Institute.

1079 **230** 60 m. blue, black & grey 30 10

231 Black-veined White

1977. Butterflies and Moths. Multicoloured.

1080 10 m. Type **231** 20 10
1081 20 m. Lappet moth 35 10
1082 30 m. Lesser clouded yellow . 50 20
1083 40 m. Dark tussock moth . . 70 20
1084 60 m. Lackey moth . . . . . 1·00 25
1085 80 m. Clouded buff . . . . . 1·40 35
1086 1 t. Scarce copper . . . . . . 1·60 50

232 Lenin Museum

1977. Inauguration of Lenin Museum, Ulan Bator.

1087 **232** 60 m. multicoloured . . . 40 20

233 Cruiser "Aurora" and Soviet Flag

1977. 60th Anniv of Russian Revolution. Mult.

1088 50 m. Type **233** 60 15
1089 60 m. Dove and globe (horiz) 50 15
1090 1 t. 50 Freedom banner around the globe (horiz) 75 35

234 Giant Pandas

1977. Giant Pandas. Multicoloured.

1091 10 m. Eating bamboo shoot (vert) 20 10
1092 20 m. Type **234** 35 10
1093 30 m. Female and cub in washtub (vert) 45 15
1094 40 m. Male and cub with bamboo shoot 60 20
1095 60 m. Female and cub (vert) 80 30
1096 80 m. Family (horiz) . . . . 1·40 50
1097 1 t. Male on hind legs (vert) 1·60 65

236 Montgolfier Brothers' Balloon

1977. Air. Airships and Balloons. Multicoloured.

1099 20 m. Type **236** 10 10
1100 30 m. Airship "Graf Zeppelin" over North Pole 10 10
1101 40 m. Airship "Osoaviakhim" over the Arctic 20 10
1102 50 m. Soviet Airship "Sever" 30 15
1103 60 m. Aereon 340 airship . . . 40 20
1104 80 m. Nestrenko's planned airship 45 20
1105 1 t. 20 "Flying Crane" airship . 70 35

237 Ferrari "312-T2"

1978. Racing Cars. Multicoloured.

1107 20 m. Type **237** 25 10
1108 30 m. Ford McLaren "M-23" 30 10
1109 40 m. Soviet experimental car 40 20
1110 50 m. Japanese Mazda 50 20
1111 60 m. Porsche "936-Turbo" . 60 25
1112 80 m. Model of Soviet car . . 65 25
1113 1 t. 20 American rocket car "Blue Flame" 95 40

238 Variegated Boletus (½-size illustration)

1978. Mushrooms. Multicoloured.

1114 20 m. Type **238** 50 15
1115 30 m. The charcoal burner . 75 20
1116 40 m. Red cap 80 25
1117 50 m. Brown birch bolete . . 1·00 30
1118 60 m. Yellow swamp russula . 1·25 35
1119 80 m. "Lactarius resimus" . . 1·50 50
1120 1 t. 20 "Flammula spumosa" . 2·00 75

239 Aleksandr Mozhaisky and his Monoplane, 1884

1978. Air. History of Aviation. Multicoloured.

1121 20 m. Type **239** 10 10
1122 30 m. Henri Farman and Farman H.F.III biplane . . 10 10
1123 40 m. Geoffrey de Havilland and De Havilland FE-1 biplane . 20 10
1124 50 m. Charles Lindbergh and "Spirit of St. Louis" . . . 30 15
1125 60 m. Shagdarsuren, Demberel, biplane and glider 40 20
1126 80 m. Chkalov, Baidukov, Belyakov and Tupolev ANT-25 airliner 45 25
1127 1 t. 20 A. N. Tupolev and Tupolev Tu-154 jetliner . . 70 35

240 Footballers and View of Rio de Janeiro

1978. World Cup Football Championship, Argentina. Multicoloured.

1129 20 m. Type **240** 10 10
1130 30 m. Footballers and Old Town Tower, Berne 10 10

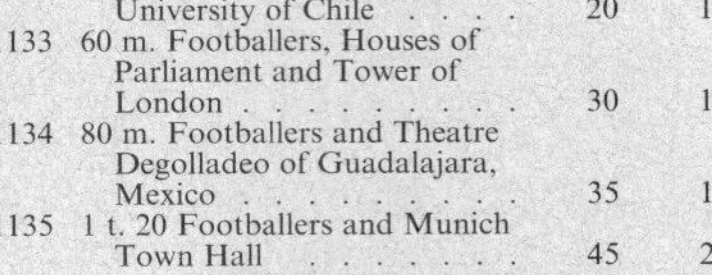

1131 40 m. Footballers and Stockholm Town Hall . . . 15 10
1132 50 m. Footballers and University of Chile 20 10
1133 60 m. Footballers, Houses of Parliament and Tower of London 30 15
1134 80 m. Footballers and Theatre Degolladeo of Guadalajara, Mexico 35 15
1135 1 t. 20 Footballers and Munich Town Hall 45 25

241 Mongolian Youth and Girl

1978. Mongolian Youth Congress, Ulan Bator.

1137 **241** 60 m. multicoloured . . . 35 15

242 Eurasian Beaver and 1954 Canadian Beaver Stamp

1978. "CAPEX '78". International Stamp Exhibition, Toronto. Multicoloured.

1138 20 m. Type **242** 20 10
1139 30 m. Tibetan sandgrouse and Canada S.G. 620 . . . . . 40 10
1140 40 m. Black-throated diver and Canada S.G. 495 . . . . . 50 10
1141 50 m. Argali and Canada S.G. 449 . . . . 70 15
1142 60 m. Brown bear and Canada S.G. 447 . . . . 80 15
1143 80 m. Elk and Canada S.G. 448 90 25
1144 1 t. 20 Herring gull and Canada S.G. 474 . . . . 1·50 35

243 Marx, Engels and Lenin

1978. 20th Anniv of Review "Problems of Peace and Socialism".

1146 **243** 60 m. red, gold and black . 35 15

244 Map of Cuba, Liner, Tupolev Tu-134 Jetliner and Emblem

1978. Air. 11th World Youth Festival, Havana.

1147 **244** 1 t. multicoloured 90 20

245 "Open-air Repose"

1978. 20th Anniv of Philatelic Co-operation between Mongolia and Hungary. Paintings by P. Angalan. Multicoloured.

1148 1 t. 50 Type **245** 40 40
1149 1 t. 50 "Winter Night" 40 40
1150 1 t. 50 "Saddling" 40 40

247 Butterfly Dog

1978. Dogs. Multicoloured.

1152 10 m. Type **247** 20 10
1153 20 m. Black Mongolian sheepdog 25 10
1154 30 m. Puli (Hungarian sheepdog) 35 15
1155 40 m. St. Bernard 40 20
1156 50 m. German shepherd dog 55 25
1157 60 m. Mongolian watchdog 65 25
1158 70 m. Semoyedic Spitz 75 35
1159 80 m. Laika (space dog) 90 35
1160 1 t. 20 Black and white poodles and cocker spaniel 1·10 55

248 Open Book showing Scenes from Mongolian Literary Works

1978. 50th Anniv of Mongolian Writers' Association.

1161 **248** 60 m. blue and red 35 15

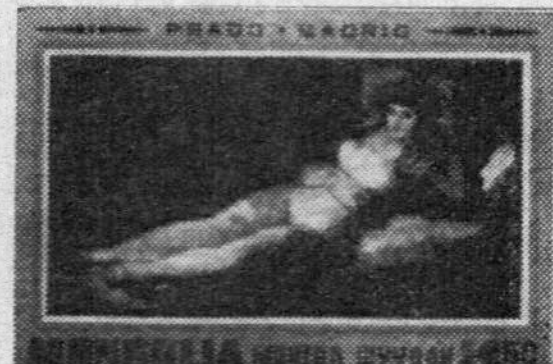

249 "Dressed Maja" (Goya, 150th death anniv)

1978. Painters' Anniversaries. Multicoloured.

1162 1 t. 50 Type **249** 1·25 1·25
1163 1 t. 50 "Ta Matete" (Gaugin - 75th death anniv) 1·25 1·25
1164 1 t. 50 "Bridge at Arles" (Van Gogh - 125th birth anniv) 1·25 1·25

250 Young Bactrian Camel

1978. Bactrian Camels. Multicoloured.

1166 20 m. Camel with Foal 25 15
1167 30 m. Type **250** 30 15
1168 40 m. Two camels 45 20
1169 50 m. Woman leading loaded camel 55 25
1170 60 m. Camel in winter coat 70 30
1171 80 m. Camel-drawn water waggon 90 45
1172 1 t. 20 Camel racing 1·25 60

251 Flags of COMECON Countries

1979. 30th Anniv of Council of Mutual Economic Assistance.

1173 **251** 60 m. multicoloured 35 15

252 Children riding Camel

1979. International Year of the Child. Multicoloured.

1174 10 m. + 5 m. Type **252** 20 15
1175 30 m. + 5 m. Children feeding chickens 30 15
1176 50 m. + 5 m. Children with deer 45 15
1177 60 m. + 5 m. Children picking flowers 55 20
1178 70 m. + 5 m. Children watering tree 65 25
1179 80 m. + 5 m. Young scientists 75 35
1180 1 t. + 5 m. Making music and dancing 1·00 50

253 Silver Tabby

1978. Domestic Cats. Multicoloured.

1182 10 m. Type **253** 20 10
1183 30 m. White Persian 35 15
1184 50 m. Red Persian 55 15
1185 60 m. Blue-cream Persian 70 20
1186 70 m. Siamese 80 30
1187 80 m. Smoke Persian 90 35
1188 1 t. Birman 1·25 50

254 "Potaninia mongolica"

1979. Flowers. Multicoloured.

1189 10 m. Type **254** 20 10
1190 30 m. "Sophora alopecuroides" 30 10
1191 50 m. "Halimodendron halodendron" 35 15
1192 60 m. "Myosotis asiatica" 50 20
1193 70 m. "Scabiosa comosa" 50 30
1194 80 m. "Leucanthemum sibiricum" 60 30
1195 1 t. "Leontopodium ochroleucum" 80 45

255 Finland v. Czechoslovakia

1979. World Ice Hockey Championships, Moscow. Multicoloured.

1196 10 m. Type **255** 10 10
1197 30 m. West Germany v. Sweden 10 10
1198 50 m. U.S.A. v. Canada 15 10
1199 60 m. Russia v. Sweden 15 10
1200 70 m. Canada v. Russia 20 15
1201 80 m. Swedish goalkeeper 20 15
1202 1 t. Czechoslovakia v. Russia 30 20

256 Lambs (Sanzhid)

1979. Agriculture Paintings. Multicoloured.

1203 10 m. Type **256** 10 10
1204 30 m. "Milking camels" (Budbazar) 20 10
1205 50 m. "Aircraft bringing help" (Radnabazar) 40 15
1206 60 m. "Herdsmen" (Budbazar) 40 15
1207 70 m. "Milkmaids" "Nanzadsguren) (vert) 55 30
1208 80 m. "Summer Evening" (Sanzhid) 75 40
1209 1 t. "Country Landscape" (Tserendondog) 90 50

257 First Mongolian and Bulgarian Stamps

1979. Death Centenary of Sir Rowland Hill, and "Philaserdica 79" International Stamp Exn, Sofia. Each black, grey and brown.

1211 1 t. Type **257** 1·50 1·00
1212 1 t. American mail coach 1·50 1·00
1213 1 t. Travelling post office, London-Birmingham railway 2·00 1·25
1214 1 t. Paddle-steamer "Hindoostan" 1·75 1·00

258 Stephenson's "Rocket"

1979. Development of Railways. Multicoloured.

1215 10 m. Type **258** 30 10
1216 20 m. Locomotive "Adler", 1835, Germany 35 10
1217 30 m. Steam locomotive, 1860, U.S.A. 45 10
1218 40 m. Class KB4 steam locomotive, 1931, Mongolia 55 15
1219 50 m. Class Er steam locomotive, 1936, Mongolia 60 20
1220 60 m. Diesel train, 1970, Mongolia 70 25
1221 70 m. "Hikari" express train, 1963, Japan 90 30
1222 80 m. Monorail aerotrain "Orleans", France 95 40
1223 1 t. 20 Experimental jet train "Rapidity", Russia 1·10 50

259 Flags of Mongolia and Russia

262 East German Flag, Berlin Buildings and "Soyuz 31"

260 Pallas's Cat

1979. 40th Anniv of Battle of Khalka River.

1224 **259** 60 m. gold, red and yellow 30 20
1225 – 60 m. red, yellow & blue 30 20

DESIGN: No. 1225, Ribbons, badge and military scene.

1979. Wild Cats. Multicoloured.

1226 10 m. Type **260** 15 10
1227 30 m. Lynx 30 15
1228 50 m. Tiger 55 25
1229 60 m. Snow leopard 65 25
1230 70 m. Leopard 75 35
1231 80 m. Cheetah 80 35
1232 1 t. Lion 1·25 50

1979. 30th Anniv of German Democratic Republic (East Germany).

1234 **262** 60 m. multicoloured 35 10

263 Demoiselle Crane

1979. Air. Protected Birds. Multicoloured.

1235 10 m. Type **263** 35 10
1236 30 m. Barred warbler 55 10
1237 50 m. Ruddy shelduck 65 15
1238 60 m. Azure-winged magpie 75 20
1239 70 m. Goldfinch 75 20
1240 80 m. Great tit 85 25
1241 1 t. Golden oriole 1·10 30

264 "Venus 5" and "6"

1979. Air. Space Research. Multicoloured.

1242 10 m. Type **264** 10 10
1243 30 m. "Mariner 5" 10 10
1244 50 m. "Mars 3" 15 10
1245 60 m. "Viking 1" and "2" 15 10
1246 70 m. "Luna 1", "2" and "3" 20 15
1247 80 m. "Lunokhod 2" 20 15
1248 1 t. "Apollo 15" Moon-rover 30 20

265 Cross-country Skiing

1980. Winter Olympic Games, Lake Placid. Multicoloured.

1250 20 m. Type **265** 10 10
1251 30 m. Biathlon 10 10
1252 40 m. Ice hockey 15 10
1253 50 m. Ski jumping 15 10
1254 60 m. Slalom 20 15
1255 80 m. Speed skating 20 15
1256 1 t. 20 Four-man bobsleigh 30 20

266 "Andrena scita" (mining bee)

1980. Air. Wasps and Bees. Multicoloured.

1258	20 m. Type **266**	10	10
1259	30 m. "Paravespula germanica" (wasp)	10	10
1260	40 m. "Perilampus ruficornis" (parasitic wasp)	20	10
1261	50 m. Buff-tailed bumble bee	30	15
1262	60 m. Honey bee	40	20
1263	80 m. "Stilbum cyanurum" (cuckoo wasp)	45	25
1264	1 t. 20 "Parnopes grandior" (cuckoo wasp)	70	35

267 Weightlifting

1980. Olympic Games, Moscow. Multicoloured.

1266	20 m. Type **267**	10	10
1267	30 m. Archery	10	10
1268	40 m. Gymnastics	15	10
1269	50 m. Running	15	10
1270	60 m. Boxing	20	15
1271	80 m. Judo	20	15
1272	1 t. 20 Cycling	30	20

268 Zlin Z-526 AFs Akrobat Special

1980. Air. World Acrobatic Championship, Oshkosh, Wisconsin. Multicoloured.

1274	20 m. Type **268**	10	10
1275	30 m. Socata RF-6B Sportsman (inscr "RS-180")	15	10
1276	40 m. Grumman A-1 Yankee	20	10
1277	50 m. MJ-2 Tempete	30	15
1278	60 m. Pitts S-2A biplane (inscr "Pits")	35	20
1279	80 m. Hirth Acrostar	45	25
1280	1 t. 20 Yakovlev Yak-50	65	35

269 Swimming

1980. Olympic Medal Winners. Multicoloured.

1282	20 m. Type **269**	10	10
1283	30 m. Fencing	10	10
1284	50 m. Judo	10	10
1285	60 m. Athletics	15	10
1286	80 m. Boxing	20	10
1287	1 t. Weightlifting	25	15
1288	1 t. 20 Kayak-canoe	30	20

270 Sukhe Bator

271 Gubarev

1980. Mongolian Politicians.

1290	**270**	60 m. brown	15	10
1291	–	60 m. blue	15	10
1292	–	60 m. turquoise	15	10
1293	–	60 m. bronze-green	15	10
1294	–	60 m. deep green	15	10
1295	–	60 m. red	15	10
1296	–	60 m. brown	15	10

DESIGNS—VERT: No. 1291, Marshal Choibalsan; No. 1292, Yu. Tsedenbal aged 13; No. 1293, Tsedenbal as soldier, 1941; No. 1294, Pres. Tsedenbal in 1979; No. 1295, Tsedenbal with children. HORIZ: No. 1296, Tsedenbal and President Brezhnev of Russia.

1980. "Intercosmos" Space Programme. Multicoloured.

1297	40 m. Type **271**	10	10
1298	40 m. Czechoslovak stamp showing Gubarev and Remek	10	10
1299	40 m. P. Klimuk	10	10
1300	40 m. Polish stamp showing M. Hermaszewski	10	10
1301	40 m. V. Bykovsky	10	10
1302	40 m. East German stamp showing S. Jahn	10	10
1303	40 m. N. Rukavishnikov	10	10
1304	40 m. Bulgarian stamp showing G. Ivanov	10	10
1305	40 m. V. Kubasov	10	10
1306	40 m. Hungarian stamp showing Kubasov and B. Farkas	10	10

272 Benz, 1885

1980. Classic Cars. Multicoloured.

1307	20 m. Type **272**	25	10
1308	30 m. "President" Czechoslovakia, 1897	30	10
1309	40 m. Armstrong Siddeley, 1904	35	25
1310	50 m. Russo-Balt, 1909	45	20
1311	60 m. Packard, 1909	50	20
1312	80 m. Lancia, 1911	70	30
1313	1 t. 60 "Marne" taxi, 1914	1·60	60

273 Adelie Penguin

276 "The Shepherd speaking the Truth"

1980. Antarctic Exploration. Multicoloured.

1315	20 m. Type **273**	75	15
1316	30 m. Blue whales	70	15
1317	40 m. Wandering albatross and Jacques Cousteau's ship "Calypso" and bathysphere	95	30
1318	50 m. Weddell seals and mobile research station	90	20
1319	60 m. Emperor penguins	1·50	35
1320	70 m. Great skuas	1·75	40
1321	80 m. Killer whales	1·75	50
1322	1 t. 20 Adelie penguins, research station, Ilyushin Il-18B airplane and tracked vehicle	2·75	75

1980. Nursery Tales. Multicoloured.

1326	20 m. Type **276**	10	10
1327	30 m. Children under umbrella and rainbow ("Above them the Sky is always clear")	10	10
1328	40 m. Children on sledge and skis ("Winter's Joys")	10	10
1329	50 m. Girl watching boy playing flute ("Little Musicians")	15	10
1330	60 m. Boys giving girl leaves ("Happy Birthday")	15	10
1331	80 m. Children with flowers and briefcase ("First Schoolday")	20	15
1332	1 t. 20 Girls dancing ("May Day")	35	25

277 Soldier

1981. 60th Anniv of Mongolian People's Army.

1334	**277**	60 m. multicoloured	40	15

MINIMUM PRICE

The minimum price quoted is 10p which represents a handling charge rather than a basis for valuing common stamps. For further notes about prices see introductory pages.

278 Economy Emblems within Party Initials

1981. 60th Anniv of Mongolian Revolutionary People's Party.

1335	**278**	60 m. gold, red and black	30	15

279 Motocross

1981. Motor Cycle Sports. Multicoloured.

1336	10 m. Type **279**	10	10
1337	20 m. Tour racing	10	10
1338	30 m. Ice racing	10	10
1339	40 m. Road racing	15	10
1340	50 m. Motocross (different)	15	10
1341	60 m. Road racing (different)	20	10
1342	70 m. Speedway	20	10
1343	80 m. Sidecar racing	25	15
1344	1 t. 20 Road racing (different)	40	20

280 Cosmonauts entering Space Capsule

1981. Soviet–Mongolian Space Flight. Mult.

1345	20 m. Type **280**	10	10
1346	30 m. Rocket and designer S. P. Korolev	10	10
1347	40 m. "Vostok 1" and Yuri Gagarin	10	10
1348	50 m. "Soyuz"–"Sallyut" space station	15	10
1349	60 m. Spectral photography	15	10
1350	80 m. Crystal and space station	20	15
1351	1 t. 20 Space complex, Moscow Kremlin and Sukhe Bator statue, Ulan Bator	35	25

281 Ulan Bator Buildings and 1961 Mongolian Stamp

1981. Stamp Exhibitions.

1353	**281**	1 t. multicoloured	2·25	1·00
1354	–	1 t. multicoloured	1·75	80
1355	–	1 t. black, blue and magenta	1·75	80
1356	–	1 t. multicoloured	2·25	1·00

DESIGNS: No. 1353, Type **281** (Mongolian stamp exhibition); No. 1354, Wurttemberg stamps of 1947 and 1949 and view of Old Stuttgart ("Naposta '81" exhibition); No. 1355, Parliament building and sculpture, Vienna, and Austrian stamp of 1933 ("WIPA 1981" exhibition); No. 1356, Japanese stamp of 1964, cherry blossom and girls in Japanese costume ("Japex '81" exhibition, Tokyo).

282 Star and Industrial and Agricultural Scenes

1981. 18th Mongolian Revolutionary People's Party Congress.

1357	**282**	60 m. multicoloured	30	10

284 Sheep Farming

1981. "Results of the People's Economy". Multicoloured.

1359	20 m. Type **284**	10	10
1360	30 m. Transport	1·25	15
1361	40 m. Telecommunications	60	15
1362	50 m. Public health service	20	10
1363	60 m. Agriculture	30	10
1364	80 m. Electrical industry	35	15
1365	1 t. 20 Housing	50	20

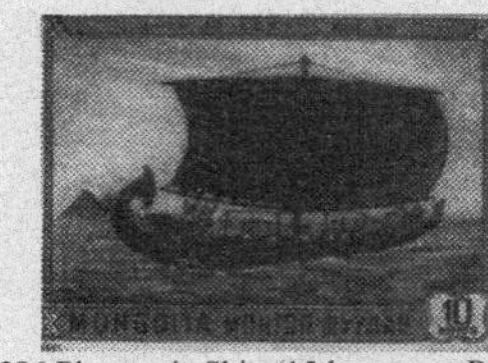

286 Pharaonic Ship (15th century B.C.)

1981. Sailing Ships. Multicoloured.

1367	10 m. Type **286**	15	10
1368	20 m. Mediterranean sailing ship (9th century)	20	10
1369	40 m. Hanse kogge (12th century) (vert)	30	10
1370	50 m. Venetian felucca (13th century) (vert)	40	15
1371	60 m. Columbus's "Santa Maria" (vert)	45	25
1372	80 m. Cook's H.M.S. "Endeavour" (vert)	50	30
1373	1 t. "Poltava" (Russian ship of the line) (vert)	70	35
1374	1 t. 20 American schooner (19th century) (vert)	80	40

287 Arms of Mongolia and Russia

1981. Soviet–Mongolian Friendship Pact.

1375	**287**	60 m. red, blue and gold	35	10

288 "Hendrickje in Bed"

290 White-tailed Sea Eagle and German 1 m. "Zeppelin" Stamp

289 Billy Goat (pawn)

1981. 375th Birth Anniv of Rembrandt (artist). Multicoloured.

1376	20 m. "Flora"	20	10
1377	30 m. Type **288**	25	15
1378	40 m. "Young Woman with Earrings"	45	20
1379	50 m. "Young girl in the Window"	50	25
1380	60 m. "Hendrickje like Flora"	60	30
1381	80 m. "Saskia with Red Flower"	80	35
1382	1 t. 20 "The Holy Family with Drape" (detail)	1·10	45

1981. Mongolian Chess Pieces. Multicoloured.
1384 20 m. Type **289** 20 10
1385 40 m. Horse-drawn cart (rook) 30 15
1386 50 m. Camel (bishop) 40 20
1387 60 m. Horse (knight) 60 25
1388 80 m. Lion (queen) 75 30
1389 1 t. 20 Man with dog (king) 1·10 40

1981. Air. 50th Anniv of "Graf Zeppelin" Polar Flight. Multicoloured.
1391 20 m. Type **290** 40 15
1392 30 m. Arctic Fox and German 2 m. "Zeppelin" stamp 40 15
1393 40 m. Walrus and German 4 m. "Zeppelin" stamp 50 15
1394 50 m. Polar Bear and Russian 30 k. "Zeppelin" stamp 60 15
1395 60 m. Snowy Owl and Russian 35 k. "Zeppelin" stamp 1·00 20
1396 80 m. Atlantic Puffin and Russian 1 r. "Zeppelin" stamp 1·25 20
1397 1 t. 20 Northern sealion and Russian 2 r. "Zeppelin" stamp 1·50 30

291 Circus Camel and Circus Building, Ulan Bator

1981. Mongolian Sport and Art. Multicoloured.
1399 10 m. Type **291** 10 10
1400 20 m. Horsemen and stadium (National holiday cavalcade) 15 10
1401 40 m. Wrestling and Ulan Bator stadium 25 15
1402 50 m. Archers and stadium 35 20
1403 60 m. Folk singer-dancer and House of Culture 45 20
1404 80 m. Girl playing jatga (folk instrument) and Ulan Bator Drama Theatre 60 30
1405 1 t. Ballet dancers and Opera House 90 40
1406 1 t. 20 Exhibition Hall and statue of man on bucking horse 1·10 65

292 Mozart and scene from "The Magic Flute"

1981. Composers. Multicoloured.
1407 20 m. Type **292** 15 10
1408 30 m. Beethoven and scene from "Fidelio" 20 10
1409 40 m. Bartok and scene from "The Miraculous Mandarin" 20 10
1410 50 m. Verdi and scene from "Aida" 30 15
1411 60 m. Tchaikovsky and scene from "The Sleeping Beauty" 35 15
1412 80 m. Dvorak and score of "New World" symphony 45 25
1413 1 t. 20 Chopin, piano, score and quill pens 60 30

293 "Mongolian Women in Everyday Life" (detail, Davaakhuu)

294 Gorbatko

1981. International Decade for Women. Mult.
1414 20 m. Type **293** 25 10
1415 30 m. "Mongolian Women in Everyday Life" (different detail) 35 15
1416 40 m. "National Day" (detail, Khishigbaiar) 40 20
1417 50 m. "National Day" (detail) (different) 50 25
1418 60 m. "National Day" (detail) (different) 60 35
1419 80 m. "Ribbon Weaver" (Ts. Baidi) 85 40
1420 1 t. 20 "Expectant Mother" (Senghesokhio) 1·25 65

1981. "Intercosmos" Space Programme. Mult.
1422 50 m. Type **294** 15 10
1423 50 m. Vietnam stamp showing Gorbatko and Pham Tuan 15 10
1424 50 m. Romanenko 15 10
1425 50 m. Cuban stamp showing Tamayo 15 10
1426 50 m. Dzhanibekov 15 10
1427 50 m. Mongolian stamp showing Dzhanibekov and Gurrugchaa 15 10
1428 50 m. Popov 15 10
1429 50 m. Rumanian stamp showing "Salyut" space station and "Soyuz" space ship 15 10

295 Karl von Drais Bicycle, 1816

1982. History of the Bicycle. Multicoloured.
1430 10 m. Type **295** 10 10
1431 20 m. Macmillan bicycle, 1838 10 10
1432 40 m. First American pedal bicycle by Pierre Lallament, 1866 15 10
1433 50 m. First European pedal bicycle by Ernest Michaux 20 10
1434 60 m. "Kangaroo" bicycle, 1877 20 10
1435 80 m. Coventry Rotary Tandem, 1870s 30 10
1436 1 t. Chain-driven bicycle, 1878 35 15
1437 1 t. 20 Modern bicycle 40 20

296 Footballers (Brazil, 1950)

1982. World Cup Football Championship, Spain. Multicoloured.
1439 10 m. Type **296** 10 10
1440 20 m. Switzerland, 1954 10 10
1441 40 m. Sweden, 1958 15 10
1442 50 m. Chile, 1962 20 10
1443 60 m. England, 1966 20 10
1444 80 m. Mexico, 1970 30 10
1445 1 t. West Germany, 1974 35 15
1446 1 t. 20 Argentina, 1978 40 20

297 Trade Union Emblem and Economic Symbols

299 Dimitrov

1982. 12th Mongolian Trade Unions Congress.
1448 **297** 60 m. multicoloured 1·00 30

1982. Birth Centenary of Georgi Dimitrov (Bulgarian statesman).
1450 **299** 60 m. black, grey & gold 35 10

300 Chicks

1982. Young Animals. Multicoloured.
1451 10 m. Type **300** 10 10
1452 20 m. Colt 10 10
1453 30 m. Lamb 15 10
1454 40 m. Roe deer fawn 20 10
1455 50 m. Bactrian camel 20 10
1456 60 m. Kid 25 10
1457 70 m. Calf 30 15
1458 1 t. 20 Wild piglet 40 20

301 Coal-fired Industry

1982. Coal Mining.
1459 **301** 60 m. multicoloured 35 10

302 Emblem

304 Revsomol Emblem within "Flower"

303 Siberian Pine

1982. 18th Revsomol Youth Congress.
1460 **302** 60 m. multicoloured 35 10

1982. Trees. Multicoloured.
1461 20 m. Type **303** 10 10
1462 30 m. Siberian fir 10 10
1463 40 m. Poplar 20 10
1464 50 m. Siberian larch 20 10
1465 60 m. Scots pine 25 10
1466 80 m. Birch 30 15
1467 1 t. 20 Spruce 50 25

1982. 60th Anniv of Revsomol Youth Organization.
1468 **304** 60 m. multicoloured 35 10

305 World Map and Satellite

1982. Air. I.T.U. Delegates' Conference, Nairobi.
1469 **305** 60 m. multicoloured 45 15

306 Japanese "Iseki-6500" Tractor

1982. Tractors. Multicoloured.
1470 10 m. Type **306** 10 10
1471 20 m. West German "Deutz-DX230" 10 10
1472 40 m. British "Bonser" 15 10
1473 50 m. American "International-884" 20 10
1474 60 m. French Renault "TX 145-14" 20 10
1475 80 m. Russian "Belarus-611" 25 10
1476 1 t. Russian "K-7100" 30 15
1477 1 t. 20 Russian "DT-75" 40 20

307 Hump-backed Whitefish and Lake Hevsgel

1982. Landscapes and Animals. Multicoloured.
1478 20 m. Type **307** 50 15
1479 30 m. Zavkhan Highlands and sheep 30 10
1480 40 m. Lake Hovd and Eurasian beaver 40 10
1481 50 m. Lake Uvs and horses 50 15
1482 60 m. Bajankhongor Steppe and goitred gazelle 60 20
1483 80 m. Bajan-Elgii Highlands and rider with golden eagle 2·25 35
1484 1 t. 20 Gobi Desert and bactrian camels 1·00 50

308 "Sputnik 1"

1982. Air. Second U.N. Conference on the Exploration and Peaceful Uses of Outer Space. Multicoloured.
1485 60 m. Type **308** 15 10
1486 60 m. "Sputnik 2" and Laika (first dog in space) 15 10
1487 60 m. "Vostok 1" and Yuri Gagarin (first man in space) 15 10
1488 60 m. "Venera 8" 15 10
1489 60 m. "Vostok 6" and V. Tereshkova (first woman in space) 15 10
1490 60 m. Aleksei Leonov and space walker 15 10
1491 60 m. Neil Armstrong and astronaut on Moon's surface 15 10
1492 60 m. V. Dzhanibekov, Jean-Loup Chretien and "Soyuz T-6" 15 10

309 Montgolfier Brothers' Balloon, 1783

1982. Air. Bicentenary of Manned Flight. Mult.
1494 20 m. Type **309** 10 10
1495 30 m. Jean-Pierre Blanchard and John Jeffries crossing the channel, 1785 15 10
1496 40 m. Charles Green's flight to Germany in balloon "Royal Vauxhall", 1836 20 10
1497 50 m. Salomon Andree's North Pole flight in balloon "Ornen", 1897 25 10
1498 60 m. First Gordon Bennett balloon race, Paris, 1906 30 15
1499 80 m. First stratosphere flight by Auguste Piccard in balloon "F.N.R.S.", Switzerland, 1931 40 20
1500 1 t. 20 Stratosphere balloon USSR-VR-62 flight, 1933 55 25

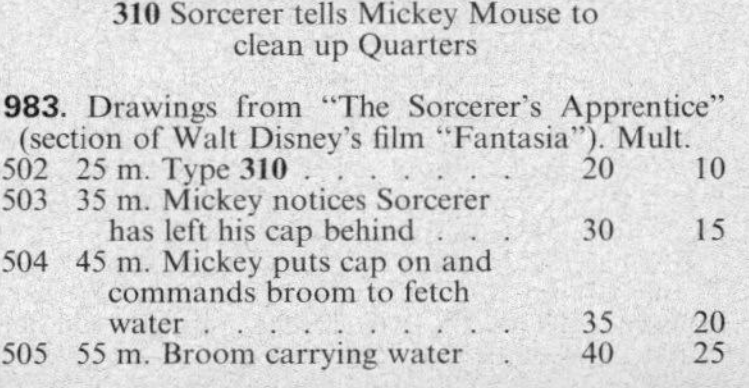

310 Sorcerer tells Mickey Mouse to clean up Quarters

1983. Drawings from "The Sorcerer's Apprentice" (section of Walt Disney's film "Fantasia"). Mult.
1502 25 m. Type **310** 20 10
1503 35 m. Mickey notices Sorcerer has left his cap behind 30 15
1504 45 m. Mickey puts cap on and commands broom to fetch water 35 20
1505 55 m. Broom carrying water 40 25

1506 65 m. Mickey sleeps while broom continues to fetch water, flooding the room . . 50 30
1507 75 m. Mickey uses axe on broom to try to stop it 55 35
1508 85 m. Each splinter becomes a broom which continues to fetch water 65 40
1509 1 t. 40 Mickey, clinging to Sorcerer's Book of Spells, caught in whirlpool . . . . 1·00 55
1510 2 t. Mickey handing cap back to Sorcerer . . . . 1·40 75

311 Foal with Mother

1983. "The Foal and the Hare" (folk tale). Mult.
1512 10 m. Type **311** 10 10
1513 20 m. Foal wanders off alone 15 10
1514 30 m. Foal finds sack 25 15
1515 40 m. Foal unties sack 30 15
1516 50 m. Wolf jumps out of sack 40 20
1517 60 m. Hare appears as wolf is about to eat foal 45 25
1518 70 m. Hare tricks wolf into re-entering sack 50 30
1519 80 m. Hare ties up sack with wolf inside 60 35
1520 1 t. 20 Hare and foal look for foal's mother 90 50

312 Antonov An-24B Aircraft

1983. Tourism. Multicoloured.
1524 20 m. Type **312** 20 10
1525 30 m. Skin tent 10 10
1526 40 m. Roe deer 15 10
1527 50 m. Argali 25 10
1528 60 m. Imperial eagle . . . . 2·00 30
1529 80 m. Khan Museum, Ulan Bator 40 20
1530 1 t. 20 Sukhe Bator statue, Ulan Bator 55 25

313 Rose

1983. Flowers. Multicoloured.
1531 20 m. Type **313** 10 10
1532 30 m. Dahlia 15 10
1533 40 m. Marigold 20 10
1534 50 m. Narcissus 25 10
1535 60 m. Viola 30 10
1536 80 m. Tulip 40 15
1537 1 t. 20 Sunflower 50 25

314 Border Guard

1983. 50th Anniv of Border Guards.
1538 **314** 60 m. multicoloured . . . 40 10

316 Karl Marx

1983. Death Centenary of Karl Marx.
1540 **316** 60 m. red, gold and blue . 35 10

317 Agriculture

1983. 18th Communist Party Congress Five Year Plan. Multicoloured.
1541 10 m. Type **317** 10 10
1542 20 m. Power industry 10 10
1543 30 m. Textile industry 10 10
1544 40 m. Science in industry and agriculture 15 10
1545 60 m. Improvement of living standards 20 10
1546 80 m. Communications . . . 2·00 50
1547 1 t. Children (education) . . . 40 20

318 Young Inventors

1983. Children's Year. Multicoloured.
1548 10 m. Type **318** 15 10
1549 20 m. In school 25 10
1550 30 m. Archery 40 15
1551 40 m. Shepherdess playing flute 50 20
1552 50 m. Girl with deer 65 30
1553 70 m. Collecting rocks and mushrooms . . . . 2·25 50
1554 1 t. 20 Girl playing lute and boy singing . . . . 1·25 60

319 Skating

1983. 10th Anniv of Children's Fund. Multicoloured.
1555 20 m. Type **319** 10 10
1556 30 m. Shepherds 10 10
1557 40 m. Tree-planting 15 10
1558 50 m. Playing by the sea . . . 20 10
1559 60 m. Carrying water 25 15
1560 80 m. Folk dancing 30 20
1561 1 t. 20 Ballet 55 25

320 Pallas's Pika

1983. Small Mammals. Multicoloured.
1563 20 m. Type **320** 35 20
1564 30 m. Long-eared jerboa . . . 45 25
1565 40 m. Eurasian red squirrel . . 55 30
1566 50 m. Daurian hedgehog . . . 65 40
1567 60 m. Harvest mouse 80 45
1568 80 m. Eurasian water shrew . 1·25 70
1569 1 t. 20 Siberian chipmunk . . 1·75 95

322 Bobsleighing

1984. Winter Olympic Games, Sarajevo. Mult.
1571 20 m. Type **322** 10 10
1572 30 m. Cross-country skiing . . 10 10
1573 40 m. Ice hockey 10 10
1574 50 m. Speed skating 15 10
1575 60 m. Ski jumping 15 10
1576 80 m. Ice dancing 20 15
1577 1 t. 20 Biathlon (horiz) . . . 35 25

323 Mail Van

1984. World Communications Year. Multicoloured.
1579 10 m. Type **323** 10 10
1580 20 m. Earth receiving station . 10 10
1581 40 m. Airliner 40 15
1582 50 m. Central Post Office, Ulan Bator 25 10
1583 1 t. Transmitter 40 15
1584 1 t. 20 Diesel train . . . . . 3·50 1·25

325 Cycling

326 Flag, Rocket and Coastal Scene

1984. Olympic Games, Los Angeles. Multicoloured.
1587 20 m. Gymnastics (horiz) . . 10 10
1588 30 m. Type **325** 10 10
1589 40 m. Weightlifting 10 10
1590 50 m. Judo 10 10
1591 60 m. Archery 15 10
1592 80 m. Boxing 20 15
1593 1 t. 20 High jumping (horiz) . . 35 25

1984. 25th Anniv of Cuban Revolution.
1595 **326** 60 m. multicoloured . . . 25 10

328 Douglas DC-10

329 Speaker, Radio and Transmitter

1984. Air. Civil Aviation. Multicoloured.
1597 20 m. Type **328** 10 10
1598 30 m. Airbus Industrie A300B2 20 10
1599 40 m. Concorde supersonic jetliner 25 10
1600 50 m. Boeing 747-200 . . . . 30 15
1601 60 m. Ilyushin Il-62M 30 20
1602 80 m. Tupolev Tu-154 . . . . 50 25
1603 1 t. 20 Ilyushin Il-86 . . . . 60 35

1984. 50th Anniv of Mongolian Broadcasting.
1605 **329** 60 m. multicoloured . . . 60 20

330 Silver and Gold Coins

1984. 60th Anniv of State Bank.
1606 **330** 60 m. multicoloured . . . 25 10

331 Donshy Mask

333 Sukhe Bator Statue

332 Golden Harp

1984. Traditional Masks. Multicoloured.
1607 20 m. Type **331** 10 10
1608 30 m. Zamandi 25 10
1609 40 m. Ulaan-Yadam 30 10
1610 50 m. Lkham 45 15
1611 60 m. Damdinchoizhoo 55 20
1612 80 m. Ochirvaan 75 25
1613 1 t. 20 Namsrai . . . . . . 1·25 40

1984. Scenes from Walt Disney's "Mickey and the Beanstalk" (cartoon film). Multicoloured.
1615 25 m. Type **332** 20 10
1616 35 m. Mickey holding box of magic beans 30 15
1617 45 m. Mickey about to eat bean 40 20
1618 55 m. Mickey looking for magic bean 50 25
1619 65 m. Goofy, Mickey and Donald at top of beanstalk 55 30
1620 75 m. Giant holding Mickey . 60 35
1621 85 m. Giant threatening Mickey 80 40
1622 140 m. Goofy, Mickey and Donald cutting down beanstalk . . . . 1·40 65
1623 2 t. Goofy and Donald rescuing golden harp . . . . 1·60 75

1984. 60th Anniv of Ulan Bator City.
1625 **333** 60 m. multicoloured . . . 60 20

334 Arms, Flag and Landscape

335 Rider carrying Flag

1984. 60th Anniv of Mongolian People's Republic.
1626 **334** 60 m. multicoloured . . . 60 20

1984. 60th Anniv of Mongolian People's Revolutionary Party.
1627 **335** 60 m. multicoloured . . . 35 10

336 Collie

1984. Dogs. Multicoloured.

1628 20 m. Type **336** 10 10
1629 30 m. German shepherd 25 10
1630 40 m. Papillon 35 10
1631 50 m. Cocker spaniel 50 15
1632 60 m. Terrier puppy (diamond-shaped) 60 20
1633 80 m. Dalmatians (diamond-shaped) 75 25
1634 1 t. 20 Mongolian shepherd 1·25 40

337 Gaetan Boucher (speed skating)

1984. Winter Olympic Gold Medal Winners. Multicoloured.

1635 20 m. Type **337** 10 10
1636 30 m. Eirik Kvalfoss (biathlon) 10 10
1637 40 m. Marja-Liisa Hamalainen (cross-country skiing) 10 10
1638 50 m. Max Julen (slalom) 15 10
1639 60 m. Jens Weissflog (ski jumping) (vert) 15 10
1640 80 m. W. Hoppe and D. Schauerhammer (two-man bobsleigh) (vert) 20 15
1641 1 t. 20 J. Valova and O. Vassiliev (pairs figure skating) (vert) 35 25

338 Four Animals and Tree

1984. "The Four Friendly Animals" (fairy tale). Multicoloured.

1643 10 m. Type **338** 15 10
1644 20 m. Animals discussing who was the oldest 20 10
1645 30 m. Monkey and elephant beside tree 20 10
1646 40 m. Elephant as calf and young tree 25 10
1647 50 m. Monkey and young tree 40 15
1648 60 m. Hare and young tree 50 20
1649 70 m. Dove and sapling 55 20
1650 80 m. Animals around mature tree 70 30
1651 1 t. 20 Animals supporting each other so that dove could reach fruit 95 40

339 Fawn

1984. Red Deer. Multicoloured.

1653 50 m. Type **339** 40 20
1654 50 m. Stag 40 20
1655 50 m. Adults and fawn by river 40 20
1656 50 m. Doe in woodland 40 20

340 Flag and Pioneers

342 Black Stork

341 Shar Tarlan

1985. 60th Anniv of Mongolian Pioneer Organization.

1657 **340** 60 m. multicoloured 40 15

1985. Cattle. Multicoloured.

1658 20 m. Type **341** 10 10
1659 30 m. Bor khalium 20 10
1660 40 m. Sarlag 30 10
1661 50 m. Dornod talin bukh 45 15
1662 60 m. Char tarlan 55 20
1663 80 m. Nutgiin uulderiin unee 65 20
1664 1 t. 20 Tsagaan tolgoit 1·10 35

1985. Birds. Multicoloured.

1666 20 m. Type **342** 20 10
1667 30 m. White-tailed sea eagle 25 10
1668 40 m. Great white crane 35 10
1669 50 m. Heude's parrotbill 50 20
1670 60 m. Hooded crane 60 20
1671 80 m. Japanese white-necked crane 75 25
1672 1 t. 20 Rough-legged buzzard 1·25 45

343 Footballers

344 Monument

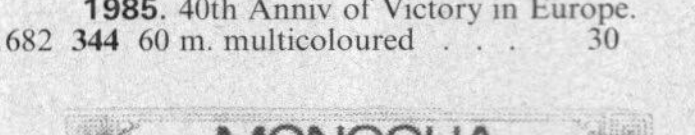

1985. World Junior Football Championship, U.S.S.R.

1674 **343** 20 m. multicoloured 10 10
1675 – 30 m. multicoloured 10 10
1676 – 40 m. multicoloured 15 10
1677 – 50 m. multicoloured 20 10
1678 – 60 m. multicoloured 25 10
1679 – 80 m. multicoloured 30 15
1680 – 1 t. 20 multicoloured 50 25

DESIGNS: 30 m. to 1 t. 20 Different footballing scenes.

1985. 40th Anniv of Victory in Europe.

1682 **344** 60 m. multicoloured 30 10

345 The Snow Leopards

1985. The Snow Leopard. Multicoloured.

1683 50 m. Type **345** 40 20
1684 50 m. Leopard 40 20
1685 50 m. Leopard on cliff ledge 40 20
1686 50 m. Mother and cubs 40 20

346 Moscow Kremlin and Girls of Different Races

347 Monument

1985. 12th World Youth and Students' Festival, Moscow.

1687 **346** 60 m. multicoloured 30 10

1985. 40th Anniv of Victory in Asia.

1688 **347** 60 m. multicoloured 35 10

348 "Rosa dahurica"

1985. Plants. Multicoloured.

1689 20 m. Type **348** 10 10
1690 30 m. False chamomile 20 10
1691 40 m. Dandelion 30 10
1692 50 m. "Saxzitraga nirculus" 45 15
1693 60 m. Cowberry 55 20
1694 80 m. "Sanguisorba officinalis" 65 20
1695 1 t. 20 "Plantago major" 1·10 35

See also Nos. 1719/25.

349 Camel

1985. The Bactrian Camel. Multicoloured.

1697 50 m. Type **349** 40 20
1698 50 m. Adults and calf 40 20
1699 50 m. Calf 40 20
1700 50 m. Adult 40 20

350 "Soyuz" Spacecraft

1985. Space. Multicoloured.

1701 20 m. Type **350** 10 10
1702 30 m. "Kosmos" satellite 10 10
1703 40 m. "Venera-9" satellite 10 10
1704 50 m. "Salyut" space station 15 10
1705 60 m. "Luna-9" landing vehicle 15 10
1706 80 m. "Soyuz" rocket on transporter 1·10 50
1707 1 t. 20 Dish aerial receiving transmission from "Soyuz" 30 15

352 U.N. and Mongolian Flags and U.N. Headquarters, New York

354 Congress Emblem

353 "Tricholoma mongolica"

1985. 40th Anniv of U.N.O.

1710 **352** 60 m. multicoloured 30 10

1985. Fungi. Multicoloured.

1711 20 m. Type **353** 20 10
1712 30 m. Chanterelle 25 10
1713 40 m. Honey fungus 30 10
1714 50 m. Caesar's mushroom 55 15
1715 70 m. Chestnut mushroom 80 20
1716 80 m. Red-staining mushroom 90 25
1717 1 t. 20 Cep 1·40 35

1986. 19th Mongolian Revolutionary People's Party Congress.

1718 **354** 60 m. multicoloured 25 10

1986. Plants. As T **348**. Multicoloured.

1719 20 m. "Valeriana officinalis" 10 10
1720 30 m. "Hyoscymus niger" 20 10
1721 40 m. "Ephedra sinica" 30 10
1722 50 m. "Thymus gobica" 45 15
1723 60 m. "Paeonia anomalia" 55 20
1724 80 m. "Achilea millefolium" 65 25
1725 1 t. 20 "Rhododendron adamsii" 1·10 35

355 Scene from Play

1986. 80th Birth Anniv of D. Natsagdorj (writer).

1726 **355** 60 m. multicoloured 25 10

356 Thalmann

357 Man wearing Patterned Robe

1986. Birth Centenary of Ernst Thalmann (German politician).

1727 **356** 60 m. multicoloured 25 10

1986. Costumes. Multicoloured.

1728 60 m. Type **357** 25 10
1729 60 m. Man in blue robe and fur-lined hat with ear flaps 25 10
1730 60 m. Woman in black and yellow dress and bolero 25 10
1731 60 m. Woman in pink dress patterned with stars 25 10
1732 60 m. Man in cream robe with fur cuffs 25 10
1733 60 m. Man in brown robe and mauve and yellow tunic 25 10
1734 60 m. Woman in blue dress with black, yellow and red overtunic 25 10

358 Footballers

1986. World Cup Football Championship, Mexico.

1735 **358** 20 m. multicoloured 10 10
1736 – 30 m. multicoloured 10 10
1737 – 40 m. multicoloured 10 10
1738 – 50 m. multicoloured 15 10
1739 – 60 m. multicoloured 15 10
1740 – 80 m. multicoloured 20 15
1741 – 1 t. 20 multicoloured 35 25

DESIGNS: 30 m. to 1 t. 20. Different footballing scenes.

359 Mink

1986. Mink. Multicoloured.

1743 60 m. Type **359** 45 15
1744 60 m. Mink on rock 45 15
1745 60 m. Mink on snow-covered branch 45 15
1746 60 m. Two mink 45 15

See also Nos. 1771/4, 1800/3, 1804/7, 1840/3 and 1844/7.

360 "Neptis coenobita"

361 Sukhe Bator Statue

1986. Butterflies and Moths. Multicoloured.

1747	20 m. Type **360**	10	10
1748	30 m. "Colias tycha"	15	10
1749	40 m. "Leptidea amurensis"	20	10
1750	50 m. "Oeneis tarpenledevi"	30	15
1751	60 m. "Mesoacidalia charlotta"	40	20
1752	80 m. Eyed hawk moth	45	25
1753	1 t. 20 Large tiger moth	75	40

1986. 65th Anniv of Independence.

1754	**361** 60 m. multicoloured	25	10

362 Yak and Goats Act

1986. Circus. Multicoloured.

1755	20 m. Type **362**	10	10
1756	30 m. Acrobat	10	10
1757	40 m. Yak act	15	10
1758	50 m. Acrobats (vert)	20	10
1759	60 m. High wire act (vert)	25	15
1760	80 m. Fire juggler on camel (vert)	30	15
1761	1 t. 20 Acrobats on camel-drawn cart (vert)	50	25

363 Morin Khuur

364 Flag and Emblem

1986. Musical Instruments. Multicoloured.

1762	20 m. Type **363**	10	10
1763	30 m. Bishguur (wind instrument)	20	10
1764	40 m. Ever buree (wind)	30	10
1765	50 m. Shudarga (string)	45	15
1766	60 m. Khiil (string)	55	20
1767	80 m. Janchir (string) (horiz)	65	25
1768	1 t. 20 Jatga (string) (horiz)	1·10	35

1986. International Peace Year.

1770	**364** 10 m. multicoloured	50	20

1986. Przewalski's Horse. As T **359**. Mult.

1771	50 m. Horses grazing on sparsely grassed plain	45	15
1772	50 m. Horses grazing on grassy plain	45	15
1773	50 m. Adults with foal	45	15
1774	50 m. Horses in snow	45	15

365 Temple

1986. Ancient Buildings. Multicoloured.

1775	60 m. Type **365**	60	20
1776	60 m. Temple with light green roof and white doors	60	20
1777	60 m. Temple with porch	60	20
1778	60 m. White building with three porches	60	20

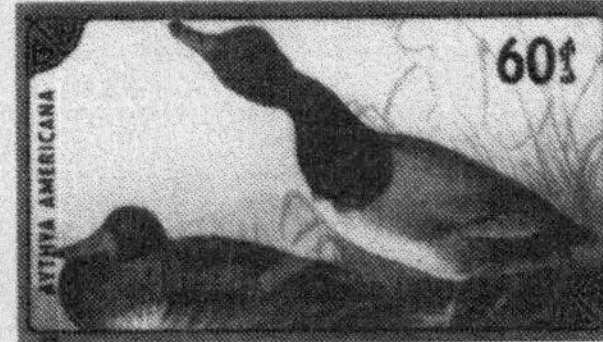

366 Redhead ("Aythya americana")

1986. Birds. Multicoloured.

1779	60 m. Type **366**	70	20
1780	60 m. Ruffed grouse ("Bonasa umbellus")	70	20
1781	60 m. Whistling swan ("Olor columbianus")	70	20
1782	60 m. Rock pipit ("Anthus spinoletta")	70	20

367 Alfa Romeo "RL Sport", 1922

1986. Cars. Multicoloured.

1783	20 m. Type **367**	10	10
1784	30 m. Stutz "Bearcat", 1912	15	10
1785	40 m. Mercedes "Simplex", 1902	20	10
1786	50 m. Tatra "11", 1923	25	10
1787	60 m. Ford Model "T", 1908	30	15
1788	80 m. Vauxhall, 1905	40	20
1789	1 t. 20 Russo-Balt "K", 1913	60	30

368 Wilhelm Steinitz and Curt von Bardeleben Game, 1895

1986. World Chess Champions. Multicoloured.

1791	20 m. Type **368**	10	10
1792	30 m. Emanuel Lasker and Harry Pilsberi game, 1895	15	10
1793	40 m. Alexander Alekhine and Richard Retti game, 1925	20	10
1794	50 m. Mikhail Botvinnik and Capablanca game, 1938	25	10
1795	60 m. Anatoly Karpov and Wolfgang Untsiker game, 1975	30	15
1796	80 m. Nona Gaprindashvili and Lasarevich game, 1961	40	20
1797	1 t. 20 Maia Chirburdanidze and Irina Levitina game, 1984	60	30

1986. Saiga Antelope. As T **359**. Multicoloured.

1800	60 m. Male	45	15
1801	60 m. Female with calf	45	15
1802	60 m. Male and female	45	15
1803	60 m. Male and female in snow	45	15

1986. Pelicans. As T **359**. Multicoloured.

1804	60 m. Dalmatian pelican ("Pelecanus crispus")	70	30
1805	60 m. Dalmatian pelican preening	70	30
1806	60 m. Eastern white pelican ("Pelecanus onocrotalus")	70	30
1807	60 m. Eastern white pelicans in flight	70	30

370 Siamese Fighting Fish

1987. Aquarium Fishes. Multicoloured.

1808	20 m. Type **370**	10	10
1809	30 m. Goldfish	15	10
1810	40 m. Glowlight rasbora	25	10
1811	50 m. Acara	35	10
1812	60 m. Platy	40	15
1813	80 m. Green swordtail	55	20
1814	1 t. 20 Freshwater angelfish (vert)	95	30

371 Lassoing Horse

1987. Traditional Equestrian Sports. Mult.

1816	20 m. Type **371**	10	10
1817	30 m. Breaking horse	15	10
1818	40 m. Mounted archer	20	10
1819	50 m. Race	25	10
1820	60 m. Horseman snatching flag from ground	35	15
1821	80 m. Tug of war	40	20
1822	1 t. 20 Racing wolf	70	25

372 Grey-headed Green Woodpecker

373 Butterfly Hunting

1987. Woodpeckers. Multicoloured.

1823	20 m. Type **372**	10	10
1824	30 m. Wryneck	15	10
1825	40 m. Great spotted woodpecker	25	10
1826	50 m. White-backed woodpecker	35	15
1827	60 m. Lesser spotted woodpecker	40	15
1828	80 m. Black woodpecker	55	20
1829	1 t. 20 Three-toed woodpecker	95	35

1987. Children's Activities. Multicoloured.

1831	20 m. Type **373**	10	10
1832	30 m. Feeding calves	10	10
1833	40 m. Drawing on ground in chalk	15	10
1834	50 m. Football	20	10
1835	60 m. Go-carting	25	15
1836	80 m. Growing vegetables	30	15
1837	1 t. 20 Playing string instrument	45	25

374 Industry and Agriculture

1987. 13th Congress and 60th Anniv of Mongolian Trade Union.

1838	**374** 60 m. multicoloured	1·00	30

375 Women in Traditional Costume

376 Flags of Member Countries

1987. 40th Anniv of Mongol–Soviet Friendship.

1839	**375** 60 m. multicoloured	40	10

1987. Argali. As T **359**. Multicoloured.

1840	60 m. On grassy rock (full face)	45	15
1841	60 m. On rock (three-quarter face)	45	15
1842	60 m. Family	45	15
1843	60 m. Close-up of head and upper body	45	15

1987. Swans. As T **359**. Multicoloured.

1844	60 m. Mute Swan ("Cygnus olor") in water	50	15
1845	60 m. Mute swan on land	50	15
1846	60 m. Whistling swan ("Cygnus bewickii")	50	15
1847	60 m. Whistling swan, "Cygnus gunus" and mute swan	50	15

1987. 25th Anniv of Membership of Council for Mutual Economic Aid.

1848	**376** 60 m. multicoloured	35	10

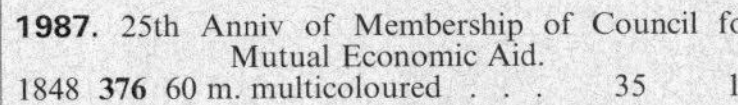

377 Sea Buckthorn

378 Couple in Traditional Costume

1987. Fruits. Multicoloured.

1849	20 m. Type **377**	10	10
1850	30 m. Blackcurrants	10	10
1851	40 m. Redcurrants	15	10
1852	50 m. Redcurrants	20	10
1853	60 m. Raspberries	25	15
1854	80 m. "Padus asiatica"	30	15
1855	1 t. 20 Strawberries	45	25

1987. Folk Art. Multicoloured.

1857	20 m. Type **378**	10	10
1858	30 m. Gold-inlaid baton and pouch	15	10
1859	40 m. Gold and jewelled ornaments	20	10
1860	50 m. Bag and dish	30	10
1861	60 m. Earrings	35	15
1862	80 m. Pipe, pouch and bottle	45	20
1863	1 t. 20 Decorative headdress	65	25

379 Dancer

1987. Dances.

1864	**379** 20 m. multicoloured	10	10
1865	– 30 m. multicoloured	15	10
1866	– 40 m. multicoloured	20	10
1867	– 50 m. multicoloured	30	10
1868	– 60 m. multicoloured	35	15
1869	– 80 m. multicoloured	45	20
1870	– 1 t. 20 multicoloured	65	25

DESIGNS: 30 m. to 1 t. 20, Different dances.

381 Scottish Fold

1987. Cats. Multicoloured.

1872	20 m. Type **381**	10	10
1873	30 m. Grey	15	10
1874	40 m. Oriental	20	10
1875	50 m. Abyssinian (horiz)	30	10
1876	60 m. Manx (horiz)	35	15
1877	80 m. Black shorthair (horiz)	45	20
1878	1 t. 20 Spotted (horiz)	65	25

382 Mil Mi-V12

1987. Helicopters. Multicoloured.

1880	20 m. Type **382**	10	10
1881	30 m. Westland WG-30	15	10
1882	40 m. Bell 206L LongRanger II	20	10
1883	50 m. Kawasaki-Hughes 369HS	25	10
1884	60 m. Kamov Ka-32	30	10
1885	80 m. Mil Mi-17	35	15
1886	1 t. 20 Mil Mi-10K	60	25

383 City Scene

384 Kremlin, Lenin and Revolutionaries

1987. 19th Mongolian People's Revolutionary Party Congress. Multicoloured.

1887 60 m. Type **383** 25 10
1888 60 m. Clothing and mining industries . . . . 1·00 25
1889 60 m. Agriculture 25 10
1890 60 m. Family 25 10
1891 60 m. Workers, factories and fields 25 10
1892 60 m. Building construction . 25 10
1893 60 m. Scientist 25 10

1987. 70th Anniv of Russian October Revolution.

1894 **384** 60 m. multicoloured . . . 35 10

385 Seven with One Blow

1987. Walt Disney Cartoons. Mult (a) "The Brave Little Tailor" (Grimm Brothers).

1895 25 m. Type **385** 10 10
1896 35 m. Brought before the King 20 10
1897 45 m. Rewards for bravery . . 25 10
1898 55 m. Fight between Mickey and the giant 30 15
1899 2 t. Happy ending . . . . . 1·00 50

(b) "The Celebrated Jumping Frog of Calaveras County" (Mark Twain).

1901 65 m. "He'd bet on anything" . 30 15
1902 75 m. "He never done nothing but...learn that frog to jump" 45 20
1903 85 m. "What might it be that you've got in that box?" . . 50 25
1904 1 t. "40 He got the frog out and filled him full of quail shot" . 80 40

386 Head

1987. The Red Fox. Multicoloured.

1906 60 m. Type **386** 45 15
1907 60 m. Vixen and cubs 45 15
1908 60 m. Stalking 45 15
1909 60 m. In the snow 45 15

388 Bobsleighing **389** Sukhe Bator

1988. Air. Winter Olympic Games, Calgary. Mult.

1911 20 m. Type **388** 10 10
1912 30 m. Ski jumping 10 10
1913 40 m. Skiing 15 10
1914 50 m. Biathlon 20 10
1915 60 m. Speed skating 25 10
1916 80 m. Figure skating 30 15
1917 1 t. 20 Ice hockey 50 25

1988. 95th Birth Anniv of Sukhe Bator.

1919 **389** 60 m. multicoloured . . . 40 10

390 "Invitation"

1988. Roses. Multicoloured.

1920 20 m. Type **390** 10 10
1921 30 m. "Meilland" 10 10
1922 40 m. "Pascali" 15 10
1923 50 m. "Tropicana" 20 10
1924 60 m. "Wendy Cussons" . . . 25 10
1925 80 m. "Rosa sp." (wrongly inscr "Blue Moon") 30 15
1926 1 t. 20 "Diorama" 50 25

391 "Ukhaant Ekhner"

1988. Puppets. Multicoloured.

1928 20 m. Type **391** 10 10
1929 30 m. "Altan Everte Mungun Turuut" 10 10
1930 40 m. "Aduuchyn Khuu" . . 15 10
1931 50 m. "Suulenkhuu" 20 10
1932 60 m. "Khonchyn Khuu" . . 25 10
1933 80 m. "Argat Byatskhan Baatar" 30 15
1934 1 t. 20 "Botgochyn Khuu" . . 50 25

393 Judo **394** Marx

1988. Olympic Games, Seoul. Multicoloured.

1936 20 m. Type **393** 10 10
1937 30 m. Archery 10 10
1938 40 m. Weightlifting 15 10
1939 50 m. Gymnastics 20 10
1940 60 m. Cycling 25 10
1941 80 m. Running 30 15
1942 1 t. 20 Wrestling 50 25

1988. 170th Birth Anniv of Karl Marx.

1944 **394** 60 m. multicoloured . . . 50 20

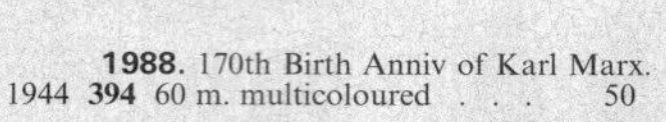

395 Couple and Congress Banner **396** "Kosmos"

1988. 19th Revsomol Youth Congress.

1945 **395** 60 m. multicoloured . . . 1·00 30

1988. Spacecraft and Satellites. Multicoloured.

1946 20 m. Type **396** 10 10
1947 30 m. "Meteor" 10 10
1948 40 m. "Salyut"–"Soyuz" space complex 10 10
1949 50 m. "Prognoz-6" 15 10
1950 60 m. "Molniya-1" 15 10
1951 80 m. "Soyuz" 20 15
1952 1 t. 20 "Vostok" 35 20

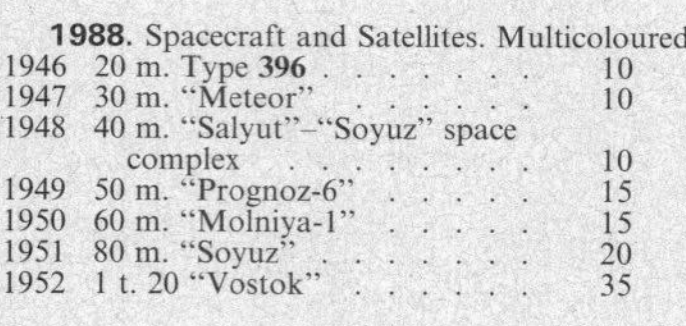

397 Buddha **398** Emblem

1988. Religious Sculptures.

1954 **397** 20 m. multicoloured . . . 10 10
1955 – 30 m. multicoloured . . . 10 10
1956 – 40 m. multicoloured . . . 20 10
1957 – 50 m. multicoloured . . . 25 10
1958 – 60 m. multicoloured . . . 30 10
1959 – 70 m. multicoloured . . . 35 10
1960 – 80 m. multicoloured . . . 40 15
1961 – 1 t. 20 multicoloured . . . 65 25

DESIGNS: 30 m. to 1 t. 20, Different buddhas.

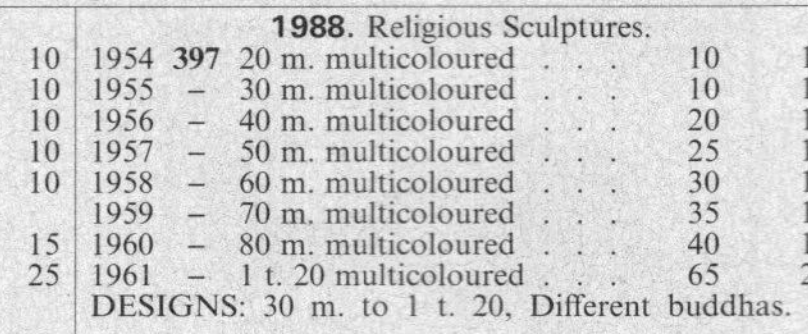

1988. 30th Anniv of Problems of "Peace and Socialism" (magazine).

1962 **398** 60 m. multicoloured . . . 50 10

399 Eagle

1988. White-tailed Sea Eagle. Multicoloured.

1963 60 m. Type **399** 45 15
1964 60 m. Eagle on fallen branch and eagle landing 45 15
1965 60 m. Eagle on rock 45 15
1966 60 m. Eagle (horiz) 45 15

400 Ass

1988. Asiatic Wild Ass. Multicoloured.

1967 60 m. Type **400** 40 15
1968 60 m. Head of ass 40 15
1969 60 m. Two adults 40 15
1970 60 m. Mare and foal 40 15

401 Athlete **403** U.S.S.R. (ice hockey)

1988. Traditional Sports. Multicoloured.

1971 10 m. Type **401** 10 10
1972 20 m. Horseman 15 10
1973 30 m. Archery 20 10
1974 40 m. Wrestling 25 10
1975 50 m. Archery (different) . . . 35 15
1976 70 m. Horsemen (national holiday cavalcade) 60 30
1977 1 t. 20 Horsemen, wrestlers and archers 95 45

1988. Winter Olympic Games Gold Medal Winners. Multicoloured.

1979 1 t. 50 Type **403** 30 10
1980 1 t. 50 Bonnie Blair (speed skating) 30 10
1981 1 t. 50 Alberto Tomba (slalom) 30 10
1982 1 t. 50 Matti Nykanen (ski jumping) (horiz) 30 10

404 Brown Goat

1988. Goats. Multicoloured.

1984 20 m. Type **404** 10 10
1985 30 m. Black goat 10 10
1986 40 m. White long-haired goats 15 10
1987 50 m. Black long-haired goat . 20 10
1988 60 m. White goat 25 10
1989 80 m. Black short-haired goat 30 15
1990 1 t. 20 Nanny and kid 50 25

405 Emblem

1989. 60th Anniv of Mongolian Writers' Association.

1992 **405** 60 m. multicoloured . . . 40 10

406 Beaver gnawing Trees

1989. Eurasian Beaver. Multicoloured.

1993 60 m. Type **406** 40 15
1994 60 m. Beaver with young . . . 40 15
1995 60 m. Beavers beside tree stump and in water 40 15
1996 60 m. Beaver rolling log . . . 40 15

407 Dancers

1989. Ballet.

1997 **407** 20 m. multicoloured . . . 10 10
1998 – 30 m. multicoloured . . . 10 10
1999 – 40 m. multicoloured (vert) 15 10
2000 – 50 m. multicoloured . . . 20 10
2001 – 60 m. multicoloured . . . 25 10
2002 – 80 m. multicoloured (vert) 30 15
2003 – 1 t. 20 multicoloured (vert) 50 25

DESIGNS: 30 m. to 1 t. 20, Different dancing scenes.

408 "Ursus pruinosis"

1989. Bears. Multicoloured.

2004 20 m. Type **408** 10 10
2005 30 m. Brown bear 20 10
2006 40 m. Asiatic black bear . . . 30 15
2007 50 m. Polar bear 40 20
2008 60 m. Brown bear 55 25
2009 80 m. Giant panda 70 35
2010 1 t. 20 Brown bear . . . . . 1·10 55

409 "Soyuz" Spacecraft

1989. Space. Multicoloured.

2012 20 m. Type **409** 10 10
2013 30 m. "Apollo"–"Soyuz" link 15 10
2014 40 m. "Columbia" space shuttle (vert) 20 10
2015 50 m. "Hermes" spacecraft . . 30 15
2016 60 m. "Nippon" spacecraft (vert) 45 20
2017 80 m. "Energy" rocket (vert) . 65 30
2018 1 t. 20 "Buran" space shuttle (vert) 95 45

411 Nehru **412** "Opuntia microdasys"

1989. Birth Centenary of Jawaharial Nehru (Indian statesman).
2021 **411** 10 m. multicoloured . . . 50 15

1989. Cacti. Multicoloured.
2022 20 m. Type **412** 10 10
2023 30 m. "Echinopsis multipiex" 10 10
2024 40 m. "Rebutia tephracanthus" 15 10
2025 50 m. "Brasilicactus haselbergii" 20 10
2026 60 m. "Gymnocalycium mihanovichii" 25 10
2027 80 m. "C. strausii" 30 15
2028 1 t. 20 "Horridocactus tuberisvicatus" 50 25

1989. 800th Anniv of Coronation of Genghis Khan. Nos. 291/4 optd **CHINGGIS KHAN CROWNATION 1189**.
2030 **67** 20 m. multicoloured . . . 2·75 2·75
2031 – 30 m. multicoloured . . . 4·25 4·25
2032 – 50 m. black, brown & red . 6·50 6·50
2033 – 60 m. buff, blue & brown . 8·50 8·50

415 Citroen "BX"

1989. Motor Cars. Multicoloured.
2035 20 m. Type **415** 10 10
2036 30 m. Volvo "760 GLF" . . . 10 10
2037 40 m. Honda "Civic" 60 25
2038 50 m. Volga 20 10
2039 60 m. Ford "Granada" . . . 25 10
2040 80 m. Baz "21099" 30 15
2041 1 t. 20 Mercedes "190" . . . 50 20

416 Monument

417 Florence Griffith-Joyner (running)

1989. 50th Anniv of Battle of Khalka River.
2043 **416** 60 m. multicoloured . . . 55 15

1989. Olympic Games Medal Winners. Mult.
2044 60 m. Type **417** (wrongly inscr "Joyner-Griffith") 25 10
2045 60 m. Stefano Cerioni (fencing) 25 10
2046 60 m. Gintautas Umaras (cycling) 25 10
2047 60 m. Kristin Otto (swimming) 25 10

418 "Malchin Zaluus" (N. Sandagsuren)

1989. 30th Anniv of Co-operative Movement. Paintings. Multicoloured.
2049 20 m. Type **418** 10 10
2050 30 m. "Tsaatny Tukhai Dursamkh" (N. Sandagsuren) (vert) 20 10
2051 40 m. "Uul Shig Tushigtei" (D. Amgalan) 30 15
2052 50 m. "Goviin Egshig" (D. Amgalan) 40 20
2053 60 m. "Tsagaan Sar" (Ts. Dagvanyam) 55 25
2054 80 m. "Tumen Aduuny Bayar" (M. Butemkh) (vert) . . . 65 30
2055 1 t. 20 "Bilcheer Deer" (N. Tsultem) . . . . 1·10 50

419 Four-man Bobsleighing

420 Victory Medal

1989. Ice Sports. Multicoloured.
2057 20 m. Type **419** 10 10
2058 30 m. Luge 10 10
2059 40 m. Figure skating 15 10
2060 50 m. Two-man bobsleighing . 20 10
2061 60 m. Ice dancing 25 10
2062 80 m. Speed skating 30 15
2063 1 t. 20 Ice speedway 50 25

1989. Orders. Designs showing different badges and medals. Multicoloured, background colour given.
2065 **420** 60 m. blue 25 10
2066 – 60 m. orange 25 10
2067 – 60 m. mauve 25 10
2068 – 60 m. violet 25 10
2069 – 60 m. green 25 10
2070 – 60 m. blue 25 10
2071 – 60 m. red 25 10

422 Chu Lha

423 Sukhe Bator Statue

1989. Buddhas. Multicoloured.
2073 20 m. Damdin Sandub 10 10
2074 30 m. Pagwa Lama 20 10
2075 40 m. Type **422** 30 15
2076 50 m. Agwanglobsan 40 20
2077 60 m. Dorje Dags Dan . . . 55 25
2078 80 m. Wangchikdorje 65 30
2079 1 t. 20 Buddha . . . . 1·10 50

1990. New Year.
2081 **423** 10 m. multicoloured . . . 75 35

424 Newspapers and City

425 Emblem

1990. 70th Anniv of "Khuvisgalt Khevlel" (newspaper).
2082 **424** 60 m. multicoloured . . . 65 30

1990. 20th Mongolian People's Revolutionary Party Congress.
2083 **425** 60 m. multicoloured . . . 50 25

426 Male Character

1990. "Mandukhai the Wise" (film).
2084 **426** 20 m. multicoloured . . . 20 10
2085 – 30 m. multicoloured . . . 30 15
2086 – 40 m. multicoloured . . . 45 20
2087 – 50 m. multicoloured . . . 55 30
2088 – 60 m. multicoloured . . . 75 35
2089 – 80 m. multicoloured . . . 90 45
2090 – 1 t. 20 multicoloured . . . 1·25 65
DESIGNS: 30 m. to 1 t. 20, Different characters from the film.

427 Trophy and Players

1990. World Cup Football Championship, Italy.
2092 **427** 20 m. multicoloured . . . 10 10
2093 – 30 m. multicoloured . . . 10 10
2094 – 40 m. multicoloured . . . 10 10
2095 – 50 m. multicoloured . . . 15 10
2096 – 60 m. multicoloured . . . 15 10
2097 – 80 m. multicoloured . . . 20 10
2098 – 1 t. 20 multicoloured . . . 35 20
DESIGNS: 30 m. to 1 t. 20, Trophy and different players.

428 Lenin

1990. 120th Birth Anniv of Lenin.
2100 **428** 60 m. black, red and gold 65 30

429 Mother with Fawn

1990. Siberian Musk Deer. Multicoloured.
2101 60 m. Type **429** 65 30
2102 60 m. Deer in wood 65 30
2103 60 m. Deer on river bank . . 65 30
2104 60 m. Deer in winter landscape 65 30

433 Russian Victory Medal

434 Crane

1990. 45th Anniv of End of Second World War.
2108 **433** 60 m. multicoloured . . . 65 30

1990. The Japanese White-necked Crane. Multicoloured.
2109 60 m. Type **434** 60 25
2110 60 m. Crane feeding (horiz) . . 60 25
2111 60 m. Cranes flying (horiz) . . 60 25
2112 60 m. Crane on river bank . . 60 25

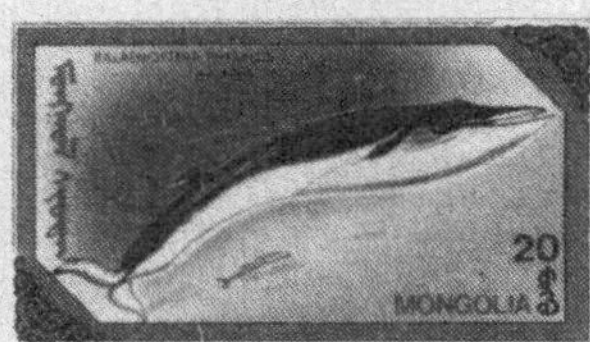
435 Fin Whale

1990. Marine Mammals. Multicoloured.
2113 20 m. Type **435** 15 10
2114 30 m. Humpback whale . . . 30 15
2115 40 m. Narwhal 40 20
2116 50 m. Risso's dolphin 50 25
2117 60 m. Bottle-nosed dolphin . . 60 30
2118 80 m. Atlantic white-sided dolphin 85 40
2119 1 t. 20 Bowhead whale . . . . 1·10 55

436 Weapons and Black Standard

437 Panda

1990. 750th Anniv of "Secret History of the Mongols" (book). Multicoloured.
2121 10 m. Type **436** 10 10
2122 10 m. Weapons and white standard 10 10
2123 40 m. Brazier (17½ × 22 mm) . 40 20
2124 60 m. Genghis Khan (17½ × 22 mm) 60 30
2125 60 m. Horses galloping . . . 60 30
2126 60 m. Tartar camp 60 30
2127 80 m. Men kneeling to ruler . 75 35
2128 80 m. Court 75 35

1990. The Giant Panda. Multicoloured.
2129 10 m. Type **437** 15 10
2130 20 m. Panda eating bamboo . 25 10
2131 30 m. Adult eating bamboo, and cub 40 20
2132 40 m. Panda on tree branch (horiz) 45 25
2133 50 m. Adult and cub resting (horiz) 55 25
2134 60 m. Panda and mountains (horiz) 75 35
2135 80 m. Adult and cub playing (horiz) 85 45
2136 1 t. 20 Panda on snow-covered river bank (horiz) . . . . . 1·60 80

438 Chasmosaurus

1990. Prehistoric Animals. Multicoloured.
2138 20 m. Type **438** 15 10
2139 30 m. Stegosaurus 25 10
2140 40 m. Probactrosaurus 35 15
2141 50 m. Opisthocoelicaudia . . 55 25
2142 60 m. Iguanodon (vert) . . . 65 30
2143 80 m. Tarbosaurus 90 45
2144 1 t. 20 Mamenchisaurus (after Mark Hallett) (60 × 22 mm) 1·10 55

439 Lighthouse, Alexandria, Egypt

440 Kea

1990. Seven Wonders of the World. Mult.
2146 20 m. Type **439** 15 10
2147 30 m. Pyramids of Egypt (horiz) 25 10
2148 40 m. Statue of Zeus, Olympia 35 20
2149 50 m. Colossus of Rhodes . . 55 25
2150 60 m. Mausoleum, Halicarnassus 65 35
2151 80 m. Temple of Artemis, Ephesus (horiz) 90 45
2152 1 t. 20 Hanging Gardens of Babylon . . . . 1·10 55

1990. Parrots. Multicoloured.
2154 20 m. Type **440** 15 10
2155 30 m. Hyacinth macaw . . . 25 10
2156 40 m. Australian king parrot . 35 15
2157 50 m. Grey parrot 45 20
2158 60 m. Kakapo 55 25
2159 80 m. Alexandrine parakeet . 75 35
2160 1 t. 20 Scarlet macaw 90 45

441 Purple Tiger Moth

1990. Moths and Butterflies. Multicoloured.
2162 20 m. Type **441** 15 10
2163 30 m. Viennese emperor moth . 25 10
2164 40 m. Comma 40 20
2165 50 m. Magpie moth 50 25
2166 60 m. Chequered moth . . . 60 30
2167 80 m. Swallowtail 85 45
2168 1 t. 20 Orange-tip . . . . . . 1·40 70

442 Jetsons in Flying Saucer

1991. The Jetsons (cartoon characters). Mult.

2170 20 m. Type **442** 10 10
2171 25 m. Family walking on planet and dragon (horiz) 15 10
2172 30 m. Jane, George, Elroy and dog Astro 20 10
2173 40 m. George, Judy, Elroy and Astro crossing river 25 10
2174 50 m. Flying in saucer (horiz) 30 15
2175 60 m. Jetsons and Cosmo Spacely (horiz) 35 20
2176 70 m. George and Elroy flying with jetpacks 45 20
2177 80 m. Elroy (horiz) 50 25
2178 1 t. 20 Judy and Astro watching Elroy doing acrobatics on tree 75 40

443 Dino and Bam-Bam meeting Mongolian Boy with Camel

1991. The Flintstones (cartoon characters). Mult.

2180 25 m. Type **443** 10 10
2181 35 m. Bam-Bam and Dino posing with boy (vert) 15 10
2182 45 m. Mongolian mother greeting Betty Rubble, Wilma Flintstone and children 20 10
2183 55 m. Barney Rubble and Fred riding dinosaurs 25 10
2184 65 m. Flintstones and Rubbles by river 30 15
2185 75 m. Bam-Bam and Dino racing boy on camel 40 20
2186 85 m. Fred, Barney and Bam-Bam with Mongolian boy 55 25
2187 1 t. 40 Flintstones and Rubbles in car 90 45
2188 2 t. Fred and Barney taking refreshments with Mongolian 1·40 70

444 Party Emblem

445 Black-capped Chickadee

1991. 70th Anniv of Mongolian People's Revolutionary Party.

2190 **444** 60 m. multicoloured 50 25

1991. "Stamp World London 90" International Stamp Exhibition. Multicoloured.

2191 25 m. Type **445** 10 10
2192 35 m. Common cardinal 15 10
2193 45 m. Crested shelduck 20 10
2194 55 m. Mountain bluebird 25 10
2195 65 m. Northern oriole 30 15
2196 75 m. Bluethroat (horiz) 35 15
2197 85 m. Eastern bluebird 45 20
2198 1 t. 40 Great reed warbler 85 30
2199 2 t. Golden eagle 1·10 45

446 Black Grouse

1991. Birds. Multicoloured.

2201 20 m. Type **446** 25 10
2202 30 m. Common shelduck 35 15
2203 40 m. Ring-necked pheasant 45 25
2204 50 m. Long-tailed duck 60 30
2205 60 m. Hazel grouse 65 30
2206 80 m. Red-breasted merganser 90 45
2207 1 t. 20 Goldeneye 1·50 70

447 Emblem

448 Superb Pink

1991. 70th Anniv of Mongolian People's Army.

2209 **447** 60 m. multicoloured 50 25

1991. Flowers. Multicoloured.

2210 20 m. Type **448** 15 10
2211 30 m. "Gentiana pneumonanthe" (wrongly inscr "puenmonanthe") 25 10
2212 40 m. Dandelion 40 20
2213 50 m. Siberian iris 55 25
2214 60 m. Turk's-cap lily 65 30
2215 80 m. "Aster amellus" 90 45
2216 1 t. 20 Thistle 1·25 60

449 Stag Beetle

1991. Beetles. Multicoloured.

2218 20 m. Type **449** 15 10
2219 30 m. "Chelorrhina polyphemus" 25 10
2220 40 m. "Coptolabrus coelestis" 40 20
2221 50 m. "Epepeotes togatus" 55 25
2222 60 m. Tiger beetle 65 30
2223 80 m. "Macrodontia cervicornis" 90 45
2224 1 t. 20 Hercules beetle 1·25 60

450 Defend

1991. Buddhas. Multicoloured.

2226 20 m. Type **450** 15 10
2227 30 m. Badmasanhava 25 10
2228 40 m. Avalokitecvara 35 15
2229 50 m. Buddha 50 25
2230 60 m. Mintugwa 60 30
2231 80 m. Shyamatara 70 35
2232 1 t. 20 Samvara 1·10 55

451 Zebras

1991. African Wildlife. Multicoloured.

2234 20 m. Type **451** 15 10
2235 30 m. Cheetah (wrongly inscr "Cheetan") 25 10
2236 40 m. Black rhinoceros 40 20
2237 50 m. Giraffe (vert) 55 25
2238 60 m. Gorilla 65 35
2239 80 m. Elephants 90 45
2240 1 t. 20 Lion (vert) 1·25 60

452 Communications

1991. Meiso Mizuhara Stamp Exhibition, Ulan Bator.

2242 **452** 1 t. 20 multicoloured 2·00 60

453 Scotch Bonnet

1991. Fungi. Multicoloured.

2243 20 m. Type **453** 15 10
2244 30 m. Oak mushroom 20 10
2245 40 m. "Hygrophorus marzuelus" 30 15
2246 50 m. Chanterelle 40 20
2247 60 m. Field mushroom 55 25
2248 80 m. Bronze boletus 70 35
2249 1 t. 20 Caesar's mushroom 1·25 60
2250 2 t. "Tricholoma terreum" 2·10 1·00

455 Green Iguana

1991. Reptiles. Multicoloured.

2253 20 m. Type **455** 15 10
2254 30 m. Flying gecko 30 15
2255 40 m. Frilled lizard 40 20
2256 50 m. Common cape lizard 55 25
2257 60 m. Common basilisk 65 30
2258 80 m. Common tegu 90 45
2259 1 t. 20 Marine iguana 1·50 50

456 Warrior

1991. Masked Costumes. Multicoloured.

2261 35 m. Type **456** 20 10
2262 45 m. Mask with fangs 30 15
2263 55 m. Bull mask 40 20
2264 65 m. Dragon mask 55 25
2265 85 m. Mask with beak 65 30
2266 1 t. 40 Old man 1·25 60
2267 2 t. Gold mask with earrings 1·50 75

457 German Shepherd

1991. Dogs. Multicoloured.

2269 20 m. Type **457** 15 10
2270 30 m. Dachshund (vert) 30 15
2271 40 m. Yorkshire terrier (vert) 40 20
2272 50 m. Standard poodle 50 25
2273 60 m. Springer spaniel 70 35
2274 80 m. Norfolk terrier 90 45
2275 1 t. 20 Keeshund 1·50 75

458 Siamese

1991. Cats. Multicoloured.

2277 20 m. Type **458** 15 10
2278 30 m. Black and white longhaired (vert) 30 15
2279 40 m. Ginger red 40 20
2280 50 m. Tabby (vert) 50 30
2281 60 m. Red and white (vert) 70 35
2282 80 m. Maine coon (vert) 90 45
2283 1 t. 20 Blue-eyed white persian (vert) 1·50 65

459 Pagoda

460 "Zegris fausti"

1991. "Phila Nippon '91" International Stamp Exhibition, Tokyo. Multicoloured.

2285 1 t. Type **459** 30 10
2286 2 t. Japanese woman 55 25
2287 3 t. Mongolian woman 85 40
2288 4 t. Temple 1·40 65

1991. Butterflies and Flowers. Multicoloured.

2289 20 m. Type **460** 10 10
2290 25 m. Yellow roses 15 10
2291 30 m. Apollo 20 10
2292 40 m. Purple tiger moth 25 10
2293 50 m. "Pseudochazara regeli" 30 15
2294 60 m. "Colotis fausta" 35 15
2295 70 m. Red rose 40 20
2296 80 m. Margueritas 50 25
2297 1 t. 20 Lily 75 35

1991. "Expo '90" International Garden and Greenery Exhibition, Osaka. Nos. 2289/97 optd **EXPO '90** and symbol.

2298 20 m. multicoloured 10 10
2299 25 m. multicoloured 15 10
2300 30 m. multicoloured 20 10
2301 40 m. multicoloured 25 10
2302 50 m. multicoloured 30 15
2303 60 m. multicoloured 35 15
2304 70 m. multicoloured 40 20
2305 80 m. multicoloured 50 25
2306 1 t. 20 multicoloured 75 35

462 Poster for 1985 Digital Stereo Re-issue

1991. 50th Anniv (1990) of Original Release of Walt Disney's "Fantasia" (cartoon film). Multicoloured.

2308 1 t. 70 Type **462** 15 10
2309 2 t. 1940 poster for original release 20 10
2310 2 t. 30 Poster for 1982 digital re-issue 25 10
2311 2 t. 60 Poster for 1981 stereo re-issue 35 15
2312 4 t. 20 Poster for 1969 "Psychedelic Sixties" release 60 30
2313 10 t. 1941 poster for original release 1·50 75
2314 15 t. Mlle. Upanova (sketch by Campbell Grant) 2·00 90
2315 16 t. Mickey as the Sorcerer's Apprentice (original sketch) 2·40 1·25

463 Speed Skating

465 Elk

1992. Winter Olympic Games, Albertville. Multicoloured.

2317 60 m. Type **463** . . . 10 10
2318 80 m. Ski jumping . . . 10 10
2319 1 t. Ice hockey . . . 15 10
2320 1 t. 20 Ice skating . . . 15 10
2321 1 t. 50 Biathlon (horiz) . . . 15 10
2322 2 t. Skiing (horiz) . . . 20 15
2323 2 t. 40 Two-man bobsleigh (horiz) . . . 25 15

1992. The Elk. Multicoloured.

2326 3 t. Type **465** . . . 70 30
2327 3 t. Female with young (horiz) 70 30
2328 3 t. Adult male (horiz) . . . 70 30
2329 3 t. Female . . . 70 30

466 Steam Locomotive, Darjeeling–Himalaya Railway, India

1992. Multicoloured. (a) Railways of the World.

2330 3 t. Type **466** . . . 70 25
2331 3 t. The "Royal Scot", Great Britain . . . 70 25
2332 6 t. Steam train on bridge over River Kwai, Burma–Siam Railway . . . 1·60 60
2333 6 t. Baltic steam locomotive No. 767, Burma . . . 1·60 60
2334 8 t. Baldwin steam locomotive, Thailand . . . 2·10 70
2335 8 t. Western Railways steam locomotive, Pakistan . . . 2·10 70
2336 16 t. Class P36 locomotive, Russia . . . 4·50 1·50
2337 16 t. Shanghai–Peking express, China . . . 4·50 1·50

(b) "Orient Express".

2339 3 t. 1931 advertising poster . 70 25
2340 3 t. 1928 advertising poster . 70 25
2341 6 t. Dawn departure . . . 1·60 60
2342 6 t. The "Golden Arrow" leaving Victoria Station, London . . . 1·60 60
2343 8 t. Standing in station, Yugoslavia . . . 2·10 70
2344 8 t. Train passing through mountainous landcape, early 1900s . . . 2·10 70
2345 16 t. "Fleche d'Or" approaching Etaples . . . 4·50 1·50
2346 16 t. Arrival in Istanbul . . . 4·50 1·50

468 Magpie

1992. Multicoloured. (a) Birds.

2349 3 t. Type **468** . . . 40 20
2350 3 t. Eagle owl . . . 40 20
2351 6 t. Black-headed gull (horiz) . 80 40
2352 6 t. Redstart (horiz) . . . 80 40
2353 8 t. Demoiselle crane . . . 1·10 55
2354 8 t. Black stork (horiz) . . . 1·10 55
2355 16 t. Rough-legged buzzard . 2·25 1·10
2356 16 t. Golden eagle (horiz) . . 2·25 1·10

(b) Butterflies and Moths.

2358 3 t. Scarce swallowtail (horiz) . 40 20
2359 3 t. Small tortoiseshell . . . 40 20
2360 6 t. "Thyria jacobaeae" (value at right) (horiz) . . . 80 40
2361 6 t. Peacock (value at left) (horiz) . . . 80 40
2362 8 t. Camberwell beauty (value at left) (horiz) . . . 1·10 55
2363 8 t. Red admiral (value at right) (horiz) . . . 1·10 55
2364 16 t. "Hyporhaia audica" (horiz) . . . 2·25 1·10
2365 16 t. Large tortoiseshell (flying over river) (horiz) . . . 2·25 1·10

472 Fleet

1992. 500th Anniv of Discovery of America by Columbus (2nd issue). Multicoloured.

2370 3 t. Type **472** . . . 15 10
2371 7 t. Amerindians' canoe approaching "Santa Maria" 25 10
2372 10 t. "Pinta" . . . 35 15
2373 16 t. "Santa Maria" in open sea (vert) . . . 55 25
2374 30 t. "Santa Maria" passing coastline . . . 1·10 50
2375 40 t. Dolphins and "Santa Maria" . . . 1·50 75
2376 50 t. "Nina" . . . 1·90 90

474 Long Jumping

1992. Olympic Games, Barcelona. Multicoloured.

2379 3 t. Type **474** . . . 10 10
2380 6 t. Gymnastics (pommel exercise) . . . 10 10
2381 8 t. Boxing . . . 10 10
2382 16 t. Wrestling . . . 10 10
2383 20 t. Archery (vert) . . . 10 10
2384 30 t. Cycling . . . 10 10
2385 40 t. Show jumping . . . 15 10
2386 50 t. High jumping . . . 20 10
2387 60 t. Weightlifting . . . 20 10

Eight designs, each 200 t. and embossed on both gold and silver foil and accompanied by matching miniature sheets, were issued in 1993 in limited printings, depicting animals, sports or transport.

476 Black Grouse

1993. Birds. Multicoloured.

2390 3 t. Type **476** . . . 10 10
2391 8 t. Moorhen . . . 30 15
2392 10 t. Golden-crowned kinglet . 40 20
2393 16 t. Common kingfisher . . 60 30
2394 30 t. Red-throated diver . . 1·10 50
2395 40 t. Grey heron . . . 1·50 75
2396 50 t. Hoopoe . . . 1·90 90
2397 60 t. Blue-throated niltava . . 2·25 1·10

477 Orange-tip

1993. Butterflies and Moths. Multicoloured.

2399 3 t. Type **477** . . . 10 10
2400 8 t. Peacock . . . 30 15
2401 10 t. High brown fritillary . . 40 20
2402 16 t. "Limenitis reducta" . . 60 30
2403 30 t. Common burnet . . . 1·10 50
2404 40 t. Common blue . . . 1·50 75
2405 50 t. Apollo . . . 1·90 90
2406 60 t. Great peacock . . . 2·25 1·10

1993. No. 1221 surch **XXX 15Ter.**

2408 15 t. on 70 m. multicoloured . 2·75 1·00

479 Nicolas Copernicus (astronomer)

1993. "Polska'93" International Stamp Exhibition, Poznan. Multicoloured.

2409 30 t. Type **479** (520th birth anniv) . . . 2·00 90
2410 30 t. Frederic Chopin (composer) . . . 2·00 90
2411 30 t. Pope John Paul II . . . 2·00 90

1993. No. 263 surch **8-Ter.**

2413 8 t. on 70 m. multicoloured . 40 20

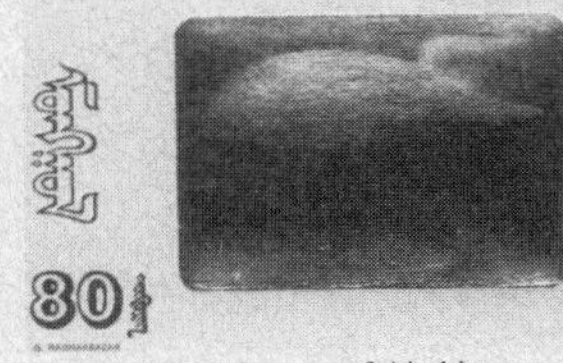

482 Hologram of Airship

1993. Airship Flight over Ulan Bator.

2415 **482** 80 t. multicoloured . . . 1·00 50

483 Buddha

1993. "Bangkok 1993" International Stamp Exhibition. Multicoloured.

2416 50 t. Buddha on throne . . . 55 25
2417 100 t. Buddha (different) . . 1·10 50
2418 150 t. Type **483** . . . 1·60 80
2419 200 t. Multi-armed Buddha . 2·25 1·10

484 Clouds, Mountains and Dog

1994. New Year. Year of the Dog. Multicoloured.

2421 60 t. Type **484** . . . 45 20
2422 60 t. Dog reclining between mountains and waves (horiz) . . . 45 20

485 Uruguay (1930, 1950)

1994. World Cup Football Championship, U.S.A. Previous Winners. Multicoloured.

2423 150 t. Type **485** . . . 30 15
2424 150 t. Italy (1934) . . . 30 15
2425 150 t. German Federal Republic (1954) . . . 30 15
2426 150 t. Brazil (1958) . . . 30 15
2427 150 t. Argentina (1978, 1986) . 30 15
2428 200 t. Italy (1938) . . . 40 20
2429 200 t. Brazil (1962) . . . 40 20
2430 200 t. German Federal Republic (1974) . . . 40 20
2431 250 t. Brazil (1970) . . . 50 25
2432 250 t. Italy (1982) . . . 50 25
2433 250 t. German Federal Republic (1990) . . . 50 25

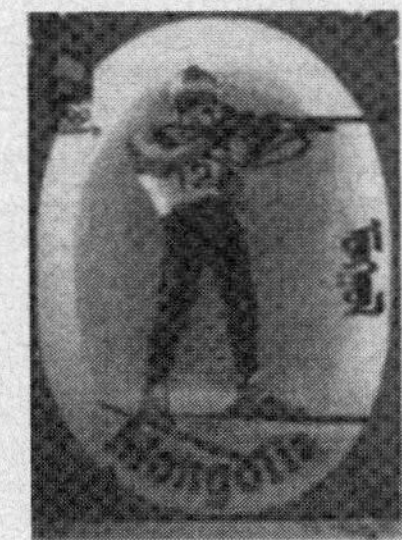

488 Biathlon

1994. Winter Olympic Games, Lillehammer, Norway. Multicoloured.

2437 50 t. Type **488** . . . 30 15
2438 60 t. Two-man bobsleigh . . 35 15
2439 80 t. Skiing . . . 45 20
2440 100 t. Ski jumping . . . 60 30
2441 120 t. Ice skating . . . 70 35
2442 200 t. Speed skating . . . 1·25 60

490 Eagle

1994. Wildlife. Multicoloured.

2445 60 t. Type **490** . . . 45 20
2446 60 t. Woodpecker on tree trunk 45 20
2447 60 t. Cranes . . . 45 20
2448 60 t. Osprey . . . 45 20
2449 60 t. Golden oriole on branch . 45 20
2450 60 t. Swallows . . . 45 20
2451 60 t. Eagle perched on rock . 45 20
2452 60 t. White birds in flight . . 45 20
2453 60 t. Squirrel on branch . . . 45 20
2454 60 t. Dragonfly . . . 45 20
2455 60 t. Black stork . . . 45 20
2456 60 t. Duck . . . 45 20
2457 60 t. Brown bird standing on rock . . . 45 20
2458 60 t. Marmot . . . 45 20
2459 60 t. Ladybird on flower . . 45 20
2460 60 t. Clutch of eggs in ground nest . . . 45 20
2461 60 t. Grasshopper . . . 45 20
2462 60 t. Butterfly . . . 45 20

Nos. 2445/62 were issued together, se-tenant, forming a composite design.

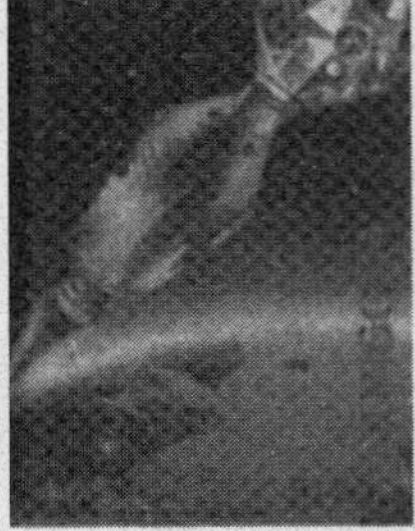

491 Command Module

492 Flowers

1994. 25th Anniv of First Manned Moon Landing. Multicoloured.

2463 200 t. Type **491** . . . 65 30
2464 200 t. Earth, astronaut in chair and shuttle wing . . . 65 30
2465 200 t. Shuttle approaching Earth . . . 65 30
2466 200 t. Astronaut on Moon . 65 30

1994.

2468 **492** 10 t. green and black . . 10 10
2469 – 18 t. purple and black . 10 10
2470 – 22 t. blue and black . . 15 10
2471 – 44 t. purple and black . 25 10

DESIGNS: 18, 44 t. Argali; 22 t. Airplane.

493 Korean Empire 1884 5 m. Stamp

1994. "Philakorea 1994" International Stamp Exhibition, Seoul. Multicoloured.

2472 600 t. Type **493** . . . 2·25 1·00
2473 600 t. Mongolia 1924 1 c. stamp . . . 2·25 1·00
2474 600 t. Mongolia 1966 Children's Day 15 m. stamp (47 × 34 mm) . . . 2·25 1·00
2475 600 t. South Korea 1993 New Year 110 w. stamp (47 × 34 mm) . . . 2·25 1·00

494 Butterfly

1994. "Singpex '94" National Stamp Exhibition, Singapore. Year of the Dog.

2477 **494** 300 t. multicoloured . . 1·00 50

496 Mammoth

1994. Prehistoric Animals. Multicoloured.

2480 60 t. Type **496** . . . 35 15
2481 80 t. Stegosaurus . . . 50 25
2482 100 t. Talararus (horiz) . . . 75 35
2483 120 t. Gorythosaurus (horiz) . 90 45
2484 200 t. Tyrannosaurus (horiz) . 1·50 75

497 National Flags

1994. Mongolia–Japan Friendship and Co-operation.

2486	**497**	20 t. multicoloured	15	10

498 Boar and Mountains

1995. New Year. Year of the Pig. Multicoloured.

2487	200 t. Type **498**	65	30
2488	200 t. Boar reclining amongst clouds (vert)	65	30

499 Dancer

1995. Tsam Religious Mask Dance.

2489	**499**	20 t. multicoloured	10	10
2490	–	50 t. multicoloured	20	10
2491	–	60 t. multicoloured	30	15
2492	–	100 t. multicoloured	50	25
2493	–	120 t. multicoloured	60	30
2494	–	150 t. multicoloured	65	30
2495	–	200 t. multicoloured	95	40

DESIGNS: 50 t. to 200 t. Different masked characters.

500 Saiga

1995. The Saiga. Multicoloured.

2497	40 t. Type **500**	20	10
2498	50 t. Male and female	30	15
2499	70 t. Male running	45	20
2500	200 t. Head and neck of male	1·00	50

502 Yellow Oranda

1995. Goldfish. Multicoloured.

2502	20 t. Type **502**	20	10
2503	50 t. Red and white veil-tailed wen-yu	35	15
2504	60 t. Brown oranda red-head	45	20
2505	100 t. Pearl-scaled	80	30
2506	120 t. Red lion-head	1·00	45
2507	150 t. Brown oranda	1·40	55
2508	200 t. Red and white oranda with narial	1·90	75

503 Bishop

1995. X-Men (comic strip). Designs showing characters. Multicoloured.

2511	30 t. Type **503**	10	10
2512	50 t. Beast	15	10
2513	60 t. Rogue	25	10
2514	70 t. Gambit	30	15
2515	80 t. Cyclops	40	20
2516	100 t. Storm	50	25
2517	200 t. Professor X	95	45
2518	250 t. Wolverine	1·25	60

505 Presley

1995. 60th Birth Anniv of Elvis Presley (entertainer). Multicoloured.

2521	60 t. Type **505**	30	15
2522	80 t. Wearing cap	35	15
2523	100 t. Holding microphone	45	20
2524	120 t. Wearing blue and white striped T-shirt	60	30
2525	150 t. With guitar and microphone	70	35
2526	200 t. On motor bike with girl	85	40
2527	250 t. On surfboard	1·10	50
2528	300 t. Pointing with left hand	1·50	70
2529	350 t. Playing guitar and girl clapping	1·90	85

Nos. 2521/9 were issued together, se-tenant, forming a composite design.

506 Monroe smiling

1995. 70th Birth Anniv (1996) of Marilyn Monroe (actress). Multicoloured.

2531	60 t. Type **506**	30	15
2532	80 t. Wearing white dress	35	15
2533	100 t. Pouting	45	20
2534	120 t. With naval officer and cello player	60	30
2535	150 t. Wearing off-the-shoulder blouse	70	35
2536	200 t. Using telephone and wearing magenta dress	85	40
2537	250 t. Man kissing Monroe's shoulder	1·10	50
2538	300 t. With white fur collar	1·50	70
2539	350 t. With Clark Gable	1·90	85

Nos. 2531/9 were issued together, se-tenant, forming a composite design.

507 Rat sitting between Mountains

1996. New Year. Year of the Rat. Multicoloured.

2541	150 t. Type **507**	70	35
2542	200 t. Rat crouching between mountains and waves (horiz)	85	40

510 Cycling

1996. Olympic Games, Atlanta, U.S.A. Mult.

2548	30 t. Type **510**	10	10
2549	60 t. Shooting	10	10
2550	80 t. Weightlifting	15	10
2551	100 t. Boxing	20	10
2552	120 t. Archery (vert)	25	10
2553	150 t. Rhythmic gymnastics (vert)	30	15
2554	200 t. Hurdling (vert)	40	20
2555	350 t. Show jumping	70	35
2556	400 t. Wrestling	80	40

x Since the above, further issues have appeared inscribed either "Mongolia" or "Mongol Post". It has so far proved impossible to discover the dates on which these stamps were issued and, indeed, if any of them were available for postal purposes in Mongolia.

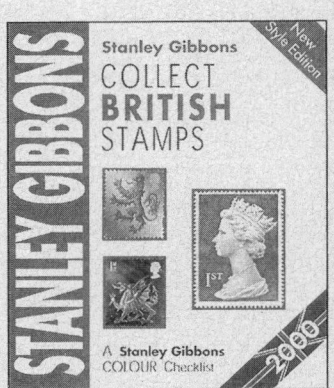

MONG-TSEU (MENGTSZ) Pt. 17

An Indo-Chinese P.O. in Yunnan province, China, closed in 1922.

1903. 100 centimes = 1 franc.
1919. 100 cents = 1 piastre.

Stamps of Indo-China surcharged.

1903. "Tablet" key-type surch **MONGTZE** and value in Chinese.
1 D 1 c. black and red on buff . 3·50 3·50
2 2 c. brown & blue on buff 2·25 2·25
3 4 c. brown & blue on grey 3·50 3·50
4 5 c. green and red . . . . 2·75 3·00
5 10 c. red and blue . . . . 4·00 4·00
6 15 c. grey and red . . . . 5·00 4·50
7 20 c. red and blue on green 5·25 5·25
8 25 c. blue and red . . . . 5·75 5·50
9 25 c. black and red on pink £400 £400
10 30 c. brown & bl on drab 4·75 5·00
11 40 c. red & blue on yellow 38·00 38·00
12 50 c. red and blue on pink £190 £190
13 50 c. brown & red on blue 60·00 60·00
14 75 c. brown & red on orge 60·00 60·00
15 1 f. green and red . . . . 60·00 60·00
16 5 f. mauve & blue on lilac 60·00 60·00

1906. Surch **Mong-Tseu** and value in Chinese.
17 8 1 c. green 90 85
18 2 c. purple on yellow 90 85
19 4 c. mauve on blue 90 85
20 5 c. green 90 85
21 10 c. pink . . . . 1·10 1·10
22 15 c. brown on blue . . . . 1·10 1·10
23 20 c. red on green . . . . 2·00 2·00
24 25 c. blue . . . . 2·25 2·25
25 30 c. brown on cream . . . . 3·50 3·50
26 35 c. black on yellow . . . . 2·50 2·50
27 40 c. black on grey . . . . 3·25 3·25
28 50 c. brown . . . . 9·50 9·50
29 D 75 c. brown & red on orange . 23·00 23·00
30 8 1 f. green . . . . 11·00 11·00
31 2 f. brown on yellow . . . 27·00 27·00
32 D 5 f. mauve and blue on lilac . 60·00 60·00
34 8 10 f. red on green . . . . 80·00 80·00

1908. Surch **MONGTSEU** and value in Chinese.
35 10 1 c. black and brown . . . 35 40
36 2 c. black and brown . . . 40 45
37 4 c. black and blue 50 55
38 5 c. black and green 60 60
39 10 c. black and red 85 90
40 15 c. black and violet . . . 95 95
41 11 20 c. black and violet . . . 2·50 2·25
42 25 c. black and blue . . . . 3·25 3·25
43 30 c. black and brown . . . 2·25 2·00
44 35 c. black and green . . . 2·25 2·00
45 40 c. black and brown . . . 2·25 2·25
46 50 c. black and red . . . . 2·25 2·25
47 12 75 c. black and orange . . . 5·50 5·50
48 – 1 f. black and red . . . . 6·00 6·25
49 – 2 f. black and green . . . 8·00 8·25
50 – 5 f. black and blue . . . . 55·00 60·00
51 – 10 f. black and violet . . . 65·00 70·00

1919. Nos. 35/51 further surch in figures and words.
52 10 ⅖ c. on 1 c. black & brown 45 45
53 ⅘ c. on 2 c. black & brown 45 40
54 1⅗ c. on 4 c. black & blue 90 90
55 2 c. on 5 c. black and green 55 55
56 4 c. on 10 c. black and red 1·10 1·00
57 6 c. on 15 c. black and violet 1·10 1·00
58 11 8 c. on 20 c. black and violet 2·00 2·00
59 10 c. on 25 c. black and blue 1·60 1·60
60 12 c. on 30 c. black & brown 1·60 1·60
61 14 c. on 35 c. black & green 1·60 1·50
62 16 c. on 40 c. black & brown 2·00 2·00
63 20 c. on 50 c. black and red 2·25 2·00
64 12 30 c. on 75 c. black & orge 2·00 2·00
65 – 40 c. on 1 f. black and red 4·25 4·25
66 – 80 c. on 2 f. black and green 2·75 2·75
67 – 2 p. on 5 f. black and blue 70·00 75·00
68 – 4 p. on 10 f. black and violet 13·00 13·00

MONTENEGRO Pt. 3

Formerly a monarchy on the Adriatic Sea, now part of Yugoslavia. In Italian and German occupation during 1939-45 war.

1874. 100 novcic = 1 florin.
1902. 100 heller = 1 krone.
1907. 100 para = 1 krone (1910 = 1 perper).

1 Prince Nicholas

Прослава
1493 1893
Штампарије
(2)

1874.
45 1 1 n. blue 40 45
38 2 n. yellow . . . . 2·00 2·00
51 2 n. green 20 15
39 3 n. green 50 50
52 3 n. red 20 15
40 5 n. red 50 50
53 5 n. orange 45 20
19 7 n. mauve . . . . 35·00 30·00
41 7 n. pink 50 50
54 7 n. grey 35 45
42 10 n. blue 50 50
55 10 n. purple 30 45
56 15 n. brown 30 45
46 20 n. brown 25 25
7 25 n. purple £250 £275
44 25 n. brown . . . . 50 2·75
57 25 n. blue 30 45
47 1 30 n. brown 40 45
48 50 n. blue 40 45
49 1 f. green . . . . 1·25 2·75
50 2 f. red . . . . 1·25 4·00

1893. 400th Anniv of Introduction of Printing into Montenegro. Optd with T **2**.
81 1 2 n. yellow . . . . 24·00 2·75
82 3 n. green . . . . 1·50 1·50
83 5 n. red . . . . 1·25 1·25
84 7 n. pink . . . . 1·00 1·00
86 10 n. blue . . . . 1·75 1·75
87 15 n. bistre . . . . 1·50 1·50
89 25 n. brown . . . . 1·90 1·90

3 Monastery near Cetinje, Royal Mausoleum

1896. Bicentenary of Petrovich Niegush Dynasty.
90 3 1 n. brown and blue . . . . 30 1·00
91 2 n. yellow and purple . . . 30 1·00
92 3 n. green and brown . . . 30 1·00
93 5 n. brown and green . . . 30 1·00
94 10 n. blue and yellow . . . 30 1·00
95 15 n. green and blue . . . . 30 1·00
96 20 n. blue and green . . . . 40 1·25
97 25 n. yellow and blue . . . . 40 1·25
98 30 n. brown and purple . . . 45 1·25
99 50 n. blue and red . . . . 50 1·50
100 1 f. blue and pink . . . . 90 1·75
101 2 f. black and brown . . . 1·00 1·50

4

УСТАВ
Constitution
1905
(5)

7

1902.
102 4 1 h. blue 30 30
103 2 h. mauve 30 30
104 5 h. green 30 20
105 10 h. red 30 30
106 25 h. blue 30 50
107 50 h. green 40 50
108 1 k. brown 35 35
109 2 k. brown 50 50
110 5 k. brown . . . . 75 1·50

1905. Granting of Constitution. Optd with T **5**.
111 4 1 h. blue 15 20
112 2 h. mauve 15 20
113 5 h. green 15 20
114 10 h. red 50 50
124a 25 h. blue 15 25
125a 50 h. green 15 25
126a 1 k. brown 15 25
127a 2 k. brown 15 25
119 5 k. orange . . . . 75 2·50

1907. New Currency.
129 7 1 pa. yellow 15 20
130 2 pa. black 15 20
131 5 pa. green . . . . 1·00 10
132 10 pa. red . . . . 1·50 10
133 15 pa. blue 20 15
134 20 pa. orange 20 20
135 25 pa. blue . . . . 20 1·25
136 35 pa. brown 25 15
137 50 pa. lilac 45 35
138 1 k. red 45 60
139 2 k. green 45 60
140 5 k. red . . . . 90 2·00

9 King Nicholas when a Youth

10 King Nicholas and Queen Milena

11 Prince Nicholas

12 Nicholas I

1910. Proclamation of Kingdom and 50th Anniv of Reign of Prince Nicholas.
141 9 1 pa. black 35 15
142 10 2 pa. purple 35 15
143 – 5 pa. green 30 15
144 – 10 pa. red 30 15
145 – 15 pa. blue 30 15
146 10 20 pa. olive 65 15
147 – 25 pa. blue 65 15
148 – 35 pa. brown 85 85
149 – 50 pa. violet 65 35
150 – 1 per. lake 65 35
151 – 2 per. green 85 50
152 11 5 per. blue . . . . 1·25 1·00
DESIGNS: As Type **9**: 5, 10, 25, 35 pa. Nicholas I in 1910; 15 pa. Nicholas I in 1878; 50 pa., 1, 2 per. Nicholas I in 1890.

1913.
153 12 1 pa. orange 15 15
154 2 pa. purple 15 15
155 5 pa. green 15 15
156 10 pa. red 15 15
157 15 pa. blue 20 20
158 20 pa. brown 20 20
159 25 pa. blue 20 20
160 35 pa. red 50 50
161 50 pa. blue 25 25
162 1 per. brown 25 25
163 2 per. purple 65 65
164 5 per. green 65 65

ITALIAN OCCUPATION

Montenegro
Црна Гора
17-IV-41-XIX
(1)

ЦРНА ГОРА
(2)

1941. Stamps of Yugoslavia optd with T **1**.
(a) Postage. On Nos. 414, etc.
1 99 25 p. black 30 65
2 1 d. green 30 65
3 1 d. 50 red 30 65
4 2 d. mauve 30 65
5 3 d. brown 30 65
6 4 d. blue 30 65
7 5 d. blue . . . . 1·50 4·75
8 5 d. 50 violet . . . . . . 1·50 4·75
9 6 d. blue . . . . 1·50 4·75
10 8 d. brown . . . . 1·75 5·50
11 12 d. violet . . . . 1·50 4·75
12 16 d. purple . . . . 1·50 4·75
13 20 d. blue . . . . 90·00 £140
14 30 d. pink . . . . 40·00 65·00

(b) Air. On Nos. 360/7.
15 80 50 p. brown . . . . 8·00 6·00
16 – 1 d. green . . . . 2·00 5·00
17 – 2 d. blue . . . . 2·00 5·50
18 – 2 d. 50 red . . . . 3·00 6·00
19 80 5 d. violet . . . . 22·00 45·00
20 – 10 d. red . . . . 22·00 45·00
21 – 20 d. green . . . . 22·00 50·00
22 – 30 d. blue . . . . 22·00 48·00

1941. Stamps of Italy optd with T **2**. (a) On Postage stamps of 1929.
28 98 5 c. brown 15 50
29 – 10 c. brown 15 50
30 – 15 c. green 15 50
31 99 20 c. red 15 50
32 – 25 c. green 15 50
33 103 30 c. brown 15 50
34 50 c. violet 15 50
35 – 75 c. red 15 50
36 – 1 l. 25 blue 15 50

(b) On Air stamp of 1930.
37 110 50 c. brown 15 50

1942. Nos. 416 etc of Yugoslavia optd **Governatorato del Montenegro Valore LIRE**.
43 99 1 d. green . . . . 75 1·40
44 1 d. 50 red . . . . 25·00 30·00
45 3 d. brown . . . . 75 1·40
46 4 d. blue . . . . 75 1·40
47 5 d. 50 violet . . . . 75 1·40
48 6 d. blue . . . . 75 1·40
49 8 d. brown . . . . 75 1·40
50 12 d. violet . . . . 75 1·40
51 16 d. purple . . . . 75 1·40

1942. Air. Nos. 360/7 of Yugoslavia optd **Governatorato del Montenegro Valore in Lire**.
52 80 0.50 l. brown . . . . 2·50 3·50
53 – 1 l. green . . . . 2·50 3·50
54 – 2 l. blue . . . . 2·50 3·50
55 – 2.50 l. red . . . . 2·50 3·50
56 80 5 l. violet . . . . 2·50 3·50
57 – 10 l. brown . . . . 2·50 3·50
58 – 20 l. green . . . . 65·00 £100
59 – 30 l. blue . . . . 20·00 32·00

4 Prince Bishop Peter Njegos and View

1943. National Poem Commemoratives. Each stamp has fragment of poetry inscr at back.
60 4 5 c. violet 25 75
61 – 10 c. green 25 75
62 – 15 c. brown 25 75
63 – 20 c. orange 25 75
64 – 25 c. green 25 75
65 – 50 c. mauve 25 75
66 – 1 l. 25 blue 25 75
67 – 2 l. green . . . . 1·00 2·00
68 – 5 l. red on buff . . . . . . 2·50 6·00
69 – 20 l. purple on grey . . . . 5·00 13·00
DESIGNS—HORIZ: 10 c. Meadow near Mt. Lovcen; 15 c. Country chapel; 20 c. Chiefs Meeting; 25, 50 c. Folk-dancing; 1 l. 25, Taking the Oath; 2 l. Moslem wedding procession; 5 l. Watch over wounded standard-bearer. VERT: 20 l. Portrait of Prince Bishop Peter Njegos.

5 Cetinje

1943. Air. With Junkers. G31 airplane (2,20 l.) or Fokker F.VIIa/3m airplane (others).
70 5 50 c. brown . . . . 35 1·25
71 – 1 l. blue . . . . 35 1·25
72 – 2 l. mauve . . . . 35 1·25
73 – 5 l. green . . . . 70 2·50
74 – 10 l. purple on buff . . . . 4·00 9·00
75 – 20 l. blue on pink . . . . 6·25 16·00
DESIGNS—HORIZ: 1 l. Coastline; 2 l. Budva; 5 l. Mt. Lovcen; 10 l. Lake of Scutari. VERT: 20 l. Mt. Durmitor.

GERMAN OCCUPATION

1943. Nos. 419/20 of Yugoslavia surch **Deutsche Militaer-Verwaltung Montenegro** and new value in lire.
76 99 50 c. on 3 d. brown . . . . 2·00 22·00
77 1 l. on 3 d. brown . . . . 2·00 22·00
78 1 l. 50 on 3 d. brown . . . 2·00 22·00
79 2 l. on 3 d. brown . . . . 5·00 45·00
80 4 l. on 3 d. brown . . . . 5·00 45·00
81 5 l. on 4 d. blue . . . . 5·00 45·00
82 8 l. on 4 d. blue . . . . 8·50 75·00
83 10 l. on 4 d. blue . . . . 12·00 £150
84 20 l. on 4 d. blue . . . . 50·00 £325

1943. Appointment of National Administrative Committee. Optd **Nationaler Verwaltungs-ausschuss 10.XI.1943**. (a) Postage. On Nos. 64/8.
85 25 c. green . . . . 8·00 £150
86 50 c. mauve . . . . 8·00 £150
87 1 l. 25 blue . . . . 8·00 £150
88 2 l. green . . . . 8·00 £150
89 5 l. red on buff £200 £2000

(b) Air. On Nos. 70/4.
90 5 50 c. brown . . . . 17·00 £160
91 1 l. blue . . . . 17·00 £160
92 2 l. mauve . . . . 17·00 £160
93 5 l. green . . . . 17·00 £160
94 10 l. purple on buff £3250 £15000

1944. Refugees Fund. Surch **Fluchtlingshilfe Montenegro** and new value in German currency.
(a) On Nos. 419/20 of Yugoslavia.
95 99 0.15 + 0.85 Rm. on 3 d. . . 7·00 £150
96 0.15 + 0.85 Rm. on 4 d. . . 7·00 £150

(b) On Nos. 46/9.
97 – 0.15 + 0.85 Rm. on 25 c. . 7·00 £150
98 – 0.15 + 1.35 Rm. on 50 c. . 7·00 £150
99 – 0.25 + 1.75 Rm. on 1 l. 25 . 7·00 £150
100 – 0.25 + 1.75 Rm. on 2 l. . . 7·00 £150

(c) Air. On Nos. A52/4.
101 5 0.15 + 0.85 Rm. on 50 c. . 9·25 £150
102 – 0.25 + 1.25 Rm. on 1 l. . . 9·25 £150
103 – 0.50 + 1.50 Rm. on 2 l. . . 9·25 £150

1944. Red Cross. Surch + **Crveni krst Montenegro** and new value in German currency.
(a) On Nos. 419/20 of Yugoslavia.
104 99 0.50 + 2.50 Rm. on 3 d. . 7·00 £100
105 0.50 + 2.50 Rm. on 4 d. . 7·00 £100

(b) On Nos. 64/5.
106 – 0.15 + 0.85 Rm. on 25 c. . 7·00 £100
107 – 0.15 + 1.35 Rm. on 50 c. . 7·00 £100

(c) Air. On Nos. 70/2.
108 5 0.25 + 1.75 Rm. on 50 c. . 10·50 £110
109 – 0.25 + 2.75 Rm. on 1 l. . . 10·50 £110
110 – 0.50 + 2 Rm. on 2 l. . . . 10·50 £110

ACKNOWLEDGEMENT OF RECEIPT STAMPS

A 3

A 4

1895.
A90 A 3 10 n. blue and red . . . 85 1·00

1902.
A111 A 4 25 h. orange and red . . 75 75

1905. Optd with T **5**.
A120 A 4 25 h. orange and red . . 60 60

1907. As T **7**, but letters "A" and "R" in top corners.
A141 7 25 p. olive 50 65

1913. As T **12**, but letters "A" and "R" in top corners.
A169 12 25 p. olive 40 70

POSTAGE DUE STAMPS

D 3

D 4

D 8

1894.
D90 D 3 1 n. red . . . . 2·25 1·40
D91 2 n. green 50 20
D92 3 n. orange 50 20
D93 5 n. green 50 20

D94	D 3	10 n. purple	50	30
D95		20 n. blue	50	30
D96		30 n. green	50	30
D97		50 n. pale green	50	30

1902.

D111	D 4	5 h. orange	20	20
D112		10 h. green	30	30
D113		25 h. purple	30	30
D114		50 h. green	30	30
D115		1 k. grey	35	35

1905. Optd with T **5**.

D120	D 4	5 h. orange	35	50
D121		10 h. olive	50	1·00
D122		25 h. purple	35	50
D123		50 h. green	35	50
D124		1 k. pale green	50	75

1907.

D141	D 8	5 p. brown	25	35
D142		10 p. violet	25	35
D143		25 p. red	25	35
D144		50 p. green	25	35

1913. As T **12** but inscr "HOPTOMAPKA" at top.

D165	5 p. grey	75	75
D166	10 p. lilac	50	50
D167	25 p. blue	50	50
D168	50 p. red	65	65

ITALIAN OCCUPATION

1941. Postage Due stamps of Yugoslavia optd **Montenegro Upha 17-IV-41-XIX**.

D23	D **56**	50 p. violet	50	1·00
D24		1 d. mauve	50	1·00
D25		2 d. blue	50	1·00
D26		5 d. orange	30·00	50·00
D27		10 d. brown	3·00	6·00

1942. Postage Due stamps of Italy optd **UPHATOPA**.

D38	D **141**	10 c. blue	15	1·25
D39		20 d. red	15	1·25
D40		30 c. orange	15	1·25
D41		50 c. violet	15	1·25
D42		1 l. orange	25	1·25

MONTSERRAT Pt. 1

One of the Leeward Is., Br. W. Indies. Used general issues for Leeward Is. concurrently with Montserrat stamps until 1 July 1956, when Leeward Is. stamps were withdrawn.

1876. 12 pence = 1 shilling;
20 shillings = 1 pound.
1951. 100 cents = 1 West Indian dollar.

1876. Stamps of Antigua as T **1** optd **MONTSERRAT**.

8c 1d. red . . . . . 15·00 14·00
2 6d. green . . . . . 55·00 40·00

3

1880.

7 **3** ½d. green . . . . . 1·00 7·00
9 2½d. brown . . . . . £225 65·00
10 2½d. blue . . . . . 19·00 18·00
5 4d. blue . . . . . £140 40·00
12 4d. mauve . . . . . 4·50 3·00

4 Device of the Colony **5**

1903.

24a **4** ½d. green . . . . . 40 1·00
15 1d. grey and red 75 40
26a 2d. grey and brown . . . . 1·75 1·00
17 2½d. grey and blue . . . . 1·50 1·75
28a 3d. orange and purple . . . 7·00 2·50
29a 6d. purple and olive . . . 7·00 5·50
30 1s. green and purple . . . 8·50 7·00
21 2s. green and brown . . . 24·00 17·00
22 2s. 6d. green and black . . . 18·00 32·00
33 **5** 5s. black and red . . . . 80·00 £110

1908.

36 **4** 1d. red . . . . . 1·40 30
38 2d. grey . . . . . 1·75 14·00
39 2½d. blue . . . . . 2·25 3·50
40 3d. purple on yellow . . . . 1·00 17·00
43 6d. purple . . . . . 6·50 48·00
44 1s. black on green . . . . 8·50 45·00
45 2s. purple and blue on blue . . 25·00 55·00
46 2s. 6d. black & red on blue . . 30·00 70·00
47 **5** 5s. red and green on yellow . . 50·00 70·00

1914. As T **5**, but portrait of King George V.

48 5s. red and green on yellow . . 55·00 85·00

8 **10** Plymouth

1916.

63 **8** ½d. brown . . . . . 15 5·50
64 ½d. green 20 30
50 1d. red 45 75
65 1d. violet 30 60
67 1½d. yellow . . . . . 1·75 9·50
68 1½d. red . . . . . 30 3·25
69 1½d. brown 90 50
70 2d. grey . . . . . 45 1·75
71a 2½d. blue 60 90
72 2½d. yellow . . . . . 1·25 19·00
74 3d. purple on yellow . . . . 1·10 4·75
73 3d. blue . . . . . 60 15·00
75 4d. black & red on yellow . . . 60 11·00
76 5d. purple and olive . . . 2·75 10·00
77 6d. purple . . . . . 2·50 7·00
78 1s. black on green . . . . 3·00 7·00
79 2s. purple and blue on blue . . 7·00 13·00
80 2s. 6d. black & red on blue . . 12·00 48·00
81 3s. green and violet . . . . 12·00 18·00
82 4s. black and red . . . . 15·00 32·00
83 5s. green and red on yellow . . 24·00 38·00

1917. Optd **WAR STAMP**.

60 **8** ½d. green . . . . . 10 1·00
62 1½d. black and orange 10 30

1932. 300th Anniv of Settlement of Montserrat.

84 **10** ½d. green . . . . . 75 6·00
85 1d. red . . . . . 75 5·50
86 1½d. brown . . . . . 1·25 2·50
87 2d. grey . . . . . 1·50 15·00
88 2½d. blue . . . . . 1·25 13·00
89 3d. orange . . . . . 1·50 14·00
90 6d. violet . . . . . 2·25 26·00
91 1s. olive . . . . . 12·00 35·00
92 2s. 6d. purple . . . . . 48·00 70·00
93 5s. brown £100 £160

1935. Silver Jubilee. As T **10a** of Gambia.

94 1d. blue and red . . . . . 85 3·25
95 1½d. blue and grey . . . . . 1·50 2·75
96 2½d. brown and blue . . . . . 2·25 3·25
97 1s. grey and purple . . . . . 3·00 14·00

1937. Coronation. As T **10b** of Gamiba.

98 1d. red 30 50
99 1½d. brown 40 30
100 2½d. blue 40 75

11 Carr's Bay

1938. King George VI.

101a **11** ½d. green 15 20
102a – 1d. red 30 30
103a – 1½d. purple 30 50
104a – 2d. orange 85 70
105a – 2½d. blue 40 30
106 **11** 3d. brown . . . . . 1·75 40
107a – 6d. violet . . . . . 2·50 60
108a **11** 1s. red . . . . . 2·00 30
109 – 2s. 6d. blue . . . . . 20·00 80
110a **11** 5s. red . . . . . 21·00 3·00
111 – 10s. blue . . . . . 13·00 17·00
112 **11** £1 black . . . . . 13·00 27·00

DESIGNS: 1d., 1½d., 2½d. Sea Island cotton; 2d., 6d., 2s. 6d., 10s. Botanic station.

1946. Victory. As T **11a** of Gamiba.

113 1½d. purple 10 10
114 3d. brown 10 10

1949. Silver Wedding. As T **11b/c** of Gambia.

115 2½d. blue 10 10
116 5s. red . . . . . 4·75 6·50

1949. U.P.U. As T **11d/g** of Gambia.

117 2½d. blue 20 30
118 3d. brown . . . . . 1·75 30
119 6d. purple 40 30
120 1s. purple 40 30

1951. Inauguration of B.W.I. University College. As T **67/8** of Jamaica.

121 3 c. black and purple 20 60
122 12 c. black and violet 20 60

14 Government House **21** Pineapple

1951.

123 **14** 1 c. black . . . . . 10 1·50
124 – 2 c. green 15 70
125 – 3 c. brown 30 70
126 – 4 c. red 30 50
127 – 5 c. violet 30 70
128 – 6 c. brown 30 30
129 – 8 c. blue 35 20
130 – 12 c. blue and brown . . . 35 30
131 – 24 c. red and green . . . 95 30
132 – 60 c. black and red . . . 6·00 2·50
133 – $1.20 green and blue . . . 6·00 4·50
134 – $2.40 black and green . . . 5·00 12·00
135 – $4.80 black and purple . . . 16·00 16·00

DESIGNS: 2 c., $1.20, Sea Island cotton: cultivation; 3 c. Map; 4 c., 24 c. Picking tomatoes; 5 c., 12 c. St. Anthony's Church; 6 c., $4.80, Badge; 8 c., 60 c. Sea Island cotton: ginning; $2.40, Government House (portrait on right).

1953. Coronation. As T **11h** of Gambia.

136 2 c. black and green 40 15

1953. As 1951 but portrait of Queen Elizabeth II.

136a ½ c. violet (As 3 c.) (I) . . . 50 10
136b ½ c. violet (II) 70 10
137 1 c. black 10 10
138 2 c. green 15 10
139 3 c. brown (I) 50 10
139a 3 c. brown (II) . . . . . 70 1·25
140 4 c. red 30 20
141 5 c. violet 30 30
142 6 c. brown (I) 30 10
142a 6 c. brown (II) 40 15
143 8 c. blue . . . . . 1·00 10
144 12 c. blue and brown . . . . 1·50 10
145 24 c. red and green . . . . 1·50 20
145a 48 c. olive & pur (As 2 c.) . . 12·00 2·25
146 60 c. black and red . . . . 7·00 2·00
147 $1.20 green and blue . . . . 14·00 4·25
148 $2.40 black and green . . . 12·00 10·00
149 $4.80 black and purple (I) . . 6·00 10·00
149a $4.80 black and purple (II) . . 12·00 7·50

I. Inscr "Presidency". II. Inscr "Colony".

1958. British Caribbean Federation. As T **79** of Jamaica.

150 3 c. green 55 20
151 6 c. blue 75 60
152 12 c. red 90 15

1963. Freedom from Hunger. As T **20a** of Gambia.

153 12 c. violet 30 15

1963. Cent of Red Cross. As T **20b** of Gambia.

154 4 c. red and black 15 20
155 12 c. red and blue 35 50

1964. 400th Birth Anniv oof Shakespeare. As T **22a** of Gambia.

156 12 c. blue 10 10

1965. Cent of I.T.U. As T **44** of Gibraltar.

158 4 c. red and violet 15 10
159 48 c. green and red 30 20

1965. Multicoloured.

160 1 c. Type **21** 10 10
161 2 c. Avocado 10 10
162 3 c. Soursop 10 10
163 4 c. Pepper 10 10
164 5 c. Mango 10 10
165 6 c. Tomatoe 10 10
166 8 c. Guava 10 10
167 10 c. Ochro 10 10
168 12 c. Lime 15 10
169 20 c. Orange 20 10
170 24 c. Banana 20 10
171 42 c. Onion 75 60
172 48 c. Cabbage . . . . . 1·50 75
173 60 c. Pawpaw . . . . . 2·25 90
174 $1.20 Pumpkin . . . . . 2·00 2·50
175 $2.40 Sweet potato . . . . . 6·00 5·50
176 $4.80 Egg plant . . . . . 6·00 9·00

1965. I.C.Y. As T **45** of Gibraltar.

177 2 c. purple and turquoise . . . 10 20
178 12 c. green and lavender . . . 25 10

1966. Churchill Commem. As T **46** of Gibraltar.

179 1 c. blue 10 10
180 2 c. green 10 10
181 24 c. brown 20 10
182 42 c. violet 25 15

1966. Royal Visit. As T **49** of Grenada.

183 14 c. black and blue 40 15
184 24 c. black and mauve 60 15

1966. Inauguration of W.H.O. Headquarters, Geneva. As T **54** of Gibraltar.

185 12 c. black, green and blue . . 15 10
186 60 c. black, purple and ochre . . 35 60

1966. 20th Anniv of U.N.E.S.C.O. As T **56a/c** of Gibraltar.

187 4 c. multicoloured 10 10
188 60 c. yellow, violet and olive . . 35 10
189 $1.80 black, purple & orange . . 1·40 70

25 Sailing Dinghies

1967. International Tourist Year. Multicoloured.

190 5 c. Type **25** 15 10
191 15 c. Waterfall near Chance Mountain 20 10
192 16 c. Fishing, skin diving and swimming 25 40
193 24 c. Playing golf . . . . . 1·60 45

No. 191 is vert.

1968. Nos. 168, 170, 172, 174/6 surch.

194 15 c. on 12 c. Lime 20 15
195 25 c. on 24 c. Banana 25 15
196 50 c. on 48 c. Cabbage 45 15
197 $1 on $1.20 Pumpkin 80 40
198 $2.50 on $2.40 Sweet potato . . 1·25 3·25
199 $5 on $4.80 Egg plant . . . . 1·40 3·75

27 Sprinting

1968. Olympic Games, Mexico.

200 **27** 15 c. mauve, green & gold . . 10 10
201 – 25 c. blue, orange & gold . . 15 10
202 – 50 c. green, red and gold . . 25 10
203 – $1 multicoloured 35 30

DESIGNS—HORIZ: 25 c. Weightlifting; 50 c. Gymnastics. VERT: $1 Sprinting and Aztec pillars.

31 Alexander Hamilton

1968. Human Rights Year. Multicoloured.

204 5 c. Type **31** 10 10
205 15 c. Albert T. Marryshow . . . 10 10
206 25 c. William Wilberforce . . . 10 10
207 50 c. Dag Hammarskjold . . . 10 10
208 $1 Dr. Martin Luther King . . . 25 30

32 "The Two Trinities" (Murillo) **34** Map showing CARIFTA Countries

1968. Christmas.

209 **32** 5 c. multicoloured 10 10
210 – 15 c. multicoloured 10 10
211 **32** 25 c. multicoloured 10 10
212 – 50 c. multicoloured 25 20

DESIGN: 15, 50 c. "The Adoration of the Kings" (detail, Botticelli).

1969. 1st Anniv of CARIFTA (Caribbean Free Trade Area). Multicoloured.

223 15 c. Type **34** 10 10
224 20 c. Type **34** 10 10
225 35 c. "Strength in Unity" . . . 10 10
226 50 c. As 35 c. 15 15

Nos. 225/6 are horiz.

36 Telephone Receiver and Map of Montserrat **41** King Caspar before the Virgin and Child (detail) (Norman 16th-cent stained glass window)

40 Dolphin (fish)

1969. Development Projects. Multicoloured.

227 15 c. Type **36** 10 10
228 25 c. School symbols and map . . 10 10
229 50 c. Hawker Siddeley H.S.748 aircraft and map 15 10
230 $1 Electricity pylon and map . . 25 50

1969. Game Fish. Multicoloured.

231 5 c. Type **40** 35 10
232 15 c. Atlantic sailfish 50 10
233 25 c. Blackfin tuna 60 10
234 40 c. Spanish mackerel 80 55

1969. Christmas. Paintings multicoloured; frame colours given.

235 **41** 15 c. black, gold & violet . . 10 10
236 25 c. black and red 10 10
237 – 50 c. black, blue & orge . . 15 15

DESIGN—HORIZ: 50 c. "Nativity" (Leonard Limosin).

43 "Red Cross Sale"

1970. Centenary of British Red Cross. Mult.

238 3 c. Type **43** 10 15
239 4 c. School for deaf children . . 10 15
240 15 c. Transport services for disabled 10 20
241 20 c. Workshop 10 60

44 Red-footed Booby

1970. Birds. Multicoloured.

242 1 c. Type **44** 10 10
243 2 c. American kestrel 15 15
244 3 c. Magnificent frigate bird . . 15 15
245 4 c. Great egret . . . . . 1·00 15
299a 5 c. Brown pelican 60 55
247 10 c. Bananaquit 40 10

248 15 c. Smooth-billed ani . . . 30 15
249 20 c. Red-billed tropic bird . . 35 15
250 25 c. Montserrat oriole . . . 50 50
251 50 c. Green-throated carib . . 5·00 1·25
252 $1 Antillean crested hummingbird . . . . . . 6·50 1·00
253 $2.20 Little blue heron . . . . 5·50 10·00
254 $5 Purple-throated carib . . . 7·50 11·00
254c $10 Forest thrush . . . . . . 15·00 15·00

The 2, 3, 4, 5, 10, 50 c. and $2.50 are vert.

45 "Madonna and Child with Animals" (Brueghel the Elder, after Durer)

1970. Christmas. Multicoloured.

255 5 c. Type **45** 10 10
256 15 c. "The Adoration of the Shepherds" (Domenichino) . 10 10
257 20 c. Type **45** 10 10
258 $1 As 15 c. . . . . 35 1·25

46 War Memorial

1970. Tourism. Multicoloured.

259 5 c. Type **46** 10 10
260 15 c. Plymouth from Fort St. George 10 10
261 25 c. Carr's Bay 15 15
262 50 c. Golf Fairway . . . . . . 1·00 1·40

47 Girl Guide and Badge

48 "Descent from the Cross" (Van Hemessen)

1970. Diamond Jubilee of Montserrat Girl Guides. Multicoloured.

264 10 c. Type **47** 10 10
265 15 c. Brownie and badge . . . 10 10
266 25 c. As 15 c. 15 10
267 40 c. Type **47** 20 60

1971. Easter. Multicoloured.

268 5 c. Type **48** 10 10
269 15 c. "Noli me tangere" (Orcagna) 10 10
270 20 c. Type **48** 10 10
271 40 c. As 15 c. 15 30

49 D.F.C. and D.F.M. in Searchlights

50 "The Nativity with Saints" (Romanino)

1971. Golden Jubilee of Commonwealth Ex-Services League. Multicoloured.

272 10 c. Type **49** 10 10
273 20 c. M.C., M.M. and jungle patrol 15 10
274 40 c. D.S.C., D.S.M. and submarine action 20 15
275 $1 V.C. and soldier attacking bunker 50 70

1971. Christmas. Multicoloured.

276 5 c. Type **50** 10 10
277 15 c. "Choir of Angels" (Simon Marmion) 10 10
278 20 c. Type **50** 10 10
279 $1 As 15 c. 35 40

51 Piper Apache

1971. 14th Anniv of Inauguration of L.I.A.T. (Leeward Islands Air Transport). Multicoloured.

280 5 c. Type **51** 10 10
281 10 c. Beech 50 Twin Bonanza . . 15 15
282 15 c. De Havilland Heron . . . 30 15
283 20 c. Britten Norman Islander . 35 15
284 40 c. De Havilland Twin Otter 100 65 45
285 75 c. Hawker Siddeley H.S.748 . 2·00 2·25

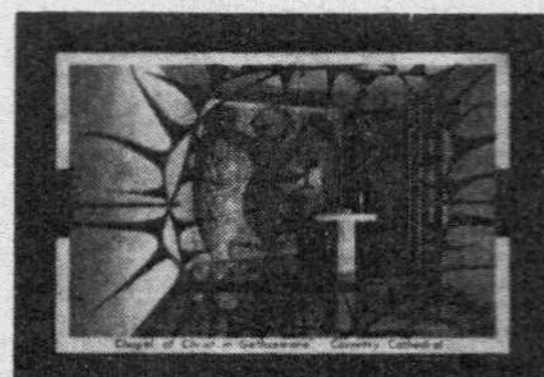

52 "Chapel of Christ in Gethsemane", Coventry Cathedral

1972. Easter. Multicoloured.

287 5 c. Type **52** 10 10
288 10 c. "The Agony in the Garden" (Bellini) 10 10
289 20 c. Type **52** 10 10
290 75 c. As 10 c. 35 50

53 Lizard

54 "Madonna of the Chair" (Raphael)

1972. Reptiles. Multicoloured.

291 15 c. Type **53** 15 10
292 20 c. Mountain chicken (frog) . 20 10
293 40 c. Iguana (horiz) 35 20
294 $1 Tortoise (horiz) . . . . . . 1·50 1·50

1972. Christmas. Multicoloured.

303 10 c. Type **54** 10 10
304 35 c. "Virgin and Child with Cherub" (Fungai) 20 10
305 50 c. "Madonna of the Magnificat" (Botticelli) . . . 30 30
306 $1 "Virgin and Child with St. John and an Angel" (Botticelli) 40 65

1972. Royal Silver Wedding. As T **98** of Gibraltar, but with lime, tomatoes and pawpaw in background.

307 35 c. pink 10 10
308 $1 blue 20 20

56 "Passiflora herbertiana"

58 "Virgin and Child" (School of Gerard David)

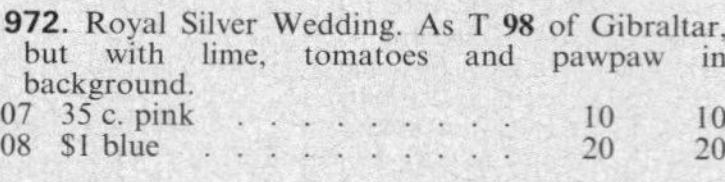

57 Montserrat Monastery, Spain

1973. Easter. Passion-flowers. Multicoloured.

309 20 c. Type **56** 25 10
310 35 c. "P. vitifolia" 30 10
311 75 c. "P. amabilis" 50 75
312 $1 "P. alata-caerulea" 60 80

1973. 480th Anniv of Columbus's Discovery of Montserrat. Multicoloured.

313 10 c. Type **57** 15 10
314 35 c. Columbus sighting Montserrat 30 15
315 60 c. "Santa Maria" off Montserrat . . . . 1·10 1·10
316 $1 Island badge and map of voyage . . . . 1·25 1·10

1973. Christmas. Multicoloured.

318 20 c. Type **58** 25 10
319 35 c. "The Holy Family with St. John" (Jordaens) 30 10
320 50 c. "Virgin and Child" (Bellini) 45 50
321 90 c. "Virgin and Child with Flowers" (Dolci) . . . . . 65 1·00

1973. Royal Wedding. As T **101a** of Gibraltar. Multicoloured, background colours given.

322 35 c. green 10 10
323 $1 blue 20 20

59 Steel Band

1974. 25th Anniv of University of West Indies. Multicoloured.

324 20 c. Type **59** 15 10
325 35 c. Masqueraders (vert) . . . 15 10
326 60 c. Student weaving (vert) . . 25 45
327 $1 University Centre, Montserrat 30 55

60 Hands with Letters

1974. Centenary of U.P.U.

329 **60** 1 c. multicoloured 10 10
330 – 2 c. red, orange and black . 10 10
331 **60** 3 c. multicoloured 10 10
332 – 5 c. orange, red and black . 10 10
333 **60** 50 c. multicoloured 20 20
334 – $1 blue, green and black . . 40 65

DESIGN: 2 c., 5 c., $1 Figures from U.P.U. Monument.

1974. Various stamps surch.

335 2 c. on $1 mult (No. 252) . . . 30 1·50
336 5 c. on 50 c. mult (No. 333) . . 30 60
337 10 c. on 60 c. mult (No. 326) . 65 1·75
338 20 c. on $1 mult (No. 252) . . 30 1·25
339 35 c. on $1 blue, green and black (No. 334) . . . . 40 1·25

62 Churchill and Houses of Parliament

1974. Birth Cent of Sir Winston Churchill. Mult.

340 35 c. Type **62** 15 10
341 70 c. Churchill and Blenheim Palace 20 20

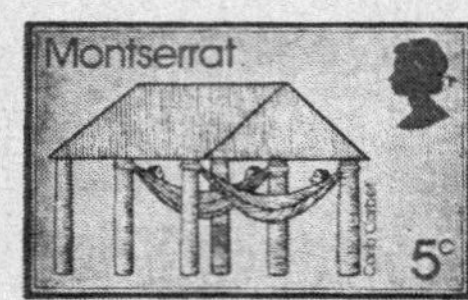

63 Carib "Carbet"

1975. Carib Artefacts.

343 **63** 5 c. brown, yellow & black . 10 10
344 – 20 c. black, brown & yell . 10 10
345 – 35 c. black, yellow & brn . . 15 10
346 – 70 c. yellow, brown & blk . 45 40

DESIGNS: 20 c. "Caracoli"; 35 c. Club or mace; 70 c. Carib canoe.

Nos. 343/46 also come self-adhesive from booklet panes.

64 One-Bitt Coin

1975. Local Coinage, 1785–1801.

351 **64** 5 c. black, blue and silver . . 10 10
352 – 10 c. black, pink and silver . 15 10
353 – 35 c. black, green & silver . 20 15
354 – $2 black, red and silver . . 90 1·50

DESIGNS: 10 c. Eighth dollar; 35 c. Quarter dollar; $2 One dollar.

65 1d. and 6d. Stamps of 1876

1976. Centenary of First Montserrat Postage Stamp.

356 **65** 5 c. red, green and black . . 15 10
357 – 10 c. yellow, red and black . 20 10
358 – 40 c. multicoloured 50 40
359 – 55 c. mauve, green & blk . . 60 50
360 – 70 c. multicoloured 70 70
361 – $1.10 green, blue and black 1·00 1·00

DESIGNS: 10 c. G.P.O. and bisected 1d. stamp; 40 c. Bisects on cover; 55 c. G.B. 6d. used in Montserrat and local 6d. of 1876; 70 c. Stamps for 2½d. rate, 1876; $1.10, Packet boat "Antelope" and 6d. stamp.

66 "The Trinity"

69 Mary and Joseph

68 White Frangipani

1976. Easter. Paintings by Orcagna. Multicoloured.

363 15 c. Type **66** 10 10
364 40 c. "The Resurrection" . . . 15 15
365 55 c. "The Ascension" 15 15
366 $1.10 "Pentecost" 30 40

1976. Nos. 244, 246 and 247 surch.

368 2 c. on 5 c. multicoloured . . . 10 15
369 30 c. on 10 c. multicoloured . . 30 20
370 45 c. on 3 c. multicoloured . . 40 25

1976. Flowering Trees. Multicoloured.

371 1 c. Type **68** 10 10
372 2 c. Cannon-ball tree 10 10
373 3 c. Lignum vitae 10 10
374 5 c. Malay apple 15 10
375 10 c. Jacaranda 30 10
376 15 c. Orchid tree 50 10
377 20 c. Manjak 30 10
378 25 c. Tamarind 60 50
379 40 c. Flame of the forest . . . 40 30
380 55 c. Pink cassia 50 30
381 70 c. Long john 50 30
382 $1 Saman 65 60
383 $2.50 Immortelle . . . . . . 1·25 1·50
384 $5 Yellow poui . . . . 1·75 2·25
385 $10 Flamboyant . . . . 2·50 4·25

1976. Christmas. Multicoloured.

386 5 c. Type **69** 10 10
387 20 c. The Shepherds 10 10
388 55 c. Mary and Jesus 15 15
389 $1.10 The Magi 30 50

MINIMUM PRICE

The minimum price quoted is 10p which represents a handling charge rather than a basis for valuing common stamps. For further notes about prices see introductory pages.

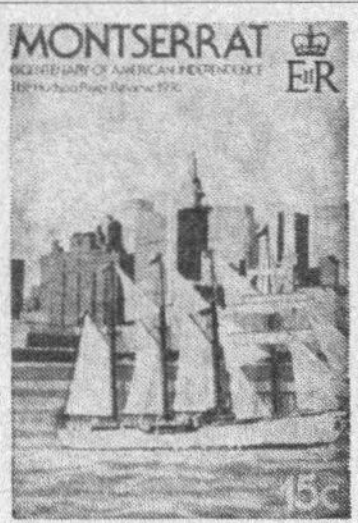

70 Hudson River Review, 1976

1976. Bicent of American Revolution. Mult.

391 15 c. Type **70** 40 20
392 40 c. "Raleigh" (American frigate), 1777* 70 40
393 75 c. H.M.S. "Druid" (frigate), 1777* 70 40
394 $1.25 Hudson River Review (different detail) . . . . . . 1·25 60

*The date is wrongly given on the stamps as "1776".

Nos. 391 and 394 and 392/3 respectively were issued in se-tenant pairs, each pair forming a composite design.

71 The Crowning

1977. Silver Jubilee. Multicoloured.

396 30 c. Royal Visit, 1966 . . . . 10 10
397 45 c. Cannons firing salute . . 15 10
398 $1 Type **71** 25 50

72 "Ipomoea alba"

75 The Stable at Bethlehem

73 Princess Anne laying Foundation Stone of Glendon Hospital

1977. Flowers of the Night. Multicoloured.

399 15 c. Type **72** 20 10
400 40 c. "Epiphyllum hookeri" (horiz) 30 30
401 55 c. "Cereus hexagonus" (horiz) 30 30
402 $1.50 "Cestrum nocturnum" . . 80 1·40

1977. Development. Multicoloured.

404 20 c. Type **73** 15 10
405 40 c. "Statesman" (freighter) in Plymouth Port 35 15
406 55 c. Glendon Hospital 35 20
407 $1.50 Jetty at Plymouth Port . . 90 1·00

1977. Royal Visit. Nos. 380/1 and 383 surch **$1.00 SILVER JUBILEE 1977 ROYAL VISIT TO THE CARIBBEAN.**

409 $1 on 55 c. Pink cassia 30 45
410 $1 on 70 c. Long john 30 45
411 $1 on $2.50 Immortelle 30 45

1977. Christmas. Multicoloured.

412 5 c. Type **75** 10 10
413 40 c. The Three Kings 15 10
414 55 c. Three Ships 20 10
415 $2 Three Angels . . . . 65 1·25

76 Four-eyed Butterflyfish

1978. Fish. Multicoloured.

417 30 c. Type **76** 55 10
418 40 c. French angelfish 60 15
419 55 c. Blue tang 70 15
420 $1.50 Queen triggerfish . . . . 1·10 1·25

77 St. Paul's Cathedral

1978. 25th Anniv of Coronation. Multicoloured.

422 40 c. Type **77** 10 10
423 55 c. Chichester Cathedral . . 10 10
424 $1 Lincoln Cathedral 20 25
425 $2.50 Llandaff Cathedral . . . 40 50

78 "Alpinia speciosa"

79 Private, 21st (Royal North British Fusiliers), 1786

1978. Flowers. Multicoloured.

427 40 c. Type **78** 20 10
428 55 c. "Allamanda cathartica" . 25 15
429 $1 "Petrea volubilis" 45 45
430 $2 "Hippeastrum puniceum" . . 70 80

1978. Military Uniforms (1st series). British Infantry Regiments. Multicoloured.

431 30 c. Type **79** 15 15
432 40 c. Corporal, 86th (Royal County Down), 1831 . . . . 20 15
433 55 c. Sergeant, 14th (Buckinghamshire), 1837 . . 30 20
434 $1.50 Officer, 55th (Westmorland), 1784 . . . . 75 80

See also Nos. 441/4.

80 Cub Scouts

1979. 50th Anniv of Boy Scout Movement on Montserrat. Multicoloured.

436 40 c. Type **80** 20 10
437 55 c. Scouts with signalling equipment 30 20
438 $1.25 Camp fire (vert) 50 55
439 $2 Oath ceremony (vert) . . . 65 1·00

1979. Military Uniforms (2nd series). As T **79**. Multicoloured.

441 30 c. Private, 60th (Royal American), 1783 . . . . . . 15 15
442 40 c. Private, 1st West India, 1819 . . . . 20 15
443 55 c. Officer, 5th (Northumberland), 1819 . . 30 25
444 $2.50 Officer, 93rd (Sutherland Highlanders), 1830 . . . . . 1·00 1·10

81 Child reaching out to Adult

1979. International Year of the Child.

446 **81** $2 black, brown and flesh . 50 55

82 Sir Rowland Hill with Penny Black and Montserrat 1876 1d. Stamp

1979. Death Cent of Sir Rowland Hill and Cent of U.P.U. Membership. Multicoloured.

448 40 c. Type **82** 20 10
449 55 c. U.P.U. emblem and notice announcing Leeward Islands entry into Union 20 15
450 $1 1883 letter following U.P.U. membership 30 50
451 $2 Great Britain Post Office Regulations Notice and Sir Rowland Hill 40 80

83 Plume Worm

1979. Marine Life. Multicoloured.

453 40 c. Type **83** 30 15
454 55 c. Sea fans 40 20
455 $2 Sponge and coral . . . . . 1·00 2·10

84 Tree Frog

1980. Reptiles and Amphibians. Mult.

456 40 c. Type **84** 20 15
457 55 c. Tree lizard 25 25
458 $1 Crapaud 45 50
459 $2 Wood slave 80 90

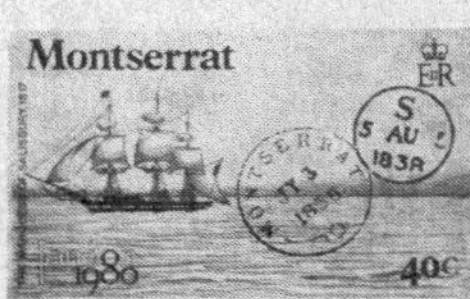

85 "Marquess of Salisbury" and 1838 Handstamps

1980. "London 1980" Int Stamp Exhibition. Mult.

460 40 c. Type **85** 20 15
461 55 c. Hawker Siddeley H.S.748 aircraft and 1976 55 c. definitive 25 25
462 $1.20 "La Plata" (liner) and 1903 5s. Stamp 30 45
463 $1.20 "Lady Hawkins" (packet steamer) and 1932 Tercentenary 5s. commem . . 30 45
464 $1.20 "Avon I" (paddle-steamer) and Penny Red stamp with "A 08" postmark 30 45
465 $1.20 Aeronca Champion 17 airplane and 1953 $1.20 definitive 30 45

1980. 75th Anniv of Rotary International. No. 383 optd **75th Anniversary of Rotary International.**

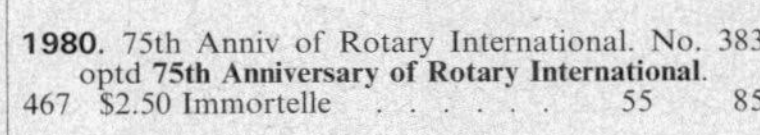

467 $2.50 Immortelle 55 85

87 Greek, French and U.S.A. Flags

1980. Olympic Games, Moscow. Multicoloured.

468 40 c. Type **87** 20 30
469 55 c. Union, Swedish and Belgian flags 20 30
470 70 c. French, Dutch and U.S.A. flags 30 40
471 $1 German, Union and Finnish flags 35 40
472 $1.50 Australian, Italian and Japanese flags 45 70
473 $2 Mexican, West German and Canadian flags 50 70
474 $2.50 "The Discus Thrower" (sculpture, Miron) . . . . . 55 1·00

1980. Nos. 371, 373, 376 and 379 surch.

476 5 c. on 3 c. Lignum vitae . . . 10 10
477 35 c. on 1 c. Type **68** 15 15
478 35 c. on 3 c. Lignum vitae . . . 15 15
479 35 c. on 15 c. Orchid tree . . . 15 15
480 55 c. on 40 c. Flame of the forest 15 15
481 $5 on 40 c. Flame of the forest 85 2·00

89 "Lady Nelson", 1928

1980. Mail Packet Boats (1st series). Mult.

482 40 c. Type **89** 30 15
483 55 c. "Chignecto", 1913 . . . 40 25
484 $1 "Solent II", 1878 . . . . . 80 60
485 $2 "Dee", 1841 . . . . 1·10 1·25

See also Nos. 615/19.

90 "Heliconius charithonia"

91 Atlantic Spadefish

1981. Butterflies. Multicoloured.

486 50 c. Type **90** 60 40
487 65 c. "Pyrgus oileus" 70 45
488 $1.50 "Phoebis agarithe" . . . 90 85
489 $2.50 "Danaus plexippus" . . 1·25 1·10

1981. Fishes. Multicoloured.

555 5 c. Type **91** 20 10
556 10 c. Hogfish and neon goby . 25 10
492 15 c. Creole wrasse 80 30
493 20 c. Three-spotted damselfish . 70 10
559 25 c. Sergeant major 35 20
560 35 c. Fin-spot wrasse 45 30
496 45 c. Schoolmaster 80 40
497 55 c. Striped parrotfish . . . . 1·10 45
498 65 c. Bigeye 80 60
564 75 c. French grunt 75 55
565 $1 Rock beauty 85 65
501 $2 Blue chromis . . . . 1·50 1·10
502 $3 Royal gramma ("Fairy basslet") and blueheads . . . 1·60 1·75
503 $5 Cherub angelfish . . . . . 2·25 2·75
504 $7.50 Long-jawed squirrelfish . 3·00 4·75
570 $10 Caribbean long-nosed butterflyfish . . . . 3·75 6·00

92 Fort St. George

1981. Montserrat National Trust. Multicoloured.

506 50 c. Type **92** 25 20
507 65 c. Bird sanctuary, Fox's Bay 45 35
508 $1.50 Museum 50 65
509 $2.50 Bransby Point Battery, c. 1780 . . . . 60 1·10

1981. Royal Wedding. Royal Yachts. As T **26/27** of Kiribati. Multicoloured.

510 90 c. "Charlotte" 25 25
511 90 c. Prince Charles and Lady Diana Spencer 85 85
512 $3 "Portsmouth" 60 60
513 $3 As No. 511 . . . . 1·50 1·50
514 $4 "Britannia" 75 75
515 $4 As No. 511 . . . . 1·75 1·75

93 H.M.S. "Dorsetshire" and Fairey Firefly Seaplane

1981. 50th Anniv of Montserrat Airmail Service. Multicoloured.

519 50 c. Type **93** 40 30
520 65 c. Beech 50 Twin Bonanza . 55 30
521 $1.50 De Havilland Dragon Rapide "Lord Shaftesbury" . 80 1·75
522 $2.50 Hawker Siddeley H.S.748 and maps of Montserrat and Antigua . . . . 1·00 2·75

94 Methodist Church, Bethel

95 Rubiaceae ("Rondeletia buxifolia")

1981. Christmas. Churches. Multicoloured.

523 50 c. Type **94** 15 15
524 65 c. St. George's Anglican Church, Harris 20 15
525 $1.50 St. Peter's Anglican Church, St. Peter's 45 60
526 $2.50 St. Patrick's R.C. Church, Plymouth . . . . 55 1·00

1982. Plant Life. Multicoloured.

No.	Description	Unused	Used
528	50 c. Type **95**	20	30
529	65 c. Boraginaceae ("Heliotropium ternatum") (horiz)	25	40
530	$1.50 Simarubaceae ("Picramnia pentandra")	50	85
531	$2.50 Ebenaceae ("Diospyrus revoluta") (horiz)	70	1·25

96 Plymouth

1982. 350th Anniv of Settlement of Montserrat by Sir Thomas Warner.

No.	Description	Unused	Used
532	**96** 40 c. green	25	30
533	55 c. red	30	35
534	65 c. brown	35	50
535	75 c. grey	40	60
536	85 c. blue	40	75
537	95 c. orange	40	80
538	$1 violet	40	80
539	$1.50 olive	45	1·25
540	$2 claret	55	1·50
541	$2.50 brown	60	1·50

The design of Nos. 532/41 is based on the 1932 Tercentenary set.

97 Catherine of Aragon, Princess of Wales, 1501

98 Local Scout

1982. 21st Birthday of Princess of Wales. Mult.

No.	Description	Unused	Used
542	75 c. Type **97**	15	15
543	$1 Coat of Arms of Catherine of Aragon	15	15
544	$5 Diana, Princess of Wales	80	1·25

1982. 75th Anniv of Boy Scout Movement. Multicoloured.

No.	Description	Unused	Used
545	$1.50 Type **98**	50	50
546	$2.20 Lord Baden-Powell	60	75

99 Annunciation

1982. Christmas. Multicoloured.

No.	Description	Unused	Used
547	35 c. Type **99**	15	15
548	75 c. Shepherds' Vision	25	35
549	$1.50 The Stable	45	85
550	$2.50 Flight into Egypt	55	1·10

100 "Lepthemis vesiculosa"

1983. Dragonflies. Multicoloured.

No.	Description	Unused	Used
551	50 c. Type **100**	40	20
552	65 c. "Orthemis ferruginea"	50	25
553	$1.50 "Triacanthagyna trifida"	1·00	1·25
554	$2.50 "Erythrodiplax umbrata"	1·40	2·00

101 Blue-headed Hummingbird

102 Montserrat Emblem

1983. Hummingbirds. Multicoloured.

No.	Description	Unused	Used
571	35 c. Type **101**	1·50	35
572	75 c. Green-throated carib	1·75	85
573	$2 Antilean crested hummingbird	2·75	2·75
574	$3 Purple-throated carib	3·00	3·75

1983.

No.	Description	Unused	Used
575	**102** $12 blue and red	4·25	5·00
576	$30 red and blue	9·00	12·00

1983. Various stamps surch. (a) Nos. 491, 494, 498/9, 501.

No.	Description	Unused	Used
577	40 c. on 25 c. Sergeant major (No. 494)	30	30
578	70 c. on 10 c. Hogfish and neon goby (No. 491)	45	45
579	90 c. on 65 c. Bigeye (No. 498)	55	60
580	$1.15 on 75 c. French grunt (No. 499)	65	70
581	$1.50 on $2 Blue chromis (No. 501)	85	90
	(b) Nos. 512/15.		
582	70 c. on $3 "Portsmouth"	40	85
583	70 c. on $3 Prince Charles and Lady Diana Spencer	1·00	2·25
584	$1.15 on $4 "Britannia"	50	1·25
585	$1.15 on $4, As No. 583	1·25	2·50

104 Montgolfier Balloon, 1783

106 Statue of Discus Thrower

105 Boys dressed as Clowns

1983. Bicentenary of Manned Flight. Mult.

No.	Description	Unused	Used
586	35 c. Type **104**	15	15
587	75 c. De Havilland Twin Otter 200/300 (horiz)	25	30
588	$1.50 Lockheed Vega V (horiz)	40	75
589	$2 Beardmore airship R.34 (horiz)	60	1·25

1983. Christmas. Carnival. Multicoloured.

No.	Description	Unused	Used
591	55 c. Type **105**	10	10
592	90 c. Girls dressed as silver star bursts	15	20
593	$1.15 Flower girls	20	35
594	$2 Masqueraders	35	80

1984. Olympic Games, Los Angeles. Mult.

No.	Description	Unused	Used
595	90 c. Type **106**	30	35
596	$1 Olympic torch	35	45
597	$1.25 Los Angeles Olympic stadium	40	50
598	$2.50 Olympic and American flags	65	1·00

107 Cattle Egret

1984. Birds of Montserrat. Multicoloured.

No.	Description	Unused	Used
600	5 c. Type **107**	30	30
601	10 c. Carib grackle	30	30
602	15 c. Moorhen	30	30
603	20 c. Brown booby	40	30
604	25 c. Black-whiskered vireo	40	40
605	40 c. Scaly-breasted thrasher	60	50
606	55 c. Laughing gull	75	30
607	70 c. Glossy ibis	90	45
608	90 c. Green heron	1·00	60
609	$1 Belted kingfisher (vert)	1·25	70
610	$1.15 Bananaquit (vert)	1·50	1·40
611	$3 American kestrel (vert)	3·25	5·00
612	$5 Forest thrush (vert)	4·50	7·00
613	$7.50 Black-crowned night heron (vert)	6·00	12·00
614	$10 Bridled quail dove (vert)	7·00	13·00

1984. Mail Packet Boats (2nd series). As T **89**. Multicoloured.

No.	Description	Unused	Used
615	55 c. "Tagus II", 1907	20	40
616	90 c. "Cobequid", 1913	30	50
617	$1.15 "Lady Drake", 1942	40	70
618	$2 "Factor", 1948	60	1·25

108 Hermit Crab and West Indian Top Shell

1984. Marine Life. Multicoloured.

No.	Description	Unused	Used
620	90 c. Type **108**	1·50	1·00
621	$1.15 Rough file shell	1·75	1·40
622	$1.50 True tulip	2·50	3·00
623	$2.50 Queen or pink conch	3·25	4·75

109 "Bull Man"

1984. Christmas. Carnival Costumes. Mult.

No.	Description	Unused	Used
624	55 c. Type **109**	50	25
625	$1.15 Masquerader Captain	1·50	1·25
626	$1.50 "Fantasy" Carnival Queen	1·75	2·25
627	$2.30 "Ebony and Ivory" Carnival Queen	2·50	4·00

110 Mango

111 "Oncidium urophyllum"

1985. National Emblems. Multicoloured.

No.	Description	Unused	Used
628	$1.15 Type **110**	30	60
629	$1.50 Lobster claw	40	1·00
630	$3 Montserrat oriole	60	2·00

1985. Orchids of Montserrat. Multicoloured.

No.	Description	Unused	Used
631	90 c. Type **111**	45	55
632	$1.15 "Epidendrum difforme"	50	80
633	$1.50 "Epidendrum ciliare"	55	1·10
634	$2.50 "Brassavola cucullata"	75	2·50

112 Queen Elizabeth the Queen Mother

115 Black-throated Blue Warbler

113 Cotton Plants

1985. Life and Times of Queen Elizabeth the Queen Mother. Various vertical portraits.

No.	Description	Unused	Used
636	**112** 55 c. multicoloured	25	30
637	– 55 c. multicoloured	25	30
638	– 90 c. multicoloured	25	40
639	– 90 c. multicoloured	25	40
640	– $1.15 multicoloured	25	40
641	– $1.15 multicoloured	25	40
642	– $1.50 multicoloured	30	40
643	– $1.50 multicoloured	30	40

Each value was issued in pairs showing a floral pattern across the bottom of the portraits which stops short of the left-hand edge on the first stamp and of the right-hand edge on the second.

1985. Montserrat Sea Island Cotton Industry. Multicoloured.

No.	Description	Unused	Used
645	90 c. Type **113**	25	45
646	$1 Operator at carding machine	25	50
647	$1.15 Threading loom	25	65
648	$2.50 Weaving with hand loom	50	2·25

1985. Royal Visit. Nos. 514/15, 543, 587/8 and 640/1 optd **CARIBBEAN ROYAL VISIT 1985** or surch also.

No.	Description	Unused	Used
650	75 c. multicoloured (No. 587)	2·75	2·50
651	$1 multicoloured (No. 543)	4·25	3·50
652	$1.15 multicoloured (No. 640)	4·25	5·00
653	$1.15 multicoloured (No. 641)	4·25	5·00
654	$1.50 multicoloured (No. 588)	6·00	6·00
655	$1.60 on $4 mult (No. 514)	2·00	3·75
656	$1.60 on $4 mult (No. 515)	13·00	16·00

No. 656 shows a new face value only, "CARIBBEAN ROYAL VISIT 1985" being omitted from the surcharge.

1985. Leaders of the World. Birth Bicentenary of John J. Audubon (ornithologist). Designs showing original paintings. Multicoloured.

No.	Description	Unused	Used
657	15 c. Type **115**	15	20
658	15 c. Palm warbler	15	20
659	30 c. Bobolink	15	30
660	30 c. Lark sparrow	15	30
661	55 c. Chipping sparrow	20	40
662	55 c. Northern oriole	20	40
663	$2.50 American goldfinch	40	1·25
664	$2.50 Blue grosbeak	40	1·25

116 Herald Angel appearing to Goatherds

1985. Christmas. Designs showing Caribbean Nativity. Multicoloured.

No.	Description	Unused	Used
665	70 c. Type **116**	15	15
666	$1.15 Three Wise Men following Star	25	40
667	$1.50 Carol singing around War Memorial, Plymouth	30	70
668	$2.30 Praying to "Our Lady of Montserrat", Church of Our Lady, St. Patrick's Village	45	1·60

117 Lord Baden-Powell

1986. 50th Anniv of Montserrat Girl Guide Movement. Multicoloured.

No.	Description	Unused	Used
669	20 c. Type **117**	15	40
670	20 c. Girl Guide saluting	15	40
671	75 c. Lady Baden-Powell	25	75
672	75 c. Guide assisting in old people's home	25	75
673	90 c. Lord and Lady Baden-Powell	30	75
674	90 c. Guides serving meal in old people's home	30	75
675	$1.15 Girl Guides of 1936	40	80
676	$1.15 Two guides saluting	40	80

1986. 60th Birthday of Queen Elizabeth II. As T **52a** of Grenadines of St. Vincent. Multicoloured.

No.	Description	Unused	Used
677	10 c. Queen Elizabeth II	10	10
678	$1.50 Princess Elizabeth in 1928	25	50
679	$3 In Antigua, 1977	40	85
680	$6 In Canberra, 1982 (vert)	65	1·75

118 King Harold and Halley's Comet, 1066 (from Bayeux Tapestry)

1986. Appearance of Halley's Comet. Multicoloured.

No.	Description	Unused	Used
682	35 c. Type **118**	25	25
683	50 c. Comet of 1301 (from Giotto's "Adoration of the Magi")	30	30
684	70 c. Edmond Halley and Comet of 1531	30	40
685	$1 Comets of 1066 and 1910	30	40
686	$1.15 Comet of 1910	40	50
687	$1.50 E.S.A. "Giotto" spacecraft and Comet	40	80
688	$2.30 U.S. space telescope and Comet	50	1·75
689	$4 Computer reconstruction of 1910 Comet	60	2·75

1986. Royal Wedding (1st isssue). As T **55a** of Grenadines of St. Vincent. Multicoloured.

No.	Description	Unused	Used
691	70 c. Prince Andrew	25	35
692	70 c. Miss Sarah Ferguson	25	35
693	$2 Prince Andrew wearing stetson (horiz)	40	80
694	$2 Miss Sarah Ferguson on skiing holiday (horiz)	40	80

See also Nos. 705/8.

119 "Antelope" being attacked by "L'Atalante"

1986. Mail Packet Sailing Ships. Mult.

696 90 c. Type **119** 2·00 1·50
697 $1.15 "Montagu" (1810) 2·25 2·00
698 $1.50 "Little Catherine" being pursued by "L'Etoile" (1813) 2·75 2·75
699 $2.30 "Hinchingbrook I" (1813) 3·50 5·00

120 Radio Montserrat Building, Dagenham — **123** Christmas Rose

122 Sailing and Windsurfing

1986. Communications. Multicoloured.

701 70 c. Type **120** 1·00 70
702 $1.15 Radio Gem dish aerial, Plymouth 1·00 1·50
703 $1.50 Radio Antilles studio, O'Garro's 1·75 2·25
704 $2.30 Cable and Wireless building, Plymouth 2·25 4·25

1986. Royal Wedding (2nd issue). Nos. 691/4 optd **Congratulations to T.R.H. The Duke & Duchess of York.**

705 70 c. Prince Andrew 70 1·25
706 70 c. Miss Sarah Ferguson 70 1·25
707 $2 Prince Andrew wearing stetson (horiz) 1·25 1·75
708 $2 Miss Sarah Ferguson on skiing holiday (horiz) 1·25 1·75

1986. Tourism. Multicoloured.

710 70 c. Type **122** 40 70
711 $1.15 Golf 80 1·50
712 $1.50 Plymouth market 80 2·00
713 $2.30 Air Recording Studios 1·25 3·00

1986. Christmas. Flowering Shrubs. Mult.

714 70 c. Type **123** 70 40
715 $1.15 Candle flower 95 85
716 $1.50 Christmas tree kalanchoe 1·50 1·50
717 $2.30 Snow on the mountain 2·00 4·50

124 Tiger Shark

1987. Sharks. Multicoloured.

719 40 c. Type **124** 1·50 55
720 90 c. Lemon shark 2·50 1·50
721 $1.15 Great white shark 2·75 2·00
722 $3.50 Whale shark 5·50 8·00

1987. Nos. 601, 603, 607/8 and 611 surch.

724 5 c. on 70 c. Glossy ibis 50 1·00
725 $1 on 20 c. Brown booby 1·75 90
726 $1.15 on 10 c. Carib grackle 2·00 1·40
727 $1.50 on 90 c. Green heron 2·25 2·50
728 $2.30 on $3 American kestrel (vert) 3·25 5·50

127 "Phoebis trite" — **128** "Oncidium variegatum"

1987. Butterflies. Multicoloured.

730 90 c. Type **127** 2·00 1·10
731 $1.15 "Biblis hyperia" 2·50 1·60
732 $1.50 "Polygonus leo" 3·00 2·50
733 $2.50 "Hypolimnas misippus" 4·50 6·50

1987. Christmas. Orchids. Multicoloured.

734 90 c. Type **128** 60 45
735 $1.15 "Vanilla planifolia" (horiz) 85 55
736 $1.50 "Gongora quinquenervis" 1·10 1·10
737 $3.50 "Brassavola nodosa" (horiz) 2·00 4·50

1987. Royal Ruby Wedding. Nos. 601, 604/5 and 608 surch **40th Wedding Anniversary HM Queen Elizabeth II HRH Duke of Edinburgh. November 1987.** and value.

739B 5 c. on 90 c. Green heron 30 40
740B $1.15 on 10 c. Carib grackle 1·00 1·00
741B $2.30 on 25 c. Black-whiskered vireo 1·75 2·25
742B $5 on 40 c. Scaly-breasted thrasher 3·50 4·50

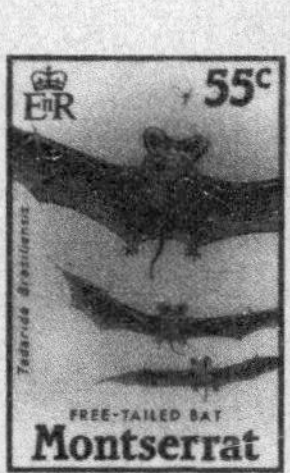
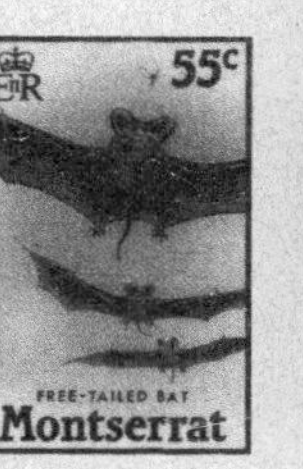

130 Free-tailed Bat — **131** Magnificent Frigate Bird

1988. Bats. Multicoloured.

743 55 c. Type **130** 80 40
744 90 c. "Chiroderma improvisum" (fruit bat) 1·25 90
745 $1.15 Fisherman bat 1·60 1·50
746 $2.30 "Brachyphylla cavernarum" (fruit bat) 3·00 5·50

1988. Easter. Birds. Multicoloured.

748 90 c. Type **131** 60 45
749 $1.15 Caribbean elaenia 80 75
750 $1.50 Glossy ibis 1·00 1·50
751 $3.50 Purple-throated carib 2·00 4·00

132 Discus throwing

1988. Olympic Games, Seoul. Multicoloured.

753 90 c. Type **132** 60 50
754 $1.15 High jumping 70 55
755 $3.50 Athletics 2·00 3·25

133 Golden Tulip

1988. Sea Shells. Multicoloured.

757 5 c. Type **133** 30 30
758 10 c. Little knobbed scallop 40 40
759 15 c. Sozoni's cone 40 40
760 20 c. Globular coral shell 50 40
761 25 c. American or common sundial 50 40
762 40 c. King helmet 60 40
763 55 c. Channelled turban 80 40
764 70 c. True tulip 1·00 75
765 90 c. Music volute 1·25 75
766 $1 Flame auger 1·40 80
767 $1.15 Rooster-tail conch 1·50 90
768 $1.50 Queen or pink conch 1·60 1·40
769 $3 Teramachi's slit shell 2·50 4·00
770 $5 Common or Florida crown conch 3·50 6·50
771 $7.50 Beau's murex 4·50 10·00
772 $10 Atlantic trumpet triton 5·50 10·00

134 University Crest

1988. 40th Anniv of University of West Indies.

773 **134** $5 multicoloured 2·40 3·25

1988. Princess Alexandra's Visit. Nos. 763, 766 and 769/70 surch **HRH PRINCESS ALEXANDRA'S VISIT NOVEMBER 1988** and new value.

774 40 c. on 55 c. Channelled turban 45 45
775 90 c. on $1 Flame auger 70 80
776 $1.15 on $3 Teramachi's slit shell 85 95
777 $1.50 on $5 Common or Florida crown conch 1·10 1·50

136 Spotted Sandpiper

1988. Christmas. Sea Birds. Multicoloured.

778 90 c. Type **136** 70 55
779 $1.15 Turnstone 85 70
780 $3.50 Red-footed booby 2·00 3·75

137 Handicapped Children in Classroom

1988. 125th Anniv of International Red Cross.

782 **137** $3.50 multicoloured 1·50 2·25

138 Drum Major in Ceremonial Uniform

1989. 75th Anniv (1986) of Montserrat Defence Force. Uniforms. Multicoloured.

783 90 c. Type **138** 70 50
784 $1.15 Field training uniform 85 75
785 $1.50 Cadet in ceremonial uniform 1·25 1·75
786 $3.50 Gazetted Police Officer in ceremonial uniform 2·50 3·50

139 Amazon Lily

1989. Easter. Lilies. Multicoloured.

788 90 c. Type **139** 50 50
789 $1.15 Salmon blood lily (vert) 70 70
790 $1.50 Amaryllis (vert) 85 1·25
791 $3.50 Amaryllis (vert) 1·90 2·75

140 "Morning Prince" (schooner), 1942

1989. Shipbuilding in Montserrat. Mult.

793 90 c. Type **140** 90 60
794 $1.15 "Western Sun" (inter-island freighter) 1·40 1·10
795 $1.50 "Kim G" (inter-island freighter) under construction 1·75 2·00
796 $3.50 "Romaris" (inter-island ferry), c. 1942 2·75 4·50

141 The Scarecrow

1989. 50th Anniv of "The Wizard of Oz" (film). Multicoloured.

797 90 c. Type **141** 40 45
798 $1.15 The Lion 55 60
799 $1.50 The Tin Man 70 85
800 $3.50 Dorothy 1·60 2·50

1989. Hurricane Hugo Relief Fund. Nos. 795/6 surch **Hurricane Hugo Relief Surcharge $2.50.**

802 $1.50 + $2.50 "Kim G" (inter-island freighter under construction) 2·25 3·00
803 $3.50 + $2.50 "Romaris" (inter-island ferry), c. 1942 2·50 4·00

143 "Apollo 11" above Lunar Surface

1989. 20th Anniv of First Manned Landing on Moon. Multicoloured.

804 90 c. Type **143** 35 40
805 $1.15 Astronaut alighting from lunar module "Eagle" 45 50
806 $1.50 "Eagle" and astronaut conducting experiment 60 80
807 $3.50 Opening "Apollo 11" hatch after splashdown 1·40 2·25

144 "Yamato" (Japanese battleship) — **145** The Empty Tomb

1990. World War II Capital Ships. Multicoloured.

809 70 c. Type **144** 1·75 70
810 $1.15 U.S.S. "Arizona" at Pearl Harbor 2·25 95
811 $1.50 "Bismarck" (German battleship) in action 2·75 2·50
812 $3.50 H.M.S. "Hood" (battle cruiser) 4·25 7·00

1990. Easter. Stained glass windows from St. Michael's Parish Church, Bray, Berkshire. Multicoloured.

814 $1.15 Type **145** 1·25 1·50
815 $1.50 The Ascension 1·50 1·75
816 $3.50 The Risen Christ with Disciples 1·75 2·25

1990. "Stamp World London '90" International Stamp Exhibition. Nos. 460/4 surch **Stamp World London 90**, emblem and value.

818 70 c. on 40 c. Type **85** 50 50
819 90 c. on 55 c. Hawker Siddeley H.S.748 aircraft and 1976 55 c. definitive 70 70
820 $1 on $1.20 "La Plata" (liner) and 1903 5s. stamp 80 90
821 $1.15 on $1.20 "Lady Hawkins" (packet steamer) and 1932 Tercentenary 5s. commem 90 1·10
822 $1.50 on $1.20 "Avon I" (paddle-steamer) and Penny Red stamp with "A 08" postmark 1·25 1·75

147 General Office, Montserrat and 1884 ½d. Stamp

1990. 150th Anniv of the Penny Black. Mult.

823 90 c. Type **147** 65 65
824 $1.15 Sorting letters and Montserrat 1d. stamp of 1876 (vert) 85 90
825 $1.50 Posting letters and Penny Black (vert) 1·25 1·75
826 $3.50 Postman delivering letters and 1840 Twopence Blue 3·00 4·50

148 Montserrat v. Antigua Match

1990. World Cup Football Championship, Italy. Multicoloured.

828	90 c. Type **148**	65	55
829	$1.15 U.S.A. v. Trinidad match	85	75
830	$1.50 Montserrat team	1·25	1·50
831	$3.50 West Germany v. Wales match	2·25	3·25

149 Spinner Dolphin

1990. Dolphins. Multicoloured.

833	90 c. Type **149**	1·50	85
834	$1.15 Common dolphin	1·75	1·25
835	$1.50 Striped dolphin	2·50	2·50
836	$3.50 Atlantic spotted dolphin	3·75	5·00

150 Spotted Goatfish

1991. Tropical Fishes. Multicoloured.

838	90 c. Type **150**	1·50	85
839	$1.15 Cushion star	1·75	1·25
840	$1.50 Rock beauty	2·50	2·50
841	$3.50 French grunt	3·75	5·00

1991. Nos. 760/1, 768 and 771 surch.

843	5 c. on 20 c. Globular coral shell	65	1·25
844	5 c. on 25 c. American or common sundial	65	1·25
845	$1.15 on $1.50 Queen or pink conch	2·75	3·25
846	$1.15 on $7.50 Beau's murex	2·75	3·25

152 Duck

1991. Domestic Birds. Multicoloured.

847	90 c. Type **152**	60	60
848	$1.15 Hen and chicks	80	90
849	$1.50 Red junglefowl	1·10	1·50
850	$3.50 Helmet guineafowl	2·40	3·50

153 "Panaeolus antillarum"

1991. Fungi

851	**153** 90 c. grey	1·25	1·00
852	– $1.15 red	1·50	1·25
853	– $1.50 brown	2·25	2·25
854	– $2 purple	2·50	3·25
855	– $3.50 blue	3·75	5·00

DESIGNS: $1.15, "Cantharellus cinnabarinus"; $1.50, "Gymnopilus chrysopellus"; $2 "Psilocybe cubensis"; $3.50, "Leptonia caeruleocapitata".

154 Red Water Lily **155** Tree Frog

1991. Lilies. Multicoloured.

856	90 c. Type **154**	65	65
857	$1.15 Shell ginger	75	85
858	$1.50 Early day lily	1·00	1·60
859	$3.50 Anthurium	2·50	3·50

1991. Frogs and Toad. Multicoloured.

860	$1.15 Type **155**	2·25	1·25
861	$2 Crapaud toad	3·25	3·75
862	$3.50 Mountain chicken (frog)	5·50	6·50

156 Black British Shorthair Cat

1991. Cats. Multicoloured.

864	90 c. Type **156**	1·50	90
865	$1.15 Seal point Siamese	1·75	1·10
866	$1.50 Silver tabby Persian	2·25	2·25
867	$2.50 Birman temple cat	3·00	3·75
868	$3.50 Egyptain mau	4·00	5·00

157 Navigational Instruments

1992. 500th Anniv of Discovery of America by Columbus. Multicoloured.

869	$1.50 Type **157**	1·25	1·50
870	$1.50 Columbus and coat of arms	1·25	1·50
871	$1.50 Landfall on the Bahamas	1·25	1·50
872	$1.50 Petitioning Queen Isabella	1·25	1·50
873	$1.50 Tropical birds	1·25	1·50
874	$1.50 Tropical fruits	1·25	1·50
875	$3 Ships of Columbus (81 × 26 mm)	1·75	2·00

158 Runner with Olympic Flame

1992. Olympic Games, Barcelona. Multicoloured.

876	$1 Type **158**	90	60
877	$1.15 Montserrat, Olympic and Spanish flags	1·25	90
878	$2.30 Olympic flame on map of Montserrat	2·25	2·75
879	$3.60 Olympic events	2·75	4·00

159 Tyrannosaurus

1992. Death Centenary of Sir Richard Owen (zoologist). Multicoloured.

880	$1 Type **159**	2·00	1·25
881	$1.15 Diplodocus	2·25	1·40
882	$1.50 Apatosaurus	2·75	2·75
883	$3.45 Dimetrodon	5·50	8·00

160 Male Montserrat Oriole

1992. Montserrat Oriole. Multicoloured.

885	$1 Type **160**	1·10	1·10
886	$1.15 Male and female orioles	1·40	1·40
887	$1.50 Female oriole with chicks	1·75	2·00
888	$3.60 Map of Montserrat and male oriole	3·50	5·00

161 "Psophus stridulus" (grasshopper)

1992. Insects. Multicoloured.

889	5 c. Type **161**	30	40
890	10 c. "Gryllus campestris" (field cricket)	35	40
891	15 c. "Lepthemis vesiculosa" (dragonfly)	40	40
892	20 c. "Orthemis ferruginea" (red skimmer)	45	45
893	25 c. "Gerris lacustris" (pond skater)	45	45
894	40 c. "Byctiscus betulae" (leaf weevil)	60	50
895	55 c. "Atta texana" (leaf-cutter ants)	60	40
896	70 c. "Polistes fuscatus" (paper wasp)	70	60
897	90 c. "Sparmopolius fulvus" (bee fly)	80	60
898	$1 "Chrysopa carnea" (lace wing)	1·25	65
899	$1.15 "Phoebis philea" (butterfly)	2·00	90
900	$1.50 "Cynthia cardui" (butterfly)	2·25	1·75
901	$3 "Utetheisa bella" (moth)	3·00	4·00
902	$5 "Alucita pentadactyla" (moth)	4·25	5·50
903	$7.50 "Anartia jatropha" (butterfly)	5·50	7·50
904	$10 "Heliconius melpomene" (butterfly)	5·50	7·50

162 Adoration of the Magi

1992. Christmas. Multicoloured.

905	$1.15 Type **162**	1·75	75
906	$4.60 Appearance of angel to shepherds	4·25	6·50

163 $1 Coin and $20 Banknote **164** Columbus meeting Amerindians

1993. East Caribbean Currency. Multicoloured.

907	$1 Type **163**	90	70
908	$1.15 10 c. and 25 c. coins with $10 banknote	1·25	85
909	$1.50 5 c. coin and $5 banknote	1·75	2·00
910	$3.60 1 c. and 2 c. coins with $1 banknote	4·00	6·00

1993. Organization of East Caribbean States. 500th Anniv of Discovery of America by Columbus. Multicoloured.

911	$1 Type **164**	1·10	90
912	$2 Ships approaching island	2·00	2·75

165 Queen Elizabeth II on Montserrat with Chief Minister W. H. Bramble, 1966

1993. 40th Anniv of Coronation. Multicoloured.

913	$1.15 Type **165**	1·50	75
914	$4.60 Queen Elizabeth II in State Coach, 1953	4·50	5·50

1993. 500th Anniv of Discovery of Montserrat. As Nos. 869/75, some with new values, each showing "500th ANNIVERSARY DISCOVERY OF MONTSERRAT" at foot and with additional historical inscr across the centre.

915	$1.15 mult (As Type **157**)	1·25	1·50
916	$1.15 multicoloured (As No. 870)	1·25	1·50
917	$1.15 multicoloured (As No. 871)	1·25	1·50
918	$1.50 multicoloured (As No. 872)	1·60	1·90
919	$1.50 multicoloured (As No. 873)	1·60	1·90
920	$1.50 multicoloured (As No. 874)	1·60	1·90
921	$3.45 multicoloured (As No. 875)	2·50	3·25

Additional inscriptions: No. 915, "PRE-COLUMBUS CARIB NAME OF ISLAND ALLIOUGANA"; No. 916, "COLUMBUS NAMED ISLAND SANTA MARIA DE MONTSERRATE"; No. 917, "COLUMBUS SAILED ALONG COASTLINE 11th NOV. 1493"; No. 918, "ISLAND OCCUPIED BY FRENCH BRIEFLY IN 1667"; No. 919, "ISLAND DECLARED ENGLISH BY TREATY OF BREDA 1667"; No. 920, "AFRICAN SLAVES BROUGHT IN DURING 1600's"; No. 921, "IRISH CATHOLICS FROM ST. KITTS AND VIRGINIA SETTLED ON ISLAND BETWEEN 1628–1634".

166 Boeing Sentry, 1993

1993. 75th Anniv of Royal Air Force. Mult.

922	15 c. Type **166**	45	20
923	55 c. Vickers Valiant B Mk1, 1962	65	40
924	$1.15 Handley Page Hastings C Mk 2, 1958	1·25	75
925	$3 Lockheed Ventura, 1943	2·50	4·00

167 Ground Beetle

1994. Beetles. Multicoloured.

927	$1 Type **167**	65	65
928	$1.15 Click beetle	80	80
929	$1.50 Harlequin beetle	1·25	1·50
930	$3.45 Leaf beetle	3·00	4·25

168 "Gossypium barbadense"

1994. Flowers. Multicoloured.

932	90 c. Type **168**	1·00	80
933	$1.15 "Hibiscus sabdariffa"	1·25	1·00
934	$1.50 "Hibiscus esculentus"	1·60	1·75
935	$3.50 "Hibiscus rosa-sinensis"	3·50	5·00

169 Coaching Young Players and Logo

1994. World Cup Football Championship, U.S.A. Multicoloured.

936	90 c. Type **169**	1·25	1·75
937	$1 United States scoring against England, 1950	1·25	1·75
938	$1.15 Rose Bowl stadium, Los Angeles, and trophy	1·25	1·75
939	$3.45 German players celebrating with trophy, 1990	2·75	3·25

170 Elasmosaurus

1994. Aquatic Dinosaurs. Multicoloured.

941	$1 Type **170**	1·75	2·00
942	$1.15 Plesiosaurus	1·75	2·00
943	$1.50 Nothosaurus	2·25	2·50
944	$3.45 Mosasaurus	3·00	3·75

1994. Space Anniversaries. Nos. 804/7 variously surch or optd, each including **Space Anniversaries**.

945	40 c. on 90 c. Type **143**	1·25	70
946	$1.15 Astronaut alighting from lunar module "Eagle"	2·00	1·25
947	$1.50 "Eagle" and astronaut conducting experiment	2·50	2·50
948	$2.30 on $3.50 Opening "Apollo 11" hatch after splashdown	3·75	5·50

Surcharges and overprints: No. 945, **Juri Gagarin First man in space April 12, 1961**; No. 946, **First Joint US Soviet Mission July 15, 1975**; No. 947 **25th Anniversary First Moon Landing Apollo XI – July 20, 1994**; No. 948, **Columbia First Space Shuttle April 12, 1981**.

172 1969 Festival Logo

1994. 25th Anniv of Woodstock Music Festival. Multicoloured.

949 $1.15 Type **172** 1·00 1·00
950 $1.50 1994 anniversary festival logo 1·25 1·25

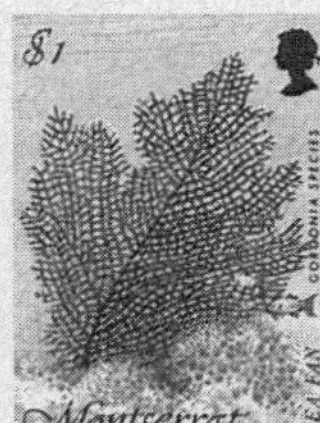

173 Sea Fan

1995. Marine Life. Multicoloured.

951 $1 Type **173** 60 50
952 $1.15 Sea lily 70 60
953 $1.50 Sea pen 90 1·00
954 $3.45 Sea fern 2·00 2·75

174 Marilyn Monroe

1995. Centenary of Cinema. Portraits of Marilyn Monroe (film star). Multicoloured.

956 $1.15 Type **174** 90 1·00
957 $1.15 Puckering lips 90 1·00
958 $1.15 Laughing in brown evening dress and earrings 90 1·00
959 $1.15 Wearing red earrings 90 1·00
960 $1.15 In brown dress without earrings 90 1·00
961 $1.15 With white boa 90 1·00
962 $1.15 In red dress 90 1·00
963 $1.15 Wearing white jumper 90 1·00
964 $1.15 Looking over left shoulder 90 1·00

176 Atmospheric Sounding Experiments using V2 Rockets

1995. 50th Anniv of End of Second World War. Scientific Achievements. Multicoloured.

967 $1.15 Type **176** 80 1·00
968 $1.15 American space shuttle "Challenger" 80 1·00
969 $1.15 Nuclear experiment, Chicago, 1942 80 1·00
970 $1.15 Calder Hall Atomic Power Station, 1956 80 1·00
971 $1.50 Radar-equipped Ju 88G 7a nightfighter 1·00 1·25
972 $1.50 Boeing E6 A.W.A.C.S. aircraft 1·00 1·25
973 $1.50 Gloster G.41 Meteor Mk III jet fighter 1·00 1·25
974 $1.50 Concorde (airliner) 1·00 1·25

177 Ears of Wheat ("Food")

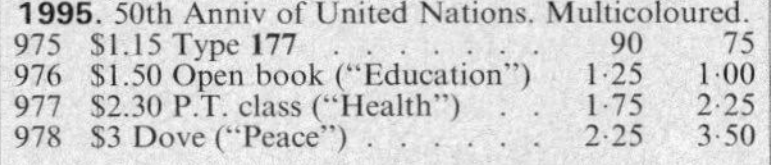

1995. 50th Anniv of United Nations. Multicoloured.

975 $1.15 Type **177** 90 75
976 $1.50 Open book ("Education") 1·25 1·00
977 $2.30 P.T. class ("Health") 1·75 2·25
978 $3 Dove ("Peace") 2·25 3·50

178 Headquarters Building

1995. 25th Anniv of Montserrat National Trust. Multicoloured.

980 $1.15 Type **178** 80 75
981 $1.50 17th-century cannons, Bransby Point 1·25 1·00
982 $2.30 Impression of Galways Sugar Mill (vert) 2·25 2·50
983 $3 Great Alps Falls (vert) 3·50 4·50

1995. 25th Anniv of Air Recording Studios. No. 713 surch **air 25TH ANNIVERSARY 1970 - 1995.**

984 $2.30 + $5 Air Recording Studios 4·25 4·75

The $5 premium on No. 984 was for relief following a volcanic eruption.

180 Bull Shark

1996. Scavengers of the Sea. Multicoloured.

985 $1 Type **180** 80 70
986 $1.15 Sea mouse 90 80
987 $1.50 Bristleworm 1·25 1·50
988 $3.45 Prawn "Xiphocaris" 2·50 3·50

181 Marconi and Radio Equipment, 1901

1996. Centenary of Radio. Multicoloured.

990 $1.15 Type **181** 90 80
991 $1.50 Marconi's steam yacht "Elettra" 1·25 1·00
992 $2.30 Receiving first Trans-atlantic radio message, Newfoundland, 1901 1·75 2·25
993 $3 Imperial Airways airplane at Croydon Airport, 1920 2·25 3·25

182 Paul Masson (France) (Cycling)

1996. Olympic Games, Atlanta. Gold Medal Winners of 1896. Multicoloured.

995 $1.15 Type **182** 80 80
996 $1.50 Robert Garrett (U.S.A.) (Discus) 1·00 1·00
997 $2.30 Spyridon Louis (Greece) (Marathon) 1·50 1·75
998 $3 John Boland (Great Britain) (Tennis) 2·00 3·00

183 James Dean

1996. James Dean (film star) Commemoration. Multicoloured.

999 $1.15 Type **183** 80 85
1000 $1.15 Wearing stetson facing right 80 85
1001 $1.15 Wearing blue sweater 80 85
1002 $1.15 Wearing black sweater 80 85
1003 $1.15 Full face portrait wearing stetson 80 85
1004 $1.15 Wearing fawn jacket 80 85
1005 $1.15 Wearing red wind-cheater 80 85
1006 $1.15 Smoking a cigarette 80 85
1007 $1.15 In open-necked shirt and green jumper 80 85

184 Leprechaun

$1.15

Montserrat

185 Blue and Green Teddybears

1996. Mythical Creatures. Multicoloured.

1009 5 c. Type **184** 10 10
1010 10 c. Pegasus 10 10
1011 15 c. Griffin 10 10
1012 20 c. Unicorn 10 10
1013 25 c. Gnomes 10 15
1014 40 c. Mermaid 15 20
1015 55 c. Cockatrice 25 30
1016 70 c. Fairy 30 35
1017 90 c. Goblin 40 45
1018 $1 Faun 45 50
1019 $1.15 Dragon 50 55
1020 $1.50 Giant 65 70
1021 $3 Elves 1·25 1·40
1022 $5 Centaur 2·10 2·25
1023 $7.50 Phoenix 3·25 3·50
1024 $10 Erin 4·75 4·50

1996. Jerry Garcia and the Grateful Dead (rock group) Commemoration. Multicoloured.

1025 $1.15 Type **185** 1·00 1·00
1026 $1.15 Green and yellow teddybears 1·00 1·00
1027 $1.15 Brown and pink teddybears 1·00 1·00
1028 $6 Jerry Garcia (37 × 50 mm) 5·50 5·50

Nos. 1025/7 were printed together, se-tenant, forming a composite design.

186 Turkey Vulture

1997. Scavengers of the Sky. Multicoloured.

1029 $1 Type **186** 75 70
1030 $1.15 American crow 90 70
1031 $1.50 Great skua 1·25 1·50
1032 $3.45 Kittiwake 2·25 3·00

1997. "HONG KONG '97" International Stamp Exhibition. Nos. 1025/7 optd **HONG KONG '97**.

1034 $1.15 Type **185** 70 90
1035 $1.15 Green and yellow teddybears 70 90
1036 $1.15 Brown and pink teddybears 70 90

1997. "PACIFIC '97" International Stamp Exhibition, San Francisco. Nos. 999/1007 optd **PACIFIC 97 World Philatelic Exhibition San Francisco, California 29 May - 8 June**.

1037 $1.15 Type **183** 80 90
1038 $1.15 Wearing stetson facing right 80 90
1039 $1.15 Wearing blue sweater 80 90
1040 $1.15 Wearing black sweater 80 90
1041 $1.15 Full-face portrait wearing stetson 80 90
1042 $1.15 Wearing fawn jacket 80 90
1043 $1.15 Wearing red wind-cheater 80 90
1044 $1.15 Smoking a cigarette 80 90
1045 $1.15 In open-necked shirt and green jumper 80 90

189 Heavy Ash Eruption over Plymouth, 1995

1997. Eruption of Soufriere Volcano. Multicoloured.

1046 $1.50 Type **189** 1·10 1·25
1047 $1.50 Burning rock flow entering sea 1·10 1·25
1048 $1.50 Double venting at Castle Peak 1·10 1·25
1049 $1.50 Mangrove cuckoo 1·10 1·25
1050 $1.50 Lava flow at night, 1996 1·10 1·25
1051 $1.50 Antillean crested hummingbird 1·10 1·25
1052 $1.50 Ash cloud over Plymouth 1·10 1·10
1053 $1.50 Lava spine, 1996 1·10 1·10
1054 $1.50 Burning rock flows forming new land 1·10 1·10

190 Elvis Presley

1997. Rock Legends. Multicoloured.

1055 $1.15 Type **190** 1·00 1·10
1056 $1.15 Jimi Hendrix 1·00 1·10
1057 $1.15 Jerry Garcia 1·00 1·10
1058 $1.15 Janis Joplin 1·00 1·10

191 Untitled Painting by Frama

1997. Frama Exhibition at Guggenheim Museum, New York.

1059 **191** $1.50 multicoloured 85 95

1997. No. 1028 surch **$1.50**.

1060 $1.50 on $6 Jerry Garcia (37 × 50 mm) 85 90

193 Prickly Pear

MONTSERRAT

194 Eva and Juan Peron (Argentine politicians)

1998. Medicinal Plants. Multicoloured.

1061 $1 Type **193** 55 50
1062 $1.15 Pomme coolie 60 55
1063 $1.50 Aloe 75 75
1064 $3.45 Bird pepper 1·75 2·00

1998. Famous People of the 20th Century. Multicoloured.

1065 $1.15 Type **194** 70 80
1066 $1.15 Pablo Picasso (painter) 70 80
1067 $1.15 Wernher von Braun (space scientist) 70 80
1068 $1.15 David Ben Gurion (Israeli statesman) 70 80
1069 $1.15 Jean Henri Dunant (founder of Red Cross) 70 80
1070 $1.15 Dwight Eisenhower (President of U.S.A.) 70 80
1071 $1.15 Mahatma Gandhi (leader of Indian Independence movement) 70 80
1072 $1.15 King Leopold III and Queen Astrid of Belgium 70 80
1073 $1.15 Grand Duchess Charlotte and Prince Felix of Luxembourg 70 80
1074 $1.50 Charles Augustus Lindbergh (pioneer aviator) 80 90
1075 $1.50 Mao Tse-tung (Chinese communist leader) 80 90
1076 $1.50 Earl Mountbatten (last Viceroy of India) 80 90
1077 $1.50 Konrad Adenauer (German statesman) 80 90
1078 $1.50 Anne Frank (Holocaust victim) 80 90
1079 $1.50 Queen Wilhelmina of the Netherlands 80 90
1080 $1.50 King George VI of Great Britain 80 90
1081 $1.50 King Christian X of Denmark 80 90
1082 $1.50 King Haakon VII and Crown Prince Olav of Norway 80 90
1083 $1.50 King Alfonso XIII of Spain 80 90
1084 $1.50 King Gustavus V of Sweden 80 90

195 Jerry Garcia

1998. Rock Music Legends. Multicoloured. (a) Jerry Garcia.

1086 $1.15 In long-sleeved blue shirt . . . 70 80
1087 $1.15 With drum kit in background . . . 70 80
1088 $1.15 Type **195** . . . 70 80
1089 $1.15 Wearing long-sleeved black t-shirt . . . 70 80
1090 $1.15 Close-up with left hand in foreground . . . 70 80
1091 $1.15 With purple and black background . . . 70 80
1092 $1.15 Holding microphone . . 70 80
1093 $1.15 In short-sleeved blue t-shirt . . . 70 80
1094 $1.15 In sunglasses with cymbal in background . . . 70 80

(b) Bob Marley. Predominant colour for each design given.

1095 $1.15 Pointing (green) . . . 70 80
1096 $1.15 Wearing neck chain (green) . . . 70 80
1097 $1.15 Singing into microphone (green) . . . 70 80
1098 $1.15 Singing with eyes closed (yellow) . . . 70 80
1099 $1.15 Facing audience (yellow) . . . 70 80
1100 $1.15 In striped t-shirt with fingers on chin (red) . . . 70 80
1101 $1.15 In Rastafarian hat (red) . 70 80
1102 $1.15 In striped t-shirt with hand closed (red) . . . 70 80

196 Ash Eruption from Soufriere Hills Volcano

1998. Total Eclipse of the Sun on 26 February. Multicoloured.

1104 $1.15 Type **196** . . . 90 90
1105 $1.15 Volcano emitting black cloud . . . 90 90
1106 $1.15 Village below volcano . . 90 90
1107 $1.15 Lava flow and wrecked house . . . 90 90

197 Princess Diana on Wedding Day, 1981

1998. Diana, Princess of Wales Commemoration. Multicoloured.

1109 $1.15 Type **197** . . . 75 70
1110 $1.50 Accepting bouquet from children . . . 90 90
1111 $3 At Royal Ascot . . . 1·75 2·00

1998. 19th World Scout Jamboree, Chile. Nos. 669/72 optd **19 th WORLD JAMBOREE MONDIAL CHILE 1999** and emblem.

1113 20 c. Type **117** . . . 20 25
1114 20 c. Girl Guide saluting . . 20 25
1115 75 c. Lady Baden-Powell . . 65 75
1116 75 c. Guide assisting in old people's home . . . 65 75

200 Jerry Garcia

1999. Jerry Garcia (rock musician) Commemoration. Multicoloured.

1117 $1.15 Type **200** . . . 75 75
1118 $1.15 In front of drum kit (bluish violet background) . 75 75
1119 $1.15 Singing into microphone . 75 75
1120 $1.15 Playing guitar, facing right (vert) . . . 75 75
1121 $1.15 Singing with eyes closed (vert) . . . 75 75
1122 $1.15 Singing in white spotlight (vert) . . . 75 75
1123 $1.15 In front of drum kit (green background) . . . 75 75
1124 $1.15 In long-sleeved black shirt . . . 75 75
1125 $1.15 In red shirt . . . 75 75
1126 $1.15 In short-sleeved black t-shirt (without frame) (vert) 75 75
1127 $1.15 In blue t-shirt (oval frame) (vert) . . . 75 75
1128 $1.15 In short-sleeved black t-shirt (oval frame) (vert) . . 75 75

1999. "iBRA '99" International Stamp Exhibition, Nuremberg. Nos. 975/6 optd **iBRA INTERNATIONALE BRIEFMARKEN WELTAUSSTELLUNG NURNBERG 27.-4.5.99.**

1130 $1.15 Type **177** . . . 50 55
1131 $1.50 Open book ("Education") 65 70

201 Mango

1999. Tropical Caribbean Fruits. Multicoloured.

1132 $1.15 Type **201** . . . 75 70
1133 $1.50 Breadfruit . . . 90 80
1134 $2.30 Papaya . . . 1·40 1·40
1135 $3 Lime . . . 1·75 1·90
1136 $6 Akee . . . 3·50 4·00

202 Yorkshire Terrier

1999. Dogs. Each black.

1138 70 c. Type **202** . . . 55 40
1139 $1 Welsh corgi . . . 65 55
1140 $1.15 King Charles spaniel . . 75 70
1141 $1.50 Poodle . . . 90 90
1142 $3 Beagle . . . 1·75 2·00

203 Pupil's Equipment and World Map

1999. World Teachers' Day. Multicoloured.

1144 $1 Type **203** . . . 65 55
1145 $1.15 Teacher and class . . 75 70
1146 $1.50 Emblems of vocational training . . . 90 90
1147 $5 Scientific equipment . . . 3·25 3·75

204 Great Hammerhead Shark

1999. Endangered Species. Great Hammerhead Shark. Multicoloured.

1148 50 c. Type **204** . . . 20 25
1149 50 c. Two hammerhead sharks among fish . . . 20 25
1150 50 c. Two hammerhead sharks on sea-bed . . . 20 25
1151 50 c. Three hammerhead sharks . . . 20 25

HAVE YOU READ THE NOTES AT THE BEGINNING OF THIS CATALOGUE?
These often provide answers to the enquiries we receive.

OFFICIAL STAMPS

1976. Various stamps, some already surch, optd **O.H.M.S.**

O1 5 c. multicoloured (No. 246) . . + 65
O2 10 c. multicoloured (No. 247) . + 75
O3 30 c. on 10 c. mult (No. 369) . + 1·50
O4 45 c. on 3 c. mult (No. 370) . + 2·00
O5 $5 multicoloured (No. 254) . + £100
O6 $10 multicoloured (No. 254a) . + £550

These stamps were issued for use on mail from the Montserrat Philatelic Bureau. They were not sold to the public, either unused or used.

1976. Nos. 372, 374/82, 384/5 and 476 optd **O.H.M.S.** or surch also.

O17 5 c. Malay apple . . . + 10
O28 5 c. on 3 c. Lignum vitae . . + 20
O18 10 c. Jacaranda . . . + 10
O19 15 c. Orchid tree . . . + 10
O20 20 c. Manjak . . . + 10
O21 25 c. Tamarind . . . + 15
O33 30 c. on 15 c. Orchid tree . . + 30
O34 35 c. on 2 c. Cannon-ball tree + 30
O35 40 c. Flame of the forest . . + 40
O22 55 c. Pink cassia . . . + 35
O23 70 c. Long john . . . + 45
O24 $1 Saman . . . + 60
O39 $2.50 on 40 c. Flame of the forest . . . + 2·00
O25 $5 Yellow poui . . . + 2·00
O16 $10 Flamboyant . . . 3·75

1981. Nos. 490/4, 496, 498, 500, 502/3 and 505 optd **O.H.M.S.**

O42 5 c. Type **91** . . . 10 10
O43 10 c. Hogfish and neon goby . 10 10
O44 15 c. Creole wrasse . . . 10 10
O45 20 c. Three-spotted damselfish . 15 15
O46 25 c. Sergeant major . . . 15 15
O47 45 c. Schoolmaster . . . 25 20
O48 65 c. Bigeye . . . 35 30
O49 $1 Rock beauty . . . 65 65
O50 $3 Royal gramma ("Fairy basslet") and blueheads . . 1·75 1·75
O51 $5 Cherub angelfish . . . 2·50 2·25
O52 $10 Caribbean long-nosed butterflyfish . . . 4·00 2·25

1983. Nos. 510/15 surch **O.H.M.S.** and value.

O53 45 c. on 90 c. "Charlotte" . . 20 30
O54 45 c. on 90 c. Prince Charles and Lady Diana Spencer . . . 60 70
O55 75 c. on $3 "Portsmouth" . . 25 35
O56 75 c. on $3 Prince Charles and Lady Diana Spencer . . . 90 1·00
O57 $1 on $4 "Britannia" . . . 35 50
O58 $1 on $4 Prince Charles and Lady Diana Spencer . . . 1·00 1·10

1983. Nos. 542/4 surch on **O.H.M.S.**

O59 70 c. on 75 c. Type **97** . . . 60 40
O60 $1 Coat of Arms of Catherine of Aragon . . . 70 50
O61 $1.50 on $5 Diana, Princess of Wales . . . 1·00 80

1985. Nos. 600/12 and 614 optd **O H M S.**

O62 5 c. Type **107** . . . 60 70
O63 10 c. Carib grackle . . . 60 70
O64 15 c. Moorhen . . . 70 70
O65 20 c. Brown booby . . . 75 60
O66 25 c. Black-whiskered vireo . . 75 60
O67 40 c. Scaly-breasted thrasher . 1·00 60
O68 55 c. Laughing gull . . . 1·25 65
O69 70 c. Glossy ibis . . . 1·40 80
O70 90 c. Green heron . . . 1·75 80
O71 $1 Belted kingfisher . . . 1·75 60
O72 $1.15 Bananaquit . . . 2·50 90
O73 $3 American kestrel . . . 3·75 2·50
O74 $5 Forest thrush . . . 4·50 2·50
O75 $10 Bridled quail dove . . . 6·50 2·50

1989. Nos. 757/70 and 772 optd **O H M S.**

O76 5 c. Type **133** . . . 25 30
O77 10 c. Little knobbed scallop . . 25 30
O78 15 c. Sozoni's cone . . . 30 30
O79 20 c. Globular coral shell . . 35 30
O80 25 c. American or common sundial . . . 35 30
O81 40 c. King helmet . . . 45 40
O82 55 c. Channelled turban . . . 50 40
O83 70 c. True tulip shell . . . 60 60
O84 90 c. Music volute . . . 75 75
O85 $1 Flame auger . . . 80 70
O86 $1.15 Rooster-tail conch . . . 90 80
O87 $1.50 Queen or pink conch . . 1·10 1·40
O88 $3 Teramachi's slit shell . . 1·75 1·90
O89 $5 Common or Florida crown conch . . . 3·00 3·00
O90 $10 Atlantic trumpet triton . . 5·50 5·50

1989. Nos. 578 and 580/1 surch **OHMS.**

O91 70 c. on 10 c. Hogfish and neon goby . . . 1·50 1·50
O92 $1.15 on 75 c. French grunt . 2·00 1·50
O93 $1.50 on $2 Blue chromis . . 2·25 2·75

1992. Nos. 838/41, 847/50, 856/9 surch or optd **OHMS.**

O 94 70 c. on 90 c. Type **150** . . . 1·25 1·25
O 95 70 c. on 90 c. Type **152** . . . 1·25 1·25
O 96 70 c. on 90 c. Type **154** . . . 1·25 1·25
O 97 70 c. on $3.50 French grunt . 1·25 1·25
O 98 $1 on $3.50 Helmeted guineafowl . . . 1·40 1·50
O 99 $1 on $3.50 Anthurium . . . 1·40 1·40
O100 $1.15 Cushion star . . . 1·40 1·40
O101 $1.15 Hen and chicks . . . 1·40 1·40
O102 $1.15 Shell ginger . . . 1·40 1·40
O103 $1.50 Rock beauty . . . 1·50 1·50
O104 $1.50 Red junglefowl . . . 1·50 1·50
O105 $1.50 Early day lily . . . 1·50 1·50

1993. Nos. 889/902 and 904 optd **OHMS.**

O106 5 c. Type **161** . . . 40 60
O107 10 c. "Gryllus campestris" (field cricket) . . . 40 60
O108 15 c. "Lepthemis vesiculosa" (dragonfly) . . . 50 60
O109 20 c. "Orthemis ferruginea" (red skimmer) . . . 50 50
O110 25 c. "Gerris lacustris" (pond skater) . . . 50 50
O111 40 c. "Byctiscus betulae" (leaf weevil) . . . 60 40
O112 55 c. "Atta texana" (leaf-cutter ants) . . . 65 40
O113 70 c. "Polistes fuscatus" (paper wasp) . . . 70 70
O114 90 c. "Sparmopolius fulvus" (bee fly) . . . 80 70
O115 $1 "Chrysopa carnea" (lace wing) . . . 1·00 70
O116 $1.15 "Phoebis philea" (butterfly) . . . 1·75 1·50
O117 $1.50 "Cynthia cardui" (butterfly) . . . 2·00 2·25
O118 $3 "Utetheisa bella" (moth) . 2·50 3·00
O119 $5 "Alucita pentadactyla" (moth) . . . 3·50 3·75
O120 $10 "Heliconius melpomene" (butterfly) . . . 5·50 6·00

1997. Nos. 1009/22 and 1024 optd **O.H.M.S.**

O121 5 c. Type **184** . . . 10 10
O122 10 c. Pegasus . . . 10 10
O123 15 c. Griffin . . . 10 10
O124 20 c. Unicorn . . . 10 10
O125 25 c. Gnomes . . . 10 10
O126 40 c. Mermaid . . . 15 20
O127 55 c. Cockatrice . . . 25 30
O128 70 c. Fairy . . . 30 35
O129 90 c. Goblin . . . 40 45
O130 $1 Faun . . . 45 50
O131 $1.15 Dragon . . . 50 55
O132 $1.50 Giant . . . 65 70
O133 $3 Elves . . . 1·25 1·40
O134 $5 Centaur . . . 2·10 2·25
O135 $10 Erin . . . 4·25 4·50

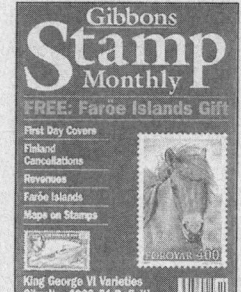

MOROCCO Pt. 13

An independent kingdom, established in 1956, comprising the former French and Spanish International Zones.

A. NORTHERN ZONE.

100 centimes = 1 peseta

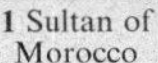
1 Sultan of Morocco

2 Polytechnic

1956.

1 **1** 10 c. brown 10 10
2 – 15 c. brown 10 10
3 **2** 25 c. violet 10 10
4 – 50 c. green 25 25
5 **1** 80 c. green 90 90
6 – 2 p. lilac . . . . 7·50 7·50
7 **2** 3 p. blue . . . . 15·00 15·00
8 – 10 p. green . . . . 31·00 31·00
DESIGNS—HORIZ: 15 c., 2 p. Villa Sanjurjo harbour. VERT: 50 c., 10 p. Cultural Delegation building, Tetuan.

3 Lockheed Super Constellation over Lau Dam

1956. Air.

9 **3** 25 c. purple 20 15
10 – 1 p. 40 mauve 90 60
11 **3** 3 p. 40 red . . . . 1·90 1·50
12 – 4 p. 80 purple . . . . 3·50 2·50
DESIGN: 1 p. 40, 4 p. 80, Lockheed Super Constellation over Rio Nekor Bridge.

1957. 1st Anniv of Independence. As T **7** but with Spanish inscriptions and currency.

13 80 c. green 65 50
14 1 p. 50 olive . . . . 1·90 1·40
15 3 p. red . . . . 4·25 3·25

1957. As T **5** but with Spanish inscriptions and currency.

16 30 c. indigo and blue 10 10
17 70 c. purple and brown 20 10
18 80 c. purple . . . . 1·60 40
19 1 p. 50 lake and green 50 15
20 3 p. green 75 50
21 7 p. red . . . . 5·25 1·50

1957. Investiture of Prince Moulay el Hassan. As T **9** but with Spanish inscriptions and currency.

22 80 c. blue 65 25
23 1 p. 50 green . . . . 1·60 80
24 3 p. red . . . . 4·75 2·50

1957. Nos. 17 and 19 surch.

25 15 c. on 70 c. purple and brown . . 75 75
26 1 p. 20 on 1 p. 50 lake and green . . 1·40 1·40

1957. 30th Anniv of Coronation of Sultan Sidi Mohammed ben Yusuf. As T **10** but with Spanish inscription and currency.

27 1 p. 20 green and black 65 50
28 1 p. 80 red and black 90 75
29 3 p. violet and black . . . . 1·60 1·50

B. SOUTHERN ZONE

100 centimes = 1 franc

5 Sultan of Morocco

6 Classroom

7 Sultan of Morocco

1956.

30 **5** 5 f. indigo and blue 20 10
31 10 f. sepia and brown 15 10
32 15 f. lake and green 25 10
33 25 f. purple . . . . 1·10 10
34 30 f. green . . . . 1·90 10
35 50 f. red . . . . 3·00 15
36 70 f. brown and sepia . . . . 4·25 60

1956. Education Campaign.

37 – 10 f. violet and purple . . . . 1·90 1·25
38 – 15 f. lake and red . . . . 2·40 1·50
39 **6** 20 f. green and turquoise . . . . 2·50 2·50
40 – 30 f. red and lake . . . . 4·50 2·75
41 – 50 f. blue and indigo . . . . 7·50 5·00
DESIGNS: 10 f. Peasants reading book; 15 f. Two girls reading; 30 f. Child reading to old man; 50 f. Child teaching parents the alphabet.

1957. 1st Anniv of Independence.

42 **7** 15 f. green . . . . 1·60 1·25
43 25 f. olive . . . . 2·25 1·25
44 30 f. red . . . . 4·00 1·90

8 Emblem over Casablanca

9 Crown Prince Moulay el Hassan

1957. Air. International Fair, Casablanca.

45 **8** 15 f. green and red . . . . 1·25 1·00
46 25 f. turquoise . . . . 2·25 1·40
47 30 f. brown . . . . 2·75 1·75

1957. Investiture of Crown Prince Moulay el Hassan.

48 **9** 15 f. blue . . . . 1·50 95
49 25 f. green . . . . 1·75 1·25
50 30 f. red . . . . 2·75 1·60

10 King Mohammed V

11 Moroccan Pavilion

1957. 30th Anniv of Coronation of King Mohammed V.

51 **10** 15 f. green and black 95 50
52 25 f. red and black . . . . 1·50 1·00
53 30 f. violet and black . . . . 1·60 1·10

C. ISSUES FOR THE WHOLE OF MOROCCO.

1958. 100 centimes = 1 franc.
1962. 100 francs = 1 dirham.

1958. Brussels International Exhibition.

54 **11** 15 f. turquoise 25 20
55 25 f. red 25 25
56 30 f. blue 35 30

12 King Mohammed V and U.N.E.S.C.O. Headquarters, Paris

1958. Inauguration of U.N.E.S.C.O. Headquarters Building, Paris.

57 **12** 15 f. green 25 20
58 25 f. lake 25 25
59 30 f. blue 35 30

13 Ben-Smine Sanatorium

14 King Mohammed V on Horseback

1959. "National Aid".

60 **13** 50 f. bistre, green and red 70 35

1959. King Mohammed V's 50th Birthday.

61 **14** 15 f. lake 65 30
62 25 f. blue 95 35
63 45 f. green . . . . 1·10 45

15 Princess Lalla Amina

16

1959. Children's Week.

64 **15** 15 f. blue 25 20
65 25 f. green 30 25
66 45 f. purple 60 30

1960. Meeting of U.N. African Economic Commission, Tangier.

67 **16** 45 f. green, brown & violet . . . . 1·10 50

(17)

18 Arab Refugees

1960. Adulterated Cooking Oil Victims Relief Fund. Surch as T **17**.

68 **5** 5 f. + 10 f. indigo and blue 35 30
69 10 f. + 10 f. sepia and brown 70 45
70 15 f. + 10 f. lake and green . . . . 1·25 95
71 25 f. + 15 f. purple . . . . 1·40 1·10
72 30 f. + 20 f. green . . . . 2·25 2·00

1960. World Refugee Year.

73 **18** 15 f. black, green and ochre 25 20
74 – 45 f. green and black 65 35
DESIGNS: 45 f. "Uprooted tree" and Arab refugees.

19 Marrakesh

20 Lantern

1960. 900th Anniv of Marrakesh.

75 **19** 100 f. green, brown and blue . . . . 1·40 95

1960. 1100th Anniv of Karaouiyne University.

76 **20** 15 f. purple 60 50
77 – 25 f. blue (Fountain) 65 55
78 – 30 f. brown (Minaret) . . . . 1·25 60
79 – 35 f. black (Frescoes) . . . . 1·60 80
80 – 45 f. green (Courtyard) . . . . 2·25 1·40

21 Arab League Centre and King Mohammed V

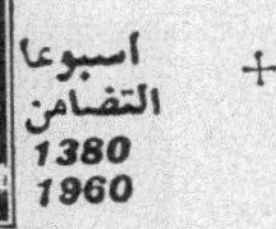

(22)

1960. Inauguration of Arab League Centre, Cairo.

81 **21** 15 f. black and green 20 20

1960. Solidarity Fund. Nos. 458/9 (Mahakma, Casablanca) of French Morocco surch as T **22**.

82 **106** 15 f. + 3 f. on 18 f. myrtle 55 55
83 + 5 f. on 20 f. lake 80 80

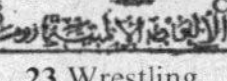
23 Wrestling

24 Runner

1960. Olympic Games.

84 **23** 5 f. purple, green and violet . . 10 10
85 – 10 f. chocolate, blue & brn . . 15 10
86 – 15 f. brown, blue and green . . 20 15
87 – 20 f. purple, blue and bistre . . 25 20
88 – 30 f. brown, violet and red . . 30 25
89 – 40 f. brown, blue and violet . . 60 25
90 – 45 f. blue, green and purple . . 75 35
91 – 70 f. black, blue and brown . . 1·40 45
DESIGNS: 10 f. Gymnastics; 15 f. Cycling; 20 f. Weightlifting; 30 f. Running; 40 f. Boxing; 45 f. Sailing; 70 f. Fencing.

1961. 3rd Pan-Arab Games, Casablanca.

92 **24** 20 f. green 20 15
93 30 f. lake 65 20
94 50 f. blue 75 60

25 Post Office and Letters

26 King Mohammed V and African Map

27 Lumumba and Congo Map

1961. African Postal and Telecommunications Conference, Tangier.

95 **25** 20 f. purple and mauve 35 30
96 – 30 f. turquoise and green 45 35
97 – 90 f. ultramarine and blue 85 60
DESIGNS—VERT: 30 f. Telephone operator. HORIZ: 90 f. Sud Aviation Caravelle mail plane over Tangier.

1962. 1st Anniv of African Charter of Casablanca.

98 **26** 20 f. purple and buff 20 20
99 30 f. indigo and blue 25 25

1962. Patrice Lumumba Commemorative.

100 **27** 20 f. black and bistre 20 20
101 30 f. black and brown 30 25

28 King Hassan II

29 "Pupils of the Nation"

1962. Air.

102 **28** 90 f. black 75 15
103 1 d. red 90 15
104 2 d. blue . . . . 1·10 45
105 3 d. green . . . . 2·25 1·10
106 5 d. violet . . . . 4·50 1·60

1962. Children's Education.

107 **29** 20 f. blue, red and green 35 25
108 30 f. sepia, brown and green 40 35
109 90 f. blue, purple and green 90 50

1962. Arab League Week. As T **76** of Libya.

110 20 f. brown 20 15

30 King Hassan II

31 Scout with Banner

1962.

111 **30** 1 f. olive 10 10
112 2 f. violet 10 10
113 5 f. sepia 10 10
114 10 f. brown 10 10
115 15 f. turquoise 15 10
116 20 f. purple (18 × 22 mm) 20 10
116a 20 f. purple (17½ × 23½ mm) 30 10
116b 25 f. red 20 10
117 30 f. green 25 10
117a 35 f. slate 65 10
117b 40 f. blue 65 10
118 50 f. purple 80 10
118a 60 f. purple . . . . 1·10 10
119 70 f. blue . . . . 1·25 10
120 80 f. lake . . . . 2·10 15

1962. 5th Arab Scout Jamboree, Rabat.

121 **31** 20 f. purple and blue 20 15

32 Campaign Emblem and Swamp

33 Aquarium, Brown Trout and Fish

1962. Malaria Eradication Campaign.

122 **32** 20 f. blue and green 20 15
123 – 50 f. lake and green 35 25
DESIGN—VERT: 50 f. Sword piercing mosquito.

1962. Casablanca Aquarium. Multicoloured.
124 20 f. Type 33 . . . . 85 25
125 30 f. Aquarium and Mediterranean moray . . . 90 25

34 Mounted Postman and 1912 Sherifian Stamp

(35)

1962. First National Philatelic Exhibition, Rabat, and Stamp Day.
126 34 20 f. green and brown . . . 75 35
127 – 30 f. black and red 90 40
128 – 50 f. bistre and blue . . . 1·25 50
DESIGNS: 30 f. Postman and circular postmark; 50 f. Sultan Hassan I and octagonal postmark. (Both stamps commemorate 70th anniv of Sherifian post.)

1963. Flood Relief Fund. Surch as T 35.
129 5 20 + 5 f. on 5 f. indigo and blue 90 85
130 30 + 10 f. on 50 f. red . . . 1·00 85

36 King Moulay Ismail

37 Ibn Batota (voyager)

1963. 300th Anniv of Meknes.
131 36 20 f. sepia 25 20

1963. "Famous Men of Maghreb".
132 37 20 f. purple 45 20
133 – 20 f. black 45 20
134 – 20 f. myrtle 25 25
134a 37 40 f. blue 30 10
PORTRAITS: No. 133, Ibn Khaldoun (historian); 134, Al Idrissi (geographer).

38 Sugar Beet and Refinery

39 Isis (bas relief)

1963. Freedom from Hunger.
135 38 20 f. black, brown & green . 25 20
136 – 50 f. black, brown & blue . . 65 35
DESIGN—VERT: 50 f. Fisherman and tuna.

1963. Nubian Monuments Preservation.
137 – 20 f. black and grey 20 15
138 39 30 f. violet 25 25
139 – 50 f. purple 60 35
DESIGNS—HORIZ: 20 f. Heads of Colossi, Abu Simbel; 50 f. Philae Temple.

40 Agadir before Earthquake

1963. Reconstruction of Agadir.
140 40 20 f. red and blue 35 35
141 30 f. red and blue 45 35
142 – 50 f. red and blue 80 40
DESIGNS: 30 f. is optd with large red cross and date of earthquake, 29th February, 1960; 50 f. Reconstructed Agadir.

41 Plan of new Agadir Hospital

42 Emblems of Morocco and Rabat

1963. Centenary of International Red Cross.
143 41 30 f. multicoloured 50 20

1963. Opening of Parliament.
144 42 20 f. multicoloured 45 20

43 Hands breaking Chain

44 National Flag

1963. 15th Anniv of Declaration of Human Rights.
145 43 20 f. brown, sepia & green . 45 20

1963. Evacuation of Foreign Troops from Morocco.
146 44 20 f. red, green and black . . 25 25

45 "Moulay Abdurrahman" (after Delacroix)

1964. 3rd Anniv of King Hassan's Coronation.
147 45 1 d. multicoloured . . . . 2·75 1·90

46 Map, Chart and W.M.O. Emblem

1964. World Meteorological Day. Multicoloured.
148 20 f. African weather map (postage) (vert) 25 20
149 30 f. Type 46 . . . . 40 35
150 90 f. Globe and weather vane (air) (vert) 90 45

47 Fair Entrance

1964. Air. 20th Anniv of Casablanca Int Fair.
151 47 1 d. red, drab and blue . . . 95 60

48 Moroccan Pavilion at Fair

1964. Air. New York World's Fair.
152 48 1 d. multicoloured . . . . 1·25 65

49 Children Playing in the Sun

50 Olympic Torch

1964. Postal Employees' Holiday Settlements.
153 49 20 f. multicoloured 25 20
154 – 30 f. multicoloured 35 25
DESIGN: 30 f. Boy, girl and holiday settlement.

1964. Olympic Games, Tokyo.
155 50 20 f. green, violet and red . . 25 25
156 30 f. purple, blue and grn . . 35 30
157 50 f. red, blue and green . . 75 35

MINIMUM PRICE

The minimum price quoted is 10p which represents a handling charge rather than a basis for valuing common stamps. For further notes about prices see introductory pages.

51 Lighthouse and Sultan Mohamed ben Abdurrahman (founder)

52 Tangier Iris

1964. Centenary of Cape Spartel Lighthouse.
158 51 25 f. multicoloured 55 45

1965. Flowers. Multicoloured.
159 25 f. Type 52 . . . . 1·00 45
160 40 f. Gladiolus (vert) . . . . 1·25 55
161 60 f. Caper (horiz) . . . . . 1·90 1·40

53 Return of King Mohammed

54 Early Telegraph Receiver

1965. 10th Anniv of Return of King Mohammed V from Exile.
162 53 25 f. green 50 20

1965. Centenary of I.T.U. Multicoloured.
163 25 f. Type 54 . . . . 20 20
164 40 f. "TIROS" weather satellite 35 30

55 I.C.Y. Emblem

59 Corn

1965. International Co-operation Year.
165 55 25 f. black and green . . . 25 20
166 60 f. lake 40 35

1965. Sea Shells. As T 52. Multicoloured, background colours given.
167 25 f. violet 55 25
168 25 f. blue 55 25
169 25 f. yellow 55 25
SEASHELLS: No. 167, Knobbed triton ("Charonia nodifera"); 168, Smooth callista ("Pitaria chione"); 169, "Cymbium tritonis".

1965. Shellfish. As T 52. Multicoloured.
170 25 f. Helmet Crab 70 50
171 40 f. Mantis shrimp . . . . . 1·60 95
172 1 d. Royal prawn (horiz) . . . 2·25 1·40

1965. Orchids. As T 52. Multicoloured.
173 25 f. "Ophrys speculum" (vert) 60 45
174 40 f. "Ophrys fusca" (vert) . . 95 50
175 60 f. "Ophrys tenthredinifera" (horiz) . . . . 1·75 1·25

1966. Agricultural Products (1st issue).
176 59 25 f. black and ochre 20 15
See also Nos. 188/9 and 211.

60 Flag, Map and Dove

1966. 10th Anniv of Independence.
177 60 25 f. red and green 20 15

61 King Hassan II and Crown

1966. 5th Anniv of King Hassan's Coronation.
178 61 25 f. blue, green and red . . 20 15

62 Cross-country Runner

1966. 53rd "Cross des Nations" (Cross-country Race).
179 62 25 f. green 20 15

63 W.H.O. Building

1966. Inaug of W.H.O. Headquarters, Geneva.
180 63 25 f. black and purple . . . 20 15
181 – 40 f. black and blue 25 20
DESIGN: 40 f. W.H.O. Building (different view).

64 King Hassan and Parachutist

65 Brooch

1966. 10th Anniv of Royal Armed Forces.
182 64 25 f. black and gold 60 25
183 – 40 f. black and gold 60 25
DESIGN: 40 f. Crown Prince Hassan kissing hand of King Mohammed.

1966. Palestine Week. As No. 110 but inscr "SEMAINE DE LA PALESTINE" at foot and dated "1966".
184 25 f. blue 20 15

1966. Red Cross Seminar. Moroccan Jewellery. Multicoloured.
185 25 f. + 5 f. Type 65 . . . . . 90 45
186 40 f. + 10 f. Pendant . . . . 1·25 55
See also Nos. 203/4, 246/7, 274/5, 287/8, 303/4, 324/5, 370/1, 397/8, 414/15, 450/1 and 493.

66 Rameses II, Abu Simbel

67 Class XDd Diesel Train

1966. Air. 20th Anniv of U.N.E.S.C.O.
187 66 1 d. red and yellow . . . . 1·25 75

1966. Agricultural Products (2nd and 3rd issue). As T 59.
188 40 f. multicoloured 25 10
189 60 f. multicoloured 35 20
DESIGNS—VERT: 40 f. Citrus fruits. HORIZ: 60 f. Olives.

1966. Moroccan Transport. Multicoloured.
190 25 f. Type 67 (postage) . . . . 1·50 60
191 40 f. Liner "Maroc" 80 40
192 1 d. Tourist coach 95 60
193 3 d. Sud Aviation Caravelle of Royal Air Maroc (48 × 27½ mm) (air) . . . . 4·50 1·90

68 Twaite Shad

1967. Fishes. Multicoloured.
194 25 f. Type 68 . . . . 1·10 25
195 40 f. Plain bonito . . . . . . 1·40 30
196 1 d. Bluefish . . . . 3·00 1·40

69 Hilton Hotel, Ancient Ruin and Map

1967. Opening of Hilton Hotel, Rabat.
197 69 25 f. black and blue 20 15
198 1 d. purple and blue 50 20

70 Ait Aadel Dam

1967. Inauguration of Ait Aadel Dam.
199 **70** 25 f. grey, blue and green 25 15
200 40 f. bistre and blue 65 20

71 Moroccan Scene and Lions Emblem

1967. 50th Anniv of Lions Int.
201 **71** 40 f. blue and gold 50 20
202 1 d. green and gold 1·00 25

1967. Moroccan Red Cross. As T **65**. Mult.
203 60 f. + 5 f. Necklace 95 95
204 1 d. + 10 f. Two bracelets 1·90 1·90

72 Three Hands and Pickaxe

73 I.T.Y. Emblem

1967. Communal Development Campaign.
205 **72** 25 f. green 20 15

1967. International Tourist Year.
206 **73** 1 d. blue and cobalt 80 35

74 Arrow and Map

75 Horse-jumping

1967. Mediterranean Games, Tunis.
207 **74** 25 f. multicoloured 25 20
208 40 f. multicoloured 30 20

1967. International Horse Show.
209 **75** 40 f. multicoloured 30 20
210 1 d. multicoloured 75 35

1967. Agricultural Products (4th issue). As T **59**.
211 40 f. mult (Cotton plant) 65 15

76 Human Rights Emblem

77 Msouffa Woman

1968. Human Rights Year.
212 **76** 25 f. slate 20 20
213 1 d. lake 35 25

1968. Moroccan Costumes. Multicoloured.
214 10 f. Ait Moussa or Ali 65 25
215 15 f. Ait Mouhad 90 30
216 25 f. Barquemaster of Rabat-Sale 1·00 35
217 25 f. Townsman 1·90 75
218 40 f. Townswoman 1·10 45
219 60 f. Royal Mokhazni 1·50 60
220 1 d. Type **77** 1·50 95
221 1 d. Riff 1·50 95
222 1 d. Zemmour woman 1·90 1·25
223 1 d. Meknassa 1·90 60

78 King Hassan

79 Red Crescent Nurse and Child

1968.
224 **78** 1 f. multicoloured 10 10
225 2 f. multicoloured 10 10
226 5 f. multicoloured 10 10
227 10 f. multicoloured 10 10
228 15 f. multicoloured 10 10
229 20 f. multicoloured 10 10
230 25 f. multicoloured 15 10
231 30 f. multicoloured 15 10
232 35 f. multicoloured 45 10
233 40 f. multicoloured 45 10
234 50 f. multicoloured 50 10
235 60 f. multicoloured 50 10
236 70 f. multicoloured 4·00 90
237 75 f. multicoloured 1·00 15
238 80 f. multicoloured 70 20
239 – 90 f. multicoloured 1·40 20
240 – 1 d. multicoloured 2·00 20
241 – 2 d. multicoloured 2·50 35
242 – 3 d. multicoloured 5·00 80
243 – 5 d. multicoloured 8·75 2·50

Nos. 239/43 bear a similar portrait of King Hassan, but are larger, $26\frac{1}{2} \times 40\frac{1}{2}$ mm.

1968. 20th Anniv of W.H.O.
244 **79** 25 f. brown, red & blue 20 10
245 40 f. brown, red & slate 25 15

1968. Red Crescent. Moroccan Jewellery. As T **65**. Multicoloured.
246 25 f. Pendant brooch 80 40
247 40 f. Bracelet 1·25 50

80 Rotary Emblem, Conference Building and Map

1968. Rotary Int District Conf, Casablanca.
248 **80** 40 f. gold, blue and green 65 20
249 1 d. gold, ultramarine & blue 75 30

81 Belt Pattern

82 Princess Lalla Meryem

1968. "The Belts of Fez". Designs showing ornamental patterns.
250 **81** 25 f. multicoloured 1·90 70
251 – 40 f. multicoloured 2·25 1·25
252 – 60 f. multicoloured 3·50 1·75
253 – 1 d. multicoloured 6·00 3·25

1968. World Children's Day. Multicoloured.
254 25 f. Type **82** 25 20
255 40 f. Princess Lalla Asmaa 65 25
256 1 d. Crown Prince Sidi Mohammed 1·10 55

83 Wrestling

1968. Olympic Games, Mexico. Multicoloured.
257 15 f. Type **83** 15 15
258 20 f. Basketball 15 15
259 25 f. Cycling 50 15
260 40 f. Boxing 60 15
261 60 f. Running 75 15
262 1 d. Football 1·25 45

84 Silver Crown

85 Costumes of Zagora, South Morocco

1968. Ancient Moroccan Coins.
263 **84** 20 f. silver & purple 55 20
264 – 25 f. gold and purple 80 25
265 – 40 f. silver and green 1·40 65
266 – 60 f. gold and red 1·60 65

COINS: 25 f. Gold dinar; 40 f. Silver dirham; 60 f. Gold piece.

See also Nos. 270/1.

1969. Traditional Women's Costumes. Mult.
267 15 f. Type **85** (postage) 1·25 75
268 25 f. Ait Adidou costumes 1·90 1·10
269 1 d. Ait Ouaouzguit costumes (air) 2·50 1·25

1969. 8th Anniv of Coronation of Hassan II. As T **84** (silver coins).
270 1 d. silver and blue 4·25 1·60
271 5 d. silver and violet 10·00 6·00

COINS: 1 d. One dirham coin of King Mohammed V; 5 d. One dirham coin of King Hassan II.

86 Hands "reading" Braille on Map

1969. Protection of the Blind Week.
272 **86** 25 f. + 10 f. multicoloured 45 15

87 "Actor"

89 King Hassan II

1969. World Theatre Day.
273 **87** 1 d. multicoloured 45 25

1969. 50th Anniv of League of Red Cross Societies. Moroccan Jewellery as T **65**. Multicoloured.
274 25 f. + 5 f. Bracelets 90 45
275 40 f. + 10 f. Pendant 1·25 55

1969. King Hassan's 40th Birthday.
276 **89** 1 d. multicoloured 1·25 35

مؤتمر القمة الاسلامي
الرباط ١٥ رجب 1389
(90)

91 Mahatma Gandhi

1969. Islamic Summit Conf, Rabat (1st issue). No. 240 optd with T **90**.
278 1 d. multicoloured 5·00 4·00

1969. Birth Centenary of Mahatma Gandhi.
279 **91** 40 f. brown and lavender 60 15

92 I.L.O. Emblem

1969. 50th Anniv of I.L.O.
280 **92** 50 f. multicoloured 50 20

93 King Hassan on Horseback

1969. Islamic Summit Conference, Rabat (2nd issue).
281 **93** 1 d. multicoloured 1·10 35

94 "Spahi Horseman" (Haram al Glaoui)

1970. Moroccan Art.
282 **94** 1 d. multicoloured 1·10 30

1970. Flood Victims Relief Fund. Nos. 227/8 surch.
283 **78** 10 f. + 25 f. multicoloured 3·50 3·50
284 15 f. + 25 f. multicoloured 3·50 3·50

96 Drainage System, Fez

97 "Dance of the Guedra" (P. Beaubrun)

1970. 50th Congress of Public and Municipal Health Officials, Rabat.
285 **96** 60 f. multicoloured 35 20

1970. Folklore Festival, Marrakesh.
286 **97** 40 f. multicoloured 75 20

1970. Red Crescent. Moroccan Jewellery as T **65**. Multicoloured.
287 25 f. + 5 f. Necklace 1·00 65
288 50 f. + 10 f. Pendant 1·50 1·40

1970. Population Census. No. 189 surch **1970 0,25** and Arabic inscr.
290 25 f. on 60 f. multicoloured 50 10

99 Dish Aerial, Souk el Arba des Sehoul Communications Station

100 Ruddy Shelduck

1970. 17th Anniv of Revolution.
291 **99** 1 d. multicoloured 80 35

1970. Nature Protection, Wild Birds. Multicoloured.
292 25 f. Type **100** 1·50 35
293 40 f. Houbara bustard 2·50 45

101 I.E.Y. Emblem and Moroccan with Book

1970. International Education Year.
294 **101** 60 f. multicoloured 65 20

102 Symbols of U.N

1970. 25th Anniv of U.N.O.
295 **102** 50 f. multicoloured 55 15

103 League Emblem, Map and Laurel

1970. 25th Anniv of Arab League.
296 **103** 50 f. multicoloured 50 15

104 Olive Grove and Extraction Plant

1970. World Olive-oil Production Year.

297 **104** 50 f. black, brown & green . . 55 15

105 Es Sounna Mosque

1971. Restoration of Es Sounna Mosque, Rabat.

298 **105** 60 f. multicoloured 60 15

106 "Heart" within Horse

107 King Hassan II and Dam

1971. European and North African Heart Week.

299 **106** 50 f. multicoloured 50 20

1971. 10th Anniv of King Hassan's Accession.

300 **107** 25 f. multicoloured 45 10

108 Palestine on Globe

1971. Palestine Week.

302 **108** 25 f. + 10 f. multicoloured 25 20

1971. Red Crescent, Moroccan Jewellery. As T **65**. Multicoloured.

303 25 f. + 5 f. "Arrow-head" brooch 75 50

304 40 f. + 10 f. Square pendant . . 1·10 90

109 Hands holding Peace Dove

1971. Racial Equality Year.

305 **109** 50 f. multicoloured 50 15

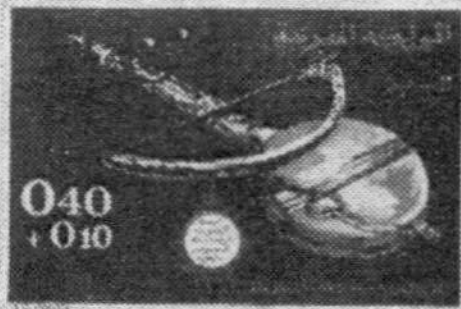

110 Musical Instrument

1971. Protection of the Blind Week.

306 **110** 40 f. + 10 f. multicoloured 60 20

111 Children at Play

112 Shah Mohammed Reza Pahlavi of Iran

1971. International Children's Day.

307 **111** 40 f. multicoloured 45 15

1971. 2,500th Anniv of Persian Empire.

308 **112** 1 d. multicoloured 70 30

113 Aerial View of Mausoleum

1971. Mausoleum of Mohammed V. Multicoloured.

309 25 f. Type **113** 15 15

310 50 f. Tomb of Mohammed V . . 20 20

311 1 d. Interior of Mausoleum (vert) 80 50

114 Football and Emblem

116 Sun and Landscape

115 A.P.U. Emblem

1971. Mediterranean Games, Izmir, Turkey. Multicoloured.

312 40 f. Type **114** 55 15

313 60 f. Athlete and emblem . . . 70 20

1971. 25th Anniv of Founding of Arab Postal Union at Sofar Conference.

314 **115** 25 f. red, blue & light blue 15 10

1971. 50th Anniv of Sherifian Phosphates Office.

315 **116** 70 f. multicoloured 55 20

117 Torch and Book Year Emblem

118 Lottery Symbol

1972. International Book Year.

316 **117** 1 d. multicoloured 65 25

1972. Creation of National Lottery.

317 **118** 25 f. gold, black & brown . 15 10

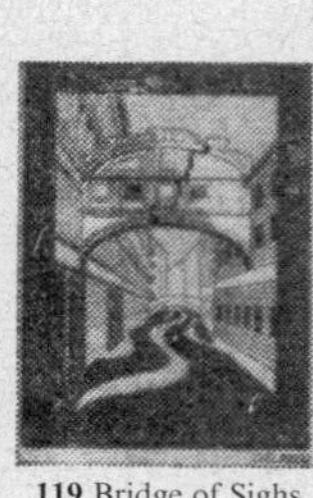

119 Bridge of Sighs

120 Mizmar (double-horned flute)

1972. U.N.E.S.C.O. "Save Venice" Campaign. Multicoloured.

318 25 f. Type **119** 15 15

319 50 f. St. Mark's Basilica (horiz) 20 15

320 1 d. Lion of St. Marks (horiz) . 65 20

1972. Protection of the Blind Week.

321 **120** 25 f. + 10 f. multicoloured . 60 20

121 Bridge and Motorway

1972. 2nd African Highways Conference, Rabat.

322 **121** 75 f. multicoloured 75 20

122 Moroccan Stamp of 1969, and Postmark

1972. Stamp Day.,

323 **122** 1 d. multicoloured 65 20

1972. Red Crescent. Moroccan Jewellery. As T **65**. Multicoloured.

324 25 f. + 5 f. Jewelled bangles . . 75 75

325 70 f. + 10 f. Filigree pendant . 1·10 1·10

123 "Betrothal of Imilchil" (Tayeb Lahlou)

124 Dove on African Map

1972. Folklore Festival, Marrakesh.

326 **123** 60 f. multicoloured 90 35

1972. 9th Organisation of African Unity Summit Conference, Rabat.

327 **124** 25 f. multicoloured 15 15

125 Polluted Beach

1972. U.N. Environmental Conservation Conference, Stockholm.

328 **125** 50 f. multicoloured 50 20

126 Running

127 "Sonchus pinnatifidus"

1972. Olympic Games, Munich.

329 **126** 25 f. red, pink & black . . 15 15

330 – 50 f. violet, lilac & black . . 20 15

331 – 75 f. green, yell and blk . . 60 20

332 – 1 d. blue, light bl & blk . . 75 25

DESIGNS: 50 f. Wrestling; 75 f. Football; 1 d. Cycling.

1972. Moroccan Flowers (1st series). Multicoloured.

333 25 f. Type **127** 45 15

334 40 f. "Amberboa crupinoides" 55 15

See also Nos. 375/6.

128 Sand Gazelle

129 Rabat Carpet

1972. Nature Protection. Fauna. Multicoloured.

335 25 f. Type **128** 75 25

336 40 f. Barbary sheep . . . . . 1·00 60

1972. Moroccan Carpets (1st series). Multicoloured.

337 50 f. Type **129** . . . . 1·00 35

338 75 f. Rabat carpet with "star-shaped" centre . . . . 1·50 50

See also Nos. 380/1, 406/7, 433/4, 485/7 and 513.

130 Mother and Child with U.N. Emblem

132 Global Weather Map

131 "Postman" and "Stamp"

1972. International Children's Day.

339 **130** 75 f. blue, yellow & green . 35 30

1973. Stamp Day.

340 **131** 25 f. multicoloured 15 10

1973. Centenary of W.M.O.

341 **132** 70 f. multicoloured 70 20

133 King Hassan and Arms

1973.

342 **133** 1 f. multicoloured 10 10

343 2 f. multicoloured 10 10

344 5 f. multicoloured 10 10

345 10 f. multicoloured . . . 10 10

346 15 f. multicoloured . . . 10 10

347 20 f. multicoloured . . . 10 10

348 25 f. multicoloured . . . 10 10

349 30 f. multicoloured . . . 15 10

350 35 f. multicoloured . . . 15 10

351 40 f. multicoloured . . . 5·00 70

352 50 f. multicoloured . . . 50 10

353 60 f. multicoloured . . . 60 15

354 70 f. multicoloured . . . 25 15

355 75 f. multicoloured . . . 30 15

356 80 f. multicoloured . . . 60 20

357 90 f. multicoloured . . . 75 15

358 1 d. multicoloured . . . . 2·00 20

359 2 d. multicoloured . . . . 4·25 55

360 3 d. multicoloured . . . . 6·25 1·25

361 5 d. mult (brown background) . . . . 4·25 1·25

361a 5 d. mult (pink background) 4·00 90

مناظرة
السياحة
1973
(134)

1973. Nat Tourist Conf. Nos. 324/5 surch with T **134**.

362 **65** 25 f. on 5 f. multicoloured . 2·50 2·50

363 70 f. on 10 f. multicoloured 2·50 2·50

On No. 363 the Arabic text is arranged in one line.

135 Tambours

1973. Protection of the Blind Week.

364 **135** 70 f. + 10 f. multicoloured 75 55

136 Kaaba, Mecca, and Mosque, Rabat

1973. Prophet Mohammed's Birthday.

365 **136** 25 f. multicoloured 15 10

INDEX

Countries can be quickly located by referring to the index at the end of this volume.

137 Roses and M'Gouna

1973. M'Gouna Rose Festival.
366 137 25 f. multicoloured 45 10

138 Handclasp and Torch 139 Folk-dancers

1973. 10th Anniv of Organization of African Unity.
367 138 70 f. multicoloured 30 15

1973. Folklore Festival, Marrakesh. Multicoloured.
368 50 f. Type **139** 50 15
369 1 d. Folk-musicians 75 25

1973. Red Crescent. Moroccan Jewellery. As T **65**. Multicoloured.
370 25 f. + 5 f. Locket . . . . . 1·00 50
371 70 f. + 10 f. Bracelet inlaid with pearls . . . . 1·10 60

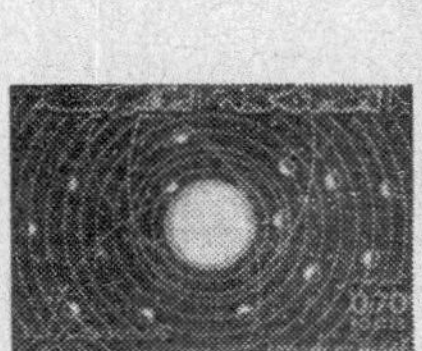

140 Solar System 141 Microscope

1973. 500th Birth Anniv of Nicholas Copernicus.
372 140 70 f. multicoloured 60 20

1973. 25th Anniv of W.H.O.
373 141 70 f. multicoloured 55 20

142 Interpol Emblem and Fingerprint

1973. 50th Anniv of International Criminal Police Organization (Interpol).
374 142 70 f. multicoloured 30 25

1973. Moroccan Flowers (2nd series). As T **127**. Multicoloured.
375 25 f. "Chrysanthemum carinatum" (horiz) 75 35
376 1 d. "Amberboa muricata" . . 1·25 55

143 Striped Hyena

1973. Nature Protection. Multicoloured.
377 25 f. Type **143** 95 40
378 50 f. Eleonora's Falcon (vert) . 3·25 55

144 Map and Arrows

1973. Meeting of Maghreb Committee for Co-ordination of Posts and Telecommunications, Tunis.
379 144 25 f. multicoloured 15 10

1973. Moroccan Carpets (2nd series). As T **129**. Multicoloured.
380 25 f. Carpet from the High Atlas 1·00 25
381 70 f. Tazenakht carpet . . . . 1·50 50

145 Golf Club and Ball

المؤتمر الاسلامي - لاهور
1394
(146)

1974. International "Hassan II Trophy" Golf Grand Prix, Rabat.
382 145 70 f. multicoloured . . . . 1·25 60

1974. Islamic Summit Conference, Lahore, Pakistan. No. 281 optd with T **146**.
383 1 d. multicoloured . . . . . . 2·75 1·60

147 Human Rights Emblem 148 Vanadinite

1974. 25th Anniv (1973) of Declaration of Human Rights.
384 147 70 f. multicoloured 50 20

1974. Moroccan Mineral Sources. Multicoloured.
385 25 f. Type **148** 95 50
386 70 f. Erythrine . . . . 1·90 1·00

149 Marrakesh Minaret 150 U.P.U. Emblem and Congress Dates

1974. 173rd District of Rotary International Annual Conference, Marrakesh.
387 149 70 f. multicoloured 70 20

1974. Centenary of U.P.U.
388 150 25 f. black, red and green . 15 10
389 – 1 d. multicoloured 70 25
DESIGN—HORIZ: 1 d. Commemorative scroll.

151 Drummers and Dancers

1974. 15th Folklore Festival, Marrakesh. Multicoloured.
390 25 f. Type **151** 35 15
391 70 f. Juggler with woman . . . 1·25 30

152 Environmental Emblem and Scenes 154 Flintlock Pistol

1974. World Environmental Day.
392 152 25 f. multicoloured 20 15

1974. Red Crescent. Moroccan Firearms. Multicoloured.
397 25 f. + 5 f. Type **154** 75 75
398 70 f. + 10 f. Gunpowder box . 1·10 1·10

155 Stamps, Postmark and Magnifying Glass

الاحصاء الفلاحي
1.00
(156)

1974. Stamp Day.
399 155 70 f. multicoloured 60 20

1974. No. D393 surch with T **156**.
400 1 d. on 5 f. orange, grn & blk . 1·90 1·25

157 World Cup Trophy 158 Erbab (two-string fiddle)

1974. World Cup Football Championship, West Germany.
401 157 1 d. multicoloured 85 65

1974. Blind Week.
402 158 70 f. + 10 f. multicoloured 1·00 50
See also No. 423.

160 Double-spurred Francolin 162 Jasmine

1974. Moroccan Animals. Multicoloured.
404 25 f. Type **160** . . . . . . 1·60 50
405 70 f. Leopard (horiz) 95 40

1974. Moroccan Carpets (3rd series). As T **129**. Multicoloured.
406 25 f. Zemmour carpet 65 10
407 1 d. Beni M'Guild carpet . . . 1·25 50

1975. Flowers (1st series). Multicoloured.
408 25 f. Type **162** 50 10
409 35 f. Orange lilies 60 10
410 70 f. Poppies 85 35
411 90 f. Carnations . . . . 1·10 50
See also Nos. 417/20.

163 Aragonite 165 "The Water-carrier" (Feu Taieb-Lalou)

1975. Minerals. Multicoloured.
412 50 f. Type **163** 75 40
413 1 d. Agate . . . . 1·50 75
See also Nos. 543 and 563/4.

1975. Red Crescent. Moroccan Jewellery. As T **65**. Multicoloured.
414 25 f. + 5 f. Pendant 75 75
415 70 f. + 10 f. Earring . . . . . 1·10 1·00

1975. "Moroccan Painters".
416 165 1 d. multicoloured . . . . 1·10 30

1975. Flowers (2nd series). As T **162**. Multicoloured.
417 10 f. Daisies 10 10
418 50 f. Pelargoniums 60 10
419 60 f. Orange blossom 75 30
420 1 d. Pansies . . . . 1·10 60

166 Collector with Stamp Album 167 Dancer with Rifle

1975. Stamp Day.
421 166 40 f. multicoloured 20 10

1975. 16th Nat Folklore Festival, Marrakesh.
422 167 1 d. multicoloured 65 30

1975. Blind Week. As T **158**. Multicoloured.
423 1 d. Mandolin 85 25

168 "Animals in Forest" (child's drawing)

1975. Children's Week.
424 168 25 f. multicoloured 15 10

169 Games Emblem and Athletes

1975. 7th Mediterranean Games, Algiers.
425 169 40 f. multicoloured 45 10

170 Waldrapp

1975. Fauna. Multicoloured.
426 40 f. Type **170** . . . . 3·00 70
427 1 d. Caracal (vert) . . . . . . 1·50 75
See also Nos. 470/71.

1975. "Green March" (1st issue). Nos. 370/1 optd **1975** and Arabic inscr.
428 25 f. (+ 5 f.) multicoloured . . 2·50 2·50
429 70 f. (+ 10 f.) multicoloured . . 2·50 2·50
The premiums on the stamps are obliterated.

172 King Mohammed V greeting Crowd

1975. 20th Anniv of Independence. Mult.
430 40 f. Type **172** 15 10
431 1 d. King Hassan (vert) 75 45
432 1 d. King Hassan V wearing fez (vert) 75 45

1975. Moroccan Carpets (4th series). As T **129**. Multicoloured.
433 25 f. Ouled Besseba carpet . . 60 35
434 1 d. Ait Ouaouzguid carpet . . 90 45
See Nos. 485/7 and 513.

173 Marchers crossing Desert 174 Fez Coin of 1883/4

1975. "Green March" (2nd issue).

435 **173** 40 f. multicoloured 15 10

1976. Moroccan Coins (1st series). Multicoloured.

436 5 f. Type **174** 10 10
437 15 f. Rabat silver coin 1774/5 . 10 10
438 35 f. Sabta coin, 13/14th centuries 75 35
439 40 f. Type **174** 50 10
440 50 f. As No. 437 . . . . 75 35
441 65 f. As No. 438 . . . . 75 50
442 1 d. Sabta coin, 12/13th centuries 1·10 60

See also Nos. 458/67a.
For Nos. 439/40 in smaller size, see Nos. 520/b.

175 Interior of Mosque

1976. Millennium of Ibn Zaidoun Mosque. Multicoloured.

443 40 f. Type **175** 15 10
444 65 f. Interior archways (vert) . 50 15

176 Moroccan Family

1976. Family Planning.

445 **176** 40 f. multicoloured 15 10

177 Bou Anania College, Fez

1976. Moroccan Architecture.

446 **177** 1 d. multicoloured 70 20

178 Temple Sculpture

1976. Borobudur Temple Preservation Campaign. Multicoloured.

447 40 f. Type **178** 15 15
448 1 d. View of Temple 60 20

179 Dome of the Rock, Jerusalem

1976. 6th Anniv of Islamic Conference.

449 **179** 1 d. multicoloured 70 20

1976. Red Crescent. Moroccan Jewellery. As T **65**. Multicoloured.

450 40 f. Jewelled purse 15 10
451 1 d. Jewelled pectoral 65 25

180 George Washington, King Hassan I, Statue of Liberty and Mausoleum of Mohammed V

181 Wrestling

1976. Bicentenary of American Revolution. Multicoloured.

452 40 f. Flags of USA and Morocco (horiz) 45 15
453 1 d. Type **180** 65 25

1976. Olympic Games, Montreal. Multicoloured.

454 35 f. Type **181** 10 10
455 40 f. Cycling 15 10
456 50 f. Boxing 50 15
457 1 d. Running 70 25

1976. Moroccan Coins (2nd series). As T **174**. Multicoloured.

458 5 f. Medieval silver mohur . . 10 10
459 10 f. Gold mohur 10 10
460 15 f. Gold coin 10 10
461 20 f. Gold coin (different) . . 10 10
461a 25 f. As No. 437 . . . . . . 1·25 50
462 30 f. As No. 459 . . . . . . 35 10
463 35 f. Silver dinar 45 10
464 60 f. As No. 458 . . . . . . 50 15
465 70 f. Copper coin 80 15
466 75 f. As No. 463 . . . . . . 50 15
466a 80 f. As No. 460 . . . . . . 2·50 75
467 75 f. As No. 465 . . . . . . 60 35
467a 3 d. As No. 461 . . . . . . 3·75 1·25

182 Early and Modern Telephones with Dish Aerial

1976. Telephone Centenary.

468 **182** 1 d. multicoloured 70 25

183 Gold Medallion

1976. Blind Week.

469 **183** 50 f. multicoloured 50 10

1976. Birds. As T **170**. Multicoloured.

470 40 f. Dark chanting goshawk . 1·75 40
471 1 d. Purple swamphen . . . . 2·50 85

Nos. 470/1 are vert designs.

185 King Hassan, Emblems and Map

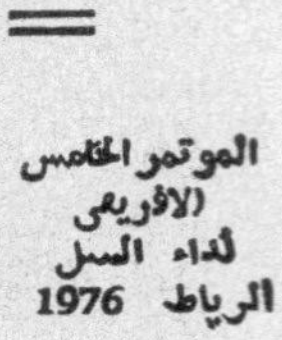

(186)

1976. 1st Anniv of "Green March".

472 **185** 40 f. multicoloured 45 10

1976. Fifth African Tuberculosis Conference. Nos. 414/15 optd with T **186**.

473 25 f. multicoloured . . . . . 1·90 1·90
474 70 f. multicoloured . . . . . 2·25 2·25

187 Globe and Peace Dove

188 African Nations Cup

1976. Conference of Non-Aligned Countries, Colombo.

475 **187** 1 d. red, black and blue . . 30 20

1976. African Nations Football Championship.

476 **188** 1 d. multicoloured 65 20

189 Letters encircling Globe

1977. Stamp Day.

477 **189** 40 f. multicoloured 40 10

INDEX

Countries can be quickly located by referring to the index at the end of this volume.

190 "Aeonium arboreum"

1977. Flowers. Multicoloured.

478 40 f. Type **190** 30 10
479 50 f. "Malope trifida" (24 × 38 mm) 95 30
480 1 d. "Hesperolaburnum platyclarpum" . . . . . . 1·10 30

191 Ornamental Candle Lamps

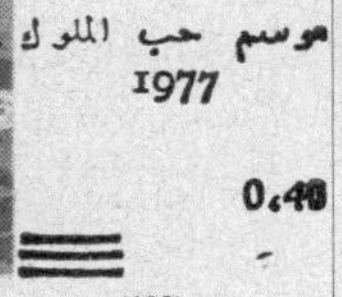

(192)

1977. Procession of the Candles, Sale.

481 **191** 40 f. multicoloured 45 10

1977. Cherry Festival. No. D394 surch with T **192**.

482 40 f. on 10 f. Cherries 75 30

193 Map and Emblem

1977. 5th Congress, Organization of Arab Towns.

483 **193** 50 f. multicoloured 15 10

194 A.P.U. Emblem

1977. 25th Anniv of Arab Postal Union.

484 **194** 1 d. multicoloured 60 20
486 40 f. Ait Haddou carpet . . . 40 20
487 1 d. Henbel rug, Sale 95 30

195 Zither

196 Mohammed Ali Jinnah

1977. Blind Week.

488 **195** 1 d. multicoloured 85 25

1977. Birth Centenary of Mohammed Ali Jinnah.

489 **196** 70 f. multicoloured 50 20

197 Marcher with Flag

1977. 2nd Anniv of "Green March".

490 **197** 1 d. multicoloured 60 20

198 Assembly Hall

1977. Opening of House of Representatives.

491 **198** 1 d. multicoloured 65 20

199 Silver Brooch

200 Bowl with Funnel

1977. Red Crescent.

493 **199** 1 d. multicoloured . . . . 1·25 60

1978. Moroccan Copperware. Multicoloured.

494 40 f. Type **200** 35 10
495 1 d. Bowl with cover 70 20

201 Development Emblem

202 Decorative Pot with Lid

1978. Sahara Development. Multicoloured.

496 40 f. Type **201** 35 10
497 1 d. Fishes in net and camels at oasis (horiz) 60 20

1978. Blind Week. Multicoloured.

498 1 d. Type **202** 90 30
499 1 d. Decorative jar 90 30

203 Map and Red Cross within Red Crescent

1978. 10th Conference of Arab Red Crescent and Red Cross Societies.

500 **203** 1 d. red and black 65 20

204 View of Fez

205 Dome of the Rock

1978. Rotary International Meeting, Fez.

501 **204** 1 d. multicoloured 65 20

1978. Palestine Welfare.

502 **205** 5 f. multicoloured 10 10
503 10 f. multicoloured 10 10

206 Flautist and Folk Dancers

208 Yacht

207 Sugar Field and Crushing Plant

1978. National Folklore Festival, Marrakesh.
504 **206** 1 d. multicoloured 55 20

1978. Sugar Industry.
505 **207** 40 f. multicoloured 15 10

1978. World Sailing Championships.
506 **208** 1 d. multicoloured 60 20

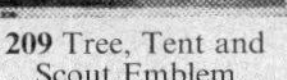

209 Tree, Tent and Scout Emblem — **211** Human Rights Emblem

210 Moulay Idriss

1978. Pan-Arab Scout Festival, Rabat.
507 **209** 40 f. multicoloured 15 10

1978. Moulay Idriss Great Festival.
508 **210** 40 f. multicoloured 15 10

1978. 30th Anniv of Declaration of Human Rights.
509 **211** 1 d. multicoloured 65 20

212 Houses in Agadir — **214** Decorated Pot

213 Player, Football and Cup

1979. Southern Moroccan Architecture (1st series). Multicoloured.
510 40 f. Type **212** 15 10
511 1 d. Old fort at Marrakesh 60 15
See also Nos. 536 and 562.

1979. Mohammed V Football Cup.
512 **213** 40 f. multicoloured 15 10

1979. Moroccan Carpets (6th series). As T **129**.
513 40 f. Marmoucha carpet 40 15

1979. Blind Week.
514 **214** 1 d. multicoloured 65 20

215 "Procession from a Mosque" — **216** Coffee Pot and Heater

1979. Paintings by Mohamed Ben Ali Rbati. Mult.
515 40 f. Type **215** 15 10
516 1 d. "Religious Ceremony in a Mosque" (horiz) 55 20

1979. Red Crescent. Brassware. Multicoloured.
517 40 f. Engraved Circular Boxes 25 15
518 1 d. Type **216** 85 30

217 Costumed Girls — **218** Curved Dagger in Jewelled Sheath

1979. National Folklore Festival, Marrakesh.
519 **217** 40 f. multicoloured 15 10

1979. Moroccan Coins. As T **174**, but smaller, $17\frac{1}{2} \times 22\frac{1}{2}$ mm.
520 40 f. multicoloured 10 10
520b 50 f. multicoloured 10 10

1979. Ancient Weapons.
521 **218** 1 d. black and yellow 75 20

219 King Hassan II — **221** King Hassan II

220 Festival Emblem

1979. King Hassan's 50th Birthday.
522 **219** 1 d. multicoloured 70 20

1979. 4th Arab Youth Festival, Rabat.
523 **220** 1 d. multicoloured 70 20

1979. "25th Anniv of Revolution of King and People".
524 **221** 1 d. multicoloured 30 20

222 World Map superimposed on Open Book

1979. 50th Anniv of International Bureau of Education.
525 **222** 1 d. brown and yellow 60 20

223 Pilgrims in Wuquf, Arafat

1979. Pilgrimage to Mecca.
526 **223** 1 d. multicoloured 70 20

استرجاع اقليم وادى الذهب
1979-8-14
(224)

1979. Recovery of Oued Eddahab Province. Design as No. 497, with face value amended (40 f.), optd with T **224**.
527 40 f. multicoloured 15 10
528 1 d. multicoloured 65 20

225 Centaurium — **226** Children around Globe

1979. Flowers. Multicoloured.
529 40 f. Type **225** 15 10
530 1 d. "Leucanthemum catanance" 55 20

1979. International Year of the Child.
531 **226** 40 f. multicoloured 60 25

227 European Otter — **228** Traffic Signs

1979. Wildlife. Multicoloured.
532 40 f. Type **227** 50 15
533 1 d. Moussier's redstart 1·50 55

1980. Road Safety. Multicoloured.
534 40 f. Type **228** 15 10
535 1 d. Children at crossing 30 20

229 Fortress

1980. South Moroccan Architecture (2nd series).
536 **229** 1 d. multicoloured 55 20

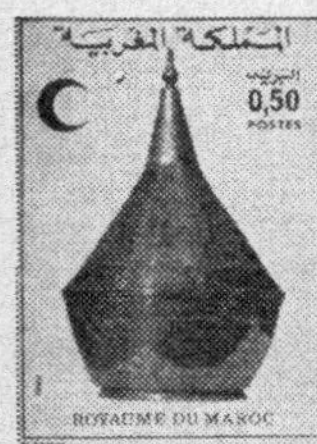

230 Copper Bowl with Lid — **231** Pot

1980. Red Crescent. Multicoloured.
537 50 f. Type **230** 50 15
538 70 f. Copper kettle and brazier 60 20

1980. Blind Week.
539 **231** 40 f. multicoloured 15 10

232 Mechanised Sorting Office, Rabat

1980. Stamp Day.
540 **232** 40 f. multicoloured 15 10

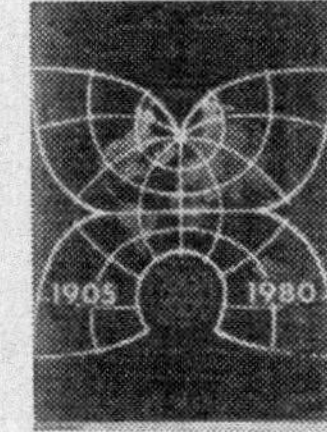
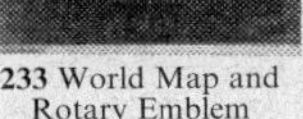

233 World Map and Rotary Emblem — **234** Leather Bag and Cloth

1980. 75th Anniv of Rotary International.
541 **233** 1 d. multicoloured 55 20

1980. 4th Textile and Leather Exhibition, Casablanca.
542 **234** 1 d. multicoloured 55 20

1980. Minerals (2nd series). As T **163**. Multicoloured.
543 40 f. Gypsum 85 10

235 Peregrine Falcon — **236** Diagram of Blood Circulation and Heart

1980. Hunting with Falcon.
544 **235** 40 f. multicoloured 1·50 45

1980. Campaign against Cardio-vascular Diseases.
545 **236** 1 d. multicoloured 65 20

237 Decade Emblem and Human Figures — **238** Harnessed Horse

1980. Decade for Women.
546 **237** 40 f. mauve and blue 15 10
547 – 1 d. multicoloured 55 20
DESIGN: 1 d. Decade and United Nations emblems.

1980. Ornamental Harnesses. Multicoloured.
548 40 f. Harnessed horse (different) 15 10
549 1 d. Type **238** 75 20

239 Satellite orbiting Earth and Dish Aerial — **240** Light Bulb and Fuel Can

1980. World Meteorological Day.
550 **239** 40 f. multicoloured 15 10

1980. Energy Conservation. Multicoloured.
551 40 f. Type **240** 15 10
552 1 d. Hand holding petrol pump 55 20

241 Conference Emblem

1980. World Tourism Conference, Manila.
553 **241** 40 f. multicoloured 15 10

242 Tree bridging Straits of Gibraltar

1980. European–African Liaison over the Straits of Gibraltar.
554 **242** 1 d. multicoloured 60 20

243 Flame and Marchers

1980. 5th Anniv of "The Green March".
555 **243** 1 d. multicoloured 60 20

244 Holy Kaaba, Mecca — **245** "Senecio antheuphorbium"

1980. 1400th Anniv of Hegira. Multicoloured.
556 40 f. Type **244** 15 10
557 1 d. Mosque, Mecca 60 20

1980. Flowers. Multicoloured.
558 40 f. Type **245** 60 10
559 1 d. "Periploca laevigata" 1·25 50

246 Painting by Aherdan

247 Nejjarine Fountain, Fez

1980. Paintings.
560 – 40 f. bistre and brown 15 10
561 **246** 1 d. multicoloured 60 20
DESIGN: 40 f. Composition of bird and feathers.

1981. Moroccan Architecture (3rd series).
562 **247** 40 f. multicoloured 10 10

1981. Minerals (3rd series). Vert designs as T **163**. Multicoloured.
563 40 f. Onyx 95 35
564 1 d. Malachite-azurite 1·60 75

248 King Hassan II

249 King Hassan II

1981. 25th Anniv of Independence. Mult.
565 60 f. Type **248** 35 10
566 60 f. Map, flags, broken chains and "25" 35 10
567 60 f. King V. Mohammed 35 10

1981. 20th Anniv of King Hassan's Coronation.
568 **249** 1 d. 30 multicoloured 50 25

250 "Source" (Jillali Gharbaoul)

1981. Moroccan Painting.
569 **250** 1 d. 30 multicoloured 75 25

251 "Anagalis monelli"

252 King Hassan as Major General

1981. Flowers. Multicoloured.
570 40 f. Type **251** 20 10
571 70 f. "Bubonium intricatum" 40 15

1981. 25th Anniv of Moroccan Armed Forces.
572 **252** 60 f. lilac, gold and green 35 10
573 – 60 f. multicoloured 35 10
574 – 60 f. lilac, gold and green 35 10
DESIGNS: No. 573, Army badge; No. 574, King Mohammed V (founder).

253 Caduceus (Telecommunications and Health)

254 Plate with Pattern

1981. World Telecommunications Day.
575 **253** 1 d. 30 multicoloured 70 20

1981. Blind Week. Multicoloured.
576 50 f. Type **254** 10 10
577 1 d. 30 Plate with ship pattern 60 20

255 Musicians and Dancers

256 "Seboula" Dagger

1981. 22nd National Folklore Festival, Marrakesh.
578 **255** 1 d. 30 multicoloured 85 25

1981. Ancient Weapons.
579 **256** 1 d. 30 multicoloured 75 20

257 Pestle and Mortar

258 Hands holding I.Y.D.P. Emblem

1981. Red Crescent. Moroccan Copperware. Mult.
580 60 f. Type **257** 25 15
581 1 d. 30 Tripod brazier 80 25

1981. International Year of Disabled People.
582 **258** 60 f. multicoloured 35 10

259 "Iphiclides feisthamelii Lotteri"

260 King Hassan and Marchers

1981. Butterflies (1st series). Multicoloured.
583 60 f. Type **259** 50 25
584 1 d. 30 "Zerynthina rumina africana" 1·25 60
See also Nos. 609/10.

1981. 6th Anniv of "Green March".
585 **260** 1 d. 30 multicoloured 70 20

261 Town Buildings and Congress Emblem

1981. 10th International Twinned Towns Congress, Casablanca.
586 **261** 1 d. 30 multicoloured 20 20

262 Dome of the Rock

264 Terminal Building and Runway

1981. Palestinian Solidarity Day.
587 **262** 60 f. multicoloured 35 10

1981. 12th Arab Summit Conference, Fez. Nos. 502/3 surch **1981 0,40**.
588 **205** 40 f. on 5 f. multicoloured 4·00 4·00
588a 40 f. on 10 f. multicoloured 2·75 2·75

1981. 1st Anniv of Mohammed V Airport.
589 **264** 1 d. 30 multicoloured 70 20

265 Al Massira Dam

266 King Hassan II

1981. Al Massira Dam.
590 **265** 60 f. multicoloured 35 10

1981.
591 **266** 5 f. red, blue and gold 10 10
592 10 f. red, yellow and gold 10 10
593 15 f. red, green and gold 10 10
594 20 f. red, pink and gold 10 10
595 25 f. red, lilac and gold 10 10
596 30 f. blue, lt bl & gold 10 10
597 35 f. blue, yellow & gold 10 10
598 40 f. blue, green and gold 10 10
599 50 f. blue, pink and gold 10 10
600 60 f. blue, lilac and gold 10 10
601 65 f. blue, lilac and gold 10 10
602 70 f. violet, yellow and gold 10 10
603 75 f. violet, green and gold 15 15
604 80 f. violet, pink and gold 15 15
605 90 f. violet, lilac and gold 15 15
605a 1 d. 25 red, mauve & gold 20 15
605b 4 d. brown, yellow and gold 1·10 55
See also Nos. 624/9, 718/22, 759/61, 866, 895/6 and 930.

267 Horse Jumping

268 Ait Quaquzguit

1981. Equestrian Sports.
606 **267** 1 d. 30 multicoloured 1·25 25

1982. Carpets (1st series). Multicoloured.
607 50 f. Type **268** 10 10
608 1 d. 30 Ouled Besseba 60 30
See also Nos. 653/4.

1982. Butterflies and Moths (2nd series). As T **259**. Multicoloured.
609 60 f. "Celerio oken lineata" 70 25
610 1 d. 30 "Mesoacidalia aglaja lyauteyi" 1·50 55

269 Tree and Emblem

270 Jug

1982. World Forestry Day.
611 **269** 40 f. multicoloured 10 10

1982. Blind Week.
612 **270** 1 d. multicoloured 50 25

271 Dancers

272 Candlestick

1982. Popular Art.
613 **271** 1 d. 40 multicoloured 60 35

1982. Red Crescent.
614 **272** 1 d. 40 multicoloured 60 35

273 Painting by M. Mezian

274 Buildings and People on Graph

1982. Moroccan Painting.
615 **273** 1 d. 40 multicoloured 60 35

1982. Population and Housing Census.
616 **274** 60 f. multicoloured 15 15

275 Dr. Koch, Lungs and Apparatus

276 I.T.U. Emblem

1982. Centenary of Discovery of Tubercle Bacillus.
617 **275** 1 d. 40 multicoloured 75 35

1982. I.T.U. Delegates' Conference, Nairobi.
618 **276** 1 d. 40 multicoloured 60 35

277 Wheat, Globe, Sea and F.A.O. Emblem

278 Class XDd Diesel Locomotive (1956) and Route Map

1982. World Food Day.
619 **277** 60 f. multicoloured 15 15

1982. Unity Railway.
620 **278** 1 d. 40 multicoloured 1·25 70

279 A.P.U. Emblem

1982. 30th Anniv of Arab Postal Union.
621 **279** 1 d. 40 multicoloured 40 15

280 Dome of the Rock and Map of Palestine

281 Red Coral

1982. Palestinian Solidarity.
622 **280** 1 d. 40 multicoloured 40 15

1982. Red Coral of Al Hoceima.
623 **281** 1 d. 40 multicoloured 70 25

1983. As T **266** but inscribed "1982".
624 1 d. maroon, blue and gold 25 10
625 1 d. 40 brown, lt brn and gold 35 10
626 2 d. maroon, green and gold 45 15
627 3 d. brown, yellow and gold 65 25
628 5 d. brown, green and gold 1·40 50
629 10 d. brown, orange and gold 2·75 90

282 Moroccan Stamps

283 King Hassan II

1983. Stamp Day.
630 **282** 1 d. 40 multicoloured 60 20

1983.
631 **283** 1 d. 40 multicoloured 25 20
632 2 d. multicoloured 35 30
633 3 d. multicoloured 80 50
634 5 d. multicoloured 1·40 45
635 10 d. multicoloured 2·75 1·10

284 Decorated Pot 286 Ornamental Stand

285 Musicians

1983. Blind Week.
636 **284** 1 d. 40 multicoloured . . . 60 20

1983. Popular Arts.
637 **285** 1 d. 40 multicoloured . . . 75 20

1983. Red Crescent.
638 **286** 1 d. 40 multicoloured . . . 75 20

287 Commission Emblem

1983. 25th Anniv of Economic Commission for Africa.
639 **287** 1 d. 40 multicoloured . . . 55 20

288 "Tecoma sp."

290 Games Emblem and Stylized Sports

289 King Hassan II, Map and Sultan of Morocco

1983. Flowers. Multicoloured.
640 60 c. Type **288** 10 10
641 1 d. 40 "Strelitzia sp." 75 20

1983. 30th Anniv of Revolution.
642 **289** 80 c. multicoloured 20 20

1983. 9th Mediterranean Games, Casablanca.
644 **290** 80 c. blue, silver and gold . 20 20
645 – 1 d. multicoloured 20 20
646 – 2 d. multicoloured 60 30
DESIGNS—VERT: 1 d. Games emblem. HORIZ: 2 d. Stylized runner.

291 Ploughing

1983. Touiza.
648 **291** 80 c. multicoloured 20 20

292 Symbol of "Green March" 293 Palestinian formed from Map and Globe

1983. 8th Anniv of "Green March".
649 **292** 80 f. multicoloured 20 15

1983. Palestinian Welfare.
650 **293** 80 f. multicoloured 20 15

294 Ouzoud Waterfall 295 Children's Emblem

1983. Ouzoud Waterfall.
651 **294** 80 f. multicoloured 20 15

1983. Children's Day. Multicoloured.
652 **295** 2 d. multicoloured 70 30

1983. Carpets (2nd series). As T **268**. Mult.
653 60 f. Zemmouri 10 10
654 1 d. 40 Zemmouri (different) . . 55 20

296 Transport and W.C.Y. Emblem

1983. World Communications Year.
655 **296** 2 d. multicoloured . . . . 1·75 70

297 Views of Jerusalem and Fez

1984. Twinned Towns.
656 **297** 2 d. multicoloured 95 20

298 Fennec Fox

1984. Animals. Multicoloured.
657 80 f. Type **298** 30 25
658 2 d. Lesser Egyptian jerboa . . 60 35

299 Map of League Members and Emblem

المهرجان
25
(300)

1984. 39th Anniv of League of Arab States.
659 **299** 2 d. multicoloured 70 20

1984. 25th National Folklore Festival, Marrakesh. No. 578 optd with T **300**.
660 **255** 1 d. 30 multicoloured . . . 75 15

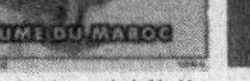

301 "Metha viridis" 302 Decorated Bowl

1984. Flowers. Multicoloured.
661 80 f. Type **301** 20 15
662 2 d. Aloe 75 30

1984. Blind Week.
663 **302** 80 f. multicoloured 20 15

303 Lidded Container

304 Sports Pictograms

1984. Red Crescent.
664 **303** 2 d. multicoloured 75 30

1984. Olympic Games, Los Angeles.
665 **304** 2 d. multicoloured 75 30

305 Dove carrying Children

306 U.P.U. Emblem and Ribbons

1984. International Child Victims' Day.
666 **305** 2 d. multicoloured 70 30

1984. Universal Postal Union Day.
667 **306** 2 d. multicoloured 40 30

307 Hands holding Ears of Wheat

308 Stylized Bird, Airplane and Emblem

1984. World Food Day.
668 **307** 80 f. multicoloured 20 15

1984. 40th Anniv of I.C.A.O.
669 **308** 2 d. multicoloured 40 30

309 Inscribed Scroll

1984. 9th Anniv of "Green March".
670 **309** 80 f. multicoloured 20 15

311 Flag and Dome of the Rock 312 Emblem and People

1984. Palestinian Welfare.
672 **311** 2 d. multicoloured 60 25

1984. 36th Anniv of Human Rights Declaration.
673 **312** 2 d. multicoloured 60 25

313 Aidi

314 Weighing Baby

1984. Dogs. Multicoloured.
674 80 f. Type **313** 50 10
675 2 d. Sloughi . . . . 1·10 25

1985. Infant Survival Campaign.
676 **314** 80 f. multicoloured 15 10

315 Children playing in Garden

316 Sherifian Mail Postal Cancellation, 1892

1985. 1st Moroccan S.O.S. Children's Village.
677 **315** 2 d. multicoloured 60 25

1985. Stamp Day.
678 **316** 2 d. grey, pink and black . 60 25
See also Nos. 698/9, 715/16, 757/8, 778/9, 796/7, 818/19, 841/2, 877/8, 910/11 and 924/5.

317 Emblem, Birds, Landscape and Fish

318 Musicians

1985. World Environment Day.
680 **317** 80 f. multicoloured 20 10

1985. National Folklore Festival, Marrakesh.
681 **318** 2 d. multicoloured 75 25

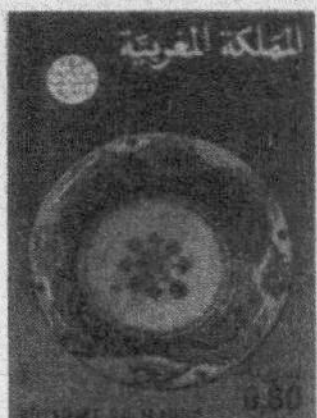

319 Decorated Plate

320 Bougainvillea

1985. Blind Week.
682 **319** 80 f. multicoloured 15 10

1985. Flowers. Multicoloured.
683 80 f. Type **320** 60 10
684 2 d. "Hibiscus rosasinensis" . . 1·25 50

321 Woman in Headdress

323 Map and Emblem

322 Musicians and Dancers

1985. Red Crescent.
685 **321** 2 d. multicoloured . . . . 1·25 50

1985. National Folklore Festival, Marrakesh.
686 **322** 2 d. multicoloured 95 25

1985. 6th Pan-Arab Games.
687 **323** 2 d. multicoloured 95 25

324 Emblem on Globe **325** Emblem

1985. 40th Anniv of U.N.O.
688 **324** 2 d. multicoloured 60 25

1986. International Youth Year.
689 **325** 2 d. multicoloured 60 25

326 Medal **327** Clasped Hands around Flag

1985. 10th Anniv of "Green March".
690 **326** 2 d. multicoloured 60 25

1985. Palestinian Welfare.
691 **327** 2 d. multicoloured 60 25

328 "Euphydryas desfontainii" **329** Arms

1985. Butterflies (1st series). Multicoloured.
692 80 f. Type **328** 45 30
693 2 d. "Colotis evagore" . . . . 1·40 90
See also Nos. 713/14.

1986. 25th Anniv of King Hassan's Coronation. Multicoloured.
694 80 f. Type **329** 15 10
695 2 d. King Hassan II (horiz) . . 60 25

330 Emblem **331** Vase

1986. 26th International Military Medicine Congress.
697 **330** 2 d. multicoloured 60 25

1986. Stamp Day. As T **316**.
698 80 f. orange and black 15 10
699 2 d. green and black 60 25
DESIGNS: 80 f. Sherifian postal seal of Maghzen-Safi; 2 d. Sherifian postal seal of Maghzen-Safi (different).

1986. Blind Week.
700 **331** 1 d. multicoloured 15 10

332 Footballer and Emblem

1986. World Cup Football Championship, Mexico. Multicoloured.
701 1 d. Type **332** 50 10
702 2 d. Cup, pictogram of footballer and emblem . . . . . . 1·00 25

333 Copper Coffee Pot **334** "Warionia saharae"

1986. Red Crescent.
703 **333** 2 d. multicoloured . . . . 1·25 50

1986. Flowers. Multicoloured.
704 1 d. Type **334** 60 10
705 2 d. "Mandragora autumnalis" 1·25 50

335 Emblem **336** Dove and Olive Branch

1986. 18th Parachute Championships.
706 **335** 2 d. multicoloured 90 25

1986. International Peace Year.
707 **336** 2 d. multicoloured 60 25

337 Horsemen **338** Book

1986. Horse Week.
708 **337** 1 d. light brown, pink and brown 60 10

1986. 11th Anniv of "Green March".
709 **338** 1 d. multicoloured 15 10

339 Stylized People and Wheat **340** Marrakesh

1986. Fight against Hunger.
710 **339** 2 d. multicoloured 60 25

1986. Aga Khan Architecture Prize.
711 **340** 2 d. multicoloured 60 25

341 Hands holding Wheat

الملتقى العالمي الاول
لخطباء الجمعة

(342)

1986. "1,000,000 Hectares of Grain".
712 **341** 1 d. multicoloured 15 10

1986. Butterflies (2nd series). As T **328**. Multicoloured.
713 1 d. "Elphinstonia charlonia" . 65 35
714 2 d. "Anthocharis belia" . . . 90 85

1987. Stamp Day. As T **316**.
715 1 d. blue and black 15 10
716 2 d. red and black 60 25
DESIGNS: 1 d. Circular postal cancellation of Tetouan; 2 d. Octagonal postal cancellation of Tetouan.

1987. Air. 1st World Reunion of Friday Preachers. Optd with T **342**.
717 **283** 2 d. multicoloured 90 60

1987. Size 25 × 32 mm. Inscribed "1986".
718 **266** 1 d. 60 red, brown and gold 25 20
719 2 d. 50 red, grey and gold . 60 25
720 6 d. 50 red, brown and gold 1·50 35
721 7 d. red, brown and gold . 1·75 45
722 8 d. 50 red, lilac and gold . 2·00 50

343 Sidi Muhammad ben Yusuf addressing Crowd

1987. 40th Anniv of Tangier Conference. Each blue, silver and black.
723 1 d. Type **343** 15 10
724 1 d. King Hassan II making speech 15 10

344 Copper Lamp **345** Woman with Baby and Packet of Salt being emptied into Beaker

1987. Red Crescent.
726 **344** 2 d. multicoloured 60 25

1987. U.N.I.C.E.F. Child Survival Campaign.
727 **345** 1 d. multicoloured 15 10

346 Decorated Pottery Jug **347** "Zygophyllum fontanesii"

1987. Blind Week.
728 **346** 1 d. multicoloured 15 10

1987. Flowers. Multicoloured.
729 1 d. Type **347** 15 10
730 2 d. "Otanthus maritimus" . . 60 25

348 Arabesque from Door, Dar Batha Palace, Fez **349** Map and King Hassan giving Blood

1987. Bicentenary of Diplomatic Relations with United States of America.
731 **348** 1 d. blue, red & black . . . 15 10

1987. Blood Transfusion Service.
732 **349** 2 d. multicoloured 95 25

350 Woman from Melhfa **351** Emblem and Irrigated Field

1987. Sahara Costumes. Multicoloured.
733 1 d. Type **350** 15 10
734 2 d. Man from Derraa 60 25

1987. 13th International Irrigation and Drainage Congress.
735 **351** 1 d. multicoloured 15 10

352 Baby on Hand and Syringe **353** Azurite

1987. United Nations Children's Fund Child Survival Campaign.
736 **352** 1 d. multicoloured 15 10

1987. Mineral Industries Congress, Marrakesh. Multicoloured.
737 1 d. Type **353** 50 10
738 2 d. Wulfenite . . . . 1·00 50

354 "12" on Scroll

1987. 12th Anniv of "Green March".
739 **354** 1 d. multicoloured 15 10

355 Activities **356** Desert Sparrow

1987. Armed Forces Social Services Month.
740 **355** 1 d. multicoloured 15 10

1987. Birds. Multicoloured.
741 1 d. Type **356** 90 30
742 2 d. Barbary partridge . . . . 1·60 70

357 1912 25 m. Stamp and Postmark

1987. 75th Anniv of Moroccan Stamps.
743 **357** 3 d. mauve, black and green 80 40

358 "Cetiosaurus mogrebiensis"

1988. Dinosaur of Tilougguite.
744 **358** 2 d. multicoloured . . . . 1·40 50

359 King Mohammed V **360** Map and Player in Arabesque Frame

1988. International Conference on King Mohammed V, Rabat.
745 **359** 2 d. multicoloured 60 25

1988. 16th African Nations Cup Football Competition.
746 **360** 3 d. multicoloured 75 40

361 Boy with Horse

1988. Horse Week.
747 **361** 3 d. multicoloured . . . . 1·50 60

362 Pottery Flask **363** Anniversary Emblem

1988. Blind Week.
748 **362** 3 d. multicoloured 75 35

1988. 125th Anniv of Red Cross.
749 **363** 3 d. black, red and pink . . 75 35

364 "Citrullus colocynthis" **365** Breastfeeding Baby

1988. Flowers. Multicoloured.
750 3 d. 60 Type **364** 90 45
751 3 d. 60 "Calotropis procera" . . 90 45

1988. U.N.I.C.E.F. Child Survival Campaign.
752 **365** 3 d. multicoloured 95 35

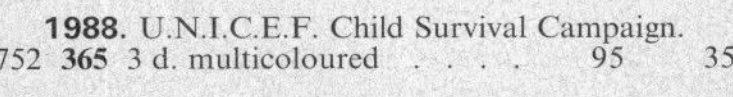

366 Olympic Medals and Rings **367** Greater Bustard

1988. Olympic Games, Seoul.
753 **366** 2 d. multicoloured 30 25

1988. Birds. Multicoloured.
754 3 d. 60 Type **367** . . . . . . 1·60 55
755 3 d. 60 Greater flamingo . . . 1·60 55

اتحاد المغرب العربي

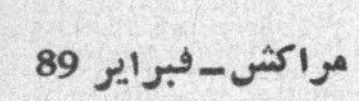

368 "13" on Scroll (370)

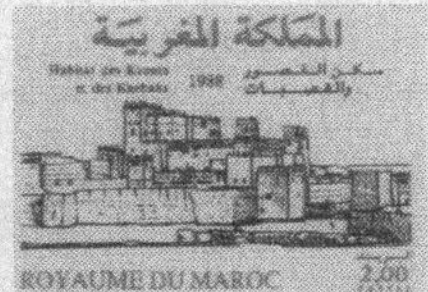

369 Housing of the Ksours and Csbaha

1988. 13th Anniv of "Green March".
756 **368** 2 d. multicoloured 60 25

1988. Stamp Day. As T **316**.
757 3 d. brown and black 95 35
758 3 d. violet and black 95 35
DESIGNS: No. 757, Octagonal postal cancellation of Maghzen el Jadida; 758, Circular postal cancellation of Maghzen el Jadida.

1988. Inscribed "1988".
759 **266** 1 d. 20 blue, lilac & gold . 15 10
760 3 d. 60 red and gold . . . 75 20
761 5 d. 20 brown, bis & gold . 1·25 30

1989. Architecture.
762 **369** 2 d. multicoloured 60 25

1989. Union of Arab Maghreb. No. 631 optd with T **370**.
763 **283** 1 d. 40 multicoloured . . . 50 15

371 King and Bishop with Chess Symbols

1989. 25th Anniv of Royal Moroccan Chess Federation.
764 **371** 2 d. multicoloured 85 25

372 Copper Vase **373** Ceramic Vase

1989. Red Crescent.
765 **372** 2 d. multicoloured 60 25

1989. Blind Week.
766 **373** 2 d. multicoloured 60 25

374 King Hassan **375** "Cerinthe major"

1989. 60th Birthday of King Hassan II. Mult.
767 2 d. Type **374** 75 25
768 2 d. King Hassan in robes . . . 75 25

1989. Flowers. Multicoloured.
770 2 d. Type **375** 75 25
771 2 d. "Narcissus papyraceus" . . 75 25

376 Telephone Handset linking Landmarks

1989. World Telecommunications Day.
772 **376** 2 d. multicoloured 60 25

377 Gender Symbols forming Globe, Woman and Eggs

1989. 1st World Fertility and Sterility Congress.
773 **377** 2 d. multicoloured 75 25

378 Desert Wheatear

1989. Birds. Multicoloured.
774 2 d. Type **378** 90 50
775 3 d. Shore lark . . . . 2·10 75

379 House of Representatives

1989. Centenary of Interparliamentary Union.
776 **379** 2 d. multicoloured 60 25

380 Scroll

1989. 14th Anniv of "Green March".
777 **380** 3 d. multicoloured 70 35

1990. Stamp Day. As T **316**.
778 2 d. orange and black 60 20
779 3 d. green and black 70 35
DESIGNS: 2 d. Round postal cancellation of Casablanca; 3 d. Octagonal postal cancellation of Casablanca.

381 Flags forming Map

1990. 1st Anniv of Union of Arab Maghreb.
780 **381** 2 d. multicoloured 65 20

382 Oil Press

1990. 3rd World Olive Year. Multicoloured.
782 2 d. Type **382** 60 15
783 3 d. King Hassan and olives . . 85 25

383 Decorated Pot

1990. Blind Week.
784 **383** 2 d. multicoloured 55 15

384 Silver Teapot

1990. Red Crescent.
785 **384** 2 d. multicoloured 60 15

385 Arabic Script and Open Book **386** Turtle Dove

1990. International Literacy Year.
786 **385** 3 d. green, yellow & blk . . 80 25

1990. Birds. Multicoloured.
787 2 d. Type **386** 85 40
788 3 d. Hoopoe (horiz) . . . . . 1·40 70

387 "15" on Scroll **388** "35", Sun's Rays and Flag

1990. 15th Anniv of "Green March".
789 **387** 3 d. multicoloured 80 25

1990. 35th Anniv of Independence.
790 **388** 3 d. multicoloured 80 25

389 Dam

1990.
791 **389** 3 d. multicoloured 80 25

390 Emblem **392** Projects and Emblem

391 Morse Code Apparatus

1990. 10th Anniv of Royal Academy of Morocco.
792 **390** 3 d. multicoloured 85 25

1990. 20th Anniv of National Postal Museum. Multicoloured.
793 2 d. Type **391** 60 15
794 3 d. Horse-drawn mail wagon, 1913 . . . . 85 25

1991. Stamp Day. As T **316**.
796 2 d. red and black 60 15
797 3 d. blue and black 85 25
DESIGNS: 2 d. Round postal cancellation of Rabat; 3 d. Octagonal postal cancellation of Rabat.

1991. 40th Anniv of United Nations Development Programme.
798 **392** 3 d. turquoise, yell & blk . . 85 25

393 King Hassan **394** Mining

1991. 30th Anniv of Enthronement of King Hassan II. Multicoloured.
799 3 d. Type **393** 85 25
800 3 d. King Hassan in robes . . . 85 25

1991. 70th Anniv of Mineral Exploitation by Sherifian Phosphates Office.
802 **394** 3 d. multicoloured 85 25

395 Kettle on Stand

396 Lantern

1991. Blind Week.
803 **395** 3 d. multicoloured 85 25

1991. Red Crescent.
804 **396** 3 d. multicoloured 85 25

397 "Cynara humilis"

398 Man

1991. Flowers. Multicoloured.
805 3 d. Type **397** 85 25
806 3 d. "Pyrus mamorensis" . . . 85 25

1991. Ouarzazate Costumes. Multicoloured.
807 3 d. Type **398** 85 20
808 3 d. Woman 85 20

1991. Inscribed "1991".
809 **266** 1 d. 35 red, green & gold . 20 10

399 Road

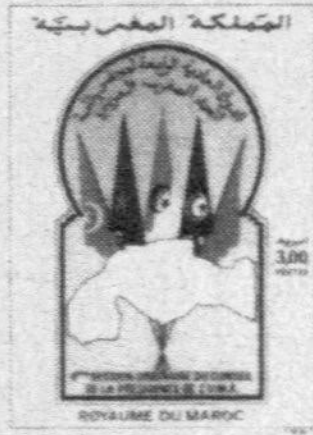
400 Members' Flags and Map

1991. 19th World Roads Congress, Marrakesh.
810 **399** 3 d. multicoloured 85 20

1991. 4th Ordinary Session of Arab Maghreb Union Presidential Council, Casablanca.
811 **400** 3 d. multicoloured 85 20

401 "16" on Scroll

402 White Stork

1991. 16th Anniv of "Green March".
812 **401** 3 d. multicoloured 85 20

1991. Birds. Multicoloured.
813 3 d. Type **402** 45 20
814 3 d. European bee eater 45 20

403 Figures and Blood Splash

405 Zebra and Map of Africa

404 Emblem

1991. World AIDS Day.
815 **403** 3 d. multicoloured 85 20

1991. 20th Anniv of Islamic Conference Organization.
816 **404** 3 d. multicoloured 85 20

1991. African Tourism Year.
817 **405** 3 d. multicoloured 85 20

1992. Stamp Day. As T **316**.
818 3 d. green and black 85 20
819 3 d. violet and black 85 20
DESIGNS: No. 818, Circular postal cancellation of Essaouira; No. 819, Octagonal postal cancellation of Essaouira.

406 Satellites around Earth

407 Bottle

1992. International Space Year.
820 **406** 3 d. multicoloured 85 20

1992. Blind Week.
821 **407** 3 d. multicoloured 85 20

408 Brass Jug

409 Quartz

1992. Red Crescent.
822 **408** 3 d. multicoloured 85 50

1992. Minerals. Multicoloured.
823 1 d. 35 Type **409** 45 10
824 3 d. 40 Calcite . . . . 1·10 60

410 Woman

411 "Campanula afra"

1992. Tata Costumes. Multicoloured.
825 1 d. 35 Type **410** 20 10
826 3 d. 40 Man . . . . 1·10 60

1992. Flowers. Multicoloured.
827 1 d. 35 Type **411** 20 10
828 3 d. 40 "Thymus broussonetii" 1·10 60

412 Olympic Rings and Torch

414 La Koutoubia, La Giralda (cathedral bell-tower) and Exhibition Emblem

413 Map of Africa and Methods of Transport and Communication

1992. Olympic Games, Barcelona.
829 **412** 3 d. 40 multicoloured . . . 1·10 20

1992. Decade of Transport and Communications in Africa.
830 **413** 3 d. 40 multicoloured . . . 3·00 1·00

1992. "Expo '92" World's Fair, Seville.
831 **414** 3 d. 40 multicoloured . . . 1·10 50

415 Columbus's Fleet and Route Map

1992. 500th Anniv of Discovery of America by Columbus.
832 **415** 3 d. 40 multicoloured . . . 1·25 50

416 Pin-tailed Sandgrouse

1992. Birds. Multicoloured.
833 3 d. Type **416** 40 20
834 3 d. Griffon vulture ("Gyps fulvus") (vert) 40 20

417 "17" on Scroll

1992. 17th Anniv of "Green March".
835 **417** 3 d. 40 multicoloured . . . 1·10 20

418 Postal Messenger, Route Map and Cancellations

1992. Centenary of Sherifian Post. Multicoloured.
836 1 d. 35 Type **418** 20 10
837 3 d. 40 Postal cancellation, "100" on scroll and Sultan Mulay al-Hassan . . . . 1·10 50

419 Conference Emblem

1992. International Nutrition Conference, Rome.
839 **419** 3 d. 40 multicoloured . . . 1·10 50

420 Douglas DC-9 Airliners on Runway

422 Satellite orbiting Earth

421 Dishes

1992. Al Massira Airport, Agadir.
840 **420** 3 d. 40 multicoloured . . . 1·10 20

1993. Stamp Day. As T **316**.
841 1 d. 70 green and black 25 10
842 3 d. 80 orange and black . . . 1·10 50
DESIGNS: 1 d. 70, Round postal cancellation of Tangier; 3 d. 80, Octagonal postal cancellation of Tangier.

1993. Blind Week.
843 **421** 4 d. 40 multicoloured . . . 1·25 25

1993. World Meteorological Day.
844 **422** 4 d. 40 multicoloured . . . 1·25 25

423 Kettle on Stand

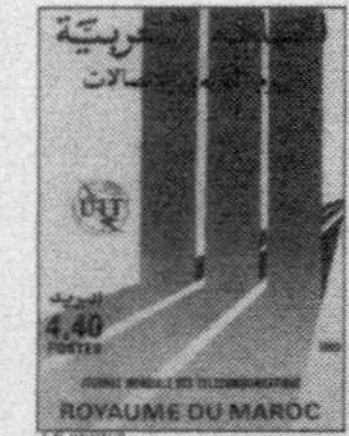

424 Emblem

1993. Red Crescent.
845 **423** 4 d. 40 multicoloured . . . 1·25 25

1993. World Telecommunications Day.
846 **424** 4 d. 40 multicoloured . . . 60 25

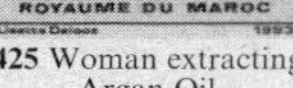
425 Woman extracting Argan Oil

426 Prince Sidi Mohammed

1993. Argan Oil. Multicoloured.
847 1 d. 70 Type **425** 25 10
848 4 d. 80 Branch and fruit of argan tree 70 30

1993. 30th Birthday of Prince Sidi Mohammed.
849 **426** 4 d. 80 multicoloured . . . 70 30

427 King Hassan and Mosque

428 Canopy, Sceptres, Flag and "40" on Sun

1993. Inauguration of King Hassan II Mosque.
850 **427** 4 d. 80 multicoloured . . . 70 30

1993. 40th Anniv of Revolution.
851 **428** 4 d. 80 multicoloured . . . 70 30

429 Post Box and Globe

430 Emblem

1993. World Post Day.
852 **429** 4 d. 80 multicoloured . . . 70 30

1993. Islamic Summer University.
853 **430** 4 d. 80 multicoloured . . . 70 30

431 "18" on Scroll

433 Flags, Scroll and "50"

432 Marbled Teal

1993. 18th Anniv of "Green March".
854 **431** 4 d. 80 multicoloured . . . 70 30

1993. Waterfowl. Multicoloured.
855 1 d. 70 Type **432** 25 10
856 4 d. 80 Red-knobbed coot . . . 70 30

1994. 50th Anniv of Istaqlal (Independence) Party.
857 **433** 4 d. 80 multicoloured . . . 70 30

434 House

435 Decorated Vase

1994. Signing of Uruguay Round Final Act of General Agreement on Tariffs and Trade, Marrakesh.
858 **434** 1 d. 70 multicoloured . . . 25 10
859 – 4 d. 80 multicoloured . . . 70 30
DESIGN: 4 d. 80, Mosque.

1994. Blind Week.
861 **435** 4 d. 80 multicoloured . . . 70 30

436 Copper Vessel

437 Couple

1994. Red Crescent.
862 **436** 4 d. 80 multicoloured . . . 70 30

1994. National Congress on Children's Rights. Children's Drawings. Multicoloured.
863 1 d. 70 Type **437** 25 10
864 4 d. 80 Couple under sun . . . 70 30

438 Ball, Moroccan and U.S.A. Flags, Pictogram and Trophy

1994. World Cup Football Championship, U.S.A.
865 **438** 4 d. 80 multicoloured . . . 70 30

1994. Size 25 × 32 mm. Inscr "1994".
866 **266** 1 d. 70 red, blue and gold . 25 10

439 King Hassan II and Arms

1994. 65th Birthday of King Hassan II. Multicoloured.
867 1 d. 70 Type **439** 25 10
868 4 d. 80 King Hassan II (vert) . 70 30

440 "100" and Rings

441 Saint-Exupery, Route Map and Biplane

1994. Centenary of International Olympic Committee.
869 **440** 4 d. 80 multicoloured . . . 70 30

1994. 50th Death Anniv of Antoine de Saint-Exupery (writer and pilot).
870 **441** 4 d. 80 multicoloured . . . 70 30

442 "Chamaeleon gummifer"

1994. Flowers. Multicoloured.
871 1 d. 70 Type **442** 25 10
872 4 d. 80 "Pancratium maritimum" (vert) 70 30

443 Curlew

1994. Birds. Multicoloured.
873 1 d. 70 Type **443** 25 10
874 4 d. 80 Audouin's gull 70 30

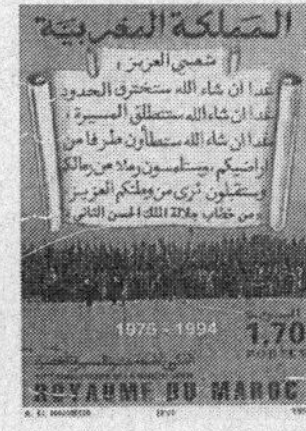
444 Scroll and March

445 Decorated Vase

1994. 19th Anniv of "Green March". Multicoloured.
875 1 d. 70 Type **444** 25 10
876 4 d. 80 Marchers and Moroccan coastline 70 30

1994. Stamp Day. As T **316**.
877 1 d. 70 blue and black 25 10
878 4 d. 80 red and black 70 30
DESIGNS: 1 d. 70, Round postal cancellation of Marrakesh; 4 d. 80, Octagonal postal cancellation of Marrakesh.

1995. Blind Week.
879 **445** 4 d. 80 multicoloured . . . 70 30

446 Anniversary Emblem

447 Copper Vessel

1995. 50th Anniv of League of Arab States.
880 **446** 4 d. 80 multicoloured . . . 70 30

1995. Red Crescent.
881 **447** 4 d. 80 multicoloured . . . 70 30

448 "Malva hispanica"

449 Common Roller

1995. Flowers. Multicoloured.
882 2 d. Type **448** 30 10
883 4 d. 80 "Phlomis crinita" . . . 70 30

1995. Birds. Multicoloured.
884 1 d. 70 Type **449** 25 10
885 4 d. 80 Goldfinch 70 30

450 Anniversary Emblem, Building and Map

1995. 50th Anniv of F.A.O.
886 **450** 4 d. 80 multicoloured . . . 70 30

451 "50" and Flags

1995. 50th Anniv of U.N.O. Multicoloured.
887 1 d. 70 Type **451** 25 10
888 4 d. 80 U.N. emblem, doves and map 70 30

452 "20" on Scroll

453 "40", National Flag and Crown

1995. 20th Anniv of "Green March". Multicoloured.
889 1 d. 70 Type **452** 25 10
890 4 d. 80 National flag, book and medal 70 30

1995. 40th Anniv of Independence.
891 **453** 4 d. 80 multicoloured . . . 70 30

1995. Stamp Day. As T **316**.
893 1 d. 70 bistre and black 25 10
894 4 d. 80 lilac and black 70 30
DESIGNS: 1 d. 70, Round postal cancellation of Meknes; 4 d. 80, Octagonal cancellation of Meknes.

1996. Size 25 × 32 mm. Dated "1996".
895 **266** 5 d. 50 brown, red and gold 80 35
896 20 d. brown, blue and gold . . . . 2·75 1·10

454 National Arms

455 Decorated Vase

1996. 35th Anniv of Enthronement of King Hassan II. Multicoloured.
897 2 d. Type **454** 30 15
898 5 d. 50 King Hassan II 80 35

1996.
900 **455** 5 d. 50 multicoloured . . . 80 35

456 Leather Flask

457 "Cleonia lusitanica"

1996.
901 **456** 5 d. 50 multicoloured . . . 80 35

1996. Flowers. Multicoloured.
902 2 d. Type **457** 30 15
903 5 d. 50 "Tulipa sylvestris" . . . 80 35

458 King Hassan II wearing Military Uniform

459 Emblem and Runners

1996. 40th Anniv of Royal Armed Forces. Multicoloured.
904 2 d. Type **458** 30 15
905 5 d. 50 King Hassan II and globe 80 35

1996. Centenary of Modern Olympic Games. Olympic Games, Atlanta, U.S.A.
906 **459** 5 d. 50 multicoloured . . . 70 30

460 Osprey

461 "21" on Scroll

1996. Birds. Multicoloured.
907 2 d. Type **460** 25 10
908 5 d. 50 Little egret 70 30

1996. 21st Anniv of "Green March".
909 **461** 5 d. 50 multicoloured . . . 70 30

1996. Stamp Day. As T **316**.
910 2 d. orange and black 25 10
911 5 d. 50 green and black . . . 70 30
DESIGNS: 2 d. Round postal cancellation of Maghzen-Fes; 5 d. 50, Octagonal postal cancellation of Maghzen-Fes.

462 Rainbow and Emblem

1996. 50th Anniv of U.N.I.C.E.F.
912 **462** 5 d. 50 multicoloured . . . 70 30

463 Terracotta Vessel

1997.
913 **463** 5 d. 50 multicoloured . . . 70 30

464 Lupin

465 King Mohammed V

1997. Flowers. Multicoloured.
914 2 d. Type **464** 25 10
915 5 d. 50 Milk thistle 70 30

1997. 50th Anniv of Tangier Talks (determining future status of Tangier).
916 2 d. Type **465** 25 10
917 2 d. King Hassan II 25 10

466 Map in Open Book and Quill

468 Copper Door Knocker

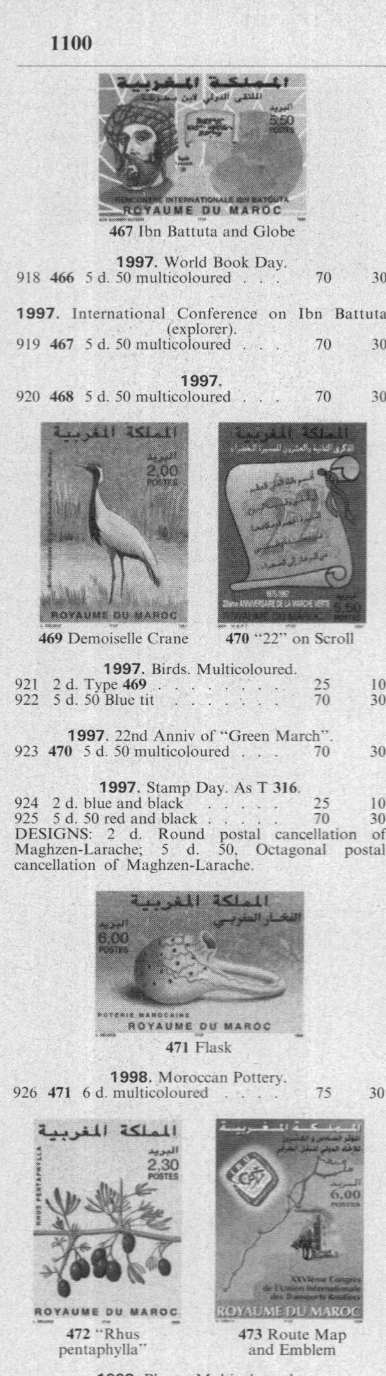

467 Ibn Battuta and Globe

1997. World Book Day.

918 **466** 5 d. 50 multicoloured . . . 70 30

1997. International Conference on Ibn Battuta (explorer).

919 **467** 5 d. 50 multicoloured . . . 70 30

1997.

920 **468** 5 d. 50 multicoloured . . . 70 30

469 Demoiselle Crane **470** "22" on Scroll

1997. Birds. Multicoloured.

921 2 d. Type **469** 25 10
922 5 d. 50 Blue tit 70 30

1997. 22nd Anniv of "Green March".

923 **470** 5 d. 50 multicoloured . . . 70 30

1997. Stamp Day. As T **316**.

924 2 d. blue and black 25 10
925 5 d. 50 red and black 70 30

DESIGNS: 2 d. Round postal cancellation of Maghzen-Larache; 5 d. 50, Octagonal postal cancellation of Maghzen-Larache.

471 Flask

1998. Moroccan Pottery.

926 **471** 6 d. multicoloured 75 30

472 "Rhus pentaphylla" 473 Route Map and Emblem

1998. Plants. Multicoloured.

927 2 d. 30 Type **472** 30 15
928 6 d. "Orchis papilionacea" . . . 75 30

1998. 26th International Road Haulage Union Congress, Marrakesh.

929 **473** 6 d. multicoloured 75 30

1998. King Hassan II. Size 25 × 32 mm. Dated "1998".

930 **266** 2 d. 30 red, green and gold 30 15

474 Sconce 475 Players and Ball

1998. Moroccan Copperware.

931 **474** 6 d. multicoloured 75 30

1998. World Cup Football Championship, France.

932 **475** 6 d. multicoloured 75 30

476 Emblem, Rainbow, World Map and Hands

1998. International Year of the Ocean.

933 **476** 6 d. multicoloured 75 30

477 King Mohammed V and King Hassan II

1998. 45th Anniv of Revolution.

934 **477** 6 d. multicoloured 75 30

478 Globe and Letter **479** Thrush Nightingale

1998. World Stamp Day.

935 **478** 6 d. multicoloured 75 30

1998. Birds. Multicoloured.

936 2 d. 30 Type **479** 30 15
937 6 d. Ostrich 75 30

480 Scroll **481** Arabic Script

1998. 23rd Anniv of "Green March".

938 **480** 6 d. multicoloured 75 30

1998. 40th Anniv of Code of Civil Liberties.

939 **481** 6 d. multicoloured 75 30

482 Anniversary Emblem

1998. 50th Anniv of Universal Declaration of Human Rights.

940 **482** 6 d. multicoloured 75 30

POSTAGE DUE STAMPS

D 53

1965.

D162 **D 53** 5 f. green . . . . . . 3·00 1·25
D163 10 f. brown 50 25
D164 20 f. red 50 25
D165 30 f. sepia . . . . . . 1·25 50

D **153** Peaches

1974.

D393 – 5 f. orge, grn & blk 10 10
D394 – 10 f. grn, red & blk 10 10
D395 – 20 f. green & black 50 10
D396 **D 153** 30 f. orge, grn & blk 60 35
D397 – 40 f. green and black 15 10
D398 – 60 f. orge, grn & blk 20 15
D399 – 80 f. orange, green and black 50 20
D399a – 1 d. multicoloured 20 15
D400 – 1 d. 20 multicoloured 50 15
D401 – 1 d. 60 multicoloured 60 20
D402 – 2 d. multicoloured 55 25
D403 – 5 d. multicoloured 65 30

DESIGNS: 60 f., 1 d. 60, Peaches. VERT: 5 f. Oranges; 10 f., 1 d. 20, Cherries; 20 f. Raisins; 40 f. Grapes; 80 f. Oranges; 1, 5 d. Apples; 2 d. Strawberries.

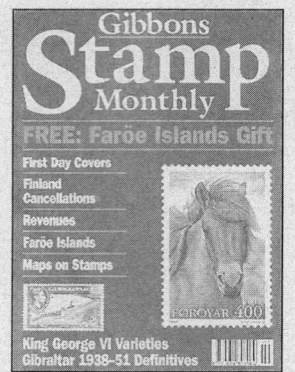

MOROCCO AGENCIES Pt. 1

Stamps used at British postal agencies in Morocco, N. Africa, the last of which closed on 30 April, 1957.

I. GIBRALTAR ISSUES OVERPRINTED.

For use at all British Post Offices in Morocco. All British P.O.'s in Morocco were under the control of the Gibraltar P.O. until 1907 when control was assumed by H.M. Postmaster-General.

1898. Stamps of Gibraltar (Queen Victoria) optd **Morocco Agencies**.

9	7	5 c. green	30	40
10		10 c. red	55	30
11		20 c. olive	4·00	70
3		20 c. olive and brown	4·00	1·25
4		25 c. blue	2·50	60
5		40 c. brown	4·00	3·25
14		50 c. lilac	6·50	3·50
7		1 p. brown and blue	12·00	26·00
8		2 p. black and red	13·00	26·00

1903. Stamps of Gibraltar (King Edward VII) optd **Morocco Agencies**.

24	8	5 c. light green and green	4·75	2·75
18		10 c. purple on red	6·00	30
26		20 c. green and red	3·00	25·00
20		25 c. purple & black on blue	5·00	20
28		50 c. purple and violet	6·00	35·00
29		1 p. black and red	24·00	75·00
30		2 p. black and blue	15·00	35·00

II. BRITISH CURRENCY.

On sale at British P.O.s throughout Morocco, including Tangier, until 1937.

PRICES. Our prices for used stamps with these overprints are for examples used in Morocco. These stamps could also be used in the United Kingdom, with official sanction, from the summer of 1950 onwards, and with U.K. postmarks are worth about 50 percent less.

Stamps of Great Britain optd **MOROCCO AGENCIES**.

1907. King Edward VII.

31	83	½d. green	1·50	7·00
32		1d. red	7·50	4·00
33	–	2d. green and red	6·50	4·50
34	–	4d. green and brown	3·75	3·25
35a	–	4d. orange	8·50	8·50
36	–	6d. purple	12·00	14·00
37	–	1s. green and red	26·00	17·00
38	–	2s. 6d. purple	65·00	£110

1914. King George V.

55	105	½d. green	60	30
43	104	1d. red	60	10
44	105	1½d. brown	2·25	11·00
45	106	2d. orange	2·25	35
58	104	2½d. blue	2·00	5·00
46	106	3d. violet	1·00	35
47		4d. green	2·25	70
60a	107	6d. purple	55	60
49	108	1s. brown	5·00	75
53	109	2s. 6d. brown	32·00	25·00
74		5s. red	23·00	85·00

1935. Silver Jubilee.

62	123	½d. green	1·25	6·50
63		1d. red	1·25	6·50
64		1½d. brown	2·25	9·00
65		2½d. blue	2·50	2·50

1935. King George V.

66	119	1d. red	3·25	8·00
67	118	1½d. brown	3·00	12·00
68	120	2d. orange	40	4·25
69	119	2½d. blue	1·75	4·25
70	120	3d. violet	40	20
71		4d. green	40	20
72	122	1s. brown	80	1·75

1936. King Edward VIII.

75	124	1d. red	10	30
76		2½d. blue	10	15

In 1937 unoverprinted Great Britain stamps replaced overprinted **MOROCCO AGENCIES** issues as stocks became exhausted. In 1949 overprinted issues reappeared and were in use at Tetuan (Spanish Zone), the only remaining British P.O. apart from that at Tangier.

1949. King George VI.

77	128	½d. green	1·75	7·00
94		½d. orange	1·75	50
78		1d. red	2·75	9·00
95		1d. blue	1·75	65
79		1½d. brown	2·75	8·50
96		1½d. green	1·75	1·75
80		2d. orange	3·00	9·00
97		2d. brown	1·75	3·25
81		2½d. blue	3·25	10·00
98		2½d. red	1·75	3·00
82		3d. violet	1·50	1·60
83	129	4d. green	45	90
84		5d. brown	3·00	15·00
85		6d. purple	1·50	1·00
86	130	7d. green	40	16·00
87		8d. red	3·00	6·50
88		9d. olive	40	11·00
89		10d. blue	40	6·00
90		11d. plum	70	6·00
91		1s. brown	2·75	6·00
92	131	2s. 6d. green	12·00	29·00
93		5s. red	28·00	55·00

1951. Pictorials.

99	147	2s. 6d. green	12·00	18·00
100	–	5s. red (No. 510)	12·00	19·00

1952. Queen Elizabeth II.

101	154	½d. orange	10	10
102		1d. blue	15	1·00
103		1½d. green	15	20
104		2d. brown	20	1·25
105	155	2½d. red	15	60
106		4d. blue	85	3·25
107	156	5d. brown	65	60
108		6d. purple	85	3·25
109	158	8d. mauve	70	1·00
110	159	1s. bistre	70	60

III. SPANISH CURRENCY.

Stamps surcharged in Spanish currency were sold at British P.O.'s throughout Morocco until the establishment of the French Zone and the Tangier International Zone, when their use was confined to the Spanish Zone.

Stamps of Great Britain surch **MOROCCO AGENCIES** and value in Spanish currency.

1907. King Edward VII.

112	83	5 c. on ½d. green	3·50	20
113		10 c. on 1d. red	6·50	10
114a	–	15 c. on 1½d. purple and green	1·75	20
115	–	20 c. on 2d. green & red	1·00	15
116a	83	25 c. on 2½d. blue	1·25	20
117	–	40 c. on 4d. grn & brn	1·00	2·00
118a	–	40 c. on 4d. orange	90	60
119a	–	50 c. on 5d. pur & blue	1·25	1·25
120a	–	1 p. on 10d. pur & red	18·00	8·00
121	–	3 p. on 2s. 6d. purple	20·00	24·00
122	–	6 p. on 5s. red	35·00	45·00
123	–	12 p. on 10s. blue	75·00	75·00

1912. King George V.

126	101	5 c. on ½d. green	2·50	10
127	102	10 c. on 1d. red	90	10

1914. King George V.

128	105	3 c. on ½d. green	50	3·25
129		5 c. on ½d. green	50	10
130	104	10 c. on 1d. red	70	10
131	105	15 c. on 1½d. brown	70	10
132	106	20 c. on 2d. orange	60	25
133	104	25 c. on 2½d. blue	1·50	25
148	106	40 c. on 4d. green	1·25	1·50
135	108	1 p. on 10d. blue	1·75	4·25
142	109	3 p. on 2s. 6d. brown	23·00	75·00
136		6 p. on 5s. red	29·00	48·00
138		12 p. on 10s. blue	£110	£160

1935. Silver Jubilee.

149	123	5 c. on ½d. green	1·00	65
150		10 c. on 1d. red	2·75	2·25
151		15 c. on 1½d. brown	5·00	16·00
152		25 c. on 2½d. blue	4·00	2·25

1935. King George V.

153	118	5 c. on ½d. green	75	14·00
154	119	10 c. on 1d. red	2·50	5·00
155	118	15 c. on 1½d. brown	4·00	3·25
156	120	20 c. on 2d. orange	40	25
157	119	25 c. on 2½d. blue	1·25	3·75
158	120	40 c. on 4d. green	45	3·00
159	122	1 p. on 10d. blue	4·00	30

1936. King Edward VIII.

160	124	5 c. on ½d. green	10	10
161		10 c. on 1d. red	50	1·50
162		15 c. on 1½d. brown	10	10
163		25 c. on 2½d. blue	10	10

1937. Coronation.

164	126	15 c. on 1½d. brown	50	30

1937. King George VI.

165	128	5 c. on ½d. green	55	15
182		5 c. on ½d. orange	2·00	2·25
166		10 c. on 1d. red	50	10
183		10 c. on 1d. blue	3·25	4·00
167		15 c. on 1½d. brown	55	25
184		15 c. on 1½d. green	1·75	12·00
168		25 c. on 2½d. blue	60	50
185		25 c. on 2½d. red	1·75	4·00
169	129	40 c. on 4d. green	28·00	10·00
186		40 c. on 4d. blue	60	9·00
170	130	70 c. on 7d. green	60	9·00
171		1 p. on 10d. blue	1·00	3·50

1940. Stamp Centenary.

172	134	5 c. on ½d. green	30	1·75
173		10 c. on 1d. red	2·75	2·00
174		15 c. on 1½d. brown	40	2·00
175		25 c. on 2½d. blue	40	60

1948. Silver Wedding.

176	137	25 c. on 2½d. blue	40	15
177	138	45 p. on £1 blue	17·00	22·00

1948. Olympic Games.

178	139	25 c. on 2½d. blue	40	60
179	140	30 c. on 3d. violet	40	60
180	–	60 c. on 6d. purple	40	60
181	–	1 p. 20 on 1s. brown	55	60

1954. Queen Elizabeth II.

189	154	5 c. on ½d. orange	15	1·00
188		10 c. on 1d. blue	50	75
190	155	40 c. on 4d. blue	70	1·75

IV. FRENCH CURRENCY.

Stamps surch in French currency were sold at British P.O.'s in the French Zone.

Stamps of Great Britain surch **MOROCCO AGENCIES** and value in French currency.

1917. King George V.

191	105	3 c. on ½d. green	60	2·50
192		5 c. on ½d. green	30	10
203	104	10 c. on 1d. red	30	85
194	105	15 c. on 1½d. brown	2·25	15
205	104	25 c. on 2½d. blue	40	40
206	106	40 c. on 4d. green	50	80
207	107	50 c. on 5d. brown	50	10
198	108	75 c. on 9d. green	60	75
209		90 c. on 9d. green	11·00	4·50
210		1 f. on 10d. blue	70	10
211		1 f. 50 on 1s. brown	6·50	2·25
200	109	3 f. on 2s. 6d. brown	7·50	1·50
226		6 f. on 5s. red	6·00	21·00

1935. Silver Jubilee.

212	123	5 c. on ½d. green	15	15
213		10 c. on 1d. red	2·25	50
214		15 c. on 1½d. brown	30	50
215		25 c. on 2½d. blue	30	15

1935. King George V.

216	118	5 c. on ½d. green	45	4·00
217	119	10 c. on 1d. red	35	30
218	118	15 c. on 1½d. brown	3·00	3·50
219	119	25 c. on 2½d. blue	30	15
220	120	40 c. on 4d. green	30	15
221	121	50 c. on 5d. brown	30	15
222	122	90 c. on 9d. olive	35	1·00
223		1 f. on 10d. blue	30	30
224		1 f. 50 on 1s. brown	40	2·25

1936. King Edward VIII.

227	124	5 c. on ½d. green	10	15
228		15 c. on 1½d. brown	10	15

1937. Coronation.

229	126	15 c. on 1½d. brown	30	20

1937. King George VI.

230	128	5 c. on ½d. green	1·25	1·40

V. TANGIER INTERNATIONAL ZONE.

This Zone was established in 1924 and the first specially overprinted stamps issued in 1927.

PRICES. Our note re U.K. usage (at beginning of Section II) also applies to **TANGIER** optd stamps.

Stamps of Great Britain optd **TANGIER**.

1927. King George V.

231	105	½d. green	1·25	10
232	104	1d. red	1·50	10
233	105	1½d. brown	3·75	2·25
234	106	2d. orange	3·25	10

1934. King George V.

235	118	½d. green	1·00	1·40
236	119	1d. red	2·00	70
237	118	1½d. brown	15	10

1935. Silver Jubilee optd **TANGIER TANGIER**.

238	123	½d. green	1·00	2·75
239		1d. red	13·50	11·00
240		1½d. brown	1·25	40

1936. King Edward VIII.

241	124	½d. green	10	15
242		1d. red	10	10
243		1½d. brown	15	10

1937. Coronation optd **TANGIER TANGIER**.

244	126	1½d. brown	40	30

1937. King George VI.

245	128	½d. green	1·25	40
280		½d. orange	60	1·00
246		1d. red	3·75	30
281		1d. blue	70	2·50
247		1½d. brown	1·00	10
282		1½d. green	70	14·00
261		2d. orange	4·00	4·00
283		2d. brown	70	2·00
262		2½d. blue	60	2·75
284		2½d. red	70	3·25
263		3d. violet	35	65
264	129	4d. green	7·50	10·00
285		4d. blue	1·50	2·50
265		5d. brown	3·50	11·00
266		6d. purple	35	30
267	130	7d. green	90	10·00
268		8d. red	3·50	8·50
269		9d. olive	70	11·00
270		10d. blue	70	11·00
271		11d. plum	70	8·50
272		1s. brown	70	1·75
273	131	2s. 6d. green	4·25	11·00
274		5s. red	13·00	38·00
275	–	10s. blue (No. 478a)	38·00	95·00

1940. Stamp Centenary.

248	134	½d. green	30	3·25
249		1d. red	45	50
250		1½d. brown	2·00	2·75

1946. Victory.

253	135	2½d. blue	30	20
254	–	3d. violet	30	55

1948. Silver Wedding.

255	137	2½d. blue	30	15
256	138	£1 blue	25·00	25·00

1948. Olympic Games.

257	139	2½d. blue	75	1·25
258	140	3d. violet	75	1·25
259	–	6d. purple	75	1·25
260	–	1s. brown	75	60

1949. U.P.U.

276	143	2½d. blue	50	1·00
277	144	3d. violet	50	85
278	–	6d. purple	50	85
279	–	1s. brown	50	1·75

1951. Pictorial stamps.

286	147	2s. 6d. green	8·00	4·50
287	–	5s. red (No. 510)	14·00	15·00
288	–	10s. blue (No. 511)	19·00	15·00

1952. Queen Elizabeth II.

313	154	½d. orange	10	20
314		1d. blue	20	30
291		1½d. green	10	30
292		2d. brown	20	30
293	155	2½d. red	10	40
294		3d. lilac	20	40
320		4d. blue	65	2·00
296	157	5d. brown	60	90
297		6d. purple	45	15
298		7d. green	80	2·00
299	158	8d. mauve	60	1·50
300		9d. olive	1·40	75
301		10d. blue	1·40	2·75
302		11d. purple	1·40	3·25
303	159	1s. brown	50	30
304		1s. 3d. green	65	2·50
305		1s. 6d. blue	1·00	1·75

1953. Coronation.

306	161	2½d. red	50	30
307	–	4d. blue	1·00	30
308	163	1s. 3d. green	1·25	1·25
309	–	1s. 6d. blue	1·25	60

1955. Pictorials.

310	166	2s. 6d. brown	3·50	6·00
311	–	5s. red	5·50	11·00
312	–	10s. blue	19·00	21·00

1957. Cent of British Post Office in Tangier. Queen Elizabeth II stamps optd **1857–1957 TANGIER**.

323	154	½d. orange	10	10
324		1d. blue	10	10
325		1½d. green	10	10
326		2d. brown	10	10
327	155	2½d. red	15	60
328		3d. lilac	15	10
329		4d. blue	30	20
330	157	5d. brown	30	35
331		6d. purple	30	15
332		7d. green	30	30
333	158	8d. mauve	30	70
334		9d. olive	30	30
335		10d. blue	30	30
336		11d. plum	30	30
337	159	1s. bistre	30	30
338		1s. 3d. green	45	2·50
339		1s. 6d. blue	50	1·00
340	166	2s. 6d. brown	2·00	3·00
341	–	5s. red	2·75	4·25
342	–	10s. blue	5·50	6·00

MORVI Pt. 1

A state of India, Bombay district. Now uses Indian stamps.

12 pies = 1 anna

1 Maharaja Lakhdirji 3

1931.

8	1	3 p. red	2·25	7·50
9b		6 p. green	3·00	7·50
5a		½ a. blue	1·90	9·50
6		1 a. brown	3·25	19·00
10		1 a. blue	2·25	8·00
7		2 a. brown	4·00	26·00
11		2 a. violet	10·00	28·00

1934.

16	3	3 p. red	70	2·50
17		6 p. green	75	2·00
14		1 a. brown	1·10	8·00
19		2 a. violet	2·50	15·00

MOSUL Pt. 19

Stamps used by Indian forces in Mesopotamia (now Iraq) at the close of the 1914–18 war.

12 pies = 1 anna; 16 annas = 1 rupee

1919. Turkish Fiscal stamps surch **POSTAGE I.E.F. 'D'** and value in annas.

1	½ a. on 1 pi. green and red	1·40	1·40
2	1 a. on 20 pa. black on red	1·40	1·75
4	2½ a. on 1 pi. mauve & yellow	1·50	1·50
5	3 a. on 20 pa. green	1·60	2·50
6	3 a. on 20 pa. green & orange	25·00	45·00
7	4 a. on 1 pi. violet	3·00	3·50
8	8 a. on 10 pa. red	4·00	5·00

MOZAMBIQUE

Pt. 9; Pt. 13; Pt. 1

Former Overseas Province of Portugal in East Africa, granted independence in 1975.
The Republic of Mozambique joined the Commonwealth on 12 November 1995.

1876. 1000 reis = 1 milreis.
1913. 100 centavos = 1 escudo.
1980. 100 centavos = 1 metical.

1876. "Crown" key-type inscr "MOCAMBIQUE".
1 P 5 r. black 50 40
11 10 r. yellow . . . . 1·60 1·40
19 10 r. green 40 30
3 20 r. bistre 50 30
20 20 r. red . . . . £100 75·00
4a 25 r. red 25 15
21 25 r. lilac . . . . 1·10 60
14 40 r. blue . . . . 4·00 2·50
22 40 r. buff 75 65
6 50 r. green . . . . 35·00 11·00
23 50 r. blue 40 30
7 100 r. lilac 40 25
8 200 r. orange . . . . 1·25 70
9 300 r. brown 95 65

1886. "Embossed" key-type inscr "PROVINCIA DE MOCAMBIQUE".
30 Q 5 r. black 50 35
32 10 r. green 45 35
34 20 r. red 50 35
48 25 r. lilac . . . . 3·25 1·75
37 40 r. brown 45 30
38 50 r. blue 70 35
40 100 r. brown 50 30
42 200 r. violet . . . . 1·10 75
43 300 r. orange . . . . 1·40 45

1893. No. 37 surch **PROVISORIO 5 5**.
53 Q 5 on 40 r. brown . . . . 32·00 23·00

1894. "Figures" key-type inscr "MOCAMBIQUE".
56 R 5 r. orange 30 20
57 10 r. mauve 30 20
58 15 r. brown 35 25
59 20 r. lilac 35 20
65 25 r. green 30 15
60 50 r. blue . . . . 1·10 25
67 75 r. pink 65 45
61 80 r. green . . . . 1·10 65
62 100 r. brown on buff 70 50
68 150 r. red on pink . . . . 3·00 1·60
64 200 r. blue on blue . . . . 1·10 90
69 300 r. blue on brown . . . . 1·60 1·25

1895. "Embossed" key-type of Mozambique optd **1195 CENTENARIO ANTONINO 1895**.
71 Q 5 r. black . . . . 2·25 1·60
72 10 r. green . . . . 2·25 1·75
73 20 r. red . . . . 2·40 2·00
74 25 r. purple . . . . 2·40 2·00
75 40 r. brown . . . . 2·40 2·25
76 50 r. blue . . . . 2·40 2·25
77 100 r. brown . . . . 2·40 2·25
78 200 r. lilac . . . . 7·50 5·50
79 300 r. orange . . . . 7·50 5·50

1897. No. 69 surch **50 reis**.
82 R 50 r. on 300 r. bl on brn . . . . 60·00 45·00

1898. Nos. 34 and 37 surch **MOCAMBIQUE** and value.
84 Q 2½ r. on 20 r. red . . . . 7·00 5·50
85 5 r. on 40 r. brown . . . . 6·00 5·50

1898. "King Carlos" key type inscr "MOCAMBIQUE". Name and value in red (500 r.) or black (others).
86 S 2½ r. grey 15 15
87 5 r. red 15 15
88 10 r. green 15 15
89 15 r. brown . . . . 1·50 75
138 15 r. green 50 40
90 20 r. lilac 50 25
91 25 r. green 50 25
139 25 r. red 40 15
92 50 r. blue 55 30
140 50 r. brown . . . . 1·25 85
141 65 r. blue . . . . 3·00 3·00
93 75 r. pink . . . . 2·50 1·50
142 75 r. purple . . . . 1·00 85
94 80 r. mauve . . . . 2·50 1·50
95 100 r. blue on blue . . . . 1·25 65
143 115 r. brown on pink . . . . 3·00 2·50
144 130 r. brown on yellow . . . . 3·00 2·50
96 150 r. brown on yellow . . . . 2·25 1·50
97 200 r. purple on pink . . . . 1·00 70
98 300 r. blue on pink . . . . 2·00 1·25
145 400 r. blue on cream . . . . 4·50 3·25
99 500 r. black on blue . . . . 4·75 3·00
100 700 r. mauve on yellow . . . . 5·50 3·50

1902. Various types surch.
146 S 50 r. on 65 r. blue . . . . 1·10 1·00
101 R 65 r. on 10 r. mauve 95 85
102 65 r. on 15 r. brown 95 85
105 Q 65 r. on 20 r. red . . . . 1·40 1·00
106 R 65 r. on 20 r. lilac 95 85
108 Q 65 r. on 40 r. brown . . . . 1·25 1·25
110 65 r. on 200 r. violet . . . . 1·50 1·00
111 V 115 r. on 2½ r. brown 95 90
113 Q 115 r. on 5 r. black 65 55
114 R 115 r. on 5 r. orange 90 75
115 115 r. on 25 r. green 95 85
117 Q 115 r. on 50 r. blue 60 50
120 130 r. on 25 r. mauve 70 45
121 R 130 r. on 75 r. red 95 90
122 130 r. on 100 r. brown on buff . . . . 2·25 2·25
123 130 r. on 150 r. red on pink . . . . 1·00 1·00
124 130 r. on 200 r. bl on bl . . . . 2·00 2·00
126 Q 130 r. on 300 r. orange 75 45
128 400 r. on 10 r. green . . . . 1·75 1·60
129 R 400 r. on 50 r. blue 60 50
130 400 r. on 80 r. green 60 50
132 Q 400 r. on 100 r. brown . . . . 12·50 8·50
133 R 400 r. on 300 r. blue on brown 60 50

1902. "King Carlos" key-type of Mozambique optd **PROVISORIO**.
134 S 15 r. brown 75 45
135 25 r. green 75 45
136 50 r. blue . . . . 1·25 95
137 75 r. pink . . . . 2·10 1·25

1911. "King Carlos" key-type of Mozambique optd **REPUBLICA**.
147 S 2½ r. grey 10 15
148 5 r. orange 15 15
149 10 r. green 40 25
150 15 r. green 15 10
151 20 r. lilac 40 20
152 25 r. red 15 10
153 50 r. brown 15 15
154 75 r. purple 30 25
155 100 r. blue on blue 30 25
156 115 r. brown on pink 40 30
157 130 r. brown on yellow 40 30
158 200 r. purple on pink 75 50
159 400 r. blue on yellow 70 45
160 500 r. black on blue 70 45
161 700 r. mauve on yellow 70 45

1912. "King Manoel" key-type inscr "MOCAMBIQUE" with opt **REPUBLICA**.
162 T 2½ r. lilac 15 10
163 5 r. black 15 10
164 10 r. green 15 10
165 20 r. red 35 25
166 25 r. brown 15 10
167 50 r. blue 20 15
168 75 r. brown 20 15
169 100 r. brown on green 20 15
170 200 r. green on orange 45 40
171 300 r. black on blue 45 40
172 500 r. brown and green 90 80

1913. Surch **REPUBLICA MOCAMBIQUE** and value on "Vasco da Gama" issues of (a) Portuguese Colonies.
173 ¼ c. on 2½ r. green 45 30
174 ½ c. on 5 r. red 40 30
175 1 c. on 10 r. purple 35 30
176 2½ c. on 25 r. green 35 30
177 5 c. on 50 r. blue 40 30
178 7½ c. on 75 r. brown 70 55
179 10 c. on 100 r. brown 50 45
180 15 c. on 150 r. brown 45 40

(b) Macao.
181 ¼ c. on ½ a. green 60 50
182 ½ c. on 1 a. red 55 50
183 1 c. on 2 a. purple 55 45
184 2½ c. on 4 a. green 55 45
185 5 c. on 8 a. blue . . . . 1·50 1·25
186 7½ c. on 12 a. brown 85 75
187 10 c. on 16 a. brown 60 50
188 15 c. on 24 a. brown 55 45

(c) Timor.
189 ¼ c. on ½ a. green 60 50
190 ½ c. on 1 a. red 60 50
191 1 c. on 2 a. purple 55 45
192 2½ c. on 4 a. green 55 45
193 5 c. on 8 a. blue 90 70
194 7½ c. on 12 a. brown 65 50
195 10 c. on 16 a. brown 50 45
196 15 c. on 24 a. brown 45 35

1914. "Ceres" key-type inscr "MOCAMBIQUE".
197 U ¼ c. green 10 10
198 ½ c. black 10 10
199 1 c. green 10 10
200 1½ c. brown 10 10
201 2 c. red 10 10
270 2 c. grey 10 10
202 2½ c. violet 10 10
255 3 c. orange 10 10
256 4 c. pink 10 10
257 4½ c. grey 10 10
203 5 c. blue 10 10
275 6 c. mauve 10 10
259 7 c. blue 10 10
260 7½ c. brown 10 10
278 8 c. grey 10 10
279 10 c. red 10 10
280 12 c. brown 10 10
281 12 c. green 10 10
283 15 c. purple 10 10
284 20 c. green 15 15
285 24 c. blue 15 15
286 25 c. brown 20 20
209 30 c. brown on green 70 50
287 30 c. green 15 15
295 30 c. lilac on pink 70 55
210 40 c. brown on pink 75 60
288 40 c. turquoise 40 15
211 50 c. orange on orange . . . . 1·40 1·10
289 50 c. mauve 15 10
297 60 c. brown on pink 70 55
290 60 c. blue 45 25
291 60 c. pink 45 25
298 80 c. brown on blue 65 45
293 80 c. red 45 25
299 1 e. green on blue . . . . 1·10 65
264 1 e. pink 50 40
301 1 e. blue 70 45
300 U 2 e. mauve on pink 80 50
302 2 e. purple 40 30
303 5 e. brown . . . . 4·50 1·90
304 10 e. pink . . . . 6·75 2·50
305 20 e. green . . . . 18·00 8·25

1915. Provisional issues of 1902 optd **REPUBLICA**.
226 S 50 r. blue (136) 30 20
227 50 r. on 65 r. blue 30 25
213 75 r. pink (137) 70 40
228 V 115 r. on 2½ r. brown 30 25
216 Q 115 r. on 5 r. black . . . . 9·00 8·50
229 R 115 r. on 5 r. orange 30 25
230 115 r. on 25 r. green 30 25
231 130 r. on 75 r. red 30 25
220 130 r. on 100 r. brown on buff 55 45
232 130 r. on 150 r. red on pink 30 25
233 130 r. on 200 r. bl on bl 30 25
223 400 r. on 50 r. blue 65 60
224 400 r. on 80 r. green 65 60
225 400 r. on 300 r. bl on brn 65 60

1918. Charity Tax stamp surch **2½ CENTAVOS**. Roul or perf.
248 C 16 2½ c. on 5 c. red 40 25

1920. Charity Tax stamps surch. (a) **CORREIOS** and value in figures.
306 C 15 1 c. on 1 c. green 30 30
307 C 16 1½ c. on 5 c. red 30 25

(b) **SEIS CENTAVOS**.
308 C 16 6 c. on 5 c. red 40 30

1921. "Ceres" stamps of 1913 surch.
309 U 10 c. on ½ c. black 70 60
310 30 c. on 1½ c. brown 70 60
316 50 c. on 4 c. pink 55 35
311 60 c. on 2½ c. violet 90 70
328 70 c. on 2 e. purple 30 20
329 1 e. 40 on 2 e. purple 35 20

1922. "Ceres" key-type of Lourenco Marques surch.
312 U 10 c. on ½ c. black 50 45
314 30 c. on 1½ c. brown 50 45

1922. Charity Tax stamp surch **2$00**.
315 C 16 $2 on 5 c. red 60 35

1924. 4th Death Centenary of Vasco da Gama. "Ceres" key-type of Mozambique optd **Vasco da Gama 1924**.
317 U 80 c. pink 50 35

1925. Nos. 129 and 130 surch **Republica 40 C.**
318 R 40 c. on 400 r. on 50 r. 35 25
319 40 c. on 400 r. on 80 r. 35 30

1929. "Due" key-type inscr "MOCAMBIQUE" optd **CORREIOS**.
320 W 50 c. lilac 55 45

23 Mousinho de Albuquerque

25 "Portugal" and Camoens' "The Lusiads"

1930. Albuquerque's Victories Commemorative. Vignette in grey.
321 23 50 c. lake and red (Macontene) . . . . 2·75 2·50
322 50 c. orange and red (Mujenga) . . . . 2·75 2·50
323 50 c. mauve and brown (Coolela) . . . . 2·25 1·90
324 50 c. grey and green (Chaimite) . . . . 2·75 2·50
325 50 c. blue and indigo (Ibrahimo) . . . . 2·25 1·90
326 50 c. blue and black (Mucuto-muno) . . . . 2·25 1·90
327 50 c. violet and lilac (Naguema) . . . . 2·25 1·90

The above were for compulsory use throughout Mozambique in place of ordinary postage stamps on certain days in 1930 and 1931. They are not listed among the Charity Tax stamps as the revenue was not applied to any charitable fund.

1938. Value in red (1, 15 c., 1 e. 40) or black (others).
330 25 1 c. brown 10 10
331 5 c. brown 10 10
332 10 c. purple 10 10
333 15 c. black 10 10
334 20 c. grey 10 10
335 30 c. green 10 10
336 35 c. green . . . . 2·50 1·40
337 40 c. red 10 10
338 45 c. blue 20 20
339 50 c. brown 15 10
340 60 c. green 20 15
341 70 c. brown 20 15
342 80 c. green 20 15
343 85 c. red 55 40
344 1 e. purple 25 15
345 1 e. 40 blue . . . . 3·75 1·25
346 1 e. 75 blue . . . . 2·40 1·10
347 2 e. lilac 65 25
348 5 e. green . . . . 1·25 30
349 10 e. brown . . . . 2·75 50
350 20 e. orange . . . . 12·50 80

1938. As 1938 issue of Macao. Name and value in black.
351 54 1 c. green (postage) 10 10
352 5 c. brown 10 10
353 10 c. red 10 10
354 15 c. purple 10 10
355 20 c. grey 10 10
356 – 30 c. purple 15 10
357 – 35 c. green 20 15
358 – 40 c. brown 20 15
359 – 50 c. mauve 20 10
360 – 60 c. black 20 10
361 – 70 c. violet 25 15
362 – 80 c. orange 25 15
363 – 1 e. red 30 15
364 – 1 e. 75 blue 90 30
365 – 2 e. red 90 30
366 – 5 e. green . . . . 2·25 30
367 – 10 e. blue . . . . 4·50 60
368 – 20 e. brown . . . . 11·00 1·00
369 56 10 c. red (air) 10 10
370 20 c. violet 10 10
371 50 c. orange 15 10
372 1 e. blue 20 10
373 2 e. red 40 15
374 3 e. green 60 20
375 5 e. brown . . . . 1·00 35
376 9 e. red . . . . 1·90 45
377 10 e. mauve . . . . 3·00 60

DESIGNS: 30 to 50 c. Mousinho de Albuquerque; 60 c. to 1 e. Dam; 1 e. 75, to 5 e. Henry the Navigator; 10, 20 e. Afonso de Albuquerque.

1938. No. 338 surch **40 centavos**.
378 25 40 c. on 45 c. blue . . . . 1·75 1·50

26a Route of President's Tour

27 New Cathedral, Lourenco Marques

1938. President Carmona's 2nd Colonial Tour.
379 26a 80 c. violet on mauve . . . . 1·50 75
380 1 e. 75 blue on blue . . . . 4·50 1·90
381 3 e. green on green . . . . 6·75 3·50
382 20 e. brown on cream . . . . 32·00 16·00

1944. 400th Anniv of Lourenco Marques.
383 27 50 c. brown 65 30
384 – 50 c. green 65 30
385 – 1 e. 75 blue . . . . 4·50 1·00
386a – 20 e. black . . . . 2·75 30

DESIGNS—HORIZ: 1 e. 75, Lourenco Marques Central Railway Station; 20 e. Town Hall, Lourenco Marques.
See also No. 405.

1946. Nos. 354, 364 and 375 surch.
387 10 c. on 15 c. purple (postage) 40 30
388 60 c. on 1 e. 75 blue 60 35
389 3 e. on 5 e. brown (air) . . . . 4·00 1·75

1947. No. 386a surch.
390 2 e. on 20 e. black . . . . 1·25 1·10

30 Lockheed L.18 Lodestar

1946. Air. Values in black.
391 30 1 e. 20 red . . . . 1·00 65
392 1 e. 60 blue . . . . 1·50 80
393 1 e. 70 purple . . . . 2·10 1·20
394 2 e. 90 brown . . . . 3·75 1·40
395 3 e. green . . . . 2·75 1·60

1947. Air. Optd **Taxe percue**. Values in red (50 c.) or black (others).
397 30 50 c. black 40 30
398 1 e. pink 50 30
399 3 e. green 80 40
400 4 e. 50 green . . . . 1·40 55
401 5 e. red . . . . 2·00 80
402 10 e. blue . . . . 5·50 1·90
403 20 e. violet . . . . 13·50 5·25
404 50 e. orange . . . . 30·00 12·00

1948. As T **27** but without commemorative inscr.
405 4 e. 50 red . . . . 1·25 40

31 Antonio Enes

33 Lourenco Marques

1948. Birth Centenary of Antonio Enes.
406 31 50 c. black and cream . . . . 1·00 20
407 5 e. purple and cream . . . . 4·25 80

1948.
408 – 5 c. brown 25 15
409 – 10 c. purple 50 15
410 – 20 c. brown 25 15
411 – 30 c. purple 25 15
412 – 40 c. green 25 15
413 **33** 50 c. grey 25 15
414 – 60 c. purple 30 15
415 **33** 80 c. violet 25 15
416 – 1 e. red 35 15
417 – 1 e. 20 grey 2·00 45
418 – 1 e. 50 violet 35 20
419 – 1 e. 75 blue 95 25
420 – 2 e. brown 60 15
421 – 2 e. 50 blue 2·10 20
422 – 3 e. green 90 20
423 – 3 e. 50 green 1·60 20
424 – 5 e. green 1·40 20
425 – 10 e. brown 3·25 35
426 – 15 e. red 8·00 1·50
427 – 20 e. orange 15·00 1·75
DESIGNS—VERT: 5, 30 c. Gogogo Peak; 20, 40 c. Zumbo River; 60 c., 3 e. 50, Nhanhangare Waterfall. HORIZ: 10 c., 1 e. 20, Railway bridge over River Zambesi at Sena; 1, 5 e. Gathering coconuts; 1 e. 50, 2 e. River Pungue at Beira; 1 e. 75, 3 e. Polana beach, Lourenco Marques; 2 e. 50, 10 e. Bird's eye view of Lourenco Marques; 15, 20 e. Malema River.

1949. Honouring the Statue of Our Lady of Fatima. As T **62** of Macao.
428 50 c. blue 1·50 50
429 1 e. 20 mauve 3·00 1·00
430 4 e. 50 green 11·00 3·50
431 20 e. brown 21·00 5·25

35 Aircraft and Globe

36 Clown Triggerfish

1949. Air.
432 **35** 50 c. brown 20 10
433 1 e. 20 violet 40 20
434 4 e. 50 blue 95 35
435 5 e. green 1·60 45
436 20 e. brown 4·75 1·00

1949. 75th Anniv of U.P.U. As T **64** of Macao.
437 4 e. 50 blue 1·50 60

1950. Holy Year. As Nos. 425/6 of Macao.
438 1 e. 50 orange 65 30
439 3 e. blue 90 45

1951. Fishes. Multicoloured.
440 5 c. Type **36** 15 10
441 10 c. Thread-finned butterflyfish 15 10
442 15 c. Racoon butterflyfish 35 20
443 20 c. Lionfish 15 10
444 30 c. Pearl puffer 15 10
445 40 c. Golden filefish 10 10
446 50 c. Spot-cheeked surgeonfish 10 10
447 1 e. Pennant coralfish (vert) 15 10
448 1 e. 50 Seagrass wrasse 15 10
449 2 e. Sombre sweetlips 15 10
450 2 e. 50 Blue-striped snapper 40 15
451 3 e. Convict tang 40 15
452 3 e. 50 Starry triggerfish 45 10
453 4 e. Cornetfish 70 20
454 4 e. 50 Vagabond butterflyfish 1·00 15
455 5 e. Sail-backed mailcheek 1·00 10
456 6 e. Dusky batfish (vert) 1·00 10
457 8 e. Moorish idol (vert) 1·75 25
458 9 e. Triangulate boxfish 1·75 20
459 10 e. Eastern flying gurnard 4·25 1·10
460 15 e. Red-toothed triggerfish 28·00 7·50
461 20 e. Picasso triggerfish 14·50 3·25
462 30 e. Long-horned cowfish 17·00 4·50
463 50 e. Spotted cowfish 26·00 10·00

1951. Termination of Holy Year. As T **69** of Macao.
464 5 e. red and orange 1·90 90

37 Victor Cordon (colonist)

39 Liner and Lockheed Constellation Airliner

1951. Birth Centenary of Cordon.
465 **37** 1 e. brown and light brown 1·25 30
466 5 e. black and blue 6·00 85

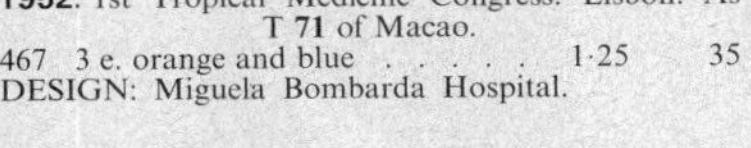
1952. 1st Tropical Medicine Congress. Lisbon. As T **71** of Macao.
467 3 e. orange and blue 1·25 35
DESIGN: Miguela Bombarda Hospital.

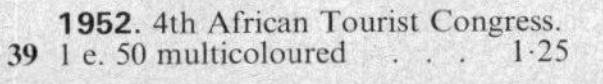
1952. 4th African Tourist Congress.
468 **39** 1 e. 50 multicoloured 1·25 35

40 Missionary

41 Citrus Butterfly

1953. Missionary Art Exhibition.
469 **40** 10 c. red and lilac 10 10
470 1 e. red and green 70 20
471 5 e. black and blue 1·40 40

1953. Butterflies and Moths. Multicoloured.
472 10 c. Type **41** 10 10
473 15 c. "Amphicallia thelwalli" 10 10
474 20 c. Forest queen 10 10
475 30 c. Western scarlet 10 10
476 40 c. Black-barred red-tip 10 10
477 50 c. Mocker swallowtail 10 10
478 80 c. "Nudaurelia hersilia dido" 15 15
479 1 e. African moon moth 15 10
480 1 e. 50 Large striped swallowtail 15 10
481 2 e. "Athletes ethica" 4·50 30
482 2 e. 30 African monarch 3·00 25
483 2 e. 50 Green swallowtail 7·50 25
484 3 e. "Arniocera ericata" 95 10
485 4 e. Apollo moth 50 10
486 4 e. 50 Peach moth 50 10
487 5 e. "Metarctica lateritia" 50 10
488 6 e. "Xanthospilopteryx mozambica" 55 15
489 7 e. 50 White bear 3·00 30
490 10 e. Flame-coloured charaxes 7·50 1·00
491 20 e. Fervid tiger moth 11·00 1·00

42 Stamps

43 Map of Mozambique

1953. Philatelic Exhibition, Lourenco Marques.
492 **42** 1 e. multicoloured 1·25 30
493 3 e. multicoloured 3·25 1·10

1953. Portuguese Postage Stamp Centenary. As T **75** of Macao.
494 50 c. multicoloured 50 35

1954. 4th Centenary of Sao Paulo. As T **76** of Macao.
495 3 e. 50 multicoloured 30 20

1954. Multicoloured map; Mozambique territory in colours given.
496 **43** 10 c. lilac 10 10
497 20 c. yellow 10 10
498 50 c. blue 10 10
499 1 e. yellow 10 10
500 2 e. 30 white 65 35
501 4 e. orange 65 25
502 10 e. green 1·90 25
503 20 e. brown 2·75 35

44 Arms of Beira

45 Mousinho de Albuquerque

1954. 1st Philatelic Exhibition, Manica and Sofala.
504 **44** 1 e. multicoloured 35 20
505 3 e. 50 multicoloured 90 35

1955. Birth Centenary of M. de Albuquerque.
506 **45** 2 e. brown and grey 50 30
507 – 2 e. 50 multicoloured 1·10 55
DESIGN: 2 e. 50, Equestrian statue of Albuquerque.

46 Arms and Inhabitants

47 Beira

1956. Visit of President to Mozambique. Multicoloured. Background in colours given.
508 **46** 1 e. cream 25 15
509 2 e. 50 blue 65 30

1957. 50th Anniv of Beira.
510 **47** 2 e. 50 multicoloured 65 25

1958. 6th International Congress of Tropical Medicine. As T **79** of Macao.
511 1 e. 50 multicoloured 1·25 70
DESIGN: 1 e. 50, "Strophanthus grandiflorus" (plant).

1958. Brussels International Exn. As T **78** of Macao.
512 3 e. 50 multicoloured 25 15

48 Caravel

49 "Arts and Crafts"

1960. 500th Death Anniv of Prince Henry the Navigator.
513 **48** 5 e. multicoloured 45 20

1960. 10th Anniv of African Technical Co-operation Commission.
514 **49** 3 e. multicoloured 45 20

50 Arms of Lourenco Marques

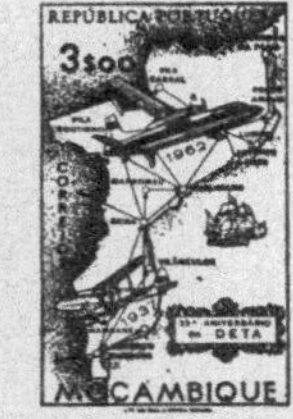

51 Fokker F.27 Friendship and De Havilland D.H.89 Dragon Rapide over Route Map

1961. Arms. Multicoloured.
515 5 c. Type **50** 15 10
516 15 c. Chibuto 15 10
517 20 c. Nampula 15 10
518 30 c. Inhambane 15 10
519 50 c. Mozambique (city) 15 10
520 1 e. Matola 30 15
521 1 e. 50 Quelimane 30 15
522 2 e. Mocuba 50 15
523 2 e. 50 Antonio Enes 1·10 15
524 3 e. Cabral 50 15
525 4 e. Manica 50 20
526 4 e. 50 Pery 50 15
527 5 e. St. Tiago de Tete 60 20
528 7 e. 50 Porto Amelia 80 35
529 10 e. Chinde 1·40 35
530 20 e. Joao Belo 2·75 50
531 50 e. Beira 4·50 1·25

1962. Sports. As T **82** of Macao. Multicoloured.
532 50 c. Water-skiing 10 10
533 1 e. Wrestling 75 20
534 1 e. 50 Gymnastics 35 15
535 2 e. 50 Hockey 60 15
536 4 e. 50 Netball 90 40
537 15 e. Outboard speedboat racing 1·60 90

1962. Malaria Eradication. Mosquito design as T **83** of Macao. Multicoloured.
538 2 e. 50 "Anopheles funestus" 50 30

1962. 25th Anniv of D.E.T.A. (Mozambique Airline).
539 **51** 3 e. multicoloured 45 20

52 Lourenco Marques in 1887 and 1962

53 Oil Refinery, Sonarep

1962. 75th Anniv of Lourenco Marques.
540 **52** 1 e. multicoloured 40 20

1962. Air. Multicoloured.
541 1 e. 50 Type **53** 50 10
542 2 e. Salazar Academy 30 10
543 3 e. 50 Aerial view of Lourenco Marques Port 40 15
544 4 e. 50 Salazar Barrage 35 15
545 5 e. Trigo de Morais Bridge and Dam 40 15
546 20 e. Marcelo Caetano Bridge and Dam 1·10 50
Each design includes an airplane in flight.

54 Arms of Mozambique and Statue of Vasco da Gama

55 Nef, 1430

1963. Bicentenary of City of Mozambique.
547 **54** 3 e. multicoloured 35 20

1963. 10th Anniv of T.A.P. Airline. As T **52** of Portuguese Guinea.
548 2 e. 50 multicoloured 35 15

1963. Evolution of Sailing Ships. Multicoloured.
549 10 c. Type **55** 10 10
550 20 c. Caravel, 1436 (vert) 10 10
551 30 c. Lateen-rigged caravel, 1460 (vert) 15 10
552 50 c. Vasco da Gama's ship "Sao Gabriel", 1497 (vert) 30 10
553 1 e. Don Manuel's nau, 1498 (vert) 55 10
554 1 e. 50 Galleon, 1530 (vert) 40 15
555 2 e. Nau "Flor de la Mer", 1511 (vert) 40 15
556 2 e. 50 Caravel "Redonda", 1519 45 15
557 3 e. 50 Nau, 1520 (vert) 45 15
558 4 e. Portuguese Indies galley, 1521 50 20
559 4 e. 50 Galleon "Santa Tereza", 1639 (vert) 50 20
560 5 e. Nau "N. Senhora da Conceicao", 1716 (vert) 10·00 30
561 6 e. Warship "N. Senhora do Bom Sucesso", 1764 80 25
562 7 e. 50 Bomb launch, 1788 90 35
563 8 e. Naval brigantine "Lebre", 1793 90 35
564 10 e. Corvette "Andorinha", 1799 95 35
565 12 e. 50 Naval schooner "Maria Teresa", 1820 1·25 60
566 15 e. Warship "Vasco da Gama", 1841 1·60 60
567 20 e. Sail frigate "Don Fernando II e Gloria", 1843 (vert) 2·00 75
568 30 e. Cadet barque "Sagres I", 1924 (vert) 3·50 1·25

1964. Centenary of National Overseas Bank. As T **84** of Macao but view of Bank building, Lourenco Marques.
569 1 e. 50 multicoloured 20 15

56 Pres. Tomas

57 State Barge of Joao V, 1728

1964. Presidential Visit.
570 **56** 2 e. 50 multicoloured 15 10

1964. Portuguese Marine, 18th and 19th Centuries. Multicoloured.
571 15 c. Type **57** 10 10
572 35 c. State barge of Jose I, 1753 10 10
573 1 e. Barge of Alfandega, 1768 35 10
574 1 e. 50 Oarsman of 1780 (vert) 30 15
575 2 e. 50 State barge "Pinto da Fonseca", 1780 20 10
576 5 e. State barge of Carlota Joaquina, 1790 25 20
577 9 e. Don Miguel's state barge, 1831 60 40

1965. I.T.U. Centenary. As T **85** of Macao.
578 1 e. multicoloured 30 20

1966. 40th Anniv of Portuguese National Revolution. As T **86** of Macao, but showing different building. Multicoloured.
579 1 e. Beira railway station and Antonio Enes Academy 85 50

58 Arquebusier, 1560

59 Luis de Camoens (poet)

1967. Portuguese Military Uniforms. Multicoloured.
580 20 c. Type **58** 10 10
581 30 c. Arquebusier, 1640 10 10
582 40 c. Infantryman, 1777 15 10
583 50 c. Infantry officer, 1777 15 10
584 80 c. Drummer, 1777 35 20
585 1 e. Infantry sergeant, 1777 30 10
586 2 e. Infantry major, 1784 30 15
587 2 e. 50 Colonial officer, 1788 30 15
588 3 e. Infantryman, 1789 40 20
589 5 e. Colonial bugler, 1801 50 30
590 10 e. Colonial officer, 1807 70 30
591 15 e. Infantryman, 1817 85 55

1967. Centenary of Military Naval Association. As T **88** of Macao. Multicoloured.
592 3 e. A. Coutinho and paddle-gunboat "Tete" 35 15
593 10 e. J. Roby and paddle-gunboat "Granada" 65 35

1967. 50th Anniv of Fatima Apparitions. As T **89** of Macao.
594 50 c. "Golden Crown" 15 10

1968. 500th Birth Anniv of Pedro Cabral (explorer). As T **90** of Macao.
595 1 e. Erecting the Cross at Porto Sequro (horiz) 10 10
596 1 e. 50 First mission service in Brazil (horiz) 20 10
597 3 e. Church of Grace, Santarem 40 15

1969. Birth Centenary of Admiral Gago Coutinho. As T **91** of Macao.
598 70 c. Admiral Gago Coutinho Airport, Lourenco Marques (horiz) 25 10

1969. 400th Anniv of Camoens' Visit to Mozambique. Multicoloured.
599 15 c. Type **59** 10 10
600 50 c. Nau of 1553 (horiz) . . . 15 10
601 1 e. Map of Mozambique, 1554 . . . . 20 15
602 2 e. 50 Chapel of Our Lady of Baluarte (horiz) 25 20
603 5 e. Part of the "Lusiad" (poem) 40 30

1969. 500th Birth Anniv of Vasco da Gama (explorer). As T **92** of Macao. Multicoloured.
604 1 e. Route map of Da Gama's Voyage to India (horiz) . . . 15 10

1969. Centenary of Overseas Administrative Reforms. As T **93** of Macao.
605 1 e. 50 multicoloured 15 10

1969. 500th Birth Anniv of King Manoel I. As T **95** of Macao. Multicoloured.
606 80 c. Illuminated arms (horiz) . 15 10

1970. Birth Centenary of Marshal Carmona. As T **96** of Macao. Multicoloured.
607 5 e. Portrait in ceremonial dress 25 15

60 Fossilized Fern

1971. Rocks, Minerals and Fossils. Mult.
608 15 c. Type **60** 15 10
609 50 c. "Lytodiscoides conduciensis" (fossilized snail) 20 10
610 1 e. Stibnite 20 10
611 1 e. 50 Pink beryl 20 10
612 2 e. Endothiodon and fossil skeleton 25 10
613 3 e. Tantalocolumbite 30 10
614 3 e. 50 Verdelite 40 15
615 4 e. Zircon 50 30
616 10 e. Petrified tree-stump . . . 1·25 65

1972. 400th Anniv of Camoens' "The Lusiads" (epic poem). As T **98** of Macao. Multicoloured.
617 4 e. Mozambique Island in 16th century . . . . 1·25 30

1972. Olympic Games, Munich. As T **99** of Macao. Multicoloured.
618 3 e. Hurdling and swimming . . 15 10

1972. 50th Anniv of 1st Flight, Lisbon–Rio de Janeiro. As T **100** of Macao. Multicoloured.
619 1 e. Fairey IIID seaplane "Santa Cruz" at Recife 15 10

61 Racing Dinghies

1973. World Championships for "Vauriens" Class Yachts, Lourenco Marques.
620 **61** 1 e. multicoloured 15 10
621 – 1 e. 50 multicoloured . . . 15 10
622 – 3 e. multicoloured 30 20
DESIGNS: Nos. 621/2 similar to Type **61**.

1973. Centenary of I.M.O./W.M.O. As T **102** of Macao.
623 2 e. multicoloured 20 20

62 Dish Aerials

1974. Inauguration of Satellite Communications Station Network.
624 **62** 50 c. multicoloured 20 20

63 Bird with "Flag" Wings

1975. Implementation of Lusaka Agreement.
625 **63** 1 e. multicoloured 10 10
626 1 e. 50 multicoloured . . . 10 10
627 2 e. multicoloured 15 10
628 3 e. 50 multicoloured . . . 25 15
629 6 e. multicoloured 65 30

1975. Independence. Optd **INDEPENDENCIA 25 JUN 75.**
631 **43** 10 c. mult (postage) 50 50
632 – 40 c. mult (No. 476) 10 10
633 **62** 50 c. multicoloured 20 15
634 **61** 1 e. multicoloured 30 25
635 – 1 e. 50 mult (No. 621) . . . 85 75
636 – 2 e. mult (No. 623) . . . . 2·40 2·40
637 – 2 e. 50 mult (No. 535) . . . 35 30
638 – 3 e. mult (No. 618) 40 35
639 – 3 e. mult (No. 622) 45 40
640 – 3 e. 50 mult (No. 614) . . . 2·40 2·40
641 – 4 e. 50 mult (No. 536) . . . 2·75 1·50
642 – 7 e. 50 mult (No. 489) . . . 80 30
643 – 10 e. mult (No. 616) . . . . 1·40 35
644 – 15 e. mult (No. 537) . . . . 1·75 1·50
645 **43** 20 e. multicoloured . . . . 4·75 4·25
646 – 3 e. 50 multicoloured (No. 543) (air) 35 25
647 – 4 e. 50 mult (No. 544) . . . 40 25
648 – 5 e. mult (No. 545) . . . . 1·25 50
649 – 20 e. mult (No. 546) . . . . 2·00 4·25

66 Workers, Farmers and Children

67 Farm Worker

1975. "Vigilance, Unity, Work". Multicoloured.
650 20 c. Type **66** 10 10
651 30 c. Type **66** 10 10
652 50 c. Type **66** 10 10
653 2 e. 50 Type **66** 15 10
654 4 e. 50 Armed family, workers and dancers 25 15
655 5 e. As No. 654 . . . . . . 35 15
656 10 e. As No. 654 . . . . . . 95 30
657 50 e. As No. 654 . . . . . . 4·25 2·10

1976. Women's Day.
659 **67** 1 e. black and green 10 10
660 – 1 e. 50 black and brown . . . 10 10
661 – 2 e. 50 black and blue . . . 15 10
662 – 10 e. black and red 90 40
DESIGNS: 1 e. 50, Teaching; 2 e. 50, Nurse; 10 e. Mother.

1976. Pres. Kaunda's First Visit to Mozambique. Optd **PRESIDENTE KENNETH KAUNDA PREMEIRA VISITA 20/4/1976.**
663 **63** 2 e. multicoloured 15 10
664 3 e. 50 multicoloured . . . 25 15
665 6 e. multicoloured 50 30

69 Arrival of President Machel

70 Mozambique Stamp of 1876 and Emblem

1976. 1st Anniv of Independence. Mult.
666 50 c. Type **69** 10 10
667 1 e. Proclamation ceremony . . 10 10
668 2 e. 50 Signing ceremony . . . 15 10
669 7 e. 50 Soldiers on parade . . . 40 20
670 20 e. Independence flame . . . 1·50 1·10

1976. Stamp Centenary.
671 **70** 1 e. 50 multicoloured 10 10
672 6 e. multicoloured 30 20

1976. "FACIM" Industrial Fair. Optd **FACIM 1976.**
673 **66** 2 e. 50 multicoloured . . . 30 15

72 Weapons and Flag

73 Thick-tailed Bush baby

1976. Army Day.
674 **72** 3 e. multicoloured 20 10

1977. Animals. Multicoloured.
675 50 c. Type **73** 15 10
676 1 e. Ratel (horiz) 15 10
677 1 e. 50 Temminck's ground pangolin 20 10
678 2 e. Steenbok (horiz) 20 10
679 2 e. 50 Diademed monkey . . . 25 10
680 3 e. Hunting dog (horiz) . . . 25 10
681 4 e. Cheetah (horiz) 35 10
682 5 e. Spotted hyena 50 15
683 7 e. 50 Warthog (horiz) . . . . 1·00 25
684 8 e. Hippopotamus (horiz) . . . 1·10 30
685 10 e. White rhinoceros (horiz) . 1·10 30
686 15 e. Sable antelope . . . . . 1·60 65

74 Congress Emblem

75 "Women" (child's drawing)

1977. 3rd Frelimo Congress, Maputo. Mult.
687 3 e. Type **74** 15 10
688 3 e. 50 Macheje Monument (site of 2nd Congress) (34 × 24 mm) 20 10
689 20 e. Maputo Monument (23 × 34 mm) . . . . 1·40 50

1977. Mozambique Women's Day.
690 **75** 5 e. multicoloured 25 10
691 15 e. multicoloured 65 25

76 Labourer and Farmer

77 Crowd with Arms and Crops

1977. Labour Day.
692 **76** 5 e. multicoloured 25 10

1977. 2nd Anniv of Independence.
693 **77** 50 c. multicoloured 10 10
694 1 e. 50 multicoloured . . . 10 10
695 3 e. multicoloured 15 10
696 15 e. multicoloured 60 25

78 "Encephalartos ferox"

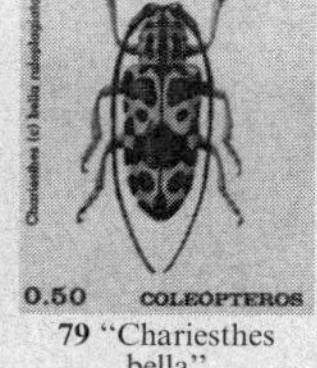

79 "Chariesthes bella"

1978. Stamp Day. Nature Protection. Mult.
697 1 e. Type **78** 10 10
698 10 e. Nyala 50 20

1978. Beetles. Multicoloured.
699 50 c. Type **79** 10 10
700 1 e. "Tragocephalus variegata" 10 10
701 1 e. 50 "Monochamus leuconotus" 10 10
702 3 e. "Prosopocera lactator" . . 25 10
703 5 e. "Dinocephalus ornatus" . . 40 10
704 10 e. "Tragiscoschema nigroscriptus" 60 20

80 Violet-crested Turaco

81 Mother and Child

1978. Birds. Multicoloured.
705 50 c. Type **80** 30 10
706 1 e. Lilac-breasted roller . . . 40 10
707 1 e. 50 Red-headed weaver . . 40 10
708 2 e. 50 Violet starling 45 15
709 3 e. Peters's twin-spot 95 20
710 15 e. European bee eater . . . 2·25 40

1978. Global Eradication of Smallpox.
711 **81** 15 e. multicoloured 45 25

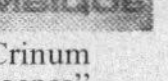

82 "Crinum delagoense"

83 First Stamps of Mozambique and Canada

1978. Flowers. Multicoloured.
712 50 c. Type **82** 10 10
713 1 e. "Gloriosa superba" . . . 10 10
714 1 e. 50 "Eulophia speciosa" . . 10 10
715 3 e. "Erithrina humeana" . . . 15 10
716 5 e. "Astripomoea malvacea" . 80 15
717 10 e. "Kigelia africana" . . . . 1·00 60

1978. "CAPEX '78" International Stamp Exhibition, Toronto.
718 **83** 15 e. multicoloured 45 25

84 Mozambique Flag

85 Boy with Books

1978. 3rd Anniv of Independence. Multicoloured.
719 1 e. Type **84** 10 10
720 1 e. 50 Coat of Arms 10 10
721 7 e. 50 People and Constitution 25 15
722 10 e. Band and National Anthem 30 20

1978. 11th World Youth Festival, Havana. Multicoloured.
724 2 e. 50 Type **85** 10 10
725 3 e. Soldiers 15 10
726 7 e. 50 Harvesting wheat . . . 25 20

86 Czechoslovakian 50 h. Stamp, 1919

1978. "PRAGA '78" International Stamp Exhibition.
727 **86** 15 e. blue, ochre and red . . 45 30

87 Football

1978. Stamp Day. Sports. Multicoloured.
729 50 c. Type **87** 10 10
730 1 e. 50 Putting the shot 10 10
731 3 e. Hurdling 15 10
732 7 e. 50 Basketball 35 20
733 12 e. 50 Swimming 45 35
734 25 e. Roller-skate hockey . . . 1·25 60

88 U.P.U. Emblem and Dove

1979. Membership of U.P.U.
735 **88** 20 e. multicoloured . . . . 1·00 45

89 Eduardo Mondlane

1979. 10th Death Anniv of Eduardo Mondlane (founder of FRELIMO). Multicoloured.

736 1 e. Soldier handing gourd to woman 10 10
737 3 e. FRELIMO soldiers 15 10
738 7 e. 50 Children learning to write 30 20
739 12 e. 50 Type **89** 40 30

90 Shaded Silver

91 I.Y.C. Emblem

1979. Domestic Cats. Multicoloured.

740 50 c. Type **90** 10 10
741 1 e. 50 Manx cat 10 10
742 2 e. 50 British blue 15 10
743 3 e. Turkish cat 20 10
744 12 e. 50 Long-haired tabby . . 85 55
745 20 e. African wild cat . . . . 1·50 90

1979. Obligatory Tax. International Year of the Child.

746 **91** 50 c. red 15 10

92 Wrestling

1979. Olympic Games, Moscow (1980). Mult.

747 1 e. Type **92** 10 10
748 2 e. Running 10 10
749 3 e. Horse jumping 15 10
750 5 e. Canoeing 15 10
751 10 e. High jump 30 20
752 15 e. Archery 50 40

93 Flowers

1979. International Year of the Child. Multicoloured.

754 50 c. Type **93** 10 10
755 1 e. 50 Dancers 10 10
756 3 e. In the city 15 10
757 5 e. Working in the country . . 15 10
758 7 e. 50 Houses 25 15
759 12 e. 50 Transport . . . . . 1·50 50

94 Flight from Colonialism

1979. 4th Anniv of Independence. Multicoloured.

760 50 c. Type **94** 10 10
761 2 e. Eduardo Mondlane (founder of FRELIMO) 10 10
762 3 e. Armed struggle, death of Mondlane 15 10
763 7 e. 50 Final fight for liberation 25 15
764 15 e. President Samora Machel proclaims victory 45 35

95 Golden Scorpionfish

1979. Tropical Fish. Multicoloured.

766 50 c. Type **95** 10 10
767 1 e. 50 Golden trevally 15 10
768 2 e. 50 Brick goby 20 10
769 3 e. Clown surgeonfish 25 15
770 10 e. Lace goby 60 25
771 12 e. 50 Yellow-edged lyretail . 95 40

96 Quartz

1979. Minerals. Multicoloured.

772 1 e. Type **96** 10 10
773 1 e. 50 Beryl 10 10
774 2 e. 50 Magnetite 15 10
775 5 e. Tourmaline 30 10
776 10 e. Euxenite 60 20
777 20 e. Fluorite . . . . 1·40 45

97 Soldier handing out Guns

1979. 15th Anniv of Fight for Independence.

778 **97** 5 e. multicoloured 25 15

98 Locomotive No. 1, 1914

1979. Early Locomotives. Multicoloured.

779 50 c. Type **98** 15 10
780 1 e. 50 Gaza Railway locomotive No. 1, 1898 . . . . . . 20 10
781 3 e. Cape Government Railway 1st Class locomotive, 1878 . 45 10
782 7 e. 50 Delagoa Bay Railway locomotive No. 9, 1892 . . . 75 20
783 12 e. 50 Locomotive No. 41, 1896 1·25 30
784 15 e. Trans Zambesia Railway Class D steam locomotive . . 1·40 35

99 Dalmatian

1979. Dogs. Multicoloured.

785 50 c. Basenji (vert) 10 10
786 1 e. 50 Type **99** 15 10
787 3 e. Boxer 15 10
788 7 e. 50 Blue gascon pointer . . 35 15
789 12 e. 50 English cocker spaniel 85 25
790 15 e. Pointer . . . . 1·25 30

100 "Papilio nireus"

1979. Stamp Day. Butterflies. Multicoloured.

791 1 e. Type **100** 10 10
792 1 e. 50 "Amauris ochlea" . . . 10 10
793 2 e. 50 "Pinacopterix eriphia" . 15 10
794 5 e. "Junonia hierta" 35 10
795 10 e. "Nephronia argia" . . . 1·00 20
796 20 e. "Catacroptera cloanthe" . 2·10 90

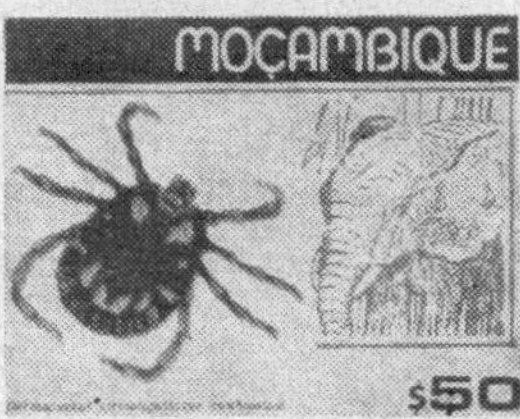

101 "Dermacentor circumguttatus cunhasilvai" and African Elephant

1980. Ticks. Multicoloured.

797 50 c. Type **101** 20 10
798 1 e. 50 "Dermacentor rhinocerinos" and black rhinoceros 30 10
799 2 e. 50 "Amblyomma hebraeum" and giraffe 40 15
800 3 e. "Amblyomma pomposum" and eland 50 15
801 5 e. "Amblyomma theilerae" and cow 60 15
802 7 e. 50 "Amblyomma eburneum" and African buffalo 85 30

102 Ford "Hercules" Bus, 1950

1980. Road Transport. Multicoloured.

803 50 c. Type **102** 10 10
804 1 e. 50 Scania "Marco-polo" bus, 1978 . . . . 10 10
805 3 e. Bussing Nag Bus, 1936 . . 15 10
806 5 e. Ikarus articulated bus, 1978 20 10
807 7 e. 50 Ford Taxi, 1929 . . . 40 15
808 12 e. 50 Fiat "131" Taxi, 1978 80 20

103 Soldier and Map of Southern Africa

1980. Zimbabwe Independence.

809 **103** 10 e. blue and brown . . . 40 15

104 Marx, Engels and Lenin

1980. International Workers' Day.

810 **104** 10 e. multicoloured 40 15

105 "Market" (Moises Simbine)

1980. "London 1980" International Stamp Exhibition. Multicoloured.

811 50 c. "Heads" (Malangatana) . 10 10
812 1 e. 50 Type **105** 10 10
813 3 e. "Heads with Helmets" (Malangatana) 15 10
814 5 e. "Women with Goods" (Machiana) 20 10
815 7 e. 50 "Crowd with Masks" (Malangatana) 25 15
816 12 e. 50 "Man and Woman with Spear" (Mankeu) 50 25

106 Telephone

1980. World Telecommunications Day.

817 **106** 15 e. multicoloured 60 25

MINIMUM PRICE

The minimum price quoted is 10p which represents a handling charge rather than a basis for valuing common stamps. For further notes about prices see introductory pages.

107 Mueda Massacre

108 Crowd waving Tools

1980. 20th Anniv of Mueda Massacre.

818 **107** 15 e. green, brown and red 60 25

1980. 5th Anniv of Independence.

819 – 1 e. black and red 10 10
820 **108** 2 e. multicoloured 10 10
821 – 3 e. multicoloured 15 10
822 – 4 e. multicoloured 20 10
823 – 5 e. black, yellow and red 20 10
824 – 10 e. multicoloured 40 15

DESIGNS—As T **108**: 1 e. Crowd, doctor tending patient, soldier and workers tilling land; 3 e. Crowd with flags and tools; 4 e. Stylised figures raising right hand; 5 e. Hand grasping flags, book and plants; 10 e. Figures carrying banners each with year date. 55 × 37 mm: 30 e. Soldiers.

109 Gymnastics

1980. Olympic Games, Moscow. Multicoloured.

826 50 c. Type **109** 10 10
827 1 e. 50 Football 10 10
828 2 e. 50 Running 10 10
829 3 e. Volleyball 20 10
830 10 e. Cycling 40 15
831 12 e. 50 Boxing 45 20

110 Narina Trogon

1980. Birds. Multicoloured.

832 1 m. Type **110** 30 10
833 1 m. 50 South African crowned crane 35 10
834 2 m. 50 Bare-throated francolin 40 10
835 5 m. Ostrich 75 20
836 7 m. 50 Spur-winged goose . . 85 20
837 12 m. 50 African fish eagle . . 1·00 30

111 Family and Census Officer

1980. First General Census.

838 **111** 3 m. 50 multicoloured . . . 25 10

112 Animals fleeing from Fire

1980. Campaign against Bush Fires.

839 **112** 3 m. 50 multicoloured . . . 25 10

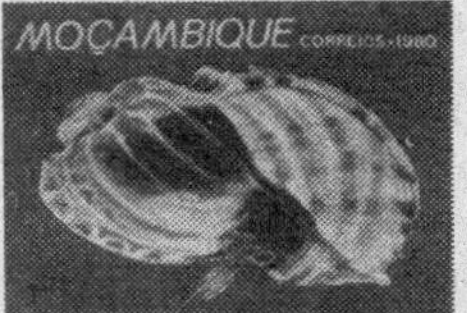

113 Common Harp

1980. Stamp Day. Shells. Multicoloured.
840 1 m. Type **113** 10 10
841 1 m. 50 Arthritic spider conch . 15 10
842 2 m. 50 Venus comb murex . . 20 10
843 5 m. Clear sundial 40 15
844 7 m. 50 Ramose murex 50 20
845 12 m. 50 Diana conch . . . . 1·10 35

114 Pres. Machel, Electricity Pylons, Aircraft and Lorry

1981. "Decade for Victory over Underdevelopment".
846 **114** 3 m. 50 blue and red . . . 2·00 75
847 – 7 m. 50 brown and green . 25 15
848 – 12 m. 50 mauve and blue . 50 30
DESIGNS: 7 m. 50, Pres. Machel and armed forces on parade; 12 m. 50, Pres. Machel and classroom scenes.

115 Footballer and Athletic de Bilbao Stadium

1981. World Cup Football Championships, Spain (1982). Multicoloured.
849 1 m. Type **115** 10 10
850 1 m. 50 Valencia, C.F. 10 10
851 2 m. 50 Oviedo C.F. 10 10
852 5 m. R. Betis Balompie 20 10
853 7 m. 50 Real Zaragoza 25 15
854 12 m. 50 R. C.D. Espanol . . . 50 25

116 Giraffe

117 Chitende

1981. Protected Animals. Multicoloured.
856 50 c. Type **116** 10 10
857 1 m. 50 Topi 10 10
858 2 m.50 Aardvark 10 10
859 3 m. African python 10 10
860 5 m. Loggerhead turtle 20 15
861 10 m. Marabou stork 70 30
862 12 m. 50 Saddle-bill stork . . 1·25 35
863 15 m. Kori bustard . . . . . 1·50 45

1981. Musical Instruments. Multicoloured.
864 50 c. Type **117** 10 10
865 2 m. Pankwe (horiz) 10 10
866 2 m. 50 Kanyembe 10 10
867 7 m. Nyanga (horiz) 30 20
868 10 m. Likuti and M'Petheni (horiz) 70 25

118 Disabled Persons making Baskets

1981. International Year of Disabled People.
869 **118** 5 m. multicoloured 25 15

119 De Havilland Dragon Rapide

1981. Air. Mozambique Aviation History. Mult.
870 50 c. Type **119** 10 10
871 1 m. 50 Junkers Ju 52/3m . . . 10 10
872 3 m. Lockheed Super Electra . 20 15
873 7 m. 50 De Havilland Dove . . 35 30
874 10 m. Douglas DC-3 . . . . . 50 35
875 12 m. 50 Fokker Friendship . . 75 50

120 Controlled Killing, Marromeu

1981. World Hunting Exhibition, Plovdiv. Mult.
876 2 m. Type **120** 30 15
877 5 m. Traditional hunting Cheringoma 20 15
878 6 m. Tourist hunting, Save . . 40 30
879 7 m. 60 Marksmanship Gorongosa 40 20
880 12 m. 50 African elephants, Gorongosa . . . . 1·50 60
881 20 m. Trap, Cabo Delgado . . 80 50

121 50 Centavos Coin

122 Sunflower

1981. 1st Anniv of New Currency. Mult.
883 50 c. Type **121** 10 10
884 1 m. One metical coin 10 10
885 2 m. 50 Two meticals 50 coin . 10 10
886 5 m. Five meticals coin 20 15
887 10 m. Ten meticals coin 50 25
888 20 m. Twenty meticals coin . . 1·40 55

1981. Agricultural Resources.
890 **122** 50 c. orange and red . . . 10 10
891 – 1 m. black and red 10 10
892 – 1 m. 50 blue and red . . . 10 10
893 – 2 m. 50 yellow and red . . 10 10
894 – 3 m. 50 green and red . . . 15 10
895 – 4 m. 50 grey and red . . . 15 10
896 – 10 m. blue and red 40 15
897 – 12 m. 50 brown and red . . 50 20
898 – 15 m. brown and red . . . 60 25
899 – 25 m. green and red . . . 1·40 40
900 – 40 m. orange and red . . . 2·00 60
901 – 60 m. brown and red . . . 2·75 1·00
DESIGNS: 1 m. Cotton; 1 m. 50, Sisal; 2 m. 50, Cashew; 3 m. 50, Tea; 4 m. 50, Sugar cane; 10 m. Castor oil; 12 m. 50, Coconut; 15 m. Tobacco; 25 m. Rice; 40 m. Maize; 60 m. Groundnut.

123 Archaeological Excavation, Manyikeni

1981. Archaeological Excavation. Mult.
902 1 m. Type **123** 10 10
903 1 m. 50 Hand-axe (Massingir Dam) 10 10
904 2 m. 50 Ninth century bowl (Chibuene) 10 10
905 7 m. 50 Ninth century pot (Chibuene) 30 20
906 12 m. 50 Gold beads (Manyikeni) 50 30
907 20 m. Gong (Manyikeni) . . . 80 50

124 Mapiko Mask

1981. Sculptures. Multicoloured.
908 50 c. Type **124** 10 10
909 1 m. Woman who suffers . . . 10 10
910 2 m. 50 Woman with a child . . 10 10
911 3 m. 50 The man who makes fire 15 10
912 5 m. Chietane 20 15
913 12 m. 50 Chietane (different) . 70 30

125 Broken Loaf on Globe

1981. World Food Day.
914 **125** 10 m. multicoloured . . . 45 25

126 Tanker "Matchedje"

1981. Mozambique Ships. Multicoloured.
915 50 c. Type **126** 15 15
916 1 m. 50 Tug "Macuti" 15 15
917 3 m. Trawler "Vega 7" 25 15
918 5 m. Freighter "Linde" 35 25
919 7 m. 50 Freighter "Pemba" . . 55 30
920 12 m. 50 Dredger "Rovuma" . 95 55

127 "Portunus pelagicus"

1981. Crustaceans. Multicoloured.
921 50 c. Type **127** 10 10
922 1 m. 50 "Scylla serrata" . . . 10 10
923 3 m. "Penacus indicus" 15 10
924 7 m. 50 "Palinurus delagoae" . 35 20
925 12 m. 50 "Lysiosquilla maculata" 55 35
926 15 m. "Panulirus ornatus" . . 80 45

128 "Hypoxis multiceps"

129 Telex Tape, Telephone and Globe

1981. Flowers. Multicoloured.
927 1 m. Type **128** 10 10
928 1 m. 50 "Pelargonium luridun" . 10 10
929 2 m. 50 "Caralluma melanathera" 10 10
930 7 m. 50 "Ansellia gigantea" . . 35 20
931 12 m. 50 "Stapelia leendertsiae" 60 35
932 25 m. "Adenium multiflorum" . 1·50 70

1982. 1st Anniv of Mozambique Post and Telecommunications. Multicoloured.
933 6 m. Type **129** 35 20
934 15 m. Winged envelope and envelope forming railway wagon . . . . 3·00 1·50

130 Diagram of Petrol Engine

1982. Fuel Saving. Multicoloured.
935 5 m. Type **130** 30 15
936 7 m. 50 Speeding car 45 25
937 10 m. Loaded truck 60 35

131 Sea-snake

1982. Reptiles. Multicoloured.
938 50 c. Type **131** 20 10
939 1 m. 50 "Naja mossambica mossambica" 10 10
940 3 m. "Thelotornis capensis mossambica" 20 15
941 6 m. "Dendroaspis polylepis polylepis" 35 25
942 15 m. "Dispholidus typus" . . 80 50
943 20 m. "Bitis arietans arietans" . 1·50 75

132 Dr. Robert Koch, Bacillus and X-Ray

1982. Centenary of Discovery of Tubercle Bacillus.
944 **132** 20 m. multicoloured . . . 1·75 1·00

133 Telephone Line

134 Player with Ball

1982. International Telecommunications Union. Plenipotentiary Conference.
945 **133** 20 m. multicoloured . . . 1·00 75

1982. World Cup Football Championship, Spain. Multicoloured.
946 1 m. 50 Type **134** 10 10
947 3 m. 50 Player heading ball . . 25 15
948 7 m. Two players fighting for ball 40 20
949 10 m. Player receiving ball . . 60 30
950 20 m. Goalkeeper . . . . . . 1·25 1·00

135 Political Rally

137 "Vangueria infausta"

1982. 25th Anniv of FRELIMO. Multicoloured.
953 4 m. Type **135** 25 15
954 8 m. Agriculture 45 25
955 12 m. Marching workers . . . 70 35

1982. Fruits. Multicoloured.
956 1 m. Type **137** 10 10
957 2 m. "Mimusops caffra" . . . 10 10
958 4 m. "Sclerocarya caffra" . . . 25 15
959 8 m. "Strychnos spinosa" . . . 45 25
960 12 m. "Salacia kraussi" 70 40
961 32 m. "Trichilia emetica" . . . 1·90 85

138 "Sputnik I"

139 Vigilantes

1982. 25th Anniv of First Artificial Satellite. Multicoloured.
962 1 m. Type **138** 10 10
963 2 m. First manned space flight . 10 10
964 4 m. First walk in space . . . 25 15
965 8 m. First manned flight to the moon 45 25
966 16 m. "Soyuz"–"Apollo" mission . . . . 1·25 70
967 20 m. "Intercosmos" rocket . . 1·50 70

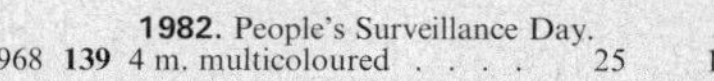

1982. People's Surveillance Day.
968 **139** 4 m. multicoloured 25 15

140 Caique

141 "Ophiomostix venosa"

1982. Traditional Boats. Multicoloured.
969 1 m. Type **140** 10 10
970 2 m. Machua 15 10
971 4 m. Calaua (horiz) 30 15
972 8 m. Chitatarro (horiz) 60 25
973 12 m. Cangaia (horiz) 80 35
974 16 m. Chata (horiz) . . . . . 1·75 60

1982. Starfishes and Sea Urchins. Multicoloured.

975	1 m. Type **141**	10	10
976	2 m. "Protoreaster lincki"	10	10
977	4 m. "Tropiometra carinata"	15	10
978	8 m. "Holothuria scabra"	35	20
979	12 m. "Prionocidaris baculosa"	60	35
980	16 m. "Colobocentrotus atnatus"	80	40

142 Soldiers defending Mozambique

1983. 4th Frelimo Party Congress. Multicoloured.

981	4 m. Type **142**	15	10
982	8 m. Crowd waving voting papers	30	20
983	16 m. Agriculture, industry and education	65	40

143 "Codium duthierae"

1983. Seaweeds. Multicoloured.

984	1 m. Type **143**	10	10
985	2 m. "Halimeda cunata"	10	10
986	4 m. "Dictyota liturata"	15	10
987	8 m. "Endorachne binghamiae"	40	20
988	12 m. "Laurencia flexuosa"	60	30
989	20 m. "Acrosorium sp."	1·25	55

144 Diving and Swimming

1983. Olympic Games, Los Angeles (1st issue). Multicoloured.

990	1 m. Type **144**	10	10
991	2 m. Boxing	10	10
992	4 m. Basketball	20	10
993	8 m. Handball	35	20
994	12 m. Volleyball	55	30
995	16 m. Running	65	40
996	20 m. Yachting	1·25	65

See also Nos. 1029/34.

145 Mallet Type Locomotive

1983. Steam Locomotives. Multicoloured.

998	1 m. Type **145**	10	10
999	2 m. Baldwin, 1915–45	20	10
1000	4 m. Class 141-148, 1950	40	15
1001	8 m. Baldwin, 1926	75	25
1002	16 m. Henschel Garratt type, 1956	1·40	50
1003	32 m. Natal Government Class H, 1899–1903	3·00	1·00

146 O.A.U. Emblem

1983. 20th Anniv of Organization of African Unity.

1004	**146**	4 m. multicoloured	20	15

147 Four-toed Elephant-shrew

150 "Communications"

148 Aiding Flood Victims

1983. Mozambique Mammals. Multicoloured.

1005	1 m. Type **147**	10	10
1006	2 m. Four-striped grass mouse	15	10
1007	4 m. Vincent's bush squirrel	25	15
1008	8 m. Hottentot mole-rat	50	25
1009	12 m. Natal red hare	75	40
1010	16 m. Straw-coloured fruit bat	1·25	75

1983. 2nd Anniv of Mozambique Red Cross. Multicoloured.

1011	4 m. Type **148**	20	10
1012	8 m. Red Cross lorry	40	20
1013	16 m. First aid demonstration	75	40
1014	32 m. Agricultural worker performing first aid	1·90	75

1983. World Communications Year.

1016	**150**	8 m. multicoloured	1·50	75

151 Line Fishing

1983. Fishery Resources. Multicoloured.

1017	50 c. Type **151**	10	10
1018	2 m. Chifonho (basket trap)	10	10
1019	4 m. Spear fishing	25	15
1020	8 m. Gamboa (fence trap)	40	25
1021	16 m. Mono (basket trap)	1·50	40
1022	20 m. Lema (basket trap)	1·60	55

152 Kudu Horn

153 Swimming

1983. Stamp Day. Multicoloured.

1023	50 c. Type **152**	10	10
1024	1 m. Drum communication	10	10
1025	4 m. Postal runners	20	15
1026	8 m. Mail canoe	40	40
1027	16 m. Mail van	75	40
1028	20 m. Steam mail train	3·25	1·50

1984. Olympic Games, Los Angeles (2nd issue). Multicoloured.

1029	50 c. Type **153**	10	10
1030	4 m. Football	20	10
1031	8 m. Hurdling	35	20
1032	16 m. Basketball	90	50
1033	32 m. Handball	1·90	80
1034	60 m. Boxing	3·00	1·75

154 "Trichilia emetica"

1984. Indigenous Trees. Multicoloured.

1035	50 c. Type **154**	10	10
1036	2 m. "Brachystegia spiciformis"	10	10
1037	4 m. "Androstachys johnsonii"	20	10
1038	8 m. "Pterocarpus angolensis"	35	20
1039	16 m. "Milletia stuhlmannii"	80	40
1040	50 m. "Dalbergia melanoxylon"	2·75	1·75

155 Dove with Olive Sprig

1984. Nkomati South Africa–Mozambique Non-aggression Pact.

1041	**155**	4 m. multicoloured	25	10

156 State Arms

1984. Emblems of the Republic. Multicoloured.

1042	4 m. Type **156**	20	10
1043	8 m. State Flag	40	20

157 Makway Dance

1984. "Lubrapex '84" Portuguese–Brazilian Stamp Exhibition, Lisbon. Traditional Mozambican dances. Multicoloured.

1044	4 m. Type **157**	20	10
1045	8 m. Mapiko dance	40	20
1046	16 m. Wadjaba dance	1·40	50

158 Nampula Museum and Statuette of Woman with Water Jug

1984. Museums. Multicoloured.

1047	50 c. Type **158**	10	10
1048	4 m. Natural History Museum and secretary bird	45	10
1049	8 m. Revolution Museum and soldier carrying wounded comrade	35	20
1050	16 m. Colonial History Museum and cannon	65	40
1051	20 m. National Numismatic Museum and coins	1·25	65
1052	30 m. St. Paul's Palace and antique chair	1·50	95

159 Imber's Tetra

1984. Fishes. Multicoloured.

1053	50 c. Type **159**	10	10
1054	4 m. Purple labeo	25	10
1055	12 m. Brown squeaker	75	35
1056	16 m. Blue-finned notho	95	55
1057	40 m. Slender serrate barb	2·50	1·40
1058	60 m. Barred minnow	3·75	1·90

160 Badge and Laurels

162 Knife and Club

161 Rural Landscape and Emblem

1984. International Fair, Maputo.

1059	**160**	16 m. multicoloured	70	50

1984. 20th Anniv of African Development Bank.

1060	**161**	4 m. multicoloured	30	10

1984. Traditional Weapons. Multicoloured.

1061	50 c. Type **162**	10	10
1062	4 m. Axes	20	10
1063	8 m. Spear and shield	35	15
1064	16 m. Bow and arrow	75	35
1065	32 m. Rifle	1·90	95
1066	50 m. Assegai and arrow	2·75	1·90

163 Workers and Emblem

1984. 1st Anniv of Organization of Mozambican Workers.

1067	**163**	4 m. multicoloured	20	10

164 Barue 1902 Postmark

1984. Stamp Day. Postmarks. Multicoloured.

1068	4 m. Type **164**	15	10
1069	8 m. Zumbo postmark and King Carlos 15 r. Mozambique "key type" stamp	35	20
1070	12 m. Mozambique Company postmark and 1935 airmail stamp	55	30
1071	16 m. Macequece postmark and 1937 2 e. Mozambique Company stamp	70	40

165 Keeper and Hive

166 Shot-putter and Emblem

1985. Bee-keeping. Multicoloured.

1072	4 m. Type **165**	15	10
1073	8 m. Worker bee	45	20
1074	16 m. Drone	1·25	40
1075	20 m. Queen bee	1·75	60

1985. "Olymphilex 85" Olympic Stamps Exhibition, Lausanne.

1076	**166**	16 m. blue, black & red	75	35

167 Forecasting Equipment and Desert

1985. World Meteorology Day.
1077 **167** 4 m. multicoloured . . . 35 10

168 Map

1985. 5th Anniv of Southern African Development Co-ordination Conference. Multicoloured.
1078 4 m. Type **168** 15 10
1079 8 m. Map and pylon 45 20
1080 16 m. Industry and transport . 2·50 1·25
1081 32 m. Member states' flags . . 1·90 95

169 Battle of Mujenga, 1896

1985. 10th Anniv of Independence. Mult.
1082 1 m. Type **169** 10 10
1083 4 m. Attack on Barue by Macombe, 1917 . . . . . 25 10
1084 8 m. Attack on Massangano, 1868 . . . . 55 20
1085 16 m. Battle of Marracuene, 1895, and Gungunhana . . 1·50 50

170 U.N. Building, New York and Flag

1985. 40th Anniv of U.N.O.
1086 **170** 16 m. multicoloured . . . 80 50

171 Mathacuzana

1985. Traditional Games and Sports. Multicoloured.
1087 50 c. Type **171** 10 10
1088 4 m. Mudzobo 20 10
1089 8 m. Muravarava (board game) 40 20
1090 16 m. N'tshuwa 90 50

172 "Rana angolensis"

1985. Frogs and Toads. Multicoloured.
1091 50 c. Type **172** 10 10
1092 1 m. "Hyperolius pictus" . . . 10 10
1093 4 m. "Ptychadena porosissima" 15 10
1094 8 m. "Afrixalus formasinii" . . 50 20
1095 16 m. "Bufo regularis" . . . 95 50
1096 32 m. "Hyperolius marmoratus" . . . . . . 2·40 95

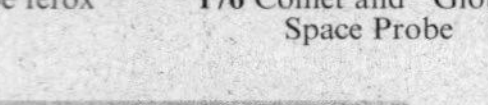

174 "Aloe ferox" **176** Comet and "Giotto" Space Probe

175 Mozambique Company 1918 10 c. Stamp

1985. Medicinal Plants. Multicoloured.
1099 50 c. Type **174** 10 10
1100 1 m. "Boophone disticha" . . 10 10
1101 3 m. 50 "Gloriosa superba" . . 15 10
1102 4 m. "Cotyledon orbiculata" . 15 10
1103 8 m. "Homeria breyniana" . . 55 20
1104 50 m. "Haemanthus coccineus" 3·75 1·90

1985. Stamp Day. Multicoloured.
1105 1 m. Type **175** . . . . 1·25 75
1106 4 m. Nyassa Co. 1911 25 r. stamp 15 10
1107 8 m. Mozambique Co. 1918 ½ c. stamp 50 20
1108 16 m. Nyassa Co. 1924 1 c. Postage Due stamp . . 1·25 50

1986. Appearance of Halley's Comet.
1109 **176** 4 m. blue & light blue . . 20 10
1110 – 8 m. violet & light violet . 50 20
1111 – 16 m. multicoloured . . . 95 50
1112 – 30 m. multicoloured . . . 2·00 95
DESIGNS: 8 m. Comet orbits; 16 m. Small and large telescopes, comet and space probe; 30 m. Comet, stars and globe.

177 Vicente

1986. World Cup Football Championship, Mexico. Multicoloured.
1113 3 m. Type **177** 15 10
1114 4 m. Coluna 20 10
1115 8 m. Costa Pereira 40 20
1116 12 m. Hilario 65 35
1117 16 m. Matateu 95 50
1118 50 m. Eusebio . . . . . . 3·25 1·90

178 Dove and Emblem **179** "Amanita muscaria"

1986. International Peace Year.
1119 **178** 16 m. multicoloured . . . 85 45

1986. Fungi. Multicoloured.
1120 4 m. Type **179** 50 20
1121 8 m. "Lactarius deliciosus" . . 95 30
1122 16 m. "Amanita phaloides" . . 2·00 65
1123 30 m. "Tricholoma nudum" . 4·25 1·25

181 Spiky Style

1986. Women's Hairstyles. Multicoloured.
1125 1 m. Type **181** 10 10
1126 4 m. Beaded plaits 25 10
1127 8 m. Plaited tightly to head . . 50 20
1128 16 m. Plaited tightly to head with ponytail . . . . . . 1·25 55

182 Dugong

1986. Marine Mammals. Multicoloured.
1129 1 m. Type **182** 10 10
1130 8 m. Common dolphin . . . 35 20
1131 16 m. "Neobalena marginata" 1·25 85
1132 50 f. Fin whale . . . . 4·25 2·75

183 Children Studying

1986. 1st Anniv of Continuadores Youth Organization.
1133 **183** 4 m. multicoloured . . . 30 15

184 50 m. Notes

1986. Savings. Multicoloured.
1134 4 m. Type **184** 25 10
1135 8 m. 100 m. notes 50 20
1136 16 m. 500 m. notes . . . . . 1·40 50
1137 30 m. 1000 m. notes . . . . . 2·75 1·25

185 Quelimane Post Office

1986. Stamp Day. Post Offices. Multicoloured.
1138 3 m. Type **185** 20 10
1139 4 m. Maputo 30 10
1140 8 m. Beira 65 20
1141 16 m. Nampula . . . . . . 1·40 50

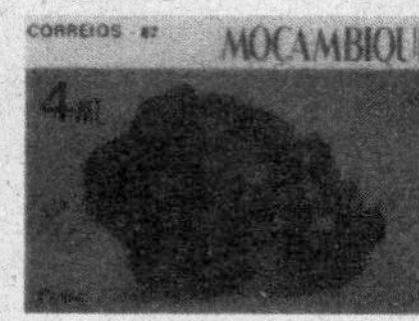

186 Pyrite

1987. Minerals. Multicoloured.
1142 4 m. Type **186** 30 10
1143 8 m. Emerald 60 20
1144 12 m. Agate 85 40
1145 16 m. Malachite . . . . . . 1·40 50
1146 30 m. Garnet . . . . 2·50 1·25
1147 50 m. Amethyst . . . . . . 4·25 2·00

187 Crowd beneath Flag

1987. 10th Anniv of Mozambique Liberation Front.
1148 **187** 4 m. multicoloured . . . 30 15

188 Little Libombos Dam

1987.
1149 **188** 16 m. multicoloured . . . 1·40 60

189 Children being Vaccinated

1987. World Health Day. Vaccination Campaign.
1150 **189** 50 m. multicoloured . . . 1·90 1·50

190 Common Grenadier **191** Football

1987. Birds. Multicoloured.
1151 3 m. Type **190** 20 10
1152 4 m. Woodland kingfisher . . 25 15
1153 8 m. White-fronted bee eater . 50 30
1154 12 m. Lesser seedcracker . . . 75 45
1155 16 m. Broad-billed roller . . . 1·00 65
1156 30 m. Neergaard's sunbird . . 2·00 1·10

1987. Olympic Games, Seoul (1988) (1st issue). Multicoloured.
1157 12 m. 50, Type **191** 10 10
1158 25 m. Running 20 10
1159 50 m. Handball 40 20
1160 75 m. Chess . . . . 1·25 30
1161 100 m. Basketball . . . . . 1·25 35
1162 200 m. Swimming . . . . . 2·00 65
See also Nos. 1176/81.

193 Work on Loom

1987. Weaving. Multicoloured.
1164 20 m. Type **193** 15 10
1165 40 m. Triangle and diamond design 40 10
1166 80 m. "Eye" design 70 20
1167 200 m. Red carpet . . . . . 2·00 60

194 Piper "Navajo"

1987. Air. History of Aviation in Mozambique. Multicoloured.
1168 20 m. Type **194** 15 10
1169 40 m. De Havilland Hornet moth 25 10
1170 80 m. Boeing 737 . . . . . . 50 20
1171 120 m. Beechcraft King Air . . 75 20
1172 160 m. Piper Aztec . . . . . 1·00 35
1173 320 m. Douglas DC-10 . . . 2·00 75

195 Early Plan

1987. Centenary of Maputo as City.
1174 **195** 20 m. multicoloured . . . 20 15

1987. No. 895 surch **4,00 MT.**

1175 4 m. on 4 m. 50 grey & red . . 15 10

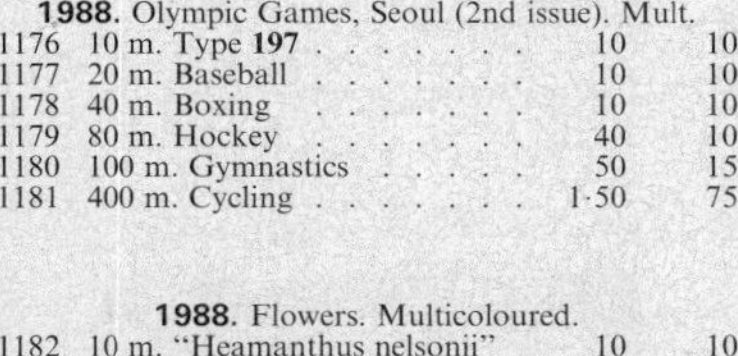

197 Javelin throwing **198** "Boophane disticha"

1988. Olympic Games, Seoul (2nd issue). Mult.

1176 10 m. Type **197** 10 10
1177 20 m. Baseball 10 10
1178 40 m. Boxing 10 10
1179 80 m. Hockey 40 10
1180 100 m. Gymnastics 50 15
1181 400 m. Cycling . . . . 1·50 75

1988. Flowers. Multicoloured.

1182 10 m. "Heamanthus nelsonii" 10 10
1183 20 m. "Crinum polyphyllum" 15 10
1184 40 m. Type **198** 15 10
1185 80 m. "Cyrtanthus contractus" 35 10
1186 100 m. "Nerine angustifolia" . 50 15
1187 400 m. "Cyrtanthus galpinnii" 2·00 75

199 Man refusing Cigarette

1988. 40th Anniv of W.H.O. Anti-smoking Campaign.

1188 **199** 20 m. multicoloured . . . 20 10

201 Mat

1988. Basketry. Multicoloured.

1190 20 m. Type **201** 10 10
1191 25 m. Basket with lid 10 10
1192 80 m. Basket with handle . . 20 10
1193 100 m. Fan 30 10
1194 400 m. Dish . . . . 1·50 1·00
1195 500 m. Conical basket . . . . 1·90 1·40

203 Percheron

1988. Horses. Multicoloured.

1197 20 m. Type **203** 15 10
1198 40 m. Arab 20 10
1199 80 m. Pure blood 40 10
1200 100 m. Pony 50 15

204 Machel

1988. 2nd Death Anniv of Samora Machel (President 1975–86).

1201 **204** 20 m. multicoloured . . . 15 10

205 Inhambane

1988. Ports. Multicoloured.

1202 20 m. Type **205** 15 10
1203 50 m. Quelimane (vert) . . . 40 10
1204 75 m. Pemba 50 10
1205 100 m. Beira 55 20
1206 250 m. Nacali (vert) . . . . . 1·10 50
1207 500 m. Maputo . . . . . . 2·75 1·25

206 Mobile Post Office

1988. Stamp Day. Multicoloured.

1208 20 m. Type **206** 10 10
1209 40 m. Posting box (vert) . . . 15 10

207 Maize **208** Mondlane

1989. 5th FRELIMO Congress. Multicoloured.

1210 25 m. Type **207** 10 10
1211 50 m. Hoe 10 10
1212 75 m. Abstract 10 10
1213 100 m. Cogwheels 20 10
1214 250 m. Right-half of cogwheel 50 25

Nos. 1210/14 were printed together, se-tenant, forming a composite design.

1989. 20th Anniv of Assassination of Pres. Mondlane.

1215 **208** 25 m. black, gold & red . 15 10

209 "Storming the Bastille" (Thevenin)

1989. Bicentenary of French Revolution. Mult.

1216 100 m. Type **209** 25 10
1217 250 m. "Liberty guiding the People" (Delacroix) 60 35

210 "Pandinus sp."

1989. Venomous Animals. Multicoloured.

1219 25 m. Type **210** 10 10
1220 50 m. Egyptian cobra 10 10
1221 75 m. "Bombus sp." (bee) . . 15 10
1222 100 m. "Paraphysa sp." (spider) 25 10
1223 250 m. Marble cone 90 40
1224 500 m. Lionfish . . . . . . 1·90 70

211 "Acropora pulchra"

1989. Corals. Multicoloured.

1225 25 m. Type **211** 10 10
1226 50 m. "Eunicella papilosa" . . 15 10
1227 100 m. "Dendrophyla migrantus" 30 10
1228 250 m. "Favia fragum" . . . 50 35

212 Footballers **213** Macuti Lighthouse

1989. World Cup Football Championship, Italy (1990). Designs showing various footballing scenes.

1229 **212** 30 m. multicoloured . . . 10 10
1230 – 60 m. multicoloured . . . 15 10
1231 – 125 m. multicoloured . . 30 10
1232 – 200 m. multicoloured . . 50 25
1233 – 250 m. multicoloured . . 65 35
1234 – 500 m. multicoloured . . 1·50 70

1989. Lighthouses. Multicoloured.

1235 30 m. Type **213** 15 10
1236 60 m. Pinda 15 10
1237 125 m. Cape Delgado 30 10
1238 200 m. Goa Island 60 25
1239 250 m. Caldeira Point 80 35
1240 500 m. Vilhena . . . . 1·50 70

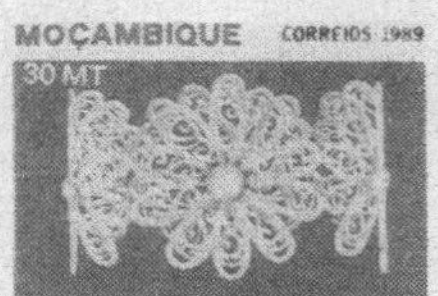

214 Bracelet

1989. Silver Filigree Work.

1241 **214** 30 m. grey, red & black . 10 10
1242 – 60 m. grey, blue & black . 15 10
1243 – 125 m. grey, red & black . 25 10
1244 – 200 m. grey, bl & black . 40 25
1245 – 250 m. grey, pur & blk . 55 35
1246 – 500 m. grey, grn & blk . . 1·25 70

DESIGNS: 60 m. Flower belt; 125 m. Necklace; 200 m. Casket; 250 m. Spoons; 500 m. Butterfly.

215 Flag and Soldiers **216** Rain Gauge

1989. 25th Anniv of Fight for Independence.

1247 **215** 30 m. multicoloured . . . 15 10

1989. Meteorological Instruments. Multicoloured.

1248 30 m. Type **216** 10 10
1249 60 m. Radar graph 15 10
1250 125 m. Sheltered measuring instruments 30 10
1251 200 m. Computer terminal . . 55 25

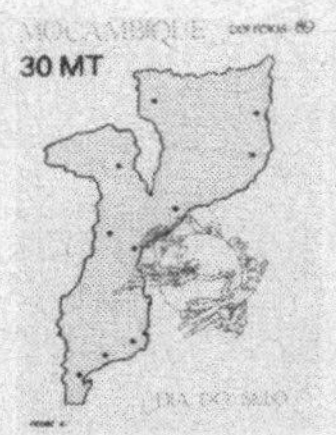

218 Map and U.P.U. Emblem **219** Railway Map

1989. Stamp Day.

1253 **218** 30 m. multicoloured . . . 15 10
1254 – 60 m. black, green & red . 15 10

DESIGN: 60 m. Map and Mozambique postal emblem.

1990. 10th Anniv of Southern Africa Development Co-ordination Conference.

1255 **219** 35 m. multicoloured . . . 1·00 50

MINIMUM PRICE

The minimum price quoted is 10p which represents a handling charge rather than a basis for valuing common stamps. For further notes about prices see introductory pages.

220 Cloth and Woman wearing Dress

1990. Traditional Dresses. Designs showing women wearing different dresses and details of cloth used.

1256 **220** 42 m. multicoloured . . . 10 10
1257 – 90 m. multicoloured . . . 15 10
1258 – 150 m. multicoloured . . 20 10
1259 – 200 m. multicoloured . . 25 15
1260 – 400 m. multicoloured . . 55 40
1261 – 500 m. multicoloured . . 65 50

221 Sena Fortress, Sofala

1990. Fortresses.

1262 **221** 45 m. blue and black . . . 10 10
1263 – 90 m. blue and black . . . 15 10
1264 – 150 m. multicoloured . . 20 10
1265 – 200 m. multicoloured . . 30 15
1266 – 400 m. red and black . . 55 40
1267 – 500 m. red and black . . 70 40

DESIGNS: 90 m. Sto. Antonio, Ibo Island; 150 m. S. Sebastiao, Mozambique Island; 200 m. S. Caetano, Sofala; 400 m. Our Lady of Conception, Maputo; 500 m. S. Luis, Tete.

223 Obverse and Reverse of 50 m. Coin

1990. 15th Anniv of Bank of Mozambique.

1269 **223** 100 m. multicoloured . . . 20 10

224 Statue of Eduardo Mondlane (founder of FRELIMO)

1990. 15th Anniv of Independence. Mult.

1270 42 m. 50 Type **224** 10 10
1271 150 m. Statue of Samora Machel (President, 1975–86) . . . 25 15

225 White Rhinoceros

1990. Endangered Animals. Multicoloured.

1272 42 m. 50 Type **225** 15 10
1273 100 m. Dugong 20 10
1274 150 m. African elephant . . . 35 15
1275 200 m. Cheetah 40 15
1276 400 m. Spotted-necked otter . 70 40
1277 500 m. Hawksbill turtle . . . 85 50

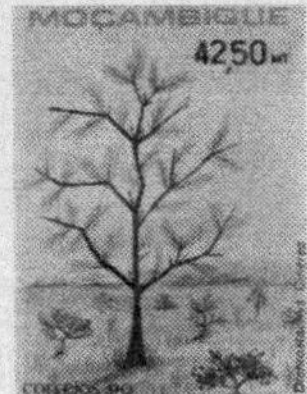

226 "Dichrostachys cinerea" **227** Pillar Box waving to Kurika

1990. Environmental Protection. Plants. Mult.

1278 42 m. 50 Type **226** 10 10
1279 100 m. Forest fire 20 10
1280 150 m. Horsetail tree 25 10
1281 200 m. Mangrove 30 15
1282 400 m. "Estrato herbaceo" (grass) 65 40
1283 500 m. Pod mahogany 80 50

1990. Kurika (post mascot) at Work. Mult.
1284 42 m. 50 Type **227** 15 10
1285 42 m. 50 Hand cancelling envelopes 15 10
1286 42 m. 50 Leaping across hurdles 15 10
1287 42 m. 50 Delivering post to chicken 15 10

228 "10" and Posts Emblem
229 Bird-of-Paradise Flower

1991. 10th Anniv of National Posts and Telecommunications Enterprises, Mozambique.
1288 **228** 50 m. blue, red & blk 15 10
1289 – 50 m. brown, green & black 15 10
DESIGN: No. 1289, "10" and telecommunications emblem.

1991. Flowers. Multicoloured.
1290 50 m. Type **229** 15 10
1291 125 m. Flamingo lily 25 15
1292 250 m. Calla lily 50 30
1293 300 m. Canna lily 55 35

230 Two Hartebeest
231 Mpompine

1991. Lichtenstein's Hartebeest. Multicoloured.
1294 50 m. Type **230** 15 10
1295 100 m. Alert hartebeest 20 10
1296 250 m. Hartebeest grazing 1·50 70
1297 500 m. Mother feeding young 2·10 1·40

1991. Maputo Drinking Fountains. Mult.
1298 50 m. Type **231** 10 10
1299 125 m. Chinhambanine 15 10
1300 250 m. S. Pedro-Zaza 25 10
1301 300 m. Xipamanine 35 15

232 Painting by Samate
233 Diving

1991. Paintings by Mozambican Artists. Mult.
1302 180 m. Type **232** 15 10
1303 250 m. Malangatana Ngwenya 20 15
1304 560 m. Malangatana Ngwenya (different) 40 30

1991. Olympic Games, Barcelona (1992). Mult.
1305 10 m. Type **233** 10 10
1306 50 m. Roller hockey 15 10
1307 100 m. Tennis 20 10
1308 200 m. Table tennis 30 10
1309 500 m. Running 50 20
1310 1000 m. Badminton 1·10 40

234 Proposed Boundaries in 1890 Treaty
236 Skipping

1991. Centenary of Settling of Mozambique Borders. Multicoloured.
1311 600 m. Type **234** 50 25
1312 800 m. Frontiers settled in English-Portuguese 1891 treaty 75 35

1991. Stamp Day. Children's Games. Multicoloured.
1314 40 m. Type **236** 10 10
1315 150 m. Spinning top 10 10
1316 400 m. Marbles 20 10
1317 900 m. Hopscotch 45 20

237 "Christ"
238 "Rhisophora mucronata"

1992. Stained Glass Windows. Multicoloured.
1318 40 m. Type **237** 10 10
1319 150 m. "Faith" 10 10
1320 400 m. "IC XC" 20 10
1321 900 m. Window in three sections 45 20

1992. Marine Flowers. Multicoloured.
1322 300 m. Type **238** 15 10
1323 600 m. "Cymodocea ciliata" 30 15
1324 1000 m. "Sophora inhambanensis" 85 25

239 Spears
240 Amethyst Sunbird

1992. "Lubrapex 92" Brazilian–Portuguese Stamp Exhibition, Lisbon. Weapons. Multicoloured.
1325 100 m. Type **239** 10 10
1326 300 m. Tridents 15 10
1327 500 m. Axe 25 10
1328 1000 m. Dagger 85 25

1992. Birds. Multicoloured.
1329 150 m. Type **240** 10 10
1330 200 m. Mosque swallow 10 10
1331 300 m. Red-capped robin chat 15 10
1332 400 m. Lesser blue-eared glossy starling 20 10
1333 500 m. Grey-headed bush shrike 50 10
1334 800 m. African golden oriole 75 20

241 Emblem
242 Phiane

1992. 30th Anniv of Eduardo Mondlane University.
1335 **241** 150 m. green and brown 10 10

1992. "Genova '92" International Thematic Stamp Exn. Musical Instruments. Multicoloured.
1336 200 m. Type **242** 10 10
1337 300 m. Xirupe (rattle) 15 10
1338 500 m. Ngulula (drum) 25 10
1339 1500 m. Malimba (drum) 75 35

243 Children Eating
244 Parachutist

1992. International Nutrition Conference, Rome.
1341 **243** 450 m. multicoloured 20 10

1992. Parachuting. Multicoloured.
1342 50 m. Type **244** 10 10
1343 400 m. Parachutist and buildings 20 10
1344 500 m. Airplane dropping parachutists 25 10
1345 1500 m. Parachutist (different) 1·10 1·10

1992. No. 890 surch **50MT**.
1346 **122** 50 m. on 50 c. orange and red 10 10

246 Order of Peace and Friendship

1993. Mozambique Decorations. Multicoloured.
1347 400 m. Type **246** 20 10
1348 800 m. Bagamoyo Medal 40 20
1349 1000 m. Order of Eduardo Mondlane 50 25
1350 1500 m. Veteran of the Struggle for National Liberation Medal 70 35

247 Tree Stumps and Girl carrying Wood

1993. Pollution. Multicoloured.
1351 200 m. Type **247** 10 10
1352 750 m. Chimneys smoking 35 15
1353 1000 m. Tanker sinking 50 25
1354 1500 m. Car exhaust fumes 70 35

248 Lion (Gorongosa Park, Sofala)

1993. National Parks. Multicoloured.
1355 200 m. Type **248** 10 10
1356 800 m. Giraffes (Banhine Park, Gaza) 40 20
1357 1000 m. Dugongs (Bazoruto Park, Inhambane) 50 25
1358 1500 m. Ostriches (Zinave Park, Inhambane) 70 35

249 Heroes Monument, Maputo

1993. "Brasiliana 93" International Stamp Exhibition, Rio de Janeiro.
1359 **249** 1500 m. multicoloured 55 25

250 Conference Emblem
251 "Cycas cercinalis"

1993. National Culture Conference, Maputo.
1360 **250** 200 m. multicoloured 10 10

1993. Forest Plants. Multicoloured.
1361 200 m. Type **251** 10 10
1362 250 m. "Cycas revoluta" 10 10
1363 900 m. "Encephalartos ferox" 25 10
1364 2000 m. "Equisetum ramosissimum" 50 25

252 "Anacardium occidentale"
254 Mozambique Rough-scaled Sand Lizard

1994. Medicinal Plants. Multicoloured.
1365 200 m. Type **252** 10 10
1366 250 m. "Sclerocarya caffra" 10 10
1367 900 m. "Annona senegalensis" 25 10
1368 2000 m. "Crinum delagoense" 50 25

1994. Various stamps surch.
1369 50 m. on 7 m. 50 multicoloured (No. 905) 10 10
1370 50 m. on 7 m. 50 multicoloured (No. 924) 10 10
1371 50 m. on 7 m. 50 multicoloured (No. 930) 10 10
1372 100 m. on 10 m. blue and red (No. 896) 10 10
1373 100 m. on 12 m. 50 mult (No. 931) 10 10
1374 200 m. on 12 m. 50 brown and red (No. 897) 10 10
1375 250 m. on 12 m. 50 mult (No. 925) 10 10

1994. "Philakorea 1994" International Stamp Exhibition, Seoul. Reptiles. Multicoloured.
1376 300 m. Type **254** 10 10
1377 500 m. Olive loggerhead turtle 10 10
1378 2000 m. Northern coppery snake 40 20
1379 3500 m. Marshall's chameleon 75 35

255 Crop-spraying

1994. 50th Anniv of I.C.A.O. Multicoloured.
1381 300 m. Type **255** 10 10
1382 500 m. Airport 10 10
1383 2000 m. Air transport 40 20
1384 3500 m. Aircraft maintenance 75 35

256 Bean Plant
257 Queue of Voters

1994. "Lubrapex'94" Portuguese–Brazilian Stamp Exhibition. World Food Day.
1385 **256** 2000 m. multicoloured 40 20

1994. 1st Multiparty Elections.
1386 **257** 900 m. multicoloured 20 10

258 Document and Handshake
259 Couple using Drugs

1994. 20th Anniv of Lusaka Accord (establishing independence).
1387 **258** 1500 m. multicoloured 30 15

1994. Anti-drugs Campaign. Multicoloured.
1388 500 m. Type **259** 10 10
1389 1000 m. Couple, syringe, cigarette and skeleton 20 10
1390 2000 m. Addict 40 20
1391 5000 m. Sniffer dog capturing man with drugs 1·00 50

260 Basket
261 Dress and Cloak

1995. Baskets and Bags. Multicoloured.

1392 250 m. Type **260** 10 10
1393 300 m. Bag with two handles . 10 10
1394 1200 m. Circular bag with one handle 20 10
1395 5000 m. Bag with flap . . . 85 40

1995. Women's Costumes. Multicoloured.

1396 250 m. Type **261** 10 10
1397 300 m. Blouse and calf-length skirt 10 10
1398 1200 m. Blouse and ankle-length skirt 20 10
1399 5000 m. Strapless top and skirt 85 40

262 State Arms

263 Bushbaby

1995. Investiture (1994) of President Joaquim Chissano. Multicoloured.

1400 900 m. Type **262** 15 10
1401 2500 m. National flag . . . 45 20
1402 5000 m. Pres. Chissano . . . 85 40

Nos. 1400/2 were issued together, se-tenant, the commemorative inscription at the foot extending across the strip.

1995. Mammals. Multicoloured.

1403 500 m. Type **263** 10 10
1404 2000 m. Greater kudu (horiz) . 25 10
1405 3000 m. Bush pig (horiz) . . . 40 20
1406 5000 m. Bushbuck 65 30

1995. Various stamps surch.

1407 250 m. on 12 m. 50 multicoloured (No. 931) . . 10 10
1408 300 m. on 10 m. blue and red (No. 896) 10 10
1409 500 m. on 12 m. 50 multicoloured (No. 925) . . 10 10
1410 900 m. on 12 e. 50 multicoloured (No. 771) 10 10
1411 1000 m. on 12 m. 50 multicoloured (No. 837) . . 15 10
1412 1500 m. on 16 m. multicoloured (No. 1064) 20 10
1413 2000 m. on 16 m. multicoloured (No. 995) 25 10
1414 2500 m. on 12 m. multicoloured (No. 880) 35 15

265 Family carrying Foodstuffs

266 Emblem

1995. 50th Anniv of F.A.O.

1415 **265** 5000 m. multicoloured . . 65 30

1995. 50th Anniv of United Nations Organization.

1416 **266** 5000 m. blue and black . 65 30

267 Child wearing Blue Cloak

1995. 20th Anniv of U.N.I.C.E.F. in Mozambique.

1417 **267** 5000 m. multicoloured . 60 65

268 Player scoring Goal

1996. Football. Multicoloured.

1418 1000 m. Type **268** 10 15
1419 2000 m. Goalkeeper holding ball 20 25
1420 4000 m. Referee admonishing players 40 45
1421 6000 m. Two players tackling for ball 60 65

269 Mask

270 "Mae Africa" (De Malangatana)

1996. Local Masks.

1422 **269** 1000 m. multicoloured . 10 15
1423 – 2000 m. multicoloured . 20 25
1424 – 4000 m. multicoloured . 40 45
1425 – 6000 m. multicoloured . 60 65

DESIGNS: 2000 to 6000 m. Different masks.

1996. 15th Anniv of Mozambique Red Cross.

1426 **270** 5000 m. multicoloured . 50 55

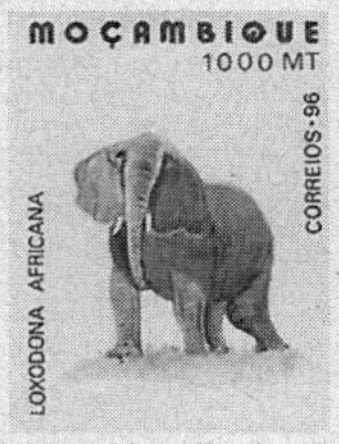

271 African Elephant

272 Mine Field

1996. Wild Animals. Multicoloured.

1427 1000 m. Type **271** 35 20
1428 2000 m. White rhinoceros . . 50 35
1429 4000 m. Leopard 70 65
1430 6000 m. Pel's fishing owl . . . 1·00 1·00

1996. Land Mine Clearance Campaign. Mult.

1431 2000 m. Type **272** 20 25
1432 6000 m. Warning sign 60 65
1433 8000 m. Soldier with mine detector 80 85
1434 10000 m. Soldier lifting mine . 1·00 1·10

273 City Street

274 5 r. Stamp of 1876 and Magnifying Glass

1996. "Keeping the City Clean".

1435 **273** 2000 m. multicoloured . 20 25

1996. 120th Anniv of Mozambique Stamps.

1436 **274** 2000 m. multicoloured . 20 25

275 Mitumbui

1997. Local Boats. Multicoloured.

1437 2000 m. Type **275** 20 25
1438 6000 m. Muterere 60 65
1439 8000 m. Lancha 80 85
1440 10000 m. Dhow . . . . . . 1·00 1·10

276 Village Scene

1997. International Children's Day.

1441 **276** 2000 m. multicoloured . 20 25

277 Enaretta Conitera

1997. Beetles. Multicoloured.

1442 2000 m. Type **277** 20 25
1443 6000 m. "Zographus hieroglyphicus 60 65
1444 8000 m. "Tragiscoschema bertolonii" 80 85
1445 10000 m. "Tragocephala ducalis" . . . . 1·00 1·10

278 Yellow-billed Stork

280 Sun and Globe

279 Abstract Patterns

1997. Aquatic Birds. Multicoloured.

1447 2000 m. Type **278** 35 25
1448 4000 m. Black-winged stilt . . 55 45
1449 8000 m. Long-toed stint (horiz) 95 85
1450 10000 m. Eastern white pelican . . . . 1·10 1·10

1997. Centenary of Joao Ferreira dos Santos Group.

1451 **279** 2000 m. multicoloured . 20 25

1997. Protection of Ozone Layer.

1452 **280** 2000 m. multicoloured . 20 25

282 Coelacanth

1998. "EXPO '98" International Stamp Exhibition, Lisbon.

1454 **282** 2000 m. multicoloured . 20 25

283 Woman with Food Products

1998. Food Production.

1455 **283** 2000 m. multicoloured . 20 25

CHARITY TAX STAMPS

The notes under this heading in Portugal also apply here.

C 15 Arms of Portugal and Mozambique and Allegorical Figures

C 16 Prow of Galley of Discoveries and Symbols of Declaration of War

1916. War Tax Fund. Imperf, roul or perf.

No.	Type	Description	Unused	Used
C234	C 15	1 c. green	35	25
C235	C 16	5 c. red	35	30

C 18 "Charity"

C 22 Society's Emblem

1920. 280th Anniv of Restoration of Portugal. Wounded Soldiers and Social Assistance Funds.

No.	Type	Description	Unused	Used
C309	C 18	¼ c. green	70	70
C310		½ c. black	75	70
C311		1 c. brown	75	70
C312		2 c. brown	75	75
C313		3 c. lilac	75	75
C314		4 c. green	75	75
C315	–	5 c. green	85	75
C316	–	6 c. blue	85	75
C317	–	7½ c. brown	85	75
C318	–	8 c. yellow	85	75
C319	–	10 c. lilac	85	85
C320	–	12 c. pink	85	85
C321	–	18 c. red	85	85
C322	–	24 c. brown	1·10	85
C323	–	30 c. green	1·10	85
C324	–	40 c. red	1·10	85
C325	–	50 c. yellow	1·10	85
C326	–	1 e. blue	1·10	85

DESIGNS: 5 c. to 12 c. Wounded soldier and nurse; 18 c. to 1 e. Family scene.

1925. Marquis de Pombal stamps of Portugal, but inscr "MOCAMBIQUE".

No.	Type	Description	Unused	Used
C327	C 73	15 c. brown	15	15
C328	–	15 c. brown	15	15
C329	C 75	15 c. brown	15	15

1925. Red Cross. Surch **50 CENTAVOS**.

No.	Type	Description	Unused	Used
C330	C 22	50 c. yellow and grey	55	40

1926. Surch **CORREIOS** and value.

No.	Type	Description	Unused	Used
C337	C 22	5 c. yellow and red	75	60
C338		10 c. yellow and green	75	60
C339		20 c. yellow and grey	75	60
C340		30 c. yellow and blue	75	60
C331		40 c. yellow and grey	80	75
C341		40 c. yellow and violet	75	60
C332		50 c. yellow and grey	80	75
C342		50 c. yellow and red	75	60
C333		60 c. yellow and grey	80	75
C343		60 c. yellow and brown	75	60
C334		80 c. yellow and grey	80	75
C344		80 c. yellow and blue	75	60
C335		1 e. yellow and grey	90	75
C345		1 e. yellow and green	75	60
C336		2 e. yellow and grey	90	75
C346		2 e. yellow and brown	75	60

C 25

1928. Surch **CORREIOS** and value in black, as in Type C **25**.

No.	Type	Description	Unused	Used
C347	C 25	5 c. yellow and green	1·10	1·00
C348		10 c. yellow and blue	1·10	1·00
C349		20 c. yellow and black	1·10	1·00
C350		30 c. yellow and red	1·10	1·00
C351		40 c. yellow and purple	1·10	1·00
C352		50 c. yellow and red	1·10	1·00
C353		60 c. yellow and brown	1·10	1·00
C354		80 c. yellow and brown	1·10	1·00
C355		1 e. yellow and grey	1·10	1·00
C356		2 e. yellow and red	1·10	1·00

C 27

C 29 Pelican

C 28 "Charity"

1929. Value in black.

No.	Type	Description	Unused	Used
C357	C 27	40 c. purple and blue	85	85
C358		40 c. violet and red	85	85
C359		40 c. violet and green	85	85
C360		40 c. red and brown	85	85
C361		(No value) red & green	1·10	1·10
C362		40 c. blue and orange	1·10	1·10
C363		40 c. blue and brown	85	85
C364		40 c. purple and green	1·10	1·00
C365		40 c. black and yellow	1·10	1·10
C366		40 c. black and brown	1·10	1·10

1942.

No.	Type	Description	Unused	Used
C383	C 28	50 c. pink and black	2·00	90

1943. Inscr "Colonia de Mocambique". Value in black.

No.	Type	Description	Unused	Used
C390	C 29	50 c. red	1·50	75
C389		50 c. blue	1·50	75
C386		50 c. violet	1·50	75
C387		50 c. brown	1·50	75
C393		50 c. green	1·50	75

1952. Inscr "Provincia de Mocambique". Value in black.

No.	Type	Description	Unused	Used
C514	C 29	30 c. yellow	45	35
C515		50 c. orange	45	35
C469		50 c. green	75	40
C470		50 c. brown	75	40

1957. No. C470 surch **$30**.

No.	Type	Description	Unused	Used
C511	C 29	30 c. on 50 c. brown	45	25

C 56 Women and Children

C 58 Telegraph Poles and Map

1963.

No.	Type	Description	Unused	Used
C569	C 56	30 c. black, green & red	15	15
C570		50 c. black, bistre & red	20	15
C571		50 c. black, pink & red	20	15
C572		50 c. black, green & red	20	15
C573		50 c. black, blue & red	20	15
C574		50 c. black, buff & red	20	15
C575		50 c. black, grey & red	20	15
C576		50 c. black, yell & red	20	15
C577		1 e. grey, blk & red	50	25
C578		1 e. black, buff & red	15	10
C578a		1 e. black, mve & red	15	10

1965. Mozambique Telecommunications Improvement.

No.	Type	Description	Unused	Used
C579	C 58	30 c. black, pink & vio	10	10
C580	–	50 c. black, brown & bl	10	10
C581	–	1 e. black, orge & grn	20	20

DESIGN—19½ × 36 mm: 50 c., 1 e. Telegraph linesman.

A 2 e. 50 in Type C **58** was also issued for compulsory use on telegrams.

NEWSPAPER STAMPS

1893. "Embossed" key-type of Mozambique surch.

(a) **JORNAES 2½ 2½**.

No.	Type	Description	Unused	Used
N53	Q	2½ r. on 40 r. brown	9·50	7·50

(b) **JORNAES 2½ REIS**.

No.	Type	Description	Unused	Used
N54	Q	2½ r. on 40 r. brown	45·00	30·00
N57		5 r. on 40 r. brown	28·00	24·00

1893. "Newspaper" key-type inscribed "MOCAMBIQUE".

No.	Type	Description	Unused	Used
N58	V	2½ r. brown	25	20

POSTAGE DUE STAMPS

1904. "Due" key-type inscr "MOCAMBIQUE".

No.	Type	Description	Unused	Used
D146	W	5 r. green	15	15
D147		10 r. grey	15	15
D148		20 r. brown	15	15
D149		30 r. orange	30	20
D150		50 r. brown	30	20
D151		60 r. brown	1·25	75
D152		100 r. mauve	1·25	75
D153		130 r. blue	70	65
D154		200 r. red	1·25	65
D155		500 r. violet	1·25	65

1911. "Due" key-type of Mozambique optd **REPUBLICA**.

No.	Type	Description	Unused	Used
D162	W	5 r. green	15	15
D163		10 r. grey	15	15
D164		20 r. brown	20	15
D165		30 r. orange	20	15
D166		50 r. brown	20	15
D167		60 r. brown	30	20
D168		100 r. mauve	30	20
D169		130 r. blue	50	40
D170		200 r. red	65	60
D171		500 r. lilac	65	60

1917. "Due" key-type of Mozambique, but currency changed.

No.	Type	Description	Unused	Used
D246	W	½ c. green	15	15
D247		1 c. grey	15	15
D248		2 c. brown	15	15
D249		3 c. orange	15	15
D250		5 c. brown	15	15
D251		6 c. brown	15	15
D252		10 c. mauve	15	15
D253		13 c. blue	30	25
D254		20 c. red	30	25
D255		50 c. lilac	30	25

1918. Charity Tax stamps optd **PORTEADO**.

No.	Type	Description	Unused	Used
D256	C 15	1 c. green	50	40
D257	C 16	5 c. red	50	40

1922. "Ceres" key-type of Lourenco Marques (½, 1½ c.) and of Mozambique (1, 2½, 4 c.) surch **PORTEADO** and value and bar.

No.	Type	Description	Unused	Used
D316	U	5 c. on ½ c. black	55	40
D318		6 c. on 1 c. green	60	40
D317		10 c. on 1½ c. brown	55	40
D319		20 c. on 2½ c. violet	60	40
D320		50 c. on 4 c. pink	60	40

1924. "Ceres" key-type of Mozambique surch **Porteado** and value.

No.	Type	Description	Unused	Used
D321	U	20 c. on 30 c. green	35	30
D323		50 c. on 60 c. blue	55	40

1925. Marquis de Pombal charity tax designs as Nos. C327/9, optd **MULTA**.

No.	Type	Description	Unused	Used
D327	C 73	30 c. brown	15	15
D328	–	30 c. brown	15	15
D329	C 75	30 c. brown	15	15

1952. As Type D **70** of Macao, but inscr "MOCAMBIQUE".

No.	Type	Description	Unused	Used
D468		10 c. multicoloured	10	10
D469		30 c. multicoloured	10	10
D470		50 c. multicoloured	10	10
D471		1 e. multicoloured	20	20
D472		2 e. multicoloured	20	20
D473		5 e. multicoloured	25	25

MOZAMBIQUE COMPANY Pt. 9

The Mozambique Company was responsible from 1891 until 1942 for the administration of Manica and Sofala territory in Portuguese East Africa. Now part of Mozambique.

1899. 1000 reis = 1 milreis.
1913. 100 centavos = 1 escudo.

1892. "Embossed" key-type inscr "PROVINCA DE MOCAMBIQUE" optd **COMPA. DE MOCAMBIQUE**.

No.	Type	Description	Unused	Used
10	Q	5 r. black	25	20
2		10 r. green	35	15
3		20 r. red	45	15
4		25 r. mauve	30	20
5		40 r. brown	30	15
6		50 r. blue	35	20
7		100 r. brown	30	45
8		200 r. violet	60	45
9		300 r. orange	60	45

2

1895. Value in black or red (500, 1000 r.).

No.	Type	Description	Unused	Used
33	2	2½ r. yellow	10	10
114		2½ r. grey	50	25
17		5 r. orange	15	10
36		10 r. mauve	15	15
115		10 r. green	30	25
39		15 r. brown	15	15
116		15 r. green	30	25
20		20 r. lilac	15	15
45		25 r. green	15	15
117		25 r. red	45	20
46		50 r. blue	20	15
118		50 r. brown	45	30
109		65 r. blue	30	25
48		75 r. red	20	15
119		75 r. mauve	90	75
50		80 r. green	20	15
52		100 r. brown on buff	25	15
120		100 r. blue on blue	90	75
110		115 r. pink on pink	80	70
121		115 r. brown on pink	1·40	90
111		130 r. green on pink	80	70
122		130 r. brown on yellow	1·40	90
54		150 r. orange on pink	25	15
55		200 r. blue on blue	25	15
123		200 r. lilac on pink	1·40	90
56		300 r. blue on brown	25	15
112		400 r. black on blue	80	70
124		400 r. blue on yellow	1·75	1·40
58		500 r. black	35	25
125		500 r. black on blue	1·75	40
126		700 r. mauve on buff	1·90	1·60
59		1000 r. mauve	45	25

1895. Surch **PROVISORIO 25**.

No.	Type	Description	Unused	Used
77	2	25 on 80 r. green	6·50	4·50

1895. No. 6 optd **PROVISORIO**.

No.	Type	Description	Unused	Used
78	Q	50 r. blue	1·60	1·25

1898. Vasco da Gama. Optd **1498 Centenario da India 1898**.

No.	Type	Description	Unused	Used
80	2	2½ r. yellow	55	55
81		5 r. orange	65	60
82		10 r. mauve	65	55
84		15 r. brown	80	70
86		20 r. lilac	90	80
87		25 r. green	1·50	90
99		50 r. blue	85	80
89		75 r. red	1·50	1·25
91		80 r. green	1·50	1·10
101		100 r. brown on buff	1·60	1·40
102		150 r. orange on pink	1·60	1·50
94		200 r. blue on blue	2·00	1·75
104		300 r. blue on brown	3·00	2·25

1899. Surch **25 PROVISORIO**.

No.	Type	Description	Unused	Used
105	2	25 on 75 r. red	1·25	1·10

1900. Surch **25 Reis** and bar.

No.	Type	Description	Unused	Used
106	2	25 r. on 5 r. orange	1·10	65

1900. Perforated through centre and surch **50 REIS**.

No.	Type	Description	Unused	Used
108	2	50 r. on half of 20 r. lilac	40	40

1911. Optd **REPUBLICA**.

No.	Type	Description	Unused	Used
145	2	2½ r. grey	15	10
147		5 r. orange	15	10
148		10 r. green	10	10
150		15 r. green	10	10
151		20 r. lilac	15	10
153		25 r. red	10	10
155		50 r. brown	10	10
156		75 r. mauve	15	10
157		100 r. blue on blue	20	10
159		115 r. brown on pink	30	20
160		130 r. brown on yellow	30	20
161		200 r. lilac on pink	30	15
162		400 r. blue on yellow	30	15
163		500 r. black on blue	30	15
164		700 r. mauve on yellow	35	30

1916. Surch **REPUBLICA** and value in figures.

No.	Type	Description	Unused	Used
166	2	¼ c. on 2½ r. grey	10	10
168		½ c. on 5 r. orange	10	10
170		1 c. on 10 r. green	15	15
173		1½ c. on 15 r. green	15	15
175		2 c. on 20 r. lilac	15	15
178		2½ c. on 25 r. red	15	15
180		5 c. on 50 r. brown	15	15
181		7½ c. on 75 r. mauve	25	15
182		10 c. on 100 r. blue on blue	25	15
183		11½ c. on 115 r. brown on pink	50	30
184		13 c. on 130 r. brown on yell	50	25
185		20 c. on 200 r. lilac on pink	40	30
186		40 c. on 400 r. blue on yell	40	30
187		50 c. on 500 r. black on blue	50	35
188		70 c. on 700 r. mauve on yell	50	35

1917. Red Cross Fund. Stamps of 1911 (optd **REPUBLICA**) optd with red cross and **31.7.17.**

No.	Type	Description	Unused	Used
189	2	2½ r. grey	1·50	1·25
190		10 r. green	2·00	1·75
191		20 r. lilac	2·00	1·75
192		50 r. brown	4·50	2·75
193		75 r. mauve	10·50	8·75
194		100 r. blue on blue	13·50	11·25
195		700 r. mauve on yellow	42·00	29·00

1918. Stamps of 1911 (optd **REPUBLICA**) surch with new value.

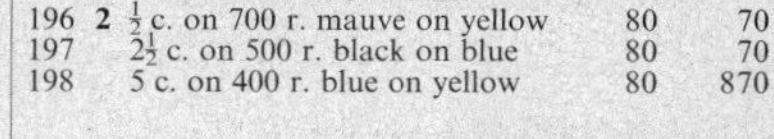

No.	Type	Description	Unused	Used
196	2	½ c. on 700 r. mauve on yellow	80	70
197		2½ c. on 500 r. black on blue	80	70
198		5 c. on 400 r. blue on yellow	80	870

14 Native Village

15 Ivory

1918.

No.	Type	Description	Unused	Used
199	14	¼ c. green and brown	15	15
233		¼ c. black and green	15	15
200	15	½ c. black	15	15
201	–	1 c. black and green	15	15
202	–	1½ c. green and black	15	15
203	–	2 c. black and red	15	15
235	–	2 c. black and grey	15	15
204	–	2½ c. black and lilac	15	15
236	–	3 c. black and orange	15	15
205	–	4 c. brown and green	15	15
237	–	4 c. black and red	15	15
227	14	4½ c. black and grey	20	15
206	–	5 c. black and blue	25	15
207	–	6 c. blue and purple	25	20
238	–	6 c. black and mauve	15	15
228	–	7 c. black and blue	75	25
208	–	7½ c. green and orange	35	30
239	–	8 c. black and lilac	30	25
210	–	10 c. black and red	45	30
229	–	12 c. black and brown	65	45
241	–	12 c. black and green	30	20
242	–	15 c. black and red	55	40
212	–	20 c. black and green	20	15
213	–	30 c. black and brown	40	30
244	–	30 c. black and green	40	30
214	–	40 c. black and green	30	20
246	–	40 c. black and blue	45	30
215	–	50 c. black and orange	40	30
247	–	50 c. black and mauve	60	40
230	–	60 c. brown and red	75	50
231	–	80 c. brown and blue	1·75	80
248	–	80 c. black and red	1·00	50

216	–	1 e. black and green	70	50
249	–	1 e. black and blue	60	50
232	–	2 e. violet and red	2·25	80
250	–	2 e. black and lilac	5·00	55

DESIGNS—HORIZ: 1, 3 c. Maize field; 2 c. Sugar factory; 5 c., 2 e. Beira; 20 c. Law Court; 40 c. Mangrove swamp. VERT: 1½ c. India-rubber; 2½ c. River Buzi; 4 c. Tobacco bushes; 6 c. Coffee bushes; 7, 15 c. Steam train, Amatongas Forest; 7½ c. Orange tree; 8, 12 c. Cotton plants; 10, 80 c. Sisal plantation; 30 c. Coconut palm; 50, 60 c. Cattle breeding; 1 e. Mozambique Co's Arms.

1920. Pictorial issue surch in words.

217	½ c. on 30 c. (No. 213)	1·10	95
218	½ c. on 1 e. (No. 216)	1·10	95
219	1½ c. on 2½ c. (No. 204)	90	90
220	1½ c. on 5 c. (No. 206)	3·25	3·25
221	2 c. on 2½ c. (No. 204)	70	55
222	4 c. on 20 c. (No. 212)	1·10	75
223	4 c. on 40 c. (No. 214)	1·10	75
224	6 c. on 8 c. (No. 239)	1·10	75
225	6 c. on 50 c. (No. 215)	1·10	75

33

36 Tea

1925.

251	**33**	24 c. black and blue	80	65
252	–	25 c. blue and brown	80	65
253	**33**	85 c. black and red	60	50
254	–	1 e. 40 black and blue	1·25	40
255	–	5 e. blue and brown	65	35
256	**36**	10 e. black and red	65	35
257	–	20 e. black and green	80	35

DESIGNS—VERT: 25 c., 1 e. 40, Beira; 5 e. Tapping rubber. HORIZ: 20 e. River Zambesi.

38 Ivory

1931.

258	**38**	45 c. blue	1·50	80
259	–	70 c. brown	1·00	50

DESIGN—VERT: 70 c. Gold mining.

40 Zambesi Bridge

1935 Opening of River Zambesi Railway Bridge at Sena.

260	**40**	1 e. black and blue	2·50	35

41 Armstrong-Whitworth Atalanta Airliner over Beira

1935. Inauguration of Blantyre–Beira–Salisbury Air Route.

261	**41**	5 c. black and blue	40	25
262		10 c. black and red	40	25
263		15 c. black and red	40	25
264		20 c. black and green	40	25
265		30 c. black and green	40	25
266		40 c. black and blue	50	35
267		45 c. black and blue	50	35
268		50 c. black and purple	50	35
269		60 c. brown and red	80	40
270		80 c. black and red	80	40

42 Armstrong-Whitworth Atalanta Airliner over Beira

1935. Air.

271	**42**	5 c. black and blue	10	10
272		10 c. black and red	10	10
273		15 c. black and red	10	10
274		20 c. black and green	10	10
275		30 c. black and green	10	10
276		40 c. black and green	10	10
277		45 c. black and blue	10	10
278		50 c. black and purple	10	10
279		60 c. brown and red	10	10
280		80 c. black and red	10	10
281		1 e. black and blue	15	10
282		2 e. black and lilac	35	20
283		5 e. blue and brown	60	35
284		10 e. black and red	65	40
285		20 e. black and green	1·40	85

43 Coastal Dhow

46 Palms at Beira

45 Crocodile

1937.

286	–	1 c. lilac and green	10	10
287	–	5 c. green and blue	10	10
288	**43**	10 c. blue and red	10	10
289	–	15 c. black and red	10	10
290	–	20 c. blue and green	10	10
291	–	30 c. blue and green	10	10
292	–	40 c. black and blue	10	10
293	–	45 c. brown and blue	10	10
294	**45**	50 c. green and violet	15	15
295	–	60 c. blue and red	15	15
296	–	70 c. green and brown	15	15
297	–	80 c. green and red	15	15
298	–	85 c. black and red	20	15
299	–	1 e. black and blue	15	15
300	**46**	1 e. 40 c. green and blue	20	15
301	–	2 e. brown and lilac	40	20
302	–	5 e. blue and brown	90	80
303	–	10 e. black and red	55	35
304	–	20 e. purple and green	85	50

DESIGNS—VERT: 21 × 29 mm—1 c. Giraffe; 20 c. Common zebra; 70 c. Native woman. 23 × 31 mm—10 e. Old Portuguese gate, Sena; 20 e. Arms. HORIZ: 29 × 21 mm—5 c. Native huts. 15 c. S. Caetano fortress, Sofala; 60 c. Leopard; 80 c. Hippopotami. 37 × 22 mm—5 e. Railway bridge over River Zambesi. TRIANGULAR: 30 c. Python; 40 c. White rhinoceros; 45 c. Lion; 85 c. Vasco da Gama's flagship "Sao Gabriel"; 1 e. Native in dugout canoe; 2 e. Greater kudu.

1939. President Carmona's Colonial Tour. Optd **28-VII-1939 Visita Presidencial**.

305	–	30 c. (No. 291)	70	50
306	–	40 c. (No. 292)	70	50
307	–	45 c. (No. 293)	70	50
308	**45**	50 c. green and violet	70	50
309	–	85 c. (No. 298)	70	50
310	–	1 e. (No. 299)	1·10	90
311	–	2 e. (No. 301)	1·40	1·10

49 King Afonso Henriques

51 "Don John IV" after Alberto de Souza

1940. 800th Anniv of Portuguese Independence.

312	**49**	1 e. 75 light blue and blue	70	40

1940. Tercentenary of Restoration of Independence.

313	**51**	40 c. black and blue	20	15
314		50 c. green and violet	20	15
315		60 c. blue and red	20	15
316		70 c. green and brown	20	15
317		80 c. green and red	20	15
318		1 e. black and blue	20	15

CHARITY TAX STAMPS

The notes under this heading in Portugal also apply here.

1932. No. 236 surch **Assistencia Publica 2 Ctvos. 2.**

C260	2 c. on 3 c. black & orge	35	35

C 41 "Charity"

C 50

1934.

C261	C **41**	2 c. black and mauve	45	1·10

1940.

C313	C **50**	2 c. blue and black	2·75	2·40

C 52

1941.

C319	C **52**	2 c. red and black	2·75	2·40

NEWSPAPER STAMP

1894. "Newspaper" key-type inscr "MOCAMBIQUE" optd **COMPA. DE MOCAMBIQUE.**

N15	V	2½ r. brown	25	20

POSTAGE DUE STAMPS

D 9

D 32

1906.

D114	D **9**	5 r. green	20	20
D115		10 r. grey	20	20
D116		20 r. brown	20	20
D117		30 r. orange	35	25
D118		50 r. brown	35	25
D119		60 r. brown	1·75	1·60
D120		100 r. mauve	50	50
D121		130 r. blue	2·50	1·75
D122		200 r. red	1·10	70
D123		500 r. lilac	1·40	1·10

1911. Optd **REPUBLICA.**

D166	D **9**	5 r. green	15	15
D167		10 r. grey	15	15
D168		20 r. brown	15	15
D169		30 r. orange	15	15
D170		50 r. brown	15	15
D171		60 r. brown	30	20
D172		100 r. mauve	30	20
D173		130 r. blue	70	75
D174		200 r. red	80	70
D175		500 r. lilac	90	80

1916. Currency changed.

D189	D **9**	½ c. green	15	15
D190		1 c. grey	15	15
D191		2 c. brown	15	15
D192		3 c. orange	15	15
D193		5 c. brown	15	15
D194		6 c. brown	15	15
D195		10 c. mauve	35	35
D196		13 c. blue	70	70
D197		20 c. red	70	70
D198		50 c. lilac	90	90

1919.

D217	D **32**	½ c. green	10	10
D218		1 c. black	10	10
D219		2 c. brown	10	10
D220		3 c. orange	10	10
D221		5 c. brown	15	10
D222		6 c. brown	20	20
D223		10 c. red	20	20
D224		13 c. blue	25	25
D225		20 c. red	25	20
D226		50 c. grey	30	30

MUSCAT — Pt. 1

Independent Sultanate in Eastern Arabia with Indian and, subsequently, British postal administration.

12 pies = 1 anna. 16 annas = 1 rupee

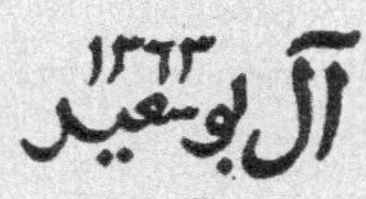

(2)

1944. Bicentenary of Al-Busaid Dynasty. Stamps of India (King George VI) optd as T **2**.

1	**100a**	3 p. slate	30	5·00
2		½ a. mauve	30	5·00
3		9 p. green	30	5·00
4		1 a. red	30	5·00
5	**101**	1½ a. plum	30	5·00
6		2 a. red	30	5·00
7		3 a. violet	50	5·00
8		3½ a. blue	50	5·00
9	**102**	4 a. brown	50	5·00
10		6 a. green	65	5·00
11		8 a. violet	65	5·00
12		12 a. red	80	5·00
13	–	14 a. purple (No. 277)	2·00	7·00
14	**93**	1 r. slate and brown	50	9·00
15		2 r. purple and brown	1·50	15·00

OFFICIAL STAMPS

1944. Bicentenary of Al-Busaid Dynasty. Official stamps of India optd as T **2**.

O 1	O **20**	3 p. slate	50	9·50
O 2		½ a. purple	50	9·50
O 3		9 p. green	50	9·50
O 4		1 a. red	50	9·50
O 5		1½ a. violet	50	9·50
O 6		2 a. orange	50	9·50
O 7		2½ a. violet	1·50	9·50
O 8		4 a. brown	1·00	9·50
O 9		8 a. violet	2·00	11·00
O10	**93**	1 r. slate and brown (No. O138)	2·25	19·00

For later issues see **BRITISH POSTAL AGENCIES IN EASTERN ARABIA**.

MUSCAT AND OMAN — Pt. 19

Independent Sultanate in Eastern Arabia. The title of the Sultanate was changed in 1971 to Oman.

1966. 64 baizas = 1 rupee.
1970. 1000 baizas = 1 rial saidi.

12 Sultan's Crest

14 Nakhal Fort

1966.

94	**12**	3 b. purple	10	10
95		5 b. brown	10	10
96		10 b. brown	10	10
97	A	15 b. black and violet	20	15
98		20 b. black and blue	30	20
99		25 b. black and orange	35	20
100	**14**	30 b. mauve and blue	45	30
101	B	50 b. green and brown	70	40
102	C	1 r. blue and orange	1·40	75
103	D	2 r. brown and green	2·75	1·50
104	E	5 r. violet and red	6·75	4·50
105	F	10 r. red and violet	11·00	9·50

DESIGNS—VERT: 21½ × 25½ mm: A, Crest and Muscat harbour. HORIZ (as Type **14**): B, Samail Fort; C, Sohar Fort; D, Nizwa Fort; E, Matrah Fort; F, Mirani Fort.

15 Mina el Fahal

1969. 1st Oil Shipment (July 1967). Multicoloured.

106	20 b. Type **15**	80	40
107	25 b. Storage tanks	70	50
108	40 b. Desert oil-rig	1·10	85
109	1 r. Aerial view from "Gemini 4"	2·75	2·00

1970. Designs as issue of 1966, but inscribed in new currency.

110	**12**	5 b. purple	10	10
111		10 b. brown	10	10
112		20 b. brown	20	10
113	A	25 b. black and violet	25	15
114		30 b. black and blue	35	20
115		40 b. black and orange	45	25
116	**14**	50 b. mauve and blue	50	30
117	B	75 b. green and brown	75	50
118	C	100 b. blue and orange	1·10	65
119	D	¼ r. brown and green	3·00	1·90
120	E	½ r. violet and red	6·00	3·75
121	F	1 r. red and violet	11·00	7·75

For later issues see **OMAN**.

MYANMAR — Pt. 21

Formerly known as Burma.

100 pyas = 1 kyat

81 Fountain, National Assembly Park (½-size illustration)

1990. State Law and Order Restoration Council.

312	**81**	1 k. multicoloured	1·00	65

1990. As Nos. 258/61 of Burma but inscr "UNION OF MYANMAR".

313	15 p. deep green and green	20	15
314	20 p. black, brown and blue	25	20
315	50 p. violet and brown	45	25
316	1 k. violet, mauve and black	90	65

82 Map and Emblem

83 Nawata Ruby

1990. 40th Anniv of United Nations Development Programme.
322 **82** 2 k. blue, yellow & black . . 1·90 1·25

1991. Gem Emporium.
323 **83** 50 p. multicoloured 95 65

84 "Grandfather giving Sword to Grandson" (statuette, Nan Win)

85 Emblem

1992. 44th Anniv of Independence. Multicoloured.
324 50 p. Warrior defending personification of Myanmar and map (poster, Khin Thein) 50 40
325 2 k. Type **84** . . . . 2·00 1·50

1992. National Sports Festival.
326 **85** 50 p. multicoloured 55 40

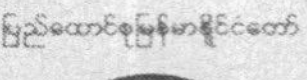

86 Campaign Emblem

87 Fish, Water Droplet and Leaf

1992. Anti-AIDS Campaign.
327 **86** 50 p. red 40 30

1992. International Nutrition Conference, Rome.
328 **87** 50 p. multicoloured 30 20
329 1 k. multicoloured 55 40
330 3 k. multicoloured . . . . 1·60 1·10
331 5 k. multicoloured . . . . 2·75 1·90

88 Statue

89 Hintha (legendary bird)

1993. National Convention for Drafting of New Constitution.
332 **88** 50 p. multicoloured 25 20
333 3 k. multicoloured . . . . 1·50 1·00

1993. Statuettes. Multicoloured.
334 5 k. Type **89** . . . . 2·50 1·75
335 10 k. Lawkanat . . . . 5·00 3·50

90 Horseman aiming Spear at Target

1993. Festival of Traditional Equestrian Sports, Sittwe.
336 **90** 3 k. multicoloured . . . . 1·60 1·10

91 Tree, Globe and Figures

92 Association Emblem

1994. World Environment Day.
337 **91** 4 k. multicoloured . . . . 2·00 1·50

1994. 1st Anniv of Union Solidarity and Development Association.
338 **92** 3 k. multicoloured . . . . 1·75 1·25

93 City and Emblem

1995. 50th Anniv of Armed Forces Day.
339 **93** 50 p. multicoloured 10 10

94 Cross through Poppy Head

95 Camera and Film

1995. International Day against Drug Abuse.
340 **94** 2 k. multicoloured 45 30

1995. 60th Anniv of Myanmar Film Industry.
341 **95** 50 p. multicoloured 10 10

96 Figures around Emblem

97 Convocation Hall

1995. 50th Anniv of United Nations Organization.
342 **96** 4 k. multicoloured 90 65

1995. 60th Anniv of Yangon University.
343 **97** 50 p. multicoloured 10 10
344 2 k. multicoloured 45 30

98 Punt

1996. Visit Myanmar Year. Multicoloured.
345 50 p. Type **98** 10 10
346 4 k. Karaweik Hall 90 65
347 5 k. Mandalay Palace . . . . 1·10 75

99 Four-man Canoe

1996. International Letter Writing Week. "Unity equals Success". Multicoloured.
348 2 k. Type **99** 40 30
349 5 k. Human pyramid holding flag aloft (vert) . . . . 1·10 75

100 Breastfeeding

101 Emblem and Map of Myanmar

1996. 50th Anniv of U.N.I.C.E.F. Multicoloured.
350 1 k. Type **100** 20 15
351 2 k. Nurse inoculating child . . 40 30
352 4 k. Children outside school . . 85 60

1997. 30th Anniv of Association of South-East Asian Nations.
353 **101** 1 k. multicoloured 25 15
354 – 2 k. multicoloured 40 30

102 Throne

103 Xylophone

1998. 50th Anniv of Independence.
355 **102** 2 k. multicoloured 40 30

1998. Musical Instruments. Multicoloured.
356 5 k. Type **103** . . . . 1·00 70
357 10 k. Mon brass gongs . . . . 2·00 1·40
358 20 k. Rakhine auspicious drum . 4·00 2·75
359 30 k. Myanmar harp . . . . . 6·00 4·25
360 50 k. Shan pot drum . . . . . 10·00 7·00

104 Emblem

105 Dove and U.P.U. Emblem

1999. Asian and Pacific Decade of Disabled Persons. Seventh Far East and South Pacific Region Disabled Games.
365 **104** 2 k. multicoloured 40 30
366 5 k. multicoloured . . . . 1·00 70

1999. 125th Anniv of Universal Postal Union.
367 **105** 2 k. multicoloured 40 30
368 5 k. multicoloured . . . . 1·00 70

106 People linking Hands around Map of Myanmar

2000. 52nd Anniv of Independence.
369 **106** 2 k. multicoloured 40 30

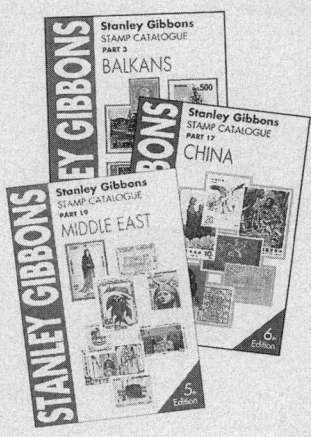

NABHA Pt. 1

A "Convention" state in the Punjab, India.

12 pies = 1 anna; 16 annas = 1 rupee

Stamps of India optd **NABHA STATE**.

1885. Queen Victoria. Vert opt.

1 **23** $\frac{1}{2}$ a. turquoise 1·75 3·25
2 – 1 a. purple 30·00 £110
3 – 2 a. blue 10·00 35·00
4 – 4 a. green (No. 96) 60·00 £150
5 – 8 a. mauve £300
6 – 1 r. grey (No. 79) £275

1885. Queen Victoria. Horiz opt.

36 **40** 3 p. red 10 15
14 **23** $\frac{1}{2}$ a. turquoise 10 10
15 – 9 p. red 50 2·50
17 – 1 a. purple 90 50
18 – 1 a. 6 p. brown 75 2·00
20 – 2 a. blue 1·25 80
22 – 3 a. orange 2·00 1·25
12 – 4 a. green (No. 69) 25·00 £130
24 – 4 a. green (No. 96) 3·50 1·60
26 – 6 a. brown (No. 80) 1·40 2·00
27 – 8 a. mauve 1·50 1·60
28 – 12 a. purple on red 2·50 3·00
29 – 1 r. grey (No. 101) 7·00 35·00
30 **37** 1 r. green and red 7·00 3·75
31 **38** 2 r. red and orange 90·00 £180
32 3 r. brown and green 90·00 £225
33 5 r. blue and violet 90·00 £325

1903. King Edward VII.

37 3 p. grey 30 15
38 $\frac{1}{2}$ a. green (No. 122) 40 30
39 1 a. red (No. 123) 80 60
40a 2 a. lilac 1·60 30
40b $2\frac{1}{2}$ a. blue 17·00 80·00
41 3 a. orange 50 30
42 4 a. olive 1·40 1·75
43 6 a. bistre 90 11·00
44 8 a. mauve 6·00 15·00
45 12 a. purple on red 2·75 17·00
46 1 r. green and red 6·00 9·00

1907. As last, but inscr "INDIA POSTAGE & REVENUE".

47 $\frac{1}{2}$ a. green (No. 149) 65 1·10
48 1 a. red (No. 150) 40 70

1913. King George V. Optd in two lines.

49 **55** 3 p. grey 20 20
50 **56** $\frac{1}{2}$ a. green 20 10
51 **57** 1 a. red 60 10
59 1 a. brown 2·75 1·50
52 **59** 2 a. lilac 50 35
53 **62** 3 a. orange 50 35
54 **63** 4 a. olive 55 95
55 **64** 6 a. bistre 55 4·25
56 **65** 8 a. mauve 1·50 3·00
57 **66** 12 a. red 1·40 17·00
58 **67** 1 r. brown and green 6·50 3·25

1928. King George V. Optd in one line.

60 **55** 3 p. grey 75 15
61 **56** $\frac{1}{2}$ a. green 30 20
73 **79** $\frac{1}{2}$ a. green 40 30
61a **80** 9 p. green 1·50 1·10
62 **57** 1 a. brown 60 15
74 **81** 1 a. brown 30 30
63 **82** $1\frac{1}{4}$ a. mauve 80 4·00
64 **70** 2 a. lilac 1·75 35
65 **61** $2\frac{1}{2}$ a. orange 45 6·00
66 **62** 3 a. blue 1·40 1·00
75 **57** 3 a. red 3·75 9·00
76 **63** 4 a. olive 2·75 2·25
67 **71** 4 a. green 1·60 1·40
71 **67** 2 r. red and orange 22·00 75·00
72 5 r. blue and purple 70·00 £200

1938. King George VI. Nos. 247/63.

77 **91** 3 p. slate 5·50 30
78 $\frac{1}{2}$ a. brown 3·25 60
79 9 p. green 17·00 3·25
80 1 a. red 1·50 30
81 **92** 2 a. red 1·00 4·25
82 – 2 a. 6 p. violet 1·00 7·00
83 – 3 a. green 1·10 3·75
84 – 3 a. 6 p. blue 1·10 14·00
85 – 4 a. brown 5·00 5·00
86 – 6 a. green 2·50 14·00
87 – 8 a. violet 1·90 14·00
88 – 12 a. red 2·25 15·00
89 **93** 1 r. slate and brown 10·00 21·00
90 2 r. purple and brown 19·00 75·00
91 5 r. green and blue 45·00 £150
92 10 r. purple and red 70·00 £300
93 15 r. brown and green £180 £550
94 25 r. slate and purple £180 £550

1942. King George VI. Optd **NABHA** only.

95 **91** 3 p. slate 28·00 2·75
105 **100a** 3 p. slate 80 55
96 **91** $\frac{1}{2}$ a. brown 65·00 3·75
106 **100a** $\frac{1}{2}$ a. mauve 4·00 65
97 **91** 9 p. green 10·00 10·00
107 **100a** 9 p. green 3·25 60
98 **91** 1 a. red 10·00 2·25
108 **100a** 1 a. red 80 2·25
109 **101** 1 a. 3 p. brown 80 1·75
110 $1\frac{1}{2}$ a. violet 1·00 1·10
111 2 a. red 80 3·00
112 3 a. violet 2·50 2·75
113 $3\frac{1}{2}$ a. blue 10·00 38·00
114 **102** 4 a. brown 1·60 75
115 6 a. green 8·00 38·00
116 8 a. violet 6·00 26·00
117 12 a. purple 4·50 38·00

OFFICIAL STAMPS

Stamps of Nabha optd **SERVICE**.

1885. Nos. 1/3 (Queen Victoria).

O1 $\frac{1}{2}$ a. turquoise 1·75 60
O2 1 a. purple 30 15
O3 2 a. blue 50·00 £100

1885. Nos. 14/30 (Queen Victoria).

O 6 $\frac{1}{2}$ a. turquoise 10 10
O 8 1 a. purple 75 25
O 9 2 a. blue 1·60 65
O11 3 a. orange 16·00 55·00
O13 4 a. green (No. 4) 2·00 65
O15 6 a. brown 12·00 20·00
O17 8 a. mauve 1·25 70
O18 12 a. purple on red 5·00 14·00
O19 1 r. grey 28·00 £180
O20 1 r. green and red 25·00 55·00

1903. Nos. 37/46 (King Edward VII).

O25 3 p. grey 70 9·50
O26 $\frac{1}{2}$ a. green 40 10
O27 1 a. red 15 10
O29 2 a. lilac 1·25 40
O30 4 a. olive 1·40 50
O32 8 a. mauve 1·10 1·25
O34 1 r. green and red 1·50 2·25

1907. Nos. 47/8 (King Edward VII inscr "INDIA POSTAGE & REVENUE").

O35 $\frac{1}{2}$ a. green 20 40
O36 1 a. red 25 25

1913. Nos. 54 and 58, (King George V).

O37 **63** 4 a. olive 10·00 45·00
O38 **67** 1 r. brown and green 55·00 £300

1913. Official stamps of India (King George V) optd **NABHA STATE**.

O39 **55** 3 p. grey 30 5·50
O40 **56** $\frac{1}{2}$ a. green 15 10
O41 **57** 1 a. red 15 10
O42 **59** 2 a. lilac 30 15
O43 **63** 4 a. olive 40 40
O44 **65** 8 a. mauve 65 90
O46 **67** 1 r. brown and green 3·25 2·25

1932. Stamps of India (King George V) optd **NABHA STATE SERVICE**.

O47 **55** 3 p. grey 10 15
O48 **81** 1 a. brown 15 15
O49 **63** 4 a. olive 19·00 2·25
O50 **65** 8 a. mauve 1·00 1·90

1938. Stamps of India (King George VI) optd **NABHA STATE SERVICE**.

O53 **91** 9 p. green 1·75 2·50
O54 1 a. red 9·00 55

1943. Stamps of India (King George VI) optd **NABHA**.

O55 **O 20** 3 p. slate 60 70
O56 $\frac{1}{2}$ a. brown 70 30
O57 $\frac{1}{2}$ a. purple 2·75 50
O58 9 p. green 1·25 20
O59 1 a. red 50 20
O61 $1\frac{1}{2}$ a. violet 60 40
O62 2 a. orange 1·40 75
O64 4 a. brown 3·50 2·00
O65 8 a. violet 5·50 13·00

1943. Stamps of India (King George VI) optd **NABHA SERVICE**.

O66 **93** 1 r. slate and brown 8·50 28·00
O67 2 r. purple and brown 24·00 £150
O68 5 r. green and blue £200 £475

NAGORNO-KARABAKH Pt. 10

The mountainous area of Nagorno-Karabakh, mainly populated by Armenians, was declared an Autonomous Region within the Azerbaijan Soviet Socialist Republic on 7 July 1923.

Following agitation for union with Armenia in 1988 Nagorno-Karabakh was placed under direct U.S.S.R. rule in 1989. On 2 September 1991 the Regional Soviet declared its independence and this was confirmed by popular vote on 10 December. By 1993 fighting between Azerbaijan forces and those of Nagorno-Karabakh, supported by Armenia, led to the occupation of all Azerbaijan territory separating Nagorno-Karabakh from the border with Armenia. A ceasefire under Russian auspices was signed on 18 February 1994.

1993. 100 kopeks = 1 rouble.
1995. 100 louma = 1 dram.

1 National Flag

1993. Inscr "REPUBLIC OF MOUNTAINOUS KARABAKH".

1 **1** 1 r. multicoloured 20 20
2 – 3 r. blue, purple and brown 60 60
3 – 15 r. red and blue 3·00 3·00

DESIGNS: 3 r. President Arthur Mkrtchian; 15 r. "We are Our Mountains" (sculpture of man and woman).

Ա (2 "A")　Ր (2a "P")　Գ (2b "K")

1995. Nos. 1 and 3 surch in Armenian script as T **2/2b**.

6 **2** (50 d.) on 1 r. multicoloured 1·25 1·25
7 **2a** (100 d.) on 15 r. red and blue 2·25 2·25
8 **2b** (200 d.) on 15 r. red and blue 4·75 4·75

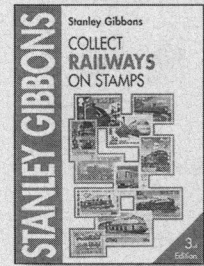

3 Dadiwank Monastery

1996. 5th Anniv of Independence. Multicoloured.

9 50 d. Type **3** 50 50
10 100 d. Parliament Building, Stepanakert 90 90
11 200 d. "We are Our Mountains" (sculpture of man and woman) 1·60 1·60

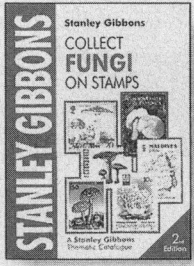

4 Boy playing Drum and Fawn (Erna Arshakyan)

1997. Festivals. Multicoloured.

13 50 d. Type **4** (New Year) 35 35
14 200 d. Madonna and Child with angels (Mihran Akopyan) (Christmas) (vert) 1·75 1·75

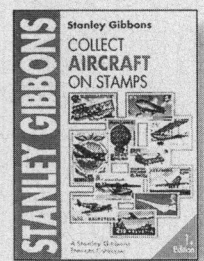

5 Eagle and Demonstrator with Flag

1998. 10th Anniv of Karabakh Movement.

15 **5** 250 d. multicoloured 75 75

6 Parliament Summer Palace

1998. 5th Anniv of Liberation of Shushi. Multicoloured.

16 100 d. Type **6** 30 30
17 250 d. Church of the Saviour (vert) 75 75

NAKHICHEVAN Pt. 10

An autonomous province of Azerbaijan, separated from the remainder of the republic by Armenian territory. Nos. 1 and 2 were issued during a period when the administration of Nakhichevan was in dispute with the central government.

100 qopik = 1 manat

1 President Aliev

1993. 70th Birthday of President H. Aliev of Nakhichevan.
1 **1** 5 m. black and red . . . . . . 3·75 3·75
2 – 5 m. multicoloured . . . . . . 3·75 3·75
DESIGN: No. 2, Map of Nakhichevan.

NAMIBIA Pt. 1

Formerly South West Africa which became independent on 21 March 1990.

1990. 100 cents = 1 rand.
1993. 100 cents = 1 Namibia dollar.

141 Pres. Sam Nujoma, Map of Namibia and National Flag

1990. Independence. Multicoloured.
538 18 c. Type **141** 30 15
539 45 c. Hands releasing dove and map of Namibia (vert) . . . 70 1·00
540 60 c. National flag and map of Africa . . . . 1·25 1·75

142 Fish River Canyon

1990. Namibia Landscapes. Multicoloured.
541 18 c. Type **142** 35 20
542 35 c. Quiver-tree forest, Keetmanshoop 65 35
543 45 c. Tsaris Mountains 75 55
544 60 c. Dolerite boulders, Keetmanshoop 85 65

143 Stores on Kaiser Street, c. 1899

1990. Centenary of Windhoek. Multicoloured.
545 18 c. Type **143** 25 20
546 35 c. Kaiser Street, 1990 . . . 45 35
547 45 c. City Hall, 1914 . . . . . 55 65
548 60 c. City Hall, 1990 . . . . . 70 1·00

144 Maizefields 145 Gypsum

1990. Farming. Multicoloured.
549 20 c. Type **144** 25 20
550 35 c. Sanga bull 45 35
551 50 c. Damara ram 60 45
552 65 c. Irrigation in Okavango . . 75 60

1991. Minerals. As Nos. 519/21 and 523/33 of South West Africa, some with values changed and new design (5 r.), inscr "Namibia" as T **145**. Multicoloured.
553 1 c. Type **145** 10 10
554 2 c. Fluorite 15 10
555 5 c. Mimetite 20 10
556 10 c. Azurite 30 10
557 20 c. Dioptase 35 10
558 25 c. Type **139** 35 15
559 30 c. Tsumeb lead and copper complex 50 20
560 35 c. Rosh Pinah zinc mine . . 50 20
561 40 c. Diamonds 65 25
562 50 c. Uis tin mine 65 25
563 65 c. Boltwoodite 65 35
564 1 r. Rossing uranium mine . . 70 50
565 1 r. 50 Wulfenite . . . . . . 1·10 70
566 2 r. Gold . . . . 1·50 1·10
567 5 r. Willemite (vert as T **145**) . 3·00 2·75

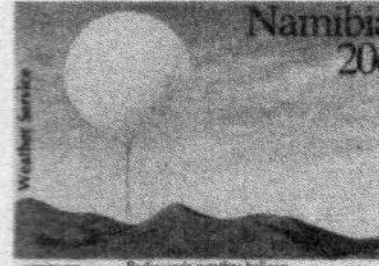

146 Radiosonde Weather Balloon

1991. Centenary of Weather Service. Mult.
568 20 c. Type **146** 30 20
569 35 c. Sunshine recorder 45 30
570 50 c. Measuring equipment . . 60 50
571 65 c. Meteorological station, Gobabeb 70 60

147 Herd of Zebras

1991. Endangered Species. Mountain Zebra. Multicoloured.
572 20 c. Type **147** . . . . 1·10 60
573 25 c. Mare and foal . . . . . 1·25 70
574 45 c. Zebras and foal . . . . . 2·00 1·75
575 60 c. Two zebras . . . . 2·50 3·00

148 Karas Mountains

1991. Mountains of Namibia. Multicoloured.
576 20 c. Type **148** 35 20
577 25 c. Gamsberg Mountains . . 40 30
578 45 c. Mount Brukkaros 70 70
579 60 c. Erongo Mountains . . . 80 1·00

149 Bernabe de la Bat Camp

1991. Tourist Camps. Multicoloured.
580 20 c. Type **149** 45 30
581 25 c. Von Bach Dam Recreation Resort 55 45
582 45 c. Gross Barmen Hot Springs 85 65
583 60 c. Namutoni Rest Camp . . 1·00 1·00

150 Artist's Pallet

1992. 21st Anniv of Windhoek Conservatoire. Multicoloured.
584 20 c. Type **150** 20 15
585 25 c. French horn and cello . . 25 20
586 45 c. Theatrical masks 50 60
587 60 c. Ballet dancers 65 60

151 Mozambique Mouthbrooder

1992. Freshwater Angling. Multicoloured.
588 20 c. Type **151** 40 20
589 25 c. Large-mouthed yellowfish 45 20
590 45 c. Common carp 85 50
591 60 c. Sharp-toothed catfish . . 95 65

152 Old Jetty

1992. Centenary of Swakopmund. Mult.
592 20 c. Type **152** 25 25
593 25 c. Recreation centre 25 25
594 45 c. State House and lighthouse 80 60
595 60 c. Sea front 85 75

153 Running 154 Wrapping English Cucumbers

1992. Olympic Games, Barcelona. Mult.
597 20 c. Type **153** 25 20
598 25 c. Map of Namibia, Namibian flag and Olympic rings . . . 30 20
599 45 c. Swimming 50 40
600 60 c. Olympic Stadium, Barcelona 65 55

1992. Integration of the Disabled. Mult.
602 20 c. Type **154** 20 15
603 25 c. Weaving mats 20 15
604 45 c. Spinning thread 40 30
605 60 c. Preparing pot plants . . . 55 50

155 Elephants in Desert

1993. Namibia Nature Foundation. Rare and Endangered Species. Multicoloured.
606 20 c. Type **155** 40 20
607 25 c. Sitatunga in swamp . . . 30 20
608 45 c. Black rhinoceros 65 50
609 60 c. Hunting dogs 65 60

156 Herd of Simmentaler Cattle

1993. Centenary of Simmentalar Cattle in Namibia. Multicoloured.
611 20 c. Type **156** 30 10
612 25 c. Cow and calf 30 15
613 45 c. Bull 60 40
614 60 c. Cattle on barge 85 75

157 Sand Dunes, Sossusvlei

1993. Namib Desert Scenery. Multicoloured.
615 30 c. Type **157** 25 20
616 40 c. Blutkuppe 25 20
617 65 c. River Kuiseb, Homeb . . 40 45
618 85 c. Desert landscape 60 65

158 Smiling Child

1993. S.O.S. Child Care in Namibia. Mult.
619 30 c. Type **158** 30 20
620 40 c. Family 35 20
621 65 c. Modern house 60 55
622 85 c. Young artist with mural . 80 80

159 "Charaxes jasius" 160 White Seabream

1993. Butterflies. Multicoloured.
707 5 c. Type **159** 10 10
624 10 c. "Acraea anemosa" . . . 20 20
625 20 c. "Papilio nireus" 30 10
626 30 c. "Junonia octavia" 30 10
627 40 c. "Hypolimnus misippus" . 30 10
708 50 c. "Physcaeneura panda" . . 40 40
629 65 c. "Charaxes candiope" . . 40 30
630 85 c. "Junonia hierta" 50 40
631 90 c. "Colotis cellmene" . . . 50 40
632 $1 "Cacyreus dicksoni" 55 35
633 $2 "Charaxes bohemani" . . . 80 80
634 $2.50 "Stugeta bowkeri" . . . 1·00 1·10
635 $5 "Byblia anvatara" . . . . . 1·50 1·75
See also No. 648.

1994. Coastal Angling. Multicoloured.
636 30 c. Type **160** 25 25
637 40 c. Kob 25 25
638 65 c. West coast steenbras . . . 40 40
639 85 c. Galjoen 60 60

161 Container Ship at Wharf

1994. Incorporation of Walvis Bay Territory into Namibia. Multicoloured.
641 30 c. Type **161** 40 30
642 65 c. Aerial view of Walvis Bay . 60 80
643 85 c. Map of Namibia . . . . 95 1·25

162 "Adenolobus pechuelii" 163 Yellow-billed Stork

1994. Flowers. Multicoloured.
644 35 c. Type **162** 30 25
645 40 c. "Hibiscus elliottiae" . . . 30 25
646 65 c. "Pelargonium cortusifolium" 55 40
647 85 c. "Hoodia macrantha" . . 75 60

1994. Butterflies. As T **159**, but inscr "STANDARDISED MAIL". Multicoloured.
648 (–) "Graphium antheus" . . . 15 20
No. 648 was initially sold at 35 c., but this was subsequently increased to reflect changes in postal rates.

1994. Storks. Multicoloured.
649 35 c. Type **163** 40 30
650 40 c. Abdim's stork 40 30
651 80 c. African open-bill stork . . 70 50
652 $1.10 White stork 80 65

164 Steam Railcar, 1908

1994. Steam Locomotives. Multicoloured.
653 35 c. Type **164** 45 30
654 70 c. Krauss side-tank locomotive No. 106, 1904 . . . . 70 50
655 80 c. Class 24 locomotive, 1948 75 55
656 $1.10 Class 7C locomotive, 1914 . . . . 1·10 80

165 Cape Cross Locomotive No. 84 "Prince Edward", 1895

1995. Cent of Railways in Namibia. Mult.
657 35 c. Type **165** 45 25
658 70 c. Steam locomotive, German South West Africa 70 35
659 80 c. South African Railways Class 8 steam locomotive . . 75 40
660 $1.10 Trans-Namib Class 33-400 diesel-electric locomotive . . 1·10 55

166 National Arms

167 Living Tortoise and "Geochelone stromeri" (fossil)

1995. 5th Anniv of Independence.

662 **166** (–) multicoloured 30 30

No. 662 is inscribed "STANDARDISED MAIL" and was initially sold for 35 c., but this was subsequently increased to reflect changes in postal rates.

1995. Fossils. Multicoloured.

663 40 c. Type **167** 50 25
664 80 c. Ward's diamond bird and "Diamantornis wardi" (fossil eggs) 80 60
665 90 c. Hyraxes and "Prohyrax hendeyi" skull 90 70
666 $1.20 Crocodiles and "Crocodylus lloydi" skull . . 1·10 90

168 Martii Rautanen and Church

169 Ivory Buttons

1995. 125th Anniv of Finnish Missionaries in Namibia. Multicoloured.

667 40 c. Type **168** 25 20
668 80 c. Albin Savola and hand printing press 50 50
669 90 c. Karl Weikkolin and wagon 60 65
670 $1.20 Dr. Selma Rainio and Onandjokwe Hospital . . . 85 95

1995. Personal Ornaments. Multicoloured.

671 40 c. Type **169** 20 20
672 80 c. Conus shell pendant . . . 45 45
673 90 c. Cowrie shell headdress . . 55 55
674 $1.20 Shell button pendant . . 85 95

170 U.N. Flag

1995. 50th Anniv of the United Nations.

676 **170** 40 c. blue and black . . . 20 20

171 Bogenfels Arch

1996. Tourism. Multicoloured.

677 (–) Type **171** 15 15
678 90 c. Ruacana Falls 30 30
679 $1 Epupa Falls 30 30
680 $1.30 Herd of wild horses . . . 35 50

No. 677 is inscribed "Standardised Mail" and was initially sold at 45 c.

172 Sister Leoni Kreitmeier and Dobra Education and Training Centre

1996. Centenary of Catholic Missions in Namibia. Multicoloured.

681 50 c. Type **172** 20 20
682 95 c. Father Johann Malinowski and Heirachabis Mission . . 30 40
683 $1 St. Mary's Cathedral, Windhoek 30 40
684 $1.30 Archbishop Joseph Gotthardt and early church, Ovamboland 35 80

173 Children and U.N.I.C.E.F. Volunteer

1996. 50th Anniv of U.N.I.C.E.F. Multicoloured.

686 (–) Type **173** 15 15
687 $1.30 Girls in school 60 60

No. 686 is inscribed "STANDARD POSTAGE" and was initially sold at 50 c.

174 Boxing

1996. Centennial Olympic Games, Atlanta. Multicoloured.

688 (–) Type **174** 15 15
689 90 c. Cycling 30 40
690 $1 Swimming 30 40
691 $1.30 Running 35 55

No. 688 is inscribed "Standard Postage" and was initially sold at 50 c.

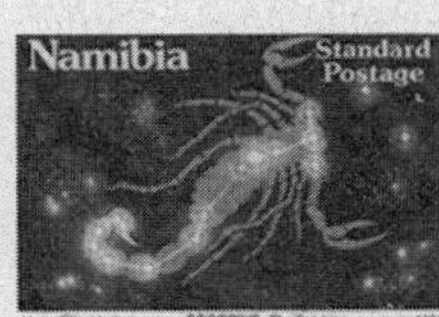

175 Scorpius

1996. Stars in the Namibian Sky. Multicoloured.

692 (–) Type **175** 15 15
693 90 c. Sagittarius 25 30
694 $1 Southern Cross 30 30
695 $1.30 Orion 35 50

No. 692 is inscribed "Standard Postage" and was initially sold at 50 c.

176 Urn-shaped Pot

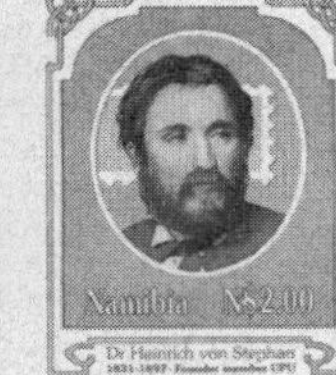

179 Heinrich von Stephan

177 Khauxa!nas Ruins

1996. Early Pottery. Multicoloured.

697 (–) Type **176** 15 15
698 90 c. Decorated storage pot . . 25 40
699 $1 Reconstructed cooking pot . . 30 40
700 $1.30 Storage pot 35 70

No. 697 is inscribed "Standard Postage" and was initially sold at 50 c.

1997. Khaux!nas Ruins.

701 **177** (–) multicoloured 25 20
702 – $1 multicoloured 50 50
703 – $1.10 multicoloured . . . 60 65
704 – $1.50 multicoloured . . . 85 1·00

DESIGNS: $1 to $1.50, Different views.

No. 701 is inscribed "Standard postage" and was initially sold at 50 c.

1997. Death Centenary of Heinrich von Stephan (founder of U.P.U.).

709 **179** $2 multicoloured 85 85

180 Cinderella Waxbill

182 Jackass Penguins calling

181 Helmet Guineafowl

1997. Waxbills. Multicoloured.

710 50 c. Type **180** 20 30
711 60 c. Black-cheeked waxbill . . 20 30

1997. Greetings Stamp.

712 **181** $1.20 multicoloured . . . 30 35

For similar designs see Nos. 743/6.

1997. Endangered Species. Jackass Penguin. Multicoloured.

713 (–) Type **182** 25 30
714 $1 Incubating egg 40 40
715 $1.10 Adult with chick 50 50
716 $1.50 Penguins swimming . . . 55 60

No. 713 is inscribed "STANDARD POSTAGE" and was initially sold at 50 c.

183 Caracal

1997. Wildcats. Multicoloured.

718 (–) Type **183** 20 20
719 $1 "Felis lybic" 30 30
720 $1.10 Serval 35 40
721 $1.50 Black-footed cat 50 55

No. 718 is inscribed "STANDARD POSTAGE" and was initially sold at 50 c.

184 "Catophractes alexandri"

1997. Greeting Stamps. Flowers and Helmet Guineafowl. Multicoloured.

723 (–) Type **184** 15 20
724 (–) "Crinum paludosum" . . . 15 20
725 (–) "Gloriosa superba" . . . 15 20
726 (–) "Tribulus zeyheri" . . . 15 20
727 (–) "Aptosimum pubescens" . . 15 20
728 50 c. Helmet guineafowl raising hat 15 20
729 50 c. Holding bouquet 15 20
730 50 c. Ill in bed 15 20
731 $1 With heart round neck . . . 25 20
732 $1 With suitcase and backpack . 25 20

Nos. 723/7 are inscribed "Standard Postage" and were initially sold at 50 c. each.

185 Collecting Bag

1997. Basket Work. Multicoloured.

733 50 c. Type **185** 20 20
734 90 c. Powder basket 30 30
735 $1.20 Fruit basket 35 35
736 $2 Grain basket 70 75

186 Veterinary Association Coat of Arms

1997. 50th Anniv of Namibian Veterinary Association.

737 **186** $1.50 multicoloured 50 50

MINIMUM PRICE

The minimum price quoted is 10p which represents a handling charge rather than a basis for valuing common stamps. For further notes about prices see introductory pages.

188 German South West Africa Postman

189 False Mopane

1997. World Post Day.

739 **188** (–) multicoloured 20 20

No. 739 is inscribed "STANDARD POSTAGE" and was initially sold at 50 c.

1997. Trees. Multicoloured.

740 (–) Type **189** 15 20
741 $1 Ana tree 30 40
742 $1.10 Shepherd's tree 35 55
743 $1.50 Kiaat 50 70

No. 740 is inscribed "STANDARD POSTAGE" and was initially sold at 50 c.

1997. Christmas. As T **181**, showing Helmet Guineafowl, each with festive frame. Multicoloured.

744 (–) Guineafowl facing right . . 15 20
745 $1 Guineafowl in grass 30 30
746 $1.10 Guineafowl on rock . . . 35 40
747 $1.50 Guineafowl in desert . . 50 55

No. 744 is inscribed "standard postage" and was initially sold at 50 c.

190 Flame Lily

191 John Muafangejo

1997. Flora and Fauna. Multicoloured.

749 5 c. Type **190** 10 10
750 10 c. Bushman poison 10 10
751 20 c. Camel's foot 10 10
752 30 c. Western rhigozum 10 10
753 40 c. Blue-cheeked bee-eater . . 10 10
754 50 c. Laughing dove 10 10
755 (–) Peach-faced lovebird . . . 10 10
756 60 c. Lappet-faced vulture . . . 10 10
757 90 c. Yellow-billed hornbill . . 20 25
758 $1 Lilac-breasted roller 20 25
759 $1.10 Hippopotamus 20 25
760 $1.20 Giraffe 30 35
761 (–) Leopard 30 35
762 $1.50 Elephant 30 35
763 $2 Lion 40 45
764 $4 Buffalo 80 85
765 $5 Black rhinoceros . . . . . 1·00 1·10
766 $10 Cheetah . . . . 2·00 2·10

No. 755 is inscribed "standard postage" and was initially sold at 50 c.; No. 761 is inscribed "postcard rate" and was initially sold at $1.20.

Nos. 755, 758 and 761 exist with ordinary or self-adhesive gum.

1997. 10th Death Anniv of John Muafangejo (artist).

770 **191** (50 c.) multicoloured . . . 30 30

No. 770 is inscribed "STANDARD POSTAGE" and was initially sold at 50 c.

192 Gabriel B. Taapopi

1998. Gabriel B. Taapopi (writer) Commemoration.

771 **192** (–) silver and brown . . . 20 20

No. 771 is inscribed "STANDARD POSTAGE" and was initially sold at 50 c.

194 Leopard

1998. Large Wild Cats. Multicoloured.

782 $1.20 Type **194** 40 25
783 $1.90 Lioness and cub 60 55
784 $2 Lion 60 60
785 $2.50 Cheetah 70 90

195 Narra Plant

196 Collecting Rain Water

1998. Narra Cultivation.
787 **195** $2.40 multicoloured . . . 35 40

1998. World Water Day.
788 **196** (–) multicoloured 30 30
No. 788 is inscribed "STANDARD POSTAGE" and was initially sold at 50 c. On 1 April 1998 the standard postage rate was increased to 55 c.

197 White-faced Scops Owl

1998. Owls of Namibia. Multicoloured.
790 55 c. Black-tailed tree rat (20 × 24 mm) 30 30
791 $1.50 Type **197** 55 55
792 $1.50 Barred owl 55 55
793 $1.90 Spotted eagle owl 55 55
794 $1.90 Barn owl (61 × 24 mm) . . 55 55

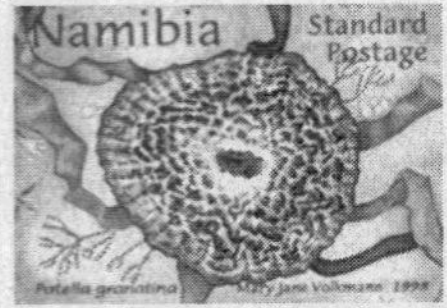

198 "Patella ganatina" (Limpet)

1998. Shells. Multicoloured.
795 (–) Type **198** 20 10
796 $1.10 "Cymatium cutaceum africanum" (Triton) 40 30
797 $1.50 "Conus mozambicus" (Cone) 60 55
798 $6 "Venus verrucosa" (Venus clam) . . . . 1·75 2·00
No. 795 is inscribed "Standard Postage" and was initially sold at 55 c.

201 Namibian Beach

1998. World Environment Day. Multicoloured.
802 (–) Type **201** 10 10
803 $1.10 Okavango sunset 20 25
804 $1.50 Sossusvlei 30 35
805 $1.90 African Moringo tree . . 40 45
No. 802 is inscribed "STANDARD POSTAGE" and was initially sold at 55 c.

204 Carmine Bee-eater

1998. Wildlife of the Caprivi Strip. Multicoloured.
808 60 c. Type **204** 20 20
809 60 c. Sable antelope (40 × 40 mm) 20 20
810 60 c. Lechwe (40 × 40 mm) . . 20 20
811 60 c. Woodland waterberry . . 20 20
812 60 c. Nile monitor (40 × 40 mm) . 20 20
813 60 c. African jacana 20 20
814 60 c. African fish eagle 20 20
815 60 c. Woodland kingfisher . . . 20 20
816 60 c. Nile crocodile (55 × 30 mm) 20 20
817 60 c. Black mamba (32 × 30 mm) 20 20
Nos. 808/17 were printed together, se-tenant, with the backgrounds forming a composite design.

207 Damara Dik-dik

208 Yoka perplexed

1999. "Fun Stamps for Children". Animals. Mult.
820 $1.80 Type **207** 50 50
821 $2.65 Striped tree squirrel (26 × 36 mm) 75 75

1999. "Yoka the Snake" (cartoon). Multicoloured. Self-adhesive.
822 $1.60 Type **208** 30 35
823 $1.60 Yoka under attack (33 × 27 mm) 30 35
824 $1.60 Yoka caught on branch . 30 35
825 $1.60 Yoka and wasps (33 × 27 mm) 30 35
826 $1.60 Yoka and footprint . . . 30 35
827 $1.60 Yoka and tail of red and white snake 30 35
828 $1.60 Mouse hunt (33 × 27 mm) . 30 35
829 $1.60 Snakes entwined 30 35
830 $1.60 Red and white snake singing 30 35
831 $1.60 Yoka sulking (33 × 27 mm) 30 35

210 Zogling Glider, 1928

1999. Gliding in Namibia. Multicoloured.
833 $1.60 Type **210** 40 40
834 $1.80 Schleicher glider, 1998 . . 50 50

212 Greater Kestrel

1999. Birds of Prey. Multicoloured.
836 60 c. Type **212** 20 15
837 $1.60 Common kestrel ("Rock Kestrel") 45 40
838 $1.80 Red-headed falcon . . . 45 45
839 $2.65 Lanner falcon 70 80

213 Wattled Crane

1999. Wetland Birds. Multicoloured.
840 $1.60 Type **213** 45 40
841 $1.80 Variegated sandgrouse ("Burchell's Sandgrouse") . . 45 45
842 $1.90 Pratincole 50 50
843 $2.65 Eastern white pelican . . 70 80

215 "Eulophia hereroensis" (orchid)

1999. "China '99" International Philatelic Exhibition, Beijing. Orchids. Multicoloured.
845 $1.60 Type **215** 45 35
846 $1.80 "Ansellia africana" . . . 45 40
847 $2.65 "Eulophia leachii" . . . 70 70
848 $3.90 "Eulophia speciosa" . . . 90 1·00

216 Johanna Gertze

1999. Johanna Gertze Commemoration.
851 **216** $20 red, pink and blue . . 4·00 4·25

217 Sunset over Namibia

1999. New Millennium. Multicoloured.
852 $2.20 Type **217** 40 45
853 $2.40 Sunrise over Namibia . . 45 50

218 South African Shelduck

2000. Ducks of Namibia. Multicoloured.
855 $2 Type **218** 40 45
856 $2.40 White-faced whistling duck 45 50
857 $3 Comb duck ("Knobbilled duck") 60 65
858 $7 Cape shoveler . . . . 1·50 1·60
No. 858 is inscribed "Cape shoveller" in error.

2000. Nos. 749/52 surch with **standard postage** (859) or new values (others).
859 (–) on 5 c. Type **190** 15 20
860 $1.80 on 30 c. Western rhigozum 35 40
861 $3 on 10 c. Bushman poison . . 60 65
862 $6 on 20 c. Camel's foot . . . . 1·10 1·25
No. 859 was initially sold at 65 c. The other surcharges show face values.

220 Namibian Children

2000. 10th Anniv of Independence. Multicoloured.
863 65 c. Type **220** 15 20
864 $3 Namibian flag 60 65

221 Actor playing Jesus wearing Crown of Thorns

2000. Easter Passion Play. Multicoloured.
865 $2.10 Type **221** 40 45
866 $2.40 On the way to Calvary . . 45 50

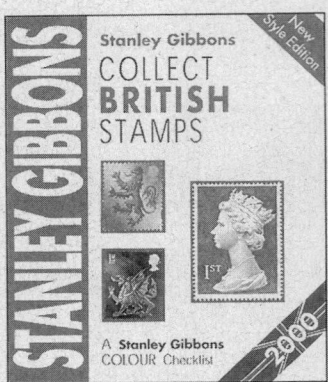

NANDGAON Pt. 1

A state of central India. Now uses Indian stamps.

12 pies = 1 anna; 16 annas = 1 rupee

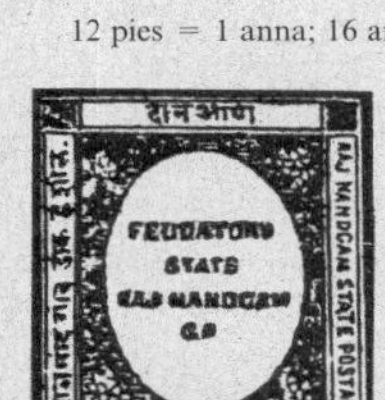

1

2 (2 a.)

1891. Imperf.
1 1 ½a. blue . . . . 4·00 £110
2 2a. pink . . . . 18·00 £325

1893. Imperf.
3 2 ½a. green . . . . 8·50 55·00
6 1a. red . . . . 40·00 90·00
4 2a. red . . . . 7·50 55·00

OFFICIAL STAMPS

1893. Optd **M.B.D.** in oval.
O1 1 ½a. blue £350
O4 2 ½a. green . . . . 4·50 7·50
O5 1a. red . . . . 7·00 26·00
O6 2a. red . . . . 6·00 16·00

NAPLES Pt. 8

A state on the S.W. coast of Central Italy, formerly part of the Kingdom of Sicily, but now part of Italy.

200 tornesi = 100 grano = 1 ducato

1 Arms under Bourbon Dynasty

4 Cross of Savoy

1858. The frames differ in each value. Imperf.
8 1 ½t. blue £120000 £8000
1 ½g. red £650 £170
2 1g. red . . . . £180 15·00
3 2g. red . . . . £110 4·25
4 5g. red . . . . £900 18·00
5 10g. red . . . . £2000 65·00
6 20g. red £1700 £275
7 50g. red £4250 £2500

1860. Imperf.
9 4 ½t. blue £16000 £3000

NATAL Pt. 1

On the east coast of S. Africa. Formerly a British Colony, later a province of the Union of S. Africa.

12 pence = 1 shilling;
20 shillings = 1 pound

1

1857. Embossed stamps. Various designs.
1 1 1d. red . . . . — £1700
2 1d. buff . . . . — £1000
3 1d. blue . . . . — £1100
4 3d. red . . . . — £400
5 – 6d. green . . . . — £1100
6 – 9d. blue . . . . — £7000
7 – 1s. buff . . . . — £5500

The 3d., 6d., 9d. and 1s. are larger. Beware of reprints.

6

7

1859.
19 6 1d. red . . . . 85·00 27·00
12 3d. blue . . . . £100 32·00
13 6d. grey . . . . £160 50·00
24 6d. violet . . . . 42·00 27·00

1867.
25 7 1s. green . . . . £130 28·00

1869. Variously optd **POSTAGE** or **Postage.**
50 6 1d. red . . . . 85·00 32·00
82 1d. yellow . . . . 70·00 70·00
53 3d. blue . . . . £140 42·00
83 6d. violet . . . . 55·00 6·00
84 7 1s. green . . . . 80·00 5·50

1870. Optd **POSTAGE** in a curve.
59 7 1s. green . . . . 70·00 10·00
108 1s. orange . . . . 3·50 85

1870. Optd **POSTAGE** twice, reading up and down.
60 6 1d. red . . . . 70·00 13·00
61 3d. blue . . . . 75·00 13·00
62 6d. violet . . . . £150 25·00

1873. Optd **POSTAGE** once, reading up.
63 7 1s. brown . . . . £150 18·00

23

28

NATAL POSTAGE
FIVE SHILLINGS

16

1874. Queen Victoria. Various frames.
97a 23 ½d. green . . . . 1·25 40
99 – 1d. red . . . . 2·00 10
107 – 2d. olive . . . . 2·25 1·40
113 28 2½d. blue . . . . 3·75 50
68 – 3d. blue . . . . 90·00 15·00
101 – 3d. grey . . . . 2·75 95
102 – 4d. brown . . . . 3·25 75
103 – 6d. lilac . . . . 3·25 80
73 16 5s. red . . . . 60·00 27·00

1877. No. 99 surch ½ **HALF.**
85 ½d. on 1d. red . . . . 23·00 65·00

POSTAGE | POSTAGE.
Half-penny | Half-Penny
(21) | (29)

1877. Surch as T **21**.
91 6 ½d. on 1d. yellow . . . . 8·00 12·00
92 1d. on 6d. violet . . . . 50·00 8·50
93 1d. on 6d. red . . . . 95·00 35·00

1885. Surch in words.
104 ½d. on 1d. red (No. 99) . . . . 16·00 11·00
105 2d. on 3d. grey (No. 101) . . . . 18·00 5·50
109 2½d. on 4d. brown (No. 102) . . . . 11·00 8·50

1895. No. 23 surch with T **29**.
114 6 ½d. on 6d. violet . . . . 1·25 2·75

1895. No. 99 surch **HALF.**
125 HALF on 1d. red . . . . 1·00 75

31

32

1902.
127 31 ½d. green . . . . 1·25 15
128 1d. red . . . . 3·50 15
129 1½d. green and black . . . . 2·00 2·00
130 2d. red and olive . . . . 1·25 25
131 2½d. blue . . . . 1·25 3·00
132 3d. purple and grey . . . . 1·00 90
152 4d. red and brown . . . . 2·75 1·00
134 5d. black and orange . . . . 1·50 2·75
135 6d. green and purple . . . . 1·50 1·75
136 1s. red and blue . . . . 2·75 1·75
137 2s. green and violet . . . . 48·00 9·00
138 2s. 6d. purple . . . . 38·00 12·00
139 4s. red and yellow . . . . 60·00 70·00
140 32 5s. blue and red . . . . 22·00 9·00
141 10s. red and purple . . . . 65·00 26·00
142 £1 black and blue . . . . £150 50·00
143 £1.10s. green and violet . . . . £300 85·00
162 £1.10s. orange & purple £1000 £1800
144 £5 mauve and black £1900 £500
145 £10 green and orange £6500 £2500
145a £20 red and green £13000 £6000

1908. As T **31/2** but inscr "POSTAGE POSTAGE".
165 31 6d. purple . . . . 4·50 2·25
166 1s. black on green . . . . 6·00 2·00
167 2s. purple & blue on blue . . . . 15·00 3·00
168 2s. 6d. black & red on blue . . . . 25·00 3·00
169 32 5s. green & red on yellow . . . . 18·00 20·00
170 10s. green & red on green . . . . 55·00 60·00
171 £1 purple & black on red £225 £200

OFFICIAL STAMPS

1904. Optd **OFFICIAL.**
O1 31 ½d. green . . . . 3·00 35
O2 1d. red . . . . 2·25 70
O3 2d. red and olive . . . . 18·00 9·50
O4 3d. purple and grey . . . . 9·50 4·00
O5 6d. green and purple . . . . 32·00 40·00
O6 1s. red and blue . . . . 95·00 £160

NAURU Pt. 1

An island in the W. Pacific Ocean, formerly a German possession and then administered by Australia under trusteeship. Became a Republic on 31 January 1968.

1916. 12 pence = 1 shilling;
20 shillings = 1 pound.
1966. 100 cents = 1 Australian dollar.

1916. Stamps of Gt. Britain (King George V) optd **NAURU.**
1 105 ½d. green . . . . 1·75 6·50
2 104 1d. red . . . . 1·50 4·50
15 105 1½d. brown . . . . 23·00 40·00
4 106 2d. orange . . . . 2·00 11·00
6 104 2½d. blue . . . . 2·75 7·00
7 106 3d. violet . . . . 2·00 3·50
8 4d. green . . . . 2·00 8·50
9 107 5d. brown . . . . 2·25 8·50
10 6d. purple . . . . 3·25 10·00
11 108 9d. black . . . . 8·50 20·00
12 1s. brown . . . . 7·00 19·00
25 109 2s. 6d. brown . . . . 65·00 95·00
22 5s. red £100 £140
23 10s. blue £250 £325

4

6

1924.
26A 4 ½d. brown . . . . 1·50 2·75
27B 1d. green . . . . 2·50 3·00
28B 1½d. red . . . . 90 1·50
29B 2d. orange . . . . 1·75 8·00
30dB 2½d. blue . . . . 2·00 4·00
31cB 3d. blue . . . . 2·75 10·00
32B 4d. green . . . . 4·25 12·00
33B 5d. brown . . . . 3·50 4·00
34B 6d. violet . . . . 3·25 4·50
35A 9d. brown . . . . 9·00 19·00
36B 1s. red . . . . 5·50 2·75
37B 2s. 6d. green . . . . 25·00 35·00
38B 5s. purple . . . . 35·00 50·00
39B 10s. yellow £100 £130

1935. Silver Jubilee. Optd **HIS MAJESTY'S JUBILEE. 1910–1935.**
40 4 1½d. red 75 80
41 2d. orange . . . . 1·25 4·00
42 2½d. blue . . . . 1·50 1·50
43 1s. red . . . . 5·00 3·50

1937. Coronation.
44 6 1½d. red . . . . 45 1·25
45 2d. orange . . . . 45 1·75
46 2½d. blue 45 60
47 1s. purple 65 90

8 Anibare Bay

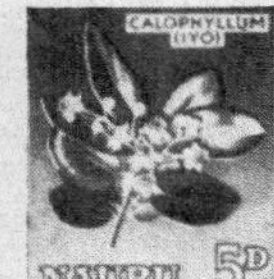

18 "Iyo" ("calophyllum")

21 White Tern

1954.
48 – ½d. violet 20 40
49a 8 1d. green 20 40
50 – 3½d. red . . . . 1·50 60
51 – 4d. blue . . . . 1·50 1·75
52 – 6d. orange 70 20
53 – 9d. red 60 20
54 – 1s. purple 30 20
55 – 2s. 6d. green . . . . 2·75 1·25
56 – 5s. mauve . . . . 9·00 3·00

DESIGNS—HORIZ: ½d. Nauruan netting fish; 3½d. Loading phosphate from cantilever; 4d. Great frigate bird; 6d. Canoe; 9d. Domaneab (meeting house); 2s. 6d. Buada Lagoon. VERT: 1s. Palm trees; 5s. Map of Nauru.

1963.
57 – 2d. multicoloured . . . . 75 2·25
58 – 3d. multicoloured 55 35
59 18 5d. multicoloured 55 75
60 – 8d. black and green . . . . 2·50 80
61 – 10d. black 50 30
62 21 1s. 3d. blue, black & green . . . . 2·75 4·00
63 – 2s. 3d. blue . . . . 3·50 55
64 – 3s. 3d. multicoloured . . . . 2·75 2·75

DESIGNS—VERT (As Type **21**): 2d. Micronesian pigeon. (26 × 29 mm): 10d. Capparis (flower). HORIZ (As Type **18**): 3d. Poison nut (flower); 8d. Black lizard; 2s. 3d. Coral pinnacles. 3s. 3d. Finsch's reed warbler.

22 "Simpson and his Donkey"

1965. 50th Anniv of Gallipoli Landing.
65 22 5d. sepia, black and green 15 10

24 Anibare Bay

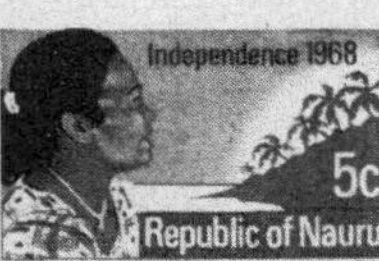

27 "Towards the Sunrise"

1966. Decimal Currency. As earlier issues but with values in cents and dollars as in T **24**. Some colours changed.
66 24 1 c. blue 15 10
67 – 2 c. purple (as No. 48) 15 40
68 – 3 c. green (as No. 50) . . . . 30 1·25
69 – 4 c. multicoloured (as T **18**) 25 10
70 – 5 c. blue (as No. 54) 25 60
71 – 7 c. black and brown (as No. 60) 30 10
72 – 8 c. green (as No. 61) 30 10
73 – 10 c. red (as No. 51) 40 10
74 – 15 c. blue, black and green (as T **21**) . . . . 80 1·50
75 – 25 c. brown (as No. 63) 45 60
76 – 30 c. mult (as No. 58) 70 30
77 – 35 c. mult (as No. 64) . . . . 1·25 35
78 – 50 c. mult (as No. 57) . . . . 2·50 80
79 – $1 mauve (as No. 56) . . . . 1·50 1·00

The 25 c. is as No. 63 but larger, 27½ × 25 mm.

1968. Nos. 66/79 optd **REPUBLIC OF NAURU.**
80 24 1 c. blue 10 30
81 – 2 c. purple 10 10
82 – 3 c. green 15 10
83 – 4 c. multicoloured 15 10
84 – 5 c. blue 15 10
85 – 7 c. black and brown 25 10
86 – 8 c. green 25 10
87 – 10 c. red 30 15
88 – 15 c. blue, black and green . . . . 2·25 2·50
89 – 25 c. brown 30 15
90 – 30 c. multicoloured 55 15
91 – 35 c. multicoloured . . . . 2·00 30
92 – 50 c. multicoloured . . . . 2·00 50
93 – $1 purple . . . . 1·25 75

1968. Independence.
94 27 5 c. multicoloured 10 10
95 – 10 c. black, green & blue 10 10

DESIGN: 10 c. Planting seedling, and Map.

29 Flag of Independent Nauru

1969.
96 29 15 c. yellow, orange & blue 50 15

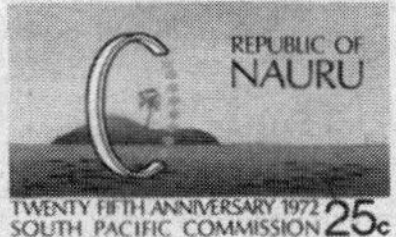

30 Island, "C" and Stars

1972. 25th Anniv of South Pacific Commission.
97 30 25 c. multicoloured 30 30

1973. 5th Anniv. of Independence. No. 96 optd **Independence 1968–1973.**
98 29 15 c. yellow, orange & blue 20 30

32 Denea

33 Artefacts and Map

1973. Multicoloured.

99 1 c. Ekwenababae 40 20
100 2 c. Kauwe iud 45 20
101 3 c. Rimone 45 20
102 4 c. Type **32** 45 40
103 5 c. Erekogo 45 40
104 7 c. Racoon butterflyfish ("Ikimago") 30 50
105 8 c. Catching flying fish 30 20
106 10 c. Itsibweb (ball game) 30 20
107 15 c. Nauruan wrestling 35 20
108 20 c. Snaring great frigate birds 50 50
109 25 c. Nauruan girl 40 30
110 30 c. Catching common noddy birds 60 40
111 50 c. Great frigate birds 80 75
112 $1 Type **33** 80 75

Nos. 104/106 and 110/111 are horiz designs.

34 Co-op Store

1973. 50th Anniv of Nauru Co-operative Society. Multicoloured.

113 5 c. Type **34** 20 30
114 25 c. Timothy Detudamo (founder) 20 15
115 50 c. N.C.S. trademark (vert) 45 55

35 Phosphate Mining

1974. 175th Anniv of First Contact with the Outside World. Multicoloured.

116 7 c. M.V. "Eigamoiya" (bulk carrier) 80 90
117 10 c. Type **35** 60 25
118 15 c. Fokker Fellowship "Nauru Chief" 80 30
119 25 c. Nauruan chief in early times 60 35
120 35 c. Capt. Fearn and 18th-century frigate (70 × 22 mm) 3·00 2·50
121 50 c. 18th-century frigate off Nauru (70 × 22 mm) 1·50 1·40

Nos. 120/1 are wrongly identified as "Hunter" (snow).

36 Map of Nauru **37** Rev. P. A. Delaporte

1974. Centenary of U.P.U. Multicoloured.

122 5 c. Type **36** 15 20
123 8 c. Nauru Post Office 15 20
124 20 c. Nauruan postman 15 10
125 $1 U.P.U. Building and Nauruan flag 40 60

1974. Christmas and 75th Anniv of Rev. Delaporte's Arrival.

127 **37** 15 c. multicoloured 20 20
128 20 c. multicoloured 30 30

38 Map of Nauru, Lump of Phosphate Rock and Albert Ellis

1975. Phosphate Mining Anniversaries. Mult.

129 5 c. Type **38** 25 40
130 7 c. Coolies and mine 35 40
131 15 c. Electric phosphate train, barges and ship 1·00 1·40
132 25 c. Modern ore extraction 1·25 1·50

ANNIVERSARIES: 5 c. 75th anniv of discovery; 7 c. 70th anniv of Mining Agreement; 15 c. 55th anniv of British Phosphate Commissioners; 25 c. 5th anniv of Nauru Phosphate Corporation.

39 Micronesian Outrigger **41** "Our Lady" (Yaren Church)

40 New Civic Centre

1975. South Pacific Commission Conf, Nauru (1st issue). Multicoloured.

133 20 c. Type **39** 75 40
134 20 c. Polynesian double-hull 75 40
135 20 c. Melanesian outrigger 75 40
136 20 c. Polynesian outrigger 75 40

1975. South Pacific Commission Conf, Nauru (2nd issue). Multicoloured.

137 30 c. Type **40** 15 15
138 50 c. Domaneab (meeting-house) 30 30

1975. Christmas. Stained-glass Windows. Multicoloured.

139 5 c. Type **41** 15 15
140 7 c. "Suffer little children" (Orro Church) 15 15
141 15 c. As 7 c. 20 55
142 25 c. Type **41** 25 70

42 Flowers floating towards Nauru

1976. 30th Anniv of Islanders' Return from Truk. Multicoloured.

143 10 c. Type **42** 10 10
144 14 c. Nauru encircled by garland 15 10
145 25 c. Finsch's reed warbler and maps 35 25
146 40 c. Return of the islanders 45 35

43 3d. and 9d. Stamps of 1916

1976. 60th Anniv of Nauruan Stamps. Mult.

147 10 c. Type **43** 15 15
148 15 c. 6d. and 1s. stamps 20 15
149 25 c. 2s. 6d. stamp 30 25
150 50 c. 5s. "Specimen" stamp 40 35

44 "Pandanus mei" and "Enna G" (cargo liner)

1976. South Pacific Forum, Nauru. Mult.

151 10 c. Type **44** 15 10
152 20 c. "Tournefortia argentea" with Boeing 737 and Fokker Fellowship aircraft 20 15
153 30 c. "Thespesia populnea" and Nauru Tracking Station 25 15
154 40 c. "Cordia subcordata" and produce 35 25

45 Nauruan Choir **46** Nauru House and Coral Pinnacles

1976. Christmas. Multicoloured.

155 15 c. Type **45** 10 10
156 15 c. Nauruan choir 10 10
157 20 c. Angel in white dress 15 15
158 20 c. Angel in red dress 15 15

1977. Opening of Nauru House, Melbourne. Multicoloured.

159 15 c. Type **46** 15 15
160 30 c. Nauru House and Melbourne skyline 25 25

47 Cable Ship "Anglia" **48** Father Kayser and First Catholic Church

1977. 75th Anniv of First Trans-Pacific Cable and 20th Anniv of First Artificial Earth Satellite.

161 **47** 7 c. multicoloured 20 10
162 – 15 c. blue, grey and black 30 15
163 – 20 c. blue, grey and black 30 20
164 – 25 c. multicoloured 30 20

DESIGNS: 15 c. Tracking station, Nauru; 20 c. Stern of "Anglia"; 25 c. Dish aerial.

1977. Christmas. Multicoloured.

165 15 c. Type **48** 10 10
166 25 c. Congregational Church, Orro 15 15
167 30 c. Catholic Church, Arubo 15 15

49 Arms of Nauru

1978. 10th Anniv of Independence.

168 **49** 15 c. multicoloured 20 15
169 60 c. multicoloured 35 30

1978. Nos. 159/60 surch.

170 **46** 4 c. on 15 c. multicoloured 55 1·50
171 5 c. on 15 c. multicoloured 55 1·50
172 – 8 c. on 30 c. multicoloured 55 1·50
173 – 10 c. on 30 c. multicoloured 55 1·50

51 Collecting Shellfish

1978.

174 **51** 1 c. multicoloured 50 30
175 – 2 c. multicoloured 50 30
176 – 3 c. multicoloured 1·00 40
177 – 4 c. brown, blue and black 50 30
178 – 5 c. multicoloured 1·75 40
179 – 7 c. multicoloured 30 65
180 – 10 c. multicoloured 30 20
181 – 15 c. multicoloured 40 30
182 – 20 c. grey, black and blue 30 30
183 – 25 c. multicoloured 30 30
184 – 30 c. multicoloured 1·50 45
185 – 32 c. multicoloured 2·25 65
186 – 40 c. multicoloured 1·50 1·75
187 – 50 c. multicoloured 85 75
188 – $1 multicoloured 70 55
189 – $2 multicoloured 95 1·00
190 – $5 grey, black and blue 1·50 2·25

DESIGNS: 2 c. Coral outcrop; 3 c. Reef scene; 4 c. Girl with fish; 5 c. Eastern reef heron; 7 c. Catching fish, Buada Lagoon; 10 c. Ijuw Lagoon; 15 c. Girl framed by coral; 20 c. Pinnacles, Anibare Bay reef; 25 c. Pinnacle at Meneng; 30 c. Head of great frigate bird; 32 c. White-capped noddy birds in coconut palm; 40 c. Wandering tattler; 50 c. Great frigate birds on perch; $1 Old coral pinnacles at Topside; $2 New pinnacles at Topside; $5 Blackened pinnacles at Topside.

52 A.P.U. Emblem **53** Virgin and Child

1978. 14th General Assembly of Asian Parliamentarians' Union, Nauru.

191 **52** 15 c. multicoloured 20 25
192 – 20 c. black, blue and gold 20 25

DESIGN: 20 c. As Type **52**, but with different background.

1978. Christmas. Multicoloured.

193 7 c. Type **53** 10 10
194 15 c. Angel in sun-rise scene (horiz) 10 10
195 20 c. As 15 c. 15 15
196 30 c. Type **53** 20 20

54 Baden-Powell and Cub Scout

1978. 70th Anniv of Boy Scout Movement. Multicoloured.

197 20 c. Type **54** 20 15
198 30 c. Scout 25 20
199 50 c. Rover Scout 35 30

55 Wright Flyer I over Nauru

1979. Flight Anniversaries. Multicoloured.

200 10 c. Type **55** 20 15
201 15 c. Fokker F.VIIa/3m "Southern Cross" superimposed on nose of Boeing 737 30 20
202 15 c. "Southern Cross" and Boeing 737 (front view) 30 20
203 30 c. Wright Flyer I over Nauru airfield 55 30

ANNIVERSARIES: Nos. 200, 203, 75th anniv of powered flight; Nos. 201/2, 50th anniv of Kingsford-Smith's Pacific flight.

56 Sir Rowland Hill and Marshall Islands 10 pf. stamp of 1901

1979. Death Cent of Sir Rowland Hill. Mult.

204 5 c. Type **56** 15 10
205 15 c. Sir Rowland Hill and "Nauru" opt on G.B. 10s. "Seahorse" stamp of 1916–23 25 20
206 60 c. Sir Rowland Hill and Nauru 60 c. 10th anniv of Independence stamp, 1978 55 40

57 Dish Antenna, Transmitting Station and Radio Mast

1979. 50th Anniv of International Consultative Radio Committee. Multicoloured.

208 7 c. Type **57** 15 10
209 32 c. Telex operator 35 25
210 40 c. Radio operator 40 25

58 Smiling Child

1979. International Year of the Child.

211 **58** 8 c. multicoloured 10 10
212 – 15 c. multicoloured 15 15
213 – 25 c. multicoloured 20 20
214 – 32 c. multicoloured 20 20
215 – 50 c. multicoloured 25 25

DESIGNS: 15 c. to 50 c. Smiling children.

59 Ekwenababae (flower), Scroll inscribed "Peace on Earth" and Star

1979. Christmas. Multicoloured.

216 7 c. Type **59** 10 10
217 15 c. "Thespia populnea" (flower), scroll inscribed "Goodwill towards Men" and star 10 10
218 20 c. Denea (flower), scroll inscribed "Peace on Earth" and star 10 10
219 30 c. Erekogo (flower), scroll inscribed "Goodwill toward Men" and star 20 20

60 Dassault Bregeut Mystere Falcon 50 over Melbourne

1980. 10th Anniv of Air Nauru. Mult.

220 15 c. Type **60** 35 15
221 20 c. Fokker F.28 Fellowship over Tarawa 40 15
222 25 c. Boeing 727-100 over Hong Kong 40 15
223 30 c. Boeing 737 over Auckland . 40 15

61 Steam Locomotive

1980. 10th Anniv of Nauru Phosphate Corporation. Multicoloured.

224 8 c. Type **61** 10 10
225 32 c. Electric locomotive 20 20
226 60 c. Diesel-hydraulic locomotive . 35 35

62 Verse 10 from Luke, Chapter 2 in English

1980. Christmas. Verses from Luke, Chapter 2. Multicoloured.

228 20 c. Type **62** 10 10
229 20 c. Verse 10 in Nauruan . . . 10 10
230 30 c. Verse 14 in English . . . 15 15
231 30 c. Verse 14 in Nauruan . . . 15 15

See also Nos. 248/51.

63 Nauruan, Australia, Union and New Zealand Flags on Aerial View of Nauru

1980. 20th Anniv of U.N. Declaration on the Granting of Independence to Colonial Countries and Peoples. Multicoloured.

232 25 c. Type **63** 15 15
233 50 c. U.N. Trusteeship Council (72 × 23 mm) 15 15
234 50 c. Nauru independence ceremony, 1968 (72 × 23 mm) 25 25

64 Timothy Detudamo

1981. 30th Anniv of Nauru Local Government Council. Head Chiefs. Multicoloured.

235 20 c. Type **64** 15 15
236 30 c. Raymond Gadabu . . . 15 15
237 50 c. Hammer DeRoburt . . . 25 25

65 Casting Net by Hand

1981. Fishing. Multicoloured.

238 8 c. Type **65** 10 10
239 20 c. Outrigger canoe 20 15
240 32 c. Outboard motor boat . . 25 20
241 40 c. Trawler 30 25

66 Bank of Nauru Emblem and Building

1981. 5th Anniv of Bank of Nauru.

243 **66** $1 multicoloured 60 60

67 Inaugural Speech

1981. U.N. Day. E.S.C.A.P. (United Nations Economic and Social Commission for Asia and the Pacific) Events. Multicoloured.

244 15 c. Type **67** 15 15
245 20 c. Presenting credentials . . 15 15
246 25 c. Unveiling plaque 20 20
247 30 c. Raising U.N. flag 25 25

1981. Christmas. Bible Verses. Designs as T **62**. Multicoloured.

248 20 c. Matthew 1, 23 in English 15 15
249 20 c. Matthew 1, 23 in Nauruan 15 15
250 30 c. Luke 2, 11 in English . . 20 20
251 30 c. Luke 2, 11 in Nauruan . . 20 20

68 Earth Satellite Station

1981. 10th Anniv of South Pacific Forum. Multicoloured.

252 10 c. Type **68** 20 15
253 20 c. "Enna G" (cargo liner) . . 25 20
254 30 c. Boeing 737 airliner . . . 25 25
255 40 c. Local produce 25 30

69 Nauru Scouts leaving for 1935 Frankston Scout Jamboree

1982. 75th Anniv of Boy Scout Movement. Multicoloured.

256 7 c. Type **69** 15 15
257 8 c. Two Nauru scouts on "Nauru Chief", 1935 (vert) . 15 15
258 15 c. Nauru scouts making pottery, 1935 (vert) 15 20
259 20 c. Lord Huntingfield addressing Nauru scouts, Frankston Jamboree, 1935 . 20 25
260 25 c. Nauru cub and scout, 1982 20 30
261 40 c. Nauru cubs, scouts and scouters, 1982 . . . . 30 45

70 100 kw Electricity Generating Plant under Construction (left side)

1982. Ocean Thermal Energy Conversion. Multicoloured.

263 25 c. Type **70** 50 30
264 25 c. 100 kw Electricity Generating Plant under construction (right side) . . 50 30
265 40 c. Completed plant (left) . . 70 40
266 40 c. Completed plant (right) . 70 40

Nos. 263/4 and 265/6 were each issued as horizontal se-tenant pairs, forming composite designs.

71 S.S. "Fido"

1982. 75th Anniv of Phosphate Shipments. Multicoloured.

267 5 c. Type **71** 55 10
268 10 c. Steam locomotive "Nellie" 80 20
269 30 c. Class "Clyde" diesel locomotive 90 50
270 60 c. M.V. "Eigamoiya" (bulk carrier) 95 80

72 Queen Elizabeth II on Horseback

1982. Royal Visit. Multicoloured.

272 20 c. Type **72** 35 30
273 50 c. Prince Philip, Duke of Edinburgh 45 60
274 $1 Queen Elizabeth II and Prince Philip (horiz) . . . . 60 1·25

73 Father Bernard Lahn

1982. Christmas. Multicoloured.

275 10 c. Type **73** 20 30
276 30 c. Reverend Itubwa Amram 20 45
277 40 c. Pastor James Aingimen . 25 70
278 50 c. Bishop Paul Mea . . . . 30 1·00

74 Speaker of the Nauruan Parliament

75 Nauru Satellite Earth Station

1983. 15th Anniv of Independence. Mult.

279 15 c. Type **74** 15 15
280 20 c. Family Court in session . 20 20
281 30 c. Law Courts building (horiz) 25 25
282 50 c. Parliamentary chamber (horiz) 40 40

1983. World Communications Year. Mult.

283 5 c. Type **75** 20 10
284 10 c. Omni-directional range installation 20 15
285 20 c. Emergency short-wave radio 25 25
286 25 c. Radio Nauru control room 40 30
287 40 c. Unloading air mail . . . 90 45

76 Return of Exiles from Truk on M.V. "Trienza", 1946

1983. Angam Day. Multicoloured.

288 15 c. Type **76** 20 25
289 20 c. Mrs. Elsie Agio (exile community leader) 20 25
290 30 c. Child on scales 35 40
291 40 c. Nauruan children 45 50

Nos. 289/91 are vert, each 25 × 41 mm.

77 "The Holy Virgin, Holy Child and St. John" (School of Raphael)

78 S.S. "Ocean Queen"

1983. Christmas. Multicoloured.

292 5 c. Type **77** 10 10
293 15 c. "Madonna on the Throne, surrounded by Angels" (School of Sevilla) 20 15
294 50 c. "The Mystical Betrothal of St. Catherine with Jesus" (School of Veronese) (horiz) . 60 40

1984. 250th Anniv of "Lloyd's List" (newspaper). Multicoloured.

295 20 c. Type **78** 40 30
296 25 c. M.V "Enna G" 45 35
297 30 c. M.V "Baron Minto" . . 50 40
298 40 c. Sinking of M.V. "Triadic", 1940 . . . . 75 55

79 1974 U.P.U. $1 Stamp

1984. Universal Postal Union Congress, Hamburg.

299 **79** $1 multicoloured . . . . . 90 1·25

80 "Hypolimnas bolina" (female)

1984. Butterflies. Multicoloured.

300 25 c. Type **80** 50 40
301 30 c. "Hypolimnas bolina" (male) 55 55
302 50 c. "Danaus plexippus" . . . 70 85

81 Coastal Scene

1984. Life in Nauru. Multicoloured.

303 1 c. Type **81** 10 40
304 3 c. Nauruan woman (vert) . . 15 40
305 5 c. Modern trawler 40 50
306 10 c. Golfer on the links . . . 90 50
307 15 c. Excavating phosphate (vert) 90 65
308 20 c. Surveyor (vert) 65 55
309 25 c. Air Nauru Boeing 727 airliner 80 55
310 30 c. Elderly Nauruan (vert) . . 50 50
311 40 c. Loading hospital patient on to Boeing 727 aircraft . . . 90 55
312 50 c. Skin-diver with fish (vert) 1·00 80
313 $1 Tennis player (vert) . . . . 2·50 3·25
314 $2 Anabar Lagoon . . . . . . 2·50 3·75

82 Buada Chapel

1984. Christmas. Multicoloured.

315 30 c. Type **82** 40 50
316 40 c. Detudamo Memorial Church 50 65
317 50 c. Candle-light service, Kayser College (horiz) 60 70

83 Air Nauru Boeing 737 Jet on Tarmac

1985. 15th Anniv of Air Nauru. Mult.

318 20 c. Type **83** 65 35
319 30 c. Stewardesses on Boeing 737 aircraft steps (vert) 85 60
320 40 c. Fokker F.28 Fellowship over Nauru . . . . 1·10 75
321 50 c. Freight being loaded onto Boeing 727 (vert) . . . . . 1·25 85

84 Open Cut Mining

1985. 15th Anniv of Nauru Phosphate Corporation. Multicoloured.

322 20 c. Type **84** 80 60
323 25 c. Diesel locomotive hauling crushed ore . . . . 1·50 1·00
324 30 c. Phosphate drying plant . . 1·50 1·00
325 50 c. Early steam locomotive . 2·25 1·75

85 Mother and Baby on Beach **86** Adult Common Noddy with Juvenile

1985. Christmas. Multicoloured.

326 50 c. Beach scene . . . . . . 1·10 2·00
327 50 c. Type **85** . . . . 1·10 2·00

Nos. 326/7 were printed se-tenant forming a composite design.

1985. Birth Bicentenary of John J. Audubon (ornithologist). Common ("Brown") Noddy. Multicoloured.

328 10 c. Type **86** 35 35
329 20 c. Adult and immature birds in flight 50 70
330 30 c. Adults in flight 65 85
331 50 c. "Brown Noddy" (John J. Audubon) . . . . 80 1·10

87 Douglas Motor Cycle

1986. Early Transport on Nauru. Mult.

332 15 c. Type **87** 80 70
333 20 c. Primitive lorry 95 95
334 30 c. German-built steam locomotive, 1910 . . . . . 1·50 1·50
335 40 c. "Baby" Austin car . . . 1·75 1·75

88 Island and Bank of Nauru

1986. 10th Anniv of Bank of Nauru. Children's Paintings. Multicoloured.

336 20 c. Type **88** 20 30
337 25 c. Borrower with notes and coins 25 35
338 30 c. Savers 30 40
339 40 c. Customers at bank counter 35 55

89 "Plumeria rubra"

1986. Flowers. Multicoloured.

340 20 c. Type **89** 55 70
341 25 c. "Tristellateia australis" . . 65 85
342 30 c. "Bougainvillea cultivar" . . 75 1·00
343 40 c. "Delonix regia" . . . . . 1·00 1·25

90 Carol Singers

1986. Christmas. Multicoloured.

344 20 c. Type **90** 40 30
345 $1 Carol singers and hospital patient . . . . 1·60 3·00

91 Young Girls Dancing

1987. Nauruan Dancers. Multicoloured.

346 20 c. Type **91** 80 80
347 30 c. Stick dance . . . . . . 1·00 1·25
348 50 c. Boy doing war dance (vert) 1·75 2·50

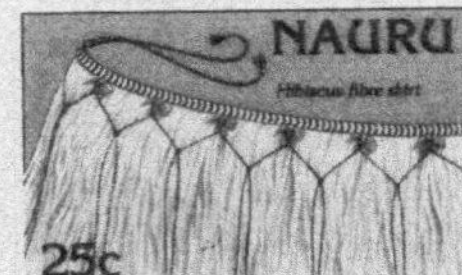

92 Hibiscus Fibre Skirt

1987. Personal Artefacts. Multicoloured.

349 25 c. Type **92** 75 75
350 30 c. Headband and necklets . 85 85
351 45 c. Decorative necklets . . . 1·10 1·10
352 60 c. Pandanus leaf fan . . . . 1·60 1·60

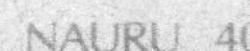

93 U.P.U. Emblem and Air Mail Label **94** Open Bible

1987. World Post Day.

353 **93** 40 c. multicoloured 90 75

1987. Centenary of Nauru Congregational Church.

355 **94** 40 c. multicoloured . . . . 75 1·00

95 Nauruan Children's Party

1987. Christmas. Multicoloured.

356 20 c. Type **95** 75 50
357 $1 Nauruan Christmas dinner . 2·75 3·25

96 Loading Phosphate on Ship

1988. 20th Anniv of Independence. Mult.

358 25 c. Type **96** . . . . 1·00 1·00
359 40 c. Tomano flower (vert) . . 1·50 1·50
360 55 c. Great frigate bird (vert) . 2·25 2·25
361 $1 Arms of Republic (35 × 35 mm) . . . . . . 2·50 3·50

97 Map of German Marshall Is. and 1901 5 m. Yacht Definitive

1988. 80th Anniv of Nauru Post Office. Mult.

362 30 c. Type **97** 75 75
363 50 c. Letter and post office of 1908 . . . . 1·00 1·25
364 70 c. Nauru Post Office and airmail letter . . . . 1·25 1·50

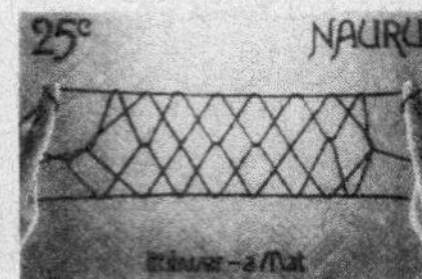

98 "Itubwer" (mat)

1988. String Figures. Multicoloured.

365 25 c. Type **98** 35 35
366 40 c. "Etegerer – the Pursuer" . 50 60
367 55 c. "Holding up the Sky" . . 65 70
368 80 c. "Manujie's Sword . . . . 1·00 1·25

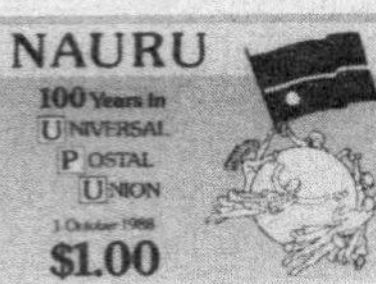

99 U.P.U. Emblem and National Flag

1988. Cent of Nauru's Membership of U.P.U.

369 **99** $1 multicoloured . . . . . 1·25 1·25

100 "Hark the Herald Angels"

1988. Christmas. Designs showing words and music from "Hark the Herald Angels Sing".

370 **100** 20 c. black, red & yellow . 40 30
371 – 60 c. black, red & mauve . 1·00 85
372 – $1 black, red and green . . 1·60 1·40

101 Logo (15th anniv of Nauru Insurance Corporation) **102** Mother and Baby

1989. Anniversaries and Events. Mult.

373 15 c. Type **101** 30 30
374 50 c. Logos (World Telecommunications Day and 10th anniv of Asian-Pacific Telecommunity) 75 85
375 $1 Photograph of island scene (150 years of photography) . 1·75 2·00
376 $2 Capitol and U.P.U. emblem (20th U.P.U. Congress, Washington) . . . . 2·75 3·75

1989. Christmas. Multicoloured.

377 20 c. Type **102** 50 30
378 $1 Children opening presents . 2·25 3·00

NAURU 25c

NAURU 50c

103 Eigigu working while Sisters play **104** Early Mining by Hand

1989. 20th Anniv of First Manned Landing on Moon. Legend of "Eigigu, the Girl in the Moon". Multicoloured.

379 25 c. Type **103** . . . . 2·50 2·50
380 30 c. Eigigu climbing tree . . . 2·75 2·75
381 50 c. Eigigu stealing toddy from blind woman . . . . 4·75 4·75
382 $1 Eigigu on Moon . . . . . 7·00 7·00

1990. 20th Anniv of Nauru Phosphate Corporation. Multicoloured.

383 50 c. Type **104** 75 75
384 $1 Modern mining by excavator 1·25 1·50

INDEX

Countries can be quickly located by referring to the index at the end of this volume.

105 Sunday School Class **106** Eoiyepiang laying Baby on Mat

1990. Christmas. Multicoloured.

385 25 c. Type **105** . . . . 90 1·00
386 25 c. Teacher telling Christmas story . . . . 90 1·00

Nos. 385/6 were printed together, se-tenant, forming a composite design.

1990. Legend of "Eoiyepiang, the Daughter of Thunder and Lightning". Multicoloured.

387 25 c. Type **106** . . . . 1·00 60
388 30 c. Eoiyepiang making floral decoration . . . . 1·25 70
389 50 c. Eoiyepiang left on snow-covered mountain . . . . . 1·75 2·00
390 $1 Eoiyepiang and warrior . . 2·75 3·50

107 Oleander

1991. Flowers. Multicoloured.

391 15 c. Type **107** 10 15
392 20 c. Lily 15 20
393 25 c. Passion flower 20 25
394 30 c. Lily (different) 25 30
395 35 c. Caesalpinia 30 35
396 40 c. Clerodendron 30 35
397 45 c. "Baubina pinnata" . . . 35 40
398 50 c. Hibiscus (vert) 40 45
399 75 c. Apocymaceae 60 65
400 $1 Bindweed (vert) 80 85
401 $2 Tristellateia (vert) . . . . . 1·60 1·75
402 $3 Impala lily (vert) . . . . . 2·40 2·50

109 Star and Symbol of Asian Development Bank

1992. 25th Annual Meeting of Asian Development Bank.

404 **109** $1.50 multicoloured . . . 2·00 2·50

110 Gifts under Christmas Tree

1992. Christmas. Children's Paintings. Mult.

405 45 c. Type **110** 75 75
406 60 c. Father Christmas in sleigh 1·00 1·50

111 Hammer DeRoburt **112** Running, Constitution Day Sports

1993. 25th Anniv of Independence and Hammer DeRoburt (former President) Commemoration.

407 **111** $1 multicoloured . . . . . 2·00 2·50

1993. 15th Anniv of Constitution Day. Mult.

408 70 c. Type **112** 75 75
409 80 c. Part of Independence Proclamation . . . . 1·00 1·25

113 Great Frigate Birds, Flying Fish and Island

1993. 24th South Pacific Forum Meeting, Nauru. Multicoloured.

410 60 c. Type **113** . . . . 1·40 1·50
411 60 c. Red-tailed tropic bird, great frigate bird, dolphin and island 1·40 1·50
412 60 c. Racoon butterflyfish ("Ikimago"), coral and sea urchins . . . . 1·40 1·50
413 60 c. Three different types of fish with corals . . . . 1·40 1·50

Nos. 410/13 were printed together, se-tenant, forming a composite design.

114 "Peace on Earth, Goodwill to Men" and Star

1993. Christmas. Multicoloured.

415 55 c. Type **114** 85 85
416 65 c. "Hark the Herald Angels Sing" and star 90 90

115 Girls with Dogs

1994. "Hong Kong '94" International Stamp Exhibition. Chinese New Year ("Year of the Dog"). Multicoloured.

417 $1 Type **115** . . . . 1·50 1·75
418 $1 Boys with dogs . . . . 1·50 1·75

116 Weightlifting

117 Peace Dove and Star over Island

1994. 15th Commonwealth Games, Victoria, Canada.

421 **116** $1.50 multicoloured . . . 1·40 1·75

1994. Christmas. Multicoloured.

422 65 c. Type **117** 60 65
423 75 c. Star over Bethlehem . . . 70 85

118 Air Nauru Airliner and Emblems

1994. 50th Anniv of I.C.A.O. Multicoloured.

424 55 c. Type **118** 50 55
425 65 c. Control tower, Nauru International Airport 60 65
426 80 c. D.V.O.R. equipment . . . 70 1·00
427 $1 Crash tenders . . . . . . 90 1·10

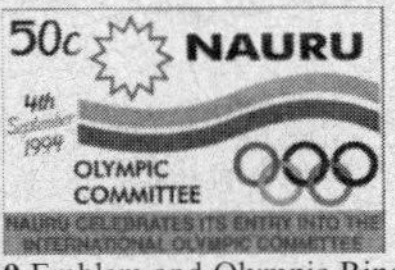

119 Emblem and Olympic Rings

1994. Nauru's Entry into International Olympic Committee.

429 **119** 50 c. multicoloured 45 50

120 Nauruan Flag

1995. 50th Anniv of United Nations (1st issue). Multicoloured.

430 75 c. Type **120** . . . . 90 1·10
431 75 c. Arms of Nauru . . . . . 90 1·10
432 75 c. Outrigger canoe on coastline . . . . 90 1·10
433 75 c. Airliner over phosphate freighter . . . . 90 1·10

Nos. 430/3 were printed together, se-tenant, forming a composite design.

See also Nos. 444/5.

121 Signing Phosphate Agreement, 1967

1995. 25th Anniv of Nauru Phosphate Corporation. Multicoloured.

435 60 c. Type **121** . . . . 80 1·00
436 60 c. Pres. Bernard Dowiyogo and Prime Minister Keating of Australia shaking hands . . 80 1·00

1995. International Stamp Exhibitions. No. 309 surch.

438 50 c. on 25 c. multicoloured (surch "at Beijing") . . . . 90 1·10
439 $1 on 25 c. multicoloured (surch "at Jakarta") . . . . 90 1·40
440 $1 on 25 c. multicoloured (surch "at Singapore") . . . . . . 90 1·40

124 Children playing on Gun

1995. 50th Anniv of Peace. Multicoloured

442 75 c. Type **124** . . . . 1·25 1·50
443 $1.50 Children making floral garlands . . . . 1·75 2·00

125 Nauru Crest, Coastline and U.N. Anniversary Emblem

126 Young Girl praying

1995. 50th Anniv of United Nations (2nd issue). Multicoloured.

444 75 c. Type **125** . . . . 90 1·00
445 $1.50 Aerial view of Nauru and U.N. Headquarters, New York 1·60 2·00

1995. Christmas. Multicoloured.

446 60 c. Type **126** . . . . 90 1·00
447 70 c. Man praying . . . . . . 90 1·00

127 Returning Refugees and Head Chief Timothy Detudamo

1996. 50th Anniv of Nauruans' Return from Truk.

448 **127** 75 c. multicoloured . . . . 90 1·00
449 $1.25 multicoloured . . . 1·60 2·00

129 Symbolic Athlete

1996. Centenary of Modern Olympic Games. Multicoloured.

452 40 c. Type **129** 70 70
453 50 c. Symbolic weightlifter . . 80 90
454 60 c. Weightlifter (horiz) . . . 90 1·00
455 $1 Athlete (horiz) . . . . . . 1·40 2·00

130 The Nativity and Angel

1996. Christmas. Multicoloured.

456 50 c. Type **130** 60 60
457 70 c. Angel, world map and wild animals . . . . 80 1·00

131 Dolphin (fish)

1997. Endangered Species. Fishes. Multicoloured.

458 20 c. Type **131** 60 60
459 30 c. Wahoo 70 70
460 40 c. Sailfish 75 75
461 50 c. Yellow-finned tuna . . . 80 80

132 Statue of Worshipper with Offering

133 Princess Elizabeth and Lieut. Philip Mountbatten, 1947

1997. "HONG KONG '97" International Stamp Exhibition. Statues of different worshippers (1 c. to 15 c.) or Giant Buddha of Hong Kong (25 c.).

462 **132** 1 c. multicoloured 20 20
463 – 2 c. multicoloured 20 20
464 – 5 c. multicoloured 25 25
465 – 10 c. multicoloured 30 30
466 – 12 c. multicoloured 30 30
467 – 15 c. multicoloured 30 30
468 – 25 c. multicoloured 40 40

1997. Golden Wedding of Queen Elizabeth and Prince Philip.

469 **133** 80 c. black and gold . . . 90 1·00
470 – $1.20 multicoloured . . . 1·40 1·60

DESIGN: $1.20, Queen Elizabeth and Prince Philip, 1997.

135 Commemorative Pillar

1997. Christmas. 110th Anniv of Nauru Congregational Church. Multicoloured.

473 60 c. Type **135** 60 55
474 80 c. Congregational Church . 80 90

137 Juan Antonio Samaranch and Aerial View

1998. Visit of International Olympic Committee President.

476 **137** $2 multicoloured . . . . . 1·75 2·00

138 Diana, Princess of Wales

139 Gymnastics

1998. Diana, Princess of Wales Commemoration. Multicoloured.

477 70 c. Type **138** 55 60
478 70 c. Wearing white shirt . . . 55 60
479 70 c. With tiara 55 60
480 70 c. In white jacket 55 60
481 70 c. Wearing pink hat 55 60
482 70 c. In white suit 55 60

1998. 16th Commonwealth Games, Kuala Lumpur, Malaysia. Multicoloured.

483 40 c. Type **139** 30 35
484 60 c. Athletics 45 50
485 70 c. Sprinting 55 60
486 80 c. Weightlifting 60 65

140 Sqn. Ldr. Hicks (Composer of Nauru's National Anthem) conducting

1998. 30th Anniv of Independence. Multicoloured.

488 $1 Type **140** 85 80
489 $2 Sqn. Ldr. Hicks and score . 1·75 2·00

141 Palm Trees, Fish, Festive Candle and Flower

1998. Christmas. Multicoloured.

491 85 c. Type **141** 80 80
492 95 c. Flower, present, fruit and island scene 85 90

142 18th-century Frigate

1998. Bicentenary of First Contact with the Outside World. Multicoloured.

493 $1.50 Type **142** . . . . . . 1·25 1·50
494 $1.50 Capt. John Fearn . . . . 1·25 1·50

No. 493 is wrongly identified as "Hunter" (snow).

1999. 30th Anniv of First Manned Landing on Moon. As T **296** of Jamaica. Multicoloured.

497 70 c. Neil Armstrong (astronaut) 65 65
498 80 c. Service and lunar module on way to Moon 70 70
499 90 c. Aldrin and "Apollo 11" on Moon's surface 85 85
500 $1 Command module entering Earth's atmosphere 90 90

144 Emblem and Forms of Transport

146 Girl holding Candle

1999. 125th Anniv of Universal Postal Union.

502 **144** $1 multicoloured 90 95

1999. Christmas. Multicoloured.

504 65 c. Type **146** 50 55
505 70 c. Candle and Christmas tree 55 60

147 Nauruan Woman in Traditional Dress and Canoes

2000. New Millennium. Multicoloured.

506 70 c. Type **147** 55 60
507 $1.10 Aspects of modern Nauru 85 90
508 $1.20 Woman holding globe and man at computer 90 95

NAWANAGAR Pt. 1

A state of India, Bombay District. Now uses Indian stamps.

6 docra = 1 anna

1 (1 docra)

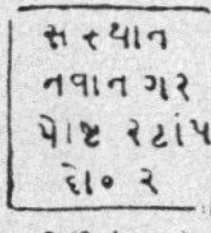
2 (2 docra)

1877. Imperf or perf.

1	1	1 doc. blue	50	22·00

1880. Imperf.

6ab	2	1 doc. lilac	2·25	5·00
8c		2 doc. green	3·00	7·50
9b		3 doc. yellow	4·25	8·50

4 (1 docra)

1893. Imperf or perf.

13	4	1 doc. black	75	3·75
14		2 doc. green	80	4·25
15b		3 doc. yellow	80	7·00

NEAPOLITAN PROVINCES Pt. 8

Temporary issues for Naples and other parts of S. Italy which adhered to the new Kingdom of Italy in 1860.

200 tornesi = 100 grano = 1 ducato

1

1861. Embossed. Imperf.

2	1	½ t. green	3·25	55·00
5		½ g. brown	£110	80·00
9		1 g. black	£200	8·00
10		2 g. blue	45·00	3·75
15		5 g. red	£130	40·00
18		10 g. orange	£110	70·00
19		20 g. yellow	£400	£700
23		50 g. slate	5·00	£6000

NEGRI SEMBILAN Pt. 1

A state of the Federation of Malaya, incorporated in Malaysia in 1963.

100 cents = 1 dollar (Straits or Malayan)

1891. Stamp of Straits Settlements optd **Negri Sembilan**.

1	5	2 c. red	2·50	4·25

2 Tiger

3

1891.

2	2	1 c. green	2·75	1·00
3		2 c. red	3·25	6·00
4		5 c. blue	28·00	40·00

1896.

5	3	1 c. purple and green	7·50	3·50
6		2 c. purple and brown	32·00	£100
7		3 c. purple and red	9·00	85
8		5 c. purple and yellow	7·50	6·00
9		8 c. purple and blue	28·00	16·00
10		10 c. purple and orange	27·00	14·00
11		15 c. green and violet	40·00	75·00
12		20 c. green and olive	48·00	38·00
13		25 c. green and red	70·00	90·00
14		50 c. green and black	55·00	60·00

1898. Surch in words and bar.

15	3	1 c. on 15 c. green & violet	80·00	£170
16	2	4 c. on 1 c. green	1·25	15·00
17	3	4 c. on 3 c. purple and red	3·00	15·00
18	2	4 c. on 5 c. blue	1·25	15·00

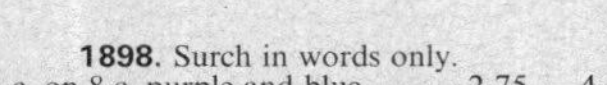

1898. Surch in words only.

19	3	4 c. on 8 c. purple and blue	2·75	4·00

6 Arms of Negri Sembilan 7

1935.

21	6	1 c. black	85	20
22		2 c. green	85	20
23		2 c. orange	3·75	60·00
24		3 c. green	6·50	8·00
25		4 c. orange	70	10
26		5 c. brown	1·50	10
27		6 c. red	9·50	2·50
28		6 c. grey	4·25	70·00
29		8 c. grey	2·00	10
30		10 c. purple	70	10
31		12 c. blue	1·40	50
32		15 c. blue	9·00	48·00
33		25 c. purple and red	90	70
34		30 c. purple and orange	3·50	2·00
35		40 c. red and purple	85	2·00
36		50 c. black on green	3·75	2·25
37		$1 black and red on blue	2·25	3·25
38		$2 green and red	26·00	16·00
39		$5 green and red on green	15·00	48·00

1948. Silver Wedding. As T **11b/c** of Gambia.

40		10 c. violet	15	50
41		$5 green	18·00	28·00

1949.

42	7	1 c. black	10	10
43		2 c. orange	10	10
44		3 c. green	10	30
45		4 c. brown	10	10
46a		5 c. purple	30	45
47		6 c. grey	30	10
48		8 c. red	30	75
49		8 c. green	1·50	1·60
50		10 c. mauve	20	10
51		12 c. red	1·50	2·50
52		15 c. blue	2·25	10
53		20 c. black and green	30	75
54		20 c. blue	80	10
55		25 c. purple and orange	30	10
56		30 c. red and purple	1·25	2·50
57		35 c. red and purple	70	1·00
58		40 c. red and purple	80	4·75
59		50 c. black and blue	80	20
60		$1 blue and purple	3·00	2·00
61		$2 green and red	12·00	15·00
62		$5 green and brown	50·00	38·00

1949. U.P.U. As T **11d/g** of Gambia.

63		10 c. purple	20	10
64		15 c. blue	1·10	2·00
65		25 c. orange	50	2·00
66		50 c. black	1·00	2·50

1853. Coronation. As T **11h** of Gambia.

67		10 c. black and purple	75	30

1957. As Nos. 92/102 of Kedah but inset Arms of Negri Sembilan.

68		1 c. black	10	10
69		2 c. red	10	10
70		4 c. sepia	10	10
71		5 c. lake	10	10
72		8 c. green	85	1·40
73		10 c. sepia	1·25	10
74		10 c. purple	3·00	10
75		20 c. blue	60	10
76a		50 c. black and blue	30	10
77		$1 blue and purple	1·50	2·00
78		$2 green and red	5·00	12·00
79		$5 brown and green	11·00	16·00

8 Tuanku Munawir

1961. Installation of Tuanku Munawir as Yang di-Pertuan Besar of Negri Sembilan.

80	8	10 c. multicoloured	30	40

9 "Vanda hookeriana"

1965. As Nos. 115/21 of Kedah but with Arms of Negri Sembilan inset and inscr "NEGERI SEMBILAN" as in T **6**.

81	9	1 c. multicoloured	10	75
82	–	2 c. multicoloured	10	85
83	–	5 c. multicoloured	40	10
84	–	6 c. multicoloured	40	40
85	–	10 c. multicoloured	40	10
86	–	15 c. multicoloured	80	10
87	–	20 c. multicoloured	1·25	75

The higher values used in Negri Sembilan were Nos. 20/7 of Malaysia (National Issues).

10 Negri Sembilan Crest and Tuanku Ja'afar

1968. Installation of Tuanku Ja'afar as Yang di-Pertuan Besar of Negri Sembilan.

88	10	15 c. multicoloured	15	40
89		50 c. multicoloured	30	1·25

11 "Hebomoia glaucippe"

1971. Butterflies. As Nos. 124/30 of Kedah but with Arms of Negri Sembilan inset as T **11** and inscr "negeri sembilan".

91	–	1 c. multicoloured	40	1·25
92	–	2 c. multicoloured	60	1·25
93	–	5 c. multicoloured	90	10
94	–	6 c. multicoloured	90	1·50
95	11	10 c. multicoloured	90	10
96	–	15 c. multicoloured	1·25	10
97	–	20 c. multicoloured	1·25	40

The higher values in use with this issue were Nos. 64/71 of Malaysia (National Issues).

12 "Hibiscus rosa-sinensis"

13 Oil Palm

1979. Flowers. As Nos. 135/41 of Kedah but with Arms of Negri Sembilan and inscr "negeri sembilan" as in T **12**.

103	1 c. "Rafflesia hasseltii"	10	75
104	2 c. "Pterocarpus indicus"	10	75
105	5 c. "Lagerstroemia speciosa"	15	20
106	10 c. "Durio zibethinus"	20	10
107	15 c. Type **12**	20	10
108	20 c. "Rhododendron scortechinii"	25	10
109	25 c. "Etlingera elatior" (inscr "Phaeomeria speciosa")	45	20

1986. As Nos. 152/8 of Kedah but with Arms of Negri Sembilan and inscr "NEGERI SEMBILAN" as T **13**.

117	1 c. Coffee	10	10
118	2 c. Coconuts	10	10
119	5 c. Cocoa	10	10
120	10 c. Black pepper	10	10
121	15 c. Rubber	10	10
122	20 c. Type **13**	10	10
123	30 c. Rice	15	20

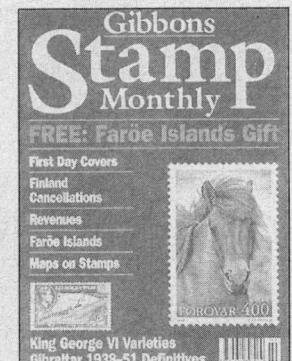

NEPAL Pt. 21

An independent Kingdom in the Himalayas N. of India.

1861. 16 annas = 1 rupee.
1907. 64 pice = 1 rupee.
1954. 100 paisa = 1 rupee.

1 (1 a.) Crown and Kukris — 2 (½ a.) Bow and Arrow and Kukris — 3 Siva Mahadeva (2 pice)

1881. Imperf or pin-perf.

34	2	½ a. black	2·00	1·00
35		½ a. orange	£300	£120
42	1	1 a. blue	4·00	1·60
14		1 a. green	26·00	26·00
16c		2 a. violet	12·00	12·00
40		2 a. brown	5·00	3·00
41		4 a. green	4·00	4·00

1907. Various sizes.

57	3	2 p. brown	20	20
58		4 p. green	60	40
59		8 p. red	40	30
60		16 p. purple	3·00	1·50
61		24 p. orange	3·00	1·00
62		32 p. blue	5·00	1·25
63		1 r. red	9·00	4·00
50		5 r. black and brown	14·00	8·00

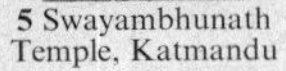

5 Swayambhunath Temple, Katmandu — 7 Guheswari Temple, Patan

8 Sri Pashupati (Siva Mahadeva)

1949.

64	5	2 p. brown	50	40
65	–	4 p. green	50	40
66	–	6 p. pink	1·00	40
67	–	8 p. red	1·00	60
68	–	16 p. purple	1·00	60
69	–	20 p. blue	2·00	1·00
70	7	24 p. red	1·60	60
71	–	32 p. blue	3·00	1·00
72	8	1 r. orange	12·00	6·00

DESIGNS—As Type 5: 4 p. Pashupatinath Temple, Katmandu; 6 p. Tri-Chundra College; 8 p. Mahabuddha Temple. 26 × 30 mm: 16 p. Krishna Mandir Temple, Patan. As Type 7: 20 p. View of Katmandu; 32 p. The twenty-two fountains, Balaju.

9 King Tribhuvana — 10 Map of Nepal

1954. (a) Size 18 × 22 mm.

73	9	2 p. brown	1·00	20
74		4 p. green	2·00	60
75		6 p. red	80	20
76		8 p. lilac	60	20
77		12 p. orange	4·00	1·00

(b) Size 25½ × 29½ mm.

78	9	16 p. brown	80	20
79		20 p. red	1·60	60
80		24 p. purple	1·40	60
81		32 p. blue	2·00	60
82		50 p. mauve	9·00	3·00
83		1 r. red	18·00	5·00
84		2 r. orange	9·00	4·00

(c) Size 30 × 18 mm.

85	10	2 p. brown	80	40
86		4 p. green	2·00	60
87		6 p. red	6·00	1·00
88		8 p. lilac	60	40
89		12 p. orange	6·00	1·00

(d) Size 38 × 21½ mm.

90	10	16 p. brown	1·00	40
91		20 p. red	1·60	40
92		24 p. purple	1·25	40
93		32 p. blue	3·00	80
94		50 p. mauve	11·00	3·00
95		1 r. red	20·00	4·00
96		2 r. orange	9·00	4·00

11 Mechanization of Agriculture — 13 Hanuman Dhoka, Katmandu

1956. Coronation.

97	11	4 p. green	2·00	1·25
98	–	6 p. red and yellow	1·25	60
99	–	8 p. violet	80	40
100	13	24 p. red	2·00	80
101	–	1 r. red	55·00	48·00

DESIGNS—As Type 11: 8 p. Processional elephant. As Type 13: 6 p. Throne; 1 r. King and Queen and mountains.

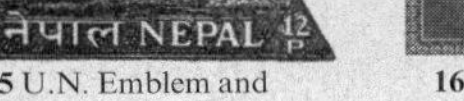

15 U.N. Emblem and Nepalese Landscape — 16 Nepalese Crown

1956. 1st Anniv of Admission into U.N.O.

102	15	12 p. blue and brown	2·75	1·60

1957. (a) Size 18 × 22 mm.

103	16	2 p. brown	40	25
104		4 p. green	60	40
105		6 p. red	40	40
106		8 p. violet	40	40
107		12 p. red	2·25	60

(b) Size 25½ × 29½ mm.

108	16	16 p. brown	3·00	1·00
109		20 p. red	5·00	1·40
110		24 p. mauve	3·00	1·25
111		32 p. blue	4·00	1·40
112		50 p. pink	7·00	3·00
113		1 r. salmon	15·00	6·00
114		2 r. orange	7·00	4·00

17 Gaunthali carrying Letter — 18 Temple of Lumbini

1958. Air. Inauguration of Nepalese Internal Airmail Service.

115	17	10 p. blue	1·10	1·10

1958. Human Rights Day.

116	18	6 p. yellow	80	80

19 Nepalese Map and Flag

1959. 1st Nepalese Elections.

117	19	6 p. red and green	30	25

20 Spinning Wheel — 21 King Mahendra

1959. Cottage Industries.

118	20	2 p. brown	25	25

1959. Admission of Nepal to U.P.U.

119	21	12 p. blue	30	25

22 Vishnu — 23 Nyatopol Temple, Bhaktapur

1959.

120	22	1 p. brown	10	10
121	–	2 p. violet	10	10
122	–	4 p. blue	30	20
123	–	6 p. pink	30	15
124	–	8 p. brown	20	10
125	–	12 p. grey	30	10
126	23	16 p. violet and brown	30	10
127		20 p. red and blue	1·00	40
128	23	24 p. red and green	1·00	40
129		32 p. blue and lilac	60	40
130		50 p. green and red	1·00	40
131	–	1 r. blue and brown	6·00	2·00
132	–	2 r. blue and purple	6·00	3·25
133	–	5 r. red and violet	45·00	38·00

DESIGNS—As Type 22. HORIZ: 2 p. Krishna; 8 p. Siberian musk deer; 12 p. Indian rhinoceros. VERT: 4 p. Himalayas; 6 p. Gateway, Bhaktapur Palace. As Type 23. VERT: 1 r., 2 r. Himalayan monal pheasant; 5 r. Satyr tragopan.

24 King Mahendra opening Parliament — 25 Sri Pashupatinath

1959. Opening of 1st Nepalese Parliament.

134	24	6 p. red	60	60

1959. Renovation of Sri Pashupatinath Temple, Katmandu.

135	25	4 p. green (18 × 25 mm)	40	40
136		8 p. red (21 × 28½ mm)	60	40
137		1 r. blue (24½ × 33½ mm)	5·00	3·25

26 Children, Pagoda and Mt. Everest — 27 King Mahendra

1960. Children's Day.

137a	26	6 p. blue	8·00	6·00

1960. King Mahendra's 41st Birthday.

138	27	1 r. purple	90	60

See also Nos. 163/4a.

28 Mt. Everest — 29 King Tribhuvana

1960. Mountain Views.

139	–	5 p. brown and purple	20	10
140	28	10 p. purple and blue	30	15
141	–	40 p. brown and violet	70	45

DESIGNS: 5 p. Machha Puchhre; 40 p. Manaslu (wrongly inscr "MANSALU").

1961. 10th Democracy Day.

142	29	10 p. orange and brown	10	10

30 Prince Gyanendra cancelling Children's Day Stamps of 1960 — 31 King Mahendra

1961. Children's Day.

143	30	12 p. orange	20·00	20·00

1961. King Mahendra's 42nd Birthday.

144	31	6 p. green	20	20
145		12 p. blue	30	30
146		50 p. red	60	60
147		1 r. brown	1·00	1·00

32 Campaign Emblem and House — 33 King Mahendra on Horseback

1962. Malaria Eradication.

148	32	12 p. blue	20	20
149	–	1 r. orange and red	60	60

DESIGN: 1 r. Emblem and Nepalese flag.

1962. King Mahendra's 43rd Birthday.

150	33	10 p. blue	15	15
151		15 p. brown	20	20
152		45 p. brown	40	40
153		1 r. grey	60	60

34 Bhana Bhakta Acharya

1962. Nepalese Poets.

154	34	5 p. brown	20	20
155	–	10 p. turquoise	20	20
156	–	40 p. green	30	30

PORTRAITS: 10 p. Moti Ram Bhakta; 40 p. Sambhu Prasad.

35 King Mahendra — 36

1962.

157	35	1 p. red	10	10
158		2 p. blue	10	10
158a		3 p. grey	30	20
159		5 p. brown	10	10
160	36	10 p. purple	10	10
161		40 p. brown	20	20
162		75 p. green	6·00	6·00
162a	35	75 p. green	80	40
163	27	2 r. red	80	80
164		5 r. green	1·60	1·60
164a		10 r. violet	6·00	5·00

No. 162a is smaller, 17½ × 20 mm.

37 Emblems of Learning — 38 Hands holding Lamps

1963. U.N.E.S.C.O. "Education for All" Campaign.

165	37	10 p. black	20	10
166		15 p. brown	30	20
167		50 p. blue	50	40

1963. National Day.

168	38	5 p. blue	10	10
169		10 p. brown	10	10
170		50 p. purple	40	30
171		1 r. green	80	40

39 Campaign Symbols — 40 Map of Nepal and Open Hand

1963. Freedom from Hunger.

172	39	10 p. orange	20	10
173		15 p. blue	30	20
174		50 p. green	60	40
175		1 r. brown	80	70

1963. Rastruya Panchayat.

176	40	10 p. green	10	10
177		15 p. purple	20	20
178		50 p. grey	50	30
179		1 r. blue	80	50

41 King Mahendra — 42 King Mahendra and Highway Map

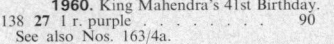

1963. King Mahendra's 44th Birthday.
180 **41** 5 p. violet 10 10
181 10 p. brown 20 10
182 15 p. green 30 20

1964. Inauguration of East–West Highway.
183 **42** 10 p. orange and blue . . . 10 10
184 15 p. orange and blue . . . 20 10
185 50 p. brown and green . . . 30 20

43 King Mahendra at Microphone

44 Crown Prince Birendra

1964. King Mahendra's 45th Birthday.
186 **43** 1 p. brown 10 10
187 2 p. grey 10 10
188 2 r. brown 60 60

1964. Crown Prince's 19th Birthday.
189 **44** 10 p. green 50 40
190 15 p. brown 50 40

45 Flag, Kukris, Rings and Torch

46 Nepalese Family

1964. Olympic Games, Tokyo.
191 **45** 10 p. blue, red and pink . . . 50 40

1965. Land Reform.
192 – 2 p. black and green 20 20
193 – 5 p. brown and green . . . 20 20
194 – 10 p. purple and grey . . . 20 20
195 **46** 15 p. brown and yellow . . . 30 30
DESIGNS: 2 p. Farmer ploughing; 5 p. Ears of wheat; 10 p. Grain elevator.

47 Globe and Letters

48 King Mahendra

1965. Introduction of International Insured and Parcel Service.
196 **47** 15 p. violet 20 20

1965. King Mahendra's 46th Birthday.
197 **48** 50 p. purple 50 40

49 Four Martyrs

50 I.T.U. Emblem

1965. "Nepalese Martyrs".
198 **49** 15 p. green 25 20

1965. I.T.U. Centenary.
199 **50** 15 p. black and purple . . . 30 20

51 I.C.Y. Emblem

52 Devkota (poet)

1965. International Co-operation Year.
200 **51** 1 r. multicoloured 60 50

1965. Devkota Commemoration.
201 **52** 15 p. brown 20 20

54 Flag and King Mahendra

1966. Democracy Day.
202 **54** 15 p. red and blue 40 30

55 Siva Parvati and Pashuvati Temple

56 "Stamp" Emblem

1966. Maha Siva-Ratri Festival.
203 **55** 15 p. violet 25 20

1966. Nepalese Philatelic Exhibition, Katmandu.
204 **56** 15 p. orange and green . . . 30 20

57 King Mahendra

58 Queen Mother

1966. King Mahendra's 47th Birthday.
205 **57** 15 p. brown and yellow . . . 25 20

1966. Queen Mother's 60th Birthday.
206 **58** 15 p. brown 20 20

59 Queen Ratna

60 Flute-player and Dancer

1966. Children's Day.
207 **59** 15 p. brown and yellow . . . 25 20

1966. Krishna Anniv.
208 **60** 15 p. violet and yellow . . . 25 20

61 "To render service..."

1966. 1st Anniv of Nepalese Red Cross.
209 **61** 50 p. red and green . . . . 2·40 80

62 W.H.O. Building on Flag

63 Paudyal

1966. Inaug of W.H.O. Headquarters, Geneva.
210 **62** 1 r. violet . . . . 1·25 80

1966. Leknath Paudyal (poet) Commemoration.
211 **63** 15 p. blue 25 20

64 Rama and Sita

65 Buddha

1967. Rama Navami, 2024, birthday of Rama.
212 **64** 15 p. brown and yellow . . 25 20

1967. Buddha Jayanti, birthday of Buddha.
213 **65** 75 p. purple and orange . . 50 50

66 King Mahendra addressing Nepalese

1967. King Mahendra's 48th Birthday.
214 **66** 15 p. brown and blue . . . 25 25

67 Queen Ratna and Children

68 Ama Dablam (mountain)

1967. Children's Day.
215 **67** 15 p. brown and cream . . . 25 20

1967. International Tourist Year.
216 **68** 5 p. violet (postage) 20 20
217 – 65 p. brown 40 40
218 – 1 r. 80 red and blue (air) . . 1·00 80
DESIGNS—38 × 20 mm: 65 p. Bhaktapur Durbar Square. $35\frac{1}{2} \times 25\frac{1}{2}$ mm: 1 r. 80, Plane over Katmandu.

69 Open-air Class

1967. Constitution Day. "Go to the Village" Educational Campaign.
219 **69** 15 p. multicoloured 25 20

70 Crown Prince Birendra, Campfire and Scout Emblem

1967. Diamond Jubilee of World Scouting.
220 **70** 15 p. blue 40 30

71 Prithvi Narayan Shah (founder of Kingdom)

72 Arms of Nepal

1968. Bicentenary of the Kingdom.
221 **71** 15 p. blue and red 40 30

1968. National Day.
222 **72** 15 p. blue and red 40 30

73 W.H.O. Emblem and Nepalese Flag

1968. 20th Anniv of W.H.O.
223 **73** 1 r. 20 blue, red & yellow . . 1·75 1·25

74 Sita and Janaki Temple

1968. Sita Jayanti.
224 **74** 15 p. brown and violet . . . 30 20

75 King Mahendra, Mountains and Himalayan Monal Pheasant

1968. King Mahendra's 49th Birthday.
225 **75** 15 p. multicoloured . . . . 1·00 30

76 Garuda and Airline Emblem

1968. Air. 10th Anniv of Royal Nepalese Airlines.
226 **76** 15 p. brown and blue . . . 20 20
227 – 65 p. blue 40 40
228 – 2 r. 50 blue and orange . . 1·50 1·25
DESIGNS—DIAMOND ($25\frac{1}{2} \times 25\frac{1}{2}$ mm): 65 p. Route-map. As Type **76**: 2 r. 50, Convair Metropolitan airliner over Mount Dhaulagiri.

77 Flag, Queen Ratna and Children

78 Human Rights Emblem and Buddha

1968. Children's Day and Queen Ratna's 41st Birthday.
229 **77** 5 p. red, yellow and green . 20 15

1968. Human Rights Year.
230 **78** 1 r. red and green . . . . . 1·60 1·25

79 Crown Prince Birendra and Dancers

1968. Crown Prince Birendra's 24th Birthday, and National Youth Festival.
231 **79** 25 p. blue 40 30

80 King Mahendra, Flags and U.N. Building, New York

81 Amsu Varma (7th-century ruler)

1969. Nepal's Election to U.N. Security Council.
232 **80** 1 r. multicoloured 60 50

1969. Famous Nepalese.
233 **81** 15 p. violet and green . . . 30 30
234 – 25 p. turquoise 40 40
235 – 50 p. brown 50 50
236 – 1 r. purple and brown . . . 60 50
DESIGNS—VERT: 25 p. Ram Shah (17th-century King of Gurkha); 50 p. Bhimsen Thapa (19th-century Prime Minister). HORIZ: 1 r. Bal Bhadra Kunwar (19th-century warrior).

82 I.L.O. Emblem

1969. 50th Anniv of I.L.O.
237 **82** 1 r. brown and mauve . . . 3·00 2·00

83 King Mahendra — **85** Queen Ratna, and Child with Toy

84 King Tribhuvana and Queens

1969. King Mahendra's 50th Birthday.
238 **83** 25 p. multicoloured 25 25

1969. 64th Birth Anniv of King Tribhuvana.
239 **84** 25 p. brown and yellow . . 25 25

1969. National Children's Day.
240 **85** 25 p. mauve and brown . . 25 25

86 Rhododendron — **87** Durga, Goddess of Victory

1969. Flowers. Multicoloured.
241 25 p. Type **86** 35 30
242 25 p. Narcissus 35 30
243 25 p. Marigold 35 30
244 25 p. Poinsettia 35 30

1969. Durga Pooja Festival.
245 **87** 15 p. black and orange . . . 20 20
246 50 p. violet and brown . . . 45 40

88 Crown Prince Birendra and Princess Aishwarya

1970. Royal Wedding.
247 **88** 25 p. multicoloured 25 20

89 Produce, Cow and Landscape

1970. Agricultural Year.
248 **89** 25 p. multicoloured 25 20

90 King Mahendra, Mt. Everest and Nepalese Crown

1970. King Mahendra's 51st Birthday.
249 **90** 50 p. multicoloured 40 30

91 Lake Gosainkunda

1970. Nepalese Lakes. Multicoloured.
250 5 p. Type **91** 20 20
251 25 p. Lake Phewa Tal 30 30
252 1 r. Lake Rara Daha 50 50

92 A.P.Y. Emblem

1970. Asian Productivity Year.
253 **92** 1 r. blue 50 40

93 Queen Ratna and Children's Palace, Taulihawa

1970. National Children's Day.
254 **93** 25 p. grey and brown . . . 25 20

94 New Headquarters Building

1970. New U.P.U. Headquarters, Berne.
255 **94** 2 r. 50 grey and brown . . . 1·00 80

95 U.N. Flag

1970. 25th Anniv of United Nations.
256 **95** 25 p. blue and purple . . . 25 20

96 Durbar Square, Patan

1970. Tourism. Multicoloured.
257 15 p. Type **96** 20 10
258 25 p. Boudhanath Stupa (temple) (vert) 30 20
259 1 r. Mt. Gauri Shankar 50 40

97 Statue of Harihar, Valmiki Ashram — **98** Torch within Spiral

1971. Nepalese Religious Art.
260 **97** 25 p. black and brown . . . 25 20

1971. Racial Equality Year.
261 **98** 1 r. red and blue 60 45

99 King Mahendra taking Salute — **100** Sweta Bhairab

1971. King Mahendra's 52nd Birthday.
262 **99** 15 p. purple and blue . . . 25 20

1971. Bhairab Statues of Shiva.
263 **100** 15 p. brown and chestnut . 20 20
264 – 25 p. brown and green . . 20 20
265 – 50 p. brown and blue . . . 40 40
DESIGNS: 25 p. Mahankal Bhairab; 50 p. Kal Bhairab.

101 Child presenting Queen Ratna with Garland

1971. National Children's Day.
266 **101** 25 p. multicoloured 25 15

102 Iranian and Nepalese Flags on Map of Iran

1971. 2,500th Anniv of Persian Empire.
267 **102** 1 r. multicoloured 60 40

103 Mother and Child

1971. 25th Anniv of U.N.I.C.E.F.
268 **103** 1 r. blue 60 40

104 Mt. Everest — **105** Royal Standard

1971. Tourism. Himalayan Peaks.
269 **104** 25 p deep brown, brown and blue 20 10
270 – 1 r. black, brown and blue 40 30
271 – 1 r. 80 green, brown and blue 70 50
DESIGNS: 1 r. Mt. Kanchenjunga; 1 r. 80, Mt. Annapurna I.

1972. National Day.
272 **105** 25 p. black and red 25 15

106 Araniko and White Dagoba, Peking — **107** Open Book

1972. Araniko (13th-century architect) Commem.
273 **106** 15 p. brown and blue . . . 15 10

1972. International Book Year.
274 **107** 2 p. brown and buff . . . 10 10
275 5 p. black and brown . . . 10 10
276 1 r. black and blue 50 40

108 Human Heart

1972. World Heart Month.
277 **108** 25 p. red and green 25 20

109 King Mahendra — **110** King Birendra

1972. 1st Death Anniv of King Mahendra.
278 **109** 25 p. brown and black . . 25 15

1972. King Birendra's 28th Birthday.
279 **110** 50 p. purple and brown . . 30 25

111 Northern Border Costumes — **112** Sri Baburam Acharya

1973. National Costumes. Multicoloured.
280 25 p. Type **111** 20 10
281 50 p. Hill-dwellers 25 20
282 75 p. Katmandu Valley 35 25
283 1 r. Inner Terai 50 35

1973. 85th Birth Anniv of Sri Baburam Acharya (historian).
284 **112** 25 p. grey and red 20 15

113 Nepalese Family

1973. 25th Anniv of W.H.O.
285 **113** 1 r. blue and orange . . . 50 40

114 Birthplace of Buddha, Lumbini

1973. Tourism. Multicoloured.
286 25 p. Type **114** 20 10
287 75 p. Mt. Makalu 30 20
288 1 r. Castle, Gurkha 40 40

115 Transplanting Rice

1973. 10th Anniv of World Food Programme.
289 **115** 10 p. brown & violet . . . 10 10

116 Interpol H.Q., Paris

1973. 50th Anniv of International Criminal Police Organization (Interpol).
290 **116** 25 p. blue and brown . . . 20 15

117 Shri Shom Nath Sigdyal — **118** Cow

1973. 1st Death Anniv of Shri Shom Nath Sigdyal (scholar).
291 **117** 1 r. 25 violet 50 40

1973. Domestic Animals. Multicoloured.
292 2 p. Type **118** 10 10
293 3 r. 25 Yak 90 60

119 King Birendra

1974. King Birendra's 29th Birthday.
294 **119** 5 p. brown and black . . . 10 10
295 15 p. brown and black . . 15 10
296 1 r. brown and black . . . 40 30

120 Text of National Anthem
121 King Janak seated on Throne

1974. National Day.
297 **120** 25 p. purple 20 10
298 – 1 r. green 30 25
DESIGN: 1 r. Anthem musical score.

1974. King Janak Commemoration.
299 **121** 2 r. 50 multicoloured . . . 1·00 80

122 Emblem and Village

1974. 25th Anniv of SOS Children's Village International.
300 **122** 25 p. blue and red 15 15

123 Football
124 W.P.Y. Emblem

1974. Nepalese Games. Multicoloured.
301 2 p. Type **123** 10 10
302 2 r. 75 Baghchal (diagram) . . 60 50

1974. World Population Year.
303 **124** 5 p. blue and brown . . . 10 10

125 U.P.U. Monument, Berne
126 Red Lacewing

1974. Centenary of U.P.U.
304 **125** 1 r. black and green . . . 40 30

1974. Nepalese Butterflies. Multicoloured.
305 10 p. Type **126** 10 10
306 15 p. Leaf butterfly 40 15
307 1 r. 25 Leaf butterfly (underside) 1·00 70
308 1 r. 75 Red-breasted jezebel . . 1·25 1·00

127 King Birendra
128 Muktinath

1974. King Birendra's 30th Birthday.
309 **127** 25 p. black and green . . . 15 15

1974. "Visit Nepal" Tourism. Multicoloured.
310 25 p. Type **128** 20 10
311 1 r. Peacock window, Bhaktapur (horiz) 40 25

129 Guheswari Temple

1975. Coronation of King Birendra. Multicoloured.
312 25 p. Type **129** 20 10
313 50 p. Lake Rara (37 × 30 mm) . 20 10
314 1 r. Throne and sceptre (46 × 26 mm) 30 20
315 1 r. 25 Royal Palace, Katmandu (46 × 26 mm) 60 30
316 1 r. 75 Pashupatinath Temple (25 × 31 mm) 40 40
317 2 r. 75 King Birendra and Queen Aishwarya (46 × 25 mm) . . 60 50

130 Tourism Year Emblem

1975. South Asia Tourism Year. Multicoloured.
319 2 p. Type **130** 10 10
320 25 p. Temple stupa (vert) . . . 20 20

131 Tiger

1975. Wildlife Conservation. Multicoloured.
321 2 p. Type **131** 20 20
322 5 p. Swamp deer (vert) 20 20
323 1 r. Lesser panda 40 40

132 Queen Aishwarya and I.W.Y. Emblem

1975. International Women's Year.
324 **132** 1 r. multicoloured 30 20

133 Rupse Falls
134 King Birendra

1975. Tourism. Multicoloured.
325 2 p. Mt. Ganesh Himal (horiz) . 10 10
326 25 p. Type **133** 10 10
327 50 p. Kumari ("Living Goddess") 30 20

1975. King Birendra's 31st Birthday.
328 **134** 25 p. violet and mauve . . 15 10

136 Flag and Map
138 Flags of Nepal and Colombo Plan

137 Transplanting Rice

1976. Silver Jubilee of National Democracy Day.
330 **136** 2 r. 50 red and blue 10 10

1976. Agriculture Year.
331 **137** 25 p. multicoloured 15 10

1976. 25th Anniv of Colombo Plan.
332 **138** 1 r. multicoloured 30 25

139 Running
140 "Dove of Peace"

1976. Olympic Games, Montreal.
333 **139** 3 r. 25 black and blue . . . 80 60

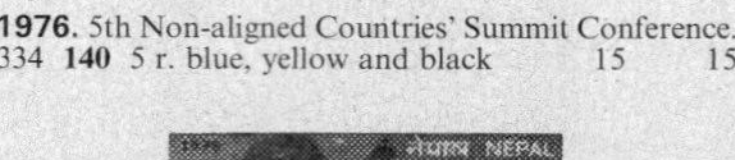

1976. 5th Non-aligned Countries' Summit Conference.
334 **140** 5 r. blue, yellow and black 15 15

141 Lakhe Dance

1976. Nepalese Dances. Multicoloured.
335 10 p. Type **141** 10 10
336 15 p. Maruni dance 10 10
337 30 p. Jhangad dance 20 10
338 1 r. Sebru dance 30 20

142 Nepalese Lily
143 King Birendra

1976. Flowers. Multicoloured.
339 30 p. Type **142** 30 10
340 30 p. "Meconopsis grandis" . . 30 10
341 30 p. "Cardiocrinum giganteum" (horiz) 30 10
342 30 p. "Megacodon stylophorus" (horiz) 30 10

1976. King Birendra's 32nd Birthday.
343 **143** 5 p. green 10 10
344 30 p. dp brown, brn & yell . 15 10

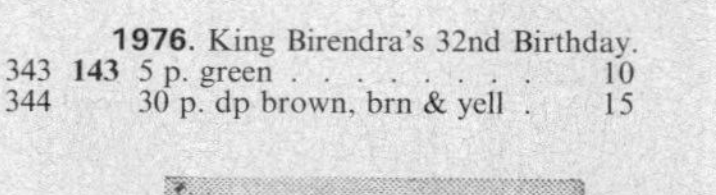

144 Liberty Bell

1976. Bicentenary of American Revolution.
345 **144** 10 r. multicoloured . . . . 1·50 1·40

145 Kaji Amarsingh Thapa

1977. Kaji Amarsingh Thapa (19th-century warrior) Commemoration
346 **145** 10 p. green and brown . . 10 10

146 Terracotta Figurine and Kapilavastu

1977. Tourism.
347 **146** 30 p. violet 10 10
348 – 5 r. green and brown . . . 80 60
DESIGN: 5 r. Ashokan pillar, Lumbini.

147 Great Indian Hornbill

148 Tukuche Himal and Police Flag

1977. Birds. Multicoloured.
349 5 p. Type **147** 45 10
350 15 p. Cheer pheasant (horiz) . . 80 15
351 1 r. Green magpie (horiz) . . . 1·25 45
352 2 r. 30 Spiny babbler . . . . . 2·25 95

1977. 1st Anniv of Ascent of Tukuche Himal by Police Team.
353 **148** 1 r. 25 multicoloured . . . 30 20

149 Map of Nepal and Scout Emblem

150 Dhanwantari, the Health-giver

1977. 25th Anniv of Scouting in Nepal.
354 **149** 3 r. 50 multicoloured . . . 60 40

1977. Health Day.
355 **150** 30 p. green 15 10

151 Map of Nepal and Flags

152 King Birendra

1977. 26th Consultative Committee Meeting of Colombo Plan, Katmandu.
356 **151** 1 r. multicoloured 20 15

1977. King Birendra's 33rd Birthday.
357 **152** 5 p. brown 10 10
358 1 r. brown 20 20

153 General Post Office, Katmandu, and Seal

1978. Centenary of Nepalese Post Office.
359 **153** 25 p. brown and agate . . 10 10
360 – 75 p. brown and agate . . 10 10
DESIGN: 75 p. General Post Office, Katmandu, and early postmark.

154 South-west Face of Mount Everest

1978. 25th Anniv of First Ascent of Mt. Everest.
361 **154** 2 r. 30 grey and brown . . 50 30
362 – 4 r. blue and green . . . 70 60
DESIGN: 4 r. South face of Mt. Everest.

155 Sun, Ankh and Landscape

1978. World Environment Day.
363 **155** 1 r. green and orange . . . 10 10

156 Queen Mother Ratna — **157** Rapids, Tripsuli River

1978. Queen Mother's 50th Birthday.
364 **156** 2 r. 30 green 10 10

1978. Tourism. Multicoloured.
365 10 p. Type **157** 10 10
366 50 p. Window, Nara Devi, Katmandu 15 10
367 1 r. Mahakali dance (vert) 25 20

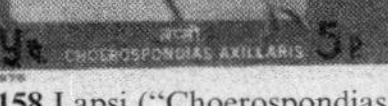

158 Lapsi ("Choerospondias axillaris") — **159** Lamp and U.N. Emblem

1978. Fruits. Multicoloured.
368 5 p. Type **158** 15 10
369 1 r. Katus (vert) 25 20
370 1 r. 25 Rudrakshya 40 25

1978. 30th Anniv of Human Rights Declaration.
371 **159** 25 p. brown and red 10 10
372 1 r. blue and red 20 15

160 Wright Flyer I and Boeing 727-100 — **161** King Birendra

1978. Air. 75th Anniv of First Powered Flight.
373 **160** 2 r. 30 blue and brown 45 30

1978. King Birendra's 34th Birthday.
374 **161** 30 p. blue and brown 10 10
375 2 r. brown and violet 10 10

162 Red Machchhindranath and Kamroop and Patan Temples

1979. Red Machchhindranath (guardian deity) Festival.
376 **162** 75 p. brown and green 20 15

163 "Buddha's Birth" (carving, Maya Devi Temple) — **164** Planting a Sapling

1979. Lumbini Year.
377 **163** 1 r. yellow and brown 20 15

1979. Tree Planting Festival.
378 **164** 2 r. 30 brown, grn & yell 10 10

165 Chariot of Red Machchhindranath — **166** Nepalese Scouts and Guides

1979. Bhoto Jatra (Vest Exhibition) Festival.
379 **165** 1 r. 25 multicoloured 25 20

1979. International Year of the Child.
380 **166** 1 r. brown 10 10

167 Mount Pabil — **168** Great Grey Shrike

1979. Tourism.
381 **167** 30 p. green 10 10
382 – 50 p. red and blue 10 10
383 – 1 r. 25 multicoloured 25 25
DESIGNS: 50 p. Yajnashala, Swargadwari. 1 r. 25, Shiva-Parbati (wood carving, Gaddi Baithak Temple).

1979. International World Pheasant Association Symposium, Katmandu. Multicoloured.
384 10 p. Type **168** (postage) 25 20
385 10 r. Fire-tailed sunbird 7·25 3·50
386 3 r. 50 Himalayan monal pheasant (horiz) (air) 2·50 1·90

169 Lichchhavi Coin (obverse) — **170** King Birendra

1979. Coins.
387 **169** 5 p. orange and brown 10 10
388 – 5 p. orange and brown 10 10
389 – 15 p. blue and indigo 10 10
390 – 15 p. blue and indigo 10 10
391 – 1 r. blue and deep blue 20 20
392 – 1 r. blue and deep blue 20 20
DESIGNS: No. 388, Lichchhavi coin (reverse); No. 389, Malla coin (obverse); No. 390, Malla coin (reverse); No. 391, Prithvi Narayan Shah coin (obverse); No. 392, Prithvi Narayan Shah coin (reverse).

1979. King Birendra's 35th Birthday. Multicoloured.
393 25 p. Type **170** 10 10
394 2 r. 30 Reservoir 40 30

171 Samyak Pooja Festival

1980. Samyak Pooja Festival, Katmandu.
395 **171** 30 p. brown, grey & pur 10 10

172 Sacred Basil

1980. Herbs. Multicoloured.
396 5 p. Type **172** 10 10
397 30 p. Valerian 10 10
398 1 r. Nepalese pepper 20 15
399 2 r. 30 Himalayan rhubarb 40 25

173 Gyandil Das — **174** Everlasting Flame and Temple, Shirsasthan

1980. Nepalese Writers.
400 **173** 5 p. lilac and brown 10 10
401 – 30 p. purple and brown 10 10
402 – 1 r. green and blue 15 15
403 – 2 r. 30 blue and green 55 25
DESIGNS: 30 p. Siddhidas Amatya; 1 r. Pahalman Singh Swanr; 2 r. 30, Jay Prithvi Bahadur Singh.

1980. Tourism. Multicoloured.
404 10 p. Type **174** 10 10
405 1 r. Godavari Pond 20 15
406 5 r. Mount Dhaulagiri 70 50

175 Bhairab Dancer — **176** King Birendra

1980. World Tourism Conference, Manila, Philippines.
407 **175** 25 r. multicoloured 3·00 2·25

1980. King Birendra's 36th Birthday.
408 **176** 1 r. multicoloured 20 15

177 I.Y.D.P. Emblem and Nepalese Flag

1981. International Year of Disabled Persons.
409 **177** 5 r. multicoloured 80 60

178 Nepal Rastra Bank — **179** One Anna Stamp of 1881

1981. 25th Anniv of Nepal Rastra Bank.
410 **178** 1 r. 75 multicoloured 10 10

1981. Nepalese Postage Stamp Centenary.
411 **179** 10 p. blue, brown and black 10 10
412 – 40 p. purple, brown and black 10 10
413 – 3 r. 40 green, brown and blk 50 40
DESIGNS: 40 p. 2 anna stamp of 1881; 3 r. 40, 4 a. stamp of 1881.

180 Nepalese Flag and Association Emblem — **181** Hand holding Stamp

1981. 70th Council Meeting of International Hotel Association, Katmandu.
415 **180** 1 r. 75 multicoloured 10 10

1981. "Nepal 81" Stamp Exhibition, Katmandu.
416 **181** 40 p. multicoloured 10 10

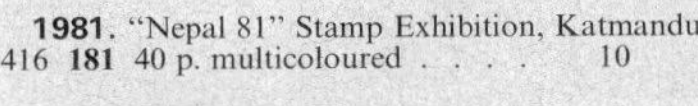

182 King Birendra — **183** Image of Hrishikesh, Ridi

1981. King Birendra's 37th Birthday.
417 **182** 1 r. multicoloured 10 10

1981. Tourism. Multicoloured.
418 5 p. Type **183** 10 10
419 25 p. Tripura Sundari Temple, Baitadi 10 10
420 2 r. Mt. Langtang Lirung 10 10

184 Academy Building — **185** Balakrishna Sama

1982. 25th Anniv of Royal Nepal Academy.
421 **184** 40 p. multicoloured 10 10

1982. 1st Death Anniv of Balakrishna Sama (writer).
422 **185** 1 r. multicoloured 10 10

186 "Intelsat V" and Dish Aerial — **187** Mount Nuptse

1982. Sagarmatha Satellite Earth Station, Balambu.
423 **186** 5 r. multicoloured 75 40

1982. 50th Anniv of Union of International Alpinist Associations. Multicoloured.
424 25 p. Type **187** 10 10
425 2 r. Mount Lhotse (31 × 31 mm) 30 20
426 3 r. Mount Everest (39 × 31 mm) 60 30
Nos. 424/6 were issued together, se-tenant, forming a composite design.

188 Games Emblem and Weights — **189** Indra Sarobar Lake

1982. 9th Asian Games, New Delhi.
427 **188** 3 r. 40 multicoloured 50 40

1982. Kulekhani Hydro-electric Project.
428 **189** 2 r. multicoloured 10 10

190 King Birendra — **191** N.I.D.C. Emblem

1982. King Birendra's 38th Birthday.
429 **190** 5 p. multicoloured 10 10

1983. 25th Anniv (1984) of Nepal Industrial Development Corporation.
430 **191** 50 p. multicoloured 10 10

192 Boeing 727 over Himalayas

1983. 25th Anniv of Royal Nepal Airlines.
431 **192** 1 r. multicoloured 40 15

193 W.C.Y. Emblem and Nepalese Flag — **194** Sarangi

1983. World Communications Year.
432 **193** 10 p. multicoloured 10 10

1983. Musical Instruments. Multicoloured.
433 5 p. Type **194** 10 10
434 10 p. Kwota (drum) 10 10
435 50 p. Narashinga (horn) 10 10
436 1 r. Murchunga 20 20

195 Chakrapani Chalise

196 King Birendra and Doves

1983. Birth Centenary of Chakrapani Chalise (poet).
437 **195** 4 r. 50 multicoloured . . . 60 45

1983. King Birendra's 39th Birthday.
438 **196** 5 r. multicoloured 70 40

197 Barahkshetra Temple and Image of Barah

1983. Tourism. Multicoloured.
439 1 r. Type **197** 15 10
440 2 r. 20 Temple, Triveni 15 15
441 6 r. Mount Cho-oyu 15 15

198 Auditing Accounts

199 Antenna and Emblem

1984. 25th Anniv of Auditor General.
442 **198** 25 p. multicoloured 10 10

1984. 20th Anniv of Asia-Pacific Broadcasting Union.
443 **199** 5 r. multicoloured 70 60

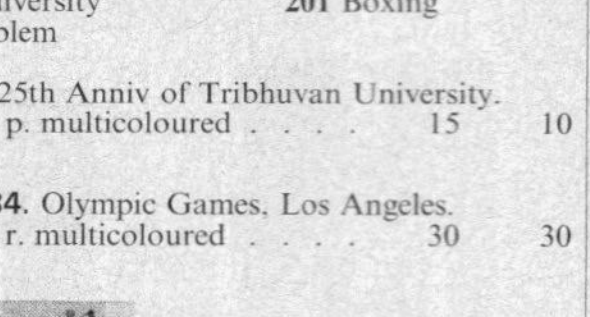

200 University Emblem

201 Boxing

1984. 25th Anniv of Tribhuvan University.
444 **200** 50 p. multicoloured 15 10

1984. Olympic Games, Los Angeles.
445 **201** 10 r. multicoloured 30 30

202 Family and Emblem

203 National Flag and Emblem

1984. 25th Anniv of Nepal Family Planning Association.
446 **202** 1 r. multicoloured 15 10

1984. Social Service Day.
447 **203** 5 p. multicoloured 10 10

204 Gharial

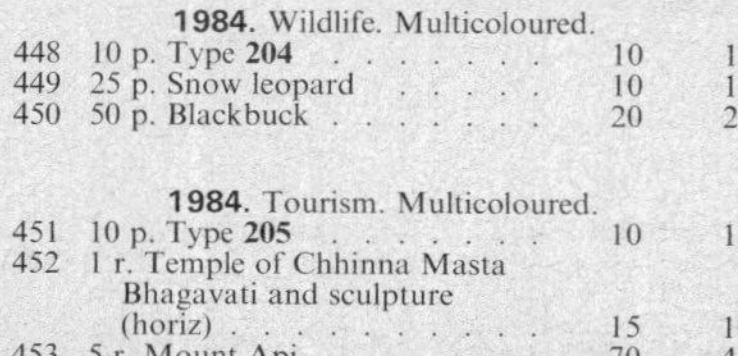

205 "Vishnu as Giant" (stone carving)

1984. Wildlife. Multicoloured.
448 10 p. Type **204** 10 10
449 25 p. Snow leopard 10 10
450 50 p. Blackbuck 20 20

1984. Tourism. Multicoloured.
451 10 p. Type **205** 10 10
452 1 r. Temple of Chhinna Masta Bhagavati and sculpture (horiz) 15 10
453 5 r. Mount Api 70 45

206 King Birendra

1984. King Birendra's 40th Birthday.
454 **206** 1 r. multicoloured 15 10

207 Animals and Mountains

208 Shiva

1985. Sagarmatha (Mt. Everest) National Park.
455 **207** 10 r. multicoloured . . . . 2·50 70

1985. Traditional Paintings. Details of cover of "Shiva Dharma Purana". Multicoloured.
456 50 p. Type **208** 10 10
457 50 p. Multi-headed Shiva talking to woman 10 10
458 50 p. Brahma and Vishnu making offering (15 × 22 mm) . . . 10 10
459 50 p. Shiva in single- and multi-headed forms 10 10
460 50 p. Shiva talking to woman . . 10 10
Nos. 456/60 were printed together, se-tenant, forming a composite design.

209 U.N. Flag

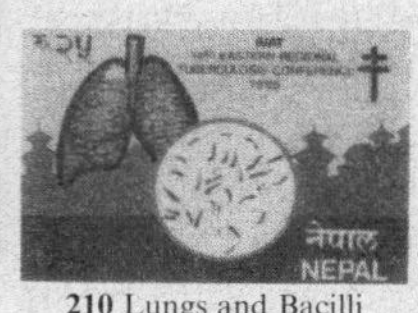

210 Lungs and Bacilli

1985. 40th Anniv of U.N.O.
461 **209** 5 r. multicoloured 15 15

1985. 14th Eastern Regional Tuberculosis Conference, Katmandu.
462 **210** 25 r. multicoloured 50 50

211 Flags of Member Countries

1985. 1st South Asian Association for Regional Co-operation Summit.
463 **211** 5 r. multicoloured 60 40

212 Jaleshwar Temple

213 I.Y.Y. Emblem

1985. Tourism. Multicoloured.
464 10 p. Type **212** 10 10
465 1 r. Temple of Goddess Shaileshwari, Silgadi 10 10
466 2 r. Phoksundo Lake 10 10

1985. International Youth Year.
467 **213** 1 r. multicoloured 15 10

214 King Birendra

215 Devi Ghat Hydro-electric Project

1985. King Birendra's 41st Birthday.
468 **214** 50 p. multicoloured 10 10

1985.
469 **215** 2 r. multicoloured 10 10

216 Emblem

217 Royal Crown

1986. 25th Anniv of Panchayat System (partyless government).
470 **216** 4 r. multicoloured 50 40

1986.
471 – 5 p. brown and deep brown . . 10 10
472 – 10 p. blue 10 10
474 – 50 p. blue 10 10
476 **217** 1 r. brown and ochre . . . 15 10
DESIGNS: 5, 50 p. Pashupati Temple; 10 p. Mayadevi Temple of Lumbini (Buddha's birthplace).

218 Pharping Hydro-electric Station

1986. 75th Anniv of Pharping Hydro-electric Power Station.
480 **218** 15 p. multicoloured 10 10

219 Emblem and Map

1986. 25th Anniv of Asian Productivity Organization.
481 **219** 1 r. multicoloured 15 10

220 Mt. Pumori, Himalayas

221 King Birendra

1986. Tourism. Multicoloured.
482 60 p. "Budhanilkantha" (sculpture of reclining Vishnu), Katmandu Valley (38 × 22 mm) 10 10
483 8 r. Type **220** 15 15

1986. King Birendra's 42nd Birthday.
484 **221** 1 r. multicoloured 10 10

222 I.P.Y. Emblem

223 National Flag and Council Emblem

1986. International Peace Year.
485 **222** 10 r. multicoloured 25 25

1987. 10th Anniv of National Social Service Co-ordination Council.
486 **223** 1 r. multicoloured 10 10

224 Emblem and Forest

1987. 1st Nepal Scout Jamboree, Katmandu.
487 **224** 1 r. brown, orange & bl . . 10 10

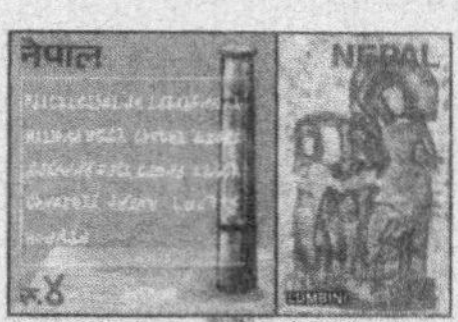

225 Ashokan Pillar and Maya Devi

1987. Lumbini (Buddha's Birthplace) Development Project.
488 **225** 4 r. multicoloured 40 30

226 Emblem

227 Emblem

1987. 3rd South Asian Association for Regional Co-operation Summit, Katmandu.
489 **226** 60 p. gold and red 10 10

1987. 25th Anniv of Rastriya Samachar Samiti (news service).
490 **227** 4 r. purple, blue & red . . 10 10

228 Kashthamandap, Katmandu

229 Gyawali

1987.
491 **228** 25 p. multicoloured 10 10

1987. 89th Birth Anniv of Surya Bikram Gyawali.
492 **229** 60 p. multicoloured 10 10

230 Emblem

231 King Birendra

1987. International Year of Shelter for the Homeless.
493 **230** 5 r. multicoloured 10 10

1987. King Birendra's 43rd Birthday.
494 **231** 25 p. multicoloured 10 10

232 Mt. Kanjiroba

1987.
495 **232** 10 r. multicoloured 25 25

233 Crown Prince Dipendra

1988. Crown Prince Dipendra's 17th Birthday.
496 **233** 1 r. multicoloured 10 10

234 Baby in Incubator

1988. 25th Anniv of Kanti Children's Hospital, Katmandu.
497 **234** 60 p. multicoloured 10 10

235 Swamp Deer

236 Laxmi, Goddess of Wealth

1988. 12th Anniv of Royal Shukla Phanta Wildlife Reserve.

498 **235** 60 p. multicoloured 20 10

1988. 50th Anniv of Nepal Bank Ltd.

499 **236** 2 r. multicoloured 10 10

237 Queen Mother

238 Hands protecting Blood Droplet

1988. 60th Birthday of Queen Mother.

500 **237** 5 r. multicoloured 15 15

1988. 25th Anniv of Nepal Red Cross Society.

501 **238** 1 r. red and brown 10 10

239 Temple and Statue

1988. Temple of Goddess Bindhyabasini, Pokhara.

502 **239** 15 p. multicoloured 10 10

240 King Birendra

241 Temple

1988. King Birendra's 44th Birthday.

503 **240** 4 r. multicoloured 10 10

1989. Pashupati Area Development Trust.

504 **241** 1 r. multicoloured 10 10

242 Emblem

243 S.A.A.R.C. Emblem

1989. 10th Anniv of Asia-Pacific Telecommunity.

505 **242** 4 r. green, black & violet . 15 15

1989. South Asian Association for Regional Co-operation Year against Drug Abuse and Trafficking.

506 **243** 60 p. multicoloured 10 10

244 King Birendra

245 Child Survival Measures

1989. King Birendra's 45th Birthday.

507 **244** 2 r. multicoloured 20 10

1989. Child Survival Campaign.

508 **245** 1 r. multicoloured 10 10

246 Lake Rara

247 Mt. Amadablam

1989. Rara National Park.

509 **246** 4 r. multicoloured 15 15

1989.

510 **247** 5 r. multicoloured 20 20

248 Crown Prince Dipendra

249 Temple of Manakamana, Gorkha

1989. Crown Prince Dipendra's Coming-of-Age.

511 **248** 1 r. multicoloured 10 10

1990.

512 **249** 60 p. black and violet . . . 10 10

250 Emblem and Children

251 Emblem

1990. 25th Anniv of Nepal Children's Organization.

513 **250** 1 r. multicoloured 10 10

1990. Centenary of Bir Hospital.

514 **251** 60 p. red, blue and yellow . 10 10

252 Emblem

253 Goddess and Bageshwori Temple, Nepalgunj

1990. 20th Anniv of Asian–Pacific Postal Training Centre, Bangkok.

515 **252** 4 r. multicoloured 30 15

1990. Tourism. Multicoloured.

516 1 r. Type **253** 10 10

517 5 r. Mt. Saipal (36 × 27 mm) . . 35 25

254 Leisure Activities

1990. South Asian Association for Regional Co-operation Girls' Year.

518 **254** 4 r. 60 multicoloured . . . 35 20

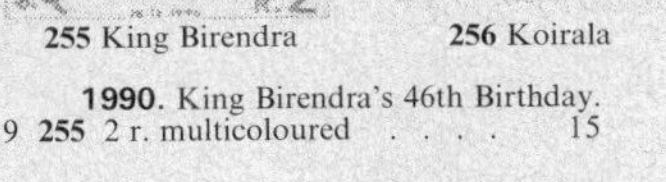

255 King Birendra

256 Koirala

1990. King Birendra's 46th Birthday.

519 **255** 2 r. multicoloured 15 10

1990. 76th Birth Anniv of Bisweswar Prasad Koirala (Prime Minister, 1959–60).

520 **256** 60 p. black, orange and red 10 10

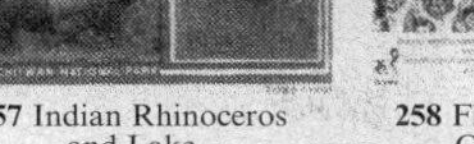

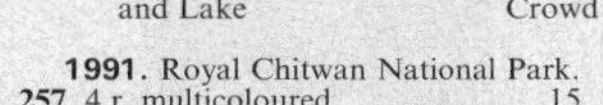

257 Indian Rhinoceros and Lake

258 Flower and Crowd

1991. Royal Chitwan National Park.

521 **257** 4 r. multicoloured 15 15

1991. 1st Anniv of Abrogation of Ban on Political Parties.

522 **258** 1 r. multicoloured 10 10

259 Official and Villagers

260 Federation and Jubilee Emblems

1991. National Population Census.

523 **259** 60 p. multicoloured 10 10

1991. 25th Anniv of Federation of Nepalese Chambers of Commerce and Industry.

524 **260** 3 r. multicoloured 15 15

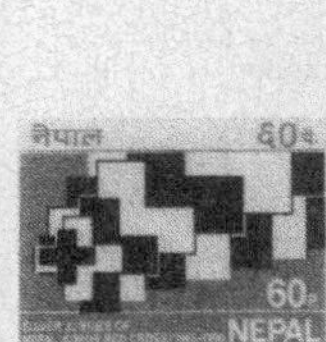

261 Crosses

262 Delegates

1991. 25th Anniv (1990) of Nepal Junior Red Cross.

525 **261** 60 p. red and grey 10 10

1991. 1st Session of Revived Parliament.

526 **262** 1 r. multicoloured 10 10

263 King Birendra making Speech

264 Rama and Janaki (statues) and Vivaha Mandap

1991. Constitution Day.

527 **263** 50 p. multicoloured 10 10

1991. 5th Anniv of Rebuilt Vivaha Mandap Pavilion, Janaki Temple.

528 **264** 1 r. multicoloured 10 10

265 Mt. Kumbhakarna

266 King Birendra

1991. Tourism.

529 **265** 4 r. 60 multicoloured . . . 15 15

1991. King Birendra's 47th Birthday.

530 **266** 8 r. multicoloured 15 15

267 Houses

268 Glass magnifying Society Emblem

1991. South Asian Association for Regional Co-operation Year of Shelter.

531 **267** 9 r. multicoloured 25 25

1992. 25th Anniv (1991) of Nepal Philatelic Society.

532 **268** 4 r. multicoloured 10 10

269 Rainbow over River and Trees

1992. Environmental Protection.

533 **269** 60 p. multicoloured 10 10

270 Nutrition, Education and Health Care

1992. Rights of the Child.

534 **270** 1 r. multicoloured 10 10

271 Thakurdwara Temple, Bardiya

272 Bank Emblem

1992. Temples. Multicoloured.

535 75 p. Type **271** (postage) . . . 10 10

536 1 r. Namo Buddha Temple, Kavre 10 10

537 2 r. Narijhowa Temple, Mustang 10 10

538 11 r. Dantakali Temple, Bijayapur (air) 20 20

1992. 25th Anniv of Agricultural Development Bank.

539 **272** 40 p. brown and green . . 10 10

273 Pin-tailed Green Pigeon

1992. Birds. Multicoloured.

540 1 r. Type **273** 10 10

541 3 r. Bohemian waxwing 15 10

542 25 r. Rufous-tailed desert (inscr "Finch") lark 60 50

274 King Birendra exchanging Swords with Goddess Sree Bhadrakali

275 Pandit Kulchandra Gautam

1992. King Birendra's 48th Birthday.

543 **274** 7 r. multicoloured 20 20

1992. Poets. Multicoloured, frame colour given in brackets.

544 1 r. Type **275** 10 10

545 1 r. Chittadhar Hridaya (drab) 10 10

546 1 r. Vidyapati (stone) 10 10

547 1 r. Teongsi Sirijunga (grey) . . 10 10

276 Shooting and Marathon

277 Golden Mahseer

1992. Olympic Games, Barcelona.

548 **276** 25 r. multicoloured 50 50

1993. Fishes. Multicoloured.

549 25 p. Type **277** 15 10

550 1 r. Marinka 15 10

551 5 r. Indian eel 40 20

552 10 r. False loach 85 45

278 Antibodies attacking Globe

279 Tanka Prasad Acharya (Prime Minister, 1956–57)

1993. World AIDS Day.
554 **278** 1 r. multicoloured 10 10

1993. Death Anniversaries. Multicoloured.
555 25 p. Type **279** (1st anniv) . . . 10 10
556 1 r. Sungdare Sherpa (mountaineer) (4th anniv) . . 10 10
557 7 r. Siddhi Charan Shrestha (poet) (1st anniv) 20 10
558 15 r. Falgunanda (religious leader) (44th anniv) 30 20

280 Bagh Bairab Temple, Kirtipur

1993. Holy Places. Multicoloured.
559 1 r. 50 Halesi Mahadev cave (hiding place of Shiva), Khotang 10 10
560 5 r. Devghat (gods' bathing place), Tanahun 10 10
561 8 r. Type **280** 20 15

281 Tushahiti Fountain, Sundari Chowk, Patan

282 King Birendra

1993. Tourism. Multicoloured.
562 5 r. Type **281** 10 10
563 8 r. White-water rafting 20 10

1993. King Birendra's 49th Birthday.
564 **282** 10 r. multicoloured 25 20

283 Monument

284 Mt. Everest

1994.
565 **283** 20 p. brown 10 10
566 – 25 p. red 10 10
567 – 30 p. green 10 10
568 **284** 1 r. multicoloured 10 10
569 – 5 r. multicoloured 20 10
DESIGNS—20 × 22 mm: 25 p. State arms. 22 × 20 mm: 30 p. Lumbini. 25 × 15 mm: 5 r. Map of Nepal, crown and state arms and flag.

285 Pasang Sherpa

1994. 1st Death Anniv of Pasang Sherpa (mountaineer).
570 **285** 10 r. multicoloured 25 20

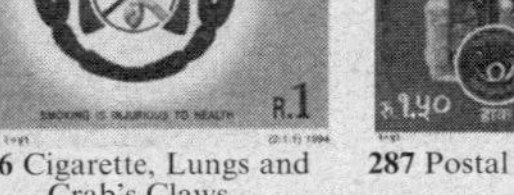
286 Cigarette, Lungs and Crab's Claws

287 Postal Delivery

1994. Anti-smoking Campaign.
571 **286** 1 r. multicoloured 10 10

1994.
572 **287** 1 r. 50 multicoloured . . . 10 10

288 Khuda

1994. Weapons. Multicoloured.
573 5 r. Kukris (three swords and two scabbards) 15 10
574 5 r. Type **288** 15 10
575 5 r. Dhaal (swords and shield) . 15 10
576 5 r. Katari (two daggers) . . . 15 10

289 Workers and Emblem

1994. 75th Anniv of I.L.O.
577 **289** 15 r. gold, blue & ultram . 30 25

290 Landscape

1994. World Food Day.
578 **290** 25 r. multicoloured 50 40

291 "Dendrobium densiflorum"

292 Family

1994. Orchids. Multicoloured.
579 10 r. Type **291** 25 15
580 10 r. "Coelogyne flaccida" . . 25 15
581 10 r. "Cymbidium devonianum" 25 15
582 10 r. "Coelogyne corymbosa" . . 25 15

1994. International Year of the Family.
583 **292** 9 r. emerald, green and red . 20 15

293 Emblem and Airplane

294 "Russula nepalensis"

1994. 50th Anniv of I.C.A.O.
584 **293** 11 r. blue, gold and deep blue 20 15

1994. Fungi. Multicoloured.
585 7 r. Type **294** 35 10
586 7 r. Morels ("Morchella conica") 35 10
587 7 r. Caesar's mushroom ("Amanita caesarea") . . . 35 10
588 7 r. "Cordyceps sinensis" . . . 35 10

295 Dharanidhar Koirala (poet)

1994. Celebrities. Multicoloured.
589 1 r. Type **295** 10 10
590 2 r. Narayan Gopal Guruwacharya (singer) . . . 10 10
591 6 r. Bahadur Shah (vert) . . . 10 10
592 7 r. Balaguru Shadananda . . . 15 10

296 King Birendra, Flag, Map and Crown

1994. King Birendra's 50th Birthday (1st issue).
593 **296** 9 r. multicoloured 20 15
See also No. 621.

297 Lake Tilicho, Manang

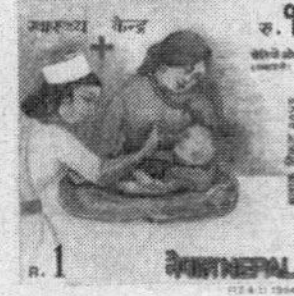
298 Health Care

1994. Tourism. Multicoloured.
594 9 r. Type **297** 20 15
595 11 r. Taleju Temple, Katmandu (vert) 20 15

1994. Children's Activities. Multicoloured.
596 1 r. Type **298** 10 10
597 1 r. Classroom 10 10
598 1 r. Playground equipment . . 10 10
599 1 r. Stamp collecting 10 10

299 Singhaduarbar

300 Crab on Lungs

1995.
600 **299** 10 p. green 10 10
601 – 50 p. blue 10 10
DESIGN—VERT: 50 p. Pashupati.

1995. Anti-cancer Campaign.
602 **300** 2 r. multicoloured 10 10

301 Chandra Man Singh Maskey (artist)

302 Bhakti Thapa (soldier)

1995. Celebrities. Multicoloured.
603 3 r. Type **301** 10 10
604 3 r. Parijat (writer) 10 10
605 3 r. Bhim Nidhi Tiwari (writer) . 10 10
606 3 r. Yuddha Prasad Mishra (writer) 10 10

1995. Celebrities. Multicoloured.
607 15 p. Type **302** 10 10
608 1 r. Madan Bhandari (politician) 10 10
609 4 r. Prakash Raj Kaphley (human rights activist) 10 10

303 Gaur ("Bos gaurus")

1995. "Singapore '95" International Stamp Exhibition. Mammals. Multicoloured.
610 10 r. Type **303** 20 10
611 10 r. Lynx ("Felis lynx") . . . 20 10
612 10 r. Assam macaque ("Macaca assamensis") 20 10
613 10 r. Striped hyena ("Hyaena hyaena") 20 10

304 Anniversary Emblem

1995. 50th Anniv of F.A.O.
614 **304** 7 r. multicoloured 15 10

305 Figures around Emblem

306 Bhimeswor Temple, Dolakha

1995. 50th Anniv of U.N.O.
615 **305** 50 r. multicoloured . . . 95 35

1995. Tourism. Multicoloured.
616 1 r. Type **306** 10 10
617 5 r. Ugra Tara Temple, Dadeldhura (horiz) 10 10
618 7 r. Mt. Nampa (horiz) 15 10
619 18 r. Nrity Aswora (traditional Pauba painting) (27 × 39 mm) . 35 10
620 20 r. Lumbini (Buddha's birthplace) (28 × 28 mm) . . 40 15

307 King Birendra

309 King Birendra

308 Anniversary Emblem

1995. King Birendra's 50th Birthday (1994) (2nd issue).
621 **307** 1 r. multicoloured 10 10

1995. 10th Anniv of South Asian Association for Regional Co-operation.
622 **308** 10 r. multicoloured 20 10

1995. King Birendra's 51st Birthday.
623 **309** 12 r. multicoloured . . . 25 10

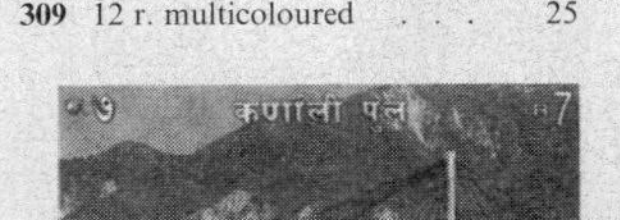

310 Karnali Bridge

1996.
624 **310** 7 r. multicoloured 15 10

311 State Arms

312 Kaji Kalu Pande (soldier and royal adviser)

1996.
625 **311** 25 p. red 10 10

1996. Political Figures. Multicoloured.
626 75 p. Type **312** 10 10
627 1 r. Pushpa Lal Shrestha (Nepal Communist Party General-Secretary) 10 10
628 5 r. Suvarna Shamsher Rana (founder of Nepal Democratic Congress Party) 10 10

313 Hem Raj Sharma (grammarian) **314** Runner and Track

1996. Writers. Multicoloured.

629		1 r. Type **313**	10	10
630		3 r. Padma Prasad Bhattarai (Sanskrit scholar)	10	10
631		5 r. Bhawani Bhikshu (novelist)	10	10

1996. Olympic Games, Atlanta.

632	**314**	7 r. multicoloured	15	10

315 Kasthamandap, Katmandu **316** Hindu Temple, Arjundhara

1996. Temples.

633	**315**	10 p. red and black	10	10
634		50 p. black and red	10	10
635	–	1 r. red and blue	10	10

DESIGN—VERT: 1 r. Nyata Pola temple, Bhaktapur.

1996. Tourism. Multicoloured.

636		1 r. Type **316**	10	10
637		2 r. Durbar, Nuwakot	10	10
638		8 r. Gaijatra Festival, Bhaktapur	15	10
639		10 r. Lake Beganas, Kaski	20	10

317 Krishna Peacock **318** Ashoka Pillar

1996. Butterflies and Birds. Multicoloured.

640		5 r. Type **317**	10	10
641		5 r. Great Himalayan barbet	10	10
642		5 r. Sarus crane	10	10
643		5 r. Northern jungle queen	10	10

Nos. 640/3 were issued together, se-tenant, forming a composite design.

1996. Centenary of Rediscovery of Ashoka Pillar, Lumbini (birthplace of Buddha).

644	**318**	12 r. multicoloured	25	10

319 King Birendra

1996. King Birendra's 52nd Birthday.

645	**319**	10 r. multicoloured	20	10

320 Mt. Annapurna South and Mt. Annapurna I

1996. The Himalayas.

646		18 r. Type **320**	35	10
647		18 r. Mt. Machhapuchhre and Mt. Annapurna III	35	10
648		18 r. Mt. Annapurna IV and Mt. Annapurna II	35	10

Nos. 646/8 were issued together, se-tenant, forming a composite design.

321 King Birendra before Throne

1997. Silver Jubilee of King Birendra's Accession.

649	**321**	2 r. multicoloured	10	10

322 Mountains and National Flags **323** Postal Emblem

1997. 40th Anniv of Nepal–Japan Diplomatic Relations.

650	**322**	18 r. multicoloured	35	10

1997.

651	**323**	2 r. red and brown	10	10

324 Campaign Emblem

1997. National Tourism Year.

652	**324**	2 r. red and blue	10	10
653	–	10 r. multicoloured	20	10
654	–	18 r. multicoloured	35	10
655	–	20 r. multicoloured	40	10

DESIGNS—HORIZ: 10 r. Upper Mustang mountain peak; 18 r. Rafting, River Sunkoshi. VERT: 20 r. Changunarayan.

325 Chepang Couple **326** National Flags and Handshake

1997. Ethnic Groups. Multicoloured.

656		5 r. Type **325**	10	10
657		5 r. Gurung couple	10	10
658		5 r. Rana Tharu couple	10	10

1997. 50th Anniv of Nepal–United States Diplomatic Relations.

659	**326**	20 r. multicoloured	40	10

327 Riddhi Bahadur Malla (writer) **328** "Jasminum gracile"

1997. Celebrities. Multicoloured.

660		2 r. Type **327**	10	10
661		2 r. Dr. K. I. Singh (politician)	10	10

1997. Flowers. Multicoloured.

662		40 p. Type **328**	10	10
663		1 r. China aster	10	10
664		2 r. "Manglietia insignis"	10	10
665		15 r. "Luculia gratissima"	30	10

329 Dhiki (corn crusher)

1997. Traditional Technology. Multicoloured.

666		5 r. Type **329**	10	10
667		5 r. Janto (mill stone)	10	10
668		5 r. Kol (oil mill) (vert)	10	10
669		5 r. Okhal (implement for pounding rice) (vert)	10	10

330 King Birendra **331** Sunrise, Shree Antudanda, Ilam

1997. King Birendra's 53rd Birthday.

670	**330**	10 r. multicoloured	20	10

1998. Tourism. Multicoloured.

671		p2 r. Type **331**	10	10
672		10 r. Maitidevi Temple, Katmandu	20	10
673		18 r. Great Renunciation Gate, Kapilavastu	35	10
674		20 r. Mt. Cholatse, Solukhumbu (vert)	35	10

332 Ram Prasad Rai (nationalist)

1998. Personalities.

675	**332**	75 p. black and brown	10	10
676	–	1 r. black and mauve	10	10
677	–	2 r. black and green	10	10
678	–	2 r. black and blue	10	10
679	–	5 r. 40 black and red	10	10

DESIGNS: No. 676, Imansing Chemjong (Kiranti language specialist); 677, Tulsi Meher Shrestha (social worker); 678, Maha Pundit Dadhi Ram Marasini (poet); 679, Mahananda Sapkota (educationalist and writer).

333 Match Scenes

1998. World Cup Football Championship, France.

680	**333**	12 r. multicoloured	20	10

334 Ganesh Man Singh

1998. 1st Death Anniv of Ganesh Man Singh (politician).

681	**334**	5 r. multicoloured	10	10

335 World Map and Nepalese Soldiers

1998. 40 Years of Nepalese Army Involvement in United Nations Peace Keeping Missions.

682	**335**	10 r. multicoloured	20	10

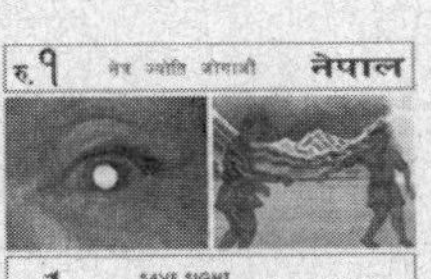

336 Cataract and Guiding of Blind Man

1998. Cataract Awareness Campaign.

683	**336**	1 r. multicoloured	10	10

337 King Cobra

1998. Snakes. Multicoloured.

684		1 r. 70 Type **337**	10	10
685		2 r. Golden tree snake	10	10
686		5 r. Asiatic rock python	10	10
687		10 r. Karan's pit viper	20	10

338 Dove and Profile

1998. 50th Anniv of Universal Declaration of Human Rights.

688	**338**	10 r. multicoloured	20	10

339 Disabled Persons **340** King Birendra

1998. Asian and Pacific Decade of Disabled Persons.

689	**339**	10 r. multicoloured	20	10

1998. King Birendra's 54th Birthday.

690	**340**	2 r. multicoloured	10	10

341 Dam and Power House

1998. River Marsyangdi Hydro-electric Power Station.

691	**341**	12 r. multicoloured	20	10

342 Hospital and Emblem

1999. 25th Anniv of Nepal Eye Hospital.

692	**342**	2 r. multicoloured	10	10

343 Kalika Bhagawati Temple, Baglung

1999. Tourism. Multicoloured.

693		2 r. Type **343**	10	10
694		2 r. Chandan Nath Temple, Jumla (vert)	10	10
695		12 r. Bajrayogini Temple, Sankhu (vert)	20	10
696		15 r. Mt. Everest	25	10
697		15 r. Ashokan Pillar, Lumbini, and English translation of its inscription (39 × 27 mm)	25	10

344 Four-horned Antelope **346** U.P.U. Emblem and Cockerel

345 Him Kanchha (mascot) and Games Emblem

1999. Mammals. Multicoloured.

698		10 r. Type **344**	10	10
699		10 r. Argali (Ovis ammon)	10	10

1999. 8th South Asian Sports Federation Games, Katmandu.

700	**345**	10 r. multicoloured	10	10

1999. 125th Anniv of Universal Postal Union.

701	**346**	15 r. multicoloured	25	10

OFFICIAL STAMPS

O **25** Nepalese Arms and Soldiers

काज सरकारी

(O **28**)

1960. (a) Size 30 × 18 mm.

O135	O **25**	2 p. brown	10	10
O136		4 p. green	10	10
O137		6 p. red	10	10
O138		8 p. violet	10	10
O139		12 p. orange	15	15

(b) Size 38 × 27 mm.

O140	O **25**	16 p. brown	20	20
O141		24 p. red	35	25
O142		32 p. purple	35	35
O143		50 p. blue	65	55
O144		1 r. red	1·40	1·25
O145		2 r. orange	2·50	2·25

1960. Optd as Type O **28**.

O146	**27**	1 r. purple	50	

1961. Optd with Type O **28**.

O148	**35**	1 p. red	10	10
O149		2 p. blue	10	10
O150		5 p. brown	10	10
O151	**36**	10 p. purple	10	10
O152		40 p. brown	10	10
O153		75 p. green	15	15
O154	**27**	2 r. red	30	30
O155		5 r. green	80	80

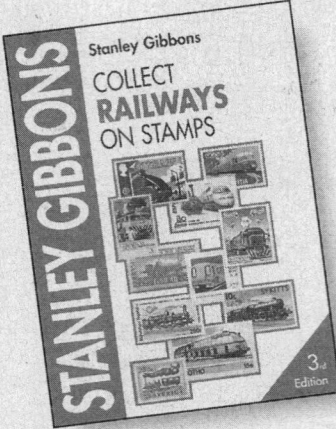

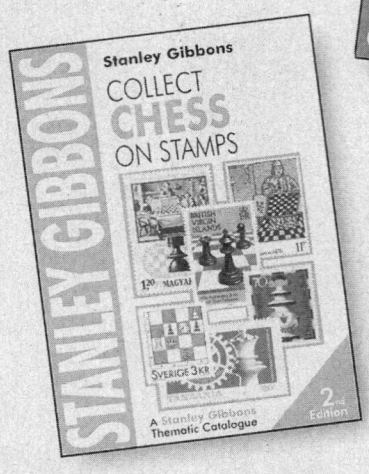

NETHERLANDS Pt. 4

A kingdom in the N.W. of Europe on the North Sea.

100 cents = 1 gulden (florin)

1 3 4
King William III

1852. Imperf.

1	1	5 c. blue	£375	29·00
2		10 c. red	£450	22·00
3b		15 c. orange	£700	£100

1864. Perf.

8	3	5 c. blue	£300	16·00
9		10 c. red	£425	8·25
10		15 c. orange	£1100	90·00

1867.

47	4	5 c. blue	75·00	2·00
30		10 c. red	£130	2·75
46		15 c. brown	£650	30·00
50		20 c. green	£550	21·00
15		25 c. purple	£2250	£100
16		50 c. gold	£2500	£150

5 6

1869.

58	5	½ c. brown	23·00	4·00
53		1 c. black	£200	70·00
59		1 c. green	11·00	2·00
60		1½ c. red	£130	75·00
61		2 c. yellow	50·00	14·50
62		2½ c. mauve	£475	70·00

1872.

91	6	5 c. blue	9·00	15
92		7½ c. brown	38·00	18·00
112		10 c. red	55·00	1·25
113		12½ c. grey	65·00	1·25
95		15 c. brown	£350	5·50
96		20 c. green	£550	5·25
97		22½ c. green	80·00	45·00
98		25 c. lilac	£550	4·00
100		50 c. bistre	£700	11·00
101		1 g. violet	£500	35·00
74	–	2 g. 50 blue and red	£900	£110

No. 74 is similar to Type **6** but larger and with value and country scrolls transposed.

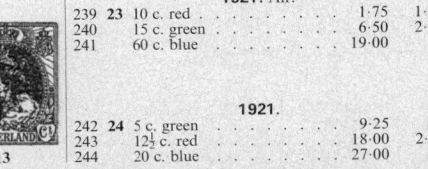

8

9 Queen Wilhelmina

1876.

138d	8	½ c. red	3·00	10
140		1 c. green	2·25	10
143		2 c. yellow	32·00	2·75
145		2½ c. mauve	14·50	15

1891.

147a	9	3 c. orange	9·25	2·10
148a		5 c. blue	4·00	10
149b		7½ c. brown	17·00	5·50
150b		10 c. red	24·00	1·25
151b		12½ c. grey	24·00	1·60
152a		15 c. brown	55·00	4·75
153b		20 c. green	60·00	3·00
154a		22½ c. green	32·00	11·50
155		25 c. mauve	£110	4·50
156a		50 c. bistre	£500	16·00
159	–	50 c. brown and green	75·00	9·25
157	9	1 g. violet	£550	75·00
160	–	1 g. green and brown	£180	18·00
161	–	2 g. 50 blue and red	£425	£130
165	–	5 g. red and green	£750	£400

Nos. 159, 160, 161 and 165 are as Type **9** but larger and with value and country scrolls transposed.

11 12 13

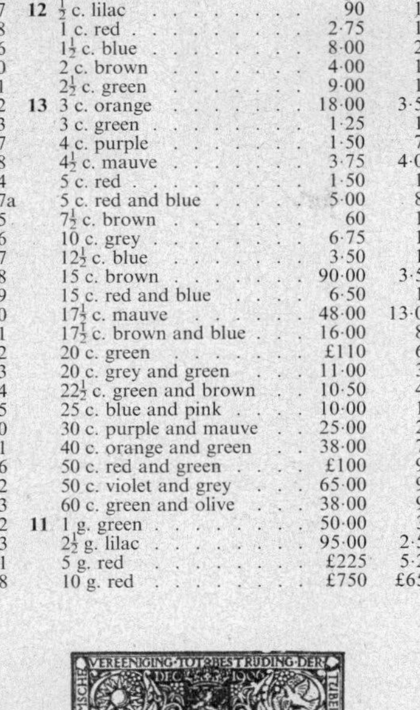

1898. Nos. 174 and 176 also exist imperf.

167	12	½ c. lilac	90	15
168		1 c. red	2·75	10
226		1½ c. blue	8·00	25
170		2 c. brown	4·00	10
171		2½ c. green	9·00	10
172	13	3 c. orange	18·00	3·50
173		3 c. green	1·25	10
227		4 c. purple	1·50	70
228		4½ c. mauve	3·75	4·00
174		5 c. red	1·50	10
187a		5 c. red and blue	5·00	80
175		7½ c. brown	60	10
176		10 c. grey	6·75	10
177		12½ c. blue	3·50	15
178		15 c. brown	90·00	3·50
179		15 c. red and blue	6·50	10
180		17½ c. mauve	48·00	13·00
181		17½ c. brown and blue	16·00	85
182		20 c. green	£110	65
183		20 c. grey and green	11·00	30
184		22½ c. green and brown	10·50	40
185		25 c. blue and pink	10·00	10
230		30 c. purple and mauve	25·00	20
231		40 c. orange and green	38·00	75
186		50 c. red and green	£100	90
232		50 c. violet and grey	65·00	95
233		60 c. green and olive	38·00	90
202	11	1 g. green	50·00	30
203		2½ g. lilac	95·00	2·50
201		5 g. red	£225	5·25
198		10 g. red	£750	£650

14

1906. Society for the Prevention of Tuberculosis.

208	14	1 c. (+ 1 c.) red	14·50	9·00
209		3 c. (+ 3 c.) green	27·00	22·00
210		5 c. (+ 5 c.) violet	27·00	13·00

15 Admiral M. A. de Ruyter

16 William I

1907. Birth Tercentenary of Admiral de Ruyter.

211	15	½ c. blue	1·75	1·40
212		1 c. red	3·50	2·25
213		2½ c. red	7·50	2·25

1913. Independence Centenary.

214	16	2½ c. green on green	60	50
215	–	3 c. yellow on cream	90	90
216	–	5 c. red on buff	90	40
217	–	10 c. grey	3·50	2·00
218	16	12½ c. blue on blue	2·75	1·50
219	–	20 c. brown	13·00	11·00
220	–	25 c. blue	13·50	8·00
221	–	50 c. green	32·00	27·00
222	16	1 g. red	48·00	20·00
223	–	2½ g. lilac	£120	48·00
224	–	5 g. yellow on cream	£275	40·00
225	–	10 g. orange	£750	£750

DESIGNS: 3 c., 20 c., 2½ g. William II; 5 c., 25 c., 5 g. William III; 10 c., 50 c., 10 g. Queen Wilhelmina.

1919. Surch **Veertig Cent** (40 c.) or **Zestig Cent** (60 c.).

234	13	40 c. on 30 c. purple & mve	25·00	3·50
235		60 c. on 30 c. purple & mve	25·00	3·50

1920. Surch in figures.

238	13	4 c. on 4½ c. mauve	4·50	1·90
236	11	2.50 on 10 g. red	£150	£120
237	–	2.50 on 10 g. red (225)	£150	95·00

23

24

1921. Air.

239	23	10 c. red	1·75	1·25
240		15 c. green	6·50	2·00
241		60 c. blue	19·00	20

1921.

242	24	5 c. green	9·25	15
243		12½ c. red	18·00	2·10
244		20 c. blue	27·00	15

25 Lion in Dutch Garden and Orange Tree (emblematical of Netherlands)

26

27

1923.

248	25	1 c. violet	50	60
249		2 c. orange	5·50	10
250	26	2½ c. green	1·75	70
251	27	4 c. blue	1·25	45

1923. Surch.

252	12	2 c. on 1 c. red	45	20
253		2 c. on 1½ c. blue	45	20
254	13	10 c. on 3 c. green	4·50	15
255		10 c. on 5 c. red	8·50	55
256		10 c. on 12½ c. blue	7·50	55
257a		10 c. on 17½ c. brown & bl	3·00	3·50
258a		10 c. on 22½ c. olive & brn	3·00	3·50

30

31

1923. 25th Anniv of Queen's Accession.

259a	31	2 c. green	15	10
260a	30	5 c. green	25	10
261a	31	7½ c. red	40	10
262b		10 c. red	30	10
263		20 c. blue	3·75	55
264		25 c. yellow	5·50	90
265b		35 c. orange	5·50	2·50
266a		50 c. black	16·00	20
267	30	1 g. red	32·00	7·50
268		2½ g. black	£225	£200
269		5 g. blue	£200	£175

1923. Surch **DIENST ZEGEL PORTEN AAN TEEKEN RECHT** and value.

270	13	10 c. on 3 c. green	90	1·00
271		1 g. on 17½ c. brown & blue	70·00	17·00

33

1923. Culture Fund.

272	33	2 c. + 5 c. blue on pink	19·00	18·00
273	–	10 c. + 5 c. red on pink	19·00	18·00

DESIGN: 10 c. Two women.

35 Carrier Pigeon

36 Queen Wilhelmina

1924.

330	35	½ c. grey	40	25
423		1 c. red	10	10
332		1½ c. mauve	20	10
424a		1½ c. grey	10	10
425		2 c. orange	10	10
426a		2½ c. green	70	20
427		3 c. green	10	10
427a		4 c. blue	10	10
428	36	5 c. green	15	10
429		6 c. brown	15	10
279		7½ c. yellow	40	10
313		7½ c. violet	2·75	10
314		7½ c. red	20	10
279c		9 c. red and black	1·75	1·60
281		10 c. red	1·40	10
317		10 c. blue	2·50	10
282		12½ c. red	1·75	35
431		12½ c. blue	30	10
320		15 c. blue	7·25	15
432		15 c. yellow	1·60	10
433		20 c. blue	7·50	10
434		21 c. brown	26·00	90
323		22½ c. brown	7·50	3·00
434a		22½ c. orange	15·00	18·00
435		25 c. green	4·50	10
346		27½ c. grey	4·50	95
437		30 c. violet	10·00	10
286c		35 c. brown	35·00	6·75
437a		40 c. brown	10·00	15
329		50 c. green	5·50	15
289		60 c. violet	32·00	85
437c		60 c. black	29·00	90
301		1 g. blue (23 × 29 mm)	9·25	30
302		2½ g. red (23 × 29 mm)	95·00	4·50
303		5 g. black (23 × 29 mm)	£180	2·75

For further stamps in Type **35**, see Nos. 546/57.

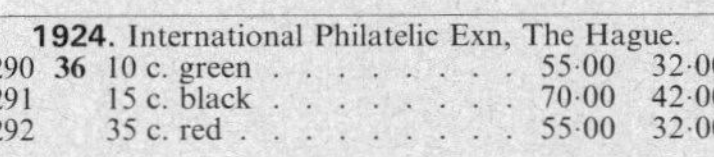

1924. International Philatelic Exn, The Hague.

290	36	10 c. green	55·00	32·00
291		15 c. black	70·00	42·00
292		35 c. red	55·00	32·00

37

38

39

1924. Dutch Lifeboat Centenary.

293	37	2 c. brown	7·50	2·75
294	38	10 c. brown on yellow	13·00	13·00

1924. Child Welfare.

295	39	2 c. + 2 c. green	2·50	1·60
296		7½ c. + 3½ c. brown	11·50	5·75
297		10 c. + 2½ c. red	8·00	1·50

40 Arms of South Holland

46 Queen Wilhelmina

47 Red Cross Allegory

1925. Child Welfare. Arms as T **40**.

298	–	2 c. + 2 c. green & yell	1·40	80
299	–	7½ c. + 3½ c. violet & blue	7·75	4·75
300	40	10 c. + 2½ c. red & yellow	7·50	65

ARMS: 2 c. North Brabant; 7½ c. Gelderland.

See also Nos. 350/3 and 359/62.

1926. Child Welfare. Arms as T **40**.

350		2 c. + 2 c. red and silver	1·25	40
351		5 c. + 3 c. green and blue	4·50	1·25
352		10 c. + 3 c. red and green	6·00	20
353		15 c. + 3 c. yellow & blue	13·50	6·00

ARMS: 2 c. Utrecht; 5 c. Zeeland; 10 c. North Holland; 15 c. Friesland.

1927. 60th Anniv of Dutch Red Cross Society.

354a	46	2 c. + 2 c. red	5·50	2·75
355	–	3 c. + 2 c. green	13·00	8·50
356	–	5 c. + 3 c. blue	1·90	1·10
357a	–	7½ c. + 3½ c. blue	11·00	1·60
358	47	15 c. + 5 c. red & blue	20·00	9·75

PORTRAITS: 2 c. King William III; 3 c. Queen Emma; 5 c. Henry, Prince Consort.

1927. Child Welfare. Arms as T **40**.

359		2 c. + 2 c. red and lilac	1·40	35
360		5 c. + 3 c. green & yellow	4·00	1·40
361		7½ c. + 3½ c. red and black	7·75	30
362		15 c. + 3 c. blue & brown	12·50	5·25

ARMS: 2 c. Drente; 5 c. Groningen; 7½ c. Limburg; 15 c. Overyssel.

48 Sculler

49 Footballer

1928. Olympic Games, Amsterdam.

363	48	1½ c. + 1 c. green	1·75	1·50
364	–	2 c. + 1 c. purple	2·50	1·75
365	49	3 c. + 1 c. green	2·50	2·10
366	–	5 c. + 1 c. blue	2·75	1·50
367	–	7½ c. + 2½ c. orange	2·75	1·60
368	–	10 c. + 2 c. red	7·50	5·75
369	–	15 c. + 2 c. blue	7·50	4·50
370	–	30 c. + 3 c. sepia	25·00	25·00

DESIGNS—HORIZ: 2 c. Fencer. VERT: 5 c. Yachting; 7½ c. Putting the weight; 10 c. Runner; 15 c. Horseman; 30 c. Boxer.

50 Lieut. Koppen

1928. Air.

371	50	40 c. red	45	45
372	–	75 c. green	45	45

DESIGN: 75 c. Van der Hoop.

52 J. P. Minckelers

53 Mercury

1928. Child Welfare.
373 52 1½ c. + 1½ c. violet 50 35
374 – 5 c. + 3 c. green . . . . . 1·75 65
375a – 7½ c. + 2½ c. red . . . . . 3·25 25
376a – 12½ c. + 3½ c. blue . . . . 10·00 7·50
PORTRAITS: 5 c. Boerhaave; 7½ c. H. A. Lorentz; 12½ c. G. Huygens.

1929. Air.
377 53 1½ g. black . . . . 2·50 1·60
378 4½ g. red . . . . 1·50 3·50
379 7½ g. green . . . . 27·00 4·50

1929. Surch 21.
380 36 21 c. on 22½ c. brown . . . . 22·00 1·40

55 "Friendship and Security"
56 Rembrandt and "De Staalmeesters" 

1929. Child Welfare.
381 55 1½ c. + 1½ c. grey . . . . . 2·25 40
382 5 c. + 3 c. green . . . . . 3·50 65
383 6 c. + 4 c. red . . . . . . 2·25 30
384 12½ c. + 3½ c. blue . . . . 14·00 13·00

1930. Rembrandt Society.
385 56 5 c. (+ 5 c.) green . . . . . 7·50 7·50
386 6 c. (+ 5 c.) black . . . . . 5·50 3·50
387 12½ c. (+ 5 c.) blue . . . . 9·25 9·25

57 Spring
58 
59 Queen Wilhelmina 

1930. Child Welfare.
388 57 1½ c. + 1½ c. red . . . . . 1·50 35
389 – 5 c. + 3 c. green . . . . . 2·25 65
390 – 6 c. + 4 c. purple . . . . . 2·25 25
391 – 12½ c. + 3½ c. blue . . . . 17·00 10·00
DESIGNS (allegorical): 5 c. Summer; 6 c. Autumn; 12½ c. Winter.

1931. Gouda Church Restoration Fund.
392 58 1½ c. + 1½ c. green . . . . 18·00 18·00
393 6 c. + 4 c. red . . . . . . 22·00 20·00

1931.
395 – 70 c. blue and red (postage) . 30·00 45
395b – 80 c. green and red . . . . £110 3·25
394 59 36 c. red and blue (air) . . . 14·00 40
DESIGNS: 70 c. Portrait and factory; 80 c. Portrait and shipyard.

61 Mentally Deficient Child
62 Windmill and Dykes, Kinderdijk 
63 Gorse (Spring) 

1931. Child Welfare.
396 – 1½ c. + 1½ c. red and blue . . 1·40 50
397 61 5 c. + 3 c. green & purple . . 2·25 1·25
398 – 6 c. + 4 c. purple & green . . 1·75 40
399 – 12½ c. + 3½ c. blue & red . . 27·00 23·00
DESIGNS: 1½ c. Deaf mute; 6 c. Blind girl; 12½ c. Sick child.

1932. Tourist Propaganda.
400 62 2½ c. + 1½ c. green & black . . 7·50 5·50
401 – 6 c. + 4 c. grey & black . . 11·00 5·50
402 – 7½ c. + 3½ c. red & black . . 38·00 23·00
403 – 12½ c. + 2½ c. blue & black . 35·00 20·00
DESIGNS: 6 c. Aerial view of Town Hall, Zierikzee; 7½ c. Bridges at Schipluiden and Moerdijk; 12½ c. Tulips.

1932. Child Welfare.
404 63 1½ c. + 1½ c. brown & yell . . 2·25 35
405 – 5 c. + 3 c. blue and red . . 3·00 65
406 – 6 c. + 4 c. green & orge . . 2·25 30
407 – 12½ c. + 3½ c. blue & orange . 30·00 22·00
DESIGNS: Child and: 5 c. Cornflower (Summer); 6 c. Sunflower (Autumn); 12½ c. Christmas rose (Winter).

64 Arms of House of Orange
65 Portrait by Goltzius 

1933. 4th Birth Centenary of William I of Orange. T 64 and portraits of William I inscr "1533", as T 65.
408 64 1½ c. black 55 15
409 65 5 c. green . . . . 1·75 20
410 – 6 c. purple . . . . 2·75 10
411 – 12½ c. blue . . . . 17·00 3·75
DESIGNS: 6 c. Portrait by Key; 12½ c. Portrait attributed to Moro.

68 Dove of Peace
69 Projected Monument at Den Helder 
70 "De Hoop" (hospital ship) 

1933. Peace Propaganda.
412 68 12½ c. blue . . . . 9·25 25

1933. Seamen's Fund.
413 69 1½ c. + 1½ c. red . . . . . 3·50 1·90
414 70 5 c. + 3 c. green and red . . 12·00 3·50
415 – 6 c. + 4 c. green . . . . . 17·00 2·75
416 – 12½ c. + 3½ c. blue . . . . 24·00 21·00
DESIGNS: 6 c. Lifeboat; 12½ c. Seaman and Seamen's Home.

73 Pander S.4 Postjager

1933. Air (Special Flights).
417 73 30 c. green 70 75

74 Child and Star of Epiphany
75 Princess Juliana 

1933. Child Welfare.
418 74 1½ c. + 1½ c. orange & grey . 1·50 45
419 5 c. + 3 c. yellow and brown . 2·25 60
420 6 c. + 4 c. gold and green . 2·75 40
421 12½ c. + 3½ c. silver & blue . 26·00 20·00

1934. Crisis stamps.
438 – 5 c. + 4 c. purple . . . . . 13·00 3·50
439 75 6 c. + 5 c. blue . . . . . . 11·00 4·50
DESIGN: 5 c. Queen Wilhelmina.

76 Dutch Warship
77 Dowager Queen Emma 

1934. Tercentenary of Curacao.
440 – 6 c. black . . . . 4·00 10
441 76 12½ c. blue . . . . 26·00 2·75
DESIGN: 6 c. Willemstad Harbour.

1934. Anti-T.B. Fund.
442 77 6 c. + 2 c. blue . . . . . . 13·00 1·60

78 Destitute child
79 H. D. Guyot 

1934. Child Welfare.
443 78 1½ c. + 1½ c. brown . . . . 1·50 50
444 5 c. + 3 c. red . . . . . 2·25 1·25
445 6 c. + 4 c. green . . . . . 2·25 25
446 12½ c. + 3½ c. blue . . . . 27·00 19·00

1935. Cultural and Social Relief Fund.
447 79 1½ c. + 1½ c. red . . . . . 1·90 1·90
448 – 5 c. + 3 c. brown . . . . . 4·50 4·75
449 – 6 c. + 4 c. green . . . . . 5·50 30
450 – 12½ c. + 3½ c. blue . . . . 28·00 5·50
PORTRAITS: 5 c. A. J. M. Diepenbrock; 6 c. F. C. Donders; 12½ c. J. P. Sweelinck.
See also Nos. 456/9, 469/72, 478/82 and 492/6.

80 Aerial Map of Netherlands
81 Child picking Fruit 

1935. Air Fund.
451 80 6 c. + 4 c. brown . . . . . 29·00 11·00

1935. Child Welfare.
452 81 1½ c. + 1½ c. red 60 30
453 5 c. + 3 c. green . . . . . 1·75 1·25
454 6 c. + 4 c. brown . . . . . 1·50 30
455 12½ c. + 3½ c. blue . . . . 24·00 8·00

1936. Cultural and Social Relief Fund. As T 79.
456 1½ c. + 1½ c. sepia . . . . . 85 1·00
457 5 c. + 3 c. green . . . . . . 4·50 3·75
458 6 c. + 4 c. red . . . . . . 3·75 35
459 12½ c. + 3½ c. blue . . . . . 15·00 3·25
PORTRAITS: 1½ c. H. Kamerlingh Onnes; 5 c. Dr. A. S. Talma; 6 c. Mgr. Dr. H. J. A. M. Schaepman; 12½ c. Desiderius Erasmus.

83 Pallas Athene

1936. Tercentenary of Utrecht University Foundation.
460 83 6 c. red . . . . 1·75 20
461 – 12½ c. blue . . . . 5·50 5·25
DESIGN: 12½ c. Gisbertus Voetius.

84 Child Herald
85 Scout Movement 

1936. Child Welfare.
462 84 1½ c. + 1½ c. slate 50 25
463 5 c. + 3 c. green . . . . . 2·50 75
464 6 c. + 4 c. brown . . . . . 2·40 20
465 12½ c. + 3½ c. blue . . . . 16·00 5·00

1937. Scout Jamboree.
466 – 1½ c. black and green . . . 15 10
467 85 6 c. brown and black . . . 1·50 10
468 – 12½ c. black and blue . . . 3·75 1·60
DESIGNS: 1½ c. Scout Tenderfoot Badge; 12½ c. Hermes.

1937. Cultural and Social Relief Fund. Portraits as T 79.
469 1½ c. + 1½ c. sepia 60 60
470 5 c. + 3 c. green . . . . . 5·00 3·75
471 6 c. + 4 c. purple . . . . . 1·10 25
472 12½ c. + 3½ c. blue . . . . 8·25 1·00
PORTRAITS: 1½ c. Jacob Maris; 5 c. F. de la B. Sylvius; 6 c. J. van den Vondel; 12½ c. A. van Leeuwenhoek.

86 "Laughing Child" by Frans Hals
87 Queen Wilhelmina 

1937. Child Welfare.
473 86 1½ c. + 1½ c. black 15 15
474 3 c. + 2 c. green . . . . . 1·75 1·25
475 4 c. + 2 c. red 60 50
476 5 c. + 3 c. green 50 15
477 12½ c. + 3½ c. blue . . . . 7·75 1·50

1938. Cultural and Social Relief Fund. As T 79.
478 1½ c. + 1½ c. sepia 40 70
479 3 c. + 2 c. green 60 35
480 4 c. + 2 c. red . . . . . . 2·00 2·25
481 5 c. + 3 c. green . . . . . 2·50 30
482 12½ c. + 3½ c. blue . . . . 9·00 1·25
PORTRAITS: 1½ c. M. van St. Aldegonde; 3 c. O. G. Heldring; 4 c. Maria Tesselschade; 5 c. Rembrandt; 12½ c. H. Boerhaave.

1938. 40th Anniv of Coronation.
483 87 1½ c. black 20 10
484 5 c. red 25 10
485 12½ c. blue . . . . 3·75 1·40

88 Carrion Crow
89 Boy with Flute 

1938. Air (Special Flights).
486 88 12½ c. blue and grey 75 65
790a 25 c. blue and grey . . . . 4·50 1·90

1938. Child Welfare.
487 89 1½ c. + 1½ c. black 15 20
488 3 c. + 2 c. brown 40 30
489 4 c. + 2 c. green 75 85
490 5 c. + 3 c. red 35 15
491 12½ c. + 3½ c. blue . . . . 9·00 2·00

1939. Cultural and Social Relief Fund. As T 79.
492 1½ c. + 1½ c. brown 60 60
493 2½ c. + 2½ c. green . . . . . 3·75 2·75
494 3 c. + 3 c. red . . . . 80 1·25
495 5 c. + 3 c. green . . . . . . 2·75 30
496 12½ c. + 3½ c. blue . . . . . 6·75 1·00
PORTRAITS: 1½ c. M. Maris; 2½ c. Anton Mauve; 3 c. Gerardus van Swieten; 5 c. Nicolas Beets; 12½ c. Pieter Stuyvesant.

91 St. Willibrord's landing in the Netherlands
92 Replica of Locomotive "De Arend" 
93 Child and Cornucopia 

1939. 12th Death Centenary of St. Willibrord.
497 91 5 c. green . . . . 1·25 10
498 – 12½ c. blue . . . . 8·75 2·40
DESIGN: 12½ c. St. Willibrord as Bishop of Utrecht.

1939. Centenary of Netherlands Railway.
499 92 5 c. green 75 15
500 – 12½ c. blue . . . . 9·50 3·50
DESIGN: 12½ c. Electric railcar.

1939. Child Welfare.
501 93 1½ c. + 1½ c. black 15 20
502 2½ c. + 2½ c. green . . . . 5·00 3·00
503 3 c. + 3 c. red 60 25
504 5 c. + 3 c. green . . . . . 1·00 10
505 12½ c. + 3½ c. blue . . . . 4·25 1·40

94 Queen Wilhelmina
95 Vincent Van Gogh 
98 Girl with Dandelion 

1940.
506 94 5 c. green 10 10
506a 6 c. brown 65 10
507 7½ c. red 10 10
508 10 c. purple 10 10
509 12½ c. blue 10 10
510 15 c. blue 15 10
510a 17½ c. blue . . . . 1·10 80
511 20 c. violet 20 10
512 22½ c. olive . . . . 1·10 95
513 25 c. red 20 10
514 30 c. ochre 45 30
515 40 c. green . . . . 1·40 85
515a 50 c. orange . . . . 7·75 60
515b 60 c. purple . . . . 7·50 2·50

1940. Cultural and Social Relief Fund.
516 95 1½ c. + 1½ c. brown . . . . 2·00 35
517 – 2½ c. + 2½ c. green . . . . 6·50 1·25
518 – 3 c. + 3 c. red . . . . . . 3·75 1·00
519 – 5 c. + 3 c. green . . . . . 8·00 25
520 – 12½ c. + 3½ c. blue . . . . 7·50 95
PORTRAITS: 1½ c. E. J. Potgieter; 3 c. Petrus Camper; 5 c. Jan Steen; 12½ c. Joseph Scaliger.
See also Nos. 558/62 and 656/60.

1940. As No. 519, colour changed. Surch.
521 7½ c. + 2½ c. on 5 c. + 3 c. red 35 25

1940. Surch with large figures and network.
522 35 2½ on 3 c. red . . . . . . 3·00 25
523 5 on 3 c. green 10 20
524 7½ on 3 c. red 10 10
525 10 on 3 c. green 10 15
526 12½ on 3 c. blue 15 30
527 17½ on 3 c. green 75 65
528 20 on 3 c. green 45 15
529 22½ on 3 c. green . . . . 90 1·10
530 25 on 3 c. green 55 30
531 30 on 3 c. green 75 50
532 40 on 3 c. green 90 70
533 50 on 3 c. green . . . . . 1·10 60
534 60 on 3 c. green . . . . . 1·90 1·25
535 70 on 3 c. green . . . . . 4·50 3·00
536 80 on 3 c. green . . . . . 6·25 5·50
537 100 on 3 c. green . . . . 38·00 35·00
538 250 on 3 c. green . . . . 42·00 42·00
539 500 on 3 c. green . . . . 42·00 40·00

1940. Child Welfare.

540 98 1½ c. + 1½ c. violet 90 20
541 2½ c. + 2½ c. olive 2·75 90
542 4 c. + 3 c. blue 3·50 1·10
543 5 c. + 3 c. green 3·75 15
544 7½ c. + 3½ c. red 90 15

1941.

546 35 5 c. green 10 10
547 7½ c. red 10 10
548 10 c. violet 10 10
549 12½ c. blue 10 30
550 15 c. blue 20 35
551 17½ c. red 10 15
552 20 c. violet 15 15
553 22½ c. olive 10 30
554 25 c. lake 15 25
555 30 c. brown 3·75 25
556 40 c. green 15 30
557 50 c. brown 10 15

1941. Cultural and Social Relief Fund. As T **95** but inscr "ZOMERZEGEL 31.12.46".

558 1½ c. + 1½ c. brown 90 30
559 2½ c. + 2½ c. green 90 30
560 4 c. + 3 c. red 90 30
561 5 c. + 3 c. green 90 30
562 7½ c. + 3½ c. purple 90 30

PORTRAITS: 1½ c. Dr. A. Mathijsen; 2½ c. J. Ingenhousz; 4 c. Aagje Deken; 5 c. Johan Bosboom; 7½ c. A. C. W. Staring.

100 "Titus Rembrandt" 101 Legionary

1941. Child Welfare.

563 100 1½ c. + 1½ c. black 25 30
564 2½ c. + 2½ c. olive 25 30
565 4 c. + 3 c. blue 25 30
566 5 c. + 3 c. green 25 30
567 7½ c. + 3½ c. red 25 30

1942. Netherlands Legion Fund.

568 101 7½ c. + 2½ c. red 90 75
569 – 12½ c. + 87½ c. blue 6·75 7·00

DESIGN—HORIZ: 12½ c. Legionary with similar inscription.

1943. 1st European Postal Congress. As T **26** but larger (21 × 27½ mm) surch **EUROPEESCHE P T T VEREENIGING 19 OCTOBER 1942 10 CENT.**

570 26 10 c. on 2½ c. yellow 10 15

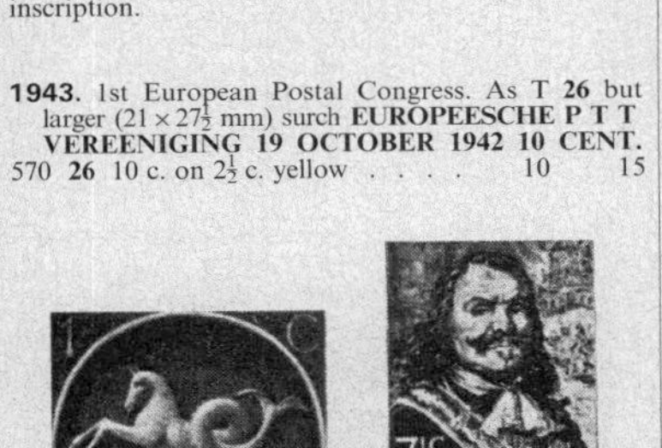

103 Seahorse 104 Michiel A. de Ruyter

1943. Old Germanic Symbols.

571 103 1 c. black 10 10
572 – 1½ c. red 10 10
573 – 2 c. blue 10 10
574 – 2½ c. green 10 10
575 – 3 c. red 10 10
576 – 4 c. brown 10 10
577 – 5 c. olive 10 10

DESIGNS—VERT: 1½ c. Triple crowned tree; 2½ c. Birds in ornamental tree; 4 c. Horse and rider. HORIZ: 2 c. Swans; 3 c. Trees and serpentine roots; 5 c. Prancing horses.

1943. Dutch Naval Heroes.

578 104 7½ c. red 10 10
579 – 10 c. green 10 10
580 – 12½ c. blue 10 15
581 – 15 c. violet 15 15
582 – 17½ c. grey 10 10
583 – 20 c. brown 10 10
584 – 22½ c. red 10 20
585 – 25 c. purple 50 50
586 – 30 c. blue 10 10
587 – 40 c. grey 10 15

PORTRAITS: 10 c. Johan Evertsen; 12½ c. Maarten H. Tromp; 15 c. Piet Hein; 17½ c. Wilhelm Joseph van Gent; 20 c. Witte de With; 22½ c. Cornelis Evertsen; 25 c. Tjerk Hiddes de Fries; 30 c. Cornelis Tromp; 40 c. Cornelis Evertsen the younger.

105 Mail Cart

106 Child and Doll's House

1943. Stamp Day.

589 105 7½ c. + 7½ c. red 10 10

1944. Child Welfare and Winter Help Funds. Inscr "WINTERHULP" (1½ c. and 7½ c.) or "VOLKSDIENST" (others).

590 106 1½ c. + 3½ c. black 10 20
591 – 4 c. + 3½ c. brown 10 20
592 – 5 c. + 5 c. green 10 20
593 – 7½ c. + 7½ c. red 10 20
594 – 10 c. + 40 c. blue 10 20

DESIGNS: 4 c. Mother and child; 5 c., 10 c. Mother and children; 7½ c. Child and wheatsheaf.

107 Infantryman 111 Queen Wilhelmina

1944.

595 107 1½ c. black 10 10
596 – 2½ c. green 10 10
597 – 3 c. brown 10 10
598 – 5 c. blue 10 10
599 111 7½ c. red 10 10
600 10 c. orange 10 10
601 12½ c. blue 10 10
602 15 c. red 1·10 1·10
603 17½ c. green 1·00 1·10
604 20 c. violet 25 20
605 22½ c. red 75 90
606 25 c. brown 1·50 1·50
607 30 c. green 20 15
608 40 c. purple 2·00 2·00
609 50 c. mauve 1·10 90

DESIGNS—HORIZ: 2½ c. "Nieuw Amsterdam" (liner); 3 c. Airman. VERT: 5 c. "De Ruyter" (cruiser).

The above set was originally for use on Netherlands warships serving with the Allied Fleet, and was used after liberation in the Netherlands.

112 Lion and Dragon 113

1945. Liberation.

610 112 7½ c. orange 10 10

1945. Child Welfare.

611 113 1½ c. + 2½ c. grey 30 25
612 2½ c. + 3½ c. green 30 25
613 5 c. + 5 c. brown 30 25
614 7½ c. + 4½ c. red 30 25
615 12½ c. + 5½ c. blue 30 25

114 Queen Wilhelmina

115 Emblem of Abundance

1946.

616 114 1 g. blue 80 20
617 2½ g. red £140 9·00
618 5 g. green £140 30·00
619 10 g. violet £140 28·00

1946. War Victims' Relief Fund.

620 115 1½ c. + 3½ c. black 50 30
621 2½ c. + 5 c. green 60 60
622 5 c. + 10 c. violet 65 60
623 7½ c. + 15 c. red 45 20
624 12½ c. + 37½ c. blue 95 60

116 Princess Irene

117 Boy on Roundabout

1946. Child Welfare.

625 116 1½ c. + 1½ c. brown 50 50
626 – 2½ c. + 1½ c. green 50 60
627 116 4 c. + 2 c. red 65 65
628 – 5 c. + 2 c. brown 65 65
629 – 7½ c. + 2½ c. red 50 15
630 – 12½ c. + 7½ c. blue 50 65

PORTRAITS: 2½ c., 5 c. Princess Margriet; 7½ c., 12½ c. Princess Beatrix.

1946. Child Welfare.

631 117 2 c. + 2 c. violet 40 40
632 4 c. + 2 c. green 45 50
633 7½ c. + 2½ c. red 45 50
634 10 c. + 5 c. purple 60 15
635 20 c. + 5 c. blue 60 65

118 Numeral

119 Queen Wilhelmina

122 Children

1946.

636 118 1 c. red 10 10
637 2 c. blue 10 10
638 2½ c. orange 6·50 1·75
638a 3 c. brown 10 10
639 4 c. green 20 10
639a 5 c. orange 10 10
639c 6 c. grey 45 10
639d 7 c. red 20 10
639f 8 c. mauve 20 10

1947.

640 119 5 c. green 1·10 10
641 6 c. black 15 10
642 6 c. blue 40 10
643 7½ c. red 15 20
644 10 c. purple 40 10
645 12½ c. red 60 40
646 15 c. violet 6·25 10
647 20 c. blue 7·50 10
648 22½ c. green 70 70
649 25 c. blue 14·50 10
650 30 c. orange 14·50 20
651 35 c. blue 14·50 50
652 40 c. brown 18·00 50
653 – 45 c. blue 22·00 12·50
654 – 50 c. brown 14·50 25
655 – 60 c. red 18·00 2·25

Nos. 653/5 are as Type **119** but have the inscriptions in colour on white ground.

1947. Cultural and Social Relief Fund. As T **95** but inscr "ZOMERZEGEL...13.12.48".

656 2 c. + 2 c. red 70 50
657 4 c. + 2 c. green 1·50 75
658 7½ c. + 2½ c. violet 1·90 85
659 10 c. + 5 c. brown 1·75 15
660 20 c. + 5 c. blue 1·40 85

PORTRAITS: 2 c. H. van Deventer; 4 c. P. C. Hooft; 7½ c. Johan de Witt; 10 c. J. F. van Royen; 20 c. Hugo Grotius.

1947. Child Welfare.

661 122 2 c. + 2 c. brown 20 10
662 – 4 c. + 2 c. green 1·10 60
663 – 7½ c. + 2½ c. brown 1·50 90
664 – 10 c. + 5 c. lake 1·25 10
665 122 20 c. + 5 c. blue 1·50 90

DESIGN: 4 c. to 10 c. Baby.

124 Ridderzaal, The Hague

125 Queen Wilhelmina

1948. Cultural and Social Relief Fund.

666 124 2 c. + 2 c. brown 1·75 40
667 – 6 c. + 4 c. green 2·00 60
668 – 10 c. + 5 c. red 1·60 15
669 – 20 c. + 5 c. blue 2·00 90

BUILDINGS: 6 c. Palace on the Dam; 10 c. Kneuterdijk Palace; 20 c. Nieuwe Kerk, Amsterdam.

1948. Queen Wilhelmina's Golden Jubilee.

670 125 10 c. red 10 10
671 20 c. blue 2·25 2·10

126 Queen Juliana

127 Boy in Canoe

1948. Coronation.

672 126 10 c. brown 1·50 10
673 20 c. blue 2·00 50

1948. Child Welfare.

674 127 2 c. + 2 c. green 15 10
675 – 5 c. + 3 c. green 2·25 80
676 – 6 c. + 4 c. grey 1·40 15
677 – 10 c. + 5 c. red 45 10
678 – 20 c. + 8 c. blue 2·25 1·10

DESIGNS: 5 c. Girl swimming; 6 c. Boy on toboggan; 10 c. Girl on swing; 20 c. Boy skating.

128 Terrace near Beach

1949. Cultural and Social Relief Fund.

679 128 2 c. + 2 c. yell & blue 2·00 20
680 – 5 c. + 3 c. yell & blue 3·50 2·00
681 – 6 c. + 4 c. green 3·00 50
682 – 10 c. + 5 c. yell & blue 3·75 10
683 – 20 c. + 5 c. blue 3·50 2·25

DESIGNS: 5 c. Hikers in cornfield; 6 c. Campers by fire; 10 c. Gathering wheat; 20 c. Yachts.

129 Queen Juliana 130

131 Hands reaching for Sunflower

1949.

684 129 5 c. green 50 10
685 6 c. blue 40 10
686 10 c. orange 30 10
687 12 c. red 1·75 1·75
688 15 c. green 4·50 10
689 20 c. blue 3·75 10
690 25 c. brown 13·00 10
691 30 c. violet 9·25 10
692 35 c. blue 22·00 15
693 40 c. purple 40·00 20
694 45 c. orange 1·75 90
695 45 c. violet 50·00 30
696 50 c. green 10·50 15
697 60 c. brown 15·00 15
697a 75 c. red 75·00 1·25
698 130 1 g. red 3·75 10
699 2½ g. brown £190 2·40
700a 5 g. brown £450 4·00
701 10 g. violet £300 16·00

1949. Red Cross and Indonesian Relief Fund.

702 131 2 c. + 3 c. yellow & grey 90 30
703 6 c. + 4 c. yellow & red 65 40
704 10 c. + 5 c. yellow & bl 3·75 25
705 30 c. + 10 c. yellow & brn 9·50 3·00

132 Posthorns and Globe

133 "Autumn"

1949. 75th Anniv of U.P.U.

706 132 10 c. lake 55 10
707 20 c. blue 9·50 2·75

1949. Child Welfare Fund. Inscr "VOOR HET KIND".

708 133 2 c. + 3 c. brown 20 10
709 – 5 c. + 3 c. red 6·75 2·00
710 – 6 c. + 4 c. green 3·75 30
711 – 10 c. + 5 c. grey 20 10
712 – 20 c. + 7 c. blue 5·50 1·60

DESIGNS: 5 c. "Summer"; 6 c. "Spring"; 10 c. "Winter"; 20 c. "New Year".

134 Resistance Monument

135 Section of Moerdijk Bridge

1950. Cultural and Social Relief Fund. Inscr "ZOMERZEGEL 1950".

713 134 2 c. + 2 c. brown 2·00 1·25
714 – 4 c. + 2 c. green 11·50 11·00
715 – 5 c. + 3 c. grey 9·00 3·25
716 – 6 c. + 4 c. violet 4·50 75
717 135 10 c. + 5 c. slate 5·00 20
718 – 20 c. + 5 c. blue 17·00 14·50

DESIGNS—VERT: 4 c. Sealing dykes; 5 c. Rotterdam skyscraper. HORIZ: 6 c. Harvesting; 20 c. "Overijssel" (canal freighter).

1950. Surch with bold figure **6**.

719 119 6 c. on 7½ c. red 2·25 10

INDEX

Countries can be quickly located by referring to the index at the end of this volume.

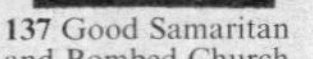

137 Good Samaritan and Bombed Church   138 Janus Dousa

1950. Bombed Churches Rebuilding Fund.
720 137 2 c. + 2 c. olive . . . . . 7·50 1·75
721 5 c. + 3 c. brown . . . . 11·00 11·00
722 6 c. + 4 c. green . . . . 7·50 3·00
723 10 c. + 5 c. red . . . . 18·00 35
724 20 c. + 5 c. blue . . . . . 32·00 30·00

1950. 375th Anniv of Leyden University.
725 138 10 c. olive . . . . . . 5·00 10
726 – 20 c. blue . . . . . . 5·00 1·40
PORTRAIT: 20 c. Jan van Hout.

139 Baby and Bees   140 Bergh Castle

1950. Child Welfare. Inscr "VOOR HET KIND".
727 139 2 c. + 3 c. red 20 10
728 – 5 c. + 3 c. olive . . . . . 10·50 4·50
729 – 6 c. + 4 c. green . . . . . 3·75 60
730 – 10 c. + 5 c. purple 20 10
731 – 20 c. + 7 c. blue . . . . 11·00 10·50
DESIGNS: 5 c. Boy and fowl; 6 c. Girl and birds; 10 c. Boy and fish; 20 c. Girl, butterfly and frog.

1951. Cultural and Social Relief Fund. Castles.
732 – 2 c. + 2 c. violet . . . . . 2·50 1·25
733 140 5 c. + 3 c. red . . . . . 9·00 7·75
734 – 6 c. + 4 c. sepia . . . . . 3·00 60
735 – 10 c. + 5 c. green . . . . . 6·00 25
736 – 20 c. + 5 c. blue . . . . . 8·50 8·50
DESIGNS—HORIZ: 2 c. Hillenraad; 6 c. Hernen. VERT: 10 c. Rechteren; 20 c. Moermond.

141 Girl and Windmill   142 Gull   143 Jan van Riebeeck

1951. Child Welfare.
737 141 2 c. + 3 c. green 30 10
738 – 5 c. + 3 c. blue . . . . . 7·50 4·50
739 – 6 c. + 4 c. brown . . . . 5·50 60
740 – 10 c. + 5 c. lake 20 10
741 – 20 c. + 7 c. blue . . . . 7·50 7·50
DESIGNS: Each shows boy or girl: 5 c. Crane; 6 c. Fishing nets; 10 c. Factory chimneys; 20 c. Flats.

1951. Air.
742 142 15 g. brown £250 £125
743 25 g. black £275 £125

1952. Tercentenary of Landing in South Africa and Van Riebeeck Monument Fund.
744 143 2 c. + 3 c. violet . . . . 5·50 3·75
745 6 c. + 4 c. green . . . . 6·50 4·50
746 10 c. + 5 c. red . . . . 7·50 4·50
747 20 c. + 5 c. blue . . . . 5·50 3·75

144 Miner   145 Wild Rose

1952. 50th Anniv of State Mines, Limburg.
748 144 10 c. blue . . . . 2·50 10

1952. Cultural and Social Relief Fund. Floral designs inscr "ZOMERZEGEL 1952".
749 145 2 c. + 2 c. green & red . . 75 50
750 – 5 c. + 3 c. yellow & green . 2·50 2·50
751 – 6 c. + 4 c. green & red . . 2·25 1·10
752 – 10 c. + 5 c. green & orge . 2·00 15
753 – 20 c. + 5 c. green & blue . 13·00 12·00
FLOWERS: 5 c. Marsh Marigold; 6 c. Tulip; 10 c. Marguerite; 20 c. Cornflower.

146 Radio Masts   147 Boy feeding Goat

1952. Netherlands Stamp Centenary and Centenary of Telegraph Service.
754 – 2 c. violet 90 20
755 146 6 c. red 20 10
756 – 10 c. green 20 10
757 – 20 c. slate . . . . 7·75 2·25
DESIGNS: 2 c. Telegraph poles and steam train; 10 c. Postman delivering letters, 1852; 20 c. Postman delivering letters, 1952.

1952. International Postage Stamp Ex, Utrecht ("ITEP"). Nos. 754/7 but colours changed.
757a – 2 c. brown . . . . 22·00 17·00
757b 146 6 c. blue . . . . 17·00 13·00
757c – 10 c. lake . . . . 17·00 13·00
757d – 20 c. blue . . . . 17·00 13·00
Nos. 757a/d were sold only in sets at the Exhibition at face + 1 g. entrance fee.

1952. Child Welfare.
758 147 2 c. + 3 c. black & olive . . 15 10
759 – 5 c. + 3 c. black & pink . . 3·00 1·25
760 – 6 c. + 4 c. black & green . 2·75 50
761 – 10 c. + 5 c. black & orge . 20 10
762 – 20 c. + 7·5 c. black & blue . 7·75 6·50
DESIGNS: 5 c. Girl riding donkey; 6 c. Girl playing with dog; 10 c. Boy and cat; 20 c. Boy and rabbit.

1953. Flood Relief Fund. Surch **19 53 10 c + 10 WATERSNOOD**.
763 129 10 c. + 10 c. orange 65 10

149 Hyacinth   150 Red Cross

1953. Cultural and Social Relief Fund.
764 149 2 c. + 2 c. green & violet . 60 35
765 – 5 c. + 3 c. green & orge . . 2·10 2·00
766 – 6 c. + 4 c. yellow & green . 2·00 55
767 – 10 c. + 5 c. green & red . . 3·25 15
768 – 20 c. + 5 c. green & blue . 13·50 13·50
FLOWERS: 5 c. African marigold; 6 c. Daffodil; 10 c. Anemone; 20 c. Dutch iris.

1953. Red Cross Fund. Inscr "RODE KRUIS".
769 150 2 c. + 3 c. red and sepia . 90 45
770 – 6 c. + 4 c. red and brown . 3·75 3·50
771 – 7 c. + 5 c. red and olive . . 1·00 50
772 – 10 c. + 5 c. red 60 10
773 – 25 c. + 8 c. red and blue . 8·00 5·50
DESIGNS: 6 c. Man with lamp; 7 c. Rescue worker in flooded area; 10 c. Nurse giving blood transfusion; 25 c. Red Cross flags.

151 Queen Juliana   152 Queen Juliana

1953.
775 151 10 c. brown 10 10
776 12 c. turquoise 10 10
777 15 c. red 10 10
777b 18 c. turquoise 20 10
778 20 c. purple 15 10
778b 24 c. olive 40 20
779 25 c. blue 20 10
780a 30 c. orange 40 15
781 35 c. brown 90 10
781a 37 c. turquoise 85 20
782 40 c. slate 35 10
783 45 c. red 40 10
784 50 c. green 35 10
785 60 c. brown 50 10
785a 62 c. red . . . . 3·25 2·75
785b 70 c. blue 60 10
786 75 c. purple 50 10
786a 80 c. violet 75 15
786b 85 c. green . . . . . . 1·40 20
786c 95 c. brown . . . . . . 2·25 25
787 152 1 g. red . . . . 1·75 10
788 2½ g. green . . . . . . 9·25 10
789 5 g. black . . . . . . 3·75 15
790 10 g. blue . . . . 18·00 1·25

153 Girl with Pigeon   154 M. Nijhoff (poet)

1953. Child Welfare. Inscr "VOOR HET KIND".
791 – 2 c. + 3 c. blue & yellow . . 10 10
792 – 5 c. + 3 c. lake & green . . 3·25 2·40
793 153 7 c. + 5 c. brown & blue . 3·25 80
794 – 10 c. + 5 c. lilac & bistre . . 10 10
795 – 25 c. + 8 c. turq & pink . . 11·00 12·00
DESIGNS: 2 c. Girl, bucket and spade; 5 c. Boy and apple; 10 c. Boy and tjalk (sailing boat); 25 c. Girl and tulip.

1954. Cultural and Social Relief Fund.
796 154 2 c. + 3 c. blue . . . . . 1·75 1·75
797 – 5 c. + 3 c. brown . . . . 2·75 1·75
798 – 7 c. + 5 c. red . . . . . 3·75 1·40
799 – 10 c. + 5 c. green . . . . 7·50 15
800 – 25 c. + 8 c. purple . . . . 11·00 11·50
PORTRAITS: 5 c. W. Pijper (composer); 7 c. H. P. Berlage (architect); 10 c. J. Huizinga (historian); 25 c. Vincent van Gogh (painter).

155 St. Boniface   156 Boy and Model Glider

1954. 1200th Anniv of Martyrdom of St. Boniface.
801 155 10 c. blue . . . . 2·75 10

1954. National Aviation Fund.
802 156 2 c. + 2 c. green . . . . . 1·40 90
803 – 10 c. + 4 c. blue . . . . . 3·50 50
PORTRAIT: 10 c. Dr. A. Plesman (aeronautical pioneer).

157 Making Paperchains   158 Queen Juliana

1954. Child Welfare.
804 157 2 c. + 3 c. brown 10 10
805 – 5 c. + 3 c. olive . . . . . 1·75 1·75
806 – 7 c. + 5 c. blue . . . . . 1·50 50
807 – 10 c. + 5 c. red 10 10
808 – 25 c. + 8 c. blue . . . . . 10·00 6·25
DESIGNS—VERT: 5 c. Girl brushing her teeth; 7 c. Boy and toy boat; 10 c. Nurse and child. HORIZ: 25 c. Invalid boy drawing in bed.

1954. Ratification of Statute for the Kingdom.
809 158 10 c. red 80 10

159 Factory, Rotterdam   160 "The Victory of Peace"

1955. Cultural and Social Relief Fund.
810 159 2 c. + 3 c. brown . . . . 1·25 1·25
811 – 5 c. + 3 c. green 55 35
812 – 7 c. + 5 c. red . . . . . 1·25 1·25
813 – 10 c. + 5 c. blue . . . . 2·10 15
814 – 25 c. + 8 c. brown . . . . 12·00 11·00
DESIGNS—HORIZ: 5 c. Post Office, The Hague; 10 c. Town Hall, Hilversum; 25 c. Office Building, The Hague. VERT: 7 c. Stock Exchange, Amsterdam.

1955. 10th Anniv of Liberation.
815 160 10 c. red . . . . 1·60 10

161 Microscope and Emblem of Cancer   162 "Willem van Loon" (D. Dircks)

1955. Queen Wilhelmina Anti-Cancer Fund.
816 161 2 c. + 3 c. black & red . . 60 50
817 5 c. + 3 c. green & red . . 1·60 1·25
818 7 c. + 5 c. purple & red . . 1·50 70
819 10 c. + 5 c. blue and red . . 85 10
820 25 c. + 8 c. olive & red . . 7·50 6·50

1955. Child Welfare Fund.
821 162 2 c. + 3 c. green 10 10
822 – 5 c. + 3 c. red . . . . . 2·10 1·00
823 – 7 c. + 5 c. brown . . . . 4·00 80
824 – 10 c. + 5 c. blue 10 10
825 – 25 c. + 8 c. lilac . . . . . 9·50 9·00
PORTRAITS: 5 c. "Portrait of a Boy" (J. A. Backer); 7 c. "Portrait of a Girl" (unknown); 10 c. "Philips Huygens" (A. Hanneman); 25 c. "Constantin Huygens" (A. Hanneman).

163 "Farmer"

1956. Cultural and Social Relief Fund and 350th Birth Anniv of Rembrandt. Details from Rembrandt's paintings.
826 163 2 c. + 3 c. slate . . . . . 2·75 2·75
827 – 5 c. + 3 c. olive . . . . . 1·90 1·50
828 – 7 c. + 5 c. brown . . . . 4·50 4·50
829 – 10 c. + 5 c. green . . . . 12·50 25
830 – 25 c. + 8 c. brown . . . . 18·00 18·00
PAINTINGS: 5 c. "Young Tobias with Angel"; 7 c. "Persian wearing Fur Cap"; 10 c. "Old Blind Tobias"; 25 c. Self-portrait 1639.

164 Yacht   165 Amphora   167 "Portrait of a Boy" (Van Scorel)

1956. 16th Olympic Games, Melbourne.
831 164 2 c. + 3 c. black & blue . . 75 75
832 – 5 c. + 3 c. black & yellow . 1·10 1·10
833 165 7 c. + 5 c. black & brown . 1·50 1·25
834 – 10 c. + 5 c. black & grey . 3·00 40
835 – 25 c. + 8 c. black & green . 6·50 6·50
DESIGNS: As Type **164**: 5 c. Runner; 10 c. Hockey player; 25 c. Water polo player.

1956. Europa. As T **110** of Luxembourg.
836 10 c. black and lake . . . . . 1·75 10
837 25 c. black and blue . . . . . 45·00 1·75

1956. Child Welfare Fund. 16th century Dutch Paintings.
838 167 2 c. + 3 c. grey & cream . 10 10
839 – 5 c. + 3 c. olive & cream . 1·25 65
840 – 7 c. + 5 c. purple & cream . 3·50 1·50
841 – 10 c. + 5 c. red & cream . 10 10
842 – 25 c. + 8 c. blue & cream . 7·50 4·25
PAINTINGS: 5 c. "Portrait of a Boy"; 7 c. "Portrait of a Girl"; 10 c. "Portrait of a Girl"; 25 c. "Portrait of Eechie Pieters".

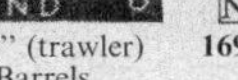

168 "Curacao" (trawler) and Fish Barrels   169 Admiral M. A. de Ruyter

1957. Cultural and Social Relief Fund. Ships.
843 – 4 c. + 3 c. blue . . . . . 1·25 90
844 – 6 c. + 4 c. lilac . . . . . 2·25 1·60
845 – 7 c. + 5 c. red . . . . . . 1·90 1·50
846 168 10 c. + 8 c. green . . . . 4·00 15
847 – 30 c. + 8 c. brown . . . . 7·50 7·00
DESIGNS: 4 c. "Gaasterland" (freighter); 6 c. Coaster; 7 c. "Willem Barendsz" (whale factory ship) and whale; 30 c. "Nieuw Amsterdam" (liner).

1957. 350th Birth Anniv of M. A. de Ruyter.
848 169 10 c. orange 75 10
849 – 30 c. blue . . . . 5·00 1·75
DESIGN: 30 c. De Ruyter's flagship, "De Zeven Provincien".

170 Blood Donors' Emblem   171 "Europa" Star

1957. 90th Anniv of Netherlands Red Cross Society and Red Cross Fund.
850 170 4 c. + 3 c. blue & red . . . 1·10 1·00
851 – 6 c. + 4 c. green & red . . 1·50 1·25
852 – 7 c. + 5 c. red & green . . 1·50 1·25
853 – 10 c. + 8 c. red & ochre . . 1·25 10
854 – 30 c. + 8 c. red & blue . . 2·75 2·75
DESIGNS: 6 c. "J. Henry Dunant" (hospital ship); 7 c. Red Cross; 10 c. Red Cross emblem; 30 c. Red Cross on globe.

1957. Europa.
855 171 10 c. black and blue . . . 65 10
856 30 c. green and blue . . . 7·50 1·75

172 Portrait by B. J. Blommers

173 Walcheren Costume

1957. Child Fund Welfare. 19th/20th Century Paintings by Dutch Masters.
857 **172** 4 c. + 4 c. red 40 10
858 – 6 c. + 4 c. green . . . . . 2·50 2·00
859 – 8 c. + 4 c. sepia . . . . . 3·25 2·00
860 – 12 c. + 9 c. purple 40 10
861 – 30 c. + 9 c. blue . . . . . 8·50 7·50
PORTRAITS: Child paintings by: W. B. Tholen (6 c.); J. Sluyters (8 c.); M. Maris (12 c.); C. Kruseman (30 c.).

1958. Cultural and Social Relief Fund. Provincial Costumes.
862 **173** 4 c. + 4 c. blue 80 60
863 – 6 c. + 4 c. ochre . . . . . 1·50 80
864 – 8 c. + 4 c. red . . . . . . 5·00 1·75
865 – 12 c. + 9 c. brown . . . . 2·00 15
866 – 30 c. + 9 c. lilac . . . . . 7·75 7·50
COSTUMES: 6 c. Marken; 8 c. Scheveningen; 12 c. Friesland; 30 c. Volendam.

1958. Surch **12 C.**
867 **151** 12 c. on 10 c. brown . . . 1·10 10

1958. Europa. As T **119a** of Luxembourg.
868 12 c. blue and red 20 10
869 30 c. red and blue 90 70

176 Girl on Stilts and Boy on Tricycle

177 Cranes

1958. Child Welfare Fund. Children's Games.
870 **176** 4 c. + 4 c. blue 10 10
871 – 6 c. + 4 c. red . . . . . . 2·50 1·75
872 – 8 c. + 4 c. green . . . . . 1·75 1·25
873 – 12 c. + 9 c. red 10 10
874 – 30 c. + 9 c. blue . . . . . 6·25 4·75
DESIGNS: 6 c. Boy and girl on scooter; 8 c. Boys playing leap-frog; 12 c. Boys on roller-skates; 30 c. Girl skipping and boy in toy car.

1959. 10th Anniv of N.A.T.O. As T **123** of Luxembourg (N.A.T.O. emblem).
875 12 c. blue and yellow 10 10
876 30 c. blue and red . . . . . . 1·00 60

1959. Cultural and Social Relief Fund. Prevention of Sea Encroachment.
877 – 4 c. + 4 c. blue on green . 1·40 1·25
878 – 6 c. + 4 c. brown on grey . 90 90
879 – 8 c. + 4 c. violet on blue . 2·25 1·75
880 **177** 12 c. + 9 c. green on yell . 4·00 15
881 – 30 c. + 9 c. black on red . 6·75 6·75
DESIGNS: 4 c. Tugs and caisson; 6 c. Dredger; 8 c. Labourers making fascine mattresses; 30 c. Sand-spouter and scoop.

1959. Europa. As T **123a** of Luxembourg.
882 12 c. red 15 10
883 30 c. green . . . . 3·00 1·90

178 Silhouette of Douglas DC-8 Airliner and World Map

179 Child in Play-pen

1959. 40th Anniv of K.L.M. (Royal Dutch Airlines).
884 **178** 12 c. blue and red 20 10
885 – 30 c. blue and green . . . 2·00 1·25
DESIGN: 30 c. Silhouette of Douglas DC-8 airliner.

1959. Child Welfare Fund.
886 **179** 4 c. + 4 c. blue & brown . 10 10
887 – 6 c. + 4 c. brown and green . . . . 1·75 1·40
888 – 8 c. + 4 c. blue and red . 3·00 1·90
889 – 12 c. + 9 c. red, black and blue 10 10
890 – 30 c. + 9 c. turquoise and yellow . . . . 4·00 4·00
DESIGNS: 6 c. Boy as "Red Indian" with bow and arrow; 8 c. Boy feeding geese; 12 c. Traffic warden escorting children; 30 c. Girl doing homework.

180 Refugee Woman

181 White Water-lily

1960. World Refugee Year.
891 **180** 12 c. + 8 c. purple 25 15
892 30 c. + 10 c. green . . . . 3·50 3·00

1960. Cultural and Social Relief Fund. Flowers.
893 – 4 c. + 4 c. red, green and grey 80 65
894 – 6 c. + 4 c. yellow, green and salmon . . . . 1·50 1·25
895 **181** 8 c. + 4 c. multicoloured . 3·25 2·50
896 – 12 c. + 8 c. red, green and buff . . . . 2·75 20
897 – 30 c. + 10 c. blue, green and yellow . . . . 6·25 6·00
FLOWERS—VERT: 4 c. "The Princess" tulip; 6 c. Gorse; 12 c. Poppy; 30 c. Blue sea-holly.

182 J. van der Kolk

183 Marken Costume

184 Herring Gull

1960. World Mental Health Year.
898 **182** 12 c. red 80 10
899 – 30 c. blue (J. Wier) . . . . 6·75 2·75

1960. Europa. As T **113a** of Norway.
900 12 c. yellow and red 25 10
901 30 c. yellow and blue . . . . . 3·00 2·25

1960. Child Welfare Fund. Costumes. Multicoloured portraits.
902 **183** 4 c. + 4 c. slate 30 10
903 – 6 c. + 4 c. ochre . . . . . 2·50 1·25
904 – 8 c. + 4 c. turquoise . . . 5·25 2·25
905 – 12 c. + 9 c. violet 30 10
906 – 30 c. + 9 c. grey . . . . . 7·50 6·75
DESIGNS: Costumes of: 6 c. Volendam; 8 c. Bunschoten; 12 c. Hindeloopen; 30 c. Huizen.

1961. Cultural and Social Relief Fund. Beach and Meadow Birds.
907 **184** 4 c. + 4 c. slate & yellow . 1·50 1·50
908 – 6 c. + 4 c. sep. & brown . 1·50 1·50
909 – 8 c. + 4 c. brn & olive . . 1·40 1·25
910 – 12 c. + 8 c. blk & blue . . 3·00 25
911 – 30 c. + 10 c. blk & green . 5·50 4·00
BIRDS—HORIZ: 6 c. Oystercatcher; 12 c. Avocet. VERT: 8 c. Curlew; 30 c. Lapwing.

185 Doves

186 St. Nicholas

1961. Europa.
912 **185** 12 c. brown 10 10
913 30 c. turquoise 30 30

1961. Child Welfare.
914 **186** 4 c. + 4 c. red 10 10
915 – 6 c. + 4 c. blue . . . . . 1·25 90
916 – 8 c. + 4 c. bistre . . . . . 1·25 1·25
917 – 12 c. + 9 c. green 10 10
918 – 30 c. + 9 c. orange . . . . 3·50 3·25
DESIGNS: 6 c. Epiphany; 8 c. Palm Sunday; 12 c. Whitsuntide; 30 c. Martinmas.

187 Queen Juliana and Prince Bernhard

188 Detail of "The Repast of the Officers of the St. Jorisdoelen" after Frans Hals

1962. Silver Wedding.
919 **187** 12 c. red 15 10
920 30 c. green . . . . 1·50 60

1962. Cultural, Health and Social Welfare Funds.
921 – 4 c. + 4 c. green . . . . . 1·25 90
922 – 6 c. + 4 c. black 65 65
923 – 8 c. + 4 c. purple . . . . 1·50 1·50
924 – 12 c. + 8 c. bistre . . . . 1·50 25
925 **188** 30 c. + 10 c. blue . . . . 2·00 2·00
DESIGNS—HORIZ: 4 c. Roman cat (sculpture). VERT: 6 c. "Pleuroceras spinatus" (ammonite); 8 c. Pendulum clock (after principle of Huygens); 12 c. Ship's figurehead.

189 Telephone Dial

190 Europa "Tree"

1962. Completion of Netherlands Automatic Telephone System. Inscr "1962".
926 **189** 4 c. red and black 10 10
927 – 12 c. drab and black . . . 55 10
928 – 30 c. ochre, blue & blk . . 2·40 2·00
DESIGNS—VERT: 12 c. Diagram of telephone network. HORIZ: 30 c. Arch and telephone dial.

1962. Europa.
929 **190** 12 c. black, yellow & bis . . 10 10
930 30 c. black, yellow & bl . . 90 60

191 "Polder" Landscape (reclaimed area)

192 Children cooking Meal

1962.
935 – 4 c. deep blue and blue . . 10 10
937 **191** 6 c. deep green & green . . 40 10
938 – 10 c. dp purple & purple . . 10 10
DESIGNS: 4 c. Cooling towers, State mines, Limburg; 10 c. Delta excavation works.

1962. Child Welfare.
940 **192** 4 c. + 4 c. red 10 10
941 – 6 c. + 4 c. bistre 70 55
942 – 8 c. + 4 c. blue . . . . . 1·75 1·50
943 – 12 c. + 9 c. green 10 10
944 – 30 c. + 9 c. lake . . . . . 2·75 2·75
DESIGNS—Children: 6 c. Cycling; 8 c. Watering flowers; 12 c. Feeding poultry; 30 c. Making music.

193 Ears of Wheat

194 "Gallery" Windmill

1963. Freedom from Hunger.
945 **193** 12 c. ochre and blue . . . 10 10
946 30 c. ochre and red . . . . 1·00 75

1963. Cultural, Health and Social Welfare Funds. Windmill types.
947 **194** 4 c. + 4 c. blue . . . . . 1·00 1·00
948 – 6 c. + 4 c. violet . . . . . 1·00 1·00
949 – 8 c. + 4 c. green . . . . . 1·40 1·40
950 – 12 c. + 8 c. brown . . . . 1·75 25
951 – 30 c. + 10 c. red . . . . . 2·40 2·40
WINDMILLS—VERT: 6 c. North Holland polder; 12 c. "Post"; 30 c. "Wip". HORIZ: 8 c. South Holland polder.

195

196 Wayside First Aid Post

1963. Paris Postal Conference Centenary.
952 **195** 30 c. blue, green & blk . . 1·25 1·00

1963. Red Cross Fund and Centenary (8 c.).
953 **196** 4 c. + 4 c. blue and red . . 40 40
954 – 6 c. + 4 c. violet and red . . 25 30
955 – 8 c. + 4 c. red & black . . 90 75
956 – 12 c. + 9 c. brown & red . . 35 15
957 – 30 c. + 9 c. green & red . . 1·60 1·60
DESIGNS: 6 c. "Books" collection-box; 8 c. Crosses; 12 c. "International Aid" (Negro children at meal); 30 c. First aid party tending casualty.

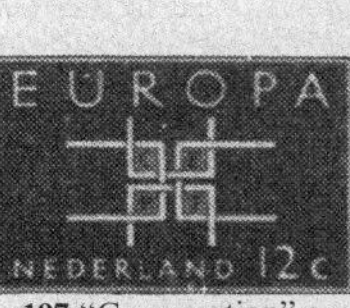

197 "Co-operation"

198 "Auntie Luce sat on a goose ..."

1963. Europa.
958 **197** 12 c. orange and brown . . 10 10
959 30 c. orange and green . . 1·25 1·00

1963. Child Welfare.
960 **198** 4 c. + 4 c. ultra & bl . . . 10 10
961 – 6 c. + 4 c. green & red . . 70 65
962 – 8 c. + 4 c. brown & green . 90 65
963 – 12 c. + 9 c. violet & yell . 10 10
964 – 30 c. + 8 c. blue & pink . . 1·75 1·75
DESIGNS (Nursery rhymes): 6 c. "In the Hague there lives a count..."; 8 c. "One day I passed a puppet's fair..."; 12 c. "Storky, storky, Billy Spoon...."; 30 c. "Ride on a little pram...".

199 William, Prince of Orange, landing at Scheveningen

200 Knights' Hall, The Hague

1963. 150th Anniv of Kingdom of the Netherlands.
965 **199** 4 c. black, bistre & blue . . 10 10
966 5 c. black, red and green . 10 10
967 – 12 c. bistre, blue & black . 10 10
968 – 30 c. red and black 50 50
DESIGNS: 12 c. Triumvirate: Van Hogendorp, Van Limburg, and Van der Duyn van Maasdam; 30 c. William I taking oath of allegiance.

1964. 500th Anniv of 1st States-General Meeting.
969 **200** 12 c. black and olive . . . 15 10

201 Guide Dog for the Blind

1964. Cultural, Health and Social Welfare Funds. Animals.
970 **201** 5 c. + 5 c. red, black and olive 60 50
971 – 8 c. + 5 c. brown, black and red 30 30
972 – 12 c. + 9 c. black, grey and bistre 55 15
973 – 30 c. + 9 c. multicoloured . 85 70
DESIGNS: 8 c. Three red deer; 12 c. Three kittens; 30 c. European bison and calf.

202 University Arms

203 Signal No. 144, Amersfoort Station

1964. 350th Anniv of Groningen University.
974 **202** 12 c. slate 10 10
975 – 30 c. brown 20 15
DESIGN: 30 c. "AG" monogram.

1964. 125th Anniv of Netherlands Railways.
976 **203** 15 c. black and green . . . 20 10
977 – 40 c. black and yellow . . 90 70
DESIGN: 40 c. Class ELD-4 electric train.

204 Bible and Dove

205 Europa "Flower"

1964. 150th Anniv of Netherlands Bible Society.
978 **204** 15 c. brown 10 10

1964. Europa.
979 **205** 15 c. green 15 10
980 20 c. brown 35 25

1964. 20th Anniv of "BENELUX". As T **150a** of Luxembourg, but smaller 35 × 22 mm.
981 15 c. violet and flesh 10 10

206 Young Artist

207 Queen Juliana

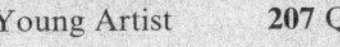

1964. Child Welfare.
982 206 7 c. + 3 c. blue & green . . 40 50
983 – 10 c. + 5 c. red, pink and green 35 40
984 – 15 c. + 10 c. yellow, black and bistre 10 10
985 – 20 c. + 10 c. red, sepia and mauve 45 45
986 – 40 c. + 15 c. green & blue 1·00 70
DESIGNS: 10 c. Ballet-dancing; 15 c. Playing the recorder; 20 c. Masquerading; 40 c. Toy-making.

1964. 10th Anniv of Statute for the Kingdom.
987 207 15 c. green 10 10

208 "Killed in Action" (Waalwijk) and "Destroyed Town" (Rotterdam) (monuments)

209 Medal of Knight (Class IV)

1965. "Resistance" Commemoration.
988 208 7 c. black and red 10 10
989 – 15 c. black and olive 10 10
990 – 40 c. black and red . . . . 1·25 75
MONUMENTS: 15 c. "Docker" (Amsterdam) and "Killed in Action" (Waalwijk); 40 c. "Destroyed Town" (Rotterdam) and "Docker" (Amsterdam).

1965. 150th Anniv of Military William Order.
991 209 1 g. grey . . . . 2·00 80

210 I.T.U. Emblem and "Lines of Communication"

1965. Centenary of I.T.U.
992 210 20 c. blue and drab 20 15
993 40 c. brown and blue . . . 65 50

211 Veere

1965. Cultural, Health and Social Welfare Funds.
994 211 8 c. + 6 c. black & yellow . . 30 45
995 – 10 c. + 6 c. black & turq . . 45 40
996 – 18 c. + 12 c. blk & brn . . 35 15
997 – 20 c. + 10 c. black & blue . . 45 40
998 – 40 c. + 10 c. black & grn . . 55 55
DESIGNS: (Dutch towns): 10 c. Thorn; 18 c. Dordrecht; 20 c. Staveren; 40 c. Medemblik.

212 Europa "Sprig"

1965. Europa.
999 212 18 c. black, red & brn . . 20 10
1000 20 c. black, red & blue . . 30 25

213 Girl's Head

1965. Child Welfare. Multicoloured.
1001 8 c. + 6 c. Type 213 . . . . 10 10
1002 10 c. + 6 c. Ship 50 50
1003 18 c. + 12 c. Boy (vert) . . . 10 10
1004 20 c. + 10 c. Duck-pond . . . 65 60
1005 40 c. + 10 c. Tractor . . . . 1·25 80

214 Marines of 1665 and 1965

215 "Help them to a safe Haven" (Queen Juliana)

1965. Tercentenary of Marine Corps.
1007 214 18 c. blue and red 10 10

1966. Intergovernmental Committee for European Migration (I.C.E.M.) Fund.
1008 215 10 c. + 7 c. yell & blk . . 30 25
1009 40 c. + 20 c. red and blk 30 15

216 Writing Materials

217 Aircraft in Flight

1966. Cultural, Health and Social Welfare Funds. Gysbert Japicx Commem and 200th Anniv of Netherlands Literary Society. Multicoloured.
1011 10 c. + 5 c. Type 216 . . . . 30 35
1012 12 c. + 8 c. Part of MS, Japicx's poem "Wobbelke" 30 35
1013 20 c. + 10 c. Part of miniature, "Knight Walewein" 40 35
1014 25 c. + 10 c. Initial "D" and part of MS, novel, "Ferguut" 50 65
1015 40 c. + 20 c. 16th-cent printery (woodcut) 40 65

1966. Air (Special Flights).
1016 217 25 c. multicoloured . . . 30 40

218 Europa "Ship"

219 Infant

1966. Europa.
1017 218 20 c. green and yellow . . 15 10
1018 40 c. deep blue & blue . . 30 15

1966. Child Welfare.
1019 219 10 c. + 5 c. red & blue . . 10 10
1020 – 12 c. + 8 c. green & red . . 10 10
1021 – 20 c. + 10 c. blue & red . . 10 10
1022 – 25 c. + 10 c. purple & bl . 80 90
1023 – 40 c. + 20 c. red & green . 95 80
DESIGNS: 12 c. Young girl; 20 c. Boy in water; 25 c. Girl with moped; 40 c. Young man with horse.

220 Assembly Hall

221 Common Northern Whelk Eggs

1967. 125th Anniv of Delft Technological University.
1025 220 20 c. sepia and yellow . . 10 10

1967. Cultural, Health and Social Welfare Funds. Marine Fauna.
1026 221 12 c. + 8 c. brown & grn 20 20
1027 – 15 c. + 10 c. blue, light blue and deep blue 20 20
1028 – 20 c. + 10 c. mult 20 15
1029 – 25 c. + 10 c. purple, brown and bistre 45 50
1030 – 45 c. + 20 c. mult 70 65
DESIGNS: 15 c. Common northern whelk; 20 c. Common blue mussel; 25 c. Jellyfish; 45 c. Crab.

222 Cogwheels

223 Netherlands 5 c. Stamp of 1852

1967. Europa.
1031 222 20 c. blue & light blue . . 40 10
1032 45 c. purple & lt purple . . 1·00 70

1967. "Amphilex 67" Stamp Exn, Amsterdam.
1035 223 20 c. blue and black . . . 2·40 2·25
1036 – 25 c. red and black . . . 2·40 2·25
1037 – 75 c. green and black . . . 2·40 2·25
DESIGNS: 25 c. Netherlands 10 c. stamp of 1864; 75 c. Netherlands 20 c. stamp of 1867.
Nos. 1035/7 were sold at the Exhibition and at post offices at 3 g. 70, which included entrance fee to the Exhibition.

INDEX
Countries can be quickly located by referring to the index at the end of this volume.

224 "1867-1967"

225 "Porcupine Lullaby"

1967. Centenary of Dutch Red Cross.
1038 12 c. + 8 c. blue and red . . . 20 20
1039 15 c. + 10 c. red 35 35
1040 20 c. + 10 c. olive and red . . 20 15
1041 25 c. + 10 c. green & red . . 35 40
1042 45 c. + 20 c. grey and red . . 60 70
DESIGNS: 12 c. Type 224; 15 c. Red crosses; 20 c. "NRK" ("Nederlandsche Rood Kruis") in the form of a cross; 25 c. Maltese cross and "red" crosses; 45 c. "100" in the form of a cross.

1967. Child Welfare. Multicoloured.
1043 12 c. + 8 c. Type 225 . . . . 10 10
1044 15 c. + 10 c. "The Whistling Kettle" 10 10
1045 20 c. + 10 c. "Dikkertje Dap" (giraffe) 10 10
1046 25 c. + 10 c. "The Flower-seller" 70 80
1047 45 c. + 20 c. "Pippeloentje" (bear) . . . . 1·10 95

226 "Financial Automation"

1968. 50th Anniv of Netherlands Postal Cheque and Clearing Service.
1049 226 20 c. red, black & yell . . 15 10

227 St. Servatius' Bridge, Maastricht

1968. Cultural, Health and Social Welfare Funds. Dutch Bridges.
1050 227 12 c. + 8 c. green 40 50
1051 – 15 c. + 10 c. brown . . . 60 70
1052 – 20 c. + 10 c. red . . . . 1·50 25
1053 – 25 c. + 10 c. blue 40 50
1054 – 45 c. + 20 c. blue 85 80
BRIDGES: 15 c. Magere ("Narrow"), Amsterdam; 20 c. Railway, Culemborg; 25 c. Van Brienenoord, Rotterdam; 45 c. Oosterschelde, Zeeland.

228 Europa "Key"

1968. Europa.
1055 228 20 c. blue 20 10
1056 45 c. red 70 60

229 "Wilhelmus van Nassouwe"

230 Wright Type A and Cessna 150F

1968. 400th Anniv of Dutch National Anthem, "Wilhelmus".
1057 229 20 c. multicoloured . . . 20 10

1968. Dutch Aviation Anniversaries.
1058 12 c. black, red & mauve . . . 10 10
1059 20 c. black, emerald & grn . . 10 10
1060 45 c. black, blue & green . . 1·25 1·25
DESIGNS AND EVENTS: 12 c. T 230 (60th anniv (1967) of Royal Netherlands Aeronautical Assn); 20 c. Fokker F.II and Fellowship aircraft (50th anniv (1969) of Royal Netherlands Aircraft Factories "Fokker"); 45 c. De Havilland D.H.9B biplane and Douglas DC-9 airliner (50th anniv (1969) of Royal Dutch Airlines "KLM").

231 "Goblin"

1968. Child Welfare.
1061 231 12 c. + 8 c. pink, black and green 10 10
1062 – 15 c. + 10 c. pink, blue and black 10 10
1063 – 20 c. + 10 c. blue, green and black 10 10
1064 – 25 c. + 10 c. red, yellow and black . . . . 1·50 1·50
1065 – 45 c. + 20 c. yellow, orange and black . . . . . 1·50 1·50
DESIGNS: 15 c. "Giant"; 20 c. "Witch"; 25 c. "Dragon"; 45 c. "Sorcerer".

232 "I A O" (Internationale Arbeidsorganisatie)

1969. 50th Anniv of I.L.O.
1067 232 25 c. red and black . . . 35 10
1068 45 c. blue and black . . . 1·00 95

233 Queen Juliana

234 Villa, Huis ter Heide (1915)

1969. (a) Type 233.
1069 233 25 c. red . . . . 1·50 10
1069c 30 c. brown 15 10
1070a 35 c. blue 20 10
1071a 40 c. red 25 10
1072a 45 c. blue 30 10
1073a 50 c. purple 25 10
1073c 55 c. red 20 10
1074a 60 c. blue 20 10
1075 70 c. brown 40 10
1076 75 c. green 45 10
1077 80 c. red 45 10
1077a 90 c. grey 50 10

(b) Size 22 × 33 mm.
1078 – 1 g. green 80 10
1079 – 1 g. 25 lake 95 10
1080 – 1 g. 50 brown . . . . . 1·10 10
1081 – 2 g. mauve . . . . 1·50 10
1082 – 2 g. 50 blue . . . . . . 1·90 10
1083 – 5 g. grey . . . . 3·75 10
1084 – 10 g. blue . . . . 7·50 1·10
DESIGNS: 1 g., 1 g. 25, 1 g. 50, 2 g., 2 g. 50, 5 g. and 10 g. similar to Type 233.

1969. Cultural, Health and Social Welfare Funds. 20th-century Dutch Architecture.
1085 234 12 c. + 8 c. black & brn . 70 70
1086 – 15 c. + 10 c. black, red and blue 70 70
1087 – 20 c. + 10 c. black & vio . 70 70
1088 – 25 c. + 10 c. brown & grn . 70 30
1089 – 45 c. + 20 c. black, blue and yellow 70 70
DESIGNS: 15 c. Private House, Utrecht (1924); 20 c. Open-Air School, Amsterdam (1930); 25 c. Orphanage, Amsterdam (1960); 45 c. Congress Building, The Hague (1969).

235 Colonnade

236 Stylised "Crab" (of Cancer)

1969. Europa.
1090 235 25 c. blue 40 10
1901 45 c. red . . . . 1·50 1·40

1969. 20th Anniv of Queen Wilhelmina Cancer Fund.
1092 236 12 c. + 8 c. violet 75 75
1093 25 c. + 10 c. orange . . . 1·00 30
1094 45 c. + 20 c. green . . . 1·75 1·75

1969. 25th Anniv of "BENELUX" Customs Union. As T 186 of Luxembourg.
1095 25 c. multicoloured 30 10

238 Erasmus

239 Child with Violin

1969. 500th Birth Anniv of Desiderius Erasmus.
1096 238 25 c. purple on green . . 30 10

1969. Child Welfare.

1097 – 12 c. + 8 c. black, yellow and blue 10 10
1098 **239** 15 c. + 10 c. black and red 10 10
1099 – 20 c. + 10 c. black, yellow and red 1·90 2·00
1100 – 25 c. + 10 c. black, red and yellow 10 10
1101 – 45 c. + 20 c. black, red and green . . . . 1·90 2·00

DESIGNS—VERT: 12 c. Child with recorder; 20 c. Child with drum. HORIZ: 25 c. Three choristers; 45 c. Two dancers.

240 Queen Juliana and "Sunlit Road"

1969. 25th Anniv of Statute for the Kingdom.

1103 **240** 25 c. multicoloured . . . 30 10

241 Prof. E. M. Meijers (author of "Burgerlijk Wetboek")

1970. Introduction of New Netherlands Civil Code ("Burgerlijk Wetboek").

1104 **241** 25 c. ultramarine, green and blue 30 10

242 Netherlands Pavilion

243 "Circle to Square"

1970. Expo 70, World Fair, Osaka, Japan.

1105 **242** 25 c. grey, blue & red . . 30 10

1970. Cultural, Health and Social Welfare Funds.

1106 **243** 12 c. + 8 c. black on yell 1·10 1·25
1107 – 15 c. + 10 c. black on silver 1·10 1·25
1108 – 20 c. + 10 c. black 1·10 1·25
1109 – 25 c. + 10 c. black on bl 1·10 70
1110 – 45 c. + 20 c. white on grey 1·10 1·25

DESIGNS: 15 c. Parallel planes in cube; 20 c. Overlapping scales; 25 c. Concentric circles in transition; 45 c. Spirals.

244 "V" Symbol

245 "Flaming Sun"

1970. 25th Anniv of Liberation.

1111 **244** 12 c. red, blue & brown . 40 10

1970. Europa.

1112 **245** 25 c. red 40 10
1113 45 c. blue . . . . 1·60 1·00

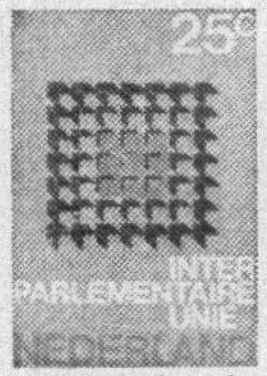

246 "Work and Co-operation"

247 Globe on Plinth

1970. Inter-Parliamentary Union Conference.

1114 **246** 25 c. green, blk & grey . . 40 10

1970. 25th Anniv of United Nations.

1115 **247** 45 c. blk, violet and bl . . 75 70

248 Human Heart

249 Toy Block

1970. Netherlands Heart Foundation.

1116 **248** 12 c. + 8 c. red, black and yellow 80 80
1117 25 c. + 10 c. red, black and mauve 80 65
1118 45 c. + 20 c. red, black and green 80 80

1970. Child Welfare. "The Child and the Cube".

1119 **249** 12 c. + 8 c. blue, violet and green 10 10
1120 – 15 c. + 10 c. green, blue and yellow . . . . 1·60 1·60
1121 **249** 20 c. + 10 c. mauve, red and violet . . . . 1·60 1·60
1122 – 25 c. + 10 c. red, yell and mauve 15 10
1123 **249** 45 c. + 20 c. grey, cream and black . . . . . 2·00 2·00

DESIGN: 15 c., 25 c. As Type **249**, but showing underside of block.

250 "Fourteenth Census 1971"

1971. 14th Netherlands Census.

1125 **250** 15 c. purple 15 10

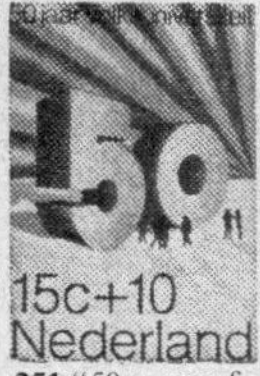

251 "50 years of Adult University Education"

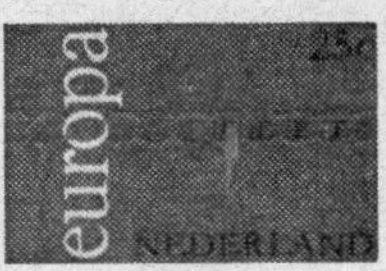

252 Europa Chain

1971. Cultural, Health and Social Welfare Funds. Other designs show 15th-century wooden statues by unknown artists.

1126 **251** 15 c. + 10 c. black, red and yellow . . . . 1·50 1·50
1127 – 20 c. + 10 c. black and green on green . . . 1·00 1·00
1128 – 25 c. + 10 c. black and orange on orge . . . 1·25 60
1129 – 30 c. + 15 c. black and blue on blue . . . . . . 1·50 1·50
1130 – 45 c. + 20 c. black and red on pink . . . . . . 1·50 1·50

STATUES: 20 c. "Apostle Paul"; 25 c. "Joachim and Ann"; 30 c. "John the Baptist and Scribes"; 45 c. "Ann, Mary and Christ-Child" (detail).

1971. Europa.

1131 **252** 25 c. yellow, red & black . 40 10
1132 45 c. yellow, blue & blk . 1·60 1·00

253 Carnation Symbol of Prince Bernhard Fund

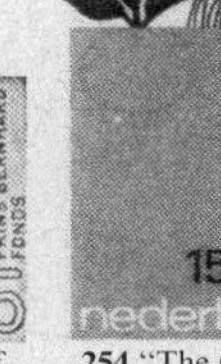

254 "The Good Earth"

1971. Prince Bernhard's 60th Birthday.

1133 **253** 15 c. yellow, grey & blk . 15 10
1134 – 20 c. multicoloured . . . 25 15
1135 – 25 c. multicoloured . . . 25 10
1136 – 45 c. + 20 c. black, purple and yellow . . . . . . 2·75 2·75

DESIGNS—HORIZ: 20 c. Panda symbol of World Wildlife Fund. VERT: 25 c. Prince Bernhard; 45 c. Statue, Borobudur Temple, Indonesia.

1971. Child Welfare.

1137 **254** 15 c. + 10 c. red, purple and black 10 10
1138 – 20 c. + 10 c. mult 30 15
1139 – 25 c. + 10 c. mult 15 10
1140 – 30 c. + 15 c. blue, violet and black 85 70
1141 – 45 c. + 20 c. blue, green and black . . . . 1·75 2·00

DESIGNS—VERT: 20 c. Butterfly; 45 c. Reflecting water. HORIZ: 25 c. Sun waving; 30 c. Moon winking.

255 Delta Map

256 "Fruits"

1972. Delta Sea-Defences Plan.

1143 **255** 20 c. multicoloured . . . 30 10

1972. Cultural, Health and Social Welfare Funds. "Floriade Flower Show" (20 c., 25 c.) and "Holland Arts Festival" (30 c., 45 c.). Mult.

1144 20 c. + 10 c. Type **256** . . . 1·25 1·00
1145 25 c. + 10 c. "Flower" . . . 1·25 1·00
1146 30 c. + 15 c. "Sunlit Landscape" . . . . 1·25 70
1147 45 c. + 25 c. "Music" . . . . 1·25 1·00

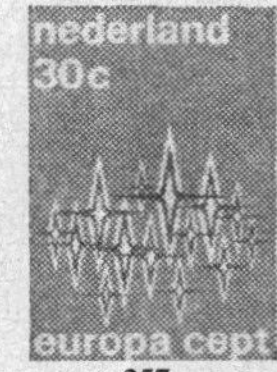

257 "Communications"

258 "There is more to be done in the world than ever before" (Thorbecke)

1972. Europa.

1148 **257** 30 c. brown and blue . . 85 10
1149 45 c. brown and orange . 1·40 1·25

1972. Death Centenary of J. R. Thorbecke (statesman).

1150 **258** 30 c. black and blue . . . 30 10

259 Netherlands Flag

260 Hurdling

1972. 400th Anniv of Netherlands Flag.

1151 **259** 20 c. multicoloured . . . 60 15
1152 25 c. multicoloured . . . 1·40 10

1972. Olympic Games, Munich. Multicoloured.

1153 20 c. Type **260** 15 10
1154 30 c. Diving 15 10
1155 45 c. Cycling . . . . 1·00 1·25

261 Red Cross

262 Prince Willem-Alexander

1972. Netherlands Red Cross.

1156 **261** 5 c. red 10 10
1157 – 20 c. + 10 c. red & pink . 60 60
1158 – 25 c. + 10 c. red & orge . 80 1·00
1159 – 30 c. + 15 c. red & black . 75 35
1160 – 45 c. + 25 c. red & blue . 85 95

DESIGNS: 20 c. Accident services; 25 c. Blood transfusion; 30 c. Refugee relief; 45 c. Child care.

1972. Child Welfare. Multicoloured.

1161 25 c. + 15 c. Type **262** . . . 15 15
1162 30 c. + 10 c. Prince Johan Friso 70 80
1163 35 c. + 15 c. Prince Constantin 70 10
1164 50 c. + 20 c. The Three Princes 2·40 2·50

Nos. 1162/4 are horiz.

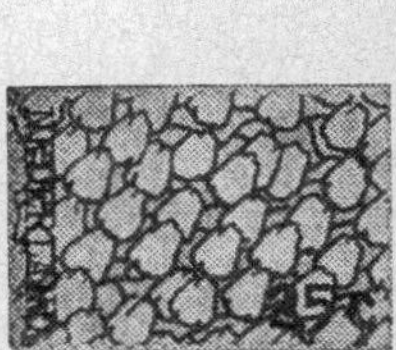

263 Tulips in Bloom

264 "De Zeven Provincien" (De Ruyter's flagship)

1973. Tulip Exports.

1166 **263** 25 c. multicoloured . . . 75 10

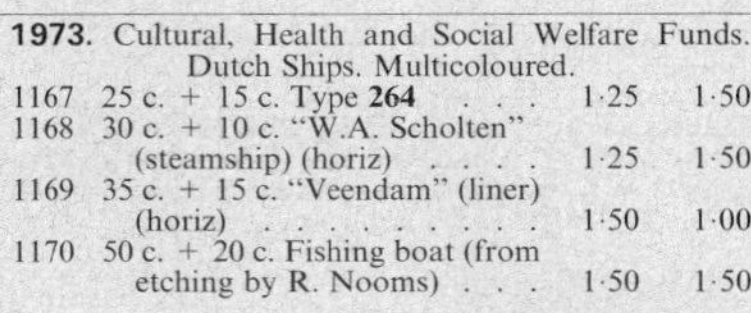

1973. Cultural, Health and Social Welfare Funds. Dutch Ships. Multicoloured.

1167 25 c. + 15 c. Type **264** . . . 1·25 1·50
1168 30 c. + 10 c. "W.A. Scholten" (steamship) (horiz) . . . 1·25 1·50
1169 35 c. + 15 c. "Veendam" (liner) (horiz) . . . . 1·50 1·00
1170 50 c. + 20 c. Fishing boat (from etching by R. Nooms) . . . 1·50 1·50

265 Europa "Posthorn"

266 Hockey-players

1973. Europa.

1171 **265** 35 c. lt blue & blue . . . 45 40
1172 50 c. blue and violet . . . 80 75

1973. Events and Anniversaries. Multicoloured.

1173 25 c. Type **266** 25 10
1174 30 c. Gymnastics . . . . . 2·25 55
1175 35 c. Dish aerial (vert) 35 10
1176 50 c. Rainbow 60 60

EVENTS—VERT: 25 c. 75th anniv of Royal Netherlands Hockey Association; 30 c. World Gymnastics Championships, Rotterdam. HORIZ: 35 c. Opening of Satellite Station, Burum; 50 c. Centenary of World Meteorological Organization.

267 Queen Juliana

268 "Co-operation"

1973. Silver Jubilee of Queen Juliana's Accession.

1177 **267** 40 c. multicoloured . . . 50 10

1973. International Development Co-operation.

1178 **268** 40 c. multicoloured . . . 1·00 10

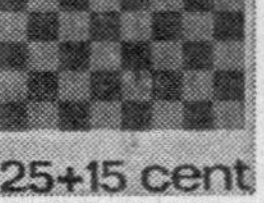

269 "Chess"

270 Northern Goshawk

1973. Child Welfare.

1179 **269** 25 c. + 15 c. red, yellow and black 65 15
1180 – 30 c. + 10 c. green, mauve and black . . . . . 1·00 70
1181 – 40 c. + 20 c. yellow, green and black 80 10
1182 – 50 c. + 20 c. blue, yellow and black . . . . . 2·25 2·25

DESIGNS: 30 c. "Noughts and crosses"; 40 c. "Maze"; 50 c. "Dominoes".

1974. "Nature and Environment". Multicoloured.

1184 25 c. Type **270** . . . . 1·90 60
1185 25 c. Tree . . . . 1·25 60
1186 25 c. Fisherman and frog . . 1·25 60

Nos. 1184/6 were issued together se-tenant forming a composite design.

271 Bandsmen (World Band Contest, Kerkrade)

NEDERLAND 25 CENT

272 Football on Pitch

1974. Cultural, Health and Social Welfare Funds.

1187 **271** 25 c. + 15 c. multicoloured 90 90
1188 – 30 c. + 10 c. multicoloured 90 90
1189 – 40 c. + 20 c. brown, black and red 90 65
1190 – 50 c. + 20 c. purple, black and red 90 90

DESIGNS: 30 c. Dancers and traffic-lights ("Modern Ballet"); 40 c. Herman Heijermans; 50 c. "Kniertje" (character from Heijermans' play "Op hoop van zegan"). The 40 c. and 50 c. commemorate the 50th death anniv of the playwright.

1974. Sporting Events.

1191 **272** 25 c. multicoloured . . . 20 10
1192 – 40 c. yellow, red & mve . 30 10

DESIGNS AND EVENTS—HORIZ: 25 c. (World Cup Football Championships, West Germany). VERT: 40 c. Hand holding tennis ball (75th anniv of Royal Dutch Lawn Tennis Association).

273 Netherlands Cattle

274 "BENELUX" (30th Anniv of Benelux (Customs Union))

1974. Anniversaries. Multicoloured.

1193 25 c. Type **273** . . . 9·25 2·25
1194 25 c. "Cancer" . . . 15 15
1195 40 c. "Suzanna" (lifeboat) seen through binoculars . . . 20 10

EVENTS AND ANNIVERSARIES: No. 1193, Cent of Netherlands Cattle Herdbook Society; No. 1194, 25th anniv of Queen Wilhelmina Cancer Research Fund; No. 1195, 150th anniv of Dutch Lifeboat Service.

1974. International Anniversaries.

1196 **274** 30 c. green, turq & bl . . 20 10
1197 – 45 c. deep blue, silver & bl 30 10
1198 – 45 c. yellow, blue & blk . 30 10

DESIGNS—VERT: No. 1197, NATO emblem (25th anniv); 1198, Council of Europe emblem (25th anniv).

275 Hands with Letters

276 Boy with Hoop

1974. Centenary of Universal Postal Union.

1199 **275** 60 c. multicoloured . . . 40 35

1974. 50th Anniv of Child Welfare Issues. Early Photographs.

1200 **276** 30 c. + 15 c. brown & blk 15 15
1201 – 35 c. + 20 c. brown . . . 40 50
1202 – 45 c. + 20 c. black . . . 40 15
1203 – 60 c. + 20 c. black . . . 1·25 1·40

DESIGNS: 35 c. Child and baby; 45 c. Two young girls; 60 c. Girl sitting on balustrade.

277 Amsterdam

278 St. Hubertus Hunting Lodge, De Hoge Veluwe National Park

1975. Anniversaries. Multicoloured.

1205 30 c. Type **277** . . . 20 10
1206 30 c. Synagogue and map . . 55 20
1207 35 c. Type **277** . . . 35 10
1208 45 c. "Window" in human brain 40 15

ANNIVERSARIES: Nos. 1205, 1207, Amsterdam (700th anniv); No. 1206, Portuguese-Israelite Synagogue, Amsterdam (300th anniv); No. 1208, Leyden University and university education (400th anniv).

1975. Cultural, Health and Social Welfare Funds. National Monument Year. Preserved Monuments. Multicoloured.

1209 35 c. + 20 c. Type **278** . . . 50 50
1210 40 c. + 15 c. Bergijnhof (Beguinage), Amsterdam (vert) . . . 50 50
1211 50 c. + 20 c. "Kuiperspoort" (Cooper's gate), Middelburg (vert) . . . 65 50
1212 60 c. + 20 c. Orvelte village, Drenthe . . . 75 90

279 Eye and Barbed Wire

280 Company Emblem and "Stad Middelburg" (schooner)

1975. 30th Anniv of Liberation.

1213 **279** 35 c. black and red . . . 30 10

1975. Centenary of Zeeland Shipping Company.

1214 **280** 35 c. multicoloured . . . 30 10

281 Dr. Albert Schweitzer crossing Lambarene River

1975. Birth Centenary of Dr. Schweitzer.

1215 **281** 50 c. multicoloured . . . 40 10

282 Man and Woman on "Playing-card"

283 Braille Reading

1975. International Events. Multicoloured.

1216 35 c. Type **282** (Int Women's Year) . . . 20 10
1217 50 c. Metric scale (Metre Convention centenary) (horiz) . . . 30 10

1975. 150th Anniv of Invention of Braille.

1218 **283** 35 c. multicoloured . . . 30 10

284 Dutch 25 c. Coins

285 "Four Orphans" (C. Simons), Torenstraat Orphanage, Medemblik

1975. Savings Campaign.

1219 **284** 50 c. grey, green & blue . 35 10

1975. Child Welfare. Historic Ornamental Stones. Multicoloured.

1220 35 c. + 15 c. Type **285** . . . 15 15
1221 40 c. + 15 c. "Milkmaid" Kooltuin Alkmaar . . . 45 45
1222 50 c. + 25 c. "Four Sons of Aymon seated on Beyaert", Herengracht . . . 30 10
1223 60 c. + 25 c. "Life at the Orphanage", Molenstraat Orphanage, Gorinchem . . 85 85

286 18th-century Lottery Ticket

287 Numeral

1976. 250th Anniv of National Lottery.

1225 **286** 35 c. multicoloured . . . 30 10

1976.

1226 **287** 5 c. grey . . . 10 10
1227 10 c. blue . . . 10 10
1228 25 c. violet . . . 10 10
1229 40 c. brown . . . 15 10
1230 45 c. blue . . . 30 10
1231 50 c. mauve . . . 30 10
1232 55 c. green . . . 45 10
1233 60 c. yellow . . . 45 10
1234 65 c. brown . . . 45 10
1235 70 c. violet . . . 45 10
1236 80 c. mauve . . . 50 10

288 West European Hedgehog

1976. Cultural, Health and Social Welfare Funds. Nature Protection (40, 75 c.) and Anniversaries. Multicoloured.

1241 40 c. + 20 c. Type **288** . . . 60 60
1242 45 c. + 20 c. Open book (vert) 60 60
1243 55 c. + 20 c. People and organization initials . . . 70 25
1244 75 c. + 25 c. Frog and spawn (vert) . . . 85 85

ANNIVERSARIES: No. 1242, 175th anniv of Primary education and centenary of Agricultural education; No. 1245, 75th anniv of Social Security Bank and legislation.

289 Admiral Michiel de Ruyter (statue)

1976. 300th Death Anniv of Admiral Michiel de Ruyter.

1245 **289** 55 c. multicoloured . . . 35 10

290 Guillaume Groen van Prinsterer

1976. Death Centenary of Guillaume Groen van Prinsterer (statesman).

1246 **290** 55 c. multicoloured . . . 35 10

291 Detail of 18th Century Calendar

1976. Bicentenary of American Revolution.

1247 **291** 75 c. multicoloured . . . 50 35

292 Long-distance Marchers

293 The Art of Printing

1976. Sport and Recreation Anniversaries. Mult.

1248 40 c. Type **292** . . . 20 15
1249 55 c. Runners "photo-finish" . 60 15

ANNIVERSARIES: 40 c. 60th Nijmegen Long-Distance March; 55 c. Royal Dutch Athletics Society (75th anniv).

1976. Anniversaries.

1250 **293** 45 c. red and blue . . . 25 10
1251 – 55 c. + 25 c. multicoloured 45 45

DESIGNS AND EVENTS: 45 c. Type **293** (75th anniv of Netherlands Printers' organization); 55 c. Rheumatic patient "Within Care" (50th anniv of Dutch Anti-Rheumatism Association).

294 Dutch Tjalk and Reclaimed Land

295 Queen Wilhelmina 4½ c. Stamp, 1919

1976. Zuider Zee Project–Reclamation and Urbanization. Multicoloured.

1252 **294** 40 c. blue, olive and red . 25 10
1253 – 75 c. yellow, red & blue . 50 35

DESIGN: 75 c. Duck flying over reclaimed land.

1976. "Amphilex '77" International Stamp Exhibition, Amsterdam (1977) (1st series). Stamp Portraits of Queen Wilhelmina. Mult.

1254 – 55 c. + 55 c. blue, deep grey and grey . . . 70 75
1255 **295** 55 c. + 55 c. purple, deep grey and grey . . . 70 75
1256 – 55 c. + 55 c. brown, deep grey and grey . . . 70 75
1257 – 75 c. + 75 c. turq, deep grey and grey . . . 70 75
1258 – 75 c. + 75 c. blue, deep grey and grey . . . 70 75

DESIGNS: No. 1254, 5 c. stamp, 1891; No. 1256, 25 c. stamp, 1924; No. 1257, 15 c. stamp, 1940; No. 1258, 25 c. stamp, 1947.

See also Nos. 1273/6.

296 "Football" (J. Raats)

1976. Child Welfare. Children's Paintings. Multicoloured.

1259 40 c. + 20 c. Type **296** . . . 25 25
1260 45 c. + 20 c. "Boat" (L Jacobs) 25 25
1261 55 c. + 20 c. "Elephant" (M. Lugtenburg) . . . 30 10
1262 75 c. + 25 c. "Caravan" (A. Seeleman) . . . 65 80

297 Ballot-paper and Pencil

1977. National Events. Multicoloured.

1264 40 c. "Energy" (vert) . . . 30 10
1265 45 c. Type **297** . . . 40 10

EVENTS: 40 c. "Be wise with energy" campaign; 45 c. Elections to Lower House of States General. See also No. 1268.

298 Spinoza

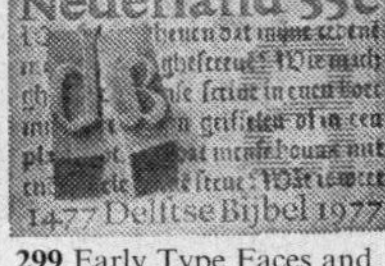

299 Early Type Faces and "a" on Bible Script

1977. 300th Death Anniv of Barach (Benedictus) de Spinoza (philosopher).

1266 **298** 75 c. multicoloured . . . 60 30

1977. 500th Anniv of Printing of "Delft Bible".

1267 **299** 55 c. multicoloured . . . 40 30

1977. Elections to Lower House of States General. As T **297** but also inscribed "25 MEI '77".

1268 45 c. multicoloured . . . 45 10

300 Altar of Goddess Nehalennia

301 "Kaleidoscope"

1977. Cultural, Health and Social Welfare Funds. Roman Archaeological Discoveries.

1269 – 40 c. + 20 c. mult . . . 30 30
1270 **300** 45 c. + 20 c. black, stone and green . . . 30 25
1271 – 55 c. + 20 c. black, blue and red . . . 30 20
1272 – 75 c. + 25 c. black, grey and yellow . . . 40 45

DESIGNS: 40 c. Baths, Heerlen; 55 c. Remains of Zwammerdam ship; 75 c. Parade helmet.

1977. "Amphilex 1977" International Stamp Exhibition, Amsterdam (2nd series). As T **295**.

1273 55 c. + 45 c. grn, brn & grey 45 50
1274 55 c. + 45 c. bl, brn & grey 45 50
1275 55 c. + 45 c. bl, brn & grey 45 50
1276 55 c. + 45 c. red, brn & grey 45 50

DESIGNS: No. 1273, Queen Wilhelmina 1 g. stamp, 1898; No. 1274, Queen Wilhelmina 20 c. stamp, 1923; No. 1275, Queen Wilhelmina 12½ c. stamp, 1938; No. 1276, Queen Wilhelmina 10 c. stamp, 1948.

1977. Bicentenary of Netherlands Society for Industry and Commerce.

1278 **301** 55 c. multicoloured . . . 30 10

302 Man in Wheelchair and Maze of Steps

303 Risk of Drowning

1977. Anniversaries.

1279 **302** 40 c. brown, green & bl . 20 10
1280 – 45 c. multicoloured . . . 25 10
1281 – 55 c. multicoloured . . . 35 10

DESIGNS—HORIZ: 40 c. Type **302** (50th anniv of A.V.O. Nederland); 45 c. Diagram of water current (50th anniv of Delft Hydraulic Laboratory). VERT: 55 c. Teeth (centenary of dentists' training in Netherlands).

1977. Child Welfare. Dangers to Children. Mult.

1282 40 c. + 20 c. Type **303** . . . 30 20
1283 45 c. + 20 c. Medicine cabinet (poisons) . . . 30 25
1284 55 c. + 20 c. Balls in road (traffic) . . . 30 20
1285 75 c. + 25 c. Matches (fire) . 55 65

304 "Postcode" 305 Makkum Dish

1978. Introduction of Postcodes.

1287 **304** 40 c. red and blue 20 10
1288 45 c. red and blue 25 10

1978. Cultural, Health and Social Welfare Funds. Multicoloured.

1289 40 c. + 20 c. Anna Maria van Schurman (writer) 30 30
1290 45 c. + 20 c. Passage from letter by Belle de Zuylen (Mme. de Charriere) 30 25
1291 55 c. + 20 c. Delft dish . . . 30 25
1292 75 c. + 25 c. Type **305** . . . 40 45

306 "Human Rights" Treaty 307 Chess

1978. European Series.

1293 **306** 45 c. grey, black and blue 25 10
1294 – 55 c. black, stone and orange 35 10

DESIGN: 55 c. Haarlem Town Hall (Europa).

1978. Sports.

1295 **307** 40 c. multicoloured . . . 50 15
1296 – 45 c. red and blue 50 15

DESIGN: 45 c. The word "Korfbal".

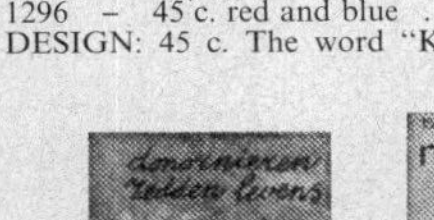

308 Kidney Donor 309 Epaulettes

1978. Health Care. Multicoloured.

1297 **308** 40 c. black, blue and red . 25 10
1298 – 45 c. multicoloured . . . 30 10
1299 – 55 c. + 25 c. red, grey and black 45 50

DESIGNS—VERT: 45 c. Heart and torch. HORIZ: 55 c. Red crosses on world map.

1978. 150th Anniv of Royal Military Academy, Breda.

1301 **309** 55 c. multicoloured . . . 30 10

310 Verkade as Hamlet

1978. Birth Centenary of Eduard Rutger Verkade (actor and producer).

1302 **310** 45 c. multicoloured . . . 30 10

311 Boy ringing Doorbell

1978. Child Welfare. Multicoloured.

1303 40 c. + 20 c. Type **311** . . . 30 20
1304 45 c. + 20 c. Child reading . . 30 20
1305 55 c. + 20 c. Boy writing (vert) 30 15
1306 75 c. + 25 c. Girl and blackboard 40 60

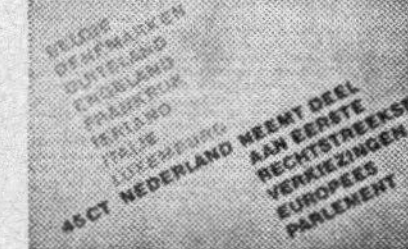

312 Clasped Hands and Arrows 313 Names of European Community Members

1979. 400th Anniv of Treaty of Utrecht.

1308 **312** 55 c. blue 35 10

1979. First Direct Elections to European Assembly.

1309 **313** 45 c. red, blue and black . 40 10

314 Queen Juliana

1979. Queen Juliana's 70th Birthday.

1310 **314** 55 c. multicoloured . . . 40 10

315 Fragment of "Psalmen Trilogie" (J. Andriessen) 316 Netherlands Stamps and Magnifying Glass

1979. Cultural, Health and Social Welfare Funds.

1311 **315** 40 c. + 20 c. grey and red 30 30
1312 – 45 c. + 20 c. grey and red 30 25
1313 – 55 c. + 20 c. multicoloured 30 20
1314 – 75 c. + 25 c. multicoloured 65 45

DESIGNS AND EVENTS: 150th anniv of Musical Society; 45 c. Choir. Restoration of St. John's Church, Gouda (stained glass windows); 55 c. Mary (detail, "Birth of Christ"); 75 c. William of Orange (detail, "Relief of Leyden").

1979. Europa and 75th Anniv of Scheveningen Radio. Multicoloured.

1315 55 c. Type **316** 35 10
1316 75 c. Liner and Morse Key . . 50 35

317 Map of Chambers of Commerce 318 Action Shot of Football Match

1979. 175th Anniv of First Dutch Chamber of Commerce, Maastricht.

1317 **317** 45 c. multicoloured . . . 40 15

1979. Anniversaries. Multicoloured.

1318 45 c. Type **318** (centenary of organized football) 35 15
1319 55 c. Women's suffrage meeting (60th anniv of Women's suffrage) (vert) 45 10

319 Porch of Old Amsterdam Theatre

1979. 300th Death Annivs of Joost van den Vondel (poet) and Jan Steen (painter). Multicoloured.

1320 40 c. Type **319** 20 10
1321 45 c. "Gay Company" (detail) (Jan Steen) 25 10

320 Hindustani Girl on Father's Shoulder (The Right to Love)

1979. Child Welfare. International Year of the Child

1322 **320** 40 c. + 20 c. grey, red and yellow 35 20
1323 – 45 c. + 20 c. grey, red and black 35 15
1324 – 55 c. + 20 c. grey, black and yellow 35 15
1325 – 75 c. + 25 c. black, blue and red 45 60

DESIGNS—HORIZ: 45 c. Chilean child from refugee camp (The Right to Medical Care). VERT: 55 c. Senegalese boy from Sahel area (The Right to Food); 75 c. Class from Albert Cuyp School, Amsterdam (The Right to Education).

321 A. F. de Savornin Lohman 322 Dunes

1980. Dutch Politicians. Multicoloured.

1327 45 c. Type **321** (Christian Historical Union) 25 10
1328 50 c. P. J. Troelstra (Socialist Party) 25 10
1329 60 c. P. J. Oud (Liberal Party) 35 10

1980. Cultural, Health and Social Welfare Funds. Multicoloured.

1330 45 c. + 20 c. Type **322** . . . 40 30
1331 50 c. + 20 c. Country estate (vert) 40 30
1332 60 c. + 25 c. Lake District . . 50 25
1333 80 c. + 35 c. Moorland . . . 65 65

323 Avro Type 683 Lancaster dropping Food Parcels 324 Queen Beatrix and New Church, Amsterdam

1980. 35th Anniv of Liberation. Multicoloured.

1334 45 c. Type **323** 40 15
1335 60 c. Anne Frank (horiz) . . . 60 10

1980. Installation of Queen Beatrix.

1336 **324** 60 c. blue, red & yellow . 45 10
1337 65 c. blue, red & yellow . 55 10

325 Young Stamp Collectors 326 "Flight"

1980. "Jupostex 1980" Stamp Exhibition, Eindhoven, and Dutch Society of Stamp Dealers Show, The Hague.

1338 **325** 50 c. multicoloured . . . 30 20

1980. Air. (Special Flights).

1339 **326** 1 g. blue and black . . . 75 45

327 Bridge Players and Cards 328 Road Haulage

1980. Sports Events. Multicoloured.

1340 50 c. Type **327** (Bridge Olympiad, Valkenburg) . . 30 10
1341 60 c. + 25 c. Sportswoman in wheelchair (Olympics for the Disabled, Arnhem and Veenendaal) 50 40

1980. Transport.

1342 **328** 50 c. multicoloured . . . 25 10
1343 – 60 c. blue, brown & blk . 55 15
1344 – 80 c. multicoloured . . . 45 25

DESIGNS: 60 c. Rail transport; 80 c. Motorised canal barge.

329 Queen Wilhelmina

1980. Europa.

1345 **329** 60 c. black, red & blue . . 35 10
1346 – 80 c. black, red & blue . . 40 20

DESIGN: 80 c. Sir Winston Churchill.

330 Abraham Kuyper (first rector) and University Seal

1980. Centenary of Amsterdam Free University.

1347 **330** 50 c. multicoloured . . . 30 10

331 "Pop-up" Book 332 Saltmarsh

1980. Child Welfare. Multicoloured.

1348 45 c. + 20 c. Type **331** . . . 35 20
1349 50 c. + 20 c. Child flying on a book (vert) 35 35
1350 60 c. + 30 c. Boy reading "Kikkerkoning" (vert) . . . 45 20
1351 80 c. + 30 c. Dreaming in a book 60 65

1981. Cultural, Health and Social Welfare Funds. Multicoloured.

1353 45 c. + 20 c. Type **332** . . . 30 30
1354 55 c. + 25 c. Dyke 30 30
1355 60 c. + 25 c. Drain 35 30
1356 65 c. + 30 c. Cultivated land 40 40

333 Parcel (Parcel Post)

1981. P.T.T. Centenaries. Multicoloured.

1357 45 c. Type **333** 25 10
1358 55 c. Telephone, dish aerial and telephone directory page (public telephone service) . 30 10
1359 65 c. Savings bank books, deposit transfer card and savings bank stamps (National Savings Bank) . . 35 10

334 Huis ten Bosch Royal Palace, The Hague

1981.

1361 **334** 55 c. multicoloured . . . 35 10

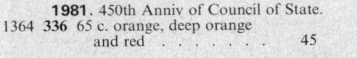

335 Carillon

1981. Europa. Multicoloured.

1362 45 c. Type **335** 35 10
1363 65 c. Barrel organ 55 10

336 Council of State Emblem and Maps of 1531 and 1981

1981. 450th Anniv of Council of State.

1364 **336** 65 c. orange, deep orange and red 45 10

337 Marshalling Yard, Excavator and Ship's Screw

1981. Industrial and Agricultural Exports. Multicoloured.

1365 45 c. Type **337** 55 15
1366 55 c. Inner port, cast-iron component and weighing machine 40 15
1367 60 c. Airport, tomato and lettuce 45 40
1368 65 c. Motorway interchange, egg and cheese 55 10

338 "Integration in Society"

1981. Child Welfare. Integration of Handicapped Children. Multicoloured.

1369 45 c. + 25 c. Type **338** . . . 40 20
1370 55 c. + 20 c. "Integration in the Family" (vert) 45 45
1371 60 c. + 25 c. Child vaccinated against polio (Upper Volta project) (vert) 50 50
1372 65 c. + 30 c. "Integration among Friends" 60 20

339 Queen Beatrix

340 Agnieten Chapel and Banners

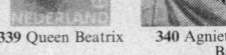

1981.

1374 **339** 65 c. brown and black . . 40 10
1375 70 c. lilac and black . . . 55 10
1376 75 c. pink and black . . . 75 10
1377 90 c. green and black . . 1·25 10
1378 1 g. lilac and black . . . 75 10
1379 1 g. 20 bistre and black . . 1·10 10
1380 1 g. 40 green and black . . 1·75 10
1381 1 g. 50 lilac and black . . 90 10
1382 2 g. bistre and black . . . 1·50 10
1383 2 g. 50 orange and black . . 1·75 15
1384 3 g. blue and black . . . 2·10 10
1385 4 g. green and black . . . 3·00 10
1386 5 g. blue and black . . . 3·75 10
1387 6 g. 50 lilac and black . . 5·50 15
1388 7 g. blue and black . . . 5·25 10
1389 7 g. 50 green and black . . 6·00 30

For this design but on uncoloured background see Nos. 1594/1605.

1982. 350th Anniv of University of Amsterdam.

1395 **340** 65 c. multicoloured . . . 50 10

341 Skater

342 Apple Blossom

1982. Centenary of Royal Dutch Skating Association.

1396 **341** 45 c. multicoloured . . . 40 20

1982. Cultural, Health and Social Welfare Funds. Multicoloured.

1397 50 c. + 20 c. Type **342** . . . 40 45
1398 60 c. + 25 c. Anemones . . . 50 45
1399 65 c. + 25 c. Roses 50 45
1400 70 c. + 30 c. African violets . . 70 75

343 Stripes in National Colours

1982. Bicentenary of Netherlands–United States Diplomatic Relations.

1401 **343** 50 c. red, blue and black . 40 10
1402 65 c. red, blue and black . 60 20

344 Sandwich Tern and Eider

345 Zebra Crossing

1982. Waddenzee. Multicoloured.

1403 50 c. Type **344** 40 15
1404 70 c. Barnacle Geese 60 15

1982. 50th Anniv of Dutch Road Safety Organization.

1405 **345** 60 c. multicoloured . . . 55 15

346 Ground Plan of Enkhuizen Fortifications

347 Aerial view of Palace and Liberation Monument

1982. Europa. Multicoloured.

1406 50 c. Type **346** 40 10
1407 70 c. Part of ground plan of Coevorden fortifications . . 60 10

1982. Royal Palace, Dam Square, Amsterdam. Multicoloured.

1408 50 c. Facade, ground plan and cross-section of Palace . . . 40 10
1409 60 c. Type **347** 45 10

348 Great Tits and Child

349 Touring Club Activities

1982. Child Welfare. Child and Animal. Mult.

1410 50 c. + 30 c. Type **348** . . . 60 30
1411 60 c. + 20 c. Child arm-in-arm with cat 65 20
1412 65 c. + 20 c. Child with drawing of rabbit 70 85
1413 70 c. + 30 c. Child with palm cockatoo . . . . 1·00 95

1983. Centenary of Royal Dutch Touring Club.

1415 **349** 70 c. multicoloured . . . 65 10

350 Johan van Oldenbarnevelt (statesman) (after J. Houbraken)

351 Newspaper

1983. Cultural, Health and Social Welfare Funds.

1416 **350** 50 c. + 20 c. pink, blue and black 50 40
1417 – 60 c. + 25 c. multicoloured 60 40
1418 – 65 c. + 25 c. multicoloured 75 60
1419 – 70 c. + 30 c. grey, black and gold 80 60

DESIGNS: 60 c. Willem Jansz Blaeu (cartographer) (after Thomas de Keijser); 65 c. Hugo de Groot (statesman) (after J. van Ravesteyn); 70 c. "Saskia van Uylenburch" (portrait of his wife by Rembrandt).

1983. Europa. Multicoloured.

1420 50 c. Type **351** (75th anniv of Netherlands Newspaper Publishers Assoc.) 40 10
1421 70 c. European Communications Satellite and European Telecommunication Satellites Organization members' flags 60 10

352 "Composition 1922" (P. Mondriaan)

353 "Geneva Conventions"

1983. De Stijl Art Movement. Multicoloured.

1422 50 c. Type **352** 40 10
1423 65 c. Contra construction from "Maison Particuliere" (C. van Eesteren and T. van Doesburg) 60 20

1983. Red Cross.

1424 **353** 50 c. + 25 c. multicoloured 45 45
1425 – 60 c. + 20 c. multicoloured 55 45
1426 – 65 c. + 25 c. multicoloured 70 45
1427 – 70 c. + 30 c. grey, black and red 80 70

DESIGNS: 60 c. Red Cross and text "charity, independence, impartiality"; 65 c. "Socio-medical work"; 70 c. Red Cross and text "For Peace".

354 Luther's Signature

355 Child looking at Donkey and Ox through Window

1983. 500th Birth Anniv of Martin Luther (Protestant Reformer).

1428 **354** 70 c. multicoloured . . . 40 10

1983. Child Welfare. Child and Christmas. Multicoloured.

1429 50 c. + 10 c. Type **355** . . . 50 50
1430 50 c. + 25 c. Child riding flying snowman 60 20
1431 60 c. + 30 c. Child in bed and star 75 75
1432 70 c. + 30 c. Children dressed as the three kings 80 20

356 Parliament

1984. Second Elections to European Parliament.

1434 **356** 70 c. multicoloured . . . 55 10

357 Lapwings

358 St. Servaas

1984. Cultural, Health and Social Welfare Funds. Pasture Birds. Multicoloured.

1435 50 c. + 20 c. Type **357** . . . 50 35
1436 60 c. + 25 c. Ruffs 70 35
1437 65 c. + 25 c. Redshanks (vert) 80 70
1438 70 c. + 30 c. Black-tailed godwits (vert) 85 80

1984. 1600th Death Anniv of St. Servaas (Bishop of Tongeren and Maastricht).

1439 **358** 60 c. multicoloured . . . 50 10

359 Bridge

1984. Europa. 25th Anniv of European Post and Telecommunications Conference.

1440 **359** 50 c. dp blue and blue . . 40 10
1441 70 c. green and lt green 70 10

360 Eye and Magnifying Glass

1984. Centenary of Organized Philately in the Netherlands and "Filacento" International Stamp Exhibition, The Hague. Multicoloured.

1442 50 c. + 20 c. Type **360** . . . 40 40
1443 60 c. + 25 c. 1909 cover . . . 50 50
1444 70 c. + 30 c. Stamp club meeting, 1949 . . . . . . 60 60

361 William of Orange (after Adriaen Thomaszoon Key)

1984. 400th Death Anniv of William of Orange.

1446 **361** 70 c. multicoloured . . . 60 10

362 Giant Pandas and Globe

363 Graph and Leaf

1984. World Wildlife Fund.

1447 **362** 70 c. multicoloured . . . 75 10

1984. 11th International Small Business Congress, Amsterdam.

1448 **363** 60 c. multicoloured . . . 55 10

364 Violin Lesson

365 Sunny, First Dutch Guide-Dog

1984. Child Welfare. Strip Cartoons. Multicoloured.

1449 50 c. + 25 c. Type **364** . . . 40 25
1450 60 c. + 20 c. At the dentist . . 75 55
1451 65 c. + 20 c. The plumber . . 85 85
1452 70 c. + 30 c. The king and money chest 65 35

1985. 50th Anniv of Royal Dutch Guide-Dog Fund.

1454 **365** 60 c. black, ochre and red 60 10

366 Plates and Cutlery on Place-mat

367 Saint Martin's Church, Zaltbommel

1985. Tourism. Multicoloured.

1455 50 c. Type **366** (centenary of Travel and Holidays Association) 40 10
1456 70 c. Kroller-Muller museum emblem, antlers and landscape (50th anniv of De Hoge Veluwe National Park) 60 10

1985. Cultural, Health and Social Welfare Funds. Religious Buildings. Multicoloured.

1457 50 c. + 20 c. Type **367** . . . 60 45
1458 60 c. + 25 c. Winterswijk synagogue and Holy Ark (horiz) 65 55
1459 65 c. + 25 c. Bolsward Baptist church 80 55
1460 70 c. + 30 c. Saint John's Cathedral, 's-Hertogenbosch (horiz) 85 35

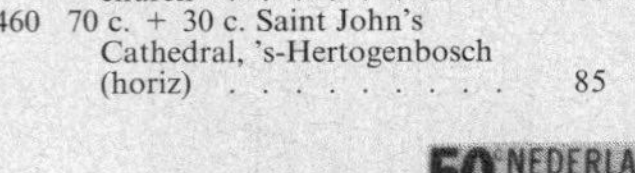

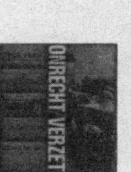

368 Star of David, Illegal Newspapers and Rifle Practice (Resistance Movement)

369 Piano Keyboard

1985. 40th Anniv of Liberation.

1461 **368** 50 c. black, stone & red . 50 10
1462 – 60 c. black, stone & blue . 55 10
1463 – 65 c. black, stone & orge . 60 25
1464 – 70 c. black, stone & grn 1·00 10

DESIGNS: 60 c. Bombers over houses, "De Vliegende Hollander" (newspaper) and soldier (Allied Forces); 65 c. Soldiers and civilians, "Parool" (newspaper) and American war cemetery, Margraten (Liberation); 70 c. Women prisoners, prison money and Burma Railway (Dutch East Indies).

1985. Europa. Music Year. Multicoloured.

1465 50 c. Type **369** 40 10
1466 70 c. Organ 60 10

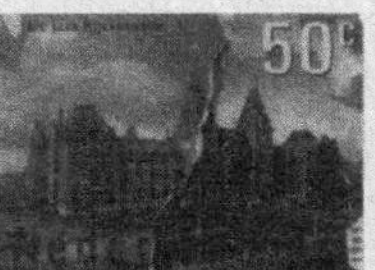

370 National Museum, Amsterdam (centenary)

1985. Anniversaries and Events. Multicoloured.
1467 50 c. Type **370** 45 10
1468 60 c. Teacher with students (bicentenary of Amsterdam Nautical College) 55 10
1469 70 c. Ship's mast and rigging ("Sail '85", Amsterdam) . . 70 10

371 Porpoise and Graph

1985. Endangered Animals.
1470 **371** 50 c. black, blue & red . . 40 10
1471 – 70 c. black, blue & red . . 85 10
DESIGN: 70 c. Seal and PCB molecule structure.

372 Ignition Key and Framed Photograph ("Think of Me")

1985. Child Welfare. Road Safety. Multicoloured.
1472 50 c. + 25 c. Type **372** . . . 60 30
1473 60 c. + 20 c. Child holding target showing speeds . . . 70 70
1474 65 c. + 20 c. Girl holding red warning triangle 85 85
1475 70 c. + 30 c. Boy holding "Children Crossing" sign . 90 20

373 Penal Code Extract

1986. Centenary of Penal Code.
1477 **373** 50 c. black, yell & pur . . 35 10

374 Surveyor with Pole and N.A.P. Water Gauge

1986. 300th Anniv of Height Gauging Marks at Amsterdam.
1478 **374** 60 c. multicoloured . . . 45 10

375 Windmill, Graph and Cloudy Sky

1986. Inaug of Windmill Test Station, Sexbierum.
1479 **375** 70 c. multicoloured . . . 60 10

376 Scales

377 Het Loo Palace Garden, Apeldoorn

1986. Cultural, Health and Social Welfare Funds. Antique Measuring Instruments. Multicoloured.
1480 50 c. + 20 c. Type **376** . . . 45 30
1481 60 c. + 25 c. Clock (vert) . . 55 30
1482 65 c. + 25 c. Barometer (vert) 70 70
1483 70 c. + 30 c. Jacob's staff . . 80 80

1986. Europa. Multicoloured.
1484 50 c. Type **377** 40 10
1485 70 c. Tree with discoloured crown 70 10

MINIMUM PRICE

The minimum price quoted is 10p which represents a handling charge rather than a basis for valuing common stamps. For further notes about prices see introductory pages.

378 Cathedral

379 Drees at Binnenhof, 1947

1986. Utrecht Events.
1486 **378** 50 c. multicoloured . . . 45 20
1487 – 60 c. blue, pink and black 65 20
1488 – 70 c. multicoloured . . . 80 10
DESIGNS—VERT: 50 c. Type **378** (completion of interior restoration); 60 c. German House (75th anniv of Heemschut Conservation Society). HORIZ: 70 c. Extract from foundation document (350th anniv of Utrecht University).

1986. Birth Centenary of Dr. Willem Drees (politician).
1489 **379** 55 c. multicoloured . . . 60 10

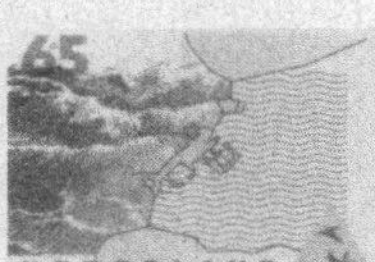

380 Draughts as Biscuits in Saucer
381 Map of Flood Barrier

1986. 75th Anniversary of Royal Dutch Draughts Association (1490) and Royal Dutch Billiards Association (1491). Multicoloured.
1490 75 c. Type **380** 90 15
1491 75 c. Player in ball preparing to play 90 15

1986. Delta Project Completion. Multicoloured.
1492 65 c. Type **381** 70 20
1493 75 c. Flood barrier 90 10

382 Children listening to Music (experiencing)

383 Engagement Picture

1986. Child Welfare. Child and Culture.
1494 55 c. + 25 c. Type **382** . . . 70 70
1495 65 c. + 35 c. Boy drawing (achieving) 80 60
1496 75 c. + 35 c. Children at theatre (understanding) 90 20

1987. Golden Wedding of Princess Juliana and Prince Bernhard.
1498 **383** 75 c. orange, black and gold 75 10

384 Block of Flats and Hut

1987. International Year of Shelter for the Homeless (65 c.) and Centenary of Netherlands Salvation Army (75 c.). Multicoloured.
1499 65 c. Type **384** 60 20
1500 75 c. Army officer, meeting and tramp 80 10

385 Eduard Douwes Dekker (Multatuli) and De Harmonie Club

1987. Writers' Death Annivs. Multicoloured.
1501 55 c. Type **385** (centenary) . . 55 20
1502 75 c. Constantijn Huygens and Scheveningseweg, The Hague (300th anniv) 85 10

386 Steam Pumping Station, Nijerk

1987. Cultural Health and Social Welfare Funds. Industrial Buildings.
1503 **386** 55 c. + 30 c. red, grey and black 70 75
1504 – 65 c. + 35 c. grey, black and blue 85 85
1505 – 75 c. + 35 c. grey, yellow and black 90 60
DESIGNS: 65 c. Water tower, Deventer; 75 c. Brass foundry, Joure.

387 Dance Theatre, Scheveningen (Rem Koolhaas)

1987. Europa. Architecture. Multicoloured.
1506 55 c. Type **387** 55 20
1507 75 c. Montessori School, Amsterdam (Herman Hertzberger) 85 10

388 Auction at Broek op Langedijk

1987. Centenary of Auction Sales (55, 75 c.) and 150th Anniv of Groningen Agricultural Society (65 c.). Multicoloured.
1508 55 c. Type **388** 55 20
1509 65 c. Groningen landscape and founders' signatures 65 20
1510 75 c. Auction sale and clock . 75 10

389 Telephone Care Circles

390 Map of Holland

1987. Dutch Red Cross. Multicoloured.
1511 55 c. + 30 c. Type **389** . . . 60 60
1512 65 c. + 35 c. Red cross and hands (Welfare work) . . . 75 75
1513 75 c. + 35 c. Red cross and drip (Blood transfusion) 85 45

1987. 75th Anniv of Netherlands Municipalities Union.
1514 **390** 75 c. multicoloured . . . 65 10

391 Noordeinde Palace, The Hague

392 Woodcutter

1987.
1515 **391** 65 c. multicoloured . . . 50 10

1987. Child Welfare. Child and Profession. Multicoloured.
1516 55 c. + 25 c. Type **392** . . . 60 60
1517 65 c. + 35 c. Woman sailor . 75 55
1518 75 c. + 35 c. Woman pilot . . 85 25

393 Star
394 "Narcissus cyclamineus" "Peeping Tom" and Extract from "I Call You Flowers" (Jan Hanlo)

1987. Christmas.
1520 **393** 50 c. red, blue and green . 60 20
1521 50 c. yellow, red and blue 60 20
1522 **393** 50 c. red, blue and yellow 60 20
1523 50 c. yellow, red and green 60 20
1524 50 c. blue, green and red . 60 20
The first colour described is that of the St. George's Cross.

1988. "Filacept" European Stamp Exhibition, The Hague. Flowers. Multicoloured.
1525 55 c. + 55 c. Type **394** . . . 90 80
1526 75 c. + 70 c. "Rosa gallica" "Versicolor" and "Roses" (Daan van Golden) . . . . 1·10 1·00
1527 75 c. + 70 c. Sea holly and 1270 map of The Hague . . . . 1·10 1·00

395 Quagga

1988. Cultural, Health and Social Welfare Funds. 150th Anniv of Natura Artis Magistra Zoological Society. Multicoloured.
1528 55 c. + 30 c. Type **395** . . . 70 70
1529 65 c. + 35 c. American manatee 80 80
1530 75 c. + 35 c. Orang-utan (vert) 90 45

396 Man's Shoulder

397 Traffic Scene with Lead Symbol crossed Through

1988. 75th Anniv of Netherlands Cancer Institute.
1531 **396** 75 c. multicoloured . . . 80 10

1988. Europa. Transport. Multicoloured.
1532 55 c. Type **397** (lead-free petrol) 50 20
1533 75 c. Cyclists reflected in car wing mirror (horiz) 75 10

398 Pendulum, Prism and Saturn

1988. 300th Anniv of England's Glorious Revolution. Multicoloured.
1534 65 c. Type **398** 50 20
1535 75 c. Queen Mary, King William III and 17th-century warship 70 10

399 "Cobra Cat" (Appel)

400 Sailing Ship and Map of Australia

1988. 40th Anniv of Founding of Cobra Painters Group. Multicoloured.
1536 55 c. Type **399** 50 50
1537 65 c. "Kite" (Corneille) . . . 55 50
1538 75 c. "Stumbling Horse" (Constant) 60 20

1988. Bicentenary of Australian Settlement.
1539 **400** 75 c. multicoloured . . . 90 10

401 Statue of Erasmus, Rotterdam

402 "Rain"

1988. 75th Anniv of Erasmus University, Rotterdam (1540) and Centenary of Concertgebouw Concert Hall and Orchestra (1541).
1540 **401** 75 c. dp green & green . . 65 20
1541 – 75 c. violet 65 20
DESIGN: No. 1541, Violin and Concertgebouw concert hall.

1988. Child Welfare. Centenary of Royal Netherlands Swimming Federation. Children's drawings. Multicoloured.
1543 55 c. + 25 c. Type **402** . . . 65 60
1544 65 c. + 35 c. "Getting Ready for the Race" 85 50
1545 75 c. + 35 c. "Swimming Test" 85 30

403 Stars

1988. Christmas.
1547 **403** 50 c. multicoloured . . . 50 10

404 Postal and Telecommunications Services

1989. Privatization of Netherlands PTT.
1548 **404** 75 c. multicoloured . . . 75 10

405 "Solidarity" **406** Members' Flags

1989. Trade Unions. Multicoloured.
1549 55 c. Type **405** 40 20
1550 75 c. Talking mouths on hands 50 10

1989. 40th Anniv of N.A.T.O.
1551 **406** 75 c. multicoloured . . . 75 10

407 Boier **408** Boy with Homemade Telephone

1989. Cultural, Health and Social Welfare Funds. Old Sailing Vessels.
1552 **407** 55 c. + 30 c. grn & blk . 30 10
1553 – 65 c. + 35 c. blue & blk . 35 10
1554 – 75 c. + 35 c. brn & blk . 40 10
DESIGNS: 65 c. Fishing smack; 75 c. Clipper.

1989. Europa. Children's Games. Multicoloured.
1555 55 c. Type **408** 50 20
1556 75 c. Girl with homemade telephone 75 10

409 Wheel on Rail **410** Boy with Ball and Diagram of Goal Scored in European Championship

1989. 150th Anniv of Netherlands' Railways. Multicoloured.
1557 55 c. Type **409** 80 25
1558 65 c. Steam, electric and diesel locomotives 90 25
1559 75 c. Diesel train, station clock and "The Kiss" (sculpture by Rodin) 95 10

1989. Centenary of Royal Dutch Football Assn.
1560 **410** 75 c. multicoloured . . . 80 10

411 Map **412** Right to Housing

1989. 150th Anniv of Division of Limburg between Netherlands and Belgium.
1561 **411** 75 c. multicoloured . . . 80 10

1989. Child Welfare. 30th Anniv of Declaration of Rights of the Child. Multicoloured.
1562 55 c. + 25 c. Type **412** . . . 60 60
1563 65 c. + 35 c. Right to food . . 80 50
1564 75 c. + 35 c. Right to education 90 30

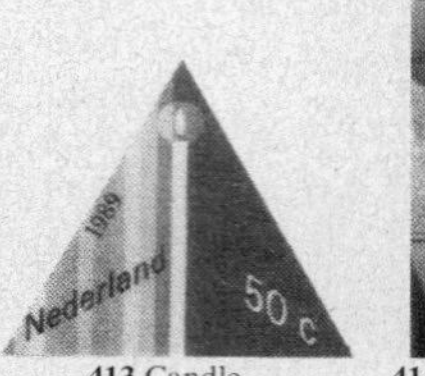

413 Candle **414** "Arms of Leiden" (tulip) and Plan of Gardens in 1601

1989. Christmas.
1566 **413** 50 c. multicoloured . . . 60 10

1990. 400th Anniv of Hortus Botanicus (botanical gardens), Leiden.
1567 **414** 65 c. multicoloured . . . 70 20

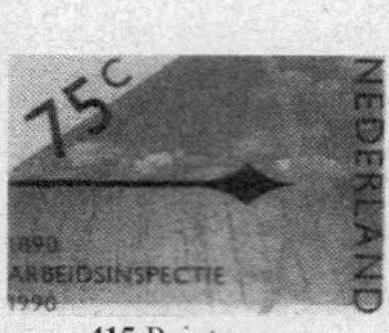

415 Pointer on Graduated Scale **416** "Self-portrait" (detail)

1990. Centenary of Labour Inspectorate.
1568 **415** 75 c. multicoloured . . . 70 10

1990. Death Centenary of Vincent van Gogh (painter). Multicoloured.
1569 55 c. Type **416** 75 20
1570 75 c. "Green Vineyard" (detail) 1·25 10

417 Summer's Day

1990. Cultural, Health and Social Welfare Funds. The Weather. Multicoloured.
1571 55 c. + 30 c. Type **417** . . . 60 50
1572 65 c. + 35 c. Clouds and isobars (vert) 75 65
1573 75 c. + 35 c. Satellite weather picture (vert) 90 30

418 Zuiderkerk Ruins

1990. 50th Anniv of German Bombing of Rotterdam.
1574 **418** 55 c. deep brown, brown and black 55 20
1575 – 65 c. multicoloured . . . 65 10
1576 – 75 c. multicoloured . . . 85 10
DESIGNS: 65 c. City plan as stage; 75 c. Girder and plans for future construction.

419 Postal Headquarters, Groningen, and Veere Post Office **420** Construction of Indiaman and Wreck of "Amsterdam"

1990. Europa. Post Office Buildings.
1577 – 55 c. grey, mauve & brn . 55 20
1578 **419** 75 c. blue, green & grey . 85 10
DESIGN: 55 c. As Type **419** but inscr "Postkantoor Veere".

1990. 3rd Anniv of Dutch East India Company Ships Association (replica ship project) (1579) and "Sail 90", Amsterdam (1580). Multicoloured.
1579 65 c. Type **420** 65 20
1580 75 c. Crew manning yards on sailing ship 95 10

421 Queens Emma, Wilhelmina, Juliana and Beatrix **422** Flames, Telephone Handset and Number

1990. Netherlands Queens of the House of Orange.
1581 **421** 150 c. multicoloured . . . 1·50 45

1990. Introduction of National Emergency Number.
1582 **422** 65 c. multicoloured . . . 60 20

423 Girl riding Horse **424** Falling Snow

1990. Child Welfare. Hobbies. Multicoloured.
1583 55 c. + 25 c. Type **423** . . . 75 60
1584 65 c. + 35 c. Girl at computer 85 50
1585 75 c. + 35 c. Young philatelist 90 30

1990. Christmas.
1587 **424** 50 c. multicoloured . . . 50 10

425 Industrial Chimneys, Exhaust Pipes and Aerosol Can (Air Pollution)

1991. Environmental Protection. Multicoloured.
1588 55 c. Type **425** 55 20
1589 65 c. Outfall pipes and chemicals (sea pollution) 70 20
1590 75 c. Agricultural chemicals, leaking drums and household landfill waste (soil pollution) 90 10

426 German Raid on Amsterdam Jewish Quarter and Open Hand

1991. 50th Anniv of Amsterdam General Strike.
1591 **426** 75 c. multicoloured . . . 75 10

427 Princess Beatrix and Prince Claus on Wedding Day **428** Queen Beatrix

1991. Royal Silver Wedding Anniversary. Mult.
1592 75 c. Type **427** 95 35
1593 75 c. Queen Beatrix and Prince Claus on horseback 95 35

1991.
1594 **428** 75 c. dp green & green . 1·40 10
1595 80 c. brown & lt brown . 60 10
1597 90 c. blue 70 10
1598 1 g. violet 75 10
1600 1 g. 30 blue and violet . . 1·00 10
1601 1 g. 40 green and olive . 1·00 10
1601a 1 g. 50 green 95 25
1602 1 g. 60 purple & mauve . 1·00 10
1603 2 g. brown . . . . . . 1·10 10
1603a 2 g. 50 purple . . . . . 1·40 10
1604 3 g. blue . . . . 1·90 10
1605 5 g. red . . . . 3·25 10
1706 7 g. 50 violet . . . . . 5·00 40
1708 10 g. green . . . . . . 6·50 70

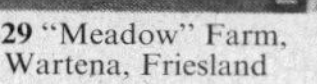

429 "Meadow" Farm, Wartena, Friesland **430** Gerard Philips's Experiments with Carbon Filaments

1991. Cultural, Health and Social Welfare Funds. Traditional Farmhouses. Multicoloured.
1610 55 c. + 30 c. Type **429** . . . 80 50
1611 65 c. + 35 c. "T-house" farm, Kesteren, Gelderland . . . 90 65
1612 75 c. + 35 c. "Courtyard" farm, Nuth, Limburg 95 30

1991. 75th Anniv of Netherlands Standards Institute (65 c.) and Centenary of Philips Organization (others). Multicoloured.
1615 55 c. Type **430** 45 20
1616 65 c. Wiring to Standard NEN 1010 (horiz) 55 20
1617 75 c. Laser beams reading video disc 70 10

431 Man raising Hat to Space **432** Sticking Plaster over Medal

1991. Europa. Europe in Space. Multicoloured.
1618 55 c. Type **431** 60 20
1619 75 c. Ladders stretching into space 80 10

1991. 75th Anniv of Nijmegen International Four Day Marches.
1620 **432** 80 c. multicoloured . . . 65 10

433 Jacobus Hendericus van't Hoff **434** Children and Open Book

1991. Dutch Nobel Prize Winners. Multicoloured.
1621 60 c. Type **433** (chemistry, 1901) 50 15
1622 70 c. Pieter Zeeman (physics, 1902) 60 20
1623 80 c. Tobias Michael Carel Asser (peace, 1911) 65 10

1991. Centenary (1992) of Public Libraries in the Netherlands.
1624 **434** 70 c. drab, black & mve . 60 20
1625 – 80 c. multicoloured . . . 65 10
DESIGN: 80 c. Books on shelf.

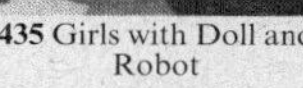

435 Girls with Doll and Robot **436** "Greetings Cards keep People in Touch"

1991. Child Welfare. Outdoor Play. Multicoloured.
1626 60 c. + 30 c. Type **435** . . . 75 50
1627 70 c. + 35 c. Bicycle race . . 85 65
1628 80 c. + 40 c. Hide and Seek . 95 30

1991. Christmas.
1630 **436** 55 c. multicoloured . . . 45 15

437 Artificial Lightning, Microchip and Oscilloscope

1992. 150th Anniv of Delft University of Technology.
1631 **437** 60 c. multicoloured . . . 50 15

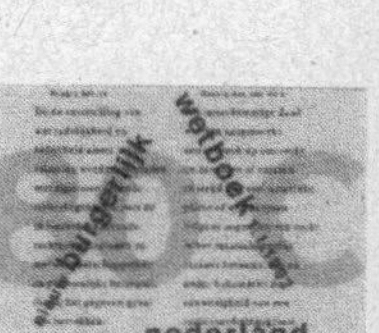

438 Extract from Code **440** Tulips ("Mondrian does not like Green")

1992. Implementation of Property Provisions of New Civil Code.
1632 **438** 80 c. multicoloured . . . 65 10

1992. "Expo '92" World's Fair, Seville. Mult.
1634 70 c. Type **440** 60 20
1635 80 c. "Netherland Expo '92" . 65 10

441 Tasman's Map of Staete Landt (New Zealand)

1992. 350th Anniv of Discovery of Tasmania and New Zealand by Abel Tasman.
1636 **441** 70 c. multicoloured . . . 60 20

442 Yellow and Purple Flowers **443** Geometric Planes

1992. Cultural, Health and Social Welfare Funds. "Floriade" Flower Show, Zoetermeer. Multicoloured.
1637 60 c. + 30 c. Water lilies . . . 75 50
1638 70 c. + 35 c. Orange and purple flowers 85 65
1639 80 c. + 40 c. Type **442** . . . 1·25 30

1992. 150th Anniv of Royal Association of Netherlands Architects (60 c.) and Inauguration of New States General Lower House (80 c.). Multicoloured.
1643 60 c. Type **443** 50 15
1644 80 c. Atrium and blue sky (symbolising sending of information into society) . . 65 10

444 Globe and Columbus **445** Moneta (Goddess of Money)

1992. Europa. 500th Anniv of Discovery of America by Columbus.
1645 **444** 60 c. multicoloured . . . 50 15
1646 – 80 c. blk, mve & yell . . . 65 10
DESIGN—VERT: 80 c. Galleon.

1992. Centenary of Royal Netherlands Numismatics Society.
1647 **445** 70 c. multicoloured . . . 60 20

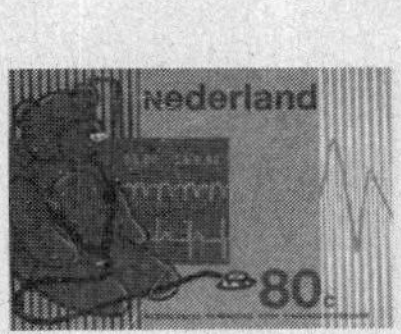

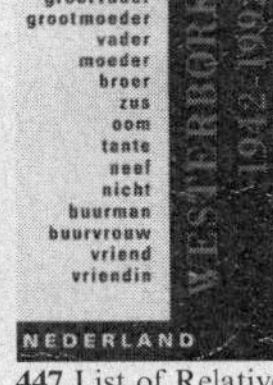

446 Teddy Bear wearing Stethoscope **447** List of Relatives and Friends

1992. Centenary of Netherlands Paediatrics Society.
1648 **446** 80 c. multicoloured . . . 65 10

1992. 50th Anniv of Departure of First Deportation Train from Westerbork Concentration Camp.
1649 **447** 70 c. multicoloured . . . 55 15

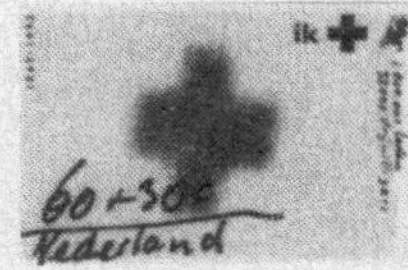

448 Cross

1992. 125th Anniv of Netherlands Red Cross. Multicoloured.
1650 60 c. + 30 c. Type **448** . . . 70 45
1651 70 c. + 35 c. Supporting injured person . . . . 1·10 55
1652 80 c. + 40 c. Red cross on dirty bandage . . . . 1·25 30

449 "United Europe" and European Community Flag **450** Queen Beatrix on Official Birthday, 1992, and at Investiture

1992. European Single Market.
1656 **449** 80 c. multicoloured . . . 60 10

1992. 12½ Years since Accession to the Throne of Queen Beatrix.
1657 **450** 80 c. multicoloured . . . 60 10

451 Saxophone Player **452** Poinsettia

1992. Child Welfare. Child and Music. Mult.
1658 60 c. + 30 c. Type **451** . . . 70 45
1659 70 c. + 35 c. Piano player . . 80 55
1660 80 c. + 40 c. Double bass player 90 30

1992. Christmas.
1662 **452** 55 c. multicoloured (centre of flower silver) 40 10
1663 55 c. multicoloured (centre red) 40 10

453 Cycling

1993. Centenary of Netherlands Cycle and Motor Industry Association.
1664 **453** 70 c. multicoloured . . . 55 15
1665 – 80 c. brown, grey & yell . 60 10
DESIGN: 80 c. Car.

454 Collages **455** Mouth to Mouth Resuscitation

1993. Greetings Stamps. Multicoloured.
1666 70 c. Type **454** 55 10
1667 70 c. Collages (different) . . . 55 10

1993. Anniversaries. Multicoloured.
1668 70 c. Type **455** (centenary of Royal Netherlands First Aid Association) 55 10
1669 80 c. Pests on leaf (75th anniv of Wageningen University of Agriculture) 55 10
1670 80 c. Lead driver and horses (bicentenary of Royal Horse Artillery) 60 10

456 Emblems

1993. 150th Anniv of Royal Dutch Notaries Association. Each red and violet.
1671 80 c. Type **456** ("150 Jaar" reading up) 60 10
1672 80 c. As Type **456** but emblems inverted and "150 Jaar" reading down 60 10
Nos. 1671/2 were issued together in horizontal tete-beche pairs, each pair forming a composite design.

457 Large White **458** Elderly Couple

1993. Butterflies. Multicoloured.
1673 70 c. Pearl-bordered fritillary . 55 15
1674 80 c. Large tortoiseshell . . . 60 10
1675 90 c. Type **457** 70 20

1993. Cultural, Health and Social Welfare Funds. Senior Citizens' Independence.
1677 70 c. + 35 c. Type **458** . . . 1·00 1·00
1678 70 c. + 35 c. Elderly man . . 1·00 1·00
1679 80 c. + 40 c. Elderly woman with dog . . . . 1·25 90

459 Radio Orange **460** Sports Pictograms

1993. Radio Orange (Dutch broadcasts from London during Second World War). Multicoloured.
1683 80 c. Type **459** 55 10
1684 80 c. Man listening to radio in secret 55 10

1993. 2nd European Youth Olympic Days. Multicoloured.
1685 70 c. Type **460** 75 15
1686 80 c. Sports pictograms (different) 80 10

461 "The Embodiment of Unity" (Wessel Couzijn) **462** Johannes Diderik van der Waals (Physics, 1910)

1993. Europa. Contemporary Art. Multicoloured.
1687 70 c. Type **461** 75 15
1688 80 c. Architectonic sculpture (Per Kirkeby) 80 10
1689 160 c. Sculpture (Naum Gabo) (vert) . . . . 1·50 1·10

1993. Nobel Prize Winners.
1690 **462** 70 c. blue, black & red . . 50 15
1691 – 80 c. mauve, blk & red . . 55 10
1692 – 90 c. multicoloured . . . 95 15
DESIGNS: 80 c. Willem Einthoven (medicine, 1924); 90 c. Christiaan Eijkman (medicine, 1929).

463 Pen and Pencils

1993. Letter Writing Campaign. Multicoloured.
1693 80 c. Type **463** 55 10
1694 80 c. Envelope 55 10

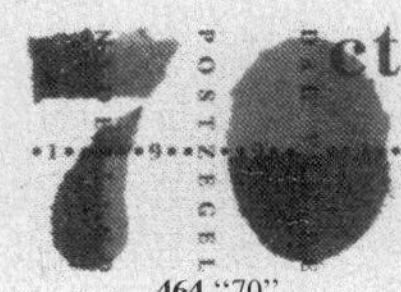

464 "70"

1993. Stamp Day (70 c.) and Netherlands PTT (80 c.). Multicoloured.
1695 70 c. Type **464** 50 15
1696 80 c. Dish aerial and dove carrying letter 55 10

465 Child in Newspaper Hat

1993. Child Welfare. Child and the Media. Multicoloured.
1697 70 c. + 35 c. Type **465** . . . 1·00 50
1698 70 c. + 35 c. Elephant listening to radio on headphones . . 1·00 50
1699 80 c. + 40 c. Television . . . 1·10 25

466 Candle

1993. Christmas. Multicoloured.
1711 55 c. Type **466** 45 15
1712 55 c. Fireworks 45 15
Both designs have a number of punched holes.

467 "Composition"

1994. 50th Death Anniv of Piet Mondriaan (artist). Multicoloured.
1713 70 c. "The Red Mill" (detail) . 55 15
1714 80 c. Type **467** 65 10
1715 90 c. "Broadway Boogie Woogie" (detail) 70 20

468 Barnacle Goose

1994. "Fepapost 94" European Stamp Exhibition, The Hague. Multicoloured.
1716 70 c. + 60 c. Type **468** . . . 1·00 65
1717 80 c. + 70 c. Bluethroat . . . 1·25 40
1718 90 c. + 80 c. Garganey . . . 1·40 95

469 Downy Rose

1994. Wild Flowers. Multicoloured.
1719 70 c. Type **469** 55 15
1720 80 c. Daisies 65 10
1721 90 c. Wood forget-me-not . . 70 20

470 Airplane

1994. 75th Aircraft Industry Anniversaries.
1723 **470** 80 c. blue and black . . . 65 10
1724 – 80 c. grey, red and black . 65 10
1725 – 80 c. multicoloured . . . 65 10
DESIGNS: No. 1723, Type **470** (KLM (Royal Dutch Airlines)); 1724, Plan and outline of aircraft and clouds (Royal Netherlands Fokker Aircraft Industries); 1725, Airplane and clouds (National Aerospace Laboratory).

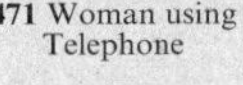

471 Woman using Telephone **472** Eisinga's Planetarium

1994. Cultural, Health and Social Welfare Funds. Senior Citizens' Security. Multicoloured.
1726 70 c. + 35 c. Type **471** . . . 85 55
1727 80 c. + 40 c. Man using telephone 95 30
1728 90 c. + 35 c. Man using telephone (different) . . . . 1·00 65

1994. Anniversaries. Multicoloured.
1732 80 c. Type **472** (250th birth anniv of Eise Eisinga) 65 10
1733 90 c. Astronaut and boot print on Moon surface (25th anniv of first manned Moon landing) 70 20

473 Players Celebrating

1994. World Cup Football Championship, U.S.A.
1734 **473** 80 c. multicoloured . . . 65 10

474 Stock Exchange

1994. Quotation of Netherlands PTT (KPN) on Stock Exchange.
1735 **474** 80 c. multicoloured . . . 65 15

475 Road Sign, Car and Bicycle

1994. Anniversaries and Events. Multicoloured.
1736 70 c. Type **475** (centenary of provision of road signs by Netherlands Motoring Association) 55 15
1737 80 c. Equestrian sports (World Equestrian Games, The Hague) 65 10

476 Footprint and Sandal

1994. Second World War. Multicoloured.
1738 80 c. Type **476** (war in Netherlands Indies, 1941–45) 65 10
1739 90 c. Soldier, children and aircraft dropping paratroops (50th anniv of Operation Market Garden (Battle of Arnhem)) (vert) 70 20

477 Brandaris Lighthouse, Terschelling

1994. Lighthouses. Multicoloured.
1740 70 c. Type **477** 55 15
1741 80 c. Ameland (vert) 65 10
1742 90 c. Vlieland (vert) 70 20

478 Decorating

479 Star and Christmas Tree

1994. Child Welfare. "Together". Multicoloured.
1744 70 c. + 35 c. Type **478** . . . 85 55
1745 80 c. + 40 c. Girl on swing knocking fruit off tree (vert) . 95 30
1746 90 c. + 35 c. Girl helping boy onto roof of playhouse (vert) . . . . 1·00 65

1994. Christmas. Multicoloured.
1748 55 c. Type **479** 45 15
1749 55 c. Candle and star . . . 45 15

480 Flying Cow

1995.
1750 **480** 100 c. multicoloured . . . 80 25

481 "Prayer" (detail)

1995. Anniversary and Events.
1751 **481** 80 c. multicoloured . . . 65 10
1752 – 80 c. multicoloured . . . 65 10
1753 – 80 c. black and red . . . 65 10
DESIGNS—VERT: No. 1751, Type **481** (50th death anniv of Hendrik Werkman (graphic designer); 1752, "Mesdag Panorama" (detail) (re-opening of Mesdag Museum). HORIZ: No. 1753, Mauritius 1847 2d. "POST OFFICE" stamp (purchase by PTT Museum of remaining mint example in private hands).

482 Joriz Ivens (documentary maker)

1995. Year of the Film (centenary of motion pictures). Multicoloured.
1754 70 c. Type **482** 55 15
1755 80 c. Scene from "Turkish Delight" 65 10

483 Mahler and Score of 7th Symphony

1995. Mahler Festival, Amsterdam.
1756 **483** 80 c. black and blue . . . 65 10

484 Dates and Acronym

1995. Centenaries. Multicoloured.
1757 80 c. Type **484** (Netherlands Institute of Chartered Accountants) 65 10
1758 80 c. Builders, bricklayer's trowel and saw (Netherlands Association of Building Contractors) 65 10

485 Postcard from Indonesia

486 "40 45"

1995. Cultural, Health and Social Welfare Funds. Mobility of the Elderly. Multicoloured.
1759 70 c. + 35 c. Type **485** . . . 85 55
1760 80 c. + 40 c. Couple reflected in mirror 95 30
1761 100 c. + 45 c. Couple with granddaughter at zoo . . . 1·10 75

1995. 50th Anniversaries. Multicoloured.
1763 80 c. Type **486** (end of Second World War) 65 10
1764 80 c. "45 95" (liberation) . . . 65 10
1765 80 c. "50" (U.N.O.) 65 10

487 Birthday Cake and Signs of the Zodiac

488 Scout

1995. Birthday Greetings.
1766 **487** 70 c. multicoloured . . . 55 15

1995. Events. Multicoloured.
1767 70 c. Type **488** (World Scout Jamboree, Dronten) 55 15
1768 80 c. Amsterdam harbour ("Sail '95" and finish of Tall Ships Race, Amsterdam) (horiz) . 65 10

489 Common Kestrel

490 Petrus Debye (Chemistry, 1936)

1995. Birds of Prey. Multicoloured.
1769 70 c. Type **489** 55 15
1770 80 c. Face of hen harrier (horiz) 65 10
1771 100 c. Red kite (horiz) 80 25

1995. Nobel Prize Winners. Multicoloured.
1773 80 c. Type **490** 65 10
1774 80 c. Frederik Zernike (Physics, 1953) 65 10
1775 80 c. Jan Tinbergen (Economics, 1969) 65 10

491 Eduard Jacobs and Jean-Louis Pisuisse

1995. Centenary of Dutch Cabaret. Multicoloured.
1776 70 c. Type **491** 55 15
1777 80 c. Wim Kan and Freek de Jonge 65 10

492 "The Schoolteacher" (Leonie Ensing)

493 Children with Stars

1995. Child Welfare. "Children and Fantasy". Children's Computer Drawings. Multicoloured.
1778 70 c. + 35 c. "Dino" (Sjoerd Stegeman) (horiz) 85 55
1779 80 c. + 40 c. Type **492** . . . 95 30
1780 100 c. + 50 c. "Children and Colours" (Marcel Jansen) (horiz) . . . . 1·10 75

1995. Christmas. Self-adhesive.
1782 **493** 55 c. red, yellow and black 45 15
1783 – 55 c. blue, yellow and black 45 15
DESIGN: No. 1783, Children looking at star through window.

494 "Woman in Blue reading a Letter"

495 Trowel, Daffodil Bulb and Glove

1996. Johannes Vermeer Exhibition, Washington and The Hague. Details of his Paintings. Multicoloured.
1784 70 c. "Lady writing a Letter with her Maid" 50 15
1785 80 c. "The Love Letter" . . . 60 10
1786 100 c. Type **494** 75 20

1996. Spring Flowers. Multicoloured.
1788 70 c. Type **495** 50 15
1789 80 c. Tulips "kissing" woman . 60 10
1790 100 c. Snake's-head fritillary (detail of painting, Charles Mackintosh) 75 20

496 Putting up "MOVED" sign

497 Swimming

1996. Change of Address Stamp.
1792 **496** 70 c. multicoloured . . . 50 15
See also No. 1826.

1996. Cultural, Health and Social Welfare Funds. The Elderly in the Community. Multicoloured.
1793 70 c. + 35 c. Type **497** . . . 75 50
1794 80 c. + 40 c. Grandad bottle-feeding baby 90 30
1795 100 c. + 50 c. Playing piano . . 1·10 75

499 Cycling

1996. Tourism. Multicoloured.
1798 70 c. Type **499** 50 15
1799 70 c. Paddling in sea 50 15
1800 80 c. Traditional architecture . 60 10
1801 100 c. Windmills 75 20

500 Parade in Traditional Costumes

1996. Bicentenary of Province of North Brabant.
1802 **500** 80 c. multicoloured . . . 60 10

501 Lighting Olympic Torch

502 Erasmus Bridge

1996. Sporting Events. Multicoloured.
1803 70 c. Type **501** (Olympic Games, Atlanta) 50 15
1804 80 c. Flag and cyclists (Tour de France cycling championship) 60 10
1805 100 c. Player, ball and Wembley Stadium (European Football Championship, England) . . . 75 20
1806 160 c. Olympic rings and athlete on starting block (Olympic Games, Atlanta) . . . . . 1·10 55

1996. Bridges and Tunnels. Multicoloured.
1807 80 c. Type **502** 60 10
1808 80 c. Wijker Tunnel (horiz) . . 60 10
1809 80 c. Martinus Nijhoff Bridge (horiz) 60 10

503 Children in School Uniforms

504 Bert and Ernie

1996. 50th Anniv of U.N.I.C.E.F. Multicoloured.
1810 70 c. Type **503** 50 15
1811 80 c. Girl carrying platter on head 60 10

1996. "Sesame Street" (children's television programme). Multicoloured.
1812 70 c. Type **504** 50 15
1813 80 c. Bears holding Big Bird's foot 60 10

505 Petrus Plancius
506 Books and Baby

1996. 16th-century Voyages of Discovery.
1814 **505** 70 c. black, yellow and red 50 15
1815 – 80 c. multicoloured . . . 60 10
1816 – 80 c. multicoloured . . . 60 10
1817 – 100 c. multicoloured . . . 75 20
DESIGNS: No. 1815, Cornelis de Houtman; 1816, Willem Barentsz; 1817, Mahu en De Cordes.

1996. Child Welfare. Multicoloured.
1818 70 c. + 35 c. Type **506** 75 50
1819 80 c. + 40 c. Animals and boy . . 90 30
1820 80 c. + 40 c. Tools and girl . . 90 30

507 Woman's Face and Hand

1996. Christmas. Multicoloured. Self-adhesive.
1822 55 c. Type **507** 40 10
1823 55 c. Woman's eyes and man shouting 40 10
1824 55 c. Bird's wing, hands and detail of man's face 40 10
1825 55 c. Men's faces & bird's wing 40 10
Nos. 1822/5 were issued together, se-tenant, forming a composite design.

1997. Change of Address Stamp. Self-adhesive.
1826 **496** 80 c. multicoloured . . . 50 10
No. 1826 was intended for use by people moving house.

508 Numeral on Envelope with Top Flap

1997. Business Stamps. Multicoloured. Self-adhesive.
1827 80 c. Type **508** 50 10
1828 160 c. Numeral on envelope with side flap 95 45

509 Skaters

1997. 15th Eleven Cities Skating Race.
1829 **509** 80 c. multicoloured . . . 50 10

510 Heart

1997. Greetings Stamps.
1830 **510** 80 c. multicoloured . . . 50 10
No. 1830 is for the stamp with the heart intact. The heart can be scratched away to reveal different messages.

511 Pony

1997. Nature and the Environment. Multicoloured.
1831 80 c. Type **511** 50 10
1832 100 c. Cow 60 15

512 Suske, Wiske, Lambik and Aunt Sidonia

1997. Suske and Wiske (cartoon by Willy Vandersteen).
1834 **512** 80 c. multicoloured . . . 50 10

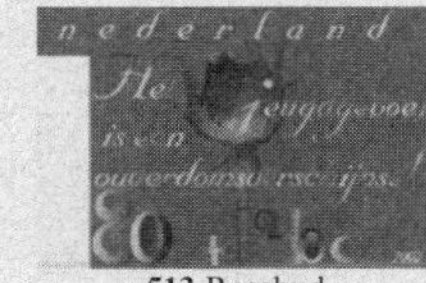

513 Rosebud

1997. Cultural, Health and Social Welfare Funds. The Elderly and their Image. Multicoloured.
1836 80 c. + 40 c. Type **513** . . . 70 25
1837 80 c. + 40 c. Rose stem . . . 70 25
1838 80 c. + 40 c. Rose 70 25

514 Birthday Cake

1997. Greetings Stamps. Multicoloured.
1840 80 c. Type **514** 50 10
1841 80 c. Cup of coffee, glasses of wine, candles, writing letter, and amaryllis 50 10

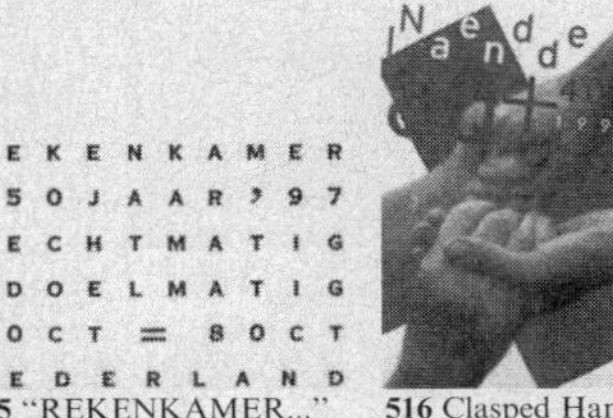

515 "REKENKAMER..." (550th anniv of Court of Audit
516 Clasped Hands over Red Cross

1997. Anniversaries.
1842 **515** 80 c. multicoloured . . . 50 10
1843 – 80 c. red, yellow and black 50 10
1844 – 80 c. red, black and blue 50 10
DESIGNS—50th anniv of Marshall Plan (post-war American aid for Europe): No. 1843, Map of Europe; 1844, Star and stripes.

1997. Red Cross.
1845 **516** 80 c. + 40 c. multicoloured . 70 20

517 "eu" and Globe

1997. European Council of Ministers' Summit, Amsterdam.
1846 **517** 100 c. multicoloured . . 60 15

518 Children playing in Boat

1997. Water Activities. Multicoloured.
1847 80 c. Type **518** 50 10
1848 1 g. Skutsje (sailing barges) races, Friesland 60 15

519 "vernuft"

1997. Anniversaries. Multicoloured.
1849 **519** 80 c. ultramarine and blue . 50 10
1850 – 80 c. ultramarine and blue . 50 10
1851 – 80 c. multicoloured . . 50 10
1852 – 80 c. multicoloured . . 50 10
DESIGNS: No. 1849, Type **519** (150th anniv of Royal Institute of Engineers); 1850, "adem" (centenary of Netherlands Asthma Centre, Davos, Switzerland); 1851, Flower (centenary of Florens College (horticultural college) and 125th anniv of Royal Botanical and Horticultural Society); 1852, Pianist accompanying singer (birth bicentenary of Franz Schubert (composer)).

520 "Nederland80"

1997. Youth. Multicoloured.
1853 **520** 80 c. red and blue . . . 50 10
1854 – 80 c. multicoloured . . . 50 10
DESIGN: No. 1854, "NEDERLAND80" in style of computer games giving appearance of three-dimensional block on race track.

521 Stork with Bundle

1997. New Baby Stamp. Ordinary or self-adhesive gum.
1855 **521** 80 c. multicoloured . . . 50 10

522 "Little Red Riding Hood"
523 Heads and Star

1997. Child Welfare. Fairy Tales. Multicoloured.
1856 80 c. + 40 c. Type **522** . . . 75 25
1857 80 c. + 40 c. Man laying loaves on ground ("Tom Thumb") . 75 25
1858 80 c. + 40 c. Woodman with bottle ("Genie in the Bottle") 75 25

1997. Christmas. Multicoloured, colour of background given.
1860 **523** 55 c. yellow 35 10
1861 55 c. blue 35 10
1862 – 55 c. orange 35 10
1863 – 55 c. red 35 10
1864 – 55 c. green 35 10
1865 **523** 55 c. green 35 10
DESIGN: Nos. 1862, 1863, 1864, Heads and heart.

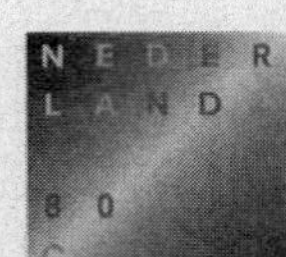

524 Light across Darkness
525 Cow and "Ship" Tiles

1998. Bereavement Stamp.
1866 **524** 80 c. blue 50 10

1998. Delft Faience.
1867 **525** 100 c. multicoloured . . . 65 15
1868 – 160 c. blue . . . . 1·00 50
DESIGN: 160 c. Ceramic tile showing boy standing on head.

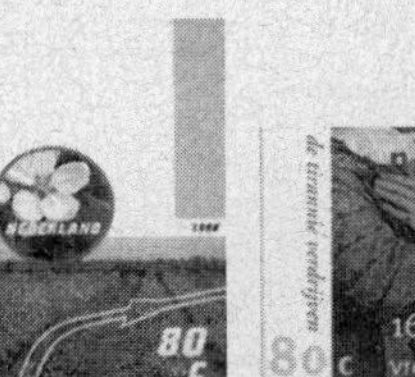

526 Strawberries in Bloom (Spring)
527 Handshake

1998. The Four Seasons. Multicoloured.
1869 80 c. Type **526** 50 45
1870 80 c. Strawberry, flan and strawberry plants (Summer) 50 45
1871 80 c. Bare trees and pruning diagram (Winter) 50 45
1872 80 c. Orchard and apple (Autumn) 50 45

1998. Anniversaries. Multicoloured.
1873 80 c. Type **527** (350th anniv of Treaty of Munster) 50 10
1874 80 c. Statue of Johan Thorbecke (politician) (150th anniv of Constitution) 50 10
1875 80 c. Child on swing (50th anniv of Declaration of Human Rights) 50 10

528 Bride and Groom
529 Shopping List

1998. Wedding Stamp. Ordinary or self-adhesive gum.
1876 **528** 80 c. multicoloured . . . 50 10

1998. Cultural, Health and Social Welfare Funds. Care and the Elderly.
1877 80 c. + 40 c. Type **529** . . . 75 25
1878 80 c. + 40 c. Sweet 75 25
1879 80 c. + 40 c. Training shoe . . 75 25

530 Letters Blowing in Wind

1998. Letters to the Future.
1881 **530** 80 c. multicoloured . . . 50 10

531 Customers

1998. Centenary of Rabobank.
1882 **531** 80 c. yellow, green and blue 50 10

532 Goalkeeper catching Boot

1998. Sport.
1883 80 c. Type **532** (World Cup Football Championship, France) 50 10
1884 80 c. Family hockey team (centenary of Royal Netherlands Hockey Federation) 50 10

533 Map of Friesland, c. 1600

1998. 500th Anniv of Central Administration of Friesland.
1885 **533** 80 c. multicoloured . . . 50 10

534 River Defences

1998. Bicentenary of Directorate-General of Public Works and Water Management. Multicoloured.
1886 80 c. Type **534** 50 10
1887 1 g. Sea defences 65 15

535 "tnt post groep"

1998. Separation of Royal Netherlands PTT into TNT Post Groep and KPN NV (telecommunications).
1888 **535** 80 c. black, blue and red . . 50 10
1889 – 80 c. black, blue and green . 50 10
DESIGN: No. 1889, "kpn nv".
Nos. 1888/9 were issued together, se-tenant, forming a composite design of the complete "160".

536 Books and Keyboard

1998. Cultural Anniversaries. Multicoloured.
1890 80 c. Type **536** (bicentenary of National Library) 50 10
1891 80 c. Maurits Escher (graphic artist, birth centenary) looking at his mural "Metamorphose" in The Hague Post Office (vert) . . . 50 10
1892 80 c. Simon Vestdijk (writer, birth centenary) and page from "Fantoches" 50 10

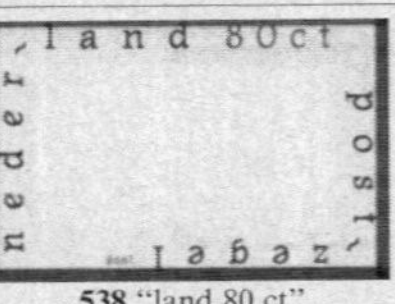

538 "land 80 ct"

1998. Greetings Stamps. Multicoloured. Self-adhesive.
1894 80 c. Type **538** (top of frame red) 50 10
1895 80 c. "80 ct post" (top of frame mauve) 50 10
1896 80 c. Type **538** (top of frame orange) 50 10
1897 80 c. "80 ct post" (top of frame orange) 50 10
1898 80 c. Type **538** (top of frame yellow) 50 10

The part of the frame used for identification purposes is above the face value.

Nos. 1894/8 were only available in sheetlets of ten stamps and 20 labels (five stamps and ten labels on each side of the card). It was intended that the sender should insert the appropriate greetings label into the rectangular space on each stamp before use.

539 Rabbits

1998. Domestic Pets. Multicoloured.
1899 80 c. Type **539** 50 10
1900 80 c. Drent partridge dog . . . 50 10
1901 80 c. Kittens 50 10

540 Cathy and Jeremy writing a Letter

1998. 25th Anniv of Jack, Jacky and the Juniors (comic strip characters).
1902 **540** 80 c. multicoloured . . . 50 45

541 St. Nicholas on Horseback

1998. Child Welfare. Celebrations. Multicoloured.
1904 80 c. + 40 c. Type **541** . . . 75 25
1905 80 c. + 40 c. Making birthday cake 75 25
1906 80 c. + 40 c. Carnival parade . 75 25

542 Hare and Snowball
543 House and Tree on Snowball

1998. Christmas. Self-adhesive.
1908 **542** 55 c. blue, red and black . 35 10
1909 – 55 c. multicoloured . . . 35 10
1910 – 55 c. blue, red and black . 35 10
1911 – 55 c. multicoloured . . . 35 10
1912 – 55 c. blue, red and black . 35 10
1913 – 55 c. green, blue and red . 35 10
1914 – 55 c. green, blue and red . 35 10
1915 – 55 c. green, blue and red . 35 10
1916 – 55 c. green, blue and red . 35 10
1917 – 55 c. green, blue and red . 35 10
1918 – 55 c. blue, green and red . 35 10
1919 – 55 c. red, green and black . 35 10
1920 – 55 c. blue, green and red . 35 10
1921 – 55 c. green, red and black . 35 10
1922 – 55 c. blue, green and red . 35 10
1923 – 55 c. blue, green and red . 35 10
1924 – 55 c. blue, green and red . 35 10
1925 – 55 c. blue, green and red . 35 10
1926 – 55 c. blue, green and red . 35 10
1927 – 55 c. blue, green and red . 35 10

DESIGNS: No. 1909, House and snowball; 1910, Dove and snowball; 1911, Christmas tree and snowball; 1912, Reindeer and snowball; 1913, Hare; 1914, House; 1915, Dove; 1916, Christmas tree; 1917, Reindeer; 1918, House and hare; 1919, House and heart; 1920, Dove and house; 1921, Christmas tree and house; 1922, House and reindeer; 1923, Christmas tree and hare; 1924, Christmas tree and house; 1925, Christmas tree and dove; 1926, Christmas tree and heart; 1927, Christmas tree and reindeer.

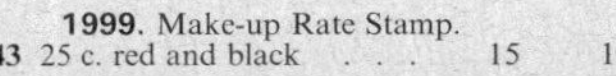

1999. Make-up Rate Stamp.
1928 **543** 25 c. red and black . . . 15 10

544 Euro Coin

1999. Introduction of the Euro (European currency).
1929 **544** 80 c. multicoloured . . . 50 10

545 Pillar Box, 1850

1999. Bicentenary of Netherlands Postal Service.
1930 **545** 80 c. multicoloured . . . 50 10

546 Richard Krajicek serving
547 White Spoonbill

1999. Centenary of Royal Dutch Lawn Tennis Federation.
1931 **546** 80 c. multicoloured . . . 45 10

1999. Protection of Bird and Migrating Waterfowl. Multicoloured.
1932 80 c. Type **547** (centenary of Dutch Bird Protection Society) 45 10
1933 80 c. Section of globe and terns (African–Eurasian Waterbird Agreement 45 10

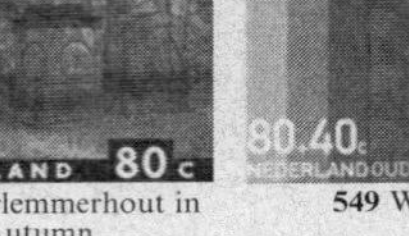

548 Haarlemmerhout in Autumn
549 Woman

1999. Parks during the Seasons. Multicoloured.
1934 80 c. Type **548** 45 10
1935 80 c. Sonsbeek in winter . . . 45 10
1936 80 c. Weerribben in summer . . 45 10
1937 80 c. Keukenhof in spring . . 45 10

1999. Cultural, Health and Social Welfare Funds. International Year of the Elderly. Multicoloured.
1938 80 c. + 40 c. Type **549** 70 10
1939 80 c. + 40 c. Man (green background) 70 10
1940 80 c. + 40 c. Man (blue background) 70 10

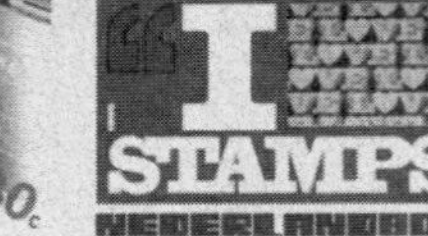

550 Lifeboats on Rough Sea
551 "I Love Stamps"

1999. Maritime Anniversaries. Multicoloured.
1942 80 c. Type **550** (175th Anniv of Royal Netherlands Lifeboat Association) 45 10
1943 80 c. Freighters in canal (150th Anniv of Royal Association of Ships' Masters "Schuttevaer") 45 10

1999.
1944 **551** 80 c. blue and red 45 10
1945 – 80 c. red and blue 45 10

DESIGN: No. 1945, "Stamps love Me".

552 "The Goldfinch" (Carel Fabritius)

1999. 17th-Century Dutch Art. Multicoloured. Self-adhesive gum (1 g.).
1946 80 c. Type **552** 45 10
1947 80 c. "Self-portrait" (Rembrandt) 45 10
1948 80 c. "Self-portrait" (Judith Leyster) 45 10
1949 80 c. "St. Sebastian" (Hendrick ter Brugghen) 45 10
1950 80 c. "Beware of Luxury" (Jan Steen) 45 10
1951 80 c. "The Sick Child" (Gabriel Metsu) 45 10
1952 80 c. "Gooseberries" (Adriaen Coorte) 45 10
1953 80 c. "View of Haarlem" (Jacob van Ruisdael) 45 10
1954 80 c. "Mariaplaats, Utrecht" (Pieter Saenredam) 45 10
1955 80 c. "Danae" (Rembrandt) . . 45 10
1956 1 g. "The Jewish Bride" (Rembrandt) 60 10

553 "80" on Computer Screen

1999. Ordinary or self-adhesive gum.
1957 **553** 80 c. multicoloured . . . 45 10

554 Amaryllis, Coffee Cup, Candles, Letter Writing and Wine Glasses

1999. Greetings Stamp. Self-adhesive.
1959 **554** 80 c. multicoloured . . . 45 10

555 Victorian Heavy Machinery and Modern Computer

1999. Centenary of Confederation of Netherlands Industry and Employers.
1962 **555** 80 c. multicoloured . . . 45 10

556 Tintin and Snowy wearing Space Suits

1999. 70th Anniv of Tintin (comic strip character by Herge). Scenes from "Explorers on the Moon". Multicoloured.
1963 **556** 80 c. multicoloured . . . 45 40

558 Digger (completion of Afsluitdijk, 1932)

1999. The Twentieth Century. Multicoloured.
1966 80 c. Type **558** 45 10
1967 80 c. Space satellite 45 10
1968 80 c. Berlage Commodity Exchange, Amsterdam (inauguration, 1903) 45 10
1969 80 c. Empty motorway (car-free Sundays during oil crisis, 1973–74) 45 10
1970 80 c. Old man (Old Age Pensions Act, 1947) 45 10
1971 80 c. Delta Flood Project, 1953–97 . . . . 45 10
1972 80 c. Players celebrating (victory of Netherlands in European Cup Football Championship, 1998) 45 10
1973 80 c. Four riders on one motor cycle (liberation and end of Second World War, 1945) . 45 10
1974 80 c. Woman posting vote (Women's Franchise, 1919) . 45 10
1975 80 c. Ice skaters (eleven cities race) 45 10

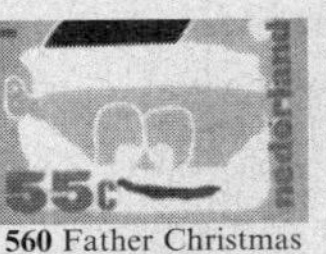

559 Pluk van de Pettevlet on Fire Engine

1999. Child Welfare. Characters created by Fiep Westendorp. Multicoloured.
1976 80 c. + 40 c. Type **559** 70 45
1977 80 c. + 40 c. Otje drinking through straw 70 45
1978 80 c. + 40 c. Jip and Janneke with cat 70 45

560 Father Christmas (Robin Knegt)
561 "25"

1999. Christmas. Winning entries in design competition. Multicoloured.
1980 55 c. Type **560** 30 10
1981 55 c. Angel singing (Davinia Bovenlander) (vert) 30 10
1982 55 c. Dutch doughnuts in box (Henk Drenth) 30 10
1983 55 c. Moon wearing Christmas hat (Lizet van den Berg) (vert) 30 10
1984 55 c. Father Christmas carrying sacks (Noortje Kruse) . . . 30 10
1985 55 c. Clock striking midnight (Hucky de Haas) (vert) . . . 30 10
1986 55 c. Ice skater (Marleen Bos) . 30 10
1987 55 c. Human Christmas tree (Mariette Strik) (vert) . . . 30 10
1988 55 c. Woman wearing Christmas tree earrings (Saskia van Oversteeg) . . . 30 10
1989 55 c. Woman vacuuming pine needles (Frans Koenis) (vert) 30 10
1990 55 c. Angel with harp and music score (Evelyn de Zeeuw) 30 10
1991 55 c. Hand balancing candle, star, hot drink, hat and Christmas tree on fingers (Aafke van Ewijk) (vert) . . . 30 10
1992 55 c. Christmas tree (Daan Roepman) (vert) 30 10
1993 55 c. Cat wearing crown (Sjoerd van der Zee) (vert) 30 10
1994 55 c. Bird flying over house (Barbara Vollers) 30 10
1995 55 c. Baby with angel wings (Rosmarijn Schmink) (vert) . 30 10
1996 55 c. Dog wearing Christmas hat (Casper Heijstek and Mirjam Cnosser) 30 10
1997 55 c. Angel flying (Patricia van der Neut) (vert) 30 10
1998 55 c. Nativity (Marco Cockx) . 30 10
1999 55 c. Christmas tree with decorations (Matthias Meiling) (vert) 30 10

2000. Make-up Rate Stamp.
2000 **561** 25 c. red, blue and yellow . 15 10

562 Guilder, Margaret of Austria (Regent of Netherlands) (after Bernard van Orley) and "Coronation of Charles V" (Juan de la Coate)

2000. 500th Birth Anniv of Charles V, Holy Roman Emperor. Multicoloured.
2001 80 c. Type **562** 45 10
2002 80 c. Map of the Seventeen Provinces, "Charles V after the Battle of Muehlberg" (Titian) and Margaret of Parma (Regent of Netherlands) (after Antonius Mohr) 45 10

MARINE INSURANCE STAMPS

M 22

1921.

No.	Type	Description	Unused	Used
M238	M 22	15 c. green	9·00	48·00
M239		60 c. red	11·00	55·00
M240		75 c. brown	13·00	65·00
M241	–	1 g. 50 blue	65·00	£500
M242	–	2 g. 25 brown	£110	£700
M243	–	4½ g. black	£180	£900
M244	–	7½ g. red	£300	£1400

DESIGNS (inscr "DRIJVENDE BRANDKAST"): 1 g. 50, 2 g. 25 "Explosion"; 4½ g., 7½ g. Lifebelt.

OFFICIAL STAMPS

1913. Stamps of 1898 optd **ARMENWET**.

No.	Type	Description	Unused	Used
O214	12	1 c. red	3·75	2·75
O215		1½ c. blue	85	2·25
O216		2 c. brown	6·25	7·50
O217		2½ c. green	16·00	13·00
O218	13	3 c. green	3·75	1·25
O219		5 c. red	3·75	4·75
O220		10 c. grey	32·00	40·00

POSTAGE DUE STAMPS

D 8

D 9

1870.

No.	Type	Description	Unused	Used
D76	D 8	5 c. brown on yellow	70·00	12·00
D77		10 c. purple on blue	£160	14·50

For same stamps in other colours, see Netherlands Indies, Nos. D1/5.

1881.

No.	Type	Description	Unused	Used
D208	D 9	½ c. black and blue	15	15
D182		1 c. black and blue	1·25	15
D183		1½ c. black and blue	45	20
D184		2½ c. black and blue	1·75	15
D209		3 c. black and blue	1·50	1·00
D210		4 c. black and blue	1·50	1·75
D185		5 c. black and blue	10·00	10
D211		6½ c. black and blue	32·00	35·00
D212		7½ c. black and blue	1·75	40
D186		10 c. black and blue	28·00	25
D187		12½ c. black and blue	23·00	1·10
D188		15 c. black and blue	28·00	90
D189		20 c. black and blue	16·00	6·50
D190		25 c. black and blue	35·00	45
D181		1 g. red and blue	80·00	22·00

No. D181 is inscribed "EEN GULDEN".

1906. Surch.

No.	Type	Description	Unused	Used
D213	D 9	3 c. on 1 g. red & blue	27·00	27·00
D215		4 on 6½ c. black & blue	4·50	5·50
D216		6½ on 20 c. black & blue	3·50	4·50
D214		50 c. on 1 g. red & blue	£130	£130

1907. De Ruyter Commem. stamps surch **PORTZEGEL** and value.

No.	Type	Description	Unused	Used
D217	15	½ c. on 1 c. red	1·25	1·25
D218		1 c. on 1 c. red	75	75
D219		1½ c. on 1 c. red	75	75
D220		2½ c. on 1 c. red	1·60	1·60
D221		5 c. on 2½ c. red	1·60	75
D222		6½ c. on 2½ c. red	2·75	2·75
D223		7½ c. on ½ c. blue	1·75	1·50
D224		10 c. on ½ c. blue	1·75	95
D225		12½ c. on ½ c. blue	4·50	4·50
D226		15 c. on 2½ c. red	6·50	3·75
D227		25 c. on ½ c. blue	8·00	7·50
D228		50 c. on ½ c. blue	40·00	35·00
D229		1 g. on ½ c. blue	60·00	50·00

1912. Re-issue of Type **D 9** in one colour.

No.	Type	Description	Unused	Used
D230	D 9	½ c. blue	10	10
D231		1 c. blue	10	10
D232		1½ c. blue	1·50	1·50
D233		2½ c. blue	10	10
D234		3 c. blue	35	35
D235		4 c. blue	10	15
D236		4½ c. blue	5·00	4·75
D237		5 c. blue	10	10
D238		5½ c. blue	4·75	4·50
D239		7 c. blue	2·25	2·25
D240		7½ c. blue	3·25	1·50
D241		10 c. blue	50	50
D242		12½ c. blue	50	50
D453		15 c. blue	50	50
D244		20 c. blue	50	50
D245		25 c. blue	65·00	95
D246		50 c. blue	40	15

D 25

D 121

1921.

No.	Type	Description	Unused	Used
D442	D 25	3 c. blue	35	15
D445		6 c. blue	35	15
D446		7 c. blue	50	50
D447		7½ c. blue	50	55
D448		8 c. blue	50	50
D449		9 c. blue	65	65
D450		11 c. blue	10·00	3·25
D247		12 c. blue	45	40
D455		25 c. blue	45	40
D456		30 c. blue	50	40
D458		1 g. red	60	40

1923. Surch in white figures in black circle.

No.	Type	Description	Unused	Used
D272	D 9	1 c. on 3 c. blue	75	75
D273		2½ c. on 7 c. blue	1·10	50
D274		25 c. on 1½ c. blue	8·25	75
D275		25 c. on 7½ c. blue	9·25	50

1924. Stamps of 1898 surch **TE BETALEN PORT** and value in white figures in black circle.

No.	Type	Description	Unused	Used
D295	13	4 c. on 3 c. green	1·50	1·10
D296	12	5 c. on 1 c. red	75	40
D297		10 c. on 1½ c. blue	1·10	45
D298	13	12½ c. on 5 c. red	1·25	45

1947.

No.	Type	Description	Unused	Used
D656	D 121	1 c. blue	10	10
D657		3 c. blue	10	15
D658		4 c. blue	10·00	80
D659		5 c. blue	10	10
D660		6 c. blue	35	35
D661		7 c. blue	15	15
D662		8 c. blue	15	15
D663		10 c. blue	15	10
D664		11 c. blue	35	35
D665		12 c. blue	90	80
D666		14 c. blue	75	70
D667		15 c. blue	30	10
D668		16 c. blue	85	85
D669		20 c. blue	30	10
D670		24 c. blue	1·25	1·25
D671		25 c. blue	30	10
D672		26 c. blue	1·60	1·75
D673		30 c. blue	65	10
D674		35 c. blue	70	10
D675		40 c. blue	75	10
D676		50 c. blue	85	10
D677		60 c. blue	1·00	25
D678		85 c. blue	15·00	35
D679		90 c. blue	2·75	40
D680		95 c. blue	2·75	35
D681		1 g. red	2·25	10
D682		1 g. 75 red	5·50	25

For stamps as Types **D 121**, but in violet, see under Surinam.

INTERNATIONAL COURT OF JUSTICE

Stamps specially issued for use by the Headquarters of the Court of International Justice. Nos. J1 to J36 were not sold to the public in unused condition.

1934. Optd **COUR PER- MANENTE DE JUSTICE INTER- NATIONALE**.

No.	Type	Description	Unused	Used
J1	35	1½ c. mauve	—	40
J2		2½ c. green	—	40
J3	36	7½ c. red	—	80
J4	68	12½ c. blue	—	25·00
J7	36	12½ c. blue	—	18·00
J5		15 c. yellow	—	1·00
J6		3 c. purple	—	2·10

1940. Optd **COUR PER- MANENTE DE JUSTICE INTER- NATIONALE**.

No.	Type	Description	Unused	Used
J 9	94	7½ c. red	—	9·00
J10		12½ c. blue	—	9·00
J11		15 c. blue	—	9·00
J12		30 c. bistre	—	9·00

1947. Optd **COUR INTERNATIONALE DE JUSTICE**.

No.	Type	Description	Unused	Used
J13	94	7½ c. red	—	1·00
J14		10 c. purple	—	1·00
J15		12½ c. blue	—	1·00
J16		20 c. violet	—	1·00
J17		25 c. red	—	1·00

J 3   J 4 Peace Palace, The Hague

J 5 Queen Juliana

1950.

No.	Type	Description	Unused	Used
J18	J 3	2 c. blue	—	8·25
J19		4 c. green	—	8·25

1951.

No.	Type	Description	Unused	Used
J20	J 4	2 c. lake	—	50
J21		3 c. blue	—	50
J22		4 c. green	—	50
J23		5 c. brown	—	50
J24	J 5	6 c. mauve	—	2·10
J25	J 4	6 c. green	—	85
J26		7 c. red	—	85
J27	J 5	10 c. green	—	15
J28		12 c. red	—	1·75
J29		15 c. red	—	15
J30		20 c. blue	—	20
J31		25 c. brown	—	20
J32		30 c. purple	—	30
J33	J 4	40 c. blue	—	30
J34		45 c. red	—	35
J35		50 c. mauve	—	35
J36	J 5	1 g. grey	—	70

J 6 Olive Branch and Peace Palace, The Hague

1989.

No.	Type	Description	Unused	Used
J37	J 6	5 c. black and yellow	10	10
J38		10 c. black and blue	10	10
J39		25 c. black and red	20	20
J41		50 c. black and green	40	40
J42		55 c. black and mauve	40	40
J43		60 c. black and bistre	45	45
J44		65 c. black and green	50	50
J45		70 c. black and blue	55	55
J46		75 c. black and yellow	55	55
J47		80 c. black and green	60	60
J49		1 g. black and orange	75	75
J50		1 g. 50 black and blue	1·10	1·10
J51		1 g. 60 black and brown	1·00	1·00
J54	–	5 g. multicoloured	3·25	3·25
J56	–	7 g. multicoloured	4·00	4·00

DESIGNS: 5, 7 g. Olive branch and column

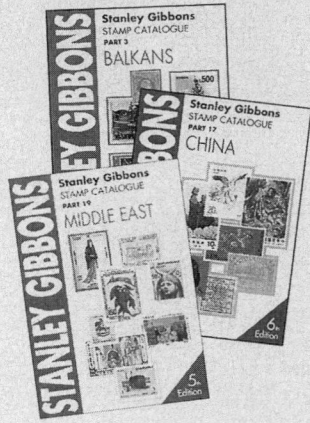

NETHERLANDS ANTILLES Pt. 4

Curacao and other Netherlands islands in the Caribbean Sea. In December 1954 these were placed on an equal footing with Netherlands under the Crown.

100 cents = 1 gulden

48 Spanish Galleon

49 Alonso de Ojeda

1949. 450th Anniv of Discovery of Curacao.
306 **48** 6 c. green . . . . 3·50 1·75
307 **49** 12½ c. red . . . . 3·75 3·50
308 **48** 15 c. blue . . . . 3·75 2·25

50 Posthorns and Globe

51 Leap-frog

1949. 75th Anniv of U.P.U.
309 **50** 6 c. red . . . . 3·00 2·25
310 25 c. blue . . . . 3·00 1·10

1950. As numeral and portrait types of Netherlands but inscr "NED. ANTILLEN".
325 **118** 1 c. brown 10 10
326 1½ c. blue 10 10
327 2 c. orange 10 10
328 2½ c. green 80 15
329 3 c. violet 10 10
329a 4 c. green 45 35
330 5 c. red 10 10
310a **129** 5 c. yellow 25 25
311 6 c. purple 85 10
311a 7½ c. brown . . . . . . 4·00 10
312a 10 c. red 30 30
313 12½ c. green . . . . . . 1·75 15
314a 15 c. blue 35 35
315a 20 c. orange 70 70
316 21 c. black . . . . . . 2·00 1·75
316a 22½ c. green . . . . . . 5·00 10
317a 25 c. violet 80 80
318 27½ c. brown . . . . . . 5·00 1·90
319a 30 c. sepia 80 80
319b 40 c. blue 80 80
320 50 c. olive . . . . . . 9·00 10
321 **130** 1½ g. green . . . . . . 32·00 20
322 2½ g. brown . . . . . . 30·00 70
323 5 g. red . . . . 50·00 8·50
324 10 g. purple . . . . . . £200 50·00

1951. Child Welfare.
331 **51** 1½ c. + 1 c. violet . . . . . 1·75 2·25
332 – 5 c. + 2½ c. brown . . . . 11·00 4·50
333 – 6 c. + 2½ c. blue . . . . 11·00 4·50
334 – 12½ c. + 5 c. red . . . . 11·00 4·50
335 – 25 c. + 10 c. turquoise . . . 11·00 4·50
DESIGNS: 5 c. Kite-flying; 6 c. Girl on swing; 12½ c. Girls playing "Oranges and Lemons"; 25 c. Bowling hoops.

52 Gull over Ship

54 Fort Beekenburg

1952. Seamen's Welfare Fund. Inscr "ZEEMANSWELVAREN".
336 **52** 1½ c. + 1 c. green . . . . 1·50 75
337 – 6 c. + 4 c. brown . . . . 8·00 3·50
338 – 12½ c. + 7 c. mauve . . . . 8·00 3·75
339 – 15 c. + 10 c. blue . . . . 10·00 4·00
340 – 25 c. + 15 c. red . . . . 8·50 3·50
DESIGNS: 6 c. Sailor and lighthouse; 12½ c. Sailor on ship's prow; 15 c. Tanker in harbour; 25 c. Anchor and compass.

1953. Netherlands Flood Relief Fund. No. 321 surch **22½ Ct. + 7½ Ct. WATERSNOOD NEDER-LAND 1953**.
341 **130** 22½ c. + 7½ c. on 1½ g. . . 1·10 1·10

1953. 250th Anniv of Fort Beekenburg.
342 **54** 22½ c. brown . . . . . . 3·50 40

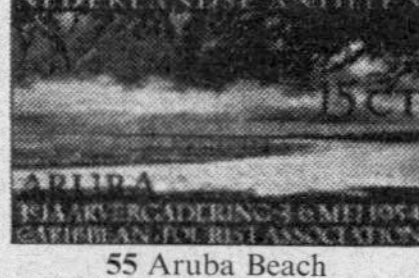

55 Aruba Beach

1954. 3rd Caribbean Tourist Assn Meeting.
343 **55** 15 c. blue and buff . . . . 3·50 2·50

1954. Ratification of Statute of the Kingdom. As No. 809 of Netherlands.
344 **158** 7½ c. green 70 65

56 "Anglo" Flower

1955. Child Welfare.
345 **56** 1½ c. + 1 c. blue, yellow & turquoise 40 50
346 – 7½ c. + 5 c. red, yellow and violet . . . . 3·25 2·25
347 – 15 c. + 5 c. red, grn & olive 3·25 2·50
348 – 22½ c. + 7½ c. red, yellow and blue . . . . 3·25 2·25
349 – 25 c. + 10 c. red, yellow and grey . . . . 3·25 2·50
FLOWERS: 7½ c. White Cayenne; 15 c. "French" flower; 22½ c. Cactus; 25 c. Red Cayenne.

57 Prince Bernhard and Queen Juliana

1955. Royal Visit.
350 **57** 7½ c. + 2½ c. red 20 20
351 22½ c. + 7½ c. blue 95 95

59 Oil Refinery

1955. 21st Meeting of Caribbean Commission.
352 – 15 c. blue, green & brown . 2·50 2·00
353 **59** 25 c. blue, green & brown . 4·00 2·50
DESIGN (rectangle, 36×25 mm): 15 c. Aruba Beach.

60 St. Anne Bay

1956. 10th Anniv of Caribbean Commission.
354 **60** 15 c. blue, red and black . . 30 25

61 Lord Baden-Powell

1957. 50th Anniv of Boy Scout Movement.
355 **61** 6 c. + 1½ c. yellow 50 50
356 7½ c. + 2½ c. green 50 50
357 15 c. + 5 c. red 50 50

62 "Dawn of Health"

1957. 1st Caribbean Mental Health Congress, Aruba.
358 **62** 15 c. black and yellow . . . 30 30

63 Saba

1957. Tourist Publicity. Multicoloured.
359 7½ c. Type **63** 35 35
360 15 c. St. Maarten 35 35
361 25 c. St. Eustatius 35 35

64 Footballer

65 Curacao Intercontinental Hotel

1957. 8th Central American and Caribbean Football Championships.
362 **64** 6 c. + 2½ c. orange 50 70
363 – 7½ c. + 5 c. red . . . . . 1·00 1·10
364 – 15 c. + 5 c. green . . . . 1·10 1·10
365 – 22½ c. + 7½ c. blue . . . . 1·10 80
DESIGNS—HORIZ: 7½ c. Caribbean map. VERT: 15 c. Goalkeeper saving ball; 22½ c. Footballers with ball.

1957. Opening of Curacao Inter-continental Hotel.
366 **65** 15 c. blue 30 25

66 Map of Curacao

67 American Kestrel

1957. International Geophysical Year.
367 **66** 15 c. deep blue and blue . . 80 65

1958. Child Welfare. Bird design inscr "VOOR HET KIND". Multicoloured.
368 2½ c. + 1 c. Type **67** 30 25
369 7½ c. + 1½ c. Yellow oriole . . 85 65
370 15 c. + 2½ c. Scaly-breasted ground doves . . . . . . 1·10 80
371 22½ c. + 2½ c. Brown-throated conure . . . . 1·25 70

68 Greater Flamingoes (Bonaire)

1958. Size 33½×22 mm.
372 **68** 6 c. pink and green . . . . 7·50 10
373 A 7½ c. yellow and brown . . 10 10
374 8 c. yellow and blue . . . 10 15
375 B 10 c. yellow and grey . . . 10 10
376 C 12 c. grey and green . . . 15 20
377 D 15 c. blue and green . . . 15 10
377a 15 c. lilac and green . . . 15 10
378 E 20 c. grey and red 20 10
379 A 25 c. green and blue . . . 25 10
380 D 30 c. green and brown . . 30 10
381 E 35 c. pink and grey 35 20
382 C 40 c. green and mauve . . 40 10
383 B 45 c. blue and violet . . . 50 20
384 **68** 50 c. pink and brown . . . 50 10
385 E 55 c. green and red 65 25
386 **68** 65 c. pink and green . . . 65 30
387 D 70 c. orange and purple . . 70 45
388 **68** 75 c. pink and violet . . . 80 45
389 B 85 c. green and brown . . 85 60
390 E 90 c. orange and blue . . . 85 70
391 C 95 c. yellow and orange . . 90 70
392 D 1 g. grey and red . . . . . 1·00 15
393 A 1½ g. brown and violet . . 1·40 20
394 C 2½ g. yellow and blue . . . 2·50 30
395 B 5 g. mauve and brown . . 4·75 85
396 **68** 10 g. pink and blue . . . . 8·50 4·00
DESIGNS: A. Dutch Colonial houses (Curacao); B. Mountain and palms (Saba); C. Town Hall (St. Maarten); D. Church tower (Aruba); E. Memorial obelisk (St. Eustatius).

For larger versions of some values see Nos. 653/6.

69

70 Red Cross Flag and Antilles Map

1958. 50th Anniv of Netherlands Antilles Radio & Telegraph Administration.
397 **69** 7½ c. lake and blue 15 15
398 15 c. blue and red 30 30

1958. Neth. Antilles Red Cross Fund. Cross in red.
399 **70** 6 c. + 2 c. brown 30 30
400 7½ c. + 2½ c. green 45 45
401 15 c. + 5 c. yellow 45 45
402 22½ c. + 7½ c. blue 45 45

71 Aruba Caribbean Hotel

1959. Opening of Aruba Caribbean Hotel.
403 **71** 15 c. multicoloured 30 20

72 Zeeland

1959. Curacao Monuments Preservation Fund. Multicoloured.
404 6 c. + 1½ c. Type **72** 80 80
405 7½ c. + 2½ c. Saba Island . . . 80 90
406 15 c. + 5 c. Molenplein (vert) . 80 90
407 22½ c. + 7½ c. Scharloobrug . . 80 90
408 25 c. + 7½ c. Brievengat . . . 80 90

73 Water-distillation Plant

74 Antilles Flag

1959. Inauguration of Aruba Water-distillation Plant.
409 **73** 20 c. light blue and blue . . 35 35

1959. 5th Anniv of Ratification of Statute of the Kingdom.
410 **74** 10 c. red, blue & lt blue . . 25 25
411 20 c. red, blue and yellow . . 30 30
412 25 c. red, blue and green . . 30 30

75 Fokker F.XVIII "De Snip" over Caribbean

76 Mgr. Niewindt

1959. 25th Anniv of K.L.M. Netherlands-Curacao Air Service. Each yellow, deep blue and blue.
413 10 c. Type **75** 40 30
414 20 c. Fokker F.XVIII "De Snip" over globe 40 30
415 25 c. Douglas DC-7C "Seven Seas" over Handelskade (bridge), Willemstad 40 15
416 35 c. Douglas DC-8 at Aruba Airport 40 40

1960. Death Centenary of Mgr. M. J. Niewindt.
417 **76** 10 c. purple 35 35
418 20 c. violet 50 50
419 25 c. olive 35 35

77 Flag and Oil-worker

78 Frogman

1960. Labour Day.
420 **77** 20 c. multicoloured 30 30

1960. Princess Wilhelmina Cancer Relief Fund. Inscr "KANKERBESTRIJDING".
421 **78** 10 c. + 2 c. blue . . . . . 1·10 1·10
422 – 20 c. + 3 c. multicoloured . 1·40 1·25
423 – 25 c. + 5 c. red, blue & blk . 1·40 1·25
DESIGNS—HORIZ: 20 c. Queen angelfish; 25 c. Big-scaled soldierfish.

79 Child on Bed

1961. Child Welfare. Inscr "voor het kind".
424 6 c. + 2 c. black and green . . 25 25
425 10 c. + 3 c. black and red . . . 30 30
426 20 c. + 6 c. black and yellow . 30 30
427 25 c. + 8 c. black and orange . 35 35
DESIGNS: 6 c. Type **79**; 10 c. Girl with doll; 20 c. Boy with bucket; 25 c. Children in classroom.

80 Governor's Salute to the American Naval Brig "Andrew Doria" at St. Eustatius

1961. 185th Anniv of 1st Salute to the American Flag.
428 **80** 20 c. multicoloured 85 60

1962. Royal Silver Wedding. As T **187** of Netherlands.
429 10 c. orange 15 15
430 25 c. blue 30 20

81 Jaja (nursemaid) and Child **82** Knight and World Map

1962. Cultural Series.
431 – 6 c. brown and yellow . . . 15 15
432 – 10 c. multicoloured 20 15
433 – 20 c. multicoloured 30 30
434 **81** 25 c. brown, green & blk . . 35 30
DESIGNS: 6 c. Corn-masher; 10 c. Benta player; 20 c. Petji kerchief.

1962. 5th International Candidates Chess Tournament, Curacao.
436 **82** 10 c. + 5 c. green 95 60
437 20 c. + 10 c. red 95 60
438 25 c. + 10 c. blue 95 60

1963. Freedom from Hunger. No. 378 surch **TEGEN DE HONGER** wheat sprig and **+10 c**.
439 20 c. + 10 c. grey and red . . . 50 50

84 Family Group

1963. 4th Caribbean Mental Health Congress, Curacao.
440 **84** 20 c. buff and blue 30 30
441 – 25 c. red and blue 30 30
DESIGN: 25 c. Egyptian Cross emblem.

85 "Freedom" **86** Hotel Bonaire

1963. Centenary of Abolition of Slavery in Dutch West Indies.
442 **85** 25 c. brown and yellow . . 25 25

1963. Opening of Hotel Bonaire.
443 **86** 20 c. brown 20 20

87 Child and Flowers **88** Test-tube and Flask

1963. Child Welfare. Child Art. Multicoloured.
444 5 c. + 2 c. Type **87** 25 35
445 6 c. + 3 c. Children and flowers 25 35
446 10 c. + 5 c. Girl with ball . . . 30 35
447 20 c. + 10 c. Men with flags . . 30 35
448 25 c. + 12 c. Schoolboy . . . 30 35
Nos. 445/7 are horiz.

1963. 150th Anniv of Kingdom of the Netherlands. As No. 968 of Netherlands, but smaller, size (26×27 mm).
449 25 c. green, red and black . . . 20 20

1963. Chemical Industry, Aruba.
450 **88** 20 c. red, light green and green 45 40

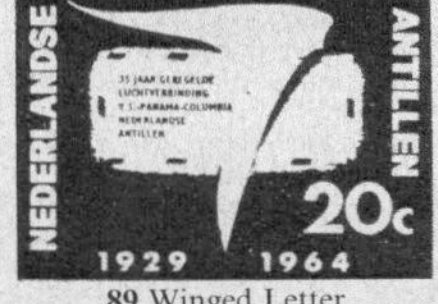

89 Winged Letter

1964. 35th Anniv of 1st U.S.–Curacao Flight. Multicoloured.
451 20 c. Type **89** 30 30
452 25 c. Route map, Sikorsky S-38 flying boat and Boeing 707 . 40 30

90 Trinitaria

1964. Child Welfare. Multicoloured.
453 6 c. + 3 c. Type **90** 20 20
454 10 c. + 5 c. Magdalena 25 25
455 20 c. + 10 c. Yellow keiki . . 30 30
456 25 c. + 11 c. Bellisima 30 30

91 Caribbean Map **92** "Six Islands"

1964. 5th Caribbean Council Assembly.
457 **91** 20 c. yellow, red & blue . . 30 20

1964. 10th Anniv of Statute for the Kingdom.
458 **92** 25 c. multicoloured 20 20

93 Princess Beatrix **94** I.T.U. Emblem and Symbols

1965. Visit of Princess Beatrix.
459 **93** 25 c. red 35 30

1965. Centenary of I.T.U.
460 **94** 10 c. deep blue and blue . . 15 15

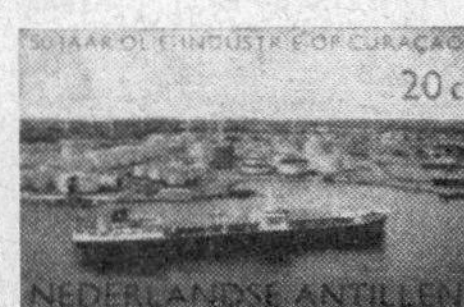

95 "Asperalla" (tanker) at Curacao

1965. 50th Anniv of Curacao's Oil Industry. Multicoloured.
461 10 c. Catalytic cracking plant (vert) 20 15
462 20 c. Type **95** 40 15
463 25 c. Super fractionating plant (vert) 25 20

96 Flag and Fruit Market, Curacao

1965.
464 **96** 1 c. blue, red & green . . . 10 10
465 – 2 c. blue, red and yellow . . 10 10
466 – 3 c. blue, red and cobalt . . 10 10
467 – 4 c. blue, red and orange . . 25 10
468 – 5 c. blue, red and blue . . . 10 10
469 – 6 c. blue, red and pink . . . 10 10
DESIGNS (Flag and): 2 c. Divi-divi tree; 3 c. Lace; 4 c. Greater flamingoes; 5 c. Church; 6 c. Lobster. Each is inscr with a different place-name.

97 Cup Sponges

1965. Child Welfare. Marine Life. Multicoloured.
470 6 c. + 3 c. Type **97** 15 15
471 10 c. + 5 c. Cup sponges (diff) 20 20
472 20 c. + 10 c. Sea anemones on star coral 20 20
473 25 c. + 11 c. Basket sponge, blue chromis and "Brain" coral . 30 35

98 Marine and Seascape **99** Budgerigars and Wedding Rings

1965. Tercentenary of Marine Corps.
474 **98** 25 c. multicoloured 20 15

1966. Intergovernmental Committee for European Migration (I.C.E.M.) Fund. As T **215** of Netherlands.
475 35 c. + 15 c. bistre & brown . . 20 25

1966. Marriage of Crown Princess Beatrix and Herr Claus von Amsberg.
476 **99** 25 c. multicoloured 40 35

100 Admiral de Ruyter and Map

1966. 300th Anniv of Admiral de Ruyter's Visit to St. Eustatius.
477 **100** 25 c. ochre, violet & blue . 20 15

101 "Grammar" **102** Cooking

1966. 25 years of Secondary Education.
478 **101** 6 c. black, blue & yellow . 10 10
479 – 10 c. black, red & green . . 10 10
480 – 20 c. black, blue & yellow . 15 15
481 – 25 c. black, red and green . 20 20
DESIGNS: The "Free Arts", figures representing: 10 c. "Rhetoric" and "Dialect"; 20 c. "Arithmetic" and "Geometry"; 25 c. "Astronomy" and "Music".

1966. Child Welfare. Multicoloured.
482 6 c. + 3 c. Type **102** 10 10
483 10 c. + 5 c. Nursing 10 10
484 20 c. + 10 c. Metal-work fitting 20 20
485 25 c. + 11 c. Ironing 25 25

103 "Gelderland" (cruiser)

1967. 60th Anniv of Royal Netherlands Navy League.
486 **103** 6 c. bronze and green . . . 10 10
487 – 10 c. ochre and yellow . . 15 15
488 – 20 c. brown and sepia . . . 20 15
489 – 25 c. blue and indigo . . . 20 20
SHIPS: 10 c. "Pioneer" (schooner); 20 c. "Oscilla" (tanker); 25 c. "Santa Rosa" (liner).

104 M. C. Piar **105** "Heads in Hands"

1967. 150th Death Anniv of Manuel Piar (patriot).
490 **104** 20 c. brown and red . . . 15 15

1967. Cultural and Social Relief Funds.
491 **105** 6 c. + 3 c. black & blue . . 10 10
492 10 c. + 5 c. black & mve . . 15 15
493 20 c. + 10 c. purple . . . 15 15
494 25 c. + 11 c. blue 15 20

106 "The Turtle and the Monkey" **107** Olympic Flame and Rings

1967. Child Welfare. "Nanzi" Fairy Tales. Mult.
495 6 c. + 3 c. "Princess Long Nose" (vert) 15 15
496 10 c. + 5 c. Type **106** 20 15
497 20 c. + 10 c. "Nanzi (spider) and the Tiger" 25 15
498 25 c. + 11 c. "Shon Arey's Balloon" (vert) 30 20

1968. Olympic Games, Mexico. Multicoloured.
499 10 c. Type **107** 20 20
500 20 c. "Throwing the discus" (statue) 20 20
501 25 c. Stadium and doves . . . 20 20

108 "Dance of the Ribbons"

1968. Cultural and Social Relief Funds.
502 **108** 10 c. + 5 c. multicoloured 15 15
503 15 c. + 5 c. multicoloured 15 15
504 20 c. + 10 c. multicoloured 15 20
505 25 c. + 10 c. multicoloured 20 25

109 Boy with Goat

1968. Child Welfare Fund. Multicoloured.
506 6 c. + 3 c. Type **109** 15 15
507 10 c. + 5 c. Girl with dog . . . 15 15
508 20 c. + 10 c. Boy with cat . . 25 25
509 25 c. + 11 c. Girl with duck . . 35 35

110 Fokker Friendship 500 **111** Radio Pylon, "Waves" and Map

1968. Dutch Antillean Airlines.
510 **110** 10 c. blue, black & yellow . 25 20
511 – 20 c. blue, black & brown . 25 20
512 – 25 c. blue, black & pink . . 25 20
DESIGNS: 20 c. Douglas DC-9; 25 c. Fokker Friendship 500 in flight and Douglas DC-9 on ground.

1969. Opening of Broadcast Relay Station, Bonaire.
513 **111** 25 c. green, dp blue & blue 20 20

112 "Code of Laws" **113** "Carnival"

1969. Centenary of Netherlands Antilles Court of Justice.
514 **112** 20 c. green, gold & lt grn . 20 20
515 – 25 c. multicoloured 20 20
DESIGN: 25 c. "Scales of Justice".

1969. Cultural and Social Relief Funds. Antilles' Festivals. Multicoloured.
516 10 c. + 5 c. Type **113** 30 30
517 15 c. + 5 c. "Harvest Festival" 30 30
518 20 c. + 10 c. "San Juan Day" 40 40
519 25 c. + 10 c. "New Years' Day" 40 40

114 I.L.O. Emblem, "Koenoekoe" House and Cacti
115 Boy playing Guitar

1969. 50th Anniv of I.L.O.

520 114 10 c. black and blue . . . 15 15
521 25 c. black and red 15 15

1969. Child Welfare.

522 115 6 c. + 3 c. violet & orge . . 25 25
523 – 10 c. + 5 c. grn & yell . . 35 35
524 – 20 c. + 10 c. red and blue 40 40
525 – 25 c. + 11 c. brn & pink . 50 50
DESIGNS: 10 c. Girl playing recorder; 20 c. Boy playing "marimula"; 25 c. Girl playing piano.

1969. 15th Anniv of Statute of the Kingdom. As T 240 of the Netherlands, but inscr "NEDERLANDSE ANTILLEN".

526 25 c. multicoloured 25 20

117 Radio Station, Bonaire
118 St. Anna Church, Otrabanda, Curacao

1970. 5th Anniv of Trans-World Religious Radio Station, Bonaire. Multicoloured.

527 10 c. Type 117 . . . . . . 15 15
528 15 c. Trans-World Radio emblem 15 15

1970. Churches of the Netherlands Antilles. Mult.

529 10 c. Type 118 . . . . . . 20 20
530 20 c. "Mikve Israel-Emanuel" Synagogue, Punda, Curacao (horiz) 20 20
531 25 c. Pulpit Fort Church Curacao 20 20

119 "The Press"
120 Mother and Child

1970. Cultural and Social Relief Funds. "Mass-media". Multicoloured.

532 10 c. + 5 c. Type 119 . . . . 40 40
533 15 c. + 5 c. "Films" 40 40
534 20 c. + 10 c. "Radio" . . . 45 45
535 25 c. + 10 c. "Television" . . 45 45

1970. Child Welfare. Multicoloured.

536 6 c. + 3 c. Type 120 . . . . 45 45
537 10 c. + 5 c. Child with piggy-bank 45 45
538 20 c. + 10 c. Children's Judo . 45 45
539 25 c. + 11 c. "Pick-a-back" . . 45 45

121 St. Theresia's Church, St. Nicolaas, Aruba
122 Lions Emblem

1971. 40th Anniv of St. Theresia Parish, Aruba.

540 121 20 c. multicoloured 20 20

1971. 25th Anniv of Curacao Lions Club.

541 122 25 c. multicoloured 35 25

123 Charcoal Stove
125 Admiral Brion

1971. Cultural and Social Relief Funds. Household Utensils. Multicoloured.

542 10 c. + 5 c. Type 123 . . . . 45 45
543 15 c. + 5 c. Earthenware water vessel 45 45
544 20 c. + 10 c. Baking oven . . . 45 45
545 25 c. + 10 c. Kitchen implements 45 45

1971. Prince Bernhard's 60th Birthday. Design as No. 1135 of Netherlands.

546 45 c. multicoloured 45 40

1971. 150th Death Anniv of Admiral Pedro Luis Brion.

547 125 40 c. multicoloured 30 30

126 Bottle Doll
127 Queen Emma Bridge, Curacao

1971. Child Welfare. Home-made Toys. Mult.

548 15 c. + 5 c. Type 126 . . . . 60 60
549 20 c. + 10 c. Simple cart . . . 65 65
550 30 c. + 15 c. Spinning-tops . . 65 65

1971. Views of the Islands. Multicoloured.

551 1 c. Type 127 . . . . 10 10
552 2 c. The Bottom, Saba 10 10
553 3 c. Greater flamingoes, Bonaire 40 10
554 4 c. Distillation plant, Aruba . 10 10
555 5 c. Fort Amsterdam, St. Maarten 10 10
556 6 c. Fort Oranje, St. Eustatius . 10 10

128 Ship in Dock
129 Steel Band

1972. Inauguration of New Dry Dock Complex, Willemstad, Curacao.

557 128 30 c. multicoloured 35 30

1972. Cultural and Social Relief Funds. Folklore. Multicoloured.

558 15 c. + 5 c. Type 129 . . . . 75 75
559 20 c. + 10 c. "Seu" festival . . 75 75
560 30 c. + 15 c. "Tambu" dance . 75 75

130 J. E. Irausquin
131 Dr. M. F. da Costa Gomez

1972. 10th Death Anniv of Juan Enrique Irausquin (Antilles statesman).

561 130 30 c. red 30 25

1972. 65th Birth Anniv of Moises F. da Costa Gomez (statesman).

562 131 30 c. black and green . . . 30 25

132 Child playing with Earth
133 Pedestrian Crossing

1972. Child Welfare. Multicoloured.

563 15 c. + 5 c. Type 132 . . . . 85 85
564 20 c. + 10 c. Child playing in water 85 85
565 30 c. + 15 c. Child throwing ball into the air 85 85

1973. Cultural and Social Relief Funds. Road Safety.

566 133 12 c. + 6 c. multicoloured 90 80
567 – 15 c. + 7 c. grn, orge & red 90 80
568 – 40 c. + 20 c. multicoloured 90 80
DESIGNS: 15 c. Road-crossing patrol; 40 c. Traffic lights.

134 William III (portrait from stamp of 1873)
135 Map of Aruba, Curacao and Bonaire

1973. Stamp Centenary.

569 134 15 c. lilac, mauve & gold 30 25
570 – 20 c. multicoloured 35 30
571 – 30 c. multicoloured 35 30
DESIGNS: 20 c. Antilles postman; 30 c. Postal Service emblem.

1973. Inauguration of Submarine Cable and Microwave Telecommunications Link. Multicoloured.

572 15 c. Type 135 . . . . 40 20
573 30 c. Six stars ("The Antilles") 40 40
574 45 c. Map of Saba, St. Maarten and St. Eustatius 40 40

136 Queen Juliana
137 Jan Eman

1973. Silver Jubilee of Queen Juliana's Reign.

576 136 15 c. multicoloured 45 45

1973. 16th Death Anniv of Jan Eman (Aruba statesman).

577 137 30 c. black and green . . . 30 25

138 "1948–1973"
139 L. B. Scott

1973. Child Welfare Fund. 25th Anniv of 1st Child Welfare Stamps.

578 138 15 c. + 5 c. light green, green and blue 85 70
579 – 20 c. + 10 c. brown, green and blue 85 75
580 – 30 c. + 15 c. violet, blue and light blue . . . . . . 1·25 90
DESIGNS: No. 579, Three Children; No. 580, Mother and child.

1974. 8th Death Anniv of Lionel B. Scott (St. Maarten statesman).

582 139 30 c. multicoloured 30 30

140 Family Meal
141 Girl combing Hair

1974. Family Planning Campaign. Multicoloured.

583 6 c. Type 140 . . . . 10 103
584 12 c. Family at home 25 20
585 15 c. Family in garden 30 20

1974. Cultural and Social Relief Funds. "The Younger Generation". Multicoloured.

586 12 c. + 6 c. Type 141 . . . . 1·00 1·00
587 15 c. + 7 c. "Pop dancers" . . 1·00 1·00
588 40 c. + 20 c. Group drummer 1·00 1·00

142 Desulphurisation Plant

1974. 50th Anniv of Lago Oil Co., Aruba. Multicoloured.

589 15 c. Type 142 . . . . 45 30
590 30 c. Fractionating towers . . . 45 30
591 45 c. Lago refinery at night . . 45 35

143 U.P.U. Emblem
144 "A Carpenter outranks a King"

1974. Centenary of Universal Postal Union.

592 143 15 c. gold, green & black . . 40 35
593 30 c. gold, blue & black . . 40 40

1974. Child Welfare. Children's Songs. Mult.

594 15 c. + 5 c. Type 144 . . . . 70 70
595 20 c. + 10 c. Footprints ("Let's Do a Ring-dance") 70 70
596 30 c. + 15 c. "Moon and Sun" 70 70

145 Queen Emma Bridge
146 Ornamental Ventilation Grid

1975. Antillean Bridges. Multicoloured.

597 20 c. Type 145 . . . . 45 40
598 30 c. Queen Juliana Bridge . . 50 40
599 40 c. Queen Wilhelmina Bridge 65 50

1975. Cultural and Social Welfare Funds.

600 146 12 c. + 6 c. multicoloured 65 65
601 – 15 c. + 7 c. brown & stone 65 65
602 – 40 c. + 20 c. multicoloured 65 65
DESIGNS: 15 c. Knight accompanied by buglers (tombstone detail); 40 c. Foundation stone.

147 Sodium Chloride Molecules

1975. Bonaire Salt Industry. Multicoloured.

603 15 c. Type 147 . . . . 55 35
604 20 c. Salt incrustation and blocks 55 45
605 40 c. Map of salt area (vert) . 65 45

148 Fokker F.XVIII "De Snip" and Old Control Tower

1975. 40th Anniv of Aruba Airport. Mult.

606 15 c. Type 148 . . . . 45 25
607 30 c. Douglas DC-9-30 and modern control tower 45 30
608 40 c. Tail of Boeing 727-200 and "Princess Beatrix" Airport buildings 45 45

149 I.W.Y. Emblem

1975. International Women's Year. Multicoloured.

609 6 c. Type 149 . . . . 20 15
610 12 c. "Social Development" . . 35 20
611 20 c. "Equality of Sexes" . . . 45 30

150 Children making Windmill

1975. Child Welfare. Multicoloured.

612 15 c. + 5 c. Type 150 . . . . 70 65
613 20 c. + 10 c. Child modelling clay 70 65
614 30 c. + 15 c. Children drawing pictures 70 65

151 Beach, Aruba **152** J. A. Abraham (statesman)

1976. Tourism. Multicoloured.
615 40 c. Type **151** 60 50
616 40 c. Fish Kiosk, Bonaire . . . 60 50
617 40 c. "Table Mountain", Curacao 60 50

1976. Abraham Commemoration.
618 **152** 30 c. purple on brown . . 40 35

153 Dyke Produce **154** Arm holding Child

1976. Agriculture, Animal Husbandry and Fisheries. Multicoloured.
619 15 c. Type **153** 35 25
620 35 c. Cattle 50 40
621 45 c. Fishes 50 50

1976. Child Welfare. "Carrying the Child".
622 **154** 20 c. + 10 c. multicoloured 60 60
623 – 25 c. + 12 c. multicoloured 60 60
624 – 40 c. + 18 c. multicoloured 60 60
DESIGNS—HORIZ: 25 c. VERT: 40 c. Both similar to Type **154** showing arm holding child.

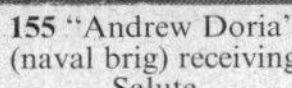

155 "Andrew Doria" (naval brig) receiving Salute **156** Carnival ostume

1976. Bicentenary of American Revolution. Multicoloured.
625 25 c. Flags and plaque, Fort Oranje 70 45
626 40 c. Type **155** 90 45
627 55 c. Johannes de Graaff, Governor of St. Eustatius . . 70 70

1977. Carnival.
628 – 25 c. multicoloured 45 35
629 **156** 35 c. multicoloured 45 35
630 – 40 c. multicoloured 45 35
DESIGNS: 25 c., 40 c. Women in Carnival costumes.

157 Tortoise (Bonaire) **158** "Ace" Playing Card

1977. Rock Paintings. Multicoloured.
631 25 c. Bird (Aruba) 60 35
632 35 c. Abstract (Curacao) . . . 60 45
633 40 c. Type **157** 75 45

1977. Sixth Central American and Caribbean Bridge Championships. Multicoloured.
634 **158** 20 c. + 10 c. red & black . 50 35
635 – 25 c. + 12 c. multicoloured 50 45
636 – 40 c. + 18 c. multicoloured 65 60
DESIGNS—VERT: 25 c. "King" playing card. HORIZ: 40 c. Bridge hand.

159 "Cordia sebestena" **160** Bells outside Main Store

1977. Flowers. Multicoloured.
639 25 c. Type **159** 40 35
640 40 c. "Albizzia lebbeck" (vert) 50 45
641 55 c. "Tamarindus indica" . . 60 55

1977. 50th Anniv of Spritzer and Fuhrmann (jewellers). Multicoloured.
642 20 c. Type **160** 40 30
643 40 c. Globe basking in sun . . 50 40
644 55 c. Antillean flag and diamond ring 60 60

161 Children with Toy Animal

1977. Child Welfare. Multicoloured.
645 15 c. + 15 c. Type **161** 35 25
646 20 c. + 10 c. Children with toy rabbit 40 40
647 25 c. + 12 c. Children with toy cat 50 45
648 40 c. + 18 c. Children with toy beetle 55 55

162 "The Unspoiled Queen" (Saba)

1977. Tourism. Multicoloured.
650 25 c. Type **162** 15 15
651 35 c. "The Golden Rock" (St. Eustatius) 20 20
652 40 c. "The Friendly Island" (St. Maarten) 25 25

1977. As Nos. 378, 381/2 and 385, but larger, (39 × 22 mm).
653 E 20 c. grey and red . . . . . 1·00 1·00
654 35 c. pink and brown . . . 2·50 3·00
655 C 40 c. green and mauve . . . 1·25 1·25
656 E 55 c. green and red . . . . 1·50 1·50

163 19th-century Chest **164** Water-skiing

1978. 150th Anniv of Netherlands Antilles' Bank. Multicoloured.
657 **163** 15 c. blue & light blue . . 10 10
658 – 20 c. orange and gold . . . 10 10
659 – 40 c. green & deep green . . 20 20
DESIGNS: 20 c. Bank emblem; 40 c. Strong-room door.

1978. Sports Funds. Multicoloured.
660 15 c. + 5 c. Type **164** 10 10
661 20 c. + 10 c. Yachting 15 15
662 25 c. + 12 c. Football 20 20
663 40 c. + 18 c. Baseball 35 35

165 "Erythrina velutina" **166** "Polythysana rubrescens"

1978. Flora of Netherlands Antilles. Multicoloured.
664 15 c. "Delconix regia" 20 15
665 25 c. Type **165** 25 25
666 50 c. "Gualacum officinale" (horiz) 35 30
667 55 c. "Gilricidia sepium" (horiz) 45 45

1978. Butterflies. Multicoloured.
668 15 c. Type **166** 25 15
669 25 c. "Caligo sp." 40 20
670 35 c. "Prepona praeneste" . . . 55 35
671 40 c. "Morpho sp." 70 50

167 "Conserve Energy" (English) **168** Red Cross

1978. Energy Conservation.
672 **167** 15 c. orange and black . . 15 15
673 – 20 c. green and black . . 20 20
674 – 40 c. red and black . . . 40 40
DESIGNS: As No. 672 but text in Dutch (20 c.) or in Papiamento (40 c.).

1978. 150th Birth Anniv of Henri Dunant (founder of Red Cross).
675 **168** 55 c. + 25 c. red & blue . . 30 30

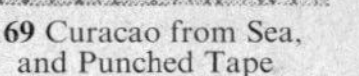

169 Curacao from Sea, and Punched Tape **170** Boy Rollerskating

1978. 70th Anniv of Antilles Telecommunications Corporation (Landsradio). Multicoloured.
677 20 c. Type **169** 25 25
678 40 c. Ship's bridge, punched tape and radio mast 35 35
679 55 c. Satellite and aerial (vert) . 50 50

1978. Child Welfare. Multicoloured.
680 15 c. + 5 c. Type **170** 40 35
681 20 c. + 10 c. Boy and girl flying kite 50 40
682 25 c. + 12 c. Boy and girl playing marbles 50 45
683 40 c. + 18 c. Girl riding bicycle 60 55

171 Ca'i Awa (pumping station) **172** Aruba Coat of Arms (float)

1978. 80th Death Anniv of Leonard Burlington Smith (entrepreneur and U.S. Consul).
685 **171** 25 c. multicoloured 20 15
686 – 35 c. black, greenish yellow and yellow 25 20
687 – 40 c. multicoloured 35 30
DESIGNS—VERT: 35 c. Leonard Burlington Smith. HORIZ: 40 c. Opening ceremony of Queen Emma Bridge, 1888.

1979. 25th Aruba Carnival. Multicoloured.
688 40 c. + 10 c. Float representing heraldic fantasy 40 35
689 75 c. + 20 c. Type **172** 65 65

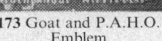

173 Goat and P.A.H.O. Emblem **174** Yacht and Sun

1979. 12th Inter-American Ministerial Meeting on Foot and Mouth Disease and Zoonosis Control, Curacao. Multicoloured.
690 50 c. Type **173** 30 30
691 75 c. Horse and conference emblem 45 45
692 150 c. Cows, flag and Pan-American Health Organization (P.A.H.O.) and W.H.O. emblems . . . . 1·00 1·00

1979. 12th International Sailing Regatta, Bonaire. Multicoloured.
694 15 c. + 5 c. Type **174** 15 15
695 35 c. + 25 c. Yachts 35 35
696 40 c. + 15 c. Yacht and globe (horiz) 50 50
697 55 c. + 25 c. Yacht, sun and flamingo 60 60

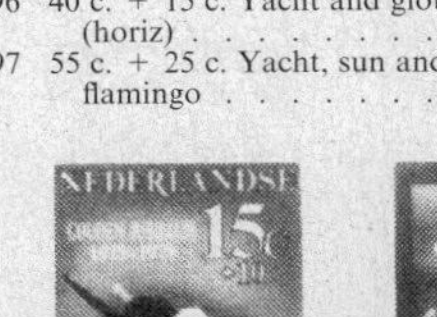

175 Corps Members **176** "Melochia tomentosa"

1979. 50th Anniv of Curacao Volunteer Corps.
699 **175** 15 c. + 10 c. blue, red and ultramarine 25 20
700 – 40 c. + 20 c. blue, violet and gold 45 40
701 – 1 g. multicoloured 70 65
DESIGNS: 40 c. Sentry in battle dress and emblem; 1 g. Corps emblem, flag and soldier in ceremonial uniform.

1979. Flowers. Multicoloured.
702 25 c. "Casearia tremula" . . . 20 15
703 40 c. "Cordia cylindrostachya" . 35 30
704 1 g. 50 Type **176** . . . . . . 1·00 1·00

177 Girls reading Book **178** Dove and Netherlands Flag

1979. International Year of the Child.
705 **177** 20 c. + 10 c. multicoloured 25 25
706 – 25 c. + 12 c. multicoloured 35 30
707 – 35 c. + 15 c. violet, brown and black 50 45
708 – 50 c. + 20 c. multicoloured 60 55
DESIGNS: 25 c. Toddler and cat; 35 c. Girls carrying basket; 50 c. Boy and girl dressing-up.

1979. 25th Anniv of Statute of the Kingdom. Multicoloured.
710 65 c. Type **178** 50 40
711 1 g. 50 Dove and Netherlands Antilles flag 80 90

179 Map of Aruba and Foundation Emblem

1979. 30th Anniv of Aruba Cultural Centre Foundation. Multicoloured.
712 95 c. Type **179** 60 60
713 1 g. Foundation headquarters . 70 70

180 Brass Chandelier

1980. 210th Anniv of Fort Church, Curacao.
714 **180** 20 c. + 10 c. yellow, black and brown 20 20
715 – 50 c. + 25 c. mult 50 50
716 – 100 c. multicoloured . . . 65 65
DESIGNS: 50 c. Pipe organ; 100 c. Cupola tower, 1910.

181 Rotary Emblem and Cogwheel

1980. 75th Anniv of Rotary International. Multicoloured.
717 45 c. Rotary emblem 35 35
718 50 c. Globe and cogwheels . . 40 40
719 85 c. Type **181** 65 65

182 Savings Box

1980. 75th Anniv of Post Office Savings Bank. Multicoloured.
721 25 c. Type **182** 20 20
722 150 c. Savings box (different) . 1·00 1·00

183 Queen Juliana Accession Stamp

1980. Accession of Queen Beatrix.
723 **183** 25 c. red, green and gold . 20 20
724 – 60 c. green, red and gold . 40 40
DESIGN: 60 c. 1965 Royal Visit stamp.

184 Sir Rowland Hill **185** Volleyball

1980. "London 1980" International Stamp Exhibition.

725 184 45 c. black and green . . . 35 35
726 – 60 c. black and red 40 40
727 – 1 g. red, black and blue . . 70 70

DESIGNS: 60 c. "London 1980" logo; 1 g. Airmail label.

1980. Sports Funds.

729 – 25 c. + 10 c. red & black . 25 25
730 – 40 c. + 15 c. yellow & blk 35 35
731 185 45 c. + 20 c. light green, green and black 50 50
732 – 60 c. + 25 c. pink, orange and black 75 75

DESIGNS: 25 c. Gymnastics (beam exercise); 30 c. Gymnastics (horse vaulting); 60 c. Basketball.

186 White-fronted Dove

1980. Birds. Multicoloured.

734 25 c. Type **186** 25 20
735 60 c. Tropical mockingbird . . 65 45
736 85 c. Bananaquit 80 70

187 "St. Maarten Landscape" **188** Rudolf Theodorus Palm

1980. Child Welfare. Children's Drawings. Multicoloured.

737 25 c. + 10 c. Type **187** 30 30
738 30 c. + 15 c. "Bonaire House" 35 40
739 40 c. + 20 c. "Child writing on Board" 45 50
740 60 c. + 25 c. "Dancing Couple" (vert) 60 65

1981. Birth Centenary (1980) of Rudolf Theodorus Palm (musician).

742 **188** 60 c. brown and yellow . . 50 45
743 – 1 g. buff and blue . . . . 1·00 85

DESIGN: 1 g. Musical score and hands playing piano.

189 Map of Aruba and TEAM Emblem **190** Boy in Wheelchair

1981. 50th Anniv of Evangelical Alliance Mission (TEAM) in Antilles. Multicoloured.

744 30 c. Type **189** 25 20
745 50 c. Map of Curacao and emblem 50 40
746 1 g. Map of Bonaire and emblem 1·00 85

1981. International Year of Disabled Persons. Multicoloured.

747 25 c. + 10 c. Blind woman . . 35 35
748 30 c. + 15 c. Type **190** . . . 45 45
749 45 c. + 20 c. Child in walking frame 70 70
750 60 c. + 25 c. Deaf girl 80 80

191 Tennis **192** Gateway

1981. Sports Funds. Multicoloured.

751 30 c. + 15 c. Type **191** 50 50
752 50 c. + 20 c. Swimming . . . 70 70
753 70 c. + 25 c. Boxing 90 90

1981. 125th Anniv of St. Elisabeth's Hospital. Multicoloured.

755 60 c. Type **192** 60 50
756 1 g. 50 St. Elisabeth's Hospital 1·40 1·40

193 Marinus van der Maarel (promoter) **194** Mother and Child

1981. 50th Anniv (1980) of Antillean Boy Scouts Association. Multicoloured.

757 45 c. + 20 c. Wolf Cub and leader 75 75
758 70 c. + 25 c. Type **193** . . . . 1·10 1·10
759 1 g. + 50 c. Headquarters, Ronde Klip . . . . 1·60 1·60

1981. Child Welfare. Multicoloured.

761 35 c. + 15 c. Type **194** 45 50
762 45 c. + 20 c. Boy and girl . . . 55 60
763 55 c. + 25 c. Child with cat . . 70 75
764 85 c. + 40 c. Girl with teddy bear 1·10 1·25

195 "Jatropha gossypifolia" **196** Pilot Gig approaching Ship

1981. Flowers. Multicoloured.

766 45 c. "Cordia globosa" 35 35
767 70 c. Type **195** 70 70
768 100 c. "Croton flavens" 85 85

1982. Centenary of Pilotage Service. Mult.

769 70 c. Type **196** 80 80
770 85 c. Modern liner and map of Antilles . . . . 1·00 1·00
771 1 g. Pilot boarding ship . . . . 1·10 1·10

197 Fencing **198** Holy Ark

1982. Sports Funds.

772 **197** 35 c. + 15 c. mauve and violet 65 50
773 – 45 c. + 20 c. blue and deep blue 85 70
774 – 70 c. + 35 c. multicoloured 1·25 95
775 – 85 c. + 40 c. brown and deep brown . . . . . . 1·40 1·10

DESIGNS: 45 c. Judo; 70 c. Football; 85 c. Cycling.

1982. 250th Anniv of Dedication of Mikve Israel-Emanuel Synagogue, Curacao. Mult.

777 75 c. Type **198** . . . . . . 1·25 90
778 85 c. Synagogue facade . . . . 1·40 90
779 150 c. Tebah (raised platform) 1·75 1·40

199 Peter Stuyvesant (Governor) and Flags of Netherlands, Netherlands Antilles and United States **200** Airport Control Tower

1982. Bicentenary of Netherlands–United States Diplomatic Relations.

780 **199** 75 c. multicoloured . . . . 1·00 80

1982. International Federation of Air Traffic Controllers.

782 – 35 c. black, ultramarine and blue 50 35
783 **200** 75 c. black, green and light green . . . . 1·00 75
784 – 150 c. black, orange and salmon . . . . . . 1·50 1·25

DESIGNS: 35 c. Radar plot trace; 150 c. Radar aerials.

201 Mail Bag **202** Brown Chromis

1982. "Philexfrance 82" International Stamp Exhibition, Paris. Multicoloured.

785 45 c. Exhibition emblem . . . 50 40
786 85 c. Type **201** 95 75
787 150 c. Netherlands Antilles and French flags . . . . . . 1·40 1·25

1982. Fishes. Multicoloured.

789 35 c. Type **202** 70 40
790 75 c. Spotted trunkfish . . . . 1·25 75
791 85 c. Blue tang . . . . . . 1·60 1·00
792 100 c. French angelfish . . . . 1·75 1·10

203 Girl playing Accordion

1982. Child Welfare. Multicoloured.

793 35 c. + 15 c. Type **203** 80 60
794 75 c. + 35 c. Boy playing guitar 1·40 1·25
795 85 c. + 40 c. Boy playing violin 1·75 1·40

204 Saba House

1982. Cultural and Social Relief Funds. Local Houses. Multicoloured.

797 35 c. + 15 c. Type **204** 70 45
798 75 c. + 35 c. Aruba House . . 1·25 95
799 85 c. + 40 c. Curacao House 1·40 1·25

205 High Jumping

1983. Sports Funds. Multicoloured.

801 35 c. + 15 c. Type **205** 65 50
802 45 c. + 20 c. Weightlifting . . 1·00 85
803 85 c. + 40 c. Wind-surfing . . 1·50 1·40

206 Natural Bridge, Aruba **207** W.C.Y. Emblem and Means of Communication

1983. Tourism. Multicoloured.

804 35 c. Type **206** 60 50
805 45 c. Lac Bay, Bonaire . . . 75 55
806 100 c. Willemstad, Curacao . . 1·25 1·10

1983. World Communications Year.

807 **207** 1 g. multicoloured . . . . 1·25 1·10

208 "Curacao" (paddle-steamer) and Post Office Building **209** Mango ("Mangifera indica")

1983. "Brasiliana 83" International Stamp Exhibition, Rio de Janeiro. Multicoloured.

809 45 c. Type **208** 70 60
810 55 c. Brazil flag, exhibition emblem and Netherlands Antilles flag and postal service emblem 75 65
811 100 c. Governor's Palace, Netherlands Antilles, and Sugarloaf Mountain, Rio de Janeiro . . . . 1·25 1·00

1983. Flowers. Multicoloured.

813 45 c. Type **209** 80 65
814 55 c. "Malpighia punicifolia" . . 95 75
815 100 c. "Citrus aurantifolia" . . 1·50 1·25

210 Boy and Lizard

1983. Child Welfare. Multicoloured.

816 45 c. + 20 c. Type **210** . . . . 1·00 85
817 55 c. + 25 c. Girl watching ants 1·25 1·10
818 100 c. + 50 c. Girl feeding donkey . . . . 2·00 1·75

211 Aruba Water Jar **212** Saba

1983. Cultural and Social Relief Funds. Pre-Columbian Pottery.

820 **211** 45 c. + 20 c. light blue, blue and black . . . . . . 1·10 1·00
821 – 55 c. + 25 c. pink, red and black . . . . 1·25 1·10
822 – 85 c. + 40 c. stone, green and black . . . . 1·50 1·25
823 – 100 c. + 50 c. light brown, brown and black . . . . 2·00 1·75

DESIGNS: 55 c. Aruba decorated bowl; 85 c. Curacao human figurine; 100 c. Fragment of Curacao female figurine.

1983. Local Government Buildings. Multicoloured.

824 20 c. Type **212** 20 20
825 25 c. St. Eustatius 25 25
826 30 c. St. Maarten 30 30
827 35 c. Aruba . . . . 1·75 35
828 45 c. Bonaire 45 45
829 55 c. Curacao 55 55
830 60 c. Type **212** 60 60
831 65 c. As No. 825 . . . . . . 65 65
832 70 c. Type **212** 75 75
833 75 c. As No. 826 . . . . . . 75 75
834 85 c. As No. 827 . . . . . . 3·00 1·10
835 85 c. As No. 828 . . . . . . 85 85
836 90 c. As No. 828 . . . . . . 90 90
837 95 c. As No. 829 . . . . . . 95 95
838 1 g. Type **212** . . . . . . 1·00 1·00
839 1 g. 50 As No. 825 . . . . . 1·40 1·40
841 2 g. 50 As No. 826 . . . . . 2·25 2·25
842 5 g. As No. 828 . . . . . . 4·25 4·25
843 10 g. As No. 829 . . . . . . 7·50 7·50
844 15 g. Type **212** . . . . . . 11·00 11·00

213 Note-taking, Type-setting and Front Page of "Amigoe"

1984. Centenary of "Amigoe de Curacao" (newspaper). Multicoloured.

845 45 c. Type **213** 65 55
846 55 c. Printing press and newspapers 75 65
847 85 c. Reading newspaper . . . 1·25 1·10

214 W.I.A. and I.C.A.O. Emblems

1984. 40th Anniv of I.C.A.O.

848 **214** 25 c. multicoloured 40 35
849 – 45 c. violet, blue & black . . 75 60
850 – 55 c. multicoloured 85 70
851 – 100 c. multicoloured . . . 1·40 1·25

DESIGNS: 45 c. I.C.A.O. anniversary emblem; 55 c. A.L.M. and I.C.A.O. emblems; 100 c. Fokker F.XIII airplane "De Snip".

215 Fielder

1984. Sports Funds. 50th Anniv of Curacao Baseball Federation. Multicoloured.
852 25 c. + 10 c. Type **215** 80 60
853 45 c. + 20 c. Batter . . . . . 1·25 1·10
854 55 c. + 25 c. Pitcher . . . . . 1·50 1·25
855 85 c. + 40 c. Running for base 1·75 1·50

216 Microphones and Radio

1984. Cultural and Social Relief Funds. Radio and Gramophone. Multicoloured.
857 45 c. + 20 c. Type **216** . . . . 1·25 1·10
858 55 c. + 25 c. Gramophones and record . . . . 1·50 1·40
859 100 c. + 50 c. Gramophone with horn . . . . 1·90 1·75

217 Bonnet-maker

1984. Centenary of Curacao Chamber of Commerce and Industry. Multicoloured.
860 45 c. Type **217** . . . . 1·10 85
861 55 c. Chamber emblem . . . . 1·10 90
862 1 g. "Southward" (liner) passing under bridge . . . . 1·75 1·50
No. 861 is an inverted triangle.

218 Black-faced Grassquit

219 Eleanor Roosevelt and Val-Kill, Hyde Park, New York

1984. Birds. Multicoloured.
863 45 c. Type **218** . . . . 1·10 75
864 55 c. Rufous-collared sparrow . 1·50 1·00
865 150 c. Blue-tailed emerald . . . 2·40 1·75

1984. Birth Centenary of Eleanor Roosevelt.
866 **219** 45 c. multicoloured . . . 70 65
867 – 85 c. black, gold & bis . . 1·00 1·00
868 – 100 c. black, yell & red . . 1·10 1·10
DESIGNS: 85 c. Portrait in oval frame; 100 c. Eleanor Roosevelt with children.

220 Child Reading

221 Adult Flamingo and Chicks

1984. Child Welfare. Multicoloured.
869 45 c. + 20 c. Type **220** . . . . 1·10 1·10
870 55 c. + 25 c. Family reading . . 1·40 1·40
871 100 c. + 50 c. Family in church 1·75 1·75

1985. Greater Flamingoes. Multicoloured.
873 25 c. Type **221** 85 60
874 45 c. Young flamingoes . . . . 1·10 80
875 55 c. Adult flamingoes . . . . 1·40 90
876 100 c. Flamingoes in various flight positions . . . . . . 2·25 1·40

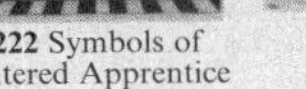
222 Symbols of Entered Apprentice

223 Players with Ball

1985. Bicentenary of De Vergenoeging Masonic Lodge, Curacao. Multicoloured.
877 45 c. Type **222** . . . . 1·10 75
878 55 c. Symbols of the Fellow Craft 1·40 1·10
879 100 c. Symbols of the Master Mason . . . . 2·50 1·60

1985. Sports Funds. Football. Multicoloured.
880 10 c. + 5 c. Type **223** 40 35
881 15 c. + 5 c. Dribbling ball . . 50 40
882 45 c. + 20 c. Running with ball 1·10 95
883 55 c. + 25 c. Tackling . . . . 1·40 1·25
884 85 c. + 40 c. Marking player with ball . . . . 1·75 1·60

224 Boy using Computer

1985. Cultural and Social Welfare Funds. International Youth Year. Multicoloured.
885 45 c. + 20 c. Type **224** . . . . 1·25 1·10
886 55 c. + 25 c. Girl listening to records . . . . 1·50 1·40
887 100 c. + 50 c. Boy break-dancing 2·25 2·00

225 U.N. Emblem

1985. 40th Anniv of U.N.O.
888 **225** 55 c. multicoloured . . . . 1·00 85
889 1 g. multicoloured . . . . 1·50 1·40

226 Pierre Lauffer and Poem

227 Eskimo

1985. Papiamentu (Creole language). Multicoloured.
890 45 c. Type **226** 50 50
891 55 c. Wave inscribe "Papiamentu" 75 75

1985. Child Welfare. Multicoloured.
892 5 c. + 5 c. Type **227** 35 20
893 10 c. + 5 c. African child . . . 45 30
894 25 c. + 10 c. Chinese girl . . . 65 50
895 45 c. + 20 c. Dutch girl . . . 1·25 85
896 55 c. + 25 c. Red Indian girl . 1·40 1·10

228 "Calotropis procera"

229 Courthouse

1985. Flowers. Multicoloured.
898 5 c. Type **228** 20 10
899 10 c. "Capparis flexuosa" . . . 20 15
900 20 c. "Mimosa distachya" . . . 45 30
901 45 c. "Ipomoea nil" 75 55
902 55 c. "Heliotropium ternatum" 90 70
903 150 c. "Ipomoea incarnata" . . 1·75 1·50

1986. 125th Anniv of Curacao Courthouse. Multicoloured.
904 5 c. Type **229** 15 10
905 15 c. States room (vert) 25 15
906 25 c. Court room 45 35
907 55 c. Entrance (vert) 80 70

230 Sprinting

231 Girls watching Artist at work

1986. Sports Funds. Multicoloured.
908 15 c. + 5 c. Type **230** 60 35
909 25 c. + 10 c. Horse racing . . 85 60
910 45 c. + 20 c. Motor racing . . 1·25 85
911 55 c. + 25 c. Football . . . . 1·40 1·25

1986. Curacao Youth Care Foundation. Multicoloured.
912 30 c. + 15 c. Type **231** 80 55
913 45 c. + 20 c. Children watching sculptor at work . . . . . 1·10 75
914 55 c. + 25 c. Children watching potter at work . . . . . 1·25 1·10

232 Chained Man

1986. 25th Anniv of Amnesty International. Multicoloured.
915 45 c. Type **232** 80 55
916 55 c. Dove behind bars 90 65
917 100 c. Man behind bars . . . . 1·40 1·10

233 Post Office Mail Box

234 Boy playing Football

1986. Mail Boxes. Multicoloured.
918 10 c. Type **233** 15 10
919 25 c. Street mail box on pole . 30 25
920 45 c. Street mail box in brick column 60 45
921 55 c. Street mail box 75 65

1986. Child Welfare. Multicoloured.
922 20 c. + 10 c. Type **234** 50 40
923 25 c. + 15 c. Girl playing tennis 65 55
924 45 c. + 20 c. Boy practising judo 90 75
925 55 c. + 25 c. Boy playing baseball . . . . 1·25 1·10

235 Brothers' First House and Mauritius Vliegendehond

236 Engagement Picture

1986. Centenary of Friars of Tilburg Mission. Multicoloured.
927 10 c. Type **235** 25 15
928 45 c. St. Thomas College and Mgr. Ferdinand E. C. Kieckens 80 55
929 55 c. St. Thomas College courtyard and Fr. F.S. de Beer 90 70

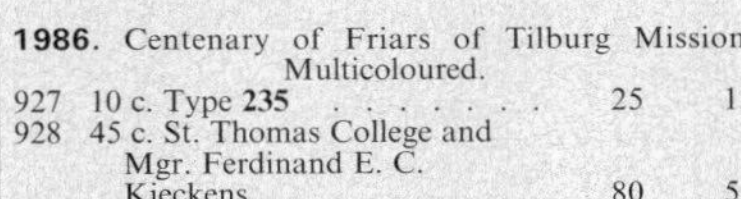

1987. Golden Wedding of Princess Juliana and Prince Bernhard.
930 **236** 1 g. 35 orange, blk & gold . 1·75 1·40

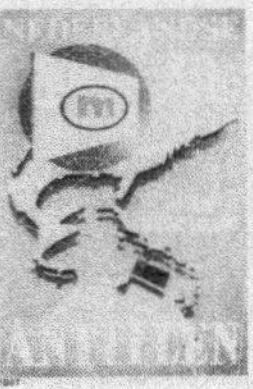
237 Map

238 Girls playing Instruments

1987. 150th Anniv of Maduro Holding Inc. Multicoloured.
932 70 c. Type **237** 80 65
933 85 c. Group activities . . . . . 1·40 80
934 1 g. 55 Saloman Elias Levy Maduro (founder) . . . . . 1·75 1·50

1987. Cultural and Social Relief Funds.
935 **238** 35 c. + 15 c. multicoloured 70 60
936 – 45 c. + 25 c. light green, green and blue . . . . . 1·00 85
937 – 85 c. + 40 c. multicoloured 1·40 1·25
DESIGNS: 45 c. Woman pushing man in wheelchair. 85 c. Bandstand.

239 Map and Emblem

1987. 50th Anniv of Curacao Rotary Club. Multicoloured.
938 15 c. Type **239** 20 15
939 50 c. Zeelandia country house (meeting venue) 65 55
940 65 c. Emblem on map of Curacao 80 65

240 Octagon (house where Bolivar's sisters lived)

1987. 175th Anniv of Simon Bolivar's Exile on Curacao (60, 80 c.) and 50th Anniv of Bolivarian Society (70, 90 c.). Multicoloured.
941 60 c. Type **240** 75 65
942 70 c. Society headquarters, Willemstad, Curacao 80 70
943 80 c. Room in Octagon . . . . 1·10 90
944 90 c. Portraits of Manuel Carlos Piar, Simon Bolivar and Pedro Luis Brion . . . . 1·25 1·10

241 Baby

1987. Child Welfare. Multicoloured.
945 40 c. + 15 c. Type **241** 80 70
946 55 c. + 25 c. Child . . . . . 1·25 1·10
947 115 c. + 50 c. Youth . . . . . 1·75 1·60

242 White-tailed Tropic Birds

1987. 25th Anniv of Netherlands Antilles National Parks Foundation. Multicoloured.
949 70 c. Type **242** . . . . 1·00 60
950 85 c. White-tailed deer 90 75
951 155 c. Iguana . . . . 1·75 1·50

243 Printing Press and Type

1987. 175th Anniv of "De Curacaosche Courant" (periodical and printing shop). Multicoloured.
952 55 c. Type **243** 65 55
953 70 c. Keyboard and modern printing press 85 65

244 William Godden (founder)

1988. 75th Anniv of Curacao Mining Company. Multicoloured.
954 40 c. Type **244** 70 45
955 105 c. Phosphate processing plant . . . . 1·50 1·10
956 155 c. Tafelberg (source of phosphate) . . . . 2·25 1·60

245 Flags, Minutes and John Horris Sprockel (first President)

246 Bridge through "100"

1988. 50th Anniv of Netherlands Antilles Staten (legislative body). Multicoloured.
957 65 c. Type **245** 75 65
958 70 c. Ballot paper and schematic representation of extension of voting rights 75 65
959 155 c. Antilles and Netherlands flags and birds representing five Antilles islands and Aruba 1·50 1·40

1988. Cultural and Social Relief Funds. Centenary of Queen Emma Bridge, Curacao. Mult.
960 55 c. + 25 c. Type **246** 70 65
961 115 c. + 55 c. Willemstad harbour (horiz) . . . . . 1·40 1·25
962 190 c. + 60 c. Leonard B. Smith (engineer) and flags (horiz) . 2·50 2·40

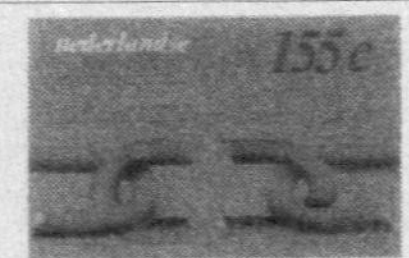

247 Broken Chain

1988. 125th Anniv of Abolition of Slavery. Mult.

963 155 c. Type **247** . . . . 1·40 1·25
964 190 c. Breach in slave wall . . 1·60 1·50

248 Flags and Map — 249 Charles Hellmund (Bonaire councillor)

1988. 3rd Inter-American Foundation of Cities "Let us Build Bridges" Conference, Curacao. Multicoloured.

965 80 c. Type **248** 90 70
966 155 c. Bridge and globe . . . . 1·40 1·25

1988. Celebrities. Multicoloured.

967 55 c. Type **249** 55 45
968 65 c. Atthelo Maud Edwards-Jackson (founder of Saba Electric Company) 60 55
969 90 c. Nicolaas Debrot (Governor of Antilles, 1962-69) . . . 1·00 90
970 120 c. William Charles de la Try Ellis (lawyer and politician) . 1·10 1·00

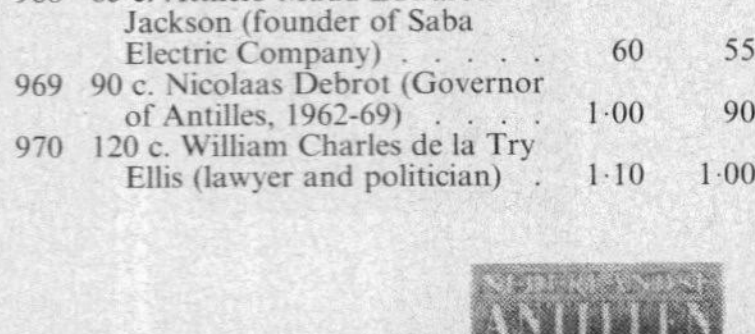

250 Child watching Television — 251 "Cereus hexagonus"

1988. Child Welfare. Multicoloured.

971 55 c. + 25 c. Type **250** 80 60
972 65 c. + 30 c. Boy with radio . 1·10 85
973 115 c. + 55 c. Girl using computer . . . . 1·50 1·25

1988. Cacti. Multicoloured.

975 55 c. Type **251** 70 45
976 115 c. Melocactus . . . . . . 1·10 85
977 125 c. "Opuntia wentiana" . . 1·25 1·00

252 Magnifying Glass over 1936 and 1980 Stamps — 253 Crested Bobwhite

1989. Cultural and Social Relief Funds. 50th Anniv of Curacao Stamp Association. Multicoloured.

978 30 c. + 10 c. Type **252** . . . 60 40
979 55 c. + 20 c. Picking up stamp with tweezers (winning design by X. Rico in drawing competition) 85 75
980 80 c. + 30 c. Barn owl and stamp album . . . . 1·50 95

Nos. 978/80 were printed together, se-tenant, forming a composite design.

1989. 40th Anniv of Curacao Foundation for Prevention of Cruelty to Animals. Multicoloured.

981 65 c. Type **253** . . . . . . 1·10 55
982 115 c. Dogs and cats . . . . . 1·40 90

254 "Sun Viking" in Great Bay Harbour, St. Maarten — 255 Paula Clementina Dorner (teacher)

1989. Tourism. Cruise Liners. Multicoloured.

983 70 c. Type **254** 90 55
984 155 c. "Eugenio C" entering harbour, St. Annabay, Curacao . . . . 1·60 1·25

1989. Celebrities. Multicoloured.

985 40 c. Type **255** 55 35
986 55 c. John Aniseto de Jongh (pharmacist and politician) . 65 45
987 90 c. Jacobo Jesus Maria Palm (musician) 95 70
988 120 c. Abraham Mendes Chumaceiro (lawyer and social campaigner) . . . . 1·25 1·00

256 Boy and Girl under Tree — 257 Hand holding "7"

1989. Child Welfare. Multicoloured.

989 40 c. + 15 c. Type **256** 75 60
990 65 c. + 30 c. Two children playing on shore . . . . . 1·10 85
991 115 c. + 35 c. Adult carrying child . . . . 1·60 1·40

1989. 40th Anniv of Queen Wilhelmina Foundation for Cancer Care. Multicoloured.

993 30 c. Type **257** 40 25
994 60 c. Seated figure and figure receiving radiation treatment 65 55
995 80 c. Figure exercising and Foundation emblem 80 70

258 Fireworks — 259 "Tephrosia cinerea"

1989. Christmas. Multicoloured.

997 30 c. Type **258** 40 25
998 100 c. Christmas tree decorations 1·10 85

1990. Flowers. Multicoloured.

999 30 c. Type **259** 35 30
1000 55 c. "Erithalis fruticosa" . . . 60 50
1001 65 c. "Evolvulus antillanus" . . 70 60
1002 70 c. "Jacquinia arborea" . . 80 65
1003 125 c. "Tournefortia onaphalodes" . . . . . . 1·40 1·25
1004 155 c. "Sesuvium portulacastrum" . . . . . 1·75 1·40

260 Girl Guides — 261 Nun with Child, Flag and Map

1990. Cultural and Social Relief Funds. Mult.

1005 30 c. + 10 c. Type **260** (60th anniv) 50 50
1006 40 c. + 15 c. Totolika (care of mentally handicapped organization) (17th anniv) . 65 65
1007 155 c. + 65 c. Boy scout (60th anniv) . . . . 2·50 2·50

1990. Centenary of Arrival of Dominican Nuns in Netherlands Antilles. Multicoloured.

1008 10 c. Type **261** 15 10
1009 55 c. St. Rose Hospital and St. Martin's Home, St. Maarten 65 55
1010 60 c. St. Joseph School, St. Maarten 70 60

262 Goal Net, Ball and Shield — 263 Carlos Nicolaas-Perez (philologist and poet)

1990. Multicoloured.

1011 65 c. + 30 c. Type **262** (65th anniv of Sport Unie Brion Trappers football club) . . 1·10 1·10
1012 115 c. + 55 c. Guiding addict from darkness towards sun (anti-drugs campaign) . . . 2·25 2·25

1990. Meritorious Antilleans. Multicoloured.

1013 40 c. Type **263** 45 40
1014 60 c. Evert Kruythoff (writer) . 65 55
1015 80 c. John de Pool (writer) . . 90 75
1016 150 c. Joseph Sickman Corsen (poet and composer) . . . 1·75 1·40

264 Queen Emma — 265 Isla Refinery

1990. Dutch Queens of the House of Orange. Multicoloured.

1017 100 c. Type **264** . . . . . . 1·50 90
1018 100 c. Queen Wilhelmina . . . 1·10 90
1019 100 c. Queen Juliana . . . . 1·10 90
1020 100 c. Queen Beatrix . . . . 1·10 90

1990. 75th Anniv of Oil Refining on Curacao.

1022 **265** 100 c. multicoloured . . . 1·40 1·25

266 Flower and Bees — 267 Parcels

1990. Child Welfare. International Literacy Year. Designs illustrating letters of alphabet. Multicoloured.

1023 30 c. + 5 c. Type **266** 40 40
1024 55 c. + 10 c. Dolphins and sun 75 75
1025 65 c. + 15 c. Donkey with bicycle 95 95
1026 100 c. + 20 c. Goat dreaming of house . . . . 1·40 1·40
1027 115 c. + 25 c. Rabbit carrying food on yoke . . . . . . 1·60 1·60
1028 155 c. + 55 c. Lizard, moon and cactus . . . . 2·40 2·40

1990. Christmas. Multicoloured.

1029 30 c. Type **267** (25th anniv of Curacao Lions Club's Good Neighbour project) 35 30
1030 100 c. Mother and child . . . 1·10 90

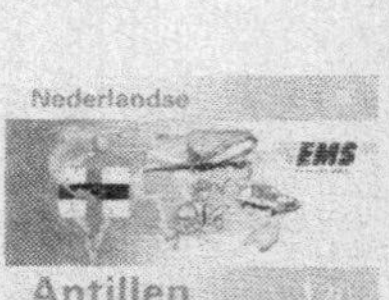

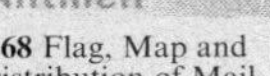

268 Flag, Map and Distribution of Mail — 269 Scuba Diver and French Grunt

1991. 6th Anniv of Express Mail Service.

1031 **268** 20 g. multicoloured . . . 18·00 14·00

1991. Fishes. Multicoloured.

1032 10 c. Type **269** 20 10
1033 40 c. Spotted trunkfish 75 50
1034 55 c. Copper sweepers . . . . 1·10 80
1035 75 c. Skindiver and yellow goatfishes . . . . 1·25 1·00
1036 100 c. Black-barred soldier-fishes . . . . 2·00 1·50

270 Children and Stamps

1991. Cultural and Social Relief Funds. Mult.

1037 30 c. + 10 c. Type **270** (12th anniv of Philatelic Club of Curacao) 50 50
1038 65 c. + 25 c. St. Vincentius Brass Band (50th anniv) . . 1·10 1·10
1039 155 c. + 55 c. Games and leisure pursuits (30th anniv of FESEBAKO) (Curacao community centres) . . . . 2·40 2·40

271 "Good Luck" — 272 Westpoint Lighthouse, Curacao

1991. Greetings Stamps. Multicoloured.

1040 30 c. Type **271** 35 30
1041 30 c. "Thank You" 35 30
1042 30 c. Couple and family ("Love You") 35 30
1043 30 c. Song birds ("Happy Day") 50 30
1044 30 c. Greater flamingo and medicines ("Get Well Soon") 50 30
1045 30 c. Flowers and balloons ("Happy Birthday") 35 30

1991. Lighthouses. Multicoloured.

1046 30 c. Type **272** 45 40
1047 70 c. Willems Toren, Bonaire . 1·00 80
1048 115 c. Klein Curacao lighthouse 1·90 1·60

273 Peter Stuyvesant College

1991. 50th Anniv of Secondary Education in Netherlands Antilles (65 c.) and "Espamer '91" Spain–Latin America Stamp Exhibition, Buenos Aires (125 c.). Multicoloured.

1049 65 c. Type **273** 75 60
1050 125 c. Dancers of Netherlands Antilles, Argentina and Portugal (vert) . . . . . . 1·40 1·25

274 Octopus with Letters and Numbers — 275 Nativity

1991. Child Welfare. Multicoloured.

1051 40 c. + 15 c. Type **274** . . . 90 90
1052 65 c. + 30 c. Parents teaching arithmetic . . . . 1·25 1·25
1053 155 c. + 65 c. Bird and tortoise with clock . . . . 2·50 2·50

1991. Christmas. Multicoloured.

1055 30 c. Type **275** 35 30
1056 100 c. Angel appearing to shepherds . . . . 1·25 1·00

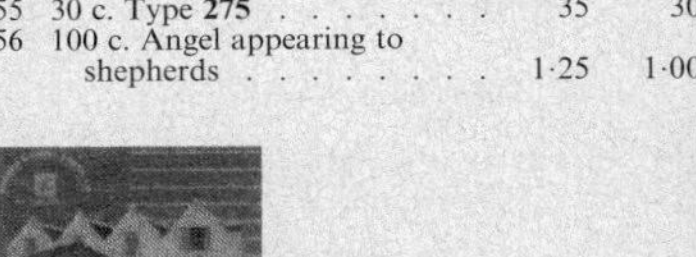

276 Joseph Alvarez Correa (founder) and Headquarters of S.E.L. Maduro and Sons — 277 Fawn

1991. 75th Anniv of Maduro and Curiel's Bank. Multicoloured.

1057 30 c. Type **276** 40 35
1058 70 c. Lion rampant (bank's emblem) and "75" 75 60
1059 155 c. Isaac Haim Capriles (Managing Director, 1954-74) and Scharloo bank branch . 1·60 1·40

1992. The White-tailed Deer. Multicoloured.

1060 5 c. Type **277** (postage) . . . 10 10
1061 10 c. Young adults 10 10
1062 30 c. Stag 30 25
1063 40 c. Stag and hind in water . 35 30
1064 200 c. Stag drinking (air) . . . 1·75 1·40
1065 355 c. Stag calling . . . . . 2·75 2·25

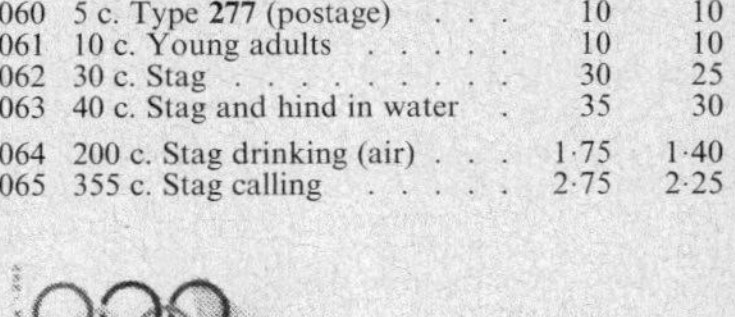

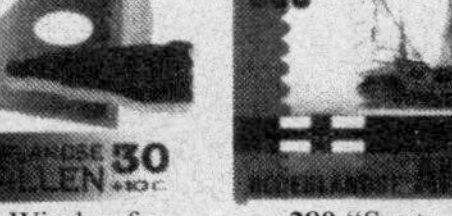

278 Windsurfer — 280 "Santa Maria"

1992. Cultural and Social Relief Funds. Olympic Games, Barcelona. Multicoloured.

1066 30 c. + 10 c. Type **278** (award of silver medal to Jan Boersma, 1988 Games) 35 35
1067 55 c. + 25 c. Globe, national flag and Olympic rings . . . 65 65
1068 115 c. + 55 c. Emblem of National Olympic Committee (60th anniv) . . . . 1·75 1·75

Nos. 1066/8 were issued together, se-tenant, forming a composite design.

1992. "World Columbian Stamp Expo '92", Chicago. Multicoloured.
1070 250 c. Type **280** . . . . . . 2·50 1·75
1071 500 c. Chart and Columbus . . . . 4·00 3·25

281 View of Dock and Town
282 Angela de Lannoy-Willems

1992. Curacao Port Container Terminal. Mult.
1072 80 c. Type **281** 85 55
1073 125 c. Crane and ship . . . . 1·25 85

1992. Celebrities.
1074 **282** 30 c. black, brown & grn 35 20
1075 – 40 c. black, brown & bl . 30 25
1076 – 55 c. black, brown & orge 40 35
1077 – 70 c. black, brown & red . 55 45
1078 – 100 c. black, brown & bl . 75 60
DESIGNS: 30 c. Type **282** (first woman Member of Parliament); 40 c. Lodewijk Daniel Gerharts (entrepreneur on Bonaire); 55 c. Cyrus Wilberforce Wathey (entrepreneur on St. Maarten); 70 c. Christian Winkel (Deputy Governor of Antilles); 100 c. Mother Joseph (founder of Roosendaal Congregation (Franciscan welfare sisterhood)).

283 Spaceship
284 Queen Beatrix and Prince Claus

1992. Child Welfare. Multicoloured.
1079 30 c. + 10 c. Type **283** . . . 30 30
1080 70 c. + 30 c. Robot 75 75
1081 100 c. + 40 c. Extra-terrestrial being . . . . 1·00 1·00

1992. $12\frac{1}{2}$ Years since Accession to the Throne of Queen Beatrix (100 c.) and Royal Visit to Netherlands Antilles (others). Designs showing photos of previous visits to the Antilles. Multi.
1083 70 c. Type **284** 55 45
1084 100 c. Queen Beatrix signing book 75 60
1085 175 c. Queen Beatrix and Prince Claus with girl . . . . . . 1·25 1·00

285 Crib
286 Hibiscus

1992. Christmas. Multicoloured.
1086 30 c. Type **285** 25 20
1087 100 c. Mary and Joseph searching for lodgings (vert) 75 60

1993. Flowers. Multicoloured.
1088 75 c. Type **286** 55 45
1089 90 c. Sunflower 70 60
1090 175 c. Ixora . . . . 1·25 1·00
1091 195 c. Rose . . . . 1·50 1·25

287 De Havilland Twin Otter and Flight Paths
288 Pekingese

1993. Anniversaries. Multicoloured.
1092 65 c. Type **287** (50th anniv of Princess Juliana International Airport, St. Maarten) . . . 50 40
1093 75 c. Laboratory worker and National Health Laboratory (75th anniv) 55 45
1094 90 c. De Havilland Twin Otter on runway at Princess Juliana International Airport . . . 70 60
1095 175 c. White and yellow cross (50th anniv of Princess Margriet White and Yellow Cross Foundation for District Nursing) . . . . 1·25 1·00

1993. Dogs. Multicoloured.
1096 65 c. Type **288** 50 40
1097 90 c. Standard Poodle 70 70
1098 100 c. Pomeranian 75 60
1099 175 c. Papillon . . . . 1·25 1·00

289 Cave Painting, Bonaire
290 "Sun and Sea"

1993. "Brasiliana '93" International Stamp Exhibition, Rio de Janeiro, and Admittance of Antilles to Postal Union of the Americas, Spain and Portugal. Multicoloured.
1100 150 c. Type **289** . . . . . . 1·10 90
1101 200 c. Exhibition emblem and Antilles flag . . . . 1·50 1·25
1102 250 c. Globe and hand signing U.P.A.E.P. agreement . . . 1·90 1·60

1993. "Carib-Art" Exhibition, Curacao. Multicoloured.
1103 90 c. Type **290** 70 60
1104 150 c. "Heaven and Earth" . . 1·10 90

291 "Safety in the Home"

1993. Child Welfare. Child and Danger. Mult.
1105 65 c. + 25 c. Type **291** . . . 70 70
1106 90 c. + 35 c. Child using seat belt ("Safety in the Car") (vert) 95 95
1107 175 c. + 75 c. Child wearing armbands ("Safety in the Water") . . . . 1·90 1·90

292 Consulate, Curacao
293 "Mother and Child" (mosaic)

1993. Bicentenary of United States Consul General to the Antilles. Multicoloured.
1109 65 c. Type **292** 50 40
1110 90 c. Arms of Netherlands Antilles and U.S.A. 70 60
1111 175 c. American bald eagle . . 2·25 1·00

1993. Christmas. Works by Lucilia Engels-Boskaljon. Multicoloured.
1112 30 c. Type **293** 20 15
1113 115 c. "Madonna and Christ" (painting) 80 65

294 Basset Hound
295 Common Caracara

1994. Dogs. Multicoloured.
1114 65 c. Type **294** 45 35
1115 75 c. Pit bull terrier 55 45
1116 90 c. Cocker spaniel 65 55
1117 175 c. Chow-chow . . . . . 1·25 1·00

1994. Birds. Multicoloured.
1118 50 c. Type **295** 35 30
1119 95 c. Green peafowl 65 55
1120 100 c. Scarlet macaw 70 60
1121 125 c. Troupial 90 75

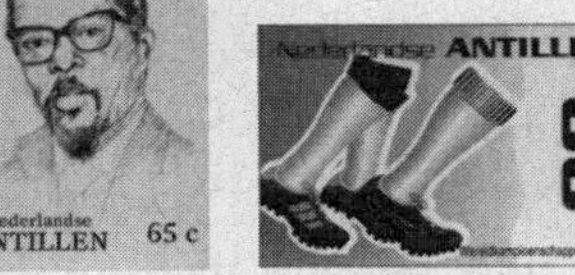

296 Joseph Husurell Lake (founder of United People's Liberation Front)
297 Players' Legs

1994. Celebrities. Multicoloured.
1122 65 c. Type **296** 45 35
1123 75 c. Efrain Jonckheer (politician and diplomat) . . 55 45
1124 100 c. Michiel Martinus Romer (teacher) 70 60
1125 175 c. Carel Nicolaas Winkel (social reformer) . . . . . 1·25 1·00

1994. World Cup Football Championship, U.S.A. Multicoloured.
1126 90 c. Type **297** 60 55
1127 150 c. Foot and ball . . . . . 1·10 90
1128 175 c. Referee's whistle and cards . . . . 1·25 1·00

298 Chair and Hammer
299 Birds and Dolphin

1994. 75th Anniv of International Labour Organization. Multicoloured.
1129 90 c. Type **298** 60 55
1130 110 c. Heart and "75" 80 65
1131 200 c. Tree . . . . 1·40 1·25

1994. Nature Protection. Multicoloured.
1132 10 c. Type **299** 10 10
1133 35 c. Dolphin, magnificent frigate bird, brown pelican and troupial 25 20
1134 50 c. Coral, iguana, lobster and fish 45 30
1135 125 c. Fish, turtle, queen conch, greater flamingos and American wigeons . . . . 1·25 1·00

300 1945 $7\frac{1}{2}$ c. Netherlands Stamp
301 Mother and Child

1994. "Fepapost '94" European Stamp Exhibition, The Hague. Multicoloured.
1137 2 g. 50 Type **300** . . . . . . 1·75 1·40
1138 5 g. 1933 6 c. Curacao stamp . 3·50 3·00

1994. Child Welfare. International Year of the Family. Multicoloured.
1140 35 c. + 15 c. Type **301** . . . 35 35
1141 65 c. + 25 c. Father and daughter reading together . 60 60
1142 90 c. + 35 c. Grandparents . . 90 90

302 Dove in Hands

1994. Christmas. Multicoloured.
1144 30 c. Type **302** 20 15
1145 115 c. Globe and planets in hands 80 65

303 Carnival and Houses
304 Handicapped and Able-bodied Children

1995. Carnival. Multicoloured.
1146 125 c. Type **303** 90 75
1147 175 c. Carnival and harbour . 1·25 1·00
1148 250 c. Carnival and rural house . . . . 1·75 1·40

1995. 50th Anniv of Mgr. Verriet Institute (for the physically handicapped). Multicoloured.
1149 65 c. Type **304** 45 35
1150 90 c. Cedric Virginie (wheelchair-bound bookbinder) 65 55

305 Dobermann

1995. Dogs. Multicoloured.
1151 75 c. Type **305** 55 45
1152 85 c. German shepherd . . . 60 50
1153 100 c. Bouvier 70 60
1154 175 c. St. Bernard . . . . . 1·25 1·00

306 Bonaire

1995. Flags and Arms of the Constituent Islands of the Netherlands Antilles. Multicoloured.
1155 10 c. Type **306** 10 10
1156 35 c. Curacao 25 20
1157 50 c. St. Maarten 35 30
1158 65 c. Saba 45 40
1159 75 c. St. Eustatius (also state flag and arms) 55 45
1160 90 c. Island flags and state arms 65 55

307 Monument to Slave Revolt of 1795
309 Sealpoint Siamese

1995. Cultural and Social Relief Funds. Bicentenary of Abolition of Slavery in the Antilles (1161/2) and Children's Drawings on Philately (1163/4). Multicoloured.
1161 30 c. + 10 c. Type **307** . . . 30 30
1162 45 c. + 15 c. Swallow and slave bell 45 45
1163 65 c. + 25 c. "Stamps" from Curacao and Bonaire (Nicole Wever and Sabine Anthonio) 65 65
1164 75 c. + 35 c. "Stamps" from St. Maarten, St. Eustatius and Saba (Chad Jacobs, Martha Hassell and Dion Humphreys) 80 80

1995. Hurricane Relief Fund. Nos. 831, 833 and 838 surch **ORKAAN LUIS** and premium.
1165 65 c. + 65 c. multicoloured . 95 95
1166 75 c. + 75 c. multicoloured . 1·10 1·10
1167 1 g. + 1 g. multicoloured . . 1·50 1·50

1995. Cats. Multicoloured.
1168 25 c. Type **309** 20 15
1169 60 c. Maine coon 45 40
1170 65 c. Silver Egyptian mau . . 45 40
1171 90 c. Angora 65 55
1172 150 c. Blue smoke Persian . . 1·10 90

310 Helping Elderly Woman across Road

1995. Child Welfare. Children and Good Deeds. Multicoloured.
1173 35 c. + 15 c. Type **310** . . . 35 35
1174 65 c. + 25 c. Reading newspaper to blind person 65 65
1175 90 c. + 35 c. Helping younger brother 90 90
1176 175 c. + 75 c. Giving flowers to the sick . . . . 1·75 1·75

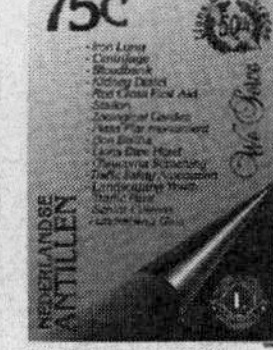

311 Wise Men on Camels
312 Serving the Community

1995. Christmas. Multicoloured.
1177 30 c. Type **311** 20 15
1178 115 c. Fireworks over houses . 85 70

1996. 50th Anniv of Curacao Lions Club. Multicoloured.
1179 75 c. Type **312** 55 45
1180 105 c. Anniversary emblem . . 75 60
1181 250 c. Handshake . . . . . . 1·90 1·60

313 Disease on Half of Leaf
314 Dish Aerial and Face

1996. 60th Anniv of Capriles Psychiatric Clinic, Otrabanda on Rif. Multicoloured.
1182 60 c. Type **313** 45 40
1183 75 c. Tornado and sun over house 55 45

1996. Centenary of Guglielmo Marconi's Patented Wireless Telegraph. Multicoloured.
1184 85 c. Type **314** 60 50
1185 175 c. Dish aerial and morse transmitter . . . . 1·25 1·00

315 Letters and Buildings
316 Gulf Fritillary

1996. Translation of Bible into Papiamentu (Creole language). Multicoloured.
1186 85 c. Type **315** 60 50
1187 225 c. Bible and alphabets . . 1·60 1·40

1996. "Capex'96" International Stamp Exhibition, Toronto, Canada. Butterflies. Multicoloured.
1188 5 c. Type **316** 10 10
1189 110 c. "Callithea philotima" . . 80 65
1190 300 c. Clipper . . . . 2·25 1·90
1191 750 c. "Euphaedra francina" . . 5·50 4·50

317 Mary Johnson-Hassell (introducer of drawn-thread work to Saba, 57th death)

1996. Anniversaries.
1193 **317** 40 c. orange and black on grey 30 25
1194 – 50 c. green and black on grey 35 30
1195 – 75 c. red and black on grey 55 45
1196 – 80 c. blue and black on grey 60 50

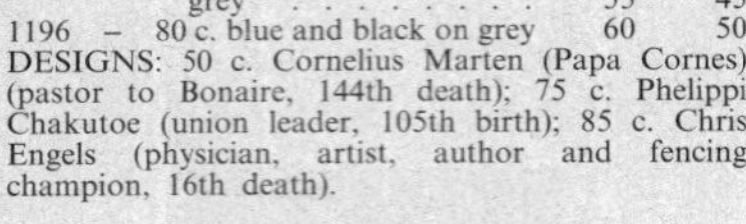

DESIGNS: 50 c. Cornelius Marten (Papa Cornes) (pastor to Bonaire, 144th death); 75 c. Phelippi Chakutoe (union leader, 105th birth); 85 c. Chris Engels (physician, artist, author and fencing champion, 16th death).

318 Shire

1996. Horses. Multicoloured.
1197 110 c. Type **318** 80 65
1198 225 c. Shetland ponies . . . . 1·60 1·40
1199 275 c. British thoroughbred . . 2·00 1·60
1200 350 c. Przewalski mare & foal . . 2·50 2·00

319 Street Child and Shanty Town
320 Straw Hat with Poinsettias and Gifts

1996. Child Welfare. 50th Anniv of U.N.I.C.E.F. Multicoloured.
1201 40 c.+15 c. Type **319** 40 40
1202 75 c.+25 c. Asian child weaver 70 70
1203 110 c.+45 c. Child in war zone of former Yugoslavia (vert) . 1·10 1·10
1204 225 c.+100 c. Impoverished Caribbean mother and child (vert) . . . . 2·25 2·25

1996. Christmas. Multicoloured. Self-adhesive.
1205 35 c. Type **320** 25 20
1206 150 c. Father Christmas . . . 1·00 80

321 Emblem
322 Deadly Galerina

1997. Cultural and Social Relief Funds.
1207 **321** 40 c.+15 c. black and yellow 40 40
1208 – 75 c.+30 c. blue, mauve and black 70 70
1209 – 85 c.+40 c. red and black 85 85
1210 – 110 c.+50 c. black, green and red . . . . 1·10 1·10
DESIGNS: 40 c. Type **321** (50th anniv of Curacao Foundation for Cure and Resettlement of Ex-prisoners); 75 c. Emblem (60th anniv (1996) of General Union of Public Servants (ABVO)); 85 c. Flag of Red Cross (65th anniv of Curacao division); 110 c. National Red Cross emblem (65th anniv of Curacao division).

1997. Fungi. Multicoloured.
1211 40 c. Type **322** 25 20
1212 50 c. Destroying angel 35 30
1213 75 c. Cep 50 40
1214 175 c. Fly agaric . . . . . . 1·25 1·00

323 Budgerigars

1997. Birds. Multicoloured.
1215 5 c. Type **323** 10 10
1216 25 c. Major Mitchell's cockatoo 15 10
1217 50 c. Yellow-shouldered Amazon 35 30
1218 75 c. Purple heron 50 40
1219 85 c. Ruby-topaz hummingbird 60 50
1220 100 c. Crowned crane 70 60
1221 110 c. Vermilion flycatcher . . 75 60
1222 125 c. Greater flamingo . . . 85 70
1223 200 c. Osprey . . . . 1·40 1·25
1224 225 c. Keel-billed toucan . . . 1·50 1·25

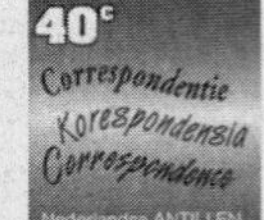

324 Parrots ("Love")
325 "Correspondence"

1997. Greetings Stamps. Multicoloured. (a) As T **324**.
1225 40 c. Type **324** 25 20
1226 75 c. Waterfall ("Positivism") 50 40
1227 85 c. Roses ("Mother's Day") . 60 50
1228 100 c. Quill pen ("Correspondence") 70 60
1229 110 c. Leaves, rainbow and heart ("Success") 75 60
1230 225 c. Ant on flower ("Congratulations") . . . . 1·50 1·25

(b) As T **325**.
1231 40 c. Motif as in Type **324** . . 25 20
1232 40 c. Type **325** 25 20
1233 75 c. Petals and moon ("Positivism") 50 40
1234 75 c. Motif as No. 1226 . . . 50 40
1235 75 c. Sun and moon ("Success") 50 40
1236 85 c. Motif as No. 1227 . . . 60 50
1237 100 c. Motif as No. 1228 . . . 70 60
1238 110 c. Motif as No. 1229 . . . 75 60
1239 110 c. Heart between couple ("Love") 75 60
1240 225 c. Motif as No. 1230 . . . 1·50 1·25

326 Rat
327 2½ Cent Coin (Plaka)

1997. "Pacific '97" International Stamp Exhibition, San Francisco. Chinese Zodiac. Designs showing Tangram (puzzle) representations and Chinese symbols for each animal. Multicoloured.
1241 5 c. Type **326** 10 10
1242 5 c. Ox 10 10
1243 5 c. Tiger 10 10
1244 40 c. Rabbit 25 20
1245 40 c. Dragon 25 20
1246 40 c. Snake 25 20
1247 75 c. Horse 50 40
1248 75 c. Goat 50 40
1249 75 c. Monkey 50 40
1250 100 c. Rooster 75 60
1251 100 c. Dog 75 60
1252 100 c. Pig 75 60

1997. Coins. Obverse and reverse of coins. Multicoloured.
1254 85 c. Type **327** 60 50
1255 175 c. 5 cent (Stuiver) . . . . 1·25 1·00
1256 225 c. 2½ gulden (Fuerte) . . . 1·50 1·25

328 Score of "Atras de Nos" and Salsa Drummer

1997. Child Welfare. The Child and Music. Multicoloured.
1257 40 c. + 15 c. Type **328** . . . 40 40
1258 75 c. + 25 c. Score of "For Elise" and pianist 70 70
1259 110 c. + 45 c. Score of "Blues for Alice" and flautist . . . 1·10 1·10
1260 225 c. + 100 c. Score of "Yesterday" and guitarist . 2·25 2·25

329 Nampu Grand Bridge, Shanghai
330 Worshippers (detail of mural by Marcolino Maas in Church of the Holy Family, Willemstad, Curacao)

1997. "Shanghai 1997" International Stamp and Coin Exhibition, China. Multicoloured.
1261 15 c. Type **329** 10 10
1262 40 c. Giant panda 25 20
1263 75 c. Tiger (New Year) (vert) . 50 40

1997. Christmas and New Year. Multicoloured.
1265 35 c. Type **330** 25 20
1266 150 c. Popping champagne cork and calendar (New Year) . 1·00 80

331 Partial Eclipse
332 Camera and Painting

1998. Total Solar Eclipse, Curacao. Multicoloured.
1267 85 c. Type **331** 60 50
1268 110 c. Close-up of sun in total eclipse 75 60
1269 225 c. Total eclipse . . . . . 1·50 1·25

1998. Cultural and Social Relief Funds. Mult.
1271 40 c. + 15 c. Type **332** (50th anniv of Curacao Museum) . 40 40
1272 40 c. + 15 c. Desalination plant and drinking water (70 years of seawater desalination) . . 40 40
1273 75 c. + 25 c. Mangrove roots and shells (Lac Cai wetlands, Bonaire) (vert) 70 70
1274 85 c. + 40 c. Lake and underwater marine life (Little Bonaire wetlands) (vert) . . 85 85

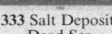

333 Salt Deposit, Dead Sea
334 Superior, 1923, and Elias Moreno Brandao

1998. "Israel 98" International Stamp Exhibition, Tel Aviv. Multicoloured.
1275 40 c. Type **333** 25 20
1276 75 c. Zion Gate, Jerusalem . . 50 40
1277 110 c. Masada 75 60

1998. 75th Anniv of E. Moreno Brandao and Sons (car dealers). Chevrolet Motor Cars. Multicoloured.
1279 40 c. Type **334** 25 20
1280 55 c. Roadster, 1934 . . . . 40 35
1281 75 c. Styleline deluxe, 1949 . . 50 40
1282 110 c. Bel Air convertible, 1957 . . . . 75 60
1283 225 c. Corvette "Stingray", 1963 . . . . 1·50 1·25
1284 500 c. Chevelle SS-454, 1970 . 3·50 3·00

335 State Flag and Arms
336 Christina Flanders (philanthropical worker)

1998. 50th Anniv of Netherlands Antilles Advisory Council. Multicoloured.
1285 75 c. Type **335** 50 40
1286 85 c. Gavel 60 50

1998. Death Anniversaries. Multicoloured.
1287 40 c. Type **336** (second anniv) . 25 20
1288 75 c. Abraham Jesurun (writer and first president of Curacao Chamber of Commerce, 80th anniv) 50 40
1289 85 c. Capt. Gerrit Newton (seaman and shipyard manager, 50th anniv (1999)) 60 50
1290 110 c. Eduardo Adriana (sportsman, first anniv) . . 75 60

337 Ireland Pillar Box
338 Globe and New Post Emblem

1998. Postboxes. Multicoloured.
1291 15 c. Type **337** 10 10
1292 40 c. Nepal postbox 25 20
1293 75 c. Uruguay postbox 50 40
1294 85 c. Curacao postbox 60 50

1998. Privatization of Postal Services.
1295 **338** 75 c. black, blue and red . . 50 40
1296 – 110 c. multicoloured . . . 75 60
1297 – 225 c. multicoloured . . . 1·50 1·25
DESIGNS—VERT: 110 c. Tree and binary code. HORIZ: 225 c. 1949 25 c. U.P.U. stamp, reproduction of No. 1296 and binary code.

339 Black Rhinoceros

1998. Endangered Species. Multicoloured.
1298 5 c. Type **339** 10 10
1299 75 c. White-tailed hawk (vert) . 50 40
1300 125 c. White-tailed deer . . . 85 70
1301 250 c. Tiger ("Tigris") (vert) . 1·75 1·40

340 Short-finned Mako ("Mako Shark")

1998. Fishes. Multicoloured.
1302 275 c. Type **340** . . . . . . 1·90 1·60
1303 350 c. Manta ray . . . . . . 2·40 2·00

341 1950 5 c. Stamp
342 Child with Family Paper Chain

1998. "70th Anniv of Dutch Stamp Dealers Club" Stamp Exhibition, The Hague. Multicoloured.
1304 225 c. Type **341** . . . . . . 1·50 1·25
1305 500 c. 1950 Queen Juliana 15 c. stamp . . . . 3·50 3·00

1998. Child Welfare. Universal Rights of the Child. Multicoloured.
1307 40 c. + 15 c. Type **342** (right to name and nationality) . . . 40 40
1308 75 c. + 25 c. Children eating water melons (right to health care) 70 70
1309 110 c. + 45 c. Children painting (right of handicapped children to special care) . . 1·10 1·10
1310 225 c. + 100 c. Children playing with can telephones (right to freedom of expression) . . . 2·25 2·25

343 Former Office, Curacao

1998. 60th Anniv of PriceWaterhouseCoopers (accountancy firm). Multicoloured.
1311 75 c. Type **343** 50 40
1312 225 c. Modern office, Curacao . 1·50 1·25

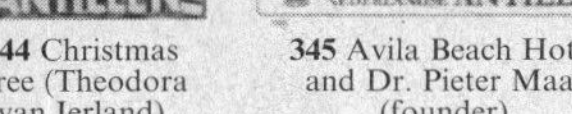
344 Christmas Tree (Theodora van Ierland)
345 Avila Beach Hotel and Dr. Pieter Maal (founder)

1998. Christmas. Children's Paintings. Multicoloured.
1313 35 c. Type **344** 25 20
1314 150 c. "Post in mail box" (Anna Sordam) . . . . 1·00 80

1999. 50th Anniv of Avila Beach Hotel. Mult.
1315 75 c. Type **345** 50 40
1316 110 c. Beach and flamboyant tree 75 60
1317 225 c. Mesquite tree . . . . . 1·50 1·20

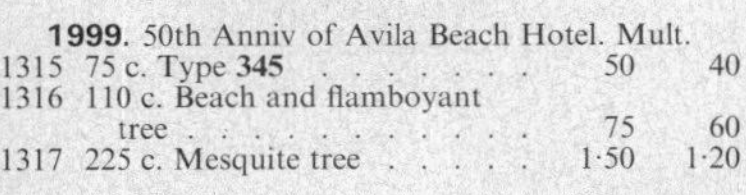

346 Rabbit and Great Wall of China
347 Girls hugging and Wiri

1999. "China 1999" International Stamp Exhibition, Peking. Year of the Rabbit. Multicoloured.
1318 75 c. Type **346** 50 40
1319 225 c. Rabbit and Jade Pagoda (vert) . . . . 1·50 1·20

1999. 50th Anniv of Government Correctional Institute. Musical instruments. Multicoloured.
1321 40 c. Type **347** 25 20
1322 75 c. Institute building and bamba 50 40
1323 85 c. Boy at lathe and triangle (horiz) 60 50

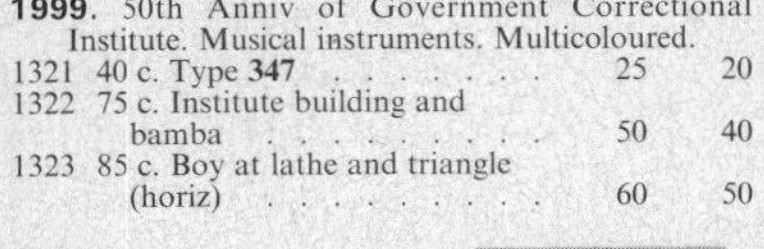

348 Launch of Ship
349 Godett

1999. 500th Anniv of First Written Record (by Amerigo Vespucci) of Curacao. Multicoloured.
1324 75 c. Type **348** 50 40
1325 110 c. Otrobanda, 1906 . . . 75 60
1326 175 c. Nos. 1324/5 and anniversary emblem . . . . 1·20 95
1327 225 c. Fort Beeckenburg, Caracasbaai . . . . 1·50 1·20
1328 500 c. 1949 $12\frac{1}{2}$ c. stamp and sailing ship . . . . 3·50 2·75

1999. Fourth Death Anniv of Wilson Godett (politician).
1329 **349** 75 c. multicoloured . . . 50 40

350 Amerindians and Old Map

1999. The Millennium. Multicoloured. (a) Size $35\frac{1}{2} \times 35\frac{1}{2}$ mm. Ordinary gum.
1330 5 c. Type **350** (arrival of Alonso de Ojeda, Amerigo Vespucci and Juan de la Cosa, 1499) . 10 10
1331 10 c. Dutch ship, indian and soldier on horseback (Dutch conquest, 1634) 10 10
1332 40 c. Flags of constituent islands of Netherlands Antilles, Autonomy Monument in Curacao and document granting autonomy, 1954 . . . . 25 20
1333 75 c. Telephone and Curacao 1873 25 c. King William III stamp (installation of telephones on Curacao, 1892) . 50 40
1334 85 c. Fokker F.XVIII airplane "De Snip" (first Amsterdam–Curacao flight, 1934) . . . 60 50
1335 100 c. Oil refinery, Curacao (inauguration, 1915) 70 55
1336 110 c. Dish aerial, undersea fibre optic cable and dolphins (telecommunications) . . . 75 60
1337 125 c. Curacao harbour, bridge and bow of cruise liner (tourism) 85 70
1338 225 c. Ka'i orgel (musical instrument) and couple in folk costume (culture) . . . 1·50 1·20
1339 350 c. Brown-throated conure, common caracara, yellow-shouldered amazon and greater flamingoes (nature) . 1·40 1·10

(b) Size 29×29 mm. Self-adhesive.
1340 5 c. Type **350** 10 10
1341 10 c. As No. 1331 . . . . . . 10 10
1342 40 c. As No. 1332 . . . . . . 25 20
1343 75 c. As No. 1333 . . . . . . 50 40
1344 85 c. As No. 1334 . . . . . . 60 50
1345 100 c. As No. 1335 . . . . . 70 55
1346 110 c. As No. 1336 . . . . . 75 60
1347 125 c. As No. 1337 . . . . . 85 70
1348 225 c. As No. 1338 . . . . . 1·50 1·20
1349 350 c. As No. 1339 . . . . . 1·40 1·10

351 Ijzerstraat, Otrobanda

1999. Cultural and Social Relief Funds. Willemstad, World Heritage Site. Multicoloured.
1350 40 c. + 15 c. Type **351** 40 40
1351 75 c. + 30 c. Oldest house in Punda (now Postal Museum) (vert) 70 70
1352 110 c. + 50 c. "The Bridal Cake" (now Central National Archives), Scharloo . . . . 1·10 1·10

352 St. Paul's Roman Catholic Church, Saba

1999. Tourist Attractions. Multicoloured.
1357 150 c. Type **352** . . . . 1·00 80
1359 250 c. Flamingoes, Bonaire . . 1·75 1·40
1361 500 c. Courthouse, St. Maarten . . . . 3·50 2·75

POSTAGE DUE STAMPS

1952. As Type D **121** of Netherlands but inscr "NEDERLANDSE ANTILLEN".
D336 1 c. green 10 10
D337 $2\frac{1}{2}$ c. green 60 60
D338 5 c. green 20 10
D339 6 c. green 65 50
D340 7 c. green 65 50
D341 8 c. green 65 50
D342 9 c. green 65 50
D343 10 c. green 30 15
D344 $12\frac{1}{2}$ c. green 30 15
D345 15 c. green 35 25
D346 20 c. green 35 45
D347 25 c. green 65 10
D348 30 c. green . . . . 1·25 1·50
D349 35 c. green . . . . 1·50 1·50
D350 40 c. green . . . . 1·25 1·50
D351 45 c. green . . . . 1·50 1·50
D352 50 c. green . . . . 1·25 1·25

NETHERLANDS INDIES Pt. 4

A former Dutch colony, consisting of numerous settlements in the East Indies, of which the islands of Java and Sumatra and parts of Borneo and New Guinea are the most important. Renamed Indonesia in 1948. Independence was granted during 1949. Netherlands New Guinea remained a Dutch possession until 1962 when it was placed under U.N. control, being incorporated with Indonesia in 1963.

100 cents = 1 gulden

1 King William III — 2

1864. Imperf.
1 1 10 c. red £275 £100

1868. Perf.
2 1 10 c. red £1000 £160

1870. Perf.
27 2 1 c. green 3·50 1·75
28 2 c. purple £100 90·00
29 2 c. brown 6·75 3·75
30 2½ c. buff 35·00 24·00
12 5 c. green 55·00 4·50
32 10 c. brown 14·50 15
51 12½ c. drab 45·00 19·00
34 15 c. brown 20·00 1·90
5 20 c. blue 90·00 2·75
36 25 c. purple 20·00 1·10
55 30 c. green 32·00 3·75
17 50 c. red 20·00 1·50
38 2 g. 50 green and purple 85·00 15·00

5 — 6 Queen Wilhelmina

1883.
89 5 1 c. green 1·10 10
90 2 c. brown 1·10 10
91 2½ c. buff 1·10 55
92 3 c. purple 1·25 10
88 5 c. green 30·00 20·00
93 5 c. blue 11·00 10

1892.
94 6 10 c. brown 4·50 15
95 12½ c. grey 8·25 14·50
96 15 c. brown 13·00 1·25
97 20 c. blue 29·00 1·50
98 25 c. purple 27·00 1·25
99 30 c. green 40·00 1·75
100 50 c. red 25·00 1·25
101 2 g. 50 blue and brown £110 32·00

1900. Netherlands stamps of 1898 surch **NED.-INDIE** and value.
111 13 10 c. on 10 c. lilac 1·75 10
112 12½ c. on 12½ c. blue 2·75 80
113 15 c. on 15 c. brown 2·75 45
114 20 c. on 20 c. green 14·50 65
115 25 c. on 25 c. blue & pink 14·50 80
116 50 c. on 50 c. red & green 23·00 90
117 11 2½ g. on 2½ g. lilac 50·00 14·50

1902. Surch.
118 5 ½ on 2 c. brown 20 20
119 2½ on 3 c. purple 25 25

1902. As T **11/13** of Surinam but inscr "NEDERLANDSCH-INDIE".
120 ½ c. lilac 30 10
121 1 c. olive 30 10
122 2 c. brown 3·50 15
123 2½ c. green 1·75 10
124 3 c. orange 2·25 1·00
125 4 c. blue 11·50 9·25
126 5 c. red 4·50 10
127 7½ c. grey 3·00 25
128 10 c. slate 1·00 10
129 12½ c. blue 1·40 10
130 15 c. brown 8·25 1·75
131 17½ c. bistre 3·00 15
132 20 c. grey 1·40 1·40
133 20 c. olive 22·00 10
134 22½ c. olive and brown 3·50 15
135 25 c. mauve 9·25 10
136 30 c. brown 25·00 10
137 50 c. red 20·00 10
138 1 g. lilac 45·00 20
206 1 g. lilac on blue 55·00 6·50
139 2½ g. grey 60·00 1·25
207 2½ g. grey on blue 80·00 29·00

1902. No. 130 optd with horiz bars.
140 15 c. brown 1·50 55

1905. No. 132 surch **10 cent.**
141 10 c. on 20 c. grey 2·40 90

1908. Stamps of 1902 optd **JAVA**.
142 ½ c. lilac 15 20
143 1 c. olive 15 15
144 2 c. brown 2·00 1·90
145 2½ c. green 1·25 10
146 3 c. orange 90 1·00
147 5 c. red 2·50 10
148 7½ c. grey 2·25 1·90
149 10 c. slate 80 10
150 12½ c. blue 2·25 40
151 15 c. brown 2·75 2·75
152 17½ c. bistre 1·75 60
153 20 c. olive 10·00 40
154 22½ c. olive and brown 4·50 2·25
155 25 c. mauve 4·50 15
156 30 c. brown 25·00 2·25
157 50 c. red 16·00 45
158 1 g. lilac 40·00 2·50
159 2½ g. grey 55·00 42·00

1908. Stamps of 1902 optd **BUITEN BEZIT**.
160 ½ c. lilac 20 20
161 1 c. olive 25 15
162 2 c. brown 1·60 1·90
163 2½ c. green 90 15
164 3 c. orange 80 90
165 5 c. red 2·50 30
166 7½ c. grey 2·75 2·25
167 10 c. slate 75 10
168 12½ c. blue 8·25 2·00
169 15 c. brown 4·00 2·40
170 17½ c. bistre 1·90 1·50
171 20 c. olive 8·00 1·75
172 22½ c. olive and brown 6·00 3·75
173 25 c. mauve 6·50 25
174 30 c. brown 14·50 1·60
175 50 c. red 6·25 55
176 1 g. lilac 48·00 3·75
177 2½ g. grey 75·00 55·00

1912. As T **18/19** of Surinam, but inscr "NEDERLANDSCH-INDIE" (T **18**) or "NEDERL-INDIE" (T **19**).
208 18 ½ c. lilac 10 10
209 1 c. green 15 10
210 2 c. brown 30 10
264 2 c. grey 30 10
211 2½ c. green 1·10 10
265 2½ c. pink 25 10
212 3 c. brown 30 10
266 3 c. green 1·10 10
213 4 c. blue 1·10 15
267 4 c. green 1·25 15
268 4 c. bistre 8·00 4·00
214 5 c. pink 1·25 10
269 5 c. green 1·10 10
270 5 c. blue 90 10
215 7½ c. brown 90 10
271 7½ c. bistre 90 10
216 19 10 c. red 1·25 10
272 18 10 c. lilac 1·25 10
217 19 12½ c. blue 1·10 10
273 12½ c. red 1·10 10
274 15 c. blue 6·50 10
218 17½ c. brown 1·10 10
219 20 c. green 1·90 10
275 20 c. blue 1·90 10
276 20 c. orange 12·00 10
220 22½ c. orange 1·90 50
221 25 c. mauve 1·90 10
222 30 c. grey 1·90 10
277 32½ c. violet and orange 1·90 15
278 35 c. brown 7·50 50
279 40 c. green 2·25 10

1913. As T **20** of Surinam but inscr "NED. INDIE".
223 50 c. green 4·50 10
280 60 c. blue 5·50 10
281 80 c. orange 4·50 10
224 1 g. brown 3·75 10
283 1 g. 75 lilac 16·00 1·75
225 2½ g. pink 12·00 35

1915. Red Cross. Stamps of 1912 surch **+5 cts.** and red cross.
243 1 c. + 5 c. green 4·50 4·50
244 5 c. + 5 c. pink 4·50 4·25
245 10 c. + 5 c. red 7·50 7·00

1917. Stamps of 1902, 1912 and 1913 surch.
246 ½ c. on 2½ c. (No. 211) 20 20
247 1 c. on 4 c. (No. 213) 45 45
250 12½ c. on 17½ c. (No. 218) 25 10
251 12½ c. on 22½ c. (No. 220) 35 10
248 17½ c. on 22½ c. (No. 134) 1·75 70
252 20 c. on 22½ c. (No. 220) 35 10
249 30 c. on 1 g. (No. 138) 6·50 1·75
253 32½ c. on 50 c. (No. 223) 1·25 10
254 40 c. on 50 c. (No. 223) 3·75 40
255 60 c. on 1 g. (No. 224) 6·00 30
256 80 c. on 1 g. (No. 224) 6·75 75

1922. Bandoeng Industrial Fair. Stamps of 1912 and 1917 optd **3de N. I. JAARBEURS BANDOENG 1922**.
285 1 c. green 6·00 5·50
286 2 c. brown 6·00 5·50
287 2½ c. pink 50·00 60·00
288 3 c. yellow 6·00 7·25
289 4 c. blue 32·00 30·00
290 5 c. green 11·00 9·00
291 7½ c. brown 7·50 5·50
292 10 c. lilac 55·00 70·00
293 12½ c. on 22½ c. orge (No. 251) 6·00 6·00
294 17½ c. brown 3·75 4·50
295 20 c. blue 6·00 4·50
Nos. 285/95 were sold at a premium for 3, 4, 5, 6, 8, 9, 10, 12½, 15, 20 and 22 c. respectively.

33 — 36 Fokker F.VIIa

1923. Queen's Silver Jubilee.
296 33 5 c. green 15 10
297 12½ c. red 15 10
298 20 c. blue 25 10
299 50 c. orange 1·25 50
300 1 g. purple 2·75 30
301 2½ g. grey 27·00 18·00
302 5 g. brown 90·00 £100

1928. Air. Stamps of 1912 and 1913 surch **LUCHTPOST**, Fokker F.VII airplane and value.
303 10 c. on 12½ c. red 1·25 1·25
304 20 c. on 25 c. mauve 2·50 2·50
305 40 c. on 80 c. orange 2·00 2·00
306 75 c. on 1 g. sepia 85 50
307 1½ g. on 2½ g. red 6·25 6·00

1928. Air.
308 36 10 c. purple 30 15
309 20 c. brown 75 50
310 40 c. red 1·00 50
311 75 c. green 2·00 15
312 1 g. 50 orange 4·00 50

1930. Air. Surch **30** between bars.
313 36 30 c. on 40 c. red 1·10 15

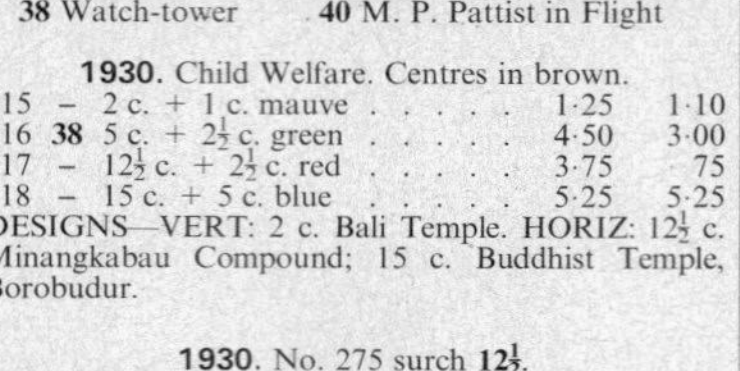

38 Watch-tower — 40 M. P. Pattist in Flight

1930. Child Welfare. Centres in brown.
315 – 2 c. + 1 c. mauve 1·25 1·10
316 38 5 c. + 2½ c. green 4·50 3·00
317 – 12½ c. + 2½ c. red 3·75 75
318 – 15 c. + 5 c. blue 5·25 5·25
DESIGNS—VERT: 2 c. Bali Temple. HORIZ: 12½ c. Minangkabau Compound; 15 c. Buddhist Temple, Borobudur.

1930. No. 275 surch **12½**.
319 12½ c. on 20 c. blue 60 10

1931. Air. 1st Java–Australia Mail.
320 40 1 g. brown and blue 13·00 11·00

41

1931. Air.
321 41 30 c. red 2·25 10
322 4½ g. blue 8·00 3·00
323 7½ g. green 10·00 3·25

42 Ploughing

1931. Lepers' Colony.
324 42 2 c. + 1 c. brown 2·75 2·00
325 – 5 c. + 2½ c. green 4·00 3·75
326 – 12½ c. + 2½ c. red 3·25 45
327 – 15 c. + 5 c. blue 8·00 6·50
DESIGNS: 5 c. Fishing; 12½ c. Native actors; 15 c. Native musicians.

1932. Air. Surch **50** on Fokker F.VIIa/3m airplane.
328 36 50 c. on 1 g. 50 c. orange 2·50 35

44 Plaiting Rattan — 45 William of Orange

1932. Salvation Army. Centres in brown.
329 – 2 c. + 1 c. purple 40 30
330 44 5 c. + 2½ c. green 2·75 2·25
331 – 12½ c. + 2½ c. red 85 25
332 – 15 c. + 5 c. blue 3·75 3·00
DESIGNS: 2 c. Weaving; 12½ c. Textile worker; 15 c. Metal worker.

1933. 400th Birth Anniv of William I of Orange.
333 45 12½ c. red 1·25 15

46 Rice Cultivation

47 Queen Wilhelmina

1933.
335 46 1 c. violet 20 10
397 2 c. purple 10 15
337 2½ c. bistre 20 10
338 3 c. green 20 15
339 3½ c. grey 15 15
340 4 c. green 75 10
401 5 c. blue 10 10
342 7½ c. violet 1·25 10
343 10 c. red 1·75 10
403 47 10 c. red 20 10
334 12½ c. brown 13·50 50
345 12½ c. red 25 10
404 15 c. blue 20 10
405 20 c. purple 20 10
348 25 c. green 2·00 10
349 30 c. blue 3·50 20
350 32½ c. bistre 11·00 8·50
408 35 c. violet 4·50 1·60
352 40 c. green 4·00 20
353 42½ c. yellow 5·00 35
354 50 c. blue 3·75 20
355 60 c. blue 4·75 40
356 80 c. red 6·25 60
357 1 g. violet 6·50 30
358 1 g. 75 green 20·00 16·00
414 2 g. green 32·00 20·00
359 2 g. 50 purple 24·00 4·00
415 5 g. bistre 30·00 8·00
The 50 c. to 5 g. are larger, 30×30 mm.

48 Pander S.4 Postjager

1933. Air. Special Flights.
360 48 30 c. blue 1·40 1·40

49 Woman and Lotus Blossom

53 Cavalryman and Wounded Soldier

1933. Y.M.C.A. Charity.
361 49 2 c. + 1 c. brown & purple 70 45
362 – 5 c. + 2½ c. brown & green 2·25 2·00
363 – 12½ c. + 2½ c. brown & orge 2·50 25
364 – 15 c. + 5 c. brown & blue 3·25 2·25
DESIGNS: 5 c. Symbolising the sea of life; 12½ c. Y.M.C.A. emblem; 15 c. Unemployed man.

1934. Surch.
365 36 2 c. on 10 c. purple 25 45
366 2 c. on 20 c. brown 20 20
367 41 2 c. on 30 c. red 35 75
368 36 42½ c. on 75 c. green 4·00 25
369 42½ c. on 1 g. 50 orange 4·00 35

1934. Anti-Tuberculosis Fund. As T **77** of Netherlands.
370 12½ c. + 2½ c. brown 1·60 45

1935. Christian Military Home.
371 – 2 c. + 1 c. brown & purple 1·40 1·50
372 53 5 c. + 2½ c. brown & grn 3·50 3·50
373 – 12½ c. + 2½ c. brown & orge 3·50 25
374 – 15 c. + 5 c. brown & blue 5·25 6·00
DESIGNS: 2 c. Engineer chopping wood; 12½ c. Artilleryman and volcano victim; 15 c. Infantry bugler.

54 Dinner-time

55 Boy Scouts

59 Sifting Rice

1936. Salvation Army.
375 54 2 c. + 1 c. purple 1·25 55
376 5 c. + 2½ c. blue 1·40 1·10
377 7½ c. + 2½ c. violet 1·40 1·40
378 12½ c. + 2½ c. orange 1·40 25
379 15 c. + 5 c. blue 2·40 2·25
Nos. 376/9 are larger, 30×27 mm.

1937. Scouts' Jamboree.
380 55 7½ c. + 2½ c. green 1·25 1·10
381 12½ c. + 2½ c. red 1·25 50

1937. Nos. 222 and 277 surch in figures.
382 10 c. on 30 c. slate 2·40 25
383 10 c. on 32½ c. vio & orge 2·40 25

1937. Relief Fund. Inscr "A.S.I.B.".
385 **59** 2 c. + 1 c. sepia & orange . . 1·25 80
386 – 3½ c. + 1½ c. grey . . . . 1·25 80
387 – 7½ c. + 2½ c. green & orge . . 1·40 85
388 – 10 c. + 2½ c. red & orange . . 1·40 20
389 – 20 c. + 5 c. blue . . . . 1·40 1·25
DESIGNS: 3½ c. Mother and children; 7½ c. Ox-team ploughing rice-field; 10 c. Ox-team and cart; 20 c. Man and woman.

1938. 40th Anniv of Coronation. As T **87** of Netherlands.
390 2 c. violet 10 15
391 10 c. red 15 10
392 15 c. blue . . . . 1·40 65
393 20 c. red 60 25

62 Douglas DC-2 Airliner

63 Nurse and Child

1938. Air Service Fund. 10th Anniv of Royal Netherlands Indies Air Lines.
394 **62** 17½ c. + 5 c. brown 85 85
395 – 20 c. + 5 c. slate 85 85
DESIGN: 20 c. As Type **62**, but reverse side of airliner.

1938. Child Welfare. Inscr "CENTRAAL MISSIE-BUREAU".
416 **63** 2 c. + 1 c. violet 65 40
417 – 3½ c. + 1½ c. green . . . . 1·10 1·10
418 – 7½ c. + 2½ c. red 80 70
419 – 10 c. + 2½ c. red . . . . 1·00 20
420 – 20 c. + 5 c. blue . . . . 1·25 80
DESIGNS—(23 × 23 mm): Nurse with child suffering from injuries to eye (3½ c.), arm (7½ c.), head (20 c.) and nurse bathing a baby (10 c.).

63a Group of Natives

64 European Nurse and Patient

1939. Netherlands Indies Social Bureau and Protestant Church Funds.
421 – 2 c. + 1 c. violet 25 15
422 – 3½ c. + 1½ c. green 35 20
423 **63a** 7½ c. + 2½ c. brown 25 20
424 – 10 c. + 2½ c. red . . . . 1·50 75
425 **64** 10 c. + 2½ c. red . . . . 1·50 75
426 – 20 c. + 5 c. blue 50 35
DESIGNS—VERT: 2 c. as Type **63a** but group in European clothes. HORIZ: 3½ c., 10 c. (No. 424) as Type **64**, but Native nurse and patient.

1940. Red Cross Fund. No. 345 surch **10+5 ct** and cross.
428 **47** 10 c. + 5 c. on 12½ c. red . . 1·00 60

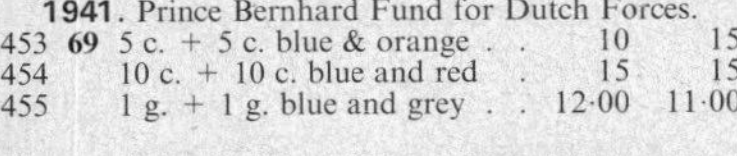

68 Queen Wilhelmina **69** Netherlands Coat of Arms

1941. As T **94** of Netherlands but inscr "NED. INDIE" and T **68**.
429 – 10 c. red 20 10
430 – 15 c. blue . . . . 2·10 1·10
431 – 17½ c. orange 35 55
432 – 20 c. mauve . . . . 27·00 29·00
433 – 25 c. green . . . . 35·00 40·00
434 – 30 c. brown . . . . 3·75 1·50
435 – 35 c. purple £140 £275
436 – 40 c. green . . . . 10·00 2·50
437 – 50 c. red . . . . 2·50 65
438 – 60 c. blue . . . . 2·25 75
439 – 80 c. red . . . . 2·25 75
440 – 1 g. violet . . . . 2·25 25
441 – 2 g. green . . . . 12·50 1·40
442 – 5 g. bistre £275 £500
443 – 10 g. green . . . . 32·00 17·00
444 **68** 25 g. orange £225 £130
Nos 429/36 measure 18 × 23 mm., Nos. 431/43 20½ × 26 mm.

1941. Prince Bernhard Fund for Dutch Forces.
453 **69** 5 c. + 5 c. blue & orange . . 10 15
454 10 c. + 10 c. blue and red . . 15 15
455 1 g. + 1 g. blue and grey . . 12·00 11·00

70 Doctor and Child

71 Wayangwong Dancer

1941. Indigent Mohammedans' Relief Fund.
456 **70** 2 c. + 1 c. green 75 50
457 – 3½ c. + 1½ c. brown . . . . 4·50 1·75
458 – 7½ c. + 2½ c. violet . . . . 3·75 2·75
459 – 10 c. + 2½ c. red . . . . 1·40 30
460 – 15 c. + 5 c. blue . . . . 11·50 5·50
DESIGNS: 3½ c. Native eating rice; 7½ c. Nurse and patient; 10 c. Nurse and children; 15 c. Basket-weaver.

1941.
461 – 2 c. red 10 15
462 – 2½ c. purple 15 20
463 – 3 c. green 15 40
464 **71** 4 c. green 15 35
465 – 5 c. blue 10 10
466 – 7½ c. violet 40 10
DESIGNS (dancers): 2 c. Menari; 2½ c. Nias; 3 c. Legon; 5 c. Padjoge; 7½ c. Dyak.
See also Nos. 514/16.

72 Paddyfield **73** Queen Wilhelmina

1945.
467 **72** 1 c. green 20 15
468 – 2 c. mauve 20 30
469 – 2½ c. purple 20 15
470 – 5 c. blue 15 10
471 – 7½ c. olive 45 10
472 **73** 10 c. brown 10 10
473 15 c. blue 10 10
474 17½ c. red 15 15
475 20 c. purple 15 10
476 30 c. grey 25 10
477 – 60 c. grey 60 10
478 – 1 g. green . . . . 1·00 10
479 – 2½ g. orange . . . . 3·75 45
DESIGNS: As Type **72**: 2 c. Lake in W. Java; 2½ c. Medical School, Batavia; 5 c. Seashore; 7½ c. Douglas DC-2 airplane over Bromo Volcano. (30 × 30 mm): 60 c. to 2½ g. Portrait as Type **73** but different frame.

76 Railway Viaduct near Soekaboemi **81** Queen Wilhelmina

1946.
484 **76** 1 c. green 30 60
485 – 2 c. brown 10 10
486 – 2½ c. red 15 15
487 – 5 c. blue 10 10
488 – 7½ c. blue 15 10
DESIGNS: 2 c. Power station; 3 c. Minangkabau house; 5 c. Tondano scene (Celebes); 7½ c. Buddhist Stupas, Java.

1947. Surch in figures.
502 – 3 c. on 2½ c. red (No. 486) . . 10 10
503 – 3 c. on 7½ c. blue (No. 488) . . 10 10
504 **76** 4 c. on 1 c. green . . . . 45 1·50
505 – 45 c. on 60 c. blue (No. 355) . . 1·60 1·40
No. 505 has three bars.

1947. Optd **1947**.
506 **47** 12½ c. red 25 25
507 25 c. green 45 25
508 – 40 c. green (No. 436) . . . 30 10
509 **47** 50 c. blue 80 40
510 80 c. red . . . . 1·25 85
511 – 2 g. green (No. 441) . . . 3·25 45
512 – 5 g. brown (No. 442) . . . 9·50 6·50

1948. Relief for Victims of the Terror. Surch **PELITA 15 + 10 Ct.** and lamp.
513 **47** 15 c. + 10 c. on 10 c. red . . . 25 50

1948. Dancers. As T **71**.
514 3 c. red (Menari) 10 10
515 4 c. green (Legon) 10 10
516 7½ c. brown (Dyak) 55 55

1948.
517 **81** 15 c. orange 60 60
518 20 c. blue 10 10
519 25 c. green 15 10
520 40 c. green 20 10
521 45 c. mauve 35 45
522 50 c. lake 25 10
523 80 c. red 30 10
524 1 g. violet 25 10
525 10 g. green . . . . 27·00 11·00
526 25 g. orange . . . . 55·00 45·00
Nos. 524/6 are larger 21 × 26 mm.

1948. Queen Wilhelmina's Golden Jubilee. As T **81** but inscr "1898 1948".
528 15 c. orange 25 15
529 20 c. blue 25 10

1948. As T **126** of Netherlands.
530 15 c. red 30 15
531 20 c. blue 30 10

MARINE INSURANCE STAMPS

1921. As Type M **22** of the Netherlands, but inscribed "NED. INDIE".
M257 15 c. green . . . . 5·50 28·00
M258 60 c. red . . . . 5·50 42·00
M259 75 c. brown . . . . 5·50 48·00
M260 1 g. 50 blue . . . . 20·00 £250
M261 2 g. 25 brown . . . . 27·00 £275
M262 4½ g. black . . . . 55·00 £475
M263 7½ g. red . . . . 65·00 £550

OFFICIAL STAMPS

1911. Stamps of 1892 optd **D** in white on a black circle.
O178 **6** 10 c. brown . . . . 1·00 50
O179 12½ c. grey . . . . 2·25 3·75
O180 15 c. bistre . . . . 2·25 2·00
O181 20 c. blue . . . . 2·25 80
O182 25 c. mauve . . . . 8·00 7·00
O183 50 c. red . . . . 1·75 1·00
O184 2 g. 50, blue and brown . . 45·00 45·00

1911. Stamps of 1902 (except No. O185) optd **DIENST**.
O186 ½ c. lilac 10 30
O187 1 c. olive 15 10
O188 2 c. brown 10 10
O185 2½ c. yellow (No. 91) . . . 50 50
O189 2½ c. green . . . . 1·10 1·00
O190 3 c. orange 30 25
O191 4 c. blue 15 10
O192 5 c. red 55 55
O193 7½ c. grey . . . . 2·00 2·25
O194 10 c. slate 15 10
O195 12½ c. blue . . . . 1·60 1·75
O196 15 c. brown 50 50
O197 15 c. brown (No. 140) . . . 26·00
O198 17½ c. bistre . . . . 2·25 1·75
O199 20 c. olive 50 40
O200 22½ c. olive and brown . . . 3·00 2·25
O201 25 c. mauve . . . . 1·75 1·50
O202 30 c. brown 70 40
O203 50 c. red . . . . 11·00 6·00
O204 1 g. lilac . . . . 2·25 1·00
O205 2½ g. grey . . . . 26·00 28·00

POSTAGE DUE STAMPS

1874. As Postage Due stamps of Netherlands. Colours changed.
D56 D **8** 5 c. yellow £250 £225
D57 10 c. green on yellow . . £100 80·00
D59 15 c. orange on yellow . . 18·00 16·00
D60 20 c. green on blue . . 30·00 11·00

1882. As Type D **2** of Surinam.
D68 2½ c. black and red 30 80
D69 5 c. black and red 20 35
D65 10 c. black and red . . . . 3·00 2·25
D70 15 c. black and red . . . . 3·25 2·75
D71 20 c. black and red . . . . 85·00 35
D82 30 c. black and red . . . . 2·10 1·90
D72 40 c. black and red . . . . 1·10 1·50
D73 50 c. black and pink . . . . 1·10 75
D74 75 c. black and red 75 75

1892. As Type D **9** of Netherlands.
D102 2½ c. black and pink 40 25
D103 5 c. black and pink . . . . 2·50 10
D104b 10 c. black and pink . . . . 2·50 40
D105 15 c. black and pink . . . . 11·50 1·75
D106b 20 c. black and pink . . . . 2·10 20
D107 30 c. black and pink . . . . 16·00 5·75
D108 40 c. black and pink . . . . 12·50 1·75
D109 50 c. black and pink . . . . 9·00 65
D110 75 c. black and pink . . . . 18·00 3·75

1913. As Type D **9** of Netherlands.
D226 1 c. orange 10 95
D489 1 c. violet 50 80
D227 2½ c. orange 10 10
D527 2½ c. brown 45 75
D228 3½ c. orange 10 95
D491 3½ c. blue 50 80
D229 5 c. orange 10 10
D230 7½ c. orange 10 10
D493 7½ c. green 60 80
D231 10 c. orange 10 10
D494 10 c. mauve 60 80
D232 12½ c. orange . . . . 2·75 10
D448 15 c. orange 65 85
D234 20 c. orange 15 10
D495 20 c. blue 60 90
D235 25 c. orange 15 10
D496 25 c. yellow 75 90
D236 30 c. orange 20 20
D497 30 c. brown . . . . 80 1·00
D237 37½ c. orange . . . . 16·00 12·50
D238 40 c. orange 20 15
D498 40 c. green . . . . 1·25 1·10
D239 50 c. orange . . . . 1·75 10
D499 50 c. yellow . . . . 1·40 1·25
D240 75 c. orange . . . . 2·75 15
D500 75 c. blue . . . . 1·40 1·25
D241 1 g. orange . . . . 4·25 5·25
D452 1 g. blue 45 55
D501 100 c. green . . . . 1·40 1·25

1937. Surch **20**.
D384 D **5** 20 c. on 37½ c. red . . . 25 25

1946. Optd **TE BETALEN PORT** or surch also.
D480 2½ c. on 10 c. red (No. 429) . . 70 70
D481 10 c. red (No. 429) . . . 1·75 1·75
D482 20 c. mauve (No. 432) . . . 4·00 4·00
D483 40 c. green (No. 436) . . . 40·00 40·00

For later issues see **INDONESIA**.

MINIMUM PRICE

The minimum price quoted is 10p which represents a handling charge rather than a basis for valuing common stamps. For further notes about prices see introductory pages.

NETHERLANDS NEW GUINEA Pt. 4

The Western half of the island of New Guinea was governed by the Netherlands until 1962, when control was transferred to the U.N. (see West New Guinea). The territory later became part of Indonesia as West Irian (q.v.).

100 cents = 1 gulden

1950. As numeral and portrait types of Netherlands but inscr "NIEUW GUINEA".
1 **118** 1 c. grey 15 15
2 2 c. orange 15 15
3 2½ c. olive 15 10
4 3 c. mauve . . . . 1·50 1·25
5 4 c. green . . . . 1·50 1·00
6 5 c. blue . . . . 3·25 15
7 7½ c. brown 35 15
8 10 c. violet . . . . 1·75 15
9 12½ c. red . . . . 1·75 1·40
10 **129** 15 c. brown . . . . 1·75 50
11 20 c. blue 70 10
12 25 c. red 70 10
13 30 c. blue . . . . 8·00 25
14 40 c. green . . . . 1·10 10
15 45 c. brown . . . . 4·50 50
16 50 c. orange 65 10
17 55 c. grey . . . . 7·50 50
18 80 c. purple . . . . 8·00 3·00
19 **130** 1 g. red . . . . 11·50 15
20 2 g. brown . . . . 9·25 1·10
21 5 g. green . . . . 12·50 1·00

1953. Netherlands Flood Relief Fund. Nos. 6, 10 and 12 surch **hulp nederland 1953** and premium.
22 **118** 5 c. + 5 c. blue . . . . . 9·00 9·00
23 **129** 15 c. + 10 c. brown . . . . 9·00 9·00
24 25 c. + 10 c. red . . . . 9·00 9·00

5 Lesser Bird of Paradise

6 Queen Juliana

1954.
25 **5** 1 c. yellow and red 30 10
26 5 c. yellow and brown 35 10
27 – 10 c. brown and blue 40 10
28 – 15 c. brown and yellow 50 10
29 – 20 c. brown and green 90 35
DESIGN: 10, 15, 20 c. Greater bird of paradise.

1954.
30 **6** 25 c. red 20 10
31 30 c. blue 20 10
32 40 c. orange . . . . 1·75 2·00
33 45 c. green 60 85
34 55 c. turquoise 45 10
35 80 c. grey 85 30
36 85 c. brown 90 45
37 1 g. purple . . . . 4·50 2·10

1955. Red Cross. Nos. 26/8 surch with cross and premium.
38 **5** 5 c. + 5 c. yellow and sepia . . 1·00 85
39 – 10 c. + 10 c. brown & blue . . 1·00 85
40 – 15 c. + 10 c. brown & lemon . . 1·00 85

8 Child and Native Hut

10 Papuan Girl and Beach Scene

1956. Anti-Leprosy Fund.
41 – 5 c. + 5 c. green 90 85
42 **8** 10 c. + 5 c. purple 90 85
43 – 25 c. + 10 c. blue 90 85
44 **8** 30 c. + 10 c. buff 90 85
DESIGN: 5 c., 25 c. Palm-trees and native hut.

1957. Child Welfare Fund.
51 **10** 5 c. + 5 c. lake 90 85
52 – 10 c. + 5 c. green 90 85
53 **10** 25 c. + 10 c. brown 90 85
54 – 30 c. + 10 c. blue 90 85
DESIGN: 10 c., 30 c. Papuan child and native hut.

11 Red Cross and Idol

12 Papuan and Helicopter

1958. Red Cross Fund.
55 **11** 5 c. + 5 c. multicoloured . . 1·00 90
56 – 10 c. + 5 c. multicoloured . . 1·00 90
57 **11** 25 c. + 10 c. multicoloured . . 1·00 90
58 – 30 c. + 10 c. multicoloured . . 1·00 90
DESIGN: 10 c., 30 c. Red Cross and Asman-Papuan bowl in form of human figure.

1959. Stars Mountains Expedition, 1959.

59	12	55 c. brown and blue	1·10	80

13 Blue-crowned Pigeon

14 "Tecomanthe dendrophila"

1959.

60	13	7 c. purple, blue and brown	50	20
61		12 c. purple, blue & green	50	20
62		17 c. purple and blue	50	15

1959. Social Welfare. Inscr "SOCIALE ZORG".

63	14	5 c. + 5 c. red and green	65	45
64	–	10 c. + 5 c. purple, yellow and olive	65	45
65	–	25 c. + 10 c. yellow, green and red	65	45
66	–	30 c. + 10 c. green & violet	65	45

DESIGNS: 10 c. "Dendrobium attennatum Lindley"; 25 c. "Rhododendron zoelleri Warburg"; 30 c. "Boea cf. urvillei".

1960. World Refugee Year. As T **180** of Netherlands.

67	25 c. blue	40	40
68	30 c. ochre	40	70

16 Paradise Birdwing

1960. Social Welfare Funds. Butterflies.

69	16	5 c. + 5 c. multicoloured	80	65
70	–	10 c. + 5 c. bl, blk & salmon	80	65
71	–	25 c. + 10 c. red, sep & yell	85	65
72	–	30 c. + 10 c. multicoloured	85	65

BUTTERFLIES: 10 c. Large green-banded blue; 25 c. Red lacewing; 30 c. Catops owl butterfly.

17 Council Building, Hollandia

1961. Opening of Netherlands New Guinea Council.

73	17	25 c. turquoise	20	30
74		30 c. red	20	30

18 "Scapanes australis"

19 Children's Road Crossing

1961. Social Welfare Funds. Beetles.

75	18	5 c. + 5 c. multicoloured	20	25
76	–	10 c. + 5 c. multicoloured	20	25
77	–	25 c. + 10 c. multicoloured	25	30
78	–	30 c. + 10 c. multicoloured	30	35

BEETLES: 10 c. Brenthid weevil; 25 c. "Neolamprima adolphinae" (stag beetle); 30 c. "Aspidomorpha aurata" (leaf beetle).

1962. Road Safety Campaign. Triangle in red.

79	19	25 c. blue	35	35
80	–	30 c. green (Adults at road crossing)	35	35

1962. Silver Wedding of Queen Juliana and Prince Bernhard. As T **187** of Netherlands.

81	55 c. brown	30	35

21 Shadow of Palm on Beach

22 Lobster

1962. 5th South Pacific Conference, Pago Pago. Multicoloured.

82	25 c. Type **21**	20	35
83	30 c. Palms on beach	20	35

1962. Social Welfare Funds. Shellfish. Multicoloured.

84	5 c. + 5 c. Crab (horiz)	20	20
85	10 c. + 5 c. Type **22**	20	20
86	25 c. + 10 c. Spiny lobster	25	25
87	30 c. + 10 c. Shrimp (horiz)	25	30

POSTAGE DUE STAMPS

1957. As Type D **121** of Netherlands but inscr "NEDERLANDS NIEUW GUINEA".

D45	1 c. red	10	20
D46	5 c. red	50	1·10
D47	10 c. red	1·50	2·25
D48	25 c. red	2·25	70
D49	40 c. red	2·25	85
D50	1 g. blue	3·00	3·75

For later issues see **WEST NEW GUINEA** and **WEST IRIAN**.

NEVIS Pt. 1

One of the Leeward Islands, Br. W. Indies. Used stamps of St. Kitts–Nevis from 1903 until June 1980 when Nevis, although remaining part of St. Kitts–Nevis, had a separate postal administration.

1861. 12 pence = 1 shilling;
20 shillings = 1 pound.
1980. 100 cents = 1 dollar.

1

2

5

(The design on the stamps refers to a medicinal spring on the Island).

1861. Various frames.
15 1 1d. red . . . . . 16·00 13·00
6 2 4d. red . . . . . 80·00 55·00
12 4d. orange . . . . . 95·00 19·00
7 – 6d. lilac . . . . . 70·00 42·00
20 – 1s. green . . . . . 70·00 90·00

1879.
25 5 ½d. green . . . . . 3·25 9·00
23 1d. mauve . . . . . 55·00 28·00
27a 1d. red . . . . . 5·00 5·50
28 2½d. brown . . . . . £100 45·00
29 2½d. blue . . . . . 13·00 11·00
30 4d. blue . . . . . £275 45·00
31 4d. grey . . . . . 6·50 2·75
32 6d. green £350 £350
33 6d. brown . . . . . 17·00 48·00
34 1s. violet . . . . . 85·00 £160

1883. Half of No. 23 surch **NEVIS. ½d.**
35 5 ½d. on half 1d. mauve . . . . £750 35·00

1980. Nos. 394/406 of St. Christopher, Nevis and Anguilla with "St. Christopher" and "Anguilla" obliterated.
37 5 c. Radio and T.V station . . . 10 10
38 10 c. Technical college 10 10
39 12 c. T.V. assembly plant . . . 10 30
40 15 c. Sugar cane harvesting . . . 10 10
41 25 c. Crafthouse (craft centre) . . 10 10
42 30 c. "Europa" (liner) 20 15
43 40 c. Lobster and sea crab . . . 20 40
44 45 c. Royal St. Kitts Hotel and golf course 80 70
45 50 c. Pinney's Beach, Nevis . . . 20 30
46 55 c. New runway at Golden Rock . 40 15
47 $1 Picking cotton 15 30
48 $5 Brewery 30 75
49 $10 Pineapples and peanuts . . 40 1·00

7a Queen Elizabeth the Queen Mother

1980. 80th Birthday of Queen Elizabeth the Queen Mother.
50 7a $2 multicoloured 20 30

8 Nevis Lighter

9 Virgin and Child

1980. Boats. Multicoloured.
51 5 c. Type **8** 10 10
52 30 c. Local fishing boat 15 10
53 55 c. "Caona" (catamaran) . . . 15 10
54 $3 "Polynesia" (cruise schooner) (39 × 53 mm) 40 40

1980. Christmas. Multicoloured.
55 5 c. Type **9** 10 10
56 30 c. Angel 10 10
57 $2.50 The Wise Men 20 30

10 Charlestown Pier

11 New River Mill

1981. Multicoloured.
58A 5 c. Type **10** 10 10
59A 10 c. Court House and Library 10 10
60A 15 c. Type **11** 10 10
61A 20 c. Nelson Museum 10 10
62A 25 c. St. James' Parish Church . 15 15
63A 30 c. Nevis Lane 15 15
64A 40 c. Zetland Plantation . . . 20 20
65A 45 c. Nisbet Plantation . . . 20 25
66A 50 c. Pinney's Beach 25 25
67A 55 c. Eva Wilkin's Studio . . . 25 30
68A $1 Nevis at dawn 30 45
69A $2.50 Ruins of Fort Charles . . 35 80
70A $5 Old Bath House . . . . . 40 1·00
71A $10 Beach at Nisbet's . . . . 50 2·00

1981. Royal Wedding. Royal Yachts. As T **26/27** of Kiribati. Multicoloured.
72 55 c. "Royal Caroline" 15 15
73 55 c. Prince Charles and Lady Diana Spencer 40 40
74 $2 "Royal Sovereign" 30 30
75 $2 As No. 73 . . . . . 80 1·25
76 $5 "Britannia" 45 80
77 $5 As No. 73 . . . . . 1·00 2·00

12 "Heliconius charithonia"

1982. Butterflies (1st series). Multicoloured.
81 5 c. Type **12** 10 10
82 30 c. "Siproeta stelenes" 15 10
83 55 c. "Marpesia petreus" . . . 20 15
84 $2 "Phoebis agarithe" 60 70
See also Nos. 105/8.

13 Caroline of Brunswick, Princess of Wales, 1793

1982. 21st Birthday of Princess of Wales. Mult.
85 30 c. Type **13** 10 10
86 55 c. Coat of arms of Caroline of Brunswick 15 15
87 $5 Diana, Princess of Wales . . 60 1·00

1982. Birth of Prince William of Wales. Nos. 85/7 optd **ROYAL BABY**.
88 30 c. As Type **13** 10 10
89 55 c. Coat of arms of Caroline of Brunswick 15 15
90 $5 Diana, Princess of Wales . . 60 1·00

14 Cyclist

1982. 75th Anniv of Boy Scout Movement. Multicoloured.
91 5 c. Type **14** 20 10
92 30 c. Athlete 25 10
93 $2.50 Camp cook 50 65

15 Santa Claus

1982. Christmas. Children's Paintings. Mult.
94 15 c. Type **15** 10 10
95 30 c. Carollers 10 10
96 $1.50 Decorated house and local band (horiz) 15 25
97 $2.50 Adoration of the Shepherds (horiz) 25 40

16 Tube Sponge

19 Montgolfier Balloon, 1783

17 H.M.S. "Boreas" off Nevis

1983. Corals (1st series). Multicoloured.
98 15 c. Type **16** 10 10
99 30 c. Stinging coral 15 10
100 55 c. Flower coral 15 10
101 $3 Sea rod and red fire sponge 50 80
See also Nos. 423/6.

1983. Commonwealth Day. Multicoloured.
103 55 c. Type **17** 15 10
104 $2 Capt. Horatio Nelson and H.M.S. "Boreas" at anchor . 45 60

1983. Butterflies (2nd series). As T **12**. Mult.
105 30 c. "Pyrgus oileus" 15 10
106 55 c. "Junonia evarete" (vert) . 20 10
107 $1.10 "Urbanus proteus" (vert) . 30 40
108 $2 "Hypolimnas misippus" . . 40 75

1983. Nos. 58 and 60/71 optd **INDEPENDENCE 1983.**
109B 5 c. Type **10** 10 10
110B 15 c. Type **11** 10 10
111B 20 c. Nelson Museum 10 10
112B 25 c. St. James' Parish Church 10 15
113B 30 c. Nevis Lane 15 15
114B 40 c. Zetland Plantation . . . 15 20
115B 45 c. Nisbet Plantation . . . 20 25
116B 50 c. Pinney's Beach 20 25
117B 55 c. Eva Wilkin's Studio . . 25 30
118B $1 Nevis at dawn 30 30
119B $2.50 Ruins of Fort Charles . . 30 45
120B $5 Old Bath House 40 55
121B $10 Beach at Nisbet's 50 70

1983. Bicentenary of Manned Flight. Mult.
122 10 c. Type **19** 10 10
123 45 c. Sikorsky S-38 flying boat (horiz) 15 10
124 50 c. Beech 50 Twin Bonanza (horiz) 15 10
125 $2.50 Hawker Siddeley Sea Harrier (horiz) 30 60

20 Mary praying over Holy Child

1983. Christmas. Multicoloured.
127 5 c. Type **20** 10 10
128 30 c. Shepherds with flock . . . 10 10
129 55 c. Three Angels 10 10
130 $3 Boy with two girls 30 60

21 "County of Oxford" (1945)

1983. Leaders of the World. Railway Locomotives (1st series). The first in each pair shows technical drawings and the second the locomotive at work.
132 21 55 c. multicoloured 10 20
133 – 55 c. multicoloured 10 20
134 – $1 red, blue and black . . . 10 20
135 – $1 multicoloured 10 20
136 – $1 purple, blue and black . . 10 20
137 – $1 multicoloured 10 20
138 – $1 red, black and yellow . . 10 20
139 – $1 multicoloured 10 20
140 – $1 multicoloured 10 20
141 – $1 multicoloured 10 20
142 – $1 yellow, black and blue . . 10 20
143 – $1 multicoloured 10 20
144 – $1 yellow, black and purple 10 20
145 – $1 multicoloured 10 20
146 – $1 multicoloured 10 20
147 – $1 multicoloured 10 20
DESIGNS: Nos. 132/3, "County of Oxford", Great Britain (1945); 134/5, "Evening Star", Great Britain (1960); 136/7, Stanier Class 5 No. 44806, Great Britain (1934); 138/9, "Pendennis Castle", Great Britain (1924); 140/1, "Winston Churchill", Great Britain (1946); 142/3, "Mallard", Great Britain (1938) (inscr "1935" in error); 144/5, "Britannia", Great Britain (1951); 146/7, "King George V", Great Britain.
See also Nos. 219/26, 277/84, 297/308, 352/9 and 427/42.

22 Boer War

1984. Leaders of the World. British Monarchs (1st series). Multicoloured.
148 5 c. Type **22** 10 10
149 5 c. Queen Victoria 10 10
150 50 c. Queen Victoria at Osborne House 10 30
151 50 c. Osborne House 10 30
152 60 c. Battle of Dettingen . . . 10 30
153 60 c. George II 10 30
154 75 c. George II at the Bank of England 10 30
155 75 c. Bank of England 10 30
156 $1 Coat of Arms of George II . 10 30
157 $1 George II (different) 10 30
158 $3 Coat of Arms of Queen Victoria 20 50
159 $3 Queen Victoria (different) . . 20 50
See also Nos. 231/6.

23 Golden Rock Inn

1984. Tourism (1st series). Multicoloured.
160 55 c. Type **23** 25 20
161 55 c. Rest Haven Inn 25 20
162 55 c. Cliffdwellers Hotel . . . 25 20
163 55 c. Pinney's Beach Hotel . . 25 20
See also Nos. 245/8.

24 Early Seal of Colony

1984.
164 24 $15 red . . . . . 1·40 4·00

25 Cadillac

1984. Leaders of the World Automobiles (1st series). As T **25**. The first design in each pair shows technical drawings and the second paintings.
165 1 c. yellow, black and mauve . 10 10
166 1 c. multicoloured 10 10
167 5 c. blue, mauve and black . . 10 10
168 5 c. multicoloured 10 10
169 15 c. multicoloured 10 15
170 15 c. multicoloured 10 15
171 35 c. mauve, yellow and black . 10 25
172 35 c. multicoloured 10 25
173 45 c. blue, mauve and black . . 10 25
174 45 c. multicoloured 10 25
175 55 c. multicoloured 10 25
176 55 c. multicoloured 10 25
177 $2.50 mauve, black and yellow 25 60
178 $2.50 multicoloured 25 60
179 $3 blue, yellow and black . . . 25 70
180 $3 multicoloured 25 70
DESIGNS: No. 165/6, Cadillac "V16 Fleetwood Convertible" (1932); 167/8, Packard "Twin Six Touring Car" (1916); 169/70, Daimler "2 Cylinder" (1886); 171/2, Porsche "911 S Targa" (1970); 173/4, Benz "Three Wheeler" (1885); 175/6, M.G. "TC" (1947); 177/8, Cobra "Roadster 289" (1966); 179/80, Aston Martin "DB6 Hardtop" (1966).
See also Nos. 203/10, 249/64, 326/37, 360/371 and 411/22.

26 Carpentry

1984. 10th Anniv of Culturama Celebrations. Multicoloured.
181 30 c. Type **26** 10 10
182 55 c. Grass mat and basket making 10 10
183 $1 Pottery firing 15 25
184 $3 Culturama Queen and dancers 40 55

27 Yellow Bell **29** C. P. Mead

28 Cotton-picking and Map

1984. Flowers. Multicoloured.
185A 5 c. Type **27** 10 10
186A 10 c. Plumbago 10 10
187A 15 c. Flamboyant 10 10
188B 20 c. Eyelash orchid 40 30
189A 30 c. Bougainvillea 10 15
190B 40 c. Hibiscus 30 30
191A 50 c. Night-blooming cereus . 15 20
192A 55 c. Yellow mahoe 20 25
193A 60 c. Spider-lily 20 25
194A 75 c. Scarlet cordia 25 30
195A $1 Shell-ginger 25 40
196A $3 Blue petrea . . . . 40 1·10
197A $5 Coral hibiscus . . . . . 60 2·00
198A $10 Passion flower . . . . . 90 3·50

1984. 1st Anniv of Independence of St. Kitts–Nevis. Multicoloured.
199 15 c. Type **28** 10 10
200 55 c. Alexander Hamilton's birthplace 10 10
201 $1.10 Local agricultural produce 20 40
202 $3 Nevis Peak and Pinney's Beach . . . . 50 1·00

1984. Leaders of the World. Automobiles (2nd series). As T **25**. The first in each pair shows technical drawings and the second paintings.
203 5 c. black, blue and brown . . 10 10
204 5 c. multicoloured 10 10
205 30 c. black, turquoise and brown 15 15
206 30 c. multicoloured 15 15
207 50 c. black, drab and brown . . 15 15
208 50 c. multicoloured 15 15
209 $3 black, brown and green . . 30 45
210 $3 multicoloured 30 45
DESIGNS: Nos. 203/4, Lagonda "Speed Model" touring car (1929); 205/6, Jaguar "E-Type" 4.2 litre (1967); 207/8, Volkswagen "Beetle" (1947); 209/10, Pierce Arrow "V12" (1932).

1984. Leaders of the World. Cricketers (1st series). As T **29**. The first in each pair shows a head portrait and the second the cricketer in action. Multicoloured.
211 5 c. Type **29** 10 10
212 5 c. C. P. Mead 10 10
213 25 c. J. B. Statham 20 30
214 25 c. J. B. Statham 20 30
215 55 c. Sir Learie Constantine . 30 40
216 55 c. Sir Learie Constantine . 30 40
217 $2.50 Sir Leonard Hutton . . . 50 1·25
218 $2.50 Sir Leonard Hutton . . . 50 1·25
See also Nos. 237/4.

1984. Leaders of the World. Railway Locomotives (2nd series). As T **21**. The first in each pair shows technical drawings and the second the locomotive at work.
219 5 c. multicoloured 10 10
220 5 c. multicoloured 10 10
221 10 c. multicoloured 10 10
222 10 c. multicoloured 10 10
223 60 c. multicoloured 15 25
224 60 c. multicoloured 15 25
225 $2 multicoloured 50 70
226 $2 multicoloured 50 70
DESIGNS: Nos. 219/20, Class EF81 electric locomotive, Japan (1968); 221/22, Class 5500 electric locomotive, France (1927); 223/4, Class 240P, France (1940); 225/6, "Hikari" express train, Japan (1964).

30 Fifer and Drummer from Honeybees Band

1984. Christmas. Local Music. Multicoloured.
227 15 c. Type **30** 15 10
228 40 c. Guitar and "barhow" players from Canary Birds Band 25 10
229 60 c. Shell All Stars steel band 30 10
230 $3 Organ and choir, St. John's Church, Fig Tree . . . . . 1·25 1·00

1984. Leaders of the World. British Monarchs (2nd series). As T **22**. Multicoloured.
231 5 c. King John and Magna Carta 10 10
232 5 c. Barons and King John . . 10 10
233 55 c. King John 10 15
234 55 c. Newark Castle 10 15
235 $2 Coat of arms 25 40
236 $2 King John (different) . . . 25 40

1984. Leaders of the World. Cricketers (2nd series). As T **29**. The first in each pair listed shows a head portrait and the second the cricketer in action. Multicoloured.
237 5 c. J. D. Love 10 10
238 5 c. J. D. Love 10 10
239 15 c. S. J. Dennis 10 15
240 15 c. S. J. Dennis 10 15
241 55 c. B. W. Luckhurst 15 20
242 55 c. B. W. Luckhurst 15 20
243 $2.50 B. L. D'Oliveira 40 60
244 $2.50 B. L. D'Oliveira 40 60

1984. Tourism (2nd series). As T **23**. Multicoloured.
245 $1.20 Croney's Old Manor Hotel 15 25
246 $1.20 Montpelier Plantation Inn 15 25
247 $1.20 Nisbet's Plantation Inn . 15 25
248 $1.20 Zetland Plantation Inn . 15 25

1985. Leaders of the World. Automobiles (3rd series). As T **25**. The first in each pair shows technical drawings and the second paintings.
249 1 c. black, green and light green 10 10
250 1 c. multicoloured 10 10
251 5 c. black, blue and light blue 10 10
252 5 c. multicoloured 10 10
253 10 c. black, green and light green 10 10
254 10 c. multicoloured 10 10
255 50 c. black, green and brown . 10 10
256 50 c. multicoloured 10 10
257 60 c. black, green and blue . . 10 10
258 60 c. multicoloured 10 10
259 75 c. black, red and orange . . 10 10
260 75 c. multicoloured 10 10
261 $2.50 black, green and blue . . 20 30
262 $2.50 multicoloured 20 30
263 $3 black, green and light green 20 30
264 $3 multicoloured 20 30
DESIGNS: Nos. 249/50, Delahaye "Type 35 Cabriolet" (1935); 251/2, Ferrari "Testa Rossa" (1958); 253/4, Voisin "Aerodyne" (1934); 255/6, Buick "Riviera" (1963); 257/8, Cooper "Climax" (1960); 259/60, Ford "999" (1904); 261/2, MG "M-Type Midget" (1930); 263/4, Rolls-Royce "Corniche" (1971).

31 Broad-winged Hawk

1985. Local Hawks and Herons. Multicoloured.
265 20 c. Type **31** . . . . 1·00 20
266 40 c. Red-tailed hawk . . . . 1·25 30
267 60 c. Little blue heron . . . . 1·25 40
268 $3 Great blue heron (white phase) . . . . 2·50 1·90

32 Eastern Bluebird

1985. Leaders of the World. Birth Bicentenary of John J. Audubon (ornithologist) (1st issue). Multicoloured.
269 5 c. Type **32** 10 10
270 5 c. Common cardinal 10 10
271 55 c. Belted kingfisher 20 55
272 55 c. Mangrove cuckoo 20 55
273 60 c. Yellow warbler 20 55
274 60 c. Cerulean warbler 20 55
275 $2 Burrowing owl . . . . . . 60 1·25
276 $2 Long-eared owl . . . . . . 60 1·25
See also Nos. 285/92.

1985. Leaders of the World. Railway Locomotives (3rd series). As T **21**, the first in each pair showing technical drawings and the second the locomotive at work.
277 1 c. multicoloured 10 10
278 1 c. multicoloured 10 10
279 60 c. multicoloured 20 20
280 60 c. multicoloured 20 20
281 90 c. multicoloured 25 25
282 90 c. multicoloured 25 25
283 $2 multicoloured 40 60
284 $2 multicoloured 40 60
DESIGNS: Nos. 277/8, Class "Wee Bogie", Great Britain (1882); 279/80, "Comet", Great Britain (1851); 281/2, Class 8H No. 6173, Great Britain (1908); 283/4, Class A No. 23, Great Britain (1866).

1985. Leaders of the World. Birth Bicentenary of John J. Audubon (ornithologist) (2nd issue). As T **32**. Multicoloured.
285 1 c. Painted bunting 10 10
286 1 c. Golden-crowned kinglet . . 10 10
287 40 c. Common flicker 25 40
288 40 c. Western tanager 25 40
289 60 c. Varied thrush 25 45
290 60 c. Evening grosbeak 25 45
291 $2.50 Blackburnian warbler . . 50 80
292 $2.50 Northern oriole 50 80

33 Guides and Guide Headquarters

1985. 75th Anniv of Girl Guide Movement. Multicoloured.
293 15 c. Type **33** 10 10
294 60 c. Girl Guide uniforms of 1910 and 1985 (vert) 15 25
295 $1 Lord and Lady Baden-Powell (vert) 20 40
296 $3 Princess Margaret in Guide uniform (vert) . . . . 50 1·25

1985. Leaders of the World. Railway Locomotives (4th series). As T **21**. The first in each pair shows technical drawings and the second the locomotive at work.
297 5 c. multicoloured 10 10
298 5 c. multicoloured 10 10
299 30 c. multicoloured 10 15
300 30 c. multicoloured 10 15
301 60 c. multicoloured 10 20
302 60 c. multicoloured 10 20
303 75 c. multicoloured 10 25
304 75 c. multicoloured 10 25
305 $1 multicoloured 10 25
306 $1 multicoloured 10 25
307 $2.50 multicoloured 20 60
308 $2.50 multicoloured 20 60
DESIGNS: Nos. 297/8, "Snowdon Ranger" (1878); 299/300, Large Belpaire locomotive, Great Britain (1904); 301/2, Class "County" No. 3821, Great Britain (1904); 303/4, "L'Outrance", France (1877); 305/6, Class PB-15, Australia (1899); 307/8, Class 64, Germany (1928).

34 The Queen Mother at Garter Ceremony **35** Isambard Kingdom Brunel

1985. Leaders of the World. Life and Times of Queen Elizabeth the Queen Mother. Various vertical portraits.
309 **34** 45 c. multicoloured 10 15
310 – 45 c. multicoloured 10 15
311 – 75 c. multicoloured 10 20
312 – 75 c. multicoloured 10 20
313 – $1.20 multicoloured 15 35
314 – $1.20 multicoloured 15 35
315 – $1.50 multicoloured 15 40
316 – $1.50 multicoloured 15 40
Each value was issued in pairs showing a floral pattern across the bottom of the portraits which stops short of the left-hand edge on the first stamp and of the right-hand edge on the second.

1985. 150th Anniv of Great Western Railway. Designs showing railway engineers and their achievements. Multicoloured.
318 25 c. Type **35** 15 35
319 25 c. Royal Albert Bridge, 1859 15 35
320 50 c. William Dean 20 45
321 50 c. Locomotive "Lord of the Isles", 1895 . . . . 20 45
322 $1 Locomotive "Lode Star", 1907 . . . . 25 65
323 $1 G. J. Churchward 25 65
324 $2.50 Locomotive "Pendennis Castle", 1924 . . . . . . 35 80
325 $2.50 C. B. Collett 35 80
Nos. 318/19, 320/1, 322/3 and 324/5 were printed together se-tenant, each pair forming a composite design.

1985. Leaders of the World. Automobiles (4th series). As T **25**. The first in each pair shows technical drawings and the second paintings.
326 10 c. black, blue and red . . . 10 10
327 10 c. multicoloured 10 10
328 35 c. black, turquoise and blue 10 25
329 35 c. multicoloured 10 25
330 75 c. black, green and brown . 10 40
331 75 c. multicoloured 10 40
332 $1.15 black, brown and green . 15 45
333 $1.15 multicoloured 15 45
334 $1.50 black, blue and red . . . 15 50
335 $1.50 multicoloured 15 50
336 $2 black, lilac and violet . . . 20 60
337 $2 multicoloured 20 60
DESIGNS: Nos. 326/7, Sunbeam "Coupe de l'Auto" (1912); 328/9, Cisitalia "Pininfarina Coupe" (1948); 330/1, Porsche "928S" (1980); 332/3, MG "K3 Magnette" (1933); 334/5, Lincoln "Zephyr" (1937); 336/7, Pontiac 2 Door (1926).

INDEX

Countries can be quickly located by referring to the index at the end of this volume.

1985. Royal Visit. Nos. 76/7, 83, 86, 92/3, 98/9 and 309/10 optd **CARIBBEAN ROYAL VISIT 1985** or surch also.
338 **16** 15 c. multicoloured . . . . 75 1·25
339 – 30 c. multicoloured (No. 92) . 1·75 1·75
340 – 30 c. multicoloured (No. 99) . 75 1·25
341 – 40 c. on 55 c. mult (No. 86) . 1·75 2·00
342 **34** 45 c. multicoloured . . . . 1·50 2·75
343 – 45 c. multicoloured (No. 310) . . . . 1·50 2·75
344 – 55 c. multicoloured (No. 83) . 1·25 1·25
345 – $1.50 on $5 multicoloured (No. 76) . . . . 2·00 2·50
346 – $1.50 on $5 multicoloured (No. 77) . . . . 10·00 13·00
347 – $2.50 mult (No. 93) . . . . 2·25 3·00

36 St. Paul's Anglican Church, Charlestown

1985. Christmas. Churches of Nevis (1st series). Multicoloured.
348 10 c. Type **36** 15 10
349 40 c. St. Theresa Catholic Church, Charlestown 35 30
350 60 c. Methodist Church, Gingerland 50 50
351 $3 St. Thomas Anglican Church, Lowland . . . . 1·25 2·75
See also Nos. 462/5.

1986. Leaders of the World. Railway Locomotives (5th series). As T **21**. The first in each pair shows technical drawings and the second the locomotive at work.
352 30 c. multicoloured 15 25
353 30 c. multicoloured 15 25
354 75 c. multicoloured 25 50
355 75 c. multicoloured 25 50
356 $1.50 multicoloured 40 70
357 $1.50 multicoloured 40 70
358 $2 multicoloured 50 80
359 $2 multicoloured 50 80
DESIGNS: Nos. 352/3, "Stourbridge Lion", U.S.A. (1829); 354/5, EP-2 Bi-Polar electric locomotive, U.S.A. (1919); 356/7, Gas turbine No. 59, U.S.A. (1953); 358/9 Class FL9 diesel locomotive No. 2039, U.S.A. (1955).

1986. Leaders of the World. Automobiles (5th series). As T **25**, the first in each pair showing technical drawings and the second paintings.
360 10 c. black, brown and green . 10 10
361 10 c. multicoloured 10 10
362 60 c. black, orange and red . . 15 25
363 60 c. multicoloured 15 25
364 75 c. black, light brown and brown 15 25
365 75 c. multicoloured 15 25
366 $1 black, light grey and grey . . 15 30
367 $1 multicoloured 15 30
368 $1.50 black, yellow and green . 20 35
369 $1.50 multicoloured 20 35
370 $3 black, light blue and blue . . 30 65
371 $3 multicoloured 30 65
DESIGNS: Nos. 360/1, Adler "Trumpf" (1936); 362/3, Maserati "Tipo 250F" (1957); 364/5, Oldsmobile "Limited" (1910); 366/7, Jaguar "C-Type" (1951); 368/9, ERA "1.5L B Type" (1937); 370/1, Chevrolet "Corvette" (1953).

37 Supermarine Spitfire Prototype, 1936

1986. 50th Anniv of Spitfire (fighter aircraft). Multicoloured.
372 $1 Type **37** 20 50
373 $2.50 Supermarine Spitfire Mk 1A in Battle of Britain, 1940 . 30 75
374 $3 Supermarine Spitfire Mk XII over convoy, 1944 . . . . . 30 75
375 $4 Supermarine Spitfire Mk XXIV, 1948 . . . . 30 1·25

38 Head of Amerindian **39** Brazilian Player

1986. 500th Anniv (1992) of Discovery of America by Columbus (1st issue). Multicoloured.
377 75 c. Type **38** 55 55
378 75 c. Exchanging gifts for food from Amerindians 55 55
379 $1.75 Columbus's coat of arms 1·25 1·75

380 $1.75 Breadfruit plant . . . . 1·25 1·75
381 $2.50 Columbus's fleet . . . . 1·25 2·00
382 $2.50 Christopher Columbus . 1·25 2·00

The two designs of each value were printed together, se-tenant, each pair forming a composite design showing charts of Columbus's route in the background.

See also Nos. 546/53, 592/99, 678/83 and 685/6.

1986. 60th Birthday of Queen Elizabeth II. As T **117a** of Montserrat. Multicoloured.

384 5 c. Queen Elizabeth in 1976 . . 10 10
385 75 c. Queen Elizabeth in 1953 . 15 25
386 $2 In Australia 20 60
387 $8 In Canberra, 1982 (vert) . . 75 2·00

1986. World Cup Football Championship, Mexico. Multicoloured.

389 1 c. Official World Cup mascot (horiz) 10 10
390 2 c. Type **39** 10 10
391 5 c. Danish player 10 10
392 10 c. Brazilian player (different) 10 10
393 20 c. Denmark v Spain 20 20
394 30 c. Paraguay v Chile 30 30
395 60 c. Italy v West Germany . . 45 55
396 75 c. Danish team (56 × 36 mm) 50 65
397 $1 Paraguayan team (56 × 36 mm) 55 70
398 $1.75 Brazilian team (56 × 36 mm) . . . . . . 75 1·25
399 $3 Italy v England . . . . . 1·10 1·90
400 $6 Italian team (56 × 36 mm) . 1·75 3·00

40 Clothing Machinist

1986. Local Industries. Multicoloured.

402 15 c. Type **40** 20 15
403 40 c. Carpentry/joinery workshop 45 30
404 $1.20 Agricultural produce market . . . . 1·25 1·50
405 $3 Fishing boats landing catch 2·50 3·25

1986. Royal Wedding. As T **118a** of Montserrat. Multicoloured.

406 60 c. Prince Andrew in midshipman's uniform . . . 15 25
407 60 c. Miss Sarah Ferguson . . 15 25
408 $2 Prince Andrew on safari in Africa (horiz) 40 60
409 $2 Prince Andrew at the races (horiz) 40 60

1986. Automobiles (6th series). As T **25**, the first in each pair showing technical drawings and the second paintings.

411 15 c. multicoloured 10 10
412 15 c. multicoloured 10 10
413 45 c. black, light blue and blue 20 25
414 45 c. multicoloured 20 25
415 60 c. multicoloured 20 30
416 60 c. multicoloured 20 30
417 $1 black, light green and green 25 40
418 $1 multicoloured 25 40
419 $1.75 black, lilac and deep lilac 30 50
420 $1.75 multicoloured 30 50
421 $3 multicoloured 50 90
422 $3 multicoloured 50 90

DESIGNS: Nos. 411/12, Riley "Brooklands Nine" (1930); 413/14, Alfa Romeo "GTA" (1966); 415/16, Pierce Arrow "Type 66" (1913); 417/18, Willys-Knight "66A" (1928); 419/20, Studebaker "Starliner" (1953); 421/2, Cunningham "V-8" (1919).

41 Gorgonia

41a Statue of Liberty and World Trade Centre, Manhattan

1986. Corals (2nd series). Multicoloured.

423 15 c. Type **41** 25 15
424 60 c. Fire coral 55 55
425 $2 Elkhorn coral . . . . . . 90 2·00
426 $3 Vase sponge and feather star 1·10 2·50

1986. Railway Locomotives (6th series). As T **21**, the first in each pair showing technical drawings and the second the locomotive at work.

427 15 c. multicoloured 10 10
428 15 c. multicoloured 10 10
429 45 c. multicoloured 15 25
430 45 c. multicoloured 15 25
431 60 c. multicoloured 20 30
432 60 c. multicoloured 20 30
433 75 c. multicoloured 20 40
434 75 c. multicoloured 20 40
435 $1 multicoloured 20 50
436 $1 multicoloured 20 50
437 $1.50 multicoloured 25 60
438 $1.50 multicoloured 25 60
439 $2 multicoloured 30 65
440 $2 multicoloured 30 65
441 $3 multicoloured 35 80
442 $3 multicoloured 35 80

DESIGNS: Nos. 427/8, Connor Single Class, Great Britain (1859); 429/30, Class P2 "Cock o' the North", Great Britain (1934); 431/2, Class 7000 electric locomotive, Japan (1926); 433/4, Class P3, Germany (1897); 435/6, "Dorchester", Canada (1836); 436/7, Class "Centennial" diesel locomotive, U.S.A. (1969); 439/40, "Lafayette", U.S.A. (1837); 441/2, Class C–16 No. 222, U.S.A. (1882).

1986. Centenary of Statue of Liberty. Multicoloured.

443 15 c. Type **41a** 20 15
444 25 c. Sailing ship passing statue 30 20
445 40 c. Statue in scaffolding . . . 30 25
446 60 c. Statue (side view) and scaffolding 30 30
447 75 c. Statue and regatta 40 40
448 $1 Tall Ships parade passing statue (horiz) 40 45
449 $1.50 Head and arm of statue above scaffolding 40 60
450 $2 Ships with souvenir flags (horiz) 55 80
451 $2.50 Statue and New York waterfront 60 90
452 $3 Restoring statue . . . . . 80 1·25

1986. Royal Wedding (2nd issue). Nos. 406/9 optd **Congratulations to T.R.H. The Duke & Duchess of York**.

454 60 c. Prince Andrew in midshipman's uniform . . . 15 40
455 60 c. Miss Sarah Ferguson . . 15 40
456 $2 Prince Andrew on safari in Africa (horiz) . . . . 40 1·00
457 $2 Prince Andrew at the races (horiz) . . . . 40 1·00

42 Dinghy sailing

1986. Sports. Multicoloured.

458 10 c. Type **42** 15 10
459 25 c. Netball 30 15
460 $2 Cricket . . . . 2·50 2·50
461 $3 Basketball . . . . 3·00 3·00

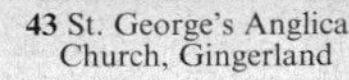

43 St. George's Anglican Church, Gingerland

44 Constitution Document, Quill and Inkwell

1986. Christmas. Churches of Nevis (2nd series). Multicoloured.

462 10 c. Type **43** 15 10
463 40 c. Trinity Methodist Church, Fountain 30 25
464 $1 Charlestown Methodist Church 60 65
465 $5 Wesleyan Holiness Church, Brown Hill . . . . 2·75 3·75

1987. Bicentenary of U.S. Constitution and 230th Birth Anniv of Alexander Hamilton (U.S. statesman). Multicoloured.

466 15 c. Type **44** 10 10
467 40 c. Alexander Hamilton and Hamilton House 20 25
468 60 c. Alexander Hamilton . . . 25 35
469 $2 Washington and his Cabinet 90 1·25

1987. Victory of "Stars and Stripes" in America's Cup Yachting Championship. No. 54 optd **America's Cup 1987 Winners 'Stars & Stripes'**.

471 $3 Windjammer S.V "Polynesia" 1·10 1·60

46 Fig Tree Church

1987. Bicentenary of Marriage of Horatio Nelson and Frances Nisbet. Multicoloured.

472 15 c. Type **46** 15 10
473 60 c. Frances Nisbet 40 30
474 $1 H.M.S. "Boreas" (frigate) . 1·25 1·00
475 $3 Captain Horatio Nelson . . 2·50 3·25

47 Queen Angelfish

1987. Coral Reef Fishes. Multicoloured.

477 60 c. Type **47** 35 60
478 60 c. Blue angelfish 35 60
479 $1 Stoplight parrotfish (male) . 40 80
480 $1 Stoplight parrotfish (female) . 40 80
481 $1.50 Red hind 45 90
482 $1.50 Rock hind 45 90
483 $2.50 Coney (bicoloured phase) 50 1·50
484 $2.50 Coney (red-brown phase) 50 1·50

Nos. 478, 480, 482 and 484 are inverted triangles.

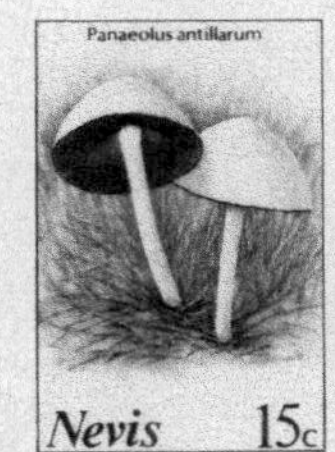

48 "Panaeolus antillarum" 50 Hawk-wing Conch

49 Rag Doll

1987. Fungi (1st series). Multicoloured.

485 15 c. Type **48** 80 30
486 50 c. "Pycnoporus sanguineus" 1·50 80
487 $2 "Gymnopilus chrysopellus" 2·75 3·25
488 $3 "Cantharellus cinnabarinus" 3·25 4·25

See also Nos. 646/53.

1987. Christmas. Toys. Multicoloured.

489 10 c. Type **49** 10 10
490 40 c. Coconut boat 20 25
491 $1.20 Sandbox cart 55 60
492 $5 Two-wheeled cart . . . . . 2·25 3·75

1988. Sea Shells and Pearls. Multicoloured.

493 15 c. Type **50** 20 15
494 40 c. Rooster-tail conch 30 20
495 60 c. Emperor helmet 50 40
496 $2 Queen or pink conch . . . 1·60 2·00
497 $3 King helmet . . . . 1·75 2·25

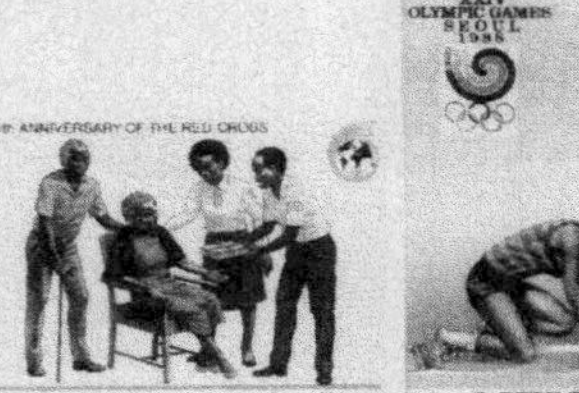

51 Visiting Pensioners at Christmas 52 Athlete on Starting Blocks

1988. 125th Anniv of International Red Cross. Multicoloured.

498 15 c. Type **51** 10 10
499 40 c. Teaching children first aid 15 20
500 60 c. Providing wheelchairs for the disabled 25 35
501 $5 Helping cyclone victim . . . 2·10 3·25

1988. Olympic Games, Seoul. Multicoloured.

502 10 c. Type **52** 10 35
503 $1.20 At start 50 85
504 $2 During race . . . . 85 1·25
505 $3 At finish . . . . 1·25 1·50

Nos. 502/5 were printed together, se-tenant, each strip forming a composite design showing an athlete from start to finish of race.

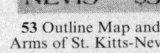

53 Outline Map and Arms of St. Kitts-Nevis 54 Poinsettia

1988. 5th Anniv of Independence.

507 **53** $5 multicoloured . . . . . 2·10 2·75

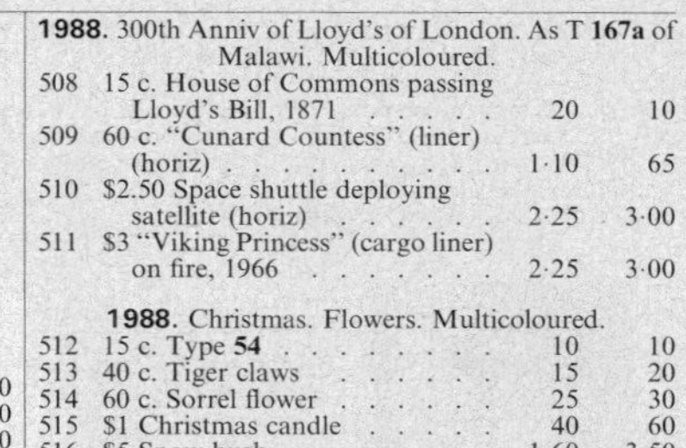

1988. 300th Anniv of Lloyd's of London. As T **167a** of Malawi. Multicoloured.

508 15 c. House of Commons passing Lloyd's Bill, 1871 . . . . . 20 10
509 60 c. "Cunard Countess" (liner) (horiz) . . . . 1·10 65
510 $2.50 Space shuttle deploying satellite (horiz) . . . . . 2·25 3·00
511 $3 "Viking Princess" (cargo liner) on fire, 1966 . . . . . . 2·25 3·00

1988. Christmas. Flowers. Multicoloured.

512 15 c. Type **54** 10 10
513 40 c. Tiger claws 15 20
514 60 c. Sorrel flower 25 30
515 $1 Christmas candle 40 60
516 $5 Snow bush . . . . 1·60 3·50

55 British Fleet off St. Kitts 56 Cicada

1989. "Philexfrance 89" International Stamp Exhibition, Paris. Battle of Frigate Bay, 1782. Multicoloured.

517 50 c. Type **55** . . . . 75 1·00
518 $1.20 Battle off Nevis . . . . 1·00 1·40
519 $2 British and French fleets exchanging broadsides . . . 1·25 1·60
520 $3 French map of Nevis, 1764 1·60 2·00

Nos. 517/19 were printed together, se-tenant, forming a composite design.

1989. "Sounds of the Night". Multicoloured.

521 10 c. Type **56** 20 15
522 40 c. Grasshopper 40 35
523 60 c. Cricket 55 50
524 $5 Tree frog . . . . 3·75 5·50

1989. 20th Anniv of First Manned Landing on Moon. As T **51a** of Kiribati. Multicoloured.

526 15 c. Vehicle Assembly Building, Kennedy Space Centre . . . 15 10
527 40 c. Crew of "Apollo 12" (30 × 30 mm) 20 20
528 $2 "Apollo 12" emblem (30 × 30 mm) . . . . . . 1·00 1·60
529 $3 "Apollo 12" astronaut on Moon . . . . 1·40 1·90

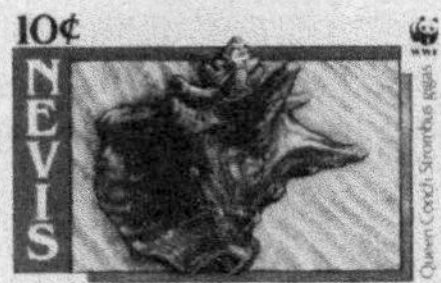

57 Queen or Pink Conch feeding

1990. Queen or Pink Conch. Multicoloured.

531 10 c. Type **57** 60 30
532 40 c. Queen or pink conch from front 90 40
533 60 c. Side view of shell . . . . 1·25 90
534 $1 Black and flare . . . . . . 1·60 2·00

58 Wyon Medal Portrait 59

1990. 150th Anniv of the Penny Black.

536 **58** 15 c. black and brown . . . 15 10
537 – 40 c. black and green . . . 30 25
538 – 60 c. black 45 55
539 – $4 black and blue . . . . . 2·50 3·25

DESIGNS: 40 c. Engine-turned background; 60 c. Heath's engraving of portrait; $4 Essay with inscriptions.

1990. 500th Anniv of Regular European Postal Services.

541 **59** 15 c. brown 20 15
542 – 40 c. green 35 25
543 – 60 c. violet 55 65
544 – $4 blue . . . . 2·75 3·50

Nos. 541/4 commemorate the Thurn and Taxis postal service and the designs are loosely based on those of the initial 1852–58 series.

1990. 500th Anniv (1992) of Discovery of America by Columbus (2nd issue). New World Natural History—Crabs. As T **354a** of Grenada, but horiz. Multicoloured.

546 5 c. Sand fiddler 10 10
547 15 c. Great land crab 15 15
548 20 c. Blue crab 15 15
549 40 c. Stone crab 30 30
550 60 c. Mountain crab 45 45
551 $2 Sargassum crab . . . . . . 1·40 1·60
552 $3 Yellow box crab . . . . . 1·75 2·00
553 $4 Spiny spider crab . . . . . 2·25 2·50

1990. 90th Birthday of Queen Elizabeth the Queen Mother. As T **103** of Grenada Grenadines.

555 $2 black, mauve and buff . . . 1·40 1·60
556 $2 black, mauve and buff . . . 1·40 1·60
557 $2 black, mauve and buff . . . 1·40 1·60

DESIGNS: No. 555, Duchess of York with corgi; 556, Queen Elizabeth in Coronation robes, 1937; 557, Duchess of York in garden.

61 MaKanaky, Cameroons

62 "Cattleya deckeri"

1990. World Cup Football Championship, Italy. Star Players. Multicoloured.

559 10 c. Type **61** 40 10
560 25 c. Chovanec, Czechoslovakia 45 15
561 $2.50 Robson, England . . . . 2·75 3·25
562 $5 Voller, West Germany . . . 3·75 5·00

1990. Christmas. Native Orchids. Mult.

564 10 c. Type **62** 55 20
565 15 c. "Epidendrum ciliare" . . 55 20
566 20 c. "Epidendrum fragrans" . . 65 20
567 40 c. "Epidendrum ibaguense" . 85 25
568 60 c. "Epidendrum latifolium" 1·10 50
569 $1.20 "Maxillaria conferta" . 1·40 1·75
570 $2 "Epidendrum strobiliferum" 1·75 2·75
571 $3 "Brassavola cucullata" . . 2·00 3·00

1991. 350th Death Anniv of Rubens. As T **273** of Antigua, showing details from "The Feast of Achelous". Multicoloured.

573 10 c. Two jugs (vert) 25 15
574 40 c. Woman at table (vert) . . 50 30
575 60 c. Two servants with fruit (vert) 65 45
576 $4 Achelous (vert) . . . . . . 2·50 3·50

63 "Agraulis vanillae"

1991. Butterflies. Multicoloured.

578B 5 c. Type **63** 20 30
579B 10 c. "Historis odius" . . . 20 20
580B 15 c. "Marpesia corinna" . . 20 20
581B 20 c. "Anartia amathea" . . 30 30
582B 25 c. "Junonia evarete" . . . 30 30
583B 40 c. "Heliconius charithonia" 40 30
584B 50 c. "Marpesia petreus" . . 45 35
585A 60 c. "Dione juno" 75 50
586B 75 c. "Heliconius doris" . . 60 60
586cB 80 c. As 60 c. 60 60
587B $1 "Hypolimnas misippus" . . 70 70
588A $3 "Danaus plexippus" . . . 2·00 2·75
589A $5 "Heliconius sara" . . . . 2·75 4·00
590A $10 "Tithorea harmonia" . . 5·00 8·00
591A $20 "Dryas julia" . . . . . 9·50 13·00

64 "Viking Mars Lander", 1976

1991. 500th Anniv of Discovery of America by Columbus (1992) (3rd issue). History of Exploration. Multicoloured.

592 15 c. Type **64** 20 15
593 40 c. "Apollo 11", 1969 . . . . 30 25
594 60 c. "Skylab", 1973 . . . . . 45 45
595 75 c. "Salyut 6", 1977 . . . . 55 55
596 $1 "Voyager 1", 1977 . . . . . 65 65
597 $2 "Venera 7", 1970 . . . . . 1·25 1·40
598 $4 "Gemini 4", 1965 . . . . 2·50 2·75
599 $5 "Luna 3", 1959 . . . . . . 2·75 3·00

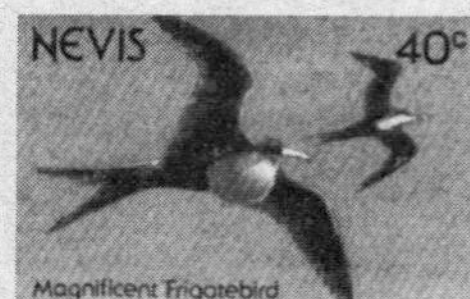

65 Magnificent Frigate Bird

1991. Island Birds. Multicoloured.

601 40 c. Type **65** 55 55
602 40 c. Roseate tern 55 55
603 40 c. Red-tailed hawk 55 55
604 40 c. Zenaida dove 55 55
605 40 c. Bananaquit 55 55
606 40 c. American kestrel 55 55
607 40 c. Grey kingbird 55 55
608 40 c. Prothonotary warbler . . 55 55
609 40 c. Blue-hooded euphonia . . 55 55
610 40 c. Antillean crested hummingbird 55 55
611 40 c. White-tailed tropic bird . 55 55
612 40 c. Yellow-bellied sapsucker . 55 55
613 40 c. Green-throated carib . . 55 55
614 40 c. Purple-throated carib . . 55 55
615 40 c. Red-billed whistling duck ("Black-bellied tree-duck") . 55 55
616 40 c. Ringed kingfisher 55 55
617 40 c. Burrowing owl 55 55
618 40 c. Turnstone 55 55
619 40 c. Great blue heron 55 55
620 40 c. Yellow-crowned night-heron 55 55

Nos. 601/20 were printed together, se-tenant, forming a composite design.

1991. 65th Birthday of Queen Elizabeth II. As T **198a** of Gambia. Multicoloured.

622 15 c. Queen Elizabeth at polo match with Prince Charles . . 30 20
623 40 c. Queen and Prince Philip on Buckingham Palace balcony . 45 35
624 $2 In carriage at Ascot, 1986 . 1·40 1·75
625 $4 Queen Elizabeth II at Windsor polo match, 1989 . . . . . 2·75 3·75

1991. 10th Wedding Anniv of Prince and Princess of Wales. As T **198b** of Gambia. Multicoloured.

627 10 c. Prince Charles and Princess Diana 20 20
628 50 c. Prince of Wales and family 50 30
629 $1 Prince William and Prince Harry 85 90
630 $5 Prince and Princess of Wales 3·00 3·50

1991. "Phila Nippon '91" International Stamp Exhibition, Tokyo. Japanese Railway Locomotives. As T **257** of Maldives. Mult.

632 10 c. Class C62 steam locomotive 50 30
633 15 c. Class C56 steam locomotive (horiz) 55 30
634 40 c. Class C55 streamlined steam locomotive (horiz) 80 50
635 60 c. Class 1400 steam locomotive (horiz) 95 80
636 $1 Class 485 diesel rail car . . 1·25 1·00
637 $2 Class C61 steam locomotive 2·00 2·00
638 $3 Class 485 diesel train (horiz) . 2·25 2·25
639 $4 Class 7000 electric train (horiz) . . . . 2·75 2·75

1991. Christmas. Drawings by Albrecht Durer. As T **211** of Lesotho.

641 10 c. black and green 10 10
642 40 c. black and orange 20 25
643 60 c. black and blue 25 30
644 $3 black and mauve . . . . . 1·40 2·40

DESIGNS: 10 c. "Mary being Crowned by an Angel"; 40 c. "Mary with the Pear"; 60 c. "Mary in a Halo"; $3 "Mary with Crown of Stars and Sceptre".

66 "Marasmius haemtocephalus"

67 Monique Knol (cycling), Netherlands

1991. Fungi (2nd series). Multicoloured.

646 15 c. Type **66** 30 20
647 40 c. "Psilocybe cubensis" . . . 40 30
648 60 c. "Hygrocybe acutoconica" . 50 40
649 75 c. "Hygrocybe occidentalis" . 60 60
650 $1 "Boletellus cubensis" . . . 70 70
651 $2 "Gymnopilus chrysopellus" . 1·25 1·50
652 $4 "Cantharellus cinnabarinus" . 2·25 2·50
653 $5 "Chlorophyllum molybdites" . 2·25 2·50

1992. 40th Anniv of Queen Elizabeth II's Accession. As T **202a** of Gambia. Multicoloured.

655 10 c. Charlestown from the sea . 25 10
656 40 c. Charlestown square . . . 40 25
657 $1 Mountain scenery 70 60
658 $5 Early cottage . . . . 2·75 3·50

1992. Olympic Games, Barcelona. Gold Medal Winners of 1988. Multicoloured.

660 20 c. Type **67** 30 30
661 25 c. Roger Kingdom (hurdles), U.S.A. 30 30
662 50 c. Yugoslavia (men's waterpolo) 50 50
663 80 c. Anja Fichtel (foil), West Germany 70 70
664 $1 Said Aouita (mid-distance running), Morocco 80 80
665 $1.50 Yuri Sedykh (hammer throw), U.S.S.R. . . . . . 1·10 1·10
666 $3 Shushunova (women's gymnastics), U.S.S.R. . . . 2·00 2·50
667 $5 Valimir Artemov (men's gymnastics), U.S.S.R. . . . 2·50 3·00

68 "Landscape" (Mariano Fortuny i Marsal)

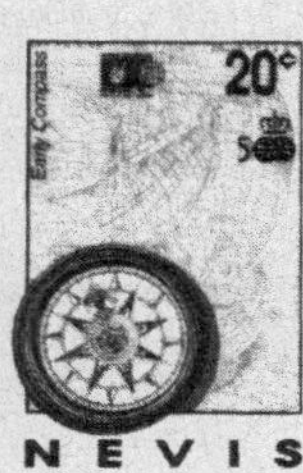

69 Early Compass and Ship

1992. "Granada '92" International Stamp Exhibition, Spain. Spanish Paintings. Multicoloured.

669 20 c. Type **68** 30 30
670 25 c. "Dona Juana la Loca" (Francisco Pradilla Ortiz) (horiz) 30 30
671 50 c. "Idyll" (Fortuny i Marsal) 50 50
672 80 c. "Old Man Naked in the Sun" (Fortuny i Marsal) . . 70 70
673 $1 "The Painter's Children in the Japanese Salon" (detail) (Fortuny i Marsal) 80 80
674 $2 "The Painter's Children in the Japanese Salon" (different detail) (Fortuny i Marsal) . . 1·25 1·25
675 $3 "Still Life: Sea Bream and Oranges" (Luis Eugenio Melendez) (horiz) . . . . . 2·00 2·50
676 $5 "Still Life: Box of Sweets, Pastry and Other Objects" (Melendez) . . . . 2·50 3·00

1992. 500th Anniv of Discovery of America by Columbus (4th issue) and "World Columbian Stamp Expo '92", Chicago. Multicoloured.

678 20 c. Type **69** 40 25
679 50 c. Manatee and fleet 75 50
680 80 c. Green turtle and "Santa Maria" . . . . 1·00 80
681 $1.50 "Santa Maria" and arms . 1·50 1·75
682 $3 Queen Isabella of Spain and commission . . . . 2·25 2·75
683 $5 Pineapple and colonists . . 3·00 4·00

1992. 500th Anniv of Discovery of America by Columbus (5th issue). Organization of East Caribbean States. As Nos. 911/12 of Montserrat. Multicoloured.

685 $1 Columbus meeting Amerindians 50 50
686 $2 Ships approaching island . . 1·25 1·40

70 Minnie Mouse

71 Care Bear and Butterfly

1992. Mickey's Portrait Gallery. Mult.

688 10 c. Type **70** 40 20
689 15 c. Mickey Mouse 40 20
690 40 c. Donald Duck 60 30
691 80 c. Mickey Mouse, 1930 . . . 80 70
692 $1 Daisy Duck 90 80
693 $2 Pluto . . . . 1·50 1·50
694 $4 Goofy . . . . 2·50 2·75
695 $5 Goofy, 1932 . . . . 2·50 2·75

1992. Christmas. Religious Paintings. As T **218** of Lesotho. Multicoloured.

697 20 c. "The Virgin and Child between Two Saints" (Giovanni Bellini) 30 15
698 40 c. "The Virgin and Child surrounded by Four Angels" (Master of the Castello Nativity) 45 25
699 50 c. "Virgin and Child surrounded by Angels with St. Frediano and St. Augustine" (detail) (Filippo Lippi) . . . 50 30
700 80 c. "The Virgin and Child between St. Peter and St. Sebastian" (Bellini) 70 70
701 $1 "The Virgin and Child with St. Julian and St. Nicholas of Myra" (Lorenzo di Credi) . . 80 80
702 $2 "St. Bernadino and a Female Saint presenting a Donor to Virgin and Child" (Francesco Bissolo) . . . . 1·50 1·50
703 $4 "Madonna and Child with Four Cherubs" (ascr Barthel Bruyn) . . . . 2·50 3·00
704 $5 "The Virgin and Child" (Quentin Metsys) . . . . . 2·75 3·25

No. 699 is inscribed "Fillipo Lippi" in error.

1993. Ecology.

706 **71** 80 c. multicoloured 60 60

1993. Bicentenary of the Louvre, Paris. As T **209b** of Gambia. Multicoloured.

708 $1 "The Card Cheat" (left detail) (La Tour) 85 85
709 $1 "The Card Cheat" (centre detail) (La Tour) 85 85
710 $1 "The Card Cheat" (right detail) (La Tour) 85 85
711 $1 "St. Joseph, the Carpenter" (La Tour) 85 85
712 $1 "St. Thomas" (La Tour) . . 85 85
713 $1 "Adoration of the Shepherds" (left detail) (La Tour) . . . 85 85
714 $1 "Adoration of the Shepherds" (right detail) (La Tour) . . . 85 85
715 $1 "Mary Magdalene with a Candle" (La Tour) 85 85

1993. 15th Death Anniv of Elvis Presley (singer). As T **209a** of Gambia. Multicoloured.

717 $1 Elvis Presley 85 85
718 $1 Elvis with guitar 85 85
719 $1 Elvis with microphone . . . 85 85

72 Japanese Launch Vehicle H-11

73 "Plumeria rubra"

1993. Anniversaries and Events. Mult.

720 15 c. Type **72** 40 20
721 50 c. Airship "Hindenburg" on fire, 1937 (horiz) 65 65
722 75 c. Konrad Adenauer and Charles de Gaulle (horiz) . . 65 65
723 80 c. Red Cross emblem and map of Nevis (horiz) 70 70
724 80 c. "Resolute" (yacht), 1920 . 70 70
725 80 c. Nelson Museum and map of Nevis (horiz) 70 70
726 80 c. St. Thomas's Church (horiz) 70 70
727 $1 Blue whale (horiz) . . . . . 1·25 80
728 $3 Mozart . . . . 1·75 1·75
729 $3 Graph and U.N. emblems (horiz) . . . . 1·60 1·60
730 $3 Lions Club emblem . . . . 1·60 1·60
731 $5 Soviet "Energia" launch vehicle SL-17 . . . . 3·00 3·50
732 $5 Lebaudy-Juillot airship No. 1 "La Jaune" (horiz) . . . . 3·00 3·50
733 $5 Adenauer and Pres. Kennedy (horiz) . . . . 3·00 3·50

ANNIVERSARIES AND EVENTS: Nos. 720, 731, International Space Year; Nos. 721, 732, 75th death anniv of Count Ferdinand von Zeppelin (airship pioneer); Nos. 722, 733, 25th death anniv of Konrad Adenauer (German statesman); No. 723, 50th anniv of St. Kitts-Nevis Red Cross; No. 724, Americas Cup Yachting Championship; No. 725, Opening of Nelson Museum; No. 726, 150th anniv of Anglican Diocese of North-eastern Caribbean and Aruba; No. 727, Earth Summit '92, Rio; No. 728, Death bicentenary of Mozart; No. 729, International Conference on Nutrition, Rome; No. 730, 75th anniv of International Association of Lions Clubs.

1993. West Indian Flowers. Multicoloured.

735 10 c. Type **73** 40 30
736 25 c. "Bougainvillea" 50 30
737 50 c. "Allamanda cathartica" . 65 50
738 80 c. "Anthurium andraeanum" 85 70
739 $1 "Ixora coccinea" 95 75
740 $2 "Hibiscus rosa-sinensis" . . 1·75 1·75
741 $4 "Justicia brandegeeana" . . 3·00 3·50
742 $5 "Antigonon leptopus" . . . 3·00 3·50

74 Antillean Blue (male)

1993. Butterflies. Multicoloured.

744 10 c. Type **74** 60 40
745 25 c. Cuban crescentspot (female) 75 40
746 50 c. Ruddy daggerwing . . . 1·00 50
747 80 c. Little yellow (male) . . . 1·25 75
748 $1 Atala . . . . 1·25 90
749 $1.50 Orange-barred giant sulphur . . . . 2·00 2·00
750 $4 Tropic queen (male) . . . . 3·25 4·25
751 $5 Malachite . . . . 3·25 4·25

1993. 40th Anniv of Coronation. As T **215a** of Gambia.

753 10 c. multicoloured 10 10
754 80 c. brown and black 35 40
755 $2 multicoloured 90 95
756 $4 multicoloured . . . . . . 1·90 2·00

DESIGNS—38 × 47 mm: 10 c. Queen Elizabeth II at Coronation (photograph by Cecil Beaton); 80 c. Queen wearing Imperial State Crown; $2 Crowning of Queen Elizabeth II; $4 Queen and Prince Charles at polo match.

75 Flag and National Anthem   76 "Annunciation of Mary"

1993. 10th Anniv of Independence of St. Kitts-Nevis. Multicoloured.
758 25 c. Type **75** 40 20
759 80 c. Brown pelican and map of St. Kitts-Nevis . . . . . . 1·00 90

1993. World Cup Football Championship 1994, U.S.A. As T **278** of Maldive Islands. Mult.
760 10 c. Imre Garaba (Hungary) and Michel Platini (France) (horiz) 40 20
761 25 c. Diego Maradona (Argentina) and Giuseppe Bergomi (Italy) (horiz) . . . 55 20
762 50 c. Luis Fernandez (France) and Vasily Rats (Russia) (horiz) 75 45
763 80 c. Victor Munez (Spain) (horiz) . . . . 1·00 55
764 $1 Preben Elkjaer (Denmark) and Andoni Goicoechea (Spain) (horiz) . . . . 1·10 70
765 $2 Elzo Coelho (Brazil) and Jean Tigana (France) (horiz) . . . 2·00 2·00
766 $3 Pedro Troglio (Argentina) and Sergei Alejnikov (Russia) (horiz) . . . . 2·25 2·50
767 $5 Jan Karas (Poland) and Antonio Luiz Costa (Brazil) (horiz) . . . . 2·75 3·50

1993. Christmas. Religious Paintings by Durer. Black, yellow and red (Nos. 769/73 and 776) or multicoloured (others).
769 20 c. Type **76** 40 10
770 40 c. "The Nativity" (drawing) . 60 25
771 50 c. "Holy Family on a Grassy Bank" 70 30
772 80 c. "The Presentation of Christ in the Temple" 90 55
773 $1 "Virgin in Glory on the Crescent" . . . . 1·00 70
774 $1.60 "The Nativity" (painting) 1·50 2·00
775 $3 "Madonna and Child" . . . 2·25 2·75
776 $5 "The Presentation of Christ in the Temple" (detail) . . . . 2·75 4·00

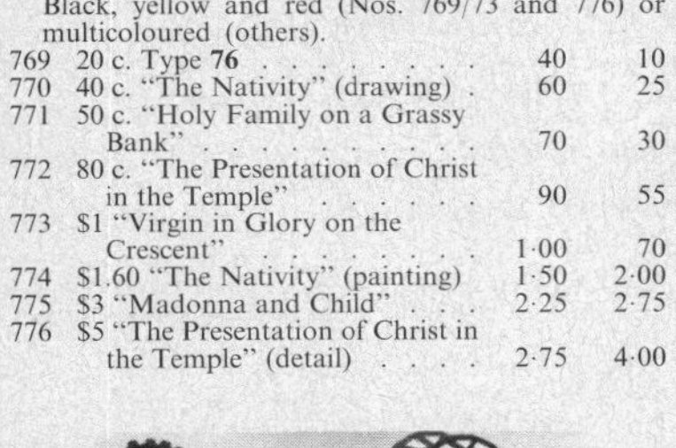

77 Mickey Mouse playing Basketball

1994. Sports and Pastimes. Walt Disney cartoon characters. Multicoloured.
778 10 c. Type **77** 40 30
779 25 c. Minnie Mouse sunbathing (vert) 50 20
780 50 c. Mickey playing volleyball . 70 40
781 80 c. Minnie dancing (vert) . . 80 60
782 $1 Mickey playing football . . 1·00 70
783 $1.50 Minnie hula hooping (vert) 1·75 1·75
784 $4 Minnie skipping (vert) . . . 2·75 3·25
785 $5 Mickey wrestling Big Pete . 2·75 3·25

1994. Hummel Figurines. As T **256** of Maldive Islands. Multicoloured.
788 5 c. Girl with umbrella 15 40
789 25 c. Boy holding beer mug and parsnips 45 15
790 50 c. Girl sitting in tree 65 35
791 80 c. Boy in hat and scarf . . . 85 60
792 $1 Boy with umbrella . . . . 1·00 70
793 $1.60 Girl with bird . . . . . 1·75 1·75
794 $2 Boy on sledge . . . . . . 2·00 2·00
795 $5 Boy sitting in apple tree . . 2·75 3·75

79 Beekeeper collecting Wild Nest

1994. Beekeeping. Multicoloured.
797 50 c. Type **79** 55 30
798 80 c. Beekeeping club 80 40
799 $1.60 Extracting honey from frames . . . . 1·60 1·75
800 $3 Keepers placing queen in hive 2·50 3·25

80 Blue Point Himalayan

1994. Persian Cats. Multicoloured.
802 80 c. Type **80** 60 60
803 80 c. Black and white Persian . 60 60
804 80 c. Cream Persian 60 60
805 80 c. Red Persian 60 60
806 80 c. Persian 60 60
807 80 c. Persian black smoke . . . 60 60
808 80 c. Chocolate smoke Persian . 60 60
809 80 c. Black Persian 60 60

81 Black Coral   83 Symbol 1. Turtles and Cloud

82 Striped Burrfish

1994. Endangered Species. Black Coral.
811 **81** 25 c. multicoloured 50 60
812 – 40 c. multicoloured 60 75
813 – 50 c. multicoloured 60 75
814 – 80 c. multicoloured 70 85
DESIGNS: 40 c. to 80 c. Different forms of coral.

1994. Fishes. Multicoloured.
815 10 c. Type **82** 20 20
816 50 c. Flame-backed angelfish . 35 35
817 50 c. Reef bass 35 35
818 50 c. Long-finned damselfish ("Honey Gregory") 35 35
819 50 c. Saddle squirrelfish . . . 35 35
820 50 c. Cobalt chromis 35 35
821 50 c. Genie's neon goby . . . 35 35
822 50 c. Slender-tailed cardinalfish . 35 35
823 50 c. Royal gramma 35 35
824 $1 Blue-striped grunt 60 60
825 $1.60 Blue angelfish . . . . 1·00 1·25
826 $3 Cocoa damselfish . . . . 1·50 1·75
Nos. 816/23 were printed together, se-tenant, forming a composite design.
No. 824 is inscribed "BLUESRIPED GRUNT" in error.

1994. "Philakorea '94" International Stamp Exhibition, Seoul. Longevity symbols. Multicoloured.
828 50 c. Type **83** 35 40
829 50 c. Symbol 2. Cranes and bamboo 35 40
830 50 c. Symbol 3. Deer and bamboo 35 40
831 50 c. Symbol 4. Turtles and Sun . 35 40
832 50 c. Symbol 5. Cranes under tree 35 40
833 50 c. Symbol 6. Deer and tree . 35 40
834 50 c. Symbol 7. Turtles and rock 35 40
835 50 c. Symbol 8. Cranes above tree 35 40

84 Twin-roofed House with Veranda

1994. Island Architecture. Multicoloured.
836 25 c. Type **84** 40 10
837 50 c. Two-storey house with outside staircase 65 30
838 $1 Government Treasury . . . 90 80
839 $5 Two-storey house with red roof . . . . 3·25 4·25

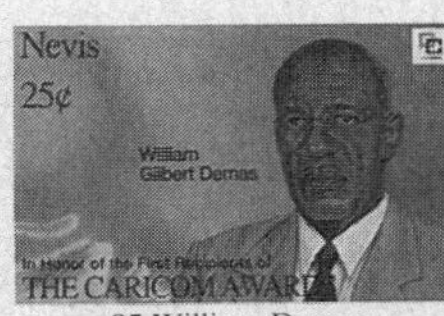

85 William Demas

1994. First Recipients of Order of Caribbean Community. Multicoloured.
841 25 c. Type **85** 30 10
842 50 c. Sir Shridath Ramphal . . 50 45
843 $1 Derek Walcott . . . . . . 1·00 80

86 "The Virgin Mary as Queen of Heaven" (detail) (Jan Provost)   88 Rufous-breasted Hermit

87 Mickey and Minnie Mouse

1994. Christmas. Religious Paintings. Multicoloured.
844 20 c. Type **86** 20 10
845 40 c. "The Virgin Mary as Queen of Heaven" (different detail) (Provost) 35 25
846 50 c. "The Virgin Mary as Queen of Heaven" (different detail) (Provost) 40 30
847 80 c. "Adoration of the Magi" (detail) (Circle of Van der Goes) 60 40
848 $1 "Adoration of the Magi" (different detail) (Circle of Van der Goes) 70 50
849 $1.60 "Adoration of the Magi" (different detail) (Circle of Van der Goes) . . . . 1·25 1·25
850 $3 "Adoration of the Magi" (different detail) (Circle of Van der Goes) . . . . 2·00 2·25
851 $5 "The Virgin Mary as Queen of Heaven" (different detail) (Provost) . . . . 3·00 3·50

1995. Disney Sweethearts (1st series). Walt Disney Cartoon Characters. Multicoloured.
853 10 c. Type **87** 20 20
854 25 c. Donald and Daisy Duck . 35 20
855 50 c. Pluto and Fifi 50 35
856 80 c. Clarabelle Cow and Horace Horsecollar 70 50
857 $1 Pluto and Figaro 85 65
858 $1.50 Polly and Peter Penguin . 1·25 1·50
859 $4 Prunella Pullet and Hick Rooster . . . . 2·50 3·00
860 $5 Jenny Wren and Cock Robin 2·50 3·00
See also Nos. 998/1006.

1995. Birds. Multicoloured.
862 50 c. Type **88** 40 40
863 50 c. Purple-throated carib . . 40 40
864 50 c. Green mango 40 40
865 50 c. Bahama woodstar 40 40
866 50 c. Hispaniolan emerald . . . 40 40
867 50 c. Antillean crested hummingbird 40 40
868 50 c. Green-throated carib . . 40 40
869 50 c. Antillean mango 40 40
870 50 c. Vervain hummingbird . . 40 40
871 50 c. Jamaican mango 40 40
872 50 c. Cuban emerald 40 40
873 50 c. Blue-headed hummingbird 40 40
874 50 c. Hooded merganser . . . 40 40
875 80 c. Green-backed heron . . . 65 50
876 $2 Double-crested cormorant . 1·25 1·40
877 $3 Ruddy duck . . . . 1·50 1·75
No. 870 is inscribed "VERVIAN" in error.

89 Pointer

1995. Dogs. Multicoloured.
879 25 c. Type **89** 30 20
880 50 c. Old Danish pointer . . . 50 50
881 80 c. Irish setter 65 65
882 80 c. Weimaraner 65 65
883 80 c. Gordon setter 65 65
884 80 c. Brittany spaniel 65 65
885 80 c. American cocker spaniel . 65 65
886 80 c. English cocker spaniel . . 65 65
887 80 c. Labrador retriever . . . 65 65
888 80 c. Golden retriever 65 65
889 80 c. Flat-coated retriever . . . 65 65
890 $1 German short-haired pointer 75 75
891 $2 English setter . . . . . . 1·40 1·40
"POINTER" is omitted from the inscription on No. 890.

INDEX
Countries can be quickly located by referring to the index at the end of this volume.

90 "Schulumbergera truncata"   92 Oriental and African People

91 Scouts backpacking

1995. Cacti. Multicoloured.
893 40 c. Type **90** 30 20
894 50 c. "Echinocereus pectinatus" 40 25
895 80 c. "Mammillaria zeilmanniana alba" 65 40
896 $1.60 "Lobivia hertriehiana" . 1·10 1·25
897 $2 "Hammatocactus setispinus" 1·40 1·50
898 $3 "Astrophytum myriostigma" 1·60 2·00

1995. 18th World Scout Jamboree, Netherlands. Multicoloured.
900 $1 Type **91** 75 90
901 $2 Scouts building aerial rope way . . . . 1·25 1·50
902 $4 Scout map reading . . . . 2·00 2·25
Nos. 900/2 were printed together, se-tenant, forming a composite design.

1995. 50th Anniv of End of Second World War in Europe. As T **317** of Maldive Islands. Multicoloured.
904 $1.25 Clark Gable and aircraft . 90 90
905 $1.25 Audie Murphy and machine-gunner 90 90
906 $1.25 Glenn Miller playing trombone 90 90
907 $1.25 Joe Louis and infantry . . 90 90
908 $1.25 Jimmy Doolittle and U.S.S. "Hornet" (aircraft carrier) 90 90
909 $1.25 John Hersey and jungle patrol 90 90
910 $1.25 John F. Kennedy in patrol boat 90 90
911 $1.25 James Stewart and bombers 90 90

1995. 50th Anniv of United Nations. Each lilac and black.
913 $1.25 Type **92** 55 60
914 $1.60 Asian people 75 80
915 $3 American and European people . . . . 1·40 1·50
Nos. 913/15 were printed together, se-tenant, forming a composite design.

1995. 50th Anniv of F.A.O. As T **92**. Multicoloured.
917 40 c. Woman wearing yellow headdress 15 20
918 $2 Babies and emblem 85 90
919 $3 Woman wearing blue headdress . . . . 1·25 1·40
Nos. 917/19 were printed together, se-tenant, forming a composite design.

93 Rotary Emblem on Nevis Flag

1995. 90th Anniv of Rotary International.
921 **93** $5 multicoloured . . . . . 2·50 3·00

1995. 95th Birthday of Queen Elizabeth the Queen Mother. As T **239a** of Gambia.
923 $1.50 brown, light brown and black . . . . 1·00 1·10
924 $1.50 multicoloured . . . . . 1·00 1·10
925 $1.50 multicoloured . . . . . 1·00 1·10
926 $1.50 multicoloured . . . . . 1·00 1·10
DESIGNS: No. 923, Queen Elizabeth the Queen Mother (pastel drawing); 924, Wearing pink hat; 925, At desk (oil painting); 926, Wearing blue hat.

1995. 50th Anniv of End of Second World War in the Pacific. United States Aircraft. As T **317** of Maldive Islands. Multicoloured.
928 $2 Grumman F4F Wildcat . . . 1·40 1·40
929 $2 Chance Vought F4U-1A Corsair . . . . 1·40 1·40
930 $2 Vought SB2U Vindicator . . 1·40 1·40
931 $2 Grumman F6F Hellcat . . . 1·40 1·40
932 $2 Douglas SDB Dauntless . . 1·40 1·40
933 $2 Grumman TBF-1 Avenger . 1·40 1·40

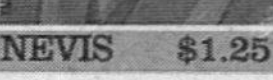

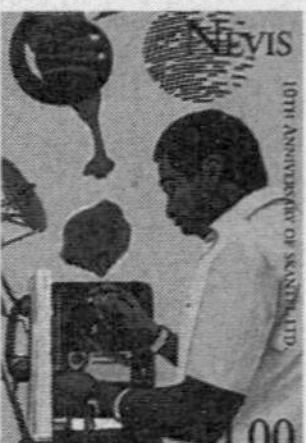

94 Emil von Behring (1901 Medicine)

97 SKANTEL Engineer

96 Great Egrets

1995. Centenary of Nobel Trust Fund. Past Prize Winners. Multicoloured.

935 $1.25 Type **94** 75 85
936 $1.25 Wilhelm Rontgen (1901 Physics) 75 85
937 $1.25 Paul Heyse (1910 Literature) 75 85
938 $1.25 Le Duc Tho (1973 Peace) . 75 85
939 $1.25 Yasunari Kawabata (1968 Literature) 75 85
940 $1.25 Tsung-dao Lee (1957 Physics) 75 85
941 $1.25 Werner Heisenberg (1932 Physics) 75 85
942 $1.25 Johannes Stark (1919 Physics) 75 85
943 $1.25 Wilhelm Wien (1911 Physics) 75 85

1995. Marine Life. Multicoloured.

946 50 c. Type **96** 35 35
947 50 c. 17th-century galleon . . . 35 35
948 50 c. Galleon and marlin 35 35
949 50 c. Herring gulls 35 35
950 50 c. Nassau groupers 35 35
951 50 c. Spotted eagleray 35 35
952 50 c. Leopard shark and hammerhead 35 35
953 50 c. Hourglass dolphins . . . 35 35
954 50 c. Spanish hogfish 35 35
955 50 c. Jellyfish and seahorses . . 35 35
956 50 c. Angelfish and buried treasure 35 35
957 50 c. Hawksbill turtle 35 35
958 50 c. Common octopus 35 35
959 50 c. Moray eel 35 35
960 50 c. Queen angelfish and butterflyfish 35 35
961 50 c. Ghost crab and sea star . . 35 35

Nos. 946/61 were printed together, se-tenant, forming a composite design.

1995. 10th Anniv of SKANTEL (telecommunications company). Multicoloured.

963 $1 Type **97** 60 50
964 $1.50 SKANTEL sign outside Nevis office . . . . 80 1·00

98 "Rucellai Madonna and Child" (detail) (Duccio)

1995. Christmas. Religious Paintings by Duccio di Buoninsegna. Multicoloured.

966 20 c. Type **98** 15 10
967 50 c. "Angel form the Rucellai Madonna" (detail) 30 25
968 80 c. "Madonna and Child" (different) 50 40
969 $1 "Angel from the Annunciation" (detail) . . . 65 50
970 $1.60 "Madonna and Child" (different) . . . . 1·00 1·00
971 $3 "Angel from the Rucellai Madonna" (different) . . . 1·60 2·00

99 View of Nevis Four Seasons Resort

1996. 5th Anniv of Four Seasons Resort, Nevis. Multicoloured.

973 25 c. Type **99** 10 15
974 50 c. Catamarans, Pinney's Beach 20 25
975 80 c. Robert Trent Jones II Golf Course 35 40
976 $2 Prime Minister Simeon Daniel laying foundation stone . . . 85 90

100 Rat, Plant and Butterfly

1996. Chinese New Year ("Year of the Rat"). Multicoloured.

978 $1 Type **100** 45 50
979 $1 Rat with prickly plant . . . 45 50
980 $1 Rat and bee 45 50
981 $1 Rat and dragonfly 45 50

101 Ancient Greek Boxers

1996. Olympic Games, Atlanta. Previous Medal Winners. Multicoloured.

984 25 c. Type **101** 10 10
985 50 c. Mark Spitz (U.S.A.) (Gold – swimming, 1972) 20 25
986 80 c. Siegbert Horn (East Germany) (Gold – single kayak slalom, 1972) 35 40
987 $1 Jim Thorpe on medal (U.S.A.), 1912 (vert) 45 50
988 $1 Glenn Morris on medal (U.S.A.), 1936 (vert) 45 50
989 $1 Bob Mathias on medal (U.S.A.), 1948 and 1952 (vert) 45 50
990 $1 Rafer Johnson on medal (U.S.A.), 1960 (vert) 45 50
991 $1 Bill Toomey (U.S.A.), 1968 (vert) 45 50
992 $1 Nikolay Avilov (Russia), 1972 (vert) 45 50
993 $1 Bruce Jenner (U.S.A.), 1976 (vert) 45 50
994 $1 Daley Thompson (Great Britain), 1980 and 1984 (vert) 45 50
995 $1 Christian Schenk (East Germany), 1988 (vert) . . . 45 50
996 $3 Olympic Stadium and Siegestor Arch, Munich (vert) . . . . 1·25 1·40

1996. Disney Sweethearts (2nd series). As T **87**. Walt Disney Cartoon Characters. Multicoloured.

998 $2 Pocahontas and John Smith . . . . 1·50 1·50
999 $2 Mowgli and the Girl . . . 1·50 1·50
1000 $2 Belle and the Beast . . . 1·50 1·50
1001 $2 Cinderella and Prince Charming . . . . 1·50 1·50
1002 $2 Pinocchio and the Dutch Girl . . . . 1·50 1·50
1003 $2 Grace Martin and Henry Coy . . . . 1·50 1·50
1004 $2 Snow White and the Prince . . . . 1·50 1·50
1005 $2 Aladdin and Jasmine . . . 1·50 1·50
1006 $2 Pecos Bill and Slue Foot Sue . . . . 1·50 1·50

102 Qian Qing Gong, Peking

1996. "CHINA '96" 9th Asian International Stamp Exhibition, Peking. Peking Pagodas. Multicoloured.

1008 $1 Type **102** 45 50
1009 $1 Temple of Heaven 45 50
1010 $1 Zhongnanhai 45 50
1011 $1 Da Zing Hall, Shehyang Palace 45 50
1012 $1 Temple of the Sleeping Buddha 45 50
1013 $1 Huang Qiong Yu, Altar of Heaven 45 50
1014 $1 The Grand Bell Temple . . 45 50
1015 $1 Imperial Palace 45 50
1016 $1 Pu Tuo Temple 45 50

1996. 70th Birthday of Queen Elizabeth II. As T **255a** of Gambia. Multicoloured.

1018 $2 Queen Elizabeth II 85 90
1019 $2 Wearing evening dress . . 85 90
1020 $2 In purple hat and coat . . 85 90

103 Children reading Book

1996. 50th Anniv of U.N.I.C.E.F. Multicoloured.

1022 25 c. Type **103** 10 10
1023 50 c. Doctor and child 20 30
1024 $4 Children . . . . 1·75 1·90

104 Cave Paintings, Tassili n'Ajjer, Algeria

1996. 50th Anniv of U.N.E.S.C.O. Multicoloured.

1026 25 c. Type **104** 10 10
1027 $2 Temple, Tikai National Park, Guatemala (vert) 85 90
1028 $3 Temple of Hera, Samos, Greece . . . . 1·25 1·40

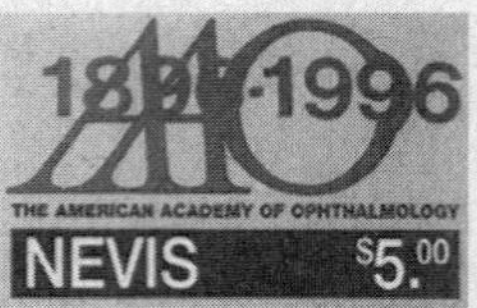

105 American Academy of Ophthalmology Logo

1996. Centenary of American Academy of Ophthalmology.

1030 **105** $5 multicoloured . . . . 2·10 2·25

106 "Rothmannia longiflora"

107 Western Meadowlark on Decoration

1996. Flowers. Multicoloured.

1031 25 c. Type **106** 10 10
1032 50 c. "Gloriosa simplex" . . . 20 25
1033 $1 "Monodora myristica" . . 45 50
1034 $1 Giraffe 45 50
1035 $1 "Adansonia digitata" . . . 45 50
1036 $1 "Ansellia gigantea" 45 50
1037 $1 "Geissorhiza rochensis" . . 45 50
1038 $1 "Arctotis venusta" 45 50
1039 $1 "Gladiotus cardinalis" . . . 45 50
1040 $1 "Eucomis bicolor" 45 50
1041 $1"Protea obtusifolia" 45 50
1042 $2 "Catharanthus roseus" . . 85 90
1043 $3 "Plumbago auriculata" . . 1·25 1·40

1996. Christmas. Birds. Multicoloured.

1045 25 c. Type **107** 10 10
1046 50 c. Bird (incorrectly inscr as "American goldfinch") with decorations (horiz) 20 25
1047 80 c. Santa Claus, sleigh and reindeer (horiz 35 40
1048 $1 American goldfinch on stocking 45 50
1049 $1.60 Mockingbird with snowman decoration . . . 70 75
1050 $5 Yellow-rumped cacique and bauble . . . . 2·10 2·25

No. 1048 is inscribed "WESTERN MEADOWLARK" and No. 1050 "YELLOW-RUMPED CAIEQUE", both in error.

109 Giant Panda eating Bamboo Shoots

110 Elquemedo Willett

1997. "HONG KONG '97" International Stamp Exhibition. Giant Pandas. Multicoloured.

1053 $1.60 Type **109** 70 75
1054 $1.60 Head of panda 70 75
1055 $1.60 Panda with new-born cub 70 75
1056 $1.60 Panda hanging from branch 70 75
1057 $1.60 Panda asleep on tree . . 70 75
1058 $1.60 Panda climbing trunk . 70 75

1997. Nevis Cricketers. Multicoloured.

1060 25 c. Type **110** 10 15
1061 80 c. Stuart Williams 35 40
1062 $2 Keith Arthurton 85 90

111 Crimson-speckled Moth

1997. Butterflies and Moths. Multicoloured.

1064 10 c. Type **111** 10 10
1065 25 c. Purple emperor 10 15
1066 50 c. Regent skipper 20 25
1067 80 c. Provence burnet moth . . 35 40
1068 $1 Common wall butterfly . . 45 50
1069 $1 Red-lined geometrid . . . 45 50
1070 $1 Boisduval's autumnal moth 45 50
1071 $1 Blue pansy 45 50
1072 $1 Common clubtail 45 50
1073 $1 Tufted jungle king 45 50
1074 $1 Lesser marbled fritillary . . 45 50
1075 $1 Peacock royal 45 50
1076 $1 Emperor gum moth . . . 45 50
1077 $1 Orange swallow-tailed moth 45 50
1078 $4 Cruiser butterfly . . . . . 1·75 1·90

No. 1073 is inscribed "TUFTED JUNGLE QUEEN" in error.

113 Paul Harris and Literacy Class

1997. 50th Death Anniv of Paul Harris (founder of Rotary International).

1081 **113** $2 multicoloured 85 90

1997. Golden Wedding of Queen Elizabeth and Prince Philip. As T **350** of Maldive Islands. Multicoloured.

1083 $1 Queen Elizabeth II 45 50
1084 $1 Royal Coat of Arms . . . 45 50
1085 $1 Queen Elizabeth wearing red hat and coat with Prince Philip 45 50
1086 $1 Queen Elizabeth in blue coat and Prince Philip 45 50
1087 $1 Caernarvon Castle 45 50
1088 $1 Prince Philip in R.A.F. uniform 45 50

1997. "Pacific '97" International Stamp Exhibition, San Francisco. Death Centenary of Heinrich von Stephan. As T **351** of Maldive Islands.

1090 $1.60 green 70 75
1091 $1.60 brown 70 75
1092 $1.60 blue 70 75

DESIGNS: No. 1090, Russian reindeer post, 1859; 1091, Von Stephan and Mercury; 1092, "City of Cairo" (paddle-steamer), Mississippi, 1800s.

1997. Birth Bicentenary of Hiroshige (Japanese painter). "One Hundred Famous Views of Edo". As T **352** of Maldive Islands. Multicoloured.

1094 $1.60 "Scattered Pines, Tone River" 70 75
1095 $1.60 "Mouth of Nakagawa River" 70 75
1096 $1.60 "Niijuku Ferry" 70 75
1097 $1.60 "Horie and Nekozane" . 70 75
1098 $1.60 "Konodai and the Tone River" 70 75
1099 $1.60 "Maple Trees, Tekona Shrine and Bridge, Mama" . 70 75

114 Augusta National Course, U.S.A.

1997. Golf Courses of the World. Multicoloured.

1101 $1 Type **114** 45 50
1102 $1 Cabo del Sol, Mexico . . . 45 50
1103 $1 Cypress Point, U.S.A. . . . 45 50
1104 $1 Lost City, South Africa . . 45 50
1105 $1 Moscow Country Club, Russia 45 50
1106 $1 New South Wales, Australia 45 50
1107 $1 Royal Montreal, Canada . . 45 50
1108 $1 St. Andrews, Scotland . . 45 50
1109 $1 Four Seasons Resort, Nevis 45 50

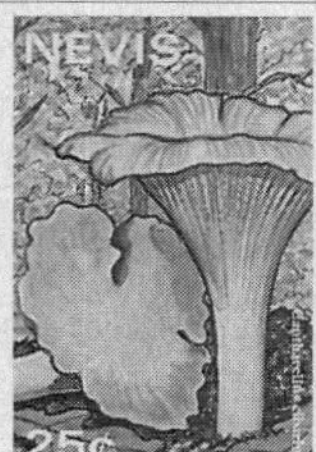

115 "Cantharellus cibarius"

116 Diana, Princess of Wales

1997. Fungi. Multicoloured.
1110 25 c. Type **115** 10 10
1111 50 c. "Stropharia aeruginosa" . 20 25
1112 80 c. "Suillus hiteus" 35 40
1113 80 c. "Amanita muscaria" . . 35 40
1114 80 c. "Lactarius rufus" . . . 35 40
1115 80 c. "Amanita rubescens" . . 35 40
1116 80 c. "Armillaria mellea" . . 35 40
1117 80 c. "Russula sardonia" . . . 35 40
1118 $1 "Boletus edulis" 45 50
1119 $1 "Pholiota lenta" 45 50
1120 $1 "Cortinarius bolaris" . . . 45 50
1121 $1 "Coprinus picaceus" . . . 45 50
1122 $1 "Amanita phalloides" . . . 45 50
1123 $1 "Cystolepiota aspera" . . . 45 50
1124 $3 "Lactarius turpis" . . . . 1·25 1·40
1125 $4 "Entoloma clypeatum" . . 1·75 1·90
Nos. 1112/17 and 1118/23 respectively were printed together, se-tenant, with the backgrounds forming composite designs.

1997. Diana, Princess of Wales Commemoration. Multicoloured.
1127 $1 Type **116** 60 70
1128 $1 Wearing white blouse . . . 60 70
1129 $1 In wedding dress, 1981 . . 60 70
1130 $1 Wearing turquoise blouse . . 60 70
1131 $1 Wearing tiara 60 70
1132 $1 Wearing blue blouse . . . 60 70
1133 $1 Wearing pearl necklace . . 60 70
1134 $1 Wearing diamond drop earrings 60 70
1135 $1 Wearing sapphire necklace and earrings 60 70

117 Victoria Govt Class S Pacific Locomotive, Australia

1997. Trains of the World. Multicoloured.
1136 10 c. Type **117** 10 10
1137 50 c. Express steam-locomotive, Japan 20 30
1138 80 c. L.M.S. steam-turbine locomotive, Great Britain . . 35 40
1139 $1 Electric locomotive, Switzerland 45 50
1140 $1.50 "Mikado" steam locomotive, Sudan 65 70
1141 $1.50 "Mohammed Ali el Kebir" steam locomotive, Egypt 65 70
1142 $1.50 Southern Region steam locomotive "Leatherhead" . 65 70
1143 $1.50 Great Southern Railway Drumm battery-powered railcar, Ireland 65 70
1144 $1.50 Pacific locomotive, Germany 65 70
1145 $1.50 Canton–Hankow Railway Pacific locomotive, China . 65 70
1146 $2 L.M.S. high-pressure locomotive, Great Britain . . 85 90
1147 $3 Great Northern Railway "Kestrel", Ireland . . . . 1·25 1·40

118 "Selection of Angels" (detail) (Durer)

1997. Christmas. Paintings. Multicoloured.
1149 20 c. Type **118** 10 10
1150 25 c. "Selection of Angels" (different detail) (Durer) . . 10 15
1151 50 c. "Andromeda and Perseus" (Rubens) 20 25
1152 80 c. "Harmony" (detail) (Raphael) 35 40
1153 $1.60 "Harmony" (different detail) (Raphael) 70 75
1154 $5 "Holy Trinity" (Raphael) . 2·10 2·25

119 Tiger (semi-circular character at top left)

1998. Chinese New Year ("Year of the Tiger"). Multicoloured.
1156 80 c. Type **119** 35 40
1157 80 c. Oblong character at bottom right 35 40
1158 80 c. Circular character at top left 35 40
1159 80 c. Square character at bottom right 35 40

120 Social Security Board Emblem

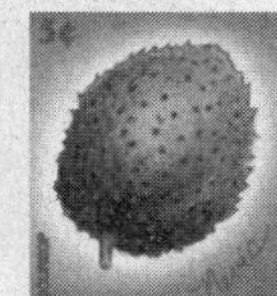
121 Soursop

1998. 20th Anniv of Social Security Board. Multicoloured.
1161 30 c. Type **120** 15 20
1162 $1.20 Opening of Social Security building, Charlestown (horiz) 50 55

1998. Fruits. Multicoloured.
1164 5 c. Type **121** 10 10
1165 10 c. Carambola 10 10
1166 25 c. Guava 10 15
1167 30 c. Papaya 15 20
1168 50 c. Mango 20 25
1169 60 c. Golden apple 25 30
1170 80 c. Pineapple 35 40
1171 90 c. Watermelon 40 45
1172 $1 Bananas 45 50
1173 $1.80 Orange 80 85
1174 $3 Honeydew . . . . . . 1·25 1·40
1175 $5 Cantelope . . . . . . 2·10 2·25
1176 $10 Pomegranate . . . . . 4·25 4·50
1177 $20 Cashew . . . . 8·75 9·00

122 African Fish Eagle

1998. Endangered Species. Multicoloured.
1178 30 c. Type **122** 15 20
1179 80 c. Summer tanager at nest . 35 40
1180 90 c. Orang Utan and young . 40 45
1181 $1 Young chimpanzee 45 50
1182 $1 Keel-billed toucan 45 50
1183 $1 Chaco peccary 45 50
1184 $1 Spadefoot toad and insect . 45 50
1185 $1 Howler monkey 45 50
1186 $1 Alaskan brown bear . . . 45 50
1187 $1 Koala bears 45 50
1188 $1 Brown pelican 45 50
1189 $1 Iguana 45 50
1190 $1.20 Tiger cub 50 55
1191 $2 Cape pangolin 85 90
1192 $3 Hoatzin . . . . 1·25 1·40
No. 1185 is inscribed "MOWLER MONKEY" and No. 1192 "MOATZIN", both in error.

123 Chaim Topol (Israeli actor)

1998. "Israel 98" International Stamp Exhibition, Tel-Aviv.
1194 **123** $1.60 multicoloured . . . 70 75

124 Boeing 747 200B (U.S.A.)

1998. Aircraft. Multicoloured.
1195 10 c. Type **124** 10 10
1196 90 c. Cessna 185 Skywagon (U.S.A.) 40 45
1197 $1 Northrop B-2 A (U.S.A.) . 45 50
1198 $1 Lockheed SR-71A (U.S.A.) 45 50
1199 $1 Beechcraft T-44A (U.S.A.) . 45 50
1200 $1 Sukhoi Su-27UB (U.S.S.R.) 45 50
1201 $1 Hawker Siddeley Harrier GR. Mk1 (Great Britain) . 45 50
1202 $1 Boeing E-3A Sentry (U.S.A.) 45 50
1203 $1 Convair B-36H (U.S.A.) . 45 50
1204 $1 IAI KFIR C2 (Israel) . . . 45 50
1205 $1.80 McDonnell Douglas DC-9 SO (U.S.A.) 75 80
1206 $5 Airbus A-300 B4 (U.S.A.) . 2·10 2·25

125 Anniversary Logo

127 Prime Minister Kennedy Simmonds receiving Constitutional Instruments from Princess Margaret, 1983

126 Butterflyfish

1998. 10th Anniv of "Voice of Nevis" Radio.
1208 **125** 20 c. violet, light violet and black 10 10
1209 – 30 c. multicoloured 15 20
1210 – $1.20 multicoloured . . . 50 55
DESIGNS: 30 c. Evered Herbert (Station Manager); $1.20, V.O.N. studio.

1998. International Year of the Ocean. Multicoloured.
1212 30 c. Type **126** 15 20
1213 80 c. Bicolor cherub 35 40
1214 90 c. Copperbanded butterfly-fish (vert) 40 45
1215 90 c. Forcepsfish (vert) . . . 40 45
1216 90 c. Double-saddled butterfly-fish (vert) 40 45
1217 90 c. Blue surgeonfish (vert) . 40 45
1218 90 c. Orbiculate batfish (vert) . 40 45
1219 90 c. Undulated triggerfish (vert) 40 45
1220 90 c. Rock beauty (vert) . . . 40 45
1221 90 c. Flamefish (vert) 40 45
1222 90 c. Queen angelfish (vert) . . 40 45
1223 $1 Pyjama cardinal fish . . . 45 50
1224 $1 Wimplefish 45 50
1225 $1 Long-nosed filefish . . . 45 50
1226 $1 Oriental sweetlips 45 50
1227 $1 Blue-spotted boxfish . . . 45 50
1228 $1 Blue-stripe angelfish . . . 45 50
1229 $1 Goldrim tang 45 50
1230 $1 Blue chromis 45 50
1231 $1 Common clownfish . . . 45 50
1232 $1.20 Silver badgerfish . . . 50 55
1233 $2 Asfur angelfish 85 90
Nos. 1214/22 and 1223/31 respectively were printed together, se-tenant, with the backgrounds forming composite designs.
No. 1223 is inscribed "Pygama" in error.

1998. 15th Anniv of Independence.
1235 **127** $1 multicoloured 45 50

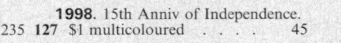

128 Stylised "50"

1998. 50th Anniv of Organization of American States.
1236 **128** $1 blue, light blue and black 45 50

129 365 "California"

1998. Birth Centenary of Enzo Ferrari (car manufacturer). Multicoloured.
1237 $2 Type **129** 85 90
1238 $2 Pininfarina's P6 . . . . . 85 90
1239 $2 250 LM 85 90

130 Scouts of Different Nationalities

1998. 19th World Scout Jamboree, Chile. Multicoloured.
1241 $3 Type **130** . . . . 1·25 1·40
1242 $3 Scout and Gettysburg veterans, 1913 . . . . . . 1·25 1·40
1243 $3 First black scout troop, Virginia, 1928 . . . . . . 1·25 1·40

131 Gandhi in South Africa, 1914

133 Princess Diana

132 Panavia Tornado F3

1998. 50th Death Anniv of Mahatma Gandhi. Multicoloured.
1244 $1 Type **131** 45 50
1245 $1 Gandhi in Downing Street, London 45 50

1998. 80th Anniv of Royal Air Force. Multicoloured.
1246 $2 Type **132** 85 90
1247 $2 Panavia Tornado F3 firing Skyflash missile 85 90
1248 $2 Tristar Mk1 Tanker refuelling Tornado GR1 . . 85 90
1249 $2 Panavia Tornado GR1 firing AIM-9L missile 85 90

1998. 1st Death Anniv of Diana, Princess of Wales.
1251 **133** $1 multicoloured 45 50

134 Kitten and Santa Claus Decoration

1998. Christmas. Multicoloured.
1252 25 c. Type **134** 10 15
1253 60 c. Kitten playing with bauble 25 30
1254 80 c. Kitten in Christmas stocking (vert) 35 40
1255 90 c. Fox Terrier puppy and presents 40 45
1256 $1 Angel with swallows . . . 45 50
1257 $3 Boy wearing Santa hat (vert) 1·25 1·40

135 Mickey Mouse

1998. 70th Birthday of Mickey Mouse. Walt Disney cartoon characters playing basketball. Mult.
1259 $1 Type **135** 70 70
1260 $1 Donald Duck bouncing ball 70 70
1261 $1 Minnie Mouse in green kit . 70 70
1262 $1 Goofy wearing purple . . . 70 70
1263 $1 Huey in green baseball cap . 70 70

1264 $1 Goofy and Mickey 70 70
1265 $1 Mickey bouncing ball . . . 70 70
1266 $1 Huey, Dewey and Louie . . 70 70
1267 $1 Mickey, in purple, shooting ball 70 70
1268 $1 Goofy in yellow shorts and vest 70 70
1269 $1 Minnie in purple 70 70
1270 $1 Mickey in yellow vest and blue shorts 70 70
1271 $1 Minnie in yellow 70 70
1272 $1 Donald spinning ball on finger 70 70
1273 $1 Donald and Mickey . . . 70 70
1274 $1 Dewey shooting for goal . . 70 70

136 Black Silver Fox Rabbits

1999. Chinese New Year ("Year of the Rabbit"). Multicoloured.
1276 $1.60 Type **136** 70 75
1277 $1.60 Dutch rabbits (brown with white "collar") 70 75
1278 $1.60 Dwarf rabbits (brown) . . 70 75
1279 $1.60 Netherlands Dwarf rabbits (white with brown markings) 70 75

137 Laurent Blanc (France)

1999. Leading Players of 1998 World Cup Football Championship, France. Multicoloured.
1281 $1 Type **137** 45 50
1282 $1 Dennis Bergkamp (Holland) 45 50
1283 $1 Davor Sukor (Croatia) . . 45 50
1284 $1 Ronaldo (Brazil) 45 50
1285 $1 Didier Deschamps (France) . 45 50
1286 $1 Patrick Kluivert (Holland) . 45 50
1287 $1 Rivaldo (Brazil) 45 50
1288 $1 Zinedine Zidane (France) . . 45 50
Nos. 1281/8 were printed together, se-tenant, with the backgrounds forming a composite design.

138 Kritosaurus

1999. "Australia '99" World Stamp Exhibition, Melbourne. Prehistoric Animals. Multicoloured.
1290 30 c. Type **138** 15 20
1291 60 c. Oviraptor 25 30
1292 80 c. Eustreptospondylus . . . 35 40
1293 $1.20 Tenontosaurus 50 55
1294 $1.20 Edmontosaurus 50 55
1295 $1.20 Avimimus 50 55
1296 $1.20 Minmi 50 55
1297 $1.20 Segnosaurus 50 55
1298 $1.20 Kentrosaurus 50 55
1299 $1.20 Deinonychus 50 55
1300 $1.20 Saltasaurus 50 55
1301 $1.20 Compsoganthus 50 55
1302 $1.20 Hadrosaurus 50 55
1303 $1.20 Tuojiangosaurus 50 55
1304 $1.20 Euoplocephalus 50 55
1305 $1.20 Anchisaurus 50 55
1306 $2 Ouranosaurus 85 90
1307 $3 Muttaburrasaurus . . . . 1·25 1·40
Nos. 1294/9 and 1300/5 respectively were printed together, se-tenant, with the backgrounds forming composite designs.

139 Emperor Haile Selassie of Ethiopia

1999. Millennium Series. Famous People of the Twentieth Century. World Leaders. Multicoloured.
1309 90 c. Type **139** 40 45
1310 90 c. Haile Selassie and Ethiopian warriors (56 × 41 mm) 40 45
1311 90 c. David Ben-Gurion, woman soldier and ancient Jewish prophet (56 × 41 mm) . . . 40 45
1312 90 c. David Ben-Gurion (Prime Minister of Israel) 40 45
1313 90 c. President Franklin D. Roosevelt of U.S.A. and Mrs. Roosevelt 40 45
1314 90 c. Franklin and Eleanor Roosevelt campaigning (56 × 41 mm) 40 45
1315 90 c. Mao Tse-tung and the Long March, 1934 (56 × 41 mm) 40 45
1316 90 c. Poster of Mao Tse-tung (founder of People's Republic of China) 40 45

140 Malachite Kingfisher

1999. Birds. Multicoloured.
1318 $1.60 Type **140** 70 75
1319 $1.60 Lilac-breasted roller . . 70 75
1320 $1.60 Swallow-tailed bee eater . 70 75
1321 $1.60 Jay 70 75
1322 $1.60 Black-collared apalis . . 70 75
1323 $1.60 Grey-backed camaroptera 70 75
1324 $1.60 Yellow warbler 70 75
1325 $1.60 Common yellowthroat . . 70 75
1326 $1.60 Painted bunting 70 75
1327 $1.60 Belted kingfisher 70 75
1328 $1.60 American kestrel 70 75
1329 $1.60 Northern oriole 70 75

141 "Phaius" hybrid

142 Miss Sophie Rhys-Jones and Prince Edward

1999. Orchids. Multicoloured.
1331 20 c. Type **141** 10 10
1332 25 c. "Cuitlauzina pendula" . . 10 15
1333 50 c. "Bletilla striata" 20 25
1334 80 c. "Cymbidium" "Showgirl" 35 40
1335 $1 "Cattleya intermedia" . . . 45 50
1336 $1 "Cattleya" "Sophia Martin" 45 50
1337 $1 "Phalaenopsis" "Little Hal" 45 50
1338 $1 "Laeliocattleya alisal" "Rodeo" 45 50
1339 $1 "Laelia lucasiana fournieri" . 45 50
1340 $1 "Cymbidium" "Red Beauty" 45 50
1341 $1 "Sobralia" sp. 45 50
1342 $1 "Promenaea xanthina" . . . 45 50
1343 $1 "Cattleya pumpernickel" . . 45 50
1344 $1 "Odontocidium artur elle" . . 45 50
1345 $1 "Neostylis lou sneary" . . . 45 50
1346 $1 "Phalaenopsis aphrodite" . . 45 50
1347 $1 "Arkundina graminieolia" . . 45 50
1348 $1 "Cymbidium" "Hunter's Point" 45 50
1349 $1 "Rhynchostylis coelestis" . . 45 50
1350 $1 "Cymbidium" "Elf's Castle" 45 50
1351 $1.60 "Zygopetalum crinitium" (horiz) 70 75
1352 $3 "Dendrobium nobile" (horiz) . . . . 1·25 1·40

1999. Royal Wedding. Multicoloured.
1354 $2 Type **142** 85 90
1355 $2 Miss Sophie Rhys-Jones at Ascot 85 90
1356 $2 Miss Sophie Rhys-Jones smiling 85 90
1357 $2 Prince Edward smiling . . . 85 90
1358 $2 Miss Sophie Rhys-Jones wearing black and white checked jacket 85 90
1359 $2 Prince Edward and Miss Sophie Rhys-Jones wearing sunglasses 85 90
1360 $2 Miss Sophie Rhys-Jones wearing black hat and jacket 85 90
1361 $2 Prince Edward wearing red-striped tie 85 90

1999. "iBRA '99" International Stamp Exhibition, Nuremberg. As T **298a** of Gambia. Multicoloured.
1363 30 c. "Beuth" (railway locomotive) and Baden 1851 1 k. stamp 15 20
1364 80 c. "Beuth" and Brunswick 1852 1 sgr. stamp 35 40
1365 90 c. "Kruzenshtern" (cadet barque) and Bergedorf 1861 ½ s. and 1 s. stamps . . . 40 45
1366 $1 "Kruzenshtern" and Bremen 1855 3 gr. stamp 45 50

1999. 150th Death Anniv of Katsushika Hokusai (Japanese artist). As T **298b** of Gambia. Mult.
1368 $1 "Women returning Home at Sunset" (women by lake) . . 45 50
1369 $1 "Blind Man" (without beard) 45 50
1370 $1 "Women returning Home at Sunset" (women descending hill) 45 50
1371 $1 "Young Man on a White Horse" 45 50
1372 $1 "Blind Man" (with beard) . 45 50
1373 $1 "Peasant crossing a Bridge" . 45 50
1374 $1.60 "Poppies" (one flower) . 70 75
1375 $1.60 "Blind Man" (with beard) 70 75
1376 $1.60 "Poppies" (two flowers) . 70 75
1377 $1.60 "Abe No Nakamaro gazing at the Moon from a Terrace" 70 75
1378 $1.60 "Blind Man" (without beard) 70 75
1379 $1.60 "Cranes on a Snowy Pine" 70 75

143 Steelband

1999. 25th Culturama Festival. Multicoloured.
1382 30 c. Type **143** 15 20
1383 80 c. Clowns 35 40
1384 $1.80 Masqueraders with band 80 85
1385 $5 Local string band . . . . . 2·10 2·25

1999. "Queen Elizabeth the Queen Mother's Century". As T **304a** of Gambia.
1386 $2 black and gold 85 90
1387 $2 multicoloured 85 90
1388 $2 black and gold 85 90
1389 $2 multicoloured 85 90
DESIGNS: No. 1386, Lady Elizabeth Bowes-Lyon on Wedding Day, 1923; 1387, Duchess of York with Princess Elizabeth, 1926; 1388, King George VI and Queen Elizabeth during Second World War; 1389, Queen Mother in 1983.

144 "The Adoration of the Magi" (Durer)

146 Boris Yeltsin (President of Russian Federation, 1991)

145 Flowers forming Top of Head

1999. Christmas. Religious Paintings. Multicoloured.
1391 30 c. Type **144** 15 20
1392 90 c. "Canigiani Holy Family" (Raphael) 40 45
1393 $1.20 "The Nativity" (Durer) . 50 55
1394 $1.80 "Madonna and Child surrounded by Angels" (Rubens) 80 85
1395 $3 "Madonna and Child surrounded by Saints" (Rubens) . . . . 1·25 1·40

1999. Faces of the Millennium: Diana, Princess of Wales. Showing collage of miniature flower photographs. Multicoloured.
1397 $1 Type **145** (face value at left) 45 50
1398 $1 Top of head (face value at right) 45 50
1399 $1 Ear (face value at left) . . . 45 50
1400 $1 Eye and temple (face value at right) 45 50
1401 $1 Cheek (face value at left) . . 45 50
1402 $1 Cheek (face value at right) . 45 50
1403 $1 Blue background (face value at left) 45 50
1404 $1 Chin (face value at right) . . 45 50
Nos. 1397/1404 were printed together, se-tenant, and when viewed as a sheetlet, forms a portrait of Diana, Princess of Wales.

2000. New Millennium. People and Events of Eighteenth Century (1700–49). As T **268** of Lesotho. Multicoloured.
1405 30 c. Jonathan Swift ("Gulliver's Travels", 1726) . 15 20
1406 30 c. Emperor Kangxi of China 15 20
1407 30 c. Bartolommeo Cristofori (invention of piano, 1709) . 15 20
1408 30 c. Captain William Kidd hanging on gibbet, 1701 . . 15 20
1409 30 c. William Herschel (astronomer) 15 20
1410 30 c. King George I of Great Britain, 1714 . . . . . . 15 20
1411 30 c. Peter the Great of Russia (trade treaty with China, 1720) 15 20
1412 30 c. "Death" (bubonic plague in Austria and Germany, 1711) 15 20
1413 30 c. "Standing Woman" (Kaigetsudo Dohan (Japanese artist)) 15 20
1414 30 c. Queen Anne of England, 1707 . . . . 15 20
1415 30 c. Anders Celcius (invention of centigrade thermometer, 1742) 15 20
1416 30 c. Vitus Bering (discovery of Alaska and Aleutian Islands, 1741) 15 20
1417 30 c. Edmund Halley (calculation of Halley's Comet, 1705) 15 20
1418 30 c. John Wesley (founder of Methodist Church, 1729) . . 15 20
1419 30 c. Sir Isaac Newton (publication of "Optick Treatise", 1704) 15 20
1420 30 c. Queen Anne (Act of Union between England and Scotland, 1707) (59 × 39 mm) 15 20
1421 30 c. Johann Sebastian Bach (composition of "The Well-tempered Klavier", 1722) . . 15 20
No. 1417 is inscribed "cometis" in error.

2000. New Millennium. People and Events of Twentieth Century (1990–99). Multicoloured.
1422 50 c. Type **146** 20 25
1423 50 c. American soldiers and burning oil wells (Gulf War, 1991) 20 25
1424 50 c. Soldiers (Bosnian Civil War, 1992) 20 25
1425 50 c. Pres. Clinton, Yitzchak Rabin and Yasser Arafat (Oslo Accords, 1993) . . . 20 25
1426 50 c. Prime Ministers John Major and Albert Reynolds (Joint Declaration on Northern Ireland, 1993) . . 20 25
1427 50 c. Frederik de Klerk and Nelson Mandela (end of Apartheid, South Africa, 1994) 20 25
1428 50 c. Cal Ripkin (record number of consecutive baseball games, 1995) 20 25
1429 50 c. Kobe from air (earthquake, 1995) 20 25
1430 50 c. Mummified Inca girl preserved in ice, 1995 . . . 20 25
1431 50 c. NASA's "Sojourner" on Mars, 1997 . . . . 20 25
1432 50 c. Dr. Ian Wilmat and cloned sheep, 1997 . . . . 20 25
1433 50 c. Death of Princess Diana, 1997 . . . . 20 25
1434 50 c. Fireworks over Hong Kong on its return to China, 1997 . . . . 20 25
1435 50 c. Mother with septuplets, 1998 . . . . 20 25
1436 50 c. Guggenheim Museum, Bilbao, 1998 . . . . 20 25
1437 50 c. "2000" and solar eclipse, 1999 (59 × 39 mm) 20 25
1438 50 c. Pres. Clinton (impeachment in 1999) 20 25
No. 1422 incorrectly identifies his office as "Prime Minister".

147 Dragon

2000. Chinese New Year ("Year of the Dragon"). Multicoloured.
1439 $1.60 Type **147** 70 75
1440 $1.60 Dragon with open claws (face value bottom left) . . 70 75
1441 $1.60 Dragon holding sphere (face value bottom right) . . 70 75
1442 $1.60 Dragon looking up (face value bottom left) 70 75

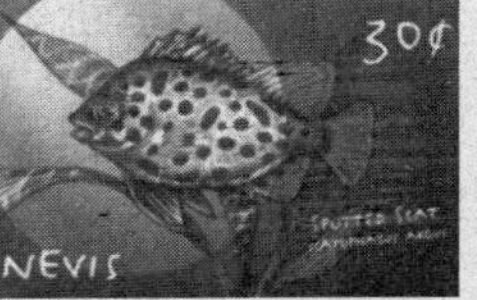

148 Spotted Scat

2000. Tropical Fish. Showing fish in spotlight. Multicoloured.

1444 30 c. Type **148** 15 20
1445 80 c. Delta topsail platy ("Platy Variatus") 35 40
1446 90 c. Emerald betta 40 45
1447 $1 Sail-finned tang 45 50
1448 $1 Black-capped basslet ("Black-capped Gramma") . 45 50
1449 $1 Sail-finned snapper ("Majestic Snapper") . . . 45 50
1450 $1 Purple fire goby 45 50
1451 $1 Clown triggerfish 45 50
1452 $1 Forceps butterflyfish ("Yellow Long-nose") . . . 45 50
1453 $1 Clown wrasse 45 50
1454 $1 Yellow-headed jawfish . . . 45 50
1455 $1 Oriental sweetlips 45 50
1456 $1 Royal gramma 45 50
1457 $1 Thread-finned butterflyfish . 45 50
1458 $1 Yellow tang 45 50
1459 $1 Bicoloured angelfish 45 50
1460 $1 Catalina goby 45 50
1461 $1 Striped mimic blenny ("False Cleanerfish") 45 50
1462 $1 Powder-blue surgeonfish . . 45 50
1463 $4 Long-horned cowfish . . . 1·75 1·90

Nos. 1447/54 and 1455/62 were each printed together, se-tenant, the backgrounds forming composite designs.

OFFICIAL STAMPS

1980. Nos. 40/49 optd **OFFICIAL**.

O 1 15 c. Sugar cane being harvested 10 10
O 2 25 c. Crafthouse (craft centre) 10 10
O 3 30 c. "Europa" (liner) 10 10
O 4 40 c. Lobster and sea crab . . 15 15
O 5 45 c. Royal St. Kitts Hotel and golf course 20 20
O 6 50 c. Pinney's Beach, Nevis . . 15 20
O 7 55 c. New runway at Golden Rock 15 20
O 8 $1 Picking cotton 15 25
O 9 $5 Brewery 45 55
O10 $10 Pineapples and peanuts . . 70 90

1981. Nos. 60/71 optd **OFFICIAL**.

O11 15 c. New River Mill 10 10
O12 20 c. Nelson Museum 10 10
O13 25 c. St. James' Parish Church 10 15
O14 30 c. Nevis Lane 15 15
O15 40 c. Zetland Plantation . . . 15 20
O16 45 c. Nisbet Plantation 20 25
O17 50 c. Pinney's Beach 20 25
O18 55 c. Eva Wilkin's Studio . . . 25 30
O19 $1 Nevis at dawn 30 30
O20 $2.50 Ruins of Fort Charles . 40 50
O21 $5 Old Bath House 50 65
O22 $10 Beach at Nisbet's . . . . 80 1·00

1983. Nos. 72/7 optd or surch **OFFICIAL**.

O23 45 c. on $2 "Royal Sovereign" 10 15
O24 45 c. on $2 Prince Charles and Lady Diana Spencer 20 25
O25 55 c. "Royal Caroline" . . . 10 15
O26 55 c. Prince Charles and Lady Diana Spencer 25 25
O27 $1.10 on $5 "Britannia" . . . 20 25
O28 $1.10 on $5 Prince Charles and Lady Diana Spencer 55 60

1985. Nos. 187/98 optd **OFFICIAL**.

O29 15 c. Flamboyant 20 20
O30 20 c. Eyelash orchid 30 30
O31 30 c. Bougainvillea 30 40
O32 40 c. Hibiscus sp 30 40
O33 50 c. Night-blooming cereus . 35 40
O34 55 c. Yellow mahoe 35 45
O35 60 c. Spider-lily 40 50
O36 75 c. Scarlet cordia 45 55
O37 $1 Shell-ginger 60 60
O38 $3 Blue petrea . . . . 1·25 1·75
O39 $5 Coral hibiscus . . . . . . 2·00 2·25
O40 $10 Passion flower . . . . . 3·00 2·50

1993. Nos. 578/91 optd **OFFICIAL**.

O41 5 c. Type **63** 30 40
O42 10 c. "Historis odius" 30 40
O43 15 c. "Marpesia corinna" . . . 30 30
O44 20 c. "Anartia amathea" . . . 30 20
O45 25 c. "Junonia evarete" . . . 30 20
O46 40 c. "Heliconius charithonia" . 40 30
O47 50 c. "Marpesia petreus" . . . 50 30
O48 75 c. "Heliconius doris" . . . 65 40
O49 80 c. "Dione juno" 65 40
O50 $1 "Hypolimnas misippus" . . 75 60
O51 $3 "Danaus plexippus" . . . 1·75 2·00
O52 $5 "Heliconius sara" . . . . 2·25 3·00
O53 $10 "Tithorea harmonia" . . . 4·50 5·50
O54 $20 "Dryas julia" . . . . . . 9·25 10·00

1999. Nos. 1166/77 optd **OFFICIAL**.

O55 25 c. Guava 10 15
O56 30 c. Papaya 15 20
O57 50 c. Mango 20 25
O58 60 c. Golden apple 25 30
O59 80 c. Pineapple 35 40
O60 90 c. Watermelon 40 45
O61 $1 Bananas 45 50
O62 $1.80 Orange 80 85
O63 $3 Honeydew . . . . 1·25 1·40
O64 $5 Cantaloupe . . . . 2·10 2·25
O65 $10 Pomegranate . . . . . . 4·25 4·50
O66 $20 Cashew . . . . 8·75 9·00

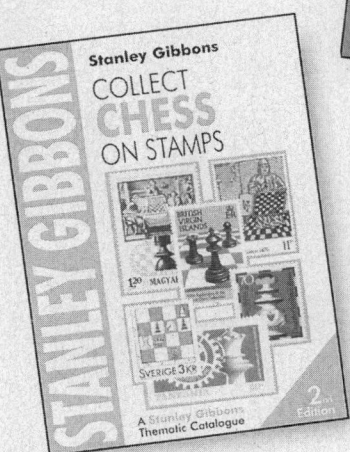

NEW BRUNSWICK Pt. 1

An eastern province of the Dominion of Canada, whose stamps are now used.

1851. 12 pence = 1 shilling;
20 shilling = 1 pound.
1860. 100 cents = 1 dollar.

1 Royal Crown and Heraldic Flowers of the United Kingdom

1851.

2 1 3d. red £2000 £325
4 6d. yellow £4500 £700
5 1s. mauve £13000 £4000

2 Locomotive

3 Queen Victoria

1860.

8 2 1 c. purple . . . . 32·00 32·00
10 3 2 c. orange . . . . 15·00 15·00
13 – 5 c. brown £4250
14 – 5 c. green . . . . 13·00 13·00
17 – 10 c. red . . . . 38·00 38·00
18 – 12½ c. blue . . . . 50·00 40·00
19 – 17 c. black . . . . 35·00 40·00

DESIGNS—VERT: 5 c. brown, Charles Connell; 5 c. green; 10 c. Queen Victoria; 17 c. King Edward VII when Prince of Wales. HORIZ: 12½ c. Steamship.

NEW CALEDONIA Pt. 6

A French Overseas Territory in the S. Pacific, E. of Australia, consisting of New Caledonia and a number of smaller islands.

100 centimes = 1 franc

1 Napoleon III

1860. Imperf.

1 1 10 c. black £190

Nos. 5/35 are stamps of French Colonies optd or surch.

1881. "Peace and Commerce" type surch **N C E** and new value. Imperf.

5 H 05 on 40 c. red on yellow . . 19·00 18·00
8a 5 on 40 c. red on yellow . . 13·50 13·50
9 5 on 75 c. red . . . . 30·00 29·00
6a 25 on 35 c. black on orge . . £110 £100
7 25 on 75 c. red £300 £250

1886. "Peace and Commerce" (imperf) and "Commerce" types surch **N.C.E. 5c**.

10 J 5 c. on 1 f. green . . . . 13·00 13·00
11 H 5 c. on 1 f. green £7500 £8500

1891. "Peace and Commerce" (imperf) and "Commerce" types surch **N.-C.E. 10 c.** in ornamental frame.

13 H 10 c. on 40 c. red on yell . . 19·00 17·00
14 J 10 c. on 40 c. red on yell . . 10·00 9·50

1892. "Commerce" type surch **N.-C.E. 10 centimes** in ornamental frame.

15 J 10 c. on 30 c. brn on drab . . 10·00 10·00

1892. Optd **NLLE CALEDONIE**. (a) "Peace and Commerce" type. Imperf.

16 H 20 c. red on green £250 £275
17 35 c. black on orange . . 50·00 50·00
19 1 f. green £200 £200

(b) "Commerce" type.

20 J 5 c. green on green . . . . 10·00 9·50
21 10 c. black on lilac . . . . 85·00 50·00
22 15 c. blue . . . . 65·00 32·00
23 20 c. red on green . . . . 65·00 35·00
24 25 c. brown on yellow . . . . 12·50 8·50
25 25 c. black on pink . . . . 70·00 9·50
26 30 c. brown on drab . . . . 48·00 42·00
27 35 c. black on orange £170 £125
29 75 c. red on pink £130 £100
30 1 f. green . . . . £110 95·00

1892. Surch **N-C-E** in ornamental scroll and new value. (a) "Peace and Commerce" type. Imperf.

31 H 10 on 1 f. green £4000 £3250

(b) "Commerce" type.

32 J 5 on 20 c. red on green . . . 13·50 9·50
34 5 on 75 c. red on pink . . . 9·00 5·75
35 10 on 1 f. green . . . . 9·00 5·75

1892. "Tablet" key-type inscr "NLLE CALEDONIE ET DEPENDANCES".

37 D 1 c. black and red on blue . . 35 30
38 2 c. brown & blue on buff . . 65 40
39 4 c. brown & blue on grey . . 90 1·00
55 5 c. green and red 85 75
41 10 c. black & blue on lilac . . 4·25 3·25
56 10 c. red and blue . . . . 5·75 1·00
42 15 c. blue and red . . . . 13·50 1·10
57 15 c. grey and red . . . . 8·00 95
43 20 c. red & blue on green . . 11·50 6·75
44 25 c. black & red on pink . . 11·50 4·75
58 25 c. blue and red . . . . 11·00 6·50
45 30 c. brown & bl on drab . . 11·50 6·75
46 40 c. red & blue on yellow . . 12·00 9·50
47 50 c. red and blue on pink . . 45·00 18·00
59 50 c. brown & red on blue . . 65·00 55·00
60 50 c. brown & blue on blue . . 38·00 32·00
48 75 c. brown & red on orge . . 22·00 13·00
49 1 f. green and red . . . . 26·00 14·50

1899. Stamps of 1892 surch (a) **N-C-E** in ornamental scroll and **5**.

50 D 5 on 2 c. brown & bl on buff . 13·00 10·50
51 5 on 4 c. brn & bl on grey . . 3·00 2·75

(b) **N.C.E.** and **15** in circle.

52 D 15 on 30 c. brown and blue on drab . . . . 3·75 3·25
53 15 on 75 c. brown and red on orange . . . . 10·50 8·00
54 15 on 1 f. green and red . . 17·00 14·50

1902. Surch **N.-C.E.** and value in figures.

61 D 5 on 30 c. brown and blue on drab . . . . 6·25 5·75
62 15 on 40 c. red and blue on yellow . . . . 4·75 4·25

1903. 50th Anniv of French Annexation. Optd **CINQUANTENAIRE 24 SEPTEMBRE 1853 1903** and eagle.

63 D 1 c. black and red on blue . . 95 75
64 2 c. brown & blue on buff . . 3·25 2·50
65 4 c. brown & blue on grey . . 4·25 2·50
66 5 c. green and red . . . . 4·25 3·00
69 10 c. black & blue on lilac . . 7·25 5·75
70 15 c. grey and red . . . . 7·75 4·25
71 20 c. red & blue on green . . 12·50 9·50
72 25 c. black & red on pink . . 12·50 11·50
73 30 c. brown & bl on drab . . 17·00 14·00
74 40 c. red & blue on yellow . . 24·00 18·00
75 50 c. red and blue on pink . . 38·00 24·00
76 75 c. brown & bl on orge . . 65·00 55·00
77 1 f. green and red . . . . 80·00 70·00

1903. Nos. 64 etc further surch with value in figures within the jubilee opt.

78 D 1 on 2 c. brn & bl on buff . . 50 45
79 2 on 4 c. brn & bl on grey . . 1·60 1·50
80 4 on 5 c. green and red . . . 1·60 1·50
82 10 on 15 c. grey and red . . . 2·00 2·10
83 15 on 20 c. red and blue on green . . . . 2·50 2·40
84 20 on 25 c. black and red on pink . . . . 4·25 4·00

15 Kagu

16

17 "President Felix Faure" (barque)

1905.

85 15 1 c. black on green 15 10
86 2 c. brown 15 10
87 4 c. blue on orange 20 25
88 5 c. green 30 20
112 5 c. blue 25 30
113 10 c. green 50 45
114 10 c. red 30 35
90 15 c. lilac 40 25
91 16 20 c. brown 30 25
92 25 c. blue on green 45 20
115 25 c. red on yellow 30 20
93 30 c. brown on orange 30 40
116 30 c. red . . . . 1·10 1·25
117 30 c. orange 35 30
94 35 c. black on yellow 55 30
95 40 c. red on green 65 55
96 45 c. red 40 45
97 50 c. red on orange . . . . 2·10 1·60
118 50 c. blue 90 85
119 50 c. grey 65 60
120 65 c. blue 35 35
98 75 c. olive 35 35
121 75 c. blue 55 65
122 75 c. violet 85 75
99 17 1 f. blue on green 85 45
123 1 f. blue . . . . 1·25 95
100 2 f. red on blue . . . . 2·10 1·50
101 5 f. black on orange . . . . 5·00 4·25

1912. Stamps of 1892 surch.

102 D 05 on 15 c. grey and red . . 40 45
103 05 on 20 c. red and blue on green 65 55
104 05 on 30 c. brown and blue on drab 65 55
105 10 on 40 c. red and blue on yellow . . . . 1·25 95
106 10 on 50 c. brown and blue on blue . . . . 1·40 1·25

1915. Surch **NCE 5** and red cross.

107 15 10 c. + 5 c. red 90 85

1915. Surch **5c** and red cross.

109 15 10 c. + 5 c. red 40 50
110 15 c. + 5 c. lilac 35 45

1918. Surch **5 CENTIMES**.

111 15 5 c. on 15 c. lilac . . . . 1·10 1·10

1922. Surch **0 05**.

124 15 0.05 on 15 c. lilac 50 45

1924. Types **15/17** (some colours changed) surch.

125 15 25 c. on 15 c. lilac 30 35
126 17 25 c. on 2 f. red on blue . . 40 50
127 25 c. on 5 f. black on orge . . 40 50
128 16 60 on 75 c. green 25 35
129 65 on 45 c. purple . . . . 1·40 1·50
130 85 on 45 c. purple . . . . 1·40 1·50
131 90 on 75 c. red 60 65
132 17 1 f. 25 on 1 f. blue 55 60
133 1 f. 50 on 1 f. blue on blue . 1·00 1·10
134 3 f. on 5 f. mauve . . . . 1·00 1·10
135 10 f. on 5 f. green on mve . 5·25 5·50
136 20 f. on 5 f. red on yellow . 10·50 10·50

22 Pointe des Paletuviers

23 Chief's Hut

24 La Perouse, De Bougainville and "L'Astrolabe"

1928.

137 22 1 c. blue and purple 10 20
138 2 c. green and brown 10 30
139 3 c. blue and red 15 25
140 4 c. blue and orange 15 35
141 5 c. brown and blue 15 35
142 10 c. brown and lilac 20 25
143 15 c. blue and brown 20 25
144 20 c. brown and red 20 35
145 25 c. brown and green 25 30
146 23 30 c. deep green and green . . 20 30
147 35 c. mauve and black 30 20
148 40 c. green and red 25 30
149 45 c. red and blue 50 60
150 45 c. green and deep green . . 65 75
151 50 c. brown and mauve 40 25
152 55 c. red and blue . . . . 2·50 1·40
153 60 c. red and blue 25 35
154 65 c. blue and brown 45 55
155 70 c. brown and mauve 30 40
156 75 c. drab and blue 80 60
157 80 c. green and purple 50 40
158 85 c. brown and green . . . . 1·25 55
159 90 c. pink and red 40 55
160 90 c. red and brown 50 60
161 24 1 f. pink and drab . . . . 4·25 2·25
162 1 f. carmine and red . . . . 1·10 1·00
163 1 f. green and red 40 50
164 1 f. 10 brown and green . . . . 9·25 7·50
165 1 f. 25 green and brown 55 65
166 1 f. 25 carmine and red 65 50
167 1 f. 40 red and blue 65 50
168 1 f. 50 light blue and blue . . 35 40
169 1 f. 60 brown and green . . . . 1·00 95
170 1 f. 75 orange and blue 45 45
171 1 f. 75 blue & ultramarine . . 45 50
172 2 f. brown and orange 40 50
173 2 f. 25 blue & ultramarine . . 45 50
174 2 f. 50 brown . . . . 1·00 1·10
175 3 f. brown and mauve 45 50
176 5 f. brown and blue 45 50
177 10 f. brown & pur on pink . . 80 80
178 20 f. brown & red on yellow . . 2·00 1·60

1931. "Colonial Exhibition" key-types.

179 E 40 c. green and black . . . 3·75 3·75
180 F 50 c. mauve and black . . . 3·75 3·75
181 G 90 c. red and black . . . 3·75 3·75
182 H 1 f. 50 blue and black . . . 3·75 3·75

1932. Paris-Noumea Flight. Optd with Couzinet 33 airplane and **PARIS-NOUMEA Verneilh-Deve-Munch 5 Avril 1932**.

183 23 40 c. olive and red £325 £350
184 50 c. brown and mauve . . £325 £350

1933. 1st Anniv of Paris-Noumea Flight. Optd **PARIS-NOUMEA Premiere liaison aerienne 5 Avril 1932** and Couzinet 33 airplane.

185 22 1 c. blue and purple . . . . 5·00 5·00
186 2 c. green and brown . . . . 5·00 5·00
187 4 c. blue and orange . . . . 5·00 5·00
188 5 c. brown and blue . . . . 5·00 5·00
189 10 c. brown and lilac . . . . 5·00 5·00
190 15 c. blue and brown . . . . 5·00 5·00
191 20 c. brown and red . . . . 5·00 5·00
192 25 c. brown and green . . . . 5·00 5·00
193 23 30 c. deep green and green . . 4·75 5·00
194 35 c. mauve and black . . . . 4·75 5·00
195 40 c. green and red . . . . 4·75 5·00
196 45 c. red and blue . . . . 4·75 5·00
197 50 c. brown and mauve . . . . 4·75 5·00
198 70 c. brown and mauve . . . . 5·75 6·00
199 75 c. drab and blue . . . . 5·75 6·00
200 85 c. brown and green . . . . 5·75 6·00
201 23 90 c. pink and red . . . . 6·00 6·25
202 24 1 f. pink and drab . . . . 6·00 6·25
203 1 f. 25 green and brown . . 6·00 6·25
204 1 f. 50 light blue & blue . . 6·00 6·25
205 1 f. 75 orange and blue . . . 6·00 6·25
206 2 f. brown and orange . . . 6·25 6·25
207 3 f. brown and mauve . . . 6·00 6·25
208 5 f. brown and blue . . . 6·00 6·25
209 10 f. brown & pur on pink . 6·00 6·25
210 20 f. brown & red on yellow . 6·00 6·25

1937. International Exhibition, Paris. As Nos. 168/73 of St.-Pierre et Miquelon.

211 20 c. violet . . . . 1·25 1·40
212 30 c. green . . . . 1·40 1·50
213 40 c. red . . . . 1·25 1·40
214 50 c. brown and blue . . . . 1·25 1·40
215 90 c. red . . . . 1·25 1·40
216 1 f. 50 blue . . . . 1·25 1·40

DESIGNS—HORIZ: 30 c. Sailing ships; 40 c. Berber, Negress and Annamite; 90 c. France extends torch of civilization; 1 f. 50, Diane de Poitiers. VERT: 50 c. Agriculture.

27 Breguet Saigon Flying Boat over Noumea

1938. Air.

217 27 65 c. violet 50 60
218 4 f. 50 red . . . . 1·10 1·10
219 7 f. green 50 50
220 9 f. blue . . . . 2·00 2·10
221 20 f. orange . . . . 1·40 1·40
222 50 f. black . . . . 2·40 2·40

1938. Int Anti-Cancer Fund. As T **22** of Mauritania.

223 1 f. 75 + 50 c. blue . . . . 9·00 9·00

1939. New York World's Fair. As T **28** of Mauritania.

224 1 f. 25 red . . . . 1·10 1·10
225 2 f. 25 blue . . . . 1·00 1·10

1939. 150th Anniv of French Revolution. As T **29** of Mauritania.

226 45 c. + 25 c. green and black (postage) . . . . 7·50 8·00
227 70 c. + 30 c. brown & black . 7·50 8·00
228 90 c. + 35 c. orange & black . 7·50 8·00
229 1 f. 25 + 1 f. red & black . . 7·50 8·00
230 2 f. 25 + 2 f. blue & black . . 8·00 8·00
231 4 f. 50 + 4 f. black and orange (air) . . . . 20·00 22·00

1941. Adherence to General de Gaulle. Optd **France Libre**.

232 22 1 c. blue and purple . . . . 10·50 10·50
233 2 c. green and brown . . . 10·50 10·50
234 3 c. blue and red . . . . 10·00 10·50
235 4 c. blue and orange . . . 10·50 10·50
236 5 c. brown and blue . . . 9·50 10·50
237 10 c. brown and lilac . . . 9·50 10·50
238 15 c. blue and brown . . . 14·00 14·00
239 20 c. brown and red . . . 14·00 14·00
240 25 c. brown and green . . . 14·00 14·00
241 23 30 c. deep green and green . 14·00 14·00
242 35 c. mauve and black . . . 14·00 14·00
243 40 c. green and red . . . 14·00 14·00
244 45 c. green & deep green . . 14·00 14·00
245 50 c. brown and mauve . . . 14·00 14·00
246 55 c. red and blue . . . 14·00 14·00
247 60 c. red and blue . . . 14·00 14·00
248 65 c. blue and brown . . . 14·00 14·00
249 70 c. brown and mauve . . . 14·00 14·00
250 75 c. drab and blue . . . 14·00 14·00
251 80 c. green and purple . . . 14·00 14·00
252 85 c. brown and green . . . 14·00 14·00
253 90 c. pink and red . . . 14·00 14·00
254 24 1 f. carmine and red . . . 14·00 14·00
255 1 f. 25 green and brown . . 14·00 14·00
256 1 f. 40 red and blue . . . 14·00 14·00
257 1 f. 50 light blue & blue . . 14·00 14·00
258 1 f. 60 brown and green . . 14·00 14·00
259 1 f. 75 orange and blue . . 14·00 14·00
260 2 f. brown and orange . . . 14·00 14·00
261 2 f. 25 blue & ultramarine . . 14·00 14·00
262 2 f. 50 brown . . . . 15·00 15·00
263 3 f. brown and mauve . . . 15·00 15·00
264 5 f. brown and blue . . . 15·00 15·00
265 10 f. brown & pur on pink . . 19·00 19·00
266 20 f. brown & red on yellow . . 20·00 20·00

29 Kagu

30 Fairey FC-1 Airliner

1942. Free French Issue. (a) Postage.

267 29 5 c. brown 20 30
268 10 c. blue 20 30
269 25 c. green 20 30
270 30 c. red 20 30
271 40 c. green 20 30
272 80 c. purple 40 30
273 1 f. mauve 50 35
274 1 f. 50 red 50 35

275 29 2 f. black 60 60
276 2 f. 50 blue 60 60
277 4 f. violet 70 45
278 5 f. yellow 80 60
279 10 f. brown . . . . 1·25 85
280 20 f. green . . . . 1·75 1·50

(b) Air.

281 30 1 f. orange 45 55
282 1 f. 50 red 45 55
283 5 f. purple 50 60
284 10 f. black 70 70
285 25 f. blue 70 70
286 50 f. green . . . . 1·25 1·00
287 100 f. red . . . . 1·40 1·25

1944. Mutual Aid and Red Cross Funds. As T **58e** of Guadeloupe.

288 5 f. + 20 f. red 80 85

1945. Eboue. As T **58f** of Guadeloupe.

289 2 f. black 40 50
290 25 f. green . . . . 1·50 1·60

1945. Surch.

291 29 50 c. on 5 c. brown 85 95
292 60 c. on 5 c. brown 85 95
293 70 c. on 5 c. brown . . . . 1·00 1·10
294 1 f. 20 on 5 c. brown 30 40
295 2 f. 40 on 25 c. green . . . 40 50
296 3 f. on 25 c. green 40 50
297 4 f. 50 on 25 c. green . . . 90 1·00
298 15 f. on 2 f. 50 blue . . . . 1·50 1·60

1946. Air. Victory. As T **63b** of Guadeloupe.

299 8 f. blue . . . . 90 1·10

1946. Air. From Chad to the Rhine. As T **63c** of Guadeloupe.

300 35 5 f. black 80 95
301 – 10 f. red . . . . 1·00 1·10
302 – 15 f. blue . . . . 95 1·10
303 – 20 f. brown . . . . 95 1·10
304 – 25 f. green . . . . 1·60 1·75
305 – 50 f. purple . . . . 2·50 2·75

DESIGNS: 5 f. Legionaries by Lake Chad; 10 f. Battle of Koufra; 15 f. Tank Battle, Mareth; 20 f. Normandy Landings; 25 f. Liberation of Paris; 50 f. Liberation of Strasbourg.

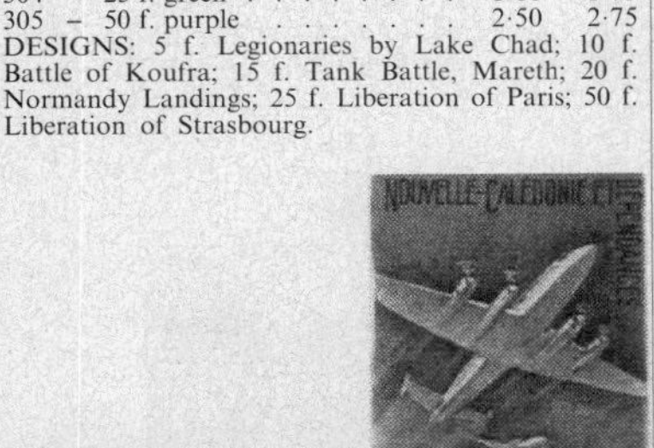

36 Two Kagus **37** Sud Est Languedoc Airliners over Landscape

1948. (a) Postage.

306 36 10 c. purple and yellow . . 10 30
307 30 c. purple and green . . . 15 30
308 40 c. purple and brown . . 15 30
309 – 50 c. purple and pink . . . 15 35
310 – 60 c. brown and yellow . . 25 35
311 – 80 c. green & light green . . 25 35
312 – 1 f. violet and orange . . . 50 35
313 – 1 f. 20 brown and blue . . . 50 35
314 – 1 f. 50 blue and yellow . . . 50 35
315 – 2 f. brown and green . . . 55 25
316 – 2 f. 40 red and purple . . . 75 35
317 – 3 f. violet and orange . . . 5·50 1·25
318 – 4 f. indigo and blue . . . . 1·50 70
319 – 5 f. violet and red . . . . . 1·75 85
320 – 6 f. brown and yellow . . . 2·10 1·25
321 – 10 f. blue and orange . . . 2·10 1·00
322 – 15 f. red and blue . . . . . 2·40 1·25
323 – 20 f. violet and yellow . . . 2·50 1·40
324 – 25 f. blue and orange . . . 3·25 2·50

(b) Air.

325 – 50 f. purple and orange . . 3·75 3·00
326 37 100 f. blue and green . . . 6·75 3·50
327 – 200 f. brown and yellow . . 12·00 7·00

DESIGNS—As T **36**: HORIZ: 50 c. to 80 c. Ducos Sanatorium; 1 f. 50, Porcupine Is; 2 f. to 4 f. Nickel foundry; 5 f. to 10 f. "The Towers of Notre Dame" Rocks. VERT: 15 f. to 25 f. Chief's hut. As T **37**: HORIZ: Sud Est Languedoc airliner over 50 f. St. Vincent Bay; 200 f. Noumea.

38 People of Five Races, Bomber and Globe

1949. Air. 75th Anniv of U.P.U.

328 38 10 f. multicoloured . . . . 5·00 3·50

INDEX

Countries can be quickly located by referring to the index at the end of this volume.

39 Doctor and Patient **40**

1950. Colonial Welfare Fund.

329 39 10 f. + 2 f. pur & brn . . . 3·50 3·75

1952. Military Medal Centenary.

330 40 2 f. red, yell & grn . . . . 4·00 4·25

41 Admiral D'Entrecasteaux

1953. French Administration Centenary. Inscr "1853 1953".

331 41 1 f. 50 lake and brown . . . 5·25 3·75
332 – 2 f. blue and turquoise . . 4·25 2·50
333 – 6 f. brown, blue and red . . 7·75 4·50
334 – 13 f. blue and green . . . . 9·00 5·25

DESIGNS: 2 f. Mgr. Douarre and church; 6 f. Admiral D'Urville and map; 13 f. Admiral Despointes and view.

42 Normandy Landings, 1944

1954. Air. 10th Anniv of Liberation.

335 42 3 f. blue and deep blue . . . 5·25 3·25

43 Towers of Notre-Dame (rocks) **44** Coffee

45 Transporting Nickel

1955.

336 43 2 f. 50 c. blue, green and sepia (postage) . . . . 1·10 70
337 3 f. blue, brown & green . . 5·50 3·00
338 44 9 f. deep blue and blue . . . 2·10 75
339 45 14 f. blue & brown (air) . . 5·75 1·75

46 Dumbea Barrage **47** "Xanthostemon"

1956. Economic and Social Development Fund.

340 46 3 f. green and blue . . . . 1·40 65

1958. Flowers.

341 47 4 f. multicoloured . . . . . 1·90 90
342 – 15 f. red, yellow & green . . 4·25 1·25

DESIGN: 15 f. Hibiscus.

48 "Human Rights" **49** Zebra Lionfish

1958. 10th Anniv of Declaration of Human Rights.

343 48 7 f. red and blue . . . . . 1·60 95

1959.

344 49 1 f. brown and grey 80 45
345 – 2 f. blue, purple and green . 70 40
346 – 3 f. red, blue and green . . 1·10 45
347 – 4 f. purple, red and green . . 1·00 50
348 – 5 f. bistre, blue and green . . 1·40 65
349 – 10 f. multicoloured . . . . 2·75 80
350 – 26 f. multicoloured . . . . 4·25 2·75

DESIGNS—HORIZ: 2 f. Outrigger canoes racing; 3 f. Harlequin tuskfish; 5 f. Sail Rock, Noumea; 26 f. Fluorescent corals. VERT: 4 f. Fisherman with spear. 10 f. Blue sea lizard and "Spirographe" (coral).

49a The Carved Rock, Bourail

1959. Air.

351 – 15 f. green, brown & red . . 3·75 1·50
352 – 20 f. brown and green . . . 8·50 2·50
353 – 25 f. black, blue & purple . . 7·50 2·75
354 – 50 f. brown, green & blue . . 5·50 3·50
355 – 50 f. brown, green & blue . . 5·00 2·00
356 – 100 f. brown, green & blue . 16·00 8·25
357 49a 200 f. brown, green & blue . 28·00 13·00

DESIGNS—HORIZ: 15 f. Fisherman with net; 20 f. New Caledonia nautilus; 25 f. Underwater swimmer shooting bump-headed unicornfish; 50 f. (No. 355), Isle of Pines; 100 f. Corbeille de Yate. VERT: 50 f. (No. 354), Yate barrage.

49b Napoleon III **49c** Port-de-France, 1859

1960. Postal Centenary.

358 15 4 f. red 75 50
359 – 5 f. brown and lake 75 50
360 – 9 f. brown and turquoise . . 90 60
361 – 12 f. black and blue . . . 90 75
362 49b 13 f. blue . . . . 3·25 1·60
363 49c 19 f. red, green & turq . . 3·50 1·10
364 – 33 f. red, green and blue . . 4·00 2·25

DESIGNS—As Type **49c**: HORIZ: 5 f. Girl operating cheque-writing machine; 12 f. Telephone receiver and exchange building; 33 f. As Type **49c** but without stamps in upper corners. VERT: 9 f. Letter-box on tree.

49d Map of Pacific and Palms

1962. 5th South Pacific Conference, Pago-Pago.

365 49d 15 f. multicoloured . . . . 2·25 1·25

49e Map and Symbols of Meteorology

1962. 3rd Regional Assembly of World Meteorological Association, Noumea.

366 49e 50 f. multicoloured . . . . 7·50 4·50

50 "Telstar" Satellite and part of Globe

1962. Air. 1st Transatlantic TV Satellite Link.

367 50 200 f. turquoise, brn & bl . . 25·00 15·00

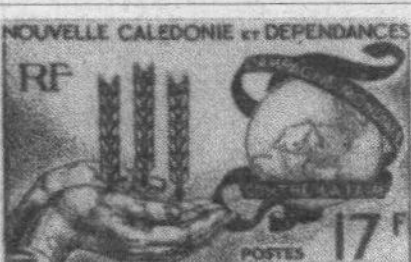

51 Emblem and Globe

1963. Freedom from Hunger.

368 51 17 f. blue and purple . . . 3·25 75

52 Relay-running **53** Centenary Emblem

1963. 1st South Pacific Games, Suva, Fiji.

369 52 1 f. red and green 65 60
370 – 7 f. brown and blue . . . . 1·60 65
371 – 10 f. brown and green . . . 2·10 1·25
372 – 27 f. blue & deep purple . . 4·00 2·25

DESIGNS: 7 f. Tennis; 10 f. Football; 27 f. Throwing the javelin.

1963. Red Cross Centenary.

373 53 37 f. red, grey and blue . . . 6·75 5·25

54 Globe and Scales of Justice **54a** "Bikkia fritillarioides"

1963. 15th Anniv of Declaration of Human Rights.

374 54 50 f. red and blue . . . . . 6·25 5·25

1964. Flowers. Multicoloured.

375 1 f. "Freycinettia" 60 40
376 2 f. Type **54a** 60 40
377 3 f. "Xanthostemon francii" . . 90 70
378 4 f. "Psidiomyrtus locellatus" . 2·40 80
379 5 f. "Callistemon suberosum" . 2·75 1·00
380 7 f. "Montrouziera sphaeroidea" 5·00 1·40
381 10 f. "Ixora collina" . . . . . 5·00 1·40
382 17 f. "Deplanchea speciosa" . . 7·00 3·00

The 7 f. and 10 f. are horiz.

54b "Ascidies polycarpa" **54c** "Philately"

1964. Corals and Marine Animals from Noumea Aquarium.

383 54b 7 f. red, brown and blue (postage) . . . . 1·50 80
384 – 10 f. red and blue . . . . 2·10 65
385 – 17 f. red, green and blue . . 3·75 2·00
388 – 13 f. bistre, black and orange (air) . . . . 3·00 1·60
389 – 15 f. green, olive & blue . . 4·25 1·60
390 – 25 f. blue and green . . . 7·50 3·75
386 – 27 f. multicoloured . . . . 5·50 2·75
387 – 37 f. multicoloured . . . . 8·00 4·00

DESIGNS—As T **54b**: VERT: 10 f. "Alcyonium catalai" (coral). HORIZ: 17 f. "Hymenocera elegans" (crab). 48 × 28 mm: 27 f. Palette surgeonfish; 37 f. "Phyllobranchus" (sea slug). 48 × 27 mm: 13 f. Twin-spotted wrasse (young); 15 f. Twin-spotted wrasse (subadult); 25 f. Twin-spotted wrasse (adult).

1964. "PHILATEC 1964" Int Stamp Exn, Paris.

391 54c 40 f. brown, green & vio . . 6·50 5·50

54d Houailou Mine

1964. Air. Nickel Production at Houailou.

392 54d 30 f. multicoloured . . . . 3·50 2·25

54e Ancient Greek Wrestling

1964. Air. Olympic Games, Tokyo.

393	**54e**	10 f. sepia, mauve & green	16·00	14·00

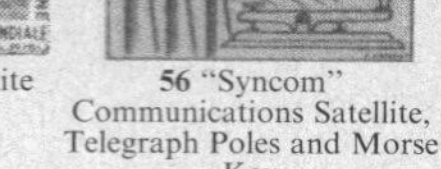

55 Weather Satellite

56 "Syncom" Communications Satellite, Telegraph Poles and Morse Key

1965. Air. World Meteorological Day.

394	**55**	9 f. multicoloured	3·25	2·25

1965. Air. Centenary of I.T.U.

395	**56**	40 f. pur, brn & blue	10·00	7·50

56a De Gaulle's Appeal of 18th June, 1940

56b Amedee Lighthouse

1965. 25th Anniv of New Caledonia's Adherence to the Free French.

396	**56a**	20 f. black, red & blue . .	10·50	6·50

1965. Inauguration of Amedee Lighthouse.

397	**56b**	8 f. bis., bl & green	1·00	60

56c Rocket "Diamant"

1966. Air. Launching of 1st French Satellite.

398	**56c**	8 f. lake, blue & turq . . .	3·00	1·50
399	–	12 f. lake, blue & turq . . .	3·50	2·00

DESIGN: 12 f. Satellite "A1".

56d Games Emblem

1966. Publicity for 2nd South Pacific Games, Noumea.

400	**56d**	8 f. black, red and blue . .	1·10	70

56e Satellite "D1"

1966. Air. Launching of Satellite "D1".

401	**56e**	10 f. brown, blue and buff	2·25	1·50

57 Noumea, 1866 (after Lebreton)

1966. Air. Centenary of Renaming of Port-de-France as Noumea.

402	**57**	30 f. slate, red and blue . .	4·00	2·75

58 Red-throated Parrot Finch

59 U.N.E.S.C.O. Allegory

1966. Birds. Multicoloured.

403	1 f. Type **58** (postage)	2·00	1·10
404	1 f. New Caledonian grass warbler	1·00	60
405	2 f. New Caledonian whistler .	1·60	1·10
406	3 f. New Caledonian pigeon ("Notou")	3·50	1·40
407	3 f. White-throated pigeon ("Collier blanc")	1·60	1·25
408	4 f. Kagu	3·75	1·60
409	5 f. Horned parakeet	5·50	2·10
410	10 f. Red-faced honeyeater . .	10·00	3·25
411	15 f. New Caledonian friarbird	5·75	2·50
412	30 f. Sacred kingfisher	8·75	4·75
413	27 f. Horned parakeet (diff) (air)	6·00	3·25
414	37 f. Scarlet honeyeater	10·00	4·50
415	39 f. Emerald dove	11·00	4·25
416	50 f. Cloven-feathered dove . .	12·50	6·25
417	100 f. Whistling hawk	22·00	9·00

Nos. 413/14 are $26 \times 45\frac{1}{2}$ mm; Nos. 415/17 are $27\frac{1}{2} \times 48$ mm.

1966. 20th Anniv of U.N.E.S.C.O.

418	**59**	16 f. purple, ochre and green	1·75	1·00

60 High Jumping

1966. South Pacific Games, Noumea.

419	**60**	17 f. violet, green & lake . .	2·50	1·10
420	–	20 f. green, purple & lake . .	3·75	1·50
421	–	40 f. green, violet & lake . .	4·75	2·25
422	–	100 f. purple, turq & lake . .	8·00	5·00

DESIGNS: 20 f. Hurdling; 40 f. Running; 100 f. Swimming.

61 Lekine Cliffs

1967.

424	**61**	17 f. grey, green and blue . .	2·10	1·00

62 Ocean Racing Yachts

1967. Air. 2nd Whangarei-Noumea Yacht Race.

425	**62**	25 f. red, blue and green . .	5·25	3·00

63 Magenta Stadium

1967. Sport Centres. Multicoloured.

426	10 f. Type **63**	1·40	60
427	20 f. Ouen-Toro swimming pool	2·50	1·10

64 New Caledonian Scenery

1967. International Tourist Year.

428	**64**	30 f. multicoloured	4·25	2·00

65 19th-century Postman

1967. Stamp Day.

429	**65**	7 f. red, green & turquoise .	1·40	1·00

66 "Papilio montrouzieri"

1967. Butterflies and Moths.

430	**66**	7 f. blue, black & green (postage)	2·50	80
431	–	9 f. blue, brown and mve . .	3·50	1·10
432	–	13 f. violet, purple & brn . .	4·25	1·40
433	–	15 f. yellow, purple & blue .	7·00	3·00
434	–	19 f. orange, brown and green (air)	5·25	3·25
435	–	29 f. purple, red and blue . .	7·50	4·25
436	–	85 f. brown, red & yellow . .	16·00	7·25

BUTTERFLIES—As T **66**: 9 f. "Polyura clitarchus"; 13 f. Common eggfly (male), and 15 f. (female). 48 × 27 mm: 19 f. Orange tiger; 29 f. Silver-striped hawk moth; 85 f. "Dellas elipsis".

67 Garnierite (mineral), Factory and Jules Garnier

1967. Air. Centenary of Garnierite Industry.

437	**67**	70 f. multicoloured	7·00	4·50

67a Lifou Island

1967. Air.

438	**67a**	200 f. multicoloured . . .	11·50	6·75

67b Skier and Snow-crystal

1967. Air. Winter Olympic Games, Grenoble.

439	**67b**	100 f. brn, blue & grn . . .	12·00	6·75

68 Bouquet, Sun and W.H.O. Emblem

69 Human Rights Emblem

1968. 20th Anniv of W.H.O.

440	**68**	20 f. blue, red and violet . .	3·25	1·50

1968. Human Rights Year.

441	**69**	12 f. red, green & yellow . .	1·90	1·00

70 Ferrying Mail-van across Tontouta River

1968. Stamp Day.

442	**70**	9 f. brown, blue and green .	2·75	1·25

71 Geography Cone

72 Dancers

1968. Sea Shells.

443	–	1 f. brn, grey & grn (postage)	1·60	45
444	–	1 f. purple and violet . . .	1·10	35
445	–	2 f. pur, red and blue . . .	1·10	60
446	–	3 f. brown and green . . .	1·60	70
447	–	5 f. red, brown & violet . .	2·10	90
448	**71**	10 f. brown, grey & blue . .	2·50	1·10
449	–	10 f. yellow, brown & red . .	4·75	1·50
450	–	10 f. black, brown & orge .	3·50	65
451	–	15 f. red, grey and green . .	3·50	2·00
452	–	21 f. brown, sepia & green .	7·25	3·00
453	–	22 f. red, brown & bl (air) .	5·25	3·00
454	–	25 f. brown and red	6·25	3·00
455	–	33 f. brown and blue . . .	7·25	3·50
456	–	34 f. violet, brown & orge .	7·25	3·50
457	–	39 f. brown, grey & green .	5·75	2·00
458	–	40 f. black, brown & red . .	5·75	2·00
459	–	50 f. red, purple & green . .	8·25	4·00
460	–	60 f. brown and green . . .	11·50	5·25
461	–	70 f. brown, grey & violet .	11·50	4·50
462	–	100 f. brown, black & bl . .	19·00	8·50

DESIGNS—VERT: 1 f. (No. 443) Swan conch ("Strombus epidromis"); 1 f. (No. 444) Scorpion conch ("Lambis scorpius"); 3 f. Common spider conch; 10 f. (No. 450) Variable conch ("Strombus variabilis"). 27 × 48 mm: 22 f. Laciniate cone; 25 f. Orange spider conch; 34 f. Vomer conch; 50 f. Chiragra spider conch. 36 × 22 mm: 2 f. Snipe's-bill murex; 5 f. Troschel's murex; 10 f. (No. 449) Sieve cowrie; 15 f. "Murex sp."; 21 f. Mole cowrie. 48 × 27 mm: 33 f. Eyed cowrie; 39 f. Lienardi's cone; 40 f. Cabrit's cone; 60 f. All-red map cowrie; 70 f. Scarlet cone; 100 f. Adusta murex.

1968. Air.

463	**72**	60 f. red, blue and green . .	6·50	4·00

73 Rally Car

1968. 2nd New Caledonian Motor Safari.

464	**73**	25 f. blue, red and green . .	6·75	2·50

74 Caudron C-60 "Aiglon" and Route Map

1969. Air. Stamp Day. 30th Anniv of 1st Noumea–Paris Flight by Martinet and Klein.

465	**74**	29 f. red, blue and violet . .	3·50	2·00

75 Concorde in Flight

1969. Air. 1st Flight of Concorde.

466	**75**	100 f. green and light green	23·00	16·00

76 Cattle-dip

1969. Cattle-breeding in New Caledonia.

467	**76**	9 f. brown, green & blue (postage)	1·25	65
468	–	25 f. violet, brown & grn . .	2·75	1·25
469	–	50 f. purple, red & grn (air)	4·75	2·75

DESIGNS: 25 f. Branding. LARGER 48 × 27 mm; 50 f. Stockman with herd.

77 Judo

1969. 3rd South Pacific Games, Port Moresby, Papua New Guinea.
470 **77** 19 f. pur, blue & red (post) . 3·00 1·50
471 – 20 f. black, red & green . . 3·00 1·50
472 – 30 f. black & blue (air) . . 4·00 1·75
473 – 39 f. brn, grn and blk . . . 5·50 2·50
DESIGNS—HORIZ: 20 f. Boxing; 30 f. Diving (38 × 27 mm). VERT: 39 f. Putting the shot (27 × 48 mm).

1969. Air. Birth Bicentenary of Napoleon Bonaparte. As T **114b** of Mauritania. Multicoloured.
474 40 f. "Napoleon in Coronation Robes" (Gerard) (vert) . . . 14·00 8·50

78 Douglas DC-4 over Outrigger Canoe

1969. Air. 20th Anniv of Regular Noumea-Paris Air Service.
475 **78** 50 f. green, brown & blue . . 4·75 2·75

79 I.L.O. Building Geneva

1969. 50th Anniv of I.L.O.
476 **79** 12 f. brown, violet & salmon 1·40 80

80 "French Wings around the World"

1970. Air. 10th Anniv of French "Around the World" Air Service.
477 **80** 200 f. brown, blue & violet . 15·00 8·50

81 New U.P.U. Building, Berne

1970. Inauguration of New U.P.U. Headquarters Building, Berne.
478 **81** 12 f. red, grey and brown . . 1·40 80

82 Packet Steamer "Natal", 1883

1970. Stamp Day.
479 **82** 9 f. black, green and blue . . 2·00 1·00

83 Cyclists on Map

1970. Air. 4th "Tour de Nouvelle Caledonie" Cycle Race.
480 **83** 40 f. brown, blue & lt bl . . 5·25 2·50

84 Mt. Fuji and Japanese "Hikari" Express Train

1970. Air. "EXPO 70" World Fair, Osaka, Japan. Multicoloured.
481 20 f. Type **84** . . . . 5·00 2·50
482 45 f. "EXPO" emblem, map and Buddha . . . . 5·25 2·50

85 Racing Yachts

1971. Air. One Ton Cup Yacht Race Auckland, New Zealand.
483 **85** 20 f. green, red and black . . 3·25 1·25

86 Steam Mail Train, Dumbea

1971. Stamp Day.
484 **86** 10 f. black, green and red . . 4·25 3·75

87 Ocean Racing Yachts

1971. 3rd Whangarei–Noumea Ocean Yacht Race.
485 **87** 16 f. turquoise, green and blue 4·00 2·25

88 Lieut.-Col. Broche and Theatre Map

1971. 30th Anniv of French Pacific Battalion's Participation in Second World War Mediterranean Campaign.
486 **88** 60 f. multicoloured . . . . 5·75 3·25

89 Early Tape Machine

90 Weightlifting

1971. World Telecommunications Day.
487 **89** 19 f. orange, pur & red . . . 2·50 1·25

1971. 4th South Pacific Games, Papeete, French Polynesia.
488 **90** 11 f. brn & red (postage) . . 2·10 1·00
489 – 23 f. violet, red & blue . . . 3·00 1·50
490 – 25 f. green and red (air) . . 3·25 2·00
491 – 100 f. blue, green and red . . 7·25 4·00
DESIGNS—VERT: 23 f. Basketball. HORIZ: 48 × 27 mm: 25 f. Pole-vaulting; 100 f. Archery.

91 Port de Plaisance, Noumea

1971. Air.
492 **91** 200 f. multicoloured . . . . 14·50 7·50

92 De Gaulle as President of French Republic, 1970

93 Publicity Leaflet showing De Havilland Gipsy Moth "Golden Eagle"

1971. 1st Death Anniv of General De Gaulle.
493 **92** 34 f. black and purple . . . 6·75 3·50
494 – 100 f. black and purple . . . 13·00 7·75
DESIGN: 100 f. De Gaulle in uniform, 1940.

1971. Air. 40th Anniv of 1st New Caledonia to Australia Flight.
495 **93** 90 f. brown, blue & orge . . 7·50 4·00

94 Downhill Skiing

1972. Air. Winter Olympic Games, Sapporo, Japan.
496 **94** 50 f. green, red & blue . . . 5·00 2·50

95 St. Mark's Basilica, Venice

1972. Air. U.N.E.S.C.O. "Save Venice" Campaign.
497 **95** 20 f. brown, grn and blue . . 3·50 1·40

96 Commission Headquarters, Noumea

1972. Air. 25th Anniv of South Pacific Commission.
498 **96** 18 f. multicoloured . . . . 1·50 1·00

97 Couzinet 33 "Le Biarritz" and Noumea Monument

1972. Air. 40th Anniv of 1st Paris–Noumea Flight.
499 **97** 110 f. black, purple & grn . 10·50 6·75

98 Pacific Island Dwelling

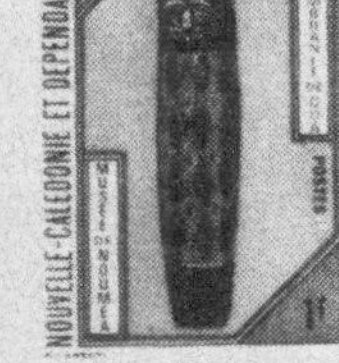

99 Goa Door-post

1972. Air. South Pacific Arts Festival, Fiji.
500 **98** 24 f. brown, blue & orange . 2·75 1·50

1972. Exhibits from Noumea Museum.
501 **99** 1 f. red, grn & grey (post) . . 75 30
502 – 2 f. black, grn & dull grn . . 1·00 60
503 – 5 f. multicoloured . . . . 1·25 80
504 – 12 f. multicoloured . . . . 3·50 1·25
505 – 16 f. multicoloured (air) . . 2·10 1·00
506 – 40 f. multicoloured . . . . 3·25 2·00
DESIGNS: 2 f. Carved wooden pillow; 5 f. Monstrance; 12 f. Tchamba mask; 16 f. Ornamental arrowheads; 40 f. Portico, chief's house.

100 Hurdling over "H" of "MUNICH"

1972. Air. Olympic Games, Munich.
507 **100** 72 f. violet, purple & blue . 6·50 3·50

101 New Head Post Office Building, Noumea

1972. Air.
508 **101** 23 f. brown, blue & green . 2·25 1·00

102 J.C.I. Emblem

1972. 10th Anniv of New Caledonia Junior Chamber of Commerce.
509 **102** 12 f. multicoloured . . . . 1·50 80

103 Forest Scene

1973. Air. Landscapes of the East Coast. Multicoloured.
510 11 f. Type **103** . . . . . . 1·50 80
511 18 f. Beach and palms (vert) . . 2·50 1·25
512 21 f. Waterfall and inlet (vert) . 3·00 1·40
See also Nos. 534/6.

104 Moliere and Characters

1973. Air. 300th Death Anniv of Moliere (playwright).
513 **104** 50 f. multicoloured . . . . 5·75 2·50

105 Tchamba Mask

1973.
514 **105** 12 f. purple (postage) . . . 5·75 2·00
515 – 23 f. blue (air) . . . . . . 9·00 4·00
DESIGN: 23 f. Concorde in flight.

106 Liner "El Kantara" in Panama Canal

1973. 50th Anniv of Marseilles–Noumea Shipping Service via Panama Canal.
516 **106** 60 f. black, brown & green 6·25 3·00

107 Globe and Allegory of Weather

1973. Air. Centenary of World Meteorological Organization.
517 **107** 80 f. multicoloured . . . . 5·75 2·75

108 DC-10 in Flight

1973. Air. Inauguration of Noumea–Paris DC-10 Air Service.
518 **108** 100 f. green, brown & blue . 6·50 3·50

109 Common Egg Cowrie

1973. Marine Fauna from Noumea Aquarium. Multicoloured.
519 8 f. Black-wedged butterflyfish (daylight) . . . . 1·75 80
520 14 f. Black-wedged butterflyfish (nocturnal) . . . . 2·50 1·40
521 3 f. Type **109** (air) 80 35
522 32 f. Orange-spotted surgeonfish (adult and young) . . . . 5·50 2·25
523 32 f. Green-lined paper bubble ("Hydatina") . . . . 3·50 1·60
524 37 f. Pacific partridge tun ("Dolium perdix") . . . . . 3·50 1·60

111 Office Emblem

1973. 10th Anniv of Central Schools Co-operation Office.
532 **111** 20 f. blue, yellow & green . 1·60 90

112 New Caledonia Mail-coach, 1880

1973. Air. Stamp Day.
533 **112** 15 f. multicoloured . . . . 2·10 1·10

1974. Air. Landscapes of the West Coast. As T **103**. Multicoloured.
534 8 f. Beach and palms (vert) . . 1·00 65
535 22 f. Trees and mountain . . . 2·00 1·40
536 26 f. Trees growing in sea . . . 2·75 1·50

113 Centre Building

1974. Air. Opening of Scientific Studies Centre, Anse-Vata, Noumea.
537 **113** 50 f. multicoloured . . . . 2·50 1·40

114 "Bird" embracing Flora

1974. Nature Conservation.
538 **114** 7 f. multicoloured 95 45

115 18th-century French Sailor

1974. Air. Discovery and Reconnaissance of New Caledonia and Loyalty Islands.
539 – 20 f. violet, red and blue . . 2·00 80
540 – 25 f. green, brown & red . . 2·10 1·00
541 **115** 28 f. brown, blue & grn . . 3·00 1·00
542 – 30 f. blue, brown & red . . 4·00 1·40
543 – 36 f. red, brown & blue . . 5·25 2·75
DESIGNS—HORIZ: 20 f. Captain Cook, H.M.S. "Endeavour" and map of Grand Terre island; 25 f. La Perouse, "L'Astrolabe" and map of Grand Terre island (reconnaissance of west coast); 30 f. Entrecasteaux, ship and map of Grand Terre island (reconnaissance of west coast); 36 f. Dumont d'Urville, "L'Astrolabe" and map of Loyalty Islands.

116 "Telecommunications"

1974. Air. Centenary of U.P.U.
544 **116** 95 f. orange, pur & grey . . 5·25 2·50

117 "Art"

1974. Air. "Arphila 75" International Stamp Exhibition, Paris (1975) (1st issue).
545 **117** 80 f. multicoloured . . . . 3·50 2·10
See also No. 554.

118 Hotel Chateau-Royal

1974. Air. Inauguration of Hotel Chateau Royal, Noumea.
546 **118** 22 f. multicoloured . . . . 1·40 80

118a Animal Skull, Burnt Tree and Flaming Landscape

1975. "Stop Bush Fires".
547 **118a** 20 f. multicoloured . . . 1·40 65

119 "Cricket"

1975. Air. Tourism. Multicoloured.
548 3 f. Type **119** 80 45
549 25 f. "Bougna" ceremony . . . 1·75 80
550 31 f. "Pilou" native dance . . . 2·50 1·00

120 "Calanthe veratrifolia" 121 Global "Flower"

1975. New Caledonian Orchids. Multicoloured.
551 8 f. Type **120** (postage) . . . 1·50 55
552 11 f. "Lyperanthus gigas" . . . 2·10 65
553 42 f. "Eriaxis rigida" (air) . . . 5·25 2·25

1975. Air. "Arphila 75" International Stamp Exhibition, Paris (2nd issue).
554 **121** 105 f. purple, green & bl . . 5·50 2·75

122 Throwing the Discus

1975. Air. 5th South Pacific Games, Guam.
555 24 f. Type **122** . . . . 2·10 1·00
556 50 f. Volleyball . . . . 3·00 2·00

123 Festival Emblem 124 Birds in Flight

1975. "Melanesia 2000" Festival, Noumea.
557 **123** 12 f. multicoloured 80 45

1975. 10th Anniv of Noumea Ornithological Society.
558 **124** 5 f. multicoloured 90 40

125 Pres. Pompidou 127 Brown Booby

126 Concordes

1975. Pompidou Commemoration.
559 **125** 26 f. grey and green . . . 2·00 1·25

1976. Air. First Commercial Flight of Concorde.
560 **126** 147 f. blue and red . . . . 10·00 6·50

1976. Ocean Birds. Multicoloured.
561 1 f. Type **127** 85 40
562 2 f. Blue-faced booby . . . . 1·25 40
563 8 f. Red-footed booby (vert) . . 3·00 1·00

128 Festival Emblem

1976. South Pacific Festival of Arts, Rotorua, New Zealand.
564 **128** 27 f. multicoloured . . . . 1·50 1·00

129 Lion and Lions' Emblem 130 Early and Modern Telephones

1976. 15th Anniv of Lions Club, Noumea.
565 **129** 49 f. multicoloured . . . . 3·00 2·00

1976. Air. Telephone Centenary.
566 **130** 36 f. multicoloured . . . . 2·00 1·25

131 Capture of Penboscт

1976. Air. Bicent of American Revolution.
567 **131** 24 f. purple and brown . . 1·50 1·00

132 Bandstand

1976. "Aspects of Old Noumea". Multicoloured.
568 25 f. Type **132** . . . . 1·10 55
569 30 f. Monumental fountain (vert) 1·40 80

133 Athletes

1976. Air. Olympic Games, Montreal.
570 **133** 33 f. violet, red & purple . 1·75 1·00

134 "Chick" with Magnifier

1976. Air. "Philately in Schools", Stamp Exhibition, Noumea.
571 **134** 42 f. multicoloured . . . . 2·50 1·50

135 Dead Bird and Trees

1976. Nature Protection.
572 **135** 20 f. multicoloured . . . . 1·40 65

136 South Pacific Heads

1976. 16th South Pacific Commission Conference.
573 **136** 20 f. multicoloured . . . . 1·50 70

137 Old Town Hall, Noumea

1976. Air. Old and New Town Halls, Noumea. Mult.
574 75 f. Type **137** . . . . 4·25 2·50
575 125 f. New Town Hall . . . . 6·25 3·00

138 Water Carnival

1977. Air. Summer Festival, Noumea.
576 **138** 11 f. multicoloured 80 40

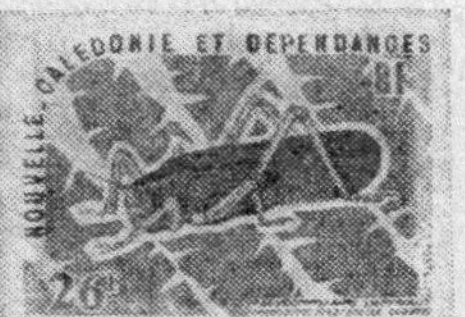

139 "Pseudophyllanax imperialis" (cricket)

1977. Insects.
577 **139** 26 f. emerald, green & brn 1·50 1·00
578 – 31 f. brown, sepia and grn 2·00 1·00
DESIGN: 31 f. "Agrianome fairmairei" (long-horn beetle).

140 Miniature Roadway

1977. Air. Road Safety.
579 **140** 50 f. multicoloured . . . . 2·50 1·50

141 Earth Station

1977. Earth Satellite Station, Noumea.
580 **141** 29 f. multicoloured . . . . 1·90 80

142 "Phajus daenikeri"

1977. Orchids. Multicoloured.
581 22 f. Type **142** . . . . 2·10 1·25
582 44 f. "Dendrobium finetianum" 3·00 1·75

143 Mask and Palms

1977. La Perouse School Philatelic Exn.
583 **143** 35 f. multicoloured . . . . 1·40 1·00

144 Trees

1977. Nature Protection.
584 **144** 20 f. multicoloured . . . . 1·00 65

145 Palm Tree and Emblem

1977. French Junior Chambers of Commerce Congress.
585 **145** 200 f. multicoloured . . . 7·75 5·00

146 Young Bird

1977. Great Frigate Birds. Multicoloured.
586 16 f. Type **146** (postage) . . . 1·60 90
587 42 f. Adult male bird (horiz) (air) 4·00 1·75

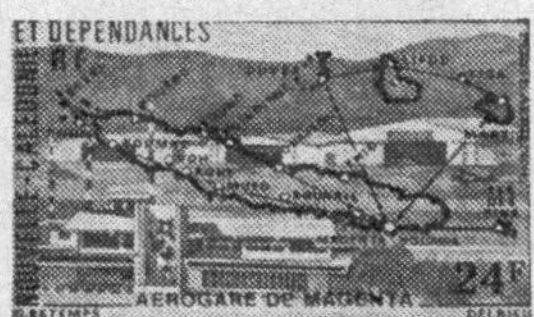

147 Magenta Airport and Map of Internal Air Network

1977. Air. Airports. Multicoloured.
588 24 f. Type **147** . . . . 1·00 90
589 57 f. La Tontout International Airport, Noumea . . . . . 2·50 1·25

1977. Air. 1st Commercial Flight of Concorde, Paris–New York. Optd **22.11.77 PARIS NEW-YORK**.
590 **126** 147 f. blue and red . . . . 11·50 9·00

149 Horse and Foal

1977. 10th Anniv of S.E.C.C. (Horse-breeding Society).
591 **149** 5 f. brown, green and blue 80 40

150 "Moselle Bay" (H. Didonna)

1977. Air. Views of Old Noumea (1st series).
592 **150** 41 f. multicoloured . . . . 2·50 1·50
593 – 42 f. purple and brown . . 2·50 1·50
DESIGN—49 × 27 mm: 42 f. "Settlers Valley" (J. Kreber).

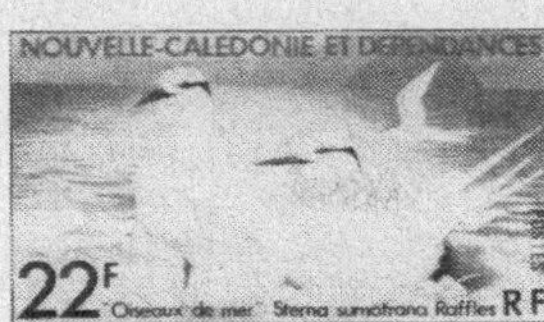

151 Black-naped Tern

1978. Ocean Birds. Multicoloured.
594 22 f. Type **151** . . . . 1·50 80
595 40 f. Sooty tern . . . . 3·00 1·50

152 "Araucaria montana"

153 "Halityle regularis"

1978. Flora. Multicoloured.
596 16 f. Type **152** (postage) . . . 85 45
597 42 f. "Amyema scandens" (horiz) (air) . . . . 3·00 1·50

1978. Noumea Aquarium.
598 **153** 10 f. multicoloured 65 30

154 Turtle

1978. Protection of the Turtle.
599 **154** 30 f. multicoloured . . . . 1·90 80

155 New Caledonian Flying Fox

1978. Nature Protection.
600 **155** 20 f. multicoloured . . . . 1·40 65

156 "Underwater Carnival"

1978. Air. Aubusson Tapestry.
601 **156** 105 f. multicoloured . . . 4·25 2·75

157 Pastor Maurice Leenhardt

1978. Birth Centenary of Pastor Maurice Leenhardt.
602 **157** 37 f. sepia, green & orge . . 1·50 1·10

158 Hare chasing "Stamp" Tortoise

1978. School Philately (1st series).
603 **158** 35 f. multicoloured . . . . 2·50 1·40

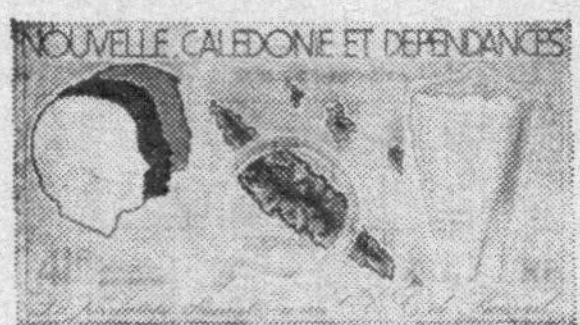

159 Heads, Map, Magnifying Glass and Cone Shell

1978. Air. Thematic Philately at Bourail.
604 **159** 41 f. multicoloured . . . . 2·10 1·10

160 Candles

161 Footballer and League Badge

1978. 3rd New Caledonian Old People's Day.
605 **160** 36 f. multicoloured . . . . 1·25 80

1978. 50th Anniv of New Caledonian Football League.
606 **161** 26 f. multicoloured . . . . 1·25 65

162 "Fauberg Blanchot" (after Lacouture)

1978. Air. Views of Old Noumea.
607 **162** 24 f. multicoloured . . . . 1·25 65

163 Map of Lifou, Solar Energy Panel and Transmitter Mast

1978. Telecommunications through Solar Energy.
608 **163** 33 f. multicoloured . . . . 1·40 80

164 Petroglyph, Mere Region

165 Ouvea Island and Outrigger Canoe

1979. Archaeological Sites.
609 **164** 10 f. red . . . . 1·00 45

1979. Islands. Multicoloured.
610 11 f. Type **165** 60 40
611 31 f. Mare Island and ornaments (horiz) 85 60
See also Nos. 629 and 649.

166 Satellite Orbit of Earth

167 19th-century Barque and Modern Container Ship

1979. Air. 1st World Survey of Global Atmosphere.
612 **166** 53 f. multicoloured . . . . 1·90 1·00

1979. Air. Centenary of Chamber of Commerce and Industry.
613 **167** 49 f. mauve, blue & brown 1·50 80

168 Child's Drawing

1979. Air. International Year of the Child.
614 **168** 35 f. multicoloured . . . . 1·40 80

169 House at Artillery Point

1979. Views of Old Noumea.
615 **169** 20 f. multicoloured 85 55

170 Skipjack Tuna

1979. Air. Sea Fishes (1st series). Multicoloured.
616 29 f. Type **170** . . . . 1·40 85
617 30 f. Black marlin . . . . . . 1·40 85
See also Nos. 632/3 and 647/8.

171 L. Tardy de Montravel (founder) and View of Port-de-France (Noumea)

1979. Air. 125th Anniv of Noumea.
618 **171** 75 f. multicoloured . . . . 3·00 2·00

172 The Eel Queen (Kanaka legend) **173** Auguste Escoffier

1979. Air. Nature Protection.
619 **172** 42 f. multicoloured . . . . 2·00 1·40

1979. Auguste Escoffier Hotel School.
620 **173** 24 f. brown, green and turquoise 85 55

174 Games Emblem and Catamarans

1979. 6th South Pacific Games, Fiji.
621 **174** 16 f. multicoloured 85 45

175 Children of Different Races, Map and Postmark

1979. Air. Youth Philately.
622 **175** 27 f. multicoloured 90 55

176 Aerial View of Centre

1979. Air. Overseas Scientific and Technical Research Office (O.R.S.T.O.M.) Centre, Noumea.
623 **176** 25 f. multicoloured 90 55

177 "Agathis ovata"

1979. Trees. Multicoloured.
624 5 f. Type **177** 75 20
625 34 f. "Cyathea intermedia" . . 1·50 65

178 Rodeo Riding

1979. Pouembout Rodeo.
626 **178** 12 f. multicoloured 80 40

179 Hill, 1860 10 c. Stamp and Post Office

1979. Air. Death Centenary of Sir Rowland Hill.
627 **179** 150 f. black, brn & orge . . 4·50 2·50

180 "Bantamia merleti"

1980. Noumea Aquarium. Fluorescent Corals (1st issue).
628 **180** 23 f. multicoloured 90 45
See also No. 646.

1980. Islands. As T **165**. Multicoloured.
629 23 f. Map of Ile des Pins and ornaments (horiz) 80 40

181 Outrigger Canoe

1980. Air.
630 **181** 45 f. blue, turq & indigo . . 1·40 1·00

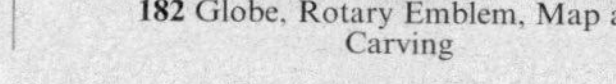
182 Globe, Rotary Emblem, Map and Carving

1980. Air. 75th Anniv of Rotary International.
631 **182** 100 f. multicoloured . . . 3·25 1·75

1980. Air. Sea Fishes (2nd series). As T **170**. Multicoloured.
632 34 f. Angler holding dolphin (fish) . . . . 1·25 80
633 39 f. Fishermen with sailfish (vert) . . . . 1·50 1·10

183 "Hibbertia virotii" **184** High Jumper, Magnifying Glass, Albums and Plimsoll

1980. Flowers. Multicoloured.
634 11 f. Type **183** . . . . 1·00 40
635 12 f. "Grevillea meisneri" . . . 1·00 40

1980. School Philately.
636 **184** 30 f. multicoloured 80 50

185 Scintex Super Emeraude Airplane and Map

1980. Air. Coral Sea Air Rally.
637 **185** 31 f. blue, green and brn . 1·25 80

186 Sailing Canoe

1980. Air. South Pacific Arts Festival, Port Moresby.
638 **186** 27 f. multicoloured . . . . 1·10 65

187 Road Signs as Road-users

1980. Road Safety.
639 **187** 15 f. multicoloured 60 25

188 "Parribacus caledonicus"

1980. Noumea Aquarium. Marine Animals (1st series). Multicoloured.
640 5 f. Type **188** 30 20
641 8 f. "Panulirus versicolor" . . 40 20
See also Nos. 668/9.

189 Kiwanis Emblem

1980. Air. 10th Anniv of Noumea Kiwanis Club.
642 **189** 50 f. multicoloured . . . . 1·50 1·00

190 Sun, Tree and Solar Panel

1980. Nature Protection. Solar Energy.
643 **190** 23 f. multicoloured 90 55

191 Old House, Poulou

1980. Air. Views of Old Noumea (4th series).
644 **191** 33 f. multicoloured . . . . 1·25 65

192 Charles de Gaulle **193** Manta Ray

1980. Air. 10th Death Anniv of Charles de Gaulle (French statesman).
645 **192** 120 f. green, olive & blue . 5·25 3·25

1981. Air. Noumea Aquarium. Fluorescent Corals (2nd series). As T **180**. Multicoloured.
646 60 f. "Trachyphyllia geoffroyi" 2·10 90

1981. Sea Fishes (3rd series). Multicoloured.
647 23 f. Type **193** . . . . 1·50 60
648 25 f. Grey reef shark . . . . . 1·50 65

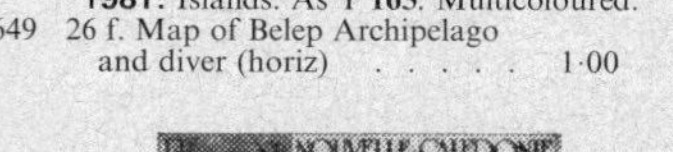
1981. Islands. As T **165**. Multicoloured.
649 26 f. Map of Belep Archipelago and diver (horiz) . . . . . 1·00 45

194 "Xeronema moorei"

1981. Air. Flowers. Multicoloured.
650 38 f. Type **194** . . . . 1·25 90
651 51 f. "Geissois pruinosa" . . . 1·25 1·10

195 Yury Gagarin and "Vostok 1"

1981. Air. 20th Anniv of First Men in Space. Multicoloured.
652 64 f. Type **195** . . . . 1·50 1·25
653 155 f. Alan Shepard and "Freedom 7" . . . . 4·00 2·50

196 Liberation Cross, "Zealandia" (troopship) and Badge

1981. Air. 40th Anniv of Departure of Pacific Battalion for Middle East.
655 **196** 29 f. multicoloured . . . . 2·50 1·60

197 Rossini's Volute **198** Sail Corvette "Constantine"

1981. Shells. Multicoloured.
656 1 f. Type **197** 15 10
657 2 f. Clouded cone 50 20
658 13 f. Stolid cowrie (horiz) 95 60

1981. Ships (1st series).
659 **198** 10 f. blue, brown and red . 1·00 55
660 – 25 f. blue, brown and red . 1·50 1·00
DESIGN: 25 f. Paddle-gunboat "Le Phoque", 1853.
See also Nos. 680/1 and 725/6.

199 "Echinometra mathaei"

1981. Air. Water Plants. Multicoloured.
661 38 f. Type **199** 90 55
662 51 f. "Prionocidaris verticillata" 1·75 65

200 Broken-stemmed Rose and I.Y.D.P. Emblems

1981. International Year of Disabled Persons.
663 **200** 45 f. multicoloured . . . . 1·40 80

201 25 c. Surcharged Stamp of 1881
202 Latin Quarter

1981. Air. Stamp Day.
664 **201** 41 f. multicoloured . . . . 1·40 65

1981. Air. Views of Old Noumea.
665 **202** 43 f. multicoloured . . . . 1·40 65

203 Trees and Unicornfish
204 Victor Roffey and "Golden Eagle"

1981. Nature Protection.
666 **203** 28 f. blue, green & brown . 1·10 65

1981. Air. 50th Anniv of First New Caledonia–Australia Airmail Flight.
667 **204** 37 f. black, violet and blue 90 60

1982. Noumea Aquarium. Marine Animals (2nd series). As T **188**. Multicoloured.
668 13 f. "Calappa calappa" . . . 65 45
669 25 f. "Etisus splendidus" . . . 1·40 1·00

205 "La Rousette"

1982. Air. New Caledonian Aircraft (1st series).
670 **205** 38 f. brown, red and green 90 55
671 – 51 f. brown, orge & grn . . 1·40 65
DESIGN: 51 f. "Le Cagou".
See also Nos. 712/13.

HAVE YOU READ THE NOTES AT THE BEGINNING OF THIS CATALOGUE?
These often provide answers to the enquiries we receive.

206 Chalcantite, Ouegoa

1982. Rocks and Minerals (1st series). Multicoloured.
672 15 f. Type **206** 90 65
673 30 f. Anorthosite, Blue River . 1·75 65
See also Nos. 688/9.

207 De Verneilh, Deve and Munch (air crew), Couzinet 33 "Le Biarritz" and Route Map

1982. Air. 50th Anniv of First Flight from Paris to Noumea.
674 **207** 250 f. mauve, blue and black 5·75 3·00

208 Scout and Guide Badges and Map

1982. Air. 50th Anniv of New Caledonian Scout Movement.
675 **208** 40 f. multicoloured . . . . 1·00 65

209 "The Rat and the Octopus" (Canaque legend)

1982. "Philexfrance 82" International Stamp Exhibition, Paris.
676 **209** 150 f. blue, mauve and deep blue . . . . 3·00 2·25

210 Footballer, Mascot and Badge

1982. Air. World Cup Football Championship, Spain.
677 **210** 74 f. multicoloured . . . . 1·60 1·00

211 Savanna Trees at Niaoulis
212 Islanders, Map and Kagu

1982. Flora. Multicoloured.
678 20 f. Type **211** 80 45
679 29 f. "Melaleuca quinquenervia" (horiz) . . . . 1·00 55

1982. Ships (2nd series). As T **198**.
680 44 f. blue, purple and brown . . 1·50 65
681 59 f. blue, light brown and brown 2·10 1·10
DESIGNS: 44 f. Naval transport barque "Le Cher"; 59 f. Sloop "Kersaint", 1902.

1982. Air. Overseas Week.
682 **212** 100 f. brown, green & bl . 2·00 1·10

213 Ateou Tribal House
214 Grey's Fruit Dove

1982. Traditional Houses.
683 **213** 52 f. multicoloured . . . . 1·40 90

1982. Birds. Multicoloured.
684 32 f. Type **214** . . . . 1·60 70
685 35 f. Rainbow lory . . . . . . 1·60 70

215 Canoe

1982. Central Office of Education Co-operation office.
686 **215** 48 f. multicoloured . . . . 1·50 65

216 Bernheim and Library

1982. Bernheim Library, Noumea.
687 **216** 36 f. brown, purple and blk 90 50

1983. Air. Rocks and Minerals (2nd series). As T **206**. Multicoloured.
688 44 f. Paya gypsum (vert) . . . 1·50 80
689 59 f. Kone silica (vert) . . . . 2·25 1·25

217 "Dendrobium oppositifolium"

1983. Orchids. Multicoloured.
690 10 f. Type **217** 30 10
691 15 f. "Dendrobium munificum" 40 15
692 29 f. "Dendrobium fractiflexum" 1·25 35

218 W.C.Y. Emblem, Map of New Caledonia and Globe

1983. Air. World Communications Year.
693 **218** 170 f. multicoloured . . . 3·25 1·60

219 "Crinum asiaticum"

1983. Flowers. Multicoloured.
694 1 f. Type **219** 10 10
695 2 f. "Xanthostemon aurantiacum" 10 10
696 4 f. "Metrosideros demonstrans" (vert) 10 10

220 Wall Telephone and Noumea Post Office, 1890

1983. 25th Anniv of Post and Telecommunications Office. Multicoloured.
697 30 f. Type **220** 70 30
698 40 f. Telephone & Noumea Post Office, 1936 . . . . 80 30
699 50 f. Push-button telephone and Noumea Post Office, 1972 . . 1·25 40

221 "Laticaudata laticaudata"
224 Volleyball

223 Bangkok Temples

1983. Noumea Aquarium. Sea Snakes. Multicoloured.
701 31 f. Type **221** . . . . 1·10 40
702 33 f. "Laticauda colubrina" . . 1·25 75

1983. Air. New Caledonian Aircraft (2nd series). As T **205**. Each red, mauve & brown.
712 46 f. Mignet HM14 "Pou du Ciel" . . . . 1·00 65
713 61 f. Caudron C-600 "Aiglon" . 1·75 80

1983. Air. "Bangkok 1983" International Stamp Exhibition.
714 **223** 47 f. multicoloured . . . . 1·10 80

1983. 7th South Pacific Games, Western Samoa.
715 **224** 16 f. purple, blue and red . 65 40

225 Oueholle

1983. Air.
716 **225** 76 f. multicoloured . . . . 1·50 1·00

226 Desert and Water Drop showing Fertile Land
227 Barn Owl

1983. Water Resources.
717 **226** 56 f. multicoloured . . . . 1·40 90

1983. Birds of Prey. Multicoloured.
718 34 f. Type **227** . . . . 2·10 1·00
719 37 f. Osprey . . . . 2·40 1·25

228 "Young Man on Beach" (R. Mascart)
229 "Conus chenui"

1983. Air. Paintings. Multicoloured.
720 100 f. Type **228** . . . . 3·00 1·50
721 350 f. "Man with Guitar" (P. Nielly) . . . . 7·75 4·50

1984. Sea Shells (1st series). Multicoloured.

No.	Description	Mint	Used
722	5 f. Type **229**	30	10
723	15 f. Molucca cone	75	50
724	20 f. "Conus optimus"	1·00	65

See also Nos. 761/2 and 810/11.

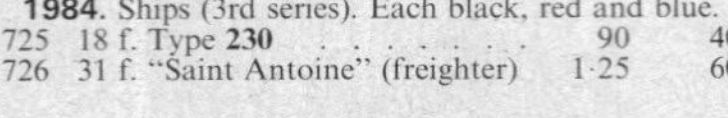

230 "St. Joseph" (freighter)

1984. Ships (3rd series). Each black, red and blue.

No.	Description	Mint	Used
725	18 f. Type **230**	90	40
726	31 f. "Saint Antoine" (freighter)	1·25	60

231 Yellow-tailed Anemonefish

1984. Air. Noumea Aquarium. Fishes. Multicoloured.

No.	Description	Mint	Used
727	46 f. Type **231**	1·40	75
728	61 f. Bicoloured angelfish	1·90	1·25

232 Arms of Noumea

233 "Araucaria columnaris"

1984.

No.	Type	Description	Mint	Used
729	**232**	35 f. multicoloured	80	45

1984. Air. Trees. Multicoloured.

No.	Description	Mint	Used
730	51 f. Type **233**	1·50	65
731	67 f. "Pritchardiopsis jeanneneyi"	2·10	80

234 Tourist Centres

1984. Nature Protection.

No.	Type	Description	Mint	Used
732	**234**	65 f. multicoloured	1·50	80

235 Swimming

1984. Air. Olympic Games, Los Angeles. Multicoloured.

No.	Description	Mint	Used
733	50 f. Type **235**	1·50	90
734	83 f. Windsurfing	2·75	1·50
735	200 f. Marathon	5·00	2·75

236 "Diplocaulobium ou-hinnae"

1984. Orchids. Multicoloured.

No.	Description	Mint	Used
736	16 f. Type **236**	65	40
737	38 f. "Acianthus atepalus"	1·25	1·00

237 Royal Exhibition Hall, Melbourne

1984. Air. "Ausipex 84" International Stamp Exhibition, Melbourne.

No.	Type	Description	Mint	Used
738	**237**	150 f. grn, brn & mve	3·50	1·60

238 School and Arrow Sign-post

239 Anchor, Rope and Stars

1984. Centenary of Public Education.

No.	Type	Description	Mint	Used
740	**238**	59 f. multicoloured	1·10	65

1984. Air. Armed Forces Day.

No.	Type	Description	Mint	Used
741	**239**	51 f. multicoloured	1·00	65

240 "Women looking for Crabs" (Mme. Bonnet de Larbogne)

1984. Air. Art. Multicoloured.

No.	Description	Mint	Used
742	120 f. Type **240**	3·00	1·50
743	300 f. "Cook discovering New Caledonia" (tapestry by Pilioko)	6·75	4·00

241 Kagu

1985.

No.	Type	Description	Mint	Used
744	**241**	1 f. blue	10	10
745		2 f. green	10	10
746		3 f. orange	10	10
747		4 f. green	15	15
748		5 f. mauve	15	15
749		35 f. red	80	45
750		38 f. red	80	60
751		40 f. red	90	35

For similar design but with "& DEPENDANCES" omitted, see Nos. 837/43.

1985. Sea Shells (2nd series). As T **229**. Multicoloured.

No.	Description	Mint	Used
761	55 f. Bubble cone	1·25	75
762	72 f. Lambert's cone	1·50	1·25

243 Weather Station transmitting Forecast to Boeing 737 and Trawler

1985. World Meteorology Day.

No.	Type	Description	Mint	Used
763	**243**	17 f. multicoloured	45	25

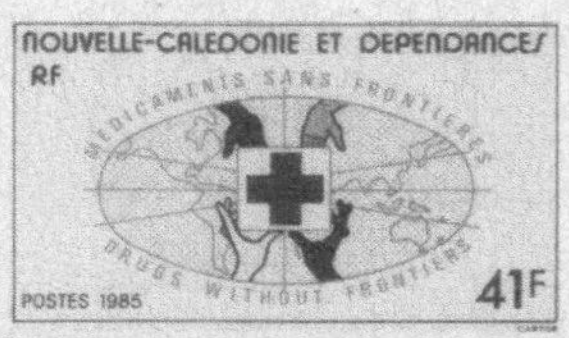

244 Map and Hands holding Red Cross

1985. International Medicines Campaign.

No.	Type	Description	Mint	Used
764	**244**	41 f. multicoloured	90	45

245 Electronic Telephone Exchange

1985. Inauguration of Electronic Telephone Equipment.

No.	Type	Description	Mint	Used
765	**245**	70 f. multicoloured	1·50	80

246 Marguerite la Foa Suspension Bridge

1985. Protection of Heritage.

No.	Type	Description	Mint	Used
766	**246**	44 f. brown, red and blue	1·00	55

247 Kagu with Magnifying Glass and Stamp

1985. "Le Cagou" Stamp Club.

No.	Type	Description	Mint	Used
767	**247**	220 f. multicoloured	4·50	3·00

248 Festival Emblem

1985. 4th Pacific Arts Festival, Papeete. Mult.

No.	Description	Mint	Used
769	55 f. Type **248**	1·25	80
770	75 f. Girl blowing trumpet triton	1·75	1·00

249 Flowers, Barbed Wire and Starving Child

1985. International Youth Year.

No.	Type	Description	Mint	Used
771	**249**	59 f. multicoloured	1·40	55

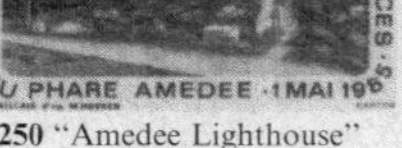

250 "Amedee Lighthouse" (M. Hosken)

251 Tree and Seedling

1985. Electrification of Amedee Lighthouse.

No.	Type	Description	Mint	Used
772	**250**	89 f. multicoloured	1·75	1·00

1985. "Planting for the Future".

No.	Type	Description	Mint	Used
773	**251**	100 f. multicoloured	2·00	1·00

252 De Havilland Dragon Rapide and Route Map

1985. Air. 30th Anniv of First Regular Internal Air Service.

No.	Type	Description	Mint	Used
774	**252**	80 f. multicoloured	1·50	1·00

253 Hands and U.N. Emblem

1985. 40th Anniv of U.N.O.

No.	Type	Description	Mint	Used
775	**253**	250 f. multicoloured	4·50	2·10

254 School, Map and "Nautilus"

1985. Air. Jules Garnier High School.

No.	Type	Description	Mint	Used
776	**254**	400 f. multicoloured	7·75	4·00

255 Purple Swamphen

1985. Birds. Multicoloured.

No.	Description	Mint	Used
777	50 f. Type **255**	1·40	70
778	60 f. Island thrush	1·60	90

256 Aircraft Tail Fins and Eiffel Tower

1986. Air. 30th Anniv of Scheduled Paris–Noumea Flights.

No.	Type	Description	Mint	Used
779	**256**	72 f. multicoloured	1·75	90

257 Merlet Scorpionfish

1986. Noumea Aquarium. Multicoloured.

No.	Description	Mint	Used
780	10 f. Emperor angelfish	50	30
781	17 f. Type **257**	75	40

258 Kanumera Bay, Isle of Pines

1986. Landscapes (1st series). Multicoloured.

No.	Description	Mint	Used
782	50 f. Type **258**	1·00	55
783	55 f. Inland village	1·10	55

See also Nos. 795/6 and 864/5.

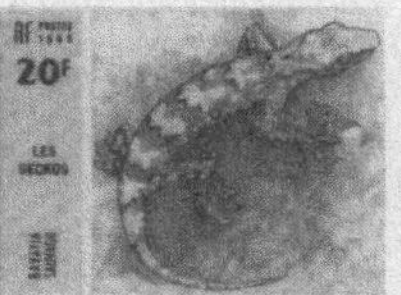

259 "Bavayia sauvagii"

1986. Geckos. Multicoloured.

No.	Description	Mint	Used
784	20 f. Type **259**	55	25
785	45 f. "Rhacodactylus leachianus"	1·00	65

260 Players and Azteca Stadium

1986. World Cup Football Championship, Mexico.
786 **260** 60 f. multicoloured . . . . 1·10 90

261 Vivarium, Nou Island

1986. Air. Protection of Heritage.
787 **261** 230 f. deep brown, blue and brown . . . . 4·50 2·75

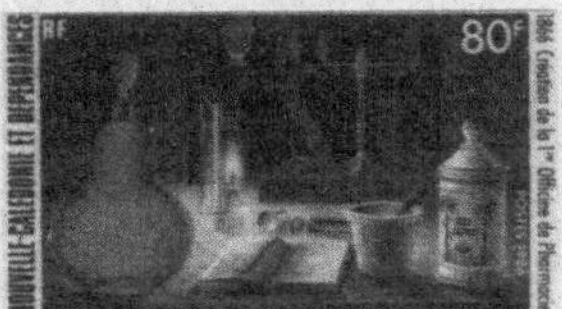

262 Pharmaceutical Equipment

1986. 120th Anniv of First Pharmacy.
788 **262** 80 f. multicoloured . . . . 1·50 1·10

263 "Coelogynae licastioides"

1986. Orchids. Multicoloured.
789 44 f. Type **263** . . . . 1·00 55
790 58 f. "Calanthe langei" . . . . 1·25 80

264 Black-backed Magpie

1986. "Stampex 86" National Stamp Exhibition, Adelaide.
791 **264** 110 f. multicoloured . . . 3·25 2·25

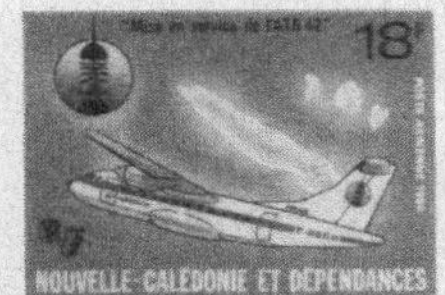

265 Airplane over New Caledonia

1986. Air. Inaugural Flight of "ATR 42".
792 **265** 18 f. multicoloured 35 25

266 Emblem and 1860 Stamp

267 Arms of Mont Dore

1986. Air. "Stockholmia 86" International Stamp Exhibition.
793 **266** 108 f. black, red and lilac . 2·25 1·50

1986.
794 **267** 94 f. multicoloured . . . . 1·75 1·10

1986. Landscapes (2nd series). As T **258**. Multicoloured.
795 40 f. West coast (vert) 80 40
796 76 f. South . . . . 1·50 90

268 Wild Flowers

269 Club Banner

1986. Association for Nature Protection.
797 **268** 73 f. multicoloured . . . . 1·50 90

1986. 25th Anniv of Noumea Lions Club.
798 **269** 350 f. multicoloured . . . 6·25 4·25

270 "Moret Bridge" (Alfred Sisley)

1986. Paintings. Multicoloured.
799 74 f. Type **270** . . . . 1·75 1·25
800 140 f. "Hunting Butterflies" (Berthe Morisot) . . . . . . 3·00 1·75

271 Emblem and Sound Waves

272 "Challenge France"

1987. Air. 25th Anniv of New Caledonia Amateur Radio Association.
801 **271** 64 f. multicoloured . . . . 1·25 80

1987. America's Cup Yacht Race. Multicoloured.
802 30 f. Type **272** . . . . 1·25 55
803 70 f. "French Kiss" . . . . . 1·75 1·00

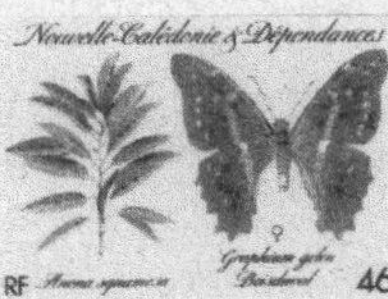

273 "Anona squamosa" and "Graphium gelon"

1987. Plants and Butterflies. Multicoloured.
804 46 f. Type **273** . . . . 1·40 65
805 54 f. "Abizzia granulosa" and "Polyura gamma" . . . . . 1·50 80

274 Peaceful Landscape, Earphones and Noisy Equipment

1987. Air. Nature Protection. Campaign against Noise.
806 **274** 150 f. multicoloured . . . 3·00 1·50

275 Isle of Pines Canoe

1987. Canoes. Each brown, green and blue.
807 72 f. Type **275** . . . . 1·40 90
808 90 f. Ouvea canoe . . . . . . 1·75 1·10

276 Town Hall

1987. New Town Hall, Mont Dore.
809 **276** 92 f. multicoloured . . . . 1·75 1·10

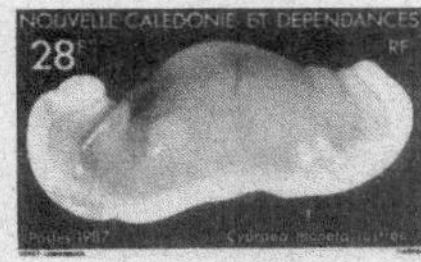

277 Money Cowrie

1987. Sea Shells (3rd series). Multicoloured.
810 28 f. Type **277** 55 45
811 36 f. Martin's cone . . . . . . 1·10 55

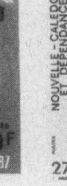

278 Games Emblem

279 Emblem

1987. 8th South Pacific Games. Noumea (1st issue).
812 **278** 40 f. multicoloured 80 55
See also Nos. 819/21.

1987. 13th Soroptimists International Convention, Melbourne.
813 **279** 270 f. multicoloured . . . 5·25 2·75

280 New Caledonia White Eye

1987. Birds. Multicoloured.
814 18 f. Type **280** 75 40
815 21 f. Peregrine falcon (vert) . . 75 45

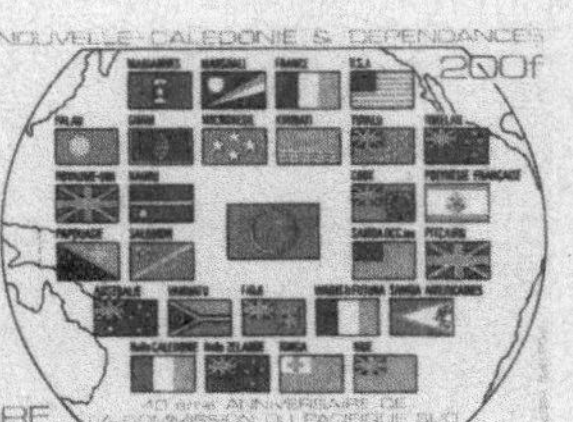

281 Flags on Globe

1987. 40th Anniv of South Pacific Commission.
816 **281** 200 f. multicoloured . . . 3·75 2·25

282 Globe and Magnifying Glass on Map of New Caledonia

1987. Schools Philately.
817 **282** 15 f. multicoloured 35 20

283 Cricketers

1987. Air. French Cricket Federation.
818 **283** 94 f. multicoloured . . . . 1·90 1·25

284 Golf

1987. 8th South Pacific Games, Noumea (2nd issue). Multicoloured.
819 20 f. Type **284** 40 20
820 30 f. Rugby football 95 35
821 100 f. Long jumping . . . . . 2·40 1·10

285 Arms of Dumbea

287 University

286 Route Map, "L'Astrolabe", "La Boussole" and La Perouse

1988. Air.
822 **285** 76 f. multicoloured . . . . 1·40 90

1988. Bicentenary of Disappearance of La Perouse's Expedition.
823 **286** 36 f. blue, brown & red . . 1·00 55

1988. French University of South Pacific, Noumea and Papeete.
824 **287** 400 f. multicoloured . . . 7·25 4·50

288 Semicircle Angelfish

289 Mwaringou House, Canala

1988. Noumea Aquarium. Fishes. Multicoloured.
825 30 f. Type **288** 65 40
826 46 f. Sapphire sergeant major . 1·25 85

1988. Traditional Huts. Each brown, green and blue.
827 19 f. Type **289** 35 20
828 21 f. Nathalo house, Lifou (horiz) 95 20

290 Anniversary Emblem

1988. 125th Anniv of International Red Cross.
829 **290** 300 f. blue, green and red . 6·00 3·25

291 "Ochrosia elliptica"

1988. Medicinal Plants. Multicoloured.
830 28 f. Type **291** (postage) . . . 60 40
831 64 f. "Rauvolfia sevenetii" (air) 1·50 80

292 "Gymnocrinus richeri"

1988.

832 **292** 51 f. multicoloured . . . . 1·50 65

293 Furnished Room and Building Exterior

1988. Bourail Museum and Historical Association.

833 **293** 120 f. multicoloured . . . 2·25 1·50

294 La Perouse sighting Phillip's Fleet in Botany Bay

1988. "Sydpex 88" Stamp Exhibition, Sydney. Multicoloured.

834 42 f. Type **294** . . . . 1·10 85
835 42 f. Phillip sighting "La Boussole" and "L'Astrolabe" 1·10 85

295 Kagu

297 Laboratory Assistant, Noumea Institute and Pasteur

296 Table Tennis

1988.

837 **295** 1 f. blue 35 10
838 2 f. green 40 10
839 3 f. orange 50 10
840 4 f. green 50 10
841 5 f. mauve 70 10
842 28 f. orange 50 20
843 40 f. red 65 20

1988. Olympic Games, Seoul.

846 **296** 150 f. multicoloured . . . 3·00 1·90

1988. Centenary of Pasteur Institute, Paris.

847 **297** 100 f. red, black and blue . 1·90 1·25

298 Georges Baudoux

1988. Writers.

848 **298** 72 f. brown, green and purple (postage) . . . . . . 1·40 80
849 – 73 f. brown, bl & blk (air) 1·40 90
DESIGN: 73 f. Jean Mariotti.

299 Map and Emblems

1988. Air. Rotary International Anti-Polio Campaign.

850 **299** 220 f. multicoloured . . . 4·00 2·75

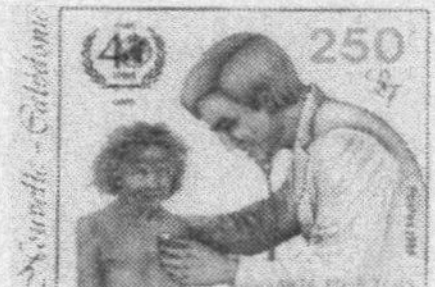

300 Doctor examining Child

1988. 40th Anniv of W.H.O.

851 **300** 250 f. multicoloured . . . 4·50 2·50

301 "Terre des Hommes" (L. Bunckley)

1988. Paintings. Multicoloured.

852 54 f. Type **301** . . . . 1·60 80
853 92 f. "Latin Quarter" (Marik) . 2·25 1·25

302 Arms of Koumac **303** "Parasitaxus ustus"

1989.

854 **302** 200 f. multicoloured . . . 3·50 2·25

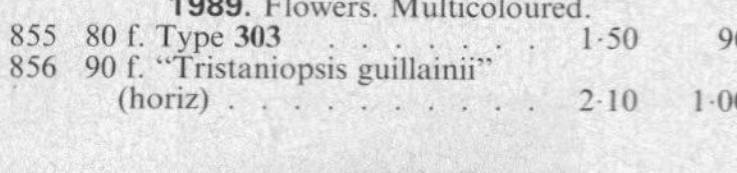

1989. Flowers. Multicoloured.

855 80 f. Type **303** . . . . 1·50 90
856 90 f. "Tristaniopsis guillainii" (horiz) . . . . 2·10 1·00

304 "Plesionika sp."

1989. Marine Life. Multicoloured.

857 18 f. Type **304** 45 20
858 66 f. Sail-backed scorpionfish . 1·50 1·00
859 110 f. Cristiate latiaxis . . . . 2·00 80

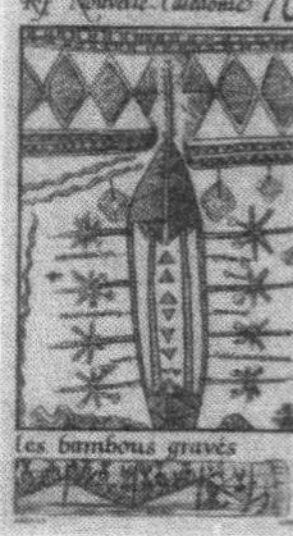

305 "Liberty" **306** Canoe and Diamond Decoration

1989. Bicentenary of French Revolution and "Philexfrance 89" International Stamp Exn, Paris. Multicoloured.

860 40 f. Type **305** (postage) . . . 80 45
861 58 f. "Equality" (air) . . . . . 1·10 65
862 76 f. "Fraternity" . . . . 1·40 90

1989. Landscapes (3rd series). As T **258**. Mult.

864 180 f. Ouaieme ferry (post) . . 3·50 1·75
865 64 f. "The Broody Hen" (rocky islet), Hienghene (air) . . . 1·25 65

1989. Bamboo Decorations by C. Ohlen. Each black, bistre and orange.

866 70 f. Type **306** (postage) . . . 1·40 80
867 44 f. Animal design (air) . . . 80 55

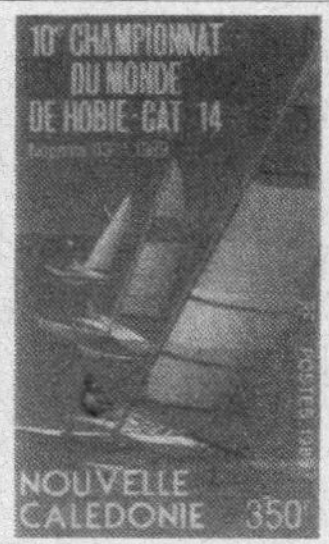

307 "Hobie Cat 14" Yachts

1989. 10th World "Hobie Cat" Class Catamaran Championship, Noumea.

868 **307** 350 f. multicoloured . . . 6·75 3·50

308 Book Title Pages and Society Members

1989. 20th Anniv of Historical Studies Society.

869 **308** 74 f. black and brown . . . 1·40 90

309 Fort Teremba

1989. Protection of Heritage.

870 **309** 100 f. green, brown & blue 2·10 1·10

310 "Rochefort's Escape" (Edouard Manet) **311** Fr. Patrick O'Reilly

1989. Paintings. Multicoloured.

871 130 f. Type **310** . . . . . . 2·50 1·75
872 270 f. "Self-portrait" (Gustave Courbet) . . . . 6·25 4·00

1990. Writers.

873 **311** 170 f. black and mauve . . 3·50 1·75

312 Grass and Female Butterfly

1990. "Cyperacea costularia" (grass) and "Paratisiphone lyrnessa" (butterfly). Multicoloured.

874 50 f. Type **312** (postage) . . . 90 55
875 18 f. Grass and female butterfly (different) (air) 35 20
876 94 f. Grass and male butterfly . 1·90 1·25

313 "Maize" Stem with Face **314** Exhibit

1990. Kanaka Money.

877 **313** 85 f. olive, orange & grn . . 1·60 80
878 – 140 f. orange, black & grn 2·75 1·40
DESIGN: 140 f. "Rope" stem with decorative end.

1990. Jade and Mother-of-pearl Exhibition.

879 **314** 230 f. multicoloured . . . 4·00 2·40

315 Ocellate Nudibranch

1990. Noumea Aquarium. Sea Slugs. Multicoloured.

880 10 f. Type **315** 25 10
881 42 f. "Chromodoris kuniei" (vert) . . . . 1·00 55

316 Head of "David" (Michelangelo) and Footballers

1990. World Cup Football Championship, Italy.

882 **316** 240 f. multicoloured . . . 4·50 2·75

317 De Gaulle

1990. Air. 50th Anniv of De Gaulle's Call to Resist.

883 **317** 160 f. multicoloured . . . 3·00 1·60

318 Neounda Site

1990. Petroglyphs.

884 **318** 40 f. brown, green and red (postage) . . . . 1·00 45
885 – 58 f. black, brown and blue (air) . . . . 1·25 65
DESIGN—HORIZ: 58 f. Kassducou site.

319 Map and Pacific International Meeting Centre

1990.

886 **319** 320 f. multicoloured . . . 5·75 2·75

320 New Zealand Cemetery, Bourail **321** Kagu

1990. Air. "New Zealand 1990" International Stamp Exhibition, Auckland. Multicoloured.

887 80 f. Type **320** . . . . 1·40 1·10
888 80 f. Brigadier William Walter Dove . . . . 1·40 1·10

1990.

890 **321** 1 f. blue 10 10
891 2 f. green 10 10
892 3 f. yellow 10 10
893 4 f. green 10 10
894 5 f. violet 10 10
895 9 f. grey 10 10
896 12 f. red 15 10
897 40 f. mauve 75 30
898 50 f. red . . . . 1·00 40
899 55 f. red . . . . 1·00 45

The 5 and 55 f. exist both perforated with ordinary gum and imperforate with self-adhesive gum.

For design with no value expressed see No. 994.

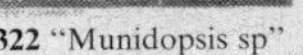

322 "Munidopsis sp" 324 "Gardenia aubryi"

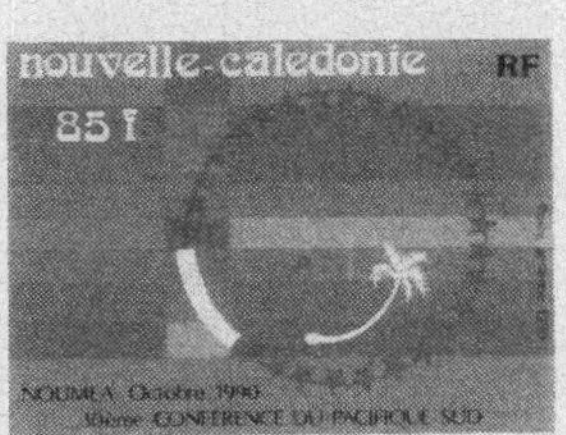

323 Emblem

1990. Air. Deep Sea Animals. Multicoloured.

900 30 f. Type **322** 55 35
901 60 f. "Lyreidius tridentatus" . . 1·40 1·00

1990. Air. 30th South Pacific Conference, Noumea.

902 **323** 85 f. multicoloured . . . . 1·40 90

1990. Flowers. Multicoloured.

903 105 f. Type **324** . . . . 2·10 1·10
904 130 f. "Hibbertia baudouinii" . 2·25 1·75

325 De Gaulle

1990. Air. Birth Centenary of Charles de Gaulle (French statesman).

905 **325** 410 f. blue . . . . 7·75 4·50

326 "Mont Dore, Mountain of Jade" (C. Degroiselle)

1990. Air. Pacific Painters. Multicoloured.

906 365 f. Type **326** (postage) . . . 6·75 3·50
907 110 f. "The Celieres House" (M. Petron) (air) . . . . 2·10 1·40

327 Fayawa-Ouvea Bay

1991. Air. Regional Landscapes. Multicoloured.

908 36 f. Type **327** 65 45
909 90 f. Coastline of Mare . . . . 1·60 1·25

328 Louise Michel and Classroom

1991. Writers.

910 **328** 125 f. mauve and blue . . 2·25 1·25
911 – 125 f. blue and brown . . . 2·25 1·25

DESIGN: No. 911, Charles B. Nething and photographer.

329 Houailou Hut 330 Northern Province

1991. Melanesian Huts. Multicoloured.

912 12 f. Type **329** 20 10
913 35 f. Hienghene hut 85 35

1991. Provinces. Multicoloured.

914 45 f. Type **330** 65 55
915 45 f. Islands Province 65 55
916 45 f. Southern Province 65 55

331 "Dendrobium biflorum"

1991. Orchids. Multicoloured.

917 55 f. Type **331** 90 55
918 70 f. "Dendrobium closterium" 1·60 1·00

332 Japanese Pineconefish

1991. Fishes. Multicoloured.

919 60 f. Type **332** . . . . 1·25 65
920 100 f. Japanese bigeye . . . . 2·00 1·25

333 Research Equipment and Sites

1991. French Scientific Research Institute for Development and Co-operation.

921 **333** 170 f. multicoloured . . . 3·50 1·90

334 Emblem 336 Emblems

335 Map and Dragon

1991. 9th South Pacific Games, Papua New Guinea.

922 **334** 170 f. multicoloured . . . 3·00 1·75

1991. Centenary of Vietnamese Settlement in New Caledonia.

923 **335** 300 f. multicoloured . . . 5·25 2·75

1991. 30th Anniv of Lions International in New Caledonia.

924 **336** 192 f. multicoloured . . . 3·50 2·50

337 Map, "Camden" (missionary brig), Capt. Robert Clark Morgan and Trees

1991. 150th Anniv of Discovery of Sandalwood.

925 **337** 200 f. blue, turquoise & grn 5·00 2·75

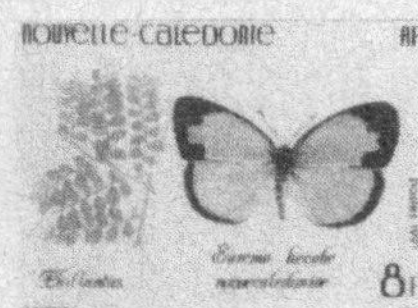

338 "Phillantus" and Common Grass Yellow

1991. "Phila Nippon '91" International Stamp Exhibition, Tokyo. Plants and Butterflies. Mult.

926 8 f. Type **338** 10 10
927 15 f. "Pipturus incanus" and "Hypolimnas octocula" . . . 20 10
928 20 f. "Stachytarpheta urticaefolia" and meadow argos 30 20
929 26 f. "Malaisia scandens" and "Cyrestis telamon" 65 45

339 Nickel Processing Plant and Dam

1991. 50th Anniv of Central Economic Co-operation Bank. Multicoloured.

931 76 f. Type **339** . . . . 1·25 75
932 76 f. Housing and hotels . . . 1·25 75

340 "Caledonian Cricket" (Marcel Moutouh)

1991. Air. Pacific Painters. Multicoloured.

933 130 f. Type **340** . . . . 2·50 2·00
934 435 f. "Saint Louis" (Janine Goetz) . . . . 8·25 4·50

341 Blue River (½ size illustration)

1992. Air. Blue River National Park.

935 **341** 400 f. multicoloured . . . 6·75 4·00

342 La Madeleine Falls

1992. Nature Protection.

937 **342** 15 f. multicoloured 20 15

343 Lapita Pot 345 "Pinta"

344 Barqueta Bridge

1992. Air. Noumea Museum.

939 **343** 25 f. black and orange . . 55 20

1992. Air. "Expo '92" World's Fair, Seville.

940 **344** 10 f. multicoloured 15 10

1992. Air. "World Columbian Stamp Expo '92", Chicago. Multicoloured.

941 80 f. Type **345** . . . . 1·40 1·00
942 80 f. "Santa Maria" . . . . . 1·40 1·00
943 80 f. "Nina" . . . . 1·40 1·00

346 Manchurian Crane and Kagu within "100"

1992. Centenary of Arrival of First Japanese Immigrants. Multicoloured, background colours given.

945 **346** 95 f. yellow . . . . 1·60 1·00
946 95 f. grey . . . . 1·60 1·00

347 Synchronised Swimming

1992. Olympic Games, Barcelona.

947 **347** 260 f. multicoloured . . . 4·50 3·00

348 Bell Airacobra, Grumman F4F Wildcat, Barrage Balloon, Harbour and Nissen Huts

1992. 50th Anniv of Arrival of American Forces in New Caledonia.

948 **348** 50 f. multicoloured . . . . 1·00 40

349 "Wahpa" (Paul Mascart)

1992. Air. Pacific Painters.

949 **349** 205 f. multicoloured . . . 3·50 2·25

350 Australian Cattle Dog

352 "Amalda fuscolingua"

351 Entrecasteaux and Fleet

1992. Air. Canine World Championships.
950 **350** 175 f. multicoloured . . . 3·50 2·25

1992. Air. Navigators. Bicentenary of Landing of Admiral Bruni d'Entrecasteaux on West Coast of New Caledonia.
951 **351** 110 f. orange, blue & grn . 3·00 1·50

1992. Air. Shells. Multicoloured.
952 30 f. Type **352** 80 35
953 50 f. "Cassis abbotti" . . . . 1·10 75

353 Deole

1992. Air. "La Brousse en Folie" (comic strip) by Bernard Berger. Multicoloured.
954 80 f. Type **353** . . . . 1·40 90
955 80 f. Tonton Marcel . . . . . . 1·40 90
956 80 f. Tathan . . . . 1·40 90
957 80 f. Joinville . . . . 1·40 90

354 Lagoon

1993. Lagoon Protection.
958 **354** 120 f. multicoloured . . . 2·10 1·25

355 Harbour (Gaston Roullet)

1993. Air. Pacific Painters.
959 **355** 150 f. multicoloured . . . 2·50 1·50

356 Symbols of New Caledonia

1993. School Philately. "Tourism my Friend".
960 **356** 25 f. multicoloured 30 20

357 Still and Plantation

1993. Air. Centenary of Production of Essence of Niaouli.
966 **357** 85 f. multicoloured . . . . 1·60 1·00

358 Planets and Copernicus

1993. Air. "Polska '93" International Stamp Exhibition, Poznan. 450th Death Anniv of Nicolas Copernicus (astronomer).
967 **358** 110 f. blue, turquoise & grey 2·25 1·25

359 Noumea Temple

1993. Air. Centenary of First Protestant Church in Noumea.
968 **359** 400 f. multicoloured . . . 6·75 4·25

1993. No. 898 surch **55F**.
969 **321** 55 f. on 50 f. red . . . . . 1·00 70

361 Malabou

1993. Air. Regional Landscapes.
970 **361** 85 f. multicoloured . . . . 1·40 1·00

362 Locomotive and Bridge

1993. Air. Centenary of Little Train of Thio.
971 **362** 115 f. red, green and lilac . 3·25 1·50

363 Rochefort

364 "Megastylis paradoxa"

1993. Air. 80th Death Anniv of Henri Rochefort (journalist).
972 **363** 100 f. multicoloured . . . 1·75 1·10

1993. Air. "Bangkok 1993" International Stamp Exhibition, Thailand. Multicoloured.
973 30 f. Type **364** 65 25
974 30 f. "Vanda coerulea" 65 25

365 Route Map and Boeing 737-300/500

1993. Air. 10th Anniv of Aircalin (national airline).
976 **365** 85 f. multicoloured . . . . 1·60 1·10

366 "Francois Arago" (cable laying ship)

1993. Air. Centenary of New Caledonia–Australia Telecommunications Cable.
977 **366** 200 f. purple, blue & turq . 3·50 2·25

367 "Oxypleurodon orbiculatus"

1993. Air. Deep-sea Life.
978 **367** 250 f. multicoloured . . . 4·00 2·50

368 Aircraft, Engine and Hangar

1993. Air. 25th Anniv of Chamber of Commerce and Industry's Management of La Tontouta Airport, Noumea.
979 **368** 90 f. multicoloured . . . . 1·60 1·00

369 First Christmas Mass, 1843 (stained glass window, Balade church)

1993. Air. Christmas.
980 **369** 120 f. multicoloured . . . 2·10 1·25

370 Bourail

1993. Town Arms. Multicoloured.
981 70 f. Type **370** . . . . 1·25 75
982 70 f. Noumea . . . . 1·25 75
983 70 f. Canala . . . . 1·25 75
984 70 f. Kone . . . . 1·25 75
985 70 f. Paita . . . . 2·75 1·10
986 70 f. Dumbea . . . . 1·25 75
987 70 f. Koumac . . . . 1·25 75
988 70 f. Ponerihouen . . . . . . 1·25 75
989 70 f. Kaamoo Hyehen . . . . 1·25 75
990 70 f. Mont Dore . . . . 2·50 1·10
991 70 f. Thio . . . . 1·25 75
992 70 f. Kaala-Gomen . . . . . . 1·25 75
993 70 f. Touho . . . . 1·25 75

1994. No value expressed.
994 **321** (60 f.) red 85 55

371 Dog, Exhibition Emblem and Chinese Horoscope Signs (New Year)

1994. Air. "Hong Kong '94" International Stamp Exhibition.
995 **371** 60 f. multicoloured . . . . 1·25 70

372 Airbus Industrie A340

1994. Air 1st Paris–Noumea Airbus Flight. Self-adhesive.
997 **372** 90 f. multicoloured . . . . 1·90 1·25

1994. "Philexjeunes '94" Youth Stamp Exhibition, Grenoble. No. 960 optd **PHILEXJEUNES'94 GRENOBLE 22–24 AVRIL**.
998 **356** 25 f. multicoloured 35 25

374 Photograph of Canala Post Office and Post Van

1994. 50th Anniv of Noumea–Canala Postal Service.
999 **374** 15 f. brown, green and blue . 20 15

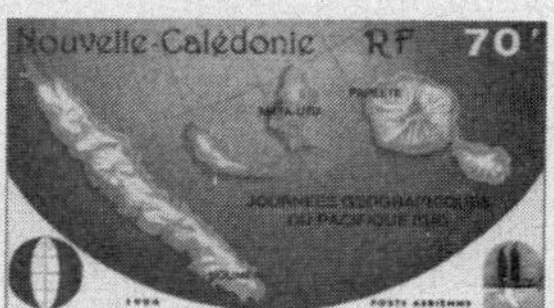

375 Pacific Islands on Globe

1994. Air. South Pacific Geographical Days.
1000 **375** 70 f. multicoloured . . . 1·25 85

376 Post Office, 1859

1994. Postal Administration Head Offices. Mult.
1001 30 f. Type **376** 40 25
1002 60 f. Posts and Telecommunications Office, 1936 . . 1·25 55
1003 90 f. Ministry of Posts and Telecommunications, 1967 . 1·60 1·25
1004 120 f. Ministry of Posts and Telecommunications, 1993 . 2·25 1·60

377 "The Mask Wearer"

1994. Pacific Sculpture.
1005 **377** 60 f. multicoloured . . . 1·25 55

378 "Legend of the Devil Fish" (Micheline Neporon)

1994. Air. Pacific Painters.
1006 **378** 120 f. multicoloured . . . 2·10 1·25

379 "Chambeyronia macrocarpa"

380 Podtanea Pot

1994.
1007 **379** 90 f. multicoloured . . . 1·60 1·00

1994. Air. Noumea Museum.
1008 **380** 95 f. multicoloured . . . 1·40 1·10

381 Trophy, U.S. Flag and Ball

1994. Air. World Cup Football Championship, U.S.A.
1009 **381** 105 f. multicoloured . . . 1·75 1·40

1994. No. D707 with "Timbre Taxe" obliterated by black bar.
1010 D **222** 5 f. multicoloured . . . 9·00 2·00

382 Timor Deer

1994. Bourail Fair.
1011 **382** 150 f. multicoloured . . . 2·50 1·40

383 Korean Family

1994. Air. "Philakorea 1994" International Stamp Exhibition, Seoul. (Int Year of the Family).
1012 **383** 60 f. multicoloured . . . 1·10 55

384 "L'Atalante" (oceanographic research vessel)

1994. Air. Evaluation Programme of Economic Zone.
1014 **384** 120 f. multicoloured . . . 2·10 1·50

385 "Nivose"

1994. Attachment of the "Nivose" (French surveillance frigate) to New Caledonia. Multicoloured.
1015 30 f. Type **385** 45 30
1016 30 f. Aircraft over frigate . . 45 30
1017 30 f. Frigate moored at quay . 45 30
1018 60 f. Frigate and map of New Caledonia on parchment . . 1·10 80
1019 60 f. Ship's bell . . . . . . 1·10 80
1020 60 f. Frigate and sailor . . . 1·10 80

386 Driving Cattle

1994. Air. 1st European Stamp Salon, Flower Gardens, Paris. Multicoloured.
1021 90 f. Aerial view of island . . 1·50 1·00
1022 90 f. Type **386** . . . . 1·50 1·00

387 Paper Darts around Girl

1994. School Philately.
1023 **387** 30 f. multicoloured . . . 45 30

388 Jaques Nervat

1994. Writers.
1024 **388** 175 f. multicoloured . . . 3·00 1·75

389 Satellite transmitting to Globe and Computer Terminal

1994. Air. 50th Anniv of Overseas Scientific and Technical Research Office.
1025 **389** 95 f. multicoloured . . . 2·10 1·25

390 Emblem and Temple

1994. Air. 125th Anniv of Freemasonary in New Caledonia.
1026 **390** 350 f. multicoloured . . . 6·25 3·00

391 Thiebaghi Mine

1994. Air.
1027 **391** 90 f. multicoloured . . . 1·60 1·00

392 Place des Cocotiers, Noumea

1994. Christmas.
1028 **392** 30 f. multicoloured . . . 45 30

No. 1028 covers any one of five stamps which were issued together in horizontal se-tenant strips, the position of the bell, tree and monument differing on each stamp. The strip is stated to produce a three-dimensional image without use of a special viewer.

393 Globe and Newspapers

1994. 50th Anniv of "Le Monde" (newspaper).
1029 **393** 90 f. multicoloured . . . 2·10 1·50

394 1988 100 f. Pasteur Institute Stamp

1995. Death Centenary of Louis Pasteur (chemist).
1030 **394** 120 f. multicoloured . . . 2·10 1·10

395 Pictorial Map

1995. Air. Tourism.
1031 **395** 90 f. multicoloured . . . 1·60 1·00

396 Profile of De Gaulle (Santucci) and Cross of Lorraine

1995. 25th Death Anniv of Charles de Gaulle (French President, 1959–69).
1032 **396** 1000 f. deep blue, blue and gold . . . . 17·00 14·00

397 Emblem

1995. Pacific University Teachers' Training Institute.
1033 **397** 100 f. multicoloured . . . 1·75 1·10

398 "Sylviornis neo-caledoniae"

1995.
1034 **398** 60 f. multicoloured . . . 1·25 55

399 Swimming, Cycling and Running

1995. Triathlon.
1035 **399** 60 f. multicoloured . . . 1·10 85

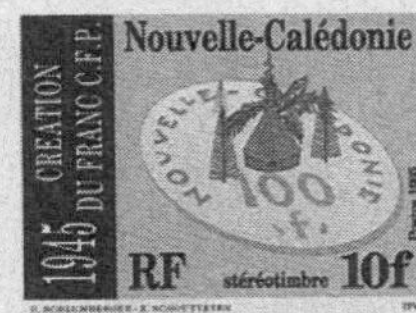

400 Tent and Trees

1995. 50th Anniv of Pacific Franc.
1036 **400** 10 f. multicoloured . . . 15 10

No. 1036 covers any one of four stamps which were issued together in horizontal se-tenant strips, the position of the central motif rotating slightly in a clockwise direction from the left to the right-hand stamp. The strip is stated to produce a three-dimensional image without use of a special viewer.

401 Bourbon Palace (Paris), Map of New Caledonia and Chamber

1995. 50th Anniversaries. Multicoloured.
1037 60 f. Type **401** (first representation of New Caledonia at French National Assembly) . . . . 1·10 55
1038 90 f. National emblems, De Gaulle and Allied flags (end of Second World War) . . 1·50 1·00
1039 90 f. U.N. Headquarters, New York (U.N.O.) . . . . . . 1·50 1·00

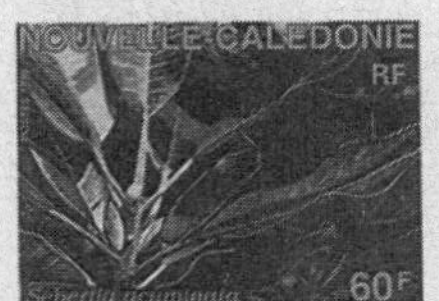

402 "Sebertia acuminata"

1995.
1040 **402** 60 f. multicoloured . . . 1·25 55

403 Common Noddy

1995. "Singapore'95" International Stamp Exhibition. Sea Birds. Multicoloured.
1041 5 f. Type **403** 10 10
1042 10 f. Silver gull 15 10
1043 20 f. Roseate tern 30 20
1044 35 f. Osprey 75 55
1045 65 f. Red-footed booby . . . 1·25 1·00
1046 125 f. Great frigate bird . . . 2·25 1·50

404 Golf

1995. 10th South Pacific Games.
1048 **404** 90 f. multicoloured . . . 1·50 1·10

405 "The Lizard Man" (Dick Bone)

1995. Pacific Sculpture.

1049 **405** 65 f. multicoloured . . . 95 60

406 Venue

1995. Air. 35th South Pacific Conference.

1050 **406** 500 f. multicoloured . . . 7·75 5·00

407 Silhouette of Francis Carco

1995. Writers.

1051 **407** 95 f. multicoloured . . . 1·50 1·10

408 Ouare

1995. Air. Kanak Dances. Multicoloured.

1052 95 f. Type **408** . . . . 1·25 75
1053 100 f. Pothe . . . . 1·40 85

409 Saw-headed Crocodilefish

1995. World of the Deep.

1054 **409** 100 f. multicoloured . . . 1·75 1·10

410 "Mekosuchus inexpectatus"

1996. Air.

1055 **410** 125 f. multicoloured . . . 2·10 1·40

411 Vessel with decorated Rim

1996. Noumea Museum.

1056 **411** 65 f. multicoloured . . . 1·10 80

412 "Captaincookia margaretae"

1996. Flowers. Multicoloured.

1057 65 f. Type **412** . . . . . . 1·00 55
1058 95 f. "Ixora cauliflora" . . . 1·50 1·00

413 Pirogue on Beach

1996. World Pirogue Championships, Noumea. Multicoloured.

1059 30 f. Type **413** 40 25
1060 65 f. Pirogue leaving shore . . 1·10 55
1061 95 f. Double-hulled pirogue . . 1·50 75
1062 125 f. Sports pirogue . . . . 2·10 1·25

Nos. 1059/62 were issued together, se-tenant, forming a composite design.

414 Red Batfish

1996. "China'96" International Stamp Exhibition, Peking. Deep Sea Life. Multicoloured.

1063 25 f. Type **414** 50 25
1064 40 f. "Perotrochus deforgesi" (slit shell) 55 35
1065 65 f. "Mursia musorstomia" (crab) . . . . . . 1·10 55
1066 125 f. Sea lily . . . . . . 2·10 1·40

415 "Sarcolchilus koghiensis"

1996. "Capex'96" International Stamp Exhibition, Toronto, Canada. Orchids. Multicoloured.

1067 5 f. Type **415** 10 10
1068 10 f. "Phaius robertsii" . . . 15 10
1069 25 f. "Megastylis montana" . . 35 25
1070 65 f. "Dendrobium macrophyllum" 85 55
1071 95 f. "Dendrobium virotii" . . 1·50 75
1072 125 f. "Ephemerantha comata" . . . . 1·90 1·00

416 Indonesian Couple beneath Tree

417 Louis Brauquier

1996. Air. Centenary of Arrival of First Indonesian Immigrants.

1073 **416** 130 f. multicoloured . . . 2·10 1·40

1996. Air. Writers.

1074 **417** 95 f. multicoloured . . . 1·50 1·00

1996. 50th Anniv of U.N.I.C.E.F. No. 1023 optd **unicef** and emblem.

1075 **387** 30 f. multicoloured . . . 40 25

419 Dish Aerial

1996. Air. Anniversaries. Multicoloured.

1076 95 f. Type **419** (20th anniv of New Caledonia's first Earth Station) . . . . 1·50 1·00
1077 125 f. Guglielmo Marconi (inventor) and telegraph masts (centenary of radio-telegraphy) . . . . . . 2·10 1·50

420 Tribal Dance

1996. Air. 7th South Pacific Arts Festival.

1078 **420** 100 f. multicoloured . . . 1·75 1·10

421 "The Woman" (Elija Trijikone)

1996. Sculptures of the Pacific.

1079 **421** 105 f. multicoloured . . . 1·75 1·10

422 Ordination, St. Joseph's Cathedral, Noumea

1996. 50th Anniv of Ordination of First Priests in New Caledonia.

1080 **422** 160 f. multicoloured . . . 2·50 1·75

423 "Man" (Paula Boi)

1996. Pacific Painters.

1081 **423** 200 f. multicoloured . . . 3·00 2·00

424 Gaica Dance

1996.

1082 **424** 500 f. multicoloured . . . 8·25 5·00

425 Great Reef

1996. Air. 50th Autumn Stamp Show, Paris. Multicoloured.

1083 95 f. Type **425** . . . . . . 1·50 1·00
1084 95 f. Mount Koghi . . . . . 1·50 1·00

426 Decorated Sandman

1996. Christmas.

1085 **426** 95 f. multicoloured . . . 1·50 75

427 Horned Tortoises

1997. Air.

1086 **427** 95 f. multicoloured . . . 1·50 1·10

428 Emblem

1997. Air. 50th Anniv of South Pacific Commission.

1087 **428** 100 f. multicoloured . . . 1·50 1·00

429 Junk, Hong Kong, Ox and Flag

1997. Air. "Hong Kong '97" Stamp Exhibition. Year of the Ox.

1088 **429** 95 f. multicoloured . . . 1·50 1·00

430 Mitterrand

1997. 1st Death Anniv of Francois Mitterrand (French President, 1981–95).

1090 **430** 1000 f. multicoloured . . 15·00 11·00

431 Windmill ("Letters from My Windmill") **432** Lapita Pot with Geometric Pattern

1997. Death Centenary of Alphonse Daudet (writer). Multicoloured.

1091 65 f. Type **431** . . . . 1·25 80
1092 65 f. Boy sitting by wall ("The Little Thing") . . . . . . 1·25 80
1093 65 f. Hunter in jungle ("Tartarin de Tarascon") . 1·25 80
1094 65 f. Daudet at work . . . . . 1·25 80

1997. Air. Melanesian Pottery in Noumea Museum. Multicoloured.

1096 95 f. Type **432** . . . . 1·50 1·00
1097 95 f. Lapita pot with "face" design . . . . 1·50 1·00

433 French Parliament Building and Lafleur

1997. Appointment of Henri Lafleur as First New Caledonian Senator in French Parliament.

1098 **433** 105 f. multicoloured . . . 1·75 1·25

434 Cotton Harlequin Bug

1997. Insects. Multicoloured.

1099 65 f. Type **434** . . . . 1·25 1·00
1100 65 f. "Kanakia gigas" . . . . . 1·25 1·00
1101 65 f. "Aenetus cohici" (moth) . 1·25 1·00

435 Iekawe

1997. 5th Death Anniv of Jacques Ieneic Iekawe (first Melanesian Prefect).

1102 **435** 250 f. multicoloured . . . 3·50 2·50

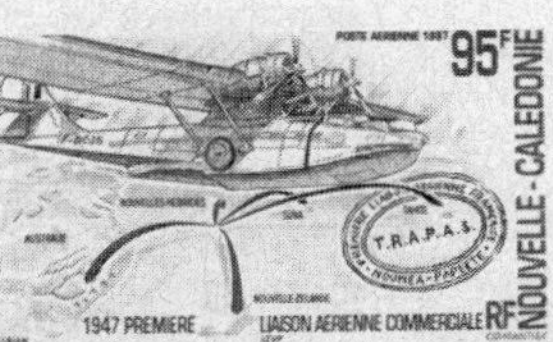

436 Consolidated Catalina Flying Boat and South Pacific Routes Map

1997. Air. 50th Anniv of Establishment by TRAPAS of First Commercial Air Routes in South Pacific. Multicoloured.

1103 95 f. Type **436** . . . . 1·25 1·00
1104 95 f. TRAPAS emblem, seaplane and New Caledonia domestic flight routes . . . 1·25 1·00

437 Kagu **438** Cup and Harness Racing

1997.

1107 **437** 30 f. orange 35 20
1113 95 f. blue . . . . 1·25 50

See also No. 1128.

1997. Equestrian Sports. Multicoloured.

1118 65 f. Type **438** . . . . 1·00 70
1119 65 f. Cup and horse racing . . 1·00 70

439 Port de France (engraving)

1997.

1120 **439** 95 f. multicoloured . . . 1·25 90

440 "Marianne", Voter and Tiki

441 Seahorses

1997. 50th Anniv of First Elections of Melanesian Representatives to French Parliament.

1121 **440** 150 f. multicoloured . . . 2·10 1·50

1997. 5th Indo-Pacific Fishes Conference.

1122 **441** 100 f. multicoloured . . . 1·25 90

442 Hammerhead Shark Dance Mask (Ken Thaiday)

1997. Pacific Art and Culture. Multicoloured.

1123 100 f. Type **442** . . . . 1·25 90
1124 100 f. Painting of traditional Melanesian images by Yvette Bouquet . . . . 1·25 90
1125 100 f. "Doka" (figurines by Frank Haikiu) . . . . . . 1·25 90

443 Father Christmas surfing to Earth

1997. Christmas. Multicoloured.

1126 95 f. Type **443** . . . . 1·10 80
1127 100 f. Dolphin with "Meilleurs Voeux" banner . . . . . . 1·10 80

1998. As Nos. 1107/13 but with no value expressed. Ordinary or self-adhesive gum.

1128 **437** (70 f.) red 80 30

444 "Lentinus tuber-regium" **445** Mask from Northern Region

1998. Edible Mushrooms. Multicoloured.

1130 70 f. Type **444** 80 60
1131 70 f. "Morchella anteridiformis" 80 60
1132 70 f. "Volvaria bombycina" . . 80 60

1998. Territorial Museum. Multicoloured.

1133 105 f. Type **445** . . . . 1·25 90
1134 110 f. Section of door frame from Central Region . . . . . . 1·25 90

446 Painting by Gauguin

1998. 150th Birth Anniv of Paul Gauguin (painter).

1135 **446** 405 f. multicoloured . . . 4·75 3·50

447 Player

1998. World Cup Football Championship, France.

1136 **447** 100 f. multicoloured . . . 1·25 90

448 "Mitimitia"

1998. Tjibaou Cultural Centre. Multicoloured.

1137 30 f. Type **448** 35 25
1138 70 f. Jean-Marie Tjibaou (politician) and Centre . . . 80 60
1139 70 f. Detail of a Centre building (Renzo Piano) (vert) 80 60
1140 105 f. "Man Bird" (Mathias Kauage) (vert) . . . . . . 1·25 90

449 Broken Chains and Slaves

1998. 150th Anniv of Abolition of Slavery.

1141 **449** 130 f. brown, blue and purple . . . . 1·50 1·10

450 Dogs watching Postman delivering Letter

1998. Stamp Day.

1142 **450** 70 f. multicoloured . . . 80 60

451 Vincent Bouquet

1998. 50th Anniv of Election of First President of Commission of Chiefs.

1143 **451** 110 f. multicoloured . . . 1·25 90

452 Noumea Fantasia, 1903

1998. 100 Years of Arab Presence.

1144 **452** 80 f. multicoloured . . . 90 65

453 Departure

1998. "Portugal 98" International Stamp Exhibition, Lisbon. 500th Anniv of Vasco da Gama's Voyage to India via Cape of Good Hope. Multicoloured.

1145 100 f. Type **453** . . . . 1·25 90
1146 100 f. Fleet at Cape of Good Hope . . . . 1·25 90
1147 100 f. Vasco da Gama meeting Indian king . . . . 1·25 90
1148 100 f. Vasco da Gama in armorial shield flanked by plants . . . . 1·25 90

454 Kagu **455** Liberty Trees

1998. Endangered Species. The Kagu. Multicoloured.

1150 5 f. Type **454** 10 10
1151 10 f. Kagu by branch 10 10
1152 15 f. Two kagus 20 15
1153 70 f. Two kagus, one with wings outspread 80 60

1998. 50th Anniv of Universal Declaration of Human Rights.

1154 **455** 70 f. green, black and blue . 80 60

456 "Prison, Nou Island" (engraving)

1998.

1155 **456** 155 f. multicoloured . . . 1·75 1·25

457 View of Island

1998. Regional Scenes. Multicoloured.

1156 100 f. Type **457** . . . . 1·25 90
1157 100 f. View of sea . . . . . . 1·25 90

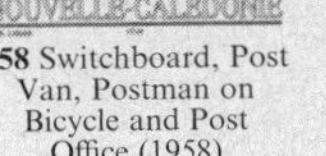

458 Switchboard, Post Van, Postman on Bicycle and Post Office (1958) **459** Marine Life forming Christmas Tree ("Merry Christmas")

1998. 40th Anniv of Posts and Telecommunications Office. Multicoloured.

1158 70 f. Type **458** 75 55
1159 70 f. Automatic service machine, woman with mobile phone, dish aerial, motor cycle courier and post office (1998) 75 55

1998. Greetings stamps. Multicoloured.

1160 100 f. Type **459** . . . . 1·10 80
1161 100 f. Treasure chest ("Best Wishes") . . . . 1·10 80
1162 100 f. Fish ("Good Holiday") . 1·10 80
1163 100 f. Fishes and reefs ("Happy Birthday") . . . . 1·10 80

460 Map, Memorial and "Monique"

1998. 20th Anniv of Erection of Memorial to the Victims of the "Monique" (inter-island freighter) Disaster.
1164 **460** 130 f. multicoloured . . . 1·40 1·00

461 "Argiope aetherea"

1999. Spiders. Multicoloured.
1165 70 f. Type **461** 75 55
1166 70 f. "Latrodectus hasselti" . . 75 55
1167 70 f. "Cyrtophora moluccensis" 75 55
1168 70 f. "Barycheloides alluvviophilus" 75 55

462 Tooth

1999. Giant-toothed Shark.
1169 **462** 100 f. multicoloured . . . 1·10 80

463 Athletics

1999. 11th South Pacific Games. Multicoloured.
1171 5 f. Type **463** 10 10
1172 10 f. Tennis 10 10
1173 30 f. Karate 75 55
1174 70 f. Baseball 75 55

464 Bwanjep

466 School Building and Computer

465 Scene from "Les Filles de la Neama" and Bloc

1999. Traditional Musical Instruments. Mult.
1175 30 f. Type **464** 30 25
1176 70 f. Bells 75 55
1177 100 f. Flutes . . . . 1·10 80

1999. 29th Death Anniv of Paul Bloc (writer).
1178 **465** 105 f. blue, green & pur . . 1·10 80

1999. 20th Anniv of Auguste Escoffier Commercial and Hotelier Professional School. Multicoloured.
1179 70 f. Type **466** 75 55
1180 70 f. School building and chef's hat 75 55

467 Unloading Supplies, Helicopters and Map

1999. Humanitarian Aid.
1181 **467** 135 f. multicoloured . . . 1·40 1·00

468 10 c. Napoleon III Stamp, 1860

1999. 140th Anniv (2000) of First New Caledonian Stamp and "Philexfrance 99" International Stamp Exhibition, Paris.
1182 **468** 70 f. multicoloured . . . 75 55

469 Food Platter

1999. Hotels and Restaurants. Multicoloured.
1184 5 f. Type **469** 10 10
1185 30 f. Seafood platter 30 25
1186 70 f. Hotel cabins by lake . . . 75 55
1187 100 f. Modern hotel and swimming pool . . . . . . 1·00 80

470 Eiffel Tower, Lighthouse with 1949 and 1999 Aircraft

1999. Air. 50th Anniv of First Paris–Noumea Scheduled Flight.
1188 **470** 100 f. multicoloured . . . 1·00 80

471 Paintings
(½-size illustration)

1999.
1189 **471** 70 f. multicoloured . . . 75 55

472 Aji Aboro (Kanak dance)

1999.
1190 **472** 70 f. multicoloured . . . 75 55

473 Chateau Hagen

1999. Historic Monuments of South Province.
1191 **473** 155 f. multicoloured . . . 1·60 1·10

474 Children protecting Tree

1999. Nature Protection: "Don't touch my Tree".
1192 **474** 30 f. multicoloured . . . 30 25

475 Children around Tree

1999. Greetings Stamps. Multicoloured.
1193 100 f. Type **475** ("Merry Christmas") . . . . 1·00 80
1194 100 f. Children with flowers and star ("Best Wishes 2000") . . 1·00 80
1195 100 f. Children and Year 2000 cake ("Happy Birthday") . . 1·00 80
1196 100 f. Children looking in pram ("Congratulations") . . . . 1·00 80

OFFICIAL STAMPS

O 49 Ancestor Pole

O 110 Carved Wooden Pillow (Noumea Museum)

1958. Inscr "OFFICIEL".
O344 **O 49** 1 f. yellow 45 40
O345 3 f. green 45 40
O346 4 f. purple 45 50
O347 5 f. blue 60 50
O348 9 f. black 70 70
O349 A 10 f. violet 85 70
O350 13 f. green . . . . . . 1·25 80
O351 15 f. blue . . . . . . 1·50 1·00
O352 24 f. mauve . . . . . 1·75 1·10
O353 26 f. orange . . . . . 2·10 1·25
O354 B 50 f. green . . . . . . 4·00 2·50
O355 100 f. brown . . . . . 7·75 4·00
O356 200 f. red . . . . . . 16·00 8·00
DESIGNS: A, B, Different idols.

1973.
O525 **O 110** 1 f. green, blk & yell 20 20
O526 2 f. red, black & grn 20 15
O527 3 f. green, blk & brn 30 20
O528 4 f. green, blk & bl 30 20
O529 5 f. green, blk & mve 45 25
O530 9 f. green, blk & bl 55 45
O531 10 f. green, blk & orge 55 45
O532 11 f. grn, blk & mve 35 20
O533 12 f. green, blk & turq 65 45
O534 15 f. green, blk & lt grn 35 25
O535 20 f. green, blk & red 35 25
O536 23 f. green, blk & red 55 45
O537 24 f. green, blk & bl 75 35
O538 25 f. green, blk & grey 95 45
O539 26 f. green, blk & yell 80 35
O540 29 f. red, black & grn 80 55
O541 31 f. red, black & yell 65 45
O542 35 f. red, black & yell 1·00 45
O543 36 f. green, blk & mve 90 45
O544 38 f. red, black & brn 1·00 45
O545 40 f. red, black & bl 90 55
O546 42 f. green, blk & brn 1·00 45
O547 50 f. green, blk & bl 90 65
O548 58 f. blue, blk & grn 1·00 65
O549 65 f. red, black & mve 1·10 65
O549a 76 f. red, blk & yell 1·40 75
O550 100 f. green, blk & red 2·10 1·25
O551 200 f. green, blk & yell 4·00 2·25

PARCEL POST STAMPS

1926. Optd **Colis Postaux** or surch also.
P137 **17** 50 c. on 5 f. green on mauve 85 90
P138 1 f. blue . . . . 1·25 1·25
P139 2 f. red on blue . . . . . 1·50 1·60

1930. Optd **Colis Postaux**.
P179 **23** 50 c. brown and mauve . . 70 70
P180 **24** 1 f. pink and drab 85 85
P181 2 f. brown and orange . . 1·25 1·25

POSTAGE DUE STAMPS

1903. Postage Due stamps of French Colonies optd **CINQUANTENAIRE 24 SEPTEMBRE 1853 1903** and eagle. Imperf.
D78 U 5 c. blue . . . . 1·40 1·25
D79 10 c. brown . . . . 5·75 5·25
D80 15 c. green . . . . 14·50 6·25
D81 30 c. red . . . . 9·50 7·25
D82 50 c. purple . . . . 45·00 11·50
D83 60 c. brown on buff . . . £200 50·00
D84 1 f. pink . . . . 23·00 11·00
D85 2 f. brown £750 £800

D 18 Outrigger Canoe **D 25** Sambar Stag **D 38**

1906.
D102 **D 18** 5 c. blue on blue . . . 25 30
D103 10 c. brown on buff . . 35 50
D104 15 c. green 40 45
D105 20 c. black on yellow . 40 45
D106 30 c. red 85 85
D107 50 c. blue on cream . . 1·40 1·40
D108 60 c. green on blue . . 1·00 1·10
D109 1 f. green on cream . . 1·60 1·60

1926. Surch.
D137 **D 18** 2 f. on 1 f. mauve . . . 3·25 3·50
D138 3 f. on 1 f. brown . . . 3·25 3·50

1928.
D179 **D 25** 2 c. brown and blue . . 15 30
D180 4 c. green and red . . . 25 35
D181 5 c. grey and orange . . 25 35
D182 10 c. blue and mauve . 20 35
D183 15 c. red and olive . . 25 35
D184 20 c. olive and red . . 75 85
D185 25 c. blue and brown . 40 45

D186	D **25**	30 c. olive and green . .	75	80
D187		50 c. red and brown . .	1·00	1·10
D188		60 c. red and mauve . .	1·10	1·10
D189		1 f. green and blue . .	1·25	1·25
D190		2 f. olive and red . . .	1·50	1·50
D191		3 f. brown and violet .	2·10	2·00

1948.

D328	D **38**	10 c. mauve	15	30
D329		30 c. brown	20	30
D330		50 c. green	30	35
D331		1 f. brown	30	35
D332		2 f. red	30	35
D333		3 f. brown	30	35
D334		4 f. blue	45	45
D335		5 f. red	55	60
D336		10 f. green	85	85
D337		20 f. blue	1·60	1·75

D **223** New Caledonian Flying Fox

1983.

D703	D **223**	1 f. multicoloured . .	10	10
D704		2 f. multicoloured . .	10	10
D705		3 f. multicoloured . .	10	10
D706		4 f. multicoloured . .	20	20
D707		5 f. multicoloured . .	20	20
D708		10 f. multicoloured . .	20	20
D709		20 f. multicoloured . .	40	40
D710		40 f. multicoloured . .	80	80
D711		50 f. multicoloured . .	90	90

NEWFOUNDLAND Pt. 1

An island off the east coast of Canada. A British Dominion merged since 1949 with Canada, whose stamps it now uses.

1857. 12 pence = 1 shilling;
20 shillings = 1 pound.
1866. 100 cents = 1 dollar.

1

2

3 Royal Crown and Heraldic Flowers of the United Kingdom

1857. Imperf.

1	**1**	1d. purple	85·00	£150
10	**2**	2d. red	£300	£375
11	**3**	3d. green	70·00	£150
12	**2**	4d. red	£2250	£800
13	**1**	5d. brown	90·00	£275
14	**2**	6d. red	£2750	£600
7		6½d. red	£2250	£2500
8		8d. red	£225	£325
9		1s. red	£13000	£4750

The frame design of Type **2** differs for each value.

1861. Imperf.

16	**1**	1d. brown	£160	£250
17	**2**	2d. lake	£150	£375
18		4d. lake	28·00	90·00
19	**1**	5d. brown	60·00	£190
20	**2**	6d. lake	21·00	£100
21		6½d. lake	65·00	£425
22		8d. lake	75·00	£500
23		1s. lake	35·00	£300

6 Codfish

7 Common Seal on Ice-floe

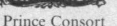

8 Prince Consort

9 Queen Victoria

10 Schooner

11 Queen Victoria

1866. Perf (2 c. also roul).

31	**6**	2 c. green	65·00	30·00
26	**7**	5 c. brown	£450	£170
32	**8**	10 c. black	£160	38·00
33	**9**	12 c. brown	42·00	42·00
29	**10**	13 c. orange	90·00	65·00
30	**11**	24 c. blue	32·00	32·00

12 King Edward VII, when Prince of Wales

14 Queen Victoria

1868. Perf or roul.

34	**12**	1 c. purple	50·00	48·00
36		3 c. orange	£250	£100
42		3 c. blue	£250	4·00
38	**7**	5 c. black	£225	£100
43		5 c. blue	£170	3·25
39	**14**	6 c. red	6·50	16·00

19 Newfoundland Dog

15 King Edward VII, when Prince of Wales

16 Codfish

17

18 Common Seal on Ice-floe

20 Atlantic Brigantine

21 Queen Victoria

1880.

49	**19**	½ c. red	9·00	7·00
59		½ c. black	9·00	4·75
44a	**15**	1 c. brown	24·00	8·00
50a		1 c. green	6·00	3·00
46	**16**	2 c. green	45·00	22·00
51		2 c. orange	14·00	4·50
47a	**17**	3 c. blue	70·00	3·00
52		3 c. brown	55·00	1·50
59a	**18**	5 c. blue	55·00	3·00
54	**20**	10 c. black	45·00	50·00

1890.

55	**21**	3 c. grey	25·00	1·25

This stamp on pink paper was stained by sea-water.

22 Queen Victoria

23 John Cabot

24 Cape Bonavista

25 Caribou-hunting

1897. 400th Anniv of Discovery of Newfoundland and 60th Year of Queen Victoria's Reign. Dated "1497 1897".

66	**22**	1 c. green	2·25	4·50
67	**23**	2 c. red	2·00	2·50
68	**24**	3 c. blue	3·25	75
69	**25**	4 c. olive	9·50	3·00
70	–	5 c. violet	13·00	3·00
71	–	6 c. brown	8·50	3·25
72	–	8 c. orange	18·00	8·00
73	–	10 c. brown	40·00	6·00
74	–	12 c. blue	35·00	5·50
75	–	15 c. red	20·00	17·00
76	–	24 c. violet	24·00	19·00
77	–	30 c. blue	45·00	60·00
78	–	35 c. red	60·00	60·00
79	–	60 c. black	17·00	12·00

DESIGNS—As Type **24**: 5 c. Mining; 6 c. Logging; 8 c. Fishing; 10 c. Cabot's ship, the "Matthew"; 15 c. Seals; 24 c. Salmon-fishing; 35 c. Iceberg. As Type **23**: 12 c. Willow/red grouse; 30 c. Seal of the Colony; 60 c. Henry VII.

1897. Surch **ONE CENT** and bar.

80	**21**	1 c. on 3 c. grey	42·00	18·00

39 Prince Edward later Duke of Windsor

40 Queen Victoria

1897. Royal portraits.

83	**39**	½ c. olive	2·25	1·50
84	**40**	1 c. red	3·25	3·50
85a	–	1 c. green	6·50	20
86	–	2 c. orange	3·25	3·00
87	–	2 c. red	14·00	40
88	–	3 c. orange	15·00	30
89	–	4 c. violet	23·00	4·00
90	–	5 c. blue	38·00	3·00

DESIGNS: 2 c. King Edward VII when Prince of Wales; 3 c. Queen Alexandra when Princess of Wales; 4 c. Queen Mary when Duchess of York; 5 c. King George V when Duke of York.

45 Map of Newfoundland

46 King James I

47 Arms of Colonisation Co

49 "Endeavour" (immigrant ship), 1610

1908.

94	**45**	2 c. lake	27·00	80

1910. Dated "1610 1910".

109	**46**	1 c. green	1·25	30
107	**47**	2 c. red	3·50	35
97	–	3 c. olive	6·00	15·00
98	**49**	4 c. violet	14·00	13·00
108	–	5 c. blue	8·00	2·75
111	–	6 c. purple	17·00	42·00
112	–	8 c. bistre	48·00	65·00
102	–	9 c. green	40·00	80·00
103	–	10 c. grey	55·00	£100
115	–	12 c. brown	60·00	60·00
105	–	15 c. black	65·00	£100

DESIGNS—HORIZ: 5 c. Cupids; 8 c. Mosquito; 9 c. Logging camp, Red Indian Lake; 10 c. Paper mills, Grand Falls. VERT: 3 c John Guy; 6 c. Sir Francis Bacon; 12 c. King Edward VII; 15 c. King George V. (Cupids and Mosquito are places).

57 Queen zzMary

58 King George V

67 Seal of Newfoundland

1911. Coronation.

117	**57**	1 c. green	6·00	30
118	**58**	2 c. red	3·50	20
119	–	3 c. brown	19·00	27·00
120	–	4 c. purple	18·00	26·00
121	–	5 c. blue	6·50	1·50
122	–	6 c. grey	13·00	25·00
123	–	8 c. blue	50·00	75·00
124	–	9 c. blue	16·00	40·00
125	–	10 c. green	28·00	40·00
126	–	12 c. plum	23·00	40·00
127	**67**	15 c. lake	18·00	45·00

PORTRAITS—VERT (As Type **57/8**): 3 c. Duke of Windsor when Prince of Wales; 4 c. King George VI when Prince Albert; 5 c. Princess Mary, the Princess Royal; 6 c. Duke of Gloucester when Prince Henry; 8 c. Duke of Kent when Prince George; 9 c. Prince John; 10 c. Queen Alexandra; 12 c. Duke of Connaught.

68 Caribou

1919. Newfoundland Contingent. 1914–18.

130	**68**	1 c. green	3·50	20
131		2 c. red	3·50	85
132		3 c. brown	5·00	20
133		4 c. mauve	5·50	60
134		5 c. blue	5·50	1·25
135		6 c. grey	5·00	32·00
136		8 c. purple	9·00	40·00
137		10 c. green	5·50	3·75
138		12 c. orange	18·00	45·00
139		15 c. blue	15·00	55·00
140		24 c. brown	22·00	28·00
141		36 c. olive	13·00	25·00

DESIGNS—Each inscr with the name of a different action: 1 c. Suvla Bay; 3 c. Gueudecourt; 4 c. Beaumont Hamel; 6 c. Monchy; 10 c. Steenbeck; 15 c. Langemarck; 24 c. Cambrai; 36 c. Combles. The 2, 5, 8 and 12 c. are inscribed "Royal Naval Reserve. Ubique".

1919. Air. Hawker Flight. No. 132a optd **FIRST TRANS- ATLANTIC AIR POST April, 1919.**

142	**68**	3 c. brown	£15000	£8000

1919. Air. Alcock and Brown Flight. Surch **Trans-Atlantic AIR POST, 1919. ONE DOLLAR.**

143		$1 on 15 c. red (No. 75)	£110	£110

1920. Surch in words between bars.

144		2 c. on 30 c. blue (No. 77)	3·50	16·00
146		3 c. on 15 c. red (No. 75)	13·00	13·00
147		3 c. on 35 c. red (No. 78)	6·00	10·00

1921. Air. Optd **AIR MAIL to Halifax, N.S. 1921.**

148a		35 c. red (No. 78)	80·00	80·00

73 Twin Hills, Tor's Cove

75 Statue of Fighting Newfoundlander, St. John's

1923.

149	**73**	1 c. green	75	20
150	–	2 c. red	60	10
151	**75**	3 c. brown	70	10
152	–	4 c. purple	90	30
153	–	5 c. blue	1·50	1·75
154	–	6 c. grey	2·75	7·50
155	–	8 c. purple	3·75	3·50
156	–	9 c. green	17·00	28·00
157	–	10 c. violet	4·50	2·75
158	–	11 c. olive	2·50	16·00
159	–	12 c. lake	2·75	9·00
160	–	15 c. blue	2·75	13·00
161	–	20 c. brown	7·00	10·00
162	–	24 c. brown	45·00	75·00

DESIGNS—HORIZ: 2 c. South-west Arm, Trinity; 6 c. Upper Steadies, Humber River; 8 c. Quidi Vidi, near St. John's; 9 c. Caribou crossing lake; 11 c. Shell Bird Island; 12 c. Mount Moriah, Bay of Islands; 20 c. Placentia. VERT: 4 c. Humber River; 5 c. Coast at Trinity; 10 c. Humber River Canon; 15 c. Humber River, near Little Rapids; 24 c. Topsail Falls.

1927. Air. Optd **Air Mail DE PINEDO 1927.**

163		60 c. black (No. 79)	£24000	£7500

88 Newfoundland and Labrador

89 S.S. "Caribou"

90 King George V and Queen Mary

91 Duke of Windsor when Prince of Wales

1928. Publicity issue.

164	**88**	1 c. green	2·25	1·25
180	**89**	2 c. red	1·50	40
181	**90**	3 c. brown	1·00	20
201	**91**	4 c. mauve	2·00	80
183	–	5 c. grey	5·50	2·00
184a	–	6 c. blue	2·25	12·00
170	–	8 c. brown	2·50	24·00
171	–	9 c. green	2·00	11·00
185	–	10 c. violet	4·00	3·00
173	–	12 c. lake	2·00	18·00
174a	–	14 c. purple	5·00	8·00
175	–	15 c. blue	3·00	27·00
176a	–	20 c. black	2·50	6·50
177	–	28 c. green	28·00	48·00
178	–	30 c. brown	6·00	16·00

DESIGNS—HORIZ: 5 c. Express train; 6 c. Newfoundland Hotel, St. John's; 8 c. Heart's Content; 10 c. War Memorial, St. John's; 15 c. Vickers Vimy aircraft; 20 c. Parliament House, St. John's. VERT: 9, 14 c. Cabot Tower, St. John's; 12, 28 c. G.P.O., St. John's; 30 c. Grand Falls, Labrador.

1929. Surch **THREE CENTS.**

188		3 c. on 6 c. (No. 154)	1·00	4·25

1930. Air. No. 141 surch **Trans-Atlantic AIR MAIL By B. M. "Columbia" September 1930** Fifty Cents.

191	**68**	50 c. on 36 c. olive	£4500	£4250

103 Westland Limousine III and Dog-team

104 Vickers-Vimy Biplane and early Sailing Packet

105 Routes of historic Trans-Atlantic Flights

1931. Air.

192	**103**	15 c. brown	4·50	11·00
193	**104**	50 c. green	30·00	45·00
194	**105**	$1 blue	48·00	85·00

107 Codfish

108 King George V

110 Duke of Windsor when Prince of Wales

111 Reindeer

112 Queen Elizabeth II when Princess

121 Corner Brook Paper Mills

1932.

209	**107**	1 c. green	2·25	30
276		1 c. grey	20	30
210	**108**	2 c. red	1·50	20
223		2 c. green	40	10
211	–	3 c. brown	1·50	20
212	**110**	4 c. lilac	5·50	2·00
224		4 c. red	1·75	40
213	**111**	5 c. purple	3·00	1·25
225c		5 c. violet	70	30
214	**112**	6 c. blue	4·00	13·00
226	–	7 c. lake	2·75	3·25
282	**121**	8 c. red	1·50	1·75
215	–	10 c. brown	70	65
216	–	14 c. black	3·75	4·50
217	–	15 c. purple	1·25	2·00
218	–	20 c. green	1·00	90
228	–	24 c. blue	85	3·00
219	–	25 c. grey	2·00	2·25
220	–	30 c. blue	28·00	28·00
289	–	48 c. brown	3·00	5·50

DESIGNS—VERT: 3 c. Queen Mary; 7 c. Queen Mother when Duchess of York. HORIZ: 10 c. Salmon; 14 c. Newfoundland dog; 15 c. Harp seal; 20 c. Cape Race; 24 c. Loading iron ore, Bell Island; 25 c. Sealing fleet; 30, 48 c. Fishing fleet.

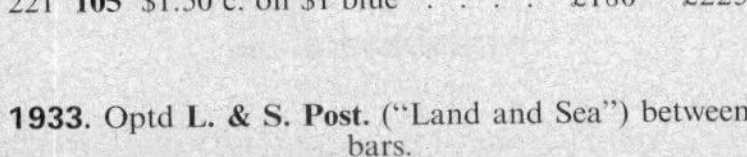

1932. Air. Surch **TRANS-ATLANTIC WEST TO EAST Per Dornier DO-X May, 1932. One Dollar and Fifty Cents.**

221	**105**	$1.50 c. on $1 blue	£180	£225

1933. Optd **L. & S. Post.** ("Land and Sea") between bars.

229	**103**	15 c. brown	3·25	9·00

124 Put to Flight

1933. Air.

230	**124**	5 c. brown	14·00	16·00
231	–	10 c. yellow	10·00	26·00
232	–	30 c. blue	28·00	40·00
233	–	60 c. green	45·00	80·00
234	–	75 c. brown	45·00	75·00

DESIGNS: 10 c. Land of Heart's Delight; 30 c. Spotting the herd; 60 c. News from home; 75 c. Labrador.

1933. Air. Balbo Trans-Atlantic Mass Formation Flight. No. 234 surch **1933 GEN. BALBO FLIGHT. $4.50.**

235	$4.50 on 75 c. brown	£250	£300

130 Sir Humphrey Gilbert

131 Compton Castle, Devon

1933. 350th Anniv of Annexation. Dated "1583 1933".

236	**130**	1 c. black	70	1·25
237	**131**	2 c. green	1·00	60
238	–	3 c. brown	2·00	1·25
239	–	4 c. red	80	50
240	–	5 c. violet	2·00	80
241	–	7 c. blue	12·00	16·00
242	–	8 c. orange	7·00	12·00
243	–	9 c. blue	7·00	10·00
244	–	10 c. brown	4·00	7·50
245	–	14 c. black	12·00	30·00
246	–	15 c. red	10·00	20·00
247	–	20 c. green	13·00	16·00
248	–	24 c. purple	13·00	22·00
249	–	32 c. black	7·00	45·00

DESIGNS—VERT: 3 c. Gilbert coat of arms; 5 c. Anchor token; 14 c. Royal Arms; 15 c. Gilbert in the "Squirrel"; 24 c. Queen Elizabeth I; 32 c. Gilbert's statue at Truro. HORIZ: 4 c. Eton College; 7 c. Gilbert commissioned by Elizabeth; 8 c. Fleet leaving Plymouth, 1583; 9 c. Arrival at St. John's; 10 c. Annexation, 5 August, 1583; 20 c. Map of Newfoundland.

1935. Silver Jubilee. As T **10a** of Gambia.

250	4 c. red	1·00	1·75
251	5 c. violet	1·25	1·75
252	7 c. blue	1·50	6·50
253	24 c. olive	5·00	7·50

1937. Coronation. As T **10b** of Gambia.

254	2 c. green	1·00	2·25
255	4 c. red	1·60	2·75
256	5 c. purple	3·00	2·75

144 Atlantic Cod

155 King George VI

1937. Coronation.

257	**144**	1 c. grey	2·25	20
258d	–	3 c. brown	3·50	3·00
259	–	7 c. blue	2·75	90
260	–	8 c. red	1·75	2·50
261	–	10 c. black	3·75	7·00
262	–	14 c. black	1·40	2·00
263	–	15 c. red	9·00	4·00
264	–	20 c. green	2·25	6·00
265	–	24 c. blue	2·25	2·50
266	–	25 c. black	2·75	1·75
267	–	48 c. purple	8·50	4·50

DESIGNS: 3 c. Map of Newfoundland; 7 c. Reindeer; 8 c. Corner Brook Paper Mills; 10 c. Atlantic salmon; 14 c. Newfoundland dog; 15 c. Harp seal; 20 c. Cape Race; 24 c. Bell Island; 25 c. Sealing fleet; 48 c. The Banks fishing fleet.

1938.

277	**155**	2 c. green	30	20
278	–	3 c. red	30	10
270	–	4 c. blue	1·75	20
271	–	7 c. blue	75	3·75

DESIGNS: 3 c. Queen Mother; 4 c. Queen Elizabeth II, aged 12; 7 c. Queen Mary.

159 King George VI and Queen Elizabeth

1938. Royal Visit.

272	**159**	5 c. blue	2·00	40

1939. Surch in figures and triangles.

273	**159**	2 c. on 5 c. blue	2·00	30
274		4 c. on 5 c. blue	1·25	60

161 Grenfell on the "Strathcona" (after painting by Gribble)

1941. 50th Anniv of Sir Wilfred Grenfell's Labrador Mission.

275	**161**	5 c. blue	30	55

162 Memorial University College

1942.

290	**162**	30 c. red	1·00	1·60

163 St. John's

165 Queen Elizabeth II when Princess

1943. Air.

291	**163**	7 c. blue	40	65

1946. Surch **TWO CENTS.**

292	**162**	2 c. on 30 c. red	30	75

1947. 21st Birthday of Princess Elizabeth.

293	**165**	4 c. blue	30	75

166 Cabot off Cape Bonavista

1947. 450th Anniv of Cabot's Discovery of Newfoundland.

294	**166**	5 c. violet	20	80

POSTAGE DUE STAMPS

D 1

1939.

D1	**D 1**	1 c. green	2·25	8·50
D2		2 c. red	13·00	7·50
D3		3 c. blue	5·00	19·00
D4		4 c. orange	9·00	17·00
D5		5 c. brown	12·00	23·00
D6		10 c. purple	6·00	17·00

NEW GUINEA Pt. 1

Formerly a German Colony, part of the island of New Guinea. Occupied by Australian forces during the 1914–18 war and subsequently joined with Papua and administered by the Australian Commonwealth under trusteeship. After the Japanese defeat in 1945 Australian stamps were used until 1952 when the combined issue appeared for Papua and New Guinea (q.v.). The stamps overprinted "N.W. PACIFIC ISLANDS" were also used in Nauru and other ex-German islands.

12 pence = 1 shilling;
20 shillings = 1 pound

1914. "Yacht" key-types of German New Guinea surch **G.R.I.** and value in English currency.

16	N	1d on 3 pf. brown	45·00	55·00
17		1d. on 5 pf. green	18·00	28·00
18		2d. on 10 pf. red	24·00	38·00
19		2d. on 20 pf. blue	28·00	42·00
5		2½d. on 10 pf. red	65·00	£140
6		2½d. on 20 pf. blue	70·00	£140
22		3d. on 25 pf. black and red on yellow	£100	£140
23		3d. on 30 pf. black and orange on buff	85·00	£120
24		4d. on 40 pf. black & red	£100	£140
25		5d. on 50 pf. black and purple on buff	£140	£180
26		8d. on 80 pf. black and red on rose	£325	£400
12	O	1s on 1 m. red	£1500	£2000
13		2s. on 2 m. blue	£1700	£2500
14		3s. on 3 m. black	£3250	£4250
15		5s. on 5 m. red and black	£6500	£8500

Nos. 3/4 surch **1.**

31	N	"1" on 2d. on 10 pf. red	£14000	£14000
32		"1" on 2d. on 20 pf. blue	£13000	£8500

4

1914. Registration labels with names of various town surch **G.R.I. 3d.**

33	**4**	3d. black and red	£150	£200

1914. "Yacht" key-types of German Marshall Islands surch **G.R.I.** and value in English currency.

50	N	1d on 3 pf. brown	48·00	80·00
51		1d. on 5 pf. green	50·00	55·00
52		2d. on 10 pf. red	17·00	26·00
53		2d. on 20 pf. blue	18·00	30·00
64g		2½d. on 10 pf. red	£7000	
64h		2½d. on 20 pf. blue	£10000	
54		3d. on 25 pf. black and red on yellow	£275	£375
55		3d. on 30 pf. black and orange on buff	£300	£400
56		4d. on 40 pf. black & red	£100	£130
57		5d. on 50 pf. black and purple on buff	£140	£180
58		8d. on 80 pf. black and red on rose	£400	£500
59	O	1s on 1 m. red	£1800	£3000
60		2s. on 2 m. blue	£1200	£2000
61		3s. on 3 m. black	£3250	£4750
62		5s. on 5 m. red & black	£6500	£8500

1915. Nos. 52 and 53 surch **1.**

63	N	"1" on 2d. on 10 pf. red	£140	£170
64		"1"on 2d. on 20 pf. blue	£3000	£2250

1915. Stamps of Australia optd **N. W. PACIFIC ISLANDS.**

102	**3**	½d. green	1·00	3·50
103		1d. red	2·50	1·60
120		1d. violet	1·25	6·50
94	**1**	2d. grey	5·00	13·00
121	**3**	2d. orange	4·50	3·25
122		2d. red	8·50	4·50
74	**1**	2½d. blue	2·75	16·00
96		3d. olive	5·00	11·00
70	**3**	4d. orange	4·00	14·00
123		4d. violet	29·00	48·00
124		4d. blue	11·00	50·00
105		5d. brown	1·75	12·00
110	**1**	6d. blue	4·50	14·00
89		9d. violet	16·00	20·00
90		1s. green	11·00	24·00
115		2s. brown	21·00	38·00
116		5s. grey and yellow	60·00	65·00
84		10s. grey and pink	£110	£160
99		£1 brown and blue	£250	£400

1918. Nos. 105 and 90 surch **One Penny.**

100	**3**	1d. on 5d. brown	90·00	80·00
101	**1**	1d. on 1s. green	90·00	75·00

12 Native Village

14 Raggiana Bird of Paradise (Dates either side of value)

1925.

125	**12**	½d. orange	2·50	6·00
126		1d. green	2·50	5·50
126a		1½d. red	3·25	2·50
127		2d. red	2·50	4·50
128		3d. blue	4·50	4·00
129		4d. olive	13·00	18·00
130b		6d. brown	4·50	48·00
131		9d. purple	13·00	45·00
132		1s. green	15·00	24·00
133		2s. lake	30·00	48·00
134		5s. brown	48·00	65·00
135		10s. red	£100	£160
136		£1 grey	£180	£250

1931. Air. Optd with biplane and **AIR MAIL.**

137	**12**	½d. orange	1·00	5·00
138		1d. green	1·60	4·50
139		1½d. red	1·00	5·00
140		2d. red	1·00	7·00
141		3d. blue	1·75	13·00
142		4d. olive	1·25	8·50
143		6d. brown	1·75	13·00
144		9d. purple	3·00	17·00
145		1s. green	3·00	17·00
146		2s. lake	7·00	40·00
147		5s. brown	20·00	65·00
148		10s. red	75·00	£100
149		£1 grey	£120	£200

1931. 10th Anniv of Australian Administration. Dated "1921–1931".

150	**14**	1d. green	3·25	80
151		1½d. red	4·25	10·00
152		2d. red	4·75	4·25
153		3d. blue	4·75	4·75
154		4d. olive	6·50	16·00
155		5d. green	4·75	17·00
156		6d. brown	4·75	17·00
157		9d. violet	8·00	17·00
158		1s. grey	6·00	15·00
159		2s. lake	10·00	27·00
160		5s. brown	40·00	50·00
161		10s. red	75·00	£120
162		£1 grey	£170	£225

1931. Air. Optd with biplane and **AIR MAIL**.
163 **14** ½d. orange 3·00 3·25
164 1d. green 3·75 4·50
165 1½d. red 3·75 9·50
166 2d. red 2·50 3·00
167 3d. blue 6·00 6·00
168 4d. olive 6·00 6·00
169 5d. green 6·00 9·50
170 6d. brown 7·00 25·00
171 9d. violet 8·00 15·00
172 1s. grey 7·00 15·00
173 2s. lake 16·00 48·00
174 5s. brown 42·00 65·00
175 10s. red 60·00 £110
176 £1 grey £100 £190

1932. As T **14**, but without dates.
177 1d. green 90 20
178 1½d. red 1·00 10·00
179 2d. red 1·25 20
179a 2½d. green 5·00 16·00
180 3d. blue 1·75 80
180a 3½d. red 11·00 9·00
181 4d. olive 90 5·00
182 5d. green 1·25 70
183 6d. brown 2·50 3·00
184 9d. violet 9·50 21·00
185 1s. grey 4·00 10·00
186 2s. lake 4·00 17·00
187 5s. brown 27·00 45·00
188 10s. red 48·00 70·00
189 £1 grey 95·00 £100

1932. Air. T **14**, but without dates, optd with biplane and **AIR MAIL**.
190 ½d. orange 50 1·50
191 1d. green 80 1·50
192 1½d. mauve 1·25 6·00
193 2d. red 90 30
193a 2½d. green 4·75 2·25
194 3d. blue 2·50 2·50
194a 3½d. red 4·00 3·25
195 4d. olive 4·25 9·00
196 5d. green 7·00 7·50
197 6d. brown 4·25 13·00
198 9d. violet 6·00 9·00
199 1s. grey 6·00 8·50
200 2s. lake 9·00 45·00
201 5s. brown 45·00 55·00
202 10s. red 75·00 75·00
203 £1 grey 75·00 55·00

16 Bulolo Goldfields **18** King George VI

1935. Air.
204 **16** £2 violet £200 £120
205 £5 green £500 £375

1935. Silver Jubilee. Nos. 177 and 179 optd **HIS MAJESTY'S JUBILEE. 1910–1935.**
206 1d. green 60 35
207 2d. red 1·75 35

1937. Coronation.
208 **18** 2d. red 50 30
209 3d. blue 50 55
210 5d. green 50 45
211 1s. purple 50 35

1939. Air. As T **16** but inscr "AIR MAIL POSTAGE".
212 ½d. orange 3·00 6·00
213 1d. green 3·25 4·00
214 1½d. red 3·25 7·50
215 2d. red 7·50 3·50
216 3d. blue 9·50 18·00
217 4d. olive 10·00 8·00
218 5d. green 8·00 2·75
219 6d. brown 19·00 15·00
220 9d. violet 19·00 20·00
221 1s. green 19·00 18·00
222 2s. red 50·00 48·00
223 5s. brown £120 95·00
224 10s. pink £325 £225
225 £1 olive £100 £110

OFFICIAL STAMPS

1915. Nos. 16 and 17 optd **O. S.**
O1 N 1d on 3 pf. brown 25·00 70·00
O2 1d. on 3 pf. green 80·00 £140

1925. Optd **O S.**
O 3 **12** 1d. green 1·00 4·50
O 4 1½d. red 5·50 17·00
O 5 2d. red 1·75 3·75
O 6 3d. blue 3·50 6·50
O 7 4d. olive 4·50 8·50
O 8a 6d. brown 7·00 35·00
O 9 9d. purple 4·00 35·00
O10 1s. green 5·50 35·00
O11 2s. lake 28·00 60·00

1931. Optd **O S.**
O12 **14** 1d. green 4·25 13·00
O13 1½d. red 5·00 12·00
O14 2d. red 8·50 7·00
O15 3d. blue 6·00 6·00
O16 4d. olive 4·25 8·50
O17 5d. green 10·00 12·00
O18 6d. brown 13·00 17·00
O19 9d. violet 16·00 28·00
O20 1s. grey 16·00 28·00
O21 2s. lake 40·00 65·00
O22 5s. brown 90·00 £150

1932. T **14**, but without dates, optd **O S.**
O23 1d. green 4·50 4·50
O24 1½d. red 5·50 12·00
O25 2d. red 5·50 3·00
O26 2½d. green 3·25 6·00
O27 3d. blue 6·50 21·00
O28 3½d. red 3·25 9·00
O29 4d. olive 5·50 15·00
O30 5d. green 5·50 15·00
O31 6d. brown 8·00 32·00
O32 9d. violet 10·00 40·00
O33 1s. grey 15·00 28·00
O34 2s. lake 35·00 75·00
O35 5s. brown £120 £160

For later issues see **PAPUA AND NEW GUINEA**.

NEW HEBRIDES Pt. 1

A group of islands in the Pacific Ocean, E. of Australia, under joint administration of Gt. Britain and France. The Condominium ended in 1980, when the New Hebrides became independent as the Republic of Vanuatu.

1908. 12 pence = 1 shilling;
20 shillings = 1 pound.
1938. 100 gold centimes = 1 gold franc.
1977. 100 centimes = 1 New Hebrides franc.

BRITISH ADMINISTRATION

1908. Stamps of Fiji optd (a) **NEW HEBRIDES. CONDOMINIUM.** (with full points).
1a **23** ½d. green 40 7·00
2 1d. red 45 40
5 2d. purple and orange 60 70
6 2½d. purple & blue on blue 60 70
7 5d. purple and green 80 2·00
8 6d. purple and red 70 1·25
3 1s. green and red 19·00 4·50

(b) **NEW HEBRIDES CONDOMINIUM** (without full points).
10 **23** ½d. green 3·50 24·00
11 1d. red 10·00 8·50
12 2d. grey 60 3·00
13 2½d. blue 65 3·75
14 5d. purple and green 1·00 5·50
15 6d. purple and deep purple 1·00 5·00
16 1s. black and green 1·00 7·50

3 Weapons and Idols

1911.
18 **3** ½d. green 85 1·75
19 1d. red 3·50 2·00
20 2d. grey 7·00 4·00
21 2½d. blue 3·00 5·50
24 5d. green 4·50 6·50
25 6d. purple 3·00 5·00
26 1s. black on green 2·25 13·00
27 2s. purple on blue 17·00 22·00
28 5s. green on yellow 32·00 48·00

1920. Surch (a) On T **3**.
40 **3** 1d. on ½d. green 4·00 20·00
30 1d. on 5d. green 7·00 60·00
31 1d. on 1s. black on green 1·25 13·00
32 1d. on 2s. purple on blue 1·00 10·00
33 1d. on 5s. green on yellow 1·00 10·00
41 3d. on 1d. red 4·00 11·00
42 5d. on 2½d. blue 7·50 20·00

(b) On No. F16 of French New Hebrides.
34 **3** 2d. on 40 c. red on yellow 1·00 15·00

5

1925.
43 **5** ½d. (5 c.) black 1·25 9·00
44 1d. (10 c.) green 1·00 9·00
45 2d. (20 c.) grey 1·75 2·50
46 2½d. (25 c.) brown 1·00 12·00
47 5d. (50 c.) blue 2·75 2·50
48 6d. (60 c.) purple 3·50 11·00
49 1s. (1 f. 25) black on green 3·25 19·00
50 2s. (2 f. 50) purple on blue 6·00 22·00
51 5s. (6 f. 25) green on yellow 6·00 25·00

6 Lopevi Islands and Outrigger Canoe

1938.
52 **6** 5 c. green 2·50 3·00
53 10 c. orange 1·25 1·50
54 15 c. violet 3·00 3·25
55 20 c. red 1·60 2·00
56 25 c. brown 1·60 2·00
57 30 c. blue 1·90 1·50
58 **6** 40 c. olive 4·50 4·25
59 50 c. purple 1·60 1·50
60 1 f. red on green 4·00 7·50
61 2 f. blue on green 30·00 17·00
62 5 f. red on yellow 70·00 48·00
63 10 f. violet on blue £200 75·00

1949. U.P.U. As No. 169 of Gambia.
64 10 c. orange 30 40
65 15 c. violet 30 40
66 30 c. blue 30 40
67 50 c. purple 40 40

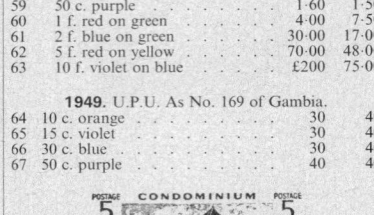

7 Outrigger Sailing Canoes

1953.
68 **7** 5 c. green 60 10
69 10 c. red 60 10
70 15 c. yellow 60 10
71 20 c. blue 60 10
72 – 25 c. olive 60 10
73 – 30 c. brown 60 10
74 – 40 c. sepia 60 10
75 – 50 c. violet 1·00 10
76 – 1 f. orange 7·50 70
77 – 2 f. purple 7·50 9·00
78 – 5 f. red 12·00 32·00
DESIGNS: 25 c. to 50 c. Native carving; 1 f. to 5 f. Two natives outside hut.

1953. Coronation. As T **11h** of Gambia.
79 10 c. black and red 60 50

10 "San Pedro y San Paulo" (Quiros) and Map

1956. 50th Anniv of Condominium. Inscr "1906 1956".
80 **10** 5 c. green 15 10
81 10 c. red 15 10
82 – 20 c. blue 10 10
83 – 50 c. lilac 15 15
DESIGN: 20, 50 c. "Marianne", "Talking Drum" and "Britannia".

12 Port Vila; Iririki Islet

1957.
84 **12** 5 c. green 40 75
85 10 c. red 30 10
86 15 c. yellow 50 75
87 20 c. blue 40 10
88 – 25 c. olive 45 10
89 – 30 c. brown 45 10
90 – 40 c. sepia 45 10
91 – 50 c. violet 45 10
92 – 1 f. orange 1·00 80
93 – 2 f. mauve 6·00 4·50
94 – 5 f. black 15·00 6·00
DESIGNS: 25 c. to 50 c. River scene and spear fisherman; 1 f. to 5 f. Woman drinking from coconut.

1963. Freedom from Hunger. As T **20a** of Gambia.
95 60 c. green 50 15

1963. Cent of Red Cross. As T **20b** of Gambia, but with British and French cyphers in place of Queen's portrait.
96 15 c. red and black 35 10
97 45 c. red and blue 45 20

17 Cocoa Beans

1963.
98 – 5 c. red, brown and blue 1·00 50
99 **17** 10 c. brown, buff & green 15 10
100 – 15 c. bistre, brown & violet 15 10
101 – 20 c. black, green and blue 55 10
102 – 25 c. violet, brown & red 50 70
103 – 30 c. brown, bistre & violet 75 10
104 – 40 c. red and blue 80 1·40
105 – 50 c. green, yellow & blue 60 10
129 – 60 c. red and blue 40 15
106 – 1 f. red, black and green 2·50 3·25
107 – 2 f. black, purple & green 2·50 1·75
108 – 3 f. multicoloured 12·00 8·00
109 – 5 f. blue, deep blue & black 14·00 21·00
DESIGNS: 5 c Exporting manganese, Forari; 15 c. Copra; 20 c. Fishing from Palikulo Point; 25 c. Picasso triggerfish; 30 c. New Caledonian nautilus shell; 40, 60 c. Lionfish; 50 c. Clown surgeonfish; 1 f. Cardinal honeyeater (bird); 2 f. Buff-bellied flycatcher; 3 f. Thicket warbler; 5 f. White-collared kingfisher.

1965. Centenary of I.T.U. As T **44** of Gibraltar, but with British and French cyphers in place of the Queen's portrait.
110 15 c. red and drab 20 10
111 60 c. blue and red 35 20

1965. I.C.Y. As T **45** of Gibraltar, but with British and French cyphers in place of the Queen's portrait.
112 5 c. purple and turquoise 15 10
113 55 c. green and lavender 20 20

1966. Churchill Commemoration. As T **46** of Gibraltar, but with British and French cyphers in place of Queen's portrait.
114 5 c. blue 20 10
115 15 c. green 40 10
116 25 c. brown 50 10
117 30 c. violet 50 10

1966. World Cup Championship. As T **47** of Gibraltar, but with British and French cyphers in place of the Queen's portrait.
118 20 c. multicoloured 20 15
119 40 c. multicoloured 30 15

1966. Inauguration of W.H.O. Headquarters, Geneva. As T **54** of Gibraltar, but with British and French cyphers in place of the Queen's portrait.
120 25 c. black, green and blue 20 10
121 60 c. black, purple and ochre 55 20

1966. 20th Anniv of U.N.E.S.C.O. As T **56a/c** of Gibraltar, but with British and French cyphers in place of the Queen's portrait.
122 15 c. multicoloured 20 10
123 30 c. yellow, violet and olive 50 10
124 45 c. black, purple & orange 60 15

36 The Coast Watchers

1967. 25th Anniv of Pacific War. Mult.
125 15 c. Type **36** 15 10
126 25 c. Map of war zone, U.S. marine and Australian soldier 50 20
127 60 c. H.M.A.S. "Canberra" (cruiser) 60 30
128 1 f. Boeing B-17 "Flying Fortress" 70 60

40 Globe and Hemispheres

1968. Bicent of Bougainville's World Voyage.
130 **40** 15 c. green, violet and red 15 10
131 – 25 c. olive, purple and blue 30 10
132 – 60 c. brown, purple & green 35 10
DESIGNS: 25 c. Ships "La Boudeuse" and "L'Etoile", and map; 60 c. Bougainville, ship's figure-head and bougainvillea flowers.

43 Concorde and Vapour Trails

1968. Anglo-French Concorde Project.
133 **43** 25 c. blue, red and blue 50 20
134 – 60 c. red, black and blue 60 25
DESIGN: 60 c. Concorde in flight.

45 Kauri Pine

1969. Timber Industry.
135 **45** 20 c. multicoloured 10 10

46 Cyphers, Flags and Relay Runner receiving Baton

1969. 3rd South Pacific Games, Port Moresby. Multicoloured.

136 25 c. Type **46** 10 10
137 1 f. Runner passing baton 20 20

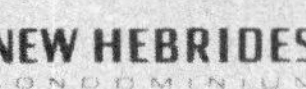
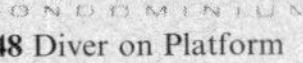

48 Diver on Platform

52 General Charles de Gaulle

51 U.P.U. Emblem and Headquarters Building

1969. Pentecost Island Land Divers. Mult.

138 15 c. Type **48** 10 10
139 25 c. Diver jumping 10 10
140 1 f. Diver at end of fall 20 20

1970. New U.P.U. Headquarters Building.

141 **51** 1 f. 05 slate, orange & purple 15 15

1970. 30th Anniv of New Hebrides' Declaration for the Free French Government.

142 **52** 65 c. multicoloured 35 70
143 1 f. 10 multicoloured 45 70

1970. No. 101 surch **35**.

144 35 c. on 20 c. black, green and blue 30 30

54 "The Virgin and Child" (Bellini)

57 Kauri Pine, Cone and Arms of Royal Society

56 Football

1970. Christmas. Multicoloured.

145 15 c. Type **54** 10 10
146 50 c. "The Virgin and Child" (Cima) 20 20

1971. Death of General Charles de Gaulle. Nos. 142/3 optd **1890-1970 IN MEMORIAM 9-11-70**.

147 **52** 65 c. multicoloured 15 10
148 1 f. 10 multicoloured 15 20

1971. 4th South Pacific Games, Papeete, French Polynesia.

149 20 c. Type **56** 10 10
150 65 c. Basketball (vert) 30 20

1971. Royal Society's Expedition to New Hebrides.

151 **57** 65 c. multicoloured 20 15

58 "The Adoration of the Shepherds" (detail, Louis le Nain)

60 Ceremonial Headdress, South Malekula

59 De Havilland Drover 3

1971. Christmas. Multicoloured.

152 25 c. Type **58** 10 10
153 50 c. "The Adoration of the Shepherds" (detail, Tintoretto) 30 60

1972. Aircraft. Multicoloured.

154 20 c. Type **59** 40 15
155 25 c. Short S.25 Sandringham 4 flying boat 40 15
156 30 c. De Havilland Dragon Rapide 40 15
157 65 c. Sud Aviation SE 210 Caravelle 1·00 1·25

1972. Multicoloured.

158 5 c. Type **60** 10 10
159 10 c. Baker's pigeon 25 10
160 15 c. Gong and carving, North Ambrym 15 15
161 20 c. Red-headed parrot finch 40 25
162 25 c. Graskoin's cowrie (shell) 40 25
163 30 c. Red-lip olive (shell) 50 30
164 35 c. Chestnut-bellied kingfisher 65 40
165 65 c. Pretty conch (shell) 75 60
166 1 f. Gong (North Malekula) and carving (North Ambrym) 70 1·00
167 2 f. Palm lorikeet 4·00 4·50
168 3 f. Ceremonial headdress, South Malekula (different) 2·00 6·00
169 5 f. Great green turban (shell) 5·50 14·00

61 "Adoration of the Kings" (Spranger)

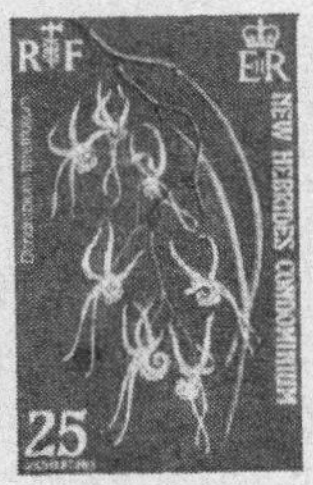

63 "Dendrobium teretifolium"

1972. Christmas. Multicoloured.

170 25 c. Type **61** 10 10
171 70 c. "The Virgin and Child in a Landscape" (Provoost) 20 20

1972. Royal Silver Wedding. As T **98** of Gibraltar, but with Royal and French cyphers in background.

172 35 c. violet 15 10
173 65 c. green 20 10

1973. Orchids. Multicoloured.

174 25 c. Type **63** 30 10
175 30 c. "Ephemerantha comata" 35 10
176 35 c. "Spathoglottis petri" 40 10
177 65 c. "Dendrobium mohlianum" 75 55

64 New Wharf at Vila

65 Wild Horses

1973. Opening of New Wharf at Villa. Multicoloured.

178 25 c. Type **64** 20 10
179 70 c. As T **64** but horiz format 40 30

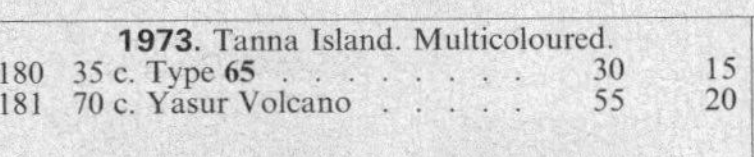

1973. Tanna Island. Multicoloured.

180 35 c. Type **65** 30 15
181 70 c. Yasur Volcano 55 20

66 Mother and Child

1973. Christmas. Multicoloured.

182 35 c. Type **66** 10 10
183 70 c. Lagoon scene 20 20

67 Pacific Pigeon

1974. Wild Life. Multicoloured.

184 25 c. Type **67** 80 25
185 35 c. "Lyssa curvata" (moth) 80 60
186 70 c. Green sea turtle 80 70
187 1 f. 15 Grey-headed flying fox 1·00 1·50

1974. Royal Visit. Nos. 164 and 167 optd **ROYAL VISIT 1974**.

188 35 c. multicoloured 30 10
189 2 f. multicoloured 50 40

69 Old Post Office

1974. Inaug of New Post Office, Vila. Mult.

190 35 c. Type **69** 15 50
191 70 c. New Post Office 15 60

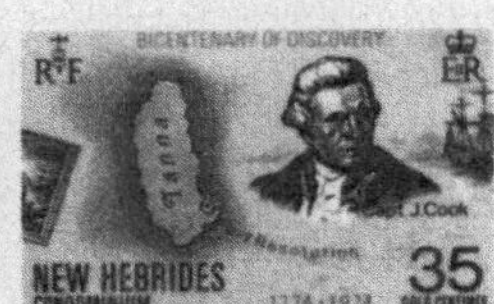

70 Capt. Cook and Map

1974. Bicent of Discovery. Multicoloured.

192 35 c. Type **70** 1·25 2·00
193 35 c. William Wales and beach landing 1·25 2·00
194 35 c. William Hodges and island scene 1·25 2·00
195 1 f. 15 Capt. Cook map and H.M.S. "Resolution" (59 × 34 mm) 2·50 3·50

71 U.P.U. Emblem and Letters

1974. Centenary of U.P.U.

196 **71** 70 c. multicoloured 30 70

72 "Adoration of the Magi" (Velazquez)

74 Canoeing

73 Charolais Bull

1974. Christmas. Multicoloured.

197 35 c. Type **72** 10 10
198 70 c. "The Nativity" (Gerard van Honthorst) 20 20

1975.

199 **73** 10 f. brown, green & blue 9·50 20·00

1975. World Scout Jamboree, Norway. Mult.

200 25 c. Type **74** 20 10
201 35 c. Preparing meal 20 10
202 1 f. Map-reading 50 15
203 5 f. Fishing 1·75 2·50

75 "Pitti Madonna" (Michelangelo)

77 Telephones of 1876 and 1976

76 Concorde in British Airways Livery

1975. Christmas. Michelangelo's Sculptures. Multicoloured.

204 35 c. Type **75** 10 10
205 70 c. "Bruges Madonna" 15 10
206 2 f. 50 "Taddei Madonna" 70 50

1976. 1st Commercial Flight of Concorde.

207 **76** 5 f. multicoloured 5·00 5·00

1976. Centenary of Telephone. Multicoloured.

208 25 c. Type **77** 15 10
209 70 c. Alexander Graham Bell 30 10
210 1 f. 15 Satellite and Noumea Earth Station 50 50

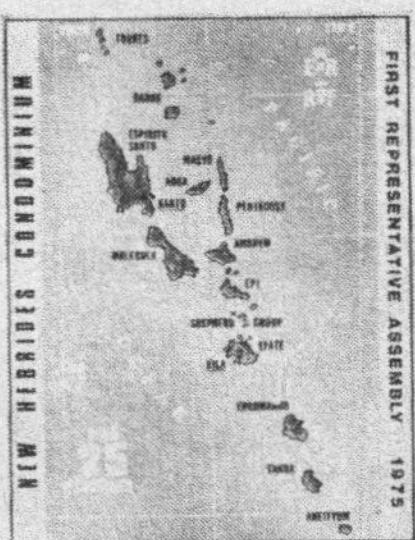

78 Map of the Islands

1976. Constitutional Changes. Multicoloured.

211 25 c. Type **78** 40 15
212 1 f. View of Santo (horiz) 75 60
213 2 f. View of Vila (horiz) 1·10 1·75

Nos. 212/13 are smaller, 36 × 26 mm.

79 "The Flight into Egypt" (Lusitano)

80 Royal Visit, 1974

1976. Christmas. Multicoloured.

214 35 c. Type **79** 10 10
215 70 c. "Adoration of the Shepherds" 15 10
216 2 f. 50 "Adoration of the Magi" 45 50

Nos. 215/16 show retables by the Master of Santos-o-Novo.

1977. Silver Jubilee. Multicoloured.

217 35 c. Type **80** 10 10
218 70 c. Imperial State Crown . . 15 10
219 2 f. The Blessing 30 65

1977. Currency change. Nos. 158/69 and 199 surch.

233 5 f. on 5 c. Type **60** 50 15
234 10 f. on 10 c. Baker's pigeon . . 50 15
222 15 f. on 15 c. Gong and carving 60 80
223 20 f. on 20 c. Red-headed parrot finch . . . . 1·25 55
224 25 f. on 25 c. Gaskoin's cowrie (shell) . . . . 1·00 1·00
225 30 f. on 30 c. Red-lip olive (shell) 1·25 50
226 35 f. on 35 c. Chestnut-bellied kingfisher . . . . 1·75 1·25
239 40 f. on 65 c. Pretty conch (shell) 1·50 55
228 50 f. on 1 f. Gong and carving 1·00 1·50
229 70 f. on 2 f. Palm lorikeet . . . 3·00 75
230 100 f. on 3 f. Ceremonial headdress . . . . 1·25 3·50
231 200 f. on 5 f. Great green turban (shell) . . . . 6·00 12·00
241 500 f. on 10 f. Type **73** . . . . 19·00 13·00

89 Island of Erromango and Kauri Pine

90 "Tempi Madonna" (Raphael)

1977. Islands. Multicoloured.

242 5 f. Type **89** 30 10
243 10 f. Territory map and copra-making 40 30
244 15 f. Espiritu Santo and cattle . 30 30
245 20 f. Efate and Vila P.O. . . . 30 25
246 25 f. Malekula and headdresses 40 40
247 30 f. Aobe, Maewo and pigs' tusks 45 50
248 35 f. Pentecost and land diver . 50 65
249 40 f. Tanna and John Frum Cross 70 60
250 50 f. Shepherd Is. and canoe . . 1·00 40
251 70 f. Banks Is. and dancers . . 1·75 2·50
252 100 f. Ambrym and idols . . . 1·75 90
253 200 f. Aneityum and baskets . . 1·75 2·50
254 500 f. Torres Is. and archer fisherman . . . . 4·00 7·50

1977. Christmas. Multicoloured.

255 10 f. Type **90** 20 15
256 15 f. "The Flight into Egypt" (Gerard David) 30 20
257 30 f. "Virgin and Child" (Batoni) 40 70

91 Concorde over New York

1978. Concorde Commemoration.

258 10 f. Type **91** . . . . 1·00 75
259 20 f. Concorde over London . 1·25 1·00
260 30 f. Concorde over Washington . . . . 1·60 1·40
261 40 f. Concorde over Paris . . . 1·90 1·60

92 White Horse of Hanover

93 "Madonna and Child"

1978. 25th Anniv of Coronation.

262 **92** 40 f. brown, blue & silver . . 15 30
263 – 40 f. multicoloured 15 30
264 – 40 f. brown, blue & silver . . 15 30

DESIGNS: No. 263, Queen Elizabeth II; No. 264, Gallic Cock.

1978. Christmas. Paintings by Durer. Multicoloured.

265 10 f. Type **93** 10 10
266 15 f. "The Virgin and Child with St. Anne" 10 10
267 30 f. "Madonna of the Siskin" 15 10
268 40 f. "Madonna of the Pear" . 20 15

1979. 1st Anniv of Internal Self-Government. Surch **166°E 11.1.79 FIRST ANNIVERSARY INTERNAL SELF-GOVERNMENT** and new value.

269 **78** 10 f. on 25 f. mult (blue background) 10 10
270 40 f. on 25 f. mult (green background) 20 20

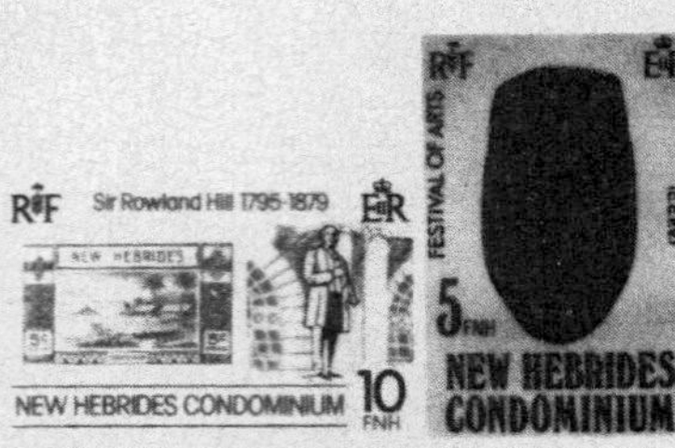

95 1938 5 c. Stamp and Sir Rowland Hill

96 Chubwan Mask

1979. Death Centenary of Sir Rowland Hill. Multicoloured.

271 10 f. Type **95** 10 10
272 20 f. 1969 25 c. Pentecost Island Land Divers commemorative 20 10
273 40 f. 1925 2d. (20 c.) . . . 25 20

1979. Arts Festival. Multicoloured.

275 5 f. Type **96** 10 10
276 10 f. Nal-Nal clubs and spears 10 10
277 20 f. Ritual puppet 15 10
278 40 f. Neqatmalow headdress . . 25 15

97 "Native Church" (Metas Masongo)

1979. Christmas and International Year of the Child. Children's Drawings. Multicoloured.

279 5 f. Type **97** 10 10
280 10 f. "Priest and Candles" (Herve Rutu) 10 10
281 20 f. "Cross and Bible" (Mark Deards) (vert) 10 10
282 40 f. "Green Candle and Santa Claus" (Dev Raj) (vert) . . . 15 15

98 White-bellied Honeyeater

1980. Birds. Multicoloured.

283 10 f. Type **98** 50 10
284 20 f. Scarlet robin 70 10
285 30 f. Yellow-fronted white eye 90 45
286 40 f. Fan-tailed cuckoo . . . 1·00 70

POSTAGE DUE STAMPS

1925. Optd **POSTAGE DUE.**

D1 **5** 1d. (10 c.) green . . . . 40·00 1·00
D2 2d. (20 c.) grey . . . . 48·00 1·00
D3 3d. (30 c.) red . . . . 50·00 2·50
D4 5d. (50 c.) blue . . . . 55·00 4·50
D5 10d. (1 c.) red on blue . . . 60·00 5·50

1938. Optd **POSTAGE DUE.**

D 6 **6** 5 c. green . . . . 22·00 29·00
D 7 10 c. orange . . . . 22·00 29·00
D 8 20 c. red . . . . 28·00 45·00
D 9 40 c. olive . . . . 35·00 60·00
D10 1 f. red on green . . . . 45·00 70·00

1953. Nos. 68/9, 71, 74 and 76 optd **POSTAGE DUE.**

D11 **7** 5 c. green . . . . 5·00 11·00
D12 10 c. red . . . . 1·75 8·00
D13 20 c. blue . . . . 6·00 17·00
D14 – 40 c. sepia (No. 74) . . . 8·50 27·00
D15 – 1 f. orange (No. 76) . . . 6·00 27·00

1957. Optd **POSTAGE DUE.**

D16 **12** 5 c. green . . . . 30 1·50
D17 10 c. red . . . . 30 1·50
D18 20 c. blue . . . . 1·25 2·00
D19 – 40 c. sepia (No. 90) . . . 2·00 3·75
D20 – 1 f. orange (No. 92) . . . 3·00 7·00

FRENCH ADMINISTRATION

1908. Stamps of New Caledonia optd **NOUVELLES HEBRIDES.**

F1 **15** 5 c. green . . . . 2·75 3·50
F2 10 c. red . . . . 3·25 3·50
F3 **16** 25 c. blue on green . . . 4·00 3·75
F4 50 c. red on green . . . 5·50 6·00
F5 **17** 1 f. blue on green . . . 11·50 11·50

1910. Nos. F1/5 further optd **CONDOMINIUM.**

F 6 **15** 5 c. green . . . . 2·00 2·00
F 7 10 c. red . . . . 2·00 80
F 8 **16** 25 c. blue on green . . . 2·25 3·75
F 9 50 c. red on orange . . . 6·50 7·00
F10 **17** 1 f. blue on green . . . 13·00 16·00

The following issues are as stamps of British Administration but are inscr "NOUVELLES HEBRIDES" except where otherwise stated.

1911.

F11 **3** 5 c. green . . . . 1·00 2·75
F12 10 c. red . . . . 45 1·25
F13 20 c. grey . . . . 1·10 2·25
F25 25 c. blue . . . . 85 4·00
F15 30 c. brown on yellow . . . 6·50 4·00
F16 40 c. red on yellow . . . 1·40 3·75
F17 50 c. olive . . . . 2·00 3·25
F18 75 c. orange . . . . 6·75 17·00
F19 1 f. red on blue . . . . 2·50 2·50
F20 2 f. violet . . . . 8·50 19·00
F21 5 f. red on green . . . . 12·00 25·00

1920. Surch in figures.

F34 5 c. on 40 c. red on yellow (No. F16) . . . . 26·00 75·00
F32a 5 c. on 50 c. red on orange (No. F4) £425 £425
F33 5 c. on 50 c. red on orange (No. F9) . . . . 2·50 7·00
F38 10 c. on 5 c. green (No. F11) 1·60 4·00
F33a 10 c. on 25 c. blue on green (No. F8) . . . . 50 1·25
F35 20 c. on 30 c. brown on yellow (No. F26) . . . . 11·00 50·00
F39 30 c. on 10 c. red (No. F12) 1·75 2·25
F41 50 c. on 25 c. blue (No. F25) 3·25 22·00

1921. Stamp of New Hebrides (British) surch **10c.**

F37 10 c. on 5d. green (No. 24) . . 15·00 42·00

1925.

F42 **5** 5 c. (½d.) black . . . . 1·50 9·50
F43 10 c. (1d.) green . . . . 1·50 9·00
F44 20 c. (2d.) grey . . . . 1·75 2·75
F45 25 c. (2½d.) brown . . . . 2·25 11·00
F46 30 c. (3d.) red . . . . 1·50 5·00
F47 40 c. (4d.) red on yellow . . 1·50 5·00
F48 50 c. (5d.) blue . . . . 1·50 3·25
F49 75 c. (7½d.) brown . . . . 2·00 11·00
F50 1 f. (10d.) red on blue . . . 2·00 3·00
F51 2 f. (1s. 8d.) violet . . . 4·25 20·00
F52 5 f. (4d.) red on green . . . 5·50 21·00

1938.

F53 **6** 5 c. green . . . . 1·60 3·25
F54 10 c. orange . . . . 1·60 2·75
F55 15 c. violet . . . . 1·25 3·25
F56 20 c. red . . . . 1·60 2·75
F57 25 c. brown . . . . 4·00 3·25
F58 30 c. blue . . . . 4·00 2·50
F59 40 c. olive . . . . 1·25 6·50
F60 50 c. purple . . . . 1·25 2·25
F61 1 f. red on green . . . . 1·60 3·75
F62 2 f. blue on green . . . . 26·00 28·00
F63 5 f. red on yellow . . . . 50·00 45·00
F64 10 f. violet and blue . . . £120 90·00

1941. Free French Issue. As last optd **France Libre.**

F65 **6** 5 c. green . . . . 2·50 22·00
F66 10 c. orange . . . . 4·00 21·00
F67 15 c. violet . . . . 6·00 30·00
F68 20 c. red . . . . 14·00 27·00
F69 25 c. brown . . . . 14·00 35·00
F70 30 c. blue . . . . 14·00 28·00
F71 40 c. olive . . . . 14·00 32·00
F72 50 c. purple . . . . 14·00 27·00
F73 1 f. red on green . . . . 14·00 27·00
F74 2 f. blue on green . . . . 14·00 32·00
F75 5 f. red on yellow . . . . 14·00 32·00
F76 10 f. violet on blue . . . . 14·00 32·00

1949. 75th Anniv of U.P.U.

F77 10 c. orange . . . . 2·25 4·25
F78 15 c. violet . . . . 3·50 7·00
F79 30 c. blue . . . . 5·00 10·00
F80 50 c. purple . . . . 6·00 10·00

1953.

F81 **7** 5 c. green . . . . 40 1·50
F82 10 c. red . . . . 90 1·00
F83 15 c. yellow . . . . 90 1·50
F84 20 c. blue . . . . 90 1·00
F85 – 25 c. olive . . . . 70 1·00
F86 – 30 c. brown . . . . 70 1·00
F87 – 40 c. sepia . . . . 70 1·50
F88 – 50 c. violet . . . . 70 1·00
F89 – 1 f. orange . . . . 19·00 6·50
F90 – 2 f. purple . . . . 21·00 45·00
F91 – 5 f. red . . . . 28·00 75·00

1956. 50th Anniv of Condominium.

F92 **10** 5 c. green . . . . 1·50 1·25
F93 10 c. red . . . . 1·50 1·25
F94 – 20 c. blue . . . . 1·50 1·50
F95 – 50 c. violet . . . . 1·50 2·00

1957.

F 96 **12** 5 c. green 80 60
F 97 10 c. red 80 40
F 98 15 c. yellow . . . . 1·25 60
F 99 20 c. blue . . . . 1·25 50
F100 – 25 c. olive . . . . 1·25 50
F101 – 30 c. brown . . . . 1·25 60
F102 – 40 c. sepia . . . . 1·25 60
F103 – 50 c. violet . . . . 1·25 50
F104 – 1 f. orange . . . . 8·00 2·75
F105 – 2 f. mauve . . . . 22·00 27·00
F106 – 5 f. black . . . . 32·00 35·00

F 7 Emblem and Globe

1963. Freedom from Hunger.

F107 **F 7** 60 c. green and brown . . 17·00 11·00

F 8 Centenary Emblem

F 9 "Syncom" Communications Satellite, Telegraph Poles and Morse Key

1963. Centenary of Red Cross.

F108 **F 8** 15 c. red, grey & orange 10·00 6·00
F109 45 c. red, grey and bistre 18·00 18·00

1963.

F110 – 5 c. lake, brown and blue . 60 30
F111 – 10 c. brown, buff & green* 80 1·00
F112 – 10 c. brown, buff & green 65 15
F113 **18** 15 c. bistre, brown and violet . . . . 10·00 40
F114 – 20 c. black, green & blue* 2·25 3·00
F115 – 20 c. black, green and blue 2·50 25
F116 – 25 c. violet, brown and red 60 60
F117 – 30 c. brown, bistre & violet 11·00 60
F118 – 40 c. red and blue . . . 3·50 6·00
F119 – 50 c. green, yellow and turquoise . . . . 11·00 60
F120 – 60 c. red and blue . . . 1·50 80
F121 – 1 f. red, black & green . . 2·00 3·50
F122 – 2 f. black, brown & olive . 24·00 10·00
F123 – 3 f. multicoloured* . . . 12·00 20·00
F124 – 3 f. multicoloured . . . 12·00 12·00
F125 – 5 f. blue, indigo & black . 22·00 28·00

The stamps indicated by an asterisk have "RF" wrongly placed on the left.

1965. Centenary of I.T.U.

F126 **F 9** 15 c. blue, green and brown . . . . 10·00 6·00
F127 60 c. red, grey & green . 22·00 22·00

1965. I.C.Y. As Nos. 112/13.

F128 5 c. purple and turquoise . . 4·00 3·00
F129 55 c. green and lavender . . 10·00 9·00

1966. Churchill Commem. As Nos. 114/17.

F130 5 c. multicoloured . . . . 1·00 75
F131 15 c. multicoloured . . . . 2·75 1·00
F132 25 c. multicoloured . . . . 3·00 3·50
F133 30 c. multicoloured . . . . 3·75 4·50

1966. World Cup Football Championships. As Nos. 118/19.

F134 20 c. multicoloured . . . . 2·75 2·75
F135 40 c. multicoloured . . . . 4·25 4·25

1966. Inauguration of W.H.O. Headquarters, Geneva. As Nos. 120/1.

F136 25 c. black, green and blue . . 3·00 2·00
F137 60 c. black, mauve and ochre 5·00 5·00

1966. 20th Anniv of U.N.E.S.C.O. As Nos. 122/4.

F138 15 c. multicoloured . . . . 1·75 1·25
F139 30 c. yellow, violet & olive . . 2·75 2·50
F140 45 c. black, purple & orange . 3·00 3·00

1967. 25th Anniv of Pacific War. As Nos. 125/8.

F141 15 c. multicoloured 85 40
F142 25 c. multicoloured . . . . 1·40 50
F143 60 c. multicoloured . . . . 2·00 1·25
F144 1 f. multicoloured . . . . 2·25 2·00

1968. Bicentenary of Bougainville's World Voyage. As Nos. 130/2.
F145 15 c. green, violet and red 20 20
F146 25 c. olive, purple and blue 40 40
F147 60 c. brown, purple & green 90 90

1968. Anglo-French Concorde Project. As Nos. 133/4.
F148 25 c. blue, red and violet 2·25 1·50
F149 60 c. red, black and blue 3·75 3·00

1969. Timber Industry. As No. 135.
F150 20 c. multicoloured 20 30

1969. 3rd South Pacific Games, Port Moresby, Papua New Guinea. As Nos. 136/7.
F151 25 c. multicoloured 50 30
F152 1 f. multicoloured 2·00 2·00

1969. Land Divers of Pentecost Island. As Nos. 138/40.
F153 15 c. multicoloured 30 30
F154 25 c. multicoloured 40 40
F155 1 f. multicoloured 1·40 1·40

1970. Inauguration of New U.P.U. Headquarters Building, Berne. As No. 141.
F156 1 f. 05 slate, orange & purple 50 70

1970. New Hebrides' Declaration for the Free French Government. As Nos. 142/3.
F157 65 c. multicoloured 85 85
F158 1 f. 10 multicoloured 1·40 1·40

1970. No. F115 surch **35**.
F159 35 c. on 20 c. black, green and blue 60 50

1970. Christmas. As Nos. 145/6.
F160 15 c. multicoloured 15 15
F161 50 c. multicoloured 25 40

1971. Death of General Charles de Gaulle. Nos. F157/8 optd **1890–1970 IN MEMORIAM 9-11-70**.
F162 65 c. multicoloured 75 55
F163 1 f. 10 multicoloured 1·50 1·50

1971. 4th South Pacific Games, Papeete, French Polynesia. As Nos. 149/50.
F164 20 c. multicoloured 35 20
F165 65 c. multicoloured 95 80

1971. Royal Society Expedition to New Hebrides. As No. 151.
F166 65 c. multicoloured 50 50

1971. Christmas. As Nos. 152/3.
F167 25 c. multicoloured 15 20
F168 50 c. multicoloured 30 35

1972. Aircraft. As Nos. 154/7.
F169 20 c. multicoloured 1·00 60
F170 25 c. multicoloured 1·00 70
F171 30 c. multicoloured 1·10 80
F172 65 c. multicoloured 3·00 4·50

1972. As Nos. 158/69.
F173 5 c. multicoloured 40 10
F174 10 c. multicoloured 1·75 50
F175 15 c. multicoloured 50 15
F176 20 c. multicoloured 2·25 30
F177 25 c. multicoloured 1·75 30
F178 30 c. multicoloured 1·75 30
F179 35 c. multicoloured 3·00 40
F180 65 c. multicoloured 2·50 60
F181 1 f. multicoloured 2·50 1·75
F182 2 f. multicoloured 15·00 10·00
F183 3 f. multicoloured 9·50 13·00
F184 5 f. multicoloured 17·00 22·00

1972. Christmas. As Nos. 170/1.
F185 25 c. multicoloured 25 20
F186 70 c. multicoloured 50 45

1972. Royal Silver Wedding. As Nos. 172/3.
F187 35 c. multicoloured 40 40
F188 65 c. multicoloured 50 1·00

1973. Orchids. As Nos. 174/7.
F189 25 c. multicoloured 2·25 60
F190 30 c. multicoloured 2·25 80
F191 35 c. multicoloured 2·25 95
F192 65 c. multicoloured 3·75 4·75

1973. Opening of New Wharf at Vila. As Nos. 178/9.
F193 25 c. multicoloured 60 50
F194 70 c. multicoloured 90 1·50

1973. Tanna Island. As No. 180/1.
F195 35 c. multicoloured 2·25 1·25
F196 70 c. multicoloured 3·25 3·25

1973. Christmas. As Nos. 182/3.
F197 35 c. multicoloured 40 35
F198 70 c. multicoloured 70 75

1974. Wild Life. As Nos. 184/7.
F199 25 c. multicoloured 3·75 1·50
F200 35 c. multicoloured 5·50 1·75
F201 70 c. multicoloured 5·50 4·00
F202 1 f. 15 multicoloured 6·00 10·00

1974. Royal Visit of Queen Elizabeth II. Nos. F179 and F182 optd **VISITE ROYALE 1974**.
F203 35 c. Chestnut-bellied kingfisher 2·50 50
F204 2 f. Green palm lorikeet 6·00 6·50

1974. Inauguration of New Post Office, Vila. As Nos. 190/1.
F205 35 c. multicoloured 50 65
F206 70 c. multicoloured 60 85

1974. Bicent of Discovery. As Nos. 192/5.
F207 35 c. multicoloured 4·50 4·00
F208 35 c. multicoloured 4·50 4·00
F209 35 c. multicoloured 4·50 4·00
F210 1 f. 15 multicoloured 10·00 8·50

1974. Centenary of U.P.U. As No. 196.
F210a 70 c. blue, red and black 1·50 1·75

1974. Christmas. As Nos. 197/8.
F211 35 c. multicoloured 25 20
F212 70 f. multicoloured 55 45

1975. Charolais Bull. As No. 199.
F213 10 f. brown, green and blue 28·00 35·00

1975. World Scout Jamboree, Norway. As Nos. 200/3.
F214 25 c. multicoloured 55 20
F215 35 c. multicoloured 65 30
F216 1 f. multicoloured 1·25 1·10
F217 5 f. multicoloured 5·50 9·00

1975. Christmas. As Nos. 204/6.
F218 35 c. multicoloured 25 15
F219 70 c. multicoloured 40 25
F220 2 f. 50 multicoloured 1·75 2·75

1976. 1st Commercial Flight of Concorde. As No. 207, but Concorde in Air France livery.
F221 5 f. multicoloured 15·00 14·00

1976. Centenary of Telephone. As Nos. 208/10.
F222 25 c. multicoloured 55 40
F223 70 c. multicoloured 1·40 1·50
F224 1 f. 15 multicoloured 1·75 2·50

1976. Constitutional Changes. As Nos. 211/13.
F225 25 c. multicoloured 50 30
F226 1 f. multicoloured 1·50 1·25
F227 2 f. multicoloured 2·50 2·25

1976. Christmas. Paintings. As Nos. 214/16.
F228 35 c. multicoloured 25 15
F229 70 c. multicoloured 40 25
F230 2 f. 50 multicoloured 1·75 2·75

1977. Silver Jubilee. As Nos. F217/9.
F231 35 c. multicoloured 30 15
F232 70 c. multicoloured 50 25
F233 2 f. multicoloured 60 60

1977. Currency change. Nos. F173/84 and F213, surch.
F234 5 f. on 5 c. multicoloured 40 40
F235 10 f. on 10 c. multicoloured 85 40
F236 15 f. on 15 c. multicoloured 70 60
F237 20 f. on 20 c. multicoloured 1·50 85
F238 25 f. on 25 c. multicoloured 1·50 1·00
F239 30 f. on 30 c. multicoloured 1·75 1·50
F240 35 f. on 35 c. multicoloured 2·50 1·50
F241 40 f. on 65 c. multicoloured 2·50 2·00
F242 50 f. on 1 f. multicoloured 2·00 2·00
F243 70 f. on 2 f. multicoloured 4·25 2·75
F244 100 f. on 3 f. multicoloured 3·25 4·50
F245 200 f. on 5 f. multicoloured 13·00 19·00
F246 500 f. on 10 f. multicoloured 22·00 35·00

1977. Islands. As Nos. 242/54.
F256 5 f. multicoloured 65 20
F257 10 f. multicoloured 75 20
F258 15 f. multicoloured 75 20
F259 20 f. multicoloured 1·00 30
F260 25 f. multicoloured 80 40
F261 30 f. multicoloured 80 45
F262 35 f. multicoloured 2·25 60
F263 40 f. multicoloured 1·25 75
F264 50 f. multicoloured 2·00 75
F265 70 f. multicoloured 4·50 3·25
F266 100 f. multicoloured 3·00 2·50
F267 200 f. multicoloured 4·75 9·00
F268 500 f. multicoloured 11·00 15·00

1977. Christmas. As Nos. 255/7.
F269 10 f. multicoloured 20 20
F270 15 f. multicoloured 35 35
F271 30 f. multicoloured 85 85

1978. Concorde. As Nos. 258/61.
F272 10 f. multicoloured 2·50 1·00
F273 20 f. multicoloured 2·75 1·50
F274 30 f. multicoloured 3·25 2·00
F275 40 f. multicoloured 3·75 3·25

1978. Coronation. As Nos. 262/4.
F276 40 f. brown, blue & silver 25 60
F277 40 f. multicoloured 25 60
F278 40 f. brown, blue & silver 25 60

1978. Christmas. As Nos. 265/8.
F279 10 f. multicoloured 15 20
F280 15 f. multicoloured 20 30
F281 30 f. multicoloured 30 60
F282 40 f. multicoloured 35 70

1979. Internal Self-Government. As T **37** surch **166°E PREMIER GOUVERNEMENT AUTONOME 11.1.78. 11.1.79** and new value.
F283 10 f. on 25 f. mult (blue background) 55 30
F284 40 f. on 25 f. mult (green background) 1·25 1·50

1979. Death Centenary of Sir Rowland Hill. As Nos. 271/3.
F285 10 f. multicoloured 25 35
F286 20 f. multicoloured 30 55
F287 40 f. multicoloured 40 75

1979. Arts Festival. As Nos. 275/8.
F288 5 f. multicoloured 20 10
F289 10 f. multicoloured 25 15
F290 20 f. multicoloured 35 40
F291 40 f. multicoloured 60 1·00

1979. Christmas and International Year of the Child. As Nos. 279/82.
F292 5 f. multicoloured 65 35
F293 10 f. multicoloured 85 35
F294 20 f. multicoloured 1·25 1·00
F295 40 f. multicoloured 2·00 2·00

1980. Birds. As Nos. 283/6.
F296 10 f. multicoloured 1·50 45
F297 20 f. multicoloured 1·75 1·00
F298 30 f. multicoloured 2·25 1·75
F299 40 f. multicoloured 2·25 2·25

POSTAGE DUE STAMPS

1925. Nos. F32 etc, optd **CHIFFRE TAXE**
FD53 **5** 10 c. (1d.) green 48·00 3·50
FD54 20 c. (2d.) grey 48·00 3·50
FD55 30 c. (3d.) red 48·00 3·50
FD56 50 c. (5d.) blue 48·00 3·50
FD57 1 f. (10d.) red on blue 48·00 3·50

1938. Optd **CHIFFRE TAXE**.
FD65 **6** 5 c. green 14·00 38·00
FD66 10 c. orange 17·00 38·00
FD67 20 c. red 23·00 48·00
FD68 40 c. olive 45·00 £100
FD69 1 f. red on green 48·00 £110

1941. Free French Issue. As last optd **France Libre**.
FD77 **6** 5 c. green 8·75 38·00
FD78 10 c. orange 8·75 38·00
FD79 20 c. red 8·75 38·00
FD80 40 c. olive 8·75 38·00
FD81 1 f. red on green 17·00 38·00

1953. Optd **TIMBRE-TAXE**.
FD92 **7** 5 c. green 4·50 18·00
FD93 10 c. red 4·50 15·00
FD94 20 c. blue 13·00 23·00
FD95 – 40 c. sepia (No. F87) 15·00 48·00
FD96 – 1 f. orange (No. F89) 25·00 48·00

1957. Optd **TIMBRE-TAXE**.
FD107 **12** 5 c. green 2·25 7·00
FD108 10 c. red 2·25 7·00
FD109 20 c. blue 5·50 9·50
FD110 – 40 c. sepia (No. F102) 11·00 17·00
FD111 – 1 f. orange (No. F104) 13·00 20·00

For later issues see **VANUATU**.

NEW REPUBLIC Pt. 1

A Boer republic originally part of Zululand. It was incorporated with the South African Republic in 1888 and annexed to Natal in 1903.

12 pence = 1 shilling;
20 shillings = 1 pound

NIEUWE REPUBLIEK 1d 8 NOV 86 ZUID-AFRIKA.

1

1886. On yellow or blue paper.
1 **1** 1d. black — £3000
2 1d. violet 10·00 12·00
73 2d. violet 8·50 8·50
74 3d. violet 13·00 13·00
75 4d. violet 13·00 13·00
81 6d. violet 8·00 8·00
82 9d. violet 8·50 8·50
83 1s. violet 8·50 8·50
77 1s. 6d. violet 14·00 14·00
85 2s. violet 18·00 16·00
86 2s. 6d. violet 23·00 23·00
87 3s. violet 42·00 42·00
88 4s. violet 11·00 11·00
89 5s. violet 13·00 13·00
90 5s. 6d. violet 12·00 12·00
91 7s. 6d. violet 14·00 17·00
92 10s. violet 12·00 12·00
93 10s. 6d. violet 16·00 16·00
44 12s. violet £300
23 13s. violet £400
94 £1 violet 45·00 45·00
25 30s. violet 95·00

Some stamps are found with Arms embossed in the paper, and others with the Arms and without a date above "ZUID-AFRIKA".

NEW SOUTH WALES Pt. 1

A S.E. state of the Australian Commonwealth, whose stamps it now uses.

12 pence = 1 shilling;
20 shillings = 1 pound

1 Seal of the Colony

8

1850. Imperf.
11 **1** 1d. red £2250 £275
25 2d. blue £1800 £130
42 3d. green £2500 £225

1851. Imperf.
47 **8** 1d. red £900 £100
83 1d. orange £170 17·00
86 2d. blue £110 8·00
87 3d. green £200 27·00
76 6d. brown £1600 £250
79 8d. yellow £3500 £600

14

15

1854. Imperf.
104 **14** 1d. red £150 22·00
107 2d. blue £130 8·00
111 3d. green £800 80·00
114 **15** 5d. green £1000 £550
116 6d. grey £400 35·00
122 6d. brown £450 35·00
126 8d. orange £3500 £800
128 1s. red £750 65·00

For these stamps perforated, see No. 134 etc.

24

1860. Perf.
173 **14** 1d. red 40·00 14·00
134 2d. blue 90·00 10·00
226 3d. green 6·00 80
243 **15** 5d. green 6·00 90
143 6d. brown £275 45·00
165 6d. violet 60·00 4·50
218 8d. orange £100 17·00
168 1s. red 75·00 7·50
297c **24** 5s. purple 32·00 12·00

26

28

1862. Queen Victoria. Various frames.
207 **26** 1d. red 5·50 30
210 **28** 2d. blue 7·50 30
230c – 4d. brown 28·00 1·00
234 – 6d. lilac 42·00 1·00
310 – 10d. lilac 12·00 3·75
237 – 1s. black 65·00 2·00

1871. As No. 310 surch **NINEPENCE**.
236d 9d. on 10d. brown 8·00 4·50

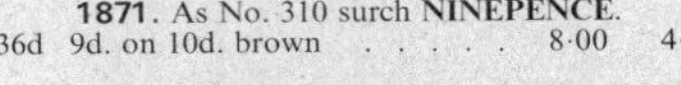

43

1885.
244b **43** 5s. green and lilac £325 80·00
251b 10s. red and violet £160 45·00
246a £1 red and lilac £2250

45 View of Sydney

46 Emu

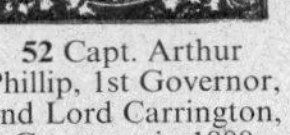
52 Capt. Arthur Phillip, 1st Governor, and Lord Carrington, Governor in 1888

55 Allegorical Figure of Australia

1888. Cent of New South Wales.

253	**45**	1d. mauve	3·75	10
254	**46**	2d. blue	4·75	10
335	–	4d. brown	9·50	3·50
256	–	6d. red	20·00	3·50
297fa	–	6d. green	22·00	8·00
339	–	6d. yellow	11·00	1·25
257	–	8d. purple	15·00	2·00
343	–	1s. brown	16·00	1·50
263	–	5s. violet	£120	27·00
346b	**52**	20s. blue	£140	60·00

DESIGNS—As Type **45**: 4d. Capt. Cook; 6d. Queen Victoria and Arms; 8d. Superb lyrebird; 1s. Kangaroo. As Type **52**: 5s. Map of Australia.

1890.

281	**55**	2½d. blue	2·50	40

1891. Types as 1862, but new value and colours, surch in words.

282	**26**	½d. on 1d. grey	3·00	3·25
283a	–	7½d. on 6d. brown	5·00	2·75
284d	–	12½d. on 1s. red	11·00	7·50

58 59

60 61

62 Superb Lyrebird 63

1892.

286	**58**	½d. grey	2·25	10
298		½d. green	1·00	10
300	**59**	1d. red	1·00	10
333	**60**	2d. blue	1·75	10
296	**61**	2½d. violet	4·50	80
303		2½d. blue	2·75	70
348	**63**	9d. brown and blue	7·00	90
345a	**62**	2s. 6d. green	27·00	18·00

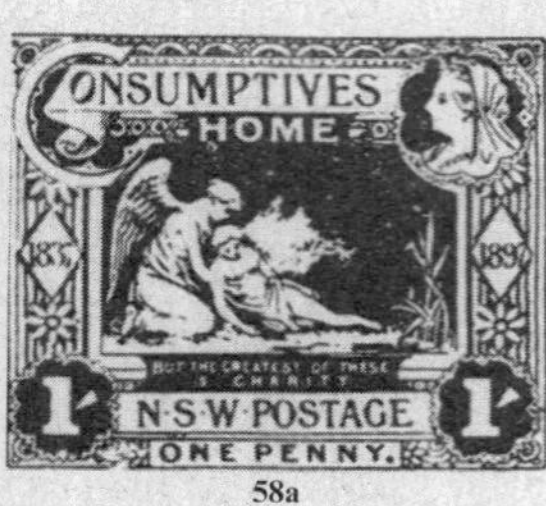

58a

1897. Diamond Jubilee and Hospital Charity.

287c	**58a**	1d. (1s.) green & brown	40·00	40·00
287d	–	2½d. (2s. 6d.) gold & blue	£150	£150

DESIGN—VERT: 2½d. Two female figures.

OFFICIAL STAMPS

1879-92. Various issues optd **O S**

A. Issues of 1854 to 1871.

O20b	**26**	1d. red	6·50	1·40
O21c	**28**	2d. blue	7·00	1·00
O25c	**14**	3d. green	5·00	3·50
O27a	–	4d. brown (No. 230c)	12·00	3·00
O28	**15**	5d. green	12·00	11·00
O31	–	6d. lilac (No. 234)	18·00	5·50
O32b	**15**	8d. orange	22·00	10·00
O11	–	9d. on 10d. (No. 236d)	£350	
O18a	–	10d. lilac (No. 310)	£130	80·00
O33	–	1s. black (No. 237)	25·00	6·50
O18	**24**	5s. purple	£170	80·00

B. Fiscal stamps of 1885.

O37	**24**	10s. red and violet	£1200	£600
O38		£1 red and violet	£5500	£3500

C. Issue of 1888 (Nos. 253/346b).

O39	1d. mauve	2·00	15
O40	2d. blue	4·25	15
O41	4d. brown	10·00	3·00
O42	6d. red	8·50	4·00
O43	8d. purple	18·00	9·00
O44	1s. brown	17·00	3·00
O49a	5s. violet	£160	70·00
O48	20s. blue	£1600	£800

D. Issues of 1890 and 1892.

O58a	**58**	½d. grey	6·00	8·00
O55	**26**	½d. on 1d. grey	50·00	45·00
O54	**55**	2½d. blue	7·00	3·00
O56	–	7½d. on 6d. (No. 283)	35·00	30·00
O57	–	12½d. on 1s. (No. 284c)	60·00	55·00

POSTAGE DUE STAMPS

D 1

1891.

D 1	**D 1**	½d. green	3·00	2·25
D 2		1d. green	5·00	90
D 3		2d. green	7·00	1·00
D 4		3d. green	12·00	2·75
D 5		4d. green	9·00	80
D 6		6d. green	18·00	2·00
D 7		8d. green	60·00	9·00
D 8		5s. green	£120	35·00
D 9a		10s. green	£180	85·00
D10b		20s. green	£225	£110

REGISTRATION STAMPS

13

1856.

88	**13**	(6d.) red and blue (Imp)	£700	£150
92		(6d.) orange and blue (Imp)	£800	£150
101		(6d.) red and blue (Perf)	75·00	15·00
94		(6d.) orange and blue (Perf)	£325	50·00

NEW ZEALAND Pt. 1

A group of islands in the south Pacific Ocean. A Commonwealth Dominion.

1855. 12 pence = 1 shilling;
20 shillings = 1 pound.
1967. 100 cents = 1 dollar.

1

3

1855. Imperf.

35	**1**	1d. red	£375	£225
34		1d. orange	£425	£190
39		2d. blue	£275	70·00
40		3d. lilac	£325	£120
43		6d. brown	£700	90·00
45		1s. green	£900	£250

1862. Perf.

110	**1**	1d. orange	£110	26·00
132		1d. brown	£100	28·00
114		2d. blue	£110	18·00
133		2d. orange	95·00	25·00
117		3d. lilac	90·00	27·00
119		4d. red	£2250	£250
120		4d. yellow	£130	90·00
122		6d. brown	£160	24·00
136		6d. blue	£110	48·00
125		1s. green	£140	80·00

1873.

151	**3**	½d. pink	8·00	70

5

6

7

8

9

10

11

1874. Inscr "POSTAGE".

180	**5**	1d. lilac	38·00	3·00
181	**6**	2d. red	38·00	1·60
154	**7**	3d. brown	£100	55·00
182	**8**	4d. purple	£140	40·00
183	**9**	6d. blue	80·00	10·00
184	**10**	1s. green	£120	35·00
185	**11**	2s. red	£325	£275
186		5s. grey	£350	£275

13

16

19

F 4

1882. Inscr "POSTAGE & REVENUE".

236	**13**	½d. black	3·25	15
237	**10**	1d. red	3·75	10
238	**9**	2d. mauve	8·00	30
239	**16**	2½d. blue	45·00	3·75
198	**10**	3d. yellow	42·00	6·50
222	**6**	4d. green	45·00	2·50
200	**19**	5d. black	42·00	9·00
224b	**8**	6d. brown	45·00	5·50
202	**9**	8d. blue	65·00	45·00
226	**7**	1s. brown	75·00	5·50

1882.

F 90	**F 4**	2s. blue	25·00	4·00
F 99		2s. 6d. brown	27·00	4·50
F100		3s. mauve	70·00	6·00
F102		5s. green	70·00	8·50
F 87		10s. brown	£130	18·00
F 77		£1 red	£170	50·00

The above are revenue stamps authorised for use as postage stamps as there were no other postage stamps available in these denominations. Other values in this and similar types were mainly used for revenue purposes.

23 Mount Cook or Aorangi

24 Lake Taupo and Mount Ruapehu

26 Lake Wakatipu and Mount Earnslaw

25 Pembroke Peak, Milford Sound

28 Sacred Huia Birds

29 White Terrace, Rotomahana

30 Otira Gorge and Mount Ruapehu

31 Brown Kiwi

32 Maori War Canoe

33 Pink Terrace, Rotomahana

34 Kea and Kaka

35 Milford Sound

1898.

246	**23**	½d. purple	4·75	60
302		½d. green	5·50	30
247	**24**	1d. blue and brown	3·50	20
248	**25**	2d. red	26·00	20
249	**26**	2½d. blue (A)*	7·00	24·00
320		2½d. blue (B)*	11·00	2·75
309	**28**	3d. brown	23·00	1·00
252	**29**	4d. red	12·00	16·00
311a	**30**	5d. brown	22·00	4·75
254	**31**	6d. green	50·00	26·00
265		6d. red	35·00	3·75
325	**32**	8d. blue	27·00	8·00
326	**33**	9d. purple	27·00	6·00
268a	**34**	1s. orange	48·00	3·00
328	**35**	2s. green	65·00	22·00
329	–	5s. red	£170	£190

DESIGN—As Type **30**: 5 s. Mount Cook.
* Type A of 2½d. is inscr "WAKITIPU", Type B "WAKATIPU".

40 Commemorative of the New Zealand Contingent in the South African War

1900.

274	**29**	1d. red	13·00	10
275b	**40**	1½d. brown	9·00	4·00
319	**25**	2d. purple	5·50	1·25
322d	**24**	4d. blue and brown	4·00	1·75

The 1d., 2d. and 4d. are smaller than the illustrations of their respective types.

42

44 Maori Canoe "Te Arawa"

1901.

303	**42**	1d. red	3·00	10

1906. New Zealand Exhibition, Christchurch. Inscr "COMMEMORATIVE SERIES OF 1906".

370	**44**	½d. green	18·00	28·00
371	–	1d. red	15·00	16·00
372	–	3d. brown and blue	48·00	75·00
373	–	6d. red and green	£170	£250

DESIGNS: 1d. Maori art; 3d. Landing of Cook; 6d. Annexation of New Zealand.

50

51 King Edward VII

53 Dominion

1907.

386	**50**	1d. red	22·00	70
383	**28**	3d. brown	35·00	14·00
376	**31**	6d. red	45·00	7·00
385	**34**	1s. orange	£120	24·00

These are smaller in size than the 1898 and 1901 issues. Type **50** also differs from Type **42** in the corner ornaments.

1909.

387	**51**	½d. green	3·75	30
405	**53**	1d. red	1·25	10
388	**51**	2d. mauve	14·00	6·50
389		3d. brown	23·00	80
390a		4d. orange	7·00	6·00
391a		5d. brown	15·00	2·00
392		6d. red	40·00	80
393		8d. blue	10·00	65
394		1s. red	48·00	1·75

1913. Auckland Industrial Exhibition. Optd **AUCKLAND EXHIBITION, 1913.**

412	**51**	½d. green	13·00	40·00
413	**53**	1d. red	19·00	38·00
414	**51**	3d. brown	£130	£250
415		6d. red	£140	£275

62 King George V

1915.

446	**62**	½d. green	50	10
416		1½d. grey	2·25	1·75
438		1½d. brown	2·25	10
417a		2d. violet	7·00	28·00
439		2d. yellow	1·75	10
419		2½d. blue	3·25	3·50
449		3d. brown	7·50	40
421		4d. yellow	4·25	48·00
422e		4d. violet	7·00	40
423		4½d. green	12·00	15·00
424		5d. blue	6·50	1·00
425		6d. red	7·00	40
426		7½d. brown	13·00	23·00
427		8d. blue	14·00	45·00
428		8d. brown	18·00	1·50
429		9d. green	17·00	2·25
430c		1s. orange	14·00	50

1915. No. 446 optd **WAR STAMP** and stars.

452	**62**	½d. green	1·60	30

64 "Peace" and Lion   **65** "Peace" and Lion

1920. Victory. Inscr "VICTORY" or dated "1914 1919" (6d.).

453	**64**	½d. green	3·00	2·25
454	**65**	1d. red	4·00	40
455	–	1½d. orange	3·50	30
456	–	3d. brown	13·00	12·00
457	–	6d. violet	15·00	16·00
458	–	1s. orange	24·00	48·00

DESIGNS—HORIZ (As Type **65**): 1½d. Maori chief. (As Type **64**): 3d. Lion; 1s. King George V. VERT (As Type **64**): 6d. "Peace" and "Progress".

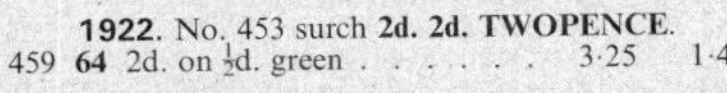

1922. No. 453 surch **2d. 2d. TWOPENCE.**

459	**64**	2d. on ½d. green	3·25	1·40

69 New Zealand   **70** Exhibition Buildings

1923. Restoration of Penny Postage.

460	**69**	1d. red	2·75	50

1925. Dunedin Exhibition.

463	**70**	½d. green on green	3·00	11·00
464		1d. red on rose	3·25	5·50
465		4d. mauve on mauve	40·00	70·00

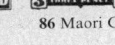

71   **73** Nurse

1926.

468	**71**	1d. red	55	10
469	–	2s. blue	48·00	20·00
470	–	3s. mauve	80·00	£130

The 2s. and 3s. are larger, 21 × 25 mm.

1929. Anti-T.B Fund.

544	**73**	1d. + 1d. red	11·00	18·00

1930. Inscr "HELP PROMOTE HEALTH".

545	**73**	1d. + 1d. red	22·00	32·00

74 Smiling Boy   **F 6** "Arms" Type

75 New Zealand Lake Scenery

1931. Health Stamps.

546	**74**	1d. + 1d. red	75·00	75·00
547		2d. + 1d. blue	75·00	60·00

1931. Air.

548	**75**	3d. brown	23·00	13·00
549		4d. purple	23·00	16·00
550		7d. orange	26·00	7·50

1931. Air. Surch **FIVE PENCE.**

551	**75**	5d. on 3d. green	11·00	7·50

1931. Various frames.

F191	**F 6**	1s. 3d. yellow	8·00	1·50
F192		1s. 3d. yellow & black	1·50	80
F193		2s. 6d. brown	8·00	60
F194		4s. red	12·00	90
F195		5s. green	17·00	80
F196		6s. red	30·00	3·25
F197		7s. blue	30·00	4·75
F198		7s. 6d. grey	60·00	50·00
F153		8s. violet	28·00	28·00
F154		9s. orange	30·00	28·00
F201		10s. red	28·00	2·25
F156		12s. 6d. purple	£140	£140
F202		15s. green	42·00	18·00
F203		£1 pink	27·00	3·75
F159		25s. blue	£250	£375
F205w		30s. brown	£200	£100
F161		35s. yellow	£2500	£2750
F206		£2 violet	80·00	20·00
F207		£2 10s. red	£250	£250
F208w		£3 green	£100	45·00
F165		£3 10s. red	£1300	£1000
F210		£4 blue	£130	95·00
F167		£4 10s. grey	£1000	£1100
F211w		£5 blue	£160	45·00

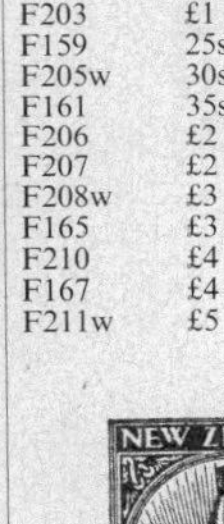

77 Hygeia Goddess of Health   **78** The Path to Health

1932. Health Stamp.

552	**77**	1d. + 1d. red	23·00	27·00

1933. Health Stamp.

553	**78**	1d. + 1d. red	13·00	17·00

1934. Air. Optd **TRANS-TASMAN AIR MAIL "FAITH IN AUSTRALIA".**

554	**75**	7d. blue	35·00	40·00

80 Crusader

1934. Health Stamp.

555	**80**	1d. + 1d. red	11·00	17·00

81 Collared Grey Fantail   **83** Maori Woman   **86** Maori Girl

85 Mt. Cook   **87** Mitre Peak

89 Harvesting   **91** Maori Panel

93 Capt. Cook at Poverty Bay

1935.

556	**81**	½d. green	1·50	50
557	–	1d. red	1·50	30
558a	**83**	1½d. brown	4·75	5·50
580	–	2d. orange	30	10
581c	**85**	2½d. brown and grey	50	4·00
561	**86**	3d. brown	12·00	1·50
583d	**87**	4d. black and brown	90	10
584c	–	5d. blue	3·00	75
585c	**89**	6d. red	1·00	10
586d	–	8d. brown	3·75	70
631	**91**	9d. red and black	3·25	2·25
588	–	1s. green	2·50	60
589e	**93**	2s. olive	10·00	1·50
590c	–	3s. chocolate and brown	5·00	2·25

DESIGNS—As Type **81**: 1d. Brown kiwi; 2d. Maori carved house; 1s. Tui. As Type **87**: 8d. Tuatara lizard. As Type **85**: 5d. Swordfish; 3s. Mt. Egmont.

95 Bell Block Aerodrome

1935. Air.

570	**95**	1d. red	1·00	50
571		3d. violet	5·00	3·00
572		6d. blue	9·50	2·50

96 King George V and Queen Mary

1935. Silver Jubilee.

573	**96**	½d. green	75	90
574		1d. red	1·25	70
575		6d. orange	21·00	23·00

97 "The Key to Health"   **99** N.Z. Soldier at Anzac Cove

1935. Health Stamp.

576	**97**	1d. + 1d. red	2·50	2·75

1936. Charity. 21st Anniv of "Anzac" Landing at Gallipoli.

591	**99**	½d. + ½d. green	60	1·75
592		1d. + 1d. red	60	1·40

100 Wool

1936. Congress of British Empire Chambers of Commerce, Wellington. Inscr as in T **100**.

593	**100**	½d. green	30	30
594	–	1d. red (Butter)	30	20
595	–	2½d. blue (Sheep)	1·00	8·00
596	–	4d. violet (Apples)	80	5·50
597	–	6d. brown (Exports)	2·00	4·50

105 Health Camp

1936. Health Stamp.

598	**105**	1d. + 1d. red	1·50	3·75

106 King George VI and Queen Elizabeth

1937. Coronation.

599	**106**	1d. red	30	10
600		2½d. blue	1·00	2·25
601		6d. orange	1·50	2·00

107 Rock climbing   **108** King George VI

1937. Health Stamp.

602	**107**	1d. + 1d. red	2·25	3·25

1938.

603	**108**	½d. green	6·50	10
604		½d. orange	20	20
605		1d. red	5·00	10
606		1d. green	20	10
607		1½d. brown	26·00	2·00
608		1½d. red	20	30
680		2d. orange	15	10
609		3d. blue	20	10
681		4d. purple	70	30
682		5d. grey	50	60
683		6d. red	40	10
684		8d. violet	65	30
685		9d. brown	1·75	30
686b	–	1s. brown and red	50	70
687	–	1s. 3d. brown and blue	1·25	80
688	–	2s. orange and green	3·00	2·00
689	–	3s. brown and grey	3·25	3·25

The shilling values are larger, 22 × 25½ mm, and "NEW ZEALAND" appears at the top.

109 Children playing   **110** Beach Ball

1938. Health Stamp.

610	**109**	1d. + 1d. red	4·00	2·50

1939. Health Stamps. Surch.

611	**110**	1d. on ½d. + ½d. green	3·75	4·00
612		2d. on 1d. + 1d. red	3·75	4·00

1939. Surch in bold figures.

F212	**F 6**	3/6 on 3s. 6d. green	20·00	7·00
F214		5/6 on 5s. 6d. lilac	48·00	18·00
F215		11/- on 11s. yellow	75·00	48·00
F216		22/- on 22s. red	£250	£130
F186		35/- on 35s. orange	£400	£225

112 "Endeavour", Chart of N.Z. and Captain Cook

1940. Centenary of Proclamation of British Sovereignty. Inscr "CENTENNIAL OF NEW ZEALAND 1840–1940".

613	–	½d. green	30	10
614	**112**	1d. brown and red	2·75	10
615	–	1½d. blue and mauve	30	30
616	–	2d. green and brown	1·50	10
617	–	2½d. green and blue	1·75	75
618	–	3d. purple and red	3·50	75
619	–	4d. brown and red	16·00	1·25
620	–	5d. blue and brown	7·00	3·50
621	–	6d. green and violet	13·00	90
622	–	7d. black and red	1·50	3·75
623	–	8d. black and red	13·00	2·00
624	–	9d. green and orange	7·50	1·75
625	–	1s. green and deep green	17·00	3·50

DESIGNS—HORIZ (as T **112**): ½d. Arrival of the Maoris, 1350; 1½d. British Monarchs; 2d. Abel Tasman with "Heemskerk" and chart; 3d. Landing of immigrants, 1840; 4d. Road, rail, ocean and air transport; 6d. "Dunedin" and "frozen mutton" sea route to London; 7, 8d. Maori council; 9d. Gold mining methods, 1861 and 1940. (25 × 21 mm): 5d. H.M.S. "Britomart" at Akaroa, 1840. VERT (21 × 25 mm): 2½d. Treaty of Waitangi. (As T **112**): 1s. Giant kauri tree.

1940. Health Stamps.

626	**110**	1d. + ½d. green	13·00	14·00
627		2d. + 1d. orange	13·00	14·00

1941. Surch.

628	**108**	1d. on ½d. green	90	10
629		2d. on 1½d. brown	90	10

1941. Health Stamps. Optd **1941**.

632	**110**	1d. + ½d. green	30	2·00
633		2d. + 1d. orange	30	2·00

125 Boy and Girl on Swing

1942. Health Stamps.

634	**125**	1d. + ½d. green	30	90
635		2d. + 1d. orange	30	90

126 Princess Margaret

1943. Health Stamps.

636	**126**	1d. + ½d. green	20	1·10
637	–	2d. + 1d. brown	20	20

DESIGN: 2d. Queen Elizabeth II as Princess.

1944. Surch **TENPENCE** between crosses.

662	–	10d. on 1½d. blue and mauve (No. 615)	15	20

129 Queen Elizabeth II as Princess and Princess Margaret

130 Peter Pan Statue, Kensington Gardens

1944. Health Stamps.

663	**129**	1d. + ½d. green	25	40
664		2d. + 1d. blue	25	30

1945. Health Stamps.zz

665	**130**	1d. + ½d. green and buff	15	20
666		2d. + 1d. red and buff	15	20

131 Lake Matheson

132 King George VI and Parliament House, Wellington

133 St. Paul's Cathedral

139 "St. George" (Wellington College War Memorial window)

1946. Peace Issue.

667	**131**	½d. green and brown	20	40
668	**132**	1d. green	10	10
669	**133**	1½d. red	10	30
670	–	2d. purple	15	10
671	–	3d. blue and grey	30	15
672	–	4d. green and orange	20	20
673	–	5d. green and blue	40	60
674	–	6d. brown and red	15	30
675	**139**	8d. black and red	15	20
676	–	9d. blue and black	15	20
677	–	1s. grey	15	20

DESIGNS—As Type **132**: 2d. The Royal Family. As Type **131**: 3d. R.N.Z.A.F. badge and airplanes; 4d. Army badge, tank and plough; 5d. Navy badge, H.M.N.Z.S. "Achilles" (cruiser) and "Dominion Monarch" (liner); 6d. N.Z. coat of arms, foundry and farm; 9d. Southern Alps and Franz Josef Glacier. As T **139**: 1s. National Memorial campanile.

142 Soldier helping Child over Stile

145 Statue of Eros

1946. Health Stamps.

678	**142**	1d. + ½d. green & orange	15	15
679		2d. + 1d. brown & orange	15	15

1947. Health Stamps.

690	**145**	1d. + ½d. green	15	15
691		2d. + 1d. red	15	15

146 Port Chalmers, 1848

1948. Centenary of Otago. Various designs inscr "CENTENNIAL OF OTAGO".

692	**146**	1d. blue and green	20	20
693	–	2d. green and brown	20	20
694	–	3d. purple	20	40
695	–	6d. black and red	20	40

DESIGNS—HORIZ: 2d. Cromwell, Otago; 6d. Otago University. VERT: 3d. First Church, Dunedin.

150 Boy sunbathing and Children playing

151 Nurse and Child

1948. Health Stamps.

696	**150**	1d. + ½d. blue and green	15	15
697		2d. + 1d. purple and red	15	15

1949. Health Stamps.

698	**151**	1d. + ½d. green	20	20
699		2d. + 1d. blue	20	20

1950. As Type F **6**, but without value, surch **1½d. POSTAGE**.

700		1½d. red	30	30

Type F **6** is illustrated next to Type **74**.

153 Queen Elizabeth II and Prince Charles

155 Cairn on Lyttleton Hills

1950. Health Stamps.

701	**153**	1d. + ½d. green	15	15
702		2d. + 1d. purple	15	15

1950. Centenary of Canterbury, N.Z.

703	–	1d. green and blue	20	40
704	**155**	2d. red and orange	20	40
705	–	3d. deep blue and blue	20	60
706	–	6d. brown and blue	20	60
707	–	1s. purple and blue	20	80

DESIGNS—VERT: 1d. Christchurch Cathedral; 3d. John Robert Godley. HORIZ: 6d. Canterbury University College; 1s. Aerial view of Timaru.

159 "Takapuna" class Yachts

1951. Health Stamps.

708	**159**	1½d. + ½d. red & yellow	15	70
709		2d. + 1d. green & yellow	15	10

160 Princess Anne

161 Prince Charles

1952. Health Stamps.

710	**160**	1½d. + ½d. red	15	30
711	**161**	2d. + 1d. brown	15	20

1952. Surch in figures.

712	**108**	1d. on ½d. orange	20	85
713		3d. on 1d. green	10	10

164 Queen Elizabeth II

166 Westminster Abbey

165 Coronation State Coach

1953. Coronation.

714	–	2d. blue	30	30
715	**164**	3d. brown	30	10
716	**165**	4d. red	1·25	2·50
717	**166**	8d. grey	80	1·60
718	–	1s. 6d. purple and blue	2·00	2·75

DESIGNS—As Type **165**: 2d. Queen Elizabeth II and Buckingham Palace; 1s. 6d. St. Edward's Crown and Royal Sceptre.

168 Girl Guides

169 Boy Scouts

1953. Health Stamps.

719	**168**	1½d. + ½d. blue	15	10
720	**169**	2d. + 1d. green	15	40

170 Queen Elizabeth II

171 Queen Elizabeth II and Duke of Edinburgh

1953. Royal Visit.

721	**170**	3d. purple	10	10
722	**171**	4d. blue	10	60

172

173

174 Queen Elizabeth II

1953. Small figures of value.

723	**172**	½d. black	15	30
724		1d. orange	15	10
725		1½d. red	20	10
726		2d. green	20	10
727		3d. red	20	10
728		4d. blue	40	40
729		6d. purple	70	1·40
730		8d. red	60	60
731	**173**	9d. brown and green	60	30
732		1s. black and red	65	10
733		1s. 6d. black and blue	1·25	50
733c		1s. 9d. black & orange	7·00	1·25
733d	**174**	2s. 6d. brown	27·00	8·00
734		3s. green	12·00	30
735		5s. red	20·00	4·25
736		10s. blue	45·00	18·00

175 Young Climber and Mts. Aspiring and Everest

176 Maori Mail-carrier

177 Queen Elizabeth II

179 Children's Health Camps Federation Emblem

1954. Health Stamps.

737	**175**	1½d. + ½d. brown and violet	15	30
738		2d. + 1d. brown and blue	15	30

1955. Centenary of First New Zealand Stamps. Inscr "1855–1955".

739	**176**	2d. brown and green	10	10
740	**177**	3d. red	10	10
741	–	4d. black and blue	35	80

DESIGN—HORIZ (As Type **176**): 4d. Douglas DC-3 airliner.

1955. Health Stamps.

742	**179**	1½d. + ½d. brown and chestnut	10	40
743		2d. + 1d. red and green	10	20
744		3d. + 1d. brown and red	15	10

180

183 Takahe

181 "The Whalers of Foveaux Strait"

1955. As 1953 but larger figures of value and stars omitted from lower right corner.

745	**180**	1d. orange	50	10
746		1½d. red	60	60
747		2d. green	40	10
748b		3d. red	75	10
749		4d. blue	1·50	70
750		6d. purple	9·50	10
751		8d. brown	6·50	8·00

1956. Southland Centennial.

752	**181**	2d. green	30	15
753	–	3d. brown	10	10
754	**183**	8d. violet and red	1·25	1·75

DESIGN—As Type **181**: 3d. Allegory of farming.

184 Children picking Apples

185 New Zealand Lamb and Map

1956. Health Stamps.
755 **184** 1½d. + ½d. brown 15 60
756 2d. + 1d. green 15 50
757 3d. + 1d. red 15 15

1957. 75th Anniv of First Export of N.Z. Lamb.
758 **185** 4d. blue . . . . 50 1·00
759 – 8d. red . . . . 75 1·25
DESIGN—HORIZ: 8d. Lamb, sailing ship "Dunedin" and "Port Brisbane" (refrigerated freighter).

187 Sir Truby King

188 Life-savers in Action

1957. 50th Anniv of Plunket Society.
760 **187** 3d. red 10 10

1957. Health Stamps.
761 **188** 2d. + 1d. black and green 15 60
762 – 3d. + 1d. blue and red . 15 10
DESIGN: 3d. Children on seashore.

1958. Surch.
763 **180** 2d. on 1½d. brown 70 10
808 2½d. on 3d. red 15 15

192 Boys' Brigade Bugler

193 Sir Charles Kingsford-Smith and Fokker F.IIa/3m Southern Cross

1958. Health Stamps.
764 – 2d. + 1d. green 20 40
765 **192** 3d. + 1d. blue 20 40
DESIGN: 2d. Girls' Life Brigade cadet.

1958. 30th Anniv of 1st Air Crossing of Tasman Sea.
766 **193** 6d. blue 50 65

194 Seal of Nelson

1958. Centenary of City of Nelson.
767 **194** 3d. red 10 10

195 "Pania" Statue, Napier

196 Australian Gannets on Cape Kidnappers

1958. Centenary of Hawke's Bay Province.
768 **195** 2d. green 10 10
769 **196** 3d. blue 20 10
770 – 8d. brown . . . . 55 1·50
DESIGN—As Type **195**: 8d. Maori sheep-shearer.

197 "Kiwi", Jamboree Badge

198 Careening H.M.S. "Endeavour" at Ship Cove

1959. Pan-Pacific Scout Jamboree, Auckland.
771 **197** 3d. brown and red 30 10

1959. Centenary of Marlborough Province. Inscr as in T **198**.
772 **198** 2d. green 30 10
773 – 3d. blue 30 10
774 – 8d. brown . . . . 1·00 2·25
DESIGNS: 3d. Shipping wool, Wairau Bar, 1857; 8d. Salt industry, Grassmere.

201 Red Cross Flag

1959. Red Cross Commemoration.
775 **201** 3d. + 1d. red and blue . . 20 10

202 Grey Teal

204 "The Explorer"

1959. Health Stamps.
776 **202** 2d. + 1d. yellow, olive and red 40 65
777 – 3d. + 1d. black, pink and blue 40 65
DESIGN: 3d. New Zealand stilt.

1960. Centenary of Westland Province.
778 **204** 2d. green 20 10
779 – 3d. salmon 20 10
780 – 8d. black . . . . 1·10 3·00
DESIGNS: 3d. "The Gold Digger"; 8d. "The Pioneer Woman".

207 Manuka (Tea Tree)

215 Timber Industry

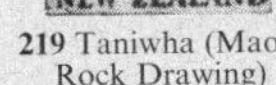

219 Taniwha (Maori Rock Drawing)

225 Sacred Kingfisher

1960.
781 **207** ½d. green and red 10 10
782 – 1d. multicoloured 10 10
783 – 2d. multicoloured 10 10
784 – 2½d. multicoloured 90 10
785 – 3d. multicoloured 30 10
786 – 4d. multicoloured 40 10
787 – 5d. multicoloured . . . . 1·25 10
788 – 6d. lilac, green & turquoise 60 10
788d – 7d. red, green and yellow 45 1·25
789 – 8d. multicoloured 40 10
790 – 9d. red and blue 40 10
791 **215** 1s. brown and green . . . 30 10
792b – 1s. 3d. red, sepia and blue 1·50 10
793 – 1s. 6d. olive and brown . . 1·00 10
794 – 1s. 9d. brown . . . . . . 16·00 15
795 – 1s. 9d. multicoloured . . 8·50 1·00
796 **219** 2s. black and buff . . . . 3·50 10
797 – 2s. 6d. yellow and brown 1·75 95
798 – 3s. sepia . . . . 32·00 75
799 – 3s. bistre, blue & green . . 6·50 1·75
800 – 5s. myrtle . . . . 5·50 80
801 – 10s. blue . . . . 9·00 3·25
802 – £1 mauve . . . . 14·00 6·00
DESIGNS—VERT (as Type **207**): 1d. Karaka; 2d. Kowhai Ngutu-kaka (Kaka Beak); 2½d. Titoki (plant); 3d. Kowhai; 4d. Puarangi (Hibiscus); 5d. Matua tikumu (Mountain daisy); 6d. Pikiarero (Clematis); 7d. Koromiko; 8d. Rata. (As T **215**): 1s. 3d. Rainbow trout; 1s. 6d. Tiki. (As T **219**): 5s. Sutherland Falls; £1 Potutu Geyser. HORIZ (as T **215**): 9d. National flag; 1s. 9d. Aerial top-dressing. (As Type **219**): 2s. 6d. Butter-making; 3s. Tongariro National Park and Chateau; 10s. Tasman Glacier.

1960. Health Stamps.
803 **225** 2d. + 1d. sepia and blue . 90 65
804 – 3d. + 1d. purple & orange 90 65
DESIGN: 3d. New Zealand pigeon.

227 "The Adoration of the Shepherds" (Rembrandt)

228 Great Egret

1960. Christmas.
805 **227** 2d. red & brown on cream 15 10

1961. Health Stamps.
806 **228** 2d. + 1d. black & purple . 65 65
807 – 3d. + 1d. sepia and green . 65 65
DESIGN: 3d. New Zealand falcon.

232 "Adoration of the Magi" (Durer)

236 Tieke Saddleback

233 Morse Key and Port Hills, Lyttleton

1961. Christmas.
809 **232** 2½d. multicoloured 10 10

1962. Telegraph Centenary.
810 **233** 3d. sepia and green 10 10
811 – 8d. black and red 90 55
DESIGN: 8d. Modern teleprinter.

1962. Health Stamps.
812 – 2½d. + 1d. multicoloured . 50 65
813 **236** 3d. + 1d. multicoloured . . 50 65
DESIGN: 2½d. Red-fronted parakeet.

237 "Madonna in Prayer" (Sassoferrato)

238 Prince Andrew

1962. Christmas.
814 **237** 2½d. multicoloured 10 10

1963. Health Stamps.
815 **238** 2½d. + 1d. blue 30 70
816 – 3d. + 1d. red 30 10
DESIGN: 3d. Prince Andrew (different).

240 "The Holy Family" (Titian)

1963. Christmas.
817 **240** 2½d. multicoloured 10 10

241 Steam Locomotive "Pilgrim" (1863) and Class DG Diesel Locomotive

1963. Centenary of New Zealand Railway. Inscr as in T **241**. Multicoloured.
818 3d. Type **241** 40 10
819 1s. 9d. Diesel express and Mt. Ruapehu . . . . 2·25 1·50

243 "Commonwealth Cable"

1963. Opening of COMPAC (Trans-Pacific Telephone Cable).
820 **243** 8d. multicoloured . . . . 50 1·25

244 Road Map and Car Steering-wheel

1964. Road Safety Campaign.
821 **244** 3d. black, yellow & blue . . 30 10

245 Silver Gulls

1964. Health Stamps. Multicoloured.
822 2½d. + 1d. Type **245** 40 50
823 3d. + 1d. Little penguin . . . 40 50

246 Rev. S. Marsden taking first Christian Service at Rangihoua Bay, 1814

1964. Christmas.
824 **246** 2½d. multicoloured 10 10

1964. Surch **7D POSTAGE**.
825 F **6** 7d. on (–) red . . . . . . 70 1·25

248 Anzac Cove

1965. 50th Anniv of Gallipoli Landing.
826 **248** 4d. brown 10 10
827 – 5d. green and red 10 60
DESIGN: 5d. Anzac Cove and poppy.

249 I.T.U. Emblem and Symbols

250 Sir Winston Churchill

1965. Centenary of I.T.U.
828 **249** 9d. blue and brown 55 35

1965. Churchill Commemoration.
829 **250** 7d. black, grey and blue . . 30 50

251 Wellington Provincial Council Building

252 Kaka

1965. Centenary of Government in Wellington.
830 **251** 4d. multicoloured 20 10

1965 Health Stamps. Multicoloured.
831 3d. + 1d. Type **252** 40 50
832 4d. + 1d. Collared grey fantail 40 50

254 I.C.Y. Emblem **255** "The Two Trinities" (Murillo)

1965. International Co-operation Year.
833 **254** 4d. red and olive 20 10

1965. Christmas.
834 **255** 3d. multicoloured 10 10

256 Arms of New Zealand

1965. 11th Commonwealth Parliamentary Conf. Multicoloured.
835 4d. Type **256** 25 20
836 9d. Parliament House, Wellington, and Badge 65 1·25
837 2s. Wellington from Mt. Victoria 4·50 6·00

259 "Progress" Arrowhead **260** New Zealand Bell Bird

1966. 4th National Scout Jamboree, Trentham.
838 **259** 4d. gold and green 15 10

1966. Health Stamps. Multicoloured.
839 3d. + 1d. Type **260** 40 65
840 4d. + 1d. Weka rail 40 65

262 "The Virgin with Child" (Maratta) **263** Queen Victoria and Queen Elizabeth II

1966. Christmas.
842 **262** 3d. multicoloured 10 10

1967. Centenary of New Zealand Post Office Savings Bank.
843 **263** 4d. black, gold & purple 10 10
844 – 9d. multicoloured 10 20
DESIGN: 9d. Half-sovereign of 1867 and commemorative dollar coin.

265 Manuka (Tea Tree) **268** Running with Ball

1967. Decimal Currency. Designs as earlier issues, but with values inscr in decimal currency as T **265**.
845 **265** ½ c. blue, green and red 10 10
846 – 1 c. mult (No. 782) 10 10
847 – 2 c. mult (No. 783) 10 10
848 – 2½ c. mult (No. 785) 10 10
849 – 3 c. mult (No. 786) 10 10
850 – 4 c. mult (No. 787) 30 10
851 – 5 c. lilac, olive and green (No. 788) 65 10
852 – 6 c. mult (No. 788d) 70 30
853 – 7 c. mult (No. 789) 85 30
854 – 8 c. red and blue (No. 790) 85 10
855 **215** 10 c. brown and green 90 10
856 – 15 c. green and brown (No. 793) 1·50 90
857 **219** 20 c. black and buff 2·50 10
858 – 25 c. yellow and brown (No. 797) 2·50 1·75
859 – 30 c. yellow, green and blue (No. 799) 2·50 25
860 – 50 c. green (No. 800) 2·75 75
861 – $1 blue (No. 801) 16·00 1·25
862 – $2 mauve (No. 802) 6·00 9·00
F219w **F 6** $4 violet 3·00 1·50
F220w $6 green 4·50 3·00
F221w $8 blue 6·00 4·50
F222w $10 blue 7·50 4·50
For 15 c. in different colours, see No. 874.

1967. Health Stamps. Rugby Football.
867 **268** 2½ c. + 1 c. multicoloured 15 15
868 – 3 c. + 1 c. multicoloured 15 15
DESIGN—HORIZ: 3 c. Positioning for place-kick.

271 Brown Trout **273** Forest and Timber

1967.
870 – 7 c. multicoloured 1·50 90
871 **271** 7½ c. multicoloured 45 70
872 – 8 c. multicoloured 75 70
873 **273** 10 c. multicoloured 50 10
874 – 15 c. green, deep green & red (as No. 793) 1·00 90
875 – 18 c. multicoloured 1·00 55
876 – 20 c. multicoloured 1·00 20
877 – 25 c. multicoloured 2·50 2·00
878 – 28 c. multicoloured 60 10
879 – $2 black, ochre & blue (as No. 802) 18·00 15·00
DESIGNS: 7 c. "Kaitia" (trawler) and catch; 8 c. Apples and orchard; 18 c. Sheep and the "Woolmark"; 20 c. Consignments of beef and herd of cattle; 25 c. Dairy farm, Mt. Egmont and butter consignment. VERT: 28 c. Fox Glacier, Westland National Park.

No. 871 was originally issued to commemorate the introduction of the brown trout into New Zealand.

No. 874 is slightly larger than No. 793, measuring 21 × 25 mm. and the inscr and numerals differ in size.

278 "The Adoration of the Shepherds" (Poussin) **279** Mount Aspiring, Aurora Australis and Southern Cross

1967. Christmas.
880 **278** 2½ c. multicoloured 10 10

1967. Cent of Royal Society of New Zealand.
881 **279** 4 c. multicoloured 25 20
882 – 8 c. multicoloured 25 80
DESIGN: 8 c. Sir James Hector (founder).

281 Open Bible **282** Soldiers and Tank

1968. Centenary of Maori Bible.
883 **281** 3 c. multicoloured 10 10

1968. New Zealand Armed Forces. Mult.
884 4 c. Type **282** 30 15
885 10 c. Airmen, Fairey Firefly and English Electric Canberra aircraft 50 70
886 28 c. Sailors and H.M.N.Z.S. "Achilles", 1939, and H.M.N.Z.S. "Waikato", 1968 70 2·25

285 Boy breasting Tape and Olympic Rings

1968. Health Stamps. Multicoloured.
887 2½ c. + 1 c. Type **285** 20 15
888 3 c. + 1 c. Girl swimming and Olympic rings 20 15

287 Placing Votes in Ballot Box **288** Human Rights Emblem

1968. 75th Anniv of Universal Suffrage in New Zealand.
890 **287** 3 c. ochre, green & blue 10 10

1968. Human Rights Year.
891 **288** 10 c. red, yellow & green 10 30

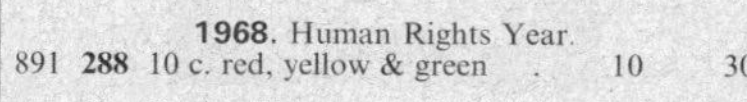

289 "Adoration of the Holy Child" (G. van Honthorst)

1968. Christmas.
892 **289** 2½ c. multicoloured 10 10

290 I.L.O. Emblem

1969. 50th Anniv of Int Labour Organization.
893 **290** 7 c. black and red 15 30

291 Supreme Court Building, Auckland

1969. Centenary of New Zealand Law Society.
894 **291** 3 c. multicoloured 10 10
895 – 10 c. multicoloured 35 60
896 – 18 c. multicoloured 45 1·25
DESIGNS—VERT: 10 c. Law Society's coat of arms; 18 c. "Justice" (from Memorial Window in University of Canterbury, Christchurch).

295 Student being conferred with Degree

1969. Centenary of Otago University. Mult.
897 3 c. Otago University (vert) 10 10
898 10 c. Type **295** 20 25

296 Boys playing Cricket

1969. Health Stamps.
899 **296** 2½ c. + 1 c. multicoloured 40 50
900 – 3 c. + 1 c. multicoloured 40 50
901 – 4 c. + 1 c. brown and ultramarine 40 2·00
DESIGNS—HORIZ: 3 c. Girls playing cricket. VERT: 4 c. Dr. Elizabeth Gunn (founder of first Children's Health Camp).

299 Oldest existing House in New Zealand, and Old Stone Mission Store, Kerikeri

1969. Early European Settlement in New Zealand, and 150th Anniv of Kerikeri. Multicoloured.
903 4 c. Type **299** 20 25
904 6 c. View of Bay of Islands 30 1·75

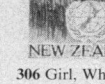

301 "The Nativity" (Federico Fiori (Barocci)) **306** Girl, Wheat Field and C.O.R.S.O. Emblem

302 Captain Cook, Transit of Venus and "Octant"

1969. Christmas.
905 **301** 2½ c. multicoloured 10 10

1969. Bicentenary of Captain Cook's Landing in New Zealand.
906 **302** 4 c. black, red and blue 1·00 35
907 – 6 c. green, brown & black 1·25 2·75
908 – 18 c. brown, green & black 2·25 2·75
909 – 28 c. red, black and blue 3·25 4·75
DESIGNS: 6 c. Sir Joseph Banks (naturalist) and outline of H.M.S. "Endeavour"; 18 c. Dr. Daniel Solander (botanist) and his plant; 28 c. Queen Elizabeth II and Cook's chart, 1769.

1969. 25th Anniv of C.O.R.S.O. (Council of Organizations for Relief Services Overseas). Multicoloured.
911 7 c. Type **306** 70 1·40
912 8 c. Mother feeding her child, dairy herd and C.O.R.S.O. emblem (horiz) 70 1·40

308 "Cardigan Bay" (champion trotter)

1970. Return of "Cardigan Bay" to New Zealand.
913 **308** 10 c. multicoloured 30 30

309 "Vanessa gonerilla" (butterfly) **310** Queen Elizabeth II and New Zealand Coat of Arms

1970.
914 – ½ c. multicoloured 10 20
915 **309** 1 c. multicoloured 10 10
916 – 2 c. multicoloured 10 10
917 – 2½ c. multicoloured 40 10
918 – 3 c. multicoloured 15 10
919 – 4 c. multicoloured 15 10
920 – 5 c. multicoloured 45 10
921 – 6 c. black, green and red 45 20
922 – 7 c. multicoloured 55 55
923 – 7½ c. multicoloured 1·00 1·50
924 – 8 c. multicoloured 65 80
925 **310** 10 c. multicoloured 40 15
926 – 15 c. black, flesh & brown 1·00 50
927 – 18 c. green, brown & black 1·00 40
928 – 20 c. black and brown 1·00 15
929 – 23 c. multicoloured 80 30
930b – 25 c. multicoloured 70 40
931 – 30 c. multicoloured 75 15
932 – 50 c. multicoloured 60 20
933 – $1 multicoloured 1·75 1·00
934 – $2 multicoloured 2·75 1·50
DESIGNS—VERT (as T **309**): ½ c. "Lycaena salustius" (butterfly); 2 c. "Argyrophenga antipodum" (butterfly); 2½ c. "Nyctemera annulata" (moth); 3 c. "Detunda egregia" (moth); 4 c. "Charagia virescens" (moth); 5 c. Scarlet wrasse ("Scarlet parrot fish"); 6 c. Big-bellied sea horses; 7 c. Leather jacket (fish); 7½ c. Intermediate halfbeak ("Garfish"); 8 c. John Dory (fish). (As T **310**): 18 c. Maori club; 25 c. Hauraki Gulf Maritime Park; 30 c Mt. Cook National Park. HORIZ (as T **310**): 15 c. Maori fish hook; 20 c. Maori tattoo pattern; 23 c. Egmont National Park; 50 c. Abel Tasman National Park; $1 Geothermal power; $2 Agricultural technology.

311 Geyser Restaurant **312** U.N. H.Q. Building

1970. World Fair, Osaka. Multicoloured.
935 7 c. Type **311** . . . . 40 1·00
936 8 c. New Zealand Pavilion . . 40 1·00
937 18 c. Bush Walk . . . . 60 1·00

1970. 25th Anniv of United Nations.
938 **312** 3 c. multicoloured 10 10
939 – 10 c. red and yellow . . . 20 20
DESIGN: 10 c. Tractor on horizon.

313 Soccer **314** "The Virgin adoring the Child" (Correggio)

1970. Health Stamps. Multicoloured.
940 $2\frac{1}{2}$ c. + 1 c. Netball (vert) . . . 30 65
941 3 c. + 1 c. Type **313** 30 65

1970. Christmas.
943 **314** $2\frac{1}{2}$ c. multicoloured 10 10
944 – 3 c. multicoloured 10 10
945 – 10 c. black, orange & silver . 30 75
DESIGNS—VERT: 3 c. Stained Glass Window, Invercargill Presbyterian Church "The Holy Family". HORIZ: 10 c. Tower of Roman Catholic Church, Seckburn.

316 Chatham Islands Lily

1970. Chatham Islands. Multicoloured.
946 1 c. Type **316** 10 35
947 2 c. Shy albatross 30 40

317 Country Women's Institute Emblem

1971. 50th Annivs of Country Women's Institutes and Rotary International in New Zealand. Multicoloured.
948 4 c. Type **317** 10 10
949 10 c. Rotary emblem and map of New Zealand 20 40

318 "Rainbow II" (yacht)

1971. One Ton Cup Racing Trophy. Mult.
950 5 c. Type **318** 25 25
951 8 c. One Ton Cup . . . . . . 35 1·25

319 Civic Arms of Palmerston North

1971. City Centenaries. Multicoloured.
952 3 c. Type **319** 10 10
953 4 c. Arms of Auckland 10 10
954 5 c. Arms of Invercargill . . . 15 90

320 Antarctica on Globe

1971. 10th Anniv of Antarctic Treaty.
955 **320** 6 c. multicoloured . . . . 1·00 1·00

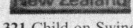

321 Child on Swing **323** Satellite-tracking Aerial

1971. 25th Anniv of U.N.I.C.E.F.
956 **321** 7 c. multicoloured 50 70

1971. No. 917 surch **4c**.
957 4 c. on $2\frac{1}{2}$ c. multicoloured . . 15 10

1971. Opening of Satellite Earth Station.
958 **323** 8 c. black, grey and red . . 60 1·25
959 – 10 c. black, green and violet 65 1·00
DESIGN: 10 c. Satellite.

324 Girls playing Hockey

1971. Health Stamps. Multicoloured.
960 3 c. + 1 c. Type **324** 45 50
961 4 c. + 1 c. Boys playing hockey 45 50
962 5 c. + 1 c. Dental health . . . 1·10 2·00

325 "Madonna bending over the Crib" (Maratta)

1971. Christmas. Multicoloured.
964 3 c. Type **325** 10 10
965 4 c. "The Annunciation" (stained-glass window) . . . 10 10
966 10 c. "The Three Kings" . . . 70 1·25
Nos. 965/6 are smaller, size $21\frac{1}{2} \times 38$ mm.

326 "Tiffany" Rose **327** Lord Rutherford and Alpha Particles

1971. 1st World Rose Convention, Hamilton. Multicoloured.
967 2 c. Type **326** 15 30
968 5 c. "Peace" 35 35
969 8 c. "Chrysler Imperial" . . . 60 1·10

1971. Birth Centenary of Lord Rutherford (scientist). Multicoloured.
970 1 c. Type **327** 25 50
971 7 c. Lord Rutherford and formula . . . . 85 1·50

328 Benz (1895) **329** Coat of Arms of Wanganui

1972. International Vintage Car Rally. Mult.
972 3 c. Type **328** 20 10
973 4 c. Oldsmobile (1904) 25 10
974 5 c. Ford "Model T" (1914) . . 25 10
975 6 c. Cadillac Service car (1915) 35 45
976 8 c. Chrysler (1924) . . . . . 75 1·90
977 10 c. Austin "7" (1923) . . . . 75 1·40

1972. Anniversaries.
978 **329** 3 c. multicoloured 15 10
979 – 4 c. orange, brown & black 15 10
980 – 5 c. multicoloured 25 10
981 – 8 c. multicoloured . . . . 65 1·25
982 – 10 c. multicoloured . . . . 65 1·25
DESIGNS AND EVENTS—VERT: 3 c. Type **329** (centenary of Wanganui Council); 5 c. De Havilland D.H.89 Dragon Rapide and Boeing 737 (25th anniv of National Airways Corp); 8 c. French frigate and Maori palisade (bicentenary of landing by Marion du Fresne). HORIZ: 4 c. Postal Union symbol (10th anniv of Asian–Oceanic Postal Union); 10 c. Stone cairn (150th anniv of New Zealand Methodist Church).

330 Black Scree Cotula **331** Boy playing Tennis

1972. Alpine Plants. Multicoloured.
983 4 c. Type **330** 30 10
984 6 c. North Island edelweiss . . 40 40
985 8 c. Haast's buttercup 60 85
986 10 c. Brown Mountain daisy . . 70 1·25

1972. Health Stamps.
987 **331** 3 c. + 1 c. grey & brown . 30 45
988 – 4 c. + 1 c. brown, grey and yellow 30 45
DESIGN: No. 988, Girl playing tennis.

332 "Madonna with Child" (Murillo) **333** Lake Waikaremoana

1972. Christmas. Multicoloured.
990 3 c. Type **332** 10 10
991 5 c. "The Last Supper" (stained-glass window, St. John's Church, Levin) 15 10
992 10 c. Pohutukawa flower . . . 35 70

1972. Lake Scenes. Multicoloured.
993 6 c. Type **333** . . . . 1·00 1·25
994 8 c. Lake Hayes . . . . 1·10 1·25
995 18 c. Lake Wakatipu . . . . . 1·50 2·25
996 23 c. Lake Rotomahana . . . 1·75 2·75

334 Old Pollen Street

1973. Commemorations.
997 **334** 3 c. multicoloured 10 10
998 – 4 c. multicoloured 15 10
999 – 5 c. multicoloured 15 15
1000 – 6 c. multicoloured 60 65
1001 – 8 c. grey, blue and gold . . 50 65
1002 – 10 c. multicoloured . . . 70 1·00
DESIGNS AND EVENTS: 3 c. (centenary of Thames Borough); 4 c. Coalmining and pasture (centenary of Westport Borough); 5 c. Cloister (centenary of Canterbury University); 6 c. Forest, birds and lake (50th anniv of Royal Forest and Bird Protection Society); 8 c. Rowers (Success of N.Z. rowers in 1972 Olympics); 10 c. Graph and people (25th anniv of E.C.A.F.E.).

335 Class W Locomotive

1973. New Zealand Steam Locomotives. Multicoloured.
1003 3 c. Type **335** 40 10
1004 4 c. Class X 40 10
1005 5 c. Class Ab 40 10
1006 10 c. Class Ja No. 1274 . . . 2·25 1·40

336 "Maori Woman and Child" **337** Prince Edward

1973. Paintings by Frances Hodgkins. Multicoloured.
1027 5 c. Type **336** 40 15
1028 8 c. "Hilltop" 60 75
1029 10 c. "Barn in Picardy" . . . 80 1·25
1030 18 c. "Self-portrait Still Life" . 1·25 2·50

1973. Health Stamps.
1031 **337** 3 c. + 1 c. green & brown 30 30
1032 4 c. + 1 c. red & brown . 30 30

338 "Tempi Madonna" (Raphael) **339** Mitre Peak

1973. Christmas. Multicoloured.
1034 3 c. Type **338** 10 10
1035 5 c. "Three Kings" (stained-glass window, St. Theresa's Church, Auckland) 10 10
1036 10 c. Family entering church . 25 50

1973. Mountain Scenery. Multicoloured.
1037 6 c. Type **339** 70 80
1038 8 c. Mt. Ngauruhoe . . . . . 80 1·00
1039 18 c. Mt. Sefton (horiz) . . . 1·10 2·25
1040 23 c. Burnett Range (horiz) . . 1·25 2·50

340 Hurdling **342** "Spirit of Napier" Fountain

1974. 10th British Commonwealth Games, Christchurch.
1041 **340** 4 c. multicoloured 10 10
1042 – 5 c. black and violet . . . 15 10
1043 – 10 c. multicoloured . . . 20 15
1044 – 18 c. multicoloured . . . 25 50
1045 – 23 c. multicoloured . . . 35 70
DESIGNS: 5 c. Ball-player (4th Paraplegic Games, Dunedin); 10 c. Cycling; 18 c. Rifle-shooting; 23 c. Bowls.

1974. Centenaries of Napier and U.P.U. Mult.
1047 4 c. Type **342** 10 10
1048 5 c. Clock Tower, Berne . . . 20 30
1049 8 c. U.P.U. Monument, Berne 80 1·60

343 Boeing Seaplane, 1919 **344** Children, Cat and Dog

1974. History of New Zealand Airmail Transport. Multicoloured.
1050 3 c. Type **343** 30 10
1051 4 c. Lockheed 10 Electra "Kauha", 1937 . . . . . . 35 10
1052 5 c. Bristol Type 170 Freighter Mk 31, 1958 . . . . . . 40 30
1053 23 c. Short S.30 modified "G" Class flying boat "Aotearoa", 1940 . . . . 1·75 2·50

1974. Health Stamps.
1054 **344** 3 c. + 1 c. multicoloured 20 35
1055 – 4 c. + 1 c. multicoloured 25 35
1056 – 5 c. + 1 c. multicoloured 1·00 1·50
Nos. 1055/6 are similar to Type **344** showing children with pets.

345 "The Adoration of the Magi" (Konrad Witz)

346 Great Barrier Island

1974. Christmas. Multicoloured.
1058 3 c. Type **345** 10 10
1059 5 c. "The Angel Window" (stained glass window, Old St. Pauls Church, Wellington) . 10 10
1060 10 c. Madonna lily 30 80

1974. Offshore Islands. Multicoloured.
1061 6 c. Type **346** 30 40
1062 8 c. Stewart Island . . . . . 50 1·25
1063 18 c. White Island . . . . . 70 1·25
1064 23 c. The Brothers . . . . . 75 1·50

347 Crippled Child

1975. Anniversaries and Events. Multicoloured.
1065 3 c. Type **347** 10 10
1066 5 c. Farming family 15 10
1067 10 c. I.W.Y. symbols 20 65
1068 18 c. Medical School Building, Otago University . . . . . 55 1·75
COMMEMORATIONS: 3 c. 40th anniv of New Zealand Crippled Children Society; 5 c. 50th anniv of Women's Division, Federated Farmers of New Zealand; 10 c. International Women's Year; 18 c. Centenary of Otago Medical School.

348 Scow "Lake Erie"

1975. Historic Sailing Ships.
1069 **348** 4 c. black and red 30 10
1070 – 5 c. black and blue 30 10
1071 – 8 c. black and yellow . . . 55 60
1072 – 10 c. black and yellow . . . 60 60
1073 – 18 c. black and brown . . . 1·00 2·00
1074 – 23 c. black and lilac . . . 1·10 2·00
SHIPS: 5 c. Schooner "Herald"; 8 c. Brigantine "New Zealander"; 10 c. Topsail schooner "Jessie Kelly"; 18 c. Barque "Tory"; 23 c. Full-rigged clipper "Rangitiki".

349 Lake Sumner Forest Park

1975. Forest Park Scenes. Multicoloured.
1075 6 c. Type **349** 50 70
1076 8 c. North-west Nelson . . . 60 1·00
1077 18 c. Kaweka . . . . 1·00 1·75
1078 23 c. Coromandel . . . . . . 1·25 2·00

350 Girl feeding Lamb

351 "Virgin and Child" (Zanobi Machiavelli)

1975. Health Stamps. Multicoloured.
1079 3 c. + 1 c. Type **350** 20 30
1080 4 c. + 1 c. Boy with hen and chicks 20 30
1081 5 c. + 1 c. Boy with duck and duckling . . . . 60 1·50

1975. Christmas. Multicoloured.
1083 3 c. Type **351** 10 10
1084 5 c. "Cross in Landscape" (stained-glass window, Greendale Church) 10 10
1085 10 c. "I saw three ships" (carol) 35 65
The 5 c. and 10 c. are horizontal.

352 "Sterling Silver"

353 Queen Elizabeth II (photograph by W. Harrison)

353a Maripi (knife)

353b Rainbow Abalone or Paua

1975. (a) Garden Roses. Multicoloured.
1086 1 c. Type **352** 10 10
1087 2 c. "Lilli Marlene" 10 10
1088 3 c. "Queen Elizabeth" . . . 60 10
1089 4 c. "Super Star" 10 20
1090 5 c. "Diamond Jubilee" . . . 10 10
1091a 6 c. "Cresset" 40 70
1092a 7 c. "Michele Meilland" . . 40 10
1093a 8 c. "Josephine Bruce" . . . 45 10
1094 9 c. "Iceberg" 30 40

(b) Type **353**.
1094ab 10 c. multicoloured 30 10

(c) Maori Artefacts.
1095 **353a** 11 c. brown, yell & blk . 30 50
1096 – 12 c. brown, yell & blk . 30 15
1097 – 13 c. brown, mve & blk . 40 65
1098 – 14 c. brown, yell & blk . 30 20
DESIGNS: 12 c. Putorino (flute); 13 c. Wahaika (club); 14 c. Kotiate (club).

(d) Sea Shells. Multicoloured.
1099 20 c. Type **353b** 15 20
1100 30 c. Toheroa clam 25 30
1101 40 c. Old woman or coarse dosinia 30 35
1102 50 c. New Zealand or spiny murex 40 45
1103 $1 New Zealand scallop . . . 70 95
1104 $2 Circular saw . . . . . . 1·00 1·75

(e) Building. Multicoloured.
1105 $5 "Beehive" (section of Parliamentary Buildings, Wellington) (22 × 26 mm) . 2·50 1·50

354 Family and League of Mothers Badge

1976. Anniversaries and Metrication. Mult.
1110 6 c. Type **354** 10 10
1111 7 c. Weight, temperature, linear measure and capacity . . . 10 10
1112 8 c. "William Bryon" (immigrant ship), mountain and New Plymouth 15 10
1113 10 c. Two women shaking hands and Y.W.C.A. badge . . . 15 50
1114 25 c. Map of the world showing cable links . . . . 30 1·25
ANNIVERSARIES: 6 c. 50th anniv of League of Mothers; 7 c. Metrication; 8 c. Centenary of New Plymouth; 10 c. 50th anniv of New Zealand Y.W.C.A.; 25 c. Link with International Telecommunications Network.

355 Gig

1976. Vintage Farm Transport. Multicoloured.
1115 6 c. Type **355** 15 40
1116 7 c. Thornycroft lorry 20 10
1117 8 c. Scandi wagon 40 20
1118 9 c. Traction engine 30 50
1119 10 c. Wool wagon 30 50
1120 25 c. Cart . . . . 85 2·25

356 Purakaunui Falls

357 Boy and Pony

1976. Waterfalls. Multicoloured.
1121 10 c. Type **356** 35 10
1122 14 c. Marakopa Falls 60 95
1123 15 c. Bridal Veil Falls . . . . 65 1·10
1124 16 c. Papakorito Falls . . . . 70 1·25

1976. Health Stamps. Multicoloured.
1125 7 c. + 1 c. Type **357** 20 30
1126 8 c. + 1 c. Girl and calf . . . 20 30
1127 10 c. + 1 c. Girls and bird . . 40 90

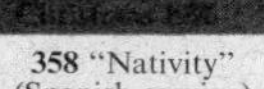
358 "Nativity" (Spanish carving)

359 Arms of Hamilton

1976. Christmas. Multicoloured.
1129 7 c. Type **358** 15 10
1130 11 c. "Resurrection" (stained-glass window, St. Joseph's Catholic Church, Grey Lynn) (horiz) 25 30
1131 18 c. Angels (horiz) 40 90

1977. Anniversaries. Multicoloured.
1132 8 c. Type **359** 15 10
1133 8 c. Arms of Gisborne 15 10
1134 8 c. Arms of Masterton . . . 15 10
1135 10 c. A.A. emblem 15 40
1136 10 c. Arms of the Royal Australasian College of Surgeons 15 40
ANNIVERSARIES: No. 1132, Cent of Hamilton; No. 1133, Cent of Gisborne; No. 1134, Cent of Masterton; No. 1135, 75th anniv of Automobile Association in New Zealand; No. 1136, 50th anniv of R.A.C.S.

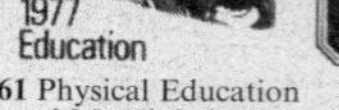
361 Physical Education and Maori Culture

363 Karitane Beach

1977. Education. Multicoloured.
1138 8 c. Type **361** 40 70
1139 8 c. Geography, science and woodwork 40 70
1140 8 c. Teaching the deaf, kindergarten and woodwork 40 70
1141 8 c. Tertiary and language classes 40 70
1142 8 c. Home science, correspondence school and teacher training 40 70

1977. Nos. 918/19 surch.
1143 7 c. on 3 c. "Detunda egregia" (moth) 40 70
1144 8 c. on 4 c. "Charagia virescens" (moth) 40 70

1977. Seascapes. Multicoloured.
1145 10 c. Type **363** 15 10
1146 16 c. Ocean Beach, Mount Maunganui 30 30
1147 18 c. Piha Beach 30 30
1148 30 c. Kaikoura Coast 35 40

364 Girl with Pigeon

365 "The Holy Family" (Correggio)

1977. Health Stamps. Multicoloured.
1149 7 c. + 2 c. Type **364** 20 30
1150 8 c. + 2 c. Boy with frog . . 25 45
1151 10 c. + 2 c. Girl with butterfly 45 1·00

1977. Christmas. Multicoloured.
1153 7 c. Type **365** 15 10
1154 16 c. "Madonna and Child" (stained-glass window, St. Michael's and All Angels, Dunedin) 25 25
1155 23 c. "Partridge in a Pear Tree" 40 1·25
The 16 c. and 23 c. are vertical.

366 Merryweather Manual Pump, 1860

1977. Fire Fighting Appliances. Mult.
1156 10 c. Type **366** 15 10
1157 11 c. 2-wheel hose, reel and ladder, 1880 . . . . 15 25
1158 12 c. Shand Mason steam fire engine, 1873 . . . . 20 30
1159 23 c. Chemical fire engine, 1888 30 70

367 Town Clock and Coat of Arms, Ashburton

368 Students and Ivey Hall, Lincoln College

1978. Centenaries.
1160 **367** 10 c. multicoloured . . . 15 10
1161 – 10 c. multicoloured . . . 15 10
1162 – 12 c. red, yellow & black . 15 15
1163 – 20 c. multicoloured . . . 20 30
DESIGNS—VERT: No. 1161, Mount Egmont (cent of Stratford); No. 1162, Early telephone (cent of telephone in New Zealand). HORIZ: No. 1163, Aerial view of the Bay of Islands (cent of the Bay of Islands County).

1978. Land Resources and Centenary of Lincoln College of Agriculture. Multicoloured.
1164 10 c. Type **368** 15 10
1165 12 c. Sheep grazing 15 25
1166 15 c. Fertiliser ground spreading 15 30
1167 16 c. Agricultural Field Days . 15 30
1168 20 c. Harvesting grain 20 40
1169 30 c. Dairy farming 30 70

369

370 Maui Gas Drilling Platform

1978. Coil Stamps.
1170 **369** 1 c. purple 10 40
1171 2 c. orange 10 40
1172 5 c. brown 10 40
1173 10 c. blue 30 75

1978. Resources of the Sea. Multicoloured.
1174 12 c. Type **370** 20 15
1175 15 c. Trawler 25 30
1176 20 c. Map of 200 mile fishing limit 30 40
1177 23 c. Humpback whale and bottle-nosed dolphins . . . 40 50
1178 35 c. Kingfish, snapper, grouper and squid 60 75

371 First Health Charity Stamp

372 "The Holy Family" (El Greco)

1978. Health Stamps.
1179 **371** 10 c. + 2 c. black, red and gold 30 35
1180 – 12 c. + 2 c. multicoloured 30 40
DESIGNS: 10 c. Type **371** (50th anniv of Health Stamps); 12 c. Heart Operation (National Heart Foundation).

1978. Christmas. Multicoloured.
1182 7 c. Type **372** 10 10
1183 16 c. All Saint's Church, Howick (horiz) 25 35
1184 23 c. Beach scene (horiz) . . . 30 50

373 Sir Julius Vogel

374 Riverlands Cottage, Blenheim

1979. Statesmen. Designs each brown and drab.
1185 10 c. Type **373** 30 65
1186 10 c. Sir George Grey 30 65
1187 10 c. Richard John Seddon . . 30 65

1979. Architecture (1st series).
1188 374 10 c. black, light blue and blue 10 10
1189 – 12 c. black, light green and green 15 25
1190 – 15 c. black and grey 20 30
1191 – 20 c. black, brown and sepia 25 30
DESIGNS: 12 c. The Mission House, Waimate North; 15 c. "The Elms", Tauranga; 20 c. Provincial Council Buildings, Christchurch.
See also Nos. 1217/20 and 1262/5.

375 Whangaroa Harbour

1979. Small Harbours. Multicoloured.
1192 15 c. Type **375** 15 10
1193 20 c. Kawau Island 20 40
1194 23 c. Akaroa Harbour (vert) 20 50
1195 35 c. Picton Harbour (vert) 30 70

376 Children with Building Bricks

1979. International Year of the Child.
1196 **376** 10 c. multicoloured 15 10

377 Two-spotted Chromis

1979. Health Stamps. Marine Life. Multicoloured.
1197 10 c. + 2 c. Type **377** 30 60
1198 10 c. + 2 c. Sea urchin 30 60
1199 12 c. + 2 c. Red goatfish and underwater cameraman (vert) 30 60

1979. Nos. 1091a/3a and 1094ab surch.
1201 4 c. on 8 c. "Josephine Bruce" 10 20
1202 14 c. on 10 c. Type **353** 30 20
1203 17 c. on 6 c. "Cresset" 30 70
1203a 20 c. on 7 c. "Michele Meilland" 30 10

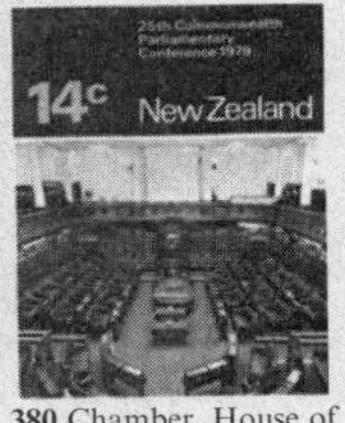

379 "Madonna and Child" (sculpture, Ghiberti) **380** Chamber, House of Representatives

1979. Christmas. Multicoloured.
1204 10 c. Type **379** 15 10
1205 25 c. Christ Church, Russell 30 40
1206 35 c. Pohutukawa (tree) 40 55

1979. 25th Commonwealth Parliamentary Conference, Wellington. Multicoloured.
1207 14 c. Type **380** 15 10
1208 20 c. Mace and Black Rod 20 30
1209 30 c. "Beehive" wall hanging 30 70

381 1855 1d. Stamp

1980. Anniversaries and Events.
1210 **381** 14 c. black, red & yellow 20 30
1211 – 14 c. black, blue & yellow 20 30
1212 – 14 c. black, green & yell 20 30
1213 – 17 c. multicoloured 20 30
1214 – 25 c. multicoloured 25 35
1215 – 30 c. multicoloured 25 40
DESIGNS: No. 1211, 1855 2d. stamp; No. 1212, 1855 1s. stamp (125th anniv of New Zealand stamps); No. 1213, Geyser, wood-carving and building (Centenary of Rotorua (town)); No. 1214, "Earina autumnalis" and "Thelymitra venosa" (International Orchid Conference, Auckland); No. 1215, Ploughing and Golden Plough Trophy (World Ploughing Championships, Christchurch).

382 Ewelme Cottage, Parnell

1980. Architecture (2nd series). Multicoloured.
1217 14 c. Type **382** 15 10
1218 17 c. Broadgreen, Nelson 15 25
1219 25 c. Courthouse, Oamaru 20 30
1220 30 c. Government Buildings, Wellington 25 35

383 Auckland Harbour

1980. Large Harbours. Multicoloured.
1221 25 c. Type **383** 25 20
1222 30 c. Wellington Harbour 30 30
1223 35 c. Lyttelton Harbour 30 35
1224 50 c. Port Chalmers 50 65

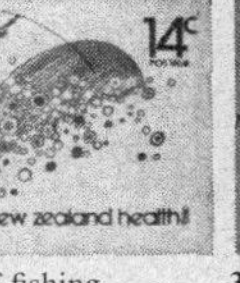

384 Surf-fishing **385** "Madonna and Child with Cherubim" (sculpture, Andrea della Robbia)

1980. Health Stamps. Fishing. Multicoloured.
1225 14 c. + 2 c. Type **384** 30 70
1226 14 c. + 2 c. Wharf-fishing 30 70
1227 17 c. + 2 c. Spear-fishing 30 55

1980. Christmas. Multicoloured.
1229 10 c. Type **385** 15 10
1230 25 c. St. Mary's Church, New Plymouth 25 25
1231 35 c. Picnic scene 40 80

386 Te Heu Heu (chief) **387** Lt. Col. the Hon. W. H. A. Feilding and Borough of Feilding Crest (cent)

1980. Maori Personalities. Multicoloured.
1232 15 c. Type **386** 10 10
1233 25 c. Te Hau (chief) 15 20
1234 35 c. Te Puea (princess) 20 10
1235 45 c. Ngata (politician) 30 20
1236 60 c. Te Ata-O-Tu (warrior) 35 25

1981. Commemorations.
1237 **387** 20 c. multicoloured 20 20
1238 – 25 c. orange and black 25 25
DESIGN AND COMMEMORATION: 25 c. I.Y.D. emblem and cupped hands (International Year of the Disabled).

388 The Family at Play **389** Kaiauai River

1981. "Family Life". Multicoloured.
1239 20 c. Type **388** 15 10
1240 25 c. The family young and old 20 20
1241 30 c. The family at home 20 30
1242 35 c. The family at church 25 45

1981. River Scenes. Multicoloured.
1243 30 c. Type **389** 25 25
1244 35 c. Mangahao 30 30
1245 40 c. Shotover (horiz) 35 40
1246 60 c. Cleddau (horiz) 55 65

390 St. Paul's Cathedral

1981. Royal Wedding. Multicoloured.
1247 20 c. Type **390** 30 30
1248 20 c. Prince Charles and Lady Diana Spencer 30 30

391 Girl with Starfish **392** "Madonna suckling the Child" (painting, d'Oggiono)

1981. Health Stamps. Children playing by the Sea. Multicoloured.
1249 20 c. + 2 c. Type **391** 25 50
1250 20 c. + 2 c. Boy fishing 25 50
1251 25 c. + 2 c. Children exploring rock pool 25 35
Nos. 1249/50 were printed together, se-tenant, forming a composite design.

1981. Christmas. Multicoloured.
1253 14 c. Type **392** 15 10
1254 30 c. St. John's Church, Wakefield 20 25
1255 40 c. Golden tainui (flower) 35 35

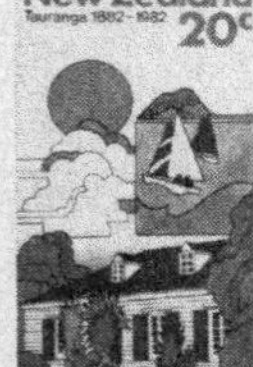

393 Tauranga Mission House **394** Map of New Zealand

1981. Commemorations. Multicoloured.
1256 20 c. Type **393** 25 10
1257 20 c. Water tower, Hawera 25 10
1258 25 c. Cat 35 35
1259 30 c. "Dunedin" (refrigerated sailing ship) 35 40
1260 35 c. Scientific research equipment 40 45
COMMEMORATIONS: No. 1256, Centenary of Tauranga (town); No. 1257, Centenary of Hawera (town); No. 1258, Centenary of S.P.C.A. (Society for the Prevention of Cruelty to Animals in New Zealand); No. 1259, Centenary of frozen meat exports; No. 1260, International Year of Science.

1982.
1261 **394** 24 c. green and blue 30 10

395 Alberton, Auckland

1982. Architecture (3rd series). Multicoloured.
1262 20 c. Type **395** 20 15
1263 25 c. Caccia Birch, Palmerston North 25 25
1264 30 c. Railway station, Dunedin 50 30
1265 35 c. Post Office, Ophir 40 40

396 Kaiteriteri Beach, Nelson (Summer)

1982. New Zealand Scenes. Multicoloured.
1266 35 c. Type **396** 30 30
1267 40 c. St. Omer Park, Queenstown (Autumn) 35 35
1268 45 c. Mt. Ngauruhoe, Tongariro National Park (Winter) 40 40
1269 70 c. Wairarapa farm (Spring) 60 60

397 Labrador **398** "Madonna with Child and Two Angels" (painting by Piero di Cosimo)

1982. Health Stamps. Dogs. Multicoloured.
1270 24 c. + 2 c. Type **397** 80 1·00
1271 24 c. + 2 c. Border collie 80 1·00
1272 30 c. + 2 c. Cocker spaniel 80 1·00

1982. Christmas. Multicoloured.
1274 18 c. Type **398** 20 10
1275 35 c. Rangiatea Maori Church, Otaki 35 30
1276 45 c. Surf life-saving 50 40

399 Nephrite **399a** Grapes

399b Kokako **400** Old Arts Building, Auckland University

1982. (a) Minerals. Multicoloured.
1277 1 c. Type **399** 10 10
1278 2 c. Agate 10 10
1279 3 c. Iron pyrites 10 10
1280 4 c. Amethyst 10 10
1281 5 c. Carnelian 10 10
1282 9 c. Native sulphur 20 10

(b) Fruits. Multicoloured.
1283 10 c. Type **399a** 50 10
1284 20 c. Citrus fruit 35 10
1285 30 c. Nectarines 30 10
1286 40 c. Apples 35 10
1287 50 c. Kiwifruit 40 10

(c) Native Birds. Multicoloured.
1288 30 c. Kakapo 50 25
1289 40 c. Mountain ("Blue") duck 60 35
1290 45 c. New Zealand falcon 1·00 35
1291 60 c. New Zealand teal 1·00 40
1292 $1 Type **399b** 1·00 30
1293 $2 Chatham Island robin 1·75 50
1294 $3 Stitchbird 1·75 1·40
1295 $4 Saddleback 2·00 2·50
1296 $5 Takahe 3·25 3·00
1297 $10 Little spotted kiwi 6·00 6·75

1983. Commemorations. Multicoloured.
1303 24 c. Salvation Army Centenary logo 20 10
1304 30 c. Type **400** 25 35
1305 35 c. Stylised kangaroo and Kiwi 30 35
1306 40 c. Rainbow trout 30 45
1307 45 c. Satellite over Earth 35 50
COMMEMORATIONS: 24 c. Salvation Army Centenary; 30 c. Auckland University Centenary; 35 c. Closer Economic Relationship agreement with Australia; 40 c. Centenary of Introduction of Rainbow Trout into New Zealand; 45 c. World Communications Year.

401 Queen Elizabeth II **402** "Boats, Island Bay" (Rita Angus)

1983. Commonwealth Day. Multicoloured.
1308 24 c. Type **401** 20 10
1309 35 c. Maori rock drawing 30 50
1310 40 c. Woolmark and woolscouring symbols 30 80
1311 45 c. Coat of arms 30 80

1983. Paintings by Rita Angus. Mult.
1312 24 c. Type **402** 35 10
1313 30 c. "Central Otago Landscape" 40 45
1314 35 c. "Wanaka Landscape" 50 50
1315 45 c. "Tree" 70 70

403 Mt. Egmont **404** Tabby

1983. Beautiful New Zealand. Mult.

1316 35 c. Type **403** 30 35
1317 40 c. Cooks Bay 35 40
1318 45 c. Lake Matheson (horiz) . . 40 45
1319 70 c. Lake Alexandrina (horiz) . 65 70

1983. Health Stamps. Cats. Multicoloured.

1320 24 c. + 2 c. Type **404** 40 50
1321 24 c. + 2 c. Siamese 40 50
1322 30 c. + 2 c. Persian 75 90

405 "The Family of the Holy Oak Tree" (Raphael) **406** Geology

1983. Christmas. Multicoloured.

1324 18 c. Type **405** 15 10
1325 35 c. St. Patrick's Church, Greymouth 40 40
1326 45 c. "The Glory of Christmas" 55 55

1984. Antarctic Research. Multicoloured.

1327 24 c. Type **406** 35 10
1328 40 c. Biology 45 40
1329 58 c. Glaciology 60 55
1330 70 c. Meteorology 70 70

407 "Mountaineer", Lake Wakatipu

1984. New Zealand Ferry Boats. Mult.

1332 24 c. Type **407** 25 10
1333 40 c. "Waikana", Otago . . . 30 45
1334 58 c. "Britannia", Waitemata . 40 1·10
1335 70 c. "Wakatere", Firth of Thames 55 85

408 Mount Hutt

1984. Ski-slope Scenery. Multicoloured.

1336 35 c. Type **408** 30 25
1337 40 c. Coronet Park 30 30
1338 45 c. Turoa 35 30
1339 70 c. Whakapapa 60 75

409 Hamilton's Frog

1984. Amphibians and Reptiles. Multicoloured.

1340 24 c. Type **409** 30 30
1341 24 c. Great Barrier skink . . . 30 30
1342 30 c. Harlequin gecko 35 35
1343 58 c. Otago skink 70 70
1344 70 c. Gold-striped gecko . . . 75 75

410 Clydesdales ploughing

1984. Health Stamps. Horses. Multicoloured.

1345 24 c. + 2 c. Type **410** 30 50
1346 24 c. + 2 c. Shetland ponies . 30 50
1347 30 c. + 2 c. Thoroughbreds . 45 50

411 "Adoration of the Shepherds" (Lorenzo di Credi)

1984. Christmas. Multicoloured.

1349 18 c. Type **411** 15 10
1350 35 c. Old St. Paul's, Wellington (vert) 30 30
1351 45 c. "The Joy of Christmas" (vert) 40 65

412 Mounted Riflemen, South Africa, 1901

1984. New Zealand Military History. Multicoloured.

1352 24 c. Type **412** 25 10
1353 40 c. Engineers, France, 1917 . 35 45
1354 58 c. Tanks of 2nd N.Z. Divisional Cavalry, North Africa, 1942 . . . . 50 90
1355 70 c. Infantryman in jungle kit, and 25-pounder gun, Korea and South-East Asia, 1950–72 60 80

413 St. John Ambulance Badge

1985. Centenary of St. John Ambulance in New Zealand.

1357 **413** 24 c. black, gold and red . 25 15
1358 30 c. black, silver & blue . 35 45
1359 40 c. black and grey . . . 40 1·10

The colours of the badge depicted are those for Bailiffs and Dames Grand Cross (24 c.). Knights and Dames of Grace (30 c.) and Officer Brothers and Sisters (40 c.).

414 Nelson Horse Tram, 1862

1985. Vintage Trams. Multicoloured.

1360 24 c. Type **414** 40 10
1361 30 c. Graham's Town steam tram, 1871 . . . . 50 60
1362 35 c. Dunedin cable car, 1881 50 70
1363 40 c. Auckland electric tram, 1902 . . . . 50 70
1364 45 c. Wellington electric tram, 1904 . . . . 60 90
1365 58 c. Christchurch electric tram, 1905 . . . . 70 1·75

415 Shotover Bridge **416** Queen Elizabeth II (from photo by Camera Press)

1985. Bridges of New Zealand. Multicoloured.

1366 35 c. Type **415** 60 60
1367 40 c. Alexandra Bridge . . . 65 60
1368 45 c. South Rangitikei Railway Bridge (vert) . . . . . . 70 1·25
1369 70 c. Twin Bridges (vert) . . . 90 1·25

1985. Mult, background colours given.

1370 **416** 25 c. red 50 10
1371 35 c. blue 90 10

417 Princess of Wales and Prince William **418** The Holy Family in the Stable

1985. Health Stamps. Designs showing photographs by Lord Snowdon. Multicoloured.

1372 25 c. + 2 c. Type **417** . . . . 90 1·10
1373 25 c. + 2 c. Princess of Wales and Prince Henry . . . . . 90 1·10
1374 35 c. + 2 c. Prince and Princess of Wales with Princes William and Henry . . . . 90 1·10

1985. Christmas. Multicoloured.

1376 18 c. Type **418** 20 10
1377 40 c. The shepherds 40 85
1378 50 c. The angels . . . . . . 45 1·00

419 H.M.N.Z.S. "Philomel" (1914–47)

1985. New Zealand Naval History. Multicoloured.

1379 25 c. Type **419** 70 15
1380 45 c. H.M.N.Z.S. "Achilles" (1936–46) . . . . 1·10 1·40
1381 60 c. H.M.N.Z.S. "Rotoiti" (1949–65) . . . . 1·40 2·00
1382 75 c. H.M.N.Z.S. "Canterbury" (from 1971) . . . . . . 1·75 2·25

420 Police Computer Operator

1986. Centenary of New Zealand Police. Designs showing historical aspects above modern police activities. Multicoloured.

1384 25 c. Type **420** 35 50
1385 25 c. Detective and mobile control room 35 50
1386 25 c. Policewoman and badge . 35 50
1387 25 c. Forensic scientist, patrol car and policeman with child 35 50
1388 25 c. Police College, Porirua, "Lady Elizabeth II" (patrol boat) and dog handler . . . 35 50

421 Indian "Power Plus" 1000cc Motor Cycle (1920)

1986. Vintage Motor Cycles. Multicoloured.

1389 35 c. Type **421** 55 45
1390 45 c. Norton "CS1" 500cc (1927) 65 65
1391 60 c. B.S.A. "Sloper" 500cc (1930) . . . . 85 1·50
1392 75 c. Triumph "Model H" 550cc (1915) . . . . 95 1·50

422 Tree of Life

1986. International Peace Year. Mult.

1393 25 c. Type **422** 30 30
1394 25 c. Peace dove 30 30

423 Knights Point **424** "Football" (Kylie Epapara)

1986. Coastal Scenery. Multicoloured.

1395 55 c. Type **423** 55 65
1396 60 c. Becks Bay 55 80
1397 65 c. Doubtless Bay 60 90
1398 80 c. Wainui Bay . . . . . . 75 1·25

1986. Health Stamps. Children's Paintings (1st series). Multicoloured.

1400 30 c. + 3 c. Type **424** 40 40
1401 30 c. + 3 c. "Children at Play" (Philip Kata) 40 40
1402 45 c. + 3 c. "Children Skipping" (Mia Flannery) (horiz) . . . 50 50

See also Nos. 1433/5.

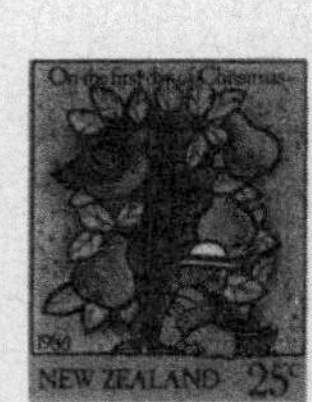

425 "A Partridge in a Pear Tree" **426** Conductor and Orchestra

1986. Christmas. "The Twelve Days of Christmas" (carol). Multicoloured.

1404 25 c. Type **425** 20 10
1405 55 c. "Two turtle doves" . . . 45 45
1406 65 c. "Three French hens" . . 50 50

1986. Music in New Zealand.

1407 **426** 30 c. multicoloured . . . 25 10
1408 – 60 c. black, blue & orange 45 70
1409 – 80 c. multicoloured . . . 70 1·40
1410 – $1 multicoloured . . . 80 1·10

DESIGNS: 60 c. Cornet and brass band; 80 c. Piper and Highland pipe band; $1 Guitar and country music group.

427 Jetboating **428** Southern Cross Cup

1987. Tourism. Multicoloured.

1411 60 c. Type **427** 50 50
1412 70 c. Sightseeing flights . . . 60 60
1413 80 c. Camping 70 75
1414 85 c. Windsurfing 70 75
1415 $1.05 Mountaineering . . . . 90 1·00
1416 $1.30 River rafting . . . . . 1·10 1·25

1987. Yachting Events. Designs showing yachts. Multicoloured.

1417 40 c. Type **428** 35 15
1418 80 c. Admiral's Cup 70 80
1419 $1.05 Kenwood Cup . . . . 85 1·25
1420 $1.30 America's Cup . . . . 1·10 1·40

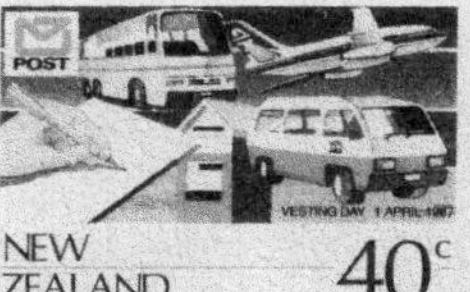

429 Hand writing Letter and Postal Transport

1987. New Zealand Post Ltd Vesting Day. Multicoloured.

1421 40 c. Type **429** . . . . . . 1·00 1·40
1422 40 c. Posting letter, train and mailbox . . . . 1·00 1·40

430 Avro Type 626 and Wigram Airfield, 1937

1987. 50th Anniv of Royal New Zealand Air Force. Multicoloured.

1423 40 c. Type **430** 65 15
1424 70 c. Curtiss Kittyhawk I over World War II Pacific airstrip 90 1·50
1425 80 c. Short S.25 Sunderland flying boat and Pacific lagoon 1·00 1·50
1426 85 c. Douglas A-4F Skyhawk and Mt. Ruapehu . . . . 1·10 1·25

431 Urewera National Park and Fern Leaf **432** "Kite Flying" (Lauren Baldwin)

1987. Centenary of National Parks Movement. Multicoloured.
1428 70 c. Type **431** 70 55
1429 80 c. Mt. Cook and buttercup 75 60
1430 85 c. Fiordland and pineapple shrub 80 65
1431 $1.30 Tongariro and tussock . 1·40 95

1987. Health Stamps. Children's Paintings (2nd series). Multicoloured.
1433 40 c. + 3 c. Type **432** . . . . 80 1·25
1434 40 c. + 3 c. "Swimming" (Ineke Schoneveld) . . . . 80 1·25
1435 60 c. + 3 c. "Horse Riding" (Aaron Tylee) (vert) . . . . 1·25 1·50

433 "Hark the Herald Angels Sing"

434 Knot ("Pona")

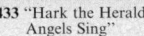

1987. Christmas. Multicoloured.
1437 35 c. Type **433** 45 10
1438 70 c. "Away in a Manger" . . 90 55
1439 85 c. "We Three Kings of Orient Are" . . . . 1·10 65

1987. Maori Fibre-work. Multicoloured.
1440 40 c. Type **434** 35 10
1441 60 c. Binding ("Herehere") . . 45 55
1442 80 c. Plait ("Whiri") 60 90
1443 85 c. Cloak weaving ("Korowai") with flax fibre ("Whitau") 65 95

435 "Geothermal"

1988. Centenary of Electricity. Each shows radiating concentric circles representing energy generation.
1444 **435** 40 c. multicoloured . . . 30 35
1445 – 60 c. black, red and brown 40 45
1446 – 70 c. multicoloured . . . 50 55
1447 – 80 c. multicoloured . . . 55 60
DESIGNS: 60 c. "Thermal"; 70 c. "Gas"; 80 c. "Hydro".

436 Queen Elizabeth II and 1882 Queen Victoria 1d. Stamp

1988. Centenary of Royal Philatelic Society of New Zealand. Multicoloured.
1448 40 c. Type **436** 35 50
1449 40 c. As Type **436**, but 1882 Queen Victoria 2d. 35 50

437 "Mangopare"

438 "Good Luck"

1988. Maori Rafter Paintings. Multicoloured.
1451 40 c. Type **437** 40 40
1452 40 c. "Koru" 40 40
1453 40 c. "Raupunga" 40 40
1454 60 c. "Koiri" 55 65

1988. Greetings Stamps. Multicoloured.
1455 40 c. Type **438** 60 70
1456 40 c. "Keeping in touch" . . . 60 70
1457 40 c. "Happy birthday" . . . 60 70
1458 40 c. "Congratulations" (41 × 27 mm) 60 70
1459 40 c. "Get well soon" (41 × 27 mm) 60 70

439 Paradise Shelduck

440 Milford Track

1988. Native Birds. Multicoloured.
1459a 5 c. Sooty crake 10 10
1460 10 c. Double-banded plover . 10 10
1461 20 c. Yellowhead 15 20
1462 30 c. Grey-backed white eye ("Silvereye") 30 30
1463 40 c. Brown kiwi 35 40
1589a 45 c. Rock wren 30 45
1464 50 c. Sacred kingfisher . . . 50 50
1465 60 c. Spotted cormorant ("Spotted shag") 50 55
1466 70 c. Type **439** 55 70
1467 80 c. Fiordland crested penguin 80 70
1467a 80 c. New Zealand falcon . . 1·00 90
1468 90 c. New Zealand robin . . 90 80
The 40 and 45 c. also exist self-adhesive.

1988. Scenic Walking Trails. Multicoloured.
1469 70 c. Type **440** 50 60
1470 80 c. Heaphy Track 55 75
1471 85 c. Copland Track 60 80
1472 $1.30 Routeburn Track . . . 90 1·25

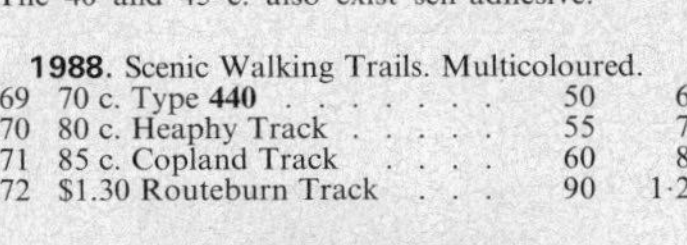

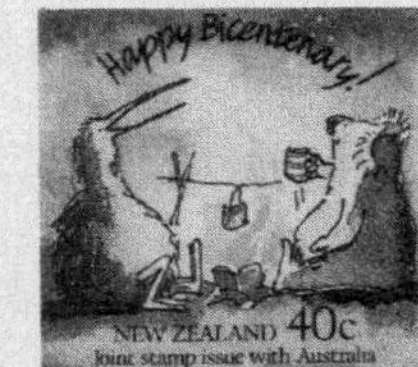

441 Kiwi and Koala at Campfire

1988. Bicent of Australian Settlement.
1474 **441** 40 c. multicoloured . . . 40 35
A stamp in a similar design was also issued by Australia.

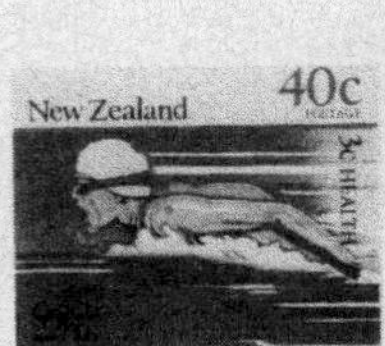

442 Swimming

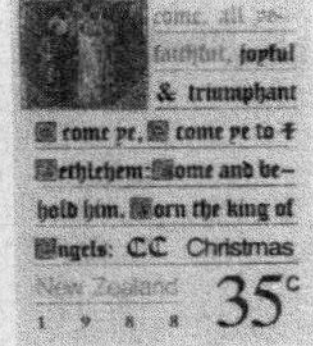

443 "O Come All Ye Faithful"

1988. Health Stamps. Olympic Games, Seoul. Multicoloured.
1475 40 c. + 3 c. Type **442** 40 65
1476 60 c. + 3 c. Athletics . . . . 60 1·00
1477 70 c. + 3 c. Canoeing . . . . 70 1·00
1478 80 c. + 3 c. Show-jumping . . 90 1·25

1988. Christmas. Carols. Designs showing illuminated verses. Multicoloured.
1480 35 c. Type **443** 30 30
1481 70 c. "Hark the Herald Angels Sing" 50 65
1482 80 c. "Ding Dong Merrily on High" 50 70
1483 85 c. "The First Nowell" . . . 55 80

444 "Lake Pukaki" (John Gully)

1988. New Zealand Heritage (1st issue). "The Land". Designs showing 19th-century paintings. Multicoloured.
1484 40 c. Type **444** 35 35
1485 60 c. "On the Grass Plain below Lake Arthur" (William Fox) 45 45
1486 70 c. "View of Auckland" (John Hoyte) 55 55
1487 80 c. "Mt. Egmont from the Southward" (Charles Heaphy) 60 60
1488 $1.05 "Anakiwa, Queen Charlotte Sound" (John Kinder) 80 80
1489 $1.30 "White Terraces, Lake Rotomahana", (Charles Barraud) 95 95
See also Nos. 1505/10, 1524/9, 1541/6, 1548/53 and 1562/7.

445 Brown Kiwi

1988.
1490 **445** $1 green . . . . 2·00 2·75
1490b $1 red . . . . 1·40 1·50
1490c $1 blue . . . . 1·00 1·25
2090 $1 violet 75 80
2090a $1.10 gold 70 75

446 Humpback Whale and Calf

1988. Whales. Multicoloured.
1491 60 c. Type **446** 80 85
1492 70 c. Killer whales . . . . . 1·00 1·10
1493 80 c. Southern right whale . . 1·10 1·25
1494 85 c. Blue whale . . . . . . 1·25 1·50
1495 $1.05 Southern bottlenose whale and calf . . . . 1·50 2·00
1496 $1.30 Sperm whale . . . . . 1·60 2·00
Although inscribed "ROSS DEPENDENCY" Nos. 1491/6 were available from post offices throughout New Zealand.

447 Clover

448 Katherine Mansfield

1989. Wild Flowers. Multicoloured.
1497 40 c. Type **447** 40 35
1498 60 c. Lotus 50 60
1499 70 c. Montbretia 60 80
1500 80 c. Wild ginger 70 90

1989. New Zealand Authors. Multicoloured.
1501 40 c. Type **448** 30 35
1502 60 c. James K. Baxter 40 50
1503 70 c. Bruce Mason 50 60
1504 80 c. Ngaio Marsh 55 70

449 Moriori Man and Map of Chatham Islands

1989. New Zealand Heritage (2nd issue). The People.
1505 **449** 40 c. multicoloured . . . 45 35
1506 – 60 c. brown, grey and deep brown 60 70
1507 – 70 c. green, grey and deep green 65 75
1508 – 80 c. blue, grey and deep blue 75 85
1509 – $1.05 grey, light grey and black . . . . 1·00 1·10
1510 – $1.30 red, grey & brown . 1·25 1·40
DESIGNS: 60 c. Gold prospector; 70 c. Settler ploughing; 80 c. Whaling; $1.05, Missionary preaching to Maoris; $1.30, Maori village.

450 White Pine (Kahikatea)

451 Duke and Duchess of York with Princess Beatrice

1989. Native Trees. Multicoloured.
1511 80 c. Type **450** 75 80
1512 85 c. Red pine (Rimu) 80 85
1513 $1.05 Totara . . . . 1·00 1·10
1514 $1.30 Kauri . . . . 1·25 1·40

1989. Health Stamps. Multicoloured.
1516 40 c. + 3 c. Type **451** . . . . 80 1·25
1517 40 c. + 3 c. Duchess of York with Princess Beatrice . . . 80 1·25
1518 80 c. + 3 c. Princess Beatrice 1·40 1·75

452 One Tree Hill, Auckland through Bedroom Window

453 Windsurfing

1989. Christmas. Designs showing Star of Bethlehem. Multicoloured.
1520 35 c. Type **452** 40 30
1521 65 c. Shepherd and dog in mountain valley 75 70
1522 80 c. Star over harbour . . . 95 90
1523 $1 Star over globe . . . . . 1·25 1·40

1989. New Zealand Heritage (3rd issue). The Sea. Multicoloured.
1524 40 c. Type **453** 40 35
1525 60 c. Fishes of many species . 70 70
1526 65 c. Striped marlin and game fishing launch 75 75
1527 80 c. Rowing boat and yachts in harbour 85 85
1528 $1 Coastal scene . . . . . . 1·10 1·10
1529 $1.50 "Rotoiti" (container ship) and tug . . . . 1·50 1·60

454 Games Logo

1989. 14th Commonwealth Games, Auckland. Multicoloured.
1530 40 c. Type **454** 40 35
1531 40 c. Goldie (games kiwi mascot) 40 35
1532 40 c. Gymnastics 40 35
1533 50 c. Weightlifting 50 55
1534 65 c. Swimming 65 70
1535 80 c. Cycling 80 90
1536 $1 Lawn bowling . . . . . . 1·00 1·25
1537 $1.80 Hurdling . . . . 1·75 1·90

455 Short S.30 modified "G" Class Flying Boat "Aotearoa" and Boeing 747-200

1990. 50th Anniv of Air New Zealand.
1539 **455** 80 c. multicoloured . . . 1·40 1·10

457 Maori Voyaging Canoe

1990. New Zealand Heritage (4th issue). The Ships. Multicoloured.
1541 40 c. Type **457** 60 35
1542 50 c. H.M.S. "Endeavour" (Cook), 1769 . . . . 85 80
1543 60 c. "Tory" (barque), 1839 . 95 90
1544 80 c. "Crusader" (full-rigged immigrant ship), 1871 . . . 1·40 1·40
1545 $1 "Edwin Fox" (full-rigged immigrant ship), 1873 . . . 1·60 1·40
1546 $1.50 "Arawa" (steamer), 1884 2·00 2·75

459 Grace Neill (social reformer) and Maternity Hospital, Wellington

1990. New Zealand Heritage (5th issue). Famous New Zealanders. Multicoloured.
1548 40 c. Type **459** 55 30
1549 50 c. Jean Batten (pilot) and Percival P.3 Gull Six aircraft 65 75
1550 60 c. Katherine Sheppard (suffragette) and 19th-century women . . . . 85 1·25
1551 80 c. Richard Pearse (inventor) and early flying machine . . 1·10 1·25
1552 $1 Lt.-Gen. Sir Bernard Freyberg and tank . . . . 1·25 1·25
1553 $1.50 Peter Buck (politician) and Maori pattern . . . . . . 1·50 2·00

460 Akaroa

461 Jack Lovelock (athlete) and Race

1990. 150th Anniv of European Settlements. Multicoloured.

1554	80 c. Type **460**	75	75
1555	$1 Wanganui	95	95
1556	$1.50 Wellington	1·40	2·25
1557	$1.80 Takapuna Beach, Auckland	1·60	2·25

1990. Health Stamps. Sportsmen (1st series). Multicoloured.

1559	40 c. + 5 c. Type **461**	50	75
1560	80 c. + 5 c. George Nepia (rugby player) and match	75	1·25

See also Nos. 1687/8.

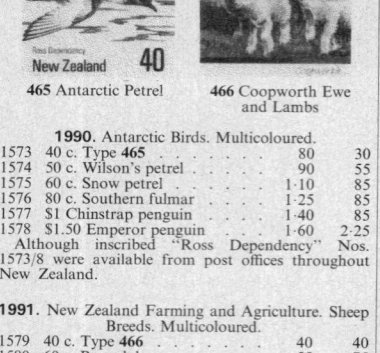

462 Creation Legend of Rangi and Papa

464 Angel

1990. New Zealand Heritage (6th issue). The Maori. Multicoloured.

1562	40 c. Type **462**	40	30
1563	50 c. Pattern from Maori feather cloak	55	70
1564	60 c. Maori women's choir	60	80
1565	80 c. Maori facial tattoos	75	90
1566	$1 War canoe prow (detail)	90	1·10
1567	$1.50 Maori haka	1·40	2·50

1990. Christmas.

1569	**464**	40 c. purple, blue & brn	40	30
1570	–	$1 purple, green & brown	80	80
1571	–	$1.50 purple, red & brown	1·40	1·75
1572	–	$1.80 purple, red & brown	1·60	1·75

DESIGNS: $1 to $1.80, Different angels.

465 Antarctic Petrel

466 Coopworth Ewe and Lambs

1990. Antarctic Birds. Multicoloured.

1573	40 c. Type **465**	80	30
1574	50 c. Wilson's petrel	90	55
1575	60 c. Snow petrel	1·10	85
1576	80 c. Southern fulmar	1·25	85
1577	$1 Chinstrap penguin	1·40	85
1578	$1.50 Emperor penguin	1·60	2·25

Although inscribed "Ross Dependency" Nos. 1573/8 were available from post offices throughout New Zealand.

1991. New Zealand Farming and Agriculture. Sheep Breeds. Multicoloured.

1579	40 c. Type **466**	40	40
1580	60 c. Perendale	55	75
1581	80 c. Corriedale	70	85
1582	$1 Drysdale	85	90
1583	$1.50 South Suffolk	1·25	2·00
1584	$1.80 Romney	1·50	2·00

467 Moriori, Royal Albatross, Nikau Palm and Artefacts

469 Tuatara on Rocks

468 Goal and Footballers

1991. Bicentenary of Discovery of Chatham Islands. Multicoloured.

1585	40 c. Type **467**	50	50
1586	80 c. Carvings, H.M.S. "Chatham", Moriori house of 1870, and Tommy Solomon	1·25	1·60

1991. Centenary of New Zealand Football Association. Multicoloured.

1587	80 c. Type **468**	1·00	1·40
1588	80 c. Five footballers and referee	1·00	1·40

Nos. 1587/8 were printed together, se-tenant, forming a composite design.

1991. Endangered Species. The Tuatara. Multicoloured.

1590	40 c. Type **469**	40	55
1591	40 c. Tuatara in crevice	40	55
1592	40 c. Tuatara with foliage	40	55
1593	40 c. Tuatara in dead leaves	40	55

470 Clown

471 Cat at Window

1991. "Happy Birthday". Multicoloured.

1594	40 c. Type **470**	55	60
1595	40 c. Balloons	55	60
1596	40 c. Party hat	55	60
1597	40 c. Birthday present (41 × 27 mm)	55	60
1598	40 c. Birthday cake (41 × 27 mm)	55	60
1599	45 c. Type **470**	55	60
1600	45 c. As No. 1595	55	60
1601	45 c. As No. 1596	55	60
1602	45 c. As No. 1597	55	60
1603	45 c. As No. 1598	55	60

1991. "Thinking of You". Multicoloured.

1604	40 c. Type **471**	55	60
1605	40 c. Cat playing with slippers	55	60
1606	40 c. Cat with alarm clock	55	60
1607	40 c. Cat in window (41 × 27 mm)	55	60
1608	40 c. Cat at door (41 × 27 mm)	55	60
1609	45 c. Type **471**	55	60
1610	45 c. As No. 1605	55	60
1611	45 c. As No. 1606	55	60
1612	45 c. As No. 1607	55	60
1613	45 c. As No. 1608	55	60

472 Punakaiki Rocks

473 Dolphins Underwater

1991. Scenic Landmarks. Multicoloured.

1614	40 c. Type **472**	40	30
1615	50 c. Moeraki Boulders	55	55
1616	80 c. Organ Pipes	85	85
1617	$1 Castle Hill	95	95
1618	$1.50 Te Kaukau Point	1·50	1·60
1619	$1.80 Ahuriri River Clay Cliffs	1·75	1·90

1991. Health Stamps. Hector's Dolphin. Multicoloured.

1620	45 c. + 5 c. Type **473**	90	1·00
1621	80 c. + 5 c. Dolphins leaping	1·25	1·75

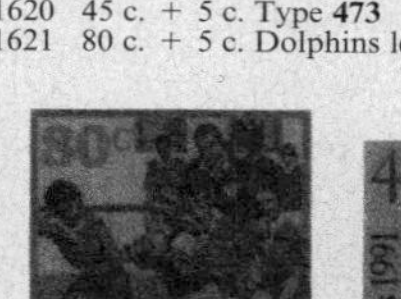

474 Children's Rugby

475 "Three Shepherds"

1991. World Cup Rugby Championship. Multicoloured.

1623	80 c. Type **474**	1·00	1·25
1624	$1 Women's rugby	1·10	95
1625	$1.50 Senior rugby	1·75	2·50
1626	$1.80 "All Blacks" (national team)	2·00	2·50

1991. Christmas. Multicoloured.

1628	45 c. Type **475**	55	75
1629	45 c. Two Kings on camels	55	75
1630	45 c. Mary and Baby Jesus	55	75
1631	45 c. King with gift	55	75
1632	65 c. Star of Bethlehem	70	80
1633	$1 Crown	85	95
1634	$1.50 Angel	1·40	2·00

476 "Dodonidia helmsii"

1991. Butterflies. Multicoloured.

1640	$1 Type **476**	90	80
1641	$2 "Zizina otis oxleyi"	2·00	1·75
1642	$3 "Vanessa itea"	2·75	3·00
1643	$4 "Lycaena salustius"	3·25	3·50
1644	$5 "Bassaris gonerilla"	3·75	4·00

479 Yacht "Kiwi Magic", 1987

1992. New Zealand Challenge for America's Cup. Multicoloured.

1655	45 c. Type **479**	45	35
1656	80 c. Yacht "New Zealand", 1988	80	70
1657	$1 Yacht "America", 1851	95	85
1658	$1.50 "America's Cup" Class yacht, 1992	1·60	1·40

480 "Heemskerk"

1992. Great Voyages of Discovery. Mult.

1659	45 c. Type **480**	55	35
1660	80 c. "Zeehan"	90	85
1661	$1 "Santa Maria"	1·25	85
1662	$1.50 "Pinta" and "Nina"	1·50	1·60

Nos. 1659/60 commemorate the 350th anniv of Tasman's discovery of New Zealand and Nos. 1661/2 the 500th anniv of discovery of America by Columbus.

481 Sprinters

1992. Olympic Games, Barcelona (1st issue).

1663	**481**	45 c. multicoloured	50	40

See also Nos. 1670/3.

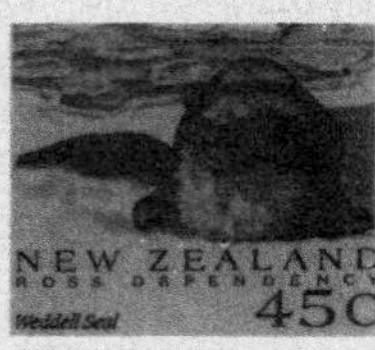

482 Weddell Seal and Pup

1992. Antarctic Seals. Multicoloured.

1664	45 c. Type **482**	70	40
1665	50 c. Crabeater seals swimming	80	40
1666	65 c. Leopard seal and Adelie penguins	1·00	85
1667	80 c. Ross seal	1·25	90
1668	$1 Southern elephant seal and harem	1·40	95
1669	$1.80 Hooker's sea lion and pup	2·25	2·25

Although inscribed "ROSS DEPENDENCY" Nos. 1664/9 were available from post offices throughout New Zealand.

483 Cycling

1992. Olympic Games, Barcelona (2nd issue). Multicoloured.

1670	45 c. Type **483**	65	35
1671	80 c. Archery	90	70
1672	$1 Equestrian three-day eventing	1·00	85
1673	$1.50 Sailboarding	1·50	1·40

484 Ice Pinnacles, Franz Josef Glacier

1992. Glaciers. Multicoloured.

1675	45 c. Type **484**	40	35
1676	50 c. Tasman Glacier	50	45
1677	80 c. Snowball glacier, Marion Plateau	70	70
1678	$1 Brewster Glacier	85	85
1679	$1.50 Fox Glacier	1·40	1·40
1680	$1.80 Franz Josef Glacier	1·50	1·60

NEW ZEALAND

485 "Grand Finale" Camellia

New Zealand Post 45c

486 Tree and Hills

1992. Camellias. Multicoloured.

1681	45 c. Type **485**	40	35
1682	50 c. "Showa-No-Sakae"	50	45
1683	80 c. "Sugar Dream"	70	70
1684	$1 "Night Rider"	85	85
1685	$1.50 "E.G. Waterhouse"	1·40	1·75
1686	$1.80 "Dr. Clifford Parks"	1·50	2·00

1992. Health Stamps. Sportsmen (2nd series). As T **461**. Multicoloured.

1687	45 c. + 5 c. Anthony Wilding (tennis player) and match	80	85
1688	80 c. + 5 c. Stewie Dempster (cricketer) and batsman	95	1·40

1992. Landscapes. Multicoloured.

1690	45 c. Type **486**	40	50
1691	45 c. River and hills	40	50
1692	45 c. Hills and mountain	40	50
1693	45 c. Glacier	40	50
1694	45 c. Hills and waterfall	40	50
1695	45 c. Tree and beach	40	50
1696	45 c. Estuary and cliffs	40	50
1697	45 c. Fjord	40	50
1698	45 c. River delta	40	50
1699	45 c. Ferns and beach	40	50

487 Reindeer over Houses

488 1920s Fashions

1992. Christmas. Multicoloured.

1700	45 c. Type **487**	70	85
1701	45 c. Santa Claus on sleigh over houses	70	85
1702	45 c. Christmas tree in window	70	85
1703	45 c. Christmas wreath and children at window	70	85
1704	65 c. Candles and fireplace	80	90
1705	$1 Family going to church	1·00	1·00
1706	$1.50 Picnic under Pohutukawa tree	1·75	2·25

1992. New Zealand in the 1920s. Mult.

1707	45 c. Type **488**	50	35
1708	50 c. Dr. Robert Jack and early radio announcer	55	55
1709	80 c. "All Blacks" rugby player, 1924	85	85
1710	$1 Swaggie and dog	95	95
1711	$1.50 Ford "Model A" car and young couple	1·75	1·75
1712	$1.80 Amateur aviators and biplane	2·00	2·50

489 "Old Charley" Toby Jug

490 Women's Fashions of the 1930s

1993. Royal Doulton Ceramics Exhibition, New Zealand. Multicoloured.

1713	45 c. Type **489**	50	35
1714	50 c. "Bunnykins" nursery plate	55	50
1715	80 c. "Maori Art" tea set	85	75
1716	$1 "Ophelia" handpainted plate	1·00	90
1717	$1.50 "St. George" figurine	1·60	2·00
1718	$1.80 "Lambeth" salt-glazed stoneware vase	1·90	2·25

1993. New Zealand in the 1930s. Mult.

1720	45 c. Type **490**	50	45
1721	50 c. Unemployed protest march	55	75
1722	80 c. "Phar Lap" (racehorse)	85	95
1723	$1 State housing project	1·00	1·00
1724	$1.50 Boys drinking free school milk	1·75	2·25
1725	$1.80 Cinema queue	1·90	2·00

491 Women signing Petition

492 Champagne Pool

1993. Centenary of Women's Suffrage. Mult.

1726 45 c. Type **491** 50 35
1727 80 c. Aircraft propeller and woman on tractor . . . . 1·00 85
1728 $1 Housewife with children . . 1·00 95
1729 $1.50 Modern women . . . . 1·60 1·60

1993. Thermal Wonders, Rotorua. Mult.

1730 45 c. Type **492** 60 40
1731 50 c. Boiling mud 60 40
1732 80 c. Emerald pool 85 70
1733 $1 Hakereteke Falls 95 80
1734 $1.50 Warbrick Terrace . . . 1·50 1·50
1735 $1.80 Pohutu Geyser . . . . 1·60 1·75

493 Yellow-eyed Penguin, Hector's Dolphin and New Zealand Fur Seal

1993. Endangered Species Conservation. Mult.

1736 45 c. Type **493** 55 70
1737 45 c. Chatham Island taiko (bird), Mount Cook lily and mountain duck 55 70
1738 45 c. Giant snail, rock wren and Hamilton's frog 55 70
1739 45 c. Kaka (bird), New Zealand pigeon and giant weta . . . 55 70
1740 45c. Tusked weta (23 × 28 mm) . 55 70

494 Boy with Puppy

495 Christmas Decorations (value at left)

1993. Health Stamps. Children's Pets. Mult.

1741 45 c. + 5 c. Type **494** 60 70
1742 80 c. + 5 c. Girl with kitten . 90 1·40

1993. Christmas. Multicoloured.

1746 45 c. Type **495** 60 80
1747 45 c. Christmas decorations (value at right) 60 80
1748 45 c. Sailboards, gifts and Christmas pudding (value at left) 60 80
1749 45 c. Sailboards, gifts and Christmas pudding (value at right) 60 80
1750 $1 Sailboards, baubles and Christmas cracker . . . . 1·50 1·25
1751 $1.50 Sailboards, present and wreath . . . . 2·00 6·50

496 Rainbow Abalone or Paua

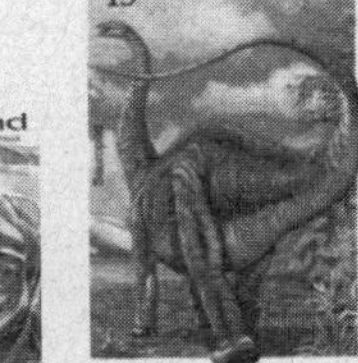

497 Sauropod

1993. Marine Life. Multicoloured.

1752 45 c. Type **496** 75 75
1753 45 c. Green mussels 75 75
1754 45 c. Tarakihi 75 75
1755 45 c. Salmon 75 75
1756 45 c. Southern blue-finned tuna, yellow-finned tuna and kahawai 75 75
1757 45 c. Rock lobster 75 75
1758 45 c. Snapper 75 75
1759 45 c. Grouper 75 75
1760 45 c. Orange roughy 75 75
1761 45 c. Squid, hoki and black oreo 75 75

1993. Prehistoric Animals. Multicoloured.

1762 45 c. Type **497** 45 45
1763 45 c. Carnosaur and sauropod (30 × 25 mm) 50 50
1764 80 c. Pterosaur 85 85
1765 $1 Ankylosaur 95 95
1766 $1.20 Mauisaurus . . . . . 1·40 1·75
1767 $1.50 Carnosaur . . . . . . 1·50 1·75

498 Soldiers, National Flag and Pyramids

499 Bungy Jumping

1993. New Zealand in the 1940s. Multicoloured.

1771 45 c. Type **498** 60 40
1772 50 c. Aerial crop spraying . . . 60 50
1773 80 c. Hydro-electric scheme . . 90 80
1774 $1 Marching majorettes . . . 1·00 90
1775 $1.50 American troops . . . 1·60 1·50
1776 $1.80 Crowd celebrating victory 1·75 1·60

1994. Tourism. Multicoloured.

1777 45 c. Type **499** 50 40
1778 45 c. White water rafting (25 × 25 mm) 50 55
1779 80 c. Trout fishing 70 70
1780 $1 Jet boating (horiz) 80 80
1781 $1.50 Tramping . . . . . . 1·40 1·40
1782 $1.80 Heli-skiing . . . . . . 1·90 2·00

500 "New Zealand Endeavour" (yacht)

503 Rock and Roll Dancers

501 Mt. Cook and New Zealand Symbols

1994. Round the World Yacht Race.

1783 **500** $1 multicoloured . . . . 1·40 1·40

1994.

1784 **501** $20 blue and gold . . . . 12·50 13·50

1994. New Zealand in the 1950s. Mult.

1787 45 c. Type **503** 45 40
1788 80 c. Sir Edmund Hillary on Mt. Everest 75 75
1789 $1 Aunt Daisy (radio personality) 85 85
1790 $1.20 Queen Elizabeth II during 1953 royal visit . . . . 1·25 1·25
1791 $1.50 Children playing with Opo the dolphin . . . . . . 1·60 1·60
1792 $1.80 Auckland Harbour Bridge 1·90 2·00

504 Mt. Cook and Mt. Cook Lily ("Winter")

1994. The Four Seasons. Mult.

1793 45 c. Type **504** 45 40
1794 70 c. Lake Hawea and Kowhai ("Spring") 65 65
1795 $1.50 Opononi Beach and Pohutukawa ("Summer") . 1·40 1·40
1796 $1.80 Lake Pukaki and Puriri ("Autumn") . . . . 1·75 1·75

505 Rainbow Abalone or Paua Shell

506 Maui pulls up Te Ika

1994. New Zealand Life. Multicoloured.

1797 45 c. Type **505** (25 × 20 mm) . 35 40
1798 45 c. Pavlova dessert (35 × 20 mm) 35 40
1799 45 c. Hokey pokey ice cream (25 × 20 mm) 35 40
1800 45 c. Fish and chips (35 × 20 mm) 35 40
1801 45 c. Jandals (30 × 20 mm) . . 35 40
1802 45 c. Bush shirt (25 × 30½ mm) . 35 40
1803 45 c. Buzzy Bee (toy) (35 × 30½ mm) 35 40
1804 45 c. Gumboots and black singlet (25 × 30½ mm) . . . 35 40
1805 45 c. Rugby boots and ball (35 × 30½ mm) 35 40
1806 45 c. Kiwifruit (30 × 30½ mm) . . 35 40

1994. Maori Myths. Multicoloured.

1807 45 c. Type **506** 50 40
1808 80 c. Rona snatched up by Marama 85 85
1809 $1 Maui attacking Tuna . . . 1·00 1·00
1810 $1.20 Tane separating Rangi and Papa . . . . 1·40 1·75
1811 $1.50 Matakauri slaying the Giant of Wakatipu . . . . 1·50 2·00
1812 $1.80 Panenehu showing crayfish to Tangaroa . . . 1·75 2·00

507 1939 2d. on 1d. + 1d. Health Stamp and Children playing with Ball

508 Astronaut on Moon (hologram)

1994. Health Stamps. 75th Anniv of Children's Health Camps. Multicoloured.

1813 45 c. + 5 c. Type **507** 50 70
1814 45 c. + 5 c. 1949 1d. + ½d. stamp and nurse holding child 50 70
1815 45 c. + 5 c. 1969 4 c. + 1 c. stamp and children reading . 50 70
1816 80 c. + 5 c. 1931 2d. + 1d. stamp and child in cap . . . 75 90

1994. 25th Anniv of First Manned Moon Landing.

1818 **508** $1.50 multicoloured . . . 1·25 1·50

509 "people reaching people"

1994. Self-adhesive.

1818ab **509** 40 c. multicoloured . . 45 40
1819 45 c. multicoloured . . 50 45

510 African Elephants

1994. Stamp Month. Wild Animals. Multicoloured.

1820 45 c. Type **510** 60 60
1821 45 c. White rhinoceros 60 60
1822 45 c. Lions 60 60
1823 45 c. Common zebras 60 60
1824 45 c. Giraffe and calf 60 60
1825 45 c. Siberian tiger 60 60
1826 45 c. Hippopotami 60 60
1827 45 c. Spider monkey 60 60
1828 45 c. Giant panda 60 60
1829 45 c. Polar bear and cub . . . 60 60

511 Children with Crib

512 Batsman

1994. Christmas. Multicoloured.

1832 45 c. Father Christmas and children (30 × 25 mm) . . . 45 40
1833 45 c. Type **511** 45 40
1834 70 c. Man and toddler with crib 65 80
1835 80 c. Three carol singers . . . 70 85
1836 $1 Five carol singers 90 90
1837 $1.50 Children and candles . . 1·25 1·75
1838 $1.80 Parents with child . . . 1·60 2·00

1994. Centenary of New Zealand Cricket Council. (a) Horiz designs, each 30 × 25 mm. Multicoloured.

1840 45 c. Bathers catching balls . . 40 60
1841 45 c. Child on surf board at top 40 60
1842 45 c. Young child with rubber ring at top 40 60
1843 45 c. Man with beach ball at top 40 60
1844 45 c. Woman with cricket bat at right 40 60
1845 45 c. Boy in green cap with bat . 40 60
1846 45 c. Man in spotted shirt running 40 60
1847 45 c. Woman in striped shorts with bat 40 60
1848 45 c. Boy in wet suit with surf board at right 40 60
1849 45 c. Sunbather with newspaper at right 40 60

(b) T **512** and similar vert designs. Multicoloured.

1850 45 c. Type **512** 45 40
1851 80 c. Bowler 80 80
1852 $1 Wicket keeper . . . . . . 1·00 1·00
1853 $1.80 Fielder . . . . 1·75 1·75

513 Auckland

1995. New Zealand by Night. Multicoloured.

1855 45 c. Type **513** 45 40
1856 80 c. Wellington 75 65
1857 $1 Christchurch 90 85
1858 $1.20 Dunedin . . . . 1·10 1·00
1859 $1.50 Rotorua . . . . 1·25 1·25
1860 $1.80 Queenstown . . . . . 1·50 1·50

514 The 15th Hole, Waitangi

515 New Zealand Pigeon and Nest

1995. New Zealand Golf Courses. Multicoloured.

1861 45 c. Type **514** 65 40
1862 80 c. The 6th hole, New Plymouth . . . . 1·00 90
1863 $1.20 The 9th hole, Rotorua . 1·50 1·75
1864 $1.80 The 5th hole, Queenstown 2·40 2·75

1995. Environment. Multicoloured.

1865 45 c. Type **515** 60 60
1866 45 c. Planting sapling 60 60
1867 45 c. Dolphins and whales . . 60 60
1868 45 c. Thunder storm 60 60
1869 45 c. Backpackers 60 60
1870 45 c. Animal pests 60 60
1871 45 c. Noxious plants 60 60
1872 45 c. Undersized fish and shellfish 60 60
1873 45 c. Pollution from factories . 60 60
1874 45 c. Family at picnic site . . 60 60

516 Teacher with Guitar and Children

517 Map of Australasia and Asia

1995. Maori Language Year. Multicoloured.

1875 45 c. Type **516** 50 45
1876 70 c. Singing group 75 75
1877 80 c. Mother and baby . . . 85 85
1878 $1 Women performing traditional welcome . . . . 1·10 1·10
1879 $1.50 Grandfather reciting family genealogy . . . . . 1·75 1·75
1880 $1.80 Tribal orator . . . . . 2·00 2·00

1995. Meetings of Asian Development Bank Board of Governors and International Pacific Basin Economic Council, Auckland. Multicoloured.

1881 $1 Type **517** . . . . 1·25 1·00
1882 $1.50 Map of Australasia and Pacific . . . . 1·75 2·50

MORE DETAILED LISTS
are given in the Stanley Gibbons Catalogues referred to in the country headings.
For lists of current volumes see Introduction.

518 "Black Magic" (yacht)

1995. New Zealand's Victory in 1995 America's Cup.
1883 **518** 45 c. multicoloured . . . 55 55

519 Boy on Skateboard

1995. Health Stamps. Children's Sports. Mult.
1884 45 c. + 5 c. Type **519** 65 70
1885 80 c. + 5 c. Girl on bicyle . . 1·25 1·40

520 Lion Red Cup and Players

1995. Centenary of Rugby League. Multicoloured.
1888 45 c. Trans Tasman test match (30 × 25 mm) 50 45
1889 45 c. Type **520** 50 45
1890 $1 Children's rugby and mascot 1·25 1·10
1891 $1.50 George Smith, Albert Baskerville and early match . 2·00 2·00
1892 $1.80 Courtney Goodwill Trophy and match against Great Britain . . . . . . 2·25 2·25

521 Sheep and Lamb

522 Archangel Gabriel

1995. Farmyard Animals. Multicoloured.
1894 40 c. Type **521** 60 65
1895 40 c. Deer 60 65
1896 40 c. Mare and foal 60 65
1897 40 c. Cow with calf 60 65
1898 40 c. Goats and kid 60 65
1899 40 c. Common turkey 60 65
1900 40 c. Ducks 60 65
1901 40 c. Red junglefowl 60 65
1902 40 c. Sow with piglets 60 65
1903 40 c. Border collie 60 65
1904 45 c. As Type **521** 60 65
1905 45 c. As No. 1895 . . . . . 60 65
1906 45 c. As No. 1896 . . . . . 60 65
1907 45 c. As No. 1897 . . . . . 60 65
1908 45 c. As No. 1898 . . . . . 60 65
1909 45 c. As No. 1899 . . . . . 60 65
1910 45 c. As No. 1900 . . . . . 60 65
1911 45 c. As No. 1901 . . . . . 60 65
1912 45 c. As No. 1902 . . . . . 60 65
1913 45 c. As No. 1903 . . . . . 60 65

1995. Christmas. Stained Glass Windows from St. Mary's Anglican Church, Merivale (Nos. 1916/18), The Lady Chapel of St. Luke's Anglican Church, Christchurch (Nos. 1919/22) or St. John the Evangelist Church, Cheviot (No. 1923). Multicoloured. (a) As T **522**.
1916 40 c. Type **522** 60 40
1917 45 c. Type **522** 60 45
1918 70 c. Virgin Mary 90 90
1919 80 c. Shepherds . . . . . 1·00 1·00
1920 $1 Virgin and Child . . . . 1·25 1·10
1921 $1.50 Two Wise Men . . . 2·00 2·50
1922 $1.80 Wise Man kneeling . . 2·25 2·50

(b) Smaller design, 25 × 30 mm.
1923 40 c. Angel with trumpet . . . 55 50

523 Face and Nuclear Disarmament Symbol

524 Mt. Cook

1995. Nuclear Disarmament.
1924 **523** $1 multicoloured . . . . 1·00 1·00

1995. New Zealand Scenery. Multicoloured.
1925 5 c. Type **524** 10 10
1926 10 c. Champagne Pool . . . 10 10
1927 20 c. Cape Reinga 15 20
1928 30 c. Mackenzie Country . . 20 25
1929 40 c. Mitre Peak (vert) . . . 25 30
1930 50 c. Mt. Ngauruhoe 30 35
1931 60 c. Lake Wanaka (vert) . . 40 45
1932 70 c. Giant kauri tree (vert) . . 45 50
1933 80 c. Doubtful Sound (vert) . . 50 55
1934 90 c. Waitomo Limestone Cave (vert) 55 60
1934a $1 Taiaroa Head (29 × 24 mm) 65 70
1934b $1.10 Kaikoura Coast (29 × 24 mm) 70 75
1934c $2 Great Barrier Island (29 × 24 mm) . . . . 1·25 1·40
1934d $3 Cape Kidnappers (29 × 24 mm) . . . . 1·90 2·00
1935 $10 Mt. Ruapela (40 × 34 mm) . . . . 6·25 6·50
For similar self-adhesive designs see Nos. 1984b/91.

525 Dame Kiri te Kanawa (opera singer)

526 National Flags, Peace Dove and "50"

1995. Famous New Zealanders. Multicoloured.
1936 40 c. Type **525** 65 40
1937 80 c. Charles Upham, V.C. (war hero) 90 85
1938 $1 Barry Crump (author) . . 1·25 1·00
1939 $1.20 Sir Brian Barratt-Boyes (surgeon) . . . . 1·50 1·25
1940 $1.50 Dame Whina Cooper (Maori leader) . . . . . . 1·75 1·75
1941 $1.80 Sir Richard Hadlee (cricketer) . . . . 2·50 2·25

1995. 50th Anniv of United Nations.
1942 **526** $1.80 multicoloured . . . 2·25 1·90

527 Fern and Globe

1995. Commonwealth Heads of Government Meeting, Auckland. Multicoloured.
1943 40 c. Type **527** 60 40
1944 $1.80 Fern and New Zealand flag . . . . 2·50 2·00

528 "Kiwi"

1996. Famous Racehorses. Multicoloured.
1945 40 c. Type **528** 55 40
1946 80 c. "Rough Habit" 95 95
1947 $1 "Blossom Lady" . . . . 1·25 1·25
1948 $1.20 "Il Vicolo" . . . . . 1·60 1·60
1949 $1.50 "Horlicks" . . . . . 1·75 1·75
1950 $1.80 "Bonecrusher" . . . . 2·50 2·50

529 Kete (basket)

530 Black-backed Gulls

1996. Maori Crafts. Multicoloured.
1952 40 c. Type **529** 50 40
1953 80 c. Head of Taiaha (spear) . 90 90
1954 $1 Taniko (embroidery) . . . 1·25 1·25
1955 $1.20 Pounamu (greenstone) . 1·50 1·50
1956 $1.50 Hue (gourd) . . . . . 1·75 1·75
1957 $1.80 Korowai (feather cloak) . 2·00 2·25

1996. Marine Life. Multicoloured. Self-adhesive or ordinary gum.
1958 40 c. Type **530** 45 50
1959 40 c. Children, sea cucumber and spiny starfish 45 50
1960 40 c. Yacht, gull and common shrimps 45 50
1961 40 c. Gaudy nudibranch . . . 45 50
1962 40 c. Large rock crab and clingfish 45 50
1963 40 c. Snake skin chiton and red rock crab 45 50
1964 40 c. Estuarine triplefin and cat's-eye shell 45 50
1965 40 c. Cushion star and sea horses 45 50
1966 40 c. Blue-eyed triplefin and Yaldwyn's triplefin 45 50
1967 40 c. Common octopus . . . 45 50

531 Fire and Ambulance Services

532 Mt. Egmont, Taranaki

1996. Rescue Services. Multicoloured.
1979 40 c. Type **531** 50 40
1980 80 c. Civil Defence 90 90
1981 $1 Air-sea rescue . . . . . 1·10 1·10
1982 $1.50 Air ambulance and rescue helicopter . . . . 1·60 1·60
1983 $1.80 Mountain rescue and Red Cross . . . . 2·25 2·40

1996. New Zealand Scenery. Self-adhesive. Multicoloured.
1984b 40 c. Type **532** 25 30
1985 40 c. Piercy Island, Bay of Islands 25 30
1986 40 c. Tory Channel, Malborough Sounds . . . 25 30
1987 40 c. "Earnslaw" (ferry), Lake Wakatipu 25 30
1988 40 c. Lake Matheson 25 30
1989 40 c. Fox Glacier 25 30
1990 80 c. Doubtful Sound (as No. 1933) 50 55
1991 $1 Pohutukawa tree (33 × 22 mm) 65 70

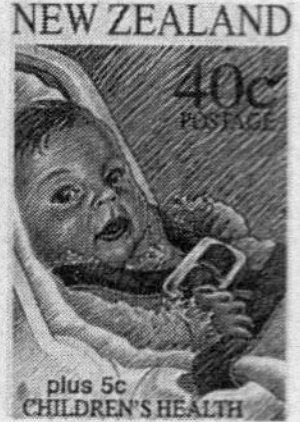

533 Yellow-eyed Penguin

534 Baby in Car Seat

1996. Marine Wildlife. Multicoloured.
1992 40 c. Type **533** 50 50
1993 80 c. Royal albatross (horiz) . 90 90
1994 $1 White herons (horiz) . . . 1·10 1·10
1995 $1.20 Flukes of sperm whale (horiz) . . . . 1·40 1·40
1996 $1.50 Fur seals . . . . . . 1·60 1·60
1997 $1.80 Bottlenose dolphin . . . 2·00 2·00

1996. Health Stamps. Child Safety. Multicoloured. Self-adhesive (1991) or ordinary (others) gum.
2000 40 c. + 5 c. Type **534** . . . 50 50
2003 40 c. + 5 c. Type **534** ($21\frac{1}{2}$ × 38 mm) 50 50
2001 80 c. + 5 c. Child and adult on zebra crossing 90 90

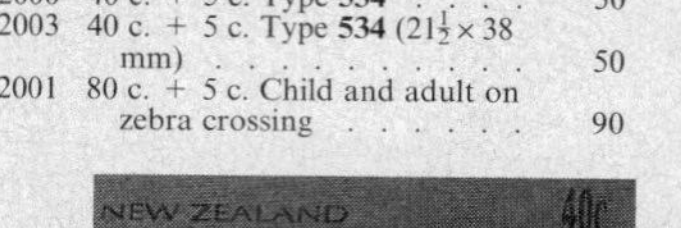

535 Violin

1996. 50th Anniv of New Zealand Symphony Orchestra. Multicoloured.
2006 40 c. Type **535** 40 40
2007 80 c. French horn . . . . . 1·00 1·50

536 Swimming

537 "Hinemoa"

1996. Centennial Olympic Games, Atlanta. Multicoloured.
2008 40 c. Type **536** 50 40
2009 80 c. Cycling . . . . 1·25 90
2010 $1 Running . . . . 1·25 1·00
2011 $1.50 Rowing . . . . . . 1·75 2·00
2012 $1.80 Dinghy racing . . . . 2·00 2·25

1996. Centenary of New Zealand Cinema. Multicoloured.
2014 40 c. Type **537** 50 40
2015 80 c. "Broken Barrier" . . . 1·00 80
2016 $1.50 "Goodbye Pork Pie" . . 1·75 2·00
2017 $1.80 "Once Were Warriors" . 1·75 2·00

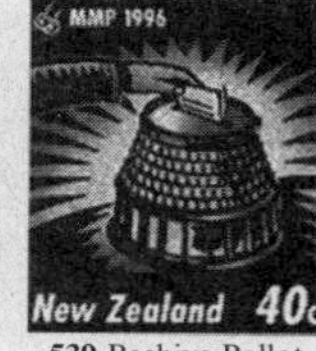

538 Danyon Loader (swimmer) and Blyth Tait (horseman)

539 Beehive Ballot Box

1996. New Zealand Olympic Gold Medal Winners, Atlanta.
2018 **538** 40 c. multicoloured . . . 45 45

1996. New Zealand's First Mixed Member Proportional Representation Election.
2019 **539** 40 c. black, red and yellow 45 45

540 King following Star

1996. Christmas. Multicoloured. (a) Size 35 × 35 mm.
2020 40 c. Type **540** 50 40
2021 70 c. Shepherd and Baby Jesus 80 80
2022 80 c. Angel and shepherd . . 90 90
2023 $1 Mary, Joseph and Baby Jesus . . . . 1·25 1·00
2024 $1.50 Mary and Joseph with donkey . . . . 2·00 2·25
2025 $1.80 The Annunciation . . 2·00 2·25

(b) Size 30 × 24 mm. Self-adhesive.
2026 40 c. Angels with trumpets . . 45 60
2027 40 c. King with gift 45 50

541 Adzebill

1996. Extinct Birds. Multicoloured. (a) Size 40 × 28 mm.
2028 40 c. Type **541** 60 40
2029 80 c. South Island whekau ("Laughing Owl") . . . . 1·25 1·25
2030 $1 Piopio . . . . 1·25 1·10
2031 $1.20 Huia . . . . 1·50 1·60
2032 $1.50 Giant eagle . . . . . 1·75 2·00
2033 $1.80 Giant moa . . . . . 2·00 2·00

(b) Size 30 × 24 mm. Self-adhesive.
2035 40 c. Stout-legged wren . . . 45 50

542 Seymour Square, Blenheim

543 Holstein Friesian Cattle

1996. Scenic Gardens. Multicoloured.
2038 40 c. Type **542** 50 40
2039 80 c. Pukekura Park, New Plymouth . . . . 1·00 1·00
2040 $1 Wintergarden, Auckland . 1·25 1·10
2041 $1.50 Botanic Garden, Christchurch . . . . . . 1·75 2·00
2042 $1.80 Marine Parade Gardens, Napier . . . . 1·90 2·00

1997. Cattle Breeds. Multicoloured.
2043 40 c. Type **543** 50 40
2044 80 c. Jersey . . . . 1·00 1·00
2045 $1 Simmental . . . . . . 1·25 1·00
2046 $1.20 Ayrshire . . . . . . 1·50 1·60
2047 $1.50 Angus . . . . 1·60 2·00
2048 $1.80 Hereford . . . . . . 1·90 2·00

544 James Cook and Sextant

1997. Millennium Series (1st issue). Discoverers of New Zealand. Multicoloured.

2051 40 c. Type **544** 70 45
2052 80 c. Kupe and ocean-going canoe . . . . 1·00 90
2053 $1 Carved panel depicting Maui (vert) . . . . 1·25 1·00
2054 $1.20 Anchor and "St. Jean Baptiste" (Jean de Surville) (vert) . . . . 1·50 1·60
2055 $1.50 Dumont d'Urville, crab and "Lastrolabe" . . . . . 1·75 2·00
2056 $1.80 Abel Tasman and illustration from journal . . 1·90 2·00

See also Nos. 2140/5, 2216/21, 2239/44, 2304/9 and 2310.

545 Rippon Vineyard, Central Otago

1997. New Zealand Vineyards. Multicoloured.

2057 40 c. Type **545** 60 40
2058 80 c. Te Mata Estate, Hawke's Bay . . . . 1·00 90
2059 $1 Cloudy Bay Vineyard, Marlborough . . . . . . 1·25 1·00
2060 $1.20 Pegasus Bay Vineyard, Waipara . . . . 1·50 1·60
2061 $1.50 Milton Vineyard, Gisborne . . . . 1·75 2·00
2062 $1.80 Goldwater Estate, Waiheke Island . . . . . 1·90 2·00

546 Cottage Letterbox

1997. Curious Letterboxes. Multicoloured. Self-adhesive.

2064 40 c. Type **546** 45 50
2065 40 c. Owl letterbox 45 50
2066 40 c. Blue whale letterbox . . 45 50
2067 40 c. "Kilroy is Back" letterbox 45 50
2068 40 c. Nesting box letterbox . . 45 50
2069 40 c. Piper letterbox 45 50
2070 40 c. Diver's helmet letterbox . 45 50
2071 40 c. Aircraft letterbox . . . 45 50
2072 40 c. Water tap letterbox . . . 45 50
2073 40 c. Indian palace letterbox . 45 50

547 "The Promised Land", 1948 (Colin McCahon)

1997. Contemporary Paintings by Colin McCahon. Multicoloured.

2074 40 c. Type **547** 50 35
2075 $1 "Six Days in Nelson and Canterbury", 1950 . . . . 1·10 90
2076 $1.50 "Northland Panels" (detail), 1958 . . . . 1·75 2·25
2077 $1.80 "Moby Dick is sighted off Muriwai Beach", 1972 . . . 2·25 2·25

548 Carrier Pigeon (based on 1899 "Pigeon-gram" local stamp)

1997. Centenary of Great Barrier Island Pigeon Post.

2078 **548** 40 c. red 50 70
2079 80 c. blue . . . . 90 1·25

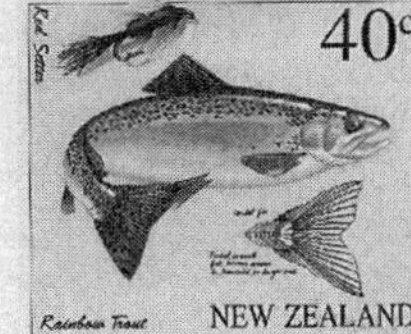
549 Rainbow Trout and Red Setter Fly

1997. Fly Fishing. Multicoloured.

2082 40 c. Type **549** 40 35
2083 $1 Sea-run brown trout and grey ghost fly 90 90
2084 $1.50 Brook charr and twilight beauty fly . . . . 1·40 1·75
2085 $1.80 Brown trout and Hare and Cooper fly . . . . 1·60 2·00

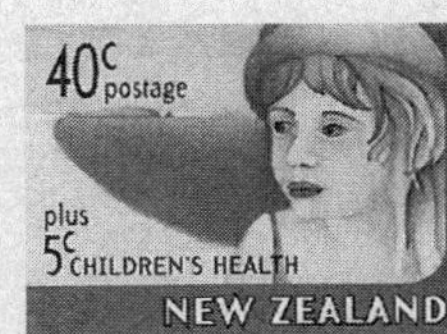
550 "Beach Scene" (Fern Petrie)

1997. Children's Health. Children's paintings. Multicoloured. (a) Ordinary gum.

2086 40 c. + 5 c. Type **550** 45 45
2087 80 c. + 5 c. "Horse-riding on the Waterfront" (Georgia Dumergue) 80 85

(b) Self-adhesive.

2089 40 c. + 5 c. "Picking Fruit" (Anita Pitcher) 45 45

551 The "Overlander" at Paremata, Wellington

1997. Scenic Railway Services. Multicoloured.

2091 40 c. Type **551** 50 35
2092 80 c. The "Tranz Alpine" in the Southern Alps 90 80
2093 $1 The "Southerner" at Canterbury . . . . 1·00 90
2094 $1.20 The "Coastal Pacific" on the Kaikoura Coast . . . . 1·40 1·75
2095 $1.50 The "Bay Express" at Central Hawke's Bay . . . 1·60 2·00
2096 $1.80 The "Kaimai Express" at Tauranga Harbour . . . . 1·75 2·00

552 Samuel Marsden's "Active", Bay of Islands

553 Huhu Beetle

1997. Christmas. Multicoloured. (a) Ordinary gum.

2097 40 c. Type **552** 45 40
2098 70 c. Revd. Marsden preaching 75 65
2099 80 c. Marsden and Maori chiefs 85 75
2100 $1 Maori family . . . . . . 1·00 90
2101 $1.50 Handshake and cross . . 1·60 1·75
2102 $1.80 Pohutukawa (flower) and Rangihoua Bay . . . . . . 1·75 2·00

(b) Smaller design, 29 × 24 mm. Self-adhesive.

2103 40 c. Memorial cross, Pohutukawa and Bay of Islands 40 40

1997. Insects. Multicoloured. Self-adhesive.

2104 40 c. Type **553** 45 45
2105 40 c. Giant land snail 45 45
2106 40 c. Giant weta 45 45
2107 40 c. Giant dragonfly 45 45
2108 40 c. Peripatus 45 45
2109 40 c. Cicada 45 45
2110 40 c. Puriri moth 45 45
2111 40 c. Veined slug 45 45
2112 40 c. Katipo 45 45
2113 40 c. Flax weevil 45 45

MORE DETAILED LISTS
are given in the Stanley Gibbons Catalogues referred to in the country headings.
For lists of current volumes see Introduction.

554 "Rosa rugosa"

555 Queen Elizabeth II and Prince Philip

1997. New Zealand–China Joint Issue. Roses. Multicoloured.

2114 40 c. Type **554** 40 40
2115 40 c. "Aotearoa" 40 40

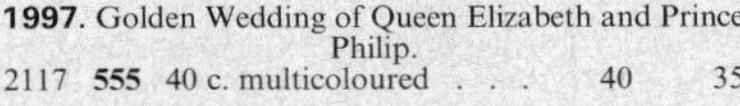

1997. Golden Wedding of Queen Elizabeth and Prince Philip.

2117 **555** 40 c. multicoloured . . . 40 35

556 Cartoon Kiwi on Busy-bee

1997. New Zealand Cartoons. "Kiwis Taking on the World". Multicoloured.

2118 40 c. Type **556** 45 35
2119 $1 "Let's have 'em for Breakfast" 85 80
2120 $1.50 Kiwi dinghy winning race 1·25 1·50
2121 $1.80 "CND" emblem cut in forest . . . . 1·60 1·75

557 Modern Dancer

1998. Performing Arts. Multicoloured.

2124 40 c. Type **557** 50 35
2125 80 c. Trombone player 85 75
2126 $1 Opera singer . . . . . . 1·00 85
2127 $1.20 Actor . . . . 1·50 1·50
2128 $1.50 Singer . . . . 1·75 1·90
2129 $1.80 Ballet dancer . . . . . 2·00 2·25

558 Museum of New Zealand

1998. Opening of Museum of New Zealand, Wellington. Multicoloured.

2131 40 c. Type **558** 30 35
2132 $1.80 Museum and seabirds . 1·40 1·40

559 Domestic Cat

560 Maoris and Canoe

1998. Cats. Multicoloured.

2133 40 c. Type **559** 40 35
2134 80 c. Burmese 75 80
2135 $1 Birman 85 80
2136 $1.20 British blue . . . . . . 1·00 1·10
2137 $1.50 Persian . . . . 1·25 1·50
2138 $1.80 Siamese . . . . 1·75 2·00

1998. Millennium Series (2nd issue). Immigrants. Multicoloured.

2140 40 c. Type **560** 30 35
2141 80 c. 19th-century European settlers and immigrant ship . 60 65
2142 $1 Gold miners and mine . . 75 80
2143 $1.20 Post 1945 European migrants and liner 90 95
2144 $1.50 Pacific islanders and hurch . . . . 1·10 1·25
2145 $1.80 Asian migrant and jumbo jet . . . . 1·25 1·40

561 "With Great Respect to the Mehmetcik" Statue, Gallipoli

562 Mother and Son Hugging

1998. Joint Issue New Zealand–Turkey. Memorial Statues. Multicoloured.

2146 40 c. Type **561** 30 35
2147 $1.80 "Mother with Children", National War Memorial, Wellington . . . . 1·25 1·40

1998. "Stay in Touch" Greetings Stamps. Multicoloured. Self-adhesive.

2148 40 c. Type **562** 25 30
2149 40 c. Couple on beach 25 30
2150 40 c. Boys striking hands . . . 25 30
2151 40 c. Grandmother and grandson 25 30
2152 40 c. Young boys in pool (horiz) 25 30
2153 40 c. "I'LL MISS YOU... PLEASE WRITE" (horiz) . 25 30
2154 40 c. Symbolic couple and clouds (horiz) 25 30
2155 40 c. Young couple kissing (horiz) 25 30
2156 40 c. Couple sat on sofa (horiz) 25 30
2157 40 c. Maoris rubbing noses (horiz) 25 30

563 Mount Cook or Aorangi

565 Girl wearing Lifejacket

564 "Wounded at Cassino"

1998. Centenary of 1898 Pictorial Stamps. Designs as T **23/26** and **28/35** with modern face values as T **563**.

2158 **563** 40 c. brown 40 40
2159 **24** 40 c. blue and brown . . 40 40
2160 **25** 40 c. brown 40 40
2161 **28** 40 c. brown 40 40
2162 **29** 40 c. red 40 40
2163 **31** 40 c. green 40 40
2164 **32** 40 c. blue 40 40
2165 **34** 40 c. orange 40 40
2166 **26** 80 c. blue (inscr "LAKE WAKITIPU") (35 × 23 mm) 75 75
2167 80 c. blue (inscr "LAKE WAKATIPU") (35 × 23 mm) 75 75
2168 **30** $1 brown (23 × 35 mm) . 85 85
2169 **33** $1.20 brown (35 × 23 mm) 90 90
2170 **35** $1.50 green (35 × 23 mm) . 1·25 1·25
2171 – $1.80 red (as No. 329) (23 × 35 mm) . . . . . 1·40 1·40

1998. Paintings by Peter McIntyre. Multicoloured.

2174 40 c. Type **564** 35 30
2175 $1 "The Cliffs of Rangitikei" . 85 75
2176 $1.50 "Maori Children, King Country" . . . . 1·25 1·40
2177 $1.80 "The Anglican Church, Kakahi" . . . . 1·40 1·50

1998. Children's Health. Water Safety. Multicoloured. (a) Ordinary gum.

2178 40 c. + 5 c. Type **565** 40 40
2179 80 c. + 5 c. Boy learning to swim 60 60

(b) Smaller design, 25 × 37 mm. Self-adhesive.

2181 40 c. + 5 c. Type **565** 30 35

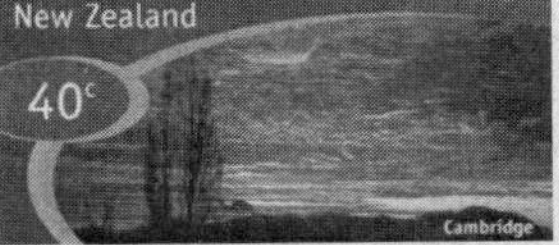
566 Sunrise near Cambridge

1998. Scenic Skies. Multicoloured.

2182	40 c. Type **566**	35	30
2183	80 c. Clouds over Lake Wanaka	65	65
2184	$1 Sunset over Mount Maunganui	75	75
2185	$1.20 Rain clouds over South Bay, Kaikoura	90	90
2186	$1.50 Sunset near Statue of Wairaka, Whakatane Harbour	1·25	1·25
2187	$1.80 Cloud formation above Lindis Pass	1·60	1·75

567 Virgin Mary and Christ Child

568 Lemon and Mineral Water Bottle, Paeroa

1998. Christmas. Multicoloured. (a) Ordinary gum.

2189	40 c. Type **567**	35	30
2190	70 c. Shepherds approaching the stable	55	55
2191	80 c. Virgin Mary, Joseph and Christ Child	65	65
2192	$1 Magi with gift of gold	80	80
2193	$1.50 Three magi	1·25	1·25
2194	$1.80 Angel and shepherds	1·40	1·50

(b) Smaller design, 24 × 29 mm. Self-adhesive.

2195	40 c. Type **567**	35	30

1998. Town Icons. Self-adhesive. Multicoloured.

2196	40 c. Type **568**	35	35
2197*	40 c. Carrot, Ohakune	35	35
2198	40 c. Brown Trout, Gore (25 × 36 mm)	35	35
2199	40 c. Crayfish, Kaikoura (25 × 36 mm)	35	35
2200	40 c. Sheep-shearer, Te Kuiti (25 × 36 mm)	35	35
2201	40 c. "Pania of the Reef" (Maori legend), Napier (25 × 36 mm)	35	35
2202	40 c. Paua Shell, Riverton (24 × 29 mm)	35	35
2203	40 c. Kiwifruit, Te Puke (24 × 29 mm)	35	35
2204	40 c. Border Collie, Lake Tekapo (24 × 29 mm)	35	35
2205	40 c. "Big Cow", Hawera (24 × 29 mm)	35	35

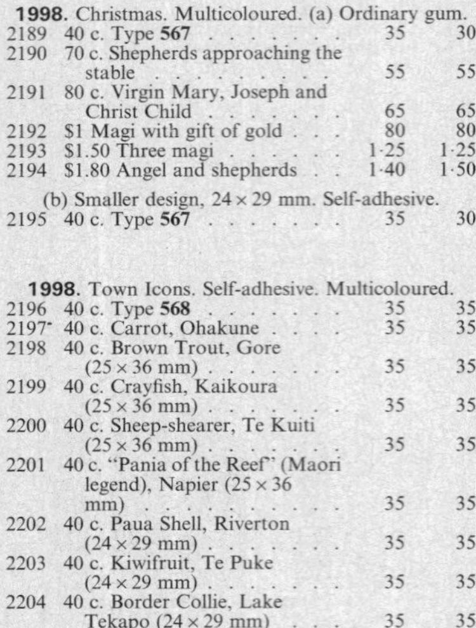

569 Moonfish

571 "Fuchsia excorticata"

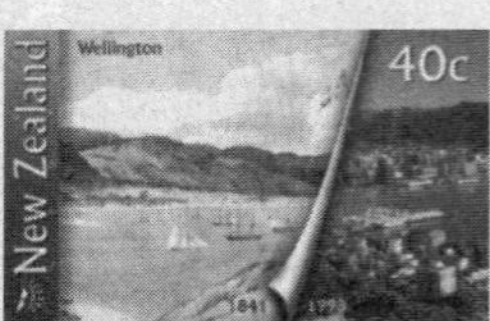

570 Wellington in 1841 and 1998

1998. International Year of the Ocean. Multicoloured.

2206	40 c. Type **569**	35	35
2207	40 c. Mako shark	35	35
2208	40 c. Yellowfin tuna	35	35
2209	40 c. Giant squid	35	35
2210	80 c. Striped marlin	60	60
2211	80 c. Porcupine fish	60	60
2212	80 c. Eagle ray	60	60
2213	80 c. Sandager's wrasse	60	60

Nos. 2206/9 and 2210/13 respectively were printed together, se-tenant, forming composite designs.

1998. Millennium Series (3rd issue). Urban Transformations. Multicoloured.

2216	40 c. Type **570**	40	30
2217	80 c. Auckland in 1852 and 1998	65	55
2218	$1 Christchurch in 1851 and 1998	75	70
2219	$1.20 Westport in 1919 and 1998	85	1·00
2220	$1.50 Tauranga in 1880 and 1998	1·25	1·40
2221	$1.80 Dunedin in 1862 and 1998	1·40	1·60

1999. Flowering Trees of New Zealand. Mult.

2222	40 c. Type **571**	40	30
2223	80 c. "Solanum laciniatum"	65	55
2224	$1 "Sophora tetraptera"	75	70
2225	$1.20 "Carmichaelia stevensonii"	85	1·00
2226	$1.50 "Olearia angustfolia"	1·25	1·40
2227	$1.80 "Metrosideros umbellata"	1·40	1·60

572 Civic Theatre, Auckland

573 Labrador Puppy and Netherland Dwarf Rabbit

1999. Art Deco Architecture. Multicoloured.

2228	40 c. Type **572**	40	30
2229	$1 Masonic Hotel, Napier	1·00	80
2230	$1.50 Medical and Dental Chambers, Hastings	1·25	1·40
2231	$1.80 Buller County Chambers, Westport	1·40	1·60

1999. Popular Pets. Multicoloured.

2232	40 c. Type **573**	40	30
2233	80 c. Netherland dwarf rabbit	80	55
2234	$1 Tabby kitten and Netherland dwarf rabbit	90	70
2235	$1.20 Lamb	1·25	1·25
2236	$1.50 Welsh pony	1·40	1·50
2237	$1.80 Two budgerigars	1·50	1·60

574 Toy Fire Engine and Marbles

1999. Millennium Series (4th issue). Nostalgia. Multicoloured.

2239	40 c. Type **574**	40	30
2240	80 c. Commemorative tin of biscuits and cereal packet	70	55
2241	$1 Tram, tickets and railway crockery	85	70
2242	$1.20 Radio and "Woman's Weekly" magazine	1·00	1·25
2243	$1.50 Coins, postcards and stamps	1·25	1·40
2244	$1.80 Lawn mower and seed packets	1·40	1·60

575 Hunter Building, Victoria University

576 Auckland Blues Player kicking Ball

1999. Centenary of Victoria University, Wellington.

2247	**575** 40 c. multicoloured	30	30

1999. New Zealand U-Bix Rugby Super 12 Championship. Multicoloured. Ordinary or self-adhesive gum.

2248	40 c. Type **576**	35	35
2249	40 c. Auckland Blues player being tackled	35	35
2250	40 c. Chiefs player being tackled	35	35
2251	40 c. Chiefs lineout jump	35	35
2252	40 c. Wellington Hurricanes player being tackled	35	35
2253	40 c. Wellington Hurricanes player passing ball	35	35
2254	40 c. Canterbury Crusaders lineout jump	35	35
2255	40 c. Canterbury Crusaders player kicking ball	35	35
2256	40 c. Otago Highlanders diving for try	35	35
2257	40 c. Otago Highlanders player running with ball	35	35

577 "The Lake, Tuai"

1999. Paintings by Doris Lusk. Multicoloured.

2268	40 c. Type **577**	35	30
2269	$1 "The Pumping Station"	80	70
2270	$1.50 "Arcade Awning, St. Mark's Square, Venice (2)"	1·10	1·25
2271	$1.80 "Tuam St. II"	1·25	1·40

578 "A Lion in the Meadow" (Margaret Mahy)

1999. Children's Health. Children's Books. Multicoloured. (a) Ordinary gum.

2272	40 c. + 5 c. Type **578**	40	40
2273	80 c. + 5 c. "Greedy Cat" (Joy Cowley)	60	60

(b) Smaller design 37 × 25 mm. Self-adhesive.

2275	40 c. + 5 c. "Hairy Maclary's Bone" (Lynley Dodd) (37 × 25 mm)	35	35

579 "APEC"

1999. 10th Asia-Pacific Economic Co-operation Meeting, New Zealand.

2278	**579** 40 c. multicoloured	30	30

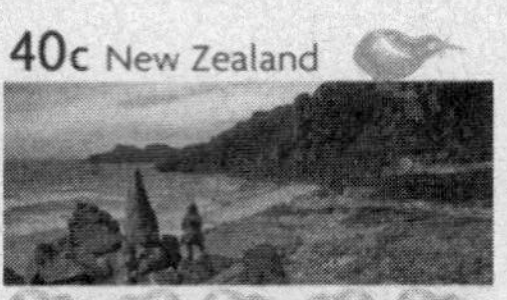

580 West Ruggedy Beach, Stewart Island

1999. Scenic Walks. Multicoloured.

2279	40 c. Type **580**	25	30
2280	80 c. Ice lake, Butler Valley, Westland	50	55
2281	$1 Tonga Bay, Abel Tasman National Park	65	70
2282	$1.20 East Matakitaki Valley, Nelson Lakes National Park	75	80
2283	$1.50 Great Barrier Island	95	1·00
2284	$1.80 Mt. Egmont, Taranki	1·10	1·25

581 Baby Jesus with Animals

1999. Christmas. Multicoloured. (a) Ordinary gum.

2288	40 c. Type **581**	25	30
2289	80 c. Virgin Mary praying	50	55
2290	$1.10 Mary and Joseph on way to Bethlehem	70	75
2291	$1.20 Angel playing harp	75	80
2292	$1.50 Three shepherds	95	1·00
2293	$1.80 Three wise men with gifts	1·10	1·25

(b) Smaller design, 23 × 28 mm. Self-adhesive.

2294	40 c. Type **581**	25	30

582 "P" Class Dinghy

1999. Yachting. Multicoloured. (a) Size 28 × 39 mm. Ordinary gum.

2296	40 c. Type **582**	25	30
2297	80 c. Laser dinghy	50	55
2298	$1.10 18' skiff	70	75
2299	$1.20 Hobie catamaran	75	80
2300	$1.50 Racing yacht	95	1·00
2301	$1.80 Cruising yacht	1·10	1·25

(b) Size 23 × 28 mm. Self-adhesive.

2303	40 c. Optimist dinghy	25	30

583 Group of Victorian Women (female suffrage, 1893)

1999. Millenium Series (5th issue). New Zealand Achievements. Multicoloured.

2304	40 c. Type **583**	25	30
2305	80 c. Richard Pearse's aircraft (powered flight, 1903)	50	55
2306	$1.10 Lord Rutherford (splitting the atom, 1919)	70	75
2307	$1.20 Boat on lake (invention of jet boat, 1953)	75	80
2308	$1.50 Sir Edmund Hillary (conquest of Everest, 1953)	95	1·00
2309	$1.80 Protesters and warship (nuclear free zone, 1987)	1·10	1·25

584 Sunrise and World Map

2000. Millennium Series (6th issue).

2310	**584** 40 c. multicoloured	25	30

585 Araiteuru (North Island sea guardian)

2000. Chinese New Year ("Year of the Dragon"). Maori Spirits and Guardians. Multicoloured.

2311	40 c. Type **585**	25	30
2312	80 c. Kurangaituku (giant bird woman)	50	55
2313	$1.10 Te Hoata and Te Pupu (volcanic taniwha sisters)	70	75
2314	$1.20 Patupaiarehe (mountain fairy tribe)	75	80
2315	$1.50 Te Ngarara-huarau (giant first lizard)	95	1·00
2316	$1.80 Tuhirangi (South Island sea guardian)	1·10	1·25

EXPRESS DELIVERY STAMPS

E 1

1903.

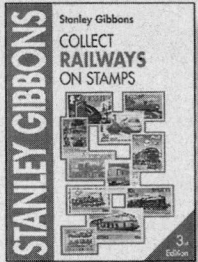

E1 E 1 6d. red and violet . . . . 35·00 22·00

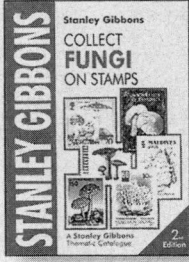

E 2 Express Mail Delivery Van

1939.

E6 E 2 6d. violet . . . . 1·50 1·75

LIFE INSURANCE DEPARTMENT

L 1 L 3 Castlepoint Lighthouse

1891.

L13 L 1 ½d. purple . . . . 55·00 3·00
L14 1d. blue . . . . 55·00 75
L15 2d. brown . . . . 75·00 3·50
L 4 3d. brown . . . . £160 20·00
L 5 6d. green . . . . £275 60·00
L 6 1s. pink £500 £120

1905. Similar type but "V.R." omitted.

L24 ½d. green . . . . 10·00 1·00
L22 1d. blue . . . . £160 30·00
L38 1d. red . . . . 3·25 2·00
L26 1½d. black . . . . 40·00 6·50
L27 1½d. brown . . . . 1·50 2·25
L21 2d. brown . . . . £1000 80·00
L28 2d. purple . . . . 48·00 26·00
L29 2d. yellow . . . . 5·50 2·00
L30 3d. brown . . . . 45·00 24·00
L35 3d. red . . . . 18·00 22·00
L41 6d. pink . . . . 11·00 32·00

1947. Lighthouses.

L42 L 3 ½d. green and orange . . . 1·00 60
L43 – 1d. olive and blue . . . 1·00 65
L44 – 2d. blue and black . . . 70 50
L45 – 2½d. black and blue . . . 9·50 13·00
L46 – 3d. mauve and blue . . . 2·50 35
L47 – 4d. brown and orange . . . 3·25 1·25
L48 – 6d. brown and blue . . . 3·50 1·75
L49 – 1s. brown and blue . . . 3·50 2·75

LIGHTHOUSES—HORIZ: 1d. Taiaroa; 2d. Cape Palliser; 6d. The Brothers. VERT: 2½d. Cape Campbell; 3d. Eddystone; 4d. Stephens Island; 1s. Cape Brett.

1967. Decimal currency. Stamps of 1947–65 surch.

L50a 1 c. on 1d. (No. L43) . . . . 1·40 4·25
L51 2 c. on 2½d. (No. L45) . . . . 11·00 13·00
L52 2½ c. on 3d. (No. L46) . . . . 2·00 4·50
L53 3 c. on 4d. (No. L47) . . . . 4·50 5·50
L54 5 c. on 6d. (No. L48) . . . . 1·00 6·00
L55a 10 c. on 1s. (No. L49) . . . . 1·00 4·00

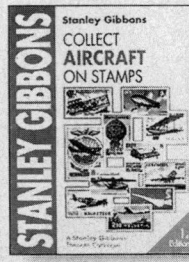

L 13 Moeraki Point Lighthouse

1969.

L56 L 13 ½ c. yellow, red & violet . 90 1·75
L57 – 2½ c. blue, green & buff . 75 1·25
L58 – 3 c. stone, yellow & brn . 75 75
L59 – 4 c. green, ochre & blue . 75 1·00
L60 – 8 c. multicoloured . . . 45 2·75
L61 – 10 c. multicoloured . . . 45 2·75
L62 – 15 c. multicoloured . . . 60 2·00

DESIGNS—HORIZ: 2½ c. Puysegur Point Lighthouse. 4 c. Cape Egmont Lighthouse. VERT: 3 c. Baring Head Lighthouse; 8 c. East Cape; 10 c. Farewell Spit; 15 c. Dog Island Lighthouse.

1978. No. L57 surch **25c**.

L63 25 c. on 2½ c. blue, green and buff . . . . 75 1·75

L 17

1981.

L64 L 17 5 c. multicoloured . . . 10 10
L65 10 c. multicoloured . . . 10 10
L66 20 c. multicoloured . . . 15 15
L67 30 c. multicoloured . . . 25 25
L68 40 c. multicoloured . . . 35 30
L69 50 c. multicoloured . . . 45 35

OFFICIAL STAMPS

1891. Optd **O.P.S.O.**

O 1 3 ½d. pink . . . . — £450
O 2 13 ½d. black . . . . — £180
O13 23 ½d. green . . . . — £180
O 4 10 1d. pink . . . . — £180
O19 42 1d. red . . . . — £180
O 6 9 2d. mauve . . . . — £325
O 8 16 2½d. blue . . . . — £225
O14 26 2½d. blue (A) . . . . . . — £400
O21 2½d. blue (B) . . . . . . — £275
O22 3d. brown . **28** . . . . — £400
O16 24 4d. blue and brown . . . — £375
O11 19 5d. black . . . . — £375
O17a 30 5d. brown . . . . — £375
O12 8 6d. brown (No. 224b) . . — £500
O18 32 8d. blue . . . . — £475
O23 34 1s. red . . . . — £800
O24 35 2s. green . . . . — £1200

Optd **OFFICIAL.**

1907. Pictorials.

O59 23 ½d. green . . . . 8·00 50
O61a 25 2d. purple . . . . 8·50 1·40
O63 28 3d. brown . . . . 42·00 1·75
O64 31 6d. red . . . . £130 18·00
O65 34 1s. orange . . . . 85·00 15·00
O66 35 2s. green . . . . 70·00 48·00
O67 – 5s. red (No. 329) £150 £170

1907. "Universal" type.

O60b 42 1d. red . . . . 8·50 30

1908.

O70 50 1d. red . . . . 65·00 2·50
O72 31 6d. red (No. 254) . . . . £110 35·00

1910. King Edward VII etc.

O73 51 ½d. green . . . . 4·25 30
O78 53 1d. red . . . . 3·25 10
O74 51 3d. brown . . . . 14·00 80
O75 6d. red . . . . 19·00 4·75
O76 8d. blue . . . . 14·00 18·00
O77 1s. orange . . . . 50·00 15·00

1913. Queen Victoria.

O82 F 4 2s. blue . . . . 48·00 38·00
O83 5s. green . . . . 75·00 90·00
O84 £1 red £550 £500

1915. King George V.

O 96 62 ½d. green 80 10
O 90 1½d. grey . . . . 4·25 80
O 91 1½d. brown . . . . 4·25 30
O 98 2d. yellow . . . . 2·00 40
O 99 3d. brown . . . . 4·00 40
O101 4d. violet . . . . 14·00 3·25
O102 6d. red . . . . 5·00 75
O103 8d. brown . . . . 70·00 £110
O104 9d. green . . . . 38·00 32·00
O105b 1s. orange . . . . 7·00 2·00

1927. King George V.

O111c 71 1d. red . . . . 1·50 10
O112 2s. blue . . . . 70·00 £100

1933. "Arms".

O113 F 6 5s. green £250 £300

Optd **OFFICIAL.**

1936. "Arms".

O133 F 6 5s. green . . . . 38·00 5·00

1936. As 1935.

O120 81 ½d. green . . . . 6·50 4·50
O115 – 1d. red (No. 557) . . . . 2·50 80
O122 83 1½d. brown . . . . 16·00 4·25
O123 – 2d. orange (No. 580) . . 2·25 10
O124a 85 2½d. brown and grey . . 14·00 21·00
O125 86 3d. brown . . . . 48·00 3·25
O126c 87 4d. black and brown . . 3·75 85
O127c 89 6d. red . . . . 8·00 30
O128a – 8d. brown (No. 586b) . . 8·00 16·00
O130 91 9d. red and black . . . 20·00 22·00
O131b – 1s. green (No. 588) . . 22·00 1·00
O132d 93 2s. olive . . . . 42·00 7·00

1938. King George VI.

O134 108 ½d. green . . . . 16·00 2·25
O135 ½d. orange . . . . 1·60 3·00
O136 1d. red . . . . 16·00 15
O137 1d. green . . . . 2·25 10
O138 1½d. brown . . . . 75·00 18·00
O139 1½d. red . . . . 9·00 5·00
O152 2d. orange . . . . 1·75 10
O140 3d. blue . . . . 2·25 10
O153 4d. purple . . . . 4·25 1·75
O154 6d. red . . . . 11·00 40
O155 8d. violet . . . . 8·00 6·50
O156 9d. brown . . . . 9·00 6·50
O157a – 1s. brn & red (No. 686b) 8·50 8·50
O158 – 2s. orange and green (No. 688) . . . . 23·00 16·00

1940. Centenary stamps.

O141 ½d. green . . . . 1·75 35
O142 1d. brown and red . . . . 4·00 10
O143 1½d. blue and mauve . . . . 2·75 2·00
O144 2d. green and brown . . . . 4·00 10
O145 2½d. green and blue . . . . 4·00 2·75
O146 3d. purple and red . . . . 8·00 90
O147 4d. brown and red . . . . 40·00 2·00
O148 6d. green and violet . . . . 25·00 2·00
O149 8d. black and red . . . . . 30·00 17·00
O150 9d. olive and red . . . . . 11·00 7·00
O151 1s. green . . . . 48·00 4·00

O 6 Queen Elizabeth II

1954.

O159 O 6 1d. orange 60 40
O160 1½d. brown . . . . . . 3·50 4·50
O161 2d. green 40 20
O162 2½d. olive . . . . . . 4·25 1·50
O163 3d. red 70 10
O164 4d. blue . . . . . . 1·25 40
O165 9d. red . . . . . . 7·00 90
O166 1s. purple . . . . . . 1·00 10
O167 3s. slate . . . . . . 35·00 48·00

1959. Surch.

O169 O 6 2½d. on 2d. green . . . 95 1·50
O168 6d. on 1½d. brown . . . 40 1·10

POSTAGE DUE STAMPS

D 1 D 2

1899.

D 9 D 1 ½d. red and green . . . 2·75 16·00
D10 1d. red and green . . . 9·50 1·25
D15 2d. red and green . . . 45·00 4·75
D12 3d. red and green . . . 13·00 3·50
D16 4d. red and green . . . 32·00 9·00
D 6 5d. red and green . . . 21·00 22·00
D 7 6d. red and green . . . 28·00 24·00
D 2 8d. red and green . . . 60·00 75·00
D 8 10d. red and green . . . 70·00 85·00
D 3 1s. red and green . . . 65·00 85·00
D 4 2s. red and green . . . £120 £140

1902.

D18 D 2 ½d. red and green . . . 1·75 1·50
D30 1d. red and green . . . 3·75 80
D22a 2d. red and green . . . 5·00 1·50
D36 3d. red and green . . . 15·00 42·00

D 3

1939.

D41 D 3 ½d. green . . . . . . 5·00 5·00
D42 1d. red . . . . . . 2·75 30
D46 2d. blue . . . . . . 7·50 1·40
D47aw 3d. brown . . . . . . 9·00 8·00

NICARAGUA Pt. 15

A republic of Central America independent since 1821.

1862. 100 centavos = 1 peso (paper currency).
1912. 100 centavos de cordoba = 1 peso de cordoba (gold currency).
1925. 100 centavos = 1 cordoba.

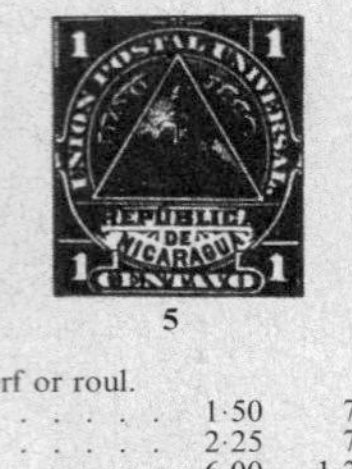

2 Volcanoes — 5

1862. Perf or roul.

13	2	1 c. brown	1·50	75
4		2 c. blue	2·25	75
14		5 c. black	6·00	1·25
18		10 c. red	2·25	1·40
19		25 c. green	2·25	2·40

1882.

20	5	1 c. green	15	20
21		2 c. red	15	20
22		5 c. blue	15	15
23		10 c. violet	15	60
24		15 c. yellow	30	1·50
25		20 c. grey	50	3·00
26		50 c. violet	70	6·00

6 Steam Locomotive and Telegraph Key — 7

1890.

27	6	1 c. brown	25	30
28		2 c. red	25	30
29		5 c. blue	25	20
30		10 c. grey	25	25
31		20 c. red	25	1·75
32		50 c. violet	25	5·50
33		1 p. brown	40	7·75
34		2 p. green	40	10·00
35		5 p. red	50	19·00
36		10 p. orange	50	27·00

1891.

37	7	1 c. brown	15	30
38		2 c. red	15	30
39		5 c. blue	15	25
40		10 c. grey	15	35
41		20 c. lake	15	1·75
42		50 c. violet	15	3·00
43		1 p. sepia	15	4·50
44		2 p. green	15	5·00
45		5 p. red	15	12·00
46		10 p. orange	15	15·00

8 First Sight of the New World — 9 Volcanoes — 10

1892. Discovery of America.

47	8	1 c. brown	15	25
48		2 c. red	15	25
49		5 c. blue	15	20
50		10 c. grey	15	25
51		20 c. red	15	1·75
52		50 c. violet	15	4·25
53		1 p. brown	15	4·25
54		2 p. green	15	5·00
55		5 p. red	15	14·00
56		10 p. orange	15	18·00

1893.

57	9	1 c. brown	15	25
58		2 c. red	15	25
59		5 c. blue	15	20
60		10 c. grey	15	25
61		20 c. brown	15	1·40
62		50 c. violet	15	3·50
63		1 p. brown	15	4·25
64		2 p. green	15	5·00
65		5 p. red	15	11·00
66		10 p. orange	15	14·00

1894.

67	10	1 c. brown	15	25
68		2 c. red	15	25
69		5 c. blue	15	20
70		10 c. grey	15	25
71		20 c. red	15	1·50
72		50 c. violet	15	3·50
73		1 p. brown	15	4·25
74		2 p. green	15	7·50
75		5 p. brown	15	9·00
76		10 p. orange	15	12·00

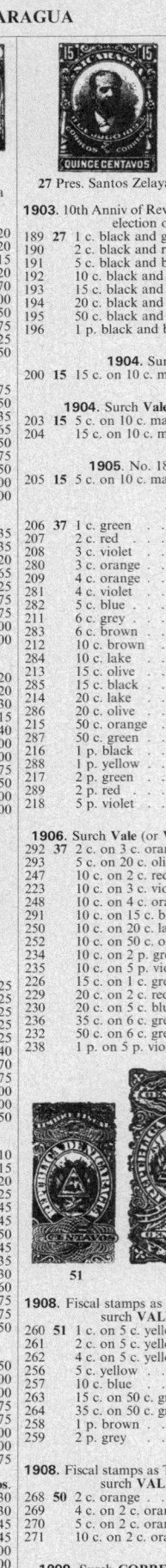

11 — 12 Map of Nicaragua — 13 Arms of Republic of Central America

1895.

77	11	1 c. brown	15	20
78		2 c. red	15	20
79		5 c. blue	15	15
80		10 c. grey	15	20
81		20 c. red	15	70
82		50 c. violet	15	3·00
83		1 p. brown	15	4·50
84		2 p. green	15	4·75
85		5 p. red	15	9·25
86		10 p. orange	15	14·50

1896. Date "1896".

90	12	1 c. violet	15	75
91		2 c. green	15	50
92		5 c. red	15	35
93		10 c. blue	30	65
94		20 c. brown	1·75	3·50
95		50 c. grey	35	4·75
96		1 p. black	35	6·50
97		2 p. red	35	9·00
98		5 p. blue	35	9·00

1897. As T 12, dated "1897".

99	12	1 c. violet	25	35
100		2 c. green	25	35
101		5 c. red	25	20
102		10 c. blue	3·75	65
103		20 c. brown	1·50	2·25
104		50 c. grey	5·25	5·75
105		1 p. black	5·25	8·75
106		2 p. red	11·50	11·00
107		5 p. blue	11·50	25·00

1898.

108	13	1 c. brown	20	20
109		2 c. grey	20	20
110		4 c. lake	20	30
122		5 c. olive	15·00	15
112		10 c. purple	8·75	40
113		15 c. blue	25	1·00
114		20 c. blue	6·00	1·00
115		50 c. yellow	6·00	5·75
116		1 p. blue	30	9·50
117		2 p. brown	11·00	13·00
118		5 p. orange	15·00	19·00

14 — 15 Mt. Momotombo

1899.

126	14	1 c. green	10	25
127		2 c. brown	10	25
128		4 c. red	20	25
129		5 c. blue	15	25
130		10 c. orange	15	25
131		15 c. brown	15	40
132		20 c. green	20	70
133		50 c. red	15	1·75
134		1 p. orange	15	5·00
135		2 p. violet	15	12·00
136		5 p. blue	15	14·50

1900.

137	15	1 c. red	35	10
138		2 c. orange	65	15
139		3 c. green	75	20
140		4 c. olive	95	25
184		5 c. red	1·50	45
185		5 c. blue	1·50	45
142		6 c. red	19·00	5·50
186		10 c. mauve	1·50	45
144		15 c. blue	10·00	35
145		20 c. brown	9·00	30
146		50 c. lake	9·00	1·60
147		1 p. yellow	20·00	6·75
148		2 p. red	8·00	75
149		5 p. black	14·00	2·50

1901. Surch **1901** and value.

151	15	2 c. on 1 p. yellow	11·00	8·50
169		3 c. on 6 c. red	8·00	5·00
163		4 c. on 6 c. red	7·00	4·00
173		5 c. on 1 p. yellow	11·50	5·75
168		10 c. on 2 p. red	8·00	1·75
152		10 c. on 5 p. black	14·00	11·00
153		20 c. on 2 p. red	22·00	20·00
176		20 c. on 5 p. black	6·00	3·75

1901. Postage Due stamps of 1900 optd **1901 Correos**.

177	D 16	1 c. red	60	30
178		2 c. orange	45	30
179		5 c. blue	55	45
180		10 c. violet	55	45
181		20 c. brown	75	1·00
182		30 c. green	70	1·00
183		50 c. lake	70	1·00

1902. Surch **1902** and value.

187	15	15 c. on 2 c. orange	4·00	1·50
188		30 c. on 1 c. red	1·50	4·25

27 Pres. Santos Zelaya — 37 Arms

1903. 10th Anniv of Revolution against Sacaza and 1st election of Pres. Zelaya.

189	27	1 c. black and green	25	45
190		2 c. black and red	50	45
191		5 c. black and blue	25	45
192		10 c. black and orange	25	70
193		15 c. black and lake	45	1·40
194		20 c. black and violet	45	1·40
195		50 c. black and olive	45	3·00
196		1 p. black and brown	45	3·50

1904. Surch **15 Centavos**.

200	15	15 c. on 10 c. mauve	5·75	3·00

1904. Surch **Vale**, value and wavy lines.

203	15	5 c. on 10 c. mauve	1·90	50
204		15 c. on 10 c. mauve	60	40

1905. No. 186 surch **5 CENTS.**

205	15	5 c. on 10 c. mauve	75	50

1905.

206	37	1 c. green	20	15
207		2 c. red	20	15
208		3 c. violet	25	20
280		3 c. orange	25	15
209		4 c. orange	25	20
281		4 c. violet	25	15
282		5 c. blue	25	15
211		6 c. grey	45	30
283		6 c. brown	1·75	1·10
212		10 c. brown	55	20
284		10 c. lake	60	10
213		15 c. olive	55	25
285		15 c. black	60	10
214		20 c. lake	45	25
286		20 c. olive	60	10
215		50 c. orange	1·75	1·40
287		50 c. green	70	35
216		1 p. black	90	90
288		1 p. yellow	70	35
217		2 p. green	90	1·25
289		2 p. red	70	35
218		5 p. violet	1·00	1·50

1906. Surch **Vale** (or **VALE**) and value in one line.

292	37	2 c. on 3 c. orange	90	75
293		5 c. on 20 c. olive	30	25
247		10 c. on 2 c. red	1·10	45
223		10 c. on 3 c. violet	30	15
248		10 c. on 4 c. orange	1·25	55
291		10 c. on 15 c. black	30	25
250		10 c. on 20 c. lake	1·90	85
252		10 c. on 50 c. orange	1·40	45
234		10 c. on 2 p. green	12·00	7·00
235		10 c. on 5 p. violet	60·00	42·00
226		15 c. on 1 c. green	30	20
229		20 c. on 2 c. red	40	25
230		20 c. on 5 c. blue	45	35
236		35 c. on 6 c. grey	1·60	1·60
232		50 c. on 6 c. grey	45	35
238		1 p. on 5 p. violet	25·00	14·50

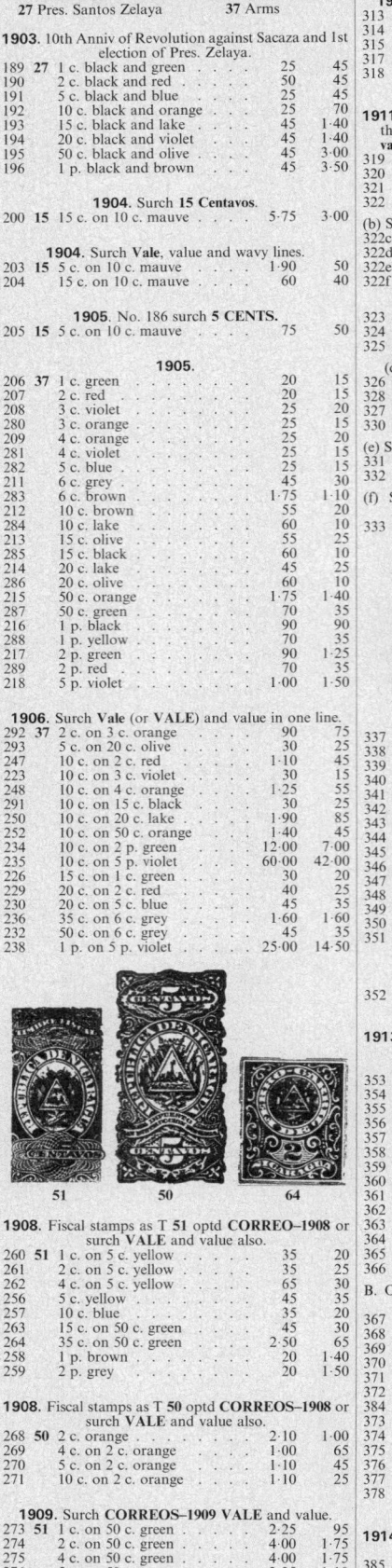

51 — 50 — 64

1908. Fiscal stamps as T 51 optd **CORREO–1908** or surch **VALE** and value also.

260	51	1 c. on 5 c. yellow	35	20
261		2 c. on 5 c. yellow	35	25
262		4 c. on 5 c. yellow	65	30
256		5 c. yellow	45	35
257		10 c. blue	35	20
263		15 c. on 50 c. green	45	30
264		35 c. on 50 c. green	2·50	65
258		1 p. brown	20	1·40
259		2 p. grey	20	1·50

1908. Fiscal stamps as T 50 optd **CORREOS–1908** or surch **VALE** and value also.

268	50	2 c. orange	2·10	1·00
269		4 c. on 2 c. orange	1·00	65
270		5 c. on 2 c. orange	1·10	45
271		10 c. on 2 c. orange	1·10	25

1909. Surch **CORREOS–1909 VALE** and value.

273	51	1 c. on 50 c. green	2·25	95
274		2 c. on 50 c. green	4·00	1·75
275		4 c. on 50 c. green	4·00	1·75
276		5 c. on 50 c. green	2·25	1·10
277		10 c. on 50 c. green	65	40

1910. Surch **Vale** and value in two lines.

296	37	2 c. on 3 c. orange	65	35
300		2 c. on 4 c. violet	25	15
301		5 c. on 20 c. olive	25	15
302		10 c. on 15 c. black	30	15
303		10 c. on 50 c. green	20	15
299		10 c. on 1 p. yellow	65	35
305		10 c. on 2 p. red	45	35

1911. Surch **Correos 1911** (or **CORREOS 1911**) and value.

307	51	2 c. on 5 p. blue	25	30
312		5 c. on 2 p. grey	90	70
308		5 c. on 10 p. pink	55	30
309		10 c. on 25 c. lilac	30	20
310		10 c. on 2 p. grey	30	20
311		35 c. on 1 p. brown	30	25

1911. Surch **VALE POSTAL de 1911** and value.

313	51	5 c. on 25 c. lilac	90	70
314		5 c. on 50 c. green	3·00	3·00
315		5 c. on 5 p. blue	4·00	4·00
317		5 c. on 50 p. red	3·00	3·00
318		10 c. on 50 c. green	70	45

1911. Railway tickets as T **64**, with fiscal surch on the front, further surch for postal use. (a) Surch **vale CORREO DE 1911** and value on back.

319	64	2 c. on 5 c. on 2nd class blue	55	65
320		05 c. on 5 c. on 2nd class blue	30	40
321		10 c. on 5 c. on 2nd class blue	30	40
322		15 c. on 10 c. on 1st class red	40	50

(b) Surch **vale CORREO DE 1911** and value on front.

322c	64	2 c. on 5 c. on 2nd class blue	8·00	8·00
322d		05 c. on 5 c. on 2nd class blue	£170	£170
322e		10 c. on 5 c. on 2nd class blue	80·00	80·00
322f		15 c. on 10 c. on 1st class red	22·00	22·00

(c) Surch **CORREO** and value on front.

323	64	2 c. on 10 c. on 1st class red	80	80
324		20 c. on 10 c. on 1st class red	4·00	4·00
325		50 c. on 10 c. on 1st class red	7·50	7·50

(d) Surch **Correo Vale 1911** and value on front.

326	64	2 c. on 10 c. on 1st class red	15	15
328		5 c. on 5 c. on 2nd class blue	90	80
327		5 c. on 10 c. on 1st class red	20	1·25
330		10 c. on 10 c. on 1st class red	70	50

(e) Surch **Vale CORREO DE 1911** and value on back.

331	64	5 c. on 10 c. on 1st class red	18·00	
332		10 c. on 10 c. on 1st class red	7·00	

(f) Surch **CORREO Vale 10 cts. 1911** and bar obliterating **oficial** on front.

333	64	10 c. on 10 c. on 1st class red	1·25	1·00

70 — 71

1912.

337	70	1 c. green	25	15
338		2 c. red	25	15
339		3 c. brown	25	15
340		4 c. purple	25	15
341		5 c. black and blue	25	15
342		6 c. brown	25	70
343		10 c. brown	25	15
344		15 c. violet	25	15
345		20 c. brown	25	15
346		25 c. black and green	25	15
347	71	35 c. brown and green	1·10	1·10
348	70	50 c. blue	65	30
349		1 p. orange	90	1·40
350		2 p. green	90	1·75
351		5 p. black	1·60	2·10

1913. Surch **Vale 15 cts Correos 1913**.

352	71	15 c. on 35 c. brown & grn	30	20

1913. Surch **VALE 1913** and value in "centavos de cordoba".

A. On stamps of 1912 issue.

353	70	$\frac{1}{2}$ c. on 3 c. brown	35	25
354		$\frac{1}{2}$ c. on 15 c. violet	20	15
355		$\frac{1}{2}$ c. on 1 p. orange	20	15
356		1 c. on 3 c. brown	55	45
357		1 c. on 4 c. purple	20	15
358		1 c. on 50 c. blue	20	15
359		1 c. on 5 p. black	20	15
360		2 c. on 4 c. purple	25	20
361		2 c. on 20 c. brown	2·25	2·75
362		2 c. on 25 c. black & grn	25	15
363	71	2 c. on 35 c. brown & grn	20	35
364	70	2 c. on 50 c. blue	20	90
365		2 c. on 2 p. green	15	15
366		3 c. on 6 c. brown	15	10

B. On Silver Currency stamps of 1912 (Locomotive type).

367	Z 1	$\frac{1}{2}$ c. on 2 c. red	3·25	2·50
368		1 c. on 3 c. brown	2·10	1·60
369		1 c. on 4 c. red	2·10	1·60
370		1 c. on 6 c. red	2·10	1·60
371		1 c. on 20 c. blue	2·10	1·60
372		1 c. on 25 c. black & grn	2·10	1·60
384		2 c. on 1 c. green	25·00	19·00
373		2 c. on 25 c. black & grn	11·25	8·50
374		5 c. on 35 c. black & grn	2·10	1·60
375		5 c. on 50 c. olive	2·10	1·60
376		6 c. on 1 p. orange	2·10	1·60
377		10 c. on 2 p. brown	2·10	1·60
378		1 p. on 5 p. green	2·10	1·60

1914. No. 352 surch with new value and **Cordoba** and thick bar over old surch.

385	71	$\frac{1}{2}$ c. on 15 c. on 35 c.	15	10
386		1 c. on 15 c. on 35 c.	20	15

1914. Official stamps of 1913 surch with new value and thick bar through "OFFICIAL".

387	70	1 c. on 25 c. blue	30	20
388	71	1 c. on 35 c. blue	30	20
389	70	1 c. on 1 p. blue	20	15
391		2 c. on 50 c. blue	30	15
392		2 c. on 2 p. blue	20	15
393		5 c. on 5 p. blue	20	15

79 National Palace, Managua

80 Leon Cathedral

1914. Various frames.
394 **79** ½ c. blue 50 15
395 1 c. green 50 15
396 **80** 2 c. orange 50 15
397 **79** 3 c. brown 80 25
398 **80** 4 c. red 80 25
399 **79** 5 c. grey 30 10
400 **80** 6 c. sepia 5·25 3·25
401 10 c. yellow 55 15
402 **79** 15 c. violet 3·50 1·40
403 **80** 20 c. grey 6·50 3·25
404 **79** 25 c. orange 85 20
405 **80** 50 c. blue 85 25
See also Nos. 465/72, 617/27 and 912/24.

1915. Surch **VALE 5 cts. de Cordoba 1915.**
406 **80** 5 c. on 6 c. sepia 1·10 35

1918. Stamps of 1914 surch **Vale–centavos de cordoba.**
407 **80** ½ c. on 6 c. sepia 2·00 75
408 ½ c. on 10 c. yellow 1·40 25
409 **79** ½ c. on 15 c. violet 1·40 45
410 ½ c. on 25 c. orange 3·00 85
411 **80** ½ c. on 50 c. blue 1·40 25
440 1 c. on 2 c. orange 90 20
413 **79** 1 c. on 3 c. brown 1·50 25
414 **80** 1 c. on 6 c. sepia 7·00 2·10
415 1 c. on 10 c. yellow 13·00 4·75
416 **79** 1 c. on 15 c. violet 2·40 55
418 **80** 1 c. on 20 c. grey 1·40 25
420 **79** 1 c. on 25 c. orange 2·40 70
421 **80** 1 c. on 50 c. blue 7·75 2·25
422 2 c. on 4 c. red 1·75 25
423 2 c. on 6 c. sepia 13·00 4·75
424 2 c. on 10 c. yellow 13·00 2·50
425 2 c. on 20 c. grey 7·00 2·10
426 **79** 2 c. on 25 c. orange 3·00 30
427 **80** 5 c. on 6 c. sepia 5·00 2·50
428 **79** 5 c. on 15 c. violet 1·75 45

1919. Official stamps of 1915 surch **Vale–centavo de cordoba** and with bar through "OFFICIAL".
444 **80** ½ c. on 2 c. blue 30 15
445 ½ c. on 4 c. blue 70 15
446 **79** 1 c. on 3 c. blue 70 25
432 1 c. on 25 c. blue 1·10 20
433 **80** 2 c. on 50 c. blue 1·10 20
443a 10 c. on 20 c. blue 1·00 40

1921. Official stamps of 1913 optd **Particular** and wavy lines through "OFFICIAL".
441 **70** 1 c. blue 90 45
442 5 c. blue 90 35

1921. No. 399 surch **Vale medio centavo.**
447 **79** ½ c. on 5 c. black 35 15

1921. Official stamp of 1915 optd **Particular R de C** and bars.
448 **79** 1 c. blue 3·50 1·00

1921. Official stamps of 1915 surch **Vale un centavo R de C** and bars.
449 **79** 1 c. on 5 c. blue 95 35
450 **80** 1 c. on 6 c. blue 50 20
451 1 c. on 10 c. blue 65 20
452 **79** 1 c. on 15 c. blue 1·10 20

90

91 Jose C. del Valle

1921. Fiscal stamps as T **23** surch **R de C Vale** and new value.
453 **90** 1 c. on 1 c. red and black 10 10
454 1 c. on 2 c. green and black 10 10
455 1 c. on 4 c. orange and black 10 10
456 1 c. on 15 c. blue and black 10 10
No. 456 is inscr "TIMBRE TELEGRAFICO".

1921. Independence Centenary.
457 – ½ c. black and blue 30 25
458 **91** 1 c. black and green 30 25
459 – 2 c. black and red 30 25
460 – 5 c. black and violet 30 25
461 – 10 c. black and orange 20 25
462 – 25 c. black and yellow 30 25
463 – 50 c. black and violet 30 25
DESIGNS: ½ c. Arce; 2 c. Larreinaga; 5 c. F. Chamorro; 10 c. Jerez; 25 c. J. P. Chamorro; 50 c. Dario.

1922. Surch **Vale un centavo R. de C.**
464 **80** 1 c. on 10 c. yellow 10 10

1922. As Nos. 394, etc., but colours changed.
465 **79** ½ c. green 15 10
466 1 c. violet 15 10
467 **80** 2 c. red 15 10
468 **79** 3 c. olive 25 15
469 **80** 6 c. brown 15 15
470 **79** 15 c. brown 25 15
471 **80** 20 c. brown 35 15
472 1 cor. brown 65 35
Nos. 465/72 are size 27 × 22¾ mm.
For later issues of these types, see Nos. 617/27 and 912/24.

1922. Optd **R. de C.**
473 **79** 1 c. violet 10 10

1922. Independence issue of 1921 surch **R. de C. Vale un centavo.**
474 **91** 1 c. on 1 c. black and green 55 45
475 – 1 c. on 5 c. black and violet 55 55
476 – 1 c. on 10 c. black and orange 55 30
477 – 1 c. on 25 c. black and yellow 55 25
478 – 1 c. on 50 c. black and violet 25 20

94 **99** F. Hernandez de Cordoba **106**

1922. Surch **Nicaragua R. de C. Vale un cent.**
479 **94** 1 c. yellow 10 10
480 1 c. mauve 10 10
481 1 c. blue 10 10

1922. Surch thus: **Vale 0.01 de Cordoba** in two lines.
482 **80** 1 c. on 10 c. yellow 70 25
483 2 c. on 10 c. yellow 70 20

1923. Surch thus: **Vale 2 centavos de cordoba** in three lines.
484 **79** 1 c. on 5 c. black 70 15
485 **80** 2 c. on 10 c. yellow 70 15

1923. Optd **Sello Postal.**
486 – ½ c. black & blue (No. 457) 5·50 4·25
487 **91** 1 c. black and green 1·40 70

1923. Independence issue of 1921 surch **R. de C. Vale un centavo de cordoba.**
488 1 c. on 2 c. black and red 30 30
489 1 c. on 5 c. black and violet 35 15
490 1 c. on 10 c. black and orge 15 15
491 1 c. on 25 c. black and yellow 25 25
492 1 c. on 50 c. black and violet 15 10

1923. Fiscal stamp optd R. de C.
493 **90** 1 c. red and black 15 10

1924. Optd **R. de C. 1924** in two lines.
494 **79** 1 c. violet 15 15

1924. 400th Anniv of Foundation of Leon and Granada.
495 **99** 1 c. green 90 25
496 2 c. red 90 25
497 5 c. blue 65 25
498 10 c. brown 65 45

1925. Optd **R. de C. 1925** in two lines.
499 **79** 1 c. violet 15 10

1927. Optd **Resello 1927.**
525 **79** ½ c. green 10 10
528 1 c. violet (No. 466) 10 10
555 1 c. violet (No. 473) 15 10
532 **80** 2 c. red 15 10
533 **79** 3 c. green 20 10
537 **80** 4 c. red 9·50 8·00
539 **79** 5 c. grey 55 20
542 **80** 6 c. brown 7·75 6·50
543 10 c. yellow 25 15
545 **79** 15 c. brown 55 25
547 **80** 20 c. brown 25 15
549 **79** 25 c. orange 30 15
551 **80** 50 c. blue 30 15
553 1 cor. brown 35 15

1928. Optd **Resello 1928.**
559 **79** ½ c. green 20 15
560 1 c. violet 10 10
561 **80** 2 c. red 15 10
562 **79** 3 c. green 15 10
563 **80** 4 c. red 15 10
564 **79** 5 c. grey 15 10
565 **80** 6 c. brown 15 10
566 10 c. yellow 20 10
567 **79** 15 c. brown 25 20
568 **80** 20 c. brown 35 20
569 **79** 25 c. orange 55 20
570 **80** 50 c. blue 90 10
571 1 cor. brown 75 25

1928. Optd **Correos 1928.**
574 **79** ½ c. green 15 10
575 1 c. violet 10 10
576 3 c. olive 55 20
577 **80** 4 c. red 25 10
578 **79** 5 c. grey 20 10
579 **80** 6 c. brown 30 15
580 10 c. yellow 35 15
581 **79** 15 c. brown 1·00 15
582 **80** 20 c. brown 1·00 15
583 **79** 25 c. orange 1·00 20
584 **80** 50 c. blue 1·00 20
585 1 cor. brown 3·00 1·50

1928. No. 577 surch **Vale 2 cts.**
586 **80** 2 c. on 4 c. red 90 25

1928. Fiscal stamp as T **90**, but inscr "TIMBRE TELEGRAFICO" and surch **Correos 1928 Vale** and new value.
587 **90** 1 c. on 5 c. blue and black 25 15
588 2 c. on 5 c. blue and black 25 15
589 3 c. on 5 c. blue and black 25 15

1928. Obligatory Tax. No. 587 additionally optd **R. de T.**
590 **90** 1 c. on 5 c. blue & black 45 10

1928. As Nos. 465/72 but colours changed.
591 **79** ½ c. red 30 15
592 1 c. orange 30 15
593 **80** 2 c. green 30 15
594 **79** 3 c. purple 30 20
595 **80** 4 c. brown 30 20
596 **79** 5 c. yellow 30 15
597 **80** 6 c. blue 30 20
598 10 c. blue 65 20
599 **79** 15 c. red 85 35
600 **80** 20 c. green 85 35
601 **79** 25 c. purple 16·00 3·75
602 **80** 50 c. brown 1·90 70
603 1 cor. violet 3·75 1·75
See also Nos. 617/27 and 912/24.

1928.
604 **106** 1 c. purple 20 10
647 1 c. red 25 10
For 1 c. green see No. 925.

1929. Optd **R. de C.**
605 **79** 1 c. orange 10 10
628 1 c. olive 15 10

1929. Optd **Correos 1929.**
606 **79** ½ c. green 20 15

1929. Optd **Correos 1928.**
607 **99** 10 c. brown 55 45

1929. Fiscal stamps as T **90**, but inscr "TIMBRE TELEGRAFICO". A. Surch **Correos 1929 R. de C. C$ 0.01** vert.
613 **90** 1 c. on 5 c. blue & black 10 15

B. Surch **Correos 1929** and value.
611 **90** 1 c. on 10 c. green and black 20 15
612 2 c. on 5 c. blue and black 20 10

C. Surch **Correos 1929** and value vert and **R. de C.** or **R. de T.** horiz.
608 **90** 1 c. on 5 c. blue and black (R. de T.) 20 15
609 2 c. on 5 c. blue and black (R. de T.) 15 15
610 2 c. on 5 c. blue and black (R. de C.) 13·00 70

1929. Air. Optd **Correo Aereo 1929. P.A.A.**
614 **79** 25 c. sepia 1·40 1·40
615 25 c. orange 1·00 1·00
616 25 c. violet 90 70

1929. As Nos. 591/603 but colours changed.
617 **79** 1 c. green 10 10
618 3 c. blue 25 15
619 **80** 4 c. blue 25 15
620 **79** 5 c. brown 30 15
621 **80** 6 c. drab 30 15
622 10 c. brown 45 15
623 **79** 15 c. red 65 20
624 **80** 20 c. orange 80 25
625 **79** 25 c. violet 20 10
626 **80** 50 c. green 35 15
627 1 cor. yellow 2·75 90
See also Nos. 912/24.

112 Mt. Momotombo **114** G.P.O. Managua

1929. Air.
629 **112** 15 c. purple 25 10
630 20 c. green 70 45
631 25 c. olive 50 30
632 50 c. sepia 80 45
633 1 cor. red 1·10 55
See also Nos. 926/30.

1930. Air. Surch **Vale** and value.
634 **112** 15 c. on 25 c. olive 40 30
635 20 c. on 25 c. olive 60 45

1930. Opening of the G.P.O., Managua.
636 **114** ½ c. sepia 80 60
637 1 c. red 80 60
638 2 c. orange 65 45
639 3 c. orange 1·00 90
640 4 c. yellow 1·00 90
641 5 c. olive 1·60 1·10
642 6 c. green 1·60 1·10
643 10 c. black 1·60 1·00
644 25 c. blue 3·25 2·40
645 50 c. blue 5·25 3·50
646 1 cor. violet 15·00 7·25

1931. Optd **1931** and thick bar obliterating old overprint "1928".
648 **99** 10 c. brown (No. 607) 45 90

1931. No. 607 surch **C $ 0.02.**
649 **99** 2 c. on 10 c. brown 55 45

1931. Optd **1931** and thick bar.
650 **99** 2 c. on 10 c. brown (498) 55 1·75

1931. Air. Nos. 614/16 surch **1931 Vale** and value.
651 **79** 15 c. on 25 c. sepia 90·00 90·00
652 15 c. on 25 c. orange 45·00 45·00
653 15 c. on 25 c. violet 9·00 9·00
654 20 c. on 25 c. violet 9·00 9·00

1931. Optd **1931.**
656 **79** ½ c. green 35 10
657 1 c. olive 35 10
665 1 c. orange (No. 605) 10 10
658 **80** 2 c. red 35 10
659 **79** 3 c. blue 35 15
660 5 c. yellow 2·10 1·40
661 5 c. sepia 65 20
662 15 c. orange 70 45
663 25 c. sepia 9·00 3·75
664 25 c. violet 3·50 1·50

1931. Air. Surch **1931** and value.
667 **80** 15 c. on 25 c. olive 4·75 4·75
668 15 c. on 50 c. sepia 36·00 36·00
669 15 c. on 1 cor. red 90·00 90·00
666 15 c. on 20 c. on 25 c. olive (No. 635) 7·50 7·50

120 G.P.O. before and after the Earthquake

1932. G.P.O. Reconstruction Fund.
670 **120** ½ c. green (postage) 90 90
671 1 c. brown 1·25 1·25
672 2 c. red 90 90
673 3 c. blue 90 90
674 4 c. blue 90 90
675 5 c. brown 1·40 1·40
676 6 c. brown 1·40 1·40
677 10 c. brown 2·25 1·50
678 15 c. red 3·50 2·25
679 20 c. orange 2·10 2·10
680 25 c. violet 2·25 2·25
681 50 c. green 2·25 2·25
682 1 cor. yellow 4·50 4·50
683 15 c. mauve (air) 90 75
684 20 c. green 1·10 1·10
685 25 c. brown 5·50 5·50
686 50 c. brown 7·00 7·00
687 1 cor. red 10·50 10·50

1932. Air. Surch **Vale** and value.
688 **112** 30 c. on 50 c. sepia 1·40 1·40
689 35 c. on 50 c. sepia 1·40 1·40
690 40 c. on 1 cor. red 1·60 1·60
691 55 c. on 1 cor. red 1·60 1·60
For similar surcharges on these stamps in different colours see Nos. 791/4 and 931/4.

1932. Air. International Air Mail Week. Optd **Semana Correo Aereo Internacional 11-17 Septiembre 1932.**
692 **112** 15 c. violet 40·00 40·00

1932. Air. Inauguration of Inland Airmail Service. Surch **Inauguracion Interior 12 Octubre 1932 Vale C$0.08.**
693 **112** 8 c. on 1 cor. red 13·00 13·00

1932. Air. Optd **Interior–1932** or surch **Vale** and value also.
705 **120** 25 c. brown 4·75 4·75
706 32 c. on 50 c. brown 5·50 5·50
707 40 c. on 1 cor. red 4·25 4·25

1932. Air. Nos. 671, etc., optd **Correo Aereo Interior** in one line and **1932**, or surch **Vale** and value also.
694 **120** 1 c. brown 12·00 12·00
695 2 c. red 12·00 12·00
696 3 c. blue 5·50 5·50
697 4 c. blue 5·50 5·50
698 5 c. brown 5·50 5·50
699 6 c. brown 5·50 5·50
700 8 c. on 10 c. brown 5·25 5·25
701 16 c. on 20 c. orange 5·25 5·25
702 24 c. on 25 c. violet 5·25 5·25
703 50 c. green 5·25 5·25
704 1 cor. yellow 5·50 5·50

1932. Air. Surch **Correo Aereo Interior–1932** in two lines and **Vale** and value below.
710 **80** 1 c. on 2 c. red 40 40
711 **79** 2 c. on 3 c. blue 40 40
712 **80** 3 c. on 4 c. blue 40 40
713 **79** 4 c. on 5 c. sepia 40 40
714 **80** 5 c. on 6 c. brown 40 40
715 6 c. on 10 c. brown 40 40
716 **79** 8 c. on 15 c. orange 40 40
717 **80** 16 c. on 20 c. orange 40 40
718 **79** 24 c. on 25 c. violet 85 60
719 25 c. on 25 c. violet 85 60
720 **80** 32 c. on 50 c. green 85 75
721 40 c. on 50 c. green 95 85
722 50 c. on 1 cor. yellow 1·25 1·25
723 100 c. on 1 cor. yellow 2·50 2·50

127 Wharf, Port San Jorge

128 La Chocolata Cutting

1932. Opening of Rivas Railway.
726 **127** 1 c. yellow (postage) . . . 19·00
727 – 2 c. red . . . . 19·00
728 – 5 c. sepia . . . . 19·00
729 – 10 c. brown . . . . . . 19·00
730 – 15 c. yellow . . . . . . 19·00

731 **128** 15 c. violet (air) . . . . . 25·00
732 – 20 c. green . . . . 25·00
733 – 25 c. brown . . . . 25·00
734 – 50 c. sepia . . . . 25·00
735 – 1 cor. red . . . . 25·00
DESIGNS—HORIZ: 2 c. El Nacascolo Halt; 5 c. Rivas Station; 10 c. San Juan del Sur; 15 c. (No. 730), Arrival platform at Rivas; 20 c. El Nacascolo; 25 c. La Cuesta cutting; 50 c. San Juan del Sur quay; 1 cor. El Estero.

1932. Surch **Vale** and value in words.
736 **79** 1 c. on 3 c. blue 35 15
737 **80** 2 c. on 4 c. blue 30 15

130 Railway Construction

1932. Opening of Leon–Sauce Railway.
739 – 1 c. yellow (postage) . . . 19·00
740 – 2 c. red . . . . 19·00
741 – 5 c. sepia . . . . 19·00
742 **130** 10 c. brown . . . . . . 19·00
743 – 15 c. yellow . . . . . . 19·00

744 – 15 c. violet (air) . . . . . 25·00
745 – 20 c. green . . . . 25·00
746 – 25 c. brown . . . . 25·00
747 – 50 c. sepia . . . . 25·00
748 – 1 cor. red . . . . 25·00
DESIGNS—HORIZ: 1 c. El Sauce; 2 c., 15 c. (No. 744), Bridge at Santa Lucia; 5 c. Santa Lucia; 15 c. (No. 743) Santa Lucia cutting; 20 c. Santa Lucia River Halt; 25 c. Malpaicillo Station; 50 c. Railway panorama; 1 cor. San Andres.

1933. Surch **Resello 1933 Vale** and value in words.
749 **79** 1 c. on 3 c. blue 20 15
750 1 c. on 5 c. sepia 20 15
751 **80** 2 c. on 10 c. brown 20 15

133 Flag of the Race

1933. 441st Anniv of Columbus' Departure from Palos. Roul.
753 **133** ½ c. green (postage) 95 95
754 1 c. green 80 80
755 2 c. red 80 80
756 3 c. red 80 80
757 4 c. orange 80 80
758 5 c. yellow 95 95
759 10 c. brown 95 95
760 15 c. brown 95 95
761 20 c. blue 95 95
762 25 c. blue 95 95
763 30 c. violet . . . . 2·40 2·40
764 50 c. purple . . . . 2·40 2·40
765 1 cor. brown . . . . . . 2·40 2·40

766 1 c. brown (air) 90 90
767 2 c. purple 90 90
768 4 c. violet . . . . 1·50 1·40
769 5 c. blue . . . . 1·40 1·40
770 6 c. blue . . . . 1·40 1·40
771 8 c. brown 45 45
772 15 c. brown 45 45
773 20 c. yellow . . . . 1·40 1·40
774 25 c. orange . . . . 1·40 1·40
775 50 c. red . . . . 1·40 1·40
776 1 cor. green . . . . 9·00 9·00

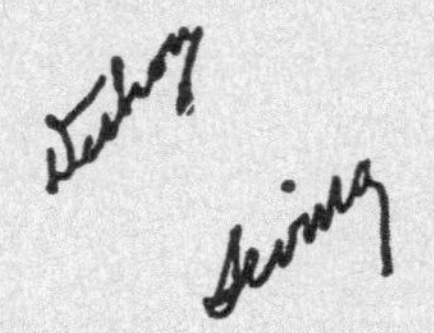
(**134**) (Facsimile signatures of R. E. Deshon, Minister of Transport and J. R. Sevilla, P.M.G.)

1933. Optd with T **134**.
777 **79** ½ c. green 30 15
778 1 c. green 15 10
779 **80** 2 c. red 40 15
780 **79** 3 c. blue 15 10
781 **80** 4 c. blue 20 15
782 **79** 5 c. brown 20 10
783 **80** 6 c. drab 25 20
784 10 c. brown 25 15
785 **79** 15 c. red 30 20
786 **80** 20 c. orange 40 30
787 **79** 25 c. violet 45 25
788 **80** 50 c. green 75 50
789 1 cor. yellow . . . . 4·00 1·60

1933. No. 605 optd with T **134**.
790 **79** 1 c. orange 25 15

1933. Air. Surch **Vale** and value.
791 **112** 30 c. on 50 c. orange . . . 35 15
792 35 c. on 50 c. blue 45 20
793 40 c. on 1 cor. yellow . . . 70 15
794 55 c. on 1 cor. green . . . 70 30

135 Lake Xolotlan

1933. Air. International Airmail Week.
795 **135** 10 c. brown 90 90
796 15 c. violet 75 75
797 25 c. red 85 85
798 50 c. blue 90 90

(**136**)

1933. Air. Surch as T **136**.
799 **80** 1 c. on 2 c. green 15 15
800 **79** 2 c. on 3 c. olive 15 15
801 **80** 3 c. on 4 c. red 15 15
802 **79** 4 c. on 5 c. blue 15 15
803 **80** 5 c. on 6 c. blue 15 15
804 6 c. on 10 c. sepia 15 10
805 **79** 8 c. on 15 c. brown 20 15
806 **80** 16 c. on 20 c. brown 20 15
807 **79** 24 c. on 25 c. red 15 15
808 25 c. on 25 c. orange . . . 30 30
809 **80** 32 c. on 50 c. violet 30 25
810 40 c. on 50 c. green 40 25
811 50 c. on 1 cor. yellow . . . 40 30
812 1 cor. on 1 cor. red 95 80

1933. Obligatory Tax. As No. 647 optd with T **134**. Colour changed.
813 **106** 1 c. orange 25 15

1934. Air. Surch **Servicio Centroamericano Vale 10 centavos**.
814 **112** 10 c. on 20 c. green 35 35
815 10 c. on 25 c. olive 35 35
See also No. 872.

1935. Optd **Resello 1935**. (a) Nos. 778/9.
816 **79** 1 c. green 10 10
817 **80** 2 c. red 15 10

(b) No. 813 but without T **134** opt.
818 **106** 1 c. orange 15 10

1935. No. 783 surch **Vale Medio Centavo**.
819 **80** ½ c. on 6 c. brown 35 15

1935. Optd with T **134** and **RESELLO-1935** in a box.
820 **79** ½ c. green 20 15
821 **80** ½ c. on 6 c. brown (No. 819) . . 15 10
822 **79** 1 c. green 25 10
823 **80** 2 c. red 55 10
824 2 c. red (No. 817) 30 10
825 **79** 3 c. blue 30 15
826 **80** 4 c. blue 30 15
827 **79** 5 c. brown 25 10
828 **80** 6 c. drab 30 10
829 10 c. brown 55 20
830 **79** 15 c. red 15 10
831 **80** 20 c. orange 90 25
832 **79** 25 c. violet 30 15
833 **80** 50 c. green 35 25
834 1 cor. yellow 45 35

1935. Obligatory Tax. No. 605 optd with **RESELLO-1935** in a box.
835 **79** 1 c. orange . . . . 25·00

1935. Obligatory Tax. Optd **RESELLO-1935** in a box.
(a) No. 813 without T **134** opt.
836 **106** 1 c. orange 25 15

(b) No. 818.
868 **106** 1 c. orange 20 15

1935. Air. Nos. 799/812 optd with **RESELLO-1935** in a box.
839 **80** 1 c. on 2 c. green 10 10
840 **79** 2 c. on 3 c. olive 20 20
879 **80** 3 c. on 4 c. red 15 15
880 **79** 4 c. on 5 c. blue 15 15
881 **80** 5 c. on 6 c. blue 15 15
882 6 c. on 10 c. sepia 15 15
883 **79** 8 c. on 15 c. brown 15 15
884 **80** 16 c. on 20 c. brown 15 15
847 **79** 24 c. on 25 c. red 35 30
848 25 c. on 25 c. orange . . . 25 25
849 **80** 32 c. on 50 c. violet 20 20
850 40 c. on 50 c. green 30 25
851 50 c. on 1 cor. yellow . . . 45 35
852 1 cor. on 1 cor. red 85 40

1935. Air. Optd with **RESELLO-1935** in a box. (a) Nos. 629/33.
853 **112** 15 c. purple 30 10
873 20 c. green 40 30
855 25 c. green 40 35
856 50 c. sepia 40 35
857 1 cor. red 65 35

(b) Nos. 791/4.
858 **112** 30 c. on 50 c. orange . . . 40 35
859 35 c. on 50 c. blue 40 25
860 40 c. on 1 cor. yellow . . . 40 35
861 55 c. on 1 cor. green . . . 40 30

(c) Nos. 814/5.
862 **112** 10 c. on 20 c. green £300 £300
863 10 c. on 25 c. olive 60 50

1935. Optd with **RESELLO-1935** in a box.
864 **79** ½ c. green (No. 465) 15 10
865 1 c. green (No. 617) 20 10
866 **80** 2 c. red (No. 467) 55 10
867 **79** 3 c. blue (No. 618) 20 15

1936. Surch **Resello 1936 Vale** and value.
869 **79** 1 c. on 3 c. blue (No. 618) . . 15 10
870 2 c. on 5 c. brown (No. 620) . 15 10

1936. Air. Surch **Servicio Centroamericano Vale diez centavos** and **RESELLO-1935** in a box.
871 **112** 10 c. on 25 c. olive 30 30

1936. Obligatory Tax. No. 818 optd **1936**.
874 **106** 1 c. orange 50 20

1936. Obligatory Tax. No. 605 optd with T **134** and **1936**.
875 **79** 1 c. orange 50 20

1936. Air. No. 622 optd **Correo Aereo Centro-Americano Resello 1936**.
876 **80** 10 c. brown 20 20

1936. Air. Nos. 799/800 and 805 optd **Resello 1936**.
885 **80** 1 c. on 2 c. green 25 20
886 **79** 2 c. on 3 c. olive 10 10
887 8 c. on 15 c. brown 25 25

1936. Optd with or without T **37**, surch **1936 Vale** and value.
888 **79** ½ c. on 15 c. red 20 15
889 **80** 1 c. on 4 c. blue 25 15
890 **79** 1 c. on 5 c. brown 25 20
891 **80** 1 c. on 6 c. drab 45 20
892 **79** 1 c. on 15 c. red 25 20
893 **80** 1 c. on 20 c. orange 20 15
895 2 c. on 10 c. brown 30 20
896 **79** 2 c. on 15 c. red 60 50
897 **80** 2 c. on 20 c. orange 55 45
898 **79** 2 c. on 25 c. violet 35 20
900 **80** 2 c. on 50 c. green 35 25
901 2 c. on 1 cor. yellow 35 30
902 3 c. on 4 c. blue 40 30

1936. Optd **Resello 1936**.
903 **79** 3 c. blue (No. 618) 35 25
904 5 c. brown (No. 620) . . . 30 15
905 **80** 10 c. brown (No. 784) . . . 30 20

1936. Air. Surch **1936 Vale and value**.
906 **112** 15 c. on 50 c. brown . . . 30 25
907 15 c. on 1 cor. red 30 25

1936. Fiscal stamps surch **RECONSTRUCCION COMUNICACIONES 5 CENTAVOS DE CORDOBA** and further surch **Vale dos centavos Resello 1936**.
908 **90** 1 c. on 5 c. green 25 10
909 2 c. on 5 c. green 25 10

1936. Obligatory Tax. Fiscal stamps surch **RECONSTRUCCION COMUNICACIONES 5 CENTAVOS DE CORDOBA** and further surch.
(a) **1936 R. de C. Vale Un Centavo**.
910 **90** 1 c. on 5 c. green 15 10

(b) **Vale un centavo R. de C. 1936**.
911 **90** 1 c. on 5 c. green 20 10

1937. Colours changed. Size $27\times22\frac{3}{4}$ mm.
912 **79** ½ c. black 15 10
913 1 c. red 15 10
914 **80** 2 c. blue 15 10
915 **79** 3 c. brown 15 10
916 **80** 4 c. yellow 20 10
917 **79** 5 c. red 15 10
918 **80** 6 c. violet 20 10
919 10 c. green 20 10
920 **79** 15 c. green 15 10
921 **80** 20 c. brown 30 10
922 **79** 25 c. orange 30 10
923 **80** 50 c. brown 35 15
924 1 cor. blue 40 25

1937. Obligatory Tax. Colour changed.
925 **106** 1 c. green 15 10

1937. Air. Colours changed.
926 **112** 15 c. orange 20 10
927 20 c. red 20 15
928 25 c. black 25 15
929 50 c. violet 45 15
930 1 cor. orange 65 15

1937. Air. Surch **Vale** and value. Colours changed.
931 **112** 30 c. on 50 c. red 30 10
932 35 c. on 50 c. olive 35 10
933 40 c. on 1 cor. green . . . 35 15
934 55 c. on 1 cor. blue 35 30

1937. Air. Surch **Servicio Centroamericano Vale Diez Centavos**.
949 **112** 10 c. on 1 cor. red 30 15

1937. Air. No. 805 (without T **134**) optd **1937**.
950 **79** 8 c. on 15 c. brown 50 15

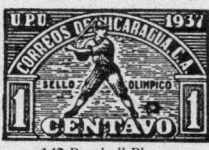

142 Baseball Player

1937. Obligatory Tax. For 1937 Central American Olympic Games. Optd with ball in red under "OLIMPICO".
951 **142** 1 c. red 35 15
952 1 c. yellow 35 15
953 1 c. blue 35 15
953a 1 c. green 35 15

1937. Nos. 799/809 optd **Habilitado 1937**.
954 **80** 1 c. on 2 c. green 10 10
955 **79** 2 c. on 3 c. olive 10 10
956 **80** 3 c. on 4 c. red 10 10
957 **79** 4 c. on 5 c. blue 10 10
658 **80** 5 c. on 6 c. blue 10 10
959 6 c. on 10 c. brown 10 10
960 **79** 8 c. on 15 c. brown 10 10
661 **80** 16 c. on 20 c. brown 20 20
962 **79** 24 c. on 25 c. red 20 20
963 25 c. on 25 c. orange . . . 20 25
664 **80** 32 c. on 50 c. violet 20 25

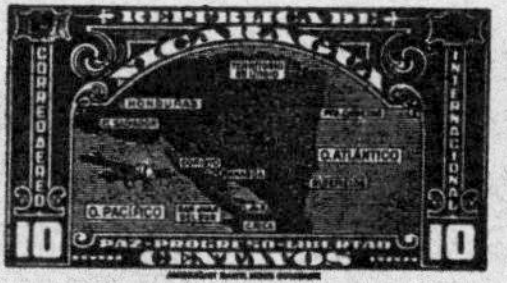
144 Presidential Palace, Managua

1937. Air. Inland.
965 **144** 1 c. red 15 10
966 2 c. blue 15 10
967 3 c. olive 15 10
968 4 c. black 15 10
969 5 c. purple 20 10
970 6 c. brown 20 10
971 8 c. violet 20 10
972 16 c. orange 35 25
973 24 c. yellow 20 15
974 25 c. green 50 25

145 Nicaragua

1937. Air. Abroad.
975 **145** 10 c. green 25 10
976 15 c. blue 25 10
977 20 c. yellow 30 25
978 25 c. violet 30 25
979 30 c. red 40 25
980 50 c. orange 60 25
981 1 cor. olive 65 45

146 Presidential Palace

1937. Air. Abroad. 150th Anniv of U.S. Constitution.
982 – 10 c. blue and green . . . 1·10 70
983 **146** 15 c. blue and orange . . . 1·10 70
984 – 20 c. blue and red 80 65
985 – 25 c. blue and brown . . . 80 65
986 – 30 c. blue and green . . . 80 65
987 – 35 c. blue and yellow . . . 35 25
988 – 40 c. blue and green . . . 55 40
989 – 45 c. blue and purple . . . 55 40
990 – 50 c. blue and mauve . . . 55 40
991 – 55 c. blue and green . . . 2·25 1·25
992 – 75 c. blue and green . . . 55 30
993 – 1 cor. red and blue . . . 75 30
DESIGNS: 10 c. Children's Park, Managua; 20 c. S. America; 25 c. C. America; 30 c. N. America; 35 c. Lake Tiscapa; 40 c. Pan American motor-road; 45 c. Priniomi Park; 50 c. Piedrecitas Park; 55 c. San Juan del Sur; 75 c. Rio Tipitapa; 1 cor. Granada landscape.

146b Diriangen

1937. Air. Day of the Race.

993a **146b** 1 c. green (inland) . . . 15 10
993b 4 c. lake . . . 15 10
993c 5 c. violet . . . 25 15
993d 8 c. blue . . . 15 10

993e 10 c. brown (abroad) . . 20 10
993f 15 c. blue . . . 20 10
993g 20 c. pink . . . 30 15

147 Letter Carrier

1937. 75th Anniv of Postal Administration.

994 **147** $\frac{1}{2}$ c. green . . . 15 10
995 – 1 c. mauve . . . 15 10
996 – 2 c. brown . . . 15 10
997 – 3 c. violet . . . 65 20
998 – 5 c. blue . . . 65 20
999 – $7\frac{1}{2}$ c. red . . . 2·50 75

DESIGNS: 1 c. Mule transport; 2 c. Diligence; 3 c. Yacht; 5 c. Packet steamer; $7\frac{1}{2}$ c. Steam mail train.

147a Gen. Tomas Martinez

1938. Air. 75th Anniv of Postal Administration.

999a **147a** 1 c. black and orange (inland) . . . 25 20
999b 5 c. black and violet . . 25 20
999c 8 c. black and blue . . . 30 30
999d 16 c. black and brown . . 40 35

999e – 10 c. black and green (abroad) . . . 30 25
999f – 15 c. black and blue . . 40 35
999g – 25 c. black and violet . . 25 25
999h – 50 c. black and red . . . 40 30

DESIGNS: 10 c. to 50 c. Gen. Anastasio Somoza.

1938. Surch **1938** and **Vale**, new value in words and **Centavos**.

1000 **79** 3 c. on 25 c. orange . . . 10 10
1001 **80** 5 c. on 50 c. brown . . . 10 10
1002 6 c. on 1 cor. blue . . . 15 15

149 Dario Park

150 Laka Managua

151 President Somoza

1939.

1003 **149** $1\frac{1}{2}$ c. green (postage) . . . 10 10
1004 2 c. red . . . 10 10
1005 3 c. blue . . . 10 10
1006 6 c. brown . . . 10 10
1007 $7\frac{1}{2}$ c. green . . . 10 10
1008 10 c. brown . . . 15 10
1009 15 c. orange . . . 15 10
1010 25 c. violet . . . 15 15
1011 50 c. green . . . 30 20
1012 1 cor. yellow . . . 60 45
1013 **150** 2 c. blue (air: inland) . . . 15 15
1014 3 c. olive . . . 15 15
1015 8 c. mauve . . . 15 15
1016 16 c. orange . . . 25 15
1017 24 c. yellow . . . 25 15
1018 32 c. green . . . 35 15
1019 50 c. red . . . 40 15

1020 **151** 10 c. brown (air: abroad) . 15 10
1021 15 c. blue . . . 15 10
1022 20 c. yellow . . . 15 20
1023 25 c. violet . . . 15 15
1024 30 c. red . . . 20 20
1025 50 c. orange . . . 30 20
1026 1 cor. olive . . . 45 35

1939. Nos. 920/1. Surch **Vale un Centavo 1939**.

1027 **79** 1 c. on 15 c. green . . . 10 10
1028 **80** 1 c. on 20 c. brown . . . 10 10

153 Will Rogers and Managua Airport

1939. Air. Will Rogers Commemorative. Inscr "WILL ROGERS/1931/1939".

1029 **153** 1 c. green . . . 10 10
1030 – 2 c. red . . . 10 10
1031 – 3 c. blue . . . 10 10
1032 – 4 c. blue . . . 15 10
1033 – 5 c. red . . . 10 10

DESIGNS: 2 c. Rogers at Managua; 3 c. Rogers in P.A.A. hut; 4 c. Rogers and U.S. Marines; 5 c. Rogers and street in Managua.

156 Senate House and Pres. Somoza

1940. Air. President's Visit to U.S.A. Inscr "AEREO INTERIOR".

1034 – 4 c. brown . . . 15 10
1035 **156** 8 c. brown . . . 10 10
1036 – 16 c. green . . . 15 10
1037 **156** 20 c. mauve . . . 30 15
1038 – 32 c. red . . . 20 20

(b) Inscr "CORREO AEREO INTERNACIONAL".

1039 – 25 c. blue . . . 20 15
1040 – 30 c. black . . . 20 10
1041 **156** 50 c. red . . . 25 40
1042 – 60 c. green . . . 30 35
1043 – 65 c. brown . . . 30 20
1044 – 90 c. olive . . . 40 35
1045 – 1 cor. violet . . . 60 30

DESIGNS: 4 c., 16 c., 25 c., 30 c., 65 c., 90 c. Pres. Somoza addressing Senate; 32 c., 60 c., 1 cor. Portrait of Pres. Somoza between symbols of Nicaragua and New York World's Fair.

158 L. S. Rowe, Statue of Liberty and Union Flags

1940. Air. 50th Anniv of Pan-American Union.

1046 **158** 1 cor. 25 multicoloured . . 40 35

159 First Issue of Nicaragua and Sir Rowland Hill

1941. Air. Centenary of First Adhesive Postage stamps.

1047 **159** 2 cor. brown . . . 2·25 75
1048 3 cor. blue . . . 7·00 80
1049 5 cor. red . . . 20·00 2·10

1941. Surch **Servicio ordinario/Vale Diez Centavos/de Cordoba**.

1050 **153** 10 c. on 1 c. green . . . 15 10

161 Rube Dario

1941. 25th Death Anniv of Ruben Dario (poet).

1051 **161** 10 c. red (postage) . . . 20 15

1052 20 c. mauve (air) . . . 25 15
1053 35 c. green . . . 30 20
1054 40 c. orange . . . 35 25
1055 60 c. blue . . . 40 35

1943. As No. 1050, but **de Cordoba** omitted.

1056 **153** 10 c. on 1 c. green . . . 10 10

162 "V" for Victory

163 Red Cross

164 Red Cross Workers and Wounded

1943. Victory.

1057 **162** 10 c. red & violet (post) . 10 10
1058 30 c. red and brown . . . 15 10

1059 40 c. red and green (air) . 15 10
1060 60 c. red and blue . . . 20 10

1944. Air. 80th Anniv of Int Red Cross Society.

1061 **163** 25 c. red . . . 40 15
1062 – 50 c. bistre . . . 65 35
1063 **164** 1 cor. green . . . 1·25 1·00

DESIGN—VERT: 50 c. Two Hemispheres.

165 Columbus and Lighthouse

166 Columbus's Fleet and Lighthouse

1945. Honouring Columbus's Discovery of America and Erection of Columbus Lighthouse near Trujillo City, Dominican Republic.

1064 **165** 4 c. black & green (post) . 15 10
1065 6 c. black and orange . . 20 10
1066 8 c. black and red . . . 20 15
1067 10 c. black and blue . . . 30 15

1068 **166** 20 c. grey & green (air) . . 60 20
1069 35 c. black and red . . . 95 25
1070 75 c. pink and green . . . 1·75 55
1071 90 c. blue and red . . . 2·00 85
1072 1 cor. blue and black . . 2·25 50
1073 2 cor. 50 red and blue . . 6·00 2·50

168 Roosevelt as a Stamp Collector

1946. President Roosevelt Commemorative Inscr "HOMENAJE A ROOSEVELT".

1074 **168** 4 c. green & black (post) . 15 15
1075 – 8 c. violet and black . . . 20 20
1076 – 10 c. blue and black . . . 30 25
1077 – 16 c. red and black . . . 40 30
1078 – 32 c. brown and black . . 50 25
1079 – 50 c. grey and black . . . 50 25

1080 – 25 c. orange & black (air) 20 10
1081 – 75 c. red and black . . . 25 20
1082 – 1 cor. green and black . . 30 30
1083 – 3 cor. violet and black . . 2·25 2·25
1084 – 5 cor. blue and black . . 3·00 3·00

DESIGNS — portraying Roosevelt HORIZ: 8 c., 25 c. with Churchill at the Atlantic Conference; 16 c., 1 cor. with Churchill, De Gaulle and Giraud at the Casablanca Conference; 32 c., 3 cor. with Churchill and Stalin at the Teheran Conference. VERT: 10 c., 75 c. Signing Declaration of War against Japan; 50 c., 5 cor. Head of Roosevelt

171 Managua Cathedral

172 G.P.O., Managua

1947. Managua Centenary Frames in black.

1085 **171** 4 c. red (postage) . . . 10 10
1086 – 5 c. blue . . . 15 10
1087 – 6 c. green . . . 20 15
1088 – 10 c. olive . . . 20 15
1089 – 75 c. brown . . . 30 25

1090 – 5 c. violet (air) . . . 10 10
1091 **172** 20 c. green . . . 15 15
1092 – 35 c. orange . . . 15 15
1093 – 90 c. purple . . . 30 20
1094 – 1 cor. brown . . . 45 35
1095 – 2 cor. 50 purple . . . 1·00 1·10

DESIGNS—POSTAGE. (as Type **171**): 5 c. Health Ministry; 6 c. Municipal Building; 10 c. College; 75 c. G.P.O., Managua. AIR (as Type **172**): 5 c. College; 35 c. Health Ministry; 90 c. National Bank; 1 cor. Municipal Building; 2 cor. 50, National Palace.

173 San Cristobal Volcano

174 Ruben Dario Monument, Managua

1947. (a) Postage.

1096 **173** 2 c. orange and black . . 10 10
1097 – 3 c. violet and black . . . 10 10
1098 – 4 c. grey and black . . . 10 10
1099 – 5 c. red and black . . . 20 10
1100 – 6 c. green and black . . . 15 10
1101 – 8 c. brown and black . . . 15 10
1102 – 10 c. red and black . . . 25 15
1103 – 20 c. blue and black . . . 1·10 25
1104 – 30 c. purple and black . . 70 25
1105 – 50 c. red and black . . . 1·90 70
1106 – 1 cor. brown and black . . 60 35

DESIGNS—as Type **173**: 3 c. Lion on Ruben Dario's tomb, Leon Cathedral; 4 c. Race Stand; 5 c. Soldiers' Monument; 6 c. Sugar cane; 8 c. Tropical fruits; 10 c. Cotton; 20 c. Horses; 30 c. Coffee plant; 50 c. Prize bullock; 1 cor. Agricultural landscape.

(b) Air.

1107 **174** 5 c. red and green . . . 10 10
1108 – 6 c. orange and black . . 10 10
1109 – 8 c. brown and red . . . 10 10
1110 – 10 c. blue and brown . . 15 10
1111 – 20 c. orange and blue . . 15 10
1112 – 25 c. green and red . . . 20 15
1113 – 35 c. brown and black . . 30 15
1114 – 50 c. black and violet . . 20 10
1115 – 1 cor. red and black . . . 45 25
1116 – 1 cor. 50 green & red . . 50 45
1117 – 5 cor. red and brown . . 3·75 3·75
1118 – 10 cor. brown and violet . 3·00 3·00
1119 – 25 cor. yellow and green . 6·00 6·00

DESIGNS—As Type **174**: 6 c. Baird's tapir; 8 c. Highway and Lake Managua; 10 c. Genizaro Dam; 20 c. Ruben Dario Monument, Managua; 25 c. Sulphur Lagoon, Nejapa; 35 c. Managua Airport; 50 c. Mouth of Rio Prinzapolka; 1 cor. Thermal Baths, Tipitapa; 1 cor. 50, Rio Tipitapa; 5 cor. Embassy building; 10 cor. Girl carrying basket of fruit; 25 cor. Franklin D. Roosevelt Monument, Managua.

175 Soft-ball

176 Pole Vaulting

177 Tennis

178 National Stadium, Managua

1949. 10th World Amateur Baseball Championships.
(a) Postage as T **175/6**.
1120 **175** 1 c. brown 10 10
1121 – 2 c. blue 50 15
1122 **176** 3 c. green 25 10
1123 – 4 c. purple 15 15
1124 – 5 c. orange 40 15
1125 – 10 c. green 40 15
1126 – 15 c. red 50 15
1127 – 25 c. blue 50 20
1128 – 35 c. green 80 20
1129 – 40 c. violet . . . . 1·75 30
1130 – 60 c. black . . . . 1·40 35
1131 – 1 cor. red . . . . 1·50 90
1132 – 2 cor. purple . . . . . . 2·75 1·50
DESIGNS—VERT: 2 c. Scout; 5 c. Cycling; 25 c. Boxing; 35 c. Basket-ball. HORIZ: 4 c. Diving; 10 c. Stadium; 15 c. Baseball; 40 c. Yachting; 60 c. Table tennis; 1 cor. Football; 2 cor. Tennis.

(b) Air as T **177**.
1133 **177** 1 c. red 10 10
1134 – 2 c. black 10 10
1135 – 3 c. red 10 10
1136 – 4 c. black 10 10
1137 – 5 c. blue 35 15
1138 – 15 c. green 65 10
1139 – 25 c. purple . . . . 1·25 25
1140 – 30 c. brown . . . . 1·00 25
1141 – 40 c. violet 50 25
1142 – 75 c. mauve . . . . 2·50 1·60
1143 – 1 cor. blue . . . . 3·00 80
1144 – 2 cor. olive . . . . 1·25 1·00
1145 – 5 cor. green . . . . 2·10 2·10
DESIGNS—SQUARE: 2 c. Football; 3 c. Table tennis; 4 c. Stadium; 5 c. Yachting; 15 c. Basket-ball; 25 c. Boxing; 30 c. Baseball; 40 c. Cycling; 75 c. Diving; 1 cor. Pole-vaulting; 2 cor. Scout; 5 cor. Soft-ball.

1949. Obligatory Tax stamps. Stadium Construction Fund.
1146 **178** 5 c. blue 20 10
1146a 5 c. red 20 10

179 Rowland Hill

180 Heinrich von Stephan

1950. 75th Anniv of U.P.U. Frames in black.
1147 **179** 20 c. red (postage) 15 10
1148 – 25 c. green 15 10
1149 – 75 c. blue 50 50
1150 – 80 c. green 30 25
1151 – 4 cor. blue 85 80
DESIGNS—VERT: 25 c. Portrait as Type **180**; 75 c. Monument, Berne; 80 c., 4 cor. Obverse and reverse of Congress Medal.

1152 – 16 c. red (air) 15 10
1153 **180** 20 c. orange 15 10
1154 – 25 c. black 15 15
1155 – 30 c. red 25 10
1156 – 85 c. green 55 50
1157 – 1 cor. 10 brown 50 35
1158 – 2 cor. 14 green . . . . . 1·25 1·25
DESIGNS—HORIZ: 16 c. Rowland Hill; 25, 30 c. U.P.U. Offices, Berne; 85 c. Monument, Berne; 1 cor. 10, and 2 cor. 14, Obverse and reverse of Congress Medal.

181 Queen Isabella and Columbus's Fleet

182 Isabella the Catholic

1952. 500th Birth Anniv of Isabella the Catholic.
1159 – 10 c. mauve (postage) . . . 10 10
1160 **181** 96 c. blue . . . . 1·50 65
1161 – 98 c. red . . . . 1·50 65
1162 – 1 cor. 20 brown 50 40
1163 **182** 1 cor. 76 purple 60 60

1164 2 cor. 30 red (air) . . . . . 1·40 1·10
1165 – 2 cor. 80 orange . . . . . 1·00 95
1166 – 3 cor. green . . . . . . 4·25 1·75
1167 **181** 3 cor. 30 blue . . . . . 4·25 2·00
1168 – 3 cor. 60 green . . . . . 1·50 1·25
DESIGNS—VERT: 10 c., 3 cor. 60, Queen facing right; 98 c., 3 cor. Queen and "Santa Maria"; 1 cor. 20, 2 cor. 80, Queen and Map of Americas.

183 O.D.E.C.A. Flag

1953. Foundation of Organization of Central American States.
1169 **183** 4 c. blue (postage) 10 10
1170 – 5 c. green 10 10
1171 – 6 c. brown 10 10
1172 – 15 c. olive 20 15
1173 – 50 c. sepia 25 15

1174 – 20 c. red (air) 10 10
1175 **183** 25 c. blue 15 10
1176 – 30 c. brown 15 15
1177 – 60 c. green 25 20
1178 – 1 cor. purple 35 45
DESIGNS: 5 c., 1 cor. Map of C. America; 6 c., 20 c. Hands holding O.D.E.C.A. arms; 15 c., 30 c. Five Presidents of C. America; 50 c., 60 c. Charter and flags.

184 Pres. Solorzano

185 Pres. Arguello

1953. Presidential Series. Portraits in black. (a) Postage. As T **184**.
1179 **184** 4 c. red 10 10
1180 – 6 c. blue (D. M. Chamorro) . . 10 10
1181 – 8 c. brown (Diaz) 10 10
1182 – 15 c. red (Somoza) 15 10
1183 – 50 c. grn (E. Chamorro) . . 20 15

(b) Air. As T **185**.
1184 **185** 4 c. red 10 10
1185 – 5 c. orange (Moncada) . . 10 10
1186 – 20 c. blue (J. B. Sacasa) . . 10 10
1187 – 25 c. blue (Zelaya) 10 10
1188 – 30 c. lake (Somoza) 10 10
1189 – 35 c. green (Martinez) . . 20 20
1190 – 40 c. plum (Guzman) . . . 20 20
1191 – 45 c. olive (Cuadra) . . . 20 20
1192 – 50 c. red (P. J. Chamorro) . . 35 25
1193 – 60 c. blue (Zavala) 40 40
1194 – 85 c. brown (Cardenas) . . 40 40
1195 – 1 cor. 10 pur (Carazo) . . 60 55
1196 – 1 cor. 20 bistre (R. Sacasa) . 65 55

186 Sculptor and U.N. Emblem

1954. U.N.O. Inscr "HOMENAJE A LA ONU".
1197 **186** 3 c. drab (postage) . . . 10 10
1198 A 4 c. green 15 10
1199 B 5 c. green 20 10
1200 C 15 c. green 55 20
1201 D 1 cor. turquoise 45 40

1202 E 3 c. red (air) 10 10
1203 F 4 c. orange 10 10
1204 C 5 c. rd 15 10
1205 D 30 c. pink 75 15
1206 B 2 cor. red 80 70
1207 A 3 cor. brown . . . . . . 1·50 1·00
1208 **186** 5 cor. purple . . . . . . 1·75 1·40
DESIGNS: A, Detail from Nicaragua's Coat of Arms; B, Globe; C, Candle and Nicaragua's Charter; D, Flags of Nicaragua and U.N.; E, Torch; F, Trusting hands.

187 Capt. D. L. Ray

188 North American Sabre

1954. National Air Force. Frames in black. (a) Postage. Frames as T **187**.
1209 **187** 1 c. black 10 10
1210 – 2 c. black 10 10
1211 – 3 c. myrtle 10 10
1212 – 4 c. orange 15 10
1213 – 5 c. green 20 10
1214 – 15 c. turquoise 15 10
1215 – 1 cor. violet 35 25

(b) Air. Frames as T **188**.
1216 – 10 c. black 10 10
1217 **188** 15 c. black 15 10
1218 – 20 c. mauve 15 10
1219 – 25 c. red 20 10
1220 – 30 c. blue 10 10
1221 – 50 c. blue 75 50
1222 – 1 cor. green 65 35
DESIGNS—POSTAGE: 2 c. North American Sabre; 3 c. Douglas Boston; 4 c. Consolidated Liberator; 5 c. North American Texan trainer; 15 c. Pres. Somoza; 1 cor. Emblem. AIR: 10 c. D. L. Ray; 20 c. Emblem; 25 c. Hangars; 30 c. Pres. Somoza; 50 c. North American Texan trainers; 1 cor. Lockheed Lightning airplanes.

189 Rotary Slogans

190a

1955. 50th Anniv of Rotary International.
1223 **189** 15 c. orange (postage) . . 10 10
1224 A 20 c. olive 15 15
1225 B 35 c. violet 15 15
1226 C 40 c. red 15 15
1227 D 90 c. black 30 25

1228 D 1 c. red (air) 10 10
1229 A 2 c. blue 10 10
1230 C 3 c. green 10 10
1231 **189** 4 c. violet 10 10
1232 B 5 c. brown 10 10
1233 25 c. turquoise 15 15
1234 **189** 30 c. black 15 10
1235 C 45 c. mauve 30 25
1236 A 50 c. green 25 20
1237 D 1 cor. blue 45 30
DESIGNS—VERT: A, Clasped hands; B, Rotarian and Nicaraguan flags; D, Paul P. Harris. HORIZ: C, World map and winged emblem.

1956. National Exhibition. Surch **Conmemoracion Exposicion Nacional Febrero 4-16, 1956** and value.
1238 5 c. on 6 c. brown (No. 1171) (postage) 10 10
1239 5 c. on 6 c. blk & blue (1180) . 10 10
1240 5 c. on 8 c. brn & blk (1101) . 10 10
1241 15 c. on 35 c. violet (1225) . . 15 10
1242 15 c. on 80 c. grn & blk (1150) . 15 10
1243 15 c. on 90 c. black (1227) . . 15 10

1244 30 c. on 35 c. black & green (1189) (air) 10 15
1245 30 c. on 45 c. blk & ol. (1191) . 25 15
1246 30 c. on 45 c. mauve (1235) . . 25 15
1247 2 cor. on 5 cor. purple (1208) . 50 35

1956. Obligatory Tax. Social Welfare Fund.
1247a **190a** 5 c. blue 10 10

191 Gen. J. Dolores Estrada

192 President Somoza

1956. Cent of War of 1856. Inscr as in T **191**.
1248 – 5 c. brown (postage) . . . 10 10
1249 – 10 c. lake 10 10
1250 – 15 c. grey 10 10
1251 – 25 c. red 15 15
1252 – 50 c. purple 30 20

1253 **191** 30 c. red (air) 10 10
1254 – 60 c. brown 20 15
1255 – 1 cor. 50 green 20 35
1256 – 2 cor. 50 blue 30 30
1257 – 10 cor. orange . . . . . 1·90 1·75
DESIGNS—VERT: 5 c. Gen. M. Jerez; 10 c. Gen. F. Chamorro; 50 c. Gen. J. D. Estrada; 1 cor. 50, E. Mangalo; 10 cor. Commodore H. Paulding. HORIZ: 15 c. Battle of San Jocinto; 25 c. Granada in flames; 60 c. Bas-relief; 2 cor. 50, Battle of Rivas.

1957. Air. National Mourning for Pres. G. A. Somoza. Various frames. Inscr as in T **192**. Centres in black.
1258 – 15 c. black 10 10
1259 – 30 c. blue 15 15
1260 **192** 2 cor. violet 80 70
1261 – 3 cor. olive . . . . 1·25 1·10
1262 – 5 cor. sepia . . . . 1·90 1·90

193 Scout and Badge

194 Clasped Hands, Badge and Globe

1957. Birth Centenary of Lord Baden-Powell.
1263 **193** 10 c. olive & violet (post) . . 10 10
1264 – 15 c. sepia and purple . . 15 15
1265 – 20 c. brown and blue . . . 15 15
1266 – 25 c. brown & turquoise . . 15 15
1267 – 50 c. olive and red 35 35
1268 **194** 3 c. olive and red (air) . . 15 15
1269 – 4 c. blue and brown . . . 15 15
1270 – 5 c. brown and green . . . 15 15
1271 – 6 c. drab and violet . . . 15 15
1272 – 8 c. red and black 15 15
1273 – 30 c. black and green . . . 15 15
1274 – 40 c. black and blue . . . 15 15
1275 – 75 c. sepia and purple . . 35 35
1276 – 85 c. grey and red 40 40
1277 – 1 cor. brown and green . . 40 40
DESIGNS—VERT: 4 c. Scout badge; 5 c., 15 c. Wolf cub; 6 c. Badge and flags; 8 c. Badge and emblems of scouting; 20 c. Scout; 25 c. A. Harrison; 75 c. Rover Scout; 85 c. Scout. HORIZ: 40 c. Presentation to Pres. Somoza.

195 Pres. Luis Somoza

197 Archbishop of Managua

196 Managua Cathedral

1957. Election of Pres. Somoza. Portrait in brown. (a) Postage. Oval frame.
1278 **195** 10 c. red 10 10
1279 15 c. blue 10 10
1280 35 c. purple 10 10
1281 50 c. brown 15 15
1282 75 c. green 40 40

(b) Air. Rectangular frame.
1283 – 20 c. blue 10 10
1284 – 25 c. mauve 15 10
1285 – 30 c. sepia 15 15
1286 – 40 c. turquoise 15 15
1287 – 2 cor. violet 95 95

1957. Churches and Priests. Centres in olive.
1288 **196** 5 c. green (postage) . . . 10 10
1289 – 10 c. purple 10 10
1290 **197** 15 c. blue 10 10
1291 – 20 c. sepia 15 10
1292 – 50 c. green 20 15
1293 – 1 cor. violet 30 30

1294 **197** 30 c. green (air) 10 10
1295 **196** 60 c. brown 15 15
1296 – 75 c. blue 25 25
1297 – 90 c. red 30 30
1298 – 1 cor. 50 turquoise . . . 35 35
1299 – 2 cor. purple 40 40
DESIGNS—HORIZ: As Type **196**: 20, 90 c. Leon Cathedral; 50 c., 1 cor. 50, La Merced, Granada Church. VERT: As Type **197**: 10, 75 c. Bishop of Nicaragua; 1, 2 cor. Father Mariano Dubon.

198 "Honduras" (freighter)

199 Exhibition Emblem

1957. Nicaraguan Merchant Marine Commemoration. Inscr as in T **198**.
1300 **198** 4 c. black, blue and myrtle (postage) 30 10
1301 – 5 c. violet, blue & brown . 30 10
1302 – 6 c. black, blue & red . . 30 10
1303 – 10 c. black, green and sepia 30 10
1304 – 15 c. brown, blue & red . 50 10
1305 – 50 c. brown, blue & violet . 60 20
1306 – 25 c. purple, blue and ultramarine (air) . . . 60 20
1307 – 30 c. grey, buff & brown . 15 10
1308 – 50 c. bistre, blue & violet . 20 20
1309 – 60 c. black, turquoise and purple 85 30
1310 – 1 cor. black, blue & red . 1·10 30
1311 – 2 cor. 50 brown, blue and black . . . . 2·25 1·25
DESIGNS: 5 c. Gen. A. Somoza, founder of Mamenic (National) Shipping Line, and "Guatemala" (freighter); 6 c. "Guatemala"; 10 c. "Salvador" (freighter); 15 c. Freighter between hemispheres; 25 c. "Managua" (freighter); 30 c. Ship's wheel and world map; 50 c. (No. 1305), Hemispheres and ship; 50 c. (No. 1308), Mamenic Shipping Line flag; 60 c. "Costa Rica" (freighter); 1 cor. "Nicarao" (freighter); 2 cor. 50, Map, freighter and flag.

1958. Air. Brussels International Exn. Inscr "EXPOSICION MUNDIAL DE BELGICA 1958".
1312 **199** 25 c. black, yell & grn . . 10 10
1313 – 30 c. multicoloured . . . 15 15
1314 – 45 c. black, ochre & blue . 15 15
1315 **199** 1 cor. black, blue and dull purple 25 25
1316 – 2 cor. multicoloured . . . 25 25
1317 – 10 cor. sepia, purple and blue . . . . 1·40 1·00
DESIGNS: As Type **199**: 30 c., 20 cor. Arms of Nicaragua; 45 c., 10 cor. Nicaraguan Pavilion.

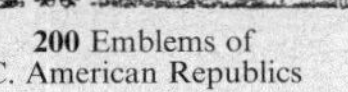

200 Emblems of C. American Republics — **201** Arms of La Salle

1958. 17th Central American Lions Convention. Inscr as in T **200**. Emblems (5 c., 60 c.) multicoloured; Lions badge (others) in blue, red, yellow (or orange and buff).

1318 **200** 5 c. blue (postage) 10 10
1319 – 10 c. blue and orange . . 10 10
1320 – 20 c. blue and green . . . 10 10
1321 – 50 c. blue and purple . . 15 15
1322 – 75 c. blue and mauve . . 30 25
1323 – 1 cor. 50, blue, salmon and drab 45 45
1324 – 30 c. blue & orge (air) . . 10 10
1325 **200** 60 c. blue and pink . . . 20 15
1326 – 90 c. blue 25 20
1327 – 1 cor. 25 blue and olive . . 35 30
1328 – 2 cor. blue and green . . 60 50
1329 – 3 cor. blue, red and violet 95 90

DESIGNS—HORIZ: 10 c., 1 cor. 25, Melvin Jones; 20, 30 c. Dr. T. A. Arias; 50, 90 c. Edward G. Barry; 75 c., 2 cor. Lions emblem; 1 cor. 50, 3 cor. Map of C. American Isthmus.

1958. Brothers of the Nicaraguan Christian Schools Commem. Inscr as in T **201**.

1330 **201** 5 c. red, blue & yellow (postage) 10 10
1331 – 10 c. sepia, blue & green . 10 10
1332 – 15 c. sepia, brown & bis . 10 10
1333 – 20 c. black, red & bistre . 10 10
1334 – 50 c. sepia, orange & bis . 15 15
1335 – 75 c. sepia, turquoise & grn 25 20
1336 – 1 cor. black, vio & bistre . 40 30
1337 **201** 30 c. blue, red & yellow (air) 10 10
1338 – 60 c. sepia, purple & grey . 25 20
1339 – 85 c. black, red & blue . . 30 25
1340 – 90 c. black, green & ochre . 35 35
1341 – 1 cor. 25 black, red and ochre 50 45
1342 – 1 cor. 50 sepia, green and grey 60 55
1343 – 1 cor. 75 blk, brn & bl . . 65 55
1344 – 2 cor. sepia, grn & grey . 65 65

DESIGNS—HORIZ: 10, 60 c. Managua Teachers Institute. VERT: 15, 85 c. De La Salle (founder); 20, 90 c. Brother Carlos; 50 c., 1 cor. 50, Brother Antonio; 75 c., 1 cor. 25, Brother Julio; 1 cor., 1 cor. 75, Brother Argeo; 2 cor. Brother Eugenio.

202 U.N. Emblem — **203** — **204**

1958. Inauguration of U.N.E.S.C.O. Headquarters Building, Paris. Inscr as in T **202**.

1345 **202** 10 c. blue & mve (postage) . 10 10
1346 – 15 c. mauve and blue . . 10 10
1347 – 25 c. brown and green . . 10 10
1348 – 40 c. black and red . . . 15 15
1349 – 45 c. mauve and blue . . 20 20
1350 **202** 50 c. green and brown . . 25 25
1351 – 60 c. blue & mauve (air) . 25 15
1352 – 75 c. brown and green . . 25 20
1353 – 90 c. green and brown . . 30 25
1354 – 1 cor. mauve and blue . . 40 30
1355 – 3 cor. red and black . . . 60 60
1356 – 5 cor. blue and mauve . . 1·00 85

DESIGNS—VERT: 15 c. Aerial view of H.Q; 25, 45 c. Facade composed of letters "UNESCO"; 40 c. H.Q. and Eiffel Tower; In oval vignettes–60 c., As 15 c; 75 c., 5 cor., As 25 c.; 90 c., 3 cor. As 40 c.; 1 cor., As Type **202**.

1959. Obligatory Tax. Consular Fiscal stamps surch Serial Nos. in red.

1357 **203** 5 c. on 50 c. blue 10 10
1358 **204** 5 c. on 50 c. blue 10 10

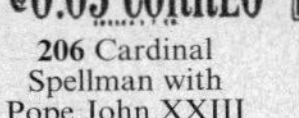

205 — **206** Cardinal Spellman with Pope John XXIII — **207** Abraham Lincoln

1959. Obligatory Tax.

1359 **205** 5 c. blue 15 10

1959. Cardinal Spellman Commemoration.

1360 **206** 5 c. flesh & grn (postage) 10 10
1361 A 10 c. multicoloured . . . 10 10
1362 B 15 c. red, black and grn . 10 10
1363 C 20 c. yellow and blue . . 10 10
1364 D 25 c. red and blue . . . 10 10
1365 E 30 c. bl, red & yellow (air) . 10 10
1366 **206** 35 c. bronze and orange . 10 10
1367 A 1 cor. multicoloured . . . 30 30
1368 B 1 cor. 5 red and black . . 35 30
1369 C 1 cor. 50 yellow & blue . . 45 35
1370 D 2 cor. blue, violet & red . 55 45
1371 E 5 cor. multicoloured . . . 75 55

DESIGNS—VERT: A, Cardinal's Arms; B, Cardinal; D, Cardinal wearing sash. HORIZ: C, Cardinal and Cross; E, Flags of Nicaragua, Vatican City and U.S.A.

1960. 150th Birth Anniv of Abraham Lincoln. Portrait in black.

1372 **207** 5 c. red (postage) 10 10
1373 10 c. green 10 10
1374 15 c. orange 10 10
1375 1 cor. purple 25 25
1376 2 cor. blue 30 45
1377 30 c. blue (air) 10 10
1378 35 c. red 15 10
1379 70 c. purple 20 20
1380 1 cor. 5 green 35 35
1381 1 cor. 50 violet 50 45
1382 – 5 cor. ochre and black . . 55 55

DESIGN—HORIZ: 5 cor. Scroll inscr "Dar al que necesite–A. Lincoln".

1960. Air. 10th Anniv of San Jose (Costa Rica) Philatelic Society. Optd **X Aniversario Club Filatelico** S. J.–C. R.

1383 2 cor. red (No. 1206) . . . 70 60
1384 2 cor. 50 blue (No. 1256) . . 75 75
1385 3 cor. green (No. 1166) . . . 1·40 90

1960. Red Cross Fund for Chilean Earthquake Relief Nos. 1372/82 optd **Resello** and Maltese Cross. Portrait in black.

1386 **207** 5 c. red (postage) 10 10
1387 10 c. green 10 10
1388 15 c. orange 10 10
1389 1 cor. purple 25 25
1390 2 cor. blue 30 25
1391 30 c. blue (air) 25 20
1392 35 c. red 20 20
1393 70 c. purple 25 25
1394 1 cor. 5 green 30 30
1395 1 cor. 50 violet 40 35
1396 – 5 cor. ochre and black . . 1·00 1·00

210

1961. Air. World Refugee Year. Inscr "ANO MUNDIAL DEL REFUGIADO".

1397 – 2 cor. multicoloured . . . 20 20
1398 **210** 5 cor. ochre, blue & grn . 60 60

DESIGN: 2 cor. Procession of refugees.

211 Pres. Roosevelt, Pres. Somoza and Officer

1961. Air. 20th Anniv of Nicaraguan Military Academy.

1399 **211** 20 c. multicoloured . . . 10 10
1400 – 25 c. red, blue and black . 10 10
1401 – 30 c. multicoloured . . . 10 10
1402 – 35 c. multicoloured . . . 10 10
1403 – 40 c. multicoloured . . . 10 10
1404 – 45 c. black, flesh and red . 15 15
1405 **211** 60 c. multicoloured . . . 15 15
1406 – 70 c. multicoloured . . . 20 20
1407 – 1 cor. 5 multicoloured . . 25 25
1408 – 1 cor. 50 multicoloured . . 35 35
1409 – 2 cor. multicoloured . . . 50 50
1410 – 5 cor. blk, flesh & grey . . 70 60

DESIGNS — VERT: 25, 70 c. Flags; 35 c., 1 cor. 50, Standard bearers; 40 c., 2 cor. Pennant and emblem. HORIZ: 30 c., 1 cor. 5 Group of officers; 45 c., 5 cor. Pres. Somoza and Director of Academy.

1961. Air. Consular Fiscal stamps as T **203/4** with serial Nos. in red, surch **Correo Aereo** and value.

1411 20 c. on 50 c. blue 15 10
1412 20 c. on 1 cor. olive 15 10
1413 20 c. on 2 cor. green 15 10
1414 20 c. on 3 cor. red 15 10
1415 20 c. on 5 cor. red 15 10
1416 20 c. on 10 cor. violet . . . 15 10
1417 20 c. on 20 cor. brown . . . 15 10
1418 20 c. on 50 cor. brown . . . 15 10
1419 20 c. on 100 cor. lake . . . 15 10

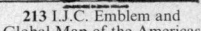

213 I.J.C. Emblem and Global Map of the Americas — **215** R. Cabezas

1961. Air. Junior Chamber of Commerce Congress.

1420 2 c. multicoloured 10 10
1421 3 c. black and yellow 10 10
1422 4 c. multicoloured 10 10
1423 5 c. black and red 10 10
1424 6 c. multicoloured 15 10
1425 10 c. multicoloured 10 10
1426 15 c. black, green and blue . . 10 10
1427 30 c. black and blue 15 10
1428 35 c. multicoloured 15 10
1429 70 c. black, red and yellow . 20 20
1430 1 cor. 5 multicoloured . . . 35 30
1431 5 cor. multicoloured 70 70

DESIGNS—HORIZ: 2 c., 15 c. Type **213**; 4 c., 35 c. "J.C.I." upon Globe. VERT: 3 c., 30 c. I.J.C. emblem; 5 c., 70 c. Scroll; 6 c., 1 cor. 5, Handclasp; 10 c., 5 cor. Regional map of Nicaragua.

1961. Air. 1st Central American Philatelic Convention, San Salvador. Optd **Convencion Filatelica - Centro - America - Panama - San Salvador - 27 Julio 1961**.

1432 **158** 1 cor. 25 multicoloured . . 25 25

1961. Air. Birth Centenary of Cabezas.

1433 **215** 20 c. blue and orange . . 10 10
1434 – 40 c. purple and blue . . 15 15
1435 – 45 c. sepia and green . . . 15 15
1436 – 70 c. green and brown . . 25 20
1437 – 2 cor. blue and pink . . . 60 40
1438 – 10 cor. purple and turquoise 1·50 1·50

DESIGNS—HORIZ: 40 c. Map and view of Cartago; 45 c. 1884 newspaper; 70 c. Assembly outside building; 2 cor. Scroll; 10 cor. Map and view of Masaya.

216 Official Gazettes — **219** "Cattleya skinneri"

1961. Centenary of Regulation of Postal Rates.

1439 **216** 5 c. brown & turquoise . . 10 10
1440 – 10 c. brown and green . . 10 10
1441 – 15 c. brown and red . . . 10 10

DESIGNS: 10 c. Envelopes and postmarks; 15 c. Martinez and Somoza.

1961. Air. Dag Hammarskjold Commem. Nos. 1351/6 optd **Homenaje a Hammarskjold Sept. 18-1961**.

1442 60 c. blue and mauve 30 30
1443 75 c. brown and green . . . 35 35
1444 90 c. green and brown . . . 45 45
1445 1 cor. mauve and blue . . . 50 50
1446 3 cor. red and black 80 80
1447 5 cor. blue and mauve . . . 1·50 1·50

1962. Air. Surch **RESELLO C$ 1.00**.

1448 – 1 cor. on 1 cor. 10 brown (No. 1157) 30 25
1449 **207** 1 cor. on 1 cor. 5 black and green 30 25

See also Nos. 1498/1500a, 1569/70, 1608/14, 1669/76 and 1748/62.

1962. Obligatory Tax. Nicaraguan Orchids. Multicoloured.

1450 5 c. Type **219** 10 10
1451 5 c. "Bletia roezlii" 10 10
1452 5 c. "Sobralia pleiantha" . . 10 10
1453 5 c. "Lycaste macrophylla" . . 10 10
1454 5 c. "Schomburgkia tibicinus" . 10 10
1455 5 c. "Maxillaria tenuifolia" . . 10 10
1456 5 c. "Stanhopea ecornuta" . . 10 10
1457 5 c. "Oncidium ascendens" and "O. cebolleta" 10 10
1458 5 c. "Cycnoches egertonianum" 10 10
1459 5 c. "Hexisia bidentata" . . . 10 10

220 U.N.E.S.C.O. "Audience" — **222** Arms of Nueva Segovia

1962. Air. 15th Anniv of U.N.E.S.C.O.

1460 **220** 2 cor. multicoloured . . . 15 15
1461 – 5 cor. multicoloured . . . 80 80

DESIGN: 5 cor. U.N. and U.N.E.S.C.O. emblems.

1962. Air. Malaria Eradication. Nos. 1425, 1428/31 optd with mosquito surrounded by **LUCHA CONTRA LA MALARIA**.

1462 – 10 c. 35 30
1463 – 35 c. 45 30
1464 – 70 c. 60 45
1465 – 1 cor. 5 . . . . 80 65
1466 – 5 cor. . . . . 1·00 1·25

1962. Urban and Provincial Arms. Arms mult; inscr black; background colours below.

1467 **222** 2 c. mauve (postage) . . . 10 10
1468 – 3 c. blue 10 10
1469 – 4 c. lilac 10 10
1470 – 5 c. yellow 10 10
1471 – 6 c. brown 10 10
1472 **222** 30 c. red (air) 10 10
1473 – 50 c. orange 15 10
1474 – 1 cor. green 25 20
1475 – 2 cor. grey 45 40
1476 – 5 cor. blue 75 60

ARMS: 3 c., 50 c. Leon; 4 c., 1 cor. Managua; 5 c., 2 cor. Granada; 6 c., 5 cor. Rivas.

223 Liberty Bell

1963. Air. 150th Anniv of Independence.

1477 **223** 30 c. drab, blue & black . 15 10

224 Blessing

1963. Air. Death Tercentenary of St. Vincent de Paul and St. Louise de Marillac.

1478 – 60 c. black and orange . . 15 10
1479 **224** 1 cor. olive and orange . . 25 20
1480 – 2 cor. black and red . . . 50 45

DESIGNS—VERT: 60 c. "Comfort" (St. Louise and woman). HORIZ: 2 cor. St. Vincent and St. Louise.

225 "Map Stamp" — **226** Cross on Globe

1963. Air. Central American Philatelic Societies Federation Commemoration.

1481 **225** 1 cor. blue and yellow . . 30 20

1963. Air. Ecumenical Council, Vatican City.

1482 **226** 20 c. red and yellow . . . 15 10

227 Ears of Wheat — **228** Boxing

1963. Air. Freedom from Hunger.
1483 **227** 10 c. green & light green . . 10 10
1484 – 25 c. sepia and yellow . . 15 10
DESIGN: 25 c. Barren tree and campaign emblem.

1963. Air. Sports. Multicoloured.
1485 2 c. Type **228** 10 10
1486 3 c. Running 10 10
1487 4 c. Underwater harpooning . 10 10
1488 5 c. Football 10 10
1489 6 c. Baseball 15 10
1490 10 c. Tennis 20 10
1491 15 c. Cycling 20 10
1492 20 c. Motor-cycling 20 10
1493 35 c. Chess 30 15
1494 60 c. Angling 45 20
1495 1 cor. Table-tennis 55 35
1496 2 cor. Basketball 75 55
1497 5 cor. Golf . . . . 1·90 1·10

1964. Air. Surch **Resello or RESELLO** (1500a) and value.
1498 – 5 c. on 6 c. (No. 1424) . 35 10
1499 – 10 c. on 30 c. (No. 1365) . 45 15
1500 **207** 15 c. on 30 c. 70 20
1500a **201** 20 c. on 30 c. 15 10
See also Nos. 1448/9, 1569/70, 1608/14 and 1669/76.

1964. Optd **CORREOS**.
1501 5 c. multicoloured (No. 1451) . 10 10

231 Flags

232 "Alliance Emblem"

1964. Air. "Centro America".
1502 **231** 40 c. multicoloured . . . 15 15

1964. Air. "Alliance for Progress". Multicoloured.
1503 5 c. Type **232** 10 10
1504 10 c. Red Cross Post 10 10
1505 15 c. Highway 10 10
1506 20 c. Ploughing 10 10
1507 25 c. Housing 15 10
1508 30 c. Presidents Somoza and Kennedy and Eugene Black (World Bank) 15 10
1509 35 c. School and adults . . . 20 15
1510 40 c. Chimneys 25 15
Nos. 1504/10 are horiz.

233 Map of Member Countries

235 Rescue of Wounded Soldier

1964. Air. Central-American "Common Market". Multicoloured.
1511 15 c. Type **233** 10 10
1512 25 c. Ears of wheat 10 10
1513 40 c. Cogwheels 10 10
1514 50 c. Heads of cattle 15 10

1964. Air. Olympic Games, Tokyo. Nos. 1485/7, 1489 and 1495/6 optd **OLIMPIADAS TOKYO-1964**.
1515 2 c. Type **108** 10 10
1516 3 c. Running 10 10
1517 4 c. Underwater harpooning . 10 10
1518 6 c. Baseball 10 10
1519 1 cor. Table-tennis . . . . . 1·10 1·10
1520 2 cor. Basketball . . . . . . 2·25 2·25

1965. Air. Red Cross Centenary. Multicoloured.
1521 20 c. Type **235** 10 10
1522 25 c. Blood transfusion . . . 15 10
1523 40 c. Red Cross and snowbound town 15 15
1524 10 cor. Red Cross and map of Nicaragua . . . . 1·50 1·50

236 Statuettes

1965. Air. Nicaraguan Antiquities. Multicoloured.
1525 5 c. Type **236** 10 10
1526 10 c. Totem 10 10
1527 15 c. Carved dog 10 10
1528 20 c. Composition of "objets d'art" 10 10
1529 25 c. Dish and vase 10 10
1530 30 c. Pestle and mortar . . . 10 10
1531 35 c. Statuettes (different) . . 10 10
1532 40 c. Deity 15 10
1533 50 c. Wine vessel and dish . . 15 10
1534 60 c. Bowl and dish 20 10
1535 1 cor. Urn 45 15
The 15, 25, 35 and 60 c. are horiz.

237 Pres. Kennedy

238 A. Bello

1965. Air. Pres. Kennedy Commemorative.
1536 **237** 35 c. black and green . . 15 10
1537 75 c. black and mauve . . 25 15
1538 1 cor. 10 black & blue . . 35 25
1539 2 cor. black & brown . . 90 55

1965. Air. Death Centenary of Andres Bello (poet and writer).
1540 **238** 10 c. black and brown . . 10 10
1541 15 c. black and blue . . . 10 10
1542 45 c. black and purple . . 15 10
1543 80 c. black and green . . 20 15
1544 1 cor. black and yellow . . 25 20
1545 2 cor. black and grey . . 45 45

1965. 9th Central-American Scout Camporee. Nos. 1450/9 optd with scout badge and **CAMPOREE SCOUT 1965**.
1546 5 c. multicoloured 20 20
1547 5 c. multicoloured 20 20
1548 5 c. multicoloured 20 20
1549 5 c. multicoloured 20 20
1550 5 c. multicoloured 20 20
1551 5 c. multicoloured 20 20
1552 5 c. multicoloured 20 20
1553 5 c. multicoloured 20 20
1554 5 c. multicoloured 20 20
1555 5 c. multicoloured 20 20

240 Sir Winston Churchill

241 Pope John XXIII

1966. Air. Churchill Commemorative.
1556 **240** 20 c. mauve and black . . 10 10
1557 – 35 c. green and black . . 15 10
1558 – 60 c. ochre and black . . 15 15
1559 – 75 c. red 20 20
1560 – 1 cor. purple 30 25
1561 **240** 2 cor. violet, lilac & blk . 60 55
1562 – 3 cor. blue and black . . 65 60
DESIGNS—HORIZ: 35 c., 1 cor. Churchill broadcasting. VERT: 60 c., 3 cor. Churchill crossing the Rhine; 75 c. Churchill in Hussars' uniform.

1966. Air. Closure of Vatican Ecumenical Council. Multicoloured.
1564 20 c. Type **241** 10 10
1565 35 c. Pope Paul VI 15 15
1566 1 cor. Archbishop Gonzalez y Robleto 30 25
1567 2 cor. St. Peter's, Rome . . . 30 25
1568 3 cor. Papal arms 60 40

1967. Air. Nos. 1533/4 surch **RESELLO** and value.
1569 10 c. on 50 c. multicoloured . . 10 10
1570 15 c. on 60 c. multicoloured . . 10 10
See also Nos. 1448/9, 1498/1500a, 1608/14 and 1669/76.

243 Dario and Birthplace

1967. Air. Birth Centenary of Ruben Dario (poet). Designs showing Dario and view. Mult.
1571 5 c. Type **243** 10 10
1572 10 c. Monument, Managua . . 10 10
1573 20 c. Leon Cathedral (site of Dario's tomb) 10 10
1574 40 c. Allegory of the centaurs . 15 10
1575 75 c. Allegory of the swans . . 2·00 75
1576 1 cor. Roman triumphal march 25 20
1577 2 cor. St. Francis and the wolf . 45 40
1578 5 cor. "Faith" opposing "Death" 65 60

244 "Megalura peleus"

1967. Air. Butterflies. Multicoloured.
1580 5 c. "Heliconius petiveranua" . 10 10
1581 10 c. "Colaenis julia" 10 10
1582 15 c. Type **244** 10 10
1583 20 c. "Aneyluris jurgensii" . . 10 10
1584 25 c. "Thecla regalis" 10 10
1585 30 c. "Doriana thia" 10 10
1586 35 c. "Lymnias pixae" 15 10
1587 40 c. "Metamorpho dido" . . 25 10
1588 50 c. "Papilio arcas" 25 15
1589 60 c. "Ananea cleomestra" . . 35 15
1590 1 cor. "Victorina epaphaus" . 60 30
1591 2 cor. "Prepona demophon" . 1·10 50
The 5, 10, 30, 35, 50 c. and 1 cor. are vert.

245 McDivitt and White

1967. Air. Space Flight of McDivitt and White. Multicoloured.
1592 5 c. Type **245** 10 10
1593 10 c. Astronauts and "Gemini 5" on launching pad . . . 10 10
1594 15 c. "Gemini 5" and White in Space 10 10
1595 20 c. Recovery operation at sea 15 10
1596 35 c. Type **245** 10 10
1597 40 c. As 10 c. 15 10
1598 75 c. As 15 c. 20 20
1599 1 cor. As 20 c. 35 25

246 National Flower of Costa Rica

1967. Air. 5th Year of Central American Economic Integration. Designs showing National Flowers of the Central-American Countries. Multicoloured.
1600 40 c. Type **246** 15 10
1601 40 c. Guatemala 15 10
1602 40 c. Honduras 15 10
1603 40 c. Nicaragua 15 10
1604 40 c. El Salvador 15 10

247 Presidents Diaz and Somoza

249 Mangoes

1968. Air. Visit of Pres. Diaz of Mexico.
1605 – 20 c. black 10 10
1606 **247** 40 c. olive 20 10
1607 – 1 cor. brown 35 20
DESIGNS—VERT: 20 c. Pres. Somoza greeting Pres. Diaz; 1 cor. Pres. Diaz of Mexico.

1968. Surch **RESELLO** and value.
1608 – 5 c. on 6 c. (No. 1180) (postage) 10 10
1609 – 5 c. on 6 c. (No. 1471) . . 10 10
1610 – 5 c. on 6 c. (No. 1424) (air) 10 10
1611 – 5 c. on 6 c. (No. 1489) . . 10 10
1612 **156** 5 c. on 8 c. (No. 1035) . . 10 10
1614 – 1 cor. on 1 cor. 50 (No. 1369) 25 20
See also Nos. 1448/9, 1498/1500a, 1569/70 and 1669/76.

1968. Air. Nicaraguan Fruits. Multicoloured.
1615 5 c. Type **249** 10 10
1616 10 c. Pineapples 10 10
1617 15 c. Oranges 10 10
1618 20 c. Pawpaws 10 10
1619 30 c. Bananas 10 10
1620 35 c. Avocado pears 15 10
1621 50 c. Water-melons 15 10
1622 75 c. Cashews 25 15
1623 1 cor. Sapodilla plums 35 20
1624 2 cor. Cocoa beans 45 20

250 "The Crucifixion" (Fra Angelico)

1968. Air. Religious Paintings. Multicoloured.
1625 10 c. Type **250** 10 10
1626 15 c. "The Last Judgement" (Michelangelo) 10 10
1627 35 c. "The Beautiful Gardener" (Raphael) 15 15
1628 2 cor. "The Spoliation of Christ" (El Greco) 45 30
1629 3 cor. "The Conception" (Murillo) 60 45
Nos. 1626/9 are vert.

1968. Air. Pope Paul's Visit to Bogota. Nos. 1625/8 optd **Visita de S. S. Paulo VI C. E. de Bogota 1968**.
1631 **250** 10 c. multicoloured . . . 10 10
1632 – 15 c. multicoloured . . . 10 10
1633 – 35 c. multicoloured . . . 10 10
1634 – 2 cor. multicoloured . . . 30 20

252 Basketball

1969. Air. Olympic Games, Mexico. Mult.
1635 10 c. Type **252** 10 10
1636 15 c. Fencing 10 10
1637 20 c. High-diving 10 10
1638 35 c. Running 10 10
1639 50 c. Hurdling 15 10
1640 75 c. Weightlifting 20 15
1641 1 cor. Boxing 35 20
1642 2 cor. Football 55 55
The 15, 50 c. and 1 cor. are horiz.

253 Midas Cichlid

1969. Air. Fishes. Multicoloured.
1644 10 c. Type **253** 10 10
1645 15 c. Moga cichlid 10 10
1646 20 c. Common carp 20 10
1647 30 c. Tropical gar 25 10
1648 35 c. Swordfish 30 10
1649 50 c. Big-mouthed sleeper . . 35 15
1650 75 c. Atlantic tarpon 40 20
1651 1 cor. Lake Nicaragua shark . 60 25
1652 2 cor. Sailfish 75 45
1653 3 cor. Small-toothed sawfish . 1·40 70

1969. Air. Various stamps surch **RESELLO** and value.
1655 10 c. on 25 c. (No. 1507) . . . 10 10
1656 10 c. on 25 c. (No. 1512) . . . 10 10
1657 15 c. on 25 c. (No. 1529) . . . 10 10
1658 50 c. on 70 c. (No. 1379) . . . 15 10

255 Scenery, Tower and Emblem

258 "Minerals"

1969. Air. "Hemisfair" (1968) Exhibition.
1659 **255** 30 c. blue and red . . . 10 10
1660 35 c. purple and red . . . 10 10
1661 75 c. red and blue 15 10
1662 1 cor. purple and black . . 30 20
1663 2 cor. purple and green . . 55 40

1969. Various stamps surch. (a) Optd **CORREO**.
1665 5 c. (No. 1450) 10 10
1666 5 c. (No. 1453) 10 10
1667 5 c. (No. 1454) 10 10
1668 5 c. (No. 1459) 10 10

(b) Optd **RESELLO** and surch.

1670	10 c. on 30 c. (No. 1324)	10	10
1671	10 c. on 30 c. (No. 1427)	10	10
1669	10 c. on 25 c. (No. 1529)	10	10
1672	10 c. on 30 c. (No. 1530)	10	10
1673	15 c. on 35 c. (No. 1531)	10	10
1674	20 c. on 30 c. (No. 1307)	10	10
1675	20 c. on 30 c. (No. 1401)	10	10
1676	20 c. on 35 c. (No. 1509)	10	10

1969. Air. Nicaraguan Products. Multicoloured.

1677	5 c. Type **258**	10	10
1678	10 c. "Fish"	10	10
1679	15 c. "Bananas"	10	10
1680	20 c. "Timber"	10	10
1681	35 c. "Coffee"	10	10
1682	40 c. "Sugar-cane"	15	10
1683	60 c. "Cotton"	20	10
1684	75 c. "Rice and Maize"	20	15
1685	1 cor. "Tobacco"	30	20
1686	2 cor. "Meat"	35	25

1969. 50th Anniv of I.L.O. Obligatory tax stamps. Nos. 1450/9, optd, **O.I.T. 1919-1969**.

1687	5 c. multicoloured	10	10
1688	5 c. multicoloured	10	10
1689	5 c. multicoloured	10	10
1690	5 c. multicoloured	10	10
1691	5 c. multicoloured	10	10
1692	5 c. multicoloured	10	10
1693	5 c. multicoloured	10	10
1694	5 c. multicoloured	10	10
1695	5 c. multicoloured	10	10
1696	5 c. multicoloured	10	10

260 Girl carrying Tinaja

261 Pele (Brazil)

1970. Air. 8th Inter-American Savings and Loans Conference, Managua.

1697	**260** 10 c. multicoloured	10	10
1698	15 c. multicoloured	10	10
1699	20 c. multicoloured	10	10
1700	35 c. multicoloured	10	10
1701	50 c. multicoloured	15	10
1702	75 c. multicoloured	20	15
1703	1 cor. multicoloured	30	20
1704	2 cor. multicoloured	60	40

1970. World Football "Hall of Fame" Poll-winners. Multicoloured.

1705	5 c. Type **261** (postage)	10	10
1706	10 c. Puskas (Hungary)	10	10
1707	15 c. Matthews (England)	10	10
1708	40 c. Di Stefano (Argentina)	10	10
1709	2 cor. Facchetti (Italy)	55	45
1710	3 cor. Yashin (Russia)	70	65
1711	5 cor. Beckenbauer (West Germany)	70	90
1712	20 c. Santos (Brazil) (air)	10	10
1713	80 c. Wright (England)	20	15
1714	1 cor. Flags of 16 World Cup Finalists	25	20
1715	4 cor. Bozsik (Hungary)	90	75
1716	5 cor. Charlton (England)	1·10	90

262 Torii (Gate)

263 Module and Astronauts on Moon

1970. Air. EXPO 70, World Fair, Osaka, Japan.

1717	**262** 25 c. multicoloured	10	10
1718	30 c. multicoloured	10	10
1719	35 c. multicoloured	10	10
1720	75 c. multicoloured	25	15
1721	1 cor. 50 multicoloured	35	30
1722	3 cor. multicoloured	45	35

1970. Air. "Apollo 11" Moon Landing. Mult.

1724	35 c. Type **263**	10	10
1725	40 c. Module landing on Moon	10	10
1726	60 c. Astronauts with U.S. Flag	20	15
1727	75 c. As 40 c.	25	15
1728	1 cor. As 60 c.	35	20
1729	2 cor. Type **263**	40	35

264 F. D. Roosevelt

265 "The Annunciation" (Grunewald)

1970. Air. 25th Death Anniv of Franklin D. Roosevelt.

1730	**264** 10 c. black	10	10
1731	– 15 c. brown and black	10	10
1732	– 20 c. green and black	10	10
1733	**264** 35 c. purple and black	10	10
1734	– 50 c. brown	15	10
1735	**264** 75 c. blue	20	15
1736	– 1 cor. red	25	20
1737	– 2 cor. black	30	35

PORTRAITS: 15 c., 1 cor. Roosevelt with stamp collection; 20 c., 50 c., 2 cor. Roosevelt (full-face).

1970. Air. Christmas. Paintings. Multicoloured.

1738	10 c. Type **265**	10	10
1739	10 c. "The Nativity" (detail, El Greco)	10	10
1740	10 c. "The Adoration of the Magi" (detail, Durer)	10	10
1741	10 c. "Virgin and Child" (J. van Hemessen)	10	10
1742	10 c. "The Holy Shepherd" (Portuguese School, 16th cent.)	10	10
1743	15 c. Type **265**	10	10
1744	20 c. As No. 1739	10	10
1745	35 c. As No. 1740	15	10
1746	75 c. As No. 1741	20	15
1747	1 cor. As No. 1742	30	20

1971. Surch **RESELLO** and new value.

1748	30 c. on 90 c. black (No. 1227) (postage)	10·00	10·00
1749	10 c. on 1 cor. 5 red, black & red (No. 1368) (air)	10	10
1750	10 c. on 1 cor. 5 mult (No. 1407)	10	10
1751	10 c. on 1 cor. 5 mult (No. 1430)	10	10
1752	15 c. on 1 cor. 50 green and red (No. 1116)	10	10
1753	15 c. on 1 cor. 50 green (No. 1255)	10	10
1754	15 c. on 1 cor. 50 yellow and blue (No. 1369)	10	10
1755	15 c. on 1 cor. 50 black and violet (No. 1381)	10	10
1756	20 c. on 85 c. black and red (No. 1276)	15	10
1757	20 c. on 85 c. black, red and blue (No. 1339)	15	10
1758	25 c. on 90 c. black, green and ochre (No. 1440)	15	15
1759	30 c. on 1 cor. 10 black and purple (No. 1195)	15	15
1760	40 c. on 1 cor. 10 brown and black (No. 1157)	65	65
1761	40 c. on 1 cor. 50 mult (No. 1408)	65	65
1762	1 cor. on 1 cor. 10 black and blue (No. 1538)	1·60	1·60

266 Basic Mathematical Equation

1971. Scientific Formulae. "The Ten Mathematical Equations that changed the Face of the Earth". Multicoloured.

1763	10 c. Type **266** (postage)	10	10
1764	15 c. Newton's Law	10	10
1765	20 c. Einstein's Law	10	10
1766	1 cor. Tsiolkovsky's Law	25	25
1767	2 cor. Maxwell's Law	90	75
1768	25 c. Napier's Law (air)	10	10
1769	30 c. Pythagoras' Law	10	10
1770	40 c. Boltzmann's Law	15	10
1771	1 cor. Broglie's Law	30	20
1772	2 cor. Archimedes' Law	55	40

267 Peace Emblem

1971. "Is There a Formula for Peace?".

1773	**267** 10 c. blue and black	10	10
1774	15 c. blue, black & vio	10	10
1775	20 c. blue, black & brn	10	10
1776	40 c. blue, black & grn	10	10
1777	50 c. blue, black & pur	15	10
1778	80 c. blue, black & red	15	15
1779	1 cor. blue, black & grn	30	20
1780	2 cor. blue, black & vio	55	35

268 Montezuma Oropendola

269 "Moses with the Tablets of the Law" (Rembrandt)

1971. Air. Nicaraguan Birds. Multicoloured.

1781	10 c. Type **268**	50	15
1782	15 c. Turquoise-browed motmot	50	15
1783	20 c. White-throated magpie-jay	60	15
1784	25 c. Scissor-tailed flycatcher	60	15
1785	30 c. Spotted-breasted oriole (horiz)	80	15
1786	35 c. Rufous-naped wren	95	15
1787	40 c. Great kiskadee	95	15
1788	75 c. Red-legged honeycreeper (horiz)	1·75	35
1789	1 cor. Great-tailed grackle (horiz)	2·10	45
1790	2 cor. Belted kingfisher	6·00	90

1971. "The Ten Commandments". Paintings. Multicoloured.

1791	10 c. Type **269** (postage)	10	10
1792	15 c. "Moses and the Burning Bush" (Botticelli) (1st Commandment)	10	10
1793	20 c. "Jepthah's Daughter" (Degas) (2nd Commandment) (horiz)	10	10
1794	30 c. "St. Vincent Ferrer preaching in Verona" (Morone) (3rd Commandment) (horiz)	10	10
1795	35 c. "Noah's Drunkenness" (Michelangelo) (4th Commandment) (horiz)	10	10
1796	40 c. "Cain and Abel" (Trevisani) (5th Commandment) (horiz)	10	10
1797	50 c. "Joseph accused by Potiphar's Wife" (Rembrandt) (6th Commandment)	10	10
1798	60 c. "Isaac blessing Jacob" (Eeckhout) (7th Commandment) (horiz)	15	10
1799	75 c. "Susannah and the Elders" (Rubens) (8th Commandment) (horiz)	25	20
1800	1 cor. "Bathsheba after her Bath" (Rembrandt) (9th Commandment) (air)	25	20
1801	2 cor. "Naboth's Vineyard" (Smetham) (10th Commandment)	40	35

270 U Thant and Pres. Somoza

1971. Air. 25th Anniv of U.N.O.

1802	**270** 10 c. brown and red	10	10
1803	15 c. green and emerald	10	10
1804	20 c. blue & light blue	10	10
1805	25 c. red and purple	10	10
1806	30 c. brown & orange	10	10
1807	40 c. green and grey	15	10
1808	1 cor. green & sage	25	20
1809	2 cor. brown & light brown	30	35

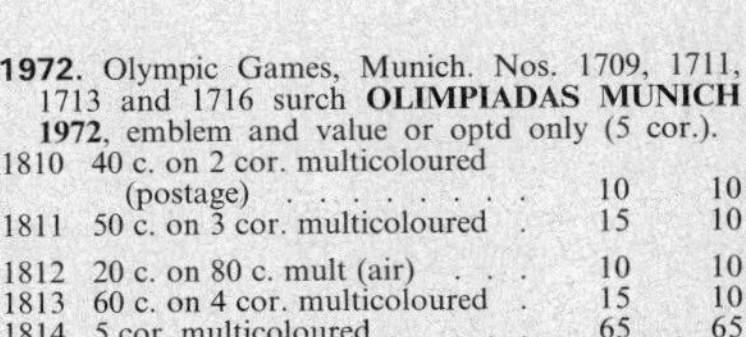

1972. Olympic Games, Munich. Nos. 1709, 1711, 1713 and 1716 surch **OLIMPIADAS MUNICH 1972**, emblem and value or optd only (5 cor.).

1810	40 c. on 2 cor. multicoloured (postage)	10	10
1811	50 c. on 3 cor. multicoloured	15	10
1812	20 c. on 80 c. mult (air)	10	10
1813	60 c. on 4 cor. multicoloured	15	10
1814	5 cor. multicoloured	65	65

272 Figurine and Apoyo Site on Map

1972. Air. Pre-Columbian Art. A. H. Heller's Pottery Discoveries. Multicoloured.

1815	10 c. Type **272**	10	10
1816	15 c. Cana Castilla	10	10
1817	20 c. Catarina	10	10
1818	25 c. Santa Helena	10	10
1819	30 c. Mombacho	10	10
1820	35 c. Tisma	10	10
1821	40 c. El Menco	10	10
1822	50 c. Los Placeres	15	10
1823	60 c. Masaya	15	15
1824	80 c. Granada	20	15
1825	1 cor. Las Mercedes	30	20
1826	2 cor. Nindiri	55	35

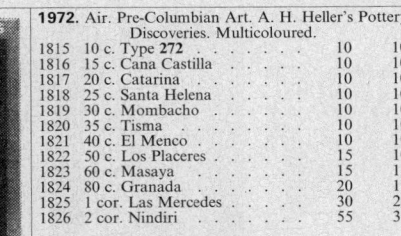

273 "Lord Peter Wimsey" (Dorothy Sayers)

1972. Air. 50th Anniv of International Criminal Police Organization (INTERPOL). Famous Fictional Detectives. Multicoloured.

1827	5 c. Type **273**	10	10
1828	10 c. "Philip Marlowe" (Raymond Chandler)	10	10
1829	15 c. "Sam Spade" (D. Hammett)	6·00	30
1830	20 c. "Perry Mason" (Erle Stanley Gardner)	10	10
1831	25 c. "Nero Wolfe" (Rex Stout)	10	10
1832	35 c. "C. Auguste Dupin" (Edgar Allan Poe)	10	10
1833	40 c. "Ellery Queen" (F. Dannay and M. Lee)	10	10
1834	50 c. "Father Brown" (G. K. Chesterton)	10	10
1835	60 c. "Charlie Chan" (Earl D. Biggers)	15	10
1836	80 c. "Inspector Maigret" (Georges Simenon)	25	15
1837	1 cor. "Hercule Poirot" (Agatha Christie)	25	20
1838	2 cor. "Sherlock Holmes" (A. Conan Doyle)	70	70

274 "The Shepherdess and her Brothers"

1972. Air. Christmas. Scenes from Legend of the Christmas Rose. Multicoloured.

1839	10 c. Type **274**	10	10
1840	15 c. Adoration of the Wise Men	10	10
1841	20 c. Shepherdess crying	10	10
1842	35 c. Angel appears to Shepherdess	10	10
1843	40 c. Christmas Rose	10	10
1844	60 c. Shepherdess thanks angel for roses	15	10
1845	80 c. Shepherdess takes roses to Holy Child	15	15
1846	1 cor. Holy Child receiving roses	20	15
1847	2 cor. Nativity Scene	45	35

275 Sir Walter Raleigh and Elizabethan Galleon

1973. Air. Causes of the American Revolution. Multicoloured.

1849	10 c. Type **275**	40	10
1850	15 c. Signing "Mayflower Compact"	10	10
1851	20 c. Acquittal of Peter Zenger (vert)	10	10
1852	25 c. Acclaiming American resistance (vert)	10	10
1853	30 c. Revenue Stamp (vert)	10	10
1854	35 c. "Serpent" slogan–"Join or die"	10	10
1855	40 c. Boston Massacre (vert)	10	10
1856	50 c. Boston Tea-party	10	10
1857	60 c. Patrick Henry on trial (vert)	15	10
1858	75 c. Battle of Bunker Hill	20	10
1859	80 c. Declaration of Independence	20	15
1860	1 cor. Liberty Bell	30	20
1861	2 cor. US seal (vert)	90	60

1973. Nos. 1450/54, 1456 and 1458/9 optd **CORREO**.

1862	**219** 5 c. multicoloured	25	10
1863	– 5 c. multicoloured	25	10
1864	– 5 c. multicoloured	25	10
1865	– 5 c. multicoloured	25	10
1866	– 5 c. multicoloured	25	10
1867	– 5 c. multicoloured	25	10
1868	– 5 c. multicoloured	25	10
1869	– 5 c. multicoloured	25	10

277 Baseball, Player and Map 278 Givenchy, Paris

1973. Air. 20th International Baseball Championships, Managua (1972).

No.	Type	Description	Unused	Used
1870	277	15 c. multicoloured	10	10
1871		20 c. multicoloured	10	10
1872		40 c. multicoloured	10	10
1873		10 cor. multicoloured	1·50	90

1973. World-famous Couturiers. Mannequins. Multicoloured.

No.	Description	Unused	Used
1875	1 cor. Type **278** (postage)	25	20
1876	2 cor. Hartnell, London	40	40
1877	5 cor. Balmain, Paris	1·00	90
1878	10 c. Lourdes, Nicaragua (air)	10	10
1879	15 c. Halston, New York	10	10
1880	20 c. Pino Lancetti, Rome	10	10
1881	35 c. Madame Gres, Paris	10	10
1882	40 c. Irene Galitzine, Rome	10	10
1883	80 c. Pedro Rodriguez, Barcelona	15	15

279 Diet Chart

1973. Air. Child Welfare. Multicoloured.

No.	Description	Unused	Used
1885	5 c. + 5 c. Type **279**	10	10
1886	10 c. + 5 c. Senora Samoza with baby, and Children's Hospital	10	10
1887	15 c. + 5 c. "Childbirth"	10	10
1888	20 c. + 5 c. "Immunisation"	10	10
1889	30 c. + 5 c. Water purification	10	10
1890	35 c. + 5 c. As No. 1886	10	10
1891	50 c. + 10 c. Alexander Fleming and "Antibiotics"	30	10
1892	60 c. + 15 c. Malaria control	15	10
1893	70 c. + 10 c. Laboratory analysis	15	15
1894	80 c. + 20 c. Gastro-enteritis	20	15
1895	1 cor. + 50 c. As No. 1886	30	25
1896	2 cor. Pediatric surgery	45	35

280 Virginia and Father

1973. Christmas. "Does Santa Claus exist?" (Virginia O'Hanlon's letter to American "Sun" newspaper). Multicoloured.

No.	Description	Unused	Used
1897	2 c. Type **280** (postage)	10	10
1898	3 c. Text of letter	10	10
1899	4 c. Reading the reply	10	10
1900	5 c. Type **280**	10	10
1901	15 c. As 3 c.	10	10
1902	20 c. As 4 c.	10	10
1903	1 cor. Type **280** (air)	20	15
1904	2 cor. As 3 c.	35	30
1905	4 cor. As 4 c.	75	65

281 Churchill making Speech, 1936

1974. Birth Cent of Sir Winston Churchill.

No.	Type	Description	Unused	Used
1907	281	2 c. multicoloured (postage)	10	10
1908	–	3 c. black, blue & brown	10	10
1909	–	4 c. multicoloured	10	10
1910	–	5 c. multicoloured	10	10
1911	–	10 c. brown, green & bl	30	10
1912	–	5 cor. multicoloured (air)	90	80
1913	–	6 cor. black, brown & bl	1·00	90

DESIGNS: 3 c. "The Four Churchills" (wartime cartoon); 4 c. Candle, cigar and "Action" stickers; 5 c. Churchill, Roosevelt and Stalin at Yalta; 10 c. Churchill landing in Normandy, 1944; 5 cor. Churchill giving "V" sign; 6 cor. "Bulldog Churchill" (cartoon).

282 Presentation of World Cup to Uruguay, 1930

1974. World Cup Football Championships. Mult.

No.	Description	Unused	Used
1915	1 c. Type **282** (postage)	10	10
1916	2 c. Victorious Italian team, 1934	10	10
1917	3 c. Presentation of World Cup to Italy, 1938	10	10
1918	4 c. Uruguay's winning goal, 1950	10	10
1919	5 c. Victorious West Germany, 1954	10	10
1920	10 c. Rejoicing Brazilian players, 1958	10	10
1921	15 c. Brazilian player holding World Cup, 1962	10	10
1922	20 c. Queen Elizabeth II presenting Cup to Bobby Moore, 1966	10	10
1923	25 c. Victorious Brazilian players, 1970	10	10
1924	10 cor. Football and flags of participating countries, 1974 (air)	1·75	1·75

283 "Malachra sp." 284 Nicaraguan 7½ c. Stamp of 1937

1974. Wild Flowers and Cacti. Multicoloured.

No.	Description	Unused	Used
1926	2 c. Type **283** (postage)	10	10
1927	3 c. "Paguira insignis"	10	10
1928	4 c. "Convolvulus sp."	10	10
1929	5 c. "Pereschia autumnalis"	10	10
1930	10 c. "Ipomea tuberosa"	10	10
1931	15 c. "Hibiscus elatus"	10	10
1932	20 c. "Plumeria acutifolia"	10	10
1933	1 cor. "Centrosema sp." (air)	20	20
1934	3 cor. "Hylocereus undatus"	60	55

1974. Centenary of U.P.U.

No.	Type	Description	Unused	Used
1935	284	2 c. red, grn & blk (postage)	10	20
1936	–	3 c. blue, green & blk	10	10
1937	–	4 c. multicoloured	10	10
1938	–	5 c. brown, mve & blk	10	10
1939	–	10 c. red, brown & blk	10	10
1940	–	20 c. green, blue & blk	10	10
1941	–	40 c. multicoloured (air)	10	10
1942	–	3 cor. green, blk & pink	50	40
1943	–	5 cor. blue, black & lilac	1·00	80

DESIGNS—VERT: 3 c. 5 c. stamp of 1937; 5 c. 2 c. stamp of 1937; 10 c. 1 c. stamp of 1937; 20 c. ½ c. stamp of 1937; 40 c. 10 c. stamp of 1961; 5 cor. 4 cor. U.P.U. stamp of 1950. HORIZ: 4 c. 10 c. air stamp of 1934; 3 cor. 85 c. U.P.U. air stamp of 1950.

1974. Air. West Germany's Victory in World Cup Football Championships. No. 1924 optd TRIUMFADOR ALEMANIA OCCIDENTAL.

No.	Description	Unused	Used
1945	10 cor. multicoloured	1·75	1·60

286 Tamandua

1974. Nicaraguan Fauna. Multicoloured.

No.	Description	Unused	Used
1947	1 c. Type **286** (postage)	10	10
1948	2 c. Puma	10	10
1949	3 c. Common raccoon	10	10
1950	4 c. Ocelot	10	10
1951	5 c. Kinkajou	10	10
1952	10 c. Coypu	10	10
1953	15 c. Collared peccary	15	10
1954	20 c. Baird's tapir	15	10
1955	3 cor. Red brocket (air)	1·50	1·40
1956	5 cor. Jaguar	2·40	2·00

287 "Prophet Zacharias" 288 Giovanni Martinelli ("Othello")

1975. Christmas. 500th Birth Anniv of Michelangelo. Multicoloured.

No.	Description	Unused	Used
1957	1 c. Type **287** (postage)	10	10
1958	2 c. "Christ amongst the Jews"	10	10
1959	3 c. "The Creation of Man" (horiz)	10	10
1960	4 c. Interior of Sistine Chapel, Rome	10	10
1961	5 c. "Moses"	10	10
1962	10 c. "Mouscron Madonna"	10	10
1963	15 c. "David"	10	10
1964	20 c. "Doni Madonna"	10	10
1965	40 c. "Madonna of the Steps" (air)	10	10
1966	80 c. "Pitti Madonna"	15	15
1967	2 cor. "Christ and Virgin Mary"	35	30
1968	5 cor. "Michelangelo" (self-portrait)	75	75

1975. Great Opera Singers. Multicoloured.

No.	Description	Unused	Used
1970	1 c. Type **288** (postage)	10	10
1971	2 c. Tito Gobbi ("Simone Boccaoegra")	10	10
1972	3 c. Lotte Lehmann ("Der Rosenkavalier")	10	10
1973	4 c. Lauritz Melchior ("Parsifal")	10	10
1974	5 c. Nellie Melba ("La Traviata")	10	10
1975	15 c. Jussi Bjoerling ("La Boheme")	10	10
1976	20 c. Birgit Nilsson ("Turandot")	10	10
1977	25 c. Rosa Ponselle ("Norma") (air)	10	10
1978	35 c. Guiseppe de Luca ("Rigoletto")	10	10
1979	40 c. Joan Sutherland ("La Figlia del Reggimiento")	10	10
1980	50 c. Enzio Pinza ("Don Giovanni")	10	10
1981	60 c. Kirsten Flagstad ("Tristan and Isolde")	15	10
1982	80 c. Maria Callas ("Tosca")	15	15
1983	2 cor. Fyodor Chaliapin ("Boris Godunov")	60	35
1984	5 cor. Enrico Caruso ("La Juive")	1·10	60

289 The First Station 290 "The Spirit of 76"

1975. Easter. The 14 Stations of the Cross.

No.	Type	Description	Unused	Used
1986	289	1 c. multicoloured (postage)	10	10
1987	–	2 c. multicoloured	10	10
1988	–	3 c. multicoloured	10	10
1989	–	4 c. multicoloured	10	10
1990	–	5 c. multicoloured	10	10
1991	–	15 c. multicoloured	10	10
1992	–	20 c. multicoloured	10	10
1993	–	25 c. multicoloured	10	10
1994	–	35 c. multicoloured	10	10
1995	–	40 c. multicoloured (air)	10	10
1996	–	50 c. multicoloured	10	10
1997	–	80 c. multicoloured	15	15
1998	–	1 cor. multicoloured	20	15
1999	–	5 cor. multicoloured	80	65

DESIGNS: 2 c. to 5 cor. Different Stations of the Cross.

1975. Bicentenary of American Independence (1st series). Multicoloured.

No.	Description	Unused	Used
2000	1 c. Type **290** (postage)	10	10
2001	2 c. Pitt addressing Parliament	10	10
2002	3 c. Paul Revere's Ride (horiz)	10	10
2003	4 c. Demolishing statue of George III (horiz)	10	10
2004	5 c. Boston Massacre	10	10
2005	10 c. Tax stamp and George III 3d. coin (horiz)	10	10
2006	15 c. Boston Tea Party (horiz)	10	10
2007	20 c. Thomas Jefferson	10	10
2008	25 c. Benjamin Franklin	10	10
2009	30 c. Signing of Declaration of Independence (horiz)	10	10
2010	35 c. Surrender of Cornwallis at Yorktown (horiz)	10	10
2011	40 c. Washington's Farewell (horiz) (air)	10	10
2012	50 c. Washington addressing Congress (horiz)	10	10
2013	2 cor. Washington arriving for Presidential Inauguration (horiz)	70	30
2014	5 cor. Statue of Liberty & flags	75	45

See also Nos. 2056/71.

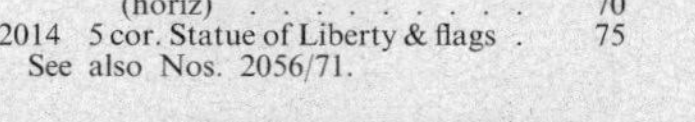

291 Saluting the Flag

1975. "Nordjamb 75" World Scout Jamboree, Norway. Multicoloured.

No.	Description	Unused	Used
2016	1 c. Type **291** (postage)	10	10
2017	2 c. Scout canoe	10	10
2018	3 c. Scouts shaking hands	10	10
2019	4 c. Scout preparing meal	10	10
2020	5 c. Entrance to Nicaraguan camp	10	10
2021	20 c. Scouts meeting	10	10
2022	35 c. Aerial view of camp (air)	10	10
2023	40 c. Scouts making music	10	10
2024	1 cor. Camp-fire	20	15
2025	10 cor. Lord Baden-Powell	1·25	1·10

292 President Somoza 293 "Chess Players" (L. Carracci)

1975. President Somoza's New Term of Office, 1974–1981.

No.	Type	Description	Unused	Used
2027	292	20 c. multicoloured (postage)	10	10
2028		40 c. multicoloured	10	10
2029		1 cor. multicoloured (air)	20	20
2030		10 cor. multicoloured	1·25	1·10
2031		20 cor. multicoloured	3·25	2·75

1975. Chess. Multicoloured.

No.	Description	Unused	Used
2032	1 c. Type **293** (postage)	10	10
2033	2 c. "Arabs playing Chess" (Delacroix)	10	10
2034	3 c. "Cardinals playing Chess" (V. Marais-Milton)	10	10
2035	4 c. "Duke Albrecht V of Bavaria and Anna of Austria at Chess" (H. Muelich) (vert)	10	10
2036	5 c. "Chess game" (14th-century Persian manuscript)	10	10
2037	10 c. "Origins of Chess" (India, 1602)	10	10
2038	15 c. "Napoleon playing Chess in Schonbrunn Palace in 1809" (A. Uniechowski) (vert)	10	10
2039	20 c. "The Chess Game in the House of Count Ingenheim" (J.E. Hummel)	10	10
2040	40 c. "The Chess-players" (T. Eakins) (air)	10	10
2041	2 cor. Fischer v Spassky match, Reykjavik, 1972	55	35
2042	5 cor. "William Shakespeare and Ben Jonson playing Chess" (K. van Mander)	60	50

294 Choir of King's College Cambridge

1975. Christmas. Famous Choirs. Multicoloured.

No.	Description	Unused	Used
2044	1 c. Type **294** (postage)	10	10
2045	2 c. Abbey Choir, Einsiedeln	10	10
2046	3 c. Regensburg Cathedral choir	10	10
2047	4 c. Vienna Boys' choir	10	10
2048	5 c. Sistine Chapel choir	10	10
2049	15 c. Westminster Cathedral choir	10	10
2050	20 c. Mormon Tabernacle choir	10	10
2051	50 c. School choir, Montserrat (air)	10	10
2052	1 cor. St. Florian children's choir	20	15
2053	2 cor. "Little Singers of the Wooden Cross" (vert)	45	35
2054	5 cor. Pope with choristers of Pueri Cantores	60	50

295 "The Smoke Signal" (F. Remington)

1976. Bicent of American Revolution (2nd series). "200 Years of Progress". Multicoloured.

No.	Description	Unused	Used
2056	1 c. Type **295** (postage)	10	10
2057	1 c. Houston Space Centre	10	10
2058	2 c. Lighting candelabra, 1976	10	10
2059	2 c. Edison's lamp and houses	10	10
2060	3 c. "Agriculture 1776"	10	10
2061	3 c. "Agriculture 1976"	10	10
2062	4 c. Harvard College, 1776	10	10
2063	4 c. Harvard University, 1976	10	10
2064	5 c. Horse and carriage	15	10
2065	5 c. Boeing 747-100 airliner	15	10
2066	80 c. Philadelphia, 1776 (air)	25	15
2067	80 c. Washington, 1976	25	15

2068 2 cor. 75 "Bonhomme Richard" (American frigate) (John Paul Jones's flagship) and H.M.S. "Seraphis" (frigate), Battle of Flamborough Head . . . . 1·50 70
2069 2 cor. 75 U.S.S. "Glenard Phipscomp" (nuclear submarine) . . . . . . 1·50 70
2070 4 cor. Wagon train 90 70
2071 4 cor. Amtrak gas turbine train, 1973 . . . . 3·25 1·75

296 Italy, 1968

1976. Olympic Games, Victors in Rowing and Sculling. Multicoloured.

2073 1 c. Denmark 1964 (postage) . 10 10
2074 2 c. East Germany 1972 . . . 10 10
2075 3 c. Type **296** 10 10
2076 4 c. Great Britain 1936 . . . 10 10
2077 5 c. France 1952 (vert) 10 10
2078 35 c. U.S.A. 1920 (vert) . . . 10 10
2079 55 c. Russia 1956 (vert) (air) . 20 10
2080 70 c. New Zealand 1972 (vert) . 20 15
2081 90 c. New Zealand 1968 . . . 25 20
2082 20 cor. U.S.A. 1956 . . . . . 2·75 2·50

1976. Air. Olympic Games, Montreal. East German Victory in Rowing Events. No. 2082 optd **REPUBLICA DEMOCRATICA ALEMANA VENCEDOR EN 1976**.

2084 20 cor. multicoloured . . . . 2·75 2·50

299 Mauritius 1847 2d. "Post Office"

1976. Rare and Famous Stamps. Multicoloured.

2087 1 c. Type **299** (postage) . . . 10 10
2088 2 c. Western Australia 1854 "Inverted Mute Swan" . . 30 10
2089 3 c. Mauritius 1847 1d. "Post Office" 10 10
2090 4 c. Jamaica 1920 1s. Inverted Frame 10 10
2091 5 c. U.S. 1918 24 c. Inverted Aircraft 10 10
2092 10 c. Swiss 1845 Basel "Dove" . 10 10
2093 25 c. Canada 1959 Seaway Inverted Centre 10 10
2094 40 c. Hawaiian 1851 2 c. "Missionary" (air) 10 10
2095 1 cor. G.B. 1840 "Penny Black" 20 20
2096 2 cor. British Guiana 1850 1 c. Black on Magenta 40 35
2097 5 cor. Honduras 1925 Airmail 25 c. on 10 c. . . . . 3·50 1·10
2098 10 cor. Newfoundland 1919 "Hawker" Airmail stamp . . 1·25 1·10

300 Olga Nunez de Saballos (Member of Parliament)

1977. Air. International Women's Year. Mult.

2100 35 c. Type **300** 10 10
2101 1 cor. Josefa Toledo de Aguerri (educator) 20 20
2102 10 cor. Hope Portocarreo de Samoza (President's wife) . 1·25 1·00

301 "Graf Zeppelin" in Hangar

1977. 75th Anniv of First Zeppelin Flight. Multicoloured.

2104 1 c. Type **301** (postage) . . . 10 10
2105 2 c. "Graf Zeppelin" in flight . 10 10
2106 3 c. Giffard's steam-powered dirigible airship, 1852 . . . 15 10
2107 4 c. "Graf Zeppelin" in mooring hangar 15 10
2108 5 c. "Graf Zeppelin" on ground 15 10
2109 35 c. Astra airship "Ville de Paris" (air) 35 15
2110 70 c. "Schwaben" 40 20
2111 3 cor. "Graf Zeppelin" over Lake Constance . . . . . 1·00 65
2112 10 cor. LZ-2 on Lake Constance . . . . 3·75 2·25

302 Lindbergh and Map

1977. 50th Anniv of Lindbergh's Transatlantic Flight. Multicoloured.

2114 1 c. Type **302** (postage) . . . 10 10
2115 2 c. Map and "Spirit of St. Louis" 10 10
2116 3 c. Charles Lindbergh (vert) . 10 10
2117 4 c. "Spirit of St. Louis" crossing Atlantic 10 10
2118 5 c. Charles Lindbergh standing by "Spirit of St. Louis" . . 10 10
2119 20 c. Lindbergh, route and "Spirit of St. Louis" . . . 20 15
2120 55 c. Lindbergh landing in Nicaragua (1928) (air) . . . 20 15
2121 80 c. "Spirit of St. Louis" and route map 35 15
2122 2 cor. "Spirit of St. Louis" flying along Nicaraguan coast 65 35
2123 10 cor. Passing Momotombo (Nicaragua) . . . . 1·90 1·25

303 Christmas Festival

1977. Christmas. Scenes from Tchaikovsky's "Nutcracker" Suite. Multicoloured.

2125 1 c. Type **303** 10 10
2126 2 c. Doll's dance 10 10
2127 3 c. Clara and snowflakes . . 10 10
2128 4 c. Snow fairy and Prince . . 10 10
2129 5 c. Snow fairies 10 10
2130 15 c. Sugar fairy and prince . 10 10
2131 40 c. Waltz of the Flowers . . 10 10
2132 90 c. Chinese dance 20 15
2133 1 cor. Senora Bonbonierre . . 20 20
2134 10 cor. Arabian dance . . . . 1·40 1·25

304 "Mr. and Mrs. Andrews". (Gainsborough)

1978. Paintings. Multicoloured.

2136 1 c. Type **304** (postage) . . . 10 10
2137 2 c. "Giovanna Bacelli" (Gainsborough) 10 10
2138 3 c. "Blue Boy" (Gainsborough) 10 10
2139 4 c. "Francis I" (Titian) . . . 10 10
2140 5 c. "Charles V at Battle of Muhlberg" (Titian) 10 10
2141 25 c. "Sacred Love" (Titian) . . 10 10
2142 5 cor. "Hippopotamus and Crocodile Hunt" (Rubens) (air) 60 50
2143 10 cor. "Duke of Lerma on Horseback" (Rubens) . . . 1·75 1·40

305 Gothic Portal with Rose Window, Small Basilica of St. Francis

1978. 750th Anniv of Canonisation of St. Francis of Assisi. Multicoloured.

2145 1 c. Type **305** (postage) . . . 10 10
2146 2 c. St. Francis preaching to birds 10 10
2147 3 c. Painting of St. Francis . . 10 10
2148 4 c. Franciscan genealogical tree 10 10
2149 5 c. Portiuncola 10 10
2150 15 c. Autographed blessing . . 10 10
2151 25 c. Windows of Large Basilica 10 10
2152 80 c. St. Francis and wolf (air) . 15 10
2153 10 cor. St. Francis . . . . . 1·60 1·50

INDEX

Countries can be quickly located by referring to the index at the end of this volume.

306 Locomotive No. 6, 1921

1978. Centenary of Railway. Multicoloured.

2155 1 c. Type **306** (postage) . . . 10 10
2156 2 c. Lightweight cargo locomotive 10 10
2157 3 c. Steam locomotive No. 10, 1909 . . . . 10 10
2158 4 c. Baldwin steam locomotive No. 31, 1906 . . . . . . 10 10
2159 5 c. Baldwin steam locomotive No. 21, 1911 . . . . . . 10 10
2160 15 c. Presidential Pullman coach 15 10
2161 35 c. Steam locomotive No. 33, 1907 (air) 20 15
2162 4 cor. Baldwin steam locomotive No. 36, 1907 . . . . . . 2·50 90
2163 10 cor. Juniata steam locomotive, 1914, U.S.A. . . 6·25 2·25

307 Mongol Warriors ("Michael Strogoff")

1978. 150th Birth Anniv of Jules Verne. Multicoloured.

2165 1 c. Type **307** (postage) . . . 10 10
2166 2 c. Sea scene ("The Mysterious Island") 10 10
2167 3 c. Sea monsters ("Journey to the Centre of the Earth") . 10 10
2168 4 c. Balloon and African elephant ("Five Weeks in a Balloon") 20 10
2169 90 c. Submarine ("Twenty Thousand Leagues Under the Sea") (air) 75 20
2170 10 cor. Balloon, Indian, steam locomotive and elephant ("Around the World in Eighty Days") . . . . . 6·50 4·00

308 Icarus

1978. 75th Anniv of History of Aviation. First Powered Flight. Multicoloured.

2172 1 c. Type **308** (postage) . . . 10 10
2173 2 c. Montgolfier balloon (vert) . 10 10
2174 3 c. Wright Flyer I 10 10
2175 4 c. Orville Wright in Wright Type A (vert) 10 10
2176 55 c. Vought-Sikorsky VS-300 helicopter prototype (air) . 30 10
2177 10 cor. Space shuttle . . . . 2·10 1·00

309 Ernst Ocwirk and Alfredo di Stefano **310** "St. Peter" (Goya)

1978. World Cup Football Championship, Argentina. Multicoloured.

2179 20 c. Type **309** (postage) . . . 10 10
2180 25 c. Ralk Edstrom and Oswaldo Piazza 10 10
2181 50 c. Franz Beckenbauer and Dennis Law (air) 10 10
2182 5 cor. Dino Zoff and Pele . . 65 50

1978. Christmas. Multicoloured.

2184 10 c. Type **310** (postage) . . . 10 10
2185 15 c. "St. Gregory" (Goya) . . 10 10
2186 3 cor. "The Apostles John and Peter" (Durer) (air) 40 30
2187 10 cor. "The Apostles Paul and Mark" (Durer) . . . . . . 1·40 1·00

311 San Cristobal

1978. Volcanoes and Lakes. Multicoloured.

2189 5 c. Type **311** (postage) . . . 10 10
2190 5 c. Lake de Cosiguina . . . 10 10
2191 20 c. Telica 10 10
2192 20 c. Lake Jiloa 10 10
2193 35 c. Cerro Negro (air) . . . 10 10
2194 35 c. Lake Masaya 10 10
2195 90 c. Momotombo 20 15
2196 90 c. Lake Asososca 20 15
2197 1 cor. Mombacho 20 15
2198 1 cor. Lake Apoyo 20 15
2199 10 cor. Concepcion . . . . . 1·60 80
2200 10 cor. Lake Tiscapa . . . . 1·60 80

312 General O'Higgins

1979. Air. Birth Bicentenary of Bernardo O'Higgins (liberation hero).

2201 **312** 20 cor. multicoloured . . 3·75 1·90

313 Ginger Plant and Broad-tailed Hummingbird

1979. Air. Flowers. Multicoloured.

2202 50 c. Type **313** . . . . 1·50 20
2203 55 c. Orchids 10 10
2204 70 c. Poinsettia 15 10
2205 80 c. "Poro poro" 15 10
2206 2 cor. "Morpho cypris" (butterfly) and Guayacan flowers 50 30
2207 4 cor. Iris 45 30

314 Children with football **315** Indian Postal Runner

316 Einstein and Albert Schweitzer

317 Loggerhead Turtle

1980. Year of Liberation (1979) and Nicaragua's Participation in Olympic Games. Unissued stamps overprinted. (a) International Year of the Child. Multicoloured.

2208 20 c. Children on roundabout (postage) 15 15
2209 90 c. Type **314** (air) 65 65
2210 2 cor. Children with stamps albums . . . . 1·50 1·50
2211 2 cor. 20 Children playing with toy steam train and aircraft . 14·00 14·00
2212 10 cor. Baseball . . . . . . 7·50 7·50

(b) Death Centenary of Sir Rowland Hill. Mult.

2214 20 c. Type **315** (postage) . . . 20 20
2215 35 c. Pony express 40 40
2216 1 cor. Pre-stamp letter (horiz) . 1·10 1·10
2217 1 cor. 80 Sir Rowland Hill examining sheet of Penny Black stamps (air) . . . . 1·90 1·90
2218 2 cor. 20 Penny Blacks (horiz) . 2·40 2·40
2219 5 cor. Nicaraguan Zeppelin flight cover (horiz) . . . . 5·50 5·50

(c) Birth Centenary of Albert Einstein (physicist). Multicoloured.

2221 5 c. Type **316** (postage) . . . 15 15
2222 10 c. Einstein and equation . . 25 25
2223 15 c. Einstein and 1939 World Fair pavilion 40 40
2224 20 c. Einstein and Robert Oppenheimer 50 50
2225 25 c. Einstein in Jerusalem . . 65 65
2226 1 cor. Einstein and Nobel Prize medal (air) . . . . 2·50 2·50
2227 2 cor. 75 Einstein and space exploration . . . . 7·00 7·00
2228 10 cor. Einstein and Mahatma Gandhi . . . . 15·00 15·00

(d) Endangered Turtles. Multicoloured.

2230 90 c. Type **317** . . . . . . 1·00 80
2231 2 cor. Leatherback turtle . . . 2·25 1·75
2232 2 cor. 30 Ridley turtle . . . . 1·75 1·75
2233 10 cor. Hawksbilled turtle . . 7·50 7·50

318 Rigoberto Lopez Perez and Crowds pulling down Statue

1980. 1st Anniv of the Revolution. Multicoloured.

2235 40 c. Type **318** 10 10
2236 75 c. Street barricade 10 10
2237 1 cor. "Learn to Read" emblem (vert) 15 10
2238 1 cor. 25 German Pomares Ordonez and jungle fighters 20 15
2239 1 cor. 85 Victory celebrations (vert) 25 15
2240 2 cor. 50 Carlos Fonesca and camp-fire 35 35
2241 5 cor. Gen. Augusto Sandino and flag (vert) 70 55

1980. Literacy Year. Unissued stamps optd **1980 ANO DE LA ALFABETIZACION**. (a) International Year of the Child. As Nos. 2208/12.

2243 – 20 c. Children on roundabout (postage) . 1·00 1·00
2244 **314** 90 c. Children with football (air) . . . . 1·00 1·00
2245 – 2 cor. Children with stamp albums . . . . 1·00 1·00
2246 – 2 cor. 20 Children playing with toy steam train and airplane . . . . 2·00 2·00
2247 – 10 cor. Baseball . . . . . 4·50 4·50

(b) Death Centenary of Sir Rowland Hill. Nos. 2214/16.

2249 **315** 20 c. Indian postal runner . 70 70
2250 – 35 c. Pony express 70 70
2251 – 1 cor. Pre-stamp letter (horiz) 70 70

(c) Birth Centenary of Albert Einstein (physicist). As Nos. 2221/8.

2253 5 c. Optd **"YURI GAGARIN/ 12/IV/1961/LER HOMBRE EN EL ESPACIO"** (postage) 1·10 1·10
2254 10 c. Optd **"LURABA 1981"** and space shuttle . . . . . 1·10 1·10
2255 15 c. Optd **"SPACE SHUTTLE"** and craft . . . 1·10 1·10
2256 20 c. Optd **ANO DE LA ALFABETIZACION** . . . 1·10 1·10
2257 25 c. Optd **"16/VII/1969/LER HOMBRE A LA LUNA" and "APOLLO XI"** . . . . . 1·10 1·10
2258 1 cor. Optd As No. 2256 (air) . 1·10 1·10
2259 2 cor. 75 Optd As No. 2256 . 1·10 1·10
2260 10 cor. 75 Optd **"LUNO-JOD 1"** and vehicle . . . . . 1·10 1·10

(d) Air. Endangered Species. Turtles. As Nos. 2230/3. Multicoloured.

2262 **317** 90 c. Loggerhead turtle . . 1·00 1·00
2263 – 2 cor. Leatherback turtle . 1·00 1·00
2264 – 2 cor. 20 Ridley turtle . . 1·00 1·00
2265 – 10 cor. Hawksbill turtle . 1·00 1·00

321 Footballer and El Molinon Stadium

1981. World Cup Football Championships, Spain. (1st issue). Venues. Multicoloured.

2268 5 c. Type **321** 10 10
2269 20 c. Sanchez Pizjuan, Seville . . 10 10
2270 25 c. San Mames, Bilbao . . . 10 10
2271 30 c. Vincent Calderon, Madrid 10 10
2272 50 c. R.C.D. Espanol, Barcelona 10 10
2273 4 cor. New Stadium, Valladolid 55 35
2274 5 cor. Balaidos, Vigo 55 35
2275 10 cor. Santiago Bernabeu, Madrid . . . . 1·10 65

See also Nos. 2325/31.

322 Adult Education

1981. 2nd Anniv of Revolution. Multicoloured.

2277 50 c. Type **322** (postage) . . . 10 10
2278 2 cor. 10 Workers marching (air) 30 15
2279 3 cor. Roadbuilding and container ship 65 30
2280 6 cor. Medical services 50 25

323 Allegory of Revolution

1981. 20th Anniv of Sandinista National Liberation Front. Multicoloured.

2281 50 c. Type **323** (postage) . . . 10 10
2282 4 cor. Sandinista guerrilla (air) . 25 10

324 Postman

1981. 12th Postal Union of the Americas and Spain Congress, Managua. Multicoloured.

2283 50 c. Type **324** (postage) . . . 10 10
2284 2 cor. 10 Pony Express (air) . 30 15
2285 3 cor. Postal Headquarters Managua 45 25
2286 6 cor. Government building, globe and flags of member countries 50 25

326 "Nymphaea capensis"

1981. Water Lilies. Multicoloured.

2288 50 c. Type **326** (postage) . . . 10 10
2289 1 cor. "Nymphaea daubenyana" 15 10
2290 1 cor. 20 "Nymphaea Marliacea Chromat" 20 10
2291 1 cor. 80 "Nymphaea Dir. Geo. T. Moore" 25 15
2292 2 cor. "Nymphaea lotus" . . . 30 15
2293 2 cor. 50 "Nymphaea B.G. Berry" 35 20
2294 10 cor. "Nymphaea Gladstoniana" (air) 60 40

328 Cardinal Tetra

1981. Tropical Fishes. Multicoloured.

2296 50 c. Type **328** (postage) . . . 15 10
2297 1 cor. Guppy 30 20
2298 1 cor. 85 Striped headstander . 50 30
2299 2 cor. 10 Skunk corydoras . . 65 35
2300 2 cor. 50 Black-finned pearlfish 75 40
2301 3 cor. 50 Long-finned killie (air) 1·10 65
2302 4 cor. Red swordtail . . . . 1·25 80

MINIMUM PRICE

The minimum price quoted is 10p which represents a handling charge rather than a basis for valuing common stamps. For further notes about prices see introductory pages.

330 Lineated Woodpecker

331 Satellite in Orbit

1981. Birds. Multicoloured.

2304 50 c. Type **330** (postage) . . . 40 15
2305 1 cor. 20 Keel-billed toucan (horiz) 80 25
2306 1 cor. 80 Finsch's conure (horiz) 95 35
2307 2 cor. Scarlet macaw . . . . 1·25 40
2308 3 cor. Slaty-tailed trogon (air) . 1·75 50
2309 4 cor. Violet sabrewing (horiz) . 2·10 60
2310 6 cor. Blue-crowned motmot . 3·75 1·00

1981. Satellite Communications. Multicoloured.

2311 50 c. Type **331** (postage) . . . 10 10
2312 1 cor. "Intelstat IVA" 15 10
2313 1 cor. 50 "Intelstat V" moving into orbit 20 15
2314 2 cor. Rocket releasing "Intelstat V" 30 20
2315 3 cor. Satellite and Space Shuttle (air) 45 25
2316 4 cor. "Intelstat V" and world maps 55 30
2317 5 cor. Tracking stations . . . 70 45

332 Steam Locomotive at Lake Granada

1981. Locomotives. Multicoloured.

2318 50 c. Type **332** (postage) . . . 20 10
2319 1 cor. Vulcan Iron Works steam locomotive No. 35, 1946 . . 40 10
2320 1 cor. 20 Baldwin steam locomotive No. 21, 1911 (inscribed "Philadelphia Iron Works") 45 10
2321 1 cor. 80 Steam crane, 1909 . . 70 10
2322 2 cor. General Electric Model "U10B" diesel locomotive, 1960s 75 10
2323 2 cor. 50 German diesel railbus, 1954 (dated "1956") 90 15
2324 6 cor. Japanese-built diesel railbus, 1967 (air) . . . . . 2·40 35

333 Heading Ball

1982. World Cup Football Championship, Spain (2nd issue). Multicoloured.

2325 5 c. Type **333** (postage) . . . 10 10
2326 20 c. Running with ball . . . 10 10
2327 25 c. Running with ball (different) 10 10
2328 2 cor. 50 Saving goal 35 20
2329 3 cor. 50 Goalkeeper diving for ball (horiz) 50 30
2330 4 cor. Kicking ball (air) . . . 55 35
2331 10 cor. Tackle (horiz) 60 40

334 Cocker Spaniel

1982. Pedigree Dogs. Multicoloured.

2333 5 c. Type **334** (postage) . . . 10 10
2334 20 c. Alsatian 10 10
2335 25 c. English setter 10 10
2336 2 cor. 50 Brittany spaniel . . 35 20
2337 3 cor. Boxer (air) 45 25
2338 3 cor. 50 Pointer 50 30
2339 6 cor. Collie 60 30

335 Satellite Communications

1982. Air. I.T.U. Congress.

2340 **335** 25 cor. multicoloured . . 2·10 1·50

336 "Dynamine myrrhina"

1982. Butterflies. Multicoloured.

2341 50 c. Type **336** (postage) . . . 20 5
2342 1 cor. 20 "Eunica alcmena" . 40 10
2343 1 cor. 50 "Callizona acesta" . 40 12
2344 2 cor. "Adelpha leuceria" . . 60 20
2345 3 cor. "Parides iphidamas" (air) 1·00 30
2346 3 cor. 50 "Consul hippona" . 1·10 35
2347 4 cor. "Morpho peleides" . . 1·25 40

337 Dog and Russian Rocket

1982. Space Exploration. Multicoloured.

2348 5 c. Type **337** (postage) . . . 10 10
2349 15 c. Satellite (vert) 10 10
2350 50 c. "Apollo-Soyuz" link . . 10 10
2351 1 cor. 50 Satellite 20 15
2352 2 cor. 50 Docking in space . . 35 20
2353 5 cor. Russian space station (air) 45 20
2354 6 cor. Space shuttle "Columbia" (vert) 60 30

338 Mailcoach

1982. Centenary of U.P.U. Membership. Multicoloured.

2355 50 c. Type **338** (postage) . . . 10 10
2356 1 cor. 20 "Victoria" (packet steamer) . . . . 1·10 35
2357 3 cor. 50 Steam locomotive, 1953 (air) . . . . 2·75 25
2358 10 cor. Boeing 727-100 airliner . . . . 1·50 1·10

339 Cyclists

1982. 14th Central American and Caribbean Games. Multicoloured.

2359 10 c. Type **339** (postage) . . . 10 10
2360 15 c. Swimming (horiz) . . . 10 10
2361 25 c. Basketball 10 10
2362 50 c. Weightlifting 10 10
2363 2 cor. 50 Handball (air) . . . 35 20
2364 3 cor. Boxing (horiz) 45 25
2365 9 cor. Football (horiz) 75 45

341 Washington passing through Trenton

1982. 250th Birth Anniv of George Washington. Multicoloured.

2368 50 c. Mount Vernon, Washington's house (39 × 49 mm) (postage) 10 10
2369 1 cor. Washington signing the Constitution (horiz) . . . 15 10
2370 2 cor. Type **341** 30 20
2371 2 cor. 50 Washington crossing the Delaware (horiz) (air) . 35 20
2372 3 cor. 50 Washington at Valley Forge (horiz) 50 30
2373 4 cor. Washington at the Battle of Trenton 55 35
2374 6 cor. Washington at Princeton 60 55

342 Carlos Fonseca, Dove and Flags

1982. 3rd Anniv of Revolution. Multicoloured.

2375 50 c. Type **342** (postage) . . 10 10
2376 2 cor. 50 Ribbons forming dove (vert) (air) 35 20
2377 1 cor. Augusto Sandino and dove (vert) 55 30
2378 6 cor. Dove 60 55

343 "Vase of Flowers" (R. Penalba)

1982. Paintings. Multicoloured.

2379 25 c. Type **343** (postage) . . . 10 10
2380 50 c. "El Gueguense" (M. Garcia) (horiz) 10 10
2381 1 cor. "The Couple" (R. Perez) 15 10
2382 1 cor. 20 "Canales Valley" (A. Mejias) (horiz) 20 10
2383 1 cor. 85 "Portrait of Senora Castellon" (T. Jerez) . . . 25 15
2384 2 cor. "The Vendors" (L. Cerrato) 30 20
2385 9 cor. "Sitting Woman" (A. Morales) (horiz) (air) . . 55 35

344 Lenin and Dimitrov, Moscow, 1921

1982. Birth Centenary of Georgi Dimitrov (Bulgarian statesman). Multicoloured.

2387 50 c. Type **344** (postage) . . . 10 10
2388 2 cor. 50 Dimitrov & Todor Yikov, Sofia, 1946 (air) . . 35 20
2389 4 cor. Dimitrov and flag . . . 55 35

345 Ausberto Narvaez

1982. 26th Anniv of State of Resistance Movement. Multicoloured.

2390 50 c. Type **345** (postage) . . . 10 10
2391 2 cor. 50 Cornelio Silva . . . 35 20
2392 4 cor. Rigoberto Lopez Perez (air) 55 35
2393 6 cor. Edwin Castro 60 55

346 Old Ruins at Leon

1982. Tourism. Multicoloured.

2394 50 c. Type **346** (postage) . . . 10 10
2395 1 cor. Ruben Dario Theatre and Park, Managua 15 10
2396 1 cor. 20 Independence Square, Granada 20 10
2397 1 cor. 80 Corn Island 25 15
2398 2 cor. Carter Santiago Volcano, Masaya 30 20
2399 2 cor. 50 El Coyotepe Fortress, Masaya (air) 35 20
2400 3 cor. 50 Luis A. Velazquez Park, Managua 50 30

347 Karl Marx and View of Trier

1982. Death Centenary of Karl Marx. Multicoloured.

2401 1 cor. Type **347** (postage) . . 15 10
2402 4 cor. Marx and grave in Highgate Cemetery (air) . . 55 35

348 Stacking Cane and Fruit

1982. World Food Day. Multicoloured.

2403 50 c. Picking Fruit (horiz) . . 10 10
2404 1 cor. Type **348** 15 10
2405 2 cor. Cutting sugar cane (horiz) 30 20
2406 10 cor. F.A.O. and P.A.N. emblems (horiz) 85 65

349 "Santa Maria"

1982. 490th Anniv of Discovery of America. Multicoloured.

2407 50 c. Type **349** (postage) . . . 65 20
2408 1 cor. "Nina" . . . . 1·25 30
2409 1 cor. 50 "Pinta" . . . . . . 1·75 45
2410 2 cor. Columbus and fleet . . 2·00 70
2411 2 cor. 50 Fleet and map of route (air) . . . . 2·00 70
2412 4 cor. Arrival in America . . 55 35
2413 7 cor. Death of Columbus . . 65 60

350 "Lobelia laxiflora"

351 "Micrurus lemniscatus"

1982. Woodland Flowers. Multicoloured.

2415 50 c. Type **350** (postage) . . . 10 10
2416 1 cor. 20 "Bombacopsis quinata" 20 10
2417 1 cor. 80 "Mimosa albida" . . 25 15
2418 2 cor. "Epidendrum alatum" . . 30 20
2419 2 cor. 50 Passion flower "Passiflora foetida" wrongly inscr "Pasiflora" (air) . . . 35 20
2420 3 cor. 50 "Clitoria sp." . . . 50 30
2421 5 cor. "Russelia sarmentosa" . 70 45

1982. Reptiles. Multicoloured.

2422 10 c. Type **351** (postage) . . . 10 10
2423 50 c. Common iguana "Iguana iguana" (horiz) 10 10
2424 2 cor. "Lachesis muta" (snake) (horiz) 30 20
2425 2 cor. 50 Hawksbill turtle "Eretmochelys imbricata" (horiz) (air) 35 20
2426 3 cor. Boa Constrictor "Constrictor constrictor" . . 45 25
2427 3 cor. 50 American crocodile "Crocodilus acutus" (horiz) 50 30
2428 5 cor. Diamond-back rattlesnake "Sistrurus catenatus" (horiz) 70 45

352 Tele-cor Building, Managua

1982. Telecommunications Day. Multicoloured.

2429 1 cor. Type **352** (postage) . . 15 10
2430 50 c. Interior of radio transmission room (air) . . 10 10

353 Girl with Dove

1983. Air. Non-Aligned States Conference.

2431 **353** 4 cor. multicoloured . . . 55 35

354 Jose Marti and Birthplace

1983. 130th Birth Anniv of Jose Marti (Cuban revolutionary).

2432 **354** 1 cor. multicoloured . . . 15 10

355 Boxing

356 "Neomarica coerulea"

1983. Olympic Games, Los Angeles (1st issue). Multicoloured.

2433 50 c. Type **355** (postage) . . . 10 10
2434 1 cor. Gymnastics 15 10
2435 1 cor. 50 Running 20 15
2436 2 cor. Weightlifting 30 20
2437 4 cor. Discus (air) 55 35
2438 5 cor. Basketball 70 45
2439 6 cor. Cycling 90 55

See also Nos. 2609/15.

1983. Flowers.

2441 **356** 1 cor. blue 15 10
2442 – 1 cor. violet 15 10
2443 – 1 cor. mauve 15 10
2444 – 1 cor. brown 15 10
2445 – 1 cor. green 15 10
2446 – 1 cor. blue 15 10
2447 – 1 cor. green 15 10
2448 – 1 cor. green 15 10
2449 – 1 cor. mauve 15 10
2450 – 1 cor. red 15 10
2451 – 1 cor. grey 15 10
2452 – 1 cor. yellow 15 10
2453 – 1 cor. brown 15 10
2454 – 1 cor. purple 15 10
2455 – 1 cor. green 15 10
2456 – 1 cor. black 15 10

DESIGNS: No. 2442, "Tabebula ochraceae"; 2443, "Laelia sp"; 2444, "Plumeria rubra"; 2445, "Brassavola nodosa"; 2446, "Stachytarpheta indica"; 2447, "Cochiospermum sp"; 2448, "Malvaviscus arboreus"; 2449, "Telecoma stans"; 2450, "Hibiscus rosa-sinensis"; 2451, "Cattleya lueddemanniana"; 2452, "Tagetes erecta"; 2453, "Senecio sp"; 2454, "Sobralia macrantha"; 2455, "Thumbergia alata"; 2456, "Bixa orellana".

See also Nos. 2739/54, 2838/53 and 3087/3102.

357 Momotombo Geo-thermal Electrical Plant

1983. Air. Energy.

2457 **357** 2 cor. 50 multicoloured . . 35 20

358 Demonstrating Crowd

1983. Papal Visit.

2458 **358** 50 c. red, black and blue (postage) 10 10
2459 – 1 cor. multicoloured . . . 15 10
2460 – 4 cor. multicoloured (air) . 55 35
2461 – 7 cor. multicoloured . . . 1·00 60

DESIGNS: 1 cor. Map of Nicaragua and girl picking coffee; 4 cor. Pres. Cordova Rivas and Pope John Paul II; 7 cor. Pope outside Managua Cathedral.

359 "Xilophanes chiron"

1983. Moths. Multicoloured.

2463 15 c. Type **359** (postage) . . . 10 10
2464 50 c. "Protoparce ochus" . . . 15 10
2465 65 c. "Pholus lasbruscae" . . 25 10
2466 1 cor. "Amphypterus gannascus" 30 10
2467 1 cor. 50 "Pholus licaon" . . 40 15
2468 2 cor. "Agrius cingulata" . . 60 25
2469 10 cor. "Rothschildia jurulla" (vert) (air) . . . . 3·25 95

360 Subriava Church, Leon

1983. Monuments. Multicoloured.

2470 50 c. Type **360** (postage) . . . 10 10
2471 1 cor. "La Immaculada" Castle, Rio San Juan 15 10
2472 2 cor. La Recoleccion Church, Leon (vert) 30 20
2473 4 cor. Ruben Dario Monument, Managua (vert) (air) . . . 55 35

361 Passenger Carriage

1983. Railway Wagons. Multicoloured.

2474 15 c. Type **361** (postage) . . . 10 10
2475 65 c. Goods wagon No. 1034 . 25 10
2476 1 cor. Tanker wagon No. 931 . 30 10
2477 1 cor. 50 Xolotlan hopper wagon 45 10
2478 4 cor. Railcar (air) . . . . . 1·25 35
2479 5 cor. Tipper truck . . . . . 1·50 40
2480 7 cor. Railbus . . . . 2·25 60

362 Aiding Flood Victims

1983. Red Cross. Multicoloured.
2481 50 c. Type **362** (postage) 10 10
2482 1 cor. Placing stretcher patient into ambulance 15 10
2483 4 cor. Helping earthquake victim (vert) (air) 55 35
2484 5 cor. Doctor examining wounded soldier 70 45

363 Raising Telephone Pole

1983. World Communications Year.
2485 **363** 1 cor. multicoloured 15 10

365 Baseball

1983. Ninth Pan-American Games. Multicoloured.
2487 15 c. Type **365** (postage) 10 10
2488 50 c. Water polo 10 10
2489 65 c. Running 15 10
2490 1 cor. Basketball (vert) 15 10
2491 2 cor. Weightlifting (vert) 30 20
2492 7 cor. Fencing (air) 65 30
2493 8 cor. Gymnastics 70 40

367 Container Ship being Unloaded

1983. 4th Anniv of Revolution. Multicoloured.
2496 1 cor. Type **367** 55 15
2497 2 cor. Telcor building, Leon 30 20

368 Carlos Fonseca

369 Simon Bolivar on Horseback

1983. Founders of Sandinista National Liberation Front. Multicoloured.
2498 50 c. Escobar, Navarro, Ubeda, Pomares and Ruiz (postage) 10 10
2499 1 cor. Santos Lopez, Borge, Buitrago and Mayorga 15 10
2500 4 cor. Type **368** (air) 55 35

1983. Birth Bicentenary of Simon Bolivar. Mult.
2501 50 c. Bolivar and Sandinista guerrilla 10 10
2502 1 cor. Type **369** 15 10

371 Movements of a Pawn

1983. Chess. Multicoloured.

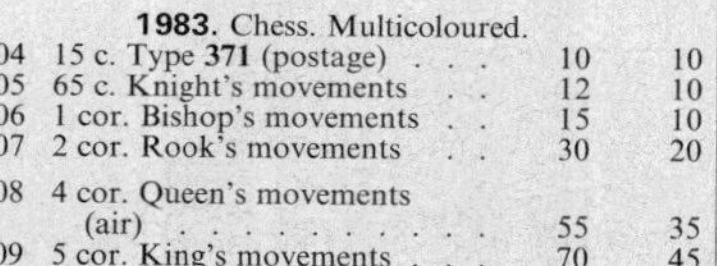

2504 15 c. Type **371** (postage) 10 10
2505 65 c. Knight's movements 12 10
2506 1 cor. Bishop's movements 15 10
2507 2 cor. Rook's movements 30 20
2508 4 cor. Queen's movements (air) 55 35
2509 5 cor. King's movements 70 45
2510 7 cor. Game in progress 75 60

372 Speed Skating

1983. Winter Olympic Games, Sarajevo (1984) (1st issue). Multicoloured.
2511 50 c. Type **372** (postage) 10 10
2512 1 cor. Slalom 15 10
2513 1 cor. 50 Luge 20 15
2514 2 cor. Ski jumping 30 20
2515 4 cor. Figure skating (air) 55 35
2516 5 cor. Downhill skiing 70 45
2517 6 cor. Biathlon 90 55

373 Soldiers with German Shepherd Dog

374 "Madonna of the Chair"

1983. Armed Forces.
2519 **373** 4 cor. multicoloured 55 35

1983. 500th Birth Anniv of Raphael. Multicoloured.
2520 50 c. Type **374** (postage) 10 10
2521 1 cor. "Esterhazy Madonna" 15 10
2522 1 cor. 50 "Sistine Madonna" 20 12
2523 2 cor. "Madonna of the Linnet" 30 20
2524 4 cor. "Madonna of the Meadow" (air) 55 35
2525 5 cor. "Madonna of the Garden" 70 45
2526 6 cor. "Adoration of the Kings" 90 55

375 Pottery Idol

1983. Archaeological Finds. Multicoloured.
2528 50 c. Type **375** (postage) 10 10
2529 1 cor. Pottery dish with ornamental lid 15 10
2530 2 cor. Vase with snake design 30 20
2531 4 cor. Pottery dish (air) 55 35

376 Metal being poured into Moulds

1983. Nationalization of Mines. Multicoloured.
2532 1 cor. Type **376** (postage) 15 10
2533 4 cor. Workers and mine (air) 55 35

377 Radio Operator and Sinking Liner

1983. "Fracap '83" Congress of Radio Amateurs of Central America and Panama. Multicoloured.
2534 1 cor. Type **377** 70 15
2535 4 cor. Congress emblem and town destroyed by earthquake 55 35

378 Tobacco

1983. Agrarian Reform.
2536 **378** 1 cor. green 15 10
2537 – 2 cor. orange 30 20
2538 – 4 cor. brown 35 35
2539 – 5 cor. blue 45 45
2540 – 6 cor. lavender 55 55
2541 – 7 cor. purple 60 60
2542 – 8 cor. purple 70 65
2543 – 10 cor. brown 90 90

DESIGNS: 2 cor. Cotton; 4 cor. Maize; 5 cor. Sugar; 6 cor. Cattle; 7 cor. Rice; 8 cor. Coffee; 10 cor. Bananas.

See also Nos. 2755/62 and 2854/61.

379 Fire Engine with Ladder

1983. Fire Engines. Multicoloured.
2544 50 c. Type **379** (postage) 10 10
2545 1 cor. Water Tanker 15 10
2546 6 cor. Crew vehicle, 1930 90 55
2547 1 cor. 50 Pump with extension fire hoses (air) 20 15
2548 2 cor. Pump with high-pressure tank 30 20
2548a 4 cor. Water tanker 60 40
2549 5 cor. Fire engine, 1910 70 45

380 Jose Marti and General Sandino

1983. Nicaragua-Cuba Solidarity. Multicoloured.
2550 1 cor. Type **380** (postage) 15 10
2551 4 cor. Teacher, doctor and welder (air) 55 35

381 "Adoration of the Shepherds" (Hugo van der Gaes)

382 Anniversary Emblem

1983. Christmas. Multicoloured.
2552 50 c. Type **381** (postage) 10 10
2553 1 cor. "Adoration of the Kings" (Domenico Ghirlandaio) 15 10
2554 2 cor. "Adoration of the Shepherds" (El Greco) 30 20
2555 7 cor. "Adoration of the Kings" (Konrad von Soest) (air) 65 30

1984. Air. 25th Anniv of Cuban Revolution.
2557 **382** 4 cor. red, blue and black 45 20
2558 – 6 cor. multicoloured 55 30

DESIGN: 6 cor. Fidel Castro and Che Guevara.

383 Bobsleigh

1984. Winter Olympic Games, Sarajevo. Mult.
2559 50 c. Type **383** (postage) 10 10
2560 50 c. Biathlon 10 10
2561 1 cor. Slalom 20 15
2562 1 cor. Speed skating 20 15
2563 4 cor. Skiing (air) 45 45
2564 5 cor. Ice dancing 55 55
2565 10 cor. Ski jumping 90 60

INDEX

Countries can be quickly located by referring to the index at the end of this volume.

384 Chinchilla

1984. Cats. Multicoloured.
2567 50 c. Type **384** (postage) 10 10
2568 50 c. Longhaired white 10 10
2569 1 cor. Red tabby 20 15
2570 2 cor. Tortoiseshell 35 20
2571 4 cor. Burmese 70 45
2572 3 cor. Siamese (air) 50 35
2573 7 cor. Longhaired silver 70 35

385 National Arms

386 Blanca Arauz

1984. 50th Death Anniv of Augusto Sandino. Multicoloured.
2574 1 cor. Type **385** (postage) 20 15
2575 4 cor. Augusto Sandino (air) 35 20

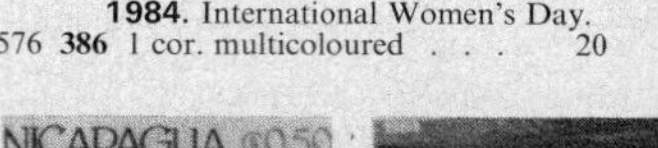

1984. International Women's Day.
2576 **386** 1 cor. multicoloured 20 15

387 Sunflower

388 "Soyuz"

1984. Agricultural Flowers. Multicoloured.
2577 50 c. Type **387** (postage) 10 10
2578 50 c. "Poinsettia pulcherrima" 10 10
2579 1 cor. "Cassia alata" 20 15
2580 2 cor. "Antigonon leptopus" 35 20
2581 3 cor. "Bidens pilosa" (air) 50 35
2582 4 cor. "Althaea rosea" 70 45
2583 5 cor. "Rivea corymbosa" 85 55

1984. Space Anniversaries. Multicoloured.
2584 50 c. Type **388** (15th anniv of "Soyuz 6", "7" and "8" flights) (postage) 10 5
2585 50 c. "Soyuz" (different) (15th anniv of "Soyuz 6", "7" and "8" flights) 10 5
2586 1 cor. "Apollo II" approaching Moon (15th anniv of 1st manned landing) 20 15
2587 2 cor. "Luna I" (25th anniv of 1st Moon satellite) 35 20
2588 3 cor. "Luna II" (25th anniv of 1st Moon landing) (air) 50 35
2589 4 cor. "Luna III" (25th anniv of 1st photographs of far side of Moon) 70 45
2590 9 cor. Rocket (50th anniv of Korolev's book on space flight) 1·25 75

389 "Noli me Tangere" (detail)

390 Daimler, 1886

1984. 450th Death Anniv of Correggio (artist). Multicoloured.
2591 50 c. Type **389** (postage) 10 10
2592 50 c. "Madonna of St. Jerome" (detail) 10 10
2593 1 cor. "Allegory of Virtue" 20 15
2594 2 cor. "Allegory of Pleasure" 35 20
2595 3 cor. "Ganymedes" (detail) (air) 50 35
2596 5 cor. "The Danae" (detail) 55 55
2597 8 cor. "Leda and the Swan" (detail) 1·00 60

1984. 150th Birth Anniv of Gottlieb Daimler (automobile designer). Multicoloured.

2599	1 cor. Type **390** (postage)	10	10
2600	1 cor. Abadal, 1914 (horiz)	10	10
2601	2 cor. Ford, 1903	1·50	45
2602	2 cor. Renault, 1899	35	20
2603	3 cor. Rolls Royce, 1910 (horiz) (air)	50	35
2604	4 cor. Metallurgique, 1907 (horiz)	70	45
2605	7 cor. Bugatti "Mod 40" (horiz)	75	50

392 Mail Transport

1984. Air. 19th Universal Postal Union Congress Philatelic Salon, Hamburg.

2607 **392**	15 cor. multicoloured	5·75	2·10

393 Basketball

1984. Olympic Games, Los Angeles (2nd issue). Multicoloured.

2609	50 c. Type **393** (postage)	10	10
2610	50 c. Volleyball	10	10
2611	1 cor. Hockey	20	15
2612	2 cor. Tennis (air)	35	20
2613	3 cor. Football (horiz)	50	35
2614	4 cor. Water polo (horiz)	70	45
2615	9 cor. Soccer (horiz)	1·10	75

395 Rural Construction Site

1984. 5th Anniv of Revolution. Multicoloured.

2618	5 c. Type **395** (postage)	10	10
2619	1 cor. Diesel locomotive, Pacific–Atlantic line	1·50	30
2620	4 cor. Ploughing with oxen and tractor (Agrarian reform) (air)	40	20
2621	7 cor. State Council building	75	35

396 "Children defending Nature" (Pablo Herrera Berrios)

1984. U.N.E.S.C.O. Environmental Protection Campaign. Multicoloured.

2622	50 c. Type **396** (postage)	10	10
2623	1 cor. Living and dead forests	20	15
2624	2 cor. Fisherman and dried river bed	35	20
2625	10 cor. Hands holding plants (vert) (air)	85	75

397 Red Cross Airplane and Ambulance

1984. 50th Anniv of Nicaraguan Red Cross. Multicoloured.

2626	1 cor. Type **397** (postage)	30	15
2627	7 cor. Battle of Solferino (125th anniv) (air)	90	45

399 Ventura Escalante and Dominican Republic Flag

1984. Baseball. Multicoloured.

2629	50 c. Type **399** (postage)	10	10
2630	50 c. Danial Herrera and Mexican flag	10	10
2631	1 cor. Adalberto Herrera and Venezuelan flag	20	15
2632	1 cor. Roberto Clemente and Nicaraguan flag	20	15
2633	3 cor. Carlos Colas and Cuban flag (air)	30	35
2634	4 cor. Stanley Cayasso and Argentinian flag	45	45
2635	5 cor. Babe Ruth and U.S.A. flag	55	55

400 Central American Tapir

1984. Wildlife Protection. Multicoloured.

2636	25 c. Type **400** (postage)	10	10
2637	25 c. Young tapir	10	10
2638	3 cor. Close-up of tapir (air)	15	10
2639	4 cor. Mother and young	20	15

401 Football in 1314

1985. World Cup Football Championship, Mexico (1986) (1st issue). Multicoloured.

2640	50 c. Type **401** (postage)	10	10
2641	50 c. Football in 1500	10	10
2642	1 cor. Football in 1872	10	10
2643	1 cor. Football in 1846	10	10
2644	2 cor. Football in 1883 (air)	10	10
2645	4 cor. Football in 1890	20	15
2646	6 cor. Football in 1953	30	20

See also Nos. 2731/7 and 2812/18.

402 "Strobilomyces retisporus"
403 Postal Runner and Map

1985. Fungi. Multicoloured.

2648	50 c. Type **402** (postage)	10	10
2649	50 c. "Boletus calopus"	10	10
2650	1 cor. "Boletus luridus"	15	10
2651	1 cor. "Xerocomus illudens" (air)	15	10
2652	4 cor. "Gyrodon merulioides"	55	25
2653	5 cor. "Tylopilus plumbeoviolaceus"	65	30
2654	8 cor. "Gyroporus castaneus"	1·10	40

1985. 13th Postal Union of the Americas and Spain Congress. Multicoloured.

2655	1 cor. Type **403** (postage)	10	10
2656	7 cor. Casa Aviocar mail plane over map (air)	45	20

406 Steam Locomotive, Oldenburg

1985. 150th Anniv of German Railway. Mult.

2659	1 cor. Type **406** (postage)	20	10
2660	1 cor. Electric locomotive, Prussia	20	10
2661	9 cor. Steam locomotive No. 88, Prussia (air)	75	15
2662	9 cor. Double-deck tram	75	15
2663	15 cor. Steam locomotive, Wurttemberg	1·10	25
2664	21 cor. Steam locomotive, Germany	1·75	40

407 Douglas, 1928

1985. Centenary of Motor Cycle. Multicoloured.

2666	50 c. Type **407** (postage)	10	10
2667	50 c. FN, 1928	10	10
2668	1 cor. Puch, 1938	10	10
2669	2 cor. Wanderer, 1939 (air)	10	10
2670	4 cor. Honda, 1949	10	10
2671	5 cor. BMW, 1984	10	10
2672	7 cor. Honda, 1984	40	10

408 "Matelea quirosii"
409 "Capitulation of German Troops" (P. Krivonogov)

1985. Flowers. Multicoloured.

2673	50 c. Type **408** (postage)	10	10
2674	50 c. "Ipomea nil"	10	10
2675	1 cor. "Lysichitum americanum"	10	10
2676	2 cor. "Clusia sp." (air)	10	10
2677	4 cor. "Vanilla planifolia"	10	10
2678	7 cor. "Stemmadenia obovata"	75	40

1985. 40th Anniv of End of World War II. Mult.

2679	9 cor. 50 Type **409** (postage)	1·00	50
2680	28 cor. Woman behind barbed wire and Nuremberg trial (air)	3·00	1·50

410 Lenin and Red Flag
413 Ring-necked Pheasant

412 Victoria de Julio Sugar Factory

1985. 115th Birth Anniv of Lenin. Multicoloured.

2681	4 cor. Type **410**	10	10
2682	21 cor. Lenin addressing crowd	45	30

1985. Air. 6th Anniv of Revolution. Multicoloured.

2684	9 cor. Type **412**	20	15
2685	9 cor. Soldier and flag	20	15

1985. Domestic Birds. Multicoloured.

2686	50 c. Type **413**	50	10
2687	50 c. Hen	50	10
2688	1 cor. Helmet guineafowl	50	10
2689	2 cor. Swan goose	50	10
2690	6 cor. Ocellated turkey	1·40	15
2691	8 cor. Duck	1·75	10

414 Luis A. Delgadillo
415 Zeledon

1985. International Music Year. Multicoloured.

2692	1 cor. Type **414** (postage)	10	10
2693	1 cor. Masked dancer with floral headdress	10	10
2694	9 cor. Masked procession (air)	65	40
2695	9 cor. Crowd outside church	65	40
2696	15 cor. Masked dancer in brimmed hat	1·10	55
2697	21 cor. Procession resting	1·50	75

1985. Air. Birth Centenary of Benjamin Zeledon.

2698 **415**	15 cor. multicoloured	1·00	55

416 Dunant and Lifeboat

1985. 75th Death Anniv of Henri Dunant (founder of Red Cross). Multicoloured.

2699	3 cor. Type **416**	40	10
2700	15 cor. Dunant and Ilyushin Il-86 and Tupolev Tu-154 aircraft	1·25	55

417 Fire Engine

1985. 6th Anniv of SINACOI Fire Service. Mult.

2701	1 cor. Type **417** (postage)	10	10
2702	1 cor. Fire station	10	10
2703	1 cor. Engine with water jet	10	10
2704	3 cor. Foam tender (air)	10	10
2705	9 cor. Airport fire engine	50	15
2706	15 cor. Engine at fire	85	45
2707	21 cor. Fireman in protective clothing	1·10	75

418 Halley, Masaya Volcano and Comet

1985. Appearance of Halley's Comet. Multicoloured.

2708	1 cor. Type **418** (postage)	10	10
2709	3 cor. Armillary sphere and 1910 trajectory	10	10
2710	3 cor. "Venus" space probe and Tycho Brahe underground observatory	10	10
2711	9 cor. Habermel's astrolabe and comet's path through solar system (air)	50	15
2712	15 cor. Hale Telescope, Mt. Palomar, and Herschel's telescope	85	45
2713	21 cor. Galileo's telescope and sections through telescopes of Newton, Cassegrain and Ritchey	1·25	60

419 Tapir eating

1985. Protected Animals. Baird's Tapir. Mult.

2714	1 cor. Type **419** (postage)	10	10
2715	3 cor. Tapir in water (air)	10	10
2716	5 cor. Tapir in undergrowth	10	10
2717	9 cor. Mother and calf	20	15

420 "Rosa spinosissima"

1986. Wild Roses. Multicoloured.

2718 1 cor. Type **420** 10 10
2719 1 cor. Dog rose ("R. canina") 10 10
2720 3 cor. "R. eglanteria" 10 10
2721 5 cor. "R. rubrifolia" 10 10
2722 9 cor. "R. foetida" 20 15
2723 100 cor. "R. rugosa" 2·00 1·10

421 Crimson Topaz

422 Footballer and Statue

1986. Birds. Multicoloured.

2724 1 cor. Type **421** 15 10
2725 3 cor. Orange-billed nightingale thrush 15 10
2726 3 cor. Troupial 15 10
2727 5 cor. Painted bunting 45 15
2728 10 cor. Frantzius's nightingale thrush 90 40
2729 21 cor. Great horned owl 1·75 1·00
2730 75 cor. Great kiskadee 6·50 3·00

1986. World Cup Football Championship, Mexico (2nd issue). Multicoloured.

2731 1 cor. Type **422** (postage) 10 10
2732 1 cor. Footballer and sculptured head 10 10
2733 3 cor. Footballer and water holder with man as stem (air) 10 10
2734 3 cor. Footballer and sculpture 10 10
2735 5 cor. Footballer and sculptured head (different) 10 10
2736 9 cor. Footballer and sculpture (different) 20 15
2737 100 cor. Footballer and sculptured snake's head 3·00 1·50

1986. (a) Flowers. As Nos. 2441/56 but values changed.

2739 5 cor. blue 10 10
2740 5 cor. violet 10 10
2741 5 cor. purple 10 10
2742 5 cor. orange 10 10
2743 5 cor. green 10 10
2744 5 cor. blue 10 10
2745 5 cor. green 10 10
2746 5 cor. green 10 10
2747 5 cor. mauve 10 10
2748 5 cor. red 10 10
2749 5 cor. grey 10 10
2750 5 cor. orange 10 10
2751 5 cor. brown 10 10
2752 5 cor. brown 10 10
2753 5 cor. green 10 10
2754 5 cor. black 10 10

DESIGNS: No. 2739, Type **356**; 2740, "Tabebula ochraceae"; 2741, "Laelia sp"; 2742, Frangipani ("Plumeria rubra"); 2743, "Brassavola nodosa"; 2744, "Strachytarpheta indica"; 2745, "Cochlospermum sp"; 2746, "Malvaviscus arboreus"; 2747, "Tecoma stans"; 2748, Chinese hibiscus ("Hibiscus rosa-sinensis"); 2749, "Cattleya lueddemanniana"; 2750, African marigold ("Tagetes erecta"); 2751, "Senecio sp"; 2752, "Sobralia macrantha"; 2753, "Thumbergia alata"; 2754, "Bixa orellana".

(b) Agrarian Reform. As T **378**.

2755 1 cor. brown 10 10
2756 9 cor. violet 20 15
2757 15 cor. purple 30 20
2758 21 cor. red 45 30
2759 33 cor. orange 65 45
2760 42 cor. green 90 55
2761 50 cor. brown 1·00 65
2762 100 cor. blue 2·00 1·50

DESIGNS: 1 cor. Type **378**; 9 cor. Cotton; 15 cor. Maize; 21 cor. Sugar; 33 cor. Cattle; 42 cor. Rice; 50 cor. Coffee; 100 cor. Bananas.

INDEX
Countries can be quickly located by referring to the index at the end of this volume.

423 Alfonso Cortes

1986. National Libraries. Latin American Writers. Multicoloured.

2763 1 cor. Type **423** (postage) 10 10
2764 3 cor. Azarias H. Pallais 10 10
2765 3 cor. Salomon de la Selva 10 10
2766 5 cor. Ruben Dario 10 10
2767 9 cor. Pablo Neruda 10 10
2768 15 cor. Alfonso Reyes (air) 45 25
2769 100 cor. Pedro Henriquez Urena 3·00 1·50

424 Great Britain Penny Black and Nicaragua 1929 25 c. Stamps

1986. Air. 125th Anniv of Nicaraguan Stamps. Designs showing G.B. Penny Black and Nicaragua stamps.

2770 **424** 30 cor. multicoloured 90 45
2771 – 40 cor. brown, black and grey 1·25 60
2772 – 50 cor. red, black and grey 1·50 75
2773 – 100 cor. blue, black and grey 3·00 1·50

DESIGNS: 40 c. 1903 1 p. stamp; 50 c. 1892 5 p. stamp; 1 p. 1862 2 c. stamp.

425 Sapodilla

426 Rainbow and Globe

1986. 40th Anniv of F.A.O. Multicoloured.

2774 1 cor. Type **425** (postage) 10 10
2775 1 cor. Maranon 10 10
2776 3 cor. Tree-cactus 10 10
2777 3 cor. Granadilla 10 10
2778 5 cor. Custard-apple (air) 10 10
2779 21 cor. Melocoton 65 35
2780 100 cor. Mamey 3·00 1·50

1986. Air. International Peace Year. Multicoloured.

2781 5 cor. Type **426** 10 10
2782 10 cor. Dove and globe 30 10

427 Lockheed L-1011 TriStar 500

1986. "Stockholmia 86" International Stamp Exhibition. Multicoloured.

2783 1 cor. Type **427** (postage) 10 10
2784 1 cor. Yakovlev Yak-40 10 10
2785 3 cor. B.A.C. One Eleven 10 10
2786 3 cor. Boeing 747-100 10 10
2787 9 cor. Airbus Industrie A300 (air) 30 10
2788 15 cor. Tupolev Tu-154 45 10
2789 100 cor. Concorde (vert) 3·00 1·50

428 "Pinta" and 16th-century Map

1986. 500th Anniv (1992) of Discovery of America by Columbus (1st issue). Multicoloured.

2791 1 cor. Type **428** (postage) 80 30
2792 1 cor. "Santa Maria" and "Nina" 80 30
2793 9 cor. Juan de la Cosa (air) 30 10
2794 9 cor. Christopher Columbus 30 10
2795 21 cor. King and Queen of Spain 65 35
2796 100 cor. Courtiers behind Columbus and Indians 3·00 1·50

The designs of the same value and Nos. 2795/6 were printed together in se-tenant pairs within their sheets, Nos. 2791/2 and 2795/6 forming composite designs.

See also Nos. 2903/8.

429 Fonseca and Flags

1986. Air. 25th Anniv of Sandinista Front and 10th Death Anniv of Carlos Fonseca (co-founder).

2798 **429** 15 cor. multicoloured 10 10

430 Rhinoceros

431 "Theritas coronata"

1986. Air. Endangered Animals. Multicoloured.

2799 15 cor. Type **430** 45 10
2800 15 cor. Zebra 45 10
2801 25 cor. Elephant 75 40
2802 25 cor. Giraffe 75 40
2803 50 cor. Tiger 1·50 75
2804 50 cor. Mandrill 1·50 75

1986. Butterflies. Multicoloured.

2805 10 cor. Type **431** (post) 20 10
2806 15 cor. "Salamis cacta" (air) 20 10
2807 15 cor. "Charayes nitebis" 20 10
2808 15 cor. "Papilio maacki" 20 10
2809 25 cor. "Palaeochrysophonus hippothoe" 20 10
2810 25 cor. "Euphaedro cyparissa" 20 10
2811 30 cor. "Ritra aurea" 20 10

432 Player and French Flag

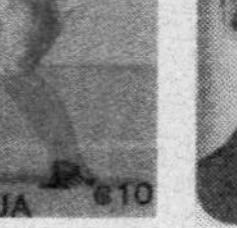

433 Ernesto Mejia Sanchez

1986. Air. World Cup Football Championship, Mexico (3rd issue). Finalists. Multicoloured. Designs showing footballers and national flags.

2812 10 cor. Type **432** 10 10
2813 10 cor. Argentina 10 10
2814 10 cor. West Germany 10 10
2815 15 cor. England 10 10
2816 15 cor. Brazil 10 10
2817 25 cor. Spain 10 10
2818 50 cor. Belgium (horiz) 10 10

1987. Ruben Dario Cultural Order of Independence. Multicoloured.

2820 10 cor. Type **433** (postage) 10 10
2821 10 cor. Fernando Gordillo 10 10
2822 10 cor. Francisco Perez Estrada 10 10
2823 15 cor. Order medal (air) 10 10
2824 30 cor. Julio Cortazar 20 20
2825 60 cor. Enrique Fernandez Morales 35 25

434 Ice Hockey

435 Development

1987. Winter Olympic Games, Calgary (1988). Multicoloured.

2826 10 cor. Type **434** (postage) 10 10
2827 10 cor. Speed skating 10 10
2828 15 cor. Downhill skiing (air) 10 10
2829 15 cor. Figure skating 10 10
2830 20 cor. Shooting 15 10
2831 30 cor. Slalom 20 10
2832 40 cor. Ski jumping 25 10

1987. U.N.I.C.E.F. Child Survival Campaign. Multicoloured.

2834 10 cor. Type **435** (postage) 10 10
2835 25 cor. Vaccination (air) 75 40
2836 30 cor. Oral rehydration therapy 90 45
2837 50 cor. Breastfeeding 1·50 75

1987. (a) Flowers. As Nos. 2441/56 and 2739/54 but values changed.

2838 10 cor. blue 10 10
2839 10 cor. violet 10 10
2840 10 cor. purple 10 10
2841 10 cor. red 10 10
2842 10 cor. green 10 10
2843 10 cor. blue 10 10
2844 10 cor. green 10 10
2845 10 cor. green 10 10
2846 10 cor. mauve 10 10
2847 10 cor. red 10 10
2848 10 cor. green 10 10
2849 10 cor. orange 10 10
2850 10 cor. brown 10 10
2851 10 cor. purple 10 10
2852 10 cor. turquoise 10 10
2853 10 cor. black 10 10

DESIGNS: No. 2838, Type **356**; 2839, "Tabebula ochraceae"; 2840, "Laelia sp"; 2841, Frangipani; 2842, "Brassavola nodosa"; 2843, "Stachytarpheta indica"; 2844, "Cochlospermum sp"; 2845, "Malvaviscus arboreus"; 2846, "Tecoma stans"; 2847, Chinese hibiscus; 2848, "Cattleya lueddemanniana"; 2849, African marigold; 2850, "Senecio sp"; 2851, "Sobralia macrantha"; 2852, "Thumbergia alata"; 2853, "Bixa orellana".

(b) Agrarian Reform. As T **378**. Dated "1987".

2854 10 cor. brown 10 10
2855 10 cor. violet 10 10
2856 15 cor. purple 10 10
2857 25 cor. red 15 10
2858 30 cor. orange 20 10
2859 50 cor. brown 30 20
2860 60 cor. green 35 25
2861 100 cor. blue 65 45

DESIGNS: No. 2854, Type **378**; 2855, Cotton; 2856, Maize; 2857, Sugar; 2858, Cattle; 2859, Coffee; 2860, Rice; 2861, Bananas.

436 Flags and Buildings

438 Tennis Player

437 "Mammuthus columbi"

1987. 77th Interparliamentary Conference, Managua.

2862 **436** 10 cor. multicoloured 10 10

1987. Prehistoric Animals. Multicoloured.

2863 10 cor. Type **437** (postage) 10 10
2864 10 cor. Triceratops 10 10
2865 10 cor. Dimetrodon 10 10
2866 15 cor. Uintaterium (air) 10 10
2867 15 cor. Dinichthys 10 10
2868 30 cor. Pteranodon 60 35
2869 40 cor. Tilosaurus 85 45

1987. "Capex 87" International Stamp Exhibition, Toronto.

2870 10 cor. multicoloured (Type **438**) (postage) 10 10
2871 10 cor. multicoloured 10 10
2872 15 cor. multicoloured (male player) (air) 45 10
2873 15 cor. multicoloured (female player) 45 10
2874 20 cor. multicoloured 60 30
2875 30 cor. multicoloured 60 45
2876 40 cor. multicoloured 85 60

DESIGNS: Nos. 2871/6, Various tennis players.

439 Dobermann Pinscher

441 Levski

440 Modern Wooden Houses

1987. Dogs. Multicoloured.
2878 10 cor. Type **439** (postage) . . 10 10
2879 10 cor. Bull mastiff 10 10
2880 15 cor. Japanese spaniel (air) . 45 10
2881 15 cor. Keeshond 45 10
2882 20 cor. Chihuahua 60 30
2883 30 cor. St. Bernard 90 45
2884 40 cor. West Gotha spitz . . . 85 60

1987. Air. International Year of Shelter for the Homeless. Multicoloured.
2885 20 cor. Type **440** 15 10
2886 30 cor. Modern brick-built houses 20 10

1987. Air. 150th Birth Anniv of Vasil Levski (revolutionary).
2887 **441** 30 cor. multicoloured . . 20 10

442 "Opuntia acanthocarpa major"

1987. Cacti. Multicoloured.
2888 10 cor. Type **442** (postage) . . 10 10
2889 10 cor. "Lophocereus schottii" 10 10
2890 10 cor. "Echinocereus engelmanii" 10 10
2891 20 cor. Saguaros (air) 60 30
2892 20 cor. "Lemaireocereus thurberi" 60 30
2893 30 cor. "Opuntia fulgida" . . . 90 45
2894 50 cor. "Opuntia ficus indica" . 1·50 75

443 High Jumping

1987. 10th Pan-American Games, Indiana. Multicoloured.
2895 10 cor. Type **443** (postage) . . 10 10
2896 10 cor. Handball 10 10
2897 15 cor. Running (air) 45 10
2898 15 cor. Gymnastics 45 10
2899 20 cor. Baseball 60 30
2900 30 cor. Synchronised swimming (vert) 90 45
2901 40 cor. Weightlifting (vert) . . 1·25 60

445 "Cosmos"

1987. Cosmonautics Day. Multicoloured.
2904 10 cor. Type **445** (postage) . . 10 10
2905 10 cor "Sputnik" 10 10
2906 15 cor. "Proton" (air) 45 10
2907 25 cor. "Luna" 75 40
2908 25 cor. "Meteor" 75 40
2909 30 cor. "Electron" 90 45
2910 50 cor. "Mars-1" . . . . . . 1·50 75

446 Native Huts and Terraced Hillside

1987. Air. 500th Anniv (1992) of Discovery of America by Christopher Columbus (2nd issue). Multicoloured.
2911 15 cor. Type **446** 45 20
2912 15 cor. Columbus's fleet . . . 90 30
2913 20 cor. Spanish soldiers in native village 60 30
2914 30 cor. Mounted soldiers killing natives 90 45
2915 40 cor. Spanish people and houses . . . . 1·25 60
2916 50 cor. Church and houses . . 1·50 75

447 Tropical Gar

1987. World Food Day. Fishes. Multicoloured.
2917 10 cor. Type **447** (postage) . . 20 10
2918 10 cor. Atlantic tarpon ("Tarpon atlanticus") . . . 20 10
2919 10 cor. Jaguar guapote ("Cichlasoma managuense") 20 10
2920 15 cor. Banded astyanax ("Astyana fasciatus") (air) . 90 45
2921 15 cor. Midas cichlid ("Cichlasoma citrimellum") 90 45
2922 20 cor. Wolf cichlid . . . . . 1·25 65
2923 50 cor. Lake Nicaragua shark . 3·00 1·50

448 Lenin

449 "Nativity"

1987. 70th Anniv of Russian Revolution. Mult.
2924 10 cor. Type **448** (postage) . . 10 10
2925 30 cor. "Aurora" (cruiser) (horiz) (air) 50 15
2926 50 cor. Russian arms 30 20

1987. Christmas. Details of Painting by L. Saenz. Multicoloured.
2927 10 cor. Type **449** 10 10
2928 20 cor. "Adoration of the Magi" 60 30
2929 25 cor. "Adoration of the Magi" (close-up detail) 75 40
2930 50 cor. "Nativity" (close-up detail) . . . . 1·50 75

1987. Surch.
2931 **435** 400 cor. on 10 cor. mult (postage) 30 15
2935 **440** 200 cor. on 20 cor. multicoloured (air) . . 15 10
2932 – 600 cor. on 50 cor. mult (No. 2837) 40 20
2933 – 1000 cor. on 25 cor. mult (No. 2835) 70 35
2936 – 3000 cor. on 30 cor. mult (No. 2886) . . . . . 2·10 1·00
2934 – 5000 cor. on 30 cor. mult (No. 2836) . . . . . 3·50 1·75

451 Cross-country Skiing

452 Flag around Globe

1988. Winter Olympic Games, Calgary. Mult.
2937 10 cor. Type **451** 10 10
2938 10 cor. Rifle-shooting (horiz) . 10 10
2939 15 cor. Ice hockey 45 10
2940 20 cor. Ice skating 60 30
2941 25 cor. Downhill skiing . . . 75 40
2942 30 cor. Ski jumping (horiz) . . 90 45
2943 40 cor. Slalom . . . . 1·25 60

1988. 10th Anniv of Nicaragua Journalists' Association. Multicoloured.
2945 1 cor. Type **452** (postage) . . 10 10
2946 5 cor. Churches of St. Francis Xavier, Sandino and Fatima, Managua, and speaker addressing journalists (42 × 27 mm) (air) . . . . 1·25 60

453 Basketball

1988. Olympic Games, Seoul. Multicoloured.
2947 10 cor. Type **453** 10 10
2948 10 cor. Gymnastics 10 10
2949 15 cor. Volleyball 45 10
2950 20 cor. Long jumping 60 30
2951 25 cor. Football 75 40
2952 30 cor. Water polo 90 45
2953 40 cor. Boxing . . . . 1·25 60

454 Brown Bear

1988. Mammals and their Young. Multicoloured.
2955 10 c. Type **454** (postage) . . . 10 10
2956 15 c. Lion 10 10
2957 25 c. Cocker spaniel 10 10
2958 50 c. Wild boar 15 10
2959 4 cor. Cheetah (air) 55 20
2960 7 cor. Spotted hyena . . . . 1·00 40
2961 8 cor. Red fox . . . . 1·25 50

455 Slide Tackle

1988. "Essen '88" International Stamp Fair and European Football Championship, Germany. Multicoloured.
2963 50 c. Type **455** (postage) . . . 10 10
2964 1 cor. Footballers 15 10
2965 2 cor. Lining up shot (vert) (air) 30 10
2966 3 cor. Challenging for ball (vert) 50 20
2967 4 cor. Heading ball (vert) . . 65 25
2968 5 cor. Tackling (vert) 80 30
2969 6 cor. Opponent winning possession . . . . 1·00 40

456 Bell JetRanger III ($\frac{1}{2}$-size illustration)

1988. "Finlandia 88" International Stamp Exhibition, Helsinki. Helicopters. Multicoloured.
2971 4 cor. Type **456** (postage) . . 15 10
2972 12 cor. MBB-Kawasaki BK-117A-3 (air) 20 10
2973 16 cor. Boeing-Vertol B-360 . 30 10
2974 20 cor. Agusta A.109 MR11 . 40 10
2975 24 cor. Sikorsky S-61N . . . 55 20
2976 28 cor. Aerospatiale SA.365 Dauphin 2 . . . . 60 25
2977 56 cor. Sikorsky S-76 Spirit . . 1·25 50

457 Flags and Map

458 Casimiro Sotelo Montenegro

1988. 9th Anniv of Revolution. Multicoloured.
2979 1 cor. Type **457** (postage) . . 20 10
2980 5 cor. Landscape and hands releasing dove (air) 80 30

1988. Revolutionaries.
2981 **458** 4 cor. blue (postage) . . . 15 10
2982 – 12 cor. mauve (air) . . . 20 10
2983 – 16 cor. green 30 10
2984 – 20 cor. red 45 15
2985 – 24 cor. brown 55 20
2986 – 28 cor. violet 65 25
2987 – 50 cor. red . . . . . . 1·25 45
2988 – 100 cor. purple . . . . . 2·40 1·00

DESIGNS: 12 cor. Ricardo Morales Aviles; 16 cor. Silvio Mayorga Delgado; 20 cor. Pedro Arauz Palacios; 24 cor. Oscar A. Turcios Chavarrias; 28 cor. Julio C. Buitrago Urroz; 50 cor. Jose B. Escobar Perez; 100 cor. Eduardo E. Contreras Escobar.

459 "Acacia baileyana"

460 West Indian Fighting Conch

1988. Flowers. Multicoloured.
2989 4 cor. Type **459** (postage) . . 15 10
2990 12 cor. "Anigozanthos manglesii" (air) 20 10
2991 16 cor. "Telopia speciosissima" 30 10
2992 20 cor. "Eucalyptus ficifolia" . 45 15
2993 24 cor. "Boronia heterophylla" 60 30
2994 28 cor. "Callistemon speciosus" 70 35
2995 30 cor. "Nymphaea caerulea" (horiz) 80 40
2996 50 cor. "Clianthus formosus" . 1·25 60

1988. Molluscs. Multicoloured.
2997 4 cor. Type **460** (postage) . . 20 10
2998 12 cor. Painted polymita (air) . 30 10
2999 16 cor. Giant sundial 40 10
3000 20 cor. Japanese baking oyster . 55 10
3001 24 cor. Yoka star shell 75 20
3002 28 cor. Gawdy frog shell . . . 80 25
3003 50 cor. Mantled top . . . . . 1·75 50

461 Zapotecan Funeral Urn

462 "Chrysina macropus"

1988. 500th Anniv (1992) of Discovery of America by Columbus (3rd issue). Multicoloured.
3004 4 cor. Type **461** (postage) . . 15 10
3005 12 cor. Mochican ceramic seated figure (air) 20 10
3006 16 cor. Mochican ceramic head 30 10
3007 20 cor. Tainan ceramic vessel . 45 10
3008 28 cor. Nazcan vessel (horiz) . 65 20
3009 100 cor. Incan ritual pipe (horiz) 2·40 1·00

1988. Beetles. Multicoloured.
3011 4 cor. Type **462** (postage) . . 15 10
3012 12 cor. "Plusiotis victoriana" (air) 20 10
3013 16 cor. "Ceratotrupes bolivari" 30 10
3014 20 cor. "Gymnetosoma stellata" 50 15
3015 24 cor. "Euphoria lineoligera" . 60 20
3016 28 cor. "Euphoria candezei" . 70 30
3017 50 cor. "Sulcophanaeus chryseicollis" . . . . . . 1·25 50

463 Dario

1988. Air. Centenary of Publication of "Blue" by Ruben Dario.
3018 **463** 25 cor. multicoloured . . 60 20

464 Simon Bolivar, Jose Marti, Gen. Sandino and Fidel Castro

1989. Air. 30th Anniv of Cuban Revolution.
3019 **464** 20 cor. multicoloured . . 50 20

465 Pochomil Tourist Centre

1989. Tourism. Multicoloured.
3020 4 cor. Type **465** (postage) . . 15 10
3021 12 cor. Granada Tourist Centre (air) 45 15
3022 20 cor. Olof Palme Convention Centre 45 15
3023 24 cor. Masaya Volcano National Park 55 20
3024 28 cor. La Boquita Tourist Centre 70 25
3025 30 cor. Xiloa Tourist Centre . 75 30
3026 50 cor. Managua Hotel . . . 1·25 50

466 Footballers **467** Downhill Skiing

1989. Air. World Cup Football Championship, Italy (1990).
3028 **466** 100 cor. multicoloured . . 10 10
3029 – 200 cor. multicoloured . . 10 10
3030 – 600 cor. multicoloured . . 10 10
3031 – 1000 cor. multicoloured . 30 10
3032 – 2000 cor. multicoloured . 60 10
3033 – 3000 cor. multicoloured . 90 40
3034 – 5000 cor. multicoloured . 1·50 50
DESIGNS: 200 cor. to 5000 cor. Different footballers.

1989. Air. Winter Olympic Games, Albertville (1992) (1st issue). Multicoloured.
3036 50 cor. Type **467** 10 10
3037 300 cor. Ice hockey 10 10
3038 600 cor. Ski jumping 10 10
3039 1000 cor. Ice skating 30 10
3040 2000 cor. Biathlon 60 10
3041 3000 cor. Slalom 90 40
3042 5000 cor. Skiing . . . . . . 1·50 50
See also Nos. 3184/90.

468 Water Polo

1989. Air. Olympic Games, Barcelona (1992). Multicoloured.
3044 100 cor. Type **468** 10 10
3045 200 cor. Running 10 10
3046 600 cor. Diving 10 10
3047 1000 cor. Gymnastics 30 10
3048 2000 cor. Weightlifting . . . 60 10
3049 3000 cor. Volleyball 90 40
3050 5000 cor. Wrestling . . . . . 1·50 50
See also Nos. 3192/8.

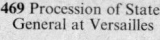

469 Procession of States General at Versailles **470** American Anhinga

1989. "Philexfrance 89" International Stamp Exhibition, Paris, and Bicentenary of French Revolution. Multicoloured.
3052 50 cor. Type **469** (postage) . . 15 10
3054 300 cor. Oath of the Tennis Court (36 × 28 mm) (air) . . 10 10
3055 600 cor. "The 14th of July" (29 × 40 mm) 10 10
3056 1000 cor. Tree of Liberty (36 × 28 mm) 30 10
3057 2000 cor. "Liberty guiding the People" (Eugene Delacroix) (29 × 40 mm) 60 10
3058 3000 cor. Storming the Bastille (36 × 28 mm) 90 40
3059 5000 cor. Lafayette taking oath (28 × 36 mm) . . . . 1·50 50

1989. Air. "Brasiliana 89" International Stamp Exhibition, Rio de Janeiro. Birds. Multicoloured.
3060 100 cor. Type **470** 10 10
3061 200 cor. Swallow-tailed kite . . 10 10
3062 600 cor. Turquoise-browed motmot 10 10
3063 1000 cor. Painted redstart . . 30 10
3064 2000 cor. Great antshrike (horiz) 60 10
3065 3000 cor. Northern royal flycatcher 90 40
3066 5000 cor. White-flanked antwren (horiz) . . . . . . 1·50 50

471 Anniversary Emblem **472** Animal-shaped Vessel

1989. Air. 10th Anniv of Revolution.
3068 **471** 300 cor. multicoloured . . 10 10

1989. Air. America. Pre-Columbian Artefacts.
3070 **472** 2000 cor. multicoloured . 60 10

Currency Reform. 150000 (old) cordoba = 1 (new) cordoba

The following issues, denominated in the old currency, were distributed by agents but were not issued (each set consists of seven values and is dated "1990"):
"London 90" International Stamp Exn. Ships
World Cup Football Championship, Italy
Olympic Games, Barcelona (1992)
Fungi
Winter Olympic Games, Albertville (1992)

473 Little Spotted Kiwi

1991. "New Zealand 1990" International Stamp Exhibition, Auckland. Birds. Multicoloured.
3071 5 c. Type **473** 10 10
3072 5 c. Takahe 10 10
3073 10 c. Red-fronted parakeet . . 15 10
3074 20 c. Weka rail 30 15
3075 30 c. Kagu (vert) 45 20
3076 60 c. Kea 85 45
3077 70 c. Kakapo . . . . . . 1·00 50

474 Jaguar

1991. 45th Anniv of Food and Agriculture Organization. Animals. Multicoloured.
3079 5 c. Type **474** 10 10
3080 5 c. Ocelot (vert) 10 10
3081 10 c. Black-handed spider monkey (vert) 15 10
3082 20 c. Baird's tapir 30 15
3083 30 c. Nine-banded armadillo . 45 20
3084 60 c. Coyote 85 45
3085 70 c. Two-toed sloth . . . . 1·00 50

HAVE YOU READ THE NOTES AT THE BEGINNING OF THIS CATALOGUE?
These often provide answers to the enquiries we receive.

475 Dr. Chamorro **476** Steam Locomotive, 1920s, Peru

1991. Dr. Pedro Joaquin Chamorro (campaigner for an independent Press).
3086 **475** 2 cor. 25 multicoloured . . 50 20

1991. Flowers. As T **356** but with currency inscribed in "oro".
3087 – 1 cor. blue 25 10
3088 – 2 cor. green 45 20
3089 – 3 cor. brown 70 30
3090 – 4 cor. purple 95 40
3091 – 5 cor. red . . . . . . 1·10 45
3092 – 6 cor. green . . . . . 1·40 55
3093 **356** 7 cor. blue . . . . . . 1·60 65
3094 – 8 cor. green . . . . . 1·90 75
3095 – 9 cor. green . . . . . 2·10 85
3096 – 10 cor. violet . . . . . 2·25 90
3097 – 11 cor. mauve . . . . . 2·50 1·00
3098 – 12 cor. yellow . . . . . 2·75 1·10
3099 – 13 cor. red . . . . . . 3·00 1·25
3100 – 14 cor. green . . . . . 3·25 1·25
3101 – 15 cor. mauve . . . . . 3·50 1·40
3102 – 16 cor. black . . . . . 3·75 1·50
DESIGNS: 1 cor. "Stachytarpheta indica"; 2 cor. "Cochlospermum sp."; 3 cor. "Senecio sp."; 4 cor. "Sobralia macrantha"; 5 cor. Frangipani; 6 cor. "Brassavola nodosa"; 8 cor. "Malvaviscus arboreus"; 9 cor. "Cattleya lueddemanniana"; 10 cor. "Tabebula ochraceae"; 11 cor. "Laelia sp."; 12 cor. African marigold; 13 cor. Chinese hibiscus; 14 cor. "Thumbergia alata"; 15 cor. "Tecoma stans"; 16 cor. "Bixa orellana".

1991. Steam Locomotives of South and Central America. Multicoloured.
3103 25 c. Type **476** 30 10
3104 25 c. Locomotive No. 508, 1917, Bolivia 30 10
3105 50 c. Class N/O locomotive, 1910s, Argentina 50 10
3106 1 cor. 50 Locomotive, 1952, Chile 90 20
3107 2 cor. Locomotive No. 61, 1944, Colombia . . . . 1·25 25
3108 3 cor. Locomotive No. 311, 1947, Brazil . . . . 2·00 35
3109 3 cor. 50 Locomotive No. 60, 1910, Paraguay . . . . . . 2·25 45

477 Match Scene (West Germany versus Netherlands)

1991. West Germany, Winners of World Cup Football Championship (1990). Multicoloured.
3111 25 c. Type **477** 10 10
3112 25 c. Match scene (West Germany versus Colombia) (vert) 10 10
3113 50 c. West German players and referee 10 10
3114 1 cor. West German players forming wall (vert) 25 10
3115 1 cor. 50 Diego Maradona (Argentina) (vert) 35 15
3116 3 cor. Argentinian players and Italian goalkeeper (vert) . . 70 30
3117 3 cor. 50 Italian players . . . 80 30

478 "Prepona praeneste"

1991. Butterflies. Multicoloured.
3119 25 c. Type **478** 10 10
3120 25 c. "Anartia fatima" 10 10
3121 50 c. "Eryphanis aesacus" . . 10 10
3122 1 cor. "Heliconius melpomene" 25 10
3123 1 cor. 50 "Chlosyne janais" . . 35 15
3124 3 cor. "Marpesia iole" 70 30
3125 3 cor. 50 Rusty-tipped page . . 80 30

479 Dove and Cross

1991. 700th Anniv of Swiss Confederation.
3127 **479** 2 cor. 25 red, black and yellow 50 20

480 Yellow-headed Amazon

1991. "Rainforest is Life". Fauna. Multicoloured.
3128 2 cor. 25 Type **480** 50 20
3129 2 cor. 25 Keel-billed toucan . . 50 20
3130 2 cor. 25 Scarlet macaw . . . 50 20
3131 2 cor. 25 Resplendent quetzal . 50 20
3132 2 cor. 25 Black-handed spider monkey 50 20
3133 2 cor. 25 White-throated capuchin 50 20
3134 2 cor. 25 Three-toed sloth . . 50 20
3135 2 cor. 25 Chestnut-headed oropendola 50 20
3136 2 cor. 25 Violet sabrewing . . 50 20
3137 2 cor. 25 Tamandua 50 20
3138 2 cor. 25 Jaguarundi 50 20
3139 2 cor. 25 Boa constrictor . . . 50 20
3140 2 cor. 25 Common iguana . . 50 20
3141 2 cor. 25 Jaguar 50 20
3142 2 cor. 25 White-necked jacobin 50 20
3143 2 cor. 25 "Doxocopa clothilda" (butterfly) 50 20
3144 2 cor. 25 "Dismorphia deione" (butterfly) 50 20
3145 2 cor. 25 Golden arrow-poison frog 50 20
3146 2 cor. 25 "Callithomia hezia" (butterfly) 50 20
3147 2 cor. 25 Chameleon 50 20
Nos. 3128/47 were issued together, se-tenant, forming a composite design.

481 "Isochilus major"

1991. Orchids. Multicoloured.
3148 25 c. Type **481** 10 10
3149 25 c. "Cycnoches ventricosum" 10 10
3150 50 c. "Vanilla odorata" . . . 10 10
3151 1 cor. "Helleriella nicaraguensis" 25 10
3152 1 cor. 50 "Barkeria spectabilis" 35 15
3153 3 cor. "Maxillaria hedwigae" . 70 30
3154 3 cor. 50 "Cattleya aurantiaca" 80 30

482 Concepcion Volcano

1991. America (1990).
3156 **482** 2 cor. 25 multicoloured . . 50 20

483 Warehouse and Flags

1991. 30th Anniv of Central American Bank of Economic Integration.
3157 **483** 1 cor. 50 multicoloured . . 35 15

484 "The One-eyed Man"

1991. Death Centenary (1990) of Vincent van Gogh (painter). Multicoloured.
3158 25 c. Type **484** 10 10
3159 25 c. "Head of Countrywoman with Bonnet" 10 10
3160 50 c. "Self-portrait" 10 10
3161 1 cor. "Vase with Carnations and other Flowers" 25 10
3162 1 cor. 50 "Vase with Zinnias and Geraniums" 35 15

3163 3 cor. "Portrait of Tanguy Father" 70 30
3164 3 cor. 50 "Portrait of a Man" (horiz) 80 30

485 Painting by Rafaela Herrera (1st-prize winner)

1991. National Children's Painting Competition.
3166 **485** 2 cor. 25 multicoloured . . 50 20

486 Golden Pavilion

1991. "Phila Nippon '91" International Stamp Exhibition, Tokyo. Multicoloured.
3167 25 c. Type **486** 10 10
3168 50 c. Himaji Castle 10 10
3169 1 cor. Head of Bunraku doll . 25 10
3170 1 cor. 50 Japanese cranes . . . 35 15
3171 2 cor. 50 Phoenix pavilion . . 60 25
3172 3 cor. "The Guardian" (statue) 70 30
3173 3 cor. 50 Kabuki actor . . . 80 30

487 Turquoise-browed Motmot
488 Columbus's Fleet

1992. Birds. Multicoloured.
3175 50 c. Type **487** 15 10
3176 75 c. Collared trogon 20 10
3177 1 cor. Broad-billed motmot . . 25 10
3178 1 cor. 50 Wire-tailed manakin . 40 15
3179 1 cor. 75 Paradise tanager (horiz) 45 20
3180 2 cor. 25 Resplendent quetzal . 60 25
3181 2 cor. 25 Black-spotted bare-eye 60 25

1992. America (1991). Voyages of Discovery.
3183 **488** 2 cor. 25 multicoloured . . 35 15

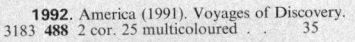

489 Ice Hockey

1992. Winter Olympic Games, Albertville (2nd issue). Multicoloured.
3184 25 c. Type **489** 10 10
3185 25 c. Four-man bobsleighing . 10 10
3186 50 c. Skiing (vert) 15 10
3187 1 cor. Speed skating 25 10
3188 1 cor. 50 Cross-country skiing . 40 15
3189 3 cor. Double luge 75 30
3190 3 cor. 50 Ski jumping (vert) . . 90 35

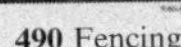

490 Fencing
491 Ceramic Vase with Face (Lorenza Pineda Co-operative)

1992. Olympic Games, Barcelona (2nd issue) Multicoloured.
3192 25 c. Type **490** 10 10
3193 25 c. Throwing the javelin (horiz) 10 10
3194 50 c. Basketball 15 10
3195 1 cor. 50 Running 40 15
3196 2 cor. Long jumping 50 20
3197 3 cor. Running 75 30
3198 3 cor. 50 Show jumping . . . 90 35

1992. Contemporary Arts and Crafts. Multicoloured.
3200 25 c. Type **491** 10 10
3201 25 c. Ceramic spouted vessel (Jose Ortiz) (horiz) 10 10
3202 50 c. Blue-patterned ceramic vase (Elio Gutierrez) . . . 15 10
3203 1 cor. "Christ" (Jose de los Santos) 25 10
3204 1 cor. 50 "Family" (sculpture, Erasmo Moya) 40 15
3205 3 cor. "Bird-fish" (Silvio Chavarria Co-operative) (horiz) 85 30
3206 3 cor. 50 Filigree ceramic vessel (Maria de los Angeles Bermudez) 90 35

492 "Picnic Table with Three Objects" (Alejandro Arostegui)
493 Magnificent Hummingbird

1992. Contemporary Paintings. Multicoloured.
3208 25 c. Type **492** 10 10
3209 25 c. "Prophetess of the New World" (Alberto Ycaza) . . 10 10
3210 50 c. "Flames of Unknown Origin" (Bernard Dreyfus) (horiz) 15 10
3211 1 cor. 50 "Owl" (Orlando Sobalvarro) (horiz) 40 15
3212 2 cor. "Pegasus at Liberty" (Hugo Palma) (horiz) . . . 50 20
3213 3 cor. "Avocados" (Omar d'Leon) (horiz) 75 30
3214 3 cor. 50 "Gueguense" (Carlos Montenegro) 90 35

1992. 2nd U.N. Conference on Environment and Development, Rio de Janeiro. Tropical Forest Wildlife. Multicoloured.
3216 1 cor. 50 Type **493** 40 15
3217 1 cor. 50 Harpy eagle ("Aguila arpia") 40 15
3218 1 cor. 50 Orchid 40 15
3219 1 cor. 50 Toucan and morpho butterfly 40 15
3220 1 cor. 50 Quetzal 40 15
3221 1 cor. 50 Guardabarranco . . 40 15
3222 1 cor. 50 Howler monkey ("Mono aullador") 40 15
3223 1 cor. 50 Sloth ("Perezoso") . . 40 15
3224 1 cor. 50 Squirrel monkey ("Mono ardilla") 40 15
3225 1 cor. 50 Macaw ("Guacamaya") 40 15
3226 1 cor. 50 Emerald boa and scarlet tanager 40 15
3227 1 cor. 50 Poison-arrow frog . 40 15
3228 1 cor. 50 Jaguar 40 15
3229 1 cor. 50 Anteater 40 15
3230 1 cor. 50 Ocelot 40 15
3231 1 cor. 50 Coati 40 15
Nos. 3216/31 were issued together, se-tenant, forming a composite design of a forest.

494 Fabretto with Children

1992. Father Fabretto, "Benefactor of Nicaraguan Children".
3232 **494** 2 cor. 25 multicoloured . . 60 25

495 "Nicaraguan Identity" (Claudia Gordillo)

1992. Winning Entry in Photography Competition.
3233 **495** 2 cor. 25 multicoloured . . 60 25

496 "The Indians of Nicaragua" (Milton Jose Cruz)

1992. Winning Entry in Children's Painting Competition.
3234 **496** 2 cor. 25 multicoloured . . 60 25

497 Eucharistical Banner
498 Rivas Cross, 1523

1993. 460th Anniv of Catholic Church in Nicaragua. Multicoloured.
3235 25 c. Type **497** 10 10
3236 50 c. "Shrine of the Immaculate Conception" 10 10
3237 1 cor. 18th-century document . 20 10
3238 1 cor. 50 16th-century baptismal font 30 10
3239 2 cor. "The Immaculate Conception" 40 15
3240 2 cor. 25 Monsignor Diego Alvarez Osorio (1st Bishop of Leon) 50 20
3241 3 cor. "Christ on the Cross" . 65 25

1993. America (1992). 500th Anniv of Discovery of America by Columbus.
3242 **498** 2 cor. 25 multicoloured . . 50 20

499 Cathedral

1993. Inauguration of Cathedral of the Immaculate Conception of Mary, Managua. Multicoloured.
3243 3 cor. Type **499** 65 25
3244 4 cor. Cross, Virgin Mary and map of Nicaragua (2nd Provincial Council) 85 35
Nos. 3243/4 were issued together, se-tenant, forming a composite design.

500 Emblem and Voters queueing outside Poll Station

1993. 23rd General Assembly of Organization of American States.
3245 **500** 3 cor. multicoloured . . . 85 45

501 Anniversary Emblem

1993. 90th Anniv of Panamerican Health Organization.
3246 **501** 3 cor. multicoloured . . . 85 45

502 "Sonatina" (Alma Iris Perez)

1993. Winning Entry in Children's Painting Competition.
3247 **502** 3 cor. multicoloured . . . 85 45

503 Racoon Buttterflyfish

1993. Butterflyfishes. Multicoloured.
3248 1 cor. 50 Type **503** 50 25
3249 1 cor. 50 Rainford's butterflyfish ("Chaetodon rainfordi") 50 25
3250 1 cor. 50 Mailed butterflyfish ("Chaetodon reticulatus") . 50 25
3251 1 cor. 50 Thread-finned butterflyfish ("Chaetodon auriga") 50 25
3252 1 cor. 50 Pennant coralfish ("Heniochus acuminatus") . 50 25
3253 1 cor. 50 Dark-banded butterflyfish ("Coradion fulvocinctus") 50 25
3254 1 cor. 50 Mirror butterflyfish ("Chaetodon speculum") . . 50 25
3255 1 cor. 50 Lined butterflyfish ("Chaetodon lineolatus") . 50 25
3256 1 cor. 50 Bennett's butterflyfish ("Chaetodon bennetti") . . 50 25
3257 1 cor. 50 Black-backed butterflyfish ("Chaetodon melanotus") . 50 25
3258 1 cor. 50 Golden butterflyfish ("Chaetodon aureus") . . . 50 25
3259 1 cor. 50 Saddle butterflyfish ("Chaetodon ephippium") . 50 25
3260 1 cor. 50 Pyramid butterflyfish ("Hemitaurichthys polylepis") 50 25
3261 1 cor. 50 Dotted butterflyfish ("Chaetodon semeion") . . 50 25
3262 1 cor. 50 Klein's butterflyfish ("Chaetodon kleinii") . . . 50 25
3263 1 cor. 50 Copper-banded butterflyfish ("Chelmon rostratus") 50 25

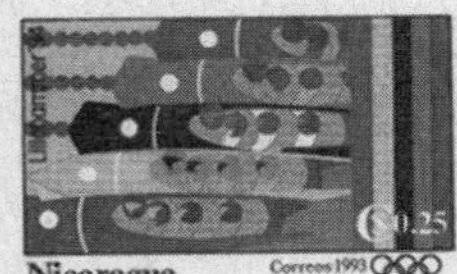

504 Four-man Bobsleighing

1993. Multicoloured. (a) Winter Olympic Games, Lillehammer, Norway (1994).
3264 25 c. Type **504** 10 10
3265 25 c. Skiing 10 10
3266 50 c. Speed skating 15 10
3267 1 cor. 50 Ski jumping 45 20
3268 2 cor. Women's figure skating . 55 25
3269 3 cor. Pairs' figure skating . . 85 45
3270 3 cor. 50 Shooting (biathlon) . 1·00 45

(b) Olympic Games, Atlanta (1996).
3271 25 c. Swimming 10 10
3272 25 c. Diving 10 10
3273 50 c. Long distance running . 15 10
3274 1 cor. Hurdling 30 15
3275 1 cor. 50 Gymnastics 45 20
3276 3 cor. Throwing the javelin . . 85 45
3277 3 cor. 50 Sprinting . . . . . 1·00 50

505 "Bromeliaceae sp."
506 Tomas Brolin (Sweden)

1994. Tropical Forest Flora and Fauna. Multicoloured.
3279 2 cor. Type **505** 50 25
3280 2 cor. Dupont's hummingbird ("Tilmatura dupontii") . . 50 25
3281 2 cor. "Anolis biporcatus" (lizard) 50 25
3282 2 cor. Lantern fly ("Fulgara laternaria") 50 25
3283 2 cor. Sloth ("Bradypus sp.") . 50 25
3284 2 cor. Ornate hawk eagle ("Spizaetus ornatus") . . . 50 25
3285 2 cor. Lovely cotinga ("Cotinga amabilis") 50 25
3286 2 cor. Schegel's lance-head snake ("Bothrops schlegelii") 50 25
3287 2 cor. "Odontoglossum sp." (orchid) and bee 50 25
3288 2 cor. Red-eyed tree frog ("Agalychnis callidryas") . 50 25
3289 2 cor. "Heliconius sapho" (butterfly) 50 25
3290 2 cor. Passion flower ("Passiflora vitifolia") . . . 50 25
Nos. 3279/90 were issued together, se-tenant, forming a composite design.

1994. World Cup Football Championship, U.S.A. Players.

3292 50 c. Type **506** 15 10
3293 1 cor. Jan Karas (Poland) and Antonio Luiz Costa (Brazil) 30 15
3294 1 cor. Maxime Bossis and Michel Platini (France) . . 30 15
3295 1 cor. 50 Harold Schumacher (Germany) 45 20
3296 2 cor. Andoni Zubizarreta (Spain) 55 30
3297 2 cor. 50 Lothar Matthaeus (Germany) and Diego Maradona (Argentine Republic) 75 35
3298 3 cor. 50 Bryan Robson (England) and Carlos Santos (Portugal) . . . . 1·00 50

507 "Four in One" (Julio Lopez)

1994. Contemporary Arts. Multicoloured.

3300 50 c. Rush mat (Rosalia Sevilla) (horiz) 15 10
3301 50 c. Type **507** 15 10
3302 1 cor. Ceramic church (Auxiliadora Bush) 30 15
3303 1 cor. Statuette of old woman (Indiana Robleto) 30 15
3304 2 cor. 50 "Santiago" (Jose de los Santos) 55 30
3305 3 cor. "Gueguense" (Ines Gutierrez de Chong) . . . 85 45
3306 4 cor. Ceramic hornet's nest (Elio Gutierrez) 95 45

508 "Callicore patelina"

1994. "Hong Kong '94" International Stamp Exhibition. Butterflies. Multicoloured.

3308 1 cor. 50 Type **508** 35 15
3309 1 cor. 50 "Chlosyne narva" . . 35 15
3310 1 cor. 50 Giant brimstone ("Anteos maerula") 35 15
3311 1 cor. 50 Diadem ("Marpesia petreus") 35 15
3312 1 cor. 50 "Pierella helvetia" . 35 15
3313 1 cor. 50 "Eurytides epidaus" . 35 15
3314 1 cor. 50 Doris ("Heliconius doris") 35 15
3315 1 cor. 50 "Smyrna blomfildia" . 35 15
3316 1 cor. 50 "Eueides lybia olympia" 35 15
3317 1 cor. 50 "Adelpha heraclea" . 35 15
3318 1 cor. 50 "Heliconius hecale zuleika" 35 15
3319 1 cor. 50 "Parides montezuma" 35 15
3320 1 cor. 50 "Morpho polyphemus" 35 15
3321 1 cor. 50 "Eresia alsina" . . 35 15
3322 1 cor. 50 "Prepona omphale octavia" 35 15
3323 1 cor. 50 "Morpho grenadensis" 35 15

509 "The Holy Family" (anonymous)

1994. Christmas (1993). Paintings. Multicoloured.

3324 1 cor. Type **509** 25 15
3325 4 cor. "Nativity" (Lezamon) . 95 45

510 Sculpture

1994. Chontal Culture Statuary. Multicoloured, colour of frame given.

3326 **510** 50 c. yellow 15 10
3327 – 50 c. yellow 15 10
3328 – 1 cor. emerald 30 15
3329 – 1 cor. green 30 15
3330 – 2 cor. 50 blue 55 35
3331 – 3 cor. blue 85 45
3332 – 4 cor. green 95 45

DESIGNS: 50 c. (3327) to 4 cor. Different sculptures.

511 "Virgin of Nicaragua" (Celia Lacayo)

1994. Contemporary Paintings. Multicoloured.

3334 50 c. Type **511** 15 10
3335 50 c. "Woman embroidering" (Guillermo Rivas Navas) . . 15 10
3336 1 cor. "Couple dancing" (June Beer) 30 15
3337 1 cor. "Song of Peace" (Alejandro Canales) 30 15
3338 2 cor. 50 "Sapodilla Plums" (Genaro Lugo) (horiz) . . . 55 30
3339 3 cor. "Figure and Fragments" (Leonel Vanegas) 85 45
3340 4 cor. "Eruption of Agua Volcano" (Asilia Guillen) (horiz) 95 45

512 Nicolas Copernicus and Satellite

1994. Astronomers. Mutlicoloured.

3342 1 cor. 50 Type **512** 35 15
3343 1 cor. 50 Tycho Brahe and astronomers 35 15
3344 1 cor. 50 Galileo Galilei and "Galileo" space probe . . . 35 15
3345 1 cor. 50 Sir Isaac Newton and telescope 35 15
3346 1 cor. 50 Edmond Halley, space probe and Halley's Comet . 35 15
3347 1 cor. 50 James Bradley and Greenwich Observatory . . 35 15
3348 1 cor. 50 William Herschel and telescope 35 15
3349 1 cor. 50 John Goodricke and Algol (star) 35 15
3350 1 cor. 50 Karl Friedrich Gauss and Gottingen Observatory . 35 15
3351 1 cor. 50 Friedrich Bessel and 1838 star telescope . . . 35 15
3352 1 cor. 50 William Cranch Bond (wrongly inscr "Granch") and Harvard College Observatory 35 15
3353 1 cor. 50 Sir George Airy and stellar disk 35 15
3354 1 cor. 50 Percival Lowell and Flagstaff Observatory, Arizona, U.S.A. 35 15
3355 1 cor. 50 George Hale (wrongly inscr "Halle") and solar spectroscope 35 15
3356 1 cor. 50 Edwin Hubble and Hubble telescope 35 15
3357 1 cor. 50 Gerard Kuiper and Miranda (Uranus moon) . . 35 15

Nos. 3342/57 were issued together, se-tenant, forming a composite design.

513 1886 Benz Tricycle

1994. Automobiles. Multicoloured.

3359 1 cor. 50 Type **513** 35 15
3360 1 cor. 50 1909 Benz Blitzen . . 35 15
3361 1 cor. 50 1923 Mercedes Benz 24/100/140 . . . . 35 15
3362 1 cor. 50 1928 Mercedes Benz SSK 35 15
3363 1 cor. 50 1934 Mercedes Benz 500K Cabriolet 35 15
3364 1 cor. 50 1949 Mercedes Benz 170S 35 15
3365 1 cor. 50 1954 Mercedes Benz W196 . . . . 35 15
3366 1 cor. 50 1954 Mercedes Benz 300SL 35 15
3367 1 cor. 50 1896 Ford Quadricycle 35 15
3368 1 cor. 50 1920 Ford taxi cab . 35 15
3369 1 cor. 50 1928 Ford Roadster . 35 15
3370 1 cor. 50 1932 Ford V-8 . . . 35 15
3371 1 cor. 50 1937 Ford V-8 78 . . 35 15
3372 1 cor. 50 1939 Ford 91 Deluxe Tudor Sedan 35 15
3373 1 cor. 50 1946 Ford V-8 Sedan Coupe 35 15
3374 1 cor. 50 1958 Ford Custom 300 35 15

514 Hugo Eckener and Count Ferdinand von Zeppelin

1994. Zeppelin Airships. Multicoloured.

3376 1 cor. 50 Type **514** 35 15
3377 1 cor. 50 "Graf Zeppelin" over New York, 1928 . . . . . 35 15
3378 1 cor. 50 "Graf Zeppelin" over Tokyo, 1929 . . . . . . 35 15
3379 1 cor. 50 "Graf Zeppelin" over house of Randolph Hearst's villa, 1929 . . . . 35 15
3380 1 cor. 50 Charles Lindbergh, Hugo Eckener and "Graf Zeppelin" at Lakehurst, 1929 . . . . 35 15
3381 1 cor. 50 "Graf Zeppelin" over St. Basil's Cathedral, Moscow (wrongly inscr "Santra Sofia") 35 15
3382 1 cor. 50 "Graf Zeppelin" over Paris, 1930 . . . . . . 35 15
3383 1 cor. 50 "Graf Zeppelin" over Cairo, Egypt, 1931 . . . 35 15
3384 1 cor. 50 "Graf Zeppelin" over Arctic Sea 35 15
3385 1 cor. 50 "Graf Zeppelin" over Rio de Janeiro, 1932 . . . 35 15
3386 1 cor. 50 "Graf Zeppelin" over St. Paul's Cathedral, London, 1935 . . . . 35 15
3387 1 cor. 50 "Graf Zeppelin" over St. Peter's Cathedral, Rome . 35 15
3388 1 cor. 50 "Graf Zeppelin" over Swiss Alps 35 15
3389 1 cor. 50 "Graf Zeppelin over Brandenburg Gate, Berlin . 35 15
3390 1 cor. 50 Hugo Eckener piloting "Graf Zeppelin" 35 15
3391 1 cor. 50 Captain Ernest Lehman, "Graf Zeppelin" and Dornier Do-X flying boat 35 15

515 Gabriel Horvilleur

1994. Nicaraguan Philatelists. Multicoloured.

3393 1 cor. Type **515** 15 10
3394 3 cor. Jose Cauadra 85 45
3395 4 cor. Alfredo Pertz 95 45

517 "Poponjoche" (Thelma Gomez)
518 Conference Emblem

1994. 1st Nicaraguan Tree Conference.

3397 **517** 4 cor. multicoloured . . . 95 45

1994. 2nd International Conference on New and Restored Democracies, Managua.

3398 **518** 3 cor. multicoloured . . . 55 55

519 Pulpit, Leon Cathedral

520 Mascot and Emblem

1994. Religious Art. Multicoloured.

3399 50 c. Type **519** 15 10
3400 50 c. "St. Anna" (porcelain figure), Chinandega Church . 15 10
3401 1 cor. "St. Joseph and Child" (porcelain figure), St. Peter's Church, Rivas 30 15
3402 1 cor. "St. James", Jinotepe Church 30 15
3403 2 cor. 50 Gold chalice, Subtiava Temple, Leon 55 30
3404 3 cor. Processional cross, Niquinohomo Church, Masaya 85 45
3405 4 cor. "Lord of Miracles" (crucifix), Lord of Miracles Temple, Managua 95 45

1994. 32nd World Amateur Baseball Championship.

3407 **520** 4 cor. multicoloured . . . 1·00 1·00

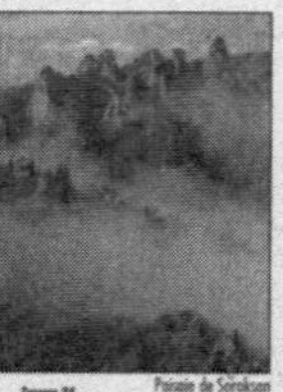

521 Mt. Sorak

1994. "Philakorea 1994" International Stamp Exhibition, Seoul. Views of South Korea. Mult.

3408 1 cor. 50 Type **521** 25 10
3409 1 cor. 50 Bronze Statue of Kim Yu-Shin 25 10
3410 1 cor. 50 Woedolgae (solitary rock) 25 10
3411 1 cor. 50 Stream, Mt. Hallasan, Cheju Island 25 10
3412 1 cor. 50 Mirukpong and Pisondae 25 10
3413 1 cor. 50 Ch'onbuldong Valley 25 10
3414 1 cor. 50 Bridge of the Seven Nymphs 25 10
3415 1 cor. 50 Piryong Waterfall . . 25 10

522 Piano on Stage

1994. 25th Anniv of Ruben Dario National Theatre, Managua.

3417 **522** 3 cor. multicoloured . . . 55 20

523 Tyrannosaurus Rex

1994. Prehistoric Animals. Multicoloured.

3418 1 cor. 50 Type **523** 25 10
3419 1 cor. 50 Plateosaurus 25 10
3420 1 cor. 50 Pteranodon 25 10
3421 1 cor. 50 Camarasaurus 25 10
3422 1 cor. 50 Euplocephalus . . . 25 10
3423 1 cor. 50 Sacuanjoche 25 10
3424 1 cor. 50 Deinonychus 25 10
3425 1 cor. 50 Chasmosaurus . . . 25 10
3426 1 cor. 50 Dimorphodon 25 10
3427 1 cor. 50 Ametriorhynchids . . 25 10
3428 1 cor. 50 Ichthyosaurus . . . 25 10
3429 1 cor. 50 Pterapsis and compsognathus 25 10
3430 1 cor. 50 Cephalopod 25 10
3431 1 cor. 50 Archelon 25 10
3432 1 cor. 50 Griphognatus and gyroptychius 25 10
3433 1 cor. 50 Plesiosaur and nautiloid 25 10

Nos. 3418/33 were issued together, se-tenant, forming a composite design.

524 Hawker Typhoon 1B

1994. 50th Anniv of D-Day. Multicoloured.
3434 3 cor. Type **524** 55 20
3435 3 cor. Douglas C-47 Skytrain transport dropping paratroops 55 20
3436 3 cor. H.M.S. "Mauritius" (cruiser) bombarding Houlgate, Normandy 55 20
3437 3 cor. Formation of Mulberry Harbours to transport supplies to beach 55 20
3438 3 cor. British AVRE Churchill tank 55 20
3439 3 cor. Tank landing craft 55 20

525 Renate Stecher (women's 200 metres, 1972)
526 Detachment of Command module "Eagle"

1994. Centenary of International Olympic Committee. Gold Medal Winners. Multicoloured.
3440 3 cor. 50 Type **525** 60 25
3441 3 cor. 50 Cassius Clay (Muhammad Ali) (boxing, 1960) 60 25

1994. 25th Anniv of First Manned Moon Landing. Multicoloured.
3443 3 cor. Type **526** 55 20
3444 3 cor. Launch of "Saturn V", Cape Canaveral, Florida 55 20
3445 3 cor. Command module orbiting Moon 55 20
3446 3 cor. Footprint on Moon 55 20
3447 3 cor. Primary space capsule separating 55 20
3448 3 cor. Command module 55 20
3449 3 cor. Lunar module landing on Moon 55 20
3450 3 cor. Astronaut on Moon 55 20

527 "The Death Cart" (Erick Joanello Montoya)

1994. 1st Prize in Children's Painting Competition.
3452 **527** 4 cor. multicoloured 70 30

528 Black-crowned Night Heron

1994. Woodland Animals. Multicoloured.
3453 2 cor. Type **528** 35 15
3454 2 cor. Scarlet macaw ("Ara macao") 35 15
3455 2 cor. Cattle egrets ("Bubulcus ibis") (wrongly inscr "Bulbulcus") 35 15
3456 2 cor. American black vultures ("Coragyps atratus") 35 15
3457 2 cor. Brazilian rainbow boa ("Epicrates cenchria") 35 15
3458 2 cor. Red-legged honeycreepers ("Cyanerpes cyaneus") 35 15
3459 2 cor. Plain chachalaca ("Ortalis vetula") 35 15
3460 2 cor. Sloth ("Bradypus griseus") 35 15
3461 2 cor. Jaguar ("Felis onca") 35 15
3462 2 cor. American anhingas ("Anhinga anhinga") 35 15
3463 2 cor. Baird's tapir ("Tapirus bairdi") 35 15
3464 2 cor. Anteater ("Myrmecophaga jubata") 35 15
3465 2 cor. Iguana ("Iguana iguana") 35 15
3466 2 cor. Snapping turtle ("Chelydra serpentina") 35 15
3467 2 cor. Red-billed whistling ducks ("Dendrocygna autumnalis") 35 15
3468 2 cor. Ocelot ("Felis pardalis") 35 15
Nos. 3453/68 were issued together, se-tenant, forming a composite design.

529 "The Kid" (dir. Charlie Chaplin)
530 "Discovery of America"

1994. Centenary of Motion Pictures. Multicoloured.
3470 2 cor. Type **529** 35 15
3471 2 cor. "Citizen Kane" (dir. Orson Welles) 35 15
3472 2 cor. "Lawrence of Arabia" (dir. David Lean) 35 15
3473 2 cor. "Ivan the Terrible" (dir. Sergio Eisenstein) 35 15
3474 2 cor. "Metropolis" (dir. Fritz Lang) 35 15
3475 2 cor. "The Ten Commandments" (dir. Cecil B. DeMille) 35 15
3476 2 cor. "Gandhi" (dir. Richard Attenborough) 35 15
3477 2 cor. "Casablanca" (dir. Michael Curtiz) 35 15
3478 2 cor. "Platoon" (dir. Oliver Stone) 35 15
3479 2 cor. "The Godfather" (dir. Francis Ford Coppola) 35 15
3480 2 cor. "2001: A Space Odyssey" (dir. Stanley Kubrick) 35 15
3481 2 cor. "The Ocean Depths" (dir. Jean Renoir) 35 15

1994. 15th Death Anniv of Rodrigo Penalba (artist). Multicoloured.
3483 50 c. Type **530** 10 10
3484 1 col. "Portrait of Mauricio" 20 10
3485 1 col. 50 "Portrait of Franco" 25 10
3486 2 col. "Portrait of Mimi Hammer" 35 15
3487 2 col. 50 "Seated Woman" 45 20
3488 3 col. "Still-life" (horiz) 55 20
3489 4 col. "Portrait of Maria Augusta" 70 30

531 Hen and Cock

1994. Endangered Species. The Highland Guan. Multicoloured.
3491 50 c. Type **531** 10 10
3492 1 col. Cock 20 10
3493 2 col. 50 Hen 45 20
3494 3 col. Cock and hen (different) 55 25

SILVER CURRENCY

The following were for use in all places on the Atlantic coast of Nicaragua where the silver currency was in use. This currency was worth about 50 c. to the peso. Earlier issues (overprints on Nicaraguan stamps) were also issued for Zelaya. These are listed in the Stanley Gibbons Part 15 (Central America) Catalogue.

Z 1 Steam Locomotive

1912.

Z 1 **Z 1** 1 c. green 1·75 90
Z 2 2 c. red 1·25 55
Z 3 3 c. brown 1·75 85
Z 4 4 c. lake 1·75 70
Z 5 5 c. blue 1·75 70
Z 6 6 c. red 9·75 5·00
Z 7 10 c. grey 1·75 70
Z 8 15 c. lilac 1·75 1·10
Z 9 20 c. blue 1·75 1·10
Z10 25 c. black and green 2·25 1·60
Z11 35 c. black and brown 3·25 1·90
Z12 50 c. green 3·25 1·90
Z13 1 p. orange 5·00 3·25
Z14 2 p. brown 9·75 6·00
Z15 5 p. green 20·00 12·50

OFFICIAL STAMPS

Overprinted **FRANQUEO OFICIAL**.

1890. Stamps of 1890.

O37 **6** 1 c. blue 30 60
O38 2 c. blue 30 60
O39 5 c. blue 30 70
O40 10 c. blue 30 75
O41 20 c. blue 35 90
O42 50 c. blue 35 1·10
O43 1 p. blue 40 1·75
O44 2 p. blue 40 2·75
O45 5 p. blue 45 6·00
O46 10 p. blue 45 11·50

1891. Stamps of 1891.

O47 **7** 1 c. green 15 40
O48 2 c. green 15 40
O49 5 c. green 15 40
O50 10 c. green 15 40
O51 20 c. green 15 70
O52 50 c. green 15 75
O53 1 p. green 15 90
O54 2 p. green 15 90
O55 5 p. green 15 2·25
O56 10 p. green 15 3·50

1892. Stamps of 1892.

O57 **8** 1 c. brown 15 30
O58 2 c. brown 15 30
O59 5 c. brown 15 30
O60 10 c. brown 15 30
O61 20 c. brown 15 50
O62 50 c. brown 15 70
O63 1 p. brown 15 1·10
O64 2 p. brown 15 1·75
O65 5 p. brown 15 2·75
O66 10 p. brown 15 3·50

1893. Stamps of 1893.

O67 **9** 1 c. black 15 30
O68 2 c. black 15 30
O69 5 c. black 15 30
O70 10 c. black 15 30
O71 20 c. black 15 50
O72 25 c. black 15 65
O73 50 c. black 15 70
O74 1 p. black 15 1·00
O75 2 p. black 15 1·25
O76 5 p. black 15 2·75
O77 10 p. black 15 3·50

1894. Stamps of 1894.

O78 **10** 1 c. orange 15 30
O79 2 c. orange 15 30
O80 5 c. orange 15 30
O81 10 c. orange 15 30
O82 20 c. orange 15 30
O83 50 c. orange 15 45
O84 1 p. orange 15 1·00
O85 2 p. orange 15 1·75
O86 5 p. orange 15 3·50
O87 10 p. orange 15 4·50

1895. Stamps of 1895.

O88 **11** 1 c. green 15 30
O89 2 c. green 15 30
O90 5 c. green 15 30
O91 10 c. green 15 30
O92 20 c. green 15 50
O93 50 c. green 15 80
O94 1 p. green 15 80
O95 2 p. green 15 1·25
O96 5 p. green 15 1·90
O97 10 p. green 15 2·40

1896. Stamps of 1896, dated "1896", optd **FRANQUEO OFICIAL** in oval frame.

O 99 **12** 1 c. red 1·50 1·90
O100 2 c. red 1·50 1·90
O101 5 c. red 1·50 1·90
O102 10 c. red 1·50 1·90
O103 20 c. red 1·90 1·90
O104 50 c. red 3·00 3·00
O105 1 p. red 7·25 7·25
O106 2 p. red 7·25 7·25
O107 5 p. red 9·50 9·50

1896. Nos. D99/103 handstamped **Franqueo Oficial**.

O108 **D 13** 1 c. orange — 4·25
O109 2 c. orange — 4·25
O110 5 c. orange — 3·00
O111 10 c. orange — 3·00
O112 20 c. orange — 3·00

1897. Stamps of 1897, dated "1897", optd **FRANQUEO OFICIAL** in oval frame.

O113 **12** 1 c. red 2·00 2·00
O114 2 c. red 2·00 2·00
O115 5 c. red 2·00 2·00
O116 10 c. red 1·90 2·10
O117 20 c. red 1·90 2·40
O118 50 c. red 3·00 3·00
O119 1 p. red 8·25 8·25
O120 2 p. red 9·75 9·75
O121 5 p. red 15·00 15·00

1898. Stamps of 1898 optd **FRANQUEO OFICIAL** in oval frame.

O124 **13** 1 c. red 2·00 2·00
O125 2 c. red 2·00 2·00
O126 4 c. red 2·00 2·00
O127 5 c. red 1·50 1·50
O128 10 c. red 2·40 2·40
O129 15 c. red 3·75 3·75
O130 20 c. red 3·75 3·75
O131 50 c. red 5·00 5·00
O132 1 p. red 6·50 6·50
O133 2 p. red 6·50 6·50
O134 5 p. red 6·50 6·50

1899. Stamps of 1899 optd **FRANQUEO OFICIAL** in scroll.

O137 **14** 1 c. green 15 60
O138 2 c. brown 15 60
O139 4 c. red 15 60
O140 5 c. blue 15 40
O141 10 c. orange 15 60
O142 15 c. brown 15 1·25
O143 20 c. green 15 2·00
O144 50 c. red 15 2·00
O145 1 p. orange 15 6·00
O146 2 p. violet 15 6·00
O147 5 p. blue 15 9·00

O 16 O 38

1900.

O148 **O 16** 1 c. purple 45 45
O149 2 c. orange 35 35
O150 4 c. olive 45 45
O151 5 c. blue 90 30
O152 10 c. violet 90 25
O153 20 c. brown 65 25
O154 50 c. lake 90 35
O155 1 p. blue 2·10 1·50
O156 2 p. orange 2·40 2·40
O157 5 p. black 3·00 3·00

1903. Stamps of 1900 surch **OFICIAL** and value, with or without ornaments.

O197 **15** 1 c. on 10 c. mauve 1·25 1·50
O198 2 c. on 3 c. green 1·50 1·90
O199 4 c. on 3 c. green 5·75 5·75
O200 4 c. on 10 c. mauve 5·75 5·75
O201 5 c. on 3 c. green 70 70

1903. Surch.

O202 **O 16** 10 c. on 20 c. brown 15 15
O203 30 c. on 20 c. brown 15 15
O204 50 c. on 20 c. brown 35 25

1905.

O219 **O 38** 1 c. green 20 20
O220 2 c. red 20 20
O221 5 c. blue 20 20
O222 10 c. brown 20 20
O223 20 c. orange 20 20
O224 50 c. olive 20 20
O225 1 p. lake 20 20
O226 2 p. violet 20 20
O227 5 p. black 20 20

1907. Surch thus: **Vale 10 c.**

O239 **O 38** 10 c. on 1 c. green 55 55
O241 10 c. on 2 c. red 15·00 11·50
O243 20 c. on 2 c. red 13·50 9·00
O245 50 c. on 1 c. green 1·10 1·10
O247 50 c. on 2 c. red 13·50 6·50

1907. Surch thus: **Vale 20 cts** or **Vale $1.00**.

O249 **O 38** 20 c. on 1 c. green 70 70
O250 $1 on 2 c. red 1·10 1·10
O251 $2 on 2 c. red 1·10 1·10
O252 $3 on 2 c. red 1·10 1·10
O253 $4 on 5 c. blue 1·40 1·40

1907. No. 206 surch **OFICIAL** and value.

O256 **49** 10 c. on 1 c. green 9·00 7·75
O257 15 c. on 1 c. green 9·00 7·75
O258 20 c. on 1 c. green 9·00 7·75
O259 50 c. on 1 c. green 9·00 7·75
O260 1 p. on 1 c. green 8·25 7·75
O261 2 p. on 1 c. green 8·25 7·75

1907. Fiscal stamps as T **50** surch thus: **10 cts. CORREOS 1907 OFICIAL 10 cts.**

O262 **50** 10 c. on 2 c. orange 10 10
O263 35 c. on 1 c. blue 10 10
O264 70 c. on 1 c. blue 10 10
O266 1 p. on 2 c. orange 10 15
O267 2 p. on 2 c. orange 10 15
O268 3 p. on 5 c. brown 10 15
O269 4 p. on 5 c. brown 15 15
O270 5 p. on 5 c. brown 15 15

1908. Stamp of 1905 surch **OFICIAL VALE** and value.

O271 **37** 10 c. on 3 c. violet 9·00 7·75
O272 15 c. on 3 c. violet 9·00 7·75
O273 20 c. on 3 c. violet 9·00 7·75
O274 35 c. on 3 c. violet 9·00 7·75
O275 50 c. on 3 c. violet 9·00 7·75

1908. Fiscal stamps as T **50** surch as last but dated 1908.

O276 **50** 10 c. on 1 c. blue 55 35
O277 10 c. on 2 c. orange 75 30
O278 35 c. on 1 c. blue 55 35
O279 35 c. on 2 c. orange 80 45
O280 50 c. on 1 c. blue 55 35
O281 50 c. on 2 c. orange 80 45
O282 70 c. on 2 c. orange 80 45
O283 1 p. on 1 c. blue 23·00 23·00
O284 1 p. on 2 c. orange 80 45
O285 2 p. on 1 c. blue 65 55
O286 2 p. on 2 c. orange 80 45

1909. Stamps of 1905 optd **OFICIAL**.

O290 **37** 10 c. lake 15 15
O291 15 c. black 45 35
O292 20 c. olive 70 55
O293 50 c. green 1·10 70
O294 1 p. yellow 1·25 90
O295 2 p. red 1·75 1·40

1911. Stamps of 1905 optd **OFICIAL** and surch **Vale** and value.

O296 **37** 5 c. on 3 c. orange 3·75 3·75
O297 10 c. on 4 c. violet 3·00 3·00

1911. Railway tickets, surch **Timbre Fiscal Vale 10 ctvs.** further surch for official postal use. Printed in red. (a) Surch **Correo oficial Vale** and value on front.

O334 **64** 10 c. on 10 c. on 1st class 5·25 4·50
O335 15 c. on 10 c. on 1st class 5·25 4·50
O336 20 c. on 10 c. on 1st class 5·25 4·50
O337 50 c. on 10 c. on 1st class 7·00 6·25
O338 $1 on 10 c. on 1st class 8·00 11·00
O339 $2 on 10 c. on 1st class 11·50 16·00

(b) Surch **CORREO OFICIAL** and new value on front.

O340 **64** 10 c. on 10 c. on 1st class 30·00 27·00
O341 15 c. on 10 c. on 1st class 30·00 27·00
O342 20 c. on 10 c. on 1st class 30·00 28·00
O343 50 c. on 10 c. on 1st class 27·00 24·00

(c) No. 322 surch on front **Correo Oficial Vale 1911** and new value and with **15 cts.** on back obliterated by heavy bar.

O344 **64** 5 c. on 10 c. on 1st class 10·00 9·50
O345 10 c. on 10 c. on 1st class 11·50 11·00
O346 15 c. on 10 c. on 1st class 13·00 12·00
O347 20 c. on 10 c. on 1st class 15·00 18·00
O348 50 c. on 10 c. on 1st class 17·00 16·00

(d) No. 322 surch on front **Correo Oficial 1912** and new value and with the whole surch on back obliterated.

O349 **64** 5 c. on 10 c. on 1st class 12·00 9·50
O350 10 c. on 10 c. on 1st class 12·00 9·50
O351 15 c. on 10 c. on 1st class 12·00 9·50
O352 20 c. on 10 c. on 1st class 12·00 9·50
O353 25 c. on 10 c. on 1st class 12·00 9·50
O354 50 c. on 10 c. on 1st class 12·00 9·50
O355 $1 on 10 c. on 1st class 12·00 9·50

1913. Stamps of 1912 optd **OFICIAL**.

O356 **70** 1 c. blue 10 10
O357 2 c. blue 10 10
O358 3 c. blue 10 10
O359 4 c. blue 10 10
O360 5 c. blue 10 10
O361 6 c. blue 10 15
O362 10 c. blue 10 15
O363 15 c. blue 10 15
O364 20 c. blue 15 20
O365 25 c. blue 15 15
O366 **71** 35 c. blue 20 20
O367 **70** 50 c. blue 1·10 1·10
O368 1 p. blue 25 25
O369 2 p. blue 25 25
O370 5 p. blue 35 35

1915. Optd **OFICIAL**.

O406 **79** 1 c. blue 15 15
O407 **80** 2 c. blue 15 15
O408 **79** 3 c. blue 15 15
O409 **80** 4 c. blue 15 15
O410 **79** 5 c. blue 15 15
O411 **80** 6 c. blue 15 15
O412 10 c. blue 15 15
O413 **79** 15 c. blue 15 15
O414 **80** 20 c. blue 15 15
O415 **79** 25 c. blue 25 25
O416 **80** 50 c. blue 45 45

1925. Optd **Oficial** or **OFICIAL**.

O513 **79** ½ c. green 10 10
O514 1 c. violet 10 10
O515 **80** 2 c. red 10 10
O516 **79** 3 c. olive 10 10
O517 **80** 4 c. red 10 10
O518 **79** 5 c. black 10 10
O519 **80** 6 c. brown 10 10
O520 10 c. yellow 10 10
O521 **79** 15 c. brown 10 10
O522 **80** 20 c. brown 10 10
O523 **79** 25 c. orange 40 40
O524 **80** 50 c. blue 45 45

1929. Air. Official stamps of 1925 additionally optd **Correo Aereo**.

O618 **79** 25 c. orange 35 35
O619 **80** 50 c. blue 55 55

1931. Stamp of 1924 surch **OFICIAL C$ 0.05 Correos 1928**.

O651 **99** 5 c. on 10 c. brown 25 25

1931. No. 648 additionally surch **OFICIAL** and value.

O652 **99** 5 c. on 10 c. brown 25 25

1931. Stamps of 1914 optd 1931 (except 6 c., 10 c.), and also optd **OFICIAL**.

O670 **79** 1 c. olive (No. 762) 20 20
O707 **80** 2 c. red 6·50 6·50
O671 **79** 3 c. blue 20 20
O672 5 c. sepia 20 20
O673 **80** 6 c. brown 25 25
O675 10 c. brown 25 25
O674 10 c. blue (No. 697) 1·10 1·10
O710 **79** 15 c. orange 70 70
O711 25 c. sepia 70 70
O712 25 c. violet 1·75 1·75

1932. Air. Optd **Correo Aereo OFICIAL** only.

O688 **79** 15 c. orange 45 45
O689 **80** 20 c. orange 50 50
O690 **79** 25 c. violet 50 50
O691 **80** 50 c. green 60 60
O692 1 cor. yellow 60 60

1932. Air. Optd **1931. Correo Aereo OFICIAL**.

O693 **79** 25 c. sepia 25·00 25·00

1932. Optd **OFICIAL**.

O694 **79** 1 c. olive 10 10
O695 **80** 2 c. red 10 10
O696 **79** 3 c. blue 15 10
O697 **80** 4 c. blue 15 10
O698 **79** 5 c. sepia 15 15
O699 **80** 6 c. brown 20 10
O700 10 c. brown 30 25
O701 **79** 15 c. orange 40 25
O702 **80** 20 c. orange 40 30
O703 **79** 25 c. violet 1·25 50
O704 **80** 50 c. green 15 15
O705 1 cor. yellow 20 20

1933. 441st Anniv of Columbus's Departure from Palos. As T **133**, but inscr "CORREO OFICIAL". Roul.

O777 1 c. yellow 60 60
O778 2 c. yellow 60 60
O779 3 c. brown 60 60
O780 4 c. brown 60 60
O781 5 c. brown 60 60
O782 6 c. blue 75 75
O783 10 c. violet 75 75
O784 15 c. purple 75 75
O785 20 c. green 75 75
O786 25 c. green 1·75 1·75
O787 50 c. red 2·25 2·25
O788 1 cor. red 3·50 3·50

1933. Optd with T **134** and **OFICIAL**.

O814 **79** 1 c. green 10 10
O815 **80** 2 c. red 10 10
O816 **79** 3 c. blue 10 10
O817 **80** 4 c. blue 10 10
O818 **79** 5 c. brown 10 10
O819 **80** 6 c. grey 10 10
O820 10 c. brown 10 10
O821 **79** 15 c. red 10 15
O822 **80** 20 c. orange 15 15
O823 **79** 25 c. violet 15 15
O824 **80** 50 c. green 25 25
O825 1 cor. yellow 50 45

1933. Air. Optd with T **134** and **CORREO Aereo OFICIAL**.

O826 **79** 15 c. violet 20 20
O827 **80** 20 c. green 20 20
O828 **79** 25 c. olive 20 20
O829 **80** 50 c. green 35 35
O830 1 cor. red 60 50

1935. Nos. O814/25 optd **RESELLO-1935** in a box.

O864 **79** 1 c. green 10 10
O865 **80** 2 c. red 10 10
O866 **79** 3 c. blue 10 10
O867 **80** 4 c. blue 10 10
O868 **79** 5 c. brown 10 10
O869 **80** 6 c. grey 10 10
O870 10 c. brown 10 10
O871 **79** 15 c. red 15 15
O872 **80** 20 c. orange 15 15
O873 **79** 25 c. violet 15 15
O874 **80** 50 c. green 20 20
O875 1 cor. yellow 35 35

1935. Air. Nos. O826/30 optd **RESELLO-1935** in a box.

O877 **79** 15 c. violet 30 25
O878 **80** 20 c. green 30 25
O879 **79** 25 c. olive 30 30
O880 **80** 50 c. green 90 90
O881 1 cor. red 90 90

(O 141) O 151 Islets in the Great Lake

1937. Nos. 913, etc., optd with Type O **141**.

O935 **79** 1 c. red 25 15
O936 **80** 2 c. blue 25 15
O937 **79** 3 c. brown 30 25
O938 5 c. red 35 30
O939 **80** 10 c. green 40 35
O940 **79** 15 c. green 50 40
O941 25 c. orange 60 45
O942 **80** 50 c. brown 85 50
O943 1 cor. blue 2·25 1·00

1937. Air. Nos. 926/30 optd with Type O **141**.

O944 **112** 15 c. orange 50 35
O945 20 c. red 50 35
O946 25 c. black 50 45
O947 50 c. violet 50 45
O948 1 cor. orange 50 45

1939.

O1020 O **151** 2 c. red 15 15
O1021 3 c. blue 15 15
O1022 6 c. brown 15 15
O1023 $7\frac{1}{2}$ c. green 15 15
O1024 10 c. brown 15 15
O1025 15 c. orange 15 15
O1026 25 c. violet 30 30
O1027 50 c. green 45 45

O **152** Pres. Somoza

1939. Air.

O1028 O **152** 10 c. brown 30 30
O1029 15 c. blue 30 30
O1030 20 c. yellow 30 30
O1031 25 c. violet 30 30
O1032 30 c. red 30 30
O1033 50 c. orange 40 40
O1034 1 cor. olive 75 75

O **175** Managua Airport

1947. Air.

O1120 O **175** 5 c. brown & black 15 10
O1121 – 10 c. blue and black 15 15
O1122 – 15 c. violet & black 15 10
O1123 – 20 c. orange & black 20 10
O1124 – 25 c. blue & black 15 15
O1125 – 50 c. red & black 15 15
O1126 – 1 cor. grey & black 40 35
O1127 – 2 cor. 50 brown and black 75 90

DESIGNS: 10 c. Sulphur Lagoon, Nejapa; 15 c. Ruben Dario Monument, Managua; 20 c. Baird's tapir; 25 c. Genizaro Dam; 50 c. Thermal Baths, Tipitapa; 1 cor. Highway and Lake Managua; 2 cor. 50, Franklin D. Roosevelt Monument, Managua.

O **181** U.P.U. Offices, Berne

1950. Air. 75th Anniv of U.P.U. Inscr as in Type O **181**. Frames in black.

O1159 – 5 c. purple 10 10
O1160 – 10 c. green 10 10
O1161 – 25 c. purple 10 10
O1162 O **181** 50 c. orange 15 10
O1163 – 1 cor. blue 35 30
O1164 – 2 cor. 60 black 2·10 1·75

DESIGNS—HORIZ: 5 c. Rowland Hill; 10 c. Heinrich von Stephan;. 25 c. Standehaus, Berne; 1 cor. Monument, Berne; 2 cor. 60, Congress Medal.

1961. Air. Consular Fiscal stamps as T **203/4** with serial Nos. in red, surch **Oficial Aereo** and value.

O1448 10 c. on 1 cor. olive 10 10
O1449 15 c. on 20 cor. brown 10 10
O1450 20 c. on 100 cor. lake 10 10
O1451 25 c. on 50 c. blue 15 10
O1452 35 c. on 50 cor. brown 15 15
O1453 50 c. on 3 cor. red 15 15
O1454 1 cor. on 2 cor. green 25 20
O1455 2 cor. on 5 cor. red 25 45
O1456 5 cor. on 10 cor. violet 60 60

POSTAGE DUE STAMPS

D **13**  D **16**

1896.

D 99 D **13** 1 c. orange 45 1·10
D100 2 c. orange 45 1·10
D101 5 c. orange 45 1·10
D102 10 c. orange 45 1·10
D103 20 c. orange 45 1·10
D104 30 c. orange 45 1·10
D105 50 c. orange 45 1·40

1897.

D108 D **13** 1 c. violet 45 1·10
D109 2 c. violet 45 1·10
D110 5 c. violet 45 1·10
D111 10 c. violet 45 1·1
D112 20 c. violet 75 1·25
D113 30 c. violet 45 90
D114 50 c. violet 45 90

1898.

D124 D **13** 1 c. green 15 1·25
D125 2 c. green 15 1·25
D126 5 c. green 15 1·25
D127 10 c. green 15 1·25
D128 20 c. green 15 1·25
D129 30 c. green 15 1·25
D130 50 c. green 15 1·25

1899.

D137 D **13** 1 c. red 15 1·25
D138 2 c. red 15 1·25
D139 5 c. red 15 1·25
D140 10 c. red 15 1·25
D141 20 c. red 15 1·25
D142 50 c. red 15 1·25

1900.

D146 D **16** 1 c. red 70
D147 2 c. orange 70
D148 5 c. blue 70
D149 10 c. violet 70
D150 20 c. brown 70
D151 30 c. green 1·40
D152 50 c. lake 1·40

NIGER Pt. 6; Pt. 14

Area south of the Sahara. In 1920 was separated from Upper Senegal and Niger to form a separate colony. From 1944 to 1959 used the stamps of French West Africa.

In 1958 Niger became an autonomous republic within the French Community and on 3 August 1960 an independent republic.

100 centimes = 1 franc

1921. Stamps of Upper Senegal and Niger optd **TERRITOIRE DU NIGER**.

1 **7** 1 c. violet and purple 10 30
2 2 c. purple and grey 10 30
3 4 c. blue and black 15 30
4 5 c. chocolate and brown 15 30
5 10 c. green and light green 50 75
25 10 c. pink on blue 10 30
6 15 c. yellow and brown 15 30
7 20 c. black and purple 15 30
8 25 c. green and black 15 30
9 30 c. carmine and red 50 65
26 30 c. red and green 30 50
10 35 c. violet and red 25 40
11 40 c. red and grey 35 50
12 45 c. brown and blue 35 50
13 50 c. blue and ultramarine 40 60
27 50 c. blue and grey 50 70
28 60 c. red 35 55
14 75 c. brown and yellow 45 85
15 1 f. purple and brown 60 80
16 2 f. blue and green 65 90
17 5 f. black and violet 1·25 1·40

1922. Stamps of 1921 surch.

18 **7** 25 c. on 15 c. yellow & brown 25 40
19 25 c. on 2 f. blue and green 25 45
20 25 c. on 5 f. black & violet 25 45
21 60 on 75 c. violet on pink 25 45
22 65 on 45 c. brown and blue 75 1·40
23 85 c. on 75 c. brown & yellow 85 1·40
24 1 f. 25 on 1 f. lt blue & blue 60 85

3 Wells  **5** Zinder Fort

4 Canoe on River Niger

1926.

29 **3** 1 c. green and purple 10 25
30 2 c. red and grey 10 30
31 3 c. brown and mauve 10 30
32 4 c. black and brown 10 30
33 5 c. green and red 10 35
34 10 c. green and blue 10 20
35 15 c. light green and green 40 40
36 15 c. red and lilac 10 25
37 **4** 20 c. brown and blue 15 30
38 25 c. pink and black 15 30
39 30 c. light green and green 35 55
40 30 c. mauve and yellow 20 40
41 35 c. blue and red on blue 15 30
42 35 c. green and deep green 35 50
43 40 c. grey and purple 25 40
44 45 c. mauve and yellow 55 70
45 45 c. green and turquoise 35 55
46 50 c. green and red on green 25 30
47 55 c. brown and red 50 70
48 60 c. brown and red 40 65
49 **4** 65 c. red and green 25 45
50 70 c. red and green 55 70
51 75 c. mauve and grn on pink 70 90
52 80 c. green and purple 80 95
53 90 c. red and carmine 55 70
54 90 c. green and red 55 70
55 **5** 1 f. green and red 3·00 3·00
56 1 f. orange and red 65 60
57 1 f. red and green 40 55
58 1 f. 10 green and brown 2·25 2·00
59 1 f. 25 red and green 70 75
60 1 f. 25 orange and red 50 70
61 1 f. 40 brown and mauve 50 70
62 1 f. 50 light blue and blue 25 35
63 1 f. 60 green and brown 75 95
64 1 f. 75 brown and mauve 1·40 1·50
65 1 f. 75 ultramarine and blue 65 85
66 2 f. brown and orange 35 50
67 2 f. 25 ultramarine and blue 55 75
68 2 f. 50 brown 65 80
69 3 f. grey and mauve 35 45
70 5 f. black & purple on pink 50 65
71 10 f. mauve and lilac 75 80
72 20 f. orange and green 75 85

1931. "Colonial Exhibition" key types inscr "NIGER".

73 E 40 c. green 2·25 2·25
74 F 50 c. mauve 2·00 2·25
75 G 90 c. red 2·50 2·75
76 H 1 f. 50 blue 2·50 2·75

1937. International Exhibition, Paris. As Nos. 168/73 of St.-Pierre et Miquelon.

77 20 c. violet 60 85
78 30 c. green 60 85
79 40 c. red 55 75
80 50 c. brown and agate 50 70
81 90 c. red 55 85
82 1 f. 50 blue 55 85

1938. Int Anti-Cancer Fund. As T **22** of Mauritania.

83 1 f. 75 + 50 c. blue 8·50 9·50

1939. Caille. As T **27** of Mauritania.

84 90 c. orange 40 55
85 2 f. violet 40 55
86 2 f. 25 blue 40 55

1939. New York World's Fair. As T **28** of Mauritania.

87 1 f. 25 red 50 60
88 2 f. 25 blue 50 60

1939. 150th Anniv of French Revolution. As T **29** of Mauritania.

89 45 c. + 25 c. green and black 4·50 5·00
90 70 c. + 30 c. brown and black 4·50 5·00
91 90 c. + 35 c. orange and black 4·75 5·00
92 1 f. 25 + 1 f. red and black 4·50 5·00
93 2 f. 25 + 2 f. blue and black 4·50 5·00

1940. Air. As T **30** of Mauritania.

94 1 f. 90 blue 50 55
95 2 f. 90 red 45 55
96 4 f. 50 green 60 70
97 4 f. 90 olive 50 60
98 6 f. 90 orange 45 60

1941. National Defence Fund. Surch **SECOURS NATIONAL** and additional value.

98a **4** + 1 f. on 50 c. green and red on green 2·00 2·00
98b + 2 f. on 80 c. green & pur 3·00 3·00
98c **5** + 2 f. on 1 f. 50 lt blue & bl 4·25 4·25
98d + 3 f. on 2 f. brown & orge 4·25 4·25

5a Zinder Fort  **5c** "Vocation"

5b Weighing Baby

1942. Marshal Petain issue.

98e **5a** 1 f. green 10
98f 2 f. 50 blue 10

1942. Air. Colonial Child Welfare Fund.

98g – 1 f. 50 + 3 f. 50 green 20
98h – 2 f. + 6 f. brown 15
98i **5b** 3 f. + 9 f. red 15

DESIGNS: 49 × 28 mm: 1 f. 50, Maternity Hospital, Dakar; 2 f. Dispensary, Mopti.

1942. Air. Imperial Fortnight.

98j **5c** 1 f. 20 + 1 f. 80 blue & red 10

1942. Air. As T **32** of Mauritania but inscr "NIGER" at foot.

98k 50 f. red and yellow 80 1·00

7 Giraffes

8 Carmine Bee Eater

1959. Wild Animals and Birds. Inscr "PROTECTION DE LA FAUNE".

99 – 50 c. turquoise, green and black (postage) 25 10
100 – 1 f. multicoloured 40 20
101 – 2 f. multicoloured 40 20
102 – 5 f. mauve, black & brown 60 20
103 – 7 f. red, black and green 75 30
104 – 10 f. multicoloured 25 10
105 – 15 f. sepia and turquoise 25 10
106 – 20 f. black and violet 35 10
107 **7** 25 f. multicoloured 45 10
108 30 f. brown, bistre & green 50 20
109 – 50 f. blue and brown 5·50 80
110 – 60 f. sepia and green 7·50 1·10
111 – 85 f. brown and bistre 2·50 85
112 – 100 f. bistre and green 3·25 85
113 **8** 200 f. multicoloured (air) 26·00 7·00
114 – 500 f. green, brown & blue 8·50 6·00

DESIGNS—As Type **7**: HORIZ: 50 c., 10 f. African manatee. VERT: 1, 2 f. Crowned Cranes; 5, 7 f. Saddle-bill Stork; 15, 20 f. Barbary sheep; 50, 60 f. Ostriches; 85, 100 f. Lion. As Type **8**: VERT: 500 f. Game animals.

1960. 10th Anniv of African Technical Co-operation Commission. As T **4** of Malagasy Republic.

115 25 f. brown and ochre 50 40

9 Conseil de l'Entente Emblem  **11** Pres. Diori Hamani

1960. 1st Anniv of Conseil de l'Entente.

116 **9** 25 f. multicoloured 50 40

1960. Independence. No. 112 surch **200 F Independance 3-8-60**.

117 – 200 f. on 100 f. 9·00 9·00

1960.

118 **11** 25 f. black and bistre 35 25

12 U.N. Emblem and Niger Flag

1961. Air. 1st Anniv of Admission into U.N.

119 **12** 25 f. red, green & orange 40 25
120 100 f. green, red & emerald 1·40 90

1962. Air. "Air Afrique" Airline. As T **42** of Mauritania.

121 100 f. violet, black and brown 1·50 75

1962. Malaria Eradication. As T **43** of Mauritania.

122 25 f. + 5 f. brown 45 45

13 Athletics

1962. Abidjan Games, 1961. Multicoloured.

123 15 f. Boxing and cycling (vert) 25 15
124 25 f. Basketball and football (vert) 35 20
125 85 f. Type **13** 1·10 55

1962. 1st Anniv of Union of African and Malagasy States. As T **45** of Mauritania.

126 **72** 30 f. mauve 40 30

14 Pres. Hamani and Map

15 Running

1962. 4th Anniv of Republic.
127 **14** 25 f. multicoloured 35 25

1963. Freedom from Hunger. As T **51** of Mauritania.
128 25 f. + 5 f. purple, brn & olive . 55 55

1963. Dakar Games.
129 – 15 f. brown and blue . . . 25 15
130 **15** 25 f. red and brown 35 20
131 – 45 f. black and green . . . 70 40
DESIGNS—HORIZ: 15 f. Swimming. VERT: 45 f. Volleyball.

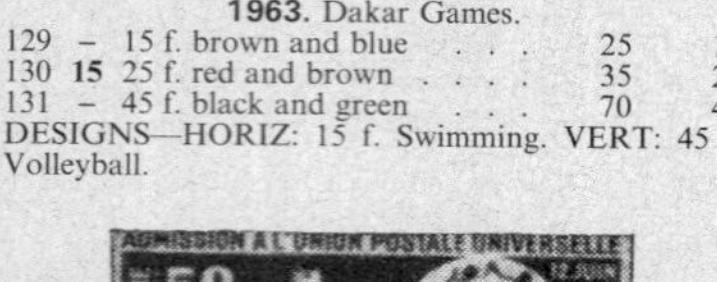

16 Agadez Mosque

1963. Air. 2nd Anniv of Admission to U.P.U. Multicoloured.
132 50 f. Type **16** 75 40
133 85 f. Gaya Bridge . . . . . . 1·25 60
134 100 f. Presidential Palace, Niamey . . . . 1·25 70

17 Wood-carving

1963. Traditional Crafts. Multicoloured.
135 5 f. Type **17** (postage) 15 15
136 10 f. Skin-tanning 20 15
137 25 f. Goldsmith 40 20
138 30 f. Mat-making 60 30
139 85 f. Potter . . . . 1·40 80
140 100 f. Canoe building (air) . . 2·00 1·10
The 10 f. and 30 f. are horiz and the 100 f. larger 47 × 27 mm.

1963. Air. African and Malagasy Posts and Telecommunications Union. As T **56** of Mauritania.
141 85 f. multicoloured 95 55

1963. Air. Red Cross Centenary. Optd with cross and **Centenaire de la Croix-Rouge** in red.
142 **12** 25 f. red, green and orange . 60 40
143 100 f. green, red and emerald . . . . 1·40 85

19 Costume Museum

1963. Opening of Costume Museum, Niamey. Vert costume designs. Multicoloured.
144 15 f. Berber woman 20 15
145 20 f. Haussa woman 35 15
146 25 f. Tuareg woman 45 20
147 30 f. Tuareg man 55 20
148 60 f. Djerma woman . . . . 1·25 50
149 85 f. Type **19** . . . . 1·50 60

20 "Europafrique"

22 Man and Globe

21 Groundnut Cultivation

1963. Air. European–African Economic Convention.
150 **20** 50 f. multicoloured . . . . 2·50 2·00

1963. Air. Groundnut Cultivation Campaign.
151 **21** 20 f. blue, brown & green . . 35 20
152 – 45 f. brown, blue & green . . 75 25
153 – 85 f. multicoloured . . . . 1·40 65
154 – 100 f. olive, brown & blue . 1·50 90
DESIGNS: 45 f. Camel transport; 85 f. Fastening sacks; 100 f. Dispatch of groundnuts by lorry.

1963. Air. 1st Anniv of "Air Afrique" and DC-8 Service Inauguration. As T **59** of Mauritania.
155 50 f. multicoloured 70 45

1963. 15th Anniv of Declaration of Human Rights.
156 **22** 25 f. blue, brown & green . . 45 25

23 "Telstar"

1964. Air. Space Telecommunications.
157 **23** 25 f. olive and violet 40 20
158 – 100 f. green and purple . . 1·10 80
DESIGN: 100 f. "Relay".

24 "Parkinsonia aculeata"

25 Statue, Abu Simbel

1964. Flowers. Multicoloured.
159 5 f. Type **24** 60 30
160 10 f. "Russelia equisetiformis" . 50 30
161 15 f. "Lantana Camara" . . . 1·00 45
162 20 f. "Agryeia nervosa" . . . 1·00 45
163 25 f. "Luffa Cylindrica" . . . 1·00 45
164 30 f. "Hibiscus rosa-sinensis" . 1·40 60
165 45 f. "Plumierai rubra" . . . 2·00 1·25
166 50 f. "Catharanthus roseus" . . 2·00 1·25
167 60 f. "Caesalpinia pulcherrima" . . . . . . 3·50 1·50
Nos. 164/7 have "REPUBLIQUE DU NIGER" at the top and the value at bottom right.

1964. Air. Nubian Monuments Preservation.
168 **25** 25 f. green and brown . . . 65 45
169 30 f. brown and blue . . . 1·00 70
170 50 f. blue and purple . . . 2·00 1·25

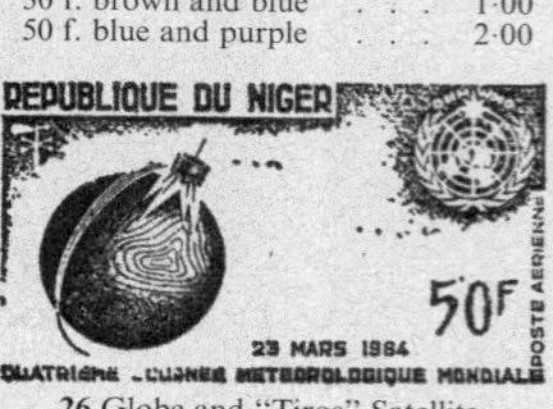
26 Globe and "Tiros" Satellite

1964. Air. World Meteorological Day.
171 **26** 50 f. brown, blue and green . 1·10 65

27 Sun Emblem and Solar Flares

28 Convoy of Lorries

1964. International Quiet Sun Years.
172 **27** 30 f. red, violet and sepia . . 50 35

1964. O.M.N.E.S. (Nigerian Mobile Medical and Sanitary Organization) Commemoration.
173 **28** 25 f. orange, olive & blue . . 40 20
174 – 30 f. multicoloured 50 20
175 – 50 f. multicoloured 80 30
176 – 60 f. purple, orange & turq . 90 35
DESIGNS: 30 f. Tending children; 50 f. Tending women; 60 f. Open-air laboratory.

29 Rocket, Stars and Stamp Outline

1964. Air. "PHILATEC 1964" Int Stamp Exn, Paris.
177 **29** 50 f. mauve and blue . . . 85 60

30 European, African and Symbols of Agriculture and Industry

31 Pres. Kennedy

1964. Air. 1st Anniv of European–African Economic Convention.
178 **30** 50 f. multicoloured 65 40

1964. Air. Pres. Kennedy Commemoration.
179 **31** 100 f. multicoloured . . . . 1·25 1·10

32 Water-polo

1964. Air. Olympic Games, Tokyo.
180 **32** 60 f. brown, deep green and purple 60 50
181 – 85 f. brown, blue and red . . 1·00 60
182 – 100 f. blue, red and green . . 1·25 70
183 – 250 f. blue, brown and grn . 2·50 1·75
DESIGNS—HORIZ: 85 f. Relay-racing. VERT: 100 f. Throwing the discus; 250 f. Athlete holding Olympic Torch.

1964. French, African and Malagasy Co-operation. As T **68** of Mauritania.
184 50 f. brown, orange & violet . . 65 40

33 Azawak Tuareg Encampment

1964. Native Villages. Multicoloured.
185 15 f. Type **33** 20 20
186 20 f. Songhai hut 25 20
187 25 f. Wogo and Kourtey tents . 30 20
188 30 f. Djerma hut 40 25
189 60 f. Sorkawa fishermen's encampment . . . . . . 1·00 30
190 85 f. Hausa urban house . . . 1·25 50

34 Doctors and Patient and Microscope Slide

35 Abraham Lincoln

1964. Anti-Leprosy Campaign.
191 **34** 50 f. multicoloured 50 45

1965. Death Centenary of Abraham Lincoln.
192 **35** 50 f. multicoloured 60 50

36 Instruction by "Radio-Vision"

1965. "Human Progress". Inscr as in T **36**.
193 **36** 20 f. brown, yellow & blue . . 30 20
194 – 25 f. sepia, brown and green . 35 20
195 – 30 f. purple, red and green . 45 25
196 – 50 f. purple, blue and brown . 70 35
DESIGNS: 25 f. Student; 30 f. Adult class; 50 f. Five tribesmen ("Alphabetisation").

37 Ader's Telephone

38 Pope John XXIII

1965. I.T.U. Centenary.
197 **37** 25 f. black, lake and green . 50 25
198 – 30 f. green, purple and red . 60 30
199 – 50 f. green, purple and red . 1·00 50
DESIGNS: 30 f. Wheatstone's telegraph; 50 f. "Telautographe".

1965. Air. Pope John Commemoration.
200 **38** 100 f. multicoloured . . . . 1·40 75

39 Hurdling

40 "Capture of Cancer" (the Crab)

1965. 1st African Games, Brazzaville.
201 **39** 10 f. purple, green & brown . 20 15
202 – 15 f. red, brown and grey . . 30 15
203 – 20 f. purple, blue & green . . 40 20
204 – 30 f. purple, green & lake . . 50 25
DESIGNS—VERT: 15 f. Running; 30 f. Long-jumping. HORIZ: 20 f. Pole-vaulting.

1965. Air. Campaign against Cancer.
205 **40** 100 f. brown, black & green . 1·40 80

41 Sir Winston Churchill

42 Interviewing

1965. Air. Churchill Commemoration.
206 **41** 100 f. multicoloured . . . . 1·40 80

1965. Radio Club Promotion.
207 **42** 30 f. brown, violet & green . 30 15
208 – 45 f. red, black and buff . . 45 25
209 – 50 f. multicoloured 55 30
210 – 60 f. purple, blue & ochre . 60 40
DESIGNS—VERT: 45 f. Recording; 50 f. Listening to broadcast. HORIZ: 60 f. Listeners debate.

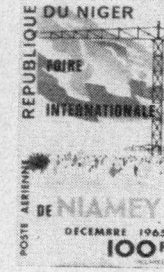

43 "Agricultural and Industrial Workers"

44 Fair Scene and Flags

1965. Air. International Co-operation Year.
211 **43** 50 f. brown, black & bistre . 70 35

1965. Air. International Fair, Niamey.
212 **44** 100 f. multicoloured . . . . 1·10 70

45 Dr. Schweitzer and Diseased Hands

1966. Air. Schweitzer Commemoration.
213 45 50 f. multicoloured 80 45

46 "Water Distribution and Control"

1966. Int Hydrological Decade Inauguration.
214 46 50 f. blue, orange & violet . 70 35

47 Weather Ship "France I"

1966. Air. 6th World Meteorological Day.
215 47 50 f. green, purple and blue . 1·50 70

48 White and "Gemini" Capsule

1966. Air. Cosmonauts.
216 48 50 f. black, brown & green . 75 40
217 – 50 f. blue, violet & orange . 75 40
DESIGN: No. 217, Leonov and "Voskhod" capsule.

49 Head-dress and Carvings

1966. World Festival of Negro Arts, Dakar.
218 49 30 f. black, brown & green . 45 25
219 – 50 f. violet, brown and blue . 60 35
220 – 60 f. lake, violet & brown . 70 40
221 – 100 f. black, red & blue . . 1·25 70
DESIGNS: 50 f. Carved figures and mosaics; 60 f. Statuettes, drums and arch; 100 f. Handicrafts and church.

50 "Diamant" Rocket and Gantry
51 Goalkeeper saving Ball

1966. Air. French Space Vehicles. Multicoloured designs each showing different Satellites.
222 45 f. Type 50 . . . . 70 40
223 60 f. "A 1" (horiz) 80 45
224 90 f. "FR 1" (horiz) . . . . 1·00 50
225 100 f. "D 1" (horiz) . . . . 1·50 75

1966. World Cup Football Championships.
226 – 30 f. red, brown and blue . . 55 25
227 51 50 f. brown, blue & green . . 75 35
228 – 60 f. blue, purple and bistre . 85 50
DESIGNS—VERT: 30 f. Player dribbling ball; 60 f. Player kicking ball.

52 Cogwheel Emblem and Hemispheres
53 Parachutist

1966. Air. Europafrique.
229 52 50 f. multicoloured 70 45

1966. 5th Anniv of National Armed Forces. Mult.
230 20 f. Type 53 . . . . 35 15
231 30 f. Soldiers with standard (vert) 45 20
232 45 f. Armoured patrol vehicle (horiz) 70 30

1966. Air. Inauguration of DC-8F Air Services. As T 87 of Mauritania.
233 30 f. olive, black and grey . . . 60 25

54 Inoculating cattle

1966. Campaign for Prevention of Cattle Plague.
234 54 45 f. black, brown & blue . . 1·00 50

55 "Voskhod 1"
56 U.N.E.S.C.O. "Tree"

1966. Air. Astronautics.
235 55 50 f. blue, indigo and lake . 65 35
236 – 100 f. violet, blue and lake . 1·25 75
DESIGN—HORIZ: 100 f. "Gemini 6" and "7".

1966. 20th Anniv of U.N.E.S.C.O.
237 56 50 f. multicoloured 70 25

57 Japanese Gate, Atomic Symbol and Cancer ("The Crab")
58 Furnace

1966. Air. International Cancer Congress, Tokyo.
238 57 100 f. multicoloured . . . . 1·40 75

1966. Malbaza Cement Works.
239 58 10 f. blue, orange & brown . 15 10
240 – 20 f. blue and green 30 15
241 – 30 f. brown, grey and blue . 45 20
242 – 50 f. indigo, brown & blue . 65 30
DESIGNS—HORIZ: 20 f. Electrical power-house; 30 f. Works and cement silos; 50 f. Installation for handling raw materials.

59 Niamey Mosque

1967. Air.
243 59 100 f. blue, green and grey . 1·10 70

60 Durer (self-portrait)

1967. Air. Paintings. Multicoloured.
244 50 f. Type 60 . . . . 80 60
245 100 f. David (self-portrait) . . 1·50 90
246 250 f. Delacroix (self-portrait) . 3·00 2·00
See also Nos. 271/2 and 277/9.

61 Red-billed Hornbill
62 Bobsleigh Course, Villard-de-Lans

1967. Birds.
247 61 1 f. bistre, red and green (postage) 20 20
248 – 2 f. black, brown and green . 20 20
249 – 30 f. multicoloured . . . . 1·10 35
249a – 40 f. purple, orange and green . . . . 1·25 60
250 – 45 f. brown, green and blue . 1·60 35
250a – 65 f. yell, brown & purple . 1·75 75
251 – 70 f. multicoloured . . . . 2·10 95
251a – 250 f. blue, purple and green (48 × 27 mm) (air) . . . 6·25 2·10
BIRDS: 2 f. Lesser pied kingfishers; 30 f. Common gonolek; 40 f. Red bishop; 45 f., 65 f. Little masked weaver; 70 f. Chestnut-bellied sandgrouse; 250 f. Splendid glossy starlings.

1967. Grenoble–Winter Olympics Town (1968).
252 62 30 f. brown, blue and green . 40 25
253 – 45 f. brown, blue and green . 60 30
254 – 60 f. brown, blue and green . 80 50
255 – 90 f. brown, blue and green . 1·10 65
DESIGNS: 45 f. Ski-jump, Autrans; 60 f. Ski-jump, St. Nizier du moucherotte; 90 f. Slalom course, Chamrousse.

63 Family and Lions Emblem
64 Weather Ship

1967. 50th Anniv of Lions International.
256 63 50 f. blue, red and green . . 60 35

1967. Air. World Meteorological Day.
257 64 50 f. red, black and blue . . 1·50 70

65 View of World Fair

1967. Air. World Fair, Montreal.
258 65 100 f. black, blue & purple . 2·75 75

66 I.T.Y. Emblem and Jet Airliner
67 Scouts around Campfire

1967. International Tourist Year.
259 66 45 f. violet, green & purple . 45 35

1967. World Scout Jamboree, Idaho, U.S.A.
260 67 30 f. brown, lake and blue . . 40 20
261 – 45 f. blue, brown & orge . . 60 30
262 – 80 f. lake, slate and bistre . 1·25 50
DESIGNS—HORIZ: 45 f. Jamboree emblem and scouts. VERT: 80 f. Scout cooking meal.

68 Audio-Visual Centre

1967. Air. National Audio-Visual Centre, Niamey.
263 68 100 f. violet, blue and green . 90 50

69 Carrying Patient
70 "Europafrique"

1967. Nigerian Red Cross.
264 69 45 f. black, red and green . . 60 20
265 – 50 f. black, red and green . . 75 25
266 – 60 f. black, red and green . . 1·00 35
DESIGNS: 50 f. Nurse with mother and child; 60 f. Doctor giving injection.

1967. Europafrique.
267 70 50 f. multicoloured 60 30

71 Dr. Konrad Adenauer
72 African Women

1967. Air. Adenauer Commemoration.
268 71 100 f. brown and blue . . . 1·40 70

1967. Air. 5th Anniv of African and Malagasy Post and Telecommunications Union (U.A.M.P.T.). As T 101 of Mauritania.
270 100 f. violet, green and red . . 1·10 60

1967. Air. Death Centenary of Jean Ingres (painter). Paintings by Ingres. As T 60. Multicoloured.
271 100 f. "Jesus among the Doctors" (horiz) . . . . 1·60 1·00
272 150 f. "Jesus restoring the Keys to St. Peter" (vert) . . . . . 2·25 1·50

1967. U.N. Women's Rights Commission.
273 72 50 f. brown, yellow and blue . 60 35

1967. 5th Anniv of West African Monetary Union. As T 103 of Mauritania.
274 30 f. green and purple 35 20

73 Nigerian Children
75 Allegory of Human Rights

74 O.C.A.M. Emblem

1967. Air. 21st Anniv of U.N.I.C.E.F.
275 73 100 f. brown, blue & green . 1·25 95

1968. Air. O.C.A.M. Conference, Niamey.
276 74 100 f. orange, green and blue . . . . 1·10 60

1968. Air. Paintings (self-portraits). As T 60. Multicoloured.
277 50 f. J.-B. Corot 70 40
278 150 f. Goya . . . . 1·90 1·00
279 200 f. Van Gogh . . . . . . 2·50 1·50

1968. Human Rights Year.
280 75 50 f. indigo, brown and blue . 60 30

76 Breguet 27 Biplane over Lake

1968. Air. 35th Anniv of 1st France-Niger Airmail Service.
281 **76** 45 f. blue, green and mauve . 95 35
282 – 80 f. slate, brown and blue . 1·60 55
283 – 100 f. black, green & blue . 2·50 75
DESIGNS—Potez 25TOE biplane: 80 f. On ground; 100 f. In flight.

77 "Joyous Health"

1968. 20th Anniv of W.H.O.
284 **77** 50 f. indigo, blue and brown . 60 35

78 Cyclists of 1818 and 1968

1968. Air. 150th Anniv of Bicycle.
285 **78** 100 f. green and red . . . . 1·50 70

79 Beribboned Rope

1968. Air. 5th Anniv of Europafrique.
286 **79** 50 f. multicoloured 65 40

80 Fencing

1968. Air. Olympic Games, Mexico.
287 **80** 50 f. purple, violet & green . 50 35
288 – 100 f. black, purple & blue . 85 50
289 – 150 f. purple and orange . 1·25 70
290 – 200 f. blue, brown & green . 1·75 1·25
DESIGNS—VERT: 100 f. High-diving; 150 f. Weight-lifting. HORIZ: 200 f. Horse-jumping.

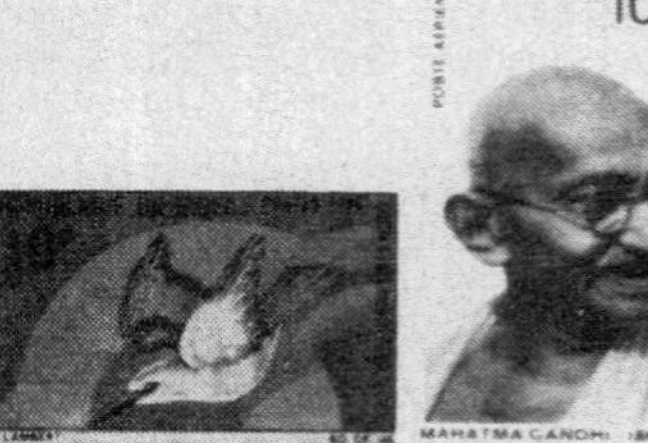

81 Woodland Kingfisher 82 Mahatma Gandhi

1969. Birds. Dated "1968". Multicoloured.
292 5 f. African grey hornbill (postage) 30 10
293 10 f. Type **81** 40 20
294 15 f. Senegal coucal 85 30
295 20 f. Rose-ringed parakeets . . 95 50
296 25 f. Abyssinian roller . . . 1·40 65
297 50 f. Cattle egret . . . . . 1·90 90
298 100 f. Violet starling (27 × 49 mm) (air) . . . . 4·25 1·75
See also Nos. 372/7, 567/8 and 714/15.

1968. Air. "Apostles of Non-Violence".
299 **82** 100 f. black and yellow . . . 1·75 60
300 – 100 f. black and turquoise . . 1·00 50
301 – 100 f. black and grey . . . 1·00 50
302 – 100 f. black and orange . . . 1·00 50
PORTRAITS: No. 300, President Kennedy; No. 301, Martin Luther King; No. 302, Robert F. Kennedy.

1968. Air. "Philexafrique" Stamp Exhibition, Abidjan (Ivory Coast, 1969) (1st issue). As T **113a** of Mauritania. Multicoloured.
304 100 f. "Pare, Minister of the Interior" (J. L. La Neuville) . 1·60 1·60

83 Arms of the Republic

1968. Air. 10th Anniv of Republic.
305 **83** 100 f. multicoloured . . . . 1·00 50

1969. Air. Napoleon Bonaparte. Birth Bicentenary. As T **114b** of Mauritania. Multicoloured.
306 50 f. "Napoleon as First Consul" (Ingres) . . . . 1·50 90
307 100 f. "Napoleon visiting the plague victims of Jaffa" (Gros) 2·50 1·25
308 150 f. "Napoleon Enthroned" (Ingres) . . . . 3·50 1·75
309 200 f. "The French Campaign" (Meissonier) . . . . 5·00 2·50

1969. Air. "Philexafrique" Stamp Exhibition, Abidjan, Ivory Coast (2nd issue). As T **114a** of Mauritania.
310 50 f. brown, blue and orange . 1·25 1·00
DESIGN: 50 f. Giraffes and stamp of 1926.

84 Boeing 707 over Rain-cloud and Anemometer

1969. Air. World Meteorological Day.
311 **84** 50 f. black, blue and green . 90 35

85 Workers supporting Globe

1969. 50th Anniv of I.L.O.
312 **85** 30 f. red and green 40 20
313 50 f. green and red 50 35

86 Panhard and Levassor (1909)

1969. Air. Veteran Motor Cars.
314 **86** 25 f. green 45 20
315 – 45 f. violet, blue and grey . . 55 25
316 – 50 f. brown, ochre and grey . 1·10 35
317 – 70 f. purple, red and grey . . 1·50 45
318 – 100 f. green, brown and grey . 1·75 65
DESIGNS: 45 f. De Dion Bouton 8 (1904); 50 f. Opel "Doktor-wagen" (1909); 70 f. Daimler (1910); 100 f. Vermorel 12/16 (1912).

87 Mother and Child 88 Mouth and Ear

1969. 50th Anniv of League of Red Cross Societies.
319 **87** 45 f. red, brown and blue . . 60 25
320 – 50 f. red, grey and green . . 70 25
321 – 70 f. red, brown and ochre . 1·00 40
DESIGNS—VERT: 70 f. Man with Red Cross parcel. HORIZ: 50 f. Symbolic Figures, Globe and Red Crosses.

1969. First French Language Cultural Conf, Niamey.
322 **88** 100 f. multicoloured . . . . 1·25 60

89 School Building

1969. National School of Administration.
323 **89** 30 f. black, green and orange 30 20

1969. Air. 1st Man on the Moon. No. 114 optd **L'HOMME SUR LA LUNE JUILLET 1969 APOLLO 11** and moon module.
324 500 f. green, brown & blue . . 6·50 6·50

91 "Apollo 8" and Rocket

1969. Air. Moon Flight of "Apollo 8". Embossed on gold foil.
325 **91** 1,000 f. gold . . . . 15·00 15·00

1969. 5th Anniv of African Development Bank. As T **122a** of Mauritania.
326 30 f. brown, green and violet . 35 15

92 Child and Toys

1969. Air. International Toy Fair, Nuremburg.
327 **92** 100 f. blue, brown and green . 2·75 75

93 Linked Squares

1969. Air. "Europafrique".
328 **93** 50 f. yellow, black & violet . 55 30

94 Trucks crossing Sahara

1969. Air. 45th Anniv of "Croisiere Noire" Trans-Africa Expedition.
329 **94** 50 f. brown, violet and mve . 75 35
330 – 100 f. violet, red and blue . 1·50 65
331 – 150 f. multicoloured . . . 2·00 1·25
332 – 200 f. green, indigo and blue . 3·00 1·50
DESIGNS: 100 f. Crossing the mountains; 150 f. African children and expedition at Lake Victoria; 200 f. Route Map, European greeting African and Citroen truck.

94a Aircraft, Map and Airport

1969. 10th Anniv of Aerial Navigation Security Agency for Africa and Madagascar (A.S.E.C.N.A.).
333 **94a** 100 f. red . . . . 1·50 70

95 Classical Pavilion

1970. National Museum.
334 **95** 30 f. blue, green and brown . 30 15
335 – 45 f. blue, green and brown . 45 25
336 – 50 f. blue, brown and green . 50 25
337 – 70 f. brown, blue and green . 70 40
338 – 100 f. brown, blue and grn . 1·10 60
DESIGNS: 45 f. Temporary Exhibition Pavilion; 50 f. Audio-visual Pavilion; 70 f. Local Musical Instruments Gallery; 100 f. Handicrafts Pavilion.

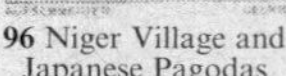

96 Niger Village and Japanese Pagodas 97 Hypodermic "Gun" and Map

1970. Air. "EXPO 70" World Fair, Osaka, Japan (1st issue).
339 **96** 100 f. multicoloured 90 45

1970. One Hundred Million Smallpox Vaccinations in West Africa.
340 **97** 50 f. blue, purple and green . 70 30

98 Education Symbols

1970. Air. International Education Year.
341 **98** 100 f. slate, red and purple . 1·00 45

99 Footballer

1970. World Cup Football Competitions, Mexico.
342 **99** 40 f. green, brown and purple 60 25
343 – 70 f. purple, brown and blue 1·00 40
344 – 90 f. red and black . . . . 1·25 60
DESIGNS: 70 f. Football and Globe; 90 f. Two footballers.

100 Rotary Emblems

1970. Air. 65th Anniv of Rotary International.
345 **100** 100 f. multicoloured . . . 1·25 55

101 Bay of Naples and Niger Stamp

1970. Air. 10th "Europafrique" Stamp Exn, Naples.
346 **101** 100 f. multicoloured . . . 1·00 60

102 Clement Ader's "Avion III" and Modern Airplane

1970. Air. Aviation Pioneers.
347 **102** 50 f. grey, blue and red . . 70 25
348 – 100 f. red, grey and blue . . 1·50 60
349 – 150 f. lt brn, brn & grn . . 1·50 75
350 – 200 f. red, bistre and violet . 2·25 1·00
351 – 250 f. violet, grey and red . 3·50 1·40
DESIGNS: 100 f. Joseph and Etienne Montgolfier balloon and rocket; 150 f. Isaac Newton and gravity diagram; 200 f. Galileo and rocket in planetary system; 250 f. Leonardo da Vinci's drawing of a "flying machine" and Chanute's glider.

103 Cathode Ray Tube illuminating Books, Microscope and Globe

1970. Air. World Telecommunications Day.
352 **103** 100 f. brown, green and red . 1·25 50

1970. Inauguration of New U.P.U. Headquarters Building, Berne. As T **81** of New Caledonia.
353 30 f. red, slate and brown . . . 35 20
354 60 f. violet, red and blue . . . 60 30

1970. Air. Safe Return of "Apollo 13". Nos. 348 and 350 optd **Solidarite Spatiale Apollo XIII 11-17 Avril 1970.**
355 100 f. red, slate and blue . . 1·00 50
356 200 f. red, bistre and violet . . 1·75 75

105 U.N. Emblem, Man, Woman and Doves

1970. Air. 25th Anniv of U.N.O.
357 **105** 100 f. multicoloured . . . 1·00 50
358 150 f. multicoloured . . . 1·50 75

106 Globe and Heads

1970. Air. International French Language Conference, Niamey. Die-stamped on gold foil.
359 **106** 250 f. gold and blue . . . 2·50 2·50

107 European and African Women

1970. Air. "Europafrique".
360 **107** 50 f. red and green 55 30

108 Japanese Girls and "EXPO 70" Skyline

1970. Air. "EXPO 70" World Fair, Osaka, Japan. (2nd issue).
361 **108** 100 f. purple, orange & grn . 90 40
362 – 150 f. blue, brown & green . 1·25 60
DESIGN: 150 f. "No" actor and "EXPO 70" by night.

109 Gymnast on Parallel Bars
111 Beethoven, Keyboard and Manuscripts

1970. Air. World Gymnastic Championships, Ljubljana.
363 **109** 50 f. blue 50 30
364 – 100 f. green . . . . . . 1·10 55
365 – 150 f. purple . . . . . 1·75 75
366 – 200 f. red . . . . . . 2·00 95
GYMNASTS—HORIZ: 100 f. Gymnast on vaulting-horse; 150 f. Gymnast in mid-air. VERT: 200 f. Gymnast on rings.

1970. Air. Moon Landing of "Luna 16". Nos. 349 and 351 surch **LUNA 16 – Sept. 1970 PREMIERS PRELEVEMENTS AUTOMATIQUES SUR LA LUNE** and value.
367 100 f. on 150 f. light brown, brown and green . . . . . 1·10 50
368 200 f. on 250 f. violet, grey and red . . . . 2·40 1·00

1970. Air. Birth Bicentenary of Beethoven. Mult.
369 100 f. Type **111** . . . . . . 1·40 55
370 150 f. Beethoven and allegory, "Hymn of Joy" . . . . . 2·25 85

112 John F. Kennedy Bridge, Niamey

1970. Air. 12th Anniv of Republic.
371 **112** 100 f. multicoloured . . . 1·10 45

1971. Birds. Designs similar to T **81**. Variously dated between 1970 and 1972. Multicoloured.
372 5 f. African grey hornbill . . . 55 25
373 10 f. Woodland kingfisher . . . 70 25
374 15 f. Senegal coucal . . . . 1·50 80
375 20 f. Rose-ringed parakeet . . 1·75 80
376 35 f. Broad-tailed paradise whydah . . . . 2·40 1·10
377 50 f. Cattle egret . . . . . 3·00 1·50
The Latin inscription on No. 377 is incorrect, reading "Bulbucus ibis" instead of "Bubulcus ibis". See also Nos. 714/15.

114 Pres. Nasser

1971. Air. Death of Pres. Gamal Nasser (Egyptian statesman). Multicoloured.
378 100 f. Type **114** 75 40
379 200 f. Nasser waving . . . . . 1·50 75

115 Pres. De Gaulle

1971. Air. De Gaulle Commemoration. Embossed on gold foil.
380 **115** 1000 f. gold . . . . 38·00 38·00

116 "MUNICH" and Olympic Rings

1971. Air. Publicity for 1972 Olympic Games, Munich.
381 **116** 150 f. purple, blue & green . 1·25 70

117 "Apollo 14" leaving Moon
118 Symbolic Masks

1971. Air. Moon Mission of "Apollo 14".
382 **117** 250 f. green, orge & blue . 2·25 1·25

1971. Air. Racial Equality Year.
383 **118** 100 f. red, green & blue . . 90 40
384 – 200 f. brown, green & blue . 1·75 80
DESIGN: 200 f. "Peoples" and clover-leaf emblem.

119 Niamey on World Map

1971. 1st Anniv of French-speaking Countries Co-operative Agency.
385 **119** 40 f. multicoloured 50 25

120 African Telecommunications Map

1971. Air. Pan-African Telecommunications Network.
386 **120** 100 f. multicoloured . . . 75 40

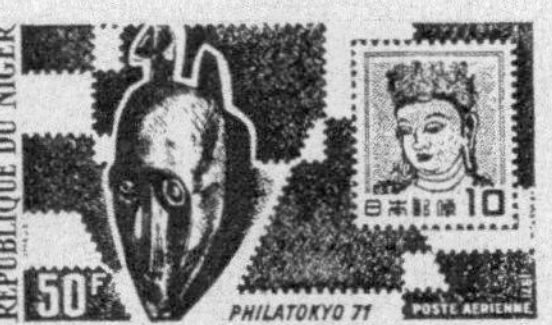

121 African Mask and Japanese Stamp

1971. Air. "PHILATOKYO 71" International Stamp Exhibition, Japan.
387 **121** 50 f. olive, purple & green . 65 30
388 – 100 f. violet, red & green . 1·10 45
DESIGN: 100 f. Japanese scroll painting and Niger stamp.

122 "Longwood House, St. Helena" (C. Vernet)

1971. Air. 150th Anniv of Napoleon's Death. Paintings. Multicoloured.
389 150 f. Type **122** . . . . . . 1·75 70
390 200 f. "Napoleon's Body on his Camp-bed" (Marryat) . . . 2·50 90

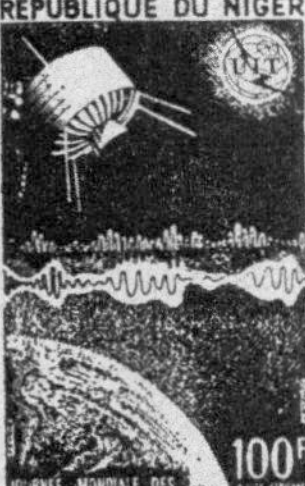

123 Satellite, Radio Waves, and Globe
125 Scout Badges and Mount Fuji

124 Pierre de Coubertin and Discus-throwers

1971. Air. World Telecommunications Day.
391 **123** 100 f. multicoloured . . . 1·10 50

1971. Air. 75th Anniv of Modern Olympic Games.
392 **124** 50 f. red and blue 50 25
393 – 100 f. multicoloured . . . 90 40
394 – 150 f. blue and purple . . . 1·40 65
DESIGNS—VERT: 100 f. Male and female athletes holding torch. HORIZ: 150 f. Start of race.

1971. 13th World Scout Jamboree, Asagiri, Japan.
395 **125** 35 f. red, purple & orange . 40 20
396 – 40 f. brown, plum and green 45 20
397 – 45 f. green, red and blue . . 60 25
398 – 50 f. green, violet and red . 70 30
DESIGNS—VERT: 40 f. Scouts and badge; 45 f. Scouts converging on Japan. HORIZ: 50 f. "Jamboree" in rope, and marquee.

126 "Apollo 15" on Moon

1971. Air. Moon Mission of "Apollo 15".
399 **126** 150 f. blue, violet & brn . . 1·50 70

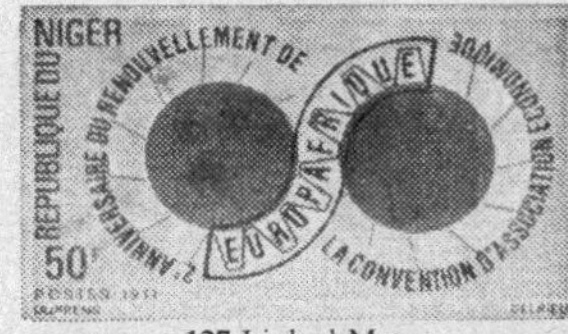

127 Linked Maps

1971. 2nd Anniv of Renewed "Europafrique" Convention, Niamey.
400 **127** 50 f. multicoloured 60 30

128 Gouroumi (Hausa)
129 De Gaulle in Uniform

1971. Musical Instruments.
401 **128** 25 f. brown, green & red . 30 10
402 – 30 f. brown, violet & grn . 35 15
403 – 35 f. blue, green & purple . 35 25
404 – 40 f. brown, orange & grn . 45 25
405 – 45 f. ochre, brown & blue . 55 35
406 – 50 f. brown, red & black . 95 45
DESIGNS: 30 f. Molo (Djerma); 35 f. Garaya (Hausa); 40 f. Godjie (Djerma-Sonrai); 45 f. Inzad (Tuareg); 50 f. Kountigui (Sonrai).

1971. Air. 1st Death Anniv of Gen. Charles De Gaulle (French statesman).
407 **129** 250 f. multicoloured . . . 5·00 4·00

1971. Air. 10th Anniv of African and Malagasy Posts and Telecommunications Union. As T **139a** of Mauritania. Multicoloured.
408 100 f. U.A.M.P.T. H.Q. and rural scene 90 45

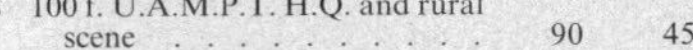

130 "Audience with Al Hariri" (Baghdad, 1237)

1971. Air. Moslem Miniatures. Multicoloured.
409 100 f. Type **130** . . . . . . 1·00 45
410 150 f. "Archangel Israfil" (Iraq, 14th-cent.) (vert) . . . . 1·50 70
411 200 f. "Horsemen" (Iraq, 1210) . 2·25 1·25

131 Louis Armstrong
132 "Children of All Races"

1971. Air. Death of Louis Armstrong (American jazz musician). Multicoloured.
412 100 f. Type **131** . . . . . . 1·50 55
413 150 f. Armstrong playing trumpet . . . . 2·00 85

1971. 25th Anniv of U.N.I.C.E.F.
414 **132** 50 f. multicoloured 60 45

133 "Adoration of the Magi" (Di Bartolo)

1971. Air. Christmas. Paintings. Multicoloured.
415 100 f. Type **133** . . . . 1·00 45
416 150 f. "The Nativity" (D. Ghirlandaio) (vert) . . . . . 1·50 70
417 200 f. "Adoration of the Shepherds" (Perugino) . . . 2·00 1·00

134 Presidents Pompidou and Hamani

1972. Air. Visit of Pres. Pompidou of France.
418 **134** 250 f. multicoloured . . . 4·75 3·50

135 Ski "Gate" and Cherry Blossom

1972. Air. Winter Olympic Games, Sapporo, Japan.
419 **135** 100 f. violet, red & green . 90 40
420 – 150 f. red, purple & violet . 1·25 70
DESIGN—HORIZ: 150 f. Snow crystals and Olympic flame.

1972. Air. U.N.E.S.C.O. "Save Venice" Campaign. As T **145** of Senegal.
422 50 f. multicoloured (vert) . . . 50 25
423 100 f. multicoloured (vert) . . . 1·00 45
424 150 f. multicoloured (vert) . . . 1·50 70
425 200 f. multicoloured . . . . 2·00 1·00
DESIGNS: Nos. 422/5 depict various details of Guardi's painting, "The Masked Ball".

136 Johannes Brahms and Music
137 Saluting Hand

1972. Air. 75th Death Anniv of Johannes Brahms (composer).
426 **136** 100 f. green, myrtle and red . 1·50 55

1972. Air. Int Scout Seminar, Cotonou, Dahomey.
427 **137** 150 f. violet, blue & orange . 1·50 60

138 Star Symbol and Open Book

1972. International Book Year.
428 **138** 35 f. purple and green . . . 35 20
429 – 40 f. blue and lake . . . 1·40 35
DESIGN: 40 f. Boy reading, 16th-century galleon and early aircraft.

139 Heart Operation

1972. Air. World Heart Month.
430 **139** 100 f. brown and red . . . 1·50 55

140 Bleriot XI crossing the Channel, 1909

1972. Air. Milestones in Aviation History.
431 **140** 50 f. brown, blue & lake . . 1·10 50
432 – 75 f. grey, brown & blue . . 1·75 60
433 – 100 f. ultramarine, blue and purple . . . . 3·25 1·40
DESIGNS: 75 f. Lindbergh crossing the Atlantic in "Spirit of St. Louis"; 100 f. First flight of Concorde, 1969.

141 Satellite and Universe

1972. Air. World Telecommunications Day.
434 **141** 100 f. brown, purple & red . 1·10 45

142 Boxing

1972. Air. Olympic Games, Munich. Sports and Munich Buildings.
435 **142** 50 f. brown and blue . . . 50 20
436 – 100 f. brown and green . . 75 40
437 – 150 f. brown and red . . . 1·25 60
438 – 200 f. brown and mauve . . 1·75 85
DESIGNS—VERT: 100 f. Long-jumping; 150 f. Football. HORIZ: 200 f. Running.

143 A. G. Bell and Telephone

1972. Air. 50th Death Anniv of Alexander Graham Bell (inventor of telephone).
440 **143** 100 f. blue, purple and red . 1·10 55

144 "Europe on Africa" Map

1972. Air. "Europafrique" Co-operation.
441 **144** 50 f. red, green and blue . . 50 25

145 Herdsman and Cattle
146 Lottery Wheel

1972. Medicinal Salt-Ponds at In-Gall. Multicoloured.
442 35 f. Type **145** 50 25
443 40 f. Cattle in salt-pond 60 25

1972. 6th Anniv of National Lottery.
444 **146** 35 f. multicoloured 35 25

147 Postal Runner

1972. Air. U.P.U. Day. Postal Transport.
445 **147** 50 f. brown, green & lake . . 60 25
446 – 100 f. green, blue & lake . . 90 45
447 – 150 f. green, violet & lake . 1·75 70
DESIGNS: 100 f. Rural mail van; 150 f. Loading Fokker Friendship mail plane.

1972. 10th Anniv of West African Monetary Union. As T **149** of Mauritania.
448 40 f. grey, violet and brown . . 40 25

1972. Air. Gold Medal Winners. Munich Olympic Games. Nos. 435/8 optd with events and names, etc.
449 **142** 50 f. brown and blue . . . 50 20
450 – 100 f. brown and green . . 85 40
451 – 150 f. brown and red . . . 1·40 60
452 – 200 f. brown and mauve . . 1·75 80
OVERPRINTS: 50 f. **WELTER CORREA MEDAILLE D'OR**; 100 f. **TRIPLE SAUT SANEIEV MEDAILLE D'OR**; 150 f. **FOOTBALL POLOGNE MEDAILLE D'OR**; 200 f. **MARATHON SHORTER MEDAILLE D'OR**.

148 "The Raven and the Fox"

1972. Air. Fables of Jean de la Fontaine.
453 **148** 25 f. black, brown & grn . 1·50 40
454 – 50 f. brown, green & pur . 60 25
455 – 75 f. brown, green & brn . 1·00 45
DESIGNS: 50 f. "The Lion and the Rat"; 75 f. "The Monkey and the Leopard".

149 Astronauts on Moon

1972. Air. Moon Flight of "Apollo 17".
456 **149** 250 f. multicoloured . . . 2·75 1·25

150 Dromedary Race
151 Pole Vaulting

1972. Niger Sports.
457 **150** 35 f. purple, red and blue . 75 40
458 – 40 f. lake, brown & green . 1·00 60
DESIGN: 40 f. Horse race.

1973. 2nd African Games, Lagos, Nigeria. Mult.
459 35 f. Type **151** 30 25
460 40 f. Basketball 35 25
461 45 f. Boxing 45 25
462 75 f. Football 70 45

152 "Young Athlete"
153 Knight and Pawn

1973. Air. Antique Art Treasures.
463 **152** 50 f. red 50 25
464 – 100 f. violet . . . . . . 1·00 40
DESIGN: 100 f. "Head of Hermes".

1973. World Chess Championships, Reykjavik, Iceland.
465 **153** 100 f. green, blue & red . . 2·50 1·00

154 "Abutilon pannosum"
155 Interpol Badge

1973. Rare African Flowers. Multicoloured.
466 30 f. Type **154** 70 30
467 45 f. "Crotalaria barkae" . . . 80 30
468 60 f. "Dichrostachys cinerea" . 1·40 45
469 80 f. "Caralluma decaisneana" . 1·60 55

1973. 50th Anniv of International Criminal Police Organization (Interpol).
470 **155** 50 f. multicoloured 85 30

156 Scout with Radio

1973. Air. Scouting in Niger.
471 **156** 25 f. brown, green & red . 25 20
472 – 50 f. brown, green & red . 55 25
473 – 100 f. brown, green & red . 1·25 50
474 – 150 f. brown, green & red . 2·25 90
DESIGNS: 50 f. First Aid; 100 f. Care of animals; 150 f. Care of the environment.

157 Hansen and Microscope
158 Nurse tending Child

1973. Centenary of Dr. Hansen's Discovery of Leprosy Bacillus.
475 **157** 50 f. brown, green & blue . 85 35

1973. 25th Anniv of W.H.O.
476 **158** 50 f. brown, red and blue . 65 25

159 "The Crucifixion" (Hugo van der Goes)

1973. Air. Easter. Paintings. Multicoloured.
477 50 f. Type **159** 55 25
478 100 f. "The Deposition" (Cima de Conegliano) (horiz) . . . . 1·10 50
479 150 f. "Pieta" (Bellini) (horiz) . 1·60 65

160 Douglas DC-8 and Mail Van

1973. Air. Stamp Day.
480 **160** 100 f. brown, red & green . 1·50 55

161 W.M.O. Emblem and "Weather Conditions"

1973. Air. Centenary of W.M.O.
481 **161** 100 f. brown, red & grn . . 1·10 45

162 "Crouching Lioness" (Delacroix)

1973. Air. Paintings by Delacroix. Multicoloured.
482 130 f. Type **162** . . . . 2·00 1·00
483 200 f. "Tigress and Cub" . . . 3·25 1·50

163 Crocodile

1973. Wild Animals from "Park W".
484 **163** 25 f. multicoloured 45 20
485 – 35 f. grey, gold and black . 75 30
486 – 40 f. multicoloured 75 30
487 – 80 f. multicoloured . . . 1·25 50
DESIGNS: 35 f. African elephant; 40 f. Hippopotamus; 80 f. Warthog.

164 Eclipse over Mountain

1973. Total Eclipse of the Sun.
488 **164** 40 f. violet 60 30

1973. Air. 24th International Scouting Congress, Nairobi, Kenya. Nos. 473/4 optd **24 Conference Mondiale du Scoutisme NAIROBI 1973**.
489 100 f. brown, green and red . . 1·00 40
490 150 f. brown, green and red . . 2·00 90

166 Palomino

1973. Horse-breeding. Multicoloured.
491 50 f. Type **166** 90 30
492 75 f. French trotter . . . . 1·40 40
493 80 f. English thoroughbred . . 1·50 55
494 100 f. Arab thoroughbred . . . 2·00 65

1973. Pan-African Drought Relief. African Solidarity. No. 436 surch **SECHERESSE SOLIDARITE AFRICAINE** and value.
495 **145** 100 f. on 35 f. multicoloured 1·40 1·00

168 Rudolf Diesel and Oil Engine

1973. 60th Death Anniv of Rudolf Diesel (engineer).
496 **168** 25 f. blue, purple & grey . . 80 45
497 – 50 f. grey, green & blue . . 1·40 65
498 – 75 f. blue, black & mauve . 2·10 1·00
499 – 125 f. blue, red & green . . 3·50 1·25
DESIGNS: 50 f. Series "BB 100" diesel locomotive; 75 f. Type "060-DB1" diesel locomotive, France; 125 f. Diesel locomotive No. 72004, France.

1973. African and Malagasy Posts and Telecommunications Union. As T **155a** of Mauritania.
500 100 f. red, green and brown . . 75 50

168a African Mask and Old Town Hall, Brussels

169 T.V. Set and Class

1973. Air. African Fortnight, Brussels.
501 **168a** 100 f. purple, blue and red . 1·00 50

1973. Schools Television Service.
502 **169** 50 f. black, red and blue . . 60 30

1973. 3rd International French Language and Culture Conf., Liege. No. 385 optd **3e CONFERENCE DE LA FRANCOPHONIE LIEGE OCTOBRE 1973**.
503 **110** 40 f. multicoloured 50 25

171 "Apollo"

172 Bees and Honeycomb

1973. Classical Sculptures.
504 **171** 50 f. green and brown . . . 60 30
505 – 50 f. black and brown . . . 60 30
506 – 50 f. brown and red . . . 60 30
507 – 50 f. purple and red . . . 60 30
DESIGNS: No. 505, "Atlas"; No. 506, "Hercules"; No. 507, "Venus".

1973. World Savings Day.
508 **172** 40 f. brown, red and blue . 45 25

173 "Food for the World"

174 Copernicus and "Sputnik 1"

1973. Air. 10th Anniv of World Food Programme.
509 **173** 50 f. violet, red and blue . . 60 30

1973. Air. 500th Birth Anniv of Copernicus (astonomer).
510 **174** 150 f. brown, blue and red . 1·40 70

175 Pres. John Kennedy

1973. Air. 10th Death Anniv of U.S. President Kennedy.
511 **175** 100 f. multicoloured . . . 1·00 50

176 Kounta Songhai Blanket

178 Lenin

177 Barges on River Niger

1973. Niger Textiles. Multicoloured.
513 35 f. Type **176** 50 30
514 40 f. Tcherka Snghai blanket (horiz) 70 40

1974. Air. 1st Anniv of Ascent of Niger by "Fleet of Hope".
515 **177** 50 f. blue, green and red . . 75 35
516 – 75 f. purple, blue and green . 1·00 45
DESIGN: 75 f. "Barban Maza" (tug) and barge.

1974. Air. 50th Death Anniv of Lenin.
517 **178** 50 c. brown 50 30

179 Slalom Skiing

1974. Air. 50th Anniv of Winter Olympic Games.
518 **179** 200 f. red, brown & blue . 2·50 1·00

180 Newly-born Baby

1974. World Population Year.
519 **180** 50 f. multicoloured 50 25

181 Footballers and "Global" Ball

1974. Air. World Cup Football Championships, West Germany.
520 **181** 75 f. violet, black and brn . 65 35
521 – 150 f. brown, green & turq . 1·40 55
522 – 200 f. blue, orange & green . 1·75 1·00
DESIGNS: 150, 200 f. Football scenes similar to Type **181**.

182 "The Crucifixion" (Grunewald)

1974. Air. Easter. Paintings. Multicoloured.
524 50 f. Type **182** 50 25
525 75 f. "Avignon Pieta" (attributed to E. Quarton) 75 35
526 125 f. "The Entombment" (G. Isenmann) . . . . . . 1·25 65

183 Class 230K Locomotive, 1948, France and Locomotive No. 5511, 1938, U.S.A.

1974. Famous Railway Locomotives of the Steam Era.
527 **183** 50 f. green, black & violet . 1·25 40
528 – 75 f. green, black & brown . 1·90 55
529 – 100 f. multicoloured . . . 2·50 85
530 – 150 f. brown, black & red . 3·75 1·25
DESIGNS: 75 f. Class 21 locomotive, 1893, France; 100 f. Locomotive, 1866, U.S.A. and "Mallard", Great Britain; 150 f. Marc Seguin locomotive, 1829, France and Stephenson's "Rocket", 1829.

184 Map of Member Countries

185 Knights

1974. 15th Anniv of Conseil de l'Entente.
531 **184** 40 f. multicoloured 40 20

1974. Air. 21st Chess Olympiad, Nice.
532 **185** 50 f. brown, blue & indigo . 1·25 65
533 – 75 f. purple, brown & green . 1·75 75
DESIGN: 75 f. Kings.

186 Marconi and "Elettra" (steam yacht)

1974. Birth Centenary of Guglielmo Marconi (radio pioneer).
534 **186** 50 f. blue, brown & mauve . 50 30

187 Astronaut on Palm of Hand

188 Tree on Palm of Hand

1974. Air. 5th Anniv of 1st Landing on Moon.
535 **187** 150 f. brown, blue & ind . 1·25 60

1974. National Tree Week.
536 **188** 35 f. turquoise, grn & brn . 40 30

189 "The Rhinoceros" (Longhi)

190 Camel Saddle

1974. Air. Europafrique.
537 **189** 250 f. multicoloured . . . 5·00 3·00

1974. Handicrafts.
538 **190** 40 f. red, blue & brown . . 45 20
539 – 50 f. blue, red and brown . 55 30
DESIGN: 50 f. Statuettes of horses.

192 Frederic Chopin

1974. 125th Death Anniv of Frederic Chopin.
541 **192** 100 f. black, red & blue . . 1·50 55

1974. Beethoven's Ninth Symphony Commemoration. As T **192**.
542 100 f. lilac, blue and indigo . . 1·50 55
DESIGN: 100 f. Beethoven.

193 European Woman and Douglas DC-8 Airliners

194 "Skylab" over Africa

1974. Air. Centenary of U.P.U.

543 **193** 50 f. turquoise, grn & pur . 50 25
544 – 100 f. blue, mauve & ultram 2·25 75
545 – 150 f. brown, blue & indigo . 1·50 80
546 – 200 f. brown, orange & red . 1·60 1·25

DESIGNS: 100 f. Japanese woman and electric locomotives; 150 f. American Indian woman and liner; 200 f. African woman and road vehicles.

1974. Air. "Skylab" Space Laboratory.

547 **194** 100 f. violet, brown & blue . 1·00 45

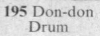

195 Don-don Drum

197 "Virgin and Child" (Correggio)

196 Tree and Compass Rose

1974.

548 **195** 60 f. purple, green & red . 90 45

1974. 1st Death Anniv of Tenere Tree (desert landmark).

549 **196** 50 f. brown, blue and ochre . 2·00 1·00

1974. Air. Christmas. Multicoloured.

550 100 f. Type **197** . . . . . . 1·00 35
551 150 f. "Virgin and Child, and St. Hilary" (F. Lippi) . . . . 1·50 55
552 200 f. "Virgin and Child" (Murillo) . . . . 2·00 95

198 "Apollo" Spacecraft

199 European and African Women

1975. Air. "Apollo–Soyuz" Space Test Project.

553 **198** 50 f. green, red and blue . . 50 25
554 – 100 f. grey, red and blue . . 80 40
555 – 150 f. purple, plum & blue . 1·25 60

DESIGNS: 100 f. "Apollo" and "Soyuz" docked; 150 f. "Soyuz" spacecraft.

1975. Air. Europafrique.

556 **199** 250 f. brown, purple & red . 2·25 1·75

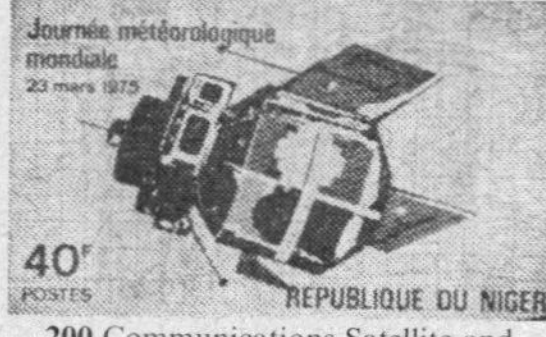

200 Communications Satellite and Weather Map

1975. World Meteorological Day.

557 **200** 40 f. red, black and blue . . 40 20

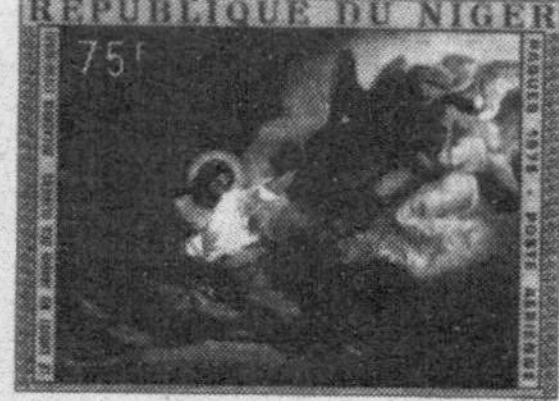

201 "Christ in the Garden of Olives" (Delacroix)

1975. Air. Easter. Multicoloured.

558 75 f. Type **201** 65 35
559 125 f. "The Crucifixion" (El Greco) (vert) . . . . . . 1·10 50
560 150 f. "The Resurrection" (Limousin) (vert) . . . . 1·25 75

202 Lt-Col. S. Kountche, Head of State

1975. Air. 1st Anniv of Military Coup.

561 **202** 100 f. multicoloured . . . 1·00 50

203 "City of Truro", 1903, Great Britain

1975. Famous Locomotives. Multicoloured.

562 50 f. Type **203** . . . . . . 1·25 35
563 75 f. Class 05 steam locomotive No. 003, 1937, Germany . . 1·60 50
564 100 f. "General", 1855, U.S.A. (dated "1863") . . . . . 2·50 75
565 125 f. Series BB 15000 electric locomotive, 1971, France . . 3·00 90

1975. Birds. As Nos. 296 and 298, but dated "1975". Multicoloured.

567 25 f. Abyssinian Roller (postage) 1·00 25
568 100 f. Violet Starlings (air) . . 2·25 65

205 "Zabira" Leather Bag

206 African Woman and Child

1975. Niger Handicrafts. Multicoloured.

569 35 f. Type **205** 30 20
570 40 f. Chequered rug 45 25
571 45 f. Flower pot 50 30
572 60 f. Gourd 75 35

1975. International Women's Year.

573 **206** 50 f. blue, brown & red . . 75 50

207 Dr. Schweitzer and Lambarene Hospital

1975. Birth Centenary of Dr. Albert Schweitzer.

574 **207** 100 f. brown, green & blk . 1·00 55

208 Peugeot, 1892

1975. Early Motor-cars.

575 **208** 50 f. blue and mauve . . . 60 30
576 – 75 f. purple and blue . . . 1·00 40
577 – 100 f. mauve and green . . 1·40 60
578 – 125 f. green and red . . . 1·50 70

DESIGNS: 75 f. Daimler, 1895; 100 f. Fiat, 1899; 125 f. Cadillac, 1903.

INDEX

Countries can be quickly located by referring to the index at the end of this volume.

209 Tree and Sun

211 Leontini Tetradrachme

210 Boxing

1975. National Tree Week.

579 **209** 40 f. green, orange and red . 40 25

1975. Traditional Sports.

580 **210** 35 f. brown, orange & blk . 35 20
581 – 40 f. brown, green & blk . 40 20
582 – 45 f. brown, blue & black . 50 25
583 – 50 f. brown, red and black . 55 30

DESIGNS—VERT: 40 f. Boxing; 50 f. Wrestling. HORIZ: 45 f. Wrestling.

1975. Ancient Coins.

584 **211** 50 f. grey, blue and red . . 60 20
585 – 75 f. grey, blue & mauve . 85 30
586 – 100 f. grey, orange & blue . 1·25 40
587 – 125 f. grey, purple & green . 1·50 60

COINS: 75 f. Athens tetradrachme; 100 f. Himer diadrachme; 125 f. Gela tetradrachme.

212 Putting the Shot

1975. Air. "Pre-Olympic Year". Olympic Games, Montreal (1976).

588 **212** 150 f. brown and red . . . 1·10 55
589 – 200 f. red, chestnut and brown . . . . 1·50 85

DESIGN: 200 f. Gymnastics.

213 Starving Family

1975. Pan-African Drought Relief.

590 **213** 40 f. blue, brown & orange . 55 30
591 – 45 f. brown and blue . . . 1·10 50
592 – 60 f. blue, green & orange . 1·00 40

DESIGNS: 45 f. Animal skeletons; 60 f. Truck bringing supplies.

214 Trading Canoe crossing R. Niger

1975. Tourism. Multicoloured.

593 40 f. Type **214** 50 25
594 45 f. Boubon Camp entrance . . 55 25
595 50 f. Boubon Camp view . . . 60 35

215 U N Emblem and Peace Dove

1975. Air. 30th Anniv of U.N.O.

596 **215** 100 f. light blue and blue . 85 40

216 "Virgin of Seville" (Murillo)

1975. Air. Christmas. Multicoloured.

597 50 f. Type **216** 50 35
598 75 f. "Adoration of the Shepherds" (Tintoretto) (horiz) 75 45
599 125 f. "Virgin with Angels" (Master of Burgo d'Osma) . 1·25 75

1975. Air. "Apollo-Soyuz" Space Link. Nos. 533/5 optd **JONCTION 17 Juillet 1975**.

600 **198** 50 f. green, red and blue . . 50 25
601 – 100 f. grey, red and blue . . 75 45
602 – 150 f. purple, plum & blue . 1·25 75

218 "Ashak"

1976. Literacy Campaign. Multicoloured.

603 25 f. Type **218** 15 10
604 30 f. "Kaska" 20 15
605 40 f. "Iccee" 25 15
606 50 f. "Tuuri-nya" 30 20
607 60 f. "Lekki" 35 25

219 Ice Hockey

1976. Winter Olympic Games, Innsbruck, Austria. Multicoloured.

608 40 f. Type **219** (postage) . . . 35 20
609 50 f. Tobogganing 40 20
610 150 f. Ski-jumping . . . . . . 1·25 50
611 200 f. Figure-skating (air) . . . 1·50 75
612 300 f. Cross-country skiing . . 2·00 1·00

220 Early Telephone and Satellite

1976. Telephone Centenary.

614 **220** 100 f. orange, blue & green . 85 50

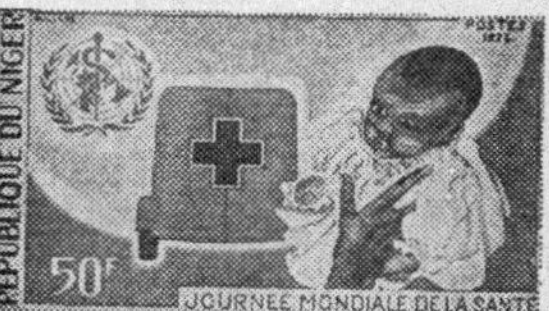

221 Baby and Ambulance

1976. World Health Day.

615 **221** 50 f. red, brown & purple . 50 25

222 Washington crossing the Delaware (after Leutze)

1976. Bicentenary of American Revolution. Mult.

616 40 f. Type **222** (postage) . . . 30 15
617 50 f. First soldiers of the Revolution 40 20
618 150 f. Joseph Warren – martyr of Bunker Hill (air) . . . . . 1·10 35
619 200 f. John Paul Jones aboard the "Bonhomme Richard" . . . 1·50 60
620 300 f. Molly Pitcher – heroine of Monmouth . . . . 2·00 90

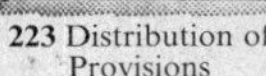

223 Distribution of Provisions **225** "Europafrique" Symbols

224 "Hindenburg" crossing Lake Constance

1976. 2nd Anniv of Military Coup. Multicoloured.

622 50 f. Type **223** 35 25
623 100 f. Soldiers with bulldozer (horiz) . . . . 1·10 45

1976. Air. 75th Anniv of Zeppelin Airships. Multicoloured.

624 40 f. Type **224** 40 15
625 50 f. LZ-3 over Wurzberg . . . 50 25
626 150 f. L-9 over Friedrichshafen . 1·40 55
627 200 f. LZ-2 over Rothenburg (vert) . . . . 1·75 70
628 300 f. "Graf Zeppelin II" over Essen . . . . 4·25 90

1976. "Europafrique".

630 **225** 100 f. multicoloured . . . 1·40 50

226 Plant Cultivation

1976. Communal Works. Multicoloured.

631 25 f. Type **226** 15 10
632 30 f. Harvesting rice 20 15

227 Boxing

1976. Olympic Games, Montreal. Multicoloured.

633 40 f. Type **227** 25 15
634 50 f. Basketball 40 20
635 60 f. Football 45 25
636 80 f. Cycling (horiz) 60 20
637 100 f. Judo (horiz) 70 30

228 Motobecane '125'

1976. Motorcycles.

639 **228** 50 f. violet, brown & turq . 60 25
640 – 75 f. green, red & turq . . 85 35
641 – 100 f. brown, orge & pur . 1·25 50
642 – 125 f. slate, olive & black . 1·50 75

DESIGNS: 75 f. Norton "Challenge"; 100 f. B.M.W. "903"; 125 f. Kawasaki "1000".

229 Cultivation Map

1976. Operation "Sahel Vert". Multicoloured.

643 40 f. Type **229** 30 15
644 45 f. Tending plants (vert) . . . 35 20
645 60 f. Planting sapling (vert) . . 55 30

1976. International Literacy Day. Nos. 603/7 optd JOURNEE INTERNATIONALE DE L'ALPHABETISATION.

646 **218** 25 f. multicoloured 15 15
647 – 30 f. multicoloured 15 15
648 – 40 f. multicoloured 20 15
649 – 50 f. multicoloured 25 20
650 – 60 f. multicoloured 30 20

231 Basket Making

1976. Niger Women's Association. Multicoloured.

651 40 f. Type **231** 35 20
652 45 f. Hairdressing (horiz) . . . 40 25
653 50 f. Making pottery 50 35

232 Wall Paintings

1976. "Archaeology". Multicoloured.

654 40 f. Type **232** 45 25
655 50 f. Neolithic statuettes . . . 50 25
656 60 f. Dinosaur skeleton 90 35

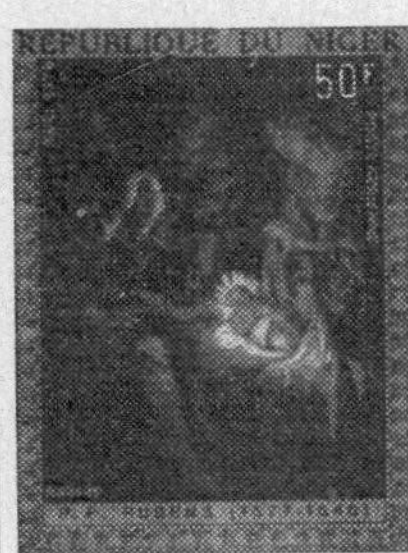

233 "The Nativity" (Rubens) **234** Benin Ivory Mask

1976. Air. Christmas. Multicoloured.

657 50 f. Type **233** 50 25
658 100 f. "Holy Night" (Correggio) . . . . 1·10 45
659 150 f. "Adoration of the Magi" (David) (horiz) . . . . . 1·50 90

1977. 2nd World Festival of Negro-African Arts, Lagos.

660 **234** 40 f. brown 40 20
661 – 50 f. blue 60 30

DESIGNS—HORIZ: 50 f. Nigerian stick dance.

235 Students in Class **236** Examining Patient

1977. Alphabetisation Campaign.

662 **235** 40 f. multicoloured 30 15
663 50 f. multicoloured 40 20
664 60 f. multicoloured 60 20

1977. Village Health. Multicoloured.

665 40 f. Type **236** 50 20
666 50 f. Examining baby 60 30

237 Rocket Launch

1977. "Viking" Space Mission. Multicoloured.

667 50 f. Type **237** (postage) . . . 45 15
668 80 f. "Viking" approaching Mars (horiz) 65 20
669 100 f. "Viking" on Mars (horiz) (air) 65 25
670 150 f. Parachute descent . . . 1·00 30
671 200 f. Rocket in flight . . . . 1·40 45

238 Marabou Stork

1977. Fauna Protection.

673 **238** 80 f. sepia, bis and red . . 2·00 85
674 – 90 f. brown and turquoise . 1·25 60

DESIGN: 90 f. Bushbuck.

239 Satellite and Weather Symbols

1977. World Meteorological Day.

675 **239** 100 f. blue, black & turq . 1·00 50

240 Gymnastic Exercise

1977. 2nd Youth Festival, Tahoua. Multicoloured.

676 40 f. Type **240** 35 20
677 50 f. High jumping 40 25
678 80 f. Choral ensemble 70 35

241 Red Cross and Children playing

1977. World Health Day. Child Immunisation Campaign.

679 **241** 80 f. red, mauve & orange . 75 35

242 Fly, Dagger, and W.H.O. Emblem in Eye

1977. Fight against Onchocerosis (blindness caused by worm infestation).

680 **242** 100 f. blue, grey and red . . 1·40 55

243 Guirka Tahoua Dance

1977. "Popular Arts and Traditions". Multicoloured.

681 40 f. Type **243** 45 25
682 50 f. Maifilafili Gaya 50 20
683 80 f. Naguihinayan Loga . . . 80 45

244 Four Cavalrymen

1977. Chiefs' Traditional Cavalry. Multicoloured.

684 40 f. Type **244** 55 25
685 50 f. Chieftain at head of cavalry 65 30
686 60 f. Chieftain and cavalry . . 90 45

245 Planting Crops

1977. "Operation Green Sahel" (recovery of desert).

687 **245** 40 f. multicoloured 50 25

247 Mao Tse-tung

246 Albert John Luthuli (Peace, 1960)

1977. Nobel Prize Winners. Multicoloured.

688 50 f. Type **246** 30 15
689 80 f. Maurice Maeterlinck (Literature, 1911) 55 20
690 100 f. Allan L. Hodgkin (Medicine, 1963) 70 25
691 150 f. Albert Camus (Literature, 1957) . . . . 1·00 35
692 200 f. Paul Ehrlich (Medicine, 1908) . . . . 1·50 40

1977. 1st Death Anniv of Mao Tse-tung (Chinese leader).
694 **247** 100 f. black and red . . . 80 50

248 Vittorio Pozzo (Italy)

1977. World Football Cup Elimination Rounds. Multicoloured.
695 40 f. Type **248** 30 10
696 50 f. Vincente Feola, Spain . . . 35 15
697 80 f. Aymore Moreira, Portugal . 50 20
698 100 f. Sir Alf Ramsey, England . 75 25
699 200 f. Helmut Schon, West Germany . . . . 1·40 45

249 Horse's Head and Parthenon

1977. U.N.E.S.C.O. Commemoration.
701 **249** 100 f. blue, red and pale blue 1·25 60

250 Carrying Water

1977. Women's Work. Multicoloured.
702 40 f. Type **250** 35 30
703 50 f. Pounding maize 40 25

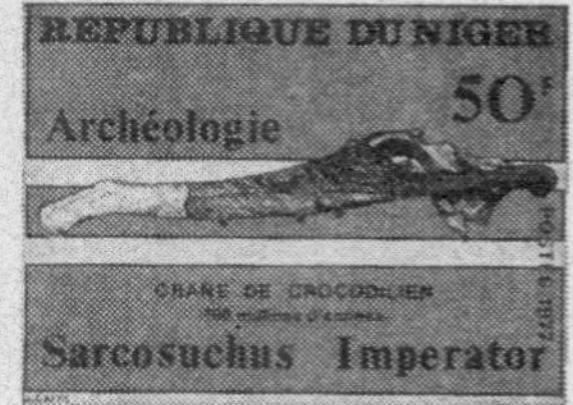

251 Crocodile Skull

1977. Archaeology. Multicoloured.
704 50 f. Type **251** 60 40
705 80 f. Neolithic tools 90 60

252 Paul Follereau and Leper
253 "The Assumption"

1978. 25th Anniv of World Leprosy Day.
706 **252** 40 f. red, blue & orange . . 30 15
707 – 50 f. black, red & orange . . 40 20
DESIGN—HORIZ: 50 f. Follereau and two lepers.

1978. 400th Birth Anniv of Peter Paul Rubens. Paintings. Multicoloured.
708 50 f. Type **253** 30 15
709 70 f. "The Artist and his Friends" (horiz) 40 20
710 100 f. "History of Maria de Medici" 70 25
711 150 f. "Alathea Talbot" . . . 1·10 35
712 200 f. "Portrait of the Marquise de Spinola" . . . . . . 1·50 40

1978. As Nos. 376/7 but redrawn and background colour of 35 f. changed to blue, 35 f. undated, 50 f. dated "1978".
714 35 f. Broad-tailed paradise whydah . . . . 1·00 50
715 50 f. Cattle egret . . . . . 2·00 60
The 50 f. is still wrongly inscribed "Balbucus".

254 Putting the Shot

1978. National Schools and University Sports Championships. Multicoloured.
716 40 f. Type **254** 20 15
717 50 f. Volleyball 30 20
718 60 f. Long-jumping 35 20
719 100 f. Throwing the javelin . . 55 35

255 Nurse assisting Patient

1978. Niger Red Cross.
720 **255** 40 f. multicoloured 30 20

256 Station and Dish Aerial

1978. Goudel Earth Receiving Station.
721 **256** 100 f. multicoloured . . . 65 40

257 Football and Flags of Competing Nations

1978. World Cup Football Championship, Argentina. Multicoloured.
722 40 f. Type **257** 25 10
723 50 f. Football in net 35 15
724 100 f. Globe and goal 75 25
725 200 f. Tackling (horiz) . . . . 1·40 55

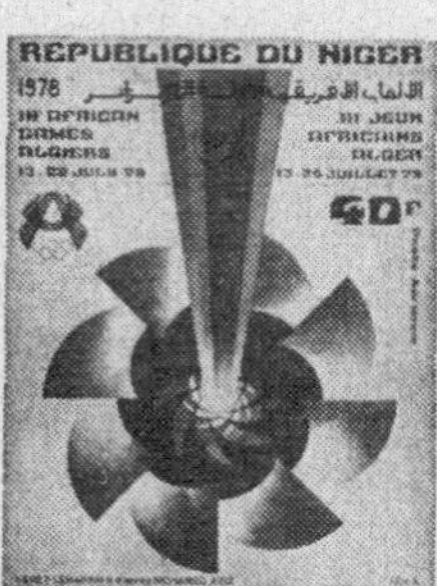

258 "Fireworks"

1978. Air. 3rd African Games, Algiers. Multicoloured.
727 40 f. Type **258** 25 20
728 150 f. Olympic rings emblem . . 1·00 60

259 Niamey Post Office

1978. Niamey Post Office. Multicoloured.
729 40 f. Type **259** 25 15
730 60 f. Niamey Post Office (different) 35 25

260 Aerial View of Water-works

1978. Goudel Water-works.
731 **260** 100 f. multicoloured . . . 55 40

261 R. T. N. Emblem

1978. Air. 20th Anniv of Niger Broadcasting.
732 **261** 150 f. multicoloured . . . 90 60

262 Golden Eagle and Oldenburg 2 g. Stamp of 1859

1978. Air. "Philexafrique" Stamp Exhibition, Libreville, Gabon (1st issue) and Int Stamp Fair, Essen, West Germany. Multicoloured.
733 100 f. Type **262** . . . . 1·75 1·25
734 100 f. Giraffes and Niger 1959 2 f. stamp . . . . 1·75 1·25
See also Nos. 769/70.

263 Giraffe
265 Dome of the Rock, Jerusalem

1978. Endangered Animals. Multicoloured.
735 40 f. Type **263** 45 25
736 50 f. Ostrich . . . . 1·50 30
737 70 f. Cheetah 75 35
738 150 f. Scimitar oryx (horiz) . . 1·50 75
739 200 f. Addax (horiz) . . . . . 2·00 95
740 300 f. Hartebeest (horiz) . . . 2·50 1·25

1978. World Cup Football Championship Finalists. Nos. 695/9 optd.
741 **248** 40 f. multicoloured 30 20
742 – 50 f. multicoloured 40 20
743 – 80 f. multicoloured 55 25
744 – 100 f. multicoloured . . . 65 40
745 – 200 f. multicoloured . . . 1·40 75
OVERPRINTS: 40 f. **EQUIPE QUATRIEME: ITALIE**; 50 f. **EQUIPE TROISIEME: BRESIL**; 80 f. **EQUIPE SECONDE: PAYS BAS**; 100 f. **EQUIPE VAINQUEUR: ARGENTINE**. 200 f. **ARGENTINE - PAYS BAS 3 - 1**.

1978. Palestinian Welfare.
747 **265** 40 f. + 5 f. multicoloured . 40 30

266 Laying Foundation Stone, and View of University

1978. Air. Islamic University of Niger.
748 **266** 100 f. multicoloured . . . 60 40

HAVE YOU READ THE NOTES AT THE BEGINNING OF THIS CATALOGUE?
These often provide answers to the enquiries we receive.

267 Tinguizi
268 "The Homecoming" (Daumier)

1978. Musicians. Multicoloured.
749 100 f. Type **267** 75 40
750 100 f. Chetima Ganga (horiz) . 75 40
751 100 f. Dan Gourmou 75 40

1979. Paintings. Multicoloured.
752 50 f. Type **268** 50 20
753 100 f. "Virgin in Prayer" (Durer) 60 20
754 150 f. "Virgin and Child" (Durer) 90 30
755 200 f. "Virgin and Child" (Durer) (different) . . . . 1·25 40

269 Feeder Tanks

1979. Solar Energy. Multicoloured.
757 40 f. Type **269** 30 20
758 50 f. Solar panels on house roofs (horiz) 40 25

270 Langha Contestants

1979. Traditional Sports. Multicoloured.
759 40 f. Type **270** 25 15
760 50 f. Langha contestants clasping hands 35 20

271 Children with Building Bricks

1979. International Year of the Child. Multicoloured.
761 40 f. Type **271** 25 15
762 100 f. Children with book . . . 60 25
763 150 f. Children with model airplane . . . . 1·25 45

272 Rowland Hill, Peugeot Mail Van and French "Ceres" Stamp of 1849

1979. Death Centenary of Sir Rowland Hill. Multicoloured.
764 40 f. Type **272** 25 15
765 100 f. Canoes and Austrian newspaper stamp, 1851 . . . 60 25
766 150 f. "DC-3" aircraft & U.S. "Lincoln" stamp, 1869 . . . 1·10 35
767 200 f. Advanced Passenger Train (APT), Great Britain and Canada 7½d. stamp, 1857 . . 2·25 40

273 Zabira Decorated Bag and Niger 45 f. Stamp, 1965

1979. "Philexafrique 2" Exhibition, Gabon (2nd issue).

769 **273** 50 f. multicoloured 65 40
770 – 150 f. blue, red & carmen . 1·60 1·10

DESIGN: 150 f. Talking Heads, world map, satellite and U.P.U. emblem.

274 Alcock and Brown Statue and Vickers Vimy aircraft

1979. 60th Anniv of First Transatlantic Flight.

771 **274** 100 f. multicoloured . . . 1·00 35

275 Djermakoye Palace

1979. Historic Monuments.

772 **275** 100 f. multicoloured . . . 55 40

276 Bororos in Festive Headdress

1979. Annual Bororo Festival. Multicoloured.

773 45 f. Type **276** 30 20
774 60 f. Bororo women in traditional costume (vert) 35 25

277 Boxing

1979. Pre-Olympic Year.

775 **277** 45 f. multicoloured 30 15
776 – 100 f. multicoloured . . . 55 25
777 – 150 f. multicoloured . . . 85 35
778 – 250 f. multicoloured . . . 1·25 45

DESIGNS: 100 f. to 250 f. Various boxing scenes.

278 Class of Learner-drivers

1979. Driving School.

780 **278** 45 f. multicoloured 30 20

279 Douglas DC-10 over Map of Niger

1979. Air. 20th Anniv of ASECNA (African Air Safety Organization).

781 **279** 150 f. multicoloured . . . 1·10 60

1979. "Apollo 11" Moon Landing. Nos. 667/8, 670/1 optd **alunissage apollo XI juillet 1969** and lunar module.

782 50 f. Type **237** (postage) . . . 30 20
783 80 f. "Viking" approaching Mars (horiz) 50 35
784 150 f. Parachute descent (air) . 90 60
785 200 f. Rocket in flight . . . . 1·25 80

281 Four-man Bobsleigh

1979. Winter Olympic Games, Lake Placid (1980). Multicoloured.

787 40 f. Type **281** 25 15
788 60 f. Downhill skiing 35 15
789 100 f. Speed skating 60 25
790 150 f. Two-man bobsleigh . . . 90 35
791 200 f. Figure skating . . . . . 1·10 45

282 Le Gaweye Hotel

1980. Air.

793 **282** 100 f. multicoloured . . . 60 40

283 Sultan and Court

1980. Sultan of Zinder's Court. Multicoloured.

794 45 f. Type **283** 30 20
795 60 f. Sultan and court (different) 40 20

284 Chain Smoker and Athlete

285 Walking

1980. World Health Day. Anti-Smoking Campaign.

796 **284** 100 f. multicoloured . . . 65 40

1980. Olympic Games, Moscow. Multicoloured.

797 60 f. Throwing the javelin . . . 35 15
798 90 f. Type **285** 50 20
799 100 f. High jump (horiz) 55 25
800 300 f. Running (horiz) . . . . 1·50 55

1980. Winter Olympic Games Medal Winners. Nos. 787/91 optd.

802 **281** 40 f. **VAINQUEUR R.D.A.** 25 15
803 – 60 f. **VAINQUEUR STENMARK SUEDE** . 30 20
804 – 100 f. **VAINQUEUR HEIDEN Etats-Unis** . 60 30
805 – 150 f. **VAINQUEURS SCHERER-BENZ Suisse** 90 45
806 – 200 f. **VAINQUEUR COUSINS Grande Bretagne** . . . . . 1·25 65

287 Village Scene

1980. Health Year.

808 **287** 150 f. multicoloured . . . 75 50

288 Class 150 (first locomotive in Japan, 1871)

1980. Steam Locomotives. Multicoloured.

809 45 f. Type **288** 80 10
810 60 f. "Fred Merril", 1848, U.S.A. 1·10 10
811 90 f. Series 61, 1934, Germany . 1·75 20
812 100 f. Type P2, 1900, Prussia . 2·25 20
813 130 f. "Aigle", 1846, France . . 3·25 30

289 Steve Biko and Map of Africa

292 U.A.P.T. Emblem

291 Footballer

1980. 4th Death Anniv of Steve Biko (South African Anti-apartheid Worker).

815 **289** 150 f. multicoloured . . . 80 60

1980. Olympic Medal Winners. Nos. 787/800 optd.

816 **285** 60 f. **KULA (URSS)** . . . 35 15
817 – 90 f. **DAMILANO (IT)** . . 55 25
818 – 100 f. **WZSOLA (POL)** . . 60 30
819 – 300 f. **YIFTER (ETH)** . . 1·60 90

1980. World Cup Football Championship, Spain (1982). Various designs showing Football.

821 **291** 45 f. multicoloured 25 15
822 – 60 f. multicoloured 30 15
823 – 90 f. multicoloured 55 20
824 – 100 f. multicoloured . . . 60 25
825 – 130 f. multicoloured . . . 80 30

1980. 5th Anniv of African Posts and Telecommunications Union.

827 **292** 100 f. multicoloured . . . 55 40

293 Earthenware Statuettes

1981. Kareygorou Culture Terracotta Statuettes. Multicoloured.

828 45 f. Type **293** 25 20
829 60 f. Head (vert) 35 20
830 90 f. Head (different) (vert) . . 50 30
831 150 f. Three heads 90 50

HAVE YOU READ THE NOTES AT THE BEGINNING OF THIS CATALOGUE?
These often provide answers to the enquiries we receive.

294 "Self-portrait"

295 Ostrich

1981. Paintings by Rembrandt. Multicoloured.

832 60 f. Type **294** 40 15
833 90 f. "Portrait of Hendrickje at the Window" 60 20
834 100 f. "Portrait of an Old Man" 65 25
835 130 f. "Maria Trip" 90 35
836 200 f. "Self-portrait" (different) . 1·25 45
837 400 f. "Portrait of Saskia" . . 2·25 1·00

1981. Animals. Multicoloured.

839 10 f. Type **295** 75 20
840 20 f. Scimitar oryx 25 15
841 25 f. Addra gazelle 20 15
842 30 f. Arabian bustard . . . . 1·25 50
843 60 f. Giraffe 50 20
844 150 f. Addax . . . . 1·00 45

296 "Apollo 11"

1981. Air. Conquest of Space. Multicoloured.

845 100 f. Type **296** 60 25
846 150 f. Boeing 747 SCA carrying space shuttle . . . . 1·00 40
847 200 f. Rocket carrying space shuttle . . . . 1·25 40
848 300 f. Space shuttle flying over planet . . . . 3·00 1·00

297 Tanks

298 Disabled Archer

1981. 7th Anniv of Military Coup.

849 **297** 100 f. multicoloured . . . . 1·00 40

1981. International Year of Disabled People.

850 **298** 50 f. dp. brown, red & brown 50 20
851 – 100 f. brown, red and green 75 40

DESIGN: 100 f. Disabled draughtsman.

299 Ballet Mahalba

1981. Ballet Mahalba. Multicoloured.

852 100 f. Type **299** 70 35
853 100 f. Ballet Mahalba (different) 70 35

300 "Portrait of Olga in an Armchair"

301 Mosque and Ka'aba

1981. Air. Birth Centenary of Pablo Picasso (artist). Multicoloured.

854 60 f. Type **300** 40 20
855 90 f. "The Family of Acrobats" . 55 25
856 120 f. "The Three Musicians" . 70 35
857 200 f. "Paul on a Donkey" . . 1·10 55
858 400 f. "Young Girl drawing in an Interior" (horiz) . . . . . . 2·40 1·25

1981. 15th Centenary of Hejira.

859 **301** 100 f. multicoloured . . . 60 35

302 Carriage

1981. British Royal Wedding.

860 **302** 150 f. multicoloured . . . 60 35
861 – 200 f. multicoloured . . . 1·00 55
862 – 300 f. multicoloured . . . 1·25 1·00

DESIGNS: 200 f., 300 f. Similar designs showing carriages.

303 Sir Alexander Fleming

305 Crops, Cattle and Fish

304 Pen-nibs, Envelope, Flower and U.P.U. Emblem

1981. Birth Centenary of Sir Alexander Fleming (discoverer of Penicillin).

864 **303** 150 f. blue, brown and green 1·50 60

1981. International Letter Writing Week.

865 **304** 65 f. on 45 f. blue and red 40 20
866 – 85 f. on 60 f. blue, orange and black 50 30

DESIGN: 85 f. Quill, hand holding pen and U.P.U. emblem.

1981. World Food Day.

867 **305** 100 f. multicoloured . . . 1·00 35

306 Tackling

1981. World Cup Football Championship, Spain (1982). Multicoloured.

868 40 f. Type **306** 25 20
869 65 f. Goal keeper fighting for ball 40 30
870 85 f. Passing ball 55 35
871 150 f. Running with ball . . . 1·00 60
872 300 f. Jumping for ball . . . . 2·25 1·10

307 Peugeot, 1912

1981. 75th Anniv of French Grand Prix Motor Race. Multicoloured.

874 20 f. Type **307** 25 15
875 40 f. Bugatti, 1924 . . . . . 35 20
876 65 f. Lotus-Climax, 1962 . . . 55 30
877 85 f. Georges Boillot 75 35
878 150 f. Phil Hill . . . . . . 1·10 60

308 "Madonna and Child" (Botticelli)

309 Children watering Plants

1981. Christmas. Various Madonna and Child Paintings by named artists. Multicoloured.

880 100 f. Type **308** 60 40
881 200 f. Botticini . . . . . . 1·25 75
882 300 f. Botticini (different) . . . 2·00 1·10

1982. School Gardens. Multicoloured.

883 65 f. Type **309** 50 30
884 85 f. Tending plants and examining produce 60 35

310 Arturo Toscanini (conductor, 25th death anniv)

1982. Celebrities' Anniversaries. Multicoloured.

885 120 f. Type **310** . . . . . . 1·00 45
886 140 f. "Fruits on a Table" (Manet, 150th birth anniv) (horiz) 80 55
887 200 f. "L'Estaque" (Braque, birth centenary) (horiz) . . . . 1·25 60
888 300 f. George Washington (250th birth anniv) . . . . . . 2·00 90
889 400 f. Goethe (poet, 150th death anniv) . . . . 2·50 1·25
890 500 f. Princess of Wales (21st birthday) . . . . 2·75 1·50

311 Palace of Congresses

1982. Palace of Congresses.

892 **311** 150 f. multicoloured . . . 90 60

312 Martial Arts

1982. 7th Youth Festival, Agadez. Multicoloured.

893 65 f. Type **312** 40 30
894 100 f. Traditional wrestling . . 60 40

313 Planting a Tree

1982. National Re-afforestation Campaign. Multicoloured.

895 150 f. Type **313** . . . . . . 1·00 60
896 200 f. Forest and desert . . . . 1·25 75

MORE DETAILED LISTS
are given in the Stanley Gibbons Catalogues referred to in the country headings.
For lists of current volumes see Introduction.

314 Scouts in Pirogue

315 Map of Africa showing Member States

1982. 75th Anniv of Boy Scout Movement. Mult.

897 65 f. Type **314** 55 30
898 85 f. Scouts inflatable dinghy . 65 30
899 130 f. Scouts in canoe . . . . 1·25 45
900 200 f. Scouts on raft . . . . . 1·75 60

1982. Economic Community of West African States.

902 **315** 200 f. yellow, black and blue 1·25 75

316 Casting Net

1982. Niger Fishermen. Multicoloured.

903 65 f. Type **316** 85 30
904 85 f. Net fishing 70 40

1982. Birth of Prince William of Wales. Nos. 860/2 optd **NAISSANCE ROYALE 1982.**

905 **302** 150 f. multicoloured . . . 75 60
906 – 200 f. multicoloured . . . 1·00 75
907 – 300 f. multicoloured . . . 1·40 1·10

318 Hands reaching towards Mosque

1982. 13th Islamic Foreign Ministers Meeting, Niamey.

909 **318** 100 f. multicoloured . . . 60 40

319 "Flautist"

1982. Norman Rockwell Paintings. Multicoloured.

910 65 f. Type **319** 40 25
911 85 f. "Clerk" 50 25
912 110 f. "Teacher and Pupil" . . 70 35
913 150 f. "Girl Shopper" 90 50

320 World Map and Satellite

1982. I.T.U. Delegates' Conference, Nairobi.

914 **320** 130 f. blue, light blue and black . . . . 1·00 50

1982. World Cup Football Championship Winners. Nos. 868/72 optd.

915 40 f. Type **306** 25 20
916 65 f. Goal keeper fighting for ball 40 30
917 85 f. Passing ball 45 25
918 150 f. Running with ball . . . 90 50
919 300 f. Jumping for ball . . . . 1·75 1·10

OVERPRINTS: 40 f. **1966 VAINQUEUR GRANDE - BRETAGNE**; 65 f. **"1970 VAINQUEUR BRESIL"**; 85 f. **"1974 VAINQUEUR ALLEMAGNE (RFA)"**; 150 f. **"1978 VAINQUEUR ARGENTINE"**; 300 f. **"1982 VAINQUEUR ITALIE"**.

322 Laboratory Workers with Microscopes

1982. Laboratory Work. Multicoloured.

921 65 f. Type **322** 60 40
922 115 f. Laboratory workers . . 80 50

323 "Adoration of the Kings"

1982. Air. Christmas. Paintings by Rubens. Multicoloured.

923 200 f. Type **323** . . . . . . 1·25 50
924 300 f. "Mystic Marriage of St. Catherine" . . . . 2·00 75
925 400 f. "Virgin and Child" . . . 2·50 1·00

324 Montgolfier Balloon

1983. Air. Bicent of Manned Flight. Mult.

926 65 f. Type **324** 45 15
927 85 f. Charles's hydrogen balloon 60 20
928 200 f. Goodyear Aerospace airship (horiz) . . . . . . 1·25 60
929 250 f. Farman H.F.III biplane (horiz) . . . . 1·50 70
930 300 f. Concorde . . . . . . 3·00 1·40
931 500 f. "Apollo 11" spacecraft . . 3·00 1·40

No. 928 is wrongly inscribed "Zeppelin".

325 Harvesting Rice

326 E.C.A. Anniversary Emblem

1983. Self-sufficiency in Food. Multicoloured.

932 65 f. Type **325** 60 30
933 85 f. Planting rice 80 40

1983. 25th Anniv of Economic Commission for Africa.

934 **326** 120 f. multicoloured . . . 75 40
935 200 f. multicoloured . . . 1·25 70

327 "The Miraculous Draught of Fishes"

1983. 500th Birth Anniv of Raphael. Multicoloured.

936 65 f. Type **327** 70 15
937 85 f. "Grand Ducal Madonna" (vert) 50 20
938 100 f. "The Deliverance of St. Peter" 60 25
939 150 f. "Sistine Madonna" (vert) 1·00 45
940 200 f. "The Fall on the Way to Calvary" (vert) . . . . . . 1·10 60
941 300 f. "The Entombment" . . . 1·75 80
942 400 f. "The Transfiguration" (vert) . . . . 2·25 1·10
943 500 f. "St. Michael fighting the Dragon" (vert) . . . . . . 3·00 1·40

328 Surveying

1983. The Army in the Service of Development. Multicoloured.
944 85 f. Type **328** 60 25
945 150 f. Road building . . . . . 1·00 50

329 Palace of Justice

1983. Palace of Justice, Agadez.
946 **329** 65 f. multicoloured 40 20

330 Javelin

1983. Air. Olympic Games, Los Angeles. Mult.
947 85 f. Type **330** 50 20
948 200 f. Shotput . . . . 1·10 60
949 250 f. Throwing the hammer (vert) . . . . 1·50 70
950 300 f. Discus . . . . 1·75 80

331 Rural Post Vehicle **332** Dome of the Rock

1983. Rural Post Service. Multicoloured.
952 65 f. Type **331** 50 20
953 100 f. Post vehicle and map . . 75 30

1983. Palestine.
954 **332** 65 f. multicoloured 65 20

333 Class watching Television

1983. International Literacy Day. Multicoloured.
955 40 f. Type **333** 25 15
956 65 f. Teacher at blackboard (vert) 40 25
957 85 f. Learning weights (vert) . . 55 30
958 100 f. Outdoor class 60 35
959 150 f. Woman reading magazine (vert) . . . . 1·00 50

334 Three Dancers

1983. Seventh Dosso Dance Festival. Multicoloured.
960 65 f. Type **334** 50 25
961 85 f. Four dancers 60 35
962 120 f. Two dancers 90 50

335 Post Van **336** Television Antenna and Solar Panel

1983. World Communications Year. Multicoloured.
963 80 f. Type **335** 60 40
964 120 f. Sorting letters 80 40
965 150 f. W.C.Y. emblem (vert) . . 1·00 50

1983. Solar Energy in the Service of Television. Multicoloured.
966 85 f. Type **336** 60 30
967 130 f. Land-rover and solar panel 90 45

337 "Hypolimnas misippus"

1983. Butterflies. Multicoloured.
968 75 f. Type **337** 70 35
969 120 f. "Papilio demodocus" . . . 1·10 50
970 250 f. "Vanessa antiopa" . . . 2·00 90
971 350 f. "Charexes jasius" . . . 2·75 1·40
972 500 f. "Danaus chrisippus" . . . 4·50 1·75

338 "Virgin and Child with Angels" **339** Samariya Emblem

1983. Air. Christmas. Paintings by Botticelli. Multicoloured.
973 120 f. Type **338** 75 40
974 350 f. "Adoration of the Magi" (horiz) . . . . 2·25 1·00
975 500 f. "Virgin of the Pomegranate" . . . . . . 3·00 1·25

1984. Samariya.
976 **339** 80 f. black, orange & grn . 50 30

340 Running

1984. Air. Olympic Games, Los Angeles. Mult.
977 80 f. Type **340** 40 20
978 120 f. Pole vault 60 30
979 140 f. High jump 80 30
980 200 f. Triple jump (vert) . . . 1·25 45
981 350 f. Long jump (vert) . . . . 2·00 1·00

341 Boubon's Tetra

1984. Fish.
983 **341** 120 f. multicoloured . . . 2·75 80

342 Obstacle Course

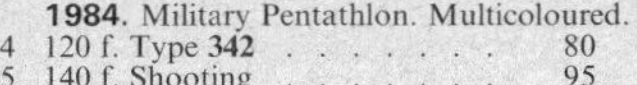
1984. Military Pentathlon. Multicoloured.
984 120 f. Type **342** 80 40
985 140 f. Shooting 95 50

343 Radio Station

1984. New Radio Station.
986 **343** 120 f. multicoloured . . . 85 40

344 Flags, Agriculture and Symbols of Unity and Growth

1984. 25th Anniv of Council of Unity.
987 **344** 65 f. multicoloured 40 25
988 85 f. multicoloured 50 40

345 "Paris" (early steamer)

1984. Ships. Multicoloured.
989 80 f. Type **345** 75 30
990 120 f. "Jacques Coeur" (full-rigged ship) 85 40
991 150 f. "Bosphorus" (full-rigged ship) . . . . 1·40 50
992 300 f. "Comet" (full-rigged ship) 2·50 1·10

346 Daimler

1984. Motor Cars. Multicoloured.
993 100 f. Type **346** 75 30
994 140 f. Renault . . . . 1·10 45
995 250 f. Delage "D 8" . . . . . . 1·75 70
996 400 f. Maybach "Zeppelin" . . 2·75 90

347 "Rickmer Rickmers" (full-rigged ship)

1984. Universal Postal Union Congress, Hamburg.
997 **347** 300 f. blue, brown and green 2·75 1·75

348 Cattle

1984. Ayerou Market. Multicoloured.
998 80 f. Type **348** 60 40
999 120 f. View of market . . . . 1·00 60

349 Viper

1984.
1000 **349** 80 f. multicoloured . . . 75 40

350 Carl Lewis (100 and 200 metres)

1984. Air. Olympic Games Medal Winners. Multicoloured.
1001 80 f. Type **350** 50 20
1002 120 f. J. Cruz (800 metres) . . 70 40
1003 140 f. A. Cova (10,000 metres) . 80 45
1004 300 f. Al Joyner (Triple jump) . 1·75 90

351 Emblem

1984. 10th Anniv of Economic Community of West Africa.
1006 **351** 80 f. multicoloured . . . 50 30

352 Emblem and Extract from General Kountche's Speech

1984. United Nations Disarmament Decennials.
1007 **352** 400 f. black and green . . 2·50 1·75
1008 500 f. black and blue . . . 3·00 1·75

353 Football

1984. Air. Preliminary Rounds of World Cup Football Championship, Mexico.
1009 **353** 150 f. multicoloured . . . 1·00 45
1010 – 250 f. multicoloured . . . 1·75 80
1011 – 450 f. multicoloured . . . 2·50 1·25
1012 – 500 f. multicoloured . . . 3·00 1·75
DESIGNS: 250 to 500 f. Footballing scenes.

354 "The Visitation" (Ghirlandaio)

1984. Air. Christmas. Multicoloured.
1013 100 f. Type **354** 60 30
1014 200 f. "Virgin and Child" (Master of Saint Verdiana) . 1·25 65
1015 400 f. "Virgin and Child" (J. Koning) . . . . 2·50 1·25

1984. Drought Relief. Nos. 895/6 optd **Aide au Sahel 84**.
1016 150 f. multicoloured . . . . 1·00 80
1017 200 f. multicoloured . . . . 1·25 1·10

356 Organization Emblem 357 Breast-feeding Baby

1985. 10th Anniv of World Tourism Organization.
1018 **356** 100 f. black, orange and green 70 40

1985. Infant Survival Campaign. Multicoloured.
1019 85 f. Type **357** 70 30
1020 110 f. Feeding baby and changing nappy 90 40

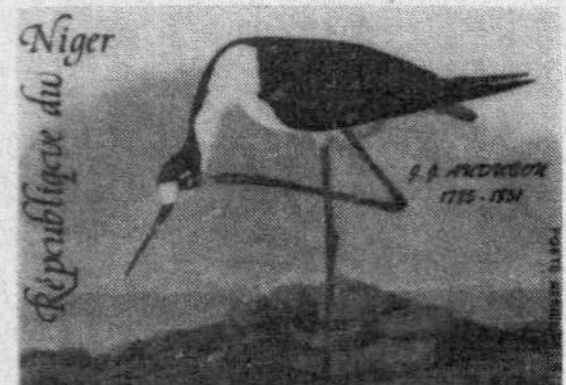

358 Black-necked Stilt

1985. Air. Birth Centenary of John J. Audubon (ornithologist). Multicoloured.
1021 110 f. Type **358** . . . . 1·25 90
1022 140 f. Greater flamingo (vert) . 1·75 1·25
1023 200 f. Atlantic puffin . . . . 2·50 1·90
1024 350 f. Arctic tern (vert) . . . 4·50 2·50

360 Profile and Emblem

1985. 15th Anniv of Technical and Cultural Co-operation Agency.
1026 **360** 110 f. brown, red & vio . 65 40

361 Dancers

1985. 8th Niamey Festival. Multicoloured.
1027 85 f. Type **361** 60 40
1028 110 f. Four dancers (vert) . . 70 50
1029 150 f. Dancers (different) . . . 1·00 65

362 Wolf ("White Fang") and Jack London

1985. International Youth Year. Multicoloured.
1030 85 f. Type **362** 60 25
1031 105 f. Woman with lion and Joseph Kessel 75 30
1032 250 f. Capt. Ahab harpooning white whale ("Moby Dick") 1·75 90
1033 450 f. Mowgli on elephant ("Jungle Book") . . . . . 2·75 1·50

363 Two Children on Leaf

1985. "Philexafrique" Stamp Exhibition, Lome, Togo (1st issue). Multicoloured.
1034 200 f. Type **363** . . . . 1·25 1·00
1035 200 f. Mining . . . . 1·25 1·00
See also Nos. 1064/5.

364 "Hugo with his Son Francois" (A. de Chatillon)

1985. Death Centenary of Victor Hugo (writer).
1036 **364** 500 f. multicoloured . . . 3·00 1·75

365 French Turbotrain TGV 001, Satellite and Boeing 737 on Map

1985. Europafrique.
1037 **365** 110 f. multicoloured . . . 2·75 55

366 Addax

1985. Endangered Animals. Multicoloured.
1038 50 f. Type **366** 40 15
1039 60 f. Addax (different) (horiz) . 45 25
1040 85 f. Two scimitar oryxes (horiz) 55 25
1041 110 f. Oryx 75 35

367 "Oedaleus sp" on Millet 368 Cross of Agadez

1985. Vegetation Protection. Multicoloured.
1042 85 f. Type **367** 55 20
1043 110 f. "Dysdercus volkeri" (beetle) 75 35
1044 150 f. Fungi attacking sorghum and millet (horiz) . . . . . 2·50 60
1045 210 f. Sudan golden sparrows in tree . . . . 3·50 1·60
1046 390 f. Red-billed queleas in tree 6·00 3·25

1985.
1047 **368** 85 f. green 45 15
1048 – 110 f. brown 55 15
DESIGN: 110 f. Girl carrying water jar on head.

369 Arms, Flags and Agriculture

1985. 25th Anniv of Independence.
1049 **369** 110 f. multicoloured . . . 70 40

370 Baobab 371 Man watching Race

1985. Protected Trees. Multicoloured.
1050 110 f. Type **370** 80 50
1051 210 f. "Acacia albida" . . . . 1·40 1·00
1052 390 f. Baobab (different) . . . 3·00 1·60

1985. Niamey–Bamako Powerboat Race. Mult.
1053 110 f. Type **371** 70 45
1054 150 f. Helicopter and powerboat 1·60 85
1055 250 f. Powerboat and map . . 1·75 1·25

1985. "Trees for Niger". As Nos. 1050/2 but new values and optd **DES ARBRES POUR LE NIGER**.
1056 **370** 30 f. multicoloured . . . 25 20
1057 – 85 f. multicoloured . . . 55 40
1058 – 110 f. multicoloured . . . 70 55

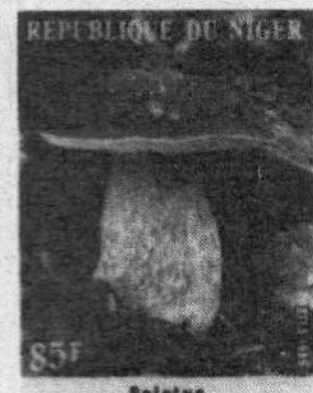

373 "Boletus"

1985. Fungi. Multicoloured.
1059 85 f. Type **373** . . . . 1·40 30
1060 110 f. "Hypholoma fasciculare" 2·10 45
1061 200 f. "Coprinus comatus" . . 3·00 1·10
1062 300 f. "Agaricus arvensis" (horiz) . . . . 4·50 1·50
1063 400 f. "Geastrum fimbriatum" (horiz) . . . . 5·75 2·10

374 First Village Water Pump

1985. "Philexafrique" Stamp Exhibition, Lome, Togo (2nd issue). Multicoloured.
1064 250 f. Type **374** . . . . 1·75 1·25
1065 250 f. Handicapped youths playing dili (traditional game) 1·75 1·25

375 "Saving Ant" and Savings Bank Emblem 376 Gouroumi

1985. World Savings Day.
1066 **375** 210 f. multicoloured . . . 1·40 85

1985. Musical Instruments. Multicoloured.
1067 150 f. Type **376** . . . . 1·10 60
1068 210 f. Gassou (drums) (horiz) . 1·60 1·00
1069 390 f. Algaita (flute) . . . . . 2·75 1·50

377 "The Immaculate Conception" 379 National Identity Card

378 Comet over Paris, 1910

1985. Air. Christmas. Paintings by Murillo. Mult.
1071 110 f. "Madonna of the Rosary" 65 35
1072 250 f. Type **377** . . . . 1·75 90
1073 390 f. "Virgin of Seville" . . . 2·50 1·25

1985. Air. Appearance of Halley's Comet. Multicoloured.
1074 110 f. Type **378** 70 35
1075 130 f. Comet over New York . 85 40
1076 200 f. "Giotto" satellite . . . 1·50 70
1077 300 f. "Vega" satellite . . . . 2·25 1·00
1078 390 f. "Planet A" space probe . 2·50 1·25

1986. Civil Statutes Reform. Each black, green and orange.
1079 85 f. Type **379** 65 30
1080 110 f. Civil registration emblem 75 40

380 Road Signs 381 Oumarou Ganda (film producer)

1986. Road Safety Campaign.
1081 **380** 85 f. black, yellow & red . 75 30
1082 – 110 f. black, red & green . 1·00 40
DESIGN: 110 f. Speed limit sign, road and speedometer ("Watch your speed").

1986. Honoured Artists. Multicoloured.
1083 60 f. Type **381** 35 20
1084 85 f. Idi na Dadaou 50 30
1085 100 f. Dan Gourmou 60 40
1086 130 f. Koungoui (comedian) . 80 45

382 Martin Luther King 384 Statue and F. A. Bartholdi

383 Footballer and 1970 40 f. Stamp

1986. Air. 18th Death Anniv of Martin Luther King (human rights activist).
1087 **382** 500 f. multicoloured . . . 3·25 1·90

1986. Air. World Cup Football Championship, Mexico. Multicoloured.
1088 130 f. Type **383** . . . . 1·00 30
1089 210 f. Footballer and 1970 70 f. stamp . . . . 1·25 45
1090 390 f. Footballer and 1970 90 f. stamp . . . . 2·75 1·00
1091 400 f. Footballer and Mexican figure on "stamp" . . . . 2·75 1·00

1986. Air. Centenary of Statue of Liberty.
1093 **384** 300 f. multicoloured . . . 2·25 1·10

385 Truck

1986. "Trucks of Hope". Multicoloured.
1094 85 f. Type **385** 75 30
1095 110 f. Mother and baby (vert) . 1·00 40

386 Nelson Mandela and Walter Sisulu **387** Food Co-operatives

1986. International Solidarity with S. African and Namibian Political Prisoners Day. Multicoloured.
1096 200 f. Type **386** . . . . 1·50 80
1097 300 f. Nelson Mandela . . . . 2·25 1·00

1986. 40th Anniv of F.A.O. Multicoloured.
1098 50 f. Type **387** 30 20
1099 60 f. Anti-desertification campaign 35 25
1100 85 f. Irrigation 50 35
1101 100 f. Rebuilding herds of livestock 60 40
1102 110 f. Reafforestation 75 45

388 Trees and Woman with Cooking Pots **389** "Sphodromantis sp."

1987. "For a Green Niger". Multicoloured.
1103 85 f. Type **388** 55 30
1104 110 f. Trees, woman and cooking pots (different) . . 70 40

1987. Protection of Vegetation. Useful Insects. Multicoloured.
1105 85 f. Type **389** 60 40
1106 110 f. "Delta sp." 85 50
1107 120 f. "Cicindela sp." 95 65

390 Transmitter, Map and Woman using Telephone

1987. Liptako–Gourma Telecommunications Network.
1108 **390** 110 f. multicoloured . . . 80 50

391 Morse Key and Operator, 19th-century

1987. 150th Anniv of Morse Telegraph. Mult.
1109 120 f. Type **391** 75 40
1110 200 f. Samuel Morse (inventor) (vert) . . . . 1·25 70
1111 350 f. Morse transmitter and receiver . . . . 2·25 1·25

392 Tennis Player

1987. Olympic Games, Seoul (1988). Multicoloured.
1112 85 f. Type **392** 50 40
1113 110 f. Pole vaulter 70 40
1114 250 f. Footballer . . . . . . 1·50 90

393 Ice Hockey

1987. Winter Olympic Games, Calgary (1988) (1st issue). Multicoloured.
1116 85 f. Type **393** 60 35
1117 110 f. Speed skating 70 35
1118 250 f. Figure skating (pairs) . 1·75 90
See also Nos. 1146/9.

394 Long-distance Running

1987. African Games, Nairobi. Multicoloured.
1120 85 f. Type **394** 50 35
1121 110 f. High jumping 60 35
1122 200 f. Hurdling . . . . 1·25 70
1123 400 f. Javelin throwing . . . 2·50 1·40

395 Chief's Stool, Sceptre and Crown

1987. 10th Anniv of National Tourism Office. Multicoloured.
1124 85 f. Type **395** 50 35
1125 110 f. Nomad, caravan and sceptre handle 60 35
1126 120 f. Houses 70 40
1127 200 f. Bridge over River Niger . 1·25 70

396 Yaama Mosque at Dawn

1987. Aga Khan Prize. Designs Showing Yaama mosque at various times of day.
1128 **396** 85 f. multicoloured . . . 50 35
1129 – 110 f. multicoloured . . . 60 35
1130 – 250 f. multicoloured . . . 1·50 90

397 Court Building **398** "Holy Family of the Sheep" (Raphael)

1987. Appeal Court, Niamey. Multicoloured.
1131 85 f. Type **397** 50 30
1132 110 f. Front entrance 60 35
1133 140 f. Side view 90 55

1987. Christmas.
1134 **398** 110 f. multicoloured . . . 65 40

399 Water Drainage

1988. Health Care. Multicoloured.
1136 85 f. Type **399** 70 40
1137 110 f. Modern sanitation . . . 80 40
1138 165 f. Refuse collection . . . 1·25 65

400 Singer and Band **402** New Great Market, Niamey

1988. Award of Dan-Gourmou Music Prize.
1139 **400** 85 f. multicoloured . . . 80 50

1988. Winter Olympic Games Winners. Nos. 1116/18 optd.
1140 85 f. **Medaille d'or URSS** . . . 50 35
1141 110 f. **Medaille d'or 5.000-10.000 m GUSTAFSON (Suede)** . 60 40
1142 250 f. **Medaille d'or C. CORDEEVA -S. GRINKOV URSS** . . . . 1·50 90

1988.
1143 **402** 85 f. multicoloured . . . 60 40

403 Mother and Child

1988. U.N.I.C.E.F. Child Vaccination Campaign and 40th Anniv of W.H.O. Multicoloured.
1144 85 f. Type **403** 70 40
1145 110 f. Doctor and villagers . . 90 50

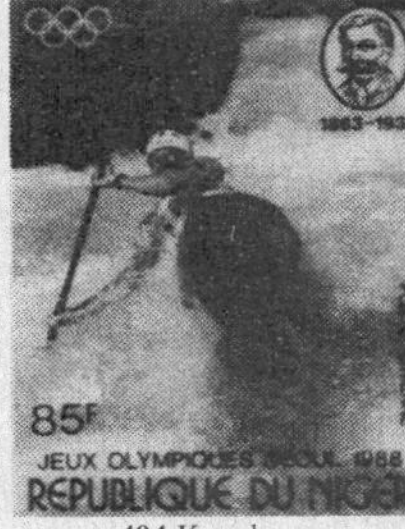

404 Kayak **405** Emblem

1988. Air. Olympic Games, Seoul (2nd issue) and 125th Birth Anniv of Pierre de Coubertin (founder of modern Olympic Games). Multicoloured.
1146 85 f. Type **404** 50 20
1147 165 f. Rowing (horiz) 90 50
1148 200 f. Two-man kayak (horiz) . 1·25 70
1149 600 f. One-man kayak . . . . 3·50 2·00

1988. 25th Anniv of Organization of African Unity.
1151 **405** 85 f. multicoloured . . . 50 30

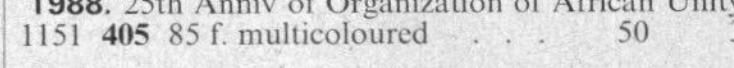

406 Team working **407** Anniversary Emblem

1988. Dune Stabilisation.
1152 **406** 85 f. multicoloured . . . 60 40

1988. 125th Anniv of International Red Cross.
1153 **407** 85 f. multicoloured . . . 60 30
1154 110 f. multicoloured . . . 80 40

409 Emblem **410** Couple, Globe and Laboratory Worker

1989. Niger Press Agency.
1159 **409** 85 f. black, orange & grn . 45 30

1989. Campaign against AIDS.
1160 **410** 85 f. multicoloured . . . 55 30
1161 110 f. multicoloured . . . 85 40

411 Radar, Tanker and Signals **412** General Ali Seybou (Pres.)

1989. 30th Anniv of International Maritime Organization.
1162 **411** 100 f. multicoloured . . . 1·75 75
1163 120 f. multicoloured . . . 2·10 1·00

1989. 15th Anniv of Military Coup. Mult.
1164 85 f. Type **412** 45 25
1165 110 f. Soldiers erecting flag . . 65 35

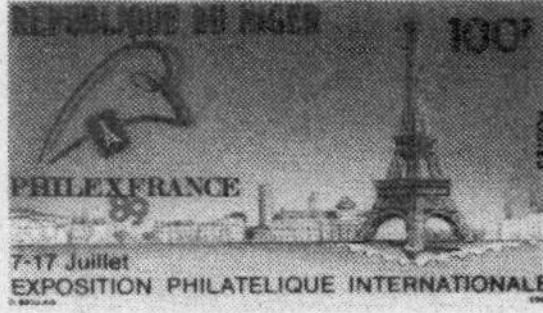

413 Eiffel Tower

1989. "Philexfrance 89" International Stamp Exhibition, Paris. Multicoloured.
1166 100 f. Type **413** 60 40
1167 200 f. Flags on stamps . . . . 1·25 65

414 "Planting a Tree of Liberty"

1989. Bicentenary of French Revolution.
1168 **414** 250 f. multicoloured . . . 1·50 1·00

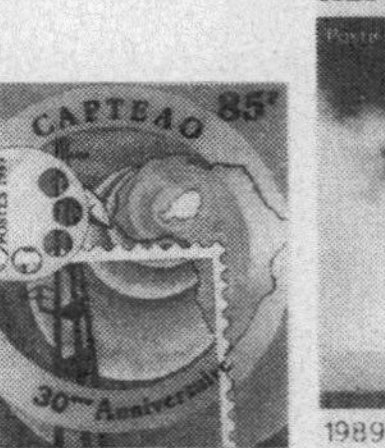

415 Telephone Dial, Radio Mast, Map and Stamp **416** "Apollo 11" Launch

1989. 30th Anniv of West African Posts and Telecommunications Association.
1169 **415** 85 f. multicoloured . . . 45 30

1989. Air. 20th Anniv of First Manned Landing on Moon. Multicoloured.
1170 200 f. Type **416** . . . . 1·25 65
1171 300 f. Crew . . . . 2·00 1·00
1172 350 f. Astronaut and module on lunar surface . . . . 2·25 1·25
1173 400 f. Astronaut and U.S. flag on lunar surface . . . . . 2·50 1·25

417 Emblem

1989. 25th Anniv of African Development Bank.
1174 **417** 100 f. multicoloured . . . 60 30

418 Before and After Attack, and "Schistocerca gregaria"

1989. Locusts.
1175 **418** 85 f. multicoloured . . . 50 30

419 Auguste Lumiere and 1st Cine Performance, 1895

1989. 35th Death Anniv of Auguste Lumiere and 125th Birth Anniv of Louis Lumiere (photography pioneers). Multicoloured.
1176 150 f. Type **419** 90 55
1177 250 f. Louis Lumiere and first cine-camera, 1894 . . . . 1·50 85
1178 400 f. Lumiere brothers and first colour cine-camera, 1920 2·50 1·25

420 Tractor, Map and Pump

1989. 30th Anniv of Agriculture Development Council.
1179 **420** 75 f. multicoloured . . . 45 30

421 Zinder Regional Museum

422 "Russelia equisetiformis"

1989. Multicoloured.
1180 85 f. Type **421** 45 30
1182 165 f. Temet dunes 90 60

1989. Flowers. Multicoloured.
1183 10 f. Type **422** 15 10
1184 20 f. "Argyreia nervosa" . . 15 10
1185 30 f. "Hibiscus rosa-sinensis" . . 20 10
1186 50 f. "Catharanthus roseus" . 35 20
1187 100 f. "Cymothoe sangaris" (horiz) 75 35

423 Emblem

424 Adults learning Alphabet

1990. 10th Anniv of Pan-African Postal Union.
1188 **423** 120 f. multicoloured . . . 70 40

1990. International Literacy Year. Multicoloured.
1189 85 f. Type **424** 45 25
1190 110 f. Adults learning arithmetic 65 35

425 Emblem

427 Leland and Child

426 Footballers and Florence

1990. 20th Anniv of Islamic Conference Organization.
1191 **425** 85 f. multicoloured . . . 50 30

1990. Air. World Cup Football Championship, Italy. Multicoloured.
1192 130 f. Type **426** . . . . . 1·00 40
1193 210 f. Footballers and Verona . 1·40 75
1194 500 f. Footballers and Bari . . 3·25 1·75
1195 600 f. Footballers and Rome . 3·75 2·00

1990. Mickey Leland (American Congressman) Commemoration.
1196 **427** 300 f. multicoloured . . . 1·75 1·00
1197 500 f. multicoloured . . . 3·00 1·75

428 Emblem

429 Flags and Envelopes on Map

1990. 1st Anniv of National Movement for the Development Society.
1198 **428** 85 f. multicoloured . . . 50 30

1990. 20th Anniv of Multinational Postal Training School, Abidjan.
1199 **429** 85 f. multicoloured . . . 65 30

430 Gymnastics

1990. Olympic Games, Barcelona (1992). Mult.
1200 85 f. Type **430** 40 25
1201 110 f. Hurdling 60 35
1202 250 f. Running . . . . . . 1·50 90
1203 400 f. Show jumping . . . . 2·75 1·40
1204 500 f. Long jumping . . . . 3·00 1·75

431 Arms, Map and Flag

432 Emblem

1990. 30th Anniv of Independence.
1206 **431** 85 f. multicoloured . . . 45 30
1207 110 f. multicoloured . . . 65 40

1990. 40th Anniv of United Nations Development Programme.
1208 **432** 100 f. multicoloured . . . 50 30

433 The Blusher

434 Christopher Columbus and "Santa Maria"

1991. Butterflies and Fungi. Multicoloured.
1209 85 f. Type **433** (postage) . . . 1·00 30
1210 110 f. "Graphium pylades" (female) 75 25
1211 200 f. "Pseudacraea hostilia" . 1·25 55
1212 250 f. Cracked green russula . 2·50 1·10
1213 400 f. "Boletus impolitus" (air) . . . . 3·75 1·60
1214 500 f. "Precis octavia" . . . . 2·75 1·25

1991. 540th Birth of Christopher Columbus. Mult.
1216 85 f. Type **434** (postage) . . . 70 25
1217 110 f. 15th-century Portuguese caravel . . . . . . 1·00 30
1218 200 f. 16th-century four-masted caravel . . . . . . 1·60 65
1219 250 f. "Estremadura" (Spanish caravel), 1511 . . . . . 2·00 85
1220 400 f. "Vija" (Portuguese caravel), 1600 (air) . . . . 3·25 1·10
1221 500 f. "Pinta" . . . . 3·50 1·50

435 Speed Skating

1991. Winter Olympic Games, Albertville (1992). Multicoloured.
1223 110 f. Type **435** 60 25
1224 300 f. Ice-hockey . . . . . 1·25 80
1225 500 f. Women's downhill skiing 2·50 1·25
1226 600 f. Two-man luge . . . . 2·75 1·25

436 Flag and Boy holding Stone

437 Hairstyle

1991. Palestinian "Intifada" Movement.
1227 **436** 110 f. multicoloured . . . 75 30

1991. Traditional Hairstyles. Multicoloured.
1228 85 f. Type **437** 20 10
1229 110 f. Netted hairstyle . . . 25 15
1230 165 f. Braided hairstyle . . . 40 20
1231 200 f. Plaited hairstyle 45 25

438 Boubon Market

1991. African Tourism Year. Multicoloured.
1232 85 f. Type **438** 20 10
1233 110 f. Timia waterfalls (vert) . 25 15
1234 130 f. Ruins at Assode 30 15
1235 200 f. Tourism Year emblem (vert) 45 25

439 Anatoly Karpov and Gary Kasparov

1991. Anniversaries and Events. Multicoloured.
1236 85 f. Type **439** (World Chess Championship) (postage) . . 20 10
1237 110 f. Ayrton Senna and Alain Prost (World Formula 1 motor racing championship) 25 15
1238 200 f. Reading of Declaration of Human Rights and Comte de Mirabeau (bicentenary of French Revolution) . . . 45 25
1239 250 f. Dwight D. Eisenhower, Winston Churchill and Field-Marshal Montgomery (50th anniv of America's entry into Second World War) . . . . 3·50 85
1240 400 f. Charles de Gaulle and Konrad Adenauer (28th anniv of Franco-German Co-operation Agreement) (air) . 95 55
1241 500 f. Helmut Kohl and Brandenburg Gate (2nd anniv of German reunification) . . 1·10 60

440 Japanese "ERS-1" Satellite

1991. Satellites and Transport. Multicoloured.
1243 85 f. Type **440** (postage) . . . 20 10
1244 110 f. Japanese satellite observing Aurora Borealis . 25 15
1245 200 f. Louis Favre and "BB 415" diesel locomotive . . . . . 2·50 45
1246 250 f. "BB-BB 301" diesel locomotive . . . . 3·00 55
1247 400 f. "BB 302" diesel locomotive (air) . . . . . 4·50 70
1248 500 f. Lockheed Stealth fighter-bomber and Concorde . . . 1·10 60

441 Crowd and Emblem on Map

443 Couple adding Final Piece to Globe Jigsaw

442 Timberless House

1991. National Conference (to determine new constitution).
1250 **441** 85 f. multicoloured . . . 20 10

1992.
1251 **442** 85 f. multicoloured . . . 20 10

1992. World Population Day. Multicoloured.
1252 85 f. Type **443** 20 10
1253 110 f. Children flying globe kite (after Robert Parker) . . . 25 15

444 Columbus and Fleet

1992. 500th Anniv of Discovery of America by Columbus.
1254 **444** 250 f. multicoloured . . . 60 35

445 Zaleye

1992. 2nd Death Anniv of Hadjia Haqua Issa (Zaleye) (singer).
1255 **445** 150 f. multicoloured . . . 35 20

446 Conference Emblem

447 College Emblem

1992. International Nutrition Conference, Rome.
1256 **446** 145 f. multicoloured . . . 35 20
1257 350 f. multicoloured . . . 80 45

1993. 30th Anniv of African Meteorology and Civil Aviation College.
1258 **447** 110 f. blue, black & green . 25 15

448 Girl planting Sapling

1993. Anti-desertification Campaign.

1259	448	85 f. multicoloured	20	10
1260		165 f. multicoloured	40	20

449 Aerosol spraying Globe (Patricia Charets)

1993. World Population Day. Children's Drawings. Multicoloured.

1261	85 f. Type 449	20	10
1262	110 f. Tree and person with globe as head looking at high-rise tower blocks (Mathieu Chevrault)	25	15

450 Jerusalem

1993. "Jerusalem, Holy City".

1268	450	110 f. multicoloured	30	15

451 People of Different Races

1994. Award of Nobel Peace Prize to Nelson Mandela and F. W. de Klerk (South African statesmen).

1269	451	270 f. multicoloured	70	40

OFFICIAL STAMPS

O 13 Djerma Women

1962. Figures of value in black.

O121	O 13	1 f. violet	10	10
O122		2 f. green	10	10
O123		5 f. blue	15	10
O124		10 f. red	15	10
O125		20 f. blue	20	15
O126		25 f. orange	25	20
O127		30 f. blue	30	25
O128		35 f. green	35	30
O129		40 f. brown	35	35
O130		50 f. slate	40	40
O131		60 f. turquoise	50	45
O132		85 f. turquoise	70	40
O133		100 f. purple	85	40
O134		200 f. blue	1·50	80

1988. As Type O 13, but figures of value in same colour as remainder of design.

O1155	O 13	5 f. blue	10	10
O1156		10 f. red	10	10
O1157		15 f. yellow	10	10
O1158		20 f. blue	20	10
O1159		45 f. orange	25	20
O1160		50 f. green	30	20

POSTAGE DUE STAMPS

1921. Postage Due stamps of Upper Senegal and Niger "Figure" key-type optd **TERRITOIRE DU NIGER**.

D18	M	5 c. green	15	50
D19		10 c. red	15	50
D20		15 c. grey	20	60
D21		20 c. brown	20	60
D22		30 c. blue	20	60
D23		50 c. black	25	65
D24		60 c. orange	30	1·00
D25		1 f. violet	50	1·10

D 6 Zinder Fort

1927.

D73	D 6	2 c. red and blue	10	25
D74		4 c. black and orange	10	25
D75		5 c. violet and yellow	15	25
D76		10 c. violet and red	15	30
D77		15 c. orange and green	15	40
D78		20 c. sepia and red	20	45
D79		25 c. sepia and black	35	50
D80		30 c. grey and violet	60	1·00
D81		50 c. red on green	60	80
D82		60 c. orge, lilac on bl	60	80
D83		1 f. violet & blue on blue	60	75
D84		2 f. mauve and red	60	80
D85		3 f. blue and brown	80	1·00

D 13 Cross of Agadez

1962.

D123	D 13	50 c. green	10	10
D124		1 f. violet	10	10
D125		2 f. myrtle	10	10
D126	A	3 f. mauve	10	10
D127		5 f. green	15	15
D128		10 f. orange	15	15
D129	B	15 f. blue	15	15
D130		20 f. red	20	20
D131		50 f. brown	40	40

DESIGNS: A, Cross of Iferouane; B, Cross of Tahoua.

D 450 Cross of Iferouane

1993.

D1263	D 450	5 f. multicoloured	10	10
D1264		10 f. orange & black	10	10
D1265	–	15 f. multicoloured	10	10
D1266	–	20 f. mve, yell & blk	10	10
D1267	–	50 f. multicoloured	10	10

DESIGN: 15 to 50 f. Cross of Tahoua.

NIGER COAST PROTECTORATE — Pt. 1

A district on the west coast of Africa. In 1900 became part of Southern Nigeria.

12 pence = 1 shilling;
20 pence = 1 pound

1892. Stamps of Gt. Britain (Queen Victoria) optd **BRITISH PROTECTORATE OIL RIVERS**.

No.	Type	Description	Unused	Used
1	**71**	½d. red	9·00	5·00
2	**57**	1d. lilac	5·50	6·50
3	**73**	2d. green and red	18·00	8·00
4	**74**	2½d. purple and blue	6·50	2·25
5	**78**	5d. purple and blue	7·50	7·50
6	**82**	1s. green	55·00	75·00

1893. Half of No. 2 surch **½d.**

No.	Type	Description	Unused	Used
7	**57**	½d. on half of 1d. lilac	£150	£140

1893. Nos. 1 to 6 surch in words (½d., 1s.) or figures (others).

No.	Type	Description	Unused	Used
20	**73**	½d. on 2d. green and red	£300	£225
21	**74**	½d. on 2½d. purple on blue	£275	£180
37	**73**	1s. on 2d. green and red	£400	£350
40		5s. on 2d. green and red	£9000	£10000
41	**78**	10s. on 5d. purple & blue	£6000	£8000
42	**82**	20s. on 1s. green	£70000	

13

14

1893. Various frames with "OIL RIVERS" barred out and "NIGER COAST" above.

No.	Type	Description	Unused	Used
45	**13**	½d. red	4·00	3·75
46		1d. blue	5·50	3·25
47d		2d. green	18·00	13·00
48		2½d. red	8·00	3·50
49b		3d. lilac	13·00	13·00
50		1s. black	14·00	12·00

1894. Various frames.

No.	Type	Description	Unused	Used
66	**14**	½d. green	3·25	1·50
67		1d. red	3·75	1·50
68		2d. red	1·75	1·25
69a		2½d. blue	7·50	1·50
55		5d. purple	6·00	5·50
71		6d. brown	7·00	6·50
56a		1s. black	30·00	7·00
73b		2s. 6d. brown	22·00	75·00
74b		10s. violet	80·00	£160

1894. Surch with large figures.

No.	Type	Description	Unused	Used
58		½ on half 1d. (No. 46)	£700	£275
59		1 on half 2d. (No. 2)	£1400	£275

1894. No. 67 bisected and surch.

No.	Type	Description	Unused	Used
64	**14**	½d. on half of 1d. red	£1700	£350

1894. Surch **ONE HALF PENNY** and bars.

No.	Type	Description	Unused	Used
65	**14**	½d. on 2½d. blue	£350	£225

NIGERIA — Pt. 1

A former British colony on the west coast of Africa, comprising the territories of Northern and Southern Nigeria and Lagos. Attained full independence within the British Commonwealth in 1960 and became a Federal Republic in 1963.

The Eastern Region (known as Biafra (q.v)) seceded in 1967, remaining independent until overrun by Federal Nigerian troops during January 1970.

1914. 12 pence = 1 shilling;
20 shillings = 1 pound.
1973. 100 kobo = 1 naira.

1

1914.

No.	Type	Description	Unused	Used
15	**1**	½d. green	1·00	40
16		1d. red	3·00	30
17		1½d. orange	3·75	15
18		2d. grey	1·50	3·75
20		2d. brown	1·25	15
21		2½d. blue	1·00	5·00
5a		3d. purple on yellow	1·50	2·75
22		3d. violet	5·00	3·25
23		3d. blue	6·00	1·50
24		4d. black & red on yellow	65	55
25a		6d. purple	7·00	8·00
26		1s. black on green	1·25	2·00
9		2s. 6d. black & red on blue	14·00	6·00
10		5s. green & red on yellow	12·00	42·00
11d		10s. green & red on green	38·00	90·00
12a		£1 purple & black on red	£160	£190

1935. Silver Jubilee. As T **10a** of Gambia.

No.	Description	Unused	Used
30	1½d. blue and grey	80	65
31	2d. green and blue	1·50	65
32	3d. brown and blue	3·00	9·00
33	1s. grey and purple	3·00	24·00

3 Apapa Wharf

5 Victoria–Buea Road

1936.

No.	Type	Description	Unused	Used
34	**3**	½d. green	1·50	1·40
35	–	1d. red	40	40
36	–	1½d. brown	1·75	40
37	–	2d. black	40	80
38	–	3d. blue	1·75	1·25
39	–	4d. brown	1·75	2·00
40	–	6d. violet	40	60
41	–	1s. green	1·50	4·50
42	**5**	2s. 6d. black and blue	3·50	19·00
43	–	5s. black and green	6·00	24·00
44	–	10s. black and grey	45·00	65·00
45	–	£1 black and orange	70·00	£140

DESIGNS—VERT: 1d. Cocoa; 1½d. Tin dredger; 2d. Timber industry; 3d. Fishing village; 4d. Cotton ginnery; 6d. Habe minaret; 1s. Fulani cattle. HORIZ: 5s. Oil palms; 10s. River Niger at Jebba; £1 Canoe pulling.

1937. Coronation. As T **10b** of Gambia.

No.	Description	Unused	Used
46	1d. red	30	1·50
47	1½d. brown	1·25	2·25
48	3d. blue	1·40	2·25

15 King George VI

1938.

No.	Type	Description	Unused	Used
49	**15**	½d. green	10	10
50a		1d. red	75	30
50b		1d. lilac	10	20
51a		1½d. brown	10	10
52		2d. black	10	1·00
52ab		2d. red	10	40
52b		2½d. orange	10	70
53		3d. blue	10	10
53b		3d. black	15	40
54		4d. orange	48·00	2·75
54a		4d. blue	15	1·75
55		6d. violet	40	10
56a		1s. olive	15	10
57		1s. 3d. blue	90	30
58b	–	2s. 6d. black and blue	2·25	3·00
59b	–	5s. black and orange	6·00	3·00

DESIGNS: 2s. 6d., 5s. As Nos. 42 and 44 but with portrait of King George VI.

1946. Victory. As T **11a** of Gambia.

No.	Description	Unused	Used
60	1½d. brown	25	10
61	4d. blue	25	1·25

1948. Royal Silver Wedding. As T **11b/c** of Gambia.

No.	Description	Unused	Used
62	1d. mauve	35	30
63	5s. orange	5·00	8·00

1949. U.P.U. As T **11d/g** of Gambia.

No.	Description	Unused	Used
64	1d. purple	20	10
65	3d. blue	1·25	2·50
66	6d. purple	70	2·25
67	1s. olive	80	1·75

1953. Coronation. As T **11h** of Gambia.

No.	Description	Unused	Used
68	1½d. black and green	40	10

18 Old Manilla Currency

26 Victoria Harbour

29 New and Old Lagos

1953.

No.	Type	Description	Unused	Used
69	**18**	½d. black and orange	15	30
70	–	1d. black and bronze	20	10
71	–	1½d. turquoise	50	40
72	–	2d. black and ochre	4·00	30
72cb	–	2d. slate	3·50	40
73	–	3d. black and purple	55	10
74	–	4d. black and blue	2·50	20
75	–	6d. brown and black	30	10
76	–	1s. black and purple	40	10
77	**26**	2s. 6d. black and green	6·00	50
78	–	5s. black and red	3·50	1·25
79	–	10s. black and brown	13·00	2·50
80	**29**	£1 black and violet	22·00	7·00

DESIGNS—HORIZ (As Type **18**): 1d. Bornu horsemen; 1½d. "Groundnuts"; 2d. "Tin"; 3d. Jebba Bridge and R. Niger; 4d. "Cocoa"; 1s. "Timber". (As Type **26**): 5s. "Palm oil"; 10s. "Hides and skins". VERT (As Type **18**): 6d. Ife bronze.

1956. Royal Visit. No. 72 optd **ROYAL VISIT 1956**.

No.	Description	Unused	Used
81	2d. black and ochre	40	30

31 Victoria Harbour

1958. Centenary of Victoria, S. Cameroons.

No.	Type	Description	Unused	Used
82	**31**	3d. black and purple	20	30

32 Lugard Hall

1959. Attainment of Self-Government. Northern Region of Nigeria.

No.	Type	Description	Unused	Used
83	**32**	3d. black and purple	15	10
84	–	1s. black and green	55	85

DESIGN: 1s. Kano Mosque.

35 Legislative Building

1960. Independence Commemoration.

No.	Type	Description	Unused	Used
85	**35**	1d. black and red	10	10
86	–	3d. black and blue	15	10
87	–	6d. green and brown	20	20
88	–	1s. 3d. blue and yellow	40	20

DESIGNS—As Type **35**: 3d. African paddling canoe; 6d. Federal Supreme Court. LARGER (40 × 24 mm): 1s. 3d. Dove, torch and map.

39 Groundnuts **48** Central Bank

1961.

No.	Type	Description	Unused	Used
89	**39**	½d. green	10	50
90	–	1d. violet	80	10
91	–	1½d. red	70	1·25
92	–	2d. blue	30	10
93	–	3d. green	40	10
94	–	4d. blue	40	75
95	–	6d. yellow and black	80	10
96	–	1s. green	4·50	10
97	–	1s. 3d. orange	1·25	10
98	**48**	2s. 6d. black and yellow	2·50	15
99	–	5s. black and green	65	85
100	–	10s. black and blue	2·00	2·25
101	–	£1 black and red	9·50	11·00

DESIGNS—VERT (as Type **39**): 1d. Coal mining; 1½d. Adult education; 2d, Pottery; 3d. Oyo carver; 4d. Weaving; 6d. Benin mask; 1s. Yellow casqued hornbill; 1s. 3d. Camel train. HORIZ (as Type **48**: 5s. Nigeria Museum; 10s. Kano airport; £1 Lagos railway station.

52 Globe and Diesel-electric Locomotive

1961. Admission into U.P.U. Inscr as in T **52**.

No.	Type	Description	Unused	Used
102	**52**	1d. orange and blue	30	10
103	–	3d. olive and black	30	10
104	–	1s. 3d. blue and red	80	20
105	–	2s. 6d. green and blue	85	2·00

DESIGNS: 3d. Globe and mail van; 1s. 3d. Globe and Bristol 175 Britannia aircraft; 2s. 6d. Globe and liner.

56 Coat of Arms

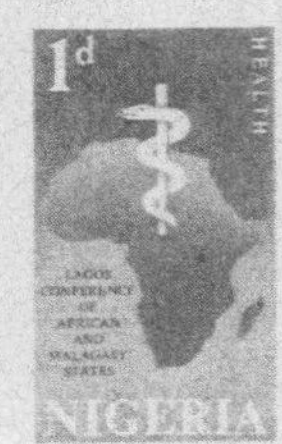

61 "Health"

1961. 1st Anniv of Independence.

No.	Type	Description	Unused	Used
106	**56**	3d. multicoloured	10	10
107	–	4d. green and orange	20	10
108	–	6d. green	30	10
109	–	1s. 3d. grey and blue	35	10
110	–	2s. 6d. green and blue	40	1·75

DESIGNS—HORIZ: 4d. Natural resources map; 6d. Nigerian eagle; 1s 3d. Eagles in flight; 2s. 6d. Nigerians and flag.

1962. Lagos Conf of African and Malagasy States.

No.	Type	Description	Unused	Used
111	**61**	1d. bistre	10	10
112	–	3d. purple	10	10
113	–	6d. green	15	10
114	–	1s. brown	20	10
115	–	1s. 3d. blue	25	20

DESIGNS: Map and emblems symbolising Culture (3d.); Commerce (6d.); Communications (1s.); Co-operation (1s. 3d.).

66 Malaria Eradication Emblem and Parasites

1962. Malaria Eradication.

No.	Type	Description	Unused	Used
116	**66**	3d. green and red	15	10
117	–	6d. blue and purple	20	10
118	–	1s. 3d. mauve and blue	20	10
119	–	2s. 6d. blue and brown	30	80

DESIGNS (embodying emblem): 6d. Insecticide-spraying; 1s. 3d. Aerial spraying; 2s. 6d. Mother, child and microscope.

70 National Monument

1962. 2nd Anniv of Independence.

No.	Type	Description	Unused	Used
120	**70**	3d. green and blue	10	10
121	–	5s. red, green and violet	1·00	70

DESIGN—VERT: 5s. Benin bronze.

72 Fair Emblem

76 "Arrival of Delegates"

1962. International Trade Fair, Lagos.

No.	Type	Description	Unused	Used
122	**72**	1d. red and olive	10	10
123	–	6d. black and red	15	10
124	–	1s. black and brown	15	10
125	–	2s. 6d. yellow and blue	60	20

DESIGNS—HORIZ: 6d. "Cogwheels of Industry"; 1s. "Cornucopia of Industry"; 2s. 6d. Oilwells and tanker.

1962. 8th Commonwealth Parliamentary Conference, Lagos.

No.	Type	Description	Unused	Used
126	**76**	2½d. blue	15	20
127	–	4d. blue and rose	15	15
128	–	1s. 3d. sepia and yellow	20	20

DESIGNS—HORIZ: 4d. National Hall. VERT: 1s. 3d. Mace as Palm Tree.

80 Tractor and Maize

81 Mercury Capsule and Kano Tracking Station

1963. Freedom from Hunger.

129	–	3d. olive	1·00	20
130	**80**	6d. mauve	1·50	20

DESIGN—VERT: 3d. Herdsman.

1963. "Peaceful Use of Outer Space".

131	**81**	6d. blue and green	25	10
132	–	1s. 3d. black & turquoise	35	20

DESIGN: 1s. 3d. Satellite and Lagos Harbour.

83 Scouts shaking Hands

1963. 11th World Scout Jamboree. Marathon.

133	**83**	3d. red and bronze	30	15
134	–	1s. black and red	95	80

DESIGN: 1s. Campfire.

85 Emblem and First Aid Team

88 President Azikiwe and State House

1963. Centenary of Red Cross.

135	**85**	3d. red and blue	75	10
136	–	6d. red and green	1·25	10
137	–	1s. 3d. red and sepia	1·75	70

DESIGNS: 6d. Emblem and "Hospital Services"; 1s. 3d. Patient and emblem.

1963. Republic Day.

138	**88**	3d. olive and green	10	10
139	–	1s. 3d. brown and sepia	10	10
140	–	2s. 6d. turquoise and blue	15	15

The buildings on the 1s. 3d. and the 2s. 6d. are the Federal Supreme Court and the Parliament Building respectively.

90 "Freedom of Worship"

93 Queen Nefertari

1963. 15th Anniv of Declaration of Human Rights.

141	–	3d. red	10	10
142	**90**	6d. green	15	10
143	–	1s. 3d. blue	30	10
144	–	2s. 6d. purple	45	30

DESIGNS—HORIZ: 3d. (Inscr "1948–1963"), Charter and broken whip. VERT: 1s. 3d. "Freedom from Want"; 2s. 6d. "Freedom of Speech".

1964. Nubian Monuments Preservation.

145	**93**	6d. olive and green	50	10
146	–	2s. 6d. brown, olive & green	2·25	2·00

DESIGN: 2s. 6d. Rameses II.

95 President Kennedy

98 President Azikiwe

1964. Pres. Kennedy Memorial Issue.

147	**95**	1s. 3d. lilac and black	50	15
148	–	2s. 6d. multicoloured	70	55
149	–	5s. multicoloured	1·25	1·60

DESIGNS: 2s. 6d. Kennedy and flags; 5s. Kennedy (U.S. coin head) and flags.

1964. 1st Anniv of Republic.

150	**98**	3d. brown	10	10
151	–	1s. 3d. green	35	10
152	–	2s. 6d. green	70	90

DESIGNS—25×42 mm: 1s. 3d. Herbert Macaulay; 2s. 6d. King Jaja of Opobo.

101 Boxing Gloves

1964. Olympic Games, Tokyo.

153	**101**	3d. sepia and green	45	10
154	–	6d. green and blue	60	10
155	–	1s. 3d. sepia and olive	1·25	15
156	–	2s. 6d. sepia and brown	2·25	3·75

DESIGNS—HORIZ: 6d. High-jumping. VERT: 1s. 3d. Running. TRIANGULAR (60×30 mm): 2s. 6d. Hurdling.

105 Scouts on Hill-top

109 "Telstar"

1965. 50th Anniv of Nigerian Scout Movement.

157	**105**	1d. brown	10	10
158	–	3d. red, black and green	15	10
159	–	6d. red, sepia and green	25	20
160	–	1s. 3d. brown, yellow and deep green	40	85

DESIGNS: 3d. Scout badge on shield; 6d. Scout badges; 1s. 3d. Chief Scout and Nigerian scout.

1965. International Quiet Sun Years.

161	**109**	6d. violet and turquoise	15	15
162	–	1s. 3d. green and lilac	15	15

DESIGN: 1s. 3d. Solar satellite.

111 Native Tom-tom and Modern Telephone

1965. Centenary of I.T.U.

163	**111**	3d. black, red and brown	20	10
164	–	1s. 3d. black, green & blue	2·00	1·00
165	–	5s. multicoloured	5·00	7·00

DESIGNS—VERT: 1s. 3d. Microwave aerial. HORIZ: 5s. Telecommunications satellite and part of globe.

114 I.C.Y. Emblem and Diesel-hydraulic Locomotive

1965. International Co-operation Year.

166	**114**	3d. green, red & orange	3·00	20
167	–	1s. black, blue & lemon	3·00	40
168	–	2s. 6d. green, blue & yell	9·00	7·00

DESIGNS: 1s. Students and Lagos Teaching Hospital; 2s. 6d. Kainji (Niger) Dam.

117 Carved Frieze

1965. 2nd Anniv of Republic.

169	**117**	3d. black, red & yellow	10	10
170	–	1s. 3d. brown, green & blue	50	10
171	–	5s. brown, sepia and green	1·00	1·25

DESIGNS—VERT: 1s. 3d. Stone Images at Ikom; 5s. Tada bronze.

121 African Elephants

1965.

172	–	½d. multicoloured	80	2·00
173	**121**	1d. multicoloured	40	15
174	–	1½d. multicoloured	6·00	7·00
222	–	2d. multicoloured	1·75	90
176	–	3d. multicoloured	1·25	30
177a	–	4d. multicoloured	30	10
225	–	6d. multicoloured	1·75	20
179	–	9d. blue and red	3·00	60
227	–	1s. multicoloured	2·00	20
181	–	1s. 3d. multicoloured	8·50	1·00
182	**227**	2s. 6d. light brown, buff and brown	75	1·25
183	–	5s. chestnut, yellow and brown	1·75	2·75
184	–	10s. multicoloured	6·50	3·00
185	–	£1 multicoloured	15·00	9·00

DESIGNS—VERT (as T **121**): ½d. Lion and cubs; 6d. Saddle-bill stork. (26½×46mm): 10s. Hippopotamus. HORIZ (as T **121**): 1½d. Splendid sunbird; 2d. Village weaver and red-headed malimbe; 3d. Cheetah; 4d. Leopards; 9d. Grey parrots. (46×26½ mm): 1s. Blue-breasted kingfishers; 1s. 3d. Crowned cranes; 2s. 6d. Kobs; 5s. Giraffes; £1 African buffalo.

The 1d., 3d., 4d., 1s., 1s. 3d., 2s. 6d., 5s. and £1 exist optd **F.G.N.** (Federal Government of Nigeria) twice in black. They were prepared in November 1968 as official stamps, but the scheme was abandoned. Some stamps held at a Head Post Office were sold in error and passed through the post. The Director of Posts then decided to put limited supplies on sale, but they had no postal validity.

1966. Commonwealth Prime Ministers' Meeting, Lagos. Optd **COMMONWEALTH P. M. MEETING 11. JAN. 1966.**

186	**48**	2s. 6d. black and yellow	30	30

135 Y.W.C.A. Emblem and H.Q., Lagos

1966. Diamond Jubilee of Nigerian Y.W.C.A.

187	**135**	4d. multicoloured	15	10
188		9d. multicoloured	15	60

137 Telephone Handset and Linesman

1966. 3rd Anniv of Republic.

189	–	4d. green	10	10
190	**137**	1s. 6d. black, brown & violet	45	50
191	–	2s. 6d. multicoloured	1·25	2·25

DESIGNS—VERT: 4d. Dove and flag. HORIZ: 2s. 6d. North Channel Bridge over River Niger, Jebba.

139 "Education, Science and Culture"

1966. 20th Anniv of U.N.E.S.C.O.

192	**139**	4d. black, lake & orange	40	10
193		1s. 6d. black, lake & turq	1·75	2·50
194		2s. 6d. black, lake & pink	2·75	5·00

140 Children drinking

1966. Nigerian Red Cross.

195	**140**	4d. + 1d. black, vio & red	40	30
196	–	1s. 6d. + 3d. multicoloured	1·00	3·75
197	–	2s. 6d. + 3d. multicoloured	1·10	4·25

DESIGNS—VERT: 1s. 6d. Tending patient. HORIZ: 2s. 6d. Tending casualties and badge.

143 Surveying

1967. Int Hydrological Decade. Mult.

198	4d. Type **143**	10	10
199	2s. 6d. Water gauge on dam (vert)	25	1·00

145 Globe and Weather Satellite

1967. World Meteorological Day.

200	**145**	4d. mauve and blue	15	10
201	–	1s. 6d. black, yellow & bl	65	90

DESIGN: 1s. 6d. Passing storm and sun.

147 Eyo Masqueraders

1967. 4th Anniv of Republic. Multicoloured.

202	4d. Type **147**	15	10
203	1s. 6d. Crowds watching acrobat	50	1·50
204	2s. 6d. Stilt dancer (vert)	75	3·00

150 Tending Sick Animal

1967. Rinderpest Eradication Campaign.

205	**150**	4d. multicoloured	15	10
206		1s. 6d. multicoloured	55	1·50

151 Smallpox Vaccination

1968. 20th Anniv of W.H.O.

207	**151**	4d. mauve and black	15	10
208	–	1s. 6d. orge, lemon & blk	55	40

DESIGN: 1s. 6d. African and mosquito.

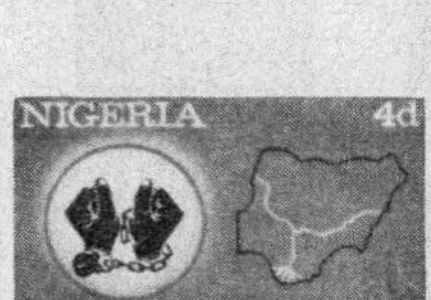

153 Chained Hands and Outline of Nigeria

155 Hand grasping at Doves of Freedom

1968. Human Rights Year.

209	**153**	4d. blue, black & yellow	10	10
210	–	1s. 6d. green, red & black	20	50

DESIGN—VERT: 1s. 6d. Nigerian flag and Human Rights emblem.

1968. 5th Anniv of Federal Republic.

211	**155**	4d. multicoloured	10	10
212		1s. 6d. multicoloured	20	20

156 Map of Nigeria and Olympic Rings

1968. Olympic Games, Mexico.

213	**156**	4d. black, green and red	10	10
214	–	1s. 6d. multicoloured	20	20

DESIGN: 1s. 6d. Nigerian athletes, flag and Olympic rings.

158 G.P.O., Lagos

1969. Inauguration of Philatelic Service.

215	**158**	4d. black and green	10	10
216		1s. 6d. black and blue	20	20

159 Yakubu Gowon and Victoria Zakari

160 Bank Emblem and "5th Anniversary"

1969. Wedding of General Gowon.

217	**159**	4d. brown and green	10	10
218		1s. 6d. black and green	50	20

1969. 5th Anniv of African Development Bank.
233 **160** 4d. orange, black & blue . . 10 10
234 – 1s. 6d. yellow, black and purple 20 50
DESIGN: 1s. 6d. Bank emblem and rays.

162 I.L.O. Emblem

1969. 50th Anniv of I.L.O.
235 **162** 4d. black and violet . . . 10 10
236 – 1s. 6d. green and black . . 75 1·00
DESIGN: 1s. 6d. World map and I.L.O. emblem.

164 Olumo Rock

1969. International Year of African Tourism.
237 **164** 4d. multicoloured 15 10
238 – 1s. black and green 20 10
239 – 1s. 6d. multicoloured . . . 1·25 50
DESIGNS—VERT: 1s. Traditional musicians; 1s. 6d. Assob Falls.

167 Symbolic Tree

169 Scroll

168 U.P.U. Headquarters Building

1970. "Stamp of Destiny". End of Civil War.
240 **167** 4d. gold, blue and black . . 10 10
241 – 1s. multicoloured 10 10
242 – 1s. 6d. green and black . . 15 10
243 – 2s. multicoloured 20 20
DESIGNS—VERT: 1s. Symbolic Wheel; 1s. 6d. United Nigerians supporting Map. HORIZ: 2s. Symbolic Torch.

1970. New U.P.U. Headquarters Building.
244 **168** 4d. violet and yellow . . . 10 10
245 1s. 6d. blue and indigo . . . 40 20

1970. 25th Anniv of United Nations.
246 **169** 4d. brown, buff and black . 10 10
247 – 1s. 6d. blue, brown & gold 30 20
DESIGN: 1s. 6d. U.N. Building.

170 Oil Rig

172 Ibibio Face Mask

171 Children and Globe

1970. 10th Anniv of Independence.
248 2d. Type **170** 25 10
249 4d. University graduate 15 10
250 6d. Durbar horsemen 30 10
251 9d. Servicemen raising flag . . 40 10
252 1s. Footballer 40 10
253 1s. 6d. Parliament building . . 40 40
254 2s. Kainji Dam 70 90
255 2s. 6d. Agricultural produce . . 70 1·00

1971. Racial Equality Year. Multicoloured.
256 4d. Type **171** 10 10
257 1s. Black and white men uprooting "Racism" (vert) . 10 10
258 1s. 6d. "The World in Black and White" (vert) 15 60
259 2s. Black and white men united 15 85

1971. Antiquities of Nigeria.
260 **172** 4d. black and blue 10 10
261 – 1s. 3d. brown and ochre . . 15 30
262 – 1s. 9d. green, brown & yell 20 80
DESIGNS: 1s. 3d. Benin bronze; 1s. 9d. Ife bronze.

173 Children and Symbol

174 Mast and Dish Aerial

1971. 25th Anniv of U.N.I.C.E.F.
263 **173** 4d. multicoloured 10 10
264 – 1s. 3d. orange, red & brn . 15 40
265 – 1s. 9d. turquoise and deep turquoise 15 85
DESIGNS: Each with U.N.I.C.E.F. symbol: 1s. 3d. Mother and child; 1s. 9d. Mother carrying child.

1971. Opening of Nigerian Earth Satellite Station.
266 **174** 4d. multicoloured 15 10
267 – 1s. 3d. green, blue & black 30 50
268 – 1s. 9d. brown, orge & blk . 40 1·00
269 – 3s. mauve, black & purple 85 2·00
DESIGNS: Nos. 267/9 as Type **174**, but showing different views of the Satellite Station.

175 Trade Fair Emblem

177 Nok Style Terracotta Head

176 Traffic

1972. All-Africa Trade Fair.
270 **175** 4d. multicoloured 10 10
271 – 1s. 3d. lilac, yellow & gold 15 35
272 – 1s. 9d. yellow, orge & blk 15 90
DESIGNS—HORIZ: 1s. 3d. Map of Africa with pointers to Nairobi. VERT: 1s. 9d. Africa on globe.

1972. Change to Driving on the Right.
273 **176** 4d. orange, brown & black 50 10
274 – 1s. 3d. multicoloured . . . 1·25 70
275 – 1s. 9d. multicoloured . . . 1·40 1·25
276 – 3s. multicoloured . . . . 2·25 3·00
DESIGNS: 1s. 3d. Roundabout; 1s. 9d. Highway; 3s. Road junction.

1972. All-Nigeria Arts Festival. Multicoloured.
277 4d. Type **177** 10 10
278 1s. 3d. Bronze pot from Igbo-Ukwu 25 60
279 1s. 9d. Bone harpoon (horiz) . 30 1·50

178 Hides and Skins

1973.
290 **178** 1 k. multicoloured 10 20
281 – 2 k. multicoloured 35 10
292 – 3 k. multicoloured 15 10
282a – 5 k. multicoloured 50 10
294 – 7 k. multicoloured . . . . 30 1·25
295 – 8 k. multicoloured 40 10
344 – 10 k. multicoloured . . . 1·00 20
297 – 12 k. black, green & blue 30 2·25
298 – 15 k. multicoloured . . . 30 60
299 – 18 k. multicoloured . . . 50 30
300 – 20 k. multicoloured . . . 65 30
301 – 25 k. multicoloured . . . 85 45
302 – 30 k. black, yellow & blue 40 1·50
303 – 35 k. multicoloured . . . 6·00 4·25
288a – 50 k. multicoloured . . . 75 90
305 – 1 n. multicoloured 50 75
306 – 2 n. multicoloured . . . . 1·25 2·25
DESIGNS—HORIZ: 2 k. Natural gas tanks; 3 k. Cement works; 5 k. Cattle-ranching; 7 k. Timber mill; 8 k. Oil refinery; 10 k. Cheetahs, Yankari Game Reserve; 12 k. New Civic Building; 15 k. Sugar-cane harvesting; 20 k. Vaccine production; 25 k. Modern wharf; 35 k. Textile machinery; 1 n. Eko Bridge; 2 n. Teaching Hos- pital, Lagos. VERT: 18 k. Palm oil production; 30 k. Argungu Fishing Festival; 50 k. Pottery.

179 Athlete

1973. Second All-African Games, Lagos.
307 **179** 5 k. lilac, blue and black . 15 10
308 – 12 k. multicoloured 25 50
309 – 18 k. multicoloured . . . . 60 1·00
310 – 25 k. multicoloured . . . . 70 1·50
DESIGNS—HORIZ: 12 k. Football; 18 k. Table tennis. VERT: 25 k. National stadium.

180 All-Africa House, Addis Ababa

1973. 10th Anniv of O.A.U. Multicoloured.
311 5 k. Type **180** 10 10
312 18 k. O.A.U. flag (vert) 30 40
313 30 k. O.A.U. emblem and symbolic flight of ten stairs (vert) 50 80

181 Dr. Hansen

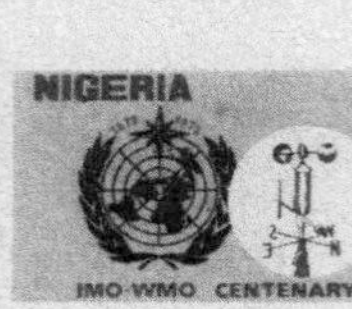

182 W.M.O. Emblem and Weather-vane

1973. Cent of Discovery of Leprosy Bacillus.
314 **181** 5 k. + 2 k. brown, pink and black 30 70

1973. Centenary of I.M.O./W.M.O.
315 **182** 5 k. multicoloured 30 10
316 30 k. multicoloured . . . . 1·50 2·25

183 University Complex

1973. 25th Anniv of Ibadan University. Multicoloured.
317 5 k. Type **183** 10 10
318 12 k. Students' population growth (vert) 15 20
319 18 k. Tower and students . . . 25 35
320 30 k. Teaching Hospital . . . 35 65

184 Lagos 1d. Stamp of 1874

1974. Stamp Centenary.
321 – 5 k. green, orange & black 15 10
322 – 12 k. multicoloured 40 40
323 **184** 18 k. green, mauve & blk . 60 70
324 – 30 k. multicoloured . . . . 1·75 2·00
DESIGNS: 5 k. Graph of mail traffic growth; 12 k. Northern Nigeria £25 stamp of 1904; 30 k. Forms of mail transport.

185 U.P.U. Emblem on Globe

1974. Centenary of U.P.U.
325 **185** 5 k. blue, orange & black . 15 10
326 – 18 k. multicoloured . . . . 2·00 60
327 – 30 k. brown, green & black 1·75 1·75
DESIGNS: 18 k. World transport map; 30 k. U.P.U. emblem and letters.

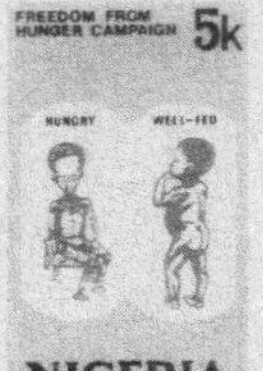

186 Starving and Well-fed Children

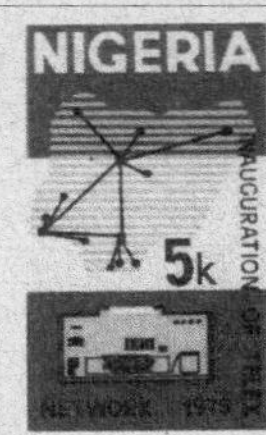

187 Telex Network and Teleprinter

1974. Freedom from Hunger Campaign.
328 **186** 5 k. green, buff and black . 10 10
329 – 12 k. multicoloured . . . 30 50
330 – 30 k. multicoloured . . . 80 1·75
DESIGNS—HORIZ: 12 k. Poultry battery. VERT: 30 k. Water-hoist.

1975. Inauguration of Telex Network.
331 **187** 5 k. black, orange & green 10 10
332 – 12 k. black, yellow & brn 20 20
333 – 18 k. multicoloured 30 30
334 – 30 k. multicoloured 50 50
DESIGNS: 12, 18, 30 k. are as Type **187** but with the motifs arranged differently.

188 Queen Amina of Zaria

190 Alexander Graham Bell

1975. International Women's Year.
335 **188** 5 k. green, yellow and blue 20 10
336 18 k. purple, blue & mauve 80 80
337 30 k. multicoloured . . . . 95 1·60

1976. Centenary of Telephone.
355 **190** 5 k. multicoloured 10 10
356 – 18 k. multicoloured 40 55
357 – 25 k. blue, light blue and brown . . . . 70 1·00
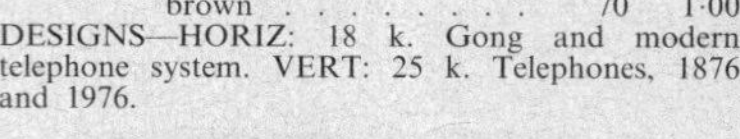
DESIGNS—HORIZ: 18 k. Gong and modern telephone system. VERT: 25 k. Telephones, 1876 and 1976.

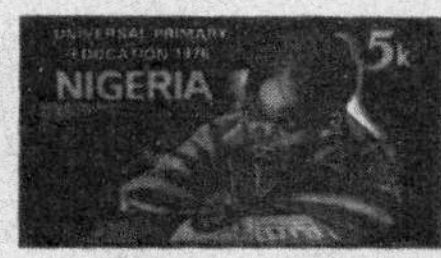

191 Child writing

1976. Launching of Universal Primary Education.
358 **191** 5 k. yellow, violet & mauve 10 10
359 – 18 k. multicoloured 45 60
360 – 25 k. multicoloured 70 85
DESIGNS—VERT: 18 k. Children entering school; 25 k. Children in class.

192 Festival Emblem

1976. 2nd World Black and African Festival of Arts and Culture, Nigeria.
361 **192** 5 k. gold and brown . . . 25 10
362 – 10 k. brown, yellow & blk 35 40
363 – 12 k. multicoloured 60 55
364 – 18 k. yellow, brown & blk 80 80
365 – 30 k. red and black . . . . 1·00 1·50
DESIGNS: 10 k. National Arts Theatre; 12 k. African hair-styles; 18 k. Musical instruments; 30 k. "Nigerian arts and crafts".

193 General Murtala Muhammed and Map of Nigeria

194 Scouts saluting

1977. 1st Death Anniv of General Muhammed (Head of State). Multicoloured.
366 5 k. Type **193** 10 10
367 18 k. General in dress uniform (vert) 20 35
368 30 k. General in battle dress (vert) 30 70

1977. 1st All-African Scout Jamboree, Jos, Nigeria. Multicoloured.
369 5 k. Type **194** 15 10
370 18 k. Scouts cleaning street (horiz) 60 70
371 25 k. Scouts working on farm (horiz) . . . . 70 1·25
372 30 k. Jamboree emblem and map of Africa (horiz) . . . . . . 80 2·00

195 Trade Fair Complex

1977. 1st Lagos Int Trade Fair.
373 **195** 5 k. black, blue & green . . 10 10
374 – 18 k. black, blue & purple 20 25
375 – 30 k. multicoloured 30 45
DESIGNS: 18 k. Globe and Trade Fair emblem; 30 k. Weaving and basketry.

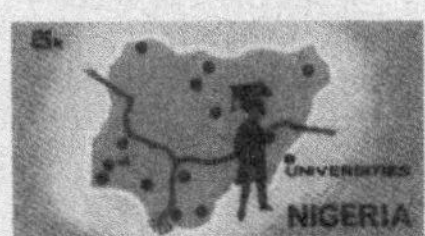

196 Map showing Nigerian Universities

1978. Global Conference on Technical Co-operation between Developing Countries, Buenos Aires.
376 **196** 5 k. multicoloured 10 10
377 – 12 k. multicoloured 15 15
378 – 18 k. multicoloured 25 25
379 – 30 k. yellow, violet & black 45 60
DESIGNS: 12 k. Map of West African highways and telecommunications; 18 k. Technologists undergoing training; 30 k. World map.

197 Microwave Antenna

1978. 10th World Telecommunications Day.
380 **197** 30 k. multicoloured 50 60

198 Students on "Operation Feed the Nation"

1978. "Operation Feed the Nation" Campaign. Multicoloured.
381 5 k. Type **198** 10 10
382 18 k. Family backyard farm . . 20 20
383 30 k. Plantain farm (vert) . . . 35 60

199 Mother with Infected Child

1978. Global Eradication of Smallpox.
384 **199** 5 k. black, brown & lilac . 15 10
385 – 12 k. multicoloured 25 20
386 – 18 k. black, brown & yell 40 40
387 – 30 k. black, silver & pink . 55 70
DESIGNS—HORIZ: 12 k. Doctor and infected child; 18 k. Group of children being vaccinated. VERT: 30 k. Syringe.

200 Nok Terracotta Human Figure Bwari, (900 B.C.–100 A.D.)
201 Anti-Apartheid Emblem

1978. Antiquities.
388 **200** 5 k. black, blue and red . . 10 10
389 – 12 k. multicoloured 15 10
390 – 18 k. black, blue and red . 20 15
391 – 30 k. multicoloured 25 20
DESIGNS—HORIZ: 12 k. Igbo-Ukwu bronze snail shell, Igbo Isaiah (9th-century A.D.). VERT: 18 k. Ife bronze statue of a king (12th–15th century A.D.); 30 k. Benin bronze equestrian figure (about 1700 A.D.).

1978. International Anti-Apartheid Year.
392 **201** 18 k. black, yellow and red 15 15

202 Wright Brothers and Wright Type A

1978. 75th Anniv of Powered Flight.
393 **202** 5 k. multicoloured 20 10
394 – 18 k. black, blue and light blue 60 20
DESIGN: 18 k. Nigerian Air Force formation.

203 Murtala Muhammed Airport

1979. Opening of Murtala Muhammed Airport.
395 **203** 5 k. black, grey and blue . 40 30

204 Child with Stamp Album

1979. 10th Anniv of National Philatelic Service.
396 **204** 5 k. multicoloured 10 10

205 Mother and Child

1979. International Year of the Child. Multicoloured.
397 5 k. Type **205** 10 10
398 18 k. Children studying 35 30
399 25 k. Children playing (vert) . . 40 50

206 Trainee Teacher making Audio Visual Aid Materials
207 Necom House

1979. 50th Anniv of International Bureau of Education. Multicoloured.
400 10 k. Type **206** 10 10
401 30 k. Adult education class . . 25 30

1979. 50th Anniv of Consultative Committee of International Radio.
402 **207** 10 k. multicoloured 15 20

208 Trainees of the Regional Air Survey School, Ile-Ife

1979. 21st Anniv of Economic Commission for Africa.
403 **208** 10 k. multicoloured 20 20

209 Football Cup and Map of Nigeria

1980. African Cup of Nations Football Competition, Nigeria. Multicoloured.
404 10 k. Type **209** 20 10
405 30 k. Footballer (vert) 60 50

210 Wrestling

1980. Olympic Games, Moscow.
406 **210** 10 k. multicoloured 10 10
407 – 20 k. black and green . . . 10 10
408 – 30 k. black, orange & blue 15 15
409 – 45 k. multicoloured 20 20
DESIGNS—VERT: 20 k. Long jump; 45 k. Netball. HORIZ: 30 k. Swimming.

211 Figures supporting O.P.E.C. Emblem

1980. 20th Anniv of O.P.E.C. (Organization of Petroleum Exporting Countries).
410 **211** 10 k. black, blue & yellow . . 15 10
411 – 45 k. black, blue & mauve . . 70 60
DESIGN—VERT: 45 k. O.P.E.C. emblem and globe.

212 Tank Locomotive No. 2, Wushishi Tramway

1980. 25th Anniv of Nigerian Railway Corporation. Multicoloured.
412 10 k. Type **212** 75 10
413 20 k. Loading goods train . . . 1·50 85
414 30 k. Freight train . . . . . . 2·00 1·25

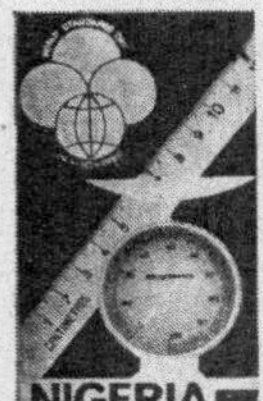

213 Metric Scales
215 Disabled Woman sweeping

214 "Communication" Symbols and Map of West Africa

1980. World Standards Day.
415 **213** 10 k. red and black 10 10
416 – 30 k. multicoloured 35 40
DESIGN—HORIZ: 30 k. Quality control.

1980. 5th Anniv of Economic Community of West African States.
417 **214** 10 k. black, orange & olive 10 10
418 – 25 k. black, green & red . . 30 10
419 – 30 k. black, yellow & brn . 20 15
420 – 45 k. black, turq & blue . . 25 25
DESIGNS: 25 k. "Transport"; 30 k. "Agriculture"; 45 k. "Industry".

1981. International Year for Disabled Persons.
421 **215** 10 k. multicoloured 20 10
422 – 30 k. black, brown & blue . 65 65
DESIGN: 30 k. Disabled man filming.

216 President launching "Green Revolution" (food production campaign)

1981. World Food Day.
423 **216** 10 k. multicoloured 10 10
424 – 25 k. black, yellow & green 20 50
425 – 30 k. multicoloured 25 55
426 – 45 k. black, brown & yell . 45 85
DESIGNS—VERT: 25 k. Food crops; 30 k. Harvesting tomatoes. HORIZ: 45 k. Pig farming.

217 Rioting in Soweto

1981. Anti-Apartheid Movement.
427 **217** 30 k. multicoloured 35 55
428 – 45 k. black, red and green 50 95
DESIGN—VERT: 45 k. "Police brutality".

218 "Preservation of Wildlife"

1982. 75th Anniv of Boy Scout Movement. Multicoloured.
429 30 k. Type **218** 50 55
430 45 k. Lord Baden-Powell taking salute 75 95

219 Early Inoculation

1982. Centenary of Robert Koch's Discovery of Tubercle Bacillus.
431 **219** 10 k. multicoloured 20 15
432 – 30 k. black, brown and green 50 65
433 – 45 k. black, brown and green 80 1·40
DESIGNS—HORIZ: 30 k. Technician and microscope. VERT: 45 k. Patient being X-rayed.

220 "Keep Your Environment Clean"

1982. 10th Anniv of U.N. Conference on Human Environment.
434 **220** 10 k. multicoloured 10 10
435 – 20 k. orange, grey and black 20 40
436 – 30 k. multicoloured 35 60
437 – 45 k. multicoloured 55 85
DESIGNS: 20 k. "Check air pollution"; 30 k. "Preserve natural environment"; 45 k. "Reafforestation concerns all".

221 "Salamis parhassus"
222 Carving of "Male and Female Twins"

1982. Nigerian Butterflies. Multicoloured.
438 10 k. Type **221** 15 10
439 20 k. "Iterus zalmoxis" 30 30
440 30 k. "Cymothoe beckeri" . . 40 40
441 45 k. "Papilio hesperus" . . . 70 70

1982. 25th Anniv of National Museum. Multicoloured.
442 10 k. Type **222** 10 10
443 20 k. Royal bronze leopard (horiz) 20 35
444 30 k. Soapstone seated figure . 35 90
445 45 k. Wooden helmet mask . . 50 1·50

223 Three Generations

1983. Family Day. Multicoloured.
446 10 k. Type **223** 15 10
447 30 k. Parents with three children (vert) 50 65

224 Satellite View of Globe

1983. Commonwealth Day.

448 **224** 10 k. brown and black . . . 10 10
449 – 25 k. multicoloured 20 30
450 – 30 k. black, purple & grey 55 35
451 – 45 k. multicoloured . . . 35 45

DESIGNS—HORIZ: 25 k. National Assembly Buildings. VERT: 30 k. Drilling for oil; 45 k. Athletics.

225 Corps Members on Building Project

226 Postman on Bicycle

1983. 10th Anniv of National Youth Service Corps. Multicoloured.

452 10 k. Type **225** 15 10
453 25 k. On the assault-course (vert) 30 30
454 30 k. Corps members on parade 40 40

1983. World Communications Year. Multicoloured.

455 10 k. Type **226** 15 10
456 25 k. Newspaper kiosk (horiz) . 30 40
457 30 k. Town crier blowing elephant tusk (horiz) . . . 35 45
458 45 k. T.V. newsreader (horiz) . 45 55

227 Pink Shrimp

1983. World Fishery Resources.

459 **227** 10 k. red, blue and black . 15 10
460 – 25 k. multicoloured 30 40
461 – 30 k. multicoloured 30 45
462 – 45 k. multicoloured 40 70

DESIGNS: 25 k. Long-necked croaker; 30 k. Barracuda; 45 k. Fishing techniques.

228 On Parade

229 Crippled Child

1983. Centenary of Boys' Brigade and 75th Anniv of Founding in Nigeria. Multicoloured.

463 10 k. Type **228** 40 10
464 30 k. Members working on cassava plantation (horiz) . . 1·50 1·50
465 45 k. Skill training (horiz) . . . 2·25 2·75

1984. Stop Polio Campaign.

466 **229** 10 k. blue, black & brown 20 15
467 – 25 k. orange, black & yell . 40 75
468 – 30 k. red, black & brown . 60 1·10

DESIGNS—HORIZ: 25 k. Child receiving vaccine. VERT: 30 k. Healthy child.

230 Waterbuck

232 Boxing

231 Obverse and Reverse of 1969 £1 Note

1984. Nigerian Wildlife.

469 **230** 10 k. green, brown & black 20 10
470 – 25 k. multicoloured 40 50
471 – 30 k. brown, black & green 50 90
472 – 45 k. blue, orange & black 60 1·25

DESIGNS—HORIZ: 25 k. Hartebeest; 30 k. African buffalo. VERT: 45 k. Diademed monkey.

1984. 25th Anniv of Nigerian Central Bank.

473 **231** 10 k. multicoloured 20 10
474 – 25 k. brown, black & green 45 50
475 – 30 k. red, black and green . 55 60

DESIGNS: 25 k. Central Bank; 30 k. Obverse and reverse of 1959 £5 note.

1984. Olympic Games, Los Angeles. Mult.

476 10 k. Type **232** 15 10
477 25 k. Discus-throwing 35 50
478 30 k. Weightlifting 40 60
479 45 k. Cycling 60 90

233 Irrigation Project, Lesotho

234 Pin-tailed Whydah

1984. 20th Anniv of African Development Bank.

480 **233** 10 k. multicoloured 15 10
481 – 25 k. multicoloured 30 50
482 – 30 k. black, yellow & blue 35 60
483 – 45 k. black, brown & blue 1·75 90

DESIGNS—HORIZ: 25 k. Bomi Hills Road, Liberia; 30 k. School building project, Seychelles; 45 k. Coal mining Niger.

1984. Rare Birds. Multicoloured.

484 10 k. Type **234** 75 20
485 25 k. Spur-winged plover . . . 1·50 70
486 30 k. Red bishop . . . . . . 1·50 1·75
487 45 k. Double-spurred francolin 1·75 2·50

235 Boeing 747 Airliner taking-off

1984. 40th Anniv of International Civil Aviation Organization. Multicoloured.

488 10 k. Type **235** 40 10
489 45 k. Boeing 707 airliner circling globe . . . . 1·50 2·25

236 Office Workers and Clocks ("Punctuality")

1985. "War against Indiscipline". Mult.

490 20 k. Type **236** 30 35
491 50 k. Cross over hands passing banknotes ("Discourage Bribery") 55 75

237 Footballers receiving Flag from Major-General Buhari

239 Globe and O.P.E.C. Emblem

238 Rolling Mill

1985. International Youth Year. Mult.

492 20 k. Type **237** 30 20
493 50 k. Girls of different tribes with flag (vert) 55 70
494 55 k. Members of youth organizations with flags (vert) 55 80

1985. 25th Anniv of Independence. Mult.

495 20 k. Type **238** 25 10
496 50 k. Map of Nigeria 40 35
497 55 k. Remembrance Arcade . . 40 40
498 60 k. Eleme, first Nigerian oil refinery . . . . 1·00 50

1985. 25th Anniv of Organization of Petroleum Exporting Countries.

500 **239** 20 k. blue and red 75 35
501 – 50 k. black and blue . . . 1·50 75

DESIGN—HORIZ: 50 k. World map and O.P.E.C. emblem.

240 Waterfall

241 Map of Nigeria and National Flag

1985. World Tourism Day. Multicoloured.

502 20 k. Type **240** 35 10
503 50 k. Pottery, carved heads and map of Nigeria (horiz) . . . 45 50
504 55 k. Calabash carvings and Nigerian flag 45 50
505 60 k. Leather work 45 55

1985. 40th Anniv of United Nations Organization and 25th Anniv of Nigerian Membership.

506 **241** 20 k. black, green & blue . 20 10
507 – 50 k. black, blue & red . . 35 50
508 – 55 k. black, blue & red . . 35 60

DESIGNS—HORIZ: 50 k. United Nations Building, New York; 55 k. United Nations logo.

242 Rock Python

243 Social Worker with Children

1986. African Reptiles.

509 **242** 10 k. multicoloured 30 10
510 – 20 k. black, brown & blue 50 70
511 – 25 k. multicoloured 50 80
512 – 30 k. multicoloured 50 80

DESIGNS: 20 k. Long snouted crocodile; 25 k. Gopher tortoise; 30 k. Chameleon.

1986. Nigerian Life. Multicoloured.

513 1 k. Type **243** 10 20
514 2 k. Volkswagen motor assembly line (horiz) . . . 10 20
515 5 k. Modern housing estate (horiz) 10 20
516 10 k. Harvesting oil palm fruit 10 10
517 15 k. Unloading freighter (horiz) 10 10
518 20 k. "Tecoma stans" (flower) 10 10
519 25 k. Hospital ward (horiz) . 10 10
519a 30 k. Birom dancers (horiz) . 10 10
520 35 k. Telephonists operating switchboard (horiz) . . . 10 10
521 40 k. Nkpokiti dancers . . . 10 10
522 45 k. Hibiscus (horiz) 10 10
523a 50 k. Post Office counter (horiz) 10 10
524 1 n. Stone quarry (horiz) . . 10 10
525a 2 n. Students in laboratory (horiz) 10 10
525ba 10 n. Lekki Beach (horiz) . . 55 60
525c 20 n. Ancient wall, Kano (horiz) . . . . 4·00 1·50
525d 50 n. Rock bridge (horiz) . . 2·75 3·00
525e 100 n. Ekpe masquerader . . 5·50 5·75
525f 500 n. National Theatre (horiz) 27·00 28·00

244 Emblem and Globe

1986. International Peace Year. Mult.

526 10 k. Type **244** 20 10
527 20 k. Hands of five races holding globe . . . . 60 1·00

245 "Goliathus goliathus" (beetle)

246 Oral Rehydration Therapy

1986. Nigerian Insects. Multicoloured.

528 10 k. Type **245** 30 10
529 20 k. "Vespa vulgaris" (wasp) . 40 40
530 25 k. "Acheta domestica" (cricket) 45 70
531 30 k. "Anthrenus verbasci" (beetle) . . . . 55 1·00

1986. 40th Anniv of U.N.I.C.E.F.

533 **246** 10 k. multicoloured 30 10
534 – 20 k. black, brown & yell . 40 40
535 – 25 k. multicoloured 45 70
536 – 30 k. multicoloured . . . . 55 1·00

DESIGNS: 20 k. Immunisation; 25 k. Breast feeding; 30 k. Mother and child.

247 Stylized Figures on Wall ("International Understanding")

1986. 25th Anniv of Nigerian Institute of International Affairs.

537 **247** 20 k. black, blue & green . 50 50
538 – 30 k. multicoloured . . . . 75 1·25

DESIGN—VERT: 30 k. "Knowledge" (bronze sculpture).

248 Freshwater Clam

1987. Shells.

539 **248** 10 k. multicoloured 65 10
540 – 20 k. black, brown & pink 1·25 1·75
541 – 25 k. multicoloured . . . . 1·25 2·00
542 – 30 k. multicoloured . . . . 1·50 2·50

DESIGNS: 20 k. Periwinkle; 25 k. Bloody cockle (inscr "BLODDY COCKLE"); 30 k. Mangrove oyster.

249 "Clitoria ternatea"

250 Doka Hairstyle

1987. Nigerian Flowers.

543 **249** 10 k. multicoloured 10 10
544 – 20 k. brown, yellow and green 15 15
545 – 25 k. multicoloured 15 20
546 – 30 k. multicoloured 20 40

DESIGNS: 20 k. "Hibiscus tiliaceus"; 25 k. "Acanthus montanus"; 30 k. "Combretum racemosum".

1987. Women's Hairstyles.

547 **250** 10 k. black, brown and grey 10 10
548 – 20 k. multicoloured 15 20
549 – 25 k. black, brown and red 20 35
550 – 30 k. multicoloured 20 40

DESIGNS: 20 k. Eting; 25 k. Agogo; 30 k. Goto.

251 Family sheltering under Tree

252 Red Cross Worker distributing Food

1987. International Year of Shelter for the Homeless. Multicoloured.

551 20 k. Type **251** 15 15
552 30 k. Family and modern house 15 30

1988. 125th Anniv of International Red Cross. Multicoloured.

553 20 k. Type **252** 65 30
554 30 k. Carrying patient to ambulance 65 95

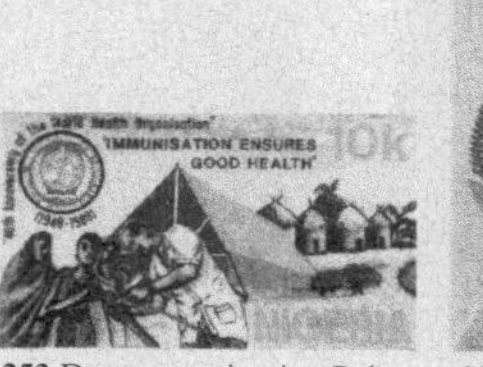

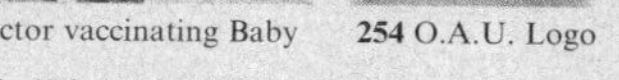

253 Doctor vaccinating Baby

254 O.A.U. Logo

1988. 40th Anniv of W.H.O. Multicoloured.

555 10 k. Type **253** 25 10
556 20 k. W.H.O. logo and outline map of Nigeria 60 60
557 30 k. Doctor and patients at mobile clinic 60 60

1988. 25th Anniv of Organization of African Unity.
558 **254** 10 k. brown, green & orge . . 15 15
559 – 20 k. multicoloured 15 15
DESIGN: 20 k. Four Africans supporting map of Africa.

255 Pink Shrimp

1988. Shrimps.
560 **255** 10 k. multicoloured 25 10
561 – 20 k. black and green . . . 40 15
562 – 25 k. black, red & brown . . 45 25
563 – 30 k. orange, brown & blk . 55 50
DESIGNS: 20 k. Tiger shrimp; 25 k. Deepwater roseshrimp; 30 k. Estuarine prawn.

256 Weightlifting

1988. Olympic Games, Seoul. Multicoloured.
565 10 k. Type **256** 25 10
566 20 k. Boxing 35 35
567 30 k. Athletics (vert) 45 55

257 Banknote Production Line (½-size illustration)

1988. 25th Anniv of Nigerian Security Printing and Minting Co. Ltd.
568 **257** 10 k. multicoloured 10 10
569 – 20 k. black, silver & green . . 20 20
570 – 25 k. multicoloured 30 30
571 – 30 k. multicoloured 45 45
DESIGNS—HORIZ (As T **257**): 20 k. Coin production line. VERT (37 × 44 mm): 25 k. Montage of products; 30 k. Anniversary logos.

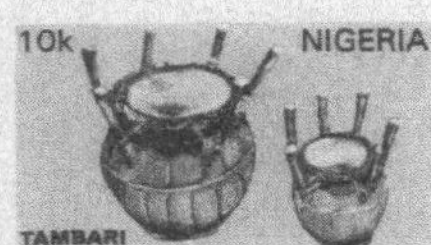

258 Tambari

1989. Nigerian Musical Instruments.
572 **258** 10 k. multicoloured 10 10
573 – 20 k. multicoloured 20 20
574 – 25 k. brown, green & black . 30 30
575 – 30 k. brown and black . . . 45 45
DESIGNS: 20 k. Kundung; 25 k. Ibid; 30 k. Dundun.

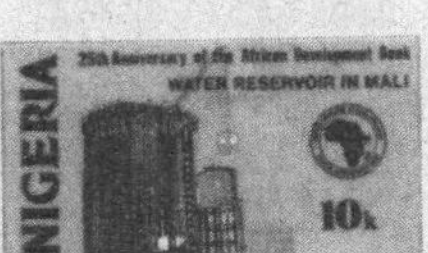

259 Construction of Water Towers, Mali

1989. 25th Anniv of African Development Bank. Multicoloured.
576 10 k. Type **259** 10 10
577 20 k. Paddy field, Gambia . . . 15 15
578 25 k. Bank Headquarters, Abidjan, Ivory Coast 25 25
579 30 k. Anniversary logo (vert) . . 35 35

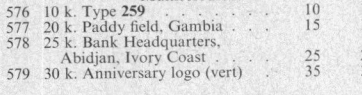

260 Lighting Campfire

1989. 70th Anniv of Nigerian Girl Guides Association. Multicoloured.
580 10 k. Type **260** 30 10
581 20 k. Guide on rope bridge (vert) . 60 60

261 Etubom Costume

262 Dove with Letter and Map of Africa

1989. Traditional Costumes. Multicoloured.
582 10 k. Type **261** 15 10
583 20 k. Fulfulde 25 25
584 25 k. Aso-Ofi 35 40
585 30 k. Fuska Kura 45 60

1990. 10th Anniv of Pan African Postal Union. Multicoloured.
586 10 k. Type **262** 25 10
587 20 k. Parcel and map of Africa . . 50 50

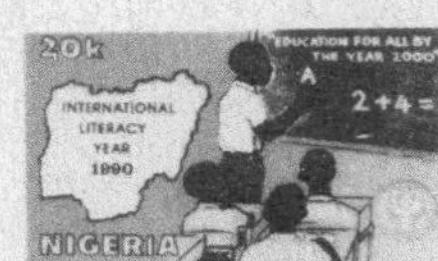

263 Oil Lamps

1990. Nigerian Pottery.
588 **263** 10 k. black, brown & violet . 10 10
589 – 20 k. black, brown & violet . 20 20
590 – 25 k. brown and violet . . 25 25
591 – 30 k. multicoloured 35 35
DESIGNS: 20 k. Water pots; 25 k. Musical pots; 50 k. Water jugs.

264 Teacher and Class

1990. International Literacy Year.
593 **264** 20 k. multicoloured 20 10
594 – 30 k. brown, blue & yellow . 30 30
DESIGN: 30 k. Globe and book.

265 Globe and OPEC Logo

1990. 30th Anniv of the Organization of Petroleum Exporting Countries. Multicoloured.
595 10 k. Type **265** 10 10
596 20 k. Logo and flags of member countries (vert) 20 20
597 25 k. World map and logo . . . 25 25
598 30 k. Logo within inscription "Co-operation for Global Energy Security" (vert) . . . 35 35

266 Grey Parrot

267 Eradication Treatment

1990. Wildlife. Multicoloured.
599 20 k. Type **266** 20 10
600 30 k. Roan antelope 20 10
601 1 n. 50 Grey-necked bald crow ("Rockfowl") 60 80
602 2 n. 50 Mountain gorilla . . . 85 1·25

1991. National Guineaworm Eradication Day. Multicoloured.
604 10 k. Type **267** 15 10
605 20 k. Women collecting water from river (horiz) 25 25
606 30 k. Boiling pot of water . . . 25 25

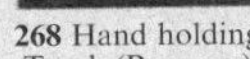
268 Hand holding Torch (Progress)

269 National Flags

1991. Organization of African Unity Heads of State and Governments Meeting, Abuja. Each showing outline map of Africa. Multicoloured.
607 20 k. Type **268** 15 10
608 30 k. Cogwheel (Unity) 20 25
609 50 k. O.A.U. flag (Freedom) . . 20 45

1991. Economic Community of West African States Summit Meeting, Abuja. Multicoloured.
610 20 k. Type **269** 15 10
611 50 k. Map showing member states 30 45

270 Electric Catfish

1991. Nigerian Fishes. Multicoloured.
612 10 k. Type **270** 15 10
613 20 k. Nile perch 25 25
614 30 k. Nile mouthbrooder ("Talapia") 35 35
615 50 k. Sharp-toothed catfish . . 50 55

271 Telecom '91 Emblem

1991. "Telecom '91" 6th World Telecommunication Exhibition, Geneva.
617 **271** 20 k. black, green & violet . 30 10
618 – 50 k. multicoloured 40 30
DESIGN—VERT: 50 k. Emblem and patchwork.

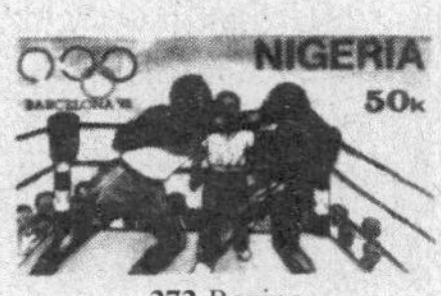

272 Boxing

1992. Olympic Games, Barcelona (1st issue). Multicoloured.
619 50 k. Type **272** 15 15
620 1 n. Nigerian athlete winning race 25 25
621 1 n. 50 Table tennis 35 35
622 2 n. Taekwondo 45 45
See also No. 624.

273 Football

274 Blood Pressure Gauge

1992. Olympic Games, Barcelona (2nd issue).
624 **273** 1 n. 50 multicoloured . . . 50 50

1992. World Health Day. Multicoloured.
625 50 k. Type **274** 15 15
626 1 n. World Health Day '92 emblem 20 20
627 1 n. 50 Heart and lungs 30 30
628 2 n. Interior of heart 40 40

275 Map of World and Stamp on Globe

1992. "Olymphilex '92" Olympic Stamp Exhibition, Barcelona. Multicoloured.
630 50 k. Type **275** 20 10
631 1 n. 50 Examining stamps . . . 40 40

276 Gathering Plantain Fruit

277 Centre Emblem

1992. 25th Anniv of International Institute of Tropical Agriculture.
633 **276** 50 k. multicoloured 10 10
634 – 1 n. multicoloured 15 15
635 – 1 n. 50 black, brown & grn . 20 20
636 – 2 n. multicoloured 25 25
DESIGNS—VERT: 1 n. 50, Harvesting cassava tubers; 2 n. Stacking yams. HORIZ: 1 n. Tropical foods.

1992. Commissioning of Maryam Babangida National Centre for Women's Development.
638 **277** 50 k. gold, emerald and green 10 10
639 – 1 n. multicoloured 15 15
640 – 1 n. 50 multicoloured . . . 20 20
641 – 2 n. multicoloured 30 30
DESIGNS—VERT: 1 n. Women working in fields; 2 n. Woman at loom. HORIZ: 1 n. 50, Maryam Babangida National Centre.
All examples of No. 641 are without a "NIGERIA" inscription.

278 Healthy Food and Emblem

279 Sabada Dance

1992. International Conference on Nutrition, Rome. Multicoloured.
642 50 k. Type **278** 10 10
643 1 n. Child eating 15 15
644 1 n. 50 Fruit (vert) 20 20
645 2 n. Vegetables 25 25

1992. Traditional Dances. Multicoloured.
647 50 k. Type **279** 10 10
648 1 n. Sato 15 15
649 1 n. 50 Asian Ubo Ikpa 20 20
650 2 n. Dundun 25 25

280 African Elephant

1993. Wildlife. Multicoloured.
652 1 n. 50 Type **280** 10 10
653 5 n. Stanley crane (vert) . . . 25 30
654 20 n. Roan antelope . . . . . 1·10 1·25
655 30 n. Lion . . . . 1·60 1·75

281 Suburban Garden

1993. World Environment Day. Multicoloured.
656 1 n. Type **281** 10 10
657 1 n. 50 Water pollution 15 10
658 5 n. Forest road 50 50
659 10 n. Rural house 90 90

282 Oni Figure

283 "Bulbophyllum distans"

1993. 50th Anniv of National Museums and Monuments Commission. Multicoloured.
660 1 n Type **282** 10 10
661 1 n. 50 Bronze head of Queen Mother 10 10
662 5 n. Bronze pendant (horiz) . . 30 35
663 10 n. Nok head 70 75

1993. Orchids. Multicoloured.
664 1 n. Type **283** 10 10
665 1 n. 50 "Eulophia cristata" . . 15 10
666 5 n. "Eulophia horsfalli" . . . 45 45
667 10 n. "Eulophia quartiniana" . 1·00 1·10

284 Children in Classroom and Adults carrying Food

1994. International Year of the Family. Mult.
669 1 n. 50 Type **284** 10 10
670 10 n. Market . . . . 1·00 1·00

285 Hand with Tweezers holding 1969 4d. Philatelic Service Stamp

1994. 25th Anniv of Nat Philatelic Service. Mult.
671 1 n. Type **285** 10 10
672 1 n. 50 Philatelic Bureau . . . 15 10
673 5 n. Stamps forming map of Nigeria 45 45
674 10 n. Philatelic counter . . . . 1·00 1·10

286 "I Love Stamps"

1994. 120th Anniv of First Postage Stamps in Nigeria. Multicoloured.
675 1 n. Type **286** 10 10
676 1 n. 50 "I Collect Stamps" . . 15 15
677 5 n. 19th-century means of communication 45 45
678 10 n. Lagos stamp of 1874 . . 1·00 1·10

287 Magnifying Glass over Globe

1994. "Philakorea '94" International Stamp Exhibition, Seoul.
679 **287** 30 n. multicoloured . . . . 1·75 2·40

288 Geryon Crab

1994. Crabs. Multicoloured.
681 1 n. Type **288** 10 10
682 1 n. 50 Spider crab 10 10
683 5 n. Red spider crab 45 45
684 10 n. Geryon maritae crab . . 90 90

289 Sewage Works **290** Letterbox

1994. 30th Anniv of African Development Bank. Multicoloured.
685 1 n. 50 Type **289** 15 10
686 30 n. Development Bank emblem and flowers . . . . 1·75 2·40

1995. 10th Anniv of Nigerian Post and Telecommunication Corporations. Multicoloured.
687 1 n. Type **290** 10 10
688 1 n. 50 Letter showing "1 JAN 1985" postmark (horiz) . . . 10 10
689 5 n. Nipost and Nitel emblems (horiz) 30 35
690 10 n. Mobile telephones . . . 60 65

291 Woman preparing Food **292** "Candlestick" Telephone

1995. Family Support Programme. Multicoloured.
691 1 n. Type **291** 10 10
692 1 n. 50 Mother teaching children 10 10
693 5 n. Family meal 30 35
694 10 n. Agricultural workers and tractor 60 65

1995. Cent of First Telephone in Nigeria. Mult.
695 1 n. 50 Type **292** 10 10
696 10 n. Early equipment 60 65

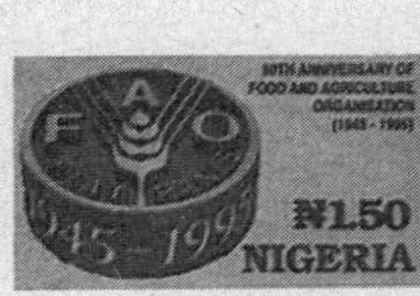
293 F.A.O. Emblem **294** "Justice" and 50th Anniversary Emblem

1995. 50th Anniv of F.A.O. Multicoloured.
697 1 n. 50 Type **293** 10 10
698 30 n. Fishing canoes . . . . . 1·90 2·00

1995. 50th Anniv of United Nations. Multicoloured.
699 1 n. Type **294** 10 10
700 1 n. 50 Toxic waste (horiz) . . 10 10
701 5 n. Tourist hut (horiz) 30 35
702 10 n. Nigerian armoured car on U.N. duty (horiz) 90 95

295 Container Ship in Dock

1996. 10th Anniv of Niger Dock. Multicoloured.
703 5 n. Type **295** 35 30
704 10 n. "Badagri" (tourist launch) on crane 65 60
705 20 n. Shipping at dock . . . . 1·25 1·50
706 30 n. "Odoragushin" (ferry) . . 2·00 2·50

296 Scientist and Crops

1996. 21st Anniv of E.C.O.W.A.S. (Economic Community of West African States). Multicoloured.
707 5 n. Type **296** 30 30
708 30 n. Queue at border crossing . . . . 1·50 2·00

297 Judo **298** Nigerian Flag and Exhibition Emblem

1996. Olympic Games, Atlanta. Multicoloured.
709 5 n. Type **297** 35 30
710 10 n. Tennis 80 60
711 20 n. Relay race . . . . 1·25 1·50
712 30 n. Football . . . . 1·75 2·25

1996. "ISTANBUL '96" International Stamp Exhibition.
713 **298** 30 n. mauve, green and black . . . . 1·50 2·00

299 "Volvariella esculenta" **300** Boy with Toys

1996. Fungi. Multicoloured.
714 5 n. Type **299** 45 30
715 10 n. "Lentinus subnudus" . . 90 60
716 20 n. "Tricholoma lobayensis" . 1·50 1·50
717 30 n. "Pleurotus tuber-regium" . 2·00 2·25

1996. 50th Anniv of U.N.I.C.E.F. Multicoloured.
718 5 n. Type **300** 30 30
719 30 n. Girl reading book (horiz) . . . . 1·50 2·00

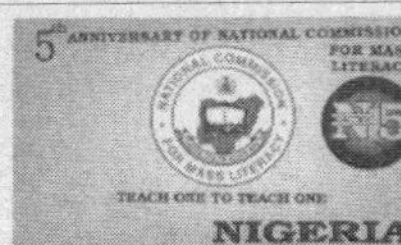
301 Literacy Logo

1996. 5th Anniv of Mass Literacy Commission.
720 **301** 5 n. emerald, green and black 30 30
721 – 30 n. emerald, green and black . . . . 1·50 2·00
DESIGN: 30 n. Hands holding book and literacy logo.

302 Three Footballers

1998. World Cup Football Championship, France. Multicoloured.
722 5 n. Type **302** 25 30
723 10 n. Player with ball (vert) . . 55 60
724 20 n. Player receiving ball (vert) 1·10 1·25
725 30 n. Two opposing players . . 1·60 1·75

303 University Tower and Complex

1998. 50th Anniv of Ibadan University. Mult.
726 5 n. Type **303** 25 30
727 30 n. Anniversary logo and University crest . . . . . . 1·60 1·75

304 Ship and Logo

1998. 8th Anniv of Economic Community of West African States Military Arm (ECOMOG). Multicoloured.
728 5 n. Type **304** 25 30
729 30 n. Logo and original member states . . . . 1·60 1·75
730 50 n. Current member states . . 2·75 3·00

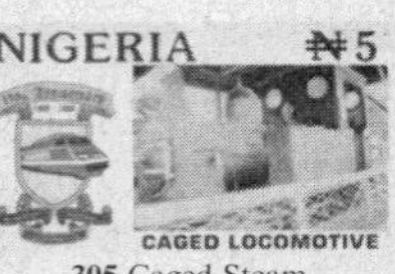
305 Caged Steam Locomotive

1999. Centenary of Nigerian Railway Corporation. Multicoloured.
731 5 n. Type **305** 25 30
732 10 n. Iddo Terminus 55 60
733 20 n. Diesel locomotive No. 2131 . . . . 1·10 1·25
734 30 n. Passenger train pulling into station . . . . 1·60 1·75

306 Football and Globe

1999. 11th World Youth Football Championship, Nigeria. Multicoloured.
735 5 n. + 5 n. Type **306** 15 20
736 10 n. + 5 n. Player throwing ball 20 25
737 20 n. + 5 n. Player scoring goal . 35 40
738 30 n. + 5 n. Map of Nigeria showing venues 50 55
739 40 n. + 5 n. World Youth Football Championship logo . 60 65
740 50 n. + 5 n. Player being tackled 75 80

307 Sea Life and F. E. P. A. Emblem **308** Nicon Emblem

1999. 10th Anniv of Federal Environmental Protection Agency. Multicoloured.
742 5 n. Type **307** 25 30
743 10 n. Forest 55 60
744 20 n. Monkeys . . . . 1·25 1·10
745 30 n. Villagers and wildlife . . . 1·60 1·75

1999. 30th Anniv of Nicon Insurance Corporation. Multicoloured.
746 5 n. Type **307** 25 30
747 30 n. Emblem and Nicon Building (horiz) . . . . . . 1·60 1·75

POSTAGE DUE STAMPS

D 1

1959.
D1 D 1 1d. orange 15 75
D2 2d. orange 20 80
D3 3d. orange . . . . 25 1·40
D4 6d. orange . . . . 25 5·00
D5 1s. black . . . . 50 6·50

1961.
D 6 D 1 1d. red 15 40
D 7 2d. blue 20 45
D 8 3d. green 25 60
D 9 6d. yellow . . . . 30 1·40
D10 1s. blue . . . . 50 2·25

1973. As Type D 1.
D11 2 k. red 10 10
D12 3 k. blue 10 10
D13 5 k. yellow 10 10
D14 10 k. green 10 10

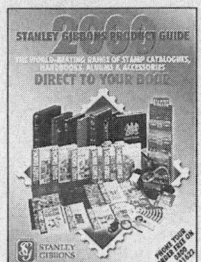

NIUAFO'OU Pt. 1

A remote island, part of the Kingdom of Tonga, with local autonomy.

100 seniti = 1 pa'anga

1 Map of Niuafo'ou **2a** SPIA De Havilland D.H.C. 6 Turin Otter 300

1983.

1 **1** 1 s. stone, black and red 30 60
2 2 s. stone, black and green 30 60
3 3 s. stone, black and blue 30 70
4 3 s. stone, black and brown 30 70
5 5 s. stone, black and purple 40 70
6 6 s. stone, black and blue 40 70
7 9 s. stone, black and green 40 70
8 10 s. stone, black and blue 40 70
9 13 s. stone, black and green 65 75
10 15 s. stone, black and brown 70 1·00
11 20 s. stone, black and blue 75 1·00
12 29 s. stone, black and purple 1·00 80
13 32 s. stone, black and green 1·00 90
14 47 s. stone, black and red 1·40 1·40

1983. No. 820 of Tonga optd **NIUAFO'OU KINGDOM OF TONGA** or surch also.

15 1 p. on 2 p. green and black 2·50 3·00
16 2 p. green 3·50 4·50

1983. Inauguration of Niuafo'ou Airport.

17 **2a** 29 s. multicoloured 80 1·00
18 1 p. multicoloured 2·50 3·25

1983. As T **1**, but without value, surch.

19 3 s. stone, black and blue 20 20
20 5 s. stone, black and blue 20 20
21 32 s. stone, black and blue 1·50 1·25
22 2 p. stone, black and blue 8·00 9·00

4 Eruption of Niuafo'ou

1983. 25th Anniv of Re-settlement. Mult.

23 5 s. Type **4** 40 30
24 29 s. Lava flow 1·00 1·00
25 32 s. Islanders fleeing to safety 1·10 1·00
26 1 p. 50 Evacuation by canoe 3·50 5·00

5 Purple Swamphen **6** Green Turtle

1983. Birds of Niuafo'ou.

27 **5** 1 s. black and mauve 80 90
28 – 2 s. black and blue 80 90
29 – 3 s. black and green 80 90
30 – 5 s. black and yellow 1·00 90
31 – 6 s. black and orange 1·25 1·10
32 – 9 s. multicoloured 1·60 1·10
33 – 10 s. multicoloured 1·60 1·60
34 – 13 s. multicoloured 2·00 1·60
35 – 15 s. multicoloured 2·00 2·00
36 – 20 s. multicoloured 2·25 2·25
37 – 29 s. multicoloured 2·50 1·50
38 – 32 s. multicoloured 2·50 1·60
39 – 47 s. multicoloured 3·00 2·25
40 – 1 p. multicoloured 5·50 7·50
41 – 2 p. multicoloured 7·50 10·00

DESIGNS—VERT (22 × 29 mm): 2 s. White collared kingfisher; 3 s. Red-headed parrot finch; 5 s. Banded rail; 6 s. Polynesian scrub hen ("Niuafo'ou megapode"); 9 s. Green honeyeater; 10 s. Purple swamphen (different). (22 × 36 mm): 29 s. Red-headed parrot finch (different); 32 s. White-collared kingfisher (different). (29 × 42 mm): 1 p. As 10 s. HORIZ (29 × 22 mm): 13 s. Banded rail (different): 15 s. Polynesian scrub hen (different). (36 × 22 mm): 20 s. As 13 s.; 47 s. As 15 s. (42 × 29 mm): 2 p. As 15 s.

1984. Wildlife and Nature Reserve. Mult.

42 29 s. Type **6** 70 70
43 32 s. Insular flying fox (vert) 70 70
44 47 s. Humpback whale 2·50 1·75
45 1 p. 50 Polynesian scrub hen ("Niuafo'ou megapode") (vert) 4·50 6·00

7 Diagram of Time Zones

1984. Cent of International Dateline. Mult.

46 47 s. Type **7** 60 50
47 2 p. Location map showing Niuafo'ou 1·90 2·75

8 Australia 1913 £2 Kangaroo Definitive **9** Dutch Brass Band entertaining Tongans

1984. "Ausipex" International Stamp Exhibition, Melbourne. Multicoloured.

48 32 s. Type **8** 75 60
49 1 p. 50 Niuafo'ou 1983 10 s. map definitive 2·25 3·00

1985. 400th Birth Anniv of Jacob Le Maire (discoverer of Niuafo'ou).

51 **9** 13 s. brown, yellow & orange 25 40
52 – 32 s. brown, yellow and blue 55 60
53 – 47 s. brown, yellow and green 75 80
54 – 1 p. 50 brown, cinnamon and yellow 2·25 3·00

DESIGNS: 32 s. Tongans preparing kava; 47 s. Tongan canoes and outriggers; 1 p. 50, "Eendracht" at anchor off Tafahi Island.

10 "Ysabel", 1902

1985. Mail Ships. Multicoloured.

56B 9 s. Type **10** 35 55
57A 13 s. "Tofua I", 1908 70 55
58B 47 s. "Mariposa", 1934 1·10 1·60
59B 1 p. 50 "Matua", 1936 2·50 4·00

11 Preparing to fire Rocket

1985. Niuafo'ou Rocket Mails. Multicoloured.

60B 32 s. Type **11** 1·00 80
61A 42 s. Rocket in flight 1·25 1·00
62B 57 s. Ship's crew watching rocket's descent 1·60 1·40
63A 1 p. 50 Islanders reading mail 3·50 4·50

12 Halley's Comet, 684 A.D.

1986. Appearance of Halley's Comet. Multicoloured.

64 42 s. Type **12** 5·00 3·00
65 42 s. Halley's Comet, 1066, from Bayeux Tapestry 5·00 3·00
66 42 s. Edmond Halley 5·00 3·00
67 42 s. Halley's Comet, 1910 5·00 3·00
68 42 s. Halley's Comet, 1986 5·00 3·00
69 57 s. Type **12** 5·00 3·50
70 57 s. As No. 65 5·00 3·50
71 57 s. As No. 66 5·00 3·50
72 57 s. As No. 67 5·00 3·50
73 57 s. As No. 68 5·00 3·50

Nos. 64/8 and 69/73 were printed together, se-tenant, forming composite designs.

1986. Nos. 32/9 surch.

74 4 s. on 9 s. Green honeyeater 75 1·25
75 4 s. on 10 s. Purple swamphen 75 1·25
76 42 s. on 13 s. Banded rail 2·00 1·50
77 42 s. on 15 s. Polynesian scrub hen 2·00 1·50
78 57 s. on 29 s. Red-headed parrot finch 2·50 2·00
79 57 s. on 32 s. White-collared kingfisher 2·50 2·00
80 2 p. 50 on 20 s. Banded rail 7·00 8·00
81 2 p. 50 on 47 s. Polynesian scrub hen 7·00 8·00

13a Peace Corps Surveyor and Pipeline

1986. "Ameripex '86" International Stamp Exhibition, Chicago. 25th Anniv of United States Peace Corps. Multicoloured.

82 57 s. Type **13a** 1·25 1·25
83 1 p. 50 Inspecting crops 2·25 2·75

14 Swimmers with Mail

1986. Centenary of First Tonga Stamps. Designs showing Niuafo'ou mail transport. Multicoloured.

85 42 s. Type **14** 90 90
86 57 s. Collecting tin can mail 1·10 1·10
87 1 p. Ship firing mail rocket 2·00 2·50
88 2 p. 50 "Collecting the Mails" (detail) (C. Mayger) 3·50 4·50

15 Woman with Nourishing Foods ("Eat a balanced diet")

1987. Red Cross. Preventive Medicine. Mult.

90 15 s. Type **15** 60 60
91 42 s. Nurse with baby ("Give them post-natal care") 1·60 1·60
92 1 p. Man with insecticide ("Insects spread disease") 2·50 3·00
93 2 p. 50 Boxer ("Say no to alcohol, drugs, tobacco") 4·00 4·75

16 Hammerhead

1987. Sharks. Multicoloured.

94 29 s. Type **16** 2·00 1·75
95 32 s. Tiger shark 2·00 1·75
96 47 s. Grey nurse shark 2·50 2·25
97 1 p. Great white shark 4·00 5·50

17 Capt. E. C. Musick and Sikorsky S.42A Flying Boat "Samoan Clipper"

1987. Air Pioneers of the South Pacific. Multicoloured.

99 42 s. Type **17** 1·40 1·40
100 57 s. Capt. J. W. Burgess and Short S.30 modified "G" Class flying boat "Aotearoa" 1·75 1·75
101 1 p. 50 Sir Charles Kingsford Smith and Fokker F.VIIa/3m "Southern Cross" 2·50 3·00
102 2 p. Amelia Earhart and Lockheed 10E Electra 3·00 3·50

18 Polynesian Scrub Hen and 1983 1 s. Map Definitive

1988. 5th Annivs of First Niuafo'ou Postage Stamp (42, 57 s.) and Niuafo'ou Airport Inauguration (1, 2 p.). Multicoloured.

103 42 s. Type **18** 80 75
104 57 s. As Type **18**, but with stamp at left 1·00 95
105 1 p. Concorde and 1983 Airport Inauguration 29 s. stamp 3·00 3·00
106 2 p. As 1 p. but with stamp at left 3·50 3·75

20 Audubon's Shearwaters and Blowholes, Houma, Tonga **23** Formation of Earth's Surface

22 Spiny Hatchetfish

1988. Islands of Polynesia. Multicoloured.

108 42 s. Type **20** 95 95
109 57 s. Brown kiwi at Akaroa Harbour, New Zealand 1·40 1·40
110 90 s. Red-tailed tropic birds at Rainmaker Mountain, Samoa 2·00 2·25
111 2 p. 50 Laysan albatross at Kapoho Volcano, Hawaii 4·50 5·50

1989. Fishes of the Deep. Multicoloured.

113 32 s. Type **22** 85 1·00
114 42 s. Snipe eel 1·00 1·00
115 57 s. Viperfish 1·25 1·50
116 1 p. 50 Football anglerfish 3·00 3·75

1989. The Evolution of the Earth. Multicoloured. (a) Size $27 \times 35\frac{1}{2}$ mm.

117 1 s. Type **23** 10 10
118 2 s. Cross-section of Earth's crust 10 10
119 5 s. Volcano 10 10
120 10 s. Cross-section of Earth during cooling 10 10
120a 13 s. Gem stones 10 15
121 15 s. Sea 10 15
122 20 s. Mountains 15 20
123 32 s. River gorge 25 30
124 42 s. Early plant life, Silurian era 30 35
124a 45 s. Early marine life 35 40
125 50 s. Fossils and Cambrian lifeforms 40 45
126 57 s. Carboniferous forest and coal seams 45 50
126a 60 s. Dinosaurs feeding 45 50
126b 80 s. Tyrannosaurus and triceratops fighting 60 65

(b) Size $25\frac{1}{2} \times 40$ mm

127 1 p. Dragonfly and amphibians, Carboniferous era 80 85
128 1 p. 50 Dinosaurs, Jurassic era 1·10 1·25
129 2 p. Archaeopteryx and mammals, Jurassic era 1·60 1·75
130 5 p. Human family and domesticated dog, Pleistocene era 4·00 4·25
130a 10 p. Mammoth and sabre-tooth tiger 7·75 8·00

24 Astronaut on Moon and Newspaper Headline

1989. "World Stamp Expo '89" International Stamp Exhibition, Washington.

131 **24** 57 s. multicoloured 1·00 1·00

25 Lake Vai Lahi

1990. Niuafo'ou Crater Lake. Multicoloured.
133 42 s. Type **25** . . . 70 90
134 42 s. Islands in centre of lake . . . 70 90
135 42 s. South-west end of lake and islet . . . 70 90
136 1 p. Type **25** . . . 1·40 1·50
137 1 p. As No. 134 . . . 1·40 1·50
138 1 p. As No. 135 . . . 1·40 1·50
Nos. 133/8 were printed together in se-tenant strips of each value, forming a composite design.

26 Penny Black and Tin Can Mail Service

1990. 150th Anniv of the Penny Black. Mult.
139 42 s. Type **26** . . . 80 80
140 57 s. U.S.A. 1847 10 c. stamp . . . 1·10 1·25
141 75 s. Western Australia 1854 1d. stamp . . . 1·25 1·50
142 2 p. 50 Mafeking Siege 1900 1d. stamp . . . 4·00 4·75

27 Humpback Whale surfacing

1990. Polynesian Whaling. Multicoloured.
143 15 s. Type **27** . . . 1·75 1·60
144 42 s. Whale diving under canoe . . . 2·25 1·90
145 57 s. Tail of Blue whale . . . 2·50 1·90
146 2 p. Old man and pair of whales . . . 6·50 7·50

27a Agriculture and Fisheries

1990. 40th Anniv of U.N. Development Programme. Multicoloured.
148 57 s. Type **27a** . . . 90 1·25
149 57 s. Education . . . 90 1·25
150 2 p. 50 Healthcare . . . 3·25 3·75
151 2 p. 50 Communications . . . 3·25 3·75

28 H.M.S. "Bounty" **30** Longhorned Beetle Grub

1991. Bicentenary of Charting of Niuafo'ou. Multicoloured.
152 32 s. Type **28** . . . 1·00 1·50
153 42 s. Chart of "Pandora's" course . . . 1·10 1·50
154 57 s. H.M.S. "Pandora" (frigate) 1·25 1·50

1991. Longhorned Beetle. Multicoloured.
157 42 s. Type **30** . . . 80 80
158 57 s. Adult beetle . . . 90 90
159 1 p. 50 Grub burrowing . . . 2·75 3·00
160 2 p. 50 Adult on tree trunk . . . 4·00 4·25

31 Heina meeting the Eel

1991. Christmas. The Legend of the Coconut Tree. Multicoloured.
161 15 s. Type **31** . . . 35 40
162 42 s. Heina crying over the eel's grave . . . 90 1·00

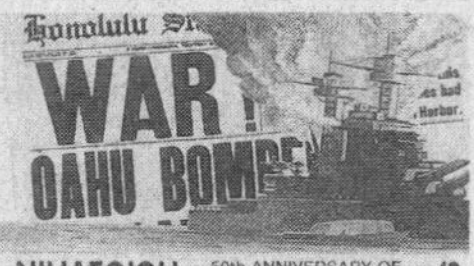

31a American Battleship Ablaze, Pearl Harbour

1992. 50th Anniv of War in the Pacific. Multicoloured.
165 42 s. Type **31a** . . . 1·10 1·25
166 42 s. Destroyed American Douglas B-18 Bolo aircraft, Hawaii . . . 1·10 1·25
167 42 s. Newspaper and Japanese Mitsubishi A6M Zero-Sen fighter . . . 1·10 1·25
168 42 s. Pres. Roosevelt signing Declaration of War . . . 1·10 1·25
169 42 s. Japanese T 95 light tank and Gen. MacArthur . . . 1·10 1·25
170 42 s. Douglas SBD Dauntless dive bomber and Admiral Nimitz . . . 1·10 1·25
171 42 s. Bren gun and Gen. Sir Thomas Blamey . . . 1·10 1·25
172 42 s. Australian mortar crew, Kokoda . . . 1·10 1·25
173 42 s. U.S.S. "Mississippi" in action and Maj. Gen. Julian C. Smith . . . 1·10 1·25
174 42 s. U.S.S. "Enterprise" (aircraft carrier) . . . 1·10 1·25
175 42 s. American marine and Maj. Gen. Curtis Lemay . . . 1·10 1·25
176 42 s. Boeing B-29 Superfortress bomber and Japanese surrender, Tokyo Bay . . . 1·10 1·25
Nos. 165/76 were printed together, se-tenant, forming a composite design.

31b King Taufa'ahau Tupou IV and Queen Halaevalu During Coronation

1992. 25th Anniv of the Coronation of King Tupou IV.
177 45 s. multicoloured . . . 75 75
178 80 s. multicoloured . . . 1·50 1·75
179 80 s. black and brown . . . 1·50 1·75
180 80 s. multicoloured . . . 1·50 1·75
181 2 p. multicoloured . . . 2·50 3·00
DESIGNS—(34 × 23 mm): No. 177, Type **31b**. (48 × 35 mm): No. 178, King Tupou IV and Tongan national anthem; 179, Extract from Investiture ceremony; 180, Tongan choir; 181, As 45 s.

32 Male and Female Scrub Hens searching for Food

1992. Endangered Species. Polynesian Scrub Hen. Multicoloured.
182 45 s. Type **32** . . . 1·00 1·25
183 60 s. Female guarding egg . . . 1·25 1·40
184 80 s. Chick . . . 1·60 1·75
185 1 p. 50 Head of male . . . 2·75 3·50

33 1983 2 s. Map Definitive and 1993 60 s. Dinosaur Definitive

1993. 10th Anniv of First Niuafo'ou Stamp. Multicoloured.
186 60 s. Type **33** . . . 1·00 1·10
187 80 s. 1983 5 s. definitive and 1993 80 s. dinosaurs definitive . . . 1·25 1·40

34 De Havilland Twin Otter 200/300 of South Pacific Island Airways **34a** King Tupou IV and "Pangai" (patrol boat)

1993. 10th Anniv of First Flight to Niuafo'ou. Multicoloured.
188 1 p. Type **34** . . . 1·50 2·00
189 2 p. 50 De Havilland Twin Otter 200/300 of Friendly Islands Airways . . . 3·50 4·25

1993. 75th Birthday of King Taufa'ahau Tupou IV. Multicoloured.
190 45 s. Type **34a** . . . 55 55
191 80 s. King Tupou IV and musical instruments (38½ × 51 mm) . . . 1·25 1·75
192 80 s. King Tupou IV and sporting events (38½ × 51 mm) . . . 1·25 1·75
193 80 s. King Tupou IV with De Havilland Twin Otter 200/300 airplane and telecommunications . . . 1·25 1·75
194 2 p. As 45 s. but larger (38½ × 51 mm) . . . 2·75 3·00

35 Blue-crowned Lorikeets **35a** "Crater Lake Megapode and Volcano" (Paea Puletau)

1993. Natural History of Lake Vai Lahi. Multicoloured.
195 60 s. Type **35** . . . 1·00 1·25
196 60 s. White-tailed tropic bird and eastern reef heron . . . 1·00 1·25
197 60 s. Black admiral (butterfly) and Niuafo'ou coconut beetle . . . 1·00 1·25
198 60 s. Niuafo'ou dragonfly, spotbill ducks and Niuafo'ou moths . . . 1·00 1·25
199 60 s. Niuafo'ou megapode . . . 1·00 1·25
Nos. 195/9 were printed together, se-tenant, forming a composite design.

1993. Children's Painting Competition Winners.
200 10 s. multicoloured . . . 40 55
201 10 s. black and grey . . . 40 55
202 1 p. multicoloured . . . 2·75 3·00
203 1 p. multicoloured . . . 2·75 3·00
DESIGNS: Nos. 200 and 202, Type **35a**; Nos. 201 and 203, "Ofato Beetle Grubs of Niuafo'ou" (Peni Finau).

36 "Scarabaeidea"

1994. Beetles. Multicoloured.
204 60 s. Type **36** . . . 85 1·00
205 80 s. "Coccinellidea" . . . 1·10 1·40
206 1 p. 50 "Cerambycidea" . . . 2·00 2·50
207 2 p. 50 "Pentatomidae" . . . 3·75 4·25

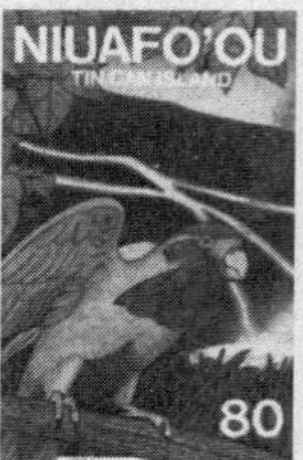

37 Stern of H.M.S. "Bounty" **38** Blue-crowned Lory and Lava Flows

1994. Sailing Ships. Multicoloured.
208 80 s. Type **37** . . . 1·75 2·00
209 80 s. Bow of H.M.S. "Bounty" . . . 1·75 2·00
210 80 s. H.M.S. "Pandora" (frigate) . . . 1·75 2·00
211 80 s. Whaling ship . . . 1·75 2·00
212 80 s. Trading schooner . . . 1·75 2·00

1994. Volcanic Eruptions on Niuafo'ou. Multicoloured.
213 80 s. Type **38** . . . 1·25 1·50
214 80 s. Spotbill ducks over lava flows . . . 1·25 1·50
215 80 s. Megapodes and palm trees . . . 1·25 1·50
216 80 s. White-tailed tropic birds and inhabitants . . . 1·25 1·50
217 80 s. Eastern heron and evacuation, 1946 . . . 1·25 1·50
Nos. 213/17 were printed together, se-tenant, forming a composite design.

1995. Visit South Pacific Year '95. Save the Whales. Nos. 143/6 surch **SAVE THE WHALES VISIT SOUTH PACIFIC YEAR '95**, emblem and value.
218 60 s. on 42 s. Whale diving under canoe . . . 1·75 1·75
219 80 s. on 15 s. Type **27** . . . 2·00 2·00
220 80 s. on 57 s. Tail of blue whale . . . 2·00 2·00
221 2 p. on 2 p. Old man and pair of whales . . . 3·75 3·75

39a American Marine

1995. 50th Anniv of End of World War II in the Pacific.
223 60 s. yellow, black and blue . . . 1·25 1·25
224 60 s. yellow, black and blue . . . 1·25 1·25
225 60 s. yellow, black and blue . . . 1·25 1·25
226 60 s. yellow, black and blue . . . 1·25 1·25
227 60 s. yellow, black and blue . . . 1·25 1·25
228 80 s. yellow, black and red . . . 1·25 1·25
229 80 s. yellow, black and red . . . 1·25 1·25
230 80 s. yellow, black and red . . . 1·25 1·25
231 80 s. yellow, black and red . . . 1·25 1·25
232 80 s. yellow, black and red . . . 1·25 1·25
DESIGNS: Nos. 223 and 228, Type **39a**; 224 and 229, Marine firing and side of tank; 225 and 230, Tank; 226 and 231, Marines leaving landing craft; 227 and 232, Beach assault and palm trees.
Nos. 223/32 were printed together, se-tenant, forming two composite designs.

39b Dinosaurs Feeding

1995. "Singapore '95" International Stamp Exhibitions. Designs showing exhibition emblem. Multicoloured.
233 45 s. Type **39b** (as No. 126a) . . . 1·00 1·25
234 60 s. Tyrannosaurus fighting Triceratops (as No. 126b) . . . 1·00 1·25

39c St. Paul's Cathedral and Searchlights

1995. 50th Anniv of United Nations and End of Second World War.
237 60 s. multicoloured . . . 1·00 1·25
238 60 s. black and blue . . . 1·00 1·25
239 60 s. multicoloured . . . 1·00 1·25
240 80 s. multicoloured . . . 1·25 1·40
241 80 s. blue and black . . . 1·25 1·40
242 80 s. multicoloured . . . 1·25 1·40
DESIGNS—No. 237, St. Paul's Cathedral and searchlights; 239, Concorde; 240, Allied prisoners of war and Burma Railway; 242, Mt. Fuji and express train. 25 × 35 mm: Nos. 238 and 241, U.N. anniversary emblem.

40 Charles Ramsay and Swimmers with Poles

1996. Tin Can Mail Pioneers. Multicoloured.
243 45 s. Type **40** . . . 90 90
244 60 s. Charles Ramsay and encounter with shark . . . 1·25 1·25
245 1 p. Walter Quensell and transferring mail from canoes to ship . . . 2·00 2·00
246 3 p. Walter Quensell and Tin Can Mail cancellations . . . 6·00 6·00

40a Cane Painting, Lake Village and Hunter

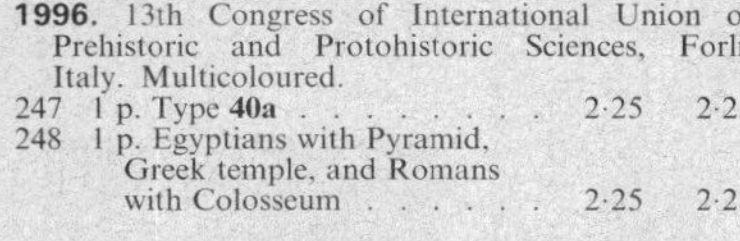

1996. 13th Congress of International Union of Prehistoric and Protohistoric Sciences, Forli, Italy. Multicoloured.

247 1 p. Type **40a** . . . . 2·25 2·25
248 1 p. Egyptians with Pyramid, Greek temple, and Romans with Colosseum . . . . . . 2·25 2·25

40b Dolls, Model Truck and Counting Balls

41 Island and Two Canoes

1996. 50th Anniv of U.N.I.C.E.F. Children's Toys. Multicoloured.

249 80 s. Type **40b** . . . . 1·25 1·50
250 80 s. Teddy bear, tricycle and model car . . . . 1·25 1·50
251 80 s. Book, model helicopter, pedal car and roller skates . 1·25 1·50

Nos. 249/51 were printed together, se-tenant, forming a composite design.

1996. 50th Anniv of Evacuation of Niuafo'ou. Multicoloured.

252 45 s. Type **41** 85 90
253 45 s. Erupting volcano and canoes 85 90
254 45 s. End of island, volcanic cloud and canoe 85 90
255 45 s. Family and livestock in outrigger canoe 70 75
256 45 s. Islanders reaching "Matua" (inter-island freighter) . . . 85 90
257 60 s. Type **41** . . . . 95 1·00
258 60 s. As No. 253 . . . . . . 95 1·00
259 60 s. As No. 254 . . . . . . 95 1·00
260 60 s. As No. 255 . . . . . . 95 1·00
261 60 s. As No. 256 . . . . . . 95 1·00

Nos. 252/6 and 257/61 respectively were printed together, se-tenant, forming the same composite design.

42 Plankton

1997. The Ocean Environment.

262 **42** 60 s. multicoloured . . . . 1·00 1·00
263 – 80 s. multicoloured . . . . 1·25 1·25
264 – 1 p. 50 multicoloured . . . 2·25 2·50
265 – 2 p. 50 multicoloured . . . 3·00 3·50

DESIGNS: 80 s. to 2 p. 50, Different plankton.

42a King and Queen on Wedding Day

1997. King and Queen of Tonga's Golden Wedding and 30th Anniv of Coronation. Multicoloured.

267 80 s. Type **42a** . . . . 1·25 1·50
268 80 s. King Tupou in Coronation robes . . . . 1·25 1·50

43 Blue-crowned Lory Nestlings

43a King Taufa'ahau Tupou IV

1998. Endangered Species. Blue-crowned Lory. Multicoloured.

270 10 s. Type **43** 50 50
271 55 s. Feeding on flowers . . . 1·00 85
272 80 s. Perched on branch . . . 1·25 1·00
273 3 p. Pair on branch . . . . . 4·00 4·50

1998. 80th Birthday of King Taufa'ahau Tupou IV.

276 **43a** 2p.70 multicoloured . . . . 2·50 3·00

43b "Amphiprion melanopus"

1998. International Year of the Ocean. Multicoloured.

278 10 s. Type **43b** 40 50
279 55 s. "Amphiprion perideraion" 80 90
280 80 s. "Amphiprion chrysopterus" 1·00 1·10

43c Angel playing lute (inscr in Tongan)

1998. Christmas. Multicoloured.

281 20 s. Type **43c** 40 40
282 55 s. Angel playing violin (inscr in English) 75 55
283 1 p. Children and bells (inscr in Tongan) . . . . 1·10 1·10
284 1 p. 60 Children and candles (inscr in English) . . . . . 1·50 2·00

44 "Eendracht" (Le Maire)

1999. Early Explorers. Multicoloured.

286 80 s. Type **44** . . . . 1·000 90
287 2 p. 70 Tongiaki (outrigger canoe) . . . . 2·50 2·75

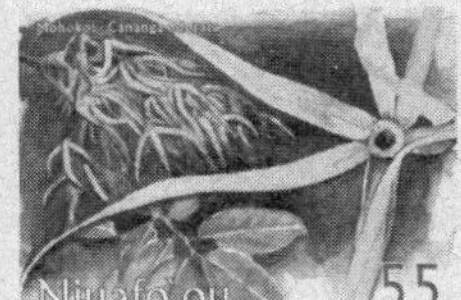

46a "Cananga odorata"

1999. Fragrant Flowers. Multicoloured.

289 55 s. Type **46a** 65 50
290 80 s. "Gardenia tannaensis" (vert) 85 80
291 1 p. "Coleus amboinicus" (vert) 1·10 1·10
292 2 p. 50 "Hernandia moerenhoutiana" . . . . 2·50 2·75

NIUE Pt. 1

One of the Cook Is. group in the S. Pacific. A dependency of New Zealand, the island achieved local self-government in 1974.

1902. 12 pence = 1 shilling;
20 shillings = 1 pound.
1967 100 cents = 1 dollar.

1902. T **42** of New Zealand optd **NIUE** only.

1	**42**	1d. red	£300	£300

Stamps of New Zealand surch **NIUE.** and value in native language.

1902. Pictorials of 1898 etc.

8	**23**	½d. green	75	80
9	**42**	1d. red	50	70
2	**26**	2½d. blue (B)	1·25	4·00
13	**28**	3d. brown	9·50	5·00
14	**31**	6d. red	12·00	11·00
16	**34**	1s. orange	35·00	35·00

1911. King Edward VII stamps.

17	**51**	½d. green	45	40
18		6d. red	2·00	7·00
19		1s. orange	6·50	45·00

1917. Dominion and King George V stamps.

21	**53**	1d. red	8·50	5·50
22	**62**	3d. brown	48·00	80·00

1917. Stamps of New Zealand (King George V, etc) optd **NIUE.** only.

23	**62**	½d. green	70	2·25
24	**53**	1d. red	8·00	7·50
25	**62**	1½d. grey	9·00	2·25
26		1½d. brown	70	3·75
28a		2½d. blue	1·25	4·00
29a		3d. brown	1·25	1·50
30a		6d. red	4·75	21·00
31a		1s. orange	5·50	21·00

1918. Stamps of New Zealand optd **NIUE.**

33	F **4**	2s. blue	15·00	32·00
34		2s. 6d. brown	21·00	48·00
35		5s. green	25·00	50·00
36		10s. red	90·00	£100
37		£1 red	£130	£160

1920. Pictorial types as Cook Islands (1920), but inscr "NIUE".

38	**9**	½d. black and green	3·75	3·75
45	–	1d. black and red	1·75	75
40	–	1½d. black and red	2·50	6·50
46	–	2½d. black and blue	4·25	11·00
41	–	3d. black and blue	60	12·00
47	**7**	4d. black and violet	7·00	17·00
42	–	6d. brown and green	1·75	18·00
43	–	1s. black and brown	1·75	18·00

1927. Admiral type of New Zealand optd **NIUE.**

49	**71**	2s. blue	18·00	32·00

1931. No. 40 surch **TWO PENCE.**

50	2d. on 1½d. black and red	2·25	1·00

1931. Stamps of New Zealand (Arms types) optd **NIUE.**

83	F **6**	2s. 6d. brown	3·50	9·00
84		5s. green	7·50	11·00
53		10s. red	35·00	85·00
86		£1 pink	42·00	55·00

1932. Pictorial stamps as Cook Islands (1932) but inscr additionally "NIUE".

89	**20**	½d. black and green	50	1·75
90	–	1d. black and red	50	80
64	**22**	2d. black and brown	40	1·25
92	–	2½d. black and blue	60	95
66	–	4d. black and blue	1·75	2·75
67	–	6d. black and orange	70	75
61	–	1s. black and violet	2·25	5·00

1935. Silver Jubilee. As Nos. 63, 92 and 67, with colours changed, optd **SILVER JUBILEE OF KING GEORGE V. 1910–1935.**

69	1d. red	60	3·00
70	2½d. blue	3·25	6·00
71	6d. green and orange	3·25	6·00

1937. Coronation. New Zealand stamps optd **NIUE.**

72	**106**	1d. red	30	10
73		2½d. blue	40	50
74		6d. orange	40	20

1938. As 1938 issue of Cook Islands, but inscr "NIUE COOK ISLANDS".

95	**29**	1s. black and violet	1·25	85
96	**30**	2s. black and brown	8·50	2·75
97	–	3s. blue and green	15·00	7·00

1940. As No. 132 of Cook Islands but inscr "NIUE COOK ISLANDS".

78	**32**	3d. on 1½d. black and purple	50	20

1946. Peace. New Zealand stamps optd **NIUE** (twice on 2d.).

98	**132**	1d. green	20	10
99	–	2d. purple (No. 670)	20	10
100	–	6d. brown & red (No. 674)	20	40
101	**139**	8d. black and red	30	40

18 Map of Niue

19 H.M.S. "Resolution"

1950.

113	**18**	½d. orange and blue	10	50
114	**19**	1d. brown and green	2·25	1·50
115	–	2d. black and red	60	60
116	–	3d. blue and violet	10	15
117	–	4d. olive and purple	10	15
118	–	6d. green and orange	60	60
119	–	9d. orange and brown	10	60
120	–	1s. purple and black	10	15
121	–	2s. brown and green	1·00	3·75
122	–	3s. blue and black	4·50	4·00

DESIGNS—HORIZ: 2d. Alofi landing; 3d. Native hut; 4d. Arch at Hikutavake; 6d. Alofi bay; 1s. Cave, Makefu. VERT: 9d. Spearing fish; 2s. Bananas; 3s. Matapa Chasm.

1953. Coronation. As Types of New Zealand but inscr "NIUE".

123	**164**	3d. brown	65	40
124	**168**	6d. grey	95	40

26

27 "Pua"

1967. Decimal Currency. (a) Nos. 113/22 surch.

125	**17**	½ c. on ½d.	10	10
126	**18**	1 c. on 1d.	1·10	15
127	–	2 c. on 2d.	10	10
128	–	2½ c. on 3d.	10	10
129	–	3 c. on 4d.	10	10
130	–	5 c. on 6d.	10	10
131	–	8 c. on 9d.	10	10
132	–	10 c. on 1s.	10	10
133	–	20 c. on 2s.	35	1·00
134	–	30 c. on 3s.	65	1·50

(b) Arms type of New Zealand without value, surch as in T **26**.

135	**26**	25 c. brown	40	55
136		50 c. green	70	80
137		$1 mauve	45	1·25
138		$2 pink	70	2·00

1967. Christmas. As T **278** of New Zealand but inscr "NIUE".

139	2½ c. multicoloured	10	10

1969. Christmas. As No. 905 of New Zealand but inscr "NIUE".

140	2½ c. multicoloured	10	10

1969. Flowers. Multicoloured; frame colours given.

141	**27**	½ c. green	10	10
142	–	1 c. red	10	10
143	–	2 c. olive	10	10
144	–	2½ c. brown	10	10
145	–	3 c. blue	10	10
146	–	5 c. red	10	10
147	–	8 c. violet	10	10
148	–	10 c. yellow	10	10
149	–	20 c. blue	75	1·25
150	–	30 c. green	1·50	1·75

DESIGNS: 1 c. "Golden Shower"; 2 c. Flamboyant; 2½ c. Frangipani; 3 c. Niue crocus; 5 c. Hibiscus; 8 c. "Passion Fruit"; 10 c. "Kampui"; 20 c. Queen Elizabeth II (after Anthony Buckley); 30 c. Tapeu orchid.

For 20 c. design as 5 c. see No. 801.

37 Kalahimu

1970. Indigenous Edible Crabs. Mult.

151	3 c. Type **37**	10	10
152	5 c. Kalavi	10	10
153	30 c. Unga	30	25

1970. Christmas. As T **314** of New Zealand, but inscr "NIUE".

154	2½ c. multicoloured	10	10

38 Outrigger Canoe, and Fokker F.27 Friendship over Jungle

1970. Opening of Niue Airport. Multicoloured.

155	3 c. Type **38**	10	15
156	5 c. "Tofua II" (cargo liner) and Fokker F.27 Friendship over harbour	15	15
157	8 c. Fokker F.27 Friendship over airport	15	20

39 Spotted Triller

1971. Birds. Multicoloured.

158	5 c. Type **39**	15	20
159	10 c. Purple-capped fruit dove	70	20
160	20 c. Blue-crowned lory	80	20

1971. Christmas. As T **325** of New Zealand, but inscr "Niue".

161	3 c. multicoloured	10	10

40 Niuean Boy

41 Octopus Lure

1971. Niuean Portraits. Multicoloured.

162	4 c. Type **40**	10	10
163	6 c. Girl with garland	10	15
164	9 c. Man	10	35
165	14 c. Woman with garland	15	60

1972. South Pacific Arts Festival, Fiji. Multicoloured.

166	3 c. Type **41**	10	10
167	5 c. War weapons	15	15
168	10 c. Sika throwing (horiz)	20	15
169	25 c. Vivi dance (horiz)	30	25

42 Alofi Wharf

1972. 25th Anniversary of South Pacific Commission. Multicoloured.

170	4 c. Type **42**	10	10
171	5 c. Medical services	15	10
172	6 c. Schoolchildren	15	10
173	18 c. Dairy cattle	25	20

1972. Christmas. As T **332** of New Zealand, but inscr "NIUE".

174	3 c. multicoloured	10	10

43 Silver Sweeper

1973. Fishes. Multicoloured.

175	8 c. Type **43**	25	25
176	10 c. Peacock hind ("Loi")	30	30
177	15 c. Yellow-edged lyretail ("Malau")	40	40
178	20 c. Ruby snapper ("Palu")	45	45

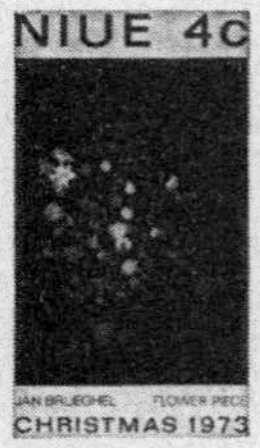

44 "Large Flower Piece" (Jan Brueghel)

46 King Fataaiki

45 Capt. Cook and Bowsprit

1973. Christmas. Flower studies by the artists listed. Multicoloured.

179	4 c. Type **44**	10	10
180	5 c. Bollongier	10	10
181	10 c. Ruysch	20	20

1974. Bicent of Capt. Cook's Visit. Mult.

182	2 c. Type **45**	20	20
183	3 c. Niue landing place	20	20
184	8 c. Map of Niue	20	30
185	20 c. Ensign of 1774 and Administration Building	30	65

1974. Self-Government. Multicoloured.

186	4 c. Type **46**	10	10
187	8 c. Annexation Ceremony, 1900	10	10
188	10 c. Legislative Assembly Chambers (horiz)	10	10
189	20 c. Village meeting (horiz)	15	15

47 Decorated Bicycles

48 Children going to Church

1974. Christmas. Multicoloured.

190	3 c. Type **47**	10	10
191	10 c. Decorated motorcycle	10	10
192	20 c. Motor transport to church	20	30

1975. Christmas. Multicoloured.

193	4 c. Type **48**	10	10
194	5 c. Child with balloons on bicycle	10	10
195	10 c. Balloons and gifts on tree	20	20

49 Hotel Buildings

1975. Opening of Tourist Hotel. Mult.

196	8 c. Type **49**	10	10
197	20 c. Ground-plan and buildings	20	20

50 Preparing Ground for Taro

1976. Food Gathering. Multicoloured.

198	1 c. Type **50**	10	10
199	2 c. Planting taro	10	10
200	3 c. Banana gathering	10	10
201	4 c. Harvesting taro	10	10
202	5 c. Gathering shell fish	30	10
203	10 c. Reef fishing	20	10
204	20 c. Luku gathering	20	15
205	50 c. Canoe fishing	30	60
206	$1 Coconut husking	35	80
207	$2 Uga gathering	60	1·40

See also Nos. 249/58 and 264/73.

51 Water

1976. Utilities. Multicoloured.

208	10 c. Type **51**	10	10
209	15 c. Telecommunications	15	15
210	20 c. Power	15	15

52 Christmas Tree, Alofi

1976. Christmas. Multicoloured.

211	9 c. Type **52**	15	15
212	15 c. Church service, Avatele	15	15

53 Queen Elizabeth II and Westminster Abbey

1977. Silver Jubilee. Multicoloured.

213	$1 Type **53**	60	50
214	$2 Coronation regalia	80	75

54 Child Care

1977. Personal Services. Multicoloured.
216 10 c. Type **54** 15 10
217 15 c. School dental clinic 20 20
218 20 c. Care of the aged 20 20

55 "The Annunciation" 58 "The Deposition of Christ" (Caravaggio)

57 "An Island View in Atooi"

1977. Christmas. Paintings by Rubens. Multicoloured.
219 10 c. Type **55** 20 10
220 12 c. "Adoration of the Magi" 20 15
221 20 c. "Virgin in a Garland" 35 40
222 35 c. "The Holy Family" 55 90

1977. Nos. 198/207, 214, 216 and 218 surch.
224 12 c. on 1 c. Type **50** 25 25
225 16 c. on 2 c. Planting taro 30 30
226 20 c. on 3 c. Banana gathering 40 40
227 35 c. on 4 c. Harvesting taro 45 45
228 40 c. on 5 c. Gathering shell fish 45 50
229 60 c. on 20 c. Luku gathering 45 55
230 70 c. on $1 Coconut husking 45 55
231 85 c. on $2 Uga gathering 45 60
232 $1.10 on 10 c. Type **22** 45 60
233 $2.60 on 20 c. Care of the aged 50 70
234 $3.20 on $2 Coronation regalia 60 80

1978. Bicent of Discovery of Hawaii. Paintings by John Webber. Multicoloured.
235 12 c. Type **57** 85 40
236 16 c. "A View of Karakaooa, in Owhyhee" 95 50
237 20 c. "An Offering before Capt. Cook in the Sandwich Islands" 1·00 60
238 30 c. "Tereoboo, King of Owhyhee bringing presents to Capt. Cook" 1·10 70
239 35 c. "A Canoe in the Sandwich Islands, the rowers masked" 1·25 80

1978. Easter. Paintings from the Vatican Galleries. Multicoloured.
241 10 c. Type **58** 30 10
242 20 c. "The Burial of Christ" (Bellini) 60 25

59 Flags of Niue and U.K.

1978. 25th Anniv of Coronation. Mult.
245 $1.10 Type **59** 60 90
246 $1.10 Coronation portrait by Cecil Beaton 60 90
247 $1.10 Queen's personal flag for New Zealand 60 90

1978. Designs as Nos. 198/207 but margin colours changed and silver frame.
249 12 c. Type **50** 20 20
250 16 c. Planting taro 20 20
251 30 c. Banana gathering 30 25
252 35 c. Harvesting taro 30 30
253 40 c. Gathering shell fish 30 40
254 60 c. Reef fishing 40 35
255 75 c. Luku gathering 40 40
256 $1.10 Canoe fishing 50 80
257 $3.20 Coconut husking 60 90
258 $4.20 Uga gathering 65 95

60 "Festival of the Rosary"

1978. Christmas. 450th Death Anniv of Durer. Multicoloured.
259 20 c. Type **60** 40 20
260 30 c. "The Nativity" 50 30
261 35 c. "Adoration of the Magi" 60 35

1979. Air. Designs as Nos. 249/58 but gold frames and additionally inscr "AIRMAIL".
264 15 c. Planting taro 20 15
265 20 c. Banana gathering 25 15
266 23 c. Harvesting taro 30 15
267 50 c. Canoe fishing 70 20
268 90 c. Reef fishing 80 35
269 $1.35 Type **50** 80 1·50
270 $2.10 Gathering shell fish 80 1·75
271 $2.60 Luku gathering 80 1·75
272 $5.10 Coconut husking 80 1·75
273 $6.35 Uga gathering 80 1·75

61 "Pieta" (Gregorio Fernandez)

1979. Easter. Paintings. Multicoloured.
274 30 c. Type **61** 30 25
275 35 c. "Burial of Christ" (Pedro Roldan) 35 25

62 "The Nurse and Child" (Franz Hals) 63 Penny Black Stamp

1979. International Year of the Child. Details of Paintings. Multicoloured.
278 16 c. Type **62** 20 15
279 20 c. "Child of the Duke of Osuna" (Goya) 20 20
280 30 c. "Daughter of Robert Strozzi" (Titian) 35 35
281 35 c. "Children eating Fruit" (Murillo) 45 40

1979. Death Cent of Sir Rowland Hill. Mult.
284 20 c. Type **63** 20 15
285 20 c. Sir Rowland Hill and original Bath mail coach 20 15
286 30 c. Basel 1845 2½ r. stamp 30 20
287 30 c. Sir Rowland Hill and Alpine village coach 30 20
288 35 c. U.S.A. 1847 5 c. stamp 35 20
289 35 c. Sir Rowland Hill and "Washington" (first transatlantic U.S.A. mail vessel) 35 20
290 50 c. France 1849 20 c. stamp 40 30
291 50 c. Sir Rowland Hill and French Post Office railway van, 1849 40 30
292 60 c. Bavaria 1849 1 k. stamp 40 30
293 60 c. Sir Rowland Hill and Bavarian coach with mail 40 30
The two versions of each value were issued se-tenant within the sheet, forming composite designs.

64 Cook's Landing at Botany Bay

1979. Death Bicentenary of Captain Cook. Multicoloured.
295 20 c. Type **64** 55 30
296 30 c. Cook's men during a landing on Erromanga 75 40
297 35 c. H.M.S. "Resolution" and H.M.S. "Discovery" in Queen Charlotte's Sound 85 45
298 75 c. Death of Captain Cook, Hawaii 1·50 70

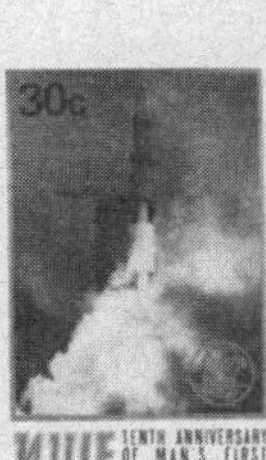

65 Launch of "Apollo 11" 66 "Virgin of Tortosa" (P. Serra)

1979. 10th Anniv of First Manned Moon Landing. Multicoloured.
300 30 c. Type **65** 35 20
301 35 c. Lunar module on Moon 45 25
302 60 c. Sikorsky Sea King helicopter, recovery ship and command module after splashdown 60 40

1979. Christmas. Paintings. Multicoloured.
304 20 c. Type **66** 10 10
305 25 c. "Virgin with Milk" (R. di Mur) 15 15
306 30 c. "Virgin and Child" (S. di G. Sassetta) 20 20
307 50 c. "Virgin and Child" (J. Huguet) 25 25

1980. Hurricane Relief. Surch **HURRICANE RELIEF Plus 2c**. (a) On Nos. 284/93 **HURRICANE RELIEF** spread over each se-tenant pair.
310 **63** 20 c. + 2 c. multicoloured 30 30
311 – 20 c. + 2 c. multicoloured (No. 285) 30 30
312 – 30 c. + 2 c. multicoloured (No. 286) 35 35
313 – 30 c. + 2 c. multicoloured (No. 287) 35 35
314 – 35 c. + 2 c. multicoloured (No. 288) 40 40
315 – 35 c. + 2 c. multicoloured (No. 289) 40 40
316 – 50 c. + 2 c. multicoloured (No. 290) 55 55
317 – 50 c. + 2 c. multicoloured (No. 291) 55 55
318 – 60 c. + 2 c. multicoloured (No. 292) 65 65
319 – 60 c. + 2 c. multicoloured (No. 293) 65 65

(b) On Nos. 295/8.
320 **64** 20 c. + 2 c. multicoloured 40 40
321 – 30 c. + 2 c. multicoloured 50 50
322 – 35 c. + 2 c. multicoloured 55 55
323 – 75 c. + 2 c. multicoloured 1·00 1·00

(c) On Nos. 300/2.
324 **65** 30 c. + 2 c. multicoloured 35 35
325 – 35 c. + 2 c. multicoloured 40 40
326 – 60 c. + 2 c. multicoloured 65 65

(d) On Nos. 304/7.
327 **66** 20 c. + 2 c. multicoloured 25 25
328 – 25 c. + 2 c. multicoloured 30 30
329 – 30 c. + 2 c. multicoloured 35 35
330 – 50 c. + 2 c. multicoloured 55 55

68 "Pieta" (Bellini)

1980. Easter. "Pieta". Paintings. Mult.
331 25 c. Type **68** 30 15
332 30 c. Botticelli 35 20
333 35 c. A. van Dyck 35 20

69 Ceremonial Stool, New Guinea 72 Queen Elizabeth the Queen Mother

1980. South Pacific Festival of Arts, New Guinea. Multicoloured.
336 20 c. Type **69** 10 10
337 20 c. Ku-Tagwa plaque, New Guinea 10 10
338 20 c. Suspension hook, New Guinea 10 10
339 20 c. Ancestral board, New Guinea 10 10
340 25 c. Platform post, New Hebrides 10 10
341 25 c. Canoe ornament, New Ireland 10 10
342 25 c. Carved figure, Admiralty Islands 10 10
343 25 c. Female with child, Admiralty Islands 10 10
344 30 c. The God A'a, Rurutu (Austral Islands) 15 15
345 30 c. Statue of Tangaroa, Cook Islands 15 15
346 30 c. Ivory pendant, Tonga 15 15
347 30 c. Tapa (Hiapo) cloth, Niue 15 15
348 35 c. Feather box (Waka), New Zealand 15 15
349 35 c. Hei-Tiki amulet, New Zealand 15 15
350 35 c. House post, New Zealand 15 15
351 35 c. Feather image of god Ku, Hawaii 15 15

1980. "Zeapex '80" International Stamp Exhibition, Auckland. Nos. 284/93 optd (A) **ZEAPEX'80 AUCKLAND** or (B) **NEW ZEALAND STAMP EXHIBITION** and emblem.
353 **63** 20 c. multicoloured (A) 30 20
354 – 20 c. multicoloured (B) 30 20
355 – 30 c. multicoloured (A) 30 20
356 – 30 c. multicoloured (B) 30 20
357 – 35 c. multicoloured (A) 30 20
358 – 35 c. multicoloured (B) 30 20
359 – 50 c. multicoloured (A) 40 25
360 – 50 c. multicoloured (B) 40 25
361 – 60 c. multicoloured (A) 40 25
362 – 60 c. multicoloured (B) 40 25

1980. 80th Birthday of The Queen Mother.
364 **72** $1.10 multicoloured 80 1·50

73 100 Metre Dash 74 "The Virgin and Child"

1980. Olympic Games, Moscow.
366 **73** 20 c. multicoloured 20 15
367 – 20 c. multicoloured 20 15
368 – 25 c. multicoloured 20 20
369 – 25 c. multicoloured 20 20
370 – 30 c. multicoloured 25 20
371 – 30 c. multicoloured 25 20
372 – 35 c. multicoloured 25 20
373 – 35 c. multicoloured 25 25
DESIGNS: No. 367, Allen Wells, Great Britain (winner 100 metre dash); 368, 400 metre freestyle 369, Ines Diers (winner, D.D.R.); 370, Soling Class; 371, Winner, Denmark; 372, Football; 373, Winner, Czechoslovakia.

Nos. 366/7, 368/9, 370/1 and 372/3 were printed se-tenant in pairs each pair forming a composite design. On the 25 c. and 35 c. stamps the face value is at right on the first design and at left on the second in each pair. For the 30 c. No. 370 has a yacht with a green sail at left and No. 371 a yacht with a red sail.

1980. Christmas. Various Virgin and Child paintings by Andrea del Sarto.
375 **74** 20 c. multicoloured 15 15
376 – 25 c. multicoloured 15 15
377 – 30 c. multicoloured 20 20
378 – 35 c. multicoloured 20 20

75 "Phalaenopsis sp." 77 Prince Charles

76 "Jesus Defiled" (El Greco)

1981. Flowers (1st series). Multicoloured.
381 2 c. Type **75** 10 10
382 2 c. Moth orchid 10 10
383 5 c. "Euphorbia pulcherrima" 10 10
384 5 c. Poinsettia 10 10
385 10 c. "Thunbergia alata" 10 10
386 10 c. Black-eyed Susan 10 10
387 15 c. "Cochlospermum hibiscoides" 15 15
388 15 c. Buttercup tree 15 15
389 20 c. "Begonia sp." 20 20
390 20 c. Begonia 20 20
391 25 c. "Plumeria sp." 25 25
392 25 c. Frangipani 25 25
393 30 c. "Strelitzia reginae" 30 30
394 30 c. Bird of Paradise 30 30
395 35 c. "Hibiscus syriacus" 30 30
396 35 c. Rose of Sharon 30 30
397 40 c. "Nymphaea sp." 35 35
398 40 c. Water lily 35 35
399 50 c. "Tibouchina sp." 45 45
400 50 c. Princess flower 45 45
401 60 c. "Nelumbo sp." 55 55
402 60 c. Lotus 55 55
403 80 c. "Hybrid hibiscus" 75 75
404 80 c. Yellow Hibiscus 75 75
405 $1 Golden shower tree ("cassia fistula") 1·25 1·00
406 $2 "Orchid var" 3·50 2·50
407 $3 "Orchid sp." 4·50 3·50
408 $4 Euphorbia pulcherrima poinsettia" 3·50 4·00
409 $6 "Hybrid hibiscus" 5·50 6·00
410 $10 Scarlet hibiscus ("hibiscus rosa-sinensis") 8·50 9·00
Nos. 405/10 are larger, 47 × 35 mm.
See also Nos. 527/36.

1981. Easter. Details of Paintings. Mult.
425 35 c. Type **76** 40 30
426 50 c. "Pieta" (Fernando Gallego) 60 50
427 60 c. "The Supper of Emmaus" (Jacopo de Pontormo) 65 55

1981. Royal Wedding. Multicoloured.
430 75 c. Type **77** 25 60
431 95 c. Lady Diana Spencer . . . 30 70
432 $1.20 Prince Charles and Lady Diana Spencer 30 80

78 Footballer Silhouettes

1981. World Cup Football Championship, Spain (1982).
434 **78** 30 c. green, gold and blue . 20 20
435 – 30 c. green, gold and blue . 20 20
436 – 30 c. green, gold and blue . 20 20
437 – 35 c. blue, gold & orange . . 20 20
438 – 35 c. blue, gold & orange . . 20 20
439 – 35 c. blue, gold & orange . . 20 20
440 – 40 c. orange, gold & green 20 20
441 – 40 c. orange, gold & green 20 20
442 – 40 c. orange, gold & green 20 20
DESIGNS—Various footballer silhouettes: 435, gold figure 3rd from left; 436, gold figure 4th from left; 437, gold figure 3rd from left; 438, gold figure 4th from left; 439, gold figure 2nd from left; 440, gold figure 3rd from left displaying close control; 441, gold figure 2nd from left; 442, gold figure 3rd from left, heading.

1982. International Year for Disabled Persons. Nos. 430/2 surch **+5c**.
444 75 c. + 5 c. Type **77** 50 85
445 95 c. + 5 c. Lady Diana Spencer 60 1·00
446 $1.20 + 5 c. Prince Charles and Lady Diana . . . . 60 1·25

80 "The Holy Family with Angels" (detail) **81** Prince of Wales

1981. Christmas. 375th Birth Anniv of Rembrandt. Multicoloured.
448 20 c. Type **80** 65 45
449 35 c. "Presentation in the Temple" 85 55
450 50 c. "Virgin and Child in Temple" . . . . 95 1·10
451 60 c. "The Holy Family" . . . 1·25 1·50

1982. 21st Birthday of Princess of Wales. Multicoloured.
454 50 c. Type **81** 40 55
455 $1.25 Prince and Princess of Wales 60 90
456 $2.50 Princess of Wales . . . . 1·50 1·40

1982. Birth of Prince William of Wales (1st issue). Nos. 430/2 optd.
458 75 c. Type **77** . . . . 1·50 2·00
459 75 c. Type **77** . . . . 1·50 2·00
460 95 c. Lady Diana Spencer . . . 2·50 2·50
461 95 c. Lady Diana Spencer . . . 2·50 2·50
462 $1.20 Prince Charles and Lady Diana Spencer . . . . . . 2·50 2·75
463 $1.20 Prince Charles and Lady Diana Spencer . . . . . . 2·50 2·75
OVERPRINTS: Nos. 458, 460 and 462 **COMMEMORATING THE ROYAL BIRTH 21 JUNE 1982**; 459, 461 and 463 **BIRTH OF PRINCE WILLIAM OF WALES 21 JUNE 1982**.

1982. Birth of Prince William of Wales (2nd issue). As Nos. 454/6, but with changed inscriptions. Multicoloured.
465 50 c. Type **81** 45 55
466 $1.25 Prince and Princess of Wales . . . . 85 1·25
467 $2.50 Princess of Wales . . . . 3·00 2·50

83 Infant

1982. Christmas. Paintings of Infants by Bronzion, Murillo and Boucher.
469 **83** 40 c. multicoloured . . . . 1·25 60
470 – 52 c. multicoloured . . . . 1·40 75
471 – 83 c. multicoloured . . . . 2·25 2·00
472 – $1.05 multicoloured . . . . 2·50 2·25

85 Prime Minister Rober Rex

1983. Commonwealth Day. Multicoloured.
475 70 c. Type **85** 50 55
476 70 c. H.M.S. "Resolution" and H.M.S. "Adventure" off Niue, 1774 . . . . 50 55
477 70 c. Passion flower 50 55
478 70 c. Limes 50 55

86 Scouts signalling

1983. 75th Anniv of Boy Scout Movement and 125th Birth Anniv of Lord Baden-Powell. Multicoloured.
479 40 c. Type **86** 35 40
480 50 c. Planting sapling 45 50
481 83 c. Map-reading 85 90

1983. 15th World Scout Jamboree, Alberta, Canada. Nos. 479/81 optd **XV WORLD JAMBOREE CANADA**.
483 40 c. Type **86** 35 40
484 50 c. Planting sapling 45 50
485 83 c. Map-reading 85 90

88 Black Right Whale

1983. Protect the Whales. Multicoloured.
487 12 c. Type **88** 75 65
488 25 c. Fin whale 95 80
489 35 c. Sei whale . . . . 1·50 1·25
490 40 c. Blue whale . . . . 1·75 1·50
491 58 c. Bowhead whale . . . . . 1·90 1·60
492 70 c. Sperm whale . . . . . . 2·25 1·75
493 83 c. Humpback whale . . . . 2·50 2·25
494 $1.05 Minke whale . . . . . . 3·00 2·50
495 $2.50 Grey whale . . . . . . 4·25 4·00

89 Montgolfier Balloon, 1783

1983. Bicentenary of Manned Flight. Mult.
496 25 c. Type **89** 35 25
497 40 c. Wright Brothers Flyer I, 1903 . . . . 80 45
498 58 c. Airship "Graf Zeppelin", 1928 . . . . 1·00 60
499 70 c. Boeing 247, 1933 . . . . 1·40 85
500 83 c. "Apollo 8", 1968 . . . . 1·40 1·00
501 $1.05 Space shuttle "Columbia", 1982 . . . . 1·60 1·40

90 "The Garvagh Madonna" **91** Morse Key Transmitter

1983. Christmas. 500th Birth Anniv of Raphael. Multicoloured.
503 30 c. Type **90** 40 30
504 40 c. "Madonna of the Granduca" 45 35
505 58 c. "Madonna of the Goldfish" 65 50
506 70 c. "The Holy Family of Francis I" 80 60
507 83 c. "The Holy Family with Saints" . . . . 1·00 70

1983. Various stamps surch. (a) Nos. 393/4, 399/404 and 407.
509 52 c. on 30 c. "Strelitzia reginae" . 60 45
510 52 c. on 30 c. Bird of paradise 60 45
511 58 c. on 50 c. "Tibouchina sp." 70 55
512 58 c. on 50 c. Princess flower . 70 55
513 70 c. on 60 c. "Nelumbo sp." . 75 60
514 70 c. on 60 c. Lotus 75 60
515 83 c. on 80 c. "Hybrid hibiscus" 90 75
516 83 c. on 80 c. Yellow hibiscus . 90 75
517 $3.70 on $3 "Orchid sp." . . . 5·00 3·25
(b) Nos. 431/2 and 455/6.
518 $1.10 on 95 c. Lady Diana Spencer . . . . 2·50 2·25
519 $1.10 on $1.25 Prince and Princess of Wales . . . . . 2·00 2·00
520 $2.60 on $1.20 Prince Charles and Lady Diana . . . . 4·00 3·50
521 $2.60 on $2.50 Princess of Wales 2·75 3·25

1984. World Communications Year. Multicoloured.
523 40 c. Type **91** 30 35
524 52 c. Wall-mounted phone . . 40 45
525 83 c. Communications satellite . 60 65

92 "Phalaenopsis sp." **93** Discus throwing

1984. Flowers (2nd series). Multicoloured.
527 12 c. Type **92** 25 15
528 25 c. "Euphorbia pulcherrima" 35 20
529 30 c. "Cochlospermum hibiscoides" 40 25
530 35 c. "Begonia sp." 40 25
531 40 c. "Plumeria sp." 50 30
532 52 c. "Strelitzia reginae" . . . 65 40
533 58 c. "Hibiscus syriacus" . . . 70 45
534 70 c. "Tibouchina sp." . . . . 1·00 60
535 83 c. "Nelumbo sp." . . . . . 1·10 70
536 $1.05 "Hybrid hibiscus" . . . 1·25 85
537 $1.75 "Cassia fistula" . . . . 2·00 1·50
538 $2.30 "Orchid var" . . . . . 3·50 2·00
539 $3.90 "Orchid sp." . . . . . 5·00 4·00
540 $5 "Euphorbia pulcherrima poinsettia" . . . . 6·50 4·50
541 $6.60 "Hybrid hibiscus" . . . 7·00 6·00
542 $8.30 "Hibiscus rosa-sinensis" . 8·00 7·00
Nos. 537/42 are larger, 39 × 31 mm.

1984. Olympic Games, Los Angeles. Multicoloured.
547 30 c. Type **93** 25 30
548 35 c. Sprinting (horiz) 30 35
549 40 c. Horse racing (horiz) . . . 35 40
550 58 c. Boxing (horiz) 50 55
551 70 c. Javelin-throwing 60 65

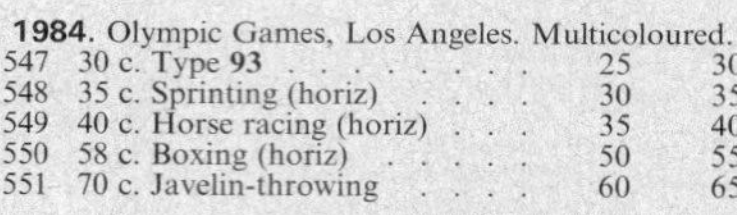

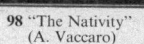

94 Koala **98** "The Nativity" (A. Vaccaro)

96 Niue National Flag and Premier Sir Robert Rex

1984. "Ausipex" International Stamp Exhibition, Melbourne. (a) Designs showing Koala Bears.
552 **94** 25 c. mult (postage) 60 30
553 – 35 c. multicoloured 65 35
554 – 40 c. multicoloured 70 40
555 – 58 c. multicoloured 90 65
556 – 70 c. multicoloured . . . . 1·10 75
(b) Vert designs showing Kangaroos.
557 – 83 c. multicoloured (air) . 1·25 85
558 – $1.05 multicoloured . . . . 1·50 1·25
559 – $2.50 multicoloured . . . . 3·00 3·50

1984. Olympic Gold Medal Winners, Los Angeles. Nos. 547/51 optd.
561 30 c. Type **93** 35 30
562 35 c. Sprinting 40 35
563 40 c. Horse racing 45 35
564 58 c. Boxing 50 50
565 70 c. Javelin-throwing 55 60
OPTS: 30 c. **Discus Throw Rolf Danneberg Germany**; 35 c. **1,500 Metres Sebastian Coe Great Britain**; 40 c. **Equestrian Mark Todd New Zealand**; 58 c. **Boxing Tyrell Biggs United States**; 70 c. **Javelin Throw Arto Haerkoenen Finland**.

1984. 10th Anniv of Self-Government. Mult.
568 40 c. Type **96** 70 35
569 58 c. Map of Niue and Premier Rex 75 50
570 70 c. Premier Rex receiving proclamation of self-government 75 60

1984. Birth of Prince Henry. Nos. 430 and 454 surch **$2 Prince Henry 15. 9. 84**.
573 $2 on 50 c. Type **81** . . . . 2·50 1·75
574 $2 on 75 c. Type **77** . . . . 2·50 1·75

1984. Christmas. Multicoloured.
575 40 c. Type **98** 50 35
576 58 c. "Virgin with Fly" (anon, 16th-century) 65 50
577 70 c. "The Adoration of the Shepherds" (B. Murillo) . . 75 60
578 80 c. "Flight into Egypt" (B. Murillo) 85 70

99 House Wren

1985. Birth Bicentenary of John J. Audubon (ornithologist). Multicoloured.
581 40 c. Type **99** . . . . 2·75 1·00
582 70 c. Veery . . . . 3·00 1·60
583 83 c. Grasshopper sparrow . . 3·25 2·00
584 $1.50 Henslow's sparrow . . . 3·50 2·25
585 $2.50 Vesper sparrow . . . . 5·00 4·25

100 The Queen Mother in Garter Robes

1985. Life and Times of Queen Elizabeth the Queen Mother. Multicoloured.
587 70 c. Type **100** 55 60
588 $1.15 In open carriage with the Queen 80 95
589 $1.50 With Prince Charles during 80th birthday celebrations . . 90 1·25

1985. South Pacific Mini Games, Rarotonga. Nos. 547/8 and 550/1 surch **MINI SOUTH PACIFIC GAMES, RAROTONGA** and emblem.
591 52 c. on 70 c. Javelin throwing 40 45
592 83 c. on 58 c. Boxing 65 70
593 95 c. on 35 c. Sprinting 75 80
594 $2 on 30 c. Type **93** . . . . . 1·50 1·60

1985. Pacific Islands Conference, Rarotonga. Nos. 475/8 optd **PACIFIC ISLANDS CONFERENCE, RAROTONGA** and emblem.
595 70 c. Type **85** 55 60
596 70 c. "Resolution" and "Adventure" off Niue, 1774 . 55 60
597 70 c. Passion flower 55 60
598 70 c. Limes 55 60
Nos. 595 also shows an overprinted amendment to the caption which now reads **Premier Sir Robert Rex K.B.E.**

103 "R. Strozzi's Daughter" (Titian) **104** "Virgin and Child"

1985. International Youth Year. Mult.
599 58 c. Type **103** . . . . 1·25 90
600 70 c. "The Fifer" (E. Manet) . 1·50 1·00
601 $1.15 "Portrait of a Young Girl" (Renoir) . . . . 2·25 1·90
602 $1.50 "Portrait of M. Berard" (Renoir) . . . . 2·50 2·50

1985. Christmas. Details of Paintings by Correggio. Multicoloured.
604 58 c. Type **104** . . . . 1·50 85
605 85 c. "Adoration of the Magi" 1·75 1·40
606 $1.05 "Virgin with Child and St. John" . . . . 2·25 2·50
607 $1.45 "Virgin and Child with St. Catherine" . . . . 2·75 3·50

105 "The Constellations" (detail)

1986. Appearance of Halley's Comet. Designs showing details from ceiling painting "The Constellations" by Giovanni de Vecchi. Nos. 611/13 show different spacecraft at top left. Multicoloured.
610 60 c. Type **105** 50 50
611 75 c. "Vega" spacecraft 65 65
612 $1.10 "Planet A" spacecraft . . 90 90
613 $1.50 "Giotto" spacecraft . . . 1·25 1·25

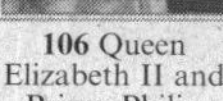

106 Queen Elizabeth II and Prince Philip
107 U.S.A. 1847 Franklin 5 c. Stamp and Washington Sculpture, Mt. Rushmore, U.S.A.

1986. 60th Birthday of Queen Elizabeth II. Multicoloured.
615 $1.10 Type **106** . . . . 80 1·00
616 $1.50 Queen and Prince Philip at Balmoral . . . . 1·00 1·25
617 $2 Queen at Buckingham Palace 1·50 1·75

1986. "Ameripex '86" International Stamp Exhibition, Chicago. Multicoloured.
620 $1 Type **107** . . . . 3·00 3·00
621 $1 Flags of Niue and U.S.A. and Mt. Rushmore sculptures . . 3·00 3·00
Nos. 620/1 were printed together, se-tenant, forming a composite design.

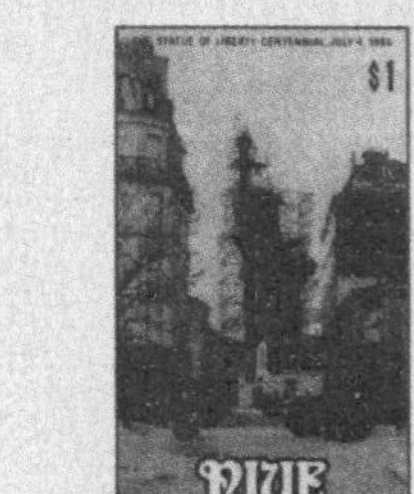

108 "Statue under Construction, Paris, 1883" (Victor Dargaud)

1986. Centenary of Statue of Liberty. Multicoloured.
622 $1 Type **108** . . . . 2·00 2·00
623 $2.50 "Unveiling of Statue of Liberty" (Edmund Morand) 2·75 2·75

109 Prince Andrew, Miss Sarah Ferguson and Westminster Abbey

1986. Royal Wedding.
625 **109** $2.50 multicoloured . . . 3·25 3·25

110 Great Egret
111 "Virgin and Child" (Perugino)

1986. "Stampex '86" Stamp Exhibition, Adelaide. Australian Birds. Multicoloured.
628 40 c. Type **110** . . . . 2·50 1·75
629 60 c. Painted finch (horiz) . . . 2·75 2·00
630 75 c. Australian king parrot . . 3·00 2·25
631 80 c. Variegated wren (horiz) . 3·25 2·50
632 $1 Peregrine falcon . . . . . . 3·75 2·75
633 $1.65 Azure kingfisher (horiz) . 5·00 4·00
634 $2.20 Budgerigars . . . . 6·00 6·00
635 $4.25 Emu (horiz) . . . . 7·50 7·50

1986. Christmas from Vatican Museum. Multicoloured.
636 80 c. Type **111** . . . . 2·00 1·75
637 $1.15 "Virgin of St. N. dei Frari" (Titian) . . . . 2·25 2·00
638 $1.80 "Virgin with Milk" (Lorenzo di Credi) . . . . . 3·25 3·50
639 $2.60 "Madonna of Foligno" (Raphael) . . . . 4·00 4·50

1986. Visit of Pope John Paul II to South Pacific. Nos. 636/9 surch **CHRISTMAS VISIT TO SOUTH PACIFIC OF POPE JOHN II NOVEMBER 21–24 1986**.
642 80 c. + 10 c. Type **111** . . . . 2·75 2·50
643 $1.15 + 10 c. "Virgin of St. N. dei Frari" (Titian) . . . . 3·25 3·00
644 $1.80 + 10 c. "Virgin with Milk" (Lorenzo di Credi) . . . . . 4·25 4·00
645 $2.60 + 10 c. "Madonna of Foligno" (Raphael) . . . . 5·50 5·00

113 Boris Becker, Olympic Rings and Commemorative Coin

1987. Olympic Games, Seoul (1988). Tennis (1st issue). Designs showing Boris Becker in play.
649 **113** 80 c. multicoloured . . . . 2·25 2·00
650 – $1.15 multicoloured . . . . 2·50 2·25
651 – $1.40 multicoloured . . . . 2·75 2·50
652 – $1.80 multicoloured . . . . 3·50 3·25

1987. Olympic Games, Seoul (1988). Tennis (2nd issue). As T **113** but showing Steffi Graf.
653 85 c. multicoloured . . . . . 1·75 1·25
654 $1.05 multicoloured . . . . . 2·00 1·50
655 $1.30 multicoloured . . . . . 2·25 1·75
656 $1.75 multicoloured . . . . . 2·75 2·00

1987. Royal Ruby Wedding. Nos. 616/17 surch **40TH WEDDING ANNIV. 4.85.**
657 $4.85 on $1.50 Queen and Prince Philip at Balmoral . . . . . 4·00 4·50
658 $4.85 on $2 Queen at Buckingham Palace . . . . 4·00 4·50

115 "The Nativity"

1987. Christmas. Religious Paintings by Durer. Multicoloured.
659 80 c. Type **115** . . . . 1·50 1·25
660 $1.05 "Adoration of the Magi" 1·75 1·75
661 $2.80 "Celebration of the Rosary" . . . . 3·25 3·50
Nos. 659/61 each include detail of an angel with lute as in T **115**.

116 Franz Beckenbauer in Action

1988. West German Football Victories. Multicoloured.
664 20 c. Type **116** 70 70
665 40 c. German "All Star" team in action 90 90
666 60 c. Bayern Munich team with European Cup, 1974 . . . . . 1·10 1·10
667 80 c. World Cup match, England, 1966 . . . . 1·40 1·40
668 $1.05 World Cup match, Mexico, 1970 . . . . 1·60 1·60
669 $1.30 Beckenbauer with pennant, 1974 . . . . 2·00 2·00
670 $1.80 Beckenbauer and European Cup, 1974 . . . . 2·25 2·25

1988. Steffi Graf's Tennis Victories. Nos. 653/6 optd.
671 85 c. mult (optd **Australia 24 Jan 88 French Open 4 June 88**) . 1·60 1·50
672 $1.05 multicoloured (optd **Wimbledon 2 July 88 U S Open 10 Sept. 88**) . . . . 1·90 1·75
673 $1.30 multicoloured (optd **Women's Tennis Grand Slam: 10 September 88**) . . . . 2·00 1·90
674 $1.75 mult (optd **Seoul Olympic Games Gold Medal Winner**) . 2·25 2·10

118 Angels

1988. Christmas. Details from "The Adoration of the Shepherds" by Rubens. Multicoloured.
675 60 c. Type **118** . . . . 1·75 1·50
676 80 c. Shepherds . . . . 2·00 1·75
677 $1.05 Virgin Mary . . . . . . 2·75 2·50
678 $1.30 Holy Child . . . . 3·50 3·00

119 Astronaut and "Apollo 11" Emblem

1989. 20th Anniv of First Manned Landing on Moon. Multicoloured.
680 $1.50 Type **119** . . . . 4·00 4·00
681 $1.50 Earth and Moon . . . . 4·00 4·00
682 $1.50 Astronaut and "Apollo 11" emblem . . . . 4·00 4·00

120 Priests

1989. Christmas. Details from "Presentation in the Temple" by Rembrandt. Multicoloured.
684 70 c. Type **120** . . . . 2·25 2·25
685 80 c. Virgin and Christ Child in Simeon's arms . . . . 2·25 2·25
686 $1.05 Joseph . . . . 2·75 2·75
687 $1.30 Simeon and Christ Child 3·25 3·25

121 Fritz Walter

1990. World Cup Football Championship, Italy. German Footballers. Multicoloured.
689 80 c. Type **121** . . . . 2·50 2·50
690 $1.15 Franz Beckenbauer . . . 2·75 2·75
691 $1.40 Uwe Seeler . . . . 3·00 3·00
692 $1.80 German team emblem and signatures of former captains 4·00 4·00

122 "Merchant Maarten Looten" (Rembrandt)
123 Queen Elizabeth the Queen Mother

1990. 150th Anniv of the Penny Black. Rembrandt Paintings. Multicoloured.
693 80 c. Type **122** . . . . 2·25 2·25
694 $1.05 "Rembrandt's Son Titus with Pen in Hand" . . . . . 2·50 2·50
695 $1.30 "The Shipbuilder and his Wife" . . . . 2·75 2·75
696 $1.80 "Bathsheba with King David's Letter" . . . . . . 3·00 3·00

1990. 90th Birthday of Queen Elizabeth the Queen Mother.
698 **123** $1.25 multicoloured . . . 4·00 3·75

124 "Adoration of the Magi" (Dirk Bouts)
129 "The Virgin and Child with Sts. Jerome and Dominic" (Lippi)

1990. Christmas. Religious Paintings. Mult.
700 70 c. Type **124** . . . . 2·25 2·25
701 80 c. "Holy Family" (Fra Bartolommeo) . . . . 2·50 2·50
702 $1.05 "Nativity" (Memling) . . 2·75 2·75
703 $1.30 "Adoration of the Kings" (Bruegel the Elder) . . . . . 3·50 3·50

1990. "Birdpex '90" Stamp Exhibition, Christchurch, New Zealand. No. 410 optd **Birdpex '90** and logo.
705 $10 Scarlet hibiscus . . . . . 11·00 12·00

1991. 65th Birthday of Queen Elizabeth II. No. 409 optd **SIXTY FIFTH BIRTHDAY QUEEN ELIZABETH II.**
706 $6 "Hybrid hibiscus" . . . . . 8·50 10·00

1991. 10th Wedding Anniv of Prince and Princess of Wales. Nos. 430/2 optd **TENTH ANNIVERSARY.**
707A 75 c. Type **77** . . . . 1·75 1·75
708A 95 c. Lady Diana Spencer . . 2·75 2·75
709A $1.20 Prince Charles and Lady Diana . . . . 2·75 2·75

1991. Christmas. Religious Paintings. Mult.
710 20 c. Type **129** 65 65
711 50 c. "The Isenheim Altarpiece" (M. Grunewald) . . . . . 1·25 1·25
712 $1 "The Nativity" (G. Pittoni) 2·25 2·50
713 $2 "Adoration of the Kings" (J. Brueghel the Elder) . . . 3·00 3·25

130 Banded Rail

1992. Birds. Multicoloured.
718 20 c. Type **130** 45 35
719 50 c. Red-tailed tropic bird . . 60 40
720 70 c. Purple swamphen 80 60
721 $1 Pacific pigeon . . . . 1·00 80
722 $1.50 White-collared kingfisher 1·50 1·50
723 $2 Blue-crowned lory . . . . . 2·00 2·00
724 $3 Purple-capped fruit dove . . 2·50 2·50
726 $5 Barn owl . . . . 3·75 3·75
727 $7 Longtailed koel ("Cockoo") ($48\frac{1}{2} \times 35$ mm) . . . . 4·50 5·00
728 $10 Eastern reef heron ($48\frac{1}{2} \times 35$ mm) . . . . 6·25 6·50
729 $15 Spotted triller ("Polynesian Triller") ($48\frac{1}{2} \times 35$ mm) . . . 9·50 9·75

131 Columbus before King Ferdinand and Queen Isabella

1992. 500th Anniv of Discovery of America by Columbus. Multicoloured.
731 $2 Type **131** . . . . 2·75 2·75
732 $3 Fleet of Columbus . . . . . 4·50 4·50
733 $5 Claiming the New World for Spain . . . . 6·00 6·00

132 Tennis and $10 Commemorative Coin

1992. Olympic Games, Barcelona. Mult.
734 $2.50 Type **132** . . . . 4·50 4·50
735 $2.50 Olympic flame and national flags . . . . 4·50 4·50
736 $2.50 Gymnastics and different $10 coin . . . . 4·50 4·50

1992. 6th Festival of Pacific Arts, Rarotonga. Nos. 336/51 surch **$1**.
738 $1 on 20 c. Type **69** . . . . . 1·00 1·00
739 $1 on 20 c. Ku-Tagwa plaque, New Guinea . . . . 1·00 1·00
740 $1 on 20 c. Suspension hook, New Guinea . . . . 1·00 1·00
741 $1 on 20 c. Ancestral board, New Guinea . . . . 1·00 1·00
742 $1 on 25 c. Platform post, New Hebrides . . . . 1·00 1·00
743 $1 on 25 c. Canoe ornament, New Ireland . . . . 1·00 1·00
744 $1 on 25 c. Carved figure, Admiralty Islands . . . . . 1·00 1·00
745 $1 on 25 c. Female with child, Admiralty Islands . . . . . 1·00 1·00
746 $1 on 30 c. The God A'a, Rurutu, Austral Islands . . . . . 1·00 1·00
747 $1 on 30 c. Statue of Tangaroa, Cook Islands . . . . . . 1·00 1·00
748 $1 on 30 c. Ivory pendant, Tonga 1·00 1·00
749 $1 on 30 c. Tapa (Hiapo) cloth, Niue . . . . 1·00 1·00
750 $1 on 35 c. Feather box (Waka), New Zealand . . . . . . 1·00 1·00
751 $1 on 35 c. Hei-Tiki amulet, New Zealand . . . . 1·00 1·00
752 $1 on 35 c. House post, New Zealand . . . . 1·00 1·00
753 $1 on 35 c. Feather image of god Ku, Hawaii . . . . 1·00 1·00

134 "St. Catherine's Mystic Marriage" (detail) (Memling)

135 Queen on Official Visit

1992. Christmas.
754 **134** 20 c. multicoloured 65 50
755 – 50 c. multicoloured . . . . 1·10 1·00
756 – $1 multicoloured . . . . . 1·75 1·75
757 – $2 multicoloured . . . . . 2·75 3·50
DESIGNS: 50 c., $1, $2 Different details from "St. Catherine's Mystic Marriage" by Hans Memling.

1992. 40th Anniv of Queen Elizabeth II's Accession. Multicoloured.
759 70 c. Type **135** . . . . 1·50 1·50
760 $1 Queen in green evening dress 2·00 2·00
761 $1.50 Queen in white embroidered evening dress . . 2·50 2·50
762 $2 Queen with bouquet . . . . 2·75 2·75

136 Rough-toothed Dolphin

1993. Endangered Species. South Pacific Dolphins. Multicoloured.
763 20 c. Type **136** . . . . . . 1·25 90
764 50 c. Fraser's dolphin . . . . . 2·00 1·60
765 75 c. Pantropical spotted dolphin 2·50 2·75
766 $1 Risso's dolphin . . . . . . 3·00 3·50

1993. Premier Sir Robert Rex Commemoration. Nos. 568/70 optd **1909 IN MEMORIAM 1992 SIR ROBERT R REX K.B.E.** or surch also.
767 40 c. Type **96** . . . . 1·25 1·25
768 58 c. Map of Niue and Premier Rex . . . . 1·50 1·50
769 70 c. Premier Rex receiving proclamation of self-government . . . . . . 1·50 1·50
770 $1 on 40 c. Type **96** . . . . . 1·75 1·75
771 $1 on 58 c. Map of Niue and Premier Rex . . . . 1·75 1·75
772 $1 on 70 c. Premier Rex receiving proclamation of self-government . . . . 1·75 1·75

138 Queen Elizabeth II in Coronation Robes and St. Edward's Crown

1993. 40th Anniv. of Coronation.
773 **138** $5 multicoloured . . . . . 7·50 8·00

139 "Virgin of the Rosary" (detail) (Guido Reni)

1993. Christmas.
774 **139** 20 c. multicoloured 65 50
775 – 70 c. multicoloured . . . . 1·50 1·00
776 – $1 multicoloured . . . . . 1·75 1·25
777 – $1. 50 multicoloured . . . 2·50 3·00
778 – $3 multicoloured (32 × 47 mm) . . . . . . 4·25 5·00
DESIGNS: 70 c. to $3 Different details of "Virgin of the Rosary" (Reni).

140 World Cup and Globe with Flags of U.S.A. and Previous Winners

1994. World Cup Football Championship, U.S.A.
779 **140** $4 multicoloured . . . . . 6·50 7·00

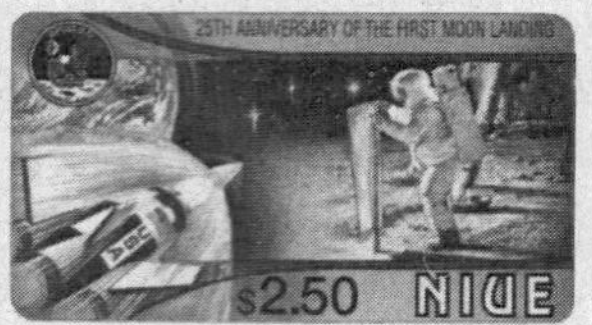

141 "Apollo 11" and Astronaut on Moon

1994. 25th Anniv of First Manned Moon Landing. Multicoloured.
780 $2.50 Type **141** . . . . . . 6·00 6·00
781 $2.50 Astronaut and flag . . . 6·00 6·00
782 $2.50 Astronaut and equipment . . . . 6·00 6·00

142 "The Adoration of the Kings" (Jan Gossaert)

1994. Christmas. Religious Paintings. Multicoloured.
783 70 c. Type **142** . . . . 1·00 1·25
784 70 c. "Madonna and Child with Sts. John and Catherine" (Titian) . . . . 1·00 1·25
785 70 c. "The Holy Family and Shepherd" (Titian) . . . . 1·00 1·25
786 70 c. "The Virgin and Child with Saints" (Gerard David) . . . 1·00 1·25
787 $1 "The Adoration of the Shepherds" (cherubs detail) (Poussin) . . . . 1·25 1·50
788 $1 "The Adoration of the Shepherds" (Holy Family detail) (Poussin) . . . . . 1·25 1·50
789 $1 "Madonna and Child with Sts. Joseph and John" (Sebastiano) . . . . . . 1·25 1·50
790 $1 "The Adoration of the Kings" (Veronese) . . . . 1·25 1·50

143 Long John Silver and Jim Hawkins ("Treasure Island")

145 Tapeu Orchid

1994. Death Centenary of Robert Louis Stevenson (author). Multicoloured.
791 $1.75 Type **143** . . . . 2·50 2·75
792 $1.75 Transformation of Dr. Jekyll ("Dr. Jekyll and Mr. Hyde") . . . . 2·50 2·75
793 $1.75 Attack on David Balfour ("Kidnapped") . . . . . . 2·50 2·75
794 $1.75 Robert Louis Stevenson, tomb and inscription . . . . 2·50 2·75

1996. Nos. 720 and 722 surch.
795 50 c. on 70 c. Purple swamphen . 2·75 1·75
796 $1 on $1.50 White-collared kingfisher . . . . 4·00 3·25

1996. Flowers. Multicoloured.
797 70 c. Type **145** 80 80
798 $1 Frangipani . . . . 1·00 1·00
799 $1.20 "Golden Shower" . . . . 1·40 1·60
800 $1.50 "Pua" . . . . 1·90 2·25

1996. Redrawn design as No. 146.
801 20 c. red and green 20 30

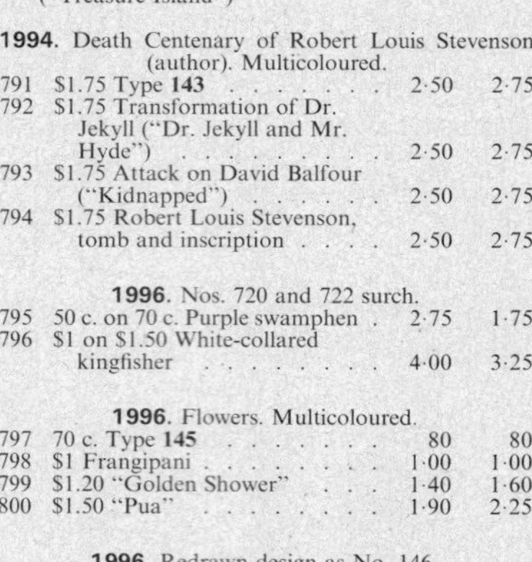

146 "Jackfish" (yacht)

1996. Sailing Ships. Multicoloured.
802 70 c. Type **146** 90 90
803 $1 "Jennifer" (yacht) . . . . . 1·40 1·40
804 $1.20 "Mikeva" (yacht) . . . . 1·75 2·00
805 $2 "Eye of the Wind" (cadet brig) . . . . 2·25 2·50

148 "Acropora gemmifera"

1996. Corals. Multicoloured.
807 20 c. Type **148** 15 20
808 50 c. "Acropora nobilis" 30 35
809 70 c. "Goniopora lobata" . . . 45 50
810 $1 "Sylaster sp." 65 70
811 $1.20 "Alveopora catalai" . . . 75 80
812 $1.50 "Fungia scutaria" . . . . 95 1·00
813 $2 "Porites solida" . . . . . . 1·25 1·40
814 $3 "Millepora sp." . . . . . . 1·90 2·00
815 $4 "Pocillopora eydouxi" . . . 2·50 2·75
816 $5 "Platygyra pini" . . . . . 3·25 3·50

150 Steps to Lagoon

1997. Island Scenes. Multicoloured.
818 $1 Type **150** . . . . 1·00 1·10
819 $1 Islands in lagoon . . . . . 1·00 1·10
820 $1 Beach with rocks in foreground . . . . 1·00 1·10
821 $1 Over-hanging rock on beach . 1·00 1·10
Nos. 818/21 were printed together, se-tenant, forming a composite design.

151 Humpback Whale

1997. Whales (1st series). Multicoloured.
822 20 c. Type **151** 30 25
823 $1 Humpback whale and calf (vert) . . . . 1·10 1·10
824 $1.50 Humpback whale surfacing (vert) . . . . 1·60 1·75
See also Nos. 827/9.

1997. Whales (2nd series). As T **151**. Multicoloured.
827 50 c. Killer whale (vert) 70 70
828 70 c. Minke whale (vert) . . . 90 90
829 $1.20 Sperm whale (vert) . . . 1·25 1·25

154 Floral Display in Woven Basket

1997. Christmas. Floral Displays. Multicoloured.
831 20 c. Type **154** 35 30
832 50 c. Display in white pot . . . 60 50
833 70 c. Display in white basket . 80 80
834 $1 Display in purple vase . . . 1·00 1·25

155 Divers and Turtle

1998. Diving. Multicoloured.
836 20 c. Type **155** 30 30
837 70 c. Diver exploring coral reef . 65 65
838 $1 Exploring underwater chasm (vert) 80 80
839 $1.20 Divers and coral fronds . . 90 90
840 $1.50 Divers in cave . . . . . 1·25 1·25

157 Pacific Black Duck

1998. Coastal Birds. Multicoloured.
841 20 c. Type **157** 45 40
842 70 c. Fairy tern 80 75
843 $1 Great frigate bird (vert) . . 1·00 1·00
844 $1.20 Lesser golden plover . . 1·25 1·40
845 $2 Brown noddy . . . . . . 1·75 2·00

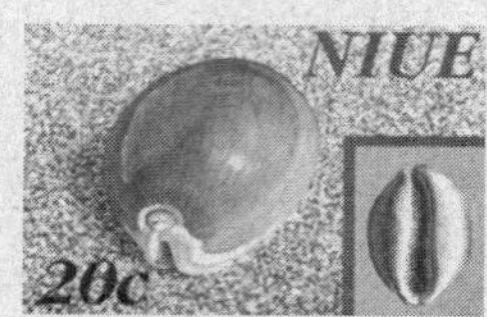

158 Golden Cowrie

1998. Shells. Multicoloured.
846 20 c. Type **158** 40 30
847 70 c. Cowrie shell 75 65
848 $1 Spider conch . . . . 1·00 1·00
849 $5 Helmet shell . . . . 5·00 5·50

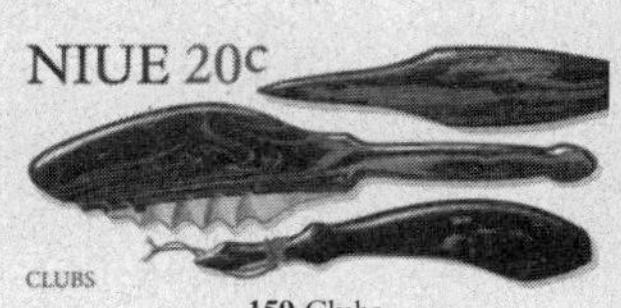

159 Clubs

1998. Ancient Weapons. Multicoloured.
850 20 c. Type **159** 30 30
851 $1.20 Three spears (59 × 24 mm) . . . . 1·00 1·00
852 $1.50 Five spears (59 × 24 mm) . 1·25 1·40
853 $2 Throwing stones . . . . . 1·50 1·75

160 Outrigger Canoe (first migration of Niue Fekai)

1999. "Australia '99" World Stamp Exhibition, Melbourne. Maritime History. Each blue.
854 70 c. Type **160** 55 50
855 $1 H.M.S. "Resolution" (Cook) 90 90
856 $1.20 "John Williams" (missionary sailing ship) . . 1·00 1·25
857 $1.50 Captain James Cook . . 1·40 1·50

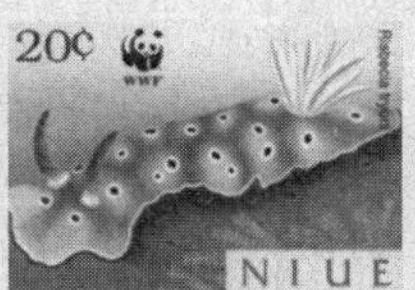

161 "Risbecia tryoni"

1999. Endangered Species. Nudibranchs. Mult.
858 20 c. Type **161** 30 30
859 $1 "Chromodoris lochi" . . . 85 85
860 $1.20 "Chromodoris elizabethina" . . . . 95 1·10
861 $1.50 "Chromodoris bullocki" . 1·25 1·40

162 Togo Chasm

1999. Scenic Views. Multicoloured.
863 $1 Type **162** 75 75
864 $1.20 Matapa Chasm 90 90
865 $1.50 Tufukia (horiz) . . . . . 1·10 1·25
866 $2 Talava Arches (horiz) . . . 1·40 1·60

163 Shallow Baskets

1999. Woven Baskets. Multicoloured.
867 20 c. Type **163** 25 30
868 70 c. Tray and bowl 65 70
869 $1 Tall basket and deep bowls (44 × 34 mm) 65 70
870 $3 Tall basket and shallow bowls (44 × 34 mm) . . . . 2·10 2·25

165 Family and Man in Canoe

1999. New Millennium. Multicoloured.
872 20 c. Type **165** 15 20
873 70 c. People pointing up 45 50
874 $4 Diver and man in traditional dress . . . . 2·50 2·60

Nos. 872/4 were printed together, se-tenant, with the backgrounds forming a composite design.

OFFICIAL STAMPS

1985. Nos. 409/10 and 527/42 optd **O.H.M.S.**
O 1 12 c. Type **92** 35 30
O 2 25 c. "Euphorbia pulcherrima" 40 35
O 3 30 c. "Cochlospermum hibiscoides" 45 35
O 4 35 c. "Begonia sp." 50 40
O 5 40 c. "Plumeria sp." 50 45
O 6 52 c. "Strelitzia reginae" . . . 60 50
O 7 58 c. "Hibiscus syriacus" . . . 60 55
O 8 70 c. "Tibouchina sp." 75 70
O 9 83 c. "Nelumbo sp." 90 80
O10 $1.05 "Hybrid hibiscus" . . . 1·25 1·00
O11 $1.75 "Cassia fistula" . . . . 1·75 1·75
O12 $2.30 Orchid var. . . . . . . 5·50 2·75
O13 $3.90 Orchid sp. . . . . . . 6·00 4·25
O14 $4 "Euphorbia pulcherrima poinsettia" . . . . 5·50 6·00
O15 $5 "Euphorbia pulcherrima poinsettia" . . . . 5·50 6·00
O16 $6 "Hybrid hibiscus" . . . . 6·50 7·50
O17 $6.60 "Hybrid hibiscus" . . . 6·50 7·50
O18 $8.30 "Hibiscus rosa-sinensis" . 7·50 8·50
O19 $10 Scarlet hibiscus . . . . . 8·50 9·50

1993. Nos. 718/29 optd **O.H.M.S.**
O20 20 c. Type **130** 50 50
O21 50 c. Red-tailed tropic bird . . 60 60
O22 70 c. Purple swamphen . . . 1·25 80
O23 $1 Pacific pigeon . . . . . . 1·50 1·25
O24 $1.50 White-collared kingfisher 1·75 1·75
O25 $2 Blue-crowned lory . . . . 2·00 2·00
O26 $3 Crimson-crowned fruit dove 2·25 2·50
O27 $5 Barn owl . . . . 5·00 5·00
O28 $7 Longtailed cuckoo ($48\frac{1}{2}$ × 35 mm) . . . . . 5·50 6·00
O29 $10 Eastern reef heron ($48\frac{1}{2}$ × 35 mm) . . . . 7·00 8·00
O30 $15 Spotted triller ("Polynesian Triller") ($48\frac{1}{2}$ × 35 mm) . . . 10·00 11·00

NORFOLK ISLAND Pt. 1

A small island East of New South Wales, administered by Australia until 1960 when local government was established.

1947. 12 pence = 1 shilling;
20 shillings = 1 pound.
1966. 100 cents = $1 Australian.

1 Ball Bay

1947.

1	**1**	½d. orange	35	60
2		1d. violet	50	60
3		1½d. green	50	70
4		2d. violet	55	40
5		2½d. red	80	30
6		3d. brown	70	70
6a		3d. green	16·00	7·00
7		4d. red	1·25	40
8		5½d. blue	70	30
9		6d. brown	70	30
10		9d. pink	1·25	40
11		1s. green	70	40
12		2s. brown	1·00	1·00
12a		2s. blue	24·00	7·50

12 "Hibiscus insularis"

2 Warder's Tower

4 Old Stores (Crankmill)

17 Queen Elizabeth II (after Annigoni and Cereus)

22 Red-tailed Tropic Bird

1953.

24	**12**	1d. green	15	10
25	–	2d. red and green	20	10
26	–	3d. green	70	15
13	**2**	3½d. red	1·00	90
27	–	5d. purple	55	20
14	–	6½d. green	2·25	3·00
15	**4**	7½d. blue	1·50	3·00
28	–	8d. red	80	50
16	–	8½d. brown	1·75	4·50
29	**17**	9d. blue	80	45
17	–	10d. violet	1·00	75
30	–	10d. brown and violet	2·00	1·25
31	–	1s. 1d. red	80	35
32	–	2s. brown	6·00	90
33	–	2s. 5d. violet	1·00	40
34	–	2s. 8d. brown and green	2·75	55
18	–	5s. brown	42·00	10·00
35	–	5s. brown and green	6·50	75
36	**22**	10s. green	45·00	26·00

DESIGNS—VERT: 2d. "Lagunaria patersonii"; 5d. Lantana; 8d. Red hibiscus; 8½d. Barracks entrance; 10d. Salt house; 1s. 1d. Fringed hibiscus; 2s. Solander's petrel; 2s. 5d. Passion-flower; 2s. 8d. Rose apple. HORIZ: 3d. White tern; 6½d. Airfield; 5s. Bloody Bridge.

For Nos. 25 and 28 with face values in decimal currency see Nos. 600/1.

8 Norfolk Is. Seal and Pitcairners Landing

1956. Cent of Landing of Pitcairners on Norfolk Is.

19	**8**	3d. green	1·50	40
20		2s. violet	2·00	75

1958. Surch.

21	**4**	7d. on 7½d. blue	75	1·00
22	–	8d. on 8½d. brown (No. 16)	75	1·00

1959. 150th Anniv of Australian P.O. No. 331 of Australia surch **NORFOLK ISLAND 5D.**

23	**143**	5d. on 4d. slate	35	30

1960. As Nos. 13 and 14/15 but colours changed and surch.

37	**2**	1s. 1d. on 3½d. blue	3·50	2·50
38		2s. 5d. on 6½d. turquoise	4·00	1·50
39	**4**	2s. 8d. on 7½d. sepia	10·00	6·00

26 Queen Elizabeth II and Map

29 Stripey

1960. Introduction of Local Government.

40	**26**	2s. 8d. purple	13·00	11·00

27 Open Bible and Candle

1960. Christmas.

41	**27**	5d. mauve	80	50

28 Open Prayer Book and Text

1961. Christmas.

42	**28**	5d. blue	30	60

1962. Fishes.

43	**29**	6d. sepia, yellow & green	75	25
44	–	11d. orange, brown & blue	2·00	80
45	–	1s. blue, pink and olive	75	25
46	–	1s. 3d. blue, brown & green	2·00	1·75
47	–	1s. 6d. sepia, violet & blue	2·75	80
48	–	2s. 3d. multicoloured	5·00	80

DESIGNS: 11d. Gold-mouthed emperor; 1s. Surge wrasse ("Po'ov"); 1s. 3d. Seachub ("Dreamfish"); 1s. 6d. Giant grouper; 2s. 3d. White trevally.

30 "Madonna and Child"

31 "Peace on Earth..."

1962. Christmas.

49	**30**	5d. blue	45	80

1963. Christmas.

50	**31**	5d. red	40	70

32 Overlooking Kingston

33 Norfolk Pine

1964. Multicoloured.

51	5d. Type **32**	75	50
52	8d. Kingston	1·00	1·25
53	9d. The Arches (Bumboras)	2·25	30
54	10d. Slaughter Bay	2·25	30

1964. 50th Anniv of Norfolk Island as Australian Territory.

55	**33**	5d. black, red and orange	40	15
56		8d. black, red and green	40	1·10

34 Child looking at Nativity Scene

35 Nativity Scene

1964. Christmas.

57	**34**	5d. multicoloured	30	40

1965. 50th Anniv of Gallipoli Landing. As T **22** of Nauru, but slightly larger (22 × 34½ mm).

58	5d. brown, black and green	15	10

1965. Christmas.

59	**35**	5d. multicoloured	15	10

38 "Hibiscus insularis"

39 Headstone Bridge

1966. Decimal Currency. As earlier issue but with values in cents and dollars. Surch in black on silver tablets obliterating old value as in T **38**.

60	**38**	1 c. on 1d.	20	10
61	–	2 c. on 2d. (No. 25)	20	10
62	–	3 c. on 3d. (No. 26)	50	50
63	–	4 c. on 5d. (No. 27)	25	10
64	–	5 c. on 8d. (No. 28)	30	10
65	–	10 c. on 10d. (No. 30)	90	15
66	–	15 c. on 1s. 1d. (No. 31)	45	50
67	–	20 c. on 2s. (No. 32)	3·50	2·75
68	–	25 c. on 2s. 5d. (No. 33)	1·50	40
69	–	30 c. on 2s. 8d. (No. 34)	1·00	50
70	–	50 c. on 5s. (No. 35)	3·50	75
71a	**22**	$1 on 10s.	2·75	2·00

1966. Multicoloured.

72	7 c. Type **39**	40	15
73	9 c. Cemetery Road	40	15

41 St. Barnabas' Chapel (interior)

43 Star over Philip Island

1966. Centenary of Melanesian Mission. Mult.

74	4 c. Type **41**	10	10
75	25 c. St. Barnabas' Chapel (exterior)	20	20

1966. Christmas.

76	**43**	4 c. multicoloured	10	10

44 H.M.S. "Resolution", 1774

1967. Multicoloured.

77	1 c. Type **44**	10	10
78	2 c. "La Boussole" and "L'Astrolabe", 1788	15	10
79	3 c. H.M.S. "Supply" (brig), 1788	15	10
80	4 c. H.M.S. "Sirius" (frigate), 1790	50	10
81	5 c. "Norfolk" (sloop), 1798	20	10
82	7 c. H.M.S. "Mermaid" (survey cutter), 1825	20	10
83	9 c. "Lady Franklin" (full-rigged ship), 1853	20	10
84	10 c. "Morayshire" (full-rigged transport), 1856	20	30
85	15 c. "Southern Cross" (missionary ship), 1866	45	30
86	20 c. "Pitcairn" (missionary schooner), 1891	60	40
87	25 c. "Black Billy" (Norfolk Island whaleboat), 1895	1·50	75
88	30 c. "Iris" (cable ship), 1907	1·50	2·00
89	50 c. "Resolution" (schooner), 1926	4·75	3·50
90	$1 "Morinda" (freighter), 1931	5·50	3·50

45 Lions Badge and 50 Stars

47 Queen Elizabeth II

46 Prayer of John Adams and Candle

1967. 50th Anniv of Lions International.

91	**45**	4 c. black, green and yellow	10	10

1967. Christmas.

92	**46**	5 c. black, olive and red	10	10

1968.

93	**47**	3 c. black, brown and red	10	10
94		4 c. black, brown and green	10	10
95		5 c. black, brown and violet	10	10
95a		6 c. black, brown and lake	30	45

59 Avro Type 691 Lancastrian and Douglas DC-4 Aircraft

1968. 21st Anniv of QANTAS Air Service, Sydney–Norfolk Island.

96	**59**	5 c. black, red and blue	15	10
97		7 c. brown, red & turq	15	10

60 Bethlehem Star and Flowers

61 Captain Cook, Quadrant and Chart of Pacific Ocean

1968. Christmas.

98	**60**	5 c. multicoloured	10	10

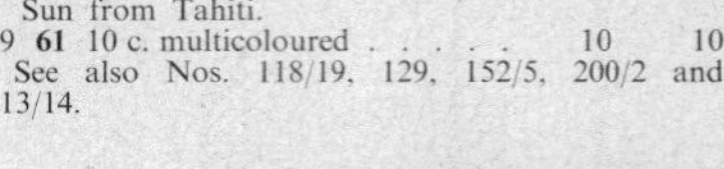

1969. Captain Cook Bicentenary (1st issue). Observation of the transit of Venus across the Sun from Tahiti.

99	**61**	10 c. multicoloured	10	10

See also Nos. 118/19, 129, 152/5, 200/2 and 213/14.

62 Van Diemen's Land, Norfolk Island and Sailing Cutter

63 "The Nativity" (carved mother-of-pearl plaque)

1969. 125th Anniv of Annexation of Norfolk Island to Van Diemen's Land.

100	**62**	5 c. multicoloured	10	10
101		30 c. multicoloured	50	80

1969. Christmas.

102	**63**	5 c. multicoloured	10	10

64 New Zealand Grey Flyeater

1970. Birds. Multicoloured.

103	1 c. Scarlet robin	30	10
104	2 c. Golden whistler	30	20
105	3 c. Type **64**	30	10
106	4 c. Long-tailed koels	60	10
107	5 c. Red-fronted parakeet	1·50	60
108	7 c. Long-tailed triller	45	10
109	9 c. Island thrush	70	10
110	10 c. Boobook owl	1·75	1·50
111	15 c. Norfolk Island pigeon	1·50	65
112	20 c. White-chested white-eye	7·00	3·25
113	25 c. Norfolk Island parrots	2·50	40
114	30 c. Collared grey fantail	7·00	1·75
115	45 c. Norfolk Island starlings	3·00	80
116	50 c. Crimson rosella	3·50	1·75
117	$1 Sacred kingfisher	10·00	10·00

Nos. 105/6, 109, 112, 114/15 and 117 are horiz; the remainder being vert.

65 Cook and Map of Australia

1970. Captain Cook Bicentenary (2nd issue). Discovery of Australia's East Coast. Mult.

118	5 c. Type **65**	15	10
119	20 c. H.M.S. "Endeavour" and aborigine	40	10

66 First Christmas Service, 1788

67 Bishop Patteson, and Martyrdom of St. Stephen

1970. Christmas.

120	**66**	5 c. multicoloured	10	10

1971. Death Cent of Bishop Patteson. Multicoloured.
121 6 c. Type **67** 10 25
122 6 c. Bible, Martyrdom of St. Stephen and knotted palm-frond 10 25
123 10 c. Bishop Patteson and stained glass 10 25
124 10 c. Cross and Bishop's Arms 10 25

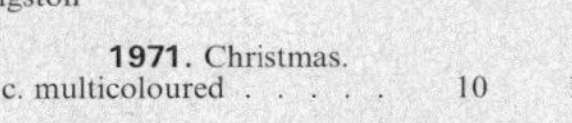
68 Rose Window, St. Barnabas Chapel, Kingston
69 Map and Flag

1971. Christmas.
125 **68** 6 c. multicoloured 10 10

1972. 25th Anniv of South Pacific Commission.
126 **69** 7 c. multicoloured 15 20

70 "St. Mark" (stained glass window) (All Saints, Norfolk Is.)
71 Cross and Pines (stained glass-window All Saints Church)

1972. Christmas.
127 **70** 7 c. multicoloured 10 10

1972. Cent of First Pitcairner-built Church.
128 **71** 12 c. multicoloured 10 10

72 H.M.S. "Resolution" in the Antarctic

1973. Capt. Cook Bicentenary (3rd issue). Crossing of the Antarctic Circle.
129 **72** 35 c. multicoloured . . . . 2·50 2·25

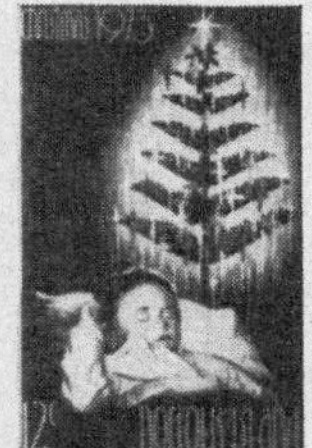

73 Child and Christmas Tree

1973. Christmas. Multicoloured.
130 7 c. Type **73** 20 10
131 12 c. Type **73** 25 10
132 35 c. Fir trees and star 70 80

74 Protestant Clergyman's Quarters

1973. Historic Buildings. Multicoloured.
133 1 c. Type **74** 10 10
134 2 c. Royal Engineers' Office . . 10 10
135 3 c. Double Quarters for Free Overseers 25 30
136 4 c. Guard House 20 20
137 5 c. Entrance to Pentagonal Gaol 25 15
138 7 c. Pentagonal Gaol 35 35
139 8 c. Prisoners' Barracks . . . . 1·25 1·75
140 10 c. Officer's Quarters, New Military Barracks 50 55
141 12 c. New Military Barracks . . 50 30
142 14 c. Beach Stores 50 70
143 15 c. The Magazine . . . . . 1·25 50
144 20 c. Entrance, Old Military Barracks 50 90
145 25 c. Old Military Barracks . . 1·25 1·00
146 30 c. Old Stores (Crankmill) . . 50 60
147 50 c. Commissariat Stores . . . 50 2·00
148 $1 Government House . . . . 1·00 4·00

75 Royal Couple and Map

1974. Royal Visit.
149 **75** 7 c. multicoloured 40 15
150 25 c. multicoloured . . . . 1·00 75

76 Chichester's De Havilland Gipsy Moth Seaplane "Madame Elijah"

1974. 1st Aircraft Landing on Norfolk Island.
151 **76** 14 c. multicoloured 75 70

77 "Captain Cook" (engraving by J. Basire)
78 Nativity Scene (pearl-shell pew carving)

1974. Capt. Cook Bicentenary (4th issue). Discovery of Norfolk Is. Multicoloured.
152 7 c. Type **77** 75 75
153 10 c. H.M.S. "Resolution" (H. Roberts) . . . . 1·75 1·75
154 14 c. Norfolk Island pine . . . 1·50 2·25
155 25 c. "Norfolk Island flax" (G. Raper) . . . . 1·50 3·00

1974. Christmas.
156 **78** 7 c. multicoloured 15 10
157 30 c. multicoloured 60 75

79 Norfolk Pine

1974. Centenary of Universal Postal Union. Multicoloured. Imperf. Self-adhesive.
158 10 c. Type **79** 25 50
159 15 c. Offshore islands 35 55
160 35 c. Crimson rosella and sacred kingfisher 75 85
161 40 c. Pacific map 75 95

80 H.M.S. "Mermaid" (survey cutter)

1975. 150th Anniv of Second Settlement. Multicoloured.
163 10 c. Type **80** 40 75
164 35 c. Kingston, 1835 (from painting by T. Seller) . . . . 60 1·00

81 Star on Norfolk Island Pine
82 Memorial Cross

1975. Christmas.
165 **81** 10 c. multicoloured 15 10
166 15 c. multicoloured 20 10
167 35 c. multicoloured 30 35

1975. Cent of St. Barnabas Chapel. Mult.
168 30 c. Type **82** 20 15
169 60 c. Laying foundation stone, and Chapel in 1975 . . . . 40 40

83 Launching of "Resolution"

1975. 50th Anniv of Launching of "Resolution" (schooner). Multicoloured.
170 25 c. Type **83** 25 40
171 45 c. "Resolution" at sea . . . 40 70

84 Whaleship "Charles W. Morgan"

1976. Bicent of American Revolution. Mult.
172 18 c. Type **84** 30 30
173 25 c. Thanksgiving Service . . . 40 30
174 40 c. Boeing B-17 Flying Fortress over Norfolk Island 75 65
175 45 c. California quail . . . . . 1·00 85

85 Swallow-tailed Tern and Sun
86 "Vanessa ita"

1976. Christmas.
176 **85** 18 c. multicoloured 30 15
177 25 c. multicoloured 55 20
178 45 c. multicoloured 90 50

1977. Butterflies and Moths. Multicoloured.
179 1 c. Type **86** 10 40
180 2 c. "Utetheisa pulchelloides" . . 10 40
181 3 c. "Agathia asterias" 10 20
182 4 c. "Cynthia kershawi" 10 25
183 5 c. "Leucania loreyimima" . . 15 40
184 10 c. "Hypolimnas bolina" . . . 30 35
185 15 c. "Pyrrhorachis pyrrhogona" 30 30
186 16 c. "Austrocarea iocephala" . . 30 30
187 17 c. "Pseudocoremia christiani" 35 30
188 18 c. "Cleora idiocrossa" . . . 35 30
189 19 c. "Simplicia caeneusalis" . . 35 30
190 20 c. "Austrocidaria ralstonae" 40 30
191 30 c. "Hippotion scrofa" . . . 50 60
192 40 c. "Papilio amynthor (ilioneus)" 55 40
193 50 c. "Tiracola plagiata" . . . 70 75
194 $1 "Precis villida" 75 75
195 $2 "Cepora perimale" . . . . 1·25 1·40

87 Queen's View, Kingston

1977. Silver Jubilee.
196 **87** 25 c. multicoloured 35 30

88 Hibiscus Flowers and Oil Lamp
89 Captain Cook (from a portrait by Nathaniel Dance)

1977. Christmas.
197 **88** 18 c. multicoloured 15 10
198 25 c. multicoloured 15 10
199 45 c. multicoloured 30 35

1978. Capt. Cook Bicentenary (5th issue). Discovery of Hawaii. Multicoloured.
200 18 c. Type **89** 30 20
201 25 c. Discovery of northern Hawaiian islands 30 30
202 80 c. British flag against island background 60 70

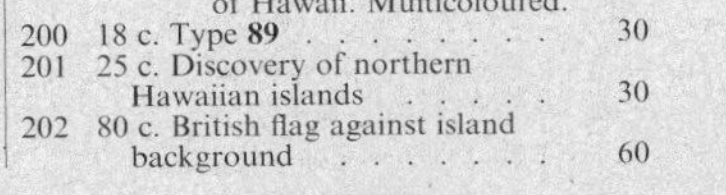

90 Guide Flag and Globe

1978. 50th Anniv of Girl Guides. Multicoloured. Imperf. Self-adhesive.
203 18 c. Type **90** 25 35
204 25 c. Trefoil and scarf badge . . 30 45
205 35 c. Trefoil and Queen Elizabeth 45 70
206 45 c. Trefoil and Lady Baden-Powell 55 70

91 St. Edward's Crown

1978. 25th Anniv of Coronation. Mult.
207 25 c. Type **91** 15 15
208 70 c. Coronation regalia . . . 40 45

92 View of Duncombe Bay with Scout at Camp Fire

1978. 50th Anniv of Boy Scout Movement. Multicoloured. Imperf. Self-adhesive.
209 20 c. Type **92** 30 45
210 25 c. View from Kingston and emblem 35 55
211 35 c. View of Anson Bay and Link Badge 50 90
212 45 c. Sunset scene and Lord Baden-Powell 55 95

93 Chart showing Route of Arctic Voyage

1978. Captain Cook Bicentenary (6th issue). Northern-most Voyages. Multicoloured.
213 25 c. Type **93** 30 30
214 90 c. "H.M.S. "Resolution" and H.M.S. "Discovery" in Pack Ice" (Webber) 80 80

94 Poinsettia and Bible
95 Cook and Village of Staithes near Marton

1978. Christmas. Multicoloured.
215 20 c. Type **94** 15 10
216 30 c. Native oak and bible . . . 20 15
217 55 c. Hibiscus and bible 30 30

1978. 250th Birth Anniv of Captain Cook. Multicoloured.
218 20 c. Type **95** 30 25
219 80 c. Cook and Whitby Harbour 70 1·25

96 H.M.S. "Resolution"

1979. Death Bicent of Captain Cook. Mult.
220 20 c. Type **96** 30 30
221 20 c. Cook (statue) 30 30
222 40 c. Cook's death 40 50
223 40 c. Cook's death (different) . 40 50

Nos. 220/1 were issued se-tenant, in horizontal pairs throughout the sheet, forming a composite design. A chart of Cook's last voyage is shown in the background. Nos. 222/3 were also issued se-tenant, the horizontal pair forming a composite design taken from an aquatint by John Clevely.

97 Assembly Building

1979. First Norfolk Island Legislative Assembly.
224 **97** $1 multicoloured 50 50

98 Tasmania 1853 1d. Stamp and Sir Rowland Hill

1979. Death Centenary of Sir Rowland Hill.
225 **98** 20 c. blue and brown . . . 20 10
226 – 30 c. red and grey 25 15
227 – 55 c. violet and indigo . . 40 30
DESIGNS: 30 c. Great Britain 1841 1d. red; 55 c. 1947 "Ball Bay" 1d. stamp.

99 I.Y.C. Emblem and Map of Pacific showing Norfolk Island as Pine Tree

1979. International Year of the Child.
229 **99** 80 c. multicoloured 40 45

100 Emily Bay **101** Lions International Emblem

1979. Christmas.
230 **100** 15 c. multicoloured 15 15
231 – 20 c. multicoloured 15 15
232 – 30 c. multicoloured 15 15
DESIGNS: 20, 30 c. Different scenes.
Nos. 230/2 were printed together, se-tenant, forming a composite design.

1980. Lions Convention.
234 **101** 50 c. multicoloured 35 30

102 Rotary International Emblem

1980. 75th Anniv of Rotary International.
235 **102** 50 c. multicoloured 35 30

103 De Havilland Gipsy Moth Seaplane "Madame Elijah"

1980. Airplanes. Multicoloured.
236 1 c. Hawker Siddeley H.S.748 15 20
237 2 c. Type **103** 15 20
238 3 c. Curtis P-40E Kittyhawk I . 15 20
239 4 c. Chance Vought F4U-1 Corsair 15 30
240 5 c. Grumman TBF Avenger . 30 30
241 15 c. Douglas SBD-5 Dauntless . 30 30
242 20 c. Cessna 172D Skyhawk . . 25 30
243 25 c. Lockheed 414 Hudson . . 30 35
244 30 c. Lockheed PV-1 Ventura . 40 90
245 40 c. Avro Type 685 York . . 50 55
246 50 c. Douglas DC-3 . . . . 65 65
247 60 c. Avro Type 691 Lancastrian 75 75
248 80 c. Douglas DC-4 . . . . . 95 95
249 $1 Beech 200 Super King Air 1·25 90
250 $2 Fokker F.27 Friendship . 2·50 2·25
251 $5 Lockheed C-130 Hercules . 6·00 2·00

104 Queen Elizabeth the Queen Mother

1980. 80th Birthday of The Queen Mother.
252 **104** 22 c. multicoloured . . . 20 20
253 60 c. multicoloured 35 40

105 Red-tailed Tropic Birds

1980. Christmas. Birds. Multicoloured.
254 15 c. Type **105** 30 25
255 22 c. White terns 30 25
256 35 c. White-capped noddys . . 30 25
257 60 c. White terns (different) . . 40 45

106 "Morayshire" and View of Norfolk Island

1981. 125th Anniv of Pitcairn Islanders' Migration to Norfolk Island. Multicoloured.
258 5 c. Type **106** 15 15
259 35 c. Islanders arriving ashore . 40 30
260 60 c. View of new settlement . . 60 45

107 Wedding Bouquet from Norfolk Island **109** Pair of White-chested White Eyes

108 Uniting Church in Australia

1981. Royal Wedding. Multicoloured.
262 35 c. Type **107** 15 15
263 55 c. Prince Charles at horse trials 25 25
264 60 c. Prince Charles and Lady Diana Spencer 25 35

1981. Christmas. Churches. Multicoloured.
265 18 c. Type **108** 15 10
266 24 c. Seventh Day Adventist Church 15 15
267 30 c. Church of the Sacred Heart 20 20
268 $1 St. Barnabas Chapel 50 70

1981. White-chested White Eye. ("Silver-eye") Mult.
269 35 c. Type **109** 35 40
270 35 c. Bird on nest 35 40
271 35 c. Bird with egg 35 40
272 35 c. Parents with chicks . . . 35 40
273 35 c. Fledgelings 35 40

110 Aerial view of Philip Island

1982. Philip and Nepean Islands. Mult.
274 24 c. Type **110** 20 20
275 24 c. Close-up view of Philip Island landscape 20 20
276 24 c. Gecko ("Phyllodactylus guentheri"), Philip Island . . 20 20
277 24 c. Sooty tern, Philip Island 20 20
278 24 c. Philip Island hibiscus ("hibiscus insularis") 20 20
279 35 c. Aerial view of Nepean Island 25 25
280 35 c. Close-up view of Nepean Island landscape 25 25
281 35 c. Gecko ("phyllodactylus guentheri"), Nepean Island. . 25 25
282 35 c. Blue-faced boobies, Nepean Island 25 25
283 35 c. "Carpobrotus glaucescens" (flower), Nepean Island . . . 25 25

111 Sperm Whale

1982. Whales.
248 **111** 24 c. multicoloured 60 35
285 – 55 c. multicoloured . . . . 1·10 95
286 – 80 c. black, mauve & stone . 1·40 2·00
DESIGNS: 55 c. Black right whale; 80 c. Humpback whale.

112 "Diocet", Wrecked 20 April 1873

1982. Shipwrecks. Multicoloured.
287 24 c. H.M.S. "Sirius", wrecked 19 March 1790 . . . . 50 50
288 27 c. Type **112** 50 50
289 35 c. "Friendship", wrecked 17 May 1835 . . . . 90 80
290 40 c. "Mary Hamilton", wrecked 6 May 1873 . . . . 90 1·25
291 55 c. "Fairlie", wrecked 14 February 1840 . . . . . . 1·25 1·25
292 65 c. "Warrigal", wrecked 18 March 1918 . . . . 1·25 1·75

113 R.N.Z.A.F. Lockheed 414 Hudson dropping Christmas Supplies, 1942

1982. Christmas. 40th Anniv of First Supply-plane Landings on Norfolk Island (Christmas Day 1942). Multicoloured.
293 27 c. Type **113** 55 35
294 40 c. R.N.Z.A.F. Lockheed 414 Hudson landing Christmas supplies 1942 . . . . 75 65
295 75 c. Christmas, 1942 . . . . . 90 1·40

114 50th (Queen's Own) Regiment **115** "Panaeolus papilionaceus"

1982. Military Uniforms. Multicoloured.
296 27 c. Type **114** 30 35
297 40 c. 58th (Rutlandshire) Regiment 40 75
298 55 c. 80th (Staffordshire Volunteers) Battalion Company 50 95
299 65 c. 11th (North Devonshire) Regiment . . . . 60 1·25

1983. Fungi. Multicoloured.
300 27 c. Type **115** 40 35
301 40 c. "Coprinus domesticus" . . 60 50
302 55 c. "Marasmius niveus" . . . 75 70
303 65 c. "Cymatoderma elegans var lamellatum" . . . . 1·00 85

116 Beechcraft 18

1983. Bicentenary of Manned Flight. Mult.
304 10 c. Type **116** 15 15
305 27 c. Fokker F.28 Fellowship 25 35
306 45 c. French military Douglas C-54 . . . . 40 60
307 75 c. Sikorsky S-61N helicopter . 60 95

117 St. Matthew **118** Cable Ship "Chantik"

1983. Christmas. 150th Birth Anniv of Sir Edward Burne-Jones.
309 5 c. Type **117** 10 10
310 24 c. St. Mark 20 30
311 30 c. Jesus Christ 25 40
312 45 c. St. Luke 35 55
313 85 c. St. John . . . . 55 1·10
DESIGNS: showing stained glass windows from St. Barnabas Chapel, Norfolk Island.

1983. World Communications Year. ANZCAN Cable. Multicoloured.
314 30 c. Type **118** 30 40
315 45 c. "Chantik" during in-shore operations 40 55
316 75 c. Cable ship "Mercury" . . 55 95
317 85 c. Diagram of cable route . . 55 1·10

119 Popwood **120** Morwong

1984. Flowers. Multicoloured.
318 1 c. Type **119** 30 70
319 2 c. Strand morning glory . . . 40 70
320 3 c. Native phreatia 45 70
321 4 c. Philip Island wisteria . . . 45 70
322 5 c. Norfolk Island palm . . . 70 70
323 10 c. Evergreen 50 70
324 15 c. Bastard oak 60 70
325 20 c. Devil's guts 60 70
326 25 c. White oak 70 80
327 30 c. Ti 70 90
328 35 c. Philip Island hibiscus . . 70 90
329 40 c. Native wisteria . . . . . 80 1·25
330 50 c. Native jasmine . . . . . 90 1·25
331 $1 Norfolk Island hibiscus . . 90 1·75
332 $3 Native oberonia . . . . . 1·75 4·00
333 $5 Norfolk Island pine . . . . 2·50 4·50

1984. Reef Fishes. Multicoloured.
334 30 c. Type **120** 40 45
335 45 c. Black-spotted goatfish . . 60 65
336 75 c. Surgeonfish . . . . . . 1·00 1·10
337 85 c. Three-striped butterflyfish . 1·25 1·40

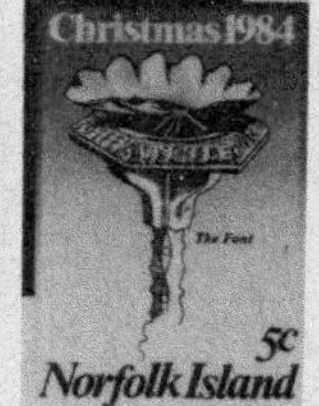

121 Owl with Eggs **123** Font, Kingston Methodist Church

122 1953 7½d. and 1974 Cook Bicent 10 c. Stamps

1984. Boobook Owl. Multicoloured.
338 30 c. Type **121** 75 70
339 30 c. Fledgeling 75 70
340 30 c. Young owl on stump . . . 75 70
341 30 c. Adult on branch 75 70
342 30 c. Owl in flight 75 70

1984. "Ausipex" International Stamp Exhibition, Melbourne. Multicoloured.
343 30 c. Type **122** 30 35
344 45 c. John Buffett commemorative postal stationery envelope 50 75
345 75 c. Design from Presentation Pack for 1982 Military Uniforms issue . . . . . . 90 1·75

1984. Christmas. Centenary of Methodist Church on Norfolk Island. Multicoloured.
347 5 c. Type **123** 10 10
348 24 c. Church service in Old Barracks, Kingston, late 1800s 25 40
349 30 c. The Revd. & Mrs. A. H. Phelps and sailing ship . . . 35 45
350 45 c. The Revd. A. H. Phelps and First Congregational Church, Chester, U.S.A. 40 65
351 85 c. Interior of Kingston Methodist Church . . . . . 80 1·40

124 The Revd. Nobbs teaching Pitcairn Islanders **125** "Fanny Fisher"

1984. Death Centenary of Revd. George Hunn Nobbs (leader of Pitcairn community). Multicoloured.
352 30 c. Type **124** 30 45
353 45 c. The Revd. Nobbs with sick islander 45 65
354 75 c. Baptising baby . . . . . 75 1·10
355 85 c. Presented to Queen Victoria, 1852 . . . . 80 1·40

1985. 19th-Century Whaling Ships (1st series). Multicoloured.
356 5 c. Type **125** 40 25
357 33 c. "Costa Rica Packet" . . 75 55
358 50 c. "Splendid" . . . . 1·25 1·25
359 90 c. "Onward" . . . . 1·50 2·00
See also Nos. 360/3.

1985. 19th-Century Whaling Ships (2nd series). As T **125**. Multicoloured.
360 15 c. "Waterwitch" 60 70
361 20 c. "Canton" 70 80
362 60 c. "Aladdin" . . . . 1·25 1·75
363 80 c. "California" . . . . . . 1·40 2·25

126 The Queen Mother (from photo by Norman Parkinson) **127** "Swimming"

1985. Life and Times of Queen Elizabeth the Queen Mother. Multicoloured.
364 5 c. The Queen Mother (from photo by Dorothy Wilding) 10 10
365 33 c. With Princess Anne at Trooping the Colour 25 25
366 50 c. Type **126** 40 55
367 90 c. With Prince Henry at his christening (from photo by Lord Snowdon) . . . . . . 60 1·00

1985. International Youth Year. Children's Paintings. Multicoloured.
369 33 c. Type **127** 40 40
370 50 c. "A Walk in the Country" 70 85

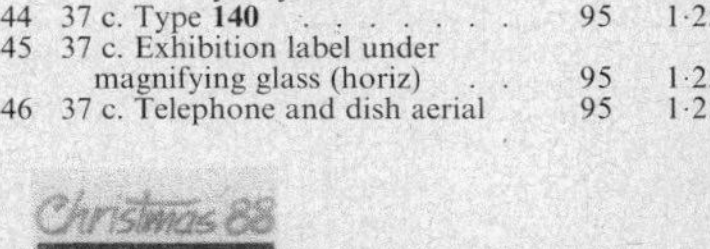

128 Prize-winning Cow and Owner **129** Shepherds with Flock

1985. 125th Anniv of Royal Norfolk Island Agricultural and Horticultural Show. Mult.
371 80 c. Type **128** 75 80
372 90 c. Show exhibits 85 90

1985. Christmas. Multicoloured.
374 27 c. Type **129** 40 30
375 33 c. Mary and Joseph with donkey 50 40
376 50 c. The Three Wise Men . . 80 65
377 90 c. The Nativity . . . . . . 1·25 1·25

130 Long-spined Sea Urchin **131** "Giotto" Spacecraft

1986. Marine Life. Multicoloured.
378 5 c. Type **130** 10 10
379 33 c. Blue starfish 30 35
380 55 c. Southern eagle ray . . . 50 85
381 75 c. Snowflake moray . . . . 70 1·25

1986. Appearance of Halley's Comet. Mult.
383 $1 Type **131** . . . . 75 1·50
384 $1 Halley's Comet . . . . . . 75 1·50
Nos. 383/4 were printed together, se-tenant, forming a composite design.

132 Isaac Robinson (U.S. Consul 1887–1908) **133** Princess Elizabeth and Dog

1986. "Ameripex '86" International Stamp Exhibition, Chicago. Multicoloured.
385 33 c. Type **132** 30 35
386 50 c. Ford "Model T" (first vehicle on island) (horiz) . . 50 50
387 80 c. Statue of Liberty 55 80
No. 387 also commemorates the Centenary of the Statue of Liberty.

1986. 60th Birthday of Queen Elizabeth II. Multicoloured.
389 5 c. Type **133** 10 10
390 33 c. Queen Elizabeth II . . . 40 35
391 80 c. Opening Norfolk Island Golf Club . . . . 1·60 1·40
392 90 c. With Duke of Edinburgh in carriage . . . . 1·25 1·60

134 Stylized Dove and Norfolk Island **135** British Convicts, 1787

1986. Christmas.
393 **134** 30 c. multicoloured 25 30
394 40 c. multicoloured 35 45
395 $1 multicoloured . . . . . 1·00 1·50

1986. Bicentenary (1988) of Norfolk Island Settlement (1st issue). Governor Phillip's Commission. Multicoloured.
396 36 c. Type **135** 80 35
397 55 c. Judge passing sentence of transportation . . . . . . 1·50 85
398 90 c. Governor Phillip meeting Home Secretary (inscr "Home Society") . . . . 2·50 3·50
399 90 c. As No. 398, but correctly inscr "Home Secretary" . . . 2·25 3·25
400 $1 Captain Arthur Phillip . . 2·50 2·50
See also Nos. 401/4, 421/4, 433/5, 436/7 and 438/43.

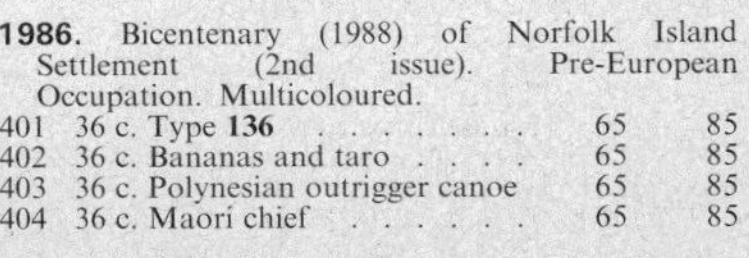

136 Stone Tools

1986. Bicentenary (1988) of Norfolk Island Settlement (2nd issue). Pre-European Occupation. Multicoloured.
401 36 c. Type **136** 65 85
402 36 c. Bananas and taro 65 85
403 36 c. Polynesian outrigger canoe 65 85
404 36 c. Maori chief 65 85

137 Philip Island from Point Ross **138** Male Red-fronted Parakeet

1987. Norfolk Island Scenes. Multicoloured.
405 1 c. Cockpit Creek Bridge . . . 50 70
406 2 c. Cemetery Bay Beach . . . 50 70
407 3 c. Island guesthouse 50 70
408 5 c. Type **137** 30 50
409 15 c. Cattle in pasture . . . . 80 1·25
410 30 c. Rock fishing . . . . . . 30 1·00
411 37 c. Old Pitcairner-style house 1·40 1·50
412 40 c. Shopping centre . . . . 35 1·25
413 50 c. Emily Bay . . . . 45 1·25
414 60 c. Bloody Bridge . . . . . 2·00 2·25
415 80 c. Pitcairner-style shop . . . 1·75 2·50
416 90 c. Government House . . . 1·25 2·00
417 $1 Melanesian Memorial Chapel 1·00 1·75
418 $2 Convict Settlement, Kingston 1·75 3·50
419 $3 Ball Bay . . . . 5·00 6·00
420 $5 Northern cliffs . . . . . . 7·00 8·50

1987. Bicentenary of Norfolk Island Settlement (1988) (3rd issue). The First Fleet. As T **135**. Multicoloured.
421 5 c. Loading supplies, Deptford 50 75
422 55 c. Fleet leaving Spithead . . 1·75 2·25
423 55 c. H.M.S. "Sirius" leaving Spithead . . . . 1·75 2·25
424 $1 Female convicts below decks 2·25 3·00
Nos. 422/3 were printed together, se-tenant, forming a composite design.

1987. Red-fronted Parakeet ("Green Parrot"). Multicoloured.
425 5 c. Type **138** . . . . 2·00 1·75
426 15 c. Adult with fledgeling and egg . . . . 2·50 2·25
427 36 c. Young parakeets . . . . 3·50 3·25
428 55 c. Female parakeet . . . . 4·50 3·75

139 Christmas Tree and Restored Garrison Barracks **140** Airliner, Container Ship and Sydney Harbour Bridge

1987. Christmas. Multicoloured.
429 30 c. Type **139** 30 30
430 42 c. Children opening presents 45 55
431 58 c. Father Christmas with children . . . . 60 1·00
432 63 c. Children's party . . . . 70 1·25

1987. Bicentenary of Norfolk Island Settlement (1988) (4th issue). Visit of La Perouse (navigator). As T **135**. Multicoloured.
433 37 c. La Perouse with King Louis XVI 95 55
434 90 c. "L'Astrolabe" and "La Boussole" off Norfolk Island 2·75 3·00
435 $1 "L'Astrolabe" wrecked in Solomon Islands . . . . . 2·75 3·00

1988. Bicentenary of Norfolk Island Settlement (5th issue). Arrival of First Fleet at Sydney. As T **135**. Multicoloured.
436 37 c. Ship's cutter approaching Port Jackson . . . . 1·25 75
437 $1 Landing at Sydney Cove . . 2·75 3·25

1988. Bicentenary of Norfolk Island Settlement (6th issue). Foundation of First Settlement. As T **135**. Multicoloured.
438 5 c. Lt. Philip Gidley King . . 20 50
439 37 c. Raising the flag, March 1788 . . . . 85 75
440 55 c. King exploring . . . . . 1·75 1·50
441 70 c. Landing at Sydney Bay, Norfolk Island . . . . . . 2·00 2·50
442 90 c. H.M.S. "Supply" (brig) . 2·25 2·75
443 $1 Sydney Bay settlement, 1788 2·25 2·75

1988. "Sydpex '88" National Stamp Exhibition, Sydney. Multicoloured.
444 37 c. Type **140** . . . . 95 1·25
445 37 c. Exhibition label under magnifying glass (horiz) . . 95 1·25
446 37 c. Telephone and dish aerial 95 1·25

141 Flowers and Decorations **142** Pier Store and Boat Shed

1988. Christmas. Multicoloured.
448 30 c. Type **141** 50 40
449 42 c. Flowers 70 70
450 58 c. Fishes and beach 85 95
451 63 c. Norfolk Island . . . . . 95 1·25

1988. Restored Buildings from the Convict Era. Multicoloured.
452 39 c. Type **142** 45 40
453 55 c. Royal Engineers Building 60 60
454 90 c. Old Military Barracks . . 1·00 1·60
455 $1 Commissariat Store and New Military Barracks . . . . . 1·10 1·60

143 "Lamprima aenea"

1989. Endemic Insects. Multicoloured.
456 39 c. Type **143** 65 40
457 55 c. "Insulascirtus nythos" . . 90 75
458 90 c. "Caedicia araucariae" . . 1·40 2·00
459 $1 "Thrincophora aridela" . . 1·60 2·00

144 H.M.S. "Bounty" off Tasmania

1989. Bicentenary of the Mutiny on the "Bounty". Multicoloured.
460 5 c. Type **144** 60 60
461 39 c. Mutineers and Polynesian women, Pitcairn Island . . . 1·75 1·25
462 55 c. Lake Windermere, Cumbria (Christian's home county) . . 2·25 2·25
463 $1.10 "Mutineers casting Bligh adrift" (Robert Dodd) . . . 3·50 4·50

145 Norfolk Island Flag **146** Red Cross

1989. 10th Anniv of Internal Self-Government. Multicoloured.
465 41 c. Type **145** 90 55
466 55 c. Old ballot box 95 65
467 $1 Norfolk Island Act, 1979 . . 1·75 2·00
468 $1.10 Island crest . . . . . . 1·75 2·75

1989. 75th Anniv of Red Cross on Norfolk Island.
469 **146** $1 red and blue . . . . . 3·00 3·00

147 "Gethsemane"

1989. Christmas. Designs showing opening lines of hymns and local scenes. Multicoloured.
470 36 c. Type **147** 90 40
471 60 c. "In the Sweet Bye and Bye" 1·75 2·00
472 75 c. "Let the Lower Lights be Burning" . . . . 2·25 2·75
473 80 c. "The Beautiful Stream" . 2·25 3·00

148 John Royle (first announcer) **149** H.M.S. "Bounty" on fire, Pitcairn Island, 1790

1989. 50th Anniv of Radio Australia. Designs each showing Kingston buildings. Mult.
474 41 c. Type **148** 95 55
475 65 c. Radio waves linking Australia and Norfolk Island 1·75 2·25
476 $1.10 Anniversary kookaburra logo . . . . 2·75 3·75

1990. History of the Norfolk Islanders (1st series). Settlement on Pitcairn Island. Mult.

477	70 c. Type **149**	2·50	2·50
478	$1.10 Arms of Norfolk Island	2·75	3·00

See also Nos. 503/4 and 516/17.

150 H.M.S. "Sirius" striking Reef

1990. Bicentenary of Wreck of H.M.S. "Sirius". Multicoloured.

479	41 c. Type **150**	1·75	2·00
480	41 c. H.M.S. "Sirius" failing to clear bay	1·75	2·00
481	65 c. Divers at work on wreck	2·50	3·00
482	$1 Recovered artifacts and chart of site	2·75	3·25

Nos. 479/80 were printed together, se-tenant, forming a composite design.

151 Unloading Lighter, Kingston

152 "Ile de Lumiere" (freighter)

1990. Ships.

483	**151**	5 c. brown	20	40
484		10 c. brown	20	40
485	–	45 c. multicoloured	80	60
486	–	50 c. multicoloured	90	1·00
487	–	65 c. multicoloured	1·00	1·25
488	**152**	70 c. multicoloured	90	1·00
489	–	75 c. multicoloured	2·00	2·00
490	–	80 c. multicoloured	2·00	2·25
491	–	90 c. multicoloured	2·00	2·25
492	–	$1 multicoloured	2·00	2·00
493	–	$2 multicoloured	2·25	3·00
494	–	$5 multicoloured	5·00	7·00

DESIGNS—As T **152**: 45 c. "La Dunkerquoise" (French patrol vessel); 50 c. "Dmitri Mendeleev" (Russian research vessel); 65 c. "Pacific Rover" (tanker); 75 c. "Norfolk Trader" (freighter); 80 c. "Roseville" (transport); 90 c. "Kalia" (container ship); $1 "Bounty" (replica); $2 H.M.A.S. "Success" (supply ship); $5 H.M.A.S. "Whyalla" (patrol vessel).

153 Santa on House Roof

154 William Charles Wentworth

1990. Christmas. Multicoloured.

499	38 c. Type **153**	75	45
500	43 c. Santa at Kingston Post Office	80	50
501	65 c. Santa over Sydney Bay, Kingston (horiz)	1·75	2·25
502	85 c. Santa on Officers' Quarters (horiz)	2·00	2·75

1990. History of the Norfolk Islanders (2nd series). The First Generation.

503	**154**	70 c. brown & cinnamon	1·25	1·50
504	–	$1.20 brown & cinnamon	2·00	2·50

DESIGN: $1.20, Thursday October Christian.

155 Adult Robin and Chicks in Nest

156 Map of Norfolk Island

1990. "Birdpex '90" Stamp Exhibition, Christchurch, New Zealand. Scarlet Robin. Multicoloured.

505	65 c. Type **155**	1·25	1·50
506	$1 Hen on branch	1·75	2·00
507	$1.20 Cock on branch	1·75	2·25

1991. Ham Radio Network. Multicoloured.

509	43 c. Type **156**	1·25	70
510	$1 Globe showing Norfolk Island	2·75	3·00
511	$1.20 Map of south-west Pacific	2·75	4·00

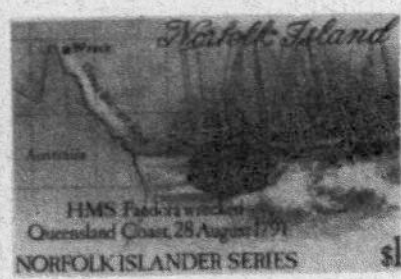

157 Display in "Sirius" Museum

158 H.M.S. "Pandora" wrecked on Great Barrier Reef (1791)

1991. Norfolk Island Museums. Mult.

512	43 c. Type **157**	90	50
513	70 c. 19th-century sitting room, House Museum (horiz)	1·75	2·00
514	$1 Carronade, "Sirius" Museum (horiz)	2·50	2·75
515	$1.20 Reconstructed jug and beaker, Archaeological Museum	2·50	3·25

1991. History of the Norfolk Islanders (3rd series). Search for the "Bounty". Multicoloured.

516	$1 Type **158**	2·75	2·50
517	$1.20 H.M.S. "Pandora" leaving bay	2·75	3·00

159 Hibiscus and Island Scene

1991. Christmas.

518	**159**	38 c. multicoloured	90	45
519		43 c. multicoloured	1·00	55
520		65 c. multicoloured	1·50	2·00
521		85 c. multicoloured	1·75	2·50

160 Tank and Soldier in Jungle

161 Coat of Arms

1991. 50th Anniv of Outbreak of Pacific War. Multicoloured.

522	43 c. Type **160**	1·25	65
523	70 c. Boeing B-17 Flying Fortress on jungle airstrip	2·25	2·75
524	$1 Warships	2·75	3·50

1992. 500th Anniv of Discovery of America by Columbus. Multicoloured.

525	45 c. Type **161**	85	55
526	$1.05 "Santa Maria"	2·00	2·75
527	$1.20 Columbus and globe	2·50	3·25

162 Deployment Map

163 Norfolk Pines above Ball Bay

1992. 50th Anniv of Battle of the Coral Sea. Multicoloured.

528	45 c. Type **162**	1·25	60
529	70 c. H.M.A.S. "Australia" (cruiser)	2·00	2·50
530	$1.05 U.S.S. "Yorktown" (aircraft carrier)	2·75	3·50

1992. 50th Anniv of Battle of Midway. As T **162**. Multicoloured.

531	45 c. Battle area	1·25	60
532	70 c. Consolidated PBY-5 Catalina flying boat over task force	2·00	2·50
533	$1.05 Douglas SBD Dauntless dive bomber and "Akagi" (Japanese aircraft carrier) burning	2·75	3·50

1992. 50th Anniv of Battle of Guadalcanal. As T **162**. Multicoloured.

534	45 c. American troops landing (horiz)	1·25	60
535	70 c. Machine-gun crew (horiz)	2·00	2·50
536	$1.05 Map of Pacific with Japanese and American flags (horiz)	2·75	3·50

1992. Christmas. Multicoloured.

537	40 c. Type **163**	70	40
538	45 c. Headstone Creek	75	45
539	75 c. South side of Ball Bay	1·50	2·25
540	$1.20 Rocky Point Reserve	2·00	3·00

164 Boat Shed and Flaghouses, Kingston

1993. Tourism. Historic Kingston. Mult.

541	45 c. Type **164**	80	1·00
542	45 c. Old Military Barracks	80	1·00
543	45 c. All Saints Church	80	1·00
544	45 c. Officers' Quarters	80	1·00
545	45 c. Quality Row	80	1·00

Nos. 541/5 were printed together, se-tenant, forming a composite design.

165 Fire Engine

1993. Emergency Services. Multicoloured.

546	45 c. Type **165**	1·00	60
547	70 c. Cliff rescue squad	1·10	1·75
548	75 c. Ambulance	1·40	1·90
549	$1.20 Police car	2·50	3·00

166 Blue-sea Lizard ("Glaucus atlanticus")

1993. Nudibranchs. Multicoloured.

550	45 c. Type **166**	80	55
551	45 c. Ocellate nudibranch ("Phyllidia ocellata")	80	55
552	75 c. "Bornella sp."	1·50	1·75
553	85 c. "Glossodoris rubroannolata"	1·75	2·25
554	95 c. "Halgerda willeyi"	2·00	2·50
555	$1.05 "Ceratosoma amoena"	2·00	3·00

167 Christmas Wreath

168 Maori Stone Clubs

1993. Christmas.

556	**167**	40 c. multicoloured	60	45
557		45 c. multicoloured	60	45
558		75 c. multicoloured	1·00	1·50
559		$1.20 multicoloured	1·90	2·50

1993. Bicentenary of Contact with New Zealand. Multicoloured.

560	70 c. Type **168**	1·25	1·50
561	$1.20 First Maori map of New Zealand, 1793	2·00	2·50

169 Alvaro de Saavedra, Route Map and "Florida"

1994. Pacific Explorers. Multicoloured.

562	5 c. Vasco Nunez de Balboa, map and "Barbara"	55	55
563	10 c. Ferdinand Magellan, map and "Vitoria"	55	55
564	20 c. Juan Sebastian del Cano, map and "Vitoria"	75	75
565	50 c. Type **169**	95	95
566	70 c. Ruy Lopez de Villalobos, map and "San Juan"	1·25	1·25
567	75 c. Miguel Lopez de Legaspi, map and "San Lesmes"	1·25	1·25
568	80 c. Sir Francis Drake, map and "Golden Hind"	1·25	1·25
569	85 c. Alvaro de Mendana, map and "Santiago"	1·25	1·25
570	90 c. Pedro Fernandes de Quiros, map and "San Pedro y Pablo"	1·25	1·25
571	$1 Luis Baez de Torres, map and "San Pedrico"	1·40	1·40
572	$2 Abel Tasman, map and "Heemskerk"	2·00	2·25
573	$5 William Dampier, map and "Cygnet"	4·25	5·00

170 Sooty Tern

171 House and Star

1994. Sea Birds. Multicoloured.

575	45 c. Type **170**	95	1·00
576	45 c. Red-tailed tropic bird	95	1·00
577	45 c. Australian gannet	95	1·00
578	45 c. Wedge-tailed shearwater	95	1·00
579	45 c. Masked booby	95	1·00

Nos. 575/9 were printed together, se-tenant, forming a composite design.

1994. Christmas. Multicoloured. Self-adhesive.

580	45 c. Type **171**	80	55
581	75 c. Figures from stained-glass windows	1·50	2·00
582	$1.20 Rainbow and "The Church of God" (missionary sailing ship)	2·50	3·00

172 Chevrolet, 1926

1995. Vintage Motor Vehicles. Multicoloured.

583	45 c. Type **172**	75	55
584	75 c. Ford Model "A", 1928	1·25	1·75
585	$1.05 Ford Model "A A/C", 1929	1·60	2·00
586	$1.20 Ford Model "A", 1930	1·75	2·25

173 Tail Flukes of Humpback Whale

1995. Humpback Whale Conservation. Multicoloured.

587	45 c. Type **173**	1·00	55
588	75 c. Mother and calf	1·50	2·00
589	$1.05 Whale breaching (vert)	1·75	2·50

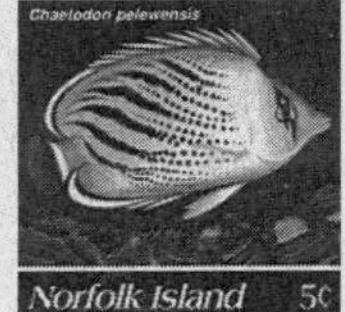

174 Dot-and-Dash Butterflyfish

1995. Butterflyfishes. Multicoloured.

591	5 c. Type **174**	30	50
592	45 c. Blue-spotted butterflyfish	85	50
593	$1.20 Three-belted butterflyfish	2·25	2·75
594	$1.50 Three-finned butterflyfish	2·50	3·00

175 International 4 × 4 Refueller, 1942

1995. Second World War Vehicles. Multicoloured.

596	5 c. Type **175**	30	40
597	45 c. Ford Sedan, 1942	75	45
598	$1.20 Ford 3 ton tipper, 1942	2·00	2·50
599	$2 D8 caterpillar with scraper	3·00	3·50

1995. Flower designs as 1960 issues, but with face values in decimal currency.

600	5 c. pink and green (as No. 25)	10	10
601	5 c. red (as No. 28)	10	10

176 Servicing Fighter

177 Peace Dove and Anniversary Emblem

1995. 50th Anniv of End of Second World War in the Pacific. Multicoloured.
602 5 c. Type **176** 40 50
603 45 c. Sgt. Tom Derrick, VC (vert) 70 45
604 75 c. Gen. Douglas MacArthur (vert) . . . . 1·25 1·50
605 $1.05 Girls celebrating victory . 1·75 2·00
606 $10 Pacific War medals (50 × 30 mm) . . . . 16·00 18·00
The $10 also includes the "Singapore '95" International stamp exhibition logo.

1995. Christmas. 50th Anniv of United Nations. Each including U.N. anniversary emblem.
607 **177** 45 c. gold and blue . . . 60 45
608 – 75 c. gold and violet . . . 1·00 1·25
609 – $1.05 gold and red . . . . 1·40 2·00
610 – $1.20 gold and green . . . 1·60 2·25
DESIGNS: 75 c. Star of Bethlehem; $1.05, Symbolic candles on cake; $1.20, Olive branch.

178 Skink on Bank

179 Sopwith Pup Biplane and Emblem

1996. Endangered Species. Skinks and Geckos. Multicoloured.
611 5 c. Type **178** 55 65
612 5 c. Gecko on branch 55 65
613 45 c. Skink facing right 70 75
614 45 c. Gecko on flower 70 75

1996. 75th Anniv of Royal Australian Air Force. Aircraft. Multicoloured.
615 45 c. Type **179** 60 60
616 45 c. Wirraway fighter 60 60
617 75 c. F-111C jet fighter . . . . 1·00 1·40
618 85 c. F/A-18 Hornet jet fighter . 1·10 1·50

181 "Naticarlus oncus"

1996. Shells. Multicoloured.
620 45 c. Type **181** 70 85
621 45 c. "Janthina janthina" . . . 70 85
622 45 c. "Cypraea caputserpentis" . 70 85
623 45 c. "Argonauta nodosa" . . 70 85

182 Shopping
183 The Nativity

1996. Tourism. Multicoloured.
624 45 c. Type **182** 50 50
625 75 c. Celebrating Bounty Day . 1·00 1·00
626 $2.50 Horse riding . . . . . . 3·75 4·25
627 $3.70 Unloading lighter . . . . 4·50 5·25

1996. Christmas. Multicoloured.
628 45 c. Type **183** 50 50
629 45 c. Star and boat sheds . . . 50 50
630 75 c. Star, bungalow and ox . . 90 1·50
631 85 c. Star, fruit, flowers and ox . . . . 1·10 1·75

184 Coat of Arms

186 "Cepora perimale"

1997.
632 **184** 5 c. blue and yellow . . . 20 30
633 – 5 c. brown 20 30
DESIGN: No. 633, Great Seal of Norfolk Island.

1997. Butterflies. Multicoloured.
636 75 c. Type **186** . . . . 1·00 85
637 90 c. "Danaus chrysippus" . . 1·25 1·50
638 $1 "Danaus hamata" . . . . 1·40 1·50
639 $1.20 "Danaus plexippus" . . 1·50 2·00

187 Dusky Dolphins

1997. Dolphins. Multicoloured.
640 45 c. Type **187** 75 60
641 75 c. Common dolphin and calf . 1·25 1·40

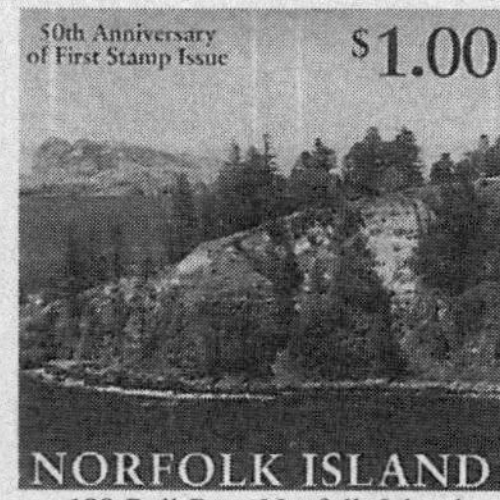

188 Ball Bay, Norfolk Island

1997. 50th Anniv of Norfolk Island Stamps. Multicoloured.
644 $1 Type **188** 80 85
645 $1.50 1947 2d. stamp . . . . . 1·10 1·40
646 $8 Ball Bay and 1947 2s. bistre stamp (90 × 45 mm) . . . . 6·50 6·75

1997. Golden Wedding of Queen Elizabeth and Prince Philip. As T **87** of Kiribati. Multicoloured.
647 20 c. Queen Elizabeth 30 40
648 25 c. Prince Philip in carriage-driving trials 30 40
649 25 c. Prince Philip 30 40
650 50 c. Queen in phaeton at Trooping the Colour 60 60

190 Christmas Tree

193 "Pepper"

1997. Annual Festivals. Multicoloured.
653 45 c. Type **190** 50 45
654 75 c. Fireworks (New Year's Eve) 80 1·00
655 $1.20 Rose (Valentine's Day) . 1·25 1·50

1998. Cats. Multicoloured.
658 45 c. Type **193** 65 65
659 45 c. "Tabitha" at window . . 65 65
660 75 c. "Midnight" . . . . . . 85 1·00
661 $1.20 "Rainbow" with flower pot 1·25 1·50

194 Entrance to Pentagonal Gaol

1998.
662 **194** 5 c. black and blue 10 15
663 – 5 c. black and green . . . 10 15
DESIGN: No. 663, Ruined First Settlement cottage.

1998. Diana, Princess of Wales Commemoration. As T **91** of Kiribati.
664 45 c. Princess Diana with bouquet, 1991 . . . . . . 40 40

195 Tweed Trousers

196 Hammer Throwing

1998. Reef Fishes. Multicoloured.
666 10 c. Type **195** 10 15
667 20 c. Conspicuous angelfish . . 15 20
668 30 c. Moon wrasse 25 30
669 45 c. Wide-striped clownfish . . 35 40
670 50 c. Racoon butterflyfish . . . 40 45
671 70 c. Artooti (juvenile) 55 60
672 75 c. Splendid hawkfish 60 65
673 85 c. Scorpion fish 65 70
674 90 c. Orange fairy basslet . . . 70 75
675 $1 Sweetlips 80 85
676 $3 Moorish idol . . . . 2·40 2·50
677 $4 Gold-ribbon soapfish . . . 3·25 3·50
Nos. 672 and 675 are incorrectly inscribed "Splendid Hawkfish" and "Sweetlip".

1998. 16th Commonwealth Games, Kuala Lumpur.
679 **196** 75 c. red and black . . . . 85 1·00
680 – 95 c. violet and black . . . 1·00 1·25
681 – $1.05 mauve and black . . 1·10 1·40
DESIGNS—HORIZ: 95 c. Trap shooting. VERT: $1.05, Lawn bowls.

197 "Norfolk" (sloop)

1998. Bicentenary of the Circumnavigation of Tasmania by George Bass and Matthew Flinders.
683 **197** 45 c. multicoloured 65 65

199 "Peace on Earth"

1998. Christmas. Multicoloured.
686 45 c. Type **199** 35 40
687 75 c. "Joy to the World" . . . 60 65
688 $1.05 "A Season of Love" . . 80 85
689 $1.20 "Light of the World" . . 90 95

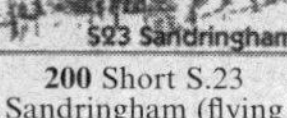

200 Short S.23 Sandringham (flying boat)

204 Solander's Petrel in Flight

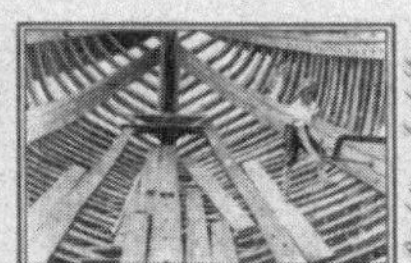

202 Hull of "Resolution" under Construction

1999. Aircraft. Each red and green.
690 5 c. Type **200** 10 10
691 5 c. DC-4 "Norfolk Trader" . . 10 10

1999. "Australia '99" International Stamp Exhibition, Melbourne. Schooner "Resolution". Multicoloured.
693 45 c. Type **202** 35 40
694 45 c. After being launched . . 35 40
695 45 c. In Emily Bay 35 40
696 45 c. Off Cascade 35 40
697 45 c. Alongside at Auckland . . 35 40

1999. Endangered Species. Solander's Petrel ("Providence Petrel"). Multicoloured.
699 75 c. Type **204** 60 65
700 $1.05 Head of Solander's petrel (horiz) 80 85
701 $1.20 Adult and fledgling (horiz) 90 95

205 "Cecile" Brunner Rose

206 Pottery

1999. Roses. Multicoloured.
703 45 c. Type **205** 35 40
704 75 c. Green rose 60 65
705 $1.05 "David Buffett" rose . . . 80 85

1999. Handicrraft of Norfolk Islands. Multicoloured.
708 45 c. Type **206** 35 40
709 45 c. Woodcarving 35 40
710 75 c. Quilting 60 65
711 $1.05 Basket-weaving 80 85

1999. "Queen Elizabeth the Queen Mother's Century". As T **304a** of Gambia. Multicoloured (except $1.20).
712 45 c. Inspecting bomb damage, Buckingham Palace, 1940 . . 35 40
713 45 c. At Abergeldy Castle sale of work, 1955 . . . . 35 40
714 75 c. Queen Mother, Queen Elizabeth and Prince William, 1994 . . . . 60 65
715 $1.20 Inspecting the King's Regiment (black) 90 95

207 Bishop George Augustus Selwyn

1999. Christmas. 150th Anniv of Melanesian Mission. Multicoloured (except 75 c.).
717 45 c. Type **207** 35 40
718 45 c. Bishop John Coleridge Patteson 35 40
719 75 c. "150 YEARS MELANESIAN MISSION" (black) 60 65
720 $1.05 Stained-glass windows . . 80 85
721 $1.20 Southern Cross (missionary ship) and religious symbols . 90 95
Nos. 717/21 were printed together, se-tenant, with the backgrounds forming a composite design.

208 Basket of Food (Thanksgiving)

2000. Festivals.
722 **208** 5 c. black and blue 10 10
723 – 5 c. black and blue 10 10
DESIGN: No. 723, Musician playing guitar (Country Music Festival).

210 Domestic Goose

2000. Ducks and Geese. Multicoloured.
725 45 c. Type **210** 35 40
726 75 c. Pacific black duck 60 65
727 $1.05 Mallard drake 80 85
728 $1.20 Aylesbury duck 90 95

211 Honour Roll for First World War

2000. Anzac Day. Multicoloured.
729 45 c. Type **211** 35 40
730 75 c. Honour rolls for Second World War and Korea . . . 60 65

NORTH BORNEO Pt. 1

A territory in the north of the Island of Borneo in the China Sea, formerly under the administration of the British North Borneo Company. A Crown Colony since 1946. Joined Malaysia in 1963 and renamed Sabah in 1964.

100 cents = 1 dollar (Malayan)

1

1883. "POSTAGE NORTH BORNEO" at top.

No.	Type	Description		
8	**1**	½ c. mauve	80·00	£170
9		1 c. orange	£170	£300
10		2 c. brown	22·00	22·00
11		4 c. pink	17·00	50·00
12		8 c. green	19·00	50·00
13		10 c. blue	25·00	45·00

1883. Surch **8 Cents.** vert.

No.	Type	Description		
2	**1**	8 c. on 2 c. brown	£900	£600

1883. Surch **EIGHT CENTS.**

No.	Type	Description		
3	**1**	8 c. on 2 c. brown	£425	£180

Where there are three price columns, prices in the second column are for postally used stamps and those in the third column are for stamps cancelled with black bars.

4

5

1883. Inscr "NORTH BORNEO".

No.	Type	Description			
4	**4**	50 c. violet	95·00	—	20·00
5	**5**	$1 red	90·00	—	9·50

For these designs with "BRITISH" in place of value in words at top, see Nos. 46/7.

1886. Optd **and Revenue**.

No.	Type	Description		
14	**1**	½ c. mauve	90·00	£170
15		10 c. blue	£130	£170

1886. Surch in words and figures.

No.	Type	Description		
18	**1**	3 c. on 4 c. pink	75·00	£110
19		5 c. on 8 c. green	80·00	£110

9

10

13

19

1886. Inscr "BRITISH NORTH BORNEO".

No.	Type	Description			
22	**9**	½ c. red	2·50	13·00	
24		1 c. orange	2·00	8·00	
25		2 c. brown	2·00	8·50	
26		4 c. pink	2·50	9·00	
27		8 c. green	8·00	16·00	
28		10 c. blue	7·00	25·00	
45	**10**	25 c. blue	40·00	80·00	75
46	–	50 c. violet	70·00	£130	75
47	–	$1 red	27·00	£110	75
48	**13**	$2 green	£110	£170	1·50
49	**19**	$5 purple	£140	£150	8·50
50	–	$10 brown	£190	£275	12·00

DESIGNS: 50 c. As Type **4**; $1, As Type **5**. $10 As Type **19** but with different frame.

14

1888. Inscr "POSTAGE & REVENUE".

No.	Type	Description			
36b	**14**	½ c. red	1·00	4·00	60
37		1 c. orange	1·60	3·50	50
38b		2 c. brown	3·00	11·00	50
39		3 c. violet	2·50	11·00	50
40		4 c. pink	4·50	24·00	50
41		5 c. grey	2·75	17·00	50
42		6 c. red	7·00	17·00	50
43a		8 c. green	15·00	21·00	50
44b		10 c. blue	6·50	18·00	50

1890. Surch in words.

No.	Type	Description		
51	**10**	2 c. on 25 c. blue	55·00	75·00
52		8 c. on 25 c. blue	85·00	£100

1891. Surch in figures and words.

No.	Type	Description		
63	**14**	1 c. on 4 c. pink	20·00	14·00
64		1 c. on 5 c. grey	6·50	6·00
54	**9**	6 c. on 8 c. green	£7000	£3750
55	**14**	6 c. on 8 c. green	16·00	9·00
56	**9**	6 c. on 10 c. blue	50·00	18·00
57	**14**	6 c. on 10 c. blue	£120	26·00
65	**10**	8 c. on 25 c. blue	£130	£150

24 Dyak Chief

25 Sambar Stag ("Cervus unicolor")

26 Sago Palm

27 Great Argus Pheasant

28 Arms of the Company

29 Malay Prau

30 Estuarine Crocodile

31 Mt. Kinabalu

32 Arms of the Company with Supporters

1894.

No.	Type	Description			
66	**24**	1 c. black & bistre	1·25	8·00	50
69	**25**	2 c. black & red	5·00	4·75	50
70	**26**	3 c. green & mauve	2·75	7·50	50
72	**27**	5 c. black & red	12·00	11·00	60
73a	**28**	6 c. black & brown	4·00	15·00	60
74	**29**	8 c. black & lilac	5·00	9·50	60
75	**30**	12 c. black & blue	27·00	80·00	2·50
78	**31**	18 c. black & green	24·00	48·00	2·00
79	**32**	24 c. blue & red	22·00	70·00	2·00

1894. As Nos. 47, etc, but inscr "THE STATE OF NORTH BORNEO".

No.	Description			
81	25 c. blue	8·50	27·00	90
82	50 c. violet	15·00	50·00	90
83	$1 red	12·00	24·00	1·00
84	$2 green	16·00	75·00	1·50
85b	$5 purple	£160	£225	5·50
86	$10 brown	£190	£275	11·00

1895. No. 83 surch in figures and words.

No.	Description			
87	4 cents on $1 red	4·50	1·50	40
88	10 cents on $1 red	12·00	1·75	40
89	20 cents on $1 red	30·00	14·00	40
90	30 cents on $1 red	23·00	22·00	40
91	40 cents on $1 red	23·00	45·00	40

37 Orang-utan

41 Sun Bear

43 Borneo Steam Train

1897. As 1894 issue with insertion of native inscriptions.

No.	Type	Description			
92a	**24**	1 c. black & bistre	8·00	2·50	40
94a	**25**	2 c. black & red	17·00	3·00	40
95		2 c. black & green	42·00	1·50	40
97	**26**	3 c. green & mauve	9·50	3·00	50
98	**37**	4 c. black & green	9·00	—	1·50
99		4 c. black & red	30·00	6·50	50
100a	**27**	5 c. black & orange	75·00	3·00	50
101a	**28**	6 c. black & brown	15·00	3·25	50
102b	**29**	8 c. black & lilac	30·00	2·75	60
104	**41**	10 c. brown & grey	70·00	35·00	2·00
106b	**30**	12 c. black & blue	80·00	32·00	1·50
107	**43**	16 c. green & brown	£120	90·00	3·00
108	**31**	18 c. black & green	17·00	60·00	1·00
110b		18 c. black & green*	60·00	12·00	1·50
109	**32**	24 c. blue & red*	16·00	75·00	1·60
111		24 c. blue & red*	55·00	35·00	2·00

*No. 110 is inscribed "POSTAGE & REVENUE" at the sides instead of "POSTAL REVENUE" as in No. 108. No. 111 has the words "POSTAGE & REVENUE" at the sides below the Arms; these words were omitted in No. 109.

1899. Stamps of 1897 and Nos. 81/6 surch **4 CENTS**.

No.	Description		
112a	4 c. on 5 c. black & orange	18·00	10·00
113	4 c. on 6 c. black & brown	18·00	23·00
114	4 c. on 8 c. black and lilac	14·00	10·00
115	4 c. on 12 c. black & blue	16·00	13·00
116	4 c. on 18 c. black and green (110)	9·50	13·00
117	4 c. on 24 c. bl & red (111)	15·00	15·00
118	4 c. on 25 c. blue	5·00	8·50
119	4 c. on 50 c. violet	7·00	14·00
121	4 c. on $1 red	5·00	10·00
122	4 c. on $2 green	5·00	12·00
125	4 c. on $5 purple	5·50	12·00
126	4 c. on $10 brown	5·50	12·00

1901. Stamps of 1897 and Nos. 81/6 optd **BRITISH PROTECTORATE.**

No.	Description			
127a	1 c. black & bistre	2·50	1·75	30
128	2 c. black & green	3·00	1·25	30
129	3 c. green & mauve	1·60	4·25	30
130	4 c. black and red	7·00	1·50	30
131a	5 c. black & orange	10·00	2·50	30
132b	6 c. black & brown	3·25	11·00	70
133	8 c. black and lilac	3·00	3·25	50
134	10 c. brown & grey	35·00	5·00	60
135	12 c. black and blue	40·00	12·00	1·50
136	16 c. green & brown	90·00	20·00	2·25
137	18 c. black & green (110)	10·00	25·00	1·25
138	24 c. blue & red (111)	16·00	40·00	1·50
139	25 c. blue	2·00	10·00	50
140	50 c. violet	2·75	11·00	55
142	$1 red	6·50	38·00	2·50
143	$2 green	30·00	95·00	3·50
144	$5 purple (with full point)	£180	£425	7·50
184	$5 purple (without full point)	£850	£950	7·50
145	$10 brown (with full point)	£300	£550	8·50
185	$10 brown (without full point)	£1100	—	7·50

1904. Stamps of 1897 and Nos. 81/6 surch **4 cents**.

No.	Description			
146	4 c. on 5 c. blk & orge	28·00	40·00	8·00
147	4 c. on 6 c. blk & brn	7·00	19·00	7·00
148	4 c. on 8 c. blk & lilac	12·00	26·00	7·50
149	4 c. on 12 c. blk & bl	22·00	40·00	8·00
150	4 c. on 18 c. black and green (110)	14·00	38·00	8·00
151a	4 c. on 24 c. bl & red (111)	16·00	48·00	8·00
152	4 c. on 25 c. blue	3·50	25·00	8·00
153	4 c. on 50 c. violet	4·00	38·00	8·00
154	4 c. on $1 red	4·50	48·00	8·00
155	4 c. on $2 green	5·50	48·00	8·00
156	4 c. on $5 purple	11·00	48·00	8·00
157	4 c. on $10 brown	11·00	48·00	8·00

51 Malayan Tapir

52 Traveller's Tree

64

(68)

1909. No. 177 is surch **20 CENTS**.

No.	Type	Description			
277	**51**	1 c. black & brown	1·00	70	—
160	**52**	2 c. black & green	1·00	70	30
278		2 c. black & red	40	60	—
162	–	3 c. black & red	2·50	1·75	40
279	–	3 c. black & green	2·75	75	—
280	–	4 c. black & red	45	10	—
281	–	5 c. black & brown	4·50	2·75	—
282	–	6 c. black & green	5·00	90	—
283	–	8 c. black & red	3·25	50	—
284	–	10 c. black & blue	3·25	90	—
285	–	12 c. black & blue	18·00	80	—
174	–	16 c. black & brown	24·00	7·00	80
175	–	18 c. black & green	90·00	30·00	1·00
177	–	20 c. on 18 c. blk & grn	6·00	95	20
176	–	24 c. black & green	27·00	3·50	90
178	**64**	25 c. black & green	6·50	4·00	1·50
179	–	50 c. black & blue	7·00	3·75	1·75
180	–	$1 black & brown	15·00	4·00	1·75
181	–	$2 black & lilac	45·00	15·00	4·25
182	–	$5 black & red	95·00	£110	24·00
183	–	$10 black & orge	£250	£300	50·00

DESIGNS—As T **51**: 3 c. Jesselton railway station; 4 c. Sultan of Sulu, his staff and W. C. Cowie, first Chairman of the Company; 5 c. Asiatic elephant; 8 c. Ploughing with buffalo; 24 c. Dwarf Cassowary. As T **52**: 6 c. Sumatran rhinoceros; 10 c. Wild boar; 12 c. Palm Cockatoo; 16 c Rhinoceros hornbill; 18 c Banteng. As T **64** but Arms with supporters: $5, $10.

1916. Stamps of 1909 surch.

No.	Description		
186	2 c. on 3 c. black and red	20·00	13·00
187	4 c. on 6 c. black and olive	16·00	16·00
188	10 c. on 12 c. black & blue	48·00	50·00

1916. Nos. 277 etc, optd with T **68**.

No.	Description		
189	1 c. black and brown	7·50	35·00
203	2 c. black and green	27·00	48·00
191	3 c. black and red	27·00	48·00
192	4 c. black and red	5·50	32·00
193	5 c. black and brown	30·00	55·00
206	6 c. black and green	42·00	65·00
207	8 c. black and red	24·00	55·00
196	10 c. black and blue	40·00	70·00
197	12 c. black and blue	85·00	90·00
198	16 c. black and brown	85·00	90·00
199	20 c. on 18 c. black & green	32·00	85·00
200	24 c. black and mauve	85·00	90·00
201	25 c. black and green	£275	£350

1918. Nos. 159, etc, surch **RED CROSS TWO CENTS**.

No.	Description		
214	1 c. + 2 c. black and brown	3·50	10·00
215	2 c. + 2 c. black and green	1·00	8·50
216	3 c. + 2 c. black and red	11·00	15·00
218	4 c. + 2 c. black and red	70	4·00
219	5 c. + 2 c. black and brown	8·00	22·00
221	6 c. + 2 c. black and olive	5·00	18·00
222	8 c. + 2 c. black and red	5·50	10·00
223	10 c. + 2 c. black and blue	7·50	23·00
224	12 c. + 2 c. black and blue	18·00	42·00
225	16 c. + 2 c. black and brown	20·00	42·00
226	24 c. + 2 c. black and mauve	20·00	42·00
229	25 c. + 2 c. black and green	10·00	38·00
230	50 c. + 2 c. black and blue	12·00	38·00
231	$1 + 2 c. black and brown	45·00	50·00
232	$2 + 2 c. black and lilac	70·00	95·00
233	$5 + 2 c. black and red	£325	£450
234	$10 + 2 c. black and orange	£325	£450

The premium of 2 c. on each value was for Red Cross Funds.

1918. Nos. 159, etc, surch **FOUR CENTS** and a red cross.

No.	Description		
235	1 c. + 4 c. black and brown	60	5·00
236	2 c. + 4 c. black and green	65	8·00
237	3 c. + 4 c. black and red	90	3·75
238	4 c. + 4 c. black and red	40	4·75
239	5 c. + 4 c. black and brown	2·00	18·00
240	6 c. + 4 c. black and olive	1·90	12·00
241	8 c. + 4 c. black and red	1·25	9·50
242	10 c. + 4 c. black and blue	3·75	12·00
243	12 c. + 4 c. black and blue	10·00	14·00
244	16 c. + 4 c. black and brown	7·00	16·00
245	24 c. + 4 c. black and mauve	9·00	20·00
246	25 c. + 4 c. black and green	5·00	48·00
248	50 c. + 4 c. black and blue	15·00	42·00
249	$1 + 4 c. black and brown	15·00	55·00
250	$2 + 4 c. black and lilac	48·00	80·00
251	$5 + 4 c. black and red	£275	£400
252	$10 + 4 c. black and orange	£275	£400

The premium of 4 c. on each value was for Red Cross Funds.

1922. Nos. 159, etc, optd **MALAYA-BORNEO EXHIBITION 1922.**

No.	Description		
253	1 c. black and brown	8·00	50·00
255	2 c. black and green	1·75	17·00
256	3 c. black and red	12·00	42·00
257	4 c. black and red	1·75	28·00
258	5 c. black and brown	9·00	48·00
260	6 c. black and green	5·00	48·00
262	8 c. black and red	5·00	42·00
263	10 c. black and blue	7·00	48·00
265	12 c. black and blue	4·75	21·00
267	16 c. black and brown	13·00	50·00
268	20 c. on 18 c. black & green	15·00	60·00
270	24 c. black and mauve	26·00	55·00
274	25 c. black and green	4·00	50·00
275	50 c. black and blue	7·50	42·00

1923. No. 280 surch **THREE CENTS** and bars.

No.	Type	Description		
276	–	3 c. on 4 c. black & red	1·00	4·75

73 Head of a Murut

76 Mount Kinabalu

1931. 50th Anniv of North Borneo Company.

No.	Type	Description		
295	**73**	3 c. black and green	90	80
296	–	6 c. black and orange	16·00	3·25
297	–	10 c. black and red	4·00	11·00
298	**76**	12 c. black and blue	4·25	8·00
299	–	25 c. black and violet	38·00	35·00
300	–	$1 black and green	27·00	95·00
301	–	$2 black and brown	48·00	£110
302	–	$5 black and purple	£140	£325

DESIGNS—VERT: 6 c. Orang-utan; 10 c. Dyak warrior; $1, $2, $5 Arms. HORIZ: 25 c. Clouded leopard.

81 Buffalo Transport

82 Palm Cockatoo

1939.

303 81 1 c. green and brown . . . 1·25 1·00
304 82 2 c. purple and blue . . . . 5·00 1·00
305 – 3 c. blue and green . . . . 2·00 2·00
306 – 4 c. green and violet . . . . 4·00 50
307 – 6 c. blue and red . . . . 3·25 5·50
308 – 8 c. red . . . . 7·50 1·50
309 – 10 c. violet and green . . . 38·00 6·00
310 – 12 c. green and blue . . . 18·00 5·00
311 – 15 c. green and brown . . . 17·00 7·50
312 – 20 c. violet and blue . . . 10·00 3·25
313 – 25 c. green and brown . . . 13·00 9·00
314 – 50 c. brown and violet . . . 16·00 7·00
315 – $1 brown and red . . . . 65·00 19·00
316 – $2 violet and olive . . . . £100 85·00
317 – $5 blue £300 £225

DESIGNS—VERT: 3 c. Native; 4 c. Proboscis monkey; 6 c. Mounted Bajaus; 10 c. Orang-utan; 15 c. Dyak; $1, $2 Arms. HORIZ: 8 c. Map of Eastern Archipelago; 12 c. Murut with blow-pipe; 20 c. River scene; 25 c. Native boat; 50 c. Mt. Kinabalu; $5 Arms with supporters.

1941. Optd **WAR TAX**.

318 81 1 c. green and brown . . . 90 2·00
319 82 2 c. purple and blue . . . . 4·75 3·50

1945. British Military Administration. Stamps of 1939 optd **BMA**.

320 81 1 c. green and brown . . . 4·25 1·75
321 82 2 c. purple and blue . . . . 12·00 1·75
322 – 3 c. blue and green . . . . 1·25 1·25
323 – 4 c. green and violet . . . . 16·00 14·00
324 – 6 c. blue and red . . . . 1·25 75
325 – 8 c. red . . . . 3·00 75
326 – 10 c. violet and green . . . 3·00 40
327 – 12 c. green and blue . . . 4·75 2·50
328 – 15 c. green and brown . . . 1·50 1·00
329 – 20 c. violet and blue . . . 3·50 1·25
330 – 25 c. green and brown . . . 5·00 1·50
331 – 50 c. brown and violet . . . 3·00 1·50
332 – $1 brown and red . . . . 45·00 30·00
333 – $2 violet and olive . . . . 38·00 24·00
334 – $5 blue . . . . 16·00 11·00

1947. Stamps of 1939 optd with Crown over GR monogram and bars obliterating "THE STATE OF" and "BRITISH PROTECTORATE".

335 81 1 c. green and brown . . . 15 1·00
336 82 2 c. purple and blue . . . . 1·75 90
337 – 3 c. blue and green 15 90
338 – 4 c. green and violet 70 40
339 – 6 c. blue and red 15 20
340 – 8 c. red 20 20
341 – 10 c. violet and green . . . 60 40
342 – 12 c. green and blue . . . 2·00 2·25
343 – 15 c. green and brown . . . 2·25 30
344 – 20 c. violet and blue . . . 1·50 85
345 – 25 c. green and brown . . . 2·50 45
346 – 50 c. brown and violet . . . 1·50 85
347 – $1 brown and red . . . . 2·50 1·25
348 – $2 violet and olive . . . . 7·50 12·00
349 – $5 blue . . . . 16·00 12·00

1948. Silver Wedding. As T **11b/c** of Gambia.

350 8 c. red 30 80
351 $10 mauve . . . . 20·00 35·00

1949. U.P.U. As T **11d/g** of Gambia.

352 8 c. red 40 30
353 10 c. brown . . . . 2·50 1·00
354 30 c. brown . . . . 90 1·75
355 55 c. blue . . . . 90 2·25

100 Mt. Kinabalu

102 Coconut Grove

1950.

356 100 1 c. brown 15 70
357 – 2 c. blue 15 50
358 102 3 c. green 15 15
359 – 4 c. purple 15 10
360 – 5 c. violet 15 10
361 – 8 c. red 75 85
362 – 10 c. purple 60 15
363 – 15 c. blue . . . . 2·00 65
364 – 20 c. brown . . . . 1·00 10
365 – 30 c. buff . . . . 2·50 20
366 – 50 c. red ("JESSLETON") . . 85 3·00
366a – 50 c. red ("JESSELTON") . . 6·50 2·00
367 – $1 orange . . . . 2·50 1·00
368 – $2 green . . . . 2·50 9·00
369 – $5 green . . . . 12·00 16·00
370 – $10 blue . . . . 35·00 45·00

DESIGNS—VERT: 4 c. Hemp drying; 5 c. Cattle at Kota Belud; 30 c. Suluk river canoe; 50 c. Clock tower, Jesselton; $1 Bajau horsemen. HORIZ: 2 c. Musician; 8 c. Map; 10 c. Log pond; 15 c. Malay prau, Sandakan; 20 c. Bajau chief; $2 Murut with blowpipe; $5 Net fishing; $10, King George VI and arms.

1953. Coronation. As T **11h** of Gambia.

371 10 c. black and red . . . . . 1·25 60

1954. As 1950 but with portrait of Queen Elizabeth II.

372 1 c. brown 10 30
373 2 c. blue 60 15
374 3 c. green . . . . 60 2·00
375 4 c. purple 75 20
376 5 c. violet 75 10
377 8 c. red 50 30
378 10 c. purple 30 10
379 15 c. blue . . . . 1·00 10
380 20 c. brown 30 15
381 30 c. buff . . . . 2·00 20
382 50 c. red (No. 366a) . . . . 5·00 20
383 $1 orange . . . . 6·50 20
384 $2 green . . . . 12·00 1·25
385 $5 green . . . . 10·00 23·00
386 $10 blue . . . . 23·00 35·00

117 Malay Prau

1956. 75th Anniv of Foundation of British North Borneo Co. Inscr "CHARTER 1ST NOVEMBER 1881".

387 – 10 c. black and red . . . . 1·00 40
388 117 15 c. black and brown . . . 30 30
389 – 35 c. black and green . . . 30 1·50
390 – $1 black and slate . . . . 65 2·50

DESIGNS—HORIZ: 10 c. Borneo Railway, 1902; 35 c. Mt. Kinabalu. VERT: $1 Arms of Chartered Company.

120 Sambar Stag

1961.

391 120 1 c. green and red 20 10
392 – 4 c. olive and orange . . . 20 90
393 – 5 c. sepia and violet . . . 30 10
394 – 6 c. black and turquoise . . 50 40
395 – 10 c. green and red 30 10
396 – 12 c. brown and myrtle . . . 30 10
397 – 20 c. turquoise and blue . . 3·50 10
398 – 25 c. black and red 70 90
399 – 30 c. sepia and olive . . . 70 20
400 – 35 c. slate and brown . . . 1·75 90
401 – 50 c. green and bistre . . . 1·75 20
402 – 75 c. blue and purple . . . 7·00 90
403 – $1 brown and green . . . 11·00 80
404 – $2 brown and slate . . . 25·00 3·00
405 – $5 green and purple . . . 38·00 15·00
406 – $10 red and blue . . . . 26·00 27·00

DESIGNS—HORIZ: 4 c. Sun bear; 5 c. Clouded leopard; 6 c. Dusun woman with gong; 10 c. Map of Borneo; 12 c. Banteng; 20 c. Butterfly orchid; 25 c. Sumatran rhinoceros; 30 c. Murut with blow-pipe; 35 c. Mt. Kinabalu; 50 c. Dusun and buffalo transport; 75 c. Bajau horseman. VERT: $1 Orang-utan; $2 Rhinoceros hornbill; $5 Crested wood partridge; $10 Arms of N. Borneo.

1963. Freedom from Hunger. As T **20a** of Gambia.

407 12 c. blue . . . . 1·50 75

POSTAGE DUE STAMPS

Overprinted **POSTAGE DUE**

1895. Issue of 1894.

D 2 25 2 c. black & red 13·00 22·00 1·50
D 3 26 3 c. green & mve 4·75 14·00 1·00
D 4 27 5 c. black & red 40·00 25·00 2·50
D 5a 28 6 c. black & brn 10·00 38·00 2·50
D 7 29 8 c. blk & lilac 35·00 45·00 2·50
D 8b 30 12 c. blk & blue 55·00 45·00 2·50
D10 31 18 c. blk & grn 55·00 60·00 4·00
D11b 32 24 c. blue & red 23·00 50·00 4·00

1897. Issue of 1897.

D12 25 2 c. black & red 7·50 8·50 1·25
D15 2 c. black & green 32·00 45·00 70
D16b 26 3 c. green & mve 11·00 20·00 50
D18 4 c. black & red 27·00 27·00 50
D19 27 5 c. black & orge 19·00 32·00 1·40
D20a 28 6 c. black & brn 4·00 23·00 70
D21a 29 8 c. blk and lilac 4·00 23·00 50
D22 30 12 c. black & bl 75·00 £170 4·00
D23a 31 18 c. black and green (No. 108) † † £450
D24 18 c. black and green (No. 110) 38·00 £170 4·00
D25 32 24 c. blue and red (No. 109) — — £180
D26a 24 c. blue and red (No. 111) 18·00 £140 2·25

1902. Issue of 1901.

D47 1 c. black & bistre 4·50 55·00 —
D36 2 c. black and green 8·50 3·00 30
D37 3 c. green & mauve 3·00 3·00 30
D38 4 c. black and red 6·00 6·00 30
D39 5 c. black & orange 15·00 4·25 30
D40 6 c. black & brown 9·00 9·00 40
D41 8 c. black and lilac 17·00 4·25 40
D42b 10 c. brown & grey 65·00 14·00 1·40
D43 12 c. black and blue 17·00 13·00 1·50
D44 16 c. green & brown 28·00 18·00 1·50
D45 18 c. black & green 6·00 18·00 1·50
D46 24 c. blue and red 9·50 22·00 1·50

1919. Issue of 1909.

D49 2 c. black and green . . . . 11·00 75·00
D57 2 c. black and red . . . . 50 1·75
D58 3 c. black and green . . . . 5·50 18·00
D51 4 c. black and red . . . . . 80 1·00
D52 5 c. black and brown . . . 8·00 17·00
D61 6 c. black and olive . . . . 4·00 2·50
D54 8 c. black and red . . . . 1·50 1·25
D55 10 c. black and blue . . . . 12·00 18·00
D56 12 c. black and blue . . . . 42·00 42·00
D56ba 16 c. black and brown . . . 6·50 50·00

D 2 Crest of the Company

1939.

D66 D 2 2 c. brown . . . . 6·50 70·00
D67 4 c. red . . . . 6·50 95·00
D68 6 c. violet . . . . 22·00 £120
D69 8 c. green . . . . 22·00 £200
D70 10 c. blue . . . . 45·00 £350

For later issues see SABAH.

JAPANESE OCCUPATION

1942. Stamps of North Borneo optd as T **1** of Japanese Occupation of Brunei. (a) Issue of 1939.

J 1 81 1 c. green and brown . . . £140 £190
J 2 82 2 c. purple and blue . . . £140 £190
J 3 – 3 c. blue and green . . . £120 £190
J 4a – 4 c. green and violet . . . 50·00 £110
J 5 – 6 c. blue and red £130 £190
J 6 – 8 c. red £130 £170
J 7 – 10 c. violet and green . . . £140 £190
J 8 – 12 c. green and blue . . . £160 £325
J 9 – 15 c. green and brown . . . £160 £325
J10 – 20 c. violet and blue . . . £190 £375
J11 – 25 c. green and brown . . . £190 £375
J12 – 50 c. brown and violet . . . £275 £425
J13 – $1 brown and red £275 £500
J14 – $2 violet and olive £375 £700
J15 – $5 blue £450 £800

(b) War Tax Issue of 1941.

J16 81 1 c. green and brown . . . £400 £250
J17 82 2 c. purple and blue . . . £1100 £350

2 Mt. Kinabalu

3 Borneo Scene

1943.

J18 2 4 c. red . . . . 14·00 32·00
J19 3 8 c. blue . . . . 14·00 32·00

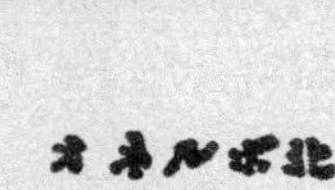

(4)

(5)

("Imperial Japanese Postal Service, North Borneo")

1944. Optd with T **4**. (a) On stamps of North Borneo.

J20 81 1 c. green and brown . . . 4·50 9·50
J21 82 2 c. purple and blue . . . 7·50 8·50
J22 – 3 c. blue and green . . . 4·25 7·50
J23 – 4 c. green and violet . . . 4·50 11·00
J24 – 6 c. blue and red . . . . 3·75 6·50
J25 – 8 c. red . . . . 5·50 17·00
J26 – 10 c. violet and green . . . 8·50 13·00
J27 – 12 c. green and blue . . . 7·00 13·00
J28 – 15 c. green and brown . . . 7·00 15·00
J29 – 20 c. violet and blue . . . 17·00 40·00
J30 – 25 c. green and brown . . . 17·00 40·00
J31 – 50 c. brown and violet . . . 55·00 £110
J32 – $1 brown and red . . . . 85·00 £150

(b) On stamps of Japanese Occupation of North Borneo.

J21a 2 c. purple and blue (J2) . . . £425
J22a 3 c. blue and green (J3) . . . £425
J25a 8 c. red (J6) £425
J26b 10 c. violet and green (J7a) . . . £180 £350
J27a 12 c. green and blue (J8) . . . £425
J28a 15 c. green and brown (J9) . . . £425

1944. No. J1 surch with T **5**.

J33 81 $2 on 1 c. green & brown . . £4500 £3750

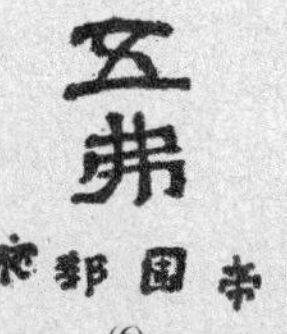

(6)

1944. No. 315 of North Borneo surch with T **6**.

J34 $5 on $1 brown and red . . . £4000 £2750

1944. Stamps of Japan optd as bottom line in T **4**.

J35 126 1 s. brown . . . . 6·00 15·00
J36 84 2 s. red . . . . 6·00 14·00
J37 – 3 s. green (No. 319) . . . 5·00 15·00
J38 129 4 s. green . . . . 6·00 13·00
J39 – 5 s. red (No. 396) . . . . 7·00 16·00
J40 – 6 s. orange (No. 322) . . . 8·00 17·00
J41 – 8 s. violet (No. 324) . . . 5·50 17·00
J42 – 10 s. red (No. 399) . . . . 5·50 17·00
J43 – 15 s. blue (No. 401) . . . 7·50 17·00
J44 – 20 s. blue (No. 328) . . . 90·00 85·00
J45 – 25 s. brown (No. 329) . . . 55·00 70·00
J46 – 30 s. blue (No. 330) . . . £160 95·00
J47 – 50 s. olive and brown (No. 331) . . . . 60·00 60·00
J48 – 1 y. brown (No. 332) . . . 60·00 80·00

NORTH GERMAN CONFEDERATION Pt. 7

The North German Confederation was set up on 1st January, 1868, and comprised the postal services of Bremen, Brunswick, Hamburg Lubeck, Mecklenburg (both), Oldenburg, Prussia (including Hanover, Schleswig-Holstein with Bergedorf and Thurn and Taxis) and Saxony.

The North German Confederation joined the German Reichspost on 4th May, 1871, and the stamps of Germany were brought into use on 1st January, 1872.

Northern District: 30 groschen = 1 thaler.
Southern District: 60 kreuzer = 1 gulden.

1

3

1868. Roul or perf. (a) Northern District.

19 1 ¼ g. mauve . . . . 15·00 12·00
22 ⅓ g. green . . . . 3·25 65
23 ½ g. orange . . . . 3·25 50
25 1 g. red . . . . 2·40 30
27 2 g. blue . . . . 3·25 40
29 5 g. bistre . . . . 7·50 4·00

(b) Southern District.

30 – 1 k. green . . . . 10·00 6·50
13 – 2 k. orange . . . . 30·00 35·00
33 – 3 k. red . . . . 5·50 60
36 – 7 k. blue . . . . 8·50 4·00
18 – 18 k. bistre . . . . 26·00 65·00

The 1 k. to 18 k. have the figures in an oval.

1869. Perf.

38 3 10 g. grey . . . . £275 50·00
39 – 30 g. blue £225 £100

The frame of the 30 g. is rectangular.

OFFICIAL STAMPS

O 5

1870. (a) Northern District.

O40 O 5 ¼ g. black and brown . . 22·00 45·00
O41 ⅓ g. black and brown . . 14·00 17·00
O42 ½ g. black and brown . . 2·00 2·50
O43 1 g. black and brown . . 2·50 35
O44 2 g. black and brown . . 5·00 2·75

(b) Southern District.

O45 1 k. black and grey . . . 32·00 £225
O46 2 k. black and grey . . . 85·00 £800
O47 3 k. black and grey . . . 28·00 35·00
O48 7 k. black and grey . . . 38·00 £250

NORTH INGERMANLAND Pt. 10

Stamps issued during temporary independence of this Russian territory, which adjoins Finland.

100 pennia = 1 mark

1 18th-century Arms of Ingermanland

4 Gathering Crops

1920.

1 1 5 p. green . . . . 2·25 3·75
2 10 p. red . . . . 2·25 3·75
3 25 p. brown . . . . 2·25 3·75
4 50 p. blue . . . . 2·25 3·75
5 1 m. black and red . . . . . 20·00 27·00
6 5 m. black and purple . . . . 65·00 £110
7 10 m. black and brown £130 £180

1920. Inscr as in T **2**.

8 – 10 p. blue and green . . . . . 3·00 6·00
9 – 30 p. green and brown . . . . 3·00 6·00
10 – 50 p. brown and blue . . . . 3·00 6·00
11 – 80 p. grey and red . . . . . 3·00 6·00
12 **4** 1 m. grey and red . . . . . 18·00 35·00
13 – 5 m. red and violet . . . . . 10·00 15·00
14 – 10 m. violet and brown . . . 11·00 17·00

DESIGNS—VERT: 10 p. Arms; 30 p. Reaper; 50 p. Ploughing; 80 p. Milking. HORIZ: 5 m. Burning church; 10 m. Zither players.

NORTH WEST RUSSIA Pt. 10

Issues made for use by the various Anti-bolshevist Armies during the Russian Civil War, 1918–20.

100 kopeks = 1 rouble

NORTHERN ARMY

1 "OKCA" = Osobiy Korpus Severnoy Armiy.—(trans "Special Corps, Northern Army")

1919. As T **1** inscr "OKCA".

1 **1** 5 k. purple 10 40
2 10 k. blue 10 40
3 15 k. yellow 10 40
4 20 k. red 10 40
5 50 k. green 10 40

NORTH-WESTERN ARMY

Сѣв. Зап.
Армiя

(2)

1919. Arms types of Russia optd as T **2**. Imperf or perf.

6 **22** 2 k. green . . . . 3·00 7·50
16 3 k. red . . . . 3·00 7·50
7 5 k. lilac . . . . 3·00 7·50
8 **23** 10 k. blue . . . . 4·50 10·00
9 **10** 15 k. blue and brown . . . . 4·00 7·50
10 **14** 20 k. red and blue . . . . 5·00 8·50
11 **10** 20 k. on 14 k. red and blue £250
12 25 k. violet and green . . . . 8·00 12·00
13 **14** 50 k. green and purple . . . 8·00 12·00
14 **15** 1 r. orange & brn on brn . . 16·00 24·00
17 **11** 3 r. 50 green and red . . . . 32·00 45·00
18 **22** 5 r. blue on green . . . . 24·00 32·00
19 **11** 7 r. pink and green . . . . 90·00 £160
15 **20** 10 r. grey and red on yell . . 60·00 85·00

1919. No. 7 surch.

20 **22** 10 k. on 5 k. lilac . . . . . 4·00 7·50

WESTERN ARMY

1919. Stamps of Latvia optd with Cross of Lorraine in circle with plain background. Imperf. (a) Postage stamps.

21 **1** 3 k. lilac . . . . 30·00 40·00
22 5 k. red . . . . 30·00 40·00
23 10 k. blue £110 £190
24 20 k. orange . . . . 30·00 40·00
25 25 k. grey . . . . 30·00 40·00
26 35 k. brown . . . . 30·00 40·00
27 50 k. violet . . . . 30·00 40·00
28 75 k. green . . . . 30·00 55·00

(b) Liberation of Riga issue.

29 **4** 5 k. red . . . . 25·00 45·00
30 15 k. green . . . . 15·00 35·00
31 35 k. brown . . . . 15·00 35·00

1919. Stamps of Latvia optd with Cross of Lorraine in circle with burele background and characters **3. A** (= "Z. A."). Imperf (a) Postage stamps.

32 **1** 3 k. lilac . . . . 4·00 8·00
33 5 k. red . . . . 4·00 8·00
34 10 k. blue . . . . 90·00 £170
35 20 k. orange . . . . 8·00 16·00
36 25 k. grey . . . . 22·00 45·00
37 35 k. brown . . . . 14·00 24·00
38 50 k. violet . . . . 14·00 24·00
39 75 k. green . . . . 14·00 24·00

(b) Liberation of Riga issue.

40 **4** 5 k. red . . . . 2·75 6·50
41 15 k. green . . . . 2·75 6·50
42 35 k. brown . . . . 2·75 6·50

1919. Arms type of Russia surch with Cross of Lorraine in ornamental frame and **LP** with value in curved frame. Imperf or perf.

43 **22** 10 k. on 2 k. green . . . . 4·50 6·00
54 20 k. on 3 k. red . . . . 4·00 7·50
44 **23** 30 k. on 4 k. red . . . . 4·50 7·00
45 **22** 40 k. on 5 k. lilac . . . . 4·50 7·00
46 **23** 50 k. on 10 k. blue . . . . 4·50 6·00
47 **10** 70 k. on 15 k. blue & brown . 4·50 6·00
48 **14** 90 k. on 20 k. red & blue . . 6·00 8·00
49 **10** 1 r. on 25 k. violet & green . 4·50 6·00
50 1 r. 50 on 35 k. green & brown 35·00 55·00
51 **14** 2 r. on 50 k. green & purple . 6·00 10·00
52 **10** 4 r. on 70 k. red & brown . . 16·00 24·00
53 **15** 6 r. on 1 r. orange, brown on brown . . . . 16·00 25·00
56 **11** 10 r. on 3 r. 50 green & pur . 40·00 48·00

NORTHERN NIGERIA Pt. 1

A British protectorate on the west coast of Africa. In 1914 incorporated into Nigeria.

12 pence = 1 shilling;
20 shillings = 1 pound

1

5

1900.

1 **1** ½d. mauve and green . . . . . 2·25 9·50
2 1d. mauve and red . . . . . 2·75 3·50
3 2d. mauve and yellow . . . . 9·00 32·00
4 2½d. mauve and blue . . . . 7·00 32·00
5 5d. mauve and brown . . . . 17·00 35·00
6 6d. mauve and violet . . . . 15·00 25·00
7 1s. green and black . . . . 20·00 60·00
8 2s. 6d. green and blue . . . . 80·00 £375
9 10s. green and brown £200 £475

1902. As T **1**, but portrait of King Edward VII.

10 ½d. purple and green . . . . . 2·00 1·00
11 1d. purple and red . . . . . 2·00 60
12 2d. purple and yellow . . . . 2·00 2·75
13 2½d. purple and blue . . . . 1·50 6·50
14 5d. purple and brown . . . . 2·00 5·00
15 6d. purple and violet . . . . 5·00 4·50
16 1s. green and black . . . . 3·00 5·50
17 2s. 6d. green and blue . . . . 8·00 35·00
18 10s. green and brown . . . . 48·00 55·00

1910. As last. New colours etc.

28 ½d. green . . . . 1·75 1·25
29 1d. red . . . . 1·75 1·00
30 2d. grey . . . . 3·25 2·25
31 2½d. blue . . . . 1·75 6·50
32 3d. purple on yellow . . . . 3·00 50
34 5d. purple and green . . . . 3·75 8·00
35a 6d. purple . . . . 3·75 6·00
36 1s. black and green . . . . 2·00 75
37 2s. 6d. black and red on blue . 9·50 27·00
38 5s. green and red on yellow . 23·00 75·00
39 10s. green and red on green . . 42·00 48·00

1912.

40 **5** ½d. green 85 60
41 1d. red 85 60
42 2d. grey . . . . 3·00 5·00
43 3d. purple on yellow . . . . 2·25 1·25
44 4d. black and red on yellow . . 75 2·00
45 5d. purple and olive . . . . 4·00 6·00
46 6d. purple and violet . . . . 4·00 4·00
47 9d. purple and red . . . . 2·00 10·00
48 1s. black on green . . . . 4·00 2·25
49 2s. 6d. black and red on blue . 7·00 32·00
50 5s. green and red on yellow . . 19·00 75·00
51 10s. green and red on green . . 38·00 48·00
52 £1 purple and black on red . . £170 £110

NORTHERN RHODESIA Pt. 1

A British territory in central Africa, north of the Zambesi. From 1954 to 1963 part of the central African Federation and using the stamps of Rhodesia and Nyasaland (q.v.). A new constitution was introduced on 3 January, 1964, with internal self-government and independence came on 24 October, 1964 when the country was renamed Zambia (q.v.).

12 pence = 1 shilling;
20 shillings = 1 pound

1

1925. The shilling values are larger and the view is in first colour.

1 **1** ½d. green . . . . 1·50 60
2 1d. brown . . . . 1·50 10
3 1½d. red . . . . 1·50 30
4 2d. orange . . . . 2·00 10
5 3d. blue . . . . 2·00 1·25
6 4d. violet . . . . 3·50 50
7 6d. grey . . . . 3·50 40
8 8d. purple . . . . 3·75 38·00
9 10d. olive . . . . 4·00 38·00
10 1s. orange and black . . . . 3·25 1·50
11 2s. brown and blue . . . . 14·00 21·00
12 **1** 2s. 6d. black and green . . . 15·00 6·50
13 3s. violet and blue . . . . 23·00 16·00
14 5s. grey and violet . . . . 26·00 17·00
15 7s. 6d. purple and black . . . 90·00 £140
16 10s. green and black . . . . 65·00 70·00
17 20s. red and purple £140 £160

1935. Silver Jubilee. As T **10a** of Gambia.

18 1d. blue and olive . . . . . 70 1·25
19 2d. green and blue . . . . . 70 1·25
20 3d. brown and blue . . . . 2·50 5·00
21 6d. grey and purple . . . . 3·00 1·25

1937. Coronation. As T **10b** of Gambia.

22 1½d. red 30 35
23 2d. brown 40 35
24 3d. blue . . . . 60 1·25

1938. As 1925, but with portrait of King George VI facing right and "POSTAGE & REVENUE" omitted.

25 ½d. green 10 10
26 ½d. brown 10 80
27 1d. brown 10 10
28 1d. green 60 90
29 1½d. red . . . . 45·00 40
30 1½d. orange 30 10
31 2d. brown . . . . 45·00 1·25
32 2d. red 30 30
33 2d. purple 45 90
34 3d. blue 30 10
35 3d. red . . . . 50 2·00
36 4d. violet 30 40
37 4½d. blue . . . . 40 4·50
38 6d. grey 30 10
39 9d. violet . . . . 40 2·25
40 1s. orange and black . . . . 2·25 40
41 2s. 6d. black and green . . . 7·00 2·25
42 3s. violet and blue . . . . 13·00 4·00
43 5s. grey and violet . . . . 9·00 6·00
44 10s. green and black . . . . 12·00 12·00
45 20s. red and purple . . . . 38·00 45·00

1946. Victory. As T **11a** of Gambia.

46 1½d. orange 10 10
47 2d. red 10 40

1948. Silver Wedding. As T **11b/c** of Gambia.

48 1½d. orange 30 10
49 20s. red . . . . 42·00 45·00

1949. U.P.U. As T **11d/g** of Gambia.

50 2d. red 30 30
51 3d. blue . . . . 1·90 1·25
52 6d. grey . . . . 1·00 1·25
53 1s. orange . . . . 1·00 1·00

5 Cecil Rhodes and Victoria Falls

1953. Birth Centenary of Cecil Rhodes.

54 **5** ½d. brown 50 50
55 1d. green 40 50
56 2d. mauve 40 15
57 4½d. blue . . . . 40 3·25
58 1s. orange and black . . . . 75 4·00

6 Arms of the Rhodesias and Nyasaland

9 Arms

1953. Rhodes Centenary Exhibition.

59 **6** 6d. violet 40 75

1953. Coronation. As T **11h** of Gambia.

60 1½d. black and orange 40 10

1953. As 1938 but with portrait of Queen Elizabeth II facing left.

61 ½d. brown 65 10
62 1d. green 65 10
63 1½d. orange 80 10
64 2d. purple 75 10
65 3d. red 60 10
66 4d. violet . . . . 1·25 1·25
67 4½d. blue . . . . 90 3·75
68 6d. grey . . . . 1·25 10
69 9d. violet . . . . 60 3·75
70 1s. orange and black 60 10
71 2s. 6d. black and green . . . 6·50 2·75
72 5s. grey and purple . . . . 6·50 12·00
73 10s. green and black . . . . 6·00 22·00
74 20s. red and purple . . . . 20·00 26·00

1963. Arms black, gold and blue; portrait and inscriptions black; background colours given.

75 **9** ½d. violet 40 60
76 1d. blue 70 10
77 2d. brown 30 10
78 3d. yellow 20 10
79 4d. green 30 20
80 6d. green 30 10
81 9d. bistre 30 90
82 1s. purple 30 10
83 1s. 3d. purple . . . . 1·75 10
84 2s. orange . . . . 1·25 2·50
85 2s. 6d. purple . . . . 1·25 1·00
86 5s. mauve . . . . 5·50 5·50
87 10s. mauve . . . . 5·00 13·00
88 20s. blue . . . . 6·00 14·00

Nos. 84/88 are larger (27 × 23 mm).

POSTAGE DUE STAMPS

D 1

D 2

1929.

D1 **D 1** 1d. black . . . . 2·50 2·50
D2 2d. black . . . . 3·00 3·00
D3 3d. black . . . . 3·00 24·00
D4 4d. black . . . . 9·50 28·00

1963.

D 5 **D 2** 1d. orange . . . . 90 3·75
D 6 2d. blue . . . . 90 4·00
D 7 3d. lake . . . . 1·00 4·50
D 8 4d. blue . . . . 1·00 6·50
D 9 6d. purple . . . . 5·50 8·00
D10 1s. green . . . . 6·50 19·00

For later issues see **ZAMBIA**.

NORWAY Pt. 11

In 1814 Denmark ceded Norway to Sweden, from 1814 to 1905 the King of Sweden was also King of Norway after which Norway was an independent Kingdom.

1855. 120 skilling = 1 speciedaler.
1877. 100 ore = 1 krone.

1

3 King Oscar I

1855. Imperf.

1 **1** 4 s. blue . . . . £3500 85·00

1856. Perf.

4 **3** 2 s. yellow . . . . £350 85·00
6 3 s. lilac . . . . £200 50·00
7 4 s. blue . . . . £130 9·50
11 8 s. red . . . . £650 24·00

4

5

1863.

12 **4** 2 s. yellow £450 £110
13 3 s. lilac £350 £300
16 4 s. blue . . . . 70·00 7·50
17 8 s. pink . . . . £500 32·00
18 24 s. brown . . . . 25·00 75·00

1867.

21 **5** 1 s. black . . . . 50·00 30·00
23 2 s. buff . . . . 13·00 30·00
26 3 s. lilac . . . . £190 60·00
27 4 s. blue . . . . 48·00 5·75
29 8 s. red . . . . £250 27·00

6

10 With background shading

A

1872. Value in "Skilling".

33 **6** 1 s. green . . . . 5·75 24·00
36 2 s. blue . . . . 9·50 42·00
39 3 s. red . . . . 32·00 7·50
42 4 s. mauve . . . . 8·50 42·00
44 6 s. brown . . . . £275 32·00
45 7 s. brown . . . . 28·00 42·00

1877. Letters without serifs as Type A. Value in "ore".

47 **10** 1 ore brown . . . . 4·25 4·25
83 2 ore brown . . . . 2·75 2·75
84c 3 ore orange . . . . 38·00 3·75
51 5 ore blue . . . . 24·00 4·75
85d 5 ore green . . . . 28·00 1·40
86a 10 ore red . . . . 32·00 75
55 12 ore green . . . . 60·00 11·50
75b 12 ore brown . . . . 15·00 13·00
76 20 ore brown . . . . 65·00 9·50
87 20 ore blue . . . . 60·00 2·10
88 25 ore mauve . . . . 9·50 7·50
61 35 ore green . . . . 11·50 8·50
62 50 ore purple . . . . 26·00 5·75
63 60 ore blue . . . . 25·00 5·75

9 King Oscar II

1878.

68 **9** 1 k. green and light green . . 19·00 5·50
69 1 k. 50 blue and ultramarine . 38·00 26·00
70 2 k. brown and pink . . . . 26·00 15·00

1888. Surch **2 Ore.**

89a **6** 2 ore on 12 ore brown . . . 1·90 1·90

D

1893. Letters with serifs as Type D.

133 **10** 1 ore drab . . . 15 25
134 2 ore brown . . . 15 15
135 3 ore orange . . . 20 10
136 5 ore green . . . 2·25 10
529 5 ore purple . . . 40 10
138 7 ore green . . . 30 10
139 10 ore red . . . 3·00 10
140 10 ore green . . . 4·00 10
529a 10 ore grey . . . 10 10
141 12 ore violet . . . 45 50
530 15 ore brown . . . 20 10
143 15 ore blue . . . 3·00 10
144 20 ore blue . . . 4·25 10
530a 20 ore green . . . 10 10
146 25 ore mauve . . . 26·00 15
147 25 ore red . . . 3·75 75
531 25 ore blue . . . 20 10
148 30 ore grey . . . 5·00 15
149 30 ore blue . . . 4·75 2·75
119 35 ore green . . . 7·50 4·00
150 35 ore brown . . . 5·75 25
151 40 ore green . . . 2·40 25
152 40 ore blue . . . 15·00 15
531ab 50 ore purple . . . 10 10
154 60 ore blue . . . 15·00 20
531ac 60 ore orange . . . 10 10
531ad 70 ore orange . . . 20 10
531ae 80 ore brown . . . 20 10
531af 90 ore brown . . . 20 10

See also Nos. 279 etc and 1100/3.

1905. Surch.

122 **5** 1 k. on 2 s. buff . . . 21·00 26·00
123 1 k. 50 on 2 s. buff . . . 42·00 50·00
124 2 k. on 2 s. buff . . . 45·00 45·00

1906. Surch.

162 **10** 5 ore on 25 ore mauve . . . 45 65
125 **6** 15 ore on 4 s. mauve . . . 2·40 2·75
126 30 ore on 7 s. brown . . . 5·25 5·75

15 King Haakon VII **16**

1907.

127 **15** 1 k. green . . . 26·00 24·00
128 1½ k. blue . . . 48·00 50·00
129 2 k. red . . . 75·00 75·00

1910.

155a **16** 1 k. green . . . 25 10
156 1½ k. blue . . . 1·00 40
157 2 k. red . . . 1·75 40
158 5 k. violet . . . 2·75 3·75

17 Constitutional Assembly (after O. Wergeland) **19**

1914. Centenary of Independence.

159 **17** 5 ore green . . . 40 15
160 10 ore red . . . 80 15
161 20 ore blue . . . 6·00 4·75

1922.

163 **19** 10 ore green . . . 5·75 10
164 20 ore purple . . . 7·50 10
165 25 ore red . . . 17·00 50
166 45 ore blue . . . 85 50

20

21

22

1925. Air. Amundsen's Polar Flight.

167 **20** 2 ore brown . . . 1·50 1·75
168 3 ore orange . . . 2·50 2·75
169 5 ore mauve . . . 5·25 8·50
170 10 ore green . . . 6·50 12·00
171 15 ore blue . . . 5·75 13·00
172 20 ore mauve . . . 9·50 16·00
173 25 ore red . . . 1·90 3·75

1925. Annexation of Spitzbergen.

183 **21** 10 ore green . . . 3·25 5·75
184 15 ore blue . . . 2·75 2·75
185 20 ore purple . . . 3·75 95
186 45 ore blue . . . 3·75 4·25

1926. Size 16×19½ mm.

187 **22** 10 ore green . . . 40 10
187a 14 ore orange . . . 90 1·75
188 15 ore brown . . . 55 10
189 20 ore purple . . . 14·00 10
189a 20 ore red . . . 45 10
190 25 ore red . . . 5·75 1·25
190a 25 ore brown . . . 60 15
190b 30 ore blue . . . 75 10
191 35 ore brown . . . 48·00 15
191a **22** 35 ore violet . . . 1·10 20
192 40 ore blue . . . 1·40 95
193 40 ore grey . . . 1·50 10
194 50 ore pink . . . 1·10 15
195 60 ore blue . . . 1·10 15

For stamps as Type **22** but size 17×21 mm, see Nos. 284, etc.

1927. Surcharged with new value and bar.

196 **22** 20 ore on 25 ore red . . . 1·00 1·10
197 **19** 30 ore on 45 ore blue . . . 7·00 80
198 **21** 30 ore on 45 ore blue . . . 1·90 3·25

24 Akershus Castle

25 Ibsen

28 Abel

1927. Air.

199a **24** 45 ore blue (with frame-lines) 2·25 2·10
323 45 ore blue (without frame-lines) 40 15

1928. Ibsen Centenary.

200 **25** 10 ore green . . . 3·25 1·50
201 15 ore brown . . . 2·10 2·10
202 20 ore red . . . 2·00 35
203 30 ore blue . . . 3·00 3·00

1929. Postage Due stamps optd **Post Frimerke** (204/6 and 211) or **POST** and thick bar (others).

204 D **12** 1 ore brown . . . 25 60
205 4 ore purple (No. D96a) . . . 20 30
206 10 ore green . . . 1·25 1·75
207 15 ore brown . . . 1·75 2·40
208 20 ore purple . . . 80 35
209 40 ore blue . . . 95 40
210 50 ore purple . . . 4·75 4·75
211 100 ore yellow . . . 2·00 1·90
212 200 ore violet . . . 3·75 2·00

1929. Death Cent of N. H. Abel (mathematician).

213 **28** 10 ore green . . . 1·25 40
214 15 ore brown . . . 1·25 1·25
215 20 ore red . . . 70 15
216 30 ore blue . . . 1·40 1·50

1929. Surch **14 ORE 14**.

217 **5** 14 ore on 2 s. buff . . . 1·90 2·75

30 St. Olaf (sculpture, Brunlanes Church)

31 Nidaros Trondhjem Cathedral

32 Death of St. Olaf (after P. N. Arbo)

1930. 9th Death Centenary of St. Olaf.

219 **30** 10 ore green . . . 5·25 25
220 **31** 15 ore sepia and brown . . . 60 30
221 **30** 20 ore red . . . 70 15
222 **32** 30 ore blue . . . 2·25 2·25

33 North Cape and "Bergensfjord" (liner)

1930. Norwegian Tourist Association Fund. Size 35½×21½ mm.

223 **33** 15 ore + 25 ore brown . . . 2·00 3·25
224 20 ore + 25 ore red . . . 20·00 23·00
225 30 ore + 25 ore blue . . . 65·00 75·00

For smaller stamps in this design see Nos. 349/51 (1938), 442/66 and 464/6.

34 Radium Hospital

1931. Radium Hospital Fund.

226 **34** 20 ore + 10 ore red . . . 5·25 3·75

35 Bjornson

36 L. Holberg

1932. Birth Cent of Bjornstjerne Bjornson (writer).

227 **35** 10 ore green . . . 5·75 25
228 15 ore brown . . . 75 85
229 20 ore red . . . 65 15
230 30 ore blue . . . 1·75 1·75

1934. 250th Birth Anniv of Holberg (writer).

231 **36** 10 ore green . . . 1·10 25
232 15 ore brown . . . 50 40
233 20 ore red . . . 7·00 15
234 30 ore blue . . . 1·75 1·75

37 Dr. Nansen

38 No background shading

38b King Haakon VII

1935. Nansen Refugee Fund.

235 **37** 10 ore + 10 ore green . . . 1·75 2·75
236 15 ore + 10 ore brown . . . 6·25 7·50
237 20 ore + 10 ore red . . . 85 90
238 30 ore + 10 ore blue . . . 5·75 7·50

See also Nos. 275/8.

1937.

279 **38** 1 ore green . . . 10 10
280 2 ore brown . . . 10 10
281 3 ore orange . . . 10 10
282 5 ore mauve . . . 20 10
283 7 ore green . . . 30 10
413 10 ore grey . . . 30 10
285 12 ore violet . . . 70 80
414 15 ore green . . . 1·40 10
415 15 ore brown . . . 40 10
416 20 ore brown . . . 2·90 1·50
417 20 ore green . . . 40 10

1937. As T **22**, but size 17×21 mm.

284 **22** 10 ore green . . . 15 10
286 14 ore orange . . . 1·90 2·50
287 15 ore green . . . 30 10
288a 20 ore red . . . 20 10
289 25 ore brown . . . 1·00 15
289a 25 ore red . . . 30 10
290 30 ore blue . . . 1·40 15
290a 30 ore grey . . . 7·50 20
291 35 ore violet . . . 1·50 10
292 40 ore grey . . . 1·10 10
292a 40 ore blue . . . 3·25 10
293 50 ore purple . . . 95 10
293a 55 ore orange . . . 23·00 10
294 60 ore blue . . . 1·10 10
294a 80 ore brown . . . 22·00 10

1937.

255 **38b** 1 k. green . . . 15 20
256 1 k. 50 blue . . . 70 1·75
257 2 k. red . . . 70 5·25
258 5 k. purple . . . 3·75 35·00

39 Reindeer **41** Joelster in Sunnfjord

1938. Tourist Propaganda.

262 **39** 15 ore brown . . . 50 30
263 – 20 ore red . . . 20 10
264 **41** 30 ore blue . . . 25 10

DESIGN—As T **39** but VERT: 20 ore, Stave Church, Borgund.

1938. Norwegian Tourist Association Fund. As T **33**, but reduced to 27×21 mm.

349 **33** 15 ore + 25 ore brown . . . 90 1·25
350 20 ore + 25 ore red . . . 1·10 2·00
351 30 ore + 25 ore blue . . . 1·60 2·50

42 Queen Maud

43 Lion Rampant

44 Dr. Nansen

1939. Queen Maud Children's Fund.

267 **42** 10 ore + 5 ore green . . . 45 7·50
268 15 ore + 5 ore brown . . . 45 7·50
269 20 ore + 5 ore red . . . 45 5·75
270 30 ore + 5 ore blue . . . 45 8·00

1940.

271 **43** 1 k. green . . . 60 10
272 1½ k. blue . . . 1·40 25
273 2 k. red . . . 1·50 1·10
274 5 k. purple . . . 2·75 2·75

See also Nos. 318/21.

1940. National Relief Fund.

275 **44** 10 ore + 10 ore green . . . 2·00 2·75
276 15 ore + 10 ore brown . . . 2·40 3·25
277 20 ore + 10 ore red . . . 60 70
278 30 ore + 10 ore blue . . . 95 2·40

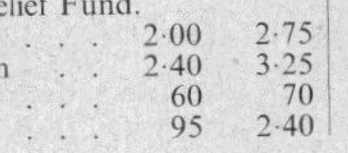

46 Femboring (fishing boat) and Iceberg

47 Colin Archer (founder) and Lifeboat "Colin Archer"

1941. Haalogaland Exhibition and Fishermen's Families Relief Fund.

295 **46** 15 ore + 10 ore blue . . . 1·00 3·75

1941. 50th Anniv of National Lifeboat Institution.

296 **47** 10 ore + 10 ore green . . . 1·00 1·25
297 15 ore + 10 ore brown . . . 1·25 1·60
298 – 20 ore + 10 ore red . . . 60 60
299 – 30 ore + 10 ore blue . . . 2·75 3·75

DESIGN—VERT: 20 ore, 30 ore, "Osloskoyta" (lifeboat).

48 Soldier and Flags

51 Oslo University

1941. Norwegian Legion Support Fund.

300 **48** 20 ore + 80 ore red . . . 32·00 55·00

1941. Stamps of 1937 optd **V** (= Victory).

301 **38** 1 ore green . . . 15 2·40
302 2 ore brown . . . 15 3·75
303 3 ore orange . . . 15 2·25
304 5 ore mauve . . . 15 20
305 7 ore green . . . 40 2·75
306 **22** 10 ore green . . . 15 15
307 **38** 12 ore violet . . . 75 11·50
308 **22** 14 ore orange . . . 75 10·50
309 15 ore green . . . 40 1·90
310 20 ore red . . . 15 10
311 25 ore brown . . . 15 30
312 30 ore blue . . . 75 1·40
313 35 ore violet . . . 40 50
314 40 ore grey . . . 20 40
315 50 ore purple . . . 75 1·75
316 60 ore blue . . . 95 1·40
317 **43** 1 k. green . . . 40 30
318 1½ k. blue . . . 2·75 10·50
319 2 k. red . . . 8·00 35·00
320 5 k. purple . . . 15·00 80·00

1941. As No. 413, but with "V" incorporated in the design.

321 10 ore green . . . 40 6·50

1941. Centenary of Foundation of Oslo University Building.

322 **51** 1 k. green . . . 22·00 35·00

52 Queen Ragnhild's Dream

53 Stiklestad Battlefield

1941. 700th Death Anniv of Snorre Sturlason (historian).

324 **52** 10 ore green . . . 15 10
325 – 15 ore brown . . . 20 30
326 – 20 ore red . . . 15 10
327 – 30 ore blue . . . 90 1·60
328 – 50 ore violet . . . 60 1·25
329 **53** 60 ore blue . . . 95 1·40

DESIGNS (illustrations from "Sagas of Kings")—As T **53**: 15 ore Einar Tambarskjelve at Battle of Svolder; 30 ore King Olav II sails to his wedding; 50 ore Svipdag's men enter Hall of the Seven Kings. As T **52**: 20 ore Snorre Sturlason.

55 Vidkun Quisling

1942. (a) Without opt.

330 **55** 20 ore + 30 ore red . . . 3·50 16·00

(b) Optd **1-2-1942**.

331 **55** 20 ore + 30 ore red . . . 3·50 16·00

See also No. 336.

56 Rikard Nordraak

57 Embarkation of the Viking Fleet

1942. Birth Centenary of Rikard Nordraak (composer).
332 **56** 10 ore green 75 1·50
333 **57** 15 ore brown 1·25 1·90
334 **56** 20 ore red 75 1·50
335 – 30 ore blue 75 1·50
DESIGN—As Type **57**: 30 ore Mountains across sea and two lines of the National Anthem.

1942. War Orphans' Relief Fund. As T **55** but inscr "RIKSTINGET 1942".
336 20 ore + 30 ore red 30 3·75

58 J. H. Wessel
59 Reproduction of Types **55** and **1** 

1942. Birth Bicentenary of Wessel (poet).
337 **58** 15 ore brown 15 15
338 20 ore red 15 15

1942. Inaug of European Postal Union, Vienna.
339 **59** 20 ore red 20 75
340 30 ore blue 20 1·50

60 Destroyer "Sleipner"
61 Edvard Grieg 

1943.
341 **60** 5 ore purple 10 20
342 – 7 ore green 20 20
343 **60** 10 ore green 10 10
344 – 15 ore green 25 40
345 – 20 ore red 10 10
346 – 30 ore blue 85 85
347 – 40 ore green 40 60
348 – 60 ore blue 40 60
DESIGNS: 7 ore, 30 ore Merchant ships in convoy; 15 ore Airman; 20 ore "Vi Vil Vinne" (We will win) written on the highway; 40 ore Soldiers on skis; 60 ore King Haakon VII.

For use on correspondence posted at sea on Norwegian merchant ships and (in certain circumstances) from Norwegian camps in Gt. Britain during the German Occupation of Norway. After liberation all values were put on sale in Norway.

1943. Birth Centenary of Grieg (composer).
352 **61** 10 ore green 30 25
353 20 ore red 30 25
354 40 ore green 30 35
355 60 ore blue 30 35

62 Soldier's Emblem
63 Fishing Station 

1943. Soldiers' Relief Fund.
356 **62** 20 ore + 30 ore red 30 3·75

1943. Winter Relief Fund.
357 **63** 10 ore + 10 ore green 70 5·25
358 – 20 ore + 10 ore red 60 4·75
359 – 40 ore + 10 ore grey 60 4·75
DESIGNS: 20 ore Mountain scenery; 40 ore Winter landscape.

64 Sinking of "Baroy" (freighter)
65 Gran's Bleriot XI "Nordsjoen" 

1944. Shipwrecked Mariners' Relief Fund.
360 **64** 10 ore + 10 ore green 70 5·25
361 – 15 ore + 10 ore brown 70 5·25
362 – 20 ore + 10 ore red 70 5·25
DESIGNS—HORIZ: 15 ore Cargo liner "Sanct Svithun" attacked by Bristol Blenheim airplane. VERT: 20 ore Sinking of freighter "Irma".

1944. 30th Anniv of First North Sea Flight, by Tryggve Gran.
363 **65** 40 ore blue 30 2·40

66 Girl Spinning
67 Arms 
68 Henrik Wergeland 

1944. Winter Relief Fund. Inscr as in T **66**.
364 **66** 5 ore + 10 ore mauve 30 4·25
365 – 10 ore + 10 ore green 30 4·25
366 – 15 ore + 10 ore purple 30 4·25
367 – 20 ore + 10 ore red 30 4·25
DESIGNS: 10 ore Ploughing; 15 ore Tree felling; 20 ore Mother and children.

1945.
368 **67** 1½ k. blue 1·10 40

1945. Death Centenary of Wergeland (poet).
369 **68** 10 ore green 25 20
370 15 ore brown 80 80
371 20 ore red 20 10

69 Red Cross Sister
70 Folklore Museum Emblem 

1945. Red Cross Relief Fund and Norwegian Red Cross Jubilee.
372 **69** 20 ore + 10 ore red 50 50

1945. 50th Anniv of National Folklore Museum.
373 **70** 10 ore green 40 30
374 20 ore red 40 20

71 Crown Prince Olav
72 "R.N.A.F." 

1946. National Relief Fund.
375 **71** 10 ore + 10 ore green 30 30
376 15 ore + 10 ore brown 30 30
377 20 ore + 10 ore red 30 30
378 30 ore + 10 ore blue 1·50 1·40

1946. Honouring Norwegian Air Force Trained in Canada.
379 **72** 15 ore red 45 40

73 King Haakon VII
74 Fridjof of Nansen, Roald Amundsen and "Fram" 

1946.
380 **73** 1 k. green 1·25 10
381 1½ k. blue 3·75 20
382 2 k. brown 26·00 10
383 5 k. violet 17·00 35

1947. Tercentenary of Norwegian Post Office.
384 – 5 ore mauve 30 10
385 – 10 ore green 30 10
386 – 15 ore brown 55 10
387 – 25 ore red 30 10
388 – 30 ore grey 1·10 30
389 – 40 ore blue 2·10 15
390 – 45 ore violet 3·75 50
391 – 50 ore brown 2·50 15
392 **74** 55 ore orange 4·50 20
393 – 60 ore grey 2·90 1·40
394 – 80 ore brown 4·25 30
DESIGNS: 5 ore Hannibal Sehested (founder of postal service) and Akershus Castle; 10 ore "Postal-peasant"; 15 ore Admiral Tordenskiold and 18th-century warship; 25 ore Christian M. Falsen; 30 ore Cleng Peerson and "Restaurationen" (emigrant sloop); 40 ore "Constitutionen" (paddle-steamer); 45 ore Steam locomotive; 50 ore Svend Foyn and "Spes et Fides" (whale catcher); 60 ore Coronation of King Haakon and Queen Maud in Nidaros Cathedral; 80 ore King Haakon and Oslo Town Hall.

75 Petter Dass
76 King Haakon VII 

1947. Birth Tercentenary of Petter Dass (poet).
395 **75** 25 ore red 35 35

1947. 75th Birthday of King Haakon VII.
396 **76** 25 ore orange 35 35

77 Axel Heiberg
80 A. L. Kielland 

1948. 50th Anniv of Norwegian Forestry Society and Birth Centenary of Axel Heiberg (founder).
397 **77** 25 ore red 75 30
398 80 ore brown 1·40 30

1948. Red Cross. Surch **25 + 5** and bars.
399 **69** 25 + 5 ore on 20 + 10 ore red 65 50

1949. Stamps of 1937 surch.
400 **22** 25 ore on 20 ore red 50 10
401 45 ore on 40 ore blue 1·90 30

1949. Birth Centenary of Alexander L. Kielland (author).
402 **80** 25 ore red 1·10 15
403 40 ore blue 1·25 25
404 80 ore brown 1·90 50

81 Symbolising Universe
82 Pigeons and Globe 

1949. 75th Anniv of U.P.U.
405 **81** 10 ore green and purple 50 40
406 **82** 25 ore red 30 15
407 – 40 ore blue 30 30
DESIGN—37 × 21 mm: 40 ore Dove, globe and signpost.

84 King Harald Haardraade and Oslo Town Hall
85 Child with Flowers 

1950. 900th Anniv of Founding of Oslo.
408 **84** 15 ore green 45 60
409 25 ore red 30 15
410 45 ore blue 40 50

1950. Infantile Paralysis Fund.
411 **85** 25 ore + 5 ore red 95 95
412 45 ore + 5 ore blue 4·75 4·75

87 King Haakon VII
88 Arne Garborg (after O. Rusti) 

1950.
418 **87** 25 ore red 45 10
419 25 ore grey 11·00 10
419a 25 ore green 85 10
420 30 ore grey 6·25 45
421 30 ore red 50 10
422a 35 ore red 3·50 10
422b 40 ore purple 1·10 10
423 45 ore blue 1·40 1·40
424 50 ore brown 2·40 10
425 55 ore orange 1·40 95
426 55 ore blue 95 30
427 60 ore blue 10·50 10
427a 65 ore blue 1·25 15
427b 70 ore brown 9·50 15
428 75 ore purple 1·40 15
429 80 ore brown 2·10 10
430 90 ore orange 95 15

1951. Birth Centenary of Garborg (author).
431 **88** 25 ore red 30 20
432 45 ore blue 1·90 1·90
433 80 ore brown 2·00 1·10
"NOREG" on the stamps was the spelling advocated by Arne Garborg.

89 Ice Skater
92 King Haakon VII 

1951. 6th Winter Olympic Games. Inscr "OSLO 1952".
434 **89** 15 ore + 5 ore green 2·40 2·40
435 – 30 ore + 10 ore red 2·40 2·40
436 – 55 ore + 20 ore blue 9·50 9·50
DESIGNS—As T **89**: 30 ore Ski jumping. 38 × 21 mm: 55 ore Winter landscape.

1951. Surch in figures.
440 **38** 20 ore on 15 ore green 40 15
437 **87** 30 ore on 25 ore red 40 10

1952. 80th Birthday of King Haakon.
438 **92** 30 ore scarlet and red 20 15
439 55 ore blue and grey 60 60

94 "Supplication"
95 Medieval Sculpture 

1953. Anti-Cancer Fund.
441 **94** 30 ore + 10 ore red and cream 1·50 1·50

1953. Norwegian Tourist Association Fund. As T **33** but smaller (27½ × 21 mm).
442 **33** 20 ore + 10 ore green 8·00 8·00
464 25 ore + 10 ore green 4·50 4·50
443 30 ore + 15 ore red 8·00 8·00
465 35 ore + 15 ore red 6·00 6·00
444 55 ore + 25 ore blue 13·50 13·50
466 65 ore + 25 ore blue 4·50 4·50

1953. 8th Cent of Archbishopric of Nidaros.
445 **95** 30 ore red 30 25

96 Locomotive, 1851 (first locomotive in Norway, 1854) and Horse-drawn Sledge
97 C. T. Nielsen (first Director) 

1954. Centenary of Norwegian Railways.
446 **96** 20 ore green 1·25 30
447 – 30 ore red 1·25 15
448 – 55 ore blue 2·25 1·50
DESIGNS: 30 ore Diesel-hydraulic express train; 55 ore Alfred Andersen (engine driver) in locomotive cab.

1954. Centenary of Telegraph Service.
449 **97** 20 ore black and green 30 30
450 – 30 ore red 30 15
451 – 55 ore blue 75 75
DESIGNS: 30 ore Radio masts at Tryvannshogda; 55 ore Telegraph lineman on skis.

98 "Posthorn" Type Stamp
100 King Haakon and Queen Maud 

1955. Norwegian Stamp Centenary.
452 – 20 ore blue and green 45 45
453 **98** 30 ore deep red and red 15 10
454 – 55 ore blue & grey 75 75
DESIGNS: 20 ore Norway's first stamp; 55 ore "Lion" type stamp.

1955. Stamp Cent and Int Stamp Exn, Oslo. Nos. 452/4 with circular opt **OSLO NORWEX**.
455 – 20 ore blue and green 7·50 7·50
456 **98** 30 ore deep red and red 7·50 7·50
457 – 55 ore blue and grey 7·50 7·50
Nos. 455/7 were only on sale at the Exhibition P.O. at face + 1 k. entrance fee.

1955. Golden Jubilee of King Haakon.
458 **100** 30 ore red 30 15
459 55 ore blue 40 40

101 Crown Princess Martha

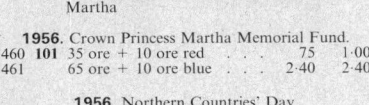

101a Whooper Swans

1956. Crown Princess Martha Memorial Fund.

460	101	35 ore + 10 ore red	75	1·00
461		65 ore + 10 ore blue	2·40	2·40

1956. Northern Countries' Day.

462	101a	35 ore red	1·00	50
463		65 ore blue	1·00	75

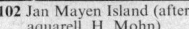

102 Jan Mayen Island (after aquarell, H. Mohn)

103 Map of Spitzbergen

1957. Int Geophysical Year. Inscr "INTERN. GEOFYSISK AR 1957–1958".

467	102	25 ore green	40	25
468	103	35 ore red and grey	40	10
469	–	65 ore green and blue	50	40

DESIGN—VERT: 65 ore Map of Antarctica showing Queen Maud Land.

104 King Haakon VII

105 King Olav V

106

1957. 85th Birthday of King Haakon.

470	104	35 ore red	15	10
471		65 ore blue	35	35

1958.

472	105	25 ore green	80	10
473		30 ore violet	1·25	10
474		35 ore red	80	10
474a		35 ore green	3·00	10
475		40 ore red	80	10
475a		40 ore grey	2·50	70
476		45 ore red	1·00	10
477		50 ore brown	4·25	10
478		50 ore red	4·75	10
479		55 ore grey	1·50	35
480		60 ore violet	3·25	45
481		65 ore blue	1·75	25
482		80 ore brown	7·50	30
483		85 ore brown	1·25	15
484		90 ore orange	85	10
485	106	1 k. green	50	10
486		1 k. 50 blue	1·90	10
487		2 k. red	1·75	10
488		5 k. purple	30·00	10
489		10 k. orange	3·50	10

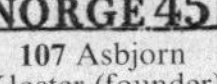

107 Asbjorn Kloster (founder)

108 Society's Centenary Medal

1959. Cent of Norwegian Temperance Movement.

490	107	45 ore brown	30	25

1959. 150th Anniv of Royal Norwegian Agricultural Society.

491	108	45 ore brown and red	25	25
492		90 ore grey and blue	1·40	1·40

109 Sower

110 White Anemone

1959. Centenary of Norwegian Royal College of Agriculture.

493	109	45 ore black and brown	25	25
494	–	90 ore black and blue	60	70

DESIGN—VERT: 90 ore Ears of Corn.

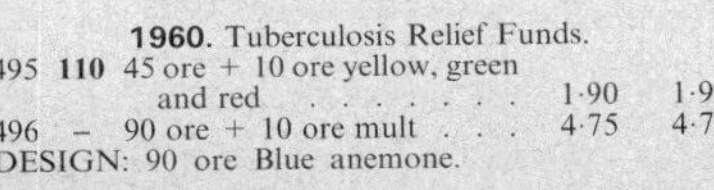

1960. Tuberculosis Relief Funds.

495	110	45 ore + 10 ore yellow, green and red	1·90	1·90
496	–	90 ore + 10 ore mult	4·75	4·75

DESIGN: 90 ore Blue anemone.

111 Society's Original Seal

112 Refugee Mother and Child

1960. Bicentenary of Royal Norwegian Society of Scientists.

497	111	45 ore red on grey	25	15
498		90 ore blue on grey	1·10	1·10

1960. World Refugee Year.

499	112	45 ore + 25 ore black and pink	3·75	3·75
500		90 ore + 25 ore black and blue	6·50	6·50

113 Viking Longship

1960. Norwegian Ships.

501	113	20 ore black and grey	1·00	80
502	–	25 ore black and green	1·00	80
503	–	45 ore black and red	1·00	15
504	–	55 ore black and brown	2·00	2·00
505	–	90 ore black and blue	2·00	90

SHIPS: 25 ore Hanse kogge; 45 ore "Skomvaer" (barque); 55 ore "Dalfon" (tanker); 90 ore "Bergensfjord" (liner).

113a Conference Emblem

113b Douglas DC-8

1960. Europa.

506	113a	90 ore blue	35	35

1961. 10th Anniv of Scandinavian Airlines System (SAS).

507	113b	90 ore blue	55	30

114 Throwing the Javelin

115 Haakonshallen Barracks and Rosencrantz Tower

1961. Centenary of Norwegian Sport.

508	114	20 ore brown	40	40
509	–	25 ore green	40	40
510	–	45 ore red	40	15
511	–	90 ore mauve	70	80

DESIGNS: 25 ore Ice skating; 45 ore Ski jumping; 90 ore Yachting.

1961. 700th Anniv of Haakonshallen, Bergen.

512	115	45 ore black and red	30	15
513		1 k. black and green	40	25

116 Oslo University

117 Nansen

1961. 150th Anniv of Oslo University.

514	116	45 ore red	25	10
515		1 k. 50 blue	45	20

1961. Birth Centenary of Fridtjof Nansen (polar explorer).

516	117	45 ore black and red	25	15
517		90 ore black and blue	50	50

118 Amundsen, "Fram" and Dog-team

119 Frederic Passy and Henri Dunant (winners in 1901)

1961. 50th Anniv of Amundsen's Arrival at South Pole.

518	118	45 ore red and grey	50	15
519	–	90 ore deep blue and blue	90	55

DESIGN: 90 ore Amundsen's party and tent at South Pole.

1961. Nobel Peace Prize.

520	119	45 ore red	30	10
521	–	1 k. green	95	20

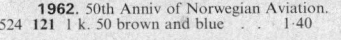

120 Prof. V. Bjerknes

121 Etrich/Rumpler Taube Monoplane "Start"

1962. Birth Centenary of Prof. Vilhelm Bjerknes (physicist).

522	120	45 ore black and red	25	10
523		1 k. 50 black and blue	45	25

1962. 50th Anniv of Norwegian Aviation.

524	121	1 k. 50 brown and blue	1·40	40

122 Branch of Fir, and Cone

123 Europa "Tree"

1962. Cent of State Forestry Administration.

525	122	45 ore grey, black & red	50	35
526		1 k. grey, black & green	4·25	20

1962. Europa.

527	123	50 ore red	30	10
528		90 ore blue	95	95

125 Reef Knot

126 Camilla Collett

127 Boatload of Wheat

1962.

531ag	–	25 ore green	90	10
532	–	30 ore drab	2·25	1·60
532a	–	30 ore green	30	10
533	125	35 ore green	40	10
533a	–	40 ore red	2·75	10
534	–	40 ore green	30	10
534a	–	45 ore green	40	25
535	125	50 ore red	2·75	10
535a		50 ore grey	30	10
536	–	55 ore brown	30	20
536a	125	60 ore green	7·00	15
537		60 ore red	60	10
537b	–	65 ore violet	2·00	10
538	125	65 ore red	30	10
538a		70 ore brown	30	10
539	–	75 ore green	30	10
539a	–	80 ore purple	2·50	1·00
539b	–	80 ore brown	35	10
540	–	85 ore brown	45	15
540a	–	85 ore buff	40	15
540b	–	90 ore blue	35	10
541	–	100 ore violet	60	10
541a	–	100 ore red	50	10
542	–	110 ore red	45	15
542a	–	115 ore brown	60	20
543	–	120 ore blue	60	20
543a	–	125 ore red	40	10
544	–	140 ore blue	60	35
544a	–	750 ore brown	80	10

DESIGNS: 25, 40, 90, 100(2), 110, 120, 125 ore, Runic drawings; 30, 45, 55, 75, 85 ore, Ear of wheat and Atlantic cod; 65 (537b), 80, 140 ore, "Stave" (wooden) church and Aurora Borealis; 115 ore Fragment of Urnes stave-church; 750 ore Sigurd Farnesbane (the Dragon killer) and Regin (the blacksmith), portal from Hylestad stave-church.

1963. 150th Birth Anniv of Camilla Collett (author).

545	126	50 ore red	20	10
546		90 ore blue	95	95

1963. Freedom from Hunger.

547	127	25 ore bistre	20	30
548		35 ore green	30	30
549	–	50 ore red	30	10
550	–	90 ore blue	95	95

DESIGN—37½ × 21 mm: 50, 90 ore Birds carrying food on cloth.

128 River Mail Boat

129 Ivar Aasen

1963. Tercentenary of Southern-Northern Norwegian Postal Services.

551	128	50 ore red	90	25
552	–	90 ore blue	1·90	2·00

DESIGN: 90 ore Femboring (Northern sailing vessel).

1963. 150th Birth Anniv of Ivar Aasen (philologist).

553	129	50 ore red and grey	20	10
554		90 ore blue and grey	95	95

The note after No. 433 re "NOREG" also applies here.

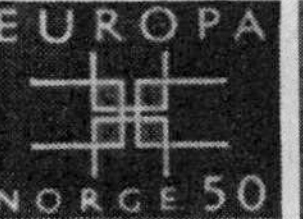

130 "Co-operation"

131 "Herringbone" Pattern

1963. Europa.

555	130	50 ore orange and purple	30	10
556		90 ore green and blue	1·40	1·40

1963. 150th Anniv of Norwegian Textile Industry.

557	131	25 ore green and bistre	30	35
558		35 ore ultramarine and blue	40	55
559		50 ore purple and red	30	20

132 Edvard Munch (self-portrait)

133 Eilert Sundt (founder)

1963. Birth Centenary of Edvard Munch (painter and engraver).

560	132	25 ore black	20	15
561	–	35 ore green	20	25
562	–	50 ore brown	20	10
563	–	90 ore blue and indigo	50	65

DESIGNS (woodcuts)—HORIZ: 35 ore "Fecundity"; 50 ore "The Solitaries". VERT: 90 ore "The Girls on the Bridge".

1964. Centenary of Oslo Workers' Society.

564	133	25 ore green	20	25
565	–	50 ore purple	20	10

DESIGN: 50 ore Beehive emblem of O.W.S.

134 C. M. Guldberg and P. Waage (chemists)

135 Eidsvoll Manor

1964. Centenary of Law of Mass Action.

566	134	35 ore green	40	30
567		55 ore stone	1·00	1·00

1964. 150th Anniv of Norwegian Constitution.

568	135	50 ore grey and red	20	10
569	–	90 ore black and blue	85	85

DESIGN: 90 ore Storting (Parliament House), Oslo.

On 1st June, 1964, a stamp depicting the U.N. refugee emblem and inscr "PORTO BETALT ... LYKKEBREVET 1964" was put on sale. It had a franking value of 50 ore but was sold for 2 k. 50, the balance being for the Refugee Fund. In addition, each stamp bore a serial number representing participation in a lottery which took place in September. The stamp was on sale until 15th July and had validity until 10th August.

136 Harbour Scene

137 Europa "Flower"

1964. Cent of Norwegian Seamen's Mission.

570	136	25 ore green and yellow	30	25
571		90 ore blue and cream	1·10	1·10

1964. Europa.

572	137	90 ore deep blue & blue	1·90	1·90

138 H. Anker and O. Arvesen (founders)

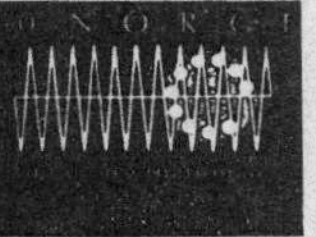

139 "Radio-telephone"

1964. Cent of Norwegian Folk High Schools.

573	138	50 ore pink	25	10
574		90 ore blue	1·75	1·75

The note after No. 433 re "NOREG" also applies here.

1965. Cent of I.T.U.

575	139	60 ore purple	25	10
576	–	90 ore grey	95	95

DESIGN: 90 ore "T.V. transmission".

140 Dove of Peace and Broken Chain

1965. 20th Anniv of Liberation.

577 **140** 30 ore + 10 ore brown, green and sepia 25 25
578 – 60 ore + 10 ore blue and red 25 20
DESIGN: 60 ore Norwegian flags.

141 Mountain Landscapes

142 Europa "Sprig"

1965. Centenary of Norwegian Red Cross.

579 **141** 60 ore brown and red . . . 20 10
580 – 90 ore blue and red . . . . 2·40 2·40
DESIGN: 90 ore Coastal view.

1965. Europa.

581 **142** 60 ore red 25 10
582 90 ore blue . . . . 1·10 1·10

143 St. Sunniva and Bergen Buildings

144 Rondane Mountains (after H. Sohlberg)

1965. Bicentenary of Harmonien Philharmonic Society.

583 – 30 ore black and green . . 25 20
584 **143** 90 ore black and blue . . . 95 95
DESIGN—VERT: 30 ore St. Sunniva.

1965. Rondane National Park.

585 **144** 1 k. 50 blue . . . . 1·75 15

145 "Rodoy Skier" (rock carving)

146 "The Bible"

1966. World Skiing Championships, Oslo. Inscr "VM OSLO 1966".

586 **145** 40 ore brown 50 50
587 – 55 ore green . . . . . . 1·25 1·25
588 – 60 ore brown 50 15
589 – 90 ore blue 90 75
DESIGNS—HORIZ: 55 ore Ski jumper; 60 ore Cross-country skier. VERT: 90 ore Holmenkollen ski jumping tower, Oslo.

1966. 150th Anniv of Norwegian Bible Society.

590 **146** 60 ore red 25 15
591 90 ore blue 85 85

147 Guilloche Pattern

148 J. Sverdrup (after C. Krohg)

1966. 150th Anniv of Bank of Norway.

592 **147** 30 ore green 35 30
593 – 60 ore red (Bank building) 25 15
No. 593 is size $27\frac{1}{2}\times21$ mm.

1966. 150th Birth Anniv of Johan Sverdrup (statesman).

594 **148** 30 ore green 35 30
595 60 ore purple 30 15

149 Europa "Ship"

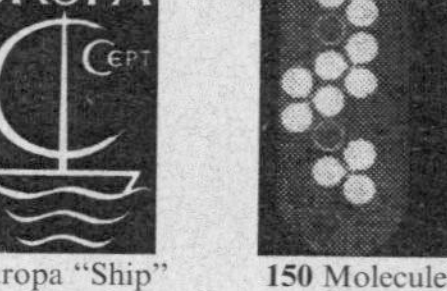
150 Molecules in Test-tube

1966. Europa.

596 **149** 60 ore red 30 10
597 90 ore blue 95 95

1966. Birth Centenaries of S. Eyde (industrialist) (1966) and K. Birkeland (scientist) (1967), founders of Norwegian Nitrogen Industry.

598 **150** 40 ore blue and lt blue . . 1·00 95
599 – 55 ore mauve and red . . . 1·40 1·40
DESIGN: 55 ore Ear of wheat and conical flask.

151 E.F.T.A. Emblem

152 "Owl" and Three Swords

1967. European Free Trade Association.

600 **151** 60 ore red 20 10
601 90 ore blue . . . . 1·40 1·40

1967. 150th Anniv of Higher Military Training.

602 **152** 60 ore brown 40 20
603 90 ore green . . . . 1·90 1·90

153 Cogwheels

154 Johanne Dybwad

1967. Europa.

604 **153** 60 ore deep plum, plum and purple 25 10
605 90 ore deep violet, violet and blue . . . . 1·00 95

1967. Birth Centenary of J. Dybwad (actress).

606 **154** 40 ore blue 20 20
607 60 ore red 20 10

155 I. Skrefsrud (missionary and founder)

156 Climbers on Mountain-top

1967. Centenary of Norwegian Santal Mission.

608 **155** 60 ore brown 20 10
609 – 90 ore blue 75 75
DESIGN—HORIZ: 90 ore Ebenezer Church, Benagaria, Santal, India.

1968. Centenary of Norwegian Mountain Touring Association.

610 **156** 40 ore brown 75 75
611 – 60 ore red 40 15
612 – 90 ore blue 80 60
DESIGNS: 60 ore Mountain cairn and scenery; 90 ore Glitretind peak.

157 "The Blacksmiths"

158 Vinje

1968. Norwegian Handicrafts.

613 **157** 65 ore brown, black & red 25 10
614 90 ore brown, black & bl . 95 95

1968. 150th Birth Anniv of Aasmund Vinje (poet).

615 **158** 50 ore brown 20 20
616 65 ore red 20 10
See note below No. 433.

159 Cross and Heart

160 Cathinka Guldberg (first deaconess)

1968. Centenary of Norwegian Lutheran Home Mission Society.

617 **159** 40 ore red and green . . . 1·90 1·90
618 65 ore red and violet . . . 25 10

1968. Centenary of Deaconess House, Oslo.

619 **160** 50 ore blue 20 20
620 65 ore red 20 10

161 K. P. Arnoldson and F. Bajer

161a Viking Ships (from old Swedish coin)

1968. Nobel Peace Prize Winners of 1908.

621 **161** 65 ore brown 30 15
622 90 ore blue 95 95

1969. 50th Anniv of Northern Countries' Union.

623 **161a** 65 ore red 20 10
624 90 ore blue 85 85

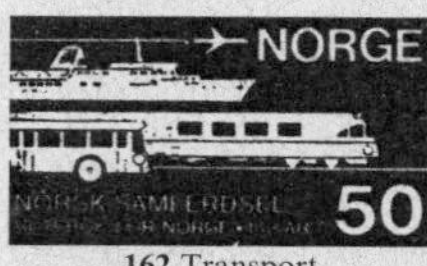
162 Transport

1969. Centenary of "Rutebok for Norge" ("Communications of Norway") and Road Safety Campaign.

625 **162** 50 ore green 60 40
626 – 65 ore red and green . . . 25 10
DESIGN: 65 ore Pedestrian-crossing.

163 Colonnade

1969. Europa.

627 **163** 65 ore black and red . . . 25 10
628 90 ore black and blue . . . 75 55

164 J. Hjort and Eggs of Atlantic Cod

165 Traena Islands

1969. Birth Centenary of Professor Johan Hjort (fisheries pioneer).

629 **164** 40 ore brown and blue . . 50 40
630 – 90 ore blue and green . . . 1·75 1·75
DESIGN: 90 ore Hjort and polyp.

1969.

631 **165** 3 k. 50 black . . . . . . 1·10 10

166 King Olav V

167 "Mother and Child"

1969.

632 **166** 1 k. green 45 10
633 1 k. 50 blue 45 10
634 2 k. red 50 10
635 5 k. blue . . . . 1·10 10
636 10 k. brown . . . . . . 2·10 10
637 20 k. brown . . . . . . 3·75 10
637a 50 k. green . . . . . . 9·50 25

1969. Birth Centenary of Gustav Vigeland (sculptor).

638 **167** 65 ore black and red . . . 30 10
639 – 90 ore black and blue . . . 70 60
DESIGN: 90 ore "Family" (sculpture).

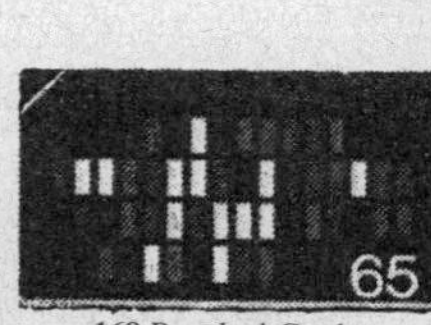
168 Punched Cards

169 Queen Maud

1969. Bicentenary of 1st National Census. Mult.

640 65 ore Type **168** 30 10
641 90 ore "People" (diagram) . . 70 60

1969. Birth Centenary of Queen Maud.

642 **169** 65 ore purple 30 10
643 90 ore blue 70 55

INDEX

Countries can be quickly located by referring to the index at the end of this volume.

170 Wolf

171 "V" Symbol

1970. Nature Conservation Year.

644 **170** 40 ore brown and blue . . 80 35
645 – 60 ore grey and brown . . 1·25 1·25
646 – 70 ore brown and blue . . 1·00 40
647 – 100 ore brown and blue . . 2·25 1·00
DESIGNS—VERT: 60 ore Pale pasque flower; 70 ore Voringsfossen Falls. HORIZ: 100 ore White-tailed sea eagle.

1970. 25th Anniv of Liberation.

648 **171** 70 ore red and violet . . . 1·25 25
649 – 100 ore blue and green . . 1·25 1·00
DESIGN—HORIZ: 100 ore Merchant ships in convoy.

172 "Citizens"

173 Hands reaching for Globe

1970. 900th Anniv of Bergen.

650 **172** 40 ore green 95 50
651 – 70 ore purple . . . . . . 1·75 20
652 – 1 k. blue . . . . 1·00 80
DESIGNS: 70 ore "City between the Mountains"; 1 k. "Ships".

1970. 25th Anniv of United Nations.

653 **173** 70 ore red . . . . 1·75 40
654 100 ore green . . . . . . 1·10 1·10

174 G. O. Sars

175 Ball-game

1970. Norwegian Zoologists.

655 **174** 40 ore brown 95 95
656 – 50 ore lilac 60 50
657 – 70 ore brown 70 15
658 – 100 ore blue 70 70
ZOOLOGISTS: 50 ore Hans Strom; 70 ore J. E. Gunnerus; 100 ore Michael Sars.

1970. Centenary of Central School of Gymnastics, Oslo.

659 **175** 50 ore brown and blue . . 45 25
660 – 70 ore brown and red . . . 55 10
DESIGN—HORIZ: 70 ore "Leapfrog" exercise.

176 Tonsberg's Seal c. 1340

1971. 1100th Anniv of Tonsberg.

661 **176** 70 ore red 30 10
662 100 ore blue 75 45

177 Parliament House, Oslo

1971. Centenary of Introduction of Annual Parliamentary Sessions.

663 **177** 70 ore lilac and red 30 10
664 100 ore green and blue . . 75 75

178 "Helping Hand"

1971. "Help for Refugees".

665 **178** 50 ore green & black . . . 40 30
666 70 ore red & black 30 10

179 "Hauge addressing Followers" (A. Tidemand)

1971. Birth Centenary of Hans Nielson Hauge (church reformer).
667 **179** 60 ore black 35 30
668 70 ore brown 25 10

180 Bishop welcoming Worshippers

1971. 900th Anniv of Oslo Bishopric.
669 – 70 ore black and red . . . 30 10
670 **180** 1 k. black and blue 95 80
DESIGN—VERT: 70 ore Masons building first church.

181 Roald Amundsen and Treaty Emblem
182 "The Preacher and the King"

1971. 10th Anniv of Antarctic Treaty.
671 **181** 100 ore red and blue . . . 1·90 1·25

1971. Norwegian Folk Tales. Drawings by Erik Werenskiold.
672 – 40 ore black and green . . 35 10
673 **182** 50 ore black and blue . . . 40 15
674 – 70 ore black and purple . . 55 10
DESIGNS—VERT: 40 ore "The Farmer and the Woman"; 70 ore "The Troll and the Girl".

183 Anniversary Symbol
184 3 s. "Posthorn" Stamp

1972. 150th Anniv of Norwegian Savings Banks.
675 **183** 80 ore gold and red 40 10
676 1 k. 20 gold and blue . . . 50 45

1972. Centenary of Norwegian "Posthorn" Stamps.
677 **184** 80 ore red and brown . . . 30 10
678 1 k. blue and violet 40 30

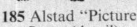

185 Alstad "Picture" Stone (detail)
186 King Haakon VII

1972. 1100th Anniv of Norway's Unification. Relics.
680 **185** 50 ore green 45 40
681 – 60 ore brown 70 65
682 – 80 ore red . . . . 1·00 50
683 – 1 k. 20 blue 70 70
DESIGNS: 60 ore Portal, Hemsedal Church (detail); 80 ore Figurehead of Oseberg Viking ship; 1 k. 20, Sword-hilt (Lodingen).

1972. Birth Centenary of King Haakon VII.
684 **186** 80 ore red . . . . 1·75 40
685 1 k. 20 blue 95 95

187 "Joy" (Ingrid Ekrem)
189 "Maud"

1972. "Youth and Leisure".
686 **187** 80 ore mauve 35 10
687 – 1 k. 20 blue 95 95
DESIGN: 1 k. 20, "Solidarity" (Ole Instefjord).

1972. "Interjunex 1972" Stamp Exhibition, Oslo. Nos. 686/7 optd **INTERJUNEX 72**.
688 **187** 80 ore mauve . . . . . . 1·90 2·00
689 – 1 k. 20 blue . . . . . . 1·90 2·00

1972. Norwegian Polar Ships.
690 **189** 60 ore olive and green . . . 1·10 60
691 – 80 ore red and black . . . 1·10 10
692 – 1 k. 20 blue and red . . . 1·40 1·40
DESIGNS: 80 ore "Fram" (Amundsen and Nansen's ship); 1 k. 20, "Gjoa".

190 "Little Man"
191 Dr. Hansen and Bacillus Diagram

1972. Norwegian Folk Tales. Drawings of Trolls by Th. Kittelsen.
693 **190** 50 ore black and green . . 30 10
694 – 60 ore black and blue . . . 40 35
695 – 80 ore black and pink . . . 30 10
TROLLS: 60 ore "The troll who wonders how old he is"; 80 ore "Princess riding on a bear".

1973. Centenary of Hansen's Identification of Leprosy Bacillus.
696 **191** 1 k. red and blue 60 10
697 – 1 k. 40 blue and red . . . 1·10 1·10
DESIGN: 1 k. 40, As Type **191** but bacillus as seen in modern microscope.

192 Europa "Posthorn"
193 King Olav V

1973. Europa.
698 **192** 1 k. red, scarlet and carmine 1·40 10
699 1 k. 40 emerald, green and blue . . . . 1·10 1·10

1973. Nordic Countries' Postal Co-operation. As T **214** of Sweden.
700 1 k. multicoloured 65 10
701 1 k. 40 multicoloured 60 55

1973. King Olav's 70th Birthday.
702 **193** 1 k. brown and purple . . 75 10
703 1 k. 40 brown and blue . . . 75 75

194 J. Aall
195 Bone Carving

1973. Birth Centenary of Jacob Aall (industrialist).
704 **194** 1 k. purple 40 10
705 1 k. 40 blue 65 65

1973. Lapp Handicrafts.
706 **195** 75 ore brown and cream . . 40 25
707 – 1 k. red and cream 55 10
708 – 1 k. 40 black and blue . . 65 50
DESIGNS: 1 k. Detail of weaving; 1 k. 40, Detail of tin-ware.

196 Yellow Wood Violet
197 Land Surveying

1973. Mountain Flowers. Multicoloured.
709 65 ore Type **196** 40 10
710 70 ore Rock speedwell 50 40
711 1 k. Mountain heath 50 10

1973. Bicentenary of Norwegian Geographical Society.
712 **197** 1 k. red 50 10
713 – 1 k. 40 blue 75 55
DESIGN: 1 k. 40, Old map of Hestbraepiggene (mountain range).

198 Lindesnes
199 "Bridal Procession on Hardanger Fjord" (A. Tidemand and H. Gude)

1974. Norwegian Capes.
714 **198** 1 k. green 50 15
715 – 1 k. 40 blue . . . . 1·40 1·40
DESIGN: 1 k. 40, North Cape.

1974. Norwegian Paintings. Multicoloured.
716 1 k. Type **199** 40 10
717 1 k. 40, "Stugunoset from Filefjell" (J. Dahl) 60 60

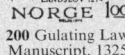

200 Gulating Law Manuscript, 1325
201 Trees and Saw Blade

1974. 700th Anniv of King Magnus Lagaboter National Legislation.
718 **200** 1 k. red and brown 30 10
719 – 1 k. 40 blue and brown . . 85 85
DESIGN: 1 k. 40, King Magnus Lagaboter (sculpture in Stavanger Cathedral).

1974. Industrial Accident Prevention.
720 **201** 85 ore green, deep green and emerald . . . . 1·75 1·75
721 – 1 k. carmine, red and orange 1·00 40
DESIGN: 1 k. Flower and cogwheel.

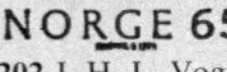

202 J. H. L. Vogt
203 Buildings of the World

1974. Norwegian Geologists.
722 **202** 65 ore brown and green . . 30 25
723 – 85 ore brown and purple . 1·25 1·25
724 – 1 k. brown and orange . . 45 10
725 – 1 k. 40 brown and blue . . 90 85
DESIGNS: 85 ore V. M. Goldschmidt; 1 k. Th. Kjerulf; 1 k. 40, W. C. Brogger.

1974. Centenary of Universal Postal Union.
726 **203** 1 k. brown and green . . . 30 10
727 – 1 k. 40 blue and brown . . 75 75
DESIGN: 1 k. 40, People of the World.

204 Detail of Chest of Drawers
205 Woman Skier, 1900

1974. Norwegian Folk Art. Rose Painting. Mult.
728 85 ore Type **204** 45 45
729 1 k. Detail of cupboard 30 10

1975. Norwegian Skiing.
730 **205** 1 k. red and green 75 15
731 – 1 k. 40 blue and brown . . 75 55
DESIGN: 1 k. 40, Skier making telemark turn.

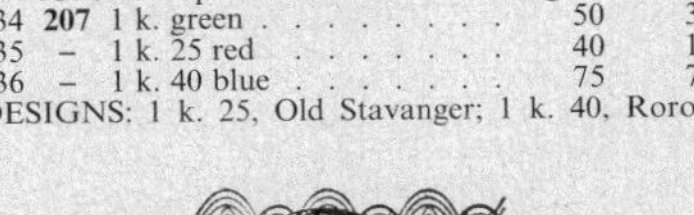

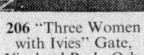

206 "Three Women with Ivies" Gate, Vigeland Park, Oslo
207 Nusfjord Fishing Harbour, Lofoten Islands

1975. International Women's Year.
732 **206** 1 k. 25 violet and purple . . 50 10
733 1 k. 40 ultramarine and blue 75 75

1975. European Architectural Heritage Year.
734 **207** 1 k. green 50 35
735 – 1 k. 25 red 40 10
736 – 1 k. 40 blue 75 75
DESIGNS: 1 k. 25, Old Stavanger; 1 k. 40, Roros.

208 Norwegian 1 k. Coin, 1875 (Monetary Convention)

1975. Cent of Monetary and Metre Conventions.
737 **208** 1 k. 25 red 30 10
738 – 1 k. 40 blue 50 40
DESIGN: 1 k. 40, O. J. Broch (original Director of the International Bureau of Weights and Measures) (Metre Convention).

209 Camping and Emblem

1975. World Scout Jamboree, Lillehammer. Mult.
739 1 k. 25 Type **209** 45 15
740 1 k. 40 Skiing and emblem . . 80 60

210 Colonist's Peat House

1975. 150th Anniv of First Emigrations to America.
741 **210** 1 k. 25 brown 40 15
742 – 1 k. 40 blue 70 50
DESIGNS: 1 k. 40, C. Peerson and extract from letter to America, 1874.

211 "Templet" (Temple Mountain), Tempelfjord, Spitzbergen
212 "Television Screen" (T. E. Johnsen)

1975. 50th Anniv of Norwegian Administration of Spitzbergen.
743 **211** 1 k. grey 50 25
744 – 1 k. 25 purple 50 10
745 – 1 k. 40 blue . . . . 1·50 1·00
DESIGNS: 1 k. 25, Miners leaving pit; 1 k. 40, Polar bear.

1975. 50th Anniv of Norwegian Broadcasting System. Multicoloured.
746 1 k. 25 Type **212** 30 10
747 1 k. 40 Telecommunications antenna (N. Davidsen) (vert) 75 75

213 "The Annunciation"
214 "Halling" (folk dance)

1975. Paintings from "Altaket" (wooden vault from "Al" (Stave Church), Hallingdal).
748 80 ore Type **213** 30 10
749 1 k. "The Visitation" 30 25
750 1 k. 25 "The Nativity" (30 × 38 mm) 30 10
751 1 k. 40 "The Adoration" (30 × 38 mm) 60 45

1976. Norwegian Folk Dances. Multicoloured.
752 80 ore Type **214** 45 25
753 1 k. "Springar" 45 25
754 1 k. 25 "Gangar" 45 10

215 Silver Sugar Caster, Stavanger, 1770
217 "The Pulpit", Lyse Fjord

216 Bishop's "Mitre" Bowl, 1760

1976. Centenary of Oslo Museum of Applied Art.
755 **215** 1 k. 25 brown, red & pink . 20 10
756 – 1 k. 40 lilac, blue and azure . 35 40
DESIGN: 1 k. 40, Goblet, Nostetangen Glass-works, 1770.

1976. Europa. Early Products of Herrebo Potteries, Halden.
757 **216** 1 k. 25 red and mauve . . 20 10
758 – 1 k. 40 ultramarine & blue . 75 75
DESIGN: 1 k. 40, Decorative plate, 1760.

1976. Norwegian Scenery. Multicoloured.
759 1 k. Type **217** 50 25
760 1 k. 25 Peak of Gulleplet ("The Golden Apple"), Balestrand, Sognefjord 50 10

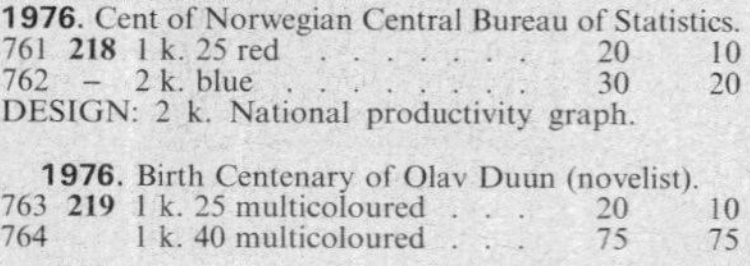

218 Social Development Graph
219 Olav Duun and Cairn, Dun Mountain, Joa Island, Namsen Fjord

1976. Cent of Norwegian Central Bureau of Statistics.
761 **218** 1 k. 25 red 20 10
762 – 2 k. blue 30 20
DESIGN: 2 k. National productivity graph.

1976. Birth Centenary of Olav Duun (novelist).
763 **219** 1 k. 25 multicoloured . . . 20 10
764 1 k. 40 multicoloured . . . 75 75

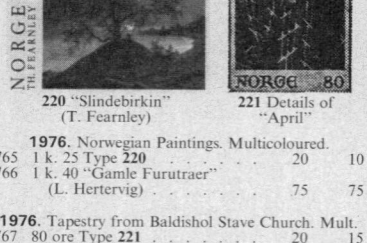

220 "Slindebirkin" (T. Fearnley)
221 Details of "April"

1976. Norwegian Paintings. Multicoloured.
765 1 k. 25 Type **220** 20 10
766 1 k. 40 "Gamle Furutraer" (L. Hertervig) 75 75

1976. Tapestry from Baldishol Stave Church. Mult.
767 80 ore Type **221** 20 15
768 1 k. Detail of "May" 20 25
769 1 k. 25 "April" and "May" section of tapestry (48 × 30 mm) 20 15

222 Five Water-lilies

1977. Nordic Countries Co-operation in Nature Conservation and Environment Protection.
770 **222** 1 k. 25 multicoloured . . . 25 10
771 1 k. 40 multicoloured . . . 25 35

223 Akershus Castle, Oslo
224 Hamnoy, Lofoten Islands

1977.
772 – 1 k. green 15 10
773 – 1 k. 10 purple 45 15
774 **223** 1 k. 25 red 20 10
775 – 1 k. 30 brown 30 10
776 – 1 k. 40 lilac 45 10
777 – 1 k. 50 red 20 10
778 – 1 k. 70 green 30 15
779 – 1 k. 75 green 30 10
780 – 1 k. 80 blue 50 10
781 – 2 k. red 30 10
782 – 2 k. 20 blue 30 15
783 – 2 k. 25 violet 55 45
784 – 2 k. 50 red 30 10
785 – 2 k. 75 red 75 65
786 – 3 k. blue 40 10
787 – 3 k. 50 violet 55 15
DESIGNS—HORIZ: 1 k. Austraat Manor; 1 k. 10, Trondenes Church, Harstad; 1 k. 30, Steinviksholm Fortress, Asen Fjord; 1 k. 40, Ruins of Hamar Cathedral; 2 k. 20, Tromsdalen Church; 2 k. 50, Loghouse, Breiland; 2 k. 75, Damsgard Palace, Laksevag, near Bergen; 3 k. Ruins of Selje Monastery; 3 k. 50, Lindesnes lighthouse. VERT: 1 k. 50, Stavanger Cathedral; 1 k. 70, Rosenkrantz Tower, Bergen; 1 k. 75, Seamen's commemoration hall, Stavern; 1 k. 80, Torungen lighthouses, Arendal; 2 k. Tofte royal estate, Dovre; 2 k. 25, Oscarshall (royal residence), Oslofjord.

1977. Europa. Multicoloured.
795 1 k. 25 Type **224** 65 10
796 1 k. 80 Huldrefossen, Nordfjord (vert) 40 40

225 Spruce
226 Paddle-Steamer "Constitutionen" at Arendal

1977. Norwegian Trees.
797 **225** 1 k. green 20 25
798 – 1 k. 25 brown 20 15
799 – 1 k. 80 black 30 35
DESIGNS: 1 k. 25, Fir; 1 k. 80, Birch.
See note below No. 433.

1977. Norwegian Coastal Routes.
800 **226** 1 k. brown 40 25
801 – 1 k. 25 red 60 10
802 – 1 k. 30 green . . . . . . 1·25 1·10
803 – 1 k. 80 blue 60 65
DESIGNS: 1 k. 25, "Vesteraalen" (coaster) off Bodo; 1 k. 30, Ferries "Kong Haakon" and "Dronningen" at Stavanger, 1893; 1 k. 80, "Nordstjernen" and "Harald Jarl" (ferries).

227 "From the Herring Fishery" (after photo by S. A. Borretzen)
228 "Saturday Evening" (H. Egedius)

1977. Fishing Industry.
804 **227** 1 k. 25 brown on orange . . 20 10
805 – 1 k. 80 blue on blue . . . 30 35
DESIGN: 1 k. 80, Saithe and fish hooks.
See note below No. 433.

1977. Norwegian Paintings. Multicoloured.
806 1 k. 25 Type **228** 20 10
807 1 k. 80 "Forest Lake in Lower Telemark" (A. Cappelen) . . 75 75

229 "David with the Bells"
230 "Peer and the Buck Reindeer" (after drawing by P. Krohg for "Peer Gynt")

1977. Miniatures from the Bible of Aslak Bolt. Multicoloured.
808 80 ore Type **229** 20 10
809 1 k. "Singing Friars" 20 20
810 1 k. 25 "The Holy Virgin with the Child" (34 × 27 mm) 20 10

1978. 150th Birth Anniv of Henrik Ibsen (dramatist).
811 **230** 1 k. 25 black and stone . . 20 10
812 – 1 k. 80 multicoloured . . . 25 30
DESIGN: 1 k. 80, Ibsen (after E. Werenskiold).

231 Heddal Stave Church, Telemark
232 Lenangstindene and Jaegervasstindene, Troms

1978. Europa.
813 **231** 1 k. 25 brown & orange . . 50 10
814 – 1 k. 80 green and blue . . 55 40
DESIGN: 1 k. 80, Borgund stave church, Sogn.

1978. Norwegian Scenery. Multicoloured.
815 1 k. Type **232** 30 15
816 1 k. 25 Gaustatoppen, Telemark 35 30

233 King Olav in Sailing-boat

1978. 75th Birthday of King Olav V.
817 **233** 1 k. 25 brown 20 10
818 – 1 k. 80 violet 55 35
DESIGN—VERT: 1 k. 80, King Olav delivering royal speech at opening of Parliament.

234 Amundsen's Polar Flight Stamp of 1925

1978. "Norwex 80" International Stamp Exhibition.
819 **234** 1 k. 25 green and grey . . 85 90
820 1 k. 25 blue and grey . . . 85 90
821 – 1 k. 25 green and grey . . 85 90
822 – 1 k. 25 blue and grey . . . 85 90
823 **234** 1 k. 25 purple and grey . . 85 90
824 1 k. 25 red and grey . . . 85 90
825 – 1 k. 25 purple and grey . . 85 90
826 – 1 k. 25 blue and grey . . . 85 90
DESIGNS: Nos. 821/2, 825/6, Annexation of Spitzbergen stamp of 1925.
On Nos. 819/26 each design incorporates a different value of the 1925 issues.

235 Willow Pipe Player
236 Wooden Doll, c. 1830

1978. Musical Instruments.
827 **235** 1 k. green 30 10
828 – 1 k. 25 red 30 10
829 – 1 k. 80 blue 30 30
830 – 7 k. 50 grey . . . . . . 2·40 25
831 – 15 k. brown . . . . . . 2·40 15
DESIGNS: 1 k. 25, Norwegian violin; 1 k. 80, Norwegian zither; 7 k. 50, Ram's horn; 15 k. Jew's harp.
See note below No. 433.

1978. Christmas. Antique Toys from Norwegian Folk Museum. Multicoloured.
835 80 ore Type **236** 20 10
836 1 k. Toy town, 1896/7 . . . . 20 20
837 1 k. 25 Wooden horse from Torpo, Hallingdal 20 10

237 Ski Jumping at Huseby, 1879
238 "Portrait of Girl" (M. Stoltenberg)

1979. Centenary of Skiing Competitions at Huseby and Holmenkollen.
838 **237** 1 k. green 30 15
839 – 1 k. 25 red 30 10
840 – 1 k. 80 blue 65 65
DESIGNS: 1 k. 25, Crown Prince Olav ski jumping at Holmenkollen, 1922; 1 k. 80, Cross-country skiing at Holmenkollen, 1976.

1979. International Year of the Child. Mult.
841 1 k. 25 Type **238** 25 10
842 1 k. 80 "Portrait of Boy" (H. C. F. Hosenfelder) 55 55

239 Road to Briksdal Glacier
240 Falkberget (after Harald Dal)

1979. Norwegian Scenery. Multicoloured.
843 1 k. Type **239** 25 15
844 1 k. 25 Skjernoysund, near Mandal 55 10

1979. Birth Centenary of Johan Falkberget (novelist).
845 **240** 1 k. 25 brown 20 10
846 – 1 k. 80 blue 65 65
DESIGN: 1 k. 80, "Ann-Magritt and the Hovi Bullock" (statue by Kristofer Leirdal).

242 Kylling Bridge, Verma, Romsdal
243 Glacier Buttercup

1979. Norwegian Engineering.
848 **242** 1 k. 25 black and brown . . 60 10
849 – 2 k. black and blue . . . 35 20
850 – 10 k. brown and bistre . . 1·90 35
DESIGNS: 2 k. Vessingsjo Dam, Nea, Sor-Trondelag; 10 k. Statfjord A offshore oil drilling and production platform.

1979. Flowers. Multicoloured.
851 80 ore Type **243** 20 10
852 1 k. Alpine cinquefoil 25 20
853 1 k. 25 Purple saxifrage 25 10
See also Nos. 867/8.

244 Leaf and Emblems
245 Oystercatcher Chick ("Haematopus ostralegus")

1980. Centenary of Norwegian Christian Youth Association. Multicoloured.
854 1 k. Type **244** 15 10
855 1 k. 80 Plant and emblems . . 55 55

1980. Birds (1st series). Multicoloured.
856 1 k. Type **245** 35 15
857 1 k. Mallard chick ("Anas platyrhynchos") 35 15
858 1 k. 25 Dipper ("Cinclus cinclus") 35 15
859 1 k. 25 Great tit ("Parus major") 35 15
See also Nos. 869/72, 894/5 and 914/15.

246 Telephone and Dish Aerial

1980. Centenary of Norwegian Telephone Service.
860 **246** 1 k. 25 brown, pur & bl . . 20 10
861 – 1 k. 80 multicoloured . . . 75 75
DESIGN: 1 k. 80, Erecting a telephone pole.

248 "Vulcan as an Armourer" (Hassel Jerverk after Bech)

1980. Nordic Countries' Postal Co-operation. Cast-iron Stove Ornaments.
863 **248** 1 k. 25 brown 15 10
864 – 1 k. 80 violet 45 30
DESIGN: 1 k. 80, "Hercules at a burning Altar" (Moss Jerverk after Henrich Bech).

249 "Jonsokbal" (N. Astrup)

1980. Norwegian Paintings. Multicoloured.
865 1 k. 25 Type **249** 35 10
866 1 k. 80 "Seljefloyten" (C. Skredsvig) 65 65

1980. Flowers. As T **243**. Multicoloured.
867 80 ore Rowan berries 15 10
868 1 k. Dog rose hips 15 10

1981. Birds (2nd series). As T **245**. Multicoloured.
869 1 k. 30 Lesser white-fronted goose ("Anser erythropus") 30 20
870 1 k. 30 Peregrine falcon ("Falco peregrinus") 30 20
871 1 k. 50 Atlantic puffin ("Fratercula arctica") . . . 50 10
872 1 k. 50 Black guillemot ("Cepphus grylle") 50 10

250 Cow
251 "The Mermaid" (painting by Kristen Aanstad on wooden dish from Hol)

1981. Centenary of Norwegian Milk Producers' National Association. Multicoloured.
873 1 k. 10 Type **250** 15 15
874 1 k. 50 Goat 20 10
See note below No. 433.

1981. Europa. Multicoloured.
875 1 k. 50 Type **251** 30 10
876 2 k. 20 "The Proposal" (painting by Ola Hansson on box from Nes) 40 45
See note below No. 433.

252 Weighing Anchor
253 Paddle Steamer "Skibladner"

1981. Sailing Ship Era.
877 **252** 1 k. 30 green 40 30
878 – 1 k. 50 red 35 15
879 – 2 k. 20 blue 70 45
DESIGNS—VERT: 1 k. 50, Climbing the rigging. HORIZ: 2 k. 20, Cadet ship "Christian Radich".

1981. Norwegian Lake Shipping.
880 **253** 1 k. 10 brown 20 20
881 – 1 k. 30 green 20 30
882 – 1 k. 50 red 20 10
883 – 2 k. 30 blue 40 30
DESIGNS: 1 k. 30, "Victoria" (ferry); 1 k. 50, "Faemund II" (ferry); 2 k. 30, "Storegut" (train ferry).

254 Handicapped People as Part of Community

1981. International Year of Disabled Persons.
884 **254** 1 k. 50 pink, red & blue 20 10
885 – 2 k. 20 blue, deep blue and red 55 35
DESIGN: 2 k. 20, Handicapped and non-handicapped people walking together.

255 "Interior in Blue" (Harriet Backer)
256 Hajalmar Branting and Christian Lange

1981. Norwegian Paintings. Multicoloured.
886 1 k. 50 Type **255** 20 10
887 1 k. 70 "Peat Moor on Jaeren" (Kitty Lange Kielland) 30 35

1981. Nobel Peace Prize Winners of 1921.
888 **256** 5 k. black 1·10 35

257 "One of the Magi" (detail from Skjak tapestry, 1625)
258 Ski Sticks

1981. Tapestries. Multicoloured.
889 1 k. 10 Type **257** 20 10
890 1 k. 30 "Adoration of Christ" (detail, Skjak tapestry, 1625) 20 15
891 1 k. 50 "Marriage in Cana" (pillow slip from Storen, 18th century) (29 × 36 mm) 45 10

1982. World Ski Championships, Oslo.
892 **258** 2 k. red and blue 30 10
893 – 3 k. blue and red 50 35
DESIGN: 3 k. Skis.

1982. Birds (3rd series). As T **245**. Multicoloured.
894 2 k. Bluethroat ("Luscinia svecica") 40 20
895 2 k. European robin ("Erithacus rubecula") 40 20

259 Nurse
260 King Haakon VII disembarking from "Heimdal" after Election, 1905

1982. Anti-tuberculosis Campaign. Mult.
896 2 k. Type **259** 25 10
897 3 k. Microscope 35 35
See note below No. 433.

1982. Europa.
898 **260** 2 k. brown 1·10 10
899 – 3 k. blue 95 35
DESIGN: 3 k. Crown Prince Olav greeting King Haakon VII after liberation, 1945.

261 "Girls from Telemark" (Erik Werenskiold)

1982. Norwegian Paintings. Multicoloured.
900 1 k. 75 Type **261** 25 25
901 2 k. "Tone Veli by Fence" (Henrik Sorenson) 25 10
See note below No. 433.

262 Consecration Ceremony, Nidaros Cathedral, Trondheim

1982. 25th Anniv of King Olav V's Reign.
902 **262** 3 k. violet 65 40

263 "Bjornstjerne Bjornson on Balcony at Aulestad" (Erik Werenskiold)

1982. Writers' Birth Anniversaries. Multicoloured.
903 1 k. 75 Type **263** (150th anniv) 25 25
904 2 k. "Sigrid Undset" (after A. C. Svarstad) (birth centenary) 25 10

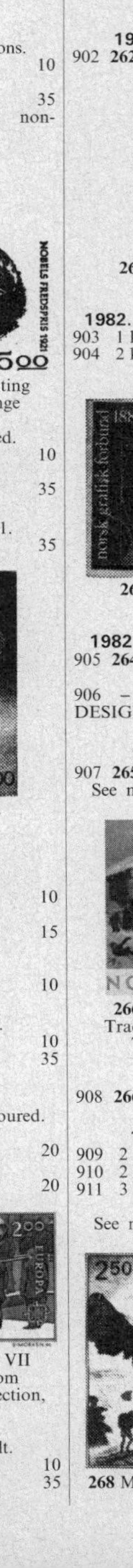

264 Construction of Letter "A"
265 Fridtjof Nansen

1982. Centenary of Graphical Union of Norway.
905 **264** 2 k. yellow, green and black 25 15
906 – 3 k. multicoloured 65 35
DESIGN: 3 k. Offset litho printing rollers.

1982. 1922 Nobel Peace Prize-Winner.
907 **265** 3 k. blue 85 35
See note below No. 433.

266 "Christmas Tradition" (Adolf Tidemand)
267 Buhund (farm dog)

1982. Christmas.
908 **266** 1 k. 75 multicoloured 25 15

1983. Norwegian Dogs. Multicoloured.
909 2 k. Type **267** 40 25
910 2 k. 50 Elkhound 60 15
911 3 k. 50 Lundehund (puffin hunter) 75 40
See note below No. 433.

268 Mountain Scenery
269 Edvard Grieg with Concerto in A minor

1983. Nordic Countries' Postal Co-operation. "Visit the North". Multicoloured.
912 2 k. 50 Type **268** 65 10
913 3 k. 50 Fjord scenery 75 35

1983. Birds (4th series). As T **245**. Mult.
914 2 k. 50 Barnacle goose ("Branta leucopsis") 50 25
915 2 k. 50 Little auk ("Alle alle") 50 25

1983. Europa.
916 **269** 2 k. 50 red 1·10 10
917 – 3 k. 50 blue & green 95 35
DESIGN—VERT: 3 k. 50, Statue of Niels Henrik Abel (mathematician) by Gustav Vigeland.

270 Arrows forming Posthorn
271 King Olav V and Royal Birch, Molde

1983. World Communications Year. Multicoloured.
918 2 k. 50 Type **270** 65 10
919 3 k. 50 Arrows circling globe 85 35

1983. 80th Birthday of King Olav V.
920 **271** 5 k. green 1·40 25

272 Lie
273 Northern Femboring

1983. 150th Birth Anniv of Jonas Lie (author).
921 **272** 2 k. 50 red 55 10

1983. North Norwegian Ships.
922 **273** 2 k. blue and brown 50 20
923 – 3 k. brown and blue 85 40
DESIGNS: 3 k. Jekt.
See note below No. 433.

274 "The Sleigh Ride" (Axel Ender)
275 Post Office Counter

1983. Christmas. Multicoloured.
924 2 k. Type **274** 65 10
925 2 k. 50 "The Guests are arriving" (Gustav Wendel) 65 10

1984. Postal Work. Multicoloured.
926 2 k. Type **275** 55 20
927 2 k. 50 Postal sorting 65 10
928 3 k. 50 Postal delivery 85 35

276 Freshwater Fishing
277 Magnetic Meridians and Parallels

1984. Sport Fishing.
929 **276** 2 k. 50 red 55 10
930 – 3 k. green 65 40
931 – 3 k. 50 blue 85 50
DESIGNS: 3 k. Atlantic salmon fishing; 3 k. 50, Sea fishing.

1984. Birth Bicentenary of Christopher Hansteen (astronomer and geophysicist).
932 **277** 3 k. 50 blue 95 30
933 – 5 k. red 1·40 30
DESIGN—VERT: 5 k. Portrait of Hansteen by Johan Gorbitz.

278 Bridge
279 Vegetables, Fruit and Herbs

1984. Europa. 25th Anniv of European Post and Telecommunications Conference.
934 **278** 2 k. 50 multicoloured 75 10
935 3 k. 50 multicoloured 95 40

1984. Centenary of Norwegian Horticultural Society. Multicoloured.
936 2 k. Type **279** 25 15
937 2 k. 50 Rose and garland of flowers 55 10

280 Honey Bees
281 Holberg (after J. M. Bernigeroth)

1984. Centenaries of Norwegian Beekeeping Society and Norwegian Poultry-breeding Society. Mult.
938 2 k. 50 Type **280** 55 10
939 2 k. 50 Leghorn cock 55 10
See note below No. 433.

1984. 300th Birth Anniv of Ludvig Holberg (writer).
940 **281** 2 k. 50 red 55 10

282 Children reading
284 Karius and Baktus (tooth decay bacteria)

283 Entering Parliamentary Chamber, 2 July 1884

1984. 150th Anniv of "Norsk Penning-Magazin" (1st weekly magazine in Norway).
941 **282** 2 k. 50 purple, blue and red 55 10
942 – 3 k. 50 orange and violet 75 35
DESIGN: 3 k. 50, 1st edition of "Norsk Penning-Magazin".

1984. Cent. of Norwegian Parliament.
943 **283** 7 k. 50 brown 2·25 45

1984. Characters from Stories by Thorbjorn Egner. Multicoloured.
944 2 k. Type **284** 1·25 15
945 2 k. The tree shrew playing guitar 1·25 15
946 2 k. 50 Kasper, Jesper and Jonatan (Rovers) in Kardemomme Town 1·40 25
947 2 k. 50 Chief Constable Bastian 1·40 15

285 Mount Sagbladet (Saw Blade)
286 Return of Crown Prince Olav, 1945

1985. Antarctic Mountains. Multicoloured.
948 2 k. 50 Type **285** 65 15
949 3 k. 50 Mount Hoggestabben (Chopping Block) 85 40

1985. 40th Anniv of Liberation.
950 **286** 3 k. 50 red and blue 95 35

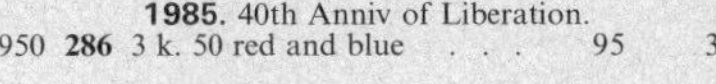

287 Kongsten Fort

1985. 300th Anniv of Kongsten Fort.
951 **287** 2 k. 50 multicoloured 75 10

288 Bronze Cannon, 1596 — **289** "Boy and Girl" (detail)

1985. Artillery Anniversaries. Multicoloured.

952 3 k. Type **288** (300th anniv of Artillery) . . . 75 55
953 4 k. Cannon on sledge carriage, 1758 (bicentenary of Artillery Officers Training School) . . 1·10 35

1985. International Youth Year. Sculptures in Vigeland Park, Oslo. Multicoloured.

954 2 k. Type **289** 55 20
955 3 k. 50 Bronze fountain (detail) . . 95 65

See note below No. 433.

290 Torgeir Augundsson (fiddler) — **291** Workers at Glomfjord

1985. Europa. Music Year.

956 **290** 2 k. 50 red 50 10
957 – 3 k. 50 blue 95 40

DESIGN: 3 k. 50, Ole Bull (composer and violinist).

1985. Centenary of Electricity in Norway.

958 **291** 2 k. 50 red and scarlet . . 75 10
959 – 4 k. blue and green . . . . 1·10 40

DESIGN: 4 k. Men working on overhead cable.

293 Carl Deichman on Book Cover — **294** Wreath

1985. Bicentenary of Public Libraries.

961 **293** 2 k. 50 sepia and brown . . 65 10
962 – 10 k. green . . . . 3·00 50

DESIGN—HORIZ: 10 k. Library interior.

1985. Christmas. Multicoloured.

963 2 k. Type **294** . . . . 1·10 10
964 2 k. 50 Bullfinches . . . . . 1·40 10

295 Dredger "Berghavn" — **296** Sun

1985. 250th Anniv of Port Authorities and Bicentenary of Hydrography in Norway.

965 **295** 2 k. 50 purple, orange & bl . 65 10
966 – 5 k. blue, green & brown . 1·50 40

DESIGN: 5 k. Sextant and detail of chart No. 1 of Lt. F.C. Grove showing Trondheim sealane, 1791.

1986.

967 **296** 2 k. 10 orange and brown . 55 10
968 – 2 k. 30 green and blue . . 55 10
969 – 2 k. 70 pink and red . . . 60 10
970 – 4 k. blue and green 65 10

DESIGNS: 2 k. 30, Atlantic cod and herring; 2 k. 70, Flowers; 4 k. Star ornaments.

297 Marksman in Prone Position

1986. World Biathlon Championships. Mult.

977 2 k. 50 Type **297** 65 10
978 3 k. 50 Marksman standing to take aim 95 65

298 Industry and Countryside — **299** Stone Cutter

1986. Europa. Multicoloured.

979 2 k. 50 Type **298** 75 10
980 3 k. 50 Dead and living forest, mountains and butterflies . . 95 35

1986. Centenary of Norwegian Craftsmen's Federation.

981 **299** 2 k. 50 lake and red . . . 65 10
982 – 7 k. blue and red . . . . . 1·90 50

DESIGN: 7 k. Carpenter.

300 Moss

1986. Nordic Countries' Postal Co-operation. Twinned Towns. Multicoloured.

983 2 k. 50 Type **300** 75 15
984 4 k. Alesund . . . . 1·10 55

See note below No. 433.

301 Han Polson Egede (missionary) and Map — **303** "Olav Kyrre founds Diocese in Nidaros"

1986. Birth Anniversaries.

985 **301** 2 k. 10 brown and red . . 55 55
986 – 2 k. 50 red, green & blue . 60 35
987 – 3 k. brown and red 75 40
988 – 4 k. purple and lilac . . . 1·10 40

DESIGNS: 2 k. 10, Type **301** (300th anniv); 2 k. 50, Herman Wildenvey (poet) and poem carved in wall at Stavern (centenary); 3 k. Tore Ojasaeter (poet) and old cupboard from Skjak (centenary); 4 k. Engebret Soot (engineer) and lock gates, Orje (centenary).

See note below No. 433.

1986. Christmas. Stained Glass Windows by Gabriel Kielland in Nidaros Cathedral, Trondheim. Multicoloured.

990 2 k. 10 Type **303** . . . . . . 1·10 20
991 2 k. 50 "The King and the Peasant at Sul" . . . . . . 1·10 15

304 Doves — **305** Numeral

1986. International Peace Year.

992 **304** 15 k. red, blue & green . . 4·75 75

1987.

993 **305** 3 k. 50 yellow, red & blue . 95 65
994 4 k. 50 blue, yellow & grn . 1·10 40

306 Wooden Building

1987. Europa. Multicoloured.

1000 2 k. 70 Type **306** 55 10
1001 4 k. 50 Building of glass and stone . . . . 1·40 45

307 The Final Vote — **309** Funnel-shaped Chanterelle ("Cantharellus tubaeformis")

1987. 150th Anniv of Laws on Local Councils (granting local autonomy).

1002 **307** 12 k. green . . . . 3·25 55

1987. Fungi (1st series). Multicoloured.

1004 2 k. 70 Type **309** . . . . . . 1·00 15
1005 2 k. 70 The gypsy ("Rozites caperata") . . . . 1·00 15

See also Nos. 1040/1 and 1052/3.

310 Bjornstad Farm from Vaga

1987. Centenary of Sandvig Collections, Maihaugen.

1006 **310** 2 k. 70 sepia and brown . 50 15
1007 – 3 k. 50 purple and blue . . 85 40

DESIGN: 3 k. 50, "Horse and Rider" (wooden carving, Christen Erlandsen Listad).

311 Valevag Churchyard

1987. Birth Centenary of Fartein Valen (composer).

1008 **311** 2 k. 30 blue and green . . 50 30
1009 – 4 k. 50 brown 90 35

DESIGN—VERT: 4 k. 50, Fartein Valen.

See note below No. 433.

312 "Storm at Sea" (Christian Krohg)

1987. Paintings. Multicoloured.

1010 2 k. 70 Type **312** 50 15
1011 5 k. "The Farm" (Gerhard Munthe) . . . . 1·00 25

314 Cat with Children making Decorations

1987. Christmas. Multicoloured.

1013 2 k. 30 Type **314** 95 15
1014 2 k. 70 Dog with children making gingersnaps 95 15

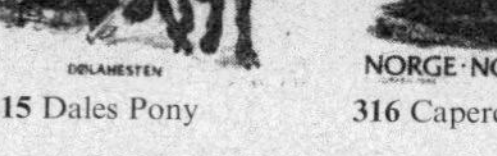

315 Dales Pony — **316** Capercaillie

1987. Native Ponies.

1015 **315** 2 k. 30 deep brown, green and brown 55 20
1016 – 2 k. 70 buff, brown & bl . 65 15
1017 – 4 k. 50 brown, red and blue . 90 45

DESIGNS: 2 k. 70, Fjord pony; 4 k. 50, Nordland pony.

See note below No. 433.

1988. Animals.

1018 – 2 k. 60 deep brown, brown and green 45 10
1019 **316** 2 k. 90 black, brn & grn . 70 15
1020 – 3 k. brown, grey & grn . . 55 10
1021 – 3 k. 20 ultramarine, green and blue 60 20
1022 – 3 k. 80 brown, bl & blk . 85 10
1023 – 4 k. brown, red & green . 95 10
1024 – 4 k. 50 brown, grn & bl . 90 10
1025 – 5 k. 50 brown, grey & grn . 1·40 25
1026 – 6 k. 40 brown, blk & grn . 1·50 50

DESIGNS: 2 k. 60, Fox; 3 k. Stoat; 3 k. 20, Mute swan; 3 k. 80, Reindeer; 4 k. Eurasian red squirrel; 4 k. 50, Beaver; 5 k. 50, Lynx; 6 k. 40, Tengmalm's owl.

317 Band

1988. Centenary of Salvation Army in Norway. Multicoloured.

1035 2 k. 90 Type **317** 75 15
1036 4 k. 80 Othilie Tonning (early social worker) and Army nurse . . . . 1·25 65

318 Building Fortress

1988. Military Anniversaries.

1037 **318** 2 k. 50 green 75 20
1038 – 2 k. 90 brown 80 15
1039 – 4 k. 60 blue . . . . . . 1·25 65

DESIGNS: 2 k. 50, Type **318** (300th anniv of Defence Construction Service); 2 k. 90, Corps members in action (centenary of Army Signals corps); 4 k. 60, Making pontoon bridge (centenary of Engineer Corps).

1988. Fungi (2nd series). As T **309**. Mult.

1040 2 k. 90 Wood blewits 75 15
1041 2 k. 90 Milk caps 75 15

319 Globe — **320** King Olav V

1988. European Campaign for Interdependence and Solidarity of North and South.

1042 **319** 25 k. multicoloured . . . 5·75 75

1988. 85th Birthday of King Olav V.

1043 **320** 2 k. 90 multicoloured . . 70 10

321 "Prinds Gustav" (paddle-steamer) — **322** King Christian IV

1988. Europa. Transport and Communications.

1045 **321** 2 k. 90 black, red & blue . 85 10
1046 – 3 k. 80 blue, red & yell . . 1·25 85

DESIGN: 3 k. 80, Heroybrua Bridge.

1988. 400th Anniv of Christian IV's Accession to Danish and Norwegian Thrones.

1047 **322** 2 k. 50 black, stone & vio . 60 10
1048 – 10 k. multicoloured . . . 2·75 45

DESIGN: 10 k. 1628 silver coin and extract from decree on mining in Norway.

324 Ludvig with Ski Stick — **325** Start and Finish of Race

1988. Christmas. Multicoloured.

1050 2 k. 90 Type **324** 95 10
1051 2 k. 90 Ludvig reading letter . 95 10

1989. Fungi (3rd series). As T **309**. Multicoloured.

1052 3 k. Chanterelle ("Cantharellus cibarius") 80 20
1053 3 k. Butter mushroom ("Suillus luteus") 80 20

1989. World Cross-country Championship, Stavanger.

1054 **325** 5 k. multicoloured . . . . 1·10 25

326 Vardo

327 Setesdal Woman

1989. Town Bicentenaries.

1055 **326** 3 k. blue, red & lt blue . . 85 10
1056 – 4 k. purple, blue & orge . 1·25 35
DESIGN: 4 k. Hammerfest.

1989. Nordic Countries' Postal Co-operation. Traditional Costumes. Multicoloured.

1057 3 k. Type **327** 85 10
1058 4 k. Kautokeino man . . . . 1·25 45

328 Children making Snowman

329 Rooster and Cover of 1804 First Reader

1989. Europa. Children's Games. Multicoloured.

1059 3 k. 70 Type **328** 85 50
1060 5 k. Cat's cradle . . . . . . 1·50 50
See note below No. 433.

1989. 250th Anniv of Primary Schools.

1061 **329** 2 k. 60 multicoloured . . 85 45
1062 – 3 k. brown 60 10
DESIGN: 3 k. Pocket calculator and child writing.

332 Arnulf Overland (poet, centenary)

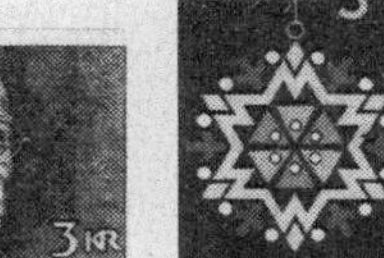
333 Star Decoration

1989. Writers' Birth Anniversaries.

1065 **332** 3 k. red and blue 60 10
1066 – 25 k. blue, orange & green 5·75 70
DESIGN: 25 k. Hanna Winsnes (pseudonym Hugo Schwartz) (bicentenary).

1989. Christmas. Tree Decorations. Mult.

1067 3 k. Type **333** 60 10
1068 3 k. Bauble 60 10

334 Larvik Manor

335 Emblem

1989. Manor Houses.

1069 **334** 3 k. brown 60 10
1070 – 3 k. green 60 10
DESIGN: No. 1070, Rosendal Barony.

1990. Winter Cities Events, Tromso.

1071 **335** 5 k. multicoloured . . . . 1·40 35

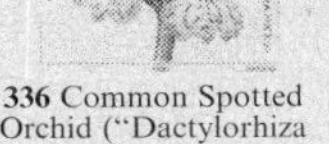
336 Common Spotted Orchid ("Dactylorhiza fuchsii")

337 Merchant Navy, Airforce, Home Guard, "Moses" (coastal gun) and Haakon VII's Monogram

1990. Orchids (1st series). Multicoloured.

1072 3 k. 20 Type **336** 60 10
1073 3 k. 20 Dark red helleborine ("Epipactis atrorubens") 60 10
See also Nos. 1141/2.

1990. 50th Anniv of Norway's Entry into Second World War. Multicoloured.

1074 3 k. 20 Type **337** 85 10
1075 4 k. Second Battle of Narvik, 1940 . . . . 1·00 45

339 Trondheim Post Office

340 "Tordenskiold" (from print by J. W. Tegner after Balthazar Denner)

1990. Europa. Post Office Buildings. Mult.

1077 3 k. 20 Type **339** 75 10
1078 4 k. Longyearbyen Post Office 1·10 45

1990. 300th Birth Anniv of Admiral Tordenskiold (Peter Wessel). Multicoloured.

1079 3 k. 20 Type **340** 75 10
1080 5 k. Tordenskiold's coat-of-arms . . . . 1·25 45

341 Svendsen

343 "Children and Snowman" (Ragni Engstrom Nilsen)

1990. 150th Birth Anniv of Johan Svendsen (composer and conductor).

1081 **341** 2 k. 70 black and red . . 85 50
1082 – 15 k. brown & yellow . . 3·00 95
DESIGN: 15 k. Svendsen Monument (Stinius Fredriksen), Oslo.

1990. Christmas. Children's Prize-winning Drawings. Multicoloured.

1084 3 k. 20 Type **343** 60 10
1085 3 k. 20 "Christmas Church" (Jorgen Ingier) 60 10

344 Nobel Medal and Soderblom

1990. 60th Anniv of Award of Nobel Peace Prize to Nathan Soderblom, Archbishop of Uppsala.

1086 **344** 30 k. brown, blue & red . 6·25 95

345 Plan and Elevation of Container Ship and Propeller

346 Satellite transmitting to Tromso

1991. Centenaries of Federation of Engineering Industries (1989) and Union of Iron and Metal Workers.

1087 **345** 5 k. multicoloured . . . . 1·00 45

1991. Europa. Europe in Space. Mult.

1088 3 k. 20 Type **346** 60 10
1089 4 k. Rocket leaving Andoya rocket range 90 25
See note below No. 433.

347 Christiansholm Fortress (late 17th-century)

348 Fountain, Vigeland Park, Oslo

1991. 350th Anniv of Kristiansand. Each black, blue and red.

1090 3 k. 20 Type **347** 60 15
1091 5 k. 50 Present day view of Christiansholm Fortress . . 1·10 60

1991. Nordic Countries' Postal Co-operation. Tourism. Multicoloured.

1092 3 k. 20 Type **348** 60 10
1093 4 k. Globe, North Cape Plateau 1·50 45

349 "Skomvaer III" (lifeboat)

352 Posthorn

1991. Centenary of Norwegian Society for Sea Rescue.

1094 **349** 3 k. 20 brown, black & grn 60 55
1095 – 27 k. brown, grey & purple 5·75 2·25
DESIGN—VERT: 27 k. "Colin Archer" (first lifeboat).

1991.

1098 **352** 1 k. black and orange . . 20 10
1099 2 k. red and green 35 10
1100 3 k. green and blue . . . 55 10
1101 4 k. red and orange . . . 75 10
1102 5 k. blue and green . . . 90 10
1103 6 k. red and green . . . . 1·10 25
1104 7 k. blue and brown . . . 1·25 25
1105 8 k. green and purple . . 1·50 35
1106 9 k. brown and blue . . . 1·60 45

353 Guisers with Goat Head

1991. Christmas. Guising. Multicoloured.

1120 3 k. 20 Type **353** 60 10
1121 3 k. 20 Guisers with lantern . 60 10

354 Queen Sonja

355 King Harald

356 King Harald

1992.

1122 **354** 2 k. 80 lake, purple & red 50 10
1123 3 k. green, deep green and turquoise 55 10
1124 **355** 3 k. 30 blue, ultramarine and light blue 60 10
1125 3 k. 50 black and grey . . 65 10
1127 4 k. 50 deep red and red . 90 10
1128 5 k. 50 brn, sepia & blk . 1·00 25
1129 5 k. 60 orange, red and vermilion . . . . 1·00 25
1131 6 k. 50 emerald, green and turquoise . . . . 1·25 55
1132 6 k. 60 maroon, purple and brown . . . . 1·25 25
1133 7 k. 50 violet, lilac and purple . . . . 1·50 60
1134 8 k. 50 chestnut, deep brown and brown . . . . 1·75 70
1135 **356** 10 k. green . . . . 1·90 45
1137 20 k. violet . . . . 3·75 1·10
1138 30 k. blue . . . . 5·75 3·75
1139 50 k. green . . . . 9·50 1·25

1992. Orchids (2nd series). As T **336**. Mult.

1141 3 k. 30 Lady's slipper orchid ("Cypripedium calceolus") . 85 10
1142 3 k. 30 Fly orchid ("Ophrys insectifera") 85 10

358 "Restauration" (emigrant sloop)

1992. Europa. 500th Anniv of Discovery of America by Columbus. Transatlantic Ships. Multicoloured.

1144 3 k. 30 Type **358** 80 15
1145 4 k. 20 "Stavangerfjord" (liner) and American skyline . . . 1·40 35
See note below No. 433.

359 Norwegian Pavilion, Rainbow and Ship

360 Molde

1992. "Expo '92" World's Fair, Seville. Mult.

1146 3 k. 30 Type **359** 70 10
1147 5 k. 20 Mountains, rainbow, fish and oil rig . . . . 1·25 25

1992. 250th Anniversaries of Molde and Kristiansund.

1148 **360** 3 k. 30 blue, green & brn 70 10
1149 – 3 k. 30 blue, brown & lt bl 70 10
DESIGN: No. 1149, Kristiansund.

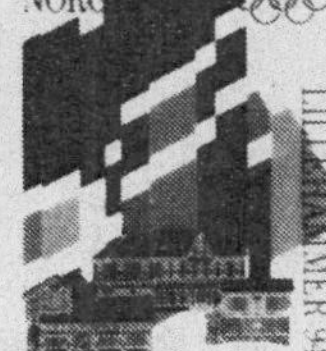
361 Banners and Lillehammer Buildings

363 Gnomes below Pillar Box

1992. Winter Olympic Games, Lillehammer (1994) (1st issue). Multicoloured.

1150 3 k. 30 Type **361** 60 10
1151 4 k. 20 Flags . . . . 1·00 35
See also Nos. 1169/70 and 1175/80.

1992. Christmas. Christmas card designs by Otto Moe. Multicoloured.

1153 3 k. 30 Type **363** 60 10
1154 3 k. 30 Gnome posting letter . 60 10

364 Orange-tip ("Anthocaris cardamines")

366 Grieg

1993. Butterflies (1st series). Multicoloured.

1155 3 k. 50 Type **364** 65 10
1156 3 k. 50 Small tortoiseshell ("Aglais urticae") 65 10
See also Nos. 1173/4.

1993. 150th Birth Anniv of Edvard Grieg (composer). Multicoloured.

1158 3 k. 50 Type **366** 95 10
1159 5 k. 50 "Spring" . . . . . . 1·40 25

367 Two-man Kayak on Lake

368 Richard With (founder) and "Vesteraalen"

1993. Nordic Countries' Postal Co-operation. Tourist Activities. Multicoloured.

1160 4 k. Type **367** . . . . 1·10 45
1161 4 k. 50 White-water rafting . . 1·50 55

1993. Centenary of Express Coaster Service.

1162 **368** 3 k. 50 blue, vio & red . . 65 10
1163 – 4 k. 50 multicoloured . . 1·50 25
DESIGN: 4 k. 50, "Kong Harald".

369 Handball

370 Johann Castberg (politician)

1993. Sports Events. Multicoloured.

1164 3 k. 50 Type **369** (Women's World Championship, Norway) 65 10
1165 5 k. 50 Cycling (World Championships, Oslo and Hamar) . . . . 1·40 40

1993. Centenary of Workforce Protection Legislation.

1166 **370** 3 k. 50 brown and blue . . 65 10
1167 – 12 k. blue and brown . . 2·90 90
DESIGN: 12 k. Betzy Kjelsberg (first woman factory inspector).

372 Torch Bearer on Skis

373 Store Mangen Chapel

1993. Winter Olympic Games, Lillehammer (1994) (2nd issue). Morgedal–Lillehammer Torch Relay. Multicoloured.

1169 3 k. 50 Type **372** 95 45
1170 3 k. 50 Lillehammer 95 45
Nos. 1169/70 were issued together, se-tenant, forming a composite design.

1993. Christmas. Multicoloured.

No.	Description		
1171	3 k. 50 Type **373**	95	10
1172	3 k. 50 Stamnes church, Sandnessjoen	95	10

1994. Butterflies (2nd series). As T **364**. Mult.

No.	Description		
1173	3 k. 50 Northern clouded yellow ("Colias hecla")	65	10
1174	3 k. 50 Freya's fritillary ("Clossiana freija")	65	10

374 Flags  **375** Cross-country Skiing

1994. Winter Olympic Games, Lillehammer (3rd issue). Multicoloured.

No.	Description		
1175	3 k. 50 Type **374**	65	10
1176	3 k. 50 Flags (different)	65	10
1177	3 k. 50 Lillehammer (church) and rings	65	10
1178	3 k. 50 Lillehammer (ski jump) and rings	65	10
1179	4 k. 50 Flags of European countries	85	25
1180	5 k. 50 Flags of non-European countries	1·00	40

Nos. 1175/8 were issued together, se-tenant, forming a composite design.

1994. Paralympic Games, Lillehammer. Mult.

No.	Description		
1181	4 k. 50 Type **375**	80	20
1182	5 k. 50 Downhill skiing	1·00	40

376 King Christian VII's Signature and Seal

1994. Bicentenary of Tromso.

No.	Description		
1183	**376** 3 k. 50 red, bistre & brn	65	10
1184	– 4 k. 50 blue, yellow and light blue	85	25

DESIGN: 4 k. 50, Tromsdalen church.

377 Mount Floy Incline Railway, Bergen

1994. Tourism. Multicoloured.

No.	Description		
1185	4 k. Type **377**	85	25
1186	4 k. 50 "Svolvaer Goat" (rock formation), Lofoten	85	25
1187	5 k. 50 Beacon, World's End, Tjome	1·00	40

378 Osterdal Farm Buildings

1994. Cent of Norwegian Folk Museum, Bygdoy.

No.	Description		
1188	**378** 3 k. multicoloured	60	10
1189	– 3 k. 50 blue, yellow and purple	70	10

DESIGN: 3 k. 50, Horse-drawn sleigh, 1750 (Torsten Hoff).

379 Technological Symbols and Formula ("Glass Flasks")

1994. EUREKA (European technology co-operation organization) Conference of Ministers, Lillehammer. Multicoloured.

No.	Description		
1190	4 k. Type **379**	80	20
1191	4 k. 50 Technological symbols ("Electronic Chips")	90	25

380 Electric Tram and Street Plan of Oslo, 1894  **382** Sledge

1994. Centenary of Electric Trams. Multicoloured.

No.	Description		
1192	3 k. 50 Type **380**	75	15
1193	12 k. Articulated tram and Oslo route map	2·75	1·10

1994. Christmas.

No.	Description		
1195	**382** 3 k. 50 red and black	70	10
1196	– 3 k. 50 ultramarine, blue and black	70	10

DESIGN: No. 1196, Kick-sledge.

383 Cowberry  **384** Swan Pharmacy, Bergen ("Vaccinium vitis-idaea")

1995. Wild Berries (1st Series). Multicoloured.

No.	Description		
1197	3 k. 50 Type **383**	70	10
1198	3 k. 50 Bilberry ("Vaccinium myrtillus")	70	10

See also Nos. 1224/5.

1995. 400th Anniv of Norwegian Pharmacies.

No.	Description		
1199	**384** 3 k. 50 green and brown	70	10
1200	– 25 k. multicoloured	4·75	2·40

DESIGN: 25 k. Scales, pestle and mortar and ingredients.

385 German Commander saluting Terje Rollem (Home Guard commander)

1995. 50th Anniv of Liberation of Norway.

No.	Description		
1201	**385** 3 k. 50 silver, green and black	70	10
1202	– 4 k. 50 silver, blue and black	90	35
1203	– 5 k. 50 silver, red and black	1·10	45

DESIGNS: 4 k. 50, King Haakon VII and family returning to Norway; 5 k. 50, Children waving Norwegian flags.

386 Old Moster Church  **387** Skudeneshavn

1995. Millenary of Christianity in Norway. Multicoloured.

No.	Description		
1204	3 k. 50 Type **386**	70	10
1205	15 k. Slettebakken Church, Bergen	3·25	1·60

1995. Nordic Countries' Postal Co-operation. Tourism. Multicoloured.

No.	Description		
1206	4 k. Type **387**	80	20
1207	4 k. 50 Hole in the Hat (coastal rock formation)	90	35

388 Flagstad as Isolde  **389** Disputants in Conflict

1995. Birth Centenary of Kirsten Flagstad (opera singer). Multicoloured.

No.	Description		
1208	3 k. 50 Type **388**	70	10
1209	5 k. 50 Flagstad in scene from "Lohengrin" (Wagner)	1·10	40

1995. Bicentenary of Conciliation Boards. Multicoloured.

No.	Description		
1210	7 k. Type **389**	1·10	55
1211	12 k. Disputants in conciliation with mediator	2·25	1·00

390 Letter and Vice-regent Hannibal Sehested (founder)

1995. 350th Anniv (1997) of Norwegian Postal Service (1st issue). Multicoloured.

No.	Description		
1212	3 k. 50 Type **390** (letter post, 1647)	95	10
1213	3 k. 50 Wax seal (registered post, 1745)	95	10
1214	3 k. 50 Postmarks (1845)	95	10
1215	3 k. 50 Banknotes, coins and money orders (transfer of funds, 1883)	95	10
1216	3 k. 50 Editions of "Norska Intelligenz-Sedler" and "Arkiv" (newspapers and magazines, 1660)	95	10
1217	3 k. 50 Address label, cancellations and "Constitutionen" (paddle-steamer) (parcel post, 1827)	95	10
1218	3 k. 50 Stamps (1855)	95	10
1219	3 k. 50 Savings book (Post Office Savings Bank, 1950)	95	10

The dates are those of the introduction of the various services.

See also Nos. 1237/44 and 1283/90.

391 Trygve Lie (first Secretary-General) and Emblem  **392** Woolly Hat

1995. 50th Anniv of U.N.O. Multicoloured.

No.	Description		
1220	3 k. 50 Type **391**	70	10
1221	5 k. 50 Relief worker, water pump and emblem	1·10	40

1995. Christmas. Multicoloured.

No.	Description		
1222	3 k. 50 Type **392**	70	10
1223	3 k. 50 Mitten	70	10

1996. Wild Berries (2nd series). As T **383**. Multicoloured.

No.	Description		
1224	3 k. 50 Wild strawberries ("Fragaria vesca")	70	10
1225	3 k. 50 Cloudberries ("Rubus chamaemorus")	70	10

393 Advent Bay  **394** Cross-country Skier (Hakon Paulsen)

1996. Svalbard Islands. Multicoloured.

No.	Description		
1226	10 k. Type **393**	1·90	75
1227	20 k. Polar bear	3·75	1·50

1996. Centenary of Modern Olympic Games. Children's Drawings. Multicoloured.

No.	Description		
1228	3 k. 50 Type **394**	65	10
1229	5 k. 50 Athlete (Emil Tanem)	1·10	40

395 Besseggen  **396** Urskog–Holand Line

1996. Tourism. U.N.E.S.C.O. World Heritage Sites. Multicoloured.

No.	Description		
1230	4 k. Type **395**	75	20
1231	4 k. 50 Stave church, Urnes	85	30
1232	5 k. 50 Rock carvings, Alta	1·10	40

See also Nos. 1291/3.

1996. Railway Centenaries. Multicoloured.

No.	Description		
1233	3 k. Type **396**	65	10
1234	4 k. 50 Setesdal line	85	30

397 Location Map and Height Indicator

1996. Natural Gas Production at Troll, near Bergen. Multicoloured.

No.	Description		
1235	3 k. 50 Type **397**	65	10
1236	25 k. Planned route map of pipelines to Europe for next 200 years	4·75	1·90

398 Postal Courier crossing Mountains

1996. 350th Anniv (1997) of Postal Service (2nd issue). Multicoloured.

No.	Description		
1237	3 k. 50 Type **398**	65	10
1238	3 k. 50 "Framnaes" (fjord steamer)	65	10
1239	3 k. 50 Postal truck in Oslo	65	10
1240	3 k. 50 Taking mail on board "Ternen" (seaplane) on Jonsvatn Lake, Trondheim	65	10
1241	3 k. 50 Loading mail train at East Station, Oslo	65	10
1242	3 k. 50 Rural postman at Mago farm, Nittedal	65	10
1243	3 k. 50 Serving customer, Elverum post office	65	10
1244	3 k. 50 Computer, letters and globe	65	10

399 Leif Juster, Sean Connery, Liv Ullmann and Olsen Gang

1996. Centenary of Motion Pictures. Multicoloured.

No.	Description		
1245	3 k. 50 Type **399**	65	10
1246	5 k. 50 Wenche Foss, Jack Fjeldstad, Marilyn Monroe, blood and gun	1·10	40
1247	7 k. Charlie Chaplin in "Modern Times", Ottar Gladvedt, Laurel and Hardy and Marlene Dietrich	1·40	55

400 Left detail  **401** Skram

1996. Christmas. Embroidery Details from Telemark Folk Costume. Multicoloured.

No.	Description		
1248	3 k. 50 Type **400**	65	10
1249	3 k. 50 Right detail	65	10

Nos. 1248/9 were issued together, se-tenant, forming a composite design.

1996. 150th Birth Anniv of Amalie Skram (writer).

No.	Description		
1250	**401** 3 k. 50 red	65	10
1251	– 15 k. violet and red	3·00	1·10

DESIGN: 15 k. Scene from dramatisation of "People of Hellemyr".

402 Posthorn 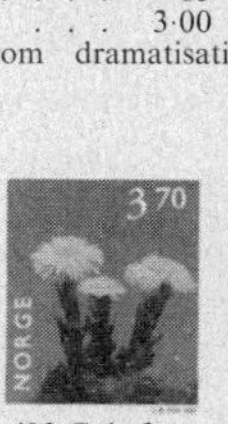 **403** Coltsfoot

1997. Multicoloured, colour of oval given.

No.	Description		
1252	**402** 10 ore red	10	10
1253	20 ore blue	10	10
1254	30 ore orange	10	10
1255	40 ore black	10	10
1256	50 ore green	10	10

1997. Flowers. Multicoloured.

No.	Description		
1263	3 k. 20 Red clover	60	10
1264	3 k. 40 Marsh marigold	55	10
1265	3 k. 60 Red campion	60	10
1266	3 k. 70 Type **403**	70	10
1267	3 k. 80 Wild pansy	60	10
1268	4 k. Wood anemone	65	15
1269	4 k. 30 Lily of the valley	85	25
1270	4 k. 50 White clover	70	15
1271	5 k. Harebell	95	35
1271a	5 k. 40 Oeder's lousewort	80	30
1272	5 k. 50 Hepatica	90	35
1273	6 k. Ox-eye daisy	1·10	40
1274	7 k. Yellow wood violet	1·10	40
1275	7 k. 50 Pale pasque flower	1·25	50
1275a	8 k. White water-lily	1·25	50
1276	13 k. Purple saxifrage	2·10	80
1276a	14 k. Globe flower	2·25	90
1276b	25 k. Melancholy thistle	4·00	1·60

404 Bumble Bee **405** Ski Jumping

1997. Insects (1st series). Multicoloured.
1277 3 k. 70 Type **404** 70 10
1278 3 k. 70 Ladybird 70 10
See also Nos. 1306/7.

1997. World Nordic Skiing Championships, Trondheim. Multicoloured.
1279 3 k. 70 Type **405** 70 10
1280 5 k. Speed skiing 95 35

406 King Harald (photo by Erik Johansen)

1997. 60th Birthdays of King Harald and Queen Sonja. Multicoloured.
1281 3 k. 70 Type **406** 65 10
1282 3 k. 70 Queen Sonja and King Harald (photo by Knut Falch) (horiz) 65 10

407 Hammer, Plumb Line and Hook (post-war reconstruction)

1997. 350th Anniv of Postal Service (3rd issue). Post-war History. Multicoloured.
1283 3 k. 70 Type **407** 65 10
1284 3 k. 70 "Kon Tiki" (replica of balsa raft) (Thor Heyerdahl's expedition from Peru to Polynesia, 1947) 65 10
1285 3 k. 70 Grouse feather (official bird of Rondane National Park (first National Park, 1962)) 65 10
1286 3 k. 70 Hands of man and woman (Welfare State (introduction of National Insurance, 1967)) 65 10
1287 3 k. 70 Drilling platform, Ekofisk oil field (discovery of oil in Norwegian sector of North Sea, 1969) 65 10
1288 3 k. 70 Grete Waitz (first women's world Marathon champion, 1983) 65 10
1289 3 k. 70 Askoy Bridge, 1992 (communications) 65 10
1290 3 k. 70 Crown Prince Haakon Magnus lighting Olympic flame (Winter Olympic Games, Lillehammer, 1994) . 65 10

1997. Tourism. As T **395**. Multicoloured.
1291 4 k. 30 Roros 75 20
1292 5 k. Faerder Lighthouse . . 85 30
1293 6 k. Nusfjord . . . . . . 1·00 40

408 University, Cathedral, Statue of King Olav, City Gate and Broadcasting Tower

409 Gerhardsen and Storting (Parliament House)

1997. Millenary of Trondheim. Multicoloured.
1294 3 k. 70 Type **408** 65 10
1295 12 k. Trees, mine, King Olav, pilgrims, burning buildings and harbour . . . . . . 2·00 80

1997. Birth Centenary of Einar Gerhardsen (Prime Minister 1945–51, 1955–63 and 1963–65).
1296 **409** 3 k. 70 black, stone and red 65 10
1297 – 25 k. black, flesh and green 4·25 1·60
DESIGN: 25 k. Gerhardsen, mountain, factory and electricity pylon.

410 Thematic Subjects **411** Harald Saeverud (composer)

1997. Inauguration of National Junior Stamp Club. Multicoloured.
1298 3 k. 70 Type **410** 65 10
1299 3 k. 70 Thematic subjects including lumpsucker (fish) and tiger 65 10

1997. Birth Centenaries.
1300 **411** 10 k. blue . . . . 1·75 70
1301 – 15 k. green . . . . 2·50 1·00
DESIGN: 15 k. Tarjei Vesaas (writer).

412 Dass in Rowing Boat

1997. 350th Birth Anniv of Petter Dass (priest and poet). Multicoloured.
1302 **412** 3 k. 20 blue and brown . . 50 10
1303 – 3 k. 70 green, blue and brown 60 10
DESIGN: 3 k. 70, Dass and Alstahaug Church.

413 Golden Calendar Stick Symbols against Candle Flames **414** Roses

1997. Christmas. Multicoloured. Self-adhesive.
1304 3 k. 70 Type **413** 60 10
1305 3 k. 70 Silver calendar stick symbols against night sky 60 10

1998. Insects (2nd series). As T **404**. Multicoloured.
1306 3 k. 80 Dragonfly 60 10
1307 3 k. 80 Grasshopper 60 10

1998. St. Valentine's Day. Self-adhesive.
1308 **414** 3 k. 80 multicoloured . . 60 10

415 "Hornelen" (passenger and mail steamer) **416** Holmenkollen Ski Jump, Oslo

1998. Nordic Countries' Postal Co-operation. Ships.
1309 **415** 3 k. 80 blue and green . . 60 10
1310 – 4 k. 50 green and blue . . 70 15
DESIGN: No. 1310, "Kommandoren" (passenger catamaran).

1998. Tourist Sights. Multicoloured.
1311 3 k. 80 Type **416** 55 10
1312 4 k. 50 Fisherman, Alesund Harbour 70 15
1313 5 k. 50 Mt. Hamaroyskaftet . . 90 35

417 Egersund Harbour

1998. Bicentenary of Egersund.
1314 **417** 3 k. 80 blue and pink . . 60 10
1315 – 6 k. blue and mauve . . . 95 35
DESIGN: No. 1315, Egersund ceramics.

418 Silver

1998. Minerals. Multicoloured.
1316 3 k. 40 Type **418** 55 10
1317 5 k. 20 Cobalt 85 30

419 "Water Rider" (Frans Widerberg)

1998. Contemporary Art. Multicoloured.
1318 6 k. Type **419** 95 35
1319 7 k. 50 "Red Moon" (carpet, Synnove Anker Aurdal) . . 1·25 50
1320 13 k. "King Haakon VII" (sculpture, Nils Aas) . . . 2·10 80

420 Hopscotch

1998. Children's Games. Multicoloured.
1321 3 k. 80 Type **420** 60 10
1322 5 k. 50 Throwing coins at a stick 90 35

421 Boeing 747, Doulas DC-3 and Junkers Ju 52 Airliners

1998. Inauguration of Oslo Airport, Gardermoen. Multicoloured.
1323 3 k. 80 Type **421** 60 10
1324 6 k. Boeing 737 airliner and map of former approaches to Gardermoen Airport . . . 95 35
1325 24 k. Terminal building, control tower and wings drawn by Leonardo da Vinci . . . . 3·75 1·50

422 Main Entrance and Guard

1998. 150th Anniv of Royal Palace, Oslo.
1326 **422** 3 k. 40 purple 55 10
1327 – 3 k. 80 blue, pink and yellow 60 10
DESIGN: 3 k. 80, Main front of palace.

423 Music Score **424** Cheese Slicer (Thor Bjorklund)

1998. Christmas. Multicoloured. Self-adhesive.
1328 3 k. 80 Type **423** (red background) 60 10
1329 3 k. 80 Music score (blue background) 60 10

1999. Norwegian Inventions. Self-adhesive.
1330 **424** 3 k. 60 black and blue . . 60 10
1331 – 4 k. black and red 65 10
DESIGN: No. 1331, Paper clip (Johan Vaaler).

425 Salmon and Fly

1999. Fishes and Fishing Flies. Multicoloured. Self-adhesive.
1332 4 k. Type **425** 65 10
1333 4 k. Cod and fly 65 10

426 Heart blowing Flowers out of Posthorn **427** "The Pioneer" (statue, Per Palle Storm)

1999. St. Valentine's Day.
1334 **426** 4 k. multicoloured . . . 60 10

1999. Centenary of Norwegian Confederation of Trade Unions.
1335 **427** 4 k. multicoloured . . . 60 10

428 Poland v Norway, Class B Championship, 1998

1999. World Ice Hockey Championships, Norway. Multicoloured.
1336 4 k. Type **428** 60 10
1337 7 k. Switzerland v Sweden, Class A Championship, 1998 . . . . 1·10 40

429 Swans

1999. Tourism. Multicoloured.
1338 4 k. Type **429** 60 10
1339 5 k. Hamar Cathedral 80 30
1340 6 k. Sami man from Troms . . 95 35

430 Emigration

1999. "Norway 2000" (1st issue). Multicoloured.
1341 4 k. Type **430** 60 10
1342 6 k. King Olav and Bible (conversion to Christianity, 11th century) 95 35
1343 14 k. Medal of King Christian IV and quarry workers (union of Norway and Denmark) . . . . 2·25 90
1344 26 k. Oslo at Beier Bridge, 1850s (industrialization) . . 4·00 1·60

431 Horse Ferry, Amli, East Agder, 1900

1999. "Norway 2000" (2nd issue). Photographs of Everyday Life. Multicoloured.
1345 4 k. Type **431** 60 10
1346 4 k. Men hewing rock during construction of Valdres railway line, 1900 . . . . . 60 10
1347 4 k. Taxi driver Aarseth Odd filling up car with petrol, Kleive, 1930 . . . . . . 60 10
1348 4 k. Dairymaid Mathea Isaksen milking cow, Karmoy, 1930 . 60 10
1349 4 k. Haymakers, Hemsedal, 1943 . . . . 60 10
1350 4 k. Cross-country skier Dagfinn Knutsen, 1932 . . . 60 10
1351 4 k. "Bolgen" (coastal fishing boat), Varanger Fjord, 1977 . 60 10
1352 4 k. Boy Jon Andre Koch holding football, 1981 . . . 60 10

432 Skateboarding **434** Family bringing in Logs

433 Wenche Foss and Per Haugen in "An Ideal Husband" (Oscar Wilde)

1999. Children's Games. Multicoloured.
1354 4 k. Type **432** 60 10
1355 6 k. Inline skating 95 35

1999. Centenary of National Theatre.
1356 **433** 3 k. 60 purple and orange . . . 55 10
1357 – 4 k. ultramarine and blue . 60 10
DESIGN: 4 k. Toralv Maurstad and Tore Segelcke in "Per Gynt" (Henrik Ibsen).

1999. Christmas. Multicoloured. Self-adhesive.
1358 4 k. Type **434** 60 10
1359 4 k. Family sitting by window . 60 10

435 "Sunset" (Sverre Simonsen)

1999. Year 2000. Winning entries in photographic competition. Multicoloured. Self-adhesive.
1360 4 k. Type **435** 60 10
1361 4 k. "Winter Nights" (Poul Christensen) 60 10

436 Eye within Heart

2000. Valentine's Day.
1362 **436** 4 k. multicoloured . . . 60 10

OFFICIAL STAMPS

O 22

O 36

1925.
O187 **O 22** 5 ore mauve 75 75
O188 10 ore green 45 15
O189 15 ore blue . . . . . 1·40 1·90
O190 20 ore purple 20 10
O191 30 ore grey . . . . . 1·90 3·75
O192 40 ore blue 95 75
O193 60 ore blue . . . . . 2·40 4·25

1929. Surch **2 2**.
O219 **O 22** 2 ore on 5 ore mauve . 45 75

1933.
O231 **O 36** 2 ore brown . . . . . 30 1·10
O243 5 ore purple . . . . . 95 1·90
O233 7 ore orange . . . . . 3·25 4·75
O245 10 ore green 30 15
O235 15 ore green 30 25
O247 20 ore red 30 10
O237 25 ore brown 40 40
O238 30 ore blue 40 30
O248 35 ore violet 40 30
O249 40 ore grey 40 15
O250 60 ore blue 40 65
O241 70 ore brown . . . . . 80 1·90
O242 100 ore blue . . . . . 1·90 1·40

O 39

O 58 Quisling Emblem

1937.
O267 **O 39** 5 ore mauve 15 10
O268 7 ore orange 30 65
O257 10 ore green 15 10
O270 15 ore brown 30 15
O271 20 ore red 15 10
O260 25 ore brown 40 50
O273 25 ore red 20 10
O261 30 ore blue 65 30
O275 30 ore grey 75 20
O276 35 ore purple 15 10
O277 40 ore grey 20 10
O278 40 ore blue . . . . . 3·75 20
O279 50 ore lilac 50 10
O280 60 ore blue 30 10
O281 100 ore blue 30 10
O282 200 ore orange . . . . 1·60 20

1942.
O336 **O 58** 5 ore mauve . . . . . 20 1·60
O337 7 ore orange . . . . . 20 1·60
O338 10 ore green 10 15
O339 15 ore brown . . . . . 1·25 11·50
O340 20 ore red 10 15
O341 25 ore brown . . . . . 1·90 16·00
O342 30 ore blue . . . . . 1·50 16·00
O343 35 ore purple . . . . . 1·10 8·00
O344 40 ore grey 15 20
O345 60 ore blue . . . . . 1·25 9·00
O346 1 k. blue . . . . 1·25 11·50

1949. Surch **25** and bar.
O402 **O 39** 25 ore on 20 ore red . . 30 15

O 89

O 99

1951.
O434 **O 89** 5 ore mauve 75 15
O435 10 ore grey 65 10
O436 15 ore brown 95 20
O437 30 ore red 40 10
O438 35 ore brown 60 40
O439 60 ore blue 85 15
O440 100 ore violet . . . . . 1·25 25

1955.
O458 **O 99** 5 ore purple 15 10
O459 10 ore grey 15 10
O460 15 ore brown 50 60
O461 20 ore green 20 10
O736 25 ore green 20 15
O463 30 ore red 80 40
O464 30 ore green 55 15
O465 35 ore red 30 10
O466 40 ore lilac 60 10
O467 40 ore green 50 15
O468 45 ore red 65 10
O469 50 ore brown . . . . . 2·00 25
O470 50 ore red 80 10
O471 50 ore blue 30 10
O738 50 ore grey 30 10
O739 60 ore blue 80 85
O473 60 ore red 60 10
O475 65 ore red 60 10
O476 70 ore brown . . . . . 3·25 60
O477 70 ore red 30 10
O478 75 ore purple . . . . . 8·50 8·50
O479 75 ore green 60 50
O481 80 ore brown 40 10
O741 **O 99** 80 ore red 30 10
O482 85 ore brown 60 80
O483 90 ore orange 60 15
O484 1 k. violet 50 10
O485 1 k. red 30 10
O486 1 k. 10 red 55 30
O744 1 k. 25 red 45 10
O745 1 k. 30 purple 45 30
O746 1 k. 50 red 30 10
O747 1 k. 75 green 60 40
O748 2 k. green 55 10
O749 2 k. red 55 10
O750 3 k. violet 75 20
O488 5 k. violet . . . . . 3·75 35
O752 5 k. blue . . . . . 1·00 20

POSTAGE DUE STAMPS

D 12

1889. Inscr "at betale" and "PORTOMAERKE".
D95 **D 12** 1 ore green 75 75
D96a 4 ore mauve 65 35
D97 10 ore red . . . . . 1·90 25
D98 15 ore brown 75 75
D99 20 ore blue . . . . . 1·10 25
D94 50 ore purple . . . . . 2·75 1·25

1922. Inscr "a betale" and "PORTOMERKE".
D162 **D 12** 4 ore purple . . . . . 3·25 6·00
D163 10 ore green . . . . . 1·25 85
D164 20 ore purple . . . . . 1·90 2·00
D165 40 ore blue . . . . . 3·75 40
D166 100 ore yellow . . . . 14·00 5·75
D167 200 ore violet . . . . 35·00 13·00

NOSSI-BE — Pt. 6

An island north-west of Madagascar, declared a French protectorate in 1840. In 1901 it became part of Madagascar and Dependencies.

100 centimes = 1 franc

1889. Stamp of French Colonies, "Peace and Commerce" type, surch.
8 H 25 c. on 40 c. red on yellow . £1400 £500

1889. Stamps of French Colonies, "Commerce" type, surch.
4 J 5 c. on 10 c. black on lilac . . £1600 £550
2 5 c. on 20 c. red on green . . . £1800 £700
6 15 on 20 c. red on green . . . £1500 £550
7 25 on 30 c. brown on drab . . £1400 £425
9 25 on 40 c. red on yellow . . £1400 £400

1890. Stamps of French Colonies, "Commerce" type, surch (a) **N S B 0 25**.
10 J 0.25 on 20 c. red on green . . £225 £160
11 0 25 on 75 c. red on pink . . . £225 £160
12 0 25 on 1 f. green £225 £160

(b) **N S B 25 c.**
13 J 25 c. on 20 c. red on green . . £225 £160
14 25 c. on 75 c. red on pink . . £225 £160
15 25 c. on 1 f. green £225 £160

(c) **N S B 25** in frame.
16 J 25 on 20 c. red on green . . . £575 £375
17 25 on 75 c. red on pink . . . £575 £375
18 25 on 1 f. green £575 £375

1893. Stamps of French Colonies, "Commerce" type, surch **NOSSI-BE** and bar over value in figures.
36 J 25 on 20 c. red on green . . . 23·00 18·00
37 50 on 10 c. black on lilac . . 25·00 18·00
38 75 on 15 c. blue £160 £120
39 1 f. on 5 c. green . . . . . . 60·00 50·00

1893. Stamps of French Colonies, "Commerce" type, optd **Nossi Be**.
40 J 10 c. black on lilac . . . . 8·00 4·50
41 15 c. blue . . . . 8·50 7·00
42 20 c. red on green . . . . . 60·00 30·00

1894. "Tablet" key-type inscr "NOSSI-BE" in red (1, 5, 15, 25, 75 c., 1 f.) or blue (others).
44 D 1 c. black on blue 60 60
45 2 c. brown on buff 85 75
46 4 c. brown on grey . . . . . 1·25 75
47 5 c. green on green . . . . . 1·40 85
48 10 c. black on lilac . . . . . 3·00 1·90
49 15 c. blue . . . . 4·75 2·25
50 20 c. red on green . . . . . 5·25 3·00
51 25 c. black on pink . . . . . 6·00 4·25
52 30 c. brown on drab . . . . 8·25 5·00
53 40 c. red on yellow . . . . . 9·00 7·75
54 50 c. red on pink . . . . . 9·00 6·25
55 75 c. brown on orange . . . 23·00 17·00
56 1 f. green . . . . 12·00 9·00

POSTAGE DUE STAMPS

1891. Stamps of French Colonies, "Commerce" type, surch **NOSSI-BE chiffre-taxe A PERCEVOIR** and value.
D19 J 0.20 on 1 c. black on blue . £210 £160
D20 0.30 on 2 c. brown on buff . £210 £160
D21 0.35 on 4 c. brown on grey . £225 £170
D22 0.35 on 20 c. red on green . £250 £170
D23 0.50 on 30 c. brn on drab . 70·00 55·00
D24 1 f. on 35 c. blk on orge . £160 £110

1891. Stamps of French Colonies, "Commerce" type, surch **Nossi-Be A PERCEVOIR** and value.
D25 J 5 c. on 20 c. red on green . . £160 £110
D26 10 c. on 15 c. blue on blue . £140 £140
D33 0.10 on 5 c. green . . . . . 10·00 8·25
D27 15 c. on 10 c. blk on lilac . 90·00 90·00
D34 0.15 on 20 c. red on green . 12·50 11·00
D28 25 c. on 5 c. green on grn . 90·00 90·00
D35 0.25 on 75 c. red on pink . . £375 £350

NOVA SCOTIA

An eastern province of the Dominion of Canada, whose stamps it now uses.

Currency: As Canada

1

2 Emblem of the United Kingdom

1853. Imperf.
1 1 1d. brown £2000 £400
4 2 3d. blue £750 £130
5 6d. green £4000 £400
8 1s. purple £14000 £2500

3

4

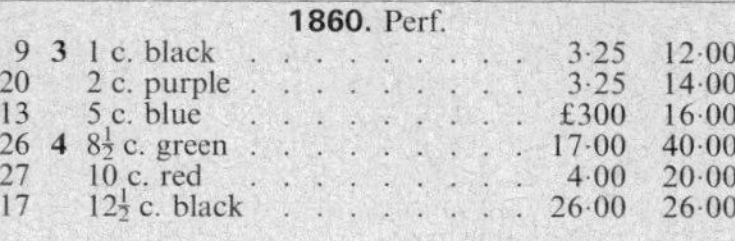
1860. Perf.
9 3 1 c. black . . . . 3·25 12·00
20 2 c. purple . . . . 3·25 14·00
13 5 c. blue . . . . £300 16·00
26 4 $8\frac{1}{2}$ c. green . . . . 17·00 40·00
27 10 c. red . . . . 4·00 20·00
17 $12\frac{1}{2}$ c. black . . . . 26·00 26·00

NYASALAND PROTECTORATE

A British Protectorate in central Africa. Formerly known as British Central Africa. From 1954 to 1963 part of the Central African Federation using the stamps of Rhodesia and Nyasaland (q.v.). From July 1964 independent within the Commonwealth under its new name of Malawi.

12 pence = 1 shilling;
20 shillings = 1 pound

1891. Stamps of Rhodesia optd **B.C.A.**
1 1 1d. black . . . . 3·50 4·00
2 2d. green and red . . . . . 3·50 4·00
3 4d. brown and black . . . . 3·75 5·00
5 6d. blue . . . . 5·50 8·00
6 8d. red and blue . . . . . . 12·00 28·00
7 1s. brown . . . . 13·00 11·00
8 2s. red . . . . 25·00 50·00
9 2s. 6d. purple . . . . 60·00 80·00
10 3s. brown and green . . . . 55·00 60·00
11 4s. black and red . . . . . 60·00 85·00
12 5s. yellow . . . . 60·00 75·00
13 10s. green £120 £180
14 – £1 blue £500 £500
15 – £2 red £800
16 – £5 olive £1400
17 – £10 brown £3250

1892. Stamps of Rhodesia surch **B.C.A.** and value in words.
18 1 3s. on 4s. black and red . . . £325 £325
19 4s. on 5s. yellow . . . . . . 70·00 85·00

1895. No. 2 surch **ONE PENNY.** and bar.
20 1 1d. on 2d. green and red . . . 6·50 26·00

5 Arms of the Protectorate 7

1895. The 2s. 6d. and higher values are larger.
32 5 1d. black . . . . 3·25 4·50
33 2d. black and green . . . . 14·00 5·00
34 4d. black and orange . . . . 21·00 17·00
35 6d. black and blue . . . . . 21·00 11·00
36 1s. black and red . . . . . 21·00 13·00
37 2s. 6d. black and mauve . . . £110 £110
38 3s. black and yellow . . . . 85·00 50·00
39 5s. black and olive £120 £150
29 £1 black and orange £900 £375
40 £1 black and blue £750 £475
30 £10 black and orange £4000 £3500
31 £25 black and green £7000

1897. The 2s. 6d. and higher values are larger.
43 7 1d. black and blue . . . . . 2·50 90
57d 1d. purple and red . . . . . 2·00 40
44 2d. black and yellow . . . . 2·00 1·75
45 4d. black and red . . . . . 5·50 1·50
57e 4d. purple and olive . . . . 8·00 11·00
46 6d. black and green . . . . 42·00 4·25
58 6d. purple and brown . . . . 3·75 3·00
47 1s. black and purple . . . . 9·50 7·00
48 2s. 6d. black and blue . . . 45·00 42·00
49 3s. black and green £190 £225
50 4s. black and red . . . . . 70·00 80·00
50a 10s. black and olive £120 £130
51 £1 black and purple £275 £160
52 £10 black and yellow £4000 £1700

1897. No. 49 surch **ONE PENNY.**
53 7 1d. on 3s. black and green . . 5·00 9·00

10

11

1898.
56a 10 1d. red and blue (imperf) . . £1800 £130
57 1d. red and blue (perf) . . . £2000 17·00

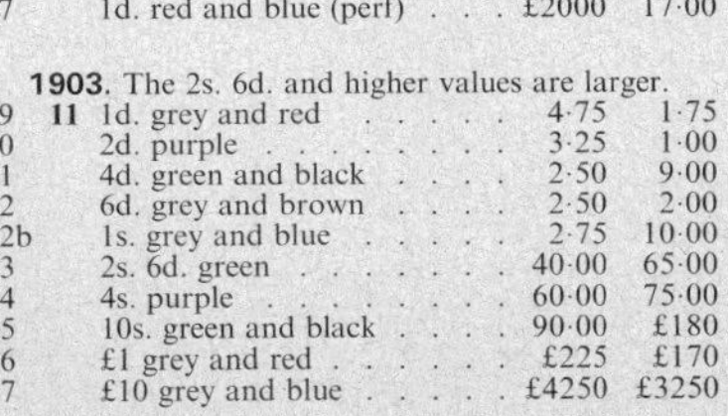
1903. The 2s. 6d. and higher values are larger.
59 11 1d. grey and red . . . . . 4·75 1·75
60 2d. purple . . . . 3·25 1·00
61 4d. green and black . . . . 2·50 9·00
62 6d. grey and brown . . . . 2·50 2·00
62b 1s. grey and blue . . . . . 2·75 10·00
63 2s. 6d. green . . . . 40·00 65·00
64 4s. purple . . . . 60·00 75·00
65 10s. green and black . . . . 90·00 £180
66 £1 grey and red £225 £170
67 £10 grey and blue £4250 £3250

13

14

1908.
73 13 $\frac{1}{2}$d. green . . . . 1·50 2·00
74 1d. red . . . . 3·50 1·00
75 3d. purple on yellow . . . . 1·50 3·75
76 4d. black & red on yellow . . 1·50 1·50
77 6d. purple . . . . 3·75 10·00
72 1s. black on green . . . . . 2·50 7·50
78 14 2s. 6d. black & red on blue . 45·00 80·00
79 4s. red and black . . . . . 80·00 £110
80 10s. green & red on green . . £110 £190
81 £1 purple & black on red . . £450 £550
82 £10 purple and blue £7000 £4500

1913. As 1908, but portrait of King George V.
100 $\frac{1}{2}$d. green . . . . 1·00 30
101 1d. red . . . . 1·50 30
102 $1\frac{1}{2}$d. orange . . . . 3·25 17·00
103 2d. grey . . . . 1·00 30
89 $2\frac{1}{2}$d. blue . . . . 2·25 6·50
90 3d. purple on yellow . . . . 4·00 4·00
91 4d. black and red on yellow . 2·00 2·50
107 6d. purple . . . . 3·00 3·25
93a 1s. black on green . . . . . 5·00 1·50
109 2s. purple and blue on blue . 14·00 11·00
94 2s. 6d. black & red on blue . 11·00 10·00
111 4s. red and black . . . . . 18·00 21·00
112 5s. green & red on yellow . . 35·00 75·00
96 10s. green and red on green . 65·00 85·00
98 £1 purple and black on red . £150 £140
99e £10 purple and blue £2750 £1700

17 King George V and Symbol of the Protectorate

1934.
114 17 $\frac{1}{2}$d. green 75 95
115 1d. brown 75 75
116 $1\frac{1}{2}$d. red . . . . 75 2·50
117 2d. grey . . . . 80 1·25
118 3d. blue . . . . 2·25 1·50
119 4d. mauve . . . . 2·25 3·00
120 6d. violet . . . . 2·25 40
121 9d. olive . . . . 5·00 9·00
122 1s. black and orange . . . . 7·50 13·00

1935. Silver Jubilee. As T **10a** of Gambia.
123 1d. blue and grey . . . . . 1·00 1·50
124 2d. green and blue . . . . . 1·00 70
125 3d. brown and blue . . . . . 7·00 14·00
126 1s. grey and purple . . . . 16·00 32·00

1937. Coronation. As T **10b** of Gambia.
127 $\frac{1}{2}$d. green 30 60
128 1d. brown 50 40
129 2d. grey . . . . 50 1·50

1938. As T **17** but with head of King George VI and "POSTAGE REVENUE" omitted.
130 $\frac{1}{2}$d. green . . . . 30 1·00
130a $\frac{1}{2}$d. brown . . . . 10 1·50
131 1d. brown 70 20
131a 1d. green 30 60
132 $1\frac{1}{2}$d. red . . . . 2·00 4·50
132a $1\frac{1}{2}$d. grey . . . . 30 4·00
133 2d. grey . . . . 4·00 1·00
133a 2d. red . . . . 30 1·25
134 3d. blue 60 40
135 4d. mauve . . . . 2·25 1·25
136 6d. violet . . . . 2·50 1·25
137 9d. olive . . . . 2·50 2·50
138 1s. black and orange . . . . 3·00 1·25

1938. As T **14** but with head of King George VI facing right.
139 2s. purple and blue on blue . . 10·00 8·50
140 2s. 6d. black and red on blue . 12·00 8·50
141 5s. green and red on yellow . . 40·00 18·00
142 10s. green and red on green . . 55·00 26·00
143 £1 purple and black on red . . 30·00 26·00

20 Lake Nyasa

21 King's African Rifles

1945.
144 20 $\frac{1}{2}$d. black and brown 30 10
145 21 1d. black and green 40 70
160 – 1d. brown and green 50 20
146 – $1\frac{1}{2}$d. black and grey 20 50
147 – 2d. black and red 50 50
148 – 3d. black and blue 20 30
149 – 4d. black and red . . . . . 1·25 45
150 – 6d. black and violet . . . . 1·25 40
151 20 9d. black and olive . . . . 1·50 2·50
152 – 1s. blue and green . . . . . 1·25 20
153 – 2s. green and purple . . . . 3·75 4·25
154 – 2s. 6d. green and blue . . . 7·50 4·25
155 – 5s. purple and blue . . . . 4·50 6·00
156 – 10s. red and green . . . . . 12·00 13·00
157 – 20s. red and black . . . . . 17·00 24·00
DESIGNS—HORIZ: $1\frac{1}{2}$d., 6d. Tea estate; 2d., 1s., 10s. Map of Nyasaland; 4d., 2s. 6d. Tobacco; 5s., 20s. Badge of Nyasaland. VERT: 1d. (No. 160), Leopard and sunrise; 3d., 2s. Fishing village.

1946. Victory. As T **11a** of Gambia.
158 1d. green 10 10
159 2d. red 30 10

1948. Silver Wedding. As T **11b/c** of Gambia.
161 1d. green 15 10
162 10s. mauve . . . . 15·00 25·00

1949. U.P.U. As T **11d/g** of Gambia.
163 1d. green 50 20
164 3d. blue . . . . 2·25 2·50
165 6d. purple . . . . 1·00 50
166 1s. blue 50 50

27 Arms in 1891 and 1951

1951. Diamond Jubilee of Protectorate.
167 27 2d. black and red . . . . . 1·00 1·00
168 3d. black and blue . . . . 1·00 1·00
169 6d. black and violet . . . . 1·00 1·50
170 5s. black and blue . . . . . 2·00 7·00

1953. Rhodes Centenary Exhibition. As T **6** of Northern Rhodesia.
171 6d. violet 20 30

1953. Coronation. As T **11h** of Gambia.
172 2d. black and orange 50 60

29 Grading Cotton

1953. As 1945 but with portrait of Queen Elizabeth II as in T **29**. Designs as for corresponding values except where stated.
173 20 $\frac{1}{2}$d. black and brown . . . 10 85
174 – 1d. brown and green (as No. 160) 65 20
175 – $1\frac{1}{2}$d. black and grey . . . . 20 1·90
176a – 2d. black and orange . . . 30 10
177 29 $2\frac{1}{2}$d. green and black . . . 20 50
178 – 3d. black & red (as 4d.) . . 30 10
179 – $4\frac{1}{2}$d. black & blue (as 3d.) . 30 40
180a – 6d. black and violet . . . 1·50 60
181 20 9d. black and olive . . . . 70 2·50
182 – 1s. blue and green . . . . 1·75 50
183 – 2s. green and red . . . . 2·00 3·00
184 – 2s. 6d. green and blue . . . 3·25 4·25
185 – 5s. purple and blue . . . . 7·00 4·50
186 – 10s. red and green . . . . 4·25 14·00
187 – 20s. red and black . . . . 15·00 18·00

30

32 Mother and Child

34 Tea Industry

1963. Revenue stamps optd **POSTAGE** as in T **30** or surch also.
188 30 $\frac{1}{2}$d. on 1d. blue 30 30
189 1d. green 30 10
190 2d. red 30 30
191 3d. blue 30 10
192 6d. purple 30 10
193 9d. on 1s. red 40 25
194 1s. purple 45 10
195 2s. 6d. black . . . . 70 1·75
196 5s. brown . . . . 2·00 1·50
197 10s. olive . . . . 3·25 5·00
198 £1 violet . . . . 4·25 5·00

1964.
199 32 $\frac{1}{2}$d. violet 10 30
200 – 1d. black and green 10 10
201 – 2d. brown 10 10
202 – 3d. brown, green & bistre . . 10 10
203 – 4d. blue and yellow 20 30

204	**34**	6d. purple, green and blue	60	30
205	–	1s. brown, blue and yellow	15	10
206	–	1s. 3d. bronze and brown	2·50	10
207	–	2s. 6d. brown and blue	2·50	50
208	–	5s. blue, green, yellow & blk	1·50	1·25
209	–	10s. green, salmon & black	2·00	3·00
210	–	£1 brown and yellow	7·00	5·50

DESIGNS—HORIZ (as Type **32**): 1d. Chambo (fish); 2d. Zebu bull; 3d. Groundnuts; 4d. Fishing. (As Type **34**): 1s. Timber; 1s. 3d. Turkish tobacco industry; 2s. 6d. Cotton industry; 5s. Monkey Bay, Lake Nyasa; 10s. Forestry, Afzelia. VERT (as Type **34**): £1 Nyala.

POSTAGE DUE STAMPS

1950. As Type D **1** of Gold Coast, but inscr "NYASALAND".

D1	1d. red	3·75	18·00
D2	2d. blue	9·00	22·00
D3	3d. green	9·50	6·00
D4	4d. purple	17·00	40·00
D5	6d. orange	23·00	95·00

For later issues see **MALAWI**.

NYASSA COMPANY Pt. 9

In 1894 Portugal granted a charter to the Nyassa Company to administer an area in the Northern part of Mozambique, including the right to issue its own stamps. The lease was terminated in 1929 and the administration was transferred to Mozambique whose stamps were used there.

1898. 1000 reis = 1 milreis.
1913. 100 centavos = 1 escudo.

1898. "Figures" and "Newspaper" key-types inscr "MOCAMBIQUE" optd **NYASSA**.

1	V	$2\frac{1}{2}$ r. brown	85	85
2	R	5 r. orange	85	85
3		10 r. mauve	85	85
4		15 r. brown	85	85
5		20 r. lilac	85	85
6		25 r. green	85	85
7		50 r. blue	85	85
8		75 r. pink	1·25	1·00
9		80 r. green	1·25	1·00
10		100 r. brown on buff	1·25	1·00
11		150 r. red on pink	2·75	2·75
12		200 r. blue on blue	1·90	1·90
13		300 r. blue on brown	1·90	1·90

1898. "King Carlos" key-type inscr "MOCAMBIQUE" optd **NYASSA**.

14	S	$2\frac{1}{2}$ r. grey	60	50
15		5 r. red	60	50
16		10 r. green	60	50
17		15 r. brown	85	60
18		20 r. lilac	85	60
19		25 r. green	85	60
20		50 r. blue	85	60
21		75 r. pink	85	60
22		80 r. mauve	1·00	85
23		100 r. blue on blue	1·00	85
24		150 r. brown on yellow	1·00	85
25		200 r. purple on pink	1·00	85
26		300 r. blue on pink	1·00	85

2 Giraffe

3 Dromedaries

1901.

27	**2**	$2\frac{1}{2}$ r. brown and black	50	25
28		5 r. violet and black	50	25
29		10 r. green and black	50	25
30		15 r. brown and black	50	25
31		20 r. red and black	50	25
32		25 r. orange and black	50	25
33		50 r. blue and black	50	25
34	**3**	75 r. red and black	60	25
35		80 r. bistre and black	60	25
36		100 r. brown and black	60	45
37		150 r. brown and black	60	45
38		200 r. green and black	60	45
39		300 r. green and black	60	45

1903. (a) Surch in figures and words.

40	**3**	65 r. on 80 r. mauve & blk	50	40
41		115 r. on 150 r. brown & blk	50	40
42		130 r. on 300 r. green & blk	50	40

(b) Optd **PROVISORIO**.

43	**2**	15 r. brown and black	50	45
44		25 r. orange and black	50	45

1910. Optd **PROVISORIO** and surch in figures and words.

50	**2**	5 r. on $2\frac{1}{2}$ r. brown and black	50	50
51	**3**	50 r. on 100 r. bistre & black	50	50

9 Dromedaries

12 Vasco de Gama's Flagship "Sao Gabriel"

1911. Optd **REPUBLICA**.

53	**9**	$2\frac{1}{2}$ r. violet and black	40	25
54		5 r. black	40	25
55		10 r. green and black	40	25
56	–	20 r. red and black	40	25
57	–	25 r. brown and black	40	25
58	–	50 r. blue and black	40	25
59	–	75 r. brown and black	40	25
60	–	100 r. brown & black on green	40	35
61	–	200 r. green & black on orge	50	50
62	**12**	300 r. black on blue	1·25	90
63		400 r. brown and black	1·40	1·00
64		500 r. violet and green	1·75	1·40

DESIGNS—HORIZ: 20, 25, 50 r. Common zebra. VERT: 75, 100, 200 r. Giraffe.

1918. Surch **REPUBLICA** and value in figures.

(a) Stamps of 1901.

65	**2**	$\frac{1}{4}$ c. on $2\frac{1}{2}$ c. brown and black	22·00	13·00
66		$\frac{1}{2}$ c. on 5 r. violet and black	22·00	13·00
67		1 c. on 10 r. green and black	22·00	13·00
68		$1\frac{1}{2}$ c. on 15 r. brown & black	1·00	50
69		2 c. on 20 r. red and black	60	50
70		$3\frac{1}{2}$ c. on 25 r. orange & black	60	50
71		5 c. on 50 r. blue and black	60	50
72	**3**	$7\frac{1}{2}$ c. on 75 r. red and black	60	50
73		8 c. on 80 r. mauve and black	60	50
74		10 c. on 100 r. bistre & black	60	50
75		15 c. on 150 r. brown & black	1·00	90
76		20 c. on 200 r. green & black	80	90
77		30 c. on 300 r. green & black	1·50	1·25

(b) Nos. 43/4 and 40/2.

78	**2**	$1\frac{1}{2}$ c. on 15 r. brown & black	2·00	1·50
79		$3\frac{1}{2}$ c. on 25 r. orange & blk	70	50
80	**3**	40 c. on 65 r. on 80 r.	4·50	4·50
81		50 c. on 115 r. on 150 r.	1·25	1·00
82		1 c. on 130 r. on 300 r.	1·25	1·00

1921. Stamps of 1911 surch in figures and words.

83	**9**	$\frac{1}{4}$ c. on $2\frac{1}{2}$ r. violet & black	60	60
85		$\frac{1}{2}$ c. on 5 r. black	60	60
86		1 c. on 10 r. green & black	60	60
87	**12**	$1\frac{1}{2}$ c. on 300 r. black on blue	60	60
88	–	2 c. on 20 r. red and black	60	60
89	–	$2\frac{1}{2}$ c. on 25 r. brown & black	60	60
90	**12**	3 c. on 400 r. brown & black	60	60
91	–	5 c. on 50 r. blue and black	60	60
92	–	$7\frac{1}{2}$ c. on 75 r. brown & black	60	60
93	–	10 c. on 100 r. brown and black on green	60	60
94	**12**	12 c. on 500 r. violet & green	60	60
95	–	20 c. on 200 r. green and black on orange	60	60

16 Giraffe

19 Common Zebra

1921.

96	**16**	$\frac{1}{4}$ c. purple	40	30
97		$\frac{1}{2}$ c. blue	40	30
98		1 c. black and green	40	30
99		$1\frac{1}{2}$ c. orange and black	40	30
100	–	2 c. black and red	40	30
101	–	$2\frac{1}{2}$ c. green and black	40	30
102	–	4 c. red and black	40	30
103	–	5 c. black and blue	40	30
104	–	6 c. violet and black	40	30
123	–	$7\frac{1}{2}$ c. brown and black	70	30
124	–	8 c. green and black	70	30
125	–	10 c. brown and black	70	30
126	–	15 c. red and black	70	30
127	–	20 c. blue and black	80	40
110	**19**	30 c. brown and black	2·25	40
111		40 c. blue and black	1·75	40
112		50 c. green and black	65	40
113		1 e. brown and black	85	40
114	–	2 e. black and brown	2·00	1·25
115	–	5 e. brown and blue	1·60	1·10

DESIGNS—As Type **16**: 2 c. to 6 c. Vasco da Gama; $7\frac{1}{2}$ c. to 20 c. Vasco da Gama's flagship "Sao Gabriel". As Type **19**: 2, 5 e. Native dhow.

CHARITY TAX STAMPS

The notes under this heading in Portugal also apply here.

1925. Marquis de Pombal Commem. Nos. C327/9 of Mozambique optd **NYASSA**.

C141	C **22**	15 c. brown	3·75	3·75
C142	–	15 c. brown	3·75	3·75
C143	C **25**	15 c. brown	3·75	3·75

POSTAGE DUE STAMPS

D **21** "Sao Gabriel"

1924.

D132	–	$\frac{1}{2}$ c. green	1·10	85
D133	–	1 c. blue	1·10	85
D134	–	2 c. red	1·10	85
D135	–	3 c. red	1·10	85
D136	D **21**	5 c. brown	1·75	1·25
D137		6 c. brown	1·75	1·25
D138		10 c. purple	1·75	1·25
D139	–	20 c. red	1·10	85
D140	–	50 c. purple	1·10	85

DESIGNS: $\frac{1}{2}$ c., 1 c. Giraffe; 2 c., 3 c. Common Zebra; 20 c., 50 c. Vasco da Gama.

1925. De Pombal stamps of Mozambique, Nos. D327/9, optd **NYASSA**.

D144	C **22**	30 c. brown	5·00	5·00
D145	–	30 c. brown	5·00	5·00
D146	C **25**	30 c. brown	5·00	5·00

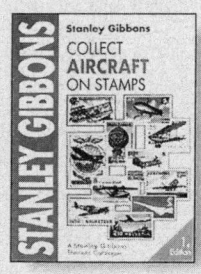

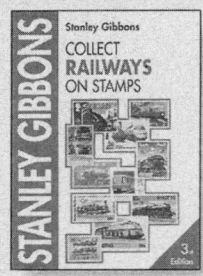

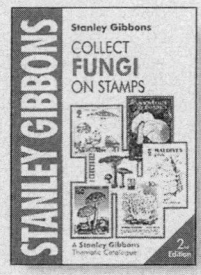

ADDENDA AND CORRIGENDA

GAMBIA

307 Flowers forming Top of Head

1999. Faces of the Millennium: Diana, Princess of Wales. Designs showing collage of miniature flower photographs. Multicoloured.

3231 3 d. Type **307** (face value at left) . . . 35 40
3232 3 d. Top of head (face value at right) . . . 35 40
3233 3 d. Ear (face value at left) . . 35 40
3234 3 d. Eye and temple (face value at right) . . . 35 40
3235 3 d. Cheek (face value at left) . 35 40
3236 3 d. Cheek (face value at right) 35 40
3237 3 d. Blue background (face value at left) . . . 35 40
3238 3 d. Chin (face value at right) . 35 40

Nos. 3231/8 were printed together, se-tenant, so that the sheetlet forms a portrait of Diana, Princess of Wales.

308 Betty Boop

2000. Betty Boop (cartoon character). Mult.

3239 5 d. Type **308** 60 65
3240 5 d. In full-length gown . . . 60 65
3241 5 d. In t-shirt and dungarees . 60 65
3242 5 d. In cropped trousers, sleeveless shirt and tie 60 65
3243 5 d. Sitting in wicker chair . . 60 65
3244 5 d. In ripped purple trousers, orange t-shirt and gilet . . . 60 65
3245 5 d. In fur coat 60 65
3246 5 d. In pink crinoline 60 65
3247 5 d. In the gym 60 65

308a Leonardo da Vinci's First Design for Flying Machine, 1480

308b Max Planck (Quantum Theory of Energy, 1900)

2000. New Millennium. People and Events of Fifteenth Century (1450–1500). Multicoloured.

3249 2 d. Type **308a** 20 25
3250 2 d. Johannes Gutenberg (first printed Bible, 1455) 20 25
3251 2 d. Capital "B" (first colour printing, 1457) 20 25
3252 2 d. Ivan III ("the Great") becomes Grand Prince of Moscow, 1462 . . . . . 20 25
3253 2 d. Walls under attack (Fall of Constantinople, 1453) . . . 20 25
3254 2 d. Great Wall of China rebuilt, 1488 . . . . . . 20 25
3255 2 d. Lorenzo de Medici (ruler of Florence) and "Pieta" (sculpture), 1479 . . . . 20 25
3256 2 d. King Henry VII of England (Foundation of Tudor dynasty, 1485) 20 25
3257 2 d. Sailing ship and meeting with Indians (Vasco da Gama's voyage to India, 1497) 20 25
3258 2 d. King Ferdinand V and Queen Isabella I (Union of Aragon and Castile, 1479) . 20 25
3259 2 d. Foetus (birth of Erasmus (Dutch scholar), 1466) . . . 20 25
3260 2 d. Sailing ship and Cross of St. George (John Cabot's voyage to North America, 1497) 20 25
3261 2 d. King Henry VI and Richard, Duke of Gloucester (Wars of the Roses, 1455) . 20 25
3262 2 d. Bartolomeu Dias and map (Discovery of Cape of Good Hope, 1487) 20 25
3263 2 d. Matthias Hunyadi (crowned King of Hungary, 1458) 20 25
3264 2 d. Christopher Columbus (Discovery of the Americas, 1492) (59 × 39 mm) . . 20 25
3265 2 d. Girolamo Savonarola (religious reformer) (executed 1498) 20 25

2000. New Millennium. People and Events of Twentieth Century (1900–09). Multicoloured.

3266 3 d. Type **308b** 35 40
3267 3 d. Zeppelin in hangar (invention of rigid airship, 1900) . 35 40
3268 3 d. Guglielmo Marconi (first transatlantic radio message, 1901) 35 40
3269 3 d. Funeral of Queen Victoria, 1901 . . . . 35 40
3270 3 d. Alfred Nobel (first Nobel Prizes awarded, 1901) . . . 35 40
3271 3 d. British infantry advancing (end of Boer War, 1902) . . 35 40
3272 3 d. Wright Brothers and aircraft (first flight, 1903) . . 35 40
3273 3 d. Early teddy bear, 1903 . . 35 40
3274 3 d. Panama Canal locks under construction, 1904 . . . . 35 40
3275 3 d. Albert Einstein (Theory of Relativity, 1905) 35 40
3276 3 d. Crowd with flags (unrest in Russia, 1905) 35 40
3277 3 d. Rescue squad and collapsed building, San Francisco earthquake, 1906 . . . . . 35 40
3278 3 d. Louis Lumiere (development of colour photography, 1907) 35 40
3279 3 d. "Les Demoiselles d'Avignon" (Pablo Picasso), 1907 . . . . 35 40
3280 3 d. Robert Peary (conquest of North Pole, 1909) 35 40
3281 3 d. Henry Ford and first Model T, 1908 (59 × 39 mm) 35 40
3282 3 d. Planting sapling (foundation of first Jewish kibbutz in Palestine, 1909) 35 40

309 Dragon

2000. Chinese New Year ("Year of the Dragon"). Multicoloured.

3283 5 d. Type **309** 60 65
3284 5 d. Multicoloured dragon . . 60 65
3285 5 d. Purple dragon 60 65
3286 5 d. Brown dragon 60 65

GERMANY

1286 Woman

2000. Prevention of Violence Against Women.

2942 **1286** 110 pf. red, grey and black 70 35

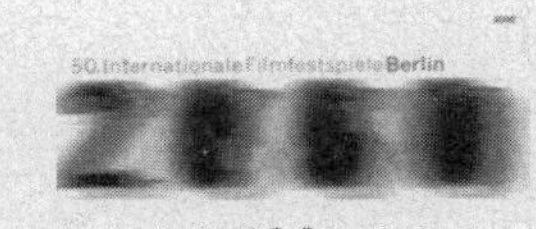

1287 "2000" in Moving Film Sequence

2000. 50th Berlin International Film Festival.

2943 **1287** 100 pf. multicoloured . . 65 30

1288 Boxing

2000. Sport Promotion Fund. Multicoloured.

2944 100 pf. + 50 pf. Type **1288** (fair play) . . . . 1·00 1·00
2945 110 pf. + 50 pf. Rhythmic gymnastics (beauty) . . . . 1·10 1·00
2946 110 pf. + 50 pf. Running (competition) . . . . 1·10 1·00
2947 300 pf. + 100 pf. Raised hands (culture of interaction) . . . 2·50 1·25

1289 Gutenberg (after engraving by A. Thevet) and Letters from Gutenberg Bible

1290 Jester

2000. 600th Birth Anniv of Johannes Gutenberg (inventor of printing press).

2948 **1289** 110 pf. black and red . . 70 35

2000. 175th Anniv of First Dusseldorf Carnival.

2949 **1290** 110 pf. multicoloured . . 70 35

1291 Ebert

2000. 75th Death Anniv of Friedrich Ebert (President, 1919–25).

2950 **1291** 110 pf. multicoloured . . 70 35

1292 Weill at Rehearsal of "One Touch of Venus" (musical), 1943

2000. Birth Centenary of Kurt Weill (composer).

2951 **1292** 300 pf. blk, stone & red . 2·00 1·00

GREAT BRITAIN

1464 Raising the Stone (Strangford Stone, Killyleagh)

2000. Millennium Projects (7th series). "Stone and Soil".

2152 **1464** (2nd) blk, grey & silver . 30 35
2153 – (1st) multicoloured . . . 40 45
2154 – 45p. multicoloured . . . 70 75
2155 – 65p. multicoloured . . . 1·00 1·10

DESIGNS: No. 2153, Horse's Hooves (Trans Pennine Trail, Derbyshire); 2154, Cyclist (Kingdom of Fife Cycle Ways, Scotland); 2155, Bluebell Wood (Groundwork's "Changing Places" Project).

GREENLAND

149 Huskies pulling Sledge

2000. 50th Anniv of "Sirius" (naval sledge patrol).

371 **149** 10 k. multicoloured . . . 85 85

GRENADINES OF GRENADA

138 George Raft

140 Kirk Douglas

139 "Sputnik I", 1957

1999. Early Cinema Actors.

2788 **138** $1 multicoloured 45 50
2789 – $1 grey and black 45 50
2790 – $1 grey and black 45 50
2791 – $1 multicoloured 45 50
2792 – $1 multicoloured 45 50
2793 – $1 black and grey 45 50
2794 – $1 black, blue and grey . 45 50
2795 – $1 multicoloured 45 50
2796 – $2 multicoloured 85 90
2797 – $2 black and grey 85 90
2798 – $2 multicoloured 85 90
2799 – $2 black and grey . . . . 2·50 2·75

DESIGNS: No. 2791, Fatty Arbuckle; 2792, Buster Keaton; 2795, Harold Lloyd; 2796, James Cagney; 2798, Edward G. Robinson. (53 × 39 mm): No. 2789, George Raft in "Scarface"; 2790, Fatty Arbuckle with nurse; 2793, Buster Keaton on locomotive cowcatcher; 2974, Harold Lloyd hanging on clockface; 2979, James Cagney in "The Public Enemy" 2799, Edward G. Robinson in "Little Caesar".

1999. Space Exploration. Multicoloured.

2801 $1.50 Type **139** 65 70
2802 $1.50 "Explorer I", 1958 . . . 65 70
2803 $1.50 "Telstar I" satellite, 1962 65 70
2804 $1.50 "Maristat I", 1976 . . . 65 70
2805 $1.50 Long Duration Exposure facility, 1984 . . . . 65 70
2806 $1.50 Hubble Space Telescope, 1990 . . . . 65 70
2807 $1.50 X-15 rocket plane, 1960 (vert) 65 70
2808 $1.50 "Freedom 7" rocket, 1961 (vert) 65 70
2809 $1.50 "Friendship 7", 1962 (vert) 65 70
2810 $1.50 "Gemini 4" rocket and Edward H. White, 1965 (vert) 65 70
2811 $1.50 Saturn V rocket and Edwin E. Aldrin stepping onto Moon, 1969 (vert) . . 65 70
2812 $1.50 Lunar Rover, "Apollo 15" mission, 1971 (vert) . . 65 70

Nos. 2801/6 and 2807/12 were each printed together, se-tenant, with the backgrounds forming composite designs.

1999. Kirk Douglas (American actor). Multicoloured.

2814 $1.50 Type **140** 65 70
2815 $1.50 As a boxer in "Champion" 65 70
2816 $1.50 As Van Gogh in "Lust for Life" 65 70
2817 $1.50 With white hair and wearing black shirt . . . 65 70
2818 $1.50 In French uniform for "Paths of Glory" 65 70
2819 $1.50 As a cowboy in "The Bad and the Beautiful" 65 70

141 Elvis Presley

1999. Elvis Presley Commemoration. Each grey, silver and black.
2821 $1.50 Type **141** 65 70
2822 $1.50 Resting chin on hand . . 65 70
2823 $1.50 Wearing roll-neck sweater 65 70
2824 $1.50 Leaning against brick wall 65 70
2825 $1.50 Singing into microphone . 65 70
2826 $1.50 Singing with eyes closed . 65 70

Christmas 1999
142 Poinsettia and Candle

1999. Christmas. Foliage and Candles. Mult.
2827 15 c. Type **142** 10 15
2828 35 c. Holly 15 20
2829 75 c. Fir tree 35 40
2830 $1.50 Ivy 65 70
2831 $3 Geranium . . . . 1·25 1·40
No. 2829 is inscribed "FUR TREE" in error.

GUYANA

565 Pres. Kennedy and "Eternal Flame"

1997. 80th Birth Anniv of Pres. John F. Kennedy.
4937 **565** $50 violet 35 40
No. 4937 is in the same design as the U.S.A. Memorial Issue of 1964.

1997. 50th Anniv of U.N.E.S.C.O. Multicoloured. As T **273a** of Gambia.
4938 $20 Hall at Horyu-ji, Japan . . 15 20
4939 $25 Coastline, Scandola Nature Reserve, France 20 25
4940 $30 Great Wall turret, China . 20 25
4941 $35 Bedroom in the Residenz, Wurzburg, Germany 20 25
4942 $60 Monastery of Batalha, Portugal 40 45
4943 $60 Cathedral of Aquisgran, Aachen, Germany (vert) . . 40 45
4944 $60 Trier Cathedral, Germany (vert) 40 45
4945 $60 Column of Augusta Treveror, Trier (vert) . . . 40 45
4946 $60 The Residenz and garden, Wurzburg (vert) 40 45
4947 $60 Interior of church, Wurzburg (vert) 40 45
4948 $60 The Residenz and lake, Wurzburg (vert) 40 45
4949 $60 Riverside houses, Inselstadt, Bamberg, Germany (vert) . . 40 45
4950 $60 Cathedral interior, Speyer, Germany (vert) 40 45
4951 $60 Monastery of Thessaloniki, Greece (vert) 40 45
4952 $60 Church tower, Monastery of Mystras, Greece (vert) . . 40 45
4953 $60 Interior of Church of Santa Sofia, Thessaloniki (vert) . . 40 45
4954 $60 Monastery and ruins, Mystras (vert) 40 45
4955 $60 Aerial view of Monastery at Mystras (vert) 40 45
4956 $60 City wall, Thessaloniki (vert) 40 45
4957 $60 Wall painting, Mystras Monastery (vert) 40 45
4958 $60 Paintings in Museum of Byzantine Art, Thessaloniki (vert) 40 45
4959 $60 Monastery of Poblet, Catalonia, Spain (vert) . . . 40 45
4960 $60 Salamanca, Spain (vert) . . 40 45
4961 $60 Toledo, Spain (vert) . . . 40 45
4962 $60 Florence Cathedral, Italy (vert) 40 45
4963 $60 Leaning Tower of Pisa, Italy (vert) 40 45
4964 $60 Courtyard and tower, Convent of Cristo in Tomas, Portugal (vert) 40 45
4965 $60 Main door, Convent of Cristo in Tomas (vert) . . . 40 45
4966 $60 Cloisters, Convent of Cristo in Tomas (vert) 40 45
4967 $80 Tower, Horyu-ji, Japan . . 55 60
4968 $80 Temple with verandah, Kyoto, Japan 55 60
4969 $80 Temple and pillar, Kyoto . 55 60
4970 $80 Temples and lake, Horyu-Ji 55 60
4971 $80 Three-storey temple, Horyu-Ji 55 60
4972 $80 University of Virginia, U.S.A. 55 60
4973 $80 Yosemite National Park, U.S.A. 55 60
4974 $80 Yellowstone National Park, U.S.A. 55 60
4975 $80 Olympic National Park, U.S.A. 55 60
4976 $80 Everglades, U.S.A. 55 60
4977 $80 Street, Cuzco, Peru . . . 55 60
4978 $80 Potosi, Bolivia 55 60
4979 $80 Fortress of San Lorenzo, Panama 55 60
4980 $80 Sangay National Park, Ecuador 55 60
4981 $80 Los Glaciares National Park, Argentina 55 60
4982 $200 City walls, Dubrovnik, Croatia . . . . 1·40 1·50

566 "Morchella hortensis"
567 Pineapple Lily 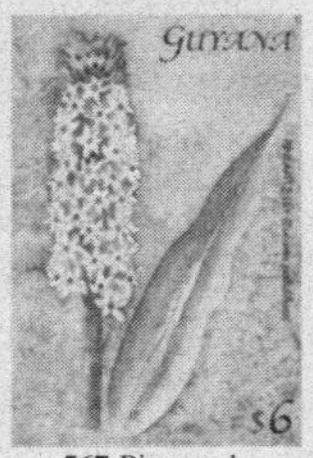

1997. Fungi of the World. Multicoloured.
4984 $6 Type **566** 10 10
4985 $20 "Boletus chrysenteron" . . 15 20
4986 $25 "Hygrophorus agathosmus" 20 25
4987 $30 "Cortinarius violaceus" . . 20 25
4988 $35 "Acanthocystis geogenius" 20 25
4989 $60 "Mycena polygramma" . . 40 45
4990 $80 "Coprinus picaceus" . . . 55 60
4991 $80 "Stropharia umbonatescens" 55 60
4992 $80 "Paxillus involutus" . . . 55 60
4993 $80 "Amanita inaurata" . . . 55 60
4994 $80 "Lepiota rhacodes" . . . 55 60
4995 $80 "Russula amoena" 55 60
4996 $80 "Volvaria volvacea" . . . 55 60
4997 $80 "Psalliota augusta" . . . 55 60
4998 $80 "Tricholoma aurantium" . . 55 60
4999 $80 "Pholiota spectabilis" . . 55 60
5000 $80 "Cortinarius armillatus" . . 55 60
5001 $80 "Agrocybe dura" 55 60
5002 $200 "Hebeloma radicosum" . . 1·40 1·50
5003 $300 "Coprinus comatus" . . 2·00 2·10

1997. Flowers. Multicoloured.
5005 $6 Type **567** 10 10
5006 $6 Blue columbine 10 10
5007 $20 Petunia 15 20
5008 $25 Lily of the Nile 20 25
5009 $30 Bird of paradise 20 25
5010 $35 African daisy 20 25
5011 $60 Cape daisy 40 45
5012 $60 Monarch slipperwort . . . 40 45
5013 $60 Passion flower 40 45
5014 $60 Butterfly iris 40 45
5015 $60 Red-hot poker 40 45
5016 $60 Water lily "Dir G. T. Moore" 40 45
5017 $60 Painted tongue "Superbissima" 40 45
5018 $60 Canariensis orchid 40 45
5019 $60 Annual chrysanthemum . . 40 45
5020 $80 Tulips 55 60
5021 $80 Liatris 55 60
5022 $80 Roses 55 60
5023 $80 Gerber daisies 55 60
5024 $80 Sunflowers 55 60
5025 $80 Chrysanthemums 55 60
5026 $80 Gazania 55 60
5027 $80 Cape water lily 55 60
5028 $200 Insigne lady's slipper . . 1·40 1·50

INDIA

1473 Dam and Pumping Station

1999. Sri Sathya Sai Water Supply Project.
1884 **1473** 3 r. multicoloured . . . 15 15

1474 Supreme Court, New Delhi

1999. 50th Anniv of Supreme Court of India.
1885 **1474** 3 r. multicoloured . . . 15 15

1475 A. Vaidyanatha Iyer and Temple Tower

1999. March of Progress.
1886 **1475** 3 r. red 15 15
1887 – 3 r. brown and green . . 15 15
1888 – 3 r. buff and black . . . 15 15
1889 – 3 r. brown and green . . 15 15
DESIGNS: No. 1887, Dr. Punjabrao Deshmukh and symbols of agriculture; 1888, Indulal Kanaiyalal Yagnik and newspaper; 1889, Kakkan and machinery.

1476 Aspects of Thermal Power

1999. Centenary of Thermal Power.
1890 **1476** 3 r. chocolate and brown 15 15

1477 "Hindustan Times" Front Pages from 1950 and 1999

1999. 75th Anniv of "Hindustan Times" Newspaper.
1891 **1477** 15 r. multicoloured . . . 40 45

1478 Three Faces ("Small Family by Choice")
1479 Hand inside Flame in front of Cross 

1999. 50th Anniv of Family Planning Association of India.
1892 **1478** 3 r. multicoloured . . . 15 15

1999. 2000th Birth Anniv of Jesus Christ.
1893 **1479** 3 r. multicoloured . . . 15 15

1480 Tabo Monastery and Mountains

1999. Tabo Monastery Commemoration. Mult.
1894 5 r. Type **1480** 15 20
1895 10 r. Traditional scene 30 35

1481 Agni II Rocket and Dove

2000. 41st Anniv of Defence Research and Development Organization.
1896 **1481** 3 r. multicoloured . . . 15 15

1482 Sunrise

2000. New Millennium.
1897 **1482** 3 r. multicoloured . . . 15 15

JERSEY

210 "Ocean Adventure" (Gemma Care)

2000. "Stampin' the Future" (children's stamp design competition) Winners. Multicoloured.
929 22p. Type **210** 45 50
930 22p. "Solar Power" (Chantal Varley-Best) 45 50
931 22p. "Floating City and Space Cars" (Nicola Singleton) . . 45 50
932 22p. "Conservation" (Carly Logan) 45 50

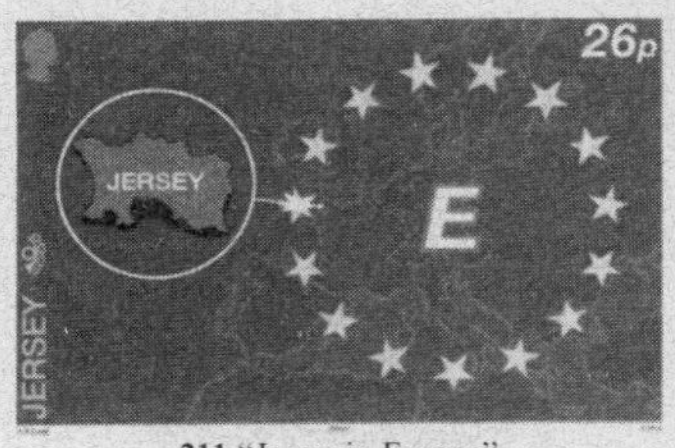

211 "Jersey in Europe"

2000. Europa. Multicoloured.
934 26p. Type **211** 50 55
935 34p. "Building Europe" (29 × 39 mm) 70 75

KOREA

NORTH KOREA

1254 Liu Shaoqi
1255 Victory in Yonsong Monument, Yonan Fortress and Banners 

1998. Birth Centenary of Liu Shaoqi (Chairman of Chinese People's Republic, 1959–68). Multicoloured.
N3812 10 ch. Type **1254** 10 10
N3813 20 ch. Liu Shaoqi and Mao Tse-tung 15 10
N3814 30 ch. Liu Shaoqi and his daughter, Xiao Xiao . . . 30 15
N3815 40 ch. Liu Shaoqi and his wife, Wang Guangmei . . 35 15

1998. 400th Anniv of Victory in Korean–Japanese War. Multicoloured.
N3817 10 ch. Type **1255** 10 10
N3818 30 ch. Naval Victory in Myongryang Monument, General Ri Sun Sin and "turtle" ship 30 15
N3819 1 wn. 60 Monument to Hyujong in Kangwon province, Hyujong (Buddhist priest), sword and helmet 90 45

1256 Dish Aerial, Artificial Satellite, Globe and Relay Tower
1257 Goat 

1998. 15th Anniv of North Korean Membership of Intersputnik.
N3821 **1256** 1 wn. deep green and green 90 45

1998.
N3822 **1257** 10 ch. black and green . 10 10
N3823 1 wn. black and red . . 90 45

1258 "A Floral Carriage of Happiness" (sculpture) and Palace
1259 Emblem 

1998. Mangyongdae Schoolchildren's Palace.
N3824 **1258** 40 ch. multicoloured . 35 15

1998. 50th Anniv of Universal Declaration of Human Rights.
N3826 **1259** 20 ch. multicoloured . 15 10

1260 Reeves's Turtle   1261 Thajong Rock

1998. Reptiles and Amphibians. Multicoloured.

N3827	10 ch. Type **1260**	10	10
N3828	40 ch. Skink	35	15
N3829	60 ch. Loggerhead turtle	55	25
N3830	1 wn. 20 Leatherback turtle	1·10	55

Nos. N3827/30 were issued together, se-tenant, forming a composite design.

1998. Mt. Chilbo. Multicoloured.

N3831	30 ch. Type **1261**	30	15
N3832	50 ch. Peasant Rock	45	20
N3833	1 wn. 70 Couple Rock	1·50	75

1262 Ri Mong Ryong marrying Song Chun Hyang   1263 Chollima Statue

1998. Tale of Chun Hyang. Multicoloured.

N3834	40 ch. Type **1262**	35	15
N3835	1 wn. 60 Pyon Hak Do watching Chun Hyang	1·50	75
N3836	2 wn. 50 Ri Mong Ryong and Chun Hyang	2·40	1·10

1998. Pyongyang Monuments.

N3838	**1263**	10 ch. red	10	10
N3839	A	10 ch. red	10	10
N3840	B	10 ch. red	10	10
N3841	A	20 ch. orange	15	10
N3842	**1263**	30 ch. orange	30	15
N3843	A	40 ch. yellow	35	15
N3844	B	40 ch. yellow	35	15
N3845	**1263**	70 ch. green	65	30
N3846	B	70 ch. green	65	30
N3847		1 wn. 20 green	1·00	50
N3848	**1263**	1 wn. 50 green	1·40	70
N3849	A	2 wn. blue	1·75	85
N3850	B	3 wn. blue	2·75	1·40
N3851	**1263**	5 wn. blue	4·50	2·25
N3852	A	10 wn. violet	9·00	4·50

DESIGNS: A, Arch of Triumph; B, Tower of Juche Idea.

NOTE. The first supplement containing new issues not in this catalogue or Addenda appeared in the September 2000 issue of *Gibbons Stamp Monthly*.

INDEX